Get Connected to ConnectED

connectED.mcgraw-hill.com

- 100% Online
- One-Stop Shop, One Personalized Password
- Easy Intuitive Navigation
- Resources, Resources, Resources

For Students

Leave your books at school. Now you can go online and interact with your **StudentWorks Plus** digital Student Edition from any place, any time!

For Teachers

ConnectED is your one-stop online center for everything you need to teach using ***Florida Algebra 2***, including: **TeacherWorks Plus** digital Teacher Edition, lesson planning and scheduling tools, pacing, and assessment.

For Parents

Get homework help, help your student prepare for testing, and review math topics.

Get Connected to the way students learn and teachers teach TODAY!

Algebra 2

Program Highlights

Vertically Aligned Content	Sample Page(s)
• Research Base for Glencoe Mathematics	T22
• PreK-12 Alignment	T24
• College and Work Readiness	T26

Balanced Instruction Delivers Rich, Rigorous Content to All Students	Sample Page(s)
• Chapter 0, Preparing for Algebra 2	P1–P19
• Friendly Lesson Design	5–12
• Engaging Algebra and Graphing Technology Labs	68, 101–102
• Step-by-Step Selected Solutions	106–109, R20–R134

Right Amount of Rigor	Sample Page(s)
• Leveled Exercise Sets	106-109
• Multiple Representations	66, 192
• **H**igher **O**rder **T**hinking Problems (H.O.T. Problems)	116, 258
• Leveled Resources	246A–246B, 249

Assessment and Tiered Intervention	Sample Page(s)
• Diagnostic Teaching	330F, 334, 339
• Formative Assessment	342, 345, 347, 367
• Summative Assessment	401
• Tier 1–3 Response to Intervention (RtI)	331, 367, 401

State-of-the-Art Technology	Sample Page(s)
• Personal Tutors for Each Example	249, 305
• FL Math Online at **glencoe.com**	246, 249, 320
• FREE! Hotmath.com Online Tutorials	R20–R134

Teacher Edition

Glencoe McGraw-Hill

Florida Algebra 2

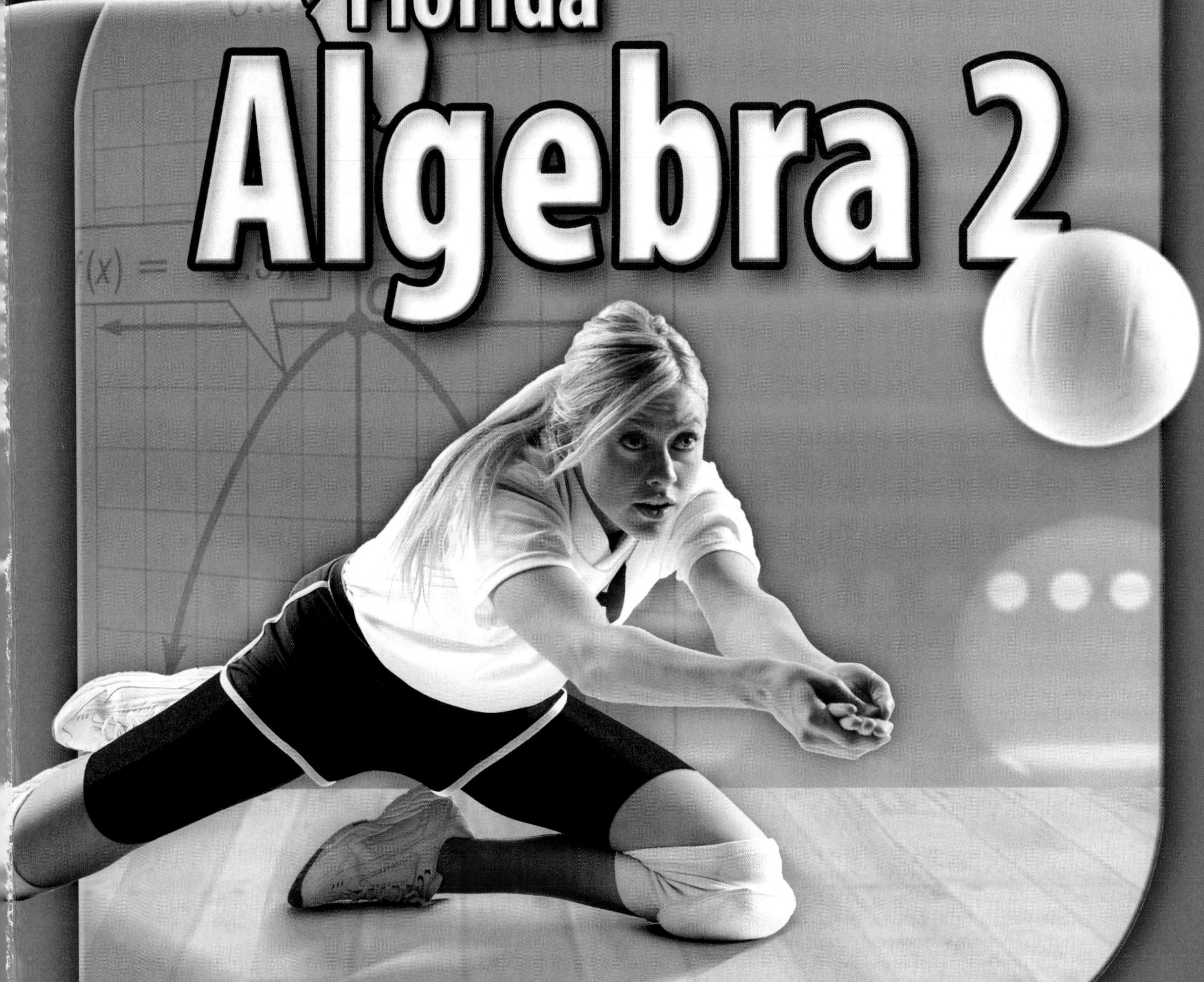

Authors

Carter • Cuevas • Day • Malloy • Casey • Holliday

McGraw Hill Glencoe

About the Cover

After a volleyball is hit upward, it travels along a path shaped like a parabola. This parabola can be modeled mathematically using a quadratic function. With a quadratic function you can find out how long the volleyball will be in the air, how high it will go, and where it will land. You will study quadratic functions in Chapter 5.

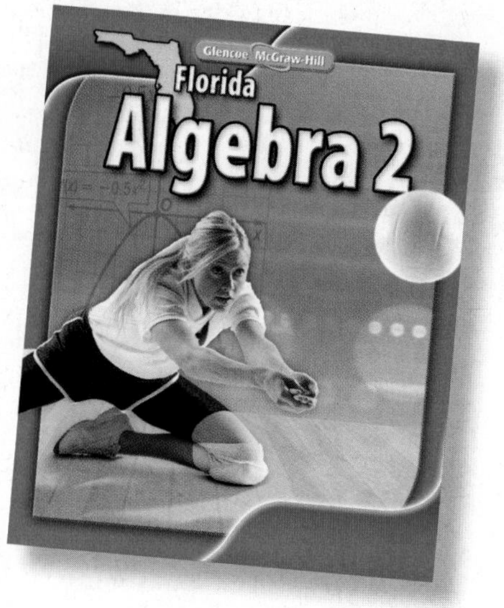

Photo Credits:

0 (t)Richard Hutchings, (c)Getty Images, (b)Jupiter Images/ThinkStock/Alamy; **T4** Aaron Haupt; **T5–T7**; The McGraw-Hill Companies; **T8–T9** Panoramic Images/Getty Images; **T10–T11** Chad Riley/Getty Images; **T11** (t)BananaStock/PictureQuest, (bl)Getty Images, (br)The McGraw-Hill Companies; **T12–T13** Richard Hutchings; **T13** (tl tr c)Richard Hutchings, (b)Getty Images; **T14, T17** Mike Kemp/Getty Images; **T18–T19** Huntstock/Getty Images; **T22** Digital Vision/Getty Images; **T23** BananaStock/PictureQuest; **T26** Getty Images; **T26–T27** (bkgd)Dynamic Graphics/JupiterImages; **T27** Getty Images; **T28** Jason Reed/Getty Images, (bkgd)RubberBall Selects/Alamy; **T32** Digital Vision/Punchstock; **i** Mark Zylber/Alamy Images; **ii** Don Farrall/Getty Images; **iii** Thinkstock/CORBIS; **iv** Tom Stewart/CORBIS; **v** Kobal/The Picture Desk; **vi** Andrew Weeks/SuperStock; **vii** Rodolfo Arpia/Alamy Images; **viii** Masterfile; **ix** Burgess Blevins/Getty Images; **x** Onne van der Wal/CORBIS; **xi** Photodisc/Alamy Images; **xii** Kim Karpeles/Alamy Images; **xiii** Digital Vision/Getty Images; **xiv** Charlie Munsey/CORBIS; **xv** Yellow Dog Productions/Getty Images; **xviii–xix** James Schwabel/Alamy

TI-Nspire is a trademark of Texas Instruments.
TI-Nspire images used by permission.

The McGraw·Hill Companies

Glencoe

Send all inquiries to:
Glencoe/McGraw-Hill
8787 Orion Place
Columbus, OH 43240-4027

ISBN: 978-0-07-892270-1 *(Florida Teacher Edition)*
MHID: 0-07-892270-4 *(Florida Teacher Edition)*
ISBN: 978-0-07-892265-7 *(Florida Student Edition)*
MHID: 0-07-892265-8 *(Florida Student Edition)*

Printed in the United States of America.

1 2 3 4 5 6 7 8 9 10 079/043 17 16 15 14 13 12 11 10 09

Designed for Florida Success

Contents in Brief

Suggested Pacing Guide

Each chapter includes multiple days for review and assessment.

Chapter 0	Optional
Chapter 1	9 days
Chapter 2	13 days
Chapter 3	8 days
Chapter 4	10 days
Chapter 5	12 days
Chapter 6	13 days
Chapter 7	11 days
Chapter 8	14 days
Chapter 9	11 days
Chapter 10	12 days
Chapter 11	13 days
Chapter 12	11 days
Chapter 13	15 days
Chapter 14	8 days
Total	**160 days**

Authors

Our lead authors ensure that the Macmillan/McGraw-Hill and Glencoe/McGraw-Hill mathematics programs are truly vertically aligned by beginning with the end in mind—success in Algebra 1 and beyond. By "backmapping" the content from the high school programs, all of our mathematics programs are well articulated in their scope and sequence.

Lead Authors

John A. Carter, Ph.D.
Assistant Principal for Teaching and Learning
Adlai E. Stevenson High School
Lincolnshire, Illinois

Areas of Expertise: Using technology and manipulatives to visualize concepts; mathematics achievement of English language learners

Gilbert J. Cuevas, Ph.D.
Professor of Mathematics Education
Texas State University—San Marcos
San Marcos, Texas

Areas of Expertise: Applying concepts and skills in mathematically rich contexts; mathematical representations

Roger Day, Ph.D., NBCT
Mathematics Department Chairperson
Pontiac Township High School
Pontiac, Illinois

Areas of Expertise: Understanding and applying probability and statistics; mathematics teacher education

Carol Malloy, Ph.D.
Associate Professor
University of North Carolina at Chapel Hill
Chapel Hill, North Carolina

Areas of Expertise: Representations and critical thinking; student success in Algebra 1

FL Math Online Meet the Authors at **glencoe.com**

Program Authors

Ruth Casey
Mathematics Consultant
Regional Teacher Partner
University of Kentucky
Lexington, Kentucky

Areas of Expertise: Graphing technology and mathematics

Dr. Berchie Holliday, Ed.D.
National Mathematics Consultant
Silver Spring, Maryland

Areas of Expertise: Using mathematics to model and understand real-world data; the effect of graphics on mathematical understanding

Contributing Author

Dinah Zike FOLDABLES
Educational Consultant
Dinah-Might Activities, Inc.
San Antonio, Texas

Florida Teacher Advisory Board

Glencoe/McGraw-Hill thanks the following professionals for their invaluable feedback during the development of the program. They reviewed instructional materials at different stages of development.

Elizabeth Anderson
Teacher
Fort Braden
Tallahassee, Florida

Eleanor Barton
Department Chair
Glades Middle School
Miami, Florida

Audrenita Blair
Teacher/Mathematics Department Head
Marion Rodgers Middle School
Riverview, Florida

Arlene Colson
Mathematics Teacher
W.C. Young Middle School
Pembroke Pines, Florida

Joi B. Davies
Instructional Staff Developer-Secondary Mathematics
Pinellas County Schools
Largo, Florida

Laurie Delikat
Professional Development Resource Teacher
Lee County
Ft. Myers, Florida

Patricia Dell Foley
Primary Mathematics Specialist, Mathematics Academy Teacher
Schwarzkopf Elementary School
Lutz, Florida

Christina Fritsch
K–5 Mathematics Specialist
Bryan Elementary
Plant City, Florida

Jeanne Garcia
Curriculum Support Specialist
District Office
Miami, Florida

Daneri Gay
Teacher
Arvida Middle School
Miami, Florida

Debbie Georgia
Staff Developer Secondary Mathematics
Area III Office
Largo, Florida

Carol A. Goehring, NBCT
Curriculum Resource Teacher
Wekiva High School
Orlando, Florida

Francine "Fran" Harvey
Teacher
Belcher Elementary School
Clearwater, Florida

Andrea A. Hernandez
Mathematics Facilitator/Part-time District Curriculum Support Specialist
Lake Stevens Elementary School
Opa-Locka, Florida

Janet Hornik
Mathematics Department Chairperson
Stranahan High School
Ft. Lauderdale, Florida

Rima Kelley, NBCT
Mathematics Teacher and Department Chairperson
Deerlake Middle School
Tallahassee, Florida

Sharon Kelley
Elementary Resource Specialist
Osceola District Schools
Kissimmee, Florida

Serena A. Kennedy
Middle School Mathematics Teacher/Department Head
Lee Middle School
Fort Myers, Florida

Kelly S. Mahaffey
Title I TOA
K–5 Mathematics EDC
Daytona Beach, Florida

Stephanie Marks
Middle Grades Mathematics Teacher
Lee Middle School
Fort Myers, Florida

Carol Newman
Retired Mathematics Curriculum Specialist K–5
Broward County Schools
Ft. Lauderdale, Florida

Jamie Pittman
K–12 Mathematics Program Specialist
Marion County Public Schools
Ocala, Florida

Michelle Richardson
Mathematics Department Chair/Teacher
McLane Middle School
Brandon, Florida

Matt Roberson
Mathematics Teacher
William J. Montford, III Middle School
Tallahassee, Florida

Maria Yaquelin Rodriguez
Assistant Principal
Lake Stevens Elementary School
Miami, Florida

Katrina Latrice Summerville
5th Grade Mathematics Instructor/Intermediate Mathematics Specialist
William S. Maxey Elementary
Winter Garden, Florida

Jim Swick
Assistant Professor of Mathematics
Palm Beach Atlantic University
West Palm Beach, Florida

Patti Thompson
Mathematics Department Head
J.M. Tate High School
Cantonment, Florida

Sandra E. van Cleef
Curriculum Specialist
Region VI
Miami, Florida

Kathleen D. Van Sise
Mathematics Teacher
Mandarin High School
Jacksonville, Florida

Consultants and Reviewers

These professionals were instrumental in providing valuable input and suggestions for improving the effectiveness of the mathematics instruction.

Consultants

Mathematical Content

Viken Hovsepian
Professor of Mathematics
Rio Hondo College
Whittier, California

Grant A. Fraser, Ph.D.
Professor of Mathematics
California State University, Los Angeles
Los Angeles, California

Arthur K. Wayman, Ph.D.
Professor of Mathematics Emeritus
California State University, Long Beach
Long Beach, California

Gifted and Talented

Shelbi K. Cole
Research Assistant
University of Connecticut
Storrs, Connecticut

College Readiness

Robert Lee Kimball, Jr.
Department Head, Math and Physics
Wake Technical Community College
Raleigh, North Carolina

English-Language Learners

Susana Davidenko
State University of New York
Cortland, New York

Alfredo Gómez
Mathematics/ESL Teacher
George W. Fowler High School
Syracuse, New York

Graphing Calculator

Jerry Cummins
Former President
National Council of Supervisors of Mathematics
Western Springs, Illinois

Mathematical Fluency

Robert M. Capraro
Associate Professor
Texas A&M University
College Station, Texas

Pre-AP

Dixie Ross
Lead Teacher for Advanced Placement Mathematics
Pflugerville High School
Pflugerville, Texas

Reading and Writing

ReLeah Cossett Lent
Author and Educational Consultant
Morganton, Georgia

Lynn T. Havens
Director of Project CRISS
Kalispell, Montana

West Palm Beach

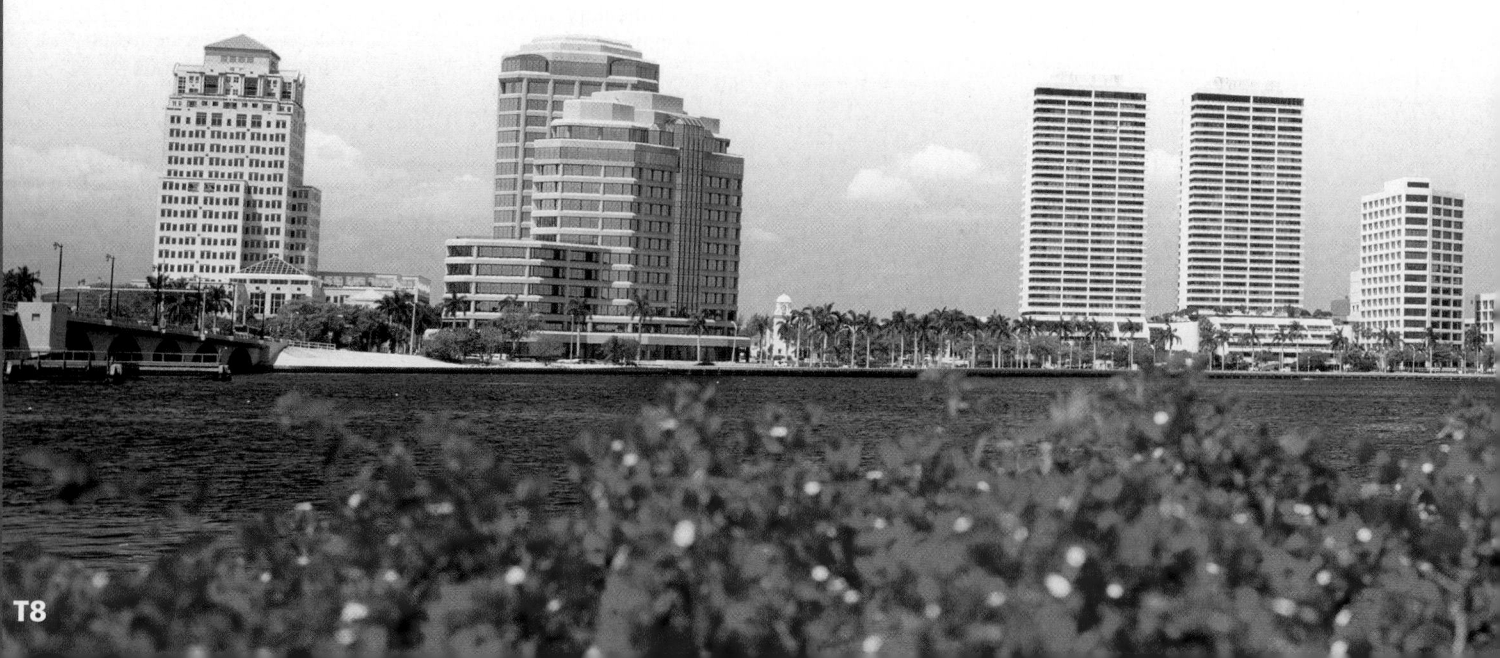

Reviewers

Corey Andreasen
Mathematics Teacher
North High School
Sheboygan, Wisconsin

Mark B. Baetz
Mathematics Coordinating Teacher
Salem City Schools
Salem, Virginia

Kathryn Ballin
Mathematics Supervisor
Newark Public Schools
Newark, New Jersey

Kevin C. Barhorst
Mathematics Department Chair
Independence High School
Columbus, Ohio

Brenda S. Berg
Mathematics Teacher
Carbondale Community High School
Carbondale, Illinois

Dawn Brown
Mathematics Department Chair
Kenmore West High School
Buffalo, New York

Sheryl Pernell Clayton
Mathematics Teacher
Hume Fogg Magnet School
Nashville, Tennessee

Bob Coleman
Mathematics Teacher
Cobb Middle School
Tallahassee, Florida

Jane E. Cotts
Mathematics Teacher
O'Fallon Township High School
O'Fallon, Illinois

Michael D. Cuddy
Mathematics Instructor
Zypherhills High School
Zypherhills, Florida

Melissa M. Dalton, NBCT
Mathematics Instructor
Rural Retreat High School
Rural Retreat, Virginia

Trina Louise Davis
Mathematics Teacher
Fort Mill High School
Fort Mill, South Carolina

Tina S. Dohm
Mathematics Teacher
Naperville Central High School
Naperville, Illinois

Laurie L.E. Ferrari
Mathematics Teacher
L'Anse Creuse High School—North
Macomb, Michigan

Steve Freshour
Mathematics Teacher
Parkersburg South High School
Parkersburg, West Virginia

Shirley D. Glover
Mathematics Teacher
TC Roberson High School
Asheville, North Carolina

Caroline W. Greenough
Mathematics Teacher
Cape Fear Academy
Wilmington, North Carolina

Michelle Hanneman
Mathematics Teacher
Moore High School
Moore, Oklahoma

Theresalynn Haynes
Mathematics Teacher
Glenbard East High School
Lombard, Illinois

Sandra Hester
Mathematics Teacher/AIG Specialist
North Henderson High School
Hendersonville, North Carolina

Jacob K. Holloway
Mathematics Teacher
Capitol Heights Junior High School
Montgomery, Alabama

Robert Hopp
Mathematics Teacher
Harrison High School
Harrison, Michigan

Eileen Howanitz
Mathematics Teacher/Department Chairperson
Valley View High School
Archbald, Pennsylvania

Charles R. Howard, NBCT
Mathematics Teacher
Tuscola High School
Waynesville, North Carolina

Sue Hvizdos
Mathematics Department Chairperson
Wheeling Park High School
Wheeling, West Virginia

Elaine Keller
Mathematics Teacher
Mathematics Curriculum Director K–12
Northwest Local Schools
Canal Fulton, Ohio

Sheila A. Kotter
Mathematics Educator
River Ridge High School
New Port Richey, Florida

Frank Lear
Mathematics Department Chair
Cleveland High School
Cleveland, Tennessee

Jennifer Lewis
Mathematics Teacher
Triad High School
Troy, Illinois

Catherine McCarthy
Mathematics Teacher
Glen Ridge High School
Glen Ridge, New Jersey

Jacqueline Palmquist
Mathematics Department Chair
Waubonsie Valley High School
Aurora, Illinois

Thom Schacher
Mathematics Teacher
Otsego High School
Otsego, Michigan

Laurie Shappee
Teacher/Mathematics Coordinator
Larson Middle School
Troy, Michigan

Jennifer J. Southers
Mathematics Teacher
Hillcrest High School
Simpsonville, South Carolina

Sue Steinbeck
Mathematics Department Chair
Parkersburg High School
Parkersburg, West Virginia

Kathleen D. Van Sise
Mathematics Teacher
Mandarin High School
Jacksonville, Florida

Karen Wiedman
Mathematics Teacher
Taylorville High School
Taylorville, Illinois

Florida Algebra 2

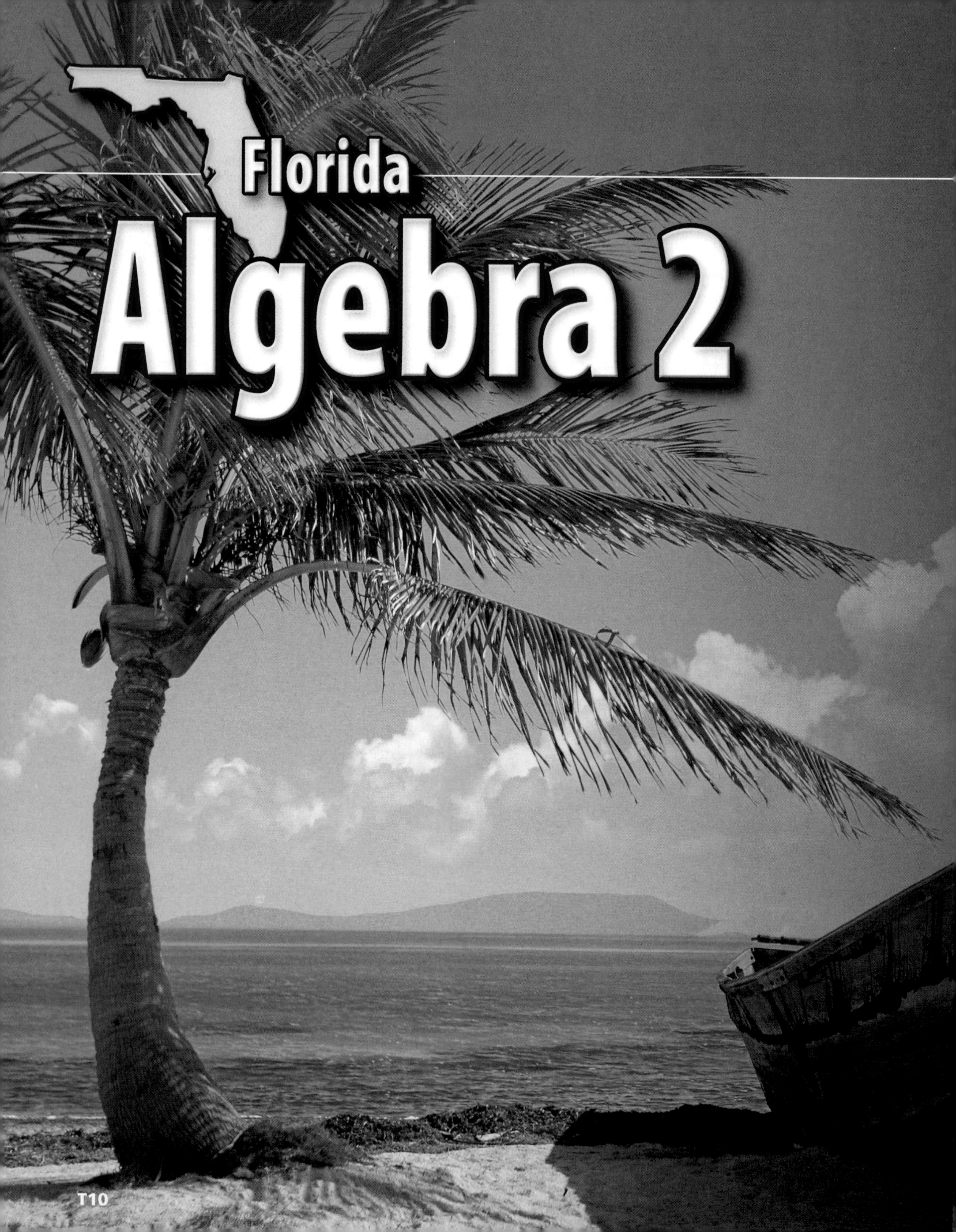

- Digital and Print Solutions
- Support for Every Learner
- Support for Every Teacher
- Data-Driven Decision Making
- Built on Research
- Preparation for College and Work
- NGSSS Correlation

FL Math Online

TURN THE PAGE
for your NEW
mathematics
curriculum solution . . .

Florida's Next Generation Classroom

Seamless Digital and Print Solutions

Whole-Class Instruction

Problem-Centered Connections

Inquiry-Based Learning

Diagnostic, Formative, and Summative Assessment

Independent Learning and Practice

Individualized Study

Fully-Supported Teacher Planning

Data Management and Reporting

Professional Development

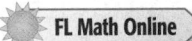

FL Math Online

Balanced Instruction

Florida Algebra 2 is designed to provide students with a balanced approach to mathematics, including: conceptual understanding, procedural fluency, strategic competence, adaptive reasoning, and productive disposition.

Concepts and Skills

In each chapter, students use multiple representations to communicate conceptual understanding. Meaningful practice helps students carry out procedures accurately and efficiently.

Depth and Rigor

Students participate in mathematics discourse and apply higher-order thinking skills. Collaborative activities, writing exercises, and multi-step word problems challenge all students to formulate, represent, reflect upon, and explain their solutions.

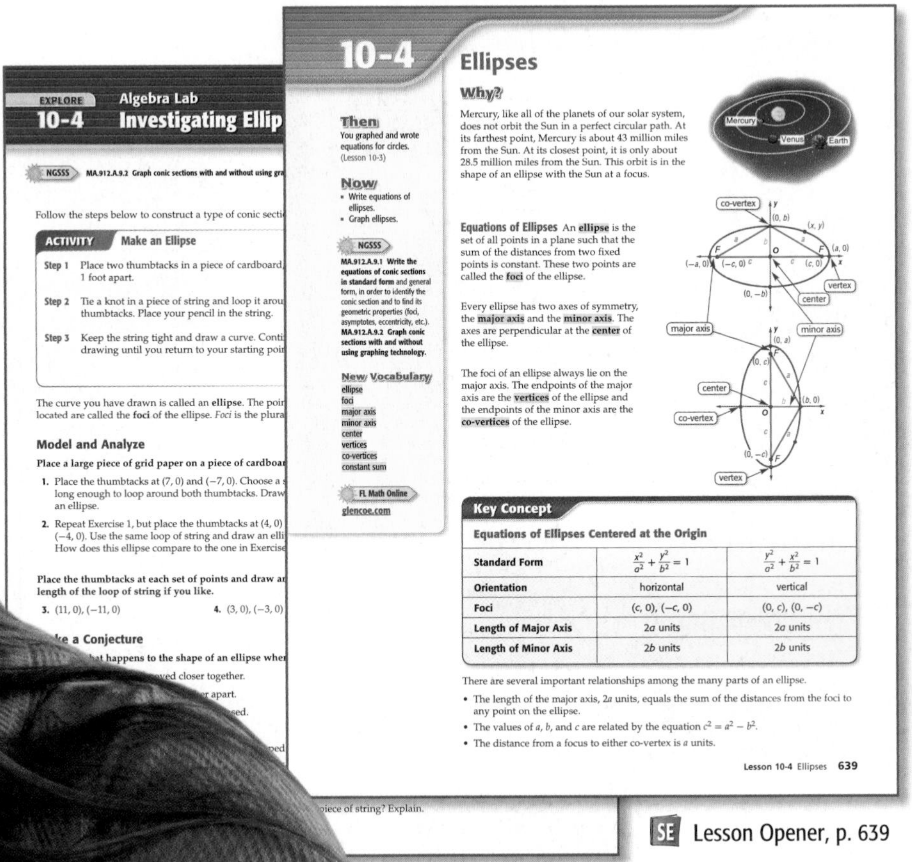

EXPLORE 10-4 Algebra Lab
Investigating Ellip

NGSSS MA.912.A.9.2 Graph conic sections with and without using gra

Follow the steps below to construct a type of conic secti

ACTIVITY Make an Ellipse

Step 1 Place two thumbtacks in a piece of cardboard, 1 foot apart.

Step 2 Tie a knot in a piece of string and loop it arou thumbtacks. Place your pencil in the string.

Step 3 Keep the string tight and draw a curve. Conti drawing until you return to your starting poi

The curve you have drawn is called an **ellipse**. The poi located are called the **foci** of the ellipse. *Foci* is the plura

Model and Analyze

Place a large piece of grid paper on a piece of cardboa

1. Place the thumbtacks at (7, 0) and (−7, 0). Choose a long enough to loop around both thumbtacks. Draw an ellipse.
2. Repeat Exercise 1, but place the thumbtacks at (4, 0) (−4, 0). Use the same loop of string and draw an elli How does this ellipse compare to the one in Exercise

Place the thumbtacks at each set of points and draw a length of the loop of string if you like.

3. (11, 0), (−11, 0)
4. (3, 0), (−3, 0)

ke a Conjecture

piece of string? Explain.

10-4 Ellipses

Why?

Mercury, like all of the planets of our solar system, does not orbit the Sun in a perfect circular path. At its farthest point, Mercury is about 43 million miles from the Sun. At its closest point, it is only about 28.5 million miles from the Sun. This orbit is in the shape of an ellipse with the Sun at a focus.

Then
You graphed and wrote equations for circles. (Lesson 10-3)

Now
- Write equations of ellipses.
- Graph ellipses.

NGSSS
MA.912.A.9.1 Write the equations of conic sections in standard form and general form, in order to identify the conic section and to find its geometric properties (foci, asymptotes, eccentricity, etc.).
MA.912.A.9.2 Graph conic sections with and without using graphing technology.

New Vocabulary
ellipse
foci
major axis
minor axis
center
vertices
co-vertices
constant sum

FL Math Online
glencoe.com

Equations of Ellipses An **ellipse** is the set of all points in a plane such that the sum of the distances from two fixed points is constant. These two points are called the **foci** of the ellipse.

Every ellipse has two axes of symmetry, the **major axis** and the **minor axis**. The axes are perpendicular at the **center** of the ellipse.

The foci of an ellipse always lie on the major axis. The endpoints of the major axis are the **vertices** of the ellipse and the endpoints of the minor axis are the **co-vertices** of the ellipse.

Key Concept

Equations of Ellipses Centered at the Origin

Standard Form	$\frac{x^2}{a^2} + \frac{y^2}{b^2} = 1$	$\frac{y^2}{a^2} + \frac{x^2}{b^2} = 1$
Orientation	horizontal	vertical
Foci	(c, 0), (−c, 0)	(0, c), (0, −c)
Length of Major Axis	$2a$ units	$2a$ units
Length of Minor Axis	$2b$ units	$2b$ units

There are several important relationships among the many parts of an ellipse.

- The length of the major axis, $2a$ units, equals the sum of the distances from the foci to any point on the ellipse.
- The values of a, b, and c are related by the equation $c^2 = a^2 - b^2$.
- The distance from a focus to either co-vertex is a units.

Lesson 10-4 Ellipses 639

SE Lesson Opener, p. 639

SE Algebra Lab, p. 638

Problem-Based Learning

A wealth of problem-solving opportunities include:

- **Multiple Representations** in every chapter
- **H**igher **O**rder **T**hinking exercises for every lesson
- Worked-out examples that follow a four-step plan
- **Problem-Solving Strategy** tips throughout the chapter
- Problem-solving/test-taking strategy in every chapter
- **Word-Problem Practice** masters for every lesson

Write each equation in standard form. Identify *A*, *B*, and *C*.

44. $\frac{x+5}{3} = -2y + 4$ 45. $\frac{4x-1}{5} = 8y - 12$ 46. $\frac{-2x-8}{3} = -12y + 18$

Find the *x*-intercept and the *y*-intercept of the graph of each equation.

47. $\frac{6x+15}{4} = 3y - 12$ 48. $\frac{-8x+12}{3} = 16y + 24$ 49. $\frac{15x+20}{4} = \frac{3y+6}{5}$

Real-World Link

Bake sales, car washes, and coupon campaigns are among the most popular ideas to make money for schools because it gives students something to offer, making it easier to approach people.

Source: School-Link

50. **FUNDRAISING** The Freshman Class Student Council wanted to raise money by giving car washes. The students spent \$10 on supplies and charged \$2 per car wash.
    a. Write an equation to model the situation.
    b. Graph the equation.
    c. How much money did they earn after 20 car washes?
    d. How many car washes are needed for them to earn \$100?

51. **MULTIPLE REPRESENTATIONS** Consider the following linear functions.

$$f(x) = -2x + 4 \qquad g(x) = 6 \qquad h(x) = \frac{1}{3}x + 5$$

   a. **GRAPHICAL** Graph the linear functions on separate graphs.
   b. **TABULAR** Use the graphs to complete the table.

Function	One-to-One	Onto
$f(x) = -2x + 4$		
$g(x) = 6$		
$h(x) = \frac{1}{3}x + 5$		

   c. **VERBAL** Are all linear functions one-to-one and/or onto? Explain your reasoning.

H.O.T. Problems Use Higher-Order Thinking Skills

52. **CHALLENGE** Write a function with an *x*-intercept of $(a, 0)$ and a *y*-intercept of $(0, b)$.

53. **OPEN ENDED** Write an equation of a line with an *x*-intercept of 3.

54. **REASONING** Determine whether an equation of the form $x = a$, where a is a constant, is *sometimes*, *always*, or *never* a function. Explain your reasoning.

55. **WHICH ONE DOESN'T BELONG?** Of the four equations shown, identify the one that does not belong. Explain your reasoning.

$y = 2x + 3$	$2x + y = 5$	$y = 5$	$y = 2xy$

56. **WRITING IN MATH** Consider the graph of the relationship between hours worked and earnings.
    a. Why do you think the graph of this relationship should only be in the first quadrant?
    b. Provide another example of a situation in which only the first quadrant is needed. Explain your reasoning.

Lesson 2-2 Linear Relations and Functions **73**

SE Multiple Representations, p. 73

Content that Connects

Labs maintain learner motivation. Algebra Labs introduce and reinforce concepts using manipulatives like algebra tiles. Graphing Technology Labs allow students to explore concepts using graphing calculators.

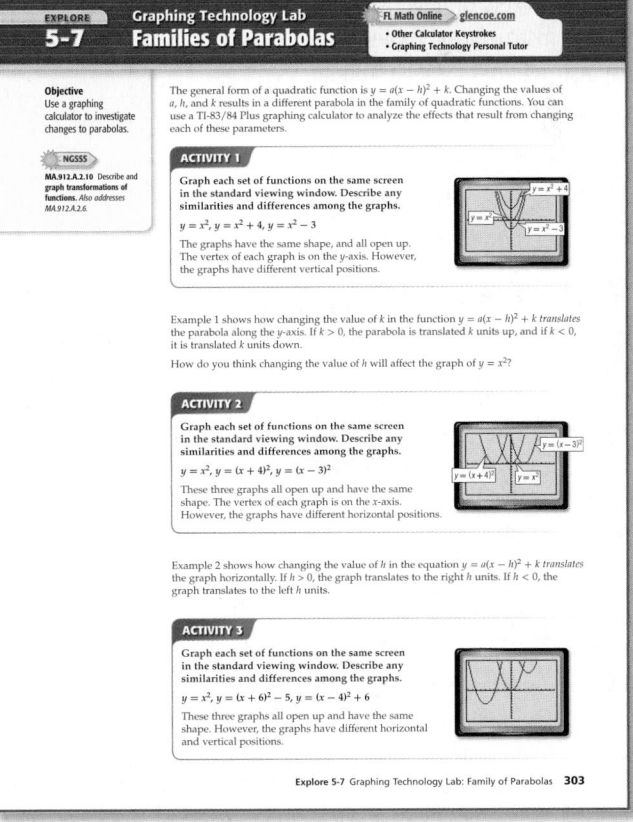

EXPLORE **5-7** Graphing Technology Lab

Families of Parabolas

FL Math Online glencoe.com
- Other Calculator Keystrokes
- Graphing Technology Personal Tutor

Objective
Use a graphing calculator to investigate changes to parabolas.

NGSSS
MA.912.A.2.10 Describe and graph transformations of functions. *Also addresses MA.912.A.2.6.*

The general form of a quadratic function is $y = a(x - h)^2 + k$. Changing the values of a, h, and k results in a different parabola in the family of quadratic functions. You can use a TI-83/84 Plus graphing calculator to analyze the effects that result from changing each of these parameters.

ACTIVITY 1

Graph each set of functions on the same screen in the standard viewing window. Describe any similarities and differences among the graphs.

$y = x^2$, $y = x^2 + 4$, $y = x^2 - 3$

The graphs have the same shape, and all open up. The vertex of each graph is on the *y*-axis. However, the graphs have different vertical positions.

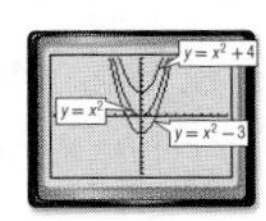

Example 1 shows how changing the value of k in the function $y = a(x - h)^2 + k$ *translates* the parabola along the *y*-axis. If $k > 0$, the parabola is translated k units up, and if $k < 0$, it is translated k units down.

How do you think changing the value of h will affect the graph of $y = x^2$?

ACTIVITY 2

Graph each set of functions on the same screen in the standard viewing window. Describe any similarities and differences among the graphs.

$y = x^2$, $y = (x + 4)^2$, $y = (x - 3)^2$

These three graphs all open up and have the same shape. The vertex of each graph is on the *x*-axis. However, the graphs have different horizontal positions.

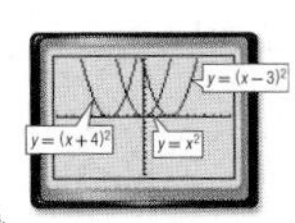

Example 2 shows how changing the value of h in the equation $y = a(x - h)^2 + k$ *translates* the graph horizontally. If $h > 0$, the graph translates to the right h units. If $h < 0$, the graph translates to the left h units.

ACTIVITY 3

Graph each set of functions on the same screen in the standard viewing window. Describe any similarities and differences among the graphs.

$y = x^2$, $y = (x + 6)^2 - 5$, $y = (x - 4)^2 + 6$

These three graphs all open up and have the same shape. However, the graphs have different horizontal and vertical positions.

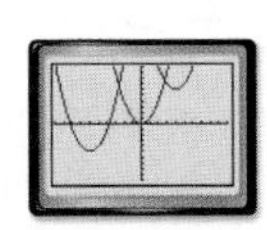

Explore 5-7 Graphing Technology Lab: Family of Parabolas **303**

SE Graphing Technology Lab, p. 303

Differentiated Instruction

AL Approaching Grade Level
OL On Grade Level
BL Beyond Grade Level
ELL English Language Learners

Florida Algebra 2 fully supports the 3-tier RtI model with print and digital resources to diagnose students, identify areas of need, and conduct short, frequent assessments for accurate data-driven decision making. Every lesson provides easy-to-use resources that consider the special needs of all students.

RtI: Response to Intervention

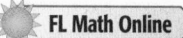

FL Math Online

TIER 1 Daily Intervention

OL ON GRADE LEVEL

Core instruction targets on-level students. Comprehensive instructional materials help you personalize instruction for every student.

- Diagnostic Teaching
- Options for Differentiated Instruction
- Leveled Exercise Sets, Resources, and Technology
- Data-Driven Decision Making

BL BEYOND GRADE LEVEL

At every step, resources and assignments are available for advanced learners.

- Higher-Order Thinking Questions
- Differentiated Homework Options
- Enrichment Masters
- Differentiated Instruction Extension

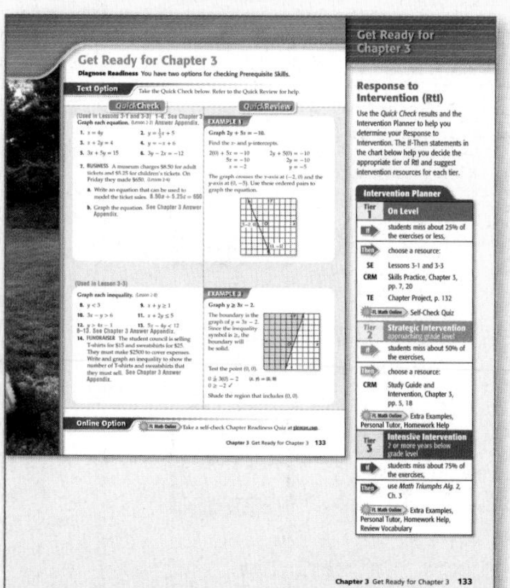

Get Ready for Chapter 3

Response to Intervention (RtI)

Intervention Planner

TE Get Ready for the Chapter, p. 133

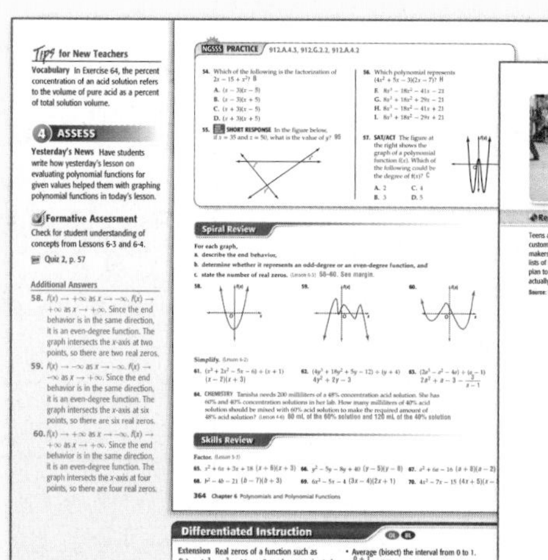

Differentiated Instruction

TE Differentiated Instruction, p. 364

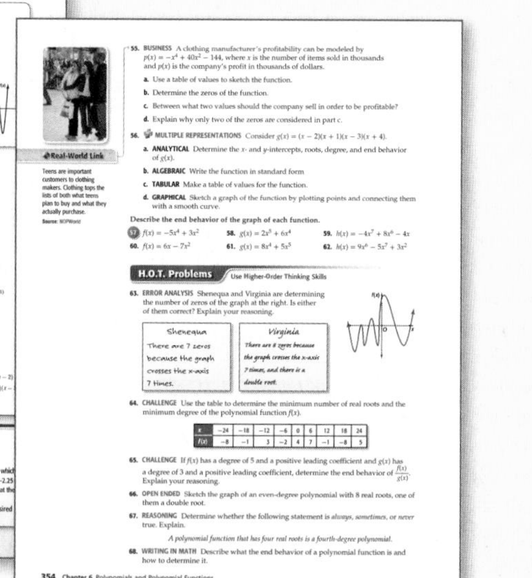

H.O.T. Problems

SE H.O.T. Problems, p. 354

ELL English Language Learners

Comprehensive resources are found throughout the program.

- Teacher Edition with strategies to modify activities and lesson content
- eGlossary with definitions for each vocabulary word in 13 languages
- Book with English and Spanish audio

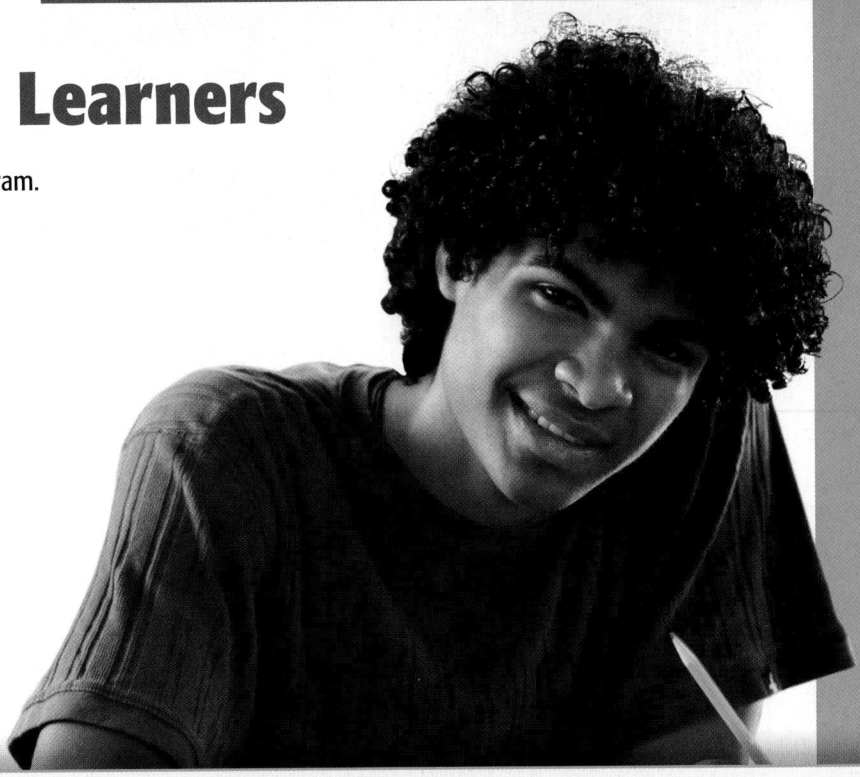

TIER 2 Strategic Intervention

AL APPROACHING GRADE LEVEL

Teachers can choose from a myriad of intervention tips and ancillary materials to support struggling learners.

- Using Manipulatives
- Alternate Teaching Strategies
- Online resources, including animations, examples, and Personal Tutors

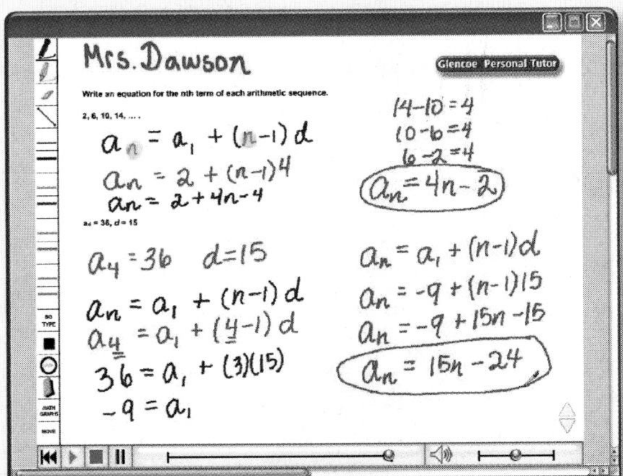

FL Math Online Online Personal Tutor

TIER 3 Intensive Intervention

AL FAR BELOW GRADE LEVEL

For students who are far below grade level, ***Math Triumphs*** provides step-by-step instruction, vocabulary support, and meaningful practice.

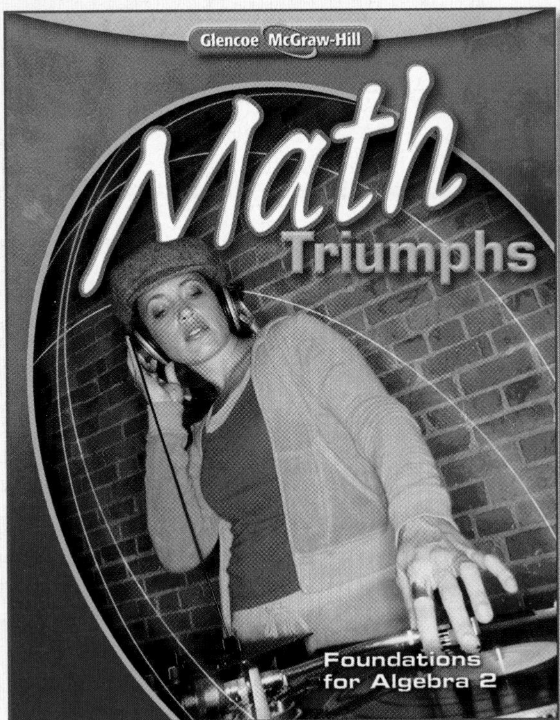

Florida Teacher Success

Florida Algebra 2 offers teachers many ways to plan and deliver quality instruction, from the Teacher Edition to online assets to quality professional development. The seamless integration of print and digital tools puts the teacher in control.

Plan

At-a-glance planning and scheduling tools show the mathematics objectives, suggested pacing, vertical alignment, and NGSSS correlations.

ConnectED is the online all-in-one portal that allows you to build lesson plans with easy-to-find print and digital resources. Search for activities to meet a variety of learning modalities, and then personalize instruction with print and digital resources.

Teach

Robust teacher materials help you build rigorous lessons that address concepts in depth.

ConnectED helps you teach with technology by providing virtual manipulatives, lesson animations, whole-class presentations, and more.

ConnectED provides students with anywhere, anytime access to student resources and tools, including eBooks, tutorials, animations, and the eGlossary.

Assess

Florida Algebra 2 helps you apply a continuous improvement model for student progress.

ConnectED includes AdvanceTracker, which allows you to assign online assessments, track student progress, generate reports, and differentiate instruction.

Exam*View*® Assessment Suite lets you create and customize assessments correlated to the NGSSS. Format tests in one or two columns, and include multiple choice, short, extended, and gridded response items.

e PROFESSIONAL DEVELOPMENT

McGraw-Hill Professional Development (MHPD) provides comprehensive programs for growth in mathematics education that target teachers, math coaches, and administrators. Support includes initial and on-going training.

eInservice

A program walkthrough of ***Florida Algebra 2*** components, technology, and ancillaries.

eClips Video Library

Videos for specific concepts and general instructional strategies including demonstrations and commentaries by experts in the field.

eConsultant Website

Provides customized, online support to educators using ***Florida Algebra 2***.

eWorkshops Onsite

Onsite, coach-led video and activity-based workshops.

eTech Training

Short animated or video modules that explain the use of ***Florida Algebra 2*** technology components.

Ready-Access Math

More than 200 lessons allows for a custom professional development series, or a special 45–60 minute after-school session.

Florida Professional Development Needs	eInservice	eClips Video Library	eConsultant Website	eWorkshops Onsite	eTech Training	Ready-Access Math	Accredited Online Courses*	Consultants
Initial Professional Development	●							●
Administration and Interpretation of Assessment	●			●				
Coaches, Mentors, Peers				●		●		
Class Modeling	●	●	●				●	
Ongoing Professional Development		●	●	●	●	●	●	

*Available for purchase at mhpdonline.com.

Comprehensive Assessment

Florida Algebra 2 offers frequent and meaningful assessment built into the curriculum structure and teacher support materials. Digital assessment solutions offer the same quality assessments, plus options to create, customize, administer, and instantly grade assessments.

1 Diagnostic

Initial Assessment

Assess students' knowledge at the beginning of the year with *Florida Diagnostic and Placement Tests.* The results and scoring guides identify students who may need additional resources to meet grade-level standards.

Entry-Level Assessment

Assess students' prior knowledge at the beginning of a chapter or lesson.

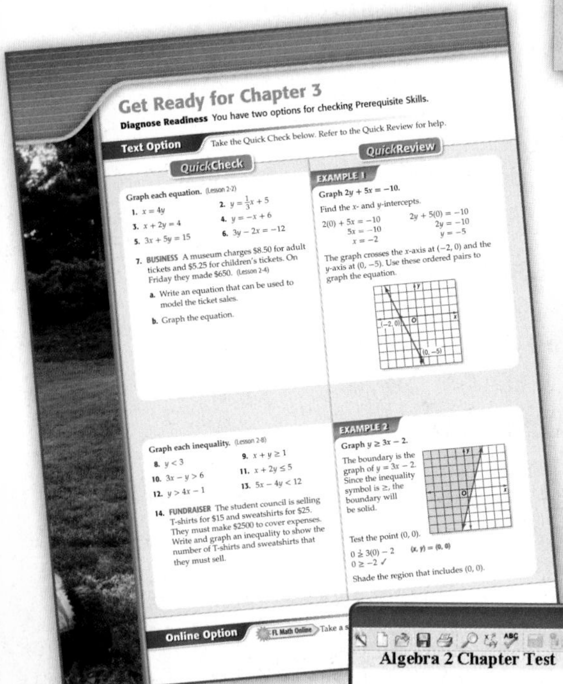

Get Ready for Chapter 3

Diagnose Readiness You have two options for checking Prerequisite Skills.

Text Option Take the Quick Check below. Refer to the Quick Review for help.

QuickCheck

Graph each equation. (Lesson 2-2)

1. $x = 4y$
2. $y = \frac{1}{3}x + 5$
3. $x + 2y = 4$
4. $y = -x + 6$
5. $3x + 5y = 15$
6. $3y - 2x = -12$
7. **BUSINESS** A museum charges $8.50 for adult tickets and $5.25 for children's tickets. On Friday they made $650. (Lesson 2-4)
   a. Write an equation that can be used to model the ticket sales.
   b. Graph the equation.

Graph each inequality. (Lesson 2-8)

8. $y < 3$
9. $x + y \geq 1$
10. $3x - y > 6$
11. $x + 2y \leq 5$
12. $y > 4x - 1$
13. $5x - 4y < 12$
14. **FUNDRAISER** The student council is selling T-shirts for $15 and sweatshirts for $25. They must make $2500 to cover expenses. Write and graph an inequality to show the number of T-shirts and sweatshirts that they must sell.

QuickReview

EXAMPLE 1

Graph $2y + 5x = -10$.

Find the x- and y-intercepts.

$2(0) + 5x = -10$, $5x = -10$, $x = -2$

$2y + 5(0) = -10$, $2y = -10$, $y = -5$

The graph crosses the x-axis at $(-2, 0)$ and the y-axis at $(0, -5)$. Use these ordered pairs to graph the equation.

EXAMPLE 2

Graph $y \geq 3x - 2$.

The boundary is the graph of $y = 3x - 2$. Since the inequality symbol is $\geq$, the boundary will be solid.

Test the point $(0, 0)$.

$0 \overset{?}{\geq} 3(0) - 2$ $\quad (x, y) = (0, 0)$

$0 \geq -2$ ✓

Shade the region that includes $(0, 0)$.

Online Option FL Math Online Take a s

SE Get Ready for the Chapter, p. 133

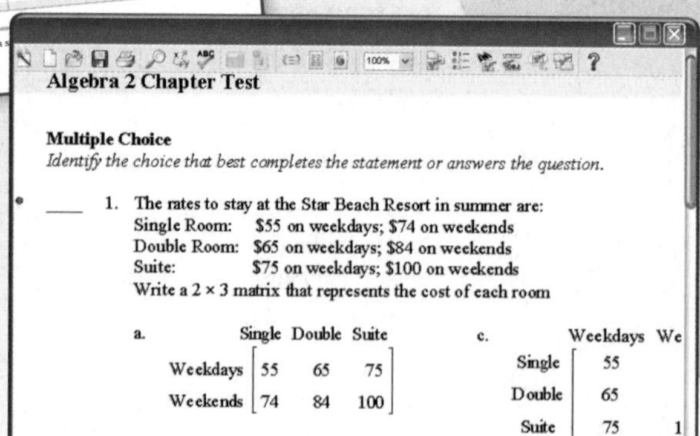

Algebra 2 Chapter Test

Multiple Choice

Identify the choice that best completes the statement or answers the question.

____ 1. The rates to stay at the Star Beach Resort in summer are:
Single Room: $55 on weekdays; $74 on weekends
Double Room: $65 on weekdays; $84 on weekends
Suite: $75 on weekdays; $100 on weekends
Write a 2 × 3 matrix that represents the cost of each room

a.

	Single	Double	Suite
Weekdays	55	65	75
Weekends	74	84	100

c.

	Weekdays	We
Single	55	
Double	65	
Suite	75	1

b.

	Single	Double	Suite
Weekdays	55	75	84

d.

	Weekdays	We
Single	55	

FL Math Online Exam*View*® Assessment Suite

2 Formative

Progress Monitoring

Determine if students are progressing adequately as you teach each lesson. Use the assessments to differentiate lesson instruction and practice.

Student Edition

- Guided Practice
- Check Your Understanding
- H.O.T. Problems
- Mid-Chapter Quiz
- Study Guide and Review

Additional Resources

- Chapter Resource Masters
- Mid-Chapter Test
- 4 Quizzes
- Standardized Test Practice

Digital Resources

ExamView Assessment Suite

FL Math Online glencoe.com

- Self-Check Quizzes
- Mid-Chapter Test
- Study Guide and Review

3 Summative

Summative Assessment

Assess student success in learning the concepts in each chapter. Use remediation suggestions to address problem areas.

Student Edition

- Practice Test
- Standardized Test Practice

Additional Resources

- Chapter Resource Masters
- Vocabulary Test
- 6 Leveled Chapter Tests
- Extended Response Test

Digital Resources

ExamView Assessment Suite

- Chapter Tests
- Cumulative Standardized Test Practice

FL Math Online glencoe.com

- Chapter Tests
- Cumulative Standardized Test Practice

Solid Foundation

Continuous research with teachers, students, academics, and leading experts builds a solid foundation for ***Florida Algebra 2***. Expert authors, reviewers, and consultants contribute their knowledge and experience throughout the program development.

Developmental

Pre-Development

- State and local standards evaluation
- Relevant data from recognized sources
- Qualitative market research
- Current academic content research

Formative

Pre-Publication

- Pedagogical research base
- Classroom field tests
- Teacher advisory boards
- Academics, authors, consultants, and reviewers

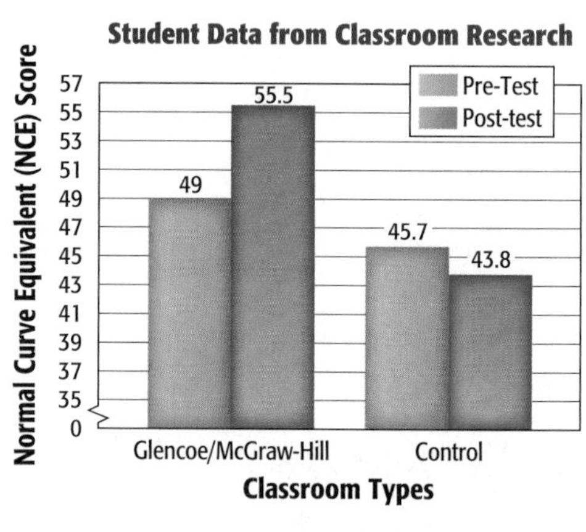

Students using a field test version of the ***Glencoe Algebra 2*** program (experimental group) had higher pre-test to post-test gains than students using other textbook programs (control group).

Summative

Post-Publication

- Evidence of increased test scores
- Quasi-experimental program efficacy research
- Longitudinal studies
- Qualitative program evaluations

FL Math Online Find detailed information about our classroom research results.

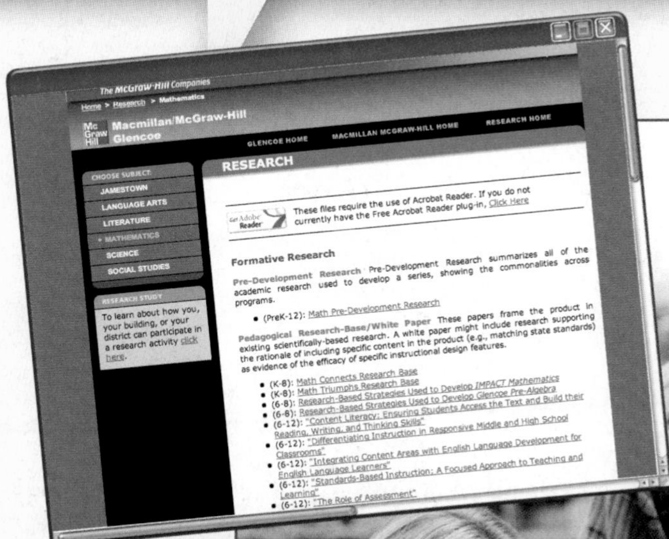

True PreK–12 Curriculum Alignment

Content

Students experience an articulated, coherent sequence of content from elementary to high school. Content is introduced, reinforced, and assessed at appropriate steps in each grade and throughout the series, eliminating gaps and unnecessary duplication.

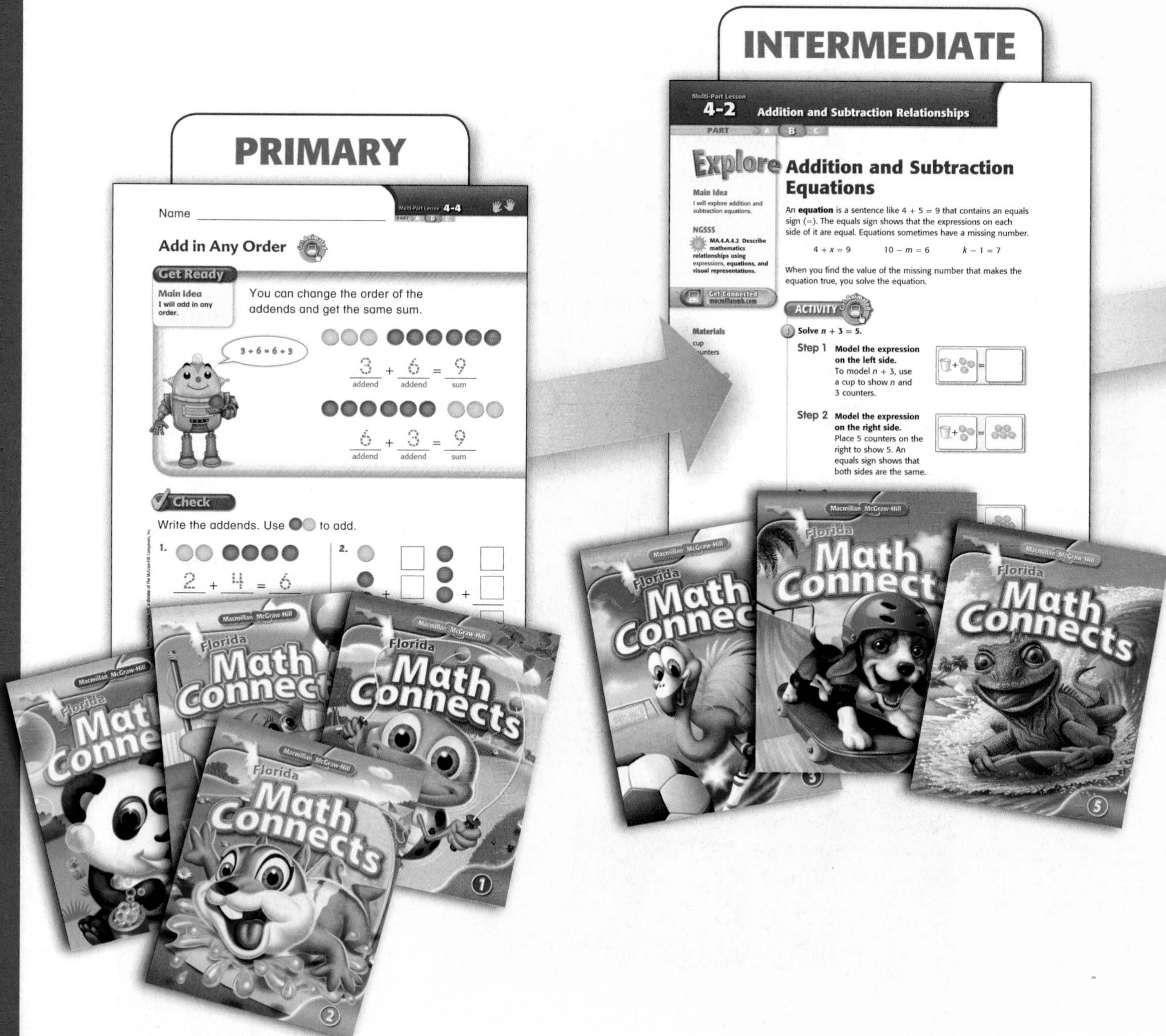

Instruction

A uniform approach to presenting concepts and skills, along with common authors, vocabulary, technology, lesson planning, and manipulatives, allows smooth transitions for students between grade levels and less reteaching for teachers.

Appearance

The student pages have a consistent visual design–elementary through high school. This logical page design makes student reading and learning easier. Common labels and color schemes support student progress from grade to grade.

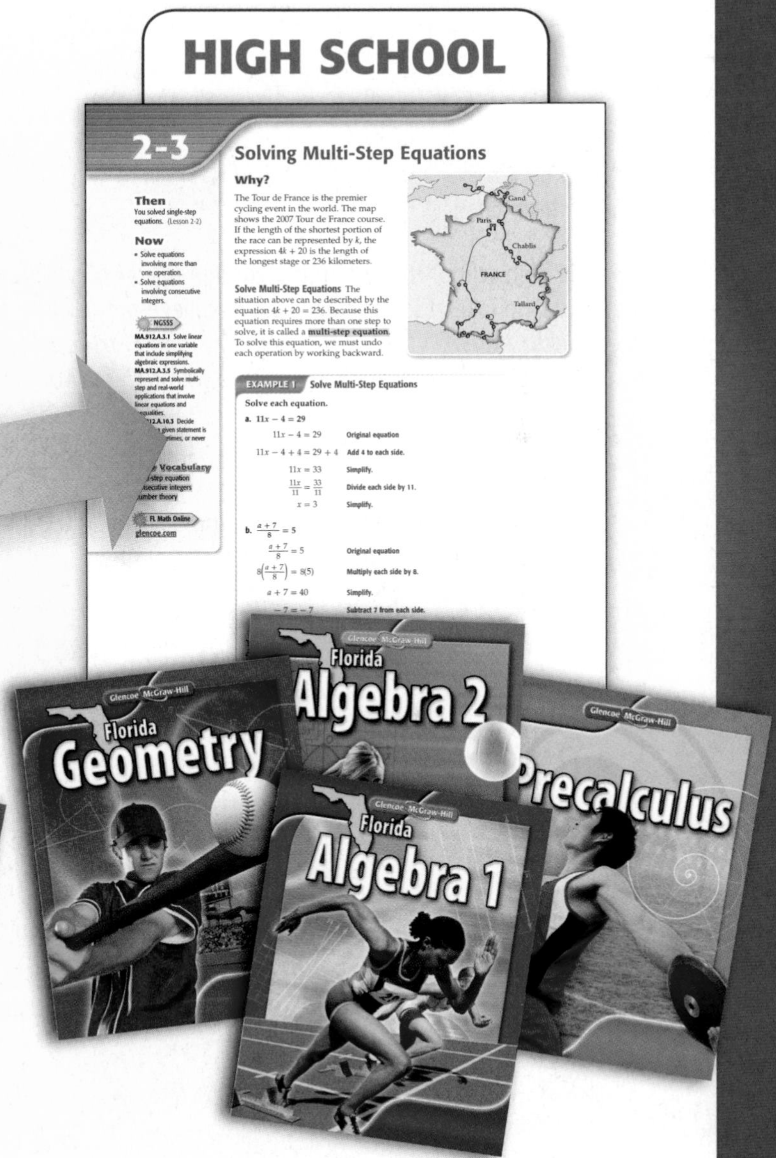

College and Work Readiness

College Readiness

A strong high school curriculum is a good predictor of college readiness (Adelman, 2006). Students who take at least three years of college-preparatory mathematics using programs like ***Florida Algebra 1***, ***Florida Geometry***, and ***Florida Algebra 2*** are less likely to need remedial courses in college than students who do not (Abraham & Creech, 2002).

David Conley at the University of Oregon developed the following criteria for college readiness:

Key Content Knowledge

Florida Algebra 1, Florida Geometry, and ***Florida Algebra 2*** have been aligned to rigorous state and national standards, including the *NCTM Principles & Standards for School Mathematics*, the College Board Standards for College Success, and the American Diploma Project's Benchmarks. Correlations to these standards can be found at **glencoe.com**.

Habits of Mind

These include critical thinking skills such as analysis, interpretation, problem solving, and reasoning. Students can hone critical higher-order thinking skills through the use of **H.O.T. (Higher Order Thinking) Problems**.

Sources:

Abraham, A. & Creech, J. (2002). *Reducing Remedial Education*. Atlanta, GA: Southern Regional Education Board.

ACT, Inc. (2006). *Readiness for College and Readiness for Work: Same or Different?* Iowa City, IA

The Conference Board, Corporate Voices for Working Families, the Partnership for 21st Century Skills, and the Society for Human Resource Management (2006). *Are They Really Ready to Work?*

Conley, D. (2007). *Toward a More Comprehensive Conception of College Readiness*. Eugene, OR: Educational Policy Improvement Center.

Work Readiness

Does College Readiness Lead to Success in the Workplace?

Work readiness is the ability of entry-level employees to add value in front-line jobs. The U.S. Chamber of Commerce has created a National Work Readiness Credential that involves nine sub-skills, one of which is using math to solve problems. In a recent study, 53.5% of employers who responded reported that high school graduate entrants into the workforce are "deficient" in mathematics, while 30.4% felt that knowledge of mathematics is "very important."
(*Are They Really Ready to Work?,* 2006)

What About Students Who Don't Plan to Go to College?

In today's technological world, math is no longer just for students who go to college. ACT compared the skills needed to succeed as a freshman in college and those needed for job-training programs. They found that students need to be educated to a comparable level in algebra, geometry, data analysis, and statistics for success in either situation (ACT, 2006).

Contextual Skills

These are practical skills like understanding the admissions process and financial aid, placement testing, and communicating with professors. Throughout each Glencoe mathematics program, students are required to write, explain, justify, prove, and analyze.

Academic Behaviors

These include general skills such as reading comprehension, time management, note-taking, and metacognition. **Reading Math** tips and **Vocabulary Links** help students with reading comprehension. **Study Notebooks** and **Anticipation Guides** help students build note-taking skills and aid with metacognition.

NGSSS Next Generation Sunshine State Standards, Algebra 2 and Algebra 2 Honors

Correlated to *Florida Algebra 2*

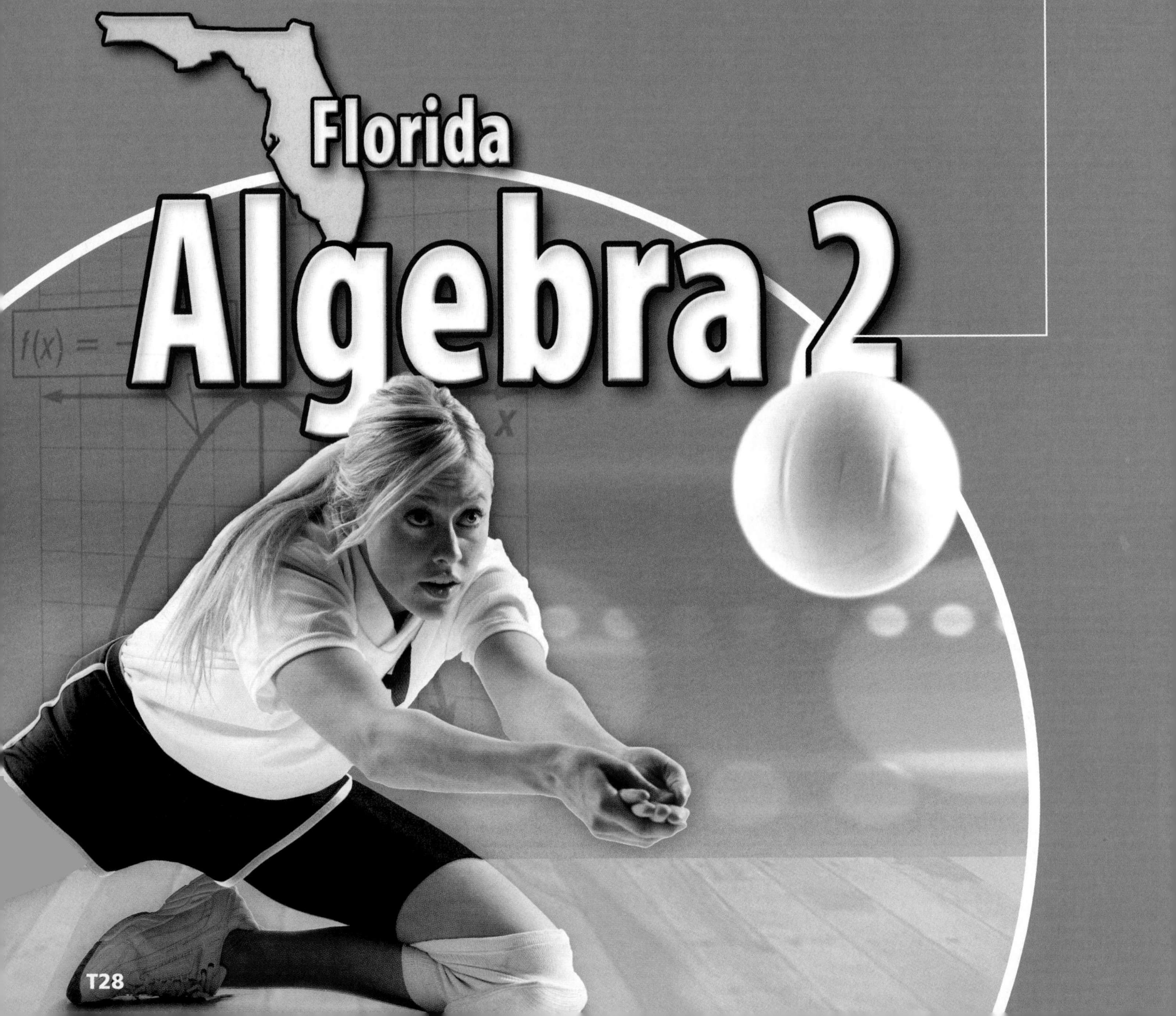

Lessons in which the benchmark is the primary focus are indicated in **bold.**
* – These benchmarks are included in the Course Description for Algebra 2 Honors only.
** – These benchmarks are not included in the Course Description for Algebra 2, but they do align with the ADP Algebra II End-of-Course Exam Content Standards.

Benchmark Code	Benchmark	Lesson(s)	Page Number(s)
LA.910.1.6.1	The student will use new vocabulary that is introduced and taught directly;	Throughout the text; for example, Explore 1-6, 4-1, Extend 6-1, 9-3, 13-2	40, 185–191, 340, 569–575, 817–823
LA.910.4.2.1	The student will write in a variety of informational/ expository forms, including a variety of technical documents (e.g., how-to-manuals, procedures, assembly directions);	Throughout the text; for example, 3-3, 6-2, 8-1, 9-2	151–157, 341–347, 475–482, 562–568
MA.912.A.1.6	Identify the real and imaginary parts of complex numbers and perform basic operations.	5-4	276–282
MA.912.A.2.5	Graph absolute value equations and inequalities in two variables.	2-6, 2-7, 2-8	101–107, 109–116, 117–121
MA.912.A.2.6	Identify and graph common functions (including but not limited to linear, rational, quadratic, cubic, radical, absolute value).	**2-2, 2-6,** Explore 2-7, 2-7, **2-8, 5-1,** Explore 5-7, 6-4, **7-3, Extend 7-4**	**69–77, 101–107,** 108, 109–116, **117–121, 249–257,** 303, 357–364, **424–430, 437**
MA.912.A.2.7	Perform operations (addition, subtraction, division and multiplication) of functions algebraically, numerically, and graphically.	7-1	409–416
MA.912.A.2.8	Determine the composition of functions.	7-1	409–416
MA.912.A.2.9*	Recognize, interpret, and graph functions defined piece-wise, with and without technology.	**2-6**	**101–107**
MA.912.A.2.10	Describe and graph transformations of functions	2-7, Explore 5-7, **5-7,** 8-1, 8-3, 9-4	**109–116,** 303–304, **305–310,** 475–482, 492–499, 577–584
MA.912.A.2.11	Solve problems involving functions and their inverses.	7-2, Extend 7-2	417–422, 423
MA.912.A.2.12	Solve problems using direct, inverse, and joint variations.	Extend 2-4, **9-5**	90, **586–593**
MA.912.A.3.3	Solve literal equations for a specified variable.	**1-3**	**18–25**
MA.912.A.3.6	Solve and graph the solutions of absolute value equations and inequalities with one variable.	**1-4, 1-6**	**27–32, 41–48**
MA.912.A.3.10	Write an equation of a line given any of the following information: two points on the line, its slope and one point on the line, or its graph. Also, find an equation of a new line parallel to a given line, or perpendicular to a given line, through a given point on the new line.	**2-4**	**83–89**
MA.912.A.3.14	Solve systems of linear equations and inequalities in two and three variables using graphical, substitution, and elimination methods.	**3-1, Extend 3-1, 3-2, 3-3, Extend 3-3**, 3-4, **3-5,** 4-5, 4-6, Extend 4-6	**135–141, 142, 143–150, 151–157, 158,** 160–166, **167–173**, 220–228, 229–235, 236

Benchmark Code	Benchmark	Lesson(s)	Page Number(s)
MA.912.A.3.15	Solve real-world problems involving systems of linear equations and inequalities in two and three variables.	**3-1, 3-2, 3-3,** 3-4, 3-5	**135–141, 143–150, 151–157,** 160–166, 167–173
MA.912.A.4.3	Factor polynomial expressions.	**5-3,** 6-5, 6-6, 6-7, 6-8	**268–275**, 368–375, 377–382, 383–390, 391–397
MA.912.A.4.4	Divide polynomials by monomials and polynomials with various techniques, including synthetic division.	**6-2**	**341–347**
MA.912.A.4.5	Graph polynomial functions with and without technology and describe end behavior.	6-3, Extend 6-3, **6-4,** Extend 6-4	348–355, 356, **357–364,** 365
MA.912.A.4.6	Use theorems of polynomial behavior (including but not limited to the Fundamental Theorem of Algebra, Remainder Theorem, the Rational Root Theorem, Descartes' Rule of Signs, and the Conjugate Root Theorem) to find the zeros of a polynomial function.	**6-6, 6-7, 6-8**	**377–382, 383–390, 391–397**
MA.912.A.4.7	Write a polynomial equation for a given set of real and/or complex roots.	**Extend 5-6,** 6-7	**301–302,** 383–390
MA.912.A.4.8	Describe the relationships among the solutions of an equation, the zeros of a function, the x-intercepts of a graph, and the factors of a polynomial expression, with and without technology	**Extend 2-2,** 6-6, 6-7, 6-8	**75,** 377–382, 383–390, 391–397
MA.912.A.4.9	Use graphing technology to find approximate solutions for polynomial equations.	**Extend 5-2, Extend 6-5**	**267, 376**
MA.912.A.4.10	Use polynomial equations to solve real-world problems.	6-5	368–375
MA.912.A.4.11*	Solve a polynomial inequality by examining the graph with and without the use of technology.	**5-8,** Extend 6-5	**312–318,** 376
MA.912.A.4.12*	Apply the Binomial Theorem.	**11-6**	**721–725**
MA.912.A.5.2	Add subtract, multiply, and divide rational expressions.	**9-1, 9-2**	**553–561, 562–568**
MA.912.A.5.3	Simplify complex fractions.	**9-1**	**553–561**
MA.912.A.5.5	Solve rational equations.	**9-6, Extend 9-6**	**594–602, 603–604**
MA.912.A.5.6*	Identify removable and non-removable discontinuities, and vertical, horizontal, and oblique asymptotes of a graph of a rational function, find the zeros, and graph the function.	9-3, **9-4, Extend 9-4**	569–575, **577–584, 585**
MA.912.A.6.2	Add, subtract, multiply and divide radical expressions (square roots and higher).	**7-5**	**439–445**
MA.912.A.6.3	Simplify expressions using properties of rational exponents.	**7-6**	**446–452**
MA.912.A.6.4	Convert between rational exponent and radical forms of expressions.	**7-6**	**446–452**
MA.912.A.6.5	Solve equations that contain radical expressions.	7-6, **7-7, Extend 7-7**	446–452, **453–459, 460–461**

Benchmark Code	Benchmark	Lesson(s)	Page Number(s)
MA.912.A.7.3	Solve quadratic equations over the real numbers by completing the square.	**5-5,** Extend 5-5	**284–290,** 291
MA.912.A.7.4	Use the discriminant to determine the nature of the roots of a quadratic equation.	**5-6**	**282–300**
MA.912.A.7.5	Solve quadratic equations over the complex number system.	5-5, 5-6	284–290, 282–300
MA.912.A.7.6	Identify the axis of symmetry, vertex, domain, range and intercept(s) for a given parabola.	**5-1,** 5-2	**249–257**, 259–266
MA.912.A.7.7*	Solve non-linear systems of equations with and without using technology.	**10-7**	**662–667**
MA.912.A.7.10*	Use graphing technology to find approximate solutions of quadratic equations.	5-2, **Extend 5-2**	259–266, **267**
MA.912.A.8.1	Define exponential and logarithmic functions and determine their relationship	**8-3**	**492–499**
MA.912.A.8.2	Define and use the properties of logarithms to simplify logarithmic expressions and to find their approximate values.	8-3, 8-4, **8-5, 8-6, 8-7**	492–499, 502–507, **509–515, 516–522, 525–531**
MA.912.A.8.3	Graph exponential and logarithmic functions.	**8-1,** 8-3	**475–482,** 492–499
MA.912.A.8.5	Solve logarithmic and exponential equations.	Explore 8-2, 8-2, **8-4,** Extend 8-6, 8-8	483–484, 485–491, **502–507,** 523–524, 533–539
MA.912.A.8.6	Use the change of base formula.	8-6	516–522
MA.912.A.8.7	Solve applications of exponential growth and decay.	8-1, 8-7, 8-8	475–482, 525–531, 533–539
MA.912.A.9.1*	Write the equations of conic sections in standard form and general form, in order to identify the conic section and to find its geometric properties (foci, asymptotes, eccentricity, etc.).	**10-2,** Explore 10-3, **10-3, 10-4, 10-5,** 10-6, Extend 10-6	**623–629,** 630, **631–637, 639–646, 648–655,** 656–660, 661
MA.912.A.9.2*	Graph conic sections with and without using graphing technology.	**10-2,** Explore 10-3, **10-3,** Explore 10-4, **10-4, 10-5,** Extend 10-6	**623–629**, 630, **631–637**, 638, **639–646, 648–655**, 661
MA.912.A.10.3	Decide whether a given statement is always, sometimes, or never true (statements involving linear or quadratic expressions, equations, or inequalities rational or radical expressions or logarithmic or exponential functions).	2-1, 2-2, 2-3, 5-1, 5-3, 5-6, 5-8, 7-4, 7-7, 8-1, 8-2, 8-7, 9-1	61–97, 69–74, 76–82, 249–257, 268–275, 292–300, 312–318, 431–436, 453–459, 475–482, 485–491, 525–531, 553–561
MA.912.D.11.1	Define arithmetic and geometric sequences and series.	**11-1, 11-2, 11-3, 11-4,** 11-5	**691–687, 688–695, 696–702, 705–711**, 714–719

Benchmark Code	Benchmark	Lesson(s)	Page Number(s)
MA.912.D.11.2*	Use sigma notation to describe series.	**11-2,** 11-3, **11-4**	**688–695,** 696–702, **705–711**
MA.912.D.11.3	Find specified terms of arithmetic and geometric sequences.	**11-1, 11-2, 11-3**	**691–687, 688–695, 696–702**
MA.912.D.11.4*	Find partial sums of arithmetic and geometric series, and find sums of infinite convergent geometric series. Use Sigma notation where applicable.	**11-2, 11-3, 11-4**	**688–695, 696–702, 705–711**
MA.912.G.6.6*	Given the center and the radius, find the equation of a circle in the coordinate plane or given the equation of a circle in center-radius form, state the center and the radius of the circle.	**Explore 10-3, 10-3**	**630, 631–637**
MA.912.G.6.7*	Given the equation of a circle in center-radius form or given the center and the radius of a circle, sketch the graph of the circle.	**10-3**	**631–637**
MA.912.A.1.1**	Know equivalent forms of real numbers (including integer exponents and radicals, percents, scientific notation, absolute value, rational numbers, irrational numbers).	**1-2, Concepts and Skills Bank 2, Concepts and Skills Bank 3**	**11–17, 995–996, 997**
MA.912.A.1.3**	Simplify real number expressions using the laws of exponents.	6-1	333–339
MA.912.A.1.4**	Perform operations on real numbers (including integer exponents, radicals, percents, scientific notation, absolute value, rational numbers, irrational numbers) using multi-step and real-world problems.	1-1, 1-2, 1-4, 6-1, 7-5, Concepts and Skills Bank 2, Concepts and Skills Bank 3	5–10, 11–17, 27–32, 333–339, 439–445, 995–996, 997
MA.912.A.1.7**	Represent complex numbers geometrically.	5-4	276–282
MA.912.A.2.9**	Recognize, interpret, and graph functions defined piece-wise with and without technology.	**2-6**	**101–107**
MA.912.A.5.6**	Identify removable and non-removable discontinuities, and vertical, horizontal, and oblique asymptotes of a graph of a rational function, find the zeros, and graph the function.	**9-4**	**577–584**
MA.912.A.5.7**	Solve real-world problems involving rational equations (mixture, distance, work, interest, and ratio).	8-2, **9-6**	485–491, **594–602**
MA.912.A.7.9**	Solve optimization problems.	**3-4**	**160–166**

Everglades National Park

CHAPTER 0

Preparing for Advanced Algebra

Chapter 0 Support

Helping You Learn

- **Vocabulary** P2, P4, P9, P12, P15
- **Key Concepts** P9, P12, P13
- **Exercises** P5, P6, P8, P10, P14, P16, P18

FL Math Online

- **Personal Tutor** P4, P5, P6, P7, P8, P9, P10, P12, P13, P14, P15, P16, P17, P18
- **Self-Check Quizzes** P4, P6, P7, P9, P12, P15, P17
- **Extra Examples** P4, P6, P7, P9, P12, P15, P17
- **Homework Help** P4, P6, P7, P9, P12, P15, P17

Unit 1
Linear Relations and Functions

CHAPTER 1

Equations and Inequalities

Chapter 1 Support

Unit 1
Linear Relations and Functions

CHAPTER 2

Linear Relations and Functions

Chapter 2 Support

Helping You Learn

FL Math Online

NGSSS PRACTICE

Unit 1
Linear Relations and Functions

CHAPTER 3

Systems of Equations and Inequalities

NGSSS

Chapter 3 Support

Helping You Learn

FL Math Online

NGSSS PRACTICE

Matrices

Chapter 4 Support

Helping You Learn

FL Math Online

NGSSS PRACTICE

Unit 2
Quadratic, Polynomial, and Radical Functions and Relations

CHAPTER 5

Quadratic Functions and Relations

Chapter 5 Support

Helping You Learn

FL Math Online

NGSSS PRACTICE

Unit 2
Quadratic, Polynomial, and Radical Functions and Relations

CHAPTER 6

Polynomials and Polynomial Functions

NGSSS

Chapter 6 Support

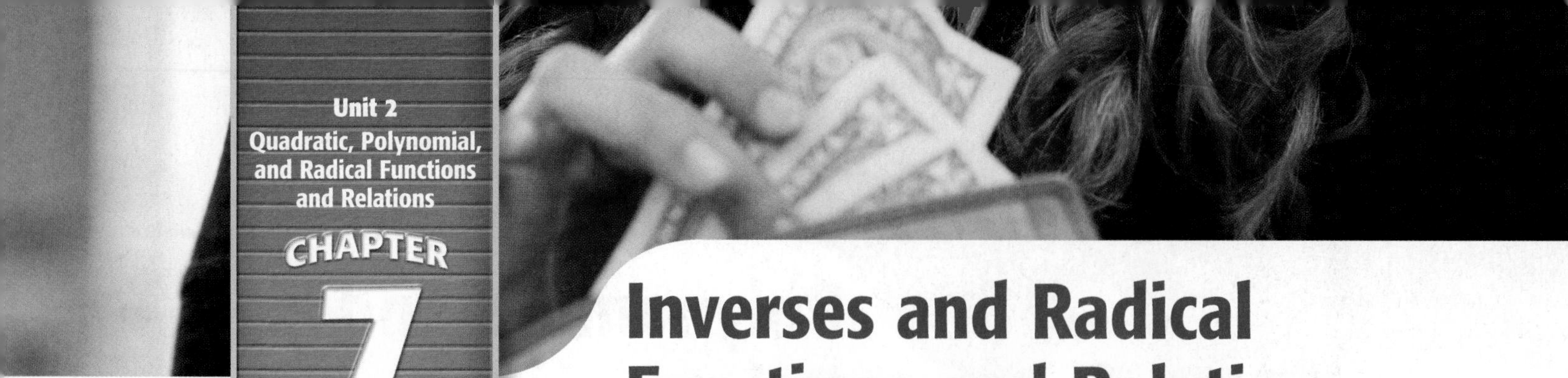

Unit 2
Quadratic, Polynomial, and Radical Functions and Relations

CHAPTER 7

Inverses and Radical Functions and Relations

NGSSS

Chapter 7 Support

Helping You Learn

FL Math Online

NGSSS PRACTICE

Unit 3
Advanced Functions and Relations

CHAPTER 8

Exponential and Logarithmic Functions and Relations

NGSSS

Chapter 8 Support

Helping You Learn

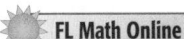

FL Math Online

NGSSS PRACTICE

Unit 3
Advanced Functions and Relations

CHAPTER 9

Rational Functions and Relations

Chapter 9 Support

Helping You Learn

FL Math Online

NGSSS PRACTICE

Unit 3
Advanced Functions and Relations

CHAPTER 10

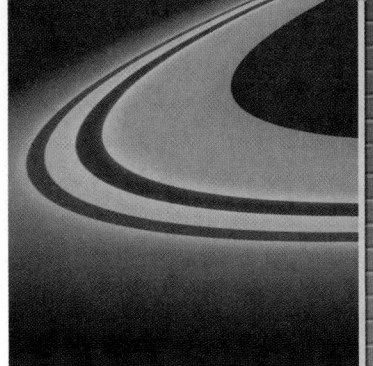

Conic Sections

Chapter 10 Support

Unit 4
Discrete Mathematics

CHAPTER 11

Sequences and Series

Chapter 11 Support

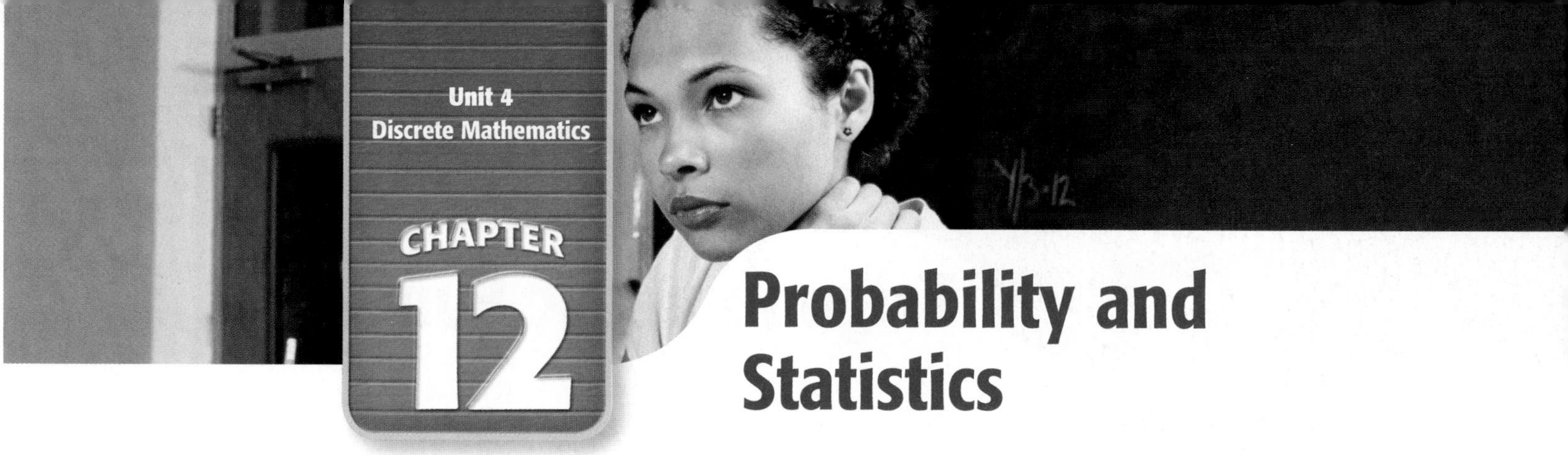

Probability and Statistics

NGSSS

Chapter 12 Support

Helping You Learn

FL Math Online

NGSSS PRACTICE

Unit 5
Trigonometry

CHAPTER 13

Trigonometric Functions

NGSSS

Chapter 13 Support

Helping You Learn

FL Math Online

NGSSS PRACTICE

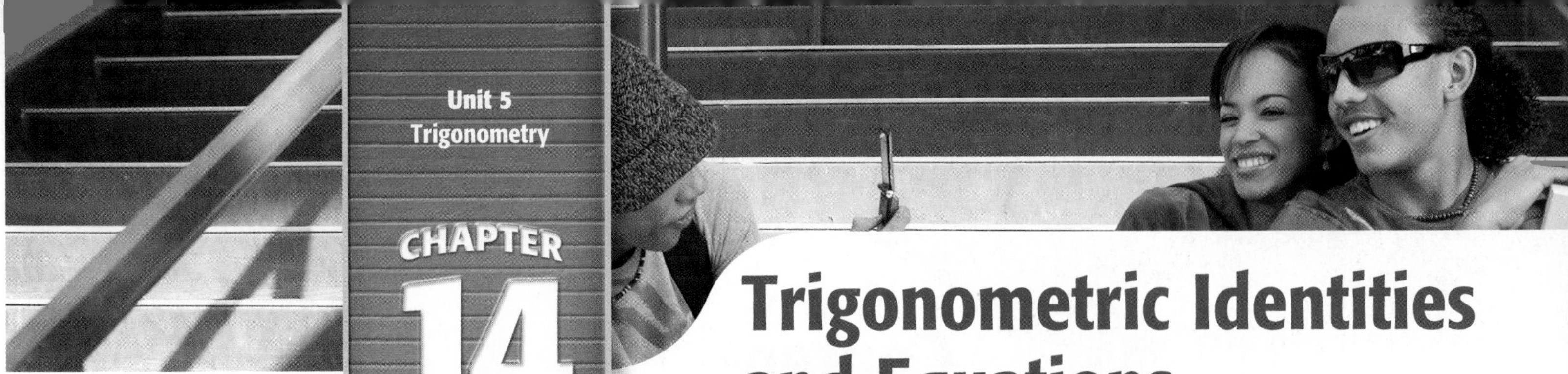

Unit 5 Trigonometry

CHAPTER 14

Trigonometric Identities and Equations

NGSSS

Chapter 14 Support

Helping You Learn

- **New Vocabulary** 891, 919
- **Key Concepts** 891, 898, 899, 904, 911, 912
- **Guided Practice** 892, 893, 898, 899, 900, 904, 905, 906, 911, 912, 913, 914, 919, 920, 921, 922
- **Check Your Understanding** 894, 900, 906, 915, 922
- **Multiple Representations** 895, 908
- **H.O.T. Problems** 896, 902, 908, 916, 924
- **Skills Review** 897, 903, 909, 917, 925

FL Math Online

- **Get Animated** 888
- **Personal Tutor** 891, 892, 893, 898, 899, 900, 904, 905, 906, 911, 912, 913, 914, 919, 920, 921, 922
- **Self-Check Quizzes** 891, 898, 904, 911, 919
- **Extra Examples** 891, 898, 904, 911, 919
- **Homework Help** 891, 898, 904, 911, 919
- **Graphing Technology Personal Tutor** 918

NGSSS PRACTICE

- **Extended Response** 925, 933
- **Multiple Choice** 897, 899, 900, 903, 909, 910, 917, 925, 929, 932
- **Short/Gridded Response** 909, 917, 930, 931, 933
- **Worked-Out Example** 899

Student Handbook

Contents

WELCOME TO

Florida Algebra 2

Master Florida's Next Generation Sunshine State Standards in 3 Easy Steps

1 Practice the Standards Daily

> **NGSSS**
>
> **Reinforcement of MA.912.A.3.4 Solve** and graph simple and **compound inequalities in one variable and be able to justify each step in a solution.**

Each lesson addresses the Florida Next Generation Sunshine State Standards covered in that lesson.

NGSSS PRACTICE Questions aligned to the standards provide you with ongoing opportunities to sharpen your test-taking skills.

2 Practice the Standards throughout the Chapter

NGSSS EXAMPLE Every chapter contains a completely worked-out NGSSS Example to help you solve problems that are similar to those you might find on Florida assessments.

NGSSS PRACTICE Every chapter contains two full pages of NGSSS Practice with Test-Taking Tips.

3 Practice the Standards

WEEKLY STANDARDS REVIEW Use pages FL1–FL20 to practice questions that review NGSSS. Lesson references are included should you need a little refresher.

Florida Reviewers

Each Florida Reviewer reviewed at least two chapters of the Student Edition, giving feedback and suggestions for improving the effectiveness of the mathematics instruction.

Candace Acosta
Mathematics Teacher
Treasure Coast High School
Pt. St. Lucie, FL

Marisol Amoedo
Mathematics Teacher
Cypress Bay High School
Weston, FL

Bob Coleman
Mathematics Teacher
Cobb Middle School
Tallahassee, Florida

Michael D. Cuddy
Mathematics Instructor
Zypherhills High School
Zypherhills, Florida

Donna A. Evans
Mathematics Teacher
B.T. Washington High School
Pensacola, FL

Deidra Jackson
Mathematics Instructor
Apopka High School
Apopka, FL

Sheila A. Kotter
Mathematics Educator
River Ridge High School
New Port Richey, Florida

Judith J. Miller
Mathematics Department Head
Leon High School
Tallahassee, FL

John H. Nygren
Math Teacher
Dunedin High School
Dunedin, FL

Kathleen A. Sklarew
Math Department Chairperson, Geometry Teacher
Indian Ridge Middle
Davie, FL

Laura R. Tulowiecki
Math Teacher/Dept. Chair
Lake Gibson High School
Lakeland, FL

Kathleen D. Van Sise
Mathematics Teacher
Mandarin High School
Jacksonville, Florida

NGSSS

Weekly Standards Review

The **Weekly Standards Review** helps your students review the NGSSS.

NGSSS Weekly Standards Review

How Should I Study?

The good news is that you've been studying all along a little bit every day. Here are some of the ways your textbook has been preparing you.

- **Every Day** Each lesson has practice questions that cover the NGSSS.
- **Every Week** The Mid-Chapter Quiz and Practice Test has several practice questions. Also, the following pages include a section called Weekly Standards Review. These pages give you practice questions that cover the NGSSS.
- **Every Chapter** Each chapter has two full pages of practice questions that review the NGSSS.

How Should I Use the Weekly Standards Review?

The Weekly Standards Review consists of 20 weeks of practice problems that cover the NGSSS. You should plan to complete one practice page each week to help you review the NGSSS.

If you are struggling with any of the items, lesson references are provided so that you can go back and review from the pages in your textbook.

Multiple-Choice Items

For multiple-choice questions, you will select the correct response from four answer choices. Your teacher will provide you with an answer sheet to fill in your answer choices.

Gridded Response Items

For gridded-response questions, you will grid in your response. Your teacher will provide an answer sheet.

Week 1

Monday

1. Solve the equation $-5x + 4 + 2x = 7x - 5 - x$. (Lesson 1-3) **(912.A.3.1)** A

Ⓐ 1
Ⓑ -3
Ⓒ 7
Ⓓ 0

Tuesday

2. Which statement is sometimes true regarding the slopes of parallel lines? (Lesson 2-3) **(912.A.10.3)** I

Ⓕ The slopes are different.
Ⓖ The slopes are opposite reciprocals.
Ⓗ The slopes are the same.
Ⓘ The slopes are undefined.

Wednesday

3. Megan and three of her friends go to the movies. They each spend \$5 on a movie ticket and \$3.25 on snacks. How much did they spend in all? (Lesson 1-2) **(912.A.3.2)** B

Ⓐ \$23.25
Ⓑ \$33.00
Ⓒ \$37.50
Ⓓ \$41.25

Thursday

4. Solve the inequality $|b - 9| < 5$. (Lesson 1-4) **(912.A.3.6)** H

Ⓕ $b < 14$
Ⓖ $b > 4$
Ⓗ $4 < b < 14$
Ⓘ $b < 4$ or $b > 14$

Friday

5. **GRIDDED RESPONSE** What is the slope of a line that is perpendicular to the one shown below? (Lesson 2-4) **(912.A.10.3)** $-1/4$

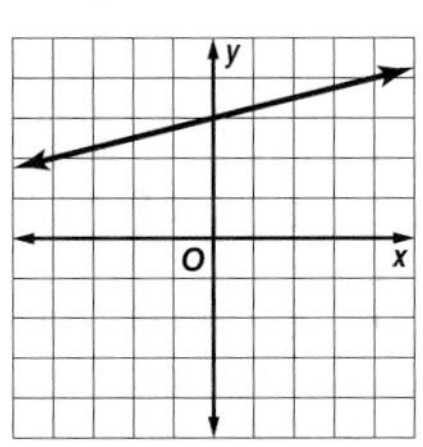

Choice Analysis

1. A. Correct
B. Arithmetic error, combine like terms on each side of equals first
C. Arithmetic error
D. Arithmetic error

2. F. This statement is never true.
G. This statement is never true.
H. This statement is always true.
I. Correct

3. A. Need snack for all 4, not just one
B. Correct
C. Need snack for 4 not 5
D. Only 4 going out not 5

4. F. Forgot that $b - 9$ could be negative
G. Forgot that $b - 9$ could be positive
H. Correct
I. Solved with the inequality $>$ instead of $<$

Week 1

NEED EXTRA HELP?					
If You Missed Question...	1	2	3	4	5
Go to Lesson...	1-3	2-3	1-2	1-4	2-4
For Help with NGSSS...	912.A.3.1	912.A.10.3	912.A.3.2	912.A.3.6	912.A.10.3

Choice Analysis

1. A. This graph would be shifted 2 units left of the origin.

B. This graph would be centered at the origin.

C. Correct

D. This graph would be shifted up 2 units.

2. F. Square root function

G. Absolute value function

H. Linear function

I. Correct

3. A. The endpoints are incorrect.

B. The endpoints are incorrect, and the second inequality sign is incorrect.

C. Correct

D. The value $t = 4$ should not be included.

4. F. Correct

G. This graph is a horizontal line.

H. This graph is a straight line.

I. This graph is shaped like a U.

Weekly Standards Review

Week 2

Monday

1. Which function is shown in the graph below? (Lesson 2-7) **(912.A.2.5)** C

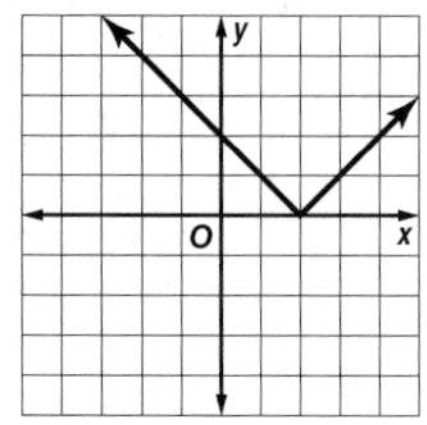

Ⓐ $y = |x + 2|$
Ⓑ $y = |x|$
Ⓒ $y = |x - 2|$
Ⓓ $y = |x| + 2$

Tuesday

2. Which of the following functions represents the parent quadratic function? (Lesson 2-2) **(912.A.2.6)** I

Ⓕ $y = \sqrt{x}$
Ⓖ $y = |x|$
Ⓗ $y = x$
Ⓘ $y = x^2$

Wednesday

3. A campground charges $8 to rent a canoe for the first hour and $4 for each additional hour. Suppose Heather spends $20 to rent a canoe. Which of the following describes how long she rents the canoe? (Lesson 2-6) **(912.A.2.9)** C

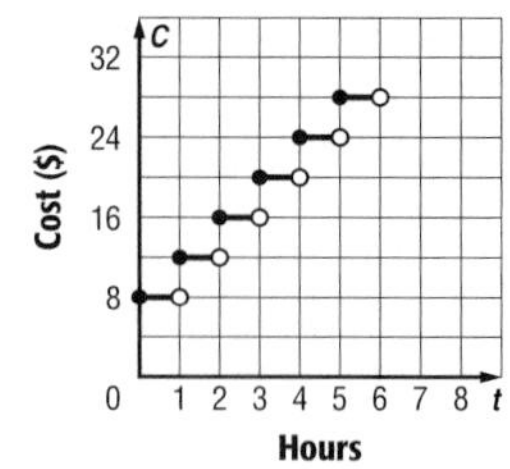

Ⓐ $2 \leq t < 3$
Ⓑ $2 \leq t \leq 3$
Ⓒ $3 \leq t < 4$
Ⓓ $3 \leq t \leq 4$

Thursday

4. Which parent function has a graph shaped like a V and a range of real numbers greater than or equal to 0? (Lesson 2-7) **(912.A.2.6)** F

Ⓕ absolute value function
Ⓖ constant function
Ⓗ linear function
Ⓘ quadratic function

Friday

5. **GRIDDED RESPONSE** Consider the point (2, 4) on $y = x^2$. If you reflect $y = x^2$ across the x-axis, what would be the y-coordinate of the reflected point? (Lesson 2-7) **(912.A.2.10)** −4

Week 2

NEED EXTRA HELP?					
If You Missed Question...	1	2	3	4	5
Go to Lesson...	2-7	2-2	2-6	2-7	2-7
For Help with NGSSS...	912.A.2.5	912.A.2.6	912.A.2.9	912.A.2.6	912.A.2.10

Week 3

Monday

1. How does the graph of the function $y = |x + 1| - 5$ compare with the graph of the parent absolute value function $y = |x|$? (Lesson 2-7) **(912.A.2.10)** D

Ⓐ translated 1 unit right and 5 units down
Ⓑ translated 1 unit left and 5 units up
Ⓒ translated 1 unit right and 5 units up
Ⓓ translated 1 unit left and 5 units down

Wednesday

3. Which inequality is shown in the graph at the right? (Lesson 2-8) **(912.A.2.5)** B

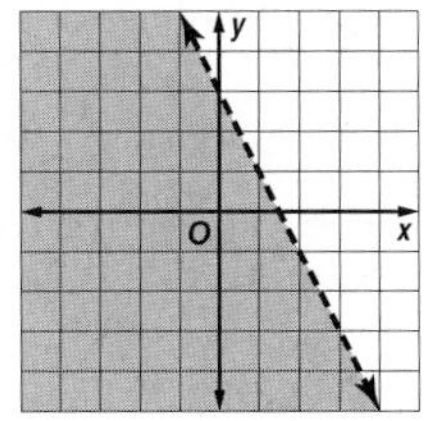

Ⓐ $y < -\frac{1}{2}x + 3$
Ⓑ $y < -2x + 3$
Ⓒ $y > -2x + 3$
Ⓓ $y > \frac{1}{2}x - 3$

Tuesday

2. Which of the following describes the parent quadratic function shifted up 3 units and right 2 units? (Lesson 2-7) **(912.A.2.10)** F

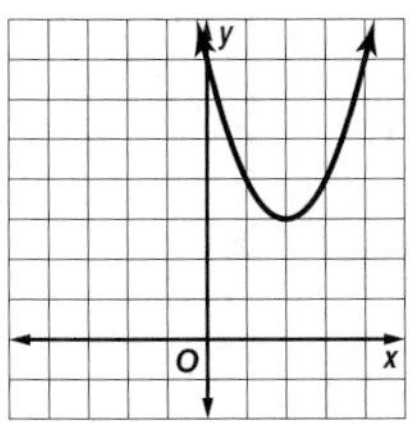

Ⓕ $y = (x - 2)^2 + 3$
Ⓖ $y = (x + 2)^2 + 3$
Ⓗ $y = (x - 2)^2 - 3$
Ⓘ $y = (x - 3)^2 + 2$

Thursday

4. The function below shows the cost of shipping a package. How much does it cost to ship a package that weighs 4 pounds 9 ounces? (Lesson 2-6) **(912.A.2.9)** H

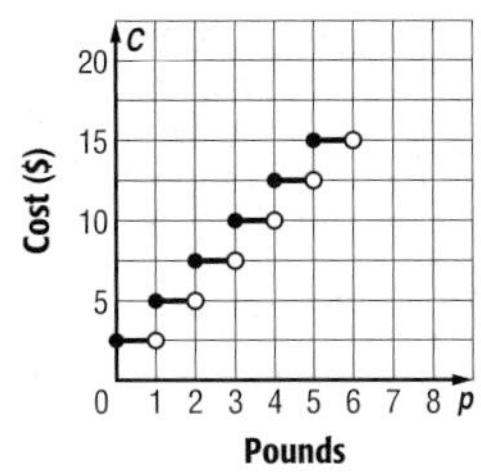

Ⓕ \$2.50
Ⓖ \$10.00
Ⓗ \$12.50
Ⓘ \$15.00

Friday

5. **GRIDDED RESPONSE** Rodrigo can spend no more than \$20 at the video arcade. He spends \$6 on snacks and \$2 on each game he plays. What is the greatest number of games Rodrigo can play? (Lesson 1-4) **(912.A.3.6)** 7

Choice Analysis

1. **A.** The function is shifted left.
B. The function is shifted down.
C. The function is shifted left and down.
D. Correct

2. **F.** Correct
G. This function is on the other side of *y*-axis
H. The vertex of this function is in the 3rd quadrant
I. This function has vertex at (3,2)

3. **A.** The slope is incorrect.
B. Correct
C. The lower half plane is shaded.
D. The line representing the inequality and the inequality symbol are incorrect.

4. **F.** This is the cost for a package that weighs less than 1 pound
G. This is the cost for a package that weighs 3 to 4 lbs
H. Correct
I. This is the cost for a package that weighs 5 lbs

Week 3

NEED EXTRA HELP?					
If You Missed Question...	1	2	3	4	5
Go to Lesson...	2-7	2-7	2-8	2-6	1-4
For Help with NGSSS...	912.A.2.10	912.A.2.10	912.A.2.5	912.A.2.9	912.A.3.6

Choice Analysis

1. **A.** The signs are incorrect.
   B. The *x*- and *y*-coordinates are reversed.
   C. There is a sign error.
   D. Correct

2. **F.** The constants of each inequality are reversed.
   G. The coefficients of *x* and *y* are incorrect.
   H. The inequality symbols are incorrect.
   I. Correct

3. **A.** The system is also independent.
   B. The system has a point of intersection, so it is consistent.
   C. Correct
   D. The lines are not the same, so they are independent.

4. **F.** The sum of the angle measures would be 45°, not 90°.
   G. This is the measure of $\angle 2$.
   H. Correct
   I. Since $m\angle 2$ would be 32° and the sum is 96°.

Weekly Standards Review

Week 4

Monday

1. Solve the system of equations.

$$y = 5x + 10$$
$$y = -3x - 14$$

(Lesson 3-2) **(912.A.3.14)** D

Ⓐ (3, 5)
Ⓑ (−5, −3)
Ⓒ (−3, 5)
Ⓓ (−3, −5)

Tuesday

2. Jennifer earns $8 per hour babysitting and $12 per hour mowing lawns. She works no more than 30 hours per week at both jobs combined. If Jennifer wants to earn at least $225 next week, which system of inequalities can she use to model the situation? Let *x* represent the number of hours spent babysitting and *y* the number of hours spent mowing lawns. (Lesson 3-3) **(912.A.3.15)** I

Ⓕ $x + y \le 225$
$8x + 12y \ge 30$
Ⓖ $x + y \le 30$
$12x + 8y \ge 225$
Ⓗ $x + y < 30$
$8x + 12y > 225$
Ⓘ $x + y \le 30$
$8x + 12y \ge 225$

Wednesday

3. Which terms best describes the system of equations shown in the graph? (Lesson 3-1) **(912.A.3.14)** C

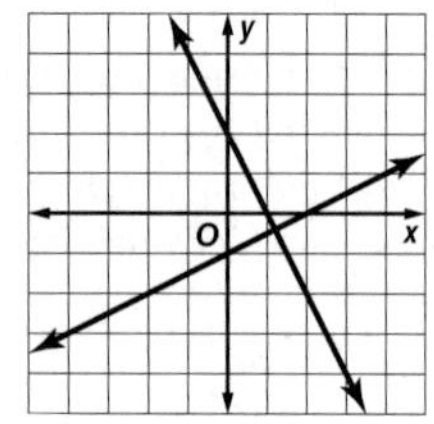

Ⓐ consistent
Ⓑ inconsistent
Ⓒ consistent and independent
Ⓓ consistent and dependent

Thursday

4. Angles 1 and 2 are complementary. If the measure of $\angle 1$ is 3° less than twice the measure of $\angle 2$, what is the measure of $\angle 1$? (Lesson 3-2) **(912.A.3.15)** H

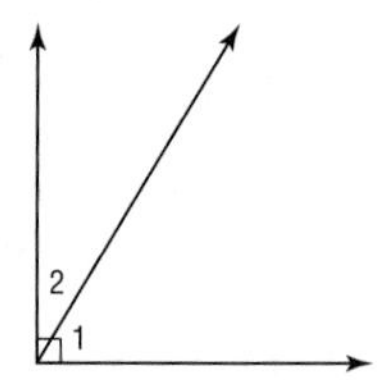

Ⓕ 29°
Ⓖ 31°
Ⓗ 59°
Ⓘ 61°

Friday

5. **GRIDDED RESPONSE** Emily scored 9 baskets for a total of 21 points. If some of the baskets were worth 2 points and the rest 3 points, how many 3-point baskets did she make? (Lesson 3-2) **(912.A.3.15)** 3

Week 4

NEED EXTRA HELP?					
If You Missed Question...	1	2	3	4	5
Go to Lesson...	3-2	3-3	3-1	3-2	3-2
For Help with NGSSS...	912.A.3.14	912.A.3.15	912.A.3.14	912.A.3.15	912.A.3.15

Weekly Standards Review

Week 5

Monday

1. Find the slope of the line that passes through the points $(-2, 7)$ and $(2, -1)$. (Lesson 2-3) **(912.A.3.9)** A

Ⓐ -2

Ⓑ $-\frac{1}{2}$

Ⓒ 2

Ⓓ 4

Tuesday

2. What is $g(-4)$? (Lesson 2-6) **(912.A.2.9)** H

$$g(x) = \begin{cases} -3x \text{ if } x < -4 \\ 4 \text{ if } -4 \leq x < 4 \\ 8x \text{ if } x \geq 4 \end{cases}$$

Ⓕ -32

Ⓖ -3

Ⓗ 4

Ⓘ 12

Wednesday

3. Solve the system of linear equations.

$$y = 3x - 1$$
$$y = -2x + 4$$

(Lesson 3-2) **(912.A.3.14)** C

Ⓐ $(0, -1)$

Ⓑ $(3, -2)$

Ⓒ $(1, 2)$

Ⓓ $(-2, -7)$

Thursday

4. Juan mows lawns during his summer break. He charges a flat rate of \$5.00 to cover the cost of his equipment and \$7.50 per hour he mows. Which equation best represents the relationship between the number of hours working n and the total cost c to mow a lawn? (Lesson 1-5) **(912.A.3.4)** I

Ⓕ $c > \$5.00n + 7.50$

Ⓖ $n \leq \$5.00c + 7.50$

Ⓗ $c \leq \$5.00 + 7.50n$

Ⓘ $c \geq \$5.00 + 7.50n$

Friday

5. **GRIDDED RESPONSE** If $f(x) = -2x + 5$, find $f(3)$. (Lesson 1-3) **(912.A.2.3)** -1

Choice Analysis

1. A. Correct
B. Transposed x and y values in slope formula
C. Missing negative sign
D. Miscalculation

2. F. Used function $g(x) = 8x$ which is when $x \geq 4$
G. Does not satisfy middle function
H. Correct
I. Does not satisfy middle function

3. A. This solution works in first equation, but not the second
B. This solution works in the second equation, but not the first
C. Correct
D. Miscalculation

4. F. The \$5 is a fixed cost, not variable
G. The \$5 is a fixed cost, not variable, and c should be on the left
H. Inequality sign the wrong direction, and c should be on the left
I. Correct

Week 5

NEED EXTRA HELP?					
If You Missed Question...	1	2	3	4	5
Go to Lesson...	2-3	2-6	3-2	1-5	1-3
For Help with NGSSS...	912.A.3.9	912.A.2.9	912.A.3.14	912.A.3.4	912.A.2.3

Choice Analysis

1. A. Correct
B. Slope is incorrect, it should be -1
C. Inequality is wrong direction, shading is above, not below
D. Slope is incorrect, it should be -1

2. F. Correct
G. Miscalculation
H. Miscalculation
I. T-shirts and sweatshirts switched

3. A. Correct
B. This function has the same output value no matter the input value.
C. This function has an output of x for any input value.
D. This function has an output of x^2 for any input value.

4. F. A dependent system does have a solution.
G. A dependent system has more than 1 solution.
H. A dependent system has more than 2 solutions.
I. Correct

Week 6

Monday

1. Which inequality is shown in the graph? (Lesson 2-7) **(912.A.2.5)** A

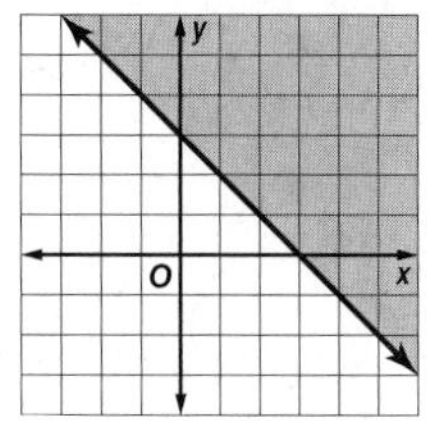

Ⓐ $y \geq -x + 3$
Ⓑ $y > -2x + 3$
Ⓒ $y < -x + 3$
Ⓓ $y \geq -2x + 3$

Tuesday

2. The school bookstore sells T-shirts for \$8 and sweatshirts for \$12. Last month, 35 T-shirts and sweatshirts were sold for \$336. How many of each were sold? (Lesson 3-3) **(912.A.3.15)** F

Ⓕ 21 T-shirts and 14 sweatshirts
Ⓖ 20 T-shirts and 15 sweatshirts
Ⓗ 18 T-shirts and 17 sweatshirts
Ⓘ 14 T-shirts and 21 sweatshirts

Wednesday

3. Which parent function is defined by

$$f(x) = \begin{cases} -x \text{ if } x < 0 \\ 0 \text{ if } x = 0 \\ x \text{ if } x > 0 \end{cases} ?$$

(Lesson 2-6) **(912.A.2.9)** A

Ⓐ absolute value function
Ⓑ constant function
Ⓒ linear function
Ⓓ quadratic function

Thursday

4. How many solutions are there to a dependent system of equations? (Lesson 3-1) **(912.A.3.14)** I

Ⓕ 0
Ⓖ 1
Ⓗ 2
Ⓘ infinitely many

Friday

5. **GRIDDED RESPONSE** What is the x-coordinate of the solution to the system of equations? (Lesson 3-1) **(912.A.3.14)** -2

$$y = -3x - 1$$
$$y = 0.5x + 6$$

Week 6

NEED EXTRA HELP?					
If You Missed Question...	1	2	3	4	5
Go to Lesson...	2-7	3-3	2-6	3-1	3-1
For Help with NGSSS...	912.A.2.5	912.A.3.15	912.A.2.9	912.A.3.14	912.A.3.14

Week 7

Monday

1. Which quadratic function is shown in the graph below? (Lesson 5-1) **(912.A.2.6)** B

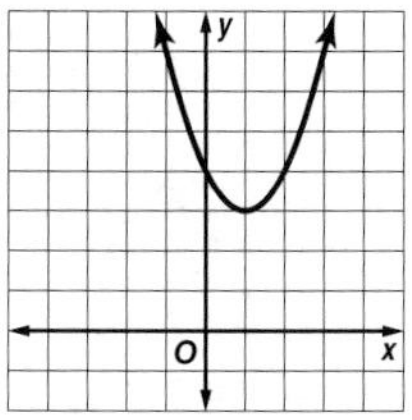

Ⓐ $y = (x + 1)^2 + 3$
Ⓑ $y = (x - 1)^2 + 3$
Ⓒ $y = (x - 1)^2 - 3$
Ⓓ $y = (x - 3)^2 + 1$

Tuesday

2. What is the imaginary part of the complex number $4 - 3i$? (Lesson 5-4) **(912.A.1.6)** I

Ⓕ 4
Ⓖ -4
Ⓗ $-3i$
Ⓘ -3

Wednesday

3. The inequality $y \leq x^2 - 3x - 4$ is shown below. Use the graph to solve $x^2 - 3x - 4 \leq 0$. (Lesson 5-8) **(912.A.4.11)** B

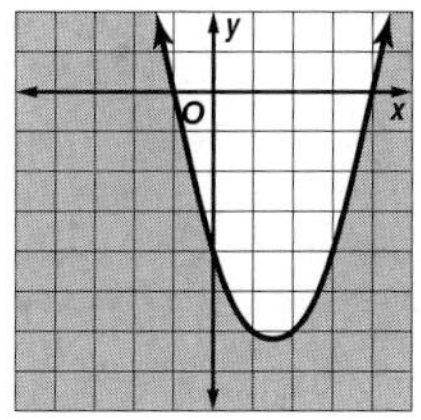

Ⓐ $\{x \mid -1 < x < 4\}$
Ⓑ $\{x \mid -1 \leq x \leq 4\}$
Ⓒ $\{x \mid -1 > x \text{ or } x > 4\}$
Ⓓ $\{x \mid -1 \geq x \text{ or } x \geq 4\}$

Thursday

4. Solve $2x^2 - 3x - 5 = 0$ by completing the square. (Lesson 5-5) **(912.A.7.3)** H

Ⓕ $x = -\frac{5}{2}, 1$
Ⓖ $x = -\frac{1}{2}, -5$
Ⓗ $x = -1, \frac{5}{2}$
Ⓘ $x = -5, \frac{1}{2}$

Friday

5. **GRIDDED RESPONSE** How many real roots does the quadratic equation $2x^2 + 12x + 18 = 0$ have? (Lesson 5-6) **(912.A.7.4)** 1

Choice Analysis

1. **A.** This function has an axis of symmetry of $x = -1$.
   B. Correct
   C. This graph would be shifted down.
   D. The values of *h* and *k* are incorrect.
2. **F.** This is the real part of the complex number.
   G. This number is not part of the complex number.
   H. The imaginary part should not include the imaginary unit *i*.
   I. Correct
3. **A.** The endpoints should be included.
   B. Correct
   C. This is the solution of $x^2 - 3x - 4 > 0$
   D. This is the solution of $x^2 - 3x - 4 \geq 0$
4. **F.** These solutions contain sign errors.
   G. The completing the square process was not completed correctly.
   H. Correct
   I. The completing the square process was not completed correctly.

Week 7

NEED EXTRA HELP?					
If You Missed Question...	1	2	3	4	5
Go to Lesson...	5-1	5-4	5-8	5-5	5-6
For Help with NGSSS...	912.A.2.6	912.A.1.6	912.A.4.11	912.A.7.3	912.A.7.4

Choice Analysis

1. **A.** The limits of the domain are reversed.
   B. Correct
   C. The value $x = -2$ should not be included in the domain.
   D. The value $x = -6$ should be included in the domain.

2. **F.** This is not equivalent to the original polynomial. You cannot factor sum of square
   G. This is not equivalent to the original polynomial.
   H. This is not equivalent to the original polynomial. All factors must be positive
   I. Correct

3. **A.** The graph shows a 4th degree polynomial, thus must have term with x^4
   B. The graph shows a 4th degree polynomial, thus must have term with x^4
   C. Correct
   D. The leading coefficient should be negative, since graph open down.

4. **F.** ± 1 is a possible rational root
   G. These are possible rational roots since $\frac{\pm 2}{\pm 1} = \pm 2$
   H. These are possible rational roots, since $\frac{\pm 3}{\pm 1} = \pm 3$
   I. Correct

Weekly Standards Review

Week 8

Monday

1. What is the domain of the piece-wise defined function below? (Lesson 2-6) **(912.A.2.9)** B

$$g(x) = \begin{cases} -2x \text{ if } x \le -6 \\ 4 \text{ if } -2 < x \le 3 \\ 9x \text{ if } x > 3 \end{cases}$$

Ⓐ $\{x \mid x \le -2 \text{ or } -6 < x\}$
Ⓑ $\{x \mid x \le -6 \text{ or } -2 < x\}$
Ⓒ $\{x \mid x \le -6 \text{ or } -2 \le x\}$
Ⓓ $\{x \mid x < -6 \text{ or } -2 < x\}$

Tuesday

2. Factor the polynomial $11x^4 + 6y^4$ completely. (Lesson 6-5) **(912.A.4.3)** I

Ⓕ $(x^2 + y^2)(11x^2 + 6y^2)$
Ⓖ $6(5x^4 + y^4)$
Ⓗ $17(x^2 + y^2)(x^2 - y^2)$
Ⓘ prime

Wednesday

3. Which polynomial function is shown below? (Lesson 6-4) **(912.A.4.5)** C

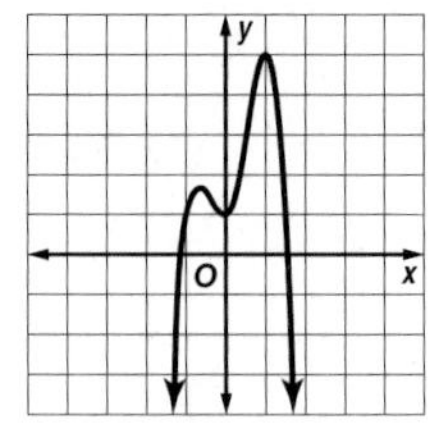

Ⓐ $f(x) = 2x^3 - x^2 + 3x + 1$
Ⓑ $f(x) = -x^3 + 2x^2 - x - 1$
Ⓒ $f(x) = -3x^4 + 2x^3 + 5x^2 + x + 1$
Ⓓ $f(x) = 4x^4 + 3x^3 - 2x^2 - x - 1$

Thursday

4. According to the Rational Root Theorem, which of the following are NOT possible rational roots of the polynomial function $f(x) = x^3 + 2x^2 - 5x - 6$? (Lesson 6-8) **(912.A.4.6)** I

Ⓕ ± 1
Ⓖ ± 2
Ⓗ ± 3
Ⓘ ± 5

Friday

5. **GRIDDED RESPONSE** What is the real root of $2x^3 - 13x^2 + 26x - 24$. (Lesson 6-2) **(912.A.4.4)** 4

Week 8

NEED EXTRA HELP?					
If You Missed Question...	1	2	3	4	5
Go to Lesson...	2-6	6-5	6-4	6-8	6-2
For Help with NGSSS...	912.A.2.9	912.A.4.3	912.A.4.5	912.A.4.6	912.A.4.4

Week 9

Monday

1. Factor the polynomial by grouping: $2ac - 3bc + 10ad - 15bd$. (Lesson 6-5) **(912.A.4.3)** A
   - (A) $(2a - 3b)(c + 5d)$
   - (B) $(a - 3b)(2c + 5d)$
   - (C) $(2a + 3b)(c - 5d)$
   - (D) $(2a + b)(3c - 5d)$

Tuesday

2. Use the Quadratic Formula to solve $-x^2 + 3x + 5 = 0$. (Lesson 5-6) **(912.A.7.5)** G
   - (F) $x = \frac{-2 \pm \sqrt{21}}{3}$
   - (G) $x = \frac{3 \pm \sqrt{29}}{2}$
   - (H) $x = \frac{-3 \pm \sqrt{29}}{2}$
   - (I) $x = \frac{2 \pm \sqrt{21}}{3}$

Wednesday

3. Which polynomial function below has roots $\pm 1, \pm\frac{i}{2}$? (Lesson 6-7) **(912.A.4.7)** C
   - (A) $f(x) = x^4 - \frac{1}{4}x^2 - \frac{1}{2}$
   - (B) $f(x) = x^4 - 2x^2 - \frac{1}{4}$
   - (C) $f(x) = x^4 - \frac{3}{4}x^2 - \frac{1}{4}$
   - (D) $f(x) = x^4 + \frac{3}{4}x^2 - \frac{1}{2}$

Thursday

4. Suppose $4 - 2i$ is a zero of the polynomial function $P(x)$. Which of the following is also a root of the function? (Lesson 6-7) **(912.A.4.6)** G
   - (F) $2 + 4i$
   - (G) $4 + 2i$
   - (H) $2 - 4i$
   - (I) not enough information

Friday

5. **GRIDDED RESPONSE** The polynomial below can be used to model the population of Florida. In the polynomial, $P(t)$ represents the population in millions, and t is the number of years since 1940. Use a graphing calculator to solve the equation $P(t) = 25$ to predict when the population of Florida will reach 25 million people. (Lesson 6-5) **(912.A.4.10)** 2021

$$P(t) = 0.0022t^2 + 0.111t + 1.73$$

Choice Analysis

1. **A.** Correct
   B. The coefficients are incorrect.
   C. There are sign errors in this answer.
   D. There are coefficient and sign errors in this answer.
2. **F.** The b term is -3 not -2
   G. Correct
   H. Missing negative in denominator
   I. The b term is -3 not 2
3. **A.** 1 is not a factor of this function, this graph has real roots
   B. 1 is not a factor of this function, this graph has real roots
   C. Correct
   D. 1 is not a factor of this function, this graph has real roots
4. **F.** This is not the complex conjugate of $4 - 2\mathbf{i}$, **i** must be with the 2 not the 4.
   G. Correct
   H. This is not the complex conjugate of $4 - 2\mathbf{i}$, **i** must be with the 2 not the 4.
   I. Imaginary roots appear in conjugate pairs.

Week 9

NEED EXTRA HELP?					
If You Missed Question...	1	2	3	4	5
Go to Lesson...	6-5	5-6	6-7	6-7	6-5
For Help with NGSSS...	912.A.4.3	912.A.7.5	912.A.4.7	912.A.4.6	912.A.4.10

Choice Analysis

1. A. This is $(f + g)(x)$.

B. This is $(fg)(x)$.

C. This is $\left(\frac{g}{f}\right)(x)$.

D. Correct

2. F. This is $(fg)(x)$.

G. Correct

H. This is $(f + g)(x)$.

I. This is $(g \circ f)(x)$.

3. A. There is a sign error, need to add 1 to each side, not subtract

B. Correct

C. The radical is over $x + 1$, not just x.

D. The radical is over $x + 1$, not just x

4. F. The a-variable and the coefficients were not simplified correctly.

G. The exponents were not simplified correctly.

H. The coefficients were switched.

I. Correct

Weekly Standards Review

Week 10

Monday

1. Given $f(x) = x - 3$ and $g(x) = 4x + 2$, find $\left(\frac{f}{g}\right)(x)$. (Lesson 7-1) **(912.A.2.7)** D

Ⓐ $\left(\frac{f}{g}\right)(x) = 5x - 1$

Ⓑ $\left(\frac{f}{g}\right)(x) = 4x^2 - 10x - 6$

Ⓒ $\left(\frac{f}{g}\right)(x) = \frac{4x + 2}{x - 3}$

Ⓓ $\left(\frac{f}{g}\right)(x) = \frac{x - 3}{4x + 2}$

Tuesday

2. Given $f(x) = x^2$ and $g(x) = x + 5$, find $(f \circ g)(x)$. (Lesson 7-1) **(912.A.2.8)** G

Ⓕ $(f \circ g)(x) = x^3 + 5x^2$

Ⓖ $(f \circ g)(x) = x^2 + 10x + 25$

Ⓗ $(f \circ g)(x) = x^2 + x + 5$

Ⓘ $(f \circ g)(x) = x^2 + 5$

Wednesday

3. What is the inverse of the function $f(x) = x^2 - 1$? (Lesson 7-2) **(912.A.2.11)** B

Ⓐ $f^{-1}(x) = \sqrt{x - 1}$

Ⓑ $f^{-1}(x) = \sqrt{x + 1}$

Ⓒ $f^{-1}(x) = \sqrt{x} + 1$

Ⓓ $f^{-1}(x) = \sqrt{x} - 1$

Thursday

4. Simplify the expression $\sqrt[4]{162a^6b^4}$. (Lesson 7-5) **(912.A.6.2)** I

Ⓕ $6a^3b\sqrt[4]{2a^2}$

Ⓖ $3a^4b^4\sqrt[4]{2a^2}$

Ⓗ $2ab\sqrt[4]{3a^2}$

Ⓘ $3ab\sqrt[4]{2a^2}$

Friday

5. **GRIDDED RESPONSE** Simplify $(-125)^{\frac{2}{3}}$. (Lesson 7-4) **(912.A.6.3)** 25

FL10

Week 10

NEED EXTRA HELP?					
If You Missed Question...	1	2	3	4	5
Go to Lesson...	7-1	7-1	7-2	7-5	7-4
For Help with NGSSS...	912.A.2.7	912.A.2.8	912.A.2.11	912.A.6.2	912.A.6.3

Week 11

Monday

1. What function is shown in the graph? (Lesson 8-1) **(912.A.8.3)** B

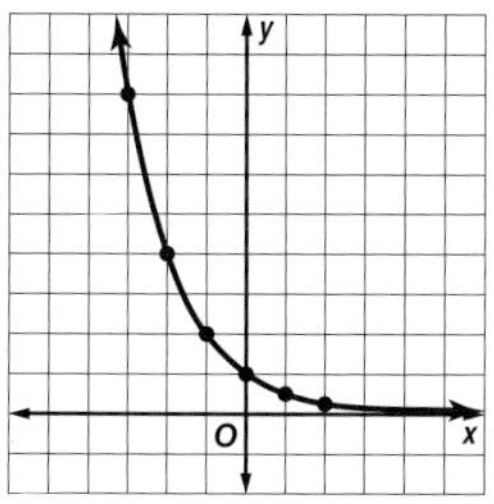

Ⓐ $y = 2^x$
Ⓑ $y = 2^{-x}$
Ⓒ $y = x^{-2}$
Ⓓ $y = x^2$

Tuesday

2. Which of the following shows how to express $\log_6 50$ in terms of common logarithms? (Lesson 8-6) **(912.A.8.6)** I

Ⓕ $\dfrac{\log_{50} 10}{\log_{50} 6}$

Ⓖ $\dfrac{\log_6 60}{\log_6 10}$

Ⓗ $\dfrac{\log_{10} 6}{\log_{10} 50}$

Ⓘ $\dfrac{\log_{10} 50}{\log_{10} 6}$

Wednesday

3. Caffeine has a half-life of about 6 hours in a typical adolescent. Suppose Carla drinks a soda that contains 55 milligrams of caffeine. How much of the caffeine remains in her system after 10 hours? Round your answer to the nearest tenth milligram. (Lesson 8-8) **(912.A.8.7)** D

Ⓐ 10.8 mg
Ⓑ 12.6 mg
Ⓒ 14.5 mg
Ⓓ 17.3 mg

Thursday

4. Write the exponential equation $2^x = 128$ in logarithmic form. (Lesson 8-3) **(912.A.8.1)** H

Ⓕ $\log_2 x = 128$
Ⓖ $\log_x 128 = 2$
Ⓗ $\log_2 128 = x$
Ⓘ $\log_x 2 = 128$

Friday

5. **GRIDDED RESPONSE** Solve the equation $2 \log x + \log 4 = 2$. (Lesson 8-4) **(912.A.8.5)** 5

Choice Analysis

1. A. The graph shows an exponential decay function, not exponential growth.
B. Correct
C. This is a rational function.
D. This is a quadratic function.

2. F. These are not common logarithms, need terms to be in $\log_{10}$
G. These are not common logarithms, need terms to be in $\log_{10}$
H. The 50 and 6 are reversed.
I. Correct

3. A. Miscalculation
B. Miscalculation
C. Miscalculation
D. Correct

4. F. This is not equivalent to the original exponential equation, *x* should be on the right.
G. This is not equivalent to the original exponential equation, should have a base of 2
H. Correct
I. This is not equivalent to the original exponential equation, should have a base of 2

Week 11

NEED EXTRA HELP?					
If You Missed Question...	1	2	3	4	5
Go to Lesson...	8-1	8-6	8-8	8-3	8-4
For Help with NGSSS...	912.A.8.3	912.A.8.6	912.A.8.7	912.A.8.1	912.A.8.5

Choice Analysis

1. **A.** This is $(f + g)(x)$.
   B. This is $\left(\frac{f}{g}\right)(x)$.
   C. Correct
   D. The constant term is incorrect.
2. **F.** This statement is true, y will always be 7 or less.
   G. This statement is true, x can be any number
   H. Correct
   I. This statement is true, the vertex is at (2, 7) thus the axis of symmetry is at $x = 2$
3. **A.** The square root of a negative number is imaginary.
   B. The sign is incorrect, it should be positive
   C. Correct
   D. This is not the simplified form, need to have the 4
4. **F.** There should only be 1 solution to the equation, since the degree is 1
   G. There should only be 1 solution to the equation, since the degree is 1
   H. Correct
   I. There is a sign error, the answer should be positive

Weekly Standards Review

Week 12

Monday

1. Given $f(x) = 2x^2 + 5$ and $g(x) = -x^2 + 4x - 1$, find $(f - g)(x)$. (Lesson 7-1) **(912.A.2.7)** C

Ⓐ $(f - g)(x) = x^2 + 4x + 4$
Ⓑ $(f - g)(x) = \frac{2x^2 + 5}{-x^2 + 4x - 1}$
Ⓒ $(f - g)(x) = 3x^2 - 4x + 6$
Ⓓ $(f - g)(x) = 3x^2 - 4x + 4$

Tuesday

2. Which of the following is NOT true for the parabola shown in the graph? (Lesson 5-1) **(912.A.7.6)** H

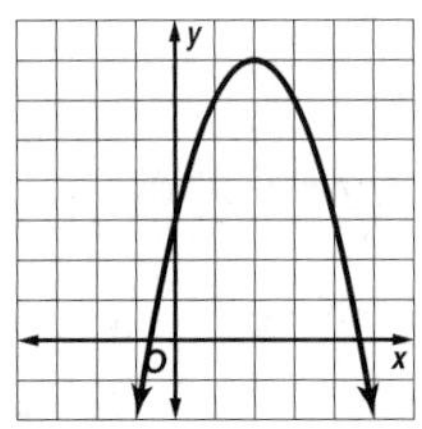

Ⓕ The range is $\{y \mid y \leq 7\}$.
Ⓖ The domain is all real numbers.
Ⓗ The vertex is (7, 2).
Ⓘ The axis of symmetry is $x = 2$.

Wednesday

3. Simplify $\sqrt{-16}$. (Lesson 5-4) **(912.A.1.6)** C

Ⓐ -4
Ⓑ $-4i$
Ⓒ $4i$
Ⓓ i

Thursday

4. Solve $\sqrt{x} - 2 = \sqrt{x - 5}$. Check for extraneous solutions. (Lesson 7-7) **(912.A.6.5)** H

Ⓕ $x = -\frac{81}{16}, 2$
Ⓖ $x = -2, \frac{81}{16}$
Ⓗ $x = \frac{81}{16}$
Ⓘ $x = -\frac{81}{16}$

Friday

5. **GRIDDED RESPONSE** If the polynomial $15x^3 + 8x^2 - 21x + 6$ is divided by $5x - 4$, what is the remainder? (Lesson 6-2) **(912.A.4.4)** 2

FL12

Week 12

NEED EXTRA HELP?					
If You Missed Question...	1	2	3	4	5
Go to Lesson...	7-1	5-1	5-4	7-7	6-2
For Help with NGSSS...	912.A.2.7	912.A.7.6	912.A.1.6	912.A.6.5	912.A.4.4

Week 13

Monday

1. Which rational function is shown in the graph below? (Lesson 9-4) **(912.A.2.6)** C

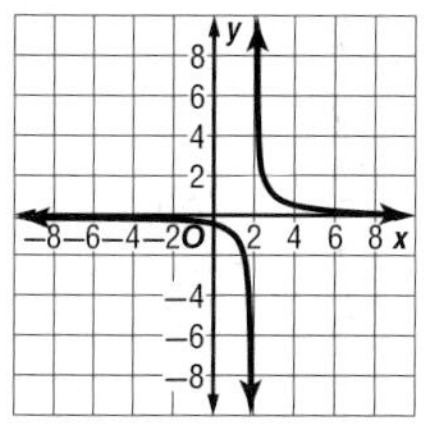

Ⓐ $y = \frac{2}{x}$

Ⓑ $y = \frac{1}{x} - 2$

Ⓒ $y = \frac{1}{x - 2}$

Ⓓ $y = \frac{1}{x + 2}$

Tuesday

2. Which of the following is not a point of discontinuity for the rational function $f(x) = \frac{x - 2}{(x - 2)(x + 5)(x - 6)}$? (Lesson 9-4) **(912.A.5.6)** F

Ⓕ $x = -6$

Ⓖ $x = -5$

Ⓗ $x = 2$

Ⓘ $x = 6$

Wednesday

3. Which rational function is shown in the graph? (Lesson 9-3) **(912.A.5.6)** D

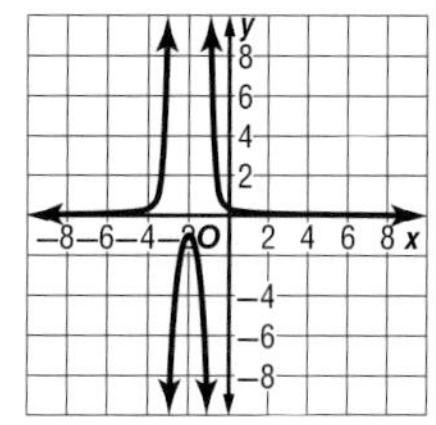

Ⓐ $y = \frac{1}{x^2 + 6x + 8}$

Ⓑ $y = \frac{1}{x^2 + x - 6}$

Ⓒ $y = \frac{1}{x^2 - 4x + 3}$

Ⓓ $y = \frac{1}{x^2 + 4x + 3}$

Thursday

4. Which of the following best describes the points of discontinuity for the rational function $f(x) = \frac{x - 3}{x^2 - 4x + 3}$? (Lesson 9-4) **(912.A.5.6)** H

Ⓕ vertical asymptotes at $x = 1, 3$

Ⓖ holes at $x = 1, 3$

Ⓗ hole at $x = 3$, vertical asymptote at $x = 1$

Ⓘ horizontal asymptote at $x = 3$, vertical asymptote at $x = 1$

Friday

5. **GRIDDED RESPONSE** The time it takes to drive a fixed distance varies inversely as the rate of speed. Suppose it takes Jamie 2.25 hours to drive to her grandmother's house driving at a rate of 50 miles per hour. How long would it take her to make the drive at a rate of 60 miles per hour? Round to the nearest thousandth place if necessary. (Lesson 9-5) **(912.A.2.12)** 1.875

Choice Analysis

1. **A.** This graph is centered about the origin.

B. This graph is centered about the origin and shifted down 2 units.

C. Correct

D. This graph has a vertical asymptote at $x = -2$.

2. **F.** Correct

G. There is a vertical asymptote at this point.

H. There is a hole at this point.

I. There is a vertical asymptote at this point.

3. **A.** The graph does not match this rational function. This one has asymptotes at –4 and –2

B. The graph does not match this rational function. This function has asymptotes at 2 and –3

C. The graph does not match this rational function.

D. Correct

4. **F.** The graph of the function has 1 hole and 1 asymptote.

G. The graph of the function has 1 hole and 1 asymptote.

H. Correct

I. The graph of the function has 1 hole and 1 asymptote.

Week 13

NEED EXTRA HELP?

If You Missed Question...	1	2	3	4	5
Go to Lesson...	9-4	9-4	9-3	9-4	9-5
For Help with NGSSS...	912.A.2.6	912.A.5.6	912.A.5.6	912.A.5.6	912.A.2.12

Choice Analysis

1. **A.** The *x*- and *y*-coordinates are reversed.
   B. Correct
   C. These points do not satisfy both equations, use elimination and multiply 1st equation by 4.
   D. These points do not satisfy both equations.

2. **F.** This answer has sign errors.
   G. The center of the hyperbola is incorrect.
   H. This hyperbola opens the wrong way.
   I. Correct

3. **A.** Wrong signs
   B. Correct
   C. Switched coordinates
   D. Wrong signs

4. **F.** This is one of the 4 solutions to the system.
   G. This is a solution to the system, (3, –4) is at an intersection of the two curves
   H. This is a solution to the system, (–3, –4) is at the intersection of the two curves
   I. Correct

Week 14

Monday

1. Solve the system of equations. (Lesson 10-7) **(912.A.7.7)** B

$$x^2 - y^2 = 4$$
$$9x^2 + 4y^2 = 36$$

Ⓐ (0, −2), (0, 2)
Ⓑ (−2, 0), (2, 0)
Ⓒ (−1, 3), (1, 3)
Ⓓ (−3, 1), (3, 1)

Wednesday

3. What are the coordinates of the center of the circle with equation $x^2 - 8x + y^2 + 4y - 5 = 0$? (Lesson 10-3) **(912.A.9.1)** B

Ⓐ (−4, 2)
Ⓑ (4, −2)
Ⓒ (−2, 4)
Ⓓ (2, −4)

Tuesday

2. What is the equation of the conic section shown in the graph below? (Lesson 10-5) **(912.A.9.2)** I

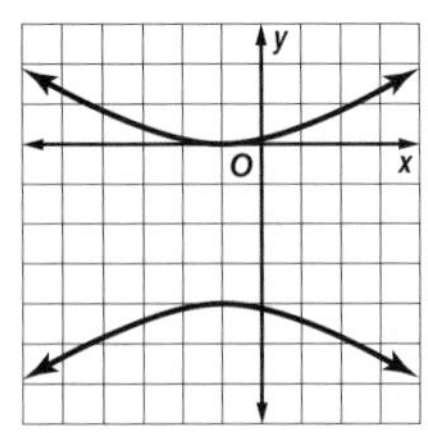

Ⓕ $\frac{(y-2)^2}{2^2} - \frac{(x-1)^2}{3^2} = 1$
Ⓖ $\frac{(y+1)^2}{2^2} - \frac{(x+2)^2}{3^2} = 1$
Ⓗ $\frac{(x+1)^2}{3^2} - \frac{(y+2)^2}{2^2} = 1$
Ⓘ $\frac{(y+2)^2}{2^2} - \frac{(x+1)^2}{3^2} = 1$

Thursday

4. The graph shows the system of equations $\begin{cases} x^2 + y^2 = 25 \\ 2x^2 - y^2 = 2 \end{cases}$. Which of the following is NOT a solution to the system? (Lesson 10-7) **(912.A.7.7)** I

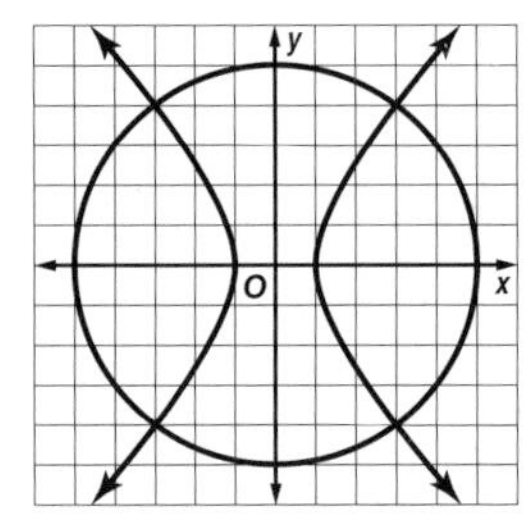

Ⓕ (−3, 4)
Ⓖ (3, −4)
Ⓗ (−3, −4)
Ⓘ (−4, 3)

Friday

5. **GRIDDED RESPONSE** Given the equation $(x - 4)^2 + (y + 3)^2 = 6^2$, what is the *y*-coordinate of the center of this circle? (Lesson 10-3) **(912.A.6.6)** −3

Week 14

NEED EXTRA HELP?					
If You Missed Question...	1	2	3	4	5
Go to Lesson...	10-7	10-5	10-3	10-7	10-3
For Help with NGSSS...	912.A.7.7	912.A.9.2	912.A.9.1	912.A.7.7	912.A.6.6

Week 15

Monday

1. Given $f(x) = x^2$ and $g(x) = x + 5$, which of the following statements is true? (Lesson 7-1) **(912.A.2.8)** A

Ⓐ The range of $(f \circ g)(x)$ is $\{y \mid y \geq 0\}$.
Ⓑ The domain of $(f \circ g)(x)$ is $\{x \mid x \geq 0\}$.
Ⓒ The range of $(f \circ g)(x)$ is $\{y \mid y \geq 5\}$.
Ⓓ The domain of $(f \circ g)(x)$ is $\{x \mid x \geq 5\}$.

Tuesday

2. Which lines below represent inverse functions? (Lesson 7-2) **(912.A.2.11)** F

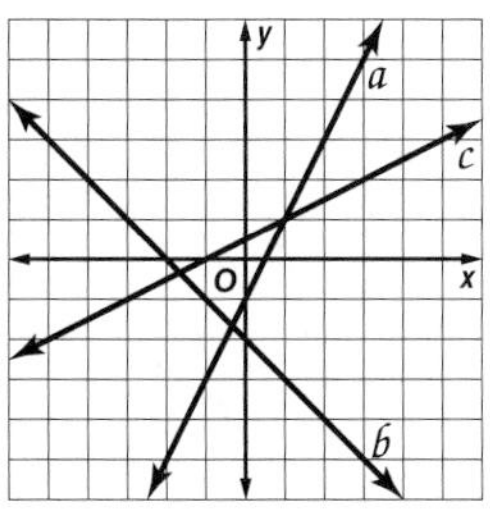

Ⓕ lines *A* and *C*
Ⓖ lines *A* and *B*
Ⓗ lines *B* and *C*
Ⓘ none of the above

Wednesday

3. If $P(x)$ can be written in factored form as $P(x) = 2(x - 5)(x + 5)(x - 2)$, which of the following is not a solution to the equation $P(x) = 0$? (Lesson 6-6) **(912.A.4.8)** B

Ⓐ -5
Ⓑ -2
Ⓒ 2
Ⓓ 5

Thursday

4. Simplify $(1 + i)(3 - i)$. (Lesson 5-4) **(912.A.1.6)** I

Ⓕ $4 - 2i$
Ⓖ $3 - i$
Ⓗ $3 + i$
Ⓘ $4 + 2i$

Friday

5. **GRIDDED RESPONSE** Suppose Mr. Gathers invests $75,000 in a money market account that pays 2.75% interest. The interest is compounded continuously. How much interest will the account earn over a period of 18 years? Round to the nearest dollar. (Lesson 8-7) **(912.A.8.7)** 48037

Choice Analysis

1. A. Correct
B. The domain is all real numbers.
C. The range is all positive real numbers.
D. The domain is all real numbers.

2. F. Correct
G. These lines are not symmetric about the line $y = x$.
H. These lines are not symmetric about the line $y = x$.
I. There are two lines that represent inverse functions in the graph.

3. A. This is a solution to the equation, solutions are ± 5 and 2
B. Correct
C. This is a solution to the equation.
D. This is a solution to the equation.

4. F. The sign of the imaginary part is incorrect.
G. The student multiplied the real and imaginary parts.
H. The FOIL procedure was not performed correctly.
I. Correct

Week 15

NEED EXTRA HELP?					
If You Missed Question...	1	2	3	4	5
Go to Lesson...	7-1	7-2	6-6	5-4	8-7
For Help with NGSSS...	912.A.2.8	912.A.2.11	912.A.4.8	912.A.1.6	912.A.8.7

Choice Analysis

1. **A.** The first term is incorrect.
   B. Correct
   C. The constant term in the formula is incorrect.
   D. The first term and constant are incorrect.
2. **F.** The exponent is off by 1.
   G. This equation represents an exponential growth sequence.
   H. Correct
   I. This equation represents an exponential growth sequence.
3. **A.** The coefficients of the expansion are incorrect, don't forget you have $3b$ not just b
   B. The coefficients of the expansion are incorrect. $a^4 + 4a^3(3b) + 6a^2(3b)^2 + 4a(3b)^3 + (3b)^4$
   C. The coefficients of the expansion are incorrect.
   D. Correct
4. **F.** Correct
   G. The last index of n is incorrect.
   H. The expression for the sequence is incorrect.
   I. The expression for the sequence is incorrect.

Weekly Standards Review

Week 16

Monday

1. Write a recursion formula for the sequence of numbers shown below. (Lesson 11-5) **(912.A.11.1)** B

$$-\frac{1}{3}, 3, -7, 23, -67, \ldots$$

Ⓐ $a_1 = -3, a_{n+1} = -3 \cdot a_n + 2$
Ⓑ $a_1 = -\frac{1}{3}, a_{n+1} = -3 \cdot a_n + 2$
Ⓒ $a_1 = -\frac{1}{3}, a_{n+1} = -3 \cdot a_n + 1$
Ⓓ $a_1 = \frac{1}{3}, a_{n+1} = -3 \cdot a_n + 3$

Tuesday

2. Write an equation for the nth term of the geometric sequence below. (Lesson 11-3) **(912.A.11.1)** H

$$192, 96, 48, 24, 12, 6, \ldots$$

Ⓕ $a_n = 192 \cdot \left(\frac{1}{2}\right)^n$
Ⓖ $a_n = -192 \cdot 2^{n-1}$
Ⓗ $a_n = 192 \cdot \left(\frac{1}{2}\right)^{n-1}$
Ⓘ $a_n = 192 \cdot 2^{n-1}$

Wednesday

3. Use the Binomial Theorem to expand $(a + 3b)^4$. (Lesson 11-6) **(912.A.4.12)** D

Ⓐ $a^4 + 6a^3b + 27a^2b^2 + 54ab^3 + 27b^4$
Ⓑ $a^4 + 4a^3b + 14a^2b^2 + 16ab^3 + 24b^4$
Ⓒ $a^4 + 6a^3b + 64a^2b^2 + 128ab^3 + 96b^4$
Ⓓ $a^4 + 12a^3b + 54a^2b^2 + 108ab^3 + 81b^4$

Thursday

4. Use sigma notation to describe the series: $12 + 16 + 20 + \cdots + 64$. (Lesson 11-2) **(912.A.11.2)** F

Ⓕ $\sum_{n=1}^{14} 4n + 8$
Ⓖ $\sum_{n=1}^{16} 4n + 8$
Ⓗ $\sum_{n=1}^{12} 8n + 4$
Ⓘ $\sum_{n=1}^{10} 8n + 4$

Friday

5. **GRIDDED RESPONSE** Maurice bought a new car 12 years ago. At the time, the value of the car was $22,560. Since he bought the car, the value has depreciated at a rate of 5% per year. What is the value of the car today? Round to the nearest whole dollar. (Lesson 11-3) **(912.A.11.3)** 12191

Week 16

NEED EXTRA HELP?					
If You Missed Question...	1	2	3	4	5
Go to Lesson...	11-5	11-3	11-6	11-2	11-3
For Help with NGSSS...	912.A.11.1	912.A.11.1	912.A.4.12	912.A.11.2	912.A.11.3

Week 17

Monday

1. Use a graphing calculator to solve the quadratic equation $3x^2 + 4x - 3 = 0$. Round your answers to the nearest hundredth if necessary. (Lesson 5-2) **(912.A.7.10)** D
   - (A) −4.16, 3.82
   - (B) −2.59, −1.12
   - (C) −0.78, 2.74
   - (D) −1.87, 0.54

Tuesday

2. Use sigma notation to describe the series: $3 + 9 + 15 + \cdots + 141$. (Lesson 11-2) **(912.A.11.2)** H
   - (F) $\sum_{n=1}^{20} 6n - 2$
   - (G) $\sum_{n=1}^{24} 6n + 3$
   - (H) $\sum_{n=1}^{24} 6n - 3$
   - (I) $\sum_{n=1}^{22} 6n - 3$

Wednesday

3. Rachael has \$224 in her savings account. She plans to save an additional \$22 per week. How much will she have in her savings account after the 15th week? (Lesson 11-1) **(912.A.11.3)** C
   - (A) \$510
   - (B) \$532
   - (C) \$554
   - (D) \$576

Thursday

4. In a jar there are 5 red, 6 black, 3 green, and 5 purple jelly beans. What is the probability that you will pick out a purple jelly bean first and a black second without replacement? (Lesson 12-3) **(912.P.2.3)** G
   - (F) $\frac{25}{342}$
   - (G) $\frac{30}{342}$
   - (H) $\frac{25}{361}$
   - (I) $\frac{30}{361}$

Friday

5. **GRIDDED RESPONSE** Jade is preparing for the cross country championship meet. Her times for this season are given in the table at the right. What was her mean time in minutes for her races this season? Round to the nearest hundredth. (Algebra 1) **(912.S.3.3)** 20.41

Time (min)
19.47
19.68
19.90
20.17
20.30
20.62
21.03
21.13
21.42

Choice Analysis

1. **A.** These are not the x-intercepts of the parabola.
   B. These are not the x-intercepts of the parabola, you should have one positive and one negative solutions
   C. These are not the x-intercepts of the parabola.
   D. Correct
2. **F.** The expression for the sequence is incorrect, all the terms of the series are odd, so an even number can't be subtracted
   G. The expression for the sequence is incorrect
   H. Correct
   I. The last index of n is incorrect, there are 24 items in the series
3. **A.** This is the amount after the 13th week.
   B. This is the amount after the 14th week.
   C. Correct
   D. This is the amount after the 16th week.
4. **F.** 5 ways for a purple times 6 for a black gives the numerator of 30
   G. Correct
   H. Calculated probability with replacement
   I. Calculated probability with replacement

Week 17

NEED EXTRA HELP?					
If You Missed Question...	1	2	3	4	5
Go to Lesson...	5-2	11-2	11-1	12-3	*Algebra 1*
For Help with NGSSS...	912.A.7.10	912.A.11.2	912.A.11.3	912.P.2.3	912.S.3.3

Weekly Standards Review

Week 18

Monday

1. What is the equation of the conic section shown in the graph below? (Lesson 10-4) **(912.A.9.2)** B

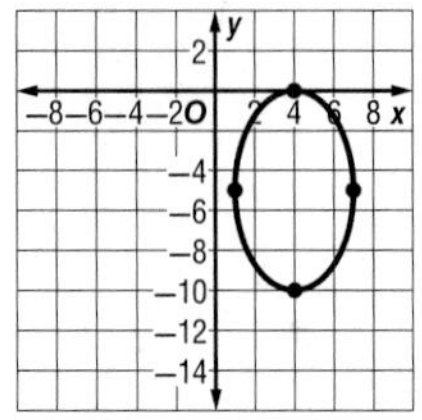

Ⓐ $\frac{(x-4)^2}{5^2} + \frac{(y+5)^2}{3^2} = 1$

Ⓑ $\frac{(x-4)^2}{3^2} + \frac{(y+5)^2}{5^2} = 1$

Ⓒ $\frac{(x+4)^2}{3^2} + \frac{(y-5)^2}{5^2} = 1$

Ⓓ $\frac{(x-4)^2}{2^2} + \frac{(y+5)^2}{3^2} = 1$

Tuesday

2. A map of Florida is scaled so that 2 inches represents 25 miles. If the distance between Miami and Palm Beach is 5.6 inches on the map, what is the actual distance between the two cities? (Lesson 9-5) **(912.A.2.12)** I

Ⓕ 62 miles

Ⓖ 65 miles

Ⓗ 68 miles

Ⓘ 70 miles

Wednesday

3. Given $f(x) = -3x + 5$ and $g(x) = 2x - 1$, find $(f \circ g)(x)$. (Lesson 7-1) **(912.A.2.7)** A

Ⓐ $(f \circ g)(x) = -6x^2 + 13x - 5$

Ⓑ $(f \circ g)(x) = -6x^2 + 3x - 5$

Ⓒ $(f \circ g)(x) = -6x^2 + 13x + 5$

Ⓓ $(f \circ g)(x) = 6x^2 - 10x - 5$

Thursday

4. Simplify $\frac{-2i}{5-i}$. (Lesson 5-4) **(912.A.1.6)** F

Ⓕ $\frac{1}{13} - \frac{5}{13}i$

Ⓖ $\frac{1}{13} + \frac{5}{13}i$

Ⓗ $-\frac{5}{13} + \frac{1}{13}i$

Ⓘ $\frac{5}{13} - \frac{1}{13}i$

Friday

5. **GRIDDED RESPONSE** Solve the system $\begin{cases} 3a + 2b - 4c = -12 \\ -2a - b + 6c = 21 \\ -3a - 2b + 2c = 4 \end{cases}$. What is the value of c? (Lesson 3-5) **(912.A.3.14)** 4

FL18

Choice Analysis

1. A. The values of a and b are reversed.

B. Correct

C. The center of the ellipse is incorrect.

D. The values of a and b are incorrect.

2. F. This value is too low, check your equation $\frac{(25 \cdot 2)}{5.6}$

G. This value is too low, this would be 5.2 inches not 5.6 inches

H. This value is too low, this would be 5.4 inches

I. Correct

3. A. Correct

B. The x-term of the function is incorrect.

C. The sign of the constant term is incorrect.

D. This is not the correct function.

4. F. Correct

G. The sign of the imaginary part is incorrect.

H. The real and imaginary parts are reversed.

I. The real and imaginary parts are reversed, and the signs are incorrect.

Week 18

NEED EXTRA HELP?					
If You Missed Question...	1	2	3	4	5
Go to Lesson...	10-4	9-5	7-1	5-4	3-5
For Help with NGSSS...	912.A.9.2	912.A.2.12	912.A.2.7	912.A.1.6	912.A.3.14

Week 19

Monday

1. Which of the following statements is sometimes true regarding the roots of a quadratic equation if the discriminant is greater than 0? (Lesson 5-6) **(912.A.10.3)** A

   Ⓐ There are 2 rational roots.
   Ⓑ There is 1 real root.
   Ⓒ There are 2 complex roots.
   Ⓓ There are no real roots.

Tuesday

2. Find the perimeter of the triangle below. (Lesson 13-5) **(912.T.2.3)** F

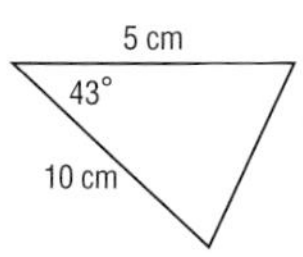

   Ⓕ 22.20 cm
   Ⓖ 25.22 cm
   Ⓗ 71.80 cm
   Ⓘ 103.14 cm

Wednesday

3. Write an equation for the nth term of the arithmetic sequence below. (Lesson 11-3) **(912.A.11.1)** A

   12, 18, 24, 30, 36, 42, …

   Ⓐ $a_n = 6n + 6$
   Ⓑ $a_n = 6n + 12$
   Ⓒ $a_n = -6n + 12$
   Ⓓ $a_n = 6n - 6$

Thursday

4. Which series is described in sigma notation as $\sum_{n=1}^{10} 7n + 1$? (Lesson 11-2) **(912.A.11.2)** I

   Ⓕ $7 + 14 + 21 + \cdots + 70$
   Ⓖ $8 + 14 + 20 + \cdots + 65$
   Ⓗ $8 + 16 + 24 + \cdots + 80$
   Ⓘ $8 + 15 + 22 + \cdots + 71$

Friday

5. **GRIDDED RESPONSE** What is $\cos \theta$, if $\sin \theta = -\frac{12}{13}$; $270° < \theta < 360°$? (Lesson 14-3) **(912.T.3.2)** 5/13

Choice Analysis

1. **A.** Correct
   B. This statement is never true, there will be two since the quadratic formula has a ± before the square root
   C. This statement is never true, there are two complex roots when the discriminant is less than 0
   D. This statement is never true, since the discriminant is greater than 0

2. **F.** Correct
   G. Miscalculation
   H. Miscalculation
   I. Forgot to take the square root after using the Law of Cosines

3. **A.** Correct
   B. Equation does not work with $n = 1$
   C. Wrong sign for first term
   D. Equation does not work with $n = 1$

4. **F.** The terms of the series do not match the sigma notation, first term should be 8 not 7
   G. The terms of the series do not match the sigma notation, the second term should be 15 not 14
   H. The terms of the series do not match the sigma notation, the last term should be 71 not 80
   I. Correct

Week 19

NEED EXTRA HELP?					
If You Missed Question...	1	2	3	4	5
Go to Lesson...	5-6	13-5	11-3	11-2	14-3
For Help with NGSSS...	912.A.10.3	912.T.2.3	912.A.11.1	912.A.11.2	912.T.3.2

Choice Analysis

1. **A.** Correct
   B. The center of the circle is at (4, 3) not (−4, −3)
   C. The radius of the circle is 3, and standard form it is r^2
   D. The radius of the circle is 3, not 4.
2. **F.** The coefficients were not simplified correctly.
   G. The *x*- and *y*-variables were not simplified correctly.
   H. The *x*-variable was not simplified correctly.
   I. Correct
3. **A.** These functions are not inverses.
   B. These functions are not inverses.
   C. Correct
   D. These functions are not inverses.
4. **F.** There are sign errors in this answer.
   G. There are sign errors in this answer.
   H. There are sign errors in this answer.
   I. Correct

Weekly Standards Review

Week 20

Monday

1. What is the equation of the circle shown in the graph? (Lesson 10-3) **(912.A.6.7)** A

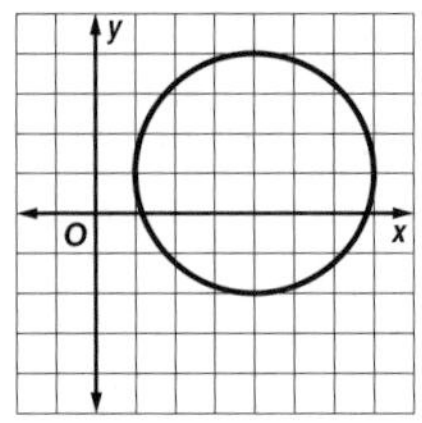

Ⓐ $(x-4)^2+(y-1)^2=3^2$
Ⓑ $(x+4)^2+(y+1)^2=3^2$
Ⓒ $(x-4)^2+(y-1)^2=3$
Ⓓ $(x-4)^2+(y-1)^2=4^2$

Tuesday

2. Simplify the expression $\frac{\sqrt{48x^5}}{\sqrt{3x^2y^6}}$. Assume that all variables are positive. (Lesson 7-5) **(912.A.6.2)** I

Ⓕ $\frac{x\sqrt{3x}}{y^3\sqrt{2}}$
Ⓖ $\frac{4x^2\sqrt{x}}{y^2}$
Ⓗ $\frac{4x}{y^3}$
Ⓘ $\frac{4x\sqrt{x}}{y^3}$

Wednesday

3. Two functions are called *inverse functions* if $(f \circ g)(x) = x$ and $(g \circ f)(x) = x$. Which pair of functions below are inverse functions? (Lesson 7-1) **(912.A.2.8)** C

Ⓐ $f(x) = x + 1$
$g(x) = 1 - x^2$
Ⓑ $f(x) = \frac{1}{4}x + 2$
$g(x) = -\frac{1}{4}x - 2$
Ⓒ $f(x) = 2x - 8$
$g(x) = \frac{1}{2}x + 4$
Ⓓ $f(x) = \sqrt{4x - 1}$
$g(x) = \frac{1}{2}x^2 + 2$

Thursday

4. What is the inverse of the function $y = \frac{x-8}{5}$? (Lesson 7-2) **(912.A.2.11)** I

Ⓕ $f^{-1}(x) = -5x - 8$
Ⓖ $f^{-1}(x) = -5x + 8$
Ⓗ $f^{-1}(x) = 5x - 8$
Ⓘ $f^{-1}(x) = 5x + 8$

Friday

5. **GRIDDED RESPONSE** Some school districts use a phone tree to notify employees of a closing due to bad weather. Suppose the first person in the chain calls two people. Then each of these people call two others, and so on. How many calls are made in the first 6 stages of the phone tree? (Lesson 11-3) **(912.A.11.4)** 126

Week 20

NEED EXTRA HELP?					
If You Missed Question...	1	2	3	4	5
Go to Lesson...	10-3	7-5	7-1	7-2	11-3
For Help with NGSSS...	912.A.6.7	912.A.6.2	912.A.2.8	912.A.2.11	912.A.11.4

CHAPTER 0

Preparing for Advanced Algebra

Now

Chapter 0 contains lessons on topics from previous courses. You can use this chapter in various ways.

- Begin the school year by taking the Pretest. If you need additional review, complete the lessons in this chapter. To verify that you have successfully reviewed the topics, take the Posttest.
- As you work through the text, you may find that there are topics you need to review. When this happens, complete the individual lessons that you need.
- Use this chapter for reference. When you have questions about any of these topics, flip back to this chapter to review definitions or key concepts.

FOLDABLES® Study Organizer

Each chapter of *Glencoe Algebra 2* features a Foldable Study Organizer students can make to organize their notes. Encourage students to use these tools to make their study time more productive.

Get Started on Chapter 0

You will review several concepts, skills, and vocabulary terms as you study Chapter 0. To get ready, identify important terms and organize your resources.

FOLDABLES® Study Organizer

Throughout this text, you will be invited to use Foldables to organize your notes.

Why should you use them?

- They help you organize, display, and arrange information.
- They make great study guides, specifically designed for you.
- You can use them as your math journal for recording main ideas, problem-solving strategies, examples, or questions you may have.
- They give you a chance to improve your math vocabulary.

How should you use them?

- Write general information–titles, vocabulary terms, concepts, questions, and main ideas–on the front tabs of your Foldable.
- Write specific information–ideas, your thoughts, answers to questions, steps, notes, and definitions–under the tabs.
- Use the tabs for:
  - math concepts in parts, like types of triangles,
  - steps to follow, or
  - parts of a problem, like *compare and contrast* (2 parts) or *what*, *where*, *when*, *why*, and *how* (5 parts).
- You may want to store your Foldables in a plastic zipper bag that you have three-hole punched to fit in your notebook.

When should you use them?

- Set up your Foldable as you begin a chapter, or when you start learning a new concept.
- Write in your Foldable every day.
- Use your Foldable to review for homework, quizzes, and tests.

New Vocabulary

English		Español
domain	• p. P4 •	dominio
range	• p. P4 •	rango
quadrants	• p. P4 •	cuadrantes
mapping	• p. P4 •	transformaciones
function	• p. P4 •	función
outcome	• p. P9 •	resultados
sample space	• p. P9 •	espacio muestral
event	• p. P9 •	evento
Fundamental Counting Principle	• p. P9 •	principio fundamental de conteo
factorial	• p. P10 •	factorial
permutation	• p. P12 •	permutación
linear permutation	• p. P12 •	permutación lineal
combination	• p. P12 •	combinacion
congruent	• p. P15 •	congruente
similar	• p. P15 •	semejantes

Multilingual eGlossary glencoe.com

FL Math Online glencoe.com

- Study the chapter online
- Explore **Get Animated**
- Get extra help from your own **Personal Tutor**
- Use **Extra Examples** for additional help
- Take a **Self-Check Quiz**
- **Review Vocabulary** in fun ways

P2 **Chapter 0** Preparing for Advanced Algebra

State the domain and range of each relation. Then determine whether each relation is a function. Write *yes* or *no*. 1. D = {−3, 8, 14}, R = {1, 4, 6}; yes

1. {(14, 1), (−3, 6), (8, 4)}

2. D = {−2, 3}, R = {−4, −2, 0, 2}; no

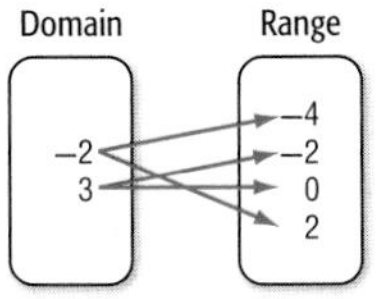

Name the quadrant in which each point is located.

3. (−6, −2) III

4. (10, 11) I

5. (4, −3) IV

6. (−5, −7) III

Find each product. 8. $a^2 + 3a - 18$

7. $(x + 1)(x + 4)$ $x^2 + 5x + 4$

8. $(a - 3)(a + 6)$

9. $(m - 2)(m - 5)$

10. $(d + 7)(d + 7)$

11. $(t - 9)(t + 4)$ $t^2 - 5t - 36$

12. $(c + 8)(c - 8)$ $c^2 - 64$

9. $m^2 - 7m + 10$ 10. $d^2 + 14d + 49$

13. **NUMBER THEORY** There are two integers. One is 5 more than a number, and the other is 1 less than the same number. a. $n + 5$, $n - 1$

a. Write expressions for the two numbers.

b. Write a polynomial expression for the product of the numbers. $n^2 + 4n - 5$

17. $(x + 3)(x + 2)$

Factor each polynomial. 15. $5b(2ab + 1)$

14. $6a^2 + 2a$ $2a(3a + 1)$

15. $10ab^2 + 5b$

16. $15d - 12cd^2$ $3d(5 - 4cd)$

17. $x^2 + 5x + 6$

18. $y^2 + 6y - 7$ $(y - 1)(y + 7)$

19. $a^2 - 13a + 36$ $(a - 4)(a - 9)$

State whether the events are *independent* or *dependent*.

20. selecting three playing cards from a standard deck without replacing any of the cards dependent

21. rolling two dice independent

22. choosing a type of car and selecting a brand of tire independent

23. selecting two baseballs from a carton of five without replacement dependent

24. **BOOKS** A bookshelf holds 4 different biographies and 5 different mystery novels. How many ways can one book of each type be selected? 20 ways

25. **ICE CREAM** An ice cream shop offers a choice of two types of cones and 15 flavors of ice cream. How many different 1-scoop ice cream cones can a customer order? 30 cones

Determine whether each situation involves a *permutation* or a *combination*. Then find the number of possibilities.

26. placing an algebra book, a geometry book, a chemistry book, an English book, and a health book on a shelf permutation; 120

27. selecting 3 of 15 flavors of juice at the grocery store combination; 455

28. Determine whether the triangles are *similar*, *congruent*, or *neither*. similar

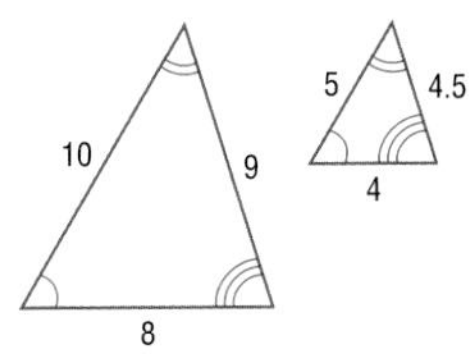

29. **PHOTOGRAPHS** A photo that is 3 inches wide by 5 inches long is being enlarged so that it is 12 inches long. How wide will the enlarged photo be? 7.2 in.

Find each missing measure. Round to the nearest tenth, if necessary.

30. 29 cm

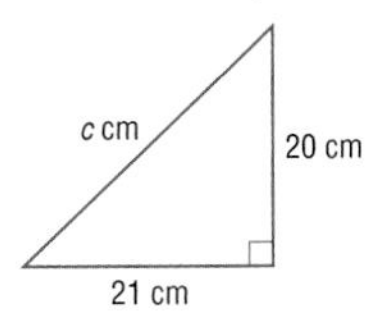

31. $a = 6$ yd, $b = 9$ yd, $c = ?$ 10.8 yd

The lengths of three sides of a triangle are given. Determine whether each triangle is a right triangle.

32. 12 yd, 14 yd, 16 yd no

33. 15 km, 20 km, 25 km yes

34. 45 mm, 60 mm, 75 mm yes

CHAPTER 0 Pretest

Using the Pretest

The Chapter 0 Pretest assesses students' understanding of the concepts presented in Chapter 0. You may use the pretest to determine whether students need to complete each lesson in Chapter 0 before beginning the content in Chapter 1.

Chapter 0 Pretest P3

0-1 Lesson Notes

1 FOCUS

Vertical Alignment

Lesson 0-1
Identify the domain and range of functions.

After Lesson 0-1
Identify the domain and range of linear, quadratic, radical, exponential, logarithmic, and rational functions.

2 TEACH

Example 1 shows how to identify the domain and range of a relation. **Example 2** shows how to identify the quadrant in which a point is located. **Example 3** shows how to use the domain and range to determine whether a relation is a function.

Additional Examples

1 State the domain and range of the relation.
{(–2, –1), (–1, 0), (1, –5), (2, 7)}
D = {–2, –1, 1, 2}
R = {–1, 0, –5, 7}

2 Name the quadrant in which the point $P(2, -6)$ is located.
Quadrant IV

Watch Out!

Student Misconceptions Remind students that a function can pair more than one element of the domain with a single element of the range. However, the reverse is not true.

0-1 Representing Functions

Objective
- Identify the domain and range of functions.

New Vocabulary
domain
range
quadrants
mapping
function

FL Math Online
glencoe.com

Recall that a *relation* is a set of ordered pairs. The **domain** of a relation is the set of all first coordinates (x-coordinates) from the ordered pairs, and the **range** is the set of all second coordinates (y-coordinates) from the ordered pairs.

EXAMPLE 1 Domain and Range

State the domain and the range of the relation.
{(–3, 3), (0, –7), (1, –5), (2, 4)}

The domain is the set of x-coordinates.
D = {–3, 0, 1, 2}

The range is the set of y-coordinates.
R = {–7, –5, 3, 4}

A relation can be graphed on a coordinate plane. A coordinate plane is formed by the intersection of the horizontal axis, or x-axis, and the vertical axis, or y-axis. The axes meet at the origin (0, 0) and divide the plane into four **quadrants**. Any ordered pair in the coordinate plane can be written in the form (x, y).

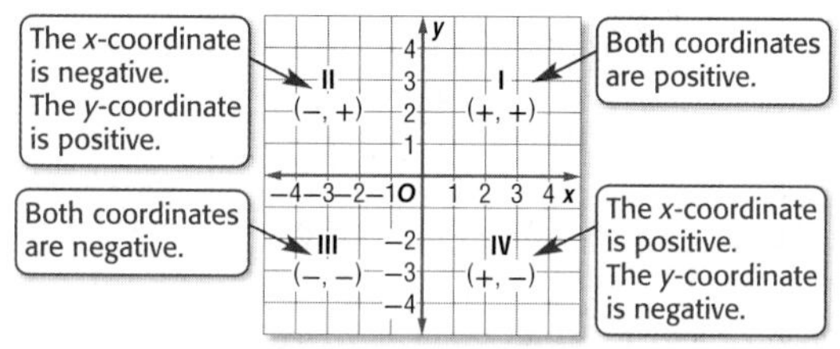

EXAMPLE 2 Locate Coordinates

Name the quadrant in which $T(-8, 5)$ is located.

Point T has a negative x-coordinate and a positive y-coordinate. The point is located in Quadrant II.

A relation can also be represented by a table or a mapping. A **mapping** illustrates how each element of the domain is paired with an element in the range.

Ordered Pairs

(1, 2)
(–2, 3)
(0, –3)

Table

x	y
1	2
–2	3
0	–3

Graph

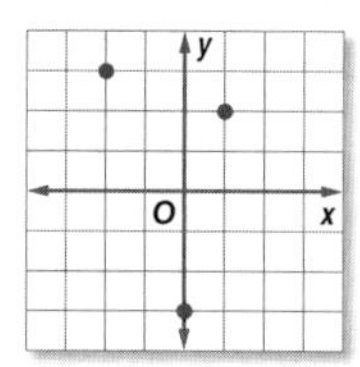

Mapping

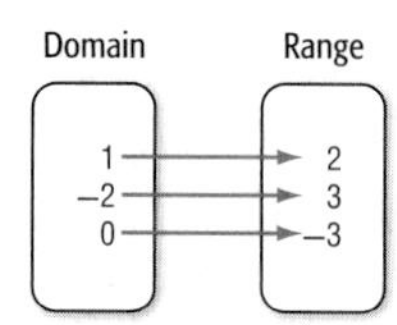

A **function** is a relation in which each element of the domain is paired with *exactly one* element of the range.

TEACH with TECH

DOCUMENT CAMERA Select a student and give him or her a set of ordered pairs. Have the student work on the document camera to show and explain how to create a table, a graph, and a mapping from the ordered pairs.

P4 Chapter 0 Preparing for Advanced Algebra

EXAMPLE 3 Identify Domain and Range

State the domain and range of each relation. Then determine whether each relation is a function.

a. {(10, 3), (6, −2), (7, 4), (−8, −9)}

D = {−8, 6, 7, 10}
R = {−9, −2, 3, 4}
For each element of the domain, there is only one corresponding element in the range. So, this relation is a function.

b.

x	y
1	3, 4
2	7
3	4

D = {1, 2, 3}
R = {3, 4, 7}

Because 1 is paired with 3 and 4, this is not a function.

c.

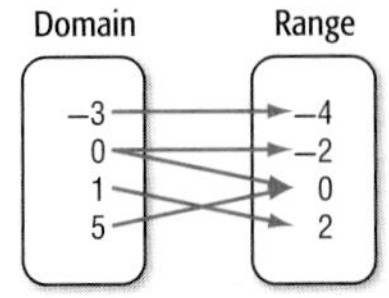

D = {−3, 0, 1, 5}
R = {−4, −2, 0, 2}
Because 0 is paired with −2 and 0, this is not a function.

d.

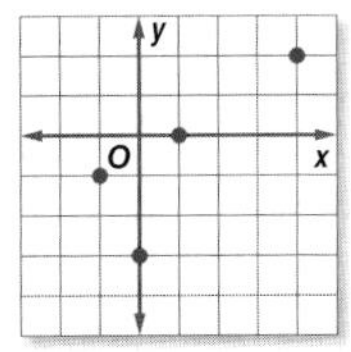

D = {−1, 0, 1, 4}
R = {−3, −1, 0, 2}
This is a function.

> **Watch Out!**
>
> **Functions** Remember that in a function, an element of the range can be paired with more than one element of the domain. But an element of the domain cannot be paired with more than one element of the range.

Exercises

State the domain and range of each relation. Then determine whether each relation is a function. Write *yes* or *no*.

1. {(2, 7), (3, 10), (1, 6)}

2. {(−6, 0), (5, 5), (9, −2), (−2, −9)}

1. D = {1, 2, 3}, R = {6, 7, 10}; yes
2. D = {−6, −2, 5, 9}, R = {−9, −2, 0, 5}; yes

3.

x	y
1	5
2	7
1	9

D = {1, 2}, R = {5, 7, 9}; no

4.

x	y
−12	0
−10	1
−8	2
−6	4

D = {−12, −10, −8, −6}, R = {0, 1, 2, 4}; yes

5.

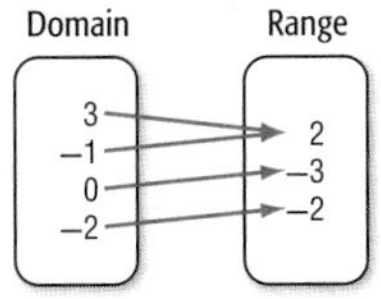

6.

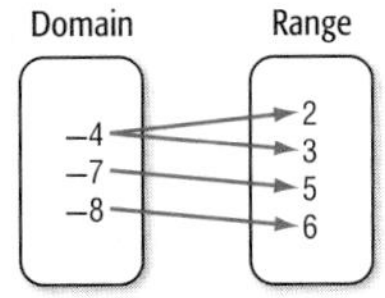

5. D = {−2, −1, 0, 3}, R = {−3, −2, 2}; yes
6. D = {−8, −7, −4}, R = {2, 3, 5, 6}; no

7.

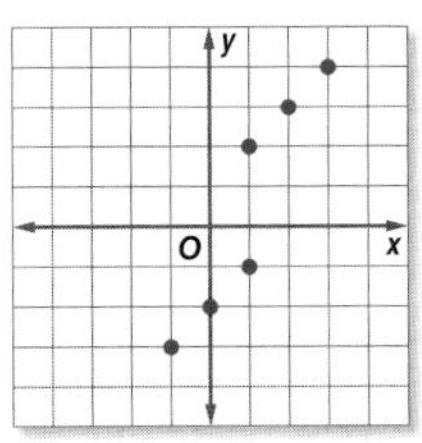

8.

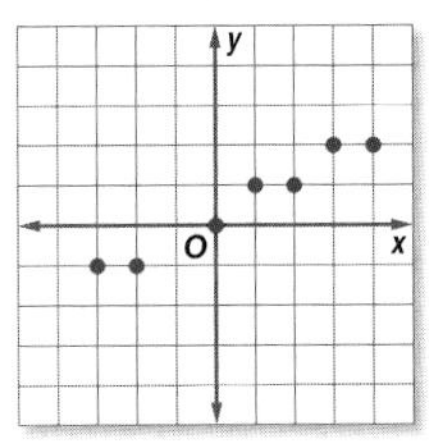

7. D = {−1, 0, 1, 2, 3}, R = {−3, −2, −1, 2, 3, 4}; no
8. D = {−3, −2, 0, 1, 2, 3, 4}, R = {−1, 0, 1, 2}; yes

Name the quadrant in which each point is located.

9. (5, 3) I
10. (8, −6) IV
11. (2, 0) none
12. (−7, −1) III

Additional Example

3 State the domain and range of each relation. Then determine whether each relation is a function.

a. {(3, 2), (4, 1), (6, 2), (8, 0)}
D = {3, 4, 6, 8}
R = {2, 1, 0}, yes

b.

x	y
0	−2
3	2
6	2

D = {0, 3, 6}
R = {−2, 2}, yes

c.

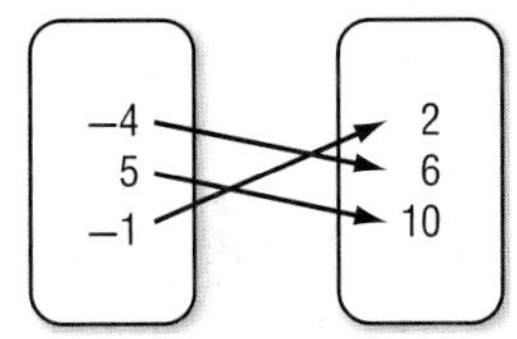

D = {−4, 5, −1}
R = {2, 6, 10}, yes

d.

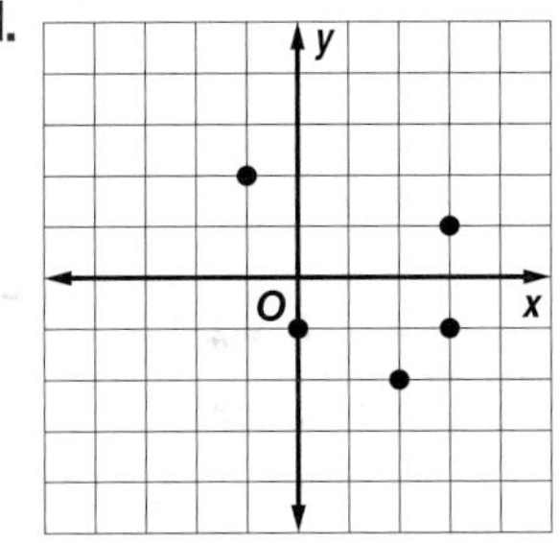

D = {−1, 0, 2, 3}
R = {2, −1, −2, 1}, no

3 ASSESS

Formative Assessment

Use Exercises 1–12 to assess whether students can identify the domain and range of a relation and determine whether the relation is a function.

Ticket Out the Door Ask students to list four ordered pairs that could be elements of a single function.

0-2 Lesson Notes

1 FOCUS

Vertical Alignment

Lesson 0-2
Use the FOIL method to multiply binomials.

After Lesson 0-2
Factor quadratic trinomials.

2 TEACH

Example 1 shows how to use the FOIL method to find the product of two binomials.

Additional Example

1 Find each product.

a. $(d - 1)(d + 6)$ $d^2 + 5d - 6$

b. $(2p - 3)(6p - 1)$ $12p^2 - 20p + 3$

Watch Out!

Preventing Errors It may help some students to write a binomial such as $(x - 5)$ in the form $(x + (-5))$ to emphasize that the sign is included as part of the constant term.

3 ASSESS

Formative Assessment

Use Exercises 1–18 to assess whether students understand how to use FOIL to multiply binomials.

Crystal Ball Ask students how they think today's lesson on multiplying binomials will help with tomorrow's lesson on factoring polynomials.

0-2 FOIL

Objective
- Use the FOIL method to multiply binomials.

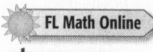

FL Math Online
glencoe.com

The product of two binomials is the sum of the products of
the *first* terms, the *outer* terms, the *inner* terms, and the *last* terms.
F O I L

EXAMPLE 1 Use the FOIL Method

Find each product.

a. $(x + 3)(x - 5)$

F L First Outer Inner Last

$(x + 3)(x - 5) = x \cdot x + x \cdot (-5) + 3 \cdot x + 3 \cdot (-5)$

I

O

$= x^2 - 5x + 3x - 15$
$= x^2 - 2x - 15$

b. $(3y + 2)(5y + 4)$

$(3y + 2)(5y + 4) = 3y \cdot 5y + 3y \cdot 4 + 2 \cdot 5y + 2 \cdot 4$
$= 15y^2 + 12y + 10y + 8$
$= 15y^2 + 22y + 8$

Exercises

Find each product.

1. $(a + 2)(a + 4)$ $a^2 + 6a + 8$

2. $(v - 7)(v - 1)$ $v^2 - 8v + 7$

3. $(h + 4)(h - 4)$ $h^2 - 16$

4. $(d - 1)(d + 1)$ $d^2 - 1$

5. $(b + 4)(b - 3)$ $b^2 + b - 12$

6. $(t - 9)(t + 11)$ $t^2 + 2t - 99$

7. $(r + 3)(r - 8)$ $r^2 - 5r - 24$

8. $(k - 2)(k + 5)$ $k^2 + 3k - 10$

9. $(p + 8)(p + 8)$ $p^2 + 16p + 64$

10. $(x - 15)(x - 15)$ $x^2 - 30x + 225$

11. $(2c + 1)(c - 5)$ $2c^2 - 9c - 5$

12. $(7n - 2)(n + 3)$ $7n^2 + 19n - 6$

13. $(3m + 4)(2m - 5)$ $6m^2 - 7m - 20$

14. $(5g + 1)(6g + 9)$ $30g^2 + 51g + 9$

15. $(2q - 17)(q + 2)$ $2q^2 - 13q - 34$

16. $(4t - 7)(3t - 12)$ $12t^2 - 69t + 84$

17. **NUMBERS** I am thinking of two integers. One is 7 less than a number, and the other is 2 greater than the same number.

a. Write expressions for the two numbers. $n - 7$, $n + 2$

b. Write a polynomial expression for the product of the numbers. $n^2 - 5n - 14$

18. **OFFICE SPACE** Monica's current office is square. Her office in the company's new building will be 3 feet wider and 5 feet longer.

a. Write expressions for the dimensions of Monica's new office. $x + 3$, $x + 5$

b. Write a polynomial expression for the area of Monica's new office. $x^2 + 8x + 15$

c. Suppose Monica's current office is 7 feet by 7 feet. How much larger will her new office be? 71 ft^2

TEACH with TECH

INTERACTIVE WHITEBOARD Work through an example of multiplying two binomials. Write an example on the board and use a different color for each of the four terms. Create a table with four columns for the four parts of FOIL. In each column, write the expression for the two terms to be multiplied using the same colors as before.

P6 Chapter 0 Preparing for Advanced Algebra

0-3 Factoring Polynomials

Objective
- Use various techniques to factor polynomials.

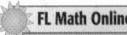

FL Math Online
glencoe.com

Some polynomials can be factored using the Distributive Property.

EXAMPLE 1 Use the Distributive Property

Factor $4a^2 + 8a$.

Find the GCF of $4a^2$ and $8a$.

$4a^2 = 2 \cdot 2 \cdot a \cdot a$ $\quad 8a = 2 \cdot 2 \cdot 2 \cdot a$ $\quad \rightarrow$ GCF: $2 \cdot 2 \cdot a$ or $4a$

$4a^2 + 8a = 4a(a) + 4a(2)$ — **Rewrite each term using the GCF.**

$= 4a(a + 2)$ — **Distributive Property**

Thus, the completely factored form of $4a^2 + 8a$ is $4a(a + 2)$.

To factor quadratic trinomials of the form $x^2 + bx + c$, find two integers m and p with a product equal to c and a sum equal to b. Then write $x^2 + bx + c$ using the pattern $(x + m)(x + p)$.

EXAMPLE 2 Use Factors and Sums

Factor each polynomial.

a. $x^2 + 5x + 6$ ← Both b and c are positive.

In this trinomial, b is 5 and c is 6. Find two numbers with a product of 6 and a sum of 5.

Factors of 6	Sum of factors	
1, 6	7	
2, 3	5	**The correct factors are 2 and 3.**

$x^2 + 5x + 6 = (x + m)(x + p)$ — **Write the pattern.**

$= (x + 2)(x + 3)$ — **$m = 2$ and $p = 3$**

b. $x^2 - 8x + 12$ ← b is negative, and c is positive.

In this trinomial, $b = -8$ and $c = 12$. This means that $m + p$ is negative and mp is positive. So m and p must both be negative.

Factors of 12	Sum of factors	
−1, −12	−13	
−2, −6	−8	**The correct factors are −2 and −6.**

$x^2 - 8x + 12 = (x + m)(x + p)$ — **Write the pattern.**

$= [x + (-2)][x + (-6)]$ — **$m = -2$ and $p = -6$**

$= (x - 2)(x - 6)$ — **Simplify.**

c. $x^2 + 14x - 15$ ← b is positive, and c is negative.

In this trinomial, $b = 14$ and $c = -15$. This means that $m + p$ is positive and mp is negative. So either m or p must be negative, but not both.

Factors of −15	Sum of factors	
1, −15	−15	
−1, 15	14	**The correct factors are −1 and 15.**

$x^2 + 14x - 15 = (x + m)(x + p)$ — **Write the pattern.**

$= [x + (-1)](x + 15)$ — **$m = -1$ and $p = 15$**

$= (x - 1)(x + 15)$ — **Simplify.**

0-3 Lesson Notes

1 FOCUS

Vertical Alignment

Lesson 0-3
Use various techniques to factor polynomials.

After Lesson 0-3
Simplify rational expressions.
Solve polynomial equations.

2 TEACH

Example 1 shows how to use the Distributive Property to factor a polynomial. **Example 2** shows how to factor quadratic trinomials of the form $x^2 + bx + c$. **Example 3** shows how to factor quadratic trinomials of the form $ax^2 + bx + c$. **Example 4** shows how to factor special products such as perfect square trinomials and the difference of squares.

Additional Examples

1 Factor $9cd^2 - 6cd^3$. $3cd^2(3 - 2d)$

2 Factor each polynomial.

a. $q^2 + 7q + 10$ $(q + 5)(q + 2)$

b. $x^2 - 7x + 12$ $(x - 3)(x - 4)$

c. $x^2 + 4x - 21$ $(x + 7)(x - 3)$

Tips for New Teachers

Sense-Making Remind students that in Algebra 1 they learned that a monomial is a number, a variable, or the product of a number and one or more variables; a binomial is the sum of two monomials; and a trinomial is the sum of three monomials. Ask students to give an example of each.

Additional Examples

3 Factor $20y^2 - 11y - 3$. $(4y - 3)(5y + 1)$

4 Factor each polynomial.

a. $9h^2 - 42h + 49$ $(3h - 7)^2$

b. $9d^2 - 64$ $(3d + 8)(3d - 8)$

Watch Out!

Preventing Errors Remind students that it is easy to confuse signs when factoring trinomials. To help prevent these mistakes, suggest that students use FOIL to check the factors.

TEACH with TECH

RSS Create a class Web page about how to factor different types of polynomials. After each class period, update the page with information from the most recent lesson, such as notes from class, video clips, and additional resources. Have students subscribe to an RSS feed so they can easily receive these updates.

3 ASSESS

Formative Assessment

Use Exercises 1–24 to assess whether students understand how to factor polynomials.

Yesterday's News Ask students to explain how yesterday's lesson on multiplying binomials helped them with today's lesson on factoring polynomials.

To factor quadratic trinomials of the form $ax^2 + bx + c$, find two integers m and p with a product equal to ac and a sum equal to b. Write $ax^2 + bx + c$ using the pattern $ax^2 + mx + px + c$. Then factor by grouping.

EXAMPLE 3 Use Factors and Sums

Factor $6x^2 + 7x - 3$.

In this trinomial, $a = 6$, $b = 7$, and $c = -3$. This means that $m + p$ is positive and mp is negative. So either m or p must be negative, but not both.

Factors of −18	Sum of factors
1, −18	−17
−1, 18	17
2, −9	−7
−2, 9	7

The correct factors are −2 and 9.

$6x^2 + 7x - 3 = 6x^2 + mx + px - 3$ **Write the pattern.**

$= 6x^2 + (-2)x + 9x - 3$ **$m = -2$ and $p = 9$**

$= (6x^2 - 2x) + (9x - 3)$ **Group terms with common factors.**

$= 2x(3x - 1) + 3(3x - 1)$ **Factor the GCF from each group.**

$= (2x + 3)(3x - 1)$ **Distributive Property**

StudyTip

Checking Solutions You can check to see that you have factored correctly by multiplying the factors and comparing the product to the original polynomial.

Here are some special products.

Perfect Square Trinomials

$(a + b)^2 = (a + b)(a + b) = a^2 + 2ab + b^2$

$(a - b)^2 = (a - b)(a - b) = a^2 - 2ab + b^2$

Difference of Squares

$a^2 - b^2 = (a + b)(a - b)$

EXAMPLE 4 Use Special Products

Factor each polynomial.

a. $4x^2 + 20x + 25$ ← The first and last terms are perfect squares. The middle term is equal to $2(2x)(5)$. This is a perfect square trinomial of the form $(a + b)^2$.

$4x^2 + 20x + 25 = (2x)^2 + 2(2x)(5) + 5^2$ **Write as $a^2 + 2ab + b^2$.**

$= (2x + 5)^2$ **Factor using the pattern.**

b. $x^2 - 4$ ← This is a difference of squares.

$x^2 - 4 = x^2 - (2)^2$ **Write in the form $a^2 - b^2$.**

$= (x + 2)(x - 2)$ **Factor the difference of squares.**

Exercises

Factor each polynomial.

1. $12x^2 + 4x$ $4x(3x + 1)$
2. $6x^2y + 2x$ $2x(3xy + 1)$
3. $8ab^2 - 12ab$ $4ab(2b - 3)$
4. $x^2 + 5x + 4$ $(x + 1)(x + 4)$
5. $y^2 + 12y + 27$
6. $x^2 + 6x + 8$ $(x + 2)(x + 4)$
7. $3y^2 + 13y + 4$
8. $7x^2 + 51x + 14$
9. $3x^2 + 28x + 32$
10. $x^2 - 5x + 6$
11. $y^2 - 5y + 4$
12. $6x^2 - 13x + 5$
13. $6a^2 - 50ab + 16b^2$
14. $11x^2 - 78x + 7$
15. $18x^2 - 31xy + 6y^2$
16. $x^2 + 4xy + 4y^2$ $(x + 2y)^2$
17. $9x^2 - 24x + 16$ $(3x - 4)^2$
18. $4a^2 + 12ab + 9b^2$
19. $x^2 - 144$
20. $4c^2 - 9$
21. $16y^2 - 1$ $(4y + 1)(4y - 1)$
22. $25x^2 - 4y^2$ $(5x + 2y)(5x - 2y)$
23. $36y^2 - 16$ $4(3y + 2)(3y - 2)$
24. $9a^2 - 49b^2$ $(3a + 7b)(3a - 7b)$

5. $(y + 3)(y + 9)$
7. $(3y + 1)(y + 4)$
8. $(7x + 2)(x + 7)$
9. $(3x + 4)(x + 8)$
10. $(x - 3)(x - 2)$
11. $(y - 4)(y - 1)$
12. $(3x - 5)(2x - 1)$
13. $2(3a - b)(a - 8b)$
14. $(11x - 1)(x - 7)$
15. $(2x - 3y)(9x - 2y)$
18. $(2a + 3b)^2$
19. $(x + 12)(x - 12)$
20. $(2c + 3)(2c - 3)$

P8 Chapter 0 Preparing for Advanced Algebra

0-4

The Counting Principle

Objective
- Use the Fundamental Counting Principle to find outcomes involving independent and dependent events.

New Vocabulary
outcome
sample space
event
Fundamental Counting Principle
factorial

FL Math Online
glencoe.com

An **outcome** is the result of a single trial. For example, the trial of tossing a coin has two outcomes: head or tail. The set of all possible outcomes is called the **sample space**. An **event** consists of one or more outcomes of a trial. When two or more events occur, the events can be independent or dependent.

Key Concept

Independent Events

Words If the outcome of an event does not affect the outcome of another event, the two events are independent.

Example tossing a coin and rolling a die

Dependent Events

Words If the outcome of an event does affect the outcome of another event, the two events are dependent.

Example taking a marble from a bag and then taking another marble from the bag without replacing the first

You can use the **Fundamental Counting Principle** to find the number of possible outcomes when two or more events occur.

Key Concept Fundamental Counting Principle

Words If event M can occur in m ways and is followed by event N that can occur in n ways, then the event M followed by event N can occur in $m \cdot n$ ways.

Example If event M can occur in 2 ways and is followed by event N that can occur in 3 ways, then the event M followed by event N can occur in $2 \cdot 3$ or 6 ways.

EXAMPLE 1 Independent Events

CONTESTS Kim won a contest on a radio station. The prize was a restaurant gift certificate and tickets to a sporting event. She can select one of three different restaurants and tickets to a football, baseball, basketball, or hockey game. How many different ways can she select a restaurant followed by a sporting event?

Her choice of a restaurant does not affect her choice of a sporting event, so these events are independent.

There are 3 ways she can choose a restaurant, and there are 4 ways she can choose the sporting event. Use the Fundamental Counting Principle to find the number of ways she can choose her two prizes.

number of restaurants		number of sporting events		number of ways to choose prizes
3	·	4	=	12

So, there are 12 different ways that Kim can choose her prizes.

0-4 Lesson Notes

1 FOCUS

Vertical Alignment

Lesson 0-4
Use the Fundamental Counting Principle to find outcomes involving independent and dependent events.

After Lesson 0-4
Solve problems involving permutations and combinations.

2 TEACH

Example 1 shows how to use the Fundamental Counting Principle to find outcomes involving two independent events. **Example 2** shows how to use the Fundamental Counting Principle to find outcomes involving more than two independent events. **Example 3** shows how to use the Fundamental Counting Principle to find outcomes involving dependent events.

Additional Example

1 **SHOPPING** Hector is planning to buy an MP3 player. He can choose from 5 different capacities and 4 colors. How many ways can he select his purchase? 20

Additional Examples

2 **RESTAURANTS** For dinner in a restaurant, Nathan can choose from 4 appetizers, 6 main courses, 5 beverages, and 3 desserts. How many different meals are possible? 360

3 **TRAVEL** Annabelle is planning to visit 5 colleges on her winter break. In how many different orders can she visit all 5 colleges? 120

Watch Out!

Preventing Errors Remind students that when counting with events that cannot occur more than once, the events are dependent.

TEACH with TECH

DIGITAL CAMERA Have students name different combinations of photo settings available on the camera (photo size, photo quality, flash on/off, etc.). Use these settings to find how many different combinations of photo settings are possible on the camera.

You can also use the Fundamental Counting Principle when there are more than two events.

EXAMPLE 2 More than Two Independent Events

CODES Many answering machines allow owners to call home and get their messages by entering a 3-digit code. How many codes are possible?

The choice of any digit does not affect the other two digits, so the choices of the digits are independent events. Each digit can be any numeral from 0 to 9.

There are 10 possible first digits in the code, 10 possible second digits, and 10 possible third digits. So, there are $10 \cdot 10 \cdot 10$ or 1000 possible different code numbers.

The mathematical notation 5! also means $5 \cdot 4 \cdot 3 \cdot 2 \cdot 1$. The symbol 5! is read five **factorial**. $n!$ means the product of all counting numbers beginning with n and counting backward to 1. By definition, $0! = 1$.

Problem-Solving Tip

Use a Diagram or Model It is sometimes helpful to sketch objects or use models such as counters to represent independent or dependent events. In Example 3, a different color counter could represent each course Charlita could take.

EXAMPLE 3 Dependent Events

SCHOOL Charlita wants to take 6 different classes next year. Assuming that each class is offered each period, how many different schedules could she have?

When Charlita schedules a class for a given period, she cannot schedule that class for any other period. Therefore, the choices of which class to schedule each period are dependent events.

There are 6 classes Charlita can take during first period. That leaves 5 classes she can take second period. After she chooses which classes to take the first two periods, there are 4 remaining choices for third period, and so on.

Period	1	2	3	4	5	6
Number of Choices	6	5	4	3	2	1

There are $6 \cdot 5 \cdot 4 \cdot 3 \cdot 2 \cdot 1$ or 720 schedules that Charlita could have. Note that $6 \cdot 5 \cdot 4 \cdot 3 \cdot 2 \cdot 1 = 6!$.

Exercises

State whether the events are *independent* or *dependent*.

1. selecting a fiction book and a nonfiction book at the library **independent**
2. choosing a president, vice president, secretary, and treasurer for Student Council, assuming that a person can hold only one office **dependent**
3. choosing a style, color, and size of mountain bike **independent**
4. selecting two pens from a box of 12 without replacing the first **dependent**

P10 Chapter 0 Preparing for Advanced Algebra

Real-World Link

"Black tie" is worn to any formal event after 6:00 P.M. The following is appropriate: traditional black tuxedo, white shirt, vest or cummerbund in black or dark color, black tie, and black patent shoes.

Source: Skeffington's FormalWear

Solve.

5. **HOMEWORK** Carlos has homework in math, chemistry, and English. How many ways can Carlos choose the order in which he does homework? **6**

6. **COMPUTERS** A mail-order computer company offers a choice of 4 amounts of memory, 2 sizes of hard drives, and 2 sizes of monitors. How many different systems are available to a customer? **16**

7. **DINING** A cafeteria offers the choices shown in the table. How many different combinations of drink and salad are possible? **12**

Drink	Salad
water	pasta
coffee	fruit
juice	chicken
milk	

8. **DANCES** Dane is renting a tuxedo for prom. Once he has chosen his jacket, he must choose from three types of pants and six colors of vests. How many different ways can he select his attire for prom? **18**

9. **MANUFACTURING** A baseball glove manufacturer makes a glove with the different options shown in the table. How many different gloves are possible? **48**

Option	Number of Choices
sizes	4
types by position	3
materials	2
levels of quality	2

10. **CLOTHES** How many different outfits can be made if Jessica chooses 1 each from 11 skirts, 9 blouses, 3 belts, and 7 pairs of shoes? **2079**

11. **PASSWORDS** Abby is registering at a Web site. She must select a password containing six digits from 1 to 9 to be able to use the site. How many passwords are allowed if no digit may be used more than once? **60,480**

12. **QUIZZES** Each question on a five-question multiple-choice quiz has answer choices labeled A, B, C, and D. How many different ways can a student answer the five questions? **1024**

13. **GAMES** The letters A through Z are written on pieces of paper and placed in a jar. Four of them are selected one after the other without replacing any of them. How many ways are there to select the letters? **358,800**

14. **LICENSE PLATES** How many different license plates are possible with two letters followed by three digits between 0 and 9? **676,000**

15. **FOOD** How many different combinations of sandwich, side, and beverage are possible for lunch? **60**

Sandwiches	Sides	Beverages
• hot dog • hamburger • veggie burger • bratwurst • grilled chicken	• chips • apple • pasta salad	• bottled water • soda • juice • milk

16. **AREA CODES** Prior to 1995, area codes were in the following format.

(ABC): $A = 2, 3, 4, 5, 6, 7, 8, 9$
$B = 0, 1$
$C = 0, 1, 2, 3, 4, 5, 6, 7, 8, 9$

a. How many area codes were possible before 1995? **160**

b. In 1995, the restriction on the middle digit was removed, allowing any digit in that position. How many total codes were possible after this change was made? **800**

3 ASSESS

Formative Assessment

Use Exercises 1–16 to assess whether students understand how to count events using the Fundamental Counting Principle.

Name the Math Ask students to describe the difference between independent and dependent events, using examples.

Lesson 0-4 The Counting Principle **P11**

0-5 Lesson Notes

1 FOCUS

Vertical Alignment

Lesson 0-5
Solve problems involving permutations and combinations.

After Lesson 0-5
Use permutations and combinations to find probabilities.

2 TEACH

Example 1 shows how to distinguish between permutations and combinations. **Example 2** shows how to evaluate permutations. **Example 3** shows how to evaluate permutations with repetition. **Example 4** shows how to evaluate combinations.

Additional Example

1 Determine whether each situation involves a permutation or a combination.

a. choosing a 4-digit password for an Internet account permutation

b. selecting 3 movies out of 20 possibilities to rent for the weekend combination

c. choosing 5 students out of a class of 28 to plan a class party combination

d. scheduling 6 students to each work for an hour selling raffle tickets permutation

0-5 Permutations and Combinations

Objective
- Solve problems involving permutations and combinations.

New Vocabulary
permutation
linear permutation
combination

FL Math Online
glencoe.com

When a group of objects or people is arranged in a certain order, the arrangement is called a **permutation**. In a permutation, the *order* of the objects is important. The arrangement of objects or people in a line is called a **linear permutation**.

An arrangement or selection of objects in which order is *not* important is called a **combination**.

When solving probability problems, it is helpful to be able to determine whether situations involve permutations or combinations. Often words in a problem give clues as to which type of arrangement is involved.

Type of Arrangement	Description	Clue Words	Examples
permutation	The order of objects or people is important.	• arranging *x* • an arrangement of first, second, and third	• arranging 4 books on a bookshelf • an arrangement of the letters in *math*
combination	The order of objects or people is not important.	• selecting *x* of *y* • choosing *x* from *y*	• selecting 3 of 8 flavors • choosing 2 people from a group of 7

EXAMPLE 1 Permutations and Combinations

Determine whether each situation involves a *permutation* or a *combination*.

a. choosing 6 students from a class of 25

Because the order of the students does not matter, this is a combination.

b. an arrangement of the letters in *drive*

Because the order of the letters is important, this is a permutation.

c. selecting 2 of 9 different side dishes

Because the order in which the side dishes are chosen does not matter, this is a combination.

d. choosing 3 classes from a list of 12 to schedule for first, second, and third periods

Because the order of the periods is important, this is a permutation.

You can use the following rule to find the number of permutations of objects.

Key Concept Permutations

The number of permutations of n distinct objects taken r at a time is given by

$${}_nP_r = \frac{n!}{(n-r)!}.$$

ReadingMath

Permutations The expression $_nP_r$ reads *the number of permutations of n objects taken r at a time.* A permutation can also be written as $P(n, r)$.

EXAMPLE 2 Permutation

There are 10 finalists in a figure skating competition. How many ways can gold, silver, and bronze medals be awarded?

Because each winner will receive a different medal, order is important. You must find the number of permutations of 10 finalists taken 3 at a time.

$_nP_r = \frac{n!}{(n-r)!}$ **Permutation formula**

$_{10}P_3 = \frac{10!}{(10-3)!}$ **$n = 10$ and $r = 3$**

$= \frac{10!}{7!}$ **Simplify.**

$= \frac{10 \cdot 9 \cdot 8 \cdot \cancel{7} \cdot \cancel{6} \cdot \cancel{5} \cdot \cancel{4} \cdot \cancel{3} \cdot \cancel{2} \cdot \cancel{1}}{\cancel{7} \cdot \cancel{6} \cdot \cancel{5} \cdot \cancel{4} \cdot \cancel{3} \cdot \cancel{2} \cdot \cancel{1}}$ **Divide by common factors.**

$= 720$ **Simplify.**

The gold, silver, and bronze medals can be awarded in 720 ways.

When some letters or objects are alike, use the rule below to find the number of permutations.

Key Concept Permutations with Repetition

The number of permutations of n of which p are alike and q are alike is

$$\frac{n!}{p!q!}.$$

EXAMPLE 3 Permutation with Repetition

How many different ways can the letters of the word *MISSISSIPPI* be arranged?

The letter *I* occurs 4 times, *S* occurs 4 times, and *P* occurs 2 times.

You need to find the number of permutations of 11 letters of which 4 of one letter, 4 of another letter, and 2 of another letter are the same.

There are 11 letters. →
There are 4 *I*s, 4 *S*s, and 2 *P*s. →
$\frac{11!}{4!4!2!} = \frac{11 \cdot 10 \cdot 9 \cdot 8 \cdot 7 \cdot 6 \cdot 5 \cdot 4!}{4!4!2!}$

$= 34{,}650$ **Use a calculator.**

There are 34,650 ways to arrange the letters.

ReadingMath

Combinations The expression $_nC_r$ reads *the number of combinations of n objects taken r at a time.* A combination can also be written as $C(n, r)$.

Key Concept Combinations

The number of combinations of n distinct objects taken r at a time is given by

$$_nC_r = \frac{n!}{(n-r)!r!}.$$

Additional Examples

2 **PASS CODES** Shaquan has a 4-digit pass code to access her computer. The code is made up of the odd digits: 1, 3, 5, 7, and 9. If each digit can be used only once, how many different pass codes could she have? 120

3 **NOTEBOOKS** In how many ways can 7 white notebook binders, 5 red binders, and 4 blue binders be arranged on a shelf? 1,441,440

Watch Out!

Student Misconceptions Some students confuse permutations and combinations. Remind them that clue words like *arrangement, sequence,* and *order* can help them decide whether a situation involves permutations.

TEACH with TECH

PORTABLE MEDIA PLAYER Ask students to find the number of songs on their portable media players from their favorite album. Then, have students calculate the number of 5-song playlists that could be created for that album (the order of the songs does matter). Discuss individual results with the class.

Additional Example

4 **CLOTHING** In how many ways can Xavier choose 3 shirts out of 12 in his closet to pack for a trip? 220

3 ASSESS

Formative Assessment

Use Exercises 1–20 to assess whether students understand how to identify and use permutations and combinations.

Yesterday's News Ask students to describe how the previous lesson on the Fundamental Counting Principle helped them with today's lesson on permutations and combinations.

EXAMPLE 4 Combination

A group of seven students working on a project needs to choose two students to present the group's report. How many ways can they choose the two students?

Because the order for choosing the students is not important, you must find the number of combinations of 7 students taken 2 at a time.

${}_nC_r = \frac{n!}{(n-r)!r!}$	**Combination formula**
${}_7C_2 = \frac{7!}{(7-2)!2!}$	**$n = 7$ and $r = 2$**
$= \frac{7!}{5!2!}$	**Subtract.**
$= \frac{\overset{3}{7 \cdot \cancel{6}} \cdot \overset{1}{\cancel{5}} \cdot \overset{1}{\cancel{4}} \cdot \overset{1}{\cancel{3}} \cdot \overset{1}{\cancel{2}} \cdot \overset{1}{\cancel{1}}}{\underset{1}{\cancel{5}} \cdot \underset{1}{\cancel{4}} \cdot \underset{1}{\cancel{3}} \cdot \underset{1}{\cancel{2}} \cdot \underset{1}{\cancel{1}} \cdot \underset{1}{\cancel{2}} \cdot \underset{1}{\cancel{1}}}$	**Divide by common factors.**
$= 21$	**Simplify.**

There are 21 possible ways to choose the two students.

Exercises

Find each permutation or combination.

1. ${}_5P_3$ **60**
2. ${}_6P_3$ **120**
3. ${}_7P_5$ **2520**
4. ${}_4C_2$ **6**
5. ${}_6C_1$ **6**
6. ${}_{10}C_4$ **210**
7. ${}_9P_5$ **15,120**
8. ${}_{12}C_7$ **792**

Determine whether each situation involves a *permutation* or a *combination*. Then find the number of possibilities.

9. 7 shoppers in line at a checkout counter **permutation; 5040**
10. an arrangement of the letters in the word *intercept* **permutation; 90,720**
11. selecting 4 of 13 different colored balloons **combination; 715**
12. an arrangement of 4 blue tiles, 2 red tiles, and 3 black tiles in a row **permutation; 1260**
13. choosing 2 different pizza toppings from a list of 6 **combination; 15**
14. the winner and first, second, and third runners-up in a contest with 10 finalists **permutation; 1260**
15. an arrangement of the letters in the word *parallel* **permutation; 3360**
16. choosing 2 CDs to buy from 10 that are on sale **combination; 45**
17. **SOFTBALL** The manager of a softball team has 7 possible players in mind for the top 4 spots in the lineup. How many ways can she choose the top 4 spots? **840 ways**
18. **NEWSPAPERS** A newspaper has 9 reporters available to cover 4 different stories. How many ways can the reporters be assigned to cover the stories? **3024 ways**
19. **READING** Jack has a reading list of 12 books. How many ways can he select 9 books from the list to check out of the library? **220 ways**
20. **BANDS** A band is choosing 3 new backup singers from a group of 18 who try out. How many ways can they choose the new singers? **816 ways**

Real-World Link

There are almost half a million words in the English language. But one third of all English writing is made up of only twenty-two words.

Source: *The Reading Solution*

P14 **Chapter 0** Preparing for Advanced Algebra

0-6 Congruent and Similar Figures

Objective
- Identify and use congruent and similar figures.

New Vocabulary
congruent
similar

FL Math Online
glencoe.com

Congruent figures have the same size and the same shape.

Two polygons are congruent if their corresponding sides are congruent and their corresponding angles are congruent.

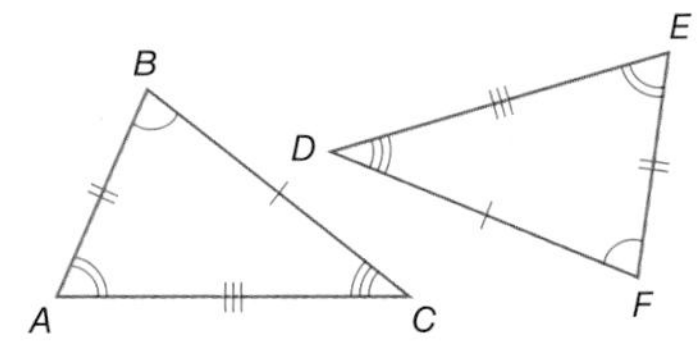

Congruent Angles	Congruent Sides
$\angle A \cong \angle E$	$\overline{AB} \cong \overline{EF}$
$\angle B \cong \angle F$	$\overline{BC} \cong \overline{FD}$
$\angle C \cong \angle D$	$\overline{AC} \cong \overline{ED}$

Read the symbol $\cong$ as *is congruent to*.

$\triangle ABC \cong \triangle EFD$

The order of the vertices indicates the corresponding parts.

EXAMPLE 1 Congruence Statements

The corresponding parts of two congruent triangles are marked on the figure. Write a congruence statement for the two triangles.

List the congruent angles and sides.

$\angle A \cong \angle D$	$\overline{AB} \cong \overline{DE}$
$\angle B \cong \angle E$	$\overline{AC} \cong \overline{DC}$
$\angle ACB \cong \angle DCE$	$\overline{BC} \cong \overline{EC}$

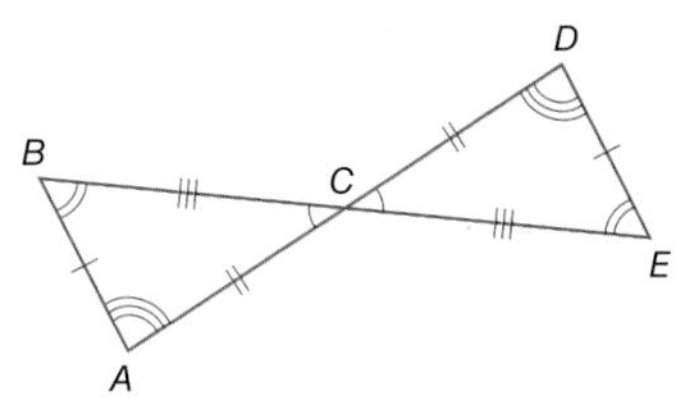

Match the vertices of the congruent angles. Therefore, $\triangle ABC \cong \triangle DEC$.

Similar figures have the same shape, but not necessarily the same size.

In similar figures, corresponding angles are congruent, and the measures of corresponding sides are proportional. (They have equivalent ratios.)

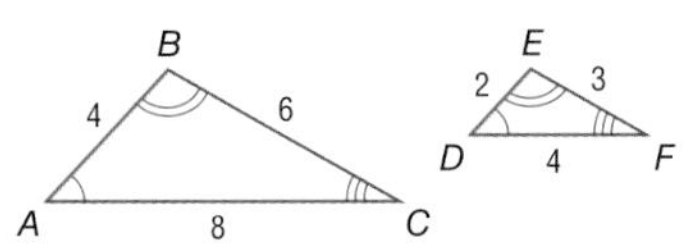

Congruent Angles
$\angle A \cong \angle D$, $\angle B \cong \angle E$, $\angle C \cong \angle F$

Proportional Sides
$\frac{AB}{DE} = \frac{BC}{EF} = \frac{AC}{DF}$

$\triangle ABC \sim \triangle DEF$ ← Read the symbol $\sim$ as *is similar to*.

EXAMPLE 2 Determine Similarity

Determine whether the polygons are similar. Justify your answer.

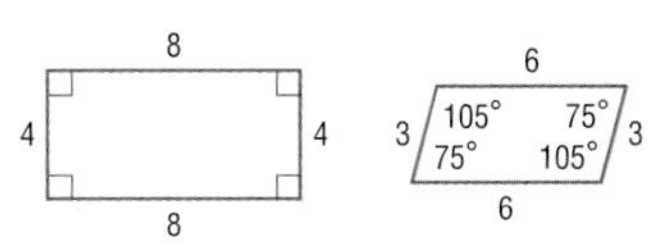

Because $\frac{4}{3} = \frac{8}{6} = \frac{4}{3} = \frac{8}{6}$, the measures of the sides are proportional. However, the corresponding angles are not congruent. The polygons are not similar.

0-6 Lesson Notes

1 FOCUS

Vertical Alignment

Lesson 0-6
Identify and use congruent and similar figures.

After Lesson 0-6
Use the Pythagorean Theorem to solve problems.

2 TEACH

Example 1 shows how to write congruence statements. **Example 2** shows how to determine whether two polygons are similar. **Example 3** shows how to use similar triangles to solve a real-world problem.

Additional Examples

1. The corresponding parts of two congruent triangles are marked on the figure. Write a congruence statement for the two triangles. $\triangle ABD \cong \triangle CBD$

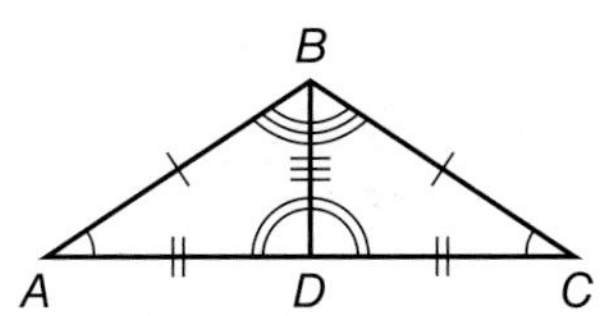

2. Determine whether the polygons are similar. Justify your answer.

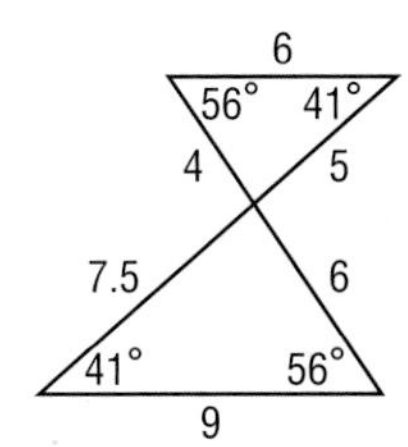

Yes; the corresponding angles are equal and the corresponding sides are proportional.

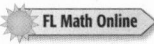

Additional Example

3 **GEOGRAPHY** A person is standing at the edge of the water, looking at an island that is 2 miles off shore. When a 5-inch long card is held 20 inches from the person's eye, the length of the island is covered exactly. How long is the island? 0.5 mile

TEACH with TECH

WIKI Have students work in pairs to create a wiki page about the different ways to prove two figures are congruent or similar. Have students review and revise each others' work as they create the page.

Watch Out!

Preventing Errors When using similarity to solve problems, students may set up the proportion incorrectly. Remind them that the order in which the vertices are named tells you which parts of the figure correspond.

3 ASSESS

Formative Assessment

Use Exercises 1–12 to assess whether students understand the concepts of congruence and similarity.

Crystal Ball Ask students how they think the concept of similarity in today's lesson will help them with tomorrow's lesson on the Pythagorean Theorem.

StudyTip

Reasonableness When solving a problem using a proportion, examine your solution for reasonableness. In Example 3, *DA* is more than twice *BA*, so *DE* should be more than twice *BC*. The solution is reasonable.

EXAMPLE 3 Solve a Problem Involving Similarity

CIVIL ENGINEERING The city of Mansfield plans to build a bridge across Pine Lake. Use the information in the diagram at the right to find the distance across Pine Lake.

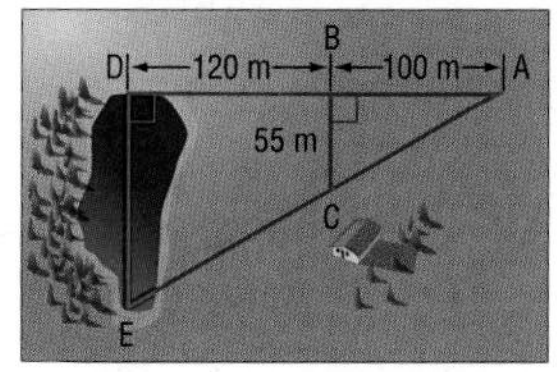

$\triangle ABC \sim \triangle ADE$

$\frac{AB}{AD} = \frac{BC}{DE}$	**Definition of similar polygons**
$\frac{100}{220} = \frac{55}{DE}$	***AB* = 100, *AD* = 100 + 120 or 220, *BC* = 55**
$100DE = 220(55)$	**Cross products**
$100DE = 12{,}100$	**Simplify.**
$DE = 121$	**Divide each side by 100.**

The distance across the lake is 121 meters.

Exercises

Determine whether each pair of figures is *similar, congruent,* or *neither*.

1. 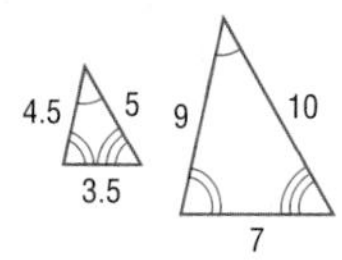 similar

2. 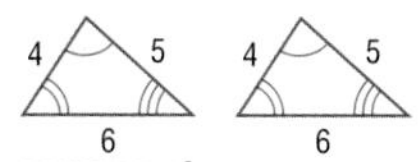 congruent

3. 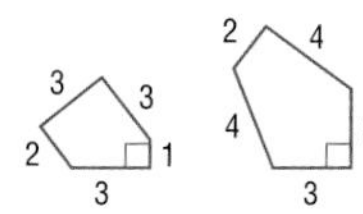 neither

4. 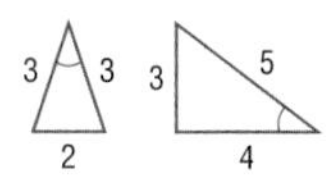 neither

5. 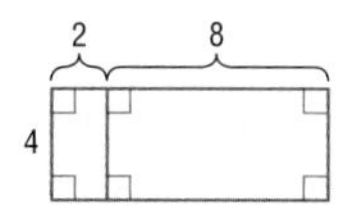 similar

6. 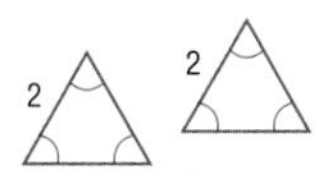 congruent

Each pair of polygons is similar. Find the values of *x* and *y*.

7. 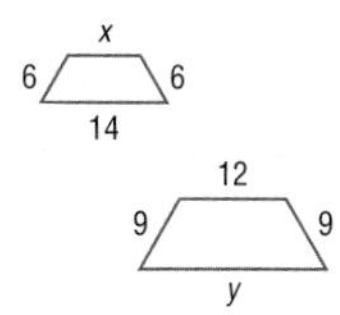 8; 21

8. 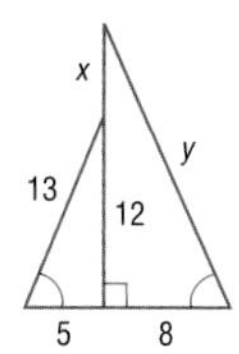 7.2; 20.8

9. 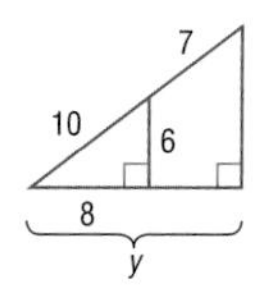 10.2; 13.6

10. SHADOWS On a sunny day, Jason measures the length of his shadow and the length of a tree's shadow. Use the figures at the right to find the height of the tree. 4.5 m

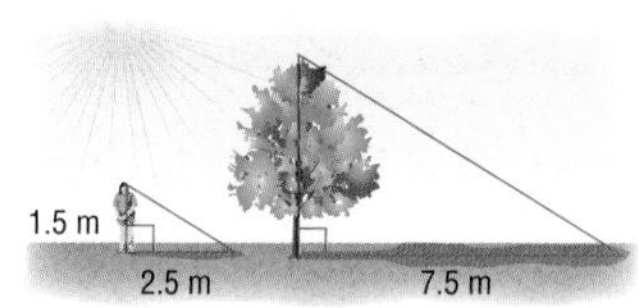

11. PHOTOGRAPHY A photo that is 4 inches wide by 6 inches long must be reduced to fit in a space 3 inches wide. How long will the reduced photo be? $4\frac{1}{2}$ in.

12. SURVEYING Surveyors use instruments to measure objects that are too large or too far away to measure by hand. They can use the shadows that objects cast to find the height of the objects without measuring them. A surveyor finds that a telephone pole that is 25 feet tall is casting a shadow 20 feet long. A nearby building is casting a shadow 52 feet long. What is the height of the building? 65 ft

0-7 The Pythagorean Theorem

Objective
- Use the Pythagorean Theorem and its converse.

FL Math Online
glencoe.com

The **Pythagorean Theorem** states that in a right triangle, the square of the length of the hypotenuse c is equal to the sum of the squares of the lengths of the legs a and b.

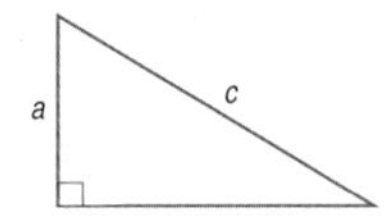

That is, in any right triangle, $c^2 = a^2 + b^2$.

EXAMPLE 1 Find Hypotenuse Measures

Find the length of the hypotenuse of each right triangle.

a.

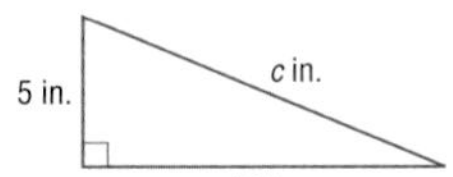

$c^2 = a^2 + b^2$	Pythagorean Theorem
$c^2 = 5^2 + 12^2$	$a = 5$ and $b = 12$
$c^2 = 25 + 144$	Simplify.
$c^2 = 169$	Add.
$c = \sqrt{169}$	Take the positive square root of each side.
$c = 13$	The length of the hypotenuse is 13 inches.

b.

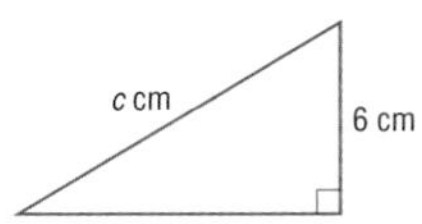

$c^2 = a^2 + b^2$	Pythagorean Theorem
$c^2 = 6^2 + 10^2$	$a = 6$ and $b = 10$
$c^2 = 36 + 100$	Simplify.
$c^2 = 136$	Add.
$c = \sqrt{136}$	Take the positive square root of each side.
$c \approx 11.7$	Use a calculator.

To the nearest tenth, the length of the hypotenuse is 11.7 centimeters.

You can also find the length of a leg of a right triangle given the lengths of the hypotenuse and the other leg.

EXAMPLE 2 Find Leg Measures

Find the length of the missing leg in each right triangle.

a.

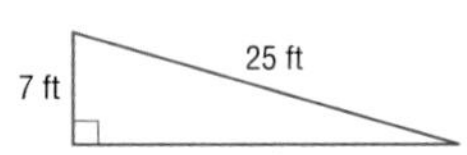

$c^2 = a^2 + b^2$	Pythagorean Theorem
$25^2 = a^2 + 7^2$	$c = 25$ and $b = 7$
$625 = a^2 + 49$	Simplify.
$625 - 49 = a^2 + 49 - 49$	Subtract 49 from each side.
$576 = a^2$	Simplify.
$\sqrt{576} = a$	Take the positive square root of each side.
$24 = a$	The length of the leg is 24 feet.

0-7 Lesson Notes

1 FOCUS

Vertical Alignment

Lesson 0-7
Use the Pythagorean Theorem and its converse.

After Lesson 0-7
Find the distance between two points on the coordinate plane.
Find the equation of a circle.

2 TEACH

Example 1 shows how to use the Pythagorean Theorem to find the length of the hypotenuse of a right triangle. **Example 2** shows how to use the Pythagorean Theorem to find the length of one of the legs of a right triangle. **Example 3** shows how to use the Pythagorean Theorem to determine whether a triangle is a right triangle.

Additional Example

1 Find the length of the hypotenuse of each right triangle.

a.

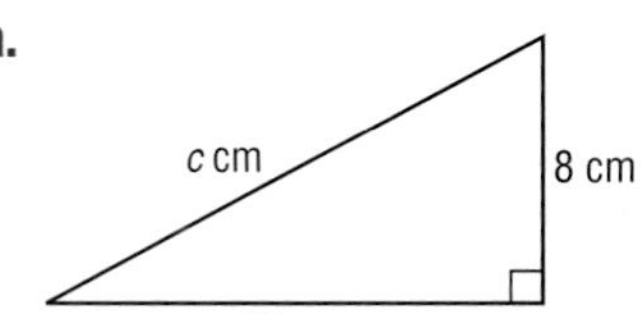

17 cm

b.

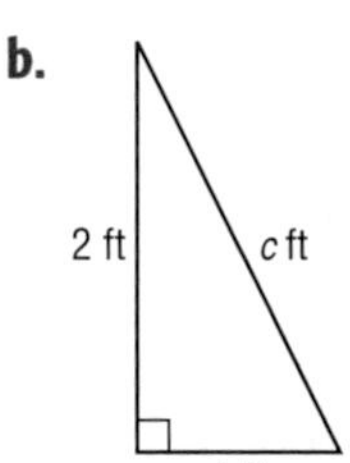

$\sqrt{5} \approx 2.2$ ft

Tips for New Teachers

Reasoning Show students that they can separate a figure with two polygons and draw a new diagram to clarify which side and angle measures of the polygons are similar.

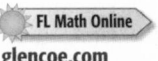

Additional Examples

2 Find the length of the missing leg in each right triangle.

a.

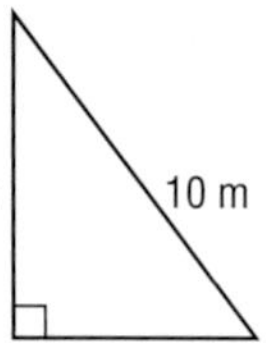

6 m

b.

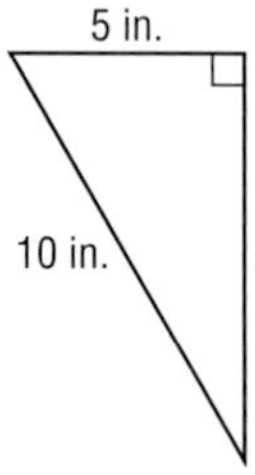

$\sqrt{75} \approx 8.7$ in.

3 The lengths of the three sides of a right triangle are 10, 24, and 26 centimeters. Determine whether this triangle is a right triangle. yes

Watch Out!

Preventing Errors Point out to students that when given three numbers that represent the lengths of the sides of a right triangle, the greatest value is always the measure of the hypotenuse, and the two lesser values are the measures of the two legs.

3 ASSESS

Formative Assessment

Use Exercises 1–17 to assess whether students understand how to use the Pythagorean Theorem.

Name the Math Have students describe the Pythagorean Theorem, including examples of when to use it or its converse.

Watch Out!

Positive Square Root When finding the length of a side using the Pythagorean Theorem, use only the positive and not the negative square root, since length cannot be negative.

b.

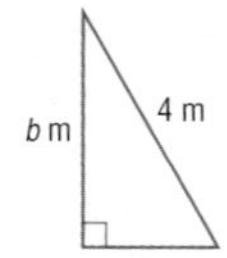

$c^2 = a^2 + b^2$	**Pythagorean Theorem**
$4^2 = 2^2 + b^2$	**$c = 4$ and $a = 2$**
$16 = 4 + b^2$	**Simplify.**
$16 - 4 = 4 - 4 + b^2$	**Subtract 4 from each side.**
$12 = b^2$	**Simplify.**
$\sqrt{12} = b$	**Take the positive square root of each side.**
$3.5 \approx b$	**Use a calculator.**

To the nearest tenth, the length of the leg is 3.5 meters.

The **converse of the Pythagorean Theorem** states that if the sides of a triangle have lengths a, b, and c, and $c^2 = a^2 + b^2$, then the triangle is a right triangle.

EXAMPLE 3 Identify a Right Triangle

The lengths of the three sides of a triangle are 5, 7, and 9 inches. Determine whether this triangle is a right triangle.

Because the longest side is 9 inches, use 9 as c, the measure of the hypotenuse.

$c^2 = a^2 + b^2$	**Pythagorean Theorem**
$9^2 \stackrel{?}{=} 5^2 + 7^2$	**$c = 9$, $a = 5$, and $b = 7$**
$81 \stackrel{?}{=} 25 + 49$	**Evaluate 9^2, 5^2, and 7^2.**
$81 \neq 74$	**Simplify.**

Because $c^2 \neq a^2 + b^2$, the triangle is *not* a right triangle.

Exercises

Find each missing measure. Round to the nearest tenth, if necessary.

1. 39 ft

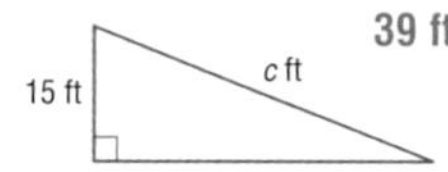

2. 24 km

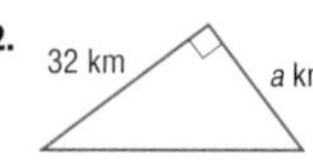

3. 8.3 cm

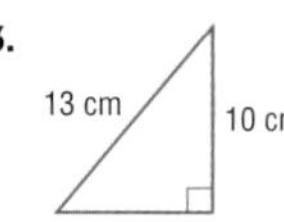

4. $a = 3, b = 4, c = ?$ 5
5. $a = ?, b = 12, c = 13$ 5
6. $a = 14, b = ?, c = 50$ 48
7. $a = 2, b = 9, c = ?$ 9.2
8. $a = 6, b = ?, c = 13$ 11.5
9. $a = ?, b = 7, c = 11$ 8.5

The lengths of three sides of a triangle are given. Determine whether each triangle is a right triangle.

10. 5 in., 7 in., 8 in. no
11. 9 m, 12 m, 15 m yes
12. 6 cm, 7 cm, 12 cm no
13. 11 ft, 12 ft, 16 ft no
14. 10 yd, 24 yd, 26 yd yes
15. 11 km, 60 km, 61 km yes

16. FLAGPOLES Mai-Lin wants to find the distance from her feet to the top of the flagpole. If the flagpole is 30 feet tall and Mai-Lin is standing a distance of 15 feet from the flagpole, what is the distance from her feet to the top of the flagpole? about 33.5 ft

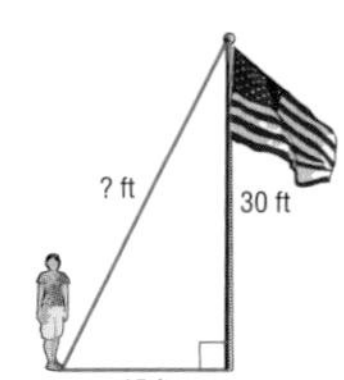

17. CONSTRUCTION The walls of a recreation center are being covered with paneling. The doorway into one room is 0.9 meter wide and 2.5 meters high. What is the length of the longest rectangular panel that can be taken through this doorway? about 2.66 m

TEACH with TECH

STUDENT RESPONSE SYSTEM Show students a set of three numbers, and ask them if these could be the side lengths of a right triangle. Have students respond with A for yes and B for no.

State the domain and range of each relation. Then determine whether each relation is a function. Write *yes* or *no*. 1. D = {0, 4, 5, 7}, R = {−2, −1, 5, 9, 12}; no

1. {(4, 5), (5, −1), (0, 12), (0, −2), (7, 9)}

2.

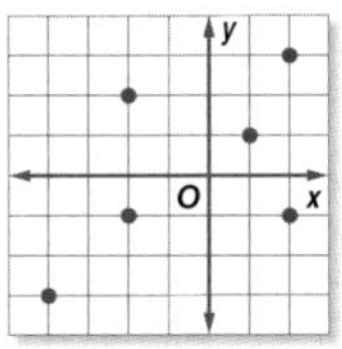

D = {−4, −2, 1, 2}, R = {−3, −1, 1, 2, 3}; no

Name the quadrant in which each point is located.

3. (−3, 7) II

4. (10, −11) IV

5. (42, 5) I

6. (−15, 3) II

Find each product. 7–12. See margin.

7. $(2r + 9)(r + 1)$

8. $(4n - 3)(2n + 2)$

9. $(5p - 1)(6p - 10)$

10. $(2r - 5)(r + 5)$

11. $(7x + 4)(7x + 4)$

12. $(3k - 2)(6k + 9)$

13. GEOMETRY The height of a rectangle is 3 millimeters less than twice the width.

a. Write an expression for each measure. w; $2w - 3$

b. Write a polynomial expression for the area of the rectangle. $2w^2 - 3w$

15. $(5a - 2)^2$ 16. $4(a + 2b)^2$ 17. $(10n - 1)(10n + 1)$

Factor each polynomial completely.

14. $4x^2 + 4xy + y^2$ $(2x + y)^2$

15. $25a^2 - 20a + 4$

16. $4a^2 + 16ab + 16b^2$

17. $100n^2 - 1$

18. $81t^2 - 36$ $9(3t - 2)(3t + 2)$

19. $16x^2 - 25y^2$ $(4x - 5y)(4x + 5y)$

State whether the events are *independent* or *dependent*.

20. choosing the color and size of a pair of shoes

21. choosing the winner and runner-up at a dog show

22. answering two multiple choice questions

23. answering two matching test questions where each solution is used only once

20, 22. independent 21, 23. dependent

24. COLLEGE For a college application, Macawi must select one of five topics on which to write a short essay. She must also select a different topic from the list for a longer essay. How many ways can she choose the topics of the two essays? 20 ways

25. STUDENT COUNCIL A student council has 6 seniors, 5 juniors, and 1 sophomore as members. In how many ways can a 3-member council committee be formed that includes one member from each class? 30 ways

Determine whether each situation involves a *permutation* or a *combination*. Then find the number of possibilities.

26. selecting 2 of 8 employees to attend a business seminar combination; 28

27. forming a team of 12 athletes from a group of 25 who try out combination; 5,200,300

28. Determine whether the rectangles are *similar*, *congruent*, or *neither*. neither

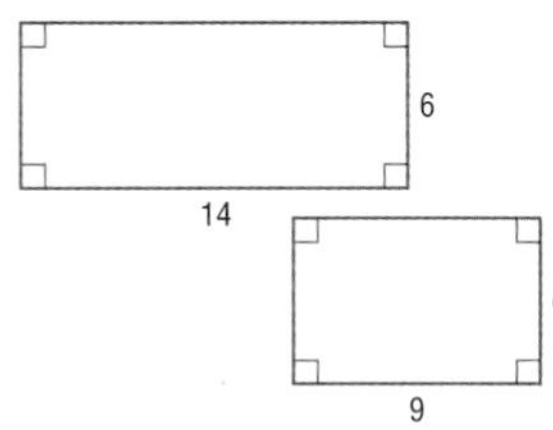

29. COMPUTERS A computer image of a painting is 320 pixels wide by 240 pixels high. If the actual painting is 42 inches wide, how high is it? 31.5 in.

Find each missing measure. Round to the nearest tenth, if necessary.

30.

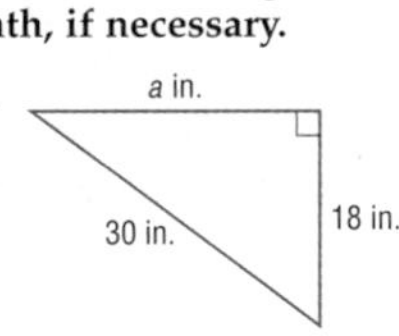

24 in.

31. $a = 33$ cm, $b = ?$ cm, $c = 45$ cm 30.6 cm

The lengths of three sides of a triangle are given. Determine whether each triangle is a right triangle.

32. 6 in., 8 in., 12 in. no

33. 30 m, 34 m, 16 m yes

34. 21 cm, 72 cm, 75 cm yes

CHAPTER 0 Posttest

Using the Posttest

Use the Chapter 0 Posttest to assess students' understanding of the concepts after you have presented the lessons in Chapter 0. If students are still having difficulty with one or more concepts, refer to *Math Triumphs 10/11* for strategies for reteaching.

Additional Answers

7. $2r^2 + 11r + 9$

8. $8n^2 + 2n - 6$

9. $30p^2 - 56p + 10$

10. $2r^2 + 5r - 25$

11. $49x^2 + 56x + 16$

12. $18k^2 + 15k - 18$

CHAPTER 1

Chapter Planner

Diagnostic Assessment
Quick Check, p. 3

	Lesson 1-1 Pacing: 1 day	Lesson 1-2 Pacing: 1 day	Lesson 1-3 Pacing: 1 day
Title	**Expressions and Formulas**	**Properties of Real Numbers**	**Solving Equations**
Objectives	• Use the order of operations to evaluate expressions. • Use formulas.	• Classify real numbers. • Use the properties of real numbers to evaluate expressions.	• Translate verbal expressions into algebraic expressions and equations, and vice versa. • Solve equations using the Properties of equality.
Key Vocabulary	variables algebraic expressions order of operations formula	real numbers rational numbers irrational numbers integers whole numbers natural numbers	open sentence equation solution
NGSSS	MA.912.A.3.1	MA.912.A.3.2	MA.912.A.3.1
Multiple Representations	p. 9	p. 16	p. 24
Lesson Resources	**Chapter 1 Resource Masters** • Study Guide and Intervention, pp. 5–6 AL OL ELL • Skills Practice, p. 7 AL OL ELL • Practice, p. 8 AL OL BL ELL • Word Problem Practice, p. 9 AL OL BL ELL • Enrichment, p. 10 OL BL **Transparencies** • 5-Minute Check Transparency 1-1 AL OL BL ELL **Additional Print Resources** • Study Notebook AL OL BL ELL	**Chapter 1 Resource Masters** • Study Guide and Intervention, pp. 11–12 AL OL ELL • Skills Practice, p. 13 AL OL ELL • Practice, p. 14 AL OL BL ELL • Word Problem Practice, p. 15 AL OL BL ELL • Enrichment, p. 16 OL BL • Quiz 1, p. 45 AL OL BL ELL **Transparencies** • 5-Minute Check Transparency 1-2 AL OL BL ELL **Additional Print Resources** • Study Notebook AL OL BL ELL	**Chapter 1 Resource Masters** • Study Guide and Intervention, pp. 17–18 AL OL ELL • Skills Practice, p. 19 AL OL ELL • Practice, p. 20 AL OL BL ELL • Word Problem Practice, p. 21 AL OL BL ELL • Enrichment, p. 22 OL BL • Graphing Calculator, p. 23 OL • Quiz 2, p. 45 AL OL BL ELL **Transparencies** • 5-Minute Check Transparency 1-3 AL OL BL ELL **Additional Print Resources** • Study Notebook AL OL BL ELL • Teaching Algebra with Manipulatives, pp. 178–179 AL OL ELL
Technology for Every Lesson	FL Math Online **glencoe.com** • Extra Examples • Self-Check Quizzes • Personal Tutor • Homework Help	**CD/DVD Resources** IWB INTERACTIVE WHITEBOARD READY IWB StudentWorks Plus IWB Interactive Classroom IWB Diagnostic and Assessment Planner	• TeacherWorks Plus • eSolutions Manual Plus • ExamView Assessment Suite
Get Animated		Animation	
Differentiated Instruction	pp. 6, 8, 10	pp. 12, 13, 17	pp. 20, 21

Formative Assessment
Mid-Chapter Quiz, p. 26

KEY: AL Approaching Level OL On Level BL Beyond Level ELL English Learners

Suggested Pacing			
Time Periods	Instruction	Review & Assessment	Total
45-minute	7	2	9
90-minute	4	1	5

Equations and Inequalities

Lesson 1-4 Pacing: 1 day	Lesson 1-5 Pacing: 1 day	Explore 1-6 Pacing: 0.5 day	Lesson 1-6 Pacing: 1.5 days
Solving Absolute Value Equations	**Solving Inequalities**	**Algebra Lab: Interval Notation**	**Solving Compound and Absolute Value Inequalities**
• Evaluate expressions involving absolute values. • Solve absolute value equations.	• Solve one-step inequalities. • Solve multi-step inequalities.	• Use interval notation to describe sets of numbers.	• Solve compound inequalities. • Solve absolute value inequalities.
absolute value empty set extraneous solution	set-builder notation		compound inequality intersection union
MA.912.A.3.6	MA.912.A.3.4	LA.910.1.6.1	MA.912.A.3.4, MA.912.A.3.6
p. 31	p. 38		
Chapter 1 Resource Masters • Study Guide and Intervention, pp. 24–25 AL OL ELL • Skills Practice, p. 26 AL OL ELL • Practice, p. 27 AL OL BL ELL • Word Problem Practice, p. 28 AL OL BL ELL • Enrichment, p. 29 OL BL • Spreadsheet Activity, p. 30 OL **Transparencies** • 5-Minute Check Transparency 1-4 AL OL BL ELL **Additional Print Resources** • Study Notebook AL OL BL ELL	**Chapter 1 Resource Masters** • Study Guide and Intervention, pp. 31–32 AL OL ELL • Skills Practice, p. 33 AL OL ELL • Practice, p. 34 AL OL BL ELL • Word Problem Practice, p. 35 AL OL BL ELL • Enrichment, p. 36 OL BL • Quiz 3, p. 46 AL OL BL ELL **Transparencies** • 5-Minute Check Transparency 1-5 AL OL BL ELL **Additional Print Resources** • Study Notebook AL OL BL ELL	**Additional Print Resources** • Teaching Algebra with Manipulatives, p.180 AL OL ELL	**Chapter 1 Resource Masters** • Study Guide and Intervention, pp. 37–38 AL OL ELL • Skills Practice, p. 39 AL OL ELL • Practice, p. 40 AL OL BL ELL • Word Problem Practice, p. 41 AL OL BL ELL • Enrichment, p. 42 OL BL • Quiz 4, p. 46 AL OL BL ELL **Transparencies** • 5-Minute Check Transparency 1-6 AL OL BL ELL **Additional Print Resources** • Study Notebook AL OL BL ELL • Teaching Algebra with Manipulatives, p. 181 AL OL ELL

FL Math Online glencoe.com
- Extra Examples
- Self-Check Quizzes
- Personal Tutor
- Homework Help

CD/DVD Resources IWB INTERACTIVE WHITEBOARD READY
- IWB StudentWorks Plus
- IWB Interactive Classroom
- IWB Diagnostic and Assessment Planner
- TeacherWorks Plus
- eSolutions Manual Plus
- ExamView Assessment Suite

			Animation
pp. 29, 32	pp. 35, 39		pp. 42, 44

Summative Assessment
- Study Guide and Review, pp. 49–52
- Practice Test, p. 53

CHAPTER 1

Assessment and Intervention

SE = Student Edition, **TE** = Teacher Edition, **CRM** = Chapter Resource Masters

	Diagnosis	Prescription
Diagnostic Assessment	**Beginning Chapter 1**	
	Get Ready for Chapter 1 **SE,** p. 3	Response to Intervention **TE,** p. 3
	Beginning Every Lesson	
	Then, Now, Why? **SE** 5-Minute Check Transparencies	Chapter 0 **SE,** pp. P1–P19 Concepts and Skills Bank **SE,** pp. 994–1007
Formative Assessment	**During/After Every Lesson**	
	Guided Practice **SE,** every example Check Your Understanding **SE** H.O.T. Problems **SE** Spiral Review **SE** Additional Examples **TE** Watch Out! **TE** Step 4, Assess **TE** Chapter 1 Quizzes **CRM,** pp. 45–46 Self-Check Quizzes glencoe.com	**Tier 1 Intervention** Concepts and Skills Bank **SE,** pp. 994–1007 Skills Practice **CRM,** Ch. 1 glencoe.com **Tier 2 Intervention** Differentiated Instruction **TE** Study Guide and Intervention Masters **CRM,** Ch. 1 **Tier 3 Intervention** *Math Triumphs, Alg. 2,* Ch. 1 and 2
	Mid-Chapter	
	Mid-Chapter Quiz **SE,** p. 26 Mid-Chapter Test **CRM,** p. 47 ExamView Assessment Suite	**Tier 1 Intervention** Concepts and Skills Bank **SE,** pp. 994–1007 Skills Practice **CRM,** Ch. 1 glencoe.com **Tier 2 Intervention** Study Guide and Intervention Masters **CRM,** Ch. 1 **Tier 3 Intervention** *Math Triumphs, Alg. 2,* Ch. 1 and 2
	Before Chapter Test	
	Chapter Study Guide and Review **SE,** pp. 49–52 Practice Test **SE,** p. 53 Standardized Test Practice **SE,** pp. 54–57 Chapter Test glencoe.com Standardized Test Practice glencoe.com Vocabulary Review glencoe.com ExamView Assessment Suite	**Tier 1 Intervention** Concepts and Skills Bank **SE,** pp. 994–1007 Skills Practice **CRM,** Ch. 1 glencoe.com **Tier 2 Intervention** Study Guide and Intervention Masters **CRM,** Ch. 1 **Tier 3 Intervention** *Math Triumphs, Alg. 2,* Ch. 1 and 2
Summative Assessment	**After Chapter 1**	
	Multiple-Choice Tests, Forms 1, 2A, 2B **CRM,** pp. 49–54 Free-Response Tests, Forms 2C, 2D, 3 **CRM,** pp. 55–60 Vocabulary Test **CRM,** p. 48 Extended Response Test **CRM,** p. 61 Standardized Test Practice **CRM,** pp. 62–64 ExamView Assessment Suite	Study Guide and Intervention Masters **CRM,** Ch. 1 glencoe.com

Differentiated Instruction

Option 1 Reaching All Learners AL OL BL ELL

KINESTHETIC Have pairs of students make up a set of real number cards. For each type of real number (rational, irrational, integer, natural, or whole), pairs should make up four cards that represent that type of real number. Then pairs will play a game of "Concentration." The first partner will turn over two cards. The two cards are removed if they represent the same type of real number. If not, both are turned back over. The other partner then takes a turn.

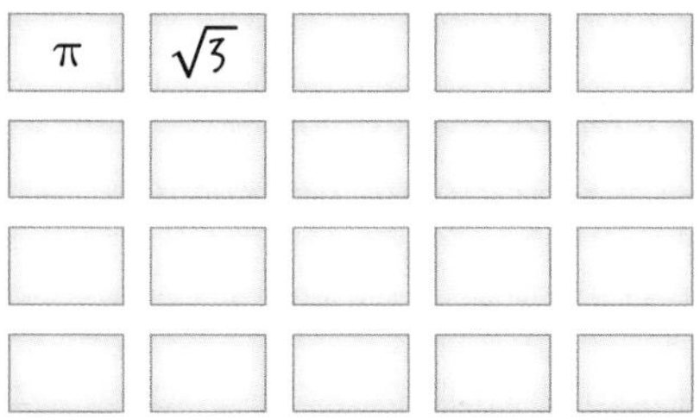

INTERPERSONAL Place students in pairs or small groups and assign inequalities such as those in Exercises 10–21 on page 37 for them to solve. Tell students to use the Key Concept Summaries on pages 33 and 34 and discuss which property is best to use to solve the inequalities they have been assigned. Make sure all group members participate in the discussion.

Option 2 Approaching Level AL

Write $x - 6 = 15$ on the board. Review the Addition and Subtraction Properties of Equality as you solve for *x*. Then erase all the equals signs and replace them with $>$.

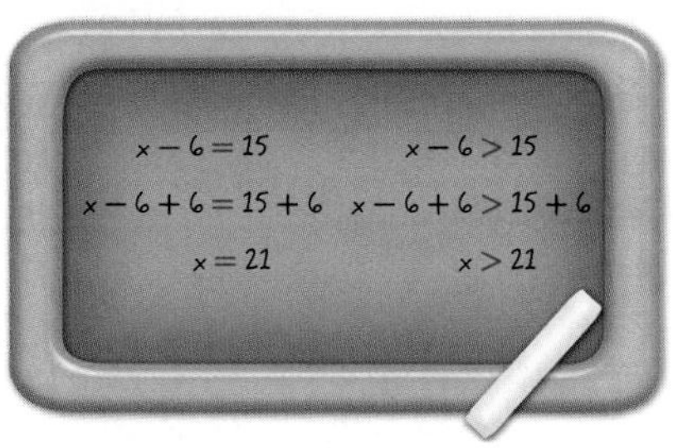

Discuss the similarities. Repeat, using $<$.

FL Math Online Access Point Activities

Option 3 English Learners ELL

Have students work in pairs to read, discuss, and plan a solution strategy for real-world problems. This interaction can help students to identify individual difficulties with word problems and also to discover new strategies used by other students.

Option 4 Beyond Level BL

Ask groups of students to write their own set of instructions for solving one- and two-step inequalities, including when to reverse the inequality sign and how to tell when the graph begins with a circle or a dot.

Focus on Mathematical Content

Vertical Alignment

Before Chapter 1

Related Topics from Algebra 1

- use symbols to represent unknowns and variables
- use the Commutative, Associative, and Distributive Properties to simplify algebraic expressions
- formulate linear equations and inequalities to solve problems, and solve the equations and inequalities

Chapter 1

- use the properties of real numbers to evaluate expressions and formulas
- classify real numbers
- use the properties of equality to solve equations
- solve absolute value equations
- solve inequalities, compound inequalities, and absolute value inequalities

After Chapter 1

Preparation for Precalculus

- define functions, describe characteristics of functions, and translate among verbal, numerical, graphical, and symbolic representations of functions

Lesson-by-Lesson Preview

1-1 Expressions and Formulas

An algebraic expression is an expression that contains at least one variable. It may also contain numbers and operations. When evaluating an algebraic expression, each variable must be replaced with a given value, and the order of operations must be followed. The order of operations is

- evaluate expressions inside grouping symbols,
- evaluate all powers,
- multiply and/or divide from left to right, and then
- add and/or subtract from left to right.

1-2 Properties of Real Numbers

Every real number corresponds to exactly one point on the number line, and every point on the number line represents exactly one real number. Real numbers are classified as either rational or irrational.

- A rational number can be expressed as a ratio $\frac{m}{n}$, where m and n are integers and $n \neq 0$.
- Any real number that is not rational is irrational.

Properties of real numbers are used to justify the steps used in solving equations and to describe mathematical relationships. The properties of real numbers include the following:

- the Commutative Properties of Addition and Multiplication,
- the Associative Properties of Addition and Multiplication, and
- the Distributive Property.

The sets of real numbers include identity elements for the operations of addition and multiplication, an additive inverse for every real number, and a multiplicative inverse for every real number except 0.

1-3 Solving Equations

An equation is a mathematical sentence stating that two mathematical expressions are equal. Solving an equation requires a series of equations, equivalent to the given equation, that result in a final equation that isolates the variable on one side of the equals sign. The Properties of Equality can be used to solve equations. The Properties of Equality include

- the Reflexive Property of Equality,
- the Symmetric Property of Equality,
- the Transitive Property of Equality, and
- Substitution.

Equations and Inequalities

Most equations can be solved by adding the same number to each side of the equation, by subtracting the same number from each side, or by multiplying or dividing each side by the same nonzero number.

1-4 Solving Absolute Value Equations

The absolute value of a number is its distance from zero on a number line. The absolute value symbols are grouping symbols like parentheses. For example, to evaluate the expression $2 \cdot |15 - 31|$, first calculate inside the absolute value symbols.

$$\begin{aligned} 2 \cdot |15 - 31| &= 2 \cdot |-16| \\ &= 2 \cdot (16) \\ &= 32 \end{aligned}$$

The equation $|a - 6| = 4$ can be interpreted as *the distance between some number* a *and 6 is 4 units.* The value $a - 6$ can be 4 or -4. So, if $a - 6 = 4$, then $a = 10$. If $a - 6 = -4$, then $a = 2$. The solutions are 10 and 2. An equation like $|x| = -2$ is *never* true, so there is no solution.

1-5 Solving Inequalities

An open sentence that contains the symbol $<$, $\leq$, $>$, or $\geq$ is called an *inequality.* For any two real numbers, a and b, exactly one of the following statements is true: $a < b$, $a = b$, or $a > b$.

Solving an inequality involves using the Properties of Inequality to write a series of equivalent inequalities, ending with one that isolates the variable. These properties include:

- the Addition Property of Inequality,
- the Subtraction Property of Inequality,
- the Multiplication Property of Inequality, and
- the Division Property of Inequality.

In general, adding the same number to (or subtracting the same number from) each side of an inequality, or multiplying or dividing each side by a positive number, does not change the truth of an inequality. Multiplying or dividing an inequality by a negative number *reverses* the order of the inequality.

There are infinitely many solutions to an inequality. These solutions can be expressed in more than one way:

- **Graphs** When the solution is graphed on a number line, an open circle indicates a value that is not included in the solution, and a closed circle indicates a value that is included. Circles are used with $<$ and $>$, and dots are used with $\leq$ and $\geq$.
- **Set Builder Notation** Solutions can be written using set-builder notation. A solution such as $x \geq 4$ would be written $\{x \mid x \geq 4\}$, and read *the set of values* x *such that* x *is greater than or equal to 4.*

1-6 Solving Compound and Absolute Value Inequalities

An inequality that consists of two inequalities joined by the word *and* or the word *or* is called a *compound inequality.* To solve a compound inequality, each part of the inequality must be solved.

- The graph of a compound inequality that contains *and* is the *intersection* of the solution sets of the two inequalities.
- The graph of a compound inequality that contains *or* is the *union* of the solution sets of the two inequalities.

There are important connections between compound inequalities and absolute value inequalities.

- An absolute value inequality using $<$ or $\leq$ is related to a compound inequality using the word *and.* For example, thinking of $|a| < 7$ as $|a - 0| < 7$, then the value of a is any number whose distance from 0 is less than 7 units.

Possible values for a

- An absolute value inequality using $>$ or $\geq$ is related to a compound inequality using the word *or.* For example, thinking of $|b| > 5$ as $|b - 0| > 5$, then the value of b is any number whose distance from 0 is greater than 5.

Possible values for b

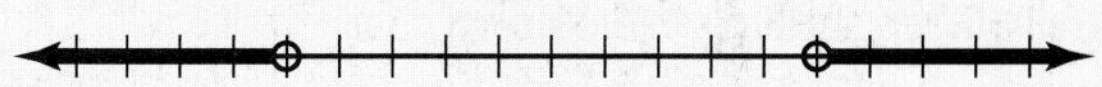

McGraw Hill Professional Development

Targeted professional development has been articulated throughout *Algebra 2.* More quality, customized professional development is available from McGraw-Hill Professional Development. Visit glencoe.com for details on each product.

- **Online Lessons** emphasize the strategies and techniques used to teach Algebra 2. Includes streaming video, interactive pages, and online tools.
- **Video Workshops** allow mentors, coaches, or leadership personnel to facilitate on-site workshops on educational strategies in mathematics and mathematical concepts.
- **MHPD Online** (www.mhpdonline.com) offers online professional development with video clips of instructional strategies, links, student activities, and news and issues in education.
- **Teaching Today** (teachingtoday.glencoe.com) gives secondary teachers practical strategies and materials that inspire excellence and innovation in teaching.

CHAPTER 1 Notes

Chapter Project

Purchasing Power

Students use what they have learned about equations and inequalities to investigate personal purchases.

- Ask each student to identify a reasonably expensive item that they would like to purchase at some point in the future. Depending on the student, the item could be an MP3 player, a prom dress, a used car, a television, etc.
- Have them research retail prices for their chosen purchase that include a variety of features and brands, and identify a range of available prices *P* from lowest to highest. Then write a compound inequality that represents the price range.
- Next, ask them to incorporate state and/or local sales taxes and write a revised inequality for the actual amount they would have to pay.
- Finally, have students write down how much money they receive per week from part-time jobs, payment for household chores, allowance, etc. Then write and solve equations in which the variable *N* is the number of weeks it would take them to save for their purchase, using both the least and most expensive amounts.

Key Vocabulary Introduce the key vocabulary in the chapter using the routine below.

Define: The absolute value of a number is its distance from zero on the number line, represented by $|x|$.

Example: $|-7| = 7$

Ask: Can the absolute value of a number ever be a negative number? Explain. No, because distance is nonnegative.

CHAPTER 1 Equations and Inequalities

Then
In Algebra 1, you wrote expressions with variables.

Now
In Chapter 1, you will:

- Simplify and evaluate algebraic expressions.
- Solve linear and absolute value equations.
- Solve and graph inequalities.

NGSSS
Reinforcement of MA.912.A.3.1
Reinforcement of MA.912.A.3.2

Why?
MONEY Connecting money to mathematics is one of the most practical skills you can learn. As long as you use money, you will be using mathematics. In this chapter, you will explore money topics such as sales tax, income, and budgeting for your first apartment.

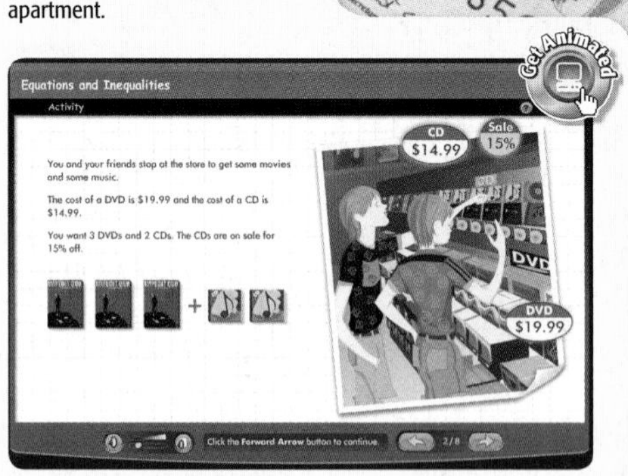

Get Ready for Chapter 1

Diagnose Readiness You have two options for checking Prerequisite Skills.

Text Option

Take the Quick Check below. Refer to the Quick Review for help.

QuickCheck

(Used in Lessons 1-1 through 1-3)

Simplify. (Prerequisite Skill)

1. $15.7 + (-3.45)$ **12.25**
2. $-18.54 - (-32.05)$ **13.51**
3. $-9.8 \cdot 6.75$ **−66.15**
4. $4 \div (-0.5)$ **−8**
5. $3\frac{2}{3} + \left(-1\frac{4}{5}\right)$ **$1\frac{13}{15}$**
6. $\frac{54}{7} - \frac{26}{6}$ **$3\frac{8}{21}$**
7. $\left(\frac{6}{5}\right)\left(-\frac{10}{9}\right)$ **$-1\frac{1}{3}$**
8. $-3 \div \frac{7}{8}$ **$-3\frac{3}{7}$**
9. **CRAFTS** Felisa needs $\frac{7}{8}$ yard of one type of material to make a quilt. How much of this material will she need to make 12 quilts? **$10\frac{1}{2}$ yd**

(Used in Lesson 1-1)

Evaluate each power. (Prerequisite Skill)

10. 6^3 **216**
11. $(-4)^3$ **−64**
12. $-(0.6)^2$ **−0.36**
13. $-(-2.5)^3$ **15.625**
14. $\left(\frac{4}{5}\right)^2$ **$\frac{16}{25}$**
15. $\left(\frac{7}{3}\right)^4$ **$\frac{2401}{81}$**
16. $\left(-\frac{7}{10}\right)^2$ **$\frac{49}{100}$**
17. $\left(-\frac{15}{2}\right)^3$ **$-\frac{3375}{8}$**
18. **FOOD** Nate's Deli offers 3 types of bread, 3 types of meat, and 3 types of cheese. How many different sandwiches can be made with 1 type each of bread, meat, and cheese? (Lesson 0-4) **3^3 or 27**

(Used in Lesson 1-5)

Identify each statement as *true* or *false*. (Prerequisite Skill)

19. $-6 \geq -7$ **true**
20. $8 > -5$ **true**
21. $\frac{1}{7} \leq \frac{1}{9}$ **false**
22. $\frac{5}{6} \leq \frac{25}{30}$ **true**
23. **MEASUREMENT** Christy has a board that is 0.6 yard long. Marissa has a board that is $\frac{2}{3}$ yard long. Marissa states that $\frac{2}{3} > 0.6$. Is she correct? **yes**

QuickReview

EXAMPLE 1

Simplify $\left(\frac{3}{16}\right)\left(-\frac{4}{5}\right)$.

$\left(\frac{3}{16}\right)\left(-\frac{4}{5}\right) = -\frac{3(4)}{16(5)}$	Multiply the numerators and the denominators.
$= -\frac{12}{80}$	Simplify.
$= -\frac{12 \div 4}{80 \div 4}$	Divide the numerator and denominator by the GCF, 4.
$= -\frac{3}{20}$	Simplify.

EXAMPLE 2

Evaluate $(-1.5)^3$.

$(-1.5)^3 = (-1.5)(-1.5)(-1.5)$	$(-1.5)^3$ means 1.5 is a factor 3 times.
$= -3.375$	Simplify.

EXAMPLE 3

Identify $\frac{3}{8} > \frac{12}{24}$ as *true* or *false*.

$\frac{3}{8} \overset{?}{>} \frac{12 \div 3}{24 \div 3}$	Divide 12 and 24 by 3 to get a denominator of 8.
$\frac{3}{8} \not> \frac{4}{8}$	Simplify.

False; $\frac{3}{8} \not> \frac{4}{8}$ because $\frac{3}{8} < \frac{4}{8}$.

Online Option

FL Math Online Take a self-check Chapter Readiness Quiz at glencoe.com.

Chapter 1 Get Ready for Chapter 1 3

Response to Intervention (RtI)

Use the *Quick Check* results and the Intervention Planner to help you determine your Response to Intervention. The If-Then statements in the chart below help you decide the appropriate tier of RtI and suggest intervention resources for each tier.

Intervention Planner

Tier 1 On Level

If students miss about 25% of the exercises or less,

Then choose a resource:

TE Chapter Project, p. 2

FL Math Online Self-Check Quiz

Tier 2 Strategic Intervention approaching grade level

If students miss about 50% of the exercises,

Then choose a resource:

FL Math Online Extra Examples, Personal Tutor, Homework Help

Tier 3 Intensive Intervention 2 or more years below grade level

If students miss about 75% of the exercises,

Then use *Math Triumphs, Alg. 2*, Ch. 1 and 2

FL Math Online Extra Examples, Personal Tutor, Homework Help, Review Vocabulary

Diagnose students' readiness for each chapter by using either the in-text **Quick Check** or the online **Chapter Readiness Quiz.** Then use the **Intervention Planner** to choose the correct program resource to reinforce each student's prerequisite skills.

FOLDABLES® Study Organizer

Dinah Zike's Foldables®

Focus As students work through this chapter, they write notes and show examples about equations and inequalities on cards to be placed in the pockets of the Foldables.

Teach Have students make and label their Foldables as illustrated. At the end of each lesson, ask students to write about their experiences with real numbers, computational skills, equations or inequalities, or other concepts presented in the lessons. Have them create study cards with notes and examples and place them in the appropriate pocket.

When to Use It Encourage students to add to their Foldables as they work through the chapter and to use them to review for the chapter test.

Differentiated Instruction

CRM Student-Built Glossary, pp. 1–2
Students should complete the chart by providing a definition of each term and an example as they progress through Chapter 1. This study tool can also be used to review for the chapter test.

Get Started on Chapter 1

You will learn several new concepts, skills, and vocabulary terms as you study Chapter 1. To get ready, identify important terms and organize your resources. You may wish to refer to **Chapter 0** to review prerequisite skills.

FOLDABLES® Study Organizer

Equations and Inequalities Make this Foldable to help you organize your Chapter 1 notes about equations and inequalities. Begin with one sheet of 11" × 17" paper.

1. **Fold** 2" tabs on each of the short sides.
2. **Then** fold in half in both directions. Open and cut as shown.
3. **Refold** along the width. Staple each pocket. Label pockets as *Algebraic Expressions, Properties of Real Numbers, Solving Equations,* and *Solve and Graph Inequalities.* Place index cards for notes in each pocket.

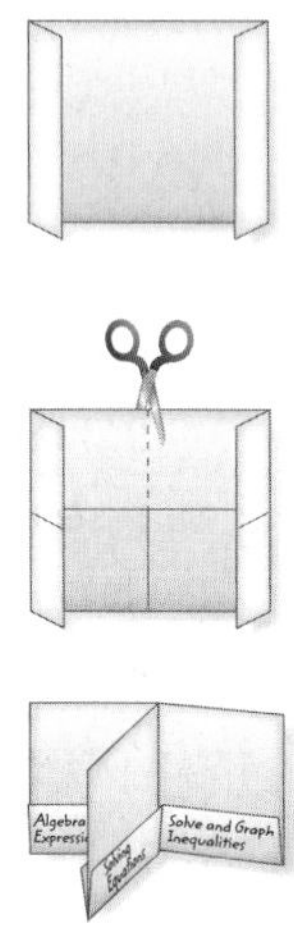

New Vocabulary

English		Español
variable	• p. 5 •	variable
algebraic expression	• p. 5 •	expressión algebraica
order of operations	• p. 5 •	orden de las operaciones
formula	• p. 6 •	formula
real numbers	• p. 11 •	números reales
rational numbers	• p. 11 •	números racional
irrational numbers	• p. 11 •	números irracional
integers	• p. 11 •	enteros
whole numbers	• p. 11 •	números enteros
natural numbers	• p. 11 •	números naturales
open sentence	• p. 18 •	enuciado abierto
equation	• p. 18 •	ecuación
solution	• p. 18 •	solución
absolute value	• p. 27 •	valor absolute
empty set	• p. 28 •	conjunto vacío
set-builder notation	• p. 35 •	notación de construcción de conjuntos
compound inequality	• p. 41 •	desigualdad compuesta
intersection	• p. 41 •	intersección
union	• p. 42 •	unión

Review Vocabulary

evaluate • p. 5 • evaluar to find the value of an expression

inequality • p. 33 • desigualdad an open sentence that contains the symbol $<$, $\leq$, $>$, or $\geq$

power • p. 6 • potencia an expression of the form x^n, read *x to the nth power*

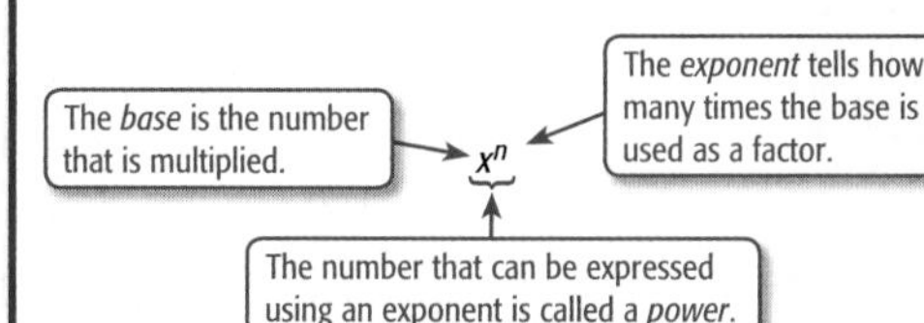
The *base* is the number that is multiplied.
x^n
The *exponent* tells how many times the base is used as a factor.
The number that can be expressed using an exponent is called a *power*.

Multilingual eGlossary glencoe.com

FL Math Online glencoe.com
- Study the chapter online
- Explore **Get Animated**
- Get extra help from your own **Personal Tutor**
- Use **Extra Examples** for additional help
- Take a **Self-Check Quiz**
- **Review Vocabulary** in fun ways

1-1 Expressions and Formulas

Then
You used the rules of exponents. (Lesson 0-3)

Now
- Use the order of operations to evaluate expressions.
- Use formulas.

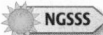

NGSSS
Reinforcement of MA.912.A.3.1 Solve linear equations in one variable that include **simplifying algebraic expressions**.

New Vocabulary
variables
algebraic expressions
order of operations
formula

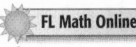

FL Math Online
glencoe.com

Why?

The following formula can be used to calculate a baseball player's on-base percentage x.

$$x = \frac{h + w + p}{b + w + p + s}$$

- h is the number of hits.
- w is the number of walks.
- p is the number of times the player has been hit by a pitch.
- b is the number of times at bat.
- s is the number of sacrifice flies.

During the first twenty games of a season, Ian has 9 hits, 2 walks, 38 at bats, 5 sacrifice flies, and he is hit by 1 pitch. The expression $\frac{9 + 2 + 1}{38 + 2 + 1 + 5}$ gives Ian's on-base percentage.

Order of Operations **Variables** are letters used to represent unknown quantities. Expressions that contain at least one variable are called **algebraic expressions**. You can evaluate an algebraic expression by replacing each variable with a number and then applying the **order of operations**.

Key Concept Order of Operations

Step 1 Evaluate expressions inside grouping symbols.
Step 2 Evaluate all powers.
Step 3 Multiply and/or divide from left to right.
Step 4 Add and/or subtract from left to right.

New Vocabulary is listed at the beginning of every lesson. Some lessons also have a Vocabulary Link, which shows how mathematical words are related to everyday words.

EXAMPLE 1 Evaluate Algebraic Expressions

Evaluate $m + (p - 1)^2$ if $m = 3$ and $p = -4$.

$m + (p - 1)^2 = 3 + (-4 - 1)^2$ — Replace m with 3 and p with -4.
$= 3 + (-5)^2$ — Add -4 and -1.
$= 3 + 25$ — Evaluate $(-5)^2$.
$= 28$ — Add 3 and 25.

Guided Practice

Evaluate each expression if $m = 12$ and $q = -1$.

1A. $m + (3 - q)^2$ 28

1B. $m \div 2q + 4$ −2

Personal Tutor glencoe.com

1-1 Lesson Notes

1 FOCUS

Vertical Alignment

Before Lesson 1-1
Use the rules of exponents.

Lesson 1-1
Use the order of operations to evaluate expressions.
Use formulas.

After Lesson 1-1
Solve linear equations.

2 TEACH

Scaffolding Questions

Have students read the *Why?* section of the lesson.

Ask:
- What does the variable b represent? number of times at bat
- What is Ian's on-base percentage? 0.261
- How would Ian's on-base percentage change if he had not been hit by any pitches? It would decrease from 0.261 to 0.244.
- Why does the formula represent on-base percentage? The numerator represents all the ways that a batter can reach first base. The denominator represents all the batter's plate appearances. (Note that at-bats does not include walks, hits by pitches, sacrifice flies, or sacrifice bunts.)

Lesson 1-1 Resources

Resource	Approaching-Level	On-Level	Beyond-Level	English Learners
Teacher Edition	• Differentiated Instruction, p. 6	• Differentiated Instruction, pp. 6, 8,10	• Differentiated Instruction, pp. 8, 10	• Differentiated Instruction, p. 6
Chapter Resource Masters	• Study Guide and Intervention, pp. 5–6 • Skills Practice, p. 7 • Practice, p. 8 • Word Problem Practice, p. 9	• Study Guide and Intervention, pp. 5–6 • Skills Practice, p. 7 • Practice, p. 8 • Word Problem Practice, p. 9 • Enrichment, p. 10	• Practice, p. 8 • Word Problem Practice, p. 9 • Enrichment, p. 10	• Study Guide and Intervention, pp. 5–6 • Skills Practice, p. 7 • Practice, p. 8 • Word Problem Practice, p. 9
Transparencies	• 5-Minute Check Transparency 1-1	• 5-Minute Check Transparency 1-1	• 5-Minute Check Transparency 1-1	• 5-Minute Check Transparency 1-1
Other	• Study Notebook	• Study Notebook	• Study Notebook	• Study Notebook

Order of Operations

Examples 1 and 2 show how to evaluate three different algebraic expressions by replacing the variables with numbers and then applying the order of operations.

TEACH with TECH

STUDENT RESPONSE SYSTEM

Write expressions on the board that use several different operations (such as $6 \times [5 - 4] \div 2 + 1$). Ask students which operation should be performed first. Give them a numerical key to use for their responses (for example, 1 for +, 2 for –, 3 for ×, and 4 for ÷).

Formative Assessment

Use the Guided Practice exercises after each example to determine students' understanding of concepts.

Additional Examples

1 Evaluate $(x - y)^3 + 3$ if $x = 1$ and $y = 4$. -24

2 a. Evaluate $n - t(n^2 - t)$ if $n = 2$ and $t = 3.4$. -0.04

b. Evaluate $\frac{8xy + z^3}{y^2 + 5}$ if $x = 5$, $y = -2$, and $z = -1$. -9

Additional Examples also in Interactive Classroom PowerPoint® Presentations

IWB INTERACTIVE WHITEBOARD READY

Tips for New Teachers

Evaluating Expressions When evaluating expressions such as $64 - 1.5(9.5)$, students often fail to follow the order of operations and instead perform the operations from left to right.

$$64 - 1.5(9.5) \neq 62.5(9.5)$$

The value of an expression can be determined only if the order of operations is followed.

ReadingMath

Exponents x^2 may be read as *x squared* or *x to the second power*. x^3 may be read as *x cubed* or *x to the third power*.

EXAMPLE 2 Evaluate Algebraic Expressions

a. Evaluate $a + b^2(b - a)$ if $a = 5$ and $b = -3.2$.

$a + b^2(b - a) = 5 + (-3.2)^2(-3.2 - 5)$	**$a = 5$ and $b = -3.2$**
$= 5 + (-3.2)^2(-8.2)$	**Subtract 5 from -3.2.**
$= 5 + 10.24(-8.2)$	**Evaluate $(-3.2)^2$.**
$= 5 + (-83.968)$	**Multiply 10.24 and -8.2.**
$= -78.968$	**Add 5 and -83.968.**

b. Evaluate $\frac{x^4 - 3wy}{y^3 + 2w}$ if $w = 4$, $x = -3$, and $y = -5$.

$\frac{x^4 - 3wy}{y^3 + 2w} = \frac{(-3)^4 - 3(4)(-5)}{(-5)^3 + 2(4)}$	**$w = 4$, $x = -3$, and $y = -5$**
$= \frac{81 - 3(4)(-5)}{-125 + 2(4)}$	**Evaluate the numerator and denominator separately.**
$= \frac{81 - (-60)}{-125 + 8}$	**Multiply in the numerator and denominator.**
$= \frac{141}{-117}$ or $-\frac{47}{39}$	**Simplify the numerator and denominator. Then simplify the fraction.**

Guided Practice

Evaluate each expression if $h = 4$, $j = -1$, and $k = 0.5$.

2A. $h^2k + h(h - k)$ 22 **2B.** $j + (3 - h)^2$ 0 **2C.** $\frac{j^2 - 3h^2k}{j^3 + 2}$ -23

Personal Tutor glencoe.com

StudyTip

Grouping Symbols Remember that in the order of operations, expressions inside of grouping symbols are evaluated first. A fraction bar is one type of grouping symbol. Evaluate the expressions in the numerator and denominator separately before dividing.

Formulas A **formula** is a mathematical sentence that expresses the relationship between certain quantities. If you know the value of every variable in the formula except one, you can find the value of the remaining variable.

Real-World EXAMPLE 3 Use a Formula

TORNADOES The formula for the volume of a cone, $V = \frac{1}{3}\pi r^2 h$, can be used to approximate the volume of a tornado. Find the approximate volume of the tornado at the right.

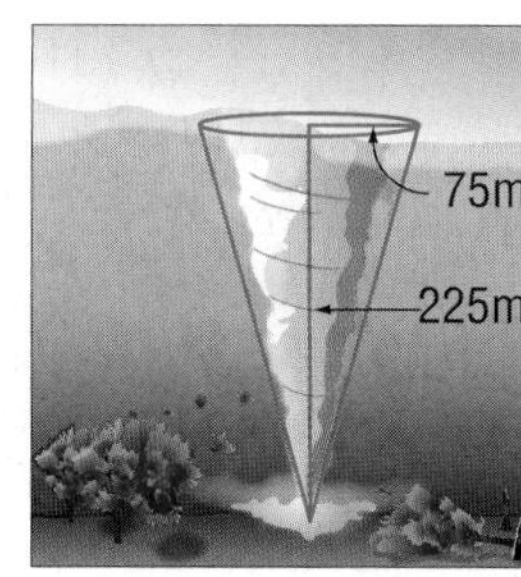

$V = \frac{1}{3}\pi r^2 h$	**Volume of a cone**
$= \frac{1}{3}\pi(75)^2(225)$	**$r = 75$ and $h = 225$**
$= \frac{1}{3}\pi(5625)(225)$	**Evaluate 75^2.**
$\approx 1{,}325{,}359$	**Multiply.**

The approximate volume of the tornado is about 1,325,359 cubic meters.

Guided Practice

3. GEOMETRY The formula for the volume V of a rectangular prism is $V = \ell wh$, where ℓ represents the length, w represents the width, and h represents the height. Find the volume of a rectangular prism with a length of 4 feet, a width of 2 feet, and a height of 3.5 feet. 28 ft^3

Personal Tutor glencoe.com

Differentiated Instruction AL OL ELL

If students have trouble memorizing the order of operations,

Then ask them to create a song, rhyme, or mnemonic device that will help them to remember the correct order of operations. **P**lease **E**xcuse **M**y **D**ear **A**unt **S**ally is an example of a mnemonic device.

Check Your Understanding

Example 1 p. 5

Evaluate each expression if $a = -2$, $b = 3$, and $c = 4.2$.

1. $a - 2b + 3c$ **4.6**
2. $2a + (b + 3)^2$ **32**
3. $a + 3[b^2 - (a + c)]$ **18.4**

Example 2 p. 6

4. $5c - 2[(b - a) + c]$ **2.6**
5. $4(2a + 3b) - 2c$ **11.6**
6. $\frac{a^2 + 4c}{3b + 2a}$ **4.16**
7. $\frac{b^3 + ac}{ab + 2bc}$ **0.96875**
8. $\frac{3b + 2a}{5 - c}$ **6.25**
9. $\frac{3a - 2c}{4ab}$ **0.6**

Example 3 p. 6

10. **VOLLEYBALL** A player's attack percentage A is calculated using the formula $A = \frac{k - e}{t}$, where k represents the number of kills, e represents the number of attack errors including blocks, and t represents the total attacks attempted. Find the attack percentage given each set of values.

a. $k = 22, e = 11, t = 35$ **0.314 or 31.4%** **b.** $k = 33, e = 9, t = 50$ **0.48 or 48%**

Practice and Problem Solving

● = **Step-by-Step Solutions** begin on page R20. **Extra Practice** begins on page 947.

Example 1 p. 5

Evaluate each expression if $w = -3$, $x = 4$, $y = 2.6$, and $z = \frac{1}{3}$.

11. $y + x - z$ $6\frac{4}{15}$
12. $w - 2x + y \div 2$ **−9.7**
13. $4(x - w)$ **28**
14. $6(y + x)$ **39.6**
15. $9z - 4y + 2w$ **−13.4**
16. $3y - 4z + x$ $10\frac{7}{15}$

17. **GAS MILEAGE** The gasoline used by a car is measured in miles per gallon and is related to the distance traveled by the following formula.

miles per gallon × number of gallons = distance traveled

a. During a trip your car used a total of 46.2 gallons of gasoline. If your car gets 33 miles to the gallon, how far did you travel? **1524.6 mi**

b. Your friend has decided to buy a hybrid car that gets 60 miles per gallon. The gasoline tank holds 12 gallons. How far can the car go on one tank of gasoline? **720 mi**

Example 2 p. 6

Evaluate each expression if $a = -4$, $b = -0.8$, $c = 5$, and $d = \frac{1}{5}$.

18. $\frac{a + b}{c - d}$ **−1**
19. $\frac{a - b}{bd}$ **20**
20. $\frac{ac}{d + b}$ $33\frac{1}{3}$
21. $\frac{b^2c^2}{ad}$ **−20**
22. $\frac{b + 6}{4(d + c)}$ **0.25**
23. $\frac{5(d + a)}{2ab^2}$ **≈ 3.71**

24. **TEMPERATURE** The formula $C = \frac{5(F - 32)}{9}$ can be used to convert temperatures in degrees Fahrenheit to degrees Celsius.

a. Room temperature commonly ranges from 64°F to 73°F. Determine room temperature range in degrees Celsius. **17.8°C to 22.8°C**

b. The normal average human body temperature is 98.6°F. A temperature above this indicates a fever. If your temperature is 42°C, do you have a fever? Explain your reasoning.

24b. Yes; Sample answer: 98.6°F = 37°C, so a temperature above 37°C indicates a fever.

Example 3 p. 6

25. **GEOMETRY** The formula for the area A of a triangle with height h and base b is $A = \frac{1}{2}bh$. Write an expression to represent the area of the triangle. $\frac{1}{2}(x + 7)(2x)$

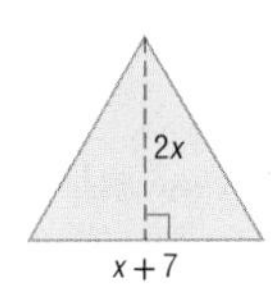

B

26. **FINANCIAL LITERACY** The profit that a business made during a year is \$536,897,000. If the business divides the profit evenly for each share, estimate how much each share made if there are 10,995,000 shares. **\$48.83**

Formulas

Example 3 shows how to find the value of a variable in a formula when the values of all the other variables are known.

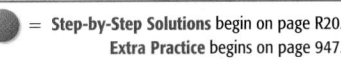

Additional Example

3 **GEOMETRY** The formula for the area A of a trapezoid is $A = \frac{1}{2}h(b_1 + b_2)$, where h represents the height, and b_1 and b_2 represent the measures of the bases. Find the area of a trapezoid with base lengths of 13 meters and 25 meters and a height of 8 meters. 152 m^2

Tips for New Teachers

Reasoning Remind students to follow the order of operations when evaluating algebraic expressions. Demonstrate with an example to show students that performing the operations using an alternative method, such as from left to right, will result in an incorrect answer.

3 PRACTICE

Formative Assessment

Use Exercises 1–10 to check for understanding.

Use the chart at the bottom of this page to customize assignments for your students.

Differentiated Homework Options

Level	Assignment	Two-Day Option	
AL Basic	11–25, 43, 45, 47–67	11–25 odd, 50–53	12–24 even, 43, 45, 47–49, 54–67
OL Core	11–25 odd, 26–28, 29–33 odd, 35–43, 45, 47–67	11–25, 50–53	26–43, 45, 47–49, 54–67
BL Advanced	26–59, (optional: 60–67)		

The **Differentiated Homework Options** provide leveled assignments. Many of the homework exercises are paired, so that students can do the odds one day and the evens the next day.

Multiple Representations In Exercise 42, students use geometric drawings, a ruler, a table of values, and an algebraic expression to compare the volume of two cylinders.

Watch Out!

Error Analysis For Exercise 43, students should see that Lauren and Rico did something different when they subtracted −12 − 20. They must now decide who subtracted correctly.

Additional Answers

42a. Sample answer:

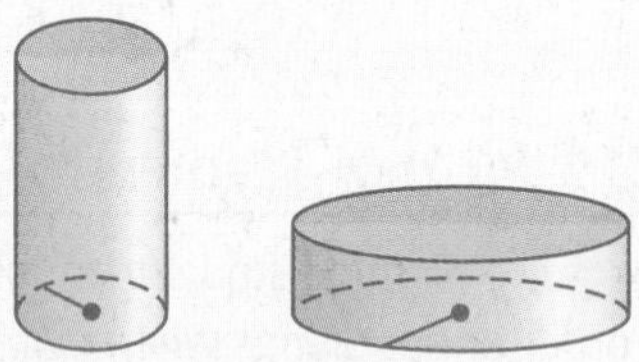

42b. Sample answer:

cylinder	radius	height	volume
1	2 in.	5 in.	$20\pi \approx 62.8 \text{ in}^3$
2	4 in.	1 in.	$16\pi \approx 50.3 \text{ in}^3$

27. EARTH The radius of Earth's orbit is 93,000,000 miles.

a. Find the circumference of Earth's orbit assuming that the orbit is a circle. The formula for the circumference of a circle is $2\pi r$. **584,336,233.6 mi**

b. Earth travels at a speed of 66,698 miles per hour around the Sun. Use the formula $T = \frac{C}{V}$, where T is time in hours, C is circumference, and V is velocity to find the number of hours it takes Earth to revolve around the Sun. **8761 h**

c. Did you prove that it takes 1 year for Earth to go around the Sun? Explain.

27c. Yes; $\frac{8761}{24}$ = 365 days or 1 year.

Real-World Link

Worldwide, over 6000 Web searches are performed every second.

Source: Nielsen Research

28. ANCIENT PYRAMID The Great Pyramid in Cairo, Egypt, is approximately 146.7 meters high, and each side of its base is approximately 230 meters.

a. Find the area of the base of the pyramid. Remember $A = \ell w$. **52,900 m²**

b. The volume of a pyramid is $\frac{1}{3}Bh$, where B is the area of the base and h is the height. What is the volume of the Great Pyramid? **2,586,810 m³**

Evaluate each expression if $w = \frac{3}{4}$, $x = 8$, $y = -2$, and $z = 0.4$.

29. $x^3 + 2y^4$ **544**

30. $(x - 6z)^2$ **31.36**

31. $2(6w - 2y) - 8z$ **13.8**

32. $\frac{(y + z)^2}{xw}$ **0.427**

33. $\frac{12w - 6y}{z^2}$ **131.25**

34. $\frac{wx + yz}{wx - yz}$ **0.765**

35. GEOMETRY The formula for the volume V of a cone with radius r and height h is $V = \frac{1}{3}\pi r^2 h$. Write an expression for the volume of the cone at the right. $6\pi x^3$

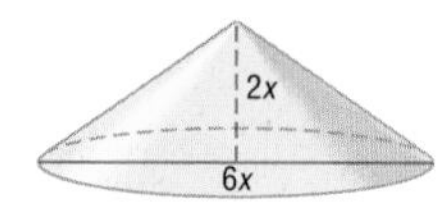

36. SEARCH ENGINES Page rank is a numerical value that represents how important a page is on the Web. One formula used to calculate the page rank for a page is $PR = 0.15 + 0.85L$, where L is the page rank of the linking page divided by the number of outbound links on the page. Determine the page rank of a page in which $L = 10$. **8.65**

37. WEATHER In 1898, A.E. Dolbear studied various species of crickets to determine their "chirp rate" based on temperatures. He determined that the formula $t = 50 + \frac{n - 40}{4}$, where n is the number of chirps per minute, could be used to find the temperature t in degrees Fahrenheit. What is the temperature if the number of chirps is 120? **70°F**

38. FOOTBALL The following formula can be used to calculate a quarterback efficiency rating.

$$\left(\frac{\frac{C}{A} - 0.3}{0.2} + \frac{\frac{Y}{A} - 3}{4} + \frac{\frac{T}{A}}{0.05} + \frac{0.095 - \frac{I}{A}}{0.04}\right) \cdot \frac{100}{6}$$

- C is the number of passes completed.
- A is the number of passes attempted.
- Y is passing yardage.
- T is the number of touchdown passes.
- I is the number of interceptions.

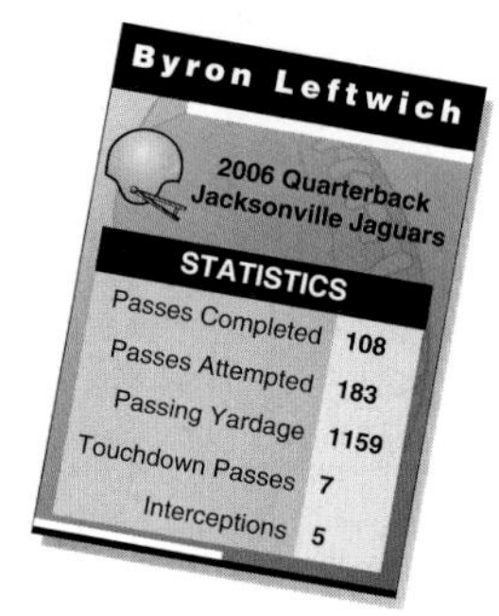

Byron Leftwich
2006 Quarterback
Jacksonville Jaguars
STATISTICS
Passes Completed 108
Passes Attempted 183
Passing Yardage 1159
Touchdown Passes 7
Interceptions 5

Find Byron Leftwich's efficiency rating to the nearest tenth for the season statistics shown. **79.0**

39. MOVIES The average price for a movie ticket can be represented by $P = \frac{y^2}{400} + \frac{7y}{100} + 2.96$ where y is the number of years since 1980.

a. Find the average price of a ticket in 1990, 2000, and 2010. **$3.91; $5.36; $7.31**

b. Another equation that can be used to represent ticket prices is $P = \frac{y^3}{2500} - \frac{y^2}{100} + \frac{6y}{25} + 2.62$. Find the price of a ticket in 1990, 2000, and 2010. How do these values compare to those you found in part a?

39b. $4.42; $6.62; $11.62; Sample answer: The average prices found in part a become increasingly higher with time.

Differentiated Instruction

OL BL

Extension Challenge students by having them convert square and cubic units. After completing Exercise 28a, convert the area of the base to square centimeters and square kilometers. 529,000,000 cm²; 0.0529 km² After completing Exercise 28b, convert the volume to cubic centimeters and cubic kilometers. 2,586,810,000,000 cm³; 0.00258681 km³

8 Chapter 1 Equations and Inequalities

StudyTip

Look Back To review simplifying square root expressions, see Concepts and Skills Bank Lesson 2.

40. **GEOMETRY** The area of a triangle can be found using Heron's Formula, $A = \sqrt{s(s-a)(s-b)(s-c)}$, where a, b, and c are the lengths of the three sides of the triangle, and $s = \frac{a+b+c}{2}$. Find the area of the triangle at the right. **31.5 in²**

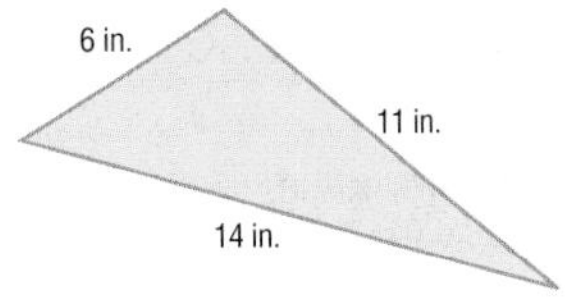

41. Evaluate $y = \sqrt{b^2\left(1 - \frac{x^2}{a^2}\right)}$ if $a = 6$, $b = 8$, and $x = 3$. Round to the nearest tenth. **6.9**

42. **MULTIPLE REPRESENTATIONS** You will write expressions using the formula for the volume of a cylinder. Recall that the volume of a cylinder can be found using the formula $v = \pi r^2 h$, in which v = volume, r = radius, and h = height.

a. **GEOMETRIC** Draw two cylinders of different sizes. **See margin.**

b. **TABULAR** Use a ruler to measure the radius and height of each cylinder. Organize the measures for each cylinder into a table. Include a column in your table to calculate the volume of each cylinder. **See margin.**

c. **VERBAL** Write a verbal expression for the difference in volume of the two cylinders.

d. **ALGEBRAIC** Write and solve an algebraic expression for the difference in volume of the two cylinders. **Sample answer: $\pi(2)^2(5) - \pi(4)^2(1) = 4\pi \approx 12.5$ in³**

42c. Sample answer: π times 2 squared times 5 minus π times 4 squared times 1

H.O.T. Problems — Use Higher-Order Thinking Skills

43. **ERROR ANALYSIS** Lauren and Rico are evaluating $\frac{-3d - 4c}{2ab}$ for $a = -2$, $b = -3$, $c = 5$, and $d = 4$. Is either of them correct? Explain your reasoning. **Lauren; −12 − 20 = −32**

Lauren

$\frac{-3d - 4c}{2ab} = \frac{-3(4) - 4(5)}{2(-2)(-3)}$

$= \frac{-12 - 20}{12} = \frac{-32}{12} = -\frac{8}{3}$

Rico

$\frac{-3d - 4c}{2ab} = \frac{-3(4) - 4(5)}{2(-2)(-3)}$

$= \frac{-12 - 20}{12} = \frac{8}{12} = \frac{2}{3}$

44. **CHALLENGE** For any three distinct numbers a, b, and c, $a\$b\$c$ is defined as $a\$b\$c = \frac{-a - b - c}{c - b - a}$. Find $-2\$(-4)\$5$. **$\frac{1}{11}$**

45. **REASONING** Explain the steps involved in finding the value of k such that $4\left(\frac{k+6}{3} - 12\right) + 8 = -48$.

46. **CHALLENGE** Let m, n, p, and q represent nonzero positive integers. Find a number in terms of m, n, p, and q that is halfway between $\frac{m}{n}$ and $\frac{p}{q}$.

47. **OPEN ENDED** Write an algebraic expression using $x = -2$, $y = -3$, and $z = 4$ and all four operations for which the value of the expression is 10.

48. **WRITING IN MATH** Provide an example of a formula used in everyday situations. Explain the usefulness of this formula and what happens if the formula is not used correctly.

49. **WRITING IN MATH** Use the information for on-base percentage given at the beginning of the lesson to explain how formulas are used in baseball to calculate a player's stats. Explain why a formula for on-base percentage is more useful than a table of specific percentages. **A table of on-base percentages is limited to those situations listed, while a formula can be used to find any on-base percentage.**

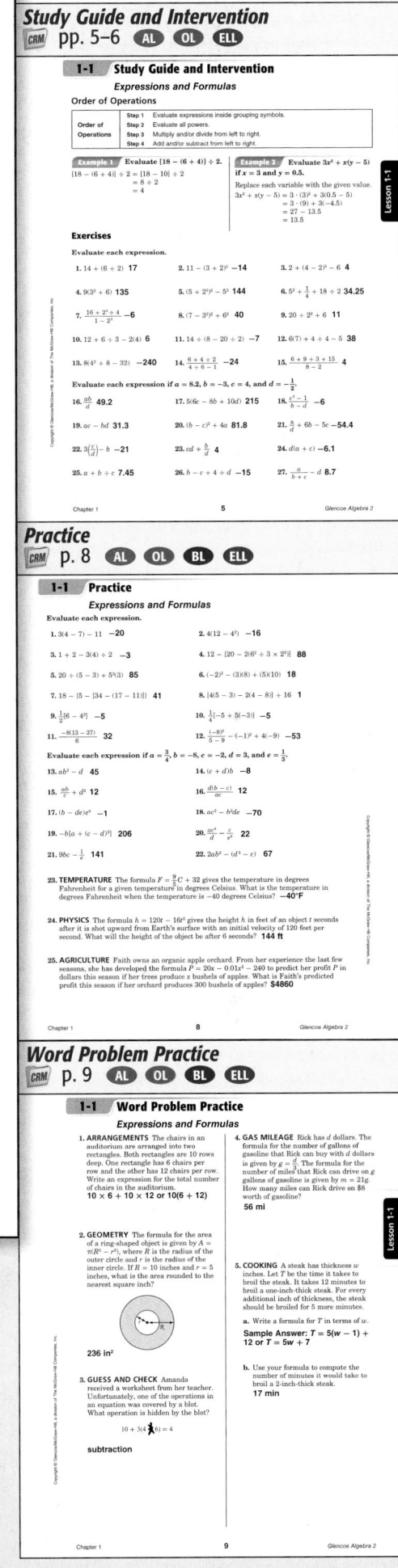

45. Subtract 8 from each side. Divide each side by 4. Add 12 to each side. Multiply each side by 3. Subtract 6 from each side. $k = -12$

46. Halfway between $\frac{m}{n}$ and $\frac{p}{q}$ is the average of the two: $\frac{1}{2}\left(\frac{m}{n} + \frac{p}{q}\right) = \frac{qm + pn}{2nq}$.

47. Sample answer: $y\left(\frac{-4z}{x^2} - x\right) + z$

48. Sample answer: A formula is used to calculate the price of filling a gasoline tank in which the price = number of gallons × price per gallon. If calculated incorrectly, you may underestimate or overestimate how much you will need to pay.

Study Guide and Intervention
CRM pp. 5–6 AL OL ELL

1-1 Study Guide and Intervention
Expressions and Formulas

Order of Operations

Order of Operations	Step 1	Evaluate expressions inside grouping symbols.
	Step 2	Evaluate all powers.
	Step 3	Multiply and/or divide from left to right.
	Step 4	Add and/or subtract from left to right.

Example 1 Evaluate $[18 - (6 + 4)] \div 2$.

$[18 - (6 + 4)] \div 2 = [18 - 10] \div 2$
$= 8 \div 2$
$= 4$

Example 2 Evaluate $3x^2 + x(y - 5)$ if $x = 3$ and $y = 0.5$.

Replace each variable with the given value.

$3x^2 + x(y - 5) = 3 \cdot (3)^2 + 3(0.5 - 5)$
$= 3 \cdot (9) + 3(-4.5)$
$= 27 - 13.5$
$= 13.5$

Lesson 1-1

Exercises

Evaluate each expression.

1. $14 + (6 \div 2)$ **17**
2. $11 - (3 + 2)^2$ **−14**
3. $2 + (4 - 2)^3 - 6$ **4**
4. $9(3^2 + 6)$ **135**
5. $(5 + 2^3)^2 - 5^2$ **144**
6. $5^2 + \frac{1}{4} + 18 \div 2$ **34.25**
7. $\frac{16 + 2^3 \div 4}{1 - 2^2}$ **−6**
8. $(7 - 3^2)^2 + 6^2$ **40**
9. $20 \div 2^2 + 6$ **11**
10. $12 + 6 \div 3 - 2(4)$ **6**
11. $14 \div (8 - 20 \div 2)$ **−7**
12. $6(7) + 4 \div 4 - 5$ **38**
13. $8(4^2 + 8 - 32)$ **−240**
14. $\frac{6 + 4 \div 2}{4 \div 6 - 1}$ **−24**
15. $\frac{6 + 9 \div 3 + 15}{8 - 2}$ **4**

Evaluate each expression if $a = 8.2$, $b = -3$, $c = 4$, and $d = -\frac{1}{2}$.

16. $\frac{ab}{d}$ **49.2**
17. $5(6c - 8b + 10d)$ **215**
18. $\frac{c^2 - 1}{b - d}$ **−6**
19. $ac - bd$ **31.3**
20. $(b - c)^2 + 4a$ **81.8**
21. $\frac{a}{d} + 6b - 5c$ **−54.4**
22. $3\left(\frac{c}{d}\right) - b$ **−21**
23. $cd + \frac{b}{d}$ **4**
24. $d(a + c)$ **−6.1**
25. $a + b \div c$ **7.45**
26. $b - c + 4 \div d$ **−15**
27. $\frac{a}{b + c} - d$ **8.7**

Chapter 1 5 Glencoe Algebra 2

Practice
CRM p. 8 AL OL BL ELL

1-1 Practice
Expressions and Formulas

Evaluate each expression.

1. $3(4 - 7) - 11$ **−20**
2. $4(12 - 4^2)$ **−16**
3. $1 + 2 - 3(4) \div 2$ **−3**
4. $12 - [20 - 2(6^2 \div 3 \times 2^2)]$ **88**
5. $20 \div (5 - 3) + 5^2(3)$ **85**
6. $(-2)^3 - (3)(8) + (5)(10)$ **18**
7. $18 - \{5 - [34 - (17 - 11)]\}$ **41**
8. $[4(5 - 3) - 2(4 - 8)] \div 16$ **1**
9. $\frac{1}{2}[6 - 4^2]$ **−5**
10. $\frac{1}{4}[-5 + 5(-3)]$ **−5**
11. $\frac{-8(13 - 37)}{6}$ **32**
12. $\frac{(-8)^2}{5 - 9} - (-1)^2 + 4(-9)$ **−53**

Evaluate each expression if $a = \frac{3}{4}$, $b = -8$, $c = -2$, $d = 3$, and $e = \frac{1}{3}$.

13. $ab^2 - d$ **45**
14. $(c + d)b$ **−8**
15. $\frac{ab}{c} + d^2$ **12**
16. $\frac{d(b - c)}{ac}$ **12**
17. $(b - de)e^2$ **−1**
18. $ac^3 - b^2de$ **−70**
19. $-b[a + (c - d)^2]$ **206**
20. $\frac{ac^4}{d} - \frac{c}{e^2}$ **22**
21. $9bc - \frac{1}{e}$ **141**
22. $2ab^2 - (d^3 - c)$ **67**

23. **TEMPERATURE** The formula $F = \frac{9}{5}C + 32$ gives the temperature in degrees Fahrenheit for a given temperature in degrees Celsius. What is the temperature in degrees Fahrenheit when the temperature is −40 degrees Celsius? **−40°F**

24. **PHYSICS** The formula $h = 120t - 16t^2$ gives the height h in feet of an object t seconds after it is shot upward from Earth's surface with an initial velocity of 120 feet per second. What will the height of the object be after 6 seconds? **144 ft**

25. **AGRICULTURE** Faith owns an organic apple orchard. From her experience the last few seasons, she has developed the formula $P = 20x - 0.01x^2 - 240$ to predict her profit P in dollars this season if her trees produce x bushels of apples. What is Faith's predicted profit this season if her orchard produces 300 bushels of apples? **$4860**

Chapter 1 8 Glencoe Algebra 2

Word Problem Practice
CRM p. 9 AL OL BL ELL

1-1 Word Problem Practice
Expressions and Formulas

1. **ARRANGEMENTS** The chairs in an auditorium are arranged into two rectangles. Both rectangles are 10 rows deep. One rectangle has 6 chairs per row and the other has 12 chairs per row. Write an expression for the total number of chairs in the auditorium. **10 × 6 + 10 × 12 or 10(6 + 12)**

2. **GEOMETRY** The formula for the area of a ring-shaped object is given by $A = \pi(R^2 - r^2)$, where R is the radius of the outer circle and r is the radius of the inner circle. If $R = 10$ inches and $r = 5$ inches, what is the area rounded to the nearest square inch?

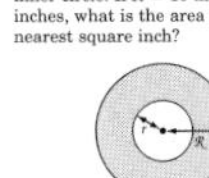

236 in²

3. **GUESS AND CHECK** Amanda received a worksheet from her teacher. Unfortunately, one of the operations in an equation was covered by a blot. What operation is hidden by the blot?

10 + 3(4 [blot] 6) = 4

subtraction

4. **GAS MILEAGE** Rick has d dollars. The formula for the number of gallons of gasoline that Rick can buy with d dollars is given by $g = \frac{d}{3}$. The formula for the number of miles that Rick can drive on g gallons of gasoline is given by $m = 21g$. How many miles can Rick drive on $8 worth of gasoline? **56 mi**

5. **COOKING** A steak has thickness w inches. Let T be the time it takes to broil the steak. It takes 12 minutes to broil a one-inch-thick steak. For every additional inch of thickness, the steak should be broiled for 5 more minutes.

a. Write a formula for T in terms of w. **Sample Answer: $T = 5(w - 1) + 12$ or $T = 5w + 7$**

b. Use your formula to compute the number of minutes it would take to broil a 2-inch-thick steak. **17 min**

Lesson 1-1

Chapter 1 9 Glencoe Algebra 2

Enrichment
CRM p. 10 OL BL

1-1 Enrichment
Traveling on a Budget

You are traveling to your aunt's house 200 miles away for a surprise birthday party. The party starts at 3 P.M. but you cannot leave from your house before 11 A.M. You must fill your gas tank before the trip. Gasoline is $3.50 per gallon and you have $18. Will you make it to the party?

1. First determine at which speed you must travel to arrive by 3:00.

a. A simple formula relates the travel time, depending on your average speed in miles per hour (mph), $T = \frac{D}{S}$, where T is time in hours, D is the distance (200 miles), and S is the speed. Determine travel time to your aunt's house at various speeds.

Speed (mph)	Time (hours)
35	5.7
40	5.0
45	4.4
50	4.0
55	3.6
60	3.3
65	3.0
70	2.8

Watch Out!

Preventing Errors Students may be reluctant to take time to show all the steps they use when evaluating an expression, such as showing the substituted values before doing the computations. Help them to see that these steps enable them to diagnose errors and prevent calculation errors that may keep them from getting correct values.

4 ASSESS

Name the Math Have each student tell a partner or write the order of operations

Standardized Test Practice exercises help students solidify their knowledge of the standards using exercises in a multiple-choice format.

NGSSS PRACTICE 912.G.2.5, 912.A.2.13, 912.G.4.2, 912.A.3.5

50. SAT/ACT If the area of a square with side x is 9, what is the area of a square of side $4x$? **B**

A. 36 C. 212
B. 144 D. 324

51. THINK SOLVE EXPLAIN **SHORT RESPONSE** A coffee shop owner wants to open a second shop when his daily customer average reaches 800 people. He has calculated the daily customer average in the table below for each month since he has opened.

Month	Daily Customer Average
1	225
2	298
3	371
4	444

If the trend continues, during what month can he open a second shop? **9**

52. GEOMETRY In $\triangle DFG$, $\overline{FH}$ and $\overline{HG}$ are angle bisectors and $m\angle D = 84$. How many degrees are in $\angle FHG$? **G**

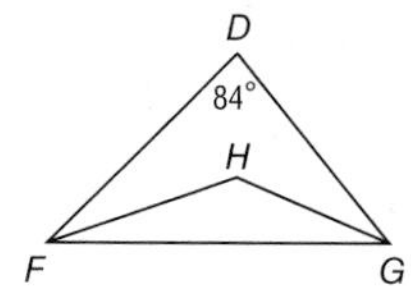

F. 96
G. 132
H. 145
I. 192

53. A skydiver in a computer game free-falls from a height of 3000 m at a rate of 55 meters per second. Which equation can be used to find h, the height of the skydiver after t seconds of free fall? **B**

A. $h = -55t - 3000$
B. $h = -55t + 3000$
C. $h = 3000t - 55$
D. $h = 3000t + 55$

Spiral Review

54. The lengths of the three sides of a triangle are 10, 14, and 18 inches. Determine whether this triangle is a right triangle. (Lesson 0-7) **no**

55. The legs of a right triangle measure 6 centimeters and 8 centimeters. Find the length of the hypotenuse. (Lesson 0-7) **10 cm**

56. MAPS On a map of the U.S., the cities of Milwaukee, Wisconsin, and Charlotte, North Carolina are $6\frac{1}{2}$ inches apart. The actual distance between Milwaukee and Charlotte is 670 miles. If Birmingham, Alabama and St. Petersburg, Florida are 465 miles apart, how far apart are they on the map? (Lesson 0-6) **$4\frac{1}{2}$ in.**

57. Factor $6x^2 + 12x$. (Lesson 0-3) **$6x(x + 2)$**

58. Find the product of $(a + 2)(a - 4)$. (Lesson 0-2) **$a^2 - 2a - 8$**

59. NUMBER An integer is 2 less than a number, and another integer is 1 greater than double that same number. What are the two integers if their sum is 14? (Lesson 0-2) **3 and 11**

Skills Review

Evaluate each expression. (Concepts and Skills Bank, Lesson 2)

60. $\sqrt{4}$ **2**
61. $\sqrt{25}$ **5**
62. $\sqrt{81}$ **9**
63. $\sqrt{121}$ **11**
64. $-\sqrt{9}$ **−3**
65. $-\sqrt{16}$ **−4**
66. $\sqrt{\frac{49}{100}}$ **$\frac{7}{10}$**
67. $\sqrt{\frac{25}{64}}$ **$\frac{5}{8}$**

Differentiated Instruction OL BL

Extension Write five numbers, all of which are between 1 and 10, on the board. Give students a "power number" between 1 and 10. Tell them to use each of the five numbers exactly once along with any operation and grouping symbols to write an expression that will make the "power number." For example, suppose the five numbers are 2, 3, 4, 7, and 8 and the "power number" is 1. Students can produce the "power number" by using the expression $4 + 7 - 2(8 - 3)$.

1-2 Properties of Real Numbers

Then
You identified and used the arithmetic properties of real numbers. (Algebra 1)

Now
- Classify real numbers.
- Use the properties of real numbers to evaluate expressions.

NGSSS
Reinforcement of MA.912.A.3.2 Identify and apply the distributive, associative, and commutative properties of real numbers and the properties of equality.

New Vocabulary
real numbers
rational numbers
irrational numbers
integers
whole numbers
natural numbers

FL Math Online
glencoe.com

Why?

The Central High School Boosters sell snacks and beverages at school functions. The items are priced the same to make determining the total cost easy.

You can use the Distributive Property to calculate the total cost when multiple items are purchased.

Real Numbers **Real numbers** consist of several different kinds of numbers.

- **Rational numbers** can be expressed as a ratio $\frac{a}{b}$, where a and b are integers and b is not zero. The decimal form of a rational number is either a terminating or repeating decimal.
- The decimal form of an **irrational number** neither terminates nor repeats. Square roots of numbers that are not perfect squares are irrational numbers.
- The sets of **integers**, $\{\ldots, -3, -2, -1, 0, 1, 2, 3, \ldots\}$, **whole numbers**, $\{0, 1, 2, 3, 4, \ldots\}$, and **natural numbers**, $\{1, 2, 3, 4, 5, \ldots\}$, are subsets of the rational numbers. These numbers are subsets of the rational numbers because every integer n is equal to $\frac{n}{1}$.

Key Concept Real Numbers (R)

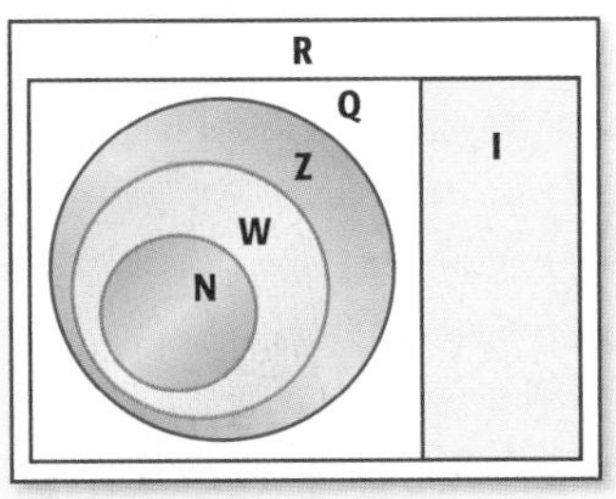

Letter	Set	Examples
Q	rationals	$0.125, -\frac{7}{8}, \frac{2}{3} = 0.66\ldots$
I	irrationals	$\pi = 3.14159\ldots$, $\sqrt{3} = 1.73205\ldots$
Z	integers	$-5, 17, -23, 8$
W	wholes	$2, 96, 0, \sqrt{36}$
N	naturals	$3, 17, 6, 86$

EXAMPLE 1 Classify Numbers

Name the sets of numbers to which each number belongs.

a. -23 integers (Z), rationals (Q), reals (R)

b. $\sqrt{50}$ irrationals (I), reals (R)

c. $-\frac{4}{9}$ rationals (Q), reals (R)

Guided Practice

1A. -185 Z, Q, R **1B.** $-\sqrt{49}$ Z, Q, R **1C.** $\sqrt{95}$ I, R **1D.** $-\frac{7}{8}$ Q, R

Personal Tutor glencoe.com

1 FOCUS

Vertical Alignment

Before Lesson 1-2
Identify and use the arithmetic properties of real numbers.

Lesson 1-2
Classify real numbers.
Use the properties of real numbers to evaluate expressions.

After Lesson 1-2
Use real number properties to solve equations and inequalities.

2 TEACH

Scaffolding Questions

Have students read the *Why?* section of the lesson.

Ask:
- How much does each item cost? $1.50
- How much would four items cost? $6.00
- Write an expression using the Distributive Property that could be used to calculate the cost of two protein bars and one popcorn. $2(1.50) + 1.50$ or $3(1.50)$

Lesson 1-2 Resources

Resource	Approaching-Level	On-Level	Beyond-Level	English Learners
Teacher Edition	• Differentiated Instruction, p. 13	• Differentiated Instruction, pp. 12, 13, 17	• Differentiated Instruction, pp. 12, 17	• Differentiated Instruction, p. 13
Chapter Resource Masters	• Study Guide and Intervention, pp. 11–12 • Skills Practice, p. 13 • Practice, p. 14 • Word Problem Practice, p. 15	• Study Guide and Intervention, pp. 11–12 • Skills Practice, p. 13 • Practice, p. 14 • Word Problem Practice, p. 15 • Enrichment, p. 16	• Practice, p. 14 • Word Problem Practice, p. 15 • Enrichment, p. 16	• Study Guide and Intervention, pp. 11–12 • Skills Practice, p. 13 • Practice, p. 14 • Word Problem Practice, p. 15
Transparencies	• 5-Minute Check Transparency 1-2	• 5-Minute Check Transparency 1-2	• 5-Minute Check Transparency 1-2	• 5-Minute Check Transparency 1-2
Other	• Study Notebook	• Study Notebook	• Study Notebook	• Study Notebook

Real Numbers

Example 1 shows how to classify numbers.

Formative Assessment

Use the Guided Practice exercises after each example to determine students' understanding of concepts.

Additional Example

1 Name the sets of numbers to which each number belongs.

a. $\sqrt{6}$ I, R

b. 5 N, W, Z, Q, R

c. $-\frac{2}{3}$ Q, R

Additional Examples also in Interactive Classroom PowerPoint® Presentations

IWB INTERACTIVE WHITEBOARD READY

TEACH with TECH

INTERACTIVE WHITEBOARD Draw a set diagram on the board showing how the set of real numbers is separated into rational and irrational numbers, integers, whole numbers, etc. Write a list of 12 real numbers, and choose students to come to the board to drag them into the correct set in the diagram.

Watch Out!

Student Misconceptions Remind students that $\sqrt{9}$, for example, means only the positive root, if one exists. So, $\sqrt{9} = 3$. To indicate both roots of the equation $x^2 = 9$, the mathematical notation is $x = \pm\sqrt{9}$ or $x = \pm 3$.

StudyTip

Real Numbers A number can belong to more than one set of numbers. For example, if a number is natural, it is also whole, an integer, rational, and real.

Properties of Real Numbers Some of the properties of real numbers are summarized below.

Concept Summary — Real Number Properties

For any real numbers a, b, and c:

Property	Addition	Multiplication
Commutative	$a + b = b + a$	$a \cdot b = b \cdot a$
Associative	$(a + b) + c = a + (b + c)$	$(a \cdot b) \cdot c = a \cdot (b \cdot c)$
Identity	$a + 0 = a = 0 + a$	$a \cdot 1 = a = 1 \cdot a$
Inverse	$a + (-a) = 0 = (-a) + a$	$a \cdot \frac{1}{a} = 1 = \frac{1}{a} \cdot a, a \neq 0$
Closure	$a + b$ is a real number.	$a \cdot b$ is a real number.
Distributive	$a(b + c) = ab + ac$ and $(b + c)a = ba + ca$	

EXAMPLE 2 Name Properties of Real Numbers

Name the property illustrated by $5 \cdot (4 \cdot 13) = (5 \cdot 4) \cdot 13$.

Associative Property of Multiplication

The Associative Property of Multiplication states that the way in which you group factors does not affect the product.

Guided Practice

2. Name the property illustrated by $2(x + 3) = 2x + 6$. Distributive Property

Personal Tutor glencoe.com

You can use the properties of real numbers to identify related values.

StudyTip

Additive and Multiplicative Inverses The additive inverse of a number has the opposite sign as the number. The multiplicative inverse of a number has the same sign as the number.

EXAMPLE 3 Additive and Multiplicative Inverses

Find the additive inverse and multiplicative inverse for $-\frac{5}{8}$.

Since $-\frac{5}{8} + \frac{5}{8} = 0$, the additive inverse of $-\frac{5}{8}$ is $\frac{5}{8}$.

Since $\left(-\frac{5}{8}\right)\left(-\frac{8}{5}\right) = 1$, the multiplicative inverse of $-\frac{5}{8}$ is $-\frac{8}{5}$.

Guided Practice

Find the additive and multiplicative inverse for each number.

3A. 1.25 -1.25; 0.8

3B. $2\frac{1}{2}$ $-2\frac{1}{2}$; $\frac{2}{5}$

Personal Tutor glencoe.com

Many real-world applications involve working with real numbers.

Differentiated Instruction OL BL

Extension Discuss with students why π is irrational. Have students investigate the history of π.

Real-World Career

Retail Store Manager Store managers are responsible for the day-to-day operations of a retail store. A store manager may range from being a high school graduate to having a 4-year degree, depending on the business.

Real-World EXAMPLE 4 Distributive Property

MONEY The prices of the components of a computer package offered by Computer Depot are shown in the table. If a 6% sales tax is added to the purchase price, how much sales tax is charged for this computer package?

Component	Price ($)
Computer	359.95
Monitor	219.99
Printer	79.00
Digital Camera	149.50
Software Bundle	99.00

There are two ways to determine the total sales tax.

Method 1 Multiply, then add.

Multiply each dollar amount by 6% or 0.06 and then add.

$T = 0.06(359.95) + 0.06(219.99) + 0.06(79.00) + 0.06(149.50) + 0.06(99.00)$

$= 21.60 + 13.20 + 4.74 + 8.97 + 5.94$

$= 54.45$

Method 2 Add, then multiply.

Find the total cost of the computer package, and then multiply the total by 0.06.

$T = 0.06(359.95 + 219.99 + 79.00 + 149.50 + 99.00)$

$= 0.06(907.44)$

$= 54.45$

The sales tax charged is $54.45. Notice that both methods result in the same answer.

Guided Practice

4. **JOBS** Kayla makes $8 per hour working at a grocery store. The number of hours Kayla worked each day in one week are 3, 2.5, 2, 1, and 4. How much money did Kayla earn this week? $100

Personal Tutor glencoe.com

The properties of real numbers can be used to simplify algebraic expressions.

EXAMPLE 5 Simplify an Expression

Simplify $3(2q + r) + 5(4q - 7r)$.

$3(2q + r) + 5(4q - 7r)$	
$= 3(2q) + 3(r) + 5(4q) - 5(7r)$	Distributive Property
$= 6q + 3r + 20q - 35r$	Multiply.
$= 6q + 20q + 3r - 35r$	Commutative Property (+)
$= (6 + 20)q + (3 - 35)r$	Distributive Property
$= 26q - 32r$	Simplify.

Guided Practice

5. Simplify $3(4x - 2y) - 2(3x + y)$. $6x - 8y$

Personal Tutor glencoe.com

Differentiated Instruction

AL OL ELL

If students have trouble remembering the names of properties,

Then have students connect the term *commutative* with *commuting,* or moving from one place to another. Have them connect the term *associative* with *associate,* "the people you associate with, or your group."

Properties of Real Numbers

Example 2 shows how to identify properties of real numbers. **Example 3** shows how to find additive and multiplicative inverses of real numbers. **Example 4** shows how to use the Distributive Property to solve a real-world problem. **Example 5** shows how properties of real numbers can be used to simplify algebraic expressions.

Additional Examples

2. Name the property illustrated by $(-8 + 8) + 15 = 0 + 15$. Additive Inverse Property

3. Find the additive inverse and multiplicative inverse for −7. additive: 7; multiplicative: $-\frac{1}{7}$

4. **STAMPS** Audrey went to a post office and bought eight 42¢ stamps and eight 27¢ postcard stamps. What was the total amount of money Audrey spent on stamps? $5.52

5. Simplify $4(3a - b) + 2(b + 3a)$. $18a - 2b$

Examples illustrate lesson concepts and closely mirror the exercises. **Guided Practice** exercises give students an opportunity to try a similar problem on their own.

Tips for New Teachers

Reading Help students to recall the Distributive Property by connecting the name to *distributing,* "handing out papers, for example, one to each person." Point out that the factor outside the parentheses acts as a multiplier for each term within the parentheses.

Focus on Mathematical Content

Irrational Numbers A non-terminating decimal whose digits show a pattern but do not repeat, such as the number 0.010010001..., is irrational. Another irrational number that shows a pattern but does not repeat is 1.232233222333....

Additive and Multiplicative Inverses Make sure students understand that additive inverses must have a sum of 0 and that multiplicative inverses must have a product of 1. Zero does not have a multiplicative inverse.

3 PRACTICE

Formative Assessment

Use Exercises 1–17 to check for understanding.

Use the chart on the next page to customize assignments for your students.

Additional Answer

13c. If she continues to mow the same number of lawns, at the end of next week she will have the money. This may not be reasonable because not all the lawns she mowed this week may need to be mowed again next week.

Check Your Understanding

Example 1 p. 11 Name the sets of numbers to which each number belongs.

1. 62 N, W, Z, Q, R **2.** $\frac{5}{4}$ Q, R **3.** $\sqrt{11}$ I, R **4.** -12 Z, Q, R

Example 2 p. 12 Name the property illustrated by each equation.

5. $(6 \cdot 8) \cdot 5 = 6 \cdot (8 \cdot 5)$ Assoc. (×) **6.** $7(9 - 5) = 7 \cdot 9 - 7 \cdot 5$ Dist.

7. $84 + 16 = 16 + 84$ Comm. (+) **8.** $(12 + 5)6 = 12 \cdot 6 + 5 \cdot 6$ Dist.

Example 3 p. 12 Find the additive inverse and multiplicative inverse for each number.

9. -7 $7; -\frac{1}{7}$ **10.** $\frac{4}{9}$ $-\frac{4}{9}; \frac{9}{4}$ **11.** 3.8 $-3.8; \frac{1}{3.8}$ **12.** $\sqrt{5}$ $-\sqrt{5}; \frac{1}{\sqrt{5}}$

Example 4 p. 13

13. MONEY Melba is mowing lawns for $22 each to earn money for a video game console that costs $550.

13a. 22(2 + 4 + 3 + 1 + 5 + 6 + 7) or 22(2) + 22(4) + 22(3) + 22(1) + 22(5) + 22(6) + 22(7)

a. Write an expression to represent the total amount of money Melba earned during this week.

b. Evaluate the expression from part a by using the Distributive Property. $616

c. When do you think Melba will earn enough for the video game console? Is this reasonable? Explain. See margin.

Lawns Mowed in One Week

Day	Lawns Mowed
Monday	2
Tuesday	4
Wednesday	3
Thursday	1
Friday	5
Saturday	6
Sunday	7

Example 5 p. 13 Simplify each expression.

14. $5(3x + 6y) + 4(2x - 9y)$ $23x - 6y$ **15.** $6(6a + 5b) - 3(4a + 7b)$ $24a + 9b$

16. $-4(6c - 3d) - 5(-2c - 4d)$ $-14c + 32d$ **17.** $-5(8x - 2y) - 4(-6x - 3y)$ $-16x + 22y$

Practice and Problem Solving

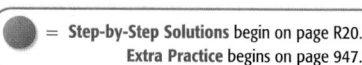

● = Step-by-Step Solutions begin on page R20.
Extra Practice begins on page 947.

Example 1 p. 11 Name the sets of numbers to which each number belongs.

18. $-\frac{4}{3}$ Q, R **19.** -8.13 Q, R **20.** $\sqrt{25}$ N, W, Z, Q, R **21.** $0.\overline{61}$ Q, R

22. $\frac{9}{3}$ N, W, Z, Q, R **23.** $-\sqrt{144}$ Z, Q, R **24.** $\frac{21}{7}$ N, W, Z, Q, R **25.** $\sqrt{17}$ I, R

Example 2 p. 12 Name the property illustrated by each equation.

26. $-7y + 7y = 0$ Inverse (+) **27.** $8\sqrt{11} + 5\sqrt{11} = (8 + 5)\sqrt{11}$ Dist.

28. $(16 + 7) + 23 = 16 + (7 + 23)$ Assoc. (+) **29.** $\left(\frac{22}{7}\right)\left(\frac{7}{22}\right) = 1$ Inverse (×)

Example 3 p. 12 Find the additive inverse and multiplicative inverse for each number.

30. -8 $8; -\frac{1}{8}$ **31.** 12.1 $-12.1; \frac{1}{12.1}$ **32.** -0.25 0.25; -4

33. $\frac{6}{13}$ $-\frac{6}{13}; \frac{13}{6}$ **34.** $-\frac{3}{8}$ $\frac{3}{8}; -\frac{8}{3}$ **35.** $\sqrt{15}$ $-\sqrt{15}; \frac{1}{\sqrt{15}}$

Example 4 p. 13

36. CONSTRUCTION Jorge needs two different kinds of concrete: quick drying and slow drying. The quick-drying concrete mix calls for $2\frac{1}{2}$ pounds of dry cement, and the slow-drying concrete mix calls for $1\frac{1}{4}$ pounds of dry cement. He needs 5 times more quick-drying concrete and 3 times more slow-drying concrete than the mixes make.

a. How many pounds of dry cement mix will he need? $16\frac{1}{4}$ lb

b. Use the properties of real numbers to show how Jorge could compute this amount mentally. Justify each step. See Chapter 1 Answer Appendix.

Example 5
p. 13

Simplify each expression.

37. $8b - 3c + 4b + 9c$ **$12b + 6c$**

38. $-2a + 9d - 5a - 6d$ **$-7a + 3d$**

39. $4(4x - 9y) + 8(3x + 2y)$ **$40x - 20y$**

40. $6(9a - 3b) - 8(2a + 4b)$ **$38a - 50b$**

41. $-2(-5g + 6k) - 9(-2g + 4k)$ **$28g - 48k$**

42. $-5(10x + 8z) - 6(4x - 7z)$ **$-74x + 2z$**

43. $53(60 + 60)$; $53(60) + 53(60)$; 6360 yd^2

B 43. **FOOTBALL** Illustrate the Distributive Property by writing two expressions for the area of a college football field. Then find the area of the football field.

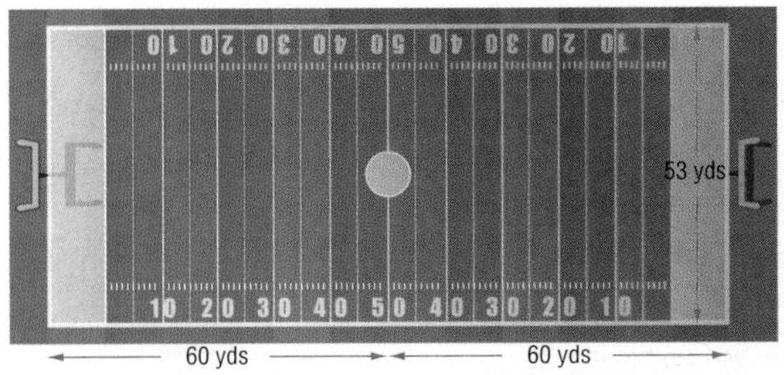

44a. $870{,}192(0.142 + 0.056 + 0.05 + 0.049) = 870{,}192(0.142) + 870{,}192(0.056) + 870{,}192(0.05) + 870{,}192(0.049)$

44. **PETS** The chart shows the percent of dogs registered with the American Kennel Club that are of the eight most popular breeds.

a. Illustrate the Distributive Property by writing two expressions to represent the number of registered dogs of the top four breeds.

b. Evaluate the expressions you wrote to find the number of registered dogs of the top four breeds. **258,447**

Top Dogs

Breed	Percent of Registered Dogs
Labrador Retrievers	14.2
Yorkshire Terriers	5.6
German Shepherds	5.0
Golden Retrievers	4.9
Beagles	4.5
Dachshunds	4.1
Boxers	4.1
Poodles	3.4
Total Registered Dogs	**870,192**

Source: American Kennel Club

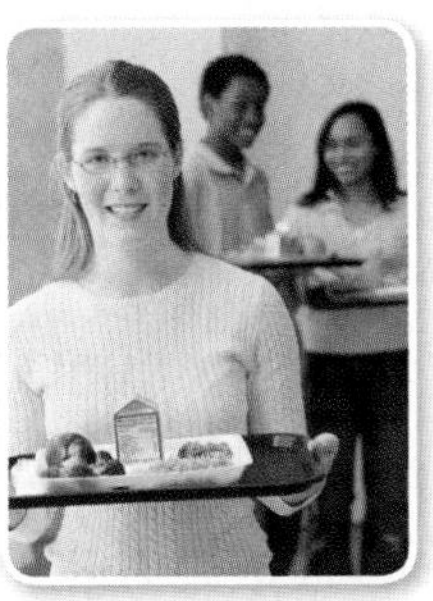

Real-World Link

The National School Lunch Program provides nutritionally balanced lunches to children each school day in more than 101,000 schools and residential childcare institutions.

Source: USDA

C 45. **FINANCIAL LITERACY** Billie is given \$20 in lunch money by her parents once every two weeks. On some days, she packs her lunch, and on other days, she buys her lunch. A hot lunch from the cafeteria costs \$4.50, and a cold sandwich from the lunch line costs \$2.

a. Billie decides that she wants to buy a hot lunch on Thursday and Friday of the first week and on Wednesday of the second week. Use the Distributive Property to determine how much that will cost. **\$13.50**

b. How many cold sandwiches can Billie buy with the amount left over? **3**

c. Assuming that both weeks are Monday through Friday, how many times will Billie have to pack her lunch? **4 times**

Simplify each expression. **48. $-36a - 30b + 24c$ 49. $-42x - 72y - 30z$**

46. $\frac{1}{3}(5x + 8y) + \frac{1}{4}(6x - 2y)$ **$\frac{19}{6}x + \frac{13}{6}y$**

47. $\frac{2}{5}(6c - 8d) + \frac{3}{4}(4c - 9d)$ **$\frac{27}{5}c - \frac{199}{20}d$**

48. $-6(3a + 5b) - 3(6a - 8c)$

49. $-9(3x + 8y) - 3(5x + 10z)$

50. **DECORATING** Mary is making curtains out of the same fabric for 5 windows. The two larger windows are the same size, and the three smaller windows are the same size. One larger window requires $3\frac{3}{4}$ yards of fabric, and one smaller window needs $2\frac{1}{3}$ yards of fabric.

a. How many yards of material will Mary need? **$14\frac{1}{2}$ yd**

b. Use the properties of real numbers to show how Mary could compute this amount mentally. **See margin.**

Watch Out!

Common Errors If students are having difficulty identifying properties, suggest that they look first at the change from one expression to the other and ask themselves if it is a change in grouping (associativity) or in position (commutativity).

Additional Answer

50b. $2\left(3\frac{3}{4}\right) + 3\left(2\frac{1}{3}\right)$

$= 2\left(3 + \frac{3}{4}\right) + 3\left(2 + \frac{1}{3}\right)$

Definition of a mixed number

$= 2(3) + 2\left(\frac{3}{4}\right) + 3(2) + 3\left(\frac{1}{3}\right)$

Distributive Property

$= 6 + \frac{3}{2} + 6 + 1$

Multiply.

$= 6 + 6 + 1 + \frac{3}{2}$

Commutative Property (+)

$= 13 + \frac{3}{2}$

Add.

$= 14\frac{1}{2}$

Add.

Differentiated Homework Options

Level	Assignment	Two-Day Option	
AL Basic	18–42, 53, 55–89	19–41 odd, 62–65	18–42 even, 53, 55–61, 66–89
OL Core	19–41 odd, 43–45, 47, 49–53, 55–89	18–42, 62–65	43–53, 55–61, 66–89
BL Advanced	43–81, (optional: 82–89)		

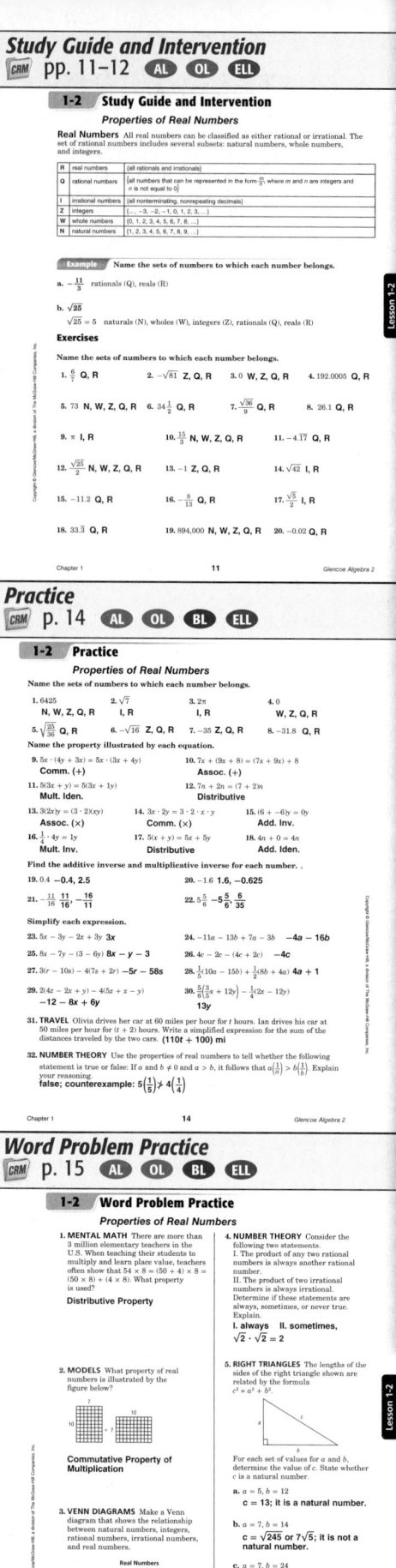

Study Guide and Intervention
CRM pp. 11–12 AL OL ELL

1-2 Study Guide and Intervention
Properties of Real Numbers

Real Numbers All real numbers can be classified as either rational or irrational. The set of rational numbers includes several subsets: natural numbers, whole numbers, and integers.

R	real numbers	{all rationals and irrationals}
Q	rational numbers	{all numbers that can be represented in the form $\frac{m}{n}$, where m and n are integers and n is not equal to 0}
I	irrational numbers	{all nonterminating, nonrepeating decimals}
Z	integers	{..., −3, −2, −1, 0, 1, 2, 3, ...}
W	whole numbers	{0, 1, 2, 3, 4, 5, 6, 7, 8, ...}
N	natural numbers	{1, 2, 3, 4, 5, 6, 7, 8, 9, ...}

Example Name the sets of numbers to which each number belongs.

a. $-\frac{11}{3}$ rationals (Q), reals (R)

b. $\sqrt{25}$
$\sqrt{25} = 5$ naturals (N), wholes (W), integers (Z), rationals (Q), reals (R)

Exercises

Name the sets of numbers to which each number belongs.

1. $\frac{6}{7}$ **Q, R** 2. $-\sqrt{81}$ **Z, Q, R** 3. 0 **W, Z, Q, R** 4. 192.0005 **Q, R**

5. 73 **N, W, Z, Q, R** 6. $34\frac{1}{2}$ **Q, R** 7. $\frac{\sqrt{36}}{9}$ **Q, R** 8. 26.1 **Q, R**

9. π **I, R** 10. $\frac{15}{3}$ **N, W, Z, Q, R** 11. $-4.\overline{17}$ **Q, R**

12. $\frac{\sqrt{25}}{2}$ **N, W, Z, Q, R** 13. −1 **Z, Q, R** 14. $\sqrt{42}$ **I, R**

15. −11.2 **Q, R** 16. $-\frac{8}{13}$ **Q, R** 17. $\frac{\sqrt{5}}{2}$ **I, R**

18. $33.\overline{3}$ **Q, R** 19. 894,000 **N, W, Z, Q, R** 20. −0.02 **Q, R**

Lesson 1-2

Chapter 1 11 Glencoe Algebra 2

Practice
CRM p. 14 AL OL BL ELL

1-2 Practice
Properties of Real Numbers

Name the sets of numbers to which each number belongs.

1. 6425 **N, W, Z, Q, R** 2. $\sqrt{7}$ **I, R** 3. 2π **I, R** 4. 0 **W, Z, Q, R**

5. $\sqrt{\frac{25}{36}}$ **Q, R** 6. $-\sqrt{16}$ **Z, Q, R** 7. −35 **Z, Q, R** 8. −31.8 **Q, R**

Name the property illustrated by each equation.

9. $5x \cdot (4y + 3x) = 5x \cdot (3x + 4y)$ **Comm. (+)**
10. $7x + (9x + 8) = (7x + 9x) + 8$ **Assoc. (+)**
11. $5(3x + y) = 5(3x + 1y)$ **Mult. Iden.**
12. $7n + 2n = (7 + 2)n$ **Distributive**
13. $3(2x)y = (3 \cdot 2)(xy)$ **Assoc. (×)**
14. $3x \cdot 2y = 3 \cdot 2 \cdot x \cdot y$ **Comm. (×)**
15. $(6 + -6)y = 0y$ **Add. Inv.**
16. $\frac{1}{4} \cdot 4y = 1y$ **Mult. Inv.**
17. $5(x + y) = 5x + 5y$ **Distributive**
18. $4n + 0 = 4n$ **Add. Iden.**

Find the additive inverse and multiplicative inverse for each number.

19. 0.4 **−0.4, 2.5**
20. −1.6 **1.6, −0.625**
21. $-\frac{11}{16}$ $\frac{11}{16}, -\frac{16}{11}$
22. $5\frac{5}{6}$ $-5\frac{5}{6}, \frac{6}{35}$

Simplify each expression.

23. $5x - 3y - 2x + 3y$ **3x**
24. $-11a - 13b + 7a - 3b$ **−4a − 16b**
25. $8x - 7y - (3 - 6y)$ **8x − y − 3**
26. $4c - 2c - (4c + 2c)$ **−4c**
27. $3(r - 10s) - 4(7s + 2r)$ **−5r − 58s**
28. $\frac{1}{5}(10a - 15b) + \frac{1}{2}(8b + 4a)$ **4a + 1**
29. $2(4z - 2x + y) - 4(5z + x - y)$ **−12 − 8x + 6y**
30. $\frac{5}{6}\left(\frac{3}{5}x + 12y\right) - \frac{1}{4}(2x - 12y)$ **13y**

31. **TRAVEL** Olivia drives her car at 60 miles per hour for t hours. Ian drives his car at 50 miles per hour for $(t + 2)$ hours. Write a simplified expression for the sum of the distances traveled by the two cars. **(110t + 100) mi**

32. **NUMBER THEORY** Use the properties of real numbers to tell whether the following statement is true or false: If a and $b \neq 0$ and $a > b$, it follows that $a\left(\frac{1}{a}\right) > b\left(\frac{1}{b}\right)$. Explain your reasoning.
false; counterexample: $5\left(\frac{1}{5}\right) \ngtr 4\left(\frac{1}{4}\right)$

Chapter 1 14 Glencoe Algebra 2

Word Problem Practice
CRM p. 15 AL OL BL ELL

1-2 Word Problem Practice
Properties of Real Numbers

1. **MENTAL MATH** There are more than 3 million elementary teachers in the U.S. When teaching their students to multiply and learn place value, teachers often show that $54 \times 8 = (50 + 4) \times 8 = (50 \times 8) + (4 \times 8)$. What property is used?
Distributive Property

2. **MODELS** What property of real numbers is illustrated by the figure below?

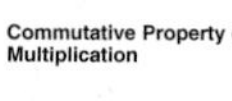

Commutative Property of Multiplication

3. **VENN DIAGRAMS** Make a Venn diagram that shows the relationship between natural numbers, integers, rational numbers, irrational numbers, and real numbers.

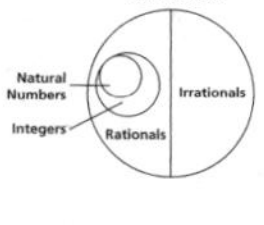

4. **NUMBER THEORY** Consider the following two statements.
I. The product of any two rational numbers is always another rational number.
II. The product of two irrational numbers is always irrational.
Determine if these statements are always, sometimes, or never true. Explain.
I. always II. sometimes, $\sqrt{2} \cdot \sqrt{2} = 2$

5. **RIGHT TRIANGLES** The lengths of the sides of the right triangle shown are related by the formula $c^2 = a^2 + b^2$.

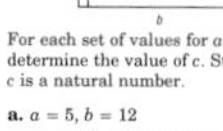

For each set of values for a and b, determine the value of c. State whether c is a natural number.

a. $a = 5, b = 12$
c = 13; it is a natural number.

b. $a = 7, b = 14$
c = $\sqrt{245}$ **or** $7\sqrt{5}$**; it is not a natural number.**

c. $a = 7, b = 24$
c = 25; it is a natural number.

Lesson 1-2

Chapter 1 15 Glencoe Algebra 2

51b. $-\sqrt{6} \approx -2.449$, $3 = 3.0$, $\frac{-15}{3} = -5$; $4.1 = 4.1$, $\pi \approx 3.14$, $0 = 0$, $\frac{3}{8} = .375$; $\sqrt{36} = 6$; $\frac{-15}{3}$, $-\sqrt{6}$, 0, $\frac{3}{8}$, π, 4.1, $\sqrt{36}$

Real-World Link

The average teen in the United States spends $3400 each year, 42% of which is for clothing.

Source: U.S. Department of Commerce

51d. Sample answer: By converting the real numbers into decimal form, they can be easily lined up and compared.
53. $\sqrt{81}$**; It is a rational number, while the other three are irrational numbers.**
55. No; Luna did not distribute the negative sign to the second term and Sophia switched the *a* and *b* terms because usually *a* comes first. The correct answer is 32*a* − 46*b*.
56. Sometimes; π and *e* are two examples of irrational numbers that do not involve the radical symbol.
57. Sample answer: $\sqrt{5} \cdot \sqrt{5} = \sqrt{25}$ **or 5, which is not irrational.**

51. **MULTIPLE REPRESENTATIONS** Consider the following real numbers.

$$-\sqrt{6}, 3, \frac{-15}{3}, 4.1, \pi, 0, \frac{3}{8}, \sqrt{36}$$

a. **TABULAR** Organize the numbers into a table according to the sets of numbers to which each belongs. **See Chapter 1 Answer Appendix.**

b. **ALGEBRAIC** Convert each number to decimal form. Then list the numbers from least to greatest.

c. **GRAPHICAL** Graph the numbers on a number line. **See Chapter 1 Answer Appendix.**

d. **VERBAL** Make a conjecture about using decimal form to list real numbers in order.

52. **CLOTHING** A department store sells shirts for $12.50 each. Dalila buys 2, Latisha buys 3, and Pilar buys 1.

a. Illustrate the Distributive Property by writing two expressions to represent the cost of these shirts. **12.50(2 + 3 + 1); 12.50 • 2 + 12.50 • 3 + 12.50 • 1**

b. Use the Distributive Property to find how much money the store received from selling these shirts. **$75**

H.O.T. Problems
Use Higher-Order Thinking Skills

53. **WHICH ONE DOESN'T BELONG?** Identify the number that does not belong with the other three. Explain your reasoning.

$\sqrt{21}$	$\sqrt{35}$	$\sqrt{67}$	$\sqrt{81}$

54. **CHALLENGE** If $12(5r + 6t) = w$, then in terms of w, what is $48(30r + 36t)$? **24w**

55. **ERROR ANALYSIS** Luna and Sophia are simplifying $4(14a - 10b) - 6(b + 4a)$. Is either of them correct? Explain your reasoning.

Luna	Sophia
$4(14a - 10b) - 6(b + 4a)$	$4(14a - 10b) - 6(b + 4a)$
$56a - 40b - 6b + 24a$	$56a - 40b - 6a - 24b$
$80a - 46b$	$50a - 64b$

56. **REASONING** Determine whether the following statement is *sometimes*, *always*, or *never* true. Explain your reasoning.

An irrational number is a real number within a radical sign.

57. **OPEN ENDED** Determine whether the Closure Property of Multiplication applies to irrational numbers. If not, provide a counterexample.

OPEN ENDED The set of all real numbers is *dense*, meaning between any two distinct members of the set there lies infinitely many other members of the set. Find an example of (a) a rational number, and (b) an irrational number between the given numbers. **58–60. See margin.**

58. 2.45 and 2.5 59. π and $\frac{10}{3}$ 60. $1.\overline{9}$ and 2.01

61. **WRITING IN MATH** Explain and provide examples to show why the Commutative Property does not hold true for subtraction or division. **See margin.**

Enrichment
CRM p. 16 OL BL

1-2 Enrichment

Properties of a Group

A set of numbers forms a group with respect to an operation if for that operation the set has (1) the Closure Property, (2) the Associative Property, (3) a member which is an identity, and (4) an inverse for each member of the set.

Example 1 Does the set {0, 1, 2, 3, ...} form a group with respect to addition?

Closure Property: For all numbers in the set, is $a + b$ in the set? $0 + 1 = 1$, and 1 is in the set; $0 + 2 = 2$, and 2 is in the set; and so on. The set has closure for addition.

Associative Property: For all numbers in the set, does $a + (b + c) = (a + b) + c$? $0 + (1 + 2) = (0 + 1) + 2$; $1 + (2 + 3) = (1 + 2) + 3$; and so on. The set is associative for addition.

Identity: Is there some number, i, in the set such that $i + a = a = a + i$ for all a? $0 + 1 = 1 = 1 + 0$; $0 + 2 = 2 = 2 + 0$; and so on. The identity for addition is 0.

Inverse: Does each number, a, have an inverse, a′, such that $a' + a = a + a' = i$? The integer inverse of 3 is −3 since $-3 + 3 = 0$, and 0 is the identity for addition. But the set does not contain −3. Therefore, there is no inverse for 3.

Multiple Representations In Exercise 51, students use information organized in a table, in a number line, and algebra to compare and order real numbers.

16 Chapter 1 Equations and Inequalities

NGSSS PRACTICE 912.A.3.15, 912.D.11.1, 912.G.3.3, 912.A.2.4

62. **EXTENDED RESPONSE** Lenora bought several pounds of cashews and several pounds of almonds for a party. The cashews cost \$8 per pound, and the almonds cost \$6 per pound. Lenora bought a total of 7 pounds and paid a total of \$48. Write and solve equations to determine the pounds of cashews and the pounds of almonds that Lenora purchased. $8c + 6a = 48$ and $c + a = 7$; $c = 3$ lb; $a = 4$ lb

63. **SAT/ACT** Find the 10th term in the series 2, 4, 7, 11, 16, … . B

A. 46
B. 56
C. 67
D. 72

64. **GEOMETRY** What are the coordinates of point A in the parallelogram? G

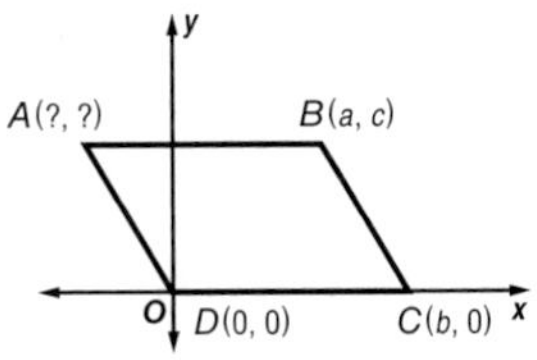

F. $(b - a, c)$
G. $(a - b, c)$
H. (b, c)
I. (c, c)

65. What is the domain of the function that contains the points $(-3, 0)$, $(0, 4)$, $(-2, 5)$, and $(6, 4)$? B

A. $\{-3, 6\}$
B. $\{-3, -2, 0, 6\}$
C. $\{0, 4, 5, 6\}$
D. $\{-3, -2, 0, 4, 5, 6\}$

Spiral Review

66. Evaluate $8(4 - 2)^3$. (Lesson 1-1) 64

67. Evaluate $a + 3(b + c) - d$, if $a = 5$, $b = 4$, $c = 3$, and $d = 2$. (Lesson 1-1) 24

68. **GEOMETRY** The formula for the area A of a circle with diameter d is $A = \pi\left(\frac{d}{2}\right)^2$. Write an expression to represent the area of the circle. (Lesson 1-1) $\pi\left(\frac{x+3}{2}\right)^2$

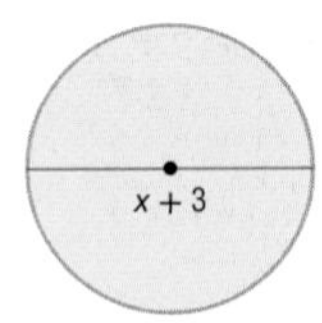

69. **CONSTRUCTION** A 10-meter ladder leans against a building so that the top is 9.64 meters above the ground. How far from the base of the wall is the bottom of the ladder? (Lesson 0-7) about 2.66 m

Factor each polynomial. (Lesson 0-3)

70. $14x^2 + 10x - 8$ $2(7x^2 + 5x - 4)$

71. $9x^2 - 3x + 18$ $3(3x^2 - x + 6)$

72. $8x^2 + 16x + 12$ $4(2x^2 + 4x + 3)$

73. $10x^2 - 20x$ $10x(x - 2)$

74. $7x^2 - 14x - 21$ $7(x - 3)(x + 1)$

75. $12x^2 - 18x - 24$ $6(2x^2 - 3x - 4)$

Find each product. (Lesson 0-2)

76. $(x + 2)(x - 3)$ $x^2 - x - 6$

77. $(y + 2)(y - 1)$ $y^2 + y - 2$

78. $(a - 5)(a + 4)$ $a^2 - a - 20$

79. $(b - 7)(b - 3)$ $b^2 - 10b + 21$

80. $(n + 6)(n + 8)$ $n^2 + 14n + 48$

81. $(p - 9)(p + 1)$ $p^2 - 8p - 9$

Skills Review

Evaluate each expression if $a = 3$, $b = \frac{2}{3}$, and $c = -1.7$. (Lesson 1-1)

82. $6b - 5$ -1

83. $\frac{1}{6}b + 1$ $\frac{10}{9}$

84. $2.3c - 7$ -10.91

85. $-8(a - 4)$ 8

86. $a + b + c$ ≈ 1.967

87. $\frac{a \cdot b}{c}$ -1.176

88. $a^2 - c$ 10.7

89. $\frac{a \cdot c}{a}$ -1.7

4 ASSESS

Ticket Out the Door Have each student write the name and an example of one of the properties in this lesson.

Formative Assessment

Check for student understanding of concepts in Lessons 1-1 and 1-2.

CRM Quiz 1, p. 45

H.O.T. Problems require students to use **H**igher **O**rder **T**hinking skills to solve problems.

Additional Answers

58. Sample answer: (a) 2.46 and (b) 2.48448444844448 . . .

59. Sample answer: (a) 3.2 and (b) $\sqrt{10}$

60. Sample answer: (a) 2.001 and (b) 2.001000100001 . . .

61. Sample answer: The Commutative Property does not hold for subtraction or division because order matters with these two operations. In addition or multiplication, the order does not matter.

For example, $2 + 4 = 4 + 2$ and $2 \cdot 4 = 4 \cdot 2$. However, with subtraction, $2 - 4 \neq 4 - 2$, and with division, $\frac{2}{4} \neq \frac{4}{2}$.

Differentiated Instruction OL BL

Extension Since the product of any two whole numbers is always a whole number, the set of whole numbers is said to be *closed* under multiplication. This is an example of the Closure Property. State whether each statement is true or false. If false, give a counterexample.

a. The set of integers is closed under multiplication. true

b. The set of whole numbers is closed under subtraction. false; $1 - 6 = -5$

c. The set of whole numbers is closed under division. false; $1 \div 5 = 0.2$

1-3 Lesson Notes

1 FOCUS

Vertical Alignment

Before Lesson 1-3
Use properties of real numbers to evaluate expressions.

Lesson 1-3
Translate verbal expressions into algebraic expressions and equations, and vice versa.
Solve equations using the properties of equality.

After Lesson 1-3
Solve systems of equations.

2 TEACH

Scaffolding Questions

Have students read the *Why?* section of the lesson.

Ask:

- What does the variable m represent? mile
- Is the length of a kilometer greater than or less than the length of a mile? less than
- About how many kilometers are in 12 miles? about 19.3 kilometers

All of the **Lesson Resources** are leveled for students who are **below grade level, on grade level,** and **above grade level,** and for students who are **English language learners.**

1-3 Solving Equations

Then
You used properties of real numbers to evaluate expressions. (Lesson 1-2)

Now
- Translate verbal expressions into algebraic expressions and equations, and vice versa.
- Solve equations using the properties of equality.

NGSSS
MA.912.A.3.3 Solve literal equations for a specified variable.

New Vocabulary
open sentence
equation
solution

FL Math Online
glencoe.com

Why?

The United States is one of the few countries in the world that measures distances in miles. When traveling by car in different countries, it is often useful to convert miles to kilometers. To find the approximate number of kilometers k in miles m, divide the number of miles by 0.62137.

$$m \text{ miles} \times \frac{1 \text{ kilometer}}{0.62137 \text{ mile}} \approx k \text{ kilometers}$$

$$\frac{m}{0.62137} \approx k \text{ kilometers}$$

Verbal Expressions and Algebraic Expressions Verbal expressions can be translated into algebraic expressions by using the language of algebra.

EXAMPLE 1 Verbal to Algebraic Expression

Write an algebraic expression to represent each verbal expression.

a. 2 more than 4 times the cube of a number $4x^3 + 2$

b. the quotient of 5 less than a number and 12 $\frac{n-5}{12}$

Guided Practice

1A. the cube of a number increased by 4 times the same number $p^3 + 4p$

1B. three times the difference of a number and 8 $3(x - 8)$

Personal Tutor glencoe.com

A mathematical sentence containing one or more variables is called an **open sentence**. A mathematical sentence stating that two mathematical expressions are equal is called an **equation**.

EXAMPLE 2 Algebraic to Verbal Sentence

Write a verbal sentence to represent each equation.

a. $6x = 72$ The product of 6 and a number is 72.

b. $n + 15 = 91$ The sum of a number and 15 is ninety-one.

Guided Practice 2A, 2B. See margin.

2A. $g - 5 = -2$

2B. $2c = c^2 - 4$

Personal Tutor glencoe.com

Open sentences are neither true nor false until the variables have been replaced by numbers. Each replacement that results in a true sentence is called a **solution** of the open sentence.

Lesson 1-3 Resources

Resource	Approaching-Level	On-Level	Beyond-Level	English Learners
Teacher Edition	• Differentiated Instruction, p. 20	• Differentiated Instruction, p. 21	• Differentiated Instruction, p. 21	• Differentiated Instruction, p. 20
Chapter Resource Masters	• Study Guide and Intervention, pp. 17–18 • Skills Practice, p. 19 • Practice, p. 20 • Word Problem Practice, p. 21	• Study Guide and Intervention, pp. 17–18 • Skills Practice, p. 19 • Practice, p. 20 • Word Problem Practice, p. 21 • Enrichment, p. 22 • Graphing Calculator Activity, p. 23	• Practice, p. 20 • Word Problem Practice, p. 21 • Enrichment, p. 22	• Study Guide and Intervention, pp. 17–18 • Skills Practice, p. 19 • Practice, p. 20 • Word Problem Practice, p. 21
Transparencies	• 5-Minute Check Transparency 1-3	• 5-Minute Check Transparency 1-3	• 5-Minute Check Transparency 1-3	• 5-Minute Check Transparency 1-3
Other	• Study Notebook • Teaching Algebra with Manipulatives	• Study Notebook • Teaching Algebra with Manipulatives	• Study Notebook	• Study Notebook • Teaching Algebra with Manipulatives

18 Chapter 1 Equations and Inequalities

Math History Link

Diophantus of Alexandria (c. 200–284)
Diophantus was famous for his work in algebra. His main work was titled *Arithmetica* and introduced symbolism to Greek algebra as well as propositions in number theory and polygonal numbers.

Properties of Equality To solve equations, we can use properties of equality. Some of these properties are listed below.

Key Concept Properties of Equality

Property	Symbols	Examples
Reflexive	For any real number a, $a = a$.	$b + 12 = b + 12$
Symmetric	For all real numbers a and b, if $a = b$, then $b = a$.	If $18 = -2n + 4$, then $-2n + 4 = 18$.
Transitive	For all real numbers a, b, and c, if $a = b$ and $b = c$, then $a = c$.	If $5p + 3 = 48$ and $48 = 7p - 15$, then $5p + 3 = 7p - 15$.
Substitution	If $a = b$, then a may be replaced by b and b may be replaced by a.	If $(6 + 1)x = 21$, then $7x = 21$.

EXAMPLE 3 Identify Properties of Equality

Name the property illustrated by each statement.

a. **If $3a - 4 = b$, and $b = a + 17$, then $3a - 4 = a + 17$.**
Transitive Property of Equality

b. **If $2g - h = 62$, and $h = 24$, then $2g - 24 = 62$.**
Substitution Property of Equality

Guided Practice

3. If $-11a + 2 = -3a$, then $-3a = -11a + 2$. Symmetric

Personal Tutor glencoe.com

StudyTip

Checking Answers When solving for a variable, you can use substitution to check your answer by replacing the variable in the original equation with your answer.

To solve most equations, you will need to perform the same operation on each side of the equals sign. The properties of equality allow for the equation to be solved in this way.

Key Concept

Addition and Subtraction Properties of Equality

Symbols For any real numbers, a, b, and c, if $a = b$, then $a + c = b + c$ and $a - c = b - c$.

Examples If $x - 6 = 14$, then $x - 6 + 6 = 14 + 6$.
If $n + 5 = -32$, then $n + 5 - 5 = -32 - 5$.

Multiplication and Division Properties of Equality

Symbols For any real numbers, a, b, and c, $c \neq 0$, if $a = b$, then $a \cdot c = b \cdot c$ and $\frac{a}{c} = \frac{b}{c}$.

Examples If $\frac{m}{8} = -7$, then $8 \cdot \frac{m}{8} = 8 \cdot (-7)$.
If $-2y = 12$, then $\frac{-2y}{-2} = \frac{12}{-2}$.

Additional Answers (Guided Practice)

2A. The difference of a number and 5 is –2.

2B. Two times a number is equal to the difference of that number squared and 4.

Verbal Expressions and Algebraic Expressions

Example 1 shows how to translate verbal expressions into algebraic expressions. **Example 2** shows how to translate algebraic expressions into verbal expressions.

Formative Assessment

Use the Guided Practice exercises after each example to determine students' understanding of concepts.

Additional Examples

1 Write an algebraic expression to represent each verbal expression.

a. 7 less than a number $n - 7$

b. the square of a number decreased by the product of 5 and the number $x^2 - 5x$

2 Write a verbal sentence to represent each equation.

a. $6 = -5 + x$ Six is equal to –5 plus a number.

b. $7y - 2 = 19$ Seven times a number minus 2 is 19.

Additional Examples also in Interactive Classroom PowerPoint® Presentations

IWB INTERACTIVE WHITEBOARD READY

Properties of Equality

Example 3 shows how to identify properties of equality.

Additional Example

3 Name the property illustrated by each statement.

a. $a - 2.03 = a - 2.03$
Reflexive Property of Equality

b. If $9 = x$, then $x = 9$.
Symmetric Property of Equality

Examples 4 and 5 show how to solve one-step and multi-step equations.

Additional Examples

4 Solve each equation. Check your solution.

a. $m - 5.48 = 0.02$ 5.5

b. $18 = \frac{1}{2}t$ 36

5 Solve $53 = 3(y - 2) - 2(3y - 1)$. −19

Tips for New Teachers

Sense-Making Help students to remember the name of the Reflexive Property by relating $a = a$ to seeing your reflection in a mirror.

Focus on Mathematical Content

Rules for Solving Equations The rules used to solve equations are based on the Properties of Equality. When a number is added to or subtracted from each side of an equation, the result is an equivalent equation. This equivalent equation will have the same solution as the original.

Tips for New Teachers

Checking Solutions Explain that checking solutions to discover possible errors is a vital procedure when you use math on the job.

Study Tips offer students helpful information about the topics they are studying.

EXAMPLE 4 Solve One-Step Equations

Solve each equation. Check your solution.

a. $n - 3.24 = 42.1$

$n - 3.24 = 42.1$	Original equation
$n - 3.24 + 3.24 = 42.1 + 3.24$	Add 3.24 to each side.
$n = 45.34$	Simplify.

The solution is 45.34.

CHECK	
$n - 3.24 = 42.1$	Original equation
$45.34 - 3.24 \stackrel{?}{=} 42.1$	Substitute 45.34 for n.
$42.1 = 42.1$ ✔	Simplify.

b. $-\frac{5}{8}x = 20$

$-\frac{5}{8}x = 20$	Original equation
$-\frac{8}{5}\left(-\frac{5}{8}\right)x = -\frac{8}{5}(20)$	Multiply each side by $-\frac{8}{5}$.
$x = -32$	Simplify.

The solution is −32.

CHECK	
$-\frac{5}{8}x = 20$	Original equation
$-\frac{5}{8}(-32) \stackrel{?}{=} 20$	Replace x with −32.
$20 = 20$ ✔	Simplify.

StudyTip

Multiplication and Division Properties of Equality Example 4b could also have been solved using the Division Property of Equality. Note that dividing each side of the equation by $-\frac{5}{8}$ is the same as multiplying each side by $-\frac{8}{5}$.

Guided Practice

4A. $x - 14.29 = 25$ 39.29

4B. $\frac{2}{3}y = -18$ −27

Personal Tutor glencoe.com

To solve an equation with more than one operation, undo operations by working backward.

EXAMPLE 5 Solve a Multi-Step Equation

Solve $5(x + 3) + 2(1 - x) = 14$.

$5(x + 3) + 2(1 - x) = 14$	Original equation
$5x + 15 + 2 - 2x = 14$	Apply the Distributive Property.
$3x + 17 = 14$	Simplify the left side.
$3x = -3$	Subtract 17 from each side.
$x = -1$	Divide each side by 3.

Guided Practice

Solve each equation.

5A. $-10x + 3(4x - 2) = 6$ 6

5B. $2(2x - 1) - 4(3x + 1) = 2$ −1

Personal Tutor glencoe.com

Differentiated Instruction

AL ELL

If students have difficulty transitioning from verbal expressions to algebraic expressions and vice versa,

Then pair these students with students who are not having trouble. Let them act as a mentor to help the students having difficulties.

You can use properties to solve an equation for a variable.

EXAMPLE 6 Solve for a Variable

GEOMETRY The formula for the area A of a trapezoid is $A = \frac{1}{2}h(b_1 + b_2)$, where h represents the height, and b_1 and b_2 represent the measures of the bases. Solve the formula for b_2.

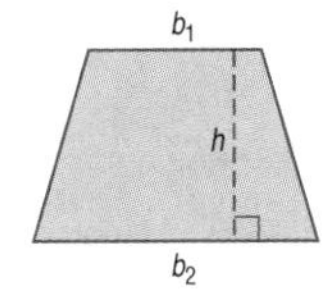

$A = \frac{1}{2}h(b_1 + b_2)$	**Area formula**
$2A = 2\left[\frac{1}{2}h(b_1 + b_2)\right]$	**Multiply each side by 2.**
$2A = h(b_1 + b_2)$	**Simplify.**
$\frac{2A}{h} = \frac{h(b_1 + b_2)}{h}$	**Divide each side by h.**
$\frac{2A}{h} = b_1 + b_2$	**Simplify.**
$\frac{2A}{h} - b_1 = b_1 + b_2 - b_1$	**Subtract b_1 from each side.**
$\frac{2A}{h} - b_1 = b_2$	**Simplify.**

Guided Practice

$6.\ h = \frac{S - 2\pi r^2}{2\pi r}$

6. The formula for the surface area S of a cylinder is $S = 2\pi r^2 + 2\pi rh$, where r is the radius of the base and h is the height of the cylinder. Solve the formula for h.

Personal Tutor glencoe.com

Test-Taking Tip

Using Properties There are often many ways to solve a problem. Using the properties of equality can help you find a simpler way.

NGSSS PRACTICE EXAMPLE 7 912.A.3.5

If $6x - 12 = 18$, what is the value of $6x + 5$?

A. 5 **B.** 11 **C.** 35 **D.** 41

Read the Test Item

You are asked to find the value of $6x + 5$. Note that you do not have to find the value of x. Instead, you can use the Addition Property of Equality to make the left side of the equation $6x + 5$.

Solve the Test Item

$6x - 12 = 18$	**Original equation**
$6x - 12 + 17 = 18 + 17$	**Add 17 to each side because $-12 + 17 = 5$.**
$6x + 5 = 35$	**Simplify.**

The answer is C.

Guided Practice

7. If $5y + 2 = \frac{8}{3}$, what is the value of $5y - 6$? G

F. $\frac{-20}{3}$ G. $\frac{-16}{3}$ H. $\frac{16}{3}$ I. $\frac{32}{3}$

Personal Tutor glencoe.com

Example 6 shows how to use properties to solve a formula for a specified variable. **Example 7** shows how to solve a standardized test question using the Addition Property of Equality.

Additional Examples

6 **GEOMETRY** The formula for the surface area S of a cone is $S = \pi r\ell + \pi r^2$, where ℓ is the slant height of the cone and r is the radius of the base. Solve the formula for ℓ. $\ell = \frac{S - \pi r^2}{\pi r}$

7 **STANDARDIZED TEST PRACTICE** If $4g + 5 = \frac{4}{9}$, what is the value of $4g - 2$? C

A $-\frac{41}{36}$ **C** $-\frac{59}{9}$

B $-\frac{41}{9}$ **D** $-\frac{67}{7}$

Every chapter includes one or more worked-out **Standardized Test Examples** that are similar to problems found on state assessments.

TEACH with TECH

BLOG Have students write a blog entry to summarize how to solve one-step equations. Make sure that students use the concept of inverse operations in their explanations.

Differentiated Instruction OL BL

Extension The formula for the perimeter of a rectangle is $P = 2\ell + 2w$. Find the area of a rectangle that has a perimeter P of 22 inches and a width w of 3 inches. (*Hint:* Begin by solving the perimeter formula for ℓ.) 24 in^2

Check Your Understanding exercises are intended to be completed in class. **Example references** show students where to look back for review.

3 PRACTICE

Formative Assessment

Use Exercises 1–21 to check for understanding.

Use the chart at the bottom of this page to customize assignments for your students.

Additional Answers

3. The sum of five times a number and 7 equals 18.
4. The difference between the square of a number and 9 is 27.
5. The difference between five times a number and the cube of that number is 12.
6. Eight more than the quotient of a number and four is -16.

Check Your Understanding

Example 1 p. 18

Write an algebraic expression to represent each verbal expression.

1. the product of 12 and the sum of a number and negative 3 $12[x + (-3)]$
2. the difference between the product of 4 and a number and the square of the number $4x - x^2$

Example 2 p. 18

Write a verbal sentence to represent each equation. 3–6. See margin.

3. $5x + 7 = 18$
4. $x^2 - 9 = 27$
5. $5y - y^3 = 12$
6. $\frac{x}{4} + 8 = -16$

Example 3 p. 19

Name the property illustrated by each statement.

7. $(8x - 3) + 12 = (8x - 3) + 12$ Reflexive Property
8. If $a = -3$ and $-3 = d$, then $a = d$. Transitive Property

Examples 4 and 5 p. 20

Solve each equation. Check your solution.

9. $z - 19 = 34$ 53
10. $x + 13 = 7$ -6
11. $-y = 8$ -8
12. $-6x = 42$ -7
13. $5x - 3 = -33$ -6
14. $-6y - 8 = 16$ -4
15. $3(2a + 3) - 4(3a - 6) = 15$ 3
16. $5(c - 8) - 3(2c + 12) = -84$ 8
17. $-3(-2x + 20) + 8(x + 12) = 92$ 4
18. $-4(3m - 10) - 6(-7m - 6) = -74$ -5

Example 6 p. 21

Solve each equation or formula for the specified variable.

19. $8r - 5q = 3$, for q $q = \frac{8r - 3}{5}$
20. $Pv = nrt$, for n $\frac{Pv}{rt} = n$

Example 7 p. 21

21. **MULTIPLE CHOICE** If $\frac{y}{5} + 8 = 7$, what is the value of $\frac{y}{5} - 2$? B

A -10 B -3 C 1 D 5

Practice and Problem Solving

● = **Step-by-Step Solutions** begin on page R20. **Extra Practice** begins on page 947.

Example 1 p. 18

Write an algebraic expression to represent each verbal expression.

22. the difference between the product of four and a number and 6 $4n - 6$
23. the product of the square of a number and 8 $8x^2$
24. fifteen less than the cube of a number $x^3 - 15$
25. five more than the quotient of a number and 4 $\frac{x}{4} + 5$

26. Four less than 8 times a number is 16.

27. The quotient of the sum of 3 and a number and 4 is 5.

28. Three less than four times the square of a number is 13.

Example 2 p. 18

Write a verbal sentence to represent each equation.

26. $8x - 4 = 16$
27. $\frac{x + 3}{4} = 5$
28. $4y^2 - 3 = 13$

29. **BASEBALL** During a recent season, Miguel Cabrera and Mike Jacobs of the Florida Marlins hit a combined total of 46 home runs. Cabrera hit 6 more home runs than Jacobs. How many home runs did each player hit? Define a variable, write an equation, and solve the problem.

29. n = number of home runs Jacobs hit; $n + 6$ = number of home runs Cabrera hit; $2n + 6 = 46$; Jacobs: 20 home runs, Cabrera: 26 home runs.

Example 3 p. 19

Name the property illustrated by each statement. 30. Subtr. (=)

30. If $x + 9 = 2$, then $x + 9 - 9 = 2 - 9$
31. If $y = -3$, then $7y = 7(-3)$ Subst.
32. If $g = 3h$ and $3h = 16$, then $g = 16$ Transitive Property
33. If $-y = 13$, then $-(-y) = -13$ Mult. (=)

Differentiated Homework Options

Level	Assignment	Two-Day Option	
AL Basic	22–50, 62, 64–82	23–49 odd, 67–70	22–50 even, 62, 64–66, 71–82
OL Core	23–51 odd, 52, 53–57 odd, 59–62, 64–82	22–50, 67–70	51–62, 64–66, 71–82
BL Advanced	51–74, (optional: 75–82)		

22 Chapter 1 Equations and Inequalities

34. **MONEY** Aiko and Kendra arrive at the state fair with \$32.50. What is the total number of rides they can go on if they each pay the entrance fee? **n = number of rides; $2(7.50) + n(2.50) = 32.50$; 7**

Examples 4 and 5 p. 20

Solve each equation. Check your solution.

35. $3y + 4 = 19$ **5**
36. $-9x - 8 = 55$ **-7**
37. $7y - 2y + 4 + 3y = -20$ **-3**
38. $5g + 18 - 7g + 4g = 8$ **-5**
39. $5(-2x - 4) - 3(4x + 5) = 97$ **-6**
40. $-2(3y - 6) + 4(5y - 8) = 92$ **8**
41. $\frac{2}{3}(6c - 18) + \frac{3}{4}(8c + 32) = -18$ **-3**
42. $\frac{3}{5}(15d + 20) - \frac{1}{6}(18d - 12) = 38$ **4**

43. **GEOMETRY** The perimeter of a regular pentagon is 100 inches. Find the length of each side. **s = length of a side; $5s = 100$; 20 in.**

44. **MEDICINE** For Nina's illness her doctor gives her a prescription for 28 pills. The doctor says that she should take 4 pills the first day and then 2 pills each day until her prescription runs out. For how many days does she take 2 pills?

44. x = the number of days she takes 2 pills; $4 + 2x = 28$; 12 days

Example 6 p. 21

Solve each equation or formula for the specified variable.

45. $E = mc^2$, for m **$m = \frac{E}{c^2}$**
46. $c(a + b) - d = f$, for a **$a = \frac{f + d}{c} - b$**
47. $z = \pi q^3 h$, for h **$h = \frac{z}{\pi q^3}$**
48. $\frac{x + y}{z} - a = b$, for y **$y = z(a + b) - x$**
49. $y = ax^2 + bx + c$, for a **$a = \frac{y - bx - c}{x^2}$**
50. $wx + yz = bc$, for z **$z = \frac{bc - wx}{y}$**

B

51. **GEOMETRY** The formula for the volume of a cylinder with radius r and height h is π times the radius times the radius times the height.

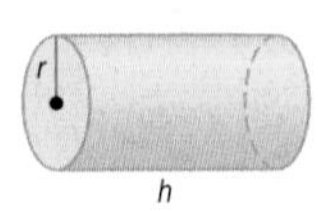

a. Write this as an algebraic expression. **$V = \pi \times r \times r \times h$**

b. Solve the expression in part a for h. **$h = \frac{V}{\pi r^2}$**

52. **AWARDS BANQUET** A banquet room can seat a maximum of 69 people. The coach, principal, and vice principal have invited the award-winning girls' tennis team to the banquet. If the tennis team consists of 22 girls, how many guests can each student bring? **n = number of guests that each student can bring; $22n + 25 = 69$; 2 guests**

Solve each equation. Check your solution.

53. $5x - 9 = 11x + 3$ **-2**
54. $\frac{1}{x} + \frac{1}{4} = \frac{7}{12}$ **3**
55. $5.4(3k - 12) + 3.2(2k + 6) = -136$ **-4**
56. $8.2p - 33.4 = 1.7 - 3.5p$ **3**
57. $\frac{4}{9}y + 5 = -\frac{7}{9}y - 8$ **$-\frac{117}{11}$**
58. $\frac{3}{4}z - \frac{1}{3} = \frac{2}{3}z + \frac{1}{5}$ **$\frac{32}{5}$**

59. **FINANCIAL LITERACY** Benjamin spent \$10,734 on his living expenses last year. Most of these expenses are listed at the right. Benjamin's only other expense last year was rent. If he paid rent 12 times last year, how much is Benjamin's rent each month? **x = the cost of rent each month; $622 + 428 + 240 + 144 + 12x = 10,734$; \$775 per month**

Expense	Annual Cost
Electric	\$622
Gas	\$428
Water	\$240
Renter's Insurance	\$144

Study Guide and Intervention
CRM pp. 17–18 AL OL ELL

1-3 Study Guide and Intervention

Solving Equations

Verbal Expressions and Algebraic Expressions The chart suggests some ways to help you translate word expressions into algebraic expressions. Any letter can be used to represent a number that is not known.

Word Expression	Operation
and, plus, sum, increased by, more than	addition
minus, difference, decreased by, less than	subtraction
times, product, of (as in $\frac{1}{2}$ of a number)	multiplication
divided by, quotient	division

Example 1 **Write an algebraic expression to represent 18 less than the quotient of a number and 3.**

$\frac{n}{3} - 18$

Example 2 **Write a verbal sentence to represent $6(n - 2) = 14$.**

Six times the difference of a number and two is equal to 14.

Exercises

Write an algebraic expression to represent each verbal expression.

1. the sum of six times a number and 25 **$6n + 25$**
2. four times the sum of a number and 3 **$4(n + 3)$**
3. 7 less than fifteen times a number **$15n - 7$**
4. the difference of nine times a number and the quotient of 6 and the same number **$9n - \frac{6}{n}$**
5. the sum of 100 and four times a number **$100 + 4n$**
6. the product of 3 and the sum of 11 and a number **$3(11 + n)$**
7. four times the square of a number increased by five times the same number **$4n^2 + 5n$**
8. 23 more than the product of 7 and a number **$7n + 23$**

Write a verbal sentence to represent each equation. Sample answers are given.

9. $3n - 35 = 79$ **The difference of three times a number and 35 is equal to 79.**
10. $2(n^3 + 3n^2) = 4n$ **Twice the sum of the cube of a number and three times the square of the number is equal to four times the number.**
11. $\frac{5n}{n + 3} = n - 8$ **The quotient of five times a number and the sum of the number and 3 is equal to the difference of the number and 8.**

Chapter 1 17 Glencoe Algebra 2

Lesson 1-3

Practice
CRM p. 20 AL OL BL ELL

1-3 Practice

Solving Equations

Write an algebraic expression to represent each verbal expression.

1. 2 more than the quotient of a number and 5 **$\frac{y}{5} + 2$**
2. the sum of two consecutive integers **$n + (n + 1)$**
3. 5 times the sum of a number and 1 **$5(m + 1)$**
4. 1 less than twice the square of a number **$2y^2 - 1$**

Write a verbal sentence to represent each equation. **5–8. Sample answers are given.**

5. $5 - 2x = 4$ **The difference of 5 and twice a number is 4.**
6. $3y = 4y^3$ **Three times a number is 4 times the cube of the number.**
7. $3c = 2(c - 1)$ **Three times a number is twice the difference of the number and 1.**
8. $\frac{m}{5} = 3(2m + 1)$ **The quotient of a number and 5 is 3 times the sum of twice the number and 1.**

Name the property illustrated by each statement.

9. If $t - 13 = 52$, then $52 = t - 13$. **Symmetric (=)**
10. If $8(2q + 1) = 4$, then $2(2q + 1) = 1$. **Division (=)**
11. If $h + 12 = 22$, then $h = 10$. **Subtraction (=)**
12. If $4m = -15$, then $-12m = 45$. **Multiplication (=)**

Solve each equation. Check your solution.

13. $14 = 8 - 6r$ **-1**
14. $9 + 4n = -59$ **-17**
15. $\frac{3}{4} - \frac{1}{2}n = \frac{5}{8}$ **$\frac{1}{4}$**
16. $\frac{5}{6}s + \frac{3}{4} = \frac{11}{12}$ **$\frac{1}{5}$**
17. $-1.6r + 5 = -7.8$ **8**
18. $6x - 5 = 7 - 9x$ **$\frac{4}{5}$**
19. $5(6 - 4v) = v + 21$ **$\frac{3}{7}$**
20. $6y - 5 = -3(2y + 1)$ **$\frac{1}{6}$**

Solve each equation or formula for the specified variable.

21. $E = mc^2$, for m **$m = \frac{E}{c^2}$**
22. $c = \frac{2d + 1}{3}$, for d **$d = \frac{3c - 1}{2}$**
23. $h = vt - gt^2$, for v **$v = \frac{h + gt^2}{t}$**
24. $E = \frac{1}{2}Iw^2 + U$, for I **$I = \frac{2(E - U)}{w^2}$**

25. **GEOMETRY** The length of a rectangle is twice the width. Find the width if the perimeter is 60 centimeters. Define a variable, write an equation, and solve the problem. **w = width; $2(2w) + 2w = 60$; 10 cm**

26. **GOLF** Luis and three friends went golfing. Two of the friends rented clubs for \$6 each. The total cost of the rented clubs and the green fees for each person was \$76. What was the cost of the green fees for each person? Define a variable, write an equation, and solve the problem. **g = green fees per person; $6(2) + 4g = 76$; \$16**

Chapter 1 20 Glencoe Algebra 2

Word Problem Practice
CRM p. 21 AL OL BL ELL

1-3 Word Problem Practice

Solving Equations

1. **AGES** Robert's father is 5 years older than 3 times Robert's age. Let Robert's age be denoted by R and let Robert's father's age be denoted by F. Write an equation that relates Robert's age and his father's age. **$F = 3R + 5$.**

2. **AIRPLANES** The Citation Sovereign is a small jet that can carry up to 2,650 pounds. The number of passengers p and the number of suitcases s that the airplane can carry are estimated by the equation $180p + 60s = 2{,}650$. If 10 people board the aircraft, how many suitcases can the airplane carry? **20 suitcases**

3. **GEOMETRY** The length of a rectangle is 10 units longer than its width. If the total perimeter of the rectangle is 44 units, what is the width?

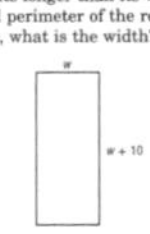

w = 6 units

4. **SAVINGS** Jason started with d dollars in his piggy bank. One week later, Jason doubled the amount in his piggy bank. Another week later, Jason was able to add \$20 to his piggy bank. At this point, the piggy bank had \$50 in it. What is d? **15**

5. **DOMINOES** Nancy is setting up a train of dominos from the front entrance straight down the hall to the kitchen entrance. The thickness of each domino is t. Nancy places the dominoes so that the space separating consecutive dominoes is $3t$. The total distance that N dominoes takes up is given by $d = t(4N + 1)$.

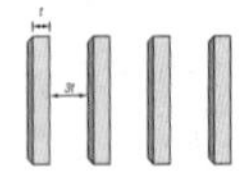

a. Nancy measures her dominoes and finds that $t = 1$ centimeter. She measures the distance of her hallway and finds that $d = 321$ centimeters. Rewrite the equation that relates d, t, and N with the given values substituted for t and d. **$321 = 4N + 1$.**

b. How many dominoes did Nancy have in her hallway? **80 dominoes**

Chapter 1 21 Glencoe Algebra 2

Lesson 1-3

Enrichment
CRM p. 22 OL BL

1-3 Enrichment

United States' Gross National Product

The Gross National Product, GNP, is an important indicator of the U.S. economy. The GNP contains information about the inflation rate, the Bond market, and the Stock market. It is composed of consumer goods, investments, government expenditures, exports, and imports.

Calculated from $GNP = C + I + G + X - M$, where

C is consumer goods (e.g. TVs, cars, food, furniture, clothes, doctors' fees, and dining)

I is investments (e.g. factories, computers, airlines, and housing)

G is government spending and investments (e.g. ships, roads, schools, NASA, and bombs)

X is exports (e.g. corn, wheat, cars, and computers)

M is for imports, (e.g. cars, computer chips, clothes, and oil)

$X - M$ is exports minus imports and equals trade surplus or deficit.

1. The most important sector of the U.S. economy is consumption. It makes up about 60% of the entire GNP. In 2000, the U.S.'s GNP was 10.5 trillion dollars. In the same year, there were 1 trillion dollars in investments, but a 1 trillion dollar trade deficit. Assuming that consumption made up 60% of the GNP, how much did the government budget for spending? **$10.5 = 6.3 + 1 + G - 1$. Therefore $G = 4.2$ trillion dollars.**

Multiple Representations In Exercise 61, students use a number line and a table of values to illustrate the workings of absolute values.

Watch Out!

Error Analysis In Exercise 62, encourage students to give a complete explanation of the error. For example, "Steven should have subtracted b from the entire left side, $\frac{2A}{h}$, in the last step of the equation."

Find the Error exercises help students identify and address common errors before they occur. Prompts in the margin of the Teacher Edition help you guide students toward understanding.

Additional Answers

60c. Yes; it seems reasonable that two crews working 4 miles apart would be able to complete the same amount of miles in the same amount of time.

61b.

Integer	Distance from Zero
−5	5
−4	4
−3	3
−2	2
−1	1
0	0
1	1
2	2
3	3
4	4
5	5

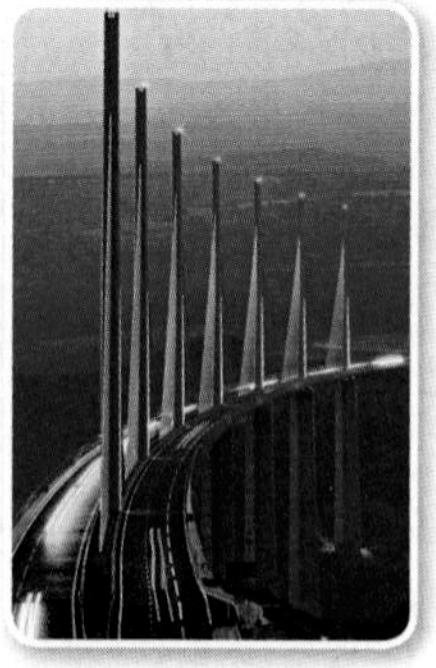

Real-World Link

The Milliau Viaduct, located in southern France, is the world's tallest vehicular bridge. The bridge stands 1122 feet tall, 1.5 miles long, and 4 lanes wide.

Source: National Geographic Society

60. BRIDGES The Sunshine Skyway Bridge spans Tampa Bay, Florida. Suppose one crew began building south from St. Petersburg, and another crew began building north from Bradenton. The two crews met 10,560 feet south of St. Petersburg approximately 5 years after construction began.

a. Suppose the St. Petersburg crew built an average of 176 feet per month. Together the two crews built 21,120 feet of bridge. Determine the average number of feet built per month by the Bradenton crew. **176 ft**

b. About how many miles of bridge did each crew build? **2 mi**

c. Is this answer reasonable? Explain. **See margin.**

61. MULTIPLE REPRESENTATIONS The absolute value of a number describes the distance of the number from zero. **a.**

a. GEOMETRIC Draw a number line. Label the integers from −5 to 5.

b. TABULAR Create a table of the integers on the number line and their distance from zero. **b–d. See margin.**

c. GRAPHICAL Make a graph of each integer x and its distance from zero y using the data points in the table.

d. VERBAL Make a conjecture about the integer and its distance from zero. Explain the reason for any changes in sign.

H.O.T. Problems
Use Higher-Order Thinking Skills

62. ERROR ANALYSIS Steven and Jade are solving $A = \frac{1}{2}h(b_1 + b_2)$ for b_2. Is either of them correct? Explain your reasoning.

Steven	Jade
$A = \frac{1}{2}h(b_1 + b_2)$	$A = \frac{1}{2}h(b_1 + b_2)$
$\frac{2A}{h} = (b_1 + b_2)$	$\frac{2A}{h} = (b_1 + b_2)$
$\frac{2A - b_1}{h} = b_2$	$\frac{2A}{h} - b_1 = b_2$

62. Sample answer: Jade; in the last step, when Steven subtracted b_1 from each side, he mistakenly put the $-b_1$ in the numerator instead of after the entire fraction.

63. CHALLENGE Solve $d = \sqrt{(x_2 - x_1)^2 + (y_2 - y_1)^2}$ for y_1. $y_1 = y_2 - \sqrt{d^2 - (x_2 - x_1)^2}$

64. REASONING Use what you have learned in this lesson to explain why the following number trick works. **Translating this number trick into an expression yields:**

- Take any number.
- Multiply it by ten.
- Subtract 30 from the result.
- Divide the new result by 5.
- Add 6 to the result.
- Your new number is twice your original.

$$\frac{(10x - 30)}{5} + 6 = 2x$$
$$\frac{(10x - 30)}{5} = 2x - 6$$
$$(2x - 6) + 6 = 2x$$

65. OPEN ENDED Provide one example of an equation involving the Distributive Property that has no solution and another example that has infinitely many solutions. **Sample answer: $3(x - 4) = 3x + 5$; $2(3x - 1) = 6x - 2$**

66. WRITING IN MATH Compare and contrast the Substitution Property of Equality and the Transitive Property of Equality.

66. Sample answer: The Transitive Property utilizes the Substitution Property. While the Substitution Property is done with two values, that is, one being substituted for another, the Transitive Property deals with three values, determining that since two values are equal to a third value, then they must be equal.

61c.

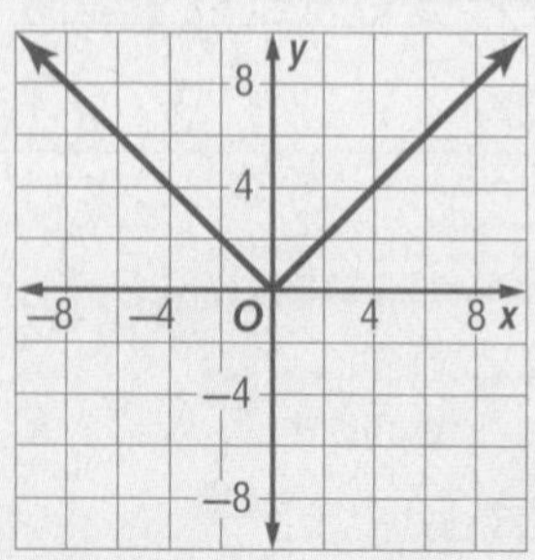

61d. For positive integers, the distance from zero is the same as the integer. For negative integers, the distance is the integer with the opposite sign because distance is always positive.

NGSSS PRACTICE 912.A.3.6, 912.G.2.4, 912.A.2.13

67. The graph shows the solution of which inequality? **D**

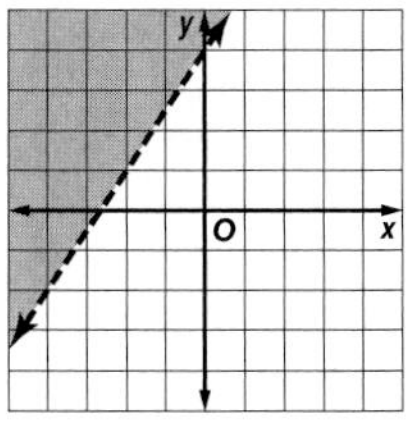

A. $y < \frac{2}{3}x + 4$ **C.** $y < \frac{3}{2}x + 4$

B. $y > \frac{2}{3}x + 4$ **D.** $y > \frac{3}{2}x + 4$

68. SAT/ACT What is $1\frac{1}{3}$ subtracted from its reciprocal? **F**

F. $-\frac{7}{12}$ **H.** $\frac{1}{4}$

G. $-\frac{1}{12}$ **I.** $\frac{3}{4}$

69. GEOMETRY Which of the following describes the transformation of $\triangle ABC$ to $\triangle A'B'C'$? **A**

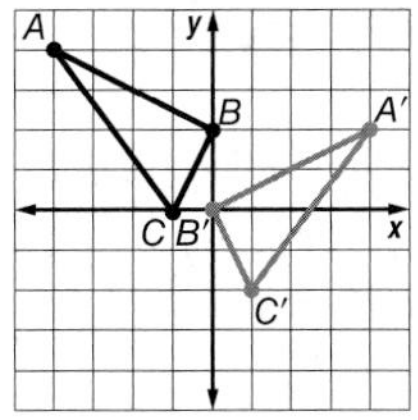

A. a reflection across the y-axis and a translation down 2 units

B. a reflection across the x-axis and a translation down 2 units

C. a rotation 90° to the right and a translation down 2 units

D. a rotation 90° to the right and a translation right 2 units

70. THINK SOLVE EXPLAIN **SHORT RESPONSE** A local theater sold 1200 tickets during the opening weekend of a movie. On the following weekend, 840 tickets were sold. What was the percent decrease of tickets sold? **30%**

Spiral Review

71. Simplify $3x + 8y + 5z - 2y - 6x + z$. (Lesson 1-2) $-3x + 6y + 6z$

72. BAKING Tamera is making two types of bread. The first type of bread needs $2\frac{1}{2}$ cups of flour, and the second needs $1\frac{3}{4}$ cups of flour. Tamera wants to make 2 loaves of the first recipe and 3 loaves of the second recipe. How many cups of flour does she need? (Lesson 1-2) $10\frac{1}{4}$ c

73. LANDMARKS Suppose the Space Needle in Seattle, Washington, casts a 220-foot shadow at the same time a nearby tourist casts a 2-foot shadow. If the tourist is $5\frac{1}{2}$ feet tall, how tall is the Space Needle? (Lesson 0-6) **605 ft**

74. Evaluate $a - [c(b - a)]$, if $a = 5$, $b = 7$, and $c = 2$. (Lesson 1-1) **1**

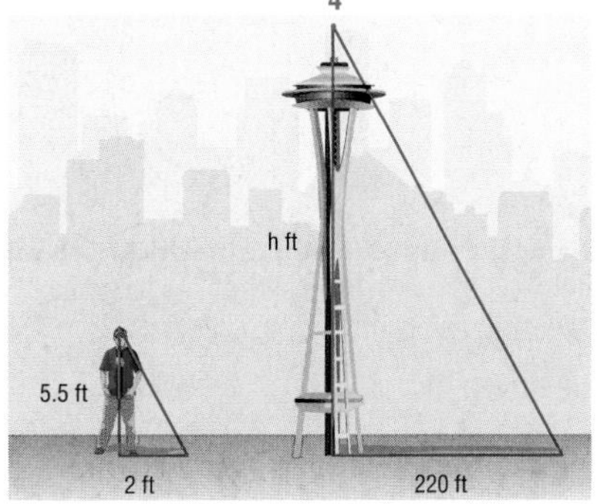

Skills Review

Identify the additive inverse for each number or expression. (Lesson 1-2)

75. $-4\frac{1}{5}$ $4\frac{1}{5}$ **76.** 3.5 **−3.5** **77.** $-2x$ $2x$ **78.** $6 - 7y$ $-6 + 7y$

79. $3\frac{2}{3}$ $-3\frac{2}{3}$ **80.** −1.25 **1.25** **81.** $5x$ $-5x$ **82.** $4 - 9x$ $-4 + 9x$

4 ASSESS

Yesterday's News Have each student write how yesterday's concepts helped with today's new material.

Formative Assessment

Check for student understanding of concepts in Lesson 1-3.

CRM Quiz 2, p. 45

CHAPTER 1

Mid-Chapter Quiz

Formative Assessment

Use the Mid-Chapter Quiz to assess students' progress in the first half of the chapter.

For problems answered incorrectly, have students review the lessons indicated in parentheses.

ExamView Assessment Suite Customize and create multiple versions of your Mid-Chapter Quiz and their answer keys.

FOLDABLES® Follow-Up

Before students complete the Mid-Chapter Quiz, encourage them to review the information for Lessons 1-1 through 1-3 in their Foldables.

CHAPTER 1

Mid-Chapter Quiz

Lessons 1-1 through 1-3

NGSSS 912.A.2.13, 912.A.3.5, 912.G.2.5, 912.G.7.5

1. Evaluate $3c - 4(a + b)$ if $a = -1$, $b = 2$ and $c = \frac{1}{3}$. (Lesson 1-1) **−3**

2. **TRAVEL** The distance that Maurice traveled in 2.5 hours riding his bicycle can be found by using the formula $d = rt$, where d is the distance traveled, r is the rate, and t is the time. How far did Maurice travel if he traveled at a rate of 16 miles per hour? (Lesson 1-1) **40 m**

3. Evaluate $(5 - m)^3 + n(m - n)$ if $m = 6$ and $n = -3$. (Lesson 1-1) **−28**

4. **GEOMETRY** The formula for the surface area of the rectangular prism below is given by the formula $S = 2xy + 2yz + 2xz$. What is the surface area of the prism if $x = 2.2$, $y = 3.5$, and $z = 5.1$? (Lesson 1-1) **73.54 units²**

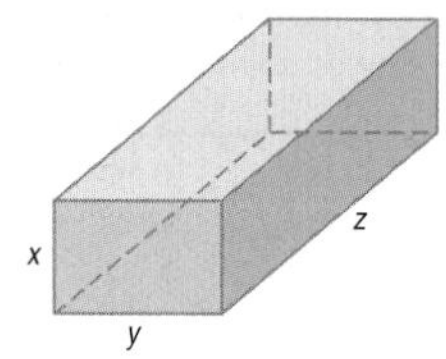

5. NGSSS **PRACTICE** What is the value of $\frac{q^2 + rt}{qr - 2t}$ if $q = -4$, $r = 3$, and $t = 8$? (Lesson 1-1) **C**

A. $-\frac{17}{6}$

B. $-\frac{1}{6}$

C. $-\frac{10}{7}$

D. $-\frac{2}{7}$

Name the sets of numbers to which each number belongs. (Lesson 1-2)

6. $\frac{25}{11}$ **Q, R**

7. $-\frac{128}{32}$ **Z, Q, R**

8. $\sqrt{50}$ **I, R**

9. -32.4 **Q, R**

10. What is the property illustrated by the equation $(4 + 15)7 = 4 \cdot 7 + 15 \cdot 7$? (Lesson 1-2) **Dist.**

11. Simplify $-3(7a - 4b) + 2(-3a + b)$. (Lesson 1-2) $\mathbf{-27a + 14b}$

12. **CLOTHES** Brittany is buying T-shirts and jeans for her new job. T-shirts cost $10.50, and jeans cost $26.50. She buys 3 T-shirts and 3 pairs of jeans. Illustrate the Distributive Property by writing two expressions representing how much Brittany spent. (Lesson 1-2) **3(10.50 + 26.50) or 3(10.50) + 3(26.50)**

13. NGSSS **PRACTICE** Which expression is equivalent to $\frac{2}{3}(4m - 5n) + \frac{1}{5}(2m + n)$? (Lesson 1-2) **F**

F. $\frac{46}{15}m - \frac{47}{15}n$

G. $46m - 47n$

H. $-\frac{mn}{15}$

I. $\frac{5}{4}m - \frac{9}{8}n$

14. Identify the additive inverse and the multiplicative inverse for $\frac{7}{6}$. (Lesson 1-2) **additive: $-\frac{7}{6}$; mult.: $\frac{6}{7}$**

15. Write a verbal sentence to represent the equation $\frac{a}{a-3} = 1$. (Lesson 1-3) **The quotient of a number *a* and the difference of a number *a* and 3 is equal to 1.**

16. Solve $6x + 4y = -1$ for x. (Lesson 1-3) $x = -\frac{2}{3}y - \frac{1}{6}$

17. NGSSS **PRACTICE** Which algebraic expression represents the verbal expression, *the product of 4 and the difference of a number and 13*? (Lesson 1-3) **B**

A. $4n - 13$

B. $4(n - 13)$

C. $\frac{4}{n - 13}$

D. $\frac{4n}{13}$

18. Solve $-3(6x + 5) + 2(4x) = 20$. (Lesson 1-3) $-\frac{7}{2}$

19. What is the height of the trapezoid below? (Lesson 1-3) **7.5 units**

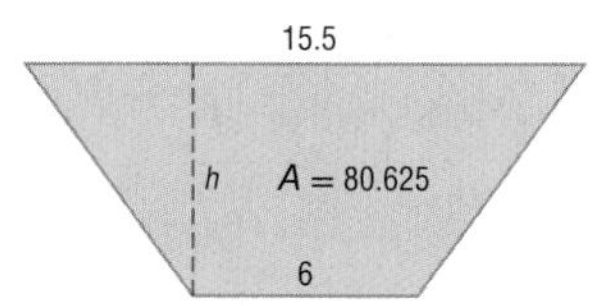

20. **GEOMETRY** The formula for the surface area of a sphere is $SA = 4\pi r^2$, and the formula for the volume of a sphere is $V = \frac{4}{3}\pi r^3$. (Lesson 1-3)

a. Find the volume and surface area of a sphere with radius 2 inches. Write your answers in terms of π. $\frac{32}{3}\pi$ **in³; 16π in²**

b. Is it possible for a sphere to have the same numerical value for the surface area and volume? If so, find the radius of such a sphere. **yes; 3 units**

Intervention Planner

Tier 1 On Level	Tier 2 Strategic Intervention approaching grade level	Tier 3 Intensive Intervention 2 or more grades below level
If students miss about 25% of the exercises or less,	**If** students miss about 50% of the exercises,	**If** students miss about 75% of the exercises,
Then choose a resource:	**Then** choose a resource:	**Then** use *Math Triumphs, Alg. 2*, Ch. 1 and 2
SE Lessons 1-1, 1-2, and 1-3	**CRM** Study Guide and Intervention, Chapter 1, pp. 5, 11, 17	
CRM Skills Practice, pp. 7, 13, and 19		
TE Chapter Project, p. 2		
FL Math Online Self-Check Quiz	FL Math Online Extra Examples, Personal Tutor, Homework Help	FL Math Online Extra Examples, Personal Tutor, Homework Help, Review Vocabulary

26 Chapter 1 Equations and Inequalities

1-4 Solving Absolute Value Equations

Why?

Sailors sometimes use a laser range finder to determine distances. Suppose one such range finder is accurate to within ±0.5 yard. This means that if a sailor estimating the distance to shore reads 323.1 yards on the laser range finder, the distance to shore might actually be as close as 322.6 or as far away as 323.6 yards. These extremes can be described by the equation $|E - 323.1| = 0.5$.

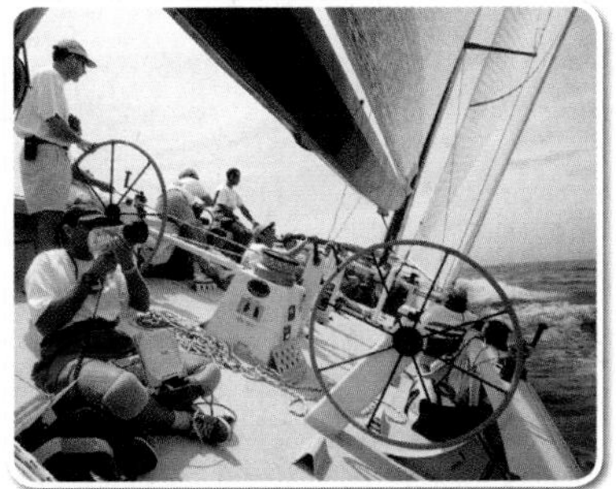

Then
You solved equations using properties of equality. (Lesson 1-3)

Now
- Evaluate expressions involving absolute values.
- Solve absolute value equations.

NGSSS
MA.912.A.3.6 **Solve** and graph the solutions **of absolute value equations and inequalities with one variable.**

New Vocabulary
absolute value
empty set
extraneous solution

FL Math Online
glencoe.com

Absolute Value Expressions The **absolute value** of a number is its distance from 0 on the number line. Since distance is nonnegative, the absolute value of a number is always nonnegative. The symbol $|x|$ is used to represent the absolute value of a number x.

Key Concept

Absolute Value

Words For any real number a, if a is positive or zero, the absolute value of a is a. If a is negative, the absolute value of a is the opposite of a.

Symbols For any real number a, $|a| = a$ if $a \geq 0$, and $|a| = -a$ if $a < 0$.

Model $|-4| = 4$ and $|4| = 4$

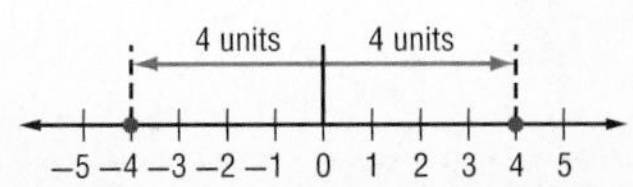

When evaluating expressions, absolute value bars act as a grouping symbol. Perform any operations inside the absolute value bars first.

EXAMPLE 1 Evaluate an Expression with Absolute Value

Evaluate $8.4 - |2n + 5|$ if $n = -7.5$.

$8.4 - |2n + 5| = 8.4 - |2(-7.5) + 5|$ — **Replace n with −7.5.**

$= 8.4 - |-15 + 5|$ — **Multiply 2 and −7.5.**

$= 8.4 - |-10|$ — **Add −15 and 5.**

$= 8.4 - 10$ — **$|-10| = 10$**

$= -1.6$ — **Subtract 10 from 8.4.**

Guided Practice

1A. Evaluate $|4x + 3| - 3\frac{1}{2}$ if $x = -2$. $1\frac{1}{2}$

1B. Evaluate $1\frac{1}{3} - |2y + 1|$ if $y = -\frac{2}{3}$. 1

Personal Tutor glencoe.com

1-4 Lesson Notes

1 FOCUS

Vertical Alignment

Before Lesson 1-4
Solve equations using properties of equality.

Lesson 1-4
Evaluate expressions involving absolute values.
Solve absolute value equations.

After Lesson 1-4
Solve absolute value inequalities.

2 TEACH

Scaffolding Questions

Have students read the *Why?* section of the lesson.

Ask:

- In $|E - 323.1| = 0.5$, what does E represent? the actual distance to shore
- What is the meaning of the number 0.5 in the equation? the degree of accuracy of the range finder
- What would be the equation for the distance to shore estimated at 962.3 yards? $|E - 962.3| = 0.5$
- How can this be shown on a number line?

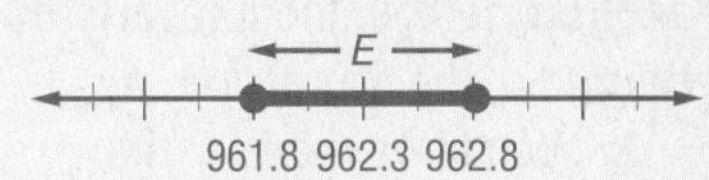

Lesson 1-4 Resources

Resource	Approaching-Level	On-Level	Beyond-Level	English Learners
Teacher Edition	• Differentiated Instruction, p. 29	• Differentiated Instruction, pp. 29, 32	• Differentiated Instruction, p. 32	• Differentiated Instruction, p. 29
Chapter Resource Masters	• Study Guide and Intervention, pp. 24–25 • Skills Practice, p. 26 • Practice, p. 27 • Word Problem Practice, p. 28	• Study Guide and Intervention, pp. 24–25 • Skills Practice, p. 26 • Practice, p. 27 • Word Problem Practice, p. 28 • Enrichment, p. 29 • Spreadsheet Activity, p. 30	• Practice, p. 27 • Word Problem Practice, p. 28 • Enrichment, p. 29	• Study Guide and Intervention, pp. 24–25 • Skills Practice, p. 26 • Practice, p. 27 • Word Problem Practice, p. 28
Transparencies	• 5-Minute Check Transparency 1-4	• 5-Minute Check Transparency 1-4	• 5-Minute Check Transparency 1-4	• 5-Minute Check Transparency 1-4
Other	• Study Notebook	• Study Notebook	• Study Notebook	• Study Notebook

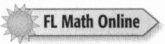

Absolute Value Expressions

Example 1 shows how to evaluate expressions that contain absolute values.

Formative Assessment

Use the Guided Practice exercises after each example to determine students' understanding of concepts.

Additional Example

1 Evaluate $2.7 + |6 - 2x|$ if $x = 4$. 4.7

Additional Examples also in Interactive Classroom PowerPoint® Presentations

IWB INTERACTIVE WHITEBOARD READY

Additional Examples parallel the examples in the text exactly. Step-by-step solutions for these examples are included in **Interactive Classroom.**

Tips for New Teachers

Reading Students may find it helpful to read the first absolute value bar as "the distance of" and the last absolute value bar as "from zero, without regard to direction." So, the expression $|6 - 2x|$ would be read as "the distance of the value of $6 - 2x$ from zero, without regard to direction."

Absolute Value Equations

Examples 2–4 show how to solve absolute value equations with two solutions, no solution, and one solution.

Additional Example

2 Solve $|y + 3| = 8$. Check your solutions. $\{-11, 5\}$

Absolute Value Equations Some equations contain absolute value expressions. The definition of absolute value is used in solving these equations. For any real numbers a and b, where $b \geq 0$, if $|a| = b$, then $a = b$ or $-a = b$. This second case is often written as $a = -b$.

Problem-Solving Tip

Write an Equation Frequently, the best way to solve a problem is to use the given information to write and solve an equation.

EXAMPLE 2 Solve an Absolute Value Equation

TENNIS A standard adult tennis racket has a 100-square-inch head, plus or minus 20 square inches. Write and solve an absolute value equation to determine the least and greatest possible sizes for the head of an adult tennis racket.

Understand We need to determine the greatest and least possible sizes for the head of a tennis racket given the middle size and the range in sizes.

Plan When writing an absolute value equation, the middle or *central* value is always placed inside the absolute value symbols. The *range* is always placed on the other side of the equality symbol.

central value → $|x - c| = r$ ← range

Solve $|x - c| = r$ **Absolute value equation**

$|x - 100| = 20$ **$c = 100$, and $r = 20$**

Case 1 $a = b$	**Case 2** $a = -b$
$x - 100 = 20$	$x - 100 = -20$
$x - 100 + 100 = 20 + 100$	$x - 100 + 100 = -20 + 100$
$x = 120$	$x = 80$

Check

$\lvert x - 100\rvert = 20$	$\lvert x - 100\rvert = 20$
$\lvert 120 - 100\rvert \stackrel{?}{=} 20$	$\lvert 80 - 100\rvert \stackrel{?}{=} 20$
$\lvert 20\rvert \stackrel{?}{=} 20$	$\lvert -20\rvert \stackrel{?}{=} 20$
$20 = 20$ ✔	$20 = 20$ ✔

On a number line, you can see that both solutions are 20 units away from 100.

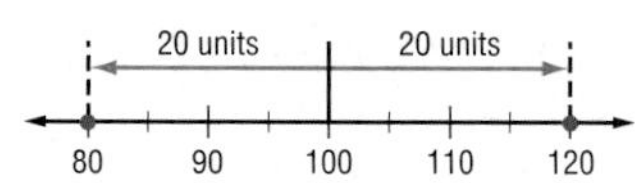

The solutions are 120 and 80. The greatest size is 120 square inches and the least is 80 square inches.

Real-World Link

Originally, players used leather gloves to hit tennis balls. Soon after, the glove was placed at the end of a stick to extend the reach of the "hand."

Source: The Cliff Richard Tennis Foundation

Guided Practice

Solve each equation. Check your solutions.

2A. $9 = |x + 12|$ $\{-21, -3\}$

2B. $8 = |y + 5|$ $\{-13, 3\}$

Personal Tutor glencoe.com

Because the absolute value of a number is always positive or zero, an equation like $|x| = -4$ is never true. Thus, it has no solution. The solution set for this type of equation is the **empty set**, symbolized by { } or ∅.

EXAMPLE 3 No Solution

Solve $|3x - 2| + 8 = 1$.

$|3x - 2| + 8 = 1$	Original equation
$|3x - 2| + 8 - 8 = 1 - 8$	Subtract 8 from each side.
$|3x - 2| = -7$	Simplify.

This sentence is *never* true. The solution set is $\varnothing$.

Guided Practice

Solve each equation. Check your solutions.

3A. $-2|3a| = 6$ $\varnothing$

3B. $|4b + 1| + 8 = 0$ $\varnothing$

Personal Tutor glencoe.com

It is important to check your answers when solving absolute value equations. Even if the correct procedure for solving the equation is used, the answers may not be actual solutions to the original equation. Such a number is called an **extraneous solution**.

StudyTip

Absolute Value It is possible for an absolute value equation to have only one solution. Remember to set up two cases. Then check your solutions.

EXAMPLE 4 One Solution

Solve $|x + 10| = 4x - 8$. Check your solutions.

Case 1 $a = b$

$x + 10 = 4x - 8$

$10 = 3x - 8$

$18 = 3x$

$6 = x$

Case 2 $a = -b$

$x + 10 = -(4x - 8)$

$x + 10 = -4x + 8$

$5x + 10 = 8$

$5x = -2$

$x = -\frac{2}{5}$

There appear to be two solutions, 6 and $-\frac{2}{5}$.

CHECK Substitute each value in the original equation.

$|x + 10| = 4x - 8$

$|6 + 10| \stackrel{?}{=} 4(6) - 8$

$|16| \stackrel{?}{=} 24 - 8$

$16 = 16$ ✔

$|x + 10| = 4x - 8$

$\left|-\frac{2}{5} + 10\right| \stackrel{?}{=} 4\left(-\frac{2}{5}\right) - 8$

$\left|9\frac{3}{5}\right| \stackrel{?}{=} -1\frac{3}{5} - 8$

$9\frac{3}{5} \neq -9\frac{3}{5}$ ✘

Because $9\frac{3}{5} \neq -9\frac{3}{5}$, the only solution is 6. The solution set is $\{6\}$.

Guided Practice

Solve each equation. Check your solutions.

4A. $2|x + 1| - x = 3x - 4$ 3

4B. $3|2x + 2| - 2x = x + 3$ −1

Personal Tutor glencoe.com

Additional Examples

3 Solve $|6 - 4t| + 5 = 0$. $\varnothing$

4 Solve $|8 + y| = 2y - 3$. Check your solutions. $\{11\}$

Focus on Mathematical Content

Absolute Value The absolute value of a number is the distance of that number from 0 on a number line. Therefore, the statement "the absolute value of x is always x" is not true. For example, if x is –3 then the absolute value of –3 is 3.

Watch Out!

Preventing Errors Remind students to think about the meaning of the mathematical sentence before they begin their calculations and again when they evaluate the reasonableness of their solution. Explain to students that they can solve verbal problems when they ask questions about words they do not understand, take time to read, understand, and plan, using a sketch to help.

TEACH with TECH

INTERACTIVE WHITEBOARD
On the board, work through several examples solving absolute value equations. Save your work to a file and send it to your students so they can use it as an additional reference.

Differentiated Instruction

AL OL ELL

If students found anything from the lesson confusing,

Then ask them to record two or three of the confusing items separately on an index card. Have them write an explanation or example for each item in their own words. This will help them review in the future.

3 PRACTICE

Formative Assessment

Use Exercises 1–13 to check for understanding.

Use the chart at the bottom of this page to customize assignments for your students.

Multiple Representations In Exercise 44, students use a number line, information organized in a table, and algebra to analyze inequalities.

Watch Out!

Error Analysis For Exercise 45, students should see that Ana and Ling have differences in their solutions. They must decide which person checked the solutions correctly.

Additional Answers

43. $|x - 100| = 245$; maximum: 345 ft above sea level; minimum: −145 ft below sea level. No, the maximum is reasonable but the minimum is not. Florida's lowest point should be at sea level where Florida meets the Atlantic Ocean and the Gulf of Mexico.

44a. Sample answer:

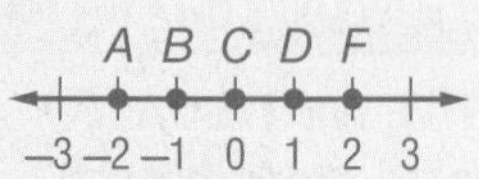

44c. Sample answer: If *A* is less than *B*, then any number added to or subtracted from *A* will be less than the same number added to or subtracted from *B*. If *B* is greater than *A*, then any number added to or subtracted from *B* is greater than the same number added to or subtracted from *A*.

Check Your Understanding

Example 1 p. 27

Evaluate each expression if $x = -4$ and $y = -9$. 4.

1. $|x - 8|$ **12**
2. $|7y|$ **63**
3. $-3|xy|$ **−108**
4. $-2|3x + 8| - 4$ **−12**

5. **FISH** Most freshwater tropical fish thrive if the water is within 2°F of 78°F.

   a. Write an equation to determine the least and greatest optimal temperatures. $|x - 78| = 2$
   b. Solve the equation you wrote in part a.
   c. If your aquarium's thermometer is accurate to within plus or minus 1°F, what should the temperature of the water be to ensure that it reaches the minimum temperature? Explain. **77°F; This would ensure a minimum temperature of 76°F.**

5b. least: 76°F, greatest: 80°F

Examples 2–4 pp. 28–29

Solve each equation. Check your solutions.

6. $|x + 8| = 12$ **{4, −20}**
7. $|y - 4| = 11$ **{15, −7}**
8. $|a - 5| + 4 = 9$ **{10, 0}**
9. $|b - 3| + 8 = 3$ **∅**
10. $3|2x - 3| - 5 = 4$ **{3, 0}**
11. $-2|5y - 1| = -10$ $\left\{\frac{6}{5}, -\frac{4}{5}\right\}$
12. $|a - 4| = 3a - 6$ **2.5**
13. $|b + 5| = 2b + 3$ **2**

Practice and Problem Solving

● = **Step-by-Step Solutions** begin on page R20.
Extra Practice begins on page 947.

Example 1 p. 27

Evaluate each expression if $a = -3$, $b = -5$, and $c = 4.2$.

14. $|-3c|$ **12.6**
15. $|5b|$ **25**
16. $|a - b|$ **2**
17. $|b - c|$ **9.2**
18. $|3b - 4a|$ **3**
19. $2|4a - 3c|$ **49.2**
20. $-|3c - a|$ **−15.6**
21. $-|abc|$ **−63**

22. **FOOD** To make cocoa powder, cocoa beans are roasted. The ideal temperature for roasting is 300°F, plus or minus 25°. Write and solve an equation describing the maximum and minimum roasting temperatures for cocoa beans. $|x - 300| = 25$; **maximum: 325°F; minimum: 275°F**

Examples 2–4 pp. 28–29

Solve each equation. Check your solutions.

23. $|z - 13| = 21$ **{34, −8}**
24. $|w + 9| = 17$ **{8, −26}**
25. $9 = |d + 5|$ **{4, −14}**
26. $35 = |x - 6|$ **{−29, 41}**
27. $5|q + 6| = 20$ **{−2, −10}**
28. $-3|r + 4| = -21$ **{3, −11}**
29. $3|2a - 4| = 0$ **2**
30. $8|5w - 1| = 0$ $\frac{1}{5}$
31. $2|3x - 4| + 8 = 6$ **∅**
32. $4|7y + 2| - 8 = -7$ $\left\{-\frac{1}{4}, -\frac{9}{28}\right\}$
33. $-3|3t - 2| - 12 = -6$ **∅**
34. $-5|3z + 8| - 5 = -20$ $\left\{-\frac{5}{3}, -\frac{11}{3}\right\}$

B

35. **MONEY** The U.S. Mint produces quarters that weigh about 5.67 grams each. After the quarters are produced, a machine weighs them. If the quarter weighs 0.02 gram more or less than the desired weight, the quarter is rejected. Write and solve an equation to find the heaviest and lightest quarters the machine will approve. $|x - 5.67| = 0.02$; **heaviest: 5.69 g; lightest: 5.65 g**

Evaluate each expression if $q = -8$, $r = -6$, and $t = 3$.

36. $12 - t|3r + 2|$ **−36**
37. $2q + |2rt + q|$ **28**
38. $-5t - q|8r - t|$ **393**

Differentiated Homework Options

Level	Assignment	Two-Day Option	
AL Basic	14–34, 45, 47–74	15–33 odd, 52–55	14–34 even, 45, 47–51, 56–74
OL Core	15–43 odd, 44, 45, 47–74	14–34, 52–55	35–45, 47–51, 56–74
BL Advanced	35–68, (optional: 69–74)		

Real-World Link

During the past century, sea levels along the Mid-Atlantic and Gulf coasts have risen about 6 inches more than the global average.

Source: Environmental Protection Agency

45. Ling; Ana included an extraneous solution. She would have caught this error if she had checked to see if her answers were correct by substituting the values into the original equation.

47. Sometimes; this is only true for certain values of a. For example, it is true for $a = 8$; if $8 > 7$, then $11 > 10$. However it is not true for $a = -8$; if $8 > 7$, then $5 \not> 10$.

48. Always; if $|x| < 3$, then x is between -3 or 3. Adding 3 to the absolute value of any of the numbers in this set will produce a positive number.

49. Always; starting with numbers between 1 and 5 and subtracting 3 will produce numbers between -2 and 2. These all have an absolute value less than or equal to 2.

50. Sample answer: $|2x + 1| = x - 3$, or $|3x + 10| = x - 5$, or $|x - 1| = \frac{1}{2}x - 4$

Solve each equation. Check your solutions.

39. $8x = 2|6x - 2|$ $\left\{1, \frac{1}{5}\right\}$

40. $-6y + 4 = |4y + 12|$ $-\frac{4}{5}$

41. $8z + 20 = -|2z + 4|$ $-\frac{8}{3}$

42. $-3y - 2 = |6y + 25|$ $\left\{-3, -\frac{23}{3}\right\}$

43. SEA LEVEL Florida is on average 100 feet above sea level. This level varies by as much as 245 feet depending on precipitation and your location. Write and solve an equation describing the maximum and minimum sea levels for Florida. Is this solution reasonable? Explain. **See margin.**

44. MULTIPLE REPRESENTATIONS Draw a number line. **a. See margin.**

a. GEOMETRIC Label any 5 integers on the number line points A, B, C, D, and F.

b. TABULAR Fill in each blank in the table with either > or < using the points from the number line.

A < B	$A + C$ < $B + C$
	$A + D$ < $B + D$
	$A + F$ < $B + F$
B > A	$B + C$ > $A + C$
	$B + D$ > $A + D$
	$B + F$ > $A + F$

A < B	$A - C$ < $B - C$
	$A - D$ < $B - D$
	$A - F$ < $B - F$
B > A	$B - C$ > $A - C$
	$B - D$ > $A - D$
	$B - F$ > $A - F$

c. VERBAL Describe the patterns in the table. **See margin.**

d. ALGEBRAIC Describe the patterns algebraically, using the variable x to replace C, D, and F. **If $A < B$, then $A + x < B + x$. If $A < B$, then $A - x < B - x$. If $B > A$, then $B + x > A + x$. If $B > A$, then $B - x > A - x$.**

H.O.T. Problems

Use Higher-Order Thinking Skills

45. ERROR ANALYSIS Ana and Ling are solving $|3x + 14| = -6x$. Is either of them correct? Explain your reasoning.

Ana	Ling
$\vert 3x + 14\vert = -6x$	$\vert 3x + 14\vert = -6x$
$3x + 14 = -6x$ or $3x + 14 = 6x$	$3x + 14 = -6x$ or $3x + 14 = 6x$
$9x = -14$ $14 = 3x$	$9x = -14$ $14 = 3x$
$x = -\frac{14}{9}$ ✓ $x = \frac{14}{3}$ ✓	$x = -\frac{14}{9}$ ✗ $x = \frac{14}{3}$ ✓

46. CHALLENGE Solve $|2x - 1| + 3 = |5 - x|$. List all cases and resulting equations. (*Hint*: There are four possible cases to examine as potential solutions.) **See Chapter 1 Answer Appendix.**

REASONING If a, x, and y are real numbers, determine whether each statement is *sometimes*, *always*, or *never* true. Explain your reasoning.

47. If $|a| > 7$, then $|a + 3| > 10$.

48. If $|x| < 3$, then $|x| + 3 > 0$.

49. If y is between 1 and 5, then $|y - 3| \le 2$.

50. OPEN ENDED Write an absolute value equation of the form $|ax + b| = cx + d$ that has no solution. Assume that a, b, c, and $d \ne 0$.

51. WRITING IN MATH Explain step by step how you solve an absolute value equation of the form $a|x - b| + c = d$ for x. **See Chapter 1 Answer Appendix.**

Study Guide and Intervention

CRM pp. 24–25 AL OL ELL

1-4 Study Guide and Intervention

Solving Absolute Value Equations

Absolute Value Expressions The **absolute value** of a number is its distance from 0 on a number line. The symbol $|x|$ is used to represent the absolute value of a number x.

Absolute Value	
• Words	For any real number a, if a is positive or zero, the absolute value of a is a. If a is negative, the absolute value of a is the opposite of a.
• Symbols	For any real number a, $\vert a\vert = a$, if $a \ge 0$, and $\vert a\vert = -a$, if $a < 0$.

Example 1 Evaluate $|-4| - |-2x|$ if $x = 6$.

$|-4| - |-2x| = |-4| - |-2 \cdot 6|$
$= |-4| - |-12|$
$= 4 - 12$
$= -8$

Example 2 Evaluate $|2x - 3y|$ if $x = -4$ and $y = 3$.

$|2x - 3y| = |2(-4) - 3(3)|$
$= |-8 - 9|$
$= |-17|$
$= 17$

Exercises

Evaluate each expression if $w = -4$, $x = 2$, $y = \frac{1}{2}$, and $z = -6$.

1. $|2x - 8|$ **4**
2. $|6 + z| - |-7|$ **−7**
3. $5 + |w + z|$ **15**
4. $|x + 5| - |2w|$ **−1**
5. $|x| - |y| - |z|$ **$-4\frac{1}{2}$**
6. $|7 - x| + |3x|$ **11**
7. $|w - 4x|$ **12**
8. $|wz| - |xy|$ **23**
9. $|z| - 3|5yz|$ **−39**
10. $5|w| + 2|z - 2y|$ **34**
11. $|z| - 4|2z + y|$ **−40**
12. $10 - |xw|$ **2**
13. $|6y + z| + |yz|$ **6**
14. $3|wx| + \frac{1}{4}|4x + 8y|$ **27**
15. $7|yz| - 30$ **−9**
16. $14 - 2|w - xy|$ **4**
17. $|2x - y| + 5y$ **6**
18. $|xyz| + |wxz|$ **54**
19. $z|z| + x|x|$ **−32**
20. $12 - |10x - 10y|$ **−3**
21. $\frac{1}{2}|5z + 8w|$ **31**
22. $|yz - 4w| - w$ **17**
23. $\frac{3}{4}|wz| + \frac{1}{2}|8y|$ **20**
24. $xz - |xz|$ **−24**

Chapter 1 24 Glencoe Algebra 2

Practice

CRM p. 27 AL OL BL ELL

1-4 Practice

Solving Absolute Value Equations

Evaluate each expression if $a = -1$, $b = -8$, $c = 5$, and $d = -1.4$.

1. $|6a|$ **6**
2. $|2b + 4|$ **12**
3. $-|10d + a|$ **−15**
4. $|17c| + |3b - 5|$ **114**
5. $-6|10a - 12|$ **−132**
6. $|2b - 1| - |-8b + 5|$ **−52**
7. $|5a - 7| + |3c - 4|$ **23**
8. $|1 - 7c| - |a|$ **33**
9. $-3|0.5c + 2| - |-0.5b|$ **−17.5**
10. $|4d| + |5 - 2a|$ **12.6**
11. $|a - b| + |b - a|$ **14**
12. $|2 - 2d| - 3|b|$ **−19.2**

Solve each equation. Check your solutions.

13. $|n - 4| = 13$ **{−9, 17}**
14. $|x - 13| = 2$ **{11, 15}**
15. $|2y - 3| = 29$ **{−13, 16}**
16. $7|x + 3| = 42$ **{−9, 3}**
17. $|3u - 6| = 42$ **{−12, 16}**
18. $|5x - 4| = -6$ **∅**
19. $-3|4x - 9| = 24$ **∅**
20. $-6|5 - 2y| = -9$ **{1.75, 3.25}**
21. $|8 + p| = 2p - 3$ **{11}**
22. $|4w - 1| = 5w + 37$ **{−38}**
23. $4|2y - 7| + 5 = 9$ **{3, 4}**
24. $-2|7 - 3y| - 6 = -14$ **$\left\{1, 3\frac{2}{3}\right\}$**
25. $2|4 - s| = -3s$ **{−8}**
26. $5 - 3|2 + 2w| = -7$ **{−3, 1}**
27. $5|2r + 3| - 5 = 0$ **{−2, −1}**
28. $3 - 5|2d - 3| = 4$ **∅**

29. **WEATHER** A thermometer comes with a guarantee that the stated temperature differs from the actual temperature by no more than 1.5 degrees Fahrenheit. Write and solve an equation to find the minimum and maximum actual temperatures when the thermometer states that the temperature is 87.4 degrees Fahrenheit.
$|x - 87.4| \le 1.5$; or $85.9 \le x \le 88.9$

30. **OPINION POLLS** Public opinion polls reported in newspapers are usually given with a margin of error. For example, a poll with a margin of error of ±5% is considered accurate to within plus or minus 5% of the actual value. A poll with a stated margin of error of 63% predicts that candidate Tonwe will receive 51% of an upcoming vote. Write and solve an equation describing the minimum and maximum percent of the vote that candidate Tonwe is expected to receive.
$|x - 51| \le 3$ or $48 \le x \le 54$

Chapter 1 27 Glencoe Algebra 2

Lesson 1-4

Word Problem Practice

CRM p. 28 AL OL BL ELL

1-4 Word Problem Practice

Solving Absolute Value Equations

1. **LOCATIONS** Identical vacation cottages, equally spaced along a street, are numbered consecutively beginning with 10. Maria lives in cottage #17. Joshua lives 4 cottages away from Maria. If n represents Joshua's cottage number, then $|n - 17| = 4$. What are the possible numbers of Joshua's cottage?

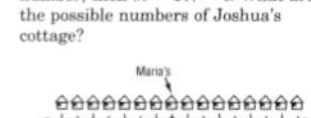

13 or 21

2. **HEIGHT** Sarah and Jessica are sisters. Sarah's height is s inches and Jessica's height is j inches. Their father wants to know how many inches separate the two. Write an equation for this difference in such a way that the result will always be positive no matter which sister is taller.
$d = |s - j|$ or $d = |j - s|$

3. **AGES** In 2005, 24.8% of all Americans were under 18 years old. Rhonda conducts a survey of the ages of students in eleventh grade at her school. On November 1, she finds the average age is 200 months. She also finds that two-thirds of the students are within 6 months of the average age. Write and solve an equation to determine the age limits for this group of students. How many months will it be till the first of these students turn 18?
$|a - 200| = 3$
$a = 197$ or 203

4. **TOLERANCE** Martin makes exercise weights. For his 10-pound dumbbells, he guarantees that the actual weight of his dumbbells is within 0.1 pound of 10 pounds. Write and solve an equation that describes the minimum and maximum weight of his 10-pound dumbbells.
$|w - 10| = 0.1$
minimum weight: 9.9 pounds
maximum weight: 10.1 pounds

5. **WALKING** Jim is walking along a straight line. An observer watches him. If Jim walks forward, the observer records the distance as a positive number, but if he walks backward, the observer records the distance as a negative number. The observer has recorded that Jim has walked a, then b, then c feet.

a. Write a formula for the total distance that Jim walked.
$T = |a| + |b| + |c|$

b. The equation you wrote in part **a** should not be $T = |a + b + c|$. What does $|a + b + c|$ represent?
The distance Jim ends up from where he started.

c. When would the formula you wrote in part **a** give the same value as the formula shown in part **b**?
They will be equal only if Jim walks in the same direction each time giving a, b, and c all the same sign.

Chapter 1 28 Glencoe Algebra 2

A Study Guide and Intervention, Practice, Word Problem Practice, and Enrichment Master are shown for every lesson. These masters can be found in the Chapter Resource Masters.

Enrichment

CRM p. 29 OL BL

1-4 Enrichment

Considering All Cases in Absolute Value Equations

You have learned that absolute value equations with one set of absolute value symbols have two cases that must be considered. For example, $|x + 3| = 5$ must be broken into $x + 3 = 5$ or $-(x + 3) = 5$. For an equation with two sets of absolute value symbols, four cases must be considered.

Consider the problem $|x + 2| + 3 = |x + 6|$. First we must write the equations for the case where $x + 6 \ge 0$ and where $x + 6 < 0$. Here are the equations for these two cases:

$|x + 2| + 3 = x + 6$
$|x + 2| + 3 = -(x + 6)$

Each of these equations also has two cases. By writing the equations for both cases of each equation above, you end up with the following four equations:

$x + 2 + 3 = x + 6$ $x + 2 + 3 = -(x + 6)$
$-(x + 2) + 3 = x + 6$ $-x - 2 + 3 = -(x + 6)$

Solve each of these equations and check your solutions in the original equation, $|x + 2| + 3 = |x + 6|$. The only solution to this equation is $-\frac{5}{2}$.

4 ASSESS

Crystal Ball Have students write how they think what they have learned in Lessons 1-3 and 1-4 will connect with Lesson 1-5, *Solving Inequalities.*

Tips for New Teachers

Looking Ahead Lesson 1-5 presents solving inequalities using steps similar to those for solving equations. Exercises 69–74 should be used to determine students' familiarity with solving equations.

New teachers, or teachers new to teaching mathematics, may especially appreciate the **Tips for New Teachers.**

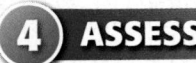

NGSSS PRACTICE 912.A.3.14, 912.P.1.2, 912.A.3.1, 912.G.1.1

52. If $4x - y = 3$ and $2x + 3y = 19$, what is the value of y? D

A. 2
B. 3
C. 4
D. 5

53. **GRIDDED RESPONSE** Two male and 2 female students from each of the 9th, 10th, 11th, and 12th grades comprise the Student Council. If a Student Council representative is chosen at random to attend a board meeting, what is the probability that the student will be either an 11th grader or male? 5/8

54. Which equation is equivalent to $4(9 - 3x) = 7 - 2(6 - 5x)$? G

F. $8x = 41$
G. $22x = 41$
H. $8x = 24$
I. $22x = 24$

55. **SAT/ACT** A square with side length 4 units has one vertex at the point (1, 2). Which one of the following points *cannot* be diagonally opposite that vertex? C

A. $(-3, -2)$
B. $(-3, 6)$
C. $(5, -3)$
D. $(5, 6)$

Spiral Review

Solve each equation. Check your solution. (Lesson 1-3)

56. $4x + 6 = 30$ 6

57. $5p - 10 = 4(7 + 6p)$ -2

58. $\frac{3}{5}y - 7 = \frac{2}{5}y + 3$ 50

59. **MONEY** Nhu is saving to buy a car. In the first 6 months, his savings were \$80 less than $\frac{3}{4}$ the price of the car. In the second six months, Nhu saved \$50 more than $\frac{1}{5}$ the price of the car. He still needs \$370. (Lesson 1-3)

a. What is the price of the car? \$6800

b. What is the average amount of money Nhu saved each month? \$535.83

c. If Nhu continues to save the average amount each month, in how many months will he be able to afford the car? 1 mo

Name the property illustrated by each equation. (Lesson 1-2)

60. $(1 + 8) + 11 = 11 + (1 + 8)$ Comm. (+)

61. $z(9 - 4) = z \cdot 9 - z \cdot 4$ Distributive

Simplify each expression. (Lesson 1-2)

62. $7a + 3b - 4a - 5b$ $3a - 2b$

63. $3x + 5y + 7x - 3y$ $10x + 2y$

64. $3(15x - 9y) + 5(4y - x)$ $40x - 7y$

65. $2(10m - 7a) + 3(8a - 3m)$ $11m + 10a$

66. $8(r + 7t) - 4(13t + 5r)$ $-12r + 4t$

67. $4(14c - 10d) - 6(d + 4c)$ $32c - 46d$

68. **GEOMETRY** The formula for the surface area of a rectangular prism is $SA = 2\ell w + 2\ell h + 2wh$, where ℓ represents the length, w represents the width, and h represents the height. Find the surface area of the rectangular prism at the right. (Lesson 1-1) 358 in^2

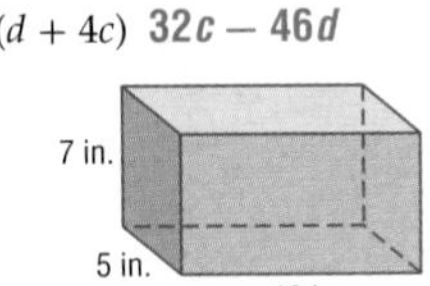

Skills Review

Solve each equation. (Lesson 1-3)

69. $15x + 5 = 35$ 2

70. $2.4y + 4.6 = 20$ ≈ 6.417

71. $8a + 9 = 6a - 7$ -8

72. $3(w - 1) = 2w - 6$ -3

73. $\frac{1}{2}(2b - 4) = 2 + 8b$ $-\frac{4}{7}$

74. $\frac{1}{3}(6p - 24) = 18 + 3p$ -26

Differentiated Instruction OL BL

Extension For equations with one set of absolute value symbols, two cases must be considered. For an equation with two sets of absolute value symbols, four cases must be considered. How many cases must be considered for an equation containing three sets of absolute value symbols? 8

1-5 Solving Inequalities

Why?

Josh is trying to decide between two text messaging plans offered by a wireless telephone company.

	Plan 1	Plan 2
Monthly Access Fee	\$25	\$40
Text Messages Included	400	650
Additional Text Messages	\$0.45	\$0.30

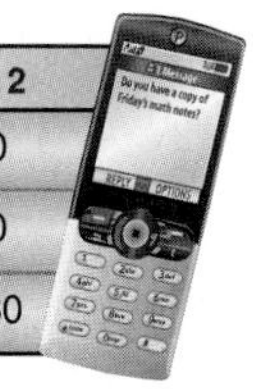

Then
You solved equations involving absolute values. (Lesson 1-4)

Now
- Solve one-step inequalities.
- Solve multi-step inequalities.

NGSSS
Reinforcement of MA.912.A.3.4 Solve and graph simple and **compound inequalities in one variable and be able to justify each step in a solution.**

New Vocabulary
set-builder notation

FL Math Online
glencoe.com

To compare these two rate plans, we can use inequalities. The monthly access fee for Plan 1 is less than the fee for Plan 2, \$25 < \$40. However, the additional text messaging fee for Plan 1 is greater than that of Plan 2, \$0.45 > \$0.30.

One-Step Inequalities For any two real numbers, a and b, exactly one of the following statements is true.

$$a < b \qquad a = b \qquad a > b$$

Adding the same number to, or subtracting the same number from, each side of an inequality does not change the truth of the inequality.

Key Concept

Addition Property of Inequality

Words For any real numbers, a, b, and c:

If $a > b$, then $a + c > b + c$.

If $a < b$, then $a + c < b + c$.

Models

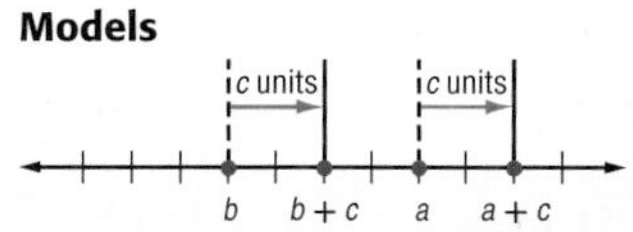

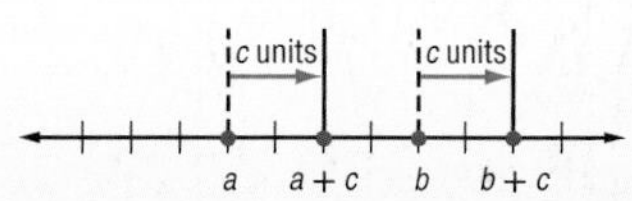

Subtraction Property of Inequality

Words For any real numbers, a, b, and c:

If $a > b$, then $a - c > b - c$.

If $a < b$, then $a - c < b - c$.

Models

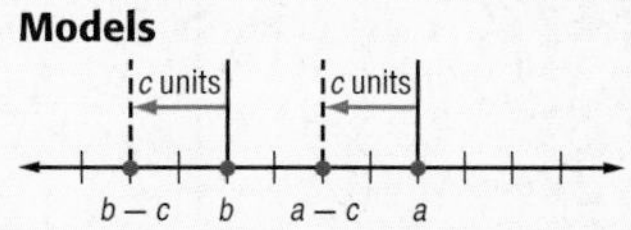

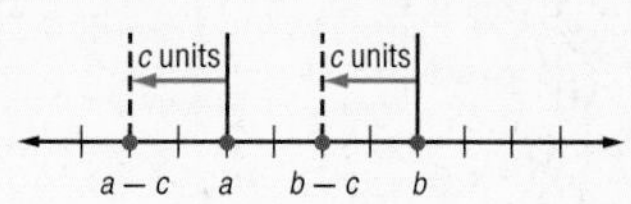

These properties are also true for $\leq$, $\geq$, and $\neq$.

These properties can be used to solve inequalities. The solution sets of inequalities in one variable can then be graphed on number lines.

1-5 Lesson Notes

1 FOCUS

Vertical Alignment

Before Lesson 1-5
Solve equations involving absolute values.

Lesson 1-5
Solve one-step inequalities.
Solve multi-step inequalities.

After Lesson 1-5
Solve systems of inequalities.

2 TEACH

Scaffolding Questions

Have students read the *Why?* section of the lesson.

Ask:

- If Josh knows that he will text no more than 400 messages per month, which plan is better for him? Plan 1
- How much would he pay if he texts 800 messages under Plan 1? Plan 2? \$205.00; \$85.00
- If he texts 500 messages per month, which plan is better for him? Plan 2

Scaffolding Questions give direction and momentum to the lesson, clarify its purpose, and keep students on task.

Lesson 1-5 Resources

Resource	Approaching-Level	On-Level	Beyond-Level	English Learners
Teacher Edition	• Differentiated Instruction, p. 35	• Differentiated Instruction, pp. 35, 39	• Differentiated Instruction, pp. 35, 39	• Differentiated Instruction, p. 35
Chapter Resource Masters	• Study Guide and Intervention, pp. 31–32 • Skills Practice, p. 33 • Practice, p. 34 • Word Problem Practice, p. 35	• Study Guide and Intervention, pp. 31–32 • Skills Practice, p. 33 • Practice, p. 34 • Word Problem Practice, p. 35 • Enrichment, p. 36	• Practice, p. 34 • Word Problem Practice, p. 35 • Enrichment, p. 36	• Study Guide and Intervention, pp. 31–32 • Skills Practice, p. 33 • Practice, p. 34 • Word Problem Practice, p. 36
Transparencies	• 5-Minute Check Transparency 1-5	• 5-Minute Check Transparency 1-5	• 5-Minute Check Transparency 1-5	• 5-Minute Check Transparency 1-5
Other	• Study Notebook	• Study Notebook	• Study Notebook	• Study Notebook

One-Step Inequalities

Example 1 shows how to solve an inequality using addition or subtraction. **Example 2** shows how to solve an inequality using multiplication or division.

Formative Assessment

Use the Guided Practice exercises after each example to determine students' understanding of concepts.

Additional Example

1 Solve $4y - 3 < 5y + 2$. Graph the solution set on a number line. $y > -5$

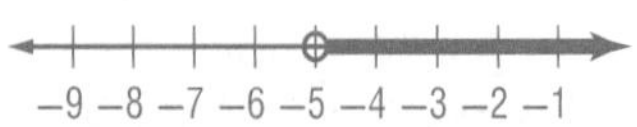

Additional Examples also in Interactive Classroom PowerPoint® Presentations

IWB INTERACTIVE WHITEBOARD READY

Watch Out!

Preventing Errors Ask students if it makes a difference whether the inequality sign is <, >, ≤, or ≥ when they use the Addition and Subtraction Properties of Inequality. There is no difference in calculations, but there is a difference in the direction and beginning of the graph of the solution set.

Review Vocabulary

Inequality Symbols
- > greater than; is more than
- < less than; is fewer than
- ≥ greater than or equal to; is at least; is no less than
- ≤ less than or equal to; is at most; is no more than

EXAMPLE 1 Solve an Inequality Using Addition or Subtraction

Solve $y - 6 < 3$. Graph the solution set on a number line.

$y - 6 < 3$	**Original inequality**
$y - 6 + 6 < 3 + 6$	**Add 6 to each side.**
$y < 9$	**Simplify.**

Any real number less than 9 is a solution of this inequality. The graph of the solution set is shown at the right.

A circle means that this point is *not* included in the solution set.

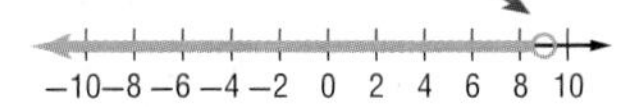

CHECK Substitute 8 and then 10 for y in $y - 6 < 3$. The inequality should be true for $y = 8$ and false for $y = 10$. ✓

Guided Practice 1A, 1B. See margin.

Solve each inequality. Graph the solution set on a number line.

1A. $5w + 3 > 4w + 9$

1B. $5x - 3 > 4x + 2$

Personal Tutor glencoe.com

StudyTip

Graphing Inequalities A circle is used for < and >. A dot is used for ≤ and ≥.

Multiplying or dividing each side of an inequality by a positive number does not change the truth of the inequality. However, multiplying or dividing each side of an inequality by a *negative* number requires that the order of the inequality be *reversed*. For example, to reverse ≤, replace it with ≥.

Key Concept boxes highlight definitions, formulas, and other important ideas. Multiple representations—words, symbols, examples, models—aid students' understanding.

Key Concept

Multiplication Property of Inequality

Words		Examples
	For any real numbers, a, b, and c,	
	where c is positive:	$-5 < -3$
	If $a > b$, then $ac > bc$.	$-5(6) < -3(6)$
	If $a < b$, then $ac < bc$.	$-30 < -18$
	where c is negative:	$12 > -7$
	If $a > b$, then $ac < bc$.	$12(-4) < -7(-4)$
	If $a < b$, then $ac > bc$.	$-48 < 28$

Division Property of Inequality

Words		Examples
	For any real numbers, a, b, and c,	
	where c is positive:	$-12 < -8$
	If $a > b$, then $\frac{a}{c} > \frac{b}{c}$.	$\frac{-12}{4} < \frac{-8}{4}$
	If $a < b$, then $\frac{a}{c} < \frac{b}{c}$.	$-3 < -2$
	where c is negative:	$-21 < -14$
	If $a > b$, then $\frac{a}{c} < \frac{b}{c}$.	$\frac{-21}{-7} > \frac{-14}{-7}$
	If $a < b$, then $\frac{a}{c} > \frac{b}{c}$.	$3 > 2$

These properties are also true for ≤, ≥, and ≠.

Additional Answers (Guided Practice)

1A. $w > 6$

1B. $x > 5$

2A. $x \leq 6$

2B. $y > -2.5$

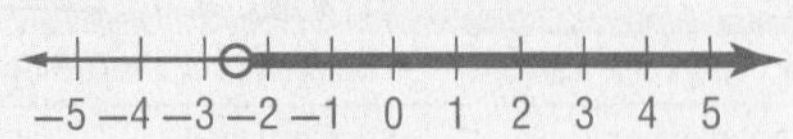

3A. $x \geq -2$

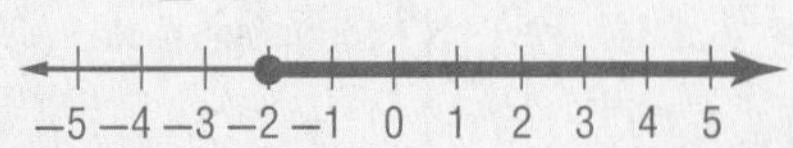

3B. $y \leq -\frac{1}{3}$

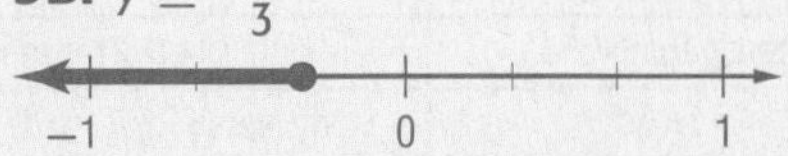

3C. $v \leq 6$

3D. $d < -\frac{1}{3}$

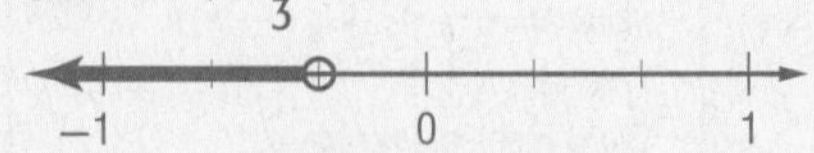

ReadingMath

Set-Builder Notation $\{y \mid y < 9\}$ is read *the set of all numbers y such that y is less than 9.*

The solution set of an inequality can be expressed by using **set-builder notation**. For example, the solution set in Example 1 can be expressed as $\{y \mid y < 9\}$.

EXAMPLE 2 Solve an Inequality Using Multiplication or Division

Solve $-4.2x \leq 29.4$. Graph the solution set on a number line.

$-4.2x \leq 29.4$	Original inequality
$\frac{-4.2x}{-4.2} \geq \frac{29.4}{-4.2}$	Divide each side by −4.2, reversing the inequality symbol.
$x \geq 7$	Simplify.

The solution set is $\{x \mid x \geq 7\}$. The graph of the solution is shown below.

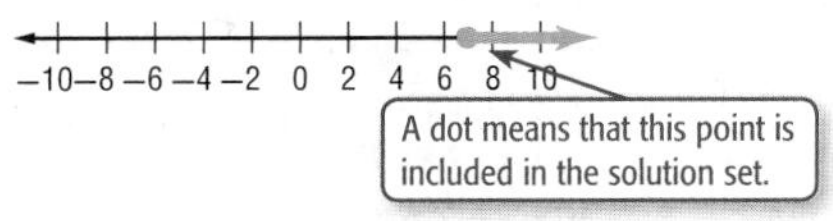

CHECK Substitute 6 and then 8 for x in $-4.2x \leq 29.4$. The inequality should be true for $x = 8$ and false for $x = 6$. ✓

Guided Practice 2A, 2B. See margin.

Solve each inequality. Graph the solution set on a number line.

2A. $-4x \geq -24$

2B. $-9.2y < 23$

Personal Tutor glencoe.com

StudyTip

When multiplying or dividing by a negative number, remember to reverse the inequality symbol.

Multi-Step Inequalities Solving multi-step inequalities is similar to solving multi-step equations.

EXAMPLE 3 Solve Multi-Step Inequalities

Solve $-4c \leq \frac{5c + 58}{6}$. Graph the solution set on a number line.

$-4c \leq \frac{5c + 58}{6}$	Original inequality
$-24c \leq 5c + 58$	Multiply each side by 6.
$-29c \leq 58$	Add −5c to each side.
$c \geq -2$	Divide each side by −29, reversing the inequality symbol.

The solution set is $\{c \mid c \geq -2\}$ and is graphed below.

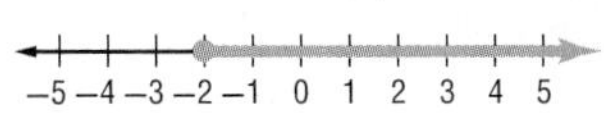

CHECK Substitute −3 and then −1 for x in $-4c \leq \frac{5c + 58}{6}$. The inequality should be true for $x = -1$ and false for $x = -3$. ✓

Guided Practice 3A–3D. See margin.

Solve each inequality. Graph the solution set on a number line.

3A. $-3x \leq \frac{-4x + 22}{5}$

3B. $8y \geq \frac{-5y + 9}{-4}$

3C. $-6(-4v + 3) \leq 2(10v + 3)$

3D. $-5(3d - 7) > 3(2d + 14)$

Personal Tutor glencoe.com

Differentiated Instruction

AL OL BL ELL

Social Have students first discuss the differences between solving an equation and solving an inequality and then discuss how the solution processes are the same.

Additional Example

2 Solve $12 \geq -0.3p$. Graph the solution set on a number line. $\{p \mid p \geq -40\}$

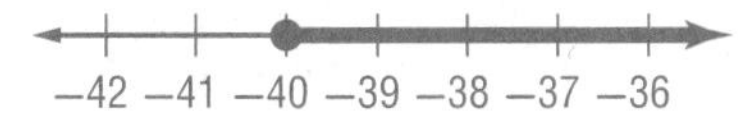

Multi-Step Inequalities

Example 3 shows how to solve a multi-step inequality. **Example 4** shows how to write and use an inequality to solve a real-world problem.

Additional Example

3 Solve $-x > \frac{x - 7}{2}$. Graph the solution set on a number line. $\left\{x \,\middle|\, x < \frac{7}{3}\right\}$

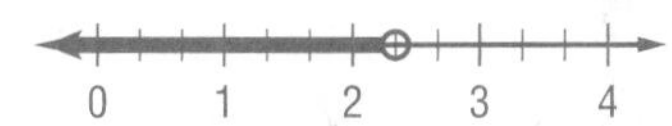

Watch Out!

Preventing Errors Remind students that in order to keep each intermediate inequality equivalent to the original, they must show the division by a negative **and** the reversal of the inequality sign in the same step.

Focus on Mathematical Content

Properties of Inequality Adding the same number to, or subtracting the same number from, each side of an inequality does not change the truth of the inequality. Multiplying or dividing each side of an inequality by a positive number also does not change the truth of the inequality. However, multiplying or dividing each side of an inequality by a negative number does change the truth of the inequality.

Additional Example

4 **CONSUMER COSTS** Javier has at most \$15.00 to spend today. He buys a bag of pretzels and a bottle of juice for \$1.59. If gasoline at this store costs \$2.89 per gallon, how many gallons of gasoline, to the nearest tenth of a gallon, can Javier buy for his car? no more than 4.6 gal

3 PRACTICE

Formative Assessment

Use Exercises 1–9 to check for understanding.

Use the chart on the bottom of the next page to customize assignments for your students.

Additional Answers

1. $b < 8$

2. $d < 20$

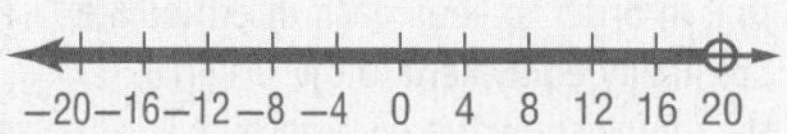

3. $x \leq -6$

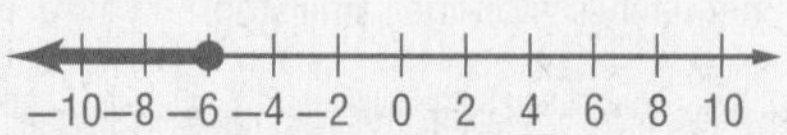

4. $y \leq 7$

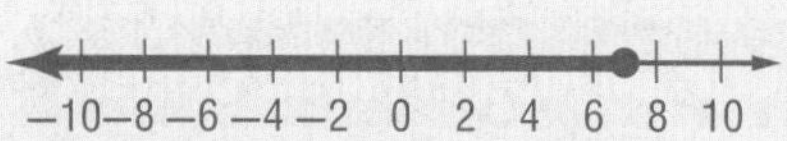

5. $w < 2$

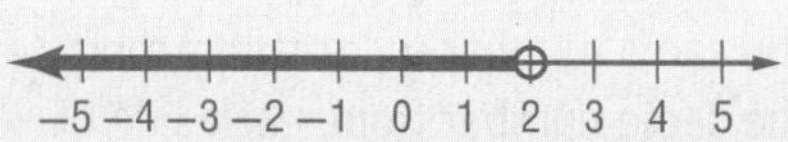

6. $z \geq -\frac{3}{4}$

7. $s \geq \frac{3}{2}$

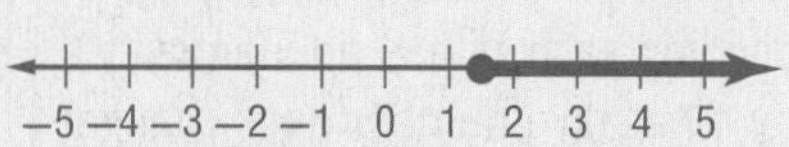

8. $x \geq -8.5$

EXAMPLE 4 Write and Solve an Inequality

Real-World Link

In 2007, the Netcraft Web Server Survey found over 108,000,000 distinct Web sites.

Source: Netcraft

WEB SITES Enrique's company pays Salim to advertise on Salim's Web site. Salim's Web site earns \$15 per month plus \$0.05 every time a visitor clicks on the advertisement. What is the least number of clicks per month that Salim needs in order to earn \$50 per month or more?

Understand Let c = the number of clicks on the advertisement. Salim earns \$15 per month and \$0.05 per click, and he wants to earn a minimum of \$50 for the advertisement.

Plan Write an inequality.

Words The monthly income is \$15 plus \$0.05 per click, and the total should be at least \$50.

Variable Let c represent the number of clicks per month.

Inequality	Flat fee	plus	fee per click	is at least	\$50.
	15	+	0.05c	≥	50

Solve

$15 + 0.05c \geq 50$ — **Original inequality**

$0.05c \geq 35$ — **Subtract 15 from each side.**

$c \geq 700$ — **Divide each side by 0.05.**

Check

$15 + 0.05c \geq 50$ — **Original inequality**

$5 + 0.05(700) \stackrel{?}{\geq} 50$ — **Replace c with 700.**

$15 + 35 \stackrel{?}{\geq} 50$ — **Multiply.**

$50 \geq 50$ ✓ — **Add.**

Visitors to Salim's Web site need to click on Enrique's advertisement at least 700 times per month in order for Salim to earn \$50 or more from Enrique's company.

Guided Practice

4. Rosa's cell phone plan costs her \$50 per month plus \$0.25 for each minute she goes beyond her free minutes. How many minutes can she go beyond her free minutes and still pay less than a total of \$70? **Rosa can go less than 80 minutes past her free minutes and still pay less than \$70.**

Personal Tutor glencoe.com

Check Your Understanding

Examples 1–3 pp. 34–35

1–8. See margin.

Solve each inequality. Then graph the solution set on a number line.

1. $b + 6 < 14$

2. $12 - d > -8$

3. $18 \leq -3x$

4. $-5y \geq -35$

5. $-4w - 13 > -21$

6. $8z - 9 \geq -15$

7. $s \geq \frac{s+6}{5}$

8. $\frac{2x-9}{4} \leq x + 2$

Example 4 p. 36

9. **YARD WORK** Tara is delivering bags of mulch. Each bag weighs 48 pounds, and the push cart weighs 65 pounds. If her flat-bed truck is capable of hauling 2000 pounds, how many bags of mulch can Tara safely take on each trip? **40 bags**

10. $m > -4$

11. $n \leq -3$

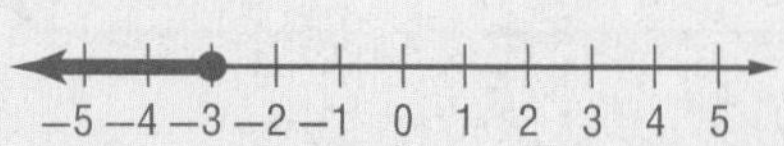

12. $r < -6$

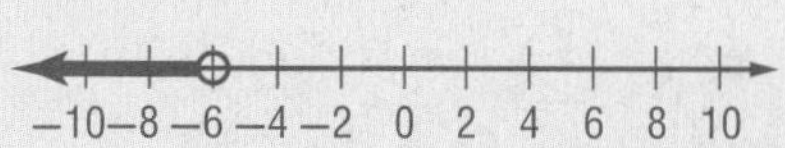

13. $t \leq \frac{1}{2}$

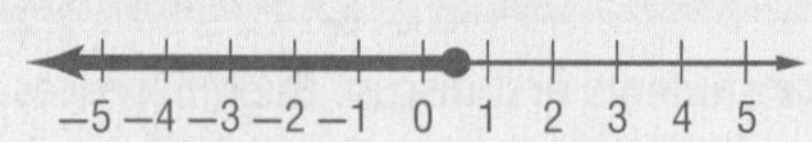

14. $w \geq 28$

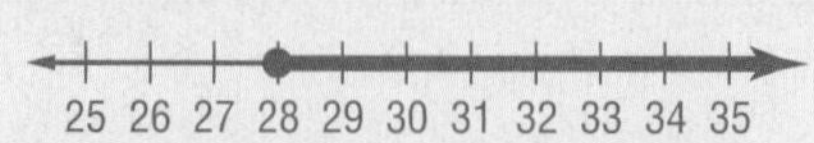

15. $k < 27$

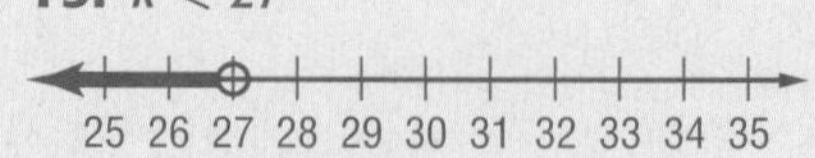

Practice and Problem Solving

● = Step-by-Step Solutions begin on page R20. Extra Practice begins on page 947.

Examples 1–3 pp. 34–35

10–21. See margin.

Solve each inequality. Then graph the solution set on a number line.

10. $m - 8 > -12$ **11.** $n + 6 \leq 3$ **12.** $6r < -36$

13. $-12t \geq -6$ **14.** $-\frac{w}{4} \leq -7$ **15.** $\frac{k}{3} - 14 < -5$

16. $4x - 15 \leq 21$ **17.** $-6z - 14 > -32$ **18.** $-16 \geq 5(2z - 11)$

19 $12 < -4(3c - 6)$ **20.** $\frac{3y - 4}{0.2} - 8 > 12$ **21.** $\frac{9z + 5}{4} + 18 < 26$

Example 4 p. 36

22. GYMNASTICS In a gymnastics competition, an athlete's final score is calculated by taking 75% of the average technical score and adding 25% of the artistic score. All scores are out of 10, and one gymnast has a 7.6 average technical score. What artistic score does the gymnast need to have a final score of at least 8.0? **9.2**

B

23. $3x - 12 < 21$; $x < 11$

Define a variable and write an inequality for each problem. Then solve.

23. Twelve less than the product of three and a number is less than 21.

24. The quotient of three times a number and 4 is at least −16. $\frac{3x}{4} \geq -16$; $x \geq -\frac{64}{3}$

25. The difference of 5 times a number and 6 is greater than the number. $5x - 6 > x$; $x > 1.5$

26. The quotient of the sum of 3 and a number and 6 is less than −2. $\frac{x + 3}{6} < -2$; $x < -15$

27. HIKING Danielle can hike 3 miles in an hour, but she has to take a one-hour break for lunch and a one-hour break for dinner. If Danielle wants to hike at least 18 miles, solve $3(x - 2) \geq 18$ to determine how many hours the hike should take. **8 hours**

Real-World Link

Stretching 2175 miles from Maine to Georgia, the Appalachian trail is the longest marked footpath in the world.

Source: Appalachian Trail Conservancy

Solve each inequality. Then graph the solution set on a number line. 28–36. See margin.

28. $18 - 3x < 12$ **29.** $-8(4x + 6) < -24$ **30.** $\frac{1}{4}n + 12 \geq \frac{3}{4}n - 4$

31. $0.24y - 0.64 > 3.86$ **32.** $10x - 6 \leq 4x + 42$ **33.** $-6v + 8 > -14v - 28$

34. $n > \frac{-3n - 15}{8}$ **35.** $-2r < \frac{6 - 2r}{5}$ **36.** $\frac{9z - 4}{5} \leq \frac{7z + 2}{4}$

37. MONEY Jin is selling advertising space in *Central City Magazine* to local businesses. Jin earns 3% commission for every advertisement he sells plus a salary of $250 a week. If the average amount of money that a business spends on an advertisement is $500, how many advertisements must he sell each week to make a salary of at least $700 that week? **37b. $a \geq 30$; He must sell at least 30 advertisements.**

a. Write an inequality to describe this situation. $250 + 0.03(500a) \geq 700$

b. Solve the inequality and interpret the solution.

C

Define a variable and write an inequality for each problem. Then solve.

38. One third of the sum of 5 times a number and 3 is less than one fourth the sum of six times that number and 5. $\frac{5n + 3}{3} < \frac{6n + 5}{4}$; $n < 1.5$

39. $\frac{x}{3} + 4 \leq 2x + 12$; $x \geq -4.8$

39. The sum of one third a number and 4 is at most the sum of twice that number and 12.

40. GEOMETRY The sides of square *ABCD* are extended to form rectangle *DEFG*. If the perimeter of the rectangle is at least twice the perimeter of the square, what is the maximum length of a side of square *ABCD*? **9 in.**

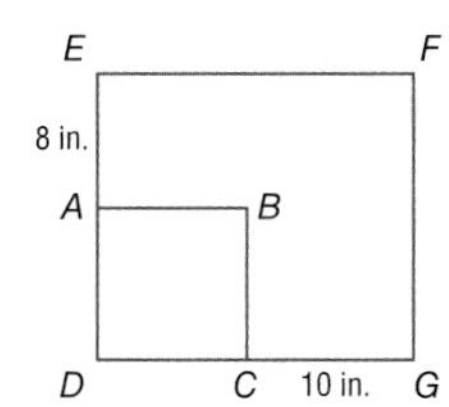

Differentiated Homework Options

Level	Assignment	Two-Day Option	
AL Basic	10–22, 45–46, 48–66	11–21 odd, 50–53	10–22 even, 45–46, 48–49, 54–66
OL Core	11–21 odd, 22–27, 29–35 odd, 37–43, 45–46, 48–66	10–22, 50–53	23–43, 45–46, 48–49, 54–66
BL Advanced	23–60, (optional: 61–66)		

Additional Answers

16. $x \leq 9$

17. $z < 3$

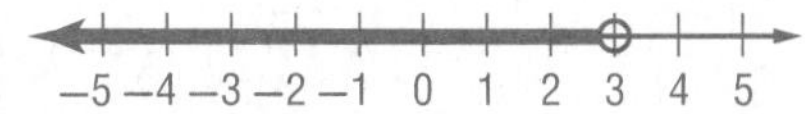

18. $z \leq 3.9$

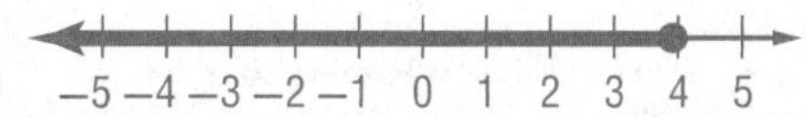

19. $c < 1$

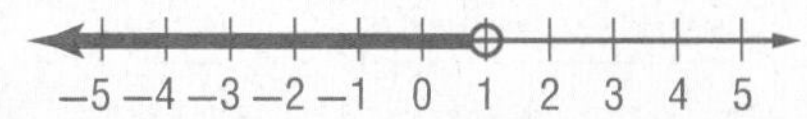

20. $y > \frac{8}{3}$

21. $z < 3$

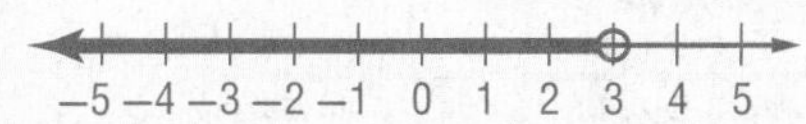

28. $x > 2$

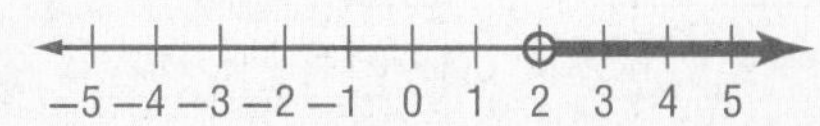

29. $x > -\frac{3}{4}$

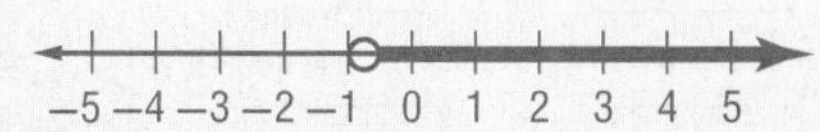

30. $n \leq 32$

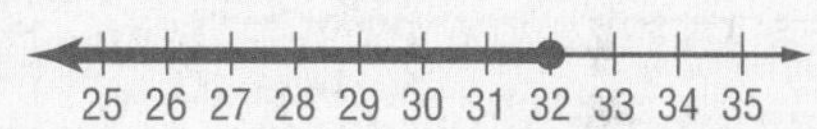

31. $y > 18.75$

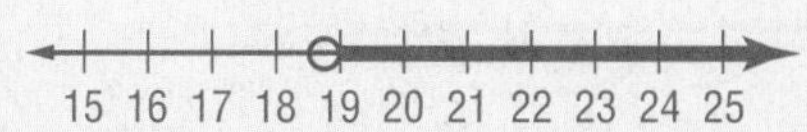

32. $x \leq 8$

33. $v > -4.5$

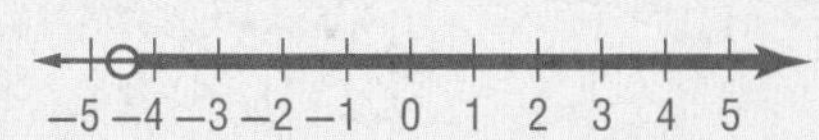

34. $n > -\frac{15}{11}$

35. $r > -\frac{3}{4}$

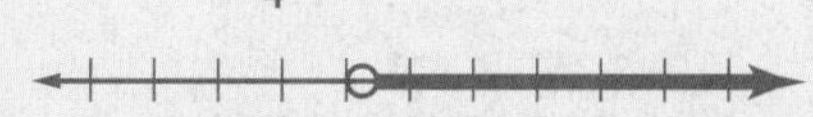

36. $z \leq 26$

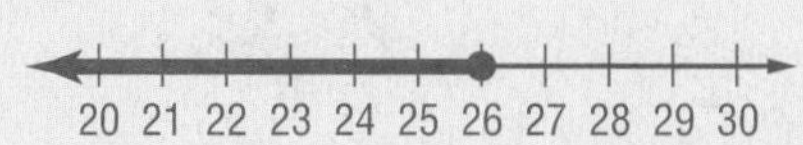

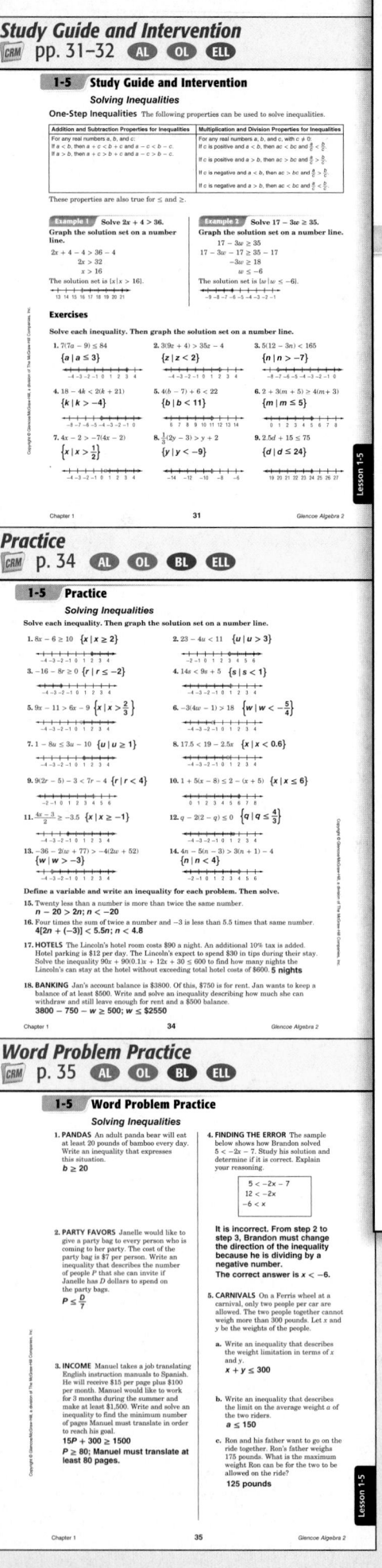

Study Guide and Intervention
CRM pp. 31–32 AL OL ELL

1-5 Study Guide and Intervention
Solving Inequalities

One-Step Inequalities The following properties can be used to solve inequalities.

Addition and Subtraction Properties for Inequalities	Multiplication and Division Properties for Inequalities
For any real numbers a, b, and c: If $a < b$, then $a + c < b + c$ and $a - c < b - c$. If $a > b$, then $a + c > b + c$ and $a - c > b - c$.	For any real numbers a, b, and c, with $c \neq 0$: If c is positive and $a < b$, then $ac < bc$ and $\frac{a}{c} < \frac{b}{c}$. If c is positive and $a > b$, then $ac > bc$ and $\frac{a}{c} > \frac{b}{c}$. If c is negative and $a < b$, then $ac > bc$ and $\frac{a}{c} > \frac{b}{c}$. If c is negative and $a > b$, then $ac < bc$ and $\frac{a}{c} < \frac{b}{c}$.

These properties are also true for $\leq$ and $\geq$.

Example 1 Solve $2x + 4 > 36$. **Graph the solution set on a number line.**

$2x + 4 - 4 > 36 - 4$
$2x > 32$
$x > 16$

The solution set is $\{x \mid x > 16\}$.

13 14 15 16 17 18 19 20 21

Example 2 Solve $17 - 3w \geq 35$. **Graph the solution set on a number line.**

$17 - 3w \geq 35$
$17 - 3w - 17 \geq 35 - 17$
$-3w \geq 18$
$w \leq -6$

The solution set is $\{w \mid w \leq -6\}$.

−9 −8 −7 −6 −5 −4 −3 −2 −1

Exercises

Solve each inequality. Then graph the solution set on a number line.

1. $7(7a - 9) \leq 84$ $\{a \mid a \leq 3\}$
2. $3(9z + 4) > 35z - 4$ $\{z \mid z < 2\}$
3. $5(12 - 3n) < 165$ $\{n \mid n > -7\}$
4. $18 - 4k < 2(k + 21)$ $\{k \mid k > -4\}$
5. $4(b - 7) + 6 < 22$ $\{b \mid b < 11\}$
6. $2 + 3(m + 5) \geq 4(m + 3)$ $\{m \mid m \leq 5\}$
7. $4x - 2 > -7(4x - 2)$ $\{x \mid x > \frac{1}{2}\}$
8. $\frac{1}{3}(2y - 3) > y + 2$ $\{y \mid y < -9\}$
9. $2.5d + 15 \leq 75$ $\{d \mid d \leq 24\}$

Lesson 1-5

Practice
CRM p. 34 AL OL BL ELL

1-5 Practice
Solving Inequalities

Solve each inequality. Then graph the solution set on a number line.

1. $8x - 6 \geq 10$ $\{x \mid x \geq 2\}$
2. $23 - 4u < 11$ $\{u \mid u > 3\}$
3. $-16 - 8r \geq 0$ $\{r \mid r \leq -2\}$
4. $14s < 9s + 5$ $\{s \mid s < 1\}$
5. $9x - 11 > 6x - 9$ $\{x \mid x > \frac{2}{3}\}$
6. $-3(4w - 1) > 18$ $\{w \mid w < -\frac{5}{4}\}$
7. $1 - 8u \leq 3u - 10$ $\{u \mid u \geq 1\}$
8. $17.5 < 19 - 2.5x$ $\{x \mid x < 0.6\}$
9. $9(2r - 5) - 3 < 7r - 4$ $\{r \mid r < 4\}$
10. $1 + 5(x - 8) \leq 2 - (x + 5)$ $\{x \mid x \leq 6\}$
11. $\frac{4x - 3}{2} \geq -3.5$ $\{x \mid x \geq -1\}$
12. $q - 2(2 - q) \leq 0$ $\{q \mid q \leq \frac{4}{3}\}$
13. $-36 - 2(w + 77) > -4(2w + 52)$ $\{w \mid w > -3\}$
14. $4n - 5(n - 3) > 3(n + 1) - 4$ $\{n \mid n < 4\}$

Define a variable and write an inequality for each problem. Then solve.

15. Twenty less than a number is more than twice the same number.
$n - 20 > 2n; n < -20$
16. Four times the sum of twice a number and −3 is less than 5.5 times that same number.
$4[2n + (-3)] < 5.5n; n < 4.8$
17. **HOTELS** The Lincoln's hotel room costs $90 a night. An additional 10% tax is added. Hotel parking is $12 per day. The Lincoln's expect to spend $30 in tips during their stay. Solve the inequality $90x + 90(0.1)x + 12x + 30 \leq 600$ to find how many nights the Lincoln's can stay at the hotel without exceeding total hotel costs of $600. **5 nights**
18. **BANKING** Jan's account balance is $3800. Of this, $750 is for rent. Jan wants to keep a balance of at least $500. Write and solve an inequality describing how much she can withdraw and still leave enough for rent and a $500 balance.
$3800 - 750 - w \geq 500; w \leq \$2550$

Word Problem Practice
CRM p. 35 AL OL BL ELL

1-5 Word Problem Practice
Solving Inequalities

1. **PANDAS** An adult panda bear will eat at least 20 pounds of bamboo every day. Write an inequality that expresses this situation.
$b \geq 20$

2. **PARTY FAVORS** Janelle would like to give a party bag to every person who is coming to her party. The cost of the party bag is $7 per person. Write an inequality that describes the number of people P that she can invite if Janelle has D dollars to spend on the party bags.
$P \leq \frac{D}{7}$

3. **INCOME** Manuel takes a job translating English instruction manuals to Spanish. He will receive $15 per page plus $100 per month. Manuel would like to work for 3 months during the summer and make at least $1,500. Write and solve an inequality to find the minimum number of pages Manuel must translate in order to reach his goal.
$15P + 300 \geq 1500$
$P \geq 80$; Manuel must translate at least 80 pages.

4. **FINDING THE ERROR** The sample below shows how Brandon solved $5 < -2x - 7$. Study his solution and determine if it is correct. Explain your reasoning.

$5 < -2x - 7$
$12 < -2x$
$-6 < x$

It is incorrect. From step 2 to step 3, Brandon must change the direction of the inequality because he is dividing by a negative number.
The correct answer is $x < -6$.

5. **CARNIVALS** On a Ferris wheel at a carnival, only two people per car are allowed. The two people together cannot weigh more than 300 pounds. Let x and y be the weights of the people.
   a. Write an inequality that describes the weight limitation in terms of x and y.
   $x + y \leq 300$
   b. Write an inequality that describes the limit on the average weight a of the two riders.
   $a \leq 150$
   c. Ron and his father want to go on the ride together. Ron's father weighs 175 pounds. What is the maximum weight Ron can be for the two to be allowed on the ride?
   125 pounds

Lesson 1-5

Real-World Link

The Boston Marathon was first held in 1897, making it the longest-running marathon in the world.

Source: Boston Athletic Association

41b. $d \geq 3.73$; In order to have enough endurance to run a marathon, Jamie should increase the distance of her average daily run by at least 3.73 miles.
42. Basic has the better deal as long as you are traveling more than 80 miles. Yes, this is the correct inequality to use. Sample explanation: It works because the inequality finds the mileage at which Ace's charge is greater than Basic's charge.
43c. Sample answer: The points on or above the line result in true statements, and the points below the line result in false statements. This is true for all points on the coordinate plane.
47–49. See Chapter 1 Answer Appendix.

41. **MARATHONS** Jamie wants to be able to run at least the standard marathon distance of 26.2 miles. A good rule for training is that runners generally have enough endurance to finish a race that is up to 3 times his or her average daily distance.
   a. If the length of her current daily run is 5 miles, write an inequality to find the amount by which she needs to increase her daily run to have enough endurance to finish a marathon. $3(5 + d) \geq 26.2$
   b. Solve the inequality and interpret the solution.

42. **MONEY** The costs for renting a car from Ace Car Rental and from Basic Car Rental are shown in the table. For what mileage does Basic have the better deal? Use the inequality $38 + 0.1x > 42 + 0.05x$. Explain why this inequality works.

Rental Car Costs

Company	Cost per Day	Cost per Mile
Ace	$38	$0.10
Basic	$42	$0.05

43. **MULTIPLE REPRESENTATIONS** In this exercise, you will explore graphing inequalities on a coordinate plane. a, b. See margin.
   a. **TABULAR** Organize the following into a table. Substitute 5 points into the inequality $y \geq -\frac{1}{2}x + 3$. State whether the resulting statement is true or false.
   b. **GRAPHICAL** Graph $y = -\frac{1}{2}x + 3$. Also graph the 5 points from the table. Label all points that resulted in a true statement with a T. Label all points that resulted in a false statement with an F.
   c. **VERBAL** Describe the pattern produced by the points you have labeled. Make a conjecture about which points on the coordinate plane would result in true and false statements.

H.O.T. Problems
Use **H**igher-**O**rder **T**hinking Skills

44. **CHALLENGE** If $-4 < x < 5$ and $0.25 < y < 4$, then $a < \frac{x}{y} < b$. What is $a + b$? 4

45. **ERROR ANALYSIS** Madlynn and Emilie were comparing their homework. Is either of them correct? Explain your reasoning. See margin.

Madlynn
$\frac{4x + 5}{-2} - 1 > -3$
$\frac{4x + 5}{-2} < -2$
$4x + 5 > 4$
$4x > -1$
$x > -\frac{1}{4}$

Emilie
$\frac{4x + 5}{-2} - 1 > -3$
$\frac{4x + 5}{-2} > -2$
$4x + 5 > 4$
$4x > -1$
$x > -\frac{1}{4}$

46. **REASONING** Determine whether the following statement is *sometimes*, *always*, or *never* true. Explain your reasoning. See margin.
The opposite of the absolute value of a negative number is less than the opposite of that number.

47. **CHALLENGE** Given $\triangle ABC$ with sides $AB = 3x + 4$, $BC = 2x + 5$, and $AC = 4x$, determine the values of x such that $\triangle ABC$ exists.

48. **OPEN ENDED** Write an inequality for which the solution is all real numbers in the form $ax + b > c(x + d)$. Explain how you know this.

49. **WRITING IN MATH** Why does the inequality symbol need to be reversed when multiplying or dividing by a negative number?

Enrichment
CRM p. 36 OL BL

1-5 Enrichment

Equivalence Relations

A relation R on a set A is an *equivalence relation* if it has the following properties.

Reflexive Property For any element a of set A, a R a.

Symmetric Property For all elements a and b of set A, if a R b, then b R a.

Transitive Property For all elements a, b, and c of set A, if a R b and b R c, then a R c.

Equality on the set of all real numbers is reflexive, symmetric, and transitive. Therefore, it is an equivalence relation.

In each of the following, a relation and a set are given. Write *yes* if the relation is an equivalence relation on the given set. If it is not, tell which of the properties it fails to exhibit.

1. <, {all numbers} no; reflexive, symmetric
2. ≅, {all triangles in a plane} yes
3. is the sister of, {all women in Tennessee} no; reflexive

TEACH with TECH

WIKI Have students create a page explaining how to solve a multi-step inequality. Be sure they explain how they decided whether or not to reverse the inequality sign.

NGSSS PRACTICE 912.A.5.4, 912.S.3.3, 912.A.3.6

50. THINK SOLVE EXPLAIN **SHORT RESPONSE** Rogelio found a cookie recipe that requires $\frac{3}{4}$ cup of sugar and 2 cups of flour. How many cups of sugar would he need if he used 6 cups of flour? **$2\frac{1}{4}$**

51. STATISTICS The mean score for Samantha's first six algebra quizzes was 88. If she scored a 95 on her next quiz, what will her mean score be for all 7 quizzes? **A**

A. 89
B. 90
C. 91
D. 92

52. SAT/ACT The average of five numbers is 9. The average of 7 other numbers is 8. What is the average of all 12 numbers? **F**

F. $8\frac{5}{12}$
G. $8\frac{7}{12}$
H. $8\frac{3}{4}$
I. $8\frac{11}{12}$

53. What is the complete solution of the equation $|8 - 4x| = 40$? **D**

A. $x = 8; x = 12$
B. $x = 8; x = -12$
C. $x = -8; x = -12$
D. $x = -8; x = 12$

Spiral Review

Solve each equation. Check your solutions. (Lesson 1-4)

54. $|x - 5| = 12$ **$\{-7, 17\}$**

55. $7|3y - 4| = 35$ **$\left\{-\frac{1}{3}, 3\right\}$**

56. $|a + 6| = a$ **$\emptyset$**

57. ASTRONOMY Pluto travels in a path that is not circular. Pluto's farthest distance from the Sun is 4539 million miles, and its closest distance is 2756 million miles. Write an equation that can be solved to find the minimum and maximum distances from the Sun to Pluto. (Lesson 1-4) **$|t - 3647.5| = 891.5$**

58. POPULATION In 2005, the population of Bay City was 19,611. For each of the next five years, the population decreased by an average of 715 people per year. (Lesson 1-3)

a. What was the population in 2010? **16,036**

b. If the population continues to decline at the same rate as from 2005 to 2010, what would you expect the population to be in 2025? **5311**

59. GEOMETRY The formula for the surface area of a cylinder is $SA = 2\pi r^2 + 2\pi rh$. (Lesson 1-2)

a. Use the Distributive Property to rewrite the formula by factoring out the greatest common factor of the two terms. **$SA = 2\pi r(r + h)$**

b. Find the surface area for a cylinder with radius 3 centimeters and height 10 centimeters using both formulas. Leave the answer in terms of π. **78π cm^2**

c. Which formula do you prefer? Explain your reasoning. **Sample answer: The formula in part b is quicker.**

60. CONSTRUCTION The Sawyers are adding a family room to their house. The dimensions of the room are 26 feet by 28 feet. Show how to use the Distributive Property to mentally calculate the area of the room. (Lesson 1-2) **$26 \cdot 28 = 26(20 + 8) = 520 + 208 = 728$**

Skills Review

Solve each equation. Check your solutions. (Lesson 1-4)

61. $|x| = 9$ **$\{-9, 9\}$**

62. $|x + 3| = 10$ **$\{-13, 7\}$**

63. $|4y - 15| = 13$ **$\left\{\frac{1}{2}, 7\right\}$**

64. $18 = |3x - 9|$ **$\{-3, 9\}$**

65. $16 = 4|w + 2|$ **$\{-6, 2\}$**

66. $|y + 3| + 4 = 20$ **$\{-19, 13\}$**

Differentiated Instruction OL BL

Extension Solve the inequality $\frac{6}{x} \geq 2$. (*Hint:* Multiply each side by *x*. Consider the cases of $x > 0$ and $x < 0$ separately.) *x* must be greater than zero but less than or equal to 3.

Differentiated Instruction: Extension activities help you cultivate skills that students will need to have success in higher mathematics.

Multiple Representations In Exercise 43, students use a table of values and a graph in the coordinate plane to explore inequalities.

4 ASSESS

Ticket Out the Door Have each student write a list for solving inequalities. Each list should include when to reverse the inequality sign and how to tell when the graph begins with a circle or with a dot.

Formative Assessment

Check for student understanding of concepts in Lessons 1-4 and 1-5.

CRM Quiz 3, p. 46

Additional Answers

43a. Sample answer:

Point	Resulting Statement	True or False
(0, 0)	$0 \geq 3$	False
(1, 1)	$1 \geq \frac{5}{2}$	False
(2, 2)	$2 \geq 2$	True
(3, 3)	$3 \geq \frac{3}{2}$	True
(4, 4)	$4 \geq 1$	True

43b. Sample answer:

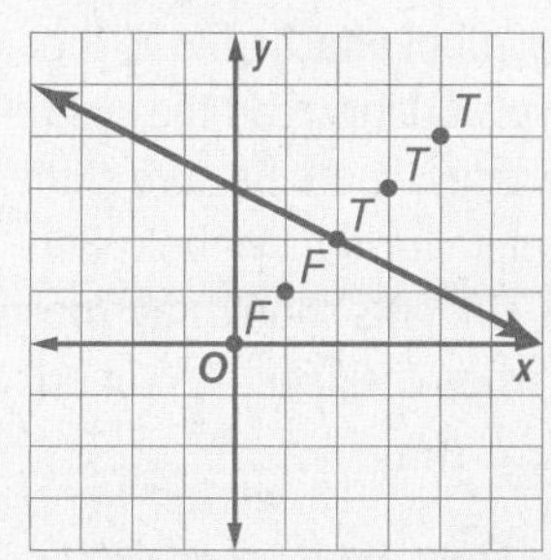

45. No; sample answer: Madlynn reversed the inequality sign when she added 1 to each side. Emilie did not reverse the inequality sign at all.

46. Sample answer: Always; the opposite of the absolute value of a negative number will always be a negative value, while the opposite of a negative number will always be a positive value. A negative value will always be less than a positive value.

EXPLORE 1-6 Lesson Notes

1 FOCUS

Objective Describe the solution set of an inequality using interval notation.

Teaching Tip

Before starting this activity, ask students to think of symbols they have used in their math studies so far.

Some examples might be a radical sign, a line segment symbol, a division sign, and so on.

2 TEACH

Working in Cooperative Groups

Put students in pairs, mixing abilities. Have groups complete Exercises 1–5.

Because symbols are used in math to represent numerical language concepts, language skills are important. One way to provide assistance with math symbols is to connect new symbols with symbols students already know. Point out, for example, that $+\infty$ has a familiar symbol attached to it, the + sign. Have students read the symbols in their exercises aloud. Be sure students use language for the symbols. For example, students should say "positive infinity" when they see $+\infty$ in an exercise.

Practice Have students complete Exercises 6–18.

3 ASSESS

Formative Assessment

Use Exercise 18 to assess whether students understand interval notation and can write a compound inequality when given interval notation.

EXPLORE 1-6 Algebra Lab: Interval Notation

Objective
Use interval notation to describe sets of numbers.

NGSSS

LA.910.1.6.1 The student will use new vocabulary that is introduced and taught directly.

The solution set of an inequality can be described by using **interval notation**. The **infinity** symbols below are used to indicate that a set is unbounded in the positive or negative direction, respectively.

Read as *positive infinity*. → $+\infty$ $-\infty$ ← Read as *negative infinity*.

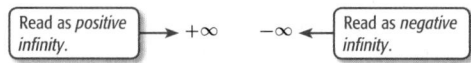

To indicate that an endpoint is *not* included in the set, a parenthesis, (or), is used. Parentheses are always used with the symbols $+\infty$ and $-\infty$, because they do not include endpoints.

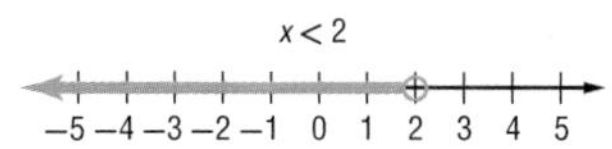

interval notation
$(-\infty, 2)$

A bracket is used to indicate that the endpoint, −2, *is* included in the solution set below.

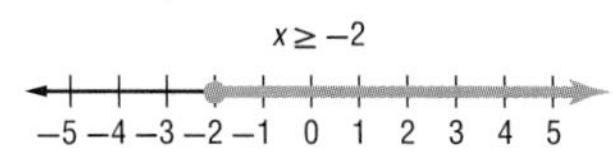

interval notation
$[-2, +\infty)$

In interval notation, the symbol for the union of the two sets is ∪. The compound inequality $y \leq -7$ or $y > -1$ is written as $(-\infty, -7] \cup (-1, +\infty)$.

Exercises

4. $(-\infty, -9] \cup (1, +\infty)$ 6. $(-\infty, -7] \cup [4, +\infty)$ 9. $(-\infty, -1) \cup (1, +\infty)$ 12. $(-\infty, -1.5] \cup [1.5, +\infty)$ 14. $(-\infty, -5) \cup (25, +\infty)$

Write each inequality using interval notation.

1. $\{a \mid a \leq -3\}$ $(-\infty, -3]$
2. $\{n \mid n > -8\}$ $(-8, +\infty)$
3. $\{y \mid y < 2 \text{ or } y \geq 14\}$ $(-\infty, 2) \cup [14, +\infty)$
4. $\{b \mid b \leq -9 \text{ or } b > 1\}$
5. $\{t \mid 1 < t < 3\}$ $(1, 3)$
6. $\{m \mid m \geq 4 \text{ or } m \leq -7\}$
7. $\{x \mid x \geq 0\}$ $[0, +\infty)$
8. $\{r \mid -3 < r < 4\}$ $(-3, 4)$
9. 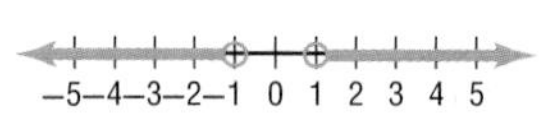

10. 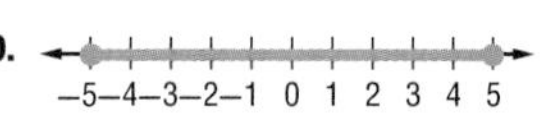

$[-5, 5]$
11. 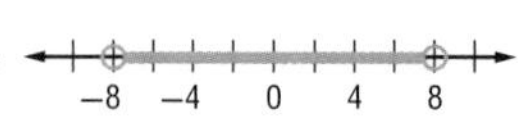

$(-8, 8)$
12. 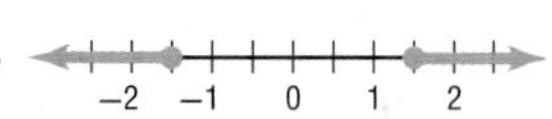

13. 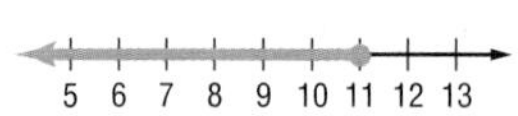

$(-\infty, 11]$
14. 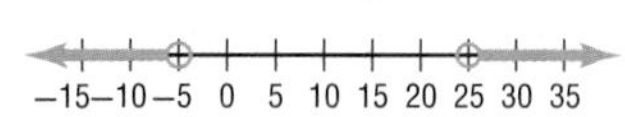

Graph each solution set on a number line. 15–17. See margin.

15. $(-1, \infty)$
16. $(-\infty, 4]$
17. $(-\infty, 5] \cup (7, +\infty)$

18. **WRITING IN MATH** Write in words the meaning of $(-\infty, 3) \cup [10, +\infty)$. Then write the compound inequality that this notation represents.

18. All values less than 3, not including 3, are part of the solution set. All values greater than and including 10 are part of the solution set; $x < 3$ or $x \geq 10$.

From Concrete to Abstract

Ask students to summarize what they have learned about the symbols used in interval notation. Ask them to cite an example of each.

Additional Answers

15. 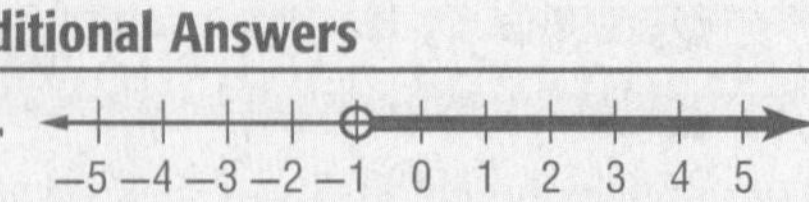

16. 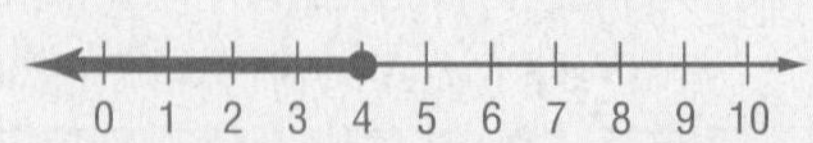

17. 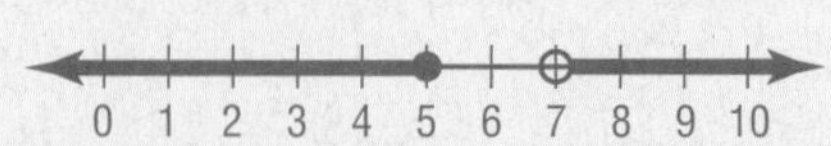

Solving Compound and Absolute Value Inequalities

Then
You solved one-step and multi-step inequalities. (Lesson 1-5)

Now
- Solve compound inequalities.
- Solve absolute value inequalities.

NGSSS
Reinforcement of MA.912.A.3.4 Solve and graph simple and compound inequalities in one variable and be able to justify each step in a solution.
MA.912.A.3.6 Solve and graph the solutions of absolute value equations and inequalities with one variable.

New Vocabulary
compound inequality
intersection
union

FL Math Online
glencoe.com

Why?

Marine biologists often have to transplant a dolphin from its natural habitat to a pool. Dolphins prefer the temperature of water to be at least 22°C but no more than 29°C. The acceptable temperature of water t for dolphins can be described by the following compound inequality.

$$t \geq 22 \text{ and } t \leq 29$$

Compound Inequalities A **compound inequality** consists of two inequalities joined by the word *and* or the word *or*. To solve a compound inequality, you must solve each part of the inequality. The graph of a compound inequality containing *and* is the **intersection** of the solution sets of the two inequalities.

Key Concept — "And" Compound Inequalities

Words A compound inequality containing the word *and* is true if and only if *both* inequalities are true.

Example

$x \geq -4$

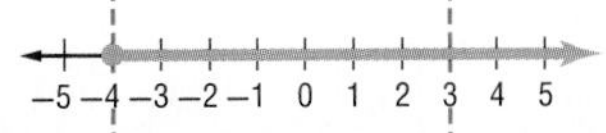

$x < 3$

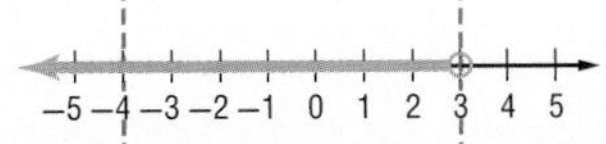

$x \geq -4$ and $x < 3$

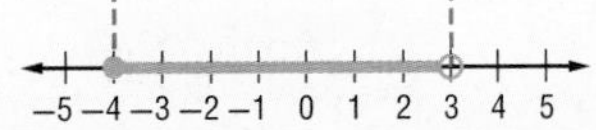

Another way of writing $x \geq -4$ and $x < 3$ is $-4 \leq x < 3$.
Both forms are read *x is greater than or equal to −4 and less than 3.*

EXAMPLE 1 Solve an "And" Compound Inequality

Solve $8 < 3y - 7 \leq 23$. Graph the solution set on a number line.

Method 1 Solve separately.
Write the compound inequality using the word *and*. Then solve each inequality.

$8 < 3y - 7$ and $3y - 7 \leq 23$
$15 < 3y$ $\quad 3y \leq 30$
$5 < y$ $\quad y \leq 10$

$5 < y \leq 10$

Method 2 Solve both together.
Solve both parts at the same time by adding 7 to each part. Then divide each part by 3.

$8 < 3y - 7 \leq 23$
$15 < 3y \leq 30$
$5 < y \leq 10$

$5 < y \leq 10$

(continued on the next page)

Web references point students to online resources such as **Extra Examples, Personal Tutor, Self-Check Quizzes, Homework Help,** and **Get Animated** features.

1-6 Lesson Notes

1 FOCUS

Vertical Alignment

Before Lesson 1-6
Solve one-step and multi-step inequalities.

Lesson 1-6
Solve compound inequalities.
Solve absolute value inequalities.

After Lesson 1-6
Solve systems of inequalities.

2 TEACH

Scaffolding Questions

Have students read the *Why?* section of the lesson.

Ask:
- Do dolphins prefer the water temperature to be greater than or less than 22°C? greater than
- Do they prefer the water temperature to be greater than or less than 29°C? less than
- Write a verbal statement describing how dolphins prefer the water that represents the compound inequality $t \geq 22$ and $t \leq 29$. Dolphins prefer the water to be between 22°C and 29°C inclusive.

Lesson 1-6 Resources

Resource	Approaching-Level	On-Level	Beyond-Level	English Learners
Teacher Edition	• Differentiated Instruction, p. 42	• Differentiated Instruction, pp. 42, 44	• Differentiated Instruction, p. 44	• Differentiated Instruction, p. 42
Chapter Resource Masters	• Study Guide and Intervention, pp. 37–38 • Skills Practice, p. 39 • Practice, p. 40 • Word Problem Practice, p. 41	• Study Guide and Intervention, pp. 37–38 • Skills Practice, p. 39 • Practice, p. 40 • Word Problem Practice, p. 41 • Enrichment, p. 42	• Practice, p. 40 • Word Problem Practice, p. 41 • Enrichment, p. 42	• Study Guide and Intervention, pp. 37–38 • Skills Practice, p. 39 • Practice, p. 40 • Word Problem Practice, p. 41
Transparencies	• 5-Minute Check Transparency 1-6	• 5-Minute Check Transparency 1-6	• 5-Minute Check Transparency 1-6	• 5-Minute Check Transparency 1-6
Other	• Study Notebook • Teaching Algebra with Manipulatives	• Study Notebook • Teaching Algebra with Manipulatives	• Study Notebook	• Study Notebook • Teaching Algebra with Manipulatives

Compound Inequalities

Example 1 shows how to solve an "and" compound inequality. **Example 2** shows how to solve an "or" compound inequality.

Formative Assessment

Use the Guided Practice exercises after each example to determine students' understanding of concepts.

Additional Examples

1 Solve $10 \le 3y - 2 < 19$. Graph the solution set on a number line. $\{y \mid 4 \le y < 7\}$

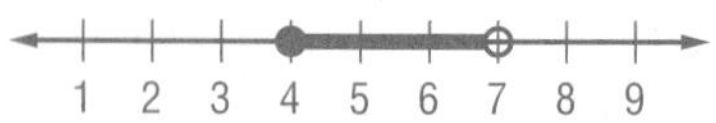

2 Solve $x + 3 < 2$ or $-x \le -4$. Graph the solution set on a number line.
$\{x \mid x < -1 \text{ or } x \ge 4\}$

Additional Examples also in Interactive Classroom PowerPoint® Presentations

IWB INTERACTIVE WHITEBOARD READY

Watch Out!

Preventing Errors Remind students that the word *and* used in Method 1 means the value for $3y - 7$ must meet *both* conditions. That is, the value must be greater than 8 *and* less than or equal to 23. An *or* compound inequality must be written as two or more separate inequalities separated by the word *or*. They cannot be shortened into one "double" inequality. Explain why it does not make sense to rewrite $x < 2$ *or* $x > 7$ as $2 > x > 7$.

Graph the solution set for each inequality and find their intersection.

$5 < y$

$y \le 10$

$5 < y \le 10$

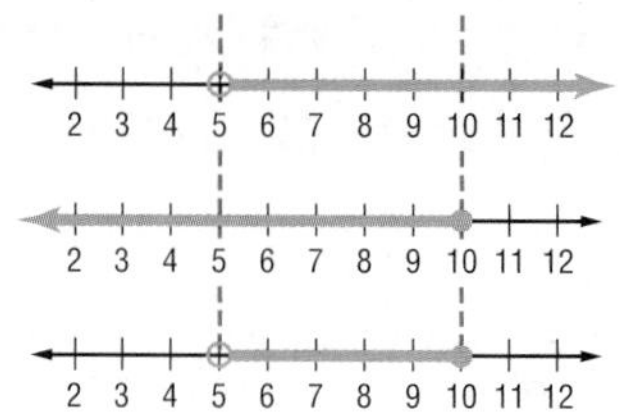

The solution set is $\{y \mid 5 < y \le 10\}$.

Guided Practice 1A, 1B. See Chapter 1 Answer Appendix.

Solve each inequality. Graph the solution set on a number line.

1A. $-12 \le 4x + 8 \le 32$

1B. $-5 \ge 3z - 2 > -14$

Personal Tutor glencoe.com

The graph of a compound inequality containing *or* is the **union** of the solution sets of the two inequalities.

Key Concept — "Or" Compound Inequalities

Words A compound inequality containing the word *or* is true if one or more of the inequalities is true.

Example

$x \ge 5$

$x < -3$

$x \ge 5$ or $x < -3$

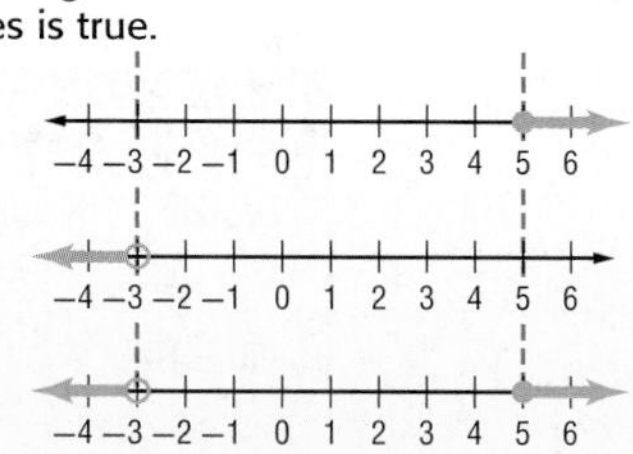

EXAMPLE 2 Solve an "Or" Compound Inequality

Solve $k + 6 < -4$ or $3k \ge 14$. Graph the solution set.

Solve each inequality separately.

$k + 6 < -4$ or $3k \ge 14$

$k < -10$ $\quad k \ge \frac{14}{3}$

$k < -10$

$k \ge \frac{14}{3}$

$k < -10$ or $k \ge \frac{14}{3}$

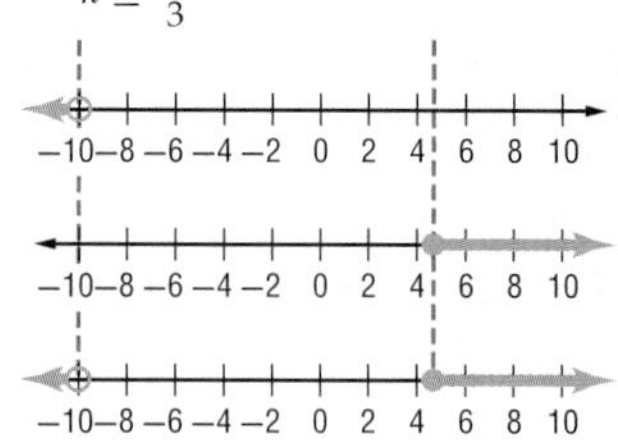

Math in Motion are online illustrations of key concepts through animations, Interactive Labs, and BrainPOPs®.

Guided Practice 2A, 2B. See Chapter 1 Answer Appendix.

Solve each inequality. Graph the solution set on a number line.

2A. $5j \ge 15$ or $-3j \ge 21$

2B. $g - 6 > -11$ or $2g + 4 < -15$

Personal Tutor glencoe.com

Differentiated Instruction

AL OL ELL

If students make the mistake of wanting to associate *union* with the word *and* because union often indicates the joining of two or more things,

Then as a memory device, point out that the word *or* begins with the letter *o,* which is found in *union,* but *and* begins with the letter *a,* which is not found in *union.*

Absolute Value Inequalities In Lesson 1-4, you learned that the absolute value of a number is its distance from 0 on the number line. You can use this definition to solve inequalities involving absolute value.

ReadingMath

within* and *between When solving problems involving inequalities, *within* is meant to be inclusive. Use $\leq$ or $\geq$.

Between is meant to be exclusive. Use $<$ or $>$.

EXAMPLE 3 Solve Absolute Value Inequalities

Solve each inequality. Graph the solution set on a number line.

a. $|x| < 3$

$|x| < 3$ means that the distance between x and 0 on a number line is less than 3 units. To make $|x| < 3$ true, substitute numbers for x that are fewer than 3 units from 0.

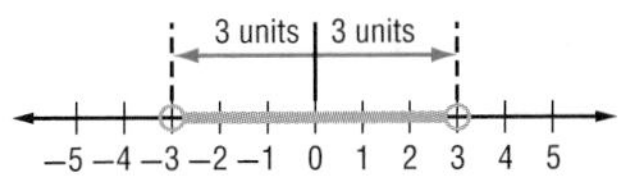

Notice that the graph of $|x| < 3$ is the same as the graph of $x > -3$ and $x < 3$.

All of the numbers between -3 and 3 are less than 3 units from 0. The solution set is $\{x \mid -3 < x < 3\}$.

b. $|x| > 5$

$|x| > 5$ means that the distance between x and 0 on a number line is more than 5 units. To make $|x| > 5$ true, substitute numbers for x that are more than 5 units from 0.

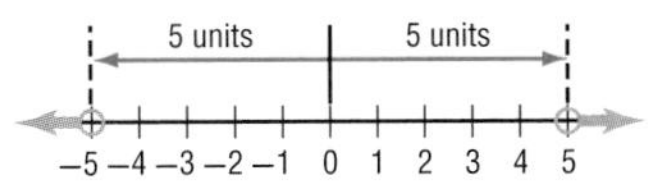

Notice that the graph of $|x| > 5$ is the same as the graph of $x < -5$ or $x > 5$.

All of the numbers between and including -5 and 5 are no more than 5 units from 0. The solution set is $\{x \mid -5 > x \text{ or } x > 5\}$.

Guided Practice 3A–3D. See margin.

Solve each inequality. Graph the solution set on a number line.

3A. $|t| < 6$ **3B.** $|u| < -3$

3C. $|t| > 3$ **3D.** $|u| > -2$

Personal Tutor glencoe.com

An absolute value inequality can be solved by rewriting it as a compound inequality.

Key Concept Absolute Value Inequalities

For all real numbers a, b, c, and x, $c > 0$, the following statements are true.

Absolute Value Inequality	Compound Inequality	Example
$\|ax + b\| > c$	$ax + b > c$ or $ax + b < -c$	If $\|4x + 5\| > 7$, then $4x + 5 > 7$ or $4x + 5 < -7$.
$\|ax + b\| < c$	$-c < ax + b < c$	If $\|4x + 5\| < 7$, then $-7 < 4x + 5 < 7$.

These statements are also true for $\leq$ and $\geq$, respectively.

Absolute Value Inequalities

Examples 3–4 show how to solve absolute value inequalities.

Additional Examples

3 **a.** Solve $2 > |d|$. Graph the solution set on a number line. $\{d \mid -2 < d < 2\}$

b. Solve $3 < |d|$. Graph the solution set on a number line. $\{d \mid d < -3 \text{ or } d > 3\}$

Tips for New Teachers

Reading Make sure students understand the meaning of Examples 3 and 4 before they go on. Have them say the problem in words (Example 3: "The distance of x from 0 without regard to direction is less than 3.") and demonstrate where x can be located on a number line.

Focus on Mathematical Content

Compound Inequalities A number is a solution to a compound inequality with *and* if the number is a solution to both inequalities. A number is a solution to a compound inequality with *or* if the number is a solution to either inequality.

Watch Out!

Preventing Errors Absolute value signs need to be interpreted so that the statement containing the absolute value signs can be rewritten as an equivalent statement without absolute value signs.

Additional Answers

3A. $\{t \mid -6 < t < 6\}$

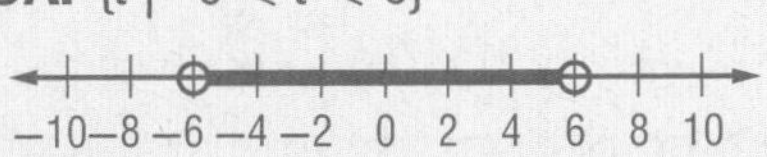

3B. $\varnothing$

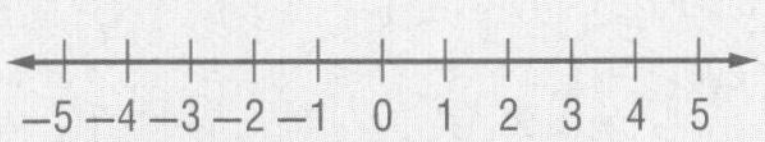

3C. $\{t \mid t > 3 \text{ or } t < -3\}$

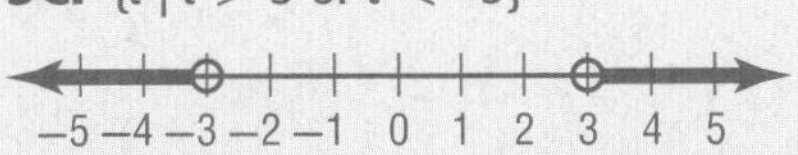

3D. $\{u \mid \text{all real numbers}\}$

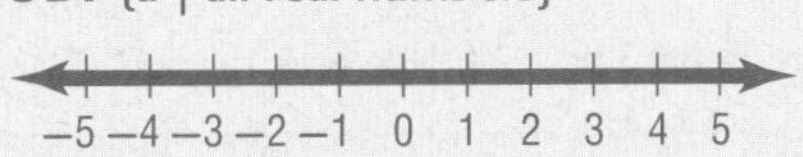

Example 5 shows how to write and solve an absolute value inequality in a real-world situation.

Additional Examples

4 Solve $|2x - 2| \geq 4$. Graph the solution set on a number line. $\{x | x \leq -1 \text{ or } x \geq 3\}$

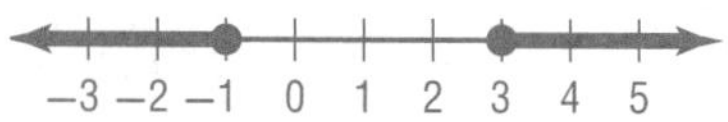

5 **JOB HUNTING** To prepare for a job interview, Hinda researches the position's requirements and pay. She discovers that the average starting salary for the position is \$38,500, but her actual starting salary could differ from the average by as much as \$2450.

a. Write an absolute value inequality to describe this situation. $|38{,}500 - x| \leq 2450$

b. Solve the inequality to find the range of Hinda's starting salary. $\{x | 36{,}050 \leq x \leq 40{,}950\}$; Hinda's starting salary will fall within \$36,050 and \$40,950.

TEACH with TECH

DOCUMENT CAMERA Choose a student to work through an example using the document camera. Be sure the student uses a graph to find the solution to the inequality.

Teach with Tech features throughout the Teacher Edition offer tips on using various types of technology such as interactive whiteboards, document cameras, blogs, and more, to enhance your teaching.

StudyTip

Absolute Value Inequalities Because the absolute value of a number is never negative, solutions involving negative numbers are as follows.
$|x| < -5$ is the empty set.
$|x| > -5$ is infinite solutions.

EXAMPLE 4 Solve a Multi-Step Absolute Value Inequality

Solve $|6y - 5| \geq 13$. Graph the solution set on a number line.

$|6y - 5| \geq 13$ is equivalent to $6y - 5 \geq 13$ or $6y - 5 \leq -13$. Solve the inequality.

$6y - 5 \geq 13$	or	$6y - 5 \leq -13$	**Rewrite the inequality.**
$6y \geq 18$		$6y \leq -8$	**Add 5 to each side.**
$y \geq 3$		$y \leq -\frac{8}{6}$ or $-\frac{4}{3}$	**Divide each side by 6.**

The solution set is $\left\{y \middle| y \leq -\frac{4}{3} \text{ or } y \geq 3\right\}$.

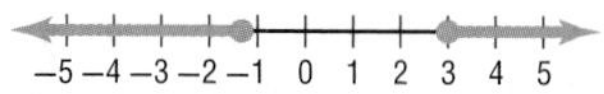

Guided Practice

Solve each inequality. Graph the solution set on a number line.

4A. $|4x - 7| > 13$ $\left\{x \middle| x < -\frac{3}{2} \text{ or } x > 5\right\}$

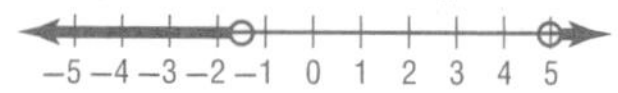

4B. $|5z + 2| \leq 17$ $\{z | -4.8 \leq z \leq 3\}$

Personal Tutor glencoe.com

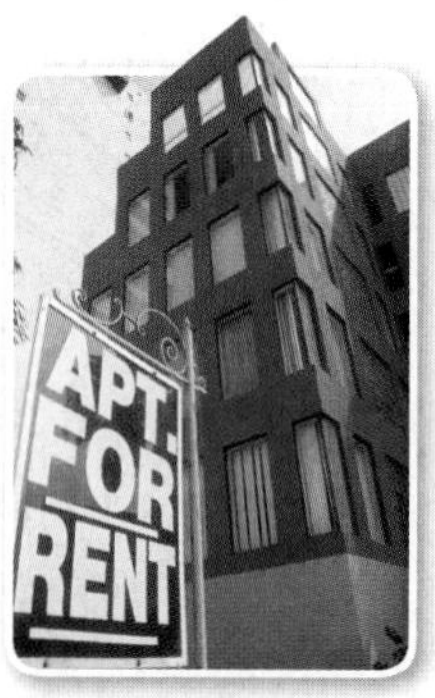

Real-World Link

Apartment costs vary greatly depending on location. Of the major U.S. cities, New York has the highest average monthly rent of \$2400, while Oklahoma City is lowest at \$543.

Source: MSN

Absolute value inequalities can be used to solve real-world problems.

EXAMPLE 5 Write and Solve an Absolute Value Inequality

MONEY **Amanda is apartment hunting in a specific area. She discovers that the average monthly rent for a 2-bedroom apartment is \$600 a month, but the actual price could differ from the average as much as \$225 a month.**

a. Write an absolute value inequality to describe this situation.

Let r = average monthly rent.

$|600 - r| \leq 225$

b. Solve the inequality to find the range of monthly rent.

Rewrite the absolute value inequality as a compound inequality. Then solve for r.

$$-225 \leq 600 - r \leq 225$$
$$-225 - 600 \leq 600 - r - 600 \leq 225 - 600$$
$$-825 \leq -r \leq -375$$
$$825 \geq r \geq 375$$

The solution set is $\{r | 375 \leq r \leq 825\}$. Thus, monthly rent could fall between \$375 and \$825, inclusive.

Guided Practice

5. TUITION Rachel is considering colleges to attend and determines that the average tuition among her choices is \$3725 per year, but the tuition at a school could differ by as much as \$1650 from the average. Write and solve an absolute value inequality to find the range of tuition. $|t - 3725| \leq 1650$; $\{t | \$2075 \leq t \leq \$5375\}$

Personal Tutor glencoe.com

Differentiated Instruction

OL BL

Extension Solve $|x - 2| > x + 4$. $\{x | x < -1\}$

Check Your Understanding

Examples 1–4 pp. 41–44

Solve each inequality. Graph the solution set on a number line. 1–10. See margin.

1. $-4 < g + 8 < 6$
2. $-9 \le 4y - 3 \le 13$
3. $z + 6 > 3$ or $2z < -12$
4. $m - 7 \ge -3$ or $-2m + 1 \ge 11$
5. $|c| \ge 8$
6. $|q| \ge -1$
7. $|z| < 6$
8. $|x| \le -4$
9. $|3v + 5| > 14$
10. $|4t - 3| \le 7$

Example 5 p. 44

11. **MONEY** Khalid is considering several types of paint for his bedroom. He estimates that he will need between 2 and 3 gallons. The table at the right shows the price per gallon for each type of paint Khalid is considering. Write a compound inequality and determine how much he could be spending.
$43.96 \le c \le 77.94$; between \$43.96 and \$77.94

Paint Type	Price per Gallon
Flat	\$21.98
Satin	\$23.98
Semi-Gloss	\$24.98
Gloss	\$25.98

Practice and Problem Solving

● = **Step-by-Step Solutions** begin on page R20. **Extra Practice** begins on page 947.

Examples 1–4 pp. 41–44

12–21. See Chapter 1 Answer Appendix.

Solve each inequality. Graph the solution set on a number line.

12. $8 < 2v - 4 < 16$
13. $-7 \le 4d - 3 \le -1$
14. $4r + 3 < -6$ or $3r - 7 > 2$
15. $6y - 3 < -27$ or $-4y + 2 < -26$
16. $|6h| < 12$
17. $|-4k| > 16$
18. $|3x - 4| > 10$
19. $|8t + 3| \le 4$
20. $|-9n - 3| < 6$
21. $|-5j - 4| \ge 12$

Example 5 p. 44

22. **ANATOMY** Forensic scientists use the equation $h = 2.6f + 47.2$ to estimate the height h of a woman given the length in centimeters f of her femur bone.
   a. Suppose the equation has a margin of error of ± 3 centimeters. Write an inequality to represent the height of a woman given the length of her femur bone.
   22a. $|2.6f + 47.2| < 3$
   b. If the length of a female skeleton's femur is 50 centimeters, write and solve an absolute value inequality that describes the woman's height in centimeters.
   $|h - 177.2| < 3$; 174.2 cm $< h <$ 180.2 cm

B Write an absolute value inequality for each graph.

23. $|x - 1| \le 5$
24. $|x - 1| \ge 5$
25. $|x + 9| \le 3$
26. $|x - 1| > 2$
27. $|x - 2| \ge 10$
28. $|x - 4| < 6$
29. $|x + 3| > 1$
30. $|x - 5| \le 3$

23. 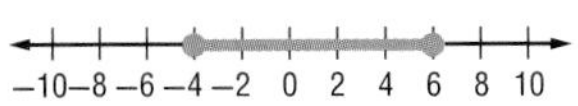

24. 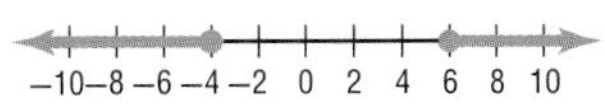

25. 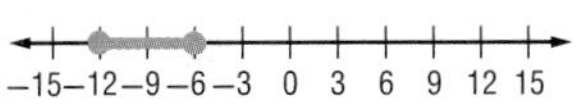

26. 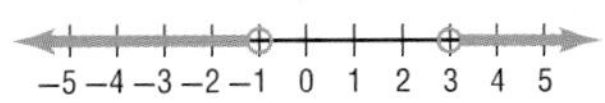

27. 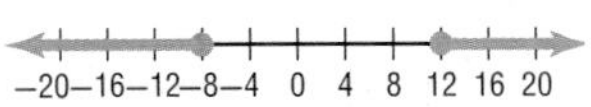

28. 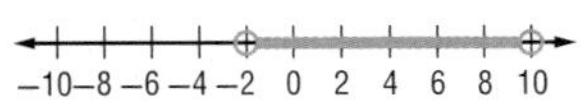

29. 

30. 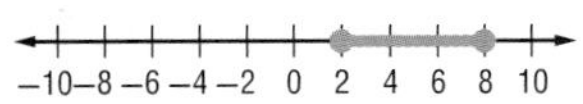

Differentiated Homework Options

Level	Assignment	Two-Day Option	
AL Basic	12–22, 53, 55–74	13–21 odd, 63–66	12–22 even, 53, 55–62, 67–74
OL Core	13–21 odd, 22, 23–31 odd, 32, 33–43 odd, 44, 45–51 odd, 52, 53, 55–74	12–22, 63–66	23–53, 55–62, 67–74
BL Advanced	23–71, (optional: 72–74)		

3 PRACTICE

Formative Assessment

Use Exercises 1–11 to check for understanding.

Use the chart on the bottom of the page to customize assignments for your students.

Additional Answers

1. $\{g \mid -12 < g < -2\}$

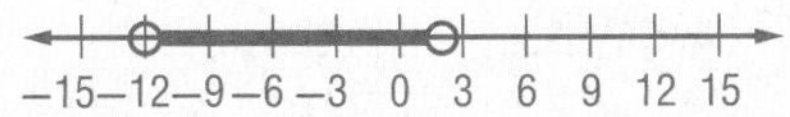

2. $\{y \mid -1.5 \le y \le 4\}$

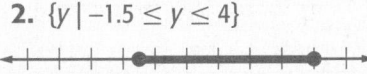

3. $\{z \mid z > -3 \text{ or } z < -6\}$

4. $\{m \mid m \ge 4 \text{ or } m \le -5\}$

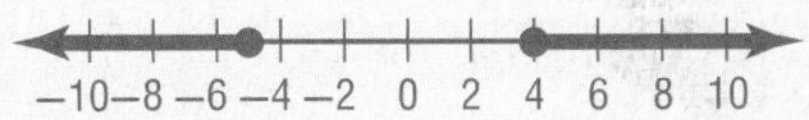

5. $\{c \mid c \ge 8 \text{ or } c \le -8\}$

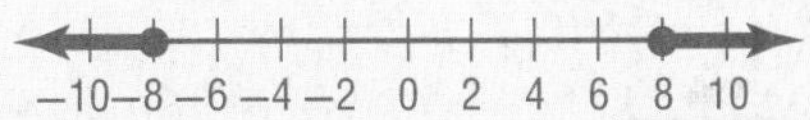

6. $\{q \mid \text{all real numbers}\}$

7. $\{z \mid -6 < z < 6\}$

8. $\varnothing$

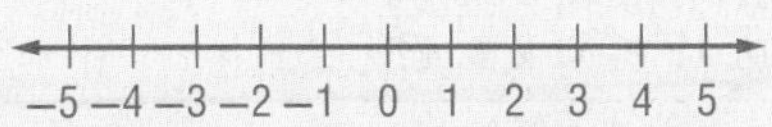

9. $\left\{v \mid v > 3 \text{ or } v < -\frac{19}{3}\right\}$

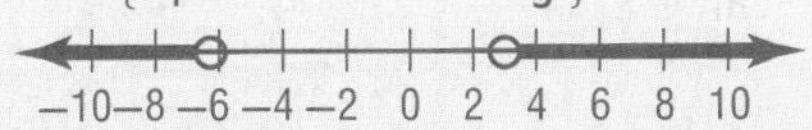

10. $\{t \mid -1 \le t \le 2.5\}$

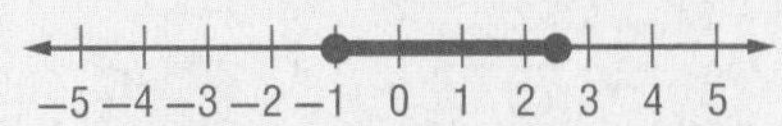

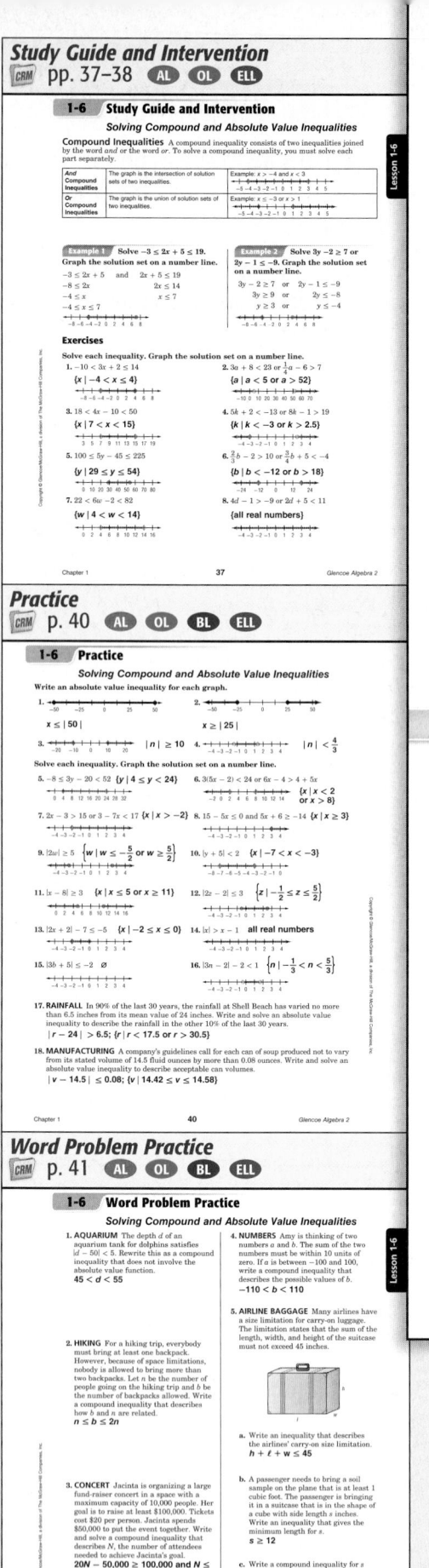

Study Guide and Intervention
CRM pp. 37–38 AL OL ELL

1-6 Study Guide and Intervention
Solving Compound and Absolute Value Inequalities

Compound Inequalities A compound inequality consists of two inequalities joined by the word *and* or the word *or*. To solve a compound inequality, you must solve each part separately.

And Compound Inequalities	The graph is the intersection of solution sets of two inequalities.	Example: $x > -4$ and $x < 3$
Or Compound Inequalities	The graph is the union of solution sets of two inequalities.	Example: $x \le -3$ or $x > 1$

Example 1 Solve $-3 \le 2x + 5 \le 19$. Graph the solution set on a number line.

$-3 \le 2x + 5$ and $2x + 5 \le 19$
$-8 \le 2x$ $\quad 2x \le 14$
$-4 \le x$ $\quad x \le 7$
$-4 \le x \le 7$

Example 2 Solve $3y - 2 \ge 7$ or $2y - 1 \le -9$. Graph the solution set on a number line.

$3y - 2 \ge 7$ or $2y - 1 \le -9$
$3y \ge 9$ or $2y \le -8$
$y \ge 3$ or $y \le -4$

Exercises

Solve each inequality. Graph the solution set on a number line.

1. $-10 < 3x + 2 \le 14$ **$\{x \mid -4 < x \le 4\}$**
2. $3a + 8 < 23$ or $\frac{1}{4}a - 6 > 7$ **$\{a \mid a < 5$ or $a > 52\}$**
3. $18 < 4x - 10 < 50$ **$\{x \mid 7 < x < 15\}$**
4. $5k + 2 < -13$ or $8k - 1 > 19$ **$\{k \mid k < -3$ or $k > 2.5\}$**
5. $100 \le 5y - 45 \le 225$ **$\{y \mid 29 \le y \le 54\}$**
6. $\frac{2}{3}b - 2 > 10$ or $\frac{3}{4}b + 5 < -4$ **$\{b \mid b < -12$ or $b > 18\}$**
7. $22 < 6w - 2 < 82$ **$\{w \mid 4 < w < 14\}$**
8. $4d - 1 > -9$ or $2d + 5 < 11$ **{all real numbers}**

Chapter 1 37 Glencoe Algebra 2

Lesson 1-6

Practice
CRM p. 40 AL OL BL ELL

1-6 Practice
Solving Compound and Absolute Value Inequalities

Write an absolute value inequality for each graph.

1. **$x \le |50|$**
2. **$x \ge |25|$**
3. **$|n| \ge 10$**
4. **$|n| < \frac{4}{3}$**

Solve each inequality. Graph the solution set on a number line.

5. $-8 \le 3y - 20 < 52$ **$\{y \mid 4 \le y < 24\}$**
6. $3(5x - 2) < 24$ or $6x - 4 > 4 + 5x$ **$\{x \mid x < 2$ or $x > 8\}$**
7. $2x - 3 > 15$ or $3 - 7x < 17$ **$\{x \mid x > -2\}$**
8. $15 - 5x \le 0$ and $5x + 6 \ge -14$ **$\{x \mid x \ge 3\}$**
9. $|2w| \ge 5$ **$\left\{w \mid w \le -\frac{5}{2} \text{ or } w \ge \frac{5}{2}\right\}$**
10. $|y + 5| < 2$ **$\{x \mid -7 < x < -3\}$**
11. $|x - 8| \ge 3$ **$\{x \mid x \le 5$ or $x \ge 11\}$**
12. $|2z - 2| \le 3$ **$\left\{z \mid -\frac{1}{2} \le z \le \frac{5}{2}\right\}$**
13. $|2x + 2| - 7 \le -5$ **$\{x \mid -2 \le x \le 0\}$**
14. $|x| > x - 1$ **all real numbers**
15. $|3b + 5| \le -2$ **$\varnothing$**
16. $|3n - 2| - 2 < 1$ **$\left\{n \mid -\frac{1}{3} < n < \frac{5}{3}\right\}$**
17. **RAINFALL** In 90% of the last 30 years, the rainfall at Shell Beach has varied no more than 6.5 inches from its mean value of 24 inches. Write and solve an absolute value inequality to describe the rainfall in the other 10% of the last 30 years. **$|r - 24| > 6.5$; $\{r \mid r < 17.5$ or $r > 30.5\}$**
18. **MANUFACTURING** A company's guidelines call for each can of soup produced not to vary from its stated volume of 14.5 fluid ounces by more than 0.08 ounces. Write and solve an absolute value inequality to describe acceptable can volumes. **$|v - 14.5| \le 0.08$; $\{v \mid 14.42 \le v \le 14.58\}$**

Chapter 1 40 Glencoe Algebra 2

Word Problem Practice
CRM p. 41 AL OL BL ELL

1-6 Word Problem Practice
Solving Compound and Absolute Value Inequalities

1. **AQUARIUM** The depth d of an aquarium tank for dolphins satisfies $|d - 50| < 5$. Rewrite this as a compound inequality that does not involve the absolute value function. **$45 < d < 55$**
2. **HIKING** For a hiking trip, everybody must bring at least one backpack. However, because of space limitations, nobody is allowed to bring more than two backpacks. Let n be the number of people going on the hiking trip and b be the number of backpacks allowed. Write a compound inequality that describes how b and n are related. **$n \le b \le 2n$**
3. **CONCERT** Jacinta is organizing a large fund-raiser concert in a space with a maximum capacity of 10,000 people. Her goal is to raise at least \$100,000. Tickets cost \$20 per person. Jacinta spends \$50,000 to put the event together. Write and solve a compound inequality that describes N, the number of attendees needed to achieve Jacinta's goal. **$20N - 50{,}000 \ge 100{,}000$ and $N \le 10{,}000$; The attendance must be between 7,500 and 10,000 people, inclusive.**
4. **NUMBERS** Amy is thinking of two numbers a and b. The sum of the two numbers must be within 10 units of zero. If a is between -100 and 100, write a compound inequality that describes the possible values of b. **$-110 < b < 110$**
5. **AIRLINE BAGGAGE** Many airlines have a size limitation for carry-on luggage. The limitation states that the sum of the length, width, and height of the suitcase must not exceed 45 inches.

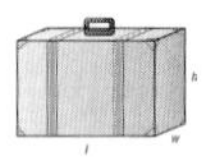

a. Write an inequality that describes the airlines' carry-on size limitation. **$h + \ell + w \le 45$**

b. A passenger needs to bring a soil sample on the plane that is at least 1 cubic foot. The passenger is bringing it in a suitcase that is in the shape of a cube with side length s inches. Write an inequality that gives the minimum length for s. **$s \ge 12$**

c. Write a compound inequality for s using parts **a** and **b**. Find the maximum and minimum values for s. **$s \ge 12$ and $3s \le 45$; s is at least 12 and at most 15**

Chapter 1 41 Glencoe Algebra 2

Lesson 1-6

---

31. **DOGS** The Labrador retriever is one of the most recognized and popular dogs kept as a pet. Using the information given, write a compound inequality to describe the range of healthy weights for a fully grown female Labrador retriever. **$55 \le w \le 70$**

Healthy Heights and Weights for Labrador Retrievers

Gender	Height (in.)	Weight
Male	22.5–24.5	65–80
Female	21.5–23.5	55–70

C 32. **GEOMETRY** The *Exterior Angle Inequality Theorem* states that an exterior angle measure is greater than the measure of either of its corresponding remote interior angles. Write two inequalities to express the relationships among the measures of the angles of $\triangle ABC$. **$m\angle4 > m\angle1$, $m\angle4 > m\angle2$**

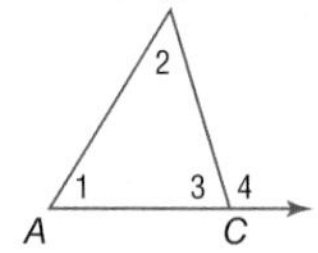

Solve each inequality. Graph the solution set on a number line. **33–40. See Chapter 1 Answer Appendix.**

33. $28 > 6k + 4 > 16$
34. $m - 7 > -12$ or $-3m + 2 > 38$
35. $|-6h| > 90$
36. $-|-5k| > 15$
37. $3|2z - 4| - 6 > 12$
38. $6|4p + 2| - 8 < 34$
39. $\frac{|5f - 2|}{6} > 4$
40. $\frac{|2w + 8|}{5} \ge 3$

Write an algebraic expression to represent each verbal expression.

41. numbers that are at least 4 units from -5 **$|x + 5| \ge 4$**
42. numbers that are no more than $\frac{3}{8}$ unit from 1 **$|x - 1| \le \frac{3}{8}$**
43. numbers that are at least 6 units but no more than 10 units from 2 **$6 \le |x - 2| \le 10$**

Real-World Link

NASCAR drivers work together. By driving in certain formations, cars create a vacuum behind them that another car can then fill. This reduces drag, which increases speed for all the drivers in the formation.

Source: *Popular Mechanics*

44. **AUTO RACING** NASCAR rules stipulate that a car must conform to a set of 32 templates, each shaped to fit a different contour of the car. When a template is placed on a car, the gap between it and the car cannot exceed the specified tolerance. Each template is marked on its edge with a colored line that indicates the tolerance for the template.

a. Suppose a certain template is 24.42 inches long. Use the information in the table at the right to write an absolute value inequality for templates with each line color.

b. Find the acceptable lengths for that part of a car if the template has each line color.

c. Graph the solution set for each line color on a number line. **See margin.**

d. The tolerance of which line color includes the tolerances of the other line colors? Explain your reasoning.

Line Color	Tolerance (in.)
Red	0.07
Blue	0.25
Green	0.5

44a.
red: $|x - 24.42| \le 0.07$;
blue: $|x - 24.42| \le 0.25$;
green: $|x - 24.42| \le 0.5$
44b.
red: $24.35 \le x \le 24.49$;
blue: $24.17 \le x \le 24.67$;
green: $23.92 \le x \le 24.92$
44d. Red; the red line color has the smallest tolerance, $0.07 < 0.25 < 0.5$, so the other line colors would be well within their tolerances.

Solve each inequality. Graph the solution set on a number line. **45–50. See margin.**

45. $n + 6 > 2n + 5 > n - 2$
46. $y + 7 < 2y + 2 < 0$
47. $2x + 6 < 3(x - 1) \le 2(x + 3)$
48. $a - 16 \le 2(a - 4) < a + 2$
49. $4g + 8 \ge g + 6$ or $7g - 14 \ge 2g - 4$
50. $5t + 7 > 2t + 4$ and $3t + 3 < 24 - 4t$

51. **HEALTH** Hypoglycemia (low blood sugar) and hyperglycemia (high blood sugar) are potentially dangerous and occur when a person's blood sugar fluctuates by more than 38 mg from the normal blood sugar level of 88 mg. Write and solve an absolute value inequality to describe blood sugar levels that are considered potentially dangerous. **$|s - 88| > 38$; $\{s \mid s > 126$ or $s < 50\}$**

Enrichment
CRM p. 42 OL BL

1-6 Enrichment

Conjunctions and Disjunctions

The compound sentence that solves an absolute value inequality is called either a *conjunction* or a *disjunction*.

Example 1 Solve $|2x| < 10$.

$|2x| < 10$ means $2x < 10$ and $2x > -10$.

Solve each inequality. $x < 5$ and $x > -5$.

Every solution for $|2x| < 10$ is a replacement for x that makes both $x < 5$ and $x > -5$ true.

A compound sentence that combines two statements by the word *and* is a *conjunction*.

Example 2 Solve $|3x - 7| \ge 11$.

$|3x - 7| \ge 11$ means $3x - 7 \ge 11$ or $3x - 7 \le -11$.

Solve each inequality. $3x \ge 18$ or $3x \le -4$
$x \ge 6$ or $x \le -\frac{4}{3}$

Every solution for the inequality is a replacement for x that makes either

Additional Answer

44c.

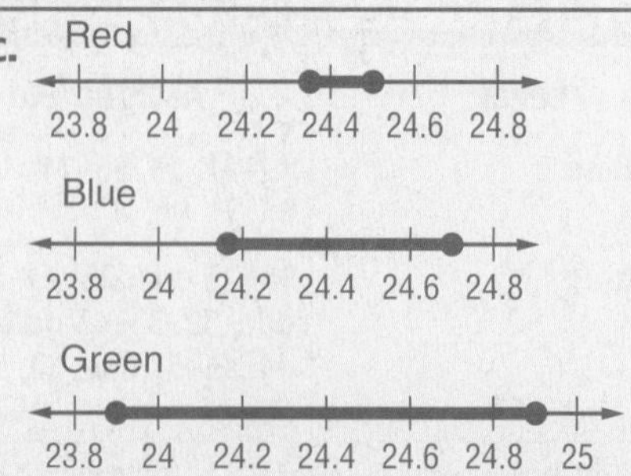

52a. $x \leq 50$; $50 < x \leq 70$; $70 < x \leq 100$; $x > 100$

52. AIR TRAVEL The airline on which Drew is flying has weight restrictions for checked baggage. Drew is checking one bag.

a. Describe the ranges of weights that would classify Drew's bag as free, \$25, \$50, and unacceptable.

b. If Drew's bag weighs 68 pounds, how much will he pay to take it on the plane? **\$25**

Cost for Checked Baggage	
Weight	**Cost**
Up to 50 lb limit	free
20 lb over limit	\$25
More than 20, but less than 50 lb over limit	\$50
More than 50 lb over limit	not accepted

53. Sample answer: David; when Sarah converted the absolute value into two inequalities, she mistakenly switched the inequality symbols.

59. Sample answer: The graph on the left indicates a solution set from −3 to 5. The graph on the right indicates a solution set of all numbers less than or equal to −3 or greater than or equal to 5.

60. Sample answer: $\left|x - \frac{a+b}{2}\right| \leq b - \frac{a+b}{2}$

61. Each of these has a non-empty solution set except for $x > 5$ and $x < 1$. There are no values of x that are simultaneously greater than 5 and less than 1.

H.O.T. Problems Use Higher-Order Thinking Skills

53. ERROR ANALYSIS David and Sarah are solving $4|-5x - 3| - 6 \geq 34$. Is either of them correct? Explain your reasoning.

David	Sarah
$4\|-5x - 3\| - 6 \geq 34$	$4\|-5x - 3\| - 6 \geq 34$
$\|-5x - 3\| \geq 10$	$\|-5x - 3\| \geq 10$
$-5x - 3 \geq 10$ or $-5x - 3 \leq -10$	$-5x - 3 \leq 10$ or $-5x - 3 \geq -10$
$-5x \geq 13$ $-5x \leq -7$	$-5x \leq 13$ $-5x \geq -7$
$x \leq -\frac{13}{5}$ $x \geq \frac{7}{5}$	$x \geq -\frac{13}{5}$ $x \leq \frac{7}{5}$

54. CHALLENGE Solve $|x - 2| - |x + 2| > x$. **$x < 0$**

REASONING **Determine whether each statement is *true* or *false*. If false, provide a counterexample.** **55–57. See margin.**

55. The graph of a compound inequality involving an *and* statement is bounded on the left and right by two values of x.

56. The graph of a compound inequality involving an *or* statement contains a region of values that are not solutions.

57. The graph of a compound inequality involving an *and* statement includes values that make all parts of the given statement true.

58. WRITING IN MATH An alternate definition of absolute value is to define $|a - b|$ as the distance between a and b on the number line. Explain how this definition can be used to solve inequalities of the form $|x - c| < r$. **See margin.**

59. REASONING The graphs of the solutions of two different absolute value inequalities are shown. Compare and contrast the absolute value inequalities.

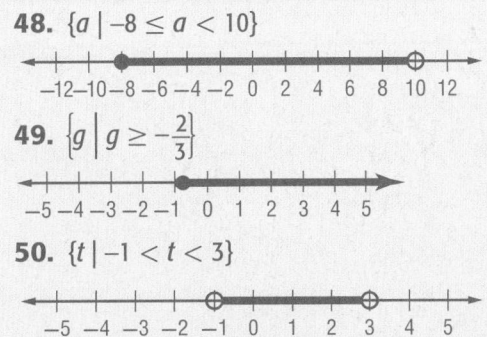

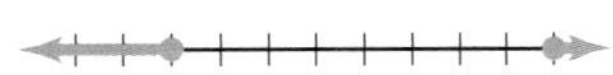

60. OPEN ENDED Write an absolute value inequality with a solution of $a \leq x \leq b$.

61. WHICH ONE DOESN'T BELONG? Identify the compound inequality that is not the same as the other three. Explain your reasoning.

$-3 < x < 5$	$x > 2$ and $x < 3$	$x > 5$ and $x < 1$	$x > -4$ and $x > -2$

62. WRITING IN MATH Summarize the difference between *and* compound inequalities and *or* compound inequalities. **See margin.**

ReadingMath

Compare to describe *similar* features or characteristics of two or more items

Contrast to describe *different* features or characteristics of two or more items

Watch Out!

Error Analysis For Exercise 53, have students pay special attention to the direction of each inequality symbol.

Every effort is made to show **answers** on the reduced Student Edition page, or in the margin of the Teacher Wraparound Edition.

Additional Answers

55. False; sample answer: the graph of $x > 2$ and $x > 5$ is a ray bounded only on one end.

56. False; sample answer: the graph of $x > 2$ or $x < 3$ includes the entire number line.

57. true

58. Sample answer: $|x - c|$ represents the distance between some unknown value of the variable x and a point c on the number line. The solution set of the inequality is the set of all numbers such that the distance from the numbers to c is less than r units. Use a number line to find the numbers that are r units from c in either direction.

62. Sample answer: A compound inequality that contains *and* is true if and only if both individual inequalities are true, while an inequality containing *or* only needs one of the individual inequalities to be true.

45. $\{n \mid -7 < n < 1\}$

46. $\varnothing$

47. $\varnothing$

48. $\{a \mid -8 \leq a < 10\}$

49. $\left\{g \mid g \geq -\frac{2}{3}\right\}$

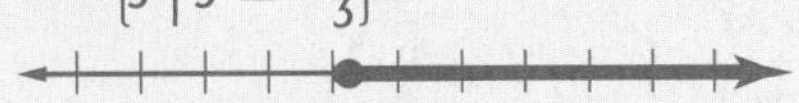

50. $\{t \mid -1 < t < 3\}$

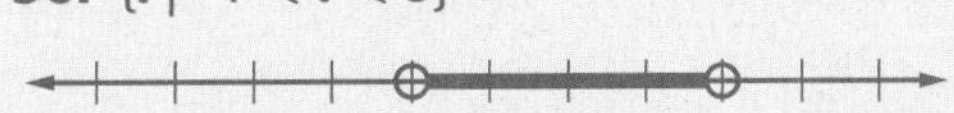

4 ASSESS

Ticket Out the Door Have each student tell a partner or write the steps used to solve $|x - 4| < 3$.

The **Four-Step Teaching Plan** shows you how to **Focus, Teach, Practice,** and **Assess** each lesson. Each lesson ends with a creative strategy for closing the lesson.

Formative Assessment

Check for student understanding of concepts in Lesson 1-6.

CRM Quiz 4, p. 46

NGSSS PRACTICE 912.A.3.12, 912.A.4.1, 912.G.7.5, 912.A.3.6

63. Which of the following best describes the graph of the equations below? **C**

$$24y = 8x + 11$$
$$36y = 12x + 11$$

A. The lines have the same x-intercept.
B. The lines have the same y-intercept.
C. The lines are parallel.
D. The lines are perpendicular.

64. SAT/ACT Find an expression equivalent to $\left(\frac{3x^3}{y}\right)^3$. **I**

F. $\frac{9x^6}{3y}$ H. $\frac{27x^6}{3y}$

G. $\frac{9x^9}{y^3}$ I. $\frac{27x^9}{y^3}$

65. **GRIDDED RESPONSE** How many cubes that measure 4 centimeters on each side can be placed completely inside the box below? **60**

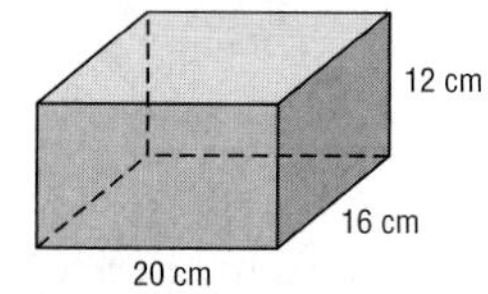

66. Which graph represents the solution set for $|3x - 6| + 8 \geq 17$? **A**

A. 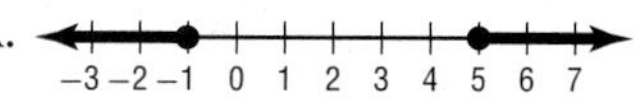

B. 

C. 

D. 

Spiral Review

67. HEALTH The National Heart Association recommends that less than 30% of a person's total daily caloric intake come from fat. One gram of fat yields nine Calories. Consider a healthy 21-year-old whose average caloric intake is between 2500 and 3300 Calories. (Lesson 1-5)

a. Write an inequality that represents the suggested fat intake for the person. **$750 \leq x \leq 990$**

b. What is the greatest suggested fat intake for the person? **110 g**

68. TRAVEL Maggie is planning a 5-day trip to a family reunion. She wants to spend no more than $1000. Her plane ticket is $375, and the hotel is $85 per night. (Lesson 1-5)

a. Let f represent the cost of food for one day. Write an inequality to represent this situation. **$800 + 5f \leq 1000$**

b. Solve the inequality and interpret the solution. **She can spend no more than $40 per day on food.**

Solve each equation. Check your solutions. (Lesson 1-4)

69. $4|x - 5| = 20$ **{0, 10}**

70. $|3y + 10| = 25$ $\left\{-\frac{35}{3}, 5\right\}$

71. $|7z + 8| = -9$ $\varnothing$

Skills Review

Name the property illustrated by each statement. (Lesson 1-3)

72. If $5x = 7$, then $5x + 3 = 7 + 3$. **Addition (=)**

73. If $-3x + 9 = 11$ and $6x + 2 = 11$, then $-3x + 9 = 6x + 2$. **Transitive (=)**

74. If $[x + (-2)] + (-4) = 5$, then $x + [-2 + (-4)] = 5$. **Assoc. (+)**

FL Math Online glencoe.com
- STUDY TO GO
- Vocabulary Review

Chapter Summary

Key Concepts

Expressions and Formulas (Lesson 1-1)

- Use the order of operations to solve equations.

Properties of Real Numbers (Lesson 1-2)

- Real numbers can be classified as rational (Q) or irrational (I). Rational numbers can be classified as integers (Z), whole numbers (W), natural numbers (N), and/or quotients of these.

Solving Equations (Lessons 1-3 and 1-4)

- Verbal expressions can be translated into algebraic expressions.
- The absolute value of a number is the number of units it is from 0 on a number line.
- For any real numbers a and b, where $b \geq 0$, if $|a| = b$, then $a = b$ or $-a = b$.

Solving Inequalities (Lessons 1-5 and 1-6)

- Adding or subtracting the same number from each side of an inequality does not change the truth of the inequality.
- When you multiply or divide each side of an inequality by a negative number, the direction of the inequality symbol must be reversed.
- The graph of an *and* compound inequality is the intersection of the solution sets of the two inequalities. The graph of an *or* compound inequality is the union of the solution sets of the two inequalities.
- An *and* compound inequality can be expressed in two different ways. For example, $-2 \leq x \leq 3$ is equivalent to $x \geq -2$ and $x \leq 3$.
- For all real numbers a and b, where $b > 0$, the following statements are true.
  1. If $|a| < b$ then $-b < a < b$.
  2. If $|a| > b$ then $a > b$ or $a < -b$.

FOLDABLES® Study Organizer

Be sure the Key Concepts are noted in your Foldable.

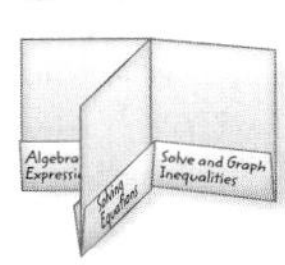

Key Vocabulary

absolute value (p. 27)
algebraic expressions (p. 5)
compound inequality (p. 41)
empty set (p. 28)
equation (p. 18)
extraneous solution (p. 29)
formula (p. 6)
infinity (p. 40)
integers (p. 11)
intersection (p. 41)
interval notation (p. 40)
irrational numbers (p. 11)
natural numbers (p. 11)
open sentence (p. 18)
order of operations (p. 5)
rational numbers (p. 11)
real numbers (p. 11)
set-builder notation (p. 35)
solution (p. 18)
union (p. 42)
variables (p. 5)
whole numbers (p. 11)

Vocabulary Check

State whether each sentence is *true* or *false*. If *false*, replace the underlined term to make a true sentence.

1. The absolute value of a number is always <u>negative</u>. **false; nonnegative**
2. $\sqrt{12}$ belongs to the set of <u>rational</u> numbers. **false; irrational**
3. An <u>equation</u> is a statement that two expressions have the same value. **true**
4. A solution of an equation is a value that makes the equation <u>false</u>. **false; true**
5. The empty set contains <u>no</u> elements. **true**
6. A mathematical sentence containing one or more variables is called an <u>open sentence</u>. **true**
7. The graph of a compound inequality containing <u>*and*</u> is the union of the solution sets of the two inequalities. **false; or**
8. Variables are used to represent <u>unknown</u> quantities. **true**
9. The set of <u>rational</u> numbers includes terminating and repeating decimals. **true**
10. Expressions that contain at least one variable are called <u>algebraic expressions</u>. **true**

CHAPTER 1 Study Guide and Review

Formative Assessment

Key Vocabulary The page references after each word denote where that term was first introduced. If students have difficulty answering questions 1–10, remind them that they can use these page references to refresh their memories about the vocabulary.

Summative Assessment

CRM Vocabulary Test, p. 48

FL Math Online glencoe.com

Vocabulary PuzzleMaker improves students' mathematics vocabulary using four puzzle formats–crossword, scramble, word search using a word list, and word search using clues. Students can work online or from a printed worksheet.

FOLDABLES® Study Organizer

Dinah Zike's Foldables®

Have students look through the chapter to make sure they have included examples in their Foldables.

Suggest that students keep their Foldables handy while completing the Study Guide and Review pages. Point out that their Foldables can serve as a quick review tool when studying for the chapter test.

Lesson-by-Lesson Review

Intervention If the given examples are not sufficient to review the topics covered by the questions, remind students that the page references tell them where to review that topic in their textbook.

Two-Day Option Have students complete the Lesson-by-Lesson Review on pp. 50–52. Then you can use ExamView® Assessment Suite to customize another review worksheet that practices all the objectives of this chapter or only the objectives on which your students need more help.

Differentiated Instruction

Super DVD: Mindjogger Videoquizzes Use this DVD as an alternative format of review for the test.

Lesson-by-Lesson Review

1-1 Expressions and Formulas (pp. 5–10)

912.A.3.1

Evaluate each expression.

11. $[28 - (16 + 3)] \div 3$ **3**

12. $\frac{2}{3}(3^3 + 12)$ **26**

13. $\frac{15(9 - 7)}{3}$ **10**

Evaluate each expression if $w = 0.2$, $x = 10$, $y = \frac{1}{2}$, and $z = -4$.

14. $4w - 8y$ **−3.2**

15. $z^2 + xy$ **21**

16. $\frac{5w - xy}{z}$ **1**

17. GEOMETRY The formula for the volume of a cylinder is $V = \pi r^2 h$, where V is volume, r is radius, and h is the height. What is the volume of a cylinder that is 6 inches high and has a radius of 3 inches? **169.65 in³**

EXAMPLE 1

Evaluate $(12 - 15) \div 3^2$.

$(12 - 15) \div 3^2 = -3 \div 3^2$ Subtract.

$= -3 \div 9$ $3^2 = 9$

$= -\frac{1}{3}$ Divide.

EXAMPLE 2

Evaluate $\frac{a^2}{2ac - b}$ if $a = -6$, $b = 5$, and $c = 0.25$.

$\frac{a^2}{2ac - b} = \frac{(-6)^2}{2(-6)(0.25) - 5}$ $a = -6$, $b = 5$, and $c = 0.25$

$= \frac{36}{2(-1.5) - 5}$ Evaluate the numerator and denominator separately.

$= \frac{36}{-8}$ or $-\frac{9}{2}$ Simplify.

1-2 Properties of Real Numbers (pp. 11–17)

912.A.3.2

Name the sets of numbers to which each value belongs.

18. $1.\overline{3}$ **Q, R** **19.** $\sqrt{4}$ **N, W, Z, Q, R** **20.** $-\frac{3}{4}$ **Q, R**

Simplify each expression.

21. $4x - 3y + 7x + 5y$ **$11x + 2y$**

22. $2(a + 3) - 4a + 8b$ **$-2a + 8b + 6$**

23. $4(2m + 5n) - 3(m - 7n)$ **$5m + 41n$**

24. MONEY At Fun City Amusement Park, hot dogs sell for \$3.50 and sodas sell for \$2.50. Dion bought 3 hot dogs and 3 sodas during one day at the park.

a. Illustrate the Distributive Property by writing two expressions to represent the cost of the hot dogs and the sodas.

b. Use the Distributive Property to find how much money Dion spent on food and drinks. **\$18**

EXAMPLE 3

Name the sets of numbers to which $\sqrt{50}$ belongs.

$\sqrt{50} = 5\sqrt{2}$ Irrationals (I), and reals (R)

EXAMPLE 4

Simplify $-4(a + 3b) + 5b$.

$-4(a + 3b) + 5b$ Original expression

$= -4(a) + -4(3b) + 5b$ Distributive Property

$= -4a - 12b + 5b$ Multiply.

$= -4a - 7b$ Simplify.

24a. 3(3.50 + 2.50) or 3(3.50) + 3(2.50)

MIXED PROBLEM SOLVING
For mixed problem-solving practice, see page 979.

1-3 Solving Equations (pp. 18–25)

912.A.3.3

Solve each equation. Check your solution.

25. $8 + 5r = -27$ -7

26. $4w + 10 = 6w - 13$ $\frac{23}{2}$

27. $\frac{x}{6} + \frac{x}{3} = \frac{3}{4}$ $\frac{3}{2}$

28. $6b - 5 = 3(b + 2)$ $\frac{11}{3}$

29. **MONEY** It cost Lori $14 to go to the movies. She bought popcorn for $3.50 and a soda for $2.50. How much was her ticket? **$8**

Solve each equation or formula for the specified variable.

30. $2k - 3m = 16$ for k $k = \frac{16 + 3m}{2}$

31. $\frac{r+5}{mn} = p$ for m $m = \frac{r+5}{pn}$

32. $A = \frac{1}{2}h(a + b)$ for h $h = \frac{2A}{a+b}$

33. **GEOMETRY** Yu-Jun wants to fill the water container at the right. He knows that the radius is 2 inches and the volume is 100.48 cubic inches. What is the height of the water bottle? Use the formula for the volume of a cylinder, $V = \pi r^2 h$, to find the height of the bottle. **8 in.**

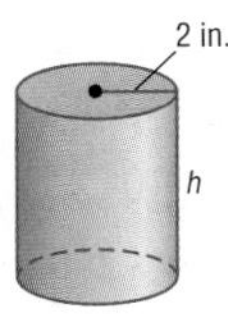

EXAMPLE 5

Solve $-3(a - 3) + 2(3a - 2) = 14$.

$-3(a - 3) + 2(3a - 2) = 14$	Original equation
$-3a + 9 + 6a - 4 = 14$	Distributive Property
$-3a + 6a + 9 - 4 = 14$	Commutative Property
$3a + 5 = 14$	Substitution Property
$3a = 9$	Subtraction Property
$a = 3$	Division Property

EXAMPLE 6

Solve each equation or formula for the specified variable.

a. $y = 2x + 3z$ for x

$y = 2x + 3z$	Original equation
$y - 3z = 2x$	Subtract $3z$ from each side.
$\frac{y - 3z}{2} = x$	Divide each side by 2.

b. $V = \frac{\pi r^2 h}{3}$ for h

$V = \frac{\pi r^2 h}{3}$	Original equation
$3V = \pi r^2 h$	Multiply each side by 3.
$\frac{3V}{\pi r^2} = h$	Divide each side by πr^2.

1-4 Solving Absolute Value Equations (pp. 27–33)

912.A.3.6

Solve each equation. Check your solution.

34. $|r + 5| = 12$ $\{-17, 7\}$

35. $4|a - 6| = 16$ $\{2, 10\}$

36. $|3x + 7| = -15$ $\varnothing$

37. $|b + 5| = 2b - 9$ $\{14\}$

38. **MEASUREMENT** Marcos is cutting ribbons for a craft project. Each ribbon needs to be $\frac{3}{4}$ yard long. If each piece is always within plus or minus $\frac{1}{16}$ yard, how long are the shortest and longest pieces of ribbon? $\frac{11}{16}$ **yd;** $\frac{13}{16}$ **yd**

EXAMPLE 7

Solve $|3m + 7| = 13$.

Case 1	Case 2
$a = b$	$a = -b$
$3m + 7 = 13$	$3m + 7 = -13$
$3m = 6$	$3m = -20$
$m = 2$	$m = -\frac{20}{3}$

The solutions are 2 and $-\frac{20}{3}$.

Chapter 1 Study Guide and Review 51

Problem Solving Review

For additional practice in problem solving for Chapter 1, see the Mixed Problem Solving Appendix, p. 980, in the Student Handbook section.

Anticipation Guide

Have students complete the Chapter 1 Anticipation Guide and discuss how their responses have changed now that they have completed Chapter 1.

Additional Answers

39. $a \geq -6$

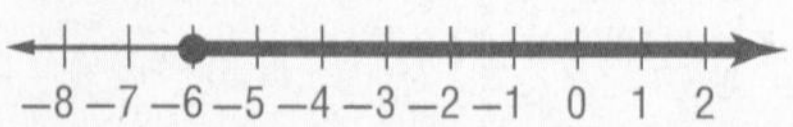

40. $r > 55$

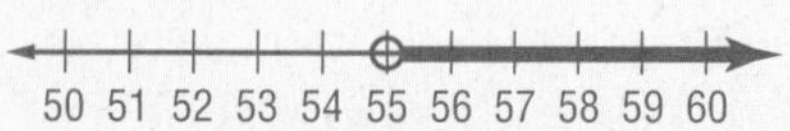

41. $x \leq -\frac{2}{9}$

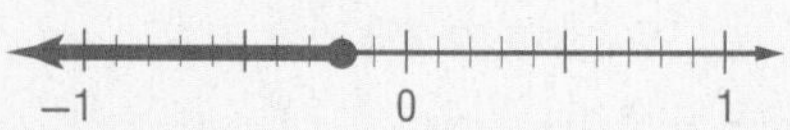

42. $p > -2$

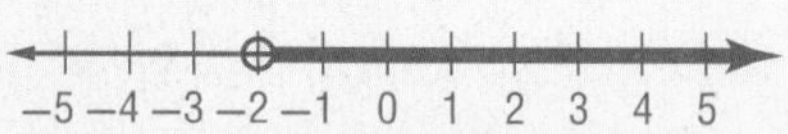

44. $\left\{m \,\middle|\, m < \frac{3}{2} \text{ or } m > 3\right\}$

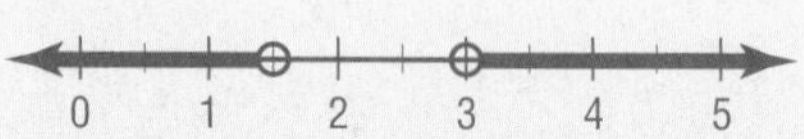

45. $\{x \mid -2 < x < 4\}$

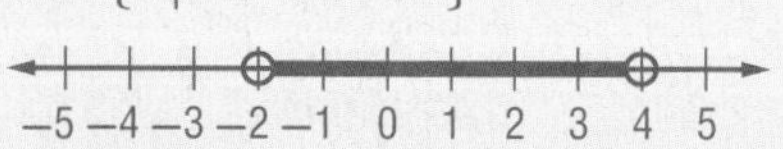

46. $\left\{y \,\middle|\, y \leq -\frac{1}{2} \text{ or } y > 3\right\}$

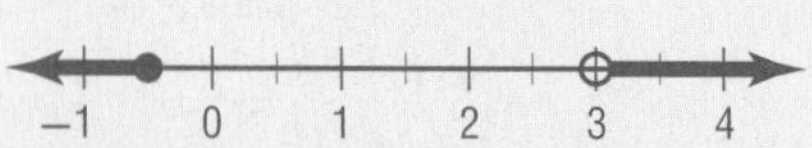

47. $\left\{m \,\middle|\, \frac{13}{5} \leq m < \frac{24}{5}\right\}$

48. $\{a \mid -13 < a < 13\}$

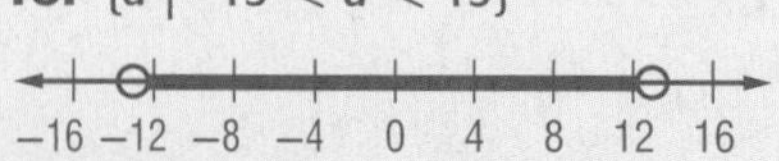

49. $\{p \mid -5 \leq p \leq 33\}$

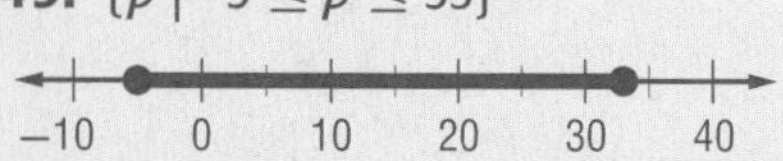

50. $\left\{k \,\middle|\, -\frac{7}{3} < k < \frac{8}{3}\right\}$

51. $\varnothing$

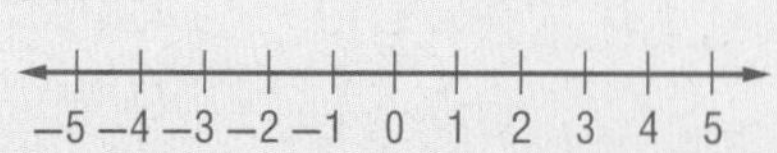

52. $\left\{q \,\middle|\, q \leq -\frac{13}{4} \text{ or } q \geq 2\right\}$

CHAPTER 1 Study Guide and Review

1-5 Solving Inequalities (pp. 34–39)

912.A.3.4

Solve each inequality. Then graph the solution set on a number line.

39. $-4a \leq 24$ **39–42. See margin.**

40. $\frac{r}{5} - 8 > 3$

41. $4 - 7x \geq 2(x + 3)$

42. $-p - 13 < 3(5 + 4p) - 2$

43. MONEY Ms. Hawkins is taking her science class on a field trip to a museum. She has $572 to spend on the trip. There are 52 students that will go to the museum. The museum charges $5 per student, and Ms. Hawkins gets in for free. If the students will have slices of pizza for lunch that cost $2 each, how many slices can each student have? **3 or fewer slices each**

EXAMPLE 8

Solve $2m - 7 < -11$. Graph the solution set on a number line.

$2m - 7 < -11$	**Original inequality**
$2m < -4$	**Add 7 to each side.**
$m < -2$	**Divide each side by 2.**

The solution set is $\{m \mid m < -2\}$.

The graph of the solution set is shown below.

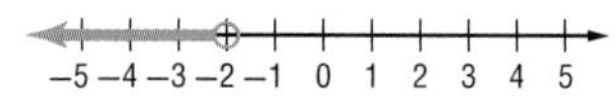

1-6 Solving Compound and Absolute Value Inequalities (pp. 41–48)

912.A.3.4, 912.A.3.6

Solve each inequality. Graph the solution set on a number line. **44–52. See margin.**

44. $2m + 4 < 7$ or $3m + 5 > 14$

45. $-5 < 4x + 3 < 19$

46. $6y - 1 > 17$ or $8y - 6 \leq -10$

47. $-2 \leq 5(m - 3) < 9$

48. $|a| + 2 < 15$

49. $|p - 14| \leq 19$

50. $|6k - 1| < 15$

51. $|2r + 7| < -1$

52. $\frac{1}{3}|8q + 5| \geq 7$

53. MONEY Cara is making a beaded necklace for a gift. She wants to spend between $20 and $30 on the necklace. The bead store charges $2.50 for large beads and $1.25 for small beads. If she buys 3 large beads, how many small beads can she buy to stay within her budget? Write and solve a compound inequality to describe the range of possible beads.
$20 \leq 2.50(3) + 1.25b \leq 30$; $10 \leq b \leq 18$

EXAMPLE 9

Solve each inequality. Graph the solution set on a number line.

a. $-14 \leq 3x - 8 < 16$

$-14 \leq 3x - 8 < 16$	**Original inequality**
$-6 \leq 3x < 24$	**Add 8 to each part.**
$-2 \leq x < 8$	**Divide each part by 3.**

The solution set is $\{x \mid -2 \leq x < 8\}$.

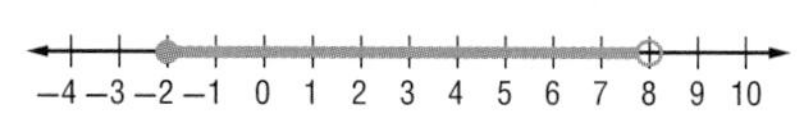

b. $|3a - 5| > 13$

$|3a - 5| > 13$ is equivalent to $3a - 5 > 13$ or $3a - 5 < -13$.

$3a - 5 > 13$	or	$3a - 5 < -13$	
$3a > 18$		$3a < -8$	**Subtract.**
$a > 6$		$a < -\frac{8}{3}$	**Divide.**

The solution set is $\left\{a \,\middle|\, a > 6 \text{ or } a < -\frac{8}{3}\right\}$.

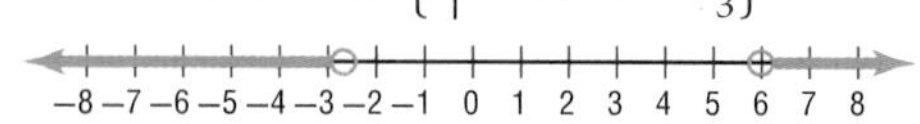

FL Math Online > glencoe.com
Chapter Test

1. Evaluate $x + y^2(2 + x)$ if $x = 3$ and $y = -1$. **8**

2. Simplify $-4(3a + b) - 2(a - 5b)$. $-14a + 6b$

3. NGSSS PRACTICE If $3m + 5 = 23$, what is the value of $2m - 3$? **B**

A. 105

B. 9

C. $\frac{47}{3}$

D. 6

4. Solve $r = \frac{1}{2}m^2p$ for p. $p = \frac{2r}{m^2}$

Write an algebraic expression to represent each verbal expression.

5. twice the difference of a number and 11 $2(n - 11)$

6. the product of the square of a number and 5 $5n^2$

7. Evaluate $2|3y - 8| + y$ if $y = 2.5$. **3.5**

8. Solve $-2b > \frac{18 - b}{5}$. Graph the solution set on a number line. **See margin.**

9. **MONEY** Carson has $35 to spend at the water park. The admission price is $25 and each soda is $2.50. Write an inequality to show how many sodas he can buy. $35 \geq 25 + 2.50s$

10. Solve $r - 3 < -5$ or $4r + 1 > 15$. Graph the solution set. **See margin.**

11. Solve $|p - 4| \leq 11$. Graph the solution set on a number line. **See margin.**

12. NGSSS PRACTICE Which graph represents the solution set for $4 < 6t + 1 \leq 43$? **F**

F. 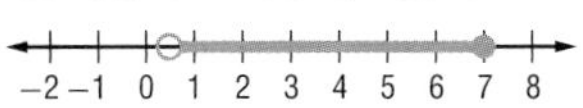

G. 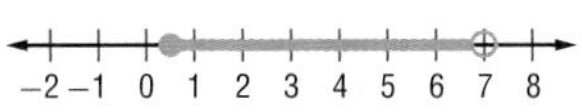

H. 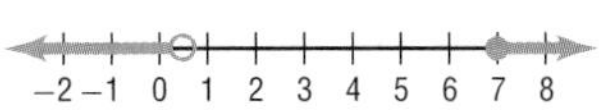

I. 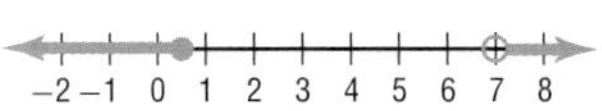

13. **MONEY** Sofia is buying new skis. She finds that the average price of skis is $500 but the actual price could differ from the average by as much as $250. Write and solve an absolute value inequality to describe this situation. $|p - 500| \leq 250$; $250 \leq p \leq 750$

14. **GARDENING** Andy is making 3 trapezoidal garden boxes for his backyard. Each trapezoid will be the size of the trapezoid below. He will place stone blocks around the borders of the boxes. How many feet of stones will Andy need? **102 ft**

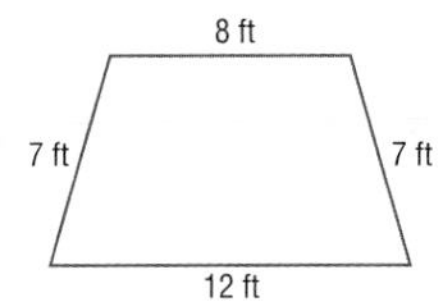

Solve each equation.

15. $|x + 4| = 3$ $\{-7, -1\}$

16. $|3m + 2| = 1$ $\left\{-1, -\frac{1}{3}\right\}$

17. $|3a + 2| = -4$ $\varnothing$

18. $|2t + 5| - 7 = 4$ $\{-8, 3\}$

19. $|5n - 2| - 6 = -3$ $\left\{-\frac{1}{5}, 1\right\}$

20. $|p + 6| + 9 = 8$ $\varnothing$

21. **GEOMETRY** The volume of a cylinder is given by the formula $V = \pi r^2 h$. What is the volume of the cylinder below? 1017.88 cm^3

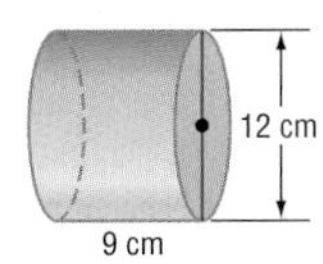

22. Solve $-3b - 5 \geq -6b - 13$. Graph the solution set on a number line. **See margin.**

23. Evaluate $\frac{3(x + y)}{4xy^2}$ if $x = \frac{2}{3}$ and $y = -2$. $-\frac{3}{8}$

24. Name the set(s) of numbers to which $-\frac{1}{3}$ belongs. **Q, R**

25. **MONEY** The costs for making necklaces at two craft stores are shown in the table. For what quantity of beads does The Accessory Store have a better deal? Use the inequality $15 + 3.25b < 20 + 2.50b$.

Shop	Cost per Chain	Cost per Bead
The Accessory Store	$15	$3.25
Finishing Touch	$20	$2.50

When you buy 6 or fewer beads, The Accessory Store is a better deal.

CHAPTER 1 Practice Test

ExamView Assessment Suite Customize and create multiple versions of your chapter test and their answer keys. All of the questions from the leveled chapter tests in the *Chapter 1 Resource Masters* are also available on ExamView® Assessment Suite.

Additional Answers

8. $b < -2$

10. $\left\{r \,\middle|\, r < -2 \text{ or } r > \frac{7}{2}\right\}$

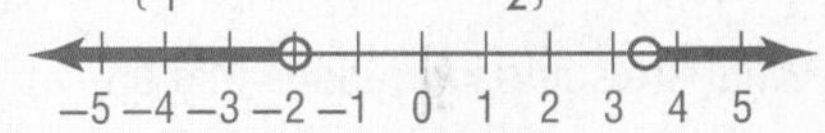

11. $\{p \mid -7 \leq p \leq 15\}$

22. $b \geq -\frac{8}{3}$

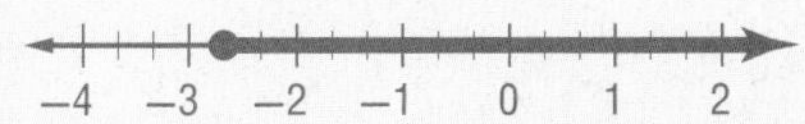

Intervention Planner

Tier 1 On Level	Tier 2 Strategic Intervention approaching grade level	Tier 3 Intensive Intervention 2 or more grades below level
If students miss about 25% of the exercises or less,	**If** students miss about 50% of the exercises,	**If** students miss about 75% of the exercises,
Then choose a resource:	**Then** choose a resource:	**Then** use *Math Triumphs, Alg. 2*, Ch. 1 and 2
SE Lessons 1-1, 1-2, 1-3, 1-4, 1-5, and 1-6	**CRM** Study Guide and Intervention, Chapter 1, pp. 5, 11, 17, 24, 31, 37	
CRM Skills Practice, pp. 7, 13, 19, 26, 33, and 39		
TE Chapter Project, p. 2		
FL Math Online > Self-Check Quiz	FL Math Online > Extra Examples, Personal Tutor, Homework Help	FL Math Online > Extra Examples, Personal Tutor, Homework Help, Review Vocabulary

1 FOCUS

Objective Use the strategy of eliminating unreasonable answers to solve standardized test problems.

2 TEACH

Scaffolding Questions

Ask:

- Have you ever noticed that some answer choices are clearly incorrect? Answers will vary.
- What are some indications that an answer choice is not the correct answer? Answers will vary. Sample answer: the wrong power is used, the wrong equality or inequality sign is used.

CHAPTER 1 Preparing for Standardized Tests

Eliminate Unreasonable Answers

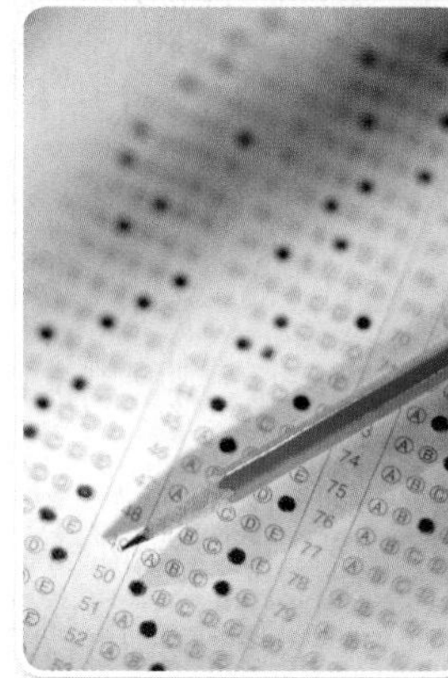

You can eliminate unreasonable answers to help you find the correct answer when solving multiple-choice test items.

Strategies for Eliminating Unreasonable Answers

Step 1

Read the problem statement carefully to determine exactly what you are being asked to find.

Ask yourself:

- What am I being asked to solve?
- In what format (that is, fraction, number, decimal, percent, type of graph) will the correct answer be?
- What units (if any) will the correct answer have?

Step 2

Carefully look over each possible answer choice and evaluate for reasonableness.

- Identify any answer choices that are clearly incorrect and eliminate them.
- Eliminate any answer choices that are not in the proper format.
- Eliminate any answer choices that do not have the correct units.

Step 3

Solve the problem and choose the correct answer from those remaining. Check your answer.

NGSSS PRACTICE EXAMPLE

Read the problem. Identify what you need to know. Then use the information in the problem to solve.

The formula for the area A of a trapezoid with height h and bases b_1 and b_2 is $A = \frac{h}{2}(b_1 + b_2)$. Write an expression to represent the area of the trapezoid at the right.

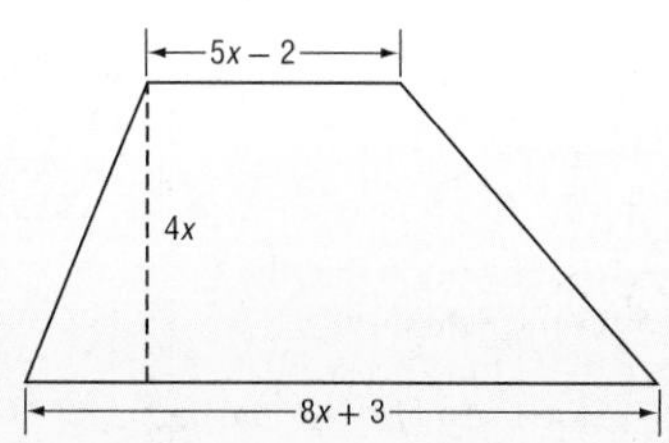

A. $26x^2 + 2x$

B. $52x^2 + 4x$

C. $13x + 1$

D. $28x + 10$

54 Chapter 1 Equations and Inequalities

To compute the area of the trapezoid, you need to multiply half the height, $2x$, by another linear factor in x. So, the correct answer will contain an x^2 term. Since choices C and D are both linear, they can be eliminated. The correct answer is either A or B. Multiply to find the expression for the area.

$$A = \frac{h}{2}(b_1 + b_2)$$
$$= \frac{4x}{2}(8x + 3 + 5x - 2)$$
$$= 2x(13x + 1)$$
$$= 26x^2 + 2x$$

The correct answer is A.

Exercises

Read each problem. Eliminate any unreasonable answers. Then use the information in the problem to solve.

1. The graph below shows the solution to which inequality? C

A. $8x - 9 \leq 5x - 3$

B. $8x - 9 < 5x - 3$

C. $8x - 9 \geq 5x - 3$

D. $8x - 9 > 5x - 3$

2. Einstein's theory of relativity relates the energy E of an object to its mass m and the speed of light c. This relationship can be represented by the formula $E = mc^2$. Solve the formula for m. G

F. $m = \frac{c^2}{E}$ **H.** $m = \frac{c}{E^2}$

G. $m = \frac{E}{c^2}$ **I.** $m = \frac{E^2}{c}$

3. A rectangle has a width of 8 inches and a perimeter of 30 inches. What is the perimeter, in inches, of a similar rectangle with a width of 12 inches? B

A. 40 **C.** 48

B. 45 **D.** 360

4. The rectangular prism below has a volume of 82 cubic inches. What will the volume be if the length, width, and height of the prism are all doubled? I

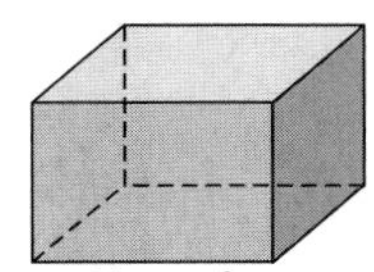

$V = 82$ in^3

F. 41 in^3

G. 164 in^3

H. 482 in^3

I. 656 in^3

5. Evaluate $a + (b + 1)^2$ if $a = 3$ and $b = 2$. C

A. −6

B. −1

C. 12

D. 15

6. At a veterinarian's office, 2 cats and 4 dogs are seen in a random order. What is the probability that the 2 cats are seen in a row? F

F. $\frac{1}{3}$ **H.** $\frac{1}{2}$

G. $\frac{2}{3}$ **I.** $\frac{3}{5}$

Additional Example

The formula for the volume V of a rectangular prism with length ℓ, width w, and height h is $V = \ell wh$. Write an expression to represent the volume of the rectangular prism below. B

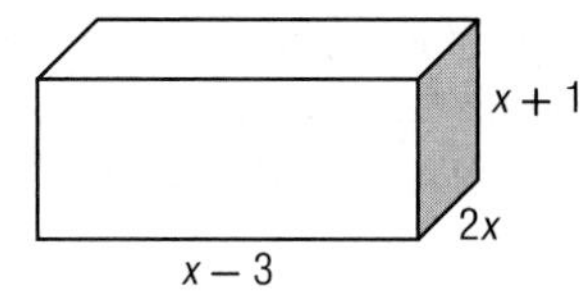

A $4x - 2$

B $2x^3 - 4x^2 - 6x$

C $2x^2 - 4x - 6$

D $2x^3 - 6x^2 - 4x$

3 ASSESS

Use Exercises 1–6 to assess students' understanding.

Chapter 1 Preparing for Standardized Tests 55

Diagnose Student Errors

Survey student responses for each item. Class trends may indicate common errors and misconceptions.

1. A. did not include the denominator
B. correct
C. did not multiply before adding
D. guess

3. F. correct
G. multiplied by 3 instead of $\frac{1}{3}$.
H. did not square *r*
I. squared *h* instead of *r*

5. A. this property says $x = x$
B. guess
C. correct
D. this property says if $x = y$ and $y = z$, then $x = z$.

7. F. used the wrong inequality
G. correct
H. guess
I. reversed the placement of 0.2 and 81.5

8. A. wrote 2 more than a quotient of a number and 5
B. wrote 5 more than the product of a number and 2
C. correct
D. wrote 5 more than a quotient of a number and 2

11. F. identified a set in which –25 does belong
G. identified a set in which –25 does belong
H. identified a set in which –25 does belong
I. correct

13. A. correct
B. simplified the inequality incorrectly
C. reversed the inequality sign
D. simplified the inequality incorrectly

Read each question. Then fill in the correct answer on the answer document provided by your teacher or on a sheet of paper.

1. Evaluate $\frac{m^2 + 2mn}{n^2 - 1}$ if $m = -3$ and $n = 2$. **B**

A. -3

B. -1

C. 2

D. 4

2. **SHORT RESPONSE** Use the absolute value equation below to answer each question.

$$|x - 3| - 2 = 0$$

a. How many solutions are there of the absolute value equation? **2**

b. Solve the equation. **$x = 1, 5$**

3. The volume of a cone with height *h* and radius *r* can be found by multiplying one-third π by the product of the height and the square of the radius. Which equation represents the volume of a cone? **F**

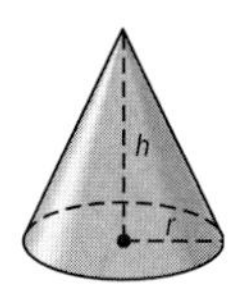

F. $V = \frac{1}{3}\pi r^2 h$

G. $V = 3\pi r^2 h$

H. $V = \frac{1}{3}\pi rh$

I. $V = \frac{1}{3}\pi rh^2$

Test-TakingTip

Question 1 Substitute –3 for *m* and 2 for *n* in the expression. Then use the order of operations to evaluate the expression.

4. **EXTENDED RESPONSE** The table at the right shows Ricardo's scores on the first 5 math quizzes this quarter. Each quiz is worth 100 points. There will be 1 more quiz this quarter.

Quiz	Score
1	86
2	79
3	80
4	85
5	77

a. In order to receive a B, Ricardo must have a quiz average of 82 or better. Write an inequality that can be solved to find the minimum score he must earn on Quiz 6. **See margin.**

b. Solve the inequality you wrote in part **a**. **$n \geq 85$**

c. What does the solution mean? **Ricardo must score at least an 85 on his last quiz to earn a B.**

5. Which property of equality is illustrated by the equation below? **C**

$$a + 2 = 4 \rightarrow 4 = a + 2$$

A. Reflexive

B. Substitution

C. Symmetric

D. Transitive

6. **GRIDDED RESPONSE** Cameron uses a laser range finder to determine distances on the golf course. Her range finder is accurate to within 0.5 yard. If Cameron measures the distance from the tee to the flag on a par 3 to be 136 yards, what is the minimum number of yards that the distance could actually be? **135.5**

7. Suppose a thermometer is accurate to within plus or minus 0.2°F. If the thermometer reads 81.5°F, which absolute value inequality represents the actual temperature *T*? **G**

F. $|T - 81.5| < 0.2$

G. $|T - 81.5| \leq 0.2$

H. $|T - 0.2| < 81.5$

I. $|T - 0.2| \leq 81.5$

8. Write an algebraic expression to represent the verbal expression below. **C**

two more than the product of a number and 5

A. $\frac{n}{5} + 2$

B. $2n + 5$

C. $5n + 2$

D. $\frac{n}{2} + 5$

9. **SHORT RESPONSE** While grilling steaks, Washington likes to keep the grill temperature at 425°, plus or minus 15°.

a. Write an absolute value inequality to model this situation. Let t represent the temperature of the grill. $|t - 425| \leq 15$

b. Within what range of temperatures does Washington like the grill to be when he cooks his steaks? $410 \leq t \leq 440$

10. **SHORT RESPONSE** Simplify the expression below. Show your work. $-18a + 19b$

$-4(3a - b) + 3(-2a + 5b)$

11. To which set of numbers does -25 *not* belong? **I**

F. integers

G. rationals

H. reals

I. wholes

12. **GRIDDED RESPONSE** The table below shows the fill amounts and tolerances of different size soft drinks at a fountain drink vending machine. What is the maximum acceptable fill amount, in fluid ounces, for a medium drink? **21.35**

Size	Amount (fl. oz)	Tolerance (fl. oz)
small	16	0.25
medium	21	0.35
large	32	0.4

13. Which number line shows the solution of the inequality $2n - 3 \geq 5n - 6$? **A**

A. 

B. 

C. 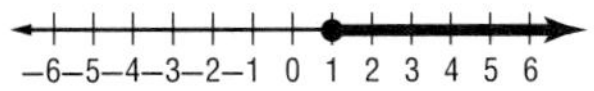

D. 

14. **EXTENDED RESPONSE** Cindy is evaluating the expression $\frac{-5m - 3n}{-2p + r}$ for $m = 1$, $n = -4$, $p = -3$, and $r = -2$. Her work is shown below.

$$\frac{-5m - 3n}{-2p + r} = \frac{-5(1) - 3(-4)}{-2(-3) + (-2)}$$
$$= \frac{-5 - 12}{6 - 2} = -\frac{17}{4} = -4\frac{1}{4}$$

a. What error did Cindy make in her computation? **See margin.**

b. What is the correct answer? $1\frac{3}{4}$

Need Extra Help?

If you missed Question...	1	2	3	4	5	6	7	8	9	10	11	12	13	14
Go to Lesson or Page...	1-1	1-4	1-3	1-5	1-3	1-4	1-6	1-3	1-6	1-2	1-2	1-6	1-5	1-1
For help with NGSSS...	912.A.3.1	912.A.3.6	912.G.7.5	912.A.3.1	912.A.3.2	912.A.3.6	912.A.3.6	912.A.3.1	912.A.3.6	912.A.3.1	912.A.3.1	912.A.3.4	912.A.3.4	912.A.3.1

Formative Assessment

You can use these two pages to benchmark student progress.

CRM Standardized Test Practice, pp. 62–64

ExamView Assessment Suite Create practice worksheets or tests that align to your state's standards as well as TIMSS and NAEP tests.

Homework Option

Get Ready for Chapter 2 Assign students the exercises on p. 59 as homework to assess whether they possess the prerequisite skills needed for the next chapter.

Additional Answers

4a. $\frac{86 + 79 + 80 + 85 + 77 + n}{6} \geq 82$

14a. Sample answer: she did not simplify the numerator of the expression correctly. She has a sign error.

Pages 14–16, Lesson 1-2

36b. $5\left(2\frac{1}{2}\right) + 3\left(1\frac{1}{4}\right)$

$= 5\left(2 + \frac{1}{2}\right) + 3\left(1 + \frac{1}{4}\right)$	Definition of a mixed number
$= 5(2) + 5\left(\frac{1}{2}\right) + 3(1) + 3\left(\frac{1}{4}\right)$	Distributive Property
$= 10 + \frac{5}{2} + 3 + \frac{3}{4}$	Multiply.
$= 10 + 3 + \frac{5}{2} + \frac{3}{4}$	Commutative Property (+)
$= 13 + \frac{5}{2} + \frac{3}{4}$	Add.
$= 13 + \left(\frac{5}{2} + \frac{3}{4}\right)$	Associative Property (+)
$= 13 + 3\frac{1}{4}$ or $16\frac{1}{4}$	Add.

51a. Sample answer:

irrational	rational	integer	whole	natural
$-\sqrt{6}$, π	3, $\frac{-15}{3}$, 4.1, 0, $\frac{3}{8}$, $\sqrt{36}$	3, $\frac{-15}{3}$, 0, $\sqrt{36}$	3, 0, $\sqrt{36}$	3, $\sqrt{36}$

51c.

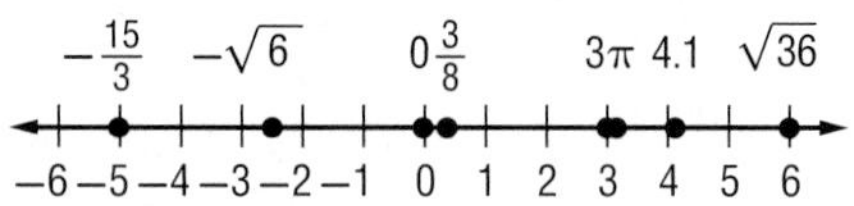

Page 31, Lesson 1-4

46. The 4 potential solutions are:
1. $(2x - 1) \geq 0$ and $(5 - x) \geq 0$
2. $(2x - 1) \geq 0$ and $(5 - x) < 0$
3. $(2x - 1) < 0$ and $(5 - x) \geq 0$
4. $(2x - 1) < 0$ and $(5 - x) < 0$

The resulting equations corresponding to these cases are:
1. $2x - 1 + 3 = 5 - x : x = 1$
2. $2x - 1 + 3 = x - 5 : x = -7$
3. $1 - 2x + 3 = 5 - x : x = -1$
4. $1 - 2x + 3 = x - 5 : x = 3$

The solutions from case 1 and case 3 work. The others are extraneous. The solution set is {–1, 1}.

51. Sample answer: First, isolate the absolute value symbol by subtracting each side by *c*, and then dividing each side by *a*. You then have $|x - b|$ equals a mathematical expression. Take away the absolute value symbol, and form two new equations by setting $x - b$ equal to both the positive and negative values of the expression. Solve each equation for *x*. Then substitute each solution into the original equation, and confirm whether they are correct.

Page 38, Lesson 1-5

47. Using the Triangle Inequality Theorem, we know that the sum of the lengths of any 2 sides of a triangle must be greater than the length of the remaining side. This generates 3 inequalities to examine.

$3x + 4 + 2x + 5 > 4x$
$x > -9$

$2x + 5 + 4x > 3x + 4$
$x > -\frac{1}{3}$

$3x + 4 + 4x > 2x + 5$
$x > 0.2$

In order for all 3 conditions to be true, *x* must be greater than 0.2.

48. Sample answer: $4x + 5 > 4(x + 1)$; This has a solution set of all real numbers because it simplifies to $4x + 5 > 4x + 4$ or $5 > 4$. This indicates that for any real value of *x* the inequality is equivalent to $1 > 0$, that is the left side will always be 1 greater than the right side.

49. Sample answer: When one number is greater than another number, it is either more positive or less negative than that number. When these numbers are multiplied by a negative value, their roles are reversed. That is, the number that was more positive is now more negative than the other number. Thus, it is now *less than* that number and the inequality symbol needs to be reversed.

Page 42, Lesson 1-6, Guided Practice

1A. $\{x \mid -5 \leq x \leq 6\}$

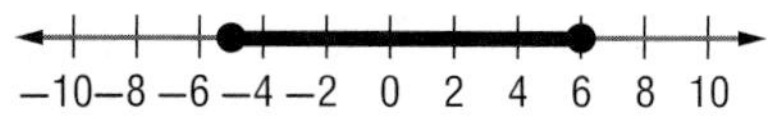

1B. $\{z \mid -4 < z \leq -1\}$

2A. $\{j \mid j \geq 3 \text{ or } j \leq -7\}$

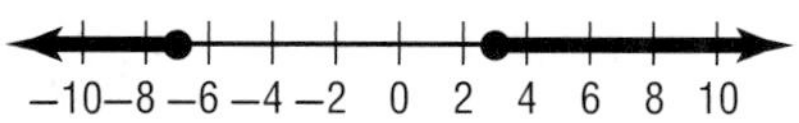

2B. $\{g \mid g > -5 \text{ or } g < -9.5\}$

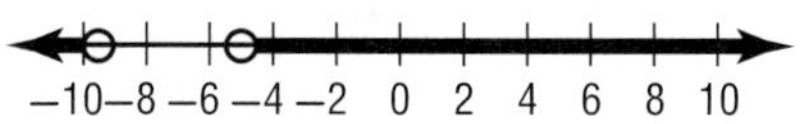

Pages 45–46, Lesson 1–6

12. $\{v \mid 6 < v < 10\}$

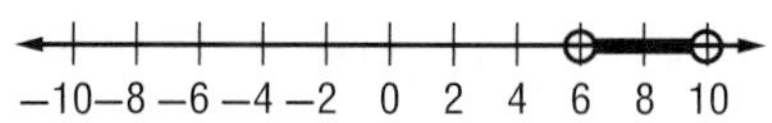

13. $\{d \mid -1 \leq d \leq 0.5\}$

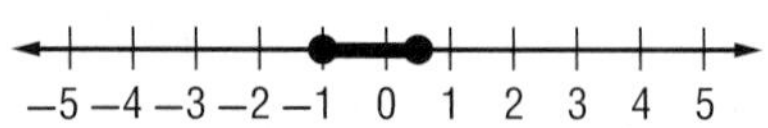

14. $\left\{r \,\middle|\, r < -\frac{9}{4} \text{ or } r > 3\right\}$

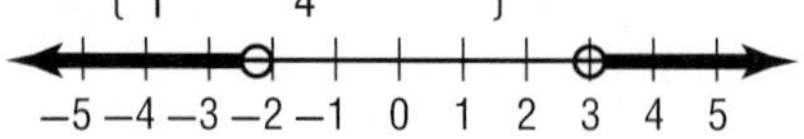

15. $\{y \mid y < -4 \text{ or } y > 7\}$

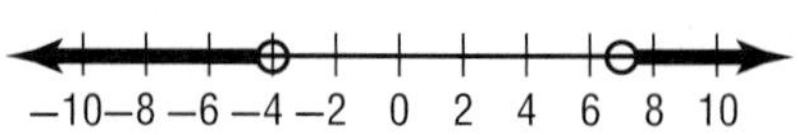

16. $\{h \mid -2 < h < 2\}$

17. $\{k \mid -4 > k \text{ or } k > 4\}$

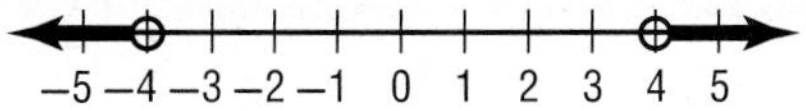

18. $\left\{x \,\middle|\, x > \frac{14}{3} \text{ or } x < -2\right\}$

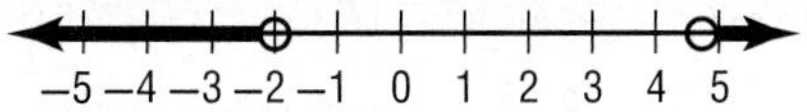

19. $\left\{t \,\middle|\, -\frac{7}{8} \leq t \leq \frac{1}{8}\right\}$

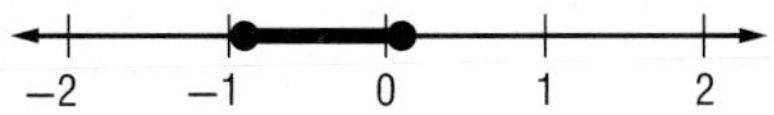

20. $\left\{n \,\middle|\, -1 < n < \frac{1}{3}\right\}$

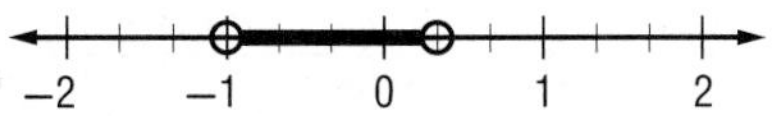

21. $\left\{j \,\middle|\, j \geq \frac{8}{5} \text{ or } j \leq -\frac{16}{5}\right\}$

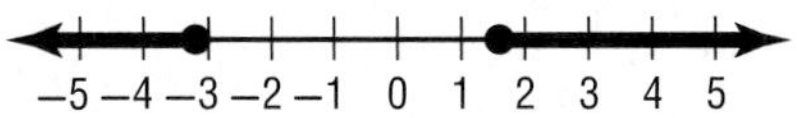

33. $\{k \mid 2 < k < 4\}$

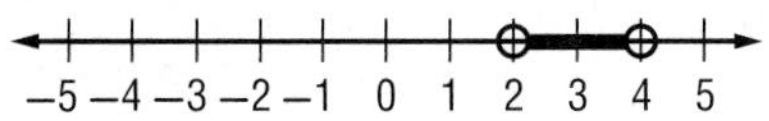

34. $\{m \mid m > -5 \text{ or } m < -12\}$

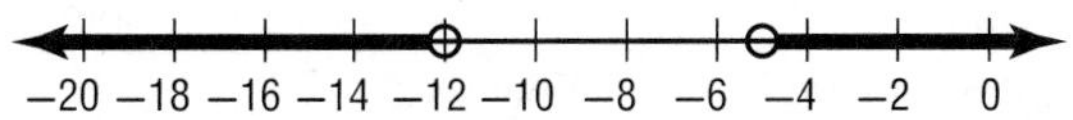

35. $\{h \mid h < -15 \text{ or } h > 15\}$

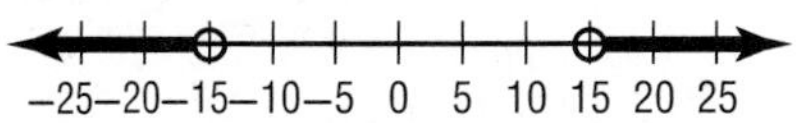

36. $\varnothing$

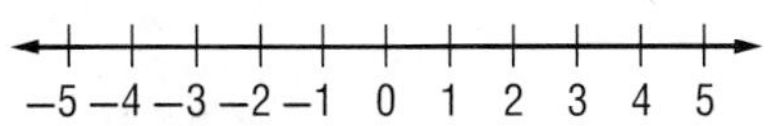

37. $\{z \mid z < -1 \text{ or } z > 5\}$

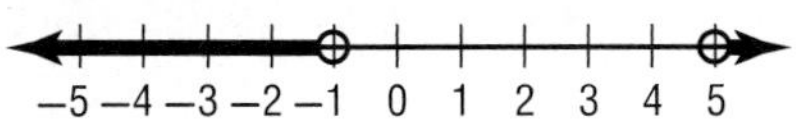

38. $\left\{p \,\middle|\, -\frac{9}{4} < p < \frac{5}{4}\right\}$

39. $\left\{f \,\middle|\, f > \frac{26}{5} \text{ or } f < -\frac{22}{5}\right\}$

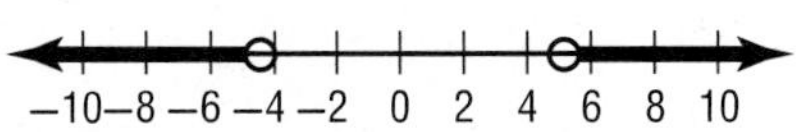

40. $\left\{w \,\middle|\, w \leq -\frac{23}{2} \text{ or } w \geq \frac{7}{2}\right\}$

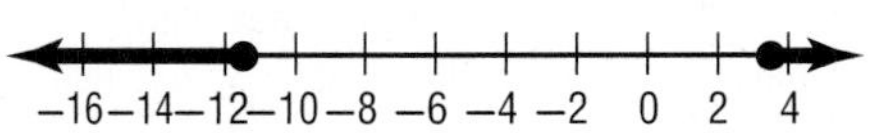

CHAPTER 2

Chapter Planner

Diagnostic Assessment
Quick Check, p. 59

	Lesson 2-1 Pacing: 1 day	Extend 2-1 Pacing: 0.5 day	Lesson 2-2 Pacing: 1 day
Title	**Relations and Functions**	**Algebra Lab: Discrete and Continuous Functions in the Real World**	**Linear Relations and Functions**
Objectives	• Analyze relations and functions. • Use equations of relations and functions.	• Use discrete and continuous functions to solve real-world problems.	• Identify linear relations and functions. • Write linear equations in standard form.
Key Vocabulary	one-to-one function onto function discrete relation continuous relation vertical line test independent variable dependent variable function notation		linear relations linear equation linear function standard form *y*-intercept *x*-intercept
NGSSS	MA.912.A.10.3		MA.912.A.2.6, MA.912.A.10.3
Multiple Representations	p. 66		p. 73
Lesson Resources	**Chapter 2 Resource Masters** • Study Guide and Intervention, pp. 5–6 AL OL ELL • Skills Practice, p. 7 AL OL ELL • Practice, p. 8 AL OL BL ELL • Word Problem Practice, p. 9 AL OL BL ELL • Enrichment, p. 10 OL BL **Transparencies** • 5-Minute Check Transparency 2-1 AL OL BL ELL **Additional Print Resources** • Study Notebook AL OL BL ELL	**Additional Print Resources** • Teaching Algebra with Manipulatives, p. 184 AL OL ELL	**Chapter 2 Resource Masters** • Study Guide and Intervention, pp. 11–12 AL OL ELL • Skills Practice, p. 13 AL OL ELL • Practice, p. 14 AL OL BL ELL • Word Problem Practice, p. 15 AL OL BL ELL • Enrichment, p. 16 OL BL • Quiz 1, p. 59 AL OL BL ELL **Transparencies** • 5-Minute Check Transparency 2-2 AL OL BL ELL **Additional Print Resources** • Study Notebook AL OL BL ELL
Technology for Every Lesson	FL Math Online **glencoe.com** • Extra Examples • Self-Check Quizzes • Personal Tutor • Homework Help	**CD/DVD Resources** IWB INTERACTIVE WHITEBOARD READY IWB StudentWorks Plus IWB Interactive Classroom IWB Diagnostic and Assessment Planner	• TeacherWorks Plus • eSolutions Manual Plus • ExamView Assessment Suite
Get Animated			
Differentiated Instruction	pp. 64, 67		pp. 71, 74

KEY: AL Approaching Level OL On Level BL Beyond Level ELL English Learners

Suggested Pacing			
Time Periods	Instruction	Review & Assessment	Total
45-minute	11	2	13
90-minute	7	1	8

Linear Relations and Functions

Extend 2-2 Pacing: 0.5 day	Lesson 2-3 Pacing: 1 day	Lesson 2-4 Pacing: 1 day	Extend 2-4 Pacing: 0.5 day
Algebra Lab: Roots of Equations and Zeros of Functions	**Rate of Change and Slope**	**Writing Linear Equations**	**Graphing Technology Lab: Direct Variation**
• Distinguish among roots, solutions, and zeros.	• Find rate of change. • Determine the slope of a line.	• Write an equation of a line given the slope and a point on the line. • Write an equation of a line parallel or perpendicular to a given line.	• Use functions to model direct variation.
	rate of change slope	slope-intercept form point-slope form parallel perpendicular	
MA.912.A.4.8	MA.912.A.10.3	MA.912.A.3.10	MA.912.A.2.12
	p. 81		
Additional Print Resources • Teaching Algebra with Manipulatives, p. 185 AL OL ELL	**Chapter 2 Resource Masters** • Study Guide and Intervention, pp. 17–18 AL OL ELL • Skills Practice, p. 19 AL OL ELL • Practice, p. 20 AL OL BL ELL • Word Problem Practice, p. 21 AL OL BL ELL • Enrichment, p. 22 OL BL **Transparencies** • 5-Minute Check Transparency 2-3 AL OL BL ELL **Additional Print Resources** • Study Notebook AL OL BL ELL	**Chapter 2 Resource Masters** • Study Guide and Intervention, pp. 23–24 AL OL ELL • Skills Practice, p. 25 AL OL ELL • Practice, p. 26 AL OL BL ELL • Word Problem Practice, p. 27 AL OL BL ELL • Enrichment, p. 28 OL BL • Spreadsheet Activity, p. 29 OL • Quiz 2, p. 59 AL OL BL ELL **Transparencies** • 5-Minute Check Transparency 2-4 AL OL BL ELL **Additional Print Resources** • Study Notebook AL OL BL ELL	**Materials** • TI-84 Plus or other graphing calculator

FL Math Online glencoe.com
- Extra Examples
- Self-Check Quizzes
- Personal Tutor
- Homework Help

CD/DVD Resources IWB INTERACTIVE WHITEBOARD READY
- IWB StudentWorks Plus
- IWB Interactive Classroom
- IWB Diagnostic and Assessment Planner
- TeacherWorks Plus
- eSolutions Manual Plus
- ExamView Assessment Suite

		Interactive Lab	
	pp. 78, 82	pp. 84, 89	

Formative Assessment
Mid-Chapter Quiz, p. 91

Chapter Planner

	Lesson 2-5 Pacing: 1 day	Extend 2-5 Pacing: 1 day	Lesson 2-6 Pacing: 1 day
Title	**Scatter Plots and Lines of Regression**	**Algebra Lab: Median Fit Lines**	**Special Functions**
Objectives	• Use scatter plots and prediction equations. • Model data using lines of regression.	• Find a median-fit line for a data set and then use the line to make a prediction. • Use median fit lines to make predictions.	• Write and graph piecewise-defined functions. • Write and graph step and absolute value functions.
Key Vocabulary	bivariate data scatter plot dot plot positive correlation negative correlation line of fit prediction equation regression line correlation coefficient		piecewise-defined function piecewise-linear function step function greatest integer function absolute value function
NGSSS	MA.912.A.3.11	MA.912.A.3.11	MA.912.A.2.5, MA.912.A.2.9
Multiple Representations			p. 106
Lesson Resources	**Chapter 2 Resource Masters** • Study Guide and Intervention, pp. 30–31 AL OL ELL • Skills Practice, p. 32 AL OL ELL • Practice, p. 33 AL OL BL ELL • Word Problem Practice, p. 34 AL OL BL ELL • Enrichment, p. 35 OL BL **Transparencies** • 5-Minute Check Transparency 2-5 AL OL BL ELL **Additional Print Resources** • Study Notebook AL OL BL ELL	**Materials** • graph paper • ruler **Additional Print Resources** • Teaching Algebra with Manipulatives, p. 186 AL OL ELL	**Chapter 2 Resource Masters** • Study Guide and Intervention, pp. 36–37 AL OL ELL • Skills Practice, p. 38 AL OL ELL • Practice, p. 39 AL OL BL ELL • Word Problem Practice, p. 40 AL OL BL ELL • Enrichment, p. 41 OL BL • Graphing Calculator Activity, p. 42 OL • Quiz 3, p. 60 AL OL BL ELL **Transparencies** • 5-Minute Check Transparency 2-6 AL OL BL ELL **Additional Print Resources** • Study Notebook AL OL BL ELL • Teaching Algebra with Manipulatives, p. 187 AL OL ELL
Technology for Every Lesson	FL Math Online glencoe.com • Extra Examples • Self-Check Quizzes • Personal Tutor • Homework Help	**CD/DVD Resources** IWB INTERACTIVE WHITEBOARD READY IWB StudentWorks Plus IWB Interactive Classroom IWB Diagnostic and Assessment Planner	• TeacherWorks Plus • eSolutions Manual Plus • ExamView Assessment Suite
Get Animated	Interactive Lab		Animation
Differentiated Instruction	pp. 94, 98		pp. 103, 104

KEY: AL Approaching Level OL On Level BL Beyond Level ELL English Learners

Explore 2-7 Pacing: 0.5 day	Lesson 2-7 Pacing: 1 day	Lesson 2-8 Pacing: 1 day
Graphing Technology Lab: Families of Lines	**Parent Functions and Transformations**	**Graphing Linear and Absolute Value Inequalities**
• Use a graphing calculator to determine how changing the parameters *m* and *b* affects the graphs of the functions.	• Identify and use parent functions. • Describe transformations of functions.	• Graph linear inequalities. • Graph absolute value inequalities.
	family of graphs parent graph parent function constant function identity function quadratic function translation reflection line of reflection dilation	linear inequality boundary
MA.912.A.2.6	MA.912.A.2.5, MA.912.A.2.10	MA.912.A.2.6, MA.912.A.2.5
Materials • TI-83/84 Plus or other graphing calculator	**Chapter 2 Resource Masters** • Study Guide and Intervention, pp. 43–44 AL OL ELL • Skills Practice, p. 45 AL OL ELL • Practice, p. 46 AL OL BL ELL • Word Problem Practice, p. 47 AL OL BL ELL • Enrichment, p. 48 OL BL • Graphing Calculator Activity, p. 49 OL **Transparencies** • 5-Minute Check Transparency 2-7 AL OL BL ELL **Additional Print Resources** • Study Notebook AL OL BL ELL	**Chapter 2 Resource Masters** • Study Guide and Intervention, pp. 50–51 AL OL ELL • Skills Practice, p. 52 AL OL ELL • Practice, p. 53 AL OL BL ELL • Word Problem Practice, p. 54 AL OL BL ELL • Enrichment, p. 55 OL BL • Quiz 4, p. 60 AL OL BL ELL **Transparencies** • 5-Minute Check Transparency 2-8 AL OL BL ELL **Additional Print Resources** • Study Notebook AL OL BL ELL

FL Math Online glencoe.com
- Extra Examples
- Self-Check Quizzes
- Personal Tutor
- Homework Help

CD/DVD Resources IWB INTERACTIVE WHITEBOARD READY
- IWB StudentWorks Plus
- IWB Interactive Classroom
- IWB Diagnostic and Assessment Planner
- TeacherWorks Plus
- eSolutions Manual Plus
- ExamView Assessment Suite

	pp. 111, 116	p. 121

Summative Assessment
- Study Guide and Review, pp. 122–126
- Practice Test, p. 127

CHAPTER 2

Assessment and Intervention

SE = Student Edition, **TE** = Teacher Edition, **CRM** = Chapter Resource Masters

	Diagnosis	Prescription
Diagnostic Assessment	**Beginning Chapter 2**	
	Get Ready for Chapter 2 **SE,** p. 59	Response to Intervention **TE,** p. 59
	Beginning Every Lesson	
	Then, Now, Why? **SE** 5-Minute Check Transparencies	Chapter 0 **SE,** pp. P1–P19 Concepts and Skills Bank **SE** pp. 994–1007
Formative Assessment	**During/After Every Lesson**	
	Guided Practice **SE,** every example Check Your Understanding **SE** H.O.T. Problems **SE** Spiral Review **SE** Additional Examples **TE** Watch Out! **TE** Step 4, Assess **TE** Chapter 2 Quizzes **CRM,** pp. 59–60 Self-Check Quizzes glencoe.com	**Tier 1 Intervention** Concepts and Skills Bank **SE,** pp. 994–1007 Skills Practice **CRM,** Ch. 1–2 glencoe.com **Tier 2 Intervention** Differentiated Instruction **TE** Study Guide and Intervention Masters **CRM,** Ch. 1–2 **Tier 3 Intervention** *Math Triumphs, Alg. 2,* Ch. 1 and 3
	Mid-Chapter	
	Mid-Chapter Quiz **SE,** p. 91 Mid-Chapter Test **CRM,** p. 61 ExamView Assessment Suite	**Tier 1 Intervention** Concepts and Skills Bank **SE,** pp. 994–1007 Skills Practice **CRM,** Ch. 1–2 glencoe.com **Tier 2 Intervention** Study Guide and Intervention Masters **CRM,** Ch. 1–2 **Tier 3 Intervention** *Math Triumphs, Alg. 2,* Ch. 1 and 3
	Before Chapter Test	
	Chapter Study Guide and Review **SE,** pp. 122–126 Practice Test **SE,** p. 127 Standardized Test Practice **SE,** pp. 128–131 Chapter Test glencoe.com Standardized Test Practice glencoe.com Vocabulary Review glencoe.com ExamView Assessment Suite	**Tier 1 Intervention** Concepts and Skills Bank **SE,** pp. 994–1007 Skills Practice **CRM,** Ch. 1–2 glencoe.com **Tier 2 Intervention** Study Guide and Intervention Masters **CRM,** Ch. 1–2 **Tier 3 Intervention** *Math Triumphs, Alg. 2,* Ch. 1 and 3
Summative Assessment	**After Chapter 2**	
	Multiple-Choice Tests, Forms 1, 2A, 2B **CRM,** pp. 63–68 Free-Response Tests, Forms 2C, 2D, 3 **CRM,** pp. 69–74 Vocabulary Test **CRM,** p. 62 Extended Response Test **CRM,** p. 75 Standardized Test Practice **CRM,** pp. 76–78 ExamView Assessment Suite	Study Guide and Intervention Masters **CRM,** Ch. 1–2 glencoe.com

Differentiated Instruction

Option 1 Reaching All Learners AL OL BL ELL

KINESTHETIC Have students work in pairs to measure the length of their arms from shoulders to finger tips and their heights in centimeters. Record the measurements as an ordered pair (arm length, height) for each student. Use the class data to create a scatter plot and a line of fit, and describe the correlation. Then use a graphing calculator to find an equation for a line of regression.

INTERPERSONAL As a class, create a word wall that contains a list of formulas and the purpose of each formula. As more and more formulas are added, ask questions about the variables such as, "Is *m* always used to represent slope?"

Option 2 Approaching Level AL

Provide each student with a ruler and a copy of a variety of graphs—some that are functions and some that are not. Ask students to draw multiple vertical lines on each graph, trying to intersect the graph in more than one point. Then have students indicate which graphs are graphs of functions.

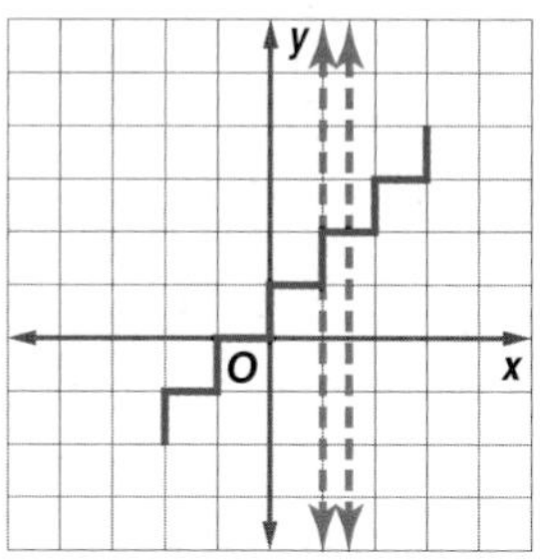

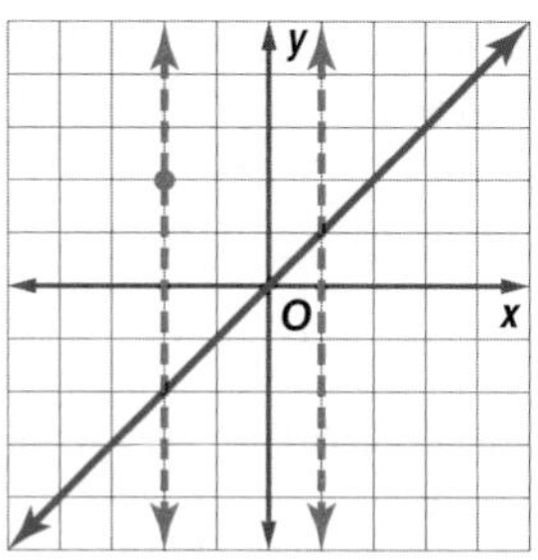

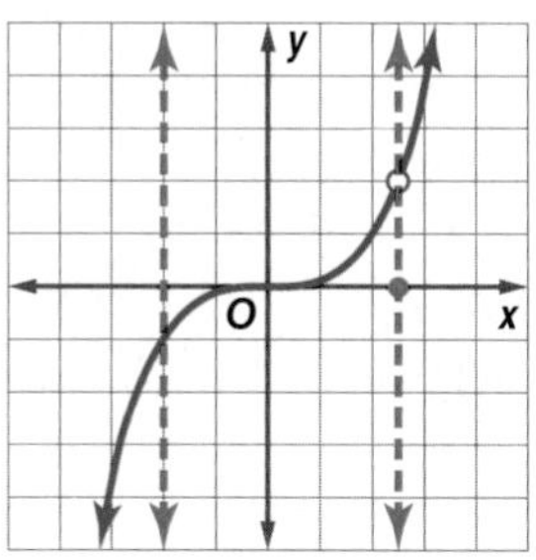

FL Math Online Access Point Activities

Option 3 English Learners ELL

Write the words *function, slope,* and *linear* on the board. For each one, have students suggest other words having similar or related meanings. Discuss when and how each of these words is used in real life versus how it is used in mathematics.

Option 4 Beyond Level BL

Create a set of vocabulary and/or formula cards from this chapter. Then ask the class to play a game of charades. One student draws a card and then must draw or act out what is on the card without uttering a word. The rest of the class tries to figure out the vocabulary word or formula written on the card.

Stretch students' understanding of data trends and linearity by analyzing real-world examples that display each trend. Ask students to create graphs that demonstrate each behavior:

- linear and continuous
- linear and discrete
- positively correlated linear trend
- negatively correlated linear trend
- linear trend based on an average increase or decrease

Focus on Mathematical Content

Vertical Alignment

Before Chapter 2

Related Topics from Algebra 1

- identify domains and ranges for given situations
- determine intercepts of the graphs of linear functions
- determine slopes from graphs, tables, and algebraic representations
- graph and write equations of lines
- use data to determine functional relationships between quantities
- formulate linear inequalities to solve problems and investigate methods for solving them

Chapter 2

- identify the mathematical domains and ranges of functions and determine reasonable domain and range values for continuous and discrete situations
- identify and sketch graphs of parent functions, including linear functions ($f(x) = x$) and absolute value functions ($f(x) = |x|$)
- collect and organize data, make and interpret scatter plots, fit the graph of a function to the data, interpret the results, and proceed to model, predict, and make decisions and critical judgments
- graph linear and absolute value inequalities

After Chapter 2

Preparation for Precalculus

- describe parent functions symbolically and graphically, including $f(x) = |x|$
- determine the domain and range of functions using graphs, tables, and symbols
- use regression to determine the appropriateness of a linear function to model real-life data

Lesson-by-Lesson Preview

2-1 Relations and Functions

Recall that a relation is a set of ordered pairs, and a function is a relation in which each element of the domain is paired with exactly one element of the range. Functions can be *one-to-one, onto,* or *both one-to-one and onto* depending on the way the elements of the domain and range are paired.

Numerical and graphical means are used to compare functions with relations. Mappings are used to show how elements of the domain are paired with elements of the range. A mapping can be used to identify relations that are functions. The vertical line test can distinguish a relation from a function.

Relations and functions in which the domain is a set of individual points are said to be *discrete.* If the domain can be graphed with a line or smooth curve, then it is *continuous.*

2-2 Linear Relations and Functions

A *linear function* is a function whose ordered pairs satisfy a related linear equation. Linear functions can be written in slope-intercept form, $f(x) = mx + b$, where m and b are real numbers.

Linear equations can be written in slope-intercept form, $y = mx + b$, or in standard form, $Ax + By = C$. Since the graph of a linear function or equation is always a straight line, one way to graph a linear function or equation is to connect the coordinates of the x- and y-intercepts.

2-3 Rate of Change and Slope

The slope (or rate of change) of a line is the ratio of the change in the y-coordinates to the corresponding change in the x-coordinates. When two points on the line are known, the slope m of a line is given by the formula $m = \frac{y_2 - y_1}{x_2 - x_1}$, where $x_1 \neq x_2$.

2-4 Writing Linear Equations

When two points or a point and the slope of a line are known, an equation of the line can be found.

- *Slope-intercept form* of a linear equation: $y = mx + b$, m represents the slope of the graph of the equation and b represents the y-intercept.
- *Point-slope form:* $y - y_1 = m(x - x_1)$, m represents the slope of the graph of the equation and (x_1, y_1) represents a point on the line.

If you know the slopes of two lines, you can determine whether they are parallel or perpendicular.

- Two nonvertical lines are parallel if and only if the lines have the same slope. (All vertical lines are parallel.)

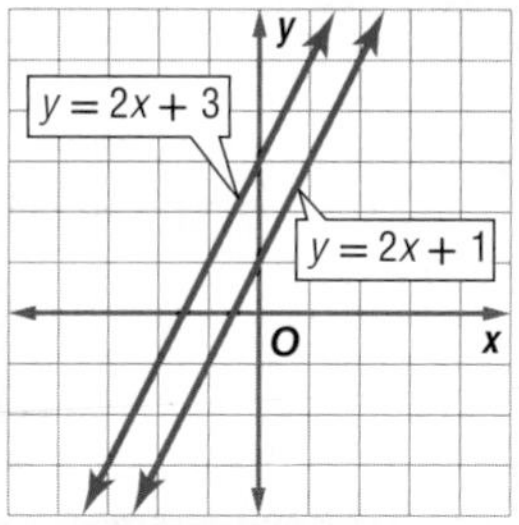

- Two nonvertical lines are perpendicular if and only if the product of their slopes is –1. (All vertical lines are perpendicular to horizontal lines.)

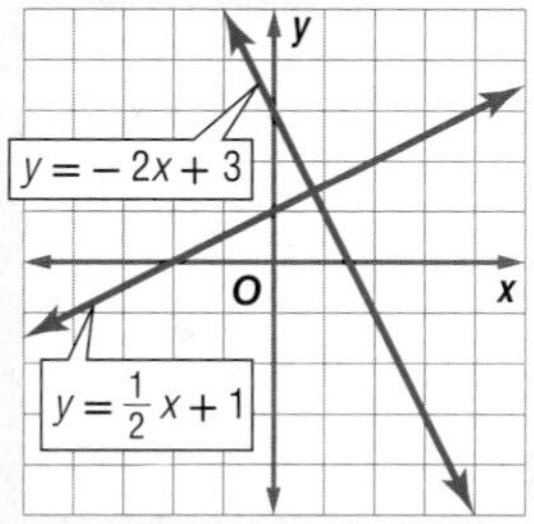

2-5 Scatter Plots and Lines of Regression

When *bivariate data* are graphed as ordered pairs in a coordinate plane, the graph is called a *scatter plot.* If a set of data exhibits a linear trend, an equation of a line of fit can be used to approximate the relation between domain values and range values of the data. This line of fit, also called a prediction equation, can be used to make predictions.

A *regression line,* a line of fit that is more precise than the one found by simply drawing a line that appears to represent the data in the scatter plot, can be determined through complex calculations. This line can be found easily using a graphing calculator.

2-6 Special Functions

This lesson examines several special functions. Special types of linear functions include the following.

- *Piecewise-defined functions* are usually written using two or more algebraic expressions.
- A common *piecewise-linear function*, called a *step function,* consists of a series of line segments that look like steps.
- The graph of an *absolute value function* is shaped like a V and is made up of portions of two lines.

2-7 Parent Functions and Transformations

A family of graphs is a group of graphs that display one or more similar characteristics. The parent graph, which is a graph of the parent function, is the simplest of the graphs in a family. This graph can be *transformed* to create other members in a family of graphs.

- A *translation* moves a figure up, down, left, or right. A constant added to or subtracted from a parent function results in a translation of the graph up or down. If a constant is added to or subtracted from x before evaluating a parent function, the result is a translation right or left.
- A *reflection* flips a figure over a line called the line of reflection. The reflection $-f(x)$ reflects the graph of $f(x)$ across the x-axis. The reflection $f(-x)$ reflects the graph of $f(x)$ across the y-axis.
- A *dilation* shrinks or enlarges a figure proportionally. When the graph of a parent function is multiplied by a nonzero number the result is a graph that is dilated.

2-8 Graphing Linear and Absolute Value Inequalities

The solution set of a linear inequality is the set of all ordered pairs that make the statement true. The graph of a linear inequality can be shown as a shaded region that is formed by a linear boundary that divides the coordinate plane into two regions. The boundary itself may or may not be included in the solution set depending on the particular inequality symbol used in the inequality. If the inequality symbol is $\geq$ or $\leq$, the boundary is included in the solution and a solid line is used in the graph. A dashed line is used when the inequality symbol is $<$ or $>$.

Graphing absolute value inequalities is similar to graphing linear inequalities. First, the inequality is graphed as if it contained an equal sign, using a dashed or solid line depending on the inequality symbol, and then the appropriate region is shaded.

McGraw Hill Professional Development

Targeted professional development has been articulated throughout *Algebra 2.* More quality, customized professional development is available from McGraw-Hill Professional Development. Visit glencoe.com for details on each product.

- **Online Lessons** emphasize the strategies and techniques used to teach Algebra 2. Includes streaming video, interactive pages, and online tools.
- **Video Workshops** allow mentors, coaches, or leadership personnel to facilitate on-site workshops on educational strategies in mathematics and mathematical concepts.
- **MHPD Online** (www.mhpdonline.com) offers online professional development with video clips of instructional strategies, links, student activities, and news and issues in education.
- **Teaching Today** (teachingtoday.glencoe.com) gives secondary teachers practical strategies and materials that inspire excellence and innovation in teaching.

CHAPTER 2 Notes

Chapter Project

Up and Down the Mountain

Students use what they have learned about linear functions and slope to describe the height of a hill or mountain.

- Obtain, or have students obtain, a topographical map of a nearby hill or mountain with which students may be familiar. (Trail maps or maps of ski areas may be available at state parks or online from state departments of recreation.)
- Have students work in small groups of two or three. Ask them to choose a hiking or ski trail to analyze. They should identify a base point to begin a climb (e.g., a parking lot or start of a trail) or ski lift, and record its altitude.
- Ask them to follow the trail and measure (using the map scale) the horizontal distance ("run") covered for each rise represented by a contour line on the map. (Contour lines typically show altitudes separated by 10 or 100 feet.) They should record these values in two columns as x and y, and continue up to the summit.
- Then have them compute cumulative x- and y-values for each contour (a spreadsheet would be helpful), and make a graph showing the height of the climb as a function of the total horizontal distance covered at any point.
- Finally, have them find the average slope of the trail and write a linear function for the altitude of the trail as a function of horizontal distance traveled.

CHAPTER 2 Linear Relations and Functions

Then

In Chapter 1, you solved equations and inequalities.

Now

In Chapter 2, you will:

- Use equations of relations and functions.
- Determine the slope of a line.
- Use scatter plots and prediction equations.
- Graph linear inequalities.

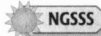

NGSSS

MA.912.A.2.6
MA.912.A.2.10.

Why?

RECREATION Linear functions can be used to model many aspects of recreational activities such as distance ridden on a bicycle, the amount of money a group of people would spend at a state fair, the height of a water slide at various points, or the amount of money you could earn from a hobby.

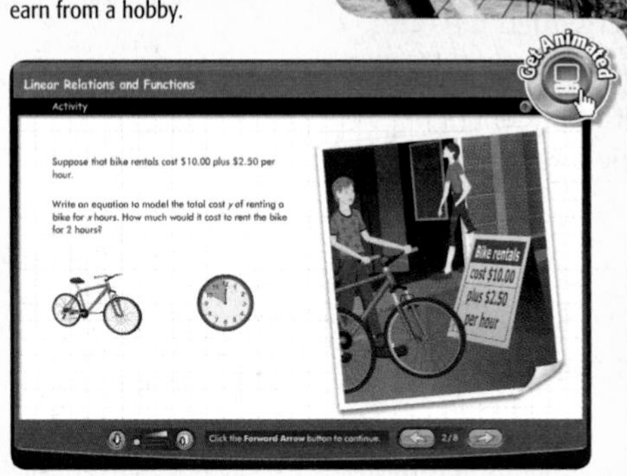

Key Vocabulary Introduce the key vocabulary in the chapter using the routine below.

Define: A linear equation is an equation that may contain one or more variables and has no operations other than addition, subtraction, and multiplication of a variable by a constant.

Example: The equation $y = 5x - 3$ is a linear equation.

Ask: Is the equation $5x^2 + 9.5 = y$ a linear equation? Explain. No, because it contains a variable with an exponent other than 1.

Get Ready for Chapter 2

Diagnose Readiness You have two options for checking Prerequisite Skills.

Text Option

Take the Quick Check below. Refer to the Quick Review for help.

QuickCheck

(Used in Lessons 2-1 through 2-8)

Write the ordered pair for each point. Then name the quadrant in which it is located. (Lesson 0-1)

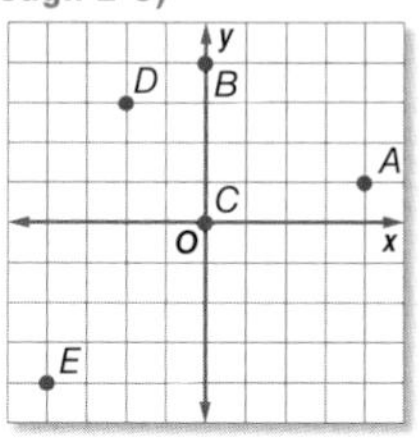

1. A 2. B
3. C 4. D
5. E (−4, −4); III

6. **BABYSITTING** Aliza earns \$6 per hour babysitting. Make a table in which the x-coordinate represents the number of hours Aliza babysits, and the y-coordinate represents the amount of money she earns. See margin.

1. (4, 1); I 2. (0, 4); y-axis
3. (0, 0); origin 4. (−2, 3); II

(Used in Lessons 2-1 through 2-8)

Evaluate each expression if $a = -3$, $b = 4$, and $c = -2$. (Lesson 1-1)

7. $4a - 3$ −15
8. $2b - 5c$ 18
9. $b^2 - 3b + 6$ 10
10. $\frac{2a + 4b}{c}$ −5

11. **PHONE SERVICE** A cell phone company uses the expression $20 + 0.25m$ to determine the monthly charge for m minutes of air time. Find the monthly charge for 80 minutes of air time.

(Used in Lessons 2-2 through 2-4)

Solve each equation for the given variable. (Lesson 1-3)

12. $4x + 2y = 12$ for y $y = 6 - 2x$
13. $a = 3b + 9$ for b $b = \frac{a}{3} - 3$
14. $15w - 10 = 5v$ for v $v = 3w - 2$
15. $3x - 4y = 8$ for x $x = \frac{8}{3} + \frac{4}{3}y$
16. $\frac{d}{6} + \frac{f}{3} = 4$ for d $d = -2f + 24$

QuickReview

EXAMPLE 1

Write the ordered pair for point M. Then name the quadrant in which it is located.

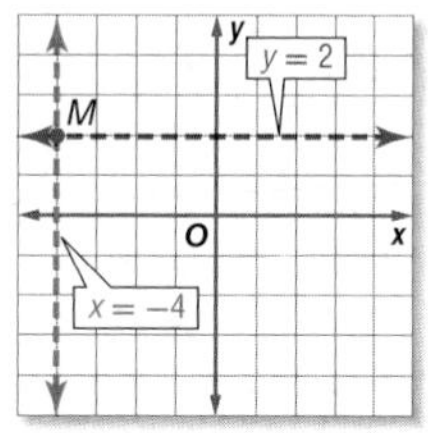

Step 1 Follow a vertical line through the point to find the x-coordinate on the x-axis.

Step 2 Follow a horizontal line through the point to find the y-coordinate on the y-axis.

Step 3 The ordered pair for point M is (−4, 2). It can also be written as $M(-4, 2)$.

The x-coordinate of M is negative, while the y-coordinate is positive. So M lies in Quadrant II.

EXAMPLE 2

Evaluate $3a^2 - 2ab + b^2$ if $a = 4$ and $b = -3$.

$$\begin{aligned} 3a^2 - 2ab + b^2 &= 3(4^2) - 2(4)(-3) + (-3)^2 \\ &= 3(16) - 2(4)(-3) + 9 \\ &= 48 - (-24) + 9 \\ &= 48 + 24 + 9 \\ &= 81 \end{aligned}$$

11. \$40

EXAMPLE 3

Solve $3x + 6y = 24$ for y.

$3x + 6y = 24$	**Original equation**
$3x + 6y - 3x = 24 - 3x$	**Subtract 3x from each side.**
$6y = 24 - 3x$	**Simplify.**
$\frac{6y}{6} = \frac{24}{6} - \frac{3x}{6}$	**Divide each side by 6.**
$y = 4 - \frac{1}{2}x$	**Simplify.**

Online Option

FL Math Online Take a self-check Chapter Readiness Quiz at glencoe.com.

Additional Answer

6.

x	y
1	6
2	12
3	18
4	24
5	30

Response to Intervention (RtI)

Use the *Quick Check* results and the Intervention Planner to help you determine your Response to Intervention. The If-Then statements in the chart below help you decide the appropriate tier of RtI and suggest intervention resources for each tier.

Intervention Planner

Tier 1 — On Level

If students miss about 25% of the exercises or less,

Then choose a resource:

SE	Lessons 0-1, 1-1, and 1-3
CRM	Skills Practice, Chapter 1, pp. 7 and 19
TE	Chapter Project, p. 58

FL Math Online Self-Check Quiz

Tier 2 — Strategic Intervention approaching grade level

If students miss about 50% of the exercises,

Then choose a resource:

CRM	Study Guide and Intervention, Chapter 1, pp. 5 and 17, 30, 36, 43, 50

FL Math Online Extra Examples, Personal Tutor, Homework Help

Tier 3 — Intensive Intervention 2 or more years below grade level

If students miss about 75% of the exercises,

Then use *Math Triumphs, Alg. 2*, Ch. 1 and 3

FL Math Online Extra Examples, Personal Tutor, Homework Help, Review Vocabulary

FOLDABLES® Study Organizer

Dinah Zike's Foldables®

Focus Students write notes as they use properties and learn about attributes of linear relations and functions in the lessons of this chapter.

Teach Have students make and label their Foldables as illustrated. As they work through the chapter, have students include the vocabulary in their notes for each lesson. Challenge students to create their own examples that illustrate the vocabulary.

When to Use It Encourage students to add to their Foldables as they work through the chapter and to use them to review for the chapter test.

Differentiated Instruction

CRM Student-Built Glossary, pp. 1–2
Students should complete the chart by providing a definition of each term and an example as they progress through Chapter 2. This study tool can also be used to review for the chapter test.

Get Started on Chapter 2

You will learn several new concepts, skills, and vocabulary terms as you study Chapter 2. To get ready, identify important terms and organize your resources. You may wish to refer to **Chapter 0** to review prerequisite skills.

FOLDABLES® Study Organizer

Linear Relations and Functions Make this Foldable to help you organize your Chapter 2 notes about linear relations and functions. Begin with four sheets of notebook paper.

1. **Fold** each sheet of paper in half from top to bottom.

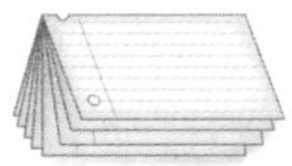

2. **Cut** along the fold. Staple the eight half-sheets together to form a booklet.

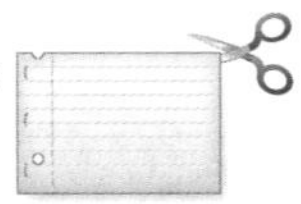

3. **Cut** tabs into the margin. The top tab is 2 lines deep, the next tab is 6 lines deep, and so on.

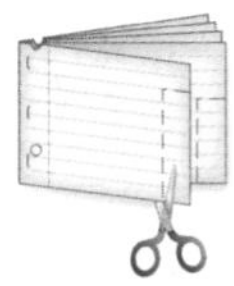

4. **Label** each of the tabs with a lesson number.

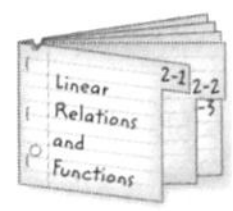

New Vocabulary

English		Español
one-to-one function	• p. 61 •	función biunívoca
onto function	• p. 61 •	función
discrete relation	• p. 62 •	relación discreta
continuous relation	• p. 62 •	relación continua
vertical line test	• p. 62 •	prueba de la recta vertical
independent variable	• p. 64 •	variable independiente
dependent variable	• p. 64 •	variable dependiente
linear equation	• p. 69 •	ecuación lineal
linear function	• p. 69 •	función lineal
rate of change	• p. 76 •	tasa de cambio
bivariate data	• p. 92 •	datos bivariados
positive correlation	• p. 92 •	correlación positiva
negative correlation	• p. 92 •	correlación negativa
line of fit	• p. 92 •	recta de ajuste
regression line	• p. 94 •	línea de regresión
piecewise-linear function	• p. 102 •	función a intervalos lineal
absolute value function	• p. 103 •	función del valor absoluto
parent function	• p. 109 •	función madre
quadratic function	• p. 109 •	función cuadrática
linear inequality	• p. 117 •	desigualdad lineal

Review Vocabulary

equation • p. 18 • ecuación a mathematical sentence stating that two mathematical expressions are equal

function • p. 7 • función a relation in which each x-coordinate is paired with exactly one y-coordinate

relation • p. 7 • relación a set of ordered pairs

Relation

Domain Range

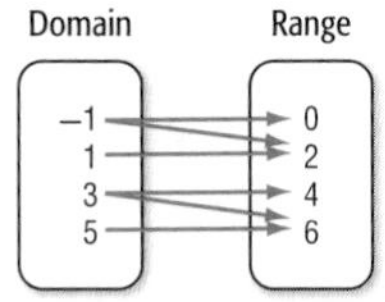

Function

Domain Range

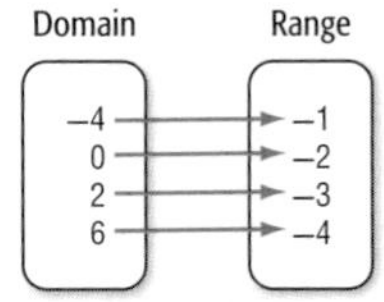

Multilingual eGlossary glencoe.com

FL Math Online glencoe.com

- Study the chapter online
- Explore **Get Animated**
- Get extra help from your own **Personal Tutor**
- Use **Extra Examples** for additional help
- Take a **Self-Check Quiz**
- **Review Vocabulary** in fun ways

2-1 Relations and Functions

Why?

Then
You identified domains and ranges for given situations. (Lesson 0-1)

Now
- Analyze relations and functions.
- Use equations of relations and functions.

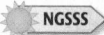

NGSSS
MA.912.A.10.3 Decide whether a given statement is always, sometimes, or never true (statements involving linear or quadratic expressions, equations, or inequalities rational or radical expressions or logarithmic or exponential functions).

New Vocabulary
one-to-one function
onto function
discrete relation
continuous relation
vertical line test
independent variable
dependent variable
function notation

FL Math Online
glencoe.com

The table shows the monthly average low and high temperatures for Charlotte, North Carolina. Each month's average temperatures can be represented by the ordered pair (average low, average high). For example, January's average temperatures can be expressed as (32, 51).

Monthly Average Temperature (°F) Charlotte, NC

Month	Jan	Feb	Mar	Apr	May	Jun	Jul	Aug	Sep	Oct	Nov	Dec
Low	32	34	42	49	58	66	71	69	63	51	42	35
High	51	56	64	73	80	87	90	88	82	73	63	54

Source: The Weather Channel

Relations and Functions Recall that a function is a relation in which each element of the domain is paired with exactly one element in the range. All functions map elements of the domain to elements of the range, but they may differ in the way the elements of the domain and range are paired.

Key Concept Functions

one-to-one function	onto function	both one-to-one and onto
Each element of the domain pairs to exactly one unique element of the range.	Each element of the range corresponds to an element of the domain.	Each element of the domain is paired to exactly one element of the range, and each element of the range corresponds to a unique element of the domain.
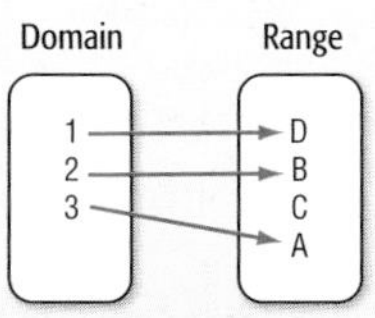	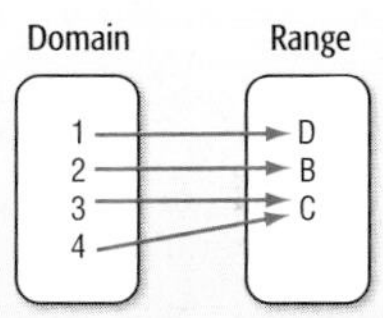	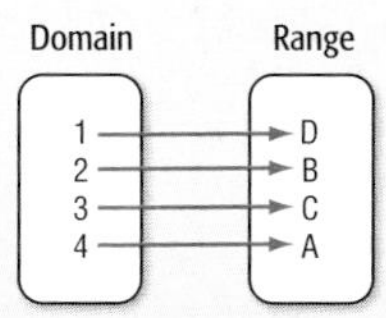

EXAMPLE 1 Domain and Range

State the domain and range of each relation. Then determine whether each relation is a *function*. If it is a function, determine if it is *one-to-one*, *onto*, *both*, or *neither*.

a. $\{(-6, -1), (-5, -9), (-3, -7), (-1, 7), (6, -9)\}$

Domain: $\{-6, -5, -3, -1, 6\}$ Range: $\{-9, -7, -1, 7\}$

function: yes, because each element of the domain is paired with one element of the range

one-to-one: no, because each element of the domain is not paired with a unique element of the range

onto: yes, because each element of the range corresponds to an element of the domain

2-1 Lesson Notes

1 FOCUS

Vertical Alignment

Before Lesson 2-1
Identify domains and ranges for given situations.

Lesson 2-1
Analyze relations and functions. Use equations of relations and functions.

After Lesson 2-1
Identify and sketch graphs of parent functions.

2 TEACH

Scaffolding Questions

Have students read the *Why?* section of the lesson.

Ask:
- What is the average low temperature in May? 58°F
- How can November's average temperatures be expressed as an ordered pair? (42, 63)
- Why can you be sure that the second number in the ordered pairs for these data are always greater than or equal to the first? The average high temperature will always be greater than or equal to the average low temperature.

Lesson 2-1 Resources

Resource	Approaching-Level	On-Level	Beyond-Level	English Learners
Teacher Edition	• Differentiated Instruction, p. 64	• Differentiated Instruction, p. 64	• Differentiated Instruction, pp. 64, 67	
Chapter Resource Masters	• Study Guide and Intervention, pp. 5–6 • Skills Practice, p. 7 • Practice, p. 8 • Word Problem Practice, p. 9	• Study Guide and Intervention, pp. 5–6 • Skills Practice, p. 7 • Practice, p. 8 • Word Problem Practice, p. 9 • Enrichment, p. 10	• Practice, p. 8 • Word Problem Practice, p. 9 • Enrichment, p. 10	• Study Guide and Intervention, pp. 5–6 • Skills Practice, p. 7 • Practice, p. 8 • Word Problem Practice, p. 9
Transparencies	• 5-Minute Check Transparency 2-1	• 5-Minute Check Transparency 2-1	• 5-Minute Check Transparency 2-1	• 5-Minute Check Transparency 2-1
Other	• Study Notebook	• Study Notebook	• Study Notebook	• Study Notebook

Relations and Functions

Example 1 illustrates the domain and range of a discrete relation and shows how to determine whether the relation is a function. It also shows how to determine if a function is *one-to-one, onto, both,* or *neither.* **Example 2** shows how to use the vertical line test to determine whether a graph represents a function. It also shows how to identify whether a relation is discrete or continuous by looking at its graph.

Formative Assessment

Use the Guided Practice exercises after each example to determine students' understanding of concepts.

Additional Example

1 State the domain and range of the relation. Then determine whether the relation is a function. If it is a function, determine if it is *one-to-one, onto, both,* or *neither.*

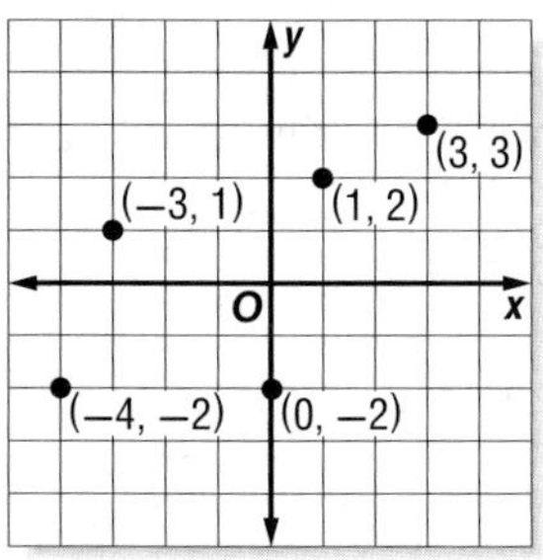

The domain is {–4, –3, 0, 1, 3}. The range is {–2, 1, 2, 3}. Each member of the domain is paired with one member of the range, so this relation is a function. It is onto, but not one-to-one.

Additional Examples also in Interactive Classroom PowerPoint® Presentations

IWB INTERACTIVE WHITEBOARD READY

b.

x	2	−1	−2	−1	2
y	−2	−1	0	1	2

Domain: {−2, −1, 2} Range: {−2, −1, 0, 1, 2}

The relation is not a function because 2 is mapped to both −2 and 2, and −1 is mapped to both −1 and 1.

Guided Practice

State the domain and range of each relation. Then determine whether each relation is a *function*. If it is a function, determine if it is *one-to-one, onto, both,* or *neither.*

1A.

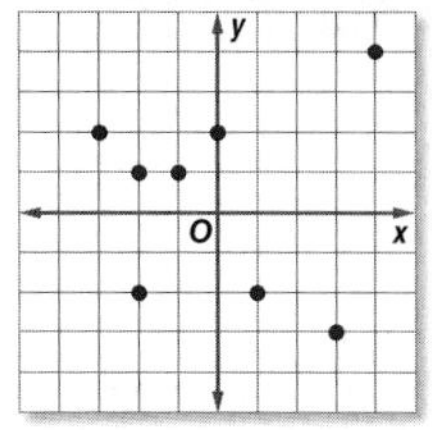

1B.

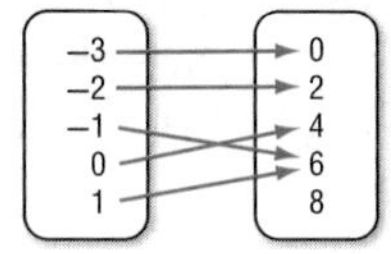

1A. D = {−3, −2, −1, 0, 1, 3, 4}, R = {−3, −2, 1, 2, 4}; not a function

1B. D = {−3, −2, −1, 0, 1}, R = {0, 2, 4, 6, 8}; function; one-to-one, not onto

Personal Tutor glencoe.com

A relation in which the domain is a set of individual points, like the relation in Graph A, is said to be a **discrete relation**. Notice that its graph consists of points that are not connected. When the domain of a relation has an infinite number of elements and the relation can be graphed with a line or smooth curve, the relation is a **continuous relation**.

StudyTip

Continuous Relations If you can draw the graph of a relation without lifting your pencil from the paper, this relation is continuous.

Graph A

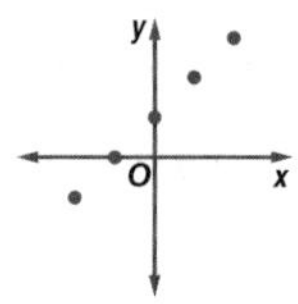

discrete relation

Graph B

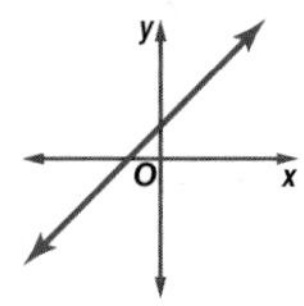

continuous relation

With both discrete and continuous graphs, you can use the **vertical line test** to determine whether the relation is a function.

Key Concept Vertical Line Test

Words	If no vertical line intersects a graph in more than one point, the graph represents a function.	If a vertical line intersects a graph in two or more points, the graph does not represent a function.
Models	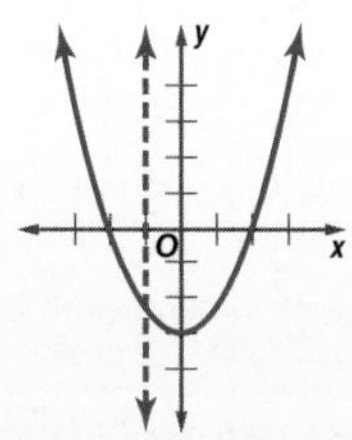	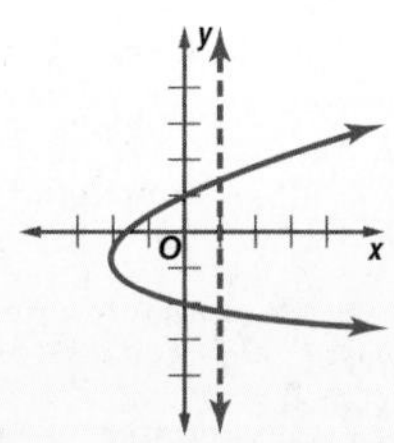

TEACH with TECH

INTERACTIVE WHITEBOARD Display a graph on the board and demonstrate the vertical line test. Draw a vertical line and drag it from left to right across the graph. Show students that if there is any place where a vertical line intersects the graph at more than one point, the graph is not a function.

Tips for New Teachers

Vertical Line Test Discuss with students why the vertical line test works. More than one point on a vertical line indicates more than one point with the same *x*-coordinate.

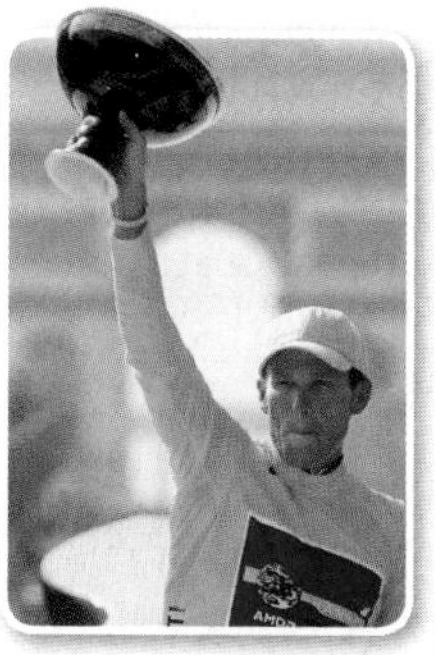

Real-World Link

Lance Armstrong has won the Tour de France more than any other rider, having won 7 consecutive races from 1999 through 2005.

Source: *USA Cycling*

Real-World EXAMPLE 2

BICYCLING The graph shows the length of the Tour de France in kilometers each year from 1998 through 2006. Is the relation *discrete* or *continuous*? Does the graph represent a function?

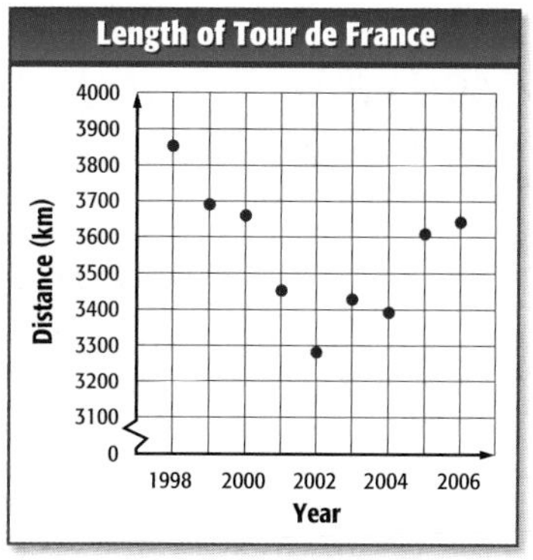

Because the graph consists of distinct points, the function is discrete. Use the vertical line test. No vertical line can be drawn that contains more than one of the data points. Therefore, the relation is a function.

Guided Practice

2. The number of employees a company had in each year from 2004 to 2009 were 25, 28, 34, 31, 27, and 29. Graph this information and determine whether the relation is *discrete* or *continuous*. Does the graph represent a function? **See margin for graph; discrete; function**

Personal Tutor glencoe.com

Equations of Relations and Functions Relations and functions can also be represented by equations. The solutions of an equation in x and y are the set of ordered pairs (x, y) that make the equation true. To determine whether an equation represents a function, it is often simplest to look at the graph of the relation.

EXAMPLE 3 Graph a Relation

Graph $y = \frac{1}{2}x - 3$, and determine the domain and range. Then determine whether the equation is a *function*, is *one-to-one*, *onto*, *both*, or *neither*. State whether it is *discrete* or *continuous*.

Make a table of values that satisfy the equation. Then graph the equation.

x	y
−4	−5
−2	−4
0	−3
2	−2
4	−1

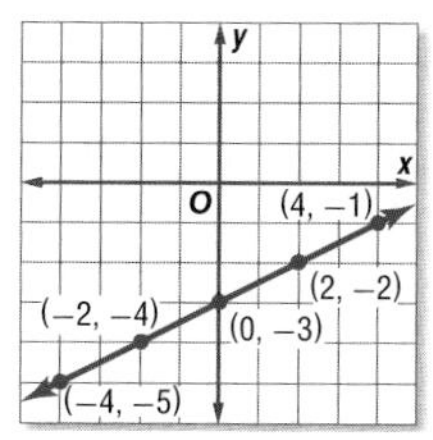

Every real number is the x-coordinate of some point on the line, and every real number is the y-coordinate of some point on the line. So the domain and range are both all real numbers.

The graph passes the vertical line test, so the equation is a function. Every x-value is paired with exactly one unique y-value, and every y-value corresponds to an x-value. Thus, the function is both one-to-one and onto.

Because the graph is a solid line without breaks, the function is continuous.

Guided Practice

3. Graph $y = x^2 + 1$, and determine the domain and range. Then determine whether the equation is a *function*, is *one-to-one*, *onto*, *both*, or *neither*. State whether it is *discrete* or *continuous*. **See margin for graph; D = {all real numbers}, R = $\{y \mid y \geq 1\}$; function; neither; continuous**

Personal Tutor glencoe.com

Additional Example

2 **TRANSPORTATION** The table shows the average fuel efficiency in miles per gallon for SUVs for several years. Graph this information and determine whether it represents a function. Is the relation *discrete* or *continuous*?

Year	Fuel Efficiency (mi/gal)
2001	20.8
2002	20.6
2003	20.8
2004	20.9
2005	21.6
2006	22.3
2007	22.6

Source: U.S. Environmental Protection Agency

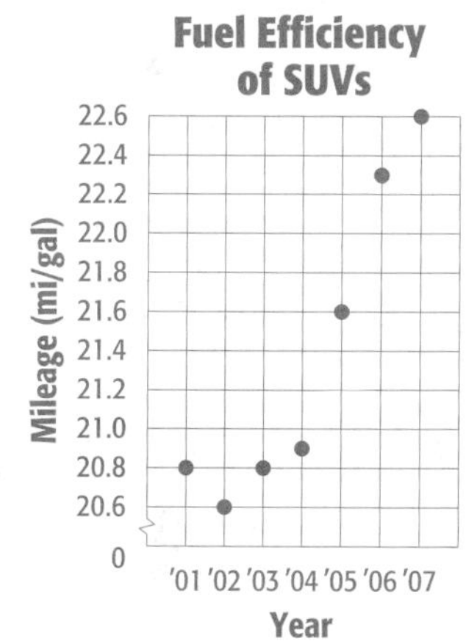

Yes, this relation is a function, and it is discrete.

Equations of Relations and Functions

Example 3 shows how to graph a relation that is a line. **Example 4** shows how to evaluate a function.

Focus on Mathematical Content

Relations and Functions A function is a special type of relation, just as a square is a special type of rectangle. All functions are relations.

Additional Answers (Guided Practice)

2.

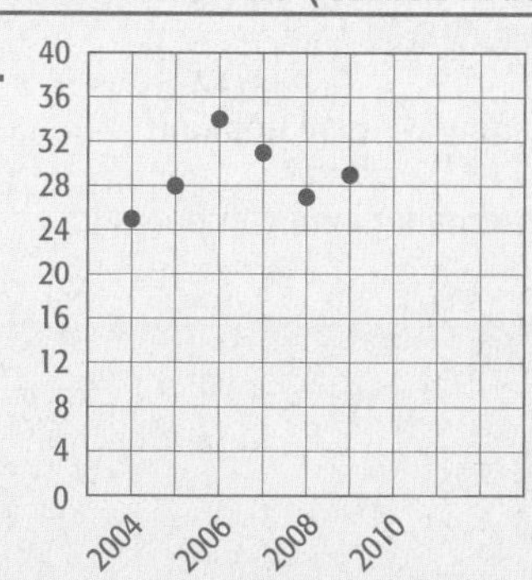

3.

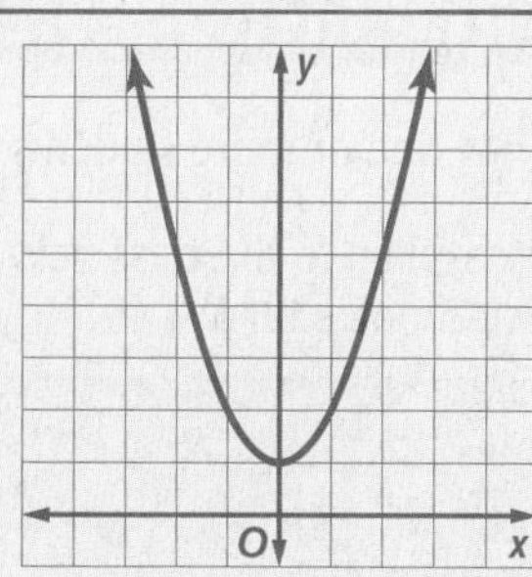

Additional Examples

3 Graph $y = 3x - 1$ and determine the domain and range. Then determine whether the equation is a *function*, is *one-to-one*, *onto*, *both*, or *neither*. State whether it is *discrete* or *continuous*.

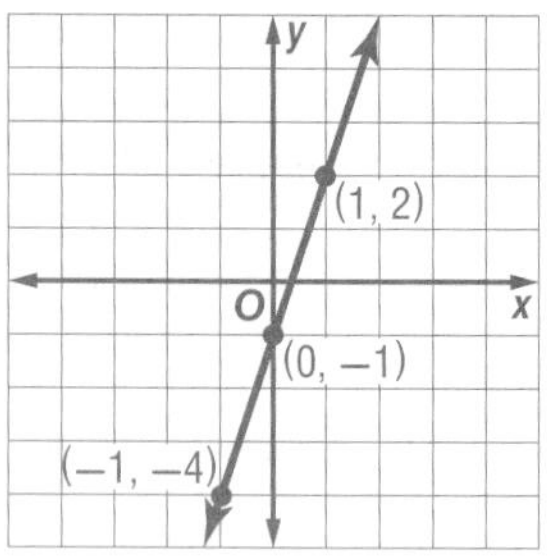

The domain is all real numbers; the range is all real numbers; the equation is a function; the equation is continuous.

4 Given $f(x) = x^3 - 3$, find each value.

a. $f(-2)$ −11

b. $f(2t)$ $8t^3 - 3$

3 PRACTICE

Formative Assessment

Use Exercises 1–10 to check for understanding.

Use the chart at the bottom of the next page to customize assignments for your students.

Additional Answer

4d. yes

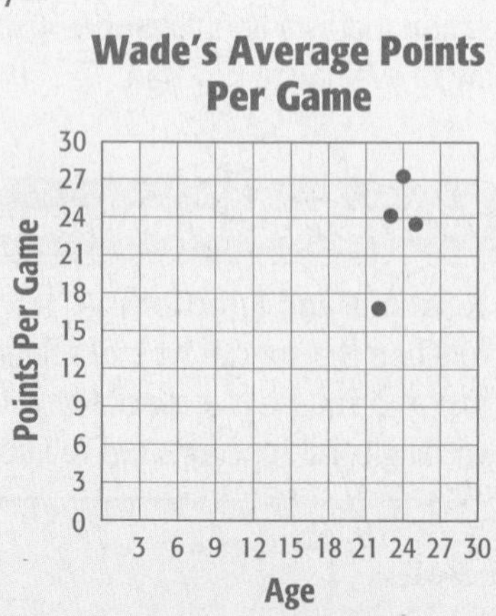

When an equation represents a function, the variable, often x, with values making up the domain is called the **independent variable**. The other variable, often y, is called the **dependent variable** because its values depend on x.

ReadingMath

Function Notation The symbol $f(x)$ replaces the y and is read "f of x." The f is just the name of the function. It is not a variable that is multiplied by x.

Equations that represent functions are often written in **function notation**. The equation $y = 5x - 1$ can be written as $f(x) = 5x - 1$. Suppose you want to find the value in the range that corresponds to the element −6 in the domain of the function. The value $f(-6)$ is found by substituting −6 for each x in the equation. Therefore, $f(-6) = 5(-6) - 1$ or −31.

EXAMPLE 4 Evaluate a Function

Given $f(x) = 2x^2 - 8$, find each value.

a. $f(6)$

$f(x) = 2x^2 - 8$	**Original function**
$f(6) = 2(6)^2 - 8$	**Substitute.**
$= 2(36) - 8$	**Evaluate 6^2.**
$= 72 - 8$ or 64	**Simplify.**

b. $f(2y)$

$f(x) = 2x^2 - 8$	**Original function**
$f(2y) = 2(2y)^2 - 8$	**Substitute.**
$= 2(4y^2) - 8$	**$(2y)^2 = 2^2y^2$**
$= 8y^2 - 8$	**Simplify.**

Guided Practice

Given $g(x) = 0.5x^2 - 5x + 3.5$, find each value.

4A. $g(2.8)$ −6.58 **4B.** $g(4a)$ $8a^2 - 20a + 3.5$

Personal Tutor glencoe.com

Check Your Understanding

Example 1 p. 61

1. D = {5, 6, −2}, R = {3, −8, 1}; function; both
2. D = {1, −2, 4}, R = {2, 5, 3, −1}; not a function
3. D = {−2, 1, 4, 8}, R = {−4, −2, 6}; function; onto

State the domain and range of each relation. Then determine whether each relation is a *function*. If it is a function, determine if it is *one-to-one*, *onto*, *both*, or *neither*.

1.

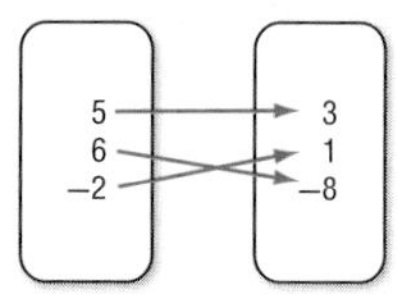

2.

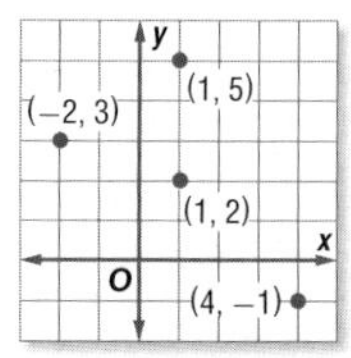

3

x	y
−2	−4
1	−4
4	−2
8	6

Example 2 p. 63

4a. D = {22, 23, 24, 25}, R = {16.2, 24.1, 27.2, 23.5}
4b. {(22, 16.2), (23, 24.1), (24, 27.2), (25, 23.5)}

4. BASKETBALL The table shows the average points per game for Dwayne Wade of the Miami Heat for four years.

SEASON	DWAYNE WADE'S AGE	AVERAGE POINTS PER GAME
2003–2004	22	16.2
2004–2005	23	24.1
2005–2006	24	27.2
2006–2007	25	23.5

a. Assume that the ages are the domain. Identify the domain and range.

b. Write a relation of ordered pairs for the data.

c. State whether the relation is *discrete* or *continuous*. discrete

d. Graph the relation. Is this relation a function? See margin.

Example 3 p. 63

Graph each equation, and determine the domain and range. Determine whether the equation is a *function*, is *one-to-one*, *onto*, *both*, or *neither*. Then state whether it is *discrete* or *continuous*. 5–8. See Chapter 2 Answer Appendix.

5. $y = 5x + 4$ **6.** $y = -4x - 2$ **7.** $y = 3x^2$ **8.** $x = 7$

Differentiated Instruction

AL OL BL

If your class has one or more students who are familiar with reading musical notation,

Then ask them to explain to the class how graphing points on a coordinate plane compares to writing musical notes on a staff.

NGSSS PRACTICE 912.A.2.13, 912.G.4.4

41. Patricia's swimming pool contains 19,500 gallons of water. She drains the pool at a rate of 6 gallons per minute. Which of these equations represents the number of gallons of water g, remaining in the pool after m minutes? **A**

A. $g = 19{,}500 - 6m$

B. $g = 19{,}500 + 6m$

C. $g = \frac{19{,}500}{6m}$

D. $g = \frac{6m}{19{,}500}$

42. **SHORT RESPONSE** Look at the pattern below.

$$-\frac{5}{2}, -2, -\frac{3}{2}, -1, \ldots$$

If the pattern continues, what will the next term be? $-\frac{1}{2}$

43. **GEOMETRY** Which set of dimensions represents a triangle similar to the triangle shown below? **I**

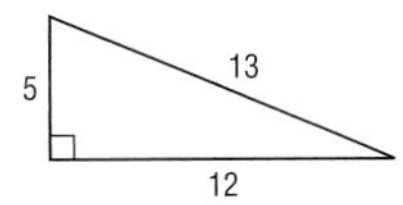

F. 1 unit, 2 units, 3 units

G. 7 units, 11 units, 12 units

H. 10 units, 23 units, 24 units

I. 20 units, 48 units, 52 units

44. **ACT/SAT** If $g(x) = x^2$, which expression is equal to $g(x + 1)$? **C**

A. 1

B. $x^2 + 1$

C. $x^2 + 2x + 1$

D. $x^2 - x$

Spiral Review

Solve each inequality. (Lesson 1-6) **46.** $z > 6$ or $z < 2$ **47.** $x > \frac{7}{4}$ or $x < -\frac{11}{4}$

45. $48 > 7y + 6 > 20$ $6 > y > 2$

46. $z + 12 > 18$ or $-2z + 16 > 12$

47. $2|4x + 2| + 3 > 21$

48. **CLUBS** Mr. Willis is starting a chess club at his high school. He sent the advertisement at the right to all of the homerooms. Write an absolute value inequality representing the situation. (Lesson 1-6) $|x - 14| \leq 8$

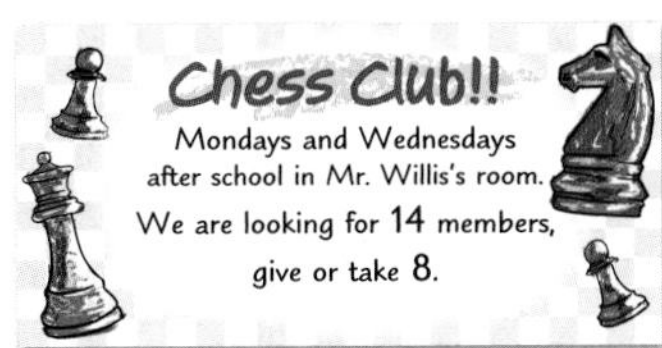

Chess Club!!
Mondays and Wednesdays after school in Mr. Willis's room.
We are looking for 14 members, give or take 8.

49. **SALES** Ling can spend no more than $120 at the summer sale of a department store. She wants to buy shirts on sale for $15 each. Write and solve an inequality to determine the number of shirts she can buy. (Lesson 1-5) $15x \leq 120$; She can buy up to 8 shirts.

Solve each equation. Check your solutions. (Lesson 1-4)

50. $18 = 2|2a + 6| - 2$ 2 or -8

51. $2 = -3|4c - 5| + 8$ $\frac{3}{4}$ or $\frac{7}{4}$

52. $-5 = 2|3b + 4| - 9$ -2 or $-\frac{2}{3}$

Simplify each expression. (Lesson 1-2)

53. $6(3a - 2b) + 3(5a + 4b)$ $33a$

54. $-4(5x - 3y) + 2(y + 3x)$ $-14x + 14y$

55. $-7(2c - 4d) + 8(3c + d)$ $10c + 36d$

Skills Review

Solve each equation. Check your solutions. (Lesson 1-3)

56. $5x + 2 = 32$ 6

57. $6a - 3 = 21$ 4

58. $-2x + 5 = 5x + 19$ -2

59. $6b + 4 = -2b - 28$ -4

60. $2(x + 5) - 3(x - 4) = 19$ 3

61. $4(2y - 3) + 5(3y + 1) = -99$ -4

62. $5c - 8 + 2c = 4c + 10$ 6

63. $8d - 4 + 3d = 2d - 100 - 7d$ -6

64. $10y - 5 - 3y = 4(2y + 3) - 20$ 3

Watch Out!

Error Analysis For Exercise 35, suggest that students rewrite the original function by substituting the expression (3*d*) for *each* occurrence of the variable *x before* they begin simplifying.

4 ASSESS

Crystal Ball In Lesson 2-2 students will be identifying linear relations and functions. Have students write about how they think today's lesson will connect with the theme of Lesson 2-2.

Tips for New Teachers

Intervention This lesson has a number of vocabulary words that may be new or challenging for some students. Make sure that all students are comfortable with the mathematical language of this lesson before they begin the next lesson.

Additional Answer

40. Sample answer: A relation is a function if each x-value only pairs with one y-value. If the vertical line test fails then there is an x-value that pairs with more than one y-value, so the relation is not a function.

Differentiated Instruction BL

Extension Some relations (and functions) are neither discrete nor completely continuous. Ask students to consider the example below as a relation between two variables. Then ask them to determine whether each is a function, and whether the domain and/or the range are discrete.

the number of bacteria in a colony and time (Assume the colony starts with one cell and each cell divides into two new cells after exactly 30 minutes.) The number of bacteria is a function of time. The domain is continuous for non-negative values of time. The dependent variable (the number of bacteria) is discrete.

EXTEND 2-1 Lesson Notes

1 FOCUS

Objective
Distinguish between discrete and continuous functions to explore real-world problems.

Materials for Each Student
- none

Teaching Tip
Begin this activity by asking students to think of examples where only whole number values for the domain make sense.

Some examples might be:

- number of wheels on a car
- number of students absent from school

2 TEACH

Working in Cooperative Groups
Divide the class into groups of two, mixing abilities. Have groups read the first four paragraphs.

Practice Have students complete Exercises 1–5.

3 ASSESS

Formative Assessment
Use Exercise 5 to assess whether students understand the difference between a discrete and a continuous function.

From Concrete to Abstract
Ask students to summarize what they learned about discrete and continuous functions. Then have them give an example of each.

EXTEND 2-1 Algebra Lab

Discrete and Continuous Functions

Objective
Use discrete and continuous functions to solve real-world problems.

A cup of frozen yogurt costs $2 at the Yogurt Shack. We might describe the cost of x cups of yogurt using the continuous function $y = 2x$, where y is the total cost in dollars. The graph of that function is shown at the right.

Buying Frozen Yogurt

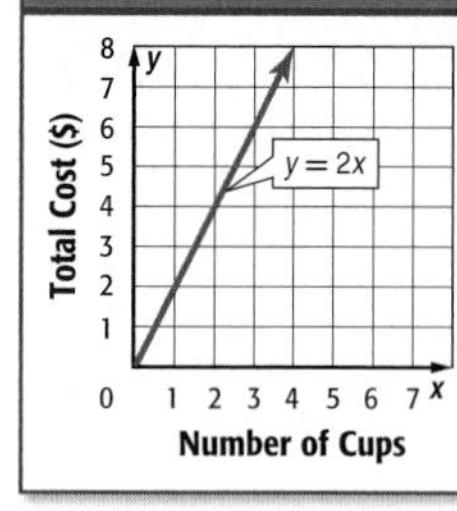

From the graph, you can see that 2 cups of yogurt cost $4, 3 cups cost $6, and so on. The graph also shows that 1.5 cups of yogurt cost 2(1.5) or $3. However, the Yogurt Shack probably will not sell partial cups of yogurt. This function is more accurately modeled with a discrete function.

The graph of the discrete function at the right also models the cost of buying cups of frozen yogurt. The domain in this graph makes sense in this situation.

Buying Frozen Yogurt

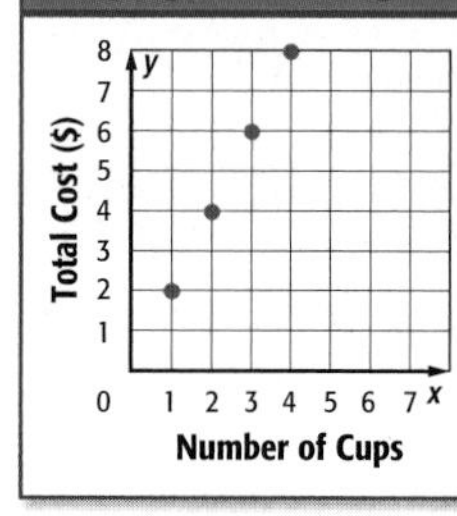

When choosing a discrete function or a continuous function to model a real-world situation, consider whether all real numbers make sense as part of the domain.

1. Continuous; there can be measures of weight that are not integers.
2. Discrete; you cannot receive a fraction of an e-mail.

Exercises

Determine whether each function is correctly modeled using a discrete or continuous function. Explain your reasoning.

1. **Converting Units**

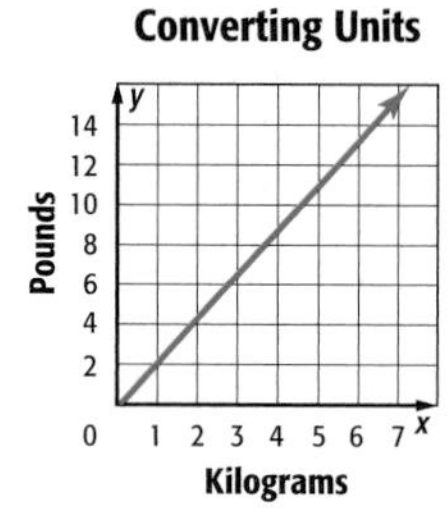

2. **E-Mails Received**

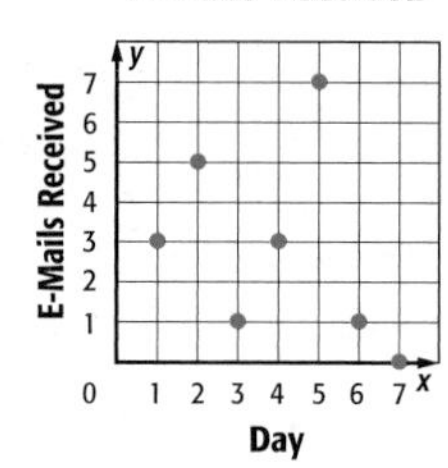

3. y represents the distance a car travels in x hours.
3–5. See Chapter 2 Answer Appendix.

4. y represents the total number of riders who have ridden on a roller coaster after x rides.

5. **WRITING IN MATH** Give an example of a real-world function that is discrete and a real-world function that is continuous. Explain your reasoning.

Extending the Concept
- Have students draw a graph of a real-life situation that is modeled by a continuous function.
- Have students draw a graph of a real-life situation that is modeled by a discrete function.

68 Chapter 2 Linear Relations and Functions

2-2 Linear Relations and Functions

Then

You analyzed relations and functions. (Lesson 2-1)

Now

- Identify linear relations and functions.
- Write linear equations in standard form.

NGSSS

MA.912.A.2.6 Identify and graph common functions (including but not limited to linear, rational, quadratic, cubic, radical, absolute value). **MA.912.A.10.3** Decide whether a given statement is always, sometimes, or never true (statements involving linear or quadratic expressions, equations, or inequalities rational or radical expressions or logarithmic or exponential functions).

New Vocabulary

linear relations
linear equation
linear function
standard form
y-intercept
x-intercept

FL Math Online

glencoe.com

Why?

Laura does yard work to earn money during the summer. She either cuts grass x or does general gardening y, and she schedules 5 jobs per day. The equation $x + y = 5$ can be used to relate how many of each task Laura can do in a day.

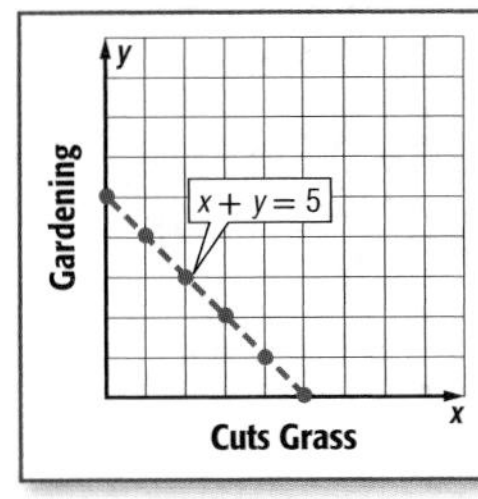

Linear Relations and Functions The points on the graph above lie along a straight line. Relations that have straight line graphs are called **linear relations**.

An equation such as $x + y = 5$ is called a linear equation. A **linear equation** has no operations other than addition, subtraction, and multiplication of a variable by a constant. The variables may not be multiplied together or appear in a denominator. A linear equation does not contain variables with exponents other than 1. The graph of a linear equation is always a line.

Linear equations	Nonlinear equations
$4x - 5y = 16$	$2x + 6y^2 = -25$
$x = 10$	$y = \sqrt{x} + 2$
$y = -\frac{2}{3}x - 1$	$x + xy = -\frac{5}{8}$
$y = \frac{1}{2}x$	$y = \frac{1}{x}$

A **linear function** is a function with ordered pairs that satisfy a linear equation. Any linear function can be written in the form $f(x) = mx + b$, where m and b are real numbers.

EXAMPLE 1 Identify Linear Functions

State whether each function is a linear function. Write *yes* or *no*. Explain.

a. $f(x) = 8 - \frac{3}{4}x$

Yes; it can be written as $f(x) = -\frac{3}{4}x + 8$.
$m = -\frac{3}{4}$, $b = 8$

b. $f(x) = \frac{2}{x}$

No; the expression includes division by the variable.

c. $g(x, y) = 3xy - 4$

No; the two variables are multiplied together.

Guided Practice

1A. $f(x) = \frac{5}{x + 6}$ No; the variable appears in the denominator.

1B. $g(x) = -\frac{3}{2}x + \frac{1}{3}$ yes; $m = -\frac{3}{2}$, $b = \frac{1}{3}$

Personal Tutor glencoe.com

You can evaluate linear functions by substituting values for x or $f(x)$.

2-2 Lesson Notes

1 FOCUS

Vertical Alignment

Before Lesson 2-2
Analyze relations and functions.

Lesson 2-2
Identify linear relations and functions and write linear equations in standard form.

After Lesson 2-2
Identify and sketch graphs of parent functions.

2 TEACH

Scaffolding Questions

Have students read the *Why?* section of the lesson.

Ask:

- What does a value of zero for x mean in this situation? Laura does not cut any grass.
- What does a negative value for x or y mean in this situation? It has no meaning. She cannot have a negative number of jobs.

Lesson 2-2 Resources

Resource	Approaching-Level	On-Level	Beyond-Level	English Learners
Teacher Edition	• Differentiated Instruction, p. 71	• Differentiated Instruction, pp. 71, 74	• Differentiated Instruction, pp. 71, 74	• Differentiated Instruction, p. 71
Chapter Resource Masters	• Study Guide and Intervention, pp. 11–12 • Skills Practice, p. 13 • Practice, p. 14 • Word Problem Practice, p. 15	• Study Guide and Intervention, pp. 11–12 • Skills Practice, p. 13 • Practice, p. 14 • Word Problem Practice, p. 15 • Enrichment, p. 16	• Practice, p. 14 • Word Problem Practice, p. 15 • Enrichment, p. 16	• Study Guide and Intervention, pp. 11–12 • Skills Practice, p. 13 • Practice, p. 14 • Word Problem Practice, p. 15
Transparencies	• 5-Minute Check Transparency 2-2	• 5-Minute Check Transparency 2-2	• 5-Minute Check Transparency 2-2	• 5-Minute Check Transparency 2-2
Other	• Study Notebook	• Study Notebook	• Study Notebook	• Study Notebook

Linear Relations and Functions

Example 1 illustrates how to determine whether a function is linear. **Example 2** shows how to evaluate a linear function by substitution.

Formative Assessment

Use the Guided Practice exercises after each example to determine students' understanding of concepts.

Additional Examples

1 State whether each function is a linear function. Write *yes* or *no*. Explain.

a. $g(x) = 2x - 5$ yes; $m = 2$, $b = -5$

b. $p(x) = x^3 + 2$ No; x has an exponent other than 1.

c. $t(x) = 4 + 7x$ yes; $m = 7$, $b = 4$

2 METEOROLOGY The linear function $f(C) = 1.8C + 32$ can be used to find the number of degrees Fahrenheit $f(C)$ that are equivalent to a given number of degrees Celsius C.

a. On the Celsius scale, normal body temperature is 37°C. What is it in degrees Fahrenheit? 98.6°F

b. There are 100 Celsius degrees between the freezing and boiling points of water and 180 Fahrenheit degrees between these two points. How many Fahrenheit degrees equal 1 Celsius degree? 1.8°F = 1°C

Additional Examples also in

Interactive Classroom PowerPoint® Presentations

IWB INTERACTIVE WHITEBOARD READY

Real-World Link

The largest member of the grass family, bamboo, is capable of growing from 1 to 4 feet per day.

Source: Infoplease

Real-World EXAMPLE 2 Evaluate a Linear Function

PLANTS **The growth rate of a sample of Bermuda grass is given by the function $f(x) = 5.9x + 3.25$, where $f(x)$ is the total height in inches x days after an initial measurement.**

a. How tall is the sample after 3 days?

$f(x) = 5.9x + 3.25$ — Original function

$f(3) = 5.9(3) + 3.25$ — Substitute 3 for *x*.

$= 20.95$ — Simplify.

The height of the sample after 3 days is 20.95 inches.

b. The term 3.25 in the function represents the height of the grass when it was initially measured. The sample is how many times as tall after 3 days?

Divide the height after 3 days by the initial height. $\frac{20.95}{3.25} \approx 6.4$

The height after 3 days is about 6.4 times as great as the initial height.

Guided Practice

2A. If the Bermuda grass is 50.45 inches tall, how many days has it been since it was last cut? 8 days

2B. Is it reasonable to think that this rate of growth can be maintained for long periods of time? Explain.

2B. Sample answer: No; the grass could not support its own weight after a long period of time.

Personal Tutor glencoe.com

Standard Form Any linear equation can be written in **standard form**, $Ax + By = C$, where A, B, and C are integers with a greatest common factor of 1.

Key Concept — Standard Form of a Linear Equation

Words The standard form of a linear equation is $Ax + By = C$, where A, B, and C are integers with a greatest common factor of 1, $A \geq 0$, and A and B are not both zero.

Examples $3x + 5y = 12$; $A = 3$, $B = 5$, and $C = 12$

EXAMPLE 3 Standard Form

Write $-\frac{3}{10}x = 8y - 15$ in standard form. Identify A, B, and C.

$-\frac{3}{10}x = 8y - 15$ — Original equation

$-\frac{3}{10}x - 8y = -15$ — Subtract 8*y* from each side.

$3x + 80y = 150$ — Multiply each side by −10.

$A = 3$, $B = 80$, and $C = 150$

Guided Practice

Write each equation in standard form. Identify A, B, and C.

3A. $2y = 4x + 5$ $4x - 2y = -5$; 4, −2, −5 **3B.** $3x - 6y - 9 = 0$ $x - 2y = 3$; 1, −2, 3

Personal Tutor glencoe.com

Focus on Mathematical Content

Linear Equations When determining whether an equation is linear, it is helpful to examine the equation for certain characteristics. A linear equation has no operations other than addition, subtraction, and multiplication of a variable by a constant. The variables may not be multiplied together or appear in a denominator. A linear equation does not contain variables with exponents other than 1.

TEACH with TECH

DOCUMENT CAMERA Give students several equations and ask them to identify each as linear or nonlinear. If the equation is linear, have students write it in standard form. Choose several students to explain and share their work with the class.

70 Chapter 2 Linear Relations and Functions

Since two points determine a line, one way to graph a linear function is to find the points at which the graph intersects each axis and connect them with a line. The y-coordinate of the point at which a graph crosses the y-axis is called the **y-intercept**. Likewise, the x-coordinate of the point at which it crosses the x-axis is called the **x-intercept**.

EXAMPLE 4 Use Intercepts to Graph a Line

Find the x-intercept and the y-intercept of the graph of $2x - 3y + 8 = 0$. Then graph the equation.

The x-intercept is the value of x when $y = 0$.

$2x - 3y + 8 = 0$	**Original equation**
$2x - 3(0) + 8 = 0$	**Substitute 0 for y.**
$2x = -8$	**Subtract 8 from each side.**
$x = -4$	**Divide each side by 2.**

The x-intercept is -4.

Likewise, the y-intercept is the value of y when $x = 0$.

$2x - 3y + 8 = 0$	**Original equation**
$2(0) - 3y + 8 = 0$	**Substitute 0 for x.**
$-3y = -8$	**Subtract 8 from each side.**
$y = \frac{8}{3}$	**Divide each side by 3.**

The y-intercept is $\frac{8}{3}$.

Use these ordered pairs to graph the equation.

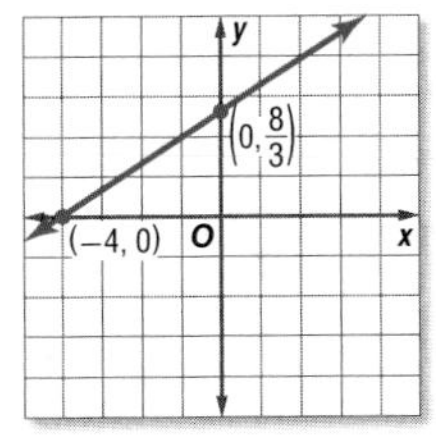

StudyTip

Vertical and Horizontal Lines When C represents a constant, an equation of the form $x = C$ represents a vertical line with only an x-intercept. The equation $y = C$ represents a horizontal line with only a y-intercept.

Guided Practice

4. Find the x-intercept and the y-intercept of the graph of $2x + 5y - 10 = 0$. Then graph the equation. See margin.

Personal Tutor glencoe.com

Check Your Understanding

1. Yes; it can be written as $f(x) = \frac{x}{5} + \frac{12}{5}$.

Example 1 p. 69 **State whether each function is a linear function. Write *yes* or *no*. Explain.**

1. $f(x) = \frac{x + 12}{5}$ **2.** $g(x) = \frac{7 - x}{x}$ **3.** $p(x) = 3x^2 - 4$ **4.** $q(x) = -8x - 21$

2. No; it cannot be written as $f(x) = mx + b$.

3. No; x has an exponent that is not 1.

4. Yes; it is written in $f(x) = mx + b$ form.

Example 2 p. 70

5. RECREATION You want to make sure that you have enough music for a car trip. If each CD is an average of 45 minutes long, the linear function $m(x) = 0.75x$ could be used to find out how many CDs you need to bring.

a. If you have 4 CDs, how many hours of music is that? 3 hours

b. If the trip you are taking is 6 hours, how many CDs should you bring? 8 CDs

Example 3 p. 70 **Write each equation in standard form. Identify A, B, and C.** 6–11. See Chapter 2 Answer Appendix.

6. $y = -4x - 7$ **7.** $y = 6x + 5$ **8.** $3x = -2y - 1$

9. $-8x = 9y - 6$ **10.** $12y = 4x + 8$ **11.** $4x - 6y = 24$

Example 4 p. 71 **Find the x-intercept and the y-intercept of the graph of each equation. Then graph the equation using the intercepts.** 12–15. See Chapter 2 Answer Appendix.

12. $y = 5x + 12$ **13.** $y = 4x - 10$ **14.** $2x + 3y = 12$ **15.** $3x - 4y - 6 = 15$

Differentiated Instruction

AL OL BL ELL

Linguistic Learners Write a letter to another student in the class explaining how to write an equation in standard form. The letter should include an explanation and an example.

Standard Form

Example 3 shows how to write a linear equation in standard form. **Example 4** explains how to find the x- and y-intercepts of a graph and use the ordered pairs to graph the equation.

Additional Examples

3 Write $y = 3x - 9$ in standard form. Identify A, B, and C. $3x - y = 9$; $A = 3, B = -1, C = 9$

4 Find the x-intercept and the y-intercept of the graph of $-2x + y - 4 = 0$. Then graph the equation. x-intercept: -2; y-intercept: 4

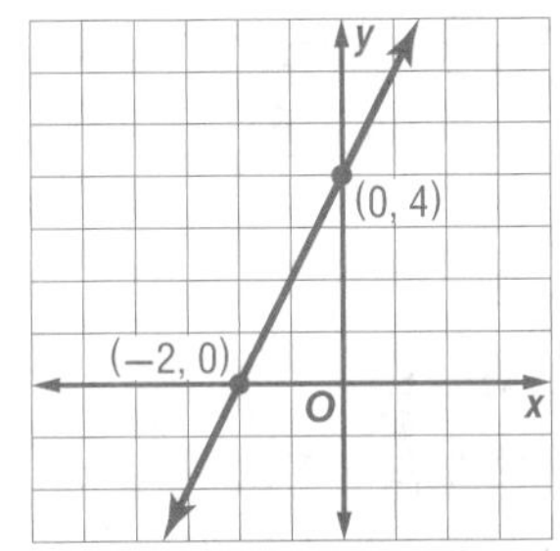

3 PRACTICE

Formative Assessment

Use Exercises 1–15 to check for understanding.

Use the chart at the bottom of the next page to customize assignments for your students.

Additional Answer (Guided Practice)

4. 5; 2

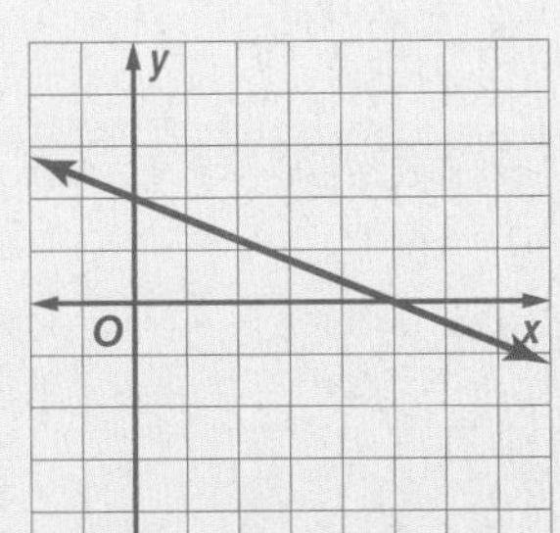

Tips for New Teachers

Graphing It may be helpful to have rulers and graph paper available for students to use as they work through the exercises.

Additional Answers

16. Yes; it can be written in $f(x) = mx + b$ form, where $m = \frac{4}{3}$ and $b = \frac{20}{3}$.

17. No; x has an exponent other than 1.

18. Yes, it can be written in $f(x) = mx + b$ form, where $m = 0$ and $b = 6$.

19. No; x has an exponent other than 1.

20. No; it cannot be written in $f(x) = mx + b$ form.

21. No; it cannot be written in $f(x) = mx + b$ form.

22. No; it cannot be written in $f(x) = mx + b$ form.

23. No; it cannot be written in $f(x) = mx + b$ form; There is an xy term.

24. Yes; it can be written in $f(x) = mx + b$ form, where $m = \frac{4}{5}$ and $b = \frac{8}{3}$.

25b. Kingda Ka; Sample answer: The Kingda Ka travels 847.5 meters in 25 seconds, so it travels a greater distance in the same amount of time.

26. $7x + 5y = -35$; $A = 7$, $B = 5$, $C = -35$

27. $8x + 3y = -6$; $A = 8$, $B = 3$, $C = -6$

28. $3x - 10y = -5$; $A = 3$, $B = -10$, $C = -5$

29. $2x + y = -11$; $A = 2$, $B = 1$, $C = -11$

30. $3x - y = 4$; $A = 3$, $B = -1$, $C = 4$

31. $6x + y = 0$; $A = 6$, $B = 1$, $C = 0$

32. $9x - 8y = 2$; $A = 9$, $B = -8$, $C = 2$

33. $5x + 32y = 160$; $A = 5$, $B = 32$, $C = 160$

34. $2x + 31y = 78$; $A = 2$, $B = 31$, $C = 78$

Practice and Problem Solving

= Step-by-Step Solutions begin on page R20.
Extra Practice begins on page 947.

Example 1 p. 69

State whether each equation or function is a linear function. Write *yes* or *no*. Explain. 16–24. See margin.

16. $3y - 4x = 20$ **17.** $y = x^2 - 6$ **18.** $h(x) = 6$

19. $j(x) = 2x^2 + 4x + 1$ **20.** $g(x) = 5 + \frac{6}{x}$ **21.** $f(x) = \sqrt{7 - x}$

22. $4x + \sqrt{y} = 12$ **23.** $\frac{1}{x} + \frac{1}{y} = 1$ **24.** $f(x) = \frac{4x}{5} + \frac{8}{3}$

Example 2 p. 70

25. ROLLER COASTERS The speed of the Steel Dragon 2000 roller coaster in Mie Prefecture, Japan, can be modeled by $y = 10.4x$, where y is the distance traveled in meters in x seconds.

a. How far does the coaster travel in 25 seconds? 260 m

b. The speed of Kingda Ka in Jackson, New Jersey, can be described by $y = 33.9x$. Which coaster travels faster? Explain your reasoning. See margin.

Example 3 p. 70

Write each equation in standard form. Identify *A*, *B*, and *C*. 26–34. See margin.

26. $-7x - 5y = 35$ **27.** $8x + 3y + 6 = 0$ **28.** $10y - 3x + 6 = 11$

29. $-6x - 3y - 12 = 21$ **30.** $3y = 9x - 12$ **31.** $2.4y = -14.4x$

32. $\frac{2}{3}y - \frac{3}{4}x + \frac{1}{6} = 0$ **33.** $\frac{4}{5}y + \frac{1}{8}x = 4$ **34.** $-0.08x = 1.24y - 3.12$

Example 4 p. 71

Find the *x*-intercept and the *y*-intercept of the graph of each equation. Then graph the equation using the intercepts. 35–40. See Chapter 2 Answer Appendix.

35. $y = -8x - 4$ **36.** $5y = 15x - 90$ **37.** $-4y + 6x = -42$

38. $-9x - 7y = -30$ **39.** $\frac{1}{3}x - \frac{2}{9}y = 4$ **40.** $\frac{3}{4}y - \frac{2}{3}x = 12$

B

41. FINANCIAL LITERACY Latonya earns a commission of \$1.75 for each magazine subscription she sells and \$1.50 for each newspaper subscription she sells. Her goal is to earn a total of \$525 in commissions in the next two weeks.

a. Write an equation that is a model for the different numbers of magazine and newspaper subscriptions that can be sold to meet the goal. $1.75m + 1.5n = 525$

b. Graph the equation. Does this equation represent a function? Explain. 41b. See Chapter 2 Answer Appendix.

c. If Latonya sells 100 magazine subscriptions and 200 newspaper subscriptions, will she meet her goal? Explain. No; the amount that Latonya will sell is $1.75 \cdot 100 + 1.5 \cdot 200$, which is \$475.

42. SNAKES Suppose the body length L in inches of a baby snake is given by $L(m) = 1.5 + 2m$, where m is the age of the snake in months until it becomes 12 months old.

a. Find the length of an 8-month-old snake. 17.5 in.

b. Find the snake's age if the length of the snake is 25.5 inches. 12 mo

43. STATE FAIR The Ohio State Fair charges \$8 for admission and \$5 for parking. After Joey pays for admission and parking, he plans to spend all of his remaining money at the ring game, which costs \$3 per game.

a. Write an equation representing the situation. $y = 3x + 13$

b. How much did Joey spend at the fair if he paid \$6 for food and drinks and played the ring game 4 times? \$31

Differentiated Homework Options

Level	Assignment	Two-Day Option	
AL Basic	16–40, 53–76	17–39 odd, 57–60	16–40 even, 53–56, 61–76
OL Core	17–39 odd, 41–43, 45–49 odd, 50–51, 53–76	16–40, 57–60	41–51, 53–56, 61–76
BL Advanced	41–68, (optional: 69–76)		

Write each equation in standard form. Identify A, B, and C. **46. See margin.**

44. $\frac{x+5}{3} = -2y + 4$ **45.** $\frac{4x-1}{5} = 8y - 12$ **46.** $\frac{-2x-8}{3} = -12y + 18$

44. $x + 6y = 7$; $A = 1$, $B = 6$, $C = 7$ **45.** $4x - 40y = -59$; $A = 4$, $B = -40$, $C = -59$

Find the x-intercept and the y-intercept of the graph of each equation.

47. $\frac{6x+15}{4} = 3y - 12$ **48.** $\frac{-8x+12}{3} = 16y + 24$ **49.** $\frac{15x+20}{4} = \frac{3y+6}{5}$

-10.5; 5.25 -7.5; -1.25 $-1\frac{1}{75}$; $6\frac{1}{3}$

Real-World Link

Bake sales, car washes, and coupon campaigns are among the most popular ideas to make money for schools because it gives students something to offer, making it easier to approach people.

Source: School-Link

50. FUNDRAISING The Freshman Class Student Council wanted to raise money by giving car washes. The students spent \$10 on supplies and charged \$2 per car wash.

a. Write an equation to model the situation. $E = 2c - 10$

b. Graph the equation. **See Chapter 2 Answer Appendix.**

c. How much money did they earn after 20 car washes? **\$30**

d. How many car washes are needed for them to earn \$100? **55**

51. MULTIPLE REPRESENTATIONS Consider the following linear functions.

$$f(x) = -2x + 4 \qquad g(x) = 6 \qquad h(x) = \frac{1}{3}x + 5$$

a. GRAPHICAL Graph the linear functions on separate graphs.

b. TABULAR Use the graphs to complete the table.

Function	One-to-One	Onto
$f(x) = -2x + 4$	yes	yes
$g(x) = 6$	no	no
$h(x) = \frac{1}{3}x + 5$	yes	yes

c. VERBAL Are all linear functions one-to-one and/or onto? Explain your reasoning.

51a. See Chapter 2 Answer Appendix.
51c. No; horizontal lines are neither one-to-one nor onto because only one y-value is used and it is repeated for every x-value. Every other linear function is one-to-one and onto because every x-value has one unique y-value that is not used by any other x-element and every possible y-value is used.
56a. Sample answer: This should only be in the first quadrant because hours worked and earnings will always be positive in this scenario.
56b. Sample answer: Number of books read and time in years; both of these values will always be positive.

H.O.T. Problems Use Higher-Order Thinking Skills

52. CHALLENGE Write a function with an x-intercept of $(a, 0)$ and a y-intercept of $(0, b)$. **Sample answer:** $f(x) = \frac{bx}{a} + b$

53. OPEN ENDED Write an equation of a line with an x-intercept of 3. **Sample answer:** $f(x) = 2(x - 3)$

54. REASONING Determine whether an equation of the form $x = a$, where a is a constant, is *sometimes*, *always*, or *never* a function. Explain your reasoning. **Sample answer: Never; the graph of $x = a$ is a vertical line.**

55. WHICH ONE DOESN'T BELONG? Of the four equations shown, identify the one that does not belong. Explain your reasoning.

$y = 2x + 3$	$2x + y = 5$	$y = 5$	$y = 2xy$

$y = 2xy$; Sample answer: $y = 2xy$ is not a linear function.

56. WRITING IN MATH Consider the graph of the relationship between hours worked and earnings.

a. Why do you think the graph of this relationship should only be in the first quadrant?

b. Provide another example of a situation in which only the first quadrant is needed. Explain your reasoning.

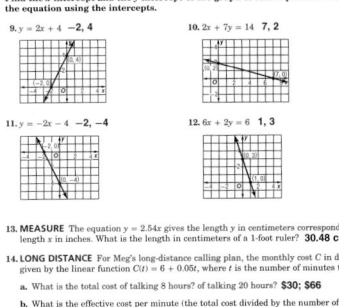

Multiple Representations In Exercise 51, students use graphs, a table, and verbal reasoning to identify properties of linear functions.

Additional Answer

46. $x - 18y = -31$; $A = 1$, $B = -18$, $C = -31$

Enrichment
CRM p. 16 OL BL

2-2 Enrichment

Diophantine Equations

The first great algebraist, Diophantus of Alexandria (about A.D. 300), devoted much of his work to the solving of indeterminate equations. An indeterminate equation has more than one variable and an unlimited number of solutions. An example is $x + 2y = 4$.

When the coefficients of an indeterminate equation are integers and you are asked to find solutions that must be integers, the equation is called a *diophantine*. Such equations can be quite difficult to solve, often involving trial and error—and some luck!

Solve each diophantine equation by finding at least one pair of positive integers that makes the equation true. Some hints are given to help you.

1. $2x + 5y = 32$
   a. First solve the equation for x. $x = 16 - \frac{5y}{2}$
   b. Why must y be an even number? **If y is odd, then x is not an integer.**
   c. Find at least one solution. **Sample answers: (11, 2), (6, 4), (1, 6)**
2. $5x + 2y = 42$

Study Guide and Intervention
CRM pp. 11–12 AL OL ELL

2-2 Study Guide and Intervention

Linear Relations and Functions

Linear Relations and Functions A **linear equation** has no operations other than addition, subtraction, and multiplication of a variable by a constant. The variables may not be multiplied together or appear in a denominator. A linear equation does not contain variables with exponents other than 1. The graph of a linear equation is always a line.

A **linear function** is a function with ordered pairs that satisfy a linear equation. Any linear function can be written in the form $f(x) = mx + b$, where m and b are real numbers.

If an equation is linear, you need only two points that satisfy the equation in order to graph the equation. One way is to find the x-intercept and the y-intercept and connect these two points with a line.

Example 1 Is $f(x) = 0.2 - \frac{x}{5}$ a linear function? Explain.

Yes; it is a linear function because it can be written in the form $f(x) = -\frac{1}{5}x + 0.2$.

Example 2 Is $2x + xy - 3y = 0$ a linear function? Explain.

No; it is not a linear function because the variables x and y are multiplied together in the middle term.

Exercises

State whether each equation or function is a linear function. Write *yes* or *no*. Explain.

1. $6y - x = 7$ **Yes; it can be written as $y = \frac{x}{6} + \frac{7}{6}$.**
2. $9x = \frac{18}{y}$ **No; the variable y appears in the denominator.**
3. $f(x) = 2 - \frac{x}{11}$ **Yes; it can be written as $f(x) = -\frac{x}{11} + 2$.**
4. $2y - \frac{x}{6} - 4 = 0$ **Yes; it can be written as $y = \frac{x}{12} + 2$.**
5. $1.6x - 2.4y = 4$ **Yes; it can be written as $y = \frac{2}{3}x - \frac{5}{3}$.**
6. $0.2x = 100 - \frac{0.4}{y}$ **No; the variable y appears in the denominator.**
7. $f(x) = 4 - x^3$ **No; the variable x is being multiplied by itself.**
8. $f(x) = \frac{4}{x}$ **No; the variable x appears in the denominator.**
9. $2yx - 3y + 2x = 0$ **No; the variables x and y are being multiplied together.**

Lesson 2-2

Chapter 2 11 Glencoe Algebra 2

Practice
CRM p. 14 AL OL BL ELL

2-2 Practice

Linear Relations and Functions

State whether each equation or function is a linear function. Write *yes* or *no*. Explain.

1. $h(x) = 23$ **Yes; there are no variables.**
2. $y = \frac{2}{3}x$ **Yes; it is in $y = mx + b$ form.**
3. $y = \frac{5}{x}$ **No; x is a denominator.**
4. $9 - 5xy = 2$ **No; x and y are multiplied.**

Write each equation in standard form. Identify A, B, and C.

5. $y = 7x - 5$ **$7x - y = 5$; 7, −1, 5**
6. $y = \frac{3}{8}x + 5$ **$3x - 8y = -40$; 3, −8, −40**
7. $3y - 5 = 0$ **$3y = 5$; 0, 3, 5**
8. $x = -\frac{2}{7}y + \frac{3}{4}$ **$28x + 8y = 21$; 28, 8, 21**

Find the x-intercept and the y-intercept of the graph of each equation. Then graph the equation using the intercepts.

9. $y = 2x + 4$ **−2, 4**

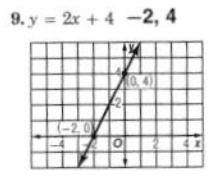

10. $2x + 7y = 14$ **7, 2**

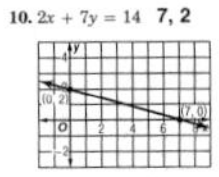

11. $y = -2x - 4$ **−2, −4**

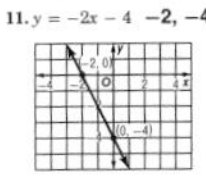

12. $6x + 2y = 6$ **1, 3**

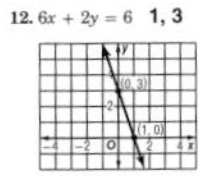

13. **MEASURE** The equation $y = 2.54x$ gives the length y in centimeters corresponding to a length x in inches. What is the length in centimeters of a 1-foot ruler? **30.48 cm**
14. **LONG DISTANCE** For Meg's long-distance calling plan, the monthly cost C in dollars is given by the linear function $C(t) = 6 + 0.05t$, where t is the number of minutes talked.
    a. What is the total cost of talking 8 hours? of talking 20 hours? **\$30; \$66**
    b. What is the effective cost per minute (the total cost divided by the number of minutes talked) of talking 8 hours? of talking 20 hours? **\$0.0625; \$0.055**

Chapter 2 14 Glencoe Algebra 2

Word Problem Practice
CRM p. 15 AL OL BL ELL

2-2 Word Problem Practice

Linear Relations and Functions

1. **WORK RATE** The linear equation $n = 10t$ describes n, the number of origami boxes that Holly can fold in t hours. How many boxes can Holly fold in 3 hours? **30 boxes**
2. **BASKETBALL** Tony tossed a basketball. Below is a graph showing the height of the basketball as a function of time. Is this the graph of a linear function? Explain.

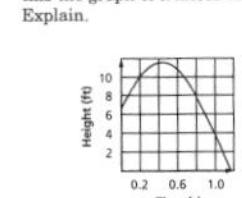

No, it is not linear because graphs of linear functions are always straight lines. This graph curves.

3. **PROFIT** Paul charges people \$25 to test the air quality in their homes. The device he uses to test air quality cost him \$500. Write an equation that describes Paul's net profit as a function of the number of clients he gets. How many clients does he need to break even? **Paul's profit is $p = 25c - 500$, if c is the number of clients and p is his profit. He needs 20 clients to break even.**
4. **RAMP** A ramp is described by the equation $5x + 7y = 35$. What is the area of the shaded region?

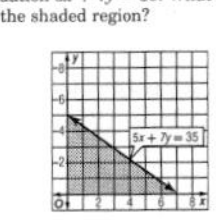

17.5 square units

5. **SWIMMING POOL** A swimming pool is shaped as shown below. The total perimeter is 500 feet.

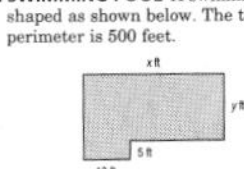

   a. Write an equation that relates x and y. **Sample answer: $2x + 2y + 10 = 500$**
   b. Write the linear equation from part a in standard form. **$x + y = 295$**
   c. Graph the equation.

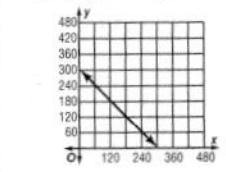

   d. Olympic swimming pools are 164 feet long. If this pool is an olympic pool, what is the value of y? **131 feet**

Lesson 2-2

Chapter 2 15 Glencoe Algebra 2

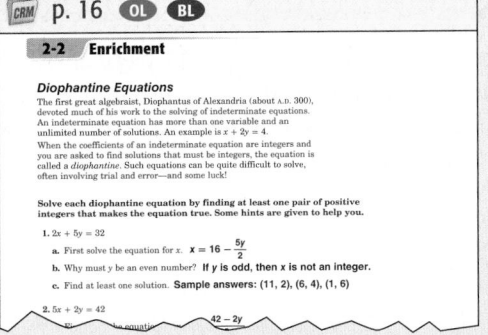

4 ASSESS

Ticket Out the Door Ask each student to write a short explanation of how to determine if an equation is linear.

Formative Assessment

Check for student understanding of concepts in Lessons 2-1 and 2-2.

CRM Quiz 1, p. 59

NGSSS PRACTICE 912.A.3.5, 912.A.3.6, 912.A.2.6

57. Tom bought n DVDs for a total cost of $15n - 2$ dollars. Which expression represents the cost of each DVD? **C**

A. $n(15n - 2)$
B. $n + (15n - 2)$
C. $(15n - 2) \div n; n \neq 0$
D. $(15n - 2) - n$

58. THINK SOLVE EXPLAIN **SHORT RESPONSE** What is the complete solution of the equation?

$|9 - 3x| = 18$ **−3, 9**

59. **NUMBER THEORY** If a, b, c, and d are consecutive odd integers and $a < b < c < d$, how much greater is $c + d$ than $a + b$? **I**

F. 2
G. 4
H. 6
I. 8

60. **ACT/SAT** Which function is linear? **B**

A. $f(x) = x^2$
B. $g(x) = 2.7$
C. $f(x) = \sqrt{9 - x^2}$
D. $g(x) = \sqrt{x - 1}$

Spiral Review

62. D = {−2, 1, 2, 4}, R = {1, 3, 5}; function; onto

State the domain and range of each relation. Then determine whether each relation is a *function*. If it is a function, determine if it is *one-to-one*, *onto*, *both*, or *neither*. (Lesson 2-1) **63. D = {−3, −4, 7}, R = {−1, −2, 9}; function; both**

61.

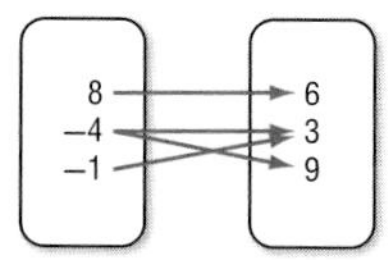

D = {8, −4, −1}, R = {6, 3, 9}; not a function

62.

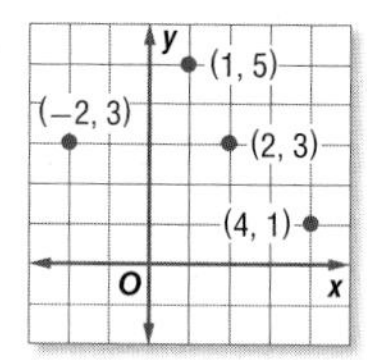

63.

x	y
−4	−2
−3	−1
−3	−1
7	9

64. **SHOPPING** Claudio is shopping for a new television. The average price of the televisions he likes is \$800, and the actual prices differ from the average by up to \$350. Write and solve an absolute value inequality to determine the price range of the televisions. (Lesson 1-6) **$|x - 800| \leq 350$; $\$450 \leq x \leq \$1150$**

Evaluate each expression if $a = -6$, $b = 5$, and $c = 3.6$. (Lesson 1-1)

65. $\frac{6a - 3c}{2ab}$ **1.78**

66. $\frac{a + 7b}{4bc}$ **$\frac{29}{72}$**

67. $\frac{b - c}{a + c}$ **$-\frac{7}{12}$**

68. **FOOD** Brandi can order a small, medium, or large pizza with pepperoni, mushrooms, or sausage. How many different one-topping pizzas can she order? (Lesson 0-4) **9**

Skills Review

Evaluate each expression. (Lesson 1-1)

69. $\frac{12 - 8}{4 - (-2)}$ **$\frac{2}{3}$**

70. $\frac{5 - 9}{-3 - (-6)}$ **$-\frac{4}{3}$**

71. $\frac{-2 - 8}{3 - (-5)}$ **$-\frac{5}{4}$**

72. $\frac{-2 - (-6)}{-1 - (-8)}$ **$\frac{4}{7}$**

73. $\frac{-7 - (-11)}{-3 - 9}$ **$-\frac{1}{3}$**

74. $\frac{-1 - 8}{7 - (-3)}$ **$-\frac{9}{10}$**

75. $\frac{-12 - (-3)}{-6 - (-5)}$ **9**

76. $\frac{4 - 3}{2 - 5}$ **$-\frac{1}{3}$**

Differentiated Instruction OL BL

Extension Have students place a piece of spaghetti or a pencil on a large coordinate plane to model the graphs of equations such as: $x = 4$, $x = -2$, $y = 0$, $y = -3$, $x = y$, and $x = -y$.

EXTEND 2-2

Algebra Lab: Roots of Equations and Zeros of Functions

NGSSS MA.912.A.4.8 **Describe the relationships among the solutions of an equation, the zeros of a function,** the *x*-intercepts of a graph, and the factors of a polynomial expression, with and **without technology.**

The *solution* of an equation is called the *root* of the equation.

EXAMPLE Determine Roots

Find the root of $0 = 5x - 10$.

$0 = 5x - 10$	**Original equation**
$10 = 5x$	**Add 10 to each side.**
$2 = x$	**Divide each side by 5.**

The root of the equation is 2.

You can also find the root of an equation by finding the *zero* of its related function. Values of x for which $f(x) = 0$ are called *zeros* of the function f.

Linear Equation	Related Linear Function
$0 = 5x - 10$	$f(x) = 5x - 10$ or $y = 5x - 10$

The zero of a function is the *x-intercept* of its graph. Since the graph of $y = 5x - 10$ intercepts the x-axis at 2, the zero of the function is 2.

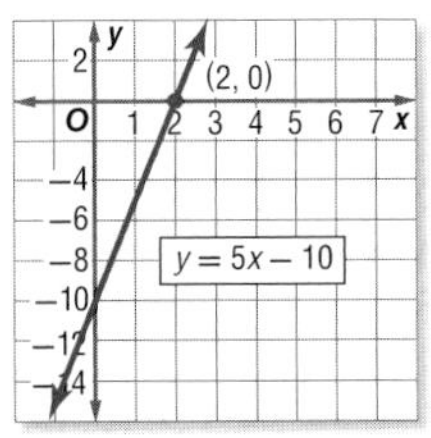

1. The root and solution of $0 = 4x + 10$ is -2.5, because it is the value of x that makes the equation a true statement. The zero of $f(x) = 4x + 10$ is -2.5 because it is the value of x for which $f(x) = 0$.

3. False; the y-intercept does not represent a zero of the function. The x-intercept -2 is the only zero.

Exercises

1. Use $0 = 4x + 10$ and $f(x) = 4x + 10$ to distinguish among roots, solutions, and zeros.
2. Relate solutions of equations and x-intercepts of graphs. The solution of an equation equals the x-intercept of the graph of the related function.

Determine whether each statement is *true* or *false*. Explain your reasoning.

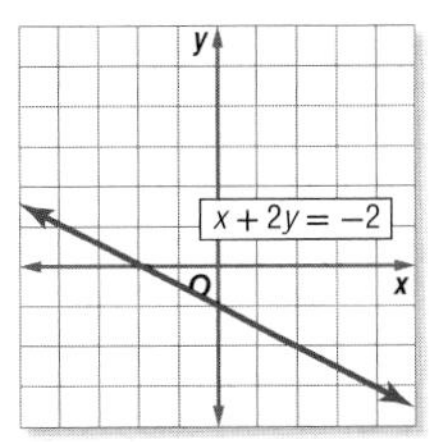

3. The function graphed at the right has two zeros, -2 and -1.
4. The root of $6x + 9 = 0$ is -1.5. True; the root of an equation is its solution.
5. $f(0)$ is a zero of the function $f(x) = -\frac{2}{3}x + 12$. False; 18 is a zero of the function because it is the value of x for which $f(x) = 0$.
6. **FUNDRAISERS** The function $y = 2x - 150$ represents the money raised y when the Boosters sell x soft drinks at a basketball game. Find the zero and describe what it means in the context of this situation. Make a connection between the zero of the function and the root of $0 = 2x - 150$. 75; After selling 75 soft drinks, the Boosters have made 0 dollars. The zero of the function equals the root of the equation because it is the value of x when $y = 0$.

From Concrete to Abstract

Ask students to summarize what they have learned about the mathematical terms, such as roots, solutions, and zeros, in everyday words. Then have them cite examples.

EXTEND 2-2

Lesson Notes

1 FOCUS

Objective

Distinguish among roots, solutions, and zeros.

Teaching Tip

Begin the lesson by asking students if they know of any words that have more than one meaning depending on how they are used. For example, the word *sentence* can mean a group of words that expresses a complete thought or a judgment by a court specifying the punishment for a crime committed.

2 TEACH

Working in Cooperative Groups

Divide the class into groups of two or three, mixing abilities. Ask each group to read about roots of equations and zeros of functions.

Explain to students that if they can relate a word they are trying to learn to something familiar, it makes it easier to remember what the new word means. By relating mathematical terms to everyday things, students can recall their meanings more readily.

Practice Have students complete Exercises 1–5.

3 ASSESS

Formative Assessment

Use Exercise 6 to assess whether students can distinguish between roots of equations and zeros of functions.

2-3 Lesson Notes

1 FOCUS

Vertical Alignment

Before Lesson 2-3
Graph linear relations.

Lesson 2-3
Find rate of change and determine the slope of a line.

After Lesson 2-3
Identify and sketch graphs of parent functions, including quadratic.

2 TEACH

Scaffolding Questions

Have students read the *Why?* section of the lesson.

Ask:

- What do the variables *r, d,* and *t* represent? *r* represents rate, *d* represents distance, and *t* represents time.
- How many miles did the car drive in the first three hours? 204 mi
- At what rate was the car traveling in the first three hours? 68 miles per hour

2-3 Rate of Change and Slope

Then
You graphed linear relations. (Lesson 2-2)

Now
- Find rate of change.
- Determine the slope of a line.

NGSSS
MA.912.A.10.3 Decide whether a given statement is always, sometimes, or never true (statements involving linear or quadratic expressions, equations, or inequalities rational or radical expressions or logarithmic or exponential functions).

New Vocabulary
rate of change
slope

FL Math Online
glencoe.com

Why?

The table at the right shows the total distance a car traveled over various time intervals. You can determine how fast the car was traveling using a formula for distance.

$$rt = d$$
$$r = \frac{d}{t}$$

Time (h)	Distance (mi)
1	68
2.5	170
3	204
4.5	306
5	340

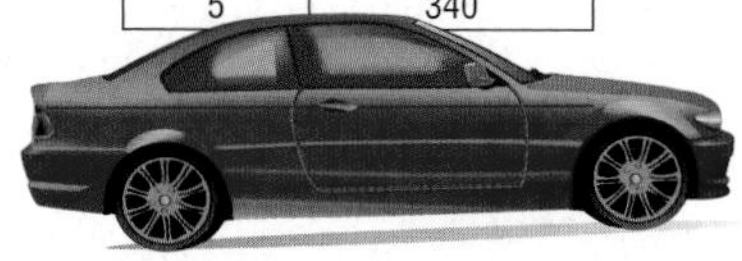

Rate of Change **Rate of change** is a ratio that compares how much one quantity changes, on average, relative to the change in another quantity. If x is the independent variable and y is the dependent variable, then rate of change $= \frac{\text{change in } y}{\text{change in } x}$. This is sometimes referred to as $\frac{\Delta y}{\Delta x}$.

Real-World EXAMPLE 1 Constant Rate of Change

CHEMISTRY The table shows the temperature of a solution after it has been removed from a heat source. Find the rate of change in temperature for the solution.

Time (min)	Temperature (°C)
0	143.6
2	139.4
5	133.1
8	126.8
12	118.4

Use the ordered pairs (2, 139.4) and (5, 133.1).

$$\text{rate of change} = \frac{\text{change in } y}{\text{change in } x}$$
$$= \frac{\text{change in temperature}}{\text{change in time}}$$
$$= \frac{133.1 - 139.4}{5 - 2}$$
$$= \frac{-6.3}{3} \text{ or } \frac{-2.1}{1}$$

The rate of change is −2.1. This means that the temperature is decreasing by 2.1°C each minute.

Guided Practice

1. **RECREATION** The graph at the right shows the number of gallons of water in a swimming pool as it is being filled. At what rate is the pool being filled? **36 gal/min**

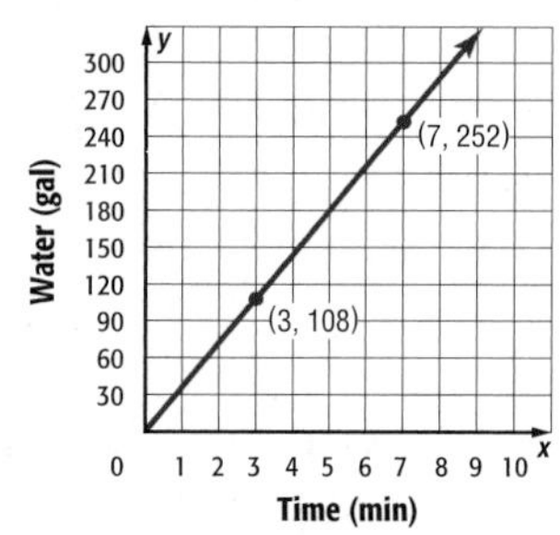

Personal Tutor glencoe.com

Lesson 2-3 Resources

Resource	Approaching-Level	On-Level	Beyond-Level	English Learners
Teacher Edition	• Differentiated Instruction, p. 78	• Differentiated Instruction, p. 78	• Differentiated Instruction, p. 82	• Differentiated Instruction, p. 78
Chapter Resource Masters	• Study Guide and Intervention, pp. 17–18 • Skills Practice, p. 19 • Practice, p. 20 • Word Problem Practice, p. 21	• Study Guide and Intervention, pp. 17–18 • Skills Practice, p. 19 • Practice, p. 20 • Word Problem Practice, p. 21 • Enrichment, p. 22	• Practice, p. 20 • Word Problem Practice, p. 21 • Enrichment, p. 22	• Study Guide and Intervention, pp. 17–18 • Skills Practice, p. 19 • Practice, p. 20 • Word Problem Practice, p. 21
Transparencies	• 5-Minute Check Transparency 2-3	• 5-Minute Check Transparency 2-3	• 5-Minute Check Transparency 2-3	• 5-Minute Check Transparency 2-3
Other	• Study Notebook	• Study Notebook	• Study Notebook	• Study Notebook

Up to this point, you have used rates of change that are constant. Many real-world situations involve rates of change that are not constant. These situations are often described using an average rate of change over a specified interval.

Real-World EXAMPLE 2 Average Rate of Change

MUSIC Refer to the graph at the right. Find the average rate of change of the percent of total music sales for both CDs and downloads from 2001 to 2006. Compare the rates.

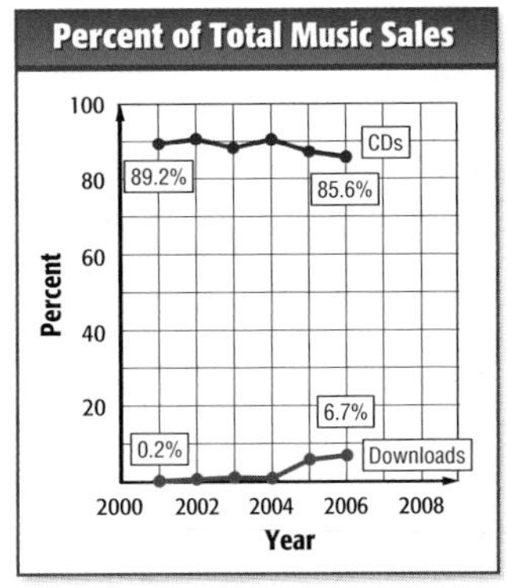

Source: Recording Industry Association of America

CDs:

$$\text{rate of change} = \frac{\text{change in } y}{\text{change in } x}$$

$$= \frac{\text{change in percent}}{\text{change in time}}$$

$$= \frac{85.6 - 89.2}{2006 - 2001}$$

$$= \frac{-3.6}{5} \text{ or } \frac{-0.72}{1}$$

Downloads:

$$\text{rate of change} = \frac{\text{change in } y}{\text{change in } x}$$

$$= \frac{\text{change in percent}}{\text{change in time}}$$

$$= \frac{6.7 - 0.2}{2006 - 2001}$$

$$= \frac{6.5}{5} \text{ or } \frac{1.3}{1}$$

The percent of CD music sales declined at an average rate of 0.72% per year, while the percent of downloaded music sales increased at an average rate of 1.3% per year.

StudyTip

Independent Quantities Rates of change often include a measure of *time* as the independent variable.

Real-World Link

As of April 2007, 36% of teens preferred to purchase CDs and 64% preferred to download music online.

Source: CNN

2. State College: average increase about 803 applicants per year; Central University: average increase about 177 applicants per year

Guided Practice

2. **EDUCATION** In 2000, 23,142 students applied to State College, and 34,689 students applied to Central University. In 2008, 29,563 students applied to State College, and 36,107 applied to Central University. Determine the average rate of change in applicants for both schools from 2000 to 2008.

Personal Tutor glencoe.com

Slope The **slope** of a line is the ratio of the change in the *y*-coordinates to the corresponding change in the *x*-coordinates. The slope of a line is the same as its rate of change.

Suppose a line passes through points at (x_1, y_1) and (x_2, y_2).

$$\text{Slope} = \frac{\text{change in } y\text{-coordinates}}{\text{change in } x\text{-coordinates}} = \frac{y_2 - y_1}{x_2 - x_1}$$

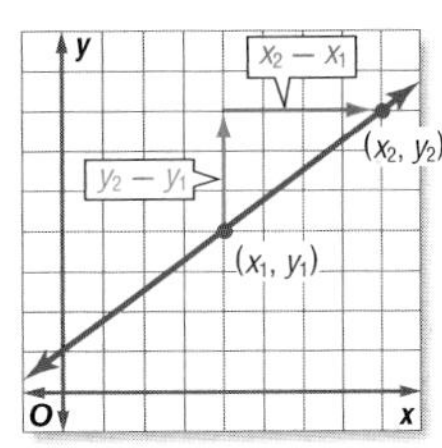

Rate of Change

Examples 1 and 2 involve finding the rate of change in real-world situations.

Formative Assessment

Use the Guided Practice exercises after each example to determine students' understanding of concepts.

Additional Examples

1 **COLLEGE ADMISSIONS** In 2004, 56,878 students applied to UCLA. In 2006, 60,291 students applied. Find the rate of change in the number of students applying for admission from 2004 to 2006. 1706.5 students per year

2 **BUSINESS** Refer to the graph below, which shows data on the fastest-growing restaurant chain in the U.S. during the time period of the graph. Find the rate of change of the number of stores from 2001 to 2006.

Between 2000 and 2006, the number of stores in the U.S. increased at an average rate of 5.4(1000), or 5400 stores per year.

Additional Examples also in Interactive Classroom PowerPoint® Presentations

IWB INTERACTIVE WHITEBOARD READY

Focus on Mathematical Content

Slope The steepness of a line is measured by its slope. The slope of a nonvertical line is found by identifying two points on the line and dividing the difference in their *y*-coordinates by the difference in their *x*-coordinates. The slope of a horizontal line is 0, and the slope of a vertical line is undefined.

Slope

Examples 3 and 4 ask students to find the slope of a line.

Additional Examples

3 Find the slope of the line that passes through (–1, 4) and (1, –2).
$\frac{-6}{2}$ or –3; The slope is –3.

4 Find the slope of the line shown below. $m = \frac{1}{2}$

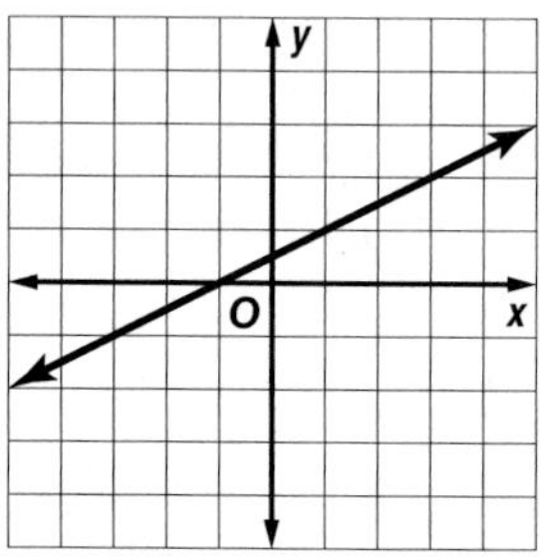

TEACH with TECH

BLOG Have students write a blog entry explaining how to find the slope of a line. Have them explain how the slope describes the appearance of the line.

StudyTip

Slope The formula for slope is often remembered as *rise over run*, where the rise is the difference in *y*-coordinates and the run is the difference in *x*-coordinates.

Key Concept — Slope of a Line

Words The slope of a line is the ratio of the change in *y*-coordinates to the change in *x*-coordinates.

Example The slope m of a line passing through (x_1, y_1) and (x_2, y_2) is given by $m = \frac{y_2 - y_1}{x_2 - x_1}$, where $x_1 \neq x_2$.

EXAMPLE 3 Find Slope Using Coordinates

Find the slope of the line that passes through (–4, 3) and (2, 5).

$m = \frac{y_2 - y_1}{x_2 - x_1}$ **Slope Formula**

$= \frac{5 - 3}{2 - (-4)}$ $(x_1, y_1) = (-4, 3), (x_2, y_2) = (2, 5)$

$= \frac{2}{6}$ or $\frac{1}{3}$ **Simplify.**

Guided Practice

Find the slope of the line that passes through each pair of points.

3A. (1, –3) and (3, 5) 4

3B. (–8, 11) and (24, –9) $-\frac{5}{8}$

Personal Tutor glencoe.com

You can choose any two points from the graph of a line to find the slope.

StudyTip

Slope is Constant The slope of a line is the same, no matter what two points on the line are used.

EXAMPLE 4 Find Slope Using a Graph

Find the slope of the line shown at the right.

The line passes through (–2, 0) and (0, –3).

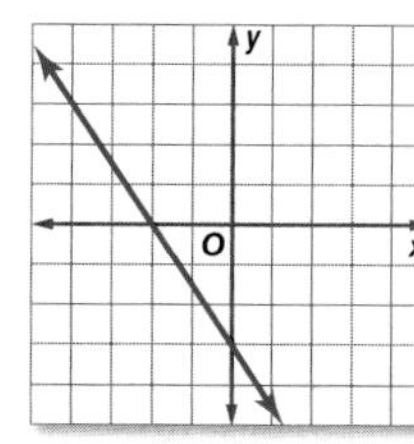

$m = \frac{y_2 - y_1}{x_2 - x_1}$ **Slope Formula**

$= \frac{-3 - 0}{0 - (-2)}$ $(x_1, y_1) = (-2, 0), (x_2, y_2) = (0, -3)$

$= \frac{-3}{2}$ or $-\frac{3}{2}$ **Simplify.**

Guided Practice

Find the slope of each line.

4A. $\frac{3}{8}$

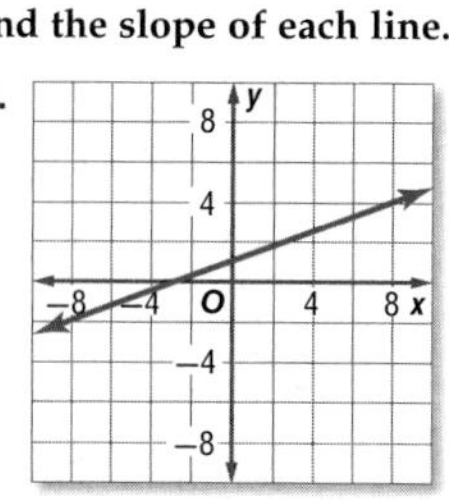

4B. –4

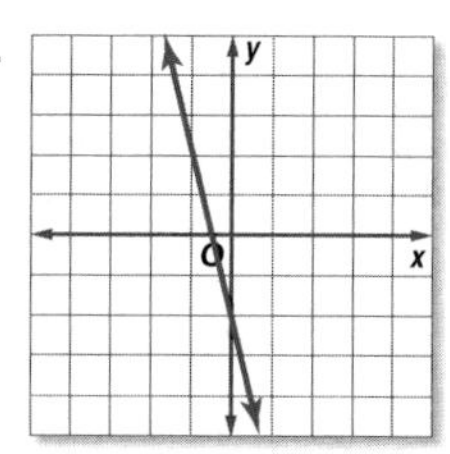

Personal Tutor glencoe.com

Differentiated Instruction AL OL ELL

If some students have trouble remembering whether a vertical line or a horizontal line has a slope of 0,

Then they can remember that a horizontal line has a slope of 0 by associating the o in the word horizontal with 0.

78 Chapter 2 Linear Relations and Functions

Check Your Understanding

Example 1 p. 76

Find the rate of change for each set of data.

1.

Time (min)	2	4	6	8	10
Distance (ft)	12	24	36	48	60

6 feet/min

2.

Time (sec)	5	10	15	20	25
Volume (cm^3)	16	32	48	64	80

3.2 cm^3/sec

Example 2 p. 77

3. **CAMERAS** The graph shows the number of digital still cameras and film cameras sold by Yellow Camera Stores in recent years.

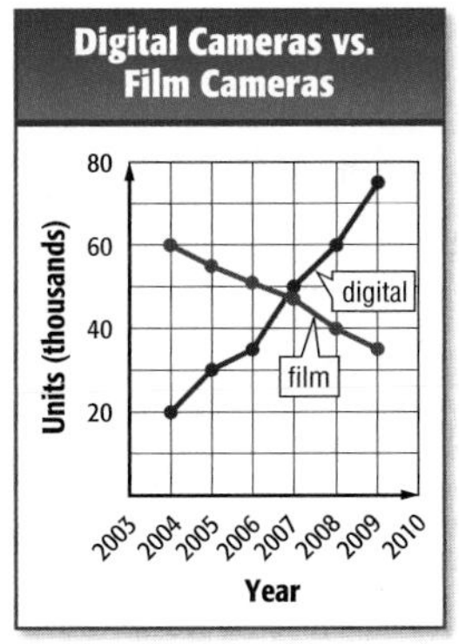

a. Find the average rate of change of the number of digital cameras sold from 2004 to 2009.

b. Find the average rate of change of the number of film cameras sold from 2004 to 2009.

c. What do the signs of each rate of change represent? The positive rate in part a represents an increase in sales of digital cameras. The negative rate in part b represents a decrease in sales of film cameras.

3a. about 11,000 per year
3b. about −5000 per year

Example 3 p. 78

Find the slope of the line that passes through each pair of points.

4. (3, 2), (8, 12) 2

5. (−1, 4), (3, −8) −3

6. (−2, −5), (−7, 10) −3

Example 4 p. 78

Determine the rate of change of each graph.

7. 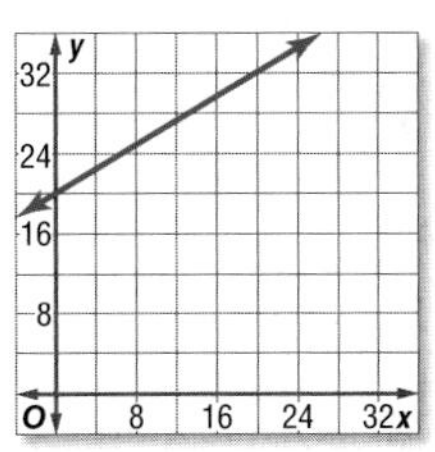

$\frac{3}{5}$

8. 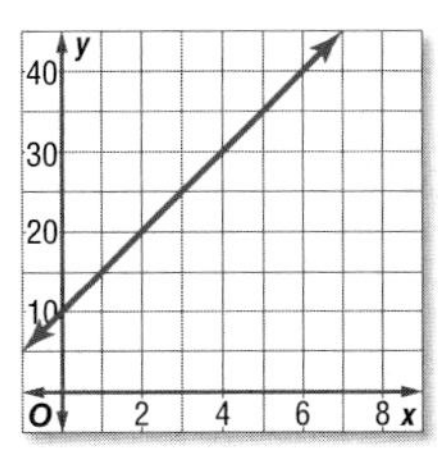

5

Practice and Problem Solving

= **Step-by-Step Solutions** begin on page R20. **Extra Practice** begins on page 947.

Example 1 p. 76

Find the rate of change for each set of data.

9.

Time (day)	3	6	9	12	15
Height (mm)	20	40	60	80	100

$\frac{20}{3}$ mm/day

10.

Weight (lb)	11	22	33	44	55
Cost ($)	8	16	24	32	40

$\frac{8}{11}$ \$/lb

3 PRACTICE

Formative Assessment

Use Exercises 1–8 to check for understanding.

Use the chart on the bottom of this page to customize assignments for your students.

Differentiated Homework Options

Level	Assignment	Two-Day Option	
AL Basic	9–21, 36, 38–57	9–21 odd, 41–44	10–20 even, 36, 38–40, 45–57
OL Core	9–29 odd, 30, 31–35 odd, 36, 38–57	9–21, 41–44	22–36, 38–41, 45–57
BL Advanced	30–54, (optional: 55–57)		

Study Guide and Intervention
CRM pp. 17–18 AL OL ELL

2-3 Study Guide and Intervention
Rate of Change and Slope

Rate of Change Rate of change is a ratio that compares how much one quantity changes, on average, relative to the change in another quantity.

Example **Find the average rate of change for the data in the table.**

Average Rate of Change $= \frac{\text{change in } y}{\text{change in } x}$

$= \frac{\text{change in Elevation of the Sun}}{\text{change in Time}}$

$= \frac{84° - 6°}{11:00 \text{ A.M.} - 7:00 \text{ A.M.}}$

$= \frac{78°}{5 \text{ hours}}$

$= 15.6$ degrees per hour

Elevation of the Sun (in degrees)	Time
6°	7:00 A.M.
26°	8:00 A.M.
45°	9:00 A.M.
64°	10:00 A.M.
84°	11:00 A.M.

Exercises

Find the rate of change for each set of data.

1.

Time P.M.	People in auditorium
7:15	26
7:22	61
7:24	71
7:30	101
7:40	151

5 people per minute

2.

Time (minutes)	Altitude of balloon (meters)
3	520
8	1,220
11	1,640
15	2,200
23	3,320

140 meters per minute

3.

Time (minutes)	Vehicles through tunnel
4	1,610
11	2,131
19	2,746
22	2,970
28	3,432

about 76 vehicles per minute

4.

Time (seconds)	Depth of sinking stone (meters)
0	3.51
7	4.77
11	5.49
21	7.29
29	8.73

0.18 meters per second

5.

Time (seconds)	Water through Channel (liters)
6	22,172
13	24,706
15	25,430
23	28,326
47	37,014

362 liters per second

6.

Time (seconds)	Distance between Two Sleds (meters)
0	37.3
3	30.2
4	27.7
7	20.8
13	7.2

−2.3 meters per second

Chapter 2 17 Glencoe Algebra 2

Lesson 2-3

Practice
CRM p. 20 AL OL BL ELL

2-3 Practice
Rate of Change and Slope

Find the slope of the line that passes through each pair of points. Express as a fraction in simplest form.

1. (3, −8), (−5, 2) $-\frac{5}{4}$
2. (−10, −3), (7, 2) $\frac{5}{17}$
3. (−7, −6), (3, −6) **0**
4. (8, 2), (8, −1) **undefined**
5. (4, 3), (7, −2) $-\frac{5}{3}$
6. (−6, −3), (−8, 4) $-\frac{7}{2}$

Determine the rate of change of each graph.

7. 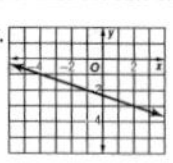 $-\frac{1}{3}$

8. 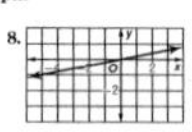 $\frac{1}{5}$

9. 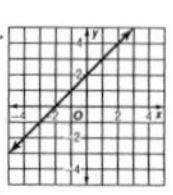 **1**

10. 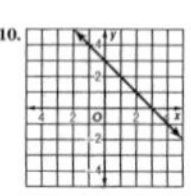 **−1**

11. 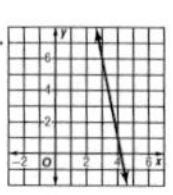 **−5**

12. 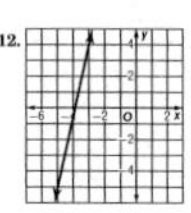 $\frac{9}{2}$

13. **DEPRECIATION** A machine that originally cost \$15,600 has a value of \$7500 at the end of 3 years. The same machine has a value of \$2800 at the end of 8 years.

a. Find the average rate of change in value (depreciation) of the machine between its purchase and the end of 3 years. **−\$2700 per year**

b. Find the average rate of change in value of the machine between the end of 3 years and the end of 8 years. **−\$940 per year**

c. Interpret the sign of your answers.
They are negative because the value is decreasing.

Chapter 2 20 Glencoe Algebra 2

Word Problem Practice
CRM p. 21 AL OL BL ELL

2-3 Word Problem Practice
Rate of Change and Slope

1. **TETHER** A tether is tied tautly to the top of a pole as shown. What is the slope of the tether?

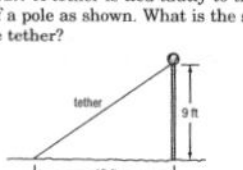

$\frac{3}{4}$

2. **AVIATION** An airplane descends along a straight-line path with a slope of −0.1 to land at an airport. Use the information in the diagram to determine the initial height of the airplane.

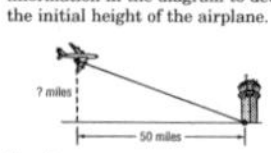

5 miles

3. **ROCK CLIMBING** Gail is climbing at a popular rock climbing spot, Boulder Canyon Sport Park in Colorado. The table below shows Gail's altitude above ground during a rock climb up a cliff.

Time	Altitude (m)
10:00	0
10:20	22
10:40	30
11:00	33

Complete the following table of Gail's average rate of ascent.

Time Period	Average rate of ascent (m/h)
10:00–10:20	**66**
10:20–10:40	**24**
10:40–11:00	**9**

4. **DESIGN** An architect is designing a window with slanted interior bars. The crossbeam is perpendicular to the other four bars. What is the slope of the crossbeam?

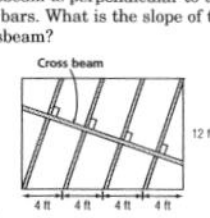

$-\frac{1}{3}$

5. **READING** The graph that shows how many pages of her book Bridget read each day.

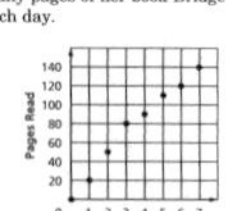

a. Find the average number of pages Bridget read per day.
20

b. On which days did Bridget read more pages than her daily average?
Day 2 and Day 3

c. If Bridget had been able to keep up the pace she had on day 3, how many days would it have taken her to reach page 140?
5 days

Chapter 2 21 Glencoe Algebra 2

Lesson 2-3

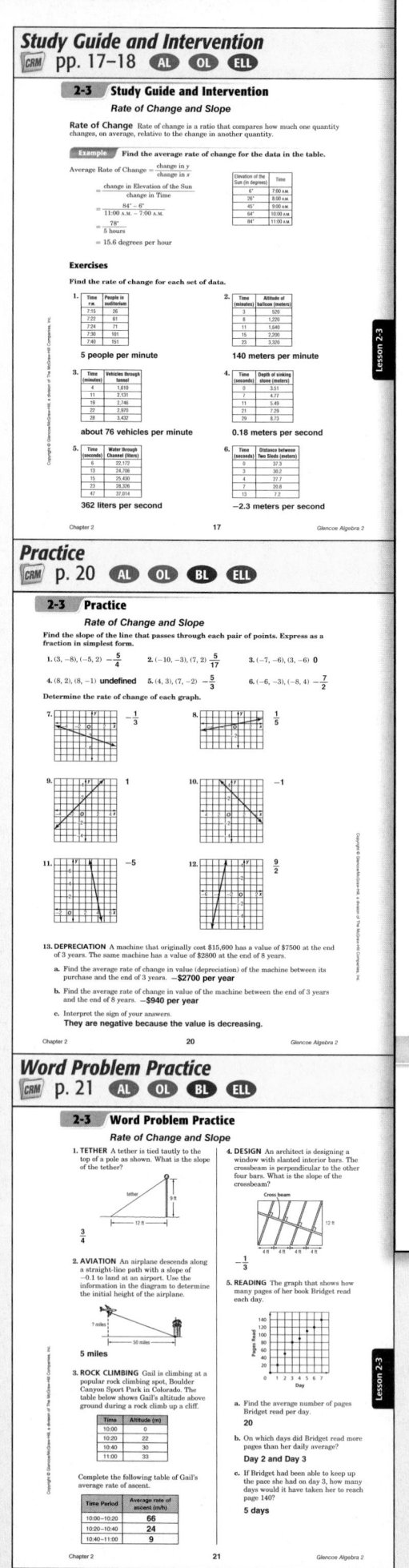

Example 2 p. 77

11. **HEALTH** The table below shows Lisa's temperature during an illness over a 3-day period.

Day	Monday		Tuesday		Wednesday	
Time	8:00 A.M.	8:00 P.M.	8:00 A.M.	8:00 P.M.	8:00 A.M.	8:00 P.M.
Temp (°F)	100.5	102.3	103.1	100.7	99.9	98.6

a. What was the average rate of change in Lisa's temperature from 8:00 A.M. on Monday to 8:00 P.M. on Monday? **0.15°/h**

b. What was the average rate of change in Lisa's temperature from 8:00 A.M. on Tuesday to 8:00 P.M. on Wednesday? Is your answer reasonable? What does the sign of the rate mean?

11b. −0.125°/h; Yes; the number should be negative because her temperature is dropping.

c. During which 12-hour period was the average rate of change in Lisa's temperature the greatest? **Tuesday 8:00 A.M.–Tuesday 8:00 P.M.**

Example 3 p. 78

Find the slope of the line that passes through each pair of points. Express as a fraction in simplest form.

12. (−2, 11), (5, 6) $-\frac{5}{7}$
13. (−9, −11), (6, 3) $\frac{14}{15}$
14. (−1.5, 3.5), (4.5, 6) $\frac{5}{12}$
15. (−4.5, 9.5), (−1, 2.5) **−2**
16. (−8, −0.5), (−4, 5) $\frac{11}{8}$
17. (−6, −2), (−1.5, 5.5) $\frac{5}{3}$

Example 4 p. 78

Determine the rate of change of each graph.

18. 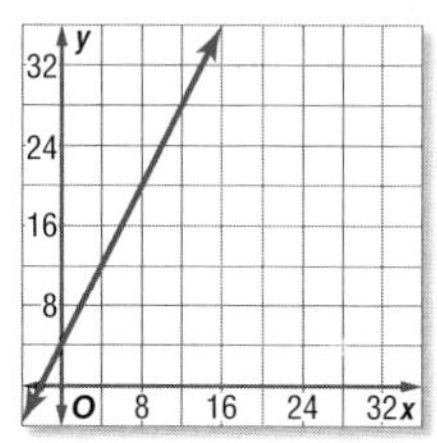 **2**

19. 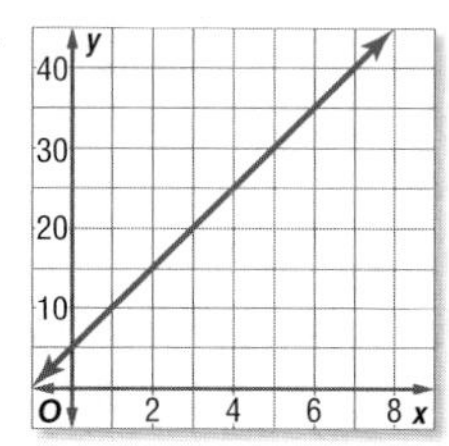 **5**

20. 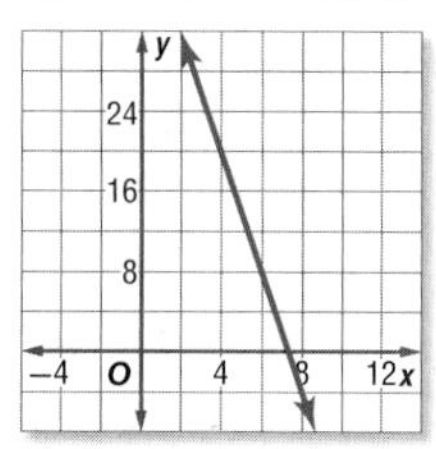 **−6**

21. 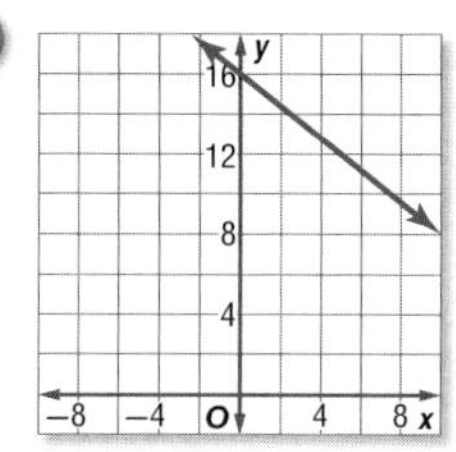 **−0.8**

Real-World Link

The Summit Plummet at Walt Disney World in Orlando, Florida, is the tallest water slide in the U.S.

Source: About, Inc.

22. **RECREATION** The table shows your height on a water slide at various time intervals. **a. See margin.**

Time (s)	Height (ft)
0	120
1	90
2	60
3	30
4	0
5	0

a. Graph the height versus the time on the water slide.

b. Find the average rate of change of a rider between 1 and 3 seconds. **−30 ft/s**

c. Find the average rate of change of a rider between 0 and 5 seconds. **−24 ft/s**

d. What is another word for *rate of change* in this situation? **speed or velocity**

Determine the rate of change for each equation.

23. $6y = 8x - 40$ $\frac{4}{3}$
24. $-2y - 16x = 41$ **−8**
25. $12x - 4y + 5 = 18$ **3**
26. $20x + 85y = 120$ $-\frac{4}{17}$
27. $\frac{3}{2}x - \frac{5}{4}y = 15$ $\frac{6}{5}$
28. $\frac{1}{6}y + \frac{3}{8}x = 24$ $-\frac{9}{4}$

Enrichment
CRM p. 22 OL BL

2-3 Enrichment
The Increase in Greenhouse Gases

The atmosphere is composed of about 50% carbon dioxide, CO_2. The level of carbon dioxide is increasing due to increased fuel consumption and housing and commercial development. The concentration of a compound is measured in parts per million (ppm). For example, if there were 500 CO_2 molecules out of one million air particles, then the CO_2 level would be 500 ppm.

1. In 1965, the concentration of CO_2 was 320 ppm. In 2007, the concentration was 383 ppm. Determine the rate at which CO_2 increased in ppm per year.
CO_2 has increased 1.5 ppm per year.

2. Carbon dioxide concentration is related to human consumption of fossil fuels and the decrease of trees due to development; therefore an increase in human population will result in an increase in carbon dioxide. In 1980 the U.S. population was 225 million. The 2000 census reported 281 million. At what rate is the population increasing per year? What do you estimate the U.S. population to be in 2020?
The U.S. population is increasing at about 2.8 million people per year. Therefore, the population in 2020 would be about 337 million.

3. Use the figures from Exercises 1 and 2 to determine about how much CO_2 is "produced" per million people in 20… Is it possible … reduce the concentration of

Additional Answer

22a. 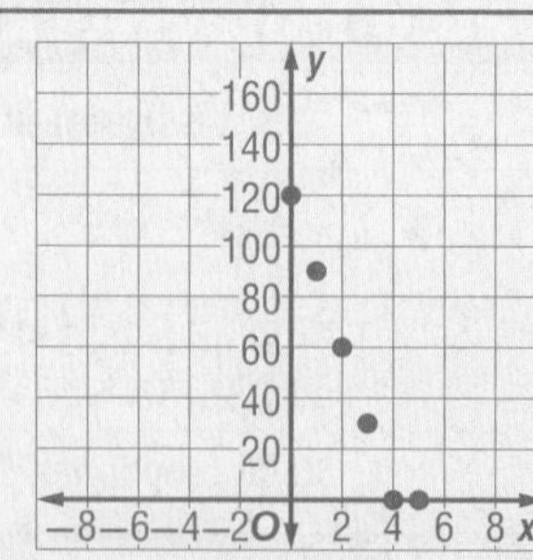

Real-World Link

Construction on the Washington Monument was begun in 1848 and ceased in 1854 due to lack of funds. Construction resumed in 1879 and was completed in 1884.

Source: National Park Service

29. **WASHINGTON MONUMENT** The Washington Monument is 555 feet $5\frac{1}{8}$ inches tall and weighs 90,854 tons. The monument is topped by an aluminum square pyramid. The sides of the pyramid's base measure 5.6 inches, and the pyramid is 8.9 inches tall. Estimate the slope that a face of the pyramid makes with its base. **about 3.2**

30. **MARINE LIFE** The illustrations show the growth of a starfish over time.

a. Find the average rate of change in the measure over time. **2 in./yr**

b. Predict the size of the starfish in 2009. **14 in.**

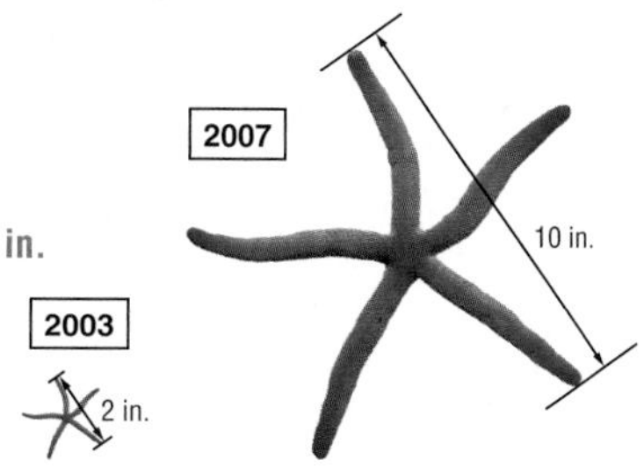

Find the value of r so that the line that passes through each pair of points has the given slope.

31. $(6, r), (3, 3), m = 2$ **9**

32. $(8, 1), (5, r), m = \frac{1}{3}$ **0**

33. $(10, r), (4, -3), m = \frac{4}{3}$ **5**

34. $(8, -2), (r, -6), m = -4$ **9**

35. **MULTIPLE REPRESENTATIONS** In this problem, you will explore the rate of change for the function $f(x) = x^2$.

a. **GRAPHICAL** Graph $f(x) = x^2$. **See margin.**

b. **TABULAR** Complete the table.

x	−4	−3	−2	−1	0	1	2	3	4
$f(x)$	16	9	4	1	0	1	4	9	16
slope		−7	−5	−3	−1	1	3	5	7

c. **VERBAL** Describe what happens to the rate of change for $f(x) = x^2$ as x increases.

36. Patty; Tim calculated slope as the ratio of the change in x to the change in y.

H.O.T. Problems

Use Higher-Order Thinking Skills

36. **ERROR ANALYSIS** Patty and Tim are asked to find the slope of the line passing through the points (4, 3) and (7, 9). Is either of them correct? Explain.

Patty	Tim
$m = \frac{9-3}{7-4}$	$m = \frac{7-4}{9-3}$
$= \frac{6}{3}$ or 2	$= \frac{3}{6}$ or $\frac{1}{2}$

37. **CHALLENGE** The graph of a line passes through the points (2, 3) and (5, 8). Explain how you would find the y-coordinate of the point $(11, y)$ on the same line. Then find y.

38. **OPEN ENDED** Write an example of a function with a rate of change four times as large as its x-intercept. **Sample answer: $y = 12x - 36$**

39. **REASONING** Determine whether the statement *A line has a slope that is a real number* is *sometimes*, *always*, or *never* true. Explain your reasoning.

40. **WRITING IN MATH** Describe the process of finding the rate of change for each.

a. a table of values

b. a graph

c. an equation

40a–c. See margin.

35c. Sample answer: The rate of change is not constant. The rate of change decreases as x approaches zero and then increases as x approaches infinity.

37. Sample answer: Because the slope from (2, 3) to (5, 8) is the same as the slope from (5, 8) to (11, y), find the slope between each pair of points and set them equal to each other. Then solve for y.

$$\frac{8-3}{5-2} = \frac{y-8}{11-5}$$
$$\frac{5}{3} = \frac{y-8}{6}$$
$$30 = 3(y-8)$$
$$10 = y-8$$
$$18 = y$$

39. Sometimes; the slope of a vertical line is undefined.

Multiple Representations In Exercise 35, students use a table of values and a graph to determine how the slope of a quadratic function changes as the input value increases.

Watch Out!

Error Analysis In Exercise 36, point out that when finding a slope, if you use $y_1 - y_2$ as the numerator, you must use $x_1 - x_2$ as the denominator. To find the slope, you can move from point A to point B, or vice versa, but you must move in a consistent direction for both the rise and the run.

Additional Answers

35a.

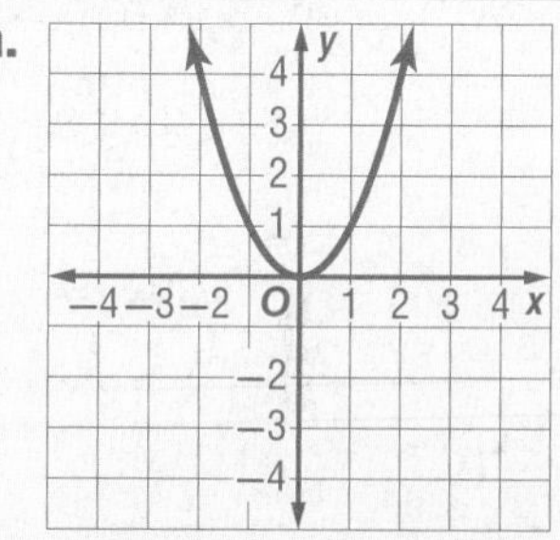

40a. Sample answer: Pick two sets of values in the table and determine the difference of the outputs (y) and the difference of the inputs (x). Divide the difference of the outputs by the difference of the inputs. This is the rate of change. Follow this process with the rest of the data to confirm the rate of change is constant and, thus, the function is linear.

40b. Sample answer: Pick two separate coordinates that fall on the graph of the straight line. Determine the difference of the outputs (y) and the difference of the inputs (x). Divide the difference of the outputs by the difference of the inputs. This is the rate of change.

40c. Sample answer: Pick two random x-values and substitute them into the equation to determine the corresponding y-values. Determine the difference of the outputs (y) and the difference of the inputs (x). Divide the difference of the outputs by the difference of the inputs. This is the rate of change.

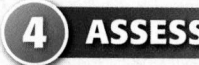

Tips for New Teachers

Pacing If there is any doubt whether your students thoroughly understand the concept of slope, consider spending an extra day on this lesson.

4 ASSESS

Name the Math Have students verbally describe the concept of slope and explain how to calculate it.

NGSSS PRACTICE 912.A.3.9, 912.A.3.5, 912.G.5.3, 912.A.3.10

41. **GRIDDED RESPONSE** What is the slope of the line shown in the graph? **3/2 or 1.5**

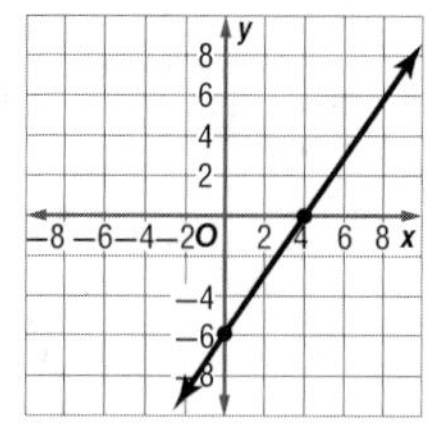

42. **ACT/SAT** In the figure below, the large square contains two smaller squares. If the areas of the two smaller squares are 4 and 25, what is the sum of the perimeters of the two shaded rectangles? **D**

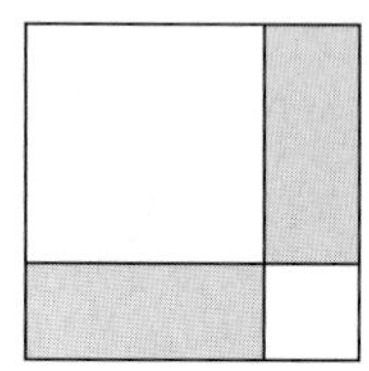

A. 14
B. 20
C. 24
D. 28

43. **GEOMETRY** In $\triangle ABC$ shown, $AC = 16$ and $m\angle DAB = 60$. What is the measure of $\overline{BD}$? **G**

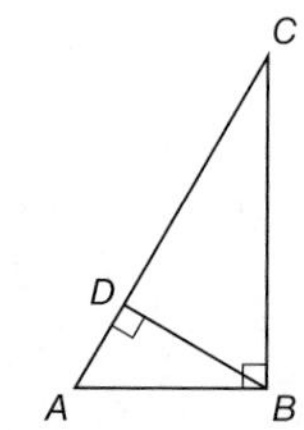

F. $9\sqrt{2}$
G. $4\sqrt{3}$
H. 9
I. 4

44. The table shows the cost of bananas depending on the amount purchased. Which conclusion can be made based on information in the table? **B**

Cost of Bananas

Number of Pounds	Cost ($)
5	1.45
20	4.60
50	10.50
100	19.00

A. The cost of 10 pounds of bananas would be more than $4.
B. The cost of 200 pounds of bananas would be at most $38.
C. The cost of bananas is always more than $0.20 per pound.
D. The cost of bananas is always less than $0.28 per pound.

45. Yes; it can be written in $f(x) = mx + b$ form. **46.** No; it cannot be written in $f(x) = mx + b$ form.

Spiral Review

47. No; it cannot be written in $f(x) = mx + b$ form.

State whether each equation or function is a linear function. Write *yes* or *no*. Explain. (Lesson 2-2)

45. $6y - 8x = 19$ **46.** $4x^2 = 2y - 9$ **47.** $18 = 2xy + 6$

Evaluate each function. (Lesson 2-1)

48. $f(-9)$ if $f(x) = -7x + 8$ **71** **49.** $g(-4)$ if $g(x) = -3x^2 + 2$ **−46** **50.** $h(12)$ if $h(x) = 4x^2 - 10x$ **456**

51. **RACING** There are 8 contestants in a 400-meter race. In how many different ways can the top three runners finish? (Lesson 0-5) **336**

Determine the quadrant of the coordinate plane where each point is located. (Lesson 0-1)

52. $(-4, -8)$ **III** **53.** $(-2, 6)$ **II** **54.** $(3, -1)$ **IV**

Skills Review

Solve each equation. (Lesson 1-3)

55. $8 = 4m - 6$ **3.5** **56.** $-6 = 3(8) + b$ **−30** **57.** $-2 = -3x + 5$ $\frac{7}{3}$

Differentiated Instruction BL

Extension Have students draw a line with a slope of 0. Let them discover that a horizontal line has a slope of 0. Ask them if all horizontal lines have a slope of 0.

Writing Linear Equations

Then

You determined slopes of lines. (Lesson 2-3)

Now

- Write an equation of a line given the slope and a point on the line.
- Write an equation of a line parallel or perpendicular to a given line.

NGSSS

MA.912.A.3.10 Write an equation of a line given any of the following information: two points on the line, its slope and one point on the line, or its graph. Also, find an equation of a new line parallel to a given line, or perpendicular to a given line, through a given point on the new line.

New Vocabulary

slope-intercept form
point-slope form
parallel
perpendicular

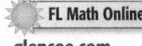

FL Math Online

glencoe.com

Why?

Medical insurance companies often require their customers to make a co-payment for every doctor's office visit in addition to an annual insurance premium.

If an insurance company charges $2280 annually and requires a copayment of $35 per doctor's office visit, then the linear equation $y = 35x + 2280$ can represent the total annual cost y for x doctor's office visits.

Forms of Equations Consider the line through $A(0, b)$ and $C(x, y)$. Notice that b is the y-intercept. You can use these two points to find the slope of $\overleftrightarrow{AC}$.

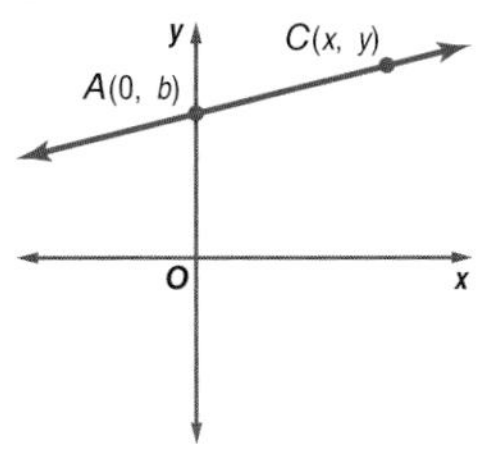

$m = \frac{y_2 - y_1}{x_2 - x_1}$	**Slope Formula**
$= \frac{y - b}{x - 0}$	$(x_1, y_1) = (0, b), (x_2, y_2) = (x, y)$
$= \frac{y - b}{x}$	**Simplify.**

Now solve the equation for y.

$mx = y - b$	**Multiply each side by x.**
$mx + b = y$	**Add b to each side.**
$y = mx + b$	**Symmetric Property of Equality**

Equations written in this format are in **slope-intercept form**.

Key Concept — Slope-Intercept Form

Words The slope-intercept form of the equation of a line is $y = mx + b$, where m is the slope and b is the y-intercept.

Model

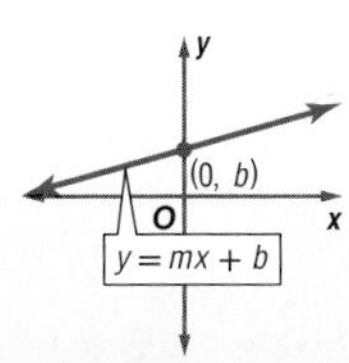

Symbols $y = mx + b$ (slope → m; b → y-intercept)

If you are given the slope and y-intercept of a line, you can find an equation of the line by substituting the values of m and b into the slope-intercept form.

1 FOCUS

Vertical Alignment

Before Lesson 2-4
Determine slopes of lines.

Lesson 2-4
Write an equation of a line given the slope and a point on the line and write an equation of a line parallel or perpendicular to a given line.

After Lesson 2-4
Apply functions to problem situations.

2 TEACH

Scaffolding Questions

Have students read the *Why?* section of the lesson.

Ask:

- What does the variable x represent in this situation? the number of doctor visits
- What does the variable y represent? the total annual cost
- What would the total annual cost be for a person who visited the doctor nine times? $2595

Lesson 2-4 Resources

Resource	Approaching-Level	On-Level	Beyond-Level	English Learners
Teacher Edition	• Differentiated Instruction, p. 84	• Differentiated Instruction, p. 84	• Differentiated Instruction, p. 89	• Differentiated Instruction, p. 84
Chapter Resource Masters	• Study Guide and Intervention, pp. 23–24 • Skills Practice, p. 25 • Practice, p. 26 • Word Problem Practice, p. 27	• Study Guide and Intervention, pp. 23–24 • Skills Practice, p. 25 • Practice, p. 26 • Word Problem Practice, p. 27 • Enrichment, p. 28 • Spreadsheet Activity, p. 29	• Practice, p. 26 • Word Problem Practice, p. 27 • Enrichment, p. 28	• Study Guide and Intervention, pp. 23–24 • Skills Practice, p. 25 • Practice, p. 26 • Word Problem Practice, p. 27
Transparencies	• 5-Minute Check Transparency 2-4	• 5-Minute Check Transparency 2-4	• 5-Minute Check Transparency 2-4	• 5-Minute Check Transparency 2-4
Other	• Study Notebook	• Study Notebook	• Study Notebook	• Study Notebook

Forms of Equations

Examples 1–3 show how to write equations for lines in slope-intercept form.

Formative Assessment

Use the Guided Practice exercises after each example to determine students' understanding of concepts.

Additional Examples

1 Write an equation in slope-intercept form for the line. $y = -\frac{1}{3}x + \frac{11}{3}$

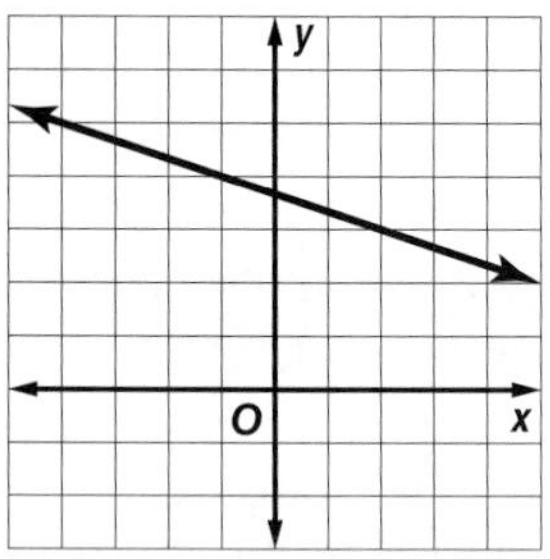

2 Write an equation of the line through (5, –2) with a slope of $-\frac{3}{5}$. $y = -\frac{3}{5}x + 1$

Additional Examples also in

Interactive Classroom PowerPoint® Presentations

IWB INTERACTIVE WHITEBOARD READY

Watch Out!

Slope-Intercept Form The equation of a vertical line cannot be written in slope-intercept form because its slope is undefined.

Sometimes it is necessary to calculate the slope before you can write an equation.

EXAMPLE 1 Write an Equation in Slope-Intercept Form

Write an equation in slope-intercept form for the line.

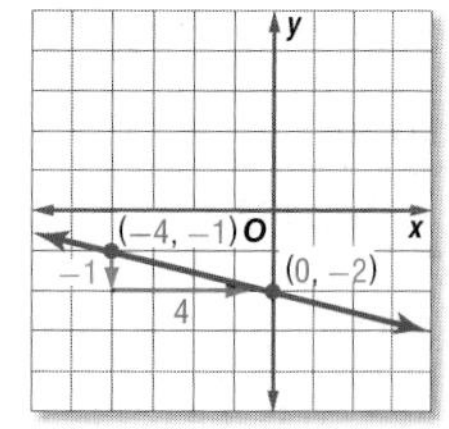

The graph intersects the y-axis at -2. So $b = -2$.

Step 1 Find the slope.

$m = \frac{y_2 - y_1}{x_2 - x_1}$ — **Slope Formula**

$= \frac{-2 - (-1)}{0 - (-4)}$ — $(x_1, y_1) = (-4, -1), (x_2, y_2) = (0, -2)$

$= \frac{-1}{4}$ or $-\frac{1}{4}$ — **Simplify.**

Step 2 Substitute the values into the slope-intercept equation.

$y = mx + b$ — **Slope-intercept form**

$y = -\frac{1}{4}x - 2$ — $m = -\frac{1}{4}, b = -2$

StudyTip

Check Your Results You can check that your equation satisfies the conditions by graphing it.

Guided Practice 1A. $y = \frac{4}{3}x + 4$ 1B. $y = -4x - 6$

Write an equation in slope-intercept form for the line described.

1A. slope $\frac{4}{3}$, passes through (0, 4)

1B. passes through (0, −6) and (−4, 10)

Personal Tutor glencoe.com

If you know the slope of a line and the coordinates of a point on the line, you can use the **point-slope form** to find an equation of the line.

Key Concept Point-Slope Form

Words The point-slope form of the equation of a line is $y - y_1 = m(x - x_1)$, where (x_1, y_1) are the coordinates of a point on the line and m is the slope of the line.

Symbols slope

$y - y_1 = m(x - x_1)$

coordinates of a point on the line

EXAMPLE 2 Write an Equation Given Slope and One Point

Write an equation of the line through (6, −2) with a slope of −4.

$y - y_1 = m(x - x_1)$ — **Point-slope form**

$y - (-2) = -4(x - 6)$ — $(x_1, y_1) = (6, -2), m = -4$

$y + 2 = -4x + 24$ — **Simplify.**

$y = -4x + 22$ — **Subtract 2 from each side.**

Guided Practice 2A. $y = \frac{1}{2}x + 2$ 2B. $y = -3x - 7$

Write an equation in slope-intercept form for the line described.

2A. passes through (2, 3); $m = \frac{1}{2}$

2B. passes through (−2, −1); $m = -3$

Personal Tutor glencoe.com

Differentiated Instruction

AL OL ELL

If students use m and b for the wrong attributes of a line,

Then make sure they understand that the letter m is always used for slope and b for the y-intercept in the slope-intercept form of an equation $y = mx + b$.

You can use any two points on a line to write an equation.

NGSSS PRACTICE EXAMPLE 3 912.A.3.10

Which is an equation of the line that passes through (−2, 7) and (3, −3)?

A. $y = -\frac{1}{2}x - \frac{3}{2}$ **C.** $y = \frac{1}{2}x + 8$

B. $y = -2x + 3$ **D.** $y = 2x + 11$

Read the Test Item

You are given the coordinates of two points on the line.

Solve the Test Item

Step 1 Find the slope of the line.

$m = \frac{y_2 - y_1}{x_2 - x_1}$ **Slope Formula**

$= \frac{-3 - 7}{3 - (-2)}$ **$(x_1, y_1) = (-2, 7)$, $(x_2, y_2) = (3, -3)$**

$= -\frac{10}{5}$ or -2 **Simplify.**

Step 2 Write an equation. Use either ordered pair for (x_1, y_1).

$y - y_1 = m(x - x_1)$ **Point-slope form**

$y - (-3) = -2(x - 3)$ **$(x_1, y_1) = (3, -3)$ and $m = -2$**

$y + 3 = -2x + 6$ **Simplify.**

$y = -2x + 3$ **Subtract 3 from each side.**

The answer is B.

Test-Taking Tip

Definitions Be certain to review key vocabulary, such as *y*-intercept, so that you understand what is being asked in a question.

Guided Practice

3. Which is an equation of the line that passes through (4, −9) and (2, −4)? F

F. $y = -\frac{5}{2}x + 1$ **H.** $y = -\frac{2}{5}x + \frac{37}{5}$

G. $y = -\frac{5}{2}x - 1$ **I.** $y = -\frac{2}{5}x - \frac{37}{5}$

Personal Tutor glencoe.com

Parallel and Perpendicular Lines Slopes can help you determine whether two lines are parallel or perpendicular.

Key Concept Parallel and Perpendicular Lines

Parallel Lines	Perpendicular Lines
Two nonvertical lines are **parallel** if and only if they have the same slope. All vertical lines are parallel.	Two nonvertical lines are **perpendicular** if and only if the product of the slopes is −1. Vertical lines and horizontal lines are perpendicular.
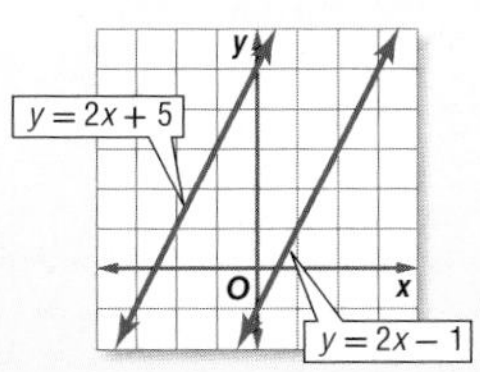	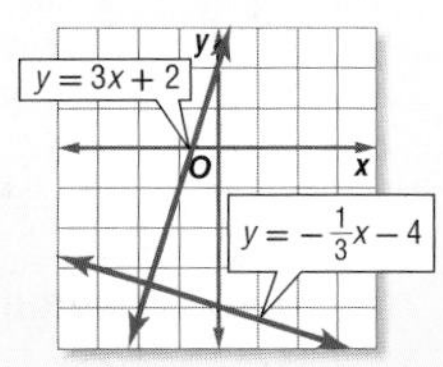
$y = 2x + 5$ and $y = 2x - 1$	$y = 3x + 2$ and $y = -\frac{1}{3}x - 4$

Additional Example

3 STANDARDIZED TEST PRACTICE What is an equation of the line through (2, −3) and (−3, 7)? D

A $y = -2x - 1$

B $y = -\frac{1}{2}x + 1$

C $y = \frac{1}{2}x + 1$

D $y = -2x + 1$

Tips for New Teachers

Reasoning Point out that finding the slope in Example 3 eliminated three of the choices. Emphasize that eliminating answer choices helps you to use your time efficiently when taking a timed test.

TEACH with TECH

INTERACTIVE WHITEBOARD Display a coordinate plane on the whiteboard. Plot two points on the plane and ask students to find the equation of the line that goes through these two points. Then, drag the points to other locations on the plane and repeat.

Focus on Mathematical Content

Point-Slope Form The point-slope form of an equation of a line is closely related to the formula for calculating slope. As an alternative to memorizing point-slope form, replace the coordinates (x_2, y_2) with (x, y) in the slope formula, $m = \frac{y - y_1}{x - x_1}$, and multiply each side by $x - x_1$.

Parallel and Perpendicular Lines

Example 4 asks students to write an equation for a line passing through a given point that is perpendicular to a line with a given equation.

Additional Example

4 Write an equation in slope-intercept form for the line that passes through (3, –2) and is perpendicular to the line with equation $y = -5x + 1$.
$y = \frac{1}{5}x - \frac{13}{5}$

Tips for New Teachers

Making Choices In Example 4, point out to students that they could choose to begin with slope-intercept form instead of point-slope form.

3 PRACTICE

Formative Assessment

Use Exercises 1–7 to check for understanding.

Use the chart at the bottom of the next page to customize assignments for your students.

EXAMPLE 4 Write an Equation of a Perpendicular Line

Write an equation in slope-intercept form for the line that passes through (5, –6) and is perpendicular to the line with equation $y = -\frac{3}{2}x + 7$.

The slope of the given line is $-\frac{3}{2}$. Because the slopes of perpendicular lines are opposite reciprocals, the slope of the line perpendicular to the given line is $\frac{2}{3}$.

Use the point-slope form and the ordered pair (5, –6).

$y - y_1 = m(x - x_1)$ **Point-slope form**

$y - (-6) = \frac{2}{3}(x - 5)$ **$(x_1, y_1) = (5, -6)$ and $m = \frac{2}{3}$**

$y + 6 = \frac{2}{3}x - \frac{10}{3}$ **Distributive Property**

$y = \frac{2}{3}x - \frac{28}{3}$ **Subtract 6 from each side and simplify.**

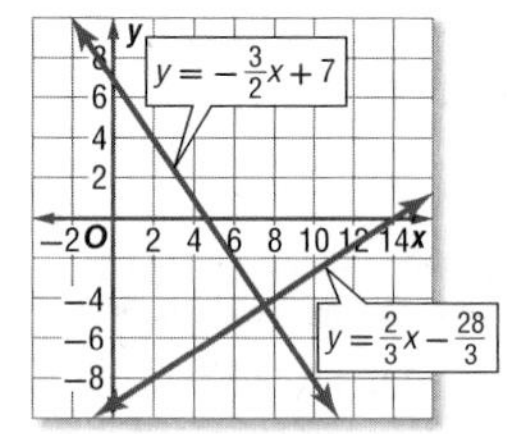

CHECK Graph both equations to verify the solution.

Guided Practice

4. Write an equation in slope-intercept form for the line that passes through (3, 7) and is parallel to the line with equation $y = \frac{3}{4}x - 5$. $y = \frac{3}{4}x + \frac{19}{4}$

Personal Tutor glencoe.com

Check Your Understanding

Example 1 p. 84 **Write an equation in slope-intercept form for the line described.**

1. slope 1.5, passes through (0, 5) $y = 1.5x + 5$

2. passes through (–2, 3) and (0, 1) $y = -x + 1$

Example 2 p. 84

3. passes through (3, 5); $m = -2$ $y = -2x + 11$

4. passes through (–8, –2); $m = \frac{5}{2}$ $y = \frac{5}{2}x + 18$

Example 3 p. 85

5. MULTIPLE CHOICE Which is an equation of the line? **A**

A $y = -4x - 25$

B $y = -\frac{2}{3}x - 5$

C $y = \frac{4}{5}x + \frac{29}{25}$

D $y = 6x + 35$

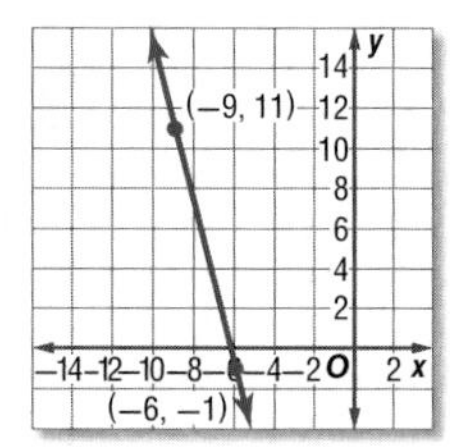

Example 4 p. 86 **Write an equation in slope-intercept form for the line that satisfies each set of conditions.**

6. passes through (–9, –3), perpendicular to $y = -\frac{5}{3}x - 8$ $y = 0.6x + 2.4$

7 passes through (4, –10), parallel to $y = \frac{7}{8}x - 3$ $y = \frac{7}{8}x - \frac{27}{2}$

86 Chapter 2 Linear Relations and Functions

Practice and Problem Solving

= **Step-by-Step Solutions** begin on page R20. **Extra Practice** begins on page 947.

Example 1 p. 84

9. $y = -\frac{1}{2}x + 5$

10. $y = -\frac{6}{5}x + 8$

Example 2 p. 84

11. $y = 4.5x - 6.5$

Write an equation in slope-intercept form for the line described.

8. slope 3, passes through (0, −2) $y = 3x - 2$
9. slope $-\frac{1}{2}$, passes through (0, 5)
10. slope $-\frac{6}{5}$, passes through (0, 8)
11. slope $\frac{9}{2}$, passes through $\left(0, -\frac{13}{2}\right)$
12. slope −2, passes through (−3, 14) $y = -2x + 8$
13. slope 4, passes through (6, 9) $y = 4x - 15$
14. slope $\frac{3}{5}$, passes through (−6, −8) $y = \frac{3}{5}x - \frac{22}{5}$
15. slope $-\frac{1}{4}$, passes through (12, −4) $y = -\frac{1}{4}x - 1$
16. **PART-TIME JOB** Each week, Carmen earns a base pay of \$15 plus \$0.17 for every pamphlet that she delivers. Write an equation that can be used to find how much Carmen earns each week. How much will she earn the week that she delivers 300 pamphlets? $y = 0.17x + 15$; \$66

Example 3 p. 85

Write an equation of the line passing through each pair of points. 17–22. See margin.

17. (−2, −6), (4, 6)
18. (−8, −5), (−3, 10)
19. (−4, 12), (−2, −4)
20. (4.6, 3.4), (2.2, 2.8)
21. (5.5, 0.6), (1.1, 2.8)
22. (−25, −16), (−29, 12)

Example 4 p. 86

Write an equation in slope-intercept form for the line that satisfies each set of conditions.

23. passes through (4, 2), perpendicular to $y = -2x + 3$ $y = \frac{1}{2}x$
24. passes through (−6, −6), parallel to $y = \frac{4}{3}x + 8$ $y = \frac{4}{3}x + 2$
25. passes through (12, 0), parallel to $y = -\frac{1}{2}x - 3$ $y = -\frac{1}{2}x + 6$
26. passes through (10, 2), perpendicular to $y = 4x + 6$ $y = -0.25x + 4.5$

27–29. See margin.

27. **FINANCIAL LITERACY** Julio buys a used car for \$5900. Monthly expenses for the car—which include insurance, maintenance, and gas—average \$180 per month. Write an equation that represents the total cost of buying and owning the car for x months.
28. **DELI** The sales of a sandwich store increased approximately linearly from \$52,000 to \$116,000 during the first five years of business. Write an equation that models the sales y after x years. Determine what the sales will be at the end of 12 years if the pattern continues.
29. **WHALES** In 2007, it was estimated that there were 250 mature right whales in existence. The population of right whales is expected to decline by at least 25 whales each generation. Write an equation that represents the number of right whales that will be in existence in x generations.

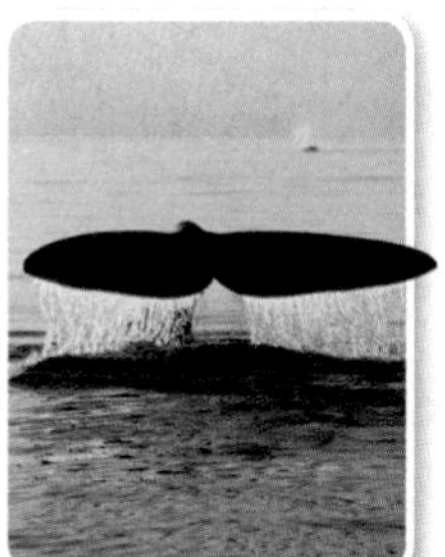

Real-World Link

The northern right whale has been listed as endangered since 1973. The eastern North Atlantic population is nearly extinct, and the western North Atlantic population numbers around 300 individuals.

Source: NOAA Fisheries Service

Write an equation in slope-intercept form for each graph. 30–32. See margin.

30.

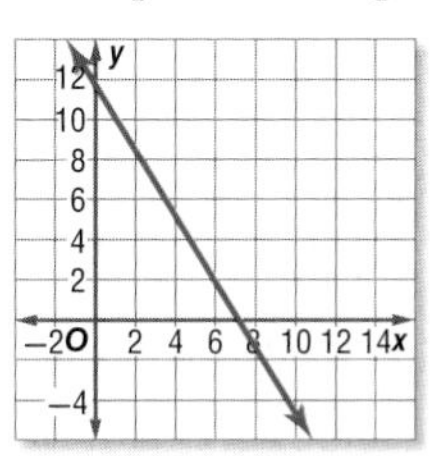

31.

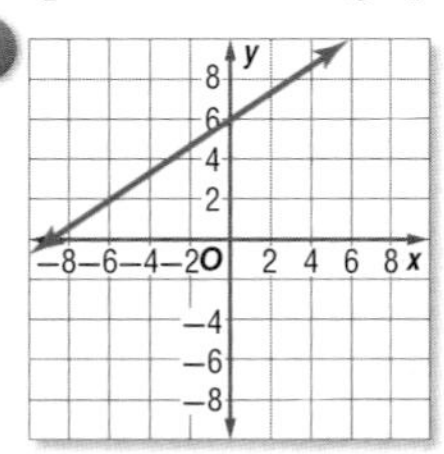

32.

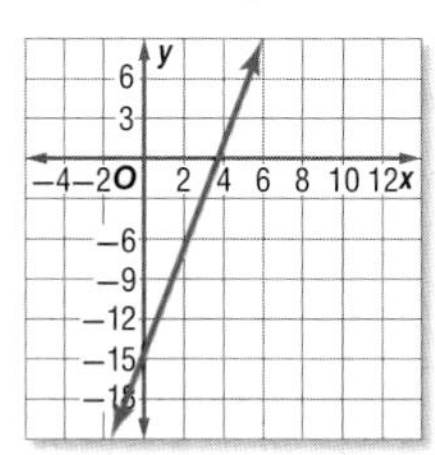

Tips for New Teachers

Slope and Steepness Point out that when the units and/or scales differ on the two axes, you *cannot* estimate the slope of the graphed line by comparing it to the slope of $y = x$.

Additional Answers

17. $y = 2x - 2$
18. $y = 3x + 19$
19. $y = -8x - 20$
20. $y = 0.25x + 2.25$
21. $y = -0.5x + 3.35$
22. $y = -7x - 191$
27. $y = 180x + 5900$
28. $y = 16{,}000x + 36{,}000$; \$228,000
29. $y = -25x + 250$
30. $y = -\frac{5}{3}x + 12$
31. $y = \frac{2}{3}x + 6$
32. $y = 4x - 15$

Differentiated Homework Options

Level	Assignment	Two-Day Option	
AL Basic	8–26, 37, 39–65	9–25 odd, 43–46	8–26 even, 37, 39–42, 47–65
OL Core	9–25 odd, 27–29, 31, 33–37, 39–65	8–26, 43–46	30–37, 39–42, 47–65
BL Advanced	27–59 (optional: 60–65)		

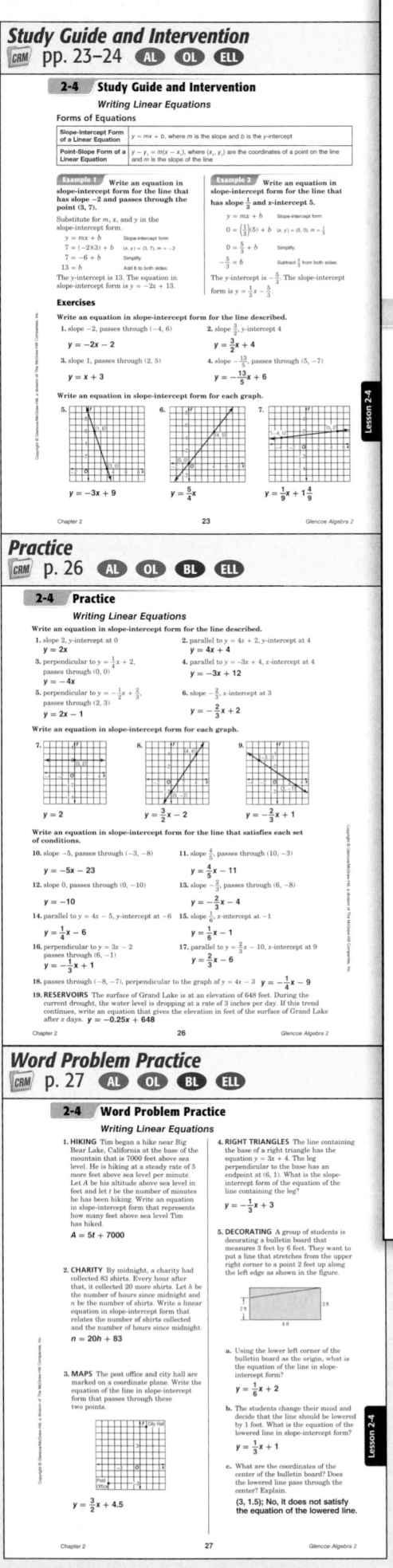

33. ROSES Brad wants to send his girlfriend Kelli a dozen roses. He visits two stores. For what distance do the two stores charge the same amount to deliver a dozen roses? **10 mi**

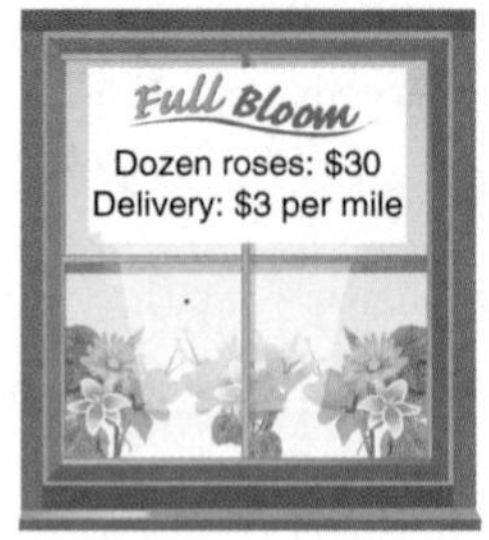

Flowers R us
Dozen roses: $40
Delivery: $2 per mile

Real-World Link

In current years, over 1,200,000,000 roses have been purchased by U.S. flower buyers. This works out to a consumption rate of 4.67 roses per person.

Source: U.S. Department of Agriculture

34. TYPING The equation $y = 55(23 - x)$ can be used to model the number of words y you have left to type after x minutes.

a. Write this equation in slope-intercept form. **$y = 1265 - 55x$**

b. Identify the slope and y-intercept. **-55; 1265**

c. Find the number of words you have left to type after 20 minutes. **165 words**

C **35. RECRUITING** As an army recruiter, Ms. Cooper is paid a daily salary plus commission. When she recruits 10 people, she earns $100. When she recruits 14 people, she earns $120.

a. Write a linear equation to model this situation. **$y = 5x + 50$**

b. What is Ms. Cooper's daily salary? **$50**

c. How much would Ms. Cooper earn in a day if she recruits 20 people? **$150**

36. TRAVEL Refer to the table at the right.

Miles	Kilometers
100	161
50	80.5

a. Write and graph the linear equation that gives the distance y in kilometers in terms of the number x in miles. **See margin.**

b. What distance in kilometers corresponds to 20 miles? **32.2 km**

c. What number is the same in kilometers and miles? Explain your reasoning.

H.O.T. Problems

Use **H**igher-**O**rder **T**hinking Skills

37. REASONING Determine whether the following statement is *always*, *sometimes*, or *never* true. Explain your reasoning.

The quadrilateral formed by any two parallel lines and two lines perpendicular to those lines is a square.

38. CHALLENGE Given $\square ABCD$ with vertices $A(a, b)$, $B(c - a, d)$, $C(c + a, d)$, and $D(c, b)$, write an equation of a line perpendicular to diagonal $\overline{BD}$ that contains A.

39. REASONING Write $y = ax + b$ in point-slope form. **Sample answer: $y - 0 = a\left(x + \frac{b}{a}\right)$**

40. OPEN ENDED Write the equations of two parallel lines with negative slopes.

41. REASONING Write an equation in point-slope form of a line with an x-intercept of c and y-intercept of d. **Sample answer: $y - d = -\frac{d}{c}(x - 0)$**

42. WRITING IN MATH Describe the process of finding the slope-intercept form of the equation of a line containing two given points. **See margin.**

36c. 0; because this is the point on the graph where the x-value and the y-value are the same

37. Sample answer: Sometimes; while the two sets of parallel and perpendicular lines will always form a quadrilateral with four 90° angles, that figure will always be a rectangle, but not necessarily a square.

38. Sample answer: $y = \frac{ax}{d - b} - \frac{a^2}{d - b} + b$ or $y = \frac{ax}{d - b} + \frac{bd - b^2 - a^2}{d - b}$

40. Sample answer: $y = -2x + 3$ and $y = -2x - 1$

Study Guide and Intervention

CRM pp. 23–24 AL OL ELL

2-4 Study Guide and Intervention

Writing Linear Equations

Forms of Equations

Slope-Intercept Form of a Linear Equation	$y = mx + b$, where m is the slope and b is the y-intercept
Point-Slope Form of a Linear Equation	$y - y_1 = m(x - x_1)$, where (x_1, y_1) are the coordinates of a point on the line and m is the slope of the line

Example 1 **Write an equation in slope-intercept form for the line that has slope −2 and passes through the point (3, 7).**

Substitute for m, x, and y in the slope-intercept form.

$y = mx + b$ Slope-intercept form
$7 = (-2)(3) + b$ $(x, y) = (3, 7)$, $m = -2$
$7 = -6 + b$ Simplify.
$13 = b$ Add 6 to both sides.

The y-intercept is 13. The equation in slope-intercept form is $y = -2x + 13$.

Example 2 **Write an equation in slope-intercept form for the line that has slope $\frac{1}{3}$ and x-intercept 5.**

$y = mx + b$ Slope-intercept form
$0 = \left(\frac{1}{3}\right)(5) + b$ $(x, y) = (5, 0)$, $m = \frac{1}{3}$
$0 = \frac{5}{3} + b$ Simplify.
$-\frac{5}{3} = b$ Subtract $\frac{5}{3}$ from both sides.

The y-intercept is $-\frac{5}{3}$. The slope-intercept form is $y = \frac{1}{3}x - \frac{5}{3}$.

Exercises

Write an equation in slope-intercept form for the line described.

1. slope −2, passes through (−4, 6) **$y = -2x - 2$**
2. slope $\frac{3}{2}$, y-intercept 4 **$y = \frac{3}{2}x + 4$**
3. slope 1, passes through (2, 5) **$y = x + 3$**
4. slope $-\frac{13}{5}$, passes through (5, −7) **$y = -\frac{13}{5}x + 6$**

Write an equation in slope-intercept form for each graph.

5. 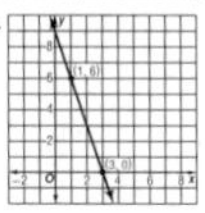 **$y = -3x + 9$**

6. 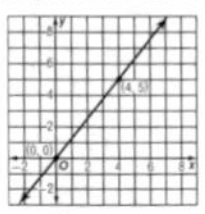 **$y = \frac{5}{4}x$**

7. 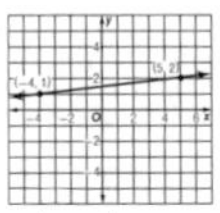 **$y = \frac{1}{9}x + 1\frac{4}{9}$**

Chapter 2 23 Glencoe Algebra 2

Lesson 2-4

Practice

CRM p. 26 AL OL BL ELL

2-4 Practice

Writing Linear Equations

Write an equation in slope-intercept form for the line described.

1. slope 2, y-intercept at 0 **$y = 2x$**
2. parallel to $y = 4x + 2$, y-intercept at 4 **$y = 4x + 4$**
3. perpendicular to $y = \frac{1}{4}x + 2$, passes through (0, 0) **$y = -4x$**
4. parallel to $y = -3x + 4$, x-intercept at 4 **$y = -3x + 12$**
5. perpendicular to $y = -\frac{1}{2}x + \frac{2}{3}$, passes through (2, 3) **$y = 2x - 1$**
6. slope $-\frac{2}{3}$, x-intercept at 3 **$y = -\frac{2}{3}x + 2$**

Write an equation in slope-intercept form for each graph.

7. 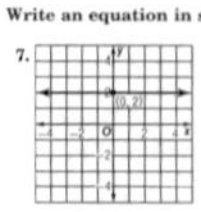 **$y = 2$**

8. 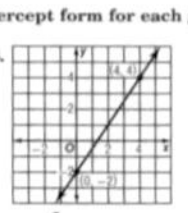 **$y = \frac{3}{2}x - 2$**

9. 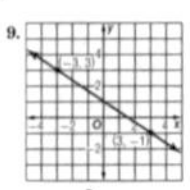 **$y = -\frac{2}{3}x + 1$**

Write an equation in slope-intercept form for the line that satisfies each set of conditions.

10. slope −5, passes through (−3, −8) **$y = -5x - 23$**
11. slope $\frac{4}{5}$, passes through (10, −3) **$y = \frac{4}{5}x - 11$**
12. slope 0, passes through (0, −10) **$y = -10$**
13. slope $-\frac{2}{3}$, passes through (6, −8) **$y = -\frac{2}{3}x - 4$**
14. parallel to $y = 4x - 5$, y-intercept at −6 **$y = \frac{1}{4}x - 6$**
15. slope $\frac{1}{6}$, x-intercept at −1 **$y = \frac{1}{6}x - 1$**
16. perpendicular to $y = 3x - 2$ passes through (6, −1) **$y = -\frac{1}{3}x + 1$**
17. parallel to $y = \frac{2}{3}x - 10$, x-intercept at 9 **$y = \frac{2}{3}x - 6$**
18. passes through (−8, −7), perpendicular to the graph of $y = 4x - 3$ **$y = -\frac{1}{4}x - 9$**
19. **RESERVOIRS** The surface of Grand Lake is at an elevation of 648 feet. During the current drought, the water level is dropping at a rate of 3 inches per day. If this trend continues, write an equation that gives the elevation in feet of the surface of Grand Lake after x days. **$y = -0.25x + 648$**

Chapter 2 26 Glencoe Algebra 2

Word Problem Practice

CRM p. 27 AL OL BL ELL

2-4 Word Problem Practice

Writing Linear Equations

1. **HIKING** Tim began a hike near Big Bear Lake, California at the base of the mountain that is 7000 feet above sea level. He is hiking at a steady rate of 5 more feet above sea level per minute. Let A be his altitude above sea level in feet and let t be the number of minutes he has been hiking. Write an equation in slope-intercept form that represents how many feet above sea level Tim has hiked.
$A = 5t + 7000$

2. **CHARITY** By midnight, a charity had collected 83 shirts. Every hour after that, it collected 20 more shirts. Let h be the number of hours since midnight and n be the number of shirts. Write a linear equation in slope-intercept form that relates the number of shirts collected and the number of hours since midnight.
$n = 20h + 83$

3. **MAPS** The post office and city hall are marked on a coordinate plane. Write the equation of the line in slope-intercept form that passes through these two points.

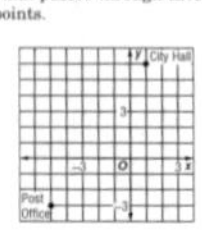

$y = \frac{3}{2}x + 4.5$

4. **RIGHT TRIANGLES** The line containing the base of a right triangle has the equation $y = 3x + 4$. The leg perpendicular to the base has an endpoint at (6, 1). What is the slope-intercept form of the equation of the line containing the leg?
$y = -\frac{1}{3}x + 3$

5. **DECORATING** A group of students is decorating a bulletin board that measures 3 feet by 6 feet. They want to put a line that stretches from the upper right corner to a point 2 feet up along the left edge as shown in the figure.

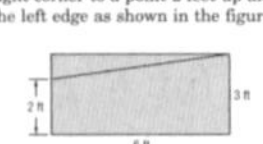

a. Using the lower left corner of the bulletin board as the origin, what is the equation of the line in slope-intercept form?
$y = \frac{1}{6}x + 2$

b. The students change their mind and decide that the line should be lowered by 1 foot. What is the equation of the lowered line in slope-intercept form?
$y = \frac{1}{3}x + 1$

c. What are the coordinates of the center of the bulletin board? Does the lowered line pass through the center? Explain.
(3, 1.5); No, it does not satisfy the equation of the lowered line.

Chapter 2 27 Glencoe Algebra 2

Lesson 2-4

Enrichment

CRM p. 28 OL BL

2-4 Enrichment

Two-Intercept Form of a Linear Equation

You are already familiar with the slope-intercept form of a linear equation, $y = mx + b$. Linear equations can also be written in the form $\frac{x}{a} + \frac{y}{b} = 1$ with x-intercept a and y-intercept b. This is called two-intercept form.

Example 1 **Draw the graph of $\frac{x}{-3} + \frac{y}{6} = 1$.**

The graph crosses the x-axis at −3 and the y-axis at 6. Graph (−3, 0) and (0, 6), then draw a straight line through them.

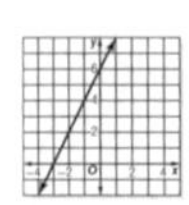

Example 2 **Write $3x + 4y = 12$ in two-intercept form.**

$\frac{3x}{12} + \frac{4y}{12} = \frac{12}{12}$ Divide by 12 to obtain 1 on the right side.
$\frac{x}{4} + \frac{y}{3} = 1$ Simplify.

The x-intercept is 4; the y-intercept is 3.

NGSSS PRACTICE 912.A.3.1, 912.P.7.2, 912.A.10.3

43. The total cost c in dollars to go to a water park and ride n water rides is given by the equation

$$c = 15 + 3n.$$

If the total cost was \$33, how many water rides were ridden? **A**

A. 6 B. 7 C. 8 D. 9

44. **SHORT RESPONSE** To raise money, the service club bought 1000 candy bars for \$0.60 each. If the club sells all of the candy bars for \$1 each, what will be their total profit? **\$400**

45. **PROBABILITY** A fair six-sided die is tossed. What is the probability that a number less than 3 will show on the face of the die? **G**

F. $\frac{1}{2}$ G. $\frac{1}{3}$ H. $\frac{2}{3}$ I. $\frac{1}{6}$

46. **ACT/SAT** What is an equation of the line through $\left(\frac{1}{2}, -\frac{3}{2}\right)$ and $\left(-\frac{1}{2}, \frac{1}{2}\right)$? **A**

A. $y = -2x - \frac{1}{2}$ C. $y = 2x - 5$

B. $y = -3x$ D. $y = \frac{1}{2}x + 1$

Spiral Review

Determine the rate of change of each graph. (Lesson 2-3)

47. 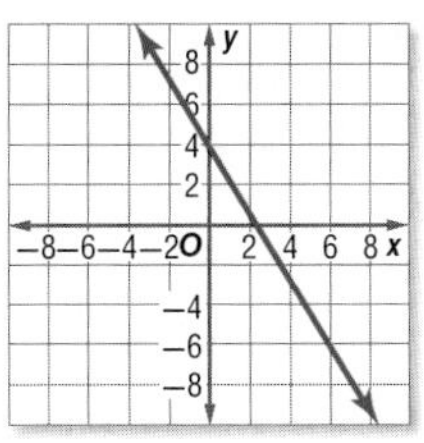 $-\frac{5}{3}$

48. 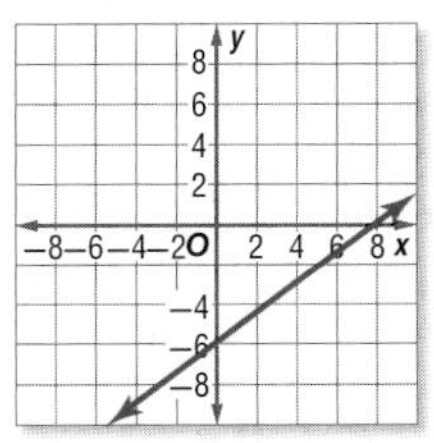 $\frac{3}{4}$

49. 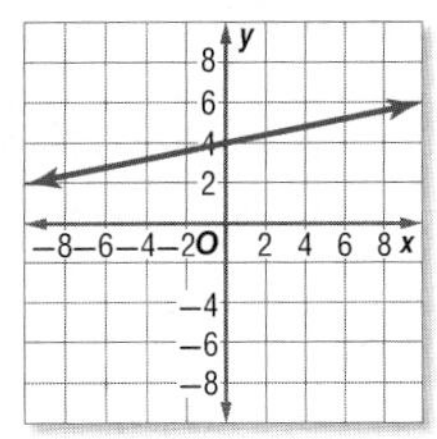 $\frac{1}{5}$

50. **RECREATION** Scott is currently on page 210 of an epic novel that is 980 pages long. He plans to read 30 pages per day until he finishes the novel. Write and solve a linear relation to determine how many days it will take Scott to complete the novel. (Lesson 2-2) **$30x + 210 = 980$; 26 days**

Solve each inequality. (Lesson 1-5)

51. $-6x - 4 \le 12 - 2x$ $x \ge -4$

52. $\frac{x+2}{5} > -3x + 1$ $x > \frac{3}{16}$

53. $\frac{5x+3}{3} \ge \frac{4x-2}{5}$ $x \ge -\frac{21}{13}$

Determine if the triangles with the following lengths are right triangles. (Lesson 0-7)

54. 5, 12, 13 **yes**

55. 36, 48, 60 **yes**

56. 7, 23, 25 **no**

Multiply. (Lesson 0-2)

57. $(4c - 6)(2c + 5)$ $8c^2 + 8c - 30$

58. $(-3b + 2)(b + 3)$ $-3b^2 - 7b + 6$

59. $(2a - 5)(-3a - 4)$ $-6a^2 + 7a + 20$

Skills Review

Find the slope of the line that passes through each pair of points. Express as a fraction in simplest form. (Lesson 2-3)

60. $(4, 8), (-2, -6)$ $\frac{7}{3}$

61. $(-6, 3), (-2, 9)$ $\frac{3}{2}$

62. $(-4, -1), (-8, -8)$ $\frac{7}{4}$

63. $(12, 4), (42, 10)$ $\frac{1}{5}$

64. $(10.5, -3), (18, -8)$ $-\frac{2}{3}$

65. $(3.5, -2.5), (-1, -2)$ $-\frac{1}{9}$

Differentiated Instruction BL

Extension Draw a set of coordinate axes on the board and label each scale with only one number. Then draw several lines with arbitrary slopes (but include a horizontal line and a vertical line). Ask students to estimate values for the slopes and intercepts of the lines and to write a reasonable equation for each line. Try this when the scales on the two axes are the same. Then try it again when the scales differ on the two axes.

Tips for New Teachers

Looking Ahead Lesson 2-5 presents modeling real-world data using scatter plots. You may want to review how to find the median of a set of numbers.

4 ASSESS

Yesterday's News Have students explain how Lesson 2-3 on slope helped prepare them for this lesson's work on writing equations.

Formative Assessment

Check for students' understanding of concepts in Lessons 2-3 and 2-4.

CRM Quiz 2, p. 59

Additional Answers

36a. 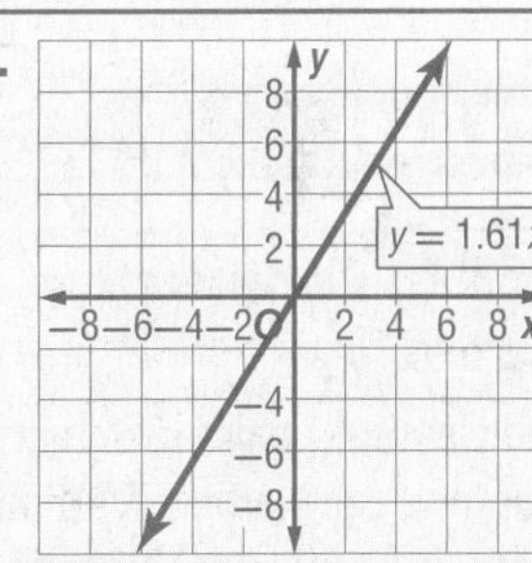

$y = 1.61x$

42. Sample answer: When given two points, A and B, find the slope of the line through the points. Divide the difference in the y-coordinates by the difference in the x-coordinates to get the slope of the line. Use the point-slope form to find the equation of the line, replacing m with the slope and (x_1, y_1) with the coordinates of A or B. Then distribute the m and subtract y_1 from both sides. After simplifying, you have the slope-intercept form of the line through A and B.

1 FOCUS

Objective
Use functions to model direct variation.

Materials for Each Student
- TI-83/84 Plus or other graphing calculator

Teaching Tip
To help students understand direct variation, give them an example with which they are familiar. As a person drives a car at a constant rate, the distance increases as the driving time increases. This is an example of direct variation.

2 TEACH

Working in Cooperative Groups
Divide the class into pairs. Give each pair a graphing calculator. Try to pair a student who is knowledgeable with a student who is less knowledgeable.

As a class, work through how to graph $y = 4x$, and discuss direct variation.

Then ask students to work with their partner to complete the Activity and Exercise 1.

Practice Have students complete Exercises 1 and 2.

3 ASSESS

Formative Assessment
Use Exercise 2 to assess whether students can graph direct variation equations.

From Concrete to Abstract
Ask students to give other examples of real-life situations that vary directly. For example: the pressure in your ears varies directly with the depth at which you are swimming.

Graphing Technology Lab
Direct Variation

FL Math Online glencoe.com
Other Calculator Keystrokes

NGSSS MA.912.A.2.12 **Solve problems using direct,** inverse, and joint **variations.**

An equation of a direct variation is a special case of a linear equation. A **direct variation** can be expressed in the form $y = kx$. This means that y is a multiple of x. The k in this equation is a constant and is called the **constant of variation**.

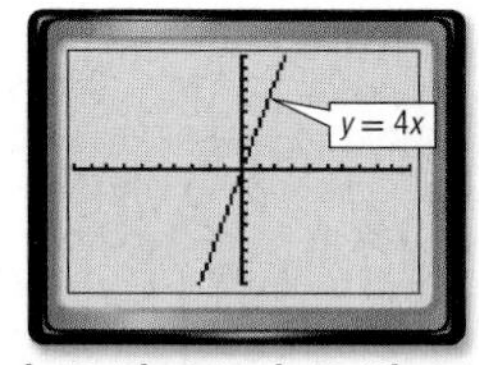

[−10, 10] scl: 1 by [−10, 10] scl: 1

Notice that the graph of $y = 4x$ is a straight line through the origin. An equation of a direct variation is a special case of an equation written in slope-intercept form, $y = mx + b$. When $m = k$ and $b = 0$, $y = mx + b$ becomes $y = kx$. So the slope of a direct variation equation is its constant of variation.

To express a direct variation, we say that y varies directly as x. In other words, as x increases, y increases or decreases at a constant rate.

Key Concept **Direct Variation**

y varies directly as x if there is some nonzero constant k such that $y = kx$. k is called the *constant of variation*.

ACTIVITY

GOLD The karat rating r of a gold object varies directly as the percentage p of gold in the object. A 14-karat ring is 58.25% gold.

a. Write and graph a direct variation equation relating r and p.

Use the point (0.5825, 14) to find the constant of variation.

$y = kx$	**Direct variation equation**
$14 = k(0.5825)$	**$x = 0.5825$, $y = 14$**
$24.03 \approx k$	**Divide each side by 0.5825.**

The direct variation equation is $r = 24.03p$.

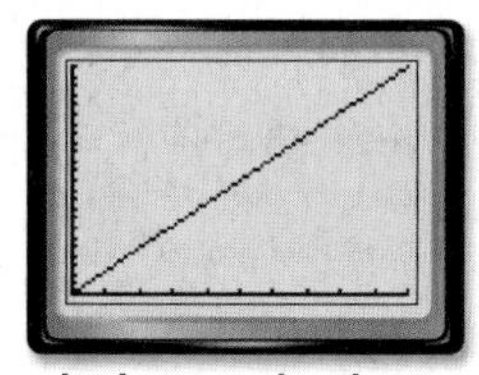
[0, 1] scl: 0.1 by [0, 24] scl: 1

b. Find the karat rating of a ring that is 75% gold.

Use the calculator to find the karat rating.

KEYSTROKES: [2nd] [CALC] 0.75 [ENTER] 18.0225

The karat rating of a ring that is 75% gold is 18 karats.

Exercises **1–2. See Chapter 2 Answer Appendix.**

1. **SWIMMING** When you swim underwater, the pressure on your ears varies directly with the depth at which you are swimming. If you are swimming in 8 feet of water, the pressure on your ears is 3.44 pounds per square inch. Write and graph a direct variation equation relating pressure and depth. Then find the pressure at a depth of 65 feet.
2. Graph the direct variation equations $y = -4x$, $y = -2x$, $y = 4x$, and $y = 2x$. Compare and contrast the graphs of the equations.

Extending the Concept
Write the equation $y = kx^3$ on the board. Ask students to describe the kind of variation modeled by this equation. Have them describe what happens to the value of y when the value of x is doubled, tripled, halved, etc. For this equation, y varies directly as the cube of x. When x is tripled, y is multiplied by 27. When x is halved, y is divided by 8.

NGSSS 912.A.2.13, 912.A.3.6, 912.A.3.10

1. State the domain and range of the relation {(−3, 2), (4, 1), (0, 3), (5, −2), (2, 7)}. Then determine whether the relation is a function. **D = {−3, 4, 0, 5, 2}; R = {2, 1, 3, −2, 7}; function**

2. Graph $y = 2x - 3$ and determine whether the equation is a *function*, is *one-to-one*, *onto*, *both*, or *neither*. State whether it is *discrete* or *continuous*. **See margin.**

Given $f(x) = 3x^3 - 2x + 7$, find each value.

3. $f(-2)$ **−13**
4. $f(2y)$ **$24y^3 - 4y + 7$**
5. $f(1.4)$ **12.432**

6. State whether $f(x) = 2x^2 - 9$ is a linear function. Explain. **No, the variable is squared.**

7. NGSSS PRACTICE The daily pricing for renting a mid-sized car is given by the function $f(x) = 0.35x + 49$, where $f(x)$ is the total rental price for a car driven x miles. Find the rental cost for a car driven 250 miles. **C**

A. $84
B. $112.50
C. $136.50
D. $215

Write each equation in standard form. Identify *A*, *B*, and *C*. **9. $10x - y = 0$; 10, −1, 0**

8. $y = -6x + 5$
9. $y = 10x$
10. $-\frac{5}{8}x = 2y + 11$ **$-5x - 16y = 88$; −5, −16, 88**
11. $0.5x = 3$ **$x = 6$; 1, 0, 6**

Find the *x*-intercept and the *y*-intercept of the graph of each equation. Then graph the equation using the intercepts. **12, 13. See Chapter 2 Answer Appendix.**

12. $4x - 3y + 12 = 0$
13. $10 - x = 2y$

14. SPEED The table shows the distance traveled by a car after each time given in minutes. Find the rate of change in distance for the car. **0.67 mi/min**

Time (min)	Distance (mi)
15	20
30	40
45	60
60	80
90	100

Find the slope of the line that passes through each pair of points. Express as a fraction in simplest form.

15. (−2, 6), (1, 15) **3**
16. (3, 5), (7, 15) **$\frac{5}{2}$**
17. (4, 8), (4, −3) **undefined**
18. (−2.5, 4), (1.5, −2) **$-\frac{3}{2}$**

19. Find the slope of the line shown. **$-\frac{1}{2}$**

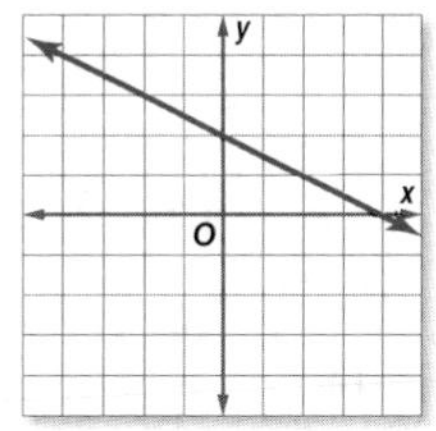

Write an equation of the line through each set of points.

20. slope $\frac{2}{3}$, passes through (3, −4) **$2x - 3y = 18$**
21. slope −2.5, passes through (1, 2) **$y = -2.5x + 4.5$**

Write an equation of the line through each set of points.

22. (−2, 3), (4, 1) **$y = -\frac{1}{3}x + \frac{7}{3}$**
23. (4.2, 3.6), (1.8, −1.2) **$y = 2x - 4.8$**

24. NGSSS PRACTICE Each week, Jaya earns $32 plus $0.25 for each newspaper she delivers. Write an equation that can be used to determine how much Jaya earns each week. How much will she earn during a week in which she delivers 240 papers? **G**

F. $75
G. $92
H. $148
I. $212

25. PART-TIME JOB Jesse is a pizza delivery driver. Each day his employer gives him $20 plus $0.50 for every pizza that he delivers.

a. Write an equation that can be used to determine how much Jesse earns each day if he delivers x pizzas. **$y = 0.5x + 20$**

b. How much will he earn the day he delivers 20 pizzas? **$30**

CHAPTER 2 Mid-Chapter Quiz

Formative Assessment

Use the Mid-Chapter Quiz to assess students' progress in the first half of the chapter.

For problems answered incorrectly, have students review the lessons indicated in parentheses.

ExamView Assessment Suite Customize and create multiple versions of your Mid-Chapter Quiz and their answer keys.

FOLDABLES Follow-Up

Before students complete the Mid-Chapter Quiz, encourage them to review the information for Lessons 2-1 through 2-4 in their Foldables.

Additional Answer

2.

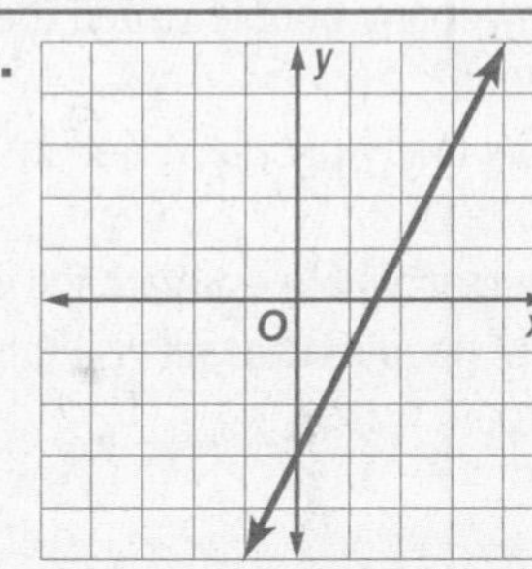

function, both, continuous

Intervention Planner

Tier 1 On Level	Tier 2 Strategic Intervention approaching grade level	Tier 3 Intensive Intervention 2 or more grades below level
If students miss about 25% of the exercises or less,	**If** students miss about 50% of the exercises,	**If** students miss about 75% of the exercises,
Then choose a resource: **SE** Lessons 2-1, 2-2, 2-3, and 2-4 **CRM** Skills Practice, pp. 7, 13, 19, and 25 **TE** Chapter Project, p. 58	**Then** choose a resource: **CRM** Study Guide and Intervention, Chapter 2, pp. 5, 11, 17, and 23	**Then** use *Math Triumphs, Alg. 2*, Ch. 1 and 3
FL Math Online Self-Check Quiz	FL Math Online Extra Examples, Personal Tutor, Homework Help	FL Math Online Extra Examples, Personal Tutor, Homework Help, Review Vocabulary

2-5 Lesson Notes

1 FOCUS

Vertical Alignment

Before Lesson 2-5
Write linear equations.

Lesson 2-5
Use scatter plots and prediction equations. Model data using lines of regression.

After Lesson 2-5
Create models from data and use the models to make decisions and critical judgments.

2 TEACH

Scaffolding Questions

Have students read the *Why?* section of the lesson.

Ask:

- About how many people visited the park in 2000? 21,000
- About how many people visited in 2005? 17,000
- What is a reasonable estimate for the number of people who will visit this park in 2008? 16,000 or 17,000

2-5 Scatter Plots and Lines of Regression

Then
You wrote linear equations. (Lesson 2-4)

Now
- Use scatter plots and prediction equations.
- Model data using lines of regression.

NGSSS
Reinforcement of MA.912.A.3.11 Write an equation of a line that models a data set and use the equation or the graph to make predictions. Describe the slope of the line in terms of the data, recognizing that the slope is the rate of change.

New Vocabulary
bivariate data
scatter plot
dot plot
positive correlation
negative correlation
line of fit
prediction equation
regression line
correlation coefficient

FL Math Online
glencoe.com

Why?

The scatter plot shows the number of visitors to Isle Royale National Park in Michigan. The linear function $f(x) = -0.43x + 24.6$ can be used to model the data.

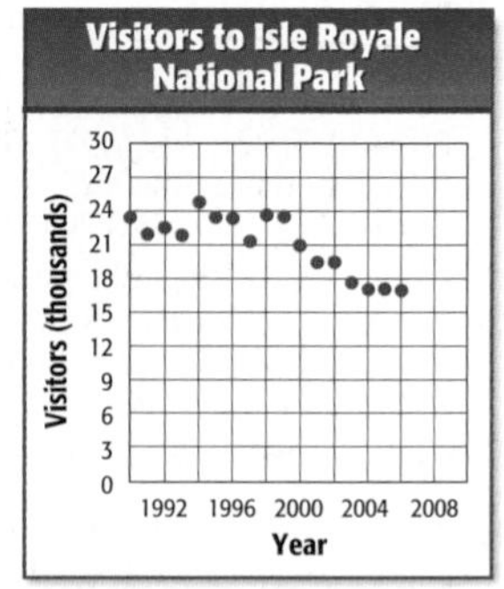

Source: National Park Service

Scatter Plots and Prediction Equations Data with two variables, such as year and number of visitors, are called **bivariate data**. A set of bivariate data graphed as ordered pairs in a coordinate plane is called a **scatter plot** or **dot plot**.

A scatter plot can show whether there is a positive, negative, or no correlation between two variables. Correlations are usually described as *strong* or *weak*. In a strong correlation, the points of the scatterplot are closer to the graph of a line than the points representing a weak correlation.

Key Concept Scatter Plots

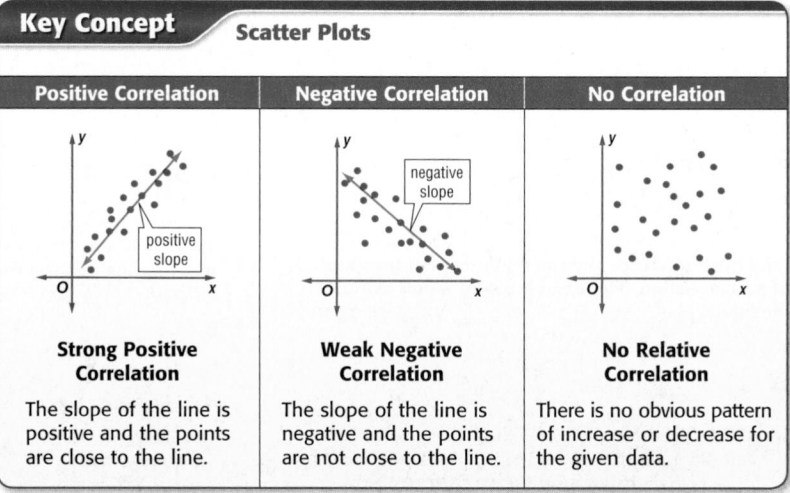

Positive Correlation

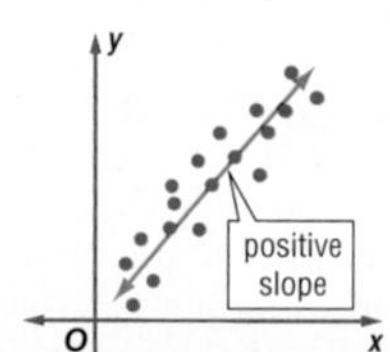

Strong Positive Correlation

The slope of the line is positive and the points are close to the line.

Negative Correlation

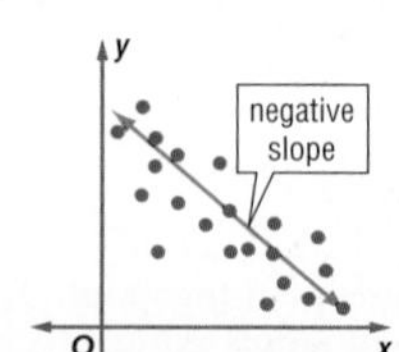

Weak Negative Correlation

The slope of the line is negative and the points are not close to the line.

No Correlation

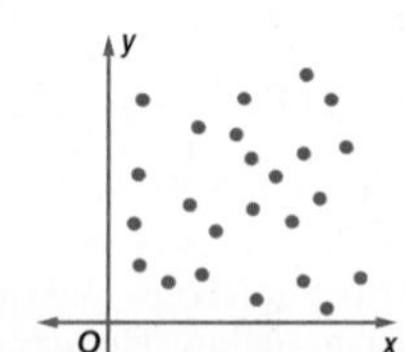

No Relative Correlation

There is no obvious pattern of increase or decrease for the given data.

When you find a line that closely approximates a set of data, you are finding a **line of fit** for the data. An equation of such a line is often called a **prediction equation** because it can be used to predict one of the variables given the other variable.

To find a line of fit and a prediction equation for a set of data, select two points that appear to represent the data well. This is a matter of personal judgment, so your line and prediction equation may be different from someone else's.

Lesson 2-5 Resources

Resource	Approaching-Level	On-Level	Beyond-Level	English Learners
Teacher Edition	• Differentiated Instruction, p. 94	• Differentiated Instruction, p. 94	• Differentiated Instruction, pp. 94, 98	
Chapter Resource Masters	• Study Guide and Intervention, pp. 30–31 • Skills Practice, p. 32 • Practice, p. 33 • Word Problem Practice, p. 34	• Study Guide and Intervention, pp. 30–31 • Skills Practice, p. 32 • Practice, p. 33 • Word Problem Practice, p. 34 • Enrichment, p. 35	• Practice, p. 33 • Word Problem Practice, p. 34 • Enrichment, p. 35	• Study Guide and Intervention, pp. 30–31 • Skills Practice, p. 32 • Practice, p. 33 • Word Problem Practice, p. 34
Transparencies	• 5-Minute Check Transparency 2-5	• 5-Minute Check Transparency 2-5	• 5-Minute Check Transparency 2-5	• 5-Minute Check Transparency 2-5
Other	• Study Notebook	• Study Notebook	• Study Notebook	• Study Notebook

Real-World Link

According to the National Technology Scan, about 70% of U.S. households have computers connected to the Internet.

Source: The National Technology Scan

Real-World EXAMPLE 1 Use a Scatter Plot and Prediction Equation

TECHNOLOGY **The table shows the percent of U.S. households with at least one personal computer.**

Year	1984	1989	1993	1997	2001	2003
Percent	8.2	15.0	22.8	36.6	56.3	61.8

Source: U.S. Census Bureau

a. Make a scatter plot and a line of fit, and describe the correlation.

Graph the data as ordered pairs with the number of years since 1984 on the horizontal axis and the percent of households on the vertical axis.

The points (5, 15.0) and (19, 61.8) appear to represent the data well. Draw a line through these two points. The data show a strong positive correlation.

Percent of Households with a PC

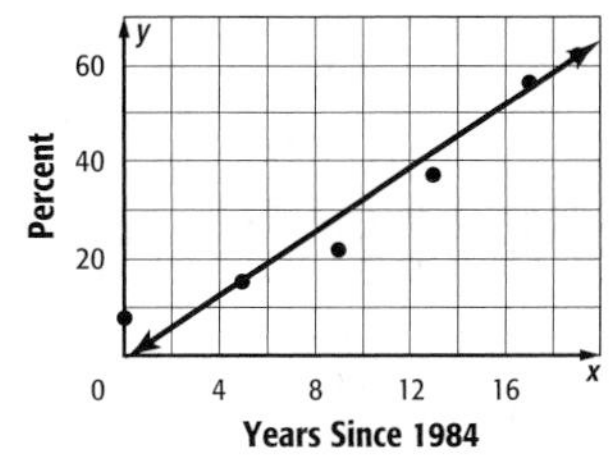

Using x = years since 1984 makes calculations simpler.

b. Use two ordered pairs to write a prediction equation.

Find an equation of the line through (5, 15.0) and (19, 61.8).

$m = \frac{y_2 - y_1}{x_2 - x_1}$ **Slope Formula**

$= \frac{61.8 - 15.0}{19 - 5}$ **Substitute.**

≈ 3.34 **Simplify.**

$y - y_1 = m(x - x_1)$ **Point-Slope form**

$y - 15 \approx 3.34(x - 5)$ **Substitute.**

$y - 15 \approx 3.34x - 16.7$ **Distributive Property**

$y \approx 3.34x - 1.7$ **Simplify.**

One prediction equation is $y = 3.34x - 1.7$.

c. Predict the percent of households with at least one personal computer in 2012.

The year 2012 is 28 years after 1984, so find y when $x = 28$.

$y \approx 3.34x - 1.7$ **Prediction equation**

$\approx 3.34(28) - 1.7$ **$x = 28$**

≈ 91.82 **Simplify.**

The model predicts that 91.82% of U.S. households will have at least one personal computer in 2012.

d. How accurate does your prediction appear to be?

Except for the outlier at (0, 8.2), the line fits the data well, so the prediction value should be fairly accurate.

Guided Practice

1. HOUSING **The table shows the mean selling price of new, privately-owned, single-family homes for some recent years.**

Year	1994	1996	1998	2000	2002	2004
Price ($1000)	154.5	166.4	181.9	207.0	228.7	273.5

Source: U.S. Census Bureau and U.S. Department of Housing and Urban Development

A. Make a scatter plot and a line of fit, and describe the correlation. **See margin.**

B. Write a prediction equation. **Sample answer: $y = 11.7x + 135.1$**

C. Predict the selling price of a new, privately-owned, single-family home in 2010.

D. How accurate does your prediction appear to be?

Personal Tutor glencoe.com

1C. Sample answer: $322,300
1D. Sample answer: The line fits the data fairly well, so the prediction is reasonably accurate.

Review Vocabulary

outlier a data point that does not appear to belong to the rest of the set

Tips for New Teachers

Scatter Plots Make sure students understand that data points must be clustered linearly to see a correlation.

Scatter Plots and Prediction Equations

Example 1 illustrates how to make a scatter plot from a table of data, draw a line of fit, and interpret the graph's meaning.

Formative Assessment

Use the Guided Practice exercises after each example to determine students' understanding of concepts.

Additional Example

1 **EDUCATION** The table below shows the approximate percent of students who sent applications to two colleges in various years since 1985.

Years Since 1985	Percent
0	20
3	18
6	15
9	15
12	14
15	13

Source: *U.S. News and World Report*

a. Make a scatter plot and a line of fit, and describe the correlation.

Percent of Students Applying to Two Colleges

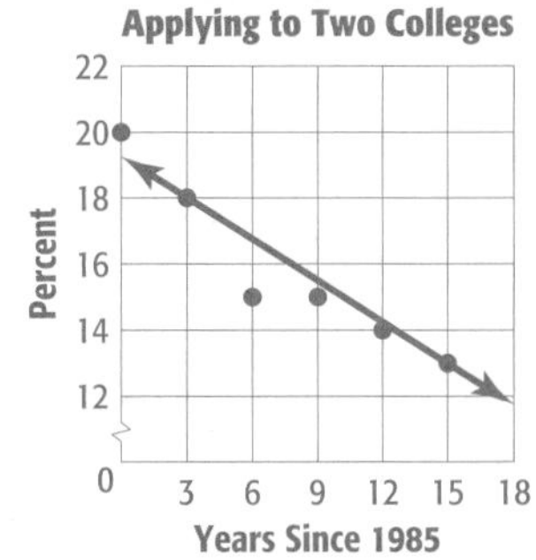

The data show a strong negative correlation.

(continued on the next page)

Additional Answer (Guided Practice)

1A. Mean House Prices

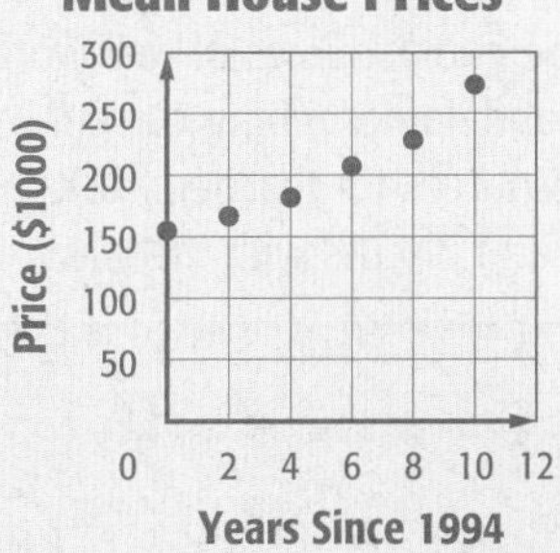

Focus on Mathematical Content

Correlation When a line is fit to a scatter plot, the type of correlation is related to the sign of the slope of the line. A positive slope indicates positive correlation, while a negative slope indicates negative correlation.

Additional Example

b. Use two ordered pairs to write a prediction equation. Using (3, 18) and (15, 13): $y = -\frac{5}{12}x + 19.25$; the slope indicates that the percent is falling by about 42% each year. The y-intercept indicates the percent in 1985 would have been about 19%.

c. Predict the percent of students who will send applications to two colleges. in 2010. about 8.83%

d. How accurate does your prediction appear to be? The fit is only approximate, so the prediction may not be very accurate.

Additional Examples also in Interactive Classroom PowerPoint® Presentations

IWB INTERACTIVE WHITEBOARD READY

Tips for New Teachers

Prediction Equations Discuss various possible prediction equations for the data in Example 1. Which equation is best? Why?

Additional Answers

1a. **Ocean Temperature**

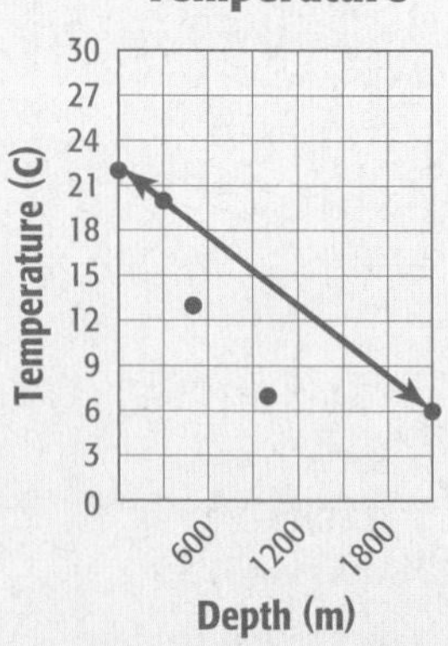

weak negative correlation

1c. Sample answer: 2°C

Lines of Regression Another method for writing a line of fit is to use a line of regression. A **regression line** is determined through complex calculations to ensure that the distance of all data points to the line of fit are at a minimum. Most graphing calculators and spreadsheets can perform these calculations easily.

The **correlation coefficient r**, $-1 \leq r \leq 1$, is a measure that shows how well data are modeled by a linear equation.

- When r is close to -1, the data have a negative correlation.
- When $r = 0$, the data have no correlation.
- When r is close to 1, the data have a positive correlation.

StudyTip

Alternate Method Letting x be the number of years since the first year in the data set simplifies the math involved in finding a function to model the data. But the rate of change and fit of the regression equation are the same. Only the y-intercept of the equation is changed.

Real-World EXAMPLE 2 Regression Line

The table shows the life expectancy for people born in the United States.

Year of Birth	1983	1990	1993	1997	2000	2003
Life Expectancy (yr)	74.6	75.4	75.5	76.5	76.9	77.5

Source: U.S. Department of Health and Human Services

Use a graphing calculator to make a scatter plot of the data. Find an equation for and graph a line of regression. Then use the equation to predict the life expectancy of a person born in 2025.

Step 1 Make a scatter plot.

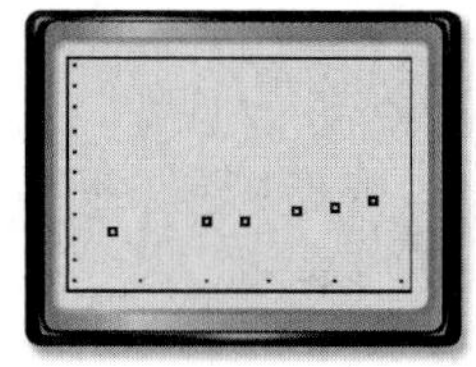

- Enter the years of birth in L1 and the ages in L2.

  KEYSTROKES: STAT ENTER 1983 ENTER 1990 ENTER 1993 ENTER …

- Set the viewing window to fit the data.

  KEYSTROKES: WINDOW 1980 ENTER 2005 ENTER 5 ENTER 70 ENTER 90 ENTER 2

- Use STAT PLOT to graph the scatter plot.

  KEYSTROKES: 2nd [STAT PLOT] ENTER ENTER Graph

Step 2 Find the equation of the line of regression.

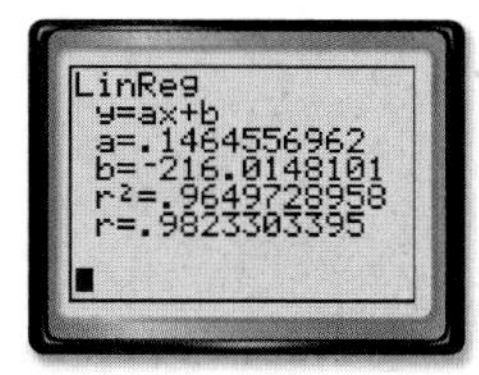

- Find the regression equation by selecting LinReg(ax + b) on the STAT CALC menu.

  KEYSTROKES: STAT ▶ 4 ENTER

The regression equation is about $y = 0.15x - 216.01$. The slope indicates that the life expectancy increases at a rate of about 0.15 per year. The correlation coefficient r is about 0.98, which is very close to 1. So, the data fit the regression line very well.

Step 3 Graph the regression equation.

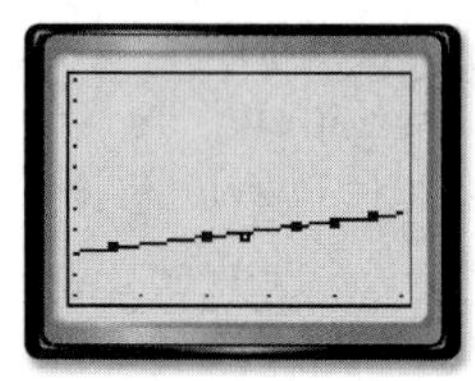

- Copy the equation to the Y= list and graph.

  KEYSTROKES: Y= VARS 5 ▶ ▶ 1 Graph

  Notice that the regression line comes close to all of the data points. As the correlation coefficient indicated, the line fits the data very well.

Differentiated Instruction

AL OL BL

Linguistic/Visual/Spatial Learners Newspapers and magazines can be good sources of real-world examples of mathematics, especially with regard to tables and graphs of data describing current issues of interest. Some publications even offer special news-related resources for teachers. Ask students to find a table of data in a newspaper or magazine to cut out and discuss with the class.

ReadingMath

Predictions When you are predicting an x-value greater than or less than any in the data set, the process is known as **extrapolation**. When you are predicting an x-value between the least and greatest in the data set, the process is known as **interpolation**.

Step 4 Predict using the function.

- Find y when $x = 2025$. Use **VALUE** on the **CALC** menu. Reset the window size to accommodate the x-value of 2025.

KEYSTROKES: [2nd] [CALC] 1 2025 [ENTER]

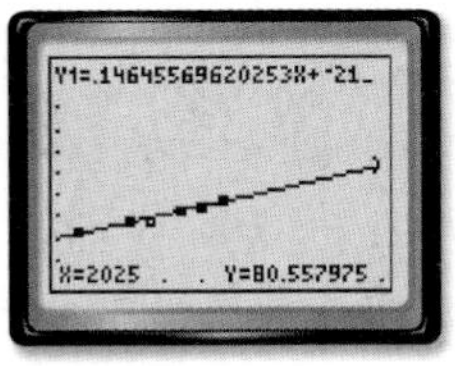

According to the function, the life expectancy of a person born in 2025 will be about 80.6 years.

Guided Practice

2. MUSIC The table at the right shows the percent of sales that were made in music stores in the United States for the period 1995–2004. Use a graphing calculator to make a scatter plot of the data. Find and graph a line of regression. Then use the function to predict the percent of sales made in a music store in 2015.

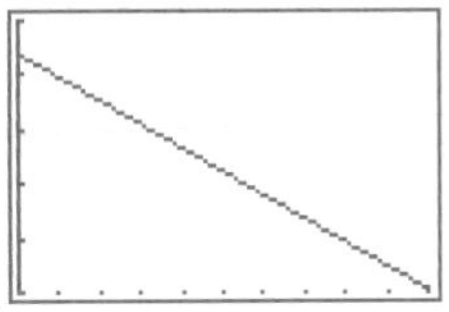

[1994, 2005] scl: 1 by [30, 55] scl: 5

$y = -2.4x + 54.4$ (x is the number of years after 1995); 6.6%

Music Store Sales

Year	Sales (percent)
1995	52.0
1996	49.9
1997	51.8
1998	50.8
1999	44.5
2000	42.4
2001	42.5
2002	36.8
2003	33.2
2004	32.5

Source: Recording Industry Association of America

Personal Tutor glencoe.com

Check Your Understanding

Example 1 p. 93

1. OCEANS The table shows the temperature in the ocean at various depths.

Depth (in meters)	0	300	500	1000	2000	2500
Temp (°C)	22	20	13	7	6	?

Source: NOAA

a. Make a scatter plot and a line of fit, and describe the correlation. See margin.

b. Use two ordered pairs to write a prediction equation.

c. Use your prediction equation to predict the missing value. Sample answer: 2°C

1b. Sample answer using (0, 22) and (2000, 6): $y = -0.008x + 22$

Example 2 p. 94

2. FINANCIAL LITERACY The table shows the median income of families in North Carolina by family size in a recent year. Use a graphing calculator to make a scatter plot of the data. Find an equation for and graph a line of regression. Then use the equation to predict the median income of a North Carolina family of 9. Sample answer: $y = 8455.1x + 25{,}837$; \$101,932; see margin for graph.

Family Size	Income ($)
1	33,265
2	44,625
3	50,528
4	59,481

Source: U.S. Department of Justice

Lines of Regression

Example 2 shows how to use a graphing calculator to make a scatter plot, graph a line of regression, and make a prediction.

Additional Examples

2 INCOME The table shows the median income of U.S. families for the period 1970–2002.

Year	Income($)
1970	9867
1980	21,023
1985	27,735
1990	35,353
1995	40,611
1998	46,737
2000	50,732
2002	51,680

Use a graphing calculator to make a scatter plot of the data. Find an equation for and graph a line of regression. Then use the equation to predict the median income in 2015.

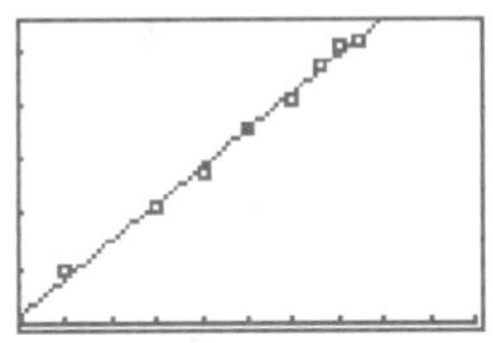

[1965, 2015] scl: 5 by [0, 55,000] scl: 10,000

$y = 1349.87x - 2{,}650{,}768.34$; median family income in 2015 will be about \$69,220.

Additional Answer

2.

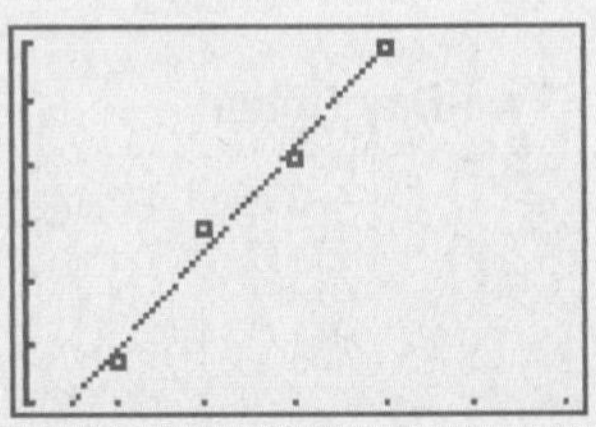

[0, 6] scl: 1 by [30,000, 60,000] scl: 5000

TEACH with TECH

VIDEO RECORDING Have students work in pairs to create a video showing how to find a regression line for a given set of data. Share each group's video with the entire class.

Tips for New Teachers

Sense-Making Encourage students to think about why trends are occurring in Example 2 and Guided Practice 2. Then ask students how problems of this type could be important in other fields such as engineering, marketing, and statistics.

3 PRACTICE

Formative Assessment

Use Exercises 1–2 to check for understanding.

Use the chart at the bottom of this page to customize assignments for your students.

Additional Answers

3a.

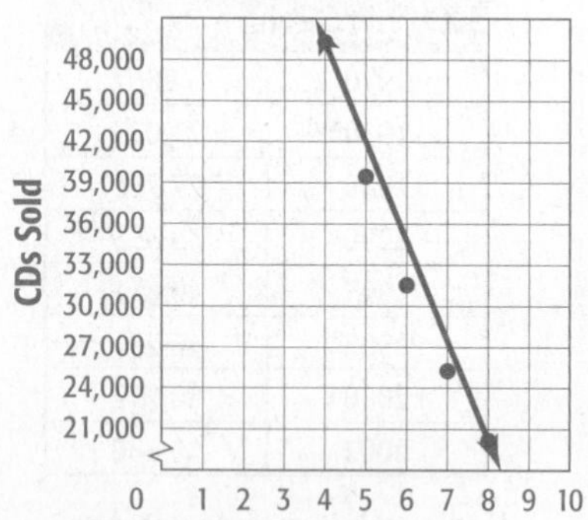

strong negative correlation

4a.

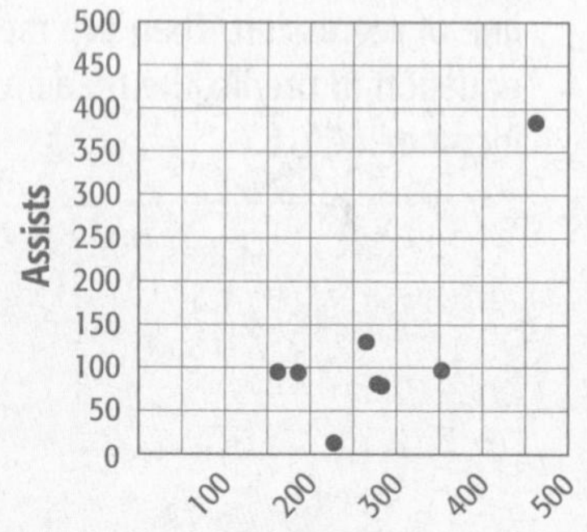

no correlation

5a.

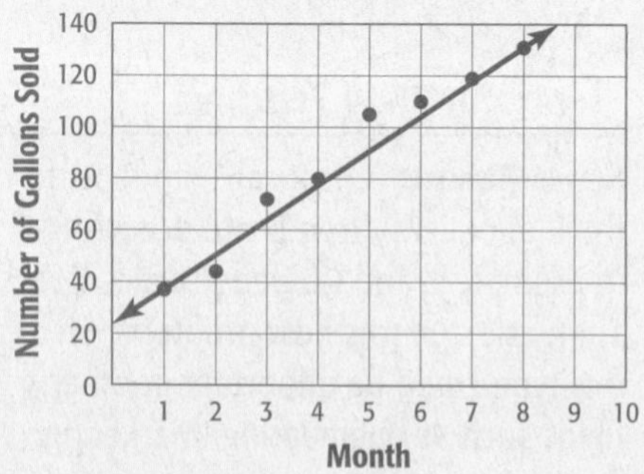

strong positive correlation

Practice and Problem Solving

● = **Step-by-Step Solutions** begin on page R20. **Extra Practice** begins on page 947.

Example 1 p. 93

For Exercises 3–6, complete parts a–c.

a. Make a scatter plot and a line of fit, and describe the correlation.

b. Use two ordered pairs to write a prediction equation.

c. Use your prediction equation to predict the missing value.

3a. See margin.
3b. Sample answer, using (4, 49,300) and (8, 20,193): $y = -7276.75x + 78{,}407$
3c. Sample answer: 12,916 CDs
4b. Sample answer: No equation can be written because there is no correlation.
4c. unpredictable

3. COMPACT DISC SALES The table shows the number of CDs sold in recent years at Jerome's House of Music.

Year	2004	2005	2006	2007	2008	2009
Number of CDs sold	49,300	39,440	31,552	25,242	20,193	?

4. BASKETBALL The table shows the number of field goals and assists for some of the members of the Miami Heat in a recent NBA season. a. See margin.

Field Goals	472	353	278	283	238	265	186	162	144
Assists	384	97	81	79	18	130	94	95	?

Source: NBA

5a. See margin. 5b. Sample answer using (1, 37) and (8, 131): $y = \frac{94}{7}x + \frac{165}{7}$

Real-World Link

The average number of licks to polish off a single scoop ice cream cone is approximately 50.

Source: Edy's®

5. ICE CREAM The table shows the amount of ice cream Sunee's Homemade Ice Creams sold for eight months.

Month	Jan	Feb	Mar	Apr	May	June	July	Aug	Sept
Gallons sold	37	44	72	80	105	110	119	131	?

5c. Sample answer: about 144 gal

6. DRAMA CLUB The table shows the total revenue of all of Central High School's plays in recent school years. a. See margin.

School Year	2002	2003	2004	2005	2006	2007
Revenue ($)	603	666	643	721	771	?

Example 2 p. 94

6b. Sample answer using (2, 603) and (6, 771): $y = 42x + 519$
6c. Sample answer: $813

7. SALES The table shows the sales of Chayton's Computers. Use a graphing calculator to make a scatter plot of the data. Find an equation for and graph a line of regression. Then use the function to predict the sales in 2012. See Chapter 2 Answer Appendix for graph; $y = 61.8x + 654$ (x is the number of years since 2002); $1.148 million in sales

Year	Sales ($ thousands)
2004	640
2005	715
2006	791
2007	852
2008	910
2009	944

8. BUSINESS The table shows the number of employees of a small company. Use a graphing calculator to make a scatter plot of the data. Find an equation for and graph a line of regression. Then use the function to predict the number of employees in 2015. See Chapter 2 Answer Appendix for graph; $y = 3.9x - 3.4$; about 43 employees

Year	Number of Employees
2002	4
2003	7
2004	11
2005	14
2006	20
2007	23

Differentiated Homework Options

Level	Assignment	Two-Day Option	
AL Basic	3–8, 12, 14–32	3–7 odd, 17–20	4–8 even, 12, 14–16, 21–32
OL Core	3–7 odd, 9–12, 14–32	3–8, 17–20	9–12, 14–32
BL Advanced	9–29, (optional: 30–32)		

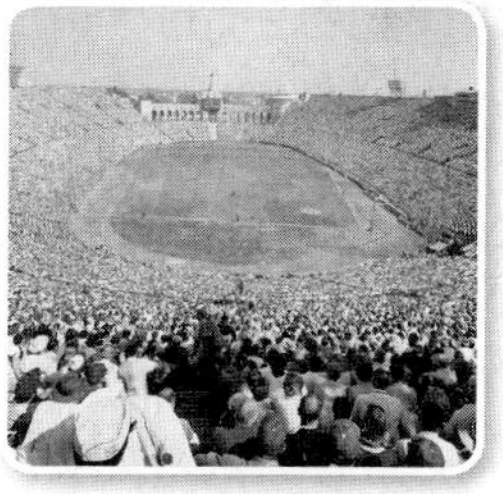

Real-World Link

The largest crowd for a single baseball game was 92,706 during the 1959 World Series between the Chicago White Sox and the Los Angeles Dodgers.

Source: Major League Baseball

9a. See Chapter 2 Answer Appendix.
9b. $y = 71{,}406.4x - 141{,}763{,}070.9$
9d. Sample answer: Unreasonable; the attendance will not increase without bound because attendance is largely dependent on the team's winning status.
10b. $r = -0.712$
10c. Sample answer: relatively accurate with a negative correlation

14a. Sample answer: years and height of a teenager
14b. Sample answer: time and capacity of a standard battery
14c. Sample answer: a person's weight and his or her income

9. BASEBALL The table at the right shows the total attendance for the Florida Marlins in some recent years.

a. Make a scatter plot of the data.

b. Find a regression equation for the data.

c. Predict the attendance in 2020. 2,477,915

d. How reasonable is your prediction? Explain.

Year	Attendance
2007	1,370,511
2006	1,164,134
2005	1,852,608
2004	1,723,105
2003	1,303,215
2002	813,118

10. CLASS SIZE The table at the right shows the relationship between the number of students in a mathematics class and the average grade for each class.

a. Make a scatter plot of the data, and find a regression equation for the data. Then sketch a graph of the regression line. See Chapter 2 Answer Appendix.

b. What is the correlation coefficient of the data?

c. Describe the correlation. How accurate is the regression equation?

Class Size	Class Average
16	81.2
19	80.6
24	82.5
26	79.9
27	78.6
29	79.3
32	77.7

11. FINANCIAL LITERACY Jocelyn is analyzing the sales of her company. The table at the right shows the total sales for each of six years.

a. Find a regression equation and correlation coefficient for the data. $y = 3.1x - 6177$; $r = 0.63$

b. Use the regression equation to predict the sales in 2015. about $64.2 million

Year	Sales ($ millions)
2003	31.2
2004	34.6
2005	18.9
2006	37.7
2007	41.3
2008	45.1

c. Remove the outlier from the data set and find a new regression equation and correlation coefficient. $y = 2.6x - 5170$; $r = 0.986$

d. Use the new regression equation to predict the sales in 2015. about $62.4 million

e. Compare the correlation coefficients for the two regression equations. Which function fits the data better? Which prediction should Jocelyn expect to be more accurate? See Chapter 2 Answer Appendix.

H.O.T. Problems

Use Higher-Order Thinking Skills

12. REASONING What is the relevance of the correlation coefficient of a linear regression line? Explain your reasoning. See Chapter 2 Answer Appendix.

13. CHALLENGE If statements a and b have a positive correlation, b and c have a negative correlation, and c and d have a positive correlation, what can you determine about the correlation between statements a and d? Explain your reasoning. See Chapter 2 Answer Appendix.

14. OPEN ENDED Provide real-world quantities that represent each of the following.

a. positive correlation **b.** negative correlation **c.** no correlation

15. CHALLENGE Draw a scatter plot for the following data set.

x	1.0	1.5	2.0	2.8	3.2	4.0	4.8	5.8
y	3.5	4.7	5.1	6.8	7.1	7.5	8.8	10.3

Which of the following best represents the correlation coefficient r for the data? Justify your answer. See Chapter 2 Answer Appendix.

a. 0.99 **b.** −0.98 **c.** 0.62 **d.** 0.08

16. WRITING IN MATH Explain why a linear equation is useful when working with data. See Chapter 2 Answer Appendix.

Study Guide and Intervention
CRM pp. 30–31 AL OL ELL

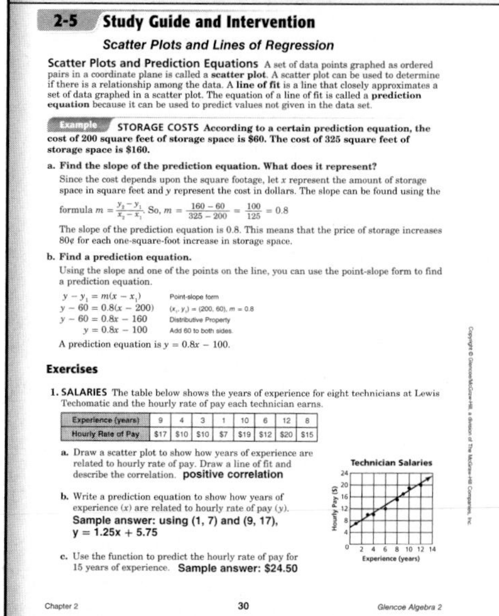

2-5 Study Guide and Intervention

Scatter Plots and Lines of Regression

Scatter Plots and Prediction Equations A set of data points graphed as ordered pairs in a coordinate plane is called a **scatter plot**. A scatter plot can be used to determine if there is a relationship among the data. A **line of fit** is a line that closely approximates a set of data graphed in a scatter plot. The equation of a line of fit is called a **prediction equation** because it can be used to predict values not given in the data set.

Example STORAGE COSTS According to a certain prediction equation, the cost of 200 square feet of storage space is $60. The cost of 325 square feet of storage space is $160.

a. Find the slope of the prediction equation. What does it represent?
Since the cost depends upon the square footage, let x represent the amount of storage space in square feet and y represent the cost in dollars. The slope can be found using the formula $m = \frac{y_2 - y_1}{x_2 - x_1}$. So, $m = \frac{160 - 60}{325 - 200} = \frac{100}{125} = 0.8$
The slope of the prediction equation is 0.8. This means that the price of storage increases 80¢ for each one-square-foot increase in storage space.

b. Find a prediction equation.
Using the slope and one of the points on the line, you can use the point-slope form to find a prediction equation.
$y - y_1 = m(x - x_1)$ Point-slope form
$y - 60 = 0.8(x - 200)$ $(x_1, y_1) = (200, 60)$, $m = 0.8$
$y - 60 = 0.8x - 160$ Distributive Property
$y = 0.8x - 100$ Add 60 to both sides.
A prediction equation is $y = 0.8x - 100$.

Exercises

1. SALARIES The table below shows the years of experience for eight technicians at Lewis Techomatic and the hourly rate of pay each technician earns.

Experience (years)	9	4	3	1	10	6	12	8
Hourly Rate of Pay	$17	$10	$10	$7	$19	$12	$20	$15

a. Draw a scatter plot to show how years of experience are related to hourly rate of pay. Draw a line of fit and describe the correlation. positive correlation

b. Write a prediction equation to show how years of experience (x) are related to hourly rate of pay (y). Sample answer: using (1, 7) and (9, 17), $y = 1.25x + 5.75$

c. Use the function to predict the hourly rate of pay for 15 years of experience. Sample answer: $24.50

Chapter 2 30 Glencoe Algebra 2

Practice
CRM p. 33 AL OL BL ELL

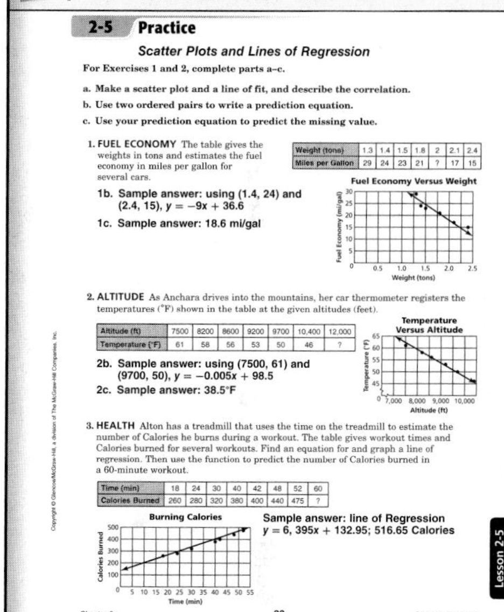

2-5 Practice

Scatter Plots and Lines of Regression

For Exercises 1 and 2, complete parts a–c.
a. Make a scatter plot and a line of fit, and describe the correlation.
b. Use two ordered pairs to write a prediction equation.
c. Use your prediction equation to predict the missing value.

1. FUEL ECONOMY The table gives the weights in tons and estimates the fuel economy in miles per gallon for several cars.

Weight (tons)	1.3	1.4	1.5	1.8	2	2.1	2.4
Miles per Gallon	29	24	23	21	?	17	15

1b. Sample answer: using (1.4, 24) and (2.4, 15), $y = -9x + 36.6$
1c. Sample answer: 18.6 mi/gal

2. ALTITUDE As Anchara drives into the mountains, her car thermometer registers the temperatures (°F) shown in the table at the given altitudes (feet).

Altitude (ft)	7500	8200	8600	9200	9700	10,400	12,000
Temperature (°F)	61	58	56	53	50	46	?

2b. Sample answer: using (7500, 61) and (9700, 50), $y = -0.005x + 98.5$
2c. Sample answer: 38.5°F

3. HEALTH Alton has a treadmill that uses the time on the treadmill to estimate the number of Calories he burns during a workout. The table gives workout times and Calories burned for several workouts. Find an equation for and graph a line of regression. Then use the function to predict the number of Calories burned in a 60-minute workout.

Time (min)	18	24	30	40	42	48	52	60
Calories Burned	260	280	320	380	400	440	475	?

Sample answer: line of Regression $y = 6.395x + 132.95$; 516.65 Calories

Chapter 2 33 Glencoe Algebra 2

Word Problem Practice
CRM p. 34 AL OL BL ELL

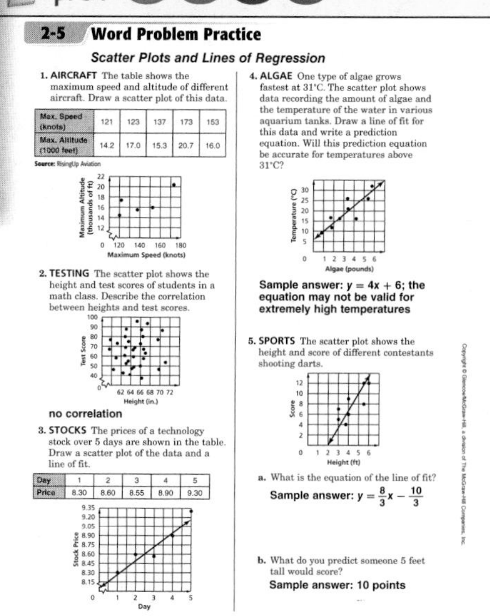

2-5 Word Problem Practice

Scatter Plots and Lines of Regression

1. AIRCRAFT The table shows the maximum speed and altitude of different aircraft. Draw a scatter plot of this data.

Max. Speed (knots)	121	123	137	173	153
Max. Altitude (1000 feet)	14.2	17.0	15.3	20.7	16.0

Source: RisingUp Aviation

2. TESTING The scatter plot shows the height and test scores of students in a math class. Describe the correlation between heights and test scores.

no correlation

3. STOCKS The prices of a technology stock over 5 days are shown in the table. Draw a scatter plot of the data and a line of fit.

Day	1	2	3	4	5
Price	8.30	8.60	8.55	8.90	9.30

4. ALGAE One type of algae grows fastest at 31°C. The scatter plot shows data recording the amount of algae and the temperature of the water in various aquarium tanks. Draw a line of fit for this data and write a prediction equation. Will this prediction equation be accurate for temperatures above 31°C?

Sample answer: $y = 4x + 6$; the equation may not be valid for extremely high temperatures

5. SPORTS The scatter plot shows the height and score of different contestants shooting darts.

a. What is the equation of the line of fit? Sample answer: $y = \frac{8}{3}x - \frac{10}{3}$

b. What do you predict someone 5 feet tall would score? Sample answer: 10 points

Chapter 2 34 Glencoe Algebra 2

6a.

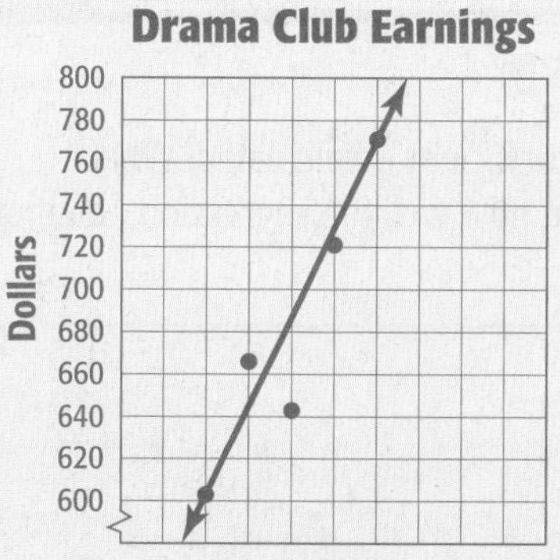

weak positive correlation

Enrichment
CRM p. 35 OL BL

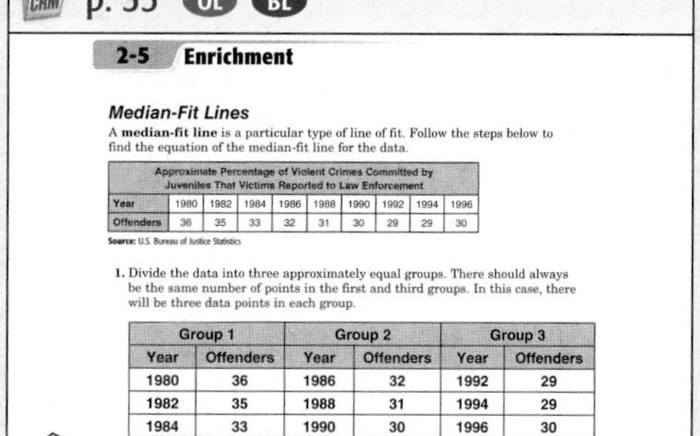

2-5 Enrichment

Median-Fit Lines

A **median-fit line** is a particular type of line of fit. Follow the steps below to find the equation of the median-fit line for the data.

Approximate Percentage of Violent Crimes Committed by Juveniles That Victims Reported to Law Enforcement

Year	1980	1982	1984	1986	1988	1990	1992	1994	1996
Offenders	36	35	33	32	31	30	29	29	30

Source: U.S. Bureau of Justice Statistics

1. Divide the data into three approximately equal groups. There should always be the same number of points in the first and third groups. In this case, there will be three data points in each group.

Group 1		Group 2		Group 3	
Year	Offenders	Year	Offenders	Year	Offenders
1980	36	1986	32	1992	29
1982	35	1988	31	1994	29
1984	33	1990	30	1996	30

Tips for New Teachers

Looking Ahead Lesson 2-6 presents the graphing of special functions, including absolute value functions. Exercises 30–32 should be used to determine your students' familiarity with solving absolute value equations.

4 ASSESS

Ticket Out the Door Give each student a small piece of paper. Have each student write three or four things to examine when reading a graph such as the one shown in the example on p. 93. Collect the papers as the students leave the room.

NGSSS PRACTICE 912.A.3.1, 912.G.3.1, 912.A.3.11

17. THINK SOLVE EXPLAIN **SHORT RESPONSE** What is the value of the expression below? **2**

$$17 - 3[-1 + 2(7 - 4)]$$

18. Anna took brownies to a club meeting. She gave half of her brownies to Selena. Selena gave a third of her brownies to Randall. Randall gave a fourth of his brownies to Trina. If Trina has 3 brownies, how many brownies did Anna have in the beginning? **C**

A. 12
B. 36
C. 72
D. 144

19. **GEOMETRY** Which is always true? **J**

F. A parallelogram is a square.
G. A parallelogram is a rectangle.
H. A quadrilateral is a trapezoid.
I. A square is a rectangle.

20. **ACT/SAT** Which line best fits the data in the graph? **D**

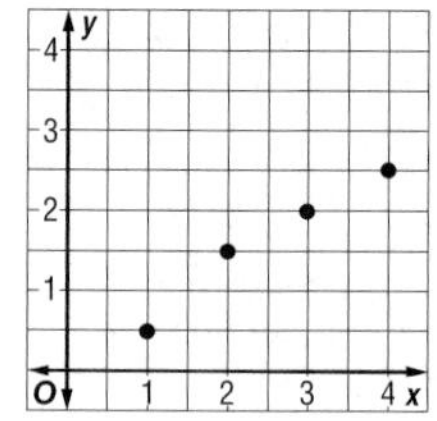

A. $y = x$
B. $y = -0.5x + 4$
C. $y = -0.5x - 4$
D. $y = 0.5x + 0.5$

Spiral Review

Write an equation in slope-intercept form for each graph. (Lesson 2-4)

21.

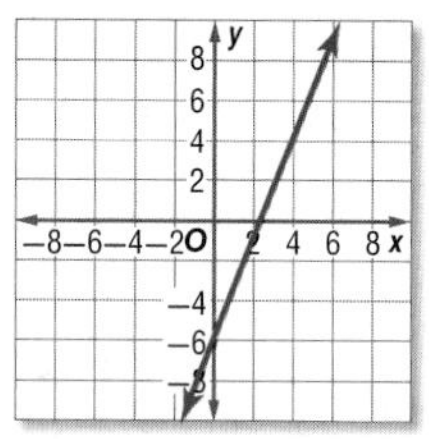

$y = 2.5x - 6$

22.

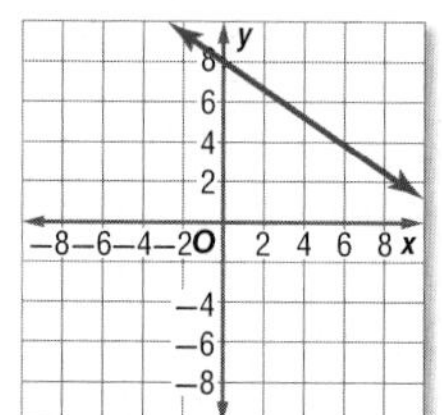

$y = -\frac{2}{3}x + 8$

23.

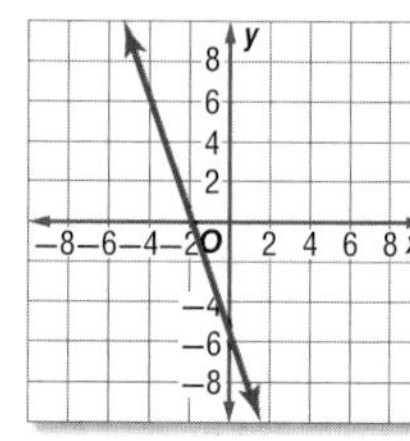

$y = -3x - 6$

Find the rate of change for each set of data. (Lesson 2-3)

24. **4 mm/day**

Time (day)	3	6	9	12	15
Height (mm)	12	24	36	48	60

25. **17.5 mi/hr**

Time (h)	2	4	6	8
Distance (mi)	35	70	105	140

26. **3.75 cm³/sec**

Time (sec)	12	16	20	24	28
Volume (cm^3)	45	60	75	90	105

27. **1.5 J/N**

Force (*N*)	32	40	48	56	64
Work (*J*)	48	60	72	84	96

28. **RECREATION** Ramona estimates that she will need 50 tennis balls for every player that signs up for the tennis club and at least 150 more just in case. Write an inequality to express the situation. (Lesson 1-5) $t \geq 50p + 150$

29. **DODGEBALL** Six teams played in a dodgeball tournament. In how many ways can the top three teams finish? (Lesson 0-5) **120**

Skills Review

Solve each equation. (Lesson 1-4)

30. $-4|x - 2| = -12$ **5, −1**

31. $|3x + 4| = 21$ $\frac{17}{3}, -\frac{25}{3}$

32. $2|4x - 1| + 3 = 9$ $1, -\frac{1}{2}$

Differentiated Instruction BL

Extension Challenge students to research how the correlation coefficient is calculated. What mathematics is involved in the calculation? Why does it represent how well the regression equation fits the data?

98 Chapter 2 Linear Relations and Functions

Real-World Link

The largest crowd for a single baseball game was 92,706 during the 1959 World Series between the Chicago White Sox and the Los Angeles Dodgers.

Source: Major League Baseball

9a. See Chapter 2 Answer Appendix.
9b. $y = 71{,}406.4x - 141{,}763{,}070.9$
9d. Sample answer: Unreasonable; the attendance will not increase without bound because attendance is largely dependent on the team's winning status.
10b. $r = -0.712$
10c. Sample answer: relatively accurate with a negative correlation

14a. Sample answer: years and height of a teenager
14b. Sample answer: time and capacity of a standard battery
14c. Sample answer: a person's weight and his or her income

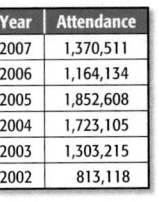

9. **BASEBALL** The table at the right shows the total attendance for the Florida Marlins in some recent years.

a. Make a scatter plot of the data.

b. Find a regression equation for the data.

c. Predict the attendance in 2020. **2,477,915**

d. How reasonable is your prediction? Explain.

Year	Attendance
2007	1,370,511
2006	1,164,134
2005	1,852,608
2004	1,723,105
2003	1,303,215
2002	813,118

10. **CLASS SIZE** The table at the right shows the relationship between the number of students in a mathematics class and the average grade for each class.

a. Make a scatter plot of the data, and find a regression equation for the data. Then sketch a graph of the regression line. **See Chapter 2 Answer Appendix.**

b. What is the correlation coefficient of the data?

c. Describe the correlation. How accurate is the regression equation?

Class Size	Class Average
16	81.2
19	80.6
24	82.5
26	79.9
27	78.6
29	79.3
32	77.7

11. **FINANCIAL LITERACY** Jocelyn is analyzing the sales of her company. The table at the right shows the total sales for each of six years.

a. Find a regression equation and correlation coefficient for the data. **$y = 3.1x - 6177$; $r = 0.63$**

b. Use the regression equation to predict the sales in 2015. **about $64.2 million**

c. Remove the outlier from the data set and find a new regression equation and correlation coefficient. **$y = 2.6x - 5170$; $r = 0.986$**

d. Use the new regression equation to predict the sales in 2015. **about $62.4 million**

e. Compare the correlation coefficients for the two regression equations. Which function fits the data better? Which prediction should Jocelyn expect to be more accurate? **See Chapter 2 Answer Appendix.**

Year	Sales ($ millions)
2003	31.2
2004	34.6
2005	18.9
2006	37.7
2007	41.3
2008	45.1

H.O.T. Problems

Use Higher-Order Thinking Skills

12. **REASONING** What is the relevance of the correlation coefficient of a linear regression line? Explain your reasoning. **See Chapter 2 Answer Appendix.**

13. **CHALLENGE** If statements a and b have a positive correlation, b and c have a negative correlation, and c and d have a positive correlation, what can you determine about the correlation between statements a and d? Explain your reasoning. **See Chapter 2 Answer Appendix.**

14. **OPEN ENDED** Provide real-world quantities that represent each of the following.

a. positive correlation **b.** negative correlation **c.** no correlation

15. **CHALLENGE** Draw a scatter plot for the following data set.

x	1.0	1.5	2.0	2.8	3.2	4.0	4.8	5.8
y	3.5	4.7	5.1	6.8	7.1	7.5	8.8	10.3

Which of the following best represents the correlation coefficient r for the data? Justify your answer. **See Chapter 2 Answer Appendix.**

a. 0.99 **b.** −0.98 **c.** 0.62 **d.** 0.08

16. **WRITING IN MATH** Explain why a linear equation is useful when working with data. **See Chapter 2 Answer Appendix.**

6a. Drama Club Earnings

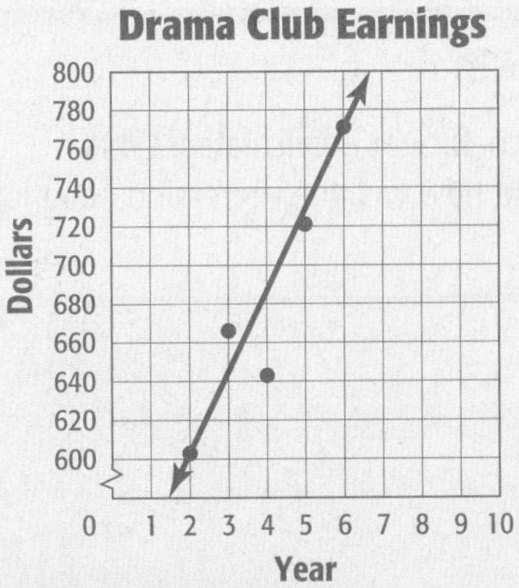

weak positive correlation

Study Guide and Intervention
CRM pp. 30–31 AL OL ELL

2-5 Study Guide and Intervention

Scatter Plots and Lines of Regression

Scatter Plots and Prediction Equations A set of data points graphed as ordered pairs in a coordinate plane is called a **scatter plot**. A scatter plot can be used to determine if there is a relationship among the data. A **line of fit** is a line that closely approximates a set of data graphed in a scatter plot. The equation of a line of fit is called a **prediction equation** because it can be used to predict values not given in the data set.

Example STORAGE COSTS **According to a certain prediction equation, the cost of 200 square feet of storage space is $60. The cost of 325 square feet of storage space is $160.**

a. Find the slope of the prediction equation. What does it represent?

Since the cost depends upon the square footage, let x represent the amount of storage space in square feet and y represent the cost in dollars. The slope can be found using the formula $m = \frac{y_2 - y_1}{x_2 - x_1}$. So, $m = \frac{160 - 60}{325 - 200} = \frac{100}{125} = 0.8$

The slope of the prediction equation is 0.8. This means that the price of storage increases 80¢ for each one-square-foot increase in storage space.

b. Find a prediction equation.

Using the slope and one of the points on the line, you can use the point-slope form to find a prediction equation.

$y - y_1 = m(x - x_1)$ Point-slope form
$y - 60 = 0.8(x - 200)$ $(x_1, y_1) = (200, 60)$, $m = 0.8$
$y - 60 = 0.8x - 160$ Distributive Property
$y = 0.8x - 100$ Add 60 to both sides.

A prediction equation is $y = 0.8x - 100$.

Exercises

1. SALARIES The table below shows the years of experience for eight technicians at Lewis Techomatic and the hourly rate of pay each technician earns.

Experience (years)	9	4	3	1	10	6	12	8
Hourly Rate of Pay	$17	$10	$10	$7	$19	$12	$20	$15

a. Draw a scatter plot to show how years of experience are related to hourly rate of pay. Draw a line of fit and describe the correlation. **positive correlation**

b. Write a prediction equation to show how years of experience (x) are related to hourly rate of pay (y). **Sample answer: using (1, 7) and (9, 17), y = 1.25x + 5.75**

c. Use the function to predict the hourly rate of pay for 15 years of experience. **Sample answer: $24.50**

Technician Salaries

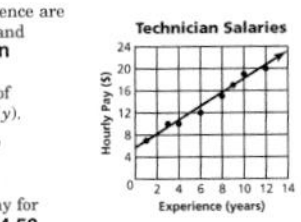

Chapter 2 30 Glencoe Algebra 2

Practice
CRM p. 33 AL OL BL ELL

2-5 Practice

Scatter Plots and Lines of Regression

For Exercises 1 and 2, complete parts a–c.

a. Make a scatter plot and a line of fit, and describe the correlation.
b. Use two ordered pairs to write a prediction equation.
c. Use your prediction equation to predict the missing value.

1. FUEL ECONOMY The table gives the weights in tons and estimates the fuel economy in miles per gallon for several cars.

Weight (tons)	1.3	1.4	1.5	1.8	2	2.1	2.4
Miles per Gallon	29	24	23	21	?	17	15

1b. Sample answer: using (1.4, 24) and (2.4, 15), y = −9x + 36.6
1c. Sample answer: 18.6 mi/gal

Fuel Economy Versus Weight

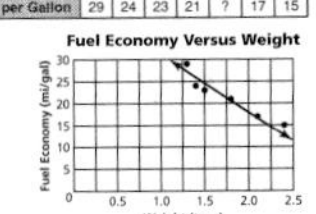

2. ALTITUDE As Anchara drives into the mountains, her car thermometer registers the temperatures (°F) shown in the table at the given altitudes (feet).

Altitude (ft)	7500	8200	8600	9200	9700	10,400	12,000
Temperature (°F)	61	58	56	53	50	46	?

2b. Sample answer: using (7500, 61) and (9700, 50), y = −0.005x + 98.5
2c. Sample answer: 38.5°F

Temperature Versus Altitude

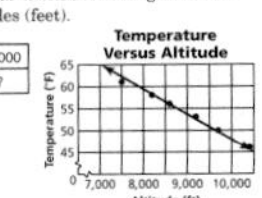

3. HEALTH Alton has a treadmill that uses the time on the treadmill to estimate the number of Calories he burns during a workout. The table gives workout times and Calories burned for several workouts. Find an equation for and graph a line of regression. Then use the function to predict the number of Calories burned in a 60-minute workout.

Time (min)	18	24	30	40	42	48	52	60
Calories Burned	260	280	320	380	400	440	475	?

Burning Calories

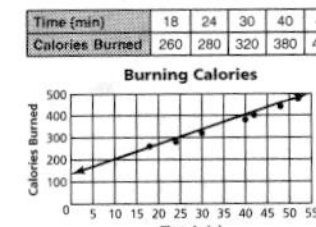

Sample answer: line of Regression y = 6, 395x + 132.95; 516.65 Calories

Chapter 2 33 Glencoe Algebra 2

Lesson 2-5

Word Problem Practice
CRM p. 34 AL OL BL ELL

2-5 Word Problem Practice

Scatter Plots and Lines of Regression

1. AIRCRAFT The table shows the maximum speed and altitude of different aircraft. Draw a scatter plot of this data.

Max. Speed (knots)	121	123	137	173	153
Max. Altitude (1000 feet)	14.2	17.0	15.3	20.7	16.0

Source: RisingUp Aviation

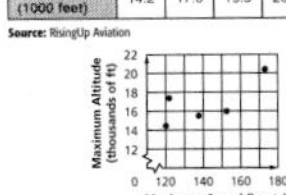

2. TESTING The scatter plot shows the height and test scores of students in a math class. Describe the correlation between heights and test scores.

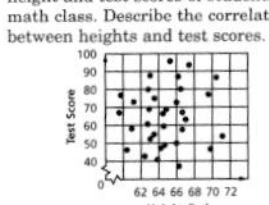

no correlation

3. STOCKS The prices of a technology stock over 5 days are shown in the table. Draw a scatter plot of the data and a line of fit.

Day	1	2	3	4	5
Price	8.30	8.60	8.55	8.90	9.30

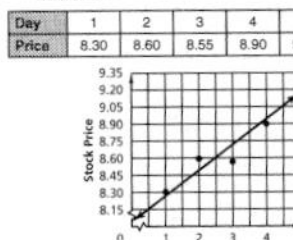

4. ALGAE One type of algae grows fastest at 31°C. The scatter plot shows data recording the amount of algae and the temperature of the water in various aquarium tanks. Draw a line of fit for this data and write a prediction equation. Will this prediction equation be accurate for temperatures above 31°C?

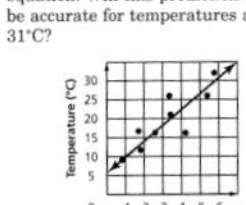

Sample answer: y = 4x + 6; the equation may not be valid for extremely high temperatures

5. SPORTS The scatter plot shows the height and score of different contestants shooting darts.

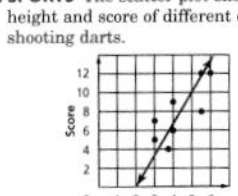

a. What is the equation of the line of fit? **Sample answer: $y = \frac{8}{3}x - \frac{10}{3}$**

b. What do you predict someone 5 feet tall would score? **Sample answer: 10 points**

Chapter 2 34 Glencoe Algebra 2

Enrichment
CRM p. 35 OL BL

2-5 Enrichment

Median-Fit Lines

A **median-fit line** is a particular type of line of fit. Follow the steps below to find the equation of the median-fit line for the data.

Approximate Percentage of Violent Crimes Committed by Juveniles That Victims Reported to Law Enforcement									
Year	1980	1982	1984	1986	1988	1990	1992	1994	1996
Offenders	36	35	33	32	31	30	29	29	30

Source: U.S. Bureau of Justice Statistics

1. Divide the data into three approximately equal groups. There should always be the same number of points in the first and third groups. In this case, there will be three data points in each group.

Group 1		Group 2		Group 3	
Year	Offenders	Year	Offenders	Year	Offenders
1980	36	1986	32	1992	29
1982	35	1988	31	1994	29
1984	33	1990	30	1996	30

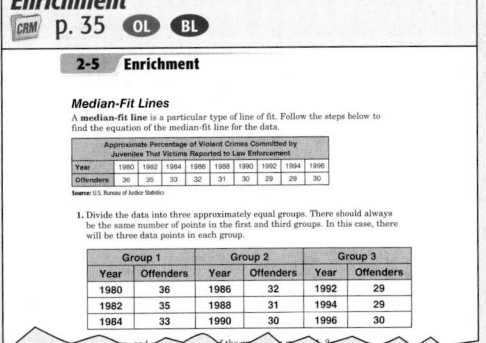

Tips for New Teachers

Looking Ahead Lesson 2-6 presents the graphing of special functions, including absolute value functions. Exercises 30–32 should be used to determine your students' familiarity with solving absolute value equations.

4 ASSESS

Ticket Out the Door Give each student a small piece of paper. Have each student write three or four things to examine when reading a graph such as the one shown in the example on p. 93. Collect the papers as the students leave the room.

NGSSS PRACTICE 912.A.3.1, 912.G.3.1, 912.A.3.11

17. **SHORT RESPONSE** What is the value of the expression below? **2**

$$17 - 3[-1 + 2(7 - 4)]$$

18. Anna took brownies to a club meeting. She gave half of her brownies to Selena. Selena gave a third of her brownies to Randall. Randall gave a fourth of his brownies to Trina. If Trina has 3 brownies, how many brownies did Anna have in the beginning? **C**

A. 12
B. 36
C. 72
D. 144

19. **GEOMETRY** Which is always true? **J**

F. A parallelogram is a square.
G. A parallelogram is a rectangle.
H. A quadrilateral is a trapezoid.
I. A square is a rectangle.

20. **ACT/SAT** Which line best fits the data in the graph? **D**

A. $y = x$
B. $y = -0.5x + 4$
C. $y = -0.5x - 4$
D. $y = 0.5x + 0.5$

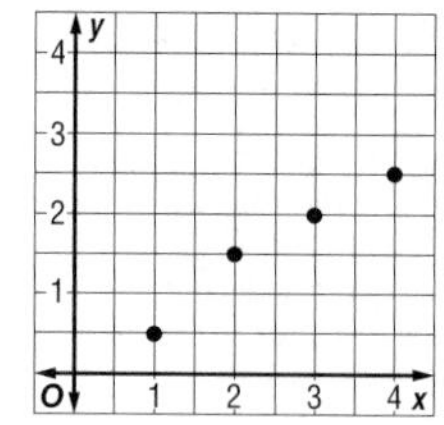

Spiral Review

Write an equation in slope-intercept form for each graph. (Lesson 2-4)

21.

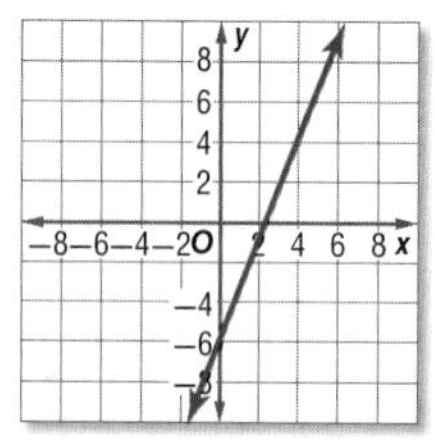

$y = 2.5x - 6$

22.

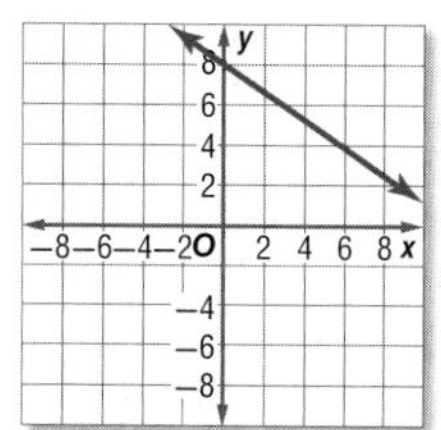

$y = -\frac{2}{3}x + 8$

23.

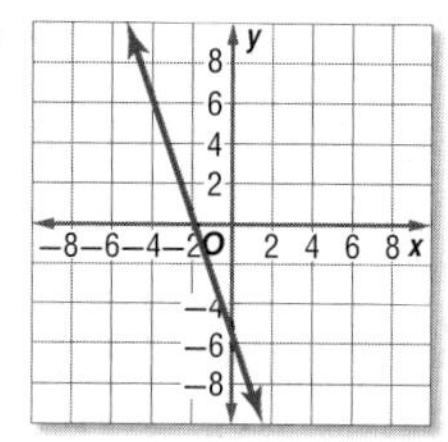

$y = -3x - 6$

Find the rate of change for each set of data. (Lesson 2-3)

24.

Time (day)	3	6	9	12	15
Height (mm)	12	24	36	48	60

4 mm/day

25.

Time (h)	2	4	6	8
Distance (mi)	35	70	105	140

17.5 mi/hr

26.

Time (sec)	12	16	20	24	28
Volume (cm^3)	45	60	75	90	105

3.75 cm^3/sec

27.

Force (*N*)	32	40	48	56	64
Work (*J*)	48	60	72	84	96

1.5 *J/N*

28. **RECREATION** Ramona estimates that she will need 50 tennis balls for every player that signs up for the tennis club and at least 150 more just in case. Write an inequality to express the situation. (Lesson 1-5) **$t \geq 50p + 150$**

29. **DODGEBALL** Six teams played in a dodgeball tournament. In how many ways can the top three teams finish? (Lesson 0-5) **120**

Skills Review

Solve each equation. (Lesson 1-4)

30. $-4|x - 2| = -12$ **5, −1**

31. $|3x + 4| = 21$ **$\frac{17}{3}, -\frac{25}{3}$**

32. $2|4x - 1| + 3 = 9$ **$1, -\frac{1}{2}$**

Differentiated Instruction BL

Extension Challenge students to research how the correlation coefficient is calculated. What mathematics is involved in the calculation? Why does it represent how well the regression equation fits the data?

2-6 Special Functions

Then
You modeled data using lines of regression. (Lesson 2-5)

Now
- Write and graph piecewise-defined functions.
- Write and graph step and absolute value functions.

NGSSS

MA.912.A.2.5 Graph absolute value equations and inequalities in two variables.
MA.912.A.2.9 Recognize, interpret, and graph functions defined piece-wise, with and without technology. *Also addresses MA.912.A.2.6.*

New Vocabulary
piecewise-defined function
piecewise-linear function
step function
greatest integer function
absolute value function

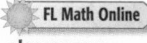

FL Math Online
glencoe.com

Why?

The table shows a recent federal income tax rate schedule. The amount of federal income tax an individual is required to pay is a function of income.

Federal Tax Rate Schedule – Filing Single

If taxable income is over	But not over	The tax is:
$0	$7,825	10% of the amount over $0
$7,825	$31,850	$782.50 plus 15% of the amount over $7,825
$31,850	$77,100	$4,386.25 plus 25% of the amount over $31,850
$77,100	$160,850	$15,698.75 plus 28% of the amount over $77,100
$160,850	$349,700	$39,148.75 plus 33% of the amount over $160,850
$349,700	no limit	$101,469.25 plus 35% of the amount over $349,700

Source: Internal Revenue Service

Piecewise-Defined Functions The function relating income and tax is not a linear function because each interval, or piece, of the function is defined by a different expression. A function that is written using two or more expressions is called a **piecewise-defined function**. On the graph of a piecewise-defined function, a dot indicates that the point is included in the graph. A circle indicates that the point is not included in the graph.

EXAMPLE 1 Piecewise-Defined Function

Graph $f(x) = \begin{cases} x - 2 \text{ if } x < -1 \\ x + 3 \text{ if } x \geq -1 \end{cases}$. Identify the domain and range.

Step 1 Graph $f(x) = x - 2$ for $x < -1$.

$f(x) = x - 2$
$= (-1) - 2$
$= -3$

Because -1 does not satisfy the inequality, begin with a circle at $(-1, -3)$.

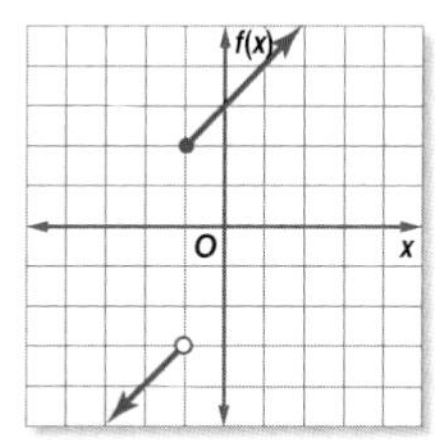

Step 2 Graph $f(x) = x + 3$ for $x \geq -1$.

$f(x) = x + 3$
$= (-1) + 3$
$= 2$

Because -1 satisfies the inequality, begin with a dot at $(-1, 2)$.

The function is defined for all values of x, so the domain is all real numbers.

The $f(x)$-coordinates of points on the graph are all real numbers less than -3 and all real numbers greater than or equal to 2, so the range is $\{f(x) \mid f(x) < -3 \text{ or } f(x) \geq 2\}$.

Guided Practice

1. Graph $f(x) = \begin{cases} x + 2 \text{ if } x < 0 \\ x \quad \text{ if } x \geq 0 \end{cases}$. Identify the domain and range. **See Chapter 2 Answer Appendix.**

Personal Tutor glencoe.com

2-6 Lesson Notes

1 FOCUS

Vertical Alignment

Before Lesson 2-6
Model data using lines of regression.

Lesson 2-6
Write and graph piecewise-defined functions and write and graph step and absolute value functions.

After Lesson 2-6
Identify and sketch graphs of parent functions, including quadratic functions.

2 TEACH

Scaffolding Questions

Have students read the *Why?* section of the lesson.

Ask:
- What is the tax for a taxable income of $50,000? $8923.75
- What is the tax for a taxable income of $31,850? $4386.25

Lesson 2-6 Resources

Resource	Approaching-Level	On-Level	Beyond-Level	English Learners
Teacher Edition	• Differentiated Instruction, p. 103	• Differentiated Instruction, p. 103	• Differentiated Instruction, p. 104	• Differentiated Instruction, p. 103
Chapter Resource Masters	• Study Guide and Intervention, pp. 36–37 • Skills Practice, p. 38 • Practice, p. 39 • Word Problem Practice, p. 40	• Study Guide and Intervention, pp. 36–37 • Skills Practice, p. 38 • Practice, p. 39 • Word Problem Practice, p. 40 • Enrichment, p. 41 • Graphing Calculator, p. 42	• Practice, p. 39 • Word Problem Practice, p. 40 • Enrichment, p. 41	• Study Guide and Intervention, pp. 36–37 • Skills Practice, p. 38 • Practice, p. 39 • Word Problem Practice, p. 40
Transparencies	• 5-Minute Check Transparency 2-6	• 5-Minute Check Transparency 2-6	• 5-Minute Check Transparency 2-6	• 5-Minute Check Transparency 2-6
Other	• Study Notebook • Teaching Algebra with Manipulatives	• Study Notebook • Teaching Algebra with Manipulatives	• Study Notebook	• Study Notebook • Teaching Algebra with Manipulatives

Piecewise-Defined Functions

Example 1 shows how to graph a piecewise-defined function. **Example 2** shows how to write a piecewise-defined function.

Formative Assessment

Use the Guided Practice exercises after each example to determine students' understanding of concepts.

Additional Example

1 Graph $f(x) = \begin{cases} x - 1 \text{ if } x \leq 3 \\ -1 \text{ if } x > 3 \end{cases}$.

Identify the domain and range.

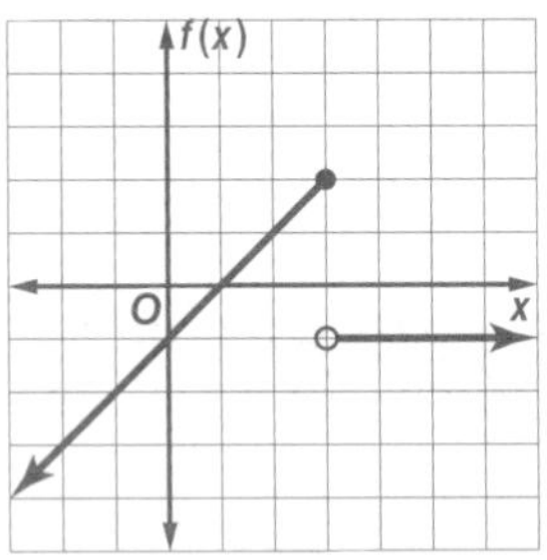

The domain is all real numbers. The range is $\{f(x) | f(x) \leq 2\}$.

2 Write the piecewise-defined function shown in the graph.

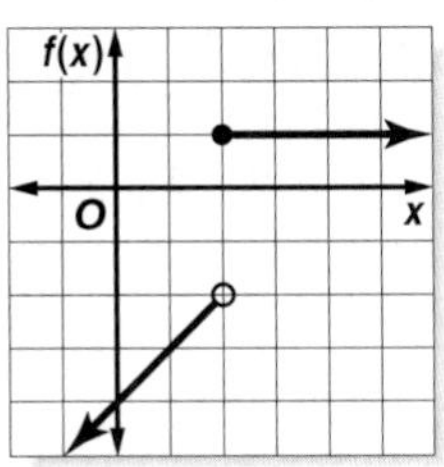

$f(x) = \begin{cases} x - 4 \text{ if } x < 2 \\ 1 \text{ if } x \geq 2 \end{cases}$

Additional Examples also in Interactive Classroom PowerPoint® Presentations

IWB INTERACTIVE WHITEBOARD READY

Piecewise-defined functions are often defined by several linear functions.

> **StudyTip**
>
> **Graphs of Piecewise-Defined Functions** The graphs of different parts of a piecewise-defined function may or may not connect. A graph may also stop at a given x-value and then begin at a different y-value for the same value of x.

EXAMPLE 2 Write a Piecewise-Defined Function

Write the piecewise-defined function shown in the graph.

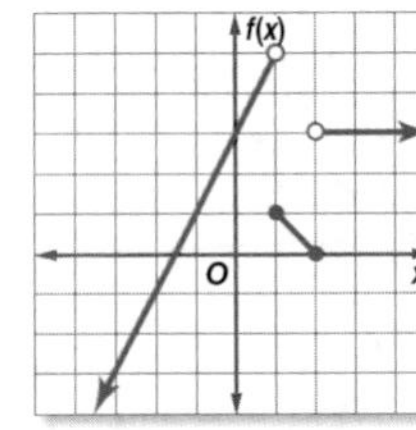

Examine and write a function for each portion of the graph.

The left portion of the graph is the graph of $f(x) = 2x + 3$. There is a circle at (1, 5), so the linear function is defined for $\{x | x < 1\}$.

The center portion of the graph is the graph of $f(x) = -x + 2$. There are dots at (1, 1) and (2, 0), so the linear function is defined for $\{x | 1 \leq x \leq 2\}$.

The right portion of the graph is the constant function $f(x) = 3$. There is a circle at (2, 3), so the constant function is defined for $\{x | x > 2\}$.

Write the piecewise-defined function.

$f(x) = \begin{cases} 2x + 3 \text{ if } x < 1 \\ -x + 2 \text{ if } 1 \leq x \leq 2 \\ 3 \text{ if } x > 2 \end{cases}$

CHECK The graph shows a portion of a line with positive slope for $x < 1$. The graph has negative slope for $1 \leq x \leq 2$ and constant slope for $x > 2$. The function is reasonable for the graph.

2A. $f(x) = \begin{cases} -\frac{1}{3}x - 2 \text{ if } x \leq -3 \\ 2 \text{ if } -3 < x < 1 \\ 4x - 2 \text{ if } x \geq 1 \end{cases}$

2B. $f(x) = \begin{cases} 3x \text{ if } x < -1 \\ -x \text{ if } -1 \leq x < 3 \\ -x + 7 \text{ if } x \geq 3 \end{cases}$

Guided Practice

Write the piecewise-defined function shown in each graph.

2A.

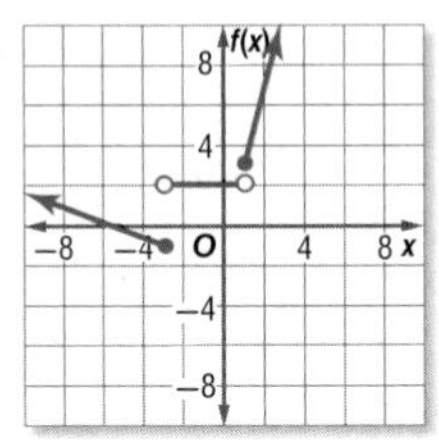

2B.

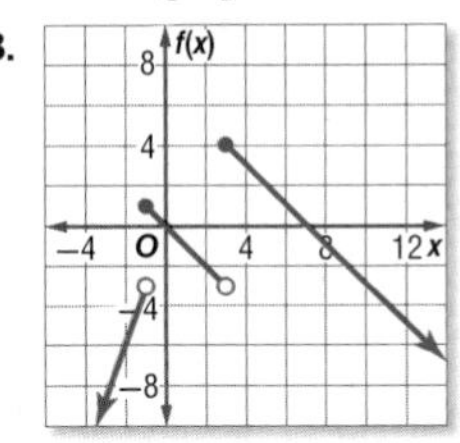

Personal Tutor glencoe.com

Step Functions and Absolute Value Functions Unlike a piecewise-defined function, a **piecewise-linear function** contains a single expression. A common piecewise-linear function is the step function. The graph of a **step function** consists of line segments.

> **StudyTip**
>
> **Greatest Integer Function** Notice that the domain of this step function is all real numbers and the range is all integers.

The **greatest integer function**, written $f(x) = [\![x]\!]$, is one kind of step function. The symbol $[\![x]\!]$ means *the greatest integer less than or equal to x*. For example, $[\![3.25]\!] = 3$ and $[\![-4.6]\!] = -5$.

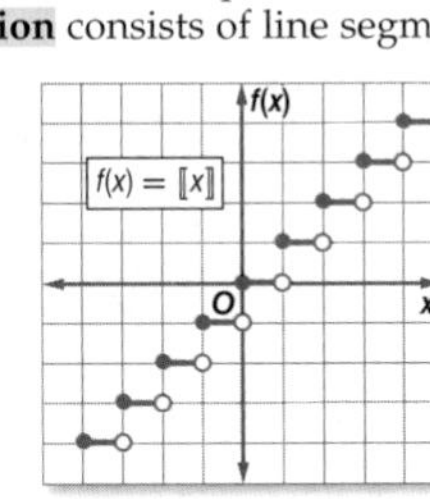

Focus on Mathematical Content

Piecewise Functions Piecewise functions are sometimes called *multi-part functions* or *split-domain functions.* For example, the absolute value function $y = |x|$ is the same as $y = -x$ for $x < 0$, and $y = x$ for $x \geq 0$.

Real-World EXAMPLE 3 Use a Step Function

BUSINESS An automotive repair center charges $50 for any part of the first hour of labor, and $35 for any part of each additional hour. Draw a graph that represents this situation.

Understand The total labor charge is $50 for the first hour plus $35 for each additional fraction of an hour, so the graph will be a step function.

Plan If the time spent on labor is greater than 0 hours, but less than or equal to 1 hour, then the labor charge is $50. If the time is greater than 1 hour but less than 2 hours, then the labor charge is $85, and so on.

Solve Use the pattern of times and costs to make a table, where x is the number of hours of labor and $T(x)$ is the total labor charge. Then graph.

x	$T(x)$
$0 < x \leq 1$	$50
$1 < x \leq 2$	$85
$2 < x \leq 3$	$120
$3 < x \leq 4$	$155
$4 < x \leq 5$	$190

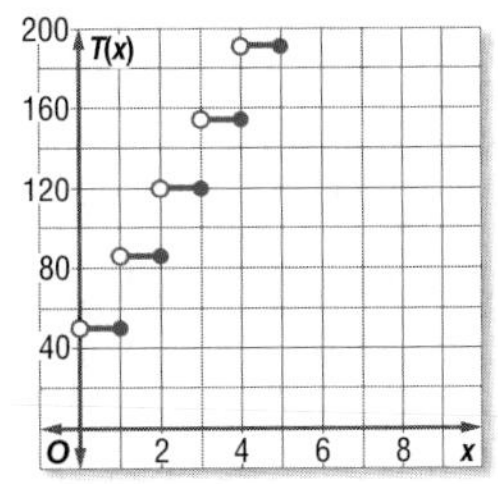

Check Since the repair center rounds any fraction of an hour up to the next whole number, each segment of the graph has a circle at the left endpoint and a dot at the right endpoint.

Guided Practice

3. See margin.

3. RECYCLING A recycling company pays $5 for every full box of newspaper. They do not give any money for partial boxes. Draw a graph that shows the amount of money $P(x)$ for the number of boxes x brought to the recycling center.

Personal Tutor glencoe.com

Math History Link

Karl Weierstrass (1815–1897)
At the wishes of his father, Weierstrass studied law, economics, and finance at the University of Bonn, but then dropped out to study his true interest, mathematics, at the University of Münster. In an 1841 essay, Weierstrass first used | | to denote absolute value.

Source: Earth 911

Another piecewise-linear function is the absolute value function. An **absolute value function** is a function that contains an algebraic expression within absolute value symbols.

Key Concept

Parent Function of Absolute Value Functions

Parent function: $f(x) = |x|$, defined as

$$f(x) = \begin{cases} x \text{ if } x > 0 \\ 0 \text{ if } x = 0 \\ -x \text{ if } x < 0 \end{cases}$$

Type of graph: V-shaped

Domain: all real numbers

Range: all nonnegative real numbers

Intercepts: $x = 0$, $f(x) = 0$

Not defined: $f(x) < 0$

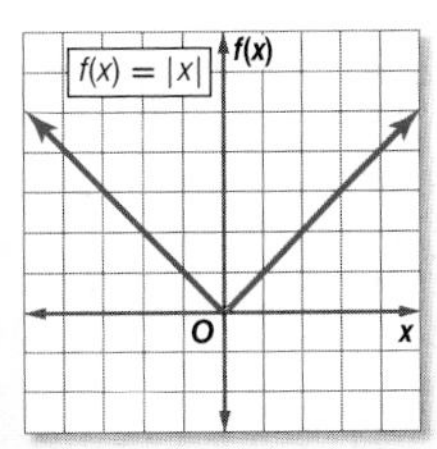

Step Functions and Absolute Value Functions

Example 3 shows how to graph and use a step function. **Example 4** shows how to graph an absolute value function and identify its domain and range.

Additional Example

3 **PSYCHOLOGY** One psychologist charges for counseling sessions at the rate of $85 per hour or any fraction thereof. Draw a graph that represents this situation.

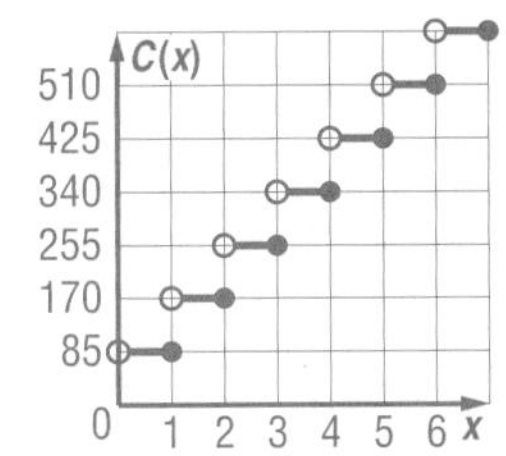

TEACH with TECH

BLOG Give students several pictures of graphs of piecewise functions. Have students write a blog entry explaining how to interpret each of the graphs.

Additional Answer (Guided Practice)

3.

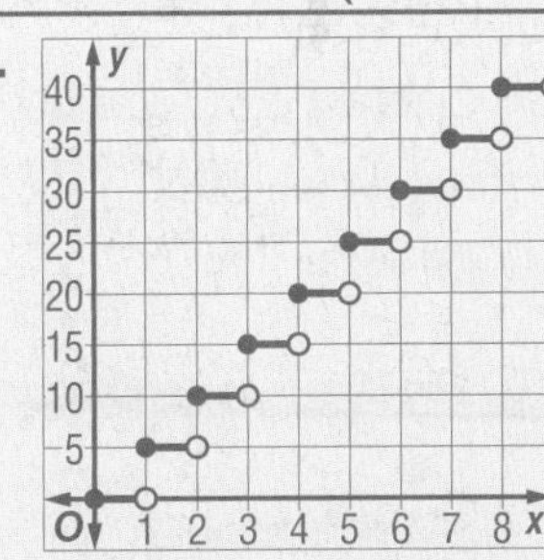

Differentiated Instruction

AL OL ELL

Verbal/Linguistic Learners Have students verbally explain to a partner how to graph one of the piecewise-defined functions they learned about in this lesson.

Additional Example

4 Graph $y = |x| + 1$. Identify the domain and range.

The domain is all real numbers.

The range is $\{y | y \geq 1\}$.

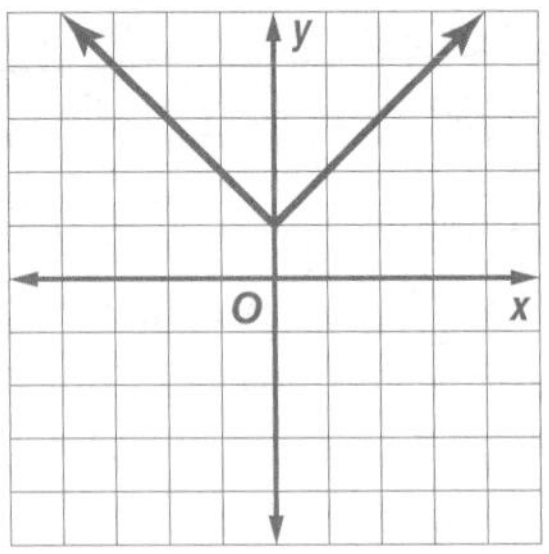

Additional Answers (Guided Practice)

4A.

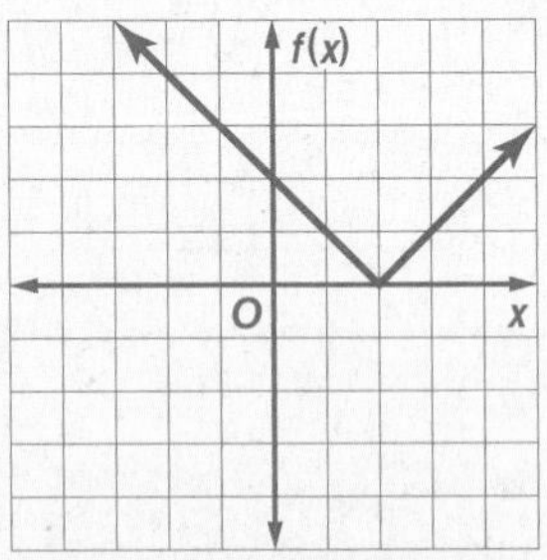

D = {all real numbers};
R = $\{f(x) | f(x) \geq 0\}$

4B.

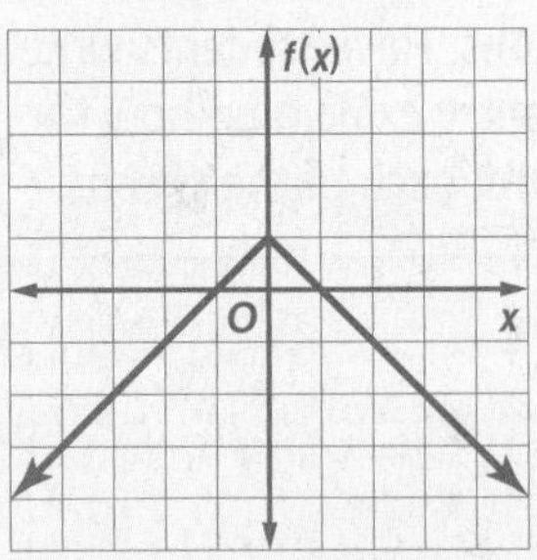

D = {all real numbers};
R = $\{f(x) | f(x) \leq 1\}$

Additional Answer

12.

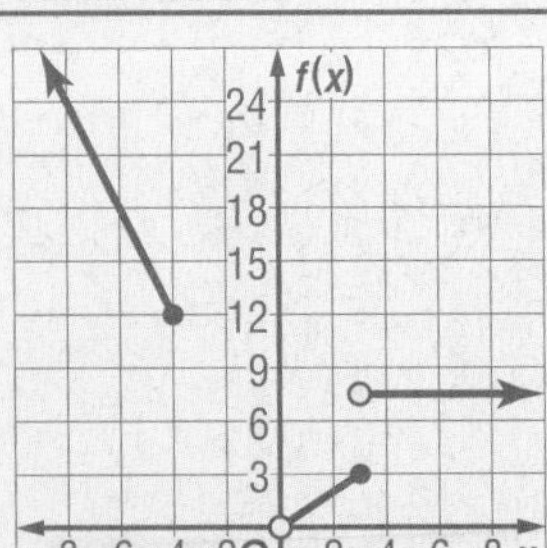

D = $\{x | x \leq -4 \text{ or } 0 < x\}$;
R = $\{f(x) | f(x) \geq 12, f(x) = 8, \text{ or } 0 < f(x) \leq 3\}$

EXAMPLE 4 **Absolute Value Functions**

Graph $f(x) = |2x| - 4$. Identify the domain and range.

Create a table of values.

x	$\|2x\| - 4$
−3	2
−2	0
−1	−2
0	−4
1	−2
2	0
3	2

Graph the points and connect them.

The domain is the set of all real numbers. The range is $\{f(x) | f(x) \geq -4\}$.

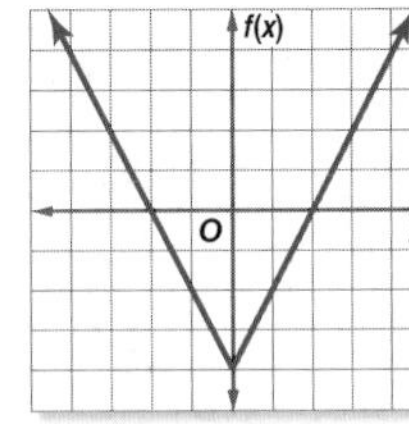

Guided Practice 4A, 4B. See margin.

Graph each function. Identify the domain and range.

4A. $f(x) = |x - 2|$

4B. $f(x) = -|x| + 1$

Personal Tutor glencoe.com

Check Your Understanding

Example 1 p. 101 — **Graph each function. Identify the domain and range.** 1, 2. See Chapter 2 Answer Appendix.

1. $g(x) = \begin{cases} -3 \text{ if } x \leq -4 \\ x \text{ if } -4 < x < 2 \\ -x + 6 \text{ if } x \geq 2 \end{cases}$

2. $f(x) = \begin{cases} 8 \text{ if } x \leq -1 \\ 2x \text{ if } -1 < x < 4 \\ -4 - x \text{ if } x \geq 4 \end{cases}$

Example 2 p. 102 — **Write the piecewise-defined function shown in each graph.** 3, 4. See Chapter 2 Answer Appendix.

3.

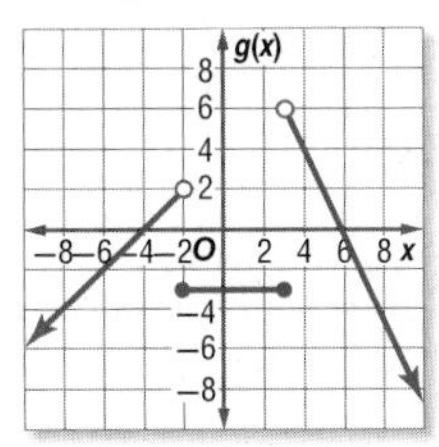

4.

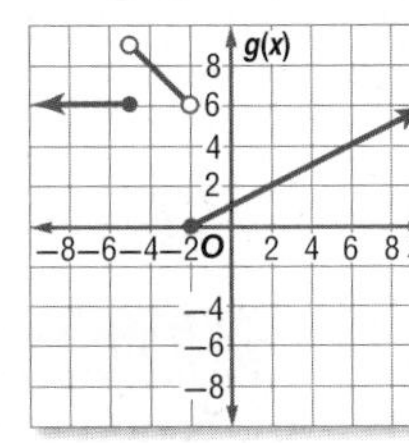

Example 3 p. 103

5 **THEATER** Springfield High School's theater can hold 250 students. The drama club is performing a play in the theater. Draw a graph of a step function that shows the relationship between the number of tickets sold x and the minimum number of performances y that the drama club must do. See Chapter 2 Answer Appendix.

Graph each function. Identify the domain and range. 6, 7. See Chapter 2 Answer Appendix.

6. $g(x) = -2[\![x]\!]$

7. $h(x) = [\![x - 5]\!]$

Example 4 p. 104 — **Graph each function. Identify the domain and range.** 8–11. See Chapter 2 Answer Appendix.

8. $g(x) = |-3x|$

9. $f(x) = 2|x|$

10. $h(x) = |x + 4|$

11. $s(x) = |-2x| + 6$

Differentiated Instruction

BL

Extension Have students draw a large coordinate plane on a sheet of paper. Then have them use toothpicks (or other similar objects) to model the general shapes of step, piecewise-defined, and absolute value functions. Students should identify each type of graph as they model it.

Practice and Problem Solving

● = **Step-by-Step Solutions** begin on page R20. **Extra Practice** begins on page 947.

Example 1 p. 101

Graph each function. Identify the domain and range. 12–15. See margin.

12. $f(x) = \begin{cases} -3x \text{ if } x \leq -4 \\ x \text{ if } 0 < x \leq 3 \\ 8 \text{ if } x > 3 \end{cases}$

13. $f(x) = \begin{cases} 2x \text{ if } x \leq -6 \\ 5 \text{ if } -6 < x \leq 2 \\ -2x + 1 \text{ if } x > 4 \end{cases}$

14. $g(x) = \begin{cases} 2x + 2 \text{ if } x < -6 \\ x \text{ if } -6 \leq x \leq 2 \\ -3 \text{ if } x > 2 \end{cases}$

15. $g(x) = \begin{cases} -2 \text{ if } x < -4 \\ x - 3 \text{ if } -1 \leq x \leq 5 \\ 2x - 15 \text{ if } x > 7 \end{cases}$

Example 2 p. 102

Write the piecewise-defined function shown in each graph. 16–19. See Chapter 2 Answer Appendix.

16.

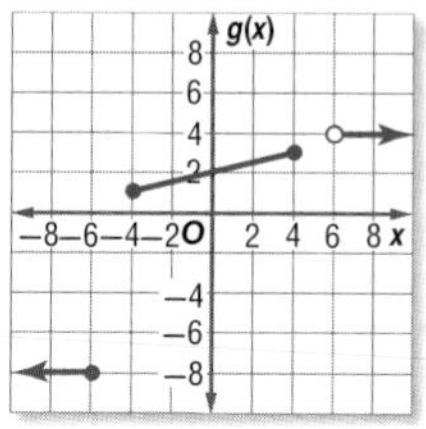

17.

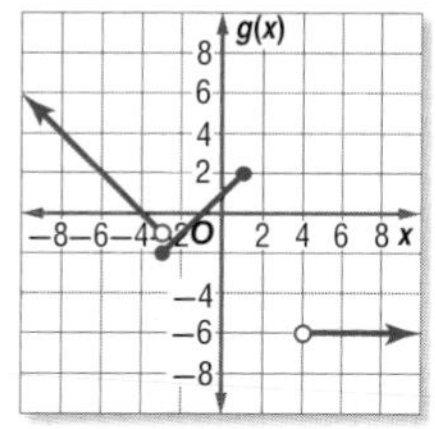

18.

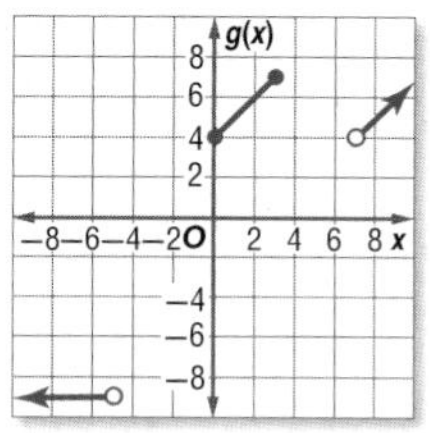

19.

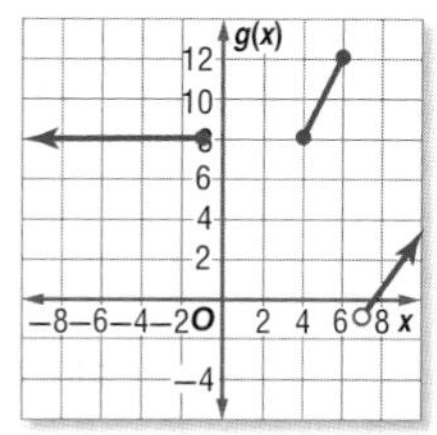

Example 3 p. 103

Graph each function. Identify the domain and range. 20–23. See Chapter 2 Answer Appendix.

20. $f(x) = [\![x]\!] - 6$

21. $h(x) = [\![3x]\!] - 8$

22. $f(x) = [\![3x + 2]\!]$

23. $g(x) = 2[\![0.5x + 4]\!]$

Example 4 p. 104

Graph each function. Identify the domain and range. 24–29. See Chapter 2 Answer Appendix.

24. $f(x) = |x - 5|$

25. $g(x) = |x + 2|$

26. $h(x) = |2x| - 8$

27. $k(x) = |-3x| + 3$

28. $f(x) = 2|x - 4| + 6$

29. $h(x) = -3|0.5x + 1| - 2$

30. VOLUNTEERING Patrick is donating and volunteering his time to an organization that restores homes for the needy. He initially donates \$10 and works on one home. He decides to donate \$4 for every additional home on which he works.

a. Identify the type of function that models this situation. piecewise

b. Write and graph a function for the situation. See Chapter 2 Answer Appendix.

31. CARS A car's speedometer reads 60 miles an hour.

a. Write an absolute value function for the difference between the car's actual speed a and the reading on the speedometer. $f(a) = |a - 60|$

b. What is an appropriate domain for the function? Explain your reasoning. $\{a \mid a \geq 0\}$

c. Use the domain to graph the function. See Chapter 2 Answer Appendix.

Differentiated Homework Options

Level	Assignment	Two-Day Option	
AL Basic	12–31, 40, 42–59	13–31 odd, 45–48	12–30 even, 40, 42–44, 49–59
OL Core	13–31 odd, 32, 33–37 odd, 39, 40, 42–59	12–31, 45–48	32–40, 42–44, 49–59
BL Advanced	32–56, (optional: 57–59)		

3 PRACTICE

Formative Assessment

Use Exercises 1–11 to check for understanding.

Use the chart on the bottom of the page to customize assignments for your students.

Tips for New Teachers

Verbal Proficiency Have students explain why step functions, absolute value functions, and piecewise-defined functions are so named.

Additional Answers

13.

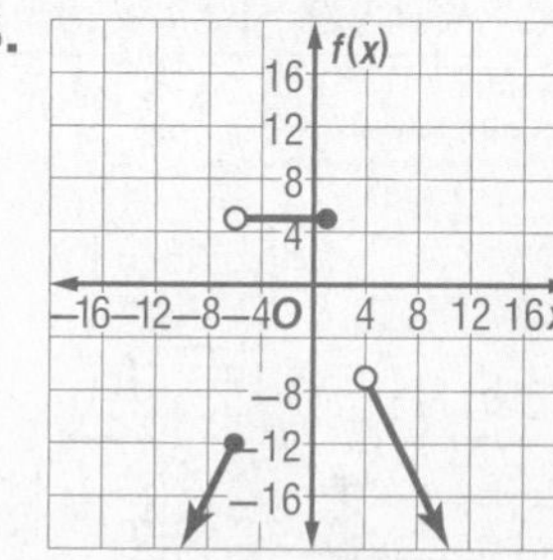

$D = \{x \mid x \leq 2 \text{ or } x > 4\}$;
$R = \{f(x) \mid f(x) < -7, \text{ or } f(x) = 5\}$

14.

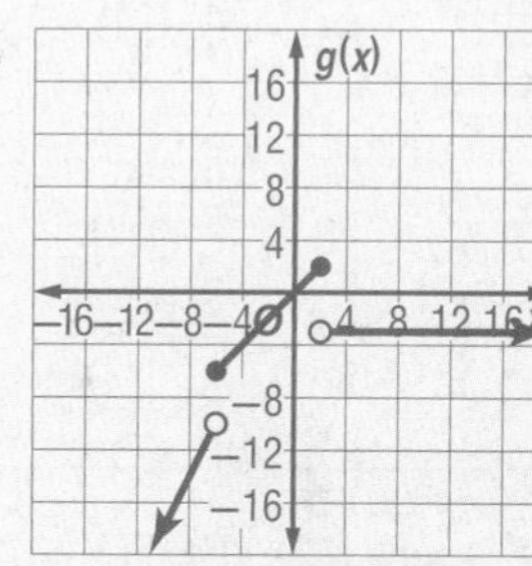

$D = \{\text{all real numbers}\}$;
$R = \{g(x) \mid g(x) < -10 \text{ or } -6 \leq g(x) \leq 2\}$

15.

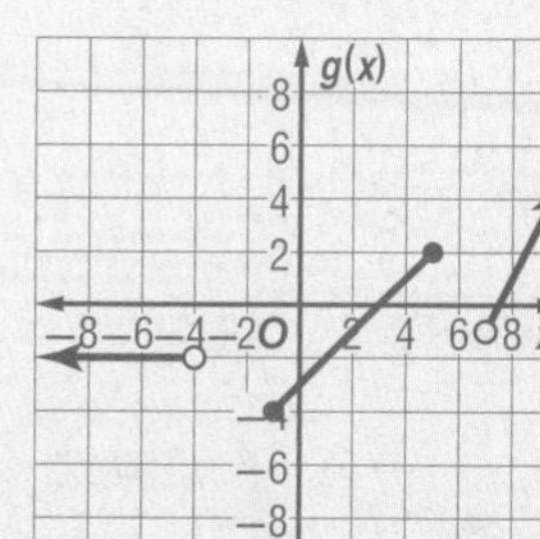

$D = \{x \mid x < -4, -1 \leq x \leq 5, \text{ or } x > 7\}$;
$R = \{g(x) \mid g(x) \geq -4\}$

Study Guide and Intervention
CRM pp. 36–37 AL OL ELL

2-6 Study Guide and Intervention

Special Functions

Piecewise-Defined Functions A **piecewise-defined function** is written using two or more expressions. Its graph is often disjointed.

Example Graph $f(x) = \begin{cases} 2x \text{ if } x < 2 \\ x - 1 \text{ if } x \geq 2. \end{cases}$

First, graph the linear function $f(x) = 2x$ for $x < 2$. Since 2 does not satisfy this inequality, stop with a circle at (2, 4). Next, graph the linear function $f(x) = x - 1$ for $x \geq 2$. Since 2 does satisfy this inequality, begin with a dot at (2, 1).

Exercises

Graph each function. Identify the domain and range.

1. $f(x) = \begin{cases} x + 2 \text{ if } x < 0 \\ 2x + 5 \text{ if } 0 \leq x \leq 2 \\ -x + 1 \text{ if } x > 2 \end{cases}$ D = {all real numbers} R = {f(x)|f(x) < 2 or 5 ≤ f(x) ≤ 9}

2. $f(x) = \begin{cases} -x - 4 \text{ if } x < -7 \\ 5x - 1 \text{ if } -7 \leq x \leq 0 \\ 2x + 1 \text{ if } x > 0 \end{cases}$ D = {all real numbers} R = {f(x)|f(x) > 1 or −36 ≤ f(x) ≤ −1}

3. $h(x) = \begin{cases} \frac{x}{2} \text{ if } x \leq 0 \\ 2x - 6 \text{ if } 0 < x < 2 \\ 1 \text{ if } x \geq 2 \end{cases}$ D = {all real numbers} R = {h(x)|h(x) = 1 or h(x) < 0}

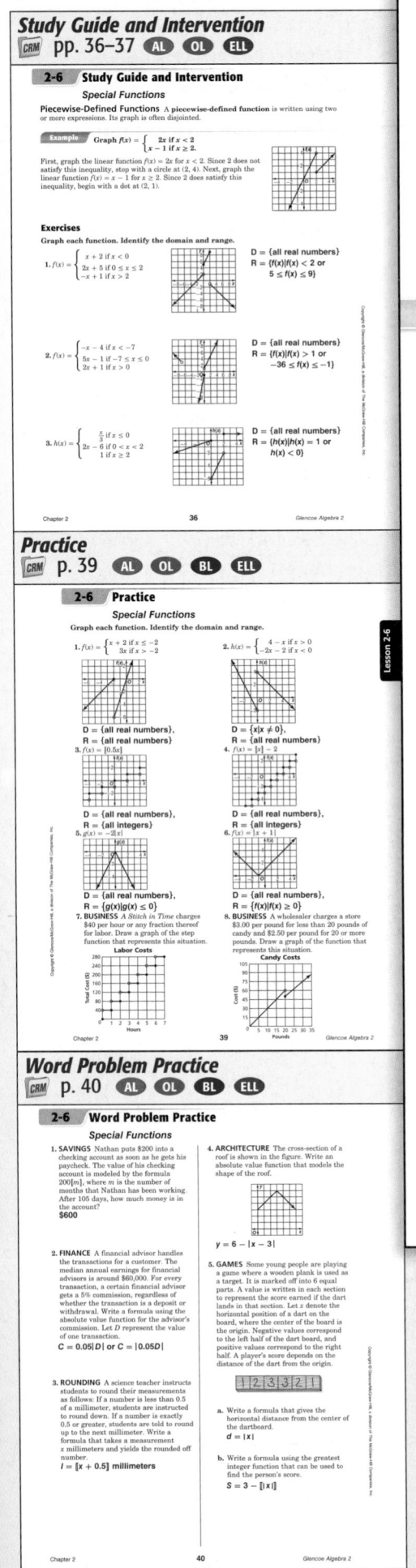

Practice
CRM p. 39 AL OL BL ELL

2-6 Practice

Special Functions

Graph each function. Identify the domain and range.

1. $f(x) = \begin{cases} x + 2 \text{ if } x \leq -2 \\ 3x \text{ if } x > -2 \end{cases}$ D = {all real numbers}, R = {all real numbers}

2. $h(x) = \begin{cases} 4 - x \text{ if } x > 0 \\ -2x - 2 \text{ if } x < 0 \end{cases}$ D = {x|x ≠ 0}, R = {all real numbers}

3. $f(x) = [\![0.5x]\!]$ D = {all real numbers}, R = {all integers}

4. $f(x) = [\![x]\!] - 2$ D = {all real numbers}, R = {all integers}

5. $g(x) = -2|x|$ D = {all real numbers}, R = {g(x)|g(x) ≤ 0}

6. $f(x) = |x + 1|$ D = {all real numbers}, R = {f(x)|f(x) ≥ 0}

7. **BUSINESS** A *Stitch in Time* charges $40 per hour or any fraction thereof for labor. Draw a graph of the step function that represents this situation.

8. **BUSINESS** A wholesaler charges a store $3.00 per pound for less than 20 pounds of candy and $2.50 per pound for 20 or more pounds. Draw a graph of the function that represents this situation.

Word Problem Practice
CRM p. 40 AL OL BL ELL

2-6 Word Problem Practice

Special Functions

1. **SAVINGS** Nathan puts $200 into a checking account as soon as he gets his paycheck. The value of his checking account is modeled by the formula 200[m], where m is the number of months that Nathan has been working. After 105 days, how much money is in the account? **$600**

2. **FINANCE** A financial advisor handles the transactions for a customer. The median annual earnings for financial advisors is around $60,000. For every transaction, a certain financial advisor gets a 5% commission, regardless of whether the transaction is a deposit or withdrawal. Write a formula using the absolute value function for the advisor's commission. Let D represent the value of one transaction. **C = 0.05|D| or C = |0.05D|**

3. **ROUNDING** A science teacher instructs students to round their measurements as follows: If a number is less than 0.5 of a millimeter, students are instructed to round down. If a number is exactly 0.5 or greater, students are told to round up to the next millimeter. Write a formula that takes a measurement x millimeters and yields the rounded off number. **l = [x + 0.5] millimeters**

4. **ARCHITECTURE** The cross-section of a roof is shown in the figure. Write an absolute value function that models the shape of the roof. **y = 6 − |x − 3|**

5. **GAMES** Some young people are playing a game where a wooden plank is used as a target. It is marked off into 6 equal parts. A value is written in each section to represent the score earned if the dart lands in that section. Let x denote the horizontal position of a dart on the board, where the center of the board is the origin. Negative values correspond to the left half of the dart board, and positive values correspond to the right half. A player's score depends on the distance of the dart from the origin.

| 1 | 2 | 3 | 3 | 2 | 1 |

a. Write a formula that gives the horizontal distance from the center of the dartboard. **d = |x|**

b. Write a formula using the greatest integer function that can be used to find the person's score. **S = 3 − [|x|]**

B **32. RECREATION** The charge for renting a bicycle from a rental shop for different amounts of time is shown at the right.

a. Identify the type of function that models this situation. **step function**

b. Write and graph a function for the situation. **See Chapter 2 Answer Appendix.**

Bicycle Rentals

Time	Price
$\frac{1}{2}$ hour	$6
1 hour	$10
2 hours	$16
Daily	$24

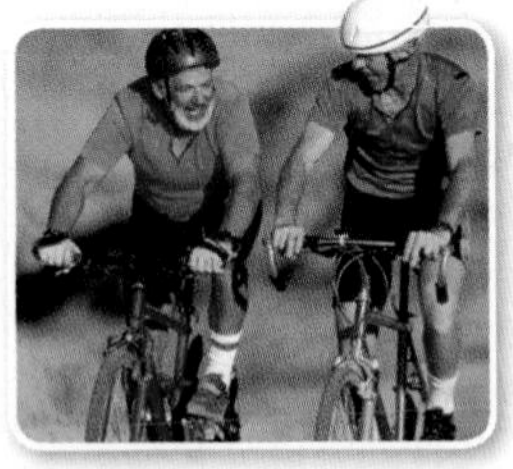

Real-World Link

Cycle tourism has begun to grow rapidly in many parts of the world. Cycle tourism is defined as recreational visits that involve leisure cycling.

Source: Cycle Tourism

Use each graph to write the absolute value function. **34. $f(x) = |x + 5| - 4$**

33 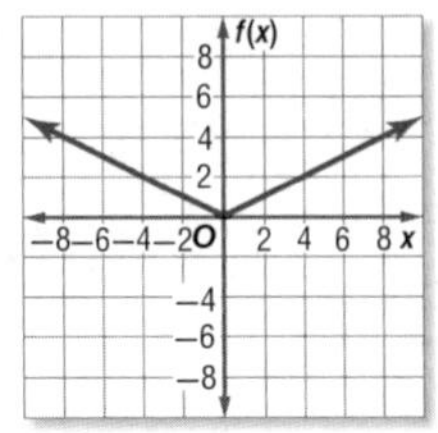 **$f(x) = |0.5x|$**

34. 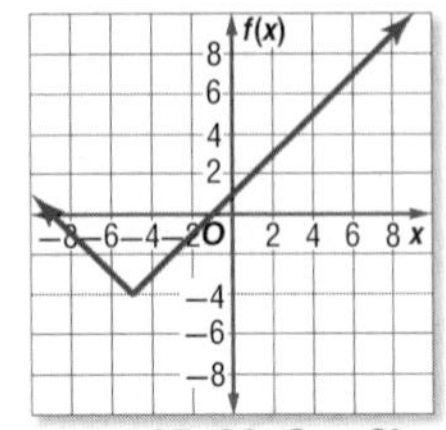

C **Graph each function. Identify the domain and range.** **35–38. See Chapter 2 Answer Appendix.**

35. $f(x) = [\![|0.5x|]\!]$

36. $g(x) = |[\![2x]\!]|$

37. $g(x) = \begin{cases} [\![x]\!] \text{ if } x < -4 \\ x + 1 \text{ if } -4 \leq x \leq 3 \\ -|x| \text{ if } x > 3 \end{cases}$

38. $h(x) = \begin{cases} -|x| \text{ if } x < -6 \\ |x| \text{ if } -6 \leq x \leq 2 \\ |-x| \text{ if } x > 2 \end{cases}$

39a–c. See Chapter 2 Answer Appendix.

42. Sample answer: 8.6; The greatest integer function asks for the greatest integer less than or equal to the given value; thus 8 is the greatest integer. If we were to round this value to the nearest integer, we would round up to 9.

39. MULTIPLE REPRESENTATIONS Consider the following absolute value functions.

$f(x) = |x| - 4$ $\qquad g(x) = |3x|$

a. TABULAR Create a table of $f(x)$ and $g(x)$ values for $x = -4$ to $x = 4$.

b. GRAPHICAL Graph the functions on separate graphs.

c. NUMERICAL Determine the slope between each two consecutive points in the table.

d. VERBAL Describe how the slopes of the two sections of an absolute value graph are related. **The two sections of an absolute value graph have opposite slopes. The slope is constant for each section of the graph.**

H.O.T. Problems
Use Higher-Order Thinking Skills

40. OPEN ENDED Write an absolute value relation in which the domain is all nonnegative numbers and the range is all real numbers. **Sample answer: $|y| = x$**

41. CHALLENGE Graph $|y| = 2|x + 3| - 5$. **See margin.**

42. REASONING Find a counterexample to the following statement and explain your reasoning.

In order to find the greatest integer function of x when x is not an integer, round x to the nearest integer.

43. OPEN ENDED Write an absolute value function in which $f(5) = -3$. **Sample answer: $f(x) = -|x - 2|$**

44. WRITING IN MATH Explain how piecewise functions can be used to accurately represent real-world problems.

44. Sample answer: Piecewise functions can be used to represent the cost of items when purchased in quantities, such as a dozen eggs.

Enrichment
CRM p. 41 OL BL

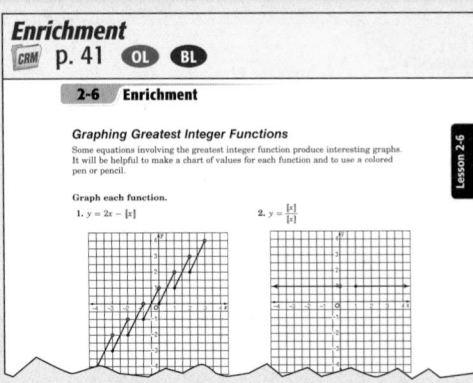

2-6 Enrichment

Graphing Greatest Integer Functions

Some equations involving the greatest integer function produce interesting graphs. It will be helpful to make a chart of values for each function and to use a colored pen or pencil.

Graph each function.

1. $y = 2x - [\![x]\!]$

2. $y = \frac{[\![x]\!]}{[\![x]\!]}$

Multiple Representations In Exercise 39, students use a table of values and a graph in the coordinate plane to compare the slopes of the two sections of an absolute-value function.

NGSSS PRACTICE 912.A.3.1, 912.A.10.3

45. **SHORT RESPONSE** What expression gives the *n*th term of the linear pattern defined by the table?

2	4	6	8	*n*
7	13	19	25	?

46. Solve: $5(x + 4) = x + 4$
Step 1: $5x + 20 = x + 4$
Step 2: $4x + 20 = 4$
Step 3: $4x = 24$
Step 4: $x = 6$

Which is the first *incorrect* step in the solution shown above? **B**

A. Step 4
B. Step 3
C. Step 2
D. Step 1

47. **NUMBER THEORY** Twelve consecutive integers are arranged in order from least to greatest. If the sum of the first six integers is 381, what is the sum of the last six integers? **I**

F. 345
G. 381
H. 387
I. 417

48. **ACT/SAT** For which function does $f\left(-\frac{1}{2}\right) \neq -1$? **B**

A. $f(x) = 2x$
B. $f(x) = |-2x|$
C. $f(x) = [\![x]\!]$
D. $f(x) = [\![2x]\!]$

Spiral Review

49. **FOOTBALL** The table shows the relationship between the total number of male students per school and the number of students who tried out for the football team. (Lesson 2-5)

a. Find a regression equation for the data. **$y = 0.10x + 30.34$**

b. Determine the correlation coefficient. **$r = 0.987$**

c. Predict how many students will try out for football at a school with 800 male students. **about 110**

Number of Male Students	Number of Tryouts
180	46
212	51
274	62
401	75
513	81
589	90

Write an equation in slope-intercept form for the line described. (Lesson 2-4) **50. $y = 0.5x - 4.5$**

50. passes through $(-3, -6)$, perpendicular to $y = -2x + 1$

51. passes through $(4, 0)$, parallel to $3x + 2y = 6$ **$y = -\frac{3}{2}x + 6$**

52. passes through the origin, perpendicular to $4x - 3y = 12$ **$y = -\frac{3}{4}x$**

Find each value if $f(x) = -4x + 6$, $g(x) = -x^2$, and $h(x) = -2x^2 - 6x + 9$. (Lesson 2-1)

53. $f(2c)$ **$-8c + 6$**

54. $g(a + 1)$ **$-a^2 - 2a - 1$**

55. $h(6)$ **-99**

56. Determine whether the figures below are similar. (Lesson 0-6) **yes**

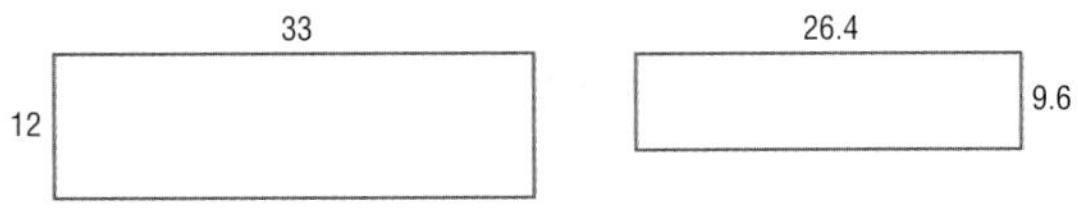

Skills Review

Graph each equation. (Lesson 2-1) **57–59. See margin.**

57. $y = -0.25x + 8$

58. $y = \frac{4}{3}x + 2$

59. $8x + 4y = 32$

4 ASSESS

Crystal Ball In Lesson 2-7 students will learn about parent funtions and transformations. Have students write about how they think today's lesson on special functions will help them with tomorrow's lesson.

Formative Assessment

Check for student understanding of concepts in Lessons 2-5 and 2-6.

CRM Quiz 3, p. 60

Additional Answers

41.

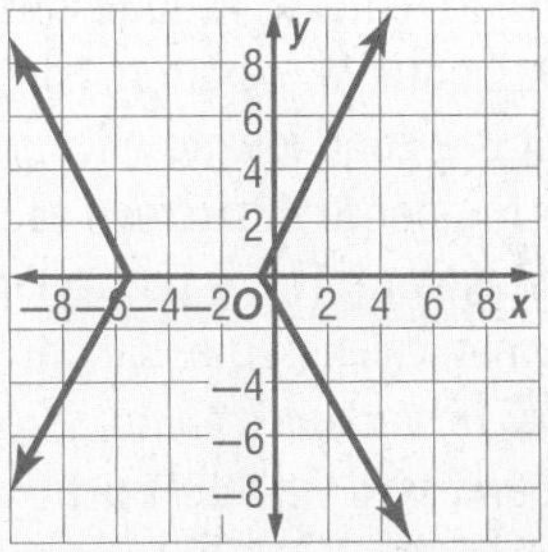

57.

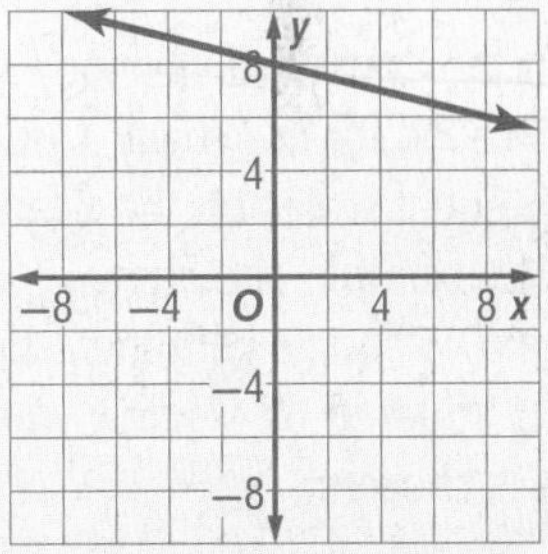

58.

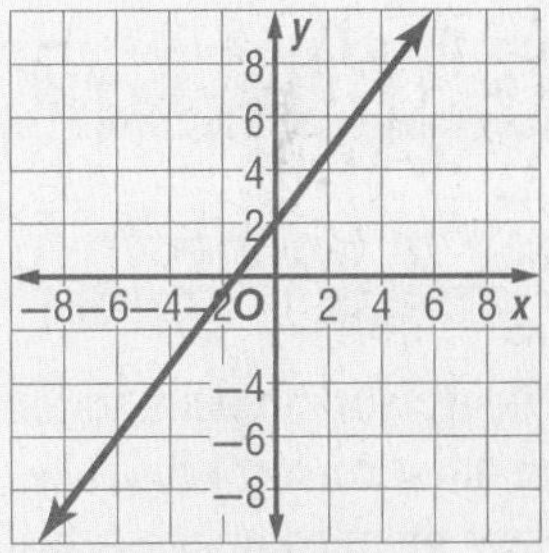

59.

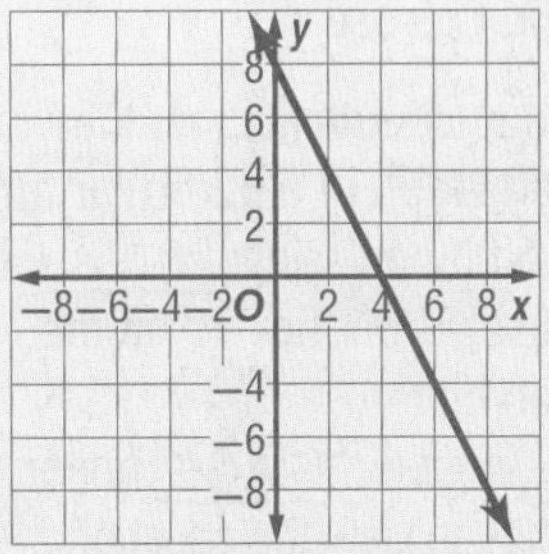

Families of Lines

FL Math Online glencoe.com
- Other Calculator Keystrokes
- Graphing Technology Personal Tutor

NGSSS **MA.912.A.2.6 Identify and graph common functions (including but not limited to linear,** rational, quadratic, cubic, radical, absolute value).

The parent function of the family of linear functions is $f(x) = x$. You can use a graphing calculator to investigate how changing the parameters m and b in $f(x) = mx + b$ affects the graphs as compared to the parent function.

ACTIVITY 1 b in $f(x) = mx + b$

Graph $f(x) = x$, $f(x) = x + 3$, and $f(x) = x - 5$ in the standard viewing window.

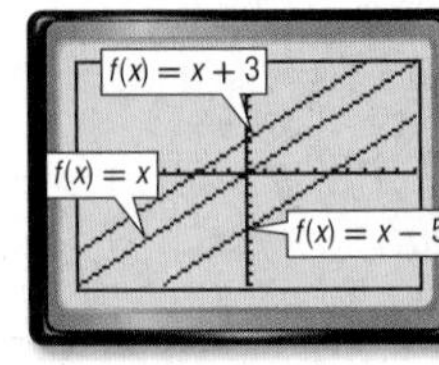

Enter the equations in the Y= list as Y1, Y2, and Y3. Then graph the equations.

KEYSTROKES: [Y=] [X,T,θ,n] [ENTER] [X,T,θ,n] [+] 3 [ENTER] [X,T,θ,n] [−] 5 [ENTER]

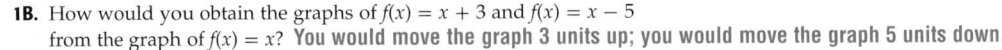

1A. Compare and contrast the graphs. **The graphs have the same slope, but different y-intercepts.**

1B. How would you obtain the graphs of $f(x) = x + 3$ and $f(x) = x - 5$ from the graph of $f(x) = x$? **You would move the graph 3 units up; you would move the graph 5 units down.**

The parameter m in $f(x) = mx + b$ affects the graphs in a different way than b.

ACTIVITY 2 m in $f(x) = mx + b$

Graph $f(x) = x$, $f(x) = 3x$, and $f(x) = \frac{1}{2}x$ in the standard viewing window.

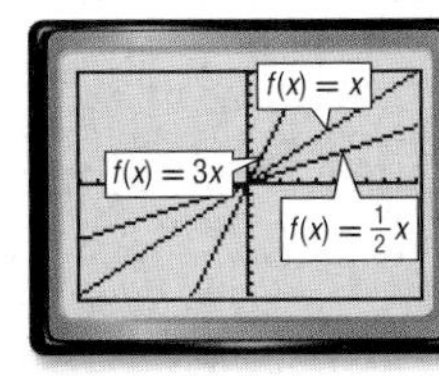

Enter the equations in the Y= list and graph. **B. $f(x) = 3x$; $f(x) = \frac{1}{2}x$**

2A. How do the graphs compare? **They have the same y-intercept.**

2B. Which graph is steepest? Which graph is the least steep?

2C. Graph $f(x) = -x$, $f(x) = -3x$, and $f(x) = -\frac{1}{2}x$ in the standard viewing window. How do these graphs compare?

2C. These graphs have the same intercept, but pass through quadrants II and IV instead of I and III.

Analyze the Results

Graph each set of equations on the same screen. Describe the similarities or differences among the graphs. **1–3. See Chapter 2 Answer Appendix.**

1. $f(x) = 3x$
$f(x) = 3x + 1$
$f(x) = 3x - 2$

2. $f(x) = x + 2$
$f(x) = 5x + 2$
$f(x) = \frac{1}{2}x + 2$

3. $f(x) = x - 3$
$f(x) = 2x - 3$
$f(x) = 0.75x - 3$

4. What do the graphs of equations of the form $f(x) = mx + b$ have in common? **They are all lines.**

5. How do the values of b and m affect the graph of $f(x) = mx + b$ as compared to the parent function $f(x) = x$? **The parameter b changes the $f(x)$-intercept and the parameter m changes the slope.**

6. Summarize your results. How can knowing about the effects of m and b help you sketch the graph of a function? **Sample answer: Knowing b tells you how much to shift the parent graph vertically. The value of m tells you whether the graph is steeper or less steep than the parent graph.**

1 FOCUS

Objective Use a graphing calculator to determine how changing the parameters m and b affects the graphs of the functions.

Materials for Each Student

- TI-83/84 Plus or other graphing calculator

Teaching Tip

Equations are entered as functions by first pressing the **Y =** button. For this reason, it is a good idea to encourage students to refer to this screen as the "Function editor." This is particularly helpful when calling up equations from the **VARS,** or Variables menu, since they are accessed via the **Function . . .** option under the **Y-VARS** submenu.

Note that the "standard viewing window" called for in Activity 1 does not show equal scales on the x- and y-axes. For example, the line $y = x$ will not make a 45° angle with the x-axis unless the squared-off viewing window **ZSquare** is chosen.

2 TEACH

Working in Cooperative Groups

Have students work in pairs so they can help each other correct keystroke errors. Have them complete Activities 1 and 2 and Exercise 1.

- Point out to students that they can turn the graph of a particular function on or off by pressing [ENTER] when the cursor is on the "=" in the function editor.
- By pressing the [TRACE] button, students can view the equation associated with each line on the graph screen. The up and down arrows can be used to switch among the different functions and their graphs. If the equations don't appear in [TRACE] mode, check the **FORMAT** screen to see if ExprOn is selected.

Practice Have students complete Exercises 2–6.

3 ASSESS

Formative Assessment

Use Exercise 3 to assess students' ability to see similarities and differences in the graphs.

From Concrete to Abstract

Use Exercise 6 to bridge the algebraic idea of solving equations from the modeling activities.

Extending the Concept

In the general form of a linear function $f(x) = mx + b$, which constant would you change to move the graph up or down? b

108 Chapter 2 Linear Relations and Functions

Parent Functions and Transformations

Then

You analyzed and used relations and functions. (Lesson 2-1)

Now

- Identify and use parent functions.
- Describe transformations of functions.

NGSSS

MA.912.A.2.5 Graph absolute value equations and inequalities in two variables.
MA.912.A.2.10 Describe and graph transformations of functions. *Also addresses MA.912.A.2.6.*

New Vocabulary

family of graphs
parent graph
parent function
constant function
identity function
quadratic function
translation
reflection
line of reflection
dilation

FL Math Online

glencoe.com

Why?

Nick makes \$8 an hour working at a pizza shop. The red line represents his wages. If he also delivers the pizzas, he is paid \$2 more per hour. The blue line represents Nick's wages when he delivers.

These graphs are examples of transformations.

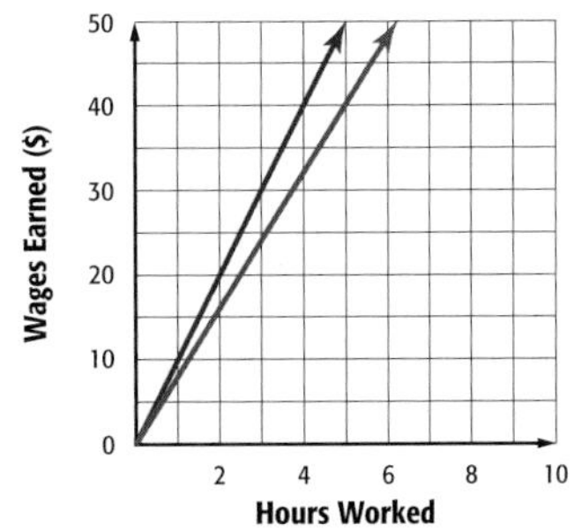

Parent Graphs A **family of graphs** is a group of graphs that display one or more similar characteristics. The **parent graph**, which is the graph of the **parent function**, is the simplest of the graphs in a family. This is the graph that is transformed to create other members in a family of graphs.

Key Concept Parent Functions

Constant Function

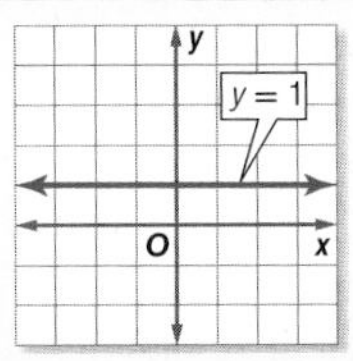

The general equation of a **constant function** is $f(x) = a$, where a is any number. The domain is all real numbers, and the range consists of a single real number a.

Identity Function

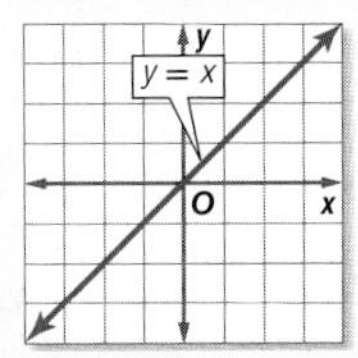

The **identity function** $f(x) = x$ passes through all points with coordinates (a, a). It is the parent function of most linear functions. Its domain and range are all real numbers.

Absolute Value Function

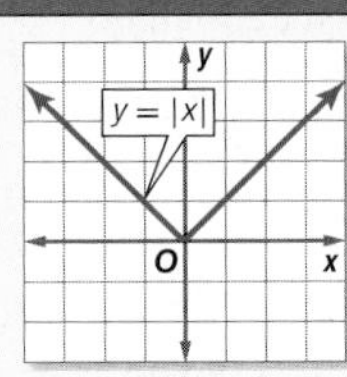

Recall that the parent function of absolute value functions is $f(x) = |x|$. The domain of $f(x) = |x|$ is the set of real numbers, and the range is the set of real numbers greater than or equal to 0.

Quadratic Function

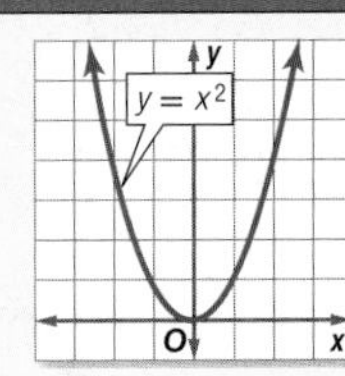

The parent function of **quadratic functions** is $f(x) = x^2$. The domain of $f(x) = x^2$ is the set of real numbers, and the range is the set of real numbers greater than or equal to 0.

2-7 Lesson Notes

1 FOCUS

Vertical Alignment

Before Lesson 2-7
Analyze and use relations and functions.

Lesson 2-7
Identify and use parent functions and describe transformations of functions.

After Lesson 2-7
Analyze a situation modeled by a rational function, formulate an equation or inequality, and solve the problem.

2 TEACH

Scaffolding Questions

Have students read the *Why?* section of the lesson.

Ask:

- If Nick works three hours at the pizza shop but does not deliver pizzas, how much will he make? \$24
- How much per hour does Nick make working at the pizza shop and delivering pizzas? \$10 an hour
- What are the slopes of the two lines? 8 and 10

Lesson 2-7 Resources

Resource	Approaching-Level	On-Level	Beyond-Level	English Learners
Teacher Edition	• Differentiated Instruction, p. 111	• Differentiated Instruction, p. 111	• Differentiated Instruction, p. 116	• Differentiated Instruction, p. 111
Chapter Resource Masters	• Study Guide and Intervention, pp. 43–44 • Skills Practice, p. 45 • Practice, p. 46 • Word Problem Practice, p. 47	• Study Guide and Intervention, pp. 43–44 • Skills Practice, p. 45 • Practice, p. 46 • Word Problem Practice, p. 47 • Enrichment, p. 48 • Graphing Calculator Activity, p. 49	• Practice, p. 46 • Word Problem Practice, p. 47 • Enrichment, p. 48	• Study Guide and Intervention, pp. 43–44 • Skills Practice, p. 45 • Practice, p. 46 • Word Problem Practice, p. 47
Transparencies	• 5-Minute Check Transparency 2-7	• 5-Minute Check Transparency 2-7	• 5-Minute Check Transparency 2-7	• 5-Minute Check Transparency 2-7
Other	• Study Notebook	• Study Notebook	• Study Notebook	• Study Notebook

Parent Graphs

Example 1 shows how to identify a function when its graph is given.

Formative Assessment

Use the Guided Practice exercises after each example to determine students' understanding of concepts.

Additional Example

1 Identify the type of function represented by each graph.

a.

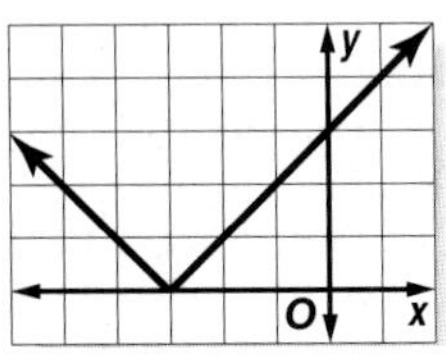

absolute value function

b.

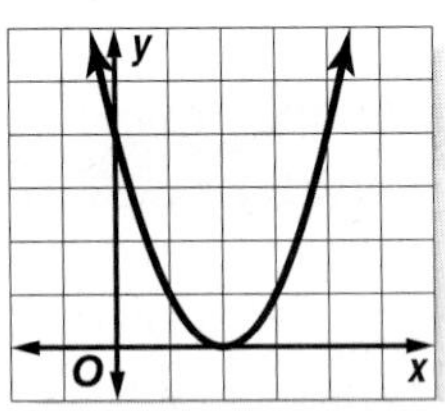

quadratic function

Additional Examples also in Interactive Classroom PowerPoint® Presentations

IWB INTERACTIVE WHITEBOARD READY

Transformations

Examples 2–4 show how to describe and graph translations, reflections, and dilations. **Example 5** shows how to identify transformations.

Additional Example

2 Describe the translation in $y = (x + 1)^2$. Then graph the function. Translates the graph $y = x^2$ 1 unit left.

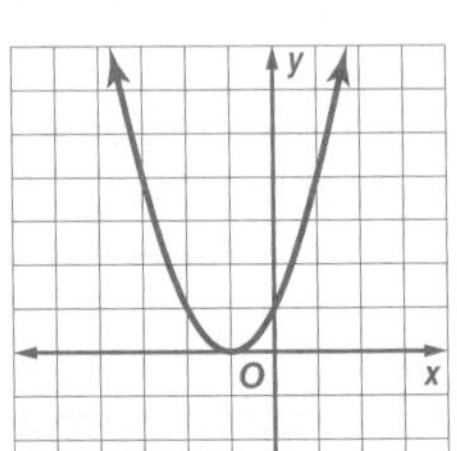

EXAMPLE 1 Identify a Function Given the Graph

Identify the type of function represented by each graph.

a.

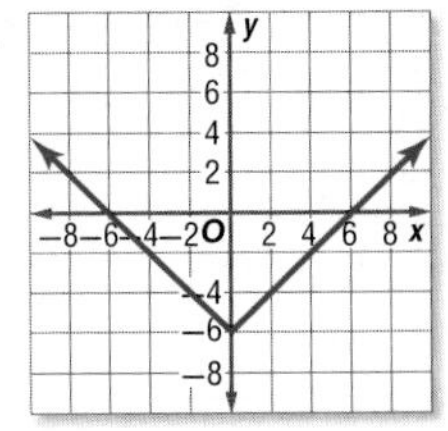

The graph is in the shape of a V. The graph represents an absolute value function.

b.

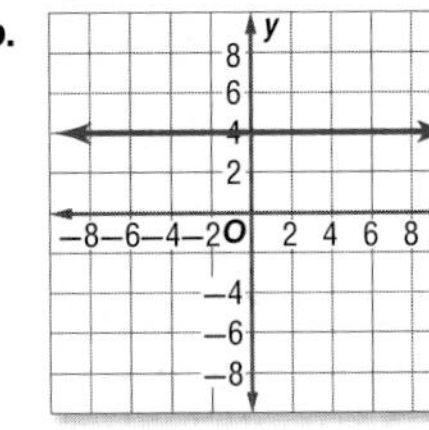

The graph is a horizontal line that crosses the y-axis at 4. The graph represents a constant function.

Guided Practice

1A.

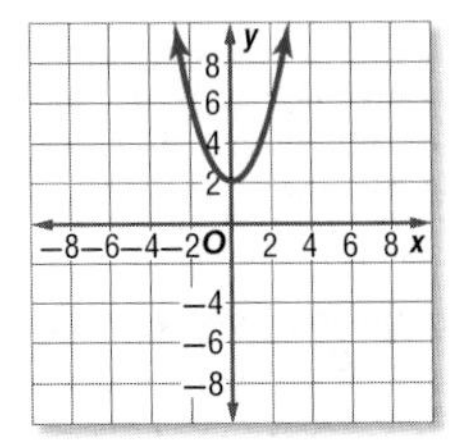

quadratic

1B.

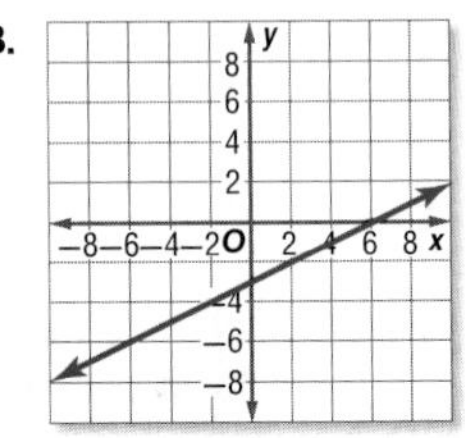

linear

Personal Tutor glencoe.com

Transformations Transformations of a parent graph may appear in a different location, flip over an axis, or appear to have been stretched or compressed. The transformed graph may resemble the parent graph, or it may not.

ReadingMath

translation A translation is also called a *slide*, a *shift*, or a *glide*.

A **translation** moves a figure up, down, left, or right.

- When a constant k is added to or subtracted from a parent function, the result $f(x) \pm k$ is a translation of the graph up or down.
- When a constant h is added to or subtracted from x before evaluating a parent function, the result, $f(x \pm h)$, is a translation left or right.

EXAMPLE 2 Describe and Graph Translations

Describe the translation in $y = |x| + 2$. Then graph the function.

The graph of $y = |x| + 2$ is a translation of the graph of $y = |x|$ up 2 units.

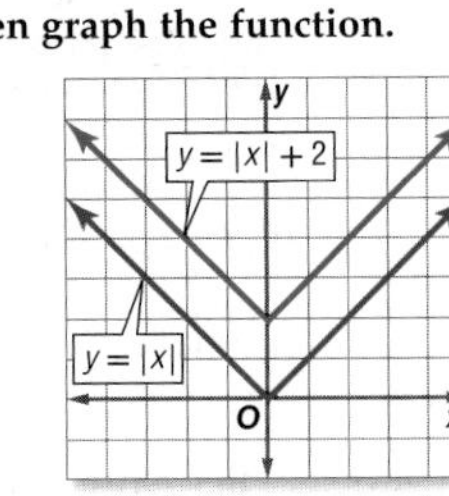

Guided Practice 2A, 2B. See margin.

Describe the translation in each function. Then graph the function.

2A. $y = |x + 3|$

2B. $y = x^2 - 4$

Personal Tutor glencoe.com

Additional Answers (Guided Practice)

2A. The graph of $y = |x + 3|$ is a translation of the graph of $y = |x|$ left 3 units.

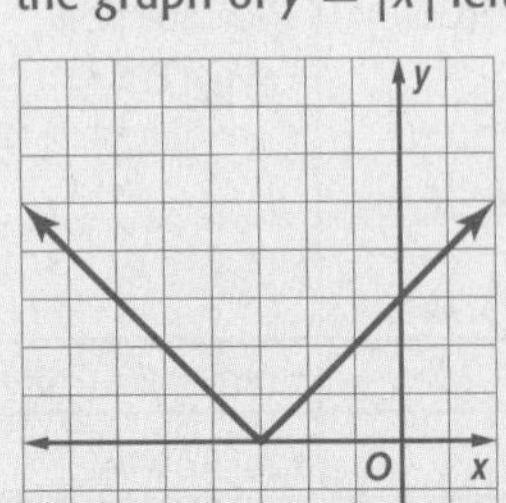

2B. The graph of $y = x^2 - 4$ is a translation of the graph of $y = x^2$ down 4 units.

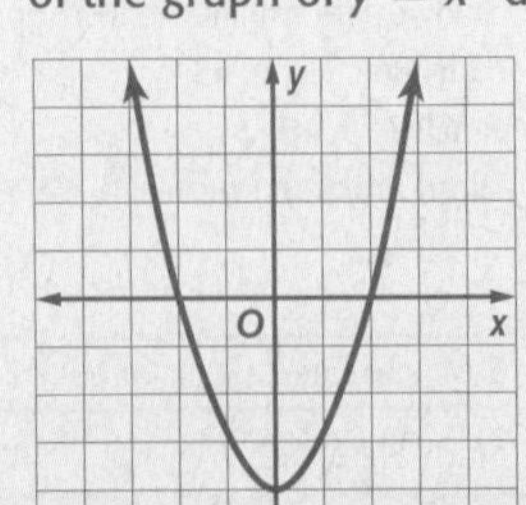

110 Chapter 2 Linear Relations and Functions

Review Vocabulary

vertex the maximum or minimum point on the graph of a quadratic or absolute value function (Lesson 2-7)

A **reflection** flips a figure over a line called the **line of reflection**.

- When a parent function is multiplied by −1, the result $-f(x)$ is a reflection of the graph in the x-axis.
- When only the variable is multiplied by −1, the result $f(-x)$ is a reflection of the graph in a line of reflection through the vertex.

EXAMPLE 3 Describe and Graph Reflections

Describe the reflection in $y = -x^2$. Then graph the function.

The graph of $y = -x^2$ is a reflection of the graph of $y = x^2$ in the x-axis.

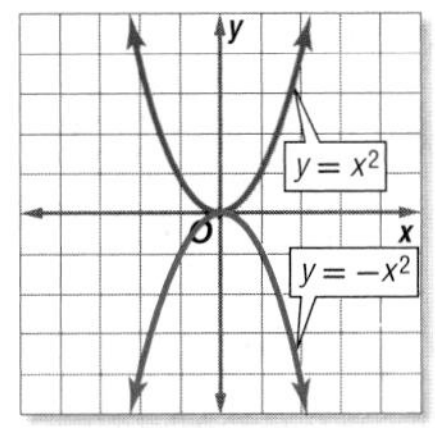

Guided Practice 3A, 3B. See margin.

Describe the reflection in each function. Then graph the function.

3A. $y = -|x|$ **3B.** $y = -x$

Personal Tutor glencoe.com

A **dilation** shrinks or enlarges a figure proportionally. When the variable in a linear parent function is multiplied by a nonzero number, the slope of the graph changes.

- When a nonlinear parent function is multiplied by a nonzero number, the function is stretched or compressed vertically.
- Coefficients greater than 1 cause the graph to be stretched vertically, and coefficients between 0 and 1 cause the graph to be compressed vertically.

EXAMPLE 4 Describe and Graph Dilations

Describe the dilation in $y = 4x$. Then graph the function.

The graph of $y = 4x$ is a dilation of the graph of $y = x$. The slope of the graph of $y = 4x$ is steeper than that of the graph of $y = x$.

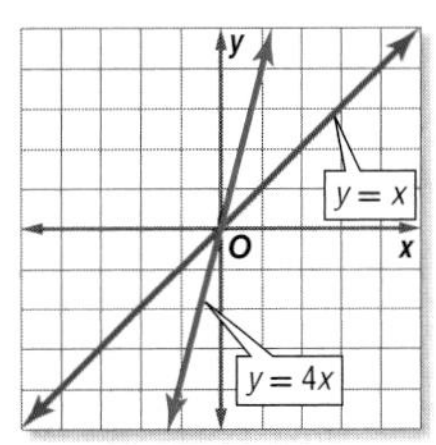

Guided Practice 4A, 4B. See Chapter 2 Answer Appendix.

Describe the dilation in each function. Then graph the function.

4A. $y = 2x^2$ **4B.** $y = \left|\frac{1}{3}x\right|$

Personal Tutor glencoe.com

Differentiated Instruction

AL OL ELL

If students have access to poster-making supplies,

Then ask them to create posters that display the four parent functions discussed in this lesson as well as the transformations. Display the posters in the room.

Additional Examples

3 Describe the reflection in $y = -|x|$. Then graph the function. It reflects the graph across the x-axis.

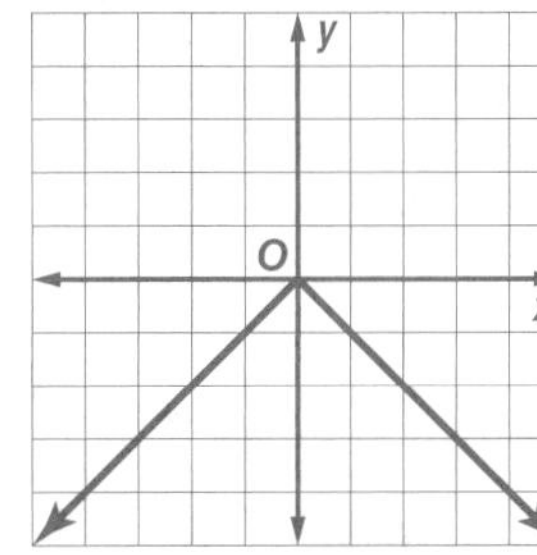

4 Describe the dilation on $y = \frac{1}{2}|x|$. Then graph the function. The graph is vertically compressed.

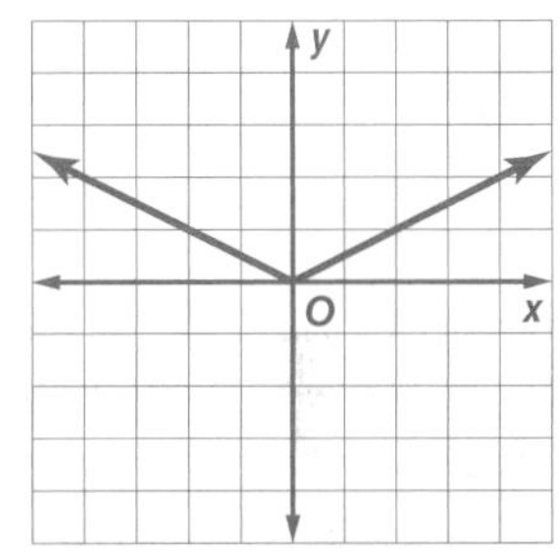

Additional Answers (Guided Practice)

3A. The graph of $y = -|x|$ is a reflection of the graph of $y = |x|$ across the x-axis.

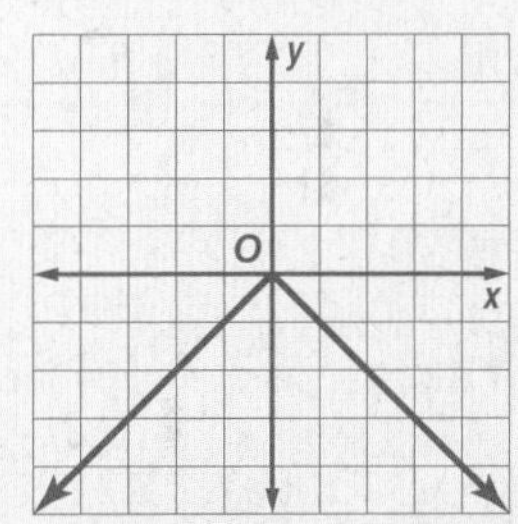

3B. The graph of $y = -x$ is a reflection of the graph of $y = x$ across the x-axis, described by $-f(x)$, or it is a reflection of the graph of $y = x$ across the y-axis, described by $f(-x)$.

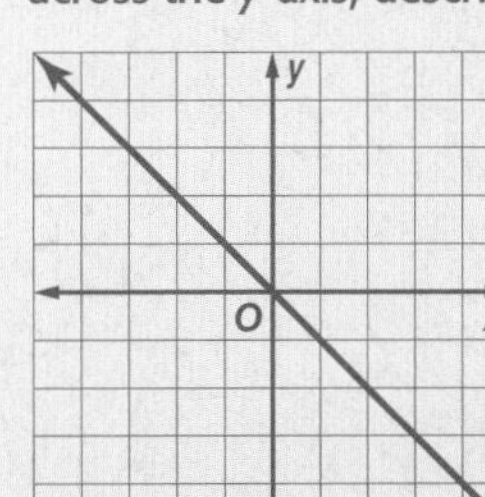

Additional Example

5 **ARCHWAYS** The function $f(x) = -\frac{1}{2}(x - 5)^2 + 12.5$ can be used to represent a parabolic archway. Describe the transformations in the function. Then graph the function. -5 translates $f(x) = x^2$ 5 units right. $+12.5$ translates $f(x) = x^2$ 12.5 units up. $-\frac{1}{2}$ reflects $f(x) = x^2$ across the x-axis and expands the graph.

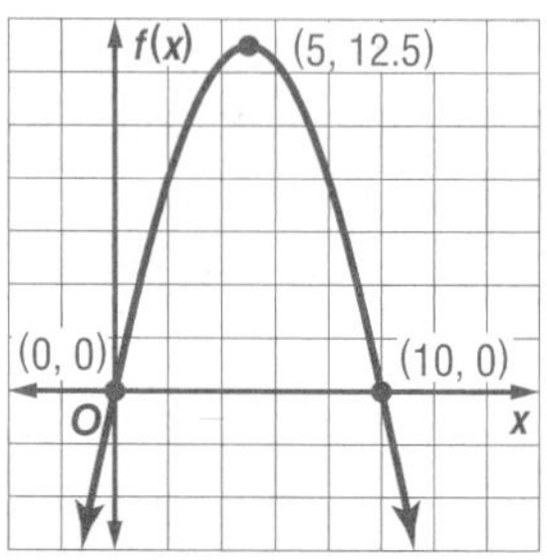

Focus on Mathematical Content

Graph Shapes A graph may exemplify a special type even if it doesn't have exactly the same shape. Stretched/flattened or inverted versions of special function graphs are still examples of special functions.

Additional Answer (Guided Practice)

5. The graph of $C(x) = \frac{5}{9}(x - 32)$ is a translation of the parent graph $C(x) = x$ right 32 units. The dilation represents a slope that is less than that of the parent graph.

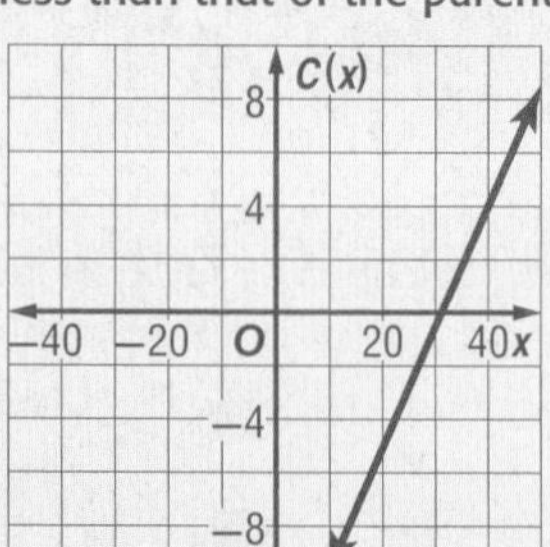

Real-World Link

The average American homeowner spends over \$350 each year on indoor and outdoor plants.

Source: American Nursery & Landscape Association

Real-World EXAMPLE 5 Identify Transformations

LANDSCAPING **Ethan is going to add a brick walkway around the perimeter of his vegetable garden. The area of the walkway can be represented by the function $f(x) = 4(x + 2.5)^2 - 25$. Describe the transformations in the function. Then graph the function.**

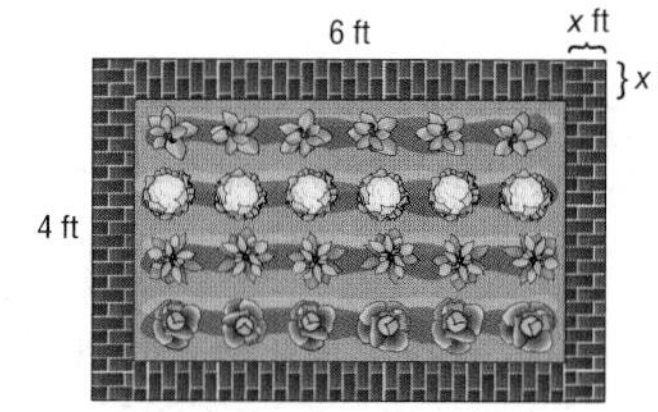

The graph of $f(x) = 4(x + 2.5)^2 - 25$ is a combination of transformations of the parent graph $f(x) = x^2$. Determine how each transformation affects the parent graph.

$f(x) = 4(x + 2.5)^2 - 25$

$+ 2.5$ translates $f(x) = x^2$ left 2.5 units.

$- 25$ translates $f(x) = x^2$ down 25 units.

4 stretches $f(x) = x^2$ vertically.

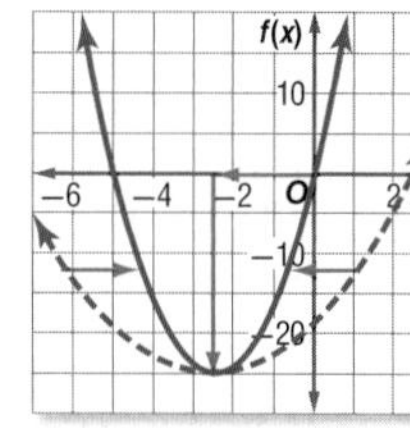

Guided Practice

5. **SCIENCE** The function $C(x) = \frac{5}{9}(x - 32)$ can be used to determine the temperature in degrees Celsius when given the temperature in degrees Fahrenheit. Describe the transformations in the function. Then graph the function. **See margin.**

Personal Tutor glencoe.com

The table summarizes the changes to the parent graph under different transformations.

Concept Summary — Transformations of Functions

Transformation	Change to Parent Graph
Translation	
$f(x + h)$	Translates graph h units left.
$f(x - h)$	Translates graph h units right.
$f(x) + k$	Translates graph k units up.
$f(x) - k$	Translates graph k units down.
Reflection	
$-f(x)$	Reflects graph in the x-axis.
$f(-x)$	Reflects graph in the y-axis.
Dilation	
$a \cdot f(x), a > 1$	Stretches graph vertically.
$a \cdot f(x), 0 < a < 1$	Compresses graph vertically
$f(bx), b > 1$	Compresses graph horizontally.
$f(bx), 0 < b < 1$	Stretches graph horizontally.

StudyTip

Describing Transformations Ask yourself these questions to help you identify transformations.

1. What type of function is it?
2. Does the graph open up or down?
3. Does the vertex lie on an axis?

3. translation of the graph of $y = x^2$ down 4 units

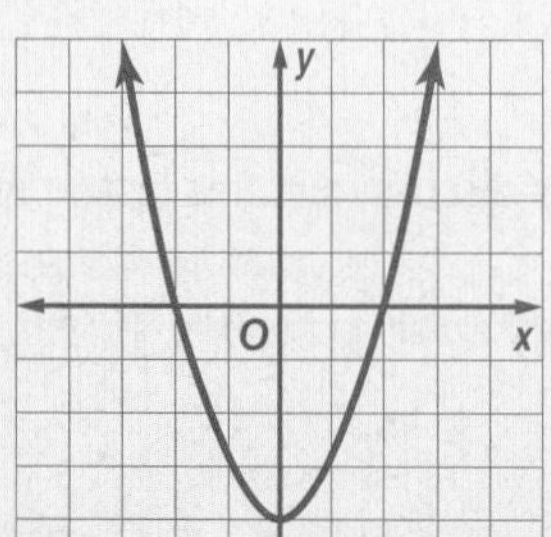

4. translation of the graph of $y = |x|$ left 1 unit

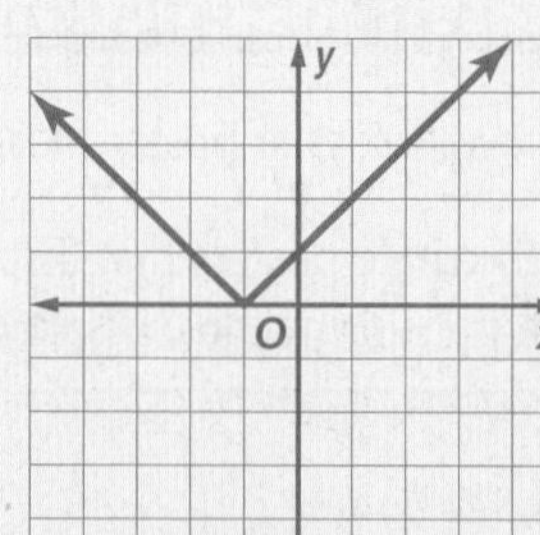

Check Your Understanding

Example 1 p. 110

Identify the type of function represented by each graph.

1. 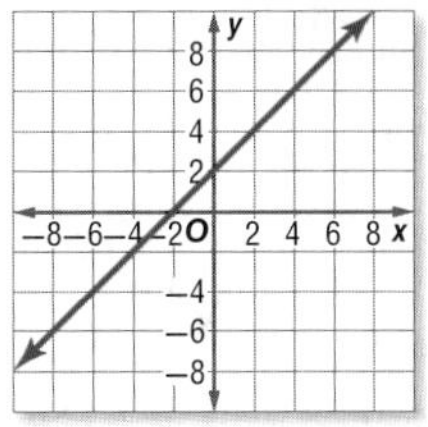

linear

2. 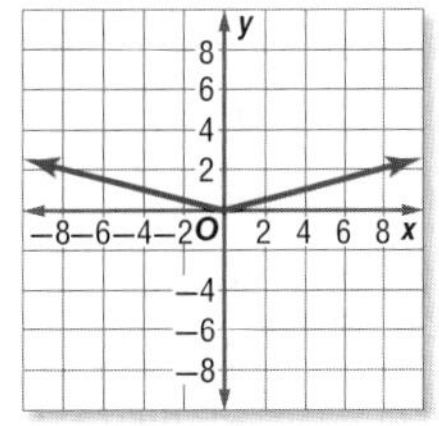

absolute value

Example 2 p. 110

Describe the translation in each function. Then graph the function. 3, 4. See margin.

3. $y = x^2 - 4$

4. $y = |x + 1|$

Example 3 p. 111

Describe the reflection in each function. Then graph the function. 5, 6. See margin.

5. $y = -|x|$

6. $y = (-x)^2$

Example 4 p. 111

Describe the dilation in each function. Then graph the function. 7, 8. See margin.

7. $y = \frac{3}{5}x$

8. $y = 3x^2$

Example 5 p. 112

9. FOOD The manager of a coffee shop is randomly checking cups of coffee drinks prepared by employees to ensure that the correct amount of coffee is in each cup. Each 12-ounce drink should contain half coffee and half steamed milk. The amount of coffee by which each drink varies can be represented by $f(x) = \frac{1}{2}|x - 12|$. Describe the transformations in the function. Then graph the function. See Chapter 2 Answer Appendix.

Practice and Problem Solving

● = **Step-by-Step Solutions** begin on page R20.
Extra Practice begins on page 947.

Example 1 p. 110

Identify the type of function represented by each graph.

10. 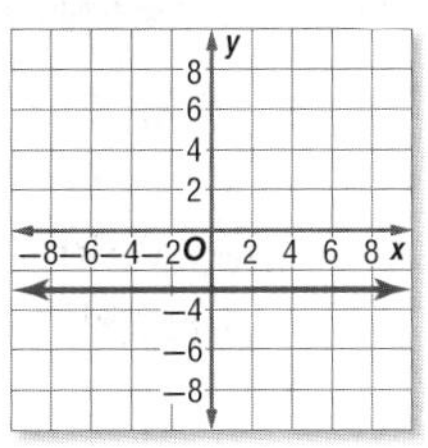

constant

11. 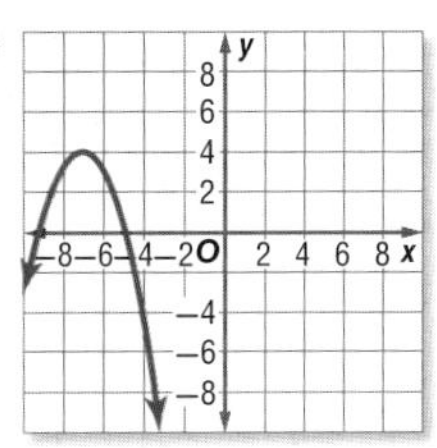

quadratic

12. 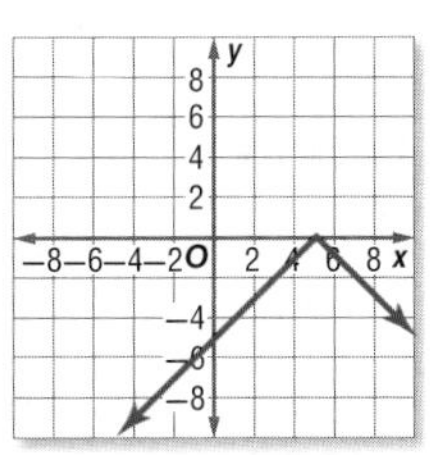

absolute value

13. 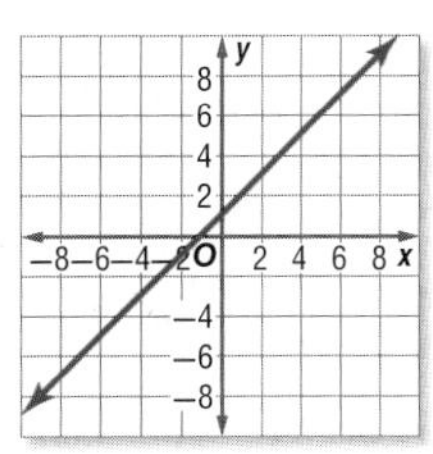

linear

Differentiated Homework Options

Level	Assignment	Two-Day Option	
AL Basic	10–32, 44–65	11–31 odd, 48–51	10–32 even, 44–47, 52–65
OL Core	11–31 odd, 32, 33–37 odd, 39–41, 44–65	10–32, 48–51	33–42, 44–47, 52–65
BL Advanced	33–62, (optional: 63–65)		

3 PRACTICE

Formative Assessment

Use Exercises 1–9 to check for understanding.

Use the chart at the bottom of this page to customize assignments for your students.

Additional Answers

5. reflection of the graph of $y = |x|$ across the x-axis

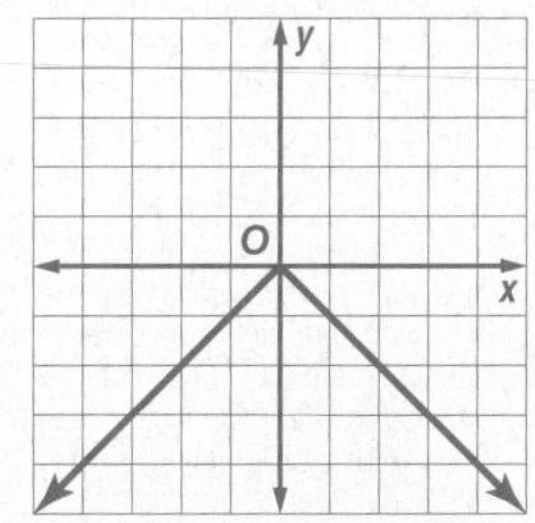

6. reflection of the graph of $y = x^2$ across the y-axis

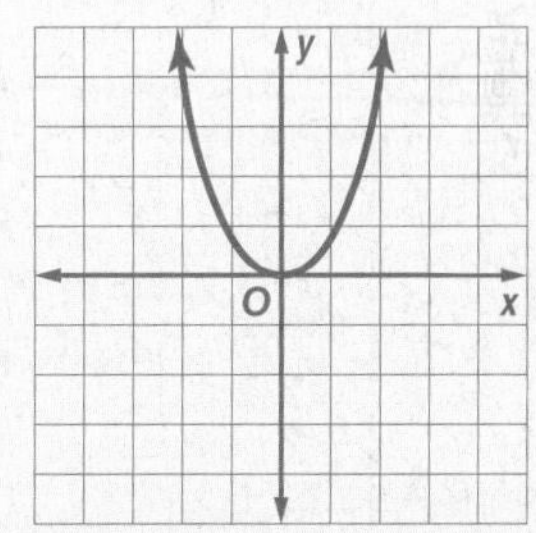

7. A vertical compression of the graph of $y = x$; the slope is not as steep as that of $y = x$.

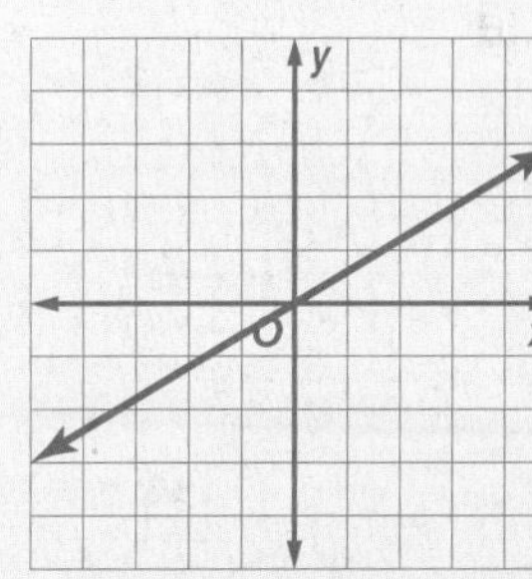

8. The dilation stretches the graph of $y = x^2$ vertically.

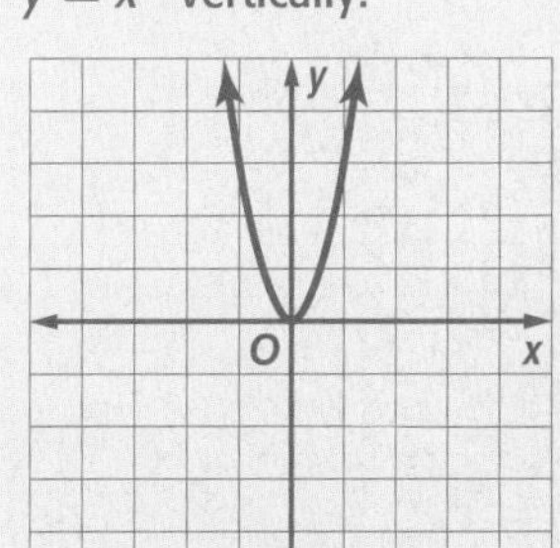

Watch Out!

Error Analysis For Exercise 44, students should remember that the identity function passes through all points with coordinates (a, a). The function $f(x) = 2x$ does not meet this requirement.

Additional Answers

14. translation of the graph of $y = x^2$ up 4 units

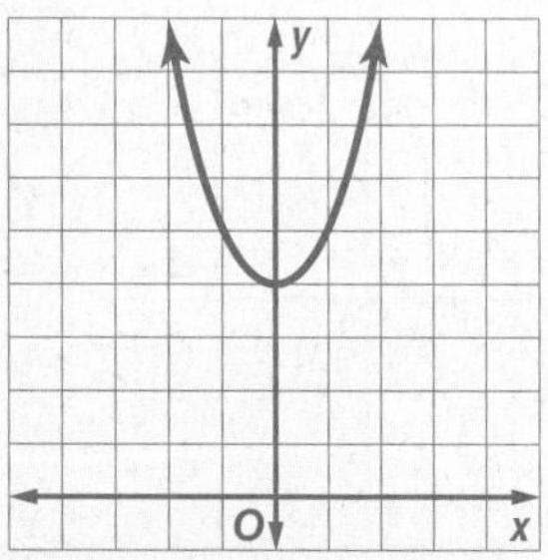

15. translation of the graph of $y = |x|$ down 3 units

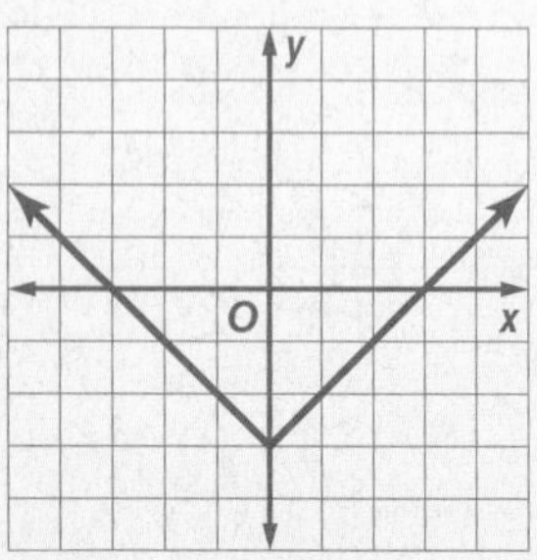

16. translation of the graph of $y = x$ down 1 unit or right 1 unit

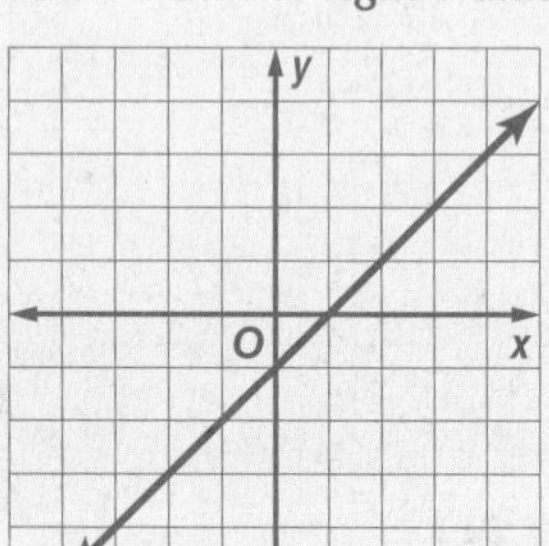

Example 2 p. 110 — **Describe the translation in each function. Then graph the function.** 14–19. See margin.

14. $y = x^2 + 4$ **15.** $y = |x| - 3$ **16.** $y = x - 1$

17. $y = x + 2$ **18.** $y = (x - 5)^2$ **19.** $y = |x + 6|$

Example 3 p. 111 — **Describe the reflection in each function. Then graph the function.** 20–25. See Chapter 2 Answer Appendix.

20. $y = -x$ **21.** $y = -x^2$ **22.** $y = (-x)^2$

23. $y = |-x|$ **24.** $y = -|x|$ **25.** $y = (-x)$

Example 4 p. 111 — **Describe the dilation in each function. Then graph the function.** 26–31. See Chapter 2 Answer Appendix.

26. $y = (3x)^2$ **27.** $y = 6x$ **28.** $y = 4|x|$

29. $y = |2x|$ **30.** $y = \frac{2}{3}x$ **31.** $y = \frac{1}{2}x^2$

Example 5 p. 112 — **32. HEALTH** A non-impact workout can burn up to 7.5 Calories per minute. The equation to represent how many Calories a person burns after m minutes of the workout is $C(m) = 7.5m$. Identify the transformation in the function. Then graph the function. See Chapter 2 Answer Appendix.

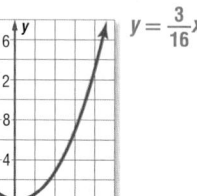

Real-World Link

Non-impact workouts usually include a sequence of exercises that combine strength, flexibility, balance, and inner awareness.

Source: *Medical Encyclopedia*

B **Write an equation for each function.**

33.

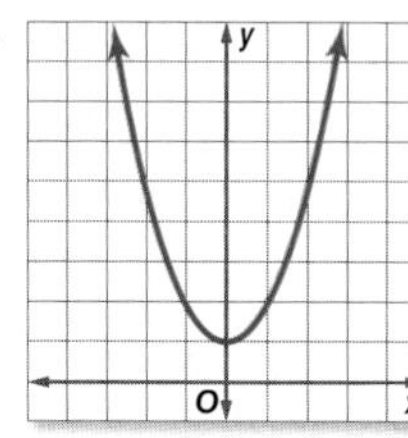

$y = x^2 + 1$

34.

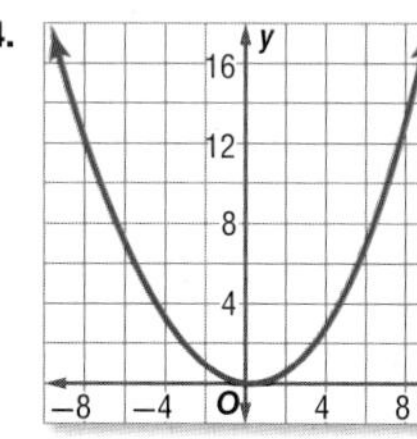

$y = \frac{3}{16}x^2$

35.

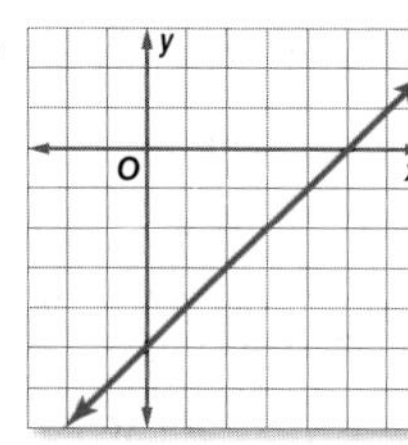

$y = x - 5$

36.

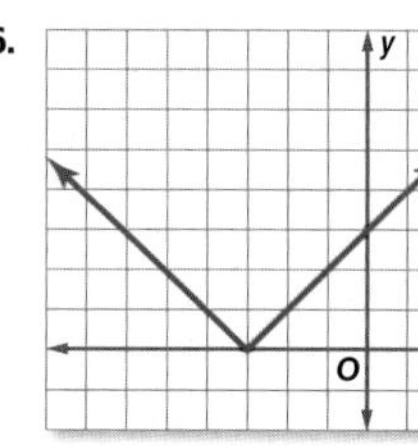

$y = |x + 3|$

37.

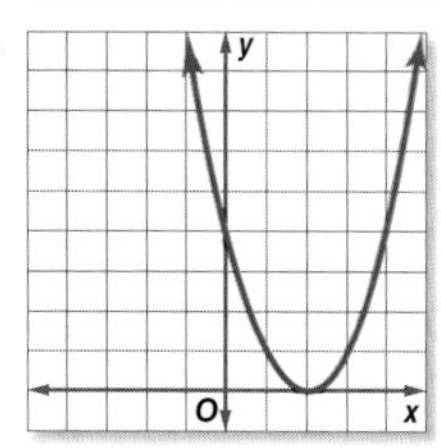

$y = (x - 2)^2$

38.

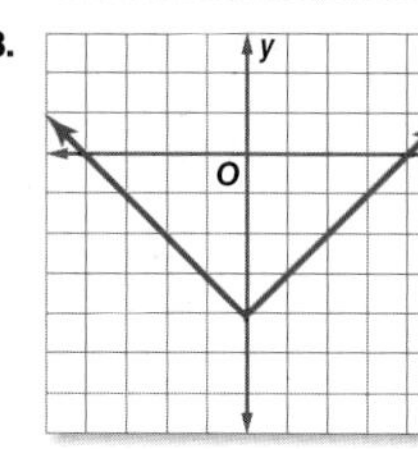

$y = |x| - 4$

39. BUSINESS The graph of the cost of producing x widgets is represented by the blue line in the graph. After hiring a consultant, the cost of producing x widgets is represented by the red line in the graph. Write the equations of both lines and describe the transformation from the blue line to the red line.

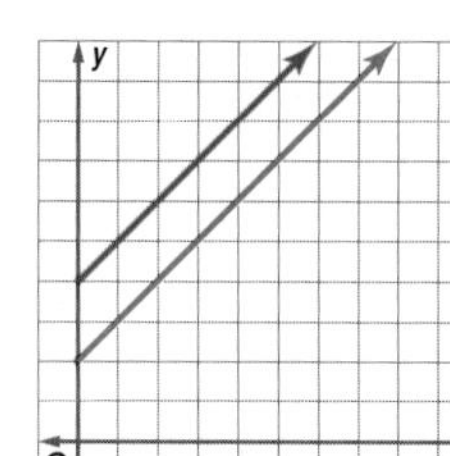

39. Blue: $y = x + 4$; red: $y = x + 2$; the red line is a translation of the blue line 2 units down.

17. translation of the graph of $y = x$ up 2 units or left 2 units

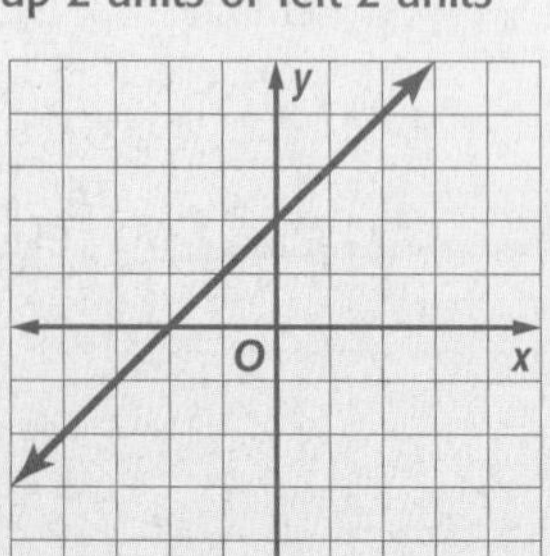

18. translation of the graph of $y = x^2$ right 5 units

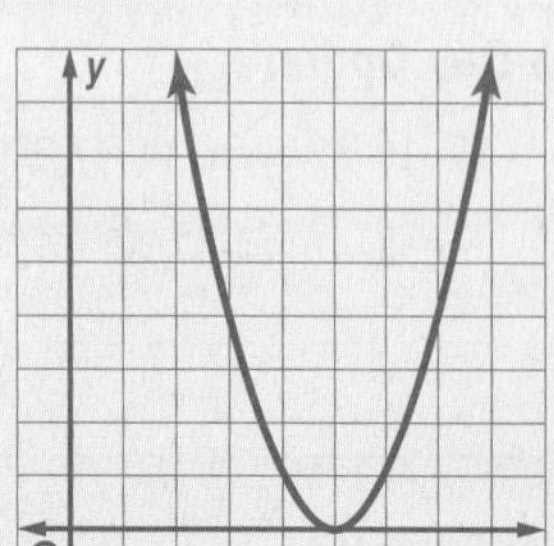

19. translation of the graph of $y = |x|$ left 6 units

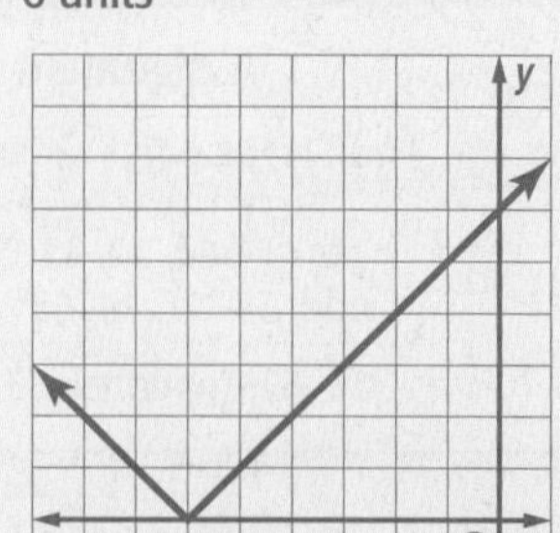

Real-World Link

Model rocketry was developed during the "space-race" era. Most rockets are constructed of cardboard, plastic, and balsa wood, and are fueled by single-use rocket motors.

40c. about 25 ft higher
40d. a dilation in which the red graph is an expansion of the blue graph

40. ROCKETRY Kenji launched a toy rocket from ground level. The height $h(t)$ of Kenji's rocket after t seconds is shown in blue. Emily believed that her rocket could fly higher and longer than Kenji's. The flight of Emily's rocket is shown in red. **a. quadratic**

a. Identify the type of function shown.

b. How much longer than Kenji's rocket did Emily's rocket stay in the air? **about 1.5 seconds**

c. How much higher than Kenji's rocket did Emily's rocket go?

d. Describe the type of transformation between the two graphs.

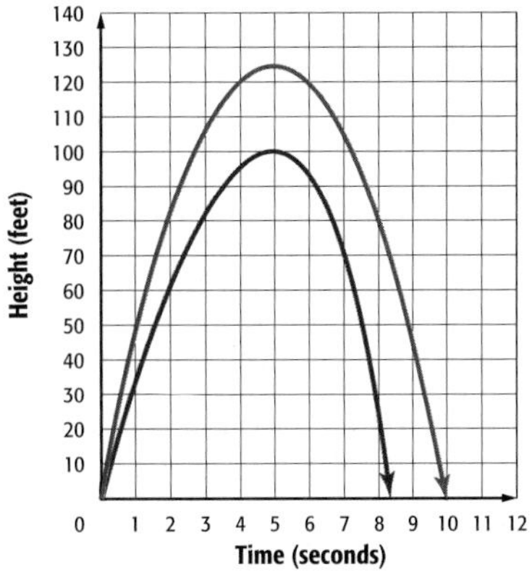

Write an equation for each function. **41. $y = (x + 4)^2 - 6$ 42. $y = |x - 5| - 2$**

41.

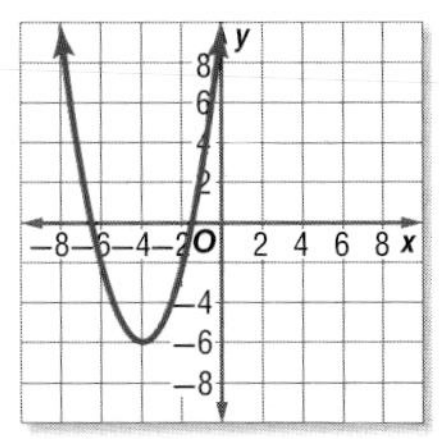

42.

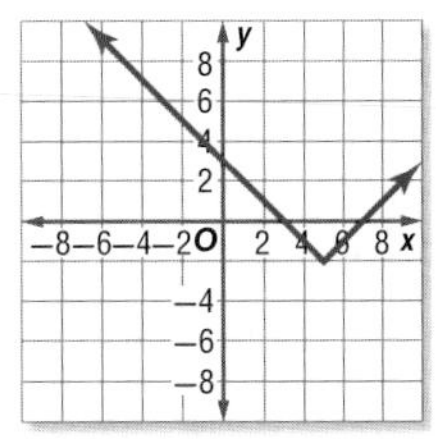

H.O.T. Problems Use Higher-Order Thinking Skills

43. Sample answer: Since a vertical translation concerns only y-values and a horizontal translation concerns only x-values, order is irrelevant.

44. Kimi; Sample answer: Linear equations that go through the origin are not always the identity. The identity linear function is $f(x) = x$.

43. CHALLENGE Explain why performing a horizontal translation followed by a vertical translation ends up being the same transformation as performing a vertical translation followed by a horizontal translation.

44. ERROR ANALYSIS Carla and Kimi are determining if $f(x) = 2x$ is the *identity function*. Is either of them correct? Explain your reasoning.

Carla	Kimi
$f(x) = 2x$ is the identity function because it is linear and goes through the origin.	*$f(x) = 2x$ is not the identity function because the values in the domain do not correspond to their duplicates in the range.*

45. OPEN ENDED Draw a figure in Quadrant II. Use any of the transformations you learned in this lesson to move your figure to Quadrant IV. Describe your transformation. **See Chapter 2 Answer Appendix.**

46. Sample answer: The graph of $y = x^2$ is positive at its rightmost points and leftmost points.

46. REASONING Study the parent graphs at the beginning of this lesson. Select a parent graph with positive y-values at its leftmost points and positive y-values at its rightmost points.

47. WRITING IN MATH Explain why the reflection of the graph of $f(x) = x^2$ in the y-axis is the same as the graph of $f(x) = x^2$. Is this true for all reflections of quadratic equations? If not, describe a case when it is false. **See margin.**

Additional Answer

47. Sample answer: It is not always true. When the axis of symmetry of the parabola is not along the y-axis, the graphs of the preimage and image will be different.

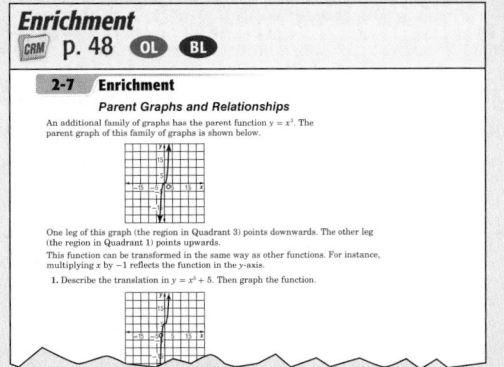

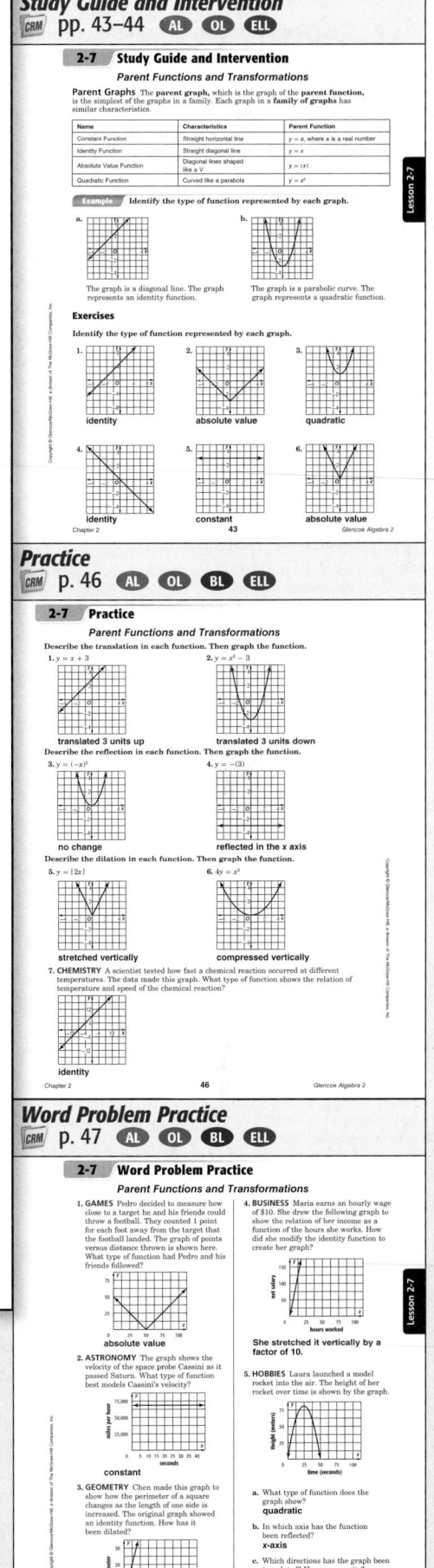

Enrichment
CRM p. 48 OL BL

2-7 Enrichment

Parent Graphs and Relationships

An additional family of graphs has the parent function $y = x^3$. The parent graph of this family of graphs is shown below.

One leg of this graph (the region in Quadrant 3) points downwards. The other leg (the region in Quadrant 1) points upwards.

This function can be transformed in the same way as other functions. For instance, multiplying x by -1 reflects the function in the y-axis.

1. Describe the translation in $y = x^3 + 5$. Then graph the function.

Study Guide and Intervention
CRM pp. 43–44 AL OL ELL

2-7 Study Guide and Intervention

Parent Functions and Transformations

Parent Graphs The **parent graph,** which is the graph of the **parent function,** is the simplest of the graphs in a family. Each graph in a **family of graphs** has similar characteristics.

Name	Characteristics	Parent Function
Constant Function	Straight horizontal line	$y = a$, where a is a real number
Identity Function	Straight diagonal line	$y = x$
Absolute Value Function	Diagonal lines shaped like a V	$y = \|x\|$
Quadratic Function	Curved like a parabola	$y = x^2$

Example Identify the type of function represented by each graph.

a. The graph is a diagonal line. The graph represents an identity function.

b. The graph is a parabolic curve. The graph represents a quadratic function.

Exercises

Identify the type of function represented by each graph.

1. **identity**
2. **absolute value**
3. **quadratic**
4. **identity**
5. **constant**
6. **absolute value**

Chapter 2 43 Glencoe Algebra 2

Lesson 2-7

Practice
CRM p. 46 AL OL BL ELL

2-7 Practice

Parent Functions and Transformations

Describe the translation in each function. Then graph the function.

1. $y = x + 3$ **translated 3 units up**
2. $y = x^2 - 3$ **translated 3 units down**

Describe the reflection in each function. Then graph the function.

3. $y = (-x)^2$ **no change**
4. $y = -(3)$ **reflected in the x axis**

Describe the dilation in each function. Then graph the function.

5. $y = |2x|$ **stretched vertically**
6. $4y = x^2$ **compressed vertically**

7. **CHEMISTRY** A scientist tested how fast a chemical reaction occurred at different temperatures. The data made this graph. What type of function shows the relation of temperature and speed of the chemical reaction? **identity**

Chapter 2 46 Glencoe Algebra 2

Word Problem Practice
CRM p. 47 AL OL BL ELL

2-7 Word Problem Practice

Parent Functions and Transformations

1. **GAMES** Pedro decided to measure how close to a target he and his friends could throw a football. They counted 1 point for each foot away from the target that the football landed. The graph of points versus distance thrown is shown here. What type of function had Pedro and his friends followed? **absolute value**

2. **ASTRONOMY** The graph shows the velocity of the space probe Cassini as it passed Saturn. What type of function best models Cassini's velocity? **constant**

3. **GEOMETRY** Chen made this graph to show how the perimeter of a square changes as the length of one side is increased. The original graph showed an identity function. How has it been dilated? **It has been stretched vertically by a factor of 4.**

4. **BUSINESS** Maria earns an hourly wage of $10. She drew the following graph to show the relation of her income as a function of the hours she works. How did she modify the identity function to create her graph? **She stretched it vertically by a factor of 10.**

5. **HOBBIES** Laura launched a model rocket into the air. The height of her rocket over time is shown by the graph.

a. What type of function does the graph show? **quadratic**

b. In which axis has the function been reflected? **x-axis**

c. Which directions has the graph been translated? How many units? **right 50 units and up 81 units**

d. What is the equation for the curve shown on the graph? **$y = -(x - 50)^2 + 81$**

Chapter 2 47 Glencoe Algebra 2

Lesson 2-7

NGSSS PRACTICE 912.A.3.6, 912.A.5.5, 912.A.2.5

48. What is the solution set of the inequality? **D**

$$6 - |x + 7| \leq -2$$

A. $\{x \mid -15 \leq x \leq 1\}$
B. $\{x \mid x \leq -1 \text{ or } x \geq 3\}$
C. $\{x \mid -1 \leq x \leq 3\}$
D. $\{x \mid x \leq -15 \text{ or } x \geq 1\}$

49. GEOMETRY The measures of two angles of a triangle are x and $4x$. Which of these expressions represents the measure of the third angle? **G**

F. $180 + x + 4x$
G. $180 - x - 4x$
H. $180 - x + 4x$
I. $180 + x - 4x$

50. GRIDDED RESPONSE Find the value of x that makes $\frac{1}{2} = \frac{x-2}{x+2}$ true. **6**

51. ACT/SAT Which could be the equation for the graph? **A**

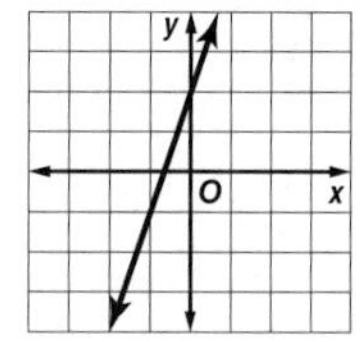

A. $y = 3x + 2$
B. $y = 3x - 2$
C. $y = -3x - 2$
D. $y = -3x + 2$

Spiral Review

Graph each function. Identify the domain and range. (Lesson 2-6) **52–54. See margin.**

52. $f(x) = |x - 3|$

53. $h(x) = [\![x]\!] - 5$

54. $f(x) = \begin{cases} -2x \text{ if } x \leq -2 \\ x \text{ if } -2 < x \leq 1 \\ 4 \text{ if } x > 1 \end{cases}$

55. ATTENDANCE The table shows the annual attendance to West High School's Summer Celebration. (Lesson 2-5)

Year	Attendance
2004	61
2005	83
2006	85
2007	92
2008	97
2009	106

a. Find a regression equation for the data. $y = 7.83x - 15{,}620.70$

b. Determine the correlation coefficient. $r = 0.953$

c. Predict how many people will attend the Summer Celebration in 2010. **about 118 people**

Solve each inequality. (Lesson 1-6)

56. $-12 \leq 2x + 4 \leq 8$ $-8 \leq x \leq 2$

57. $-4 < -3y + 2 < 11$ $2 > y > -3$

58. $|x - 3| > 7$ $x < -4$ or $x > 10$

59. CARS Loren is buying her first car. She is considering 4 different models and 5 different colors. How many different cars could she buy? (Lesson 0-4) **20**

Determine if each relation is a function. (Lesson 0-1)

60. **no**

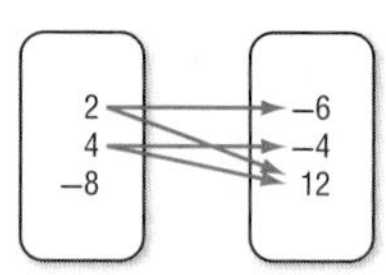

61. **yes**

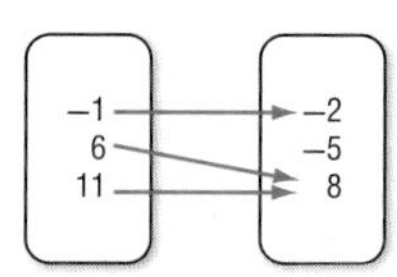

62. **yes**

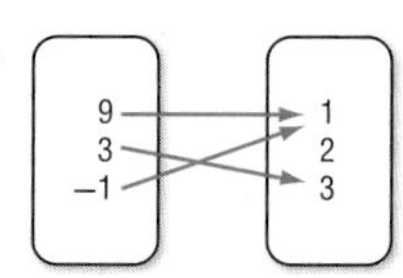

Skills Review

Evaluate each expression if $x = -4$ and $y = 6$. (Lesson 1-1)

63. $4x - 8y + 12$ -52

64. $5y + 3x - 8$ 10

65. $-12x + 10y - 24$ 84

4 ASSESS

Ticket Out the Door Have students write the names of the parent functions on separate slips of paper. Then have them describe the characteristics of one function's graph.

TEACH with TECH

STUDENT RESPONSE SYSTEM Show students a slide show of graphs of different types of functions, and ask them to identify what type of function is shown. Give students a key to use for their responses.

Additional Answers

52.

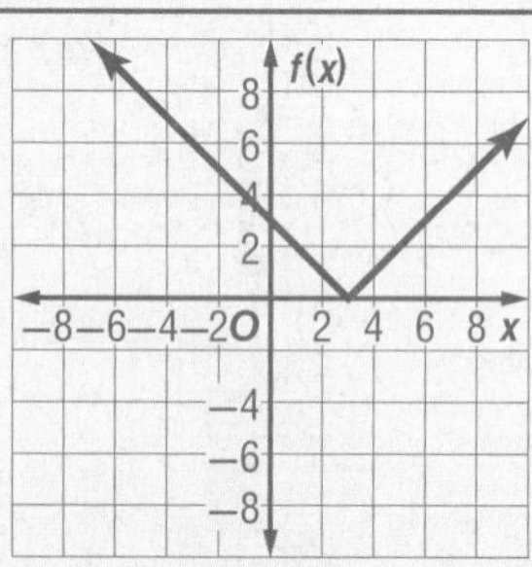

D = {all real numbers}
R = $\{f(x) \mid f(x) \geq 0\}$

53.

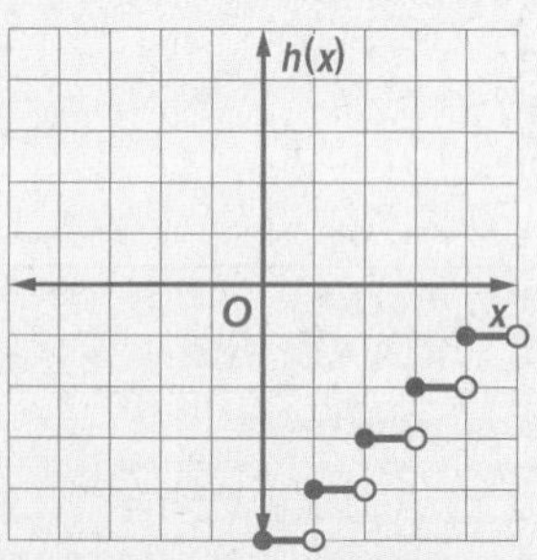

D = {all real numbers}
R = {all integers}

54.

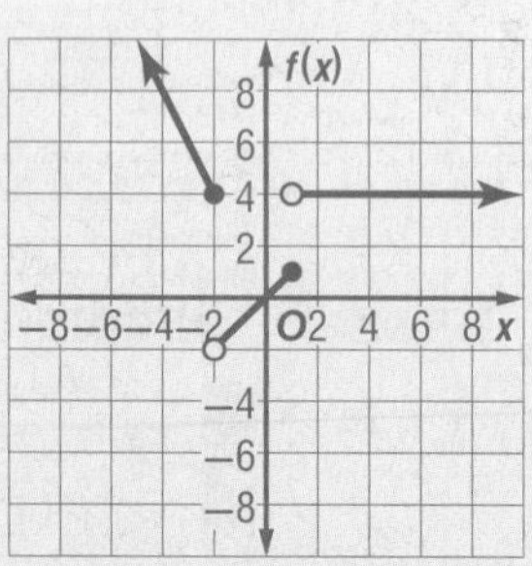

D = {all real numbers}
R = $\{f(x) \mid -2 < f(x) \leq 1$ or $f(x) \geq 4\}$

Differentiated Instruction BL

Extension Ask students to describe how different parent functions could be combined to create more complex functions and to visualize what their graphs might look like. For instance, an absolute value function added to a constant function would exhibit a graph of the absolute value function shifted up or down.

116 Chapter 2 Linear Relations and Functions

2-8 Graphing Linear and Absolute Value Inequalities

Then

You described transformations on functions. (Lesson 2-7)

Now

- Graph linear inequalities.
- Graph absolute value inequalities.

NGSSS

MA.912.A.2.6 Identify and graph common functions (including but not limited to linear, rational, quadratic, cubic, radical, absolute value).
MA.912.A.2.5 Graph absolute value equations and inequalities **in two variables.**

New Vocabulary

linear inequality
boundary

FL Math Online
glencoe.com

Why?

Randy is planning to treat his lacrosse team to a pizza party after the championship game, but he does not want to spend more than \$200.

Randy can use the linear inequality $11p + 2.25d \leq 200$, where p represents the number of pizzas and d represents the number of soft drinks, to check whether certain combinations of pizzas and drinks will fall within his budget.

Graph Linear Inequalities A **linear inequality** resembles a linear equation, but with an inequality symbol instead of an equals symbol. For example, $y > -3x - 2$ is a linear inequality and $y = -3x - 2$ is the related linear equation.

The graph of the inequality $y > -3x - 2$ is shown at the right as a shaded region. Every point in the shaded region satisfies the inequality. The graph of $y = -3x - 2$ is the **boundary** of the region. It is drawn as a dashed line to show that points on the line do not satisfy the inequality. If the symbol were $\leq$ or $\geq$, then points on the boundary would satisfy the inequality, so the boundary would be drawn as a solid line.

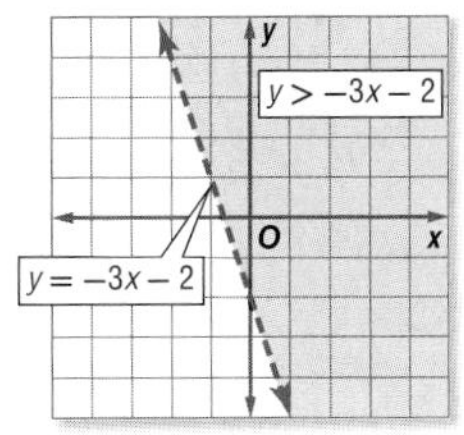

EXAMPLE 1 Dashed Boundary

Graph $x + 4y > 2$.

Step 1 The boundary of the graph is the graph of $x + 4y = 2$. Since the inequality symbol is $>$, the boundary will be dashed.

Step 2 Test the point (0, 0) because it is not on the boundary.

$x + 4y > 2$ **Original inequality**
$0 + 4(0) \overset{?}{>} 2$ **$(x, y) = (0, 0)$**
$0 > 2$ ✗ **False**

The region that does *not* contain (0, 0) is shaded.

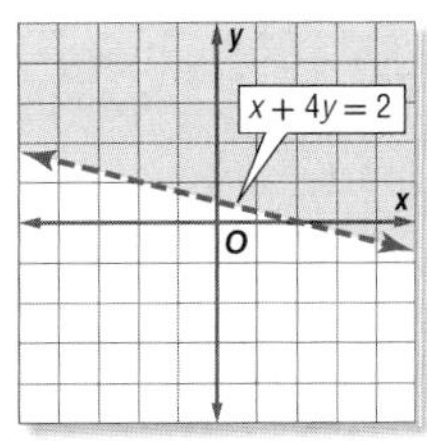

CHECK The graph indicates that (0, 3) is a solution.

$x + 4y > 2$ **Original inequality**
$0 + 4(3) \overset{?}{>} 2$ **$(x, y) = (0, 3)$**
$12 > 2$ ✓ **True**

The solution checks.

Guided Practice 1A, 1B. See Chapter 2 Answer Appendix.

1A. Graph $3x + \frac{1}{2}y < 2$. **1B.** Graph $-x + 2y > 4$.

Personal Tutor glencoe.com

2-8 Lesson Notes

1 FOCUS

Vertical Alignment

Before Lesson 2-8
Describe transformations on functions.

Lesson 2-8
Graph linear and absolute value inequalities.

After Lesson 2-8
Formulate systems of inequalities.

2 TEACH

Scaffolding Questions

Have students read the *Why?* section of the lesson.

Ask:

- Explain what the inequality $11p + 2.25d \leq 200$ means. The number of pizzas times \$11 each plus the number of drinks times \$2.25 each must be less than or equal to \$200.
- Would Randy have enough money to buy 10 large pizzas and 20 drinks? yes
- If Randy bought 15 large pizzas, what is the maximum number of drinks he could buy without spending more than \$200? 15 drinks

Lesson 2-8 Resources

Resource	Approaching-Level	On-Level	Beyond-Level	English Learners
Teacher Edition	• Differentiated Instruction, p. 121	• Differentiated Instruction, p. 121		• Differentiated Instruction, p. 121
Chapter Resource Masters	• Study Guide and Intervention, pp. 50–51 • Skills Practice, p. 52 • Practice, p. 53 • Word Problem Practice, p. 54	• Study Guide and Intervention, pp. 50–51 • Skills Practice, p. 52 • Practice, p. 53 • Word Problem Practice, p. 54 • Enrichment, p. 55	• Practice, p. 53 • Word Problem Practice, p. 54 • Enrichment, p. 55	• Study Guide and Intervention, pp. 50–51 • Skills Practice, p. 52 • Practice, p. 53 • Word Problem Practice, p. 54
Transparencies	• 5-Minute Check Transparency 2-8	• 5-Minute Check Transparency 2-8	• 5-Minute Check Transparency 2-8	• 5-Minute Check Transparency 2-8
Other	• Study Notebook	• Study Notebook	• Study Notebook	• Study Notebook

Graph Linear Inequalities

Example 1 shows how to graph a linear inequality. In **Example 2,** a linear inequality and its graph are used to model and analyze a real-world situation.

Formative Assessment

Use the Guided Practice exercises after each example to determine students' understanding of concepts.

Additional Examples

1 Graph $x - 2y < 4$.

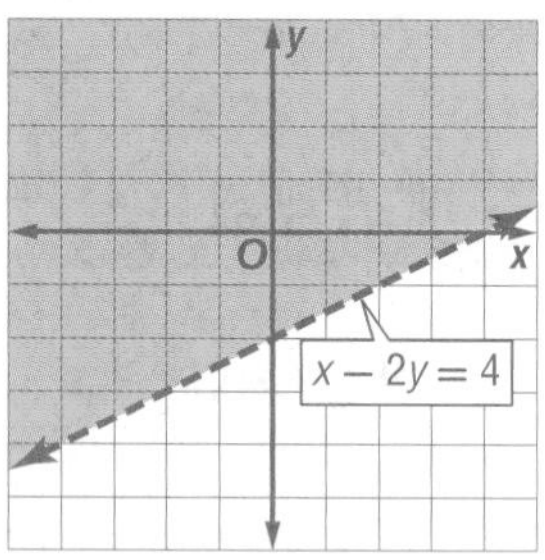

2 **EDUCATION** One tutoring company advertises that it specializes in helping students who have a combined SAT verbal and math score of 900 or less.

a. Write an inequality to describe the combined scores of students who are prospective tutoring clients. Let x represent the verbal score and y the math score. $x + y \le 900$

b. Does a student with a verbal score of 480 and a math score of 410 fit the tutoring company's guidelines? yes

Additional Examples also in Interactive Classroom PowerPoint® Presentations

IWB INTERACTIVE WHITEBOARD READY

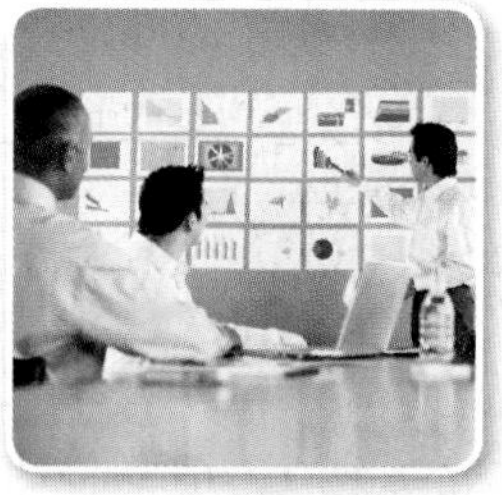

Real-World Career

Recreation Workers Recreation workers plan, organize, and manage recreational activities to meet the needs of a variety of people. Educational requirements range from a high school diploma to a graduate degree.

Real-World EXAMPLE 2 Solid Boundary

RECREATION A recreation center offers various 30-minute and 60-minute art classes. The recreation director has allotted up to 20 hours per week for art classes.

a. Write an inequality to represent the number of classes that can be offered per week. Graph the inequality.

Let x represent the number of 30-minute or $\frac{1}{2}$-hour art classes, and let y represent the number of 60-minute or 1-hour art classes. Because the sum can equal the maximum, the inequality symbol is $\le$, and the boundary is solid. The inequality is $\frac{1}{2}x + y \le 20$.

Step 1 Graph the boundary $\frac{1}{2}x + y = 20$.

Step 2 Test the point (0, 0).

$\frac{1}{2}x + y \le 20$	**Original inequality**
$\frac{1}{2}(0) + (0) \overset{?}{\le} 20$	**(x, y) = (0, 0)**
$0 \le 20$ ✓	**True**

The region that contains (0, 0) is shaded.

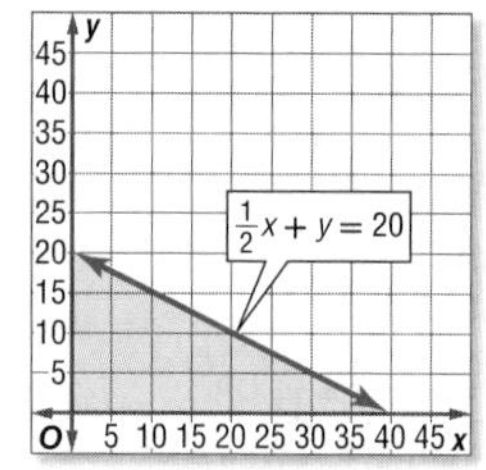

b. Can the recreation director schedule 25 of the 30-minute classes and 15 of the 60-minute classes during a given week? Explain your reasoning.

The point (25, 15) lies outside the shaded region, so it does not satisfy the inequality. Thus, the recreation director cannot schedule 25 30-minute and 15 60-minute classes.

Guided Practice 2. See Chapter 2 Answer Appendix.

2. Manuel has \$15 to spend at the county fair. The fair costs \$5 for admission, \$0.75 for each ride ticket, and \$0.25 for each game ticket. Write an inequality, and draw a graph that represents the number of ride and game tickets that Manuel can buy.

Personal Tutor glencoe.com

Graph Absolute Value Inequalities Graphing absolute value inequalities is similar to graphing linear inequalities. First you graph the absolute value equation. Then you determine whether the boundary is dashed or solid and which region should be shaded.

EXAMPLE 3 Absolute Value Inequality

Graph $y \ge |x| - 4$.

Since the inequality symbol is $\ge$, the boundary is solid. Graph the equation. Then test (0, 0).

$y \ge \lvert x \rvert - 4$	**Original inequality**
$0 \overset{?}{\ge} \lvert 0 \rvert - 4$	**(x, y) = (0, 0)**
$0 \ge -4$ ✓	**True**

The region that includes (0, 0) is shaded.

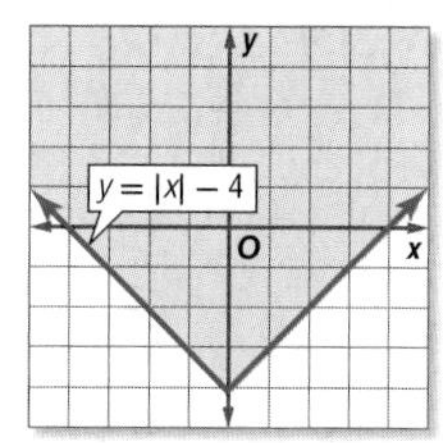

Guided Practice 3A, 3B. See Chapter 2 Answer Appendix.

3A. Graph $y \le 2|x| + 3$.

3B. Graph $y \ge 3|x + 1|$.

Personal Tutor glencoe.com

TEACH with TECH

PORTABLE MEDIA PLAYER Create a video showing your students how to graph absolute value inequalities. Load the video onto your students' portable media players for use as an additional reference outside of class.

Additional Answer

1.

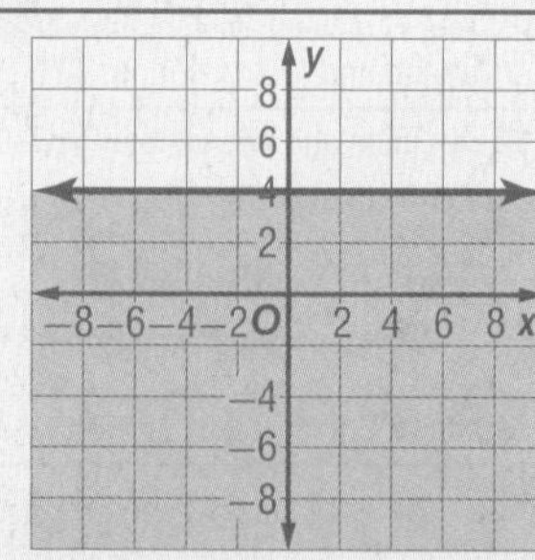

Check Your Understanding

Example 1 p. 117

Graph each inequality. 1–4. See margin.

1. $y \leq 4$
2. $x \geq -6$
3. $x + 4y \leq 2$
4. $3x + y > -8$

Example 2 p. 118

5. **CAR MAINTENANCE** Gregg needs to buy gas and oil for his car. Gas costs \$3.45 a gallon, and oil costs \$2.41 a quart. He has \$50 to spend.
   a. Write an inequality to represent the situation, where g is the number of gallons of gas he buys and q is the number of quarts of oil. $3.45g + 2.41q \leq 50$
   b. Graph the inequality. See Chapter 2 Answer Appendix.
   c. Can Gregg buy 10 gallons of gasoline and 8 quarts of oil? Explain.

5c. No; (10, 8) is not in the shaded region.

Example 3 p. 118

Graph each inequality. 6, 7. See Chapter 2 Answer Appendix.

6. $y \geq |x + 3|$
7. $y - 6 < |x|$

Practice and Problem Solving

● = **Step-by-Step Solutions** begin on page R20. **Extra Practice** begins on page 947.

Example 1 p. 117

Graph each inequality. 8–13. See Chapter 2 Answer Appendix.

8. $x + 2y > 6$
9. $y \geq -3x - 2$
10. $2y + 3 \leq 11$
11. $4x - 3y > 12$
12. $6x + 4y \leq -24$
13. $y \geq \frac{3}{4}x + 6$

Example 2 p. 118

14. **COLLEGE** April's guidance counselor says that she needs a combined score of at least 1700 on her college entrance exams to be eligible for the college of her choice. The highest possible score is 2400—1200 on the math portion and 1200 on the verbal portion.
    a. The inequality $x + y \geq 1700$ represents this situation, where x is the verbal score and y is the math score. Graph this inequality. See Chapter 2 Answer Appendix.
    b. Refer to your graph. If she scores a 680 on the math portion of the test and 910 on the verbal portion of the test, will April be eligible for the college of her choice? no

Example 3 p. 118

Graph each inequality. 15–20. See Chapter 2 Answer Appendix.

15. $y > |3x|$
16. $y + 4 \leq |x - 2|$
17. $y - 6 < |-2x|$
18. $y + 8 < 2\left|\frac{2}{3}x + 6\right|$
19. $2y > |4x - 5|$
20. $-y \leq |3x - 4|$

21. **SCHOOL DANCE** Carlos estimates that he will need to earn at least \$700 to take his girlfriend to the prom. Carlos works two jobs as shown in the table.

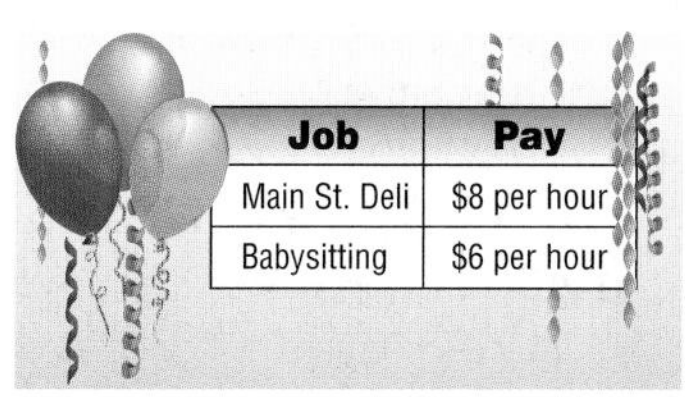

Job	Pay
Main St. Deli	\$8 per hour
Babysitting	\$6 per hour

   a. Write an inequality to represent this situation. $8a + 6b \geq 700$
   b. Graph the inequality. See Chapter 2 Answer Appendix.
   c. Will he make enough working 50 hours at each job? yes

B **Graph each inequality.** 22–26. See Chapter 2 Answer Appendix.

22. $y \geq |-2x - 6|$
23. $y \leq |x - 3| + 4$
24. $y - 3 > -2|x + 4|$
25. $|y| > |x|$
26. $|x - y| > 5$
27. $|x + 3y| \geq -2$

27. all real numbers (The graph would be shaded everywhere.)

Differentiated Homework Options

Level	Assignment	Two-Day Option	
AL Basic	8–21, 33, 35–57	9–21 odd, 38–41,	8–20 even, 33, 35–37, 42–57
OL Core	9–27 odd, 28, 29, 31, 33, 35–57	8–21, 38–41	22–33, 35–37, 42–57
BL Advanced	22–54, (optional: 55–57)		

Graph Absolute Value Inequalities

Example 3 illustrates the graph of an absolute value inequality.

Additional Example

3 Graph $y \geq |x| - 2$.

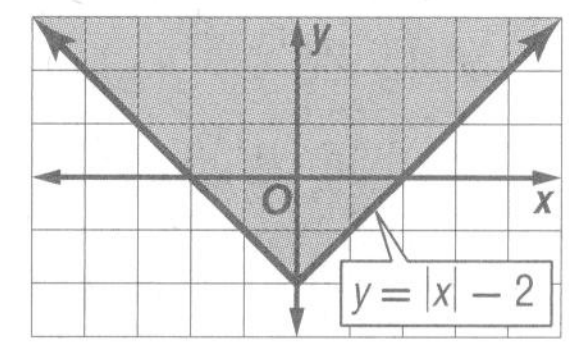

3 PRACTICE

Formative Assessment

Use Exercises 1–7 to check for understanding.

Use the chart on the bottom of this page to customize assignments for your students.

Additional Answers

2.

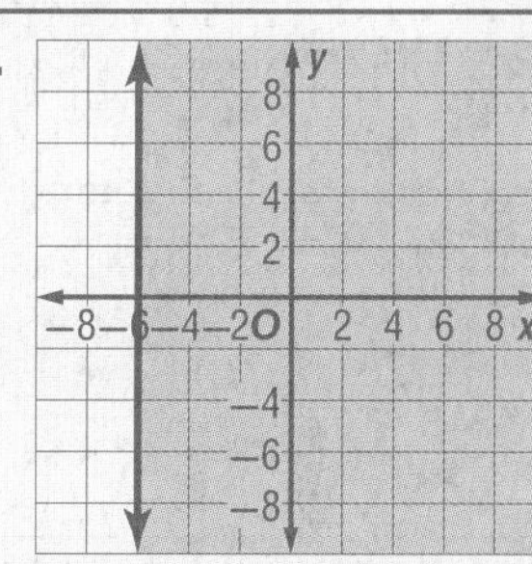

3.

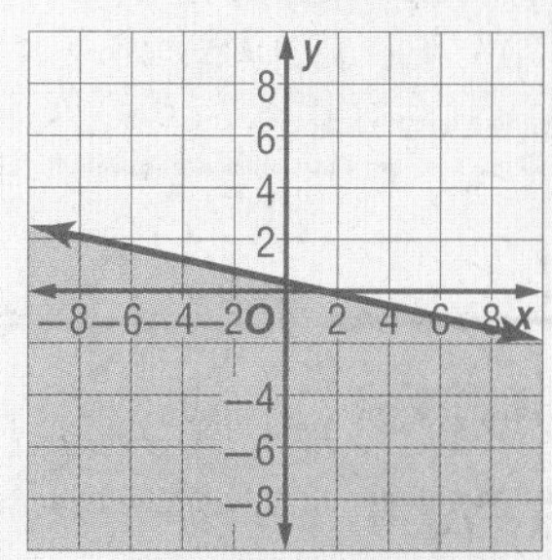

4.

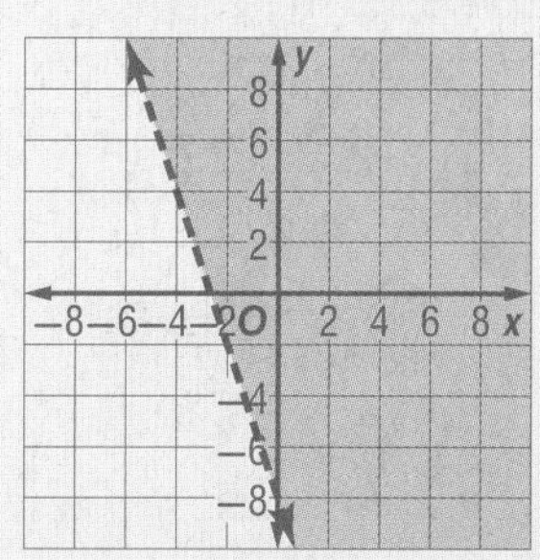

Study Guide and Intervention

CRM pp. 50–51 AL OL ELL

2-8 Study Guide and Intervention

Graphing Linear and Absolute Value Inequalities

Graph Linear Inequalities A **linear inequality**, like $y \geq 2x - 1$, resembles a linear equation, but with an inequality sign instead of an equals sign. The graph of the related linear equation separates the coordinate plane into two half-planes. The line is the boundary of each half-plane.

To graph a linear inequality, follow these steps.

Step 1 Graph the boundary; that is, the related linear equation. If the inequality symbol is $\leq$ or $\geq$, the boundary is solid. If the inequality symbol is $<$ or $>$, the boundary is dashed.

Step 2 Choose a point not on the boundary and test it in the inequality. (0, 0) is a good point to choose if the boundary does not pass through the origin.

Step 3 If a true inequality results, shade the half-plane containing your test point. If a false inequality results, shade the other half-plane.

Example Graph $x + 2y \geq 4$.

The boundary is the graph of $x + 2y = 4$.

Use the slope-intercept form, $y = -\frac{1}{2}x + 2$, to graph the boundary line.

The boundary line should be solid.

Test the point (0, 0).

$0 + 2(0) \overset{?}{\geq} 4$ $(x, y) = (0, 0)$

$0 \geq 4$ false

Shade the region that does *not* contain (0, 0).

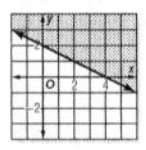

Exercises

Graph each inequality.

1. $y < 3x + 1$
2. $y \geq x - 5$
3. $4x + y \leq -1$
4. $y < \frac{x}{2} - 4$
5. $x + y > 6$
6. $0.5x - 0.25y < 1.5$

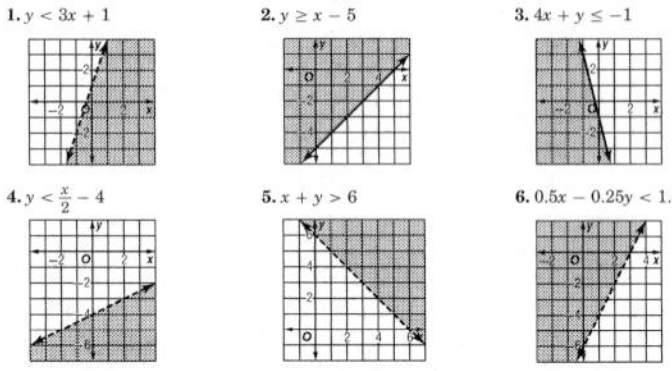

Practice

CRM p. 53 AL OL BL ELL

2-8 Practice

Graphing Linear and Absolute Value Inequalities

Graph each inequality.

1. $y \leq -3$
2. $x > 2$
3. $x + y \leq -4$
4. $y < -3x + 5$
5. $y < \frac{1}{2}x + 3$
6. $y - 1 \geq -x$
7. $x - 3y \leq 6$
8. $y > |x| - 1$
9. $y > -3|x + 1| - 2$

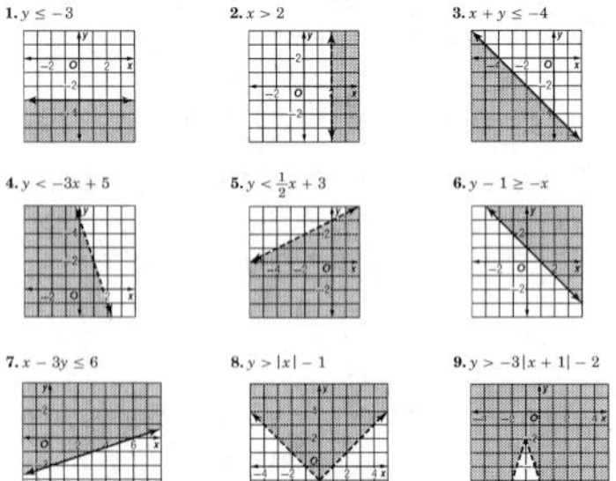

10. **COMPUTERS** A school system is buying new computers. They will buy desktop computers costing \$1000 per unit, and notebook computers costing \$1200 per unit. The total cost of the computers cannot exceed \$80,000.

a. Write an inequality that describes this situation. **$1000d + 1200n \leq 80{,}000$**

b. Graph the inequality.

c. If the school wants to buy 50 of the desktop computers and 25 of the notebook computers, will they have enough money? **yes**

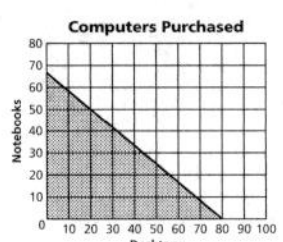

Word Problem Practice

CRM p. 54 AL OL BL ELL

2-8 Word Problem Practice

Graphing Linear and Absolute Value Inequalities

1. **FRAMES** The dimensions of a rectangular frame that can be made from a 50 inch plank of wood are limited by the inequality $\ell + w \leq 25$. Graph this inequality.

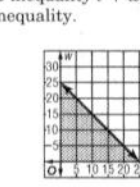

2. **BUILDING CODE** A city has a building code that limits the height of buildings around the central park. The code says that all buildings must be less than $0.1x$ in height where x is the distance of the building from the center of the park. Assume that the park center is located at 0. Graph the inequality that represents the building code.

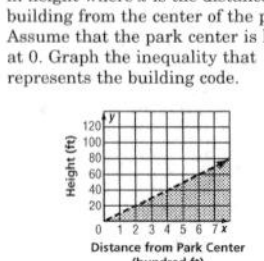

3. **LIVESTOCK** During the winter, a horse requires about 36 liters of water per day and a sheep requires about 3.6 liters per day. A farmer is able to supply his horses and sheep with a total of 300 liters of water each day. Write an inequality that represents the possible number of horses and sheep this farmer can keep.

$36h + 3.6s \leq 300$

4. **WEIGHT** A delivery crew is going to load a truck with tables and chairs. The trucks weight limitations are represented by the inequality $200t + 60c < 1200$, where t is the number of tables and c is the number of chairs. Graph this inequality.

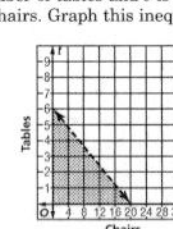

5. **ART** An artist can sell each drawing for \$100 and each painting for \$400. He hopes to make at least \$2000 every month.

a. Write an inequality that expresses how many paintings and/or drawings the artist needs to sell each month to reach his goal.

$100d + 400p \geq 2000$

b. Graph the inequality.

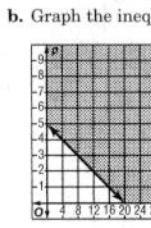

c. If David sells three paintings one month, how many drawings would he have to sell in the same month to reach \$2000?

8

Real-World Link

Making art jewelry is one of the top nine businesses for teen entrepreneurs.

Source: *Entrepreneur Magazine*

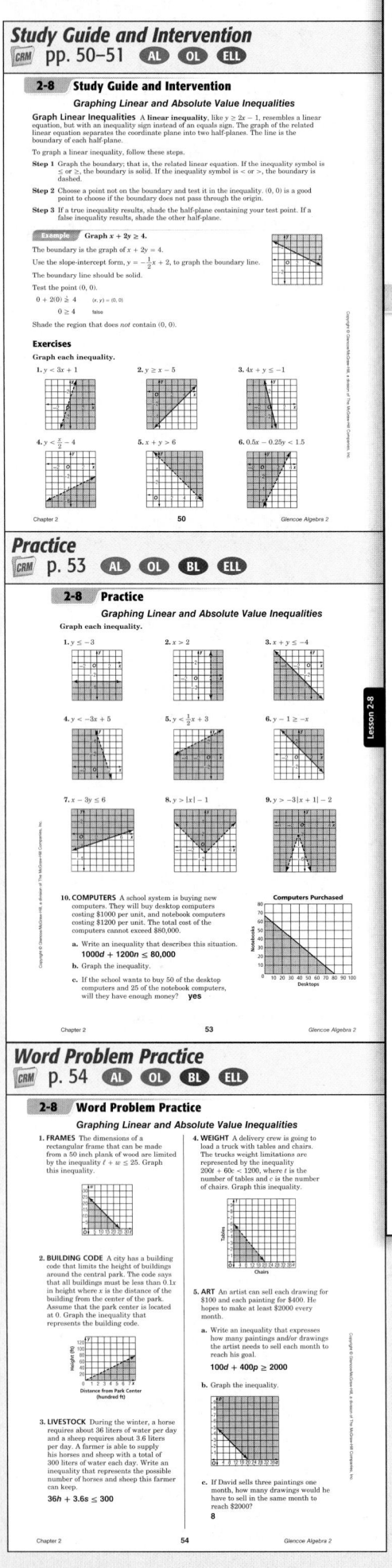

28. **JEWELRY** Mei is making necklaces and bracelets to sell at a craft show. She has enough beads to make 50 pieces. Let x represent the number of bracelets and y represent the number of necklaces.

a. Write an inequality that shows the possible number of necklaces and bracelets Mei can make. **$x + y \leq 50$**

b. Graph the inequality. **See Chapter 2 Answer Appendix.**

c. Give three possible solutions for the number of necklaces and bracelets that can be made.

29. **GIFT CARDS** Susan received a gift card from an electronics store for \$400. She wants to spend the money on DVDs, which cost \$20 each, and CDs, which cost \$15 each.

a. Let d equal the number of DVDs, and let c equal the number of CDs. Write an inequality that shows the possible combinations of DVDs and CDs that Susan can purchase. **$20d + 15c \leq 400$**

b. Graph the inequality. **See Chapter 2 Answer Appendix.**

c. Give three possible solutions for the number of DVDs and CDs she can buy. **Sample answer: 18 CDs and 5 DVDs, 12 CDs and 10 DVDs, or 6 CDs and 15 DVDs**

C **Graph each inequality. 30–32. See Chapter 2 Answer Appendix.**

30. $y \geq [\![x]\!]$
31. $y < [\![x + 2]\!]$
32. $y \geq |[\![x]\!]|$

H.O.T. Problems

Use **H**igher-**O**rder **T**hinking Skills

33. **OPEN ENDED** Create an absolute value inequality in which none of the possible solutions fall in the second or third quadrant. **Sample answer: $|y| < x$**

34. **CHALLENGE** Graph the following inequality. **See margin.**

$$g(x) > \begin{cases} |x + 1| \text{ if } x \leq -4 \\ -|x| \text{ if } -4 < x < 2 \\ |x - 4| \text{ if } x \geq 2 \end{cases}$$

35. **ERROR ANALYSIS** Paulo and Janette are graphing $x - y \geq 2$. Is either of them correct? Explain your reasoning.

Paulo

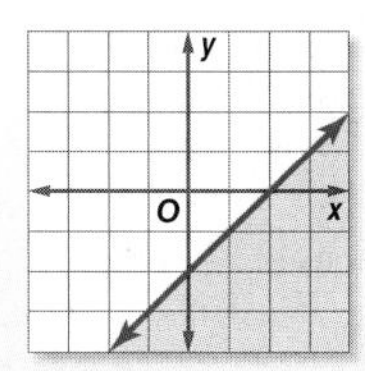

Janette

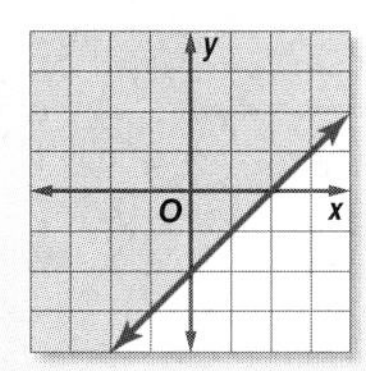

36. **REASONING** When will it be possible to shade two different areas when graphing a linear absolute value inequality? Explain your reasoning.

37. **WRITING IN MATH** Describe a situation in which there are no solutions to an absolute value inequality. Explain your reasoning.

28c. Sample answers: 0 bracelets and 50 necklaces, 25 necklaces and 25 bracelets, or 30 bracelets and 20 necklaces

35. Paulo; $x - y \geq 2$ can be written as $y \leq x - 2$.

36. Sample answer: It will be possible when we have a situation where y and x are both inside an absolute value. An example is $|y| = |x|$. When this happens, positive and negative values of y will need to be considered, as well as the positive and negative values of x.

37. Sample answer: One possibility is when $|y| < 0$. In order for there to be a solution, the absolute value of y will need to be less than 0, and, by definition of absolute value, this is impossible.

Lesson 2-8

Enrichment

CRM p. 55 OL BL

2-8 Enrichment

Limits

The concept of the limit is central to many areas of mathematics, especially to calculus. For example, consider the expression, $3x + 2$. As the value of x approaches 1, the value of the expression approaches 5, as shown in the table below. The process of systematically choosing values closer to 1 and producing values closer to 5 demonstrates finding the limit of the expression.

x	3x + 2
0.900	4.700
0.950	4.850
0.990	4.970
0.999	4.997
0.9999	4.9997

Find the limits for each expression as x approaches the value given.

1. $2x + 2$ as x approaches 5 **12**
2. $x - 5$ as x approaches 11 **6**
3. $\frac{3x + 5}{x - 6}$ as x approaches 1
4. $\frac{5x + 2}{x - 1}$ as x approaches 1

Additional Answer

34.

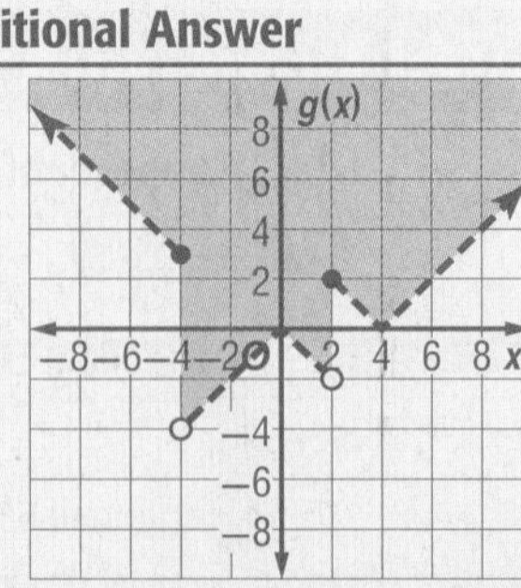

NGSSS PRACTICE 912.A.3.14, 912.A.3.2, 912.G.4.3, 912.A.2.4

38. **EXTENDED RESPONSE** Craig scored 85%, 96%, 79%, and 81% on his first four math tests. He hopes to score high enough on the final test to earn a 90% average. If the final test is worth twice as much as one of the other tests, determine if Craig can earn a 90% average. If so, what score does Craig need to get on the final test to accomplish this? Explain how you found your answer. **See margin.**

39. Which of the following sets of numbers represents an infinite set? **C**

A. {2, 4, 6}

B. {whole numbers between −50 and 50}

C. {integers}

D. $\left\{\frac{1}{2}, \frac{3}{4}, \frac{4}{5}, \frac{5}{6}\right\}$

40. **SHORT RESPONSE** Which theorem of congruence should be used to prove $\triangle ABC \cong \triangle XYZ$? **SAS**

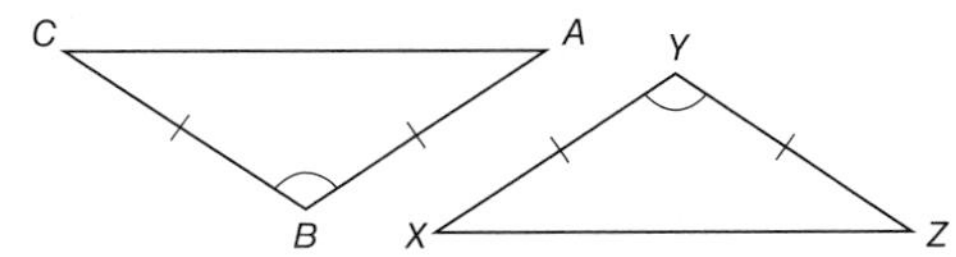

41. **ACT/SAT** For which function is the range $\{f(x) \mid f(x) \leq 0\}$? **J**

F. $f(x) = -x$

G. $f(x) = [\![x]\!]$

H. $f(x) = |x|$

I. $f(x) = -|x|$

Spiral Review

42. $y = (x - 3)^2 - 2$ 43. $y = |x + 4| - 5$ 44. $y = -|x - 2| + 4$

Write an equation for each graph. (Lesson 2-7)

42.

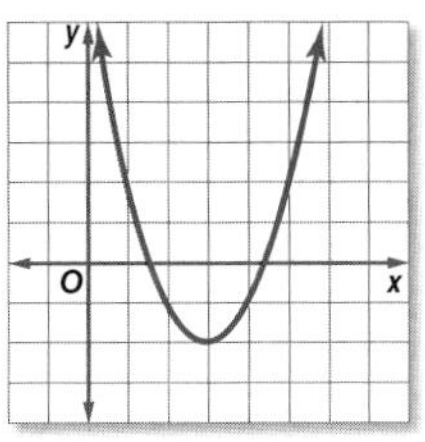

43.

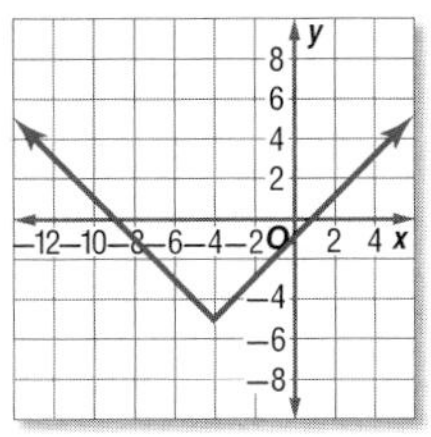

44.

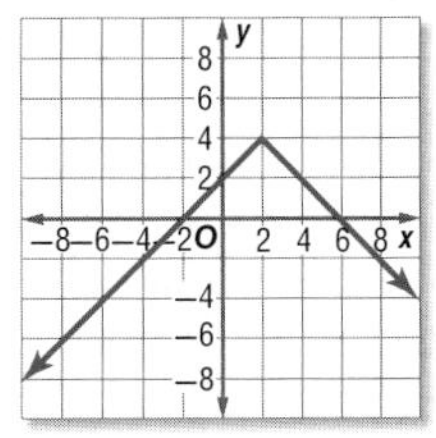

Graph each function. (Lesson 2-6) **45–47. See Chapter 2 Answer Appendix.**

45. $f(x) = \begin{cases} x \text{ if } x < 1 \\ 3 \text{ if } 1 \leq x \leq 3 \\ -2x \text{ if } x > 3 \end{cases}$

46. $f(x) = \begin{cases} x + 3 \text{ if } x < -2 \\ 2x \text{ if } -2 \leq x \leq 2 \\ -3x \text{ if } x > 2 \end{cases}$

47. $f(x) = \begin{cases} -2x \text{ if } x \leq -2 \\ x + 1 \text{ if } 0 < x \leq 6 \\ x - 5 \text{ if } x > 6 \end{cases}$

Write each equation in standard form. Identify *A*, *B*, and *C*. (Lesson 2-2)

48. $-6y = 8x - 3$ **$8x + 6y = 3$; $A = 8$, $B = 6$, $C = 3$**

49. $12y + x = -3y + 5x - 6$ **$4x - 15y = 6$; $A = 4$, $B = -15$, $C = 6$**

50. $\frac{x + 3}{4} + \frac{y - 1}{2} = 3$ **$x + 2y = 11$; $A = 1$, $B = 2$, $C = 11$**

51. **TENNIS** Sixteen players signed up for tennis lessons. The instructor plans to use 50 tennis balls for every player and have 200 extra. How many tennis balls are needed for the lessons? (Lesson 1-3) **1000**

Multiply. (Lesson 0-2)

52. $(3x - 4)(2x + 1)$ **$6x^2 - 5x - 4$**

53. $(6x + 5)(-x - 3)$ **$-6x^2 - 23x - 15$**

54. $(5x + 2)(-2x + 3)$ **$-10x^2 + 11x + 6$**

Skills Review

Graph each linear equation. (Lesson 2-2) **55–57. See Chapter 2 Answer Appendix.**

55. $y = 2x - 8$

56. $y = -\frac{3}{4}x + 2$

57. $3y - 4x = 24$

Differentiated Instruction

AL OL ELL

If students sometimes confuse equations and inequalities,

Then have them discuss the differences and similarities of solving an equation and solving an inequality. Also discuss how the solution processes are the same.

4 ASSESS

Name the Math Have students write how they know when the graph of an inequality has a dashed boundary and when it has a solid boundary.

Watch Out!

Preventing Errors Have students explain how to tell just from looking at an inequality, with *y* isolated on the left of the inequality symbol, whether the shaded area will be below or above the boundary, as well as whether the boundary is solid or dashed. The shaded area of a "less than" inequality is below the boundary, while that of a "greater than" inequality is above the boundary. The boundary is solid if the inequality includes the equality relationship.

Formative Assessment

Check for student understanding of concepts in Lessons 2-7 and 2-8.

CRM Quiz 4, p. 60

Watch Out!

Error Analysis In Exercise 35, students must decide which graph is shaded correctly. Tell students to solve the inequality for *y* before deciding who is correct.

Additional Answer

38. Sample answer: Craig can earn a 90% average by scoring a 99.5% or higher on his last test. This was determined by finding the sum of the first 4 tests. By making each original test worth 100 points, then so far he has 341 out of 400 points. If the last test is worth twice as much, then it is worth 200, so overall he has 600 possible points. In order to earn a 90%, he needs 0.90 • 600 or 540 points. So, Craig needs 540 − 341 or 199 out of 200 on the last test: 99.5%.

Formative Assessment

Key Vocabulary The page references after each word denote where that term was first introduced. If students have difficulty answering questions 1–6, remind them that they can use these page references to refresh their memories about the vocabulary.

Summative Assessment

CRM Vocabulary Test, p. 62

FL Math Online glencoe.com

Vocabulary PuzzleMaker improves students' mathematics vocabulary using four puzzle formats–crossword, scramble, word search using a word list, and word search using clues. Students can work online or from a printed worksheet.

CHAPTER 2 Study Guide and Review

FL Math Online glencoe.com
- STUDY TO GO
- Vocabulary Review

Chapter Summary

Key Concepts

Relations and Functions (Lesson 2-1)

- A function is a relation where each member of the domain is paired with exactly one member of the range.

Linear Equations and Slope (Lessons 2-2 to 2-4)

- Standard Form: $Ax + By = C$, where A, B, and C are integers whose greatest common factor is 1, $A \geq 0$, and A and B are not both zero.
- Slope-Intercept Form: $y = mx + b$
- Point-Slope Form: $y - y_1 = m(x - x_1)$

Scatter Plots and Lines of Regression (Lesson 2-5)

- A prediction equation can be used to predict the value of one of the variables given the value of the other variable.
- A line of regression can be used to model data.

Special Functions and Parent Functions (Lessons 2-6 and 2-7)

- A piecewise-defined function is made up of two or more expressions.
- Translations, reflections, and dilations to a parent graph form a family of graphs.

Graphing Linear and Absolute Value Inequalities (Lesson 2-8)

- You can graph an inequality by following these steps.

  Step 1 Determine whether the boundary is solid or dashed. Graph the boundary.

  Step 2 Choose a point not on the boundary and test it in the inequality.

  Step 3 If a true inequality results, shade the region containing your test point. If a false inequality results, shade the other region.

FOLDABLES® Study Organizer

Be sure the Key Concepts are noted in your Foldable.

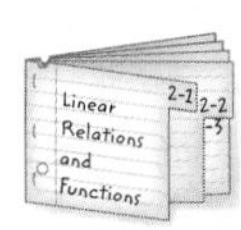

Key Vocabulary

absolute value function (p. 103)
bivariate data (p. 92)
continuous relation (p. 62)
correlation coefficient (p. 94)
dependent variable (p. 64)
dilation (p. 111)
direct variation (p. 90)
discrete relation (p. 62)
family of graphs (p. 109)
greatest integer function (p. 102)
independent variable (p. 64)
linear equation (p. 69)
linear function (p. 69)
linear inequality (p. 117)
line of fit (p. 92)
negative correlation (p. 92)
parent function (p. 109)
piecewise-defined function (p. 101)
point-slope form (p. 84)
positive correlation (p. 92)
prediction equation (p. 92)
quadratic function (p. 109)
rate of change (p. 76)
reflection (p. 111)
regression line (p. 94)
scatter plot (p. 92)
slope (p. 77)
slope-intercept form (p. 83)
standard form (p. 70)
step function (p. 102)
translation (p. 110)
vertical line test (p. 62)

Vocabulary Check

Choose the correct term to complete each sentence.

1. A function is (discrete, one-to-one) if each element of the domain is paired to exactly one unique element of the range.
2. The (domain, range) of a relation is the set of all first coordinates from the ordered pairs which determine the relation.
3. The (constant, identity) function is a linear function described by $f(x) = x$.
4. If you are given the coordinates of two points on a line, you can use the (slope-intercept, point-slope) form to find the equation of the line that passes through them.
5. A set of bivariate data graphed as ordered pairs in a coordinate plane is called a (scatter plot, line of fit).
6. A function that is written using two or more expressions is called a (linear, piecewise) function.

FOLDABLES® Study Organizer

Dinah Zike's Foldables®

Have students look through the chapter to make sure they have included examples in their Foldables.

Suggest that students keep their Foldables handy while completing the Study Guide and Review pages. Point out that their Foldables can serve as a quick review tool when studying for the chapter test.

Lesson-by-Lesson Review

2-1 Relations and Functions (pp. 61–67)

912.A.10.3

State the domain and range of each relation. Then determine whether the relation is a function. If it is a function, determine if it is *one-to-one*, *onto*, *both*, or *neither*. 7–10. See margin.

7. {(1, 2), (3, 4), (5, 6), (7, 8)}
8. {(−3, 0), (0, 2), (2, 4), (4, 5), (5, 2)}
9. {(−4, 1), (3, 3), (1, 1), (−2, 5), (3, −4)}
10. {(7, −4), (5, −2), (3, 0), (1, 2), (−1, 4)}

Find each value if $f(x) = -3x + 2$.

11. $f(4)$ −10
12. $f(-3)$ 11
13. $f(0)$ 2
14. $f(y)$ $-3y + 2$
15. $f(-a)$ $3a + 2$
16. $f(2w)$ $-6w + 2$

17. **BOWLING** A bowling alley charges $2.50 for shoe rental and $3.25 per game bowled. The amount a bowler is charged can be expressed as $y = 2.50 + 3.25x$, when $x \geq 1$, and is an integer. Find the domain and range. Then determine whether the equation is a function. Is the equation discrete or continuous? See margin.

EXAMPLE 1

State the domain and range of the relation {(−4, 3), (−1, 0), (−2, 4), (3, −1), (2, 6)}. Then determine whether the relation is a function. If it is a function, determine if it is *one-to-one*, *onto*, *both*, or *neither*.

Domain: {−4, −1, −2, 3, 2}
Range: {3, 0, 4, −1, 6}

Each element of the domain is paired with one element of the range, so the relation is a function. The function is both because each element of the domain is paired with a unique element of the range and each element of the range is paired with a unique element of the domain.

EXAMPLE 2

Find $f(-2)$ if $f(x) = 4x - 3$.

$f(-2) = 4(-2) - 3$ Substitute −3 for *x*.
$= -8 - 3$ Multiply.
$= -11$ Simplify.

2-2 Linear Relations and Functions (pp. 69–74)

912.A.2.6, 912.A.10.3

19. No; the variables have an exponent other than 1.
20. not linear

State whether each function is a linear function. Write *yes* or *no*. Explain.

18. $3x + 4y = 12$ yes
19. $x^2 + y^2 = 4$
20. $y = x^3 - 6$
21. $y = 6x - 19$ yes
22. $f(x) = -2x + 9$ yes
23. $\frac{1}{x} + 3y = -5$

23. No; *x* appears in a denominator.

Write each equation in standard form. Identify *A*, *B*, and *C*. 25. $12x - y = 0$; 12, −1, 0

24. $2x + 5y = 10$ 2, 5, 10
25. $y = 12x$
26. $-4y = 3x - 24$ 3, 4, 24
27. $4x = 8y - 12$ $x - 2y = -3$; 1, −2, −3

28. **TRAVEL** The distance the Green family traveled during their family vacation is given by the equation $y = 65x$, where x represents the number of hours spent driving. How far does the Green family travel in 8 hours? 520 miles

EXAMPLE 3

State whether $f(x) = 3x^2$ is a linear function. Write *yes* or *no*. Explain.

No, because the expression includes a variable raised to the second power.

EXAMPLE 4

Write the equation $y = -5x + 8$ in standard form. Identify *A*, *B*, and *C*.

$y = -5x + 8$ Original equation
$5x + y = 8$ Add 5*x* to each side.
$A = 5$, $B = 1$, and $C = 8$

Lesson-by-Lesson Review

Intervention If the given examples are not sufficient to review the topics covered by the questions, remind students that the page references tell them where to review that topic in their textbook.

Two-Day Option Have students complete the Lesson-by-Lesson Review on pp. 123–126. Then you can use ExamView® Assessment Suite to customize another review worksheet that practices all the objectives of this chapter or only the objectives on which your students need more help.

Differentiated Instruction

Super DVD: MindJogger Videoquizzes Use this DVD as an alternative format of review for the test.

Additional Answers

7. D = {1, 3, 5, 7}, R = {2, 4, 6, 8}; a function; both
8. D = {−3, 0, 2, 4, 5}, R = {0, 2, 4, 5}; a function; onto
9. D = {−4, −2, 1 3}, R = {−4, 1, 3, 5}; not a function
10. D = {−1, 1, 3, 5, 7}, R = {−4, −2, 0, 2, 4}; a function; both
17. D = {1, 2, 3, 4, 5, . . .}, R = {5.75, 9, 12.25, 15.5, 18.75, . . .}; a function; discrete

Additional Answers

37. $y = 4x + 25$

38. $y = \frac{3}{5}x + \frac{22}{5}$

42.

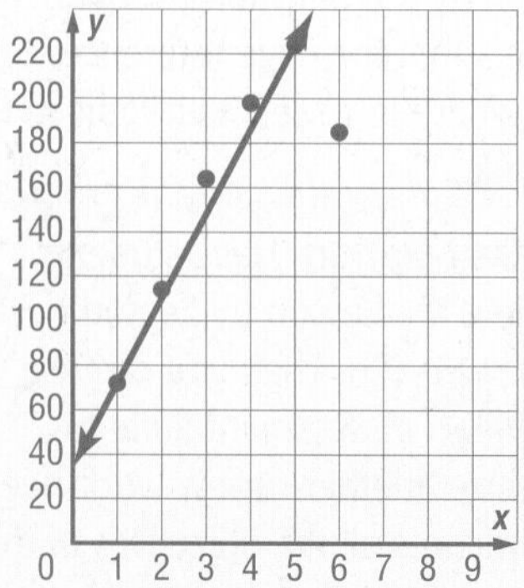

Sample answer: using (1, 72) and (5, 224): $y = 38x + 34$

2-3 Rate of Change and Slope (pp. 76–82)

912.A.10.3

29. **RETAIL** The table shows the number of DVDs sold each week at the Super Movie Store. Find the average rate of change of the number of DVDs sold from week 2 to week 5. 18

Week	1	2	3	4	5
DVDs Sold	76	58	94	83	112

Find the slope of the line that passes through each pair of points.

30. (2, 5), (6, −3) −2

31. (8, 2), (2, 8) −1

32. Determine the rate of change of the graph. 2

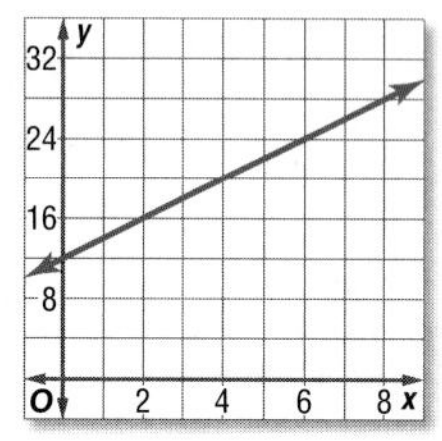

EXAMPLE 5

Find the slope of the line that passes through each pair of points.

a. (−2, 9), (1, 4)

$m = \frac{y_2 - y_1}{x_2 - x_1}$ **Slope Formula**

$= \frac{4 - 9}{1 - (-2)}$ **$(x_1, y_1) = (-2, 9), (x_2, y_2) = (1, 4)$**

$= -\frac{5}{3}$ **Simplify.**

b. (−3, 6), (4, 6)

$m = \frac{y_2 - y_1}{x_2 - x_1}$ **Slope Formula**

$= \frac{6 - 6}{4 - (-3)}$ **$(x_1, y_1) = (-3, 6), (x_2, y_2) = (4, 6)$**

$= \frac{0}{7}$ or 0 **Simplify.**

2-4 Writing Linear Equations (pp. 83–89)

912.A.3.10

Write an equation in slope-intercept form for the line that satisfies each set of conditions.

33. slope −2, passes through (−3, −5) $y = -2x - 11$

34. slope $\frac{2}{3}$, passes through (4, −1) $y = \frac{2}{3}x - \frac{11}{3}$

35. passes through (−2, 4) and (0, 8) $y = 2x + 8$

36. passes through (3, 5) and (−1, 5) $y = 5$

Write an equation of the line passing through each pair of points. 37, 38. See margin.

37. (6, 1), (4, 9)

38. (−4, 2), (6, 8)

Write an equation in slope-intercept form for the line that satisfies each set of conditions.

39. through (1, 2), parallel to $y = 4x - 3$ $y = 4x - 2$

40. through (−3, 5), perpendicular to $y = \frac{2}{3}x - 8$

41. **PETS** Drew paid a $250 fee when he adopted a puppy. The average monthly cost of feeding and caring for the puppy is $32. Write an equation that represents the total cost of adopting and caring for the puppy for x months.

EXAMPLE 6

Write an equation of the line through (−2, 5) and (0, −9).

Find the slope of the line.

$m = \frac{y_2 - y_1}{x_2 - x_1}$ **Slope Formula**

$= \frac{-9 - 5}{0 - (-2)}$ **$(x_1, y_1) = (-2, 5), (x_2, y_2) = (0, -9)$**

$= \frac{-14}{2}$ or −7 **Simplify.**

Write an equation.

$y - y_1 = m(x - x_1)$ **Point-slope form**

$y - 5 = -7(x - (-2))$ **Substitute.**

$y - 5 = -7(x + 2)$ **Simplify.**

$y - 5 = -7x - 14$ **Distributive Property**

$y = -7x - 9$ **Add 5 to each side.**

The equation is $y = -7x - 9$.

40. $y = -\frac{3}{2}x + \frac{1}{2}$ 41. $y = 32x + 250$

MIXED PROBLEM SOLVING
For mixed problem-solving practice, see page 980.

2-5 Scatter Plots and Lines of Regression (pp. 92–98)

912.A.3.11

Make a scatter plot and a line of fit and describe the correlation for each set of data. Then, use two ordered pairs to write a prediction equation.

42. HEATING The table shows the monthly heating cost for a large home. **See margin.**

Month	Sep	Oct	Nov	Dec	Jan	Feb
Bill ($)	72	114	164	198	224	185

43. AMUSEMENT PARK The table shows the annual attendance in thousands at an amusement park during the last 5 years. **See margin.**

Year	1	2	3	4	5
People (thousands)	44	42	39	31	24

EXAMPLE 7

SCHOOL ENROLLMENT The table shows the number of students each year at a school.

Year	'00	'01	'02	'03	'04	'05
Students	125	116	142	154	146	175

Use (2000, 125) and (2005, 175) to find a prediction equation.

$m = \frac{y_2 - y_1}{x_2 - x_1}$ **Slope Formula**

$= \frac{175 - 125}{2005 - 2000}$ **Substitution**

$= \frac{50}{5}$ or 10 **Simplify.**

$y - y_1 = m(x - x_1)$ **Point-slope form**

$y - 125 = 10(x - 2000)$ **Substitution**

$y - 125 = 10x - 20{,}000$ **Distributive Property**

$y = 10x - 19{,}875$ **Add 125 to each side.**

2-6 Special Functions (pp. 101–107)

912.A.2.5, 912.A.2.9

Graph each function. Identify the domain and range. **44–46. See margin.**

44. $f(x) = \begin{cases} -2x \text{ if } x \leq -1 \\ x + 1 \text{ if } -1 < x < 3 \\ x \text{ if } x \geq 3 \end{cases}$

45. $f(x) = \begin{cases} -3 \text{ if } x < -1 \\ 4x - 3 \text{ if } -1 \leq x \leq 3 \\ x \text{ if } x > 3 \end{cases}$

46. Write the piecewise function shown in the graph.

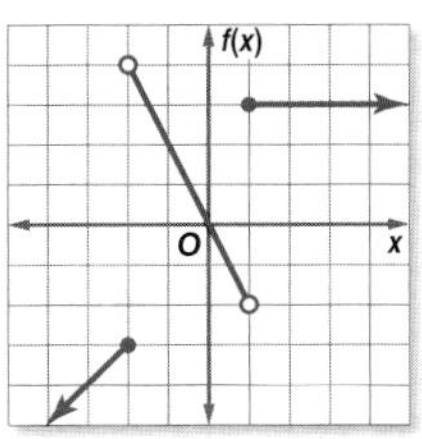

Graph each function. Identify the domain and range. **47, 48. See margin.**

47. $f(x) = [\![x]\!] + 2$

48. $f(x) = [\![x + 3]\!]$

EXAMPLE 8

Write the piecewise function shown in the graph.

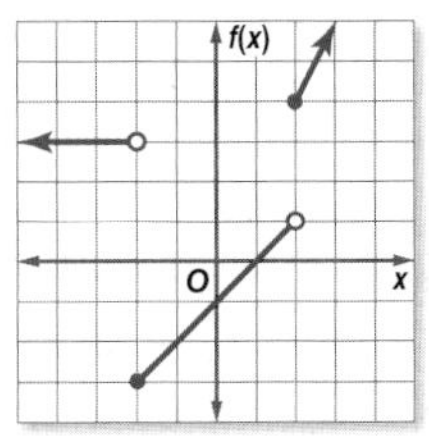

The left portion of the graph is the graph of $f(x) = 3$. There is a circle at $(-2, 3)$, so the linear function is defined for $x < -2$.

The center portion of the graph is the graph of $f(x) = x - 1$. There is a dot at $(-2, -3)$ and a circle at $(2, 1)$, so the linear function is defined for $-2 \leq x < 2$.

The right portion of the graph is the graph of $f(x) = 2x$. There is a dot at $(2, 4)$, so the linear function is defined for $x \geq 2$.

$f(x) = \begin{cases} 3 \text{ if } x < -2 \\ x - 1 \text{ if } -2 \leq x < 2 \\ 2x \text{ if } x \geq 2 \end{cases}$

Additional Answers

44.

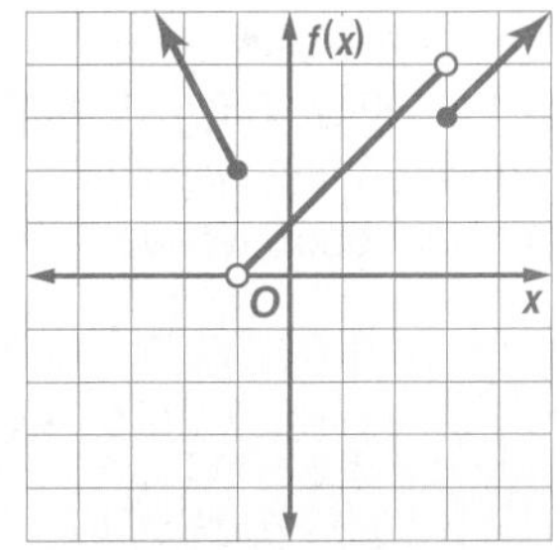

D = {all real numbers};
R = $\{f(x) \mid f(x) > 0\}$

45.

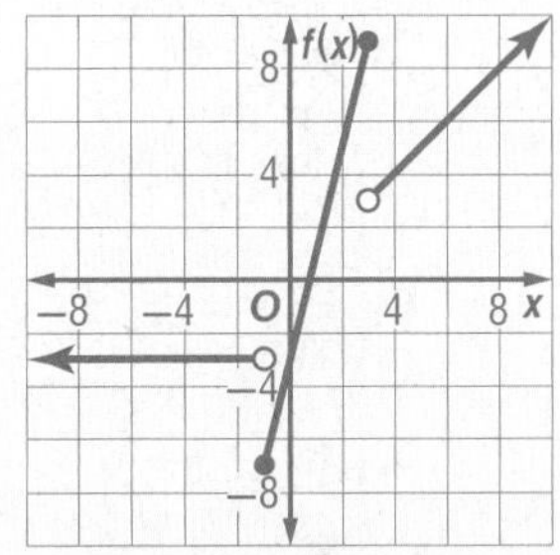

D = {all real numbers};
R = $\{f(x) \mid f(x) \geq -7\}$

46. $f(x) = \begin{cases} x - 1 \text{ if } x \leq -2 \\ -2x \text{ if } -2 < x < 1 \\ 3 \text{ if } x \geq 1 \end{cases}$

47.

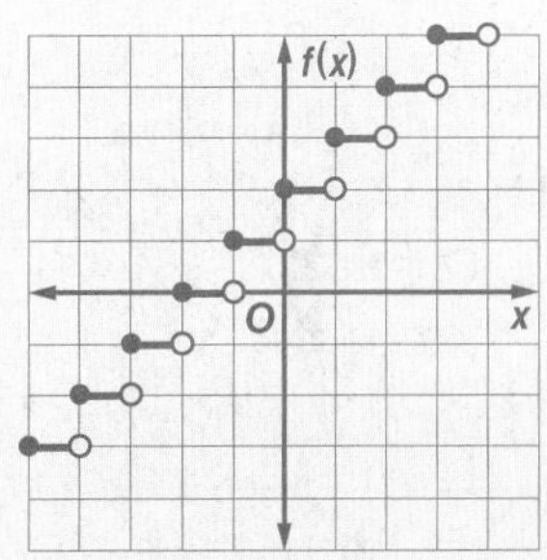

D = {all real numbers};
R = {all integers}

48.

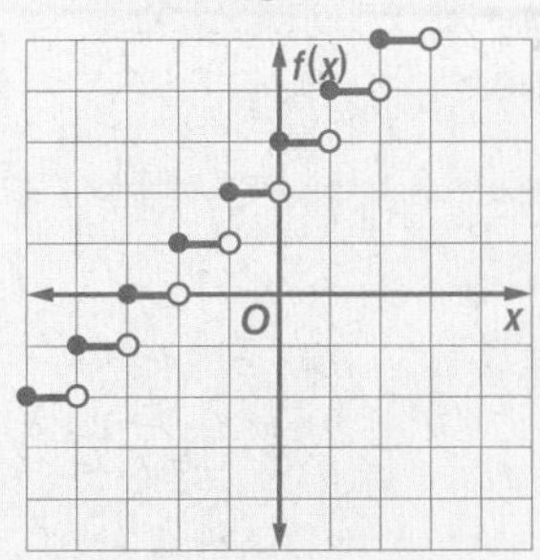

D = {all real numbers};
R = {all integers}

43.

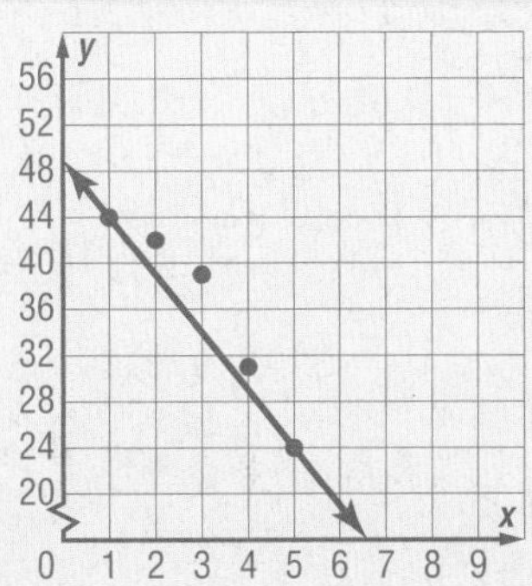

Sample answer using (1, 44) and (5, 24): $y = -5x + 49$

Problem Solving Review

For additional practice in problem solving for Chapter 2, see the Mixed Problem Solving Appendix, p. 981, in the Student Handbook section.

Additional Answers

54.

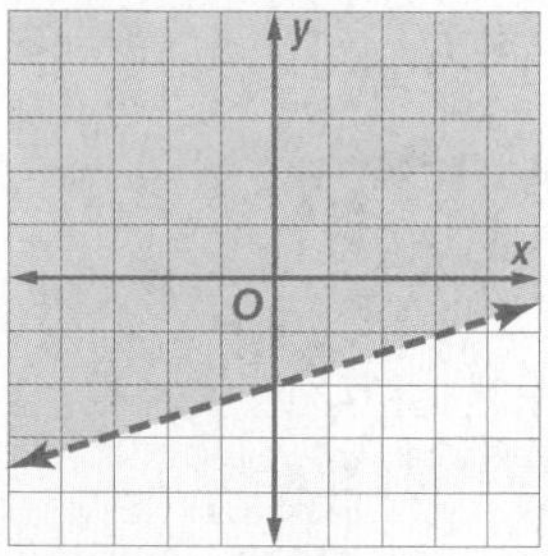

55.

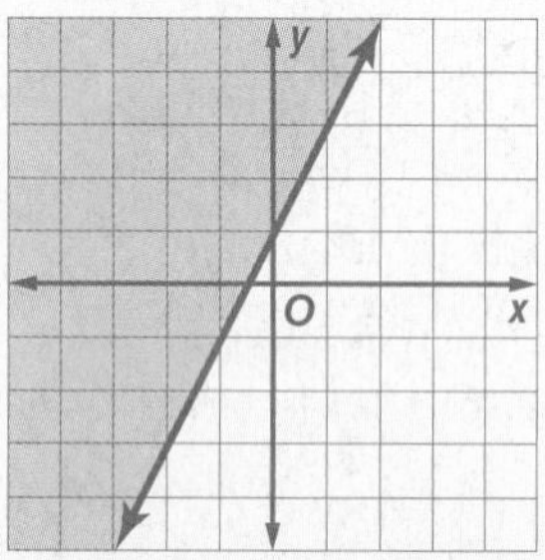

56.

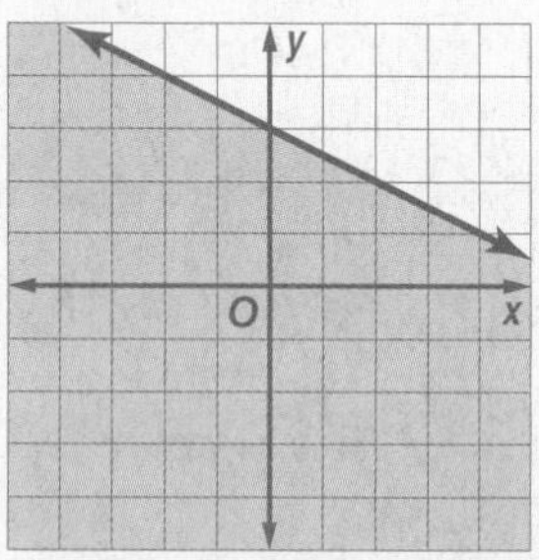

57.

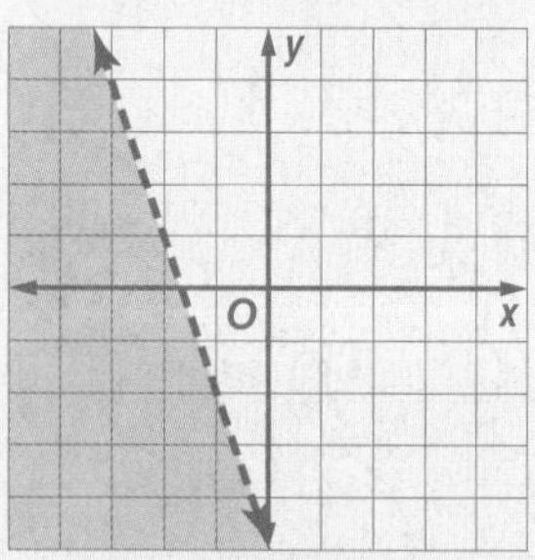

58.

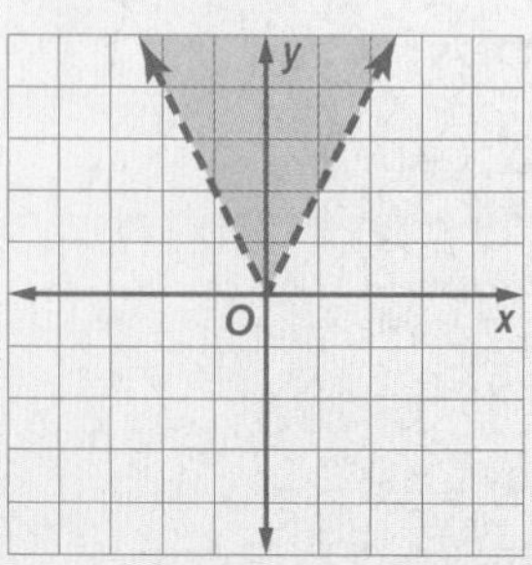

CHAPTER 2 Study Guide and Review

2-7 Parent Functions and Transformations (pp. 109–116)

912.A.2.5, 912.A.2.10

Identify the type of function represented by each graph.

49.

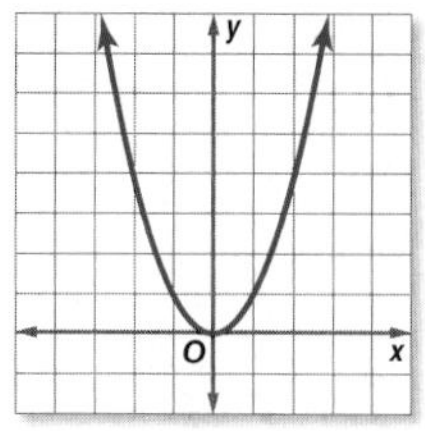

quadratic

50.

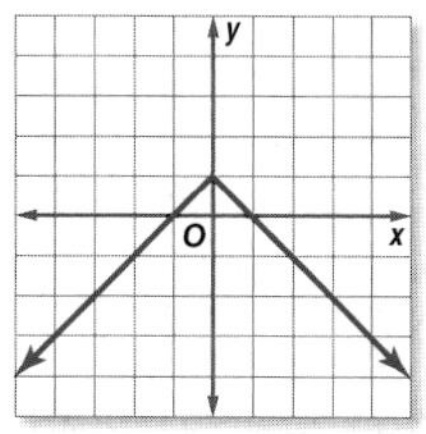

absolute value

51. $y = x^2$ shifted down 3 units

52. $y = x^2$ reflected over the x-axis

51. Describe the translation in $y = x^2 - 3$.

52. Describe the reflection in $y = -x^2$.

53. **CONSTRUCTION** A large arch is being constructed at the entrance of a new city hall building. The shape of the arch resembles the graph of the function $f(x) = -0.025x^2 + 3.64x - 0.038$. Describe the shape of the arch. parabola

EXAMPLE 9

Identify the type of function represented by the graph.

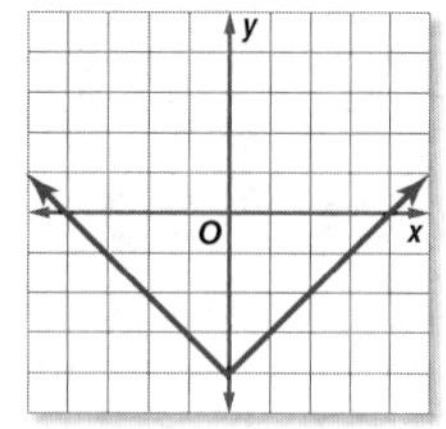

The graph is in the shape of a V. The graph represents an absolute value function.

EXAMPLE 10

Describe the translation in $y = |x + 6|$.

The graph of $y = |x + 6|$ is a translation of the graph of $y = |x|$ 6 units left.

2-8 Graphing Linear and Absolute Value Inequalities (pp. 117–121)

912.A.2.6, 912.A.2.5

Graph each inequality. 54–61. See margin.

54. $x - 3y < 6$	55. $y \geq 2x + 1$
56. $2x + 4y \leq 12$	57. $y < -3x - 5$
58. $y > \|2x\|$	59. $y \geq \|2x - 2\|$
60. $y + 3 < \|x + 1\|$	61. $2y \leq \|x - 3\|$

62. **BOOKS** Spencer has saved \$96 for a trip to his favorite bookstore. Each paperback book costs \$8 and each hardback book costs \$12. Write and graph an inequality that shows the number of paperback books and hardback books Spencer can purchase. $8x + 12y \leq 96$; See Chapter 2 Answer Appendix.

EXAMPLE 11

Graph $x - 2y > 6$.

Since the inequality symbol is >, the graph of the boundary line should be dashed. Graph $x - 2y = 6$.

Test $x - 2y > 6$ at (0, 0).

$$x - 2y > 6$$
$$0 - 2(0) \stackrel{?}{>} 6$$
$$0 > 6 \; ✗$$

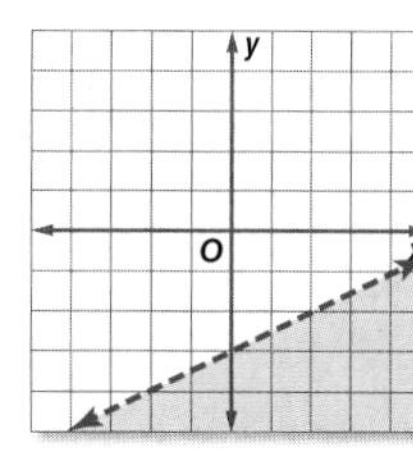

59.

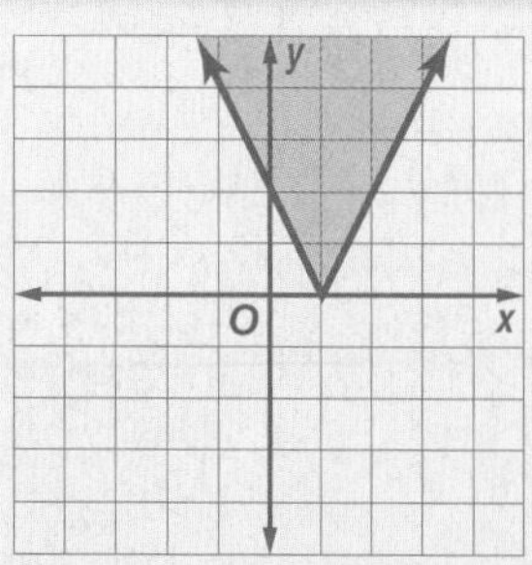

60.

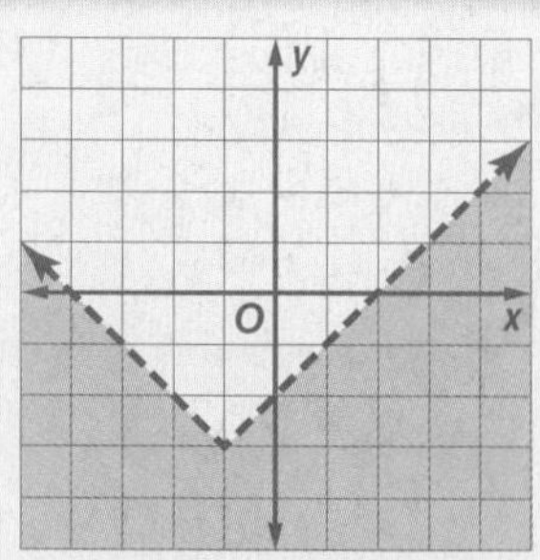

61.

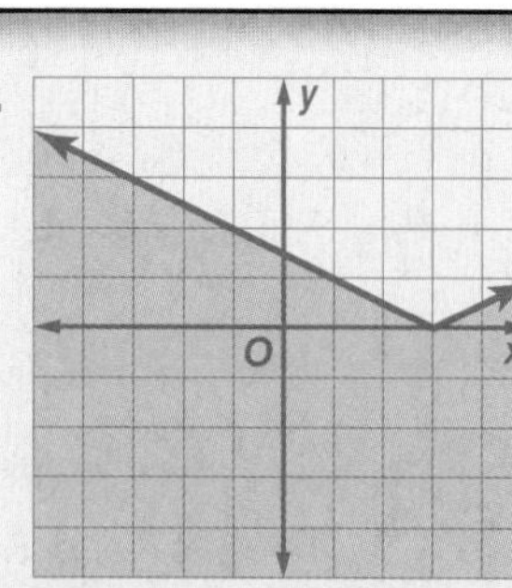

FL Math Online glencoe.com

1. State the domain and range of the relation shown in the table. Then determine if it is a function. If it is a function, determine if it is *one-to-one*, *onto*, *both*, or *neither*. D = {−2, 4, 3, 6}; R = {3, −1, 2}; onto

x	y
−2	3
4	−1
3	2
6	3

Find each value if $f(x) = -2x + 3$.

2. $f(-4)$ 11

3. $f(3y)$ $-6y + 3$

4. Write $2y = -6x + 4$ in standard form. Identify *A*, *B* and *C*. $6x + 2y = 4$; 6, 2, 4

5. Find the *x*-intercept and the *y*-intercept for $3x - 4y = -24$. (−8, 0), (0, 6)

6. **NGSSS PRACTICE** The cost of producing *x* pumpkin pies at a small bakery is given by $C(x) = 49 + 1.75x$. Find the cost of producing 25 pies. C

A. \$74.00

B. \$81.50

C. \$92.75

D. \$108.25

Find the slope of the line that passes through each pair of points.

7. (1, 6), (3, 10) 2

8. (−2, 7), (3, −1) $-\frac{8}{5}$

9. **NGSSS PRACTICE** Find the equation of the line that passes through (0, −3) and (4, 1). H

F. $y = -x + 3$

G. $y = -x - 3$

H. $y = x - 3$

I. $y = x + 3$

10. Write an equation in slope-intercept form for the line that has slope −2 and passes through the point (3, −4). $y = -2x + 2$

11. Write an equation of the line that passes through the points (2, −4) and (1, 6). $y = -10x + 16$

12. Write an equation in slope-intercept form for the line that passes through (−3, 5) and is parallel to $y = -6x + 1$. $y = -6x - 13$

13. **EMERGENCY ROOM** **A hospital tracks the number of emergency room visits during the fall and winter months.** a. See margin.

Month	Oct	Nov	Dec	Jan	Feb
Visits	124	163	155	171	192

a. Make a scatter plot and describe the correlation.

b. Use two ordered pairs to write a prediction equation. $y = 17x + 107$

c. Use your prediction equation to predict the number of emergency room visits for March. 209

14. Graph $f(x) = \begin{cases} -x \text{ if } x < -2 \\ x + 2 \text{ if } -2 \le x \le 2 \\ 5 \text{ if } x > 2 \end{cases}$. See margin.

15. Write the piecewise function shown. See margin.

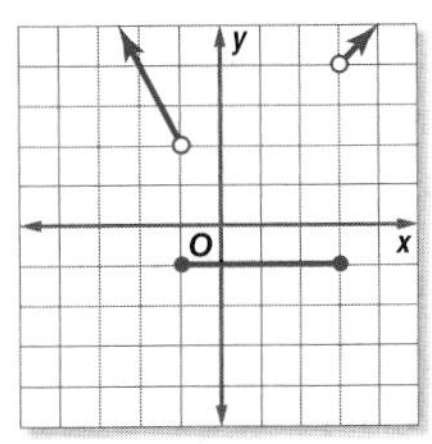

16. Identify the domain and range of $y = [\![x]\!] + 2$. D = {all real numbers}; R = {all integers}

17. Describe the translation to $y = x^2 + 5$. $y = x^2$ shifted 5 units up

18. Describe the reflection in $y = -|x|$. over the *x*-axis

Graph each inequality. 19, 20. See Chapter 2 Answer Appendix.

19. $y \ge 4x - 1$

20. $2x + 6y < -12$

CHAPTER 2 Practice Test

ExamView® Assessment Suite Customize and create multiple versions of your chapter test and their answer keys. All of the questions from the leveled chapter tests in the *Chapter 2 Resource Masters* are also available on ExamView® Assessment Suite.

Additional Answers

13a.

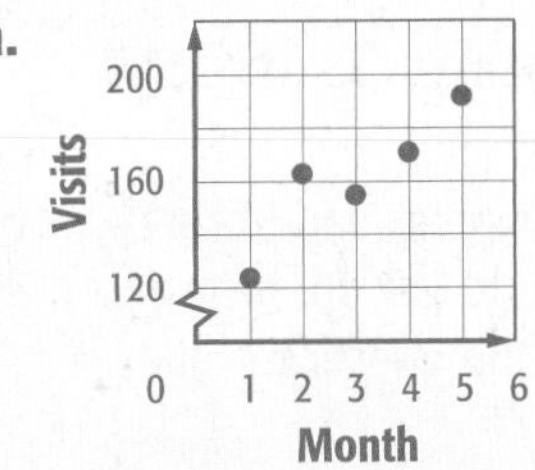

positive correlation

14.

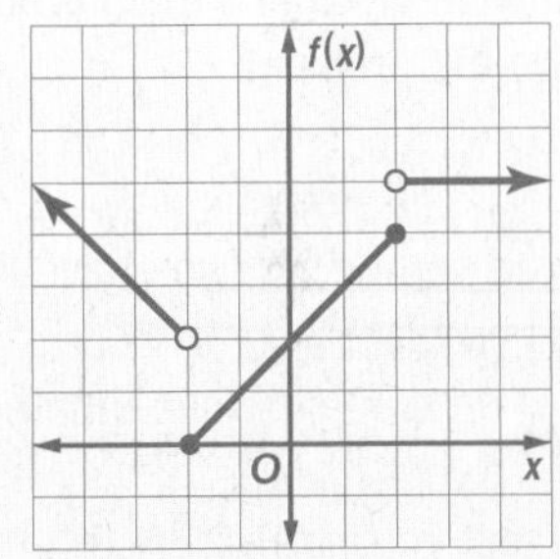

15. $y = \begin{cases} -2x \text{ if } x < -1 \\ -1 \text{ if } -1 \le x \le 3 \\ x + 1 \text{ if } x > 3 \end{cases}$

Intervention Planner

Tier 1 **On Level**	Tier 2 **Strategic Intervention** approaching grade level	Tier 3 **Intensive Intervention** 2 or more grades below level
If students miss about 25% of the exercises or less,	**If** students miss about 50% of the exercises,	**If** students miss about 75% of the exercises,
Then choose a resource: **SE** Lessons 2-1, 2-2, 2-3, 2-4, 2-5, 2-6, 2-7, and 2-8 **CRM** Skills Practice, pp. 7, 13, 19, 25, 32, 38, 45, 52 **TE** Chapter Project, p. 58 FL Math Online Self-Check Quiz	**Then** choose a resource: **CRM** Study Guide and Intervention, Chapter 2, pp. 5, 11, 17, 23, 30, 36, 43, 50 FL Math Online Extra Examples, Personal Tutor, Homework Help	**Then** use *Math Triumphs, Alg. 2*, Ch. 1 and 3 FL Math Online Extra Examples, Personal Tutor, Homework Help, Review Vocabulary

1 FOCUS

Objective Use the strategy of reading math problems to solve standardized test problems.

2 TEACH

Scaffolding Questions

Ask:

- Have you ever had to reread a math problem to get the facts you need to answer the question? Answers will vary.
- Will you always use all the information given in a math problem to solve the problem? Answers will vary. Sample answer: No, there is often extra information given.
- How can you be sure you have the correct answer? Answers will vary. Sample answer: quickly estimate and compare your answer to the estimate; check that your answer has the correct units of measure.

CHAPTER 2 Preparing for Standardized Tests

Reading Math Problems

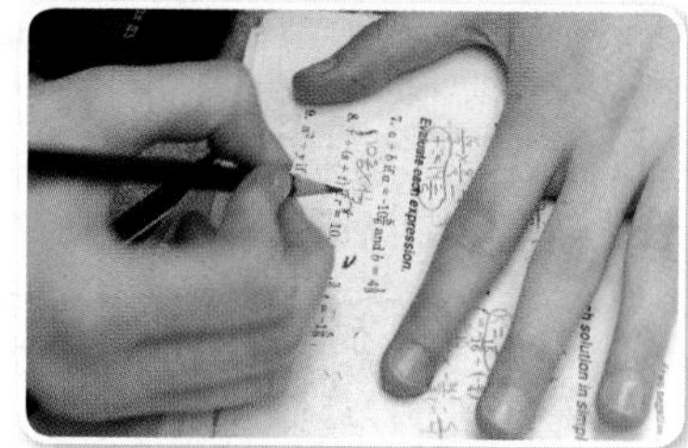

The first step to solving any math problem is to read the problem. When reading a math problem to get the information you need to solve, it is helpful to use special reading strategies.

Strategies for Reading Math Problems

Step 1

Read the problem quickly to gain a general understanding of it.

- **Ask yourself:** "What do I know?" "What do I need to find out?"
- **Think:** "Is there enough information to solve the problem? Is there extra information?"
- **Highlight:** If you are allowed to write in your test booklet, underline or highlight important information. Cross out any information you do not need.

Step 2

Reread the problem to identify relevant facts.

- **Analyze:** Determine how the facts are related.
- **Key Words:** Look for key words to solve the problem.
- **Vocabulary:** Identify mathematical terms. Think about the concepts and how they are related.
- **Plan:** Make a plan to solve the problem.
- **Estimate:** Quickly estimate the answer.

Step 3

Identify any obvious wrong answers.

- **Eliminate:** Eliminate any choices that are very different from your estimate.
- **Units of Measure:** Identify choices that are possible answers based on the units of measure in the question. For example, if the question asks for area, only answers in square units will work.

Step 4

Look back after solving the problem.

Check: Make sure you have answered the question.

128 Chapter 2 Linear Relations and Functions

NGSSS PRACTICE EXAMPLE

Read the problem. Identify what you need to know. Then use the information in the problem to solve.

Sandy heated a solution over a burner and then removed it from the heat source. The temperature of the solution decreased linearly as it cooled. The temperatures after 0, 2, 5, and 9 minutes are shown in the table. What is the rate of change in the temperature of the solution as it cools?

Time (min)	Temperature (°C)
0	133.2
2	130.4
5	126.2
9	120.6

A. −1.4 degrees per minute
B. −0.8 degrees per minute
C. 0.8 degrees per minute
D. 1.4 degrees per minute

Read the problem carefully. There is extra information in the problem. To determine the slope, you only need information from two points on the linear function. Use two of the points to find the slope.

$$m = \frac{130.4 - 133.2}{2 - 0} = -1.4$$

The correct answer is A.

Exercises

Read each question. Then fill in the correct answer on the answer document provided by your teacher or on a sheet of paper.

1. The graph shows the cost of shipping packages. How much would it cost to ship a package that weighs 2 pounds 8 ounces? B

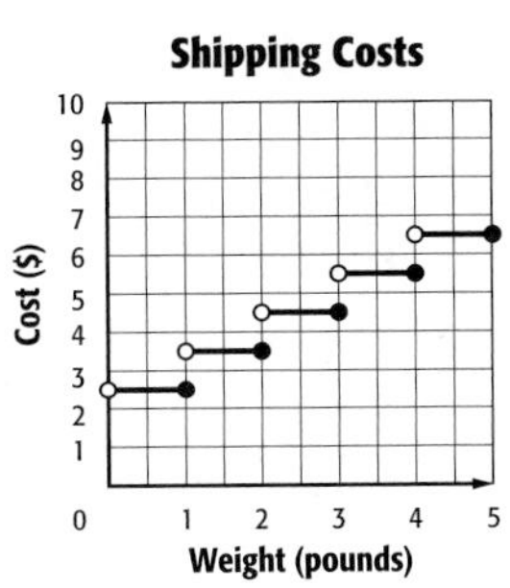

A. $3.50
B. $4.50
C. $5.00
D. $5.50

2. What is the slope of the line shown in the graph? I

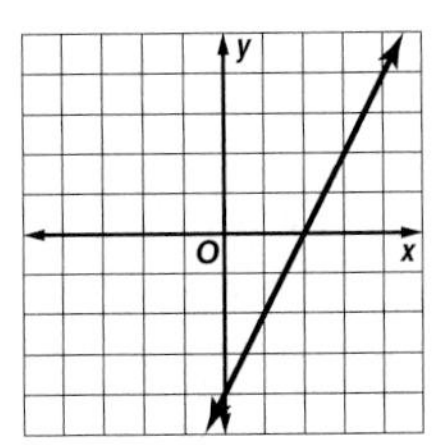

F. −2
G. $-\frac{1}{2}$
H. $\frac{1}{2}$
I. 2

Additional Example

STANDARDIZED TEST PRACTICE
The number of cups of milk in a pitcher decreases linearly as it is poured. The graph below shows the number of cups of milk remaining in the pitcher as the milk is being poured. At what rate is the milk being poured? C

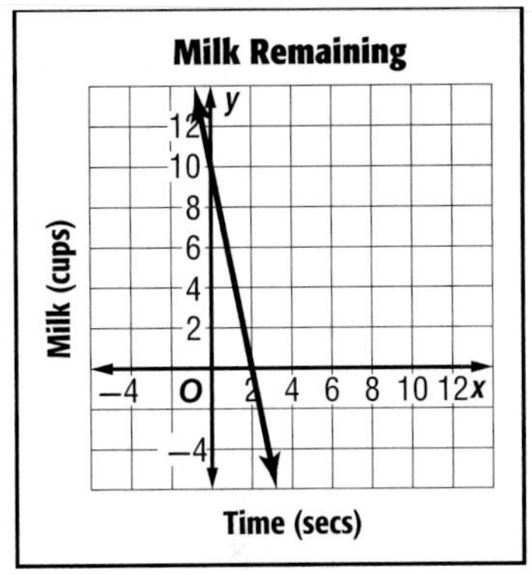

A 2 cups/min
B 2 sec/cup
C 5 cups/sec
D 10 cups/sec

3 ASSESS

Use Exercises 1 and 2 to assess students' understanding.

Diagnose Student Errors

Survey student responses for each item. Class trends may indicate common errors and misconceptions.

1. A. these are the positive values
   B. these are the values in the range
   C. correct
   D. these are the negative values
2. F. correct
   G. guess
   H. does not know which value is the value of the slope
   I. does not know that the slope of perpendicular lines are opposite reciprocals of each other
3. A. correct
   B. found the reciprocal of the slope
   C. found the inverse of the reciprocal of the slope
   D. simplified incorrectly
6. F. incorrectly divided 32 by 4
   G. correct
   H. incorrectly solved absolute value equation for case where expression inside the absolute value symbols is negative
   I. incorrectly solved absolute value equation for case where expression inside the absolute value bars is positive
9. A. guess
   B. did not identify 450 as a constant
   C. correct
   D. changed % to a decimal incorrectly
10. F. did not solve for the case in which the value inside the absolute value symbols is negative
    G. correct
    H. incorrectly solved for the case in which the value inside the absolute value symbols is positive
    I. guess
12. A. did not include the first 100 messages
    B. guess
    C. correct
    D. rounded the value up
14. F. incorrectly subtracted the years
    G. correct
    H. found only the difference in the values of the home
    I. guess

CHAPTER 2 NGSSS Practice

Cumulative, Chapters 1 and 2

Read each question. Then fill in the correct answer on the answer document provided by your teacher or on a sheet of paper.

1. What is the domain of the relation shown below? C

x	y
−3	4
1	−1
2	0
6	−3

A. {0, 1, 2, 4, 6}

B. {−3, −1, 0, 4}

C. {−3, 1, 2, 6}

D. {−3, −1}

2. Given $y = 2.24x + 16.45$, which statement best describes the effect of decreasing the y-intercept by 20.25? F

F. The x-intercept increases.

G. The y-intercept increases.

H. The new line has a greater rate of change.

I. The new line is perpendicular to the original.

3. What is the slope of the line? A

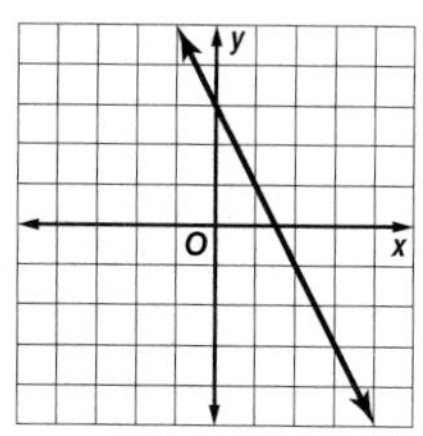

A. −2

B. $-\frac{1}{2}$

C. $\frac{1}{2}$

D. 2

Test-TakingTip

Question 3 Since the graph slopes downward from left to right, you know the slope is negative. So, answer choices C and D can be eliminated.

4. **GRIDDED RESPONSE** Evaluate the piecewise function shown in Exercise 8 for $x = -3$. 1

5. **SHORT RESPONSE** The graph of the absolute value parent function is shown below. a. $y = |x|$

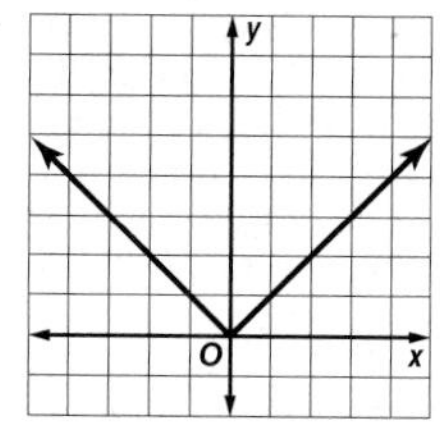

a. What is the equation of this parent function?

b. What equation would result in the graph of the parent function being reflected over the x-axis and shifted up 2 units? $y = -|x| + 2$

c. What equation would result in the graph of the parent function being shifted left 3 units and down 1 unit? $y = |x + 3| - 1$

6. Solve the absolute value equation $|4x - 8| - 24 = 0$. G

F. −4, 6

G. −4, 8

H. 4, 8

I. −8, −4

7. **EXTENDED RESPONSE** Use the scatter plot to answer each question.

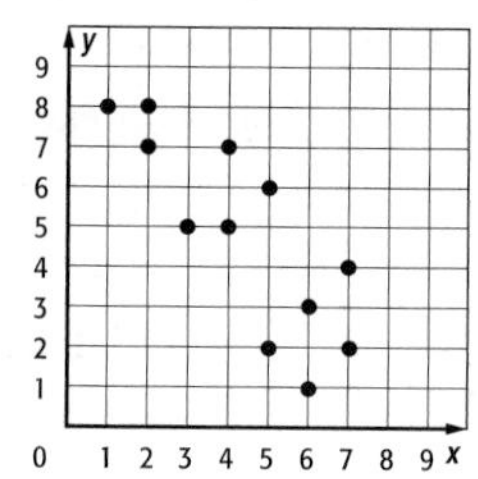

a. What type of correlation is shown by the data in the plot? negative

b. Determine a regression line for the data. Sample answer: $y = -0.99x + 9.13$

c. Use your regression line to predict the value of y when $x = 12$. Sample answer: −2.75

8. **SHORT RESPONSE** Write an equation for the piecewise function shown in the graph below. **See margin.**

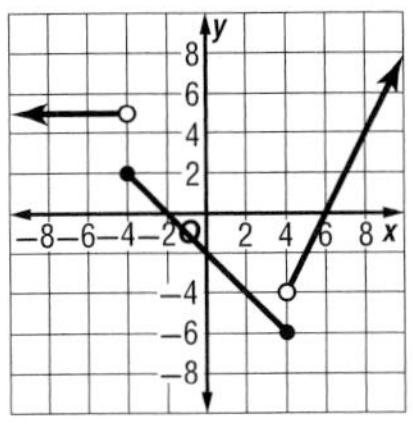

9. Carmen works for an electronics retailer. She earns a weekly salary of \$450 plus a commission of 4.5% on her weekly sales. Write a linear equation for Carmen's weekly earnings E if she has d dollars in sales. **C**

A. $E = (450 + 4.5)d$

B. $E = (450 + 0.045)d$

C. $E = 450 + 0.045d$

D. $E = 450 + 4.5d$

10. Which of the graphs represents the solution set for $|x - 3| - 4 = 0$? **G**

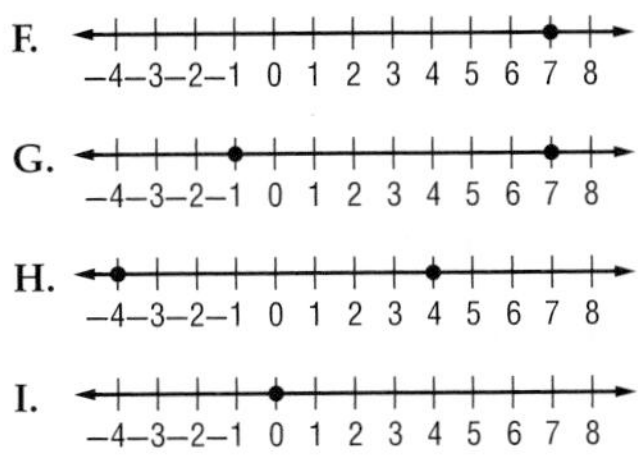

11. **SHORT RESPONSE** Solve the inequality $2(x - 2) - 1 < 17$. $x < 11$

12. Karissa has \$10 per month to spend text messaging on her cell phone. The phone company charges \$4.95 for the first 100 messages and \$0.10 for each additional message. How many text messages can Karissa afford to send each month? **C**

A. 50

B. 100

C. 150

D. 151

13a. $0.45x + 0.5y \geq 150$

13. **EXTENDED RESPONSE** The soccer team is having a bake sale this week to raise money for the program. For each cookie sold, the profit is \$0.45, and for each brownie sold, the profit is \$0.50.

a. The team hopes to earn \$150 in profits from the bake sale. Let x represent the number of cookies sold and y the number of brownies sold. Write an inequality to model the situation.

b. Graph the inequality. **See margin.**

c. If the team sells 180 cookies and 160 brownies this week, will they meet their goal? Explain. **Yes, the profit earned will be \$161.**

14. The Robinson family bought their home in 1996 for \$152,400. When they sold it in 2008, the value was \$174,900. What was the annual rate of change in the value of the home? **G**

F. \$1225

G. \$1875

H. \$22,500

I. \$27,275

Need Extra Help?

If you missed Question...	1	2	3	4	5	6	7	8	9	10	11	12	13	14
Go to Lesson or Page...	2-1	2-7	2-3	2-6	2-7	1-4	2-5	2-6	2-4	1-4	1-5	1-3	2-8	2-3
For help with NGSSS...	912.A.4.2	912.A.3.9	912.A.3.9	912.A.2.6	912.A.2.6	912.A.2.6	912.A.3.11	912.A.2.6	912.A.2.13	912.A.2.5	912.A.3.4	912.A.3.1	912.A.3.4	912.A.2.13

Formative Assessment

You can use these two pages to benchmark student progress.

CRM Standardized Test Practice, pp. 76–78

ExamView Assessment Suite Create practice worksheets or tests that align to your state's standards as well as TIMSS and NAEP tests.

Homework Option

Get Ready for Chapter 3 Assign students the exercises on p. 133 as homework to assess whether they possess the prerequisite skills needed for the next chapter.

Additional Answers

8. $y = \begin{cases} 5 & \text{if } x < -4 \\ -x - 2 & \text{if } -4 \leq x \leq 4 \\ 2x - 12 & \text{if } x > 4 \end{cases}$

13b.

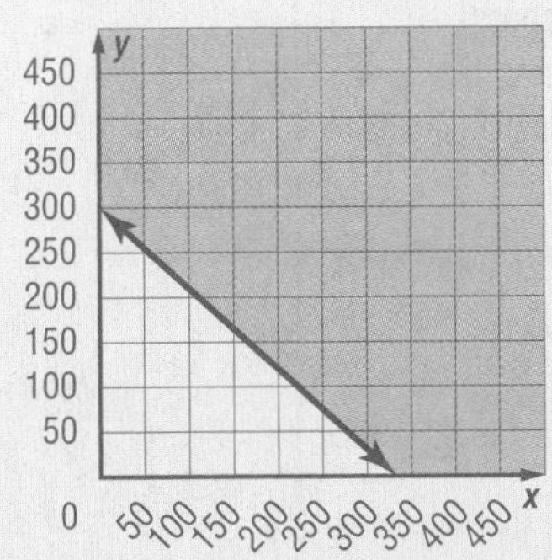

Pages 64–66, Lesson 2-1

5.

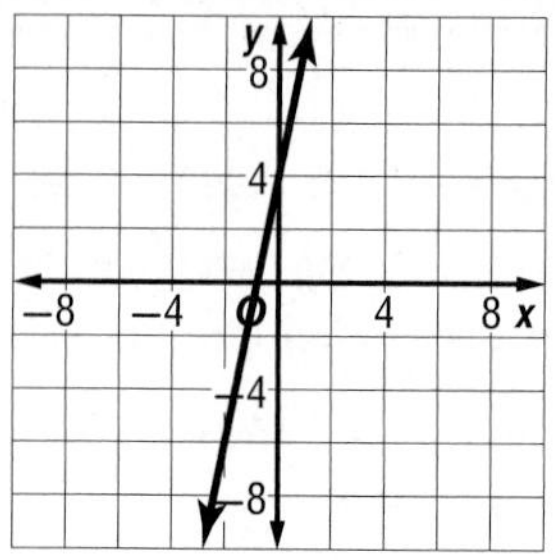

D = {all real numbers};
R = {all real numbers};
function; both; continuous

6.

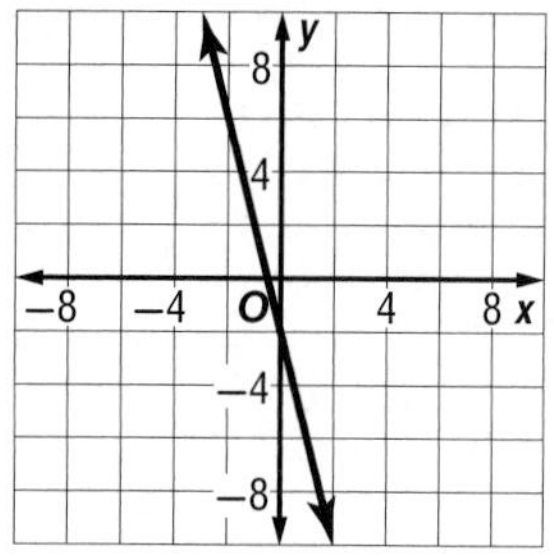

D = {all real numbers};
R = {all real numbers};
function; both; continuous

7.

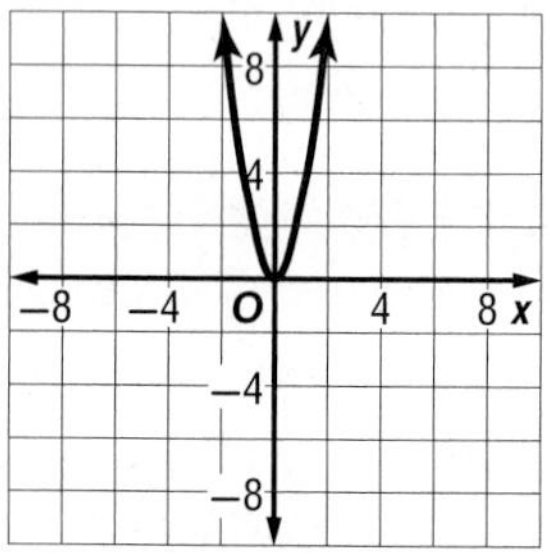

D = {all real numbers};
R = $\{y \mid y \geq 0\}$;
function; neither; continuous

8.

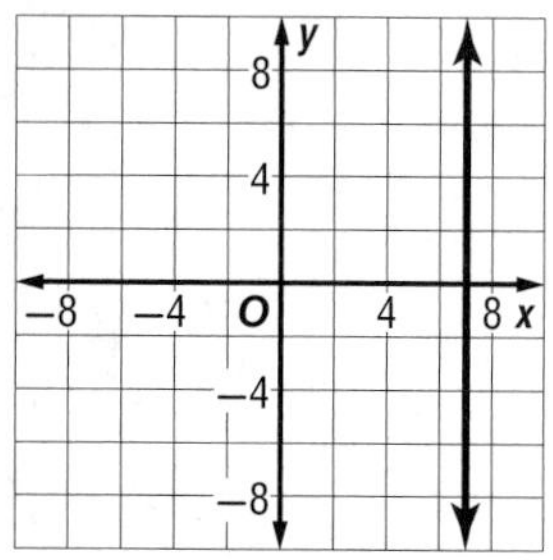

D = {7}; R = {all real numbers};
not a function; not continuous

15.

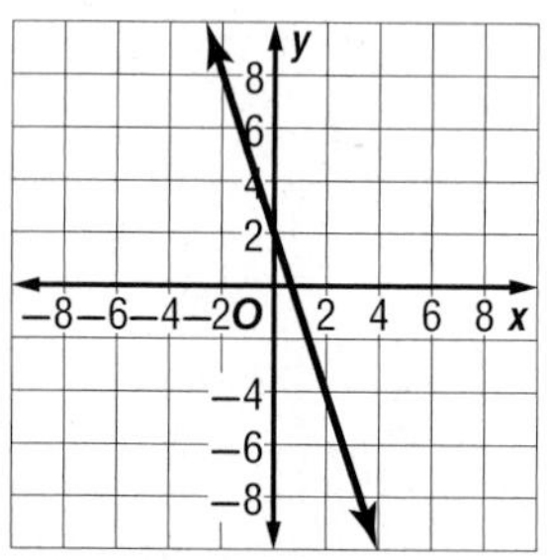

D = {all real numbers};
R = {all real numbers};
function; both; continuous

16.

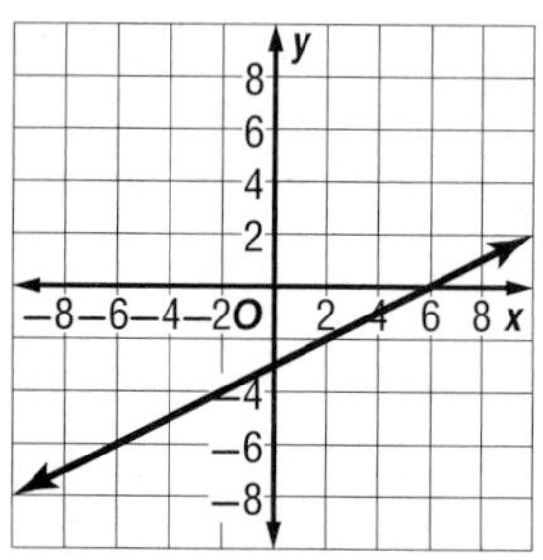

D = {all real numbers };
R = {all real numbers};
function; both; continuous

17.

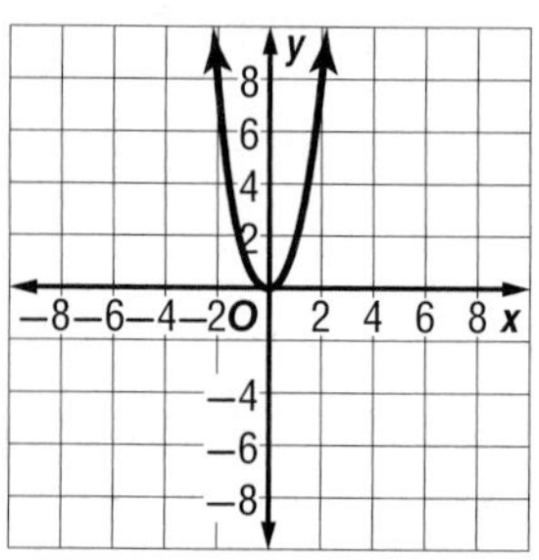

D = {all real numbers};
R = $\{y \mid y \geq 0\}$;
function; neither; continuous

18.

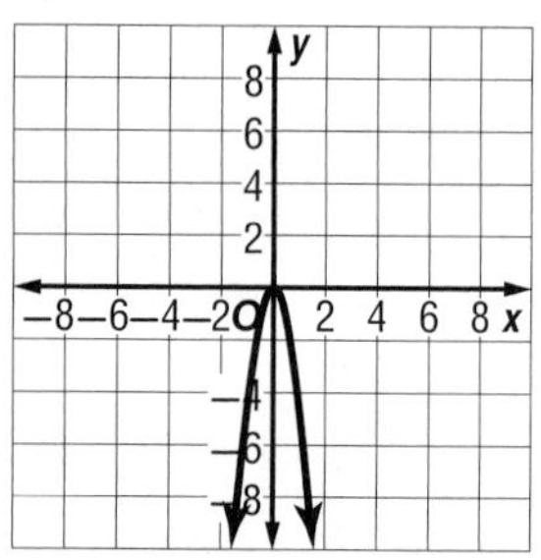

D = {all real numbers};
R = $\{y \mid y \leq 0\}$; function;
neither; continuous

19.

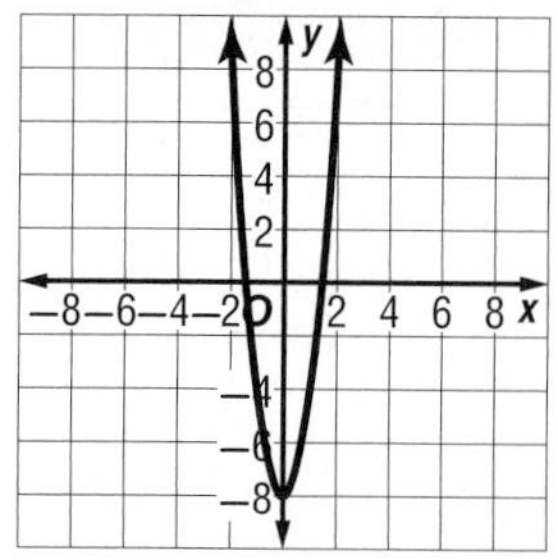

D = {all real numbers};
R = $\{y \mid y \geq -8\}$;
function; neither; continuous

20.

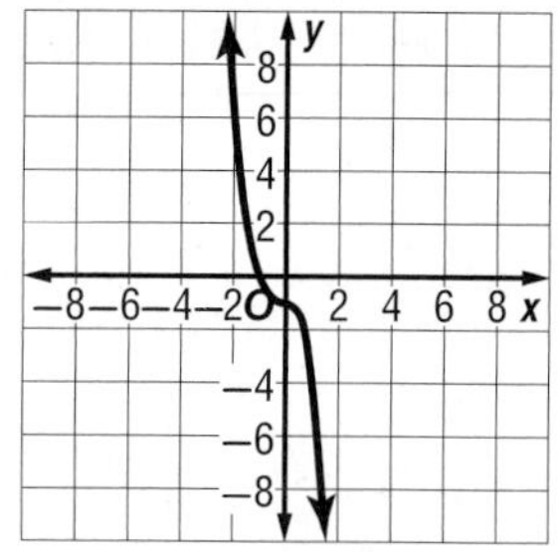

D = {all real numbers};
R = {all real numbers};
function; both; continuous

34a.

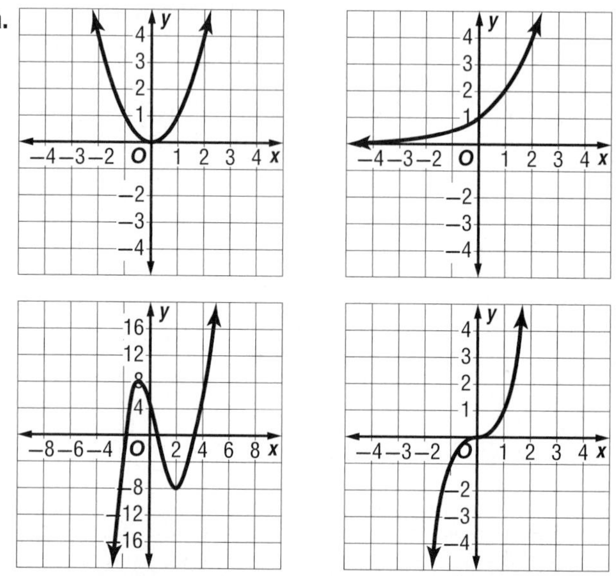

34b.

Function	Possible Intersection Points
$f(x) = x^2$	0, 1, 2
$g(x) = 2^x$	0, 1
$h(x) = x^3 - 3x^2 - 5x + 6$	1, 2, 3
$j(x) = x^3$	1

34c. $g(x)$ and $j(x)$ are one-to-one, and $f(x)$ and $n(x)$ are not.

34d. $h(x)$ and $j(x)$ are onto, and $f(x)$ and $g(x)$ are not.

34e.

Function	One-to-one	Onto
$f(x) = x^2$	no	no
$g(x) = 2^x$	yes	no
$h(x) = x^3 - 3x^2 - 5x + 6$	no	yes
$j(x) = x^3$	yes	yes

38a. Sample answer:

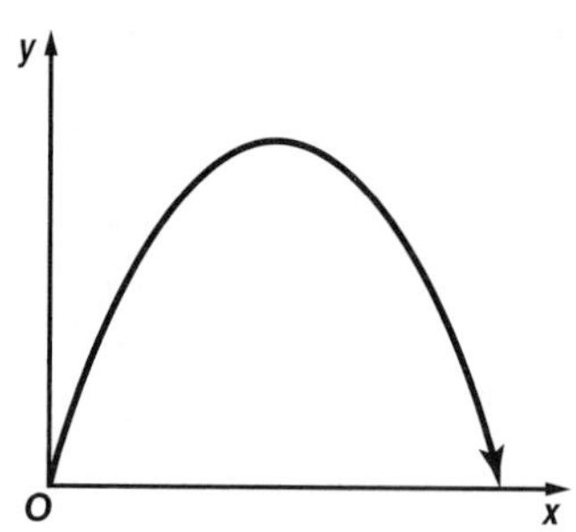

38b. Sample answer:

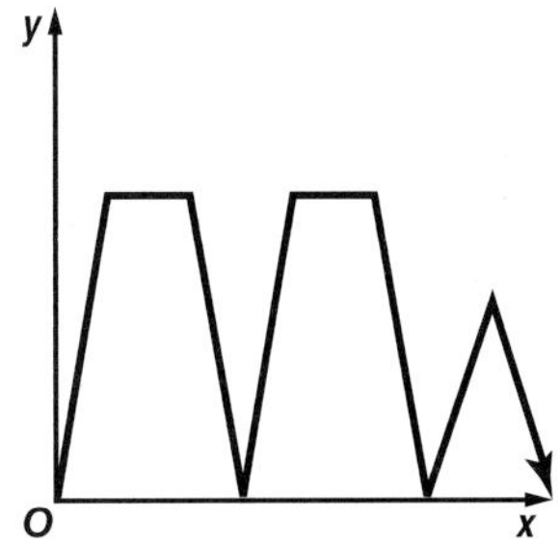

38c. Sample answer:

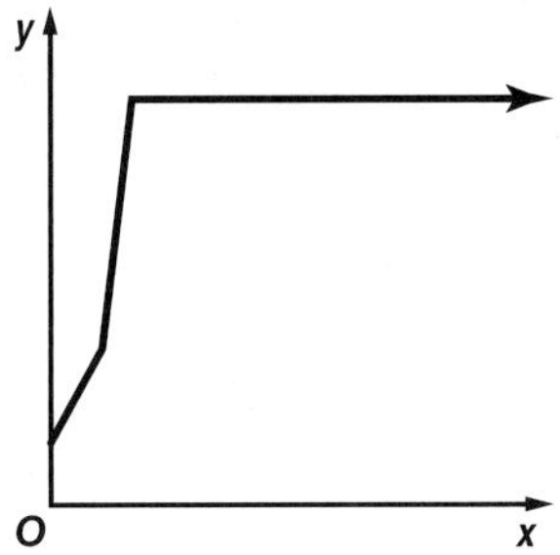

38d. Sample answer:

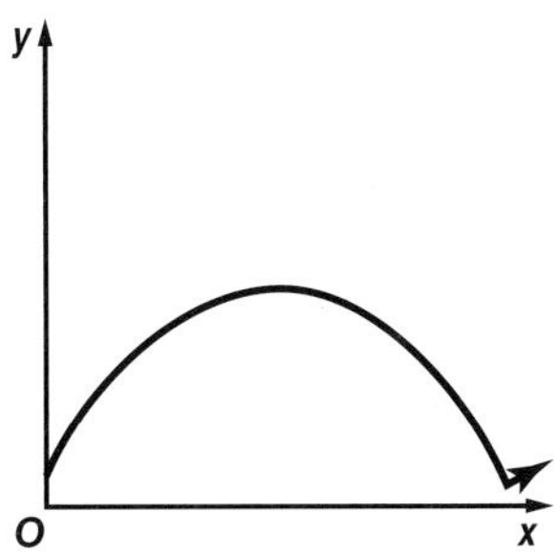

Page 68, Extend 2-1

3. Continuous; the domain, the number of hours, is the set of values greater than or equal to 0, so the graph of the function is a straight line.

4. Discrete; the domain, the number of rides, is the set of whole numbers, so the graph of the function consists of individual points.

5. Sample answer: A function describing the cost y of x football tickets is discrete because only whole-number values make sense for the domain, the number of tickets. A function describing the cost y of x pounds of grapes is continuous because the domain, the pounds of grapes, is the set of values greater than or equal to 0.

Pages 71–72, Lesson 2-2

6. $4x + y = -7$; $A = 4$, $B = 1$, $C = -7$

7. $6x - y = -5$; $A = 6$, $B = -1$, $C = -5$

8. $3x + 2y = -1$; $A = 3$, $B = 2$, $C = -1$

9. $8x + 9y = 6$; $A = 8$, $B = 9$, C, 6

10. $x - 3y = -2$; $A = 1$, $B = -3$, $C = -2$

11. $2x - 3y = 12$; $A = 2$, $B = -3$, $C = 12$

12. $-\frac{12}{5}$; 12

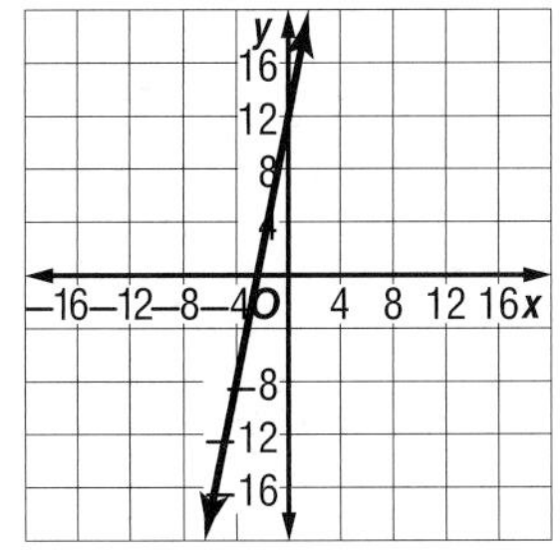

13. $\frac{5}{2}$; –10

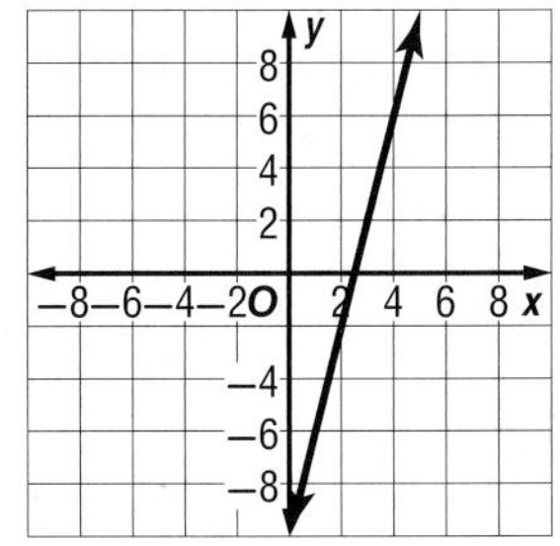

14. 6; 4

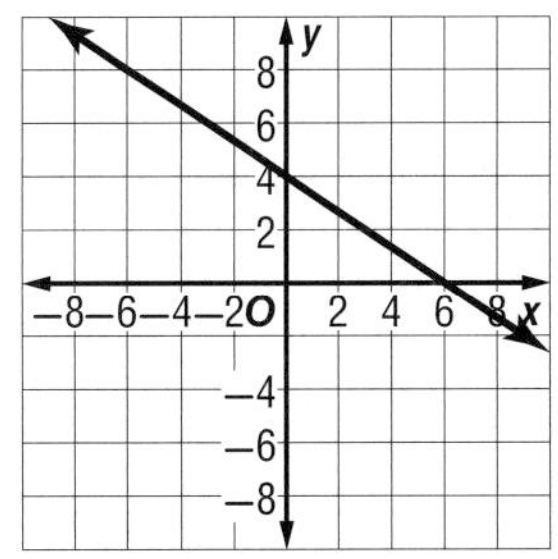

15. 7; $-\frac{21}{4}$

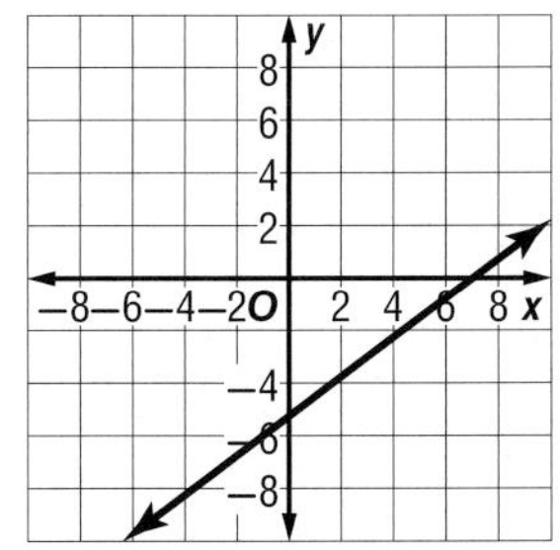

35. –0.5; –4

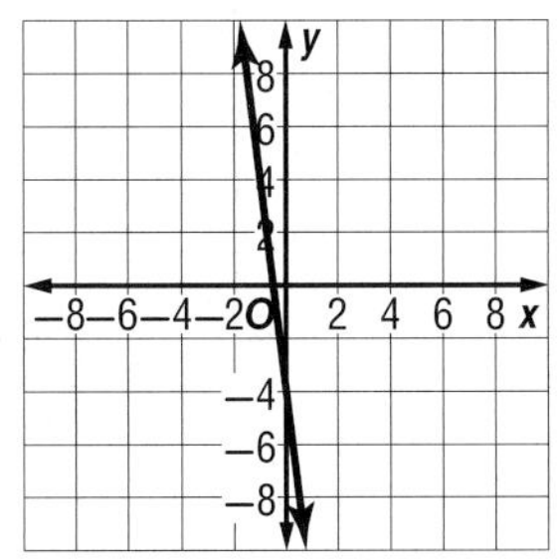

36. 6; –18

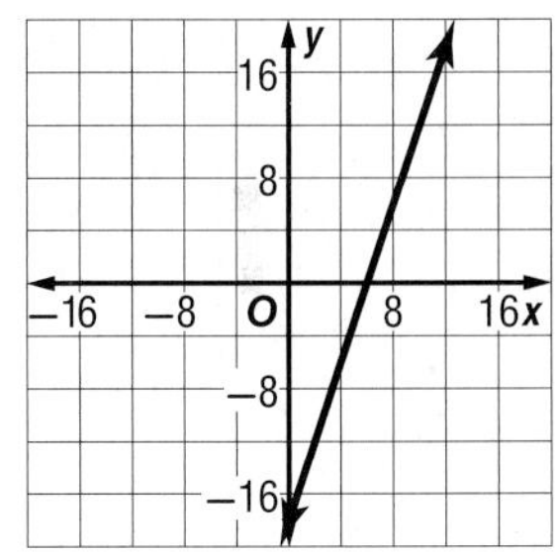

37. –7; 10.5

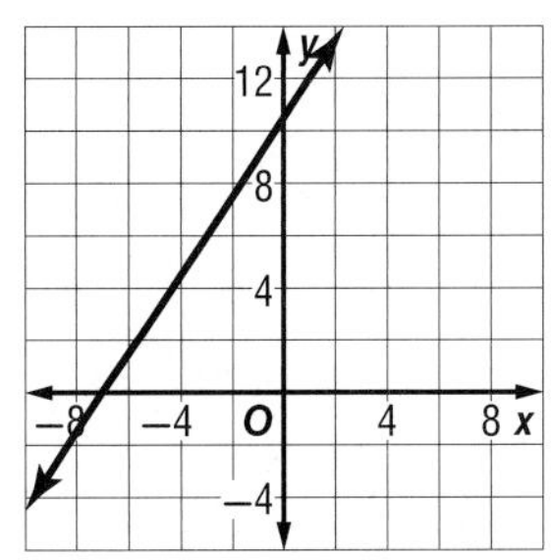

38. $\frac{10}{3}$; $\frac{30}{7}$

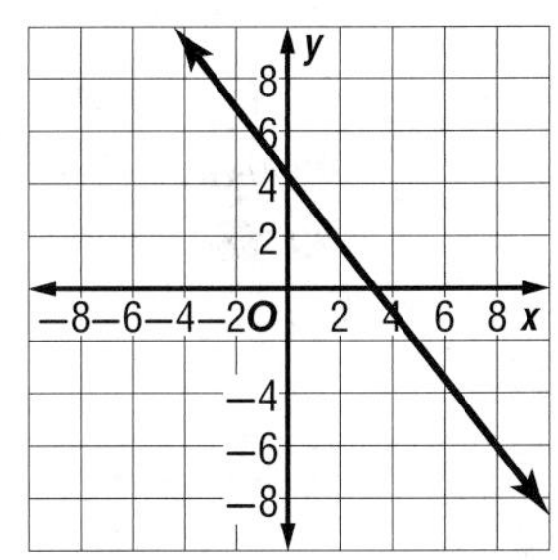

39. 12; –18

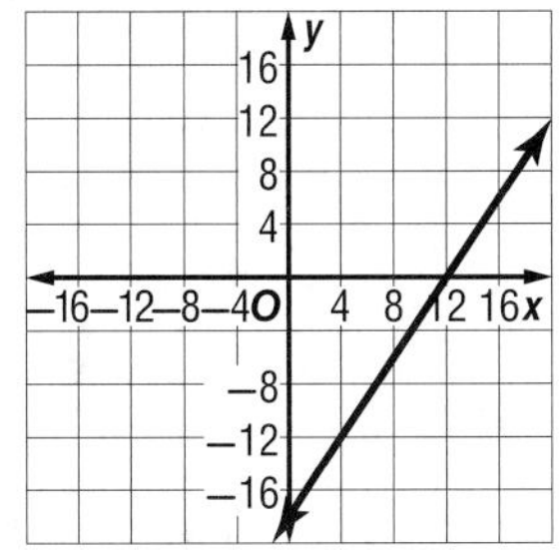

40. –18; 16

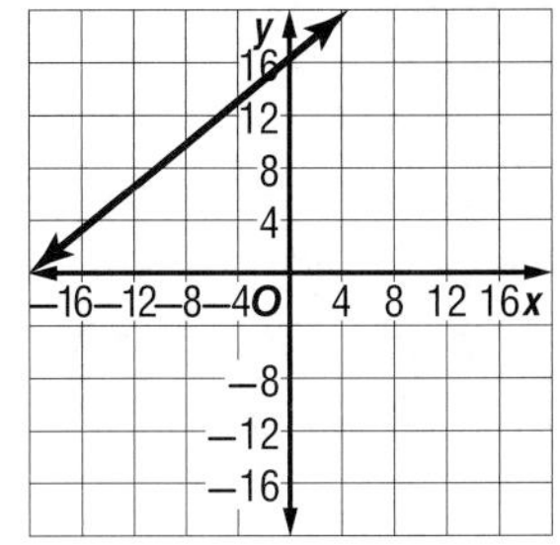

41b.

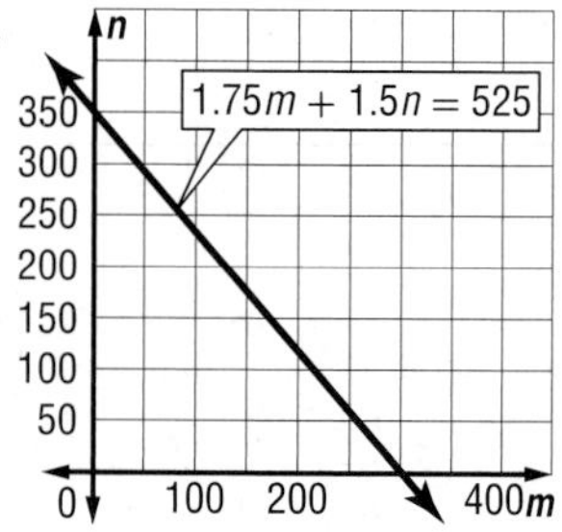

Yes; the graph passes the vertical line test.

50b.

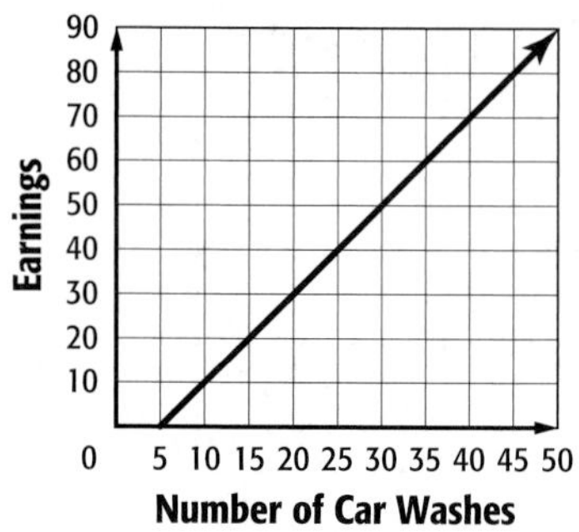

51a.

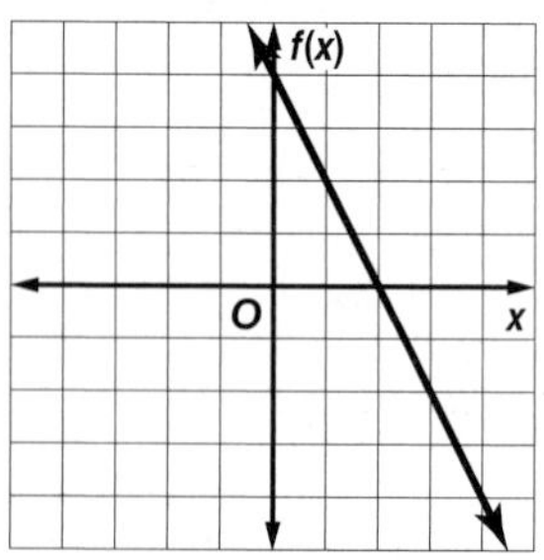

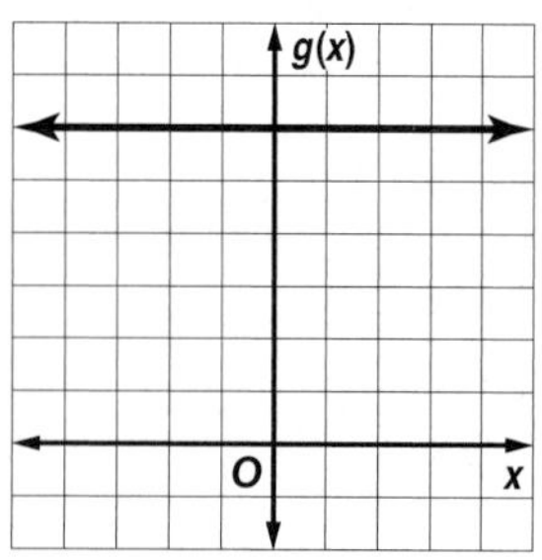

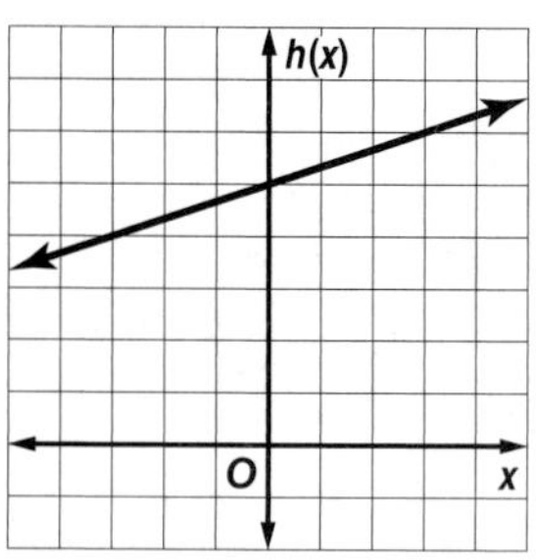

Page 90, Extend 2-4

1. $p = 0.43d$; 27.95 lb/in^2

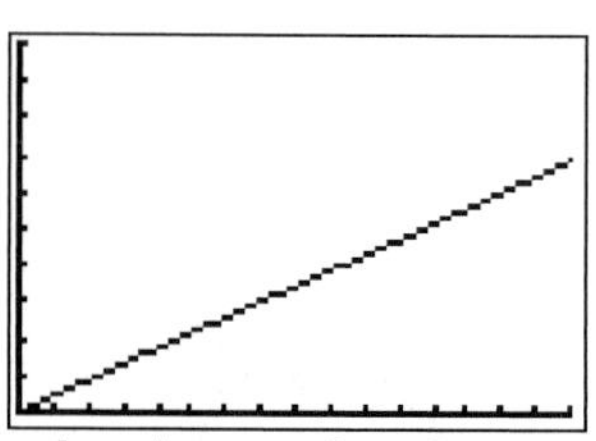

[0, 80] scl: 5 by [0, 50] scl: 5

2.

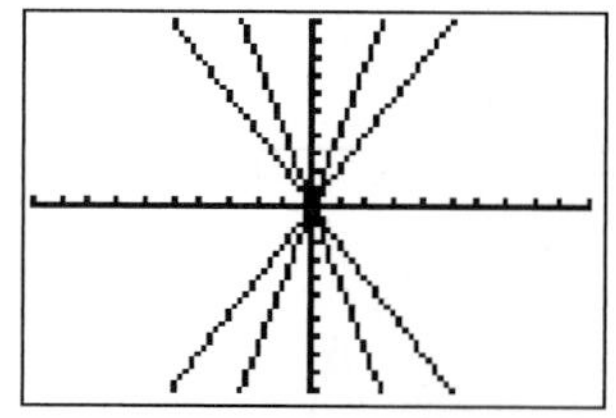

[–10, 10] scl: 1 by [–10, 10] scl: 1

The graphs of $y = -4x$ and $y = -2x$ have negative slope. As x increases, y decreases. The graphs of $y = 4x$ and $y = 2x$ have positive slope. As x increases, y increases. All of the graphs are lines, all have a constant rate of change, and all pass through the origin.

Page 91, Mid-Chapter Quiz

12. –3, 4

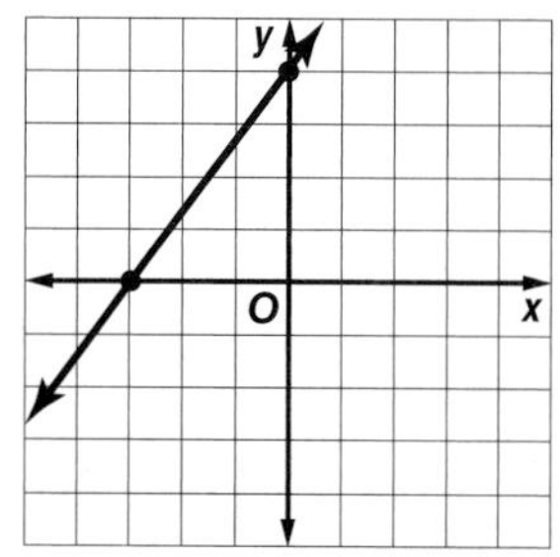

13. 10, 5

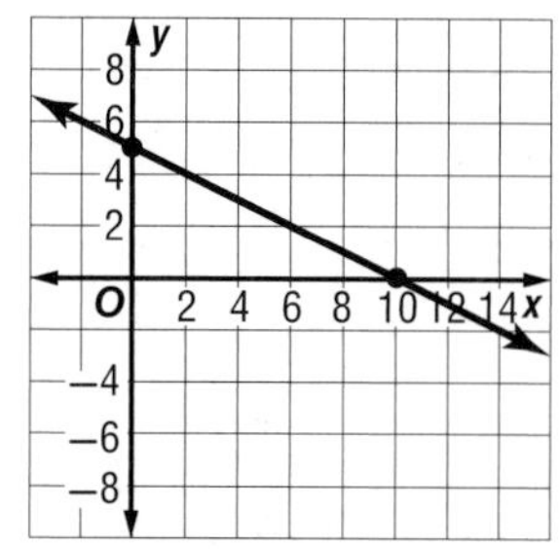

Pages 96–97, Lesson 2-5

7.

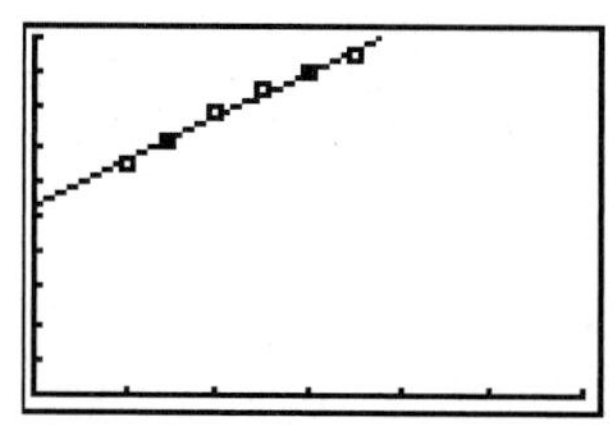

[0,12] scl: 1 by [0, 1000] scl: 100

$y = 61.9x + 530.2$ (x is the number of years since 2002); $1.149 million in sales.

8.

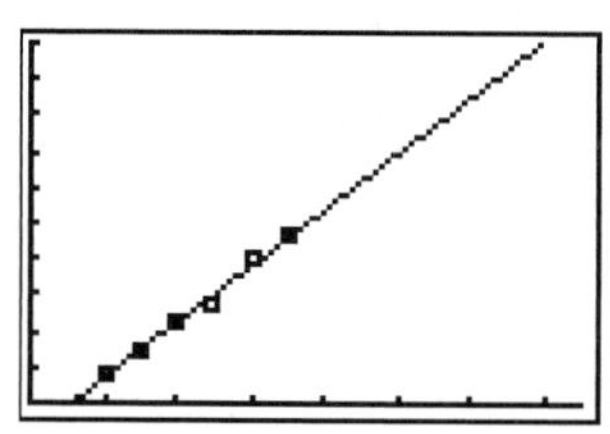

[0,15] scl: 2 by [0, 50] scl: 5

$y = 3.91x - 4.45$ (x is the number of years since 2000); 54 employees is 2015.

9a.

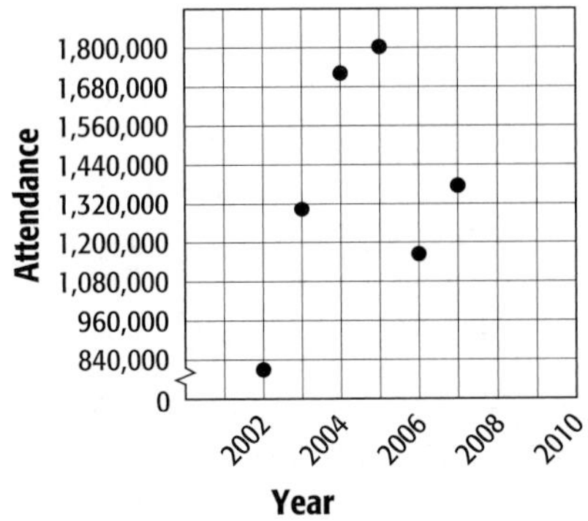

10a. $y = -0.21x + 85.1$

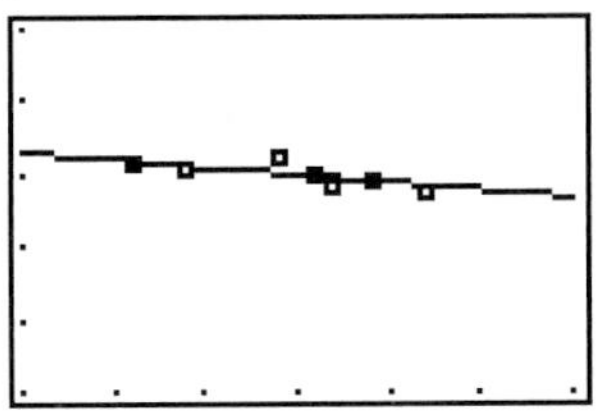

[10, 40] scl: 5 by [50, 100] scl: 10

11e. Sample answer: The new equation has a correlation coefficient, 0.986, that is extremely close to 1, so this equation should accurately represent the data.

12. Sample answer: The correlation coefficient is very valuable to a linear regression line because it determines how close the actual data points are to the regression line. The closer the points are to the line, or the closer the correlation coefficient is to 1 or –1, the more accurate the regression line is.

13. Sample answer: If *a* and *b* have a positive correlation, then they are both increasing. If *b* and *c* have a negative correlation and *b* is increasing, then *c* must be decreasing. If *c* and *d* have a positive correlation and *c* is decreasing, then *d* must be decreasing. If *a* is increasing and *d* is decreasing, then they must have a negative correlation.

15.

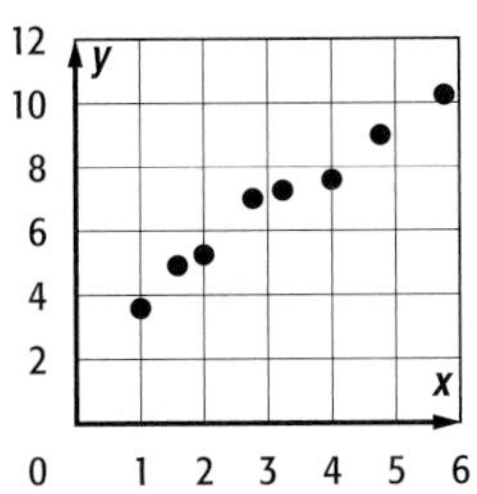

a; Sample answer: The data show a strong positive correlation which means that the correlation coefficient *r* should be close to 1.

16. Sample answer: A linear equation that represents the data is useful in that it can show whether data is increasing or decreasing. It is also helpful when using data to make predictions.

Page 101, Lesson 2-6, Guided Practice

1.

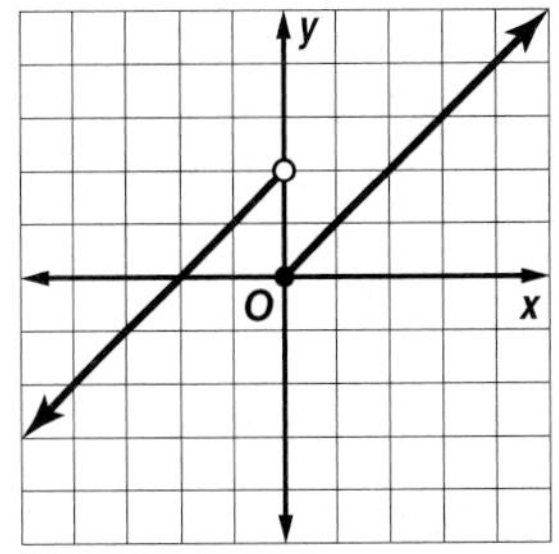

D = {all real numbers}, R = {all real numbers}

Pages 104–106, Lesson 2-6

1.

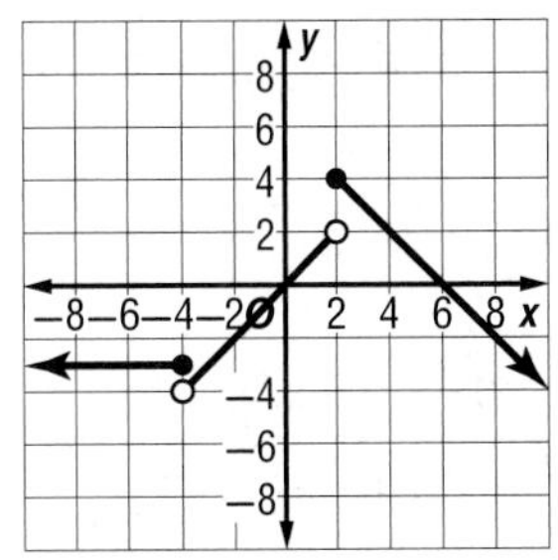

D = {all real numbers};
R = $\{y \mid y \leq 4\}$

2.

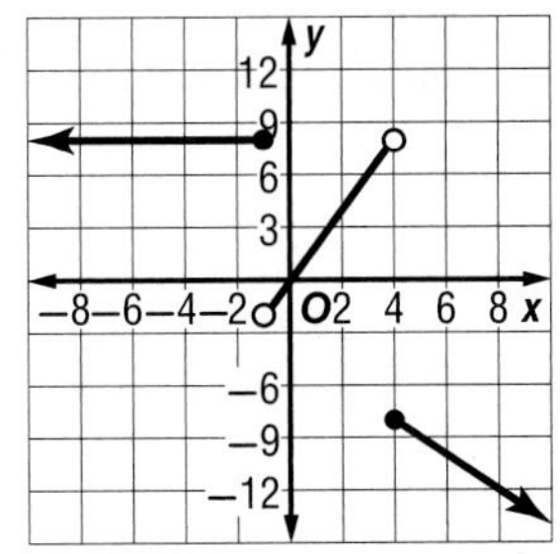

D = {all real numbers};
R = $\{y \mid 8 \geq y > -2 \text{ or } y \leq -8\}$

3. $g(x) = \begin{cases} x + 4 & \text{if } x < -2 \\ -3 & \text{if } -2 \leq x \leq 3 \\ -2x + 12 & \text{if } x > 3 \end{cases}$

4. $g(x) = \begin{cases} 6 \text{ if } x \leq -5 \\ -x + 4 \text{ if } -5 < x < -2 \\ \frac{1}{2}x + 1 \text{ if } x \geq -2 \end{cases}$

5.

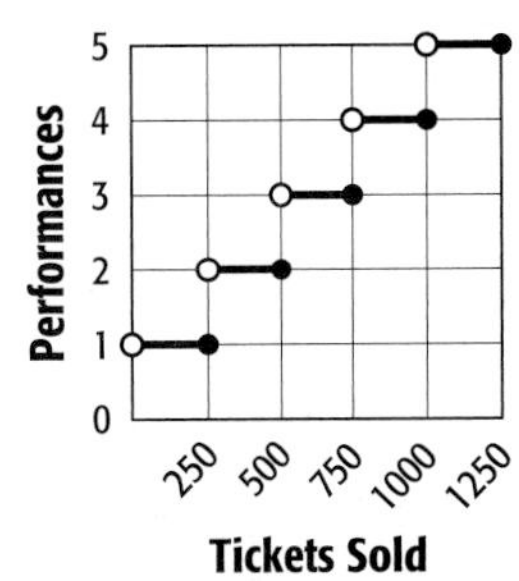

6.

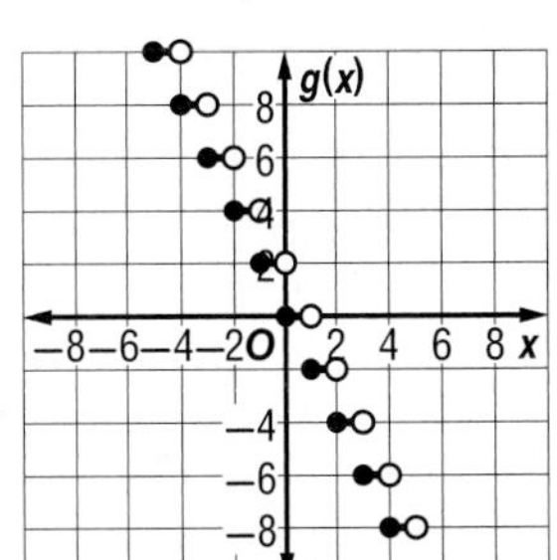

D = {all real numbers};
R = {all even integers}

7.

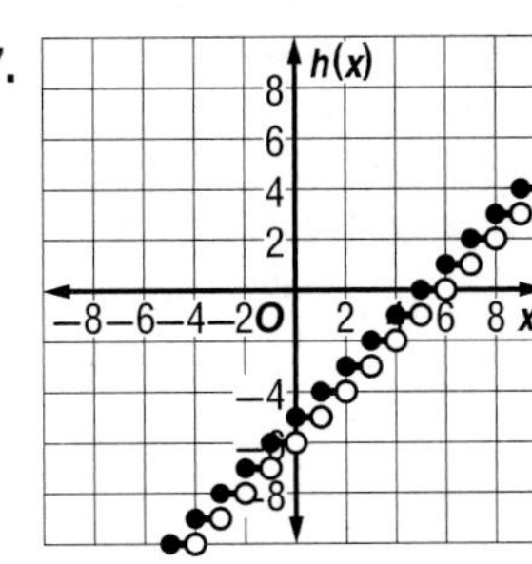

D = {all real numbers};
R = {all integers}

8.

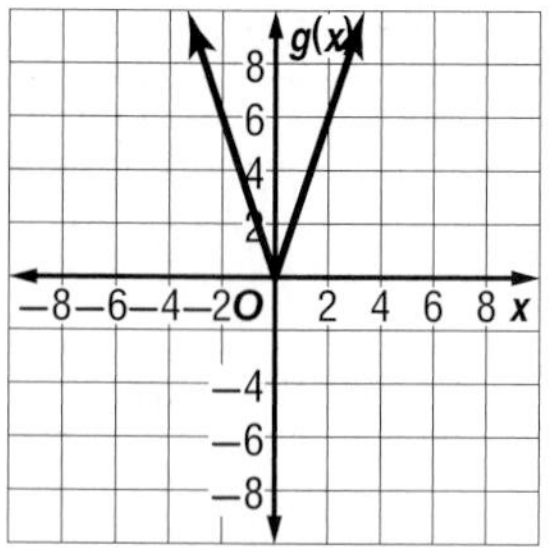

D = {all real numbers};
R = $\{g(x) \mid g(x) \geq 0\}$

9.

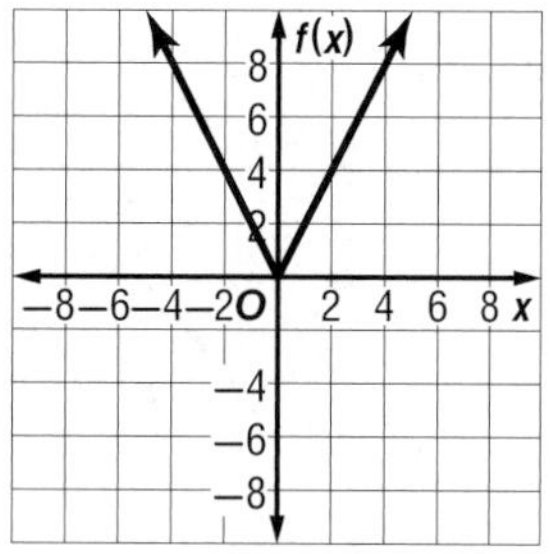

D = {all real numbers};
R = $\{f(x) \mid f(x) \geq 0\}$

10.

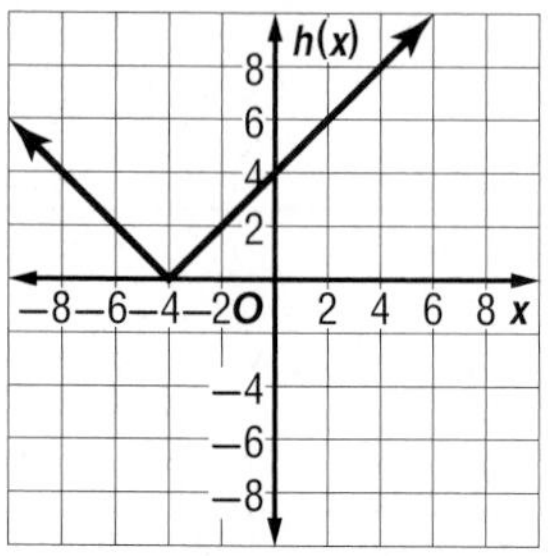

D = {all real numbers};
R = $\{h(x) \mid h(x) \geq 0\}$

11.

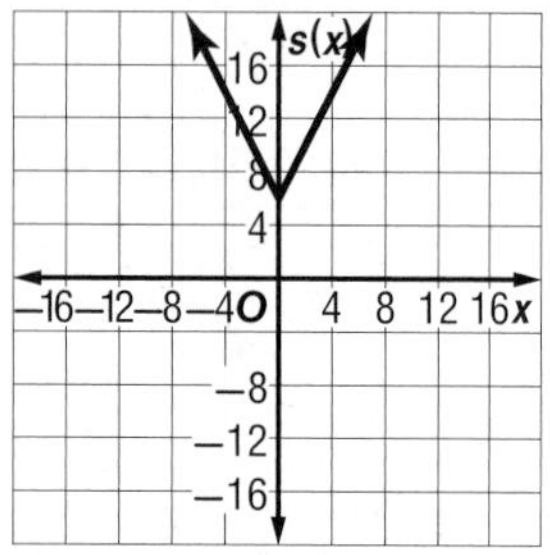

D = {all real numbers};
R = $\{s(x) \mid s(x) \geq 6\}$

16. $g(x) = \begin{cases} -8 & \text{if } x \leq -6 \\ 0.25x + 2 & \text{if } -4 \leq x \leq 4 \\ 4 & \text{if } x > 6 \end{cases}$

17. $g(x) = \begin{cases} -x - 4 & \text{if } x < -3 \\ x + 1 & \text{if } -3 \leq x \leq 1 \\ -6 & \text{if } x > 4 \end{cases}$

18. $g(x) = \begin{cases} -9 & \text{if } x < -5 \\ x + 4 & \text{if } 0 \leq x \leq 3 \\ x - 3 & \text{if } x > 7 \end{cases}$

19. $g(x) = \begin{cases} 8 & \text{if } x \leq -1 \\ 2x & \text{if } 4 \leq x \leq 6 \\ 2x - 15 & \text{if } x > 7 \end{cases}$

20.

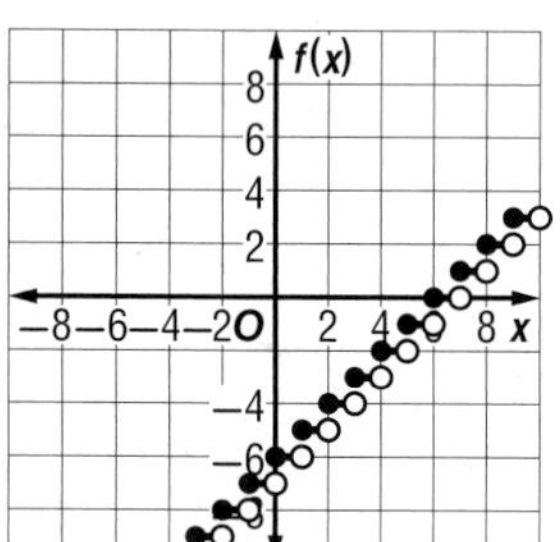

D = {all real numbers};
R = {all integers}

21.

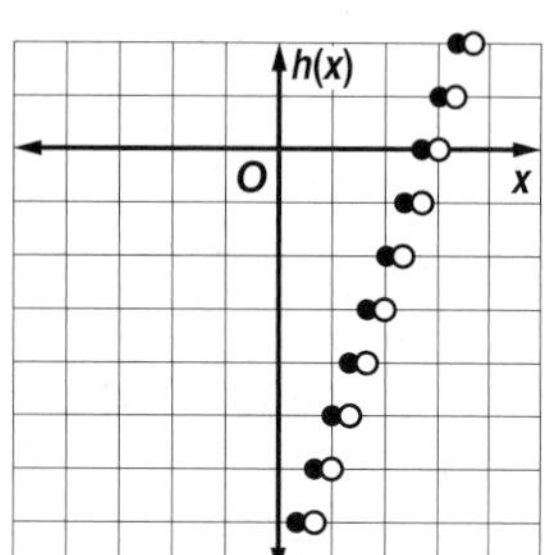

D = {all real numbers};
R = {all integers}

22.

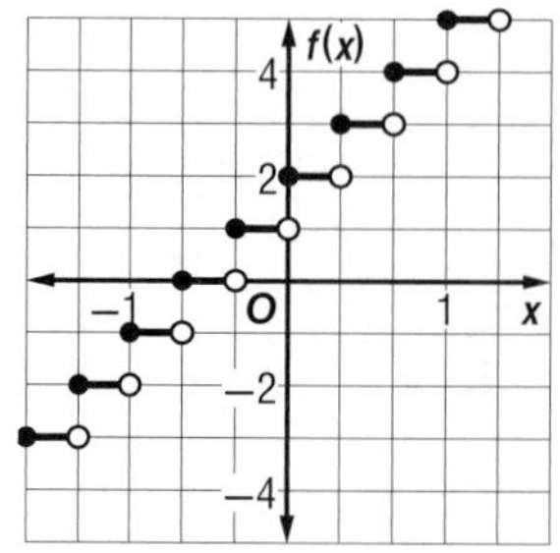

D = {all real numbers};
R = {all integers}

23.

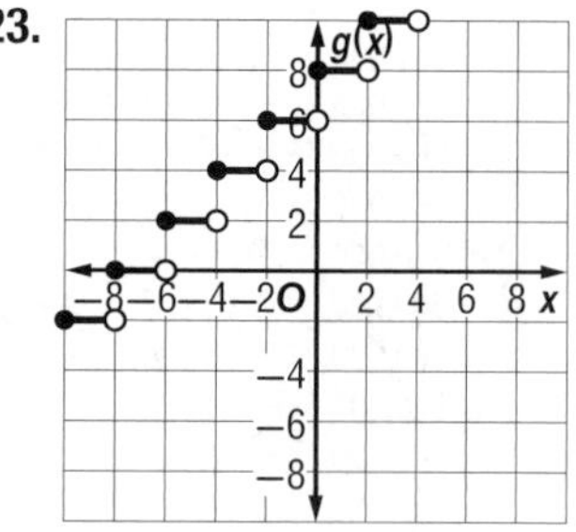

D = {all real numbers};
R = {all even integers}

24.

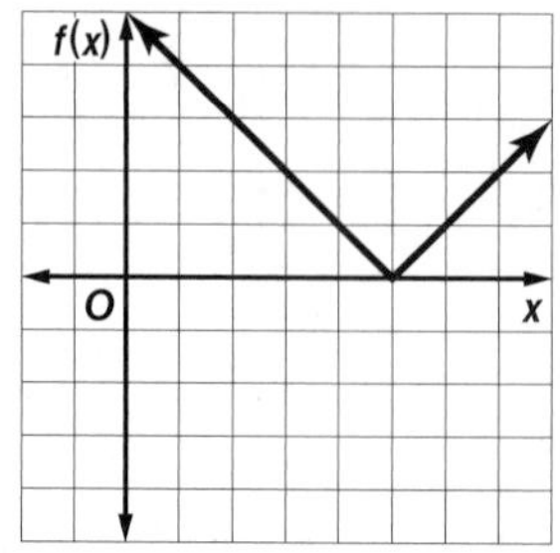

D = {all real numbers};
R = $\{f(x) \mid f(x) \geq 0\}$

25.

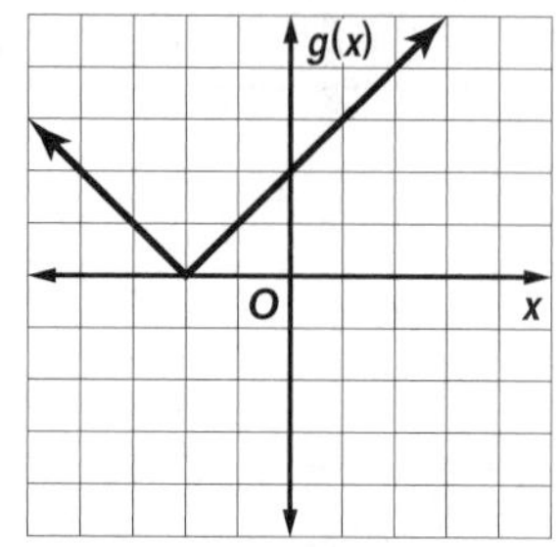

D = {all real numbers};
R = $\{g(x) \mid g(x) \geq 0\}$

26.

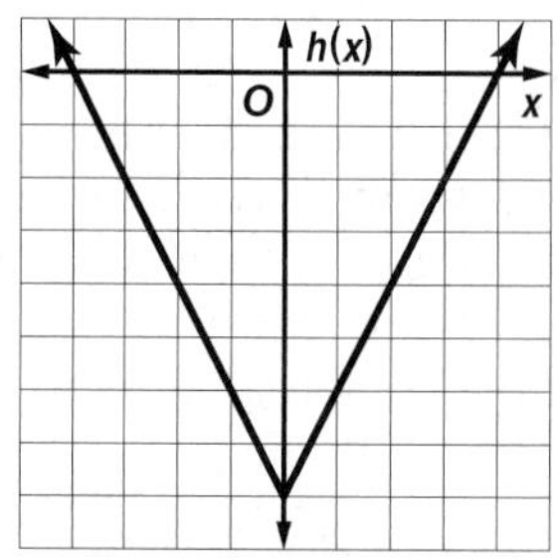

D = {all real numbers};
R = $\{h(x) \mid h(x) \geq -8\}$

27.

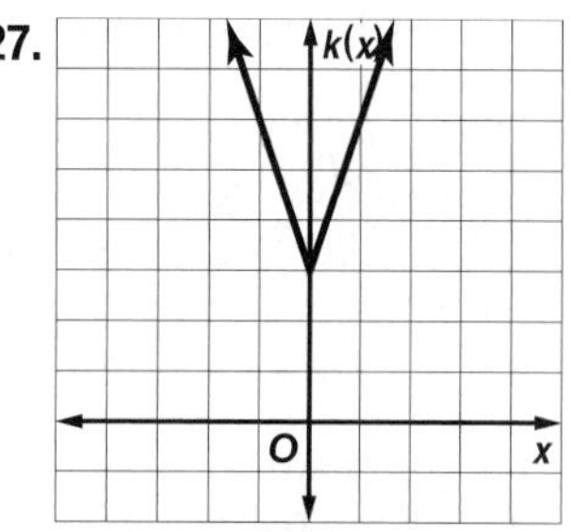

D = {all real numbers};
R = $\{k(x) \mid k(x) \geq 3\}$

28.

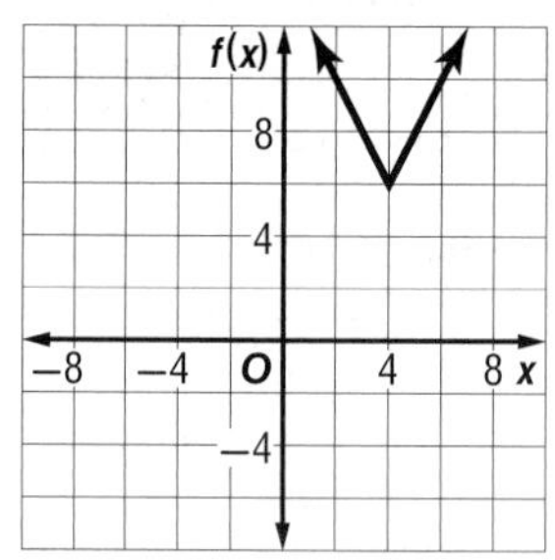

D = {all real numbers};
R = $\{f(x) \mid f(x) \geq 6\}$

29.

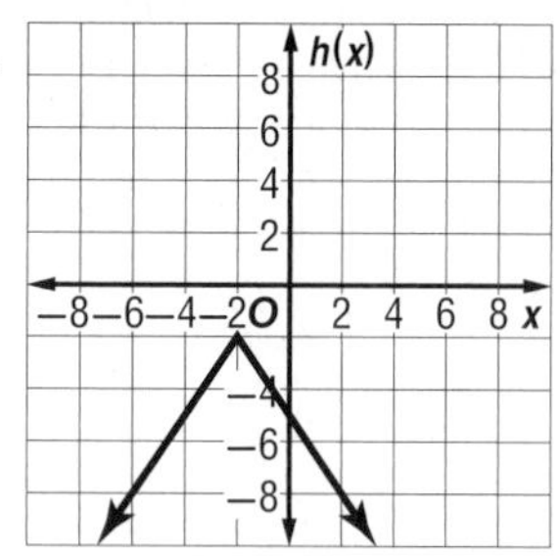

D = {all real numbers};
R = $\{h(x) \mid h(x) \leq -2\}$

30b. $f(x) = \begin{cases} 2x & \text{if } 0 < x \le 100 \\ x + 100 & \text{if } x > 100 \end{cases}$

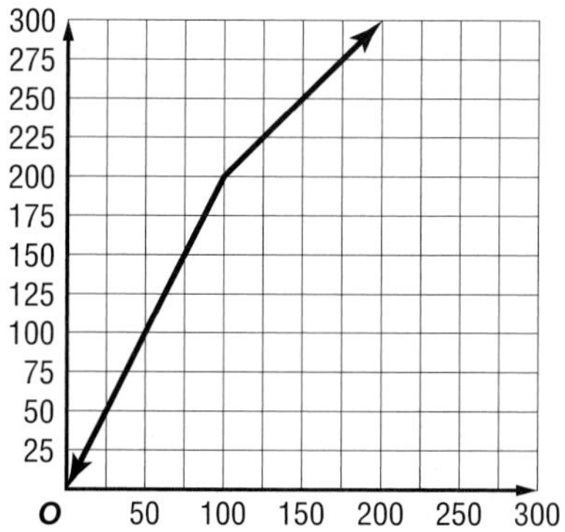

31c.

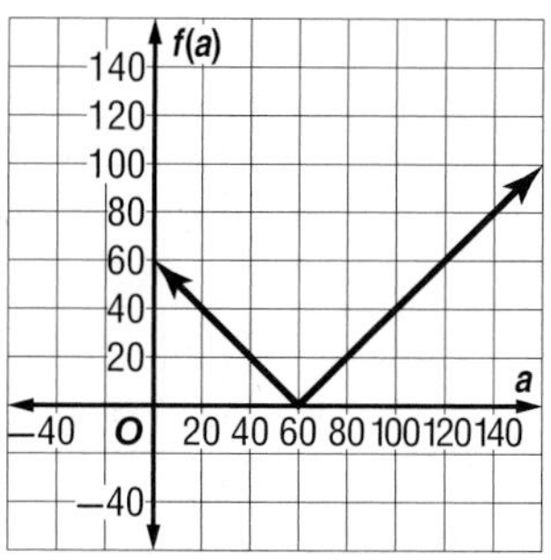

32b. $c(t) = \begin{cases} 6 & \text{if } t \le \frac{1}{2} \\ 10 & \text{if } \frac{1}{2} < t \le 1 \\ 16 & \text{if } 1 < t \le 2 \\ 24 & \text{if } 2 < t \le 24 \end{cases}$

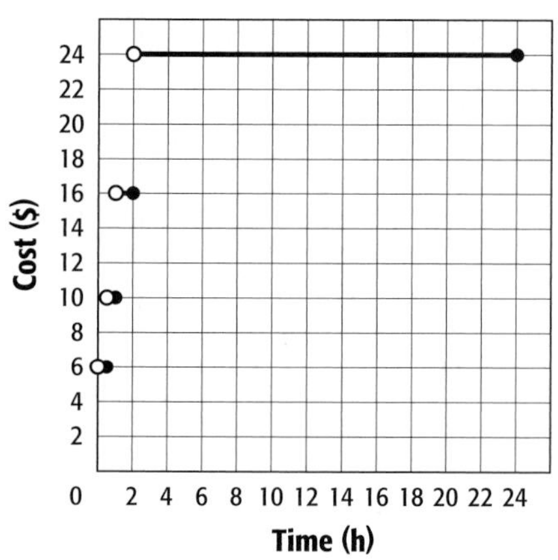

35.

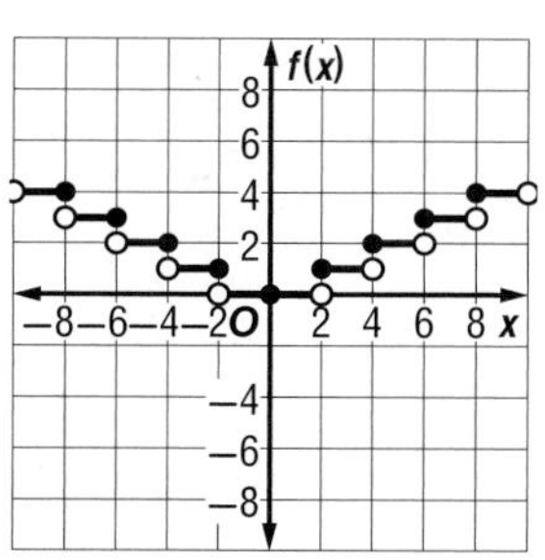

D = {all real numbers}; R = {all whole numbers}

36.

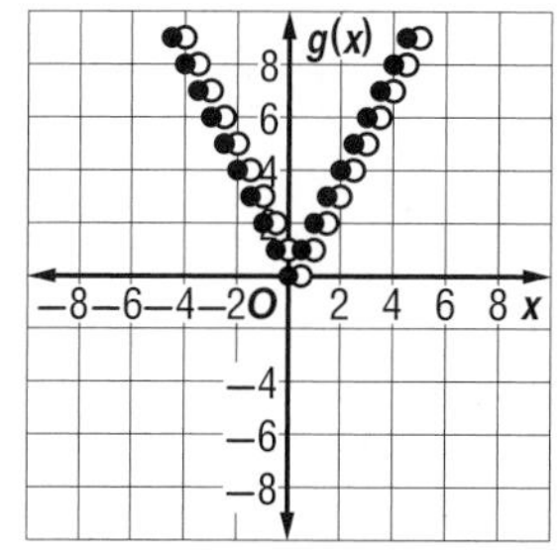

D = {all real numbers}; R = {non-negative integers}

37.

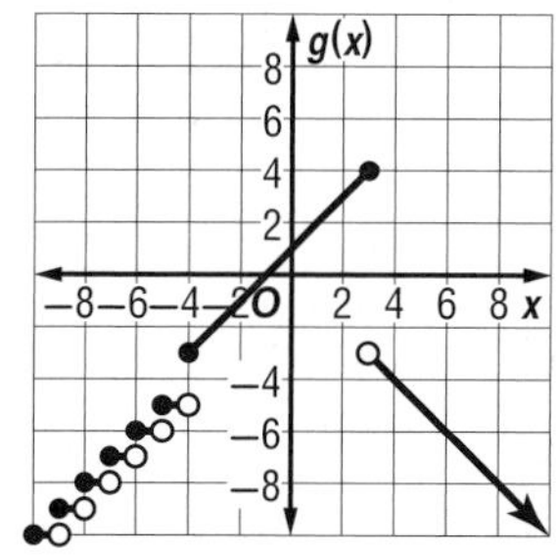

D = {all real numbers}; R = $\{g(x) \mid g(x) \le 4\}$

38.

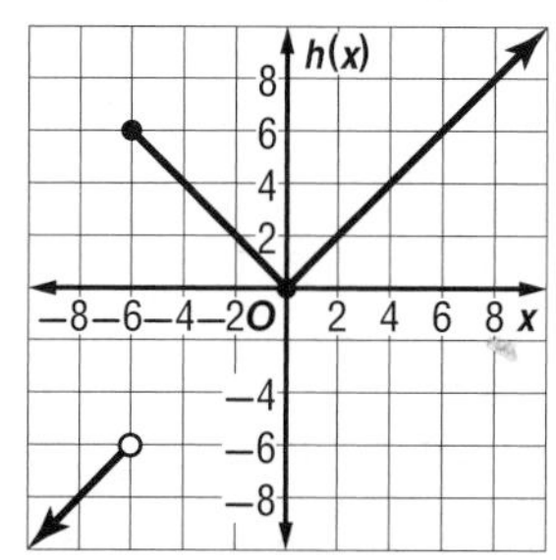

D = {all real numbers}; R = $\{h(x) \mid h(x) \le -6 \text{ or } 0 \le h(x)\}$

39a.

x	−4	−3	−2	−1	0	1	2	3	4
$f(x)$	0	−1	−2	−3	−4	−3	−2	−1	0

x	−4	−3	−2	−1	0	1	2	3	4
$g(x)$	12	9	6	3	0	3	6	9	12

39b.

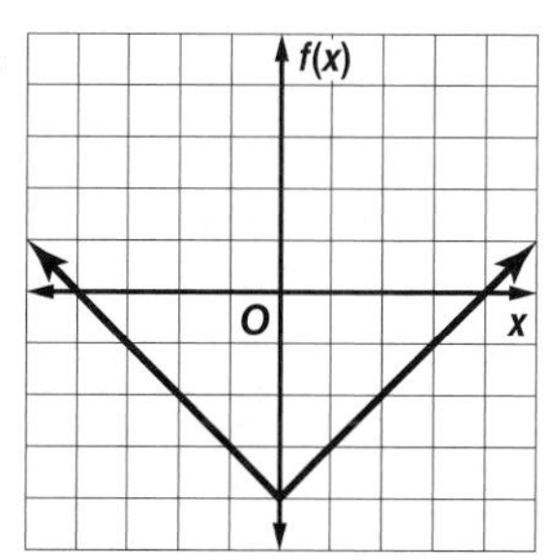

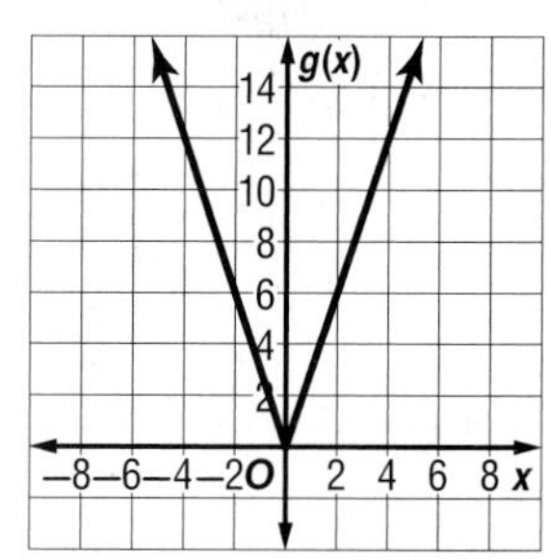

39c.

x	−4	−3	−2	−1	0	1	2	3	4
$f(x)$	0	−1	−2	−3	−4	−3	−2	−1	0
slope		−1	−1	−1	−1	1	1	1	1

x	−4	−3	−2	−1	0	1	2	3	4
$g(x)$	12	9	6	3	0	3	6	9	12
slope		−3	−3	−3	−3	3	3	3	3

Page 108, Explore 2-7

1.

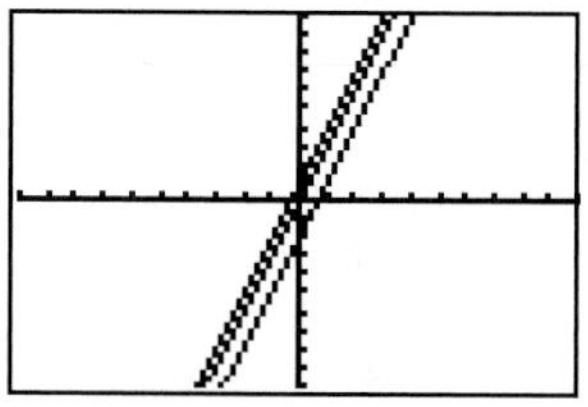

The slopes are the same, and the y-intercepts vary.

2.

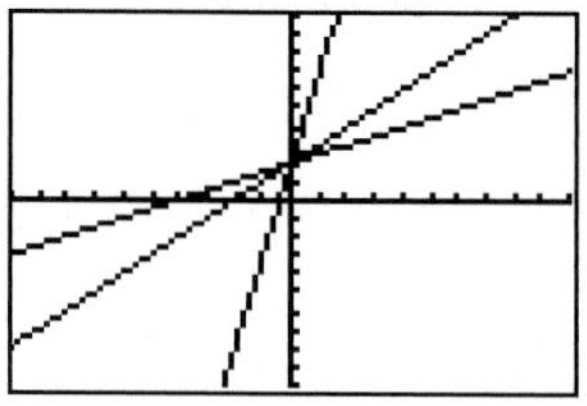

The y-intercepts are the same, and the slopes vary.

3.

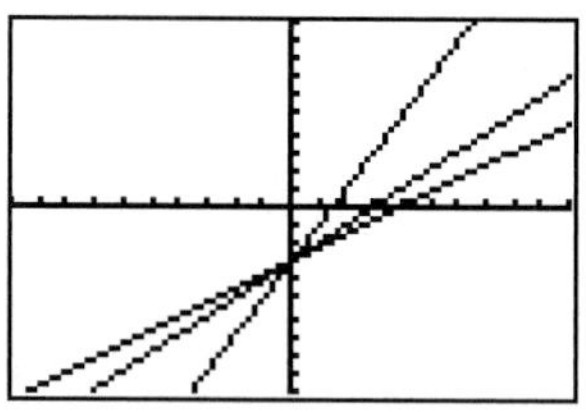

The y-intercepts are the same, and the slopes vary.

Page 111, Lesson 2-7, Guided Practice

4A. The graph of $y = 2x^2$ is a dilation, stretching the graph of $y = x^2$ vertically.

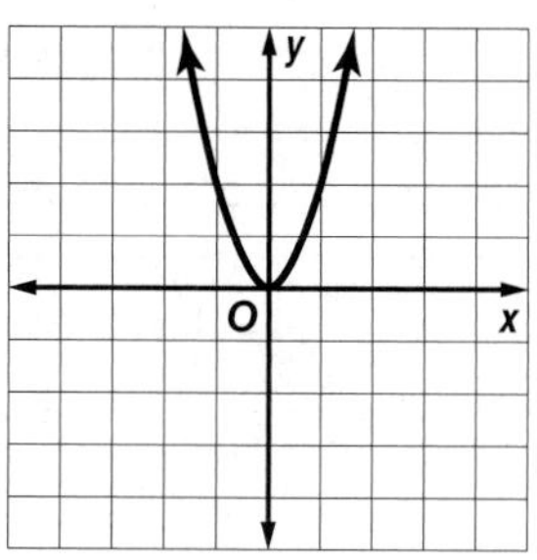

4B. The graph of $y = \left|\frac{1}{3}x\right|$ is a dilation, stretching the graph of $y = |x|$ horizontally.

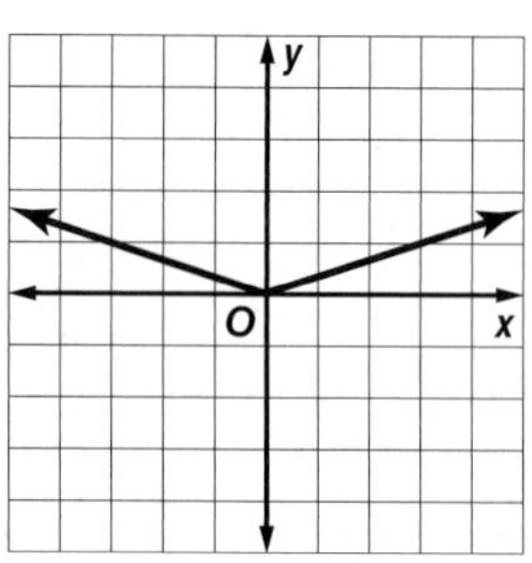

Pages 113–115, Lesson 2-7

9. The function is a dilation and translation. The graph of $f(x) = \frac{1}{2}|x - 12|$ compresses the graph $f(x) = |x|$ vertically and translates it 12 units to the right.

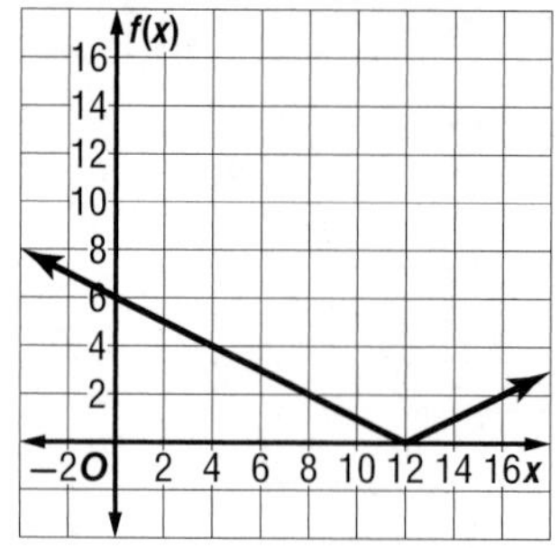

20. reflection of the graph of $y = x$ across the x-axis

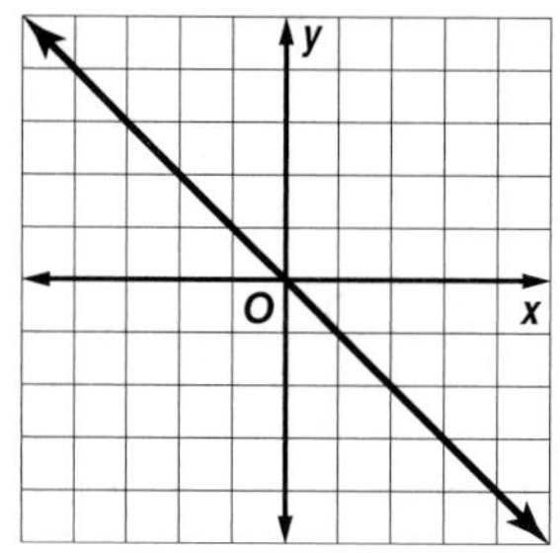

21. reflection of the graph of $y = x^2$ across the x-axis

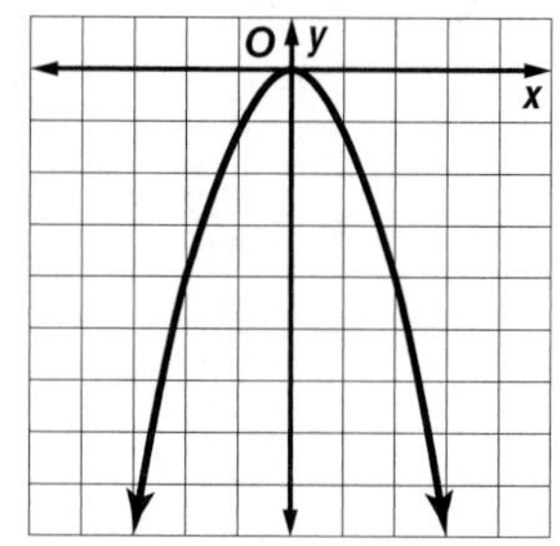

22. reflection of the graph of $y = x^2$ across the y-axis

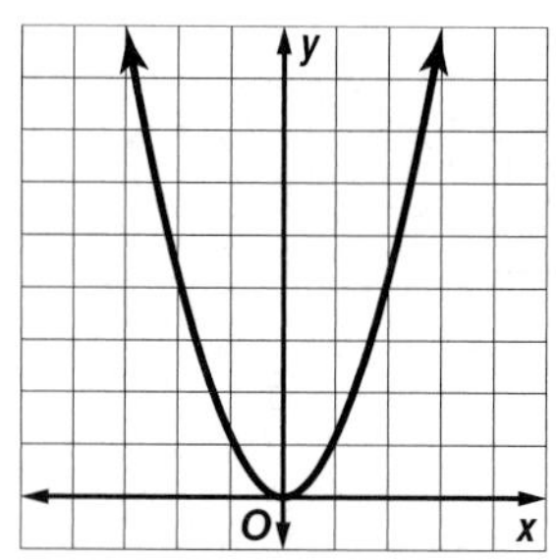

23. reflection of the graph of $y = |x|$ across the y-axis

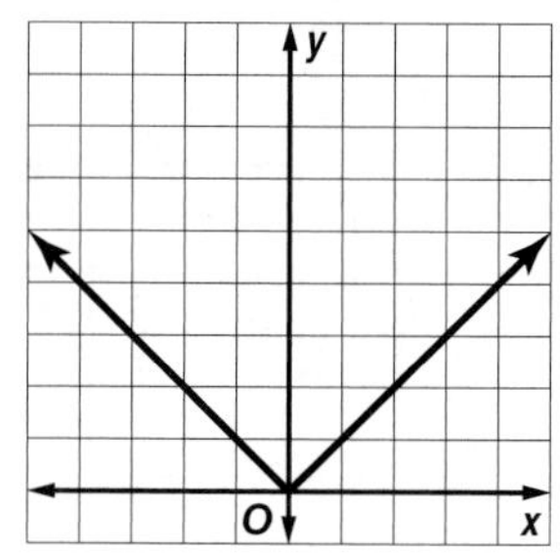

24. reflection of the graph of $y = |x|$ across the x-axis

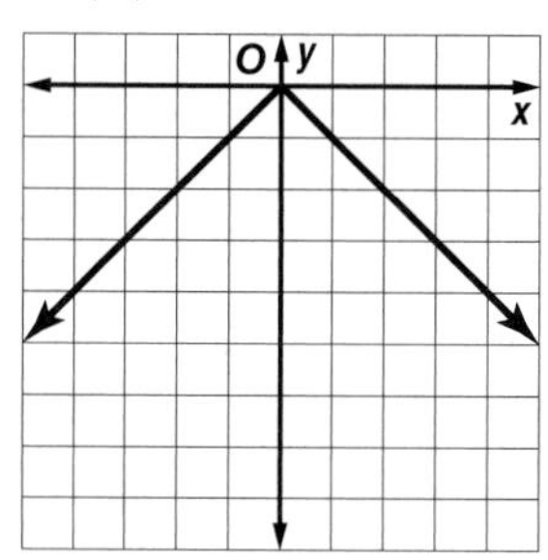

25. reflection of the graph of $y = x$ across the y-axis

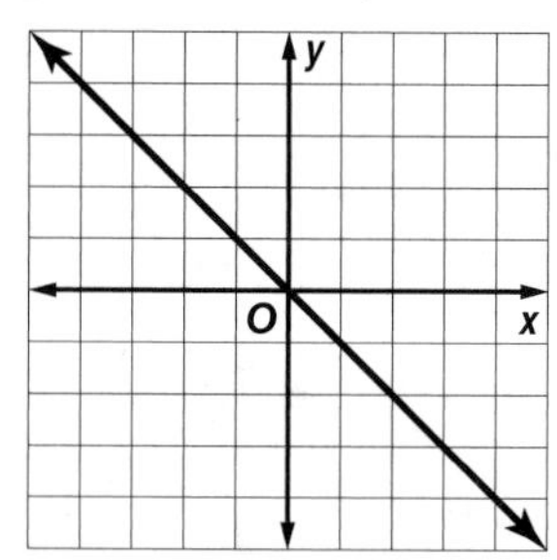

26. horizontal compression of the graph of $y = x^2$

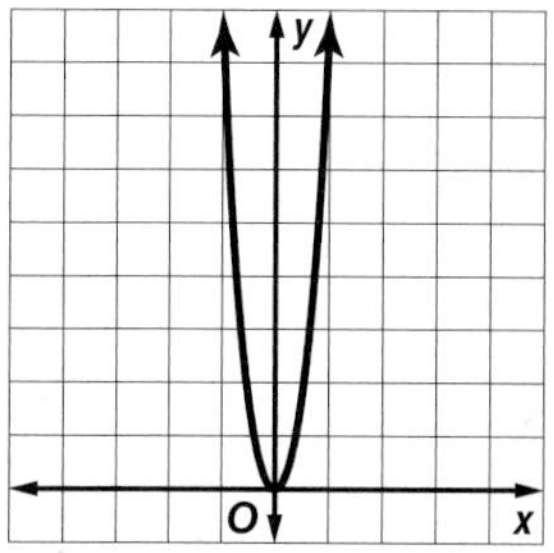

27. vertical expansion of the graph of $y = x$; The slope is steeper than that of $y = x$.

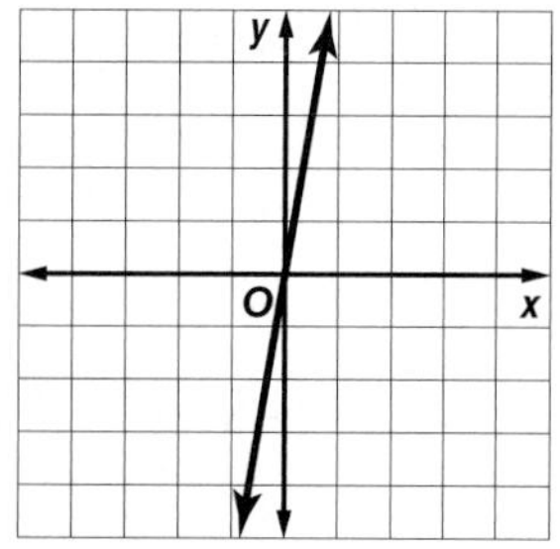

28. The dilation stetches the graph of $y = |x|$ vertically.

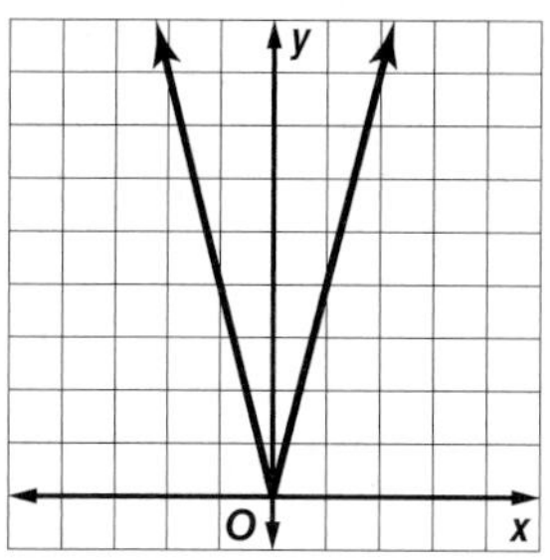

29. The dilation compresses the graph of $y = |x|$ horizontally.

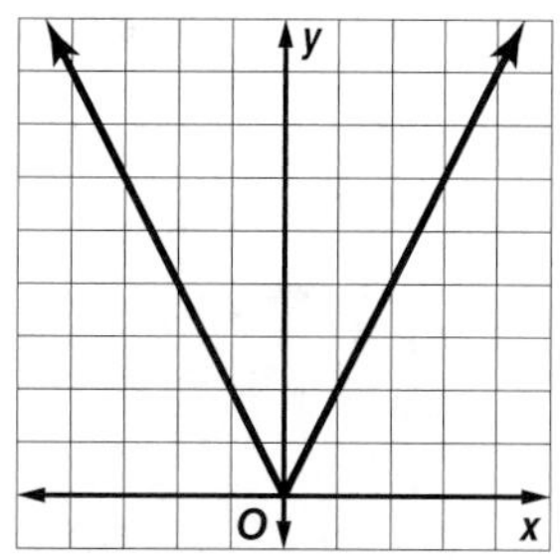

30. The dilation compresses the graph of $y = x$ vertically; the slope is not as steep as that of $y = x$.

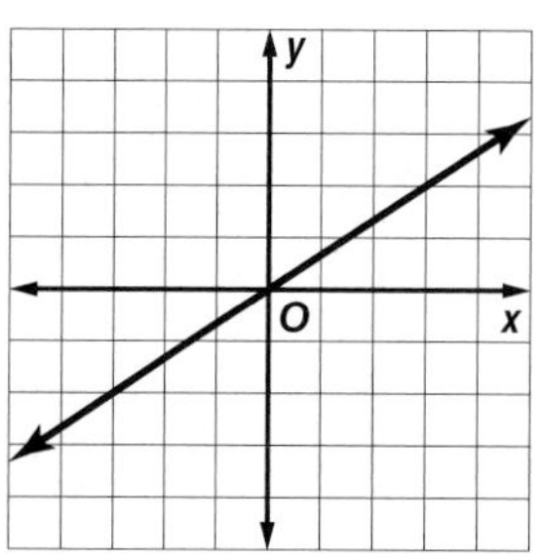

31. vertical compression of the graph of $y = x^2$

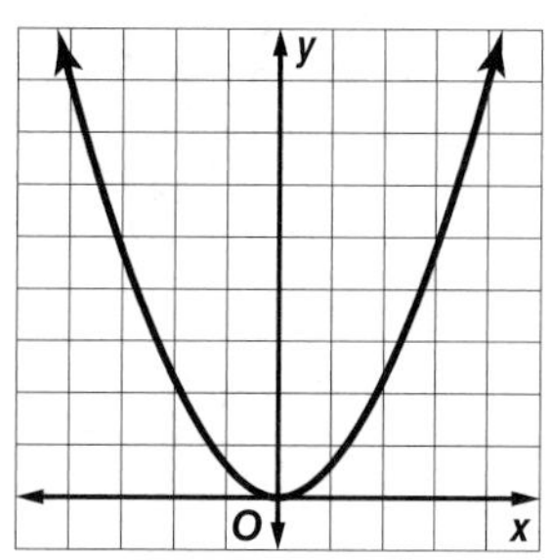

32. The graph is a dilation of the graph of $y = x$. The dilation stretches the graph vertically.

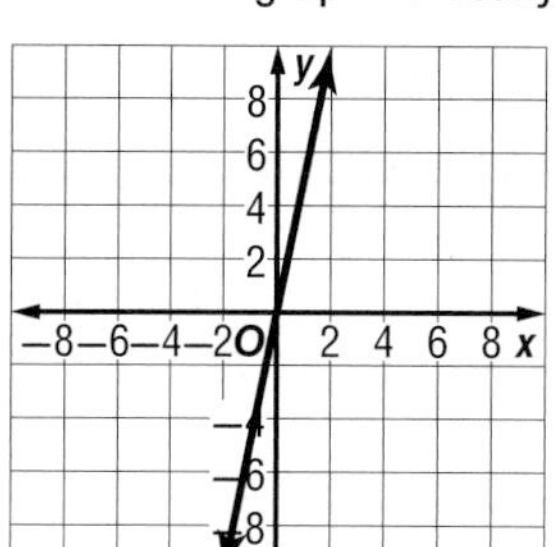

45. Sample graph:

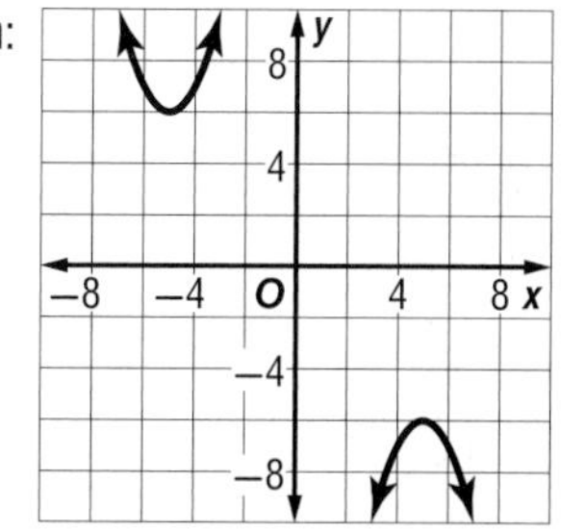

Sample answer: The figure in Quadrant II has been reflected and moved right 10 units.

Pages 117–118, Lesson 2-8, Guided Practice

1A.

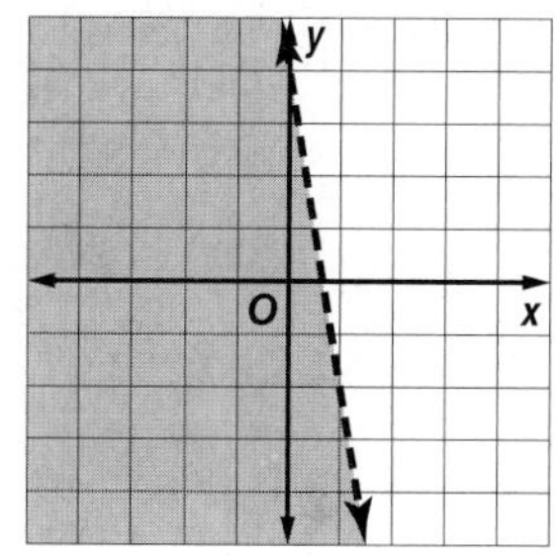

1B.

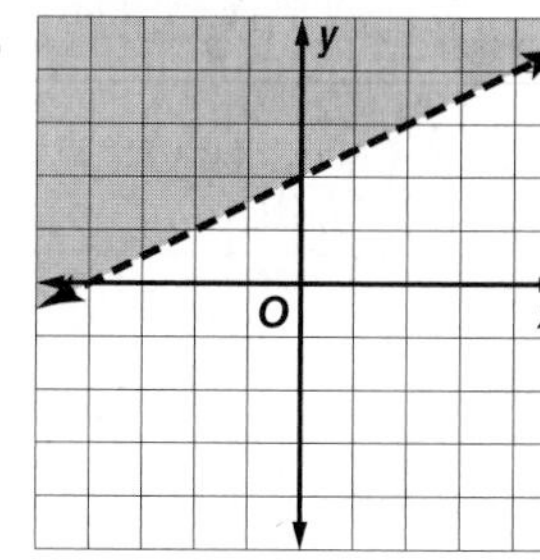

2. $g \leq -3r + 40$

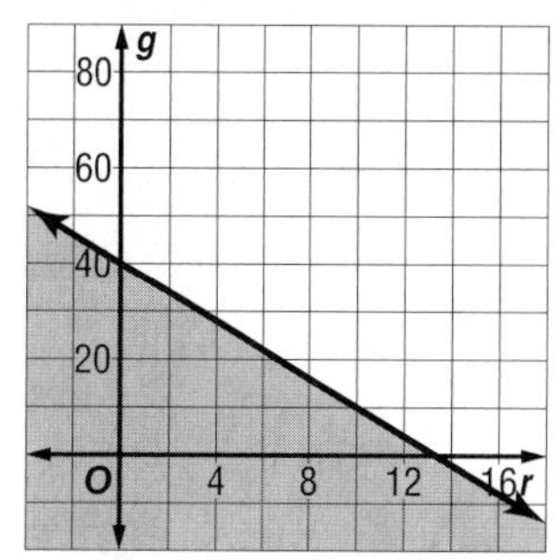

3A.

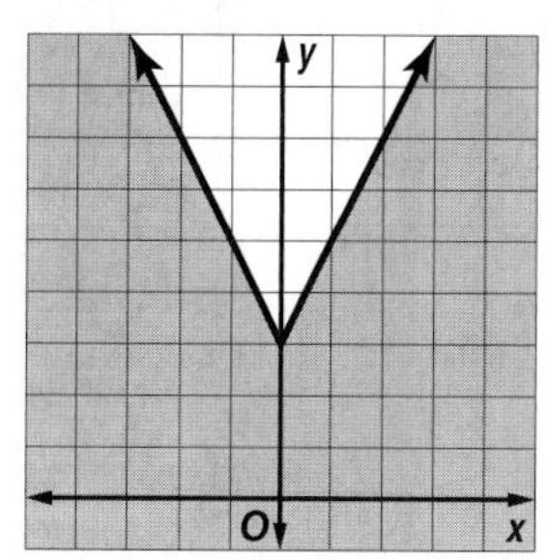

3B.

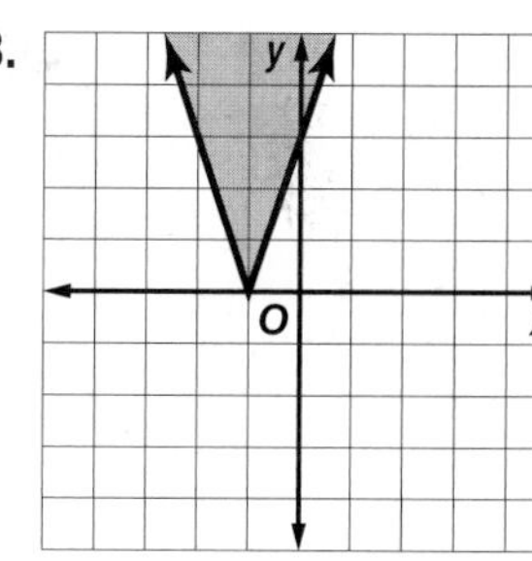

Pages 119–121, Lesson 2-8

5b.

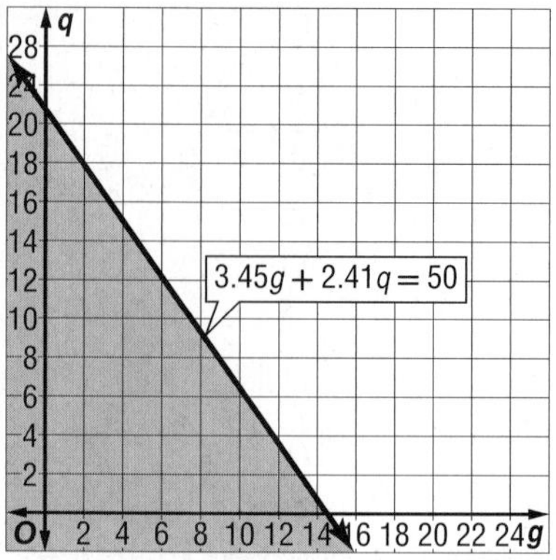

6.

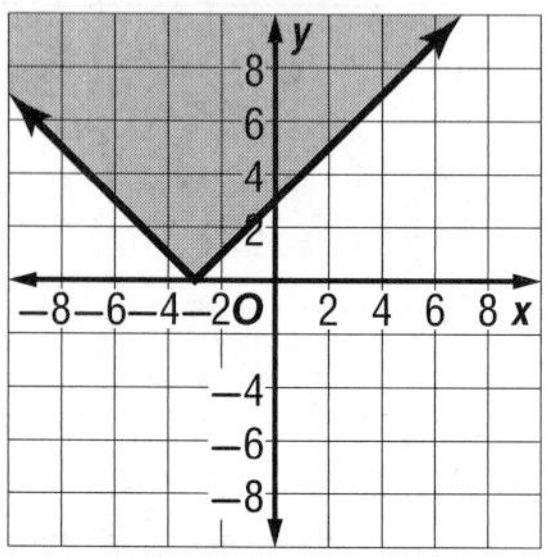

7.

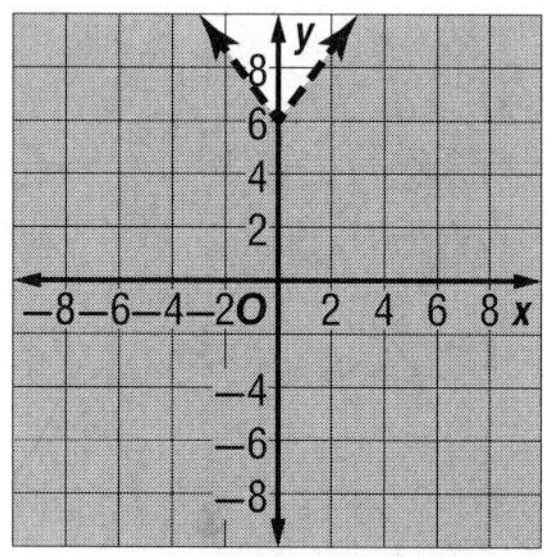

8.

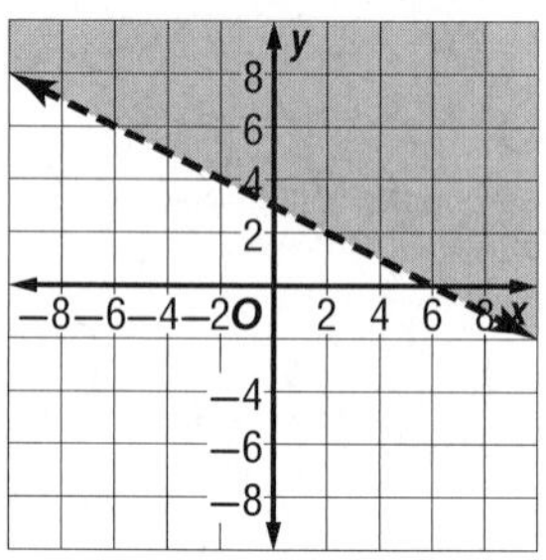

9.

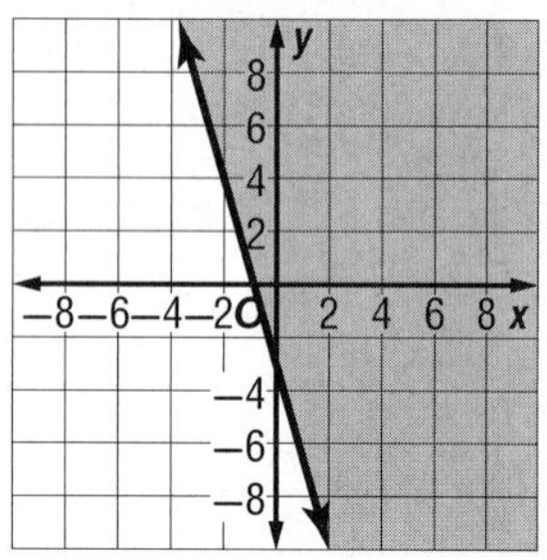

10.

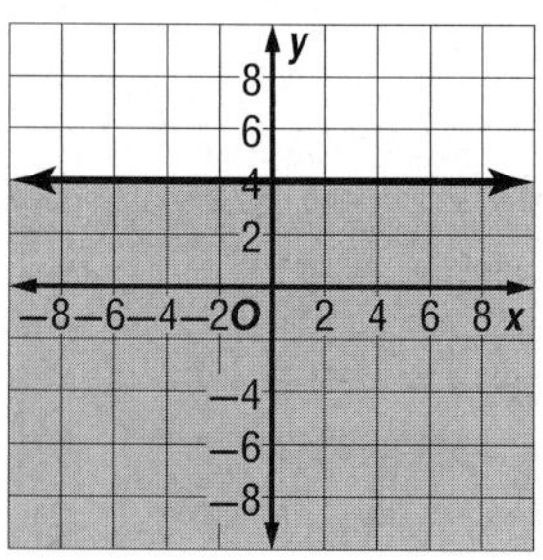

11.

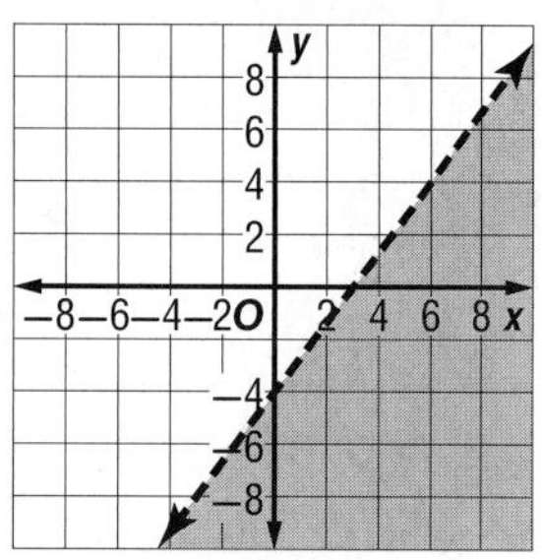

12.

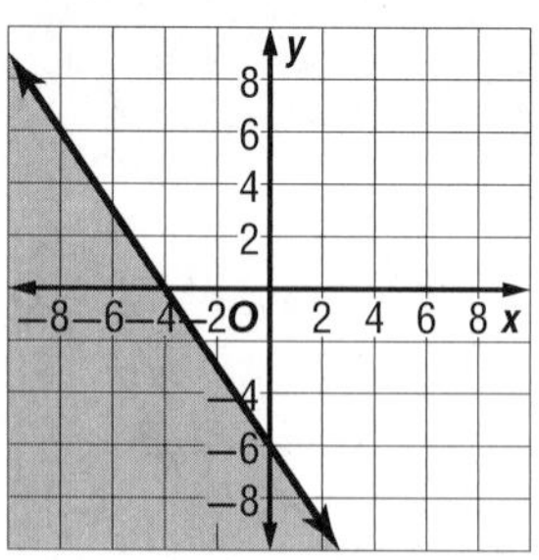

13.

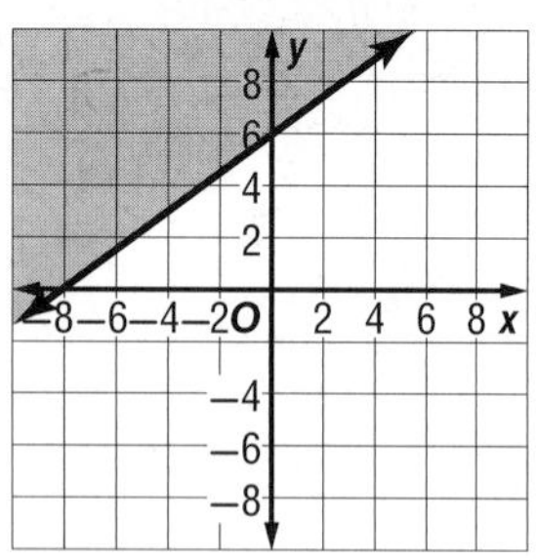

14a.

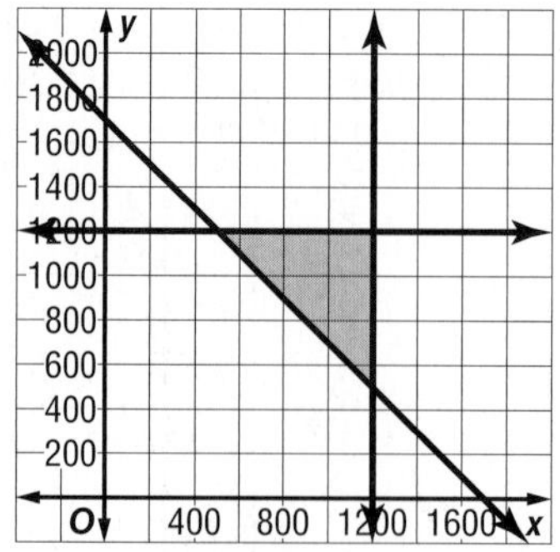

15.

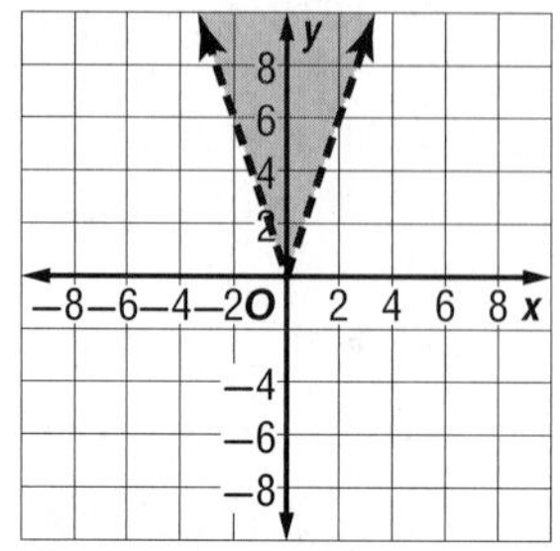

16.

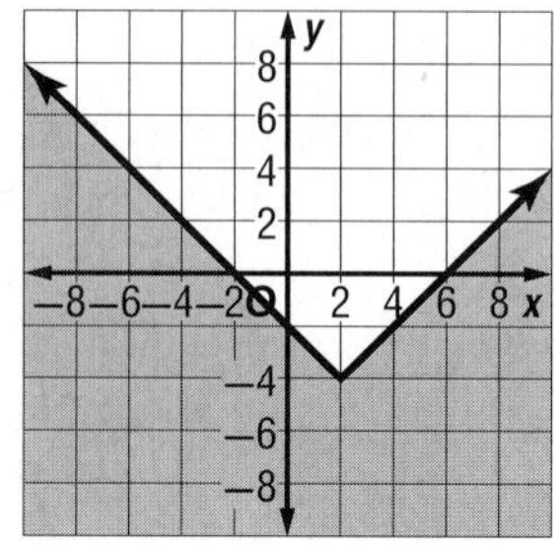

17.

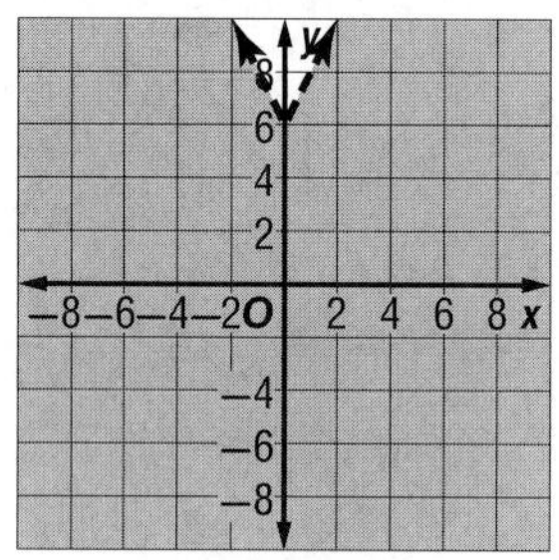

18.

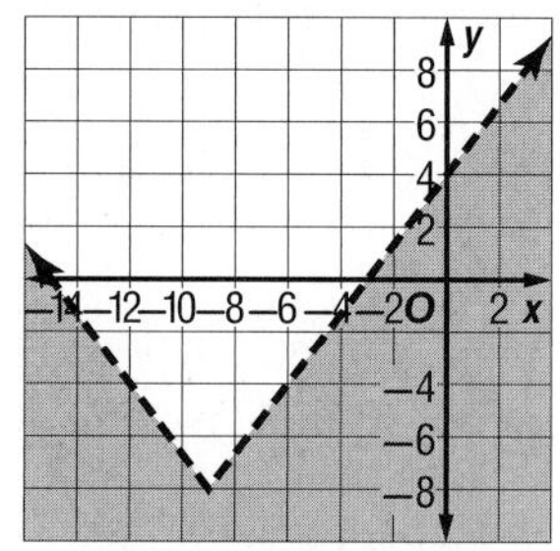

19.

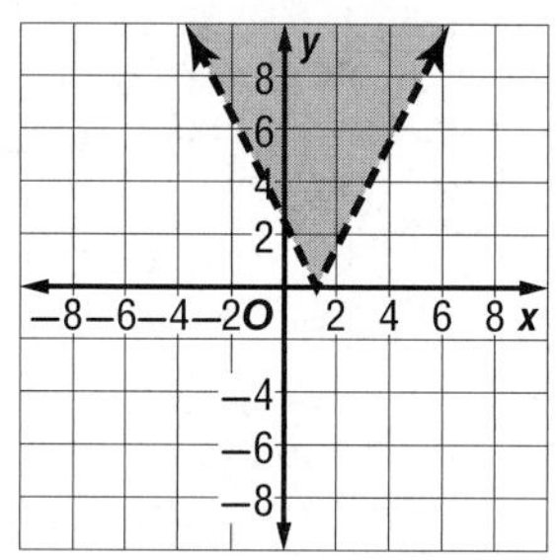

20.

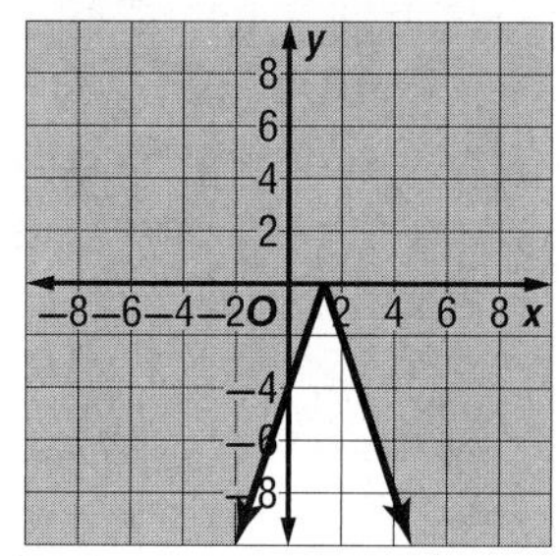

21b.

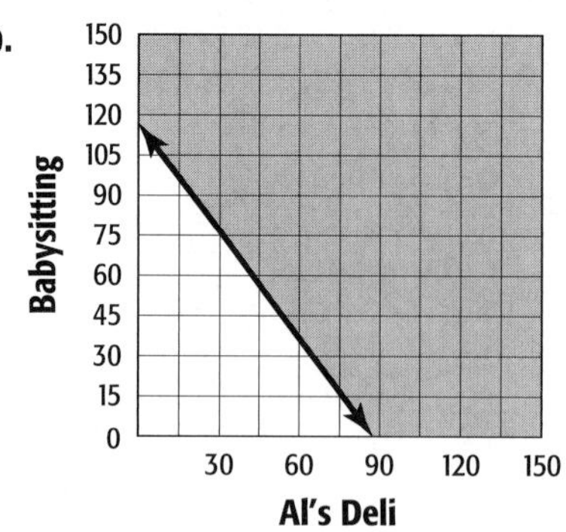

22.

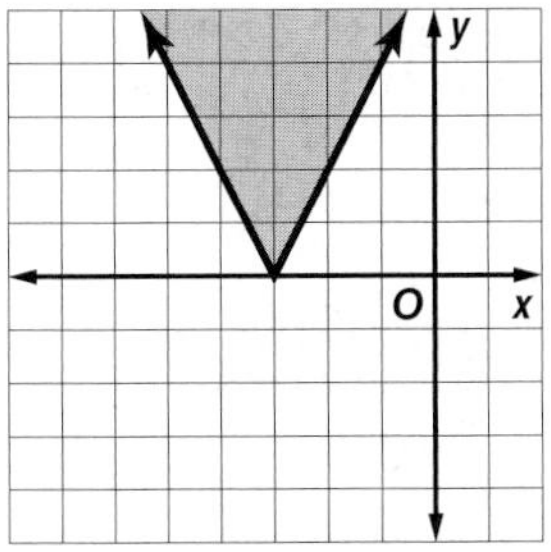

23.

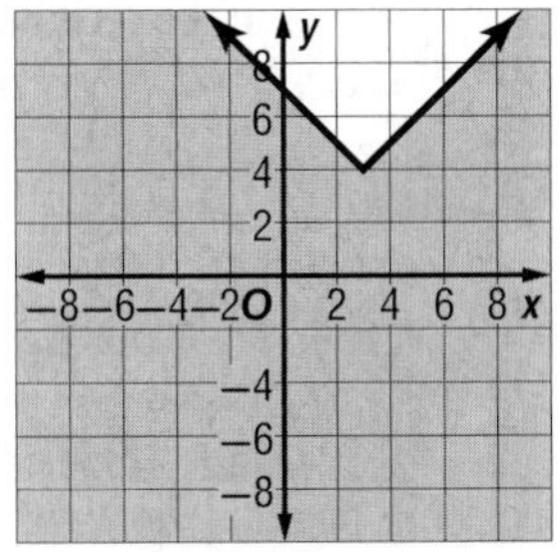

24.

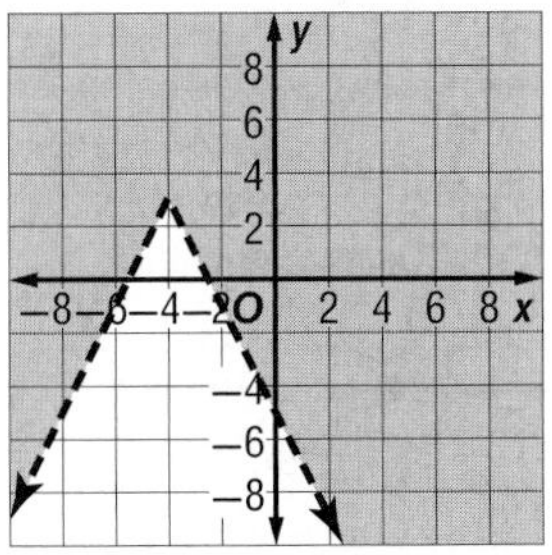

25.

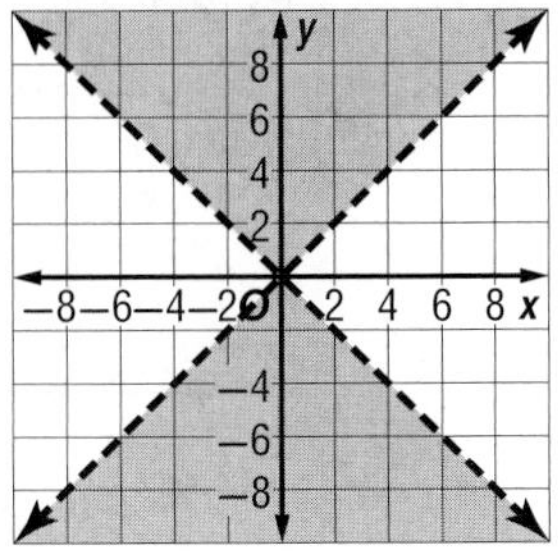

26.

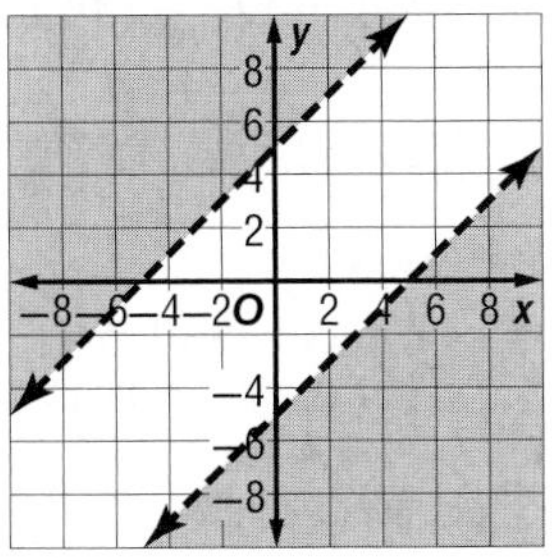

28b.

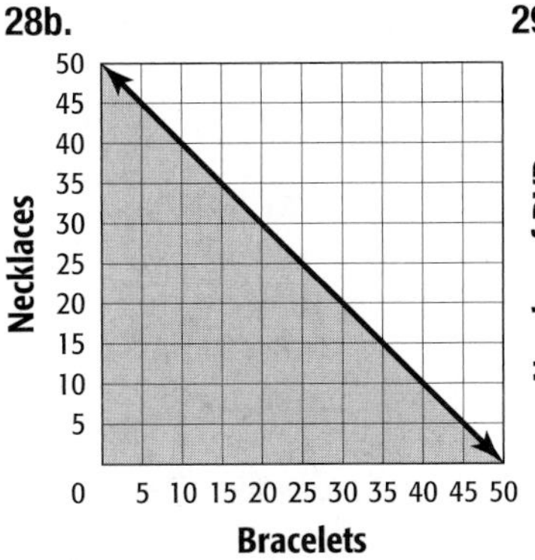

29b.

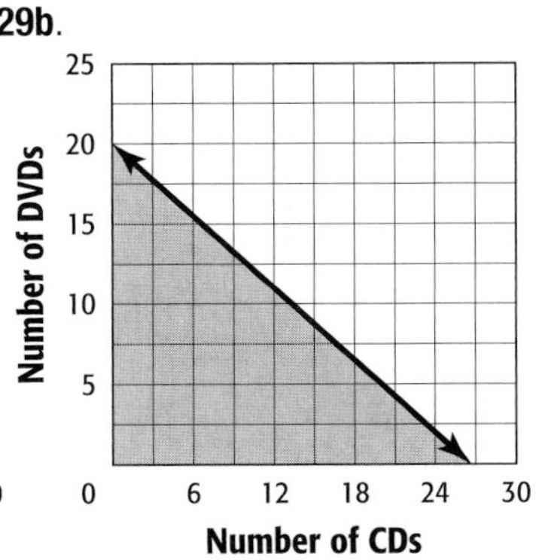

30.

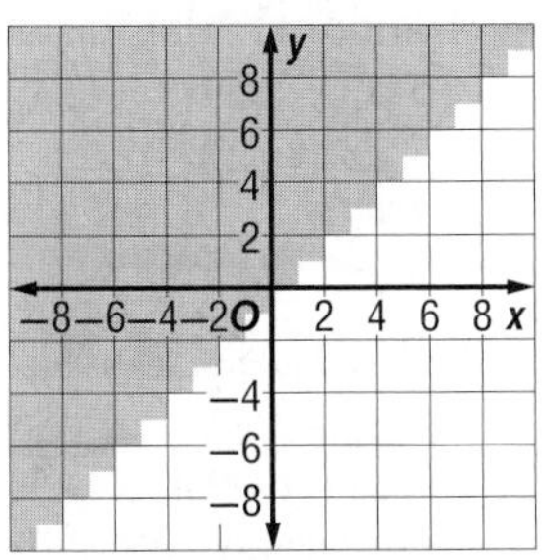

31.

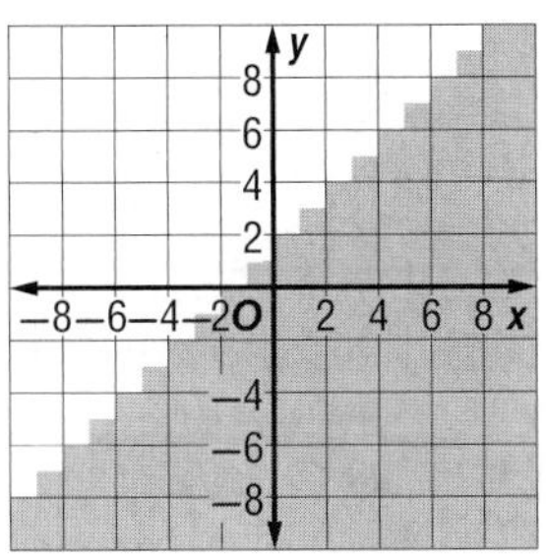

32.

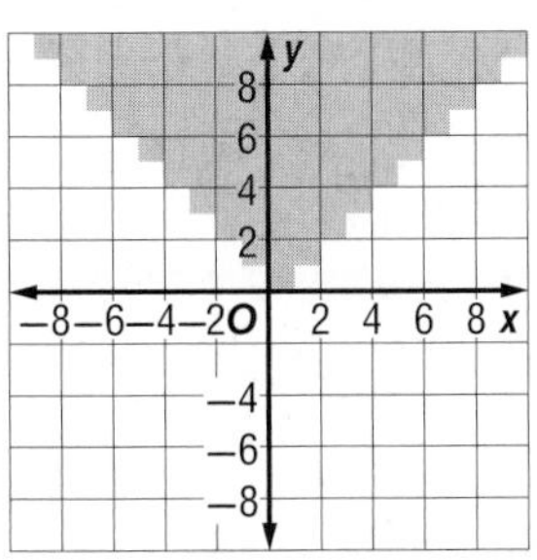

45.

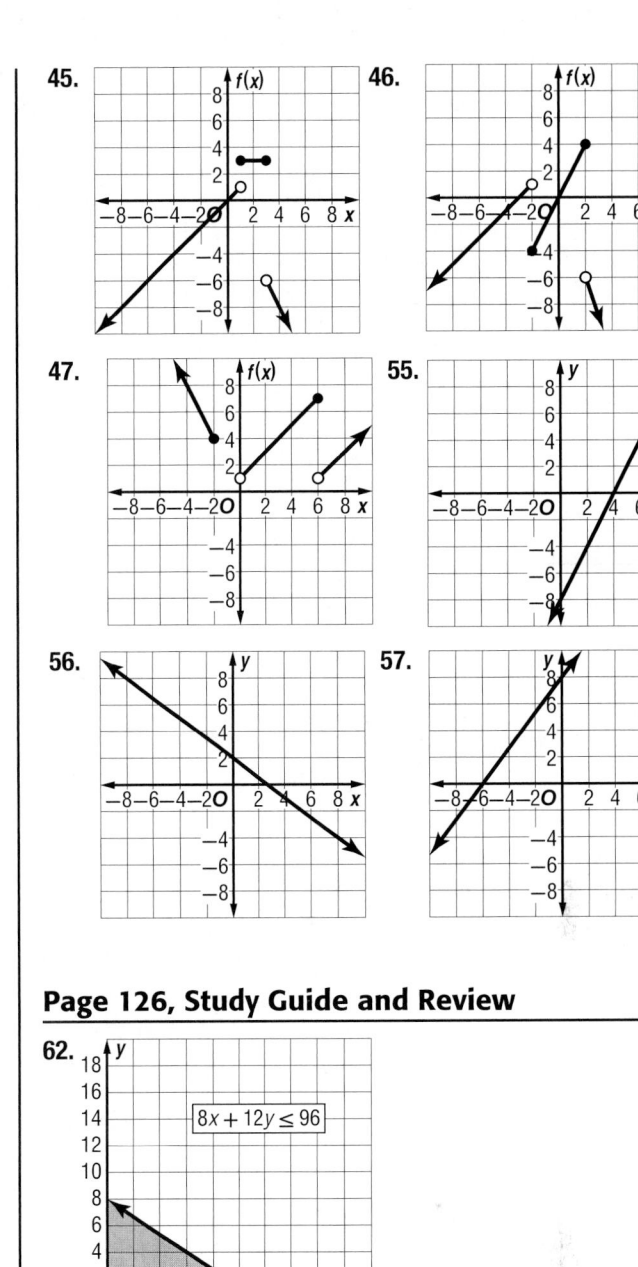

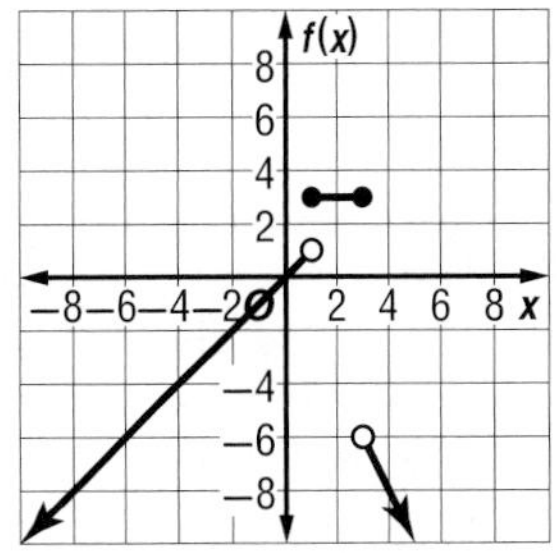

46.

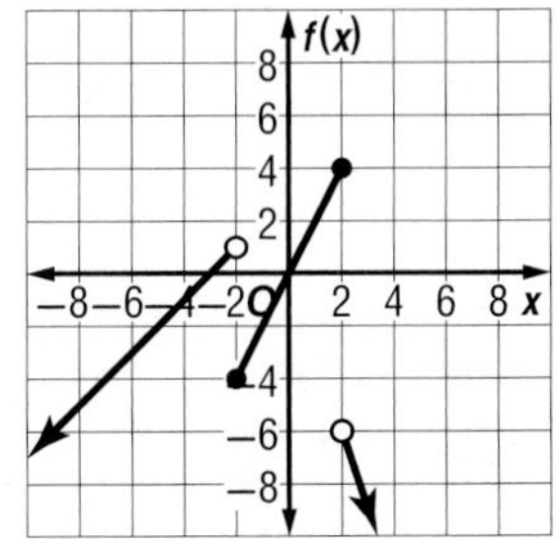

47.

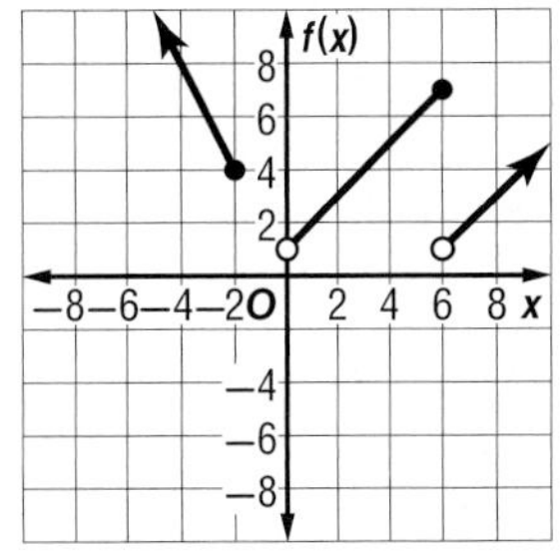

55.

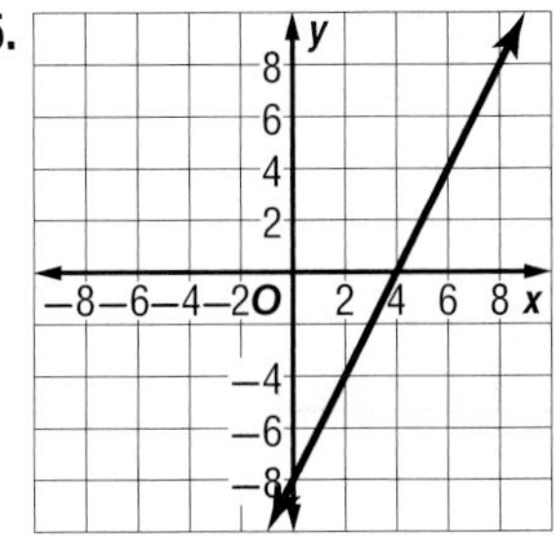

56.

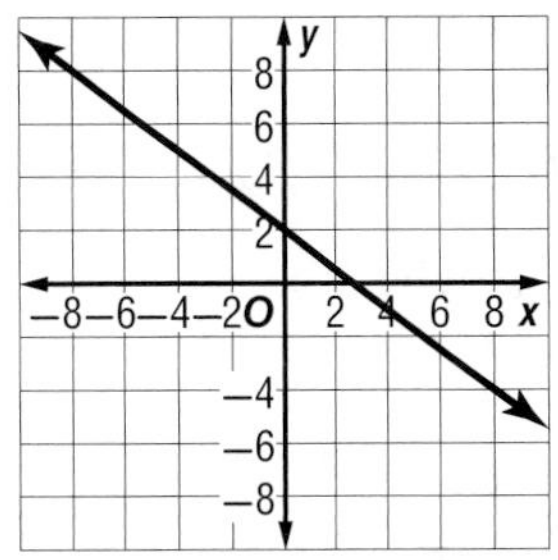

57.

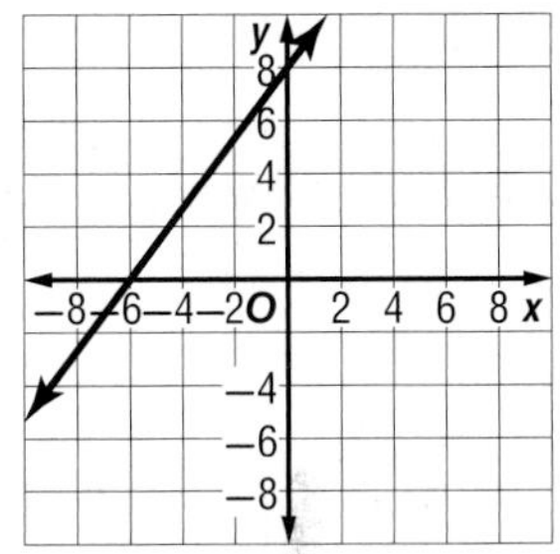

Page 126, Study Guide and Review

62.

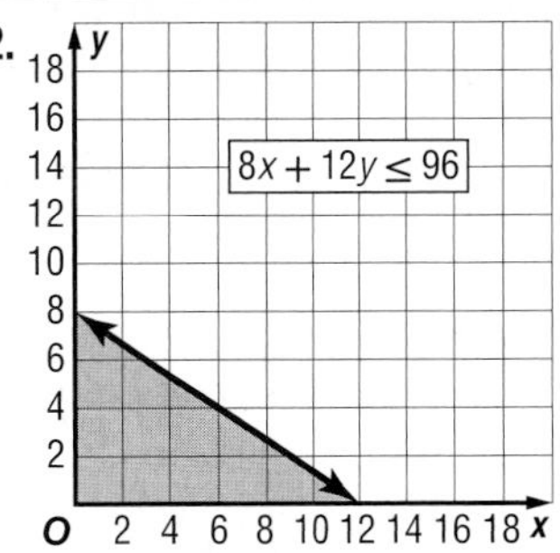

Page 127, Practice Test

19.

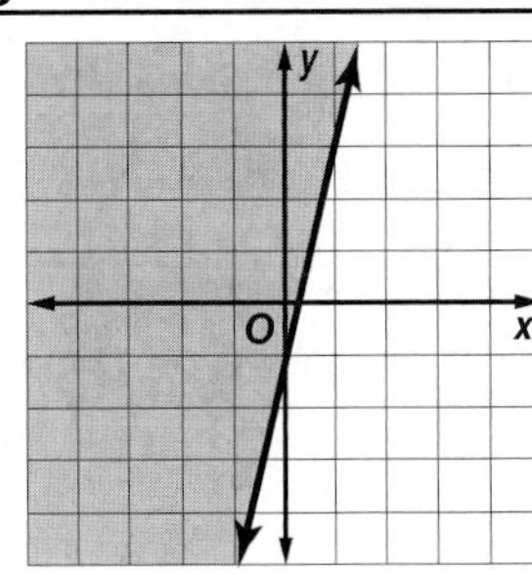

20.

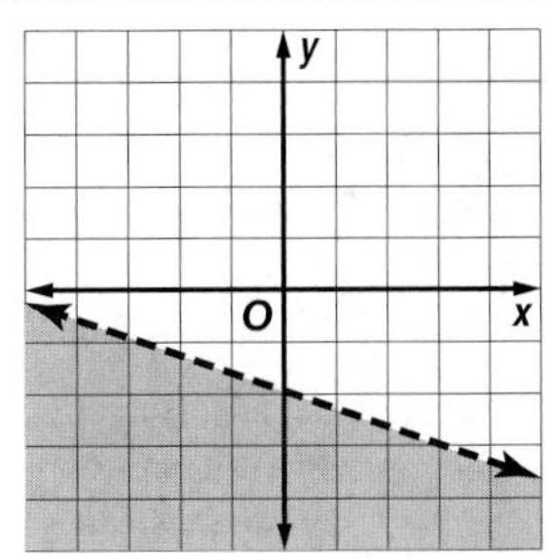

CHAPTER 3

Chapter Planner

Diagnostic Assessment
Quick Check, p. 133

	Lesson 3-1 Pacing: 1 day	Extend 3-1 Pacing: 0.5 day	Lesson 3-2 Pacing: 1 day
Title	**Solving Systems of Equations by Graphing**	**Graphing Technology Lab: Systems of Equations**	**Solving Systems of Equations Algebraically**
Objectives	• Solve systems of linear equations by using tables and graphs. • Classify systems of linear equations	• Solve systems of equations using a graphing calculator.	• Solve systems of linear equations by using substitution. • Solve systems of linear equations by using elimination.
Key Vocabulary	system of equations consistent independent dependent		substitution method elimination method
NGSSS	MA.912.A.3.14, MA.912.A.3.15	MA.912.A.3.14	MA.912.A.3.14, MA.912.A.3.15
Multiple Representations			p. 149
Lesson Resources	**Chapter 3 Resource Masters** • Study Guide and Intervention, pp. 5–6 AL OL ELL • Skills Practice, p. 7 AL OL ELL • Practice, p. 8 AL OL BL ELL • Word Problem Practice, p. 9 AL OL BL ELL • Enrichment, p. 10 OL BL • Spreadsheet Activity, p. 11 OL • Quiz 1, p. 39 AL OL BL ELL **Transparencies** • 5-Minute Check Transparency 3-1 AL OL BL ELL **Additional Print Resources** • Study Notebook AL OL BL ELL	**Materials** • TI-83/84 Plus or other graphing calculator	**Chapter 3 Resource Masters** • Study Guide and Intervention, pp. 12–13 AL OL ELL • Skills Practice, p. 14 AL OL ELL • Practice, p. 15 AL OL BL ELL • Word Problem Practice, p. 16 AL OL BL ELL • Enrichment, p. 17 OL BL • Quiz 1, p. 39 AL OL BL ELL **Transparencies** • 5-Minute Check Transparency 3-2 AL OL BL ELL **Additional Print Resources** • Study Notebook AL OL BL ELL • *Teaching Algebra with Manipulatives*, p. 190 AL OL ELL
Technology for Every Lesson	FL Math Online glencoe.com • Extra Examples • Self-Check Quizzes • Personal Tutor • Homework Help	**CD/DVD Resources** IWB INTERACTIVE WHITEBOARD READY IWB StudentWorks Plus IWB Interactive Classroom IWB Diagnostic and Assessment Planner	• TeacherWorks Plus • eSolutions Manual Plus • ExamView Assessment Suite
Get Animated			
Differentiated Instruction	pp. 136, 138, 141		pp. 146, 150

KEY: AL Approaching Level OL On Level BL Beyond Level ELL English Learners

Suggested Pacing			
Time Periods	Instruction	Review & Assessment	Total
45-minute	6	2	8
90-minute	4	1	5

Systems of Equations and Inequalities

Lesson 3-3 Pacing: 1 day	Extend 3-3 Pacing: 0.5 day	Lesson 3-4 Pacing: 1 day	Lesson 3-5 Pacing: 1 day
Solving Systems of Inequalities by Graphing	**Graphing Technology Lab: Systems of Linear Inequalities**	**Optimization with Linear Programming**	**Systems of Equations in Three Variables**
• Solve systems of inequalities by graphing. • Determine the coordinates of the vertices of a region formed by the graph of a system of inequalities.	• Graph systems of linear inequalities using a graphing calculator.	• Find the maximum and minimum values of a function over a region. • Solve real-world optimization problems using linear programming.	• Solve systems of linear equations in three variables. • Solve real-world problems using systems of linear equations in three variables.
system of inequalities		linear programming feasible region constraints unbounded optimize	ordered triple
MA.912.A.3.14, MA.912.A.3.15	MA.912.A.3.14	MA.912.A.3.14, MA.912.A.3.15	MA.912.A.3.14, MA.912.A.3.15
Chapter 3 Resource Masters • Study Guide and Intervention, pp. 18–19 AL OL ELL • Skills Practice, p. 20 AL OL ELL • Practice, p. 21 AL OL BL ELL • Word Problem Practice, p. 22 AL OL BL ELL • Enrichment, p. 23 OL BL AL OL BL ELL • Quiz 2, p. 39 AL OL BL ELL **Transparencies** • 5-Minute Check Transparency 3-3 AL OL BL ELL **Additional Print Resources** • Study Notebook AL OL BL ELL • *Teaching Algebra with Manipulatives*, p. 191 AL OL ELL	**Materials** • TI-83/84 Plus or other graphing calculator	**Chapter 3 Resource Masters** • Study Guide and Intervention, pp. 24–25 AL OL ELL • Skills Practice, p. 26 AL OL ELL • Practice, p. 27 AL OL BL ELL • Word Problem Practice, p. 28 AL OL BL ELL • Enrichment, p. 29 OL BL • Graphing Calculator Activity, p. 30 OL • Quiz 3, p. 40 AL OL BL ELL **Transparencies** • 5-Minute Check Transparency 3-4 AL OL BL ELL **Additional Print Resources** • Study Notebook AL OL BL ELL	**Chapter 3 Resource Masters** • Study Guide and Intervention, pp. 31–32 AL OL ELL • Skills Practice, p. 33 AL OL ELL • Practice, p. 34 AL OL BL ELL • Word Problem Practice, p. 35 AL OL BL ELL • Enrichment, p. 36 OL BL • Quiz 4, p. 40 AL OL BL ELL **Transparencies** • 5-Minute Check Transparency 3-5 AL OL BL ELL **Additional Print Resources** • Study Notebook AL OL BL ELL • *Teaching Algebra with Manipulatives*, p. 193 AL OL ELL

FL Math Online glencoe.com
- Extra Examples
- Self-Check Quizzes
- Personal Tutor
- Homework Help

CD/DVD Resources IWB INTERACTIVE WHITEBOARD READY
- IWB StudentWorks Plus
- IWB Interactive Classroom
- IWB Diagnostic and Assessment Planner
- TeacherWorks Plus
- eSolutions Manual Plus
- ExamView Assessment Suite

Animation		Animation	Interactive Lab
pp. 153, 155, 157		pp. 162, 166	pp. 170, 173

Formative Assessment
Mid-Chapter Quiz, p. 159

Summative Assessment
- Study Guide and Review, pp. 174–176
- Practice Test, p. 177

CHAPTER 3

Assessment and Intervention

SE = Student Edition, **TE** = Teacher Edition, **CRM** = Chapter Resource Masters

	Diagnosis	Prescription
Diagnostic Assessment	**Beginning Chapter 3**	
	Get Ready for Chapter 3 **SE,** p. 123	Response to Intervention **TE,** p. 133
	Beginning Every Lesson	
	Then, Now, Why? **SE** 5-Minute Check Transparencies	Chapter 3 **SE,** p. 1 through p.19 Concepts and Skills Bank **SE** pp. 994–1007
Formative Assessment	**During/After Every Lesson**	
	Guided Practice **SE,** every example Check Your Understanding **SE** H.O.T. Problems **SE** Spiral Review **SE** Additional Examples **TE** Watch Out! **TE** Step 4, Assess **TE** Chapter 3 Quizzes **CRM,** pp. 39–40 Self-Check Quizzes glencoe.com	**Tier 1 Intervention** Concepts and Skills Bank **SE,** pp. 994–1007 Skills Practice **CRM,** Ch. 1–3 glencoe.com **Tier 2 Intervention** Differentiated Instruction **TE** Study Guide and Intervention Masters **CRM,** Ch. 1–3 **Tier 3 Intervention** *Math Triumphs, Alg. 2,* Ch. 3
	Mid-Chapter	
	Mid-Chapter Quiz **SE,** p. 159 Mid-Chapter Test **CRM,** p. 41 ExamView Assessment Suite	**Tier 1 Intervention** Concepts and Skills Bank **SE,** pp. 994–1007 Skills Practice **CRM,** Ch. 1–3 glencoe.com **Tier 2 Intervention** Study Guide and Intervention Masters **CRM,** Ch. 1–3 **Tier 3 Intervention** *Math Triumphs, Alg. 2,* Ch. 3
	Before Chapter Test	
	Chapter Study Guide and Review **SE,** pp. 174–176 Practice Test **SE,** p. 177 Standardized Test Practice **SE,** pp. 178–181 Chapter Test glencoe.com Standardized Test Practice glencoe.com Vocabulary Review glencoe.com ExamView Assessment Suite	**Tier 1 Intervention** Concepts and Skills Bank **SE,** pp. 994–1007 Skills Practice **CRM**, Ch. 1–3 glencoe.com **Tier 2 Intervention** Study Guide and Intervention Masters **CRM,** Ch. 1–3 **Tier 3 Intervention** *Math Triumphs, Alg. 2,* Ch. 3
Summative Assessment	**After Chapter 3**	
	Multiple-Choice Tests, Forms 1, 2A, 2B **CRM,** pp. 43–48 Free-Response Tests, Forms 2C, 2D, 3 **CRM,** pp. 49–54 Vocabulary Test **CRM,** p. 42 Extended Response Test **CRM,** p. 55 Standardized Test Practice **CRM,** pp. 56–58 ExamView Assessment Suite	Study Guide and Intervention Masters **CRM,** Ch. 1–3 glencoe.com

Differentiated Instruction

Option 1 Reaching All Learners AL OL BL ELL

KINESTHETIC Put students into pairs. Give each pair a system of equations that is consistent and independent. Ask pairs to graph each equation on a separate transparency coordinate grid. Then have students combine the graphs by overlapping them. Have each student tell one point that is a solution and one point that is not a solution.

INTERPERSONAL Give pairs of students a system of equations. Ask them to explain which method they would use to solve the system, how they decided on that method, and what steps that method will involve when they are actually solving the system.

Option 2 Approaching Level AL

On a coordinate grid, draw a pair of intersecting lines. Discuss with the class how to find the slope, y-intercept, point of intersection, and equation for each line. Explain that since these equations have been graphed on the same coordinate grid, they are called a system of equations. Demonstrate how the point of intersection is a solution to both equations. Then, shade the graph above one line and below the other. Discuss with students how the shading changes the equals signs in the system of equations to inequality signs. Discuss how the shading affects the solution set.

Option 3 English Learners ELL

Create a set of flashcards to help students understand the vocabulary in the first lesson of this chapter. On one side of the card, draw a graph of intersecting lines, one line, or a pair of parallel lines. On the other side, write *consistent and independent, consistent and dependent,* or *inconsistent.*

Option 4 Beyond Level BL

Have students use three different colored index cards or sheets of lightweight cardboard to model the graphs of system of equations in three variables. Once a model is constructed, have students indicate the number of solutions their system has. Below are four such models.

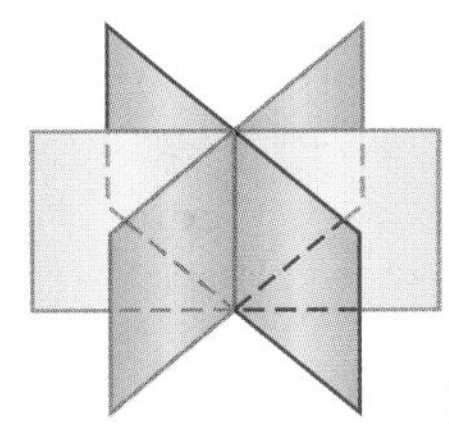

Infinitely many solutions

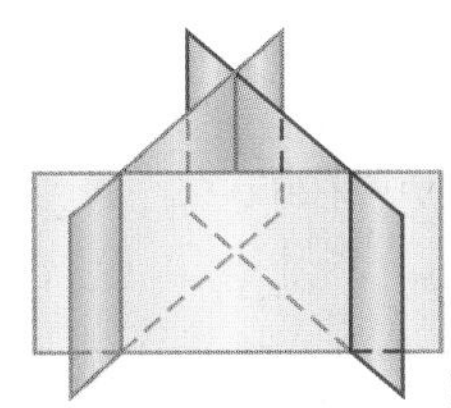

No solution

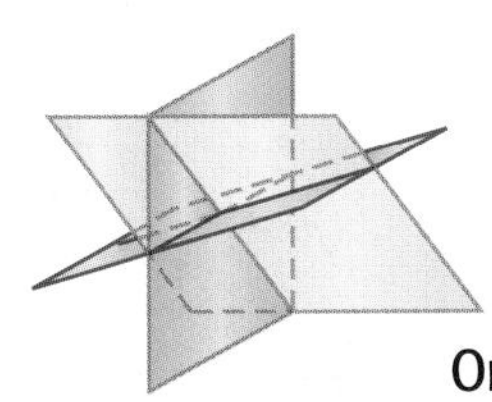

One solution

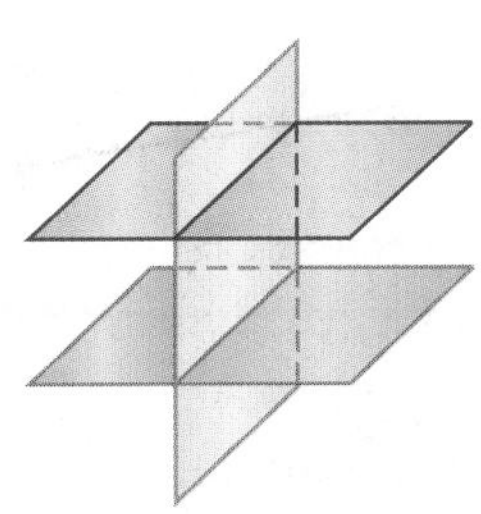

No solution

FL Math Online Access Point Activities

Focus on Mathematical Content

Vertical Alignment

Before Chapter 3

Related Topics from Algebra 1

- graph equations of lines
- transform and solve equations

Chapter 3

Related Topics from Algebra 2

- analyze situations and formulate systems of equations in two or more unknowns to solve problems
- use algebraic methods, graphs, or tables to solve systems of equations or inequalities
- interpret and determine the reasonableness of solutions to systems of equations for given contexts

After Chapter 3

Preparation for Precalculus

- define functions, describe characteristics of functions, and translate among verbal, numerical, graphical, and symbolic representations of functions
- use functions and their properties to model and solve real-life problems

Lesson-by-Lesson Preview

3-1 Solving Systems of Equations by Graphing

Two or more equations with the same variables are called a *system of equations.* A system of equations can be solved by graphing each equation on the same coordinate plane.
A solution to a system is an ordered pair that represents a point on both lines and satisfies both equations.

For any two lines in a plane, the lines must be intersecting, coincident, or parallel.

consistent and independent

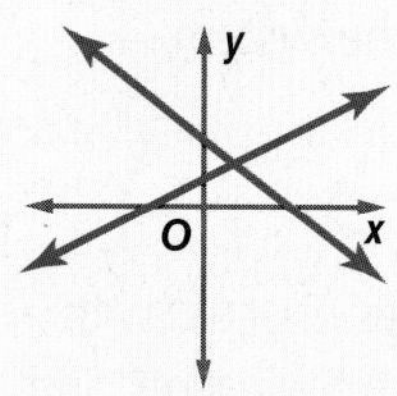

- intersecting lines
  If the two lines intersect, then the system has exactly one solution and is *consistent and independent.*

consistent and dependent

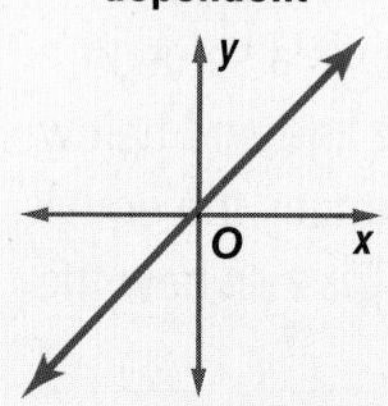

- coincident lines
  If the two lines coincide, then the system has an infinite number of solutions and is *consistent and dependent.*

inconsistent

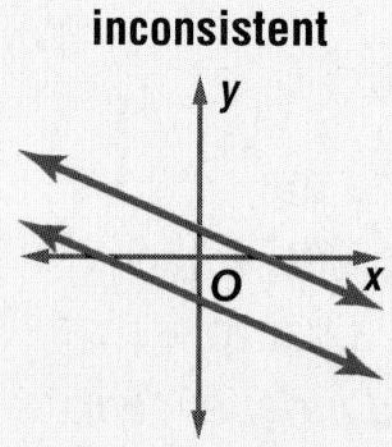

- parallel lines
  If the two lines are parallel, then the system has no solution and is *inconsistent.*

3-2 Solving Systems of Equations Algebraically

The methods of substitution and elimination can be used to solve systems of equations algebraically.

- To use the substitution method, solve one of the equations for one of the two variables. Then substitute the resulting expression into the other equation. This results in a single equation in one variable that can be solved. Then substitute to solve for the other variable.
- The elimination method is used when the coefficients of one of the variables in both equations are the same or additive inverses. To use this method, add or subtract the two equations. Solve the resulting equation, and then solve for the other variable.

- If the two equations, when in standard form, do not have one variable with coefficients that are the same or additive inverses, then multiplication is used to write equivalent equations so that the result is a system of equations in which one of the variables has coefficients that are the same or additive inverses.

3-3 Solving Systems of Inequalities by Graphing

Solving a system of inequalities by graphing is similar to solving a system of equations by graphing. The inequalities in the system are graphed on the same coordinate plane, and the ordered pairs that satisfy all of the inequalities in the system are found. For a system of two inequalities, the region that is common to the two inequalities must be determined. If the two regions do not intersect, the solution is the empty set, and no solution exists.

If the graph of a system of three or more linear inequalities forms an enclosed bounded region, the vertices of the region can be found by determining the coordinates of where the boundary lines intersect.

3-4 Optimization with Linear Programming

Solving a linear programming problem builds on the skills learned in Lesson 3-3. After the system of inequalities has been graphed and the coordinates of the vertices of the feasible region determined, a given function must be evaluated using the vertex coordinates. The solution to the problem is the point that maximizes or minimizes the function.

In a linear programming problem,

- The inequalities in the system are called *constraints.*
- The region that represents the system's solution is called the *feasible region.*
- The intersections of pairs of boundary lines are referred to as the *vertices of the feasible region.*

A bounded feasible region is one whose outline is a polygon, and an unbounded feasible region is one whose boundary is not enclosed by the constraints.

3-5 Systems of Equations in Three Variables

The graph of a first-degree equation in three variables is a plane. There are several possibilities for the solution to a system of equations in three variables, since the three planes can intersect in a variety of ways.

- at a *point* — The ordered triple for that point is a single solution to the system.
- in a *line* — The system has an infinite number of solutions, any point on that line.
- in the same *plane* — This system would also have an infinite number of solutions, all points in the plane.
- *no points in common* — The solution is the empty set.

Solving a system of equations in three variables algebraically is similar to solving systems of equations in two variables. The elimination method can be used to make a system of two equations in two variables, and then solve the system of two equations to find the two variables. Finally, substitute the values of the two variables into any of the original equations to find the value of the third variable.

When solving systems of equations in three variables,

- If there is a statement–such as $0 = 1$–that is always false, then at least two of the planes are parallel. The system has no solution.
- If there is a statement–such as $0 = 0$–that is always true, then at least two of the planes coincide. If the third plane intersects or coincides with that plane, then the number of solutions is infinite; if the third plane is parallel to the first plane, then the system has no solution.

CHAPTER 3 Notes

Chapter Project

Breaking Even

Students use what they have learned about linear systems to investigate relationships between quantitative measures in business.

- Ask students to imagine that they are setting up a small business to sell T-shirts in the summer in a resort town. They will buy plain T-shirts from a distributor for $2 each, print a logo on them, and then sell them to tourists.
- Assume space rental and permits cost $1500 for the summer, and materials for printing cost $1.25 per shirt. Write a linear function giving total cost C as a function of number of shirts sold x. Then graph the function.
- If each shirt can be sold for $8, write a function for total income as a function of number of shirts sold x. Then graph this function.
- The intersection of the two lines represents the *break-even point,* where total income equals total cost. Estimate the number of shirts that must be sold to break even for the summer, then solve algebraically to find the exact answer.
- Finally, write a function that gives the total profit (which equals total income minus total cost) for the summer as a function of the number of shirts sold.

CHAPTER 3 Systems of Equations and Inequalities

Then

In Chapter 2, you graphed equations of lines, transformed functions, and solved equations.

Now

In Chapter 3, you will:

- Solve systems of linear equations graphically and algebraically.
- Solve systems of linear inequalities graphically.
- Solve problems by using linear programming.

NGSSS

MA.912.A.3.14
MA.912.A.3.15

Why?

BUSINESS Most of the time, being successful in business means that you have to have good math skills. In this chapter, you will learn how to maximize your profits and minimize your costs. By doing this you will earn the most money possible.

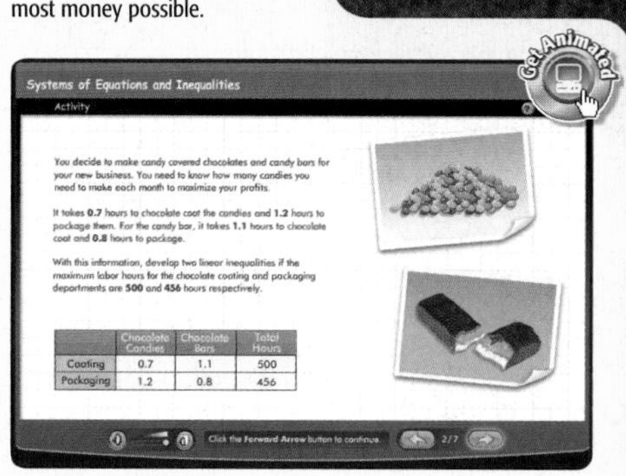

Key Vocabulary Introduce the key vocabulary in the chapter using the routine below.

Define: A consistent system of equations is one that has at least one solution.

Example: The system of equations shown has one solution, so it is consistent.

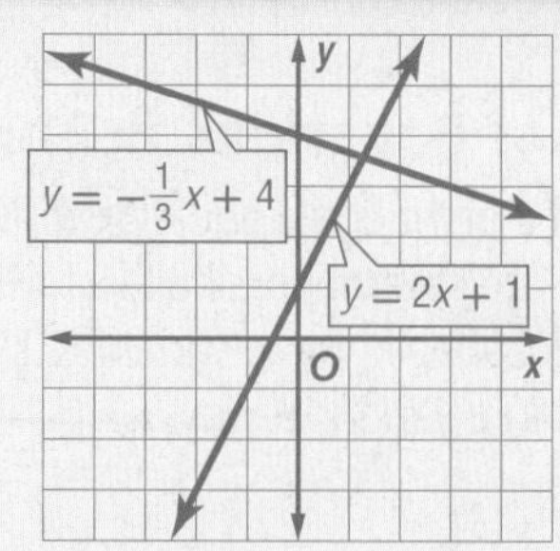

Ask: Would a system of equations that has infinitely many solutions be considered consistent? Explain.

Yes; because it would have more than one solution.

Get Ready for Chapter 3

Diagnose Readiness You have two options for checking Prerequisite Skills.

Text Option Take the Quick Check below. Refer to the Quick Review for help.

*Quick*Check

(Used in Lessons 3-1 and 3-3) 1–6. See Chapter 3 Answer Appendix.

Graph each equation. (Lesson 2-2)

1. $x = 4y$

2. $y = \frac{1}{3}x + 5$

3. $x + 2y = 4$

4. $y = -x + 6$

5. $3x + 5y = 15$

6. $3y - 2x = -12$

7. BUSINESS A museum charges $8.50 for adult tickets and $5.25 for children's tickets. On Friday they made $650. (Lesson 2-4)

a. Write an equation that can be used to model the ticket sales. $8.50a + 5.25c = 650$

b. Graph the equation. See Chapter 3 Answer Appendix.

(Used in Lesson 3-3)

Graph each inequality. (Lesson 2-8)

8. $y < 3$

9. $x + y \geq 1$

10. $3x - y > 6$

11. $x + 2y \leq 5$

12. $y > 4x - 1$

13. $5x - 4y < 12$

8–13. See Chapter 3 Answer Appendix.

14. FUNDRAISER The student council is selling T-shirts for $15 and sweatshirts for $25. They must make $2500 to cover expenses. Write and graph an inequality to show the number of T-shirts and sweatshirts that they must sell. See Chapter 3 Answer Appendix.

*Quick*Review

EXAMPLE 1

Graph $2y + 5x = -10$.

Find the x- and y-intercepts.

$$2(0) + 5x = -10 \qquad 2y + 5(0) = -10$$
$$5x = -10 \qquad 2y = -10$$
$$x = -2 \qquad y = -5$$

The graph crosses the x-axis at $(-2, 0)$ and the y-axis at $(0, -5)$. Use these ordered pairs to graph the equation.

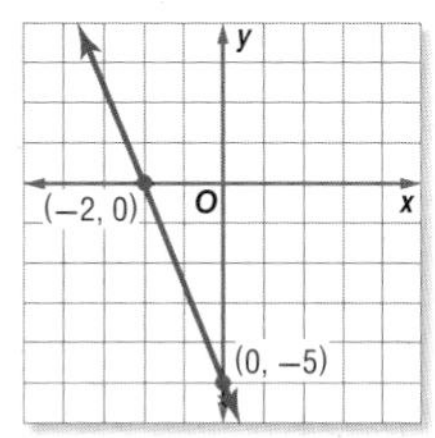

EXAMPLE 2

Graph $y \geq 3x - 2$.

The boundary is the graph of $y = 3x - 2$. Since the inequality symbol is $\geq$, the boundary will be solid.

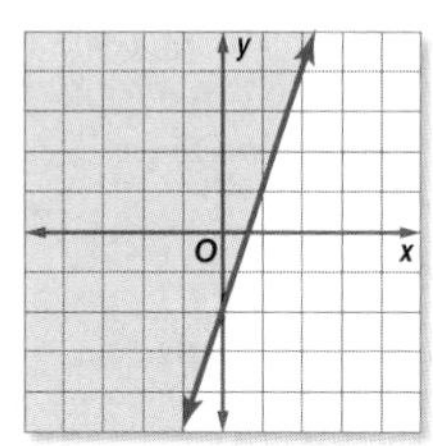

Test the point (0, 0).

$0 \overset{?}{\geq} 3(0) - 2 \qquad (x, y) = (0, 0)$

$0 \geq -2$ ✓

Shade the region that includes (0, 0).

Online Option FL Math Online Take a self-check Chapter Readiness Quiz at glencoe.com.

Response to Intervention (RtI)

Use the *Quick Check* results and the Intervention Planner to help you determine your Response to Intervention. The If-Then statements in the chart below help you decide the appropriate tier of RtI and suggest intervention resources for each tier.

Intervention Planner

Tier 1 On Level

If students miss about 25% of the exercises or less,

Then choose a resource:

- **SE** Lessons 3-1 and 3-3
- **CRM** Skills Practice, Chapter 3, pp. 7, 20
- **TE** Chapter Project, p. 132
- FL Math Online Self-Check Quiz

Tier 2 Strategic Intervention approaching grade level

If students miss about 50% of the exercises,

Then choose a resource:

- **CRM** Study Guide and Intervention, Chapter 3, pp. 5, 18
- FL Math Online Extra Examples, Personal Tutor, Homework Help

Tier 3 Intensive Intervention 2 or more years below grade level

If students miss about 75% of the exercises,

Then use *Math Triumphs Alg. 2,* Ch. 3

FL Math Online Extra Examples, Personal Tutor, Homework Help, Review Vocabulary

FOLDABLES® Study Organizer

Dinah Zike's Foldables®

Focus Students write notes about the vocabulary and concepts in the lessons of this chapter.

Teach Have students make and label their Foldables as illustrated. For each tab, have students develop their own example of the concept that is indicated. Above each example, encourage students to write a definition of the concept in their own words.

When to Use It Encourage students to add to their Foldables as they work through the chapter and to use them to review for the chapter test.

Differentiated Instruction

CRM Student-Built Glossary, pp. 1–2 Students should complete the chart by providing a definition of each term and an example as they progress through Chapter 3. This study tool can also be used to review for the chapter test.

Get Started on Chapter 3

You will learn several new concepts, skills, and vocabulary terms as you study Chapter 3. To get ready, identify important terms and organize your resources. You may wish to refer to **Chapter 0** to review prerequisite skills.

FOLDABLES® Study Organizer

Systems of Equations and Inequalities Make this Foldable to help you organize your Chapter 3 notes about systems of equations and inequalities. Begin with a sheet of $8\frac{1}{2}$" by 11" paper.

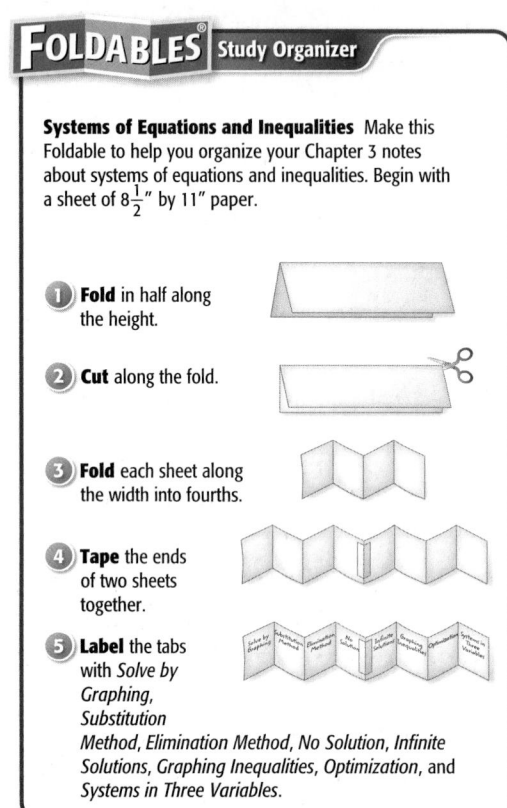

1. **Fold** in half along the height.

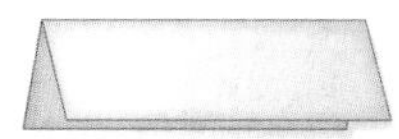

2. **Cut** along the fold.

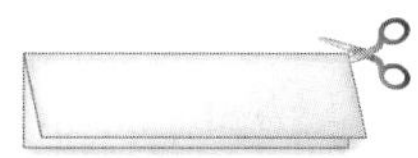

3. **Fold** each sheet along the width into fourths.

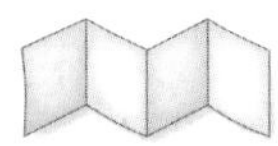

4. **Tape** the ends of two sheets together.

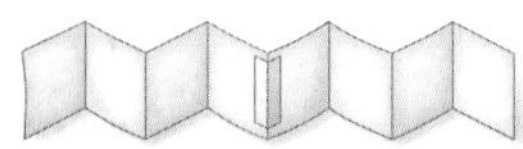

5. **Label** the tabs with *Solve by Graphing, Substitution Method, Elimination Method, No Solution, Infinite Solutions, Graphing Inequalities, Optimization*, and *Systems in Three Variables*.

FL Math Online glencoe.com

- Study the chapter online
- Explore **Get Animated**
- Get extra help from your own **Personal Tutor**
- Use **Extra Examples** for additional help
- Take a **Self-Check Quiz**
- **Review Vocabulary** in fun ways

New Vocabulary

English		Español
system of equations	• p. 135 •	sistema de ecuaciones
break-even point	• p. 136 •	punto de equilibrio
consistent	• p. 137 •	consistente
inconsistent	• p. 137 •	inconsistente
independent	• p. 137 •	independiente
dependent	• p. 137 •	dependiente
substitution method	• p. 143 •	método de substitución
elimination method	• p. 144 •	método de eliminación
system of inequalities	• p. 151 •	sistema de desigualdades
constraints	• p. 160 •	restricciones
linear programming	• p. 160 •	programación lineal
feasible region	• p. 160 •	región viable
bounded	• p. 160 •	acotada
unbounded	• p. 160 •	no acotado
optimize	• p. 162 •	optimizer
ordered triple	• p. 167 •	triple ordenado

Review Vocabulary

equation • p. 135 • ecuación a mathematical sentence stating that two mathematical expressions are equal

inequality • p. 151 • desigualdad an open sentence that contains the symbol $<$, $\leq$, $>$, or $\geq$

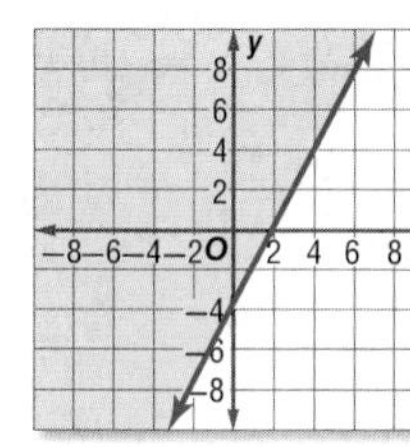

linear equation • p. 135 • ecuación lineal an equation that has no operations other than addition, subtraction, and multiplication of a variable by a constant

solution • p. 135 • solución a replacement for the variable in an open sentence that results in a true sentence

Multilingual eGlossary glencoe.com

3-1

Solving Systems of Equations by Graphing

Then

You graphed and solved linear equations. (Lesson 2-2)

Now

- Solve systems of linear equations by using tables and graphs.
- Determine whether a system of linear equations is inconsistent, consistent and dependent, or consistent and independent.

NGSSS

MA.912.A.3.14 Solve systems of linear equations and inequalities **in two** and three **variables using graphical,** substitution, and elimination **methods.**
MA.912.A.3.15 Solve real-world problems involving systems of linear equations and inequalities in two and three variables.

New Vocabulary

system of equations
break-even point
consistent
inconsistent
independent
dependent

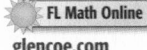

FL Math Online
glencoe.com

Why?

Miguel is moving and needs to rent a moving truck. Rico's Truck Rental charges a flat fee of \$50 plus \$0.29 per mile. Home Movers charges a flat fee of \$30 plus \$0.34 per mile. If Miguel expects to put 500 miles on the rental truck, from which company should he rent the truck? This situation can be modeled by a system of linear equations.

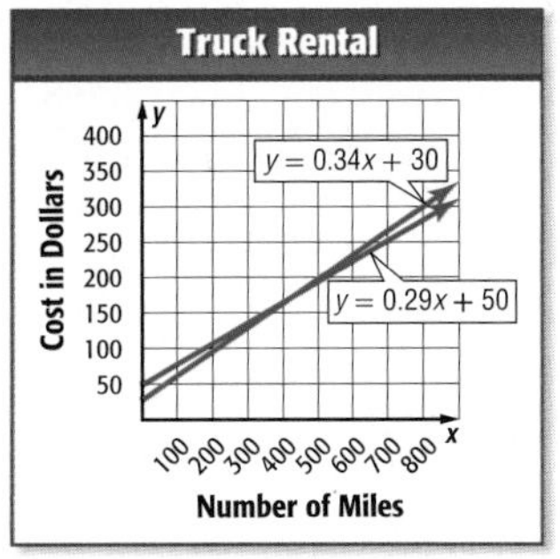

Solve Systems Using Tables and Graphs A **system of equations** is two or more equations with the same variables. To solve a system of equations with two variables, find the ordered pair that satisfies all of the equations.

To solve a system of equations by using a table, first write each equation in slope-intercept form. Then substitute different values for x and solve for the corresponding y-values. For ease of use, choose 0 and 1 as your first x-values.

$y_1 = -2x + 8$
$y_2 = 4x - 7$

x	y_1	y_2	Difference
0	8	−7	15
1	6	−3	9
2	4	1	3
3	2	5	−3

Because the difference between the y-values is closer to 0 for $x = 1$ than $x = 0$, a value greater than 1 should be tried next.

Because the difference between the y-values changed signs from $x = 2$ to $x = 3$, a value between these should be tried next.

The solution is between 2 and 3.

EXAMPLE 1 Solve by Using a Table

Solve the system of equations.

$3x + 2y = -2$
$-4x + 5y = -28$

Write each equation in slope-intercept form.

$3x + 2y = -2 \rightarrow y = -1.5x - 1$
$-4x + 5y = -28 \rightarrow y = 0.8x - 5.6$

Use a table to find the solution that satisfies both equations.

x	y_1	y_2	(x, y_1)	(x, y_2)
0	−1	−5.6	(0, −1)	(0, −5.6)
1	−2.5	−4.8	(1, −2.5)	(1, −4.8)
2	**−4**	**−4**	**(2, −4)**	**(2, −4)**

The solution of the system is (2, −4).

Guided Practice

1A. $2x - 5y = 11$
$-3x + 4y = -13$ (3, −1)

1B. $4x + 3y = -17$
$-7x - 2y = 20$ (−2, −3)

Personal Tutor glencoe.com

1 FOCUS

Vertical Alignment

Before Lesson 3-1
Graph and solve linear equations.

Lesson 3-1
Solve systems of linear equations by using tables and graphs. Determine whether a system of linear equations is inconsistent, consistent and dependent, or consistent and independent.

After Lesson 3-1
Use algebraic methods to solve systems of linear equations.

2 TEACH

Scaffolding Questions

Have students read the *Why?* section of the lesson.

Ask:

- Which company's flat fee is less? Home Movers
- How can you tell which company's cost increases at a faster rate? The slope of Home Movers, 0.34, is greater than the slope of Rico's Truck Rental, 0.29, which means Home Movers' cost increases at a faster rate.
- For what number of miles are the two companies' costs equal? 400 miles

Lesson 3-1 Resources

Resource	Approaching-Level	On-Level	Beyond-Level	English Learners
Teacher Edition		• Differentiated Instruction, pp. 136, 138, 141	• Differentiated Instruction, pp. 136, 138, 141	
Chapter Resource Masters	• Study Guide and Intervention, pp. 5–6 • Skills Practice, p. 7 • Practice, p. 8 • Word Problem Practice, p. 9	• Study Guide and Intervention, pp. 5–6 • Skills Practice, p. 7 • Practice, p. 8 • Word Problem Practice, p. 9 • Enrichment, p. 10 • Spreadsheet Activity, p. 11	• Practice, p. 8 • Word Problem Practice, p. 9 • Enrichment, p. 10	• Study Guide and Intervention, pp. 5–6 • Skills Practice, p. 7 • Practice, p. 8 • Word Problem Practice, p. 9
Transparencies	• 5-Minute Check Transparency 3-1	• 5-Minute Check Transparency 3-1	• 5-Minute Check Transparency 3-1	• 5-Minute Check Transparency 3-1
Other	• Study Notebook	• Study Notebook	• Study Notebook	• Study Notebook

Solve Systems Using Tables and Graphs

Example 1 shows how to solve a system of equations by completing a table. **Example 2** shows how to solve a system of equations by graphing. **Example 3** shows how to use systems of equations to determine the break-even point.

Formative Assessment

Use the Guided Practice exercises after each example to determine students' understanding of concepts.

Additional Examples

1 Solve the system of equations by completing a table. (3, 0)

$x + y = 3$

$-2x + y = -6$

2 Solve the system of equations by graphing. (4, 2)

$x - 2y = 0$

$x + y = 6$

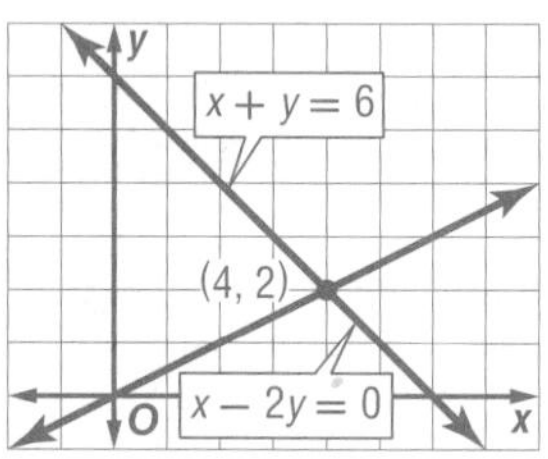

3 **SALES** A service club is selling copies of its holiday cookbook to raise funds for a project. The printer's set-up charge is $200, and each book costs $2 to print. The cookbooks will sell for $6 each. How many cookbooks must the club sell before it makes a profit? The club must sell 51 or more cookbooks to make a profit.

Additional Examples also in Interactive Classroom PowerPoint® Presentations

IWB INTERACTIVE WHITEBOARD READY

Another method for solving a system of equations is to graph the equations on the same coordinate plane. The point of intersection represents the solution.

EXAMPLE 2 Solve by Graphing

Solve the system of equations by graphing.

$2x - y = -1$
$2y + 5x = -16$

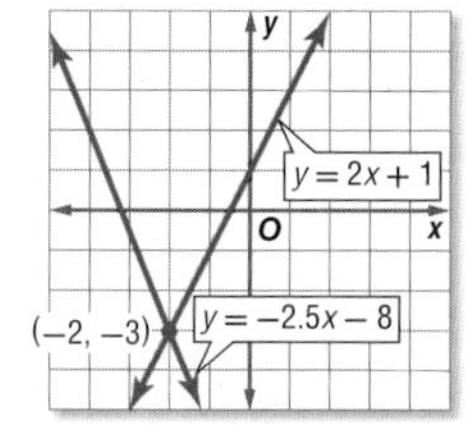

Write each equation in slope-intercept form.

$2x - y = -1 \rightarrow y = 2x + 1$
$2y + 5x = -16 \rightarrow y = -2.5x - 8$

The graphs of the lines appear to intersect at (−2, −3).

CHECK Substitute the coordinates into each original equation.

$2x - y = -1$	$2y + 5x = -16$	**Original equations**
$2(-2) - (-3) \stackrel{?}{=} -1$	$2(-3) + 5(-2) \stackrel{?}{=} -16$	**$x = -2$ and $y = -3$**
$-1 = -1$ ✓	$-16 = -16$ ✓	**Simplify.**

The solution of the system is (−2, −3).

StudyTip

Checking Solutions Always check to see if the values work for *both* of the original equations.

Guided Practice

2A. $4x + 3y = 12$
$-6x + 4y = -1$ **(1.5, 2)**

2B. $-3y + 8x = 36$
$6x + y = -21$ **(−4, 3)**

Personal Tutor glencoe.com

Systems of equations are used by businesses to determine the break-even point. The **break-even point** is the point at which the income equals the cost.

Real-World EXAMPLE 3 Break-Even Point Analysis

BUSINESS Libby borrowed $450 to start a lawn-mowing business. She charges $35 per lawn and incurs $8 in operating costs per lawn. How many lawns must she mow to make a profit?

Let x = the number of lawns Libby mows, and let y = the number of dollars.

Total Income	Total Cost
$y = 35x$	$y = 8x + 450$

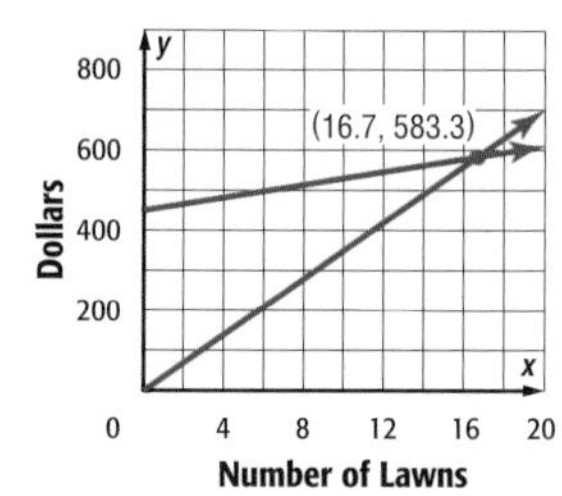

The graphs intersect at (16.7, 583.3). This is the break-even point. She can only mow a whole number of lawns. If she mows 17 lawns, she will make a profit of $595 − $586 or $9. If she mows fewer than 17 lawns, she will lose money.

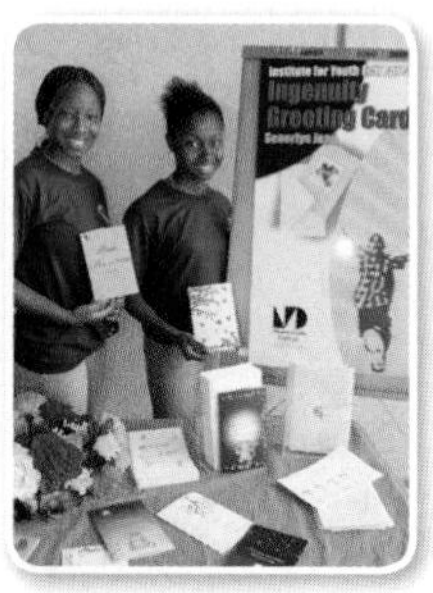

Real-World Link

The Internet provides countless business opportunities for teenage entrepreneurs. Roughly 1.6 million U.S. teens make some money using the Internet.

Source: *Business Week*

Guided Practice

3. Southeast Publishing paid $96,000 to an author for the rights to publish her book. If one book costs $12 to produce and they plan to sell them for $24 each, how many books must Southeast Publishing sell to break even? Show your results by graphing. **See Chapter 3 Answer Appendix.**

Personal Tutor glencoe.com

Differentiated Instruction OL BL

If students demonstrate an understanding of how to graph a system of inequalities and find the point of intersection,

Then have them create a list of tips to help someone draw the graphs for a system of equations and find the point of intersection easily and efficiently.

Classify Systems of Equations Systems of equations can be classified by the number of solutions. A system of equations is **consistent** if it has at least one solution and **inconsistent** if it has no solutions. If it has exactly one solution, it is **independent**, and if it has an infinite number of solutions, it is **dependent**.

EXAMPLE 4 Classify Systems

Graph each system of equations and describe them as *consistent and independent*, *consistent and dependent*, or *inconsistent*.

a. $4x + 3y = 24$
$-3x + 5y = 30$

$y = -\frac{4}{3}x + 8$

$y = \frac{3}{5}x + 6$

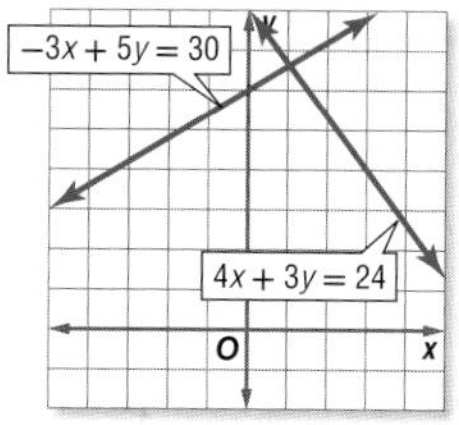

The graphs of the lines intersect at one point, so there is one solution. The system is consistent and independent.

b. $-2x + 5y = 10$
$4x - 10y = -20$

$y = \frac{2}{5}x + 2$

$y = \frac{2}{5}x + 2$

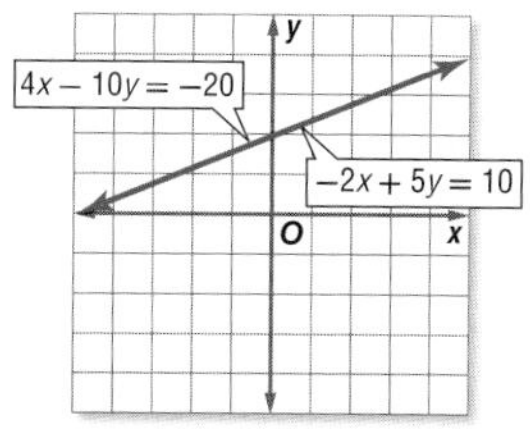

Because the equations are equivalent, their graphs are the same line. The system is consistent and dependent.

c. $-8x + 2y = 20$
$-4x + y = 12$

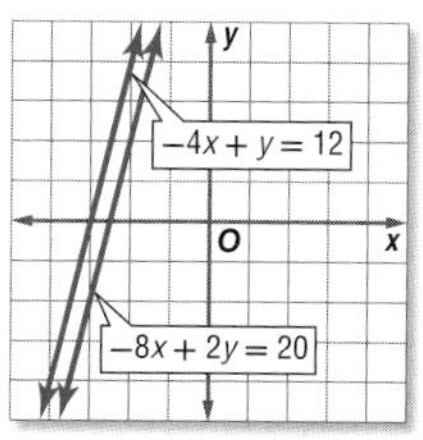

The graphs of the lines do not intersect, so the graphs are parallel and there is no solution. The system is inconsistent.

d. $f(x) = 2x - 8$
$g(x) = 2x - 4$
$h(x) = -3x + 4$

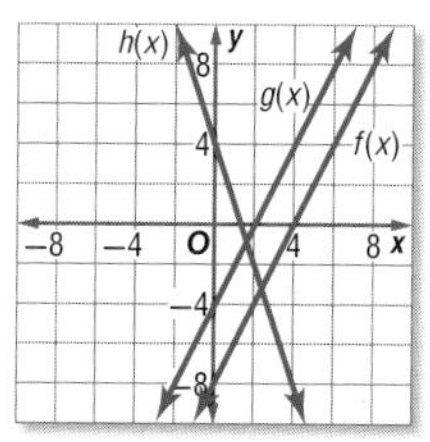

$f(x)$ and $g(x)$ are inconsistent. $f(x)$ and $h(x)$ are consistent and independent. $g(x)$ and $h(x)$ are consistent and independent.

StudyTip

Slope and Classifying Systems If the equations have different slopes, then the system is consistent and independent.

StudyTip

Graphing Calculator Most graphing calculators have a function for determining a point of intersection of two lines.

Guided Practice 4A–4D. See Chapter 3 Answer Appendix.

4A. $6x - 4y = 15$
$-6x + 4y = 18$

4B. $-4x + 5y = -17$
$-4x - 2y = 15$

4C. $10x - 12y = 40$
$-5x + 6y = -20$

4D. $6x + y = -13$
$6x - y = 13$

Personal Tutor glencoe.com

Classify Systems of Equations

Example 4 shows how to classify systems of linear equations as *consistent and independent, consistent and dependent,* or *inconsistent.*

Additional Example

4 Graph each system of equations and describe it as *consistent and independent, consistent and dependent,* or *inconsistent.*

a. $x - y = 5$

$x + 2y = -4$

consistent and independent

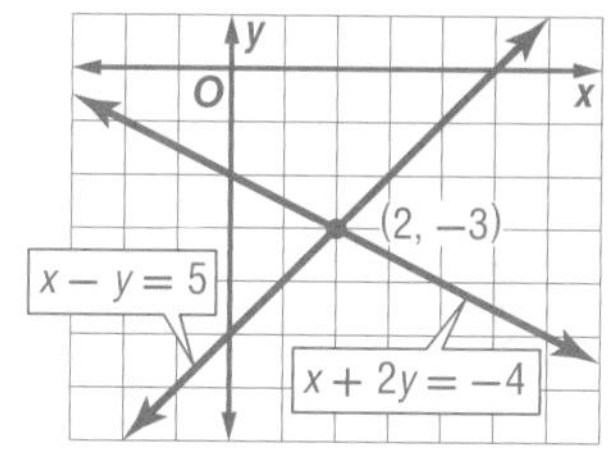

b. $9x - 6y = -6$

$6x - 4y = -4$

consistent and dependent

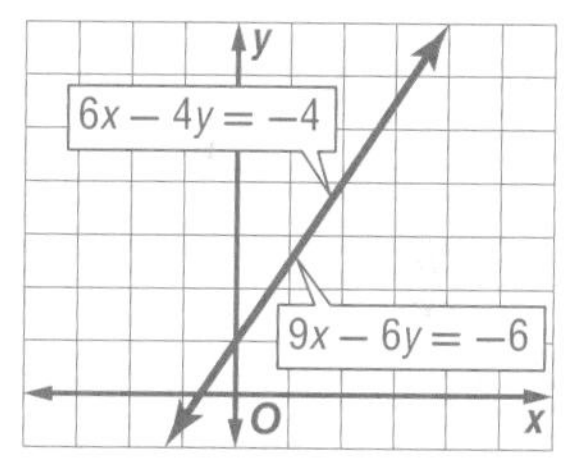

c. $15x - 6y = 0$

$5x - 2y = 10$

inconsistent

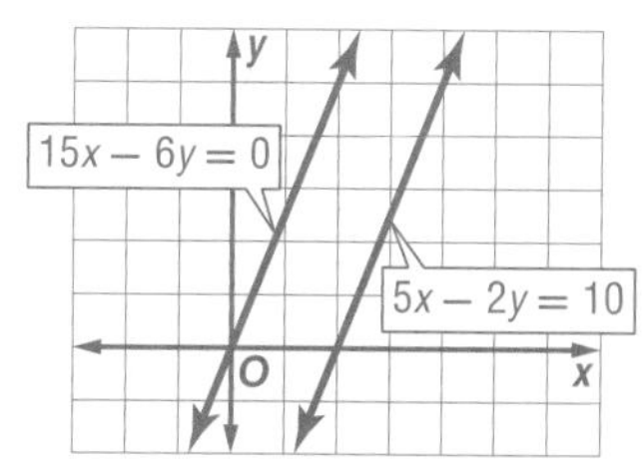

(continued on the next page)

Focus on Mathematical Content

Graphs of Systems of Equations When describing systems of equations, it is helpful to know what the graphs of each type look like. The graphs of the equations in a system that is *consistent and independent* have different slopes and different y-intercepts. The graphs of the equations of a system that is *consistent and dependent* have the same slope and same y-intercept. The graphs of the equations of a system that is *inconsistent* have the same slope and different y-intercepts.

Additional Example

d. $f(x) = -0.5x + 2$

$g(x) = -0.5x + 2$

$h(x) = 0.5x + 2$

$f(x)$ and $g(x)$are consistent and dependent.

$f(x)$ and $h(x)$ are consistent and independent $g(x)$ and $h(x)$ are consistent and independent.

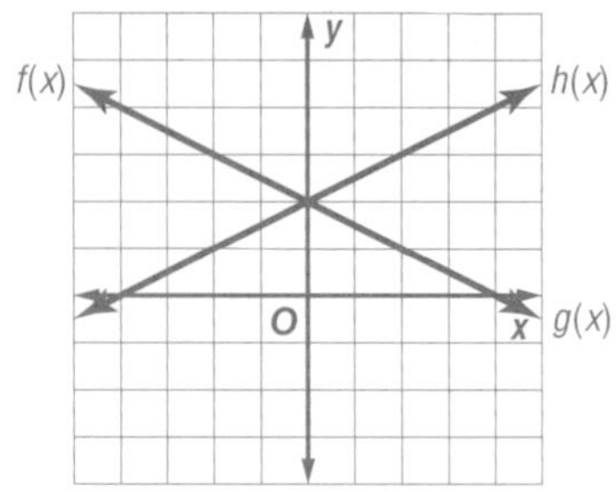

Watch Out!

Parallel Lines Remind students that the graphs of equations with the same slope and different intercepts are, by definition, parallel.

TEACH with TECH

STUDENT RESPONSE SYSTEM Write a system of equations on the board. Ask students to graphically determine the number of solutions for this system. Have them reply with A for no solutions, B for one solution, or C for infinitely many solutions. Discuss students' responses with the class.

The relationship between the graph of a system of equations and the number of solutions is summarized below.

Concept Summary — Characteristics of Linear Systems

Consistent and Independent	Consistent and Dependent	Inconsistent
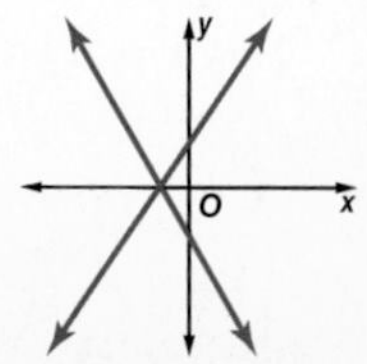	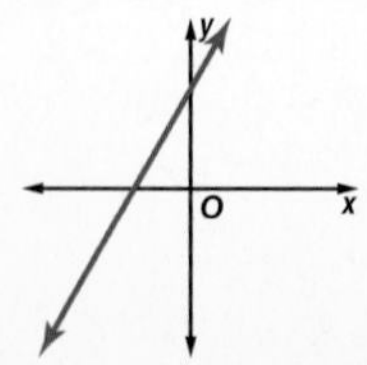	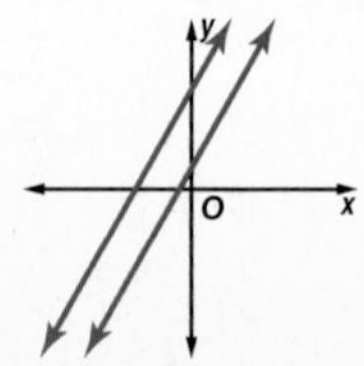
intersecting lines; one solution	same line; infinitely many solutions	parallel lines; no solution

Check Your Understanding

Example 1 p. 135 **Solve each system of equations by using a table.**

1. $y = 3x - 4$
$y = -2x + 11$ (3, 5)

2. $4x - y = 1$
$5x + 2y = 24$ (2, 7)

Example 2 p. 136 **Solve each system of equations by graphing.**

3. $y = -3x + 6$
$2y = 10x - 36$ (3, −3)

4. $y = -x - 9$
$3y = 5x + 5$ (−4, −5)

5. $y = 0.5x + 4$
$3y = 4x - 3$ (6, 7)

6. $-3y = 4x + 11$
$2x + 3y = -7$ (−2, −1)

7 $4x + 5y = -41$
$3y - 5x = 5$ (−4, −5)

8. $8x - y = 50$
$x + 4y = -2$ (6, −2)

Example 3 p. 136

9. DIGITAL PHOTOS Refer to the graphic at the right. a. $y = 0.15x + 2.70$, $y = 0.25x$

a. Write equations that represent the cost of printing digital photos at each lab.

b. Under what conditions is the cost to print digital photos the same at both stores? $6.75 for 27 photos

c. When is it best to use EZ Online Digital Photos and when is it best to use the local pharmacy?

9c. You should use EZ Online Digital Photos if you are printing more than 27 digital photos, and the local pharmacy if you are printing fewer than 27 photos.

Developing Digital Photos
EZ Online Digital Photos charges
$0.15
per digital photo
$2.70
for shipping
Local Pharmacy charges
$0.25
per digital photo

Example 4 p. 137 **Graph each system of equations and describe it as** ***consistent and independent, consistent and dependent,*** **or** ***inconsistent.*** 10–12. See margin.

10. $y + 4x = 12$
$3y = 8 - 12x$

11. $-2x - 3y = 9$
$4x + 6y = -18$

12. $9x - 2y = 11$
$5x + 4y = 13$

Differentiated Instruction OL BL

Extension Engage students in the real world applications of the content by extending the idea presented in Exercise 23 on page 139. Ask students to search the Internet for coupon offers specifically looking for two from the same company, one offering a percentage reduction and another offering a flat amount reduction. Students can then determine for which total costs they would use each coupon. Extend the task further by having students create and analyze their own discount coupons.

Practice and Problem Solving

● = **Step-by-Step Solutions** begin on page R20.
Extra Practice begins on page 947.

Example 1 p. 135

Solve each system of equations by using a table.

13. $y = 5x + 3$
$y = x - 9$ (−3, −12)

14. $3x - 4y = 16$
$-6x + 5y = -29$ (4, −1)

15. $2x - 5 = y$
$-3x + 4y = 0$ (4, 3)

16. $x + y = 6$
$-y + 8x = -15$ (−1, 7)

Example 2 p. 136

Solve each system of equations by graphing. 19. infinite solutions

17. $4x + 3y = -24$
$8x - 2y = -16$ (−3, −4)

18. $-3x + 2y = -6$
$-5x + 10y = 30$ (6, 6)

19. $-3x - 8y = 12$
$12x + 32y = -48$

20. $6x - 5y = 17$
$6x + 2y = 31$ (4.5, 2)

21. $-10x + 4y = 7$
$2x - 5y = 7$ (−1.5, −2)

22. $y - 3x = -29$
$9x - 6y = 102$ (8, −5)

Example 3 p. 136

23. SHOPPING Jerilyn has a $10 coupon and a 15% discount coupon for her favorite store. The store has a policy that only one coupon may be used per purchase. When is it best for Jerilyn to use the $10 coupon, and when is it best for her to use the 15% discount coupon? $10 coupon for a purchase less than $66.67 and 15% discount coupon for a purchase over $66.67

24. HABITATS A zoo is building a new habitat for the wolves. The boundaries for the habitat are $y = 8$, $x = 4$, $y = 2x + 2$, and $y = 0.5x - 1$. a. See margin.

a. Graph the system of equations that models the area of the new wolf enclosure.

b. Find the coordinates of the vertices of the quadrilateral that represents the wolves' new habitat. (4, 8), (4, 1), (−2, −2), (3, 8)

c. What is the approximate area of the wolves' new home? 26 square units

25. WATER SKIING A water ski jump is in the shape of a triangle. The graphs of $y - 2x = 1$, $4x + y = 7$, and $2y - x = -4$ contain the sides of the triangle. Find the coordinates of the vertices of the triangle. (1, 3), (2, −1), (−2, −3)

Example 4 p. 137

Graph each system of equations and describe it as *consistent and independent*, *consistent and dependent*, or *inconsistent*. 26–34. See Chapter 3 Answer Appendix.

26. $y = 2x - 1$
$y = 2x + 6$

27. $y = 3x - 4$
$y = 6x - 8$

28. $x - 6y = 12$
$3x + 18y = 14$

29. $2x + 5y = 10$
$-4x - 10y = 20$

30. $8y - 3x = 15$
$-16y + 6x = -30$

31 $-5x - 6y = 13$
$12y + 10x = -26$

32. $3.2x - 2.4y = 28$
$0.6y = -0.8x + 7$

33. $4.9x - 7.7y = -14$
$-1.4x + 2.2y = 4$

34. $3.5x - 1.2y = 8.2$
$-5.25x + 1.8y = 12.3$

B **Solve each system of equations by graphing.**

35. $y - \frac{3}{4}x = -\frac{5}{2}$
$\frac{3}{2}x + 6y = 9$ (4, 0.5)

36. $5x + 2y = -\frac{5}{2}$
$\frac{3}{2}y + \frac{1}{2}x = 3$ (−1.5, 2.5)

37. $\frac{5}{6}x + \frac{4}{3}y = -1$
$\frac{1}{4}x + \frac{5}{3}y = \frac{7}{2}$ (−6, 3)

Use a graphing calculator to solve each system of equations. Round the coordinates of the intersection to the nearest hundredth.

38. $12y = 5x - 15$
$4.2y + 6.1x = 11$
(2.07, −0.39)

39. $5.8x - 6.3y = 18$
$-4.3x + 8.8y = 32$
(15.03, 10.98)

40. $-3.8x + 2.9y = 19$
$6.6x - 5.4y = -23$
(−26.01, −27.54)

3 PRACTICE

Formative Assessment

Use Exercises 1–12 to check for understanding.

Use the chart on the bottom of the page to customize assignments for your students.

Additional Answers

10.

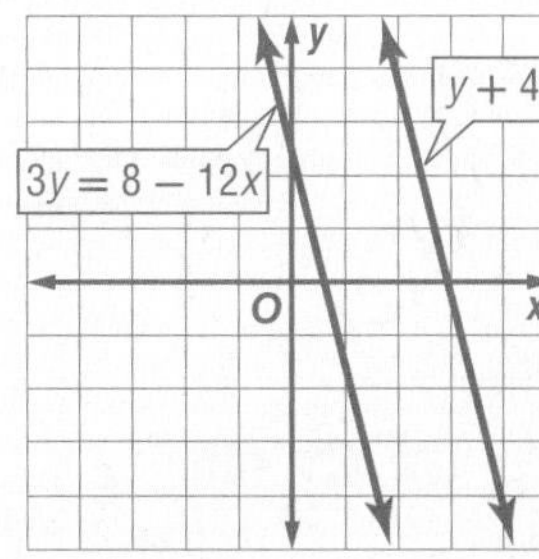

inconsistent

11.

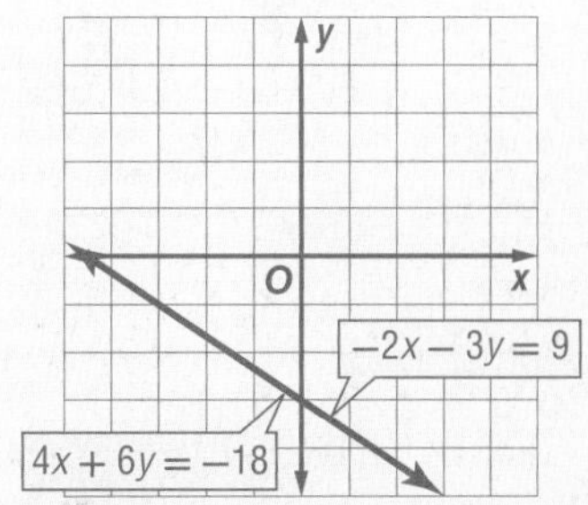

consistent, dependent

12.

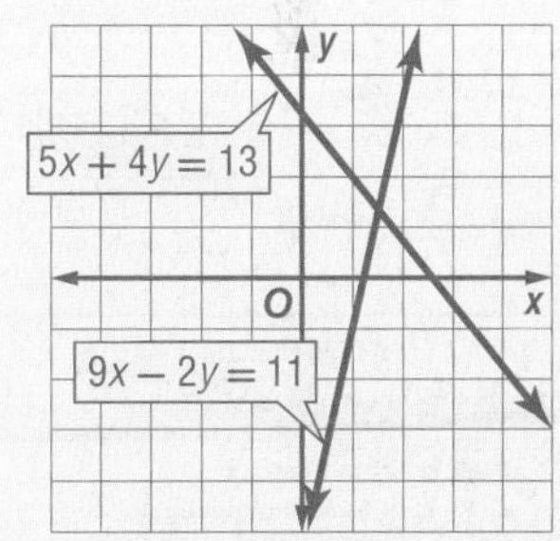

consistent, independent

24a.

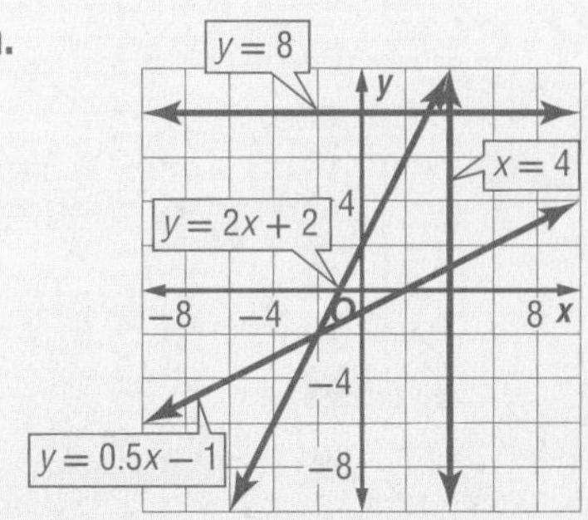

Differentiated Homework Options

Level	Assignment	Two-Day Option	
AL Basic	13–32, 42–43, 45, 47–50, 51–66	13–31 odd, 47–50	14–32 even, 42–43, 45, 51–66
OL Core	13–31 odd, 35–41 odd, 42–43, 45, 47–66	13–32, 47–50	35–43, 45, 47–66
BL Advanced	35–60, (optional: 61–66)		

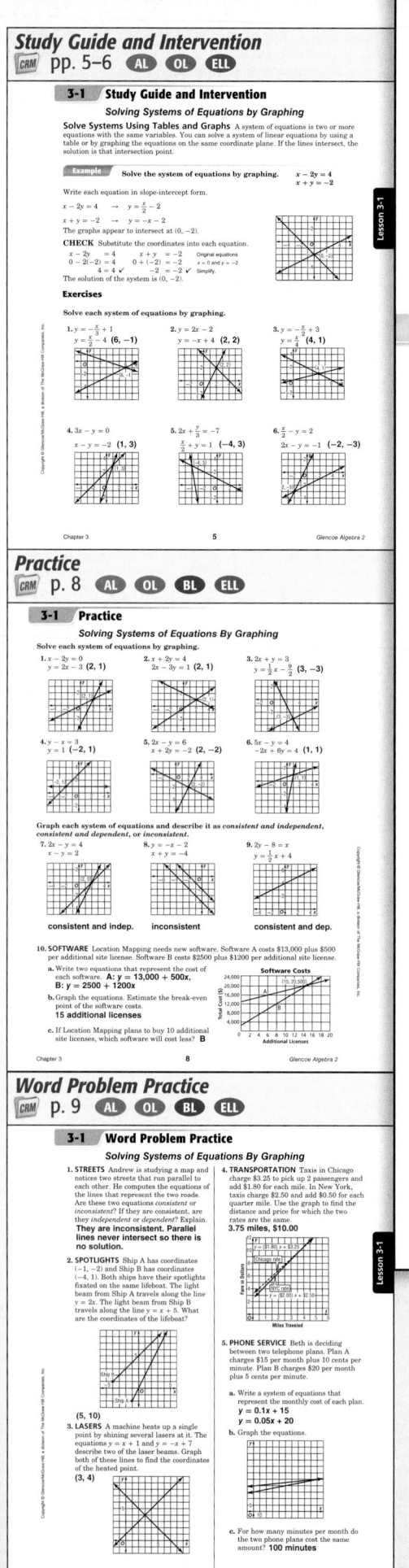

Study Guide and Intervention
CRM pp. 5–6 AL OL ELL

3-1 Study Guide and Intervention
Solving Systems of Equations by Graphing

Solve Systems Using Tables and Graphs A system of equations is two or more equations with the same variables. You can solve a system of linear equations by using a table or by graphing the equations on the same coordinate plane. If the lines intersect, the solution is that intersection point.

Example Solve the system of equations by graphing. $x - 2y = 4$, $x + y = -2$

Write each equation in slope-intercept form.

$x - 2y = 4 \rightarrow y = \frac{x}{2} - 2$

$x + y = -2 \rightarrow y = -x - 2$

The graphs appear to intersect at (0, −2).

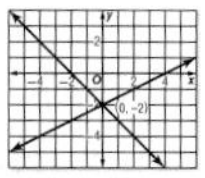

CHECK Substitute the coordinates into each equation.

$x - 2y = 4$	$x + y = -2$	Original equations
$0 - 2(-2) = 4$	$0 + (-2) = -2$	$x = 0$ and $y = -2$
$4 = 4$ ✓	$-2 = -2$ ✓	Simplify.

The solution of the system is (0, −2).

Lesson 3-1

Exercises

Solve each system of equations by graphing.

1. $y = -\frac{x}{3} + 1$, $y = \frac{x}{2} - 4$ **(6, −1)**
2. $y = 2x - 2$, $y = -x + 4$ **(2, 2)**
3. $y = -\frac{x}{2} + 3$, $y = \frac{x}{4}$ **(4, 1)**

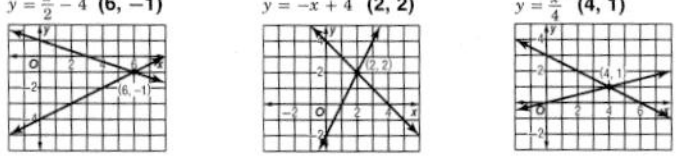

4. $3x - y = 0$, $x - y = -2$ **(1, 3)**
5. $2x + \frac{y}{3} = -7$, $\frac{x}{2} + y = 1$ **(−4, 3)**
6. $\frac{x}{2} - y = 2$, $2x - y = -1$ **(−2, −3)**

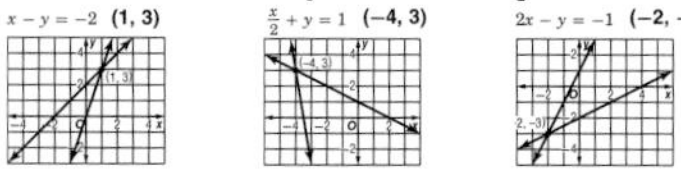

Practice
CRM p. 8 AL OL BL ELL

3-1 Practice
Solving Systems of Equations By Graphing

Solve each system of equations by graphing.

1. $x - 2y = 0$, $y = 2x - 3$ **(2, 1)**
2. $x + 2y = 4$, $2x - 3y = 1$ **(2, 1)**
3. $2x + y = 3$, $y = \frac{1}{2}x - \frac{9}{2}$ **(3, −3)**

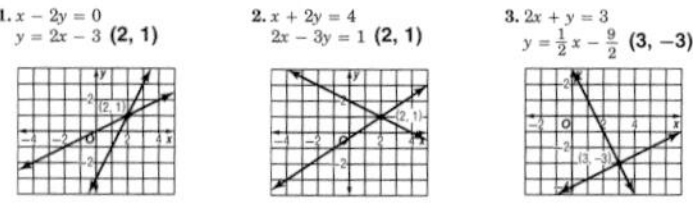

4. $y - x = 3$, $y = 1$ **(−2, 1)**
5. $2x - y = 6$, $x + 2y = -2$ **(2, −2)**
6. $5x - y = 4$, $-2x + 6y = 4$ **(1, 1)**

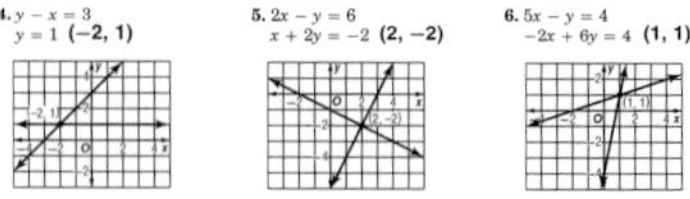

Graph each system of equations and describe it as *consistent and independent*, *consistent and dependent*, or *inconsistent*.

7. $2x - y = 4$, $x - y = 2$
8. $y = -x - 2$, $x + y = -4$
9. $2y - 8 = x$, $y = \frac{1}{2}x + 4$

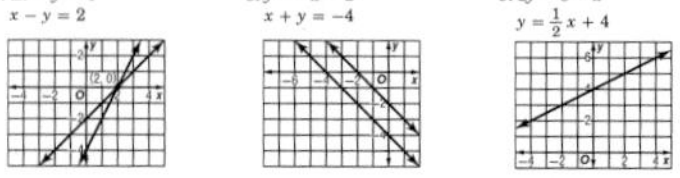

consistent and indep. **inconsistent** **consistent and dep.**

10. **SOFTWARE** Location Mapping needs new software. Software A costs $13,000 plus $500 per additional site license. Software B costs $2500 plus $1200 per additional site license.
    a. Write two equations that represent the cost of each software. **A: y = 13,000 + 500x, B: y = 2500 + 1200x**
    b. Graph the equations. Estimate the break-even point of the software costs. **15 additional licenses**
    c. If Location Mapping plans to buy 10 additional site licenses, which software will cost less? **B**

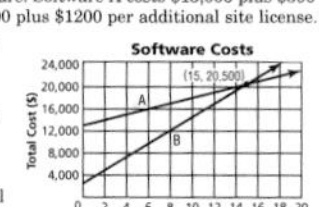

Word Problem Practice
CRM p. 9 AL OL BL ELL

3-1 Word Problem Practice
Solving Systems of Equations By Graphing

1. **STREETS** Andrew is studying a map and notices two streets that run parallel to each other. He computes the equations of the lines that represent the two roads. Are these two equations *consistent* or *inconsistent*? If they are consistent, are they *independent* or *dependent*? Explain. **They are inconsistent. Parallel lines never intersect so there is no solution.**

2. **SPOTLIGHTS** Ship A has coordinates (−1, −2) and Ship B has coordinates (−4, 1). Both ships have their spotlights fixated on the same lifeboat. The light beam from Ship A travels along the line $y = 2x$. The light beam from Ship B travels along the line $y = x + 5$. What are the coordinates of the lifeboat?

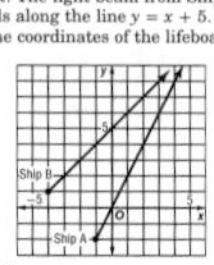

(5, 10)

3. **LASERS** A machine heats up a single point by shining several lasers at it. The equations $y = x + 1$ and $y = -x + 7$ describe two of the laser beams. Graph both of these lines to find the coordinates of the heated point. **(3, 4)**

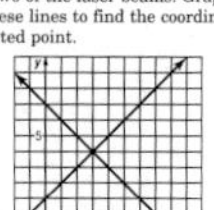

4. **TRANSPORTATION** Taxis in Chicago charge $3.25 to pick up 2 passengers and add $1.80 for each mile. In New York, taxis charge $2.50 and add $0.50 for each quarter mile. Use the graph to find the distance and price for which the two rates are the same. **3.75 miles, $10.00**

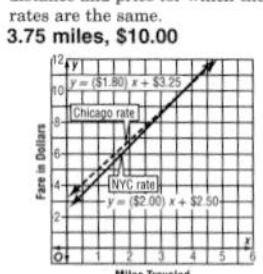

5. **PHONE SERVICE** Beth is deciding between two telephone plans. Plan A charges $15 per month plus 10 cents per minute. Plan B charges $20 per month plus 5 cents per minute.
    a. Write a system of equations that represent the monthly cost of each plan. **$y = 0.1x + 15$, $y = 0.05x + 20$**
    b. Graph the equations.

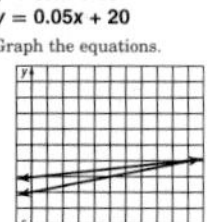

    c. For how many minutes per month do the two phone plans cost the same amount? **100 minutes**

Lesson 3-1

Real-World Link

Track and Field runners Paavo Nurmi (Finland) and Carl Lewis (U.S.) along with gymnast Larisa Latynina (former Soviet Union) currently hold the record for the most Olympic gold medals with 9 each. Latynina also holds the record for the most Olympic medals with 18.

Source: NBC Sports

41. **OLYMPICS** The table shows the winning times in seconds for the 100-meter dash at the Olympics between 1964 and 2004. **a–c. See margin.**

Years Since 1964, x	Men's Gold Medal Time	Women's Gold Medal Time
0	10.0	11.4
4	9.90	11.0
8	10.14	11.07
12	10.06	11.08
16	10.25	11.06
20	9.99	10.97
24	9.92	10.54
28	9.96	10.82
32	9.84	10.94
36	9.87	10.75
40	9.85	10.93

a. Write equations that represent the winning times for men and women since 1964. Assume that both times continue along the same trend.

b. Graph both equations. Estimate when the women's performance will catch up to the men's performance.

c. Do you think that your prediction is reasonable? Explain.

H.O.T. Problems
Use Higher-Order Thinking Skills

42. **REASONING** If *a* is consistent and dependent with *b*, *b* is inconsistent with *c*, and *c* is consistent and independent with *d*, then *a* will *sometimes*, *always*, or *never* be consistent and independent with *d*. Explain your reasoning.

42. Sample answer: Always; *a* and *b* are the same line. *b* is parallel to *c*, so *a* is also parallel to *c*. Since *c* and *d* are consistent and independent, then *c* is not parallel to *d* and, thus, intersects *d*. Since *a* and *c* are parallel, then *a* cannot be parallel to *d*, so, *a* must intersect *d* and must be consistent and independent with *d*.

43. **ERROR ANALYSIS** Victor and Alvin are using their calculators to solve the system $y = 3x - 1$ and $x + y = 4$. Is either of them correct? Explain your reasoning.

43. Alvin; sample answer: Alvin used the Intersect command, while Victor used Trace.

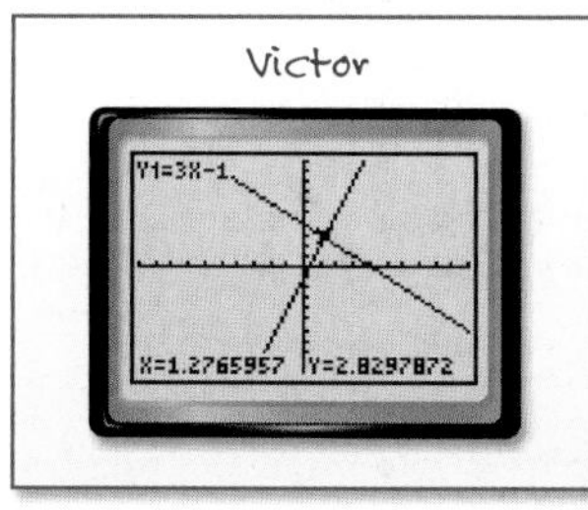

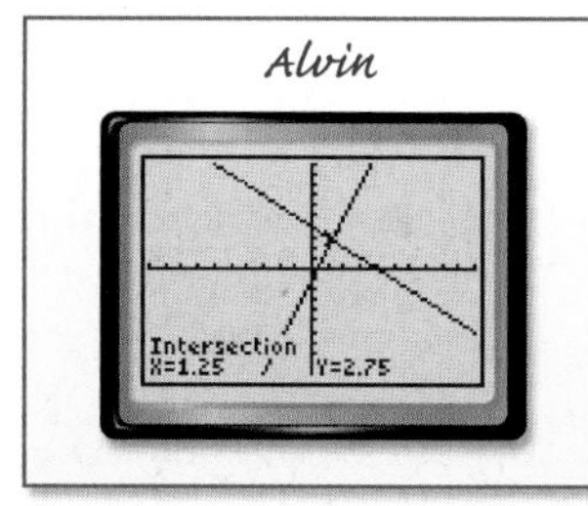

44. **CHALLENGE** Consider the system of equations $kx + 3y = 6$ and $8x + 5y = k$. Find a value of k, if it exists, for each condition. **c. No value of *k* exists to meet this condition.**
    a. The system is inconsistent. $k = \frac{24}{5}$
    b. The system is consistent and independent. **This condition is met for** $\left\{k \mid k \neq \frac{24}{5}\right\}$.
    c. The system is consistent and dependent.

45. **OPEN ENDED** Write a system to illustrate each of the following.
    a. an inconsistent system **Sample answer:** $y = 2x$; $y = 2x + 1$
    b. a consistent and dependent system **Sample answer:** $y = x$; $y = x$
    c. a consistent and independent system **Sample answer:** $y = x$; $y = 3x - 1$

46. **WRITING IN MATH** Explain how you can determine the consistency and dependence of a system without graphing the system. **See Chapter 3 Answer Appendix.**

Enrichment
CRM p. 10 OL BL

3-1 Enrichment

Solutions to Nonlinear Equations

Real-life situations are often not capable of being represented by a linear equation. Systems of nonlinear equations are often used in the study of population dynamics, modeling carbon monoxide exposure, and determining the height of an object in free fall.

Nonlinear equations have one variable raised to a power other than one or multiplication of two or more variables.

Examples

a. $xy = 1$ or $y = \frac{1}{x}$ The first equation has a product of two variables. The second is the same equation solved for *y*.

b. $y = x^3 - 2x + 1$ The variable *x* is raised to the third power.

Systems of nonlinear equations consist of two or more equations, where at least one is nonlinear.

Solutions to these systems are typically difficult to find. One useful method for finding solutions to systems of nonlinear equations is the same as the method for finding solutions to systems of linear equations—use technology to graph the system and find the point(s) of intersection. The graph of the system is shown at the right.

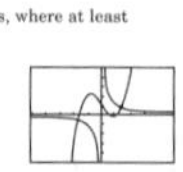

NGSSS PRACTICE 912.A.4.2, 912.A.3.10, 912.G.4.4, 912.A.2.13

47. THINK SOLVE EXPLAIN **SHORT RESPONSE** Simplify $3y(4x + 6y - 5)$. **$12xy + 18y^2 - 15y$**

48. ACT/SAT Which of the following best describes the graph of the equations? **A**

$$4y = 3x + 8$$
$$-6x = -8y + 24$$

A. The lines are parallel.
B. The lines are perpendicular.
C. The lines have the same x-intercept.
D. The lines have the same y-intercept.

49. GEOMETRY Which set of dimensions corresponds to a triangle similar to the one shown at the right? **I**

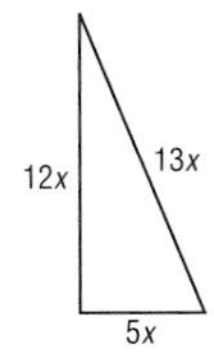

F. 1 unit, 2 units, 3 units
G. 7 units, 11 units, 12 units
H. 10 units, 23 units, 24 units
I. 20 units, 48 units, 52 units

50. Move-A-Lot Rentals will rent a moving truck for \$100 plus \$0.10 for every mile it is driven. Which equation can be used to find C, the cost of renting a moving truck and driving it for m miles? **B**

A. $C = 0.1(100 + m)$
B. $C = 100 + 0.1m$
C. $C = 100m + 0.1$
D. $C = 100(m + 0.1)$

Spiral Review

51. CRAFTS Priscilla sells stuffed animals at a local craft show. She charges \$10 for the small ones and \$15 for the large. To cover her expenses, she needs to sell at least \$350 worth of animals. (Lesson 2-8)

a. Write an inequality for this situation. **$10s + 15\ell \geq 350$**
b. Graph the inequality. **See Chapter 3 Answer Appendix.**
c. If she sells 10 small and 15 large animals, will she cover her expenses? **no**

Write an equation for each function. (Lesson 2-7)

52.

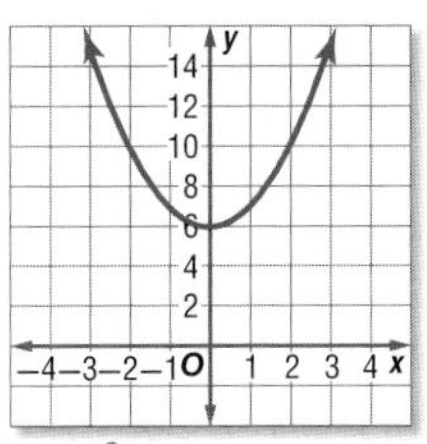

$y = x^2 + 6$

53.

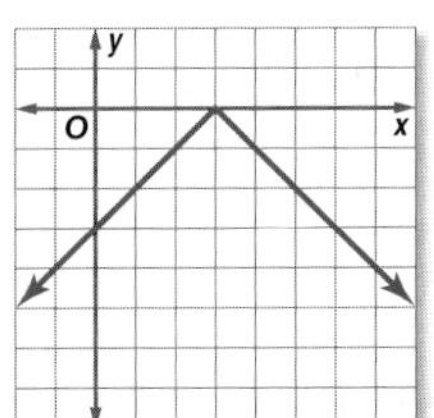

$y = -|x - 3|$

54.

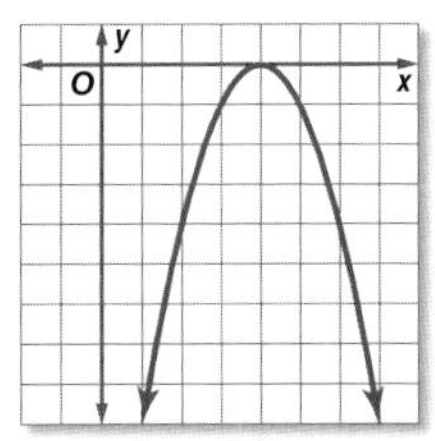

$y = -(x - 4)^2$

Solve each equation. Check your solution. (Lesson 1-3)

55. $2p = 14$ **7**
56. $-14 + n = -6$ **8**
57. $7a - 3a + 2a - a = 16$ **3.2**
58. $x + 9x - 6x + 4x = 20$ **2.5**
59. $27 = -9(y + 5) + 6(y + 8)$ **−8**
60. $-7(p + 7) + 3(p - 4) = -17$ **−11**

Skills Review

Simplify each expression. (Lesson 1-2)

61. $(2x + 4) - (3x + 2)$ **$-x + 2$**
62. $(y - 10) + (5y + 2)$ **$6y - 8$**
63. $(4x - 2y) + (-6x + 5y)$ **$-2x + 3y$**
64. $3(6x + 2y - 1)$ **$18x + 6y - 3$**
65. $4(5x + 2y - 2x + 8)$ **$12x + 8y + 32$**
66. $6(x + 4y) - 5(x + 9y)$ **$x - 21y$**

Watch Out!

Error Analysis For Exercise 43, students should see that Victor's ordered pair, (1.3, 2.9), is on the line with equation $y = 3x - 1$ but is NOT on the line with equation $x + y = 4$. Explain to students that they should use the *trace* feature of their calculators to identify the point that is on *both* lines. The graph labeled "Alvin" includes the word "Intersection," which indicates that (1.25, 2.75) is on both lines. Alvin is correct.

4 ASSESS

Ticket Out the Door Give each student a small piece of paper. Have the student show what the graph of a consistent and independent system of equations might look like.

CRM Quiz 1, p. 39

Additional Answers

41a. Sample answer for men using (0, 10) and (40, 9.85): $y_m = -0.00375x + 10$; sample answer for women using (0, 11.4) and (40, 10.93): $y_w = -0.01175x + 11.4$

41b.

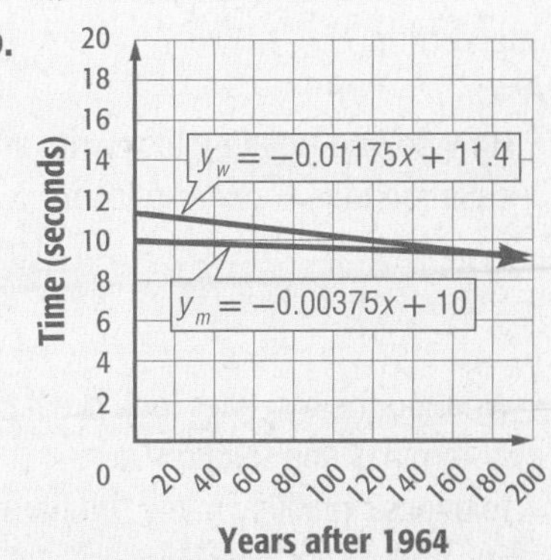

Based on these data, the women's performance will catch up to the men's performance 175 years after 1964, or in the year 2139. The next Olympic year would be 2140.

41c. Sample answer: No; it is unlikely that women's times will ever catch up to men's times because the times cannot continue to increase and decrease infinitely.

Differentiated Instruction OL BL

Extension As a preparation for the study of systems of inequalities, ask students to graph the following inequalities on the same coordinate system and then shade the region for which all three are satisfied: $x + y \leq 4, x \geq 0, y \geq 0$.

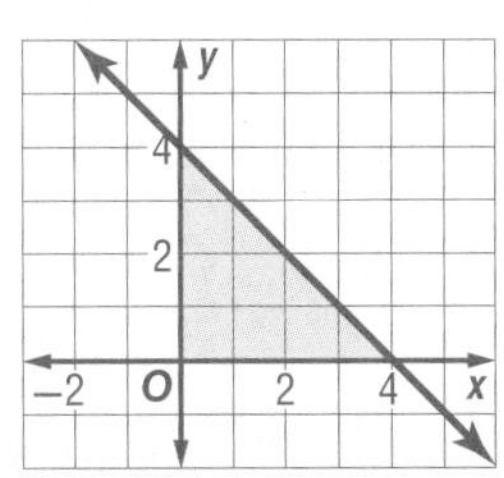

EXTEND 3-1 Lesson Notes

1 FOCUS

Objective Solve systems of equations using a graphing calculator.

Materials for Each Student

- TI-83/84 Plus or other graphing calculator

Teaching Tip

Be sure students know how to find, use, and clear the Y = screen, and that they know how to graph the equation(s) entered.

2 TEACH

Working in Cooperative Groups

Have students work in small groups. Then, for each exercise, have one student rewrite the system's equations in $y = mx + b$ form, have another student enter the equations in the Y = screen, and have a third student enter the keystrokes to find the point(s) of intersection.

Ask:

- How do you isolate y to rewrite an equation in $y = mx + b$ form? Isolate the y term on one side of the equation. Then divide both sides of the equation by the coefficient of y.
- What do the two lines look like if the system has one solution? zero solutions? infinitely many solutions? two intersecting lines; two parallel lines; one line (or two coinciding lines)

Practice Have students complete Exercises 1–10.

3 ASSESS

Formative Assessment

Use Exercises 1–3 to assess whether students can use a graphing calculator to solve systems of equations.

EXTEND 3-1

Graphing Technology Lab
Systems of Equations

FL Math Online glencoe.com
- Other Calculator Keystrokes
- Graphing Technology Personal Tutor

Objective
Use a graphing calculator to solve systems of equations.

NGSSS
MA.912.A.3.14 Solve systems of linear equations and inequalities **in two** and three **variables using graphical,** substitution, and elimination **methods.**

You can use a TI-83/84 Plus graphing calculator to solve systems of equations. You can use the Y= menu to graph each equation on the same set of axes.

EXAMPLE Intersection of Two Graphs

Graph the system of equations in the standard viewing window.

$3x + y = 9$

$x - y = -1$

Step 1 Write each equation in the form $y = mx + b$.

$3x + y = 9$	$x - y = 1$
$y = -3x + 9$	$-y = -x - 1$
	$y = x + 1$

Step 2 Enter $y = -3x + 9$ as **Y1** and $y = x + 1$ as **Y2**. Then graph the lines.

KEYSTROKES: [Y=] [(–)] 3 [X,T,θ,n] [+] 9 [ENTER] [X,T,θ,n] [+] 1 [ENTER] [ZOOM] 6

Step 3 Find the intersection of the lines.

KEYSTROKES: [2nd] [CALC] 5 [ENTER] [ENTER] [ENTER]

The solution is (2, 3).

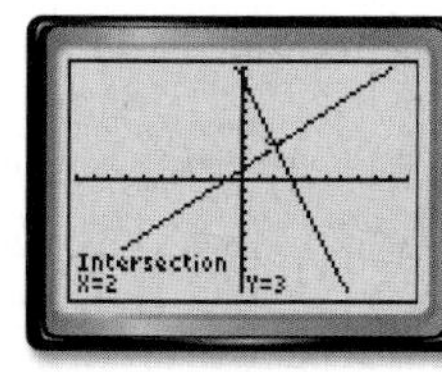

Exercises

Use a graphing calculator to solve each system of equations.

1. $2x + 4y = 36$
   $10y - 5x = 0$ **(9, 4.5)**
2. $2y - 3x = 7$
   $5x = 4y - 12$ **(−2, 0.5)**
3. $4x - 2y = 16$
   $7x + 3y = 15$ **(3, −2)**
4. $2x + 4y = 4$
   $x + 3y = 13$ **(−20, 11)**
5. $5x + y = 13$
   $3x = 15 - 3y$ **(2, 3)**
6. $4y - 5 = 20 - 3x$
   $4x - 7y + 16 = 0$ **(3, 4)**
7. $\frac{1}{4}x + y = \frac{11}{4}$
   $x - \frac{1}{2}y = 2$ **(3, 2)**
8. $3x + 2y = -3$
   $x + \frac{1}{3}y = -4$ **(−7, 9)**
9. $3x - 6y = 6$
   $2x - 4y = 4$ **infinitely many**
10. $6x + 8y = -16$
    $3x + 4y = 12$ **no solution**

From Concrete to Abstract

For each exercise, ask students which equation represents each line. Then, ask them to identify, in the graph, the solution to the system.

3-2 Solving Systems of Equations Algebraically

Then
You solved systems of linear equations by using tables and graphs. (Lesson 3-1)

Now
- Solve systems of linear equations by using substitution.
- Solve systems of linear equations by using elimination.

NGSSS
MA.912.A.3.14 Solve systems of linear equations and inequalities **in two** and three **variables using** graphical, **substitution, and elimination methods.**
MA.912.A.3.15 Solve real-world problems involving systems of linear equations and inequalities in two and three variables.

New Vocabulary
substitution method
elimination method

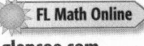

FL Math Online
glencoe.com

Why?

Alejandro has a computer support business. He estimates that the cost to run his business can be represented by $y = 48x + 500$, where x is the number of customers. He also estimates that his income can be represented by $y = 65x - 145$. A system of equations can be used to determine the number of customers he will need in order to break even.

Substitution Algebraic methods are used to find exact solutions of systems of equations. One algebraic method is called the **substitution method**.

Key Concept — Substitution Method

Step 1 Solve one equation for one of the variables.

Step 2 Substitute the resulting expression into the other equation to replace the variable. Then solve the equation.

Step 3 Substitute to solve for the other variable.

Real-World EXAMPLE 1 Use the Substitution Method

BUSINESS How many customers will Alejandro need in order to break even? What will his profit be if he has 60 customers?

Understand Alejandro wants to know how many customers he needs for his income to equal his costs. He also wants to know what his profit will be if he has 60 customers.

Plan Solve the system of equations. Income: $y = 65x - 145$
Cost: $y = 48x + 500$

Solve

$y = 65x - 145$	**Income equation**
$48x + 500 = 65x - 145$	**Substitute 48x + 500 for y.**
$500 = 17x - 145$	**Subtract 48x from each side.**
$645 = 17x$	**Add 145 to each side.**
$37.9 \approx x$	**Divide each side by 17.**

Alejandro needs 38 customers to break even. If he has 60 customers, his income will be 65(60) − 145 or \$3755, and his costs will be 48(60) + 500 or \$3380, so his profit will be 3755 − 3380 or \$375.

Check You can use a graphing calculator to check this solution. The break-even point is near (37.9, 2321.2). Use the CALC function to find the cost and income with 60 customers.

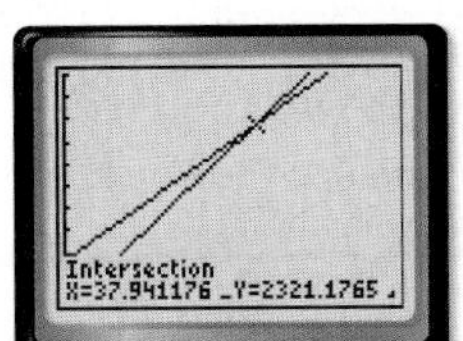

[0, 65] scl: 5 by [0, 3000] scl: 300

1 FOCUS

Vertical Alignment

Before Lesson 3-2
Solve systems of linear equations by using tables and graphs.

Lesson 3-2
Solve systems of linear equations by using substitution.
Solve systems of linear equations by using elimination.

After Lesson 3-2
Solve systems of inequalities.

2 TEACH

Scaffolding Questions

Have students read the *Why?* section of the lesson.

Ask:
- What is Alejandro's cost if he has 15 customers? \$1220
- What is his income if he has 25 customers? \$1480
- What happens if he has 38 customers? His cost and income are almost equal.

Lesson 3-2 Resources

Resource	Approaching-Level	On-Level	Beyond-Level	English Learners
Teacher Edition	• Differentiated Instruction, p. 146	• Differentiated Instruction, p. 146	• Differentiated Instruction, p. 150	
Chapter Resource Masters	• Study Guide and Intervention, pp. 12–13 • Skills Practice, p. 14 • Practice, p. 15 • Word Problem Practice, p. 16	• Study Guide and Intervention, pp. 12–13 • Skills Practice, p. 14 • Practice, p. 15 • Word Problem Practice, p. 16 • Enrichment, p. 17	• Practice, p. 15 • Word Problem Practice, p. 16 • Enrichment, p. 17	• Study Guide and Intervention, pp. 12–13 • Skills Practice, p. 14 • Practice, p. 15 • Word Problem Practice, p. 16
Transparencies	• 5-Minute Check Transparency 3-2	• 5-Minute Check Transparency 3-2	• 5-Minute Check Transparency 3-2	• 5-Minute Check Transparency 3-2
Other	• Study Notebook • Teaching Algebra with Manipulatives	• Study Notebook • Teaching Algebra with Manipulatives	• Study Notebook	• Study Notebook • Teaching Algebra with Manipulatives

Substitution

Example 1 shows how to solve a system of linear equations by using the algebraic method of substitution.

Formative Assessment

Use the Guided Practice exercises after each example to determine students' understanding of concepts.

Additional Example

1 **FURNITURE** Lancaster Woodworkers Furniture Store builds two types of wooden outdoor chairs. A rocking chair sells for $265, and an Adirondack chair with footstool sells for $320. The books show that last month, the business earned $13,930 for the 48 outdoor chairs sold. How many rocking chairs were sold? 26

Additional Examples also in Interactive Classroom PowerPoint® Presentations

IWB INTERACTIVE WHITEBOARD READY

Elimination

Examples 2–4 show how to solve systems of linear equations by using the algebraic method of elimination.

Additional Example

2 Use the elimination method to solve the system of equations.

$x + 2y = 10$

$x + y = 6$

(2, 4)

Guided Practice

Use substitution to solve each system of equations.

1A. $5x - 3y = 23$
$2x + y = 7$ (4, −1)

1B. $x - 7y = 11$
$5x + 4y = -23$ (−3, −2)

1C. $-6x - y = 27$
$3x + 8y = 9$ (−5, 3)

Personal Tutor glencoe.com

Elimination You can use the **elimination method** to solve a system when one of the variables has the same coefficient in both equations.

Key Concept — Elimination Method

Step 1 Multiply one or both equations by a number to result in two equations that contain opposite terms.

Step 2 Add the equations, eliminating one variable. Then solve the equation.

Step 3 Substitute to solve for the other variable.

Variables can be eliminated by addition or subtraction.

EXAMPLE 2 Solve by Using Elimination

Use the elimination method to solve the system of equations.

$5x + 3y = -19$
$8x + 3y = -25$

Notice that solving by substitution would involve fractions.

Step 1 Multiply one equation by −1 so the equations contain $3y$ and $-3y$.

$8x + 3y = -25$ **Multiply by −1.** $-8x - 3y = 25$

Step 2 Add the equations to eliminate one variable.

$5x + 3y = -19$	Equation 1
$(+)\ -8x - 3y = 25$	Equation 2 × (−1)
$-3x = 6$	Add the equations.
$x = -2$	Divide each side by −3.

Step 3 Substitute −2 for x into either original equation.

$8x + 3y = -25$	Equation 2
$8(-2) + 3y = -25$	$x = -2$
$-16 + 3y = -25$	Multiply.
$3y = -9$	Add 16 to each side.
$y = -3$	Divide each side by 3.

The solution is (−2, −3).

StudyTip

Elimination Remember when you add or subtract one equation from another to add or subtract *every* term, including the constant on the other side of the equal sign.

Review Vocabulary

Least Common Multiple the least number that is a common multiple of two or more numbers

Guided Practice

2A. $4x - 3y = -22$
$2x + 3y = 16$ (−1, 6)

2B. $6x - 5y = -8$
$4x - 5y = -12$ (2, 4)

2C. $2x - 9y = 34$
$-2x + 6y = -28$ (8, −2)

Personal Tutor glencoe.com

Sometimes, adding or subtracting equations will not eliminate either variable. You can use multiplication and least common multiples to find a common coefficient.

Watch Out!

Preventing Errors In Example 1, recommend to students that when they find a solution, they check their answers against the facts presented in the original problem.

144 Chapter 3 Systems of Equations and Inequalities

NGSSS PRACTICE EXAMPLE 3 912.A.3.14

Solve the system of equations. $5x + 3y = 52$
$9x - 4y = 56$

A. (4, 1) **B.** (8, 4) **C.** (8, 0) **D.** (12, 3)

Read the Test Item

You are given a system of two linear equations and are asked to find the solution.

Solve the Test Item

Neither variable has a common coefficient. The coefficients of the y-variables are 3 and 4 and their least common multiple is 12, so multiply each equation by the value that will make the y-coefficient 12.

$5x + 3y = 52$ **Multiply by 4.** $20x + 12y = 208$

$9x - 4y = 56$ **Multiply by 3.** $(+)\ 27x - 12y = 168$

$47x = 376$ **Add the equations.**

$x = 8$ **Divide each side by 47.**

Solve for y by substituting $x = 8$ into either of the original equations.

$5x + 3y = 52$ **Equation 1**
$5(8) + 3y = 52$ **Replace x with 8.**
$40 + 3y = 52$ **Multiply.**
$3y = 12$ **Subtract 40 from each side.**
$y = 4$ **Divide each side by 3.**

The correct answer is B.

Guided Practice

3. Solve the system of equations. $6a - 5b = -62$
$8a + 7b = 54$ I

F. (4, 6) **G.** (2, −12) **H.** (0, −8) **I.** (−2, 10)

Personal Tutor glencoe.com

StudyTip

Adding and Subtracting Equations If you add or subtract two equations in a system and the result is an equation that is never true, then the system is inconsistent. When you add or subtract two equations in a system and the result is an equation that is always true, then the system is dependent.

EXAMPLE 4 No Solution and Infinite Solutions

Use the elimination method to solve each system of equations.

a. $5x + 6y = 45$
$-5x - 6y = 38$

$5x + 6y = 45$
$(+)\ -5x - 6y = 38$
$0 = 83$

Because $0 = 83$ is not true, this system has no solutions.

b. $2x + 3y = 5$
$6x + 9y = 15$

$3(2x + 3y = 5) = 6x + 9y = 15$ **Multiply by 3.**
$6x + 9y = 15$
$(-)\ 6x + 9y = 15$
$0 = 0$

Because the equation $0 = 0$ is always true, there are an infinite number of solutions.

Guided Practice

4A. $9a - 7b = 14$ infinite solutions
$-18a + 14b = -28$

4B. $-6c + 12d = 81$ no solution
$-5c + 10d = -61$

Personal Tutor glencoe.com

StudyTip

Subtraction When a variable has identical coefficients in two equations, it can be eliminated by subtraction.

Additional Example

3 STANDARDIZED TEST PRACTICE Solve the system of equations.

$2x + 3y = 12$
$5x - 2y = 11$

A (2, 3) **C** (0, 5.5)
B (6, 0) **D** (3, 2)

The correct choice is D.

Tips for New Teachers

Reasoning Remind students to take time to plan a problem-solving strategy before starting calculations. Advise students that they may find it easier to eliminate one of the variables rather than the other using this technique.

Focus on Mathematical Content

Solving Systems of Equations If the coefficients for one of the variables in the equation are already the same or opposite, that variable can be easily eliminated by subtracting or adding the given equations. If this is not the case, it may be a better choice to use the method of substitution. Substitution and elimination will both solve a system of equations. You will get the same solution no matter which method you choose.

Additional Example

4 Use the elimination method to solve each system of equations.

a. $-3x + 5y = 12$
$6x - 10y = -21$

There is no solution.

b. $-3x + 4y = 7$
$9x - 12y = -21$

There are an infinite number of solutions.

TEACH with TECH

DOCUMENT CAMERA Choose two students to share their work with the class. Select students who solved the same system of equations in different ways (by solving for different variables).

Math History Link

Nina Karlovna Bari (1901–1961)
Russian mathematician Nina Karlovna Bari was considered the principal leader of mathematics at Moscow State University, shown above. She is best known for her textbooks *Higher Algebra* and *The Theory of Series*.

The following summarizes the various methods for solving systems.

Concept Summary — Solving Systems of Equations

Method	The Best Time to Use
Table	to estimate the solution, since a table may not provide an exact solution
Graphing	to estimate the solution, since graphing usually does not give an exact solution
Substitution	if one of the variables in either equation has a coefficient of 1 or −1
Elimination Using Addition	if one of the variables has opposite coefficients in the two equations
Elimination Using Subtraction	if one of the variables has the same coefficient in the two equations
Elimination Using Multiplication	if none of the coefficients are 1 or −1 and neither of the variables can be eliminated by simply adding or subtracting the equations

Check Your Understanding

Example 1 p. 143

1. **FUNDRAISER** To raise money for new uniforms, the band boosters sell T-shirts and hats. The cost and sale price of each item is shown. The boosters spend a total of $2000 on T-shirts and hats. They sell all of the merchandise, and make $3375. How many T-shirts did they sell? **250 T-shirts**

Item	Cost	Sale Price
T-Shirt	$6	$10
Hat	$4	$7

Solve each system of equations by using substitution.

2. $y = 2x - 10$
   $y = -4x + 8$ **(3, −4)**
3. $x + 5y = 3$
   $3x - 2y = -8$ **(−2, 1)**
4. $a - 3b = -22$
   $4a + 2b = -4$ **(−4, 6)**
5. $2a + 8b = -8$
   $3a - 5b = 22$ **(4, −2)**
6. $9c - 3d = -33$
   $6c + 5d = -8$ **(−3, 2)**
7. $6x - 7y = 23$
   $8x + 4y = 44$ **(5, 1)**

Examples 2–4 pp. 144–145

Solve each system of equations by using elimination.

8. $4x - 3y = 29$
   $4x + 3y = 35$ **(8, 1)**
9. $-6w - 8z = -44$
   $3w + 6z = 36$ **(−2, 7)**
10. $8a - 3b = -11$
    $5a + 2b = -3$ **(−1, 1)**
11. $3a + 5b = -27$
    $4a + 10b = -46$ **(−4, −3)**
12. $6x - 4y = 30$
    $12x + 5y = -18$ **(1, −6)**
13. $5a + 15b = -24$
    $-2a - 6b = 28$ **no solution**

14. **NGSSS PRACTICE** What is the solution of the linear system? **B**

$$4x + 3y = 2$$
$$4x - 2y = 12$$

A. (8, −10) **B.** (2, −2) **C.** (−10, 14) **D.** no solution

Differentiated Instruction AL OL

Logical Learners Have students summarize the various algebraic methods for solving a system of equations using if-then statements and examples. Sample: If one of the equations has a variable with a coefficient of 1 (such as $x + 3y = 9$ or $5x + y = 13$), then consider the substitution method.

Practice and Problem Solving

● = **Step-by-Step Solutions** begin on page R20. **Extra Practice** begins on page 947.

Example 1 p. 143

Solve each system of equations by using substitution.

15. $-4r - 3t = -26$, $5r + t = 27$ **(5, 2)**

16. $6u + 3v = -15$, $8u - 5v = 7$ **(−1, −3)**

17. $4x + 12y = 0$, $-3x - 4y = -10$ **(6, −2)**

18. $c - 5d = -16$, $3c + 2d = -14$ **(−6, 2)**

19. $-5p - t = 17$, $4p + 6t = 2$ **(−4, 3)**

20. $-6y + 5z = -35$, $7y - z = 36$ **(5, −1)**

21. $9y + 3x = 18$, $-3y - x = -6$ **infinite solutions**

22. $5x - 20y = 70$, $6x + 5y = -32$ **(−2, −4)**

23. $-4x - 16y = -96$, $7x + 3y = 68$ **(8, 4)**

24. $-4a - 5b = 14$, $9a + 3b = -48$ **(−6, 2)**

25. $-9c - 4d = 31$, $6c + 6d = -24$ **(−3, −1)**

26. $8f + 3g = 12$, $-32f - 12g = 48$ **no solution**

27. TENNIS At a park, there are 38 people playing tennis. Some are playing doubles, and some are playing singles. There are 13 matches in progress. A doubles match requires 4 players, and a singles match requires 2 players.

a. Write a system of two equations that represents the number of singles and doubles matches going on. **$x + y = 13$ and $4x + 2y = 38$**

b. How many matches of each kind are in progress? **6 doubles games and 7 singles games**

Examples 2–4 pp. 144–145

Solve each system of equations by using elimination. **31. no solution**

28. $8x + y = 27$, $-3x + 4y = 3$ **(3, 3)**

29. $2a - 5b = -20$, $2a + 5b = 20$ **(0, 4)**

30. $6j + 4k = -46$, $2j + 4k = -26$ **(−5, −4)**

31. $3x - 8y = 24$, $-12x + 32y = 96$

32. $5a - 2b = -19$, $8a + 5b = -55$ **(−5, −3)**

33. $r - 6t = 44$, $9r + 12t = 0$ **(8, −6)**

34. $6d + 5f = -32$, $5d - 9f = 26$ **(−2, −4)**

35. $11u = 5v + 35$, $8v = -6u + 62$ **(5, 4)**

36. $-1.2c + 3.4d = 6$, $6c = -30 + 17d$ **infinite solutions**

37. $6g + 8h = 16$, $-4g - 7h = -19$ **(−4, 5)**

38. $15j - 3k = 129$, $-6j + 8k = -72$ **(8, −3)**

39. $-4m - 9n = 30$, $10m + 3n = 42$ **(6, −6)**

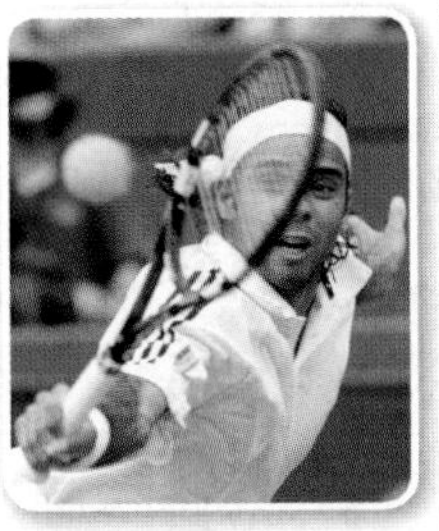

Real-World Link

The Wimbledon Championship is broadcast to over 170 countries with an audience of over 1 billion people.

Source: *Tennis Magazine*

40. The sum of four times a number and six times a second number is 36. The difference of five times the second number and three times the first number is 49. Find the numbers. **(−3, 8)**

41. Twice the sum of a number and 3 times a second number is 4. The difference of ten times the second number and five times the first is 90. Find the numbers. **(−10, 4)**

42. Three times the difference of four times a number and three times a second number is 117. Four times the sum of 6 times the second number and 8 times the first number is 72. Find the numbers. **no solution**

43. CYCLING The total distance of the cycling course is 104.8 miles. Julian starts the course at 8:00 A.M. and rides at 12 miles an hour. Peter starts two hours later than Julian but decides to try to catch up with him. Peter rides at a speed of 16 miles an hour.

a. Solve the system of equations to find when Peter will catch up to Julian. **4:00 P.M.**

b. Peter wants to reduce the time it takes him to catch up to Julian by 1 hour. Explain how he could do this by changing his starting time. Explain how he could do this by changing his speed. Are your answers reasonable?

43b. Peter could start sooner or he could increase his speed, or a combination of both; both answers are reasonable; he could change his starting time and he could increase his speed.

3 PRACTICE

Formative Assessment

Use Exercises 1–14 to check for understanding.

Use the chart at the bottom of this page to customize assignments for your students.

Differentiated Homework Options

Level	Assignment	Two-Day Option	
AL Basic	15–43, 64, 66–83	15–43 odd, 69–72	16–42 even, 64, 66–68, 73–83
OL Core	15–49 odd, 51–55, 57–61 odd, 62–64, 66–83	15–43, 69–72	44–49, 50–55, 56–64, 66–68, 73–83
BL Advanced	44–80, (optional: 81–83)		

B **Solve each system of equations.**

44. $11p + 3q = 6$
$-0.75q - 2.75p = -1.5$ **infinite solutions**

45. $8r - 5t = -60$
$6r + 3t = -18$ **(−5, 4)**

46. $10t + 4v = 13$
$-4t - 7v = 11$ **(2.5, −3)**

47. $6w = 12 - 4x$
$6x = -9w + 18$ **infinite solutions**

48. $\frac{3}{2}y + z = 3$
$-y - \frac{2}{3}z = -2$ **infinite solutions**

49. $\frac{5}{2}a - \frac{3}{4}b = 46$
$-\frac{7}{8}a - 3b = 10$ **(16, −8)**

50. ROWING Allison can row a boat 1 mile upstream (against the current) in 24 minutes. She can row the same distance downstream in 13 minutes. Assume that both the rowing speed and the speed of the current are constant. **a. 3.56 mph; 1.06 mph**

a. Find the speed at which Allison is rowing and the speed of the current.

b. If Allison plans to meet her friends 3 miles upstream one hour from now, will she be on time? Explain. **No; she will be 12 minutes late.**

51. EARTH WEEK To reduce waste, The Green Café offers a reduced refill rate on coffee for anyone buying a Green mug. The mug costs \$2.95 and is filled with 16 ounces of coffee. The refill price is \$0.50. A 16-ounce coffee in a disposable cup costs \$0.85.

a. What is the approximate break-even point for buying the mug and refills in comparison to buying coffee in disposable cups? What does this mean?

b. Which offer do you think is better? Explain your reasoning. **See margin.**

c. How would your decision change if the refillable mug offer was extended for a year? **Over a year's time, the refillable mug would be more economical.**

51a. 7 16-ounce servings; If you drink 7 coffees, the price for each option is almost the same.

Real-World Link

Earth Day began in San Francisco in 1969 and is now observed by over 500 million people worldwide.

Source: *Earth Week Charlottesville*

52. SKATING PARTY Anita invites 21 friends to the skating rink for a birthday party. The rink rents roller skates for \$3 and inline skates for \$5. The total rental bill for all 22 students is \$96.

a. Write a system of equations that represents the number of students who rented the two types of skates. **$x + y = 22$ and $3x + 5y = 96$**

b. How many students rented roller skates and how many rented inline skates? **7 students rented roller skates, and 15 students rented inline skates.**

53. GEOMETRY Angles A and B are supplementary and the measure of angle A is 18 degrees greater than the measure of angle B. Find the angle measures. **$m\angle A = 99$, $m\angle B = 81$**

54. JOBS Levi has a job offer in which he will receive \$800 per month plus a commission of 2% of the total price of cars he sells. At his current job, he receives \$1200 per month plus a commission of 1.5% of his total sales. How much must he sell per month to make the new job a better deal? **more than \$80,000**

55. TRAVEL A youth group went on a trip to an amusement park, travelling in two vans. The number of people in each van and the total cost of admission are shown in the table. Find the adult price and student price of admission. **adult: \$16; student: \$9**

	Adults	Students	Total Cost
Van A	2	5	\$77
Van B	2	7	\$95

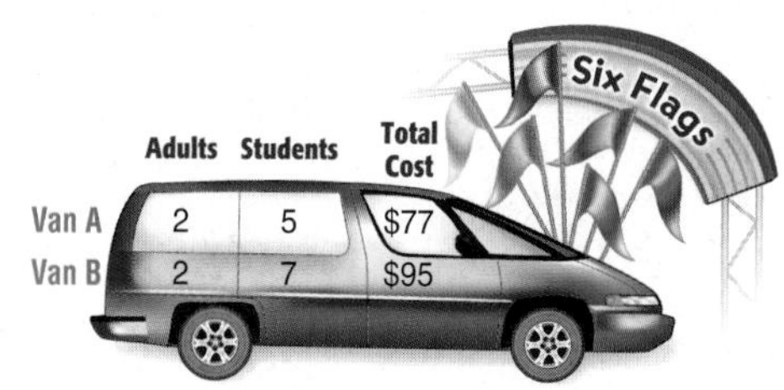

Solve each system of equations.

56. $4.1x - 3.4y = 19.97$
$6.3x + 2.2y = 7.67$ **(2.3, −3.1)**

57. $3.7x - 4.6y = 15.37$
$-5.1x - 2.8y = 40.97$ **(−4.3, −6.8)**

58. $3.65x + 6.83y = -34.526$
$-41.3x - 2.68y = 77.336$ **(−1.6, −4.2)**

59. $-6.79a + 3.29b = -43.792$
$-9.14a - 6.28b = 10.658$ **(3.3, −6.5)**

Study Guide and Intervention

CRM pp. 12–13 AL OL ELL

3-2 Study Guide and Intervention

Solving Systems of Equations Algebraically

Substitution To solve a system of linear equations by **substitution**, first solve for one variable in terms of the other in one of the equations. Then substitute this expression into the other equation and simplify.

Example **Use substitution to solve the system of equations.** $2x - y = 9$, $x + 3y = -6$

Solve the first equation for y in terms of x.

$2x - y = 9$ First equation
$-y = -2x + 9$ Subtract $2x$ from both sides.
$y = 2x - 9$ Multiply both sides by −1.

Substitute the expression $2x - 9$ for y into the second equation and solve for x.

$x + 3y = -6$ Second equation
$x + 3(2x - 9) = -6$ Substitute $2x - 9$ for y.
$x + 6x - 27 = -6$ Distributive Property
$7x - 27 = -6$ Simplify.
$7x = 21$ Add 27 to each side.
$x = 3$ Divide each side by 7.

Now, substitute the value 3 for x in either original equation and solve for y.

$2x - y = 9$ First equation
$2(3) - y = 9$ Replace x with 3.
$6 - y = 9$ Simplify.
$-y = 3$ Subtract 6 from each side.
$y = -3$ Multiply each side by −1.

The solution of the system is (3, −3).

Exercises

Solve each system of equations by using substitution.

1. $3x + y = 7$, $4x + 2y = 16$ **(−1, 10)**
2. $2x + y = 5$, $3x - 3y = 3$ **(2, 1)**
3. $2x + 3y = -3$, $x + 2y = 2$ **(−12, 7)**
4. $2x - y = 7$, $6x - 3y = 14$ **no solution**
5. $4x - 3y = 4$, $2x + y = -8$ **(−2, −4)**
6. $5x + y = 6$, $3 - x = 0$ **(3, −9)**
7. $x + 8y = -2$, $x - 3y = 20$ **(14, −2)**
8. $2x - y = -4$, $4x + y = 1$ **$\left(-\frac{1}{2}, 3\right)$**
9. $x - y = -2$, $2x - 3y = 2$ **(−8, −6)**
10. $x - 4y = 4$, $2x + 12y = 13$ **$\left(5, \frac{1}{4}\right)$**
11. $x + 3y = 2$, $4x + 12y = 8$ **infinitely many**
12. $2x + 2y = 4$, $x - 2y = 0$ **$\left(\frac{4}{3}, \frac{2}{3}\right)$**

Chapter 3 12 Glencoe Algebra 2

Practice

CRM p. 15 AL OL BL ELL

3-2 Practice

Solving Systems of Equations Algebraically

Solve each system of equations by using substitution.

1. $2x + y = 4$, $3x + 2y = 1$ **(7, −10)**
2. $x - 3y = 9$, $x + 2y = -1$ **(3, −2)**
3. $g + 3h = 8$, $\frac{1}{3}g + h = 9$ **no solution**
4. $2a - 4b = 6$, $-a + 2b = -3$ **infinitely many**
5. $2m + n = 6$, $5m + 6n = 1$ **(5, −4)**
6. $4x - 3y = -6$, $-x - 2y = 7$ **(−3, −2)**
7. $u - 2v = \frac{1}{2}$, $-u + 2v = 5$ **no solution**
8. $x - 3y = 16$, $4x - y = 9$ **(1, −5)**
9. $w + 3z = 1$, $3w - 5z = -4$ **$\left(-\frac{1}{2}, \frac{1}{2}\right)$**

Solve each system of equations by using elimination.

10. $2r + s = 5$, $3r - s = 20$ **(5, −5)**
11. $2m - n = -1$, $3m + 2n = 30$ **(4, 9)**
12. $6x + 3y = 6$, $8x + 5y = 12$ **(−1, 4)**
13. $3j - k = 10$, $4j - k = 16$ **(6, 8)**
14. $2x - y = -4$, $-4x + 2y = 6$ **no solution**
15. $2g + h = 6$, $3g - 2h = 16$ **(4, −2)**
16. $2t + 4v = 6$, $-t - 2v = -3$ **infinitely many**
17. $3x - 2y = 12$, $2x + \frac{2}{3}y = 14$ **(6, 3)**
18. $\frac{1}{2}x + 3y = 11$, $8x - 5y = 17$ **(4, 3)**

Solve each system of equations.

19. $8x + 3y = -5$, $10x + 6y = -13$ **$\left(\frac{1}{2}, -3\right)$**
20. $8q - 15r = -40$, $4q + 2r = 56$ **(10, 8)**
21. $3x - 4y = 12$, $\frac{1}{3}x - \frac{4}{9}y = \frac{4}{3}$ **infinitely many**
22. $4b - 2d = 5$, $-2b + d = 1$ **no solution**
23. $s + 3y = 4$, $s = 1$ **(1, 1)**
24. $4m - 2p = 0$, $-3m + 9p = 5$ **$\left(\frac{1}{3}, \frac{2}{3}\right)$**
25. $5g + 4k = 10$, $-3g - 5k = 7$ **(6, −5)**
26. $0.5x + 2y = 5$, $x - 2y = -8$ **(−2, 3)**
27. $h - z = 3$, $-3h + 3z = 6$ **no solution**

28. **SPORTS** Last year the volleyball team paid \$5 per pair for socks and \$17 per pair for shorts on a total purchase of \$315. This year they spent \$342 to buy the same number of pairs of socks and shorts because the socks now cost \$6 a pair and the shorts cost \$18.

a. Write a system of two equations that represents the number of pairs of socks and shorts bought each year. **$5x + 17y = 315$, $6x + 18y = 342$**

b. How many pairs of socks and shorts did the team buy each year? **socks: 12, shorts: 15**

Chapter 3 15 Glencoe Algebra 2

Lesson 3-2

Word Problem Practice

CRM p. 16 AL OL BL ELL

3-2 Word Problem Practice

Solving Systems of Equations Algebraically

1. **SUPPLIES** Kirsta and Arthur both need pens and blank CDs. The equation that represents Kirsta's purchases is $y = 27 - 3x$. The equation that represents Arthur's purchases is $y = 17 - x$. If x represents the price of the pens, and y represents the price of the CDs, what are the prices of the pens and the CDs?
pens are \$5 a pack, CDs are \$12 a pack

2. **WALKING** Amy is walking a straight path that can be represented by the equation $y = 2x + 3$. At the same time Kendra is walking the straight path that has the equation $3y = 6x + 6$. What is the solution to the system of equations that represents the paths the two girls walked? Explain.
There is no solution. Their paths never cross.

3. **CAFETERIA** To furnish a cafeteria, a school can spend \$5200 on tables and chairs. Tables cost \$200 and chairs cost \$40. Each table will have 8 chairs around it. How many tables and chairs will the school purchase?
10 tables and 80 chairs

4. **PRICES** At a store, toothbrushes cost x dollars and bars of soap cost y dollars. One customer bought 2 toothbrushes and 1 bar of soap for \$11. Another customer bought 6 toothbrushes and 5 bars of soap for \$38. Both amounts do not include tax. Write and solve a system of equations for x and y.
$2x + y = 11$
$6x + 5y = 38$
$x = 4.25$ and $y = 2.50$

5. **GAMES** Mark and Stephanie are playing darts according to World Darts Federation rules. Each toss earns points depending on where the dart lands. Each ring and sector is worth a different number of points. Mark and Stephanie both toss three darts in the first round. It happens that their darts only land in two areas of the board.

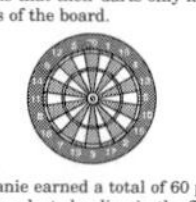

a. Stephanie earned a total of 60 points with two darts landing in the first area and one dart landing in the second area. One of Mark's darts landed in the first area and two in the second. He scored 75 points. Write a system of equations for their scores. Use x for the first area and y for the second area.
$2x + y = 60$; $x + 2y = 75$

b. Solve the equations. How many points is the first area worth? How many points is the second area worth?
$x = 15$; $y = 30$

c. If Mark and Stephanie are playing to 150 points and their darts continue to land in only the two areas, which different combinations of darts landing in the two areas will add up to 150? How many darts landing in the first area would total 150 points? How many darts landing in the second area?
10 darts in first area; 5 darts in second area; also 2 darts in first and 4 in second; 4 darts in first and 3 in second; 6 darts in first and 2 in second; 8 darts in first and 1 in second. 10 darts. 5 darts.

Chapter 3 16 Glencoe Algebra 2

Enrichment

CRM p. 17 OL BL

3-2 Enrichment

Using Coordinates

From one observation point, the line of sight to a downed plane is given by $y = x - 1$. This equation describes the distance from the observation point to the plane in a straight line. From another observation point, the line of sight is given by $x + 3y = 21$. What are the coordinates of the point at which the crash occurred?

Solve the system of equations $\begin{cases} y = x - 1 \\ x + 3y = 21 \end{cases}$

$x + 3y = 21$
$x + 3(x - 1) = 21$ Substitute $x - 1$ for y.
$x + 3x - 3 = 21$
$4x = 24$
$x = 6$

$x + 3y = 21$
$6 + 3y = 21$ Substitute 6 for x.
$3y = 15$
$y = 5$

The coordinates of the crash are (6, 5).

Lesson 3-2

Additional Answer

51b. Sample answer: If you drink fewer than 7 coffees during that week, the disposable cup price is better. If you drink more than 7 coffees, the refillable mug price is better.

StudyTip

Reasonable Answers For Exercises 60 and 61, you can use the graphs to determine whether your answers are reasonable.

GEOMETRY Find the point at which the diagonals of the quadrilaterals intersect.

60. 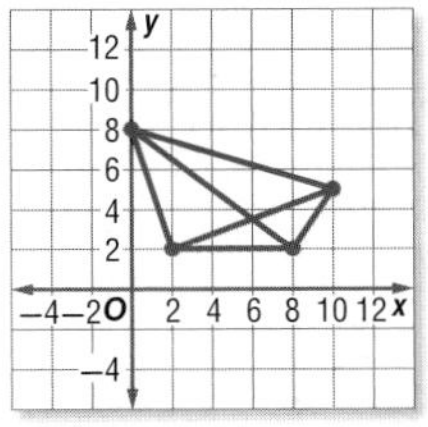

(6, 3.5)

61. 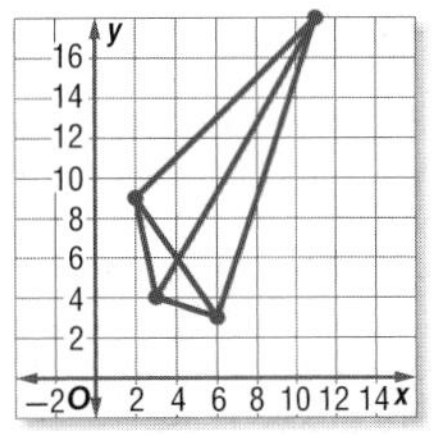

$\left(\frac{53}{13}, \frac{153}{26}\right)$

62. **ELECTIONS** In the election for student council, Candidate A received 55% of the total votes, while Candidate B received 1541 votes. If Candidate C received 40% of the votes that Candidate A received, how many total votes were cast? **6700 votes**

63. **MULTIPLE REPRESENTATIONS** In this problem, you will explore systems of equations with three lines and two variables. **a–d. See margin.**

$$3y + x = 16$$
$$y - 2x = -4$$
$$y + 5x = 10$$

a. **TABULAR** Make a table of x- and y-values for each equation.

b. **ANALYTICAL** Which values from the table indicate intersections? Is there a solution that satisfies all three equations?

c. **GRAPHICAL** Graph the three equations on a single coordinate plane.

d. **VERBAL** What conditions must be met for a system of three equations with two variables to have a solution? What conditions result in no solution?

H.O.T. Problems Use Higher-Order Thinking Skills

64. **ERROR ANALYSIS** Gloria and Syreeta are solving the system $6x - 4y = 26$ and $-3x + 4y = -17$. Is either of them correct? Explain your reasoning.

Gloria

$6x - 4y = 26$
$-3x + 4y = -17$
$3x = 9$
$x = 3$

$6(3) - 4y = 26$
$18 - 4y = 26$
$-4y = 8$
$y = -2$

The solution is (3, −2).

Syreeta

$6x - 4y = 26$
$-3x + 4y = -17$
$3x = -9$
$x = -3$

$6(-3) - 4y = 26$
$-18 - 4y = 26$
$-4y = 44$
$y = -11$

The solution is (−3, −11).

65. **CHALLENGE** Find values of a and b for which the following system has a solution of $(b - 1, b - 2)$. $a \neq 0$, $b = \pm 3$

$$-8ax + 4ay = -12a$$
$$2bx - by = 9$$

66. **REASONING** Katie says that if the coefficients of each variable are identical, then she does not need to solve the system since it will always have infinite solutions. Is she correct? Explain your reasoning.

67. **OPEN ENDED** Write a system of equations in which one equation needs to be multiplied by 3 and the other needs to be multiplied by 4 in order to solve the system with elimination. Then solve your system. **See Chapter 3 Answer Appendix.**

68. **WRITING IN MATH** Explain why substitution is sometimes more helpful than elimination and why elimination is sometimes more helpful than substitution.

64. Sample answer: Gloria; Syreeta subtracted 26 from 17 instead of 17 from 26 and got $3x = -9$ instead of $3x = 9$. She proceeded to get a value of −11 for y. She would have found her error if she substituted the solution into the original equations.

66. Sample answer: Katie is incorrect because if the constant values are different, then the system will have no solution.

68. Sample answer: It is more helpful to use substitution when one of the variables has a coefficient of 1 or if a coefficient can be reduced to 1 without turning other coefficients into fractions. Otherwise, elimination is more helpful because it will avoid the use of fractions in solving the system.

Multiple Representations In Exercise 63, students use a table of values and a graph in the coordinate plane to find solutions for a system of equations and interpret the results.

Watch Out!

Error Analysis For Exercise 64, students should see that in Syreeta's solution, the sum of 26 and −17 is incorrectly written as −9. Explain to students that when the two equations are added, the left side should be $3x$ and the right side should be 9.

Additional Answers

63a.

Equation 1		Equation 2	
x	y	x	y
0	$\frac{16}{3}$	0	−4
1	5	1	−2
2	$\frac{14}{3}$	2	0
3	$\frac{13}{3}$	3	2
4	4	4	4

Equation 3	
x	y
0	10
1	5
2	0
3	−5
4	−10

63b. Equations 1 and 2 intersect at (4, 4), equations 2 and 3 intersect at (2, 0), and equations 1 and 3 intersect at (1, 5); there is no solution that satisfies all three equations.

63c. 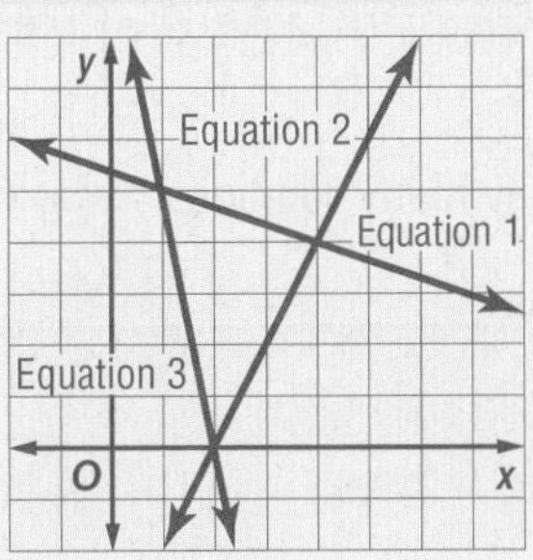

63d. If all three lines intersect at the same point, then the system has a solution. The system has no solution if the lines intersect at 3 different points, or if two or three lines are parallel.

4 ASSESS

Name the Math Have students either write on a piece of paper or tell you whether elimination or substitution would be better to solve this system of equations.

$$2m - n = 2$$
$$2m + 3n = 22$$

Formative Assessment

Check for student understanding of concepts in Lessons 3-1 and 3-2.

CRM Quiz 1, p. 39

Additional Answers

73b.

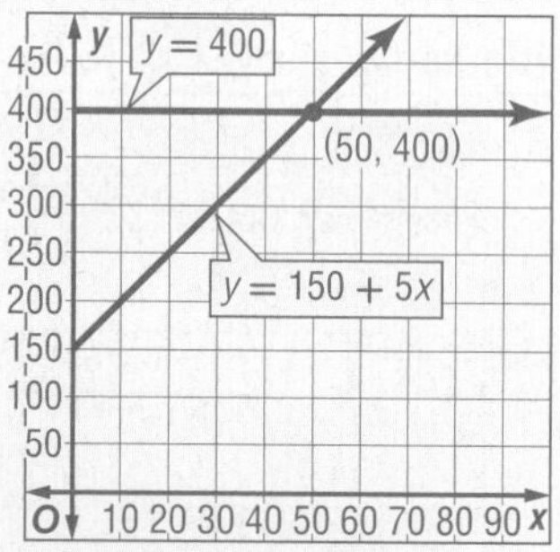

74.

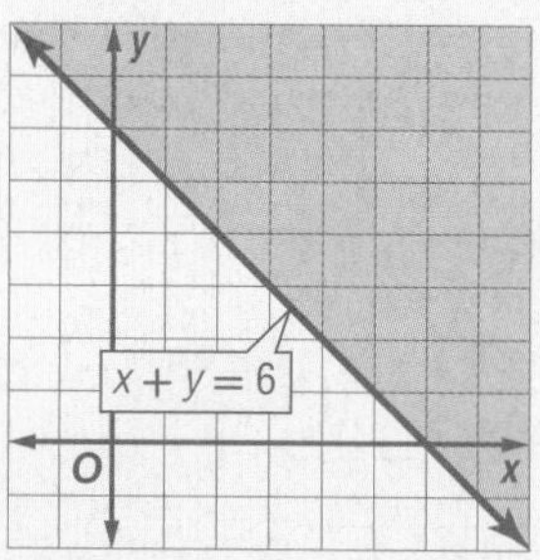

75.

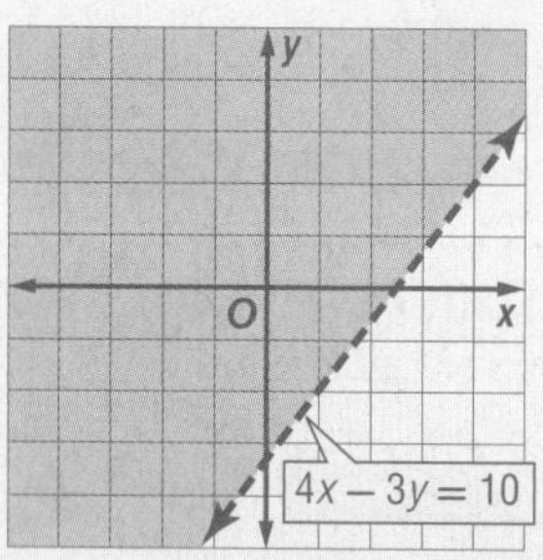

76.

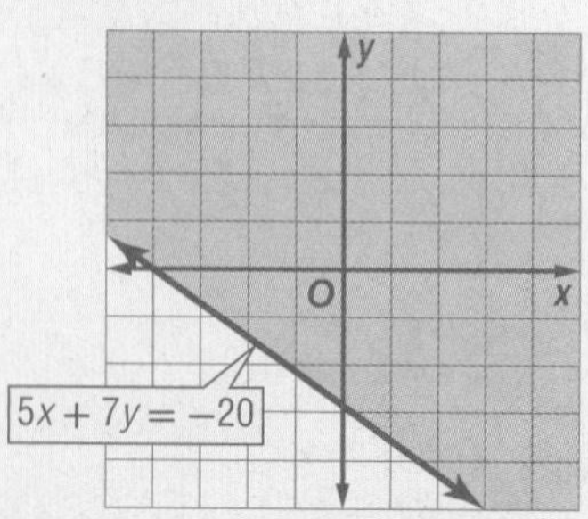

NGSSS PRACTICE 912.A.3.14, 912.A.4.2, 912.P.1.2, 912.A.3.15

69. **GRIDDED RESPONSE** A caterer bought several pounds of chicken salad and several pounds of tuna salad. The chicken salad costs \$9 per pound, and the tuna salad costs \$6 per pound. He bought a total of 14 pounds of salad and paid a total of \$111. How many pounds of chicken salad did he buy? **9**

70. A rectangular room is shown below. Which expression represents the width of the door? **A**

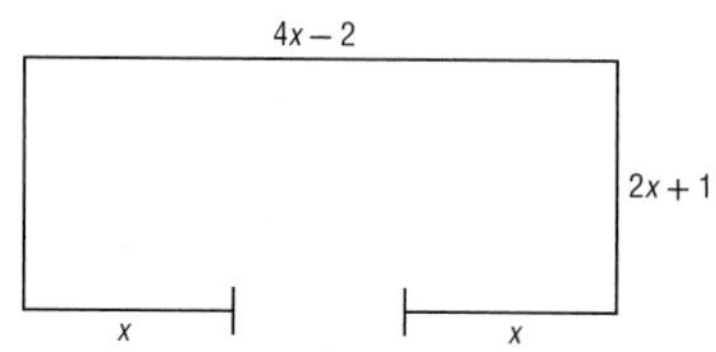

A. $(4x - 2) - x - x$
B. $(2x + 1) - x - x$
C. $(4x - 2) - (2x + 1)$
D. $(4x - 2) + x + x$

71. **PROBABILITY** Which of the following is an example of dependent events? **I**

F. rolling a 6-sided die twice and getting different numbers
G. choosing two cards from a stack of colored cards, with replacement, and both cards are red
H. flipping a coin twice and getting heads both times
I. choosing the starting line-up for a football game

72. **ACT/SAT** Peni bought a basketball and a volleyball that cost a total of \$67. If the price of the basketball b is \$4 more than twice the cost of the volleyball v, which system of linear equations could be used to determine the cost of each ball? **B**

A. $b + v = 67$, $b = 2v - 4$
B. $b + v = 67$, $b = 2v + 4$
C. $b + v = 4$, $b = 2v - 67$
D. $b + v = 4$, $b = 2v + 67$

73c. It means that the options cost the same if you visit 50 times in a year.

Spiral Review

73. **EXERCISE** Refer to the graphic. (Lesson 3-1)

a. For each option, write an equation that represents the cost of belonging to the gym. **$y = 400$; $y = 150 + 5x$**

b. Graph the equations. Estimate the break-even point for the gym memberships. **See margin.**

c. Explain what the break-even point means.

d. If you plan to visit the gym at least once per week during the year, which option should you chose? **\$400 per year**

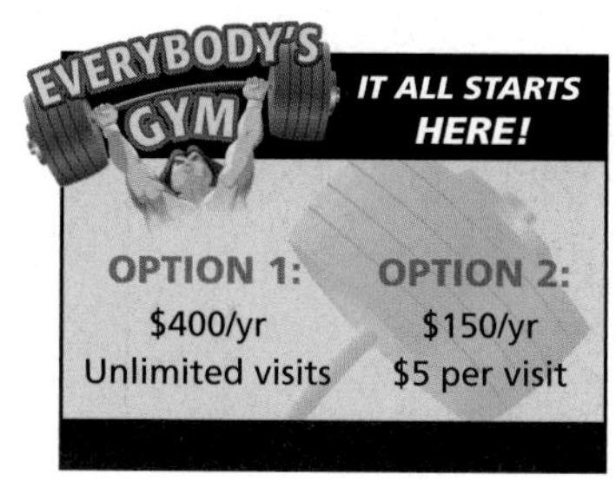

Graph each inequality. (Lesson 2-8) **74–76. See margin.**

74. $x + y \geq 6$
75. $4x - 3y < 10$
76. $5x + 7y \geq -20$

Write an equation of the line passing through each pair of points. (Lesson 2-4)

77. $(3, 5), (7, -3)$ **$y = -2x + 11$**
78. $(8, -2), (4, 8)$ **$y = -2.5x + 18$**
79. $(-6, -1), (-9, 11)$ **$y = -4x - 25$**
80. $(-4, -4), (12, -8)$ **$y = -0.25x - 5$**

Skills Review

Determine whether the given point satisfies each inequality. (Lesson 2-8)

81. $4x + 5y \leq 15$; $(2, -2)$ **yes**
82. $3x + 5y \geq 8$; $(1, 1)$ **yes**
83. $6x + 9y < -1$; $(0, 0)$ **no**

Differentiated Instruction

BL

Extension Give an example of a system of equations that has infinitely many solutions. Sample answer: $x + y = 3$ and $2x + 2y = 6$

3-3 Solving Systems of Inequalities by Graphing

Then

You solved systems of linear equations using tables and graphs. (Lesson 3-1)

Now

- Solve systems of inequalities by graphing.
- Determine the coordinates of the vertices of a region formed by the graph of a system of inequalities.

NGSSS

MA.912.A.3.14 Solve systems of linear equations and **inequalities in two** and three **variables using graphical,** substitution, and elimination **methods.**
MA.912.A.3.15 Solve real-world problems involving systems of linear equations and inequalities in two and three variables.

New Vocabulary

system of inequalities

FL Math Online

glencoe.com

Why?

Many weather conditions need to be met before a space shuttle can launch. The temperature must be greater than 35°F and less than 100°F, and the wind speed cannot exceed 30 knots. These three conditions can be represented by the system of inequalities shown at the right.

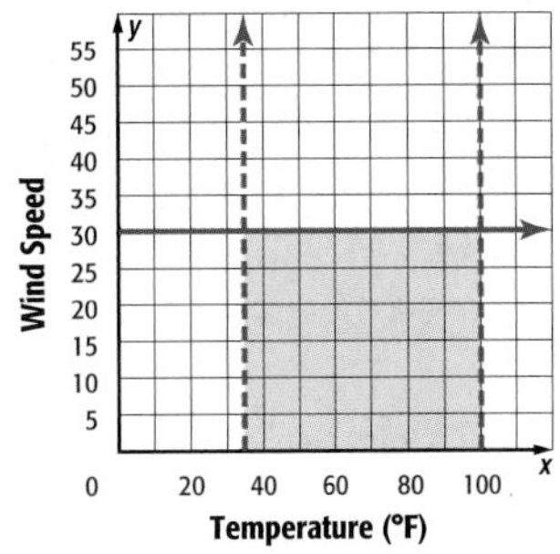

Systems of Inequalities Solving a **system of inequalities** means finding the ordered pairs that satisfy all of the inequalities in the system.

Key Concept **Solving Systems of Inequalities**

Step 1 Graph each inequality, shading the correct area.

Step 2 Identify the region that is shaded for all of the inequalities. This is the solution of the system.

EXAMPLE 1 **Intersecting Regions**

Solve the system of inequalities.
$y > 2x - 4$
$y \leq -0.5x + 3$

Solution of $y > 2x - 4 \rightarrow$ Regions 1 and 3

Solution of $y \leq -0.5x + 3 \rightarrow$ Regions 2 and 3

Region 3 is part of the solution of both inequalities, so it is the solution of the system.

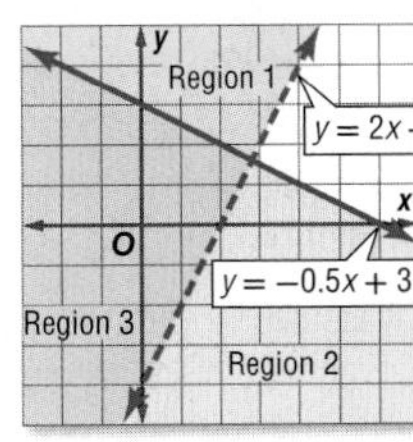

CHECK

Notice that the origin is part of the solution of the system. The origin can be used as a test point. You can test the solution by substituting (0, 0) for x and y in each equation.

$y > 2x - 4$	$y \leq -0.5x + 3$
$0 \overset{?}{>} 2(0) - 4$	$0 \overset{?}{\leq} -0.5(0) + 3$
$0 \overset{?}{>} 0 - 4$	$0 \overset{?}{\leq} 0 + 3$
$0 > -4$ ✓	$0 \leq 3$ ✓

Guided Practice 1A, 1B. See Chapter 3 Answer Appendix.

1A. $y \leq -2x + 5$
$y > -\frac{1}{4}x - 6$

1B. $y \geq |x|$
$y < \frac{4}{3}x + 5$

Personal Tutor glencoe.com

1 FOCUS

Vertical Alignment

Before Lesson 3-3
Solve systems of linear equations using tables and graphs.

Lesson 3-3
Solve systems of inequalities by graphing.
Determine the coordinates of the vertices of a region formed by the graph of a system of inequalities.

After Lesson 3-3
Solve real-world optimization problems using systems of inequalities.

2 TEACH

Scaffolding Questions

Have students read the *Why?* section of the lesson.

Ask:

- What does "°F" represent? °F indicates that temperature is measured using the Fahrenheit scale.
- Why is the horizontal line not dotted? The wind speed can be equal to 30 knots.
- Does the condition "Temperature 65°F, wind speed 34 knots" lie in the shaded region? Explain. No. The wind speed is greater than 30 knots, so this reading would be between the two vertical lines but above the horizontal line.

Lesson 3-3 Resources

Resource	Approaching-Level	On-Level	Beyond-Level	English Learners
Teacher Edition		• Differentiated Instruction, p. 153	• Differentiated Instruction, pp. 153, 155, 157	
Chapter Resource Masters	• Study Guide and Intervention, pp. 18–19 • Skills Practice, p. 20 • Practice, p. 21 • Word Problem Practice, p. 22	• Study Guide and Intervention, pp. 18–19 • Skills Practice, p. 20 • Practice, p. 21 • Word Problem Practice, p. 22 • Enrichment, p. 23	• Practice, p. 21 • Word Problem Practice, p. 22 • Enrichment, p. 23	• Study Guide and Intervention, pp. 18–19 • Skills Practice, p. 20 • Practice, p. 21 • Word Problem Practice, p. 22
Transparencies	• 5-Minute Check Transparency 3-3	• 5-Minute Check Transparency 3-3	• 5-Minute Check Transparency 3-3	• 5-Minute Check Transparency 3-3
Other	• Study Notebook • Teaching Algebra with Manipulatives	• Study Notebook • Teaching Algebra with Manipulatives	• Study Notebook	• Study Notebook • Teaching Algebra with Manipulatives

Systems of Inequalities

Examples 1 and **2** show how to solve systems of inequalities. **Example 3** shows how to write and use a system of inequalities in a real-world situation.

Formative Assessment

Use the Guided Practice exercises after each example to determine students' understanding of concepts.

Additional Examples

1 Solve the system of inequalities by graphing.

$y \geq 2x - 3$

$y < -x + 2$

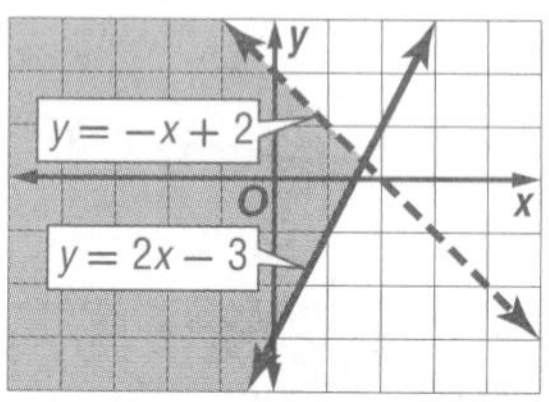

2 Solve the system of inequalities by graphing. Ø

$y \geq -\frac{3}{4}x + 1$

$y \leq -\frac{3}{4}x - 2$

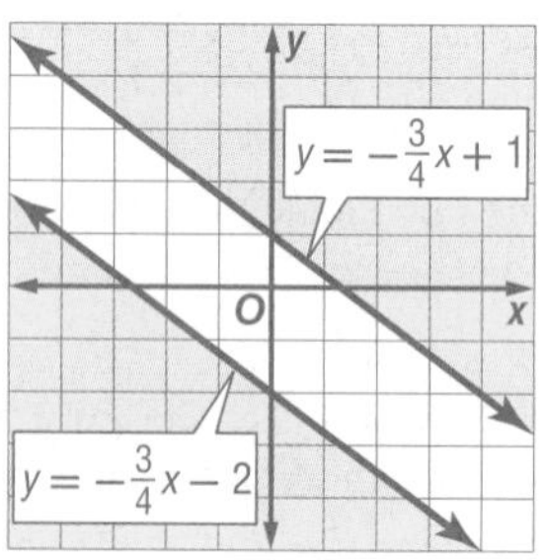

Additional Examples also in Interactive Classroom PowerPoint® Presentations

IWB INTERACTIVE WHITEBOARD READY

Tips for New Teachers

Sense-Making Make sure that students understand that the solution of an inequality must be true for all of the inequalities of the system. Have them test the coordinates of points in different regions of the graph and analyze the results.

ReadingMath

Empty Set The empty set is also called the *null set*. It can be represented by Ø or {}.

It is possible that the regions do not intersect. When this occurs, there is no solution of the system or the solution set is the *empty set*.

EXAMPLE 2 Separate Regions

Solve the system of inequalities by graphing.

$y \geq x + 5$

$y < x - 4$

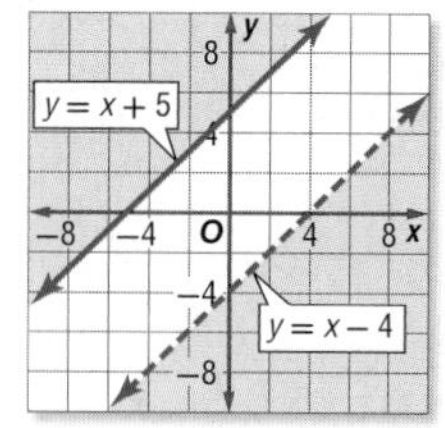

Graph both inequalities.

Since the graphs of the inequalities do not overlap, there are no points in common and there is no solution to the system.

The solution set is the empty set.

Guided Practice 2A, 2B. See Chapter 3 Answer Appendix.

2A. $y \geq -4x + 8$
$y < -4x + 4$

2B. $y \geq |x|$
$y < 2x - 24$

Personal Tutor glencoe.com

Real-World Link

Typical incoming freshmen will spend more than 3 times as many hours studying in college as in high school.

Source: *National Survey of Student Engagement*

Real-World EXAMPLE 3 Write and Use a System of Inequalities

TIME MANAGEMENT **Chelsea has final exams in calculus, physics, and history. She has up to 25 hours to study for the exams. She plans to study history for 2 hours. She needs to spend at least 7 hours studying for calculus, but over 14 is too much. She hopes to spend between 8 and 12 hours on physics. Write and graph a system of inequalities to represent the situation.**

Calculus: at least 7 hours, but no more than 14
$7 \leq c \leq 14$

Physics: at least 8 hours, but no more than 12
$8 \leq p \leq 12$

Chelsea has 25 hours available, and 2 of those will be spent on history. She has up to 23 hours left for calculus and physics.
$c + p \leq 23$

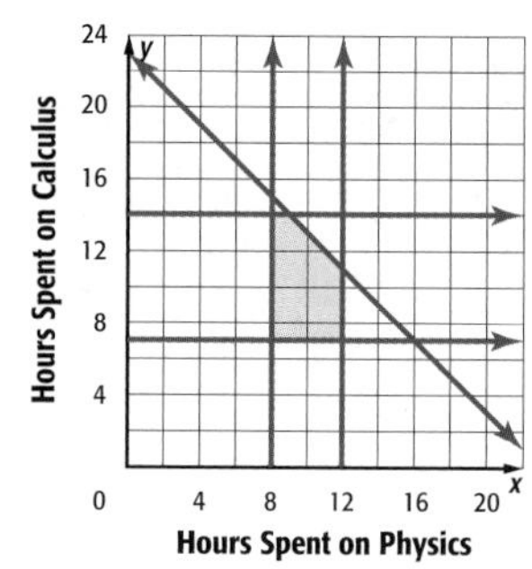

Graph all of the inequalities. Any ordered pair in the intersection is a solution of the system. One solution is 10 hours on physics and 12 hours on calculus.

Guided Practice

3. TRAVEL Mr. and Mrs. Rodriguez are driving across the country with their two children. They plan on driving a maximum of 10 hours each day. Mr. Rodriguez wants to drive at least 4 hours a day but no more than 8 hours a day. Mrs. Rodriguez can drive in between 2 and 5 hours per day. Write and graph a system of inequalities that represents this information. See margin.

Personal Tutor glencoe.com

Additional Answer, Guided Practice

3. Let j = the number of hours Mr. Rodriguez drives, and let d = the number of hours Mrs. Rodriguez drives.

$j + d \leq 10$

$4 \leq j \leq 8$

$2 \leq d \leq 5$

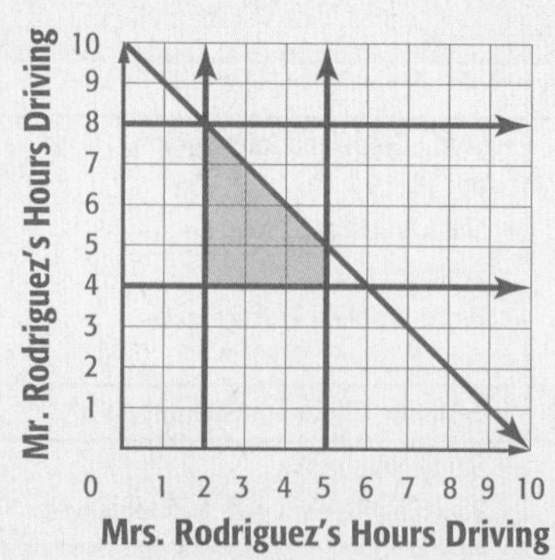

StudyTip

Boundaries If the inequality that forms the boundary is < or >, then the boundary is not included in the solution, and the line should be dashed.

Find Vertices of an Enclosed Region Sometimes the graph of a system of inequalities produces an enclosed region in the form of a polygon. To find the vertices of the region, determine the coordinates of the points at which the boundaries intersect.

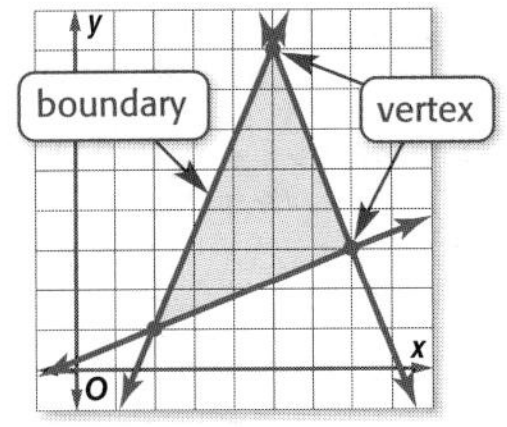

EXAMPLE 4 Find Vertices

Find the coordinates of the vertices of the triangle formed by $y \geq 2x - 8$, $y \leq -\frac{1}{4}x + 6$, and $4y \geq -15x - 32$.

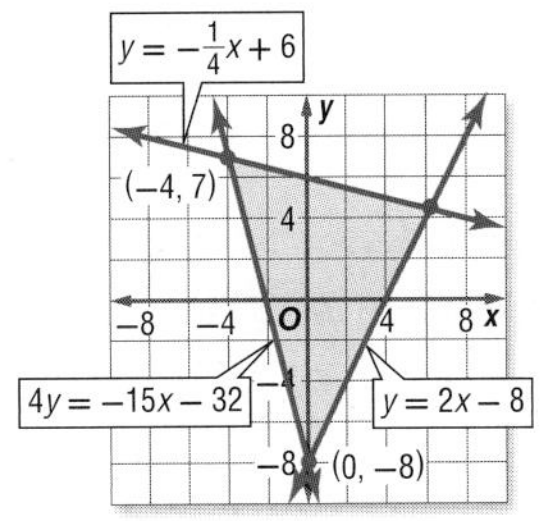

Step 1 Graph each inequality.
The coordinates (−4, 7) and (0, −8) can be determined from the graph. To find the coordinates of the third vertex, solve the system of equations $y = 2x - 8$ and $y = -\frac{1}{4}x + 6$.

Step 2 Substitute for y in the second equation.

$2x - 8 = -\frac{1}{4}x + 6$ **Replace y with $2x - 8$.**

$2x = -\frac{1}{4}x + 14$ **Add 8 to each side.**

$\frac{9}{4}x = 14$ **Add $\frac{1}{4}x$ to each side.**

$x = \frac{56}{9}$ or $6\frac{2}{9}$ **Divide each side by $\frac{9}{4}$.**

Step 3 Find y.

$y = 2\left(6\frac{2}{9}\right) - 8$ **Replace x with $6\frac{2}{9}$.**

$= 12\frac{4}{9} - 8$ **Distributive Property**

$= 4\frac{4}{9}$ **Simplify.**

CHECK Compare the coordinates to the coordinates on the graph. The x-coordinate of the third vertex is between 6 and 7, so $6\frac{2}{9}$ is reasonable. The y-coordinate of the third vertex is between 4 and 5, so $4\frac{4}{9}$ is reasonable.

The vertices of the triangle are at (−4, 7), (0, −8), and $\left(6\frac{2}{9}, 4\frac{4}{9}\right)$.

Guided Practice

Find the coordinates of the vertices of the triangle formed by each system of inequalities. 4A, 4B. See margin.

4A. $y \geq -3x - 6$
$2y \geq x - 16$
$11y + 7x \leq 12$

4B. $5y \leq 2x + 9$
$y \leq -x + 6$
$9y \geq -2x + 5$

Personal Tutor glencoe.com

Differentiated Instruction OL BL

If students demonstrate an understanding of how to solve a system of inequalities by graphing,

Then have them write a list of tips to help someone draw the graphs of systems of inequalities and find the vertices easily and efficiently.

Additional Example

3 **MEDICINE** Medical professionals recommend that patients have a cholesterol level below 200 milligrams per deciliter (mg/dL) of blood and a triglyceride level below 150 mg/dL. Write and graph a system of inequalities that represents the range of cholesterol levels c and triglyceride levels t for patients.

$0 < c < 200, 0 < t < 150$

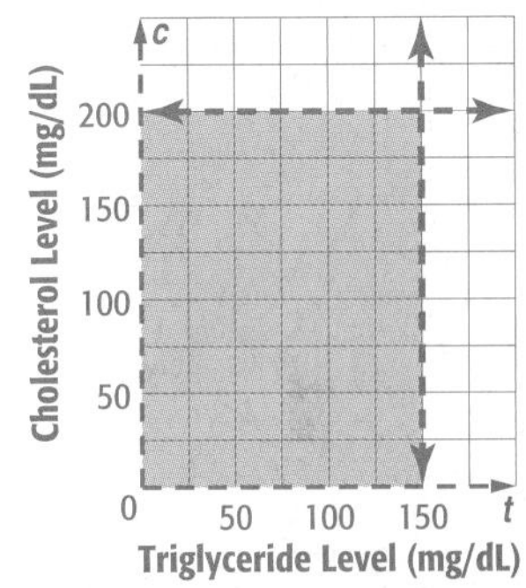

Find Vertices of an Enclosed Region

Example 4 shows how to find the vertices of the region formed by a system of inequalities.

Additional Example

4 Find the coordinates of the vertices of the triangle formed by $2x - y \geq -1$, $x + y \leq 4$, and $x + 4y \geq 4$.

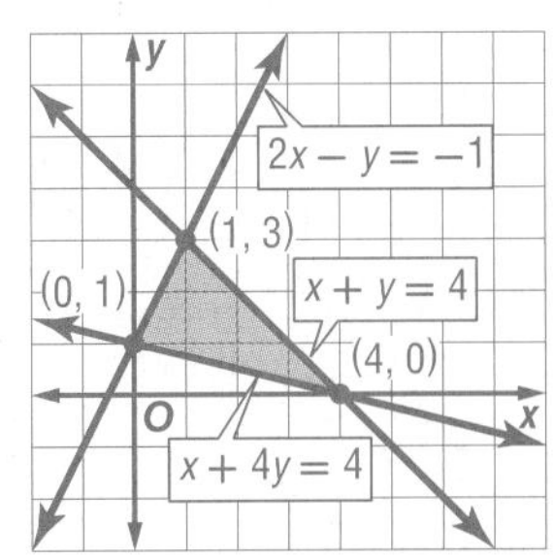

Additional Answers, Guided Practice

4A. (8, −4), (−3, 3), $\left(\frac{4}{7}, -\frac{54}{7}\right)$

4B. (−2, 1), (3, 3), (7, −1)

3 PRACTICE

Formative Assessment

Use Exercises 1–6 to check for understanding.

Use the chart on the bottom of this page to customize assignments for your students.

Additional Answers

1.

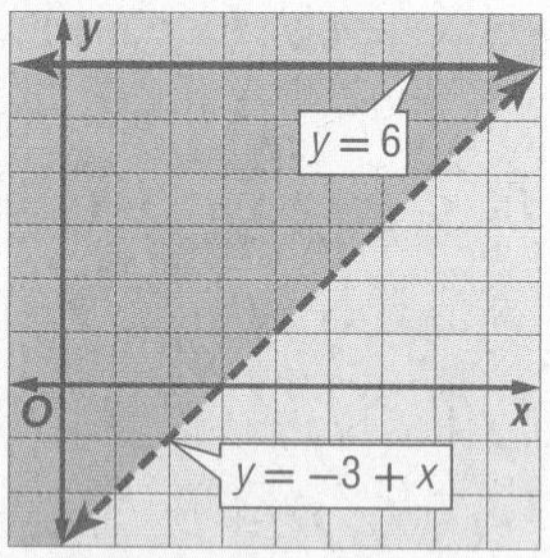

2.

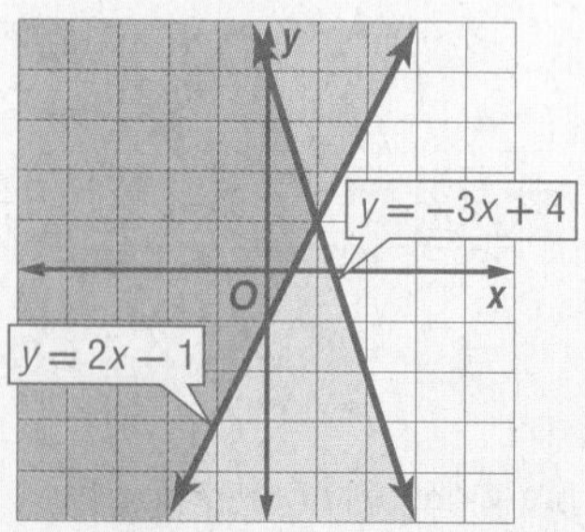

3.

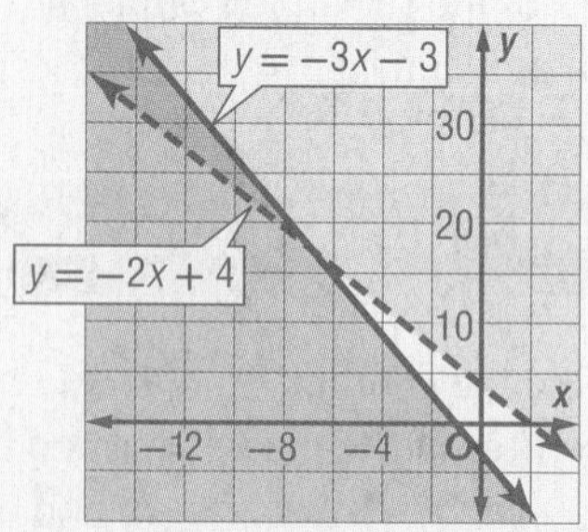

4a.

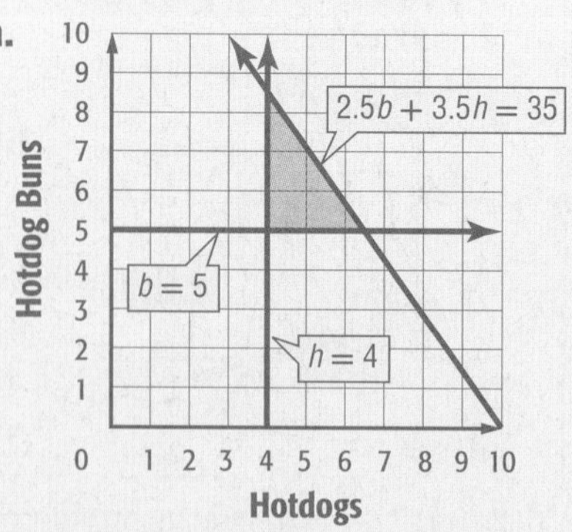

4b. Sample answer: 4 packages of hotdogs, 5 packages of buns; 5 packages of hotdogs, 6 packages of buns; 6 packages of hotdogs, 5 packages of buns

Check Your Understanding

Examples 1 and 2 pp. 151–152

Solve each system of inequalities by graphing. 1–3. See margin.

1. $y \le 6$
 $y > -3 + x$

2. $y \le -3x + 4$
 $y \ge 2x - 1$

3. $y > -2x + 4$
 $y \le -3x - 3$

Example 3 p. 152

4. **COOKOUT** The most Kala can spend on hot dogs and buns for her cookout is \$35. A package of 10 hot dogs costs \$3.50. A package of buns costs \$2.50 and contains 8 buns. She needs to buy at least 40 hot dogs and 40 buns. a, b. See margin.
   - **a.** Graph the region that shows how many packages of each item she can purchase.
   - **b.** Give an example of three different purchases she can make.

Example 4 p. 153

Find the coordinates of the vertices of the triangle formed by each system of inequalities. 5, 6. See Chapter 3 Answer Appendix for graphs.

5. $y \ge 2x + 1$
 $y \le 8$
 $4x + 3y \ge 8$
 (3.5, 8), (−4, 8), (0.5, 2)

6. $y \ge -2x - 4$
 $6y \le x + 28$
 $y \ge 13x - 34$
 (2, −8), (3, 5), (−4, 4)

Practice and Problem Solving

● = **Step-by-Step Solutions** begin on page R20. **Extra Practice** begins on page 947.

Examples 1 and 2 pp. 151–152

Solve each system of inequalities by graphing. 7–15. See Chapter 3 Answer Appendix.

7. $x < 3$
 $y \ge -4$

8. $y > 3x - 5$
 $y \le 4$

9. $y < -3x + 4$
 $3y + x > -6$

10. $y \ge 0$
 $y < x$

11. $6x - 2y \ge 12$
 $3x + 4y > 12$

12. $-8x > -2y - 1$
 $-4y \ge 2x - 5$

13. $5y < 2x + 10$
 $y - 4x > 8$

14. $3y - 2x \le -24$
 $y \ge \frac{2}{3}x - 1$

15. $y > -\frac{2}{5}x + 2$
 $5y \le -2x - 15$

Example 3 p. 152

16. **RECORDING** Jane's band wants to spend no more than \$575 recording their first CD. The studio charges at least \$35 an hour to record. Graph a system of inequalities to represent this situation. See Chapter 3 Answer Appendix.

17. **SUMMER TRIP** Rondell has to save at least \$925 to go to Rome with his Latin class in 8 weeks. He earns \$9 an hour working at the Pizza Palace and \$12 an hour working at a car wash. By law, he cannot work more than 25 hours per week. Graph two inequalities that Rondell can use to determine the number of hours he needs to work at each job if he wants to make the trip. See Chapter 3 Answer Appendix.

Example 4 p. 153

Find the coordinates of the vertices of the triangle formed by each system of inequalities. 18–23. See Chapter 3 Answer Appendix for graphs.

18. $x \ge 0$
 $y \ge 0$
 $x + 2y < 4$
 (0, 2), (4, 0), (0, 0)

19. $y \ge 3x - 7$
 $y \le 8$
 $x + y > 1$
 (2, −1), (5, 8), (−7, 8)

20. $x \le 4$
 $y > -3x + 12$
 $y \le 9$
 (1, 9), (4, 0), (4, 9)

21. $-3x + 4y \le 15$
 $2y + 5x > -12$
 $10y + 60 \ge 27x$
 (−3, 1.5), (5, 7.5), (0, −6)

22. $8y - 19x < 74$
 $38y + 26x \le 119$
 $54y - 12x \ge -198$
 (−6, −5), (−2, 4.5), (7.5, −2)

23. $6y - 24x \ge -168$
 $8y + 7x > 10$
 $20y - 2x \le 64$
 (8, 4), (6, −4), (−2, 3)

24. **BAKING** Rebecca wants to bake cookies and cupcakes for a bake sale. She can bake 15 cookies at a time and 12 cupcakes at a time. She needs to make at least 120 baked goods, but no more than 360, and she wants to have at least three times as many cookies as cupcakes. What combination of batches of each could Rebecca make? Sample answer: 15 batches of cookies and 6 batches of cupcakes.

Differentiated Homework Options

Level	Assignment	Two-Day Option	
AL Basic	7–25, 46, 48–68	7–25 odd, 51–54	8–24 even, 46, 48–50, 55–68
OL Core	7–25 odd, 29–35 odd, 41, 46, 48–68	7–25, 51–54	28–36, 40–42, 43–44, 46, 48–50, 55–68
BL Advanced	26–62, (optional: 63–68)		

25 **CELL PHONES** Dale has a maximum of 800 minutes on his cell phone plan that he can use each month. Daytime minutes cost \$0.15, and nighttime minutes cost \$0.10. Dale plans to use at least twice as many daytime minutes as nighttime minutes. If Dale uses at least 200 nighttime minutes and does not go over his limit, what is his maximum bill? his minimum bill? **maximum = \$110, minimum = \$80**

B

26. **TREES** Trees are divided into four categories according to height and trunk circumference. In one forest, the trees are categorized by the heights and circumferences described in the table.

Crown Class	dominant	co-dominant	intermediate	suppressed
Height (in feet)	over 72	56–72	40–55	under 39
Trunk Circumference (in inches)	over 60	48–60	34–48	under 33

Source: USDA Forest Service

a. Write and graph the system of inequalities that represents the range of heights h and circumferences c for a co-dominant tree. **See margin.**

b. Determine the crown class of a basswood that is 48 feet tall. Find the expected trunk circumference. **intermediate; 34–48 in.**

Real-World Link

The four crown classes are:

- dominant (D): trees well above the general canopy of the forest
- co-dominant (CD): part of the general canopy that receives sunlight from above and the sides
- intermediate (I): trees below the general canopy that only receive sunlight from above
- suppressed (S): trees well below the general canopy

Source: Silva Ecosystem Consultants

27. **CAMPING** On a camping trip, Jessica needs at least 3 pounds of food and 0.5 gallon of water per day. Marc needs at least 5 pounds of food and 0.5 gallon of water per day. Jessica's equipment weighs 10 pounds, and Marc's equipment weighs 20 pounds. A gallon of water weighs approximately 8 pounds. Each of them carries their own supplies, and Jessica is capable of carrying 35 pounds while Marc can carry 50 pounds.

a. Graph the inequalities that represent how much they can carry. **See margin.**

b. How many days can they camp, assuming that they bring all their supplies in at once? **$3\frac{1}{3}$ days**

c. Who will run out of supplies first? **Marc; Jessica could last about a quarter of a day longer than Marc.**

Solve each system of inequalities by graphing. **28–36. See Chapter 3 Answer Appendix.**

28. $y \geq |2x + 4| - 2$
$3y + x \leq 15$

29. $y \geq |6 - x|$
$|y| \leq 4$

30. $|y| \geq x$
$y < 2x$

31. $y > -3x + 1$
$4y \leq x - 8$
$3x - 5y < 20$

32. $6y + 2x \leq 9$
$2y + 18 \geq 5x$
$y > -4x - 9$

33. $|x| > y$
$y \leq 6$
$y \geq -2$

34. $2x + 3y \geq 6$
$y \leq |x - 6|$

35. $8x + 4y < 10$
$y > |2x - 1|$

36. $y \geq |x - 2| + 4$
$y \leq [\![x]\!] - 3$

37. **MUSIC** Steve is trying to decide what to put on his MP3 player. Audio books are 3 hours long and songs are 2.5 minutes long. Steve wants no more than 4 audio books on his MP3 player, but at least ten songs and one audio book. Each book costs \$15.00 and each song costs \$0.95. Steve has \$63 to spend on books and music. Graph the inequalities to show possible combinations of books and songs that Steve can have. **See Chapter 3 Answer Appendix.**

38. **JOBS** Louie has two jobs and can work no more than 25 total hours per week. He wants to earn at least \$150 per week. Graph the inequalities to show possible combinations of hours worked at each job that will help him reach his goal. **See Chapter 3 Answer Appendix.**

Job	Pay
Busboy	\$6.50
Clerk	\$8.00

Lesson 3-3 Solving Systems of Inequalities by Graphing **155**

Focus on Mathematical Content

Solving Systems of Inequalities A solution to a system of linear inequalities is any ordered pair that is a solution of each inequality in the system. The graph of a system is a region that contains all of the solutions.

TEACH with TECH

WIKI Have students work in pairs to create a wiki describing how to graph a system of inequalities. Be sure they describe how to decide whether to use a solid or dashed line and how to decide which region to shade. Be sure they also explain how to interpret the graph to find solutions of the system of inequalities.

Additional Answers

26a. $h \geq 56, h \leq 72, c \geq 48, c \leq 60$

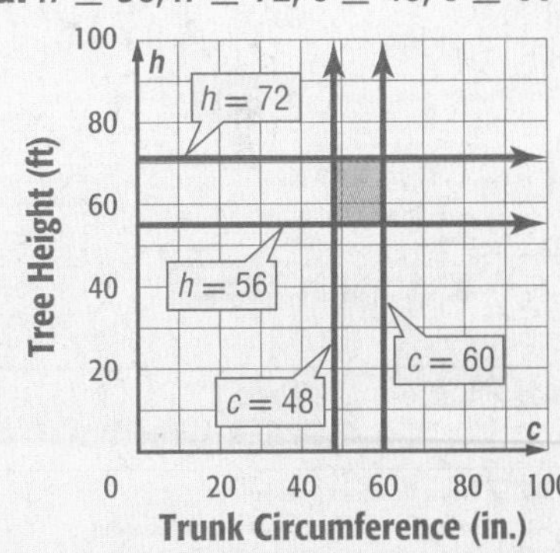

27a.

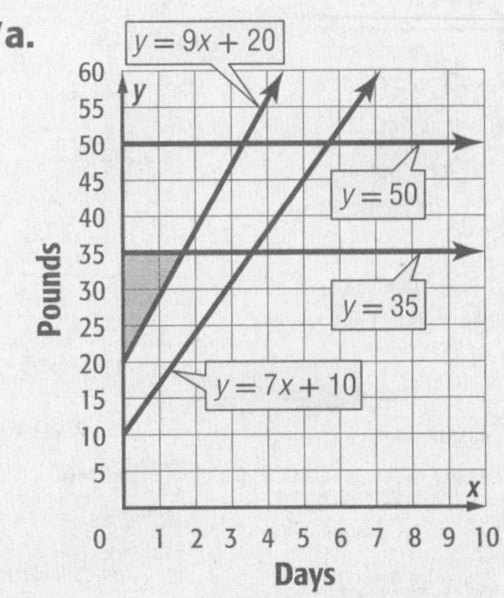

Differentiated Instruction

BL

Intrapersonal Learners For Exercises 16–17, tell students that systems of inequalities are often used to solve real-world problems. Challenge students to search newspapers, magazines, and the Internet for real-world information and use that information to write a real-world problem that can be solved using a system of inequalities. This will help students to better understand the concept of solving systems of inequalities.

Study Guide and Intervention
CRM pp. 18–19 AL OL ELL

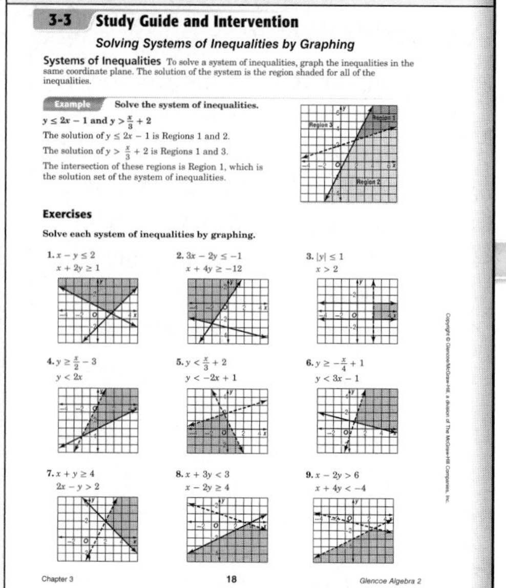
3-3 Study Guide and Intervention

Solving Systems of Inequalities by Graphing

Chapter 3 18 Glencoe Algebra 2

Practice
CRM p. 21 AL OL BL ELL

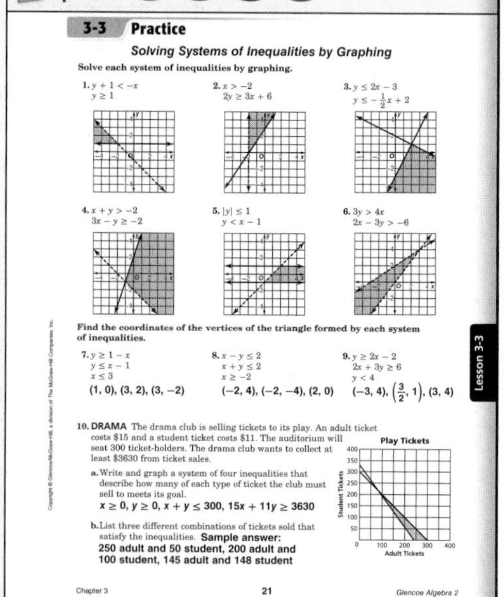
3-3 Practice

Solving Systems of Inequalities by Graphing

Chapter 3 21 Glencoe Algebra 2

Word Problem Practice
CRM p. 22 AL OL BL ELL

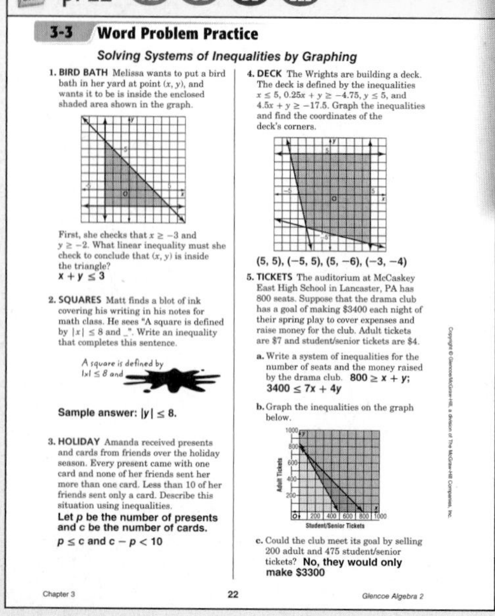
3-3 Word Problem Practice

Solving Systems of Inequalities by Graphing

Chapter 3 22 Glencoe Algebra 2

Real-World Link

Dodgeball has been played in the United States for over 100 years and is still played in schools today.

Source: Kidzworld

44a. See Chapter 3 Answer Appendix.

44b. (6, 4), (6, 5), (7, 3), (7, 4), (7, 5), (7, 6), (8, 2), (8, 3), (8, 4), (8, 5), (8, 6), (8, 7), (9,1), (9, 2), (9, 3), (9, 4), (9, 5), (9, 6), (10, 0), (10, 1), (10, 2), (10, 3), (10, 4), (10, 5), (11, 0), (11, 1), (11, 2), (11, 3), (11, 4), (12, 0), (12, 1), (12, 2), (12, 3), (13, 0), (13, 1), (13, 2), (14, 0), (14, 1), (15, 0)

47. Sample answer: $y \geq 2x - 6$; $y \leq -0.5x + 4$; $y \geq -3x - 6$

49. Sample answer: Shade each inequality in its standard way, by shading above the line if $y >$ and shading below the line if $y <$ (or you can use test points). Once you determine where to shade for each inequality, the area where *every* inequality needs to be shaded is the actual solution. This is only the shaded area.

C

39. TIME MANAGEMENT Ramir uses his spare time to write a novel and to exercise. He has budgeted 35 hours per week. He wants to exercise at least 7 hours a week but no more than 15. He also hopes to write between 20 and 25 hours per week. Write and graph a system of inequalities that represents this situation. **See margin.**

Find the coordinates of the vertices of the figure formed by each system of inequalities. 40–42. See margin.

40. $y \geq 2x - 12$
$y \leq -4x + 20$
$4y - x \leq 8$
$y \geq -3x + 2$

41. $y \geq -x - 8$
$2y \geq 3x - 20$
$4y + x \leq 24$
$y \leq 4x + 22$

42. $2y - x \geq -20$
$y \geq -3x - 6$
$y \leq -2x + 2$
$y \leq 2x + 14$

43. FINANCIAL LITERACY Mr. Hoffman is investing $10,000 in two funds. One fund will pay 6% interest, and a riskier second fund will pay 10% interest. What is the least amount Mr. Hoffman can invest in the risky fund and still earn at least $740 after one year? **$3500**

44. DODGEBALL A high school is selecting a dodgeball team to play in a fund-raising exhibition against their rival. There can be between 10 and 15 players on the team and there must be more girls than boys on the team.

a. Write and graph a system of inequalities to represent the situation.

b. List all of the possible combinations of boys and girls for the team.

c. Explain why there is not an infinite number of possibilities. **Sample answer: You cannot have a fraction of a person.**

H.O.T. Problems
Use Higher-Order Thinking Skills

45. CHALLENGE Find the area of the region defined by the following inequalities. **75 units²**

$$y \geq -4x - 16$$
$$4y \leq 26 - x$$
$$3y + 6x \leq 30$$
$$4y - 2x \geq -10$$

46. OPEN ENDED Write a system of two inequalities in which the solution:

a. lies only in the third quadrant. **Sample answer: $y < -2$, $x < -1$**

b. does not exist. **Sample answer: $y > 2$, $y < -2$**

c. lies only on a line. **Sample answer: $y \geq x$, $y \leq x$**

d. lies on exactly one point. **Sample answer: $y \geq |x|$, $y < -|x|$; solution at (0, 0)**

47. CHALLENGE Write a system of inequalities to represent the solution shown at the right.

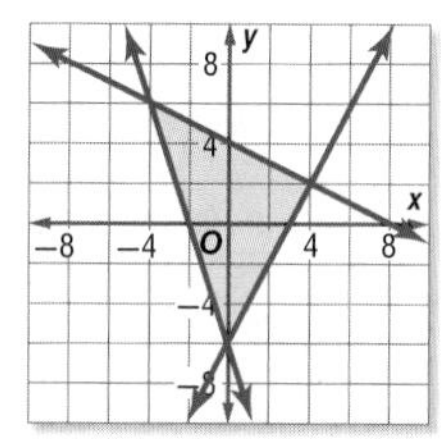

48. REASONING Determine whether the following statement is *true* or *false*. If false, give a counterexample. **true**

A system of two linear inequalities has either no points or infinitely many points in its solution.

49. WRITING IN MATH Write a how-to manual for determining where to shade when graphing a system of inequalities.

50. WRITING IN MATH Explain how you would test to see whether (−4, 6) is a solution of a system of inequalities. **See margin.**

Enrichment
CRM p. 23 OL BL

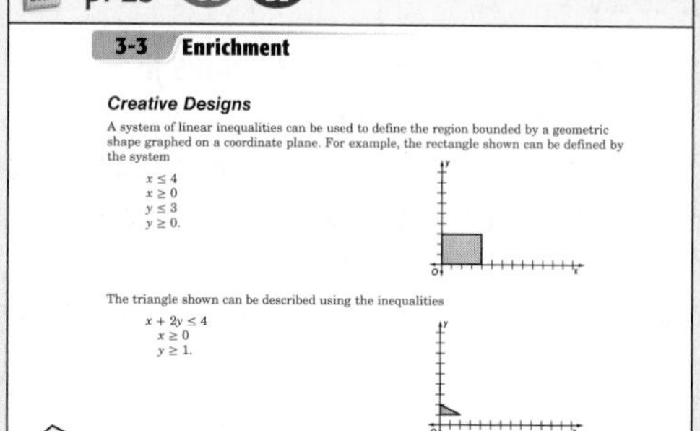
3-3 Enrichment

Creative Designs

NGSSS PRACTICE 912.A.3.15, 912.A.3.1, 912.A.3.2

51. To be a member of the marching band, a student must have a grade-point average of at least 2.0 and must have attended at least five after-school practices. Choose the system of inequalities that best represents this situation. **A**

A. $x \geq 2$, $y \geq 5$
B. $x \leq 2$, $y \leq 5$
C. $x < 2$, $y < 5$
D. $x > 2$, $y > 5$

52. ACT/SAT The table at the right shows a relationship between x and y. Which equation represents this relationship? **G**

x	y
1	5
2	8
3	11
4	14
5	17
6	20

F. $y = 3x - 2$
G. $y = 3x + 2$
H. $y = 4x + 1$
I. $y = 4x - 1$

53. THINK SOLVE EXPLAIN **SHORT RESPONSE** If $3x = 2y$ and $5y = 6z$, what is the value of x in terms of z? $\frac{4}{5}z$

54. GEOMETRY Look at the graph below. Which of these statements describes the relationship between the two lines? **D**

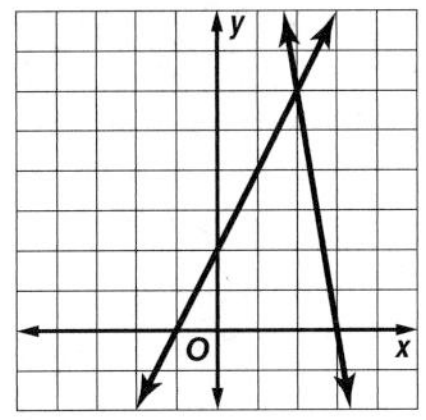

A. They intersect at (6, 2).
B. They intersect at (0, 2).
C. They intersect at (3.5, 0).
D. They intersect at (2, 6).

Spiral Review

55. (1.5, 3), (3.5, 7), (8, 3), (10, 7)

55. GEOMETRY Find the coordinates of the vertices of the parallelogram whose sides are contained in the lines with equations $y = 3$, $y = 7$, $y = 2x$, and $y = 2x - 13$. (Lesson 3-2)

Solve each system of equations by graphing. (Lesson 3-1)

56. $y = 6 - x$
$y = x + 4$ **(1, 5)**

57. $x + 2y = 2$
$2x + 4y = 8$ **no solution**

58. $x - 2y = 8$
$\frac{1}{2}x - y = 4$ **infinite solutions**

Graph each function. Identify the domain and range. (Lesson 2-7) **59–61. See Chapter 3 Answer Appendix.**

59. $g(x) = \begin{cases} 0 \text{ if } x < 0 \\ -x + 2 \text{ if } x \geq 0 \end{cases}$

60. $h(x) = \begin{cases} x + 3 \text{ if } x \leq -1 \\ 2x \text{ if } x > -1 \end{cases}$

61. $h(x) = \begin{cases} -1 \text{ if } x < -2 \\ 1 \text{ if } x > 2 \end{cases}$

62. EXTENDED RESPONSE For each meeting of the Putnam High School book club, \$25 is taken from the activities account to buy snacks and materials. After their sixth meeting, there will be \$350 left in the activities account. (Lesson 2-4)

a. If no money is put back into the account, what equation can be used to show how much money is left in the activities account after having x number of meetings? $y = 500 - 25x$

b. How much money was originally in the account? **\$500**

c. After how many meetings will there be no money left in the activities account? **20**

Skills Review

Find each value if $f(x) = 2x + 5$ and $g(x) = 3x - 4$. (Lesson 2-1)

63. $f(-3)$ **−1**
64. $g(-2)$ **−10**
65. $f(-1)$ **3**
66. $g(-0.5)$ **−5.5**
67. $f(-0.25)$ **4.5**
68. $g(-0.75)$ **−6.25**

Differentiated Instruction BL

Extension Plot the points (–2, 0), (0, 2), and (2, 0). Draw line segments connecting the points to form a triangular region. Write a system of inequalities that defines the region.
$y \geq 0$, $y \leq -x + 2$, $y \leq x + 2$

4 ASSESS

Crystal Ball Have students look ahead to Lesson 3-4. Have them write how they think what they learned today will connect with the theme in Lesson 3-4.

Formative Assessment

Check for student understanding of the concepts in Lesson 3-3.

CRM Quiz 2, p. 39

Additional Answers

39. Let w = the number of hours writing, and let e = the number of hours exercising.
$w + e \leq 35$
$7 \leq e \leq 15$
$20 \leq w \leq 25$

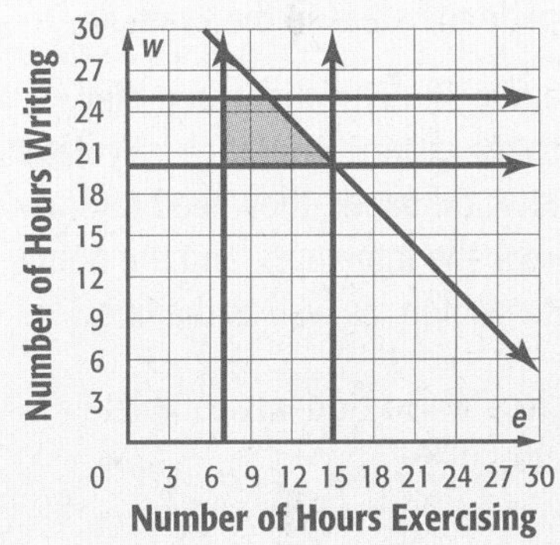

40. (0, 2), $\left(5\frac{1}{3}, -1\frac{1}{3}\right)$, $\left(4\frac{4}{17}, 3\frac{1}{17}\right)$ (2.8, –6.4)

41. (–6, –2), $\left(-3\frac{13}{17}, 6\frac{16}{17}\right)$, $\left(9\frac{1}{7}, 3\frac{5}{7}\right)$, (0.8, –8.8)

42. (–4, 6), (–3, 8), (4.8, –7.6), $\left(1\frac{1}{7}, -9\frac{3}{7}\right)$

50. Sample answer: Determine whether the point falls in the shaded area of the graphs and/or determine whether the values satisfy each inequality.

EXTEND 3-3 Lesson Notes

1 FOCUS

Objective Graph systems of linear inequalities using a graphing calculator.

Materials for Each Student

- TI-83/84 Plus or other graphing calculator

2 TEACH

Working in Cooperative Groups

Put students into groups of two, mixing abilities. Then have each group complete the steps in the Example.

Explain to students that when they sketch the graphs from their calculator windows on paper, they need to draw the axes, the intercepts, and the points of intersection, as well as the lines.

Practice Have students complete Exercises 1–9.

3 ASSESS

Formative Assessment

Use Exercise 6 to assess whether students comprehend how to graph systems of linear inequalities with a graphing calculator.

From Concrete to Abstract

Ask the students how many points are in the solution set of a system of inequalities such as those in this activity. infinitely many

EXTEND 3-3

Graphing Technology Lab

Systems of Linear Inequalities

FL Math Online glencoe.com
- Other Calculator Keystrokes
- Graphing Technology Personal Tutor

Objective
Use a graphing calculator to solve systems of inequalities.

NGSSS

MA.912.A.3.14 Solve systems of linear equations and **inequalities in two** and three **variables using graphical,** substitution, and elimination **methods.**

You can graph systems of linear inequalities with a graphing calculator by using the Y= menu. You can choose different graphing styles to shade above or below a line.

EXAMPLE Intersection of Two Graphs

Graph the system of inequalities in the standard viewing window.
$y \geq -3x + 4$
$y \leq 2x - 1$

Step 1 Enter $-3x + 4$ as Y1. Because y is greater than $-3x + 4$, shade above the line.

KEYSTROKES: Y= ◄ ◄ ENTER ENTER ► ► (−) 3 X,T,θ,n + 4 ENTER

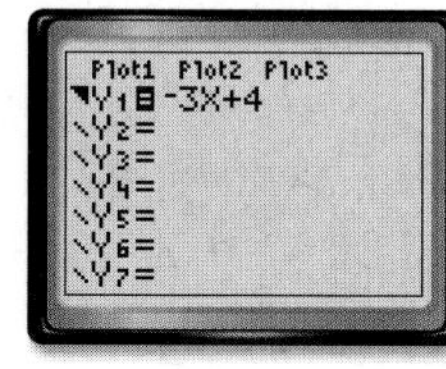

Step 2 Enter $2x - 1$ as Y2. Because y is less than $2x - 1$, shade below the line.

KEYSTROKES: ◄ ◄ ENTER ENTER ENTER ► ► 2 X,T,θ,n − 1 ENTER

Step 3 Display the graphs in the standard viewing window.

KEYSTROKES: ZOOM 6

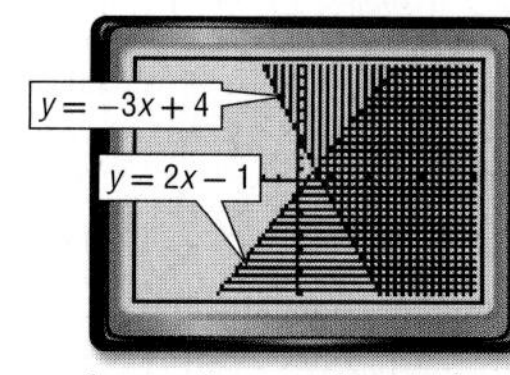

[−10, 10] scl: 1 by [−10, 10] scl: 1

Notice the shading pattern above the line $y = -2x + 3$ and the shading pattern below the line $y = x + 5$. The intersection of the graphs is the region where the patterns overlap. This region includes all the points that satisfy the system $y \geq -2x + 3$ and $y \leq x + 5$.

Exercises

Use a graphing calculator to solve each system of inequalities. 1–9. See Chapter 3 Answer Appendix.

1. $y \geq 3$, $y \leq -x + 1$

2. $y \geq -4x$, $y \leq -5$

3. $y \geq 2 - x$, $y \leq x + 3$

4. $y \geq 2x + 1$, $y \leq -x - 1$

5. $2y \geq 3x - 1$, $3y \leq -x + 7$

6. $y + 5x \geq 12$, $y - 3 \leq 10$

7. $5y + 3x \geq 11$, $3y - x \leq -8$

8. $10y - 7x \geq -19$, $7y - 5x \leq 11$

9. $\frac{1}{6}y - x \geq -3$, $\frac{1}{5}y + x \leq 7$

Extending the Concept

Ask:

- When is the point of intersection of the two boundary lines included in the solution set? The point of intersection is in the solution set when both boundary lines on the graph are solid, and when the symbol in both inequalities is either ≥ or ≤.

NGSSS 912.A.3.14, 912.A.3.15

Solve each system of equations by graphing. (Lesson 3-1)

1. $y = 2x + 4$
$y = -x - 2$ **(−2, 0)**

2. $5x + 2y = 3$
$5x - 4y = 9$ **(1, −1)**

3. $x = 2y - 4$
$x = -3y + 1$ **(−2, 1)**

4. $2x - 5y = 14$
$4x + 3y = -24$ **(−3, 4)**

5. **NGSSS PRACTICE** What type of system is shown? (Lesson 3-1) **C**

$$2x + 4y = 5$$
$$3x + 6y = 11$$

A. consistent and dependent

B. consistent and independent

C. inconsistent

D. none of the above

Solve each system of equations by using either substitution or elimination. (Lesson 3-2) **7. $\left(-\frac{2}{3}, -1\right)$**

6. $y = x + 4$
$x + y = -12$ **(−8, −4)**

7. $3x + 5y = -7$
$6x - 4y = 0$

8. $\frac{1}{3}x - \frac{3}{8}y = 28$
$\frac{1}{7}x + \frac{5}{7}y = -37$ **(21, −56)**

9. $\frac{1}{3}x = y + 2$
$x = 5y - 2$ **(18, 4)**

10. $5x + 2y = 4$
$3y - 4x = -40$ **(4, −8)**

11. $8x - 3y = -13$
$-3x + 5y = 1$ **(−2, −1)**

12. $6x - 5y = 92$
$9x + 2y = 100$ **(12, −4)**

13. $4y + 7x = -92$
$5x - 6y = 14$ **(−8, −9)**

14. **SHOPPING** Main St. Media sells all DVDs for one price and all books for another price. Alex bought 4 DVDs and 6 books for \$170, while Matt bought 3 DVDs and 8 books for \$180. What is the cost of a DVD and the cost of a book? (Lesson 3-2) **DVD: \$20; book: \$15**

15. **NGSSS PRACTICE** On Thursday, the art museum sold 56 fewer tickets than they sold on Friday. They sold a total of 406 tickets on Thursday and Friday. Which system of equations can be used to find the number of tickets sold on each day? (Lesson 3-2) **F**

F. $f - t = 56$
$f + t = 406$

H. $f - t = 406$
$f + t = 56$

G. $t - 56 = f$
$f + t = 406$

I. $f - t = 56$
$f + 406 = t$

16. **NGSSS PRACTICE** Which graph shows the solution of the system of inequalities? (Lesson 3-3) **B**

$$y \le 2x + 3$$
$$y < \frac{1}{3}x + 5$$

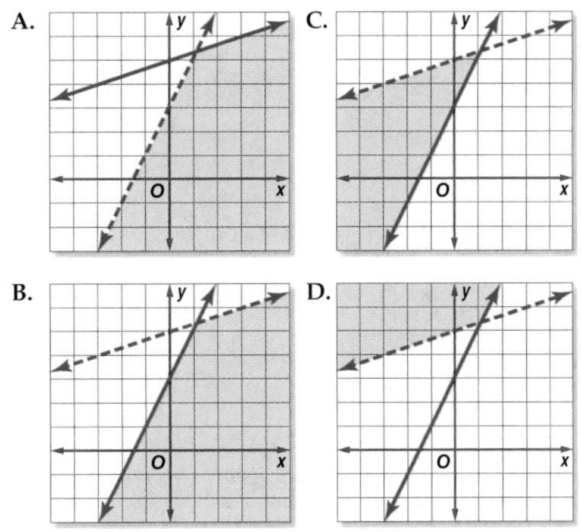

Solve each system of inequalities by graphing. (Lesson 3-3) **17–20. See Chapter 3 Answer Appendix.**

17. $x + y > 6$
$x - y < 0$

18. $y \ge 2x - 5$
$y \le x + 4$

19. $3x + 4y \le 12$
$6x - 3y \ge 18$

20. $5y + 2x \le 20$
$4x + 3y > 12$

21. **NGSSS PRACTICE** Tia spent \$42 on 2 cans of primer and 1 can of paint for her room. If the price of paint p is 150% of the price of primer r, which system of equations can be used to find the price of paint and primer? (Lesson 3-1) **F**

F. $p = r + \frac{1}{2}r$
$p + 2r = 42$

H. $r = p + \frac{1}{2}p$
$p + 2p = 42$

G. $p = r + 2r$
$p + \frac{1}{2}r = 42$

I. $r = p + 2p$
$p + \frac{1}{2} = 42$

22. **ART** Rai can spend no more than \$225 on the art club's supply of brushes and paint. A box of 3 brushes costs \$7.50. A box of 10 tubes of paint costs \$21.45. She needs at least 20 brushes and 56 tubes of paint. Graph the region that shows how many boxes of each item can be purchased. (Lesson 3-3) **See margin.**

CHAPTER 3 Mid-Chapter Quiz

Formative Assessment

Use the Mid-Chapter Quiz to assess students' progress in the first half of the chapter.

For problems answered incorrectly, have students review the lessons indicated in parentheses.

ExamView Assessment Suite Customize and create multiple versions of your Mid-Chapter Quiz and their answer keys.

FOLDABLES Follow-Up

Before students complete the Mid-Chapter Quiz, encourage them to review the information for Lessons 3-1 through 3-3 in their Foldables.

Additional Answer

22.

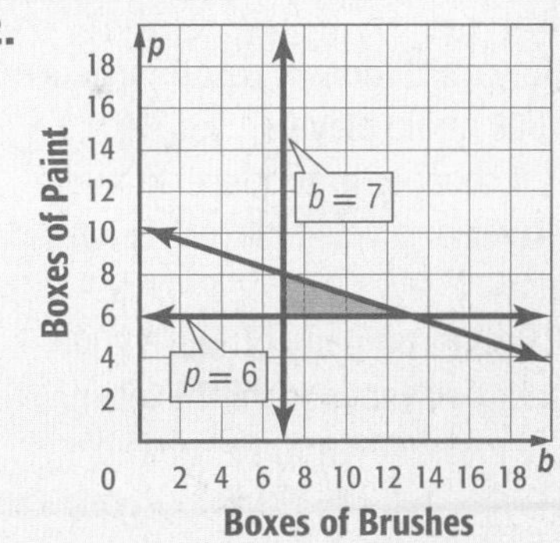

Intervention Planner

Tier 1 On Level	Tier 2 Strategic Intervention approaching grade level	Tier 3 Intensive Intervention 2 or more grades below level
If students miss about 25% of the exercises or less,	**If** students miss about 50% of the exercises,	**If** students miss about 75% of the exercises,
Then choose a resource:	**Then** choose a resource:	**Then** use *Math Triumphs, Alg. 2,* Ch. 3
SE Lessons 3-1, 3-2, and 3-3 **CRM** Skills Practice, pp. 7, 14, and 20 **TE** Chapter Project, p. 132	**CRM** Study Guide and Intervention, Chapter 3, pp. 5, 12, 18	
FL Math Online Self-Check Quiz	**FL Math Online** Extra Examples, Personal Tutor, Homework Help	**FL Math Online** Extra Examples, Personal Tutor, Homework Help, Review Vocabulary

3-4 Lesson Notes

1 FOCUS

Vertical Alignment

Before Lesson 3-4
Solve systems of linear inequalities by using graphs.

Lesson 3-4
Find the maximum and minimum values of a function over a region.
Solve real-world optimization problems using linear programming.

After Lesson 3-4
Formulate systems of equations in more than two unknowns.

2 TEACH

Scaffolding Questions

Have students read the *Why?* section of the lesson.

Ask:

- How much does it cost to produce 1000 audio players? $55,000
- Is it cheaper to produce an audio player or a video player? an audio player
- Can the company produce 2000 audio players per shift? Explain. No; the maximum number of audio players that can be produced is 1500.

3-4 Optimization with Linear Programming

Then
You solved systems of linear inequalities by using graphs. (Lesson 3-3)

Now
- Find the maximum and minimum values of a function over a region.
- Solve real-world optimization problems using linear programming.

NGSSS
MA.912.A.3.14 Solve systems of linear equations and inequalities in two and three variables using graphical, substitution, and elimination methods.
MA.912.A.3.15 Solve real-world problems involving systems of linear equations and inequalities in two and three variables.

New Vocabulary
constraints
linear programming
feasible region
bounded
unbounded
optimize

FL Math Online
glencoe.com

Why?

An electronics company produces digital audio players and digital video players. A sign on the company bulletin board is shown.

Keeping Costs Down: We Can Do It!

Our Goal: Production per Shift			
Player	Minimum	Maximum	Cost per Unit
audio	600	1500	$55
video	800	1700	$95

If at least 2000 items must be produced per shift, how many of each type should be made to minimize costs?

The company is experiencing limitations, or **constraints**, on production caused by customer demand, shipping, and the productivity of their factory. A system of inequalities can be used to represent these constraints.

Maximum and Minimum Values Situations often occur in business in which a company hopes to either maximize profits or minimize costs and many constraints need to be considered. These issues can often be addressed by the use of systems of inequalities in linear programming.

Linear programming is a method for finding maximum or minimum values of a function over a given system of inequalities with each inequality representing a constraint. After the system is graphed and the vertices of the solution set, called the **feasible region**, are substituted into the function, you can determine the maximum or minimum value.

Key Concept Feasible Regions

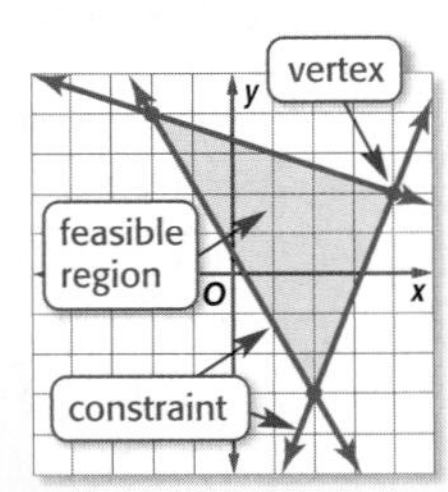

The feasible region is enclosed, or **bounded**, by the constraints. The maximum or minimum value of the related function *always* occurs at a vertex of the feasible region.

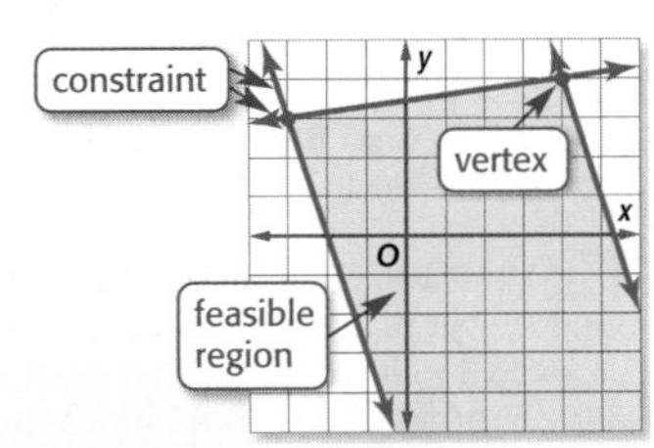

The feasible region is open and can go on forever. It is **unbounded**. Unbounded regions have either a maximum or a minimum.

Lesson 3-4 Resources

Resource	Approaching-Level	On-Level	Beyond-Level	English Learners
Teacher Edition	• Differentiated Instruction, p. 162	• Differentiated Instruction, pp. 162, 166	• Differentiated Instruction, p. 166	
Chapter Resource Masters	• Study Guide and Intervention, pp. 24–25 • Skills Practice, p. 26 • Practice, p. 27 • Word Problem Practice, p. 28	• Study Guide and Intervention, pp. 24–25 • Skills Practice, p. 26 • Practice, p. 27 • Word Problem Practice, p. 28 • Enrichment, p. 29 • Graphing Calculator, p. 30	• Practice, p. 27 • Word Problem Practice, p. 28 • Enrichment, p. 29	• Study Guide and Intervention, pp. 24–25 • Skills Practice, p. 26 • Practice, p. 27 • Word Problem Practice, p. 28
Transparencies	• 5-Minute Check Transparency 3-4	• 5-Minute Check Transparency 3-4	• 5-Minute Check Transparency 3-4	• 5-Minute Check Transparency 3-4
Other	• Study Notebook • Teaching Algebra with Manipulatives	• Study Notebook • Teaching Algebra with Manipulatives	• Study Notebook	• Study Notebook • Teaching Algebra with Manipulatives

ReadingMath

Function Notation The notation $f(x, y)$ is used to represent a function with two variables, x and y. It is read *f of x and y*.

EXAMPLE 1 Bounded Region

Graph the system of inequalities. Name the coordinates of the vertices of the feasible region. Find the maximum and minimum values of the function for this region.

$3 \le y \le 6$
$y \le 3x + 12$
$y \le -2x + 6$
$f(x, y) = 4x - 2y$

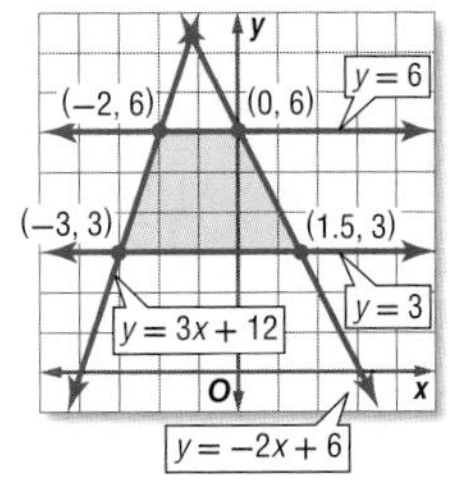

Step 1 Graph the inequalities and locate the vertices.

Step 2 Evaluate the function at each vertex.

(x, y)	4x − 2y	f(x, y)	
(−3, 3)	4(−3) − 2(3)	−18	
(1.5, 3)	4(1.5) − 2(3)	0	← maximum
(0, 6)	4(0) − 2(6)	−12	
(−2, 6)	4(−2) − 2(6)	−20	← minimum

The maximum value is 0 at (1.5, 3). The minimum value is −20 at (−2, 6).

Guided Practice 1A, 1B. See Chapter 3 Answer Appendix.

1A. $-2 \le x \le 6$
$1 \le y \le 5$
$y \le x + 3$
$f(x, y) = -5x + 2y$

1B. $-6 \le y \le -2$
$y \le -x + 2$
$y \le 2x + 2$
$f(x, y) = 6x + 4y$

Personal Tutor glencoe.com

When a system of inequalities does not form a closed region, it is unbounded.

Watch Out!

Maximum Value Do not assume that there is no maximum if the feasible region is unbounded above the vertices. Test points are needed to determine if there is a minimum or maximum.

EXAMPLE 2 Unbounded Region

Graph the system of inequalities. Name the coordinates of the vertices of the feasible region. Find the maximum and minimum values of the function for this region.

$2y + 3x \ge -12$
$y \le 3x + 12$
$y \ge 3x - 6$
$f(x, y) = 9x - 6y$

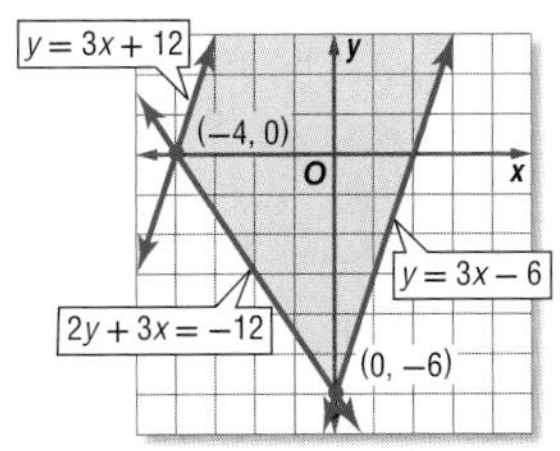

Graph the inequalities and evaluate the function at each vertex.

(x, y)	9x − 6y	f(x, y)
(−4, 0)	9(−4) − 6(0)	−36
(0, −6)	9(0) − 6(−6)	36

The maximum value is 36 at (0, −6). There is no minimum value. Notice that another point in the feasible region, (0, 8), yields a value of −48, which is less than −36.

Guided Practice 2A, 2B. See Chapter 3 Answer Appendix.

2A. $y \le 8$
$y \ge -x + 4$
$y \le -x + 10$
$f(x, y) = -6x + 8y$

2B. $y \ge x - 9$
$y \le -4x + 16$
$y \ge -4x - 4$
$f(x, y) = 10x + 7y$

Personal Tutor glencoe.com

Maximum and Minimum Values

Examples 1 and **2** show how to find the maximum and minimum values of a function for a bounded and an unbounded region.

Formative Assessment

Use the Guided Practice exercises after each example to determine students' understanding of concepts.

Additional Examples

1 Graph the following system of inequalities. Name the coordinates of the vertices of the feasible region. Find the maximum and minimum values of the function for this region.

$x \le 5$ $\quad$ $x + y \ge 2$
$y \le 4$ $\quad$ $f(x, y) = 3x - 2y$

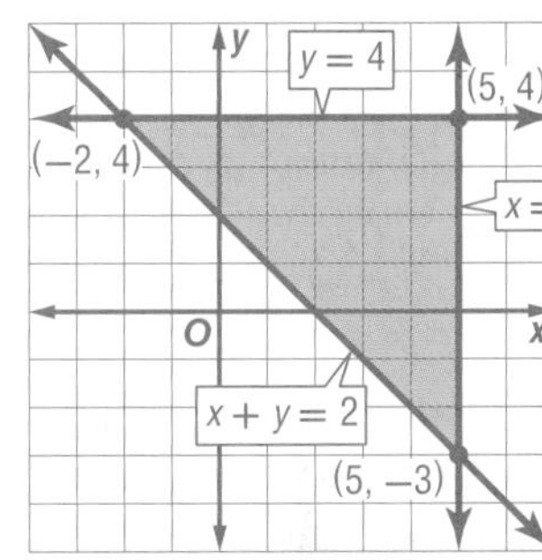

max at (5, −3) = 21;
min at (−2, 4) = −14

2 Graph the following system of inequalities. Name the coordinates of the vertices of the feasible region. Find the maximum and minimum values of the function for this region.

$-x + 2y \le 2$
$x - 2y \le 4$
$x + y \ge -2$
$f(x, y) = 2x + 3y$

See bottom margin for graph.
max: none; min at (0, −2) = −6

Additional Examples also in Interactive Classroom PowerPoint® Presentations

IWB INTERACTIVE WHITEBOARD READY

Answer for Additional Example 2

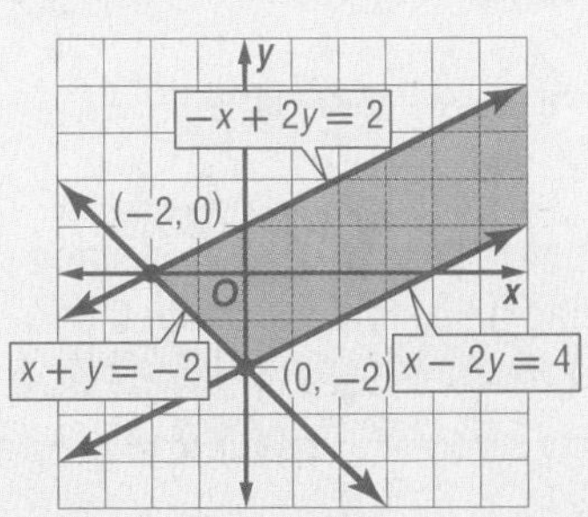

TEACH with TECH

INTERACTIVE WHITEBOARD Work through the examples on the whiteboard and save your work as notes pages. Send your notes to students to use as an additional reference outside of class.

Optimization

Example 3 shows how to use linear programming to solve a real-world problem.

Additional Example

3 **LANDSCAPING** A landscaping company has crews who mow lawns and prune shrubbery. The company schedules one hour for mowing jobs and three hours for pruning jobs. Each crew is scheduled for no more than two pruning jobs per day. Each crew's schedule is set up for a maximum of nine hours per day. On the average, the charge for mowing a lawn is $40, and the charge for pruning shrubbery is $120. Find a combination of mowing lawns and pruning shrubs that will maximize the income the company receives per day for one of its crews. either three mowings and two prunings, or nine mowings and zero prunings

Focus on Mathematical Content

Linear Programming The process of finding maximum or minimum values of a function for a region defined by linear inequalities is called linear programming. Linear programming is a very useful tool for solving many real-world problems.

Optimization To **optimize** means to seek the best price or amount to minimize costs or maximize profits. This is often obtained with the use of linear programming.

Key Concept — Optimization with Linear Programming

Step 1 Define the variables.
Step 2 Write a system of inequalities.
Step 3 Graph the system of inequalities.
Step 4 Find the coordinates of the vertices of the feasible region.
Step 5 Write a linear function to be maximized or minimized.
Step 6 Substitute the coordinates of the vertices into the function.
Step 7 Select the greatest or least result. Answer the problem.

Real-World Career

Operations Manager Operations management is an area of business that is concerned with the production of goods and services, and involves the responsibility of ensuring that business operations are efficient and effective. A master's degree in business and experience in operations are preferred.

Real-World EXAMPLE 3 Optimization with Linear Programming

BUSINESS Refer to the application at the beginning of the lesson. Use linear programming to determine how many of each type of digital player should be made per shift.

Step 1 Let a = number of audio players produced.
Let v = number of video players produced.

Step 2 $600 \leq a \leq 1500$
$800 \leq v \leq 1700$
$a + v \geq 2000$

Steps 3 and 4 The system is graphed at the right. Note the vertices of the feasible region.

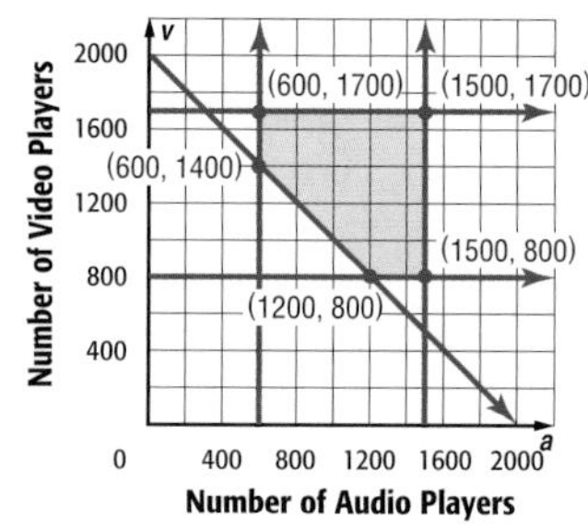

Step 5 The function to be minimized is $f(a, v) = 55a + 95v$.

Step 6

(a, v)	$55a + 95v$	$f(a, v)$	
(600, 1700)	55(600) + 95(1700)	194,500	
(600, 1400)	55(600) + 95(1400)	166,000	
(1500, 1700)	55(1500) + 95(1700)	244,000	← maximum
(1500, 800)	55(1500) + 95(800)	158,500	
(1200, 800)	55(1200) + 95(800)	142,000	← minimum

Step 7 1200 audio players and 800 video players should be produced to minimize costs.

StudyTip

Reasonableness Check your solutions for reasonableness by thinking of the context of the problem.

Guided Practice

3. JEWELRY Each week, Mackenzie can make between 10 and 25 necklaces and 15 to 40 pairs of earrings. If she earns profits of $3 on each pair of earrings and $5 on each necklace, and she plans to sell at least 30 pieces of jewelry, how many earrings and necklaces should she make to maximize profit? **40 earrings and 25 necklaces**

Personal Tutor glencoe.com

Watch Out!

Preventing Errors When using linear programming to solve real-world problems, it is important for all students to follow the seven steps from p. 162. Encourage students to show their work and label each step as they work through the problem.

Differentiated Instruction AL OL

If students have trouble with the relationship between the different regions of a graph of a system of inequalities,

Then have students use different colored pencils to shade the different regions of a graph defined by the inequalities in a linear programming problem. This should help students clarify the relationship between the various regions in these graphs.

162 Chapter 3 Systems of Equations and Inequalities

Check Your Understanding

Examples 1 and 2 p. 161

Graph each system of inequalities. Name the coordinates of the vertices of the feasible region. Find the maximum and minimum values of the given function for this region. 1–6. See margin.

1. $y \le 5$
   $x \le 4$
   $y \ge -x$
   $f(x, y) = 5x - 2y$
2. $y \le -3x + 6$
   $-y \le x$
   $y \le 3$
   $f(x, y) = 8x + 4y$
3. $y \ge -3x + 2$
   $9x + 3y \le 24$
   $y \ge -4$
   $f(x, y) = 2x + 14y$
4. $-2 \le y \le 6$
   $3y \le 4x + 26$
   $y \le -2x + 2$
   $f(x, y) = -3x - 6y$
5. $-3 \le y \le 7$
   $4y \ge 4x - 8$
   $6y + 3x \le 24$
   $f(x, y) = -12x + 9y$
6. $y \le 2x + 6$
   $y \ge 2x - 8$
   $y \ge -2x - 18$
   $f(x, y) = 5x - 4y$

Example 3 p. 162

7. **FINANCIAL LITERACY** The total number of workers' hours per day available for production in a skateboard factory is 85 hours. There are 40 hours available for finishing decks and quality control each day. The table shows the number of hours needed in each department for two different types of skateboards.

Skateboard Manufacturing Time

Board Type	Production Time	Deck Finishing/Quality Control
Pro Boards	1.5 hours	2 hours
Specialty Boards	1 hour	0.5 hour

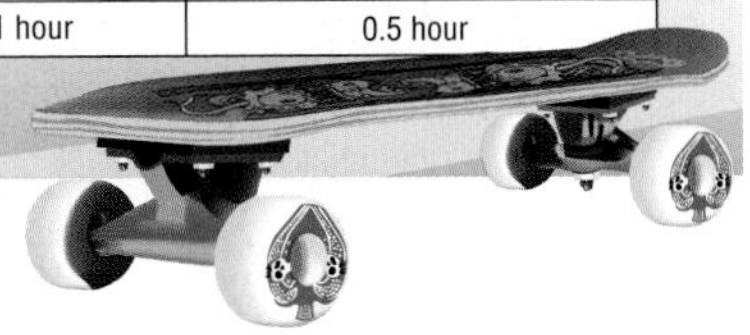

7a. $g \ge 0$, $c \ge 0$, $1.5g + c \le 85$, $2g + 0.5c \le 40$

a. Write a system of inequalities to represent the situation.

b. Draw the graph showing the feasible region. See Chapter 3 Answer Appendix.

c. List the coordinates of the vertices of the feasible region. (0, 0), (0, 20), (80, 0)

d. If the profit on a pro board is \$50 and the profit on a specialty board is \$65, write a function for the total profit on the skateboards. $f(c, g) = 65c + 50g$

e. Determine the number of each type of skateboard that needs to be made to have a maximum profit. What is the maximum profit? 80 specialty boards, 0 pro boards; \$5200

Practice and Problem Solving

● = Step-by-Step Solutions begin on page R20. Extra Practice begins on page 947.

Examples 1 and 2 p. 161

Graph each system of inequalities. Name the coordinates of the vertices of the feasible region. Find the maximum and minimum values of the given function for this region. 8–13. See Chapter 3 Answer Appendix.

8. $1 \le y \le 4$
   $4y - 6x \ge -32$
   $2y \ge -x + 4$
   $f(x, y) = -6x + 3y$
9. $2 \ge x \ge -3$
   $y \ge -2x - 6$
   $4y \le 2x + 32$
   $f(x, y) = -4x - 9y$
10. $-2 \le x \le 4$
    $5 \le y \le 8$
    $2x + 3y \le 26$
    $f(x, y) = 8x - 10y$
11. $-8 \le y \le -2$
    $y \le x$
    $y \le -3x + 10$
    $f(x, y) = 5x + 14y$
12. $x + 4y \ge 2$
    $2x + 4y \le 24$
    $2 \le x \le 6$
    $f(x, y) = 6x + 7y$
13. $3 \le y \le 7$
    $2y + x \le 8$
    $y - 2x \le 23$
    $f(x, y) = -3x + 5y$

3 PRACTICE

Formative Assessment

Use Exercises 1–7 to check for understanding.

Use the chart on the bottom of the next page to customize assignments for your students.

Additional Answers

1.

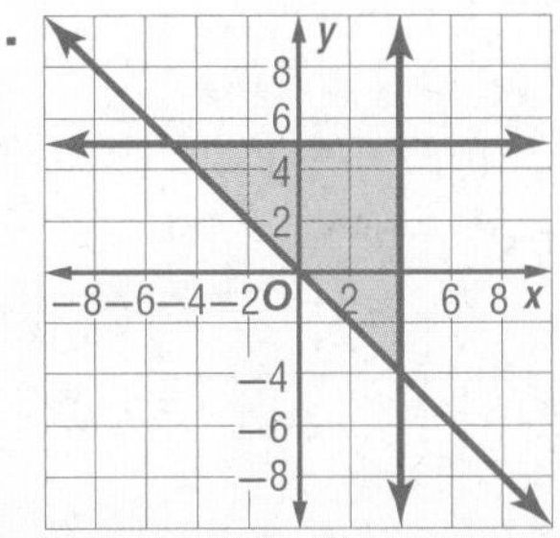

(4, 5), (4, –4), (–5, 5); max = 28, min = –35

2.

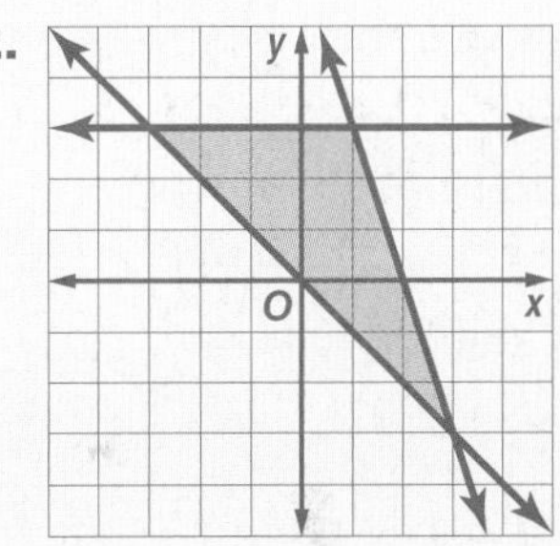

(1, 3), (3, –3), (–3, 3); max = 20, min = –12

3.

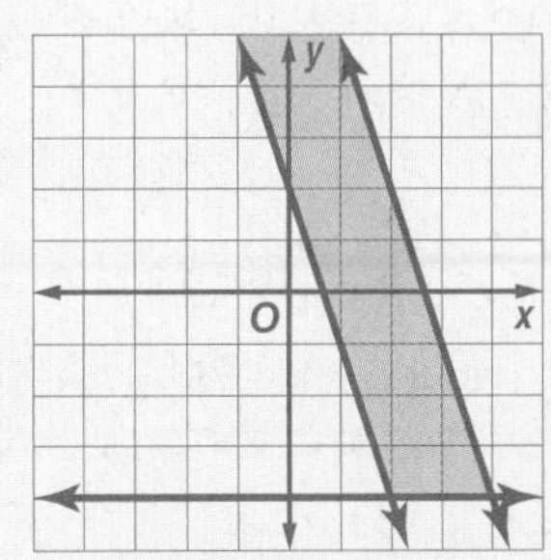

(2, –4), (4, –4); max does not exist, min = –52

4.

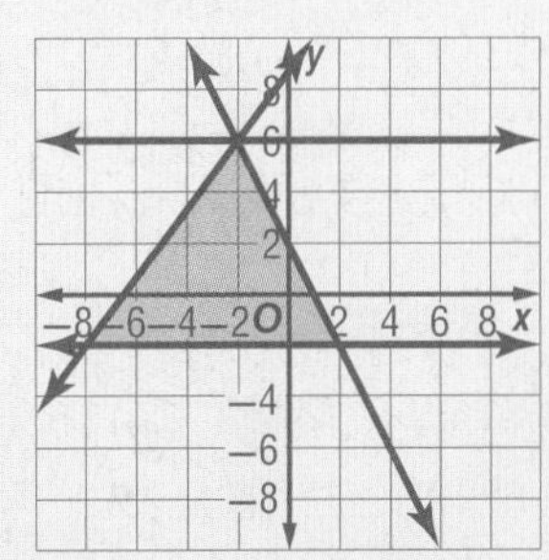

(2, –2), (–8, –2), (–2, 6); max = 36, min = –30

5.

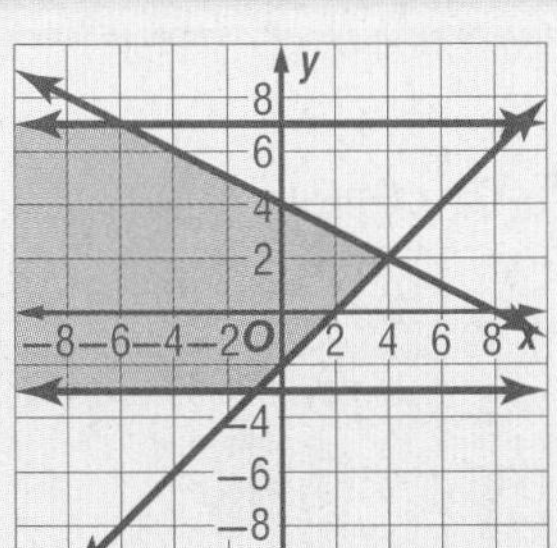

(4, 2), (–1, –3), (–6, 7); max does not exist; min = –30

6.

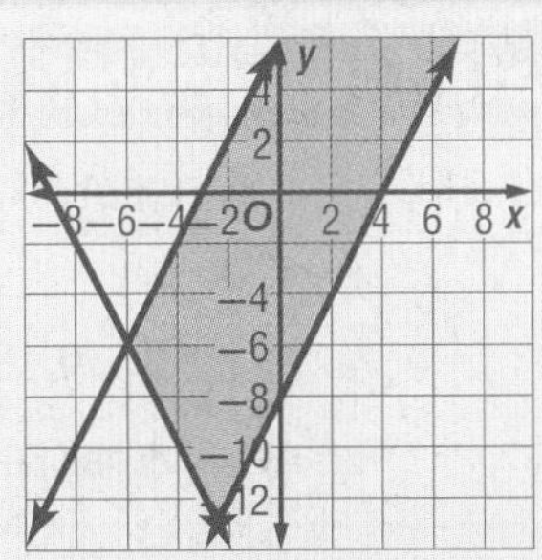

(–6, –6), (–2.5, –13), no min, max = 39.5

Tips for New Teachers

Problem Solving Tip Remind students that neither the maximum nor minimum automatically occurs at the smallest/largest (x, y) coordinate. The max/min depend on the $f(x, y)$ function in the situation.

Additional Answers

14–22. See Ch. 3 Answer Appendix for graphs.

14. (–9, –9), (–4, –9), (–5, –5), (–9, –5); max = –140, min = –252

15. (6, 3), (–8, 10), (–8, –18); max = 42, min = –140

16. (2, 0), (5, 3), (–3, 8), (–6, 8), max = –10, min = –105

17. (–6, 1), (6, –7), (–6, 5); max = 48, min = 0

18. (5, –5), (8, –17), (–12, –17), (–8, –5); max = 115, min = –49

19. (–8, 44), (16, 32), (–8, –26), (16, 22); max = 672, min = –486

20. (3, 7), (7, 3), (–3, –7), (–7, –3); max = 43, min = –43

21. (5, –1), (1, 6), (–2, –8), (–4, –8), (–4, 6), max = 60, min = –112

22. (–4, 6), (2, 4), (2, 1), (1, 0), (–3, 0), (–6, 3), (–6, 6); max = 26, min = –18

Examples 1 and 2 p. 161

Graph each system of inequalities. Name the coordinates of the vertices of the feasible region. Find the maximum and minimum values of the given function for this region. **14–22. See margin.**

14. $-9 \le x \le -3$
$-9 \le y \le -5$
$3y + 12x \le -75$
$f(x, y) = 20x + 8y$

15. $x \ge -8$
$3x + 6y \le 36$
$2y + 12 \ge 3x$
$f(x, y) = 10x - 6y$

16. $y \ge |x - 2|$
$y \le 8$
$8y + 5x \le 49$
$f(x, y) = -5x - 15y$

17. $x \ge -6$
$y + x \le -1$
$2x + 3y \ge -9$
$f(x, y) = -10x - 12y$

18. $-5 \ge y \ge -17$
$y \le 3x + 19$
$y \le -4x + 15$
$f(x, y) = 8x - 3y$

19. $-8 \le x \le 16$
$y \ge 2x - 10$
$2y + x \le 80$
$f(x, y) = 12x + 15y$

20. $y \le x + 4$
$y \ge x - 4$
$y \le -x + 10$
$y \ge -x - 10$
$f(x, y) = -10x + 9y$

21. $-4 \le x \le 8$
$-8 \le y \le 6$
$y \ge x - 6$
$4y + 7x \le 31$
$f(x, y) = 12x + 8y$

22. $y \ge |x + 1| - 2$
$0 \le y \le 6$
$-6 \le x \le 2$
$x + 3y \le 14$
$f(x, y) = 5x + 4y$

Example 3 p. 162

23. COOKING Jenny's Bakery makes two types of birthday cakes: yellow cake, which sells for \$25, and strawberry cake, which sells for \$35. Both cakes are the same size, but the decorating and assembly time required for the yellow cake is 2 hours, while the time is 3 hours for the strawberry cake. There are 450 hours of labor available for production. How many of each type of cake should be made to maximize revenue? **225 yellow cakes, 0 strawberry cakes**

24. BUSINESS The manager of a travel agency is printing brochures and fliers to advertise special discounts on vacation spots during the summer months. Each brochure costs \$0.08 to print, and each flier costs \$0.04 to print. A brochure requires 3 pages, and a flier requires 2 pages. The manager does not want to use more than 600 pages, and she needs at least 50 brochures and 150 fliers. How many of each should she print to minimize the cost? **50 brochures, 150 fliers**

B

25. PAINTING Sean has 20 days to paint as many play houses and sheds as he is able. The sheds can be painted at a rate of 2.5 per day, and the play houses can be painted at a rate of 2 per day. He has 45 structures that need to be painted.

a. Write a system of inequalities to represent the possible ways Sean can paint the structures. $a \ge 0$, $b \ge 0$, $a + b \le 45$, $4a + 5b \le 200$

b. Draw a graph showing the feasible region and list the coordinates of the vertices of the feasible region. **See Chapter 3 Answer Appendix.**

c. If the profit is \$26 per shed and \$30 per play house, how many of each should he paint? **25 sheds, 20 play houses**

d. What is the maximum profit? **\$1250**

Real-World Link

43–47% of teens see a movie in theaters at least once a month. The average American sees 5.8 movies per year in theaters.

Source: Chapel Hill

26. MOVIES Employees at a local movie theater work 8-hour shifts from noon to 8 P.M. or from 4 P.M. to midnight. The table below shows the number of employees needed and their corresponding pay. Find the numbers of day-shift workers and night-shift workers that should be scheduled to minimize the cost. What is the minimal cost? **8 day-shift and 6 night-shift workers; \$776**

Time	noon to 4 P.M.	4 P.M. to 8 P.M.	8 P.M. to midnight
Number of Employees Needed	at least 5	at least 14	6
Rate per Hour	\$5.50	\$7.50	\$7.50

Differentiated Homework Options

Level	Assignment	Two-Day Option	
AL Basic	8–24, 29–55	9–23 odd, 34–37	8–24 even, 29–33, 38–55
OL Core	9–23 odd, 25–29, 31–55	8–24, 34–37	25–29, 31–33, 38–55
BL Advanced	25–49, (optional: 50–55)		

Real-World Link

Plastic bottles can be recycled into rugs, swimming goggles, dog bowls, back packs, skateboard wheels, winter jackets, and more.

Source: Earth 911

C **27.** **BUSINESS** Each car on a freight train can hold 4200 pounds of cargo and has a capacity of 480 cubic feet. The freight service handles two types of packages: small —which weigh 25 pounds and are 3 cubic feet each, and large—which are 50 pounds and are 5 cubic feet each. The freight service charges \$5 for each small package and \$8 for each large package.

a. Find the number of each type of package that should be placed on a train car to maximize revenue. **160 small packages, 0 large packages**

b. What is the maximum revenue per train car? **\$800**

c. In this situation, is maximizing the revenue necessarily the best thing for the company to do? Explain. **See margin.**

28. **RECYCLING** A recycling plant processes used plastic into food or drink containers. The plant processes up to 1200 tons of plastic per week. At least 300 tons must be processed for food containers, while at least 450 tons must be processed for drink containers. The profit is \$17.50 per ton for processing food containers and \$20 per ton for processing drink containers. What is the profit if the plant maximizes processing? **\$23,250**

H.O.T. Problems Use Higher-Order Thinking Skills

29. **OPEN ENDED** Create a set of inequalities that forms a bounded region with an area of 20 units^2 and lies only in the fourth quadrant.

30. **CHALLENGE** Find the area of the bounded region formed by the following constraints: $y \geq |x| - 3$, $y \leq -|x| + 3$, and $x \geq |y|$. **4.5 units^2**

31. **WHICH ONE DOESN'T BELONG?** Identify the system of inequalities that is not the same as the other three. Explain your reasoning.

a.
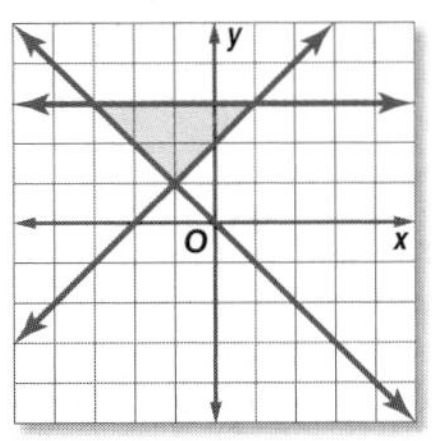

c.
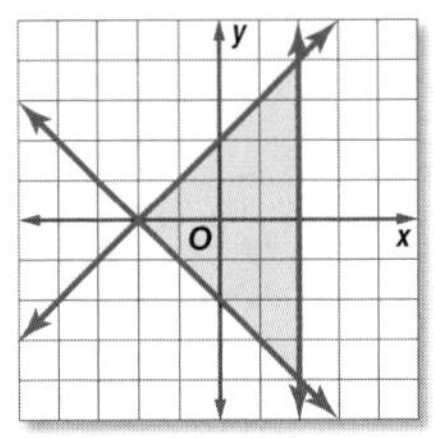

b.
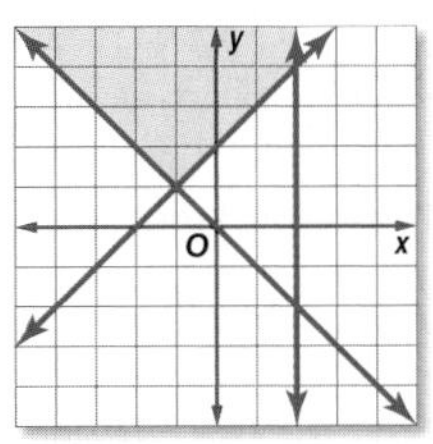

d.
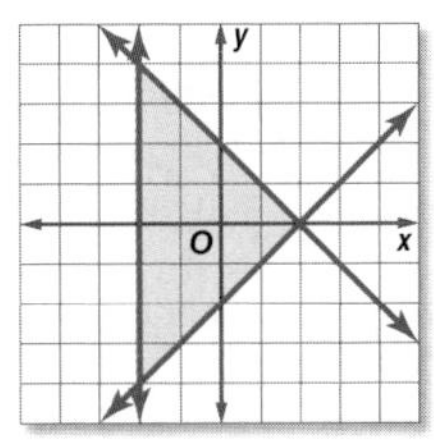

32. **REASONING** Determine whether the following statement is *sometimes*, *always*, or *never* true. Explain your reasoning.

An unbounded region will not have both a maximum and minimum value.

33. **WRITING IN MATH** Upon determining a bounded feasible region, Ayumi noticed that vertices $A(-3, 4)$ and $B(5, 2)$ yielded the same maximum value for $f(x, y) = 16y + 4x$. Kelvin confirmed that her constraints were graphed correctly and her vertices were correct. Then he said that those two points were not the only maximum values in the feasible region. Explain how this could have happened.

29. Sample answer: $-2 \geq y \geq -6$, $4 \leq x \leq 9$

31. b; The feasible region of Graph b is unbounded while the other three are bounded.

32. Sample answer: Always; if a point on the unbounded region forms a minimum, then a maximum cannot also be formed because of the unbounded region. There will always be a value in the solution that will produce a higher value than any projected maximum.

33. Sample answer: Even though the region is bounded, multiple maximums occur at *A* and *B* and all of the points on the boundary of the feasible region containing both *A* and *B*. This happened because that boundary of the region has the same slope as the function.

Additional Answer

27c. No; if revenue is maximized, the company will not deliver any large packages, and customers with large packages to ship will probably choose another carrier.

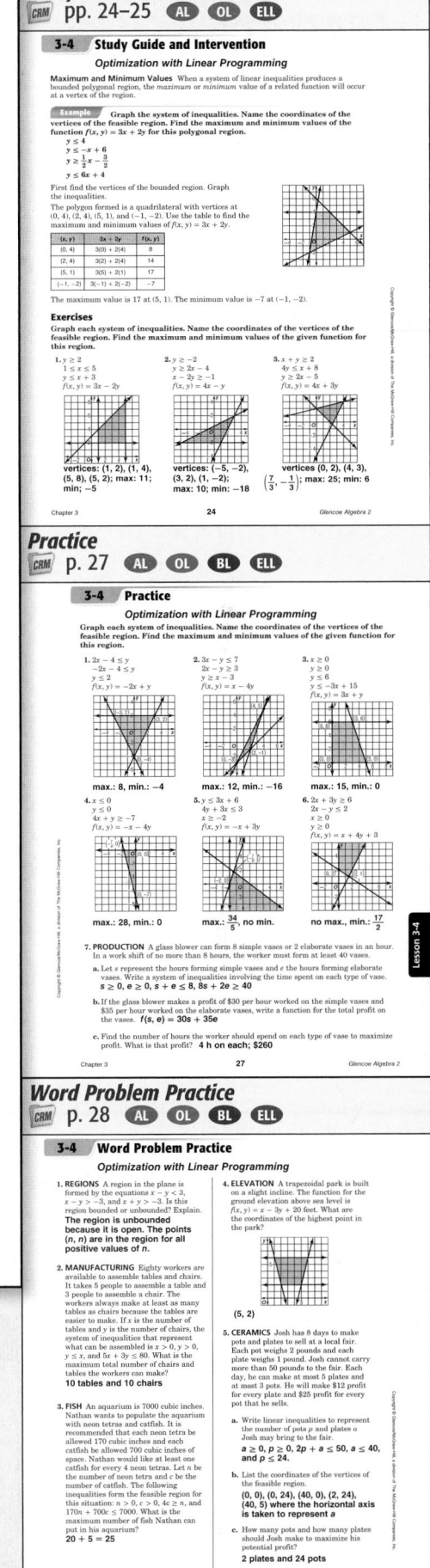

Study Guide and Intervention

CRM pp. 24–25 AL OL ELL

3-4 Study Guide and Intervention

Optimization with Linear Programming

Maximum and Minimum Values When a system of linear inequalities produces a bounded polygonal region, the *maximum* or *minimum* value of a related function will occur at a vertex of the region.

Example **Graph the system of inequalities. Name the coordinates of the vertices of the feasible region. Find the maximum and minimum values of the function $f(x, y) = 3x + 2y$ for this polygonal region.**

$y \leq 4$
$y \leq -x + 6$
$y \geq \frac{1}{2}x - \frac{3}{2}$
$y \leq 6x + 4$

First find the vertices of the bounded region. Graph the inequalities.

The polygon formed is a quadrilateral with vertices at (0, 4), (2, 4), (5, 1), and (−1, −2). Use the table to find the maximum and minimum values of $f(x, y) = 3x + 2y$.

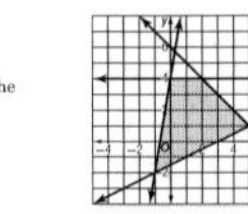

(x, y)	3x + 2y	f(x, y)
(0, 4)	3(0) + 2(4)	8
(2, 4)	3(2) + 2(4)	14
(5, 1)	3(5) + 2(1)	17
(−1, −2)	3(−1) + 2(−2)	−7

The maximum value is 17 at (5, 1). The minimum value is −7 at (−1, −2).

Exercises

Graph each system of inequalities. Name the coordinates of the vertices of the feasible region. Find the maximum and minimum values of the given function for this region.

1. $y \geq 2$, $1 \leq x \leq 5$, $y \leq x + 3$, $f(x, y) = 3x - 2y$
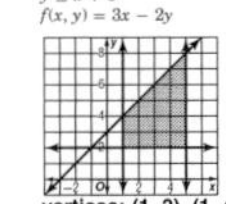
vertices: (1, 2), (1, 4), (5, 8), (5, 2); max: 11; min; −5

2. $y \geq -2$, $y \geq 2x - 4$, $x - 2y \geq -1$, $f(x, y) = 4x - y$
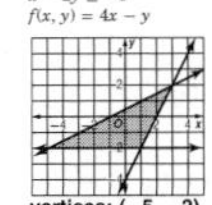
vertices: (−5, −2), (3, 2), (1, −2); max: 10; min: −18

3. $x + y \geq 2$, $4y \leq x + 8$, $y \geq 2x - 5$, $f(x, y) = 4x + 3y$
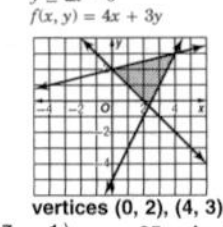
vertices (0, 2), (4, 3), $\left(\frac{7}{3}, -\frac{1}{3}\right)$; max: 25; min: 6

Chapter 3 24 Glencoe Algebra 2

Practice

CRM p. 27 AL OL BL ELL

3-4 Practice

Optimization with Linear Programming

Graph each system of inequalities. Name the coordinates of the vertices of the feasible region. Find the maximum and minimum values of the given function for this region.

1. $2x - 4 \leq y$, $-2x - 4 \leq y$, $y \leq 2$, $f(x, y) = -2x + y$
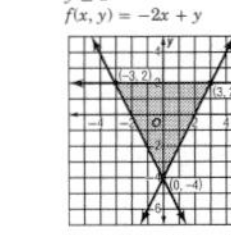
max.: 8, min.: −4

2. $3x - y \leq 7$, $2x - y \geq 3$, $y \geq x - 3$, $f(x, y) = x - 4y$
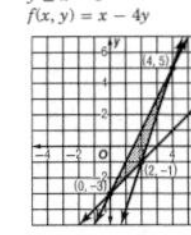
max.: 12, min.: −16

3. $x \geq 0$, $y \geq 0$, $y \leq 6$, $y \leq -3x + 15$, $f(x, y) = 3x + y$
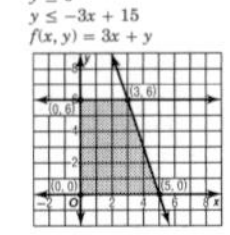
max.: 15, min.: 0

4. $x \leq 0$, $y \leq 0$, $4x + y \geq -7$, $f(x, y) = -x - 4y$
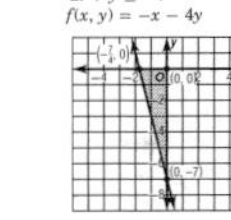
max.: 28, min.: 0

5. $y \leq 3x + 6$, $4y + 3x \leq 3$, $x \geq -2$, $f(x, y) = -x + 3y$
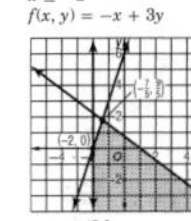
max.: $\frac{34}{5}$, no min.

6. $2x + 3y \geq 6$, $2x - y \leq 2$, $x \geq 0$, $y \geq 0$, $f(x, y) = x + 4y + 3$
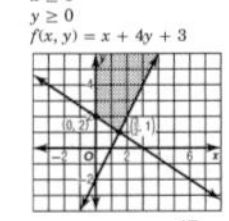
no max., min.: $\frac{17}{2}$

7. **PRODUCTION** A glass blower can form 8 simple vases or 2 elaborate vases in an hour. In a work shift of no more than 8 hours, the worker must form at least 40 vases.

a. Let s represent the hours forming simple vases and e the hours forming elaborate vases. Write a system of inequalities involving the time spent on each type of vase. **$s \geq 0$, $e \geq 0$, $s + e \leq 8$, $8s + 2e \geq 40$**

b. If the glass blower makes a profit of \$30 per hour worked on the simple vases and \$35 per hour worked on the elaborate vases, write a function for the total profit on the vases. **$f(s, e) = 30s + 35e$**

c. Find the number of hours the worker should spend on each type of vase to maximize profit. What is that profit? **4 h on each; \$260**

Chapter 3 27 Glencoe Algebra 2

Lesson 3-4

Word Problem Practice

CRM p. 28 AL OL BL ELL

3-4 Word Problem Practice

Optimization with Linear Programming

1. **REGIONS** A region in the plane is formed by the equations $x - y < 3$, $x - y > -3$, and $x + y > -3$. Is this region bounded or unbounded? Explain. **The region is unbounded because it is open. The points (*n*, *n*) are in the region for all positive values of *n*.**

2. **MANUFACTURING** Eighty workers are available to assemble tables and chairs. It takes 5 people to assemble a table and 3 people to assemble a chair. The workers always make at least as many tables as chairs because the tables are easier to make. If x is the number of tables and y is the number of chairs, the system of inequalities that represent what can be assembled is $x > 0$, $y > 0$, $y \leq x$, and $5x + 3y \leq 80$. What is the maximum total number of chairs and tables the workers can make? **10 tables and 10 chairs**

3. **FISH** An aquarium is 7000 cubic inches. Nathan wants to populate the aquarium with neon tetras and catfish. It is recommended that each neon tetra be allowed 170 cubic inches and each catfish be allowed 700 cubic inches of space. Nathan would like at least one catfish for every 4 neon tetras. Let n be the number of neon tetra and c be the number of catfish. The following inequalities form the feasible region for this situation: $n > 0$, $c > 0$, $4c \geq n$, and $170n + 700c \leq 7000$. What is the maximum number of fish Nathan can put in his aquarium? **20 + 5 = 25**

4. **ELEVATION** A trapezoidal park is built on a slight incline. The function for the ground elevation above sea level is $f(x, y) = x - 3y + 20$ feet. What are the coordinates of the highest point in the park?
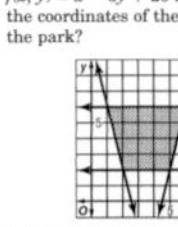
(5, 2)

5. **CERAMICS** Josh has 8 days to make pots and plates to sell at a local fair. Each pot weighs 2 pounds and each plate weighs 1 pound. Josh cannot carry more than 50 pounds to the fair. Each day, he can make at most 5 plates and at most 3 pots. He will make \$12 profit for every plate and \$25 profit for every pot that he sells.

a. Write linear inequalities to represent the number of pots p and plates a Josh may bring to the fair. **$a \geq 0$, $p \geq 0$, $2p + a \leq 50$, $a \leq 40$, and $p \leq 24$.**

b. List the coordinates of the vertices of the feasible region. **(0, 0), (0, 24), (40, 0), (2, 24), (40, 5) where the horizontal axis is taken to represent *a***

c. How many pots and how many plates should Josh make to maximize his potential profit? **2 plates and 24 pots**

Chapter 3 28 Glencoe Algebra 2

Enrichment

CRM p. 29 OL BL

3-4 Enrichment

Sensitivity Analysis

A linear programming model has specific objective coefficients. For example, if the value of a model is found by $2x + 3y = 5$, the objective coefficients are {2, 3}. What if these coefficients were {2.1, 2.9} or {2.5, 3.1}? How would these changes affect the optimal linear program value? This type of investigation is called **sensitivity analysis**.

In general, the objective function in two-variable linear programming problem can be written as: maximize (or minimize) $Ax + By = C$, subject to a set of constraint equations. Changes to the *parameters* A and B could change the slope of the line. This change of slope could lead to a change in the optimum solution to a different corner point (Recall, the optimum solution occurs at a *corner point*).

There is a range in the slope value that will produce this change, thus there is a range of variation for both A and B that will keep the optimal solution the same (see graph).

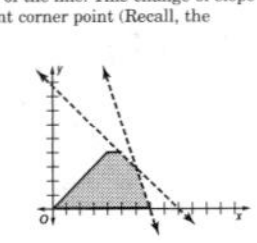

1. Find the slope of $Ax + By = C$ and observe how changes to the parameters A and B can change the slope of the line. **The slope, m, of $Ax + By = C$ is $m = \frac{-A}{B}$.**

Consider the Linear Programming problem:

4 ASSESS

Yesterday's News Have students write how yesterday's lesson helped them with today's new material.

Formative Assessment

Check for student understanding of the concepts in Lesson 3-4.

CRM Quiz 3, p. 40

Additional Answers

38.

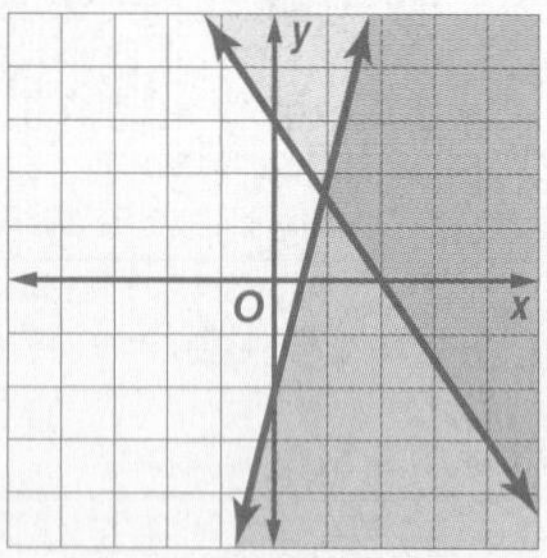

39.

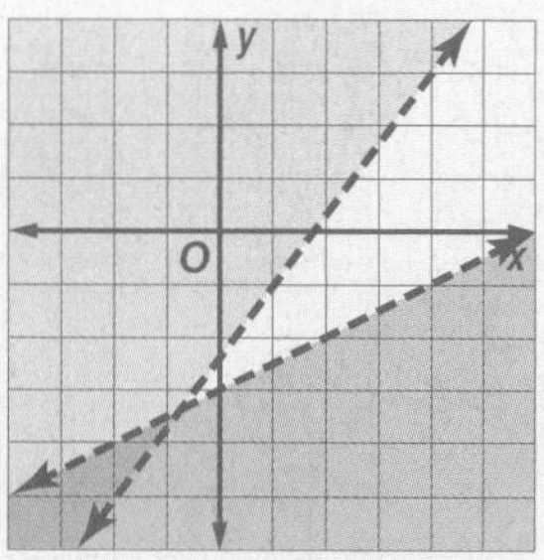

40.

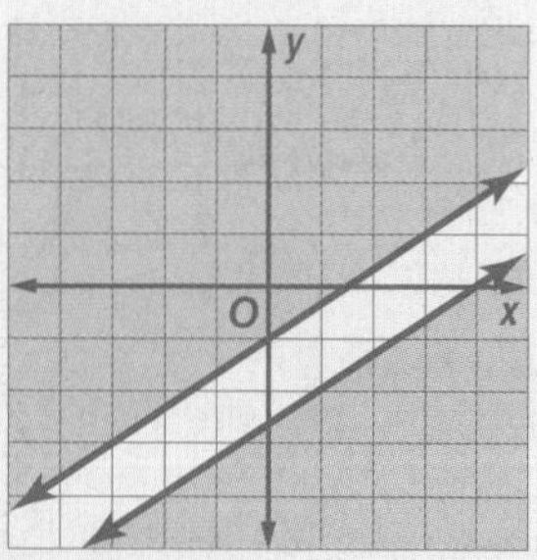

no solution

NGSSS PRACTICE 912.A.3.15, 912.A.3.1, 912.P.3.1, 912.A.3.14

34. Kelsey worked 350 hours during the summer and earned \$2978.50. She earned \$6.85 per hour when she worked at a video store and \$11 per hour as an architectural intern. Let x represent the number of hours she worked at the video store and y represent the number of hours that she interned. Which system of equations represents this situation? B

A. $x + y = 350$
$11x + 6.85y = 2978.50$

B. $x + y = 350$
$6.85x + 11y = 2978.50$

C. $x + y = 2978.50$
$6.85x + 11y = 350$

D. $x + y = 2978.50$
$11x + 6.85y = 350$

35. **SHORT RESPONSE** A family of four went out to dinner. Their bill, including tax, was \$60. They left a 17% tip on the total cost of their bill. What is the total cost of the dinner including tip? \$70.20

36. **ACT/SAT** For a game she is playing, Liz must draw a card from a deck of 26 cards, one with each letter of the alphabet on it, and roll a die. What is the probability that Liz will draw a letter in her name and roll an odd number? I

F. $\frac{2}{3}$

G. $\frac{1}{13}$

H. $\frac{1}{26}$

I. $\frac{3}{52}$

37. **GEOMETRY** Which of the following best describes the graphs of $y = 3x - 5$ and $4y = 12x + 16$? D

A. The lines have the same y-intercept.

B. The lines have the same x-intercept.

C. The lines are perpendicular.

D. The lines are parallel.

Spiral Review

Solve each system of inequalities by graphing. (Lesson 3-3) 38–40. See margin.

38. $3x + 2y \geq 6$
$4x - y \geq 2$

39. $4x - 3y < 7$
$2y - x < -6$

40. $3y \leq 2x - 8$
$y \geq \frac{2}{3}x - 1$

41. **BUSINESS** Last year the chess team paid \$7 per hat and \$15 per shirt for a total purchase of \$330. This year they spent \$360 to buy the same number of shirts and hats because the hats now cost \$8 and the shirts cost \$16. Write and solve a system of two equations that represents the number of hats and shirts bought each year. (Lesson 3-2) $7x + 15y = 330$, $8x + 16y = 360$; hats: 15, shirts: 15

Write an equation in slope-intercept form for the line that satisfies each set of conditions. (Lesson 2-4)

42. passes through (5, 1) and (8, −4) $y = -\frac{5}{3}x + \frac{28}{3}$

43. passes through (−3, 5) and (3, 2) $y = -\frac{1}{2}x + \frac{7}{2}$

Find the x-intercept and the y-intercept of the graph of each equation. Then graph the equation. (Lesson 2-2) 44–49. See Chapter 3 Answer Appendix for graphs.

44. $5x + 3y = 15$ 3; 5

45. $2x - 6y = 12$ 6; −2

46. $3x - 4y - 10 = 0$ $\frac{10}{3}$; $-\frac{5}{2}$

47. $2x + 5y - 10 = 0$ 5; 2

48. $y = x$ 0; 0

49. $y = 4x - 2$ $\frac{1}{2}$; −2

Skills Review

Evaluate each expression if $x = -1$, $y = 3$, and $z = 7$. (Lesson 1-1)

50. $x + y + z$ 9

51. $2x - y + 2z$ 9

52. $-x + 4y - 3z$ −8

53. $4x + 2y - z$ −5

54. $5x - y + 4z$ 20

55. $-3x - 3y + 3z$ 15

Differentiated Instruction

OL BL

Extension Linear programming is a great lens for looking at effective business practice. Ask students to create a business similar to those mentioned in the Exercises. Students must determine their costs and profits for the chosen business and analyze the information to determine maximum profit options. Make the task more authentic by having students pursue a business that is of personal interest to them and estimate profit margins using the Internet as a resource.

3-5 Systems of Equations in Three Variables

Then

You solved linear equations with two variables. (Lesson 3-2)

Now

- Solve systems of linear equations in three variables.
- Solve real-world problems using systems of linear equations in three variables.

NGSSS

MA.912.A.3.14 Solve systems of linear equations and inequalities in two **and three variables using** graphical, substitution, and **elimination methods.**
MA.912.A.3.15 Solve real-world problems involving systems of linear equations and inequalities in two and three variables.

New Vocabulary

ordered triple

FL Math Online

glencoe.com

Why?

Seats closest to an amphitheater stage cost \$30. The seats in the next section cost \$25, and lawn seats are \$20. There are twice as many seats in section B as in section A. When all 19,200 seats are sold, the amphitheater makes \$456,000.

A system of equations in three variables can be used to determine the number of seats in each section.

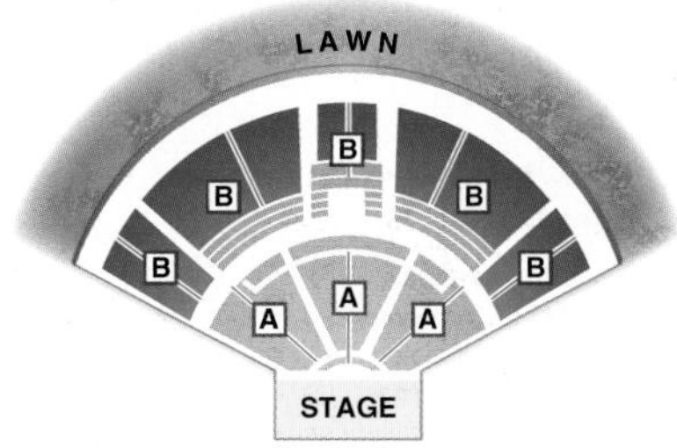

Systems in Three Variables Like systems of equations in two variables, systems in three variables can have one solution, infinite solutions, or no solution. A solution of such a system is an **ordered triple** (x, y, z).

The graph of an equation in three variables is a three-dimensional graph in the shape of a plane. The graphs of a system of equations in three variables form a system of planes.

One Solution

The three individual planes intersect at a specific point.

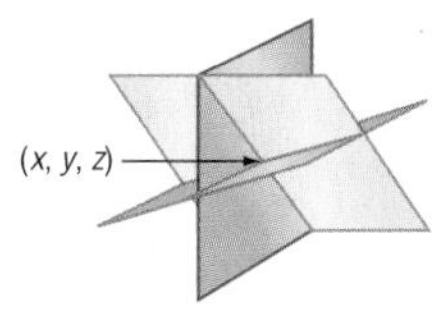

Infinitely Many Solutions

The planes intersect in a line.

Every coordinate on the line represents a solution of the system.

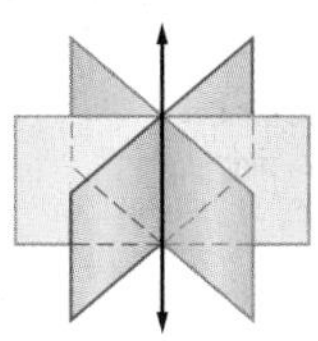

The planes intersect in the same plane.

Every equation is equivalent.
Every coordinate in the plane represents a solution of the system.

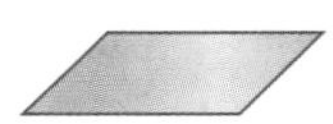

No Solution

There are no points in common with all three planes.

3-5 Lesson Notes

1 FOCUS

Vertical Alignment

Before Lesson 3-5
Solve linear equations with two variables.

Lesson 3-5
Solve systems of linear equations in three variables.
Solve real-world problems using systems of linear equations in three variables.

After Lesson 3-5
Use matrices to solve systems of equations.

2 TEACH

Scaffolding Questions

Have students read the *Why?* section of the lesson.

Ask:

- How many seats are in the amphitheater? 19,200
- How much do the seats in section A cost? \$30 in section B? \$25
- Suppose the amphitheater sells 3100 seats in section A, 5050 seats in section B, and 7200 lawn seats. How much money is taken in? \$363,250

Lesson 3-5 Resources

Resource	Approaching-Level	On-Level	Beyond-Level	English Learners
Teacher Edition	• Differentiated Instruction, p. 170	• Differentiated Instruction, p. 170	• Differentiated Instruction, p. 173	• Differentiated Instruction, p. 170
Chapter Resource Masters	• Study Guide and Intervention, pp. 31–32 • Skills Practice, p. 33 • Practice, p. 34 • Word Problem Practice, p. 35	• Study Guide and Intervention, pp. 31–32 • Skills Practice, p. 33 • Practice, p. 34 • Word Problem Practice, p. 35 • Enrichment, p. 36	• Practice, p. 34 • Word Problem Practice, p. 35 • Enrichment, p. 36	• Study Guide and Intervention, pp. 31–32 • Skills Practice, p. 33 • Practice, p. 34 • Word Problem Practice, p. 35
Transparencies	• 5-Minute Check Transparency 3-5	• 5-Minute Check Transparency 3-5	• 5-Minute Check Transparency 3-5	• 5-Minute Check Transparency 3-5
Other	• Study Notebook • Teaching Algebra with Manipulatives	• Study Notebook • Teaching Algebra with Manipulatives	• Study Notebook	• Study Notebook • Teaching Algebra with Manipulatives

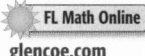

Systems in Three Variables

Examples 1 and **2** show how to solve systems of equations in three variables.

Formative Assessment

Use the Guided Practice exercises after each example to determine students' understanding of concepts.

Additional Example

1 Solve the system of equations.

$5x + 3y + 2z = 2$
$2x + y - z = 5$
$x + 4y + 2z = 16$
$(-2, 6, -3)$

Additional Examples also in Interactive Classroom PowerPoint® Presentations

IWB INTERACTIVE WHITEBOARD READY

Watch Out!

Preventing Errors Suggest that when solving systems of equations in three variables, students should take a few moments before beginning their calculations to examine the equations and make a plan for solving the system. Also, remind students that the three values of the solution represent a point in space that is contained in all three planes.

Tips for New Teachers

Eliminination Ask students what happens to the graph of an equation when it is multiplied by a constant. The graph is unchanged because the new equation is equivalent to the original equation.

Solving systems of equations in three variables is similar to solving systems of equations in two variables. Use the strategies of substitution and elimination to find the ordered triple that represents the solution of the system.

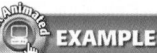

EXAMPLE 1 A System with One Solution

Solve the system of equations.

$$3x - 2y + 4z = 35$$
$$-4x + y - 5z = -36$$
$$5x - 3y + 3z = 31$$

The coefficient of 1 in the second equation makes y a good choice for elimination.

Step 1 Eliminate one variable by using two pairs of equations.

$3x - 2y + 4z = 35$
$-4x + y - 5z = -36$ **Multiply by 2.**

$$\begin{array}{rl} 3x - 2y + 4z = 35 & \textbf{Equation 1} \\ (+)\ -8x + 2y - 10z = -72 & \textbf{Equation 2} \times 2 \\ \hline -5x \qquad - 6z = -37 & \end{array}$$

$-4x + y - 5z = -36$ **Multiply by 3.**
$5x - 3y + 3z = 31$

$$\begin{array}{rl} -12x + 3y - 15z = -108 & \textbf{Equation 2} \times 3 \\ (+)\ 5x - 3y + 3z = 31 & \textbf{Equation 1} \\ \hline -7x \qquad - 12z = -77 & \end{array}$$

The y-terms in each equation have been eliminated. We now have a system of two equations and two variables, x and z.

Step 2 Solve the system of two equations.

$-5x - 6z = -37$ **Multiply by −2.**
$-7x - 12z = -77$

$$\begin{array}{rl} 10x + 12z = 74 & \\ (+)\ -7x - 12z = -77 & \\ \hline 3x \qquad = -3 & \textbf{Eliminate } z. \\ x = -1 & \textbf{Divide by 3.} \end{array}$$

Use substitution to solve for z.

$$\begin{array}{rl} -5x - 6z = -37 & \text{Equation with two variables} \\ -5(-1) - 6z = -37 & \text{Substitution} \\ 5 - 6z = -37 & \text{Multiply.} \\ -6z = -42 & \text{Subtract 5 from each side.} \\ z = 7 & \text{Divide each side by } -6. \end{array}$$

The result is $x = -1$ and $z = 7$.

Step 3 Substitute the two values into one of the original equations to find y.

$$\begin{array}{rl} -4x + y - 5z = -36 & \text{Equation 1} \\ -4(-1) + y - 5(7) = -36 & \text{Substitution} \\ 4 + y - 35 = -36 & \text{Multiply.} \\ y = -5 & \text{Add 31 to each side.} \end{array}$$

CHECK

$$\begin{array}{rl} -4x + y - 5z = -36 & \text{Equation 2} \\ -4(-1) + (-5) - 5(7) \stackrel{?}{=} -36 & x = -1, y = -5, z = 7 \\ 4 + (-5) - 35 \stackrel{?}{=} -36 & \text{Simplify.} \\ -36 = -36\ \checkmark & \end{array}$$

The solution is $(-1, -5, 7)$.

StudyTip

Choosing Variables If one of the equations is missing a variable already, use the other two equations and eliminate the same variable.

StudyTip

Checking Solutions Always substitute your answer into all of the original equations to confirm your answer.

Guided Practice

1A. $2x + 4y - 5z = 18$
$-3x + 5y + 2z = -27$
$-5x + 3y - z = -17$ $(3, -2, -4)$

1B. $4x - 3y + 6z = 18$
$-x + 5y + 4z = 48$
$6x - 2y + 5z = 0$ $(-6, 2, 8)$

Personal Tutor glencoe.com

TEACH with TECH

VIDEO RECORDING Have students work in groups to create a video showing how to solve a system of equations in three variables. Be sure students show how to check the solution in the original system of equations. Share each group's video with the entire class.

When solving a system of three linear equations with three variables, it is important to check your answer using all three of the original equations. This is necessary because it is possible for a solution to work for two of the equations but not the third.

EXAMPLE 2 No Solution and Infinite Solutions

Solve each system of equations.

a. $5x + 4y - 5z = -10$
$-4x - 10y - 8z = -16$
$6x + 15y + 12z = 24$

Eliminate x in the second two equations.

$-4x - 10y - 8z = -16$ **Multiply by 3.** $-12x - 30y - 24z = -48$

$6x + 15y + 12z = 24$ **Multiply by 2.** $(+)\ 12x + 30y + 24z = 48$

$0 = 0$

The equation $0 = 0$ is always true. This indicates that the last two equations represent the same plane. Check to see if this plane intersects the first plane.

$5x + 4y - 5z = -10$ **Multiply by 4.** $20x + 16y - 20z = -40$

$-4x - 10y - 8z = -16$ **Multiply by 5.** $(+)\ -20x - 50y - 40z = -80$

$-34y - 60z = -120$

The planes intersect in a line. So, there are an infinite number of solutions.

b. $-6a + 9b - 12c = 21$
$-2a + 3b - 4c = 7$
$10a - 15b + 20c = -30$

Eliminate a in the first two equations.

$-6a + 9b - 12c = 21$ → $-6a + 9b - 12c = 21$

$-2a + 3b - 4c = 7$ **Multiply by −3.** $(+)\ 6a - 9b + 12c = -21$

$0 = 0$

The equation $0 = 0$ is always true. This indicates that the first two equations represent the same plane. Check to see if this plane intersects the last plane.

$-2a + 3b - 4c = 7$ **Multiply by 5.** $-10a + 15b - 20c = 35$

$10a - 15b + 20c = -30$ → $(+)\ 10a - 15b + 20c = -30$

$0 = 5$

The equation $0 = 5$ is never true. So, there is no solution of this system.

Guided Practice

2A. $-4x - 2y - z = 15$ **no solution**
$12x + 6y + 3z = 45$
$2x + 5y + 7z = -29$

2B. $3x + 5y - 2z = 13$ **infinite solutions**
$-5x - 2y - 4z = 20$
$-14x - 17y + 2z = -19$

Personal Tutor glencoe.com

StudyTip

Infinite and No Solutions When solving a system of more than two equations, $0 = 5$ will always yield no solution, while $0 = 0$ may not always yield infinite solutions.

Real-World Problems When solving problems involving three variables, use the four-step plan to help organize the information. Identify the three variables and what they represent. Then use the information in the problem to form equations using the variables. Once you have three equations and all three variables are represented, you can solve the problem.

Additional Example

2 Solve each system of equations.

a. $2x + y - 3z = 5$
$x + 2y - 4z = 7$
$6x + 3y - 9z = 15$
There are an infinite number of solutions.

b. $3x - y - 2z = 4$
$6x + 4y + 8z = 11$
$9x + 6y - 12z = 23$
There is no solution to this system.

Watch Out!

Preventing Errors To help students visualize a system with no solutions, ask them to sketch a drawing of three planes whose equations form a system with no solutions.

Watch Out!

Preventing Errors Some students may think that *any* ordered triple will be a solution to a system in three variables where there are an infinite number of solutions (as in Example 2a). Ask students to discuss why only the infinite set of ordered triples that names points on the line (or plane) of intersection contains solutions of the system of equations.

Real-World Problems

Example 3 shows how to solve a real-world problem involving three variables.

Additional Example

3 **SPORTS** There are 49,000 seats in a sports stadium. Tickets for the seats in the upper level sell for \$25, the ones in the middle level cost \$30, and the ones in the bottom level are \$35 each. The number of seats in the middle and bottom levels together equals the number of seats in the upper level. When all of the seats are sold for an event, the total revenue is \$1,520,500. How many seats are there in each level? bottom level: 14,400 seats; middle level: 10,100 seats; upper level: 24,500 seats

Focus on Mathematical Content

Systems in Three Variables To graph equations in three variables, it is necessary to add a third dimension to the coordinate system. Ordered triples such as (x, y, z) represent a point in space just as ordered pairs such as (x, y) represent a point in a plane. The graph of an equation of the form $Ax + By + Cz = D$, where A, B, C, and D are not all equal to zero, is a plane.

Real-World Career

Music Management
Music management involves acting as the talent manager to the artists. Other duties include negotiating with record labels, music promoters, and tour promoters. Managers usually earn a percentage of the artist's income. A bachelor's degree is usually required.

Problem-Solving Tip

Look for a Pattern Looking for a pattern can help to identify a function and write an equation.

EXAMPLE 3 Write and Solve a System of Equations

CONCERTS Refer to the application at the beginning of the lesson. Write and solve a system of equations to determine how many seats are in each section of the amphitheater.

Understand Define the variables.
x = seats in section A
y = seats in section B
z = lawn seats

Plan There are 19,200 seats.
$x + y + z = 19{,}200$ **Equation 1**

The total revenue is \$456,000.
$30x + 25y + 20z = 456{,}000$ **Equation 2**

There are twice as many seats in section B as in section A.
$y = 2x$ **Equation 3**

Solve Solve the system.

Step 1 Substitute $y = 2x$ in the first two equations.

$x + y + z = 19{,}200$ **Equation 1**
$x + 2x + z = 19{,}200$ **$y = 2x$**
$3x + z = 19{,}200$ **Add.**
$30x + 25y + 20z = 456{,}000$ **Equation 2**
$30x + 25(2x) + 20z = 456{,}000$ **$y = 2x$**
$80x + 20z = 456{,}000$ **Simplify.**

Step 2 Solve the system of two equations in two variables.

$3x + z = 19{,}200$ **Multiply by −20.** $-60x - 20z = -384{,}000$
$80x + 20z = 456{,}000$ $(+)\ 80x + 20z = 456{,}000$
$20x = 72{,}000$
$x = 3600$

Step 3 Substitute to find z.

$3x + z = 19{,}200$ **Remaining equation in two variables**
$3(3600) + z = 19{,}200$ **$x = 3600$**
$10{,}800 + z = 19{,}200$ **Distribute.**
$z = 8400$ **Simplify.**

Step 4 Substitute to find y.

$y = 2x$ **Equation 3**
$y = 2(3600)$ or 7200 **$x = 3600$**

The solution is (3600, 7200, 8400). There are 3600 seats in section A, 7200 in section B, and 8400 lawn seats.

Check Substitute the values into either of the first two equations.

Guided Practice

3. Ms. Garza invested \$50,000 in three different accounts. She invested three times as much money in an account that paid 8% interest than an account that paid 10% interest. The third account earned 12% interest. If she earned a total of \$5160 in interest in a year, how much did she invest in each account? **6000 at 10%; 18,000 at 8%; 26,000 at 12%**

Personal Tutor glencoe.com

Differentiated Instruction

AL OL ELL

If some students struggle with solving real-world problems using systems of equations in three variables,

Then pair those students with students that are having success. Encourage students to explain to partners their explorations and plans for solving real-world problems using systems of three equations in three variables. Suggest that the listening partner take notes about the speaking partner's strategies, asking questions as needed for clarification.

170 Chapter 3 Systems of Equations and Inequalities

Check Your Understanding

Examples 1 and 2 pp. 168–169

1. (−2, −3, 5)
2. (4, −6, 1)
3. (−4, 3, 6)
4. (−2, 2, −5)
5. infinite solutions
6. (3, −4, 8)

Solve each system of equations.

1. $-3a - 4b + 2c = 28$; $a + 3b - 4c = -31$; $2a + 3c = 11$
2. $3y - 5z = -23$; $4x + 2y + 3z = 7$; $-2x - y - z = -3$
3. $3x + 6y - 2z = -6$; $2x + y + 4z = 19$; $-5x - 2y + 8z = 62$
4. $-4r - s + 3t = -9$; $3r + 2s - t = 3$; $r + 3s - 5t = 29$
5. $3x + 5y - z = 12$; $-2x - 3y + 5z = 14$; $4x + 7y + 3z = 38$
6. $2a - 3b + 5c = 58$; $-5a + b - 4c = -51$; $-6a - 8b + c = 22$

Example 3 p. 170

7a. $s + d + t = 7$, $d = 2s$, $0.3s + 0.6d + 0.6t = 3.6$

7. **DOWNLOADING** Heather downloaded some television shows. A sitcom uses 0.3 gigabyte of memory; a drama, 0.6 gigabyte; and a talk show, 0.6 gigabyte. She downloaded 7 programs totaling 3.6 gigabytes. There were twice as many episodes of the drama as the sitcom.
   a. Write a system of equations for the number of episodes of each type of show.
   b. How many episodes of each show did she download? **2 sitcoms, 4 dramas, 1 talk show**

● = **Step-by-Step Solutions** begin on page R20. **Extra Practice** begins on page 947.

Practice and Problem Solving

Examples 1 and 2 pp. 168–169

8. (−8, 4, −4)
9. (−3, −2, −4)
10. (8, −3, 2)
11. (−2, −1, 4)
12. no solution
13. infinite solutions
14. (−1, 3, 7)
15. (−4, −1, 6)
16. (−8, −7, −5)
17. no solution
18. (6, 3, −4)
19. infinite solutions

Solve each system of equations.

8. $-5x + y - 4z = 60$; $2x + 4y + 3z = -12$; $6x - 3y - 2z = -52$
9. (●) $4a + 5b - 6c = 2$; $-3a - 2b + 7c = -15$; $-a + 4b + 2c = -13$
10. $-2x + 5y + 3z = -25$; $-4x - 3y - 8z = -39$; $6x + 8y - 5z = 14$
11. $4r + 6s - t = -18$; $3r + 2s - 4t = -24$; $-5r + 3s + 2t = 15$
12. $-2x + 15y + z = 44$; $4x + 3y + 3z = 18$; $-3x + 6y - z = 8$
13. $4x + 2y + 6z = 13$; $-12x + 3y - 5z = 8$; $-4x + 7y + 7z = 34$
14. $8x + 3y + 6z = 43$; $-3x + 5y + 2z = 32$; $5x - 2y + 5z = 24$
15. $-6x - 5y + 4z = 53$; $5x + 3y + 2z = -11$; $8x - 6y + 5z = 4$
16. $-9a + 3b - 2c = 61$; $8a + 7b + 5c = -138$; $5a - 5b + 8c = -45$
17. $2x - y + z = 1$; $x + 2y - 4z = 3$; $4x + 3y - 7z = -8$
18. $x + 2y = 12$; $3y - 4z = 25$; $x + 6y + z = 20$
19. $r - 3s + t = 4$; $3r - 6s + 9t = 5$; $4r - 9s + 10t = 9$

Example 3 p. 170

20b. 7 swimmers placed third, 5 swimmers placed second, and 12 swimmers placed first.
20c. The statement is false because when you solve for second place, you get a negative as an answer and you cannot have a negative person.

20. **SWIMMING** A friend e-mails you the results of a recent high school swim meet. The e-mail states that 24 individuals placed, earning a combined total of 53 points. First place earned 3 points, second place earned 2 points, and third place earned 1 point. There were as many first-place finishers as second- and third-place finishers combined.
    a. Write a system of three equations that represents how many people finished in each place. $x + y + z = 24$, $3x + 2y + z = 53$, $x = y + z$
    b. How many swimmers finished in first place, in second place, and in third place?
    c. Suppose the e-mail had said that the athletes scored a combined total of 47 points. Explain why this statement is false and the solution is unreasonable.

21. (B) **AMUSEMENT PARKS** Nick goes to the amusement park to ride roller coasters, bumper cars, and water slides. The wait for the roller coasters is 1 hour, the wait for the bumper cars is 20 minutes long, and the wait for the water slides is only 15 minutes long. Nick rode 10 total rides during his visit. Because he enjoys roller coasters the most, the number of times he rode the roller coasters was the sum of the times he rode the other two rides. If Nick waited in line for a total of 6 hours and 20 minutes, how many of each ride did he go on? **roller coasters: 5; bumper cars: 1; water slides: 4**

3 PRACTICE

Formative Assessment

Use Exercises 1–7 to check for understanding.

Use the chart at the bottom of this page to customize assignments for your students.

Tips for New Teachers

Using Models Some students have difficulty visualizing situations in three dimensions. Encourage them to use paper, pencils, and other objects to help them model the situations they encounter in the lesson. If you or some of your students have access to computer software that draws models in three dimensions, encourage them to use this tool to demonstrate what happens visually with these systems.

Differentiated Homework Options

Level	Assignment	Two-Day Option	
AL Basic	8–20, 24, 26–42	9–19 odd, 30–33	8–20 even, 24, 26–29, 34–42
OL Core	9–19 odd, 21–24, 26–42	8–20, 30–33	21–24, 26–29, 34–42
BL Advanced	21–38, (optional: 39–42)		

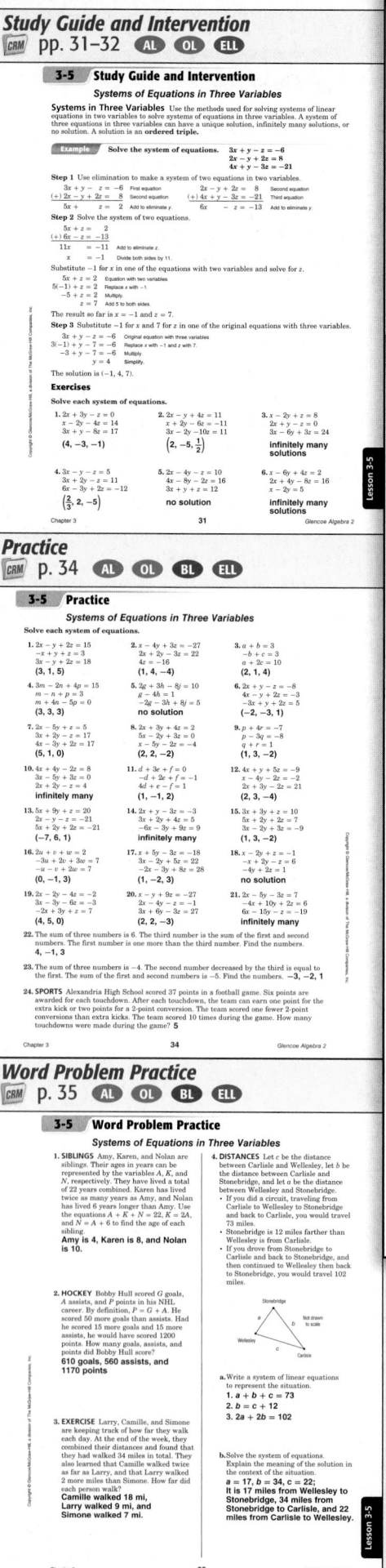

Study Guide and Intervention
CRM pp. 31–32 AL OL ELL

3-5 Study Guide and Intervention
Systems of Equations in Three Variables

Systems in Three Variables Use the methods used for solving systems of linear equations in two variables to solve systems of equations in three variables. A system of three equations in three variables can have a unique solution, infinitely many solutions, or no solution. A solution is an **ordered triple.**

Example **Solve the system of equations.** $3x + y - z = -6$, $2x - y + 2z = 8$, $4x + y - 3z = -21$

Step 1 Use elimination to make a system of two equations in two variables.

$3x + y - z = -6$ First equation
$(+)\ 2x - y + 2z = 8$ Second equation
$5x + z = 2$ Add to eliminate y.

$2x - y + 2z = 8$ Second equation
$(+)\ 4x + y - 3z = -21$ Third equation
$6x - z = -13$ Add to eliminate y.

Step 2 Solve the system of two equations.

$5x + z = 2$
$(+)\ 6x - z = -13$
$11x = -11$ Add to eliminate z.
$x = -1$ Divide both sides by 11.

Substitute -1 for x in one of the equations with two variables and solve for z.

$5x + z = 2$ Equation with two variables
$5(-1) + z = 2$ Replace x with -1.
$-5 + z = 2$ Multiply.
$z = 7$ Add 5 to both sides.

The result so far is $x = -1$ and $z = 7$.

Step 3 Substitute -1 for x and 7 for z in one of the original equations with three variables.

$3x + y - z = -6$ Original equation with three variables
$3(-1) + y - 7 = -6$ Replace x with -1 and z with 7.
$-3 + y - 7 = -6$ Multiply.
$y = 4$ Simplify.

The solution is $(-1, 4, 7)$.

Exercises

Solve each system of equations.

1. $2x + 3y - z = 0$, $x - 2y - 4z = 14$, $3x + y - 8z = 17$ **(4, –3, –1)**
2. $2x - y + 4z = 11$, $x + 2y - 6z = -11$, $3x - 2y - 10z = 11$ **$\left(2, -5, \frac{1}{2}\right)$**
3. $x - 2y + z = 8$, $2x + y - z = 0$, $3x - 6y + 3z = 24$ **infinitely many solutions**
4. $3x - y - z = 5$, $3x + 2y - z = 11$, $6x - 3y + 2z = -12$ **$\left(\frac{2}{3}, 2, -5\right)$**
5. $2x - 4y - z = 10$, $4x - 8y - 2z = 16$, $3x + y + z = 12$ **no solution**
6. $x - 6y + 4z = 2$, $2x + 4y - 8z = 16$, $x - 2y = 5$ **infinitely many solutions**

Lesson 3-5

Chapter 3 31 Glencoe Algebra 2

Practice
CRM p. 34 AL OL BL ELL

3-5 Practice
Systems of Equations in Three Variables

Solve each system of equations.

1. $2x - y + 2z = 15$, $-x + y + z = 3$, $3x - y + 2z = 18$ **(3, 1, 5)**
2. $x - 4y + 3z = -27$, $2x + 2y - 3z = 22$, $4z = -16$ **(1, 4, –4)**
3. $a + b = 3$, $-b + c = 3$, $a + 2c = 10$ **(2, 1, 4)**
4. $3m - 2n + 4p = 15$, $m - n + p = 3$, $m + 4n - 5p = 0$ **(3, 3, 3)**
5. $2g + 3h - 8j = 10$, $g - 4h = 1$, $-2g - 3h + 8j = 5$ **no solution**
6. $2x + y - z = -8$, $4x - y + 2z = -3$, $-3x + y + 2z = 5$ **(–2, –3, 1)**
7. $2x - 5y + z = 5$, $3x + 2y - z = 17$, $4x - 3y + 2z = 17$ **(5, 1, 0)**
8. $2x + 3y + 4z = 2$, $5x - 2y + 3z = 0$, $x - 5y - 2z = -4$ **(2, 2, –2)**
9. $p + 4r = -7$, $p - 3q = -8$, $q + r = 1$ **(1, 3, –2)**
10. $4x + 4y - 2z = 8$, $3x - 5y + 3z = 0$, $2x + 2y - z = 4$ **infinitely many**
11. $d + 3e + f = 0$, $-d + 2e + f = -1$, $4d + e - f = 1$ **(1, –1, 2)**
12. $4x + y + 5z = -9$, $x - 4y - 2z = -2$, $2x + 3y - 2z = 21$ **(2, 3, –4)**
13. $5x + 9y + z = 20$, $2x - y - z = -21$, $5x + 2y + 2z = -21$ **(–7, 6, 1)**
14. $2x + y - 3z = -3$, $3x + 2y + 4z = 5$, $-6x - 3y + 9z = 9$ **infinitely many**
15. $3x + 3y + z = 10$, $5x + 2y + 2z = 7$, $3x - 2y + 3z = -9$ **(1, 3, –2)**
16. $2u + v + w = 2$, $-3u + 2v + 3w = 7$, $-u - v + 2w = 7$ **(0, –1, 3)**
17. $x + 5y - 3z = -18$, $3x - 2y + 5z = 22$, $-2x - 3y + 8z = 28$ **(1, –2, 3)**
18. $x - 2y + z = -1$, $-x + 2y - z = 6$, $-4y + 2z = 1$ **no solution**
19. $2x - 2y - 4z = -2$, $3x - 3y - 6z = -3$, $-2x + 3y + z = 7$ **(4, 5, 0)**
20. $x - y + 9z = -27$, $2x - 4y - z = -1$, $3x + 6y - 3z = 27$ **(2, 2, –3)**
21. $2x - 5y - 3z = 7$, $-4x + 10y + 2z = 6$, $6x - 15y - z = -19$ **infinitely many**

22. The sum of three numbers is 6. The third number is the sum of the first and second numbers. The first number is one more than the third number. Find the numbers. **4, –1, 3**

23. The sum of three numbers is –4. The second number decreased by the third is equal to the first. The sum of the first and second numbers is –5. Find the numbers. **–3, –2, 1**

24. **SPORTS** Alexandria High School scored 37 points in a football game. Six points are awarded for each touchdown. After each touchdown, the team can earn one point for the extra kick or two points for a 2-point conversion. The team scored one fewer 2-point conversions than extra kicks. The team scored 10 times during the game. How many touchdowns were made during the game? **5**

Chapter 3 34 Glencoe Algebra 2

Word Problem Practice
CRM p. 35 AL OL BL ELL

3-5 Word Problem Practice
Systems of Equations in Three Variables

1. **SIBLINGS** Amy, Karen, and Nolan are siblings. Their ages in years can be represented by the variables A, K, and N, respectively. They have lived a total of 22 years combined. Karen has lived twice as many years as Amy, and Nolan has lived 6 years longer than Amy. Use the equations $A + K + N = 22$, $K = 2A$, and $N = A + 6$ to find the age of each sibling.
Amy is 4, Karen is 8, and Nolan is 10.

2. **HOCKEY** Bobby Hull scored G goals, A assists, and P points in his NHL career. By definition, $P = G + A$. He scored 50 more goals than assists. Had he scored 15 more goals and 15 more assists, he would have scored 1200 points. How many goals, assists, and points did Bobby Hull score?
610 goals, 560 assists, and 1170 points

3. **EXERCISE** Larry, Camille, and Simone are keeping track of how far they walk each day. At the end of the week, they combined their distances and found that they had walked 34 miles in total. They also learned that Camille walked twice as far as Larry, and that Larry walked 2 more miles than Simone. How far did each person walk?
Camille walked 18 mi, Larry walked 9 mi, and Simone walked 7 mi.

4. **DISTANCES** Let c be the distance between Carlisle and Wellesley, let b be the distance between Carlisle and Stonebridge, and let a be the distance between Wellesley and Stonebridge.
- If you did a circuit, traveling from Carlisle to Wellesley to Stonebridge and back to Carlisle, you would travel 73 miles.
- Stonebridge is 12 miles farther than Wellesley is from Carlisle.
- If you drove from Stonebridge to Carlisle and back to Stonebridge, and then continued to Wellesley then back to Stonebridge, you would travel 102 miles.

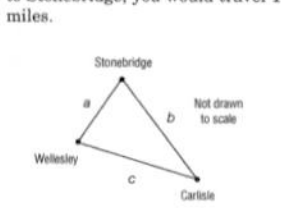

a. Write a system of linear equations to represent the situation.
1. $a + b + c = 73$
2. $b = c + 12$
3. $2a + 2b = 102$

b. Solve the system of equations. Explain the meaning of the solution in the context of the situation.
$a = 17$, $b = 34$, $c = 22$; It is 17 miles from Wellesley to Stonebridge, 34 miles from Stonebridge to Carlisle, and 22 miles from Carlisle to Wellesley.

Lesson 3-5

Chapter 3 35 Glencoe Algebra 2

Real-World Link

Most mechanics would recommend you get an oil change every 6 months and a radiator flush every other year.

Source: *Popular Mechanics*

22. **BUSINESS** Ramón usually gets one of the routine maintenance options at Annie's Garage. Today however, he needs a different combination of work than what is listed.

ANNIE'S GARAGE
ROUTINE MAINTENANCE OPTIONS
1 Oil Change & Radiator Flush $29.99
2 Brake Pads & Oil Change $39.99
3 Oil Change, Radiator Flush & Brake Pads $49.99

a. Assume that the price of an option is the same price as purchasing each item separately. Find the prices for an oil change, a radiator flush, and a brake pad replacement. **oil change: \$19.99; brake pad replacement: \$20; radiator flush: \$10**

b. If Ramón wants his brake pads replaced and his radiator flushed, how much should he plan to spend? **\$30**

23. **FINANCIAL LITERACY** Kate invested \$100,000 in three different accounts. If she invested \$30,000 more in account A than account C and is expected to earn \$6300 in interest, how much did she invest in each account? **A: \$55,000; B: \$20,000; C: \$25,000**

Account	Expected Interest
A	4%
B	8%
C	10%

H.O.T. Problems
Use Higher-Order Thinking Skills

24. **REASONING** Write a system of equations to represent the three rows of figures below. Use the system to find the number of red triangles that will balance one green circle.

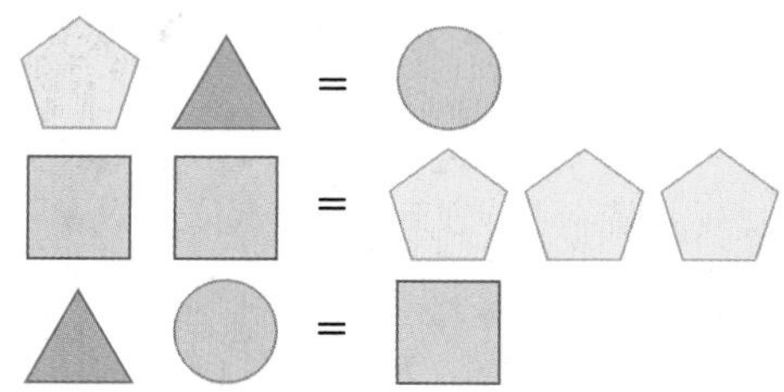

24. $t + c = s$, $p + t = c$, $2s = 3p$ where t represents triangle, c represents circle, s represents square, and p represents pentagon; 5 red triangles

25. **CHALLENGE** The general form of an equation for a parabola is $y = ax^2 + bx + c$, where (x, y) is a point on the parabola. If three points on a parabola are $(2, -10)$, $(-5, -101)$, and $(6, -90)$, determine the values of a, b, and c and write the general form of the equation. **$y = -3x^2 + 4x - 6$; $a = -3$, $b = 4$, $c = -6$**

26. **PROOF** Consider the following system and prove that if $b = c = -a$, then $ty = a$.

$$rx + ty + vz = a$$
$$rx - ty + vz = b$$
$$rx + ty - vz = c$$

See Chapter 3 Answer Appendix.

27. **OPEN ENDED** Write a system of three linear equations that has a solution of $(-5, -2, 6)$. Show that the ordered triple satisfies all three equations. **See margin.**

28. **REASONING** Use the diagrams of solutions of systems of equations on page 167 to consider a system of inequalities in three variables. Describe the solution of such a system. **See margin.**

29. **WRITING IN MATH** Use your knowledge of solving a system of three linear equations with three variables to explain how to solve a system of four equations with four variables. **See Chapter 3 Answer Appendix.**

Enrichment
CRM p. 36 OL BL

3-5 Enrichment

Homogenous Systems

A system of equations is called homogeneous if it is of the form:

$gx + hy + kz = 0$
$dx + ey + fz = 0$
$ax + by + cz = 0$

Homogeneous systems have some unique characteristics that set them apart from general systems of equations. The following exercises will explore some of these unique characteristics.

1. Evaluate the following statement. Is this statement *always*, *sometimes*, or *never* true? Expalin your reasoning.
Every homogeneous system of equations will have at least one trivial solution: (0, 0, 0).
Always; Sample answer: if you replace each variable with 0, you will always get each equation equal to 0.

2. Find a non-trivial solution to the following homogenous system of equations.
$x + y + 5z = 0$
$2x + y + 7z = 0$
$x + 2z = 0$

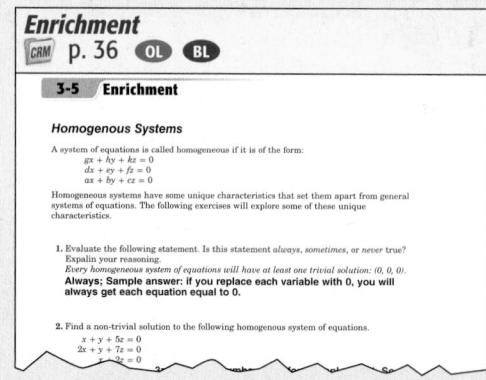

NGSSS PRACTICE 912.A.3.15, 912.A.3.1, 912.A.3.14

30. What is the solution of the system of equations shown below? **B**

$$\begin{cases} x - y + z = 0 \\ -5x + 3y - 2z = -1 \\ 2x - y + 4z = 11 \end{cases}$$

A. (0, 3, 3)
B. (2, 5, 3)
C. no solution
D. infinitely many solutions

31. Which of the following represents a correct procedure for solving each equation? **I**

F. $-3(x - 7) = -16$
$-3x - 21 = -16$
$-3x = 5$
$x = -\frac{5}{3}$

G. $7 - 4x = 3x + 27$
$7 - 7x = 27$
$-7x = -\frac{20}{7}$
$x = 20$

H. $2(x - 4) = 20$
$2x - 8 = 20$
$2x = 12$
$x = 6$

I. $6(2x + 1) = 30$
$12x + 6 = 30$
$12x = 24$
$x = 2$

32. **EXTENDED RESPONSE** Use the graph to find the solution of the systems of equations. Describe one way to check the solution. **See margin.**

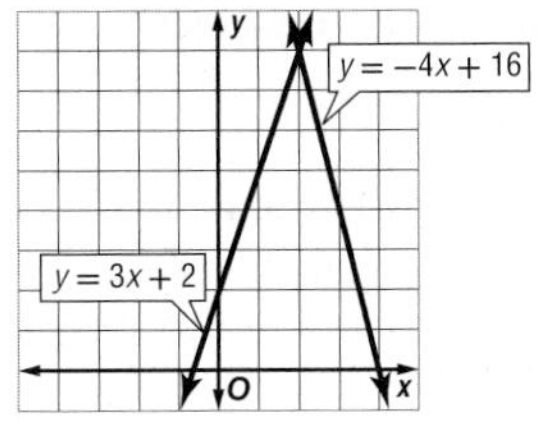

33. ACT/SAT The graph shows which system of equations? **A**

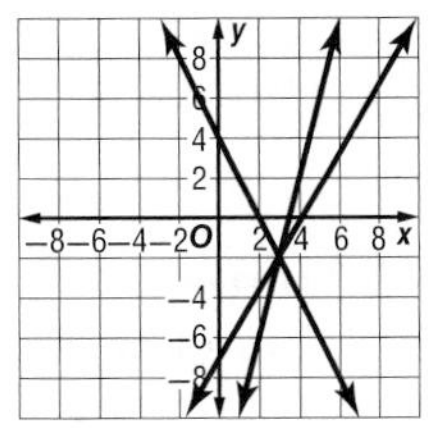

A. $y + 14 = 4x$
$y = 4 - 2x$
$-7 = y - \frac{5}{3}x$

B. $y - 14 = 4x$
$y = 4 + 2x$
$-7 = y + \frac{5}{3}x$

C. $y + 14x = 4$
$-2y = 4 + y$
$-7 = y - \frac{5}{3}x$

D. $y - 14x = 4$
$2x = 4 + y$
$7 = y - \frac{5}{3}x$

Spiral Review

A feasible region has vertices at (−3, 2), (1, 3), (6, 1), and (2, −2). Find the maximum and minimum values of each function. (Lesson 3-4)

34. $f(x, y) = 2x - y$ **11; −8**
35. $f(x, y) = x + 5y$ **16; −8**
36. $f(x, y) = y - 4x$ **14; −23**
37. $f(x, y) = -x + 3y$ **9; −8**

38. SKI CLUB The ski club's budget for the year is $4250. They are able to find skis for $75 per pair and boots for $40 per pair. They know they should buy more boots than skis because the skis are adjustable to several sizes of boots. (Lesson 3-3)

a. Give an example of three different purchases that the ski club can make.

38a. Sample answer: 40 boots, 35 skis; 45 boots, 32 skis; 50 boots, 30 skis

b. Suppose the ski club wants to spend all of its budget. What combination of skis and boots should they buy? Explain. **50 boots and 30 skis cost exactly $4250.**

Skills Review

Solve each system of equations. (Lesson 3-2)

39. $x = y + 5$
$3x + y = 19$ **(6, 1)**

40. $3x - 2y = 1$
$4x + 2y = 20$ **(3, 4)**

41. $5x + 3y = 25$
$4x + 7y = -3$ **(8, −5)**

42. $y = x - 7$
$2x - 8y = 2$ **(9, 2)**

Differentiated Instruction BL

Extension Ask students to write the various ways that three planes can intersect, explaining what will occur when solving the system of equations in three variables in each situation.

4 ASSESS

Name the Math Have students name the four steps they used in solving problems involving three variables.

Formative Assessment

Check for student understanding of the concepts in Lesson 3-5.

CRM Quiz 4, p. 40

Additional Answers

27. Sample answer:

$$3x + 4y + z = -17$$
$$3(-5) + 4(-2) + 6 = -17$$
$$-15 + (-8) + 6 = -17$$
$$-23 + 6 = -17$$
$$2x - 5y - 3z = -18$$
$$2(-5) - 5(-2) - 3(6) = -18$$
$$-10 + 10 - 18 = -18$$
$$-18 = -18$$
$$-x + 3y + 8z = 47$$
$$-(-5) + 3(-2) + 8(6) = 47$$
$$5 - 6 + 48 = 47$$
$$-1 + 48 = 47$$

28. Sample answer: The solution of an inequality in 3 variables would be the region of space on one side or the other of a plane, with the plane included if the inequality is $\leq$ or $\geq$. The solution of a system of inequalities in 3 variables would be the intersection of the regions of space that are solutions to the individual inequalities in the system.

32. (2, 8); Sample answer: You can substitute (2, 8) into each of the equations and make sure the equations are true.

Formative Assessment

Key Vocabulary The page references after each word denote where that term was first introduced. If students have difficulty answering questions 1–10, remind them that they can use these page references to refresh their memories about the vocabulary.

Summative Assessment

CRM Vocabulary Test, p. 42

FL Math Online glencoe.com

Vocabulary PuzzleMaker improves students' mathematics vocabulary using four puzzle formats–crossword, scramble, word search using a word list, and word search using clues. Students can work online or from a printed worksheet.

FL Math Online glencoe.com
- STUDY TO GO
- Vocabulary Review

Chapter Summary

Key Concepts

Systems of Equations (Lessons 3-1 and 3-2)

- The solution of a system of equations can be found by graphing the two equations and determining at what point they intersect.
- In the substitution method, one equation is solved for a variable and substituted to find the value of another variable.
- In the elimination method, one variable is eliminated by adding or subtracting the equations.

Systems of Inequalities (Lesson 3-3)

- The solution of a system of inequalities is found by graphing the inequalities and determining the intersection of the graphs.

Linear Programming (Lesson 3-4)

- Finding maximum or minimum values of a function over a given system of inequalities with each inequality representing a constraint.
- To optimize means to seek the optimal price or amount that is desired to minimize costs or maximize profits.

Systems of Equations in Three Variables (Lesson 3-5)

- A system of equations in three variables can be solved algebraically by using the substitution method or the elimination method.

FOLDABLES® Study Organizer

Be sure the Key Concepts are noted in your Foldable.

Key Vocabulary

bounded (p. 160)
break-even point (p. 136)
consistent (p. 137)
constraints (p. 160)
dependent (p. 137)
elimination method (p. 144)
feasible region (p. 160)
inconsistent (p. 137)
independent (p. 137)
linear programming (p. 160)
optimize (p. 162)
ordered triple (p. 167)
substitution method (p. 143)
system of equations (p. 135)
system of inequalities (p. 151)
unbounded (p. 160)

Vocabulary Check

Choose the term from the list above to complete each sentence. 2. elimination method

1. ________ is a method for finding maximum or minimum values of a function over a given system of inequalities with each inequality representing a constraint. linear programming
2. The ________ is an algebraic method for solving systems of linear equations that eliminates a variable by adding or subtracting the equations.
3. A system of equations is ________ if it has at least one solution. consistent
4. To ________ means to seek the best price or profit using linear programming. optimize
5. A feasible region that is open and can go on forever is called ________. unbounded
6. The ________ is the point at which the income equals the cost. break-even point
7. A system of equations is ________ if it has an infinite number of solutions. dependent
8. A(n) ________ is two or more equations with the same variables. system of equations
9. A system of equations is ________ if it has no solutions. inconsistent
10. To solve a system of equations by the ________, solve one equation for one variable in terms of the other. Then substitute in the other equation. substitution method

FOLDABLES® Study Organizer

Dinah Zike's Foldables®

Have students look through the chapter to make sure they have included examples in their Foldables.

Suggest that students keep their Foldables handy while completing the Study Guide and Review pages. Point out that their Foldables can serve as a quick review tool when studying for the chapter test.

MIXED PROBLEM SOLVING
For mixed problem-solving practice, see page 981.

Lesson-by-Lesson Review

3-1 Solving Systems of Equations by Graphing (pp. 135–141)

912.A.3.14, 912.A.3.15

Solve each system of equations by graphing.

11. $3x + 4y = 8$ (0, 2)
$x - 3y = -6$

12. $x + \frac{8}{3}y = 12$
$\frac{1}{2}x + \frac{4}{3}y = 6$

13. $y - 3x = 13$ (−3, 4)
$y = \frac{1}{3}x + 5$

14. $6x - 14y = 5$
$3x - 7y = 5$

15. **LAWN CARE** André and Paul each mow lawns. André charges a \$30 service fee and \$10 per hour. Paul charges a \$10 service fee and \$15 per hour. After how many hours will André and Paul charge the same amount? 4 hours

EXAMPLE 1

Solve the system of equations by graphing.
$x + y = 4 \qquad x + 2y = 5$

Graph both equations on the coordinate plane.

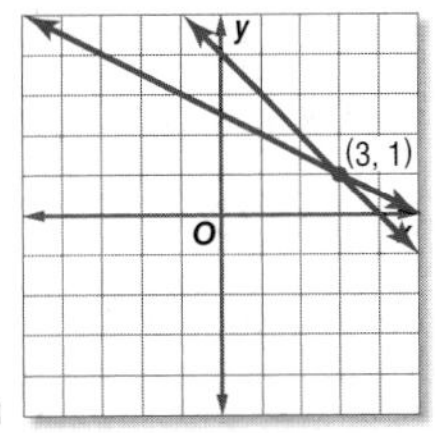

The solution of the system is (3, 1).

12. infinitely many solutions 14. no solution

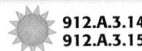

3-2 Solving Systems of Equations Algebraically (pp. 143–150)

912.A.3.14, 912.A.3.15

Solve each system of equations by using either substitution or elimination. 18. (5.25, −1.75)

16. $x + y = 6$ (2, 4)
$3x - 2y = -2$

17. $5x - 2y = 4$ (−2, −7)
$-2y + x = 12$

18. $x + y = 3.5$
$x - y = 7$

19. $3y - 5x = 0$ (3, 5)
$2y - 4x = -2$

20. **SCHOOL SUPPLIES** At an office supply store, Emilio bought 3 notebooks and 5 pens for \$13.75. If a notebook costs \$1.25 more than a pen, how much does a notebook cost? How much does a pen cost? notebook: \$2.50; pen: \$1.25

EXAMPLE 2

Solve the system of equations by using either substitution or elimination.
$3x + 2y = 1 \qquad y = -x + 1$

Substitute $-x + 1$ for y in the first equation. Then solve for y.

$$\begin{aligned} 3x + 2y &= 1 \\ 3x + 2(-x + 1) &= 1 \\ 3x - 2x + 2 &= 1 \\ x + 2 &= 1 \\ x &= -1 \end{aligned}$$

$$\begin{aligned} y &= -x + 1 \\ &= -(-1) + 1 \text{ or } 2 \end{aligned}$$

The solution is (−1, 2).

3-3 Solving Systems of Inequalities by Graphing (pp. 151–157)

912.A.3.14, 912.A.3.15

Solve each system of inequalities by graphing.

21. $y < 2x - 3$
$y \geq 4$

22. $|y| > 2$
$x > 3$

23. $y \geq x + 3$
$2y \leq x - 5$

24. $y > x + 1$
$x < -2$

25. **JEWELRY** Payton makes jewelry to sell at her mother's clothing store. She spends no more than 3 hours making jewelry on Saturdays. It takes her 15 minutes to set up her supplies and 25 minutes to make each bracelet. Draw a graph that represents this.
21–25. See margin.

EXAMPLE 3

Solve the system of inequalities by graphing.
$y \geq \frac{3}{2}x - 3$
$y < 4 - 2x$

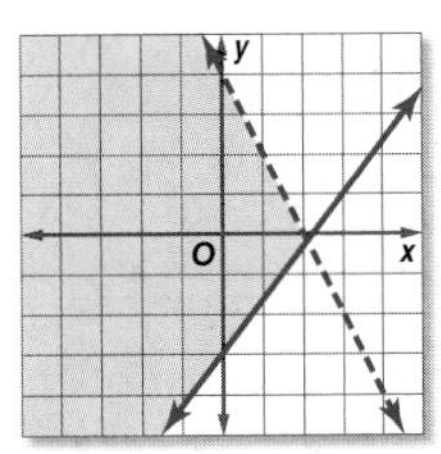

The solution of the system is the region that satisfies both inequalities. The solution of this system is the shaded region.

Lesson-by-Lesson Review

Intervention If the given examples are not sufficient to review the topics covered by the questions, remind students that the page references tell them where to review that topic in their textbooks.

Two-Day Option Have students complete the Lesson-by-Lesson Review on pp. 175–176. Then you can use ExamView® Assessment Suite to customize another review worksheet that practices all the objectives of this chapter or only the objectives on which your students need more help.

Differentiated Instruction

Super DVD: Mindjogger Videoquizzes
Use this DVD as an alternative format of review for the test.

Additional Answers

21.
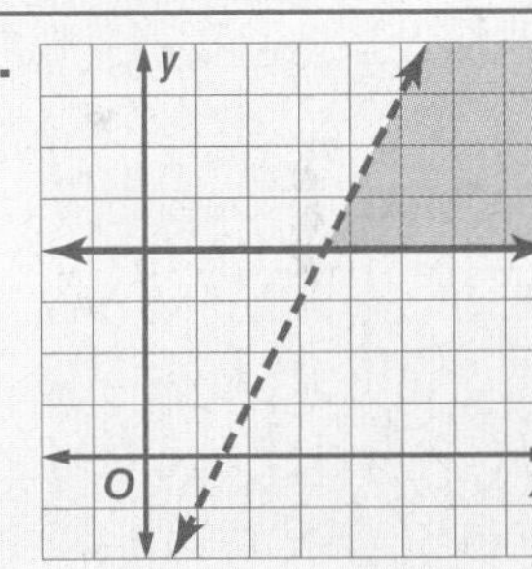

22.
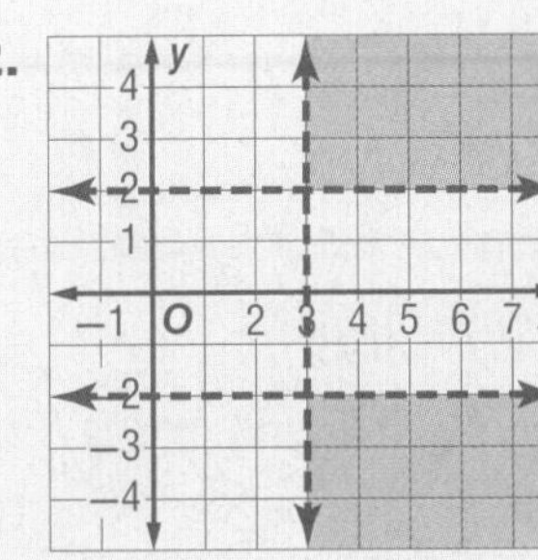

23.
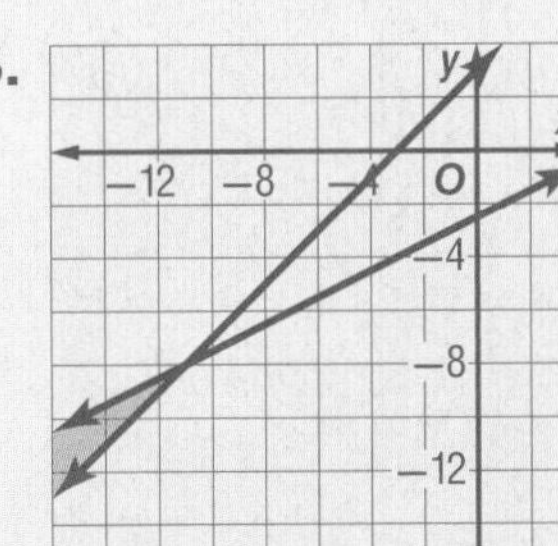

24.
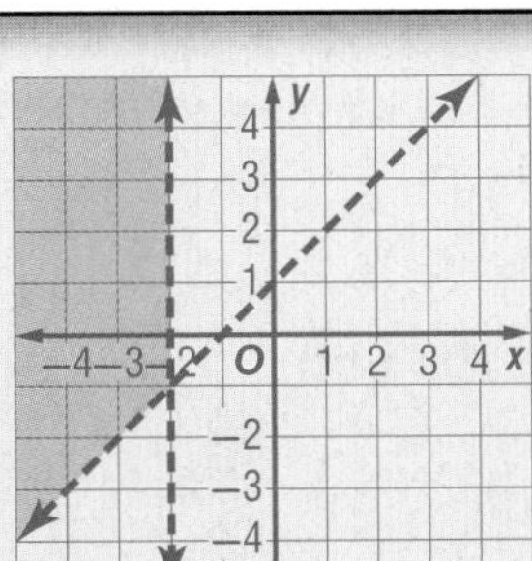

25.
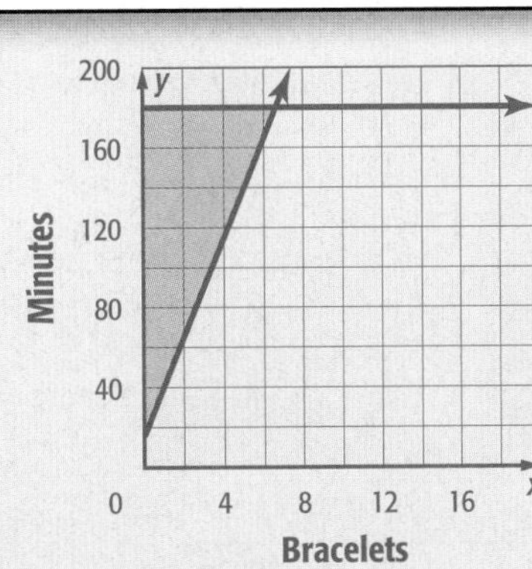

Problem Solving Review

For additional practice in problem solving for Chapter 3, see the Mixed Problem Solving Appendix, p. 982, in the Student Handbook section.

Anticipation Guide

Have students complete the Chapter 3 Anticipation Guide and discuss how their responses have changed now that they have completed Chapter 3.

Additional Answers (Practice Test)

5. 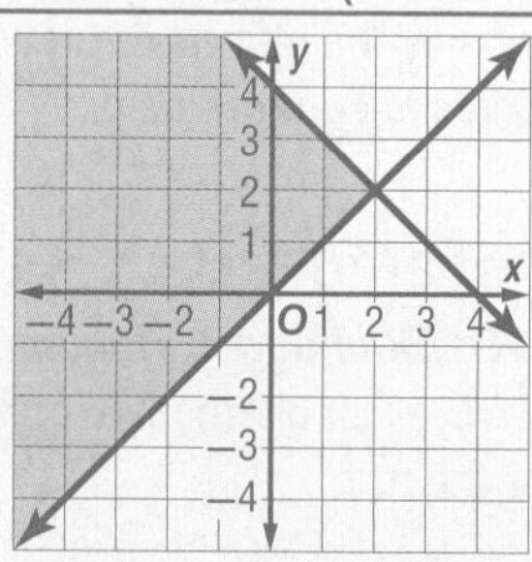

6. 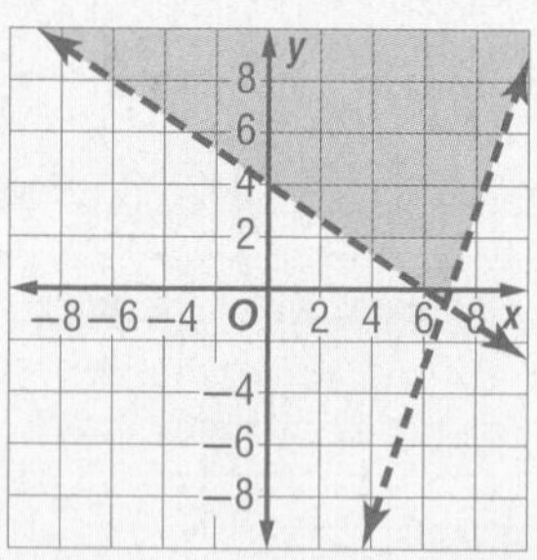

7. 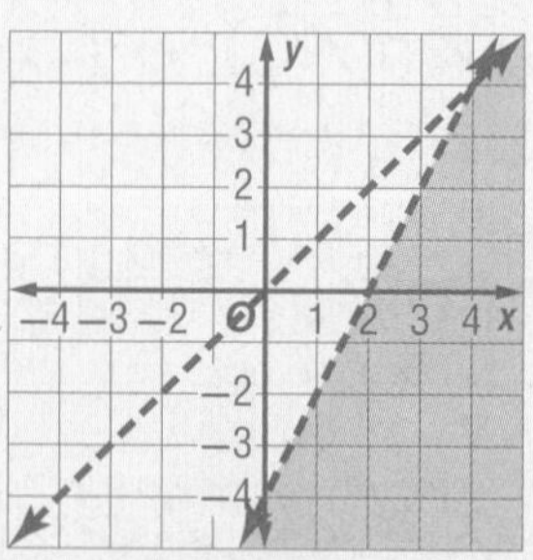

8. 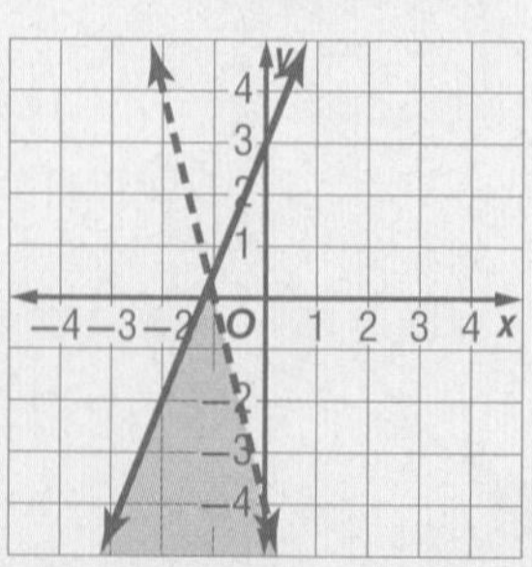

15a. $c \geq 0; t \geq 0; 3c + 2t \leq 108; 0.5c + t \leq 20$

15b. 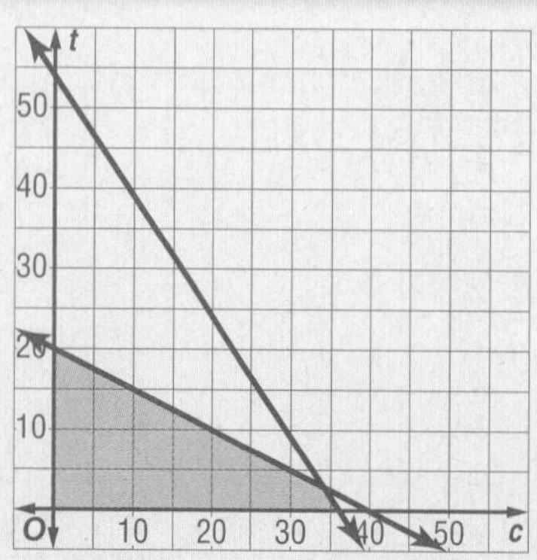

15c. 34 chairs and 3 tables will give a maximum profit of $955

CHAPTER 3 Study Guide and Review

3-4 Linear Programming (pp. 160–166)

912.A.3.14, 912.A.3.15

26. FLOWERS A florist can make a grand arrangement in 18 minutes or a simple arrangement in 10 minutes. The florist makes at least twice as many of the simple arrangements as the grand arrangements. The florist can work only 40 hours per week. The profit on the simple arrangements is $10 and the profit on the grand arrangements is $25. Find the number and type of arrangements that the florist should produce to maximize profit. **126 simple and 63 grand**

27. MANUFACTURING A shoe manufacturer makes outdoor and indoor soccer shoes. There is a two-step process for both kinds of shoes. Each pair of outdoor shoes requires 2 hours in step one and 1 hour in step two, and produces a profit of $20. Each pair of indoor shoes requires 1 hour in step one and 3 hours in step 2, and produces a profit of $15. The company has 40 hours of labor available per day for step one and 60 hours available for step two. What is the manufacturer's maximum profit? What is the combination of shoes for this profit? **$480; 12 outdoor, 16 indoor**

EXAMPLE 4

A gardener is planting two types of herbs in a 5184-square-inch garden. Herb A requires 6 square inches of space, and herb B requires 24 square inches of space. The gardener will plant no more than 300 plants. If herb A can be sold for $8 and herb B can be sold for $12, how many of each herb should be sold to maximize income?

Let a = the number of herb A and b = the number of herb B.

$a \geq 0, b \geq 0,$
$6a + 24b \leq 5184,$
and $a + b \leq 300$

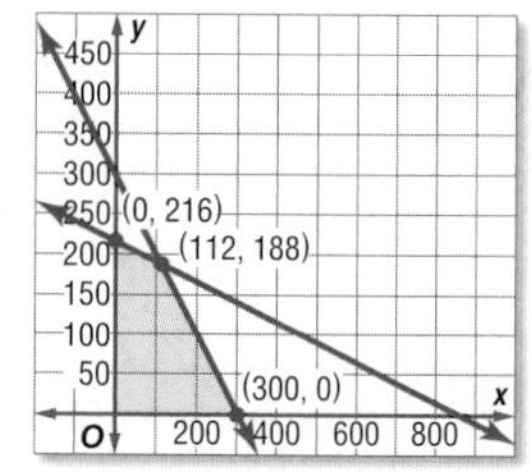

Graph the inequalities. The vertices of the feasible region are (0, 0), (300, 0), (0, 216), and (112, 188).

The profit function is $f(a, b) = 8a + 12b$.

The maximum value of $3152 occurs at (112, 188). So the gardener should plant 112 of herb A and 188 of herb B.

3-5 Solving Systems of Equations in Three Variables (pp. 167–173)

912.A.3.14, 912.A.3.15

Solve each system of equations.

28. $a - 4b + c = 3$
$b - 3c = 10$
$3b - 8c = 24$
(−23, −8, −6)

29. $2x - z = 14$
$3x - y + 5z = 0$
$4x + 2y + 3z = -2$
(5, −5, −4)

30. AMUSEMENT PARKS Dustin, Luis, and Marci went to an amusement park. They purchased snacks from the same vendor. Their snacks and how much they paid are listed in the table. How much did each snack cost?

Name	Hot Dogs	Popcorn	Soda	Price
Dustin	1	2	3	$15.25
Luis	2	0	3	$14.00
Marci	1	2	1	$10.25

hot dog: $3.25; popcorn: $2.25; soda: $2.50

EXAMPLE 5

Solve the system of equations. $x + y + 2z = 6$
$2x + 5z = 12$
$x + 2y + 3z = 9$

$2x + 2y + 4z = 12$ **Equation 1 ×2**
$(-)\ x + 2y + 3z = 9$ **Equation 3**
$x + z = 3$ **Subtract.**

Solve the system of two equations.

$2x + 5z = 12$ **Equation 1**
$(-)\ 2x + 2z = 6$ **2 × (x + z = 3)**
$3z = 6$ **Subtract.**
$z = 2$ **Divide each side by 2.**

Substitute 2 for z in one of the equations with two variables, and solve for y. Then, substitute 2 for z and the value you got for y into an equation from the original system to solve for x.

The solution is (1, 1, 2).

FL Math Online glencoe.com
Chapter Test

Solve each system of equations.

1. $2x - 3y = 9$ $4x + 3y = 9$ **(3, −1)**
2. $x + 2y = 7$ $y = 5x - 2$ **(1, 3)**
3. $-x + y = 2$ $4x - 3y = -3$ **(3, 5)**
4. $\frac{1}{2}x + \frac{1}{3}y = 7$ $\frac{1}{5}x - \frac{2}{3}y = -2$ **(10, 6)**

5–8. See margin.

Solve each system of inequalities by graphing.

5. $x + y \leq 4$ $y \geq x$
6. $2x + 3y > 12$ $3x - y < 21$
7. $x - y > 0$ $4 + y \leq 2x$
8. $2y - 5x \leq 6$ $4x + y < -4$

9. **NGSSS PRACTICE** Which statement best describes the graphs of the two equations? **A**

$$x + 4y = 8$$
$$3x + 12y = 2$$

A. The lines are parallel.

B. The lines are the same.

C. The lines intersect in only one point.

D. The lines intersect in more than one point, but are not the same.

Solve each system of equations.

10. $x - 2y + 3z = 1$ $4y - 4z = 12$ $8y - 14z = 0$ **(3, 7, 4)**
11. $x + y + z = 4$ $x + 3y + 3z = 10$ $2x + y - z = 3$ **(1, 2, 1)**
12. $2x - y - 2z = 5$ $10x + 8z = -4$ $3x - y = 1$ **(2, 5, −3)**
13. $2x + 3y + z = 0$ $3x + y = 1$ $x - 2y + z = 9$ **(1, −2, 4)**

14. **NGSSS PRACTICE** Seela rented a raft from River Rafter's Inc. She paid $100 to rent the raft and $25 for each hour. Martin rented a raft from Oscar's Outdoor Shop. He paid $50 to rent the raft and $35 per hour. For what number of hours will both rafting companies charge the same amount? **H**

F. 0

G. 4

H. 5

I. 10

15. **CARPENTRY** Cal's Carpentry makes tables and chairs. The process involves some carpentry time and some finishing time. The carpentry times and finishing times are listed in the table below.

Product	Carpentry Time (hr)	Finishing Time (hr)
chair	3	0.5
table	2	1

Cal's Carpentry can work for a maximum of 108 carpentry hours and 20 finishing hours per day. The profit is $35 for a table and $25 for a chair. How many tables and chairs should be made each day to maximize profit?

a. Using c for the number of chairs and t for the number of tables, write a system of inequalities to represent this situation. **a–c. See margin.**

b. Draw the graph showing the feasible region.

c. Determine the number of tables and chairs that need to be made to maximize profit. What is the maximum profit?

16. **DRAMA** On opening night of the drama club's play, they made $1366. They sold a total of 199 tickets. They charged $8.50 for each adult ticket and $5.00 for each child's ticket. Write a system of equations that can be used to find the number of adult tickets and the number of children's tickets sold. **$a + c = 199$, $8.50a + 5.00c = 1366$**

Graph each system of inequalities. Name the coordinates of the vertices of the feasible region. Find the maximum and the minimum values of the given function. **17, 18. See margin.**

17. $5 \geq y \geq -3$ $4x + y \leq 5$ $-2x + y \leq 5$ $f(x, y) = 4x - 3y$
18. $x \geq -10$ $1 \geq y \geq -6$ $3x + 4y \leq -8$ $2y \geq x - 10$ $f(x, y) = 2x + y$

19a. $a = 11$ in., $b = 10$ in., $c = 27$ in.

19. **GEOMETRY** An isosceles trapezoid has shorter base of measure a, longer base of measure c, and congruent legs of measure b. The perimeter of the trapezoid is 58 inches. The average of the bases is 19 inches and the longer base is twice the leg plus 7.

a. Find the lengths of the sides of the trapezoid.

b. Find the area of the trapezoid. **114 in^2**

CHAPTER 3 Practice Test

ExamView Assessment Suite Customize and create multiple versions of your chapter tests and their answer keys. All of the questions from the leveled chapter tests in the *Chapter 3 Resource Masters* are also available on ExamView® Assessment Suite.

Additional Answers (Practice Test)

17. vertices: (–4, –3), (0, 5), (2, –3); max: $f(2, -3) = 17$; min: $f(0, 5) = -15$

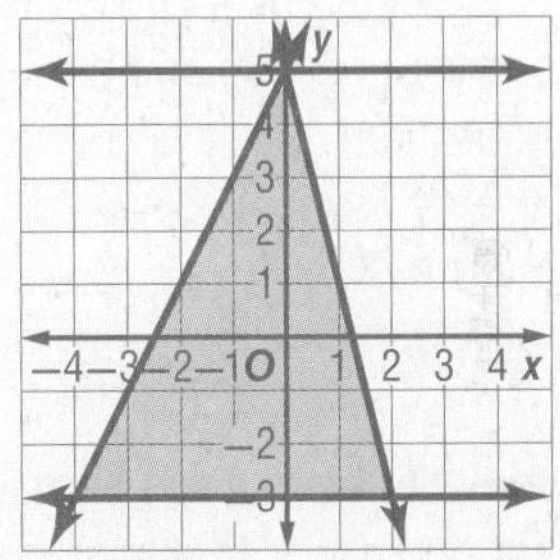

18. vertices: (–10, 1), (–4, 1), (2.4, –3.8), (–2, –6), (–10, –6); max: $f(2.4, -3.8) = 1$; min: $f(-10, -6) = -26$

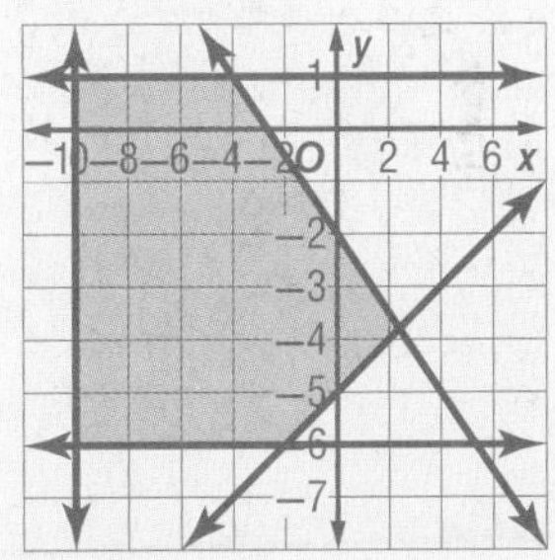

Intervention Planner

Tier 1 On Level	Tier 2 Strategic Intervention approaching grade level	Tier 3 Intensive Intervention 2 or more grades below level
If students miss about 25% of the exercises or less,	**If** students miss about 50% of the exercises,	**If** students miss about 75% of the exercises,
Then choose a resource: **SE** Lessons 3-1, 3-2, 3-3, 3-4, and 3-5; **CRM** Skills Practice, pp. 7, 14, 20, 26, and 33; **TE** Chapter Project, p. 132; FL Math Online Self-Check Quiz	**Then** choose a resource: **CRM** Study Guide and Intervention, Chapter 3, pp. 5, 12, 18, 24, and 31; FL Math Online Extra Examples, Personal Tutor, Homework Help	**Then** use *Math Triumphs, Alg. 2,* Ch. 3; FL Math Online Extra Examples, Personal Tutor, Homework Help, Review Vocabulary

1 FOCUS

Objective Use the strategy of short answer questions to solve standardized test problems.

2 TEACH

Scaffolding Questions

Ask:

- What is the difference between a short answer question and a multiple choice question? Sample answer: A short answer question does not provide a list of possible answers to choose from. The answer must be written.
- Have you ever been given partial credit for an answer to a short answer question? If so, explain how the partial credit might be determined. Sample answer: giving the correct number but the wrong label, giving an answer but not showing an explanation or the steps in the solution

Short Answer Questions

Short answer questions require you to provide a solution to the problem, along with a method, explanation, and/or justification used to arrive at the solution.

Strategies for Solving Short Answer Questions

Step 1

Short answer questions are typically graded using a **rubric**, or a scoring guide. The following is an example of a short answer question scoring rubric.

Scoring Rubric

Criteria	Score
Full Credit: The answer is correct and a full explanation is provided that shows each step.	2
Partial Credit: • The answer is correct but the explanation is incomplete. • The answer is incorrect but the explanation is correct.	1
No Credit: Either an answer is not provided or the answer does not make sense.	0

Step 2

In solving short answer questions, remember to…

- explain your reasoning or state your approach to solving the problem.
- show all of your work or steps.
- check your answer if time permits.

NGSSS PRACTICE EXAMPLE

Read the problem. Identify what you need to know. Then use the information in the problem to solve.

> Company A charges a monthly fee of $14.50 plus $0.05 per minute for cell phone service. Company B charges $20.00 per month plus $0.04 per minute. For what number of minutes would the total monthly charge be the same with each company?

Read the problem carefully. You are given information about two different cell phone companies and their monthly charges. Since the situation involves a fixed amount and a variable rate, you can set up and solve a system of equations.

Example of a 2-point response:

Set up and solve a system of equations.

flat fee + rate × minutes = total charges
y = total charges, x = minutes used

$y = 14.5 + 0.05x$ (Company A)
$y = 20 + 0.04x$ (Company B)

Solve the system by graphing.

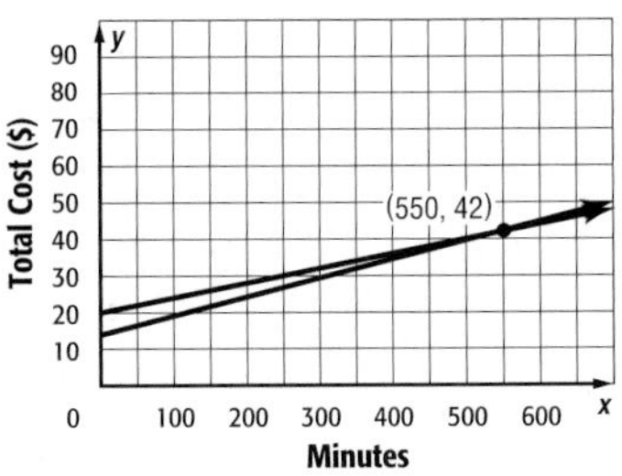

The solution is (550, 42). So, with each company, if the customer uses 550 minutes the total monthly charge is $42.

The steps, calculations, and reasoning are clearly stated. The student also arrives at the correct answer. So, this response is worth the full 2 points.

3. Sample answer: 4 brushes and 4 pencils, 5 brushes and 4 pencils, 6 brushes and 3 pencils

Exercises

Read each problem. Eliminate any unreasonable answers. Then use the information in the problem to solve.

1. Shawn and Jerome borrowed $1400 to start a lawn mowing business. They charge their customers $45 per lawn, and with each lawn that they mow, they incur $10.50 in operating expenses. How many lawns must they mow in order to start earning a profit? **41**

2. A circle of radius r is circumscribed about a square. What is the exact ratio of the area of the circle to the area of the square? $\frac{\pi}{2}$

3. Mr. Williams can spend no more than $50 on art supplies. Packages of paint brushes cost $4.75 each, and boxes of colored pencils cost $6.50 each. He wants to buy at least 2 packages of each supply. Write a system of inequalities and plot the feasible region on a coordinate grid. Give three different solutions to the system.

4. Marla sells engraved necklaces over the Internet. She purchases 50 necklaces for $400, and it costs her an additional $3 for each personalized engraving. If she charges $20 for each necklace, how many will she need to sell in order to make a profit of at least $225? **39**

Additional Example

Samuel borrowed $35 to purchase a used graphing calculator. He charges $9 an hour to tutor others on how to use a graphing calculator. He tutors only one client for one hour per day at the community library. He spends $2 for parking at the library. How many hours must he tutor to make a profit?

Set up and solve a system of equations.

Let x = the number of hours tutoring, and let y = number of dollars.

Total Income	Total Cost
$9x = y$	$2x + 35 = y$

Solve the system by graphing:

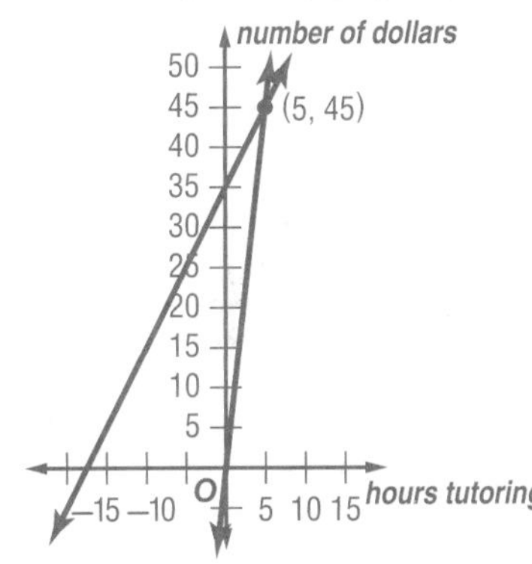

The solution is (5, 45). This is the break-even point. If Samuel tutors more than 5 hours, he will make money.

3 ASSESS

Use Exercises 1–4 to assess students' understanding.

Diagnose Student Errors

Survey student responses for each item. Class trends may indicate common errors and misconceptions.

1. A. correct
   B. did not graph the equations correctly
   C. did not use the process of elimination correctly
   D. guess
2. F. read the x-coordinate incorrectly
   G. reversed the x- and y-coordinates
   H. correct
   I. read the y-coordinate incorrectly
4. A. shaded both inequalities incorrectly
   B. shaded the second inequality incorrectly
   C. correct
   D. shaded the first inequality incorrectly
5. F. error in calculating
   G. error in calculating
   H. error in calculating
   I. correct
8. A. miscalculated the cost per inch of pizza
   B. correct
   C. miscalculated the cost per inch of pizza
   D. miscalculated the cost per inch of pizza
9. F. correct
   G. reversed the p and j in the second equation
   H. wrote the sum of the two items incorrectly
   I. guess
11. A. found a value that is a vertex
    B. correct
    C. found a value that is a vertex
    D. found a value that is a vertex

CHAPTER 3 NGSSS Practice

Cumulative, Chapters 1 through 3

Read each question. Then fill in the correct answer on the answer document provided by your teacher or on a sheet of paper.

1. Use the system of equations shown below.

$$8x - 2y = -18$$
$$-5x + 3y = 20$$

Which ordered pair is the solution of the system of linear equations? **A**

A. $(-1, 5)$

B. $\left(\frac{1}{2}, -4\right)$

C. $\left(-3, -\frac{2}{3}\right)$

D. $(-2, 2)$

2. What is the solution of the system of equations graphed below? **H**

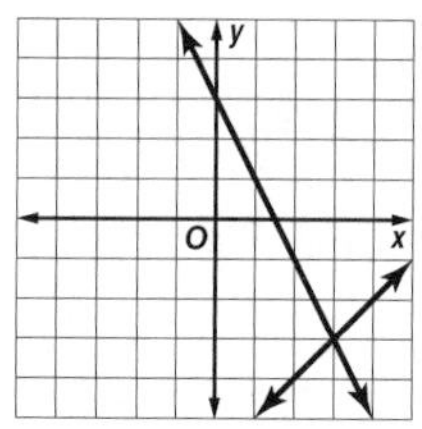

F. $(-3, -3)$

G. $(-3, 3)$

H. $(3, -3)$

I. $(3, 3)$

3. **GRIDDED RESPONSE** Miranda traveled half of her trip by train. She then traveled one fourth of the rest of the distance by bus. She rented a car and drove the remaining 120 miles. How many miles away was her destination? **320**

Test-TakingTip

Question 1 If time is short, you can test each possible answer choice in the equations to find the correct answer. This might be faster than solving the system algebraically.

4. Which region represents the solution of the system of inequalities below? **C**

$y \leq \frac{1}{2}x - 2$

$y \leq -\frac{2}{3}x - 1$

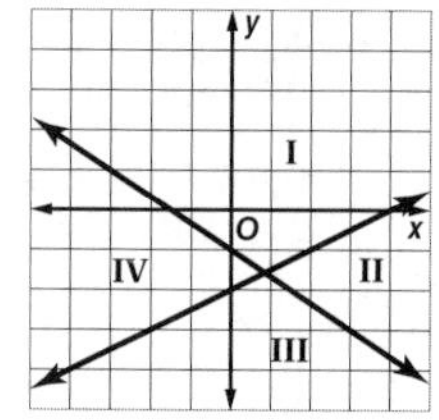

A. Region I

B. Region II

C. Region III

D. Region IV

5. A bakery sells cookies, doughnuts, and bagels. Cindy bought 3 cookies, 2 doughnuts, and 1 bagel for \$4.84. Andrew bought 10 cookies, 12 doughnuts, and 6 bagels for \$25.12. Linda bought 12 doughnuts and 10 bagels for \$27.38. How much does a doughnut cost? **I**

F. \$0.49 H. \$0.69

G. \$0.59 I. \$0.79

6. **SHORT RESPONSE** Which of the following terms does *not* describe the system of equations graphed below: consistent, dependent, independent, or intersecting? **dependent**

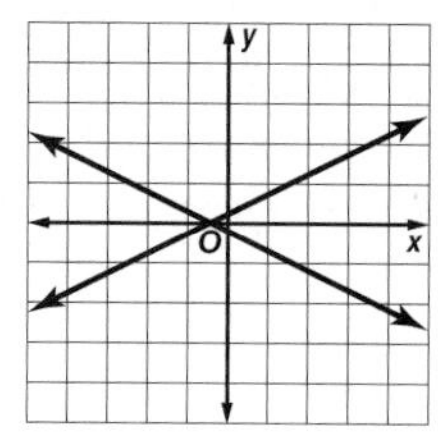

7. **GRIDDED RESPONSE** Heather is starting a small business giving tennis lessons on the weekends and evenings. Considering equipment expenses, travel, and court rental fees, she determines that the cost of running her business will be represented by the function $C(x) = 25x + 345$. The function C represents her cost, in dollars, when she has x clients taking lessons. Heather's income from giving lessons is given by the function $I(x) = 50x - 105$. How many clients will Heather need in order to break even? **18**

180 Chapter 3 Systems of Equations and Inequalities

10a. Sample answer: He has a sign error when he combines the equations; $12 + (-19) = -7$, not 7.

8. The table at the right shows the cost of a pizza depending on the diameter of the pizza.

Diameter (in.)	Cost ($)
6	5.00
10	8.10
15	11.70
20	15.00

Which conclusion can be made based on the information in the table? B

A. A 12-inch would be less than \$9.00.

B. A 24-inch would be less than \$18.00.

C. An 18-inch would be more than \$13.70.

D. An 8-inch would be less than \$6.00.

9. Marilyn bought a pair of jeans and a sweater at her favorite clothing store. She spent \$120, not including tax. If the price of the sweater p was \$12 less than twice the cost of the jeans j, which system of linear equations could be used to determine the price of each item? F

F. $j + p = 120$
$p = 2j - 12$

G. $j + p = 120$
$j = 2p - 12$

H. $j + 120 = p$
$p = 2j - 12$

I. $j + p = 12$
$p = 2j - 120$

10. THINK SOLVE EXPLAIN **SHORT RESPONSE** Julio is solving the system of equations $8x - 2y = 12$ and $-15x + 2y = -19$ by using elimination. His work is shown below.

$$\begin{aligned} 8x - 2y &= 12 \\ -15x + 2y &= -19 \\ \hline -7x &= 7 \\ x &= -1 \end{aligned} \qquad \begin{aligned} 8x - 2y &= 12 \\ 8(-1) - 2y &= 12 \\ -8 - 2y &= 12 \\ -2y &= 20 \\ y &= -10 \end{aligned}$$

The solution is $(-1, -10)$.

a. What error does Julio make?

b. What is the correct solution of the system of equations? Show your work. $(1, -2)$

11. Which of the following points is ***not*** a vertex of the feasible region for the system of linear inequalities below? B

$$x \geq 0, y \geq 0$$
$$y \leq -2x + 6$$

A. (0, 0)

B. (0, 3)

C. (0, 6)

D. (3, 0)

12. THINK SOLVE EXPLAIN **SHORT RESPONSE** Write the equation of the line, in slope-intercept form, that passes through the points (0, 2) and (2, 0). $y = -x + 2$

13b. See students' graphs; (0, 0), (0, 8), (7.5, 0), (7, 1)

13. THINK SOLVE EXPLAIN **EXTENDED RESPONSE** Suppose Tonya is baking cookies and muffins for a bake sale. Each tray of cookies uses 5 cups of flour and 2 cups of sugar. Each tray of muffins uses 5 cups of flour and 1 cup of sugar. She has 40 cups of flour and 15 cups of sugar available for baking. Tonya will make \$12 profit for each tray of cookies that is sold and \$8 profit for each tray of muffins sold.

a. Let x represent the number of trays of cookies baked, and let y represent the number of trays of muffins baked. Write a system of inequalities to model the different number of trays Tonya can bake. $x \geq 0$, $y \geq 0$, $5x + 5y \leq 40$, $2x + y \leq 15$

b. Graph the system of inequalities to show the feasible region. List the coordinates of the vertices of the feasible region.

c. Write a profit function for selling x trays of cookies and y trays of muffins. $P = 12x + 8y$

d. How any trays of cookies and muffins should Tonya bake to maximize the profit? What will the total profit be? 7 trays of cookies and 1 tray of muffins; \$92

Need Extra Help?

If you missed Question...	1	2	3	4	5	6	7	8	9	10	11	12	13
Go to Lesson or Page...	3-2	3-1	2-4	3-3	3-5	3-1	3-3	1-3	2-4	3-2	3-4	2-3	3-4
For help with NGSSS...	912.A.3.15	912.A.3.14	912.A.3.1	912.A.3.14	912.A.3.15	912.A.3.14	912.A.3.15	912.A.3.1	912.A.3.15	912.A.3.14	912.A.3.14	912.A.3.10	912.A.3.14

Formative Assessment

You can use these two pages to benchmark student progress.

CRM Chapter 3 Resource Masters

- Standardized Test Practice, pp. 56–58

ExamView Assessment Suite Create practice worksheets or tests that align to your state's standards as well as TIMSS and NAEP tests.

Homework Option

Get Ready for Chapter 4 Assign students the exercises on p. 183 as homework to assess whether they possess the prerequisite skills needed for the next chapter.

Page 133, Get Ready for Chapter 3

1. 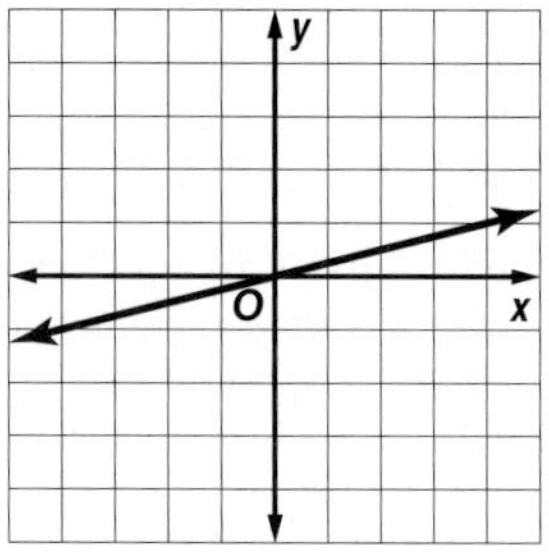

2. 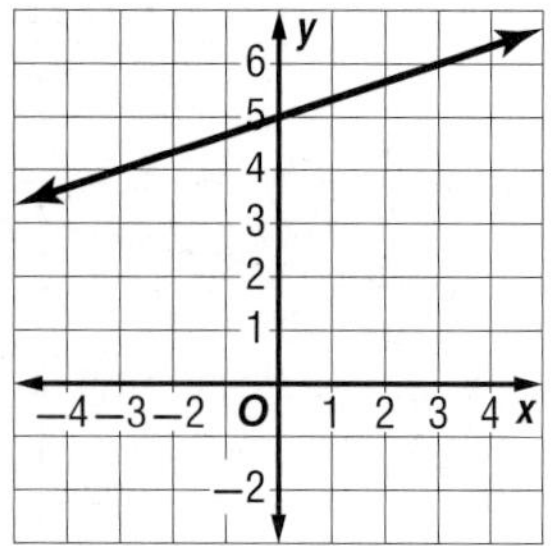

3. 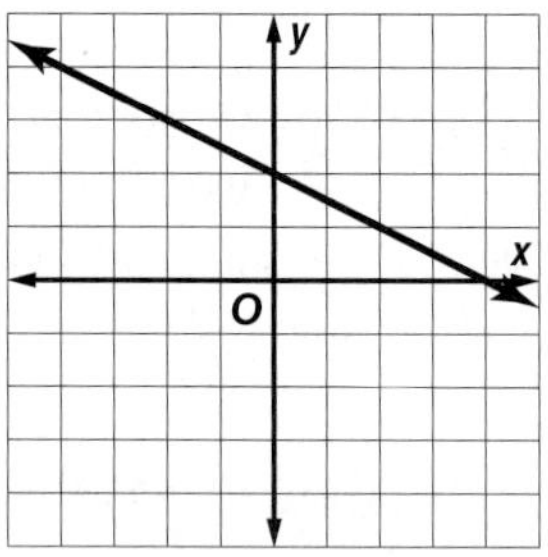

4. 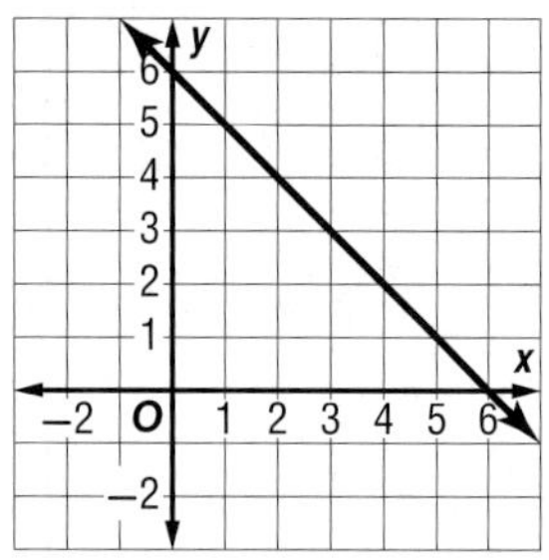

5. 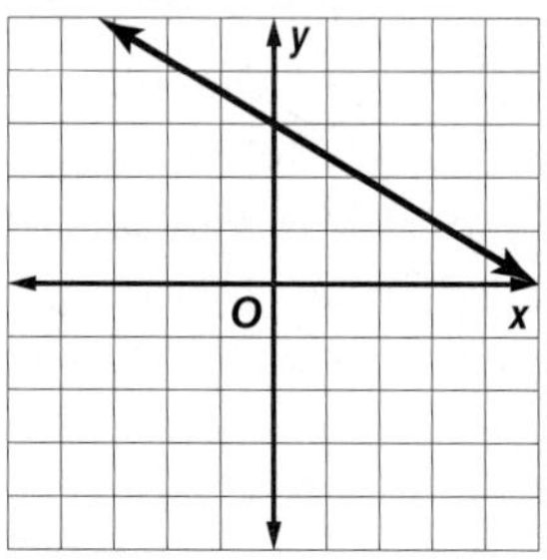

6. 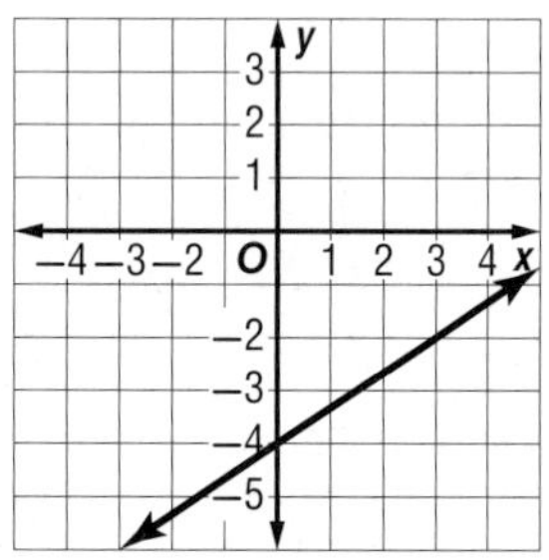

7b. 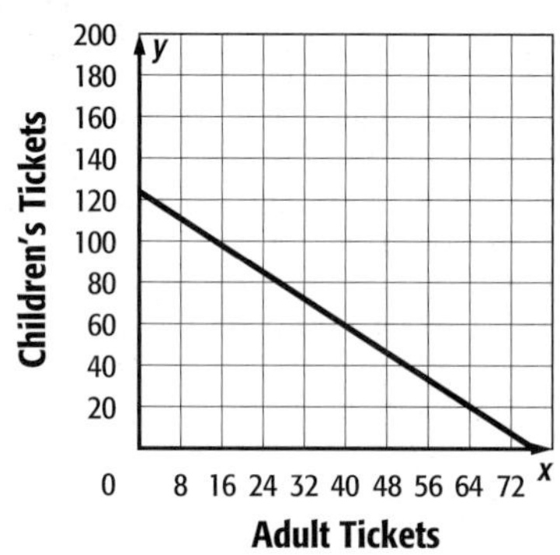

8. 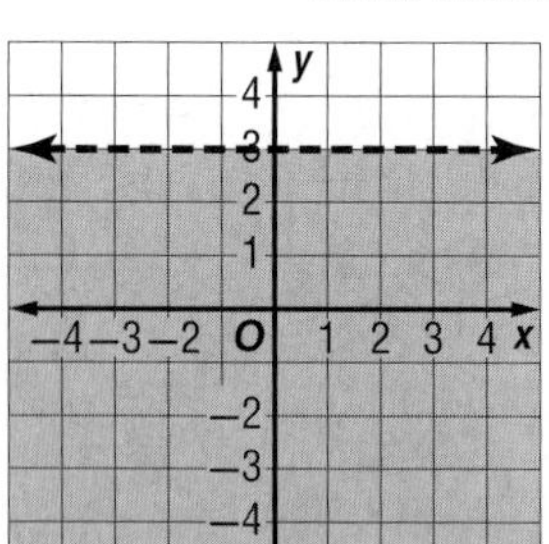

9. 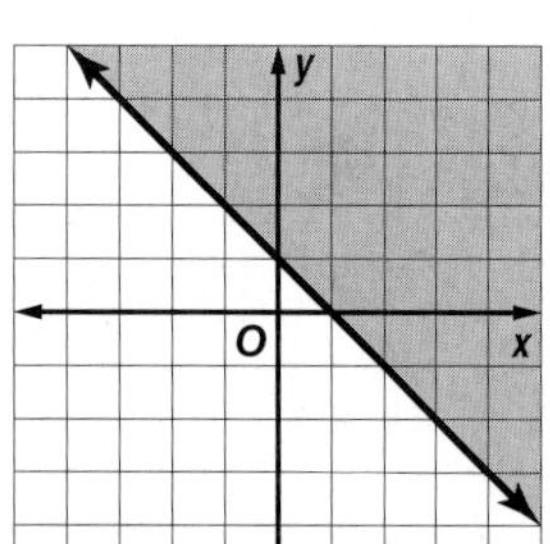

10. 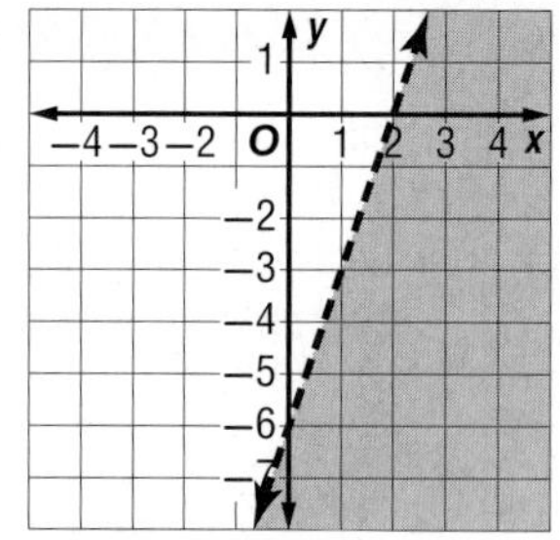

11. 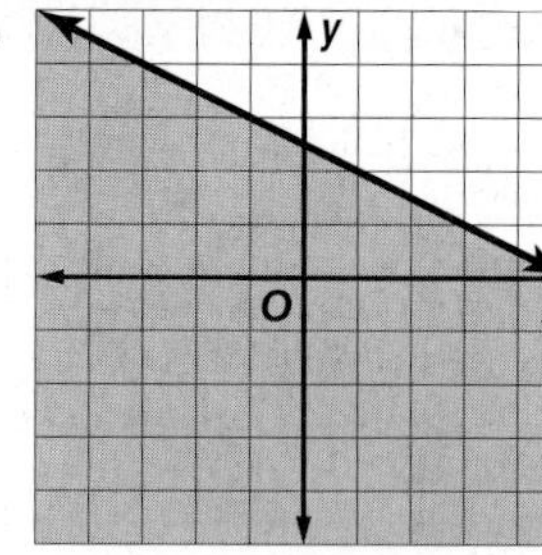

12. 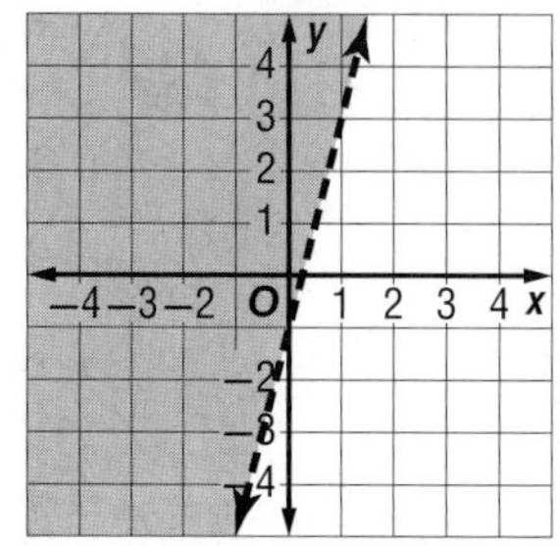

13. 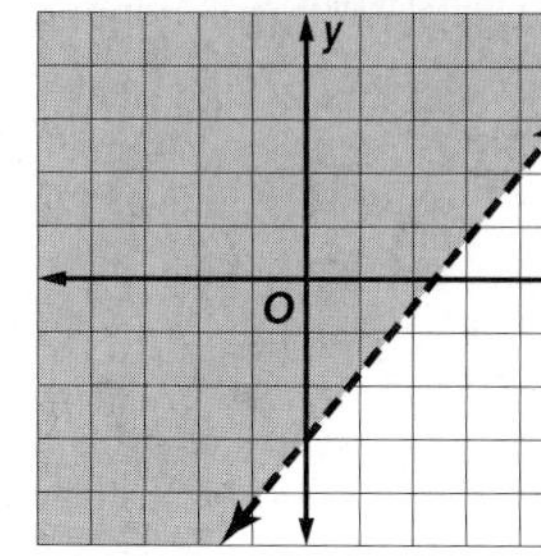

14. $15t + 25w \geq 2500$

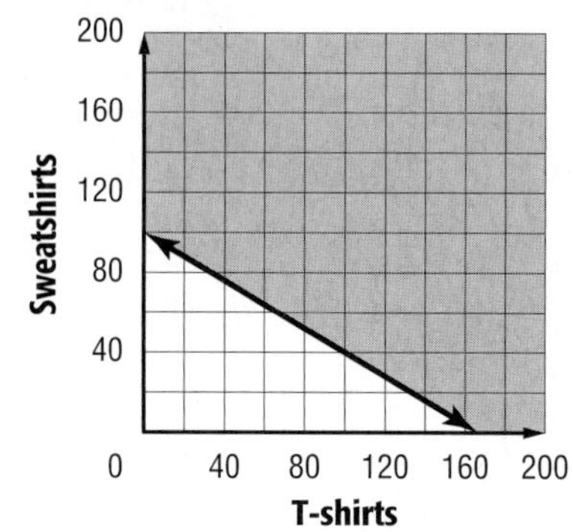

Pages 136–137, Lesson 3-1 Guided Practice

3. 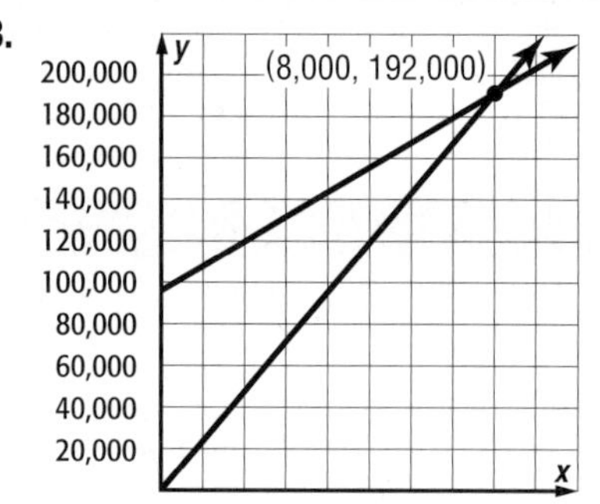

4A. 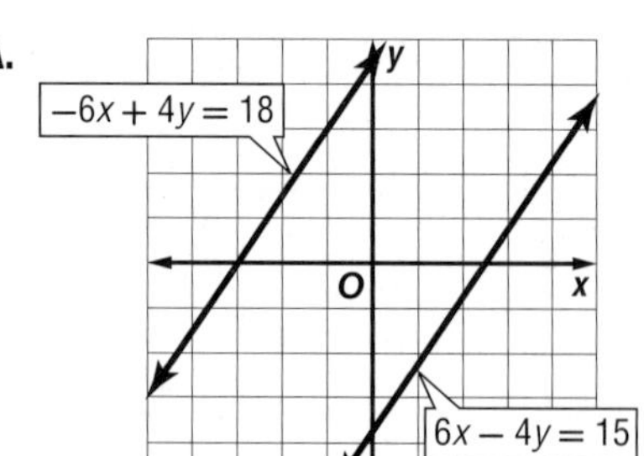

inconsistent

4B.

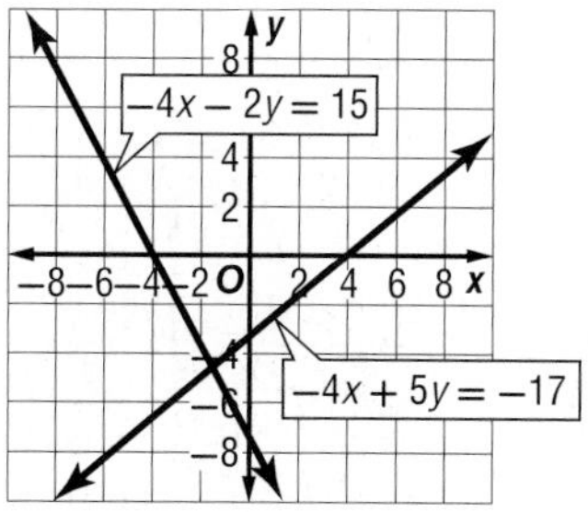

consistent, independent

4C.

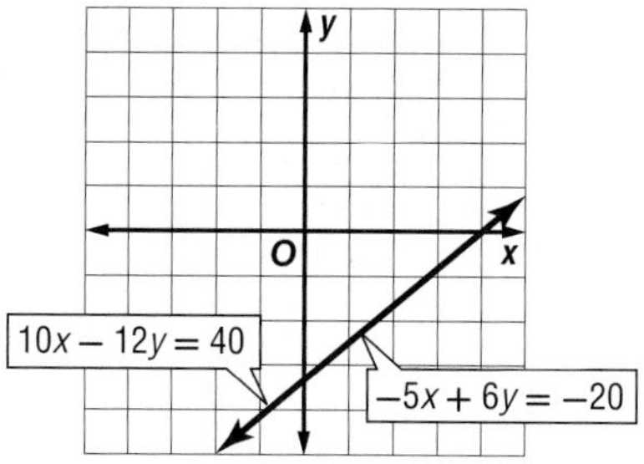

consistent, dependent

4D.

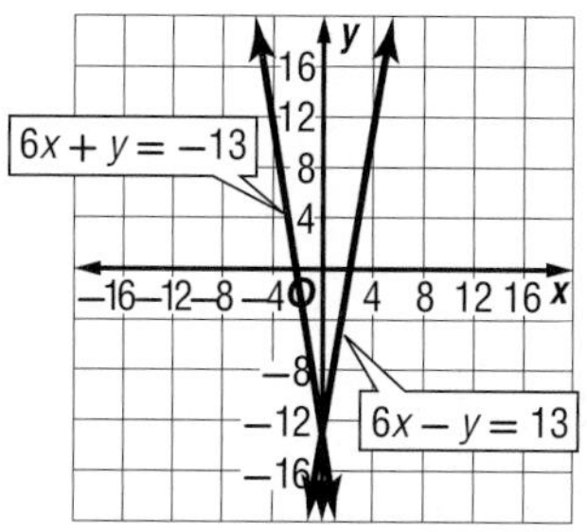

consistent, independent

Pages 139–141, Lesson 3-1

26.

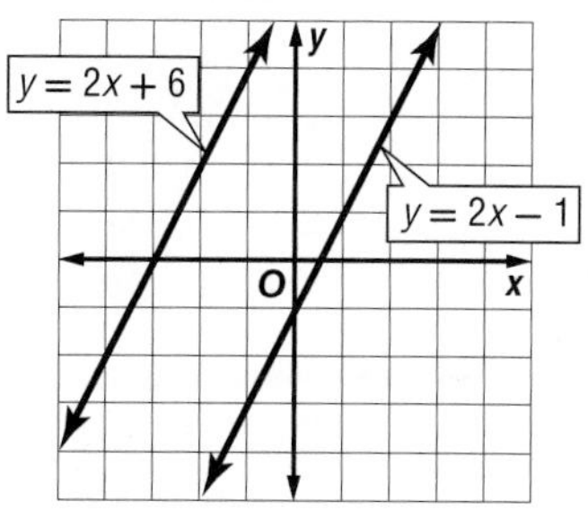

inconsistent

27.

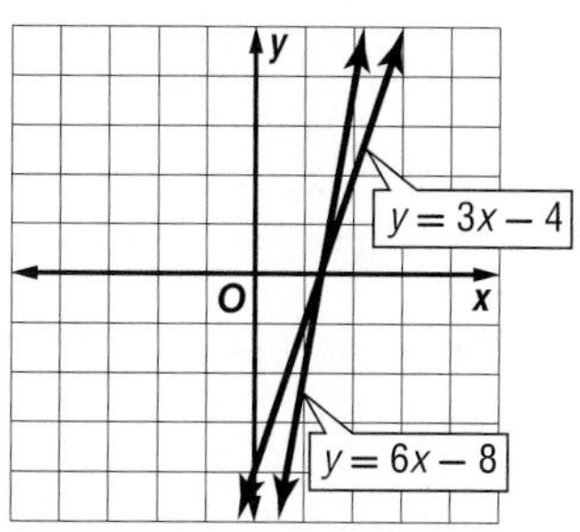

consistent and independent

28.

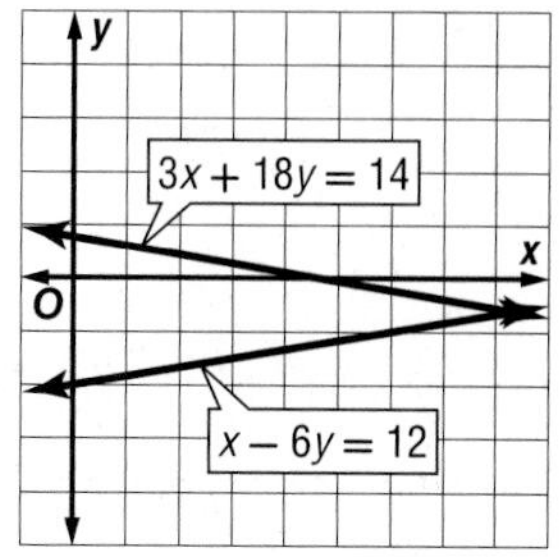

consistent and independent

29.

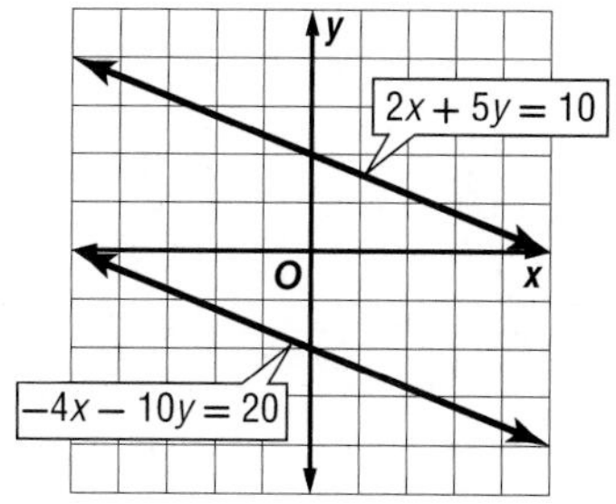

inconsistent

30.

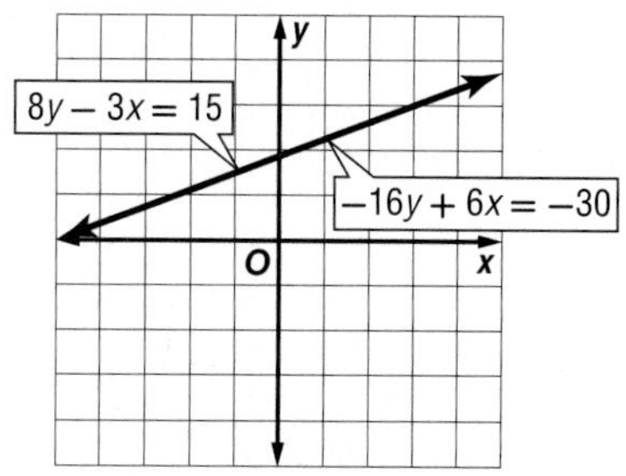

consistent and dependent

31.

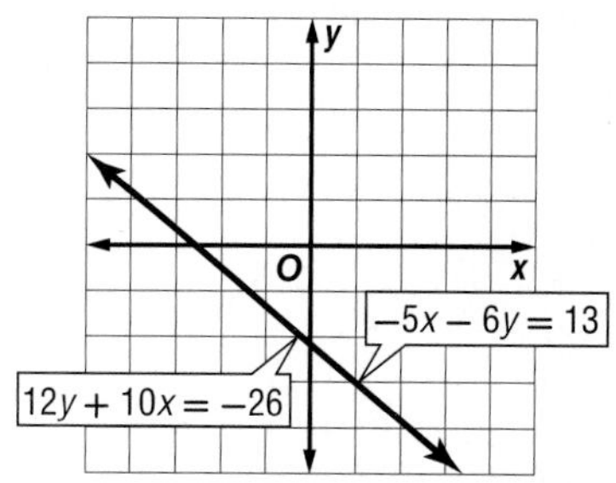

consistent and dependent

32.

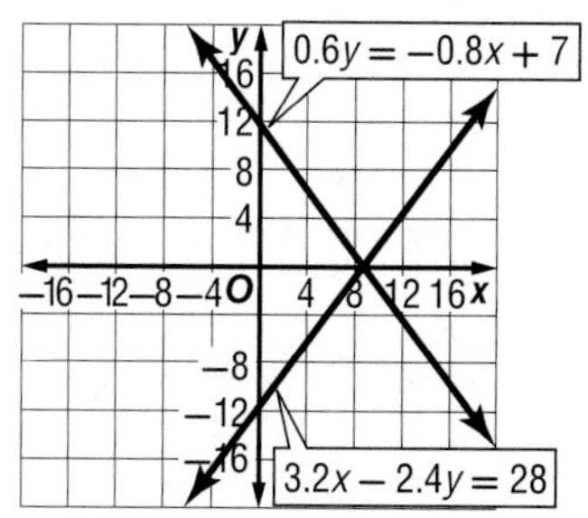

consistent and independent

33. 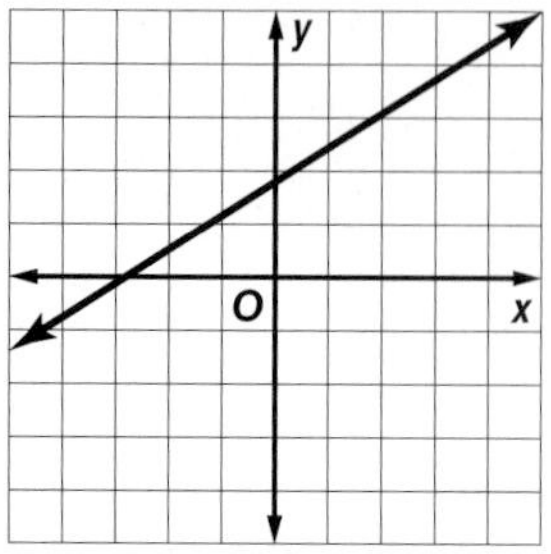
consistent and dependent

34. 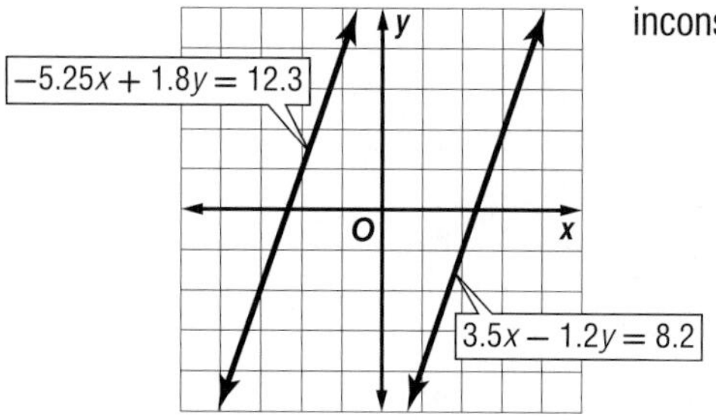

inconsistent

42. Sample answer: Always; *a* and *b* are the same line. *b* is parallel to *c*, so *a* is also parallel to *c*. Since *c* and *d* are consistent and independent, then *b* is not parallel to *d* and, thus, intersects *d*. Since *b* and *c* are parallel, then *a* cannot be parallel to *d*, so, *a* must intersect *d* and must be consistent and independent with *d*.

46. Sample answer: One method is to convert both equations into slope-intercept form. If the slopes differ, then the system is automatically consistent and independent. If the slopes are the same and the *y*-intercepts are different, then the system is inconsistent. If both the slopes and *y*-intercepts are the same, then the system is consistent and dependent.

51b. 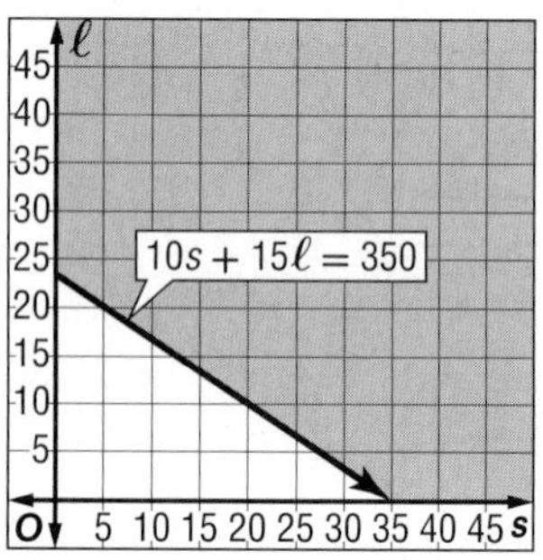

Page 149, Lesson 3-2

67. Sample answer:

$$\begin{aligned} 4x + 5y &= 21 \\ 3x - 2y &= 10 \end{aligned} \rightarrow \begin{aligned} 3(4x + 5y &= 21) \\ 4(3x - 2y &= 10) \end{aligned} \rightarrow$$

$$\begin{aligned} 12x + 15y &= 63 \\ (-)\ 12x - 8y &= 40 \\ \hline 23y &= 23 \\ y &= 1 \end{aligned}$$

$$\begin{aligned} 4x + 5(1) &= 21 \\ 4x + 5 &= 21 \\ 4x &= 16 \\ x &= 4 \end{aligned}$$ The solution is (4, 1).

Pages 151–153, Lesson 3-3, Guided Practice

1A. 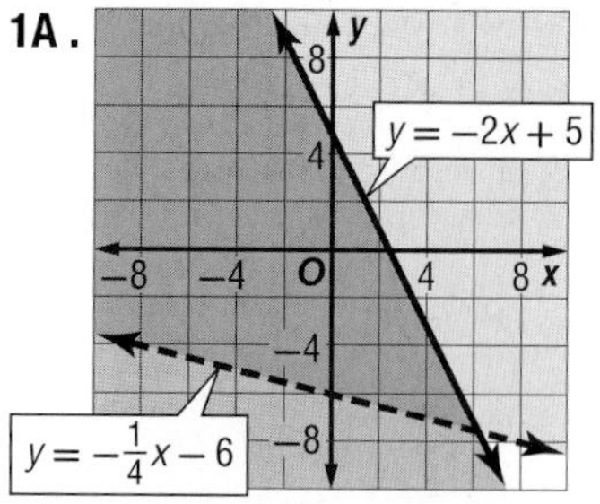

1B. 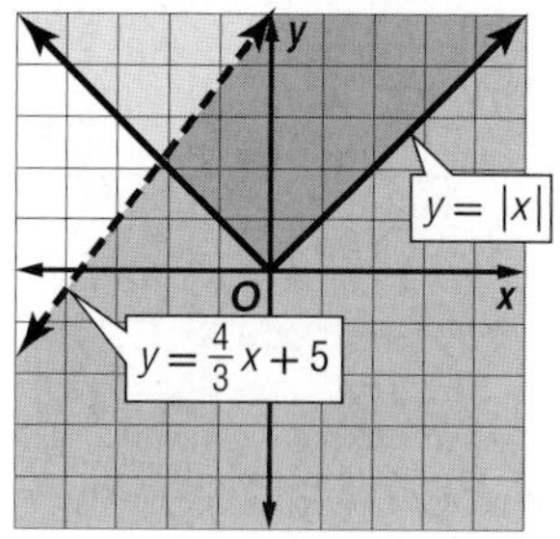

2A. 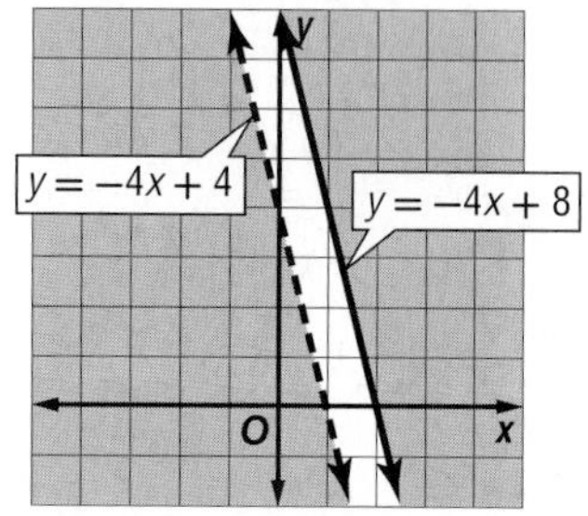

2B. 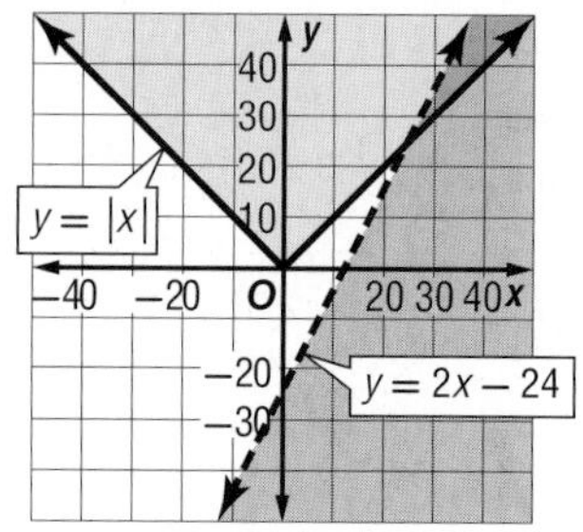

Pages 154–157, Lesson 3-3

5. 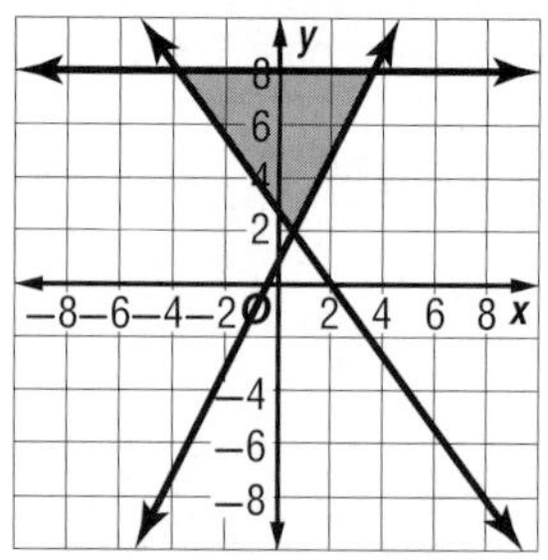

6. 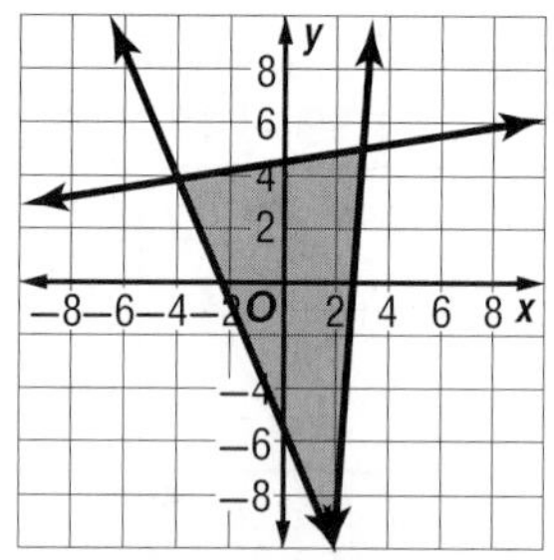

7. 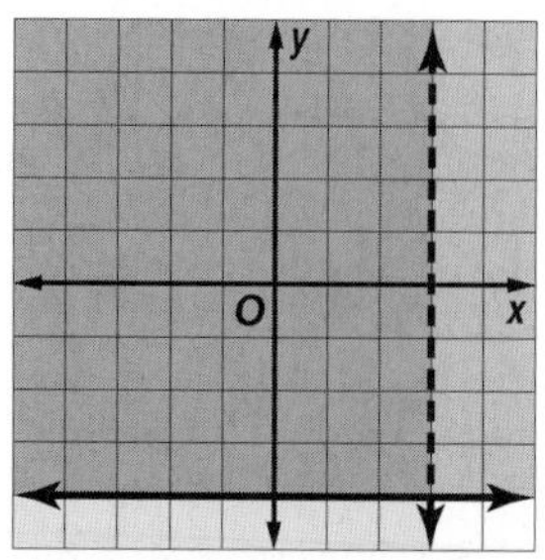

8. 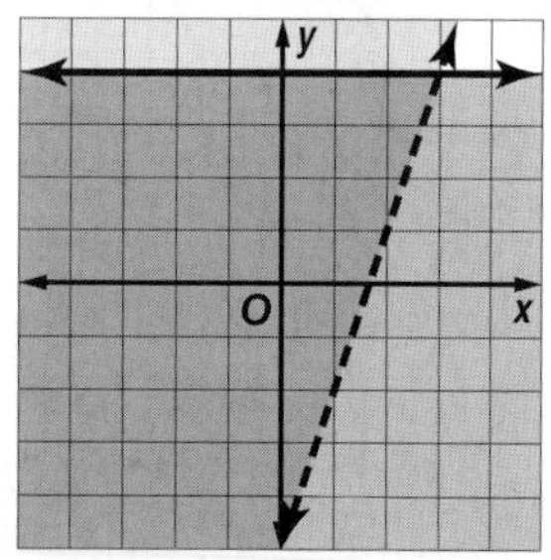

9. 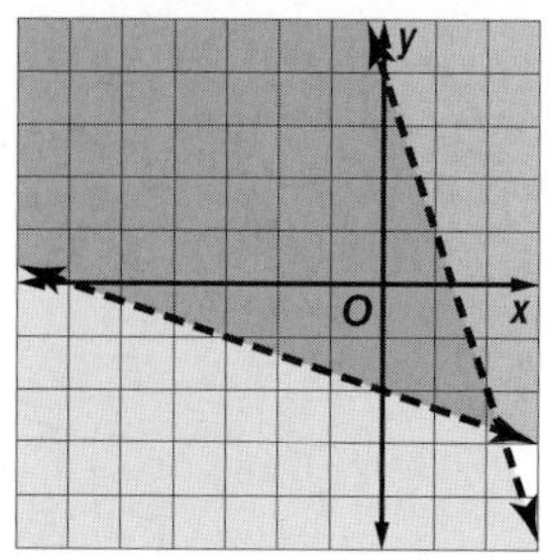

10. 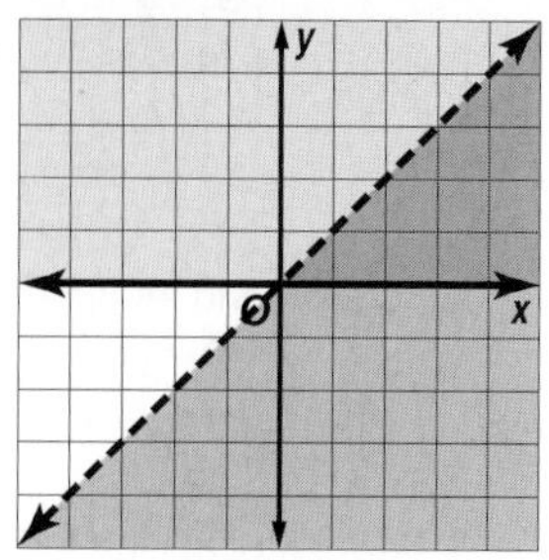

11.

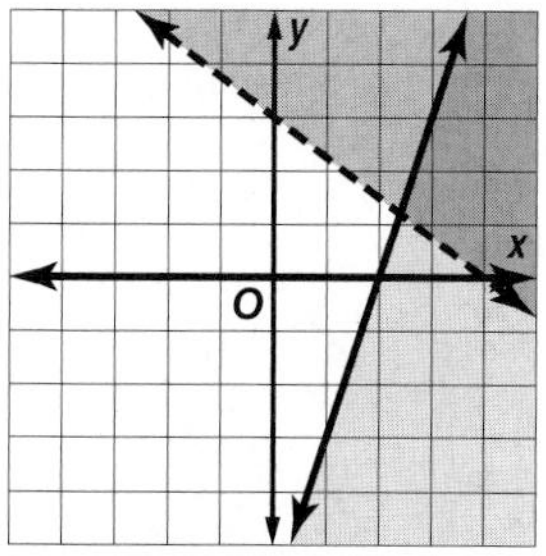

12.

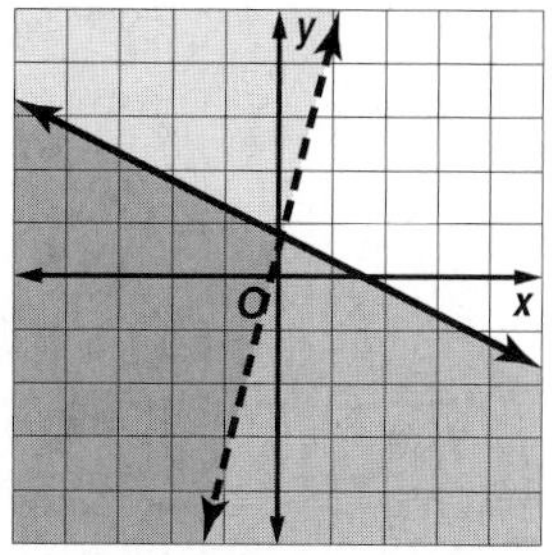

13.

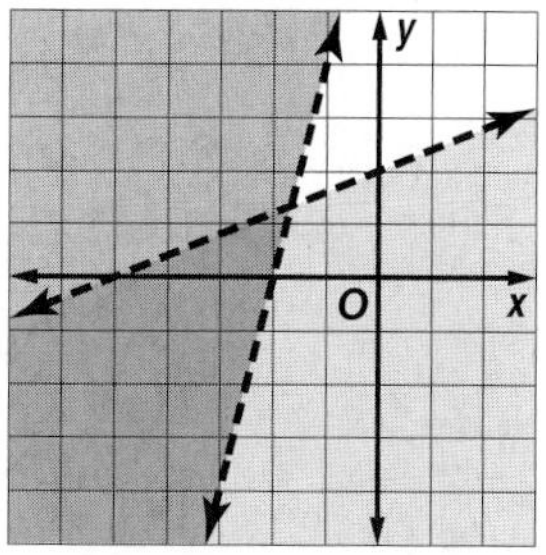

14.

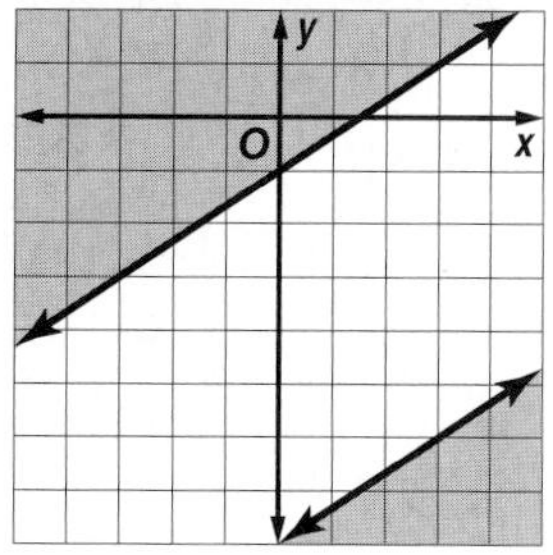

15.

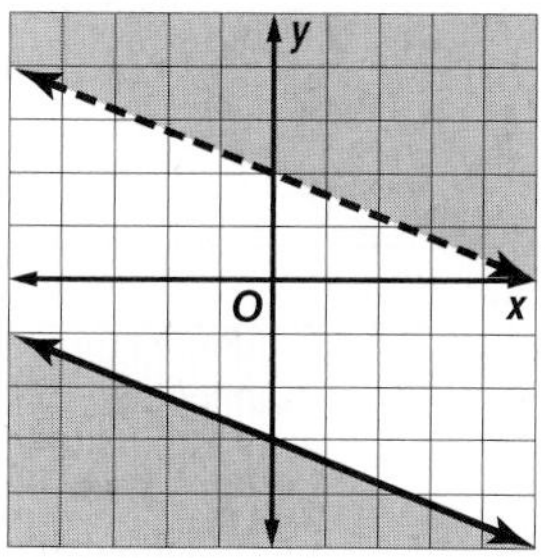

16.

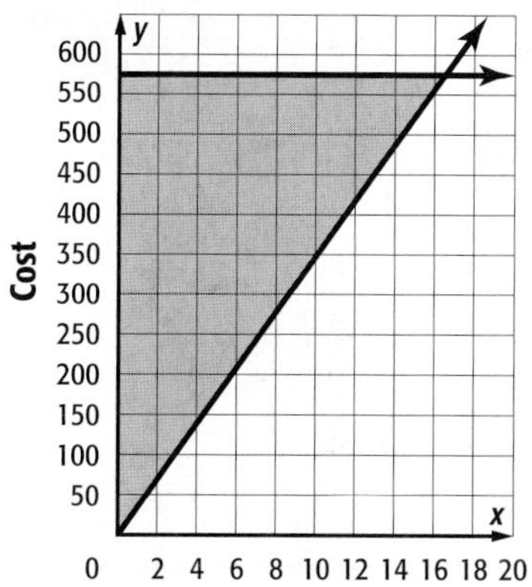

17.

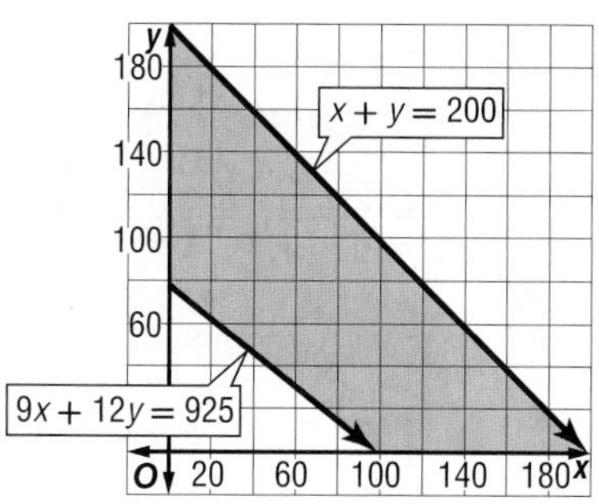

18.

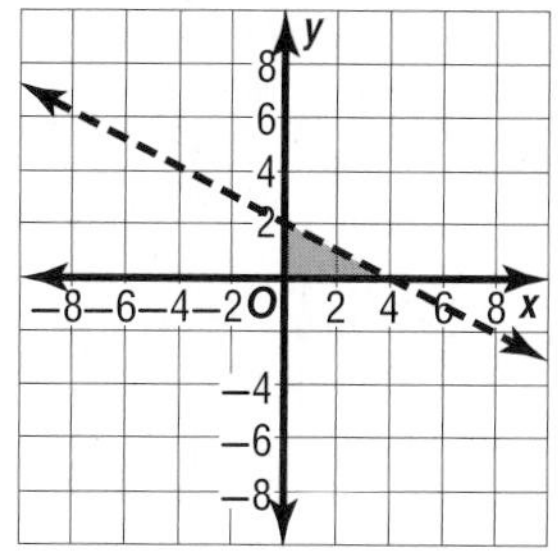

19.

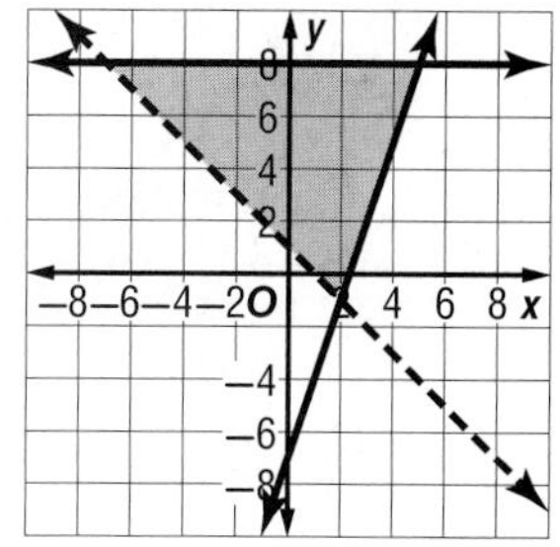

20.

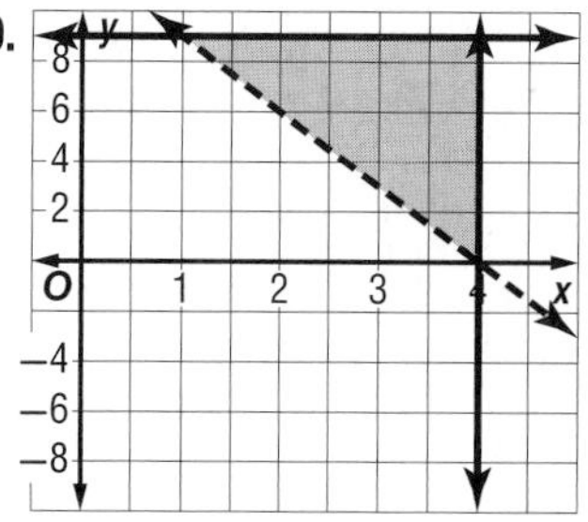

21.

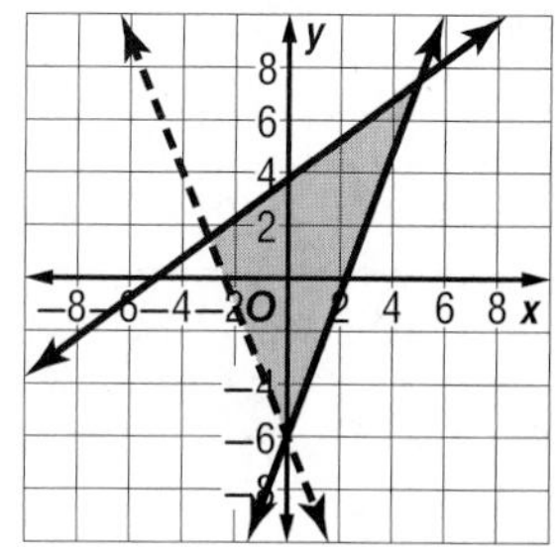

22.

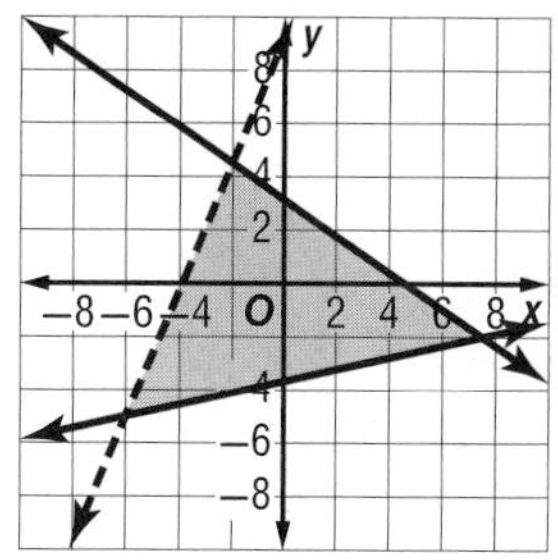

23.

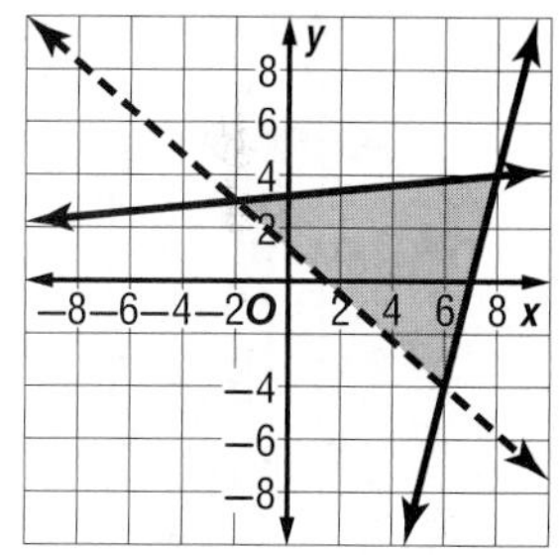

28.

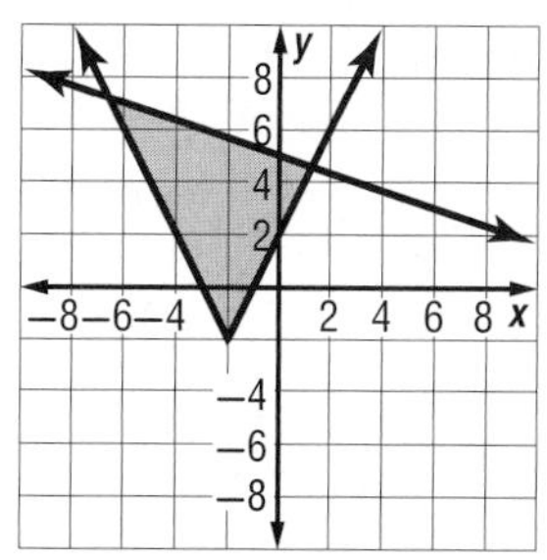

29.

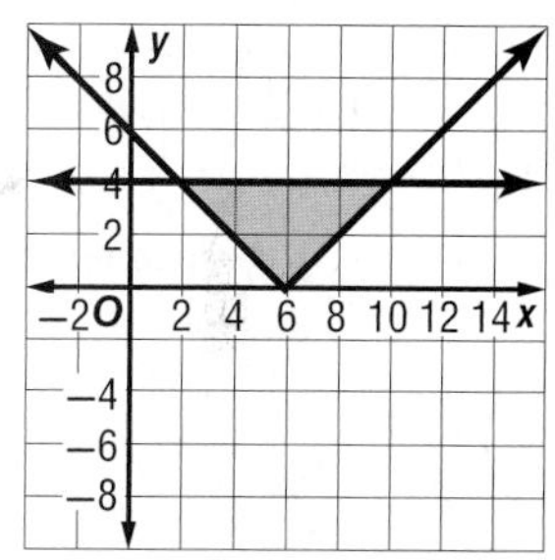

30.

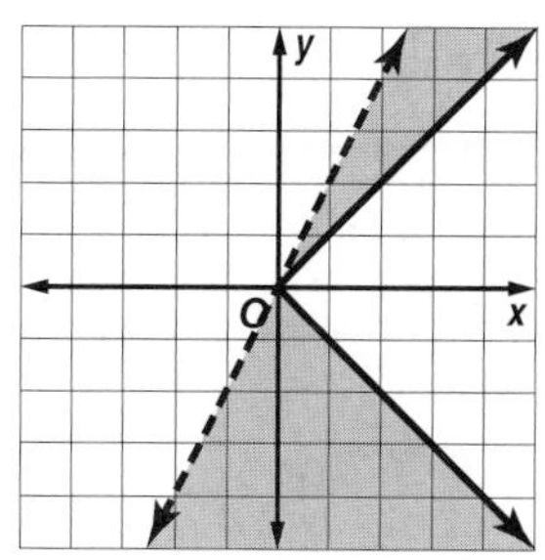

31.

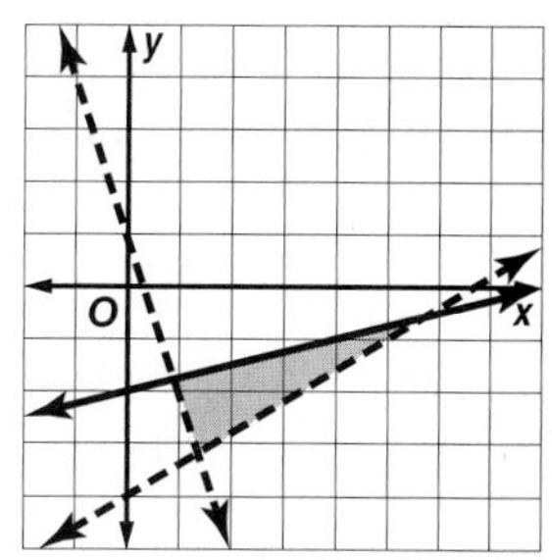

32.

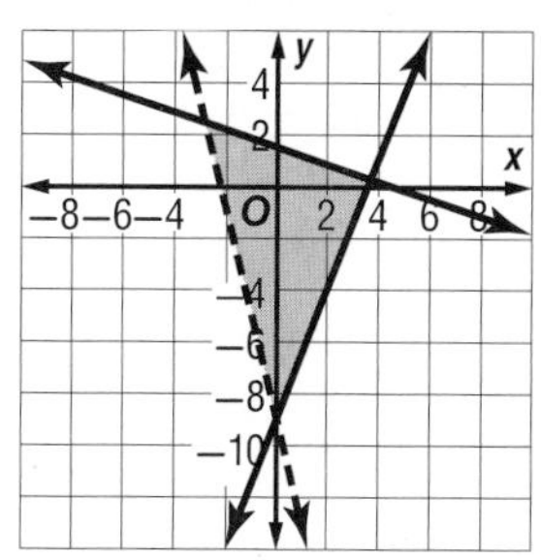

33.

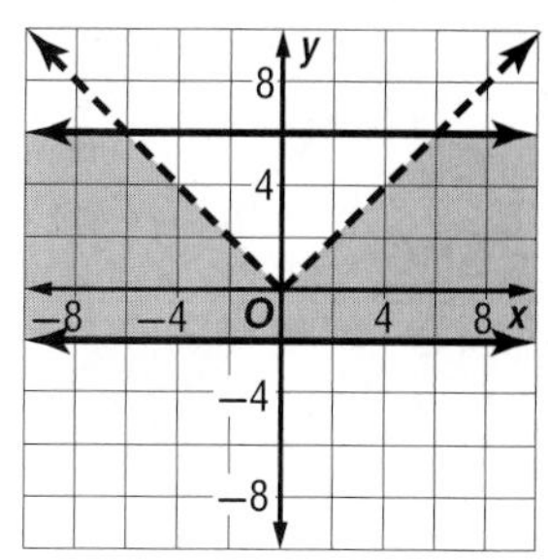

34.

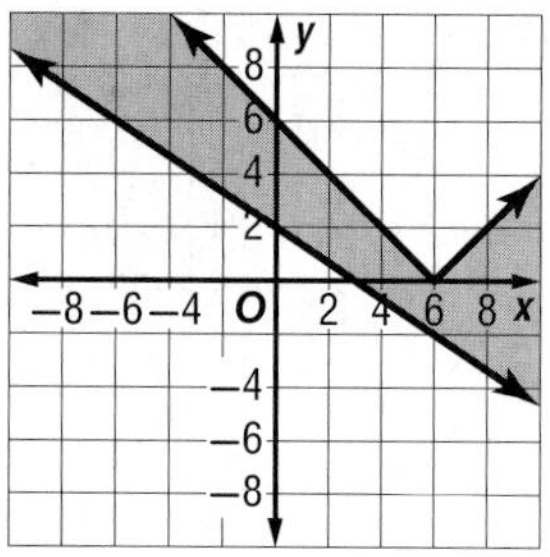

35.

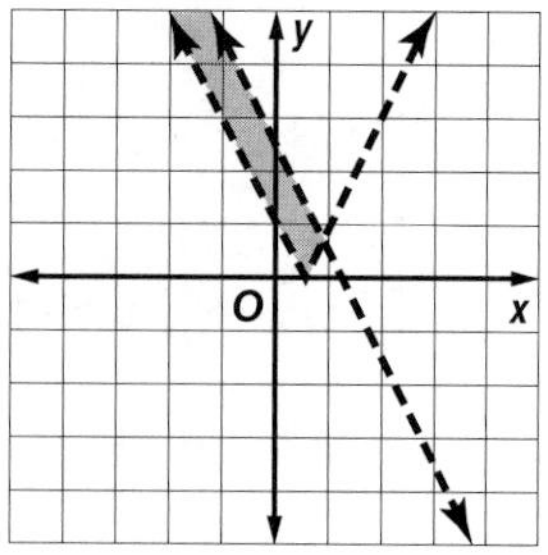

36.

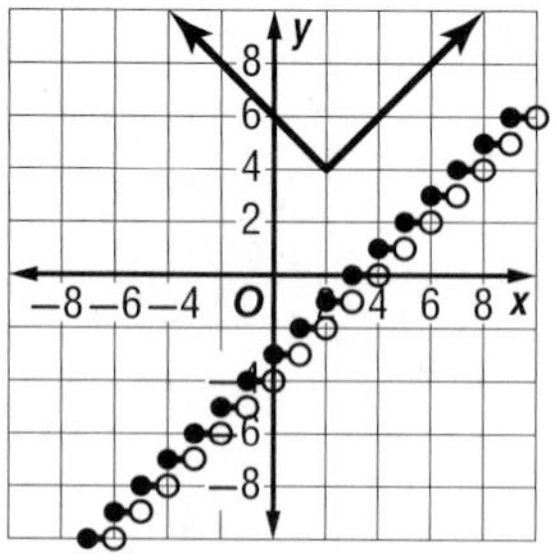

no solution

37.

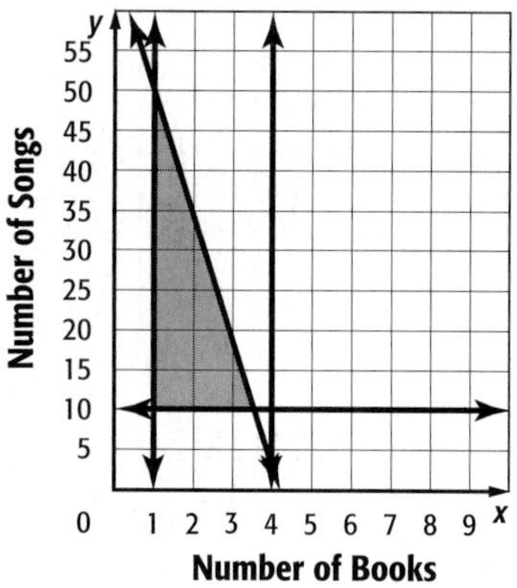

38.

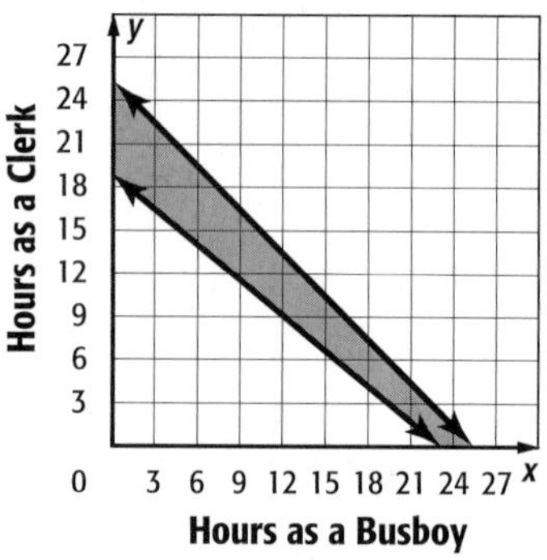

44a. $10 \le g + b \le 15$; $g > b$; $g \ge 0$; $b \ge 0$;

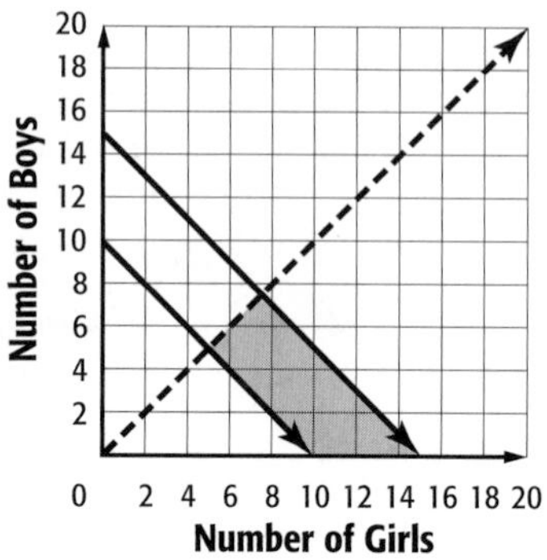

59. D = {all real numbers}, R = $\{g(x) \mid g(x) \le 2\}$

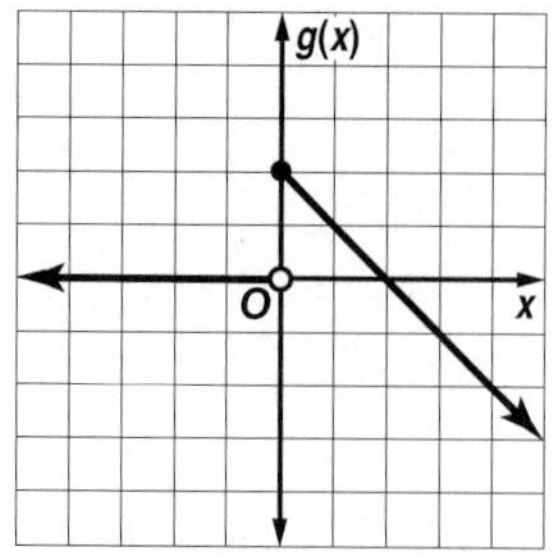

60. D = {all real numbers}, R = {all real numbers}

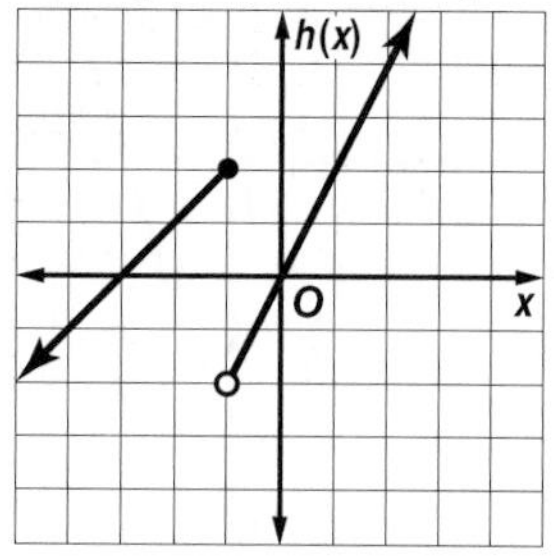

61. D = $\{x \mid x < -2$ or $x > 2\}$, R = $\{-1, 1\}$

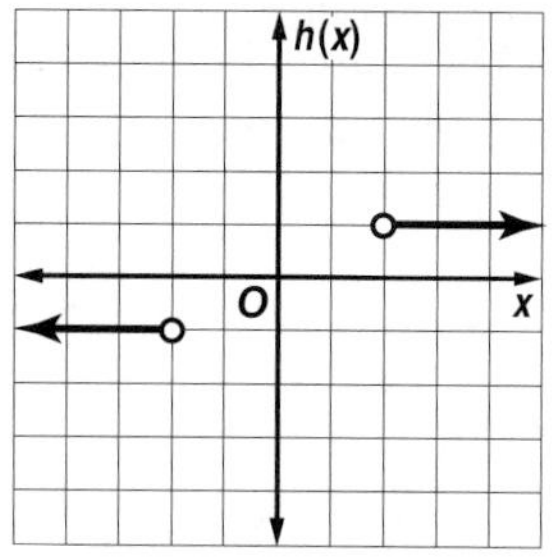

Page 158, Extend 3-3

1.

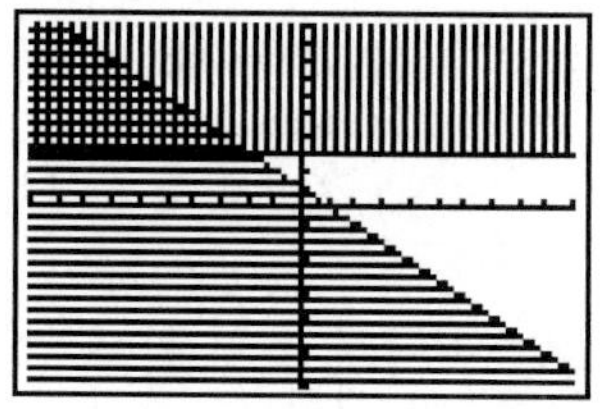

[–10, 10] scl: 1 by [–10, 10] scl: 1

2.

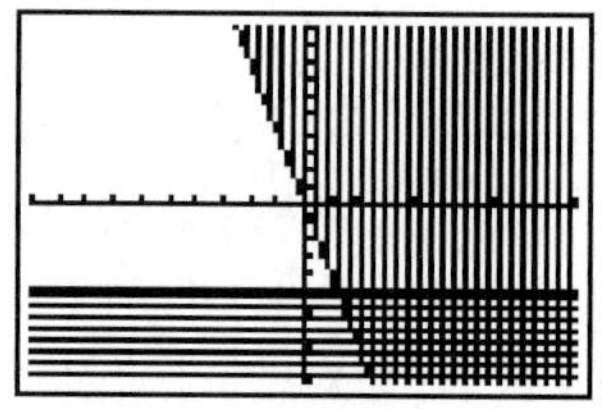

[–10, 10] scl: 1 by [–10, 10] scl: 1

3.

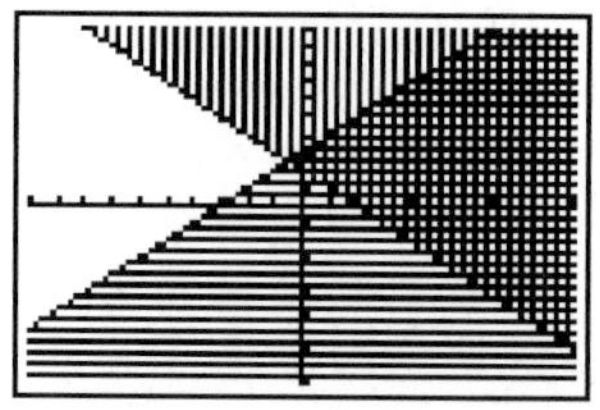

[–10, 10] scl: 1 by [–10, 10] scl: 1

4.

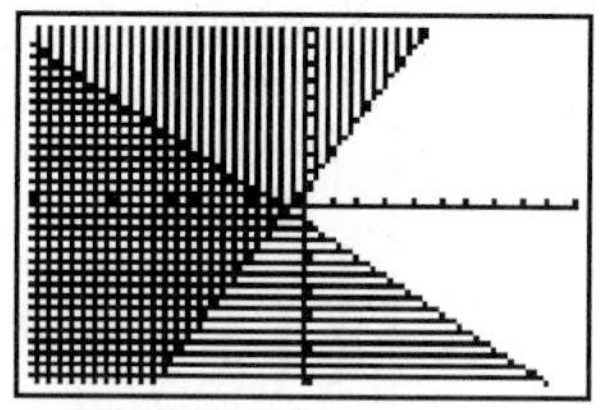

[–10, 10] scl: 1 by [–10, 10] scl: 1

5.

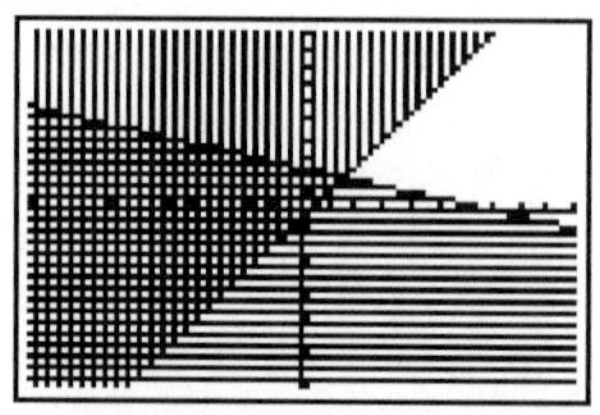

[–10, 10] scl: 1 by [–10, 10] scl: 1

6.

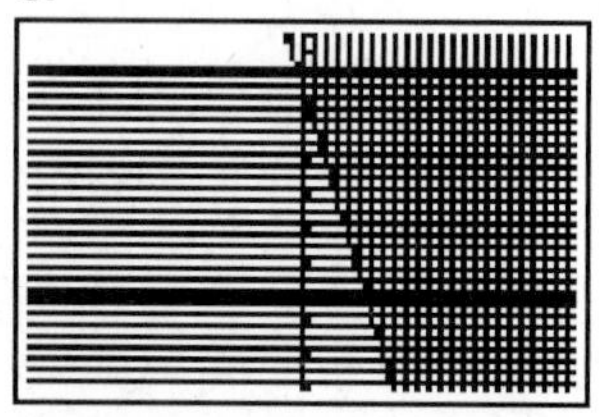

[–10, 10] scl: 1 by [–5, 15] scl: 1

7.

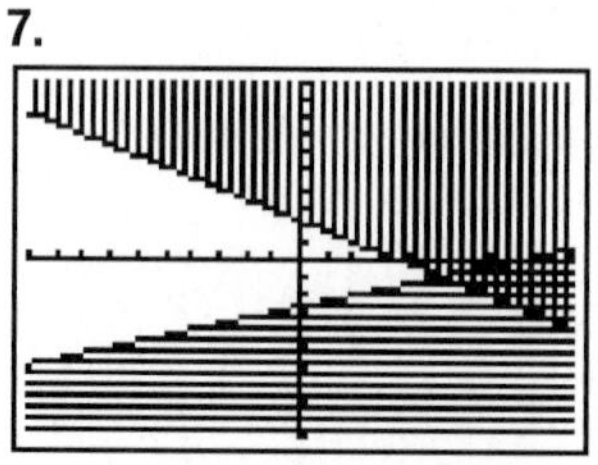

[–10, 10] scl: 1 by [–10, 10] scl: 1

8.

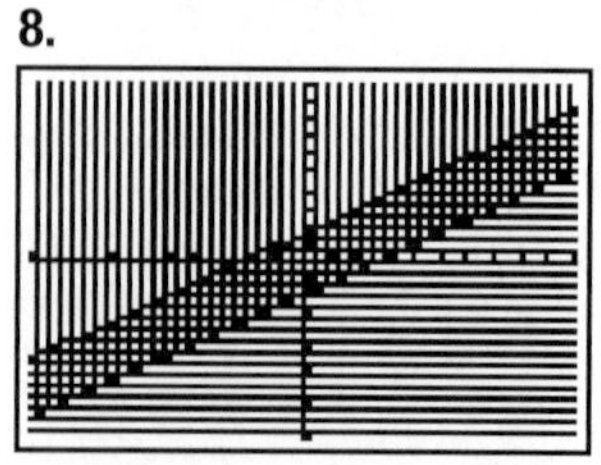

[–10, 10] scl: 1 by [–10, 10] scl: 1

9. 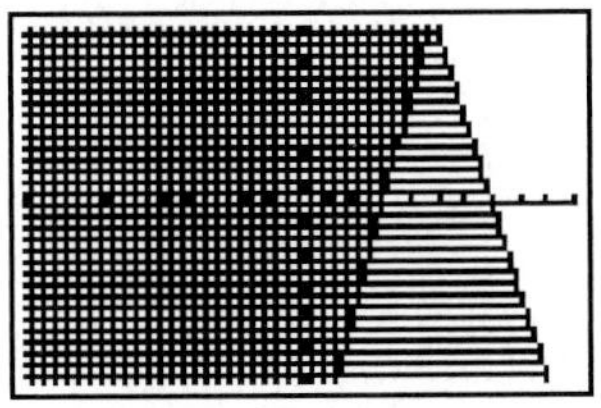

[–10, 10] scl: 1 by [–10, 10] scl: 1

Page 159, Mid-Chapter Quiz

17. 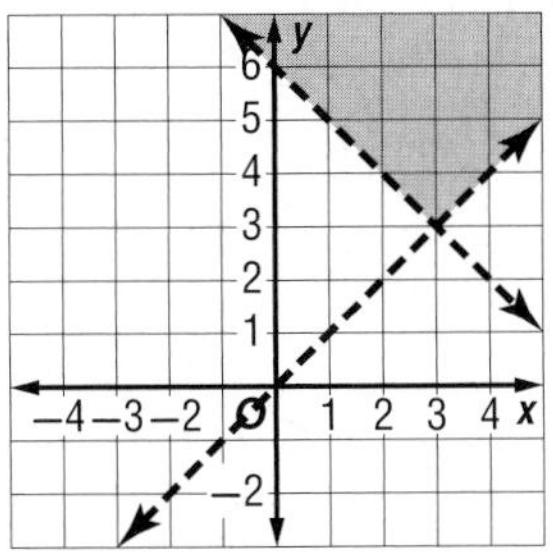

18. 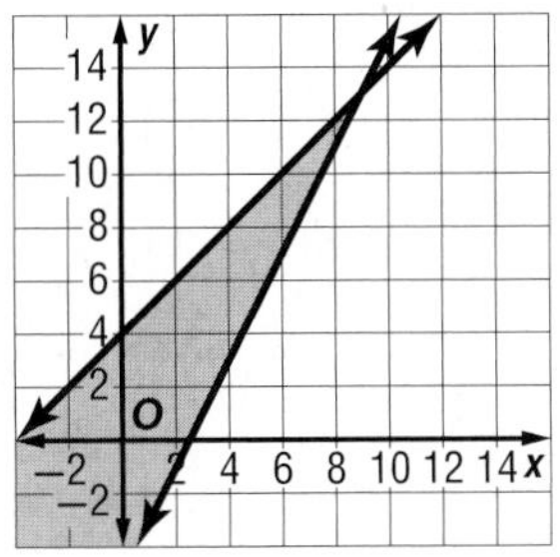

19. 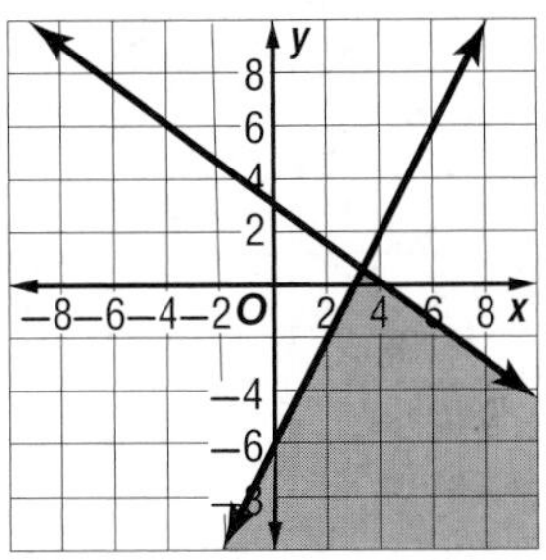

20. 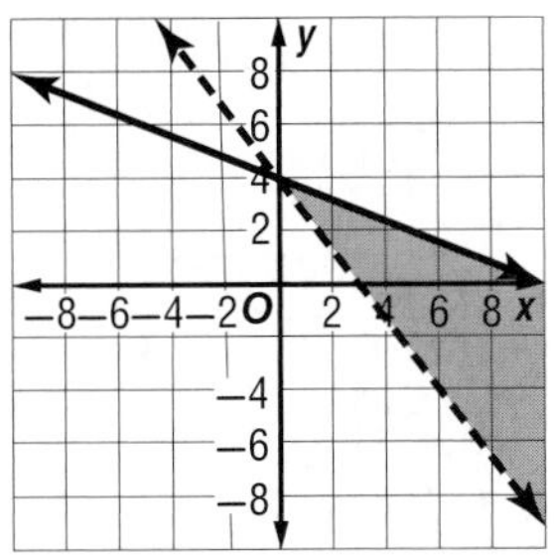

Page 161, Lesson 3-4, Guided Practice

1A. 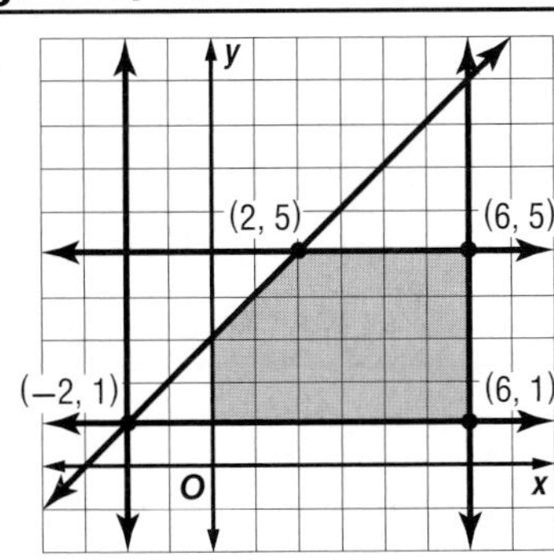

min at (6, 1) = –28;
max at (0, 3) = 12

1B. 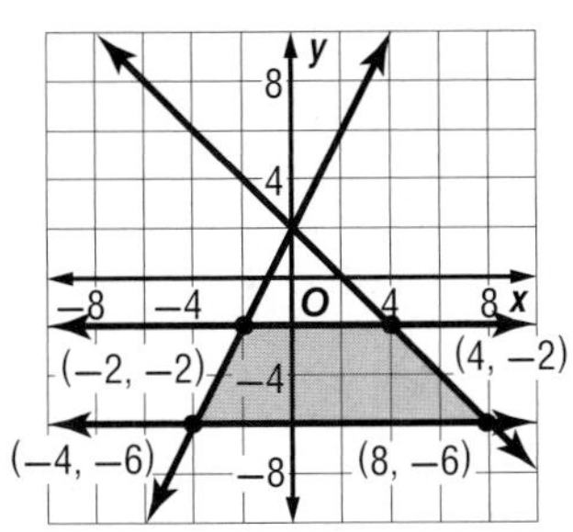

min at (–4, –6) = –48;
max at (8, –6) = 24

2A. 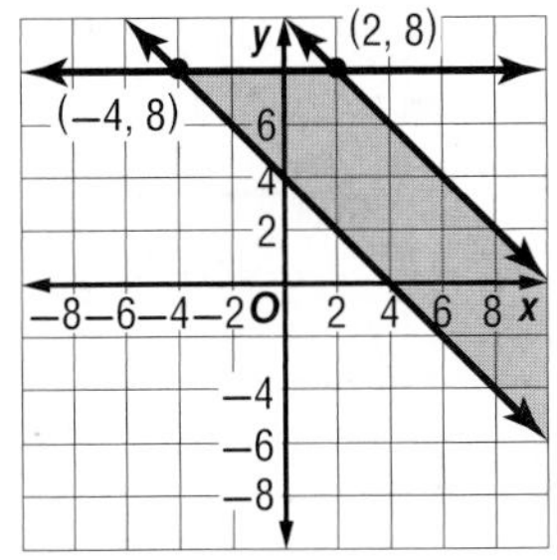

max at (–4, 8) = 88; no min

2B. 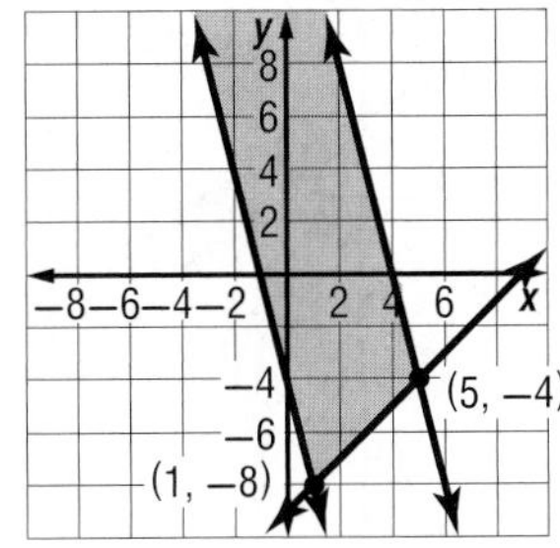

min at (1, –8) = –46; no max

Pages 163–166, Lesson 3-4

7b. 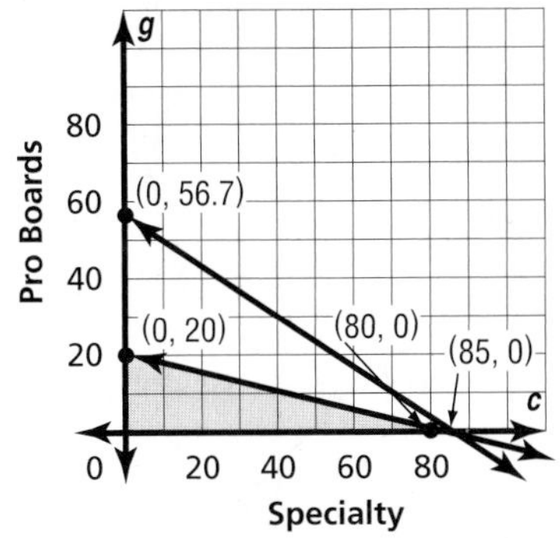

8. 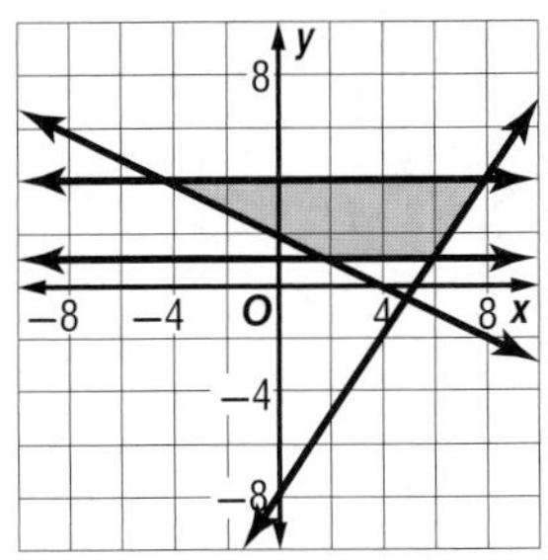

(8, 4), (6, 1), (2, 1), (–4, 4);
max = 36, min = –36

9. 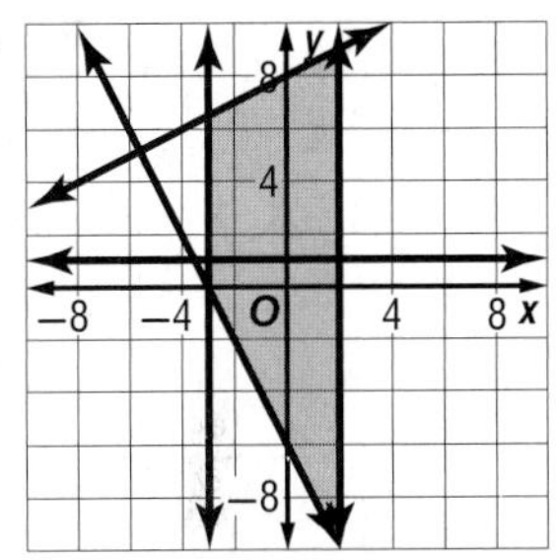

(2, –10), (–3, 0), (–3, 6.5),
(2, 9); max = 82, min = –89

10. 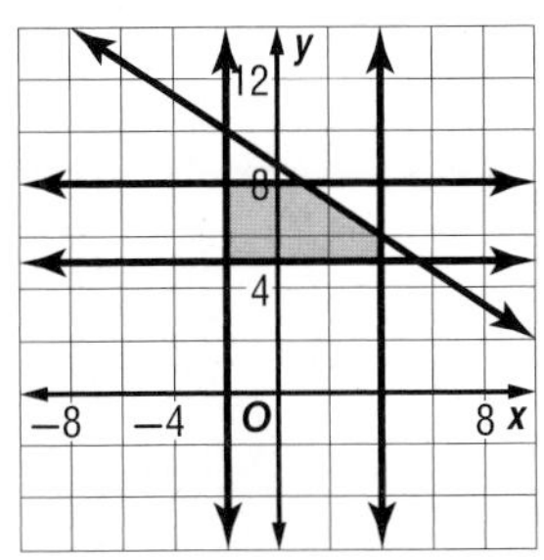

(1, 8), (4, 6), (4, 5),
(–2, 5), (–2, 8);
max = –18, min = –96

11. 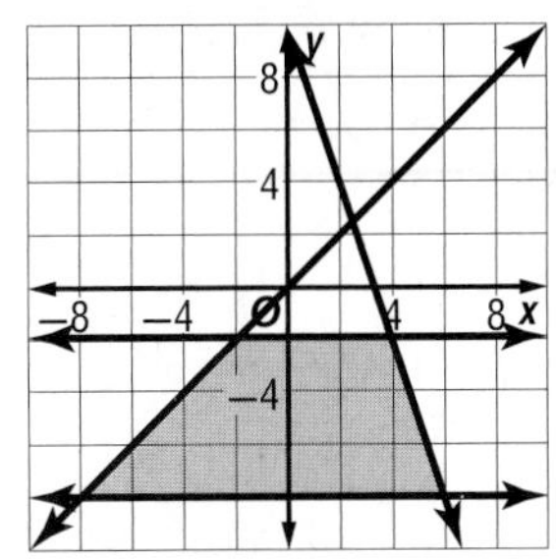

(6, –8), (4, –2),
(–2, –2), (–8, –8);
max = –8, min = –152

Chapter 3 Answer Appendix

12.

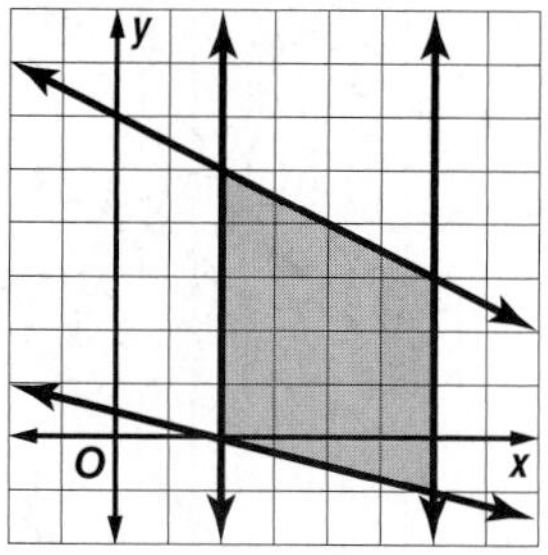

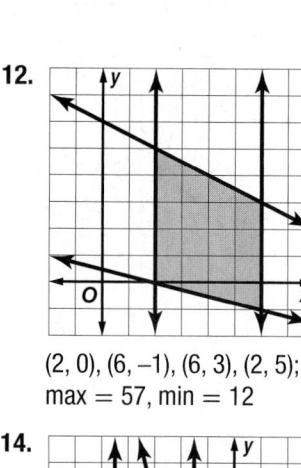

(2, 0), (6, –1), (6, 3), (2, 5); max = 57, min = 12

13.

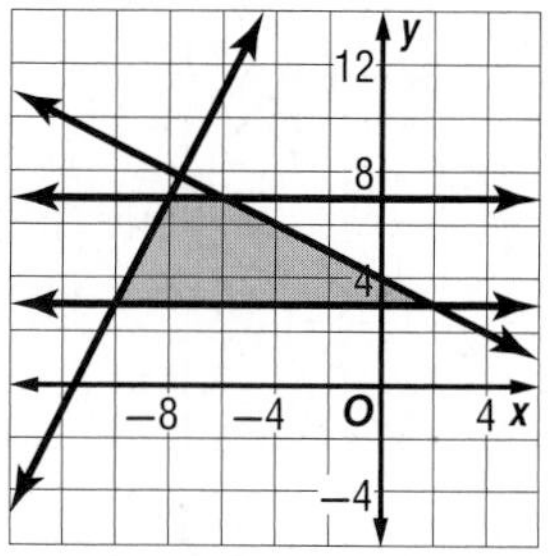

(–10, 3), (2, 3), (–6, 7), (–8, 7); max = 59, min = 9

14.

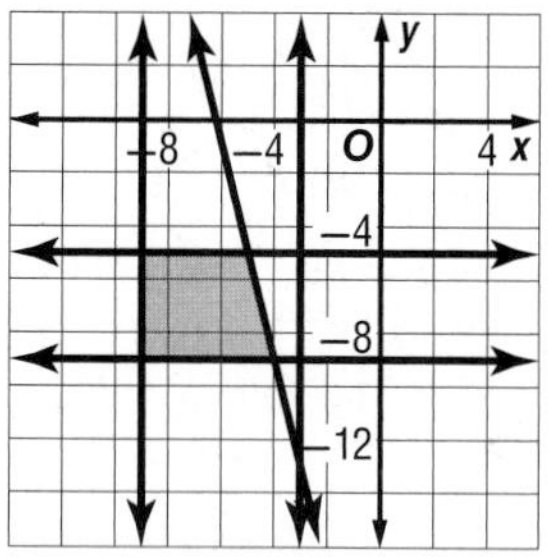

15.

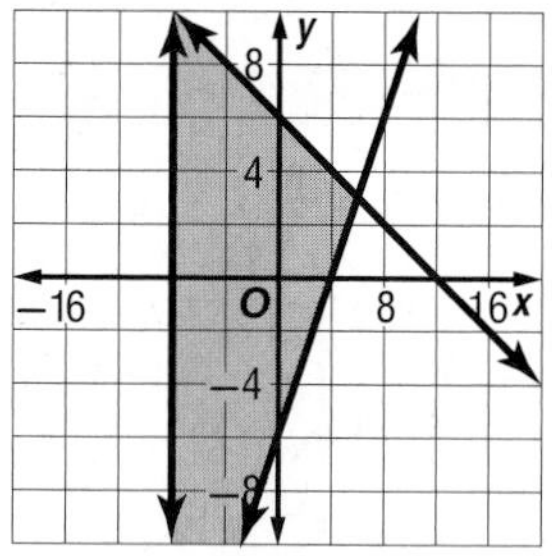

16.

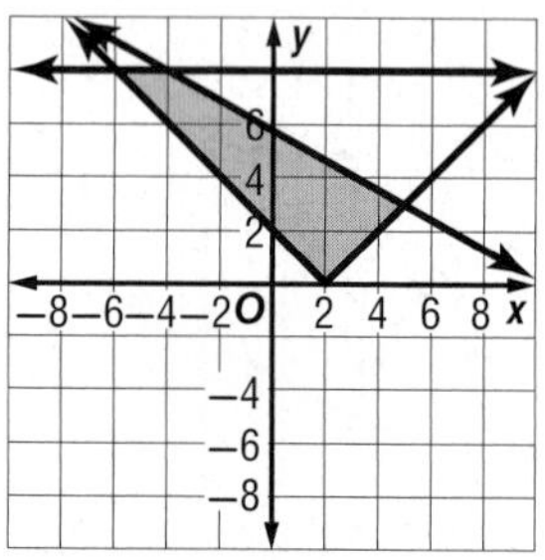

17.

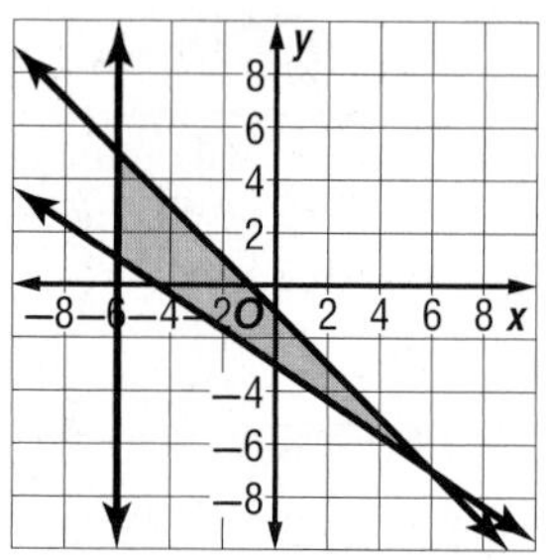

18.

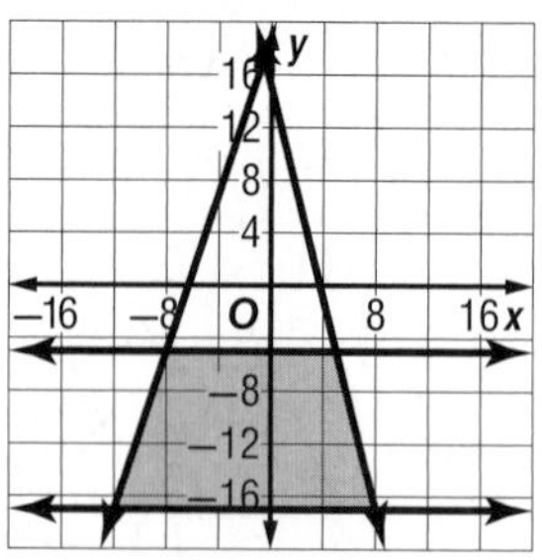

19.

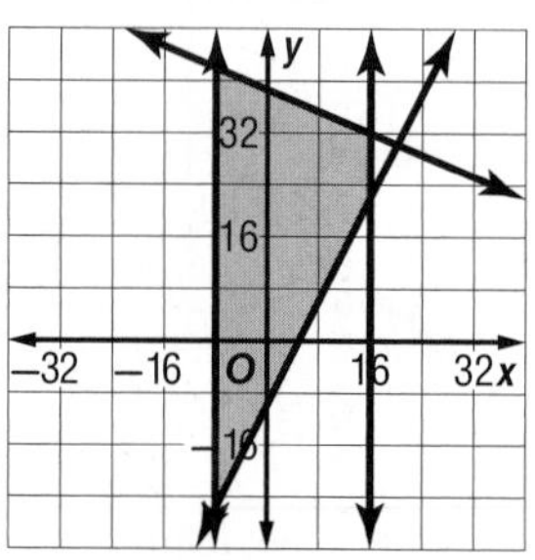

20.

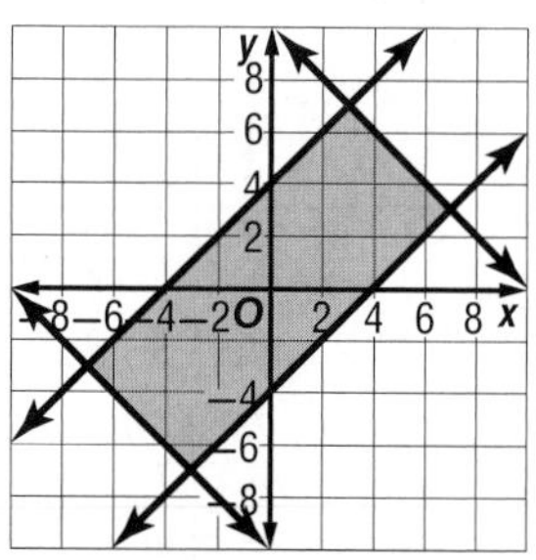

21.

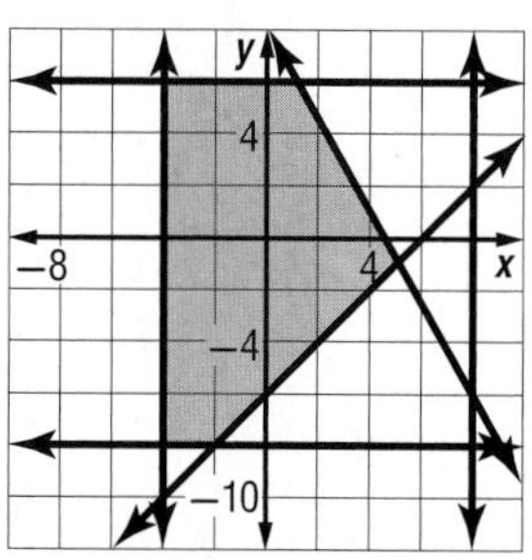

22.

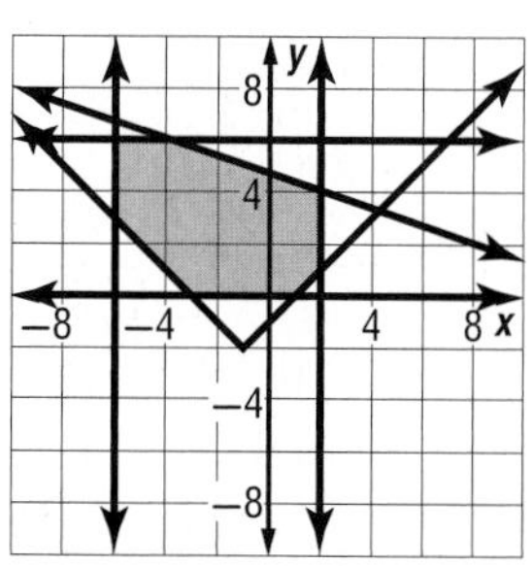

25b.

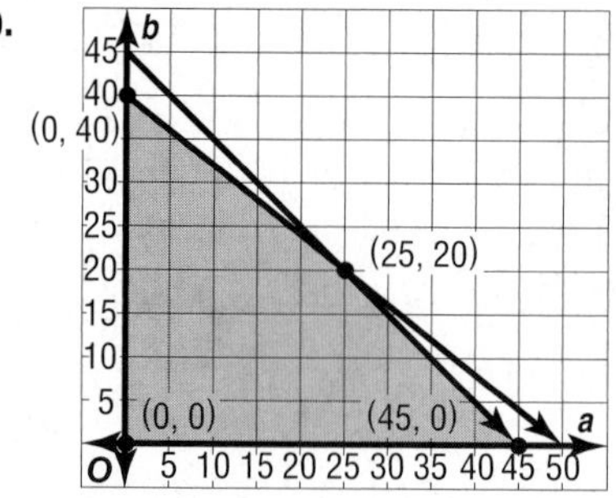

44.

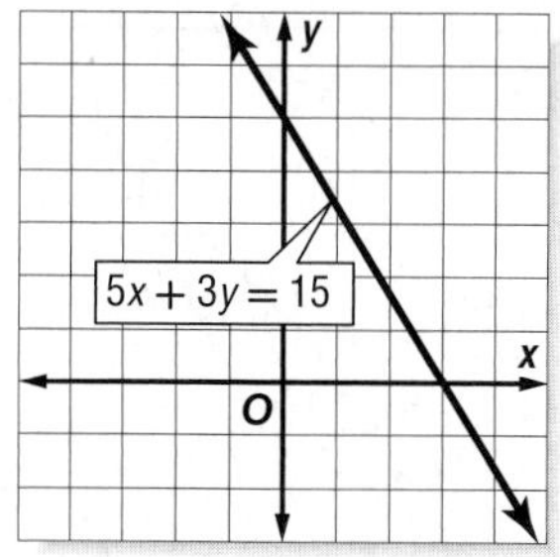

45.

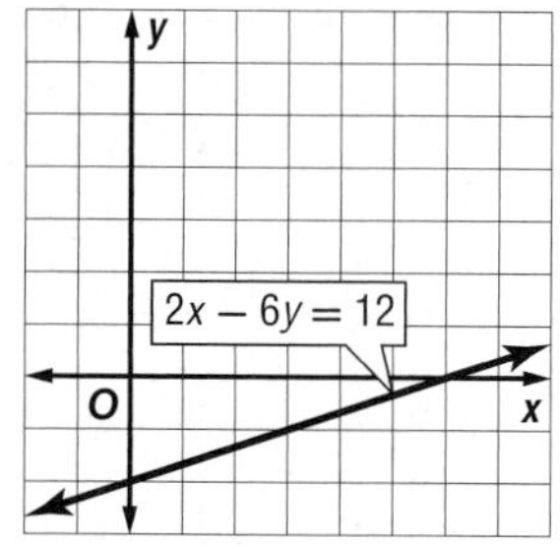

46.

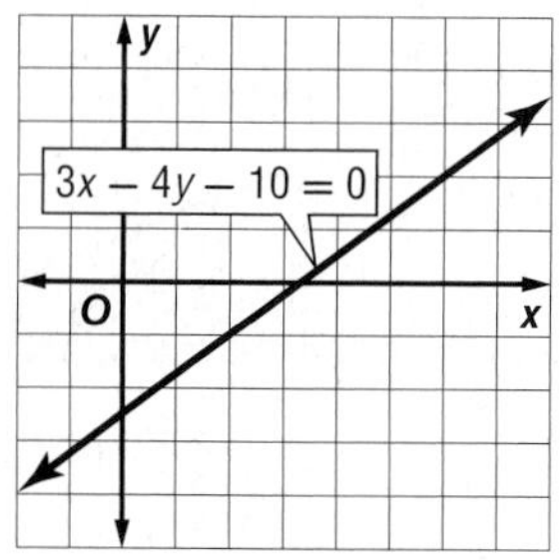

47.

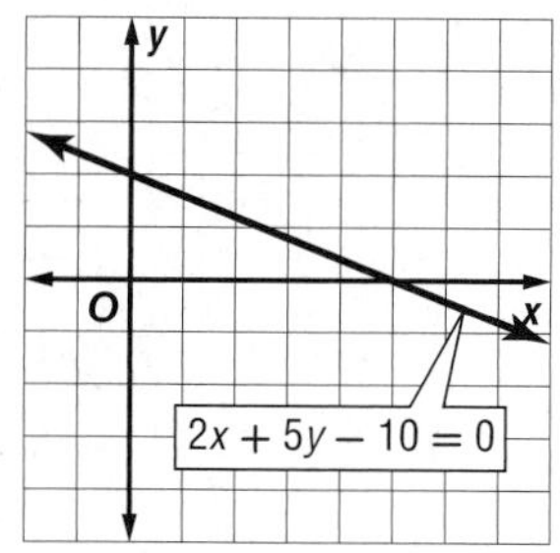

48.

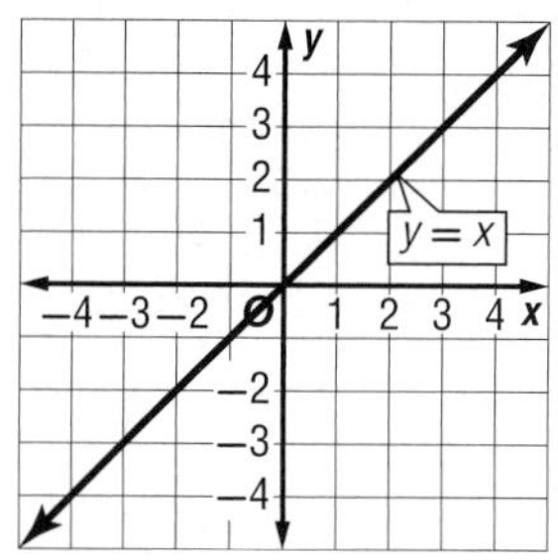

49.

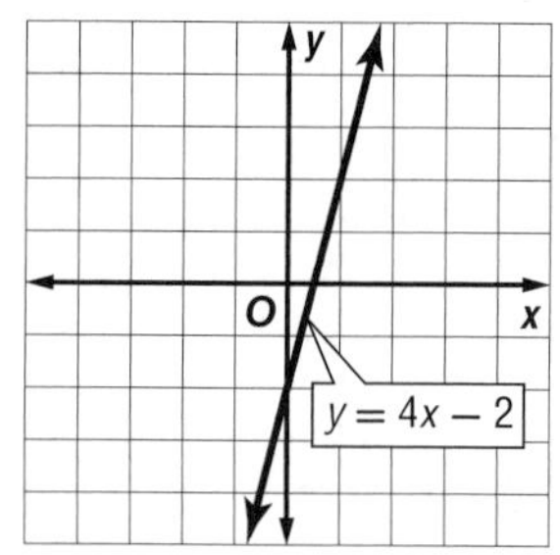

Chapter 3 Answer Appendix

Page 172, Lesson 3-5

26. Sample answer:

$a + b = (rx + ty + vz) + (rx - ty + vz)$

Replace a with $rx + ty + vz$, and b with $rx - ty + vz$.

$a + b = 2rx + 2vz$	Simplify.
$a + (-a) = 2rx + 2vz$	Replace b with $-a$.
$0 = 2rx + 2vz$	Simplify.
$0 = rx + vz$	Divide each side by 2.

$rx + ty + vz = a$	Given
$ty + (rx + vz) = a$	Commutative and Associative Properties of Addition
$ty + 0 = a$	Substitution
$ty = a$	Simplify.

29. Sample answer: First, combine two of the original equations using elimination to form a new equation with three variables. Next, combine a different pair of the original equations using elimination to eliminate the same variable and form a second equation with three variables. Do the same thing with a third pair of the original equations. You now have a system of three equations with three variables. Follow the same procedure you learned in this section. Once you find the three variables, you need to use them to find the eliminated variable.

CHAPTER 4

Chapter Planner

Diagnostic Assessment Quick Check, p. 183

	Lesson 4-1 Pacing: 1 day	Extend 4-1 Pacing: 0.5 day	Lesson 4-2 Pacing: 1 day	Lesson 4-3 Pacing: 1 day
Title	**Introduction to Matrices**	**Spreadsheet Lab: Organizing Data**	**Operations with Matrices**	**Multiplying Matrices**
Objectives	• Organize data in matrices. • Use matrix row and column operations to analyze data.	• Use a spreadsheet to organize and display data.	• Add and subtract matrices. • Multiply a matrix by a scalar.	• Multiply matrices. • Use the properties of matrix multiplication.
Key Vocabulary	matrix, element, dimensions, row matrix, column matrix, square matrix, zero matrix, equal matrices		scalar scalar multiplication	
NGSSS	LA.910.1.6.1		MA.912.D.8.2	MA.912.D.8.2
Multiple Representations	p. 190		p. 198	
Lesson Resources	**Chapter 4 Resource Masters** • Study Guide and Intervention, pp. 5–6 AL OL ELL • Skills Practice, p. 7 AL OL ELL • Practice, p. 8 AL OL BL ELL • Word Problem Practice, p. 9 AL OL BL ELL • Enrichment, p. 10 OL BL **Transparencies** • 5-Minute Check Transparency 4-1 AL OL BL ELL **Additional Print Resources** • Study Notebook AL OL BL ELL • Teaching Algebra with Manipulatives, pp. 197-198 AL OL ELL	**Materials** • computer with spreadsheet program	**Chapter 4 Resource Masters** • Study Guide and Intervention, pp. 11–12 AL OL ELL • Skills Practice, p. 13 AL OL ELL • Practice, p. 14 AL OL BL ELL • Word Problem Practice, p. 15 AL OL BL ELL • Enrichment, p. 16 OL BL • Quiz 1, p. 45 AL OL BL ELL **Transparencies** • 5-Minute Check Transparency 4-2 AL OL BL ELL **Additional Print Resources** • Study Notebook AL OL BL ELL	**Chapter 4 Resource Masters** • Study Guide and Intervention, pp. 17–18 AL OL ELL • Skills Practice, p. 19 AL OL ELL • Practice, p. 20 AL OL BL ELL • Word Problem Practice, p. 21 AL OL BL ELL • Enrichment, p. 22 OL BL • Quiz 2, p. 45 AL OL BL ELL **Transparencies** • 5-Minute Check Transparency 4-3 AL OL BL ELL **Additional Print Resources** • Study Notebook AL OL BL ELL
Technology for Every Lesson	FL Math Online glencoe.com • Extra Examples • Personal Tutor • Self-Check Quizzes • Homework Help	**CD/DVD Resources** IWB INTERACTIVE WHITEBOARD READY IWB StudentWorks Plus IWB Interactive Classroom IWB Diagnostic and Assessment Planner		• TeacherWorks Plus • eSolutions Manual Plus • ExamView Assessment Suite
Get Animated				Animation
Differentiated Instruction	pp. 189, 191		pp. 195, 199	pp. 201, 202

Formative Assessment Mid-Chapter Quiz, p. 208

KEY: AL Approaching Level OL On Level BL Beyond Level ELL English Learners

Suggested Pacing

Time Periods	Instruction	Review & Assessment	Total
45-minute	8	2	10
90-minute	5	1	6

Matrices

Lesson 4-4 Pacing: 1 day	Extend 4-4 Pacing: 1 day	Lesson 4-5 Pacing: 1 day	Lesson 4-6 Pacing: 1 day	Extend 4-6 Pacing: 0.5 day
Transformations with Matrices	**Algebra Lab: Vectors and Matrices**	**Determinants and Cramer's Rule**	**Inverse Matrices and Systems of Equations**	**Graphing Technology Lab: Augmented Matrices**
• Use matrices for translations and dilations. • Use matrices for reflections and rotations.	• Use matrices to express the component form of a vector and to add two vectors.	• Evaluate determinants. • Solve systems of linear equations by using Cramer's Rule.	• Find the inverse of a 2×2 matrix. • Write and solve matrix equations for a system of equations.	• Use a graphing calculator and the augmented matrix for a system of equations to solve the system.
vertex matrix, preimage, image, translation, dilation, rotation		determinant, second-order determinant, third-order determinant, diagonal rule, Cramer's Rule, coefficient matrix	identity matrix inverses matrix equation variable matrix constant matrix	
MA.912.G.2.4		MA.912.A.3.14	MA.912.A.3.14	MA.912.A.3.14
p. 216				
Chapter 4 Resource Masters • Study Guide and Intervention, pp. 23–24 AL OL ELL • Skills Practice, p. 25 AL OL ELL • Practice, p. 26 AL OL BL ELL • Word Problem Practice, p. 27 AL OL BL ELL • Enrichment, p. 28 OL BL • Graphing Calculator Activity, p. 29 OL **Transparencies** • 5-Minute Check Transparency 4-4 AL OL BL ELL **Additional Print Resources** • Study Notebook AL OL BL ELL	**Materials** • grid paper **Additional Print Resources** • Teaching Algebra with Manipulatives, pp. 1, 199–200 AL OL ELL	**Chapter 4 Resource Masters** • Study Guide and Intervention, pp. 30–31 AL OL ELL • Skills Practice, p. 32 AL OL ELL • Practice, p. 33 AL OL BL ELL • Word Problem Practice, p. 34 AL OL BL ELL • Enrichment, p. 35 OL BL • Spreadsheet Activity, p. 36 OL • Quiz 3, p. 46 AL OL BL ELL **Transparencies** • 5-Minute Check Transparency 4-5 AL OL BL ELL **Additional Print Resources** • Study Notebook AL OL BL ELL • Teaching Algebra with Manipulatives, p. 201 AL OL ELL	**Chapter 4 Resource Masters** • Study Guide and Intervention, pp. 37–38 AL OL ELL • Skills Practice, p. 39 AL OL ELL • Practice, p. 40 AL OL BL ELL • Word Problem Practice, p. 41 AL OL BL ELL • Enrichment, p. 42 OL BL • Quiz 4, p. 46 AL OL BL ELL **Transparencies** • 5-Minute Check Transparency 4-6 AL OL BL ELL **Additional Print Resources** • Study Notebook AL OL BL ELL	**Materials** • TI-83/84 Plus or other graphing calculator

FL Math Online glencoe.com
- Extra Examples
- Self-Check Quizzes
- Personal Tutor
- Homework Help

CD/DVD Resources IWB INTERACTIVE WHITEBOARD READY
- IWB StudentWorks Plus
- IWB Interactive Classroom
- IWB Diagnostic and Assessment Planner
- TeacherWorks Plus
- eSolutions Manual Plus
- ExamView Assessment Suite

Interactive Lab				
p. 217		pp. 221, 224, 228	pp. 231, 235	

Summative Assessment
- Study Guide and Review, pp. 237–240
- Practice Test, p. 241

CHAPTER 4 Assessment and Intervention

SE = Student Edition, **TE** = Teacher Edition, **CRM** = Chapter Resource Masters

	Diagnosis	Prescription
Diagnostic Assessment	**Beginning Chapter 4**	
	Get Ready for Chapter 4 **SE,** p. 183	Response to Intervention **TE,** p. 183
	Beginning Every Lesson	
	Then, Now, Why? **SE** 5-Minute Check Transparencies	Chapter 0 **SE,** pp. P1–P19 Concepts and Skills Bank **SE** pp. 994–1007
Formative Assessment	**During/After Every Lesson**	
	Guided Practice **SE,** every example Check Your Understanding **SE** H.O.T. Problems **SE** Spiral Review **SE** Additional Examples **TE** Watch Out! **TE** Step 4, Assess **TE** Chapter 4 Quizzes **CRM,** pp. 45–46 Self-Check Quizzes glencoe.com	**Tier 1 Intervention** Concepts and Skills Bank **SE,** pp. 994–1007 Skills Practice **CRM,** Ch. 1–4 glencoe.com **Tier 2 Intervention** Differentiated Instruction **TE** Study Guide and Intervention Masters **CRM,** Ch. 1–4 **Tier 3 Intervention** *Math Triumphs, Alg. 2*
	Mid-Chapter	
	Mid-Chapter Quiz **SE,** p. 208 Mid-Chapter Test **CRM,** p. 47 ExamView Assessment Suite	**Tier 1 Intervention** Concepts and Skills Bank **SE,** pp. 994–1007 Skills Practice **CRM,** Ch. 1–4 glencoe.com **Tier 2 Intervention** Study Guide and Intervention Masters **CRM,** Ch. 1–4 **Tier 3 Intervention** *Math Triumphs, Alg. 2*
	Before Chapter Test	
	Chapter Study Guide and Review **SE,** pp. 237–240 Practice Test **SE,** p. 241 Standardized Test Practice **SE,** pp. 242–245 Chapter Test glencoe.com Standardized Test Practice glencoe.com Vocabulary Review glencoe.com ExamView Assessment Suite	**Tier 1 Intervention** Concepts and Skills Bank **SE,** pp. 994–1007 Skills Practice **CRM,** Ch. 1–4 glencoe.com **Tier 2 Intervention** Study Guide and Intervention Masters **CRM,** Ch. 1–4 **Tier 3 Intervention** *Math Triumphs, Alg. 2*
Summative Assessment	**After Chapter 4**	
	Multiple-Choice Tests, Forms 1, 2A, 2B **CRM,** pp. 49–54 Free-Response Tests, Forms 2C, 2D, 3 **CRM,** pp. 55–60 Vocabulary Test **CRM,** p. 48 Extended Response Test **CRM,** p. 61 Standardized Test Practice **CRM,** pp. 63–64 ExamView Assessment Suite	Study Guide and Intervention Masters **CRM,** Ch. 1–4 glencoe.com

Differentiated Instruction

Option 1 Reaching All Learners AL OL BL ELL

LOGICAL Identify those students who know how to perform matrix operations using their graphing calculators. Ask these students to make a list of the series of keystrokes needed. Then have these students demonstrate, to classmates experiencing difficulty, how to use the graphing calculator to perform matrix operations.

VISUAL/SPATIAL When students are drawing a figure and its images in a coordinate plane, have them consistently use one color for the original figure, a different color for the image found when translating, a third color when rotating, a fourth when dilating, and a fifth when reflecting.

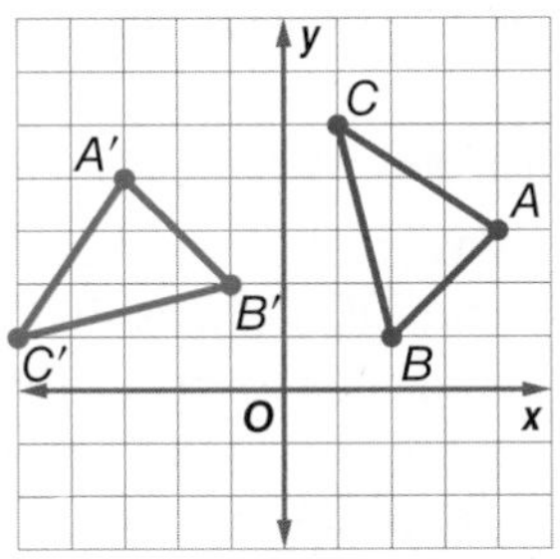

Option 2 Approaching Level AL

On the board, draw a table of data having at least three columns and two rows. As you tell students that the data in your table can be represented efficiently in a matrix, erase the column and row titles and draw matrix brackets around the data. Use this matrix to introduce the vocabulary pertaining to matrices: *element, dimensions, row, column, etc.*

Option 3 English Learners ELL

When introducing transformations of polygons on a coordinate plane using matrices, review with students other ways they know how to say translate (side, move), reflect (flip), dilate (enlarge, reduce) and rotate (turn, clockwise, counterclockwise). Demonstrate these movements as you review the terms.

Option 4 Beyond Level BL

Challenge students to use a system of equations to derive Cramer's Rule. The following method is one way to do this. Using the following system, $\begin{cases} ax + by = c \\ dx + ey = f \end{cases}$, solve for x in both equations to get $x = \frac{c - by}{a}$ and $x = \frac{f - ey}{d}$.

Equate these two values and solve for y.

$\frac{c - by}{a} = \frac{f - ey}{d}$, so $y = \frac{dc - af}{db - ae}$.

In a similar way, solve for y in both original equations. Then equate the two values and solve for x.

$y = \frac{c - ax}{b}$ and $y = \frac{f - dx}{e}$, so $\frac{c - ax}{b} = \frac{f - dx}{e}$ and $x = \frac{ce - bf}{ae - bd}$.

Then have students compare these values for x and y with the matrices formed when using Cramer's Rule.

FL Math Online Access Point Activities

CHAPTER 4

Focus on Mathematical Content

Vertical Alignment

Before Chapter 4

Related Topics before Algebra 1

- use appropriate operations to solve problems involving rational numbers
- graph dilations, reflections, and translations on a coordinate plane

Related Topics from Algebra 1

- represent relationships among quantities using tables

Previous Topics from Algebra 2

- transform and solve equations

Chapter 4

Related Topics from Algebra 2

- organize data
- analyze situations and formulate systems of equations in two or more unknowns to solve problems
- use matrices to solve systems of equations

After Chapter 4

Preparation for Precalculus

- define functions, describe characteristics of functions, and translate among verbal, numerical, graphical, and symbolic representations of functions
- use functions and their properties to model and solve real-life problems

Lesson-by-Lesson Preview

4-1 Introduction to Matrices

Matrices are introduced as a way to organize and analyze data. A matrix can be described by its dimensions. For example, a matrix with m rows and n columns is an $m \times n$ matrix.

- A *row matrix* is a matrix with only one row.
- A *column matrix* is a matrix with only one column.
- A *square matrix* is a matrix that has the same number of rows and columns.
- A *zero matrix* is a matrix in which every element is zero.
- *Equal matrices* are matrices that have the same dimensions, and each element of one matrix is equal to the corresponding element of the others. Students use equal matrices to solve equations.

4-2 Operations with Matrices

To add or subtract two matrices, first check to see that the matrices have the same dimensions. Then calculate the sum or difference of corresponding elements. The sum or difference of the two matrices will have the same dimensions as the two matrices being added or subtracted.

The product of a scalar and a matrix is found by multiplying every element in the matrix by the scalar. The product is a matrix that has the same dimensions as the matrix being multiplied. For example,

$$2\begin{bmatrix} -2 & 1 & 0 \\ 4 & -1 & 3 \end{bmatrix} = \begin{bmatrix} 2(-2) & 2(1) & 2(0) \\ 2(4) & 2(-1) & 2(3) \end{bmatrix} = \begin{bmatrix} -4 & 2 & 0 \\ 8 & -2 & 6 \end{bmatrix}.$$

Properties of matrix operations are examined. Students look at examples that illustrate the Commutative and Associative Properties of matrix addition and the Distributive Property of scalar multiplication.

4-3 Multiplying Matrices

When multiplying two matrices, it is important to first determine whether the matrix product is defined. Two matrices can only be multiplied if the number of columns in the first matrix is equal to the number of rows in the second column. For example, the product of $A_{m \times n}$ and $B_{n \times t}$ is a matrix with dimensions $m \times t$.

Matrix multiplication combines all the elements of a row in one matrix with all the elements of a column in the second matrix. Like matrix addition and subtraction, the result of the combination is a single element. For example,

$$\begin{bmatrix} 3 & -2 \\ 1 & 4 \end{bmatrix} \cdot \begin{bmatrix} 2 & 4 \\ 5 & 1 \end{bmatrix} = \begin{bmatrix} 3(2) + -2(5) & 3(4) + -2(1) \\ 1(2) + 4(5) & 1(4) + 4(1) \end{bmatrix}$$

$$= \begin{bmatrix} -4 & 10 \\ 22 & 8 \end{bmatrix}.$$

The Associative Property of Multiplication and the Distributive Property hold true for matrix multiplication, but the Commutative Property of Multiplication does not.

4-4 Transformations with Matrices

A column matrix can be used to represent a point on a coordinate plane.

- To describe a *translation* of a polygon, the coordinates of the *n* vertices of the polygon are written as the *n* columns of a 2-by-*n* matrix. The translation is written as a 2-by-*n* matrix, where each column is the same. The sum of the two matrices gives the coordinates of the result of the translation.
- Scalar multiplication can be used to describe a *dilation* (change of size) of a figure.
- Matrix multiplication can be used to *reflect* and *rotate* figures. When a matrix of the coordinates of a figure is multiplied by a *reflection matrix* or a *rotation matrix,* the resulting matrix gives coordinates of the reflected or rotated figure.

4-5 Determinants and Cramer's Rule

Every square matrix has a determinant. The determinant of a 2×2 matrix can be evaluated by calculating the difference of the products of the two diagonals. The determinant of a 3×3 can be evaluated using the diagonal rule.

If the coordinates of the vertices of a triangle are known, a determinant can be used to find the area of the triangle. For example, the area of a triangle having vertices at (a, b), (c, d), and (e, f) is $|A|$, where $A = \frac{1}{2}\begin{vmatrix} a & b & 1 \\ c & d & 1 \\ e & f & 1 \end{vmatrix}$.

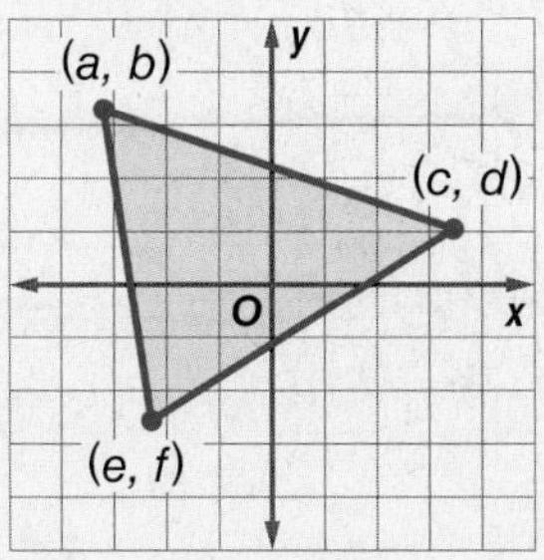

Cramer's Rule can be used to solve systems of equations. To use Cramer's Rule to solve a system of equations,

- write each equation in standard form,
- then set each variable equal to a fraction whose denominator and numerator are both determinants. The determinant in the denominator contains the coefficients of the variables. The determinant in the numerator is different for each variable.

A system has no solution if the value of the determinant in the denominator is zero.

4-6 Inverse Matrices and Systems of Equations

The identity matrix for multiplication is a square matrix with 1 for every element of the main diagonal and 0 in all other positions. When a matrix is multiplied by an identity matrix, the result is the same as the original matrix.

Two square matrices are inverses of each other if their product is the identity matrix. The multiplicative inverse for a 2×2 matrix is given by a product of two factors.

- One factor is a fraction whose numerator is 1 and whose denominator is the determinant of the given matrix.
- The second factor is the given matrix modified. The elements along the left-to-right diagonal are switched and the elements along the other diagonal are multiplied by –1.

A single matrix equation can be written to represent a system of equations. One side of the matrix equation shows the matrix of coefficients times a column matrix of variables. On the other side of the equation is a column matrix of the constants. To solve the system, multiply each side of the matrix equation by the inverse of the coefficient matrix.

McGraw Hill Professional Development

Targeted professional development has been articulated throughout *Algebra 2.* More quality, customized professional development is available from McGraw-Hill Professional Development. Visit glencoe.com for details on each product.

- **Online Lessons** emphasize the strategies and techniques used to teach Algebra 2. Includes streaming video, interactive pages, and online tools.
- **Video Workshops** allow mentors, coaches, or leadership personnel to facilitate on-site workshops on educational strategies in mathematics and mathematical concepts.
- **MHPD Online** (www.mhpdonline.com) offers online professional development with video clips of instructional strategies, links, student activities, and news and issues in education.
- **Teaching Today** (teachingtoday.glencoe.com) gives secondary teachers practical strategies and materials that inspire excellence and innovation in teaching.

Chapter Project

Animation

Students use what they have learned about matrices and matrix operations to perform transformations on geometric figures.

- Have students work in pairs to draw a figure on graph paper that consists only of line segments, with one vertex of the figure being at the origin.
- Have them identify the *x*- and *y*-coordinates of each vertex of the figure and write them in a two-column matrix called *C*.
- Ask them to choose a factor *m* by which to magnify or reduce the size of their figure. Then they write a magnification matrix $M = \begin{bmatrix} m & 0 \\ 0 & m \end{bmatrix}$. Find the matrix product *CM*, and read new coordinates for all vertices from the resulting matrix. Then plot the transformed figure.
- Have them investigate what happens to the transformed figure when the two numbers in the *M* matrix are different, or when one or both are negative.

CHAPTER 4 Matrices

Then
In Chapter 3, you solved systems of equations.

Now
In Chapter 4, you will:
- Organize data in matrices.
- Perform operations with matrices and determinants.
- Find inverses of matrices.
- Use matrices to solve systems of equations.

NGSSS
MA.912.A.3.14

Why?
GRAPHICS Computer graphics and animation use complex models for characters, objects, and scenery. These computer models describe the shapes of objects and the motions of characters. The animation models use matrices to describe the locations of specific points in the images.

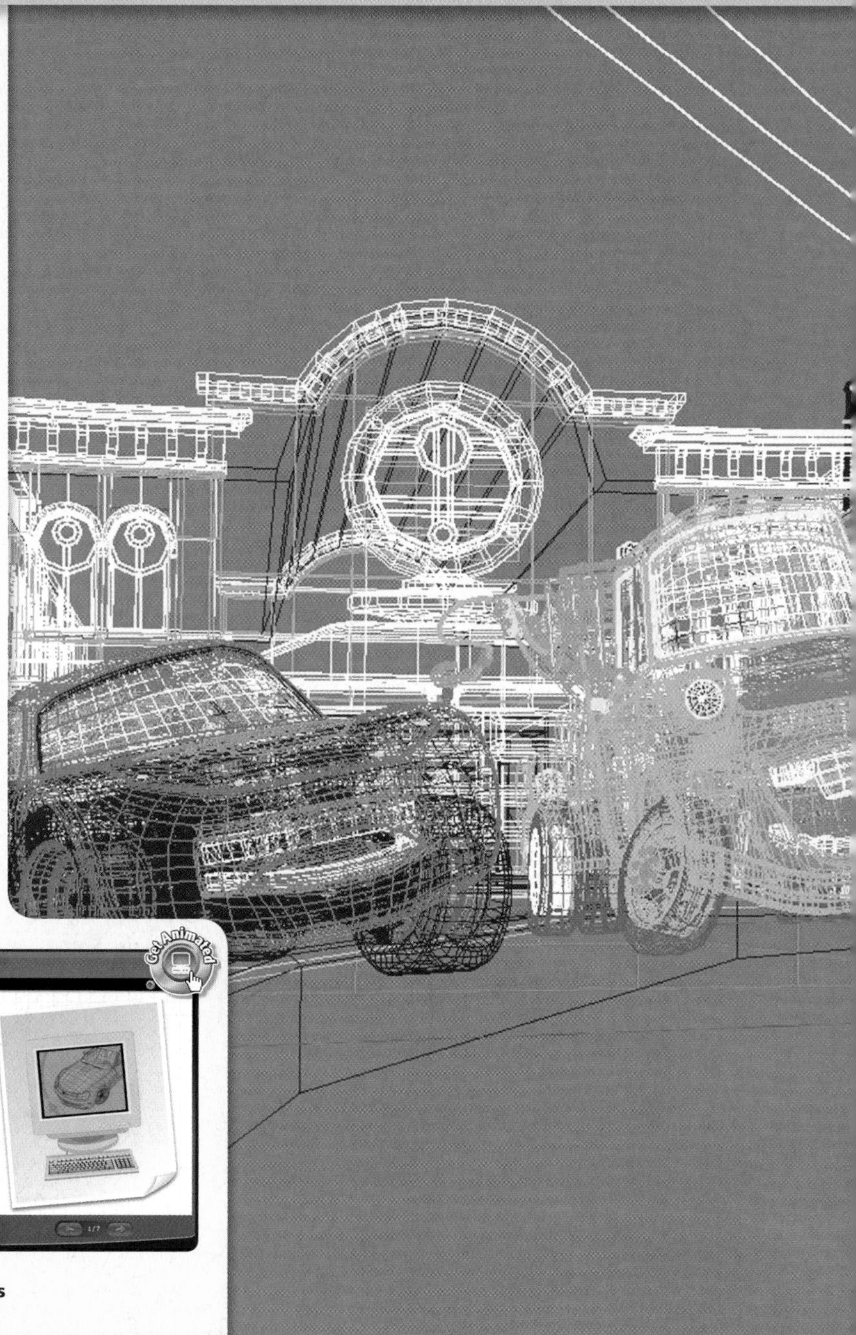

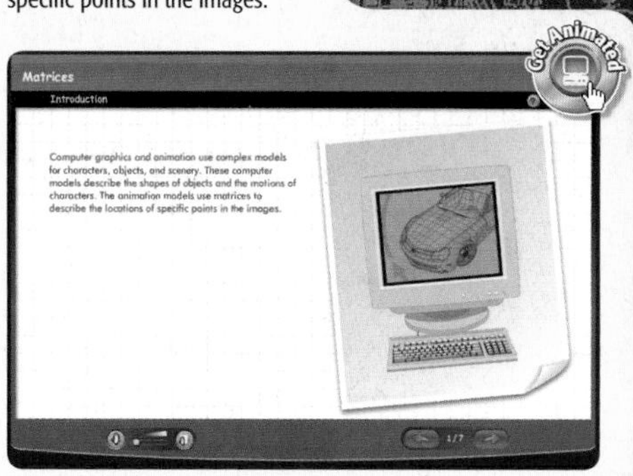

Key Vocabulary Introduce the key vocabulary in the chapter using the routine below.

Define: A scalar is a constant by which a matrix is multiplied.

Example: If $t = \begin{bmatrix} 5 & 11 \\ -3 & 7 \end{bmatrix}$, then

$$3t = \begin{bmatrix} (3)(5) & (3)(11) \\ (3)(-3) & (3)(7) \end{bmatrix} \text{ or } \begin{bmatrix} 15 & 33 \\ -9 & 21 \end{bmatrix}$$

Ask: What is a scalar? A constant that is multiplied by each element in the matrix.

Get Ready for Chapter 4

Diagnose Readiness You have two options for checking Prerequisite Skills.

Text Option Take the Quick Check below. Refer to the Quick Review for help.

QuickCheck

(Used in Lessons 4-2 and 4-6)

Name the additive inverse and the multiplicative inverse for each number. (Lesson 1-2)

1. 4 $-4, \frac{1}{4}$
2. -15 $15, -\frac{1}{15}$
3. 0.2 $-0.2, 5$
4. -1.35 $1.35, -\frac{20}{27}$
5. $-\frac{3}{4}$ $\frac{3}{4}, -\frac{4}{3}$
6. $2\frac{1}{3}$ $-2\frac{1}{3}, \frac{3}{7}$

(Used in Lessons 4-1 through 4-6)

Simplify each expression. (Lesson 1-2)

7. $6(x + 2y)$ $6x + 12y$
8. $4(x + 5) - 3$ $4x + 17$
9. $-4(3x) - (7x - 6)$ $-19x + 6$
10. $5(2x - 5) - \frac{1}{3}(4x + 1)$ $\frac{26}{3}x - \frac{76}{3}$
11. $6(2x - 1) - 3(y - x) + 0.5(4x - 6)$ $17x - 3y - 9$

(Used in Lessons 4-6 and 4-8)

Solve each system of equations by using either substitution or elimination. (Lesson 3-2)

12. $y = x + 3$, $2x - y = -1$ $(2, 5)$
13. $2x - 5y = -18$, $3x + 4y = 19$ $(1, 4)$
14. $4y + 6x = -6$, $5y - x = 35$ $(-5, 6)$
15. $x = y - 8$, $4x + 2y = 4$ $(-2, 6)$
16. **MONEY** The student council paid $15 per registration for a conference. They also paid $10 for T-shirts for a total of $180. Last year, they spent $12 per registration and $9 per T-shirt for a total of $150 to buy the same number of registrations and T-shirts. Write and solve a system of two equations that represents the number of registrations and T-shirts bought each year. See margin.

QuickReview

EXAMPLE 1

Name the additive inverse and the multiplicative inverse for −5.

The additive inverse of -5 is a number x such that $-5 + x = 0$. So, $x = 5$.

The multiplicative inverse of -5 is a number x, such that $-5x = 1$. So, $x = -\frac{1}{5}$.

EXAMPLE 2

Simplify $\frac{3}{4}(8x - 4) + 3x$.

$\frac{3}{4}(8x - 4) + 3x$

$= \frac{3}{4}(8x) - \frac{3}{4}(4) + 3x$ Distributive Property

$= 6x - 3 + 3x$ Simplify.

$= 9x - 3$ Add.

EXAMPLE 3

Solve the system of equations algebraically.

$3y = x - 9$

$4x + 5y = 2$

Since x has a coefficient of 1 in the first equation, use the substitution method. First, solve that equation for x.

$3y = x - 9 \rightarrow x = 3y + 9$

$4(3y + 9) + 5y = 2$ Substitute $3y + 9$ for x.

$12y + 36 + 5y = 2$ Distributive Property

$17y = -34$ Combine like terms.

$y = -2$ Divide each side by 17.

To find x, use $y = -2$ in the first equation.

$3(-2) = x - 9$ Substitute -2 for y.

$-6 = x - 9$ Multiply.

$3 = x$ Add 9 to each side.

The solution is $(3, -2)$.

Online Option FL Math Online Take a self-check Chapter Readiness Quiz at glencoe.com.

Additional Answer

16. $15x + 10y = 180$
$12x + 9y = 150$
number of registrations = 8
number of T-shirts = 6

Get Ready for Chapter 4

Response to Intervention (RtI)

Use the *Quick Check* results and the Intervention Planner to help you determine your Response to Intervention. The If-Then statements in the chart below help you decide the appropriate tier of RtI and suggest intervention resources for each tier.

Intervention Planner

Tier 1 On Level

If students miss about 25% of the exercises or less,

Then choose a resource:

- **SE** Lessons 1-2 and 3-2
- **CRM** Skills Practice, Chapter 1, p. 13, Chapter 3, p. 14
- **TE** Chapter Project, p. 182
- FL Math Online Self-Check Quiz

Tier 2 Strategic Intervention approaching grade level

If students miss about 50% of the exercises,

Then choose a resource:

- **CRM** Study Guide and Intervention, Chapter 1, pp. 11–12, Chapter 3, pp. 12–13
- FL Math Online Extra Examples, Personal Tutor, Homework Help

Tier 3 Intensive Intervention 2 or more years below grade level

If students miss about 75% of the exercises,

Then use *Math Triumphs, Alg. 2*

FL Math Online Extra Examples, Personal Tutor, Homework Help, Review Vocabulary

CHAPTER 4 Notes

FOLDABLES® Study Organizer

Dinah Zike's Foldables®

Focus As students read and study this chapter, they show examples and write notes about matrices on cards that are placed in the pockets of the Foldables.

Teach Have students make and label their Foldables as illustrated. At the end of each lesson, ask students to write down each vocabulary word on a separate index card. On the opposite side of the card, have students write the word's definition. Point out to students that these cards can be used as flashcards to review the vocabulary as they work through the lessons.

When to Use It Encourage students to add to their Foldables as they work through the chapter and to use them to review for the chapter test.

Differentiated Instruction

CRM Student-Built Glossary, pp. 1–2
Students should complete the chart by providing a definition of each term and an example as they progress through Chapter 4. This study tool can also be used to review for the chapter test.

Get Started on Chapter 4

You will learn several new concepts, skills, and vocabulary terms as you study Chapter 4. To get ready, identify important terms and organize your resources. You may wish to refer to **Chapter 0** to review prerequisite skills.

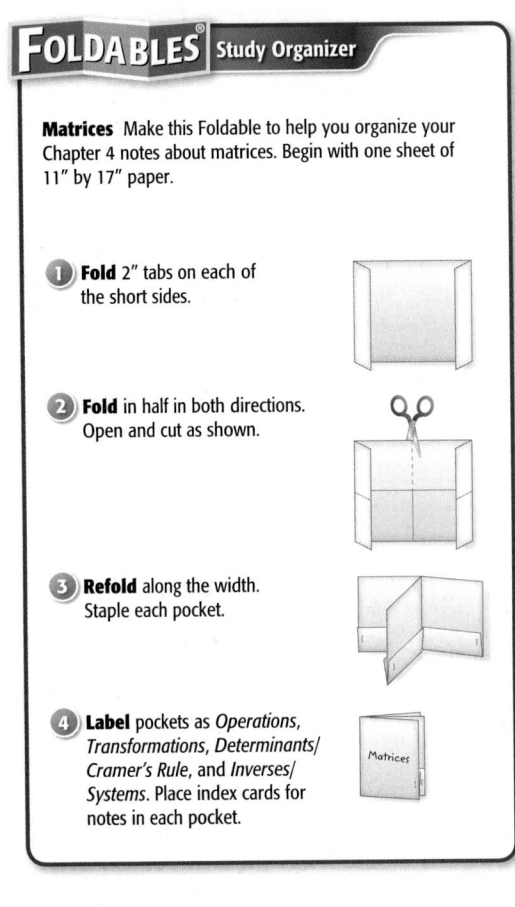

FOLDABLES® Study Organizer

Matrices Make this Foldable to help you organize your Chapter 4 notes about matrices. Begin with one sheet of 11″ by 17″ paper.

1. **Fold** 2″ tabs on each of the short sides.

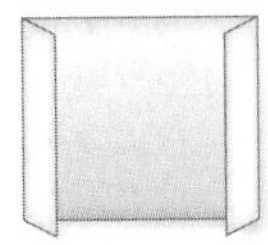

2. **Fold** in half in both directions. Open and cut as shown.

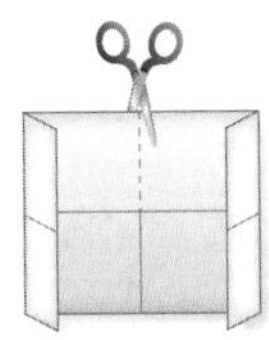

3. **Refold** along the width. Staple each pocket.

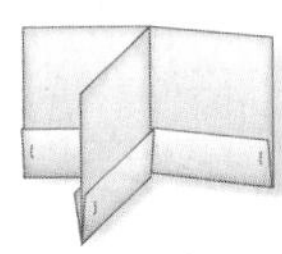

4. **Label** pockets as *Operations*, *Transformations*, *Determinants/Cramer's Rule*, and *Inverses/Systems*. Place index cards for notes in each pocket.

FL Math Online glencoe.com

- Study the chapter online
- Explore **Get Animated**
- Get extra help from your own **Personal Tutor**
- Use **Extra Examples** for additional help
- Take a **Self-Check Quiz**
- **Review Vocabulary** in fun ways

New Vocabulary

English		Español
element	• p. 185 •	elemento
dimensions	• p. 185 •	tamaño
row matrix	• p. 186 •	matriz fila
column matrix	• p. 186 •	matriz columna
square matrix	• p. 186 •	matriz cuadrada
zero matrix	• p. 186 •	matriz nula
equal matrices	• p. 186 •	matrices iguales
scalar	• p. 194 •	escalar
vertex matrix	• p. 209 •	matriz de vértice
preimage	• p. 209 •	preimagen
image	• p. 209 •	imagen
rotation	• p. 212 •	rotación
determinant	• p. 220 •	determinante
Cramer's Rule	• p. 223 •	regula de Crámer
coefficient matrix	• p. 223 •	matriz coefficiente
identity matrix	• p. 229 •	matriz identidad
inverse matrix	• p. 229 •	matriz inversa
matrix equation	• p. 231 •	ecuación matriz
variable matrix	• p. 231 •	matriz variables
constant matrix	• p. 231 •	matriz constante

Review Vocabulary

coordinate plane • Algebra 1 • plano de coordenadas the plane connecting the x- and y-axes

system of equations • p. 135 • sistema de ecuaciones a set of equations with the same variables

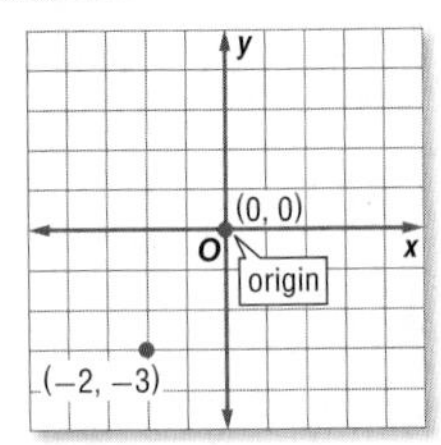

Multilingual eGlossary glencoe.com

4-1 Introduction to Matrices

Why?

SHOPPING Julie is shopping for a new smartphone and discovers that many different options are available. She wants to be able to easily compare the options, so she decides to organize the data in a matrix.

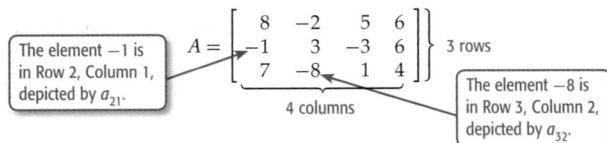

	Price	Memory	Color	Interface
Choice 1	$420	512	24	infrared
Choice 2	$399	512	24	Bluetooth
Choice 3	$315	256	24	infrared
Choice 4	$289	128	18	wi-fi

Then
You solved problems by organizing data in tables.

Now
- Organize data in matrices.
- Use matrix row and column operations to analyze data.

NGSSS

LA.910.1.6.1 The student will use new vocabulary that is introduced and taught directly.

New Vocabulary
matrix
element
dimensions
row matrix
column matrix
square matrix
zero matrix
equal matrices

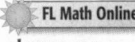

FL Math Online
glencoe.com

Organize Data A **matrix** is a rectangular array of variables or constants in horizontal rows and vertical columns, usually enclosed in brackets. In a matrix, the numbers or data are organized so that each position in the matrix has a purpose. Each value in the matrix is called an **element**. A matrix is usually named using an uppercase letter.

$$A = \begin{bmatrix} 8 & -2 & 5 & 6 \\ -1 & 3 & -3 & 6 \\ 7 & -8 & 1 & 4 \end{bmatrix} \text{ 3 rows, 4 columns}$$

The element −1 is in Row 2, Column 1, depicted by a_{21}.

The element −8 is in Row 3, Column 2, depicted by a_{32}.

A matrix can be described by its **dimensions**. A matrix with m rows and n columns is an $m \times n$ matrix (read "m by n"). Matrix A above is a 3×4 matrix because it has 3 rows and 4 columns. **a_{12} refers to an element of A, whereas b_{12} refers to an element of B.**

EXAMPLE 1 Dimensions and Elements of a Matrix

Use $A = \begin{bmatrix} -18 & 6 & 38 \\ 9 & -9 & 22 \end{bmatrix}$ to answer the following.

a. State the dimensions of A.

$$\begin{bmatrix} -18 & 6 & 38 \\ 9 & -9 & 22 \end{bmatrix} \text{ 2 rows, 3 columns}$$

Since A has 2 rows and 3 columns, the dimensions of A are 2×3.

b. Find the value of a_{21}.

$$\begin{bmatrix} -18 & 6 & 38 \\ 9 & -9 & 22 \end{bmatrix}$$

Row 2, Column 1

Since a_{21} is the element in row 2, column 1, the value of a_{21} is 9.

Guided Practice

Use $B = \begin{bmatrix} 10 & -8 \\ -2 & 19 \\ 6 & -1 \end{bmatrix}$ to answer the following.

1A. State the dimensions of B. 3×2

1B. Find the value of b_{32}. −1

Personal Tutor glencoe.com

4-1 Lesson Notes

1 FOCUS

Vertical Alignment

Before Lesson 4-1
Solve problems by organizing data in tables.

Lesson 4-1
Organize data in matrices.
Use matrix row and column operations to analyze data.

After Lesson 4-1
Use matrices to solve systems of equations.

2 TEACH

Scaffolding Questions

Have students read the *Why?* section of the lesson.

Ask:
- How many rows appear in the smartphone matrix? 4
- How many columns are there in the smartphone matrix? 4
- What number appears in row 3, column 2? 256

Organize Data

Example 1 shows how to determine the dimensions and identify the elements of a matrix. **Example 2** shows how to organize real-world data in a matrix.

Lesson 4-1 Resources

Resource	Approaching-Level	On-Level	Beyond-Level	English Learners
Teacher Edition	• Differentiated Instruction, p. 189	• Differentiated Instruction, pp. 189, 191	• Differentiated Instruction, p. 191	• Differentiated Instruction, p. 189
Chapter Resource Masters	• Study Guide and Intervention, pp. 5–6 • Skills Practice, p. 7 • Practice, p. 8 • Word Problem Practice, p. 9	• Study Guide and Intervention, pp. 5–6 • Skills Practice, p. 7 • Practice, p. 8 • Word Problem Practice, p. 9 • Enrichment, p. 10	• Practice, p. 8 • Word Problem Practice, p. 9 • Enrichment, p. 10	• Study Guide and Intervention, pp. 5–6 • Skills Practice, p. 7 • Practice, p. 8 • Word Problem Practice, p. 9
Transparencies	• 5-Minute Check Transparency 4-1	• 5-Minute Check Transparency 4-1	• 5-Minute Check Transparency 4-1	• 5-Minute Check Transparency 4-1
Other	• Study Notebook • Teaching Algebra with Manipulatives	• Study Notebook • Teaching Algebra with Manipulatives	• Study Notebook	• Study Notebook • Teaching Algebra with Manipulatives

Formative Assessment

Use the Guided Practice exercises after each example to determine students' understanding of concepts.

Additional Examples

1 **a.** State the dimensions of matrix G if $G = \begin{bmatrix} 2 & -1 & 0 & 3 \\ 1 & 5 & -3 & 1 \end{bmatrix}$. 2×4

b. Find the value of a_{12}. -1

2 **COLLEGE** Kaitlin wants to attend one of three Iowa universities next year. She has gathered information about tuition (T), room and board (R/B), and enrollment (E) for the universities.

Iowa State University
T–$6160, R/B–$5958, E–26,160

University of Iowa
T–$6293, R/B–$7250, E–30,409

University of Northern Iowa
T–$5352, R/B–$6280, E–12,609

a. Organize the data as a matrix, with columns in the order of tuition, room and board, and enrollment.

	T	R/B	E
ISU	6160	5958	26,160
UI	6293	7250	30,409
UNI	5352	6280	12,609

b. What are the dimensions of the matrix? 3×3 What is the value of a_{32}? 6280

Additional Examples also in Interactive Classroom PowerPoint® Presentations

IWB INTERACTIVE WHITEBOARD READY

Tips for New Teachers

Understanding Notation Stress that matrix dimensions are always given as "rows by columns."

Certain matrices have special names.

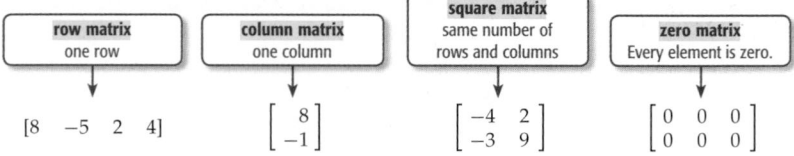

- **row matrix** one row: $[8 \quad -5 \quad 2 \quad 4]$
- **column matrix** one column: $\begin{bmatrix} 8 \\ -1 \end{bmatrix}$
- **square matrix** same number of rows and columns: $\begin{bmatrix} -4 & 2 \\ -3 & 9 \end{bmatrix}$
- **zero matrix** Every element is zero.: $\begin{bmatrix} 0 & 0 & 0 \\ 0 & 0 & 0 \end{bmatrix}$

StudyTip

Corresponding Elements *Corresponding* refers to elements that are in the exact same position in each matrix.

Two matrices are considered **equal matrices** if they have the same dimensions and if each element of one matrix is equal to the corresponding element in the other matrix.

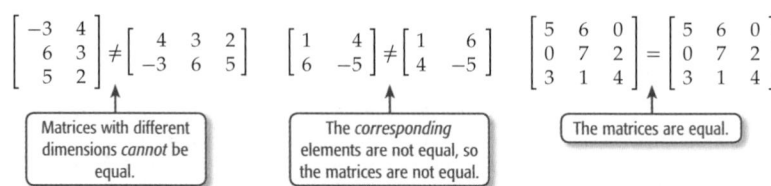

$$\begin{bmatrix} -3 & 4 \\ 6 & 3 \\ 5 & 2 \end{bmatrix} \neq \begin{bmatrix} 4 & 3 & 2 \\ -3 & 6 & 5 \end{bmatrix}$$

Matrices with different dimensions *cannot* be equal.

$$\begin{bmatrix} 1 & 4 \\ 6 & -5 \end{bmatrix} \neq \begin{bmatrix} 1 & 6 \\ 4 & -5 \end{bmatrix}$$

The *corresponding* elements are not equal, so the matrices are not equal.

$$\begin{bmatrix} 5 & 6 & 0 \\ 0 & 7 & 2 \\ 3 & 1 & 4 \end{bmatrix} = \begin{bmatrix} 5 & 6 & 0 \\ 0 & 7 & 2 \\ 3 & 1 & 4 \end{bmatrix}$$

The matrices are equal.

Matrices are used to organize and analyze data.

Real-World Link

In 2000, Tyler Ebell of Ventura, California, rushed for a high school record 4494 yards in one season.

Source: National Football League

Real-World EXAMPLE 2 Organize Data into a Matrix

FOOTBALL The West High School football team used five running backs throughout its season. Coach Williams wanted to compare the statistics of each player.

Joey: 11 games, 72 attempts, 439 yards, 6.10 average, 8 TDs

DeShawn: 9 games, 143 attempts, 1024 yards, 7.16 average, 12 TDs

Dario: 11 games, 164 attempts, 885 yards, 5.40 average, 15 TDs

Leo: 11 games, 84 attempts, 542 yards, 6.45 average, 7 TDs

Alex: 10 games, 151 attempts, 966 yards, 6.40 average, 11 TDs

a. Organize the data in a matrix, listing players in the first column, in order from most attempts to least attempts.

b. What are the dimensions of the matrix? What value is a_{34}?

a.

Player	Games	Attempts	Yards	Average	TDs
Dario	11	164	885	5.40	15
Alex	10	151	966	6.40	11
DeShawn	9	143	1024	7.16	12
Leo	11	84	542	6.45	7
Joey	11	72	439	6.10	8

b. There are five rows and five columns, so the dimensions are 5×5. The value a_{34}, which is in the third row and fourth column, is 7.16.

$$\begin{bmatrix} 11 & 164 & 885 & 5.40 & 15 \\ 10 & 151 & 966 & 6.40 & 11 \\ 9 & 143 & 1024 & 7.16 & 12 \\ 11 & 84 & 542 & 6.45 & 7 \\ 11 & 72 & 439 & 6.10 & 8 \end{bmatrix}$$

TEACH with TECH

WEB SEARCH Have students search the Web to find data that interests them such as the home attendance for 3 baseball teams on 3 days. Then show students how to use a matrix to organize this data.

Guided Practice

2. **SUBS** The figure at the right shows the prices of small, medium, and large subs.

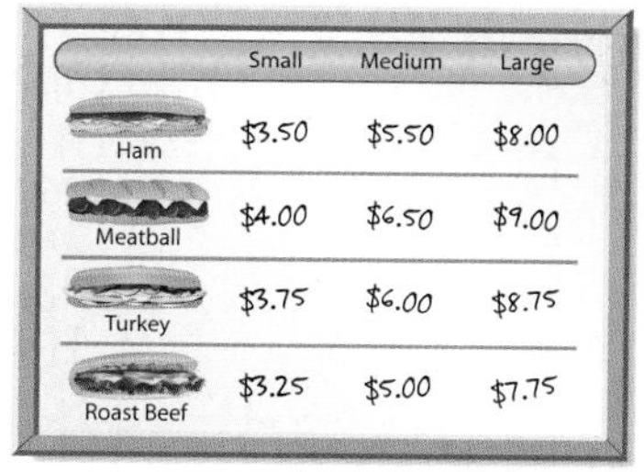

Small
Medium
Large
Ham
$3.50
$5.50
$8.00
Meatball
$4.00
$6.50
$9.00
Turkey
$3.75
$6.00
$8.75
Roast Beef
$3.25
$5.00
$7.75

   A. Organize the data in a matrix, listing the subs from least to most expensive. See margin.

   B. What are the dimensions of the matrix? 4×3

   C. What is the value of a_{21}? $3.50

Personal Tutor glencoe.com

Analyze Data Once data are organized in a matrix, they can be analyzed and interpreted. Sometimes, the sums or averages of rows or columns provide further analysis. Other times, the sums or averages provide data that are meaningless.

StudyTip

Displaying Data Matrices displaying real-world data can often be flipped, with the rows changing places with the columns.

EXAMPLE 3 Analyze Data with Matrices

FOOTBALL Coach Williams would like to use the matrix from Example 2 to further analyze his players' statistics.

G	Att	Yd	Avg.	TD
11	164	885	5.40	15
10	151	966	6.40	11
9	143	1024	7.16	12
11	84	542	6.45	7
11	72	439	6.10	8

a. Add the elements in columns 2 and 3 and interpret the results.

The sum of column 2 is 614.
This is the total number of attempts for the players.

The sum of column 3 is 3856.
This is the total number of yards gained.

b. Coach Williams wants to determine the average yards per attempt for his five running backs combined. He decides to add the elements in column 4 and divide by 5, the number of players. What is this average?

The average is 6.302.

c. Is this an accurate average? Explain.

No. The players did not have the same number of attempts, so finding the average of column 4 would not determine an accurate average. Instead, Coach Williams needs to divide the sum of column 3 by the sum of column 2. The accurate average is about 6.28.

d. Would adding the rows provide any meaningful data for Coach Williams? Explain your reasoning.

No. The sum of a row includes five different forms of data.

Guided Practice

3. **POPULATION** The table displays some of the U.S. Census data.

Latino Population in the U.S. (millions)		
Age	**Male**	**Female**
0–19	7.1	6.6
20–39	6.8	5.9
40–59	3.2	2.2
60+	1.1	1.4

   A. Organize the data in a matrix. See margin.

   B. Add the elements in the columns and interpret the results.

   C. Add the elements in the rows and interpret the results.

   D. Would finding the average of the rows or columns provide any meaningful data?

Personal Tutor glencoe.com

3B. Column 1: 18.2 million Hispanic males in the U.S.; Column 2: 16.1 million Hispanic females in the U.S.
3C. Row 1: 13.7 million Hispanics aged 0–19 in the U.S.; Row 2: 12.7 million Hispanics aged 20–39 in the U.S.; Row 3: 5.4 million Hispanics aged 40–59 in the U.S.; Row 4: 2.5 million Hispanics aged 60+ in the U.S.
3D. Sample answer: The average of the columns or the rows would not be meaningful.

Additional Answers (Guided Practice)

2A.

$$\begin{array}{r} \\ \text{Roast Beef} \\ \text{Ham} \\ \text{Turkey} \\ \text{Meatball} \end{array} \begin{array}{c} \text{Small Medium Large} \\ \begin{bmatrix} \$3.25 & \$5.00 & \$7.75 \\ \$3.50 & \$5.50 & \$8.00 \\ \$3.75 & \$6.00 & \$8.75 \\ \$4.00 & \$6.50 & \$9.00 \end{bmatrix} \end{array}$$

3A.

$$\begin{array}{r} 0\text{–}19 \\ 20\text{–}39 \\ 40\text{–}59 \\ 60+ \end{array} \begin{bmatrix} 7.1 & 6.6 \\ 6.8 & 5.9 \\ 3.2 & 2.2 \\ 1.1 & 1.4 \end{bmatrix}$$

Analyze Data

Example 3 shows how to use matrices to analyze data using row and column operations.

Additional Example

3 Use the matrix from Additional Example 2.

$$\begin{bmatrix} \$6160 & \$5958 & 26{,}160 \\ \$6293 & \$7250 & 30{,}409 \\ \$5352 & \$6280 & 12{,}609 \end{bmatrix}$$

a. Find the average of the elements in column 1, and interpret the result. The average tuition at the three universities is $5935.

b. Which university's total cost is the lowest? University of Northern Iowa

c. Would adding the elements of the rows provide meaningful data? Explain. No, the first two elements of a row are in dollars and the third is in numbers of people.

d. Would adding the elements of the third column provide meaningful data? Yes, the sum of the elements of the third column would be the total enrollment of all three schools.

Focus on Mathematical Content

Matrices A matrix provides a way to organize data. Each element in the matrix has a specific purpose. In order for matrices to be equal, they must have the same dimensions, and each element in one matrix must be equal to the corresponding element in the other matrix.

3 PRACTICE

Formative Assessment

Use Exercises 1–8 to check for understanding.

Use the chart at the bottom of this page to customize assignments for your students.

Check Your Understanding

Example 1 p. 185

State the dimensions of each matrix.

1. $\begin{bmatrix} 1 & 4 & -4 & 0 \\ -2 & 3 & 6 & -8 \end{bmatrix}$ 2×4

2. $\begin{bmatrix} 1 \\ -2 \\ 5 \\ -7 \end{bmatrix}$ 4×1

3. $\begin{bmatrix} -1 & 4 \\ 2 & 9 \\ 17 & 21 \end{bmatrix}$ 3×2

Identify each element of matrix $A = \begin{bmatrix} 1 & -6 & x & -4 \\ -2 & 3 & -1 & 9 \\ 5 & -8 & 2 & 12 \end{bmatrix}$.

4. a_{32} -8

5. a_{11} 1

6. a_{33} 2

7. a_{24} 9

Examples 2 and 3 pp. 186–187

8. **FINANCIAL LITERACY** Use the table that shows the city and highway gas mileage of five different types of vehicles.

Vehicle	SUV	Mini-van	Sedan	Compact	APV
City	23	21	21	42	61
Highway	25	24	32	49	70

Source: Auto Hoppers

a. Organize the gas mileages in a matrix. $\begin{bmatrix} 23 & 21 & 21 & 42 & 61 \\ 25 & 24 & 32 & 49 & 70 \end{bmatrix}$

b. Which type of vehicle has the best gas mileage? APV

c. Add the elements of each row and interpret the results.

d. Add the elements of each column and interpret the results. Sample answer: The sums are 48, 45, 53, 91, and 131. These values are irrelevant since they are the sums of 2 different types of data.

8c. Sample answer: City: The sum is 168. However, this value is irrelevant since it is the sum of 5 different types of data. Highway: The sum is 200. However, this value is irrelevant since it is the sum of 5 different types of data.

Practice and Problem Solving

● = **Step-by-Step Solutions** begin on page R20. **Extra Practice** begins on page 947.

Example 1 p. 185

State the dimensions of each matrix.

9. $\begin{bmatrix} -9 & 6 \end{bmatrix}$ 1×2

10. $\begin{bmatrix} 15 & y \\ 8 & -9 \end{bmatrix}$ 2×2

11. $\begin{bmatrix} 6 & 11 & -4 & -2 \\ -8 & 5 & -1 & 0 \end{bmatrix}$ 2×4

12. $\begin{bmatrix} 4 & -3 & -1 \\ x & 3y & 0 \\ 8 & 12 & 11 \end{bmatrix}$ 3×3

13. $\begin{bmatrix} 2 \\ x \\ -3 \end{bmatrix}$ 3×1

14. $\begin{bmatrix} 115 \end{bmatrix}$ 1×1

Identify each element for the following matrices.

$A = \begin{bmatrix} 6 & y \\ -9 & 31 \\ 11 & 5 \end{bmatrix}, B = \begin{bmatrix} 10 & -8 & 2x \\ -2 & 19 & 4 \end{bmatrix}$

15. a_{21} -9

16. b_{22} 19

17. b_{13} $2x$

18. a_{12} y

Example 2 p. 186

Organize the information in a matrix.

19.

Name	Game 1	Game 2	Game 3	Series
John	221	201	185	607
Hideo	168	233	159	560
Paulo	187	189	211	587

$\begin{matrix} \text{John} \\ \text{Hideo} \\ \text{Paulo} \end{matrix} \begin{bmatrix} 221 & 201 & 185 & 607 \\ 168 & 233 & 159 & 560 \\ 187 & 189 & 211 & 587 \end{bmatrix}$

Differentiated Homework Options

Level	Assignment	Two-Day Option	
AL Basic	9–21, 35–37, 39–40, 41–44, 45–55	9–21 odd, 41–44	10–20 even, 35–37, 39–40, 45–55
OL Core	9–25 odd, 26–29, 31, 33–37, 39–55	9–21, 41–44	22–37, 39–40, 45–55
BL Advanced	22–52, (optional: 53–55)		

20.

Name	Cell Phone Minutes	Text Messages	Picture Messages
Chee	95	227	138
Emelia	83	213	189
Lina	101	199	202

$\begin{matrix}\text{Chee}\\ \text{Emelia}\\ \text{Lina}\end{matrix}\begin{bmatrix}95 & 227 & 138\\ 83 & 213 & 189\\ 101 & 199 & 202\end{bmatrix}$

Example 3 p. 187

21b. Sample answer: Brand C; it was given the highest rating possible for cost and comfort, and a high rating for looks, and it will last a fairly long time.

21c. Sample answer: Yes; finding the sum of the rows and then calculating the average will provide an easy way to compare the data.

21. SHOES A consumer service company rated several pairs of shoes by cost, level of comfort, look, and longevity using a scale of 1–5, with 1 being low and 5 being high.

Brand	Cost	Comfort	Look	Longevity
A	3	2	2	1
B	4	3	2	3
C	5	5	4	4
D	1	5	5	2

a. Write a 4×4 matrix to organize this information. See margin.

b. Which shoe would you buy based on this information, and why?

c. Would finding the sum of the rows or columns provide any useful information? Explain your reasoning.

B **Identify each element for the following matrices.**

$$A = \begin{bmatrix} 23 & 11 \\ x & -5 \\ -12 & 15 \end{bmatrix}, B = \begin{bmatrix} 9 & -3 & 7 \\ 4x & 18 & -6 \end{bmatrix}$$

22. a_{32} 15 **23.** b_{21} $4x$ **24.** b_{12} -3 **25.** a_{21} x

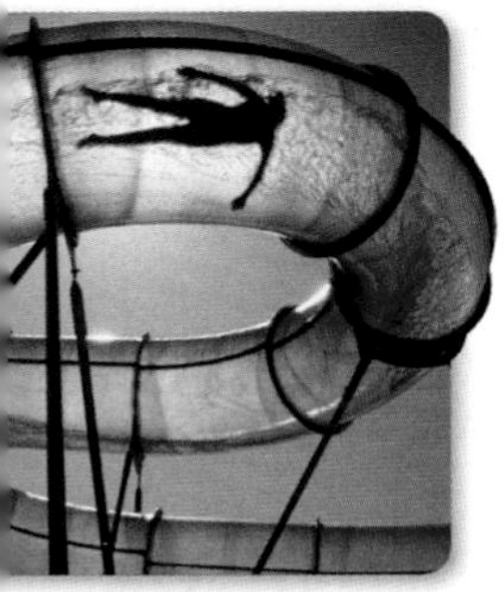

Real-World Link

There are more than 1000 waterparks in the U.S., with about 70 million visitors each year. The first waterpark to open was Wet 'N Wild in Orlando, Florida.

Source: World Waterpark Association

26. WATER PARK Use the sign at the entrance of the park shown at the right.

a. Write a matrix for the prices of admission for adults, children, and students. See margin.

b. What are the dimensions of the matrix? 3×2

Fun Time Water Park Ticket Information	
Before 5 P.M.	**After 5 P.M.**
Adult $34	Adult $24
Child $19	Child $9
Student .. $27	Student .. $17

27. TRAVEL Use the following flight costs for a flight to a certain city.

Coach: $249 weekday; $259 weekend
Business class: $279 weekday; $289 weekend
First class: $319 weekday; $339 weekend

a. Write a 3×2 matrix that represents the cost of each flight.

b. Write a 2×3 matrix that represents the cost of each flight.

27a. $\begin{bmatrix} 249 & 259 \\ 279 & 289 \\ 319 & 339 \end{bmatrix}$

27b. $\begin{bmatrix} 249 & 279 & 319 \\ 259 & 289 & 339 \end{bmatrix}$

28. INVENTORY Mr. Kelley owns three golf supply stores. Store 1 has 200 white, 100 red, and 150 yellow golf balls. Store 2 has 300 white, 175 red, and 225 yellow golf balls. Store 3 has 275 white, 150 red, and 220 yellow golf balls. a, c. See margin.

a. Organize this information into a matrix with store numbers as the column heads.

b. Find the sum of the columns. What does the sum represent?

c. Find the sum of the rows. What does the sum represent?

28b. Store 1: 450, Store 2: 700, Store 3: 645; the number of golf balls each store has

Identify each element for the following matrices.

$$A = \begin{bmatrix} x^2 + 4 & y + 6 \\ x - y & 2 - y \end{bmatrix}, B = \begin{bmatrix} 0 & x & -2y \\ 5x & 3y & -4x \\ -y & 0 & 0 \end{bmatrix}$$

29. a_{11} $x^2 + 4$ **30.** a_{22} $2 - y$ **31.** b_{31} $-y$ **32.** b_{23} $-4x$

Additional Answers

21a. $\begin{bmatrix} 3 & 2 & 2 & 1 \\ 4 & 3 & 2 & 3 \\ 5 & 5 & 4 & 4 \\ 1 & 5 & 5 & 2 \end{bmatrix}$

26a. $\begin{bmatrix} 34 & 24 \\ 19 & 9 \\ 27 & 17 \end{bmatrix}$

28a. $\begin{matrix} & \text{Store 1} & \text{Store 2} & \text{Store 3} \end{matrix}$

$\begin{matrix}\text{white}\\ \text{red}\\ \text{yellow}\end{matrix}\begin{bmatrix} 200 & 300 & 275 \\ 100 & 175 & 150 \\ 150 & 225 & 220 \end{bmatrix}$

28c. white: 775, red: 425, yellow: 595; the number of balls of each color Mr. Kelley has in his inventory

Differentiated Instruction

AL OL ELL

Social Learners Have students discuss examples that they have seen in which data are presented in rows and columns.

Real-World Link

In 2006, after a redefinition of the word "planet," it was decided that Pluto would no longer be considered a planet. It is now one of more than 40 dwarf planets.

Source: *National Geographic*

34b. goals: 19, assists: 18

33. PLANETS Use the table that shows the distance of the other planets from Earth and the Sun.

a. Organize the distances in a matrix. **See margin.**

b. What are the dimensions of the matrix? **7 × 2**

c. What is the value of a_{42}? **370**

Planet	Distance from Sun (millions of miles)	Distance from Earth (millions of miles)
Mercury	36.00	57
Venus	67.24	26
Mars	141.71	35
Jupiter	483.88	370
Saturn	887.14	744
Uranus	1783.98	1607
Neptune	2796.46	2680

Source: FactMonster

34. MULTIPLE REPRESENTATIONS In this problem, you will explore reversing rows and columns of matrices.

Name	Goals	Assists
Amy	8	3
Tama	6	5
Kristen	1	8
Catalina	4	2

a. **TABULAR** Convert the data into a matrix with the names of the players along the columns. **See margin.**

b. **ALGEBRAIC** Find the sums of the columns.

c. **TABULAR** Switch the data in the matrix, now having the names of the players along the rows. **See margin.**

d. **ALGEBRAIC** Find the sums of the rows. **goals: 19, assists: 18**

e. **ANALYTICAL** Make a conjecture about the effect on the data when the rows and columns of a matrix are switched. **Sample answer: When the rows and columns of a matrix are switched, the data are unaffected.**

H.O.T. Problems Use Higher-Order Thinking Skills

C

REASONING Determine whether each statement is *true* or *false*. Explain.

35. C is a square matrix with 4 columns. It contains element c_{53}.

36. D is a square matrix with 3 rows. It contains element c_{22}.

35. Sample answer: False; a square matrix with 4 columns has only 4 rows and cannot contain an element in a fifth row.

36. Sample answer: False; matrix D will not contain any c elements.

37. ERROR ANALYSIS Kyla and Jay were asked to identify b_{32} for $B = \begin{bmatrix} -6 & 7 \\ 0 & 5 \\ 8 & 2 \end{bmatrix}$. Is either of them correct? Explain your answer.

No; element b_{32} is the second element in the third row, which is 2.

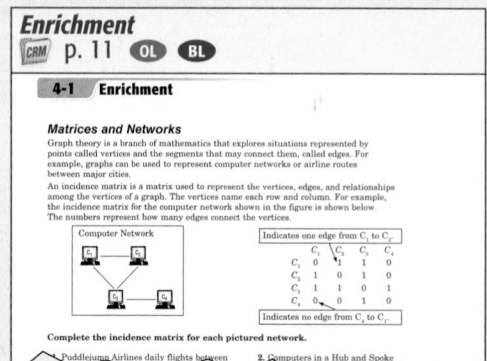

Kyla
There is no element b_{32} for B because B is a 2 × 3 matrix.

Jay
The value of b_{32} is 5.

38. CHALLENGE Solve the following for x, y, and z. **(−8, −12, −5)**

$$\begin{bmatrix} 2x - y & 3x + 4z \\ 7x - 8z & 5y + 12z \end{bmatrix} = \begin{bmatrix} 9z - 5x + 1 & 5y - 2x \\ 3y - 4z & 12x + 2y \end{bmatrix}$$

39. OPEN ENDED Form a matrix using real-world data in which the sum of the columns is relevant and the sum of the rows is irrelevant. **See margin.**

40. WRITING IN MATH Explain how a matrix can be helpful when deciding what college you want to attend.

40. Sample answer: A matrix can be beneficial when looking for colleges because you can organize all of the data for each college and compare them all at the same time.

Study Guide and Intervention
CRM pp. 5–6 AL OL ELL

4-1 Study Guide and Intervention
Introduction to Matrices

Organize and Analyze Data

Matrix	a rectangular array of variables or constants in horizontal rows and vertical columns, usually enclosed in brackets.

A matrix can be described by its **dimensions**. A matrix with m rows and n columns is an $m \times n$ matrix.

Example 1 Owls' eggs incubate for 30 days and their fledgling period is also 30 days. Swifts' eggs incubate for 20 days and their fledgling period is 44 days. Pigeon eggs incubate for 15 days, and their fledgling period is 17 days. Eggs of the king penguin incubate for 53 days, and the fledgling time for a king penguin is 360 days. Write a 2 × 4 matrix to organize this information. Source: *The Cambridge Factfinder*

	Owl	Swift	Pigeon	King Penguin
Incubation	30	20	15	53
Fledgling	30	44	17	360

Example 2 What are the dimensions of matrix A if $A = \begin{bmatrix} 13 & 10 & -3 & 45 \\ 2 & 8 & 15 & 80 \end{bmatrix}$?

Since matrix A has 2 rows and 4 columns, the dimensions of A are 2 × 4.

Exercises

State the dimensions of each matrix.

1. $\begin{bmatrix} 15 & 5 & 27 & -4 \\ 23 & 6 & 0 & 5 \\ 14 & 70 & 24 & -3 \\ 63 & 3 & 42 & 90 \end{bmatrix}$ **4 × 4**

2. $[16\ \ 12\ \ 0]$ **1 × 3**

3. $\begin{bmatrix} 71 & 44 \\ 39 & 27 \\ 45 & 16 \\ 92 & 53 \\ 78 & 65 \end{bmatrix}$ **5 × 2**

4. A travel agent provides for potential travelers the normal high temperatures for the months of January, April, July, and October for various cities. In Boston these figures are 36°, 56°, 82°, and 63°. In Dallas they are 54°, 76°, 97°, and 79°. In Los Angeles they are 68°, 72°, 84°, and 79°. In Seattle they are 46°, 58°, 74°, and 60°. In St. Louis they are 38°, 67°, 89°, and 69°. Organize this information in a 4 × 5 matrix. Source: *The New York Times Almanac*

	Boston	Dallas	Los Angeles	Seattle	St. Louis
January	36	54	68	46	38
April	56	76	72	58	67
July	82	97	84	74	89
October	63	79	79	60	89

Chapter 4 5 Glencoe Algebra 2

Practice
CRM p. 8 AL OL BL ELL

4-1 Practice
Introduction to Matrices

State the dimensions of each matrix.

1. $[-3\ \ -3\ \ 7]$ **1 × 3**

2. $\begin{bmatrix} 5 & 8 & -1 \\ -2 & 1 & 8 \end{bmatrix}$ **2 × 3**

3. $\begin{bmatrix} -2 & 2 & -2 & 3 \\ 5 & 16 & 0 & 0 \\ 4 & 7 & -1 & 4 \end{bmatrix}$ **3 × 4**

Identify each element for the following matrices.

$A = \begin{bmatrix} 4 & 7 & 0 \\ 9 & 8 & -4 \\ 3 & 0 & 5 \\ -1 & 2 & 6 \end{bmatrix}$, $B = \begin{bmatrix} 2 & 6 & -1 & 0 \\ 9 & 5 & 7 & 2 \end{bmatrix}$.

4. b_{23} **7**

5. a_{42} **2**

6. b_{11} **2**

7. a_{32} **0**

8. b_{14} **0**

9. a_{23} **−4**

10. **TICKET PRICES** The table at the right gives ticket prices for a concert. Write a 2 × 3 matrix that represents the cost of a ticket.

	Child	Student	Adult
Cost Purchased in Advance	$6	$12	$18
Cost Purchased at the Door	$8	$15	$22

$\begin{bmatrix} 6 & 12 & 18 \\ 8 & 15 & 22 \end{bmatrix}$

11. **CONSTRUCTION** During each of the last three weeks, a road-building crew has used three truckloads of gravel. The table at the right shows the amount of gravel in each load.

Week 1		Week 2		Week 3	
Load 1	40 tons	Load 1	40 tons	Load 1	32 tons
Load 2	32 tons	Load 2	40 tons	Load 2	24 tons
Load 3	24 tons	Load 3	32 tons	Load 3	24 tons

a. Write a matrix for the amount of gravel in each load.

$\begin{bmatrix} 40 & 32 & 24 \\ 40 & 40 & 32 \\ 32 & 24 & 24 \end{bmatrix}$ or $\begin{bmatrix} 40 & 40 & 32 \\ 32 & 40 & 24 \\ 24 & 32 & 24 \end{bmatrix}$

b. What are the dimensions of the matrix? **3 × 3**

Chapter 4 8 Glencoe Algebra 2

Word Problem Practice
CRM p. 9 AL OL BL ELL

4-1 Word Problem Practice
Introduction to Matrices

1. **HAWAII** The table shows the population and area of some of the islands in Hawaii. What would be the dimensions of a matrix that represented this information?

Island	Population	Area
Hawaii	120,317	4,038
Maui	91,361	729
Oahu	836,231	594
Kauai	50,947	549
Lanai	2,426	140

Source: www.vthawaii.com

5 by 2 or 2 by 5

2. **LAUNDRY** Carl is looking for a Laundromat. SuperWash has 20 small washers, 10 large washers, and 20 dryers. QuickClean has 40 small washers, 5 large washers, and 50 dryers. ToughSuds has 15 small washers, 40 large washers, and 100 dryers. Write a matrix to organize this information.

Sample answer: $\begin{bmatrix} 20 & 10 & 20 \\ 40 & 5 & 50 \\ 15 & 40 & 100 \end{bmatrix}$

3. **CITY DISTANCES** The incomplete matrix shown gives the approximate distances between Chicago, Los Angeles, and New York City. Complete the matrix.

	NYC	Chicago	Los Angeles
NYC	0	810	2790
Chicago	810	0	2050
Los Angeles	2790	2050	0

4. **INVENTORY** A store manager records the number of light bulbs in stock for 3 different brands over a five-day period. The manager decides to make a matrix of this information. Each row represents a different brand, and each column represents a different day. The entry in column N represents the inventories at the beginning of day N.

$\begin{bmatrix} 25 & 24 & 22 & 20 & 19 \\ 30 & 27 & 25 & 22 & 21 \\ 28 & 25 & 21 & 19 & 19 \end{bmatrix}$

Assuming that the inventories were never replenished, which brand holds the record for most light bulbs sold on a given day?

the third row brand

5. **SHOE SALES** A shoe store manager keeps track of the amount of money made by each of three salespeople for each day of a workweek. Monday through Friday, Carla made $40, $70, $35, $50, and $20. John made $30, $60, $20, $45, and $30. Mary made $35, $90, $30, $40, and $30.

a. Organize this data in a 3 by 5 matrix.

Sample answer:

	M	Tu	W	Th	F
Carla	40	70	30	50	20
John	30	60	20	45	30
Mary	35	90	30	40	30

b. Which salesperson made the most money that week?

Mary

Chapter 4 9 Glencoe Algebra 2

Enrichment
CRM p. 11 OL BL

4-1 Enrichment

Matrices and Networks

Graph theory is a branch of mathematics that explores situations represented by points called vertices and the segments that may connect them, called edges. For example, graphs can be used to represent computer networks or airline routes between major cities.

An incidence matrix is a matrix used to represent the vertices, edges, and relationships among the vertices of a graph. The vertices name each row and column. For example, the incidence matrix for the computer network shown in the figure is shown below. The numbers represent how many edges connect the vertices.

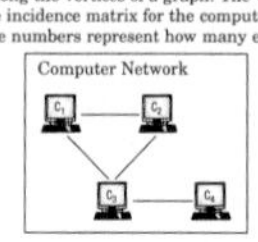

Indicates one edge from C_1 to C_2.

	C_1	C_2	C_3	C_4
C_1	0	1	1	0
C_2	1	0	1	0
C_3	1	1	0	1
C_4	0	0	1	0

Indicates no edge from C_4 to C_1.

Complete the incidence matrix for each pictured network.

1. Puddlejump Airlines daily flights between

2. Computers in a Hub and Spoke

Multiple Representations In Exercise 34, students use a table of values, a matrix, and algebraic operations to make use of information organized in a matrix.

NGSSS PRACTICE 912.A.3.10, 912.G.2.5, 912.D.8.2

41. What is the equation of the line that has a slope of 3 and passes through the point (2, −9)? **D**

A. $y = 3x + 11$
B. $y = 3x + 15$
C. $y = 3x - 11$
D. $y = 3x - 15$

42. GEOMETRY Line q is shown below. Which equation best represents a line parallel to line q? **H**

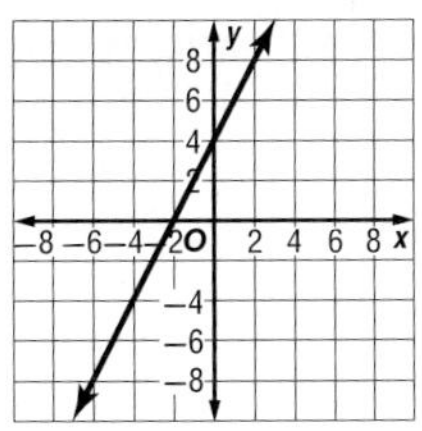

F. $y = x + 2$
G. $y = 2x + 4$
H. $y = 2x - 3$
I. $y = -2x + 2$

43. SHORT RESPONSE What is the area of the shaded part of the rectangle below? **780,000 ft^2**

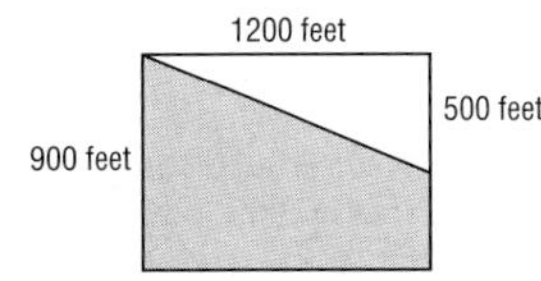

44. SAT/ACT The results of a recent poll are organized in the matrix.

$$\begin{array}{l} \\ \text{Proposition 1} \\ \text{Proposition 2} \\ \text{Proposition 3} \end{array} \begin{array}{c} \text{For} \quad \text{Against} \\ \begin{bmatrix} 1553 & 771 \\ 689 & 1633 \\ 2088 & 229 \end{bmatrix} \end{array}$$

Based on these results, which conclusion is *not* valid? **D**

A. There were 771 votes cast against Proposition 1.
B. More people voted against Proposition 1 than voted for Proposition 2.
C. Proposition 2 has little chance of passing.
D. More people voted for Proposition 1 than for Proposition 3.

Spiral Review

45. COLLEGE FOOTBALL In a recent year, Darren McFadden of Arkansas placed second overall in the Heisman Trophy voting. Players are given 3 points for every first-place vote, 2 points for every second-place vote, and 1 point for every third-place vote. McFadden received 490 total votes for first, second, and third place, for a total of 878 points. If he had 4 more than twice as many second-place votes as third-place votes, how many votes did he receive for each place? (Lesson 3-5) **45 first, 298 second, 147 third**

46. PACKAGING The Cookie Factory sells chocolate chip and peanut butter cookies in combination packages that contain between six and twelve cookies. At least three of each type of cookie should be in each package. How many of each type of cookie should be in each package to maximize the profit? (Lesson 3-4)
3 chocolate chip, 9 peanut butter

Cookie	chocolate chip	peanut butter
Cost	\$0.19	\$0.13
Price	\$0.44	\$0.39

Find the slope of the line that passes through each pair of points. (Lesson 2-3)

47. (−3, −6), (−1, −9) $-\frac{3}{2}$ **48.** (−2, 6), (4, −1) $-\frac{7}{6}$ **49.** (5, −3), (8, 2) $\frac{5}{3}$

Multiply. (Lesson 0-2)

50. $(2x + 1)(-3x - 2)$ $-6x^2 - 7x - 2$ **51.** $(y + 6)(y - 8)$ $y^2 - 2y - 48$ **52.** $(x + y)(x - 2y)$ $x^2 - xy - 2y^2$

Skills Review

Evaluate each expression if $w = 3$, $x = -2$, $y = 4$, and $z = 0.5$. (Lesson 1-2)

53. $4x - 6y + 2z$ -31 **54.** $5w + 2(x - z) + 2y$ 18 **55.** $4[3(2z + y) - 2(w + x)]$ 52

Differentiated Instruction OL BL

Extension Ask each student to write a matrix M where the matrix dimensions are 2×3. No elements in the first row are the same, and all elements in the second row are twice the element M_{12}. Sample answer: $M = \begin{bmatrix} 1 & 2 & 3 \\ 4 & 4 & 4 \end{bmatrix}$

Watch Out!

Error Analysis In Exercise 37, remind students that when identifying an item in a matrix, the row number is always listed before the column number.

4 ASSESS

Crystal Ball Ask students to name other properties of matrices they expect to study.

Additional Answers

33a.
$$\begin{array}{r} \\ \text{Mercury} \\ \text{Venus} \\ \text{Mars} \\ \text{Jupiter} \\ \text{Saturn} \\ \text{Uranus} \\ \text{Neptune} \end{array} \begin{array}{c} \text{Sun} \quad \text{Earth} \\ \begin{bmatrix} 36.00 & 57 \\ 67.24 & 26 \\ 141.71 & 35 \\ 483.88 & 370 \\ 887.14 & 744 \\ 1783.98 & 1607 \\ 2796.46 & 2680 \end{bmatrix} \end{array}$$

34a.
$$\begin{array}{r} \\ \text{Goals} \\ \text{Assists} \end{array} \begin{array}{c} \text{A T K C} \\ \begin{bmatrix} 8 & 6 & 1 & 4 \\ 3 & 5 & 8 & 2 \end{bmatrix} \end{array}$$

34c.
$$\begin{array}{r} \\ \text{Amy} \\ \text{Tama} \\ \text{Kristin} \\ \text{Catalina} \end{array} \begin{array}{c} \text{G A} \\ \begin{bmatrix} 8 & 3 \\ 6 & 5 \\ 1 & 8 \\ 4 & 2 \end{bmatrix} \end{array}$$

39. Sample answer:
$$\begin{array}{r} \\ \text{Joe} \\ \text{John} \\ \text{Jim} \end{array} \begin{array}{c} \text{Hits Walks HR} \\ \begin{bmatrix} 95 & 12 & 8 \\ 102 & 16 & 5 \\ 109 & 13 & 12 \end{bmatrix} \end{array}$$

EXTEND 4-1 Lesson Notes

1 FOCUS

Objective Use a spreadsheet to organize and display data.

Materials for Each Student

- computer with spreadsheet program

Teaching Tip

Have students practice their skills in using a spreadsheet by entering the data in the example. Suggest that students type descriptive labels in cells at the tops of columns. This makes it easier to understand and interpret results.

2 TEACH

Working in Cooperative Groups

Have students work with partners, mixing abilities so that a student with more knowledge of spreadsheets is paired with one who has less experience.

Practice Have students complete Exercises 1 and 2.

3 ASSESS

Formative Assessment

Use Exercise 3 to assess whether students comprehend how to enter data into a spreadsheet.

From Concrete to Abstract

Ask students about the structure of a given spreadsheet. For example, ask them which cells contain data values and which contain labels to identify the data. Ask students to compare the structure of a spreadsheet and the structure of a matrix.

EXTEND 4-1 Spreadsheet Lab: Organizing Data

FL Math Online glencoe.com
• Graphing Technology Personal Tutor

People in the workforce often use computer **spreadsheets** to organize, display, and analyze data. Similar to a matrix, data in a spreadsheet are entered into rows and columns. Then the data can be used to create graphs or perform calculations.

EXAMPLE

The manager of a gourmet food store has gathered data on the number of pounds of bulk coffees they have sold each week in January. Enter the data into a spreadsheet.

Weekly Sales for January

Coffee	1/5	1/12	1/19	1/26
Hawaiian Kona	17	22	11	23
Mocha Java	31	34	22	29
House Blend	55	61	44	71
Espresso	41	36	60	77
Decaf Espresso	23	29	19	44
Breakfast Blend	8	18	19	31
Decaf Breakfast Blend	22	18	30	32
Organic Italian Roast	26	16	31	39

Use Column A for the types of coffee, Column B for the sales in the week starting 1/5, Column C for sales in the week starting 1/12, and Columns D and E for the sales in the weeks starting 1/19 and 1/26.

January Weekly Sales

◇	A	B	C	D	E
1	Hawaiian Kona	17	22	11	23
2	Mocha Java	31	34	22	29
3	House Blend	55	61	44	71
4	Espresso	41	36	60	77
5	Decaf Espresso	23	29	19	44
6	Breakfast Blend	8	18	19	31
7	Decaf Breakfast Blend	22	18	30	32
8	Organic Italian Roast	26	16	31	39

Sheet 1 | Sheet 2 | Sheet 3

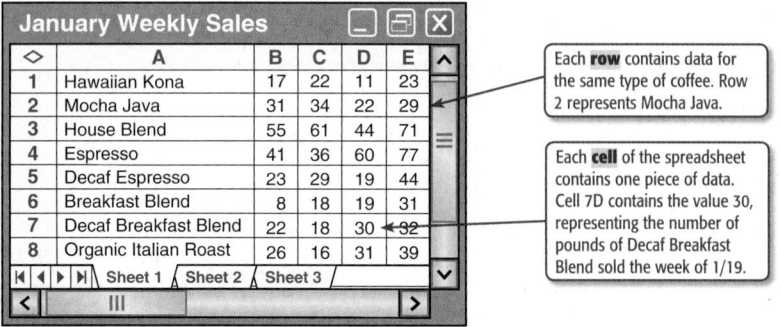

Each **row** contains data for the same type of coffee. Row 2 represents Mocha Java.

Each **cell** of the spreadsheet contains one piece of data. Cell 7D contains the value 30, representing the number of pounds of Decaf Breakfast Blend sold the week of 1/19.

Exercises

1. Enter the data on smartphones on page 185 into a spreadsheet. **See students' work.**
2. Compare and contrast how data are organized in a spreadsheet and in a matrix. **See margin.**
3. A SUM formula allows you to find the sum of the entries in a column or row. **a–c. See margin.**
   a. The formula =SUM(B1:B8) finds the sum of column B. Enter formulas in cells B9, C9, D9, and E9 to find the sums of those columns. What do the sums of the columns represent in the situation?
   b. Enter formulas in cells F1 through F8 to find the sums of rows 1 through 8. What do the sums of the rows represent in the situation?
   c. Find the sum of row 9 and the sum of column F. What do you observe? Explain.

Additional Answers

2. Both use rows and columns. In a spreadsheet, the rows are designated by numbers and the columns are designated by letters. In a matrix, both rows and columns are designated by numbers.

3a. 1/5 total 223, 1/12 total 234, 1/19 total 236, 1/26 total 346; The column sums represent the total pounds of coffee sold each week.

3b. Hawaiian Kona 73, Mocha Java 116, House Blend 231, Espresso 214, Decaf Espresso 115, Breakfast Blend 76, Decaf Breakfast Blend 102, Organic Italian Roast 112; The row sums represent the total pounds of each type of coffee sold.

3c. Both sums are 1039. The row sum and the column sum are equal because both represent the total coffee of all types sold in all weeks.

4-2 Operations with Matrices

Why?

Coastal Sales Company has three locations in Florida. The matrices below show the average daily wages and sales of all of the representatives.

	Miami Wages	Miami Sales	Tampa Wages	Tampa Sales	Tallahassee Wages	Tallahassee Sales
Entry	900	145,000	900	122,000	1050	109,500
Assistant	2400	225,000	1800	145,500	1800	135,000
Associate	2700	290,000	1800	160,000	1800	150,500

Then
You organized data into matrices.

Now
- Add and subtract matrices.
- Multiply a matrix by a scalar.

NGSSS
Preparation for MA.912.D.8.2 Use matrix operations to solve problems.

New Vocabulary
scalar
scalar multiplication

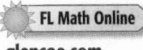

FL Math Online
glencoe.com

Add and Subtract Matrices Matrices can be added or subtracted if and only if they have the same dimensions.

Key Concept — Adding and Subtracting Matrices

Words To add or subtract two matrices with the same dimensions, add or subtract their corresponding elements.

Symbols

$$\underset{A}{\begin{bmatrix} a & b \\ c & d \end{bmatrix}} + \underset{B}{\begin{bmatrix} e & f \\ g & h \end{bmatrix}} = \underset{A+B}{\begin{bmatrix} a+e & b+f \\ c+g & d+h \end{bmatrix}}$$

$$\underset{A}{\begin{bmatrix} a & b \\ c & d \end{bmatrix}} - \underset{B}{\begin{bmatrix} e & f \\ g & h \end{bmatrix}} = \underset{A-B}{\begin{bmatrix} a-e & b-f \\ c-g & d-h \end{bmatrix}}$$

Example

$$\begin{bmatrix} 3 & -5 \\ 1 & 7 \end{bmatrix} + \begin{bmatrix} 2 & 0 \\ -9 & 10 \end{bmatrix} = \begin{bmatrix} 3+2 & -5+0 \\ 1+(-9) & 7+10 \end{bmatrix}$$

EXAMPLE 1 Add and Subtract Matrices

Find each of the following for $A = \begin{bmatrix} 16 & 2 \\ -9 & 8 \end{bmatrix}$, $B = \begin{bmatrix} -4 & -1 \\ -3 & -7 \end{bmatrix}$, and $C = \begin{bmatrix} 8 \\ 6 \end{bmatrix}$.

a. $A + B$

$A + B = \begin{bmatrix} 16 & 2 \\ -9 & 8 \end{bmatrix} + \begin{bmatrix} -4 & -1 \\ -3 & -7 \end{bmatrix}$ **Substitution**

$= \begin{bmatrix} 16+(-4) & 2+(-1) \\ -9+(-3) & 8+(-7) \end{bmatrix}$ **Add corresponding elements.**

$= \begin{bmatrix} 12 & 1 \\ -12 & 1 \end{bmatrix}$ **Simplify.**

b. $B - C$

$B - C = \begin{bmatrix} -4 & -1 \\ -3 & -7 \end{bmatrix} - \begin{bmatrix} 8 \\ 6 \end{bmatrix}$ **Substitution**

Since the dimensions of B and C are different, you cannot subtract the matrices.

Guided Practice

1A. $\begin{bmatrix} -3 & 4 \\ -9 & -5 \end{bmatrix} - \begin{bmatrix} -4 & 12 \\ 8 & -7 \end{bmatrix}$

1B. $\begin{bmatrix} -9 & 8 & 3 \\ -2 & 4 & -7 \end{bmatrix} + \begin{bmatrix} -4 & -3 & 6 \\ -9 & -5 & 18 \end{bmatrix}$

Personal Tutor glencoe.com

1A. $\begin{bmatrix} 1 & -8 \\ -17 & 2 \end{bmatrix}$

1B. $\begin{bmatrix} -13 & 5 & 9 \\ -11 & -1 & 11 \end{bmatrix}$

4-2 Lesson Notes

1 FOCUS

Vertical Alignment

Before Lesson 4-2
Organize data into matrices.

Lesson 4-2
Add and subtract matrices.
Multiply a matrix by a scalar.

After Lesson 4-2
Use matrices to solve systems of equations.

2 TEACH

Scaffolding Questions

Have students read the *Why?* section of the lesson.

Ask:
- What are the average daily wages of associate representatives in Tampa? $1800
- What is the location for average daily sales for entry-level representatives in each matrix? row 1, column 2
- How could you find the total average daily sales for all assistant representatives in the company? Add the elements in position row 2, column 2 for all three matrices.

Lesson 4-2 Resources

Resource	Approaching-Level	On-Level	Beyond-Level	English Learners
Teacher Edition	• Differentiated Instruction, p. 195	• Differentiated Instruction, p. 195	• Differentiated Instruction, pp. 195, 199	• Differentiated Instruction, p. 195
Chapter Resource Masters	• Study Guide and Intervention, pp. 11–12 • Skills Practice, p. 13 • Practice, p. 14 • Word Problem Practice, p. 15	• Study Guide and Intervention, pp. 11–12 • Skills Practice, p. 13 • Practice, p. 14 • Word Problem Practice, p. 15 • Enrichment, p. 16	• Practice, p. 14 • Word Problem Practice, p. 15 • Enrichment, p. 16	• Study Guide and Intervention, pp. 11–12 • Skills Practice, p. 13 • Practice, p. 14 • Word Problem Practice, p. 15
Transparencies	• 5-Minute Check Transparency 4-2	• 5-Minute Check Transparency 4-2	• 5-Minute Check Transparency 4-2	• 5-Minute Check Transparency 4-2
Other	• Study Notebook	• Study Notebook	• Study Notebook	• Study Notebook

Add and Subtract Matrices

Example 1 shows how to add or subtract two matrices.

Formative Assessment

Use the Guided Practice exercises after each example to determine students' understanding of concepts.

Additional Example

1 **a.** Find $A + B$ if $A = \begin{bmatrix} 6 & 4 \\ -1 & 0 \end{bmatrix}$ and $B = \begin{bmatrix} -3 & 1 \\ 0 & 3 \end{bmatrix}$. $\begin{bmatrix} 3 & 5 \\ -1 & 3 \end{bmatrix}$

b. Find $A - B$ if $A = \begin{bmatrix} 4 & -2 & 0 \\ 1 & 5 & -1 \end{bmatrix}$ and $B = \begin{bmatrix} -6 & 7 \\ -9 & 3 \end{bmatrix}$. Since their dimensions are different, these matrices cannot be subtracted.

Additional Examples also in Interactive Classroom PowerPoint® Presentations

IWB INTERACTIVE WHITEBOARD READY

Scalar Multiplication

Example 2 shows how to multiply a matrix by a scalar.

Additional Example

2 If $A = \begin{bmatrix} 2 & 1 \\ -1 & 3 \\ 0 & 5 \end{bmatrix}$, find $2A$. $\begin{bmatrix} 4 & 2 \\ -2 & 6 \\ 0 & 10 \end{bmatrix}$

Tips for New Teachers

Building on Prior Knowledge Point out that scalar multiplication of matrices is similar to using the Distributive Property to multiply the expression $3(x + y)$.

Scalar Multiplication You can multiply any matrix by a constant called a **scalar**. When you do this, you multiply each individual element by the value of the scalar. This operation is called **scalar multiplication**.

ReadingMath

Scalar Think of a scalar as a coefficient for a variable, but instead it is for a matrix.

Key Concept — Multiplying by a Scalar

Words To multiply a matrix by a scalar k, multiply each element by k.

Symbols $k \cdot A = kA$

$$k\begin{bmatrix} a & b \\ c & d \end{bmatrix} = \begin{bmatrix} ka & kb \\ kc & kd \end{bmatrix}$$

Example $-3\begin{bmatrix} 4 & 1 \\ 7 & -2 \end{bmatrix} = \begin{bmatrix} -3(4) & -3(1) \\ -3(7) & -3(-2) \end{bmatrix}$

StudyTip

Scalar Multiplication The bracket of a matrix is treated just like a regular grouping symbol. So when multiplying by a scalar, distribute the same way as with a grouping symbol.

EXAMPLE 2 Multiply a Matrix by a Scalar

If $R = \begin{bmatrix} -12 & 8 & 6 \\ -16 & 4 & 19 \end{bmatrix}$, find $5R$.

$5R = 5\begin{bmatrix} -12 & 8 & 6 \\ -16 & 4 & 19 \end{bmatrix}$ Substitution

$= \begin{bmatrix} 5(-12) & 5(8) & 5(6) \\ 5(-16) & 5(4) & 5(19) \end{bmatrix}$ Distribute the scalar.

$= \begin{bmatrix} -60 & 40 & 30 \\ -80 & 20 & 95 \end{bmatrix}$ Multiply.

Guided Practice

2. If $T = \begin{bmatrix} 8 & 0 & 3 & -2 \\ -1 & -4 & -2 & 9 \end{bmatrix}$, find $-4T$. $\begin{bmatrix} -32 & 0 & -12 & 8 \\ 4 & 16 & 8 & -36 \end{bmatrix}$

Personal Tutor glencoe.com

Many properties of real numbers also hold true for matrices. A summary of these properties is listed below.

Key Concept — Properties of Matrix Operations

For any matrices A, B, and C for which the matrix sum and product are defined and any scalar k, the following properties are true.

Commutative Property of Addition	$A + B = B + A$
Associative Property of Addition	$(A + B) + C = A + (B + C)$
Left Scalar Distributive Property	$k(A + B) = kA + kB$
Right Scalar Distributive Property	$(A + B)k = kA + kB$

Multi-step operations can be performed on matrices. The order of these operations is the same as with real numbers.

Focus on Mathematical Content

Adding and Subtracting Matrices In order to add or subtract matrices, they must have the same dimensions. To add or subtract two matrices, simply add or subtract the corresponding elements of the matrices. Both the Commutative and Associative Properties hold for matrix addition.

Watch Out!

Unlocking Misconceptions In order to help students see why matrices must have the same dimensions if they are to be added or subtracted, suggest that they try to add a 2 × 3 matrix to a 3 × 2 matrix.

EXAMPLE 3 Multi-Step Operations

If $A = \begin{bmatrix} -9 & 12 \\ 2 & -6 \end{bmatrix}$ and $B = \begin{bmatrix} -4 & -8 \\ 2 & -3 \end{bmatrix}$, find $-4B - 3A$.

$$-4B - 3A = -4\begin{bmatrix} -4 & -8 \\ 2 & -3 \end{bmatrix} - 3\begin{bmatrix} -9 & 12 \\ 2 & -6 \end{bmatrix}$$ **Substitution**

$$= \begin{bmatrix} -4(-4) & -4(-8) \\ -4(2) & -4(-3) \end{bmatrix} - \begin{bmatrix} 3(-9) & 3(12) \\ 3(2) & 3(-6) \end{bmatrix}$$ **Distribute the scalars in each matrix.**

$$= \begin{bmatrix} 16 & 32 \\ -8 & 12 \end{bmatrix} - \begin{bmatrix} -27 & 36 \\ 6 & -18 \end{bmatrix}$$ **Multiply.**

$$= \begin{bmatrix} 16-(-27) & 32-36 \\ -8-6 & 12-(-18) \end{bmatrix}$$ **Subtract corresponding elements.**

$$= \begin{bmatrix} 43 & -4 \\ -14 & 30 \end{bmatrix}$$ **Simplify.**

Guided Practice

3. If $A = \begin{bmatrix} -5 & 3 \\ 6 & -8 \\ 2 & 9 \end{bmatrix}$ and $B = \begin{bmatrix} 12 & 5 \\ 5 & -4 \\ 4 & -7 \end{bmatrix}$, find $-6B + 7A$. $\begin{bmatrix} -107 & -9 \\ 12 & -32 \\ -10 & 105 \end{bmatrix}$

Personal Tutor glencoe.com

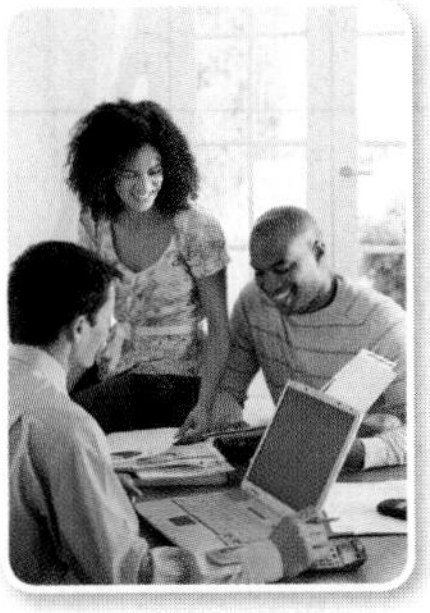

Real-World Career

Financial Planner Financial planners often use matrices to organize and describe the data they use. Financial planners need a bachelor's degree. Usually they have degrees in accounting, finance, economics, business, marketing, or commerce.

Matrices can be used in many business applications.

EXAMPLE 4 Use Multi-Step Operations with Matrices

BUSINESS Refer to the application at the beginning of the lesson. Express the average wages and sales for the entire company for a 5-day week.

To calculate the 5-day sales for the entire company, each matrix needs to be multiplied by 5 and the totals added together.

$$5\begin{bmatrix} 900 & 145{,}000 \\ 2400 & 225{,}000 \\ 2700 & 290{,}000 \end{bmatrix} + 5\begin{bmatrix} 900 & 122{,}000 \\ 1800 & 145{,}500 \\ 1800 & 160{,}000 \end{bmatrix} + 5\begin{bmatrix} 1050 & 109{,}500 \\ 1800 & 135{,}000 \\ 1800 & 150{,}500 \end{bmatrix}$$ **Write matrices.**

$$= \begin{bmatrix} 4500 & 725{,}000 \\ 12{,}000 & 1{,}125{,}000 \\ 13{,}500 & 1{,}450{,}000 \end{bmatrix} + \begin{bmatrix} 4500 & 610{,}000 \\ 9000 & 727{,}500 \\ 9000 & 800{,}000 \end{bmatrix} + \begin{bmatrix} 5250 & 547{,}500 \\ 9000 & 675{,}000 \\ 9000 & 752{,}500 \end{bmatrix}$$ **Multiply scalars.**

$$= \begin{array}{r} \\ \text{Entry} \\ \text{Assistant} \\ \text{Associate} \end{array} \begin{array}{c} \text{Wages} \quad \text{Sales} \\ \begin{bmatrix} 14{,}250 & 1{,}882{,}500 \\ 30{,}000 & 2{,}527{,}500 \\ 31{,}500 & 3{,}002{,}500 \end{bmatrix} \end{array}$$ **Add matrices.**

The final matrix indicates the average weekly sales and wages for all of the representatives of the company.

StudyTip

Corresponding Elements When representing quantities with multiple matrices, make sure the corresponding elements represent corresponding quantities.

Guided Practice

4. Use the data above to calculate the average yearly sales and wages for the company, assuming 260 working days. See margin.

Personal Tutor glencoe.com

Differentiated Instruction

AL OL BL ELL

Verbal/Linguistic Learners Students may find it helpful to talk softly, or even silently, to themselves as they work with matrices. For example, they might recite the words "row by column" to remind themselves how to write the dimensions of a matrix. When multiplying by a scalar, students may find it helps to say, for example, "5 times 1 is 5, and 5 times negative 3 is negative 15." In this way, students use more than one of their senses to check their calculations.

Properties of Matrices

Examples 3 and 4 show how to perform a combination of matrix operations.

Additional Examples

3 If $A = \begin{bmatrix} 2 & 3 \\ -1 & 0 \end{bmatrix}$ and $B = \begin{bmatrix} -2 & 1 \\ 0 & -1 \end{bmatrix}$, find $4A - 3B$. $\begin{bmatrix} 14 & 9 \\ -4 & 3 \end{bmatrix}$

4 **BUSINESS** A small company makes unfinished desks and cabinets. Each item requires different amounts of hardware as shown in the matrices.

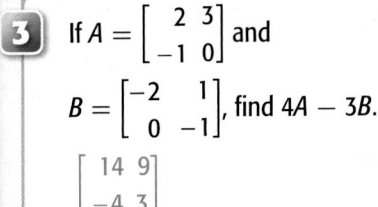

DESK: $\begin{array}{r} \\ \text{nails} \\ \text{screws} \end{array} \begin{array}{c} \text{short} \quad \text{long} \\ \begin{bmatrix} 10 & 6 \\ 8 & 4 \end{bmatrix} \end{array}$ CABINET: $\begin{array}{r} \\ \text{nails} \\ \text{screws} \end{array} \begin{array}{c} \text{short} \quad \text{long} \\ \begin{bmatrix} 4 & 8 \\ 3 & 4 \end{bmatrix} \end{array}$

The company has orders for 3 desks and 4 cabinets. Express the company's total needs for hardware in a single matrix. $\begin{bmatrix} 46 & 50 \\ 36 & 28 \end{bmatrix}$

Tips for New Teachers

Reasoning Adding and subtracting matrices can be challenging for many students. Encourage students to develop strategies for keeping track of where they are in a matrix. Students may find it helpful to circle the elements they are adding or subtracting, use color coding, or point with their fingers to the two elements as they do the calculations.

Additional Answer (Guided Practice)

4. $\begin{array}{r} \\ \text{Entry} \\ \text{Assistant} \\ \text{Associate} \end{array} \begin{array}{c} \text{Wages} \quad \text{Sales} \\ \begin{bmatrix} 741{,}000 & 97{,}890{,}000 \\ 1{,}560{,}000 & 131{,}430{,}000 \\ 1{,}638{,}000 & 156{,}130{,}000 \end{bmatrix} \end{array}$

3 PRACTICE

Formative Assessment

Use Exercises 1–11 to check for understanding.

Use the chart at the bottom of this page to customize assignments for your students.

Additional Answers

1. $\begin{bmatrix} 3 & -5 & 7 \end{bmatrix}$
2. impossible
3. $\begin{bmatrix} -2 & -18 \\ 11 & 13 \end{bmatrix}$
4. $\begin{bmatrix} 7 & 31 & -14 \\ 1 & -6 & 2 \end{bmatrix}$
5. $\begin{bmatrix} 18 & 12 & 0 \\ -6 & 42 & -24 \\ -12 & -18 & 21 \end{bmatrix}$
6. $\begin{bmatrix} -90 & 54 & -12 & -18 \\ -36 & 66 & -84 & 12 \\ -24 & 48 & 60 & -162 \end{bmatrix}$
7. $\begin{bmatrix} 20 & 4 \\ -14 & 38 \end{bmatrix}$
8. $\begin{bmatrix} 50 & 36 \\ -87 & 41 \end{bmatrix}$
9. impossible
10. $\begin{bmatrix} -24 & 29 \\ -38 & -7 \end{bmatrix}$

14a. $\begin{bmatrix} \$0.95 & \$1.00 & \$1.05 \\ \$0.75 & \$0.80 & \$0.85 \\ \$0.75 & \$0.80 & \$0.85 \\ \$1.00 & \$1.10 & \$1.20 \end{bmatrix}$

14b. 1.1

14c. $\begin{bmatrix} \$1.05 & \$1.10 & \$1.16 \\ \$0.83 & \$0.88 & \$0.94 \\ \$0.83 & \$0.88 & \$0.94 \\ \$1.10 & \$1.21 & \$1.32 \end{bmatrix}$

14d. $\begin{bmatrix} \$0.10 & \$0.10 & \$0.11 \\ \$0.08 & \$0.08 & \$0.09 \\ \$0.08 & \$0.08 & \$0.09 \\ \$0.10 & \$0.11 & \$0.12 \end{bmatrix}$

Sample answer: this matrix represents the price increases for each item.

Check Your Understanding

Example 1 p. 193

1–4. See margin.

Perform the indicated operations. If the matrix does not exist, write *impossible*.

1. $\begin{bmatrix} -8 & 2 & 6 \end{bmatrix} + \begin{bmatrix} 11 & -7 & 1 \end{bmatrix}$

2. $\begin{bmatrix} 9 & -8 & 4 \end{bmatrix} + \begin{bmatrix} 12 & 2 \end{bmatrix}$

3. $\begin{bmatrix} 7 & -12 \\ 15 & 4 \end{bmatrix} - \begin{bmatrix} 9 & 6 \\ 4 & -9 \end{bmatrix}$

4. $\begin{bmatrix} 5 & 13 & -6 \\ 3 & -17 & 2 \end{bmatrix} - \begin{bmatrix} -2 & -18 & 8 \\ 2 & -11 & 0 \end{bmatrix}$

Example 2 p. 194

5, 6. See margin.

Perform the indicated operations. If the matrix does not exist, write *impossible*.

5. $3\begin{bmatrix} 6 & 4 & 0 \\ -2 & 14 & -8 \\ -4 & -6 & 7 \end{bmatrix}$

6. $-6\begin{bmatrix} 15 & -9 & 2 & 3 \\ 6 & -11 & 14 & -2 \\ 4 & -8 & -10 & 27 \end{bmatrix}$

Example 3 p. 195

Use matrices A, B, C, and D to find the following.

$A = \begin{bmatrix} 6 & -4 \\ 3 & -5 \end{bmatrix}$ $B = \begin{bmatrix} 8 & -1 \\ -2 & 7 \end{bmatrix}$ $C = \begin{bmatrix} -4 & -6 \\ 12 & -7 \end{bmatrix}$ $D = \begin{bmatrix} 9 & 6 & 0 \\ -2 & 8 & 0 \end{bmatrix}$

7–10. See margin.

7. $4B - 2A$

8. $-8C + 3A$

9. $-5B - 2D$

10. $-4C - 5B$

Example 4 p. 195

11. GRADES Geraldo, Olivia, and Nikki have had two tests in their math class. The table shows the test grades for each student.

11a. Test 1: $\begin{bmatrix} 85 \\ 75 \\ 96 \end{bmatrix}$ Test 2: $\begin{bmatrix} 72 \\ 74 \\ 83 \end{bmatrix}$

11b. $\begin{bmatrix} 157 \\ 149 \\ 179 \end{bmatrix}$ 11c. $\begin{bmatrix} 13 \\ 1 \\ 13 \end{bmatrix}$

Student	Test 1	Test 2
Geraldo	85	72
Olivia	75	74
Nikki	96	83

a. Write a matrix for the information.

b. Find the sum of the scores from the two tests expressed as a matrix.

c. Express the difference in scores from test 1 to test 2 as a matrix.

Practice and Problem Solving

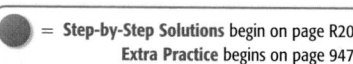

= **Step-by-Step Solutions** begin on page R20. **Extra Practice** begins on page 947.

Example 1 p. 193

Perform the indicated operations. If the matrix does not exist, write *impossible*.

12. $\begin{bmatrix} 6 & 6 \\ -15 & -1 \end{bmatrix}$

12. $\begin{bmatrix} 12 & -5 \\ -8 & -3 \end{bmatrix} + \begin{bmatrix} -6 & 11 \\ -7 & 2 \end{bmatrix}$

13. $\begin{bmatrix} 9 & 5 \\ -2 & 16 \end{bmatrix} + \begin{bmatrix} -6 & -3 & 7 \\ 12 & 2 & -4 \end{bmatrix}$ impossible

Examples 2 and 3 pp. 194–195

14. BUSINESS The drink menu from a fast-food restaurant is shown at the right. The store owner has decided that all of the prices must be increased by 10%. a–d. See margin.

Drink	Small	Medium	Large
Soda	$0.95	$1.00	$1.05
Iced tea	$0.75	$0.80	$0.85
Lemonade	$0.75	$0.80	$0.85
Coffee	$1.00	$1.10	$1.20

a. Write matrix C to represent the current prices.

b. What scalar can be used to determine a matrix N to represent the new prices?

c. Find N.

d. What is $N - C$? What does this represent in this situation?

Differentiated Homework Options

Level	Assignment	Two-Day Option	
AL Basic	12–21, 35–36, 38–58	13–21 odd, 41–44	12–20 even, 35–36, 38–40, 45–58
OL Core	13–27 odd, 28, 29, 31, 33–36, 38–58	12–21, 41–44	22–36, 38–40, 45–58
BL Advanced	22–55, (optional: 56–58)		

Example 4 p. 195

15–20. See margin.

Perform the indicated operations. If the matrix does not exist, write *impossible*.

15. $\begin{bmatrix}-5\\8\\1\\0\end{bmatrix} - \begin{bmatrix}19\\-2\\4\\7\end{bmatrix}$

16. $\begin{bmatrix}4&-3&3\\-8&12&1\\0&-1&5\\7&-9&4\end{bmatrix} - \begin{bmatrix}-3&-8&12\\-11&-5&3\\-1&22&-9\\-6&31&9\end{bmatrix}$

17. $\begin{bmatrix}62\\-37\\-4\end{bmatrix} + \begin{bmatrix}34&76&-13\end{bmatrix}$

18. $\begin{bmatrix}2&4&11\\-6&12&-3\end{bmatrix} - \begin{bmatrix}8&-9&-3\\5&14&0\end{bmatrix}$

19. $\begin{bmatrix}5\\-9\end{bmatrix} + \begin{bmatrix}-3\\-7\end{bmatrix} - \begin{bmatrix}9\\16\end{bmatrix}$

20. $\begin{bmatrix}5\\3\end{bmatrix} - \begin{bmatrix}-4\\2\end{bmatrix} + \begin{bmatrix}-2&3\\8&-3\end{bmatrix}$

Real-World Link

The Library of Congress in Washington, D.C., is the largest library in the world. The library has more than 32 million books, 2.8 million recordings, 12.5 million photographs, 5.3 million maps, and 59.5 million manuscripts.

Source: The Library of Congress

21. BOOKS Library A has 10,000 novels, 5000 biographies, and 5000 children's books. Library B has 15,000 novels, 10,000 biographies, and 2500 children's books. Library C has 4000 novels, 700 biographies, and 800 children's books. **a–d. See margin.**

a. Express each library's number of books as a matrix. Label the matrices *A*, *B*, and *C*.

b. Find the total number of each type of book in all 3 libraries. Express as a matrix.

c. How many more books of each type does Library *A* have than Library *C*?

d. Find *A* + *B*. Does the matrix have meaning in this situation? Explain.

22–27. See margin.

B **Perform the indicated operations. If the matrix does not exist, write *impossible*.**

22. $-3\begin{bmatrix}18&-6&-8\\-5&-3&12\\0&3x&-y\end{bmatrix}$

23. $8\begin{bmatrix}-a&4b&c-b\\-13&10&-5c\end{bmatrix}$

24. $-4\begin{bmatrix}-7\\4\\-3\end{bmatrix} + 3\begin{bmatrix}-8\\3x\\-9\end{bmatrix} - 5\begin{bmatrix}4\\x-6\\12\end{bmatrix}$

25. $-5\left(\begin{bmatrix}4&-8\\8&-9\end{bmatrix} + \begin{bmatrix}4&-2\\-3&-6\end{bmatrix}\right)$

26. $-6\left(\begin{bmatrix}6&3y\\4x+1&-2\\-9&xy\end{bmatrix} + \begin{bmatrix}-5&-6\\8&-7\\x+2&2x\end{bmatrix}\right)$

27. $-4\begin{bmatrix}9&-5y\\11&-3\\-1&2-x\end{bmatrix} - 7\begin{bmatrix}8&-y&12\\-4&-8&9\\3x&2+x&-y\end{bmatrix}$

28a, b. See margin.
28c. A negative number means the city was below normal on snowfall for the month; a positive number means the city's snowfall was above normal for the month. Sample answer: All the cities had below normal snowfall in January. Grand Rapids and Buffalo had snowfall well above normal in February.

28. WEATHER The table shows snowfall in inches.

City	Normal Snowfall			2007 Snowfall		
	Jan	Feb	Mar	Jan	Feb	Mar
Grand Rapids, MI	21.1	12.2	9.0	15.4	33.6	13.6
Boston, MA	13.3	11.3	8.3	1.0	4.6	10.2
Buffalo, NY	26.1	17.8	12.4	15.5	33.5	5.4
Pittsburgh, PA	12.3	8.5	7.9	11.3	14.0	9.3

Source: National Weather Service

a. Express the normal snowfall data and the 2007 data in two 4 × 3 matrices.

b. Subtract the matrix of normal data from the matrix of 2007 data. What does the difference represent in the context of the situation?

c. Explain the meaning of positive and negative numbers in the difference matrix. What trends do you see in the data?

29–32. See margin.

Perform the indicated operations. If the matrix does not exist, write *impossible*.

29. $\begin{bmatrix}12.5&-16.4\\4.31&-2.43\\-6.8&-14.1\end{bmatrix} - 3\begin{bmatrix}-18.7&-11.8\\8.1&-6.91\\-6.21&-17.6\end{bmatrix}$

30. $-2\begin{bmatrix}-9.2&-8.4\\5.6&-4.3\end{bmatrix} - 4\begin{bmatrix}4.1&-2.9\\7.2&-8.2\end{bmatrix}$

31. $-\frac{3}{4}\begin{bmatrix}12&-16\\15&8\end{bmatrix} + \frac{2}{3}\begin{bmatrix}21&18\\-4&-6\end{bmatrix}$

32. $-4\begin{bmatrix}\frac{4}{5}&2&-\frac{3}{4}\\-1&-\frac{2}{5}&-6\end{bmatrix} + 3\begin{bmatrix}\frac{1}{5}&-4&\frac{1}{8}\\4&\frac{2}{3}&-3\end{bmatrix}$

Additional Answers

15. $\begin{bmatrix}-24\\10\\-3\\-7\end{bmatrix}$ **16.** $\begin{bmatrix}7&5&-9\\3&17&-2\\1&-23&14\\13&-40&-5\end{bmatrix}$

17. impossible

18. $\begin{bmatrix}-6&13&14\\-11&-2&-3\end{bmatrix}$ **19.** $\begin{bmatrix}-7\\-32\end{bmatrix}$

21a. Library A: $\begin{bmatrix}10{,}000\\5000\\5000\end{bmatrix}$; Library B: $\begin{bmatrix}15{,}000\\10{,}000\\2500\end{bmatrix}$; Library C: $\begin{bmatrix}4000\\700\\800\end{bmatrix}$

21b. $\begin{bmatrix}29{,}000\\15{,}700\\8300\end{bmatrix}$ **21c.** $\begin{bmatrix}6000\\4300\\4200\end{bmatrix}$

21d. $\begin{bmatrix}25{,}000\\15{,}000\\7500\end{bmatrix}$; The sum represents the combined size of the two libraries.

22. $\begin{bmatrix}-54&18&24\\15&9&-36\\0&-9x&3y\end{bmatrix}$

23. $\begin{bmatrix}-8a&32b&8c-8b\\-104&80&-40c\end{bmatrix}$

24. $\begin{bmatrix}-16\\4x+14\\-75\end{bmatrix}$ **25.** $\begin{bmatrix}-40&50\\-25&75\end{bmatrix}$

26. $\begin{bmatrix}-6&-18y+36\\-24x-54&54\\-6x+42&-6xy-12x\end{bmatrix}$

28a.

	Jan	Feb	Mar
Grand Rapids	21.1	12.2	9.0
Boston	13.3	11.3	8.3
Buffalo	26.1	17.8	12.4
Pittsburgh	12.3	8.5	7.9

Grand Rapids	15.4	33.6	13.6
Boston	1.0	4.6	10.2
Buffalo	15.5	33.5	5.4
Pittsburgh	11.3	14.0	9.3

28b.

Grand Rapids	−5.7	21.4	4.6
Boston	−12.3	−6.7	1.9
Buffalo	−10.6	15.7	−7.0
Pittsburgh	−1.0	5.5	1.4

; The matrix represents the difference from normal for each city and month.

29. $\begin{bmatrix}68.6&19\\-19.99&18.3\\11.83&38.7\end{bmatrix}$

30. $\begin{bmatrix}2&28.4\\-40&41.4\end{bmatrix}$

31. $\begin{bmatrix}5&24\\-\frac{167}{12}&-10\end{bmatrix}$

32. $\begin{bmatrix}-\frac{13}{5}&-20&\frac{27}{8}\\16&\frac{18}{5}&15\end{bmatrix}$

Study Guide and Intervention
CRM pp. 11–12 AL OL ELL

4-2 Study Guide and Intervention

Operations with Matrices

Add and Subtract Matrices Matrices with the same dimensions can be added together or one can be subtracted from the other.

Addition of Matrices	$\begin{bmatrix} a & b & c \\ d & e & f \\ g & h & i \end{bmatrix} + \begin{bmatrix} j & k & l \\ m & n & o \\ p & q & r \end{bmatrix} = \begin{bmatrix} a+j & b+k & c+l \\ d+m & e+n & f+o \\ g+p & h+q & i+r \end{bmatrix}$
Subtraction of Matrices	$\begin{bmatrix} a & b & c \\ d & e & f \\ g & h & i \end{bmatrix} - \begin{bmatrix} j & k & l \\ m & n & o \\ p & q & r \end{bmatrix} = \begin{bmatrix} a-j & b-k & c-l \\ d-m & e-n & f-o \\ g-p & h-q & i-r \end{bmatrix}$

Example 1 Find $A + B$ if $A = \begin{bmatrix} 6 & -7 \\ 2 & -12 \end{bmatrix}$ and $B = \begin{bmatrix} 4 & 2 \\ -5 & -6 \end{bmatrix}$.

$$A + B = \begin{bmatrix} 6 & -7 \\ 2 & -12 \end{bmatrix} + \begin{bmatrix} 4 & 2 \\ -5 & -6 \end{bmatrix} = \begin{bmatrix} 6+4 & -7+2 \\ 2+(-5) & -12+(-6) \end{bmatrix} = \begin{bmatrix} 10 & -5 \\ -3 & -18 \end{bmatrix}$$

Example 2 Find $A - B$ if $A = \begin{bmatrix} -2 & 8 \\ 3 & -4 \\ 10 & 7 \end{bmatrix}$ and $B = \begin{bmatrix} 4 & -3 \\ -2 & 1 \\ -6 & 8 \end{bmatrix}$.

$$A - B = \begin{bmatrix} -2 & 8 \\ 3 & -4 \\ 10 & 7 \end{bmatrix} - \begin{bmatrix} 4 & -3 \\ -2 & 1 \\ -6 & 8 \end{bmatrix} = \begin{bmatrix} -2-4 & 8-(-3) \\ 3-(-2) & -4-1 \\ 10-(-6) & 7-8 \end{bmatrix} = \begin{bmatrix} -6 & 11 \\ 5 & -5 \\ 16 & -1 \end{bmatrix}$$

Exercises

Perform the indicated operations. If the matrix does not exist, write *impossible*.

1. $\begin{bmatrix} 8 & 7 \\ -10 & -6 \end{bmatrix} - \begin{bmatrix} -4 & 3 \\ 2 & -12 \end{bmatrix}$ **$\begin{bmatrix} 12 & 4 \\ -12 & 6 \end{bmatrix}$**

2. $\begin{bmatrix} 6 & -5 & 9 \\ -3 & 4 & 5 \end{bmatrix} + \begin{bmatrix} -4 & 3 & 2 \\ 6 & 9 & -4 \end{bmatrix}$ **$\begin{bmatrix} 2 & -2 & 11 \\ 3 & 13 & 1 \end{bmatrix}$**

3. $\begin{bmatrix} 6 \\ -3 \\ 2 \end{bmatrix} + [-6 \ 3 \ -2]$ **impossible**

4. $\begin{bmatrix} 5 & -2 \\ -4 & 6 \\ 7 & 9 \end{bmatrix} + \begin{bmatrix} -11 & 6 \\ 2 & -5 \\ 4 & -7 \end{bmatrix}$ **$\begin{bmatrix} -6 & 4 \\ -2 & 1 \end{bmatrix}$**

5. $\begin{bmatrix} 8 & 0 & -6 \\ 4 & 5 & -11 \\ -7 & 3 & 4 \end{bmatrix} - \begin{bmatrix} -2 & 1 & 7 \\ 3 & -4 & 3 \\ -8 & 5 & 6 \end{bmatrix}$ **$\begin{bmatrix} 10 & -1 & -13 \\ 1 & 9 & -14 \\ 1 & -2 & -2 \end{bmatrix}$**

6. $\begin{bmatrix} \frac{3}{4} & \frac{2}{5} \\ -\frac{1}{2} & \frac{4}{3} \end{bmatrix} - \begin{bmatrix} \frac{1}{2} & \frac{2}{3} \\ \frac{2}{3} & -\frac{1}{2} \end{bmatrix}$ **$\begin{bmatrix} \frac{1}{4} & -\frac{4}{15} \\ -\frac{7}{6} & \frac{11}{6} \end{bmatrix}$**

Chapter 4 11 Glencoe Algebra 2

Lesson 4-2

Practice
CRM p. 14 AL OL BL ELL

4-2 Practice

Operations with Matrices

Perform the indicated operations. If the matrix does not exist, write *impossible*.

1. $\begin{bmatrix} 2 & -1 \\ 3 & 7 \\ 14 & -9 \end{bmatrix} + \begin{bmatrix} -6 & 9 \\ 7 & -11 \\ -8 & 17 \end{bmatrix}$ **$\begin{bmatrix} -4 & 8 \\ 10 & -4 \\ 6 & 8 \end{bmatrix}$**

2. $\begin{bmatrix} 4 \\ -71 \\ 18 \end{bmatrix} - \begin{bmatrix} -67 \\ 45 \\ -24 \end{bmatrix}$ **$\begin{bmatrix} 71 \\ -116 \\ 42 \end{bmatrix}$**

3. $-3\begin{bmatrix} -1 & 0 \\ 17 & -11 \end{bmatrix} + 4\begin{bmatrix} -3 & 16 \\ -21 & 12 \end{bmatrix}$ **$\begin{bmatrix} -9 & 64 \\ -135 & 81 \end{bmatrix}$**

4. $7\begin{bmatrix} 2 & -1 & 8 \\ 4 & 7 & 9 \end{bmatrix} - 2\begin{bmatrix} -1 & 4 & -3 \\ 7 & 2 & -6 \end{bmatrix}$ **$\begin{bmatrix} 16 & -15 & 62 \\ 14 & 45 & 75 \end{bmatrix}$**

5. $-2\begin{bmatrix} 1 \\ 2 \end{bmatrix} + 4\begin{bmatrix} 0 \\ 5 \end{bmatrix} - \begin{bmatrix} 10 \\ 18 \end{bmatrix}$ **$\begin{bmatrix} -12 \\ -2 \end{bmatrix}$**

6. $\frac{3}{4}\begin{bmatrix} 8 & 12 \\ -16 & 20 \end{bmatrix} + \frac{2}{3}\begin{bmatrix} 27 & -9 \\ 54 & -18 \end{bmatrix}$ **$\begin{bmatrix} 24 & 3 \\ 24 & 3 \end{bmatrix}$**

Use matrices $A = \begin{bmatrix} 4 & -1 & 0 \\ -3 & 6 & 2 \end{bmatrix}$, $B = \begin{bmatrix} -2 & 4 & 5 \\ 1 & 0 & 9 \end{bmatrix}$, and $C = \begin{bmatrix} 10 & -8 & 6 \\ -6 & -4 & 20 \end{bmatrix}$ to find the following.

7. $A - B$ **$\begin{bmatrix} 6 & -5 & -5 \\ -4 & 6 & 11 \end{bmatrix}$**

8. $A - C$ **$\begin{bmatrix} -6 & 7 & -6 \\ 3 & 10 & -18 \end{bmatrix}$**

9. $-3B$ **$\begin{bmatrix} 6 & -12 & -15 \\ -3 & 0 & 27 \end{bmatrix}$**

10. $4B - A$ **$\begin{bmatrix} -12 & 17 & 20 \\ 7 & -6 & -38 \end{bmatrix}$**

11. $-2B - 3C$ **$\begin{bmatrix} -26 & 16 & -28 \\ 16 & 12 & -42 \end{bmatrix}$**

12. $A + 0.5C$ **$\begin{bmatrix} 9 & -5 & 3 \\ -6 & 4 & 12 \end{bmatrix}$**

13. **ECONOMICS** Use the table that shows loans by an economic development board to women and men starting new businesses.

	Women		Men	
	Businesses	Loan Amount ($)	Businesses	Loan Amount ($)
2003	27	$567,000	36	$864,000
2004	41	$902,000	32	$672,000
2005	35	$777,000	28	$562,000

a. Write two matrices that represent the number of new businesses and loan amounts, one for women and one for men. **$\begin{bmatrix} 27 & 567{,}000 \\ 41 & 902{,}000 \\ 35 & 777{,}000 \end{bmatrix}, \begin{bmatrix} 36 & 864{,}000 \\ 32 & 672{,}000 \\ 28 & 562{,}000 \end{bmatrix}$**

b. Find the sum of the numbers of new businesses and loan amounts for both men and women over the three-year period expressed as a matrix. **$\begin{bmatrix} 63 & 1{,}431{,}000 \\ 73 & 1{,}574{,}000 \\ 63 & 1{,}339{,}000 \end{bmatrix}$**

14. **PET NUTRITION** Use the table that gives nutritional information for two types of dog food. Find the difference in the percent of protein, fat, and fiber between Mix B and Mix A expressed as a matrix. **[2 −4 3]**

	% Protein	% Fat	% Fiber
Mix A	22	12	5
Mix B	24	8	8

Chapter 4 14 Glencoe Algebra 2

Word Problem Practice
CRM p. 15 AL OL BL ELL

4-2 Word Problem Practice

Operations with Matrices

1. **FARES** The matrix below gives general admission and film fares at New York's Museum of Modern Art.

	Child	Adult
General Admission	20	12
Film	12	8.5

What can you do to this matrix in order to create another matrix that represents fares for 5 people?

SOURCE: *Museum of Modern Art*

Multiply the matrix by 5.

2. **NEGATION** Two engineers need to negate all the entries of a matrix. One engineer tries to do this by multiplying the matrix by −1. The other engineer tries to do this by subtracting twice the matrix from itself. Which engineer, if either, will get the correct result? **Both engineers' methods work. For any matrix, $-M = M - 2M$.**

3. **PLANE FARES** The airfares for travel between New York, Chicago, and Los Angeles are organized in the first matrix. The second matrix gives the tax surcharges for corresponding flights.

	NYC	Chicago	Los Angeles
NYC	0	440	700
Chicago	460	0	660
Los Angeles	850	700	0

	NYC	Chicago	Los Angeles
NYC	0	40	70
Chicago	46	0	60
Los Angeles	85	70	0

Write a matrix that represents the full cost for travel between these cities.

–	NYC	Chicago	Los Angeles
NYC	**0**	**480**	**770**
Chicago	**506**	**0**	**720**
Los Angeles	**935**	**770**	**0**

4. **SUNFLOWERS** Matrix H is a 3 by 1 matrix that contains the initial heights of three sunflowers. Matrix G is a 3 by 1 matrix that contains the numbers of inches the corresponding sunflowers grow in a week. What does matrix $H + 4G$ represent? **the heights of the three sunflowers in four weeks time**

5. **DINNER** The menu shows prices for some dishes at a restaurant.

Il Ristorante Menu

	Regular	Half-portion
Lamb	$17.00	$9.00
Chicken	$14.00	$7.00
Steak	$22.00	$11.00

a. Make a 3 by 2 matrix to organize these data. **Sample answer: $\begin{bmatrix} 17 & 9 \\ 14 & 7 \\ 22 & 11 \end{bmatrix}$**

b. Let M be the matrix you wrote for part **a**. Write an expression involving M that would give prices that include an additional 20% to cover tax and tip. **$M + 0.2M$ or $1.2M$**

c. Compute the matrix you described in part **b**. **$\begin{bmatrix} 20.40 & 10.80 \\ 16.80 & 8.40 \\ 26.40 & 13.20 \end{bmatrix}$**

Chapter 4 15 Glencoe Algebra 2

Lesson 4-2

Real-World Link

At the age of 40, Dara Torres eclipsed her own American record in winning the women's 50-meter freestyle during the U.S. Swimming Championships in 2007.

33. **SWIMMING** The table shows some of the world, Olympic, and American women's freestyle swimming records.

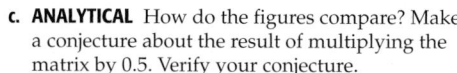

Distance (m)	World	Olympic	American
50	24.13 s	24.13 s	24.63 s
100	53.52 s	53.52 s	53.99 s
200	1:56.54 min	1:57.65 min	1:57.41 min
800	8:16.22 min	8:19.67 min	8:16.22 min

Source: USA Swimming

a. Find the difference between the American and World records expressed as a column matrix. **33a. $\begin{bmatrix} 0.5 \text{ s} \\ 0.47 \text{ s} \\ 0.87 \text{ s} \\ 0 \text{ s} \end{bmatrix}$**

b. What is the meaning of each row in the column?

c. In which events were the fastest times set at the Olympics? **50-m and 100-m**

33b. In the 50-m, the fastest American time is 0.5 second behind the world record. In the 100-m, the fastest American time is 0.47 second behind the world record. In the 200-m, the fastest American time is 0.87 second behind the world record. In the 800-m, it was an American who set the world record.

34. **MULTIPLE REPRESENTATIONS** In this problem, you will investigate using matrices to represent transformations.

a. **ALGEBRAIC** The matrix $\begin{bmatrix} -3 & -4 & 1 \\ 8 & 6 & 0 \end{bmatrix}$ represents a triangle with vertices at (−3, 8), (−4, 6), and (1, 0). Write a matrix to represent △ABC. **See margin.**

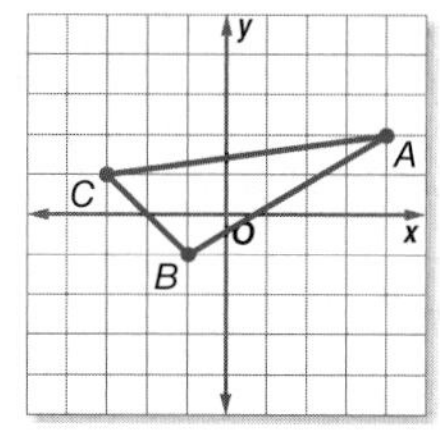

b. **GEOMETRIC** Multiply the vertex matrix you wrote by 2. Then graph the figure represented by the new matrix. **See margin.**

c. **ANALYTICAL** How do the figures compare? Make a conjecture about the result of multiplying the matrix by 0.5. Verify your conjecture.

34c. The new triangle is similar to the original, with sides twice as long as the original. The result of multiplying the matrix by 0.5 would be a figure similar to the original with sides half as long.

H.O.T. Problems
Use Higher-Order Thinking Skills

35. **PROOF** Prove that matrix addition is commutative for 2 × 2 matrices. **See Chapter 4 Answer Appendix.**

36. **PROOF** Prove that matrix addition is associative for 2 × 2 matrices. **See Chapter 4 Answer Appendix.**

37. **CHALLENGE** Find the elements of C if:

$A = \begin{bmatrix} -3 & -4 \\ 8 & 6 \end{bmatrix}$, $B = \begin{bmatrix} 5 & -1 \\ 2 & -4 \end{bmatrix}$, and $3A - 4B + 6C = \begin{bmatrix} 13 & 22 \\ 10 & 4 \end{bmatrix}$. **$\begin{bmatrix} 7 & 5 \\ -1 & -5 \end{bmatrix}$**

38. **REASONING** Determine whether each statement is *sometimes*, *always*, or *never* true for matrices A and B. Explain your reasoning. **a–e. See margin.**

a. If $A + B$ exists, then $A - B$ exists.

b. If k is a real number, then kA and kB exist.

c. If $A - B$ does not exist, then $B - A$ does not exist.

d. If A and B have the same number of elements, then $A + B$ exists.

e. If kA exists and kB exists, then $kA + kB$ exists.

39. **OPEN ENDED** Give an example of matrices A and B if $4B - 3A = \begin{bmatrix} -6 & 5 \\ -2 & -1 \end{bmatrix}$. **39. See margin.**

40. **WRITING IN MATH** Explain how to find $4D - 3C$ for two given matrices, C and D with the same dimensions. **See Chapter 4 Answer Appendix.**

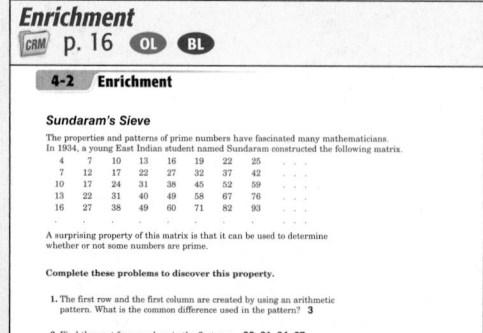

Enrichment
CRM p. 16 OL BL

4-2 Enrichment

Sundaram's Sieve

The properties and patterns of prime numbers have fascinated many mathematicians. In 1934, a young East Indian student named Sundaram constructed the following matrix.

4	7	10	13	16	19	22	25	. . .
7	12	17	22	27	32	37	42	. . .
10	17	24	31	38	45	52	59	. . .
13	22	31	40	49	58	67	76	. . .
16	27	38	49	60	71	82	93	. . .
.	.	.	.	.	.	.	.	. . .

A surprising property of this matrix is that it can be used to determine whether or not some numbers are prime.

Complete these problems to discover this property.

1. The first row and the first column are created by using an arithmetic pattern. What is the common difference used in the pattern? **3**

2. Find the next four numbers in the first row. **28, 31, 34, 37**

TEACH with TECH

VIDEO RECORDING Separate the class into groups. Have each group create a video showing how to perform one of the operations with matrices: addition, subtraction, or scalar multiplication.

NGSSS PRACTICE 912.A.3.14, 912.D.8.2, 912.P.1.2

41. What is the solution of the system of equations? **C**

$$0.06p + 4q = 0.88$$
$$p - q = -2.25$$

A. $(-0.912, -1.338)$ **C.** $(-2, 0.25)$
B. $(0.912, -3.162)$ **D.** $(-2, -4.25)$

42. **SHORT RESPONSE** Find $A + B$ if $A = \begin{bmatrix} -7 & 3 \\ 2 & 6 \end{bmatrix}$ and $B = \begin{bmatrix} 4 & 2 \\ 0 & 1 \end{bmatrix}$. $\begin{bmatrix} -3 & 5 \\ 2 & 7 \end{bmatrix}$

43. **SAT/ACT** Solve for x and y. **F**

$$x + 3y = 16$$
$$7 - x = 12$$

F. $x = -5, y = 7$ **H.** $x = 7, y = 5$
G. $x = 7, y = 3$ **I.** $x = 5, y = 7$

44. **PROBABILITY** A local pizzeria offers 5 different meat toppings and 6 different vegetable toppings. You decide to get two vegetable toppings and one meat topping. How many different types of pizzas can you order? **B**

A. 60 **C.** 120
B. 75 **D.** 150

Spiral Review

Identify each element for the following matrices. (Lesson 4-1)

$$A = \begin{bmatrix} -3 & 6 \\ -5 & x \\ 8 & 4y \end{bmatrix}, B = \begin{bmatrix} 16 & 4 & x \\ -2 & 9 & y \end{bmatrix}, C = \begin{bmatrix} 9 & -5 & 3 & 2 \\ 0 & -6 & 8 & 1 \end{bmatrix}$$

45. a_{32} **4y**

46. c_{13} **3**

47. b_{32} **does not exist**

Solve each system of equations. (Lesson 3-5)

48. $2x + 3y - z = -1$, $5x + y + 4z = 30$, $-8x - 2y + 5z = -2$ **(3, −1, 4)**

49. $3x - 4y + 6z = 26$, $5x + 3y + 2z = 5$, $-2x + 5y - 3z = -9$ **(−2, 1, 6)**

50. $5x + 2y - 4z = 22$, $6x + 3y + 5z = 5$, $-2x - 4y + z = 2$ **(4, −3, −2)**

Solve each system of inequalities by graphing. (Lesson 3-3) **51–53. See Chapter 4 Answer Appendix.**

51. $x - 2y > -4$, $y < -2x - 3$

52. $y \geq -4x + 6$, $3y < 2x + 9$

53. $4x + 2y > 8$, $4y - 3x \leq 12$

54. **RAKING LEAVES** A student can earn $20 plus an extra $5 for each trash bag he or she completely fills with leaves. Write and solve an equation to determine how many bags the student will need to fill in order to earn $100. (Lesson 2-4) **16 bags**

55. **SPORTS** There are 15,991 more student athletes in New York than in Illinois. Write and solve an equation to find the number of student athletes in Illinois. (Lesson 1-3) **350,349 − x = 15,991; 334,358**

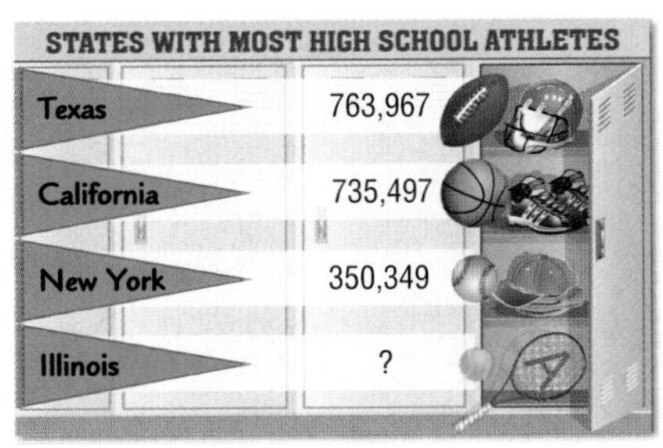

STATES WITH MOST HIGH SCHOOL ATHLETES
Texas
763,967
California
735,497
New York
350,349
Illinois
?

Skills Review

Simplify each expression. (Lesson 1-2)

56. $4(2x - 3y) + 2(5x - 6y)$ **18x − 24y**

57. $-3(2a - 5b) - 4(4b + a)$ **−10a − b**

58. $-7(x - y) + 5(y - x)$ **−12x + 12y**

Differentiated Instruction BL

Extension The following matrix shows the amount of money in six bank accounts.

$$\begin{bmatrix} 586 & 1255 \\ 9833 & 476 \\ 2981 & 1045 \end{bmatrix}$$

What scalar multiplier should be used to produce a product matrix that represents the amount in each account after one year if the interest rate is 5%? 1.05

4 ASSESS

Yesterday's News Have students write how yesterday's concepts helped them with today's lesson on adding and subtracting matrices.

Formative Assessment

Check for student understanding of concepts in Lessons 4-1 and 4-2.

CRM Quiz 1, p. 45

Additional Answers

34a. $\begin{bmatrix} 4 & -1 & -3 \\ 2 & -1 & 1 \end{bmatrix}$

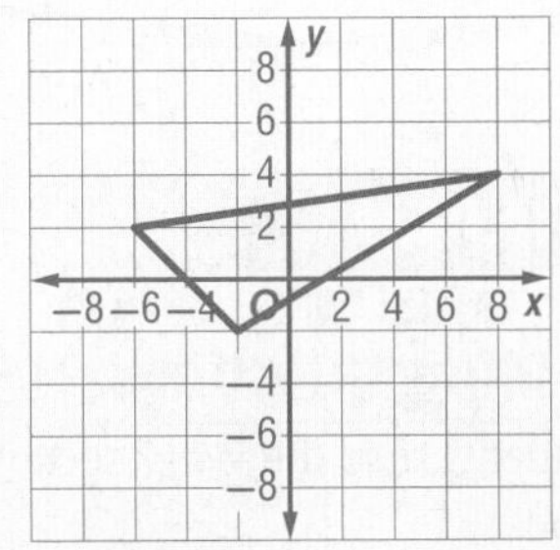

34b. $\begin{bmatrix} 8 & -2 & -6 \\ 4 & -2 & 2 \end{bmatrix}$

38a. Always; if $A + B$ exists, A and B have the same dimensions. If A and B have the same dimensions, then $A - B$ exists.

38b. Always; if k is a real number, then by the definition of scalar multiplication, $kA = \begin{bmatrix} -3k & -4k \\ 8k & 6k \end{bmatrix}$ and $kB = \begin{bmatrix} 5k & -k \\ 2k & -4k \end{bmatrix}$.

38c. Always; if $A - B$ does not exist, then A and B must have different dimensions. If A and B have different dimensions, then $A + B$ does not exist.

38d. Sometimes; matrices must have the same dimensions for their sum to exist.

38e. Sometimes; matrices must have the same dimensions for their sum to exist.

39. Sample Answer: $A = \begin{bmatrix} 6 & 1 \\ 6 & 3 \end{bmatrix}$, $B = \begin{bmatrix} 3 & 2 \\ 4 & 2 \end{bmatrix}$

4-3 Lesson Notes

1 FOCUS

Vertical Alignment

Before Lesson 4-3
Multiply matrices by a scalar.

Lesson 4-3
Multiply matrices.
Use the properties of matrix multiplication.

After Lesson 4-3
Use matrices to solve systems of equations.

2 TEACH

Scaffolding Questions

Have students read the *Why?* section of the lesson.

Ask:

- The table shows that Leslie made six 3-point field goals in 2004. How many points did she score by 3-point field goals? 18
- A field goal is worth 2 points. How many total points did Leslie score by field goals from 2003 to 2006? 1632

4-3 Multiplying Matrices

Then
You multiplied matrices by a scalar. (Lesson 4-2)

Now
- Multiply matrices.
- Use the properties of matrix multiplication.

NGSSS
Preparation for MA.912.D.8.2 Use matrix operations to solve problems.

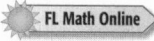

FL Math Online
glencoe.com

Why?

The table shows the scoring summary for Lisa Leslie, the WNBA's all-time scoring leader, during her highest scoring seasons. Her total baskets can be summarized in the baskets matrix B. The point values for each type of basket made can be organized in the point value matrix P.

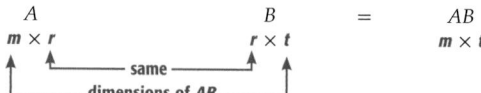

Lisa Leslie Regular Season Scoring

Type	2003	2004	2005	2006
Field Goal	153	217	197	249
3-Point Field Goal	12	6	7	8
Free Throw	82	146	102	158

Source: WNBA

You can use matrix multiplication to find the points scored during each season.

Baskets **Point Values**

$$\begin{bmatrix} 153 & 217 & 197 & 249 \\ 12 & 6 & 7 & 8 \\ 82 & 146 & 102 & 158 \end{bmatrix} \qquad P = [2 \quad 3 \quad 1]$$

Multiply Matrices You can multiply two matrices A and B if and only if the number of columns in A is equal to the number of rows in B. When you multiply two matrices $A_{m \times r}$ and $B_{r \times t}$, the resulting matrix AB is an $m \times t$ matrix.

$$\underset{m \times r}{A} \cdot \underset{r \times t}{B} = \underset{m \times t}{AB}$$

same (r and r); dimensions of AB (m and t)

EXAMPLE 1 Dimensions of Matrix Products

Determine whether each matrix product is defined. If so, state the dimensions of the product.

a. $A_{3 \times 4}$ and $B_{4 \times 2}$

$$\underset{3 \times 4}{A} \cdot \underset{4 \times 2}{B} = \underset{3 \times 2}{AB}$$

The inner dimensions are equal, so the product is defined. Its dimensions are 3×2.

b. $A_{5 \times 3}$ and $B_{5 \times 4}$

$$\underset{5 \times 3}{A} \cdot \underset{5 \times 4}{B}$$

The inner dimensions are not equal, so the matrix product is not defined.

Guided Practice

1A. $A_{4 \times 6}$ and $B_{6 \times 2}$ 4×2

1B. $A_{3 \times 2}$ and $B_{3 \times 2}$ not defined

Personal Tutor glencoe.com

Lesson 4-3 Resources

Resource	Approaching-Level	On-Level	Beyond-Level	English Learners
Teacher Edition	• Differentiated Instruction, p. 201	• Differentiated Instruction, p. 201	• Differentiated Instruction, pp. 201, 202	
Chapter Resource Masters	• Study Guide and Intervention, pp. 17–18 • Skills Practice, p. 19 • Practice, p. 20 • Word Problem Practice, p. 21	• Study Guide and Intervention, pp. 17–18 • Skills Practice, p. 19 • Practice, p. 20 • Word Problem Practice, p. 21 • Enrichment, p. 22	• Practice, p. 20 • Word Problem Practice, p. 21 • Enrichment, p. 22	• Study Guide and Intervention, pp. 17–18 • Skills Practice, p. 19 • Practice, p. 20 • Word Problem Practice, p. 21
Transparencies	• 5-Minute Check Transparency 4-3	• 5-Minute Check Transparency 4-3	• 5-Minute Check Transparency 4-3	• 5-Minute Check Transparency 4-3
Other	• Study Notebook	• Study Notebook	• Study Notebook	• Study Notebook

The product of two matrices is found by multiplying columns and rows.

Key Concept — Multiplying Matrices

Words The element in the *m*th row and *r*th column of matrix *AB* is the sum of the products of the corresponding elements in row *m* of matrix *A* and column *r* of matrix *B*.

Symbols

$$\underset{A}{\begin{bmatrix} a & b \\ c & d \end{bmatrix}} \cdot \underset{B}{\begin{bmatrix} e & f \\ g & h \end{bmatrix}} = \underset{AB}{\begin{bmatrix} ae+bg & af+bh \\ ce+dg & cf+dh \end{bmatrix}}$$

Watch Out!

Saving Your Place It is easy to lose your place as you multiply matrices. It may help to cover rows or columns not being multiplied as you find elements of the product matrix.

EXAMPLE 2 Multiply Square Matrices

Find XY if $X = \begin{bmatrix} 6 & -3 \\ -10 & -2 \end{bmatrix}$ and $Y = \begin{bmatrix} -5 & -4 \\ 3 & 3 \end{bmatrix}$.

$$XY = \begin{bmatrix} 6 & -3 \\ -10 & -2 \end{bmatrix} \cdot \begin{bmatrix} -5 & -4 \\ 3 & 3 \end{bmatrix}$$

Step 1 Multiply the numbers in the first row of X by the numbers in the first column of Y, add the products, and put the result in the first row, first column of XY.

$$\begin{bmatrix} 6 & -3 \\ -10 & -2 \end{bmatrix} \cdot \begin{bmatrix} -5 & -4 \\ 3 & 3 \end{bmatrix} = \begin{bmatrix} 6(-5)+(-3)(3) & \\ & \end{bmatrix}$$

Step 2 Follow the same procedure as in Step 1 using the first row and the second column numbers. Write the result in the first row, second column.

$$\begin{bmatrix} 6 & -3 \\ -10 & -2 \end{bmatrix} \cdot \begin{bmatrix} -5 & -4 \\ 3 & 3 \end{bmatrix} = \begin{bmatrix} 6(-5)+(-3)(3) & 6(-4)+(-3)(3) \\ & \end{bmatrix}$$

Step 3 Follow the same procedure with the second row and the first column numbers. Write the result in the second row, first column.

$$\begin{bmatrix} 6 & -3 \\ -10 & -2 \end{bmatrix} \cdot \begin{bmatrix} -5 & -4 \\ 3 & 3 \end{bmatrix} = \begin{bmatrix} 6(-5)+(-3)(3) & 6(-4)+(-3)(3) \\ -10(-5)+(-2)(3) & \end{bmatrix}$$

Step 4 The procedure is the same for the numbers in the second row, second column.

$$\begin{bmatrix} 6 & -3 \\ -10 & -2 \end{bmatrix} \cdot \begin{bmatrix} -5 & -4 \\ 3 & 3 \end{bmatrix} = \begin{bmatrix} 6(-5)+(-3)(3) & 6(-4)+(-3)(3) \\ -10(-5)+(-2)(3) & -10(-4)+(-2)(3) \end{bmatrix}$$

Step 5 Simplify the product matrix.

$$\begin{bmatrix} 6(-5)+(-3)(3) & 6(-4)+(-3)(3) \\ -10(-5)+(-2)(3) & -10(-4)+(-2)(3) \end{bmatrix} = \begin{bmatrix} -39 & -33 \\ 44 & 34 \end{bmatrix}$$

Guided Practice

2. Find UV if $U = \begin{bmatrix} 5 & 9 \\ -3 & -2 \end{bmatrix}$ and $V = \begin{bmatrix} 2 & -1 \\ 6 & -5 \end{bmatrix}$. $\begin{bmatrix} 64 & -50 \\ -18 & 13 \end{bmatrix}$

Personal Tutor glencoe.com

Multiply Matrices

Example 1 shows how to determine the dimensions of matrix products.
Example 2 shows how to find the product of two square matrices.
Example 3 shows how to solve a real-world problem by multiplying two matrices with different dimensions.

Formative Assessment

Use the Guided Practice exercises after each example to determine students' understanding of concepts.

Additional Examples

1 Determine whether each matrix product is defined. If so, state the dimensions of the product.

a. $A_{3 \times 4}$ and $B_{4 \times 2}$ The matrix product is defined. The dimensions are 3×2.

b. $A_{3 \times 2}$ and $B_{4 \times 3}$ The matrix product is not defined.

2 Find RS if $R = \begin{bmatrix} 3 & 2 \\ -1 & 0 \end{bmatrix}$ and $S = \begin{bmatrix} -2 & 1 \\ 1 & -1 \end{bmatrix}$. $\begin{bmatrix} -4 & 1 \\ 2 & -1 \end{bmatrix}$

Additional Examples also in Interactive Classroom PowerPoint® Presentations

IWB INTERACTIVE WHITEBOARD READY

Watch Out!

Preventing Errors Encourage students to show all of their work while multiplying matrices. This will allow them to find computation errors if any are made.

Differentiated Instruction (AL OL BL)

If students need more practice with matrices,

Then have them use the class seating arrangement to form matrices, with each student's desk as an element. Have students make 24 large cards showing the values for the elements of two matrices. Form two matrices $A_{4 \times 3}$ and $B_{3 \times 4}$ with student seats and give each student sitting in these "matrices" a card to show the element in that position. Have students model the matrix multiplication $AB = C$. Begin by drawing a blank 4×4 matrix on the board. For each element on matrix C, have students walk out the products, compute the sums, and then write the results in the correct locations of the matrix on the board.

Additional Example

3 **CHESS** Three teams competed in the final round of the Chess Club's championships. For each win, a team was awarded 3 points, and for each draw a team received 1 point. Which team won the tournament?

Team	Wins	Draws
Blue	5	4
Red	6	3
Green	4	5

The Red Team won the tournament with a total of 21 points.

TEACH with TECH

STUDENT RESPONSE SYSTEM Show students slides of different matrix multiplication problems. For each, ask students if this matrix multiplication is possible. Have students reply with A for yes and B for no. For each example, choose students to explain why it is or is not possible.

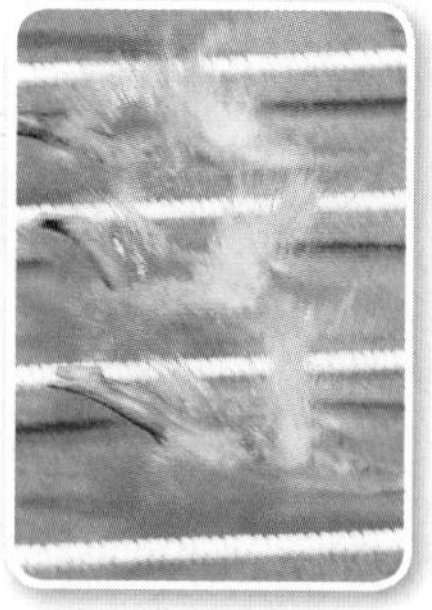

Real-World Link

Swim meets consist of racing and diving competitions. There are more than 241,000 high schools that participate each year.

Source: National Federation of State High School Associations

Matrix multiplication can be used in many real-world situations.

Real-World EXAMPLE 3 Multiply Matrices

SWIM MEET At a particular swim meet, 7 points were awarded for each first-place finish, 4 points for second, and 2 points for third. Find the total number of points for each school. Which school won the meet?

School	First Place	Second Place	Third Place
Central	4	7	3
Franklin	8	9	1
Hayes	10	5	3
Lincoln	3	3	6

Understand The final scores can be found by multiplying the swim results for each school by the points awarded for each first-, second-, and third-place finish.

Plan Write the results of the races and the points awarded in matrix form. Set up the matrices so that the number of rows in the points matrix equals the number of columns in the results matrix.

$$\text{Results} \quad R = \begin{bmatrix} 4 & 7 & 3 \\ 8 & 9 & 1 \\ 10 & 5 & 3 \\ 3 & 3 & 6 \end{bmatrix} \qquad \text{Points} \quad P = \begin{bmatrix} 7 \\ 4 \\ 2 \end{bmatrix}$$

Solve Multiply the matrices.

$$RP = \begin{bmatrix} 4 & 7 & 3 \\ 8 & 9 & 1 \\ 10 & 5 & 3 \\ 3 & 3 & 6 \end{bmatrix} \cdot \begin{bmatrix} 7 \\ 4 \\ 2 \end{bmatrix}$$ **Write an equation.**

$$= \begin{bmatrix} 4(7) + 7(4) + 3(2) \\ 8(7) + 9(4) + 1(2) \\ 10(7) + 5(4) + 3(2) \\ 3(7) + 3(4) + 6(2) \end{bmatrix}$$ **Multiply columns by rows.**

$$= \begin{bmatrix} 62 \\ 94 \\ 96 \\ 45 \end{bmatrix}$$ **Simplify.**

The product matrix shows the scores for Central, Franklin, Hayes, and Lincoln, respectively. Hayes won the swim meet with a total of 96 points.

Check R is a 4×3 matrix and P is a 3×1 matrix, so their product should be a 4×1 matrix.

Guided Practice

3. BASKETBALL Refer to the beginning of the lesson. Use matrix multiplication to determine in which season Lisa Leslie scored the most points. How many points did she score that season? **2006; 680 points**

Personal Tutor glencoe.com

Multiplicative Properties Recall that the properties of real numbers also held true for matrix addition. However, some of these properties do *not* always hold true for matrix multiplication.

Differentiated Instruction

BL

Extension Write the following problems on the board: $A = \begin{bmatrix} 1 & 0 \\ 0 & 1 \end{bmatrix} \cdot \begin{bmatrix} 2 & 6 \\ 1 & -2 \end{bmatrix}$ $B = \begin{bmatrix} 1 & 0 \\ 0 & 1 \end{bmatrix} \cdot \begin{bmatrix} -5 & 0 \\ 5 & 8 \end{bmatrix}$. Have students find each product. Then predict the product $C = \begin{bmatrix} 1 & 0 \\ 0 & 1 \end{bmatrix} \cdot \begin{bmatrix} 6 & -3 \\ 5 & 2 \end{bmatrix}$. Have them multiply to check their prediction. $A = \begin{bmatrix} 2 & 6 \\ 1 & -2 \end{bmatrix}$ $B = \begin{bmatrix} -5 & 0 \\ 5 & 8 \end{bmatrix}$; $\begin{bmatrix} 6 & -3 \\ 5 & 2 \end{bmatrix}$

EXAMPLE 4 Test of the Commutative Property

Find each product if $G = \begin{bmatrix} 1 & 3 & -5 \\ 4 & -2 & 0 \end{bmatrix}$ and $H = \begin{bmatrix} 2 & 3 \\ -2 & -8 \\ 1 & 7 \end{bmatrix}$.

a. GH

$$GH = \begin{bmatrix} 1 & 3 & -5 \\ 4 & -2 & 0 \end{bmatrix} \cdot \begin{bmatrix} 2 & 3 \\ -2 & -8 \\ 1 & 7 \end{bmatrix} \quad \text{Substitution}$$

$$= \begin{bmatrix} 2-6-5 & 3-24-35 \\ 8+4+0 & 12+16+0 \end{bmatrix} \text{ or } \begin{bmatrix} -9 & -56 \\ 12 & 28 \end{bmatrix}$$

b. HG

$$HG = \begin{bmatrix} 2 & 3 \\ -2 & -8 \\ 1 & 7 \end{bmatrix} \cdot \begin{bmatrix} 1 & 3 & -5 \\ 4 & -2 & 0 \end{bmatrix} \quad \text{Substitution}$$

$$= \begin{bmatrix} 2+12 & 6-6 & -10+0 \\ -2-32 & -6+16 & 10+0 \\ 1+28 & 3-14 & -5+0 \end{bmatrix} \text{ or } \begin{bmatrix} 14 & 0 & -10 \\ -34 & 10 & 10 \\ 29 & -11 & -5 \end{bmatrix}$$

Notice that $GH \neq HG$.

Guided Practice

4. Determine if $AB = BA$ is true for $A = \begin{bmatrix} 4 & -1 \\ 5 & -2 \end{bmatrix}$ and $B = \begin{bmatrix} -3 & 6 \\ -4 & 5 \end{bmatrix}$.

Personal Tutor glencoe.com

4. $AB = \begin{bmatrix} -8 & 19 \\ -7 & 20 \end{bmatrix}$ and $BA = \begin{bmatrix} 18 & -9 \\ 9 & -6 \end{bmatrix}$, so $AB \neq BA$.

StudyTip

Proof and Counterexamples To show that a property is true for all cases, you must show it is true for the general case. To show that a property is *not* always true, you need to find only one counterexample.

Example 4 demonstrates that the Commutative Property of Multiplication does not hold for matrix multiplication. The order in which you multiply matrices is very important.

EXAMPLE 5 Test of the Distributive Property

Find each product if $J = \begin{bmatrix} -2 & 4 \\ -5 & -2 \end{bmatrix}$, $K = \begin{bmatrix} 3 & 2 \\ -1 & 3 \end{bmatrix}$, and $L = \begin{bmatrix} -4 & -1 \\ 3 & 0 \end{bmatrix}$.

a. $J(K + L)$

$$J(K+L) = \begin{bmatrix} 2 & 4 \\ -5 & -2 \end{bmatrix} \cdot \left(\begin{bmatrix} 3 & 2 \\ -1 & 3 \end{bmatrix} + \begin{bmatrix} -4 & -1 \\ 3 & 0 \end{bmatrix} \right) \quad \text{Substitution}$$

$$= \begin{bmatrix} 2 & 4 \\ -5 & -2 \end{bmatrix} \cdot \begin{bmatrix} -1 & 1 \\ 2 & 3 \end{bmatrix} \quad \text{Add.}$$

$$= \begin{bmatrix} -2+8 & 2+12 \\ 5-4 & -5-6 \end{bmatrix} \text{ or } \begin{bmatrix} 6 & 14 \\ 1 & -11 \end{bmatrix} \quad \text{Multiply.}$$

b. $JK + JL$

$$JK + JL = \begin{bmatrix} 2 & 4 \\ -5 & -2 \end{bmatrix} \cdot \begin{bmatrix} 3 & 2 \\ -1 & 3 \end{bmatrix} + \begin{bmatrix} 2 & 4 \\ -5 & -2 \end{bmatrix} \cdot \begin{bmatrix} -4 & -1 \\ 3 & 0 \end{bmatrix}$$

$$= \begin{bmatrix} 2(3)+4(-1) & 2(2)+4(3) \\ -5(3)+(-2)(-1) & -5(2)+(-2)(3) \end{bmatrix} + \begin{bmatrix} 2(-4)+4(3) & 2(-1)+4(0) \\ -5(-4)+(-2)(3) & -5(-1)+(-2)(0) \end{bmatrix}$$

$$= \begin{bmatrix} 2 & 16 \\ -13 & -16 \end{bmatrix} + \begin{bmatrix} 4 & -2 \\ 14 & 5 \end{bmatrix} \text{ or } \begin{bmatrix} 6 & 14 \\ 1 & -11 \end{bmatrix}$$

Notice that $J(K + L) = JK + JL$.

Guided Practice

5. Use the matrices $R = \begin{bmatrix} 2 & -1 \\ 1 & 3 \end{bmatrix}$, $S = \begin{bmatrix} 4 & 6 \\ -2 & 5 \end{bmatrix}$, and $T = \begin{bmatrix} -3 & 7 \\ -4 & 8 \end{bmatrix}$ to determine if $(S + T)R = SR + TR$.

Personal Tutor glencoe.com

5. $(S + T)R = \begin{bmatrix} 15 & 38 \\ 1 & 45 \end{bmatrix}$ and $SR + TR = \begin{bmatrix} 15 & 38 \\ 1 & 45 \end{bmatrix}$, so $(S + T)R = SR + TR$.

Multiplicative Properties

Example 4 shows that the Commutative Property of Multiplication does not hold for matrix multiplication. **Example 5** shows how the Distributive Property is used with matrices.

Additional Examples

4 Find each product if $K = \begin{bmatrix} -3 & 2 & 2 \\ -1 & -2 & 0 \end{bmatrix}$ and $L = \begin{bmatrix} 1 & -2 \\ 4 & 3 \\ 0 & -1 \end{bmatrix}$.

a. KL $\begin{bmatrix} 5 & 10 \\ -9 & -4 \end{bmatrix}$

b. LK $\begin{bmatrix} -1 & 6 & 2 \\ -15 & 2 & 8 \\ 1 & 2 & 0 \end{bmatrix}$

5 Find each product if $A = \begin{bmatrix} -1 & 2 \\ 2 & 1 \end{bmatrix}$, $B = \begin{bmatrix} 1 & 0 \\ 3 & -2 \end{bmatrix}$, and $C = \begin{bmatrix} -3 & 1 \\ -1 & 0 \end{bmatrix}$.

a. $A(B + C)$ $\begin{bmatrix} 6 & -5 \\ -2 & 0 \end{bmatrix}$

b. $AB + AC$ $\begin{bmatrix} 6 & -5 \\ -2 & 0 \end{bmatrix}$

Tips for New Teachers

Building on Prior Knowledge Ask students to compare the process in Example 5 to the procedures they have used previously when applying the Distributive Property to real numbers and algebraic expressions.

Focus on Mathematical Content

Multiplying Matrices Before you multiply two matrices, you must determine whether the matrix product is defined. Two matrices can be multiplied if and only if the number of columns in the first matrix is equal to the number of rows in the second matrix.

3 PRACTICE

Formative Assessment

Use Exercises 1–14 to check for understanding.

Use the chart at the bottom of the next page to customize assignments for your students.

Additional Answers

12a. $[165\ 110\ 239]\ \begin{bmatrix} 35 & 28 \\ 32 & 17 \\ 18 & 12 \end{bmatrix}$

13. No; $\begin{bmatrix} 53 & -87 \\ -2 & -60 \end{bmatrix} \neq \begin{bmatrix} 62 & -33 \\ 28 & -69 \end{bmatrix}$.

14. Yes; $X(YZ) = \begin{bmatrix} 431 & 295 \\ 490 & 242 \end{bmatrix}$ and $(XY)Z = \begin{bmatrix} 431 & 295 \\ 490 & 242 \end{bmatrix}$.

The previous example suggests that the Distributive Property is true for matrix multiplication. Some properties of matrix multiplication are shown below.

Key Concept — Properties of Matrix Multiplication

For any matrices A, B, and C for which the matrix product is defined and any scalar k, the following properties are true.

Associative Property of Matrix Multiplication	$(AB)C = A(BC)$
Associative Property of Scalar Multiplication	$k(AB) = (kA)B = A(kB)$
Left Distributive Property	$C(A + B) = CA + CB$
Right Distributive Property	$(A + B)C = AC + BC$

Check Your Understanding

Example 1 p. 200

Determine whether each matrix product is defined. If so, state the dimensions of the product.

1. $A_{2 \times 4} \cdot B_{4 \times 3}$ 2 × 3 **2.** $C_{5 \times 4} \cdot D_{5 \times 4}$ undefined **3.** $E_{8 \times 6} \cdot F_{6 \times 10}$ 8 × 10

Examples 2 and 3 pp. 201–202

Find each product, if possible.

4. $\begin{bmatrix} 2 & 1 \\ 7 & -5 \end{bmatrix} \cdot \begin{bmatrix} -6 & 3 \\ -2 & -4 \end{bmatrix}$ $\begin{bmatrix} -14 & 2 \\ -32 & 41 \end{bmatrix}$

5. $\begin{bmatrix} 10 & -2 \\ -7 & 3 \end{bmatrix} \cdot \begin{bmatrix} 1 & 4 \\ 5 & -2 \end{bmatrix}$ $\begin{bmatrix} 0 & 44 \\ 8 & -34 \end{bmatrix}$

6. $[9\ \ -2] \cdot \begin{bmatrix} -2 & 4 \\ 6 & -7 \end{bmatrix}$ $[-30\ \ 50]$

7. $\begin{bmatrix} -9 \\ 6 \end{bmatrix} \cdot [-1\ \ -10\ \ 1]$

7. $\begin{bmatrix} 9 & 90 & -9 \\ -6 & -60 & 6 \end{bmatrix}$

8. $\begin{bmatrix} -8 & 7 & 4 \\ -5 & -3 & 8 \end{bmatrix} \cdot \begin{bmatrix} 10 & 6 \\ 8 & 4 \end{bmatrix}$ undefined

9. $\begin{bmatrix} 2 & 8 \\ 3 & -1 \end{bmatrix} \cdot \begin{bmatrix} 6 \\ -7 \end{bmatrix}$ $\begin{bmatrix} -44 \\ 25 \end{bmatrix}$

10. $\begin{bmatrix} -4 & 3 & 2 \\ -1 & -5 & 4 \end{bmatrix} \cdot \begin{bmatrix} 2 & 1 & 6 \\ 8 & 4 & -1 \\ 5 & 3 & -2 \end{bmatrix}$ $\begin{bmatrix} 26 & 14 & -31 \\ -22 & -9 & -9 \end{bmatrix}$

11. $\begin{bmatrix} 2 & 5 & 3 & -1 \\ -3 & 1 & 8 & -3 \end{bmatrix} \cdot \begin{bmatrix} 6 & -3 \\ -7 & 1 \\ 2 & 0 \\ -1 & 0 \end{bmatrix}$ $\begin{bmatrix} -16 & -1 \\ -6 & 10 \end{bmatrix}$

12. **FITNESS** The table shows the number of people registered for aerobics for the first quarter. **a.** See margin.

Quinn's Gym charges the following registration fees: class-by-class, \$165; 11-class pass, \$110; unlimited pass, \$239.

Quinn's Gym

Payment	Aerobics	Step Aerobics
class-by-class	35	28
11-class pass	32	17
unlimited pass	18	12

a. Write a matrix for the registration fees and a matrix for the number of students.

b. Find the total amount of money the gym received from aerobics and step aerobic registrations. \$22,955

Examples 4 and 5 p. 203

Use $X = \begin{bmatrix} -10 & -3 \\ 2 & -8 \end{bmatrix}$, $Y = \begin{bmatrix} -5 & 6 \\ -1 & 9 \end{bmatrix}$, **and** $Z = \begin{bmatrix} -5 & -1 \\ -8 & -4 \end{bmatrix}$ **to determine whether the following equations are true for the given matrices.** 13, 14. See margin.

13. $XY = YX$ **14.** $X(YZ) = (XY)Z$

Practice and Problem Solving

● = **Step-by-Step Solutions** begin on page R20. **Extra Practice** begins on page 947.

Example 1 p. 200

Determine whether each matrix product is defined. If so, state the dimensions of the product.

15. $P_{2 \times 3} \cdot Q_{3 \times 4}$ 2×4
16. $A_{5 \times 5} \cdot B_{5 \times 5}$ 5×5
17. $M_{3 \times 1} \cdot N_{2 \times 3}$ undefined
18. $X_{2 \times 6} \cdot Y_{6 \times 3}$ 2×3
19. $J_{2 \times 1} \cdot K_{2 \times 1}$ undefined
20. $S_{5 \times 2} \cdot T_{2 \times 4}$ 5×4

Examples 2 and 3 pp. 201–202

Find each product, if possible.

21. $\begin{bmatrix} 1 & 6 \end{bmatrix} \cdot \begin{bmatrix} -10 \\ 6 \end{bmatrix}$ $\begin{bmatrix} 26 \end{bmatrix}$

22. $\begin{bmatrix} 6 \\ -3 \end{bmatrix} \cdot \begin{bmatrix} 2 & -7 \end{bmatrix}$ $\begin{bmatrix} 12 & -42 \\ -6 & 21 \end{bmatrix}$

23. $\begin{bmatrix} -3 & -7 \\ -2 & -1 \end{bmatrix} \cdot \begin{bmatrix} 4 & 4 \\ 9 & -3 \end{bmatrix}$ $\begin{bmatrix} -75 & 9 \\ -17 & -5 \end{bmatrix}$

24. $\begin{bmatrix} -1 & 0 \\ 5 & 2 \end{bmatrix} \cdot \begin{bmatrix} 6 & -3 \\ 7 & -2 \end{bmatrix}$ $\begin{bmatrix} -6 & 3 \\ 44 & -19 \end{bmatrix}$

25. $\begin{bmatrix} -1 & 0 & 6 \\ -4 & -10 & 4 \end{bmatrix} \cdot \begin{bmatrix} 5 & -7 \\ -2 & -9 \end{bmatrix}$

26. $\begin{bmatrix} -6 & 4 & -9 \\ 2 & 8 & 7 \end{bmatrix} \cdot \begin{bmatrix} 7 \\ 2 \\ 4 \end{bmatrix}$ $\begin{bmatrix} -70 \\ 58 \end{bmatrix}$

27. $\begin{bmatrix} 2 & 9 & -3 \\ 4 & -1 & 0 \end{bmatrix} \cdot \begin{bmatrix} 4 & 2 \\ -6 & 7 \\ -2 & 1 \end{bmatrix}$

28. $\begin{bmatrix} -4 \\ 8 \end{bmatrix} \cdot \begin{bmatrix} -3 & -1 \end{bmatrix}$ $\begin{bmatrix} 12 & 4 \\ -24 & -8 \end{bmatrix}$

25. undefined

27. $\begin{bmatrix} -40 & 64 \\ 22 & 1 \end{bmatrix}$

29. **TRAVEL** The Wolf family owns three bed and breakfasts in a vacation spot. A room with a single bed is \$220 a night, a room with two beds is \$250 a night, and a suite is \$360.
   a. Write a matrix for the number of each type of room at each bed and breakfast. Then write a room-cost matrix. See margin.
   b. Write a matrix for total daily income, assuming that all the rooms are rented.
   c. What is the total daily income from all three bed and breakfasts, assuming that all the rooms are rented? \$5060

Available Rooms at a Wolf Bed and Breakfast

B & B	Single	Double	Suite
1	3	2	2
2	2	3	1
3	4	3	0

29b. $\begin{bmatrix} \$1880 \\ \$1550 \\ \$1630 \end{bmatrix}$

Examples 4 and 5 p. 203

Use $P = \begin{bmatrix} 4 & -1 \\ 1 & 2 \end{bmatrix}$, $Q = \begin{bmatrix} 6 & 4 \\ -2 & -5 \end{bmatrix}$, $R = \begin{bmatrix} 4 & 6 \\ -6 & 4 \end{bmatrix}$, **and** $k = 2$ **to determine whether the following equations are true for the given matrices.** 30–33. See margin.

30. $k(PQ) = P(kQ)$
31. $PQR = RQP$
32. $PR + QR = (P + Q)R$
33. $R(P + Q) = PR + QR$

34. **FLOWERS** Student Council is selling flowers for Mother's Day. They bought 200 roses, 150 daffodils, and 100 orchids for the purchase prices shown. They sold all of the flowers for the sales prices shown.
   a. Organize the data in two matrices, and use matrix multiplication to find the total amount that was spent on the flowers. \$747.50
   b. Write two matrices, and use matrix multiplication to find the total amount the student council received for the flower sale. \$1387.50
   c. Use matrix operations to find how much money the student council made on their project. \$640

Flower	Purchase Price	Sales Price
rose	\$1.67	\$3.00
daffodil	\$1.03	\$2.25
orchid	\$2.59	\$4.50

Real-World Link

Retailers report that Mother's Day is the second highest gift-giving holiday in the United States.

Source: Hallmark

Watch Out!

Preventing Errors In applications involving matrix products, even if the order of the matrices can be reversed, the product may only make sense in one direction.

Additional Answers

29a. $I = \begin{bmatrix} 3 & 2 & 2 \\ 2 & 3 & 1 \\ 4 & 3 & 0 \end{bmatrix}$, $C = \begin{bmatrix} 220 \\ 250 \\ 360 \end{bmatrix}$

30. Yes; $k(PQ) = \begin{bmatrix} 52 & 42 \\ 4 & -12 \end{bmatrix}$ and $P(kQ) = \begin{bmatrix} 52 & 42 \\ 4 & -12 \end{bmatrix}$.

31. No; $PQR = \begin{bmatrix} -22 & 240 \\ 44 & -12 \end{bmatrix}$ and $RQP = \begin{bmatrix} 34 & -40 \\ -220 & -44 \end{bmatrix}$.

32. Yes; $PR + QR = \begin{bmatrix} 22 & 72 \\ 44 & -18 \end{bmatrix}$ and $(P + Q)R = \begin{bmatrix} 22 & 72 \\ 14 & -18 \end{bmatrix}$.

33. No; $R(P + Q) = \begin{bmatrix} 34 & -6 \\ -64 & -30 \end{bmatrix}$ and $PR + QR = \begin{bmatrix} 22 & 72 \\ 14 & -18 \end{bmatrix}$.

Differentiated Homework Options

Level	Assignment	Two-Day Option	
AL Basic	15–33, 46–48, 50–65	15–33 odd, 51–54	16–32 even, 46–48, 50, 55–65
OL Core	15–33 odd, 34, 35, 37–43 odd, 44–48, 50–65	15–33, 51–54	34–45, 46–48, 50, 55–65
BL Advanced	34–62, (optional: 63–65)		

Study Guide and Intervention
CRM pp. 18–19 AL OL ELL

4-3 Study Guide and Intervention *(continued)*
Multiplying Matrices

Multiplicative Properties The Commutative Property of Multiplication does *not* hold for matrices.

Properties of Matrix Multiplication	For any matrices A, B, and C for which the matrix product is defined, and any scalar c, the following properties are true.
Associative Property of Matrix Multiplication	$(AB)C = A(BC)$
Associative Property of Scalar Multiplication	$c(AB) = (cA)B = A(cB)$
Left Distributive Property	$C(A + B) = CA + CB$
Right Distributive Property	$(A + B)C = AC + BC$

Example Use $A = \begin{bmatrix} 4 & -3 \\ 2 & 1 \end{bmatrix}$, $B = \begin{bmatrix} 2 & 0 \\ 5 & -3 \end{bmatrix}$, and $C = \begin{bmatrix} 1 & -2 \\ 6 & 3 \end{bmatrix}$ to find each product.

a. $(A + B)C$

$$(A+B)C = \left(\begin{bmatrix} 4 & -3 \\ 2 & 1 \end{bmatrix} + \begin{bmatrix} 2 & 0 \\ 5 & -3 \end{bmatrix}\right) \cdot \begin{bmatrix} 1 & -2 \\ 6 & 3 \end{bmatrix} = \begin{bmatrix} 6 & -3 \\ 7 & -2 \end{bmatrix} \cdot \begin{bmatrix} 1 & -2 \\ 6 & 3 \end{bmatrix} = \begin{bmatrix} 6(1) + (-3)(6) & 6(-2) + (-3)(3) \\ 7(1) + (-2)(6) & 7(-2) + (-2)(3) \end{bmatrix} = \begin{bmatrix} -12 & -21 \\ -5 & -20 \end{bmatrix}$$

b. $AC + BC$

$$AC + BC = \begin{bmatrix} 4 & -3 \\ 2 & 1 \end{bmatrix} \cdot \begin{bmatrix} 1 & -2 \\ 6 & 3 \end{bmatrix} + \begin{bmatrix} 2 & 0 \\ 5 & -3 \end{bmatrix} \cdot \begin{bmatrix} 1 & -2 \\ 6 & 3 \end{bmatrix} = \begin{bmatrix} 4(1) + (-3)(6) & 4(-2) + (-3)(3) \\ 2(1) + 1(6) & 2(-2) + 1(3) \end{bmatrix} + \begin{bmatrix} 2(1) + 0(6) & 2(-2) + 0(3) \\ 5(1) + (-3)(6) & 5(-2) + (-3)(3) \end{bmatrix} = \begin{bmatrix} -14 & -17 \\ 8 & -1 \end{bmatrix} + \begin{bmatrix} 2 & -4 \\ -13 & -19 \end{bmatrix} = \begin{bmatrix} -12 & -21 \\ -5 & -20 \end{bmatrix}$$

Note that although the results in the example illustrate the Right Distributive Property, they do not prove it.

Exercises

Use $A = \begin{bmatrix} 3 & 2 \\ 5 & -2 \end{bmatrix}$, $B = \begin{bmatrix} 6 & 4 \\ 2 & 1 \end{bmatrix}$, $C = \begin{bmatrix} -\frac{1}{2} & -2 \\ 1 & -3 \end{bmatrix}$, and scalar $c = -4$ to determine whether the following equations are true for the given matrices.

1. $c(AB) = (cA)B$ **yes**
2. $AB = BA$ **no**
3. $BC = CB$ **no**
4. $(AB)C = A(BC)$ **yes**
5. $C(A + B) = AC + BC$ **no**
6. $c(A + B) = cA + cB$ **yes**

Practice
CRM p. 20 AL OL BL ELL

4-3 Practice
Multiplying Matrices

Determine whether each matrix product is defined. If so, state the dimensions of the product.

1. $A_{7\times4} \cdot B_{4\times3}$ **7 × 3**
2. $A_{3\times5} \cdot M_{5\times8}$ **3 × 8**
3. $M_{2\times1} \cdot A_{1\times6}$ **2 × 6**
4. $M_{3\times2} \cdot A_{3\times2}$ **undefined**
5. $P_{1\times9} \cdot Q_{9\times1}$ **1 × 1**
6. $P_{9\times1} \cdot Q_{1\times9}$ **9 × 9**

Find each product, if possible.

7. $\begin{bmatrix} 2 & 4 \\ 3 & -1 \end{bmatrix} \cdot \begin{bmatrix} 3 & -2 & 7 \\ 6 & 0 & -5 \end{bmatrix}$ $\begin{bmatrix} 30 & -4 & -6 \\ 3 & -6 & 26 \end{bmatrix}$
8. $\begin{bmatrix} 2 & 4 \\ 7 & -1 \end{bmatrix} \cdot \begin{bmatrix} -3 & 0 \\ 2 & 5 \end{bmatrix}$ $\begin{bmatrix} 2 & 20 \\ -23 & -5 \end{bmatrix}$
9. $\begin{bmatrix} -3 & 0 \\ 2 & 5 \end{bmatrix} \cdot \begin{bmatrix} 2 & 4 \\ 7 & -1 \end{bmatrix}$ $\begin{bmatrix} -6 & -12 \\ 39 & 3 \end{bmatrix}$
10. $\begin{bmatrix} 3 & -2 & 7 \\ 6 & 0 & -5 \end{bmatrix} \cdot \begin{bmatrix} 3 & -2 & 7 \\ 6 & 0 & -5 \end{bmatrix}$ **undefined**
11. $[4 \ 0 \ 2] \cdot \begin{bmatrix} 1 \\ 3 \\ -1 \end{bmatrix}$ $[2]$
12. $\begin{bmatrix} 1 \\ 3 \\ -1 \end{bmatrix} \cdot [4 \ 0 \ 2]$ $\begin{bmatrix} 4 & 0 & 2 \\ 12 & 0 & 6 \\ -4 & 0 & -2 \end{bmatrix}$
13. $\begin{bmatrix} -6 & 2 \\ 3 & -1 \end{bmatrix} \cdot \begin{bmatrix} 5 & 0 \\ 0 & 5 \end{bmatrix}$ $\begin{bmatrix} -30 & 10 \\ 15 & -5 \end{bmatrix}$
14. $[-15 \ -9] \cdot \begin{bmatrix} 6 & 11 \\ 23 & -10 \end{bmatrix}$ $[-297 \ -75]$

Use $A = \begin{bmatrix} 1 & 3 \\ 3 & 1 \end{bmatrix}$, $B = \begin{bmatrix} 4 & 0 \\ -2 & -1 \end{bmatrix}$, $C = \begin{bmatrix} -1 & 0 \\ 0 & -1 \end{bmatrix}$, and $c = 3$ to determine whether the following equations are true for the given matrices.

15. $AC = CA$ **yes**
16. $A(B + C) = BA + CA$ **no**
17. $(AB)c = c(AB)$ **yes**
18. $(A + C)B = B(A + C)$ **no**

19. **RENTALS** For their one-week vacation, the Montoyas can rent a 2-bedroom condominium for $1796, a 3-bedroom condominium for $2165, or a 4-bedroom condominium for $2538. The table shows the number of units in each of three complexes.

	2-Bedroom	3-Bedroom	4-Bedroom
Sun Haven	36	24	22
Surfside	29	32	42
Seabreeze	18	22	18

a. Write a matrix that represents the number of each type of unit available at each complex and a matrix that represents the weekly charge for each type of unit. $\begin{bmatrix} 36 & 24 & 22 \\ 29 & 32 & 42 \\ 18 & 22 & 18 \end{bmatrix}$, $\begin{bmatrix} \$1796 \\ \$2165 \\ \$2538 \end{bmatrix}$

b. If all of the units in the three complexes are rented for the week at the rates given the Montoyas, express the income of each of the three complexes as a matrix. $\begin{bmatrix} 172,452 \\ 227,960 \\ 125,642 \end{bmatrix}$

c. What is the total income of all three complexes for the week? **$526,054**

Word Problem Practice
CRM p. 21 AL OL BL ELL

4-3 Word Problem Practice
Multiplying Matrices

1. **FIND THE ERROR** Both A and B are 2 by 2 matrices. Maggie made the following derivation. Is this derivation valid? If not, what error did she make?

a. $(A + B)^2 = (A + B)(A + B)$
b. $= (A + B)A + (A + B)B$
c. $= AA + BA + AB + BB$
d. $= A^2 + BA + AB + B^2$
e. $= A^2 + AB + AB + B^2$
f. $= A^2 + 2AB + B^2$

From step d to step e, Maggie commuted *A* and *B*; but for matrices, *AB* does not typically equal *BA*.

2. **EXAM SCORES** Mr. Farey recorded the exam scores of his students in a 20 by 3 matrix. Each row listed the scores of a different student. The first exam scores were listed in the first column, and the second exam scores were listed in the second column. The final exam scores were listed in the third column. Mr. Farey needed to create a 20 by 1 matrix that contained the weighted scores of each student. The first two exams account for 25% of the weighted score, and the final exam counted 50%. To make the matrix of weighted scores, what matrix can Mr. Farey multiply his 20 by 3 matrix by on the right?

$\begin{bmatrix} 0.25 \\ 0.25 \\ 0.50 \end{bmatrix}$

3. **SPECIAL MATRICES** Mandy has a 3 by 3 matrix M. She notices that for any 3 by 3 matrix X, $MX = X$. What must M be?

$\begin{bmatrix} 1 & 0 & 0 \\ 0 & 1 & 0 \\ 0 & 0 & 1 \end{bmatrix}$

4. **POWERS** Thad just learned about matrix multiplication. He began to wonder what happens when you take powers of a matrix. He computed the first few powers of the matrix $M = \begin{bmatrix} 1 & 1 \\ 0 & 1 \end{bmatrix}$ and noticed a pattern. What is M^n?

$\begin{bmatrix} 1 & n \\ 0 & 1 \end{bmatrix}$

5. **COST COMPARISONS** The average family spends more than $500 on school supplies at the beginning of each school year. Barbara and Lance need to buy pens, pencils, and erasers. They make a 2 by 3 matrix that represents the numbers of each item they would like to purchase.

	Pens	Pencils	Erasers
Barbara	10	15	3
Lance	5	20	5

They call this matrix M. Barbara and Lance find two stores that sell the items at different prices and record this information in a second matrix that they call P.

	Store 1	Store 2
Pens	2.20	1.90
Pencils	0.85	0.95
Erasers	0.60	0.65

a. Compute MP.

$\begin{bmatrix} 36.55 & 35.2 \\ 31 & 31.75 \end{bmatrix}$

b. What do the entries in MP mean? **The first row represents the total cost of Barbara's items at stores 1 and 2, respectively, and the second row represents the total cost of Lance's items at stores 1 and 2, respectively.**

Lesson 4-3

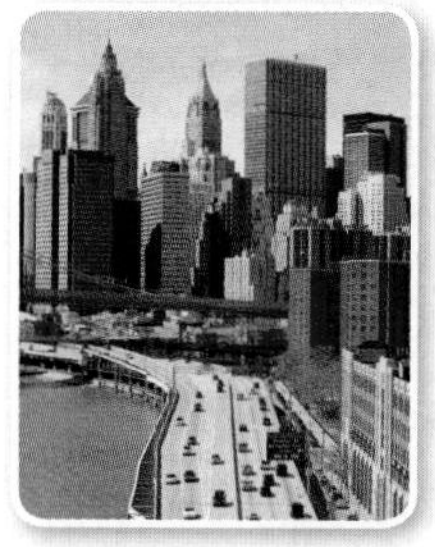

Real-World Link

There are approximately 245 million passenger vehicles registered in the U.S.

Source: Bureau of Transportation Statistics

35. **AUTO SALES** A car lot has four sales associates. At the end of the year, each sales associate gets a bonus of $1000 for every new car they have sold and $500 for every used car they have sold.

a. Use a matrix to determine which sales associate earned the most money. **See margin.**

b. What is the total amount of money the car lot spent on bonuses for the sales associates this year? **$187,500**

Cars Sold by Each Associate

Sales Associate	New Cars	Used Cars
Mason	27	49
Westin	35	36
Gallagher	9	56
Stadler	15	62

Use matrices $X = \begin{bmatrix} 2 & -6 \\ 3y & -4.5 \end{bmatrix}$, $Y = \begin{bmatrix} -5 & -1.5 \\ x+2 & y \\ 13 & 1.2 \end{bmatrix}$, and $Z = \begin{bmatrix} -3 \\ x+y \end{bmatrix}$ to find each of the following. If the matrix does not exist, write *undefined*. **37, 39, 40, 43. See margin.**

36. XY **undefined**
37. YX
38. ZY **undefined**
39. YZ
40. $(YX)Z$
41. $(XZ)X$ **undefined**
42. $X(ZZ)$ **undefined**
43. $(XX)Z$

44. **CAMERAS** Prices of digital cameras depend on features like optical zoom, digital zoom, and megapixels.

Optical Zoom	6 MP	7 MP	10 MP
3 to 4	$189.99	$249.99	$349.99
5 to 6	$199.99	$289.99	$399.99
10 to 12	$299.99	$399.99	$499.99

a. The 10-mp cameras are on sale for 20% off, and the other models are 10% off. Write a new matrix for these changes. **a, b. See margin.**

b. Write a new matrix allowing for a 6.25% sales tax on the discounted prices.

c. Describe what the differences in these two matrices represent. **sales tax**

45. **BUSINESS** The Kangy Studio has packages available for senior portraits.

a. Use matrices to determine the total cost of each package.

b. The studio offers an early bird discount of 15% off any package. Find the early bird price for each package. **A: $357.85; B: $232.90; C: $127.50; D: $57.80**

45a. A: $421; B: $274; C: $150; D: $68

Size (price)	Packages A	B	C	D
4 × 5 ($7)	10	10	8	0
5 × 7 ($10)	4	4	4	4
8 × 10 ($14)	2	2	2	2
11 × 14 ($45)	1	1	0	0
16 × 20 ($95)	1	0	0	0
Wallets (8 for $13)	88	56	16	0

H.O.T. Problems
Use Higher-Order Thinking Skills

46. **REASONING** If the product matrix AB has dimensions 5×8, and A has dimensions 5×6, what are the dimensions of matrix B? **6 × 8**

47. **PROOF** Show that each property of matrices is true for all 2×2 matrices.

a. Scalar Distributive Property **a–d. See Chapter 4 Answer Appendix.**
b. Matrix Distributive Property
c. Associative Property of Multiplication
d. Associative Property of Scalar Multiplication

48. **OPEN ENDED** Write two matrices A and B such that $AB = BA$.

48. Sample answer: $A = \begin{bmatrix} 2 & 2 \\ 2 & 2 \end{bmatrix}$, $B = \begin{bmatrix} 3 & 3 \\ 3 & 3 \end{bmatrix}$

49. **CHALLENGE** Find the missing values in $\begin{bmatrix} a & b \\ c & d \end{bmatrix} \cdot \begin{bmatrix} 4 & 3 \\ 2 & 5 \end{bmatrix} = \begin{bmatrix} 10 & 11 \\ 20 & 29 \end{bmatrix}$. **$a = 2, b = 1, c = 3, d = 4$**

50. **WRITING IN MATH** Use the data on Lisa Leslie found at the beginning of the lesson to explain how matrices can be used in sports statistics. Describe a matrix that represents the total number of points she has scored during her career and an example of a sport in which different point values are used in scoring. **See margin.**

Enrichment
CRM p. 22 OL BL

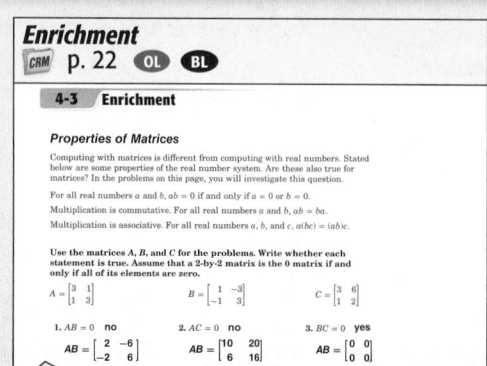

4-3 Enrichment

Properties of Matrices

Computing with matrices is different from computing with real numbers. Stated below are some properties of the real number system. Are these also true for matrices? In the problems on this page, you will investigate this question.

For all real numbers a and b, $ab = 0$ if and only if $a = 0$ or $b = 0$.

Multiplication is commutative. For all real numbers a and b, $ab = ba$.

Multiplication is associative. For all real numbers a, b, and c, $a(bc) = (ab)c$.

Use the matrices A, B, and C for the problems. Write whether each statement is true. Assume that a 2-by-2 matrix is the 0 matrix if and only if all of its elements are zero.

$A = \begin{bmatrix} 3 & 1 \\ 1 & 3 \end{bmatrix}$ $B = \begin{bmatrix} 1 & -3 \\ -1 & 3 \end{bmatrix}$ $C = \begin{bmatrix} 3 & 6 \\ 1 & 2 \end{bmatrix}$

1. $AB = 0$ **no** $AB = \begin{bmatrix} 2 & -6 \\ -2 & 6 \end{bmatrix}$
2. $AC = 0$ **no** $AB = \begin{bmatrix} 10 & 20 \\ 6 & 16 \end{bmatrix}$
3. $BC = 0$ **yes** $AB = \begin{bmatrix} 0 & 0 \\ 0 & 0 \end{bmatrix}$

Additional Answers

35a. $\begin{bmatrix} 27 & 49 \\ 35 & 36 \\ 9 & 56 \\ 15 & 62 \end{bmatrix} \cdot \begin{bmatrix} 1000 \\ 500 \end{bmatrix} = \begin{bmatrix} 51{,}500 \\ 53{,}000 \\ 37{,}000 \\ 46{,}000 \end{bmatrix}$; Westin

37. $\begin{bmatrix} -10 - 4.5y & 36.75 \\ 2x + 4 + 3y^2 & -6x - 4.5y - 12 \\ 3.6y + 26 & -83.4 \end{bmatrix}$

NGSSS PRACTICE 912.A.3.14, 912.A.3.15, 912.G.1.1, 912.D.8.2

51. **GRIDDED RESPONSE** The average (arithmetic mean) of r, w, x, and y is 8, and the average of x and y is 4. What is the average of r and w? **12**

52. Carla, Meiko, and Kayla went shopping to get ready for college. Their purchases and total amounts spent are shown in the table below.

Person	Shirts	Pants	Shoes	Total Spent
Carla	3	4	2	$149.79
Meiko	5	3	3	$183.19
Kayla	6	5	1	$181.14

Assume that all of the shirts were the same price, all of the pants were the same price, and all of the shoes were the same price. What was the price of each item? **A**

A. shirt, $12.95; pants, $15.99; shoes, $23.49
B. shirt, $15.99; pants, $12.95; shoes, $23.49
C. shirt, $15.99; pants, $23.49; shoes, $12.95
D. shirt, $23.49; pants, $15.99; shoes, $12.95

53. **GEOMETRY** Rectangle $LMNQ$ has diagonals that intersect at point P.

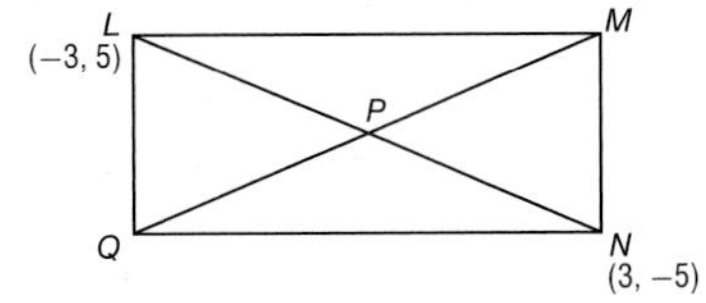

Which of the following represents point P? **H**

F. (2, 2) **H.** (0, 0)
G. (1, 1) **I.** (−1, −1)

54. **SAT/ACT** What are the dimensions of the matrix that results from the multiplication shown? **C**

$$\begin{bmatrix} a & b & c \\ d & e & f \\ g & h & i \\ j & k & l \end{bmatrix} \cdot \begin{bmatrix} 7 \\ 4 \\ 6 \end{bmatrix}$$

A. 1×4 **C.** 4×1
B. 3×3 **D.** 4×3

Spiral Review

Perform the indicated operations. If the matrix does not exist, write *impossible*. (Lesson 4-2) **55–57. See margin.**

55. $4\begin{bmatrix} 8 & -1 \\ -3 & -4 \end{bmatrix} - 5\begin{bmatrix} -2 & 4 \\ 6 & 3 \end{bmatrix}$

56. $5\left(2\begin{bmatrix} -2 & -5 \\ -1 & 3 \end{bmatrix} - 3\begin{bmatrix} -1 & -2 \\ 6 & 4 \end{bmatrix}\right)$

57. $-4\left(\begin{bmatrix} 8 & 9 \\ -5 & 5 \end{bmatrix} - 2\begin{bmatrix} -6 & -1 \\ 6 & 3 \end{bmatrix}\right)$

State the dimensions of each matrix. (Lesson 4-1)

58. $[\,-2 \quad 1\,]$ **1×2**

59. $\begin{bmatrix} 1 & 6 \\ -8 & -3 \end{bmatrix}$ **2×2**

60. $\begin{bmatrix} 9 & 1 \\ 2 & 3 \\ 5 & -3 \\ -9 & 0 \end{bmatrix}$ **4×2**

61. **MEDICINE** The graph shows how much Americans spent on doctors' visits in some recent years and a prediction for 2014. (Lesson 2-5)

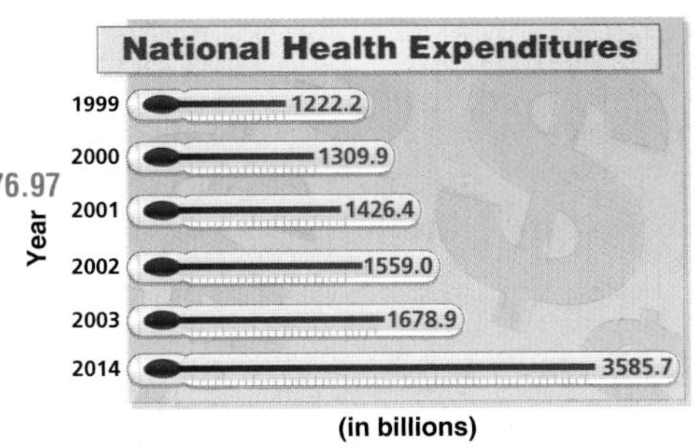

a. Find a regression equation for the data without the predicted value. **Sample answer: $y = 116.25x - 231{,}176.97$**

b. Use your equation to predict the expenditures for 2014. **Sample answer: $2950.53**

c. Compare your prediction to the one given in the graph. **The value predicted by the equation is significantly lower than the one given in the graph.**

62. How many different ways can the letters of the word *MATHEMATICS* be arranged? (Lesson 0-5) **4,989,600**

Skills Review

Describe the transformation in each function. Then graph the function. (Lesson 2-7) **63–65. See Chapter 4 Answer Appendix.**

63. $f(x) = |x - 4| + 3$

64. $f(x) = 2|x + 3| - 5$

65. $f(x) = (x + 2)^2 - 6$

4 ASSESS

Ticket Out the Door Have students write on pieces of paper whether or not a 4×3 matrix can be multiplied by a 2×3 matrix. Ask them to explain their answers.

Formative Assessment

Check for student understanding of Lesson 4-3.

CRM Quiz 2, p. 45

Additional Answers

39. $\begin{bmatrix} -1.5x - 1.5y + 15 \\ y^2 + xy - 3x - 6 \\ 1.2x + 1.2y - 39 \end{bmatrix}$

40. $\begin{bmatrix} 36.75x + 50.25y + 30 \\ -6x^2 - 18x - 10.5xy - 13.5y^2 - 12y - 12 \\ -83.4x - 94.2y - 78 \end{bmatrix}$

43. $\begin{bmatrix} 15x + 69y - 12 \\ -18y^2 + 42.75y - 18xy + 20.25x \end{bmatrix}$

44a. $\begin{bmatrix} \$170.99 & \$224.99 & \$279.99 \\ \$179.99 & \$260.99 & \$319.99 \\ \$269.99 & \$359.99 & \$399.99 \end{bmatrix}$

44b. $\begin{bmatrix} \$181.68 & \$239.05 & \$297.49 \\ \$191.24 & \$277.30 & \$339.99 \\ \$286.86 & \$382.49 & \$424.99 \end{bmatrix}$

50. Sports statistics are often listed in columns and matrices. In this case, you can find the total number of points scored by multiplying the point value matrix, which does not change, by the scoring matrix, which changes after each season. The total number of points for her career can be found by multiplying the scoring matrix S by the point matrix P. Basketball and wrestling use different point values in scoring.

55. $\begin{bmatrix} 42 & -24 \\ -42 & -31 \end{bmatrix}$

56. $\begin{bmatrix} -5 & -20 \\ -100 & -30 \end{bmatrix}$

57. $\begin{bmatrix} -80 & -44 \\ 68 & 4 \end{bmatrix}$

Formative Assessment

Use the Mid-Chapter Quiz to assess students' progress in the first half of the chapter.

For problems answered incorrectly, have students review the lessons indicated in parentheses.

ExamView Assessment Suite Customize and create multiple versions of your Mid-Chapter Quiz and their answer keys.

FOLDABLES Follow-Up

Before students complete the Mid-Chapter Quiz, encourage them to review the information for Lessons 4-1 through 4-3 in their Foldables.

Additional Answers

5a. First week: $\begin{bmatrix} 25 & 14 & 18 & 5 \\ 44 & 10 & 13 & 8 \end{bmatrix}$

Second week: $\begin{bmatrix} 32 & 26 & 15 & 4 \\ 18 & 38 & 17 & 2 \end{bmatrix}$

5b. $\begin{bmatrix} 57 & 40 & 33 & 9 \\ 62 & 48 & 30 & 10 \end{bmatrix}$

14a. $\begin{bmatrix} 10 & 10 & 15 \\ 25 & 35 & 45 \end{bmatrix}$

14b. $2\begin{bmatrix} 10 & 10 & 15 \\ 25 & 35 & 45 \end{bmatrix} = \begin{bmatrix} 20 & 20 & 30 \\ 50 & 70 & 90 \end{bmatrix}$

14c. $\begin{bmatrix} 10 & 10 & 15 \\ 25 & 35 & 45 \end{bmatrix}$; The number of shirts that he needs to stock additionally.

CHAPTER 4 Mid-Chapter Quiz

Lessons 4-1 through 4-3

NGSSS 912.A.3.15, 912.D.8.2

State the dimensions of each matrix. (Lesson 4-1)

1. $[\,3 \quad 4 \quad 5 \quad 6 \quad 7\,]$ **1 × 5**

2. $\begin{bmatrix} 10 & -6 & 18 & 0 \\ -7 & 5 & 2 & 4 \\ 3 & 11 & 9 & 7 \end{bmatrix}$ **3 × 4**

Identify each element for the following matrices. (Lesson 4-1)

$$A = \begin{bmatrix} 4 & 3 \\ -5 & 1 \\ -3 & 7 \end{bmatrix}, B = \begin{bmatrix} 1 & -9 & 2 \\ 0 & 10 & 4 \end{bmatrix}$$

3. a_{21} **−5**

4. b_{22} **10**

5. **FUNDRAISER** The ninth and tenth grade classes sold different types of clothing to raise money. Two weeks of sales are shown in the table. (Lesson 4-2)

Grade	Week	Type of Clothing			
		T-shirt	Sweatshirt	Hat	Coat
9	1	25	14	18	5
	2	32	26	15	4
10	1	44	10	13	8
	2	18	38	17	2

a. Write a matrix for each week's sales.

b. Find the sum of the two weeks' sales using matrix addition. **a, b. See margin.**

Perform the indicated operations. If the matrix does not exist, write *impossible*. (Lessons 4-2 and 4-3)

6. $\begin{bmatrix} 0 & 15 \\ -6 & -10 \end{bmatrix} - \begin{bmatrix} 8 & 0 \\ -3 & 5 \end{bmatrix}$ $\begin{bmatrix} -8 & 15 \\ -3 & -15 \end{bmatrix}$

7. $-3\begin{bmatrix} 3 & 5 & 12 \\ 0 & -1 & 3 \\ 9 & 6 & -5 \end{bmatrix}$ $\begin{bmatrix} -9 & -15 & -36 \\ 0 & 3 & -9 \\ -27 & -18 & 15 \end{bmatrix}$

8. $2\begin{bmatrix} -1 \\ 5 \\ -6 \end{bmatrix} + 4\begin{bmatrix} -3x \\ 2 \\ x \end{bmatrix} - 3\begin{bmatrix} x-2 \\ 3 \\ 1 \end{bmatrix}$ $\begin{bmatrix} -15x+4 \\ 9 \\ 4x-15 \end{bmatrix}$

9. **NGSSS PRACTICE** Find $2\begin{bmatrix} 3 & 5 \\ -6 & 0 \end{bmatrix} + 4\begin{bmatrix} 9 & -1 \\ 2 & 3 \end{bmatrix}$. (Lesson 4-2) **A**

A. $\begin{bmatrix} 42 & 6 \\ -4 & 12 \end{bmatrix}$

B. $\begin{bmatrix} 21 & 3 \\ -2 & 6 \end{bmatrix}$

C. $\begin{bmatrix} 12 & 4 \\ -4 & 3 \end{bmatrix}$

D. $\begin{bmatrix} 27 & -5 \\ -12 & 0 \end{bmatrix}$

Find each product if possible. (Lesson 4-3)

10. $\begin{bmatrix} -2 & 3 \\ 1 & 6 \end{bmatrix} \cdot \begin{bmatrix} 3 & -1 & 4 \\ 0 & 5 & -6 \end{bmatrix}$ $\begin{bmatrix} -6 & 17 & -26 \\ 3 & 29 & -32 \end{bmatrix}$

11. $\begin{bmatrix} -4 & 0 & -1 \\ 0 & 1 & 8 \end{bmatrix} \cdot \begin{bmatrix} -1 & 0 \\ 0 & 4 \end{bmatrix}$ **impossible**

12. $\begin{bmatrix} 4 & -2 & -7 \\ 6 & 3 & 5 \end{bmatrix} \cdot \begin{bmatrix} -2 \\ 5 \\ 3 \end{bmatrix}$ $\begin{bmatrix} -39 \\ 18 \end{bmatrix}$

13. **NGSSS PRACTICE** If the product matrix XY has dimensions 3 × 2 and X has dimensions 3 × 4, what are the dimensions of matrix Y? (Lesson 4-3) **I**

F. 2 × 3

G. 3 × 2

H. 3 × 4

I. 4 × 2

14. **SALES** Alex is in charge of stocking shirts for the concession stand at the high school football game. The number of shirts needed for a regular season game is listed in the matrix. Alex plans to double the number of shirts stocked for a playoff game. (Lesson 4-3)

Size	small	medium	large
Child	10	10	15
Adult	25	35	45

a. Write a matrix A to represent the regular season stock. **a–c. See Chapter 4 Answer Appendix.**

b. What scalar can be used to determine a matrix M to represent the new numbers? Find M.

c. What is $M - A$? What does this represent in this situation?

15. **NGSSS PRACTICE** What is the product of $[\,4 \quad 0 \quad -2\,]$ and $\begin{bmatrix} 2 & -1 \\ -3 & 0 \\ 0 & 4 \end{bmatrix}$? (Lesson 4-3) **A**

A. $[\,8 \quad -12\,]$

B. $\begin{bmatrix} 8 \\ -12 \end{bmatrix}$

C. $\begin{bmatrix} 8 & -4 \\ 0 & 0 \\ 0 & -8 \end{bmatrix}$

D. impossible

Determine whether each matrix product is defined. If so, state the dimensions of the product.

16. $A_{2 \times 3} \cdot B_{3 \times 2}$ **2 × 2**

17. $A_{4 \times 1} \cdot B_{2 \times 1}$ **undefined**

18. $A_{2 \times 5} \cdot B_{5 \times 5}$ **2 × 5**

19. $A_{1 \times 5} \cdot B_{5 \times 3}$ **1 × 3**

Intervention Planner

Tier 1 On Level	Tier 2 Strategic Intervention approaching grade level	Tier 3 Intensive Intervention 2 or more grades below level
If students miss about 25% of the exercises or less,	**If** students miss about 50% of the exercises,	**If** students miss about 75% of the exercises,
Then choose a resource:	**Then** choose a resource:	**Then** use *Math Triumphs, Alg. 2*
SE Lessons 4-1, 4-2, and 4-3	**CRM** Study Guide and Intervention, Chapter 4, pp. 5–6, 11–12, 17–18	
CRM Skills Practice, pp. 7, 13, and 19		
TE Chapter Project, p. 182		
FL Math Online Self-Check Quiz	FL Math Online Extra Examples, Personal Tutor, Homework Help	FL Math Online Extra Examples, Personal Tutor, Homework Help, Review Vocabulary

4-4 Transformations with Matrices

Why?

Video game designers often create detailed settings to add effects to games. One way they do this is to make reflections of objects on a shiny surface, such as a glass table top. To make a reflection, the game designers copy the original object and flip the copy. Matrices are frequently used to define the positions of the objects and to reposition and reorient them.

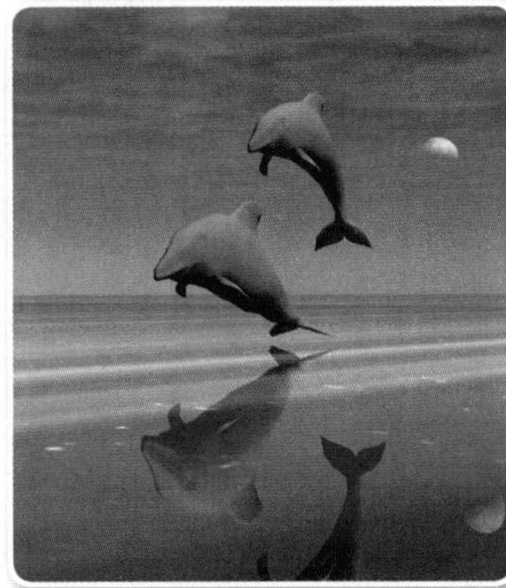

Then
You added, subtracted, and multiplied matrices. (Lessons 4-2 and 4-3)

Now
- Use matrices to determine the coordinates of a translated or dilated image.
- Use matrix multiplication to determine the coordinates of a reflected or rotated image.

NGSSS

Reinforcement of MA.912.G.2.4 Apply transformations to polygons to determine congruence, similarity, and symmetry.

New Vocabulary
vertex matrix
coordinate matrix
preimage
image
rotation

FL Math Online
glencoe.com

Translations and Dilations Points on a coordinate plane can be represented by matrices. The ordered pair (x, y) can be represented by the column matrix $\begin{bmatrix} x \\ y \end{bmatrix}$. Likewise, polygons can be represented by placing all of the column matrices of the coordinates of the vertices into one matrix. This is called a **vertex matrix** or **coordinate matrix**.

Triangle ABC with vertices $A(-4, -3)$, $B(-2, 2)$, and $C(3, -1)$ can be represented by the following vertex matrix.

$$\triangle ABC = \begin{matrix} & A & B & C & \\ & \begin{bmatrix} -4 & -2 & 3 \\ -3 & 2 & -1 \end{bmatrix} & & & \begin{matrix} \leftarrow \text{x-coordinates} \\ \leftarrow \text{y-coordinates} \end{matrix} \end{matrix}$$

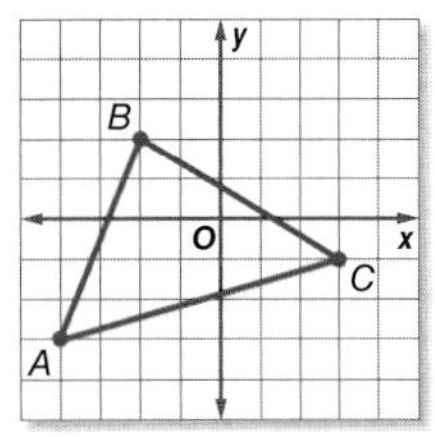

Matrices can be used to perform transformations. Transformations are functions that map points of a **preimage** onto its **image**.

Recall that one type of transformation is a translation. A translation occurs when a figure is moved from one location to another without changing its size, shape, or orientation. You can use matrix addition and a *translation matrix* to determine the coordinates of a translation image. The dimensions of a translation matrix should be the same as the dimensions of the vertex matrix.

Preimage

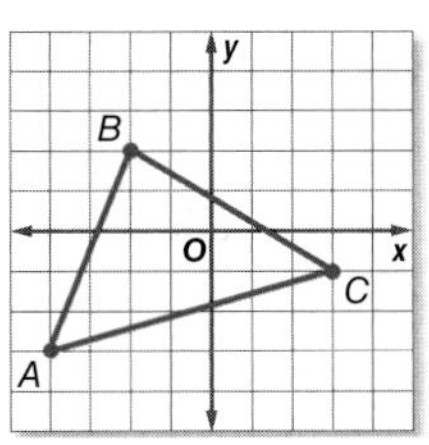

Translation

1 unit down,
2 units right

Image

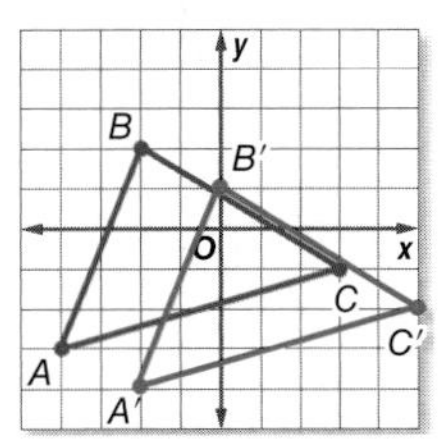

$$\begin{bmatrix} -4 & -2 & 3 \\ -3 & 2 & -1 \end{bmatrix} + \begin{bmatrix} 2 & 2 & 2 \\ -1 & -1 & -1 \end{bmatrix} = \begin{bmatrix} -2 & 0 & 5 \\ -4 & 1 & -2 \end{bmatrix}$$

4-4 Lesson Notes

1 FOCUS

Vertical Alignment

Before Lesson 4-4
Add, subtract, and multiply matrices.

Lesson 4-4
Use matrices for translations and dilations.
Use matrices for reflections and rotations.

After Lesson 4-4
Use matrices to solve systems of equations.

2 TEACH

Scaffolding Questions

Have students read the *Why?* section of the lesson.

Ask:
- When you look at yourself in a mirror, do you see yourself as others see you? No, the image is reversed.
- What does the reflection of the letter "b" look like? d

Lesson 4-4 Resources

Resource	Approaching-Level	On-Level	Beyond-Level	English Learners
Teacher Edition	• Differentiated Instruction, p. 216		• Differentiated Instruction, p. 217	
Chapter Resource Masters	• Study Guide and Intervention, pp. 23–24 • Skills Practice, p. 25 • Practice, p. 26 • Word Problem Practice, p. 27	• Study Guide and Intervention, pp. 23–24 • Skills Practice, p. 25 • Practice, p. 26 • Word Problem Practice, p. 27 • Enrichment, p. 28	• Practice, p. 26 • Word Problem Practice, p. 27 • Enrichment, p. 28	• Study Guide and Intervention, pp. 23–24 • Skills Practice, p. 25 • Practice, p. 26 • Word Problem Practice, p. 27
Transparencies	• 5-Minute Check Transparency 4-4	• 5-Minute Check Transparency 4-4	• 5-Minute Check Transparency 4-4	• 5-Minute Check Transparency 4-4
Other	• Study Notebook	• Study Notebook	• Study Notebook	• Study Notebook

Lesson 4-4 Transformations with Matrices 209

Translations and Dilations

Example 1 shows how to use addition of matrices to translate a figure. **Example 2** shows how to work backward to find a translation matrix and then find the coordinates of an unknown vertex. **Example 3** shows how to determine the coordinates of an image of a triangle by multiplying the vertex matrix of the pre-image of the triangle by a scalar.

Formative Assessment

Use the Guided Practice exercises after each example to determine students' understanding of concepts.

Additional Example

1 Determine the coordinates of the vertices of the image of quadrilateral *ABCD* with *A*(−5, −1), *B*(−2, −1), *C*(−1, −4), *D*(−3, −5), if it is translated 3 units to the right and 4 units up. Then graph *ABCD* and its image *A′B′C′D′*. *A′*(−2, 3), *B′*(1, 3), *C′*(2, 0), *D′*(0, −1);

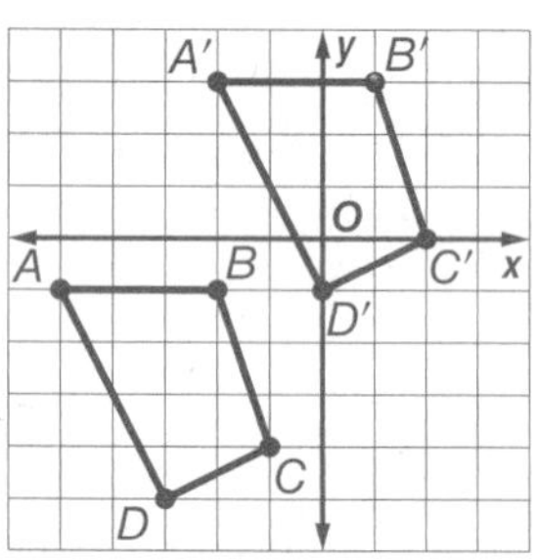

Additional Examples also in Interactive Classroom PowerPoint® Presentations

IWB INTERACTIVE WHITEBOARD READY

ReadingMath

Image Coordinates The notation *D′E′F′G′* indicates the vertices of the image of *DEFG* and is read *quadrilateral D prime E prime F prime G prime.*

EXAMPLE 1 Translation

Find the coordinates of the vertices of the image of quadrilateral *DEFG* with *D*(−4, −2), *E*(0, −1), *F*(2, −4), and *G*(−2, −5) if it is translated 1 unit left and 4 units up. Then graph *DEFG* and its image *D′E′F′G′*.

Write the vertex matrix for quadrilateral *DEFG*. $\begin{bmatrix} -4 & 0 & 2 & -2 \\ -2 & -1 & -4 & -5 \end{bmatrix}$

To translate the quadrilateral 1 unit to the left, add −1 to each *x*-coordinate. To translate the figure 4 units up, add 4 to each *y*-coordinate. This can be done by adding the translation matrix $\begin{bmatrix} -1 & -1 & -1 & -1 \\ 4 & 4 & 4 & 4 \end{bmatrix}$ to the vertex matrix of *DEFG*.

Vertex Matrix of *DEFG* + Translation Matrix = Vertex Matrix of *D′E′F′G′*

$$\begin{bmatrix} -4 & 0 & 2 & -2 \\ -2 & -1 & -4 & -5 \end{bmatrix} + \begin{bmatrix} -1 & -1 & -1 & -1 \\ 4 & 4 & 4 & 4 \end{bmatrix} = \begin{bmatrix} -5 & -1 & 1 & -3 \\ 2 & 3 & 0 & -1 \end{bmatrix}$$

The vertices of *D′E′F′G′* are *D′*(−5, 2), *E′*(−1, 3), *F′*(1, 0), and *G′*(−3, −1).

DEFG and *D′E′F′G′* have the same size, shape, and orientation.

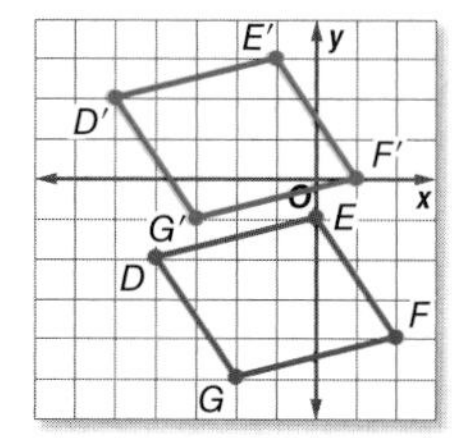

Guided Practice

1. Find the coordinates of the vertices of the image of triangle *RST* with *R*(−1, 5), *S*(2, 1), and *T*(−3, 2) if it is moved 3 units to the right and 4 units up. Then graph *RST* and its image *R′S′T′*. **See margin.**

Personal Tutor glencoe.com

You can work backward to find a translation matrix.

NGSSS PRACTICE EXAMPLE 2 912.G.2.4

Rectangle *H′J′K′L′* is an image of rectangle *HJKL*. A table of the vertices of each rectangle is shown. What are the coordinates of *K′*?

Rectangle *HJKL*	Rectangle *H′J′K′L′*
H(4, −5)	*H′*(−1, −8)
J(2, −8)	*J′*(−3, −11)
K(−4, −4)	*K′*(?, ?)
L(−2, −1)	*L′*(−7, −4)

A. (−5, −3) **B.** (−9, −7) **C.** (1, −1) **D.** (−7, −9)

Read the Test Item

You are given the coordinates of the preimage and image of points *H*, *J*, and *L*. Use this information to find the translation matrix. Then you can use the translation matrix to find the coordinates of *K′*.

Real-World Link

Translation matrices are used for modeling cartoon characters.

Additional Answer (Guided Practice)

1. *R′*(2, 9), *S′*(5, 5), and *T′*(0, 6)

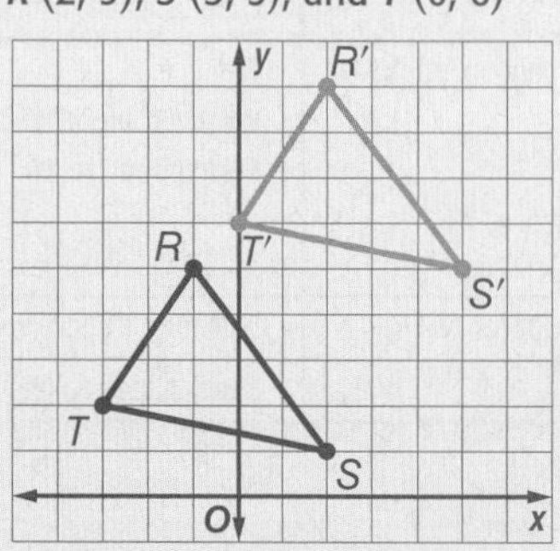

TEACH with TECH

DOCUMENT CAMERA Choose several students to work through examples and explain how to use a matrix to find the image of a figure after a transformation. Have the student find the coordinates of the image first, and then graph the preimage and the image on a coordinate plane to check the answer.

Test-Taking Tip

Two-Step Solutions Sometimes you need to solve for unknown value(s) before you can solve for the value(s) requested in the question.

Solve the Test Item

Step 1 Write a matrix equation. Let (a, b) represent the coordinates of K'.

$$\begin{bmatrix} 4 & 2 & -4 & -2 \\ -5 & -8 & -4 & -1 \end{bmatrix} + \begin{bmatrix} x & x & x & x \\ y & y & y & y \end{bmatrix} = \begin{bmatrix} -1 & -3 & a & -7 \\ -8 & -11 & b & -4 \end{bmatrix}$$

$$\begin{bmatrix} 4+x & 2+x & -4+x & -2+x \\ -5+y & -8+y & -4+y & -1+y \end{bmatrix} = \begin{bmatrix} -1 & -3 & a & -7 \\ -8 & -11 & b & -4 \end{bmatrix}$$

Step 2 The matrices are equal, so corresponding elements are equal. Use the elements from the first row in each matrix.

$4 + x = -1$ **Solve for *x*.**
$x = -5$

$-5 + y = -8$ **Solve for *y*.**
$y = -3$

Step 3 Use the values for x and y to find the values for $K'(a, b)$.

$-4 + (-5) = a$
$-9 = a$

$-4 + (-3) = b$
$-7 = b$

So, the coordinates of K' are $(-9, -7)$ and the answer is B.
Check by solving different equations for x and y.

Guided Practice

2. Triangle $X'Y'Z'$ is the image of triangle XYZ. Find the coordinates of Z' using the information shown in the table. F

Triangle *XYZ*	Triangle *X'Y'Z'*
X(3, −1)	X'(1, 0)
Y(−4, 2)	Y'(−6, 3)
Z(5, 1)	Z'(?, ?)

F. (3, 2) **H.** (7, 0)
G. (7, 2) **I.** (3, 0)

Personal Tutor glencoe.com

A dilation is always performed relative to its center. Unless otherwise specified, the center is always the origin. You can use scalar multiplication to perform dilations.

Study Tip

Dilations In dilation, the image is similar to the preimage. All linear measures of the image change in the same ratio.

EXAMPLE 3 Dilation

Dilate $\triangle MNP$ with $M(-1, 1)$, $N(2, 3)$, and $P(1, -2)$ so that the perimeter of the image is twice that of the preimage. Find the coordinates of the vertices of $\triangle M'N'P'$. Then graph $\triangle MNP$ and $\triangle M'N'P'$.

If the perimeter of the image is twice that of the preimage, then the lengths of the sides of the figure will be twice the measure of the original lengths. Multiply the vertex matrix by the scale factor 2.

$$2\begin{bmatrix} -1 & 2 & 1 \\ 1 & 3 & -2 \end{bmatrix} = \begin{bmatrix} -2 & 4 & 2 \\ 2 & 6 & -4 \end{bmatrix}$$

The coordinates of the vertices of $\triangle M'N'P'$ are $M'(-2, 2)$, $N'(4, 6)$, and $P'(2, -4)$.

The preimage and image are similar. Both figures have the same shape.

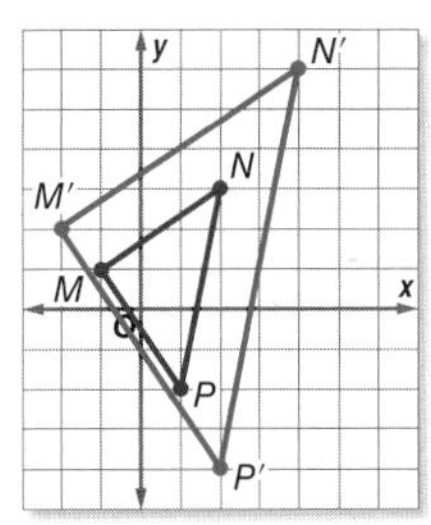

Guided Practice

3. Dilate rectangle $WXYZ$ with $W(4, 4)$, $X(4, 12)$, $Y(8, 4)$, and $Z(8, 12)$ so that the perimeter of the image is one fourth that of the preimage. Find the coordinates of the vertices of rectangle $W'X'Y'Z'$. $W'(1, 1)$, $X'(1, 3)$, $Y'(2, 1)$, $Z'(2, 3)$

Personal Tutor glencoe.com

Additional Examples

2 **STANDARD TEST PRACTICE** Rectangle $E'F'G'H'$ is the result of a translation of rectangle $EFGH$. A table of the vertices of each rectangle is shown.

Rectangle *EFGH*	Rectangle *E'F'G'H'*
E(−2, 2)	E'(−5, 0)
F(4, 2)	F'(1, 0)
G(4, −2)	G'(?, ?)
H(−2, −2)	H'(−5, −4)

Find the coordinates of G'. B

A (1, 0) **C** (7, 0)
B (1, −4) **D** (7, −4)

3 Dilate $\triangle XYZ$ with $X(1, 2)$, $Y(3, -1)$, and $Z(-1, -2)$ so that the perimeter of the image is twice that of the preimage. State the coordinates of the vertices of $\triangle X'Y'Z'$. Then graph $\triangle XYZ$ and $\triangle X'Y'Z'$. $X'(2, 4)$, $Y'(6, -2)$, $Z'(-2, -4)$

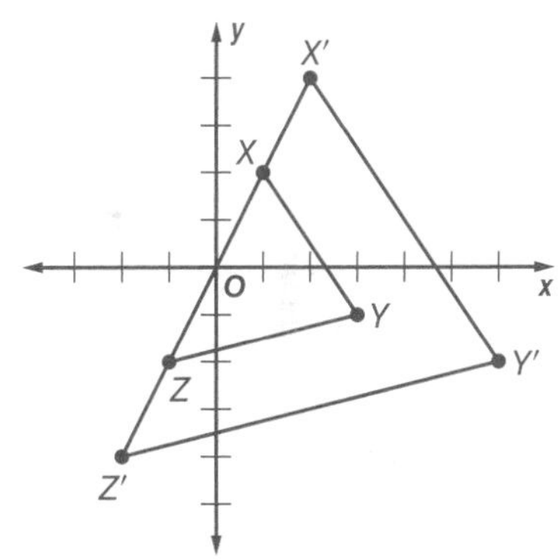

Watch Out!

Preventing Errors When students are drawing figures and their images in coordinate planes in this lesson, have them use different colored pencils for the original figures and their images.

Tips for New Teachers

Test-Taking Tip Test items involving figures in coordinate planes such as the one in Example 2 can often be solved quickly by sketching the figure. After plotting points H, J, K, and L, students can plot points H', J', or L', determine the direction of the translation, and then apply it to point K to find the coordinates of point K'.

Lesson 4-4 Transformations with Matrices 211

Reflections and Rotations

Example 4 shows how to find the coordinates of the vertices of the image of a polygon after a reflection across the line $y = x$. **Example 5** shows how to find the coordinates of the vertices of the image of a triangle after it is rotated about the origin.

Additional Example

4 Determine the coordinates of the vertices of the image of pentagon $PENTA$ with $P(-3, 1)$, $E(0, -1)$, $N(-1, -3)$, $T(-3, -4)$, and $A(-4, -1)$ after a reflection across the y-axis. Then graph the preimage and image. $P'(3, 1)$, $E'(0, -1)$, $N'(1, -3)$, $T'(3, -4)$, $A'(4, -1)$

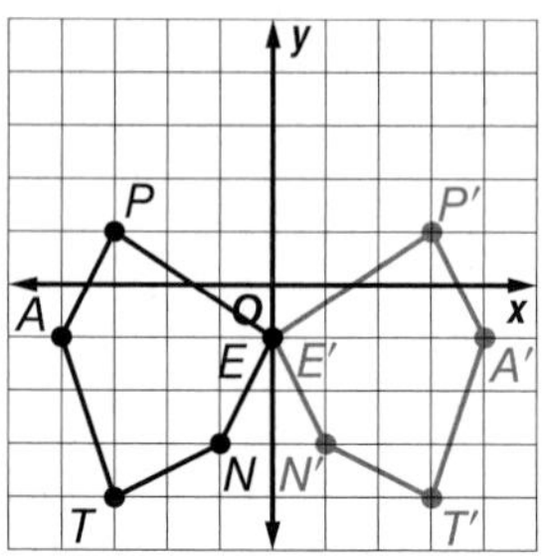

Focus on Mathematical Content

Rigid and Nonrigid Transformations A *transformation* is a process of moving all the points of a geometric figure according to a rule. If the new figure *(image)* is congruent to the original figure *(preimage)*, the transformation is called a *rigid transformation* or *isometry*. Translations, rotations, and reflections are rigid transformations. Dilations are examples of nonrigid transformations.

Reflections and Rotations A reflection maps every point of a preimage to an image in a line of symmetry using a *reflection matrix*.

StudyTip

Reflection In a reflection, the preimage and image are congruent.

Key Concept Reflection Matrices

To reflect in the given line, multiply the vertex matrix by the given matrix.

Line of Reflection	x-axis	y-axis	line $y = x$
Multiply on the left by:	$\begin{bmatrix} 1 & 0 \\ 0 & -1 \end{bmatrix}$	$\begin{bmatrix} -1 & 0 \\ 0 & 1 \end{bmatrix}$	$\begin{bmatrix} 0 & 1 \\ 1 & 0 \end{bmatrix}$
Models	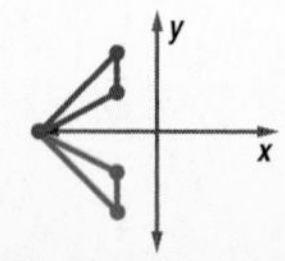	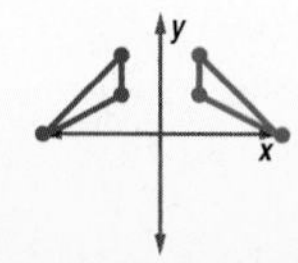	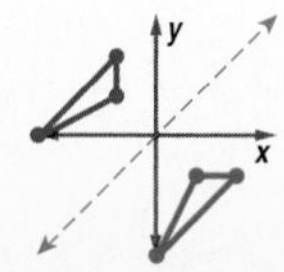

EXAMPLE 4 Reflection

Find the coordinates of the vertices of the image of $QRST$ with $Q(3, 2)$, $R(4, -3)$, $S(-3, -4)$, and $T(-2, 1)$ after reflection in $y = x$. Graph the preimage and image.

Write the ordered pairs as a vertex matrix. Then multiply the vertex matrix by the reflection matrix for the line $y = x$.

$$\begin{bmatrix} 0 & 1 \\ 1 & 0 \end{bmatrix} \cdot \begin{bmatrix} 3 & 4 & -3 & -2 \\ 2 & -3 & -4 & 1 \end{bmatrix} = \begin{bmatrix} 2 & -3 & -4 & 1 \\ 3 & 4 & -3 & -2 \end{bmatrix}$$

The coordinates of the vertices of quadrilateral $Q'R'S'T'$ are $Q'(2, 3)$, $R'(-3, 4)$, $S'(-4, -3)$, and $T'(1, -2)$.

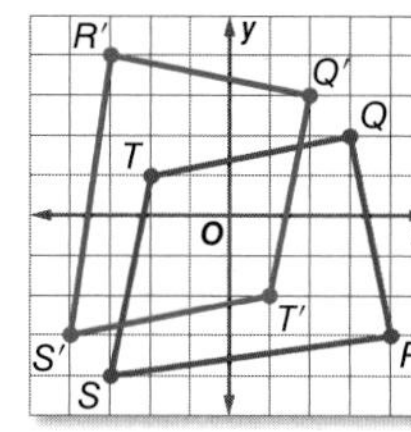

Guided Practice

4. Find the coordinates of the vertices of the image of pentagon $ABCDE$ with $A(1, 3)$, $B(3, 2)$, $C(3, -1)$, $D(1, -2)$, and $E(-1, 1)$ reflected across the x-axis.

4. $A'(1, -3)$, $B'(3, -2)$, $C'(3, 1)$, $D'(1, 2)$, $E'(-1, -1)$

Personal Tutor glencoe.com

A **rotation** maps every point of a preimage to an image rotated about a center point, usually the origin, using a *rotation matrix*.

StudyTip

Rotation Unless otherwise indicated, all rotations in this text will be counterclockwise.

Key Concept Rotation Matrices

To rotate counterclockwise about the origin, multiply the vertex matrix by the given matrix.

Angle of Rotation	90°	180°	270°
Multiply on the left by:	$\begin{bmatrix} 0 & -1 \\ 1 & 0 \end{bmatrix}$	$\begin{bmatrix} -1 & 0 \\ 0 & -1 \end{bmatrix}$	$\begin{bmatrix} 0 & 1 \\ -1 & 0 \end{bmatrix}$
Models	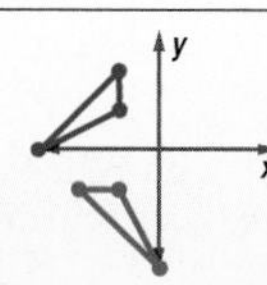	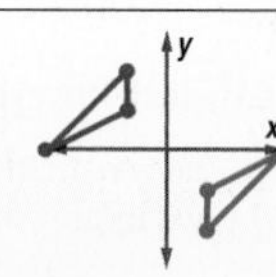	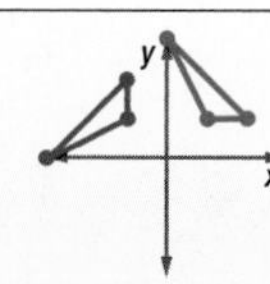

Watch Out!

Preventing Errors Ask students to describe the pattern of coordinates for corresponding points after a reflection over either axis. When a figure is reflected over the x-axis, the sign of the y-coordinate for each point on the figure changes. When a figure is reflected over the y-axis, the sign of the x-coordinate for each point on the figure changes. Then ask them to describe the pattern after a reflection over the line $y = x$. The x- and y-coordinates of each point are transposed.

StudyTip

Rotation In a rotation, like a reflection, the preimage and image are congruent.

EXAMPLE 5 Rotation

Find the coordinates of the vertices of the image of $\triangle VWX$ with $V(3, 2)$, $W(4, 1)$, and $X(2, 1)$ after it is rotated 270° counterclockwise about the origin.

Write the ordered pairs in a vertex matrix. Then multiply the vertex matrix by the rotation matrix.

$$\begin{bmatrix} 0 & 1 \\ -1 & 0 \end{bmatrix} \cdot \begin{bmatrix} 3 & 4 & 2 \\ 2 & 1 & 1 \end{bmatrix} = \begin{bmatrix} 2 & 1 & 1 \\ -3 & -4 & -2 \end{bmatrix}$$

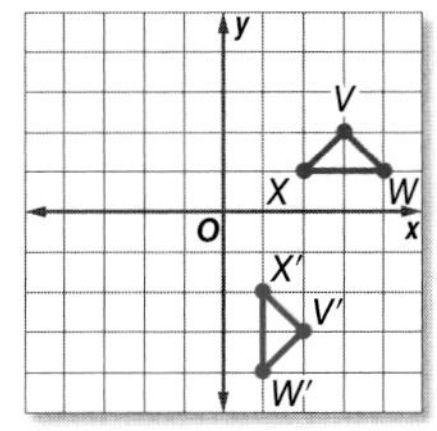

The coordinates of the vertices of $\triangle V'W'X'$ are $V'(2, -3)$, $W'(1, -4)$, and $X'(1, -2)$.

The image is congruent to the preimage. Both figures have the same size and shape.

Guided Practice

5. Find the coordinates of the vertices of the image of $\triangle XYZ$ with $X(-5, -6)$, $Y(-1, -3)$, and $Z(-2, -4)$ after it is rotated 180° counterclockwise about the origin. $X'(5, 6)$, $Y'(1, 3)$, $Z'(2, 4)$

Personal Tutor glencoe.com

Check Your Understanding

Example 1 p. 210

Find the coordinates of the vertices of the image for each figure after the given translation. Then graph the preimage and image. 1, 2. See margin.

1. $\triangle ABC$ with vertices $A(-3, -3)$, $B(-4, 2)$, and $C(1, 0)$, translated 5 units right and down 3 units

2. quadrilateral $WXYZ$ with vertices $W(1, -3)$, $X(0, 2)$, $Y(1, 2)$, and $Z(2, 1)$, translated 2 units left and up 4 units

Example 2 p. 210

3. **MULTIPLE CHOICE** Rectangle $RSTU$ with vertices $R(-3, 2)$, $S(1, 2)$, $T(-3, -1)$, and $U(1, -1)$ is translated so that T' is at $(-4, 1)$. What are the coordinates of R' and U'? A

A $R'(-4, 4)$, $U'(0, 1)$

B $R'(0, 1)$, $U'(-4, 4)$

C $R'(-2, 0)$, $U'(0, -3)$

D $R'(0, -2)$, $U'(-3, 0)$

Example 3 p. 211

Find the coordinates of the vertices of the image after the given dilation. State the coordinates of the vertices of the image. Then graph the preimage and image.

4, 5. See margin.

4. $\triangle DEF$ with vertices $D(-2, -1)$, $E(0, 3)$, and $F(2, -1)$, dilated so that its perimeter is three times the original perimeter

5. square $STUV$ with vertices $S(1, 0)$, $T(4, -3)$, $U(1, -6)$, and $V(-2, -3)$, dilated so that its perimeter is one half the original perimeter

Example 4 p. 212

Find the coordinates of the vertices of the image of each figure after a reflection in the given axis of symmetry. Then graph the preimage and image.

6, 7. See Chapter 4 Answer Appendix.

6. rectangle $GHJK$ with vertices $G(1, 5)$, $H(3, 4)$, $J(0, -2)$, and $K(-2, -1)$; x-axis

7. $\triangle PQR$ with vertices $P(-1, 2)$, $Q(4, -4)$, and $R(-1, -4)$; $y = x$

Additional Example

5 Find the coordinates of the vertices of the image of $\triangle DEF$ with $D(4, 3)$, $E(1, 1)$, and $F(2, 5)$ after it is rotated 90° counterclockwise about the origin. $D'(-3, 4)$, $E'(-1, 1)$, and $F'(-5, 2)$

3 PRACTICE

Formative Assessment

Use Exercises 1–9 to check for understanding.

Use the chart at the bottom of the next page to customize assignments for your students.

Additional Answers

1. $A'(2, -6)$, $B'(1, -1)$, $C'(6, -3)$

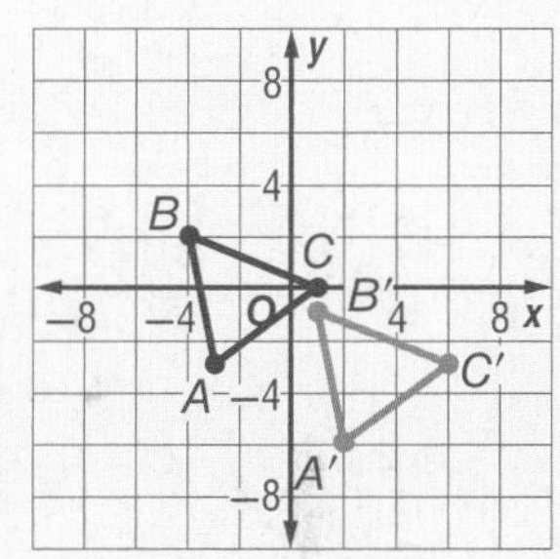

2. $W'(-1, 1)$, $X'(-2, 6)$, $Y'(-1, 6)$, $Z'(0, 5)$

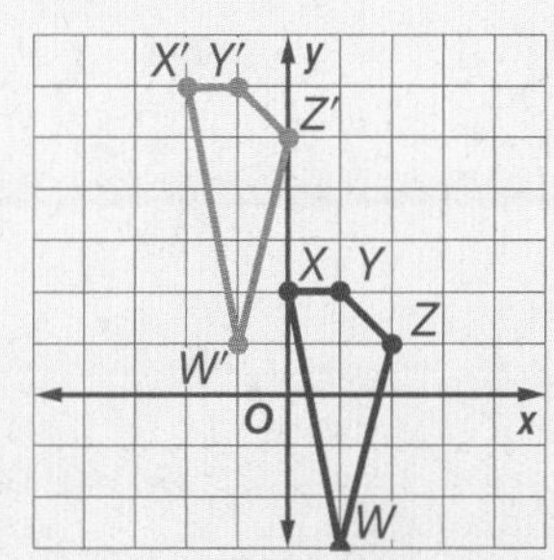

4. $D'(-6, -3)$, $E'(0, 9)$, $F'(6, -3)$

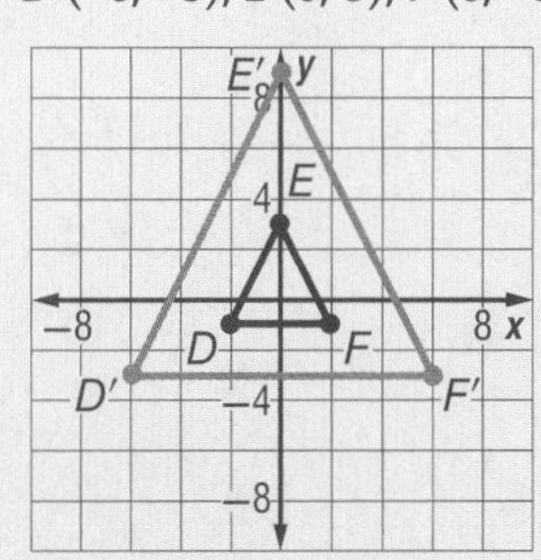

5. $S'\left(\frac{1}{2}, 0\right)$, $T'\left(2, -1\frac{1}{2}\right)$, $U'\left(\frac{1}{2}, -3\right)$, $V'\left(-1, -1\frac{1}{2}\right)$

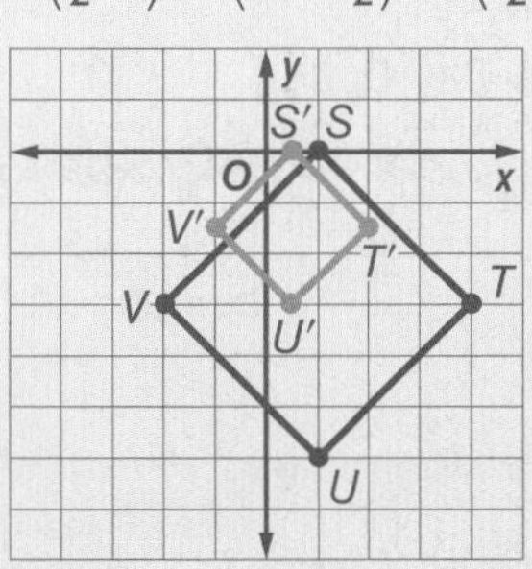

Additional Answers

8. $L'(-3, 5), M'(-1, -2), N'(-3, -3)$

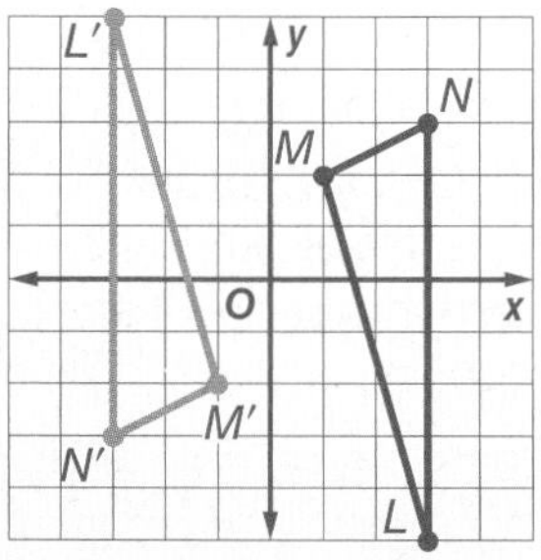

9. $A'(-1, -4), B'(-4, -3), C'(-4, 0), D'(-1, 1)$

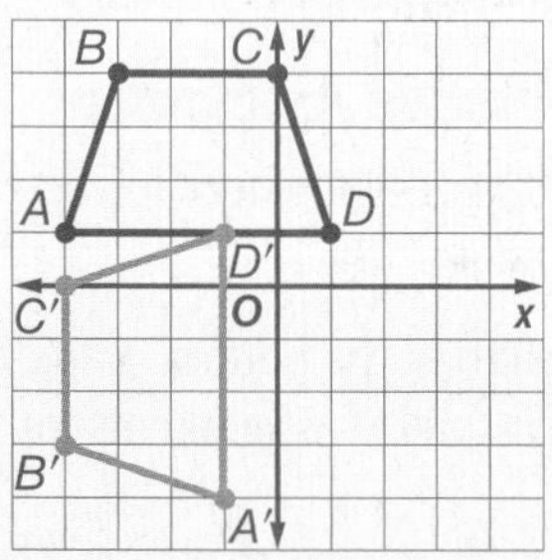

28. (3, 5), (3, 7), (−5, 5), (−5, 7)

36. $A''(1, -2), B''(2, -4), C''(5, -1)$

37. $X''(-8, -5), Y''(-6, -3), Z''(-5, -7)$

38. $D''(3, 2), E''(2, 5), F''(-2, 4), G''(-1, 1)$

39. $A''(4, -4), B''(-4, -4), C''(-4, 4), D''(4, 4)$

Example 5 p. 213

Find the coordinates of the vertices of the image of each figure after the given rotation. Then graph the preimage and image. 8, 9. See margin.

8. $\triangle LMN$ with vertices $L(3, -5)$, $M(1, 2)$, and $N(3, 3)$; 180° about the origin

9. quadrilateral $ABCD$ with $A(-4, 1)$, $B(-3, 4)$, $C(0, 4)$, and $D(1, 1)$; 90° about the origin

Practice and Problem Solving

= **Step-by-Step Solutions** begin on page R20.
Extra Practice begins on page 947.

Example 1 p. 210

Find the coordinates of the vertices of the image of each figure after the given translation. Then graph the preimage and image. 10–15. See Chapter 4 Answer Appendix.

10. $\triangle MNO$ with vertices $M(-7, 6)$, $N(1, 7)$, and $O(-3, 1)$, translated 2 units right and 6 units down

11. quadrilateral $EFGH$ with vertices $E(-4, 3)$, $F(2, -2)$, $G(-2, -4)$, and $H(-3, -3)$, translated 4 units left and 1 unit up

12. rectangle $PQRS$ with vertices $P(-2, -3)$, $Q(-2, 2)$, $R(1, 2)$, and $S(1, -3)$, translated 2 units left and 5 units down

13. $\triangle JKL$ with vertices $J(1, 4)$, $K(2, 1)$, and $L(-1, -2)$, translated 3 units right and 4 units down

14. $\triangle ABC$ with vertices $A(-1, 2)$, $B(2, 4)$, and $C(3, -2)$, translated 5 units left and 3 units down

15. square $WXYZ$ with vertices $W(3, 1)$, $X(3, 5)$, $Y(7, 5)$, and $Z(7, 1)$, translated 2 units left and 4 units up

Example 2 p. 210

16. Quadrilateral $A'B'C'D'$ is an image after a translation of quadrilateral $ABCD$. A table of the vertices of each quadrilateral is shown.

Quadrilateral *ABCD*	Quadrilateral *A′B′C′D′*
A(4, 8)	A′(−1, −2)
B(11, −10)	B′(?, ?)
C(?, ?)	C′(−17, −14)
D(−4, 6)	D′(−9, −4)

a. Find the coordinates of B'. $B'(6, -20)$

b. What are the coordinates of C? $(-12, -4)$

Problem-Solving Tip

Draw a Diagram When you solve problems, it may be helpful to draw a diagram to visualize the situation. In Exercise 17, a drawing can really help.

17 **MAPS** Camila looks at a map of a city she is visiting to find the way to a mall. Currently Camila is standing at an intersection with coordinates (5.5, 7). She figures out that she must go 3 blocks east and 4 blocks north to get to the mall.

a. Write a translation matrix that Camila can use to find the coordinates of the mall.

b. Using the translation matrix, what are the coordinates of the mall? $\begin{bmatrix} 8.5 \\ 11 \end{bmatrix}$

17a. $\begin{bmatrix} 3 \\ 4 \end{bmatrix}$

18–21. See Chapter 4 Answer Appendix.

Example 3 p. 211

Find the coordinates of the vertices of the image after the given dilation. State the coordinates of the vertices of the image. Then graph the preimage and image.

18. $\triangle TUV$ with vertices $T(-3, -1)$, $U(2, -1)$, and $V(1, -5)$, dilated so that the perimeter of the image is twice that of the preimage

19. square $DEFG$ with vertices $D(0, 4)$, $E(2, 2)$, $F(0, 0)$, and $G(-2, 2)$, dilated by a scale factor of 4

20. rectangle $KLMN$ with vertices $K(-3, 8)$, $L(-3, 2)$, $M(-6, 2)$, and $N(-6, 8)$, dilated by a scale factor of $\frac{1}{3}$

21. $\triangle QRS$ with vertices $Q(6, 4)$, $R(8, 0)$, and $S(0, 1)$, dilated so that the perimeter of the image is one fourth that of the preimage

Differentiated Homework Options

Level	Assignment	Two-Day Option	
AL Basic	10–35, 42–43, 45–64	11–35 odd, 49–52	10–34 even, 42–43, 45–48, 53–64
OL Core	11–39 odd, 40–43, 45–64	10–35, 49–52	36–43, 45–48, 53–64
BL Advanced	36–61, (optional: 62–64)		

Example 4
p. 212

22–27. See Chapter 4 Answer Appendix.

Find the coordinates of the vertices of the image of each figure after a reflection in the given axis of symmetry. Then graph the preimage and image.

22. $\triangle ABC$ with vertices $A(9, -10)$, $B(-5, -6)$, and $C(7, 7)$; y-axis

23. $\triangle DEF$ with vertices $D(7, 4)$, $E(4, 0)$, and $F(-3, 2)$; x-axis

24. quadrilateral $GHJK$ with vertices $G(-5, 6)$, $H(-2, 10)$, $J(0, 8)$, and $K(-4, -4)$; $y = x$

25. square $LMNP$ with vertices $L(1, -2)$, $M(-5, -1)$, $N(-4, 5)$, and $P(2, 4)$; y-axis

26. $\triangle QRS$ with vertices $Q(-2, 2)$, $R(4, 2)$, and $S(2, -6)$; x-axis

27. $\triangle TUV$ with vertices $T(-4, 5)$, $U(1, 3)$, and $V(-2, 0)$; $y = x$

28. See margin.

28. ANIMATION Yori has plotted all of the locations for her cartoon on a coordinate plane. The vertices of the outline of a character's house have coordinates $(-3, 5)$, $(-3, 7)$, $(5, 7)$, and $(5, 5)$. Yori decides that she wants to move all of the locations so that they are reflected across the y-axis. What will be the new coordinates of the house?

Example 5
p. 213

Find the coordinates of the vertices of the image of each figure after the given rotation. Then graph the preimage and image. 29–34. See Chapter 4 Answer Appendix.

29. $\triangle XYZ$ with vertices $X(1, 2)$, $Y(1, 4)$, and $Z(5, 2)$; 180° about the origin

30. quadrilateral $ABCD$ with vertices $A(-1, 1)$, $B(-4, 1)$, $C(-6, 5)$, and $D(-3, 5)$; 270° about the origin

31. rectangle $EFGH$ with vertices $E(3, 2)$, $F(3, -4)$, $G(2, -4)$, and $H(2, 2)$; 270° about the origin

32. square $JKLM$ with vertices $J(-3, 3)$, $K(1, 3)$, $L(1, -1)$, and $M(-3, -1)$; 90° about the origin

33. quadrilateral $NPQR$ with vertices $N(-2, -1)$, $P(-3, -5)$, $Q(-6, -5)$, and $R(-6, -1)$; 90° about the origin

Real-World Link

The Singapore Flyer is 42 stories tall.

34. $\triangle STU$ with vertices $S(-4, 2)$, $T(1, 5)$, and $U(-2, -1)$; 180° about the origin

35. RIDES The world's tallest Ferris wheel, the Singapore Flyer, is 165 meters across. Jeremy and Nicole take a ride on it while on vacation. When they are at the top of the Ferris wheel, they have coordinates (0, 165). Find their coordinates after the wheel has turned 90° counterclockwise.

35. (−165, 0)

36–39. See margin.

B **Find the coordinates of the vertices of the image after the given transformations.**

36. reflected in $y = x$, then rotated 270° about the origin

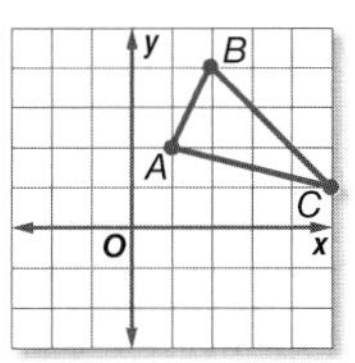

37. translated 4 units left and 2 units up, then reflected in the x-axis

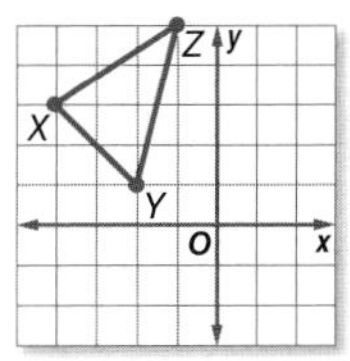

38. rotated 90° about the origin after being reflected in the y-axis

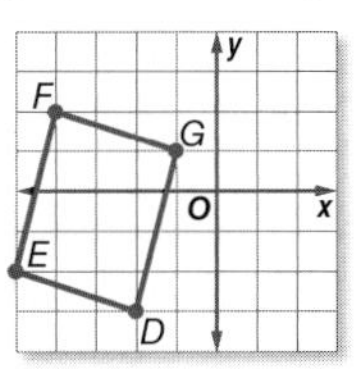

39. rotated 180° about the origin

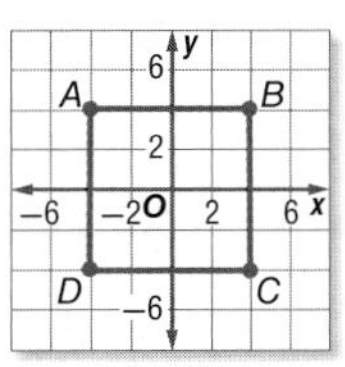

Study Guide and Intervention
CRM pp. 23–24 AL OL ELL

4-4 Study Guide and Intervention

Transformations with Matrices

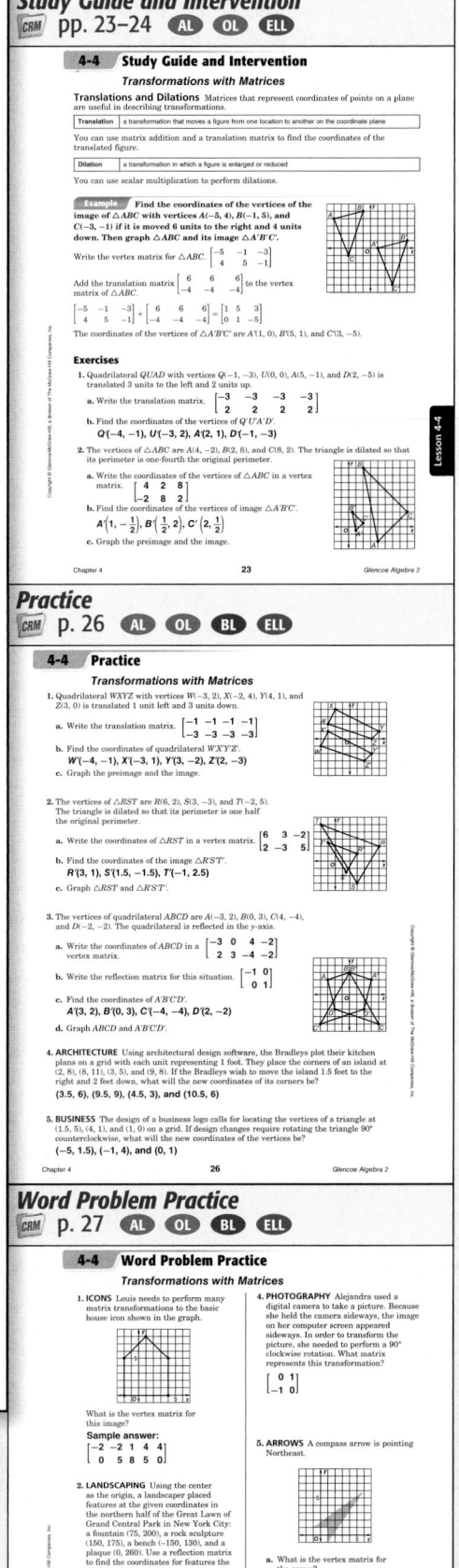

Translations and Dilations Matrices that represent coordinates of points on a plane are useful in describing transformations.

Translation	a transformation that moves a figure from one location to another on the coordinate plane

You can use matrix addition and a translation matrix to find the coordinates of the translated figure.

Dilation	a transformation in which a figure is enlarged or reduced

You can use scalar multiplication to perform dilations.

Example **Find the coordinates of the vertices of the image of $\triangle ABC$ with vertices $A(-5, 4)$, $B(-1, 5)$, and $C(-3, -1)$ if it is moved 6 units to the right and 4 units down. Then graph $\triangle ABC$ and its image $\triangle A'B'C'$.**

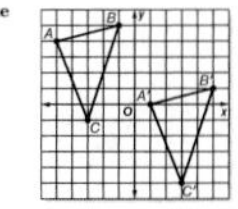

Write the vertex matrix for $\triangle ABC$. $\begin{bmatrix} -5 & -1 & -3 \\ 4 & 5 & -1 \end{bmatrix}$

Add the translation matrix $\begin{bmatrix} 6 & 6 & 6 \\ -4 & -4 & -4 \end{bmatrix}$ to the vertex matrix of $\triangle ABC$.

$\begin{bmatrix} -5 & -1 & -3 \\ 4 & 5 & -1 \end{bmatrix} + \begin{bmatrix} 6 & 6 & 6 \\ -4 & -4 & -4 \end{bmatrix} = \begin{bmatrix} 1 & 5 & 3 \\ 0 & 1 & -5 \end{bmatrix}$

The coordinates of the vertices of $\triangle A'B'C'$ are $A'(1, 0)$, $B'(5, 1)$, and $C'(3, -5)$.

Exercises

1. Quadrilateral $QUAD$ with vertices $Q(-1, -3)$, $U(0, 0)$, $A(5, -1)$, and $D(2, -5)$ is translated 3 units to the left and 2 units up.
   a. Write the translation matrix. $\begin{bmatrix} -3 & -3 & -3 & -3 \\ 2 & 2 & 2 & 2 \end{bmatrix}$
   b. Find the coordinates of the vertices of $Q'U'A'D'$.
   $Q'(-4, -1)$, $U'(-3, 2)$, $A'(2, 1)$, $D'(-1, -3)$

2. The vertices of $\triangle ABC$ are $A(4, -2)$, $B(2, 8)$, and $C(8, 2)$. The triangle is dilated so that its perimeter is one-fourth the original perimeter.
   a. Write the coordinates of the vertices of $\triangle ABC$ in a vertex matrix. $\begin{bmatrix} 4 & 2 & 8 \\ -2 & 8 & 2 \end{bmatrix}$
   b. Find the coordinates of the vertices of image $\triangle A'B'C'$.
   $A'\left(1, -\frac{1}{2}\right)$, $B'\left(\frac{1}{2}, 2\right)$, $C'\left(2, \frac{1}{2}\right)$
   c. Graph the preimage and the image.

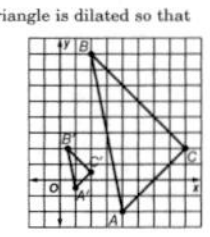

Lesson 4-4

Chapter 4 23 Glencoe Algebra 2

Practice
CRM p. 26 AL OL BL ELL

4-4 Practice

Transformations with Matrices

1. Quadrilateral $WXYZ$ with vertices $W(-3, 2)$, $X(-2, 4)$, $Y(4, 1)$, and $Z(3, 0)$ is translated 1 unit left and 3 units down.
   a. Write the translation matrix. $\begin{bmatrix} -1 & -1 & -1 & -1 \\ -3 & -3 & -3 & -3 \end{bmatrix}$
   b. Find the coordinates of quadrilateral $W'X'Y'Z'$.
   $W'(-4, -1)$, $X'(-3, 1)$, $Y'(3, -2)$, $Z'(2, -3)$
   c. Graph the preimage and the image.

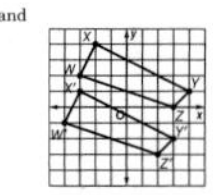

2. The vertices of $\triangle RST$ are $R(6, 2)$, $S(3, -3)$, and $T(-2, 5)$. The triangle is dilated so that its perimeter is one half the original perimeter.
   a. Write the coordinates of $\triangle RST$ in a vertex matrix. $\begin{bmatrix} 6 & 3 & -2 \\ 2 & -3 & 5 \end{bmatrix}$
   b. Find the coordinates of the image $\triangle R'S'T'$.
   $R'(3, 1)$, $S'(1.5, -1.5)$, $T'(-1, 2.5)$
   c. Graph $\triangle RST$ and $\triangle R'S'T'$.

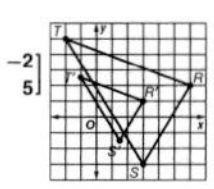

3. The vertices of quadrilateral $ABCD$ are $A(-3, 2)$, $B(0, 3)$, $C(4, -4)$, and $D(-2, -2)$. The quadrilateral is reflected in the y-axis.
   a. Write the coordinates of $ABCD$ in a vertex matrix. $\begin{bmatrix} -3 & 0 & 4 & -2 \\ 2 & 3 & -4 & -2 \end{bmatrix}$
   b. Write the reflection matrix for this situation. $\begin{bmatrix} -1 & 0 \\ 0 & 1 \end{bmatrix}$
   c. Find the coordinates of $A'B'C'D'$.
   $A'(3, 2)$, $B'(0, 3)$, $C'(-4, -4)$, $D'(2, -2)$
   d. Graph $ABCD$ and $A'B'C'D'$.

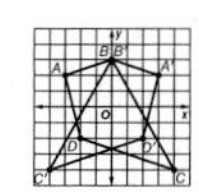

4. **ARCHITECTURE** Using architectural design software, the Bradleys plot their kitchen plans on a grid with each unit representing 1 foot. They place the corners of an island at (2, 8), (8, 11), (3, 5), and (9, 8). If the Bradleys wish to move the island 1.5 feet to the right and 2 feet down, what will the new coordinates of its corners be?
   (3.5, 6), (9.5, 9), (4.5, 3), and (10.5, 6)

5. **BUSINESS** The design of a business logo calls for locating the vertices of a triangle at (1.5, 5), (4, 1), and (1, 0) on a grid. If design changes require rotating the triangle 90° counterclockwise, what will the new coordinates of the vertices be?
   (−5, 1.5), (−1, 4), and (0, 1)

Chapter 4 26 Glencoe Algebra 2

Word Problem Practice
CRM p. 27 AL OL BL ELL

4-4 Word Problem Practice

Transformations with Matrices

1. **ICONS** Louis needs to perform many matrix transformations to the basic house icon shown in the graph.

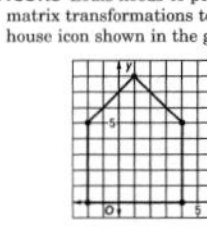

   What is the vertex matrix for this image?
   Sample answer: $\begin{bmatrix} -2 & -2 & 1 & 4 & 4 \\ 0 & 5 & 8 & 5 & 0 \end{bmatrix}$

2. **LANDSCAPING** Using the center as the origin, a landscaper placed features at the given coordinates in the northern half of the Great Lawn of Grand Central Park in New York City: a fountain (75, 200), a rock sculpture (150, 175), a bench (−150, 130), and a plaque (0, 260). Use a reflection matrix to find the coordinates for features the landscaper can place so that the south half will be a reflection of the north.
   fountain (75, −200), rock sculpture (150, −175), bench (−150, −130), plaque (0, −260)

3. **MIRROR SYMMETRY** A detective found only half of an image with mirror symmetry about the line $y = x$. The vertex matrix of the visible part is $\begin{bmatrix} 4 & 5 & -2 \\ 2 & -5 & -4 \end{bmatrix}$. What are the coordinates of the hidden vertices?
   (2, 4), (−5, 5), (−4, −2)

4. **PHOTOGRAPHY** Alejandra used a digital camera to take a picture. Because she held the camera sideways, the image on her computer screen appeared sideways. In order to transform the picture, she needed to perform a 90° clockwise rotation. What matrix represents this transformation?
   $\begin{bmatrix} 0 & 1 \\ -1 & 0 \end{bmatrix}$

5. **ARROWS** A compass arrow is pointing Northeast.

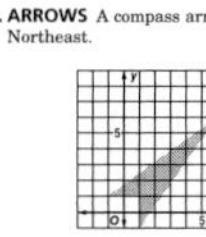

   a. What is the vertex matrix for the arrow?
   Sample answer: $\begin{bmatrix} 6 & -1 & 1 & 1 \\ 6 & 1 & 1 & -1 \end{bmatrix}$
   b. What would the vertex matrix be for the arrow if it were pointing Northwest? (Hint: Rotate 90° around the origin.)
   Sample answer: $\begin{bmatrix} -6 & -1 & -1 & 1 \\ 6 & -1 & 1 & 1 \end{bmatrix}$

Lesson 4-4

Chapter 4 27 Glencoe Algebra 2

Enrichment
CRM p. 28 OL BL

4-4 Enrichment

Computer Graphics Using Matrix Transformations

Computer animation creates a sensation of movement by slowly changing the position of pixels of an image on a two-dimensional video screen. By selecting the center of the screen as the origin, each pixel can be located using ordered pairs. A series of delayed matrix transformations (transformation, pause, transformation, pause) applied to the coordinates of the point (pixel) produces the desired animation effect.

Two computer programmers, Nate and Daniel, are writing a computer animation program using only the two matrices $A = \begin{bmatrix} 1 & 0 \\ 0 & -1 \end{bmatrix}$ and $B = \begin{bmatrix} 0 & -1 \\ 1 & 0 \end{bmatrix}$. Nate argues that it does not make a difference which matrix is applied first. Daniel disagrees.

1. What transformation does each matrix represent?
   Matrix A represents a reflection about the x-axis, and matrix B represents a 90° counterclockwise rotation.

2. Find AB and BA. Determine whether Nate or Daniel is correct.
   AB = [1 −1 …] BA = [0 1 …] … is correct because order does matter.

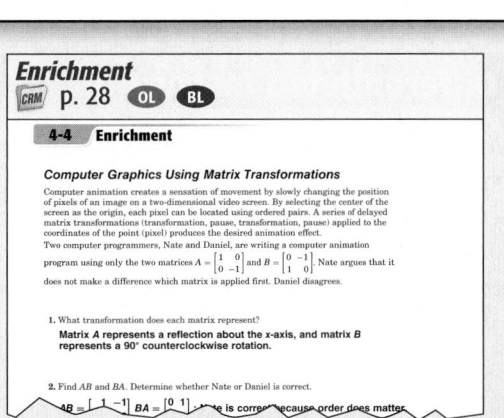

Multiple Representations

In Exercise 41, students use matrices, graphs, and matrix algebra to show the effects of multiple transformations on a plane figure.

Additional Answers

41a. $\begin{bmatrix} -2 & 4 & 2 \\ 3 & 0 & -5 \end{bmatrix}, \begin{bmatrix} -2 & 4 & 2 \\ -3 & 0 & 5 \end{bmatrix}$

41b.

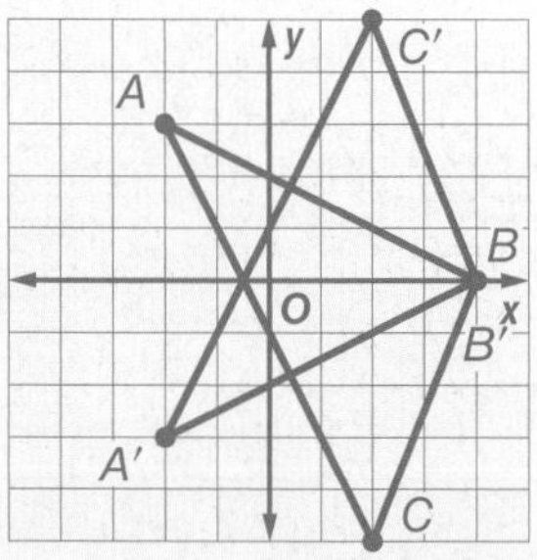

41c. The reflection of $\triangle A'B'C'$ across the x-axis is $\triangle ABC$.

41d. $\begin{bmatrix} 1 & 0 \\ 0 & -1 \end{bmatrix} \begin{bmatrix} 1 & 0 \\ 0 & -1 \end{bmatrix} = \begin{bmatrix} 1 & 0 \\ 0 & 1 \end{bmatrix}$; The matrix is the identity matrix because reflecting a triangle across the same line twice produces the original figure.

42. Sample answer: A dilation by a scale factor of 3 and a 90° counterclockwise rotation about the origin could be performed using the matrix $\begin{bmatrix} 0 & -3 \\ 3 & 0 \end{bmatrix}$.

48. Matrices can be used to translate a figure left, right, up, or down, dilate a figure so that it is enlarged or reduced, reflect a figure over a given line, and rotate a figure. Under translations, an image is congruent to the preimage and has the same orientation. Under dilation, an image is similar to the preimage. Under reflections and rotations, the image is congruent to the preimage but has different orientation.

Real-World Link

Blueprint floor plans are typically drawn to a $\frac{1}{4}$ inch per 1 foot scale of the actual size of the home.

Source: The House Designers

40. ARCHITECTURE On the blueprint for a new house, the coordinates of the corners of the garage are (1, 25), (1, 5), (31, 5), and (31, 25). If the scale of the blueprint is $\frac{1}{48}$ that of the actual structure, find the coordinates of the garage when it is built.

41. MULTIPLE REPRESENTATIONS In this problem, you will investigate the results of multiple reflections. **a–d. See margin.**

a. **SYMBOLIC** Write the vertex matrices for $\triangle ABC$ with vertices $A(-2, 3)$, $B(4, 0)$, and $C(2, -5)$ and its image $\triangle A'B'C'$ after reflection in the x-axis.

b. **GRAPHICAL** Graph $\triangle ABC$ and $\triangle A'B'C'$.

c. **VERBAL** Make a conjecture about the reflection of $\triangle A'B'C'$ in the x-axis. Perform the matrix multiplication to verify in conjecture.

d. **ANALYTICAL** Find one matrix that could be used to reflect a triangle in the x-axis twice. How does the matrix relate to in observations?

H.O.T. Problems
Use Higher-Order Thinking Skills

42. OPEN ENDED A *composite transformation* is a transformation involving two or more transformations performed in sequence. Write a transformation matrix that could be used to perform a composite transformation involving dilation and rotation of a figure. **See margin.**

43. REASONING Determine whether the following statement is *sometimes*, *always*, or *never* true. Explain your reasoning.

The image of a dilation is congruent to its preimage.

44. CHALLENGE Write a transformation matrix for each of the following.

a. reflection in the line $y = -x$

b. rotation 90° clockwise about the origin

45. OPEN ENDED Consider the point represented by the matrix $\begin{bmatrix} 3 \\ -2 \end{bmatrix}$. Give an example of a translation matrix and a reflection matrix that when applied separately to the point produce the same image point.

46. WHICH ONE DOESN'T BELONG? Determine which of the transformations is not the same as the others. Explain your reasoning.

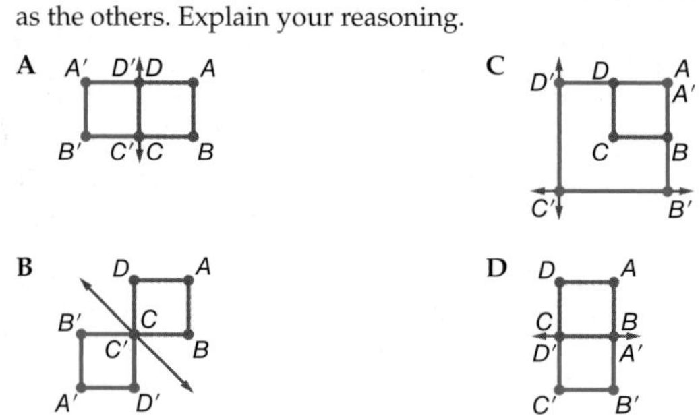

47. PROOF Show that rotating $\triangle ABC$ with vertices $A(x_1, y_1)$, $B(x_2, y_2)$, and $C(x_3, y_3)$ 180° counterclockwise about the origin is the same as reflecting the figure in the x-axis, then in the y-axis. See Chapter 4 Answer Appendix.

48. WRITING IN MATH Use the information in this lesson to describe how matrices can be used to transform figures in two-dimensional space. Describe the physical characteristics of a figure after each transformation. **See margin.**

40. (48, 240), (48, 1200), (1488, 240), (1488, 1200)

43. Sometimes; the image and preimage are only congruent if the scale factor is 1 or –1.

44a. $\begin{bmatrix} 0 & -1 \\ -1 & 0 \end{bmatrix}$

44b. $\begin{bmatrix} 0 & 1 \\ -1 & 0 \end{bmatrix}$

45. Sample answer: A reflection in the x-axis produces an image of $\begin{bmatrix} 3 \\ 2 \end{bmatrix}$. This is the same as applying the translation $\begin{bmatrix} 0 \\ 4 \end{bmatrix}$.

46. C; sample answer: Transformation C is a dilation, and the image is not the same size as the preimage. In the other three transformations, the image is congruent to the preimage.

Differentiated Instruction
AL

Visual/Spatial Learners Have students draw their own cartoon figures consisting of line segments on a coordinate grid. Then have them "animate" their figures by moving them successively to a sequence of different positions and then write a corresponding sequence of matrix transformations to accomplish the animation.

NGSSS PRACTICE 912.A.3.1, 912.P.3.1, 912.D.8.2, 912.G.2.4

49. Tonya wanted to find 5 consecutive whole numbers that add up to 95. She wrote the equation $(n-2)+(n-1)+n+(n+1)+(n+2)=95$. What does the variable n represent in the equation? **B**

A. the least of the 5 whole numbers
B. the middle of the 5 whole numbers
C. the greatest of the 5 whole numbers
D. the difference between the least and the greatest of the 5 whole numbers

50. PROBABILITY There are 12 songs on your MP3 player. The player is set to shuffle, but not repeat—that is, to play the songs in random order without repeating any. What is the probability that any two of the four country songs will be the first two played? **G**

F. $P \approx 20\%$
G. $P \approx 11.1\%$
H. $P \approx 9.09\%$
I. $P \approx 0.83\%$

51. THINK SOLVE EXPLAIN **EXTENDED RESPONSE** The following types of vehicles are rented at The Auto Store. Organize the data into a 4 × 2 matrix. Then write a new matrix providing the prices after a 15% markup. **See margin.**

	Daily	Weekly
Economy	$29.99	$149.99
Mid-Size	$39.99	$179.99
Full-Size	$49.99	$209.99
SUV	$69.99	$349.99

52. SAT/ACT Triangle ABC has vertices $A(-4, 2)$, $B(-4, -3)$, and $C(3, -2)$. After a dilation, triangle $A'B'C'$ has vertices $A'(-12, 6)$, $B'(-12, -9)$, $C'(9, -6)$. How many times as great is the perimeter of $\triangle A'B'C'$ as that of $\triangle ABC$? **A**

A. 3
B. 6
C. 12
D. $\frac{1}{3}$

Spiral Review

Find each product, if possible. (Lesson 4-3)

53. $\begin{bmatrix} 4 & 2 \\ -1 & -3 \end{bmatrix} \cdot \begin{bmatrix} 6 & 2 \\ 5 & 1 \end{bmatrix}$ 53. $\begin{bmatrix} 34 & 10 \\ -21 & -5 \end{bmatrix}$

54. $\begin{bmatrix} 8 & -2 \\ -4 & -5 \end{bmatrix} \cdot \begin{bmatrix} -2 \\ 3 \end{bmatrix}$ $\begin{bmatrix} -22 \\ -7 \end{bmatrix}$

55. $\begin{bmatrix} -3 \\ -4 \end{bmatrix} \cdot \begin{bmatrix} -6 & -8 \\ -4 & 5 \end{bmatrix}$ impossible

56. BUSINESS The table lists the prices at the Sandwich Shoppe. (Lesson 4-2) **a–c. See margin.**

a. List the prices in a 4 × 3 matrix.
b. The manager decides to cut the prices of every item by 20%. List this new set of data in a 4 × 3 matrix.
c. Subtract the second matrix from the first and determine the savings to the customer for each sandwich.

Sandwich	Small	Medium	Large
ham	$4.50	$6.75	$9.50
salami	$4.50	$6.75	$9.50
veggie	$4.00	$6.25	$8.75
meatball	$4.75	$7.50	$10.25

Graph each inequality. (Lesson 2-8) **57–59. See margin.**

57. $|2x+5|+3 \geq y$
58. $y \leq 2|x-4|$
59. $y \geq -2|x+3|+1$

State whether the events are *independent* or *dependent*. (Lesson 0-4)

60. choosing a president, vice president, secretary, and treasurer for Key Club, assuming that a person can hold only one office **dependent**

61. selecting a horror movie and a comedy at the video store **independent**

Skills Review

Solve each system of equations. (Lesson 3-2)

62. $y = 3x - 10$, $4x - 3y = 20$ **(2, −4)**

63. $4y + 5x = 21$, $2x + 7y = 3$ **(5, −1)**

64. $-5x - 2y = 27$, $8x + 5y = -54$ **(−3, −6)**

Differentiated Instruction

BL

Extension Have students use a matrix to translate triangle ABC with vertices $A(-2, 0)$, $B(4, 0)$, and $C(1, 4)$ four units to the right and down 2 units. Then have them translate the image $A'B'C'$ to the left 3 units and up 7 units. Ask students to write a translation matrix for the first translation and the second translation. $\begin{bmatrix} 4 & 4 & 4 \\ -2 & -2 & -2 \end{bmatrix}$, $\begin{bmatrix} -3 & -3 & -3 \\ 7 & 7 & 7 \end{bmatrix}$ Then ask them to write a single translation matrix for the composition of these two translations. $\begin{bmatrix} 1 & 1 & 1 \\ 5 & 5 & 5 \end{bmatrix}$

4 ASSESS

Yesterday's News Have students write how multiplying matrices helped them find the coordinates of a reflected or rotated figure.

Additional Answers

51. $\begin{bmatrix} \$29.99 & \$149.99 \\ \$39.99 & \$179.99 \\ \$49.99 & \$209.99 \\ \$69.99 & \$349.99 \end{bmatrix}$, $\begin{bmatrix} \$34.49 & \$172.49 \\ \$45.99 & \$206.99 \\ \$57.49 & \$241.49 \\ \$80.49 & \$402.49 \end{bmatrix}$

56a. $\begin{bmatrix} \$4.50 & \$6.75 & \$9.50 \\ \$4.50 & \$6.75 & \$9.50 \\ \$4.00 & \$6.25 & \$8.75 \\ \$4.75 & \$7.50 & \$10.25 \end{bmatrix}$

56b. $\begin{bmatrix} \$3.60 & \$5.40 & \$7.60 \\ \$3.60 & \$5.40 & \$7.60 \\ \$3.20 & \$5.00 & \$7.00 \\ \$3.80 & \$6.00 & \$8.20 \end{bmatrix}$

56c. $\begin{bmatrix} \$0.90 & \$1.35 & \$1.90 \\ \$0.90 & \$1.35 & \$1.90 \\ \$0.80 & \$1.25 & \$1.75 \\ \$0.95 & \$1.50 & \$2.05 \end{bmatrix}$

57.

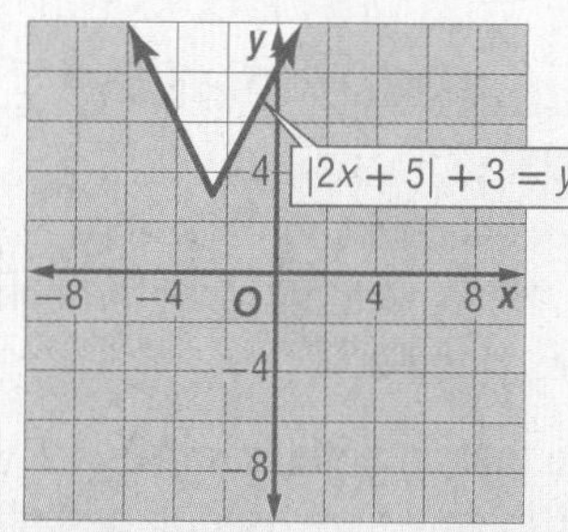

58.

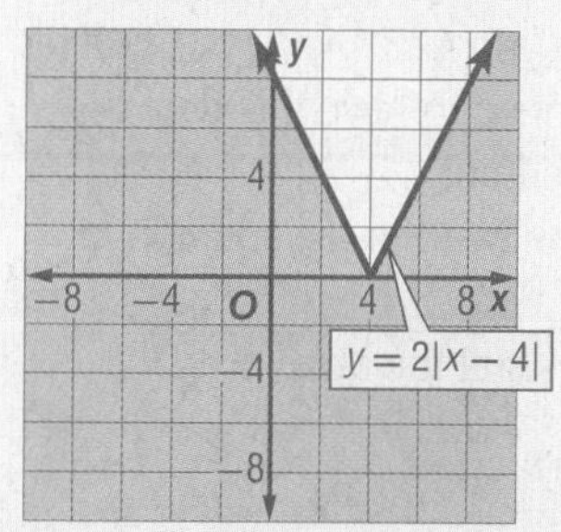

59.

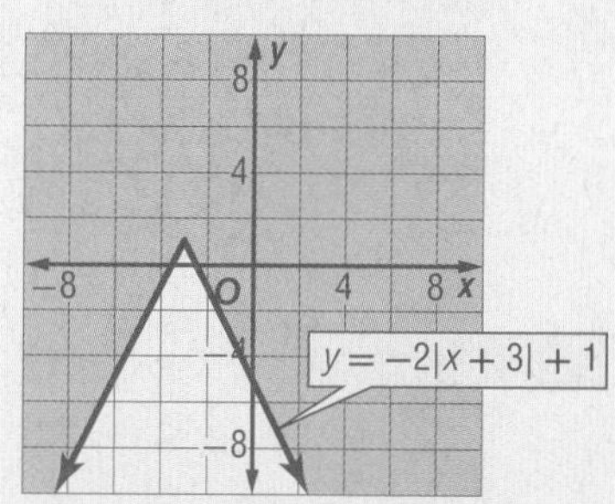

1 FOCUS

Objective Use matrices to express the component form of a vector and to add two vectors.

Materials for Each Student

- grid paper

Easy to Make Manipulatives

Teaching Algebra with Manipulatives

- template for grid paper, p. 1

Teaching Tip

Make sure students see the distinction between the use of triangular brackets to indicate a vector, such as ⟨2, 3⟩, and the use of parentheses to indicate a point, such as (2, 3).

2 TEACH

Working in Cooperative Groups

Have students work in pairs, mixing abilities. Have partners work through Examples 1 and 2.

- Notice that, in both Examples 1 and 2, 2 × 1 matrices are used to describe points as well as vectors. Students may need to have this dual use pointed out.
- For the head-to-tail addition in Example 2, $\overrightarrow{GH}$ is translated so that its tail is at the head of $\overrightarrow{CD}$.

Vectors and Matrices

A 1 × 2 or 2 × 1 matrix can be represented by a vector. A **vector** is a quantity that has both **magnitude**, or length, and **direction**. They are represented as directed segments such as $\overrightarrow{AB}$, read *vector AB*.

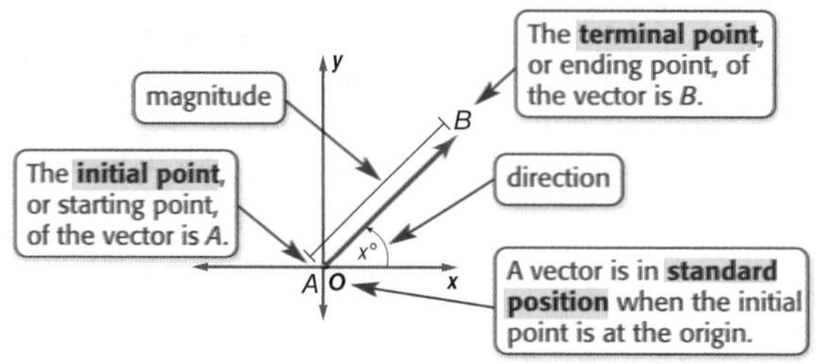

A vector on a coordinate grid can be described in **component form**, or in terms of its horizontal and vertical components. The notation for a vector in component form is ⟨*x* component, *y* component⟩. The vector ⟨2, 3⟩ has initial point (0, 0) and terminal point (2, 3).

Matrix operations can be used to determine the component form of a vector.

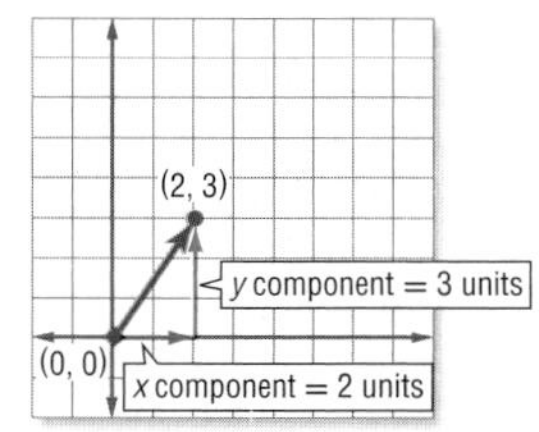

EXAMPLE 1 Determine Component Form

If $A = \begin{bmatrix} -2 \\ 1 \end{bmatrix}$ and $B = \begin{bmatrix} 4 \\ 3 \end{bmatrix}$, express $\overrightarrow{AB}$ in component form. Then graph $\overrightarrow{AB}$.

Step 1 Determine the *x*- and *y*-components by finding $B - A$.

$$B - A = \begin{bmatrix} 4 \\ 3 \end{bmatrix} - \begin{bmatrix} -2 \\ 1 \end{bmatrix}$$

$$= \begin{bmatrix} 4 - (-2) \\ 3 - 1 \end{bmatrix} \text{ or } \begin{bmatrix} 6 \\ 2 \end{bmatrix}$$

Step 2 Express $\overrightarrow{AB}$ in component form.

$$\begin{bmatrix} 6 \\ 2 \end{bmatrix} \begin{matrix} \leftarrow x \text{ component} \\ \leftarrow y \text{ component} \end{matrix} \Bigg\} \langle 6, 2 \rangle$$

Step 3 Graph $\overrightarrow{AB}$.

Because $\overrightarrow{AB} = \langle 6, 2 \rangle$, begin the vector at (0, 0) and extend it to (6, 2).

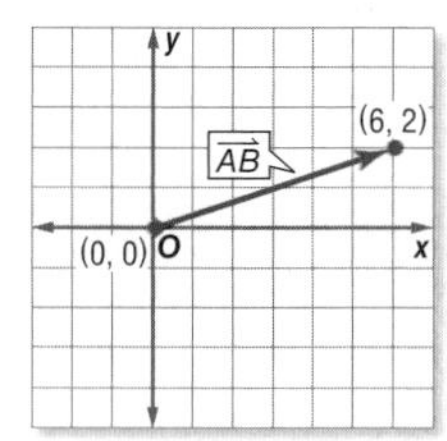

Additional Answers

1. ⟨−15, −11⟩

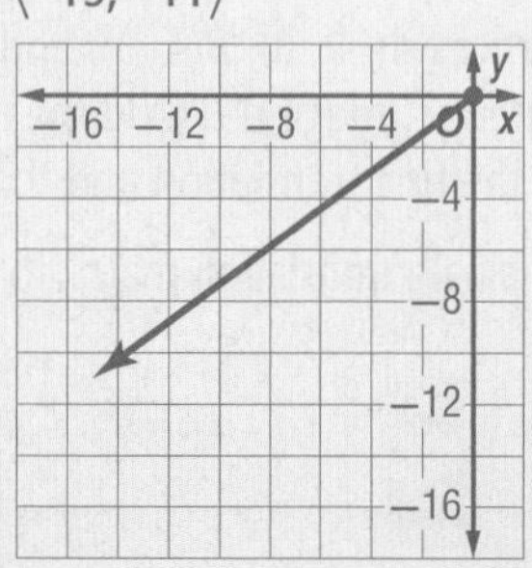

2. ⟨−5, −5⟩

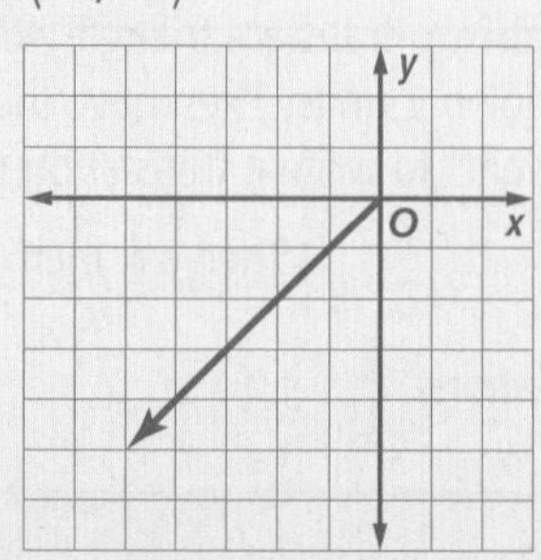

EXAMPLE 2 Add Vectors

Find $\overrightarrow{CD} + \overrightarrow{GH}$ for $C(-2, -2)$, $D(1, 3)$, $G(2, 5)$, and $H(4, -1)$.

Step 1 Express the ordered pairs as matrices.

$$C = \begin{bmatrix} -2 \\ -2 \end{bmatrix}, D = \begin{bmatrix} 1 \\ 3 \end{bmatrix}, G = \begin{bmatrix} 2 \\ 5 \end{bmatrix}, H = \begin{bmatrix} 4 \\ -1 \end{bmatrix}$$

Step 2 Use matrix operations to represent each vector.

$$\overrightarrow{CD}: D - C = \begin{bmatrix} 1-(-2) \\ 3-(-2) \end{bmatrix} = \begin{bmatrix} 3 \\ 5 \end{bmatrix} \qquad \overrightarrow{GH}: H - G = \begin{bmatrix} 4-2 \\ -1-5 \end{bmatrix} = \begin{bmatrix} 2 \\ -6 \end{bmatrix}$$

Step 3 Add the matrices to represent $\overrightarrow{CD} + \overrightarrow{GH}$.

$$\begin{bmatrix} 3 \\ 5 \end{bmatrix} + \begin{bmatrix} 2 \\ -6 \end{bmatrix} = \begin{bmatrix} 3+2 \\ 5+(-6) \end{bmatrix} = \begin{bmatrix} 5 \\ -1 \end{bmatrix}$$

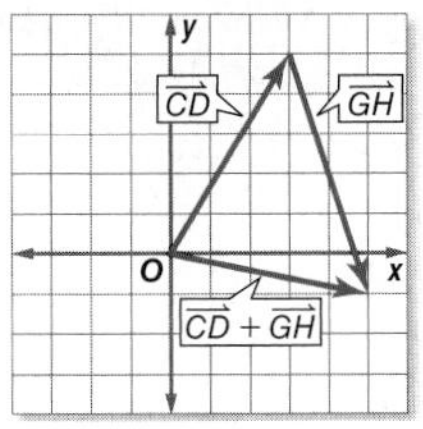

Step 4 Write the matrix as a component vector.

$$\begin{bmatrix} 5 \\ -1 \end{bmatrix} \rightarrow \langle 5, -1 \rangle$$

Thus, $\overrightarrow{CD} + \overrightarrow{GH} = \langle 5, -1 \rangle$.

Exercises 1–4. See margin.

Express $\overrightarrow{XY}$ in component form. Then graph $\overrightarrow{XY}$.

1. $X = \begin{bmatrix} 5 \\ 9 \end{bmatrix}, Y = \begin{bmatrix} -10 \\ -2 \end{bmatrix}$
2. $X = \begin{bmatrix} 8 \\ 0 \end{bmatrix}, Y = \begin{bmatrix} 3 \\ -5 \end{bmatrix}$
3. $X = [\,-8 \quad -9\,], Y = [\,8 \quad 9\,]$
4. $X = [\,-4 \quad -7\,], Y = [\,-4 \quad 6\,]$

Find $\overrightarrow{PQ} + \overrightarrow{RS}$.

5. $P(-1, -3), Q(8, -6), R(-5, -7), S(4, 2)$ **⟨18, 6⟩**
6. $P(0, 10), Q(-5, 2), R(-5, 0), S(3, 4)$ **⟨3, −4⟩**
7. $P(1, -6), Q(-9, 0), R(6, -6), S(1, 9)$ **⟨−15, 21⟩**
8. $P(5, -8), Q(2, 5), R(-6, 2), S(-7, 3)$ **⟨−4, 14⟩**

Vectors can be subtracted by using the same method as addition. Find $\overrightarrow{JK} - \overrightarrow{LM}$.

9. $J(7, -1), K(-3, 9), L(-9, 4), M(6, 0)$ **⟨−25, 14⟩**
10. $J(6, 7), K(10, -4), L(-2, 8), M(3, 1)$ **⟨−1, −4⟩**

11. **MAKE A CONJECTURE** Is addition of vectors commutative? Justify your reasoning. **See margin.**

12. **WRITING IN MATH** Explain how you could apply scalar multiplication of matrices to vectors. Describe how a vector is affected by scalar multiplication. **See margin.**

Practice Have students complete Exercises 1–12.

3 ASSESS

Formative Assessment

Use Exercise 1 to assess whether students understand how to determine the component form of a vector when given its endpoints.

From Concrete to Abstract

For Exercise 12, ask students to give a specific example to demonstrate the application of scalar multiplication to changing the size of a vector.

Additional Answers

3. ⟨16, 18⟩

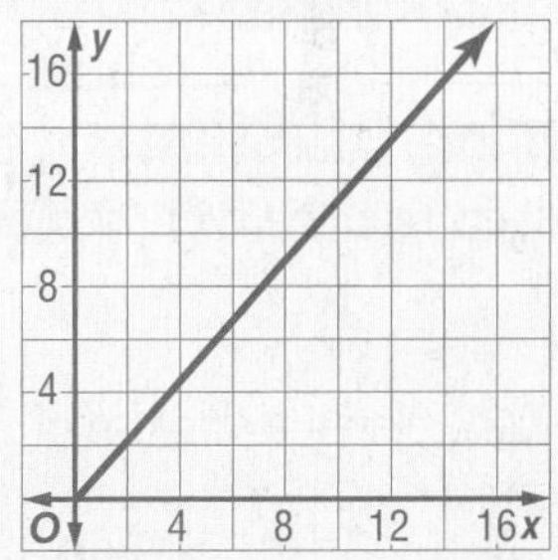

4. ⟨0, 13⟩

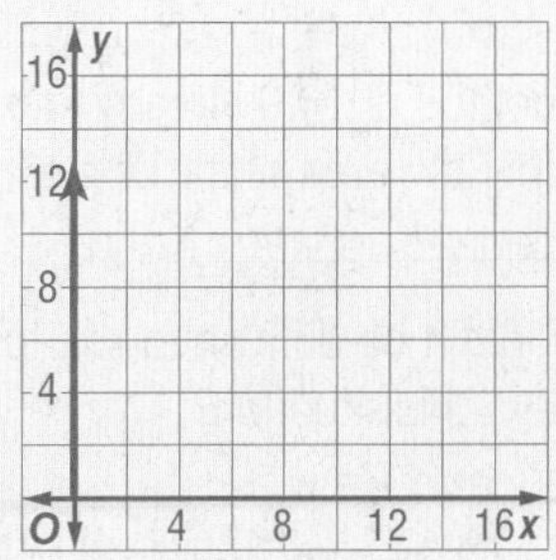

Additional Answers

11. Yes; Sample answer: Let $\overrightarrow{AB} = \langle x_1, y_1 \rangle$ and $\overrightarrow{CD} = \langle x_2, y_2 \rangle$. Then $\overrightarrow{AB} + \overrightarrow{CD} = \langle x_1 + x_2, y_1 + y_2 \rangle$ and $\overrightarrow{CD} + \overrightarrow{AB} = \langle x_2 + x_1, y_2 + y_1 \rangle$. Because $x_1 + x_2 = x_2 + x_1$ and $y_1 + y_2 = y_2 + y_1$, $\overrightarrow{AB} + \overrightarrow{CD} = \overrightarrow{CD} + \overrightarrow{AB}$.

12. Sample answer: A vector $\langle x, y \rangle$ can be represented by the matrix $\begin{bmatrix} x \\ y \end{bmatrix}$. So, $a\begin{bmatrix} x \\ y \end{bmatrix} = \begin{bmatrix} ax \\ ay \end{bmatrix}$ can be written as $\langle ax, ay \rangle$. When a vector is multiplied by a positive scalar, its magnitude changes, but its direction is the same. When a vector is multiplied by a negative scalar, its magnitude changes and its direction is opposite.

4-5 Lesson Notes

1 FOCUS

Vertical Alignment

Before Lesson 4-5
Solve systems of equations algebraically.

Lesson 4-5
Evaluate determinants.
Solve systems of linear equations by using Cramer's Rule.

After Lesson 4-5
Use matrices to solve systems of equations.

2 TEACH

Scaffolding Questions

Have students read the *Why?* section of the lesson.

Ask:

- How is GPS related to the use of coordinates? Sample answer: A GPS tracker shows the latitude and longitude coordinates of a point on Earth's surface.
- What method do you already know for finding the area of a triangle? the formula $A = \frac{1}{2}bh$
- Why would it be difficult to use this method in this situation? The height of the triangle would be difficult to find.

4-5 Determinants and Cramer's Rule

Then
You solved systems of equations algebraically. (Lesson 3-2)

Now
- Evaluate determinants.
- Solve systems of linear equations by using Cramer's Rule.

NGSSS
MA.912.A.3.14 Solve systems of linear equations and inequalities **in two and three variables using graphical,** substitution, and elimination **methods**.

New Vocabulary
determinant
second-order determinant
third-order determinant
diagonal rule
Cramer's Rule
coefficient matrix

FL Math Online
glencoe.com

Why?

A zoologist tagged a tiger with a GPS tracker so that she could determine the tiger's territory. After several days, the zoologist determined that the tiger's territory was a triangular region. By using the coordinates of the vertices of this triangle, she could use matrices and determinants to determine the size of the tiger's territory.

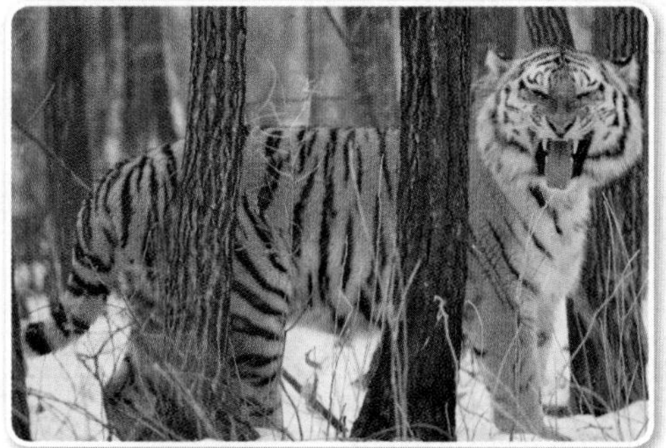

Determinants Every square matrix has a **determinant**. The determinant of a 2 × 2 matrix is called a **second-order determinant**.

Key Concept — Second-Order Determinant

Words The value of a second-order determinant is the difference of the products of the two diagonals.

Symbols $\det \begin{bmatrix} a & b \\ c & d \end{bmatrix} = \begin{vmatrix} a & b \\ c & d \end{vmatrix} = ad - bc$

Example $\begin{vmatrix} 4 & 5 \\ -3 & 6 \end{vmatrix} = 4(6) - (-3)(5) = 39$

EXAMPLE 1 Second-Order Determinant

Evaluate each determinant.

a. $\begin{vmatrix} 5 & -4 \\ 8 & 9 \end{vmatrix}$

$\begin{vmatrix} 5 & -4 \\ 8 & 9 \end{vmatrix} = 5(9) - 8(-4)$ — **Definition of determinant**

$= 45 + 32$ — **Simplify.**

$= 77$

b. $\begin{vmatrix} 0 & 6 \\ 4 & -11 \end{vmatrix}$

$\begin{vmatrix} 0 & 6 \\ 4 & -11 \end{vmatrix} = 0(-11) - 4(6)$ — **Definition of determinant**

$= 0 - 24$ — **Simplify.**

$= -24$

Guided Practice

1A. $\begin{vmatrix} -6 & -7 \\ 10 & 8 \end{vmatrix}$ 22

1B. $\begin{vmatrix} 7 & 5 \\ 9 & -4 \end{vmatrix}$ −73

Personal Tutor glencoe.com

Lesson 4-5 Resources

Resource	Approaching-Level	On-Level	Beyond-Level	English Learners
Teacher Edition	• Differentiated Instruction, p. 221	• Differentiated Instruction, pp. 221, 224	• Differentiated Instruction, pp. 224, 228	
Chapter Resource Masters	• Study Guide and Intervention, pp. 30–31 • Skills Practice, p. 32 • Practice, p. 33 • Word Problem Practice, p. 34	• Study Guide and Intervention, pp. 30–31 • Skills Practice, p. 32 • Practice, p. 33 • Word Problem Practice, p. 34 • Enrichment, p. 35 • Spreadsheet Activity, p. 36	• Practice, p. 33 • Word Problem Practice, p. 34 • Enrichment, p. 35	• Study Guide and Intervention, pp. 30–31 • Skills Practice, p. 32 • Practice, p. 33 • Word Problem Practice, p. 34
Transparencies	• 5-Minute Check Transparency 4-5	• 5-Minute Check Transparency 4-5	• 5-Minute Check Transparency 4-5	• 5-Minute Check Transparency 4-5
Other	• Study Notebook • Teaching Algebra with Manipulatives	• Study Notebook • Teaching Algebra with Manipulatives	• Study Notebook	• Study Notebook • Teaching Algebra with Manipulatives

StudyTip

Diagonal Rule The diagonal rule can only be used for 3×3 matrices.

Determinants of 3×3 matrices are called **third-order determinants**. They can be evaluated by using the **diagonal rule**.

Key Concept **Diagonal Rule**

Step 1 Rewrite the first two columns to the right of the determinant.

Step 2 Draw diagonals, beginning with the upper left-hand element. Multiply the elements in each diagonal. Repeat the process, beginning with the upper right-hand element.

Step 3 Find the sum of the products of the elements in each set of diagonals.

Step 4 Subtract the second sum from the first sum.

EXAMPLE 2 **Use Diagonals**

Evaluate $\begin{vmatrix} 4 & -8 & 3 \\ -3 & 2 & 6 \\ -4 & 5 & 9 \end{vmatrix}$ using diagonals.

Step 1 Rewrite the first two columns to the right of the determinant.

$$\left|\begin{matrix} 4 & -8 & 3 \\ -3 & 2 & 6 \\ -4 & 5 & 9 \end{matrix}\right| \begin{matrix} 4 & -8 \\ -3 & 2 \\ -4 & 5 \end{matrix}$$

Step 2 Find the products of the elements of the diagonals.

$$\left|\begin{matrix} 4 & -8 & 3 \\ -3 & 2 & 6 \\ -4 & 5 & 9 \end{matrix}\right| \begin{matrix} 4 & -8 \\ -3 & 2 \\ -4 & 5 \end{matrix} \qquad \left|\begin{matrix} 4 & -8 & 3 \\ -3 & 2 & 6 \\ -4 & 5 & 9 \end{matrix}\right| \begin{matrix} 4 & -8 \\ -3 & 2 \\ -4 & 5 \end{matrix}$$

$4(2)(9) = 72$ | $-4(2)(3) = -24$

$-8(6)(-4) = 192$ | $5(6)(4) = 120$

$3(-3)(5) = -45$ | $9(-3)(-8) = 216$

Step 3 Find the sum of each group.

$72 + 192 + (-45) = 219$ $\qquad$ $-24 + 120 + 216 = 312$

Step 4 Subtract the sum of the second group from the sum of the first group.

$219 - 312 = -93$

The value of the determinant is -93.

Guided Practice

Evaluate each determinant.

2A. $\begin{vmatrix} -5 & 9 & 4 \\ -2 & -1 & 5 \\ -4 & 6 & 2 \end{vmatrix}$ -48 $\qquad$ **2B.** $\begin{vmatrix} -8 & -4 & 4 \\ 0 & -5 & -8 \\ 3 & 4 & 1 \end{vmatrix}$ -60

Personal Tutor glencoe.com

Determinants

Example 1 shows how to find the value of a second-order determinant.
Example 2 shows how to use diagonals to evaluate a third-order determinant.
Example 3 shows how to use a determinant to evaluate the area of a triangle in a real-world situation.

Formative Assessment

Use the Guided Practice exercises after each example to determine students' understanding of concepts.

Additional Examples

1 Evaluate the determinant $\begin{vmatrix} 6 & 4 \\ -1 & 0 \end{vmatrix}$. 4

2 Evaluate $\begin{vmatrix} 3 & -2 & -1 \\ 2 & -1 & 0 \\ 1 & 2 & -3 \end{vmatrix}$ using diagonals. -8

Additional Examples also in Interactive Classroom PowerPoint® Presentations

IWB INTERACTIVE WHITEBOARD READY

TEACH with TECH

INTERACTIVE WHITEBOARD Work through several examples with the class, and save your work as several notes pages. At the end of class, email your notes to students or post them on a class Web page. This may help students to focus during the lesson rather than trying to copy the computations from the board.

Differentiated Instruction AL OL

If students are using evaluation by diagonals for the first time,

Then urge them to write down each step in the procedure. Have them compare their work with classmates to find any errors in either their calculations or their use of the procedure.

Additional Example

3 **SURVEYING** A surveying crew located three points on a map that formed the vertices of a triangular area. A coordinate grid in which one unit corresponds to 10 miles is placed over the map so that the vertices are located at (0, –1), (–2, –6), and (3, –2). Use a determinant to find the area of the triangle. 850 square miles

Focus on Mathematical Content

Determinants Every square matrix has a real number that is associated with it called the determinant of the matrix. The determinant of a 2×2 matrix is called a second-order determinant and is equal to the difference of the products of the elements on the two diagonals. The determinant of a 3×3 matrix is called a third-order determinant and can be evaluated using a method called the *diagonal rule.*

Watch Out!

Preventing Errors Have students make posters that show the process for finding the determinant of a 3×3 matrix, using colored markers to clearly identify the diagonals.

Determinants can also be used to find the areas of triangles. If the coordinates of the vertices of the triangle are known, the formula below can be used to calculate the area of the triangle.

Key Concept — Area of a Triangle

Words The area of a triangle with vertices (a, b), (c, d), and (e, f) is $|A|$, where

$$A = \frac{1}{2}\begin{vmatrix} a & b & 1 \\ c & d & 1 \\ e & f & 1 \end{vmatrix}.$$

Example $A = \frac{1}{2}\begin{vmatrix} -4 & 3 & 1 \\ 3 & 1 & 1 \\ -2 & -2 & 1 \end{vmatrix}$

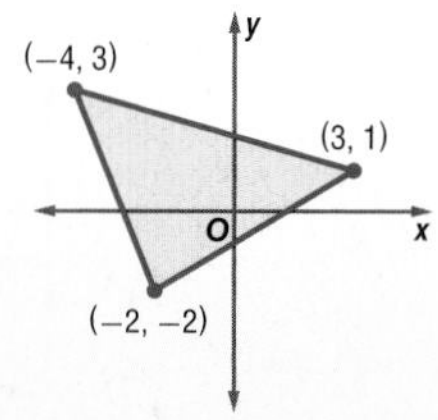

Real-World Link

Tigers are very territorial, solitary animals. Their territories can measure up to 100 square kilometers.

Source: *National Geographic*

Real-World EXAMPLE 3 Use Determinants

ZOOLOGY Refer to the application at the beginning of the lesson. The coordinates of the vertices of the tiger's territory are shown to the right. Use determinants to find the area of the tiger's territory.

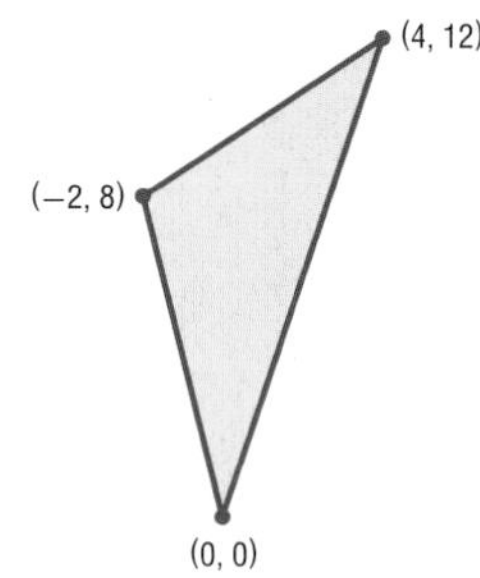

$$A = \frac{1}{2}\begin{vmatrix} a & b & 1 \\ c & d & 1 \\ e & f & 1 \end{vmatrix}$$

$$= \frac{1}{2}\begin{vmatrix} 0 & 0 & 1 \\ 4 & 12 & 1 \\ -2 & 8 & 1 \end{vmatrix}$$ **(a, b) = (0, 0)**, **(c, d) = (4, 12)**, **(e, f) = (–2, 8)**

$$\left|\begin{matrix} 0 & 0 & 1 \\ 4 & 12 & 1 \\ -2 & 8 & 1 \end{matrix}\right|\begin{matrix} 0 & 0 \\ 4 & 12 \\ -2 & 8 \end{matrix} \qquad \left|\begin{matrix} 0 & 0 & 1 \\ 4 & 12 & 1 \\ -2 & 8 & 1 \end{matrix}\right|\begin{matrix} 0 & 0 \\ 4 & 12 \\ -2 & 8 \end{matrix}$$ **Diagonal Rule**

$0 + 0 + 32 = 32$ $\qquad -24 + 0 + 0 = -24$ **Sum of products of diagonals**

$$A = \frac{1}{2}\begin{vmatrix} 0 & 0 & 1 \\ 4 & 12 & 1 \\ -2 & 8 & 1 \end{vmatrix}$$ **Area of a Triangle**

$$= \left(\frac{1}{2}\right)[32 - (-24)] \text{ or } 28$$ **Simplify.**

The area of the tiger's territory is 28 square kilometers.

Guided Practice

3. CAR WASH To raise money for their rowing club, Hannah, Christina, and Dario are advertising a car wash at three different street corners in a neighborhood. On a map, the coordinates for the corners are (3, 15), (6, 4), and (11, 9). Each unit represents 0.5 kilometer. What is the area of the neighborhood in which they are advertising? 8.75 km^2

Personal Tutor glencoe.com

ReadingMath

Determinants The determinant is used to *determine* whether a system has a unique solution.

Cramer's Rule You can use determinants to solve systems of equations. If a determinant is nonzero, then the system has a unique solution. If a determinant is 0, then the system either has no solution or infinite solutions. A method called **Cramer's Rule** uses the coefficient matrix. The **coefficient matrix** is a matrix that contains only the coefficients of the system.

Key Concept Cramer's Rule

Let C be the coefficient matrix of the system $\begin{aligned} ax + by &= m \\ fx + gy &= n \end{aligned} \rightarrow \begin{vmatrix} a & b \\ f & g \end{vmatrix}$

The solution of this system is $x = \dfrac{\begin{vmatrix} m & b \\ n & g \end{vmatrix}}{|C|}$ and $y = \dfrac{\begin{vmatrix} a & m \\ f & n \end{vmatrix}}{|C|}$, if $C \neq 0$.

StudyTip

Cramer's Rule When the determinant of the coefficient matrix C is 0, the system does not have a unique solution.

EXAMPLE 4 Solve a System of Two Equations

Solve the system by using Cramer's Rule.

$5x - 6y = 15$
$3x + 4y = -29$

$x = \dfrac{\begin{vmatrix} m & b \\ n & g \end{vmatrix}}{\lvert C\rvert}$	**Cramer's Rule**	$y = \dfrac{\begin{vmatrix} a & m \\ f & n \end{vmatrix}}{\lvert C\rvert}$
$= \dfrac{\begin{vmatrix} 15 & -6 \\ -29 & 4 \end{vmatrix}}{\begin{vmatrix} 5 & -6 \\ 3 & 4 \end{vmatrix}}$	**Substitute values.**	$= \dfrac{\begin{vmatrix} 5 & 15 \\ 3 & -29 \end{vmatrix}}{\begin{vmatrix} 5 & -6 \\ 3 & 4 \end{vmatrix}}$
$= \dfrac{15(4) - (-29)(-6)}{5(4) - (3)(-6)}$	**Evaluate.**	$= \dfrac{5(-29) - 3(15)}{5(4) - (3)(-6)}$
$= \dfrac{60 - 174}{20 + 18}$	**Multiply.**	$= \dfrac{-145 - 45}{20 + 18}$
$= -\dfrac{114}{38}$	**Add and subtract.**	$= -\dfrac{190}{38}$
$= -3$	**Simplify.**	$= -5$

The solution of the system is $(-3, -5)$.

CHECK

$5(-3) - 6(-5) \stackrel{?}{=} 15$	$x = -3, y = -5$
$-15 + 30 \stackrel{?}{=} 15$	**Simplify.**
$15 = 15$ ✓	
$3(-3) + 4(-5) \stackrel{?}{=} -29$	$x = -3, y = -5$
$-9 - 20 \stackrel{?}{=} -29$	**Simplify.**
$-29 = -29$ ✓	

Guided Practice

Solve each system using Cramer's Rule.

4A. $7x + 3y = 37$ (4, 3)
$-5x - 7y = -41$

4B. $8x - 5y = 70$ (5, −6)
$9x + 7y = 3$

Personal Tutor glencoe.com

Cramer's Rule

Example 4 shows how to use Cramer's Rule to solve a system of two linear equations. **Example 5** shows how to use Cramer's Rule to solve a system of three linear equations.

Additional Example

4 Use Cramer's Rule to solve the system of equation.

$5x + 4y = 28$
$3x - 2y = 8$

(4, 2)

Additional Example

5 Solve the system by using Cramer's Rule.

$2x + y - z = -2$

$-x + 2y + z = -0.5$

$x + y + 2z = 3.5$

(0.5, –1, 2)

Watch Out!

Preventing Errors When solving a system of three equations in three variables, it is important to point out that the numerator for x is found by replacing the coefficients of x with the constant terms of the system. Similarly, the numerators for y and z are found by replacing the coefficients of y and z, respectively, with the constant terms of the system.

Focus on Mathematical Content

Cramer's Rule One advantage of using Cramer's rule to solve a system of three linear equations in three variables is that if the system has a unique solution, Cramer's rule can give the value of any one of the variables without having to solve for the others. If the determinant is zero, then Cramer's rule does not give the solution, but it does indicate that the system is either dependent or inconsistent.

Cramer's Rule can also be used for systems of three equations.

Key Concept

Cramer's Rule for a System of Three Equations

Let C be the coefficient matrix of the system $\begin{aligned} ax + by + cz &= m \\ fx + gy + hz &= n \\ jx + ky + \ell z &= p \end{aligned} \rightarrow \begin{vmatrix} a & b & c \\ f & g & h \\ j & k & \ell \end{vmatrix}$.

The solution of this system is $x = \dfrac{\begin{vmatrix} m & b & c \\ n & g & h \\ p & k & \ell \end{vmatrix}}{|C|}$, $y = \dfrac{\begin{vmatrix} a & m & c \\ f & n & h \\ j & p & \ell \end{vmatrix}}{|C|}$,

and $z = \dfrac{\begin{vmatrix} a & b & m \\ f & g & n \\ j & k & p \end{vmatrix}}{|C|}$, if $C \neq 0$.

EXAMPLE 5 Solve a System of Three Equations

Solve the system by using Cramer's Rule.

$4x + 5y - 6z = -14$
$3x - 2y + 7z = 47$
$7x - 6y - 8z = 15$

$$x = \frac{\begin{vmatrix} m & b & c \\ n & g & h \\ p & k & \ell \end{vmatrix}}{|C|} = \frac{\begin{vmatrix} -14 & 5 & -6 \\ 47 & -2 & 7 \\ 15 & -6 & -8 \end{vmatrix}}{\begin{vmatrix} 4 & 5 & -6 \\ 3 & -2 & 7 \\ 7 & -6 & -8 \end{vmatrix}} = \frac{3105}{621} \text{ or } 5$$

$$y = \frac{\begin{vmatrix} a & m & c \\ f & n & h \\ j & p & \ell \end{vmatrix}}{|C|} = \frac{\begin{vmatrix} 4 & -14 & -6 \\ 3 & 47 & 7 \\ 7 & 15 & -8 \end{vmatrix}}{\begin{vmatrix} 4 & 5 & -6 \\ 3 & -2 & 7 \\ 7 & -6 & -8 \end{vmatrix}} = -\frac{1242}{621} \text{ or } -2$$

$$z = \frac{\begin{vmatrix} a & b & m \\ f & g & n \\ j & k & p \end{vmatrix}}{|C|} = \frac{\begin{vmatrix} 4 & 5 & -14 \\ 3 & -2 & 47 \\ 7 & -6 & 15 \end{vmatrix}}{\begin{vmatrix} 4 & 5 & -6 \\ 3 & -2 & 7 \\ 7 & -6 & -8 \end{vmatrix}} = \frac{2484}{621} \text{ or } 4$$

The solution of the system is (5, –2, 4).

CHECK

$4(5) + 5(-2) - 6(4) \stackrel{?}{=} -14$
$20 - 10 - 24 \stackrel{?}{=} -14$
$-14 = -14$ ✓

$3(5) - 2(-2) + 7(4) \stackrel{?}{=} 47$
$15 + 4 + 28 \stackrel{?}{=} 47$
$47 = 47$ ✓

$7(5) - 6(-2) - 8(4) \stackrel{?}{=} 15$
$35 + 12 - 32 \stackrel{?}{=} 15$
$15 = 15$ ✓

StudyTip

Check for Accuracy Always substitute your answers into the initial equations to confirm accuracy.

Guided Practice

Solve each system using Cramer's Rule.

5A. $3x + 5y + 2z = -7$
$-4x + 3y - 5z = -19$
$5x + 4y - 7z = -15$
$\left(\frac{23}{22}, -\frac{57}{22}, \frac{31}{22}\right)$

5B. $6x + 5y + 2z = -1$
$-x + 3y + 7z = 12$
$5x - 7y - 3z = -52$
(–4, 5, –1)

Personal Tutor glencoe.com

Differentiated Instruction OL BL

If students wish to review the process of the manipulation of matrices,

Then ask students to write a brief reflection on their reactions to the various methods they have learned involving the manipulation of matrices. Ask them to comment on what aspects they found efficient and helpful, and what aspects they found to be difficult or confusing.

Check Your Understanding

Example 1 p. 220

Evaluate each determinant.

1. $\begin{vmatrix} 8 & 6 \\ 5 & 7 \end{vmatrix}$ **26**
2. $\begin{vmatrix} -6 & -6 \\ 8 & 10 \end{vmatrix}$ **−12**
3. $\begin{vmatrix} -4 & 12 \\ 9 & 5 \end{vmatrix}$ **−128**
4. $\begin{vmatrix} 16 & -10 \\ -8 & 5 \end{vmatrix}$ **0**

Example 2 p. 221

Evaluate each determinant using diagonals.

5. $\begin{vmatrix} 3 & -2 & 2 \\ -4 & 2 & -5 \\ -3 & 1 & 4 \end{vmatrix}$ **−19**
6. $\begin{vmatrix} 2 & -3 & 5 \\ -4 & 6 & -2 \\ 4 & -1 & -6 \end{vmatrix}$ **−80**
7. $\begin{vmatrix} 8 & 4 & 0 \\ -2 & -6 & -1 \\ 5 & -3 & 6 \end{vmatrix}$ **−284**
8. $\begin{vmatrix} -5 & -3 & 4 \\ -2 & -4 & -3 \\ 8 & -2 & 4 \end{vmatrix}$ **302**
9. $\begin{vmatrix} 8 & 3 & 4 \\ 2 & 4 & 2 \\ 1 & 6 & 5 \end{vmatrix}$ **72**
10. $\begin{vmatrix} -4 & 3 & 0 \\ 1 & 5 & -2 \\ -1 & -8 & -3 \end{vmatrix}$ **139**
11. $\begin{vmatrix} 2 & -6 & -3 \\ 7 & 9 & -4 \\ -6 & 4 & 9 \end{vmatrix}$ **182**
12. $\begin{vmatrix} -5 & -6 & 7 \\ 4 & 0 & 5 \\ -3 & 8 & 2 \end{vmatrix}$ **562**

Example 3 p. 222

Use Cramer's Rule to solve each system of equations.

13. $4x - 5y = 39$, $3x + 8y = -6$ **(6, −3)**
14. $5x + 6y = 20$, $-3x - 7y = -29$ **(−2, 5)**
15. $-8a - 5b = -27$, $7a + 6b = 22$ **(4, −1)**
16. $10c - 7d = -59$, $6c + 5d = -63$ **(−8, −3)**

Examples 4 and 5 pp. 223–224

17. **GEOGRAPHY** The "Bermuda Triangle" is an area located off the southeastern Atlantic coast of the United States, and noted for reports of unexplained losses of ships, small boats, and aircraft. **a. 15.75 units²**
    a. Find the area of the triangle on the map.
    b. Suppose each grid represents 175 miles. What is the area of the Bermuda Triangle? **482,343.75 mi²**

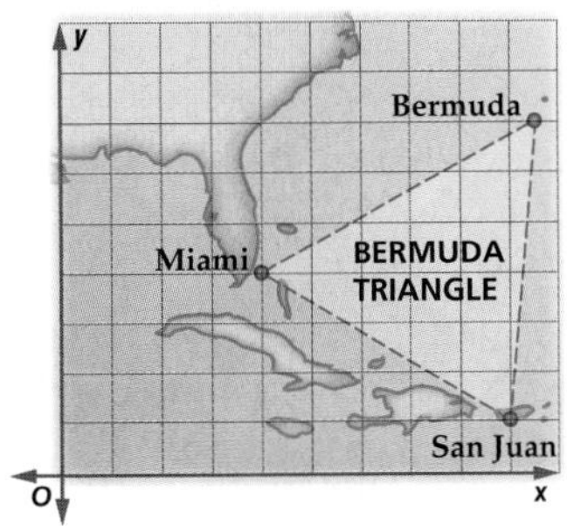

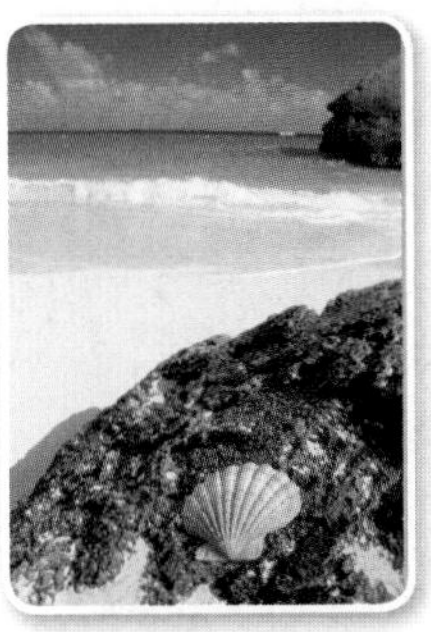

Real-World Link

The Bermuda Islands is a British territory located about 640 miles from Cape Hatteras, North Carolina. Although commonly referred to just as Bermuda, the territory consists of about 140 islands.

Use Cramer's Rule to solve each system of equations.

18. $4x - 2y + 7z = 26$, $5x + 3y - 5z = -50$, $-7x - 8y - 3z = 49$ **(−3, −5, 4)**
19. $-3x - 5y + 10z = -4$, $-8x + 2y - 3z = -91$, $6x + 8y - 7z = -35$ **$\left(\frac{66}{7}, -\frac{116}{7}, -\frac{41}{7}\right)$**
20. $6x - 5y + 2z = -49$, $-5x - 3y - 8z = -22$, $-3x + 8y - 5z = 55$ **(−3, 7, 2)**
21. $-9x + 5y + 3z = 50$, $7x + 8y - 2z = -60$, $-5x + 7y + 5z = 46$ **(−4, −2, 8)**
22. $x + 2y = 12$, $3y - 4z = 25$, $x + 6y + z = 20$ **(6, 3, −4)**
23. $9a + 7b = -30$, $8b + 5c = 11$, $-3a + 10c = 73$ **(−1, −3, 7)**
24. $2n + 3p - 4w = 20$, $4n - p + 5w = 13$, $3n + 2p + 4w = 15$ **(5, 2, −1)**
25. $x + y + z = 12$, $6x - 2y - z = 16$, $3x + 4y + 2z = 28$ **(4, 0, 8)**

3 PRACTICE

Formative Assessment

Use Exercises 1–25 to check for understanding.

Use the chart at the bottom of the next page to customize assignments for your students.

Tips for New Teachers

Sense-Making Remind students that Cramer's Rule does not apply when the determinant of the coefficient matrix is 0, because the solution would have a denominator of 0, which is undefined.

Watch Out!

Error Analysis In Exercise 58, remind students that products along "upward-sloping" diagonals are subtracted when evaluating a determinant.

Additional Answers

56a. $\begin{vmatrix} a & b \\ f & g \end{vmatrix} = ag - bf$; If $ag - bf = 0$, then $ag = bf$.

56b. Sample answer: $x + 3y = 8$ and $2x + 6y = 12$; The system is dependent or inconsistent depending on the values of m and n.

60a. Sample answer: $\begin{bmatrix} 6 & 7 \\ 6 & 7 \end{bmatrix}$

60b. Sample answer: $\begin{bmatrix} 4 & 3 \\ -3 & 4 \end{bmatrix}$

60c. Sample answer: $\begin{bmatrix} -4 & -6 \\ -8 & -4 \end{bmatrix}$

Practice and Problem Solving

= **Step-by-Step Solutions** begin on page R20.
Extra Practice begins on page 947.

Examples 1 and 2 pp. 220–221

Evaluate each determinant.

26. $\begin{vmatrix} -7 & 12 \\ 5 & 6 \end{vmatrix}$ −102

27. $\begin{vmatrix} -8 & -9 \\ 11 & 12 \end{vmatrix}$ 3

28. $\begin{vmatrix} -5 & 8 \\ -6 & -7 \end{vmatrix}$ 83

29. $\begin{vmatrix} 3 & 5 & -2 \\ -1 & -4 & 6 \\ -6 & -2 & 5 \end{vmatrix}$ −135

30. $\begin{vmatrix} 2 & 0 & -6 \\ -3 & -4 & -5 \\ -2 & 5 & 8 \end{vmatrix}$ 124

31. $\begin{vmatrix} -5 & -1 & -2 \\ 1 & 8 & 4 \\ 0 & -6 & 9 \end{vmatrix}$ −459

32. $\begin{vmatrix} 6 & -3 & -5 \\ 0 & -7 & 0 \\ 3 & -6 & -4 \end{vmatrix}$ 63

33. $\begin{vmatrix} -8 & -3 & -9 \\ 0 & 0 & 0 \\ 8 & -2 & -4 \end{vmatrix}$ 0

34. $\begin{vmatrix} 1 & 6 & 7 \\ -2 & -5 & -8 \\ 4 & 4 & 9 \end{vmatrix}$ −13

35. $\begin{vmatrix} 1 & -8 & -9 \\ 6 & 5 & -6 \\ -2 & -8 & 10 \end{vmatrix}$ 728

36. $\begin{vmatrix} 5 & -5 & -5 \\ -8 & -3 & -2 \\ -2 & 4 & 6 \end{vmatrix}$ −120

37. $\begin{vmatrix} -4 & 1 & -2 \\ 10 & 12 & 9 \\ -6 & 0 & 13 \end{vmatrix}$ −952

38. TRAVEL Mr. Smith's art class took a bus trip to an art museum. The bus averaged 65 miles per hour on the highway and 25 miles per hour in the city. The art museum is 375 miles away from the school, and it took the class 7 hours to get there. Use Cramer's Rule to find how many hours the bus was on the highway and how many hours it was driving in the city. 5 hours on the highway, 2 hours in the city

Examples 3 and 5 pp. 222–224

Use Cramer's Rule to solve each system of equations.

39. $6x - 5y = 73$, $-7x + 3y = -71$ (8, −5)

40. $10a - 3b = -34$, $3a + 8b = -28$ (−4, −2)

41. $-4c - 5d = -39$, $5c + 8d = 54$ (6, 3)

42. $-6f - 8g = -22$, $-11f + 5g = -60$ (5, −1)

43. $9r + 4s = -55$, $-5r - 3s = 36$ (−3, −7)

44. $-11u - 7v = 4$, $9u + 4v = -24$ (−8, 12)

45. $5x - 4y + 6z = 58$, $-4x + 6y + 3z = -13$, $6x + 3y + 7z = 53$ (4, −2, 5)

46. $8x - 4y + 7z = 34$, $5x + 6y + 3z = -21$, $3x + 7y - 8z = -85$ (−3, −4, 6)

Real-World Link

Archaeologists use grids at digs to record the locations of their finds.

Source: College of Staten Island Library

47. DOUGHNUTS Mi-Ling is ordering doughnuts for a class party. The box contains 2 dozen doughnuts, some of which are plain and some of which are jelly-filled. The plain doughnuts each cost \$0.50, and the jelly-filled cost \$0.60. If the total cost is \$12.60, use Cramer's Rule to find how many jelly-filled doughnuts Mi-Ling ordered. 6

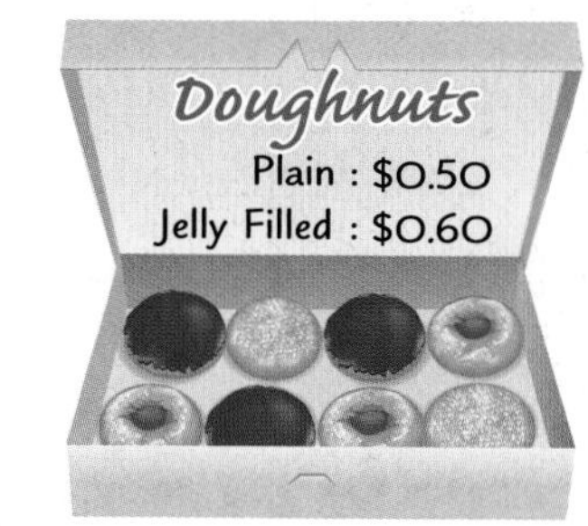

Example 4 p. 223

48. MOVIES The salary for each of the stars of a new movie is \$5 million, and the supporting actors each receive \$1 million. The total amount spent for the salaries of the actors and actresses is \$19 million. If the cast has 7 members, use Cramer's Rule to find the number of stars in the movie. 3

49. ARCHAEOLOGY Archaeologists found whale bones at coordinates (0, 3), (4, 7), and (5, 9). If the units of the coordinates are meters, find the area of the triangle formed by these finds. 2 m^2

Differentiated Homework Options

Level	Assignment	Two-Day Option	
AL Basic	26–49, 56–58, 60–76	27–49 odd, 62–65	26–48 even, 56–58, 60–61, 66–76
OL Core	27–53 odd, 54–58, 60, 76	26–49, 62–65	50–58, 60–61, 66–76
BL Advanced	50–73, (optional: 74–76)		

B Use Cramer's Rule to solve each system of equations. 53. $\left(-\frac{6187}{701}, -\frac{2904}{701}, -\frac{4212}{701}\right)$

50. $6a - 7b = -55$ **(−1, 7, −3)**
$2a + 4b - 3c = 35$
$-5a - 3b + 7c = -37$

51. $3a - 5b - 9c = 17$ **(4, 8, −5)**
$4a - 3c = 31$
$-5a - 4b - 2c = -42$

52. $4x - 5y = -2$ **(−8, −6, 3)**
$7x + 3z = -47$
$8y - 5z = -63$

53. $7x + 8y + 9z = -149$
$-6x + 7y - 5z = 54$
$4x + 5y - 2z = -44$

54. GARDENING Rob wants to build a triangular flower garden. To plan out his garden he uses a coordinate grid where each of the squares represents one square foot. The coordinates for the vertices of his garden are (−1, 7), (2, 6), and (4, −3). Find the area of the garden. **12.5 ft²**

Real-World Link

Names for soft drinks vary widely depending on where you live. *Soda* is popular in the southwest and northeast United States; *pop* is used more in the northwest and midwest; *coke* is common in the south.

C **55 FINANCIAL LITERACY** A vendor sells small drinks for \$1.15, medium drinks for \$1.75, and large drinks for \$2.25. During a week in which he sold twice as many small drinks as medium drinks, his total sales were \$2,238.75 for 1385 drinks.

a. Use Cramer's Rule to determine how many of each drink were sold.

b. The vendor decided to increase the price for small drinks to \$1.25 the next week. The next week, he sold 140 fewer small drinks, 125 more medium drinks, and 35 more large drinks. Calculate his sales for that week. **\$2426.25**

c. Was raising the price of the small drink a good business move for the vendor? Explain your reasoning.

55a. small: 650; medium: 325; large: 410
55c. It seems like it was a good move for the vendor. Although he sold fewer small drinks, he sold more medium and large drinks and on the whole, made more money this week than in the previous week.
57. Sample answer: There is no unique solution of the system. There are either infinite or no solutions.
61. Sample answer: Given a 2 × 2 system of linear equations, if the determinant of the matrix of coefficients is 0, then the system does not have a unique solution. The system may have no solution and the graphical representation shows two parallel lines. The system may have infinitely many solutions in which the graphical representation will be the same line.

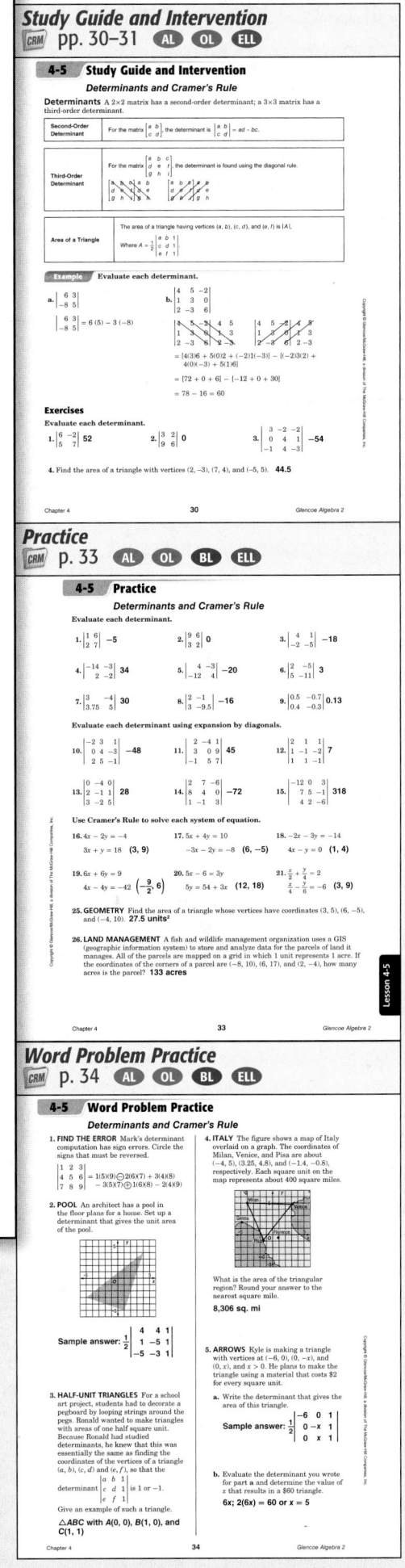

H.O.T. Problems
Use Higher-Order Thinking Skills

56. REASONING Some systems of equations cannot be solved by using Cramer's Rule.

a. Find the value of $\begin{vmatrix} a & b \\ f & g \end{vmatrix}$. When is the value 0? **a, b. See margin.**

b. Choose values for $a, b, f,$ and g to make the determinant of the coefficient matrix 0. What type of system is formed?

57. REASONING What can you determine about the solution of a system of linear equations if the determinant of the coefficients is 0?

58. ERROR ANALYSIS James and Amber are finding the value of $\begin{vmatrix} 8 & 3 \\ -5 & 2 \end{vmatrix}$.
James; because 3(−5) = −15

James	Amber
$\begin{vmatrix} 8 & 3 \\ -5 & 2 \end{vmatrix} = 16 - (-15)$ $= 31$	$\begin{vmatrix} 8 & 3 \\ -5 & 2 \end{vmatrix} = 16 - 15$ $= 1$

Is either of them correct? Explain your reasoning.

59. CHALLENGE Find the determinant of a 3 × 3 matrix defined by

$$a_{mn} = \begin{cases} 0 & \text{if } m + n \text{ is even} \\ m + n & \text{if } m + n \text{ is odd} \end{cases}. \quad \mathbf{0}$$

60. OPEN ENDED Write a 2 × 2 matrix with each of the following characteristics.

a. The determinant equals 0. **a–c. See margin.**

b. The determinant equals 25.

c. The elements are all negative numbers and the determinant equals −32.

61. WRITING IN MATH Describe the possible graphical representations of a 2 × 2 system of linear equations if the determinant of the matrix of coefficients is 0.

Study Guide and Intervention
CRM pp. 30–31 AL OL ELL

4-5 Study Guide and Intervention

Determinants and Cramer's Rule

Determinants A 2×2 matrix has a second-order determinant; a 3×3 matrix has a third-order determinant.

Second-Order Determinant	For the matrix $\begin{bmatrix} a & b \\ c & d \end{bmatrix}$, the determinant is $\begin{vmatrix} a & b \\ c & d \end{vmatrix} = ad - bc$.
Third-Order Determinant	For the matrix $\begin{bmatrix} a & b & c \\ d & e & f \\ g & h & i \end{bmatrix}$, the determinant is found using the diagonal rule. $\begin{bmatrix} a & b & c \\ d & e & f \\ g & h & i \end{bmatrix} \begin{matrix} a & b \\ d & e \\ g & h \end{matrix}$ $\begin{bmatrix} a & b & c \\ d & e & f \\ g & h & i \end{bmatrix} \begin{matrix} a & b \\ d & e \\ g & h \end{matrix}$
Area of a Triangle	The area of a triangle having vertices (a, b), (c, d), and (e, f) is $\lvert A \rvert$, Where $A = \frac{1}{2}\begin{vmatrix} a & b & 1 \\ c & d & 1 \\ e & f & 1 \end{vmatrix}$.

Example Evaluate each determinant.

a. $\begin{vmatrix} 6 & 3 \\ -8 & 5 \end{vmatrix}$

$\begin{vmatrix} 6 & 3 \\ -8 & 5 \end{vmatrix} = 6(5) - 3(-8)$

b. $\begin{vmatrix} 4 & 5 & -2 \\ 1 & 3 & 0 \\ 2 & -3 & 6 \end{vmatrix}$

$\begin{vmatrix} 4 & 5 & -2 \\ 1 & 3 & 0 \\ 2 & -3 & 6 \end{vmatrix} \begin{matrix} 4 & 5 \\ 1 & 3 \\ 2 & -3 \end{matrix}$ $\begin{vmatrix} 4 & 5 & -2 \\ 1 & 3 & 0 \\ 2 & -3 & 6 \end{vmatrix} \begin{matrix} 4 & 5 \\ 1 & 3 \\ 2 & -3 \end{matrix}$

$= [4(3)6 + 5(0)2 + (-2)1(-3)] - [(-2)3(2) + 4(0)(-3) + 5(1)6]$

$= [72 + 0 + 6] - [-12 + 0 + 30]$

$= 78 - 16 = 60$

Exercises

Evaluate each determinant.

1. $\begin{vmatrix} 6 & -2 \\ 5 & 7 \end{vmatrix}$ **52** **2.** $\begin{vmatrix} 3 & 2 \\ 9 & 6 \end{vmatrix}$ **0** **3.** $\begin{vmatrix} 3 & -2 & -2 \\ 0 & 4 & 1 \\ -1 & 4 & -3 \end{vmatrix}$ **−54**

4. Find the area of a triangle with vertices (2, −3), (7, 4), and (−5, 5). **44.5**

Practice
CRM p. 33 AL OL BL ELL

4-5 Practice

Determinants and Cramer's Rule

Evaluate each determinant.

1. $\begin{vmatrix} 1 & 6 \\ 2 & 7 \end{vmatrix}$ **−5** **2.** $\begin{vmatrix} 9 & 6 \\ 3 & 2 \end{vmatrix}$ **0** **3.** $\begin{vmatrix} 4 & 1 \\ -2 & -5 \end{vmatrix}$ **−18**

4. $\begin{vmatrix} -14 & -3 \\ 2 & -2 \end{vmatrix}$ **34** **5.** $\begin{vmatrix} 4 & -3 \\ -12 & 4 \end{vmatrix}$ **−20** **6.** $\begin{vmatrix} 2 & -5 \\ 5 & -11 \end{vmatrix}$ **3**

7. $\begin{vmatrix} 3 & -4 \\ 3.75 & 5 \end{vmatrix}$ **30** **8.** $\begin{vmatrix} 2 & -1 \\ 3 & -9.5 \end{vmatrix}$ **−16** **9.** $\begin{vmatrix} 0.5 & -0.7 \\ 0.4 & -0.3 \end{vmatrix}$ **0.13**

Evaluate each determinant using expansion by diagonals.

10. $\begin{vmatrix} -2 & 3 & 1 \\ 0 & 4 & -3 \\ 2 & 5 & -1 \end{vmatrix}$ **−48** **11.** $\begin{vmatrix} 2 & -4 & 1 \\ 3 & 0 & 9 \\ -1 & 5 & 7 \end{vmatrix}$ **45** **12.** $\begin{vmatrix} 2 & 1 & 1 \\ 1 & -1 & -2 \\ 1 & 1 & -1 \end{vmatrix}$ **7**

13. $\begin{vmatrix} 0 & -4 & 0 \\ 2 & -1 & 1 \\ 3 & -2 & 5 \end{vmatrix}$ **28** **14.** $\begin{vmatrix} 2 & 7 & -6 \\ 8 & 4 & 0 \\ 1 & -1 & 3 \end{vmatrix}$ **−72** **15.** $\begin{vmatrix} -12 & 0 & 3 \\ 7 & 5 & -1 \\ 4 & 2 & -6 \end{vmatrix}$ **318**

Use Cramer's Rule to solve each system of equation.

16. $4x - 2y = -4$, $3x + y = 18$ **(3, 9)** **17.** $5x + 4y = 10$, $-3x - 2y = -8$ **(6, −5)** **18.** $-2x - 3y = -14$, $4x - y = 0$ **(1, 4)**

19. $6x + 6y = 9$, $4x - 4y = -42$ $\left(-\frac{9}{2}, 6\right)$ **20.** $5x - 6 = 3y$, $5y = 54 + 3x$ **(12, 18)** **21.** $\frac{x}{2} + \frac{y}{4} = 2$, $\frac{x}{4} - \frac{y}{6} = -6$ **(3, 9)**

25. GEOMETRY Find the area of a triangle whose vertices have coordinates (3, 5), (6, −5), and (−4, 10). **27.5 units²**

26. LAND MANAGEMENT A fish and wildlife management organization uses a GIS (geographic information system) to store and analyze data for the parcels of land it manages. All of the parcels are mapped on a grid in which 1 unit represents 1 acre. If the coordinates of the corners of a parcel are (−8, 10), (6, 17), and (2, −4), how many acres is the parcel? **133 acres**

Lesson 4-5

Word Problem Practice
CRM p. 34 AL OL BL ELL

4-5 Word Problem Practice

Determinants and Cramer's Rule

1. FIND THE ERROR Mark's determinant computation has sign errors. Circle the signs that must be reversed.

$\begin{vmatrix} 1 & 2 & 3 \\ 4 & 5 & 6 \\ 7 & 8 & 9 \end{vmatrix} = 1(5)(9) \ominus 2(6)(7) + 3(4)(8) - 3(5)(7) \oplus 1(6)(8) - 2(4)(9)$

2. POOL An architect has a pool in the floor plans for a home. Set up a determinant that gives the unit area of the pool.

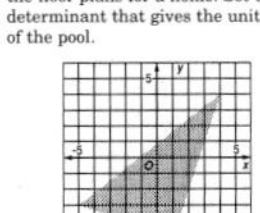

Sample answer: $\frac{1}{2}\begin{vmatrix} 4 & 4 & 1 \\ 1 & -5 & 1 \\ -5 & -3 & 1 \end{vmatrix}$

3. HALF-UNIT TRIANGLES For a school art project, students had to decorate a pegboard by looping strings around the pegs. Ronald wanted to make triangles with areas of one half square unit. Because Ronald had studied determinants, he knew that this was essentially the same as finding the coordinates of the vertices of a triangle (a, b), (c, d) and (e, f), so that the determinant $\begin{vmatrix} a & b & 1 \\ c & d & 1 \\ e & f & 1 \end{vmatrix}$ is 1 or −1.

Give an example of such a triangle.

△ABC with A(0, 0), B(1, 0), and C(1, 1)

4. ITALY The figure shows a map of Italy overlaid on a graph. The coordinates of Milan, Venice, and Pisa are about (−4, 5), (3.25, 4.8), and (−1.4, −0.8), respectively. Each square unit on the map represents about 400 square miles.

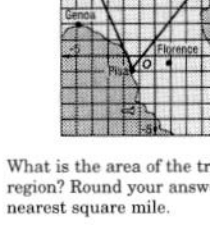

What is the area of the triangular region? Round your answer to the nearest square mile.

8,306 sq. mi

5. ARROWS Kyle is making a triangle with vertices at (−6, 0), (0, −x), and (0, x), and x > 0. He plans to make the triangle using a material that costs \$2 for every square unit.

a. Write the determinant that gives the area of this triangle.

Sample answer: $\frac{1}{2}\begin{vmatrix} -6 & 0 & 1 \\ 0 & -x & 1 \\ 0 & x & 1 \end{vmatrix}$

b. Evaluate the determinant you wrote for part **a** and determine the value of x that results in a \$60 triangle.

6x; 2(6x) = 60 or x = 5

Enrichment
CRM p. 35 OL BL

4-5 Enrichment

Matrix Transpose and Determinants

In Lesson 4-1, you learned how to represent information in matrices. A matrix contains elements of the form a_{ij} where i is the row number of the element and j is the columns number of the element.

Consider the following matrix.

$A = \begin{bmatrix} 2 & -1 \\ 3 & 4 \end{bmatrix}$

In this matrix, $a_{11} = 2$, $a_{12} = -1$, $a_{21} = 3$, and $a_{22} = 4$.

The matrix transpose can be found by switching the elements around. Element a_{ij} becomes element a_{ji}. So, the matrix transpose of A, denoted by A^T is:

$A^T = \begin{bmatrix} 2 & 3 \\ -1 & 4 \end{bmatrix}$

Calculate the determinant of A and A^T.

$\det(A) = 2(4) - 3(-1) = 11$

$\det(A^T) = 2(4) - (-1)(3) = 11$

1. Find each matrix transpose.

Tips for New Teachers

Vocabulary Point out to students that "lateral" means "side." Lateral area refers to the sum of the areas of all of the surfaces of the figure except the base or bases.

4 ASSESS

Name the Math Have each student tell a partner tips and techniques for remembering the current order of the calculations to be performed in the multi-step process discussed in this lesson.

Formative Assessment

Check for student understanding of Lessons 4-4 and 4-5.

CRM Quiz 3, p. 46

Additional Answers

66. $A'(1, 6)$, $B'(-1, 5)$, $C'(2, -1)$, $D'(4, 0)$

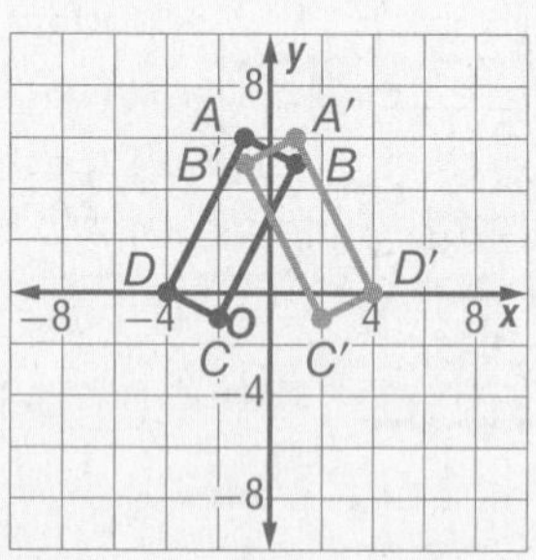

67. $E'(5, -2)$, $(-3, 5)$, $G'(-6, -1)$

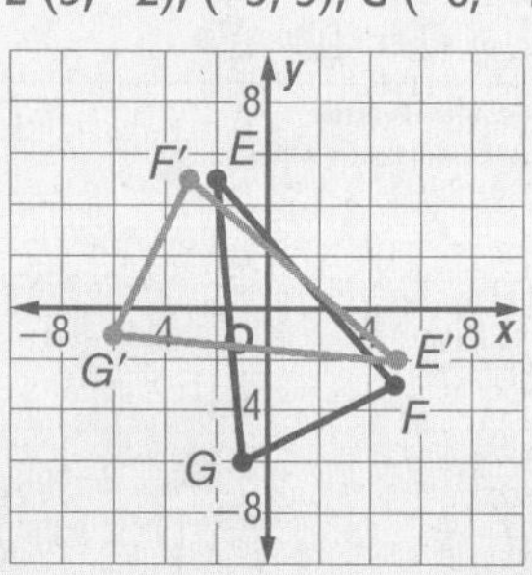

NGSSS PRACTICE 912.A.3.15, 912.A.3.1, 912.G.7.5, 912.A.2.5

62. Tyler paid \$25.25 to play three games of miniature golf and two rides on go-karts. Brent paid \$25.75 for four games of miniature golf and one ride on the go-karts. How much does one game of miniature golf cost? **C**

A. \$4.25 **C.** \$5.25
B. \$4.75 **D.** \$5.75

63. Use the table to determine the expression that best represents the number of faces of any prism having a base with n sides. **H**

Base	Sides of Base	Faces of Prisms
triangle	3	5
quadrilateral	4	6
pentagon	5	7
hexagon	6	8
heptagon	7	9
octagon	8	10

F. $2(n - 1)$ **H.** $n + 2$
G. $2(n + 1)$ **I.** $2n$

64. THINK SOLVE EXPLAIN **SHORT RESPONSE** A right circular cone has radius 4 inches and height 6 inches.

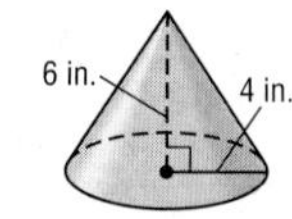

What is the lateral area of the cone? (lateral area of cone $= \pi r\ell$, where ℓ = slant height) **$8\sqrt{13}\pi$ in^2**

65. **SAT/ACT** Find the area of $\triangle ABC$. **B**

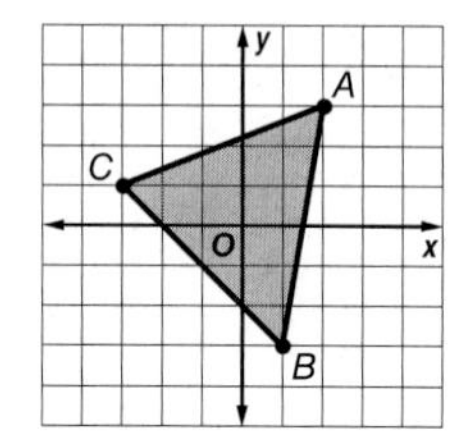

A. 10 units^2 **C.** 12 units^2
B. 14 units^2 **D.** 16 units^2

Spiral Review

66, 67. See margin.

Determine the coordinates of the vertices of the image of each figure after a reflection in the given axis of symmetry. Then graph the preimage and image. (Lesson 4-4)

66. Rectangle $ABCD$ with vertices $A(-1, 6)$, $B(1, 5)$, $C(-2, -1)$, and $D(-4, 0)$; y-axis

67. $\triangle EFG$ with vertices $E(-2, 5)$, $F(5, -3)$, and $G(-1, -6)$; $y = x$

Determine whether each matrix product is defined. If so, state the dimensions of the product. (Lesson 4-3)

68. $A_{4 \times 2} \cdot B_{2 \times 6}$ **yes; 4 × 6**

69. $C_{5 \times 4} \cdot D_{5 \times 3}$ **no**

70. $E_{2 \times 7} \cdot F_{7 \times 1}$ **yes; 2 × 1**

Graph each function. (Lesson 2-6) **71–73. See Chapter 4 Answer Appendix.**

71. $f(x) = 2|x - 3| - 4$

72. $f(x) = -3|2x| + 4$

73. $f(x) = |3x - 1| + 2$

Skills Review

Solve each system of equations. (Lesson 3-2)

74. $2x - 5y = -26$, $5x + 3y = -34$ **(−8, 2)**

75. $4y + 6x = 10$, $2x - 7y = 22$ **$\left(\frac{79}{25}, -\frac{56}{25}\right)$**

76. $-3x - 2y = 17$, $-4x + 5y = -8$ **(−3, −4)**

228 Chapter 4 Matrices

Differentiated Instruction BL

Extension Write the following system on the board.

$$2x + 4y = 10$$
$$-x - 2y = 3$$

Ask students if they can use Cramer's rule to solve the system. Have them explain why or why not.
Cramer's rule cannot be used because the determinant is zero.
Then have them graph each equation and explain why there is no solution to the system.
The graphs of the two equations are parallel.

4-6 Inverse Matrices and Systems of Equations

Then

You solved systems of linear equations algebraically. (Lesson 3-2)

Now

- Find the inverse of a 2×2 matrix.
- Write and solve matrix equations for a system of equations.

NGSSS

MA.912.A.3.14 Solve systems of linear equations and inequalities **in two and three variables using graphical,** substitution, and elimination **methods.**

New Vocabulary

identity matrix
inverse matrix
matrix equation
variable matrix
constant matrix

FL Math Online

glencoe.com

Why?

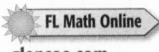

Maria's Sandwich Shop offers three lunch options as shown at the right.

To determine how much each individual item costs, you can solve the following matrix equation in which w represents the cost of a sandwich, s the cost of a side, and d the cost of a drink.

$$\begin{bmatrix} 1 & 2 & 0 \\ 2 & 2 & 2 \\ 4 & 3 & 4 \end{bmatrix} \begin{bmatrix} w \\ s \\ d \end{bmatrix} = \begin{bmatrix} 9 \\ 16.50 \\ 30.75 \end{bmatrix}$$

Lunch Options
Basic Brown Bag $9.00
Includes sandwich and 2 sides
Lunch for Two $16.50
Includes 2 sandwiches, 2 sides, and 2 drinks
Family $30.75
Includes 4 sandwiches, 3 sides, and 4 drinks

Identity and Inverse Matrices Recall that in real numbers, two numbers are multiplicative inverses if their product is the identity, 1. Similarly, for matrices, the **identity matrix** is a square matrix that, when multiplied by another matrix, equals that same matrix.

2 × 2 Identity Matrix

$$\begin{bmatrix} 1 & 0 \\ 0 & 1 \end{bmatrix}$$

3 × 3 Identity Matrix

$$\begin{bmatrix} 1 & 0 & 0 \\ 0 & 1 & 0 \\ 0 & 0 & 1 \end{bmatrix}$$

Key Concept — **Identity Matrix for Multiplication**

Words The identity matrix for multiplication I is a square matrix with 1 for every element of the main diagonal, from upper left to lower right, and 0 in all other positions. For any square matrix A of the same dimension as I, $A \cdot I = I \cdot A = A$.

Symbols If $A = \begin{bmatrix} a & b \\ c & d \end{bmatrix}$, then $I = \begin{bmatrix} 1 & 0 \\ 0 & 1 \end{bmatrix}$ such that

$$\begin{bmatrix} a & b \\ c & d \end{bmatrix} \cdot \begin{bmatrix} 1 & 0 \\ 0 & 1 \end{bmatrix} = \begin{bmatrix} 1 & 0 \\ 0 & 1 \end{bmatrix} \cdot \begin{bmatrix} a & b \\ c & d \end{bmatrix} = \begin{bmatrix} a & b \\ c & d \end{bmatrix}.$$

Two $n \times n$ matrices are **inverses** of each other if their product is the identity matrix. If matrix A has an inverse symbolized by A^{-1}, then $A \cdot A^{-1} = A^{-1} \cdot A = I$.

4-6 Lesson Notes

1 FOCUS

Vertical Alignment

Before Lesson 4-6
Solve systems of linear equations algebraically.

Lesson 4-6
Find the inverse of a 2×2 matrix.
Write and solve matrix equations for a system of equations.

After Lesson 4-6
Use augmented matrices to solve systems of equations.

2 TEACH

Scaffolding Questions

Have students read the *Why?* section of the lesson.

Ask:

- What is represented by the number 3 in the first matrix? There are 3 sides in a Family lunch.
- What are the dimensions of the product of a 3×3 matrix and a 3×1 matrix? 3×1
- Evaluate the product of the matrices $[1\ 2\ 0]$ and $\begin{bmatrix} w \\ s \\ d \end{bmatrix}$. $w + 2s$

Lesson 4-6 Resources

Resource	Approaching-Level	On-Level	Beyond-Level	English Learners
Teacher Edition		• Differentiated Instruction, p. 231	• Differentiated Instruction, p. 235	
Chapter Resource Masters	• Study Guide and Intervention, pp. 37–38 • Skills Practice, p. 39 • Practice, p. 40 • Word Problem Practice, p. 41	• Study Guide and Intervention, pp. 37–38 • Skills Practice, p. 39 • Practice, p. 40 • Word Problem Practice, p. 41 • Enrichment, p. 42	• Practice, p. 40 • Word Problem Practice, p. 41 • Enrichment, p. 42	• Study Guide and Intervention, pp. 37–38 • Skills Practice, p. 39 • Practice, p. 40 • Word Problem Practice, p. 41
Transparencies	• 5-Minute Check Transparency 4-6	• 5-Minute Check Transparency 4-6	• 5-Minute Check Transparency 4-6	• 5-Minute Check Transparency 4-6
Other	• Study Notebook	• Study Notebook	• Study Notebook	• Study Notebook

Identity and Inverse Matrices

Example 1 shows how to determine whether two matrices are inverses.

Formative Assessment

Use the Guided Practice exercises after each example to determine students' understanding of concepts.

Additional Example

1 Determine whether each pair of matrices are inverses of each other.

a. $X = \begin{bmatrix} 3 & -2 \\ -1 & 1 \end{bmatrix}$ and $Y = \begin{bmatrix} 1 & 2 \\ 1 & 3 \end{bmatrix}$ Yes, they are inverses.

b. $P = \begin{bmatrix} 3 & -1 \\ 4 & -2 \end{bmatrix}$ and $Q = \begin{bmatrix} 1 & -3 \\ 2 & 4 \end{bmatrix}$ No, they are not inverses.

Additional Examples also in Interactive Classroom PowerPoint® Presentations

IWB INTERACTIVE WHITEBOARD READY

Focus on Mathematical Content

Identity Matrices For an $n \times n$ square matrix, the entries located in row i, column i are called the diagonal entries. An identity matrix is a square matrix whose diagonal entries are 1s while all other entries are 0s.

StudyTip

Verifying Inverses Since multiplication of matrices is not commutative, it is necessary to check the product in both orders.

EXAMPLE 1 Verify Inverse Matrices

Determine whether the matrices in each pair are inverses.

a. $A = \begin{bmatrix} -4 & 2 \\ -2 & 1 \end{bmatrix}$ **and** $B = \begin{bmatrix} \frac{1}{4} & -\frac{1}{2} \\ \frac{1}{2} & -1 \end{bmatrix}$

If A and B are inverses, then $A \cdot B = B \cdot A = I$.

$A \cdot B = \begin{bmatrix} -4 & 2 \\ -2 & 1 \end{bmatrix} \cdot \begin{bmatrix} \frac{1}{4} & -\frac{1}{2} \\ \frac{1}{2} & -1 \end{bmatrix}$ **Write an equation.**

$= \begin{bmatrix} -1+1 & 2-2 \\ -\frac{1}{2}+\frac{1}{2} & 1-1 \end{bmatrix}$ or $\begin{bmatrix} 0 & 0 \\ 0 & 0 \end{bmatrix}$ **Matrix multiplication**

Since $A \cdot B \neq I$, they are *not* inverses.

b. $F = \begin{bmatrix} 3 & -5 \\ -2 & 6 \end{bmatrix}$ **and** $G = \begin{bmatrix} \frac{3}{4} & \frac{5}{8} \\ \frac{1}{4} & \frac{3}{8} \end{bmatrix}$

If F and G are inverses, then $F \cdot G = G \cdot F = I$.

$F \cdot G = \begin{bmatrix} 3 & -5 \\ -2 & 6 \end{bmatrix} \cdot \begin{bmatrix} \frac{3}{4} & \frac{5}{8} \\ \frac{1}{4} & \frac{3}{8} \end{bmatrix}$ **Write an equation.**

$= \begin{bmatrix} \frac{9}{4}-\frac{5}{4} & \frac{15}{8}-\frac{15}{8} \\ -\frac{6}{4}+\frac{6}{4} & -\frac{10}{8}+\frac{18}{8} \end{bmatrix}$ or $\begin{bmatrix} 1 & 0 \\ 0 & 1 \end{bmatrix}$ **Matrix multiplication**

$G \cdot F = \begin{bmatrix} \frac{3}{4} & \frac{5}{8} \\ \frac{1}{4} & \frac{3}{8} \end{bmatrix} \cdot \begin{bmatrix} 3 & -5 \\ -2 & 6 \end{bmatrix}$ **Write an equation.**

$= \begin{bmatrix} \frac{9}{4}-\frac{10}{8} & -\frac{15}{4}+\frac{30}{8} \\ \frac{3}{4}-\frac{6}{8} & -\frac{5}{4}+\frac{18}{8} \end{bmatrix}$ or $\begin{bmatrix} 1 & 0 \\ 0 & 1 \end{bmatrix}$ **Matrix multiplication**

Since $F \cdot G = G \cdot F = I$, F and G are inverses.

Guided Practice

1. Determine whether $X = \begin{bmatrix} 4 & -1 \\ 2 & -2 \end{bmatrix}$ and $Y = \begin{bmatrix} \frac{1}{3} & -\frac{1}{6} \\ \frac{1}{3} & -\frac{2}{3} \end{bmatrix}$ are inverses of each other. yes

Personal Tutor glencoe.com

Some matrices do not have inverses. You can determine whether a matrix has an inverse by using the determinant.

Key Concept Inverse of a 2 × 2 Matrix

The inverse of matrix $A = \begin{bmatrix} a & b \\ c & d \end{bmatrix}$ is $A^{-1} = \frac{1}{ad - bc}\begin{bmatrix} d & -b \\ -c & a \end{bmatrix}$, where $ad - bc \neq 0$.

Notice that $ad - bc$ is the value of det A. Therefore, if the value of the determinant of a matrix is 0, the matrix cannot have an inverse.

TEACH with TECH

BLOG Have students write blog entries explaining what it means when the coefficient matrix for a system of equations does not have an inverse. Be sure students use examples in their explanations.

EXAMPLE 2 Find the Inverse of a Matrix

Find the inverse of each matrix, if it exists.

a. $P = \begin{bmatrix} 7 & -5 \\ 2 & -1 \end{bmatrix}$

$\begin{vmatrix} 7 & -5 \\ 2 & -1 \end{vmatrix} = -7 - (-10) \text{ or } 3$ **Find the determinant.**

Since the determinant does not equal 0, P^{-1} exists.

$P^{-1} = \frac{1}{ad - bc}\begin{bmatrix} d & -b \\ -c & a \end{bmatrix}$ **Definition of inverse**

$= \frac{1}{7(-1) - (-5)(2)}\begin{bmatrix} -1 & 5 \\ -2 & 7 \end{bmatrix}$ **$a = 7, b = -5, c = 2, d = -1$**

$= \frac{1}{3}\begin{bmatrix} -1 & 5 \\ -2 & 7 \end{bmatrix} \text{ or } \begin{bmatrix} -\frac{1}{3} & \frac{5}{3} \\ -\frac{2}{3} & \frac{7}{3} \end{bmatrix}$ **Simplify.**

CHECK Find the product of the matrices. If the product is I, then they are inverses.

$$\begin{bmatrix} 7 & -5 \\ 2 & -1 \end{bmatrix} \cdot \begin{bmatrix} -\frac{1}{3} & \frac{5}{3} \\ -\frac{2}{3} & \frac{7}{3} \end{bmatrix} = \begin{bmatrix} -\frac{7}{3} + \frac{10}{3} & \frac{35}{3} - \frac{35}{3} \\ -\frac{2}{3} + \frac{2}{3} & \frac{10}{3} - \frac{7}{3} \end{bmatrix} \text{ or } \begin{bmatrix} 1 & 0 \\ 0 & 1 \end{bmatrix} \checkmark$$

b. $Q = \begin{bmatrix} -8 & -6 \\ 12 & 9 \end{bmatrix}$

$\begin{vmatrix} -8 & -6 \\ 12 & 9 \end{vmatrix} = -72 - (-72) = 0$ **Find the determinant.**

Since the determinant equals 0, Q^{-1} does not exist.

Guided Practice

2A. $\begin{bmatrix} 3 & 7 \\ 1 & -4 \end{bmatrix}$ **2B.** $\begin{bmatrix} 2 & 1 \\ -4 & 3 \end{bmatrix}$

Personal Tutor glencoe.com

Matrix Equations Matrices can be used to represent and solve systems of equations. Consider the system of equations below. You can write a **matrix equation** to solve this system.

$$\begin{aligned} x + 2y &= 9 \\ 3x - 6y &= 3 \end{aligned} \rightarrow \begin{bmatrix} x + 2y \\ 3x - 6y \end{bmatrix} = \begin{bmatrix} 9 \\ 3 \end{bmatrix}$$

Write the left side of the matrix equation as the product of the coefficient matrix and the variable matrix. Write the right side as a constant matrix.

$$\begin{matrix} A & \cdot & X & = & B \\ \begin{bmatrix} 1 & 2 \\ 3 & -6 \end{bmatrix} & \cdot & \begin{bmatrix} x \\ y \end{bmatrix} & = & \begin{bmatrix} 9 \\ 3 \end{bmatrix} \end{matrix}$$

coefficient matrix | **variable matrix** only the variables of a system | **constant matrix** only the constants of a system

Math History Link

Seki Kowa (1642–1708) Known as The Arithmetical Sage, Seki Kowa was the first to develop the theory of determinants.

2A. $\begin{bmatrix} \frac{4}{19} & \frac{7}{19} \\ \frac{1}{19} & -\frac{3}{19} \end{bmatrix}$

2B. $\begin{bmatrix} \frac{3}{10} & \frac{-1}{10} \\ \frac{2}{5} & \frac{1}{5} \end{bmatrix}$

Additional Example

2 Find the inverse of each matrix, if it exists.

a. $B = \begin{bmatrix} -1 & 0 \\ 8 & -2 \end{bmatrix}$ $\begin{bmatrix} -1 & 0 \\ -4 & -\frac{1}{2} \end{bmatrix}$

b. $T = \begin{bmatrix} -4 & 6 \\ -2 & 3 \end{bmatrix}$ No inverse exists.

Matrix Equations

Example 3 shows how to write a system of equations to model a real-world situation and then use a matrix equation for the system.

Differentiated Instruction

OL

Logical Learners Ask each student to write a comparison of the inverse of a matrix to the multiplicative and additive inverses of a number.

Lesson 4-6 Inverse Matrices and Systems of Equations 231

Additional Example

3 **RENTAL COSTS** The Booster Club for North High School plans a picnic. The rental company charges \$15 to rent a popcorn machine and \$18 to rent a water cooler. The club spends \$261 for a total of 15 items. How many of each do they rent? 3 popcorn machines, 12 water coolers

Focus on Mathematical Content

Solving a System of Equations Using A^{-1} If a system of equations has a unique solution, then the solution is given by $X = A^{-1}B$, where A is the coefficient matrix, B is the constant matrix, and X is the variable matrix. If there is no solution, or there are infinitely many solutions to the system, the matrix of coefficients does not have an inverse, or is not invertible.

StudyTip

Inverse You can use this method to solve systems of equations only if A has an inverse. If A does not have an inverse, then the system either has no solution or infinitely many solutions.

Then solve the matrix equation in the same way that you would solve any other equation.

$ax = b$	**Write the equation.**	$AX = B$
$\left(\frac{1}{a}\right)ax = \left(\frac{1}{a}\right)b$	**Multiply each side by the inverse of the coefficient, if it exists.**	$A^{-1}AX = A^{-1}B$
$1x = \frac{b}{a}$	$\left(\frac{1}{a}\right)a = 1$, $A^{-1}A = I$	$IX = A^{-1}B$
$x = \frac{b}{a}$	$1x = x$, $IX = X$	$X = A^{-1}B$

Notice that the solution of the matrix equation is the product of the inverse of the coefficient matrix and the constant matrix.

Real-World EXAMPLE 3 Solve a System of Equations

TRAVEL Helena stopped for gasoline twice during a car trip. The price of gasoline at the first station where she stopped was \$3.75 per gallon. At the second station, the price was \$3.50 per gallon. Helena bought a total of 24.2 gallons of gasoline and spent \$88.05. How much gasoline did Helena buy at each gas station?

Real-World Link

Average gas prices increased fivefold from \$0.70 per gallon in 1977 to \$3.50 per gallon in 2007.

Source: U.S. Department of Energy

A system of equations to represent the situation is as follows.

$x + y = 24.2$
$3.75x + 3.50y = 88.05$

The matrix equation is $\begin{bmatrix} 1 & 1 \\ 3.75 & 3.50 \end{bmatrix} \cdot \begin{bmatrix} x \\ y \end{bmatrix} = \begin{bmatrix} 24.2 \\ 88.05 \end{bmatrix}$.

Step 1 Find the inverse of the coefficient matrix.

$$A^{-1} = \frac{1}{3.50 - 3.75}\begin{bmatrix} 3.50 & -1 \\ -3.75 & 1 \end{bmatrix} \text{ or } -\frac{1}{0.25}\begin{bmatrix} 3.50 & -1 \\ -3.75 & 1 \end{bmatrix}$$

Step 2 Multiply each side of the matrix equation by the inverse matrix.

$$-\frac{1}{0.25}\begin{bmatrix} 3.50 & -1 \\ -3.75 & 1 \end{bmatrix} \cdot \begin{bmatrix} 1 & 1 \\ 3.75 & 3.50 \end{bmatrix} \cdot \begin{bmatrix} x \\ y \end{bmatrix} = -\frac{1}{0.25}\begin{bmatrix} 3.50 & -1 \\ -3.75 & 1 \end{bmatrix} \cdot \begin{bmatrix} 24.2 \\ 88.05 \end{bmatrix}$$

$$\begin{bmatrix} 1 & 0 \\ 0 & 1 \end{bmatrix} \cdot \begin{bmatrix} x \\ y \end{bmatrix} = -\frac{1}{0.25}\begin{bmatrix} -3.35 \\ -2.70 \end{bmatrix}$$

$$\begin{bmatrix} x \\ y \end{bmatrix} = \begin{bmatrix} 13.4 \\ 10.8 \end{bmatrix}$$

The solution is (13.4, 10.8), where x represents the amount of gas Helena purchased at the first gas station, and y represents the amount purchased at the second gas station.

CHECK You can check your answer by using inverses.

Enter $\begin{bmatrix} 1 & 1 \\ 3.75 & 3.50 \end{bmatrix}$ as matrix A.

Enter $\begin{bmatrix} 24.2 \\ 88.05 \end{bmatrix}$ as matrix B.

Multiply the inverse of A by B.

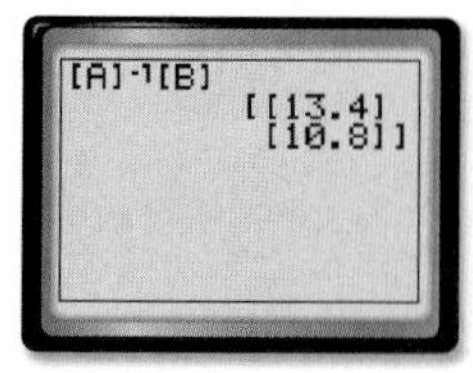

Guided Practice

3. COMIC BOOKS Dante and Erica just returned from a comic book store that sells new and used comics. Dante spent \$11.25 on 3 new and 4 old books, and Erica spent \$15.75 on 10 used and 3 new ones. If comics of one type are sold at the same price, what is the price in dollars of a new comic book? \$2.75

Personal Tutor glencoe.com

Check Your Understanding

Example 1 p. 230

Determine whether the matrices in each pair are inverses.

1. $A = \begin{bmatrix} 2 & 1 \\ -1 & 0 \end{bmatrix}, B = \begin{bmatrix} 1 & 2 \\ 2 & 1 \end{bmatrix}$ no
2. $C = \begin{bmatrix} 2 & 1 \\ 5 & 3 \end{bmatrix}, D = \begin{bmatrix} 2 & 1 \\ 5 & -3 \end{bmatrix}$ no
3. $F = \begin{bmatrix} -1 & 1 \\ 0 & -1 \end{bmatrix}, G = \begin{bmatrix} -1 & -1 \\ 0 & -1 \end{bmatrix}$ yes
4. $H = \begin{bmatrix} -3 & -1 \\ -4 & -2 \end{bmatrix}, J = \begin{bmatrix} -1 & 2 \\ 3 & -4 \end{bmatrix}$ no

Example 2 p. 231

Find the inverse of each matrix, if it exists. 5–8. See margin.

5. $\begin{bmatrix} 6 & -3 \\ -1 & 0 \end{bmatrix}$
6. $\begin{bmatrix} 2 & -4 \\ -3 & 0 \end{bmatrix}$
7. $\begin{bmatrix} -3 & 0 \\ 5 & 2 \end{bmatrix}$
8. $\begin{bmatrix} 2 & 4 \\ 1 & 2 \end{bmatrix}$

Example 3 p. 232

Use a matrix equation to solve each system of equations.

9. $-2x + y = 9$, $x + y = 3$ (−2, 5)
10. $4x - 2y = 22$, $6x + 9y = -3$ (4, −3)
11. $-2x + y = -4$, $3x + y = 1$ (1, −2)

Example 3 p. 232

12. **MONEY** Kevin had 25 quarters and dimes. The total value of all the coins was \$4. How many quarters and dimes did Kevin have? 10 quarters and 15 dimes

Practice and Problem Solving

● = **Step-by-Step Solutions** begin on page R20. **Extra Practice** begins on page 947.

Example 1 p. 230

Determine whether each pair of matrices are inverses of each other.

13. $K = \begin{bmatrix} 1 & 2 \\ 3 & 0 \end{bmatrix}, L = \begin{bmatrix} 0 & 1 \\ 2 & -1 \end{bmatrix}$ no
14. $M = \begin{bmatrix} 0 & 2 \\ 4 & 5 \end{bmatrix}, N = \begin{bmatrix} 1 & 1 \\ 0 & 0 \end{bmatrix}$ no
15. $P = \begin{bmatrix} 4 & 0 \\ 3 & 0 \end{bmatrix}, Q = \begin{bmatrix} -1 & -1 \\ \frac{2}{3} & 5 \end{bmatrix}$ no
16. $R = \begin{bmatrix} \frac{1}{2} & -\frac{1}{4} \\ \frac{1}{4} & -\frac{1}{2} \end{bmatrix}, S = \begin{bmatrix} 2 & 4 \\ 4 & 2 \end{bmatrix}$ no

Example 2 p. 231

Find the inverse of each matrix, if it exists. 17–25. See margin.

17. $\begin{bmatrix} 3 & 0 \\ 0 & 2 \end{bmatrix}$
18. $\begin{bmatrix} 2 & 3 \\ 3 & 2 \end{bmatrix}$
19. $\begin{bmatrix} 3 & 0 \\ 5 & 1 \end{bmatrix}$
20. $\begin{bmatrix} 1 & -1 \\ -6 & -1 \end{bmatrix}$
21. $\begin{bmatrix} -5 & -4 \\ 4 & 2 \end{bmatrix}$
22. $\begin{bmatrix} -5 & 9 \\ 4 & -8 \end{bmatrix}$
23. $\begin{bmatrix} 6 & -5 \\ 4 & 9 \end{bmatrix}$
24. $\begin{bmatrix} -4 & -2 \\ 7 & 8 \end{bmatrix}$
25. $\begin{bmatrix} -6 & 8 \\ 8 & -7 \end{bmatrix}$

Example 3 p. 232

26. **BAKING** Peggy is preparing a colored frosting for a cake. For the right shade of purple, she needs 25 milliliters of a 44% concentration food coloring. The store has a 25% red and a 50% blue concentration of food coloring. How many milliliters each of blue food coloring and red food coloring should be mixed to make the necessary amount of purple food coloring?

26. 6 mL of the red food coloring and 19 mL of the blue food coloring

Use a matrix equation to solve each system of equations.

27. $-x + y = 4$, $-x + y = -4$ no solution
28. $-x + y = 3$, $-2x + y = 6$ (−3, 0)
29. $x + y = 4$, $-4x + y = 9$ (−1, 5)
30. $3x + y = 3$, $5x + 3y = 6$ $\left(\frac{3}{4}, \frac{3}{4}\right)$
31. $y - x = 5$, $2y - 2x = 8$ no solution
32. $4x + 2y = 6$, $6x - 3y = 9$ (1.5, 0)
33. $1.6y - 0.2x = 1$, $0.4y - 0.1x = 0.5$ (−5, 0)
34. $4y - x = -2$, $3y - x = 6$ (−30, −8)
35. $2y - 4x = 3$, $4x - 3y = -6$ $\left(\frac{3}{4}, 3\right)$

3 PRACTICE

Formative Assessment

Use Exercises 1–12 to check for understanding.

Use the chart at the bottom of this page to customize assignments for your students.

Additional Answers

5. $\begin{bmatrix} 0 & -1 \\ -\frac{1}{3} & -2 \end{bmatrix}$

6. $\begin{bmatrix} 0 & -\frac{1}{3} \\ -\frac{1}{4} & -\frac{1}{6} \end{bmatrix}$

7. $\begin{bmatrix} -\frac{1}{3} & 0 \\ \frac{5}{6} & \frac{1}{2} \end{bmatrix}$

8. does not exist

17. $\begin{bmatrix} \frac{1}{3} & 0 \\ 0 & \frac{1}{2} \end{bmatrix}$

18. $\begin{bmatrix} -\frac{2}{5} & \frac{3}{5} \\ \frac{3}{5} & -\frac{2}{5} \end{bmatrix}$

19. $\begin{bmatrix} \frac{1}{3} & 0 \\ -\frac{5}{3} & 1 \end{bmatrix}$

20. $\begin{bmatrix} \frac{1}{7} & -\frac{1}{7} \\ -\frac{6}{7} & -\frac{1}{7} \end{bmatrix}$

21. $\begin{bmatrix} \frac{1}{3} & \frac{2}{3} \\ -\frac{2}{3} & -\frac{5}{6} \end{bmatrix}$

22. $\begin{bmatrix} -2 & -\frac{9}{4} \\ -1 & -\frac{5}{4} \end{bmatrix}$

23. $\begin{bmatrix} \frac{9}{74} & \frac{5}{74} \\ -\frac{2}{37} & \frac{3}{37} \end{bmatrix}$

24. $\begin{bmatrix} -\frac{4}{9} & -\frac{1}{9} \\ \frac{7}{18} & \frac{2}{9} \end{bmatrix}$

25. $\begin{bmatrix} \frac{7}{22} & \frac{4}{11} \\ \frac{4}{11} & \frac{3}{11} \end{bmatrix}$

Differentiated Homework Options

Level	Assignment	Two-Day Option	
AL Basic	13–36, 38, 40–54	13–35 odd, 43–46	14–38 even, 40–42, 47–54
OL Core	13–37 odd, 38, 40–54	13–35, 43–46	37, 38, 40–42, 47–54
BL Advanced	37–51, (optional: 52–54)		

Study Guide and Intervention

CRM pp. 37–38 AL OL ELL

4-6 Study Guide and Intervention

Inverse Matrices and Systems of Equations

Identity and Inverse Matrices The identity matrix for matrix multiplication is a square matrix with 1s for every element of the main diagonal and zeros elsewhere.

Identity Matrix for Multiplication	If A is an $n \times n$ matrix and I is the identity matrix, then $A \cdot I = A$ and $I \cdot A = A$.

If an $n \times n$ matrix A has an inverse A^{-1}, then $A \cdot A^{-1} = A^{-1} \cdot A = I$.

Example Determine whether $X = \begin{bmatrix} 7 & 4 \\ 10 & 6 \end{bmatrix}$ and $Y = \begin{bmatrix} 3 & -2 \\ -5 & \frac{7}{2} \end{bmatrix}$ are inverse matrices.

Find $X \cdot Y$.

$$X \cdot Y = \begin{bmatrix} 7 & 4 \\ 10 & 6 \end{bmatrix} \cdot \begin{bmatrix} 3 & -2 \\ -5 & \frac{7}{2} \end{bmatrix} = \begin{bmatrix} 21-20 & -14+14 \\ 30-30 & -20+21 \end{bmatrix} \text{ or } \begin{bmatrix} 1 & 0 \\ 0 & 1 \end{bmatrix}$$

Find $Y \cdot X$.

$$Y \cdot X = \begin{bmatrix} 3 & -2 \\ -5 & \frac{7}{2} \end{bmatrix} \cdot \begin{bmatrix} 7 & 4 \\ 10 & 6 \end{bmatrix} = \begin{bmatrix} 21-20 & 12-12 \\ -35+35 & -20+21 \end{bmatrix} \text{ or } \begin{bmatrix} 1 & 0 \\ 0 & 1 \end{bmatrix}$$

Since $X \cdot Y = Y \cdot X = I$, X and Y are inverse matrices.

Exercises

Determine whether the matrices in each pair are inverses of each other.

1. $\begin{bmatrix} 4 & 5 \\ 3 & 4 \end{bmatrix}$ and $\begin{bmatrix} 4 & -5 \\ -3 & 4 \end{bmatrix}$ **yes**
2. $\begin{bmatrix} 3 & 2 \\ 5 & 4 \end{bmatrix}$ and $\begin{bmatrix} 2 & -1 \\ -\frac{5}{2} & \frac{3}{2} \end{bmatrix}$ **yes**
3. $\begin{bmatrix} 2 & 3 \\ 5 & -1 \end{bmatrix}$ and $\begin{bmatrix} 2 & 3 \\ -1 & -2 \end{bmatrix}$ **no**
4. $\begin{bmatrix} 8 & 11 \\ 3 & 14 \end{bmatrix}$ and $\begin{bmatrix} -4 & 11 \\ 3 & -8 \end{bmatrix}$ **yes**
5. $\begin{bmatrix} 4 & -1 \\ 5 & 3 \end{bmatrix}$ and $\begin{bmatrix} 1 & 2 \\ 3 & 8 \end{bmatrix}$ **no**
6. $\begin{bmatrix} 5 & 2 \\ 11 & 4 \end{bmatrix}$ and $\begin{bmatrix} -2 & 1 \\ \frac{11}{2} & -\frac{5}{2} \end{bmatrix}$ **yes**
7. $\begin{bmatrix} 4 & 2 \\ 6 & -2 \end{bmatrix}$ and $\begin{bmatrix} -\frac{1}{5} & -\frac{1}{10} \\ \frac{3}{10} & \frac{1}{10} \end{bmatrix}$ **no**
8. $\begin{bmatrix} 5 & 8 \\ 4 & 6 \end{bmatrix}$ and $\begin{bmatrix} -3 & 4 \\ 2 & -\frac{5}{2} \end{bmatrix}$ **yes**
9. $\begin{bmatrix} 3 & 7 \\ 2 & 4 \end{bmatrix}$ and $\begin{bmatrix} \frac{7}{2} & -\frac{3}{2} \\ 1 & -2 \end{bmatrix}$ **no**
10. $\begin{bmatrix} 3 & 2 \\ 4 & -6 \end{bmatrix}$ and $\begin{bmatrix} 3 & 2 \\ -4 & -3 \end{bmatrix}$ **no**
11. $\begin{bmatrix} 7 & 2 \\ 17 & 5 \end{bmatrix}$ and $\begin{bmatrix} 5 & -2 \\ -17 & 7 \end{bmatrix}$ **yes**
12. $\begin{bmatrix} 4 & 3 \\ 7 & 5 \end{bmatrix}$ and $\begin{bmatrix} -5 & 3 \\ 7 & -4 \end{bmatrix}$ **yes**

Lesson 4-6

Chapter 4 37 Glencoe Algebra 2

Practice

CRM p. 40 AL OL BL ELL

4-6 Practice

Inverse Matrices and Systems of Equations

Determine whether each pair of matrices are inverses.

1. $M = \begin{bmatrix} 2 & 1 \\ 3 & 2 \end{bmatrix}, N = \begin{bmatrix} -2 & 1 \\ 3 & -2 \end{bmatrix}$ **no**
2. $X = \begin{bmatrix} -3 & 2 \\ 5 & -3 \end{bmatrix}, Y = \begin{bmatrix} 3 & 2 \\ 5 & 3 \end{bmatrix}$ **yes**
3. $A = \begin{bmatrix} 3 & 1 \\ -4 & 2 \end{bmatrix}, B = \begin{bmatrix} \frac{1}{5} & -\frac{1}{10} \\ \frac{2}{5} & \frac{3}{10} \end{bmatrix}$ **yes**
4. $P = \begin{bmatrix} 6 & -2 \\ -2 & 3 \end{bmatrix}, Q = \begin{bmatrix} \frac{3}{14} & \frac{1}{7} \\ \frac{1}{7} & \frac{3}{7} \end{bmatrix}$ **yes**

Determine whether each statement is *true* or *false*.

5. All square matrices have multiplicative inverses. **false**
6. All square matrices have multiplicative identities. **true**

Find the inverse of each matrix, if it exists.

7. $\begin{bmatrix} 4 & 5 \\ -4 & -3 \end{bmatrix}$ $\frac{1}{8}\begin{bmatrix} -3 & -5 \\ 4 & 4 \end{bmatrix}$
8. $\begin{bmatrix} 2 & 0 \\ 3 & 5 \end{bmatrix}$ $\frac{1}{10}\begin{bmatrix} 5 & 0 \\ -3 & 2 \end{bmatrix}$
9. $\begin{bmatrix} -1 & 3 \\ 4 & -7 \end{bmatrix}$ $-\frac{1}{5}\begin{bmatrix} -7 & -3 \\ -4 & -1 \end{bmatrix}$
10. $\begin{bmatrix} 2 & 5 \\ -1 & 3 \end{bmatrix}$ $\frac{1}{11}\begin{bmatrix} 3 & -5 \\ 1 & 2 \end{bmatrix}$
11. $\begin{bmatrix} 2 & -5 \\ 3 & 1 \end{bmatrix}$ $\frac{1}{17}\begin{bmatrix} 1 & 5 \\ -3 & 2 \end{bmatrix}$
12. $\begin{bmatrix} 4 & 6 \\ 6 & 9 \end{bmatrix}$ **no inverse exists**

13. **GEOMETRY** Use the figure at the right.

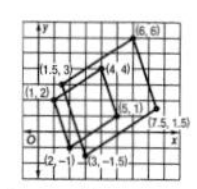

a. Write the vertex matrix A for the rectangle. $\begin{bmatrix} 1 & 4 & 5 & 2 \\ 2 & 4 & 1 & -1 \end{bmatrix}$

b. Use matrix multiplication to find BA if $B = \begin{bmatrix} 1.5 & 0 \\ 0 & 1.5 \end{bmatrix}$. $\begin{bmatrix} 1.5 & 6 & 7.5 & 3 \\ 3 & 6 & 1.5 & -1.5 \end{bmatrix}$

c. Graph the vertices of the transformed quadrilateral on the previous graph. Describe the transformation. **dilation by a scale factor of 1.5**

d. Make a conjecture about what transformation B^{-1} describes on a coordinate plane. **dilation by a scale factor of $\frac{2}{3}$**

14. **CODES** Use the alphabet table below and the inverse of coding matrix $C = \begin{bmatrix} 1 & 2 \\ 2 & 1 \end{bmatrix}$ to decode this message:
19 | 14 | 11 | 13 | 11 | 22 | 55 | 65 | 57 | 60 | 2 | 1 | 52 | 47 | 33 | 51 | 56 | 55.

CODE													
A	1	B	2	C	3	D	4	E	5	F	6	G	7
H	8	I	9	J	10	K	11	L	12	M	13	N	14
O	15	P	16	Q	17	R	18	S	19	T	20	U	21
V	22	W	23	X	24	Y	25	Z	26	–	0		

CHECK_YOUR_ANSWERS

Chapter 4 40 Glencoe Algebra 2

Word Problem Practice

CRM p. 41 AL OL BL ELL

4-6 Word Problem Practice

Inverse Matrices and Systems of Equations

1. **TEACHING** Paula is explaining matrices to her father. She writes down the following system of equations.

$$2x + y = 4$$
$$3x + y = 5.$$

Next, Paula shows her father the matrices that correspond to this system of equations. What are the matrices?

$\begin{bmatrix} 2 & 1 \\ 3 & 1 \end{bmatrix}\begin{bmatrix} x \\ y \end{bmatrix} = \begin{bmatrix} 4 \\ 5 \end{bmatrix}$

2. **TRANSPORTATION** Paula wrote the following matrix equation to show the costs of two trips by water taxi to Logan Airport in Boston. She used x for the cost of round trips and y for the cost one one-way trips.

$\begin{bmatrix} 3 & 1 \\ 2 & 2 \end{bmatrix}\begin{bmatrix} x \\ y \end{bmatrix} = \begin{bmatrix} 61 \\ 54 \end{bmatrix}$

Next, she found the inverse.

$\begin{bmatrix} 3 & 1 \\ 2 & 2 \end{bmatrix}^{-1} = \frac{1}{4}\begin{bmatrix} 2 & -1 \\ -2 & 3 \end{bmatrix}$

Then she computed her answer.

$\begin{bmatrix} x \\ y \end{bmatrix} = \begin{bmatrix} \frac{1}{2} & -\frac{1}{4} \\ -\frac{1}{2} & \frac{3}{4} \end{bmatrix}\begin{bmatrix} 61 \\ 54 \end{bmatrix} = \begin{bmatrix} 34 \\ 10 \end{bmatrix}$

When she checked her answer, the total cost of the trips came out as $112 and $88. Where did she make a mistake?
in multiplying the matrixes in the final step $\frac{1}{2}(61) + \left(-\frac{1}{2}\right)(54) = 17$, not 34

3. **AGES** Hank, Laura, and Ned are ages h, l, and n, respectively. The sum of their ages is 15 years. Laura is one year younger than the sum of Hank and Ned's ages. Ned is three times as old as Hank. Use matrices to determine the age of each sibling.
Hank is 2, Laura is 7, and Ned is 6.

4. **SELF-INVERSES** Phillip notices that any matrix with ones and negative ones on the diagonal and zeroes everywhere else has the property that it is its own inverse. Give an example of a 2 by 2 matrix that is its own inverse but has at least 1 nonzero number off the diagonal.
$\begin{bmatrix} 0 & 1 \\ 1 & 0 \end{bmatrix}$

5. **MATRIX OPERATIONS** Garth is studying determinants and inverses of matrices in math class. His teacher suggests that there are some matrices with unique properties, and challenges the class to find such matrices and describe the properties found. Garth is curious about the matrix $G = \begin{bmatrix} 0 & 1 \\ 0 & 0 \end{bmatrix}$.

a. What is the determinant of G?
The determinant of G is 0.

b. Does the inverse of G exist? Explain.
The inverse of the matrix does not exist because $ad - bc = 0$.

c. Determine a matrix operation that could be used to transform G into its Additive Identity matrix.
G^2

Lesson 4-6

Chapter 4 41 Glencoe Algebra 2

36. **POPULATIONS** The diagram shows the annual percent migration between a city and its suburbs.

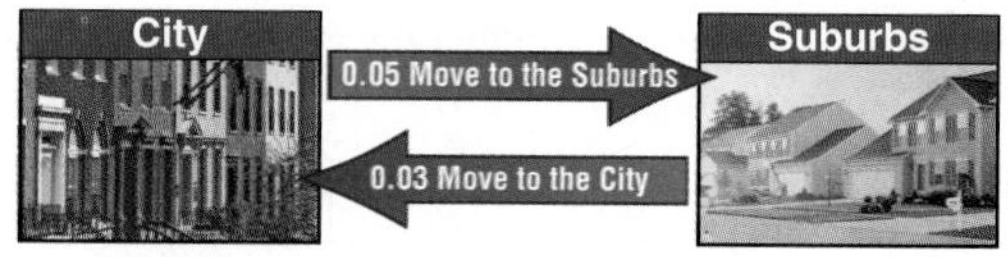

a. Write a matrix to represent the transitions in city population and suburb population. **See margin.**

b. There are currently 16,275 people living in the city and 17,552 people living in the suburbs. Assuming that the trends continue, predict the number of people who will live in the suburbs next year. **about 17,839**

c. Use the inverse of the matrix from part **b** to find the number of people who lived in the city last year. **about 17,240**

37. **MUSIC** The diagram shows the trends in digital audio player and portable CD player ownership over the past five years for Central City. Every person in Central City has either a digital audio player or a portable CD player. Central City has a stable population of 25,000 people, of whom 17,252 own digital audio players and 7748 own portable CD players.

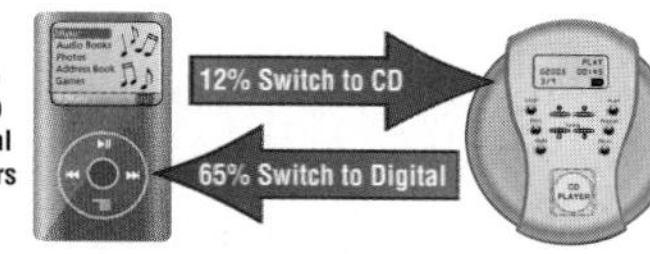

a. Write a matrix to represent the transitions in player ownership. **See margin.**

b. Assume that the trends continue. Predict the number of people who will own digital audio players next year. **about 20,218**

c. Use the inverse of the matrix from part **b** to find the number of people who owned digital audio players last year. **about 4357**

Real-World Link

The first commercially successful digital audio player was released in 1998 and weighed less than three ounces.

Source: CNet

38. Megan; Cody put 3 for x in the second equation instead of 4.
39. The system would have to consist of two equations that are the same or one equation that is a multiple of the other.
40. Sometimes; sample answer: A square matrix has a multiplicative inverse if its determinant does not equal 0.
41. Sample answer: $\begin{bmatrix} 2 & 3 \\ 4 & 6 \end{bmatrix} \cdot \begin{bmatrix} x \\ y \end{bmatrix} = \begin{bmatrix} 9 \\ 10 \end{bmatrix}$; any matrix that has a determinant equal to 0, such as $\begin{bmatrix} 1 & 1 \\ 0 & 0 \end{bmatrix}$

H.O.T. Problems

Use Higher-Order Thinking Skills

38. **ERROR ANALYSIS** Cody and Megan are setting up matrix equations for the system $5x + 7y = 19$ and $3y + 4x = 10$. Is either of them correct? Explain your reasoning.

Cody	Megan
$\begin{bmatrix} 5 & 7 \\ 3 & 4 \end{bmatrix}\begin{bmatrix} x \\ y \end{bmatrix} = \begin{bmatrix} 19 \\ 10 \end{bmatrix}$	$\begin{bmatrix} 5 & 7 \\ 4 & 3 \end{bmatrix}\begin{bmatrix} x \\ y \end{bmatrix} = \begin{bmatrix} 19 \\ 10 \end{bmatrix}$

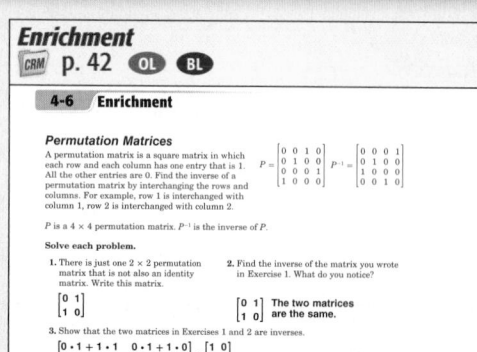

39. **CHALLENGE** Describe what a matrix equation with infinite solutions looks like.

40. **REASONING** Determine whether the following statement is *always*, *sometimes*, or *never* true. Explain your reasoning.

A square matrix has a multiplicative inverse.

41. **OPEN ENDED** Write a matrix equation that does not have a solution.

42. **WRITING IN MATH** Explain how matrix equations can be used to solve systems of equations. **See margin.**

Enrichment

CRM p. 42 OL BL

4-6 Enrichment

Permutation Matrices

A permutation matrix is a square matrix in which each row and each column has one entry that is 1. All the other entries are 0. Find the inverse of a permutation matrix by interchanging the rows and columns. For example, row 1 is interchanged with column 1, row 2 is interchanged with column 2.

$$P = \begin{bmatrix} 0 & 0 & 1 & 0 \\ 0 & 1 & 0 & 0 \\ 0 & 0 & 0 & 1 \\ 1 & 0 & 0 & 0 \end{bmatrix} \quad P^{-1} = \begin{bmatrix} 0 & 0 & 0 & 1 \\ 0 & 1 & 0 & 0 \\ 1 & 0 & 0 & 0 \\ 0 & 0 & 1 & 0 \end{bmatrix}$$

P is a 4×4 permutation matrix. P^{-1} is the inverse of P.

Solve each problem.

1. There is just one 2×2 permutation matrix that is not also an identity matrix. Write this matrix.
$\begin{bmatrix} 0 & 1 \\ 1 & 0 \end{bmatrix}$

2. Find the inverse of the matrix you wrote in Exercise 1. What do you notice?
$\begin{bmatrix} 0 & 1 \\ 1 & 0 \end{bmatrix}$ **The two matrices are the same.**

3. Show that the two matrices in Exercises 1 and 2 are inverses.
$\begin{bmatrix} 0 \cdot 1 + 1 \cdot 1 & 0 \cdot 1 + 1 \cdot 0 \\ 1 \cdot 0 + 0 \cdot 1 & 1 \cdot 1 + 0 \cdot 0 \end{bmatrix} = \begin{bmatrix} 1 & 0 \\ 0 & 1 \end{bmatrix}$

Watch Out!

Error Analysis In Exercise 38, point out that all the equations in a system of equations must be written with the variables in the same order before using matrix form.

NGSSS PRACTICE 912.A.3.15, 912.A.3.14

43. The Yogurt Shoppe sells cones in three sizes: small, \$0.89; medium, \$1.19; and large, \$1.39. One day Santos sold 52 cones. He sold seven more medium cones than small cones. If he sold \$58.98 in cones, how many medium cones did he sell? C

A. 11 B. 17 C. 24 D. 36

44. The chart shows an expression evaluated for different values of x.

x	$x^2 + x + 1$
1	3
2	7
3	13
4	31

A student concludes that for all values of x, $x^2 + x + 1$ produces a prime number. Which value of x serves as a counterexample to prove this conclusion false? I

F. −4 G. −3 H. 2 I. 4

45. THINK SOLVE EXPLAIN **SHORT RESPONSE** What is the solution of the system of equations $6a + 8b = 5$ and $10a - 12b = 2$? $\left(\frac{1}{2}, \frac{1}{4}\right)$

46. **SAT/ACT** Each year at Capital High School the students vote to choose the theme of the homecoming dance. The theme "A Night Under the Stars" received 225 votes, and "The Time of My Life" received 480 votes. If 40% of girls voted for "A Night Under the Stars" and 75% of boys voted for "The Time of My Life," how many girls and boys voted? D

A. 854 boys and 176 girls
B. 705 boys and 325 girls
C. 395 boys and 310 girls
D. 380 boys and 325 girls

Spiral Review

Evaluate each determinant. (Lesson 4-5)

47. $\begin{vmatrix} 8 & -3 \\ 6 & -9 \end{vmatrix}$ −54

48. $\begin{vmatrix} 9 & -7 \\ -5 & -3 \end{vmatrix}$ −62

49. $\begin{vmatrix} 8 & 6 & -1 \\ -4 & 5 & 1 \\ -3 & -2 & 9 \end{vmatrix}$ 551

50. Quadrilateral $A'B'C'D'$ is an image after a translation of quadrilateral $ABCD$. A table of the vertices of each rectangle is shown. (Lesson 4-4)

Quadrilateral *ABCD*	Quadrilateral *A'B'C'D'*
$A(2, 5)$	$A'(-1, 13)$
$B(9, -15)$	$B'(?, ?)$
$C(-14, -9)$	$C'(?, ?)$
$D(-6, 1)$	$D'(-9, 9)$

a. Determine the coordinates of C'. (−17, −1)

b. Determine the coordinates of B'. (6, −7)

51. **MILK** The Yoder Family Dairy produces at most 200 gallons of skim and whole milk each day for delivery to large bakeries and restaurants. Regular customers require at least 15 gallons of skim and 21 gallons of whole milk each day. If the profit on a gallon of skim milk is \$0.82 and the profit on a gallon of whole milk is \$0.75, how many gallons of each type of milk should the dairy produce each day to maximize profits? (Lesson 3-4) 179 gal of skim and 21 gal of whole milk

Skills Review

Identify the type of function represented by each graph. (Lesson 2-7)

52.
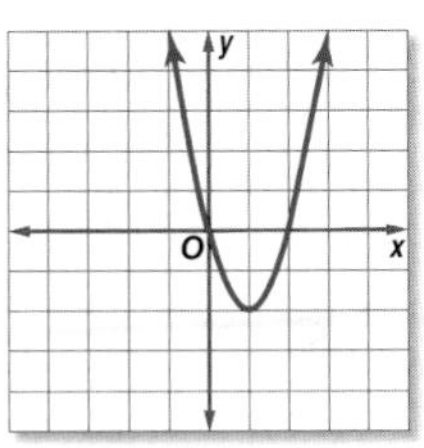

quadratic

53.
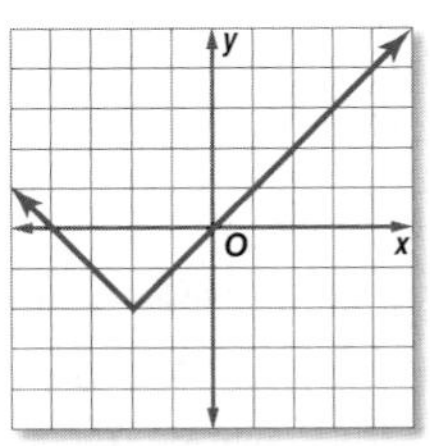

absolute value

54.
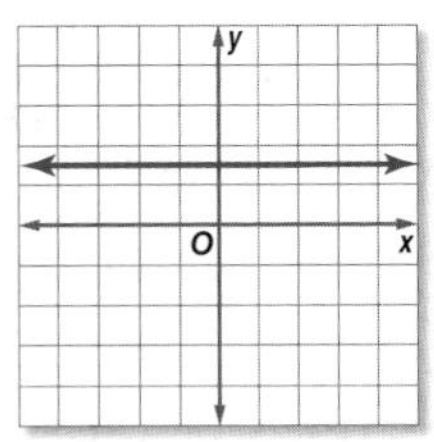

constant

4 ASSESS

Ticket Out the Door Have students describe how matrix equations can be used to solve systems of two equations in two variables.

Formative Assessment

Check for student understanding of concepts in Lesson 4-6.

CRM Quiz 4, p. 46

Additional Answers

36a.

	From city	From suburbs
To city	0.95	0.03
Suburbs	0.05	0.97

37a.

	From CD	From MP3
To CD	0.35	0.12
Mp3	0.65	0.88

42. Sample answer: First, arrange all the coefficients of the system in a coefficient matrix. Second, arrange the variables in a variable matrix. Third, arrange the constants in a constant matrix. Fourth find the inverse of the coefficient matrix. Fifth, multiply each side of the matrix equation by the inverse matrix. Sixth, check the solution in the original equation. It is more efficient to use a matrix equation when you have a system with coefficients that don't easily multiply, such as fractions, decimals, or large numbers, or there are more than three variables. It is more efficient to solve systems using substitution or elimination when the numbers are small, there are only two or three variables, or one of the variables can be defined by another variable.

Differentiated Instruction BL

Extension Write the following system on the board.

$-3x + y = 5$
$-4x - 2y = 20$

Have students use four different methods (graphing, by hand, Cramer's rule, and inverse matrices) to solve the system. Then ask them to compare and contrast the methods using criteria such as ease of use and quickness. The solution to the system is (−3, −4).

EXTEND 4-6 Lesson Notes

1 FOCUS

Objective Use a graphing calculator and the augmented matrix for a system of equations to solve the system.

Materials

- TI-83/84 Plus or other graphing calculator

Teaching Tip

Point out that the TI-83/84 Plus allows you to perform row operations on matrices. These row operations are items C through F on the [MATRIX] **Math** menu. Successive use of row operations allows you to transform a matrix to reduced row echelon form. The **rref(** function performs all the steps at once, thereby saving a great deal of time.

2 TEACH

Working in Cooperative Groups

Put students in groups of two, mixing abilities. Then have groups use their calculators to complete Steps 1 and 2 of the Example and Exercise 1.

- Point out that if one of the variables is absent from an equation in a system of equations, then its coefficient is zero.
- In order to determine the correct augmented matrix in Exercise 6, students may find it helpful to rewrite the equation, showing 0 as the coefficient of the missing variables in the second and third equations.

Practice Have students complete Exercises 2–6.

EXTEND 4-6 Graphing Technology Lab: Augmented Matrices

FL Math Online glencoe.com
- Other Calculator Keystrokes
- Graphing Technology Personal Tutor

NGSSS **MA.912.A.3.14 Solve systems of linear equations** and inequalities **in two and three variables using graphical,** substitution, and elimination **methods.**

Using a TI-83/84 Plus graphing calculator, you can solve a system of linear equations using the MATRIX function. An **augmented matrix** contains the coefficient matrix with an extra column containing the constant terms. You can use a graphing calculator to reduce the augmented matrix so that the solution of the system of equations can be easily determined.

EXAMPLE

Write an augmented matrix for the following system of equations. Then solve the system by using a graphing calculator.

$2x + y + z = 1$
$3x + 2y + 3z = 12$
$4x + y + 2z = -1$

Step 1 Write the augmented matrix and enter it into a calculator.

The augmented matrix $B = \left[\begin{array}{ccc:c} 2 & 1 & 1 & 1 \\ 3 & 2 & 3 & 12 \\ 4 & 1 & 2 & -1 \end{array}\right]$.

Begin by entering the matrix.

KEYSTROKES: [2nd] [MATRIX] [▶] [▶] [ENTER] 3 [ENTER] 4 [ENTER] 2 [ENTER] 1 [ENTER] 1 [ENTER] 1 [ENTER] 3 [ENTER] 2 [ENTER] 3 [ENTER] 12 [ENTER] 4 [ENTER] 1 [ENTER] 2 [ENTER] [(–)] 1 [ENTER]

Step 2 Find the reduced row echelon form (rref) using the graphing calculator.

KEYSTROKES: [2nd] [QUIT] [2nd] [MATRIX] [▶] [ALPHA] [B] [2nd] [MATRIX] [ENTER] [ )] [ENTER]

Study the reduced echelon matrix. The first three columns are the same as a 3×3 identity matrix. The first row represents $x = -4$, the second row represents $y = 3$, and the third row represents $z = 6$. The solution is $(-4, 3, 6)$.

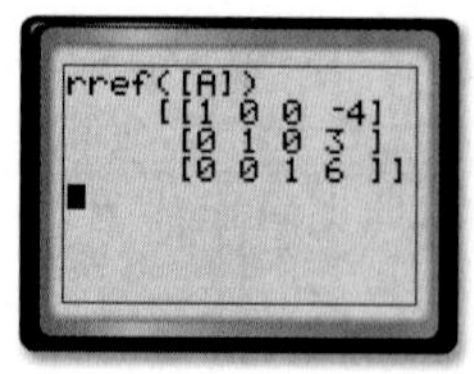

Exercises

Write an augmented matrix for each system of equations. Then solve with a graphing calculator. 1–6. See Chapter 4 Answer Appendix.

1. $3x + 2y = -4$
   $4x + 7y = 13$
2. $2x + y = 6$
   $6x - 2y = 0$
3. $2x + 2y = -4$
   $7x + 3y = 10$
4. $4x + 6y = 0$
   $8x - 2y = 7$
5. $6x - 4y + 2z = -4$
   $2x - 2y + 6z = 10$
   $2x + 2y + 2z = -2$
6. $5x - 5y + 5z = 10$
   $5x - 5z = 5$
   $5y + 10z = 0$

3 ASSESS

Formative Assessment

Use Exercise 6 to assess whether students comprehend how to solve a system of equations using a graphing calculator.

From Concrete to Abstract

Ask students which method they prefer for solving systems of two equations in two variables, the graphing calculator method shown in this investigation, or the method presented in Lesson 4-6. Have them choose their preferred methods for solving systems of equations. Have them explain their choices.

FL Math Online glencoe.com
- STUDY TO GO
- Vocabulary Review

Chapter Summary

Key Concepts

Matrices (Lesson 4-1)

- A matrix is a rectangular array of variables or constants in horizontal rows and vertical columns.
- Equal matrices have the same dimensions and corresponding elements are equal.

Operations (Lessons 4-2 and 4-3)

- Matrices can be added or subtracted if they have the same dimensions. Add or subtract corresponding elements.
- To multiply a matrix by a scalar k, multiply each element in the matrix by k.
- Two matrices can be multiplied if and only if the number of columns in the first matrix is equal to the number of rows in the second matrix.

Transformations (Lesson 4-4)

- Use matrix addition and a translation matrix to find the coordinates of a translated figure.
- Use scalar multiplication to perform dilations.
- To rotate a figure counterclockwise about the origin, multiply the vertex matrix on the left by a rotation matrix.

Identity and Inverse Matrices (Lesson 4-6)

- An identity matrix is a square matrix with ones on the diagonal and zeros in the other positions.
- Two matrices are inverses of each other if their product is the identity matrix.

Matrix Equations (Lesson 4-6)

- To solve a matrix equation, find the inverse of the coefficient matrix. Then multiply each side of the equation by the inverse matrix.

FOLDABLES® Study Organizer

Be sure the Key Concepts are noted in your Foldable.

Key Vocabulary

coefficient matrix (p. 223)
column matrix (p. 186)
constant matrix (p. 231)
Cramer's rule (p. 223)
determinant (p. 220)
diagonal rule (p. 221)
dimension (p. 185)
element (p. 185)
equal matrices (p. 186)
identity matrix (p. 229)
image (p. 209)
inverse matrix (p. 229)
matrix (p. 185)
matrix equation (p. 231)
preimage (p. 209)
rotation (p. 212)
row matrix (p. 186)
scalar (p. 194)
scalar multiplication (p. 194)
second-order determinant (p. 220)
square matrix (p. 186)
third-order determinant (p. 221)
variable matrix (p. 231)
vertex matrix (p. 209)
zero matrix (p. 186)

Vocabulary Check

Choose the correct term from the list above to complete each sentence. 4. element 8. zero

1. A(n) __________ is a rectangular array of constants or variables. matrix
2. A matrix can be multiplied by a constant called a(n) __________. scalar
3. A matrix that contains the constants in a system of equations is called a(n) __________. constant matrix
4. Each value in a matrix is called a(n) __________.
5. The __________ of a matrix with 4 rows and 3 columns are 4×3. dimensions
6. A(n) __________ occurs when a figure is moved about a center point, usually the origin. rotation
7. The __________ matrix is a square matrix that, when multiplied by another matrix, equals that same matrix. identity
8. In a(n) __________ matrix, every element is zero.
9. The __________ of $\begin{bmatrix} -1 & 2 \\ 2 & -3 \end{bmatrix}$ is -1. determinant
10. If the product of two matrices is the identity matrix, they are __________. inverses

Formative Assessment

Key Vocabulary The page references after each word denote where that term was first introduced. If students have difficulty answering questions 1–10, remind them that they can use these page references to refresh their memories about the vocabulary.

Summative Assessment

CRM Vocabulary Test, p. 54

FL Math Online glencoe.com

Vocabulary PuzzleMaker improves students' mathematics vocabulary using four puzzle formats–crossword, scramble, word search using a word list, and word search using clues. Students can work online or from a printed worksheet.

FOLDABLES® Study Organizer

Dinah Zike's Foldables®

Have students look through the chapter to make sure they have included examples in their Foldables.

Suggest that students keep their Foldables handy while completing the Study Guide and Review pages. Point out that their Foldables can serve as a quick review tool when studying for the chapter test.

Lesson-by-Lesson Review

Intervention If the given examples are not sufficient to review the topics covered by the questions, remind students that the page references tell them where to review that topic in their textbook.

Two-Day Option Have students complete the Lesson-by-Lesson Review on pp. 238–241. Then you can use ExamView® Assessment Suite to customize another review worksheet that practices all the objectives of this chapter or only the objectives on which your students need more help.

Differentiated Instruction

Super DVD: MindJogger Videoquizzes Use this DVD as an alternative format of review for the test.

Additional Answer

14a. buying price: $\begin{bmatrix}15\\25\\30\end{bmatrix}$;

14b. selling price: $\begin{bmatrix}35\\55\\85\end{bmatrix}$;

14c. $\begin{bmatrix}35\\55\\85\end{bmatrix} - \begin{bmatrix}15\\25\\30\end{bmatrix} = \begin{bmatrix}20\\30\\55\end{bmatrix}$

CHAPTER 4 Study Guide and Review

Lesson-by-Lesson Review

4-1 Introduction to Matrices (pp. 185–191)

a. $\begin{bmatrix}64 & 108 & 31\\42 & 9 & 68\end{bmatrix}$

910.1.6.1

11. SALES Three competing retail stores recorded the number and type of customers that purchased items at their stores one day. The following table shows the numbers.

Type of Customer	Store A	Store B	Store C
adult (18 and older)	64	108	31
student (under 18)	42	9	68

a. Write a matrix for the numbers of customers.

b. What are the dimensions of the matrix? **2 × 3**

c. What value is a_{23}? **68**

d. What value is a_{11}? **64**

e. Add the elements in columns 1 and 2 and interpret the results.

f. Would finding the sum of the rows provide any meaningful data? Explain. **No, the stores are competing.**

EXAMPLE 1

A movie house has three theatres; each theatre shows a different movie. The number of people who attended each movie is shown.

Type of Movie	Theatre 1	Theatre 2	Theatre 3
matinee	37	19	26
evening	69	58	75

a. Write a matrix for the number of customers. $\begin{bmatrix}37 & 19 & 26\\69 & 58 & 75\end{bmatrix}$

b. What are the dimensions of the matrix? 2 × 3

c. Add the elements in rows 1 and 2, and interpret the results.
The sum of row 1 is 82, which is the total number of customers at the matinee. The sum of row 2 is 202, which is the total number of customers at the evening show.

11e. The sum of column 1 is 106. This is the total number of customers for Store A. The sum of column 2 is 117. This is the total number of customers for Store B.

4-2 Operations with Matrices (pp. 193–199)

912.D.8.2

Perform the indicated operations. If the matrix does not exist, write *impossible*.

12. $\begin{bmatrix}2\\-6\end{bmatrix} - \begin{bmatrix}-3\\2\end{bmatrix} + \begin{bmatrix}6\\0\end{bmatrix}$ $\begin{bmatrix}11\\-8\end{bmatrix}$

13. $3\left(\begin{bmatrix}-2 & 0\\6 & 8\end{bmatrix} + \begin{bmatrix}1 & 9\\-3 & -4\end{bmatrix}\right)$ $\begin{bmatrix}-3 & 27\\9 & 12\end{bmatrix}$

14. RETAIL Current Fashions buys shirts, jeans and shoes from a manufacturer, marks them up, and then sells them. The table shows the purchase price and the selling price. **a–c. See margin.**

Item	Purchase Price	Selling Price
shirts	\$15	\$35
jeans	\$25	\$55
shoes	\$30	\$85

a. Write a matrix for the purchase price.

b. Write a matrix for the selling price.

c. Use matrix operations to find the profit on 1 shirt, 1 pair of jeans, and 1 pair of shoes.

EXAMPLE 2

Find $2B + 3A$ if $A = \begin{bmatrix}9 & 1\\1 & 2\end{bmatrix}$ and $B = \begin{bmatrix}1 & 4\\3 & 7\end{bmatrix}$.

$2B = 2\begin{bmatrix}1 & 4\\3 & 7\end{bmatrix}$ or $\begin{bmatrix}2 & 8\\6 & 14\end{bmatrix}$

$3A = 3\begin{bmatrix}9 & 1\\1 & 2\end{bmatrix}$ or $\begin{bmatrix}27 & 3\\3 & 6\end{bmatrix}$

$2B + 3A = \begin{bmatrix}2 & 8\\6 & 14\end{bmatrix} + \begin{bmatrix}27 & 3\\3 & 6\end{bmatrix}$ or $\begin{bmatrix}29 & 11\\9 & 20\end{bmatrix}$

4-3 Multiplying Matrices (pp. 200–207)

912.D.8.2

Find each product, if possible.

15. $\begin{bmatrix} 3 & -7 \end{bmatrix} \cdot \begin{bmatrix} 9 \\ -5 \end{bmatrix}$ $[\ 42\ ]$

16. $\begin{bmatrix} -3 & 0 & 2 \\ 6 & -1 & 5 \end{bmatrix} \cdot \begin{bmatrix} 8 & -1 \\ -4 & 3 \\ 6 & 7 \end{bmatrix}$ $\begin{bmatrix} -12 & 17 \\ 82 & 26 \end{bmatrix}$

17. $\begin{bmatrix} 2 & 11 \\ 0 & -3 \\ -6 & 7 \end{bmatrix} \cdot \begin{bmatrix} 0 & 8 & -5 \\ 12 & 0 & 9 \\ 4 & -6 & 7 \end{bmatrix}$ not possible

18. **GROCERIES** Martin bought 1 gallon of milk, 2 apples, 4 frozen dinners, and 1 box of cereal. The following matrix shows the prices for each item respectively.

$[\ \$2.59 \quad \$0.49 \quad \$5.25 \quad \$3.99\ ]$

Use matrix multiplication to find the total amount of money Martin spent at the grocery store. $28.56

EXAMPLE 3

Find XY if $X = \begin{bmatrix} 0 & -6 \\ 3 & 5 \end{bmatrix}$ and $Y = \begin{bmatrix} 8 \\ -1 \end{bmatrix}$.

$XY = \begin{bmatrix} 0 & -6 \\ 3 & 5 \end{bmatrix} \cdot \begin{bmatrix} 8 \\ -1 \end{bmatrix}$ **Write an equation.**

$= \begin{bmatrix} 0(8) + (-6)(-1) \\ 3(8) + 5(-1) \end{bmatrix}$ **Multiply columns by rows.**

$= \begin{bmatrix} 6 \\ 19 \end{bmatrix}$ **Simplify.**

4-4 Transformations with Matrices (pp. 209–217)

912.G.2.4

Use $\triangle ABC$ to find the coordinates of the image after each transformation.

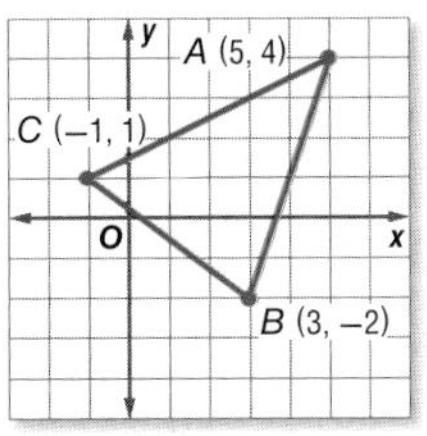

19. translation 2 units left and 3 units up
20. dilation by a scale factor of 3
21. reflection in the x-axis 19–23. See margin.
22. rotation of 180 degrees
23. **QUILTS** Carol used the pattern of a rectangle shown at the right for a quilt piece.

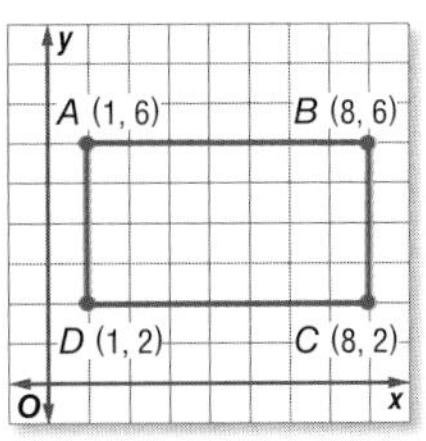

Carol wants to make a rectangle pattern that is twice as long and twice as wide. What will the new coordinates of the rectangle be?

EXAMPLE 4

Find the coordinates of the vertices of the image of $\triangle XYZ$ with $X(-2, 3)$, $Y(6, 6)$, and $Z(8, -3)$ after a rotation of 270° counterclockwise about the origin.

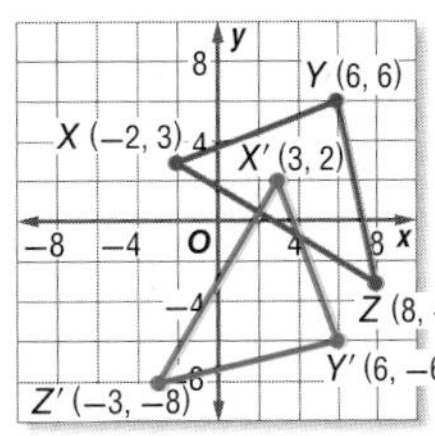

Write the ordered pairs in a vertex matrix. Then multiply by the rotation matrix.

$$\begin{bmatrix} 0 & 1 \\ -1 & 0 \end{bmatrix} \cdot \begin{bmatrix} -2 & 6 & 8 \\ 3 & 6 & -3 \end{bmatrix} = \begin{bmatrix} 3 & 6 & -3 \\ 2 & -6 & -8 \end{bmatrix}$$

The vertices of $\triangle X'Y'Z'$ are $X'(3, 2)$, $Y'(6, -6)$, and $Z'(-3, -8)$.

Additional Answers

19. $A'(3, 7)$, $B'(1, 1)$, $C'(-3, 4)$
20. $A'(15, 12)$, $B'(9, -6)$, $C'(-3, 3)$
21. $A'(5, -4)$, $B'(3, 2)$, $C'(-1, -1)$
22. $A'(-5, -4)$, $B'(-3, 2)$, $C'(1, -1)$
23. $A'(2, 12)$, $B'(16, 12)$, $C'(16, 4)$, $D'(2, 4)$

Problem Solving Review

For additional practice in problem solving for Chapter 4, see the Mixed Problem Solving Appendix, p. 983, in the Student Handbook section.

Anticipation Guide

Have students complete the Chapter 4 Anticipation Guide and discuss how their responses have changed now that they have completed Chapter 4.

4-5 Determinants and Cramer's Rule (pp. 220–228)

912.A.3.14

Evaluate each determinant.

24. $\begin{vmatrix} 2 & 4 \\ 7 & -3 \end{vmatrix}$ −34

25. $\begin{vmatrix} 2 & 3 & -1 \\ 0 & 2 & 4 \\ -2 & 5 & 6 \end{vmatrix}$ −44

Use Cramer's Rule to solve each system of equations.

26. $3x - y = 0$
$5x + 2y = 22$ (2, 6)

27. $5x + 2y = 4$
$3x + 4y + 2z = 6$
$7x + 3y + 4z = 29$ (2, −3, 6)

28. JEWELRY Alana paid \$98.25 for 3 necklaces and 2 pairs of earrings. Petra paid \$133.50 for 2 necklaces and 4 pairs of earrings. Use Cramer's Rule to find out how much 1 necklace costs and how much 1 pair of earrings costs. necklace: \$15.75; pair of earrings: \$25.50

EXAMPLE 5

Evaluate $\begin{vmatrix} 4 & -6 \\ 2 & 5 \end{vmatrix}$.

$\begin{vmatrix} 4 & -6 \\ 2 & 5 \end{vmatrix} = 4(5) - 2(-6)$ **Definition of determinant**

$= 20 + 12$ or 32 **Simplify.**

EXAMPLE 6

Use Cramer's Rule to solve $2a + 6b = -1$ and $a + 8b = 2$.

$a = \dfrac{\begin{vmatrix} -1 & 6 \\ 2 & 8 \end{vmatrix}}{\begin{vmatrix} 2 & 6 \\ 1 & 8 \end{vmatrix}}$ **Cramer's Rule** $b = \dfrac{\begin{vmatrix} 2 & -1 \\ 1 & 2 \end{vmatrix}}{\begin{vmatrix} 2 & 6 \\ 1 & 8 \end{vmatrix}}$

$= \dfrac{-8 - 12}{16 - 6}$ **Evaluate each determinant.** $= \dfrac{4 + 1}{16 - 6}$

$= \dfrac{-20}{10}$ or -2 **Simplify.** $= \dfrac{5}{10}$ or $\dfrac{1}{2}$

The solution is $\left(-2, \frac{1}{2}\right)$.

4-6 Inverse Matrices and Systems of Equations (pp. 229–235)

912.A.3.14

Find the inverse of each matrix, if it exists.

29. $\begin{bmatrix} 7 & 4 \\ 3 & 2 \end{bmatrix}$ $\frac{1}{2}\begin{bmatrix} 2 & -4 \\ -3 & 7 \end{bmatrix}$

30. $\begin{bmatrix} 2 & 5 \\ -5 & -13 \end{bmatrix}$ $\begin{bmatrix} 13 & 5 \\ -5 & -2 \end{bmatrix}$

31. $\begin{bmatrix} 6 & -3 \\ -8 & 4 \end{bmatrix}$ No inverse exists.

Use a matrix equation to solve each system of equations.

32. $\begin{bmatrix} 5 & 3 \\ 3 & 2 \end{bmatrix} \cdot \begin{bmatrix} x \\ y \end{bmatrix} = \begin{bmatrix} 4 \\ 0 \end{bmatrix}$ (8, −12)

33. $\begin{bmatrix} 3 & -1 \\ 1 & 2 \end{bmatrix} \cdot \begin{bmatrix} a \\ b \end{bmatrix} = \begin{bmatrix} 5 \\ 4 \end{bmatrix}$ (2, 1)

34. HEALTH FOOD Heath sells nuts and raisins by the pound. Sonia bought 2 pounds of nuts and 2 pounds of raisins for \$23.50. Drew bought 3 pounds of nuts and 1 pound of raisins for \$22.25. What is the cost of 1 pound of nuts and 1 pound of raisins? nuts: \$5.25 per pound; raisins: \$6.50 per pound

EXAMPLE 7

Solve $\begin{bmatrix} 2 & -5 \\ 3 & -6 \end{bmatrix} \cdot \begin{bmatrix} x \\ y \end{bmatrix} = \begin{bmatrix} 15 \\ 36 \end{bmatrix}$.

Step 1 Find the inverse of the coefficient matrix.

$A^{-1} = \dfrac{1}{-12 - (-15)}\begin{bmatrix} -6 & 5 \\ -3 & 2 \end{bmatrix}$ or $\dfrac{1}{3}\begin{bmatrix} -6 & 5 \\ -3 & 2 \end{bmatrix}$

Step 2 Multiply each side by the inverse matrix.

$\frac{1}{3}\begin{bmatrix} -6 & 5 \\ -3 & 2 \end{bmatrix} \cdot \begin{bmatrix} 2 & -5 \\ 3 & -6 \end{bmatrix} \cdot \begin{bmatrix} x \\ y \end{bmatrix} = \frac{1}{3}\begin{bmatrix} -6 & 5 \\ -3 & 2 \end{bmatrix} \cdot \begin{bmatrix} 15 \\ 36 \end{bmatrix}$

$\begin{bmatrix} 1 & 0 \\ 0 & 1 \end{bmatrix} \cdot \begin{bmatrix} x \\ y \end{bmatrix} = \frac{1}{3}\begin{bmatrix} 90 \\ 27 \end{bmatrix}$

$\begin{bmatrix} x \\ y \end{bmatrix} = \begin{bmatrix} 30 \\ 9 \end{bmatrix}$

FL Math Online glencoe.com Chapter Test

Identify each element of matrix

$A = \begin{bmatrix} 2 & 2 & 7 \\ 9 & 1 & 1 \\ 8 & 0 & 8 \end{bmatrix}$.

1. a_{22} 1

2. a_{31} 8

Perform the indicated operations. If the matrix does not exist, write *impossible*. 3–6. See margin.

3. $-3\begin{bmatrix} 4a \\ 0 \\ -3 \end{bmatrix} + 4\begin{bmatrix} -2 \\ 3 \\ -1 \end{bmatrix}$

4. $\begin{bmatrix} -3 & 0 \\ 1 & 5 \end{bmatrix} \cdot \begin{bmatrix} 2 & 4 \\ -6 & 0 \end{bmatrix}$

5. $\begin{bmatrix} 2 & 0 \\ -3 & 5 \\ 1 & 4 \end{bmatrix} \cdot \begin{bmatrix} 3 \\ -2 \end{bmatrix}$

6. $\begin{bmatrix} -5 & 7 \\ 6 & 8 \end{bmatrix} - \begin{bmatrix} 4 & 0 & -2 \\ 9 & 0 & 1 \end{bmatrix}$

7. **FINANCIAL LITERACY** Soren sells children's educational books door to door to save for college. The following table shows the cost of a set of books and the selling price. He sold 20 sets of encyclopedias, 32 sets of science books, and 14 sets of literature books.

Type of Book	Cost	Selling Price
Encyclopedia set	\$35	\$105
Science books	\$25	\$85
Literature books	\$40	\$125

a. Organize the data into two matrices. Then use matrix multiplication to find the total amount that Soren paid for the books. a, b. See margin.

b. Use matrix multiplication to find the total amount that buyers paid for the books.

c. Use matrix operations to find how much money Soren made on his sales. \$4510

8. Find $AB - AC$ if $A = \begin{bmatrix} 3 & 8 \\ -3 & -4 \end{bmatrix}$, $B = \begin{bmatrix} -7 & 5 \\ 5 & -4 \end{bmatrix}$, and $C = \begin{bmatrix} -4 & 7 \\ 2 & 0 \end{bmatrix}$. $\begin{bmatrix} 15 & -38 \\ -3 & 22 \end{bmatrix}$

9. Triangle ABC with $A(0, 2)$, $B(1.5, -1.5)$, and $C(-2.5, 0)$ is dilated so that its perimeter is three times the original perimeter. Write the vertex matrix for $\triangle ABC$. Then find the coordinates of the image after the dilation. See margin.

10. **NGSSS PRACTICE** Triangle $A'B'C'$ is an image of $\triangle ABC$. A table of the vertices of each triangle is shown. What are the coordinates of C'? B

△ABC	△A′B′C′
A(3, 4)	A′(5, 3)
B(1, −2)	B′(3, −3)
C(5, −4)	C′(?, ?)

A. (−5, 7)
B. (7, −5)
C. (4, −2)
D. (7, −3)

Triangle XYZ has vertices $X(1, 2)$, $Y(3, 6)$, and $Z(-1, 4)$.

11. Find the coordinates of the vertices of a triangle that is a dilation of $\triangle XYZ$ with a perimeter two times that of $\triangle XYZ$. $X(2, 4)$, $Y(6, 12)$, $Z(-2, 8)$

12. Find the coordinates of the vertices of $\triangle XYZ$ after it is rotated 90 degrees counterclockwise about the origin. $X(-2, 1)$, $Y(-6, 3)$, $Z(-4, -1)$

13. Use a determinant to find the area of $\triangle XYZ$. 6 square units

14. **NGSSS PRACTICE** What is the value of $\begin{vmatrix} 2 & 3 & -1 \\ 0 & 2 & 4 \\ -2 & 5 & 6 \end{vmatrix}$? F

F. −44
G. 44
H. $\frac{1}{44}$
I. $-\frac{1}{44}$

Find the inverse of each matrix, if it exists.

15. $\begin{bmatrix} 5 & 0 \\ 0 & 1 \end{bmatrix}$ $\begin{bmatrix} \frac{1}{5} & 0 \\ 0 & 1 \end{bmatrix}$

16. $\begin{bmatrix} 1 & 2 \\ 2 & 1 \end{bmatrix}$ $\begin{bmatrix} -\frac{1}{3} & \frac{2}{3} \\ \frac{2}{3} & -\frac{1}{3} \end{bmatrix}$

17. $\begin{bmatrix} 6 & 3 \\ 8 & 4 \end{bmatrix}$ No inverse exists.

18. $\begin{bmatrix} -3 & -2 \\ 6 & 4 \end{bmatrix}$ No inverse exists.

Use Cramer's Rule to solve the following system of equations.

19. $2x - y = -9$; $x + 2y = 8$ $(-2, 5)$

20. $x - y + 2z = 0$; $3x + z = 11$; $-x + 2y = 0$ $(4, 2, -1)$

21. $6x + 2y + 4z = 2$; $3x + 4y - 8z = -3$; $-3x - 6y + 12z = 5$ $\left(\frac{1}{3}, -\frac{1}{2}, \frac{1}{4}\right)$

ExamView Assessment Suite Customize and create multiple versions of your chapter test and their answer keys. All of the questions from the leveled chapter tests in the *Chapter 4 Resource Masters* are also available on ExamView® Assessment Suite.

Additional Answers

3. $\begin{bmatrix} -12a - 8 \\ 12 \\ 5 \end{bmatrix}$

4. $\begin{bmatrix} -6 & -12 \\ -28 & 4 \end{bmatrix}$

5. $\begin{bmatrix} 6 \\ -19 \\ -5 \end{bmatrix}$

6. impossible

7a. $[20\ \ 32\ \ 14] \cdot \begin{bmatrix} 35 \\ 25 \\ 40 \end{bmatrix} = [2060]$

\$2060

7b. $[20\ \ 32\ \ 14] \cdot \begin{bmatrix} 105 \\ 85 \\ 125 \end{bmatrix} = [6570]$

\$6570

9. $\begin{bmatrix} 0 & 1.5 & -2.5 \\ 2 & -1.5 & 0 \end{bmatrix}$; $A'(0, 6)$, $B'(4.5, -4.5)$, $C'(-7.5, 0)$

Intervention Planner

Tier 1 On Level	Tier 2 Strategic Intervention approaching grade level	Tier 3 Intensive Intervention 2 or more grades below level
If students miss about 25% of the exercises or less,	**If** students miss about 50% of the exercises,	**If** students miss about 75% of the exercises,
Then choose a resource:	**Then** choose a resource:	**Then** use *Math Triumphs, Alg. 2*
SE Lessons 4-1, 4-2, 4-3, 4-4, 4-5, and 4-6	**CRM** Study Guide and Intervention, Chapter 4, pp. 5–6, 11–12, 17–18, 23–24, 30–31, and 37–38	
CRM Skills Practice, Chapter 4, pp. 7, 13, 19, 25, 32, and 39		
TE Chapter Project, p. 182		
FL Math Online Self-Check Quiz	FL Math Online Extra Examples, Personal Tutor, Homework Help	FL Math Online Extra Examples, Personal Tutor, Homework Help, Review Vocabulary

1 FOCUS

Objective Use the strategy of gridded response questions to solve standardized test problems.

2 TEACH

Scaffolding Questions

Ask:

- Have you ever taken a test for which you had to darken a circle that corresponds to the correct answer on an answer sheet? Answers will vary.
- What sort of errors have you been prone to making when using this type of answer sheet? Possible answers: skip an answer, shade too many circles, make stray marks, input the digits incorrectly

CHAPTER 4 Preparing for Standardized Tests

Gridded Response Questions

In addition to multiple choice, short answer, and extended response questions, you will likely encounter gridded response questions on standardized tests. For gridded response questions, you must print your answer on an answer sheet and mark in the correct circles on the grid to match your answer.

Strategies for Solving Gridded Response Questions

Step 1

Read the problem carefully and solve.

- Be sure your answer makes sense.
- If time permits, check your answer

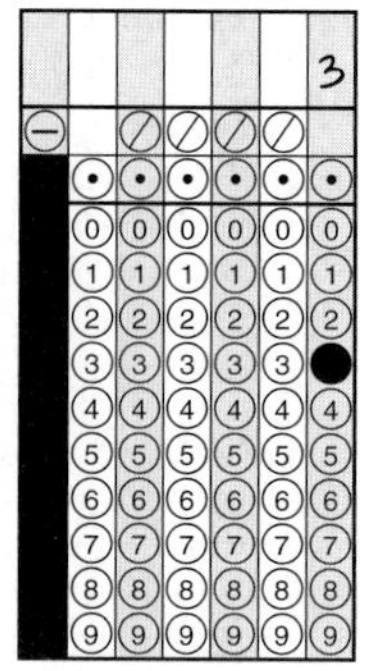

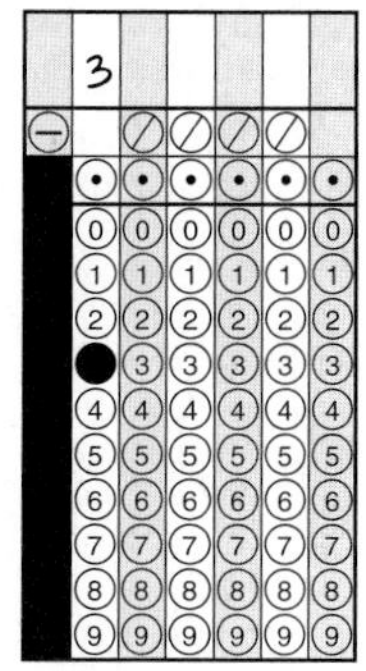

Step 2

Print your answer in the answer boxes.

- Print only one digit or symbol in each answer box.
- Do not write any digits or symbols outside the answer boxes.
- Answers to gridded response questions may be whole numbers, decimals, or fractions.

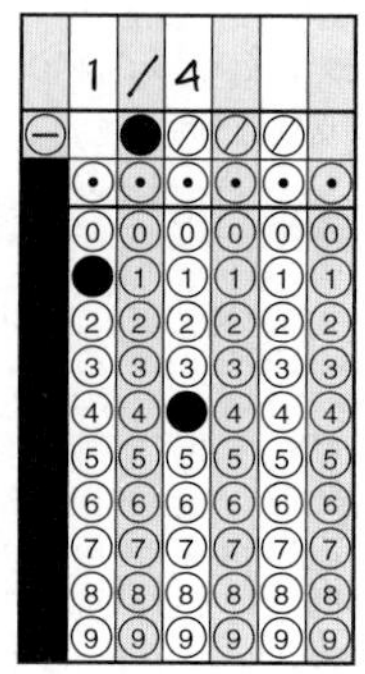

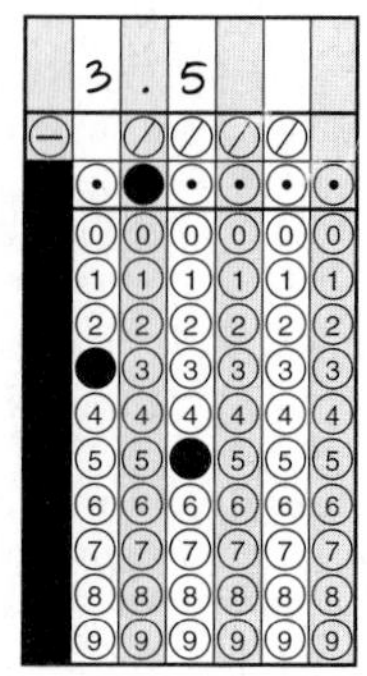

Step 3

Fill in the grid.

- Fill in only one bubble for every answer box that you have written in. Be sure not to fill in a bubble under a blank answer box.
- Fill in each bubble completely and clearly.

NGSSS PRACTICE EXAMPLE

Read the problem. Identify what you need to know. Then use the information in the problem to solve.

GRIDDED RESPONSE Christopher stopped for gas twice during a trip. The price at the first station was $2.96 per gallon. At the second, the price was $3.15 per gallon. He bought a total of 28.3 gallons of gas between the two stops and spent a total of $86.39. How many gallons did he buy at the first station?

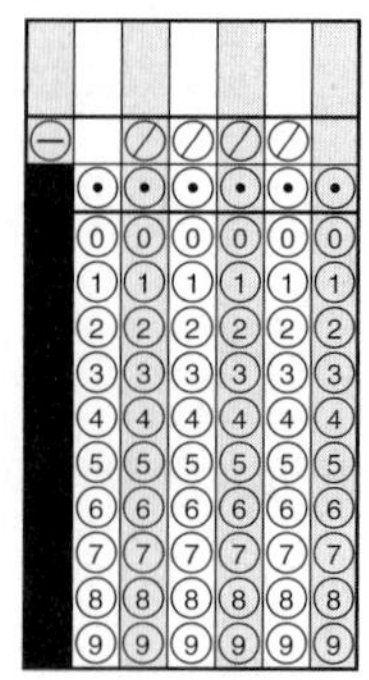

Read the problem carefully. The problem can be solved using a system of equations. Let x represent the number of gallons bought at the first gas station, and let y represent the number of gallons bought at the second station. The following system models the situation.

$$x + y = 28.3$$
$$2.96x + 3.15y = 86.39$$

The system of equations can be solved algebraically. However, if time is a concern, it may be faster and simpler to use matrices and a calculator to solve the system.

Solve the Problem

Enter the coefficient and constant matrices into a graphing calculator and solve using inverses.

$$\begin{bmatrix} 1 & 1 \\ 2.96 & 3.15 \end{bmatrix}\begin{bmatrix} x \\ y \end{bmatrix} = \begin{bmatrix} 28.3 \\ 86.39 \end{bmatrix}$$

$$A = \begin{bmatrix} 1 & 1 \\ 2.96 & 3.15 \end{bmatrix}, B = \begin{bmatrix} 28.3 \\ 86.39 \end{bmatrix}$$

$$\begin{bmatrix} x \\ y \end{bmatrix} = A^{-1}B = \begin{bmatrix} 14.5 \\ 13.8 \end{bmatrix}$$

So, Christopher bought 14.5 gallons of gasoline at the first gas station. Carefully fill in the grid to show 14.5.

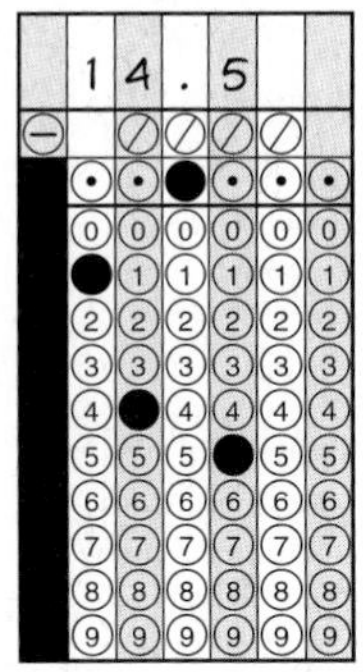

Exercises

Read each problem. Identify what you need to know. Then use the information in the problem to solve. Copy and complete an answer grid on your paper.

1. Heather has 23 nickels, dimes, and quarters. The total value of all the coins is $3.40. If she has twice as many quarters as dimes, how many nickels does Heather have? **8**

2. Find the value of the determinant $\begin{vmatrix} -1 & 4 \\ -3 & 0 \end{vmatrix}$. **12**

3. Kendra is displaying eight sweaters in a store window. There are four identical red sweaters, three identical brown sweaters, and one white sweater. How may different arrangements of the eight sweaters are possible? **280**

4. Evaluate the determinant of matrix H.

$$H = \begin{bmatrix} -2 & 0 & 3 \\ -5 & -7 & -1 \\ 4 & -8 & 1 \end{bmatrix}$$ **234**

5. Polygon $DABC$ is rotated 90° counterclockwise and then reflected over the line $y = x$. What is the x-coordinate of the final image of A? **3**

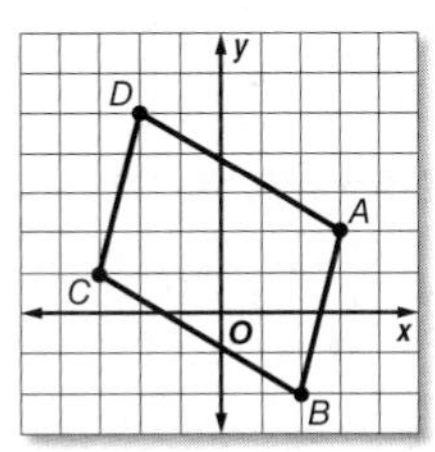

Additional Example

GRIDDED RESPONSE Maureen picked beans and tomatoes at a local u-pick farm. The price of the beans is $0.75 per pound. The price of the tomatoes is $0.50 per pound. Maureen picked a total of 47 pounds and spent $28.25. How many pounds of tomatoes did Maureen pick?

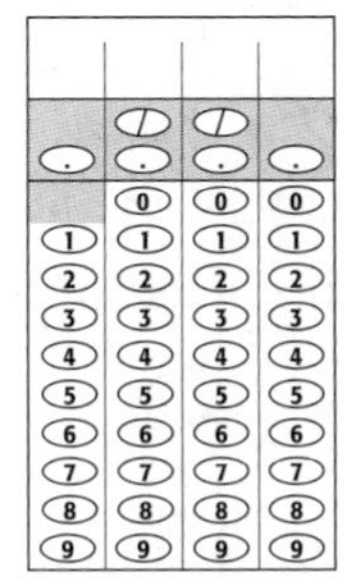

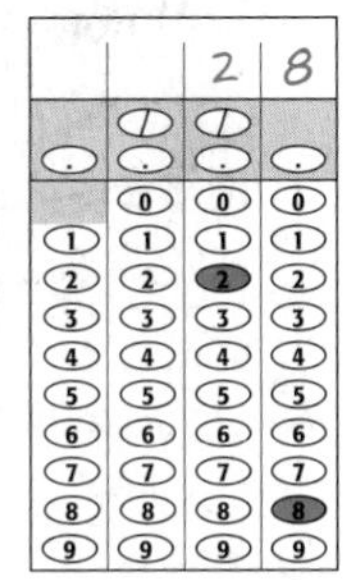

3 ASSESS

Use Exercises 1–5 to assess students' understanding.

Chapter 4 Preparing for Standardized Tests 243

Diagnose Student Errors

Survey student responses for each item. Class trends may indicate common errors and misconceptions.

1. A. misinterpreted the key word for the operation
B. correct
C. misinterpreted the key word for the operation
D. reversed the two matrices

3. F. added the elements instead of multiplying
G. correct
H. guess
I. did not understand when a matrix product is defined

4. A. found the number of tomatoes sold
B. used an incorrect matrix equation
C. used an incorrect matrix equation
D. correct

5. F. correct
G. did not substitute correctly
H. did not substitute correctly
I. guess

7. A. incorrectly found the sum of the products of the diagonals
B. incorrectly found the sum of the products of the diagonals
C. incorrectly found the sum of the products of the diagonals
D. correct

11. A. correct
B. reversed the rows with the columns
C. counted the elements instead of the columns
D. guess

13. F. did not reverse the inequality sign when multiplying or dividing by a negative
G. guess
H. subtracted 6–7 before finding the value of absolute value expression
I. correct

Read each question. Then fill in the correct answer on the answer document provided by your teacher or on a sheet of paper.

1. Matrix L shows the average low temperature, in degrees Fahrenheit, each month where Terrance lives. Matrix H shows the monthly average high temperature.

$$L = \begin{bmatrix} 24.1 & 27.7 & 35.9 \\ 44.1 & 53.6 & 62.2 \\ 66.4 & 64.9 & 57.9 \\ 46.4 & 37.3 & 28.4 \end{bmatrix}$$

$$H = \begin{bmatrix} 39.9 & 45.2 & 55.3 \\ 65.1 & 74.0 & 82.3 \\ 85.9 & 84.6 & 78.1 \\ 66.9 & 54.5 & 44.3 \end{bmatrix}$$

Which operation would you use to find the difference between the average high temperature and the average low temperature each month? **B**

A. $L + H$

B. $H - L$

C. $H \times L$

D. $L - H$

2. **SHORT RESPONSE** Does matrix B have an inverse? Explain why or why not.

$$B = \begin{bmatrix} 3 & -2 \\ -9 & 6 \end{bmatrix}$$

Sample answer: No; the determinant of the matrix is 0, so it does not have an inverse.

3. Find $[3 \quad 1] \cdot \begin{bmatrix} 2 \\ 5 \end{bmatrix}$, if possible. **G**

F. $[-3]$

G. $[-1]$

H. $\begin{bmatrix} 8 & -4 \\ 12 & 6 \end{bmatrix}$

I. undefined

Test-Taking Tip

Question 3 The product of a 1-by-2 matrix and a 2-by-1 matrix is a 1-by-1 matrix. So, answer choices H and I can be eliminated.

4. Suppose Kendall sells apples and tomatoes at a farmer's market. If he sold 280 items one morning and earned \$65.20, how many apples did he sell? **D**

Item	Cost
apple	\$0.25
tomato	\$0.20

A. 96

B. 126

C. 168

D. 184

5. What are the coordinates of the x- and y-intercepts of the graph of $2y = 4x + 3$? **F**

F. $\left(-\frac{3}{4}, 0\right), \left(0, \frac{3}{2}\right)$

G. $\left(\frac{2}{3}, 0\right), (0, 3)$

H. $(-2, 0), \left(0, \frac{1}{2}\right)$

I. $(2, 0), \left(0, \frac{3}{2}\right)$

6. **EXTENDED RESPONSE** Use the triangle shown on the coordinate grid to answer each question.

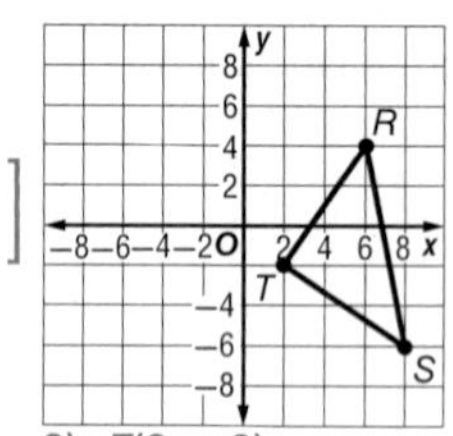

b. $\begin{bmatrix} 6 & 8 & 2 \\ 4 & -6 & -2 \end{bmatrix}$

c. $\begin{bmatrix} 0 & 1 \\ 1 & 0 \end{bmatrix}$

a. $R(6, 4)$, $S(8, -6)$, $T(2, -2)$

a. What are the vertices of $\triangle RST$?

b. Write the coordinates in a vertex matrix.

c. Suppose the triangle is reflected across the line $y = x$. What matrix can you multiply by the vertex matrix to find the reflected vertices?

d. What are the vertices of the reflected triangle?
$R'(4, 6)$, $S'(-6, 8)$, $T'(-2, 2)$

7. Triangle DEF has vertices $D(-6, 2)$, $E(3, 5)$, and $F(8, -7)$. Evaluate the determinant below to find the area of the triangle. D

$$A = \frac{1}{2}\begin{vmatrix} -6 & 2 & 1 \\ 3 & 5 & 1 \\ 8 & -7 & 1 \end{vmatrix}$$

A. 54.5 square units

B. 58 square units

C. 60 square units

D. 61.5 square units

8. **GRIDDED RESPONSE** Evaluate the determinant of $W = \begin{bmatrix} 3 & 1 & 0 \\ 2 & 5 & -4 \\ 0 & -1 & 1 \end{bmatrix}$. 1

9. Which equation is equivalent to $4x - 3(2x + 7) = 5x$? F

F. $-2x - 21 = 5x$

G. $-2x + 7 = 5x$

H. $-2x + 21 = 5x$

I. $6x - 7 = 5x$

10. **GRIDDED RESPONSE** Andrea is using a coordinate grid to design a new deck for her backyard. The deck is represented by the intersection of $y \leq 20$, $x \leq 16$, $y \geq 0$, $x \geq 0$ and $y \leq -x + 32$. If each unit of the coordinate grid represents 1 foot, what is the area of the deck? Express your answer in square feet. 312

11. What are the dimensions of $D = \begin{bmatrix} 4 & -6 \\ 9 & 2 \\ 1 & 0 \\ -3 & -5 \end{bmatrix}$? (Lesson 4-1) A

A. 4 by 2

B. 2 by 4

C. 4 by 8

D. 8 by 4

12. **SHORT RESPONSE** Valeria has 14 quarters and dimes. The total value of all the coins is \$2.75. Use this information to answer each question.

a. Let d represent the number of dimes that Valeria has, and let q represent the number of quarters. Write a system of equations to model the situation. $d + q = 14$; $0.1d + 0.25q = 2.75$

b. Write a matrix equation that can be used to solve for d and q. See margin.

c. Solve your matrix equation using inverses. How many dimes and quarters does Valeria have? 5 dimes, 9 quarters

13. What is the solution set of $6 - |x + 7| \leq -2$? I

F. $\{x \mid -15 \leq x \leq 1\}$

G. $\{x \mid -1 \leq x \leq 3\}$

H. $\{x \mid x \leq -1 \text{ or } x \geq 3\}$

I. $\{x \mid x \leq -15 \text{ or } x \geq 1\}$

14. **EXTENDED RESPONSE** Describe in your own words when two matrices can be multiplied. Describe when two matrices cannot be multiplied. Give an example. See margin.

Need Extra Help?

If you missed Question...	1	2	3	4	5	6	7	8	9	10	11	12	13	14
Go to Lesson or Page...	4-2	4-6	4-3	3-2	2-2	4-4	4-5	4-5	1-2	3-1	4-1	4-6	2-8	4-1
For help with NGSSS...	912.D.8.2	912.D.8.2	912.D.8.2	912.A.3.15	912.A.3.10	912.G.2.6	912.D.8.2	912.D.8.2	912.A.3.1	912.A.3.14	912.D.8.2	912.D.8.2	912.A.3.4	912.D.8.2

Formative Assessment

You can use these two pages to benchmark student progress.

Chapter 4 Resource Masters

- Standardized Test Practice, pp. 68–70

ExamView Assessment Suite Create practice worksheets or tests that align to your state's standards as well as TIMSS and NAEP tests.

Homework Option

Get Ready for Chapter 5 Assign students the exercises on p. 247 as homework to assess whether they possess the prerequisite skills needed for the next chapter.

Additional Answers

12b. $\begin{bmatrix} 1 & 1 \\ 0.1 & 0.25 \end{bmatrix}\begin{bmatrix} d \\ q \end{bmatrix} = \begin{bmatrix} 14 \\ 2.75 \end{bmatrix}$

14. Sample answer: If the dimensions of A are m by n, and the dimensions of B are c by d, AB exists if and only if $n = c$. Check students' examples.

Pages 198–199, Lesson 4-2

35. To show that the Commutative Property of Matrix Addition is true for 2 × 2 matrices, let $A = \begin{bmatrix} a & b \\ c & d \end{bmatrix}$ and $B = \begin{bmatrix} e & f \\ g & h \end{bmatrix}$. Show that $A + B = B + A$.

$A + B = \begin{bmatrix} a & b \\ c & d \end{bmatrix} + \begin{bmatrix} e & f \\ g & h \end{bmatrix}$	Substitution
$= \begin{bmatrix} a+e & b+f \\ c+g & d+h \end{bmatrix}$	Definition of matrix addition
$= \begin{bmatrix} e+a & f+b \\ g+c & h+d \end{bmatrix}$	Commutative Property of Addition for Real Numbers
$= \begin{bmatrix} e & f \\ g & h \end{bmatrix} + \begin{bmatrix} a & b \\ c & d \end{bmatrix}$	Definition of matrix addition
$= B + A$	Substitution

36.

$(A + B) + C = \left(\begin{bmatrix} a & b \\ c & d \end{bmatrix} + \begin{bmatrix} e & f \\ g & h \end{bmatrix}\right) + \begin{bmatrix} j & k \\ m & n \end{bmatrix}$	Substitution
$= \begin{bmatrix} a+e & b+f \\ c+g & d+h \end{bmatrix} + \begin{bmatrix} j & k \\ m & n \end{bmatrix}$	Definition of matrix addition
$= \begin{bmatrix} a+e+j & b+f+k \\ c+g+m & d+h+n \end{bmatrix}$	Definition of matrix addition
$= \begin{bmatrix} a+(e+j) & b+(f+k) \\ c+(g+m) & d+(h+n) \end{bmatrix}$	Associative Property of Addition
$= \begin{bmatrix} a & b \\ c & d \end{bmatrix} + \begin{bmatrix} e+j & f+k \\ g+m & h+n \end{bmatrix}$	Definition of matrix addition
$= \begin{bmatrix} a & b \\ c & d \end{bmatrix} + \left(\begin{bmatrix} e & f \\ g & h \end{bmatrix} + \begin{bmatrix} j & k \\ m & n \end{bmatrix}\right)$	Definition of matrix addition
$= A + (B + C)$	Substitution

40. Sample answer: First, multiply every element in D by 4. Then, multiply every element in C by 3. Finally, subtract the elements in $3C$ from the corresponding elements in $4D$. The result is a matrix equivalent to $4D - 3C$.

51.

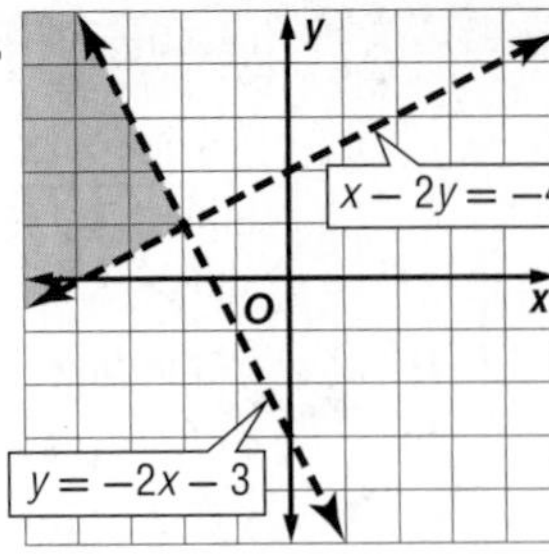

52.

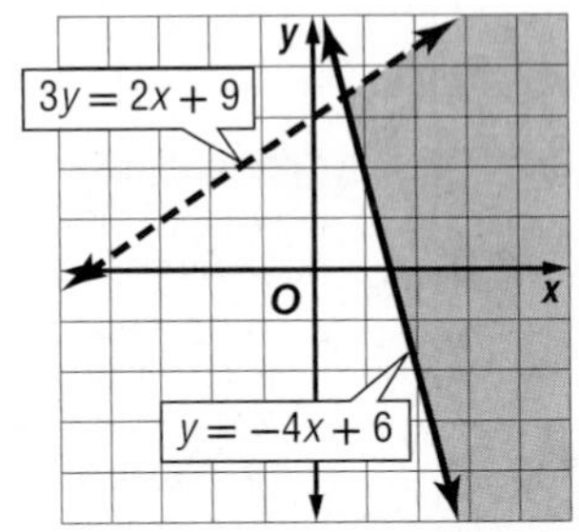

53.

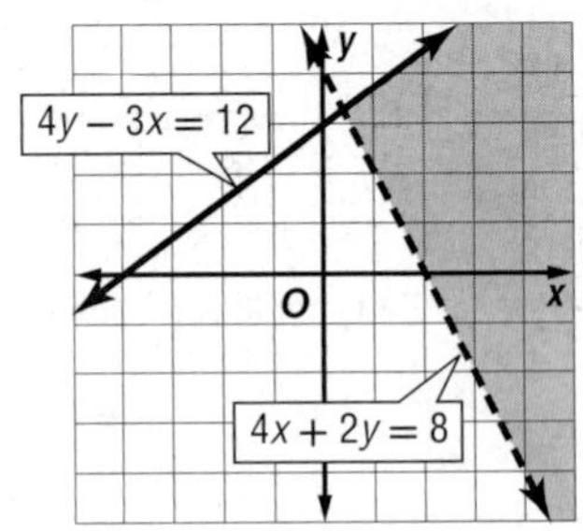

Pages 206–207, Lesson 4-3

47a.

$c(A + B) = c\left(\begin{bmatrix} a & b \\ d & e \end{bmatrix} + \begin{bmatrix} w & x \\ y & z \end{bmatrix}\right)$	Substitution
$= c\begin{bmatrix} a+w & b+x \\ d+y & e+z \end{bmatrix}$	Definition of matrix addition
$= \begin{bmatrix} ca+cw & cb+cx \\ cd+cy & ce+cz \end{bmatrix}$	Definition of scalar multiplication
$= \begin{bmatrix} ca & cb \\ cd & ce \end{bmatrix} + \begin{bmatrix} cw & cx \\ cy & cz \end{bmatrix}$	Definition of matrix addition
$= cA + cB$	Substitution

47b. $C(A+B) = \begin{bmatrix} a & b \\ c & d \end{bmatrix}\left(\begin{bmatrix} e & f \\ g & h \end{bmatrix} + \begin{bmatrix} j & k \\ m & n \end{bmatrix}\right)$ Substitution

$= \begin{bmatrix} a & b \\ c & d \end{bmatrix}\begin{bmatrix} e+j & f+k \\ g+m & h+n \end{bmatrix}$ Definition of matrix addition

$= \begin{bmatrix} a(e+j)+b(g+m) & a(f+k)+b(h+n) \\ c(e+j)+d(g+m) & c(f+k)+d(h+n) \end{bmatrix}$ Definition of matrix multiplication

$= \begin{bmatrix} ea+ja+gb+mb & fa+ka+hb+nb \\ ec+jc+gd+md & fc+kc+hd+nd \end{bmatrix}$ Distributive Property

$= \begin{bmatrix} ea+gb+ja+mb & fa+hb+ka+nb \\ ec+gd+jc+md & fc+hd+kc+nd \end{bmatrix}$ Commutative Property of Addition

$= \begin{bmatrix} ea+gb & fa+hb \\ ec+gd & fc+hd \end{bmatrix} + \begin{bmatrix} ja+mb & ka+nb \\ jc+md & kc+nd \end{bmatrix}$ Definition of matrix addition

$= CA + CB$ Definition of matrix multiplication

$(A+B)C = \left(\begin{bmatrix} a_{11} & a_{12} \\ a_{21} & a_{22} \end{bmatrix} + \begin{bmatrix} b_{11} & b_{12} \\ b_{21} & b_{22} \end{bmatrix}\right)\begin{bmatrix} c_{11} & c_{12} \\ c_{21} & c_{22} \end{bmatrix}$ Substitution

$= \begin{bmatrix} a_{11}+b_{11} & a_{12}+b_{12} \\ a_{21}+b_{21} & a_{22}+b_{22} \end{bmatrix}\begin{bmatrix} c_{11} & c_{12} \\ c_{21} & c_{22} \end{bmatrix}$ Definition of Matrix Addition

$= \begin{bmatrix} (a_{11}+b_{11})c_{11}+(a_{12}+b_{12})c_{21} & (a_{11}+b_{11})c_{12}+(a_{12}+b_{12})c_{22} \\ (a_{21}+b_{21})c_{11}+(a_{22}+b_{22})c_{21} & (a_{21}+b_{21})c_{12}+(a_{22}+b_{22})c_{22} \end{bmatrix}$ Definition of Matrix Multiplication

$= \begin{bmatrix} a_{11}c_{11}+b_{11}c_{11}+a_{12}c_{21}+b_{12}c_{21} & a_{11}c_{12}+b_{11}c_{12}+a_{12}c_{22}+b_{12}c_{22} \\ a_{21}c_{11}+b_{21}c_{11}+a_{22}c_{21}+b_{22}c_{21} & a_{21}c_{12}+b_{21}c_{12}+a_{22}c_{22}+b_{22}c_{22} \end{bmatrix}$ Distributive Property

$= \begin{bmatrix} a_{11}c_{11}+a_{12}c_{21}+b_{11}c_{11}+b_{12}c_{21} & a_{11}c_{12}+a_{12}c_{22}+b_{11}c_{12}+b_{12}c_{22} \\ a_{21}c_{11}+a_{22}c_{21}+b_{21}c_{11}+b_{22}c_{21} & a_{21}c_{12}+a_{22}c_{22}+b_{21}c_{12}+b_{22}c_{22} \end{bmatrix}$ Commutative Property of Addition

$= \begin{bmatrix} a_{11}c_{11}+a_{12}c_{21} & a_{11}c_{12}+a_{12}c_{22} \\ a_{21}c_{11}+a_{22}c_{21} & a_{21}c_{12}+a_{22}c_{22} \end{bmatrix} + \begin{bmatrix} b_{11}c_{11}+b_{12}c_{21} & b_{11}c_{12}+b_{12}c_{22} \\ b_{21}c_{11}+b_{22}c_{21} & b_{21}c_{12}+b_{22}c_{22} \end{bmatrix}$ Definition of Matrix Addition

$= AC + BC$ Definition of Matrix Multiplication

47c. $(AB)C = \left(\begin{bmatrix} a_{11} & a_{12} \\ a_{21} & a_{22} \end{bmatrix}\begin{bmatrix} b_{11} & b_{12} \\ b_{21} & b_{22} \end{bmatrix}\right)\begin{bmatrix} c_{11} & c_{12} \\ c_{21} & c_{22} \end{bmatrix}$ Substitution

$= \begin{bmatrix} a_{11}b_{11}+a_{12}b_{21} & a_{11}b_{12}+a_{12}b_{22} \\ a_{21}b_{11}+a_{22}b_{21} & a_{21}b_{12}+a_{22}b_{22} \end{bmatrix}\begin{bmatrix} c_{11} & c_{12} \\ c_{21} & c_{22} \end{bmatrix}$ Definition of Matrix Multiplication

$= \begin{bmatrix} (a_{11}b_{11}+a_{12}b_{21})c_{11}+(a_{11}b_{12}+a_{12}b_{22})c_{21} & (a_{11}b_{11}+a_{12}b_{21})c_{12}+(a_{11}b_{12}+a_{12}b_{22})c_{22} \\ (a_{21}b_{11}+a_{22}b_{21})c_{11}+(a_{21}b_{12}+a_{22}b_{22})c_{21} & (a_{21}b_{11}+a_{22}b_{21})c_{12}+(a_{21}b_{12}+a_{22}b_{22})c_{22} \end{bmatrix}$ Definition of Matrix Multiplication

$= \begin{bmatrix} a_{11}b_{11}c_{11}+a_{12}b_{21}c_{11}+a_{11}b_{12}c_{21}+a_{12}b_{22}c_{21} & a_{11}b_{11}c_{12}+a_{12}b_{21}c_{12}+a_{11}b_{12}c_{22}+a_{12}b_{22}c_{22} \\ a_{21}b_{11}c_{11}+a_{22}b_{21}c_{11}+a_{21}b_{12}c_{21}+a_{22}b_{22}c_{21} & a_{21}b_{11}c_{12}+a_{22}b_{21}c_{12}+a_{21}b_{12}c_{22}+a_{22}b_{22}c_{22} \end{bmatrix}$ Distributive Property

$= \begin{bmatrix} a_{11}b_{11}c_{11}+a_{11}b_{12}c_{21}+a_{12}b_{21}c_{11}+a_{12}b_{22}c_{21} & a_{11}b_{11}c_{12}+a_{11}b_{12}c_{22}+a_{12}b_{21}c_{12}+a_{12}b_{22}c_{22} \\ a_{21}b_{11}c_{11}+a_{21}b_{12}c_{21}+a_{22}b_{21}c_{11}+a_{22}b_{22}c_{21} & a_{21}b_{11}c_{12}+a_{21}b_{12}c_{22}+a_{22}b_{21}c_{12}+a_{22}b_{22}c_{22} \end{bmatrix}$ Commutative Property of Addition

$= \begin{bmatrix} a_{11}(b_{11}c_{11}+b_{12}c_{21})+a_{12}(b_{21}c_{11}+b_{22}c_{21}) & a_{11}(b_{11}c_{12}+b_{12}c_{22})+a_{12}(b_{21}c_{12}+b_{22}c_{22}) \\ a_{21}(b_{11}c_{11}+b_{12}c_{21})+a_{22}(b_{21}c_{11}+b_{22}c_{21}) & a_{21}(b_{11}c_{12}+b_{12}c_{22})+a_{22}(b_{21}c_{12}+b_{22}c_{22}) \end{bmatrix}$ Definition of Distributive property

$= \begin{bmatrix} a_{11} & a_{12} \\ a_{21} & a_{22} \end{bmatrix}\begin{bmatrix} b_{11}c_{11}+b_{12}c_{21} & b_{11}c_{12}+b_{12}c_{22} \\ b_{21}c_{11}+b_{22}c_{21} & b_{21}c_{12}+b_{22}c_{22} \end{bmatrix}$ Definition of Matrix Multiplication

$= \begin{bmatrix} a_{11} & a_{12} \\ a_{21} & a_{22} \end{bmatrix}\left(\begin{bmatrix} b_{11} & b_{12} \\ b_{21} & b_{22} \end{bmatrix}\begin{bmatrix} c_{11} & c_{12} \\ c_{21} & c_{22} \end{bmatrix}\right)$ Definition of Matrix Multiplication

$= A(BC)$ Substitution

47d. $$\begin{aligned} c(AB) &= c\left(\begin{bmatrix} a_{11} & a_{12} \\ a_{21} & a_{22} \end{bmatrix}\begin{bmatrix} b_{11} & b_{12} \\ b_{21} & b_{22} \end{bmatrix}\right) && \text{Substitution} \\ &= c\begin{bmatrix} a_{11}b_{11} + a_{12}b_{21} & a_{11}b_{12} + a_{12}b_{22} \\ a_{21}b_{11} + a_{22}b_{21} & a_{21}b_{12} + a_{22}b_{22} \end{bmatrix} && \text{Definition of Matrix Multiplication} \\ &= \begin{bmatrix} c(a_{11}b_{11} + a_{12}b_{21}) & c(a_{11}b_{12} + a_{12}b_{22}) \\ c(a_{21}b_{11} + a_{22}b_{21}) & c(a_{21}b_{12} + a_{22}b_{22}) \end{bmatrix} && \text{Definition of Scalar Multiplication} \\ &= \begin{bmatrix} ca_{11}b_{11} + ca_{12}b_{21} & ca_{11}b_{12} + ca_{12}b_{22} \\ ca_{21}b_{11} + ca_{22}b_{21} & ca_{21}b_{12} + ca_{22}b_{22} \end{bmatrix} && \text{Distributive Property} \\ &= \begin{bmatrix} ca_{11} & ca_{12} \\ ca_{21} & ca_{22} \end{bmatrix}\begin{bmatrix} b_{11} & b_{12} \\ b_{21} & b_{22} \end{bmatrix} && \text{Definition of Matrix Multiplication} \\ &= c\begin{bmatrix} a_{11} & a_{12} \\ a_{21} & a_{22} \end{bmatrix}\begin{bmatrix} b_{11} & b_{12} \\ b_{21} & b_{22} \end{bmatrix} && \text{Definition of Scalar Multiplication} \\ &= (cA)B && \text{Substitution} \end{aligned}$$

$$\begin{aligned} c(AB) &= c\left(\begin{bmatrix} a_{11} & a_{12} \\ a_{21} & a_{22} \end{bmatrix}\begin{bmatrix} b_{11} & b_{12} \\ b_{21} & b_{22} \end{bmatrix}\right) && \text{Substitution} \\ &= c\begin{bmatrix} a_{11}b_{11} + a_{12}b_{21} & a_{11}b_{12} + a_{12}b_{22} \\ a_{21}b_{11} + a_{22}b_{21} & a_{21}b_{12} + a_{22}b_{22} \end{bmatrix} && \text{Definition of Matrix Multiplication} \\ &= \begin{bmatrix} c(a_{11}b_{11} + a_{12}b_{21}) & c(a_{11}b_{12} + a_{12}b_{22}) \\ c(a_{21}b_{11} + a_{22}b_{11}) & c(a_{21}b_{12} + a_{22}b_{22}) \end{bmatrix} && \text{Definition of Scalar Multiplication} \\ &= \begin{bmatrix} ca_{11}b_{11} + ca_{12}b_{21} & ca_{11}b_{12} + ca_{12}b_{22} \\ ca_{21}b_{11} + ca_{22}b_{21} & ca_{21}b_{12} + ca_{22}b_{22} \end{bmatrix} && \text{Distributive Property} \\ &= \begin{bmatrix} a_{11}cb_{11} + a_{12}cb_{21} & a_{11}cb_{12} + a_{12}cb_{22} \\ a_{21}cb_{11} + a_{22}cb_{21} & a_{21}cb_{12} + a_{22}cb_{22} \end{bmatrix} && \text{Commutative Property} \\ &= \begin{bmatrix} a_{11} & a_{12} \\ a_{21} & a_{22} \end{bmatrix}\begin{bmatrix} cb_{11} & cb_{12} \\ cb_{21} & cb_{22} \end{bmatrix} && \text{Definition of Matrix Multiplication} \\ &= A(cB) && \text{Substitution} \end{aligned}$$

63. Translated 4 units to the right and 3 units up.

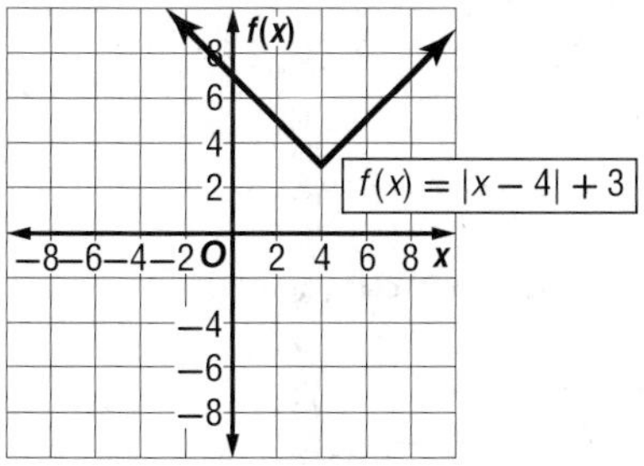

64. Translated 3 units to the left and 5 units down and stretched vertically.

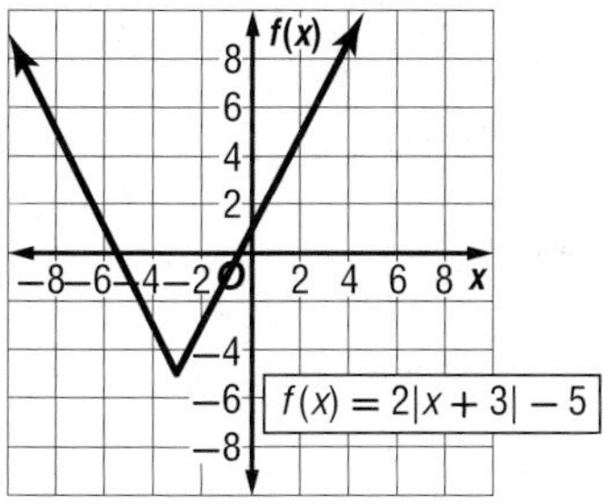

65. Translated 2 units to the left and 6 units down.

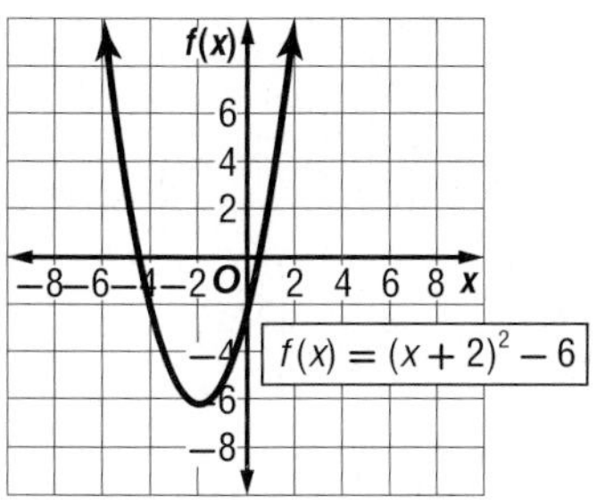

Page 213, Lesson 4-4

6. $G'(1, -5)$, $H'(3, -4)$, $J'(0, 2)$, $K'(-2, 1)$

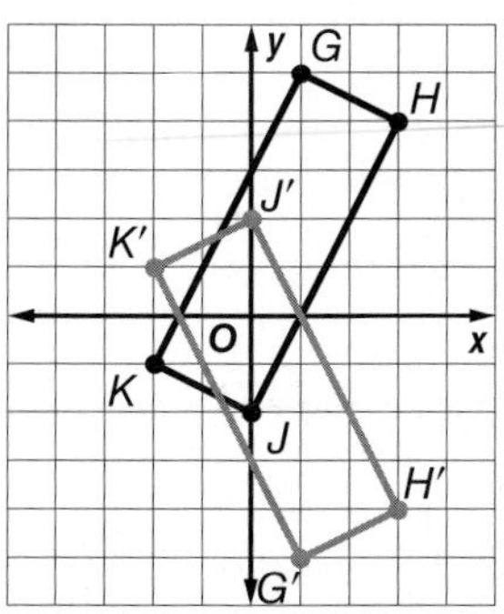

7. $P'(2, -1)$, $Q'(-4, 4)$, $R'(-4, -1)$

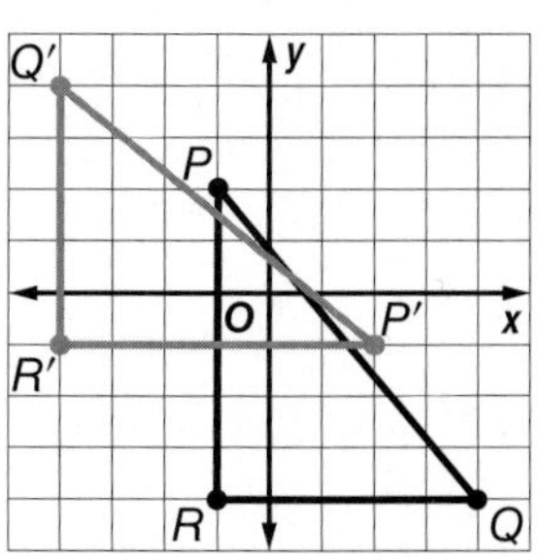

Page 214, Lesson 4-4

10. $M'(-5, 0)$, $N'(3, 1)$, $O'(-1, -5)$

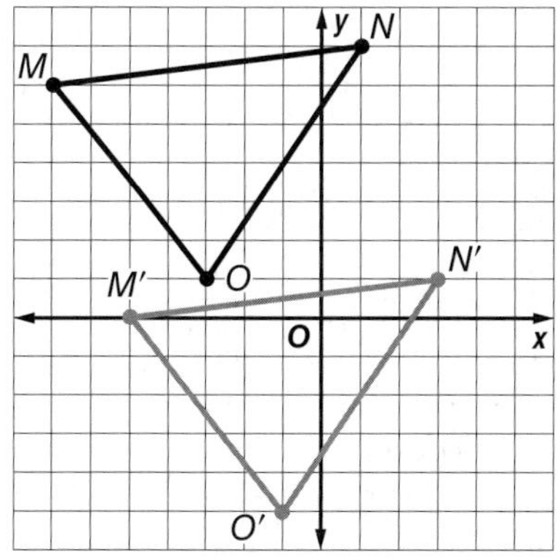

11. $E'(-8, 4)$, $F'(-2, -1)$, $G'(-6, -3)$, $H'(-7, -2)$

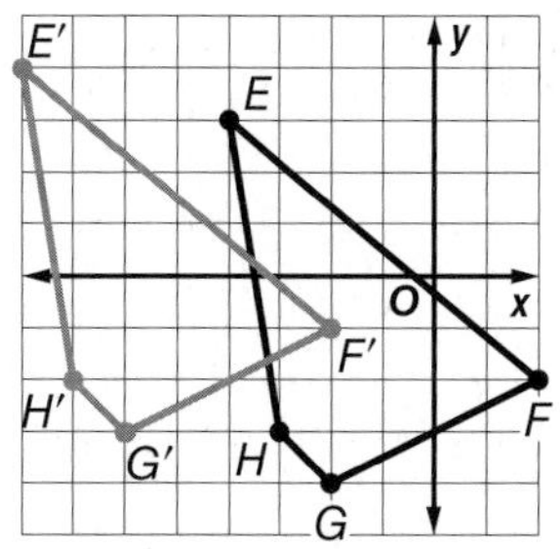

12. $P'(-4, -8)$, $Q'(-4, -3)$, $R'(-1, -3)$, $S'(-1, -8)$

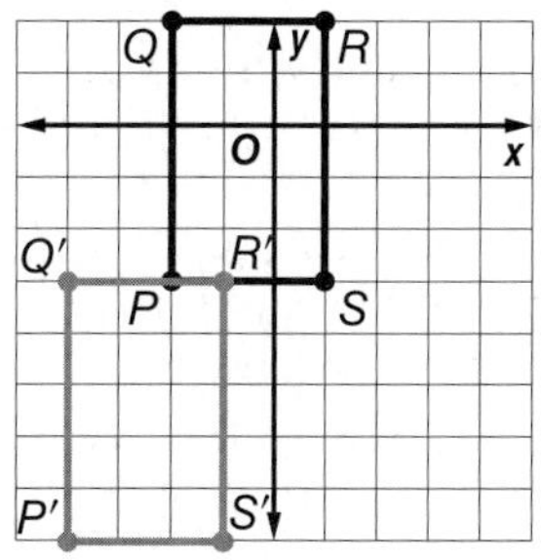

13. $J'(4, 0)$, $K'(5, -3)$, $L'(2, -6)$

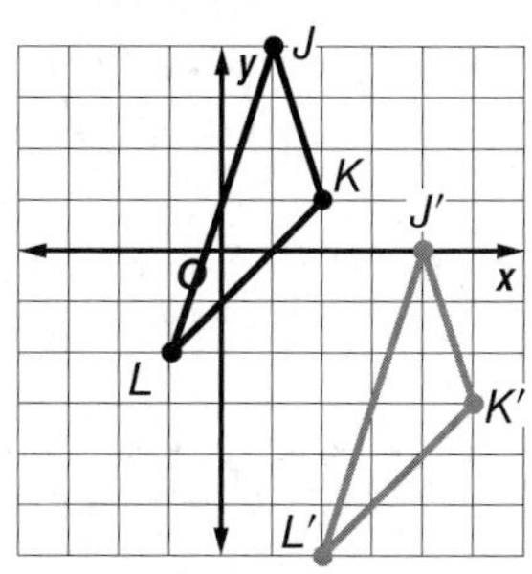

14. $A'(-6, -1)$, $B'(-3, 1)$, $C'(-2, -5)$

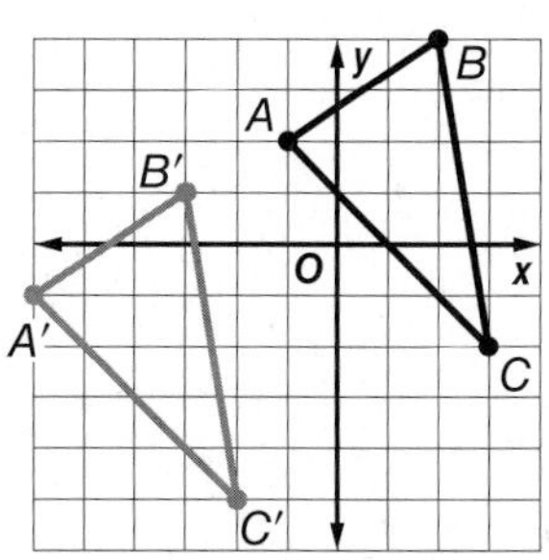

15. $W'(1, 5), X'(1, 9), Y'(5, 9), Z'(5, 5)$

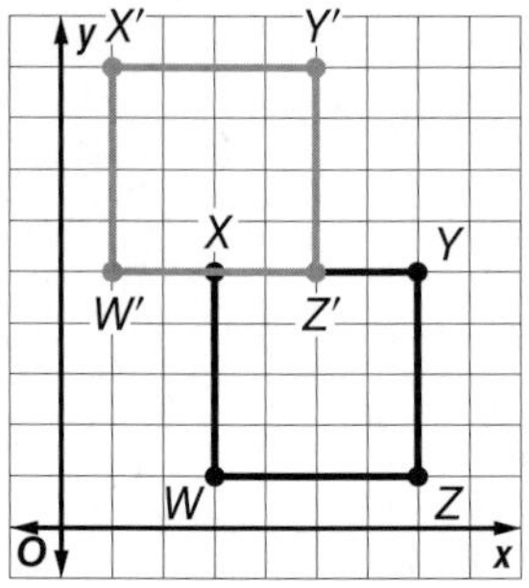

18. $T'(-6, -2), U'(4, -2), V'(2, -10)$

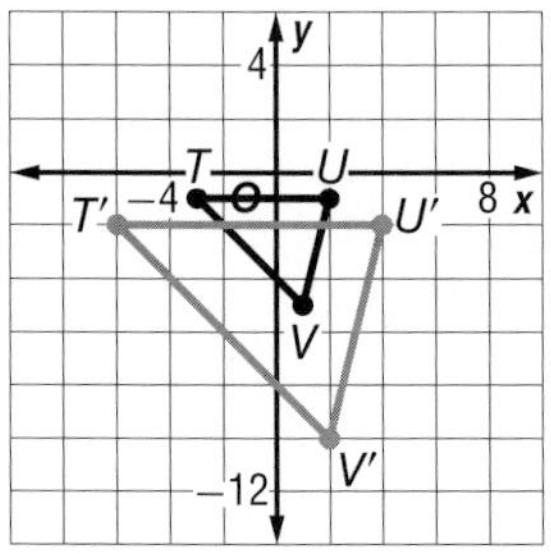

19. $D'(0, 16), E'(8, 8), F'(0, 0), G'(-8, 8)$

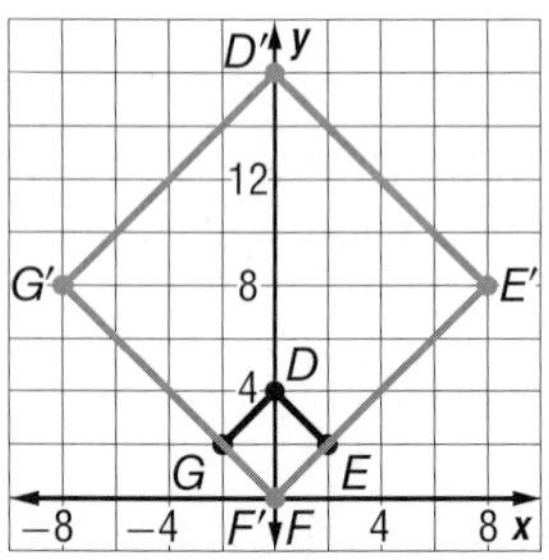

20. $K'\left(-1, 2\frac{2}{3}\right), L'\left(-1, \frac{2}{3}\right), M'\left(-2, \frac{2}{3}\right), N'\left(-2, 2\frac{2}{3}\right)$

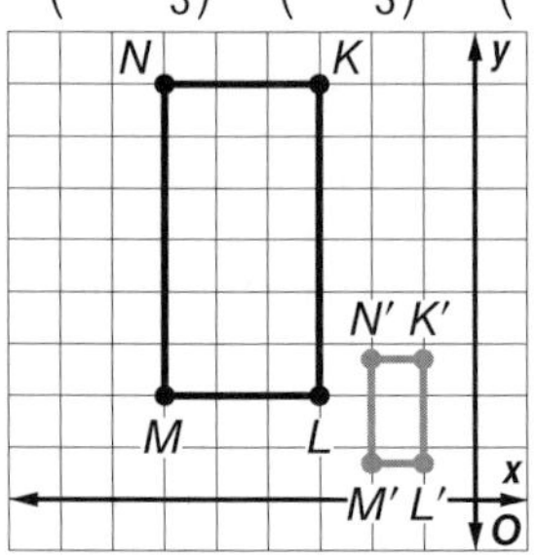

21. $Q'\left(1\frac{1}{2}, 1\right), R'(2, 0), S'\left(0, \frac{1}{4}\right)$

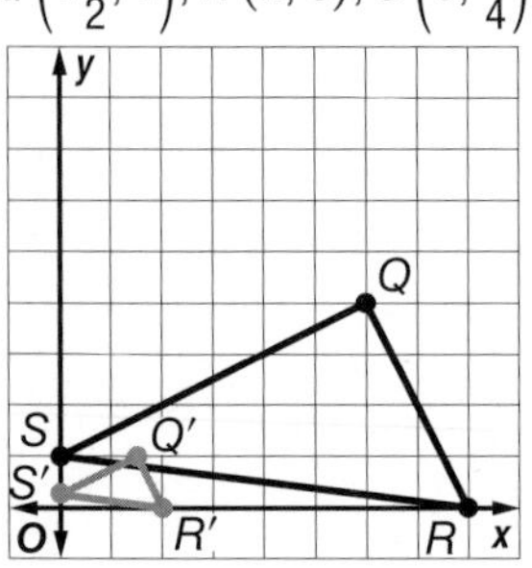

22. $A'(-9, -10), B'(5, -6), C'(-7, 7)$

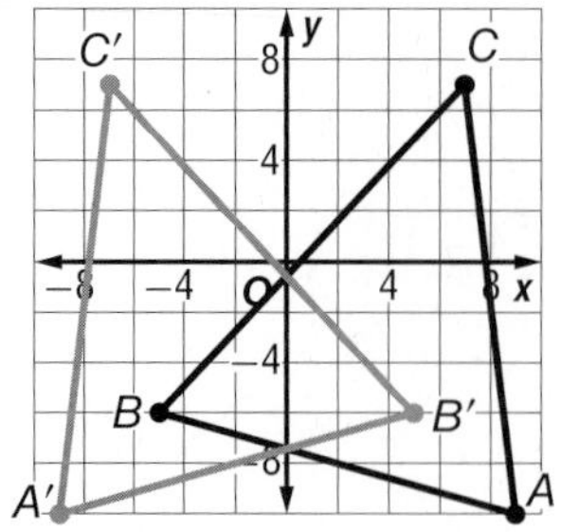

23. $D'(7, -4), E, (4, 0), F(-3, -2)$

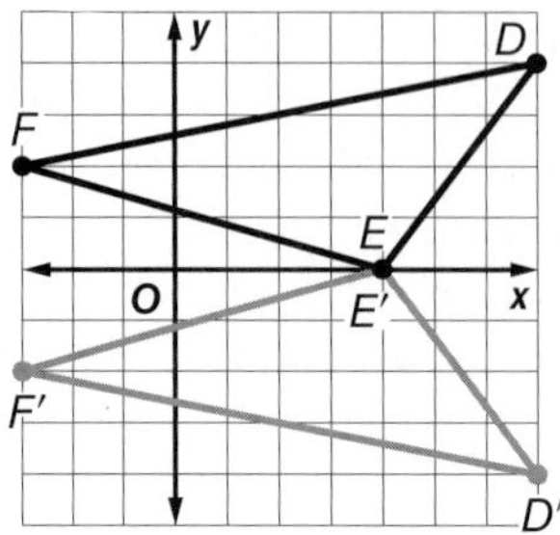

24. $G'(6, -5), H'(10, -2), J'(8, 0), K'(-4, -4)$

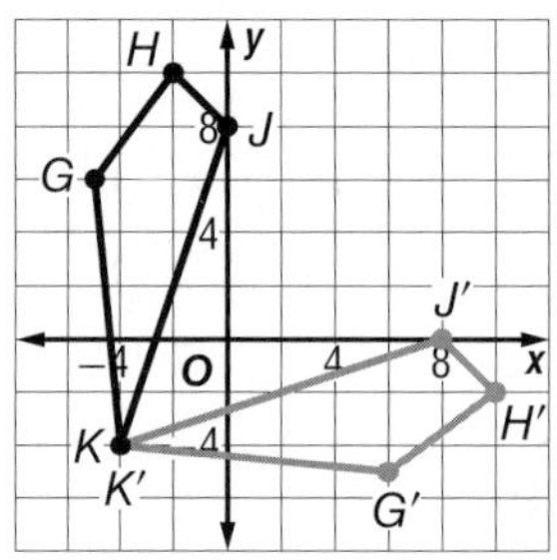

25. $L'(-1, -2), M'(5, -1), N'(4, 5), P'(-2, 4)$

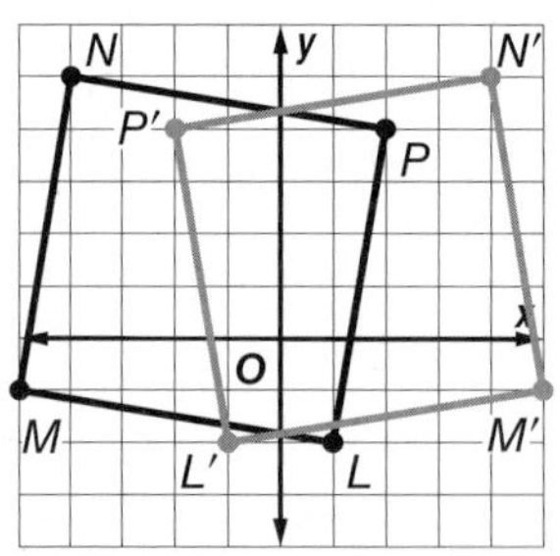

26. $Q'(-2, -2), R'(4, -2), S'(2, 6)$

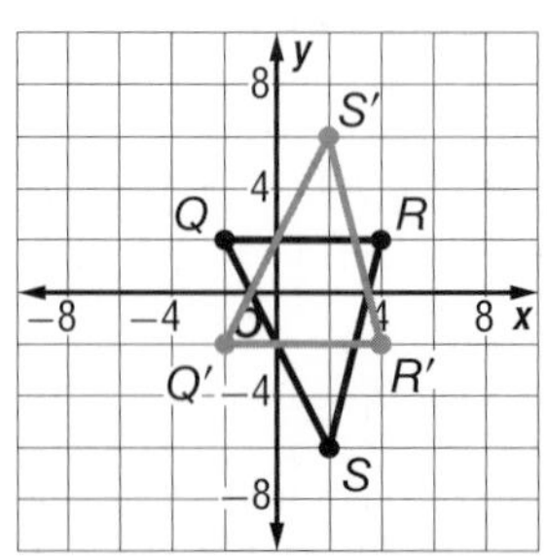

27. $T'(5, -4)$, $U'(3, 1)$, $V'(0, -2)$

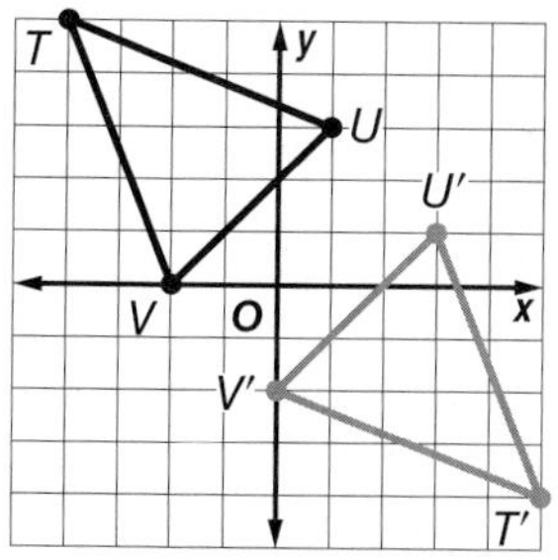

29. $X'(-1, -2)$, $Y'(-1, -4)$, $Z'(-5, -2)$

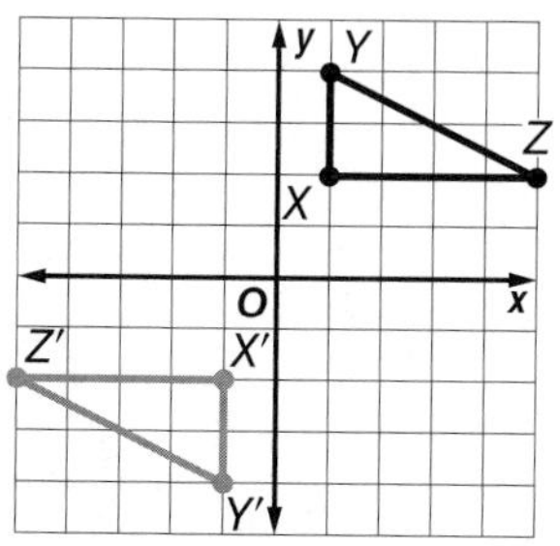

30. $A'(1, 1)$, $B'(1, 4)$, $C'(5, 6)$, $D'(5, 3)$

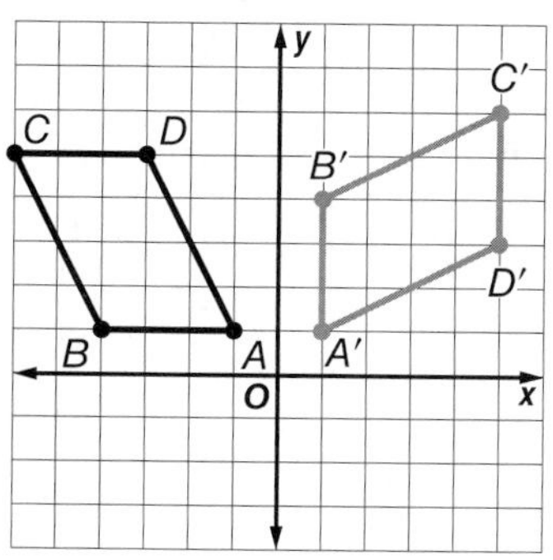

31. $E'(2, -3)$, $F'(-4, -3)$, $G'(-4, -2)$, $H'(2, -2)$

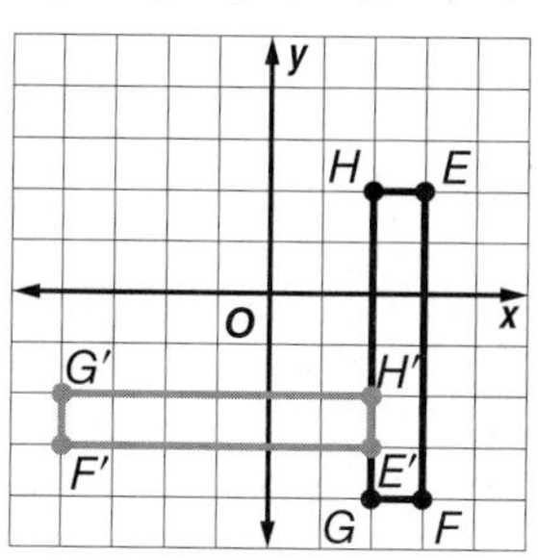

32. $J'(-3, -3)$, $K'(-3, 1)$, $L'(1, 1)$, $M'(1, -3)$

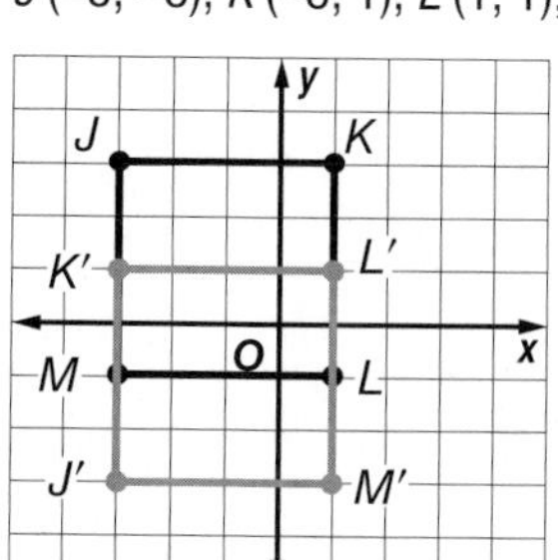

33. $N'(1, -2)$, $P'(5, -3)$, $Q'(5, -6)$, $R'(1, -6)$

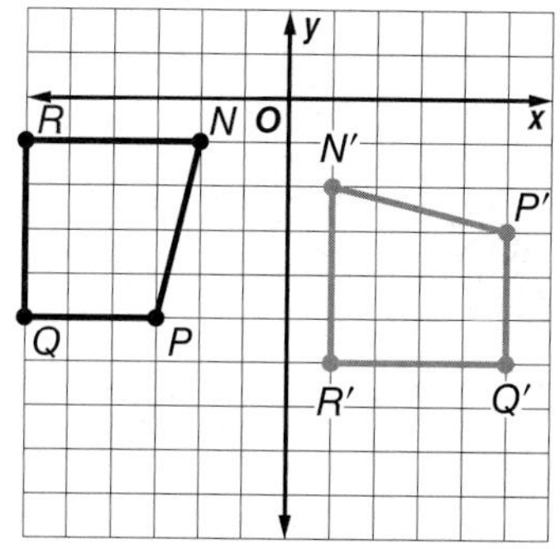

34. $S'(4, -2)$, $T'(-1, -5)$, $U'(2, 1)$

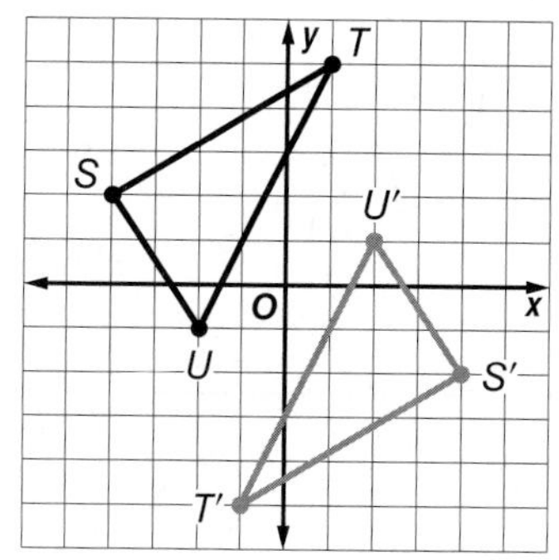

47. 180° counterclockwise rotation:

$$\begin{bmatrix} -1 & 0 \\ 0 & -1 \end{bmatrix} \cdot \begin{bmatrix} x_1 & x_2 & x_3 \\ y_1 & y_2 & y_3 \end{bmatrix} = \begin{bmatrix} -1(x_1) + 0(y_1) & -1(x_2) + 0(y_2) & -1(x_3) + 0(y_3) \\ 0(x_1) - 1(y_1) & 0(x_2) - 1(y_2) & 0(x_3) - 1(y_3) \end{bmatrix}$$

$$= \begin{bmatrix} -x_1 & -x_2 & -x_3 \\ -y_1 & -y_2 & -y_3 \end{bmatrix}$$

Reflection across the x-axis:

$$\begin{bmatrix} 1 & 0 \\ 0 & -1 \end{bmatrix} \cdot \begin{bmatrix} x_1 & x_2 & x_3 \\ y_2 & y_2 & y_3 \end{bmatrix} = \begin{bmatrix} 1(x_1) + 0(y_1) & 1(x_2) + 0(y_2) & 1(x_3) + 0(y_3) \\ 0(x_1) - 1(y_1) & 0(x_2) - 1(y_2) & 0(x_3) - 1(y_3) \end{bmatrix}$$

$$= \begin{bmatrix} x_1 & x_2 & x_3 \\ -y_1 & -y_2 & -y_3 \end{bmatrix}$$

followed by a reflection across the y-axis:

$$\begin{bmatrix} -1 & 0 \\ 0 & 1 \end{bmatrix} \cdot \begin{bmatrix} x_1 & x_2 & x_3 \\ -y_1 & -y_2 & -y_3 \end{bmatrix} = \begin{bmatrix} -1(x_1) + 0(y_1) & -1(x_2) + 0(y_2) & -1(x_3) + 0(y_3) \\ 0(x_1) + 1(-y_1) & 0(x_2) + 1(-y_2) & 0(x_3) + 1(-y_3) \end{bmatrix}$$

$$= \begin{bmatrix} -x_1 & -x_2 & -x_3 \\ -y_1 & -y_2 & -y_3 \end{bmatrix}$$

Page 228, Lesson 4-5

71.

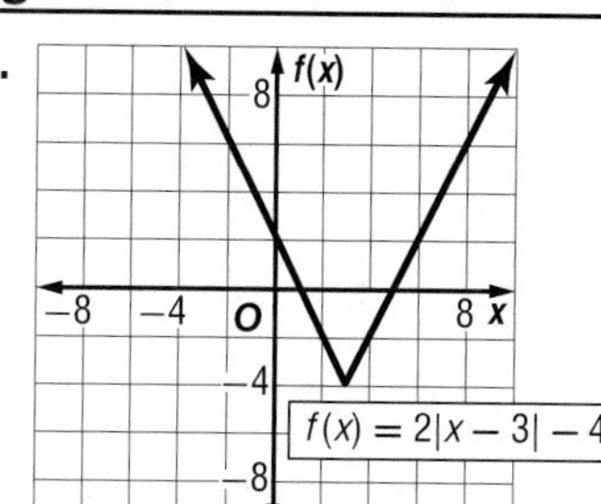

72.

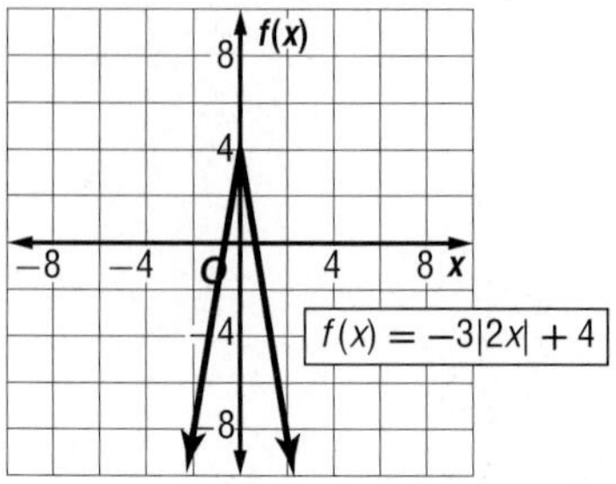

73.

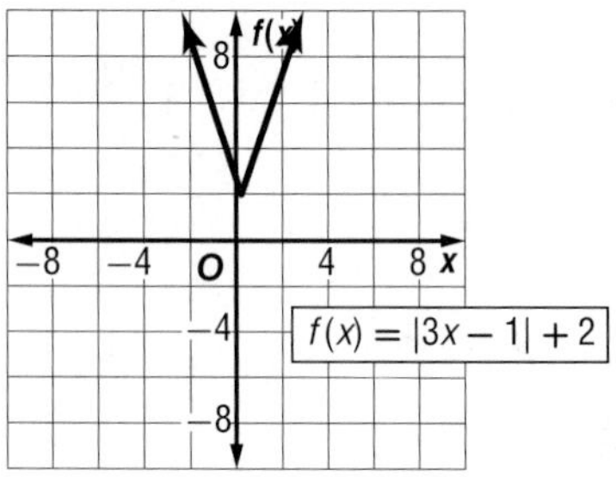

Page 236, Extend 4-6

1. $\left[\begin{array}{cc|c} 3 & 2 & -4 \\ 4 & 7 & 13 \end{array}\right]$; $\left(-\frac{54}{13}, \frac{55}{13}\right)$

2. $\left[\begin{array}{cc|c} 2 & 1 & 6 \\ 6 & -2 & 0 \end{array}\right]$; (1.2, 3.6)

3. $\left[\begin{array}{cc|c} 2 & 2 & -4 \\ 7 & 3 & 10 \end{array}\right]$; (4, –6)

4. $\left[\begin{array}{cc|c} 4 & 6 & 0 \\ 8 & -2 & 7 \end{array}\right]$; $\left(\frac{3}{4}, -\frac{1}{2}\right)$

5. $\left[\begin{array}{ccc|c} 6 & -4 & 2 & -4 \\ 2 & -2 & 6 & 10 \\ 2 & 2 & 2 & -2 \end{array}\right]$; (–2, –1, 2)

6. $\left[\begin{array}{ccc|c} 5 & -5 & 5 & 10 \\ 5 & 0 & -5 & 5 \\ 0 & 5 & 10 & 0 \end{array}\right]$; (1.25, –0.5, 0.25)

NOTES

CHAPTER 5

Chapter Planner

KEY: AL Approaching Level · OL On Level · BL Beyond Level · ELL English Learners

Diagnostic Assessment
Quick Check, p. 247

	Lesson 5-1 (Pacing: 1 day)	Extend 5-1 (Pacing: 0.5 day)	Lesson 5-2 (Pacing: 1 day)	Extend 5-2 (Pacing: 0.5 day)
Title	**Graphing Quadratic Functions**	**Graphing Technology Lab: Modeling Real-World Data**	**Solving Quadratic Equations by Graphing**	**Graphing Technology Lab: Solving Quadratic Equations by Graphing**
Objectives	• Graph quadratic functions. • Find and interpret the maximum and minimum values of a quadratic function.	• Use a graphing calculator to model data points for which the curve of best fit is a quadratic function.	• Solve quadratic equations by graphing. • Estimate solutions of quadratic equations by graphing.	• Use a graphing calculator to solve quadratic equations.
Key Vocabulary	quadratic function, quadratic, linear, constant terms, parabola, axis of symmetry, vertex, maximum value, minimum value		quadratic equations standard form root zero	
NGSSS	MA.912.A.2.6, MA.912.A.7.6		MA.912.A.7.6, MA.912.A.7.10	MA.912.A.7.10
Multiple Representations	p. 256			
Lesson Resources	**Chapter 5 Resource Masters** • Study Guide and Intervention, pp. 5–6 AL OL ELL • Skills Practice, p. 7 AL OL ELL • Practice, p. 8 AL OL BL ELL • Word Problem Practice, p. 9 AL OL BL ELL • Enrichment, p. 10 OL BL **Transparencies** • 5-Minute Check Transparency 5-1 AL OL BL ELL **Additional Print Resources** • Study Notebook AL OL BL ELL	**Materials** • TI-83/84 Plus or other graphing calculator	**Chapter 5 Resource Masters** • Study Guide and Intervention, pp. 11–12 AL OL ELL • Skills Practice, p. 13 AL OL ELL • Practice, p. 14 AL OL BL ELL • Word Problem Practice, p. 15 AL OL BL ELL • Enrichment, p. 16 OL BL • Quiz 1, p. 59 AL OL BL ELL **Transparencies** • 5-Minute Check Transparency 5-2 AL OL BL ELL **Additional Print Resources** • Study Notebook AL OL BL ELL • Teaching Algebra with Manipulatives, p. 205 AL OL ELL	**Materials** • TI-83/84 Plus or other graphing calculator
Technology for Every Lesson	FL Math Online glencoe.com • Extra Examples • Self-Check Quizzes • Personal Tutor • Homework Help	**CD/DVD Resources** IWB INTERACTIVE WHITEBOARD READY IWB StudentWorks Plus IWB Interactive Classroom IWB Diagnostic and Assessment Planner	• TeacherWorks Plus • eSolutions Manual Plus • ExamView Assessment Suite	
Get Animated				
Differentiated Instruction	pp. 253, 257		pp. 262, 266	

Quadratic Functions and Relations

Suggested Pacing			
Time Periods	Instruction	Review & Assessment	Total
45-minute	10	2	12
90-minute	6	1	7

Lesson 5-3 Pacing: 1 day	Lesson 5-4 Pacing: 1 day	Lesson 5-5 Pacing: 1 day	Extend 5-5 Pacing: 1 day	Lesson 5-6 Pacing: 1 day
Solving Quadratic Equations by Factoring	**Complex Numbers**	**Completing the Square**	**Graphing Technology Lab: Solving Quadratic Equations**	**The Quadratic Formula and the Discriminant**
• Write quadratic equations in intercept form. • Solve quadratic equations by factoring.	• Perform operations with pure imaginary numbers. • Perform operations with complex numbers.	• Solve quadratic equations by using the Square Root Property. • Solve quadratic equations by completing the square.	• Use a calculator containing a computer algebra system to solve quadratic equations.	• Solve quadratic equations by using the Quadratic Formula. • Use the discriminant to determine the number and type of roots of a quadratic equation.
factored form FOIL method	imaginary unit pure imaginary number complex number complex conjugates	completing the square		Quadratic Formula discriminant
MA.912.A.4.3, MA.912.A.10.3	MA.912.A.1.6	MA.912.A.7.3, MA.912.A.7.5	MA.912.A.7.3	MA.912.A.7.4, MA.912.A.7.5
p. 273	p. 281	p. 289		
Chapter 5 Resource Masters • Study Guide and Intervention, pp. 17–18 AL OL ELL • Skills Practice, p. 19 AL OL ELL • Practice, p. 20 AL OL BL ELL • Word Problem Practice, p. 21 AL OL BL ELL • Enrichment, p. 22 OL BL • Graphing Calculator Activity, p. 23 OL **Transparencies** • 5-Minute Check Transparency 5-3 AL OL BL ELL **Additional Print Resources** • Study Notebook AL OL BL ELL	**Chapter 5 Resource Masters** • Study Guide and Intervention, pp. 24–25 AL OL ELL • Skills Practice, p. 26 AL OL ELL • Practice, p. 27 AL OL BL ELL • Word Problem Practice, p. 28 AL OL BL ELL • Enrichment, p. 29 OL BL • Quiz 2, p. 59 AL OL BL ELL **Transparencies** • 5-Minute Check Transparency 5-4 AL OL BL ELL **Additional Print Resources** • Study Notebook AL OL BL ELL • Teaching Algebra with Manipulatives, p. 206 AL OL ELL	**Chapter 5 Resource Masters** • Study Guide and Intervention, pp. 30–31 AL OL ELL • Skills Practice, p.32 AL OL ELL • Practice, p. 33 AL OL BL ELL • Word Problem Practice, p. 34 AL OL BL ELL • Enrichment, p. 35 OL BL **Transparencies** • 5-Minute Check Transparency 5-5 AL OL BL ELL **Additional Print Resources** • Study Notebook AL OL BL ELL • Teaching Algebra with Manipulatives, pp. 207–208 AL OL ELL	**Materials** • TI-Nspire CAS calculator	**Chapter 5 Resource Masters** • Study Guide and Intervention, pp. 36–37 AL OL ELL • Skills Practice, p. 38 AL OL ELL • Practice, p. 39 AL OL BL ELL • Word Problem Practice, p. 40 AL OL BL ELL • Enrichment, p. 41 OL BL • Spreadsheet Activity, p. 42 OL • Quiz 3, p. 60 AL OL BL ELL **Transparencies** • 5-Minute Check Transparency 5-6 AL OL BL ELL **Additional Print Resources** • Study Notebook AL OL BL ELL

FL Math Online glencoe.com
- Extra Examples
- Self-Check Quizzes
- Personal Tutor
- Homework Help

CD/DVD Resources IWB INTERACTIVE WHITEBOARD READY
- IWB StudentWorks Plus
- IWB Interactive Classroom
- IWB Diagnostic and Assessment Planner
- TeacherWorks Plus
- eSolutions Manual Plus
- ExamView Assessment Suite

	Interactive Lab	Animation		
pp. 269, 275	pp. 277, 282	pp. 287, 290		pp. 293, 296

Formative Assessment
Mid-Chapter Quiz, p. 283

Chapter Planner

	Extend 5-6 Pacing: 0.5 day	Explore 5-7 Pacing: 0.5 day	Lesson 5-7 Pacing: 1 day
Title	**Algebra Lab: Sums and Products of Roots**	**Graphing Technology Lab: Families of Parabolas**	**Transformations with Quadratic Functions**
Objectives	• Use sums and products of roots to write quadratic equations.	• Use a graphing calculator to investigate changes to parabolas.	• Write a quadratic function in the form $y = a(x - h)^2 + k$. • Transform graphs of quadratic functions of the form $y = a(x - h)^2 + k$.
Key Vocabulary			vertex form
NGSSS	MA.912.A.4.7	MA.912.A.2.10	MA.912.A.2.10
Multiple Representations			
Lesson Resources	**Additional Print Resources** • Teaching Algebra with Manipulatives, pp. 209–210 AL OL ELL	**Materials** • TI-83/84 Plus or other graphing calculator	**Chapter 5 Resource Masters** • Study Guide and Intervention, pp. 43–44 AL OL ELL • Skills Practice, p. 45 AL OL ELL • Practice, p. 46 AL OL BL ELL • Word Problem Practice, p. 47 AL OL BL ELL • Enrichment, p. 48 OL BL • Quiz 4, p. 60 AL OL BL ELL **Transparencies** • 5-Minute Check Transparency 5-7 AL OL BL ELL **Additional Print Resources** • Study Notebook AL OL BL ELL • Teaching Algebra with Manipulatives, pp. 211–212 AL OL ELL
Technology for Every Lesson	FL Math Online glencoe.com • Extra Examples • Self-Check Quizzes • Personal Tutor • Homework Help	**CD/DVD Resources** IWB INTERACTIVE WHITEBOARD READY IWB StudentWorks Plus IWB Interactive Classroom IWB Diagnostic and Assessment Planner	• TeacherWorks Plus • eSolutions Manual Plus • ExamView Assessment Suite
Get Animated			Animation
Differentiated Instruction			pp. 307, 310

KEY: AL Approaching Level OL On Level BL Beyond Level ELL English Learners

Extend 5-7 Pacing: 0.5 day	Lesson 5-8 Pacing: 1 day	Extend 5-8 Pacing: 0.5 day
Algebra Lab: Quadratics and Rate of Change	**Quadratic Inequalities**	**Graphing Technology Lab: Modeling Motion**
• Investigate the rate of change of a quadratic function by examining first- and second-order differences.	• Graph quadratic inequalities in two variables. • Solve quadratic inequalities in one variable.	• Use a data collection device to investigate the relationship between the time and the distance traveled by a car on a ramp.
	quadratic inequality	
	MA.912.A.4.11, MA.912.A.10.3	
Additional Print Resources • Teaching Algebra with Manipulatives, pp. 213–217 AL OL ELL	**Chapter 5 Resource Masters** • Study Guide and Intervention, pp. 49–50 AL OL ELL • Skills Practice, p. 51 AL OL ELL • Practice, p. 52 AL OL BL ELL • Word Problem Practice, p. 53 AL OL BL ELL • Enrichment, p. 54 OL BL • Graphing Calculator, p. 55 OL • Quiz 4, p. 60 AL OL BL ELL **Transparencies** • 5-Minute Check Transparency 5-8 AL OL BL ELL **Additional Print Resources** • Study Notebook AL OL BL ELL	**Materials** • long, flat, smooth-surface board • stack of books • data collection device (TI CBR Motion Detector) • TI-83/84 Plus graphing calculator • medium-size toy car

FL Math Online glencoe.com
- Extra Examples
- Self-Check Quizzes
- Personal Tutor
- Homework Help

CD/DVD Resources IWB INTERACTIVE WHITEBOARD READY

- IWB StudentWorks Plus
- IWB Interactive Classroom
- IWB Diagnostic and Assessment Planner
- TeacherWorks Plus
- eSolutions Manual
- ExamView Assessment Suite

	pp. 315, 318	

Summative Assessment
- Study Guide and Review, pp. 320–324
- Practice Test, p. 325

CHAPTER 5 Assessment and Intervention

SE = Student Edition, **TE** = Teacher Edition, **CRM** = Chapter Resource Masters

	Diagnosis	Prescription
Diagnostic Assessment	**Beginning Chapter 5**	
	Get Ready for Chapter 5 **SE,** p. 247	Response to Intervention **TE,** p. 247
	Beginning Every Lesson	
	Then, Now, Why? **SE** 5-Minute Check Transparencies	Chapter 0 **SE,** pp. P1 through P19 Concepts and Skills Bank **SE** pp. 996–997
Formative Assessment	**During/After Every Lesson**	
	Guided Practice **SE,** every example Check Your Understanding **SE** H.O.T. Problems **SE** Spiral Review **SE** Additional Examples **TE** Watch Out! **TE** Step 4, Assess **TE** Chapter 5 Quizzes **CRM,** pp. 59–60 Self-Check Quizzes glencoe.com	**Tier 1 Intervention** Concepts and Skills Bank **SE,** pp. 996–997 Skills Practice **CRM,** Ch. 1–5 glencoe.com **Tier 2 Intervention** Differentiated Instruction **TE** Study Guide and Intervention Masters **CRM,** Ch. 1–5 **Tier 3 Intervention** *Math Triumphs., Alg. 2,* Chs. 1, 3, and 4
	Mid-Chapter	
	Mid-Chapter Quiz **SE,** p. 283 Mid-Chapter Test **CRM,** p. 61 ExamView Assessment Suite	**Tier 1 Intervention** Concepts and Skills Bank **SE,** pp. 996–997 Skills Practice **CRM,** Ch. 1–5 glencoe.com **Tier 2 Intervention** Study Guide and Intervention Masters **CRM,** Ch. 1–5 **Tier 3 Intervention** *Math Triumphs., Alg. 2,* Chs. 1, 3, and 4
	Before Chapter Test	
	Chapter Study Guide and Review **SE,** pp. 320–324 Practice Test **SE,** p. 325 Standardized Test Practice **SE,** pp. 326–329 Chapter Test glencoe.com Standardized Test Practice glencoe.com Vocabulary Review glencoe.com ExamView Assessment Suite	**Tier 1 Intervention** Concepts and Skills Bank **SE,** pp. 996–997 Skills Practice **CRM,** Ch. 1–5 glencoe.com **Tier 2 Intervention** Study Guide and Intervention Masters **CRM,** Ch. 1–5 **Tier 3 Intervention** *Math Triumphs., Alg. 2,* Chs. 1, 3, and 4
Summative Assessment	**After Chapter 5**	
	Multiple-Choice Tests, Forms 1, 2A, 2B **CRM,** pp. 63–68 Free-Response Tests, Forms 2C, 2D, 3 **CRM,** pp. 69–74 Vocabulary Test **CRM,** p. 62 Extended Response Test **CRM,** p. 75 Standardized Test Practice **CRM,** pp. 76–78 ExamView Assessment Suite	Study Guide and Intervention Masters **CRM,** Ch. 1–5 glencoe.com

CHAPTER 5 Differentiated Instruction

Option 1 Reaching All Learners AL OL BL ELL

KINESTHETIC Have pairs of students work with algebra tiles to help them write five equations that can be solved by completing the square. Provide each pair with x^2, x, and unit tiles. Have pairs begin by creating a square arrangement of their tiles, then writing the expression modeled by the tiles. Then pairs replace the constant with c. Finally, have pairs trade their five expressions with pair of students to solve for the value of c that will make the expression a perfect square.

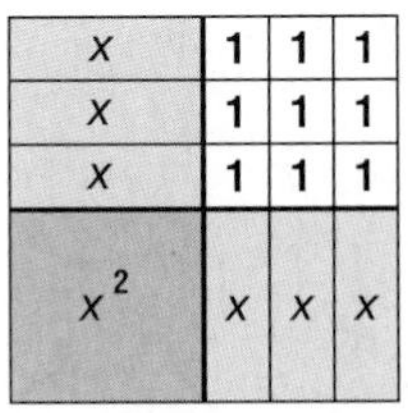

$x^2 + 6x + 9$
$x^2 + 6x + c$

VISUAL Have students make a poster listing the four different number and types of roots that can result when solving a quadratic equation. Tell students to include a sample equation, a graph that results in each number and type of root, and an explanation of how the value of the discriminant is indicative of the number and root type.

Option 2 Approaching Level AL

Provide students with grid paper and tracing paper or a transparency. Have them place a piece of tracing paper over the grid paper and graph $y = x^2$. Then have students slide the tracing paper in order to translate the graph up, down, to the right, or to the left. Discuss the equation of each new graph.

Option 3 English Learners ELL

Have students research the root words that form the words *quadratic* and *discriminant.* Discuss how the root words relate to the mathematical meanings of *quadratic* and *discriminant.*

Option 4 Beyond Level BL

Play a section of a song that rises to a crescendo and then gradually returns to its previous volume for the class. Ask students to describe how the song can be modeled by a parabola. Then have students write or find a music score that might model the path of a parabola. Ask students to indicate if the music has a maximum value or a minimum value.

FL Math Online Access Point Activities

CHAPTER 5 Focus on Mathematical Content

Vertical Alignment

Before Chapter 5

Related Topics before Algebra 1
- approximate the value of irrational numbers

Related Topics from Algebra 1
- analyze graphs of quadratic functions and draw conclusions
- solve linear inequalities using graphs

Previous Topics from Algebra 2
- use tools including factoring to transform and solve equations

Chapter 5

Related Topics from Algebra 2
- determine reasonable domain and range values of quadratic functions
- analyze situations involving quadratic functions and formulate quadratic equations and inequalities to solve problems
- solve quadratic equations and inequalities using graphs, tables, and algebraic methods, including the Quadratic Formula
- use complex numbers to describe the solutions of quadratic equations
- determine a quadratic function from its roots
- identify and sketch graphs of parent functions, including quadratic functions
- use the parent function to investigate, describe, and predict the effects of changes in *a, h,* and *k* on the graphs of the $y = a(x - h)^2 + k$ form of a function

After Chapter 5

Preparation for Precalculus
- determine the domain and range of functions using graphs, tables, and symbols
- recognize and use connections among significant values of a function, points on the graph of a function, and the symbolic representation of a function
- apply basic transformations to the parent functions

Lesson-by-Lesson Preview

5-1 Graphing Quadratic Functions

The graph of a quadratic function is called a *parabola.* All parabolas have an axis of symmetry, a vertex, and a *y*-intercept. Some parabolas open up, and others open down.

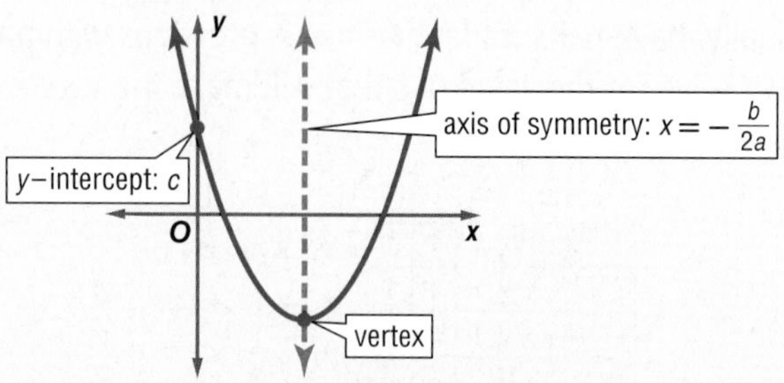

One way to graph a quadratic function is to create a table of values. It is helpful to include the vertex of the graph and the *y*-intercept in that table. After the points in the table have been plotted, they should be connected with a smooth curve. The graph should have a U-shape and not a V-shape at the vertex of the graph. Unlike the letter U, however, the graph should become progressively wider and have arrows indicating that the graph continues to infinity.

5-2 Solving Quadratic Equations by Graphing

A quadratic equation in the form $ax^2 + bx + c = 0$ has a related function $f(x) = ax^2 + bx + c$. The *zeros* of the function are the *x*-intercepts of its graph. These *x*-values are the solutions or *roots* of the related quadratic equation. A quadratic equation can have *one real* solution, *two real* solutions, or *no real* solutions. Finding the *x*-intercepts (roots) from a graph without the use of a graphing calculator usually provides a rather imprecise estimate of the solutions. Solutions that appear to be integers can be verified by substituting them into the original equation.

5-3 Solving Quadratic Equations by Factoring

To solve a quadratic equation by factoring,

- make sure the equation is in the form, $ax^2 + bx + c = 0$,
- factor the polynomial expression,
- set each factor equal to zero,
- and then solve the resulting equations.

When factoring, a polynomial of degree two or more is rewritten as a product of polynomials each having a lesser degree. Techniques used to solve quadratic equations include the techniques for factoring general trinomials, perfect square trinomials, and a difference of squares.

5-4 Complex Numbers

Introduced in this lesson is not only a new symbol *i*, but a new number system called the *complex number* system. The real number system is a subset of this new number system. Complex numbers are numbers of the form $a + bi$, where a and b are real numbers and i is a number whose square is -1, that is $i = \sqrt{-1}$. A complex number of the form bi is called a *pure imaginary number.*

The complex number $a + bi$ can be treated as if it is a binomial, and operations on complex numbers follow properties for adding, subtracting, multiplying, and dividing binomials, with one exception. That exception is to replace i^2 with -1 whenever i^2 appears in an expression.

5-5 Completing the Square

The *Square Root Property* can be used to solve an equation of the form $ax^2 + bx + c = d$ when $ax^2 + bx + c$ is a perfect square. If the trinomial is not a perfect square trinomial, a method called *completing the square* can be used to rewrite the equation so that the trinomial is a perfect square.

To complete the square for any quadratic expression of the form $x^2 + bx$,

- find half of b and square it
- add this amount to $x^2 + bx$.

When you solve a quadratic equation by completing the square, add the value you used to complete the square to each side of the equation and solve the resulting equation by taking the square root of each side.

If the coefficient of x^2 is not 1, divide each term by this coefficient before completing the square and solving the equation.

5-6 The Quadratic Formula and the Discriminant

The *Quadratic Formula* can be used to solve any equation in the form $ax^2 + bx + c = 0$, where $a \neq 0$. To determine the roots of the equation, substitute the coefficients a and b and the constant c into the formula $x = \frac{-b \pm \sqrt{b^2 - 4ac}}{2a}$ and then simplify the resulting expression.

The expression in the Quadratic Formula that appears under the radical sign, $b^2 - 4ac$, is called the *discriminant.* This value can be used to determine the number and type of roots of the equation.

- If $b^2 - 4ac > 0$, there are two real roots.
- If $b^2 - 4ac = 0$, there is one real root.
- If $b^2 - 4ac < 0$, there are two complex roots.

Checking the discriminant can provide a quick check when solving quadratic equations.

5-7 Transformations with Quadratic Functions

Quadratic equations can be written in *vertex form,* $y = a(x - h)^2 + k$, where the vertex of the graph of the equation is at (h, k) and the axis of symmetry is the line $x = h$. The value of k determines the graph's vertical translation. The value of h determines the graph's horizontal translation. The value of a determines the direction of opening of the graph and the shape of the parabola.

- If $a > 0$, the graph opens up.
- If $a < 0$, the graph opens down.

The information learned from a quadratic equation written in vertex form is very helpful when sketching its graph.

5-8 Quadratic Inequalities

The approach to graphing quadratic inequalities is similar to graphing linear inequalities. First, the related quadratic equation is graphed and then a point inside the parabola is checked. If the point is a solution to the inequality, then the region inside of the parabola is shaded. Otherwise, the region outside is shaded.

Solving a quadratic inequality in one variable algebraically is similar to solving a linear inequality. The difference lies in the fact that many quadratic inequalities have not one but two solutions. This means that the number line is divided in three intervals. Testing a value from each interval on the number line reveals which solution set or sets are correct. The solution set of a quadratic inequality will often be a compound inequality.

CHAPTER 5 Notes

Chapter Project

How High Will it Go?

Students use what they have learned about quadratic equations to predict the heights and paths of balls that have been thrown or hit into the air.

- Working in pairs, students choose a favorite baseball pitcher or tennis player. Using the Internet or other resources, find how fast the chosen player can throw or hit a ball. (For example, Serena Williams can serve a tennis ball at a speed of 202 kilometers per hour.) If the speed is not given in meters per second, convert the speed to those units.
- If the ball could be hit (or thrown) vertically upward at that same speed v, its height in meters h at any time (in seconds) would be given by $h = vt - 4.9t^2$, assuming no air resistance. Have students calculate how long the ball would be in the air.
- Then ask students to find when the ball would be at heights of 50, 100, 150, and 200 meters.
- When solving the quadratic equation for different heights, students may find one or two real roots, or they may find complex roots. Ask them to interpret the meaning for each situation.

CHAPTER 5 Quadratic Functions and Relations

Then

In Chapter 2, you graphed linear equations and inequalities.

Now

In Chapter 5, you will:

- Graph quadratic functions.
- Solve quadratic equations.
- Perform operations with complex numbers.
- Graph and solve quadratic inequalities.

NGSSS

MA.912.A.7.3
MA.912.A.7.4
MA.912.A.7.5

Why?

MOTION The path that a soccer ball or a firework takes can be modeled by a quadratic function. Quadratic functions can map an object in motion. In this chapter you will look at a pumpkin catapult, an amusement park ride, and a diver in motion.

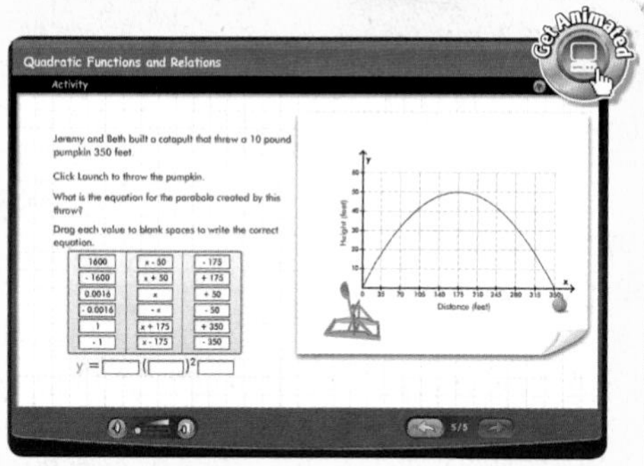

Key Vocabulary Introduce the key vocabulary in the chapter using the routine below.

Define: A quadratic inequality is an inequality in the form $y > ax^2 + bx + c$; $y \geq ax^2 + bx + c$; $y < ax^2 + bx + c$; $y \leq ax^2 + bx + c$.

Example: The graph shows the inequality $y < x^2 - 5x + 4$.

Ask: What is the boundary of a quadratic inequality called?
a parabola

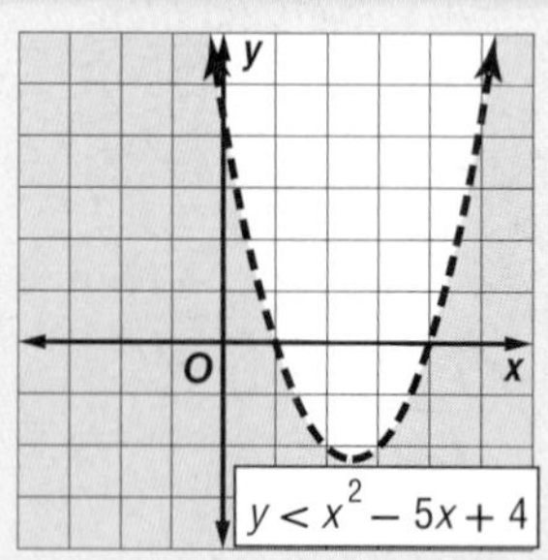

Get Ready for Chapter 5

Diagnose Readiness You have two options for checking Prerequisite Skills.

Text Option

Take the Quick Check below. Refer to the Quick Review for help.

QuickCheck

(Used in Lessons 5-1 and 5-2)

Given $f(x) = 2x^2 + 4$ and $g(x) = -x^2 - 2x + 3$, find each value. (Lesson 2-1)

1. $f(-1)$ **6**

2. $f(3)$ **22**

3. $f(0)$ **4**

4. $g(4)$ **−21**

5. $g(0)$ **3**

6. $g(-3)$ **0**

7. FISH Tuna swim at a steady rate of 9 miles per hour until they die, and they never stop moving.

a. Write a function that is a model for the situation. $f(x) = 9x$

b. Evaluate the function to estimate how far a 2-year old tuna has traveled. **157,680 mi**

8. BUDGET Marla has budgeted \$65 per day on food during a business trip. Write a function that is a model for the situation and evaluate what she would spend on a 2 week business trip. (Lesson 2-4) $f(x) = 65x$; **\$910**

(Used in Lessons 5-3 and 5-5) **9–12. See margin.**

Factor completely. If the polynomial is not factorable, write *prime*. (Lesson 0-3)

9. $x^2 + 13x + 40$

10. $x^2 - 10x + 21$

11. $2x^2 + 7x - 4$

12. $2x^2 - 7x - 15$

13. $x^2 - 11x + 15$ **prime**

14. $x^2 + 12x + 36$ $(x + 6)^2$

15. FLOOR PLAN The rectangular room pictured below has an area of $x^2 + 14x + 48$ square feet. If the width of the room is $(x + 6)$ feet, what is the length? $(x + 8)$ **feet**

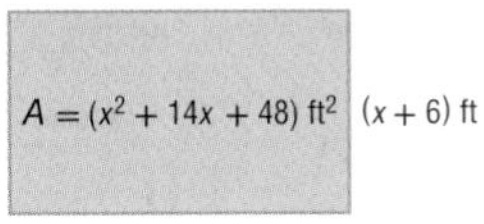

QuickReview

EXAMPLE 1

Given $f(x) = -2x^2 + 3x - 1$ and $g(x) = 3x^2 - 5$, find each value.

a. $f(2)$

$f(x) = -2x^2 + 3x - 1$ **Original function**

$f(2) = -2(2)^2 + 3(2) - 1$ **Substitute 2 for x.**

$= -8 + 6 - 1$ or -3 **Simplify.**

b. $g(-2)$

$g(x) = 3x^2 - 5$ **Original function**

$g(-2) = 3(-2)^2 - 5$ **Substitute −2 for x.**

$= 12 - 5$ or 7 **Simplify.**

EXAMPLE 2

Factor $2x^2 - x - 3$ completely. If the polynomial is not factorable, write *prime*.

To find the coefficients of the x-terms, you must find two numbers whose product is $2(-3)$ or -6, and whose sum is -1. The two coefficients must be 2 and -3 since $2(-3) = -6$ and $2 + (-3) = -1$. Rewrite the expression and factor by grouping.

$2x^2 - x - 3$

$= 2x^2 + 2x - 3x - 3$ **Substitute $2x - 3x$ for $-x$.**

$= (2x^2 + 2x) + (-3x - 3)$ **Associative Property**

$= 2x(x + 1) + -3(x + 1)$ **Factor out the GCF.**

$= (2x - 3)(x + 1)$ **Distributive Property**

Online Option

FL Math Online Take a self-check Chapter Readiness Quiz at glencoe.com.

Additional Answers

9. $(x + 8)(x + 5)$

10. $(x - 3)(x - 7)$

11. $(2x - 1)(x + 4)$

12. $(2x + 3)(x - 5)$

Response to Intervention (RtI)

Use the *Quick Check* results and the Intervention Planner to help you determine your Response to Intervention. The If-Then statements in the chart below help you decide the appropriate tier of RtI and suggest intervention resources for each tier.

Intervention Planner

Tier 1 — On Level

If students miss about 25% of the exercises or less,

Then choose a resource:

SE Concepts and Skills Bank, p. 996
Lessons 0-3, 2-1, and 2-4

CRM Skills Practice, Chapter 2, pp. 7 and 19

TE Chapter Project, p. 246

FL Math Online Self-Check Quiz

Tier 2 — Strategic Intervention approaching grade level

If students miss about 50% of the exercises,

Then choose a resource:

CRM Study Guide and Intervention, Chapter 2, pp. 5–6 and 23–24

FL Math Online Extra Examples, Personal Tutor, Homework Help

Tier 3 — Intensive Intervention 2 or more years below grade level

If students miss about 75% of the exercises,

Then use *Math Triumphs, Alg. 2*, Chs. 1, 3, and 4

FL Math Online Extra Examples, Personal Tutor, Homework Help, Review Vocabulary

FOLDABLES® Study Organizer

Dinah Zike's Foldables®

Focus Students write about the different ways quadratic functions and relations can be solved as these methods are presented in the lessons of this chapter.

Teach Have students make and label their Foldables as illustrated. Students should fill in the appropriate sections with their notes, diagrams, and examples as they cover each lesson in this chapter.

Have students use the appropriate tabs as they cover each lesson in this chapter.

When to Use It Encourage students to add to their Foldables as they work through the chapter and to use them to review for the chapter test.

Differentiated Instruction

CRM Student-Built Glossary, p. 1
Students should complete the chart by providing a definition of each term and an example as they progress through Chapter 5. This study tool can also be used to review for the chapter test.

Additional Answers (Guided Practice)

1A.

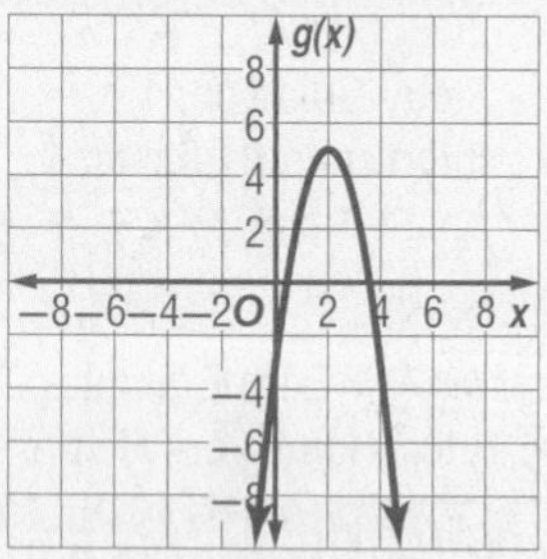

1B.

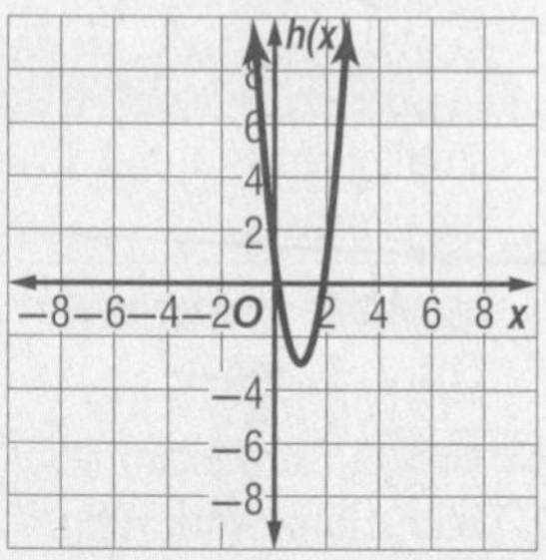

Get Started on Chapter 5

You will learn several new concepts, skills, and vocabulary terms as you study Chapter 5. To get ready, identify important terms and organize your resources. You may wish to refer to **Chapter 0** to review prerequisite skills.

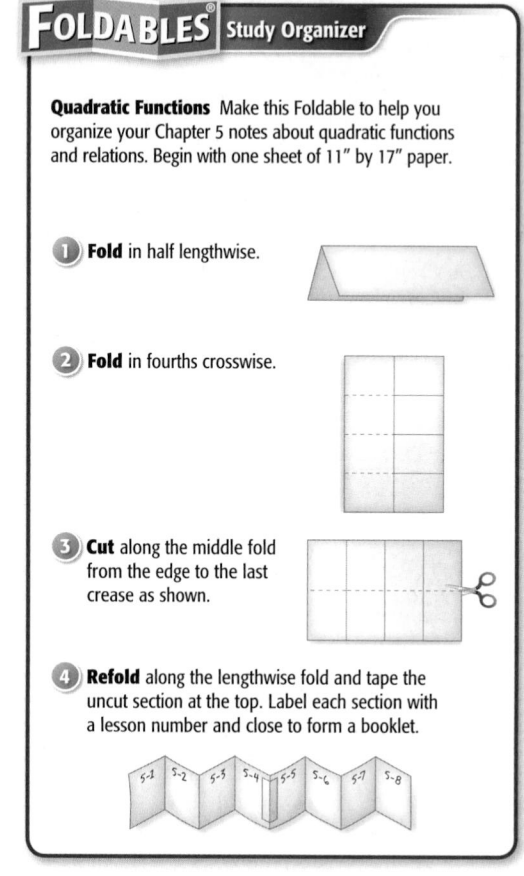

FOLDABLES® Study Organizer

Quadratic Functions Make this Foldable to help you organize your Chapter 5 notes about quadratic functions and relations. Begin with one sheet of 11″ by 17″ paper.

1. **Fold** in half lengthwise.

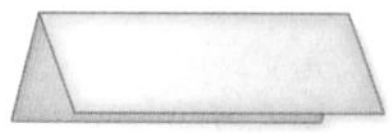

2. **Fold** in fourths crosswise.

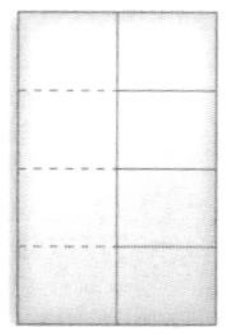

3. **Cut** along the middle fold from the edge to the last crease as shown.

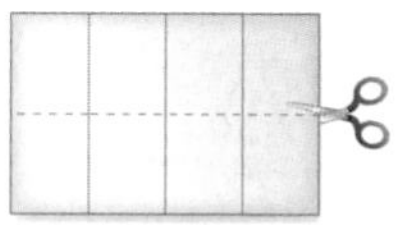

4. **Refold** along the lengthwise fold and tape the uncut section at the top. Label each section with a lesson number and close to form a booklet.

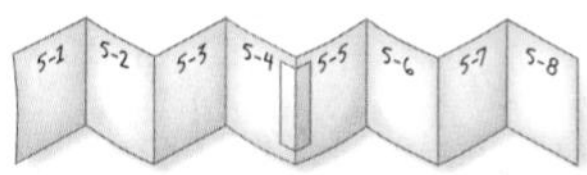

FL Math Online glencoe.com

- Study the chapter online
- Explore **Get Animated**
- Get extra help from your own **Personal Tutor**
- Use **Extra Examples** for additional help
- Take a **Self-Check Quiz**
- **Review Vocabulary** in fun ways

New Vocabulary

English		Español
quadratic term	• p. 249 •	término cuadrático
linear term	• p. 249 •	término lineal
constant term	• p. 249 •	término constante
vertex	• p. 250 •	vértice
maximum value	• p. 252 •	valor máximo
minimum value	• p. 252 •	valor mínimo
quadratic equation	• p. 259 •	ecuación cuadrática
standard form	• p. 259 •	forma estándar
root	• p. 259 •	raíz
zero	• p. 259 •	cero
imaginary unit	• p. 276 •	unidad imaginaria
pure imaginary number	• p. 276 •	número imaginario puro
complex number	• p. 277 •	número complejo
complex conjugates	• p. 279 •	conjugados complejos
completing the square	• p. 285 •	completar el cuadrado
Quadratic Formula	• p. 292 •	fórmula cuadrática
discriminant	• p. 295 •	discriminante
vertex form	• p. 305 •	forma de vértice
quadratic inequality	• p. 312 •	desigualdad cuadrática

Review Vocabulary

domain • p. P7 • dominio the set of all x-coordinates of the ordered pairs of a relation

function • p. P7 • función a relation in which each x-coordinate is paired with exactly one y-coordinate

range • p. P7 • rango the set of all y-coordinates of the ordered pairs of a relation

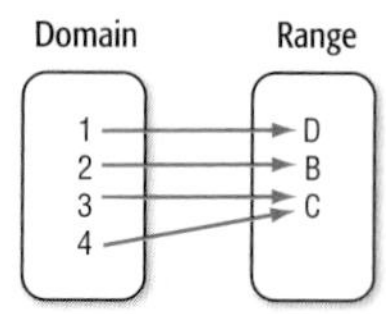

Multilingual eGlossary glencoe.com

Graphing Quadratic Functions

Then
You identified and manipulated graphs of functions. (Lesson 2-6)

Now
- Graph quadratic functions.
- Find and interpret the maximum and minimum values of a quadratic function.

NGSSS
MA.912.A.2.6 Identify and graph common functions (including but not limited to linear, rational, **quadratic**, cubic, radical, absolute value). **MA.912.A.7.6 Identify the axis of symmetry, vertex, domain, range and intercept(s) for a given parabola.** *Also addresses MA.912.A.10.3.*

New Vocabulary
quadratic function
quadratic term
linear term
constant term
parabola
axis of symmetry
vertex
maximum value
minimum value

FL Math Online
glencoe.com

Why?

Eddie is organizing a charity tournament. He plans to charge a $20 entry fee for each of the 80 players. He recently decided to raise the entry fee by $5, and 5 fewer players entered with the increase. He used this information to determine how many fee increases will maximize the money raised.

The quadratic function at the right represents this situation. The tournament prize pool increases when he first increases the fee, but eventually the pool starts to decrease as the fee gets even higher.

Tournament Prize Pool

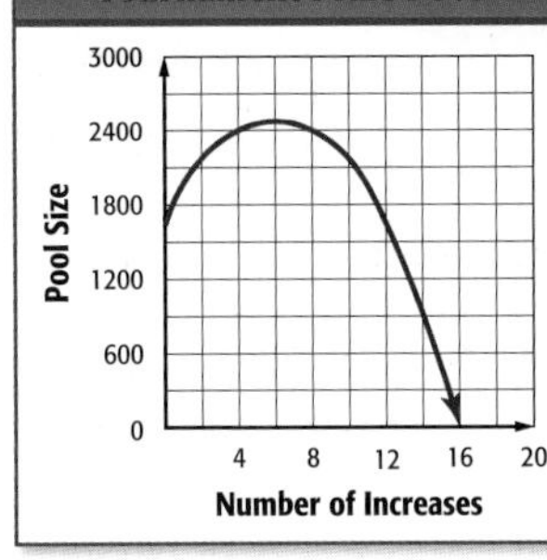

Graph Quadratic Functions In a **quadratic function**, the greatest exponent is 2. These functions can have a **quadratic term**, a **linear term**, and a **constant term**. The general quadratic function is shown below.

$$f(x) = ax^2 + bx + c, \text{ where } a \neq 0$$

quadratic term (ax^2), linear term (bx), constant term (c)

The graph of a quadratic function is called a **parabola**. To graph a quadratic function, graph ordered pairs that satisfy the function.

EXAMPLE 1 Graph a Quadratic Function by Using a Table

Graph $f(x) = 3x^2 - 12x + 6$ by making a table of values.

Choose integer values for x, and evaluate the function for each value. Graph the resulting coordinate pairs, and connect the points with a smooth curve.

x	$3x^2 - 12x + 6$	$f(x)$	$(x, f(x))$
0	$3(0)^2 - 12(0) + 6$	6	(0, 6)
1	$3(1)^2 - 12(1) + 6$	−3	(1, −3)
2	$3(2)^2 - 12(2) + 6$	−6	(2, −6)
3	$3(3)^2 - 12(3) + 6$	−3	(3, −3)
4	$3(4)^2 - 12(4) + 6$	6	(4, 6)

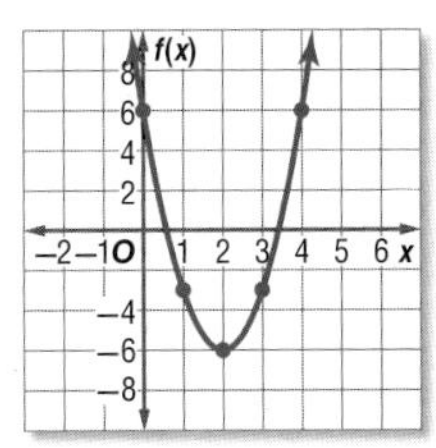

Guided Practice

1. Graph each function by making a table of values. **1A, 1B. See margin.**
   A. $g(x) = -2x^2 + 8x - 3$
   B. $h(x) = 4x^2 - 8x + 1$

Personal Tutor glencoe.com

5-1 Lesson Notes

1 FOCUS

Vertical Alignment

Before Lesson 5-1
Indentify and manipulate graphs of functions.

Lesson 5-1
Graph quadratic functions. Find and interpret the maximum and minimum values of quadratic functions.

After Lesson 5-1
Solve quadratic equations using graphs.

2 TEACH

Scaffolding Questions

Have students read the *Why?* section of the lesson.

Ask:
- What is the independent variable for this function? number of increases
- What is the dependent variable? pool size
- What is significant about the value of the expected pool size for 6 entry fee increases? The value of pool size is greatest for 6 increases, on the pool size it is at its maximum for 6 increases.

Lesson 5-1 Resources

Resource	Approaching-Level	On-Level	Beyond-Level	English Learners
Teacher Edition	• Differentiated Instruction, p. 253	• Differentiated Instruction, pp. 253, 257	• Differentiated Instruction, pp. 253, 257	• Differentiated Instruction, pp. 253, 257
Chapter Resource Masters	• Study Guide and Intervention, pp. 5–6 • Skills Practice, p. 7 • Practice, p. 8 • Word Problem Practice, p. 9	• Study Guide and Intervention, pp. 5–6 • Skills Practice, p. 7 • Practice, p. 8 • Word Problem Practice, p. 9 • Enrichment, p. 10	• Practice, p. 8 • Word Problem Practice, p. 9 • Enrichment, p. 10	• Study Guide and Intervention, pp. 5–6 • Skills Practice, p. 7 • Practice, p. 8 • Word Problem Practice, p. 9
Transparencies	• 5-Minute Check Transparency 5-1	• 5-Minute Check Transparency 5-1	• 5-Minute Check Transparency 5-1	• 5-Minute Check Transparency 5-1
Other	• Study Notebook	• Study Notebook	• Study Notebook	• Study Notebook

Graph Quadratic Functions

Example 1 shows how to graph a quadratic function by making a table of values. **Example 2** shows how the axis of symmetry, the y-intercept, and the vertex can be used to graph a quadratic function.

TEACH with TECH

COMPUTER PROJECTOR Display a coordinate grid on the board. Use this throughout the lesson as you work through examples graphing quadratic functions.

Formative Assessment

Use the Guided Practice exercises after each example to determine students' understanding of concepts.

Additional Example

1 Graph $f(x) = x^2 + 3x - 1$ by making a table of values.

x	−3	−2	−1	0	1
$f(x)$	−1	−3	−3	−1	3

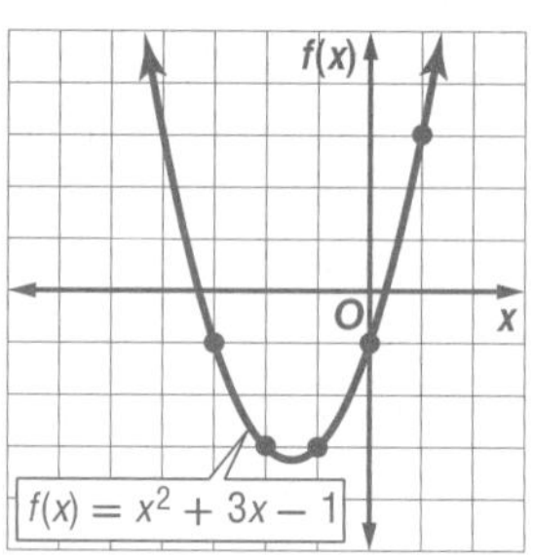

Additional Examples also in Interactive Classroom PowerPoint® Presentations

IWB INTERACTIVE WHITEBOARD READY

Notice in Example 1 that there seemed to be a pattern in the values for $f(x)$. This is due to the axis of symmetry of parabolas. The **axis of symmetry** is a line through the graph of a parabola that divides the graph into two congruent halves. Each side of the parabola is a reflection of the other side.

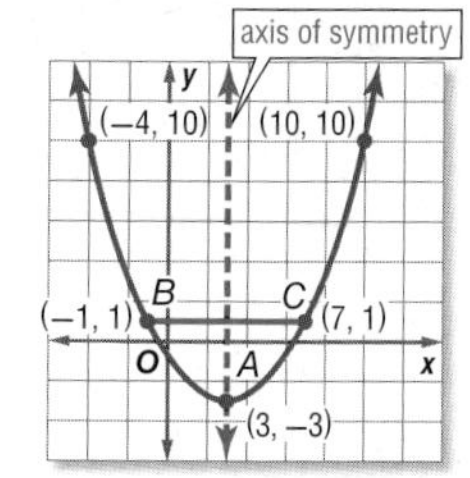

The axis of symmetry will intersect a parabola at only one point, called the **vertex**. The vertex of the graph at the right is $A(3, -3)$.

Review Vocabulary

Symmetry When something is symmetrical, its opposite sides are mirror images of each other.

Notice that the x-coordinates of points B and C are both 4 units away from the x-coordinate of the vertex, and they have the same y-coordinate. This is due to the symmetrical nature of the graph.

Key Concept

Graph of a Quadratic Function—Parabola

Words Consider the graph of $y = ax^2 + bx + c$, where $a \neq 0$.

- The y-intercept is $a(0)^2 + b(0) + c$ or c.
- The equation of the axis of symmetry is $x = -\frac{b}{2a}$.
- The x-coordinate of the vertex is $-\frac{b}{2a}$.

Model

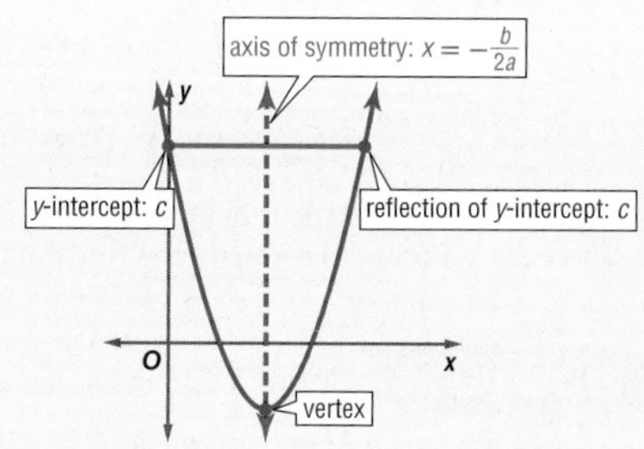

Now you can use the axis of symmetry to help plot points and graph a parabola. For $y = x^2 + 6x - 2$ below, the axis of symmetry is $x = -\frac{b}{2a} = -\frac{6}{2(1)}$ or $x = -3$.

StudyTip

Plotting Reflections The reflection of a point is its mirror image on the other side of the axis of symmetry.

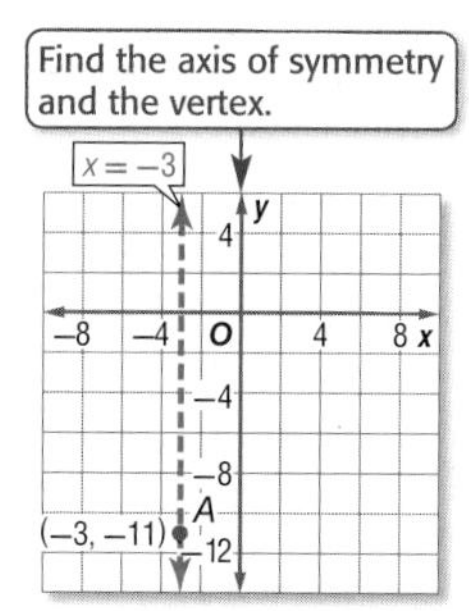

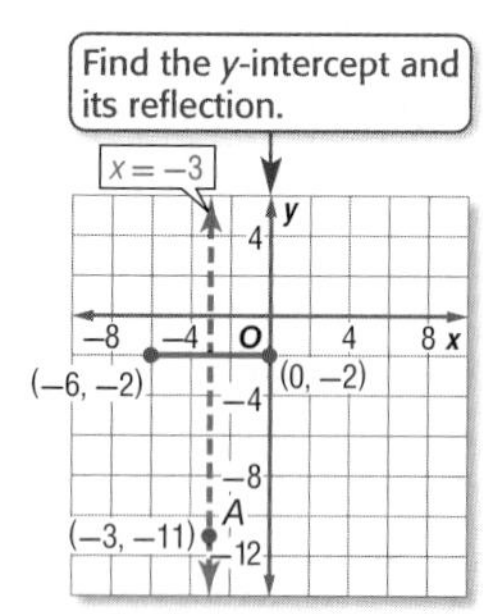

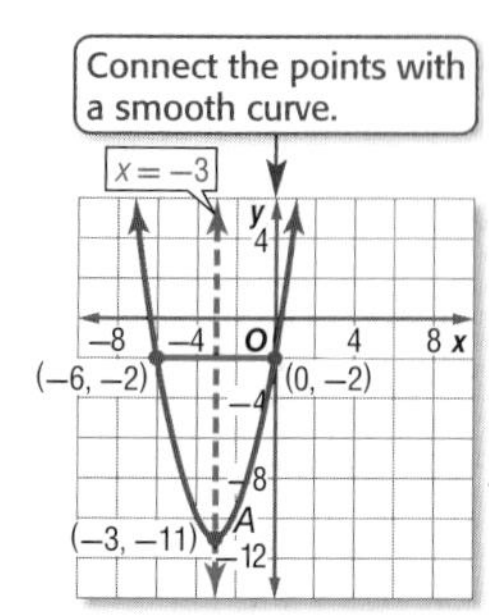

EXAMPLE 2 Axis of Symmetry, y-intercept, and Vertex

Consider $f(x) = x^2 + 4x - 3$.

StudyTip

Quadratic Form Make sure the function is in standard quadratic form, $y = ax^2 + bx + c$, before graphing.

a. Find the y-intercept, the equation of the axis of symmetry, and the x-coordinate of the vertex.

The function is of the form $f(x)$ is $ax^2 + bx + c$, so we can identify a, b, and c.

$$f(x) = ax^2 + bx + c$$

$$f(x) = 1x^2 + 4x - 3 \quad \rightarrow \quad a = 1, b = 4, \text{and } c = 3$$

The y-intercept is $c = -3$.

Use a and b to find the equation of the axis of symmetry.

$x = -\frac{b}{2a}$ **Equation of the axis of symmetry**

$= -\frac{4}{2(1)}$ **$a = 1$ and $b = 4$**

$= -2$ **Simplify.**

The equation of the axis of symmetry is $x = -2$. Therefore, the x-coordinate of the vertex is -2.

StudyTip

Fractions When the x-coordinate of the vertex is a fraction, select the nearest integer for the next point to avoid using fractions and simplify the calculations.

b. Make a table of values that includes the vertex.

Select five specific points, with the vertex in the middle and two points on either side of the vertex, including the y-intercept and its reflection. Use symmetry to determine the y-values of the reflections.

x	$x^2 + 4x - 3$	$f(x)$	$(x, f(x))$
-6	$(-6)^2 + 4(-6) - 3$	9	$(-6, 9)$
-4	$(-4)^2 + 4(-4) - 3$	-3	$(-4, -3)$
-2	$(-2)^2 + 4(-2) - 3$	-7	$(-2, -7)$
0	$(0)^2 + 4(0) - 3$	-3	$(0, -3)$
2	$(2)^2 + 4(2) - 3$	9	$(2, 9)$

c. Use this information to graph the function.

Graph the points from the table and the y-intercept, connecting them with a smooth curve.

Draw the axis of symmetry, $x = -2$, as a dashed line. The graph should be symmetrical about this line.

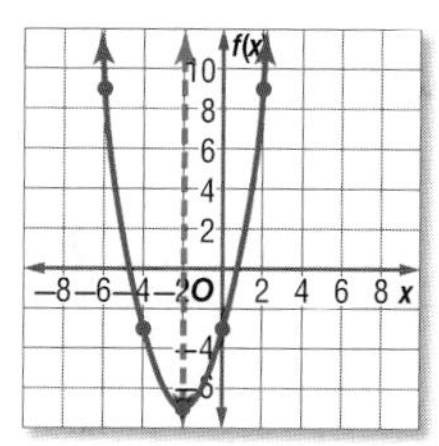

Guided Practice

2B.

x	$f(x)$
-3	-9
-2	6
-1	11
0	6
1	-9

2. Consider $f(x) = -5x^2 - 10x + 6$.

A. Find the y-intercept, the equation of the axis of symmetry, and the x-coordinate of the vertex. y-intercept $= 6$; axis of symmetry: $x = -1$; x-coordinate $= -1$

B. Make a table of values that includes the vertex.

C. Use this information to graph the function. See margin.

Personal Tutor glencoe.com

Additional Example

2 Consider $f(x) = 2 - 4x + x^2$.

a. Find the y-intercept, the equation of the axis of symmetry, and the x-coordinate of the vertex. $2; x = 2; 2$

b. Make a table of values that includes the vertex.

x	0	1	2	3	4
$f(x)$	2	-1	-2	-1	2

c. Use this information to graph the function.

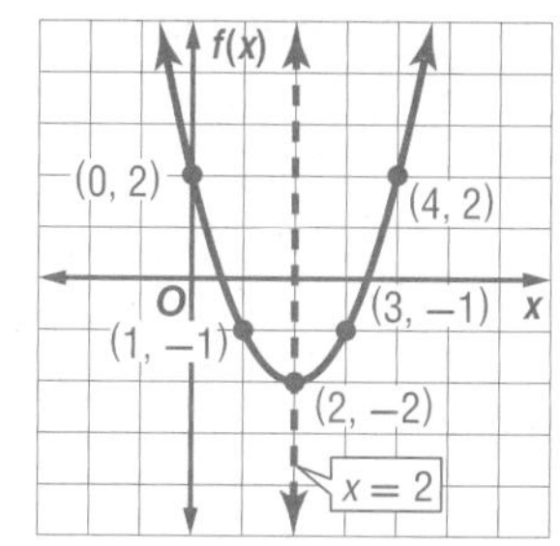

Tips for New Teachers

Extending the Concept Make sure students understand that the graph shows values for all the points that satisfy the function, even when the x-value is not an integer.

Watch Out!

Common Misconceptions When working through Example 2, make sure students realize that $f(x)$ and y can be used interchangeably, and also that the maximum or minimum value of the function is given by the y-coordinate of the vertex of the parabola.

Additional Answer (Guided Practice)

2C.

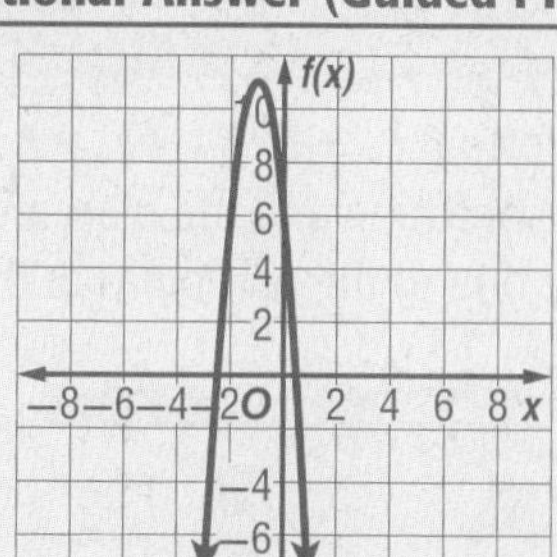

Maximum and Minimum Values

Example 3 shows how to determine whether a quadratic function has a maximum or minimum value and to state that value. **Example 4** shows how to find a maximum value for a real-world situation.

Additional Example

3 Consider $f(x) = -x^2 + 2x + 3$.

a. Determine whether the function has a maximum or minimum value. maximum

b. State the maximum or minimum value of the function. 4

c. State the domain and range of the function. D = {all real numbers}, R = $\{f(x) \mid f(x) \leq 4\}$

Watch Out!

Preventing Errors Make sure students understand that a parabola which opens upward is the graph of a function with a minimum value, and that a parabola that opens downward is the graph of a function with a maximum value. Compare these parabolas to valleys (where the altitude of the valley floor is a minimum) and hills (where the peak of the hill is the maximum altitude).

Watch Out!

Maxima and Minima The terms *minimum point* and *minimum value* are not interchangeable. The minimum point on the graph of a quadratic function is the ordered pair that describes the location of the vertex. The minimum value of a function is the y-coordinate of the minimum point. It is the smallest value obtained when $f(x)$ is evaluated for all values of x.

Maximum and Minimum Values The y-coordinate of the vertex of a quadratic function is the **maximum value** or the **minimum value** of the function. These values represent the greatest or lowest possible value the function can reach.

Key Concept — Maximum and Minimum Value

Words The graph of $f(x) = ax^2 + bx + c$, where $a \neq 0$,
- opens up and has a minimum value when $a > 0$, and
- opens down and has a maximum value when $a < 0$.

Models

a is positive.

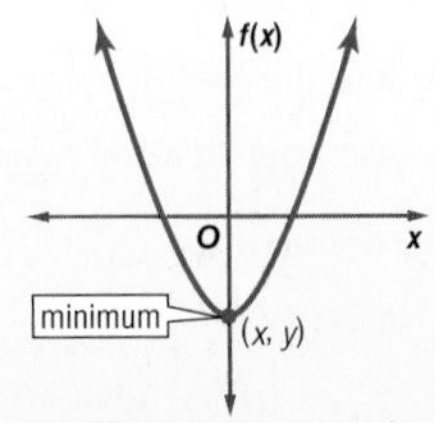

The y-coordinate is the minimum value.

a is negative.

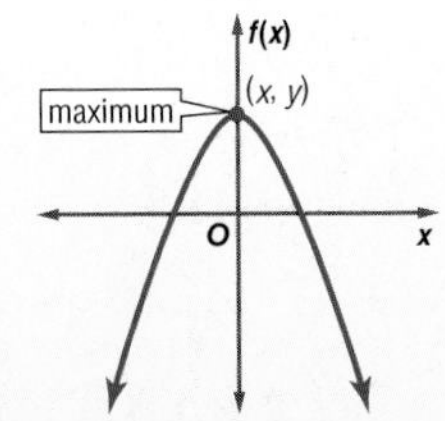

The y-coordinate is the maximum value.

EXAMPLE 3 Maximum or Minimum Values

Consider $f(x) = -4x^2 + 12x + 18$.

a. Determine whether the function has a *maximum* or *minimum* value.

For this function, $a = -4$, so the graph opens down and the function has a maximum value.

b. State the maximum or minimum value of the function.

The maximum value of the function is the y-coordinate of the vertex.

The x-coordinate of the vertex is $\frac{12}{2(-4)}$ or 1.5.

Find the y-coordinate of the vertex by evaluating the function for $x = 1.5$.

$f(x) = -4x^2 + 12x + 18$	**Original function**
$= -4(1.5)^2 + 12(1.5) + 18$	$x = 1.5$
$= -9 + 18 + 18$ or 27	The maximum value of the function is 27.

c. State the domain and range of the function.

The domain is all real numbers. The range is all real numbers less than or equal to the maximum value, or $\{f(x) \mid f(x) \leq 27\}$.

StudyTip

Domain and Range The domain of a quadratic function will always be all real numbers. The range will either be all real numbers less than or equal to the maximum or all real numbers greater than or equal to the minimum.

Guided Practice

3. Consider $f(x) = 4x^2 - 24x + 11$.

A. Determine whether the function has a maximum or minimum value. minimum

B. State the maximum or minimum value of the function. minimum = −25

C. State the domain and range of the function.
D = {all real numbers}; R = $\{f(x) \mid f(x) \geq -25\}$

Personal Tutor glencoe.com

Focus on Mathematical Content

Graphs of Quadratic Functions Graphs of quadratic functions of the form $f(x) = ax^2 + bx + c$, where $a \neq 0$, are called parabolas. Except possibly for compression or stretching and the placement of the axes, the shape of the graph of a quadratic function will look like one of the parabolas at the bottom of p. 252.

Real-World Link

As of 2006, there were approximately 900,000 public charities in the United States.

Source: National Center for Charitable Statistics

Real-World EXAMPLE 4 Quadratic Equations in the Real World

CHARITY **Refer to the beginning of the lesson.**

a. How much should Eddie charge in order to maximize charity income?

Words	Total	equals	fee	times	number of entrants.
Variables	Let x = the number of price increases. Let $P(x)$ = the total pool as a function of x.				
Equation	$P(x)$	$=$	$20 + 5x$	$\cdot$	$(80 - 5x)$

Solve for the x-value of the vertex.

$P(x) = (20 + 5x) \cdot (80 - 5x)$

$= 20(80) + 20(-5x) + 5x(80) + 5x(-5x)$ **Distribute.**

$= 1600 - 100x + 400x - 25x^2$ **Multiply.**

$= 1600 + 300x - 25x^2$ **Simplify.**

$= -25x^2 + 300x + 1600$ **$ax^2 + bx + c$ form**

Use the formula for the axis of symmetry, $x = -\frac{b}{2a}$, to find the x-coordinate.

$x = -\frac{300}{2(-25)}$ or 6 **$a = -25$ and $b = 300$**

Eddie needs to have 6 price increases, so he should charge 20 + 6(5) or \$50.

b. What will be the maximum value of the pool?

Find the maximum value of the quadratic function $P(x)$ by evaluating $P(6)$.

$P(x) = -25x^2 + 300x + 1600$ **Total pool function**

$P(6) = -25(6)^2 + 300(6) + 1600$ **$x = 6$**

$= -900 + 1800 + 1600$ or 2500 **Simplify.**

Thus, the maximum prize pool is \$2500 after 6 price increases.

CHECK Graph the function on a graphing calculator and use the CALC:Maximum function to confirm the solution.

Select a left bound of 0 and a right bound of 10. The calculator will display the coordinates of the maximum at the bottom of the screen.

The domain is $\{x \mid x \geq 0\}$ because there can be no negative increases in price. The range is $\{y \mid 0 \leq y \leq 2500\}$ because the prize pool cannot have a negative monetary value.

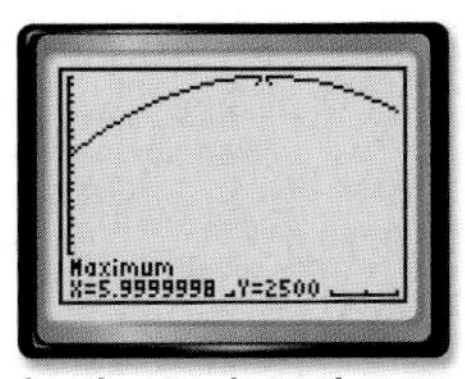

[0, 10] scl: 1 by [0, 2500] scl: 100

StudyTip

Domain and Range in Real-World Problems Use logic and the information from the problem to determine the domain and range that are reasonable in the situation.

Guided Practice

4. Suppose a different tournament that Eddie organizes has 120 players and the entry fee is \$40. Each time he increases the fee by \$5, he loses 10 players. Determine what the entry fee should be to maximize the value of the pool. \$50

Personal Tutor glencoe.com

Additional Example

4 **ECONOMICS** A souvenir shop sells about 200 coffee mugs each month for \$6 each. The shop owner estimates that for each \$0.50 increase in the price, he will sell about 10 fewer coffee mugs per month.

a. How much should the owner charge for each mug in order to maximize the monthly income from their sales? \$8

b. What is the maximum monthly income the owner can expect to make from the mugs? \$1280

Watch Out!

Preventing Errors Remind students to use the equation for the axis of symmetry to determine the x-coordinate of the vertex and then find the y-coordinate of the vertex.

Differentiated Instruction

AL OL BL ELL

If students struggle to solve real-world problems involving maximum or minimum values,

Then encourage students to explain to partners their plans for solving. Suggest that the listening partner take notes about the speaking partner's strategies, asking questions as needed for clarification.

3 PRACTICE

Formative Assessment

Use Exercises 1–11 to check for understanding.

Use the chart at the bottom of this page to customize assignments for your students.

Additional Answers

23. max = −12;
D = {all real numbers},
R = $\{f(x) \mid f(x) \leq -12\}$

Check Your Understanding

Examples 1 and 2 pp. 249–251

Complete parts a–c for each quadratic function. **1–6. See Chapter 5 Answer Appendix.**

a. Find the y-intercept, the equation of the axis of symmetry, and the x-coordinate of the vertex.

b. Make a table of values that includes the vertex.

c. Use this information to graph the function.

1. $f(x) = 3x^2$ **2.** $f(x) = -6x^2$

3. $f(x) = x^2 - 4x$ **4.** $f(x) = -x^2 - 3x + 4$

5. $f(x) = 4x^2 - 6x - 3$ **6.** $f(x) = 2x^2 - 8x + 5$

Example 3 p. 252

Determine whether each function has a *maximum* or *minimum* value, and find that value. Then state the domain and range of the function.

7. $f(x) = -x^2 + 6x - 1$ **8.** $f(x) = x^2 + 3x - 12$

9. $f(x) = 3x^2 + 8x + 5$ **10.** $f(x) = -4x^2 + 10x - 6$

7. max = 8; D = {all real numbers}, R = $\{f(x) \mid f(x) \leq 8\}$
8. min = −14.25; D = {all real numbers}, R = $\{f(x) \mid f(x) \geq -14.25\}$
9. min = $-\frac{1}{3}$; D = {all real numbers}, R = $\left\{f(x) \mid f(x) \geq -\frac{1}{3}\right\}$
10. max = 0.25; D = {all real numbers}, R = $\{f(x) \mid f(x) \leq 0.25\}$

Example 4 p. 253

11. BUSINESS A store rents 1400 videos per week at \$2.25 per video. The owner estimates that they will rent 100 fewer videos for each \$0.25 increase in price. What price will maximize the income of the store? **\$2.88**

Practice and Problem Solving

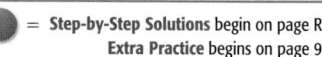

● = **Step-by-Step Solutions** begin on page R20.
Extra Practice begins on page 947.

Examples 1 and 2 pp. 249–251

Complete parts a–c for each quadratic function. **12–21. Chapter 5 Answer Appendix.**

a. Find the y-intercept, the equation of the axis of symmetry, and the x-coordinate of the vertex.

b. Make a table of values that includes the vertex.

c. Use this information to graph the function.

12. $f(x) = 4x^2$ **13.** $f(x) = -2x^2$

14. $f(x) = x^2 - 5$ **15.** $f(x) = x^2 + 3$

16. $f(x) = 4x^2 - 3$ **17.** $f(x) = -3x^2 + 5$

18. $f(x) = x^2 - 6x + 8$ **19.** $f(x) = x^2 - 3x - 10$

20. $f(x) = -x^2 + 4x - 6$ **21.** $f(x) = -2x^2 + 3x + 9$

Example 3 p. 252

Determine whether each function has a *maximum* or *minimum* value, and find that value. Then state the domain and range of the function.

22. $f(x) = 5x^2$ **23.** $f(x) = -x^2 - 12$ **See margin.**

24. $f(x) = x^2 - 6x + 9$ **25.** $f(x) = -x^2 - 7x + 1$

26. $f(x) = 8x - 3x^2 + 2$ **27.** $f(x) = 5 - 4x - 2x^2$

28. $f(x) = 15 - 5x^2$ **29.** $f(x) = x^2 + 12x + 27$

30. $f(x) = -x^2 + 10x + 30$ **31.** $f(x) = 2x^2 - 16x - 42$

22. min = 0; D = {all real numbers}, R = $\{f(x) \mid f(x) \geq 0\}$
24. min = 0; D = {all real numbers}, R = $\{f(x) \mid f(x) \geq 0\}$
25. max = 13.25; D = {all real numbers}, R = $\{f(x) \mid f(x) \leq 13.25\}$
26. max = $\frac{22}{3}$; D = {all real numbers}, R = $\left\{f(x) \mid f(x) \leq \frac{22}{3}\right\}$
27. max = 7; D = {all real numbers}, R = $\{f(x) \mid f(x) \leq 7\}$
28. max = 15; D = {all real numbers}, R = $\{f(x) \mid f(x) \leq 15\}$
29. min = −9; D = {all real numbers}, R = $\{f(x) \mid f(x) \geq -9\}$
30. max = 55; D = {all real numbers}, R = $\{f(x) \mid f(x) \leq 55\}$
31. min = −74; D = {all real numbers}, R = $\{f(x) \mid f(x) \geq -74\}$

Example 4 p. 253

32. PRODUCTION A financial analyst determined the cost in thousands of dollars of producing bicycle frames is $C = 0.000025f^2 - 0.04f + 40$, where f is the number of frames produced.

a. Find the number of frames that minimizes cost. **800**

b. What is the total cost for that number of frames? **\$24,000**

Differentiated Homework Options

Level	Assignment	Two-Day Option	
AL Basic	12–32, 61, 62, 64–82	13–31 odd, 66–69	12–32 even, 61, 62, 64, 65, 70–82
OL Core	13–39 odd, 42, 58–62, 64–82	12–32, 66–69	33–65, 70–82
BL Advanced	33–79, (optional: 80–82)		

41c. $11; Because the function has a maximum at $x = 3$, it is in the domain. Therefore, three $0.50 increases is reasonable.

B **Complete parts a–c for each quadratic function.** 33–40. See Chapter 5 Answer Appendix.

a. Find the y-intercept, the equation of the axis of symmetry, and the x-coordinate of the vertex.

b. Make a table of values that includes the vertex.

c. Use this information to graph the function.

33. $f(x) = 2x^2 - 6x - 9$

34. $f(x) = -3x^2 - 9x + 2$

35. $f(x) = -4x^2 + 5x$

36. $f(x) = 2x^2 + 11x$

37. $f(x) = 0.25x^2 + 3x + 4$

38. $f(x) = -0.75x^2 + 4x + 6$

39. $f(x) = \frac{3}{2}x^2 + 4x - \frac{5}{2}$

40. $f(x) = \frac{2}{3}x^2 - \frac{7}{3}x + 9$

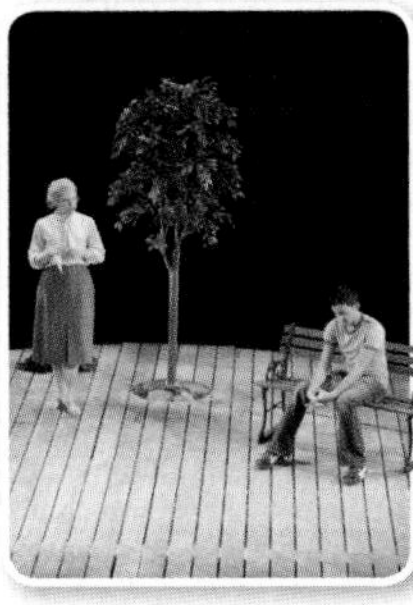

41. FINANCIAL LITERACY A babysitting club sits for 50 different families. They would like to increase their current rate of $9.50 per hour. After surveying the families, the club finds that the number of families will decrease by about 2 for each $0.50 increase in the hourly rate. b. $D = \{x \mid 0 \le x \le 25\}$, $R = \{y \mid 0 \le y \le 484\}$

a. Write a quadratic function that models this situation. $y = -x^2 + 6x + 475$

b. State the domain and range of this function as it applies to the situation.

c. What hourly rate will maximize the club's income? Is this reasonable?

d. What is the maximum income the club can expect to make? $484

42. ACTIVITIES Last year, 300 people attended the Franklin High School Drama Club's winter play. The ticket price was $8. The advisor estimates that 20 fewer people would attend for each $1 increase in ticket price.

a. What ticket price would give the greatest income for the Drama Club? $11.50

b. If the Drama Club raised its tickets to this price, how much income should it expect to bring in? $2645

Real-World Link

Participation in a drama club is not limited to acting. Other involvement includes set construction, lighting and sound, promotion, and business management.

GRAPHING CALCULATOR **Use a calculator to find the maximum or minimum of each function. Round to the nearest hundredth if necessary.**

43. $f(x) = -9x^2 - 12x + 19$ max = 23

44. $f(x) = 12x^2 - 21x + 8$ min = −1.19

45. $f(x) = -8.3x^2 + 14x - 6$ max = −0.10

46. $f(x) = 9.7x^2 - 13x - 9$ min = −13.36

47. $f(x) = 28x - 15 - 18x^2$ max = −4.11

48. $f(x) = -16 - 14x - 12x^2$ max = −11.92

Determine whether each function has a *maximum* or *minimum* value, and find that value. Then state the domain and range of the function.

49. $f(x) = -5x^2 + 4x - 8$

50. $f(x) = -4x^2 - 3x + 2$

51. $f(x) = -9 + 3x + 6x^2$

52. $f(x) = 2x - 5 - 4x^2$

53. $f(x) = \frac{2}{3}x^2 + 6x - 10$

54. $f(x) = -\frac{3}{5}x^2 + 4x - 8$

49. max = −7.2; D = {all real numbers}, R = $\{f(x) \mid f(x) \le -7.2\}$

50. max = 2.5625; D = {all real numbers}, R = $\{f(x) \mid f(x) \le 2.5625\}$

51. min = −9.375; D = {all real numbers}, R = $\{f(x) \mid f(x) \ge -9.375\}$

52. max = −4.75; D = {all real numbers}, R = $\{f(x) \mid f(x) \le -4.75\}$

53. min = −23.5; D = {all real numbers}, R = $\{f(x) \mid f(x) \ge -23.5\}$

54. max = $-\frac{4}{3}$; D = {all real numbers}, R = $\left\{f(x) \mid f(x) \le -\frac{4}{3}\right\}$

Determine the function represented by each graph.

55.

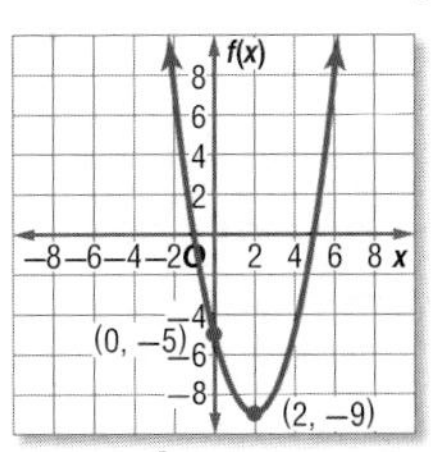

$f(x) = x^2 - 4x - 5$

56.

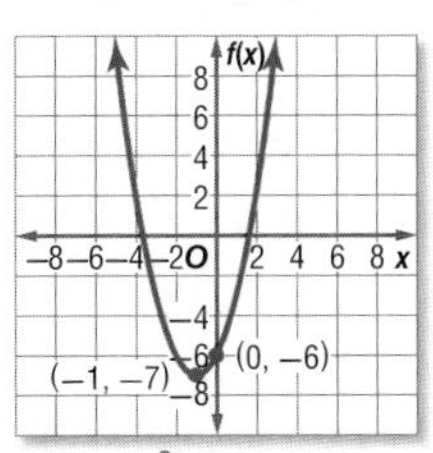

$f(x) = x^2 + 2x - 6$

57.

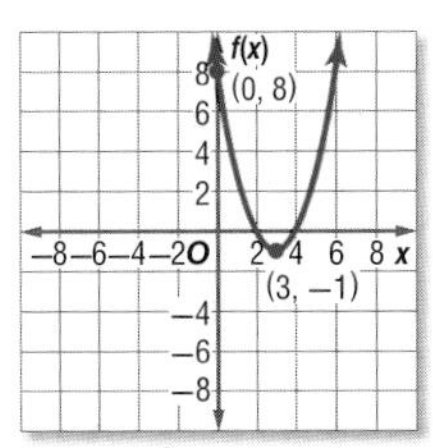

$f(x) = x^2 - 6x + 8$

Study Guide and Intervention

CRM pp. 5–6 AL OL ELL

5-1 Study Guide and Intervention

Graphing Quadratic Functions

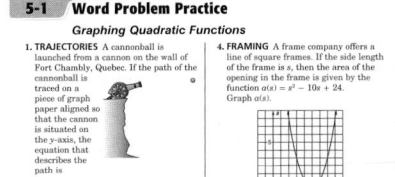

Graph Quadratic Functions

Quadratic Function	A function defined by an equation of the form $f(x) = ax^2 + bx + c$, where $a \ne 0$
Graph of a Quadratic Function	A **parabola** with these characteristics: y-intercept: c; axis of symmetry: $x = \frac{-b}{2a}$; x-coordinate of vertex: $\frac{-b}{2a}$

Example **Find the y-intercept, the equation of the axis of symmetry, and the x-coordinate of the vertex for the graph of $f(x) = x^2 - 3x + 5$. Use this information to graph the function.**

$a = 1$, $b = -3$, and $c = 5$, so the y-intercept is 5. The equation of the axis of symmetry is $x = \frac{-(-3)}{2(1)}$ or $\frac{3}{2}$. The x-coordinate of the vertex is $\frac{3}{2}$.

Next make a table of values for x near $\frac{3}{2}$.

x	$x^2 - 3x + 5$	$f(x)$	$(x, f(x))$
0	$0^2 - 3(0) + 5$	5	(0, 5)
1	$1^2 - 3(1) + 5$	3	(1, 3)
$\frac{3}{2}$	$\left(\frac{3}{2}\right)^2 - 3\left(\frac{3}{2}\right) + 5$	$\frac{11}{4}$	$\left(\frac{3}{2}, \frac{11}{4}\right)$
2	$2^2 - 3(2) + 5$	3	(2, 3)
3	$32 - 3(3) + 5$	5	(3, 5)

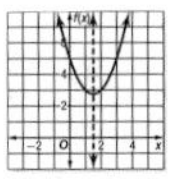

Lesson 5-1

Exercises

Complete parts a–c for each quadratic function.

a. Find the y-intercept, the equation of the axis of symmetry, and the x-coordinate of the vertex.

b. Make a table of values that includes the vertex.

c. Use this information to graph the function.

1. $f(x) = x^2 + 6x + 8$
8, x = −3, −3

x	−3	−2	−1	−4
f(x)	−1	0	3	0

2. $f(x) = -x^2 - 2x + 2$
2, x = −1, −1

x	−1	0	−2	1
f(x)	3	2	2	−1

3. $f(x) = 2x^2 - 4x + 3$
3, x = 1, 1

x	1	0	2	3
f(x)	1	3	3	9

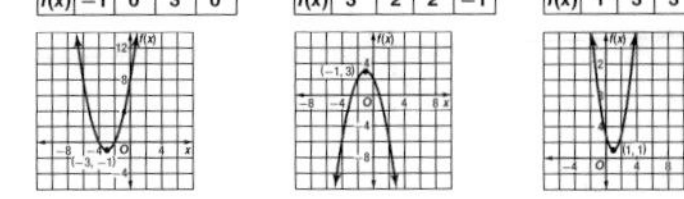

Chapter 5 5 Glencoe Algebra 2

Practice

CRM p. 8 AL OL BL ELL

5-1 Practice

Graphing Quadratic Functions

Complete parts a–c for each quadratic function.

a. Find the y-intercept, the equation of the axis of symmetry, and the x-coordinate of the vertex.

b. Make a table of values that includes the vertex.

c. Use this information to graph the function.

1. $f(x) = x^2 - 8x + 15$
15; x = 4; 4

x	0	2	4	6	8
f(x)	15	3	−1	3	15

2. $f(x) = -x^2 - 4x + 12$
12; x = −2; −2

x	−6	−4	−2	0	2
f(x)	0	12	16	12	0

3. $f(x) = 2x^2 - 2x + 1$
1; x = 0.5; 0.5

x	−1	0	0.5	1	2
f(x)	5	1	0.5	1	5

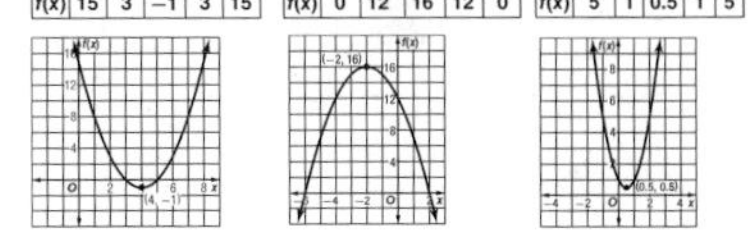

Determine whether each function has a *maximum* or *minimum* value, and find that value. Then state the domain and range of the function.

4. $f(x) = x^2 + 2x - 8$
min.; −9; all reals; $\{f(x) \mid f(x) \ge -9\}$

5. $f(x) = x^2 - 6x + 14$
min.; 5; all reals; $\{f(x) \mid f(x) \ge 5\}$

6. $v(x) = -x^2 + 14x - 57$
max.; −8; all reals; $\{f(x) \mid f(x) \le -8\}$

7. $f(x) = 2x^2 + 4x - 6$
min.; −8; all reals; $\{f(x) \mid f(x) \ge -8\}$

8. $f(x) = -x^2 + 4x - 1$
max.; 3; all reals; $\{f(x) \mid f(x) \le 3\}$

9. $f(x) = -\frac{2}{3}x^2 + 8x - 24$
max.; 0; all reals; $\{f(x) \mid f(x) \le 0\}$

10. GRAVITATION From 4 feet above a swimming pool, Susan throws a ball upward with a velocity of 32 feet per second. The height $h(t)$ of the ball t seconds after Susan throws it is given by $h(t) = -16t^2 + 32t + 4$. For $t \ge 0$, find the maximum height reached by the ball and the time that this height is reached. 20 ft; 1 s

11. HEALTH CLUBS Last year, the SportsTime Athletic Club charged $20 to participate in an aerobics class. Seventy people attended the classes. The club wants to increase the class price this year. They expect to lose one customer for each $1 increase in the price.

a. What price should the club charge to maximize the income from the aerobics classes? $45

b. What is the maximum income the SportsTime Athletic Club can expect to make? $2025

Chapter 5 8 Glencoe Algebra 2

Word Problem Practice

CRM p. 9 AL OL BL ELL

5-1 Word Problem Practice

Graphing Quadratic Functions

1. TRAJECTORIES A cannonball is launched from a cannon on the wall of Fort Chambly, Quebec. If the path of the cannonball is traced on a piece of graph paper aligned so that the cannon is situated on the y-axis, the equation that describes the path is

$$y = -\frac{1}{1600}x^2 + \frac{1}{2}x + 20,$$

where x is the horizontal distance from the cliff and y is the vertical distance above the ground in feet. How high above the ground is the cannon? 20 ft

2. TICKETING The manager of a symphony computes that the symphony will earn $-40P^2 + 1100P$ dollars per concert if they charge P dollars for tickets. What ticket price should the symphony charge in order to maximize its profits? $13.75

3. ARCHES An architect decides to use a parabolic arch for the main entrance of a science museum. In one of his plans, the top edge of the arch is described by the graph of $y = -\frac{1}{4}x^2 + \frac{5}{2}x + \frac{75}{5}$. What are the coordinates of the vertex of this parabola? (5, 25)

4. FRAMING A frame company offers a line of square frames. If the side length of the frame is s, then the area of the opening in the frame is given by the function $a(s) = s^2 - 10s + 24$. Graph $a(s)$.

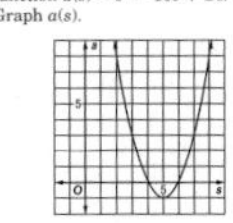

5. WALKING Canal Street and Walker Street are perpendicular to each other. Evita is driving south on Canal Street and is currently 5 miles north of the intersection with Walker Street. Jack is at the intersection of Canal and Walker Streets and heading east on Walker. Jack and Evita are both driving 30 miles per hour.

a. When Jack is x miles east of the intersection, where is Evita? 5 − x mi north of the intersection

b. The distance between Jack and Evita is given by the formula $\sqrt{x^2 + (5 - x)^2}$. For what value of x are Jack and Evita at their closest? (Hint: Minimize the square of the distance.) x = 2.5

c. What is the distance of closest approach? $\frac{5\sqrt{2}}{2}$ mi

Lesson 5-1

Chapter 5 9 Glencoe Algebra 2

Enrichment

CRM p. 10 OL BL

5-1 Enrichment

Finding the x-intercepts of a Parabola

As you know, if $f(x) = ax^2 + bx + c$ is a quadratic function, the values of x that make $f(x)$ equal to zero are $\frac{-b + \sqrt{b^2 - 4ac}}{2a}$ and $\frac{-b - \sqrt{b^2 - 4ac}}{2a}$.

The average of these two number values is $-\frac{b}{2a}$.

The function $f(x)$ has its maximum or minimum value when $x = -\frac{b}{2a}$. The x-intercepts of the parabola, when they exist, are $\frac{\sqrt{b^2 - 4ac}}{2a}$ units to the left and right of the axis of symmetry.

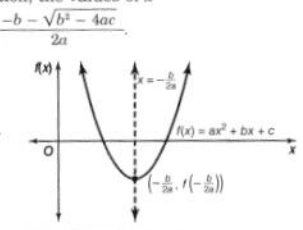

Example **Find the vertex, axis of symmetry, and x-intercepts for $f(x) = 5x^2 + 10x - 7$.**

Use $x = -\frac{b}{2a}$.

$x = -\frac{10}{2(5)} = -1$ The x-coordinate of the vertex is −1.

Substitute $x = -1$ in $f(x) = 5x^2 + 10x - 7$.

$f(-1) = 5(-1)^2 + 10(-1) - 7 = -12$. The vertex is (−1, −12).

Multiple Representations In Exercise 58, students use a table of values, a graph, and analytical observation to show how a change in values changes the shape of a graphed function.

Watch Out!

Error Analysis For Exercise 61, suggest that students follow the signs through each arithmetic operation in computing the x-coordinate of the maximum point.

Additional Answers

58a.

x	$f(x)$	$g(x)$
−4	40	88
−3	29	56
−2	20	32
−1	13	16
0	8	8
1	5	8
2	4	16
3	5	32
4	8	56

58b.

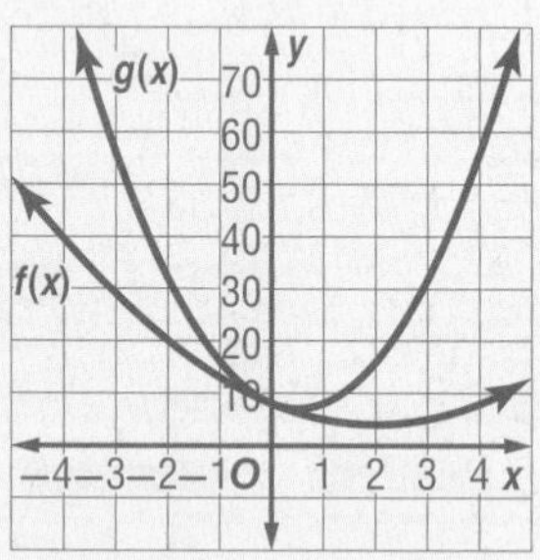

58c. Sample answer: $g(x)$ is much narrower than $f(x)$. The value of a changed from 1 to 4.

58d. Sample answer: The graph of $h(x)$ will be wider than $f(x)$.

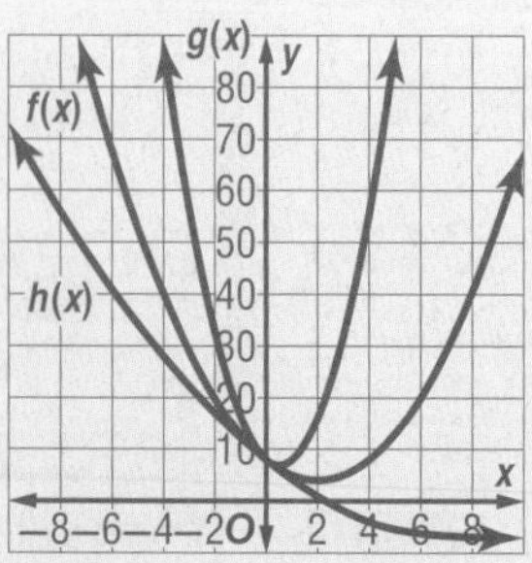

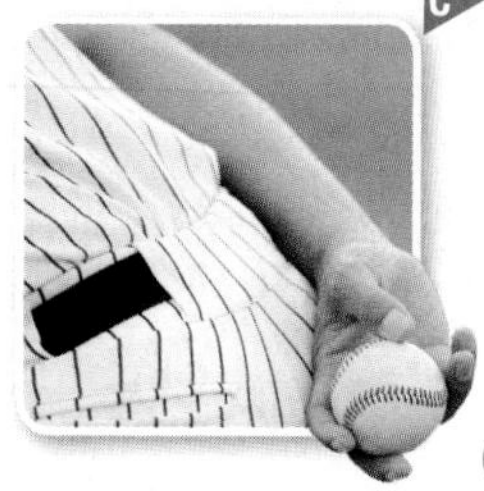

Real-World Link

To get the most distance and velocity when throwing a baseball, experienced baseball players grip a ball with their fingertips across the seams.

Source: QCBaseball

58. **MULTIPLE REPRESENTATIONS** Consider $f(x) = x^2 - 4x + 8$ and $g(x) = 4x^2 - 4x + 8$.

a. **TABULAR** Make a table of values for $f(x)$ and $g(x)$ if $-4 \leq x \leq 4$. **a–d. See margin.**

b. **GRAPHICAL** Graph $f(x)$ and $g(x)$.

c. **VERBAL** Explain the difference in the shapes of the graphs of $f(x)$ and $g(x)$. What value was changed to cause this difference?

d. **ANALYTICAL** Predict the appearance of the graph of $h(x) = 0.25x^2 - 4x + 8$. Confirm your prediction by graphing all three functions if $-10 \leq x \leq 10$.

59. **VENDING MACHINES** Omar owns a vending machine in a bowling alley. He currently sells 600 cans of soda per week at \$0.65 per can. He estimates that he will lose 100 customers for every \$0.05 increase in price and gain 100 customers for every \$0.05 decrease in price. (*Hint*: The charge *must* be a multiple of 5.) **a–c. See margin.**

a. Write and graph the related quadratic equation for a price increase.

b. If Omar lowers the price, what price should he charge in order to maximize his income?

c. What will be his income per week from the vending machine?

60. **BASEBALL** Lolita throws a baseball into the air and the height h of the ball in feet at a given time t in seconds after she releases the ball is given by the function $h(t) = -16t^2 + 30t + 5$.

a. State the domain and range for this situation. $D = \{t \mid 0 < t \leq 2.09\}$, $R = \{h(t) \mid h(t) \geq 0\}$

b. Find the maximum height the ball will reach. **19.0625 ft**

H.O.T. Problems Use Higher-Order Thinking Skills

61. **ERROR ANALYSIS** Trent and Madison are asked to find the maximum of $f(x) = -4x^2 + 8x - 6$. Is either of them correct? Explain your reasoning.

Madison	Trent
$x = -\frac{8}{2(-4)} = 1$	$x = -\frac{8}{2(-4)} = -1$
$f(1) = -4(1)^2 + 8(1) - 6$ or -2	$f(-1) = -4(-1)^2 + 8(-1) - 6$ or -18
The maximum is −2.	The maximum is −18.

61. Sample answer: Madison; when Trent found the x-coordinate of the vertex, he multiplied two negatives and mistakenly kept a negative.

62. **REASONING** Determine whether the following is *sometimes*, *always*, or *never* true. Explain your reasoning.

In a quadratic function, if two x-coordinates are equidistant from the axis of symmetry, then they will have the same y-coordinate.

62. Sample answer: Always; the coordinates of a quadratic function are symmetrical, so x-coordinates equidistant from the vertex will have the same y-coordinate.

63. **CHALLENGE** The table at the right represents some points on the graph of a quadratic function.

x	y
−20	−377
c	−13
−5	−2
−1	22
$d - 1$	a
5	$a - 24$
7	$-b$
15	−202
$14 - c$	−377

a. Find the values of a, b, c, and d. $a = 22$; $b = 26$; $c = -6$; $d = 2$

b. What is the x-coordinate of the vertex? **0**

c. Does the function have a maximum or a minimum? **maximum**

64. **OPEN ENDED** Give an example of a quadratic function with a

a. maximum of 8. **b.** minimum of −4. **c.** vertex of (−2, 6).

64a. Sample answer: $f(x) = -x^2 + 8$
64b. Sample answer: $f(x) = x^2 - 4$
64c. Sample answer: $f(x) = x^2 + 4x + 10$

65. **WRITING IN MATH** Describe how you determine whether a function is quadratic and if it has a maximum or minimum value. **See margin.**

59a. $f(x) = 39{,}000 - 3500x - 500x^2$

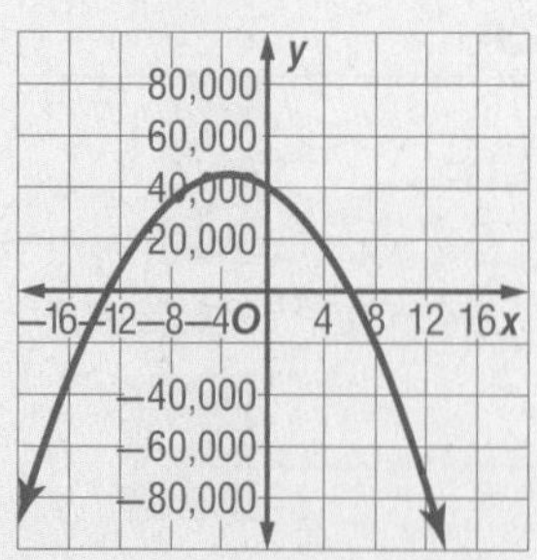

59b. Omar can charge at 45 cents or 50 cents.

59c. \$450 per week.

65. Sample answer: A function is quadratic if it has no other terms than a quadratic term, linear term, and constant term. The function has a maximum if the coefficient of the quadratic term is negative and has a minimum if the coefficient of the quadratic term is positive.

NGSSS PRACTICE 912.G.7.5, 912.A.3.14

66. Which expression is equivalent to $\frac{8!}{5!}$? **B**

A. $\frac{8}{5}$ C. 3!

B. $8 \cdot 7 \cdot 6$ D. $8 \cdot 7 \cdot 6 \cdot 5$

67. SAT/ACT The price of coffee beans is d dollars for 6 ounces, and each ounce makes c cups of coffee. In terms of c and d, what is the cost of the coffee beans required to make 1 cup of coffee? **I**

F. $\frac{cd}{6}$ H. $6cd$

G. $\frac{6c}{d}$ I. $\frac{d}{6c}$

68. THINK SOLVE EXPLAIN **SHORT RESPONSE** Each side of the square base of a pyramid is 20 feet, and the pyramid's height is 90 feet. What is the volume of the pyramid? **12,000 ft^3**

69. Which ordered pair is the solution of the following system of equations? **C**

$$3x - 5y = 11$$
$$3x - 8y = 5$$

A. (2, 1) C. (7, 2)

B. (7, −2) D. $\left(\frac{1}{3}, -2\right)$

Spiral Review

Find the inverse of each matrix, if it exists. (Lesson 4-6)

70. $\begin{bmatrix} 3 & -4 \\ 2 & -1 \end{bmatrix}$ **See margin.**

71. $\begin{bmatrix} -4 & -1 \\ 0 & 6 \end{bmatrix}$ $\begin{bmatrix} -\frac{1}{4} & -\frac{1}{24} \\ 0 & \frac{1}{6} \end{bmatrix}$

72. $\begin{bmatrix} 2 & 8 \\ -3 & -5 \end{bmatrix}$ $\begin{bmatrix} -\frac{5}{14} & -\frac{4}{7} \\ \frac{3}{14} & \frac{1}{7} \end{bmatrix}$

Evaluate each determinant. (Lesson 4-5)

73. $\begin{vmatrix} 6 & -3 \\ -1 & 8 \end{vmatrix}$ **45**

74. $\begin{vmatrix} -3 & -5 \\ -1 & -9 \end{vmatrix}$ **22**

75. $\begin{vmatrix} 8 & 6 \\ 4 & 3 \end{vmatrix}$ **0**

76. MANUFACTURING The Community Service Committee is making canvas tote bags and leather tote bags for a fundraiser. They will line both types of bags with canvas and use leather handles on both. For the canvas bags, they need 4 yards of canvas and 1 yard of leather. For the leather bags, they need 3 yards of leather and 2 yards of canvas. The committee leader purchased 56 yards of leather and 104 yards of canvas. (Lesson 3-4)

a. Let c represent the number of canvas bags, and let ℓ represent the number of leather bags. Write a system of inequalities for the number of bags that can be made. $c \geq 0$, $\ell \geq 0$, $c + 3\ell \leq 56$, $4c + 2\ell \leq 104$

b. Draw the graph showing the feasible region. **See margin.**

c. List the coordinates of the vertices of the feasible region. **(0, 0), (26, 0), (20, 12), $\left(0, 18\frac{2}{3}\right)$**

d. If the club plans to sell the canvas bags at a profit of \$20 each and the leather bags at a profit of \$35 each, write a function for the total profit on the bags. $f(c, \ell) = 20c + 35\ell$

e. How can the club make the maximum profit? **Make 20 canvas tote bags and 12 leather tote bags.**

f. What is the maximum profit? **\$820**

State whether each function is a linear function. Write *yes* or *no*. Explain. (Lesson 2-2)

77. $y = 4x^2 - 3x$ **78.** $y = -2x - 4$ **79.** $y = 4$

77. No; it cannot be written as $y = mx + b$. 78. Yes; it is written in $y = mx + b$ form.
79. Yes; it is written in $y = mx + b$ form, $m = 0$.

Skills Review

Evaluate each function for the given value. (Lesson 2-1)

80. $f(x) = 3x^2 - 4x + 6, x = -2$ **26** **81.** $f(x) = -2x^2 + 6x - 5, x = 4$ **−13** **82.** $f(x) = 6x^2 + 18, x = -5$ **168**

4 ASSESS

Name the Math Have students explain how to tell by examining a quadratic function whether its graph will have a maximum or minimum value. Then have them give examples of what such values might mean in a real-world problem.

Additional Answers

70. $\begin{bmatrix} -\frac{1}{5} & \frac{4}{5} \\ -\frac{2}{5} & \frac{3}{5} \end{bmatrix}$

76b.

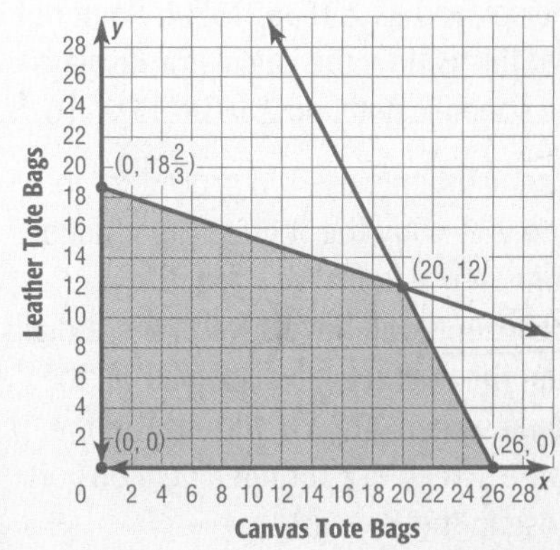

Differentiated Instruction BL OL

Extension Write the following quadratic functions on the board. Have students write each function in the form $f(x) = ax^2 + bx + c$.

$f(x) = x(x - 2) - 1$ $f(x) = x^2 - 2x - 1$

$f(x) = 2x\left(\frac{1}{2}x + 2\right) - 3$ $f(x) = x^2 + 4x - 3$

$f(x) = 2x(x - 4)$ $f(x) = 2x^2 - 8x$

EXTEND 5-1 Lesson Notes

1 FOCUS

Objective Use a graphing calculator to model data points for which the curve of best fit is a quadratic function.

Materials for Each Group

- TI-83/84 Plus or other graphing calculator

Teaching Tip

In Step 2, the value of the coefficient a is displayed as 2.1035215E-4. Point out that this is how the calculator displays the scientific notation 2.1035215×10^{-4}.

When students use the procedure in Step 2 to copy the regression equation from Step 1 to the **Y** = list, the coefficients will have several more digits than the coefficients displayed on the home screen. The coefficients on the home screen are rounded versions of those in the **Y** = list.

2 TEACH

Working in Cooperative Groups

Put students in groups of two or three, mixing abilities. Have groups work through the activity.

- Make sure students have cleared the $\mathbf{L_1}$ and $\mathbf{L_2}$ lists before entering new data. Also have them enter the **WINDOW** dimensions shown.
- For Step 1, point out that you can use the same keystrokes shown in Step 2, substituting 4 for the first 5, to select **LinReg**.
- If an error message appears in Step 2, have students clear the **Y** = list before trying Step 2 again.

Practice Have students complete Exercises 1–4.

EXTEND 5-1 Graphing Technology Lab: Modeling Real-World Data

FL Math Online glencoe.com
- Other Calculator Keystrokes
- Graphing Technology Personal Tutor

You can use a TI-83/84 Plus graphing calculator to model data points for which a curve of best fit is a quadratic function.

WATER A bottle is filled with water. The water is allowed to drain from a hole made near the bottom of the bottle. The table shows the level of the water *y* measured in centimeters from the bottom of the bottle after *x* seconds.

Time (s)	0	20	40	60	80	100	120	140	160	180	200	220
Water level (cm)	42.6	40.7	38.9	37.2	35.8	34.3	33.3	32.3	31.5	30.8	30.4	30.1

Find and graph a linear regression equation and a quadratic regression equation. Determine which equation is a better fit for the data.

Step 1 Find and graph a linear regression equation.

- Enter the times in L1 and the water levels in L2. Then find a linear regression equation.

KEYSTROKES: *Refer to Lesson 2-5.*

- Use STAT PLOT to graph a scatter plot. Copy the equation to the Y= list and graph.

KEYSTROKES: *Review statistical plots and graphing a regression equation in Lesson 2-5.*

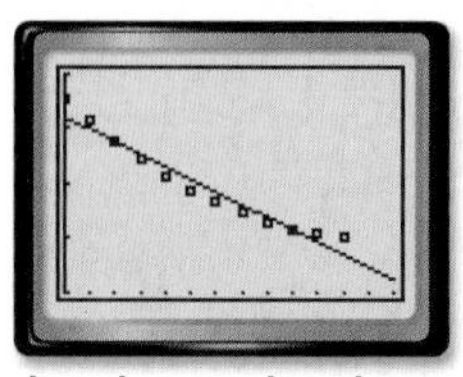

[0, 260] scl: 20 by [25, 45] scl: 5

Step 2 Find and graph a quadratic regression equation.

- Find the quadratic regression equation. Then copy the equation to the Y= list and graph.

KEYSTROKES: STAT ▶ 5 ENTER Y= VARS 5 ▶ ▶ ENTER Graph

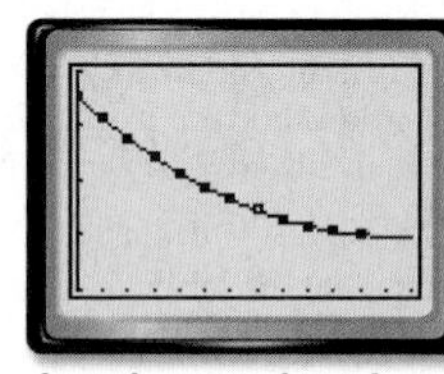

[0, 260] scl: 20 by [25, 45] scl: 5

Notice that the graph of the linear regression equation appears to pass through just two data points. However, the graph of the quadratic regression equation fits the data very well.

Exercises

Refer to the table.

Height of Player Making a Slam Dunk

Time (s)	Height (ft)
0.1	3.04
0.2	5.76
0.3	8.16
0.4	10.24
0.5	12
0.6	13.44
0.7	14.56

1. Find and graph a linear regression equation and a quadratic regression equation for the data. Determine which equation is a better fit for the data. **See Chapter 5 Answer Appendix.**
2. Use the CALC menu with each regression equation to estimate the height of the player after 1 second and 1.5 seconds. **Linear equation predictions: At 1 second, the height of the player will be 21.12 feet; at 1.5 seconds, the height of the player will be 30.72 feet. Quadratic equation predictions: At 1 second, the height of the player will be 16 feet; at 1.5 seconds, the height of the player will be 12 feet.**
3. Compare and contrast the estimates you found in Exercise 2. **See Chapter 5 Answer Appendix.**
4. How might choosing a regression equation that does not fit the data well affect predictions made by using the equation? **It could give misleading predictions.**

3 ASSESS

Formative Assessment

Use Exercise 4 to assess whether students understand that a regression equation that does not fit data well is a poor model of the given data and that it will most likely be a poor predictor.

From Concrete to Abstract

Have students explain how a scatter plot is useful for gaining insight into possible relationships between two variables. If the scatter plot shows that the data are in a straight line, a linear equation might be a good model. If they appear curved, a nonlinear model should be explored.

258 Chapter 5 Quadratic Functions and Relations

Solving Quadratic Equations by Graphing

Then

You solved systems of equations by graphing. (Lesson 3-1)

Now

- Solve quadratic equations by graphing.
- Estimate solutions of quadratic equations by graphing.

NGSSS

MA.912.A.7.6 **Identify** the axis of symmetry, vertex, domain, range and **intercept(s)** for a given parabola.
MA.912.A.7.10 Use graphing technology to find approximate solutions of quadratic equations.

New Vocabulary

quadratic equation
standard form
root
zero

FL Math Online

glencoe.com

Why?

Arielle works in the marketing department of a major retailer. Her job is to set prices for new products sold in the stores. Arielle determined that for a certain product, the function $f(p) = -6p^2 + 192p - 1440$ tells the profit $f(p)$ made at price p.

Arielle can determine the price range by finding the prices for which the profit is equal to \$0. This can be done by finding the solution of the related quadratic equation, which is zero.

The graph of the function indicates that the profit is zero at 12 and 20, so the profitable price range of the item is between \$12 and \$20.

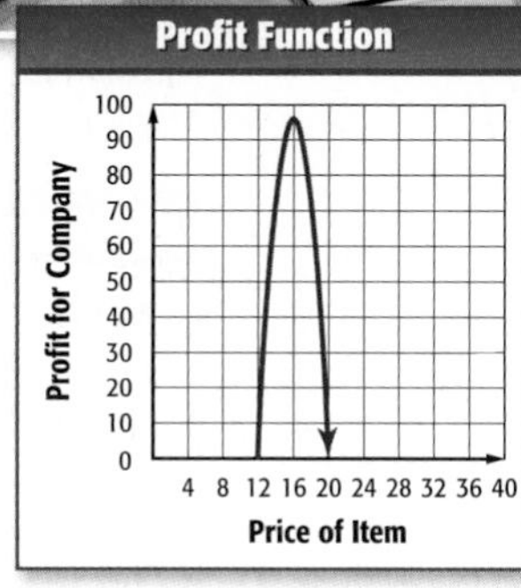

Solve Quadratic Equations **Quadratic equations** are quadratic functions that are set equal to a value. The **standard form** of a quadratic equation is $ax^2 + bx + c = 0$, where $a \neq 0$ and a, b, and c are integers.

The solutions of a quadratic equation are called the **roots** of the equation. One method for finding the roots of a quadratic equation is to find the **zeros** of the related quadratic function.

The zeros of the function are the x-intercepts of its graph.

Quadratic Function

$$f(x) = x^2 - x - 6$$

$$f(-2) = (-2)^2 - (-2) - 6 \text{ or } 0$$
$$f(3) = 3^2 - 3 - 6 \text{ or } 0$$

−2 and 3 are zeros of the function.

Quadratic Equation

$$x^2 - x - 6 = 0$$

$$(-2)^2 - (-2) - 6 \text{ or } 0$$
$$3^2 - 3 - 6 \text{ or } 0$$

−2 and 3 are roots of the equation.

Graph of Function

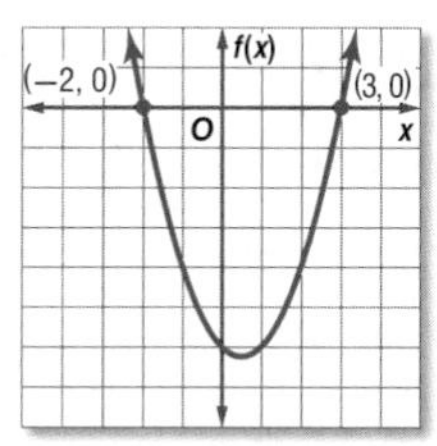

The x-intercepts are −2 and 3.

1 FOCUS

Vertical Alignment

Before Lesson 5-2
Solve systems of equations by graphing.

Lesson 5-2
Solve quadratic equations by graphing. Estimate solutions of quadratic equations by graphing.

After Lesson 5-2
Solve quadratic equations using algebraic methods.

2 TEACH

Scaffolding Questions

Have students read the *Why?* section of the lesson.

Ask:

- How can you tell by looking at the profit function's equation that the parabola opens downward? The coefficient of the p^2 term is negative.
- What item price yields the greatest profit? \$16
- Explain how you can verify that a \$12 item will give a \$0 profit? Substitute 12 for p in the function $f(p) = -6p^2 + 192p - 1440$.

Lesson 5-2 Resources

Resource	Approaching-Level	On-Level	Beyond-Level	English Learners
Teacher Edition	• Differentiated Instruction, p. 262	• Differentiated Instruction, p. 266	• Differentiated Instruction, p. 266	• Differentiated Instruction, p. 262
Chapter Resource Masters	• Study Guide and Intervention, pp. 11–12 • Skills Practice, p. 13 • Practice, p. 14 • Word Problem Practice, p. 15	• Study Guide and Intervention, pp. 11–12 • Skills Practice, p. 13 • Practice, p. 14 • Word Problem Practice, p. 15 • Enrichment, p. 16	• Practice, p. 14 • Word Problem Practice, p. 15 • Enrichment, p. 16	• Study Guide and Intervention, pp. 11–12 • Skills Practice, p. 13 • Practice, p. 14 • Word Problem Practice, p. 15
Transparencies	• 5-Minute Check Transparency 5-2	• 5-Minute Check Transparency 5-2	• 5-Minute Check Transparency 5-2	• 5-Minute Check Transparency 5-2
Other	• Study Notebook • Teaching Algebra with Manipulatives	• Study Notebook • Teaching Algebra with Manipulatives	• Study Notebook	• Study Notebook • Teaching Algebra with Manipulatives

Solve Quadratic Equations

Example 1 shows how to solve a quadratic equation with two real solutions by graphing. **Example 2** shows how to solve a quadratic equation with one real solution by graphing. **Example 3** shows how to solve a quadratic equation with no real solutions by graphing.

Formative Assessment

Use the Guided Practice exercises after each example to determine students' understanding of concepts.

Additional Examples

1 Solve $x^2 + 6x + 8 = 0$ by graphing. −4 and −2;

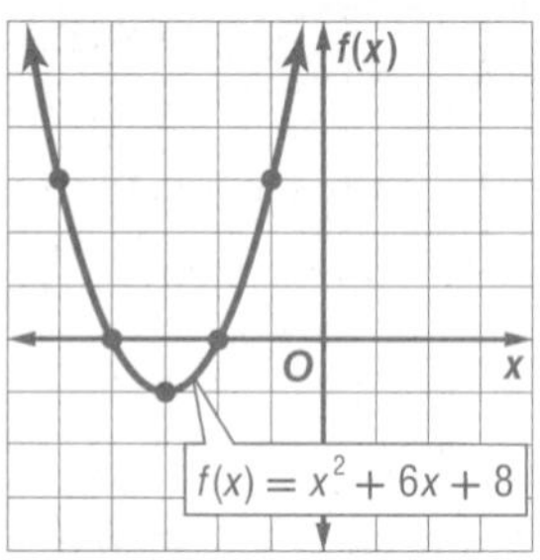

2 Solve $x^2 - 4x = -4$ by graphing. 2

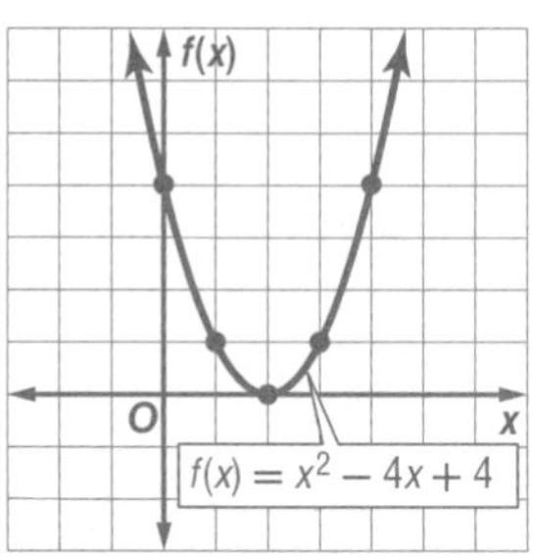

Additional Examples also in Interactive Classroom PowerPoint® Presentations

IWB INTERACTIVE WHITEBOARD READY

StudyTip

Graphing Sometimes more than five points will be needed before the zeros are located.

EXAMPLE 1 Two Real Solutions

Solve $x^2 - 3x - 4 = 0$ by graphing.

Graph the related function, $f(x) = x^2 - 3x - 4$. The equation of the axis of symmetry is $x = -\frac{-3}{2(1)}$ or 1.5. Make a table using x-values around 1.5. Then graph each point.

x	−1	0	1	1.5	2	3	4
f(x)	0	−4	−6	−6.25	−6	−4	0

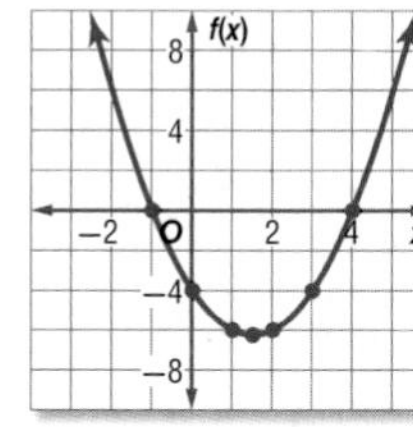

The zeros of the function are −1 and 4.
Therefore, the solutions of the equation are −1 and 4.

Guided Practice

1. Solve each equation by graphing. **1A, 1B. See margin.**

A. $x^2 + 2x - 15 = 0$ **B.** $x^2 - 8x = -12$

Personal Tutor glencoe.com

The graph of the related function in Example 1 has two zeros; therefore, the quadratic equation has two real solutions. This is one of the three possible outcomes when solving a quadratic equation.

Key Concept Solutions of a Quadratic Equation

Words A quadratic equation can have one real solution, two real solutions, or no real solutions.

Models

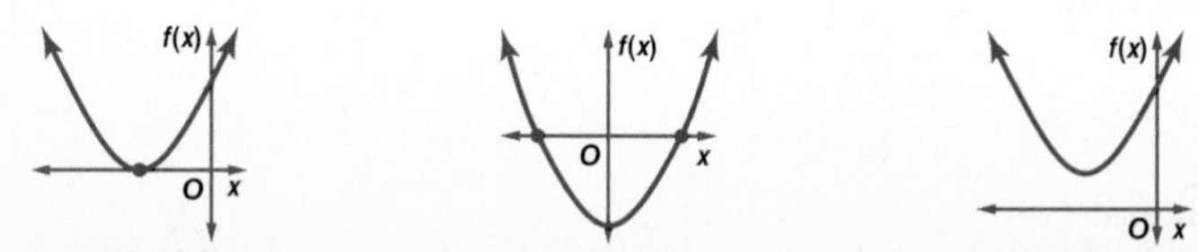

one real solution two real solutions no real solution

EXAMPLE 2 One Real Solution

Solve $14 - x^2 = -6x + 23$ by graphing.

$14 - x^2 = -6x + 23$	**Original equation**
$14 = x^2 - 6x + 23$	**Add x^2 to each side.**
$0 = x^2 - 6x + 9$	**Subtract 14.**

Graph the related function $f(x) = x^2 - 6x + 9$.

x	1	2	3	4	5
f(x)	4	1	0	1	4

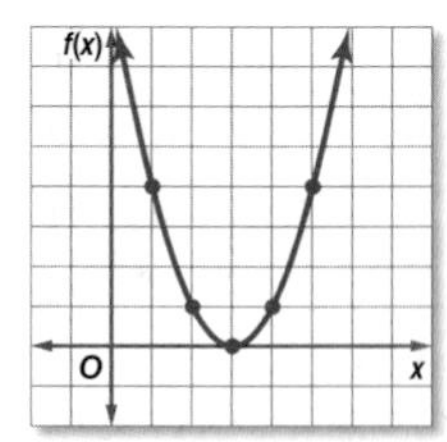

Notice that the function has only one zero, 3. Therefore, the only solution is 3.

Guided Practice **2A, 2B. See Chapter 5 Answer Appendix for graphs.**

2. Solve each equation by graphing.

A. $x^2 + 5 = -8x - 11$ **−4** **B.** $12 - x^2 = 48 - 12x$ **6**

Personal Tutor glencoe.com

StudyTip

Optional Graph $f(x) = -x^2 + 6x - 9$ could also have been graphed for this example. The graph would appear different, but it would have the same solution.

Additional Answers for Guided Practice

1A.

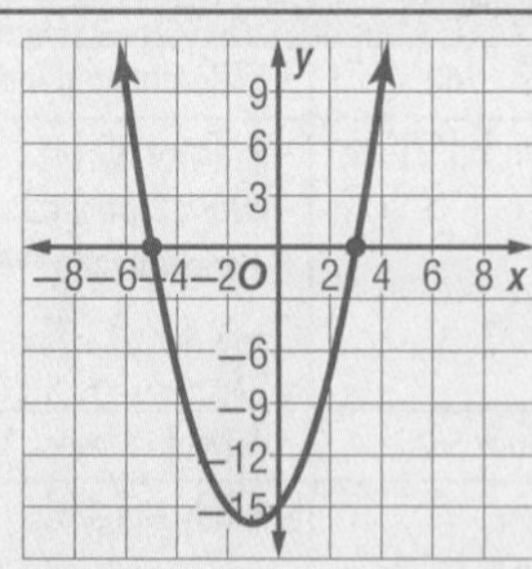

−5, 3

1B.

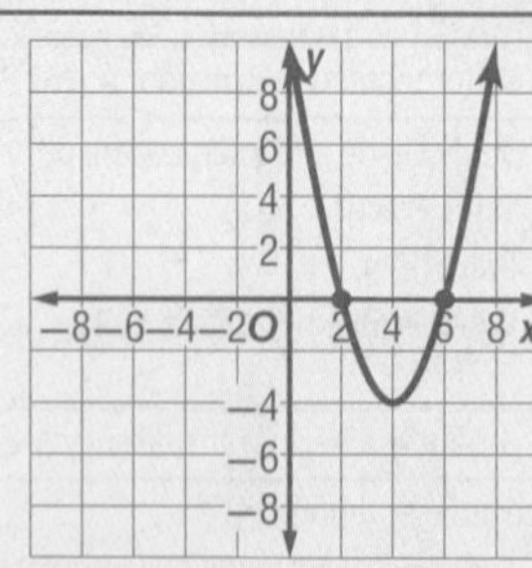

6, 2

EXAMPLE 3 No Real Solution

NUMBER THEORY Use a quadratic equation to find two real numbers with a sum of 15 and a product of 63.

Understand Let x represent one of the numbers. Then $15 - x$ is the other number.

Plan

$x(15 - x) = 63$	**The product of the numbers is 63.**
$15x - x^2 = 63$	**Distributive Property**
$-x^2 + 15x - 63 = 0$	**Subtract 63.**

Solve Graph the related function.

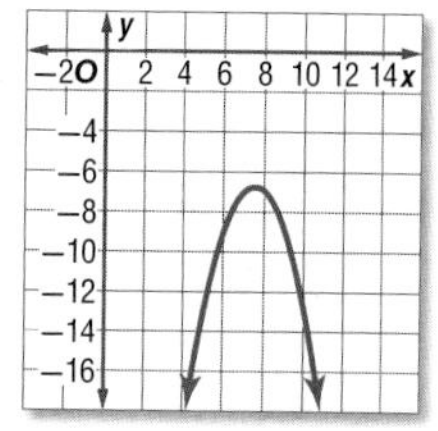

The graph has no x-intercepts. This means the original equation has no real solution. Thus, it is not possible for two real numbers to have a sum of 15 and a product of 63.

Check Try finding the product of several pairs of numbers with sums of 15. Is each product less than 63 as the graph suggests?

Guided Practice

3. Find two real numbers with a sum of 6 and a product of −55, or show that no such numbers exist. **11 and −5**

Personal Tutor glencoe.com

Additional Example

3 **NUMBER THEORY** Use a quadratic equation to find two real numbers with a sum of 4 and a product of 5.

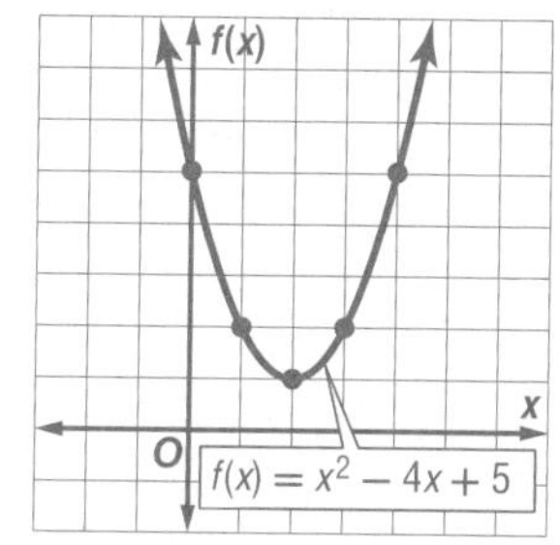

The graph of the related function does not intersect the x-axis. Thus, no such numbers exist.

Estimate Solutions Often exact roots cannot be found by graphing. You can estimate the solutions by stating the integers between which the roots are located.

When the value of the function is positive for one value and negative for a second value, then there is at least one zero between those two values.

x	−3	−2	−1	0	1	2	3
$f(x)$	12	3	−6	−2	4	8	14

zero (between −2 and −1)   zero (between 0 and 1)

Watch Out!

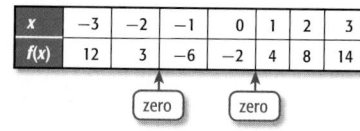

Zeros You will see in later chapters that many zeros can appear within small intervals.

Estimate Solutions

Example 4 shows how to estimate the roots of a quadratic equation when the exact roots cannot be found. **Example 5** shows how to use a table to approximate the roots of a quadratic equation. **Example 6** shows how to use a graphing calculator to approximate the solutions of a quadratic equation in a real-world situation.

EXAMPLE 4 Estimate Roots

Solve $x^2 - 6x + 4 = 0$ by graphing. If exact roots cannot be found, state the consecutive integers between which the roots are located.

x	0	1	2	3	4	5	6
$f(x)$	4	−1	−4	−5	−4	−1	4

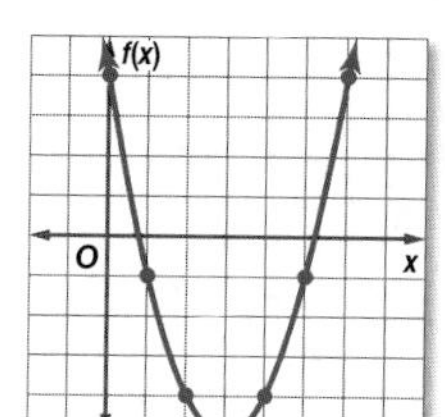

The x-intercepts of the graph indicate that one solution is between 0 and 1, and the other solution is between 5 and 6.

Guided Practice

4. Solve $x^2 - x - 10 = 0$ by graphing. If exact roots cannot be found, state the consecutive integers between which the roots are located. **between 3 and 4; between −3 and −2**

Personal Tutor glencoe.com

Additional Example

4 Solve $-x^2 + 4x - 1 = 0$ by graphing. If exact roots cannot be found, state the consecutive integers between which the roots are located. One solution is between 0 and 1; the other is between 3 and 4.

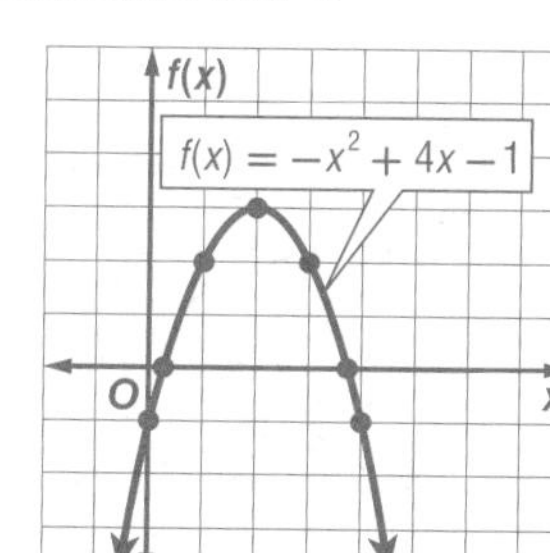

Focus on Mathematical Content

Solutions of a Quadratic Equation In a complex number system, a quadratic equation with real coefficients can have one real solution (a double root), two unequal real solutions, or two complex solutions that are not real. If the graph of the related quadratic function has one x-intercept, then there is one real solution (double root). If the graph of the related quadratic function has two x-intercepts, then there are two real solutions. If the graph of the related quadratic function does not intersect the x-axis, then there are no real solutions, but two imaginary solutions.

Additional Examples

5 Solve $x^2 + 5x - 7 = 0$. To the nearest thousandth, the solutions are –6.140 and 1.140.

6 **ROYAL GORGE BRIDGE** The highest bridge in the U.S. is the Royal Gorge Bridge in Colorado. The deck is 1053 feet above the river. Suppose a marble is dropped over the railing from a height of 3 feet above the bridge deck. How long will it take the marble to reach the surface of the water, assuming there is no air resistance? Use the formula $h(t) = -16t^2 + h_0$, where t is time in seconds and h_0, is the initial height above the water in feet. about 8 s

TEACH with TECH

PORTABLE MEDIA PLAYER Load images of graphs of quadratic functions onto students' portable media players. For each graph, have students find the zeros of the function.

You can also use tables to solve quadratic equations. After entering the equation in your calculator, scroll through the table to locate the solutions.

EXAMPLE 5 Solve by Using a Table

Solve $x^2 - 6x + 2 = 0$.

Enter $y_1 = x^2 - 6x + 2$ in your graphing calculator. Use the **TABLE** window to find where the sign of **Y1** changes. Change **△Tbl** to 0.1 and look again for the sign change. Repeat the process with 0.01 and 0.001 to get a more accurate location of the zero.

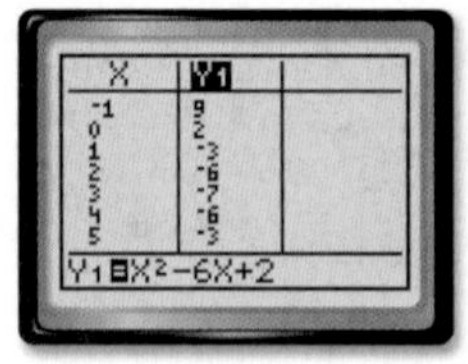

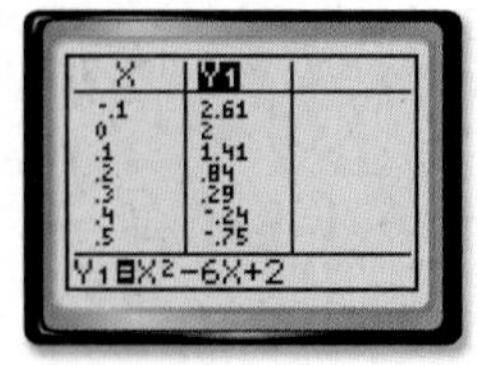

X
Y1
-.1 0 .1 .2 .3 .4 .5
2.61 2 1.41 .84 .29 -.24 -.75
Y1=X²-6X+2

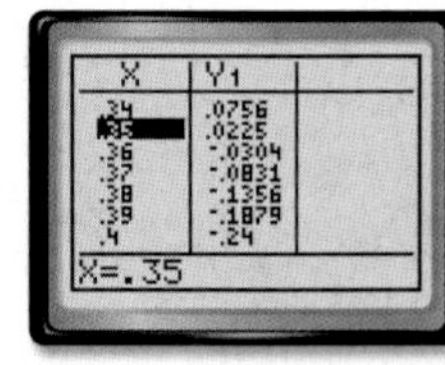

One solution is approximately 0.354.

Guided Practice

5. Locate the second zero in the function above to the nearest thousandth. 5.646

Personal Tutor glencoe.com

Quadratic equations can be solved with a calculator as well. After entering the equation, use the **ZERO** operation in the **CALC** menu.

Real-World Link

Each year, the American Red Cross responds to over 70,000 disaster situations ranging from house fires to natural disasters such as hurricanes and earthquakes.

Real-World EXAMPLE 6 Solve by Using a Calculator

RELIEF A package of supplies is tossed from a helicopter at an altitude of 200 feet. The package's height above the ground is modeled by $h(t) = -16t^2 + 28t + 200$, where t is the time in seconds after it is tossed. How long will it take the package to reach the ground?

We need to find t when $h(t)$ is 0. Solve $0 = -16t^2 + 28t + 200$. Then graph the related function $f(t) = -16t^2 + 28t + 200$ on a graphing calculator.

- Use the **ZERO** feature in the **CALC** menu to find the positive zero of the function, since time cannot be negative.
- Use the arrow keys to select a left bound and press **ENTER**.
- Locate a right bound and press **ENTER** twice.
- The positive zero of the function is about 4.52. The package would take about 4.52 seconds to reach the ground.

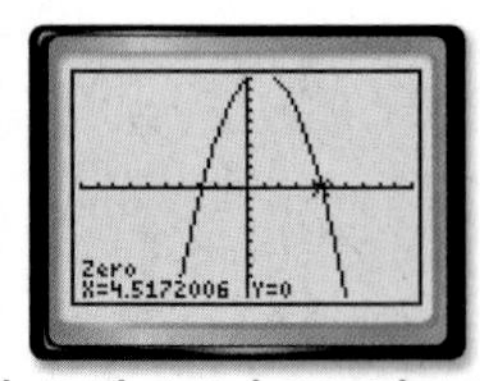

[−10, 10] scl: 1 by [−200, 200] scl: 20

Guided Practice

6. How long would it take to reach the ground if the height was modeled by $h(t) = -16t^2 + 48t + 400$? about 6.7 seconds

Personal Tutor glencoe.com

Differentiated Instruction

AL ELL

Visual/Spatial Learners Provide students with a variety of parabolas. Ask students to sort the parabolas into three piles: those that model a quadratic equation with one real solution, those that model a quadratic equation with two real solutions, and those that model a quadratic equation with no solutions. Finally, ask students to name the real solutions for those in the piles having real solutions.

Check Your Understanding

Example 1 p. 260

Use the related graph of each equation to determine its solutions.

1. no real solution

1. $x^2 + 2x + 3 = 0$

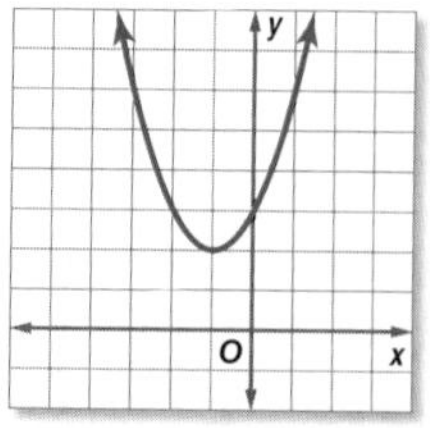

2. $x^2 - 3x - 10 = 0$ **−2, 5**

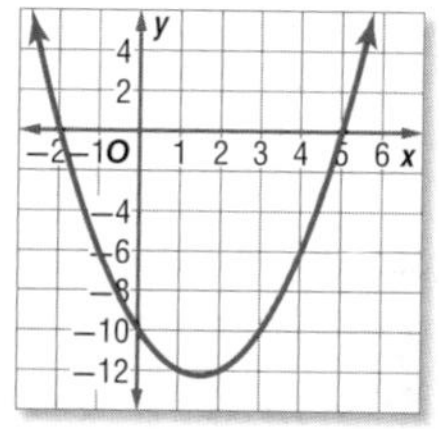

3. $-x^2 - 8x - 16 = 0$ **−4**

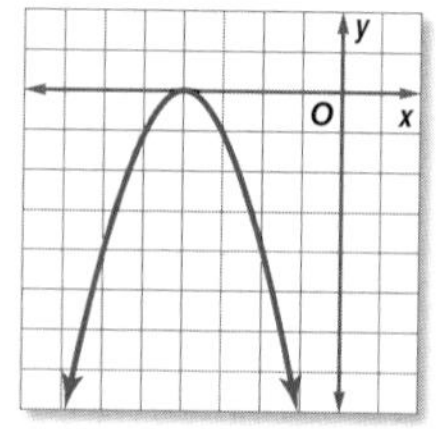

Examples 2–5 pp. 260–262

Solve each equation. If exact roots cannot be found, state the consecutive integers between which the roots are located. **4–11. See margin.**

4. $x^2 + 8x = 0$

5 $x^2 - 3x - 18 = 0$

6. $4x - x^2 + 8 = 0$

7. $-12 - 5x + 3x^2 = 0$

8. $x^2 - 6x + 4 = -8$

9. $9 - x^2 = 12$

10. $5x^2 + 10x - 4 = -6$

11. $x^2 - 20 = 2 + x$

12. **NUMBER THEORY** Use a quadratic equation to find two real numbers with a sum of 2 and a product of −24. **6 and −4**

Example 6 p. 262

13. **PHYSICS** How long will it take an object to fall from the roof of a building 400 feet above ground? Use the formula $h(x) = -16t^2 + h_0$, where t is the time in seconds and the initial height h_0 is in feet. **5 seconds**

Practice and Problem Solving

● = **Step-by-Step Solutions** begin on page R20. **Extra Practice** begins on page 947.

Example 1 p. 260

Use the related graph of each equation to determine its solutions.

15. no real solution

14. $x^2 + 4x = 0$ **−4, 0**

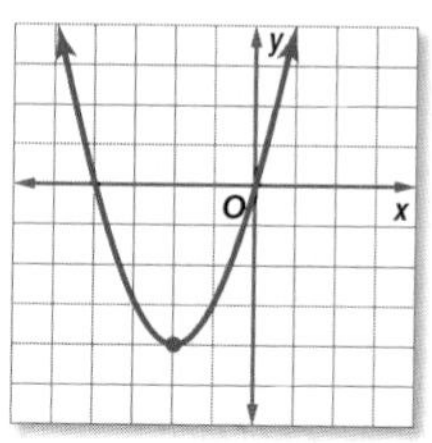

15. $-2x^2 - 4x - 5 = 0$

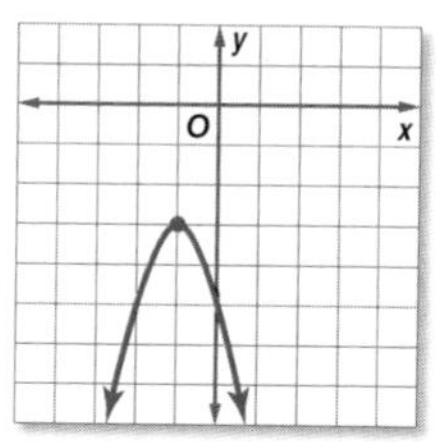

16. $0.5x^2 - 2x + 2 = 0$ **2**

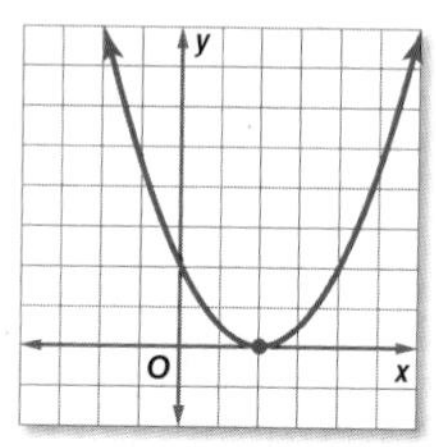

18. no real solution

19. −3, 4

17. $-0.25x^2 - x - 1 = 0$ **−2**

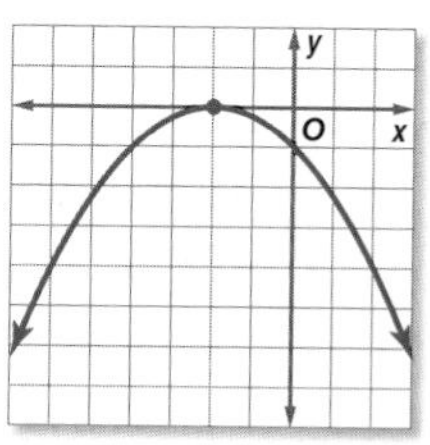

18. $x^2 - 6x + 11 = 0$

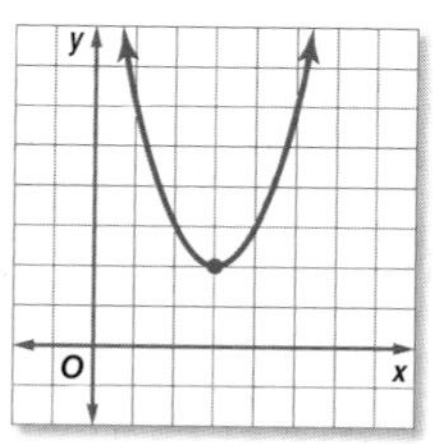

19. $-0.5x^2 + 0.5x + 6 = 0$

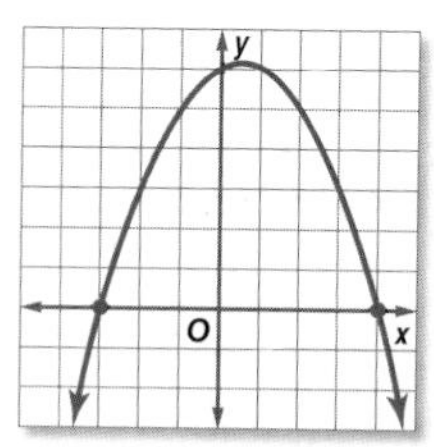

3 PRACTICE

Formative Assessment

Use Exercises 1–13 to check for understanding.

Use the chart on the bottom of this page to customize assignments for your students.

Tips for New Teachers

Reasoning Some students may notice in Exercise 3 that $-x^2 - 8x - 16 = 0$ is equivalent to $x^2 + 8x + 16 = 0$. Although the two equations have the same solution of −4, the related functions $f(x) = -x^2 - 8x - 16$ and $f(x) = x^2 + 8x + 16$ are not equivalent. This can be seen by looking at their graphs, which open in opposite directions.

Additional Answers

4–11. See Ch. 5 Answer Appendix for graphs.

4. 0, −8

5. −3, 6

6. between −2 and −1, between 5 and 6

7. between −2 and −1, 3

8. no real solution

9. no real solution

10. between −2 and −1, between −1 and 0

11. between −5 and −4, between 5 and 6

Differentiated Homework Options

Level	Assignment	Two-Day Option	
AL Basic	14–37, 52, 54–76	15–37 odd, 57–60	14–36 even, 52, 54–56, 61–76
OL Core	5–37 odd, 38–40, 41–47 odd, 49–52, 54–76	14–37, 57–60	38–52, 54–56, 61–76
BL Advanced	38–73, (optional: 74–76)		

Study Guide and Intervention

CRM pp. 11–12 AL OL ELL

5-2 Study Guide and Intervention

Solving Quadratic Equations by Graphing

Solve Quadratic Equations

Quadratic Equation	A quadratic equation has the form $ax^2 + bx + c = 0$, where $a \neq 0$.
Roots of a Quadratic Equation	solution(s) of the equation, or the zero(s) of the related quadratic function

The zeros of a quadratic function are the x-intercepts of its graph. Therefore, finding the x-intercepts is one way of solving the related quadratic equation.

Example Solve $x^2 + x - 6 = 0$ by graphing.

Graph the related function $f(x) = x^2 + x - 6$.

The x-coordinate of the vertex is $\frac{-b}{2a} = -\frac{1}{2}$, and the equation of the axis of symmetry is $x = -\frac{1}{2}$.

Make a table of values using x-values around $-\frac{1}{2}$.

x	−1	$-\frac{1}{2}$	0	1	2
f(x)	−6	$-6\frac{1}{4}$	−6	−4	0

From the table and the graph, we can see that the zeros of the function are 2 and −3.

Exercises

Use the related graph of each equation to determine its solution.

1. $x^2 + 2x - 8 = 0$ 2, −4
2. $x^2 - 4x - 5 = 0$ 5, −1
3. $x^2 - 5x + 4 = 0$ 1, 4
4. $x^2 - 10x + 21 = 0$ 3, 7
5. $x^2 + 4x + 6 = 0$ no real solutions
6. $4x^2 + 4x + 1 = 0$ $-\frac{1}{2}$

Chapter 5 11 Glencoe Algebra 2

Practice

CRM p. 14 AL OL BL ELL

5-2 Practice

Solving Quadratic Equations By Graphing

Use the related graph of each equation to determine its solutions.

1. $-3x^2 + 3 = 0$ −1, 1
2. $3x^2 + x + 3 = 0$ no real solutions
3. $x^2 - 3x + 2 = 0$ 1, 2

Solve each equation. If exact roots cannot be found, state the consecutive integers between which the roots are located.

4. $-2x^2 - 6x + 5 = 0$ between 0 and 1; between −4 and −3
5. $x^2 + 10x + 24 = 0$ −6, −4
6. $2x^2 - x - 6 = 0$ between −2 and −1, 2
7. $-x^2 + x + 6 = 0$ 3, −2
8. $-x^2 + 5x - 8 = 0$ no such real numbers exist

9. GRAVITY Use the formula $h(t) = v_0t - 16t^2$, where $h(t)$ is the height of an object in feet, v_0 is the object's initial velocity in feet per second, and t is the time in seconds.

a. Marta throws a baseball with an initial upward velocity of 60 feet per second. Ignoring Marta's height, how long after she releases the ball will it hit the ground? 3.75 s

b. A volcanic eruption blasts a boulder upward with an initial velocity of 240 feet per second. How long will it take the boulder to hit the ground if it lands at the same elevation from which it was ejected? 15 s

Chapter 5 14 Glencoe Algebra 2

Word Problem Practice

CRM p. 15 AL OL BL ELL

5-2 Word Problem Practice

Solving Quadratic Equations by Graphing

1. TRAJECTORIES David threw a baseball into the air. The function of the height of the baseball in feet is $h = 80t - 16t^2$, where t represents the time in seconds after the ball was thrown. Use this graph of the function to determine how long it took for the ball to fall back to the ground. 5 seconds

2. BRIDGES In 1895, a brick arch railway bridge was built on North Avenue in Baltimore, Maryland. The arch is described by the equation $h = 9 - \frac{1}{50}x^2$, where h is the height in yards and x is the distance in yards from the center of the bridge. Graph this equation and describe, to the nearest yard, where the bridge touches the ground. 21 yards from the center of the bridge on either side at (−21, 0) and (21, 0)

3. LOGIC Wilma is thinking of two numbers. The sum is 2 and the product is −24. Use a quadratic equation to find the two numbers. 6 and −4

4. RADIO TELESCOPES The cross-section of a large radio telescope is a parabola. The dish is set into the ground. The equation that describes the cross-section is $d = \frac{2}{75}x^2 - \frac{4}{3}x - \frac{32}{3}$, where d gives the depth of the dish below ground and x is the distance from the control center, both in meters. If the dish does not extend above the ground level, what is the diameter of the dish? Solve by graphing. 64 m

5. BOATS The distance between two boats is $d = \sqrt{t^2 - 10t + 35}$, where d is distance in meters and t is time in seconds.

a. Make a graph of d^2 versus t.

b. Do the boats ever collide? No

Chapter 5 15 Glencoe Algebra 2

Enrichment

CRM p. 16 OL BL

5-2 Enrichment

Graphing Absolute Value Equations

You can solve absolute value equations in much the same way you solved quadratic equations. Graph the related absolute value function for each equation using a graphing calculator. Then use the ZERO feature in the CALC menu to find its real solutions, if any. Recall that solutions are points where the graph intersects the x-axis.

For each equation, make a sketch of the related graph and find the solutions rounded to the nearest hundredth.

1. $|x + 5| = 0$ −5
2. $|4x - 3| + 5 = 0$ No solutions
3. $|x - 7| = 0$ 7
4. $|x + 3| - 8 = 0$
5. $-|x + 3| + 6 = 0$
6. $|x - 2| - 3 = 0$

Examples 2–4 pp. 260–261

Solve each equation. If exact roots cannot be found, state the consecutive integers between which the roots are located. 20–29. See Chapter 5 Answer Appendix for graphs.

26. between −3 and −2 and between 3 and 4
27. between −1 and 0 and between 1 and 2
28. between −1 and 0 and between 10 and 11

20. $x^2 = 5x$ 0, 5
21. $-2x^2 - 4x = 0$ −2, 0
22. $x^2 - 5x - 14 = 0$ −2, 7
23. $-x^2 + 2x + 24 = 0$ −4, 6
24. $x^2 - 18x = -81$ 9
25. $2x^2 - 8x = -32$ no real solution
26. $2x^2 - 3x - 15 = 4$
27. $-3x^2 - 7 + 2x = -11$
28. $-0.5x^2 + 3 = -5x - 2$
29. $-2x + 12 = x^2 + 16$ no real solution

Example 5 p. 262

Use the tables to determine the location of the zeros of each quadratic function.

30.

x	−7	−6	−5	−4	−3	−2	−1	0
f(x)	−8	−1	4	4	−1	−8	−22	−48

between −6 and −5; between −4 and −3

31.

x	−2	−1	0	1	2	3	4	5
f(x)	32	14	2	−3	−3	2	14	32

between 0 and 1; between 2 and 3

32.

x	−6	−3	0	3	6	9	12	15
f(x)	−6	−1	3	5	3	−1	−6	−14

between −3 and 0; between 6 and 9

Example 6 p. 262

NUMBER THEORY Use a quadratic equation to find two real numbers that satisfy each situation, or show that no such numbers exist.

33. Their sum is −15, and their product is −54. 3 and −18
34. Their sum is 4, and their product is −117. 13 and −9
35. Their sum is 12, and their product is −84. about −5 and 17
36. Their sum is −13, and their product is 42. −6 and −7
37. Their sum is −8 and their product is −209. 11 and −19

B For Exercises 38–40, use the formula $h(t) = v_0t - 16t^2$, where $h(t)$ is the height of an object in feet, v_0 is the object's initial velocity in feet per second, and t is the time in seconds.

38. **BASEBALL** A baseball is hit with an initial velocity of 80 feet per second. Ignoring the height of the baseball player, how long does it take for the ball to hit the ground? 5 seconds

39. **CANNONS** A cannonball is shot with an initial velocity of 55 feet per second. Ignoring the height of the cannon, how long does it take for the cannonball to hit the ground? about 3.4375 seconds

40. **GOLF** A golf ball is hit with an initial velocity of 100 feet per second. How long will it take for it to hit the ground? 6.25 seconds

43. between −3 and −2, between 1 and 2
45. between −1 and 0, between 4 and 5
46. between −2 and −1, between 2 and 3
47. between 3 and 4, between 8 and 9

Solve each equation. If exact roots cannot be found, state the consecutive integers between which the roots are located. 41–48. See Chapter 5 Answer Appendix for graphs.

41. $2x^2 + x = 15$ −3, between 2 and 3
42. $-5x - 12 = -2x^2$ $-\frac{3}{2}$, 4
43. $4x^2 - 15 = -4x$
44. $-35 = -3x - 2x^2$ −5, between 3 and 4
45. $-3x^2 + 11x + 9 = 1$
46. $13 - 4x^2 = -3x$
47. $-0.5x^2 + 18 = -6x + 33$
48. $0.5x^2 + 0.75 = 0.25x$ no real solution

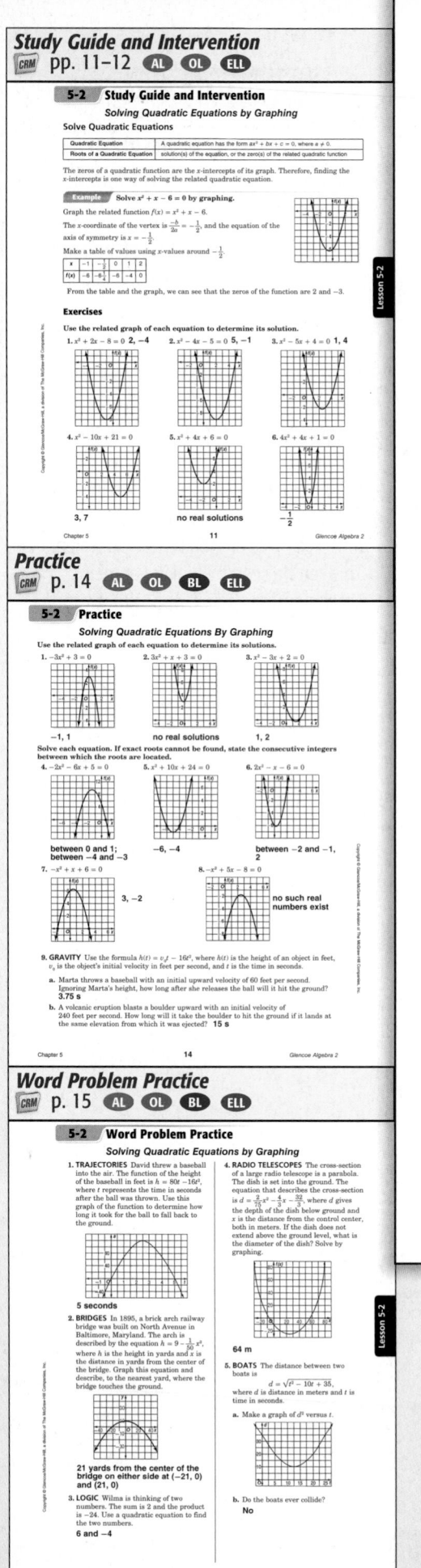

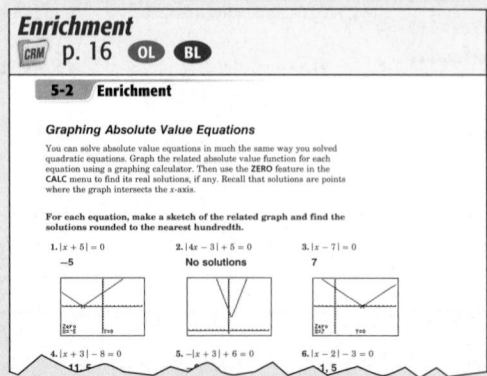

49. **WATER BALLOONS** Tony wants to drop a water balloon so that it splashes on his brother. Use the formula $h(t) = -16t^2 + h_0$, where t is the time in seconds and the initial height h_0 is in feet, to determine how far his brother should be from the target when Tony lets go of the balloon. **about 8.5 ft**

C

50. **WATER HOSES** A water hose can spray water at an initial velocity of 40 feet per second. Use the formula $h(t) = v_0t - 16t^2$, where $h(t)$ is the height of the water in feet, v_0 is the initial velocity in feet per second, and t is the time in seconds.

   a. How long will it take the water to hit the nozzle on the way down? **2.5 seconds**

   b. Assuming the nozzle is 5 feet up, what is the maximum height of the water? **30 ft**

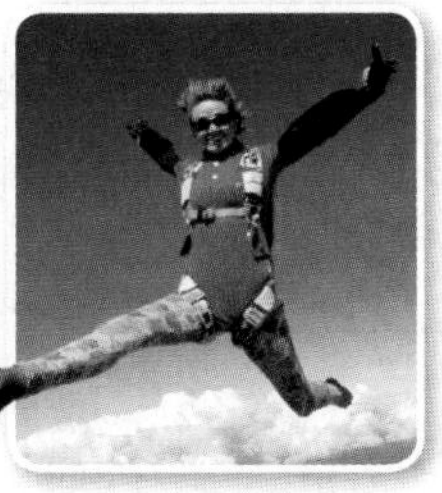

Real-World Link

The longest free fall distance by one person is 24,500 meters.

Source: Fédération Aéronautique Internationale

51. **SKYDIVING** In 2003, John Fleming and Dan Rossi became the first two blind skydivers to be in free fall together. They jumped from an altitude of 14,000 feet and free fell to an altitude of 4000 feet before their parachutes opened. Ignoring air resistance and using the formula $h(t) = -16t^2 + h_0$, where t is the time in seconds and the initial height h_0 is in feet, determine how long they were in free fall. **25 seconds**

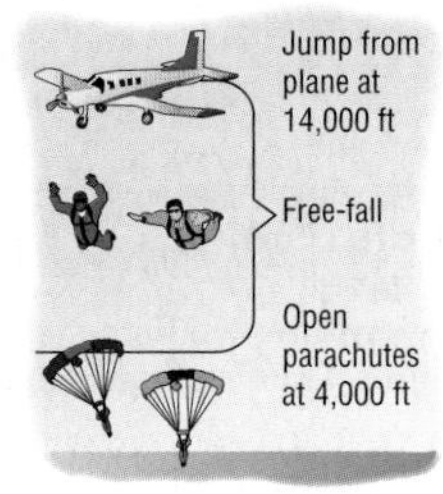

H.O.T. Problems Use Higher-Order Thinking Skills

52. **ERROR ANALYSIS** Hakeem and Tanya were asked to find the location of the roots of the quadratic function represented by the table. Is either of them correct? Explain.

x	−4	−2	0	2	4	6	8	10
$f(x)$	52	26	8	−2	−4	2	16	38

Hakeem

The roots are between 4 and 6 because f(x) stops decreasing and begins to increase between x = 4 and x = 6.

Tanya

The roots are between −2 and 0 because x changes signs at that location.

53. **CHALLENGE** Find the value of a positive integer k such that $f(x) = x^2 - 2kx + 55$ has roots at $k + 3$ and $k - 3$. $k = 8$

54. **REASONING** If a quadratic function has a minimum at $(-6, -14)$ and a root at $x = -17$, what is the other root? Explain your reasoning.

55. **OPEN ENDED** Write a quadratic function with a maximum at $(3, 125)$ and roots at -2 and 8.

56. **WRITING IN MATH** Explain how to solve a quadratic equation by graphing its related quadratic function.

52. Sample answer: No; roots are located where $f(x)$ changes signs.
54. Sample answer: The other root is at $x = 5$ because the x-coordinates of the roots need to be equidistant from the x-value of the vertex.
55. $f(x) = -5x^2 + 30x + 80$
56. Sample answer: Graph the function using the axis of symmetry. Determine where the graph intersects the x-axis. The x-coordinates of those points are solutions to the quadratic equation.

Watch Out!

Error Analysis For Exercise 52, have students think about the graph of a quadratic function, and contrast behavior near an intercept with behavior near a maximum or minimum.

Lesson 5-2 Solving Quadratic Equations by Graphing 265

4 ASSESS

Crystal Ball Have students write how what they learned today about solving quadratic equations by graphing will connect with tomorrow's theme of solving quadratic equations by factoring.

Formative Assessment

Check for student understanding of concepts in Lessons 5-1 and 5-2.

CRM Quiz 1, p. 59

Additional Answers

61. maximum, –12; D: {all real numbers}, R: $\{f(x) \mid f(x) \leq -12\}$

62. minimum, –30; D: {all real numbers}, R: $\{f(x) \mid f(x) \geq -30)\}$

63. maximum, 15; D: {all real numbers}, R: $\{f(x) \mid f(x) \leq 15\}$

67a. The object is reflected over the *x*-axis, and then translated 6 units to the right.

67b. Multiply the coordinates by $\begin{bmatrix} 1 & 0 \\ 0 & -1 \end{bmatrix}$, and then add the result to $\begin{bmatrix} 6 \\ 0 \end{bmatrix}$.

67c. Sample answer: No; since the translation does not change the *y*-coordinate, it does not matter whether or not you do the translation or reflection first. However, if the translation did change the *y*-coordinate, the order would be important.

NGSSS PRACTICE 912.P.3.1, 912.A.3.14, 912.D.11.1

57. THINK SOLVE EXPLAIN **SHORT RESPONSE** A bag contains five different colored marbles. The colors of the marbles are black, silver, red, green, and blue. A student randomly chooses a marble. Then, without replacing it, chooses a second marble. What is the probability that the student chooses the red and then the green marble? $\frac{1}{20}$

58. Which number would be closest to zero on the number line? **B**

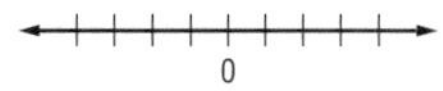

A. –0.6 C. $\frac{\sqrt{2}}{2}$

B. $\frac{2}{5}$ D. 0.5

59. **SAT/ACT** A salesman's monthly gross pay consists of \$3500 plus 20 percent of the dollar amount of his sales. If his gross pay for one month was \$15,500, what was the dollar amount of his sales for that month? **H**

F. \$12,000 H. \$60,000

G. \$16,000 I. \$70,000

60. Find the next term in the sequence below. **A**

$$\frac{2x}{5}, \frac{3x}{5}, \frac{4x}{5}, \ldots$$

A. x C. $\frac{x}{5}$

B. $5x$ D. $\frac{5x}{4}$

Spiral Review

Determine whether each function has a *maximum* or *minimum* value, and find that value. Then state the domain and range of the function. (Lesson 5-1) **61–63. See margin.**

61. $f(x) = -4x^2 + 8x - 16$ **62.** $f(x) = 3x^2 + 12x - 18$ **63.** $f(x) = 4x + 13 - 2x^2$

Determine whether each pair of matrices are inverses of each other. (Lesson 4-6)

64. $\begin{bmatrix} 4 & -3 \\ -1 & -6 \end{bmatrix}$ and $\begin{bmatrix} \frac{3}{13} & -\frac{1}{18} \\ -\frac{1}{26} & -\frac{2}{13} \end{bmatrix}$ no

65. $\begin{bmatrix} 6 & -3 \\ 4 & 8 \end{bmatrix}$ and $\begin{bmatrix} \frac{1}{10} & \frac{1}{20} \\ -\frac{1}{15} & \frac{2}{15} \end{bmatrix}$ no

66. $\begin{bmatrix} 2 & 4 \\ -3 & -2 \end{bmatrix}$ and $\begin{bmatrix} -\frac{1}{4} & -\frac{1}{2} \\ \frac{3}{8} & \frac{1}{4} \end{bmatrix}$ yes

67. **FOOTPRINTS** The combination of a reflection and a translation is called a *glide reflection*. An example is a set of footprints. (Lesson 4-4)

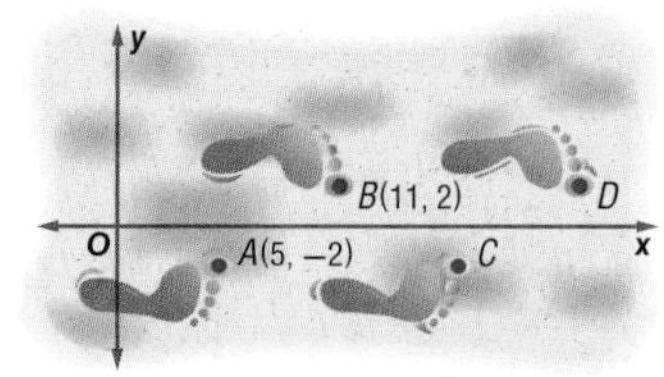

a. Describe the reflection and transformation combination shown at the right. **a–c. See margin.**

b. Write two matrix operations that can be used to find the coordinates of point *C*.

c. Does it matter which operation you do first? Explain.

d. What are the coordinates of the next two footprints? **(17, –2), (23, 2)**

Solve each system of equations. (Lesson 3-2)

68. $4x - 7y = -9$, $5x + 2y = -22$ **(–4, –1)**

69. $8y - 2x = 38$, $5x - 3y = -27$ **(–3, 4)**

70. $3x + 8y = 24$, $-16y - 6x = 48$ **no solution**

Solve each inequality. (Lesson 1-5)

71. $3x - 6 \leq -14$ $x \leq -\frac{8}{3}$

72. $6 - 4x \leq 2$ $x \geq 1$

73. $-6x + 3 \geq 3x - 16$ $x \leq \frac{19}{9}$

Skills Review

Find the GCF of each set of numbers.

74. 16, 48, 128 **16** **75.** 15, 21, 49 **1** **76.** 12, 28, 36 **4**

Differentiated Instruction BL OL

Extension Tell students that they can solve absolute value equations by graphing just as they solve quadratic equations by graphing. Write the following equations on the board:

$|x + 1| = 0$ $|x - 4| - 1 = 0$

Have students use a graphing calculator to graph the related absolute value function for each equation. Then have them use the **ZERO** feature from the **CALCULATE** menu to find its real solutions, if any, rounded to the nearest hundredth. –1; 3, 5

266 Chapter 5 Quadratic Functions and Relations

EXTEND **5-2**

Graphing Technology Lab: Solving Quadratic Equations by Graphing

FL Math Online glencoe.com
- Other Calculator Keystrokes
- Graphing Technology Personal Tutor

NGSSS **MA.912.A.7.10 Use graphing technology to find approximate solutions of quadratic equations.** *Also addresses MA.912.A.4.9.*

You can use a TI-83/84 Plus graphing calculator to solve quadratic equations.

ACTIVITY Solving Quadratic Equations

Solve $x^2 - 8x + 15 = 0$.

Step 1 Rewrite the equation in the form $y = ax^2 + bx + c$.
$y = x^2 - 8x + 15$

Step 2 Graph $y = x^2 - 8x + 15$ in a standard viewing window.
KEYSTROKES: [Y=] [X,T,θ,n] [x^2] [(−)] 8 [X,T,θ,n] [+] 15 [ZOOM] 6

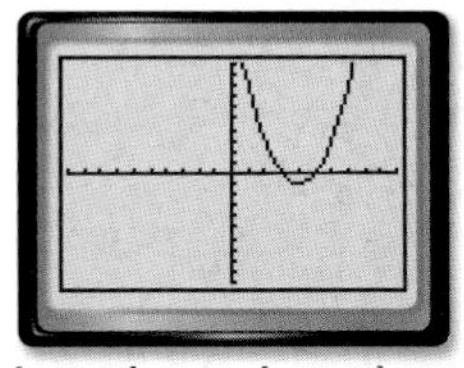
[−10, 10] scl: 1 by [−10, 10] scl: 1

Step 3 Find an x-intercept.
KEYSTROKES: [2nd] [CALC] 2
Use [◄] or [►] to position the cursor to the left of the first x-intercept. Press [ENTER]. Then use [►] to position the cursor to the right of the first x-intercept. Press [ENTER] [ENTER] to display the x-intercept.

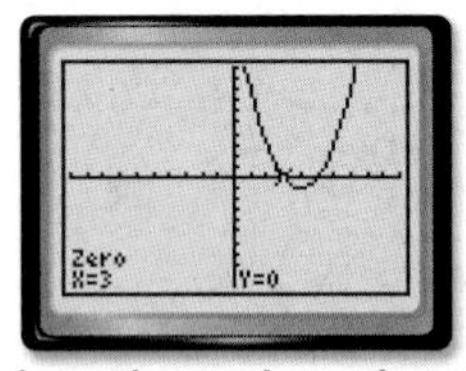

[−10, 10] scl: 1 by [−10, 10] scl: 1

Step 4 Find the second x-intercept.
KEYSTROKES: Use [►] to position the cursor to the left of the second x-intercept. Press [ENTER]. Then use [►] to position the cursor to the right of the second x-intercept. Press [ENTER] [ENTER] to display the x-intercept.

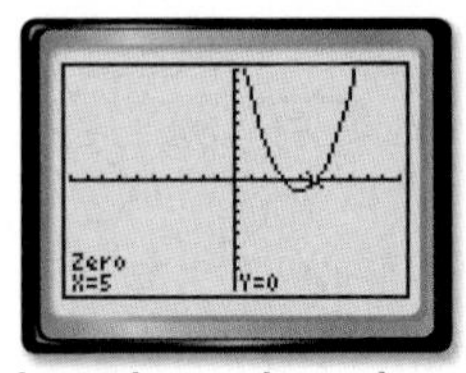

[−10, 10] scl: 1 by [−10, 10] scl: 1

The x-intercepts are 3 and 5, so $x = 3$ and $x = 5$.

Exercises

Solve each equation. Round to the nearest tenth if necessary.

1. $x^2 - 7x + 12 = 0$ **3, 4**
2. $x^2 + 5x + 6 = 0$ **−3, −2**
3. $x^2 - 3 = 2x$ **−1, 3**
4. $x^2 + 5x + 6 = 12$ **−6, 1**
5. $x^2 + 5x = 0$ **0, −5**
6. $x^2 - 4 = 0$ **−2, 2**
7. $x^2 + 8x + 16 = 0$ **−4**
8. $x^2 - 10x = -25$ **5**
9. $9x^2 + 48x + 64 = 0$ **−2.7**
10. $2x^2 + 3x - 1 = 0$ **−1.8, 0.3**
11. $5x^2 - 7x = -2$ **0.4, 1**
12. $6x^2 + 2x + 1 = 0$ **no real solution**

EXTEND **5-2**

Lesson Notes

1 FOCUS

Objective Use a graphing calculator to solve quadratic equations.

Materials for Each Student

- TI-83/84 Plus or other graphing calculator

Teaching Tips

In order to use a graph to solve the quadratic equation $ax^2 + bx + c = 0$, students must graph the related function $y = ax^2 + bx + c$.

2 TEACH

Working in Cooperative Groups

Put students in groups of two or three, mixing abilities. Have each group work through the Activity, comparing screens with each other as they go.

- Steps 3 and 4 can only be done while the graph is showing on the screen. If students try to do these steps from the home screen, remind them to display the graph first.
- When using [TRACE], the cursor's initial position is at the y-intercept, so it may not appear on the screen.

Practice Have students complete Exercises 1–12.

3 ASSESS

Formative Assessment

Use Exercise 3 to assess whether students understand that a quadratic equation should first be written in the form $ax^2 + bx + c = 0$ before solving.

From Concrete to Abstract

Have students explain why the intercepts of the graph of a function can be used to identify the roots of an equation. The x-intercepts of a graph occur where $y = 0$. At these points, the equation of the function reduces to a single-variable equation in x.

Extending the Concept

Ask:

- The x-intercepts in the Activity are 3 and 5. Have students multiply $(x - 3)(x - 5)$ and ask them to compare the result to the equation they have solved.

Extend 5-2 Graphing Technology Lab: Solving Quadratic Equations by Graphing **267**

5-3 Lesson Notes

1 FOCUS

Vertical Alignment

Before Lesson 5-3
Find the greatest common factors of sets of numbers.

Lesson 5-3
Write quadratic equations in intercept form. Solve quadratic equations by factoring.

After Lesson 5-3
Solve quadratic equations using the Quadratic Formula.

2 TEACH

Scaffolding Questions

Have students read the *Why?* section of the lesson.

Ask:

- Does $x^2 - 8x + 12$ have a maximum or minimum value? minimum
- Solve $y = x^2 - 8x + 12 = 0$ by graphing. 2, 6
- Compare the soultions to $x^2 - 8x + 12 = 0$ and $(x - 6)(x - 2) = 0$ The solutions are the same because the equations are equivalent.

5-3 Solving Quadratic Equations by Factoring

Then
You found the greatest common factors of sets of numbers. (Lesson ?-?)

Now
- Write quadratic equations in intercept form.
- Solve quadratic equations by factoring.

NGSSS
MA.912.A.4.3 Factor polynomial expressions.
MA.912.A.10.3 Decide whether a given statement is always, sometimes, or never true (statements involving linear or quadratic expressions, equations or inequalities, rational or radical expressions, or logarithmic or exponential functions).

New Vocabulary
factored form
FOIL method

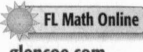

FL Math Online
glencoe.com

Why?

The **factored form** of a quadratic equation is $0 = a(x - p)(x - q)$. In the equation, p and q represent the x-intercepts of the graph of the equation.

The x-intercepts of the graph at the right are 2 and 6. In this lesson, you will learn how to change a quadratic equation in factored form into standard form and vice versa.

Standard Form	Factored Form
$0 = x^2 - 8x + 12$	$0 = (x - 6)(x - 2)$

Factors

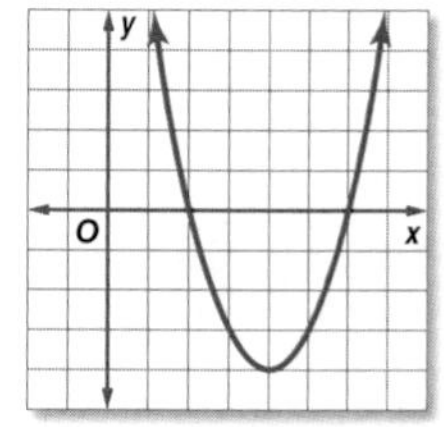

Related Graph
2 and 6 are x-intercepts.

Factored Form You can use the FOIL method to write a quadratic equation that is in factored form in standard form. The **FOIL method** uses the Distributive Property to multiply binomials.

Key Concept

FOIL Method for Multiplying Binomials

Words To multiply two binomials, find the sum of the products of ***F*** the *First* terms, ***O*** the *Outer* terms, ***I*** the *Inner* terms, and ***L*** the *Last* terms.

Examples

	Product of First Terms		Product of Outer Terms		Product of Inner Terms		Product of Last Terms
F O / I L: $(x - 6)(x - 2) =$	$(x)(x)$	+	$(x)(-2)$	+	$(-6)(x)$	+	$(-6)(-2)$

$= x^2 - 2x - 6x + 12$ or $x^2 - 8x + 12$

EXAMPLE 1 Write an Equation Given Roots

Write a quadratic equation in standard form with $-\frac{1}{3}$ and 6 as its roots.

$(x - p)(x - q) = 0$ **Write the pattern.**

$\left[x - \left(-\frac{1}{3}\right)\right](x - 6) = 0$ **Replace p with $-\frac{1}{3}$ and q with 6.**

$\left(x + \frac{1}{3}\right)(x - 6) = 0$ **Simplify.**

$x^2 - \frac{17}{3}x - 2 = 0$ **Multiply.**

$3x^2 - 17x - 6 = 0$ **Multiply each side by 3 so that b and c are integers.**

Guided Practice

1. Write a quadratic equation in standard form with $\frac{3}{4}$ and -5 as its roots.
$4x^2 + 17x - 15 = 0$

Personal Tutor glencoe.com

Lesson 5-3 Resources

Resource	Approaching-Level	On-Level	Beyond-Level	English Learners
Teacher Edition	• Differentiated Instruction, p. 269	• Differentiated Instruction, pp. 269, 275	• Differentiated Instruction, pp. 269, 275	
Chapter Resource Masters	• Study Guide and Intervention, pp. 17–18 • Skills Practice, p. 19 • Practice, p. 20 • Word Problem Practice, p. 21	• Study Guide and Intervention, pp. 17–18 • Skills Practice, p. 19 • Practice, p. 20 • Word Problem Practice, p. 21 • Enrichment, p. 22 • Graphing Calculator Activity, p. 23	• Practice, p. 20 • Word Problem Practice, p. 21 • Enrichment, p. 22	• Study Guide and Intervention, pp. 17–18 • Skills Practice, p. 19 • Practice, p. 20 • Word Problem Practice, p. 21
Transparencies	• 5-Minute Check Transparency 5-3	• 5-Minute Check Transparency 5-3	• 5-Minute Check Transparency 5-3	• 5-Minute Check Transparency 5-3
Other	• Study Notebook	• Study Notebook	• Study Notebook	• Study Notebook

StudyTip

Writing Equations $(x - p)(x - q) = 0$ produces one equation with roots p and q. In fact, there are an infinite number of equations that have these same roots. This is represented by the a coefficient.

Solve Equations by Factoring You have learned various techniques for factoring polynomials. A summary of them is listed below.

Concept Summary Factoring Techniques

Factoring Technique	General Case
Greatest Common Factor (GCF)	$a^3b^2 - nab^2 = ab^2(a^2 - n)$
General Trinomials	$acx^2 + (ad + bc)x + bd = (ax + b)(cx + d)$
Difference of Two Squares	$a^2 - b^2 = (a + b)(a - b)$
Perfect Square Trinomials	$a^2 \pm 2ab + b^2 = (a \pm b)^2$

EXAMPLE 2 Factor GCF and by Grouping

Factor each polynomial.

a. $16x^2 + 8x$

$16x^2 + 8x = 8x(2x) + 8x(1)$ — Factor the GCF.

$= 8x(2x + 1)$ — Distributive Property

b. $7x^2 + 6xy^2 + 14xy + 12y^3$

$7x^2 + 6xy^2 + 14xy + 12y^3$ — Original expression

$= (7x^2 + 14xy) + (6xy^2 + 12y^3)$ — Group terms with common factors.

$= 7x(x + 2y) + 6y^2(x + 2y)$ — Factor the GCF from each group.

$= (7x + 6y^2)(x + 2y)$ — Distributive Property

Guided Practice 2C. $(ab + 3cd)(1 + 4a)$

2A. $20x^2y - 15xy^2$ $5xy(4x - 3y)$ **2B.** $4x^2y - 16xy - y^2$ $y(4x^2 - 16x - y)$ **2C.** $ab + 3cd + 4a^2b + 12acd$

Personal Tutor glencoe.com

Review Vocabulary

perfect square a number with a positive square root that is a whole number

Trinomials and binomials that are perfect squares have special factoring rules. In order to use these rules, the first and last terms need to be perfect squares and the middle term needs to be twice the product of the square roots of the first and last terms.

EXAMPLE 3 Perfect Squares and Differences of Squares

Factor each polynomial.

a. $x^2 + 16x + 64$

$x^2 = (x)^2$; $64 = (8)^2$ — First and last terms are perfect squares.

$16x = 2(x)(8)$ — Middle term equals $2ab$.

$x^2 + 16x + 64$ is a perfect square trinomial.

$x^2 + 16x + 64 = (x + 8)^2$ — Factor using the pattern.

b. $36a^2 - 64y^4$

$36a^2 - 64y^4 = 4(9a^2 - 16y^4)$ — Factor the GCF.

$= 4[(3a)^2 - (4y^2)^2]$ — Write in form $a^2 - b^2$.

$= 4(3a + 4y^2)(3a - 4y^2)$ — Factor the difference of squares.

Guided Practice 3B. $(9x + y^3)(9x - y^3)$ 3C. $3y(5x + 3)(5x - 3)$

3A. $4x^2 - 12x + 9$ $(2x - 3)^2$ **3B.** $81x^2 - y^6$ **3C.** $75x^2y - 27y$

Personal Tutor glencoe.com

Factored Form

Example 1 shows how to write a quadratic equation for a given pair of roots.

Formative Assessment

Use the Guided Practice exercises after each example to determine students' understanding of concepts.

Additional Example

1 Write a quadratic equation in standard form with $\frac{1}{2}$ and -5 as its roots. Sample answer: $2x^2 + 9x - 5 = 0$

Additional Examples also in Interactive Classroom PowerPoint® Presentations

IWB INTERACTIVE WHITEBOARD READY

Solve Equations by Factoring

Examples 2–4 show how to factor polynomials. **Example 5** shows how to solve a real-world problem using factoring to solve a quadratic equation.

Additional Examples

2 Factor each polynomial.

a. $9y^3 - 6y^2 + 3y$ $3y(3y^2 - 2y + 1)$

b. $8a^2 + 10ab^2 + 4ab + 5b^3$ $(4a + 5b^2)(2a + b)$

3 Factor each polynomial.

a. $x^2 + 10x + 25$ $(x + 5)^2$

b. $12b^8 - 27c^2$ $3(2b^4 + 3c)(2b^4 - 3c)$

Differentiated Instruction

AL OL BL

If students think that the steps in Example 1 provide the only possible equation for the given roots,

Then provide each student with a sheet of grid paper. Have students begin by drawing a coordinate grid with two points on the x-axis plotted as the roots of a quadratic equation. Ask students to draw several parabolas that might be the graphs of different equations having those two points as their solutions. Point out that this demonstrates that the steps shown in Example 1 yield just *one* of the possible equations having the given roots.

Additional Example

4 Factor each polynomial.

a. $x^2 + 2x - 24$
$(x + 6)(x - 4)$

b. $2m^2 - 9m - 18$
$(2m + 3)(m - 6)$

StudyTip

Trinomials If values for m and p exist, then the trinomial can always be factored.

A special pattern is used when factoring trinomials of the form $ax^2 + bx + c$. First, multiply the values of a and c. Then, we must find two values, m and p, such that their product equals ac and their sum equals b.

Consider $6x^2 + 13x - 5$: $ac = 6(-5) = -30$.

Factors of −30	Sum	Factors of −30	Sum
1, −30	−29	−1, 30	29
2, −15	−13	**−2, 15**	**13**
3, −10	−7	−3, 10	7
5, −6	−1	−5, 6	1

Now the middle term, $13x$, can be rewritten as $-2x + 15x$.

This polynomial can now be factored by grouping.

$6x^2 + 13x - 5 = 6x^2 + mx + px - 5$ **Write the pattern.**
$= 6x^2 - 2x + 15x - 5$ **$m = -2$ and $p = 15$**
$= (6x^2 - 2x) + (15x - 5)$ **Group terms.**
$= 2x(3x - 1) + 5(3x - 1)$ **Factor the GCF.**
$= (2x + 5)(3x - 1)$ **Distributive Property**

EXAMPLE 4 Factor Trinomials

Factor each polynomial.

a. $x^2 + 9x + 20$

$ac = 20$ **$a = 1, c = 20$**

Factors of 20	Sum	Factors of 20	Sum
1, 20	21	−1, −20	−21
2, 10	12	−2, −10	−12
4, 5	**9**	−4, −5	−9

StudyTip

Trinomials It does not matter if the values of m and p are switched when grouping.

$x^2 + 9x + 20$ **Original expression**
$= x^2 + mx + px + 20$ **Write the pattern.**
$= x^2 + 4x + 5x + 20$ **$m = 4, p = 5$**
$= (x^2 + 4x) + (5x + 20)$ **Group terms with common factors.**
$= x(x + 4) + 5(x + 4)$ **Factor the GCF from each grouping.**
$= (x + 5)(x + 4)$ **Distributive Property**

b. $6y^2 - 23y + 20$

$ac = 120$ **$a = 6, c = 20$**
$m = -8, p = -15$ **$-8(-15) = 120; -8 + (-15) = -23$**

$6y^2 - 23y + 20$ **Original expression**
$= 6y^2 + my + py + 20$ **Write the pattern.**
$= 6y^2 - 8y - 15y + 20$ **$m = -8, p = -15$**
$= (6y^2 - 8y) + (-15y + 20)$ **Group terms with common factors.**
$= 2y(3y - 4) - 5(3y - 4)$ **Factor the GCF from each grouping.**
$= (2y - 5)(3y - 4)$ **Distributive Property**

Guided Practice

4A. $x^2 - 11x + 30$ $(x - 5)(x - 6)$

4B. $x^2 - 4x - 21$ $(x - 7)(x + 3)$

4C. $15x^2 - 8x + 1$ $(5x - 1)(3x - 1)$

4D. $-12x^2 + 8x + 15$ $-1(2x - 3)(6x + 5)$

Personal Tutor glencoe.com

Focus on Mathematical Content

Solving Quadratics by Factoring Quadratic equations can be solved using several different methods. Factoring can be a quick method. Once a polynomial has been factored, the Zero Product Property may be used to find the roots of the equation. If the polynomial is difficult to factor or not factorable, then other methods must be used.

Solving quadratic equations by factoring is an application of the Zero Product Property.

Key Concept **Zero Product Property**

Words For any real numbers a and b, if $ab = 0$, then either $a = 0$, $b = 0$, or both a and b equal zero.

Examples If $(x + 3)(x - 5) = 0$, then $x + 3 = 0$ or $x - 5 = 0$.

Real-World Link

Cuba's Osleidys Menendez broke the javelin world record in 2002 with a distance of 234 feet 8 inches.

Source: *New York Times*

Real-World EXAMPLE 5 Solve Equations by Factoring

TRACK AND FIELD **The height of a javelin in feet is modeled by $h(t) = -16t^2 + 79t + 5$, where t is the time in seconds after the javelin is thrown. How long is it in the air?**

To determine how long the javelin is in the air, we need to find when the height equals 0. We can do this by solving $-16t^2 + 79t + 5 = 0$.

$-16t^2 + 79t + 5 = 0$	Original equation
$m = 80; p = -1$	$-16(5) = -80, 80 \cdot (-1) = -80, 80 + (-1) = 79$
$-16t^2 + 80t - t + 5 = 0$	Write the pattern.
$(-16t^2 + 80t) + (-t + 5) = 0$	Group terms with common factors.
$16t(-t + 5) + 1(-t + 5) = 0$	Factor GCF from each group.
$(16t + 1)(-t + 5) = 0$	Distributive Property
$16t + 1 = 0$ or $-t + 5 = 0$	Zero Product Property
$16t = -1$ $-t = -5$	Solve both equations.
$t = -\frac{1}{16}$ $t = 5$	Solve.

CHECK We have two solutions.

- The first solution is negative and since time cannot be negative, this solution can be eliminated.
- The second solution of 5 seconds seems reasonable for the time a javelin spends in the air.
- The answer can be confirmed by substituting back into the original equation.

$$-16t^2 + 79t + 5 = 0$$
$$-16(5)^2 + 79(5) + 5 \stackrel{?}{=} 0$$
$$-400 + 395 + 5 \stackrel{?}{=} 0$$
$$0 = 0 \checkmark$$

The javelin is in the air for 5 seconds.

Guided Practice

5. **BUNGEE JUMPING** Juan recorded his brother bungee jumping from a height of 1100 feet. At the time the cord lifted his brother back up, he was 76 feet above the ground. If Juan started recording as soon as his brother fell, how much time elapsed when the cord snapped back? Use $f(t) = -16t^2 + c$, where c is the height in feet. 8 seconds

Personal Tutor glencoe.com

Additional Example

5 **ARCHITECTURE** The entrance to an office building is an arch in the shape of a parabola whose vertex is the height of the arch. The height of the arch is given by $h = 9 - x^2$, where x is the horizontal distance from the center of the arch. Both h and x are measured in feet. How wide is the arch at ground level? 6 ft

Watch Out!

Common Misconceptions In Example 5, some students may suggest solving the equation by dividing both sides by t. Point out that this cannot be done because the value of t could be zero, and division by zero is undefined.

TEACH with TECH

DOCUMENT CAMERA Choose several students to share their work with the class and explain their answers. Have students check their work by substituting their solutions into the original equation.

3 PRACTICE

Formative Assessment

Use Exercises 1–16 to check for understanding.

Use the chart at the bottom of this page to customize assignments for your students.

Additional Answers

68a.

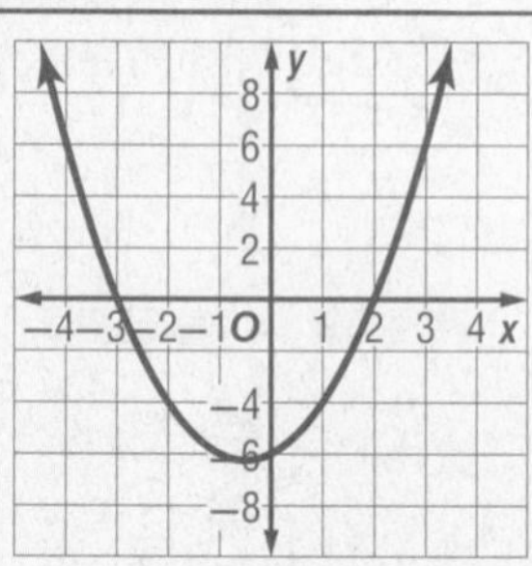

68c.

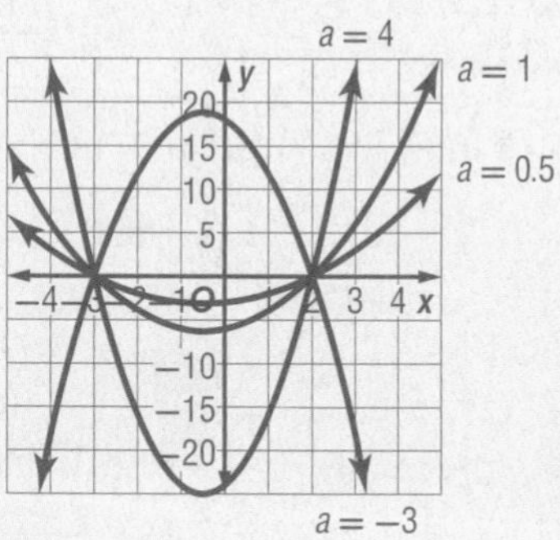

Check Your Understanding

Example 1 p. 268

Write a quadratic equation in standard form with the given root(s).

1. $-8, 5$ $x^2 + 3x - 40 = 0$ **2.** $\frac{3}{2}, \frac{1}{4}$ $8x^2 - 14x + 3 = 0$ **3.** $-\frac{2}{3}, \frac{5}{2}$ $6x^2 - 11x - 10 = 0$

Examples 2–4 pp. 269–270

Factor each polynomial.

4. $35x^2 - 15x$ $5x(7x - 3)$ **5.** $18x^2 - 3x + 24x - 4$ **6.** $x^2 - 12x + 32$

7. $x^2 - 4x - 21$ **8.** $2x^2 + 7x - 30$ **9.** $16x^2 - 16x + 3$

10. $x^2 - 36$ $(x + 6)(x - 6)$ **11.** $12x^2y - 18xy$ $6xy(2x - 3)$ **12.** $12x^2 - 2x - 2$

5. $(6x - 1)(3x + 4)$
6. $(x - 8)(x - 4)$
7. $(x - 7)(x + 3)$
8. $(2x - 5)(x + 6)$

Example 5 p. 271

Solve each equation by factoring.

13. $x^2 - 9x = 0$ $0, 9$ **14.** $x^2 - 3x - 28 = 0$ $-4, 7$ **15.** $2x^2 - 24x = -72$ 6

9. $(4x - 3)(4x - 1)$
12. $2(2x - 1)(3x + 1)$

16. GARDENING Tamika wants to double the area of her garden by increasing the length and width by the same amount. What will be the dimensions of her garden then? 9 m by 12 m

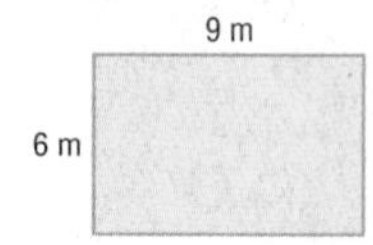

Practice and Problem Solving

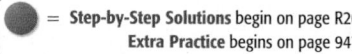

= **Step-by-Step Solutions** begin on page R20.
Extra Practice begins on page 947.

Example 1 p. 268

Write a quadratic equation in standard form with the given root(s).

17. 7 $x^2 - 14x + 49 = 0$ **18.** $-5, \frac{1}{2}$ $2x^2 + 9x - 5 = 0$ **19.** $\frac{1}{5}, 6$ $5x^2 - 31x + 6 = 0$

Examples 2–4 pp. 269–270

Factor each polynomial.

20. $40a^2 - 32a$ $8a(5a - 4)$ **21.** $51c^3 - 34c$ $17c(3c^2 - 2)$ **22.** $32xy + 40bx - 12ay - 15ab$

23. $3x^2 - 12$ $3(x + 2)(x - 2)$ **24.** $15y^2 - 240$ **25.** $48cg + 36cf - 4dg - 3df$

26. $x^2 + 13x + 40$ **27.** $x^2 - 9x - 22$ **28.** $3x^2 + 12x - 36$

29. $15x^2 + 7x - 2$ **30.** $4x^2 + 29x + 30$ **31.** $18x^2 + 15x - 12$

32. $8x^2z^2 - 4xz^2 - 12z^2$ **33.** $9x^2 - 25$ **34.** $18x^2y^2 - 24xy^2 + 36y^2$

35. $15x^2 - 84x - 36$ $3(5x + 2)(x - 6)$ **36.** $12x^2 + 13x - 14$ $(4x + 7)(3x - 2)$ **37.** $12xy^2 - 108x$ $12x(y + 3)(y - 3)$

22. $(8x - 3a)(4y + 5b)$
24. $15(y + 4)(y - 4)$
25. $(12c - d)(4g + 3f)$
26. $(x + 8)(x + 5)$
27. $(x - 11)(x + 2)$
28. $3(x + 6)(x - 2)$

Example 5 p. 271

Solve each equation by factoring.

38. $x^2 + 4x - 45 = 0$ $5, -9$ **39.** $x^2 - 5x - 24 = 0$ $8, -3$ **40.** $x^2 = 121$ $11, -11$

41. $x^2 + 13 = 17$ $2, -2$ **42.** $-3x^2 - 10x + 8 = 0$ $-4, \frac{2}{3}$ **43.** $-8x^2 + 46x - 30 = 0$ $5, \frac{3}{4}$

29. $(5x - 1)(3x + 2)$
30. $(4x + 5)(x + 6)$
31. $3(2x - 1)(3x + 4)$
32. $4z^2(2x - 3)(x + 1)$
33. $(3x + 5)(3x - 5)$
34. $6y^2(3x^2 - 4x + 6)$

44. GEOMETRY The hypotenuse of a right triangle is 1 centimeter longer than one side and 4 centimeters longer than three times the other side. Find the dimensions of the triangle. 7 cm, 24 cm, 25 cm

45. NUMBER THEORY Find two consecutive even integers with a product of 624. 24 and 26 or −24 and −26

GEOMETRY Find x and the dimensions of each rectangle. 48. $x = 12$; 14 ft by 32 ft

46.

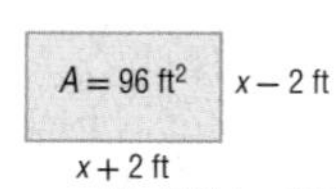

$x = 10$; 8 ft by 12 ft

47.

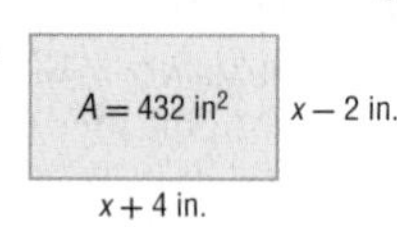

$x = 20$; 24 in. by 18 in.

48.

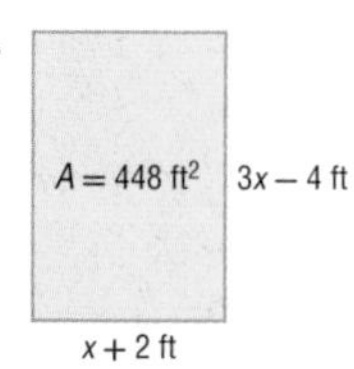

Differentiated Homework Options

Level	Assignment	Two-Day Option	
AL Basic	17–48, 79, 82–100	17–47 odd, 87–90	18–48 even, 79, 82–85, 91–100
OL Core	17–43 odd, 44, 45–65 odd, 66–70, 71–79 odd, 82–100	17–48, 86–89	49–79, 82–99
BL Advanced	49–97, (optional: 98–100)		

B Solve each equation by factoring.

49. $12x^2 - 4x = 5$ $-\frac{1}{2}, \frac{5}{6}$ **50.** $5x^2 = 15x$ **0, 3** **51.** $16x^2 + 36 = -48x$ $-\frac{3}{2}$

52. $75x^2 - 60x = -12$ $\frac{2}{5}$ **53.** $4x^2 - 144 = 0$ **6, −6** **54.** $-7x + 6 = 20x^2$

54. $\frac{2}{5}, -\frac{3}{4}$

Real-World Link

The average movie theater costs approximately $1 million per screen to build.

Source: *National Real Estate Investor*

55 **MOVIE THEATER** A company plans to build a large multiplex theater. The financial analyst told her manager that the profit function for their theater was $P(x) = -x^2 + 48x - 512$, where x is the number of movie screens, and $P(x)$ is the profit earned in thousands of dollars. Determine the range of production of movie screens that will guarantee that the company will not lose money. **16 to 32 screens**

Write a quadratic equation in standard form with the given root(s).

56. $-\frac{4}{7}, \frac{3}{8}$ $56x^2 + 11x - 12 = 0$ **57.** 3.4, 0.6 $25x^2 - 100x + 51 = 0$ **58.** $\frac{2}{11}, \frac{5}{9}$ $99x^2 - 73x + 10 = 0$

Solve each equation by factoring.

59. $10x^2 + 25x = 15$ $-3, \frac{1}{2}$ **60.** $27x^2 + 5 = 48x$ $\frac{5}{3}, \frac{1}{9}$ **61.** $x^2 + 0.25x = 1.25$ $1, -\frac{5}{4}$

62. $48x^2 - 15 = -22x$ $\frac{3}{8}, -\frac{5}{6}$ **63.** $3x^2 + 2x = 3.75$ $-\frac{3}{2}, \frac{5}{6}$ **64.** $-32x^2 + 56x = 12$ $\frac{1}{4}, \frac{3}{2}$

65. DESIGN A square is cut out of the figure at the right. Write an expression for the area of the figure that remains, and then factor the expression. $x^2 - 6^2$; $(x + 6)(x - 6)$

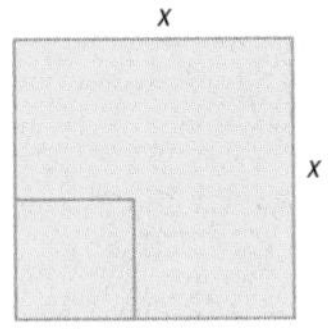

66. FINANCIAL LITERACY After analyzing the market, a company that sells Web sites determined the profitability of their product was modeled by $P(x) = -16x^2 + 368x - 2035$, where x is the price of each Web site and $P(x)$ is the company's profit. Determine the price range of the Web sites that will be profitable for the company. **\$9.25 to \$13.75**

67. PAINTINGS Enola wants to add a border to her painting, distributed evenly, that has the same area as the painting itself. What are the dimensions of the painting with the border included? **20 in. by 15 in.**

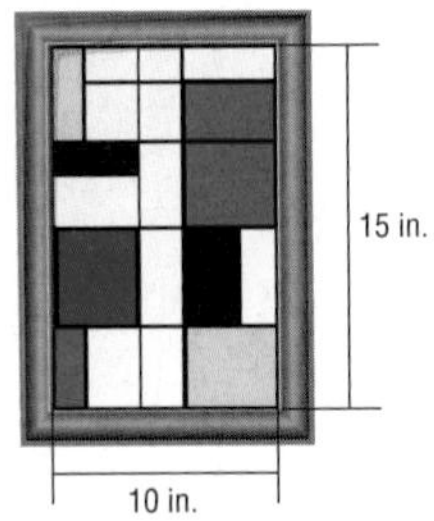

68. MULTIPLE REPRESENTATIONS In this problem, you will consider $a(x - p)(x - q) = 0$.

a. **GRAPHICAL** Graph the related function for $a = 1$, $p = 2$, and $q = -3$. **See margin.**

b. **ANALYTICAL** What are the solutions of the equation? **2 and −3**

c. **GRAPHICAL** Graph the related functions for $a = 4, -3$, and $\frac{1}{2}$ on the same graph. **See margin.**

d. **VERBAL** What are the similarities and differences between the graphs?

e. **VERBAL** What conclusion can you make about the relationship between the factored form of a quadratic equation and its solutions?

68d. Sample answer: They all have the same roots, p and q. Therefore, they all have the same solutions. The graphs are shaped differently due to the value of a. The graph with $a = -3$ is flipped due to the negative.

68e. When quadratic equations have the same factors, they will have the same solutions, regardless of the value of a, which only affects the shape of the graphs.

69. GEOMETRY The area of the triangle is 26 square centimeters. Find the length of the base. **13 cm**

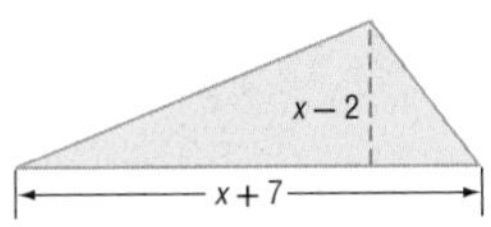

Study Guide and Intervention

CRM pp. 17–18 AL OL ELL

5-3 Study Guide and Intervention

Solving Quadratic Equations by Factoring

Factored Form To write a quadratic equation with roots p and q, let $(x - p)(x - q) = 0$. Then multiply using FOIL.

Example Write a quadratic equation in standard form with the given roots.

a. 3, −5

$(x - p)(x - q) = 0$ Write the pattern.

$(x - 3)[x - (-5)] = 0$ Replace p with 3, q with −5.

$(x - 3)(x + 5) = 0$ Simplify.

$x^2 + 2x - 15 = 0$ Use FOIL.

The equation $x^2 + 2x - 15 = 0$ has roots 3 and −5.

b. $-\frac{7}{8}, \frac{1}{3}$

$(x - p)(x - q) = 0$

$\left[x - \left(-\frac{7}{8}\right)\right]\left(x - \frac{1}{3}\right) = 0$

$\left(x + \frac{7}{8}\right)\left(x - \frac{1}{3}\right) = 0$

$\frac{(8x + 7)}{8} \cdot \frac{(3x - 1)}{3} = 0$

$\frac{24 \cdot (8x + 7)(3x - 1)}{24} = 24 \cdot 0$

$24x^2 + 13x - 7 = 0$

The equation $24x^2 + 13x - 7 = 0$ has roots $-\frac{7}{8}$ and $\frac{1}{3}$.

Exercises

Write a quadratic equation in standard form with the given root(s).

1. 3, −4 $x^2 + x - 12 = 0$
2. −8, −2 $x^2 + 10x + 16 = 0$
3. 1, 9 $x^2 - 10x + 9 = 0$
4. −5 $x^2 + 10x + 25 = 0$
5. 10, 7 $x^2 - 17x + 70 = 0$
6. −2, 15 $x^2 - 13x - 30 = 0$
7. $-\frac{1}{3}, 5$ $3x^2 - 14x - 5 = 0$
8. $2, \frac{2}{3}$ $3x^2 - 8x + 4 = 0$
9. $-7, \frac{3}{4}$ $4x^2 + 25x - 21 = 0$
10. $3, \frac{2}{5}$ $5x^2 - 17x + 6 = 0$
11. $-\frac{4}{9}, -1$ $9x^2 + 13x + 4 = 0$
12. $9, \frac{1}{6}$ $6x^2 - 55x + 9 = 0$
13. $\frac{2}{3}, -\frac{2}{3}$ $9x^2 - 4 = 0$
14. $\frac{5}{4}, -\frac{1}{2}$ $8x^2 - 6x - 5 = 0$
15. $\frac{3}{7}, \frac{1}{5}$ $35x^2 - 22x + 3 = 0$
16. $-\frac{7}{8}, \frac{7}{2}$ $16x^2 - 42x - 49 = 0$
17. $\frac{1}{2}, \frac{3}{4}$ $8x^2 - 10x + 3 = 0$
18. $\frac{1}{8}, \frac{1}{6}$ $48x^2 - 14x + 1 = 0$

Lesson 5-3

Chapter 5 17 Glencoe Algebra 2

Practice

CRM p. 20 AL OL BL ELL

5-3 Practice

Solving Quadratic Equations by Factoring

Write a quadratic equation in standard form with the given root(s).

1. 7, 2 $x^2 - 9x + 14 = 0$
2. 0, 3 $x^2 - 3x = 0$
3. −5, 8 $x^2 - 3x - 40 = 0$
4. −7, −8 $x^2 + 15x + 56 = 0$
5. −6, −3 $x^2 + 9x + 18 = 0$
6. 3, −4 $x^2 + x - 12 = 0$
7. $1, \frac{1}{2}$ $2x^2 - 3x + 1 = 0$
8. $\frac{1}{3}, 2$ $3x^2 - 7x + 2 = 0$
9. $0, -\frac{7}{2}$ $2x^2 + 7x = 0$

Factor each polynomial.

10. $r^3 + 3r^2 - 54r$ $r(r + 9)(r - 6)$
11. $8a^2 + 2a - 6$ $2(4a - 3)(a + 1)$
12. $c^2 - 49$ $(c - 7)(c + 7)$
13. $x^3 + 8$ $(x + 2)(x^2 - 2x + 4)$
14. $16r^2 - 169$ $(4r + 13)(4r - 13)$
15. $b^4 - 81$ $(b^2 + 9)(b + 3)(b - 3)$

Solve each equation by factoring.

16. $x^2 - 4x - 12 = 0$ {6, −2}
17. $x^2 - 16x + 64 = 0$ {8}
18. $x^2 - 6x + 8 = 0$ {2, 4}
19. $x^2 + 3x + 2 = 0$ {−2, −1}
20. $x^2 - 4x = 0$ {0, 4}
21. $7x^2 = 4x$ $\left\{0, \frac{4}{7}\right\}$
22. $10x^2 = 9x$ $\left\{0, \frac{9}{10}\right\}$
23. $x^2 = 2x + 99$ {−9, 11}
24. $x^2 + 12x = -36$ {−6}
25. $5x^2 - 35x + 60 = 0$ {3, 4}
26. $36x^2 = 25$ $\left\{\frac{5}{6}, -\frac{5}{6}\right\}$
27. $2x^2 - 8x - 90 = 0$ {9, −5}
28. **NUMBER THEORY** Find two consecutive even positive integers whose product is 624. **24, 26**
29. **NUMBER THEORY** Find two consecutive odd positive integers whose product is 323. **17, 19**
30. **GEOMETRY** The length of a rectangle is 2 feet more than its width. Find the dimensions of the rectangle if its area is 63 square feet. **7 ft by 9 ft**
31. **PHOTOGRAPHY** The length and width of a 6-inch by 8-inch photograph are reduced by the same amount to make a new photograph whose area is half that of the original. By how many inches will the dimensions of the photograph have to be reduced? **2 in.**

Chapter 5 20 Glencoe Algebra 2

Word Problem Practice

CRM p. 21 AL OL BL ELL

5-3 Word Problem Practice

Solving Quadratic Equations by Factoring

1. **FLASHLIGHTS** When Dora shines her flashlight on the wall at a certain angle, the edge of the lit area is in the shape of a parabola. The equation of the parabola is $y = 2x^2 + 2x - 60$. Factor this quadratic equation. **$2(x - 5)(x + 6)$**

2. **SIGNS** David was looking through an old algebra book and came across this equation.

x^2 ■ $6x + 8 = 0$

The sign in front of the 6 was blotted out. How does the missing sign depend on the signs of the roots? **The missing sign is the same as the sign of the two roots, because their product is a positive number, 8.**

3. **ART** The area in square inches of the drawing *Maisons près de la mer* by Claude Monet is approximated by the equation $y = x^2 - 23x + 130$. Factor the equation to find the two roots, which are equal to the approximate length and width of the drawing. **10 inches by 13 inches**

4. **PROGRAMMING** Ray is a computer programmer. He needs to find the quadratic function of this graph for an algorithm related to a game involving dice. Provide such a function.

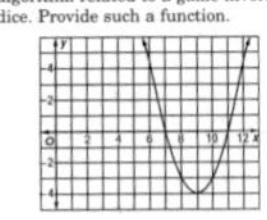

$f(x) = x^2 - 18x + 77$

5. **ANIMATION** A computer graphics animator would like to make a realistic simulation of a tossed ball. The animator wants the ball to follow the parabolic trajectory represented by the quadratic equation $f(x) = -0.2(x + 5)(x - 5)$.

a. What are the solutions of $f(x) = 0$? **$x = -5$ or $x = 5$**

b. Write $f(x)$ in standard form. **$f(x) = -0.2x^2 + 5$**

c. If the animator changes the equation to $f(x) = -0.2x^2 + 20$, what are the solutions of $f(x) = 0$? **$x = -10$ or $x = 10$**

Lesson 5-3

Chapter 5 21 Glencoe Algebra 2

Multiple Representations In Exercise 68, students use algebra and a graph in the coordinate plane to relate the factors of a quadratic equation to its solutions.

Enrichment

CRM p. 22 OL BL

5-3 Enrichment

Using Patterns to Factor

Study the patterns below for factoring the sum and the difference of cubes.

$a^3 + b^3 = (a + b)(a^2 - ab + b^2)$

$a^3 - b^3 = (a - b)(a^2 + ab + b^2)$

This pattern can be extended to other odd powers. Study these examples.

Example 1 Factor $a^5 + b^5$.

Extend the first pattern to obtain $a^5 + b^5 = (a + b)(a^4 - a^3b + a^2b^2 - ab^3 + b^4)$.

Check: $(a + b)(a^4 - a^3b + a^2b^2 - ab^3 + b^4) = a^5 - a^4b + a^3b^2 - a^2b^3 + ab^4$
$+ a^4b - a^3b^2 + a^2b^3 - ab^4 + b^5$
$= a^5 + b^5$

Example 2 Factor $a^5 - b^5$.

Extend the second pattern to obtain $a^5 - b^5 = (a - b)(a^4 + a^3b + a^2b^2 + ab^3 + b^4)$.

Check: $(a - b)(a^4 + a^3b + a^2b^2 + ab^3 + b^4) = a^5 + a^4b + a^3b^2 + a^2b^3 + ab^4$
$- a^4b - a^3b^2 - a^2b^3 - ab^4 - b^5$
$= a^5 - b^5$

Watch Out!

Error Analysis For Exercise 79 remind students that when a polynomial is subtracted, every term in the polynomial is subtracted. Always check answers by substitution in the original equation.

Additional Answers

83. Sample answer:

$(x - p)(x - q) = 0$

Original equation

$x^2 - px - qx + pq = 0$

Multiply.

$x^2 - (p + q)x + pq = 0$

Simplify.

$x = -\frac{b}{2a}$

Formula for axis of symmetry

$x = -\frac{-(p + q)}{2(1)}$

$a = 1$ and $b = -(p + q)$

$x = \frac{p + q}{2}$

Simplify.

x is midway between p and q.

Definition of midpoint

86. Sample answer: In standard form, we have $ax^2 + bx + c$. Multiply a and c. Then find a pair of integers, g and h, that multiply to equal ac and add to equal b. Then write out the quadratic, turning the middle term, bx, into $gx + hx$. We now have $ax^2 + gx + hx + c$. Now factor the GCF from the first two terms and then factor the GCF from the second two terms. So we now have $\text{GCF}(x - q) + \text{GCF}_2(x - q)$. Simplifying, we get $(\text{GCF} + \text{GCF}_2)(x - q)$ or $(x - p)(x - q)$.

Real-World Link

Kicking accuracy is usually highest when the velocity of the ball is about 80% of the maximum. Professional players can kick a ball between 32 to 35 meters per second.

Source: Coach's Information Service

71. $2(3 - 4y)(3a + 8b)$
72. $(3x + 2y)(x + 5)$
73. $6b^2(a^2 - 2a - 3b)$
74. $6a(2a - 3b + 5b^3)$
75. $2(2x - 3y)(8a + 3b)$
76. $10(a + 2b)(3c + 4d)$
79. Sample answer: Morgan; Gwen did not have like terms in the parentheses in the third line.

85. Sample answer: Always; in order to factor using perfect square trinomials, the coefficient of the linear term, bx, must be a multiple of 2, or even.

70. SOCCER When a ball is kicked in the air, its height in meters above the ground can be modeled by $h(t) = -4.9t^2 + 14.7t$ and the distance it travels can be modeled by $d(t) = 16t$, where t is the time in seconds.

a. How long was the ball in the air? **3 seconds**

b. How far did it travel before it hit the ground? (*Hint*: Ignore air resistance.) **48 m**

c. What was the maximum height of the ball? **11.025 m**

C

Factor each polynomial.

71. $18a - 24ay + 48b - 64by$	**72.** $3x^2 + 2xy + 10y + 15x$
73 $6a^2b^2 - 12ab^2 - 18b^3$	**74.** $12a^2 - 18ab + 30ab^3$
75. $32ax + 12bx - 48ay - 18by$	**76.** $30ac + 80bd + 40ad + 60bc$
77. $5ax^2 - 2by^2 - 5ay^2 + 2bx^2$ **$(x + y)(x - y)(5a + 2b)$**	**78.** $12c^2x + 4d^2y - 3d^2x - 16c^2y$ **$(2c + d)(2c - d)(3x - 4y)$**

H.O.T. Problems

Use Higher-Order Thinking Skills

79. ERROR ANALYSIS Gwen and Morgan are solving $-12x^2 + 5x + 2 = 0$. Is either of them correct? Explain your reasoning.

Gwen	Morgan
$-12x^2 + 5x + 2 = 0$	$-12x^2 + 5x + 2 = 0$
$-12x^2 + 8x - 3x + 2 = 0$	$-12x^2 + 8x - 3x + 2 = 0$
$4x(-3x + 2) - (3x + 2) = 0$	$4x(-3x + 2) + (-3x + 2) = 0$
$(4x - 1)(3x + 2) = 0$	$(4x + 1)(-3x + 2) = 0$
$x = \frac{1}{4}$ or $-\frac{2}{3}$	$x = -\frac{1}{4}$ or $\frac{2}{3}$

80. CHALLENGE Solve $3x^6 - 39x^4 + 108x^2 = 0$ by factoring. **0, 3, −3, 2, or −2**

81. CHALLENGE The rule for factoring a difference of cubes is shown below. Use this rule to factor $40x^5 - 135x^2y^3$. **$5x^2(2x - 3y)(4x^2 + 6xy + 9y^2)$**

$$a^3 - b^3 = (a - b)(a^2 + ab + b^2)$$

82. OPEN ENDED Choose two integers. Then write an equation in standard form with those roots. How would the equation change if the signs of the two roots were switched? **Sample answer: 3 and 6 → $x^2 - 9x + 18 = 0$. −3 and −6 → $x^2 + 9x + 18 = 0$. The linear term changes sign.**

83. CHALLENGE For a quadratic equation of the form $(x - p)(x - q) = 0$, show that the axis of symmetry of the related quadratic function is located halfway between the x-intercepts p and q. **See margin.**

84. WRITE A QUESTION A classmate is using the guess-and-check strategy to factor trinomials of the form $x^2 + bx + c$. Write a question to help him think of a way to use that strategy for $ax^2 + bx + c$. **Sample answer: What do you know about $a \cdot c$ to use guess-and-check to factor trinomials of the form $ax^2 + bx + c$?**

85. REASONING Determine whether the following statement is *sometimes*, *always*, or *never* true. Explain your reasoning.

In a quadratic equation in standard form where a, b, and c are integers, if b is odd, then the quadratic cannot be a perfect square trinomial.

86. WRITING IN MATH Explain how to factor a trinomial in standard form with $a > 1$. **See margin.**

NGSSS PRACTICE 912.A.2.10, 912.A.3.6, 912.P.3.1

87. THINK SOLVE EXPLAIN **SHORT RESPONSE** If *ABCD* is transformed by $(x, y) \rightarrow (3x, 4y)$, determine the area of $A'B'C'D'$. 192 square units

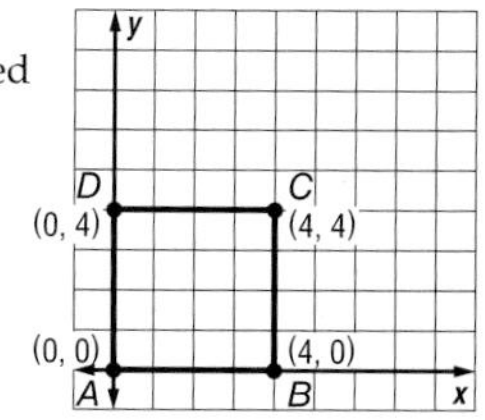

88. For $y = 2|6 - 3x| + 4$, which set describes x when $y < 6$? A

A. $\left\{x \middle| \frac{5}{3} < x < \frac{7}{3}\right\}$ **C.** $\left\{x \middle| x < \frac{5}{3}\right\}$

B. $\left\{x \middle| x < \frac{5}{3} \text{ or } x > \frac{7}{3}\right\}$ **D.** $\left\{x \middle| x > \frac{7}{3}\right\}$

89. PROBABILITY A 5-character password can contain the numbers 0 through 9 and 26 letters of the alphabet. None of the characters can be repeated. What is the probability that the password begins with a consonant? H

F. $\frac{21}{26}$ **H.** $\frac{21}{36}$

G. $\frac{21}{35}$ **I.** $\frac{5}{36}$

90. SAT/ACT If $c = \frac{8a^3}{b}$, what happens to the value of c when both a and b are doubled? D

A. c is unchanged.
B. c is halved.
C. c is doubled.
D. c is multiplied by 4.

Spiral Review

Use the related graph of each equation to determine its solutions. (Lesson 5-2)

91. $x^2 - 2x - 8 = 0$ −2, 4

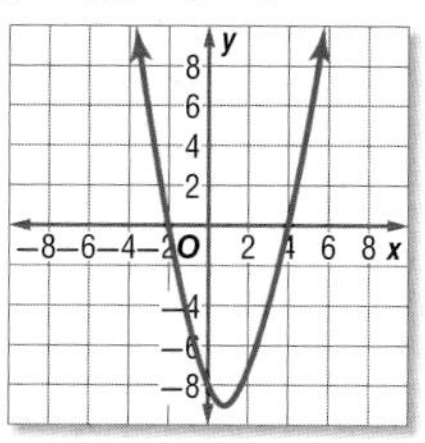

92. $x^2 + 4x = 12$ −6, 2

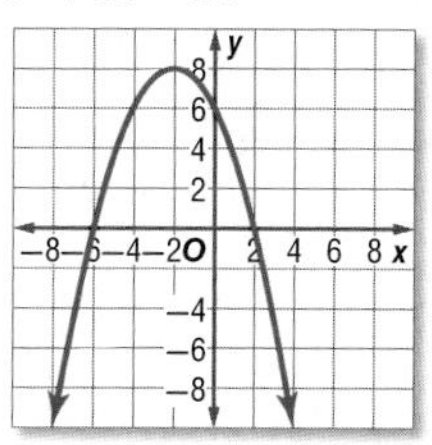

93. $x^2 + 4x + 4 = 0$ −2

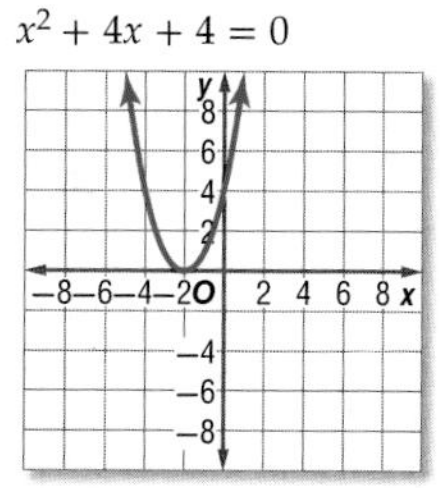

Graph each function. (Lesson 5-1) 94–96. See margin.

94. $f(x) = x^2 - 6x + 2$ **95.** $f(x) = -2x^2 + 4x + 1$ **96.** $f(x) = (x - 3)(x + 4)$

97. FUNDRAISING Lawrence High School sold wrapping paper and boxed cards for their fundraising event. The school gets \$1.00 for each roll of wrapping paper sold and \$0.50 for each box of cards sold. (Lesson 4-3)

a. Write a matrix that represents the amounts sold for each class and a matrix that represents the amount of money the school earns for each item sold. See margin.

b. Write a matrix that shows how much each class earned. See margin.

c. Which class earned the most money? juniors

d. What is the total amount of money the school made from the fundraiser? \$431

Total Amounts for Each Class

Class	Wrapping Paper	Cards
Freshmen	72	49
Sophomores	68	63
Juniors	90	56
Seniors	86	62

Skills Review

Simplify. (Prerequisite Skills 2)

98. $\sqrt{5} \cdot \sqrt{15}$ $5\sqrt{3}$ **99.** $\sqrt{8} \cdot \sqrt{32}$ 16 **100.** $2\sqrt{3} \cdot \sqrt{27}$ 18

Differentiated Instruction OL BL

Extension Pose the following question to students:
If the roots of a quadratic equation are 6 and −3, what is the equation of the axis of symmetry? $x = \frac{3}{2}$

4 ASSESS

Name the Math Have students explain the Zero Product Property. Have them discuss why it is true and how it is used in finding the roots of a quadratic equation.

Additional Answers

94.

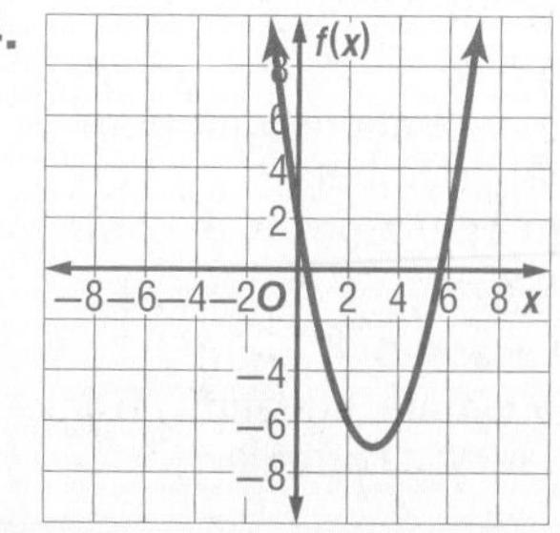

95.

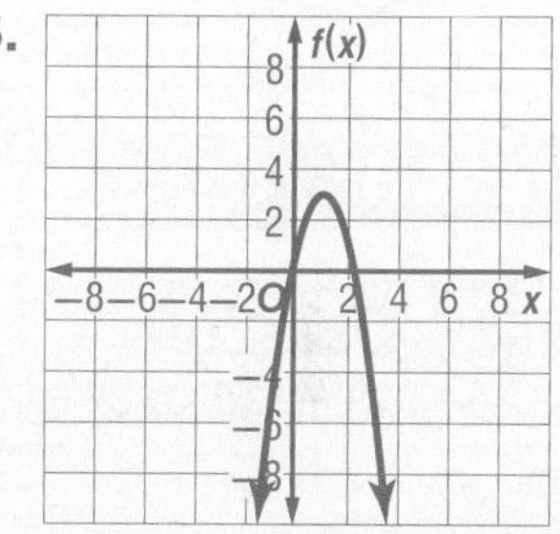

96.

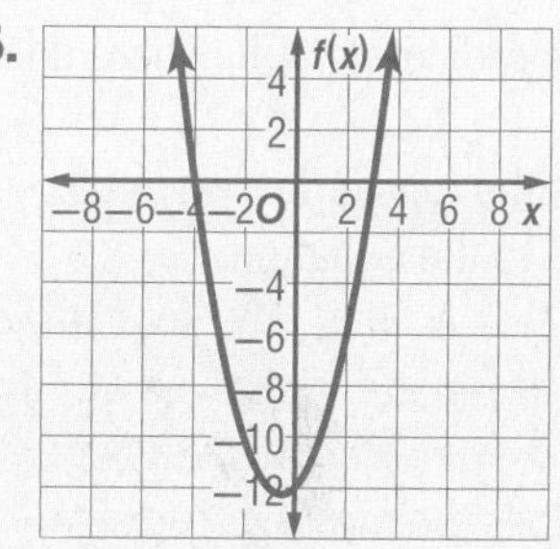

97a. $\begin{bmatrix} 72 & 49 \\ 68 & 63 \\ 90 & 56 \\ 86 & 62 \end{bmatrix}, \begin{bmatrix} 1.00 \\ 0.50 \end{bmatrix}$

97b. $\begin{bmatrix} 96.50 \\ 99.50 \\ 118 \\ 117 \end{bmatrix}$

5-4 Lesson Notes

1 FOCUS

Vertical Alignment

Before Lesson 5-4
Simplify square roots.

Lesson 5-4
Perform operations with pure imaginary numbers.
Perform operations with complex numbers.

After Lesson 5-4
Solve quadratic equations using the Quadratic Formula.

2 TEACH

Scaffolding Questions

Have students read the *Why?* section of the lesson.

Ask:

- On a coordinate graph, where does $y = 0$? on the x-axis
- How is the function $y = x^2 + 2x + 4$ related to the equation $x^2 + 2x + 4 = 0$? The solutions of the equation are the values of x that make the function equal to zero.
- Why does the message "no sign change" mean that there are no solutions to the equation? Sample answer: If the graph of a function passes through the x-axis, the value of the function usually goes from positive to negative, or vice-versa.

5-4 Complex Numbers

Then
You simplified square roots. (Prior Course)

Now
- Perform operations with pure imaginary numbers.
- Perform operations with complex numbers.

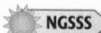

NGSSS
MA.912.A.1.6 Identify the real and imaginary parts of complex numbers and perform basic operations.

New Vocabulary
imaginary unit
pure imaginary number
complex number
complex conjugates

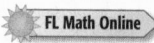

FL Math Online
glencoe.com

Why?

Consider the graph of $y = x^2 + 2x + 4$ at the right. Notice how this graph has no x-intercepts and therefore does not have any roots. Does this mean there are no solutions?

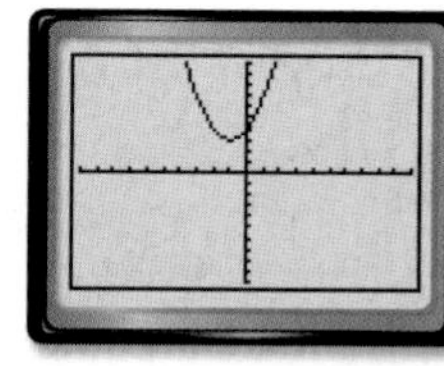

Use the Solver function located in the math menu of a graphing calculator. Enter the equation and select $x = 2$ as your *guess* to a solution.

Press ALPHA ENTER and the calculator will attempt to solve the equation. The calculator indicates there is no solution with the error message. So there are no real solutions. However, there are *imaginary* solutions.

Pure Imaginary Numbers In your math studies so far, you have worked with real numbers. Equations like the one above led mathematicians to define imaginary numbers. The **imaginary unit** i is defined to be $i^2 = -1$. The number i is the principal square root of -1; that is, $i = \sqrt{-1}$.

Numbers of the form $6i$, $-2i$, and $i\sqrt{3}$ are called **pure imaginary numbers**. Pure imaginary numbers are square roots of negative real numbers. For any positive real number b, $\sqrt{-b^2} = \sqrt{b^2} \cdot \sqrt{-1}$ or bi.

EXAMPLE 1 Square Roots of Negative Numbers

Simplify.

a. $\sqrt{-27}$

$\sqrt{-27} = \sqrt{-1 \cdot 3^2 \cdot 3}$
$= \sqrt{-1} \cdot \sqrt{3^2} \cdot \sqrt{3}$
$= i \cdot 3 \cdot \sqrt{3}$ or $3i\sqrt{3}$

b. $\sqrt{-216}$

$\sqrt{-216} = \sqrt{-1 \cdot 6^2 \cdot 6}$
$= \sqrt{-1} \cdot \sqrt{6^2 \cdot 6}$
$= i \cdot 6 \cdot \sqrt{6}$ or $6i\sqrt{6}$

Guided Practice

1A. $\sqrt{-18}$ $3i\sqrt{2}$

1B. $\sqrt{-125}$ $5i\sqrt{5}$

Personal Tutor glencoe.com

The Commutative and Associative Properties of Multiplication hold true for pure imaginary numbers. The first few powers of i are shown below.

$i^1 = i$	$i^2 = -1$	$i^3 = i^2 \cdot i$ or $-i$	$i^4 = (i^2)^2$ or 1
$i^5 = i^4 \cdot i$ or i	$i^6 = i^4 \cdot i^2$ or -1	$i^7 = i^4 \cdot i^3$ or $-i$	$i^8 = (i^2)^4$ or 1

Lesson 5-4 Resources

Resource	Approaching-Level	On-Level	Beyond-Level	English Learners
Teacher Edition	• Differentiated Instruction, p. 277	• Differentiated Instruction, pp. 277, 282	• Differentiated Instruction, pp. 277, 282	• Differentiated Instruction, p. 277
Chapter Resource Masters	• Study Guide and Intervention, pp. 24–25 • Skills Practice, p. 26 • Practice, p. 27 • Word Problem Practice, p. 28	• Study Guide and Intervention, pp. 24–25 • Skills Practice, p. 26 • Practice, p. 27 • Word Problem Practice, p. 28 • Enrichment, p. 29	• Practice, p. 27 • Word Problem Practice, p. 28 • Enrichment, p. 29	• Study Guide and Intervention, pp. 24–25 • Skills Practice, p. 26 • Practice, p. 27 • Word Problem Practice, p. 28
Transparencies	• 5-Minute Check Transparency 5-4	• 5-Minute Check Transparency 5-4	• 5-Minute Check Transparency 5-4	• 5-Minute Check Transparency 5-4
Other	• Study Notebook • Teaching Algebra with Manipulatives	• Study Notebook • Teaching Algebra with Manipulatives	• Study Notebook	• Study Notebook • Teaching Algebra with Manipulatives

EXAMPLE 2 Products of Pure Imaginary Numbers

Simplify.

a. $-5i \cdot 3i$

$-5i \cdot 3i = -15i^2$ **Multiply.**

$= -15(-1)$ $i^2 = -1$

$= 15$ **Simplify.**

b. $\sqrt{-6} \cdot \sqrt{-15}$

$\sqrt{-6} \cdot \sqrt{-15} = i\sqrt{6} \cdot i\sqrt{15}$ $i = \sqrt{-1}$

$= i^2\sqrt{90}$ **Multiply.**

$= -1 \cdot \sqrt{9} \cdot \sqrt{10}$ **Simplify.**

$= -3\sqrt{10}$ **Multiply.**

StudyTip

Square Root Property Refer to Concepts and Skills Lesson 3 to review the Square Root Property.

Guided Practice

2A. $3i \cdot 4i$ -12 **2B.** $\sqrt{-20} \cdot \sqrt{-12}$ $-4\sqrt{15}$ **2C.** i^{31} $-i$

Personal Tutor glencoe.com

You can solve some quadratic equations by using the **Square Root Property**.

EXAMPLE 3 Equation with Pure Imaginary Solutions

Solve $4x^2 + 256 = 0$.

$4x^2 + 256 = 0$ **Original equation**

$4x^2 = -256$ **Subtract 256 from each side.**

$x^2 = -64$ **Divide each side by 4.**

$x = \pm\sqrt{-64}$ **Square Root Property**

$x = \pm 8i$ $\sqrt{-64} = \sqrt{64} \cdot \sqrt{-1}$ **or** $8i$

Guided Practice

Solve each equation.

3A. $4x^2 + 100 = 0$ $\pm 5i$ **3B.** $x^2 + 4 = 0$ $\pm 2i$

Personal Tutor glencoe.com

Operations with Complex Numbers Consider $2 + 3i$. Since 2 is a real number and $3i$ is a pure imaginary number, the terms are not like terms and cannot be combined. This type of expression is called a **complex number**.

Key Concept Complex Numbers

Get Animated

Words	A complex number is any number that can be written in the form $a + bi$, where a and b are real numbers and i is the imaginary unit. a is called the real part, and b is called the imaginary part.
Examples	$5 + 2i$ $\quad$ $1 - 3i = 1 + (-3)i$

Pure Imaginary Numbers

Example 1 shows how to simplify expressions that involve square roots of negative numbers. **Example 2** shows how to find the product of pure imaginary numbers. **Example 3** shows how to solve a quadratic equation with pure imaginary solutions.

Formative Assessment

Use the Guided Practice exercises after each example to determine students' understanding of concepts.

Additional Examples

1 Simplify.

a. $\sqrt{-28}$ $2i\sqrt{7}$

b. $\sqrt{-32}$ $4i\sqrt{2}$

2 Simplify.

a. $-3i \cdot 2i$ 6

b. $\sqrt{-12} \cdot \sqrt{-2}$ $-2\sqrt{6}$

3 Solve $5y^2 + 20 = 0$. $y = \pm 2i$

Additional Examples also in Interactive Classroom PowerPoint® Presentations

IWB INTERACTIVE WHITEBOARD READY

Watch Out!

Preventing Errors Make sure students understand that when they take the square root of both sides of an equation, they must use the ± symbol in front of the radical sign.

Differentiated Instruction

AL OL BL ELL

If students need help remembering the mathematical characteristics of i,

Then have students write poems about the imaginary number i and the repeating values of its powers, perhaps including wordplay with the terms *real* and *imaginary*. The content of the poems should be helpful for remembering the mathematical characteristics of i.

Operations with Complex Numbers

Example 4 shows how to equate complex numbers. **Example 5** shows how to add and subtract complex numbers. **Examples 6–7** show how to multiply and divide complex numbers.

Additional Examples

4 Find the values of x and y that make the equation $2x + yi = -14 - 3i$ true. $x = -7, y = -3$

5 Simplify.

a. $(3 + 5i) + (2 - 4i)$ $5 + i$

b. $(4 - 6i) - (3 - 7i)$ $1 + i$

Watch Out!

Preventing Errors Emphasize that two complex numbers are equal if and only if their real parts are equal and their imaginary parts are equal.

The Venn diagram shows the set of complex numbers.

- If $b = 0$, the complex number is a real number.
- If $b \neq 0$, the complex number is imaginary.
- If $a = 0$, the complex number is a pure imaginary number.

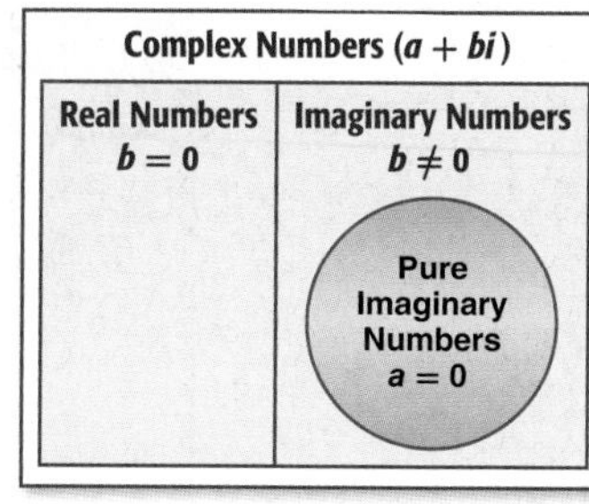

Two complex numbers are equal if and only if their real parts are equal and their imaginary parts are equal. That is, $a + bi = c + di$ if and only if $a = c$ and $b = d$.

StudyTip

Complex Numbers Whereas all real numbers are also complex, the term *complex number* usually refers to a number that is not real.

EXAMPLE 4 Equate Complex Numbers

Find the values of x and y that make $3x - 5 + (y - 3)i = 7 + 6i$ true.

Set the real parts equal to each other and the imaginary parts equal to each other.

$3x - 5 = 7$	**Real parts**	$y - 3 = 6$	**Imaginary parts**
$3x = 12$	**Add 5 to each side.**	$y = 9$	**Add 3 to each side.**
$x = 4$	**Divide each side by 3.**		

Guided Practice 4. $x = -1, y = -9$

4. Find the values of x and y that make $5x + 1 + (3 + 2y)i = 2x - 2 + (y - 6)i$ true.

Personal Tutor glencoe.com

The Commutative, Associative, and Distributive Properties of Multiplication and Addition hold true for complex numbers. To add or subtract complex numbers, combine like terms. That is, combine the real parts, and combine the imaginary parts.

EXAMPLE 5 Add and Subtract Complex Numbers

Simplify.

a. $(5 - 7i) + (2 + 4i)$

$(5 - 7i) + (2 + 4i) = (5 + 2) + (-7 + 4)i$ **Commutative and Associative Properties**

$= 7 - 3i$ **Simplify.**

b. $(4 - 8i) - (3 - 6i)$

$(4 - 8i) - (3 - 6i) = (4 - 3) + [-8 - (-6)]i$ **Commutative and Associative Properties**

$= 1 - 2i$ **Simplify.**

Guided Practice

5A. $(-2 + 5i) + (1 - 7i)$ $-1 - 2i$

5B. $(4 + 6i) - (-1 + 2i)$ $5 + 4i$

Personal Tutor glencoe.com

StudyTip

Reading Math Electrical engineers use j as the imaginary unit to avoid confusion with the i for current.

Complex numbers are used with electricity. In these problems, j usually represents the imaginary unit. In a circuit with alternating current, the voltage, current, and impedance, or hindrance to current, can be represented by complex numbers. To multiply these numbers, use the FOIL method.

278 Chapter 5 Quadratic Functions and Relations

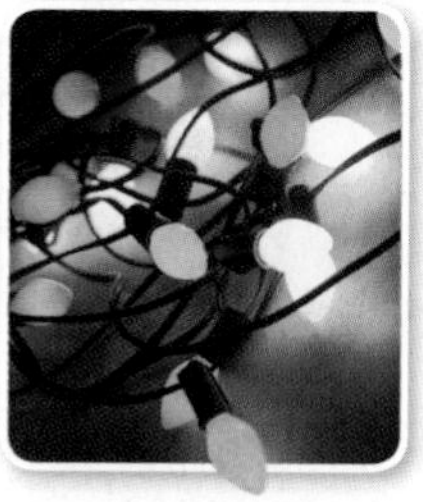

Real-World Link

An example of a series circuit is a string of holiday lights. The number of bulbs on a circuit affects the strength of the current, which in turn affects the brightness of the lights.

Source: *Popular Science*

Real-World EXAMPLE 6 Multiply Complex Numbers

ELECTRICITY In an AC circuit, the voltage V, current C, and impedance I are related by the formula $V = C \cdot I$. Find the voltage in a circuit with current $2 + 4j$ amps and impedance $9 - 3j$ ohms.

$V = C \cdot I$	**Electricity formula**
$= (2 + 4j) \cdot (9 - 3j)$	**$C = 2 + 4j$ and $I = 9 - 3j$**
$= 2(9) + 2(-3j) + 4j(9) + 4j(-3j)$	**FOIL Method**
$= 18 - 6j + 36j - 12j^2$	**Multiply.**
$= 18 + 30j - 12(-1)$	**$j^2 = -1$**
$= 30 + 30j$	**Add.**

The voltage is $30 + 30j$ volts.

Guided Practice 6. $-2 - 16j$ volts

6. Find the voltage in a circuit with current $2 - 4j$ amps and impedance $3 - 2j$ ohms.

Personal Tutor glencoe.com

Two complex numbers of the form $a + bi$ and $a - bi$ are called **complex conjugates**. The product of complex conjugates is always a real number. You can use this fact to simplify the quotient of two complex numbers.

EXAMPLE 7 Divide Complex Numbers

Simplify.

a. $\frac{2i}{3 + 6i}$

$\frac{2i}{3 + 6i} = \frac{2i}{3 + 6i} \cdot \frac{3 - 6i}{3 - 6i}$	**$3 + 6i$ and $3 - 6i$ are complex conjugates.**
$= \frac{6i - 12i^2}{9 - 36i^2}$	**Multiply.**
$= \frac{6i - 12(-1)}{9 - 36(-1)}$	**$i^2 = -1$**
$= \frac{6i + 12}{45}$	**Simplify.**
$= \frac{4}{15} + \frac{2}{15}i$	**$a + bi$ form**

b. $\frac{4 + i}{5i}$

$\frac{4 + i}{5i} = \frac{4 + i}{5i} \cdot \frac{i}{i}$	**Multiply by $\frac{i}{i}$.**
$= \frac{4i + i^2}{5i^2}$	**Multiply.**
$= \frac{4i - 1}{-5}$	**$i^2 = -1$**
$= \frac{1}{5} - \frac{4}{5}i$	**$a + bi$ form**

Guided Practice

7A. $\frac{-2i}{3 + 5i}$ $-\frac{5}{17} - \frac{3}{17}i$

7B. $\frac{2 + i}{1 - i}$ $\frac{1}{2} + \frac{3}{2}i$

Personal Tutor glencoe.com

TEACH with TECH

INTERACTIVE WHITEBOARD Work through an example multiplying two complex numbers. Write an example on the board using red for the imaginary part and blue for the real part of each complex number. In each calculation, continue to use red and blue to show the imaginary and real parts of the complex numbers.

Additional Examples

6 **ELECTRICITY** In an AC circuit, the voltage E, current I, and impedance Z are related by the formula $E = I \cdot Z$. Find the voltage in a circuit with current $1 + 4j$ amps and impedance $3 - 6j$ ohms. $27 + 6j$

7 Simplify.

a. $\frac{5i}{3 + 2i}$ $\frac{10}{13} + \frac{15}{13i}$

b. $\frac{5 + i}{2i}$ $\frac{1}{2} - \frac{5}{2i}$

Focus on Mathematical Content

Complex Numbers A complex number is any number that can be written in the form $a + bi$, where a and b are real numbers and i is the imaginary unit. If $b = 0$, the complex number is a real number. If $b \neq 0$, the complex number is imaginary. If $a = 0$, the complex number is a pure imaginary number. Pure imaginary and real numbers are both subsets of the set of complex numbers. Hence, every real number is complex, and every pure imaginary number is complex.

3 PRACTICE

Formative Assessment

Use Exercises 1–17 to check for understanding.

Use the chart at the bottom of this page to customize assignments for your students.

Multiple Representations In Exercise 65, students use a graph in the complex plane and logical analysis to represent complex numbers.

Additional Answers

65a.

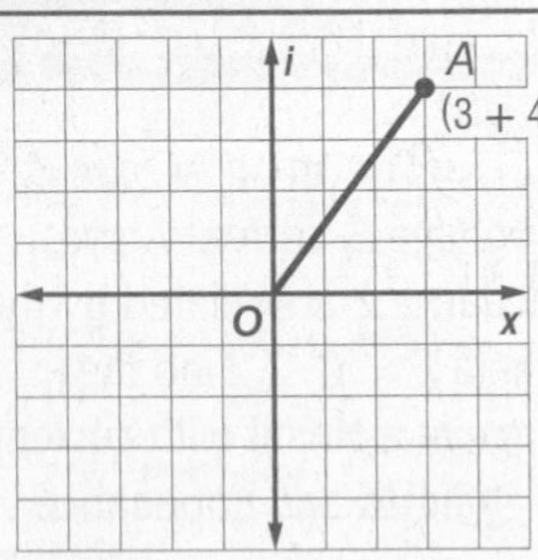

65b.

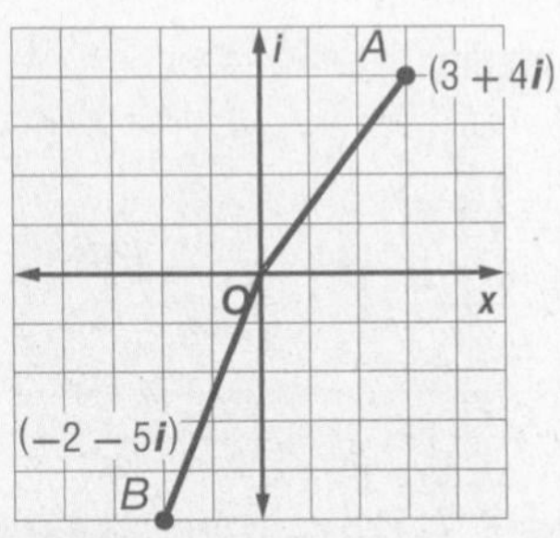

65c.

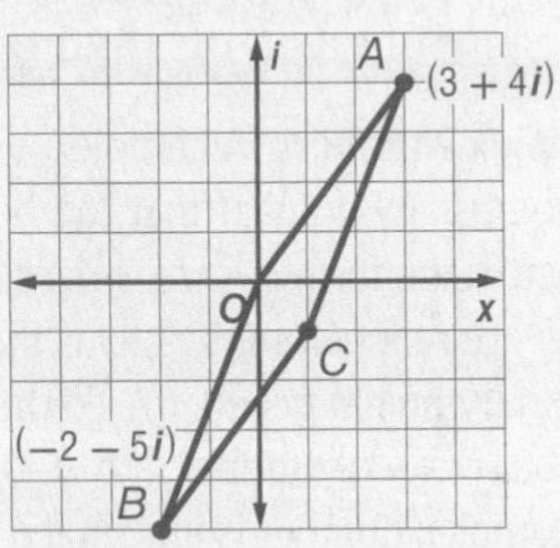

Check Your Understanding

Examples 1 and 2 pp. 276–277

Simplify.

1. $\sqrt{-81}$ $9i$
2. $\sqrt{-32}$ $4i\sqrt{2}$
3. $(4i)(-3i)$ 12
4. $3\sqrt{-24} \cdot 2\sqrt{-18}$ $-72\sqrt{3}$
5. i^{40} 1
6. i^{63} $-i$

Example 3 p. 277

Solve each equation.

7. $4x^2 + 32 = 0$ $\pm 2i\sqrt{2}$
8. $2x^2 + 24 = 0$ $\pm 2i\sqrt{3}$

Example 4 p. 278

Find the values of a and b that make each equation true.

9. $3a + (4b + 2)i = 9 - 6i$ $3, -2$
10. $4b - 5 + (-a - 3)i = 7 - 8i$ $5, 3$

Examples 5 and 7 pp. 278–279

Simplify.

11. $(-1 + 5i) + (-2 - 3i)$ $-3 + 2i$
12. $(7 + 4i) - (1 + 2i)$ $6 + 2i$
13. $(6 - 8i)(9 + 2i)$ $70 - 60i$
14. $(3 + 2i)(-2 + 4i)$ $-14 + 8i$
15. $\frac{3 - i}{4 + 2i}$ $\frac{1}{2} - \frac{1}{2}i$
16. $\frac{2 + i}{5 + 6i}$ $\frac{16}{61} - \frac{7}{61}i$

Example 6 p. 279

17. **ELECTRICITY** The current in one part of a series circuit is $5 - 3j$ amps. The current in another part of the circuit is $7 + 9j$ amps. Add these complex numbers to find the total current in the circuit. $12 + 6j$ amps

Practice and Problem Solving

● = **Step-by-Step Solutions** begin on page R20. **Extra Practice** begins on page 947.

Examples 1 and 2 pp. 276–277

Simplify. 26. $16 + 2i$ 28. $3 + 7i$

18. $\sqrt{-121}$ $11i$
19. $\sqrt{-169}$ $13i$
20. $\sqrt{-100}$ $10i$
21. $\sqrt{-81}$ $9i$
22. $(-3i)(-7i)(2i)$ $-42i$
23. $4i(-6i)^2$ $-144i$
24. i^{11} $-i$
25. i^{25} i
26. $(10 - 7i) + (6 + 9i)$
27. $(-3 + i) + (-4 - i)$ -7
28. $(12 + 5i) - (9 - 2i)$
29. $(11 - 8i) - (2 - 8i)$ 9
30. $(1 + 2i)(1 - 2i)$ 5
31. $(3 + 5i)(5 - 3i)$ $30 + 16i$
32. $(4 - i)(6 - 6i)$ $18 - 30i$
33. $\frac{2i}{1 + i}$ $1 + i$
34. $\frac{5}{2 + 4i}$ $\frac{1}{2} - i$
35. $\frac{5 + i}{3i}$ $\frac{1}{3} - \frac{5}{3}i$

Example 3 p. 277

Solve each equation.

36. $4x^2 + 4 = 0$ $\pm i$
37. $3x^2 + 48 = 0$ $\pm 4i$
38. $2x^2 + 50 = 0$ $\pm 5i$
39. $2x^2 + 10 = 0$ $\pm i\sqrt{5}$
40. $6x^2 + 108 = 0$ $\pm 3i\sqrt{2}$
41. $8x^2 + 128 = 0$ $\pm 4i$

Example 4 p. 278

Find the values of x and y that make each equation true.

42. $9 + 12i = 3x + 4yi$ $3, 3$
43. $x + 1 + 2yi = 3 - 6i$ $2, -3$
44. $2x + 7 + (3 - y)i = -4 + 6i$ $-\frac{11}{2}, -3$
45. $5 + y + (3x - 7)i = 9 - 3i$ $\frac{4}{3}, 4$
46. $a + 3b + (3a - b)i = 6 + 6i$ $\frac{12}{5}, \frac{6}{5}$
47. $(2a - 4b)i + a + 5b = 15 + 58i$ $25, -2$

Differentiated Homework Options

Level	Assignment	Two-Day Option	
AL Basic	18–60, 66, 68–89	19–59 odd, 71–74	18–60 even, 66, 68–89
OL Core	19–59 odd, 61–89	18–60, 71–74	61–66, 68–70, 75–89
BL Advanced	61–83, (optional: 84–89)		

Examples 5 and 7 pp. 278–279

Simplify. 53. $-21 + 15i$ 56. $-118 + 34i$

48. $\sqrt{-10} \cdot \sqrt{-24}$ $-4\sqrt{15}$ **49.** $4i\left(\frac{1}{2}i\right)^2(-2i)^2$ $4i$ **50.** i^{41} i

51. $(4 - 6i) + (4 + 6i)$ 8 **52.** $(8 - 5i) - (7 + i)$ $1 - 6i$ **53.** $(-6 - i)(3 - 3i)$

54. $\frac{(5 + i)^2}{3 - i}$ $\frac{31}{5} + \frac{27}{5}i$ **55.** $\frac{6 - i}{2 - 3i}$ $\frac{15}{13} + \frac{16}{13}i$ **56.** $(-4 + 6i)(2 - i)(3 + 7i)$

57. $(1 + i)(2 + 3i)(4 - 3i)$ $11 + 23i$ **58.** $\frac{4 - i\sqrt{2}}{4 + i\sqrt{2}}$ $\frac{7}{9} - \frac{4i\sqrt{2}}{9}$ **59.** $\frac{2 - i\sqrt{3}}{2 + i\sqrt{3}}$ $\frac{1}{7} - \frac{4\sqrt{3}}{7}i$

Example 6 p. 279

60. ELECTRICITY The impedance in one part of a series circuit is $7 + 8j$ ohms, and the impedance in another part of the circuit is $13 - 4j$ ohms. Add these complex numbers to find the total impedance in the circuit. $20 + 4j$ ohms

B

ELECTRICITY Use the formula $V = C \cdot I$. 63. $(3 + i)x^2 + (-2 + i)x - 8i + 7$

61 The current in a circuit is $3 + 6j$ amps, and the impedance is $5 - j$ ohms. What is the voltage? $21 + 27j$ Volts

62. The voltage in a circuit is $20 - 12j$ volts, and the impedance is $6 - 4j$ ohms. What is the current? $\frac{42}{13} + \frac{2}{13}j$ Amps

63. Find the sum of $ix^2 - (4 + 5i)x + 7$ and $3x^2 + (2 + 6i)x - 8i$.

64. Simplify $[(2 + i)x^2 - ix + 5 + i] - [(-3 + 4i)x^2 + (5 - 5i)x - 6]$. $(5 - 3i)x^2 + (-5 + 4i)x + i + 11$

C

65. MULTIPLE REPRESENTATIONS In this problem, you will explore adding complex numbers in the complex plane. The *complex plane* is a lot like the *real plane*, but it has real numbers along the x-axis and the imaginary numbers along the y-axis.

a. **GRAPHICAL** Graph $3 + 4i$ in the complex plane by drawing a segment from the origin to (3, 4). Label this point A. a–c. See margin.

b. **GRAPHICAL** Graph $-2 - 5i$ in the complex plane by drawing a segment from the origin to (−2, −5). Label this point B.

c. **GRAPHICAL** Given three vertices of a parallelogram, complete it by adding a point C.

d. **ANALYTICAL** What complex number does C represent? What is the relationship between A, B, and C? $1 - i$; $A + B = C$

Real-World Link

Electricity is the flow of an electrical charge. The electricity we use is a secondary energy source converted from fossil fuels, nuclear reactors, and natural sources.

Source: Energy Information Administration

68. Sample answer: Always; the value of 5 can be represented by $5 + 0i$, and the value of $3i$ can be represented by $0 + 3i$.

H.O.T. Problems

Use Higher-Order Thinking Skills

66. ERROR ANALYSIS Joe and Sue are simplifying $(2i)(3i)(4i)$. Is either of them correct? Explain your reasoning. Sue; $i^3 = -i$, not -1.

Joe	Sue
$24i^3 = -24$	$24i^3 = -24i$

67. CHALLENGE Simplify $(1 + 2i)^3$. $-11 - 2i$

68. REASONING Determine whether the following statement is *always*, *sometimes*, or *never* true. Explain your reasoning.

Every complex number has both a real part and an imaginary part.

69. OPEN ENDED Write two complex numbers with a product of 20. Sample answer: $(4 + 2i)(4 - 2i)$

70. WRITING IN MATH Explain how complex numbers are related to quadratic equations. How do you know when a quadratic equation will have only complex solutions?

70. Some quadratic equations have complex solutions and cannot be solved using only the real numbers. You know that a quadratic equation is going to have only complex solutions when the graph of the related function has no x-intercepts.

Watch Out!

Error Analysis For Exercise 66, since i^2 always equals −1, rewrite i^3 as $i(i^2)$.

Study Guide and Intervention

CRM pp. 24–25 AL OL ELL

5-4 Study Guide and Intervention

Complex Numbers

Pure Imaginary Numbers A **square root** of a number n is a number whose square is n. For nonnegative real numbers a and b, $\sqrt{ab} = \sqrt{a} \cdot \sqrt{b}$ and $\sqrt{\frac{a}{b}} = \frac{\sqrt{a}}{\sqrt{b}}, b \neq 0$.

- The **imaginary unit** i is defined to have the property that $i^2 = -1$.
- Simplified square root expressions do not have radicals in the denominator, and any number remaining under the square root has no perfect square factor other than 1.

Example 1

a. Simplify $\sqrt{-48}$.
$\sqrt{-48} = \sqrt{16 \cdot (-3)} = \sqrt{16} \cdot \sqrt{3} \cdot \sqrt{-1} = 4i\sqrt{3}$

b. Simplify $\sqrt{-63}$.
$\sqrt{-63} = \sqrt{-1 \cdot 7 \cdot 9} = \sqrt{-1} \cdot \sqrt{7} \cdot \sqrt{9} = 3i\sqrt{7}$

Example 2

a. Simplify $-3i \cdot 4i$.
$-3i \cdot 4i = -12i^2 = -12(-1) = 12$

b. Simplify $\sqrt{-3} \cdot \sqrt{-15}$.
$\sqrt{-3} \cdot \sqrt{-15} = i\sqrt{3} \cdot i\sqrt{15} = i^2\sqrt{45} = -1 \cdot \sqrt{9} \cdot \sqrt{5} = -3\sqrt{5}$

Example 3 Solve $x^2 + 5 = 0$.

$x^2 + 5 = 0$ Original equation.
$x^2 = -5$ Subtract 5 from each side.
$x = \pm\sqrt{5}i$ Square Root Property.

Exercises

Simplify.

1. $\sqrt{-72}$ $6i\sqrt{2}$
2. $\sqrt{-24}$ $2i\sqrt{6}$
3. $\sqrt{-84}$ $2i\sqrt{21}$
4. $(2 + i)(2 - i)$ 5

Solve each equation.

5. $5x^2 + 45 = 0$ $\pm 3i$
6. $4x^2 + 24 = 0$ $\pm i\sqrt{6}$
7. $-9x^2 = 9$ $\pm i$
8. $7x^2 + 84 = 0$ $\pm 2i\sqrt{3}$

Practice

CRM p. 27 AL OL BL ELL

5-4 Practice

Complex Numbers

Simplify.

1. $\sqrt{-36}$ $6i$
2. $\sqrt{-8} \cdot \sqrt{-32}$ -16
3. $\sqrt{-15} \cdot \sqrt{-25}$ $-5\sqrt{15}$
4. $(-3i)(4i)(-5i)$ $-60i$
5. $(7i)^2(6i)$ $-294i$
6. i^{42} -1
7. i^{55} $-i$
8. i^{89} i
9. $(5 - 2i) + (-13 - 8i)$ $-8 - 10i$
10. $(7 - 6i) + (9 + 11i)$ $16 + 5i$
11. $(-12 + 48i) + (15 + 21i)$ $3 + 69i$
12. $(10 + 15i) - (48 - 30i)$ $-38 + 45i$
13. $(28 - 4i) - (10 - 30i)$ $18 + 26i$
14. $(6 - 4i)(6 + 4i)$ 52
15. $(8 - 11i)(8 - 11i)$ $-57 - 176i$
16. $(4 + 3i)(2 - 5i)$ $23 - 14i$
17. $(7 + 2i)(9 - 6i)$ $75 - 24i$
18. $\frac{6 + 5i}{-2i}$ $\frac{-5 + 6i}{2}$
19. $\frac{2}{7 - 8i}$ $\frac{14 + 16i}{113}$
20. $\frac{3 - i}{2 - i}$ $\frac{7 + i}{5}$
21. $\frac{2 - 4i}{1 + 3i}$ $-1 - i$

Solve each equation.

22. $5n^2 + 35 = 0$ $\pm i\sqrt{7}$
23. $2m^2 + 10 = 0$ $\pm i\sqrt{5}$
24. $4m^2 + 76 = 0$ $\pm i\sqrt{19}$
25. $-2m^2 - 6 = 0$ $\pm i\sqrt{3}$
26. $-5m^2 - 65 = 0$ $\pm i\sqrt{13}$
27. $\frac{3}{4}x^2 + 12 = 0$ $\pm 4i$

Find the values of m and n that make each equation true.

28. $15 - 28i = 3m + 4ni$ 5, −7
29. $(6 - m) + 3ni = -12 + 27i$ 18, 9
30. $(3m + 4) + (3 - n)i = 16 - 3i$ 4, 6
31. $(7 + n) + (4m - 10)i = 3 - 6i$ 1, −4
32. **ELECTRICITY** The impedance in one part of a series circuit is $1 + 3j$ ohms and the impedance in another part of the circuit is $7 - 5j$ ohms. Add these complex numbers to find the total impedance in the circuit. $8 - 2j$ ohms
33. **ELECTRICITY** Using the formula $E = IZ$, find the voltage E in a circuit when the current I is $3 - j$ amps and the impedance Z is $3 + 2j$ ohms. $11 + 3j$ volts

Lesson 5-4

Word Problem Practice

CRM p. 28 AL OL BL ELL

5-4 Word Problem Practice

Complex Numbers

1. **SIGN ERRORS** Jennifer and Jessica come up with different answers to the same problem. They had to multiply $(4 + i)(4 - i)$ and give their answer as a complex number. Jennifer claims that the answer is 15 and Jessica claims that the answer is 17. Who is correct? Explain.
Jessica is correct; $(4 + i)(4 - i) = 16 + 4i - 4i - i^2 = 16 - (-1) = 16 + 1 = 17$.

2. **COMPLEX CONJUGATES** You have seen that the product of complex conjugates is always a real number. Show that the sum of complex conjugates is also always a real number.
$a + bi$ and $a - bi$ are complex conjugates and their sum is $2a$, which is real.

3. **PYTHAGOREAN TRIPLES** If three integers a, b, and c satisfy $a^2 + b^2 = c^2$, then they are called a *Pythagorean triple*. Suppose that a, b, and c are a Pythagorean triple. Show that the real and imaginary parts of $(a + bi)^2$, together with the number c^2, form another Pythagorean triple.
$(a + bi)^2 = a^2 - b^2 + 2abi$; $a^2 - b^2$ and $2ab$ are integers and $(a^2 - b^2)^2 + (2ab)^2 = a^4 - 2a^2b^2 + b^4 + 4a^2b^2 = a^4 + 2a^2b^2 + b^4 = (a^2 + b^2)^2 = (c^2)^2$, so $a^2 + b^2 = c^2$ as desired.

4. **ROTATIONS** Complex numbers can be used to perform rotations in the plane. For example, if (x, y) are the coordinates of a point in the plane, then the real and imaginary parts of $i(x + yi)$ are the horizontal and vertical coordinates of the 90° counterclockwise rotation of (x, y) about the origin. What are the real and imaginary parts of $i(x + yi)$?
The real part is $-y$ and imaginary part is x.

5. **ELECTRICAL ENGINEERING** Alternating current (AC) in an electrical circuit can be described by complex numbers. In any electrical circuit, Z, the impedance in the circuit, is related to the voltage V and the current I by the formula $Z = \frac{V}{I}$. The standard electrical voltage in Europe is 220 volts, so in these problems use $V = 220$.
a. Find the impedance in a standard European circuit if the current is $22 - 11i$ amps. **$8 + 4i$**
b. Find the current in a standard European circuit if the impedance is $10 - 5i$ watts. **$18 - 8i$ amps**
c. Find the impedance in a standard European circuit if the current is $20i$ amps. **$-11i$ amps**

Enrichment

CRM p. 29 OL BL

5-4 Enrichment

Conjugates and Absolute Value

When studying complex numbers, it is often convenient to represent a complex number by a single variable. For example, we might let $z = x + yi$. We denote the conjugate of z by $\bar{z}$. Thus, $\bar{z} = x - yi$.

We can define the absolute value of a complex number as follows.

$|z| = |x + yi| = \sqrt{x^2 + y^2}$

There are many important relationships involving conjugates and absolute values of complex numbers.

Example 1 Show $|z|^2 = z\bar{z}$ for any complex number z.

Let $z = x + yi$. Then,
$z\bar{z} = (x + yi)(x - yi) = x^2 + y^2 = \sqrt{(x^2 + y^2)^2} = |z|^2$

Show ... multiplic... inver... for an... nzero

4 ASSESS

Ticket Out the Door Have students write two complex numbers that have a product of 10 on small pieces of paper and hand them to you as they leave the classroom. Sample answer: $1 + 3i$ and $1 - 3i$

Formative Assessment

Check for student understanding of concepts in Lessons 5-3 and 5-4.

CRM Quiz 2, p. 59

Additional Answers

71b. $\angle AED \cong \angle CEB$ (Vertical angles) $\overline{DE} \cong \overline{BE}$ (Both have length x.) $\angle ADE \cong \angle CBE$ (Given) Consecutive angles and the included side are all congruent, so the triangles are congruent by the ASA Property.

71c. $\overline{EC} \cong \overline{EA}$ by CPCTC (corresponding parts of congruent triangles are congruent). $EA = 7$, so $EC = 7$.

82a. Residents: $\begin{matrix} \text{Child} & \text{Adult} \end{matrix}$ $\begin{bmatrix} 3.00 & 4.50 \\ 2.00 & 3.50 \end{bmatrix}$,

Nonresidents: $\begin{matrix} \text{Child} & \text{Adult} \end{matrix}$ $\begin{bmatrix} 4.50 & 6.75 \\ 3.00 & 5.25 \end{bmatrix}$

82b. Child Adult

$\begin{matrix} \text{Before 6} \\ \text{After 6} \end{matrix} \begin{bmatrix} 1.50 & 2.25 \\ 1.00 & 1.75 \end{bmatrix}$

82c. Child Adult

$\begin{matrix} \text{Resident} \\ \text{Nonresident} \end{matrix} \begin{bmatrix} 1.00 & 1.00 \\ 1.50 & 1.50 \end{bmatrix}$

83.

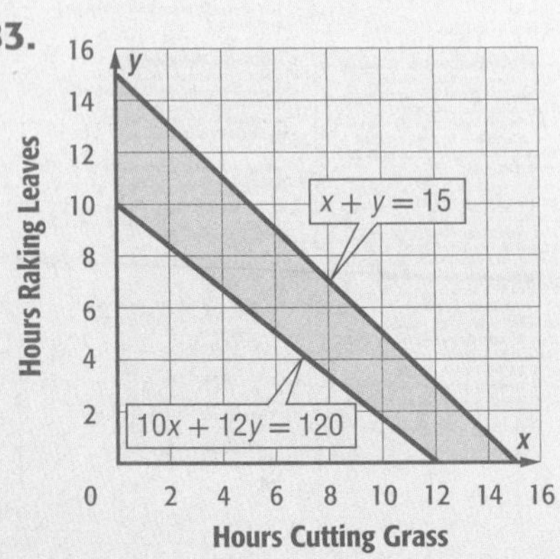

NGSSS PRACTICE 912.G.1.3, 912.A.3.15, 912.A.1.6

71. **EXTENDED RESPONSE** Refer to the figure to answer the following. **b, c. See margin.**

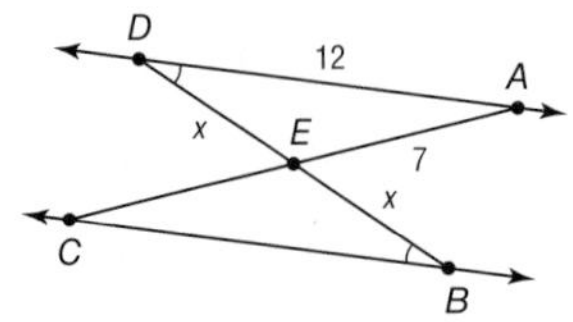

a. Name two congruent triangles with vertices in correct order. $\triangle CBE \cong \triangle ADE$

b. Explain why the triangles are congruent.

c. What is the length of $\overline{EC}$? Explain your procedure.

72. $(3 + 6)^2 =$ **B**

A. $2 \times 3 + 2 \times 6$
B. 9^2
C. $3^2 + 6^2$
D. $3^2 \times 6^2$

73. **SAT/ACT** A store charges $49 for a pair of pants. This price is 40% more than the amount it costs the store to buy the pants. After a sale, any employee is allowed to purchase any remaining pairs of pants at 30% off the store's cost.

How much would it cost an employee to purchase the pants after the sale? **H**

F. $12.50
G. $13.72
H. $24.50
I. $35.00

74. What are the values of x and y when $(5 + 4i) - (x + yi) = (-1 - 3i)$? **A**

A. $x = 6, y = 7$
B. $x = 4, y = i$
C. $x = 6, y = i$
D. $x = 4, y = 7$

Spiral Review

Solve each equation by factoring. (Lesson 5-3)

75. $2x^2 + 7x = 15$ $-5, \frac{3}{2}$
76. $4x^2 - 12 = 22x$ $-\frac{1}{2}, 6$
77. $6x^2 = 5x + 4$ $-\frac{1}{2}, \frac{4}{3}$

NUMBER THEORY **Use a quadratic equation to find two real numbers that satisfy each situation, or show that no such numbers exist.** (Lesson 5-2)

78. Their sum is −3, and their product is −40. **−8, 5**
79. Their sum is 19, and their product is 48. **3, 16**
80. Their sum is−15, and their product is 56. **−7 and −8**
81. Their sum is −21, and their product is 108. **−9, −12**

82. **RECREATION** Refer to the table. (Lesson 4-2) **a–c. See margin.**

a. Write a matrix that represents the cost of admission for residents and a matrix that represents the cost of admission for nonresidents.

b. Write the matrix that represents the additional cost for nonresidents.

c. Write a matrix that represents the difference in cost if a child or adult goes after 6:00 P.M. instead of before 6:00 P.M.

Daily Admission Fees		
Residents		
Time of day	**Child**	**Adult**
Before 6:00 P.M.	$3.00	$4.50
After 6:00 P.M.	$2.00	$3.50
Nonresidents		
Time of day	**Child**	**Adult**
Before 6:00 P.M.	$4.50	$6.75
After 6:00 P.M.	$3.00	$5.25

83. **PART-TIME JOBS** Terrell makes $10 an hour cutting grass and $12 an hour for raking leaves. He cannot work more than 15 hours per week. Graph two inequalities that Terrell can use to determine how many hours he needs to work at each job if he wants to earn at least $120 per week. (Lesson 3-3) **See margin.**

Skills Review

Determine whether each trinomial is a perfect square trinomial. Write *yes* or *no*. (Lesson 5-3)

84. $x^2 + 16x + 64$ **yes**
85. $x^2 - 12x + 36$ **yes**
86. $x^2 + 8x - 16$ **no**
87. $x^2 - 14x - 49$ **no**
88. $x^2 + x + 0.25$ **yes**
89. $x^2 + 5x + 6.25$ **yes**

Differentiated Instruction

BL OL

Extension Tell students that you are thinking of two complex numbers that have a sum of $3 + i$ and a difference of $-5 + 7i$. Ask them to find the product of the two numbers. $8 + 19i$

Additional Answer (Mid-Chapter Quiz)

1.

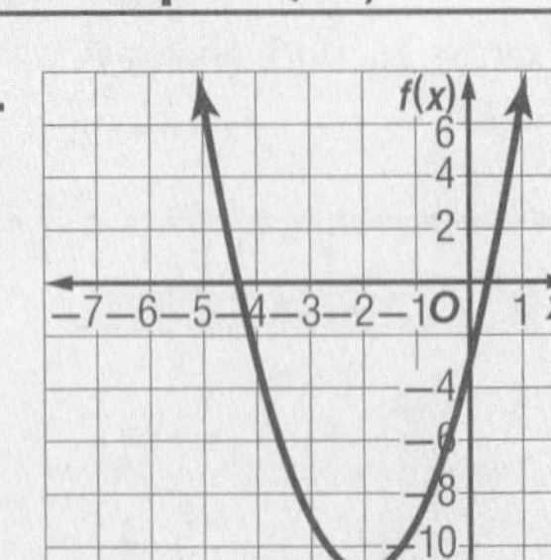

CHAPTER 5

Mid-Chapter Quiz

Lessons 5-1 through 5-4

NGSSS 912.A.7.6, 912.A.4.3

1. Find the y-intercept, the equation of the axis of symmetry, and the x-coordinate of the vertex for $f(x) = 2x^2 + 8x - 3$. Then graph the function by making a table of values. (Lesson 5-1) **See margin.**

2. **NGSSS PRACTICE** For which equation is the axis of symmetry $x = 5$? (Lesson 5-1) **B**
   - A. $f(x) = x^2 - 5x + 3$
   - B. $f(x) = x^2 - 10x + 7$
   - C. $f(x) = x^2 + 10x - 3$
   - D. $f(x) = x^2 + 5x + 2$

3. Determine whether $f(x) = 5 - x^2 + 2x$ has a maximum or a minimum value. Then find this maximum or minimum value and state the domain and range of the function. (Lesson 5-1) **max.; 6; D = {all real numbers}; R = $\{f(x) \mid f(x) \leq 6\}$**

4. **PHYSICAL SCIENCE** From 4 feet above the ground, Maya throws a ball upward with a velocity of 18 feet per second. The height $h(t)$ of the ball t seconds after Maya throws the ball is given by $h(t) = -16t^2 + 18t + 4$. Find the maximum height reached by the ball and the time that this height is reached. (Lesson 5-1) **9.0625 feet at 0.5625 seconds**

5. Solve $3x^2 - 17x + 5 = 0$ by graphing. If exact roots cannot be found, state the consecutive integers between which the roots are located. (Lesson 5-2) **between 0 and 1, and between 5 and 6**

Use a quadratic equation to find two real numbers that satisfy each situation, or show that no such numbers exist. (Lesson 5-2)

6. Their sum is 15, and their product is 36. **3 and 12**
7. Their sum is 7, and their product is 15. **See margin.**

8. **NGSSS PRACTICE** Using the graph of the function $f(x) = x^2 + 6x - 7$, what are the solutions to the equation $x^2 + 6x - 7 = 0$? (Lesson 5-2) **I**

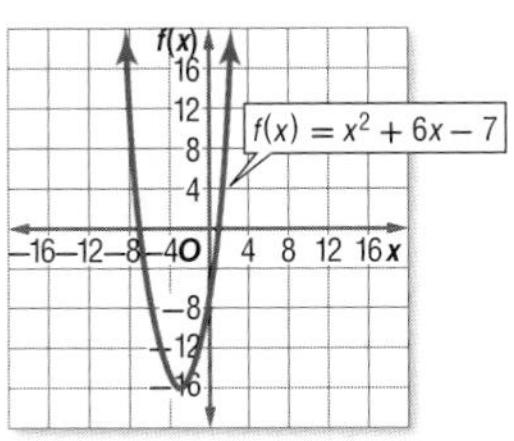

   - F. $-1, 6$
   - G. $1, -6$
   - H. $-1, 7$
   - I. $1, -7$

9. **BASEBALL** A baseball is hit upward with a velocity of 40 feet per second. Ignoring the height of the baseball player, how long does it take for the ball to fall to the ground? Use the formula $h(t) = v_0 t - 16t^2$ where $h(t)$ is the height of an object in feet, v_0 is the object's initial velocity in feet per second, and t is the time in seconds. (Lesson 5-2) **2.5 seconds**

Solve each equation by factoring. (Lesson 5-3)

10. $x^2 - x - 12 = 0$ **$\{-3, 4\}$**
11. $3x^2 + 7x + 2 = 0$ **$\left\{-2, -\frac{1}{3}\right\}$**
12. $x^2 - 2x - 15 = 0$ **$\{-3, 5\}$**
13. $2x^2 + 5x - 3 = 0$ **$\left\{-3, \frac{1}{2}\right\}$**

14. Write a quadratic equation in standard form with roots -6 and $\frac{1}{4}$. (Lesson 5-3) **$0 = 4x^2 + 23x - 6$**

15. **TRIANGLES** Find the dimensions of a triangle if the base is $\frac{2}{3}$ the measure of the height and the area is 12 square centimeters. (Lesson 5-3) **base = 4 cm, height = 6 cm**

16. **PATIO** Eli is putting a cement slab in his backyard. The original slab was going to have dimensions of 8 feet by 6 feet. He decided to make the slab larger by adding x feet to each side. The area of the new slab is 120 square feet. (Lesson 5-3)

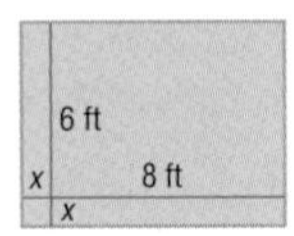

   a. Write a quadratic equation that represents the area of the new slab. **$120 = x^2 + 14x + 48$**

   b. Find the new dimensions of the slab. **12 feet by 10 feet**

Simplify. (Lesson 5-4) **19. $11 + 9i$**

17. $\sqrt{-81}$ **$9i$**
18. $\sqrt{-25x^4y^5}$ **$5x^2y^2i\sqrt{y}$**
19. $(15 - 3i) - (4 - 12i)$
20. i^{37} **i**
21. $(5 - 3i)(5 + 3i)$ **34**
22. $\frac{3 - i}{2 + 5i}$ **$\frac{1}{29} - \frac{17}{29}i$**

23. The impedance in one part of a series circuit is $3 + 4j$ ohms and the impedance in another part of the circuit is $6 - 7j$ ohms. Add these complex numbers to find the total impedance in the circuit. (Lesson 5-4) **$9 - 3j$ ohms**

CHAPTER 5 Mid-Chapter Quiz

Formative Assessment

Use the Mid-Chapter Quiz to assess students' progress in the first half of the chapter.

For problems answered incorrectly, have students review the lessons indicated in parentheses.

ExamView Assessment Suite Customize and create multiple versions of your Mid-Chapter Quiz and their answer keys.

FOLDABLES Follow-Up

Before students complete the Mid-Chapter Quiz, encourage them to review the information for Lessons 5-1 through 5-4 in their Foldables.

Additional Answers

1. y-intercept = −3; axis of symmetry $x = -2$; x-coordinate of vertex = −2; See p. 282 for graph.
7. Let x, be the first number. Then $7 - x$ is the other number. $x(7 - x) = 15$; $-x^2 + 7x - 15 = 0$. Since the graph of the related function does not intersect the x-axis, this equation has no real solutions. Therefore, no such numbers exist.

Intervention Planner

Tier 1 On Level	Tier 2 Strategic Intervention Approaching grade level	Tier 3 Intensive Intervention 2 or more grades below level
If students miss about 25% of the exercises or less,	**If** students miss about 50% of the exercises,	**If** students miss about 75% of the exercises,
Then choose a resource: **SE** Lessons 5-1–5-4 **CRM** Skills Practice, pp. 7, 13, 19, and 26 **TE** Chapter Project, p. 246	**Then** choose a resource: **CRM** Study Guide and Intervention, pp. 5, 11, 17, and 24 *Quick Review Math Handbook*	**Then** use *Math Triumphs, Alg. 2,* Chs. 1, 3, and 4
FL Math Online Self-Check Quiz	**FL Math Online** Extra Examples, Personal Tutor, Homework Help	**FL Math Online** Extra Examples, Personal Tutor, Homework Help, Review Vocabulary

5-5 Lesson Notes

1 FOCUS

Vertical Alignment

Before lesson 5-5
Factor perfect square trinomials.

Lesson 5-5
Solve quadratic equations by using the Square Root Property.
Solve quadratic equations by completing the square.

After Lesson 5-5
Solve quadratic equations using the Quadratic Formula.

2 TEACH

Scaffolding Questions

Have students read the *Why?* section of the lesson.

Ask:

- How are the equations $t^2 + 2t + 8 = 16$ and $t^2 + 2t + 1 = 9$ related? They are equivalent equations.
- What is the factored form of $t^2 + 2t + 1$? $(t + 1)^2$
- Would you expect the solution to the equation to be positive or negative? Why? positive; time is positive

5-5 Completing the Square

Then
You factored perfect square trinomials.
(Lesson 5-3)

Now
- Solve quadratic equations by using the Square Root Property.
- Solve quadratic equations by completing the square.

NGSSS
MA.912.A.7.3 Solve quadratic equations over the real numbers by completing the square.
MA.912.A.7.5 Solve quadratic equations over the complex number system.

New Vocabulary
completing the square

FL Math Online
glencoe.com

Why?

When going through a school zone, drivers must slow to a speed of 20 miles per hour. Once they are out of the school zone, the drivers can increase their speed.

Suppose Arturo is leaving school to go home for lunch, and he lives 5000 feet from the school zone. If Arturo accelerates at a constant rate of 8 feet per second squared, the equation $t^2 + 2t + 8 = 16$ represents the time t it takes him to reach home.

To solve this equation, you can use the Square Root Property.

Square Root Property You have solved equations like $x^2 - 25 = 0$ by factoring. You have also used the Square Root Property to solve such an equation. This method can be useful with equations like the one above that describes the car's speed. In this case, the quadratic equation contains a perfect square trinomial set equal to a constant.

EXAMPLE 1 Equation with Rational Roots

Solve $x^2 + 6x + 9 = 36$ by using the Square Root Property.

$x^2 + 6x + 9 = 36$	Original equation
$(x + 3)^2 = 36$	Factor the perfect square trinomial.
$x + 3 = \pm\sqrt{36}$	Square Root Property
$x + 3 = \pm 6$	$\sqrt{36} = 6$
$x = -3 \pm 6$	Subtract 3 from each side.
$x = -3 + 6$ or $x = -3 - 6$	Write as two equations.
$= 3$ $\quad = -9$	Simplify.

The solution set is $\{3, -9\}$.

CHECK Substitute both values into the original equation.

$x^2 + 6x + 9 = 36$	Original equation	$x^2 + 6x + 9 = 36$
$3^2 + 6(3) + 9 \stackrel{?}{=} 36$	Substitute 3 and −9.	$(-9)^2 + 6(-9) + 9 \stackrel{?}{=} 36$
$9 + 18 + 9 \stackrel{?}{=} 36$	Simplify.	$81 - 54 + 9 \stackrel{?}{=} 36$
$36 = 36$ ✓	Both solutions are correct.	$36 = 36$ ✓

Guided Practice

1. Solve each equation by using the Square Root Property.
   A. $x^2 - 12x + 36 = 25$ {1, 11} **B.** $x^2 - 16x + 64 = 49$ {1, 15}

Personal Tutor glencoe.com

Lesson 5-5 Resources

Resource	Approaching-Level	On-Level	Beyond-Level	English Learners
Teacher Edition	• Differentiated Instruction, p. 287	• Differentiated Instruction, pp. 287, 290	• Differentiated Instruction, p. 290	• Differentiated Instruction, p. 287
Chapter Resource Masters	• Study Guide and Intervention, pp. 30–31 • Skills Practice, p. 32 • Practice, p. 33 • Word Problem Practice, p. 34	• Study Guide and Intervention, pp. 30–31 • Skills Practice, p. 32 • Practice, p. 33 • Word Problem Practice, p. 34 • Enrichment, p. 35	• Practice, p. 33 • Word Problem Practice, p. 34 • Enrichment, p. 35	• Study Guide and Intervention, pp. 30–31 • Skills Practice, p. 32 • Practice, p. 33 • Word Problem Practice, p. 34
Transparencies	• 5-Minute Check Transparency 5-5	• 5-Minute Check Transparency 5-5	• 5-Minute Check Transparency 5-5	• 5-Minute Check Transparency 5-5
Other	• Study Notebook • Teaching Algebra with Manipulatives	• Study Notebook • Teaching Algebra with Manipulatives	• Study Notebook	• Study Notebook • Teaching Algebra with Manipulatives

Roots that are irrational numbers may be written as exact answers in radical form or as *approximate* answers in decimal form when a calculator is used.

StudyTip

Plus or Minus When using the Square Root Property, remember to put a $\pm$ sign before the radical.

EXAMPLE 2 Equation with Irrational Roots

Solve $x^2 - 10x + 25 = 27$ by using the Square Root Property.

$x^2 - 10x + 25 = 27$	**Original equation**
$(x - 5)^2 = 27$	**Factor the perfect square trinomial.**
$x - 5 = \pm\sqrt{27}$	**Square Root Property**
$x = 5 \pm 3\sqrt{3}$	**Add 5 to each side; $\sqrt{27} = 3\sqrt{3}$.**
$x = 5 + 3\sqrt{3}$ or $x = 5 - 3\sqrt{3}$	**Write as two equations.**
≈ 10.2 $\quad\quad \approx -0.2$	**Use a calculator.**

The exact solutions of this equation are $5 + 3\sqrt{3}$ and $5 - 3\sqrt{3}$. The approximate solutions are -0.2 and 10.2. Check these results by finding and graphing the related quadratic function.

$x^2 - 10x + 25 = 27$	**Original equation**
$x^2 - 10x - 2 = 0$	**Subtract 27 from each side.**
$y = x^2 - 10x - 2$	**Related quadratic function**

CHECK Use the ZERO function of a graphing calculator. The approximate zeros of the related function are -0.2 and 10.2.

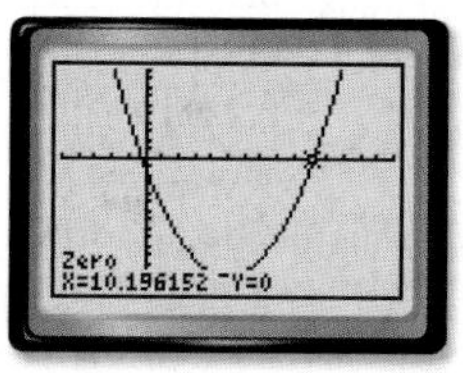

Guided Practice

2. Solve each equation by using the Square Root Property.

A. $x^2 + 8x + 16 = 20$ **{0.47, −8.47}** **B.** $x^2 - 6x + 9 = 32$ **{−2.66, 8.66}**

Personal Tutor glencoe.com

Complete the Square All quadratic equations can be solved using the Square Root Property by manipulating the equation until one side is a perfect square. This method is called **completing the square**.

Consider $x^2 + 16x = 9$. Remember to perform each operation on each side of the equation.

$x^2 + 16x + \blacksquare = 9$	**What value is needed for the perfect square?**
$x^2 + 16x + 64 = 9 + 64$	**$\left(\frac{16}{2}\right)^2 = 64$; add 64 to each side.**
$x^2 + 16x + 64 = 73$	**We can now use the Square Root Property.**
$(x + 8)^2 = 73$	**Square Root Property**

Use this pattern of coefficients to complete the square of a quadratic expression.

Square Root Property

Example 1 shows how to solve a quadratic equation using the Square Root Property. **Example 2** shows how to use the Square Root Property to solve a quadratic equation with irrational roots.

Formative Assessment

Use the Guided Practice exercises after each example to determine students' understanding of concepts.

Additional Examples

1 Solve $x^2 + 14x + 49 = 64$ by using the Square Root Property. $\{-15, 1\}$

2 Solve $x^2 - 4x + 4 = 13$ by using the Square Root Property. $\{2 \pm \sqrt{13}\}$

Additional Examples also in Interactive Classroom PowerPoint® Presentations

IWB INTERACTIVE WHITEBOARD READY

Watch Out!

Preventing Errors In Example 1, point out that both constants in the equation, 9 and 36, are perfect squares.

Watch Out!

Common Misconceptions Point out that the constant, 27, on the right side of the equation given in Example 2 is not a perfect square. Stress that this occurrence means the roots will be irrational numbers involving radicals. Also emphasize the use of the $\pm$ symbol in the step where the Square Root Property is utilized.

Focus on Mathematical Content

Completing the Square To complete the square for an expression of the form $x^2 + bx$, add the square of one half of the coefficient b to $x^2 + bx$. Written in symbols:

$x^2 + bx + \left(\frac{b}{2}\right)^2 = \left(x + \frac{b}{2}\right)^2$

TEACH with TECH

INTERACTIVE WHITEBOARD
Show a trinomial on the board where the constant term is c, and find the value that makes the trinomial a perfect square. Drag and copy the coefficient of x to a new line, and divide it by 2. Then drag and copy this quotient to a new line and square it. Take this result and drag it to replace c in the original trinomial.

Watch Out!

Preventing Errors When discussing the steps for completing the square, emphasize that the coefficient of the quadratic term must be 1.
Common Errors Remind students to think carefully about the difference between multiplying a quantity by 2 and squaring a quantity.

Additional Examples

3 Find the value of c that makes $x^2 + 12x + c$ a perfect square. Then write the trinomial as a perfect square. $36; (x + 6)^2$

4 Solve $x^2 + 4x - 12 = 0$ by completing the square. $\{-6, 2\}$

Key Concept — Completing the Square

Words To complete the square for any quadratic expression of the form $x^2 + bx$, follow the steps below.

Step 1 Find one half of b, the coefficient of x.
Step 2 Square the result in Step 1.
Step 3 Add the result of Step 2 to $x^2 + bx$.

Symbols $x^2 + bx + \left(\frac{b}{2}\right)^2 = \left(x + \frac{b}{2}\right)^2$

EXAMPLE 3 Complete the Square

Find the value of c that makes $x^2 + 16x + c$ a perfect square. Then write the trinomial as a perfect square.

Step 1 Find one half of 16. $\frac{16}{2} = 8$

Step 2 Square the result in Step 1. $8^2 = 64$

Step 3 Add the result of Step 2 to $x^2 + 16x$. $x^2 + 16x + 64$

The trinomial $x^2 + 16x + 64$ can be written as $(x + 8)^2$.

Guided Practice

3. Find the value of c that makes $x^2 - 14x + c$ a perfect square. Then write the trinomial as a perfect square. $49; (x - 7)^2$

Personal Tutor glencoe.com

You can solve any quadratic equation by completing the square. Because you are solving an equation, add the value you use to complete the square to each side.

EXAMPLE 4 Solve an Equation by Completing the Square

Solve $x^2 + 10x - 11 = 0$ by completing the square.

$x^2 + 10x - 11 = 0$	Notice that $x^2 + 10x - 11 = 0$ is not a perfect square.
$x^2 + 10x = 11$	Rewrite so the left side is of the form $x^2 + bx$.
$x^2 + 10x + 25 = 11 + 25$	Since $\left(\frac{10}{2}\right)^2 = 25$, add 25 to each side.
$(x + 5)^2 = 36$	Write the left side as a perfect square.
$x + 5 = \pm 6$	Square Root Property
$x = -5 \pm 6$	Subtract 5 from each side.
$x = -5 + 6$ or $x = -5 - 6$	Write as two equations.
$= 1$ $= -11$	Simplify.

The solution set is $\{-11, 1\}$. Check the result by using factoring.

Watch Out!
Each Side When solving equations by completing the square, don't forget to add $\left(\frac{b}{2}\right)^2$ to *each* side of the equation.

Guided Practice

4. Solve each equation by completing the square.

A. $x^2 - 10x + 24 = 0$ $\{4, 6\}$ **B.** $x^2 + 10x + 9 = 0$ $\{-9, -1\}$

Personal Tutor glencoe.com

When the coefficient of the quadratic term is not 1, you must divide the equation by that coefficient before completing the square.

EXAMPLE 5 **Equation with $a \neq 1$**

Solve $2x^2 - 7x + 5 = 0$ by completing the square.

$2x^2 - 7x + 5 = 0$	Notice that $2x^2 - 7x + 5 = 0$ is not a perfect square.
$x^2 - \frac{7}{2}x + \frac{5}{2} = 0$	Divide by the coefficient of the quadratic term, 2.
$x^2 - \frac{7}{2}x = -\frac{5}{2}$	Subtract $\frac{5}{2}$ from each side.
$x^2 - \frac{7}{2}x + \frac{49}{16} = -\frac{5}{2} + \frac{49}{16}$	Since $\left(-\frac{7}{2} \div 2\right)^2 = \frac{49}{16}$, add $\frac{49}{16}$ to each side.
$\left(x - \frac{7}{4}\right)^2 = \frac{9}{16}$	Write the left side as a perfect square by factoring. Simplify the right side.
$x - \frac{7}{4} = \pm\frac{3}{4}$	Square Root Property
$x = \frac{7}{4} \pm \frac{3}{4}$	Add $\frac{7}{4}$ to each side.
$x = \frac{7}{4} + \frac{3}{4}$ or $x = \frac{7}{4} - \frac{3}{4}$	Write as two equations.
$= \frac{5}{2}$ $\quad = 1$	

The solution set is $\left\{1, \frac{5}{2}\right\}$.

Guided Practice

5. Solve each equation by completing the square.

A. $3x^2 + 10x - 8 = 0$ $\left\{-4, \frac{2}{3}\right\}$ **B.** $3x^2 - 14x + 16 = 0$ $\left\{2, \frac{8}{3}\right\}$

Personal Tutor glencoe.com

Not all solutions of quadratic equations are real numbers. In some cases, the solutions are complex numbers of the form $a + bi$, where $b \neq 0$.

StudyTip

Check by Graphing A graph of the related function shows that the equation has no real solutions since the graph has no x-intercepts. Imaginary solutions must be checked algebraically by substituting them in the original equation.

EXAMPLE 6 **Equation with Imaginary Solutions**

Solve $x^2 + 8x + 22 = 0$ by completing the square.

$x^2 + 8x + 22 = 0$	Notice that $x^2 + 8x + 22$ is not a perfect square.
$x^2 + 8x = -22$	Rewrite so the left side is of the form $x^2 + bx$.
$x^2 + 8x + 16 = -22 + 16$	Since $\left(\frac{8}{2}\right)^2 = 16$, add 16 to each side.
$(x + 4)^2 = -6$	Write the left side as a perfect square.
$x + 4 = \pm\sqrt{-6}$	Square Root Property
$x + 4 = \pm i\sqrt{6}$	$\sqrt{-1} = i$
$x = -4 \pm i\sqrt{6}$	Subtract 4 from each side.

The solution set is $\{-4 + i\sqrt{6}, -4 - i\sqrt{6}\}$.

Guided Practice

6. Solve each equation by completing the square.

A. $x^2 + 2x + 2 = 0$ $\{-1 + i, -1 - i\}$ **B.** $x^2 - 6x + 25 = 0$ $\{3 + 4i, 3 - 4i\}$

Personal Tutor glencoe.com

Additional Examples

5 Solve $3x^2 - 2x - 1 = 0$ by completing the square. $\left\{-\frac{1}{3}, 1\right\}$

6 Solve $x^2 + 4x + 11 = 0$ by completing the square. $\{-2 \pm i\sqrt{7}\}$

Watch Out!

Preventing Misconceptions Some students may notice that the left side of the equation in Example 5 can be factored into the product of two binomials: $(2x - 5)(x - 1)$. Then the Zero Product Property can be used to obtain the same solutions. This is a good time to point out that more than one method of solution is often possible when solving a quadratic equation.

Complete the Square

Example 3 shows how to find a value for the constant in a quadratic expression so that the expression will be a perfect square. **Example 4** shows how to solve a quadratic equation by completing the square. **Example 5** shows how to solve a quadratic equation by completing the square when the coefficient of the quadratic term is not 1. **Example 6** shows how to solve a quadratic equation whose solutions are complex numbers of the form $a + bi$, where $b \neq 0$.

Differentiated Instruction

AL OL ELL

Verbal/Linguistic Learners Have students solve the equation $x^2 + 6x - 40 = 0$ by completing the square. Then have them discuss with a partner as many ways as they can to check their solutions.

3 PRACTICE

Formative Assessment

Use Exercises 1–13 to check for understanding.

Use the chart on the bottom of this page to customize assignments for your students.

Exercise Alert

For Exercise 57, students will need a straightedge and a compass.

Multiple Representations In Exercise 57, students use geometric constructions, algebra, a table of values, and logical analysis to investigate golden rectangles and the golden ratio.

4 ASSESS

Name the Math Prepare two paper bags containing pieces of paper: one containing equations that can be solved using the Square Root Property, and the other with equations to be solved by completing the square. Have each student select an equation from each bag. Then have students tell how to solve the equations.

Additional Answers

57c.

CQ	x
2	$1 + \sqrt{5}$
3	$\frac{3 + 3\sqrt{5}}{2}$
4	$2 + 2\sqrt{5}$

57d. Sample answer: the x-values are multiples of $\frac{1 + \sqrt{5}}{2}$; $x = \frac{n(1 + \sqrt{5})}{2}$

Check Your Understanding

Examples 1 and 2 pp. 284–285

Solve each equation by using the Square Root Property. Round to the nearest hundredth if necessary.

1. $x^2 + 12x + 36 = 6$ {−8.45, −3.55}
2. $x^2 - 8x + 16 = 13$ {0.39, 7.61}
3. $x^2 + 18x + 81 = 15$ {−12.87, −5.13}
4. $9x^2 + 30x + 25 = 11$ {−2.77, −0.56}
5. **LASER LIGHT SHOW** The area A in square feet of a projected laser light show is given by $A = 0.16d^2$, where d is the distance from the laser to the screen in feet. At what distance will the projected laser light show have an area of 100 square feet? 25 ft

Example 3 p. 286

Find the value of c that makes each trinomial a perfect square. Then write the trinomial as a perfect square.

6. $x^2 - 10x + c$ 25; $(x - 5)^2$
7. $x^2 - 5x + c$ 6.25; $(x - 2.5)^2$

Examples 4–6 pp. 286–287

Solve each equation by completing the square.

9. $\{2 - i\sqrt{5}, 2 + i\sqrt{5}\}$
10. {−0.69, 2.19}

8. $x^2 + 2x - 8 = 0$ {−4, 2}
9. $x^2 - 4x + 9 = 0$
10. $2x^2 - 3x - 3 = 0$
11. $2x^2 + 6x - 12 = 0$ {−4.37, 1.37}
12. $x^2 + 4x + 6 = 0$ $\{-2 - i\sqrt{2}, -2 + i\sqrt{2}\}$
13. $x^2 + 8x + 10 = 0$ {−6.45, −1.55}

Practice and Problem Solving

● = **Step-by-Step Solutions** begin on page R20.
Extra Practice begins on page 947.

Examples 1 and 2 pp. 284–285

Solve each equation by using the Square Root Property. Round to the nearest hundredth if necessary. 14. {−5.16, 1.16} 15. {−1.47, 7.47} 16. {−8.24, 0.24}

21. {4.67, 10.33}
31. {−4.61, 2.61}
34. $\left\{-\frac{3}{2}, 1\right\}$
35. $\left\{\frac{3 - i\sqrt{31}}{4}, \frac{3 + i\sqrt{31}}{4}\right\}$
36. $\left\{\frac{-5 - i\sqrt{31}}{4}, \frac{-5 + i\sqrt{31}}{4}\right\}$

14. $x^2 + 4x + 4 = 10$
15. $x^2 - 6x + 9 = 20$
16. $x^2 + 8x + 16 = 18$
17. $x^2 + 10x + 25 = 7$ {−7.65, −2.35}
18. $x^2 + 12x + 36 = 5$ {−8.24, −3.76}
19. $x^2 - 2x + 1 = 4$ {−1, 3}
20. $x^2 - 5x + 6.25 = 4$ {0.5, 4.5}
21. $x^2 - 15x + 56.25 = 8$
22. $x^2 + 32x + 256 = 1$ {−17, −15}
23. $x^2 - 3x + \frac{9}{4} = 6$ {−0.95, 3.95}
24. $x^2 + 7x + \frac{49}{4} = 4$ {−5.5, −1.5}
25. $x^2 - 9x + \frac{81}{4} = \frac{1}{4}$ {4, 5}

Example 3 p. 286

Find the value of c that makes each trinomial a perfect square. Then write the trinomial as a perfect square.

26. $x^2 + 8x + c$ 16; $(x + 4)^2$
27. $x^2 + 16x + c$ 64; $(x + 8)^2$
28. $x^2 - 11x + c$ $\frac{121}{4}$; $\left(x - \frac{11}{2}\right)^2$
29. $x^2 + 9x + c$ 20.25; $(x + 4.5)^2$

Examples 4–6 pp. 286–287

Solve each equation by completing the square. 30. $\{2 - 2i\sqrt{2}, 2 + 2i\sqrt{2}\}$

38. $\{1 - i\sqrt{2}, 1 + i\sqrt{2}\}$
39. $\{-2 - i\sqrt{7}, -2 + i\sqrt{7}\}$
40. $\{3 - 3i, 3 + 3i\}$
41. $\{5 - 2i, 5 + 2i\}$
42. {−0.39, 1.72}
43. $\left\{\frac{7 - i\sqrt{47}}{4}, \frac{7 + i\sqrt{47}}{4}\right\}$
44. {−0.71, 3.11}
45. $\{2.65 - i\sqrt{1.5775}, 2.65 + i\sqrt{1.5775}\}$

30. $x^2 - 4x + 12 = 0$
31. $x^2 + 2x - 12 = 0$
32. $x^2 + 6x + 8 = 0$ {−4, −2}
33. $x^2 - 4x + 3 = 0$ {1, 3}
34. $2x^2 + x - 3 = 0$
35. $2x^2 - 3x + 5 = 0$
36. $2x^2 + 5x + 7 = 0$
37. $3x^2 - 6x - 9 = 0$ {−1, 3}
38. $x^2 - 2x + 3 = 0$
39. $x^2 + 4x + 11 = 0$
40. $x^2 - 6x + 18 = 0$
41. $x^2 - 10x + 29 = 0$
42. $3x^2 - 4x = 2$
43. $2x^2 - 7x = -12$
44. $x^2 - 2.4x = 2.2$
45. $x^2 - 5.3x = -8.6$
46. $x^2 - \frac{1}{5}x - \frac{11}{5} = 0$ {−1.39, 1.59}
47. $x^2 - \frac{9}{2}x - \frac{24}{5} = 0$ {−0.89, 5.39}
48. **ARCHITECTURE** An architect's blueprints call for a dining room measuring 13 feet by 13 feet. The customer would like the dining room to be a square, but with an area of 250 square feet. How much will this add to the dimensions of the room? about 2.81 ft

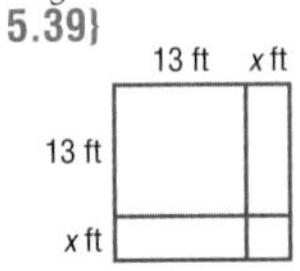

B **Solve each equation. Round to the nearest hundredth if necessary.**

49. $4x^2 - 28x + 49 = 5$ {2.38, 4.62}
50. $9x^2 + 30x + 25 = 11$ {−2.77, −0.56}
51. $x^2 + x + \frac{1}{3} = \frac{2}{3}$ {−1.26, 0.26}
52. $x^2 + 1.2x + 0.56 = 0.91$ {−1.44, 0.24}

Differentiated Homework Options

Level	Assignment	Two-Day Option	
AL Basic	14–48, 58, 60–83	15–47 odd, 63–66	14–48 even, 58, 60–62, 67–83
OL Core	15–57 odd, 58, 60–83	14–48, 63–66	49–58, 60–62, 67–83
BL Advanced	49–80, (optional: 81–83)		

Real-World Link

Each year, 250 to 300 million pounds of fireworks are used in the U.S.

Source: American Pyrotechnics Association

54. 0.1225; $(x + 0.35)^2$
55. 2.56; $(x - 1.6)^2$
56. $\frac{81}{100}$; $\left(x - \frac{9}{10}\right)^2$

57a.

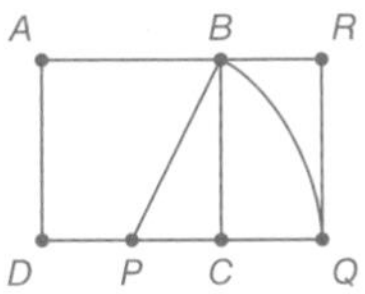

58. Alonso; Aida did not add 16 to each side; she added it only to the left side.

59. $x = \frac{-b}{2} \pm \sqrt{\frac{b^2}{4} - c}$

60. Since the expression is prime, the solutions cannot be obtained by factoring.

61. Sample answer: $x^2 - \frac{2}{3}x + \frac{1}{9} = \frac{1}{4}$; $\left\{\frac{5}{6}, -\frac{1}{6}\right\}$

62. Completing the square allows you to rewrite one side of a quadratic equation in the form of a perfect square. Once in this form, the equation can be solved by using the Square Root Property.

53. FIREWORKS A firework's distance d meters from the ground is given by $d = -1.5t^2 + 25t$, where t is the number of seconds after the firework has been lit.

a. How many seconds have passed since the firework was lit when the firework explodes if it explodes at the maximum height of its path? **$8\frac{1}{3}$ seconds**

b. What is the height of the firework when it explodes? **about 104.2 ft**

C

Find the value of c that makes each trinomial a perfect square. Then write the trinomial as a perfect square.

54. $x^2 + 0.7x + c$ **55.** $x^2 - 3.2x + c$ **56.** $x^2 - 1.8x + c$

57. MULTIPLE REPRESENTATIONS In this problem, you will use quadratic equations to investigate golden rectangles and the golden ratio.

a. **GEOMETRIC**

- Draw square $ABCD$.
- Locate the midpoint of $\overline{CD}$. Label the midpoint P.
- Draw $\overline{PB}$.
- Construct an arc with a radius of $\overline{PB}$ from B clockwise past the bottom of the square.
- Extend $\overline{CD}$ until it intersects the arc. Label this point Q.
- Construct rectangle $ARQD$.

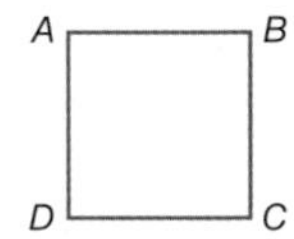

b. **ALGEBRAIC** Let $AD = x$ and $CQ = 1$. Use completing the square to solve $\frac{DQ}{AD} = \frac{QR}{CQ}$ for x. $x = \frac{1 + \sqrt{5}}{2}$

c. **TABULAR** Make a table of x and values for $CQ = 2$, 3, and 4. **See margin.**

d. **VERBAL** What do you notice about the x-values? Write an equation you could use to determine x for $CQ = n$, where n is a nonzero real number. **See margin.**

H.O.T. Problems

Use **H**igher-**O**rder **T**hinking Skills

58. ERROR ANALYSIS Alonso and Aida are solving $x^2 + 8x - 20 = 0$ by completing the square. Is either of them correct? Explain your reasoning.

Alonso	Aida
$x^2 + 8x - 20 = 0$	$x^2 + 8x - 20 = 0$
$x^2 + 8x = 20$	$x^2 + 8x = 20$
$x^2 + 8x + 16 = 20 + 16$	$x^2 + 8x + 16 = 20$
$(x + 4)^2 = 36$	$(x + 4)^2 = 20$
$x + 4 = \pm 6$	$x + 4 = \pm\sqrt{20}$
$x = -4 \pm 6$	$x = -4 \pm \sqrt{20}$

59. CHALLENGE Solve $x^2 + bx + c = 0$ by completing the square. Your answer will be an expression for x in terms of b and c.

60. REASONING Explain why certain quadratic equations such as $x^2 + 22x + 121 = 246$ cannot be solved by factoring.

61. OPEN ENDED Write a perfect square trinomial equation in which the linear coefficient is negative and the constant term is a fraction. Then solve the equation.

62. WRITING IN MATH Explain what it means to complete the square. Include a description of the steps you would take.

Study Guide and Intervention

CRM pp. 30–31 AL OL ELL

5-5 Study Guide and Intervention

Completing the Square

Square Root Property Use the Square Root Property to solve a quadratic equation that is in the form "perfect square trinomial = constant."

Example **Solve each equation by using the Square Root Property. Round to the nearest hundredth if necessary.**

a. $x^2 - 8x + 16 = 25$

$x^2 - 8x + 16 = 25$

$(x - 4)^2 = 25$

$x - 4 = \sqrt{25}$ or $x - 4 = -\sqrt{25}$

$x = 5 + 4 = 9$ or $x = -5 + 4 = -1$

The solution set is {9, −1}.

b. $4x^2 - 20x + 25 = 32$

$4x^2 - 20x + 25 = 32$

$(2x - 5)^2 = 32$

$2x - 5 = \sqrt{32}$ or $2x - 5 = -\sqrt{32}$

$2x - 5 = 4\sqrt{2}$ or $2x - 5 = -4\sqrt{2}$

$x = \frac{5 \pm 4\sqrt{2}}{2}$

The solution set is $\left\{\frac{5 \pm 4\sqrt{2}}{2}\right\}$.

Exercises

Solve each equation by using the Square Root Property. Round to the nearest hundredth if necessary.

1. $x^2 - 18x + 81 = 49$ **{2, 16}**
2. $x^2 + 20x + 100 = 64$ **{−2, −18}**
3. $4x^2 + 4x + 1 = 16$ $\left\{\frac{3}{2}, -\frac{5}{2}\right\}$
4. $36x^2 + 12x + 1 = 18$ $\left\{\frac{-1 \pm 3\sqrt{2}}{6}\right\}$
5. $9x^2 - 12x + 4 = 4$ $\left\{0, \frac{4}{3}\right\}$
6. $25x^2 + 40x + 16 = 28$ $\left\{\frac{-4 \pm 2\sqrt{7}}{5}\right\}$
7. $4x^2 - 28x + 49 = 64$ $\left\{\frac{15}{2}, -\frac{1}{2}\right\}$
8. $16x^2 + 24x + 9 = 81$ $\left\{\frac{3}{2}, -3\right\}$
9. $100x^2 - 60x + 9 = 121$ **−{0.8, 1.4}**
10. $25x^2 + 20x + 4 = 75$ $\left\{\frac{-2 \pm 5\sqrt{3}}{5}\right\}$
11. $36x^2 + 48x + 16 = 12$ $\left\{\frac{-2 \pm \sqrt{3}}{3}\right\}$
12. $25x^2 - 30x + 9 = 96$ $\left\{\frac{3 \pm 4\sqrt{6}}{5}\right\}$

Chapter 5 30 Glencoe Algebra 2

Practice

CRM p. 33 AL OL BL ELL

5-5 Practice

Completing the Square

Solve each equation by using the Square Root Property. Round to the nearest hundredth if necessary.

1. $x^2 + 8x + 16 = 1$ **−5, −3**
2. $x^2 + 6x + 9 = 1$ **−4, −2**
3. $x^2 + 10x + 25 = 16$ **−9, −1**
4. $x^2 - 14x + 49 = 9$ **4, 10**
5. $4x^2 + 12x + 9 = 4$ $-\frac{1}{2}, -\frac{5}{2}$
6. $x^2 - 8x + 16 = 8$ $4 \pm 2\sqrt{2}$
7. $x^2 - 6x + 9 = 5$ $3 \pm \sqrt{5}$
8. $x^2 - 2x + 1 = 2$ $1 \pm \sqrt{2}$
9. $9x^2 - 6x + 1 = 2$ $\frac{1 \pm \sqrt{2}}{3}$

Find the value of c that makes each trinomial a perfect square. Then write the trinomial as a perfect square.

10. $x^2 + 12x + c$ **36; $(x + 6)^2$**
11. $x^2 - 20x + c$ **100; $(x - 10)^2$**
12. $x^2 + 11x + c$ $\frac{121}{4}$; $\left(x + \frac{11}{2}\right)^2$
13. $x^2 + 0.8x + c$ **0.16; $(x + 0.4)^2$**
14. $x^2 - 2.2x + c$ **1.21; $(x - 1.1)^2$**
15. $x^2 - 0.36x + c$ **0.0324; $(x - 0.18)^2$**
16. $x^2 + \frac{5}{6}x + c$ $\frac{25}{144}$; $\left(x + \frac{5}{12}\right)^2$
17. $x^2 - \frac{1}{4}x + c$ $\frac{1}{64}$; $\left(x - \frac{1}{8}\right)^2$
18. $x^2 - \frac{5}{3}x + c$ $\frac{25}{36}$; $\left(x - \frac{5}{6}\right)^2$

Solve each equation by completing the square.

19. $x^2 + 6x + 8 = 0$ **−4, −2**
20. $3x^2 + x - 2 = 0$ $\frac{2}{3}, -1$
21. $3x^2 - 5x + 2 = 0$ $1, \frac{2}{3}$
22. $x^2 + 18 = 9x$ **6, 3**
23. $x^2 - 14x + 19 = 0$ $7 \pm \sqrt{30}$
24. $x^2 + 16x - 7 = 0$ $-8 \pm \sqrt{71}$
25. $2x^2 + 8x - 3 = 0$ $\frac{-4 \pm \sqrt{22}}{2}$
26. $x^2 + x - 5 = 0$ $\frac{-1 \pm \sqrt{21}}{2}$
27. $2x^2 - 10x + 5 = 0$ $\frac{5 \pm \sqrt{15}}{2}$
28. $x^2 + 3x + 6 = 0$ $\frac{-3 \pm i\sqrt{15}}{2}$
29. $2x^2 + 5x + 6 = 0$ $\frac{-5 \pm i\sqrt{23}}{4}$
30. $7x^2 + 6x + 2 = 0$ $\frac{-3 \pm i\sqrt{5}}{7}$

31. **GEOMETRY** When the dimensions of a cube are reduced by 4 inches on each side, the surface area of the new cube is 864 square inches. What were the dimensions of the original cube? **16 in. by 16 in. by 16 in.**

32. **INVESTMENTS** The amount of money A in an account in which P dollars are invested for 2 years is given by the formula $A = P(1 + r)^2$, where r is the interest rate compounded annually. If an investment of \$800 in the account grows to \$882 in two years, at what interest rate was it invested? **5%**

Lesson 5-5

Chapter 5 33 Glencoe Algebra 2

Word Problem Practice

CRM p. 34 AL OL BL ELL

5-5 Word Problem Practice

Completing the Square

1. **COMPLETING THE SQUARE** Samantha needs to solve the equation
$x^2 - 12x = 40.$
What must she do to each side of the equation to complete the square?
Add 36.

2. **ART** The area in square inches of the drawing *Foliage* by Paul Cézanne is approximated by the equation $y = x^2 - 40x + 396$. Complete the square and find the two roots, which are equal to the approximate length and width of the drawing.
18 inches by 22 inches

3. **COMPOUND INTEREST** Nikki invested \$1000 in a savings account with interest compounded annually. After two years the balance in the account is \$1210. Use the compound interest formula $A = P(1 + r)^t$ to find the annual interest rate.
10%

4. **REACTION TIME** Lauren was eating lunch when she saw her friend Jason approach. The room was crowded and Jason had to lift his tray to avoid obstacles. Suddenly, a glass on Jason's lunch tray tipped and fell off the tray. Lauren lunged forward and managed to catch the glass just before it hit the ground. The height h, in feet, of the glass t seconds after it was dropped is given by $h = -16t^2 + 4.5$. Lauren caught the glass when it was six inches off the ground. How long was the glass in the air before Lauren caught it?
0.5 second

5. **PARABOLAS** A parabola is modeled by $y = x^2 - 10x + 28$. Jane's homework problem requires that she find the vertex of the parabola. She uses the completing square method to express the function in the form $y = (x - h)^2 + k$, where (h, k) is the vertex of the parabola. Write the function in the form used by Jane.
$y = (x - 5)^2 + 3 = 0$

6. **AUDITORIUM SEATING** The seats in an auditorium are arranged in a square grid pattern. There are 45 rows and 45 columns of chairs. For a special concert, organizers decide to increase seating by adding n rows and n columns to make a square pattern of seating $45 + n$ seats on a side.

a. How many seats are there after the expansion?
$n^2 + 90n + 2025$

b. What is n if organizers wish to add 1000 seats?
10

c. If organizers do add 1000 seats, what is the seating capacity of the auditorium?
3025

Chapter 5 34 Glencoe Algebra 2

Watch Out!

Error Analysis For Exercise 58, remind students that when a number is added to one side of an equation, it must also be added to the other side to produce an equivalent equation.

Enrichment

CRM p. 35 OL BL

5-5 Enrichment

The Golden Quadratic Equations

A **golden rectangle** has the property that its length can be written as $a + b$, where a is the width of the rectangle and $\frac{a + b}{a} = \frac{a}{b}$. Any golden rectangle can be divided into a square and a smaller golden rectangle, as shown.

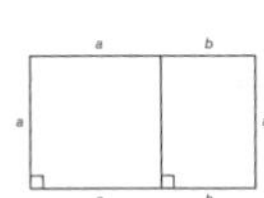

The proportion used to define golden rectangles can be used to derive two quadratic equations. These are sometimes called *golden quadratic equations.*

Solve each problem.

1. In the proportion for the golden rectangle, let a equal 1. Write the resulting quadratic equation and solve for b.
$b^2 + b - 1 = 0$
$b = \frac{-1 + \sqrt{5}}{2}$

2. In the proportion, let b equal 1. Write the resulting quadratic equation and solve for a.
$- 1 = 0$

Additional Answers

73a. Evening Matinee Twilight

$$\begin{matrix} \text{Adult} \\ \text{Child} \\ \text{Senior} \end{matrix} \begin{bmatrix} 7.50 & 5.50 & 3.75 \\ 4.50 & 4.50 & 3.75 \\ 5.50 & 5.50 & 3.75 \end{bmatrix}$$

74. 1 \$100, 3 \$50, and 6 \$20 checks

75.

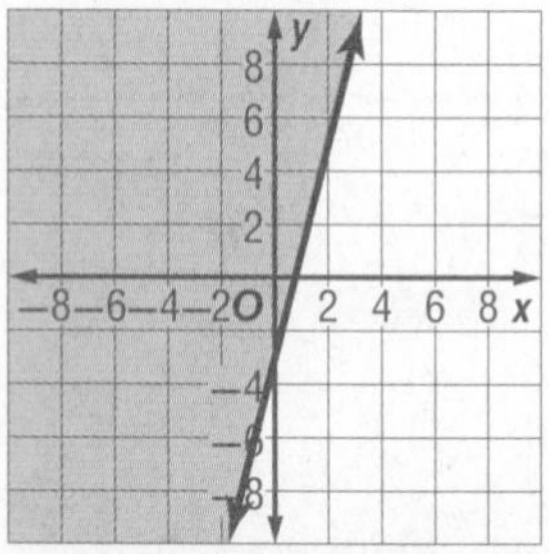

76.

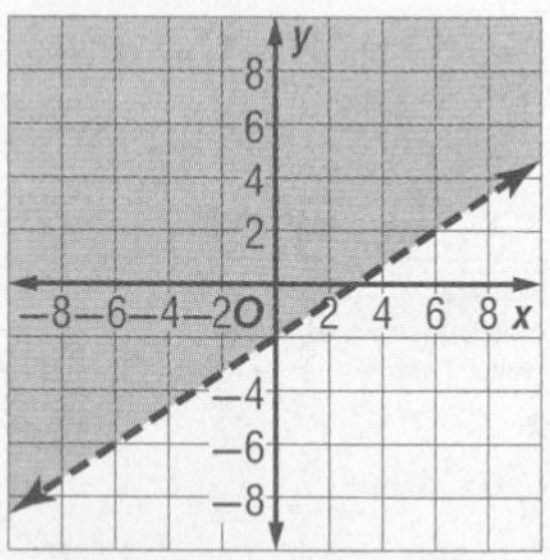

77.

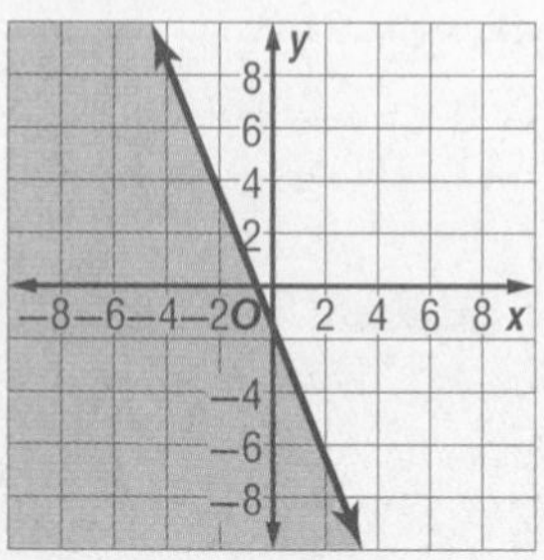

78. $y = \begin{cases} -4 \text{ if } x \leq -2 \\ -2x + 3 \text{ if } -2 < x < 1 \\ x - 5 \text{ if } x \geq 2 \end{cases}$

79. $y = \begin{cases} -8 \text{ if } x \leq -2 \\ 2x - 6 \text{ if } -2 < x \leq 5 \\ 2x - 18 \text{ if } x > 5 \end{cases}$

80. $y = \begin{cases} x + 12 \text{ if } x \leq -6 \\ 8 \text{ if } -6 < x < 2 \\ -2.5x + 15 \text{ if } x \geq 2 \end{cases}$

NGSSS PRACTICE 912.A.7.3, 912.G.2.5, 912.A.7.3, 912.A.7.5

63. SAT/ACT If $x^2 + y^2 = 2xy$, then y must equal **D**

A. -1 B. 1 C. $-x$ D. x

64. GEOMETRY Find the area of the shaded region. **H**

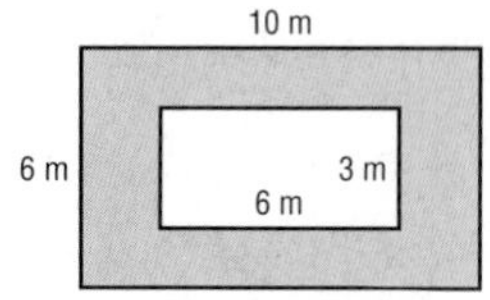

F. 14 m² G. 18 m² H. 42 m² I. 60 m²

65. SHORT RESPONSE What value of c should be used to solve the following equation by completing the square? **125**

$$5x^2 - 50x + c = 12 + c$$

66. If $5 - 3i$ is a solution for $x^2 + ax + b = 0$, where a and b are real numbers, what is the value of b? **C**

A. 10 C. 34
B. 14 D. 40

Spiral Review

Simplify. (Lesson 5-4)

67. $(8 + 5i)^2$ **$39 + 80i$**

68. $4(3 - i) + 6(2 - 5i)$ **$24 - 34i$**

69. $\frac{5 - 2i}{6 + 9i}$ **$\frac{4}{39} - \frac{19}{39}i$**

Write a quadratic equation in standard form with the given root(s). (Lesson 5-3)

70. $\frac{4}{5}, \frac{3}{4}$ **$20x^2 - 31x + 12 = 0$**

71. $-\frac{2}{5}, 6$ **$5x^2 - 28x - 12 = 0$**

72. $-\frac{1}{4}, -\frac{6}{7}$ **$28x^2 + 31x + 6 = 0$**

73. MOVIES Refer to the table. (Lesson 4-1)

a. Write a matrix for the prices of movie tickets for adults, children, and seniors. **See margin.**

b. What are the dimensions of the matrix? **3×3**

NOW PLAYING
Ticket Information
Evening Shows
Adult.......$7.50
Child.......$4.50
Senior......$5.50
Matinee Shows
Adult.......$5.50
Child.......$4.50
Senior......$5.50
Twilight Shows
All tickets....$3.75

74. TRAVEL Yoko is going with the Spanish Club to Costa Rica. She buys 10 traveler's checks in denominations of \$20, \$50, and \$100, totaling \$370. She has twice as many \$20 checks as \$50 checks. How many of each denomination of traveler's checks does she have? (Lesson 3-5) **See margin.**

Graph each inequality. (Lesson 2-8) **75–77. See margin.**

75. $y \geq 4x - 3$

76. $2x - 3y < 6$

77. $5x + 2y + 3 \leq 0$

Write the piecewise function shown in each graph. (Lesson 2-6) **78–80. See margin.**

78.

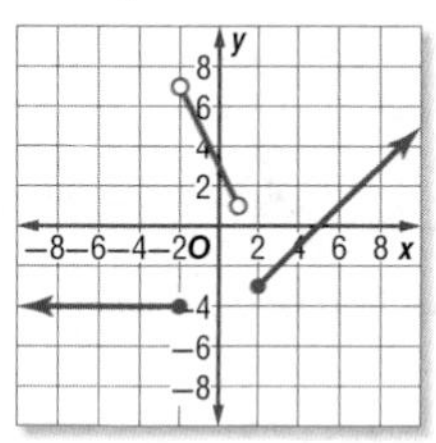

79.

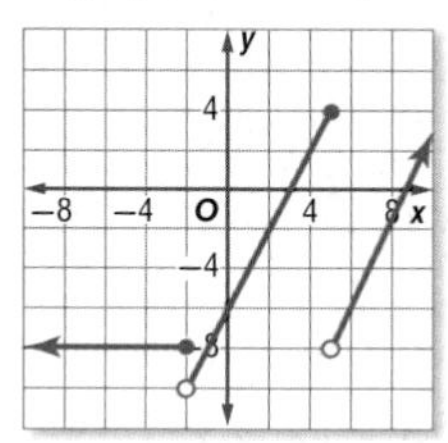

80.

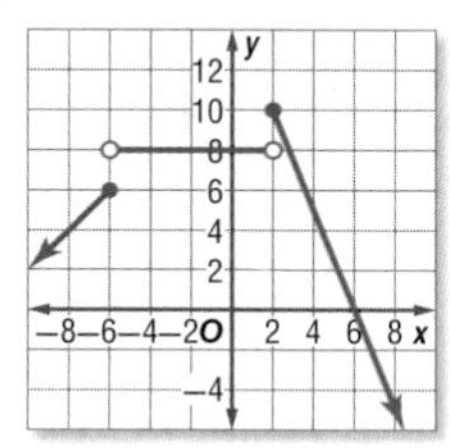

Skills Review

Evaluate $b^2 - 4ac$ for the given values of a, b, and c. (Lesson 1-2)

81. $a = 5, b = 6, c = 2$ **-4**

82. $a = -2, b = -7, c = 3$ **73**

83. $a = -5, b = -8, c = -10$ **-136**

Differentiated Instruction

OL BL

Extension Write $x^4 + 10x^2 + 25 = 49$ on the board. Explain that this is a quartic equation. Ask students to use what they have learned from this lesson to solve the equation for x. Point out that a quadratic equation (degree 2) has at most 2 solutions and a quartic equation (degree 4) has at most 4 solutions.

$$x^4 + 10x^2 + 25 = 49$$
$$(x^2 + 5)^2 = 49$$
$$x^2 + 5 = \pm\sqrt{49}$$
$$x^2 + 5 = \pm 7$$
$$x^2 = -5 \pm 7$$
$$x^2 = -12 \text{ or } x^2 = 2$$
$$x = \pm\sqrt{-12} \text{ or } x = \pm\sqrt{2}$$
$$x = \pm 2i\sqrt{3}, x = \pm\sqrt{2}$$

Graphing Technology Lab
Solving Quadratic Equations

FL Math Online glencoe.com
• Graphing Technology Personal Tutor

NGSSS MA.912.A.7.3 Solve quadratic equations over the real numbers by completing the square.

You can use a TI-Nspire™ CAS to solve quadratic equations.

ACTIVITY Finding Roots

Solve each equation.

a. $3x^2 - 4x + 1 = 0$

Step 1 From the Home screen, select **New Document**. Then select **Add Calculator**.

Step 2 Under menu, select **Algebra**, then select **Solve**.

Step 3 Enter the equation.

KEYSTROKES: 3 X x^2 − 4 X + 1 = 0 , X enter

The solutions are $x = \frac{1}{3}$ or $x = 1$.

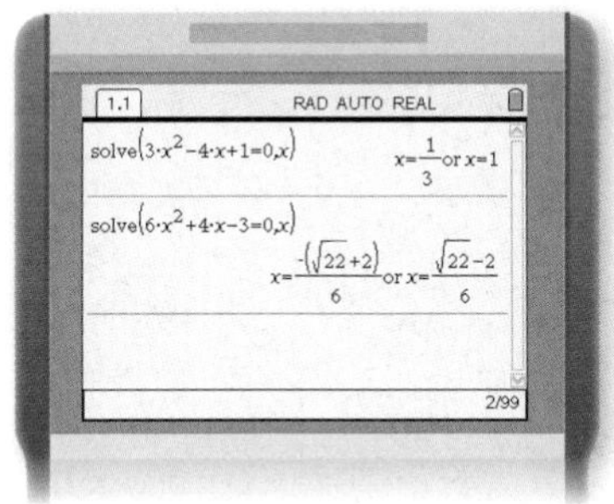

b. $6x^2 + 4x - 3 = 0$

Step 1 Under menu, select **Algebra**, then select **Solve**.

Step 2 Enter the equation.

KEYSTROKES: 6 X x^2 + 4 X − 3 = 0 , X enter

The solutions are $x = \frac{-2 \pm \sqrt{22}}{6}$.

c. $x^2 - 6x + 10 = 0$.

Step 1 Under menu, select **Algebra**, then select **Solve**.

Step 2 Enter the equation.

KEYSTROKES: X x^2 − 6 X + 10 = 0 , X enter

The calculator returns a value of *false*, meaning that there are no real solutions.

Step 3 Under menu, select **Algebra**, **Complex**, then **Solve**. Reenter the equation.

The solutions are $x = 3 \pm i$.

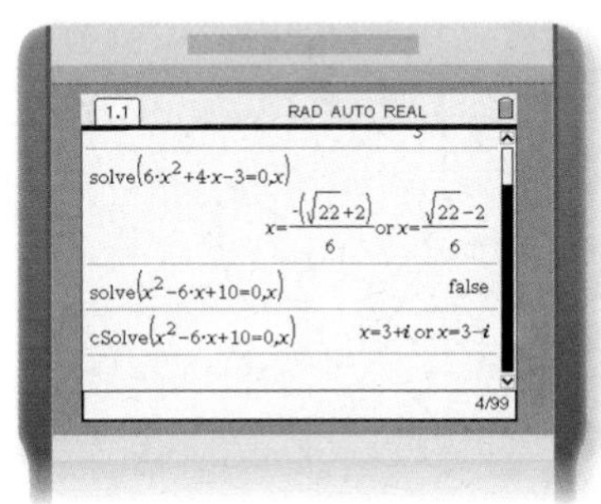

Exercises

Solve each equation.

1. $x^2 - 2x - 24 = 0$ **−4, 6**
2. $-x^2 + 4x - 1 = 0$ **$2 \pm \sqrt{3}$**
3. $0 = -3x^2 - 6x + 9$ **−3, 1**
4. $x^2 - 2x + 5 = 0$ **$1 \pm 2i$**
5. $0 = 4x^2 - 8$ **$\pm\sqrt{2}$**
6. $0 = 2x^2 - 4x + 1$ **$\frac{2 \pm \sqrt{2}}{2}$**
7. $x^2 + 3x + 8 = 5$ **$\frac{-3 \pm i\sqrt{3}}{2}$**
8. $25 + 4x^2 = -20x$ **$-\frac{5}{2}$**
9. $x^2 - x = -6$ **$\frac{1 \pm i\sqrt{23}}{2}$**

Extending the Concept

Ask:

- Do the signs of the numbers in a quadratic equation in standard form provide any clues as to whether its solutions are complex? Sample answer: If the coefficient of x^2 and the constant term are the same sign, the solutions might be complex.

EXTEND 5-5 Lesson Notes

1 FOCUS

Objective Use a calculator containing a computer algebra system to solve quadratic equations.

Materials for Each Student

- TI-Nspire CAS calculator

Teaching Tip

- The graphing calculator opens on the same screen as when it was turned off. Have students press the **Home** button to begin the lab.

2 TEACH

Working in Cooperative Groups

Have students work in groups of two or three, mixing abilities, to complete Activity and Exercises 1–3.

- The **X**'s indicated in the **KEYSTROKES** steps refer to the letter **X** key. Make sure that students do not mistake these for multiplication symbols, which are not needed in these examples.
- Solutions are displayed in exact form. To convert to decimal form: Under **menu**, select **Number,** then select **Convert to Decimal.**

Practice Have students complete Exercises 4–9.

3 ASSESS

Formative Assessment

Use Exercise 1 to assess whether students can correctly use menu selections and then solve the quadratic equation.

From Concrete to Abstract

The TI-Nspire can solve Exercises 7–9 without first writing equations in standard form ($ax^2 + bx + c = 0$).

5-6 Lesson Notes

1 FOCUS

Vertical Alignment

Before Lesson 5-6
Solve equations by completing the square.

Lesson 5-6
Solve quadratic equations by using the Quadratic Formula. Use the discriminant to determine the number and type of roots of a quadratic equation.

After Lesson 5-6
Solve quadratic inequalities using graphs and algebraic methods.

2 TEACH

Scaffolding Questions

Have students read the *Why?* section of the lesson.

Ask:

- As the value of t increases in this equation, what happens to the value of h? It increases then decreases.
- What shape does the graph of this equation have? a parabola
- Which way does the parabola open? downward

5-6 The Quadratic Formula and the Discriminant

Then
You solved equations by completing the square. (Lesson 5-5)

Now
- Solve quadratic equations by using the Quadratic Formula.
- Use the discriminant to determine the number and type of roots of a quadratic equation.

NGSSS
MA.912.A.7.4 Use the discriminant to determine the nature of the roots of a quadratic equation. MA.912.A.7.5 Solve quadratic equations over the complex number system. *Also addresses MA.912.A.10.3.*

New Vocabulary
Quadratic Formula
discriminant

FL Math Online
glencoe.com

Why?

Pumpkin catapult is an event in which a contestant builds a catapult and launches a pumpkin at a target.

The path of the pumpkin can be modeled by the quadratic function $h = -4.9t^2 + 117t + 42$, where h is the height of the pumpkin and t is the number of seconds.

To predict when the pumpkin will hit the target, you can solve the equation $0 = -4.9t^2 + 117t + 42$. This equation would be difficult to solve using factoring, graphing, or completing the square.

Quadratic Formula You have found solutions of some quadratic equations by graphing, by factoring, and by using the Square Root Property. There is also a formula that can be used to solve any quadratic equation. This formula can be derived by solving the standard form of a quadratic equation.

General Case		Specific Case
$ax^2 + bx + c = 0$	**Standard quadratic equation**	$2x^2 + 8x + 1 = 0$
$x^2 + \frac{b}{a}x + \frac{c}{a} = 0$	**Divide each side by *a*.**	$x^2 + 4x + \frac{1}{2} = 0$
$x^2 + \frac{b}{a}x = -\frac{c}{a}$	**Subtract $\frac{c}{a}$ from each side.**	$x^2 + 4x = -\frac{1}{2}$
$x^2 + \frac{b}{a}x + \frac{b^2}{4a^2} = -\frac{c}{a} + \frac{b^2}{4a^2}$	**Complete the square.**	$x^2 + 4x + \left(\frac{4}{2}\right)^2 = -\frac{1}{2} + \left(\frac{4}{2}\right)^2$
$\left(x + \frac{b}{2a}\right)^2 = -\frac{c}{a} + \frac{b^2}{4a^2}$	**Factor the left side.**	$(x + 2)^2 = -\frac{1}{2} + \left(\frac{4}{2}\right)^2$
$\left(x + \frac{b}{2a}\right)^2 = \frac{b^2 - 4ac}{4a^2}$	**Simplify the right side.**	$(x + 2)^2 = \frac{7}{2}$
$x + \frac{b}{2a} = \pm\frac{\sqrt{b^2 - 4ac}}{2a}$	**Square Root Property**	$x + 2 = \pm\sqrt{\frac{7}{2}}$
$x = -\frac{b}{2a} \pm \frac{\sqrt{b^2 - 4ac}}{2a}$	**Subtract $\frac{b}{2a}$ from each side.**	$x = -2 \pm \sqrt{\frac{7}{2}}$
$x = \frac{-b \pm \sqrt{b^2 - 4ac}}{2a}$	**Simplify.**	$x = \frac{-4 \pm \sqrt{14}}{2}$

The equation $x = \frac{-b \pm \sqrt{b^2 - 4ac}}{2a}$ is known as the **Quadratic Formula**.

Lesson 5-6 Resources

Resource	Approaching-Level	On-Level	Beyond-Level	English Learners
Teacher Edition	• Differentiated Instruction, p. 293	• Differentiated Instruction, pp. 293, 296	• Differentiated Instruction, p. 296	• Differentiated Instruction, p. 293
Chapter Resource Masters	• Study Guide and Intervention, pp. 36–37 • Skills Practice, p. 38 • Practice, p. 39 • Word Problem Practice, p. 40	• Study Guide and Intervention, pp. 36–37 • Skills Practice, p. 38 • Practice, p. 39 • Word Problem Practice, p. 40 • Enrichment, p. 41 • Spreadsheet Activity, p. 42	• Practice, p. 39 • Word Problem Practice, p. 40 • Enrichment, p. 41	• Study Guide and Intervention, pp. 36–37 • Skills Practice, p. 38 • Practice, p. 39 • Word Problem Practice, p. 40
Transparencies	• 5-Minute Check Transparency 5-6	• 5-Minute Check Transparency 5-6	• 5-Minute Check Transparency 5-6	• 5-Minute Check Transparency 5-6
Other	• Study Notebook	• Study Notebook	• Study Notebook	• Study Notebook

StudyTip

Quadratic Formula Although factoring may be an easier method to solve some of the equations, the Quadratic Formula can be used to solve any quadratic equation.

Key Concept — Quadratic Formula

Words The solutions of a quadratic equation of the form $ax^2 + bx + c = 0$, where $a \neq 0$, are given by the following formula.

$$x = \frac{-b \pm \sqrt{b^2 - 4ac}}{2a}$$

Example $x^2 + 5x + 6 = 0 \rightarrow x = \frac{-5 \pm \sqrt{5^2 - 4(1)(6)}}{2(1)}$

EXAMPLE 1 Two Rational Roots

Solve $x^2 - 10x = 11$ by using the Quadratic Formula.

First, write the equation in the form $ax^2 + bx + c = 0$ and identify a, b, and c.

$$x^2 - 10x = 11 \rightarrow \underset{\uparrow\, a}{1x^2} - \underset{\uparrow\, b}{10x} - \underset{\uparrow\, c}{11} = 0$$

Then, substitute these values into the Quadratic Formula.

$x = \frac{-b \pm \sqrt{b^2 - 4ac}}{2a}$	Quadratic Formula
$= \frac{-(-10) \pm \sqrt{(-10)^2 - 4(1)(-11)}}{2(1)}$	Replace a with 1, b with -10, and c with -11.
$= \frac{10 \pm \sqrt{100 + 44}}{2}$	Multiply.
$= \frac{10 \pm \sqrt{144}}{2}$	Simplify.
$= \frac{10 \pm 12}{2}$	$\sqrt{144} = 12$
$x = \frac{10 + 12}{2}$ or $x = \frac{10 - 12}{2}$	Write as two equations.
$= 11$ $\quad = -1$	Simplify.

The solutions are -1 and 11.

CHECK Substitute both values into the original equation.

$x^2 - 10x = 11$	$x^2 - 10x = 11$
$(-1)^2 - 10(-1) \stackrel{?}{=} 11$	$(11)^2 - 10(11) \stackrel{?}{=} 11$
$1 + 10 \stackrel{?}{=} 11$	$121 - 110 \stackrel{?}{=} 11$
$11 = 11$ ✓	$11 = 11$ ✓

Guided Practice

1. Solve each equation by using the Quadratic Formula.

A. $x^2 + 6x = 16$ $2, -8$ **B.** $2x^2 + 25x + 33 = 0$ $-11, -\frac{3}{2}$

Personal Tutor glencoe.com

Review Vocabulary

radicand the value underneath the radical symbol (Concepts and Skills Bank, Lesson 2)

When the value of the radicand in the Quadratic Formula is 0, the quadratic equation has exactly one rational root.

Quadratic Formula

Example 1 shows how to solve a quadratic equation using the Quadratic Formula. **Example 2** shows how to solve a quadratic equation when the radicand in the Quadratic Formula simplifies to 0. **Example 3** shows how to express irrational roots of a quadratic equation by writing them in radical form. **Example 4** shows how to solve a quadratic equation for complex solutions when the radicand in the Quadratic Formula simplifies to a negative value.

Formative Assessment

Use the Guided Practice exercises after each example to determine students' understanding of concepts.

Additional Example

1 Solve $x^2 - 8x = 33$ by using the Quadratic Formula. $\{-3, 11\}$

Additional Examples also in Interactive Classroom PowerPoint® Presentations

IWB INTERACTIVE WHITEBOARD READY

Focus on Mathematical Content

The Quadratic Formula Any quadratic equation written in the form $ax^2 + bx + c = 0$, where $a \neq 0$, can be solved using the Quadratic Formula. Substitute the values for a, b, and c into the Quadratic Formula to find the value(s) for x. The Quadratic Formula is $x = \frac{-b \pm \sqrt{b^2 - 4ac}}{2a}$ where $a \neq 0$.

Differentiated Instruction

AL OL ELL

If students substitute values into the Quadratic Formula incorrectly,

Then encourage students to write down the values of a, b, and c from the standard form of the quadratic equation before they begin substituting them into the formula.

Watch Out!

Common Misconceptions Some students may have commented that the equations in Examples 1 and 2 could have been solved by factoring. Before beginning Example 3, stress that many quadratic equations cannot be solved easily by factoring. State that the quadratic equation presented in Example 3 is such an equation. Emphasize that the Quadratic Formula provides a way to find the roots for *any* quadratic equation.

Additional Examples

2 Solve $x^2 - 34x + 289 = 0$ by using the Quadratic Formula. $\{17\}$

3 Solve $x^2 - 6x + 2 = 0$ by using the Quadratic Formula. $\{3 \pm \sqrt{7}\}$, or approximately 0.4 and 5.6

Math History Link

Brahmagupta (598–668) Indian mathematician Brahmagupta offered the first general solution of the quadratic equation $ax^2 + bx = c$, now know as the Quadratic Formula.

EXAMPLE 2 One Rational Root

Solve $x^2 + 8x + 16 = 0$ by using the Quadratic Formula.

Identify a, b, and c. Then, substitute these values into the Quadratic Formula.

$x = \dfrac{-b \pm \sqrt{b^2 - 4ac}}{2a}$	**Quadratic Formula**
$= \dfrac{-(8) \pm \sqrt{(8)^2 - 4(1)(16)}}{2(1)}$	**Replace *a* with 1, *b* with 8, and *c* with 16.**
$= \dfrac{-8 \pm \sqrt{0}}{2}$	**Simplify.**
$= \dfrac{-8}{2}$ or -4	$\sqrt{0} = 0$

The solution is -4.

CHECK A graph of the related function shows that there is one solution at $x = -4$.

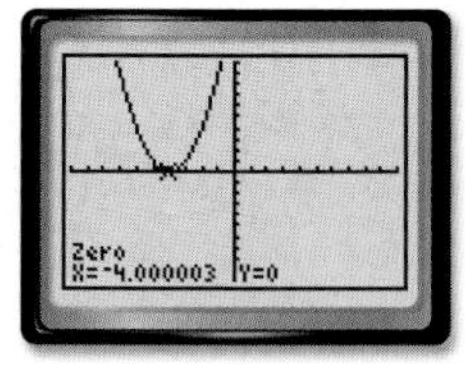

Guided Practice

2. Solve each equation by using the Quadratic Formula.

A. $x^2 - 16x + 64 = 0$ 8

B. $x^2 + 34x + 289 = 0$ -17

Personal Tutor glencoe.com

You can express irrational roots exactly by writing them in radical form.

EXAMPLE 3 Irrational Roots

Solve $2x^2 + 6x - 7 = 0$ by using the Quadratic Formula.

$x = \dfrac{-b \pm \sqrt{b^2 - 4ac}}{2a}$	**Quadratic Formula**
$= \dfrac{-(6) \pm \sqrt{(6)^2 - 4(2)(-7)}}{2(2)}$	**Replace *a* with 2, *b* with 6, and *c* with -7.**
$= \dfrac{-6 \pm \sqrt{92}}{4}$	**Simplify.**
$= \dfrac{-6 \pm 2\sqrt{23}}{4}$ or $\dfrac{-3 \pm \sqrt{23}}{2}$	$\sqrt{92} = \sqrt{4 \cdot 23}$ **or** $2\sqrt{23}$

The approximate solutions are -3.9 and 0.9.

CHECK Check these results by graphing the related quadratic function, $y = 2x^2 + 6x - 7$. Using the ZERO function of a graphing calculator, the approximate zeros of the related function are -3.9 and 0.9.

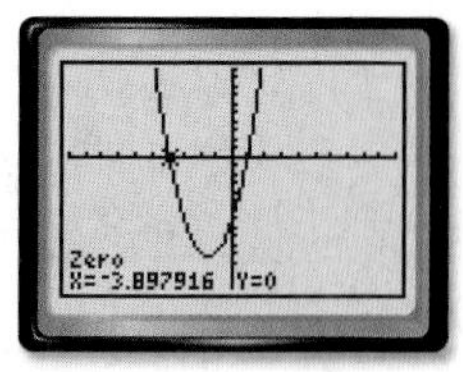

Guided Practice

3. Solve each equation by using the Quadratic Formula.

A. $3x^2 + 5x + 1 = 0$ $\dfrac{-5 \pm \sqrt{13}}{6}$

B. $x^2 - 8x + 9 = 0$ $4 \pm \sqrt{7}$

Personal Tutor glencoe.com

294 Chapter 5 Quadratic Functions and Relations

When using the Quadratic Formula, if the value of the radicand is negative, the solutions will be complex. Complex solutions always appear in conjugate pairs.

StudyTip

Complex Numbers Remember to write your solutions in the form $a + bi$, sometimes called the **standard form** of a complex number.

EXAMPLE 4 Complex Roots

Solve $x^2 - 6x = -10$ by using the Quadratic Formula.

$x = \frac{-b \pm \sqrt{b^2 - 4ac}}{2a}$	**Quadratic Formula**
$= \frac{-(-6) \pm \sqrt{(-6)^2 - 4(1)(10)}}{2(1)}$	**Replace a with 1, b with −6, and c with 10.**
$= \frac{6 \pm \sqrt{-4}}{2}$	**Simplify.**
$= \frac{6 \pm 2i}{2}$	**$\sqrt{-4} = \sqrt{4 \cdot (-1)}$ or $2i$**
$= 3 \pm i$	**Simplify.**

The solutions are the complex numbers $3 + i$ and $3 - i$.

CHECK A graph of the related function shows that the solutions are complex, but it cannot help you find them. To check complex solutions, substitute them into the original equation.

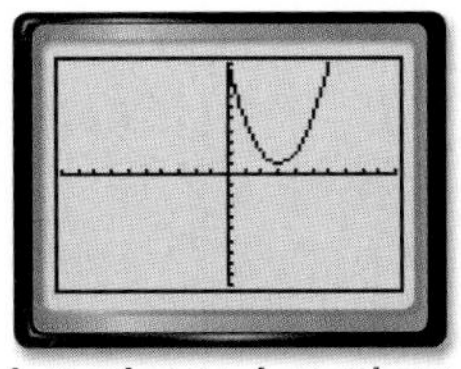

[−10, 10] scl: 1 by [−10, 10] scl: 1

$x^2 - 6x = -10$	**Original equation**
$(3 + i)^2 - 6(3 + i) \stackrel{?}{=} -10$	**$x = 3 + i$**
$9 + 6i + i^2 - 18 - 6i \stackrel{?}{=} -10$	**Square of a sum; Distributive Property**
$-9 + i^2 \stackrel{?}{=} -10$	**Simplify.**
$-9 - 1 = -10$ ✓	**$i^2 = -1$**
$x^2 - 6x = -10$	**Original equation**
$(3 - i)^2 - 6(3 - i) \stackrel{?}{=} -10$	**$x = 3 - i$**
$9 - 6i + i^2 - 18 + 6i \stackrel{?}{=} -10$	**Square of a sum; Distributive Property**
$-9 + i^2 \stackrel{?}{=} -10$	**Simplify.**
$-9 - 1 = -10$ ✓	**$i^2 = -1$**

Guided Practice

4. Solve each equation by using the Quadratic Formula.

A. $3x^2 + 5x + 4 = 0$ $\frac{-5 \pm i\sqrt{23}}{6}$ **B.** $x^2 - 4x = -13$ $2 \pm 3i$

Personal Tutor glencoe.com

Roots and the Discriminant In the previous examples, observe the relationship between the value of the expression under the radical and the roots of the quadratic equation. The expression $b^2 - 4ac$ is called the **discriminant**.

$$x = \frac{-b \pm \sqrt{b^2 - 4ac}}{2a} \leftarrow \text{discriminant}$$

The value of the discriminant can be used to determine the number and type of roots of a quadratic equation. The table on the following page summarizes the possible types of roots.

The discriminant can also be used to confirm the number and type of solutions after you solve the quadratic equation.

Additional Example

4 Solve $x^2 + 13 = 6x$ by using the Quadratic Formula. $\{3 \pm 2i\}$

Watch Out!

Preventing Errors Remind students that conjugate pairs are two complex numbers of the form $a + bi$ and $a - bi$.

Roots and the Discriminant

Example 5 shows how to find the value of the discriminant for a quadratic equation and use it to describe the number and type of roots for the equation.

Focus on Mathematical Content

Roots The value of the discriminant can be used to determine the number and type of roots of a quadratic equation. Consider a quadratic equation with rational coefficients. If the discriminant is a nonzero perfect square, there are 2 rational roots. If it is 0, there is 1 rational root. If it is positive, but not a perfect square, there are 2 irrational roots. If it is a negative number, there are 2 complex roots.

Lesson 5-6 The Quadratic Formula and the Discriminant 295

Additional Example

5 Find the value of the discriminant for each quadratic equation. Then describe the number and type of roots for the equation.

a. $x^2 + 3x + 5 = 0$ -11; two complex roots

b. $x^2 - 11x + 10 = 0$ 81; two rational roots

TEACH with TECH

STUDENT RESPONSE SYSTEM Give students a quadratic equation, and ask them to use the discriminant to determine the number of real roots for the equation. Have them respond with A for two complex roots, B for one real root, and C for two real roots.

StudyTip

Roots Remember that the solutions of an equation are called *roots* or *zeros* and are the value(s) where the graph crosses the *x*-axis.

Key Concept Discriminant

Consider $ax^2 + bx + c = 0$, where a, b, and c are real numbers and $a \neq 0$.

Value of Discriminant	Type and Number of Roots	Example of Graph of Related Function
$b^2 - 4ac > 0$; $b^2 - 4ac$ is a perfect square.	2 real, rational roots	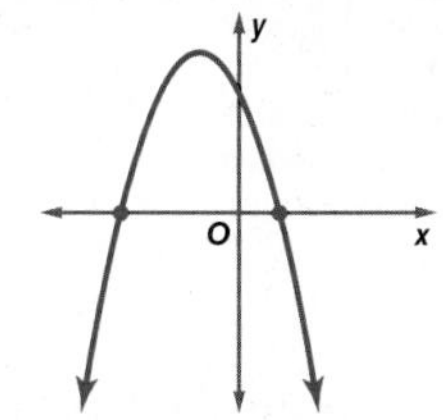
$b^2 - 4ac > 0$; $b^2 - 4ac$ is *not* a perfect square.	2 real, irrational roots	
$b^2 - 4ac = 0$	1 real root	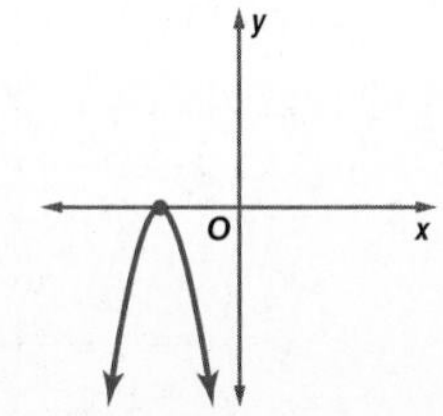
$b^2 - 4ac < 0$	2 complex roots	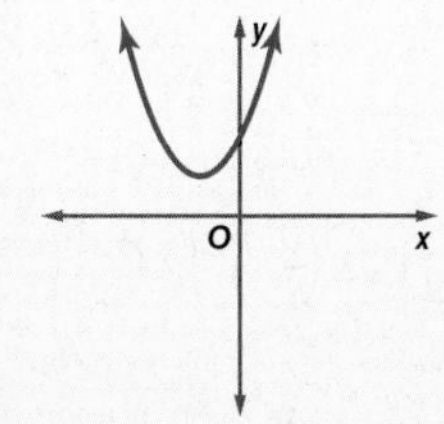

EXAMPLE 5 Describe Roots

Find the value of the discriminant for each quadratic equation. Then describe the number and type of roots for the equation.

a. $7x^2 - 11x + 5 = 0$

$a = 7, b = -11, c = 5$

$b^2 - 4ac = (-11)^2 - 4(7)(5)$
$= 121 - 140$
$= -19$

The discriminant is negative, so there are two complex roots.

b. $x^2 + 22x + 121 = 0$

$a = 1, b = 22, c = 121$

$b^2 - 4ac = (22)^2 - 4(1)(121)$
$= 484 - 484$
$= 0$

The discriminant is 0, so there is one rational root.

Guided Practice 5A. 44; 2 irrational roots 5B. 289; 2 rational roots

5A. $-5x^2 + 8x - 1 = 0$

5B. $-7x + 15x^2 - 4 = 0$

Personal Tutor glencoe.com

Differentiated Instruction OL BL

Extension Write $x^3 - 8 = 0$ on the board. Explain that this is a cubic equation. Ask students to use what they have learned from this lesson to solve this equation for x.
Point out that a quadratic equation (degree 2) has at most 2 solutions, while a cubic equation (degree 3) has at most 3 solutions.

$x^3 - 8 = 0$

$(x - 2)(x^2 + 2x + 4) = 0$

$x - 2 = 0$ or $(x^2 + 2x + 4) = 0$

$x = 2$ or $x = \dfrac{-2 \pm \sqrt{2^2 - 4(1)(4)}}{2(1)}$

$x = \dfrac{-2 \pm \sqrt{-12}}{2}$

$x = -1 \pm \boldsymbol{i}\sqrt{3}$

The solutions are $2, -1 + \boldsymbol{i}\sqrt{3}, -1 - \boldsymbol{i}\sqrt{3}$.

296 Chapter 5 Quadratic Functions and Relations

StudyTip

Study Notebook You may wish to copy this list of methods to your math notebook or Foldable to keep as a reference as you study.

You have studied a variety of methods for solving quadratic equations. The table below summarizes these methods.

Concept Summary — Solving Quadratic Equations

Method	Can be Used	When to Use
graphing	sometimes	Use only if an exact answer is not required. Best used to check the reasonableness of solutions found algebraically.
factoring	sometimes	Use if the constant term is 0 or if the factors are easily determined. **Example** $x^2 - 7x = 0$
Square Root Property	sometimes	Use for equations in which a perfect square is equal to a constant. **Example** $(x - 5)^2 = 18$
completing the square	always	Useful for equations of the form $x^2 + bx + c = 0$, where b is even. **Example** $x^2 + 6x - 14 = 0$
Quadratic Formula	always	Useful when other methods fail or are too tedious. **Example** $2.3x^2 - 1.8x + 9.7 = 0$

Check Your Understanding

3. $\frac{5 \pm \sqrt{57}}{8}$ 4. $\frac{-1 \pm \sqrt{5}}{3}$

Examples 1–4 pp. 293–295

1. $-6 \pm 3\sqrt{5}$
2. $-4 \pm \sqrt{11}$

Solve each equation by using the Quadratic Formula.

1. $x^2 + 12x - 9 = 0$
2. $x^2 + 8x + 5 = 0$
3. $4x^2 - 5x - 2 = 0$
4. $9x^2 + 6x - 4 = 0$
5. $10x^2 - 3 = 13x$ $(1.5, -0.2)$
6. $22x = 12x^2 + 6$ $\left(1.5, \frac{1}{3}\right)$
7. $-3x^2 + 4x = -8$ $\frac{2 \pm 2\sqrt{7}}{3}$
8. $x^2 + 3 = -6x + 8$ $-3 \pm \sqrt{14}$

Examples 3 and 4 pp. 294–295

9. **AMUSEMENT PARK** An amusement park ride takes riders to the top of a tower and drops them at speeds reaching 80 feet per second. A function that models this ride is $h = -16t^2 - 64t + 60$, where h is the height in feet and t is the time in seconds. About how many seconds does it take for riders to drop from 60 feet to 0 feet? about 0.78 seconds

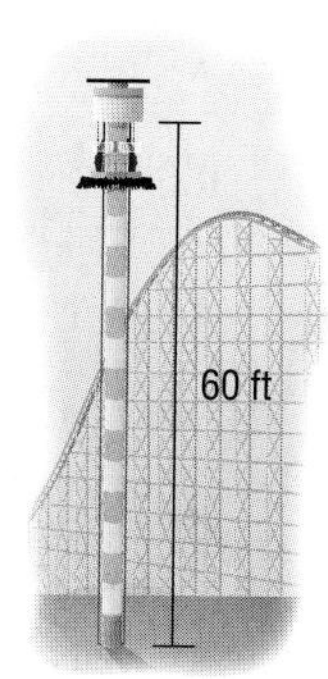

10a. 40
10b. 2 irrational roots
11a. −36
11b. 2 complex roots

Example 5 p. 296

12a. 0
12b. 1 rational root
13a. −76
13b. 2 complex roots

Complete parts a and b for each quadratic equation.

a. Find the value of the discriminant.

b. Describe the number and type of roots.

10. $3x^2 + 8x + 2 = 0$
11. $2x^2 - 6x + 9 = 0$
12. $-16x^2 + 8x - 1 = 0$
13. $5x^2 + 2x + 4 = 0$

3 PRACTICE

Formative Assessment

Use Exercises 1–13 to check for understanding.

Use the chart on the bottom of the next page to customize assignments for your students.

Tips for New Teachers

Sense-Making While the chart on this page offers suggestions for when to use each method to solve a quadratic equation, every student may not be able to analyze each equation and determine the best method to use to save time.

Lesson 5-6 The Quadratic Formula and the Discriminant 297

Watch Out!

Error Analysis For Exercise 43, remind students that a quadratic equation must be written in standard form $ax^2 + bx + c = 0$ before the discriminant can be identified.

Additional Answers

21a. 33

21b. 2 irrational

21c. $\frac{-3 \pm \sqrt{33}}{4}$

22a. 4

22b. 2 rational

22c. $\frac{1}{2}$, 1

23a. 49

23b. 2 rational

23c. $\frac{1}{6}$, −1

24a. 121

24b. 2 rational

24c. 1, $-\frac{5}{6}$

25a. −87

25b. 2 complex

25c. $\frac{3 \pm i\sqrt{87}}{6}$

26a. −40

26b. 2 complex

26c. $\frac{-2 \pm i\sqrt{10}}{2}$

27a. 36

27b. 2 rational

27c. 1, $-\frac{1}{5}$

28a. 0

28b. 1 rational

28c. 3

29a. 1

29b. 2 rational

29c. −1, $-\frac{4}{3}$

30a. 176

30b. 2 irrational

30c. $\frac{1 \pm \sqrt{11}}{4}$

Practice and Problem Solving

= **Step-by-Step Solutions** begin on page R20.
Extra Practice begins on page 947.

Examples 1–4 pp. 293–295

Solve each equation by using the Quadratic Formula.

14. $x^2 + 45x = -200$ **−5, −40**

15. $4x^2 - 6 = -12x$ $\frac{-3 \pm \sqrt{15}}{2}$

16. $3x^2 - 4x - 8 = -6$ $\frac{2 \pm \sqrt{10}}{3}$

17. $4x^2 - 9 = -7x - 4$ $\frac{-7 \pm \sqrt{129}}{8}$

18. $5x^2 - 9 = 11x$

19. $12x^2 + 9x - 2 = -17$ $\frac{-3 \pm i\sqrt{71}}{8}$

18. $\frac{11 \pm \sqrt{301}}{10}$

20. DIVING Competitors in the 10-meter platform diving competition jump upward and outward before diving into the pool below. The height h of a diver in meters above the pool after t seconds can be approximated by the equation $h = -4.9t^2 + 3t + 10$.

a. Determine a domain and range for which this function makes sense.

b. When will the diver hit the water? **about 1.77 seconds**

20a. $D = \{t \mid 0 \le t \le 2\}$, $R = \{h \mid 0 \le h \le 10\}$

Example 5 p. 296

Complete parts a–c for each quadratic equation.
a. Find the value of the discriminant.
b. Describe the number and type of roots.
c. Find the exact solutions by using the Quadratic Formula. **21–32. See margin.**

21. $2x^2 + 3x - 3 = 0$	**22.** $4x^2 - 6x + 2 = 0$	**23.** $6x^2 + 5x - 1 = 0$
24. $6x^2 - x - 5 = 0$	**25.** $3x^2 - 3x + 8 = 0$	**26.** $2x^2 + 4x + 7 = 0$
27. $-5x^2 + 4x + 1 = 0$	**28.** $x^2 - 6x = -9$	**29.** $-3x^2 - 7x + 2 = 6$
30. $-8x^2 + 5 = -4x$	**31.** $x^2 + 2x - 4 = -9$	**32.** $-6x^2 + 5 = -4x + 8$

B

33. VIDEO GAMES While Darnell is grounded his friend Jack brings him a video game. Darnell stands at his bedroom window, and Jack stands directly below the window. If Jack tosses a game cartridge to Darnell with an initial velocity of 35 feet per second, an equation for the height h feet of the cartridge after t seconds is $h = -16t^2 + 35t + 5$.

a. If the window is 25 feet above the ground, will Darnell have 0, 1, or 2 chances to catch the video game cartridge? **0**

b. If Darnell is unable to catch the video game cartridge, when will it hit the ground? **about 2.3 seconds**

34. ENGINEERING Civil engineers are designing a section of road that is going to dip below sea level. The road's curve can be modeled by the equation $y = 0.00005x^2 - 0.06x$, where x is the horizontal distance in feet between the points where the road is at sea level and y is the elevation. The engineers want to put stop signs at the locations where the elevation of the road is equal to sea level. At what horizontal distances will they place the stop signs? **0 ft and 1200 ft**

Complete parts a–c for each quadratic equation.
a. Find the value of the discriminant.
b. Describe the number and type of roots.
c. Find the exact solutions by using the Quadratic Formula.

35. $5x^2 + 8x = 0$	**36.** $8x^2 = -2x + 1$	**37.** $4x - 3 = -12x^2$
38. $0.8x^2 + 2.6x = -3.2$	**39.** $0.6x^2 + 1.4x = 4.8$	**40.** $-4x^2 + 12 = -6x - 8$

35a. 64
35b. 2 rational
35c. 0, $-\frac{8}{5}$
36a. 36
36b. 2 rational
36c. $\frac{1}{4}$, $-\frac{1}{2}$
37a. 160
37b. 2 irrational
37c. $\frac{-1 \pm \sqrt{10}}{6}$
38a. −3.48
38b. imaginary
38c. $\frac{-1.3 \pm i\sqrt{0.87}}{0.8}$
39a. 13.48
39b. 2 irrational
39c. $\frac{-0.7 \pm \sqrt{3.37}}{0.6}$
40a. 356
40b. 2 irrational
40c. $\frac{3 \pm \sqrt{89}}{4}$

Differentiated Homework Options

Level	Assignment	Two-Day Option	
AL Basic	14–32, 43, 45, 46, 48–63	15–31 odd, 49–52	14–32 even, 43, 45, 46, 48, 53–63
OL Core	15–33 odd, 34, 35–39 odd, 41–43, 45, 46, 48–63	14–32, 49–52	33–43, 45, 46, 48, 53–63
BL Advanced	33–60, (optional: 61–63)		

41c. 2017; Sample answer: No; the death rate from cancer will never be 0 unless a cure is found. If and when a cure will be found cannot be predicted.

Real-World Link

In 1965, 42% of American adults smoked, compared with fewer than 22% in 2003.

Source American Lung Association

43. Jonathan; you must first write the equation in the form $ax^2 + bx + c = 0$ to determine the values of a, b, and c. Therefore, the value of c is -7, not 7.

45a. Sample answer: Always; when a and c are opposite signs, then ac will always be negative and $-4ac$ will always be positive. Since b^2 will also always be positive, then $b^2 - 4ac$ represents the addition of two positive values, which will never be negative. Hence, the discriminant can never be negative and the solutions can never be imaginary.

45b. Sample answer: Sometimes; the roots will only be irrational if $b^2 - 4ac$ is not a perfect square.

41. SMOKING A decrease in smoking in the United States has resulted in lower death rates caused by lung cancer. The number of deaths per 100,000 people y can be approximated by $y = -0.26x^2 - 0.55x + 91.81$, where x represents the number of years after 2000.

Year	Deaths per 100,000
2000	91.9
2002	89.4
2004	85.3
2010	?
2015	?

a. Calculate the number of deaths per 100,000 people for 2010 and 2015. **60.31, 25.06**

b. Use the Quadratic Formula to solve for x when $y = 50$. **11.7**

c. According to the quadratic function, when will the death rate be 0 per 100,000? Do you think that this prediction is reasonable? Why or why not?

42. NUMBER THEORY The sum S of consecutive integers 1, 2, 3, …, n is given by the formula $S = \frac{1}{2}n(n + 1)$. How many consecutive integers, starting with 1, must be added to get a sum of 666? **36**

H.O.T. Problems

Use **H**igher-**O**rder **T**hinking Skills

44. $\frac{1 \pm 2i}{2}$

43. ERROR ANALYSIS Tama and Jonathan are determining the number of solutions of $3x^2 - 5x = 7$. Is either of them correct? Explain your reasoning.

Tama

$3x^2 - 5x = 7$

$b^2 - 4ac = (-5)^2 - 4(3)(7)$

$= -59$

Since the discriminant is negative, there are no real solutions.

Jonathan

$3x^2 - 5x = 7$

$3x^2 - 5x - 7 = 0$

$b^2 - 4ac = (-5)^2 - 4(3)(-7)$

$= 109$

Since the discriminant is positive, there are two real roots.

44. CHALLENGE Find the solutions of $4ix^2 - 4ix + 5i = 0$ by using the Quadratic Formula.

45. REASONING Determine whether each statement is *sometimes*, *always*, or *never* true. Explain your reasoning.

a. In a quadratic equation in standard form, if a and c are different signs, then the solutions will be real.

b. If the discriminant of a quadratic equation is greater than 1, the two roots are real irrational numbers.

46. OPEN ENDED Sketch the corresponding graph and state the number and type of roots for each of the following. **a–e. See Chapter 5 Answer Appendix.**

a. $b^2 - 4ac = 0$

b. A quadratic function in which $f(x)$ never equals zero.

c. A quadratic function in which $f(a) = 0$ and $f(b) = 0$; $a \neq b$.

d. The discriminant is less than zero.

e. a and b are both solutions and can be represented as fractions.

47. CHALLENGE Find the value(s) of m in the quadratic equation $x^2 + x + m + 1 = 0$ such that it has one solution. **−0.75**

48. WRITING IN MATH Describe three different ways to solve $x^2 - 2x - 15 = 0$. Which method do you prefer, and why? **See Chapter 5 Answer Appendix.**

Study Guide and Intervention

CRM pp. 36–37 AL OL ELL

5-6 Study Guide and Intervention

The Quadratic Formula and the Discriminant

Quadratic Formula The **Quadratic Formula** can be used to solve *any* quadratic equation once it is written in the form $ax^2 + bx + c = 0$.

Quadratic Formula	The solutions of $ax^2 + bx + c = 0$, with $a \neq 0$, are given by $x = \frac{-b \pm \sqrt{b^2 - 4ac}}{2a}$.

Example **Solve $x^2 - 5x = 14$ by using the Quadratic Formula.**

Rewrite the equation as $x^2 - 5x - 14 = 0$.

$x = \frac{-b \pm \sqrt{b^2 - 4ac}}{2a}$ Quadratic Formula

$= \frac{-(-5) \pm \sqrt{(-5)^2 - 4(1)(-14)}}{2(1)}$ Replace a with 1, b with −5, and c with −14.

$= \frac{5 \pm \sqrt{81}}{2}$ Simplify.

$= \frac{5 \pm 9}{2}$

$= 7$ or -2

The solutions are −2 and 7.

Exercises

Solve each equation by using the Quadratic Formula.

1. $x^2 + 2x - 35 = 0$ **5, −7**
2. $x^2 + 10x + 24 = 0$ **−4, −6**
3. $x^2 - 11x + 24 = 0$ **3, 8**
4. $4x^2 + 19x - 5 = 0$ $\frac{1}{4}, -5$
5. $14x^2 + 9x + 1 = 0$ $-\frac{1}{2}, -\frac{1}{7}$
6. $2x^2 - x - 15 = 0$ $3, -\frac{5}{2}$
7. $3x^2 + 5x = 2$ $-2, \frac{1}{3}$
8. $2y^2 + y - 15 = 0$ $\frac{5}{2}, -3$
9. $3x^2 - 16x + 16 = 0$ $4, \frac{4}{3}$
10. $8x^2 + 6x - 9 = 0$ $-\frac{3}{2}, \frac{3}{4}$
11. $r^2 - \frac{3r}{5} + \frac{2}{25} = 0$ $\frac{2}{5}, \frac{1}{5}$
12. $x^2 - 10x - 50 = 0$ $5 \pm 5\sqrt{3}$
13. $x^2 + 6x - 23 = 0$ $-3 \pm 4\sqrt{2}$
14. $4x^2 - 12x - 63 = 0$ $\frac{3 \pm 6\sqrt{2}}{2}$
15. $x^2 - 6x + 21 = 0$ $3 \pm 2i\sqrt{3}$

Chapter 5 36 Glencoe Algebra 2

Practice

CRM p. 39 AL OL BL ELL

5-6 Practice

The Quadratic Formula and the Discriminant

Solve each equation by using the Quadratic Formula.

1. $7x^2 - 5x = 0$ $0, \frac{5}{7}$
2. $4x^2 - 9 = 0$ $\pm\frac{3}{2}$
3. $3x^2 + 8x = 3$ $\frac{1}{3}, -3$
4. $x^2 - 21 = 4x$ **−3, 7**
5. $3x^2 - 13x + 4 = 0$ $\frac{1}{3}, 4$
6. $15x^2 + 22x = -8$ $-\frac{2}{3}, -\frac{4}{5}$
7. $x^2 - 6x + 3 = 0$ $3 \pm \sqrt{6}$
8. $x^2 - 14x + 53 = 0$ $7 \pm 2i$
9. $3x^2 = -54$ $\pm 3i\sqrt{2}$
10. $25x^2 - 20x - 6 = 0$ $\frac{2 \pm \sqrt{10}}{5}$
11. $4x^2 - 4x + 17 = 0$ $\frac{1 \pm 4i}{2}$
12. $8x - 1 = 4x^2$ $\frac{2 \pm \sqrt{3}}{2}$
13. $x^2 = 4x - 15$ $2 \pm i\sqrt{11}$
14. $4x^2 - 12x + 7 = 0$ $\frac{3 \pm \sqrt{2}}{2}$

Complete parts a–c for each quadratic equation.
a. Find the value of the discriminant.
b. Describe the number and type of roots.
c. Find the exact solutions by using the Quadratic Formula.

15. $x^2 - 16x + 64 = 0$ **0; 1 rational; 8**
16. $x^2 = 3x$ **9; 2 rational; 0, 3**
17. $9x^2 - 24x + 16 = 0$ **0; 1 rational;** $\frac{4}{3}$
18. $x^2 - 3x = 40$ **169; 2 rational; −5, 8**
19. $3x^2 + 9x - 2 = 0$ **2 irrational;** $\frac{-9 \pm \sqrt{105}}{6}$
20. $2x^2 + 7x = 0$ **49; 2 rational;** $0, -\frac{7}{2}$
21. $5x^2 - 2x + 4 = 0$ **2 complex;** $\frac{1 \pm i\sqrt{19}}{5}$
22. $12x^2 - x - 6 = 0$ **2 rational;** $\frac{3}{4}, -\frac{2}{3}$
23. $7x^2 + 6x + 2 = 0$ **2 complex;** $\frac{-3 \pm i\sqrt{5}}{7}$
24. $12x^2 + 2x - 4 = 0$ **2 rational;** $\frac{1}{2}, -\frac{2}{3}$
25. $6x^2 - 2x - 1 = 0$ **2 irrational;** $\frac{1 \pm \sqrt{7}}{6}$
26. $x^2 + 3x + 6 = 0$ **2 complex;** $\frac{-3 \pm i\sqrt{15}}{2}$
27. $4x^2 - 3x^2 - 6 = 0$ **2 irrational;** $\frac{3 \pm \sqrt{105}}{8}$
28. $16x^2 - 8x + 1 = 0$ **0; 1 rational;** $\frac{1}{4}$
29. $2x^2 - 5x - 6 = 0$ **2 irrational;** $\frac{5 \pm \sqrt{73}}{4}$

30. **GRAVITATION** The height $h(t)$ in feet of an object t seconds after it is propelled straight up from the ground with an initial velocity of 60 feet per second is modeled by the equation $h(t) = -16t^2 + 60t$. At what times will the object be at a height of 56 feet? **1.75 s, 2 s**

31. **STOPPING DISTANCE** The formula $d = 0.05s^2 + 1.1s$ estimates the minimum stopping distance d in feet for a car traveling s miles per hour. If a car stops in 200 feet, what is the fastest it could have been traveling when the driver applied the brakes? **about 53.2 mi/h**

Lesson 5-6

Chapter 5 39 Glencoe Algebra 2

Word Problem Practice

CRM p. 40 AL OL BL ELL

5-6 Word Problem Practice

The Quadratic Formula and the Discriminant

1. **PARABOLAS** The graph of a quadratic equation of the form $y = ax^2 + bx + c$ is shown below.

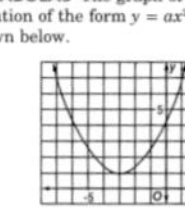

Is the discriminant $b^2 - 4ac$ positive, negative, or zero?
negative

2. **TANGENT** Kathleen is trying to find b so that the x-axis is tangent to the parabola $y = x^2 + bx + 4$. She finds one value that works, $b = 4$. Is this the only value that works? Explain.
No, $b = -4$ also works; the x-axis will be tangent when the discriminant $b^2 - 16$ is zero. This happens when $b = 4$ or -4.

3. **SPORTS** In 1990, American Randy Barnes set the world record for the shot put. His throw can be described by the equation $y = -16x^2 + 368x$. Use the Quadratic Formula to find how far his throw was to the nearest foot.
23 ft

4. **EXAMPLES** Give an example of a quadratic function $f(x)$ that has the following properties.

I. The discriminant of f is zero.

II. There is no real solution of the equation $f(x) = 10$.

Sketch the graph of $x = f(x)$.
Sample answer: $f(x) = -x^2$

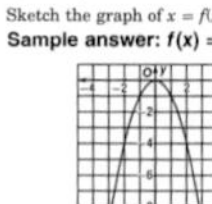

5. **TANGENTS** The graph of $y = x^2$ is a parabola that passes through the point at (1, 1). The line $y = mx - m + 1$, where m is a constant, also passes through the point at (1, 1).

a. To find the points of intersection between the line $y = mx - m + 1$ and the parabola $y = x^2$, set $x^2 = mx - m + 1$ and then solve for x. Rearranging terms, this equation becomes $x^2 - mx + m - 1 = 0$. What is the discriminant of this equation?
$x^2 - 4m + 4$

b. For what value of m is there only one point of intersection? Explain the meaning of this in terms of the corresponding line and the parabola.
$m = 2$; the parabola $y = x^2$ and the line $y = 2x - 1$ have exactly one point of intersection at (1, 1). In other words, this line is tangent to the parabola at (1, 1).

Chapter 5 40 Glencoe Algebra 2

Additional Answers

31a. −16

31b. 2 complex

31c. $-1 \pm 2i$

32a. −56

32b. 2 complex

32c. $\frac{2 \pm i\sqrt{14}}{6}$

Enrichment

CRM p. 41 OL BL

5-6 Enrichment

Sum and Product of Roots

Sometimes you may know the roots of a quadratic equation without knowing the equation itself. Using your knowledge of factoring to solve an equation, you can work backward to find the quadratic equation. The rule for finding the sum and product of roots is as follows:

Sum and Product of Roots	If the roots of $ax^2 + bx + c = 0$, with $a \neq 0$, are s_1 and s_2, then $s_1 + s_2 = -\frac{a}{b}$ and $s_1 \cdot s_2 = \frac{c}{a}$.

Example **Write a quadratic equation that has the roots 3 and −8.**

The roots are $x = 3$ and $x = -8$.

$3 + (-8) = -5$ Add the roots.

$3(-8) = -24$ Multiply the roots.

Equation: $x^2 + 5x - 24 = 0$

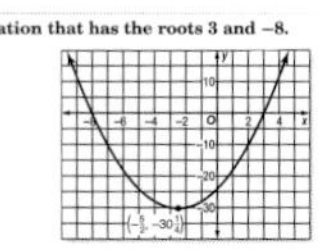

Lesson 5-6

4 ASSESS

Yesterday's News Ask students to write how an earlier lesson on simplifying radical expressions helped them with today's lesson.

Formative Assessment

Check for student understanding of concepts in Lessons 5-5 and 5-6.

CRM Quiz 3, p. 60

Additional Answers

60a. $I = \begin{bmatrix} 290 & 165 & 210 \\ 175 & 240 & 190 \\ 110 & 75 & 0 \end{bmatrix}, C = \begin{bmatrix} 22 \\ 25 \\ 18 \end{bmatrix}$

60b. $\begin{bmatrix} 14{,}285 \\ 13{,}270 \\ 4295 \end{bmatrix}$

NGSSS PRACTICE 912.A.7.5, 912.S.3.3, 912.G.6.5, 912.A.3.1

49. A company determined that its monthly profit P is given by $P = -8x^2 + 165x - 100$, where x is the selling price for each unit of product. Which of the following is the best estimate of the maximum price per unit that the company can charge without losing money? **B**

A. \$10 B. \$20 C. \$30 D. \$40

50. SAT/ACT For which of the following sets of numbers is the mean greater than the median? **H**

F. {4, 5, 6, 7, 8}
G. {4, 6, 6, 6, 8}
H. {4, 5, 6, 7, 9}
I. {3, 5, 6, 7, 8}

51. THINK SOLVE EXPLAIN **SHORT RESPONSE** In the figure below, P is the center of the circle with radius 15 inches. What is the area of $\triangle APB$? **112.5 in^2**

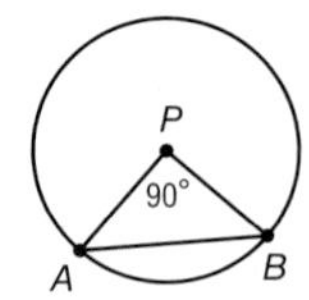

52. 75% of 88 is the same as 60% of what number? **D**

A. 100 B. 101 C. 108 D. 110

Spiral Review

Find the value of c that makes each trinomial a perfect square. Then write the trinomial as a perfect square. (Lesson 5-5)

53. $x^2 + 13x + c$ **42.25; $(x + 6.5)^2$**

54. $x^2 + 2.4x + c$ **1.44; $(x + 1.2)^2$**

55. $x^2 + \frac{4}{5}x + c$ **$\frac{4}{25}$; $\left(x + \frac{2}{5}\right)^2$**

Simplify. (Lesson 5-4)

56. i^{26} **−1**

57. $\sqrt{-16}$ **$4i$**

58. $4\sqrt{-9} \cdot 2\sqrt{-25}$ **−120**

59. PILOT TRAINING Evita is training for her pilot's license. Flight instruction costs \$105 per hour, and the simulator costs \$45 per hour. She spent 4 more hours in airplane training than in the simulator. If Evita spent \$3870, how much time did she spend training in an airplane and in a simulator? (Lesson 4-6) **27 hours of flight instruction and 23 hours in the simulator**

60. BUSINESS Ms. Larson owns three fruit farms on which she grows apples, peaches, and apricots. She sells apples for \$22 a case, peaches for \$25 a case, and apricots for \$18 a case. (Lesson 4-3) **a, b. See margin.**

Number of Cases in Stock of Each Type of Fruit

Fruit	Farm 1	Farm 2	Farm 3
apples	290	175	110
peaches	165	240	75
apricots	210	190	0

a. Write an inventory matrix for the number of cases for each type of fruit for each farm and a cost matrix for the price per case for each type of fruit.

b. Find the total income of the three fruit farms expressed as a matrix.

c. What is the total income from all three fruit farms? **\$31,850**

Skills Review

Write an equation for each graph. (Lesson 2-7) **63. $y = |x + 3|$**

61.

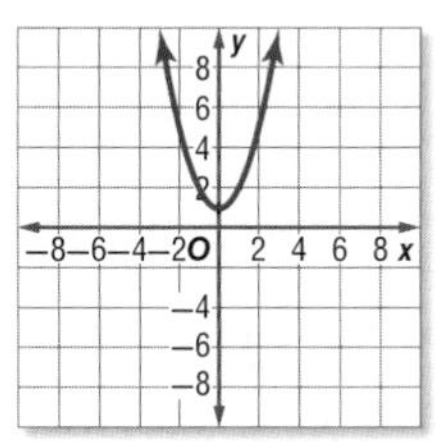

$y = x^2 + 1$

62.

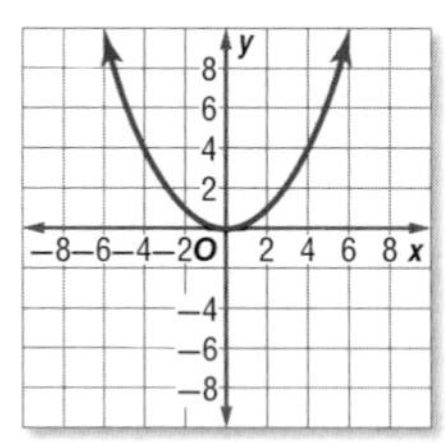

$y = 0.25x^2$

63.

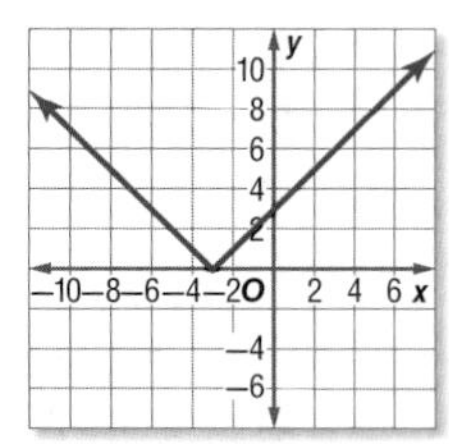

300 Chapter 5 Quadratic Functions and Relations

Algebra Lab
Sums and Products of Roots

Objective
Use sums and products of roots to write quadratic equations.

NGSSS
MA.912.A.4.7 Write a polynomial equation for a given set of real and/or complex roots.

If you know the roots of a quadratic equation, you can use the sum and product of the roots to determine the equation.

Write a quadratic equation that has roots 3 and −8.

When you factored quadratic equations, you used the Zero Product Property to determine the roots. You can use the roots and work backward to find the equation.

$x = 3$ or $x = -8$		**Start with the solutions.**
$x - 3 = 0$	$x + 8 = 0$	**Rewrite equations equal to 0.**
$(x - 3)(x + 8) = 0$		**Multiplicative Property of Zero**
$x^2 + 5x - 24 = 0$		**Multiply.**

The equation $x^2 + 5x - 24 = 0$ has roots 3 and −8 and is written in standard form. The sum and product of the roots can also be used to determine the equation.

Add the roots. $3 + (-8) = -5$ **−5 is the opposite of the coefficient of x.**

$$x^2 + 5x - 24 = 0$$

Multiply the roots. $3(-8) = -24$ **−24 is the constant term.**

The pattern above can be generalized for any quadratic equation by using the Quadratic Formula. Let r_1 and r_2 represent the roots of a quadratic equation.

$$r_1 = \frac{-b + \sqrt{b^2 - 4ac}}{2a} \qquad r_2 = \frac{-b - \sqrt{b^2 - 4ac}}{2a}$$

Add the roots.

$$r_1 + r_2 = \frac{-b + \sqrt{b^2 - 4ac}}{2a} + \frac{-b - \sqrt{b^2 - 4ac}}{2a} \quad \textbf{Add the roots.}$$

$$= \frac{-2b + 0}{2a} \text{ or } -\frac{b}{a} \quad \textbf{Simplify.}$$

The sum of the roots is $-\frac{b}{a}$.

Multiply the roots.

$$r_1 \cdot r_2 = \frac{-b + \sqrt{b^2 - 4ac}}{2a} \cdot \frac{-b - \sqrt{b^2 - 4ac}}{2a} \quad \textbf{Multiply the roots.}$$

$$= \frac{b^2 - (b^2 - 4ac)}{4a^2} \quad \textbf{Multiply.}$$

$$= \frac{b^2 - b^2 + 4ac)}{4a^2} \quad \textbf{Distributive Property}$$

$$= \frac{4ac}{4a^2} \text{ or } \frac{c}{a} \quad \textbf{Simplify.}$$

The product of the roots is $\frac{c}{a}$.

The following rule can be used to write a quadratic equation when you know the roots.

Key Concept **Sum and Product of Roots**

If the roots of $ax^2 + bx + c = 0$, with $a \neq 0$, are r_1 and r_2, then

$$r_1 + r_2 = -\frac{b}{a} \text{ and } r_1 \cdot r_2 = \frac{c}{a}.$$

1 FOCUS

Objective Use sums and products of roots to write quadratic equations.

Teaching Tip

Students should be familiar with factoring quadratic trinomials before attempting this lab.

2 TEACH

Working in Cooperative Groups

Have students work in pairs, mixing abilities. Then have pairs work through the Activities.

Ask:

- In generalizing the method by adding roots, what happens to the radicals? The same radical is added and subtracted, leaving a 0 term in the numerator of the fraction.
- What happens to the radical when the roots are multiplied? When the sum and difference of two expressions are multiplied, the result is the difference of the squares. Since the radical is squared, the result contains no radical.

Practice Have students complete Exercises 1–10.

3 ASSESS

Formative Assessment

Use Exercise 4 to assess whether students can write a quadratic equation given its roots.

From Concrete to Abstract

Exercises 9 and 10 require that students understand the pattern for identifying the numbers *a*, *b*, and *c* from the sum and product of roots.

Ask:

- If you know the sum of the roots, what do you know? $-\frac{b}{a}$, the opposite of the quotient of the coefficient of first degree term divided by the coefficient of the second degree term
- If you know the product of the roots, what do you know? $\frac{c}{a}$, the quotient of the constant term divided by the coefficient of the second degree term

ACTIVITY 1 Use the Sum and Product of Roots

Write a quadratic equation that has roots 2 and −7.

Step 1 Find the sum of the roots.

$$r_1 + r_2 = 2 + (-7)$$
$$= -5$$

Step 2 Find the product of the roots.

$$r_1 \cdot r_2 = 2 \cdot (-7)$$
$$= -14$$

Step 3 Write the equation.

$-5 = -\frac{b}{a}$ and $-14 = \frac{c}{a}$. So, $a = 1$, $b = 5$, and $c = -14$.

Thus, the equation is $x^2 + 5x - 14 = 0$.

ACTIVITY 2 Use the Sum and Product of Roots

Write a quadratic equation that has roots $\frac{3}{4}$ and $-\frac{12}{5}$.

Step 1 Find the sum of the roots.

$$r_1 + r_2 = \frac{3}{4} + \left(-\frac{12}{5}\right)$$
$$= \frac{15}{20} - \frac{48}{20} \text{ or } -\frac{33}{20}$$

Step 2 Find the product of the roots.

$$r_1 \cdot r_2 = \frac{3}{4} \cdot \left(-\frac{12}{5}\right)$$
$$= -\frac{36}{20}$$

Step 3 Write the equation.

$-\frac{33}{20} = -\frac{b}{a}$ and $-\frac{36}{20} = \frac{c}{a}$

So, $a = 20$, $b = 33$, and $c = -36$. Thus, the equation is $20x^2 + 33x - 36 = 0$.

Exercises

Write a quadratic equation that has the given roots.

1. $-\frac{3}{4}, \frac{5}{8}$ $32x^2 + 4x - 15 = 0$
2. $-7, \frac{2}{3}$ $3x^2 + 19x - 14 = 0$
3. $\pm\frac{2}{5}$ $25x^2 - 4 = 0$
4. $4 \pm \sqrt{3}$ $x^2 - 8x + 13 = 0$
5. $1 \pm \sqrt{6}$ $x^2 - 2x - 5 = 0$
6. $\frac{-2 \pm 3\sqrt{5}}{7}$ $49x^2 + 28x - 41 = 0$
7. $7 \pm 3i$ $x^2 - 14x + 58 = 0$
8. $\sqrt{5} \pm 8i$ $x^2 - 2\sqrt{5}x + 69 = 0$

Write a quadratic equation with roots that satisfy the following conditions.

9. The sum of the roots is 4. The product of the roots is $\frac{13}{12}$. $12x^2 - 48x + 13 = 0$
10. The sum of the roots is $\frac{1}{6}$. The product of the roots is $\frac{5}{21}$. $42x^2 - 7x + 10 = 0$

EXPLORE 5-7 Graphing Technology Lab
Families of Parabolas

FL Math Online glencoe.com
- Other Calculator Keystrokes
- Graphing Technology Personal Tutor

Objective
Use a graphing calculator to investigate changes to parabolas.

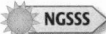

NGSSS
MA.912.A.2.10 Describe and **graph transformations of functions.** *Also addresses MA.912.A.2.6.*

The general form of a quadratic function is $y = a(x - h)^2 + k$. Changing the values of a, h, and k results in a different parabola in the family of quadratic functions. You can use a TI-83/84 Plus graphing calculator to analyze the effects that result from changing each of these parameters.

ACTIVITY 1

Graph each set of functions on the same screen in the standard viewing window. Describe any similarities and differences among the graphs.

$y = x^2$, $y = x^2 + 4$, $y = x^2 - 3$

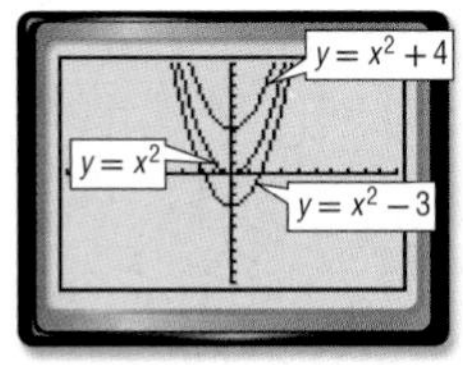

The graphs have the same shape, and all open up. The vertex of each graph is on the y-axis. However, the graphs have different vertical positions.

Example 1 shows how changing the value of k in the function $y = a(x - h)^2 + k$ *translates* the parabola along the y-axis. If $k > 0$, the parabola is translated k units up, and if $k < 0$, it is translated k units down.

How do you think changing the value of h will affect the graph of $y = x^2$?

ACTIVITY 2

Graph each set of functions on the same screen in the standard viewing window. Describe any similarities and differences among the graphs.

$y = x^2$, $y = (x + 4)^2$, $y = (x - 3)^2$

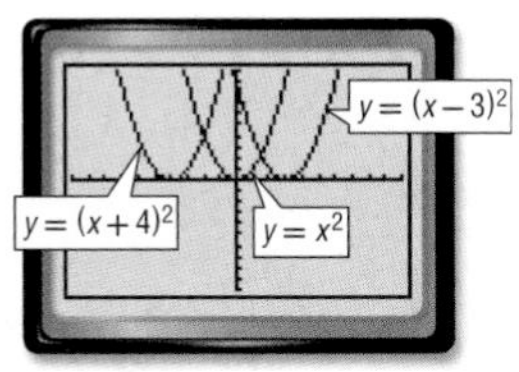

These three graphs all open up and have the same shape. The vertex of each graph is on the x-axis. However, the graphs have different horizontal positions.

Example 2 shows how changing the value of h in the equation $y = a(x - h)^2 + k$ *translates* the graph horizontally. If $h > 0$, the graph translates to the right h units. If $h < 0$, the graph translates to the left h units.

ACTIVITY 3

Graph each set of functions on the same screen in the standard viewing window. Describe any similarities and differences among the graphs.

$y = x^2$, $y = (x + 6)^2 - 5$, $y = (x - 4)^2 + 6$

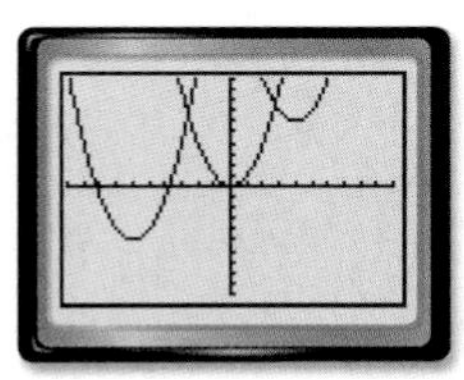

These three graphs all open up and have the same shape. However, the graphs have different horizontal and vertical positions.

EXPLORE 5-7 Lesson Notes

1 FOCUS

Objective Use a graphing calculator to investigate changes to parabolas.

Materials for Each Group

- TI-83/84 Plus or other graphing calculator

Teaching Tip

Students can use the calculator to confirm the location of the vertex of each parabola. A good way to do this is to change the window settings for the x-axis to $[-9.4, 9.4]$. Use the **TRACE** feature and symmetry properties of parabolas to check that the graph is symmetric with respect to the vertical line through the point that appears to be the vertex.

2 TEACH

Working in Cooperative Groups

Put students in pairs, mixing abilities. Then have pairs work through Activities 1–4 and Exercises 1–3.

- Ask students to describe the three constants (a, h, and k) in the general form of a quadratic function $y = a(x - h)^2 + k$. Sample answer: a: coefficient of the squared quantity involving the variable x; h: value subtracted from x in the quantity being squared and then multiplied by a; k: value added at the end.
- Before discussing the examples, have students make conjectures about the effect of the value of each of the constants a, h, and k on the graph of the parabola.

- After completing the discussion of Activity 4, have students compare the conjectures they made at the beginning of the lab to the knowledge they gained during the discussions.

Practice Have students complete Exercises 4–15.

3 ASSESS

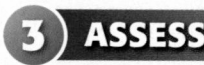

Formative Assessment

Use Exercise 15 to assess whether students comprehend how changing the constants *a*, *h*, and *k* affects the graph of $y = a(x - h)^2 + k$.

From Concrete to Abstract

Ask:

- In the general form of a quadratic function, which constant would you change to move the graph left or right? *h*
- Which constant would you change to move the graph up or down? *k*
- Which constant would you change to make the graph wider or narrower? *a*

Additional Answers

1. Changing the value of *h* moves the graph to the left and the right. If $h > 0$, the graph translates to the right, and if $h < 0$, it translates to the left. In $y = x^2$, the vertex is at (0, 0) and in $y = (x - 2)^2$, the vertex is at (2, 0). The graph has been translated to the right.
2. Changing the value of *k* moves the graph up and down. If $k > 0$, the graph translates upward, and if $k < 0$, it translates downward. In $y = x^2$, the vertex is at (0, 0) and in $y = x^2 - 3$, the vertex is at (0, –3). The graph has been translated downward.
3. Using $-a$ instead of *a* reflects the graph over the *x*-axis. The graph of $y = x^2$ opens upward, while the graph of $y = -x^2$ opens downward.

How does the value *a* affect the graph of $y = x^2$?

ACTIVITY 4

Graph each set of functions on the same screen in the standard viewing window. Describe any similarities and differences among the graphs.

a. $y = x^2$, $y = -x^2$

The graphs have the same vertex and the same shape. However, the graph of $y = x^2$ opens up and the graph of $y = -x^2$ opens down.

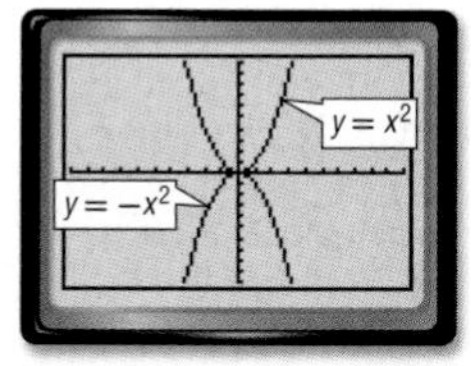

b. $y = x^2$, $y = 5x^2$, $y = \frac{1}{5}x^2$

The graphs have the same vertex, (0, 0), but each has a different shape. The graph of $y = 5x^2$ is narrower than the graph of $y = x^2$. The graph of $y = \frac{1}{5}x^2$ is wider than the graph of $y = x^2$.

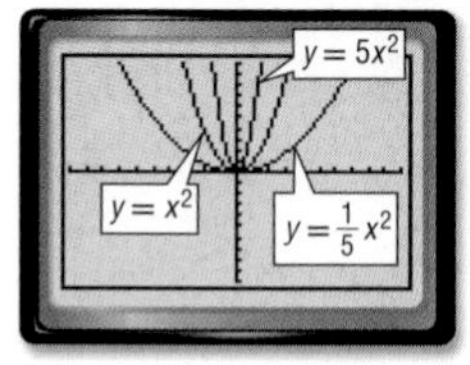

Changing the value of *a* in the function $y = a(x - h)^2 + k$ can affect the direction of the opening and the shape of the graph. If $a > 0$, the graph opens up, and if $a < 0$, the graph opens down or is *reflected* over the *x*-axis. If $|a| > 1$, the graph is expanded vertically and is narrower than the graph of $y = x^2$. If $|a| < 1$, the graph is compressed vertically and is wider than the graph of $y = x^2$. Thus, a change in the absolute value of *a* results in a *dilation* of the graph of $y = x^2$.

Analyze the Results 1–3. See margin.

1. How does changing the value of *h* in $y = a(x - h)^2 + k$ affect the graph? Give an example.
2. How does changing the value of *k* in $y = a(x - h)^2 + k$ affect the graph? Give an example.
3. How does using $-a$ instead of *a* in $y = a(x - h)^2 + k$ affect the graph? Give an example.

Examine each pair of functions and predict the similarities and differences in their graphs. Use a graphing calculator to confirm your predictions. Write a sentence or two comparing the two graphs. 4–15. See Chapter 5 Answer Appendix.

4. $y = x^2$, $y = x^2 + 3.5$
5. $y = -x^2$, $y = x^2 - 7$
6. $y = x^2$, $y = 4x^2$
7. $y = x^2$, $y = -8x^2$
8. $y = x^2$, $y = (x + 2)^2$
9. $y = -\frac{1}{6}x^2$, $y = -\frac{1}{6}x^2 + 2$
10. $y = x^2$, $y = (x - 5)^2$
11. $y = x^2$, $y = 2(x + 3)^2 - 6$
12. $y = x^2$, $y = -\frac{1}{8}x^2 + 1$
13. $y = (x + 5)^2 - 4$, $y = (x + 5)^2 + 7$
14. $y = 2(x + 1)^2 - 4$, $y = 5(x + 3)^2 - 1$
15. $y = 5(x - 2)^2 - 3$, $y = \frac{1}{4}(x - 5)^2 - 6$

304 Chapter 5 Quadratic Functions and Relations

5-7 Transformations with Quadratic Functions

Then
You transformed graphs of functions. (Lesson 2-7)

Now
- Write a quadratic function in the form $y = a(x - h)^2 + k$.
- Transform graphs of quadratic functions of the form $y = a(x - h)^2 + k$.

NGSSS
MA.912.A.2.10 Describe and graph transformations of functions.

New Vocabulary
vertex form

FL Math Online
glencoe.com

Why?

Recall that a family of graphs is a group of graphs that display one or more similar characteristics. The parent graph is the simplest graph in the family. For the family of quadratic functions, $y = x^2$ is the parent graph.

Other graphs in the family of quadratic functions, such as $y = (x - 2)^2$ and $y = x^2 - 4$, can be drawn by transforming the graph of $y = x^2$.

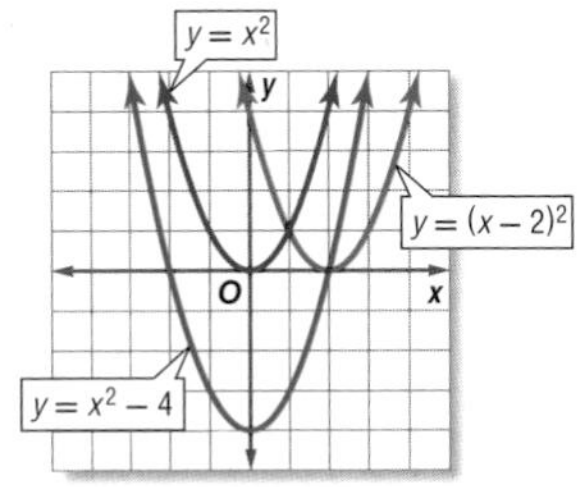

Write Quadratic Functions in Vertex Form Each function above is written in **vertex form**, $y = a(x - h)^2 + k$, where (h, k) is the vertex of the parabola, $x = h$ is the axis of symmetry, and a determines the shape of the parabola and the direction in which it opens.

When a quadratic function is in the form $y = ax^2 + bx + c$, you can complete the square to write the function in vertex form. If the coefficient of the quadratic term is not 1, then factor the coefficient from the quadratic and linear terms *before* completing the square.

EXAMPLE 1 Write Functions in Vertex Form

Write each function in vertex form.

a. $y = x^2 + 6x - 5$

$y = x^2 + 6x - 5$	$x^2 + 6x - 5$ is not a perfect square. Complete the square by adding $\left(\frac{6}{2}\right)^2$ or 9.
$y = (x^2 + 6x + 9) - 5 - 9$	Balance the equation by subtracting 9.
$y = (x + 3)^2 - 14$	Write $x^2 + 6x + 9$ as a perfect square.

b. $y = -2x^2 + 8x - 3$

$y = -2x^2 + 8x - 3$	Original function
$y = -2(x^2 - 4x) - 3$	Group $ax^2 + bx$ and factor, dividing by a.
$y = -2(x^2 - 4x + 4) - 3 - (-2)(4)$	Complete the square by adding 4 inside the parentheses. This is an overall addition of $-2(4)$. Balance the equation by subtracting $-2(4)$.
$y = -2(x - 2)^2 + 5$	Write $x^2 - 4x + 4$ as a perfect square.

Guided Practice

1A. $y = x^2 + 4x + 6$ $y = (x + 2)^2 + 2$ **1B.** $y = 2x^2 - 12x + 17$ $y = 2(x - 3)^2 - 1$

Personal Tutor glencoe.com

5-7 Lesson Notes

1 FOCUS

Vertical Alignment

Before Lesson 5-7
Transform graphs of functions.

Lesson 5-7
Write a quadratic function in the form $y = a(x - h)^2 + k$.
Transform graphs of quadratic functions of the form $y = a\,(x - h)^2 + k$.

After Lesson 5-7
Solve quadratic inequalities using graphs and algebraic methods.

2 TEACH

Scaffolding Questions

Have students read the *Why?* section of the lesson.

Ask:
- For the function $y = x^2$, what value of x makes y equal 0? $x = 0$
- What value of x makes y equal 0 if the function is $y = (x - 2)^2$? $x = 2$
- Compare the graph of $y = (x - 2)^2$ with $y = x^2$. What difference does subtracting 2 within the parentheses make? The graph of $y = x^2$ moves 2 units to the right.

Lesson 5-7 Resources

Resource	Approaching-Level	On-Level	Beyond-Level	English Learners
Teacher Edition	• Differentiated Instruction, p. 307	• Differentiated Instruction, p. 307	• Differentiated Instruction, pp. 307, 310	• Differentiated Instruction, p. 307
Chapter Resource Masters	• Study Guide and Intervention, pp. 43–44 • Skills Practice, p. 45 • Practice, p. 46 • Word Problem Practice, p. 47	• Study Guide and Intervention, pp. 43–44 • Skills Practice, p. 45 • Practice, p. 46 • Word Problem Practice, p. 47 • Enrichment, p. 48	• Practice, p. 46 • Word Problem Practice, p. 47 • Enrichment, p. 48	• Study Guide and Intervention, pp. 43–44 • Skills Practice, p. 45 • Practice, p. 46 • Word Problem Practice, p. 47
Transparencies	• 5-Minute Check Transparency 5-7	• 5-Minute Check Transparency 5-7	• 5-Minute Check Transparency 5-7	• 5-Minute Check Transparency 5-7
Other	• Study Notebook • Teaching Algebra with Manipulatives	• Study Notebook • Teaching Algebra with Manipulatives	• Study Notebook	• Study Notebook • Teaching Algebra with Manipulatives

Write Quadratic Equations in Vertex Form

Example 1 shows how to write quadratic equations in vertex form. **Example 2** shows how the coefficient of the quadratic term in a function changes the width of the graph in a multiple-choice test format.

Formative Assessment

Use the Guided Practice exercises after each example to determine students' understanding of concepts.

Additional Example

1 Write each equation in vertex form.

a. $y = x^2 - 2x + 4$
$y = (x - 1)^2 + 3$

b. $y = -3x^2 - 18x + 10$
$y = -3(x + 3)^2 + 37$

Additional Examples also in Interactive Classroom PowerPoint® Presentations

IWB INTERACTIVE WHITEBOARD READY

Watch Out!

Preventing Errors As $|a|$ increases, the graph gets narrower, because a greater multiplier for the quantity $(x - h)^2$ will make the corresponding y-value greater. Greater values of y result in a steeper (and thus narrower) graph.

TEACH with TECH

INTERACTIVE WHITEBOARD Show a coordinate grid on the board. Draw a graph of a quadratic function, give students the equation of the graph, and show students how to write the equation of the graph in vertex form. Drag the graph to move its vertex to other locations on the grid and have students find the equations of the new graphs. Discuss how the equations are similar and different.

Test-Taking Tip

The Meaning of a The sign of a in the vertex form does not determine the width of the parabola. The sign indicates whether the parabola opens up or down. The width of a parabola is determined by the absolute value of a.

If the vertex and one additional point on the graph of a parabola are known, you can write the equation of the parabola in vertex form.

NGSSS PRACTICE EXAMPLE 2 912.A.4.5

Which is an equation of the function shown in the graph?

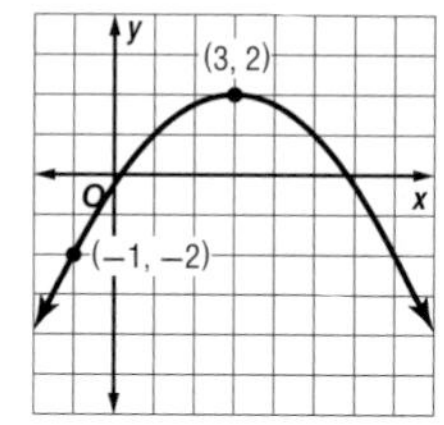

A. $y = -4(x - 3)^2 + 2$

B. $y = -\frac{1}{4}(x - 3)^2 + 2$

C. $y = \frac{1}{4}(x + 3)^2 - 2$

D. $y = 4(x + 3)^2 - 2$

Read the Test Item

You are given a graph of a parabola with the vertex and a point on the graph labeled. You need to find an equation of the parabola.

Solve the Test Item

The vertex of the parabola is at (3, 2), so $h = 3$ and $k = 2$. Since $(-1, -2)$ is a point on the graph, let $x = -1$ and $y = -2$. Substitute these values into the vertex form of the equation and solve for a.

$y = a(x - h)^2 + k$	**Vertex form**
$-2 = a(-1 - 3)^2 + 2$	**Substitute −2 for y, −1 for x, 3 for h and 2 for k.**
$-2 = a(16) + 2$	**Simplify.**
$-4 = 16a$	**Subtract 2 from each side.**
$-\frac{1}{4} = a$	**Divide each side by 16.**

The equation of the parabola in vertex form is $y = -\frac{1}{4}(x - 3)^2 + 2$.

The answer is B.

Guided Practice

2. Which is an equation of the function shown in the graph? **H**

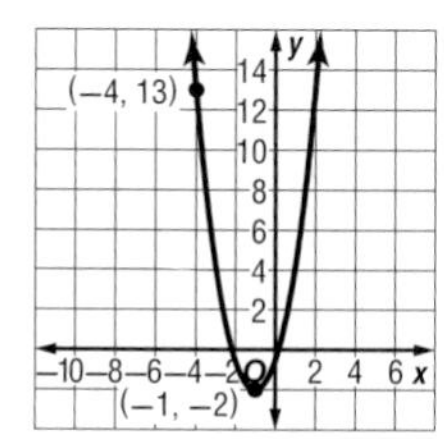

F $y = \frac{9}{25}(x - 1)^2 + 2$

G $y = \frac{3}{5}(x + 1)^2 - 2$

H $y = \frac{5}{3}(x + 1)^2 - 2$

J $y = \frac{25}{9}(x - 1)^2 + 2$

Personal Tutor glencoe.com

Transformations of Quadratic Functions In Lesson 2-7, you learned how different transformations affect the graphs of parent functions. The following summarizes these transformations for quadratic functions.

Focus on Mathematical Content

Quadratic Function in Vertex Form The values of a, k, and h, in the vertex form of a quadratic function, $y = a(x - h)^2 + k$, affect the graph of the parabola. The vertex is at (h, k). The value of a determines the direction in which the parabola opens and the width of the parabola. The value of h determines the direction in which the parabola is translated horizontally. The value of k determines the direction in which the parabola is translated vertically. The function must first be rewritten in the vertex form before a, h, and k can be determined and analyzed.

StudyTip

Absolute Value
$0 < |a| < 1$ means that a is a rational number between 0 and 1, such as $\frac{3}{4}$, or a rational number between -1 and 0, such as -0.3.

Concept Summary — Transformations of Quadratic Functions

$f(x) = a(x - h)^2 + k$

h, Horizontal Translation
$|h|$ units to the right if h is positive
$|h|$ units to the left if h is negative

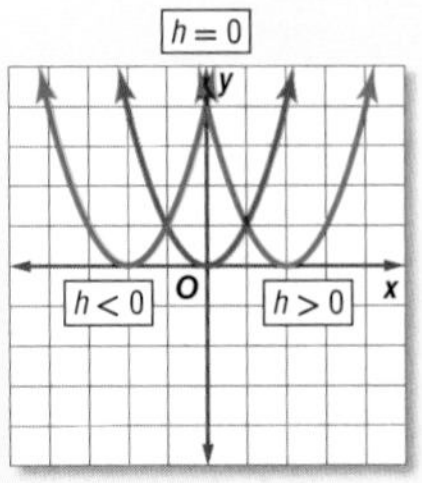

k, Vertical Translation
$|k|$ units up if k is positive
$|k|$ units down if k is negative

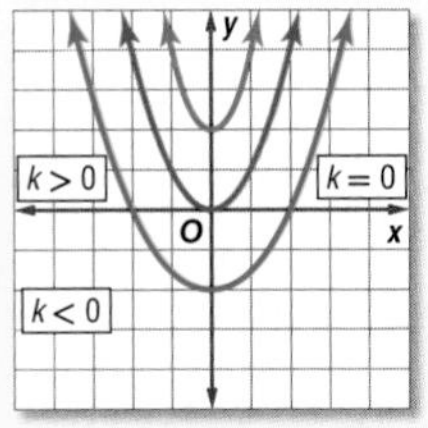

a, Reflection
If $a > 0$, the graph opens up.
If $a < 0$, the graph opens down.

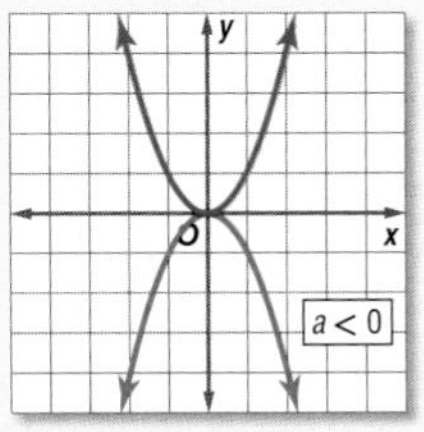

a, Dilation
If $|a| > 1$, the graph is stretched vertically. If $0 < |a| < 1$, the graph is compressed vertically.

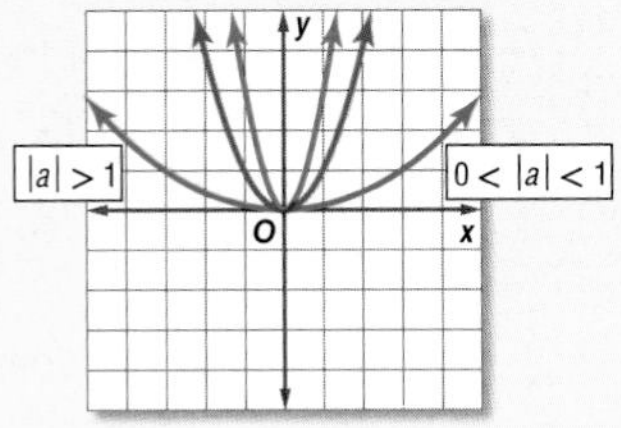

EXAMPLE 3 Graph Equations in Vertex Form

Graph $y = 4x^2 - 16x - 40$

Step 1 Rewrite the equation in vertex form.

$y = 4x^2 - 16x - 40$	**Original equation**
$y = 4(x^2 - 4x) - 40$	**Distributive Property**
$y = 4(x - 4x + 4) - 40 - 4(4)$	**Complete the square.**
$y = 4(x - 2)^2 - 56$	**Simplify.**

Step 2 The vertex is at $(2, -56)$. The axis of symmetry is $x = 2$. Because $a = 4$, the graph is narrower than the graph of $y = x^2$.

Step 3 Plot additional points to help you complete the graph.

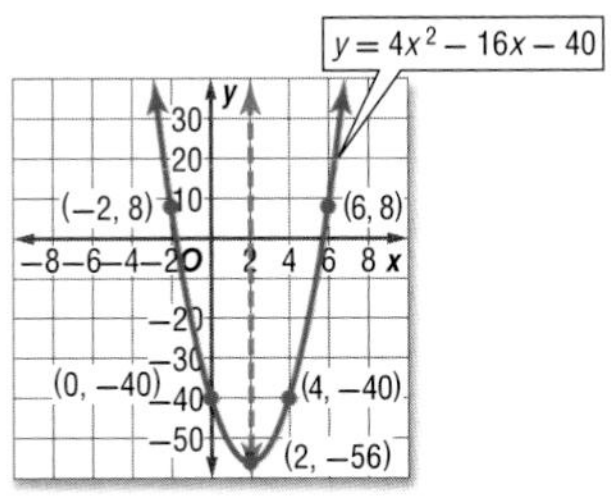

Guided Practice

3A, 3B. See Chapter 5 Answer Appendix.

3A. $y = (x - 3)^2 - 2$

3B. $y = 0.25(x + 1)^2$

Personal Tutor glencoe.com

Additional Example

2 STANDARDIZED TEST PRACTICE Which is an equation of the function shown in the graph? B

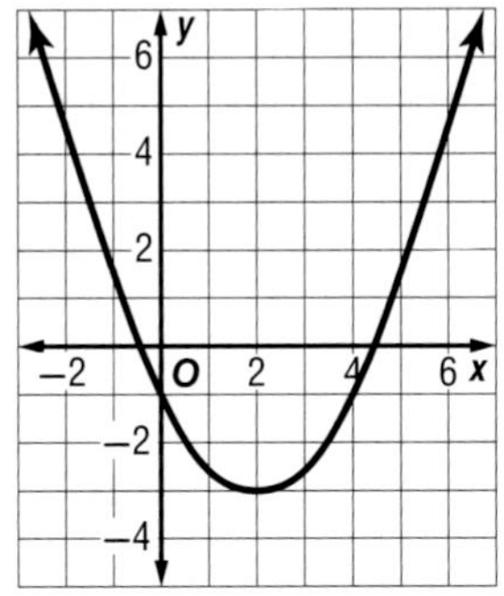

A $y = -\frac{1}{2}(x - 2)^2 + 3$

B $y = \frac{1}{2}(x - 2)^2 - 3$

C $y = -2(x - 2)^2 + 3$

D $y = 2(x - 2)^2 - 3$

Transformations of Quadratic Functions

Example 3 shows how to graph an equation after rewriting it in vertex from.

Additional Example

3 Graph $y = -2x^2 + 4x + 1$.

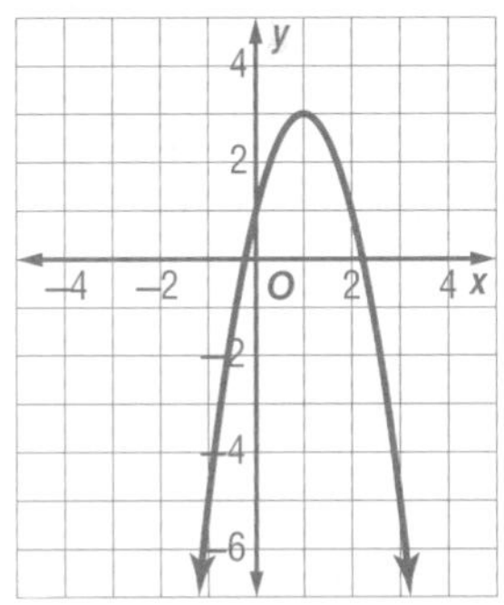

Differentiated Instruction

AL OL BL ELL

Intrapersonal Learners Have students observe or research some natural events that can be modeled by parabolas. Students should report their observations and findings to the class. If students are able to determine a quadratic function that models the event, they should present the function and explain how the characteristics of the equation can be used to analyze its graph.

3 PRACTICE

Formative Assessment

Use Exercises 1–7 to check for understanding.

Use the chart on the bottom of this page to customize assignments for your students.

Additional Answers

5.

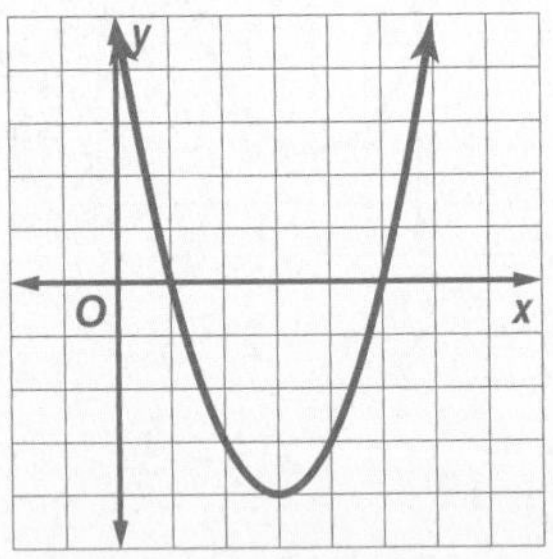

6.

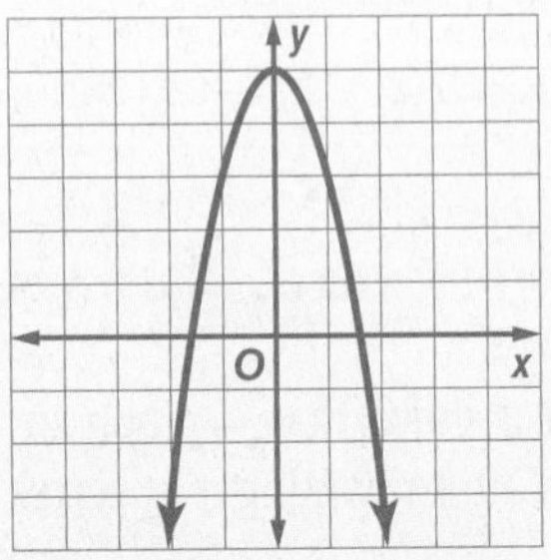

7.

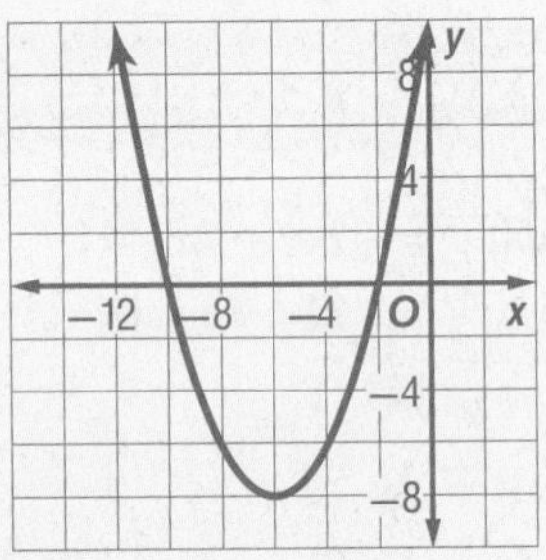

20.

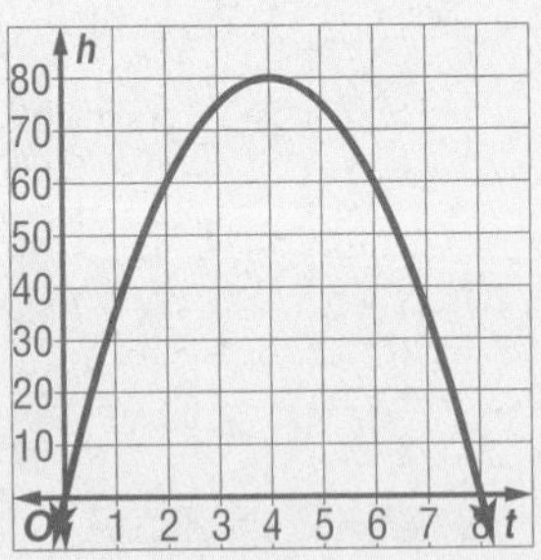

Check Your Understanding

Example 1 p. 305

Write each function in vertex form.

1. $y = x^2 + 6x + 2$
2. $y = -2x^2 + 8x - 5$
3. $y = 4x^2 + 24x + 24$

1. $y = (x + 3)^2 - 7$
2. $y = -2(x - 2)^2 + 3$
3. $y = 4(x + 3)^2 - 12$

Example 2 p. 306

4. **NGSSS PRACTICE** Which function is shown in the graph? **A**

A. $y = -(x + 3)^2 + 6$

B. $y = -(x - 3)^2 - 6$

C. $y = -2(x + 3)^2 + 6$

D. $y = -2(x - 3)^2 - 6$

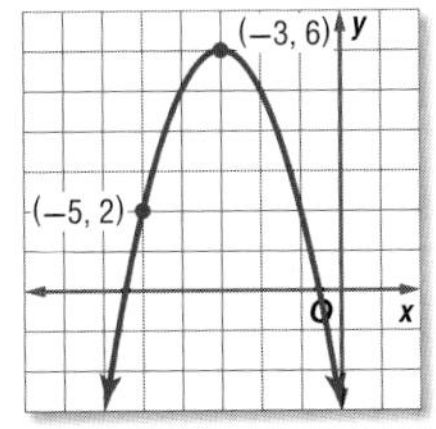

Example 3 p. 307

Graph each function. **5–7. See margin.**

5. $y = (x - 3)^2 - 4$
6. $y = -2x^2 + 5$
7. $y = \frac{1}{2}(x + 6)^2 - 8$

● = **Step-by-Step Solutions** begin on page R20. **Extra Practice** begins on page 947.

Practice and Problem Solving

Example 1 p. 305

Write each function in vertex form. **8.** $y = \left(x + \frac{9}{2}\right)^2 - \frac{49}{4}$ **9.** $y = (x - 3)^2 - 6$

8. $y = x^2 + 9x + 8$
9. $y = x^2 - 6x + 3$
10. $y = -2x^2 + 5x$
11. $y = x^2 + 2x + 7$
12. $y = -3x^2 + 12x - 10$
13. $y = x^2 + 8x + 16$
14. $y = 2x^2 - 4x - 3$
15. $y = 3x^2 + 10x$
16. $y = x^2 - 4x + 9$
17. $y = -4x^2 - 24x - 15$ **$y = -4(x + 3)^2 + 21$**
18. $y = x^2 - 12x + 36$ **$y = (x - 6)^2$**
19. $y = -x^2 - 4x - 1$ **$y = -(x + 2)^2 + 3$**

10. $y = -2\left(x - \frac{5}{4}\right)^2 + \frac{25}{8}$
11. $y = (x + 1)^2 + 6$
12. $y = -3(x - 2)^2 + 2$
13. $y = (x + 4)^2$

Example 2 p. 306

20. **FIREWORKS** During an Independence Day fireworks show, the height h in meters of a specific rocket after t seconds can be modeled by $h = -4.9(t - 4)^2 + 80$. Graph the function. **See margin.**

21. **FINANCIAL LITERACY** A bicycle rental shop rents an average of 120 bicycles per week and charges $25 per day. The manager estimates that there will be 15 additional bicycles rented for each $1 reduction in the rental price. The maximum income the manager can expect can be modeled by $y = -15x^2 + 255x + 3000$, where y is the weekly income and x is the number of bicycles rented. Write this function in vertex form. Then graph. **$y = -15(x - 8.5)^2 + 4083.75$; See Chapter 5 Answer Appendix for graph.**

14. $y = 2(x - 1)^2 - 5$
15. $y = 3\left(x + \frac{5}{3}\right)^2 - \frac{25}{3}$
16. $y = (x - 2)^2 + 5$

Example 3 p. 307

Graph each function. **22–33. See Chapter 5 Answer Appendix.**

22. $y = (x - 5)^2 + 3$
23. $y = 9x^2 - 8$
24. $y = -2(x - 5)^2$
25. $y = \frac{1}{10}(x + 6)^2 + 6$
26. $y = -3(x - 5)^2 - 2$
27. $y = -\frac{1}{4}x^2 - 5$
28. $y = 2x^2 + 10$
29. $y = -(x + 3)^2$
30. $y = \frac{1}{6}(x - 3)^2 - 10$
31. $y = (x - 9)^2 - 7$
32. $y = -\frac{5}{8}x^2 - 8$
33. $y = -4(x - 10)^2 - 10$

34. **SAILBOARDING** A sailboard manufacturer uses an automated process to manufacture the masts for its sailboards. The function $f(x) = \frac{1}{250}x^2 + \frac{3}{5}x$ is programmed into a computer to make one such mast. **a. See Chapter 5 Answer Appendix.**
    a. Write the quadratic function in vertex form. Then graph the function.
    b. Describe how the manufacturer can adjust the function to make its masts with a greater or smaller curve. **They can adjust the coefficient of x^2.**

Differentiated Homework Options

Level	Assignment	Two-Day Option	
AL Basic	8–34, 48, 51–76	9–33 odd, 53–56	8–34 even, 48, 51, 52, 57–76
OL Core	9–33 odd, 34, 35–45 odd, 47, 48, 51–76	8–34, 53–56	35–48, 51, 52, 57–76
BL Advanced	35–73, (optional: 74–76)		

$37.\ y = -\frac{2}{3}(x-3)^2$

B Write an equation in vertex form for each parabola.

35.

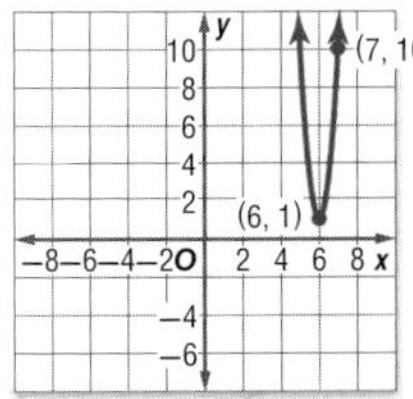

$y = 9(x-6)^2 + 1$

36.

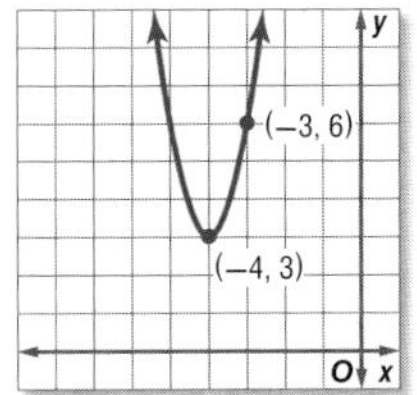

$y = 3(x+4)^2 + 3$

37.

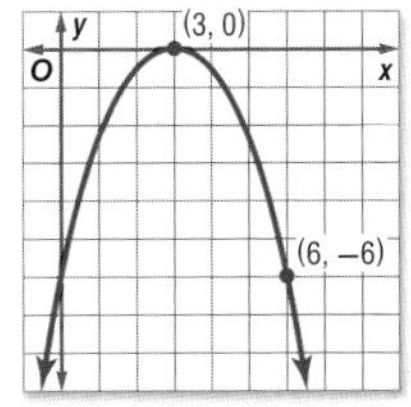

38.

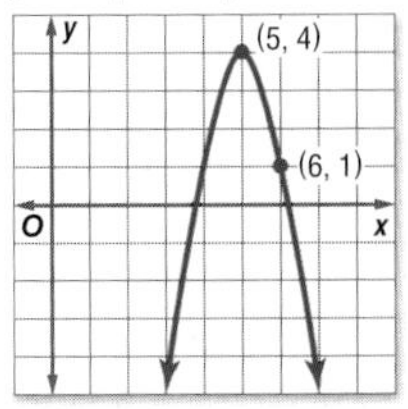

$y = -3(x-5)^2 + 4$

39.

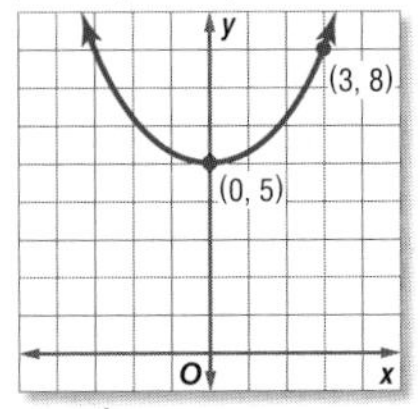

$y = \frac{1}{3}x^2 + 5$

40.

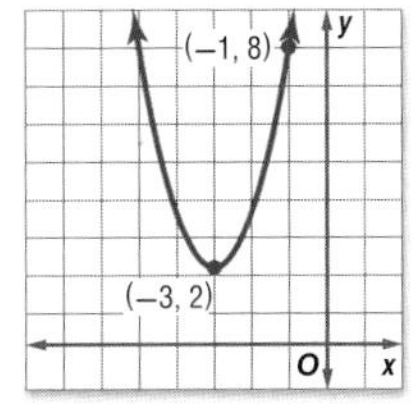

$y = \frac{3}{2}(x+3)^2 + 2$

Write each function in vertex form. Then identify the vertex, axis of symmetry, and direction of opening. **41–46. See Chapter 5 Answer Appendix.**

41. $3x^2 - 4x = 2 + y$ **42.** $-2x^2 + 7x = y - 12$ **43.** $-x^2 - 4.7x = y - 2.8$

44. $x^2 + 1.4x - 1.2 = y$ **45.** $x^2 - \frac{2}{3}x - \frac{26}{9} = y$ **46.** $x^2 + 7x + \frac{49}{4} = y$

47 **CARS** The formula $S(t) = \frac{1}{2}at^2 + v_0t$ can be used to determine the position $S(t)$ of an object after t seconds at a rate of acceleration a with initial velocity v_0. Valerie's car can accelerate 0.002 miles per second squared.

a. Express $S(t)$ in vertex form as she accelerates from 35 miles per hour to enter highway traffic. $S(t) = 0.001(t + 4.861)^2 - 0.024$

b. How long will it take Valerie to match the average speed of highway traffic of 68 miles per hour? (*Hint*: Use acceleration • time = velocity.) **4.58 seconds**

c. If the entrance ramp is $\frac{1}{8}$-mile long, will Valerie have sufficient time to match the average highway speed? Explain.

Real-World Link

Exceeding the posted speed limit or driving at an unsafe speed is the most common error in accidents.

Source: National Safety Council

47c. Yes; if we substitute $\frac{1}{8}$ for $S(t)$ and solve for t we get 7.35 seconds. This is how long Valerie will be on the ramp. Since it will take her 4.58 seconds to accelerate to 68 mph, she will be on the ramp long enough to accelerate to match the average expressway speed.

H.O.T. Problems

Use **H**igher-**O**rder **T**hinking Skills

48. OPEN ENDED Write an equation for a parabola that has been translated, compressed, **C** and reflected in the x-axis. **Sample answer:** $y = -\frac{1}{2}(x-4)^2$

49. CHALLENGE Explain how you can find an equation of a parabola using the coordinates of three points on the graph. **See Chapter 5 Answer Appendix.**

50. CHALLENGE Write the standard form of a quadratic function $ax^2 + bx + c = y$ in vertex form. Identify the vertex and the axis of symmetry. **See Chapter 5 Answer Appendix.**

51. See Chapter 5 Answer Appendix.

51. REASONING Describe the graph of $f(x) = a(x-h)^2 + k$ when $a = 0$. Is the graph the same as that of $g(x) = ax^2 + bx + c$ when $a = 0$? Explain.

52. WRITING IN MATH Explain how the graph of $y = x^2$ can be used to graph any quadratic function. Include a description of the effects produced by changing a, h, and k in the equation $y = a(x-h)^2 + k$, and a comparison of the graph of $y = x^2$ and the graph of $y = a(x-h)^2 + k$ using values you choose for a, h, and k. **See Chapter 5 Answer Appendix.**

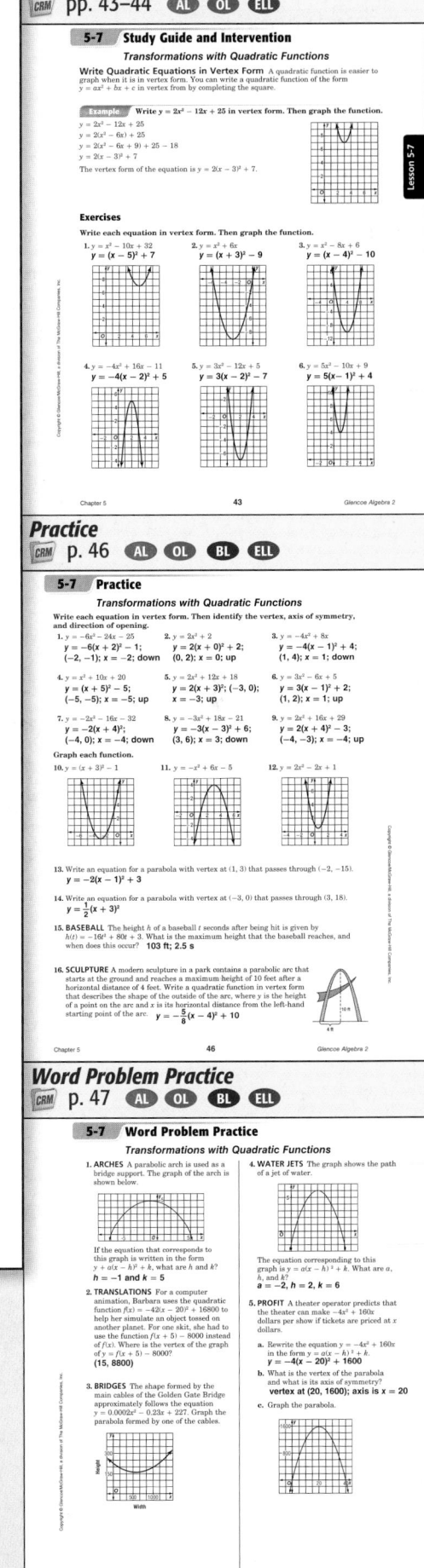

Study Guide and Intervention

CRM pp. 43–44 AL OL ELL

5-7 Study Guide and Intervention

Transformations with Quadratic Functions

Write Quadratic Equations in Vertex Form A quadratic function is easier to graph when it is in vertex form. You can write a quadratic function of the form $y = ax^2 + bx + c$ in vertex from by completing the square.

Example Write $y = 2x^2 - 12x + 25$ in vertex form. Then graph the function.

$y = 2x^2 - 12x + 25$
$y = 2(x^2 - 6x) + 25$
$y = 2(x^2 - 6x + 9) + 25 - 18$
$y = 2(x-3)^2 + 7$

The vertex form of the equation is $y = 2(x-3)^2 + 7$.

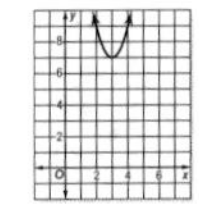

Lesson 5-7

Exercises

Write each equation in vertex form. Then graph the function.

1. $y = x^2 - 10x + 32$ $y = (x-5)^2 + 7$
2. $y = x^2 + 6x$ $y = (x+3)^2 - 9$
3. $y = x^2 - 8x + 6$ $y = (x-4)^2 - 10$

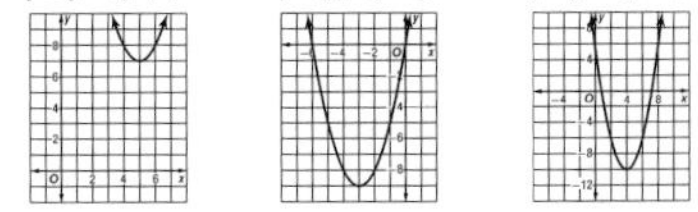

4. $y = -4x^2 + 16x - 11$ $y = -4(x-2)^2 + 5$
5. $y = 3x^2 - 12x + 5$ $y = 3(x-2)^2 - 7$
6. $y = 5x^2 - 10x + 9$ $y = 5(x-1)^2 + 4$

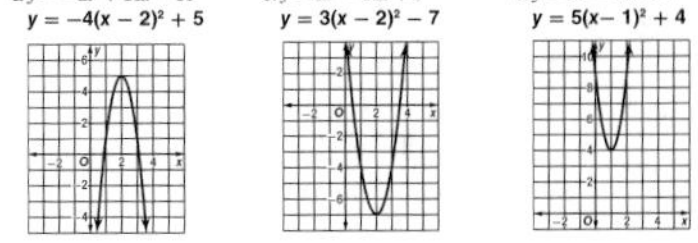

Practice

CRM p. 46 AL OL BL ELL

5-7 Practice

Transformations with Quadratic Functions

Write each equation in vertex form. Then identify the vertex, axis of symmetry, and direction of opening.

1. $y = -6x^2 - 24x - 25$ $y = -6(x+2)^2 - 1$; $(-2, -1)$; $x = -2$; down
2. $y = 2x^2 + 2$ $y = 2(x+0)^2 + 2$; $(0, 2)$; $x = 0$; up
3. $y = -4x^2 + 8x$ $y = -4(x-1)^2 + 4$; $(1, 4)$; $x = 1$; down
4. $y = x^2 + 10x + 20$ $y = (x+5)^2 - 5$; $(-5, -5)$; $x = -5$; up
5. $y = 2x^2 + 12x + 18$ $y = 2(x+3)^2$; $(-3, 0)$; $x = -3$; up
6. $y = 3x^2 - 6x + 5$ $y = 3(x-1)^2 + 2$; $(1, 2)$; $x = 1$; up
7. $y = -2x^2 - 16x - 32$ $y = -2(x+4)^2$; $(-4, 0)$; $x = -4$; down
8. $y = -3x^2 + 18x - 21$ $y = -3(x-3)^2 + 6$; $(3, 6)$; $x = 3$; down
9. $y = 2x^2 + 16x + 29$ $y = 2(x+4)^2 - 3$; $(-4, -3)$; $x = -4$; up

Graph each function.

10. $y = (x+3)^2 - 1$ 11. $y = -x^2 + 6x - 5$ 12. $y = 2x^2 - 2x + 1$

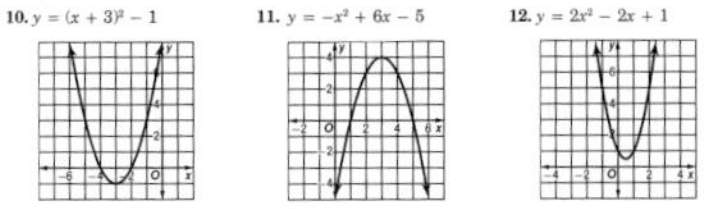

13. Write an equation for a parabola with vertex at (1, 3) that passes through (−2, −15). $y = -2(x-1)^2 + 3$

14. Write an equation for a parabola with vertex at (−3, 0) that passes through (3, 18). $y = \frac{1}{2}(x+3)^2$

15. **BASEBALL** The height h of a baseball t seconds after being hit is given by $h(t) = -16t^2 + 80t + 3$. What is the maximum height that the baseball reaches, and when does this occur? **103 ft; 2.5 s**

16. **SCULPTURE** A modern sculpture in a park contains a parabolic arc that starts at the ground and reaches a maximum height of 10 feet after a horizontal distance of 4 feet. Write a quadratic function in vertex form that describes the shape of the outside of the arc, where y is the height of a point on the arc and x is its horizontal distance from the left-hand starting point of the arc. $y = -\frac{5}{8}(x-4)^2 + 10$

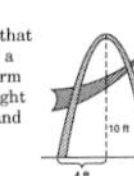

Word Problem Practice

CRM p. 47 AL OL BL ELL

5-7 Word Problem Practice

Transformations with Quadratic Functions

1. **ARCHES** A parabolic arch is used as a bridge support. The graph of the arch is shown below.

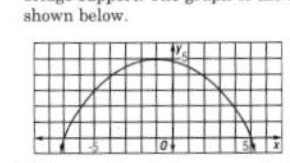

If the equation that corresponds to this graph is written in the form $y + a(x-h)^2 + k$, what are h and k? **$h = -1$ and $k = 5$**

2. **TRANSLATIONS** For a computer animation, Barbara uses the quadratic function $f(x) = -42(x-20)^2 + 16800$ to help her simulate an object tossed on another planet. For one skit, she had to use the function $f(x+5) - 8000$ instead of $f(x)$. Where is the vertex of the graph of $y = f(x+5) - 8000$? **(15, 8800)**

3. **BRIDGES** The shape formed by the main cables of the Golden Gate Bridge approximately follows the equation $y = 0.0002x^2 - 0.23x + 227$. Graph the parabola formed by one of the cables.

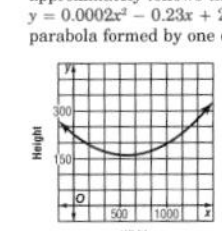

4. **WATER JETS** The graph shows the path of a jet of water.

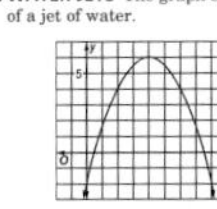

The equation corresponding to this graph is $y = a(x-h)^2 + k$. What are a, h, and k? **$a = -2$, $h = 2$, $k = 6$**

5. **PROFIT** A theater operator predicts that the theater can make $-4x^2 + 160x$ dollars per show if tickets are priced at x dollars.

a. Rewrite the equation $y = -4x^2 + 160x$ in the form $y = a(x-h)^2 + k$. **$y = -4(x-20)^2 + 1600$**

b. What is the vertex of the parabola and what is its axis of symmetry? **vertex at (20, 1600); axis is $x = 20$**

c. Graph the parabola.

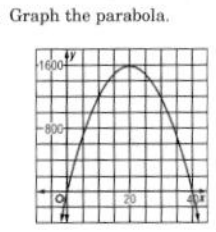

Enrichment

CRM p. 48 OL BL

5-7 Enrichment

A Shortcut to Complex Roots

When graphing a quadratic function, the real roots are shown in the graph. You have learned that quadratic functions can also have imaginary roots that cannot be seen on the graph of the function. However, there is a way to graphically represent the complex roots of a quadratic function.

Example Find the complex roots of the quadratic function $y = x^2 - 4x + 5$.

Step 1 Graph the function.

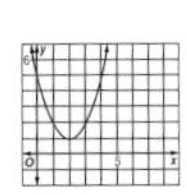

Step 2 Reflect the graph over the horizontal line containing the vertex. In this example, the vertex is (2, 1).

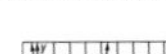

4 ASSESS

Crystal Ball Ask students to write how today's lesson on analyzing and graphing quadratic functions will help them with tomorrow's lesson on graphing and solving quadratic inequalities.

Additional Answers

66. about 20 ft^2

67a.

$$\begin{array}{l} \quad\quad\quad\ \text{Weekday Weekend} \\ \begin{array}{r} \text{Single} \\ \text{Double} \\ \text{Suite} \end{array} \begin{bmatrix} 60 & 79 \\ 70 & 89 \\ 75 & 95 \end{bmatrix} \end{array}$$

67b.

$$\begin{array}{l} \quad\quad\quad\ \text{Single Double Suite} \\ \begin{array}{r} \text{Weekday} \\ \text{Weekend} \end{array} \begin{bmatrix} 60 & 70 & 75 \\ 79 & 89 & 95 \end{bmatrix} \end{array}$$

68.

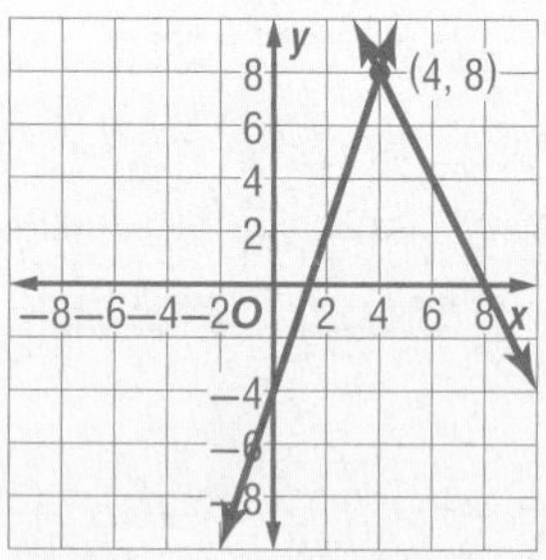

69.

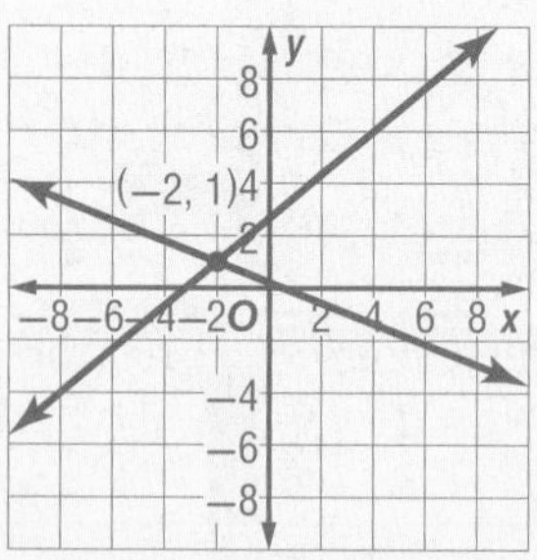

70.

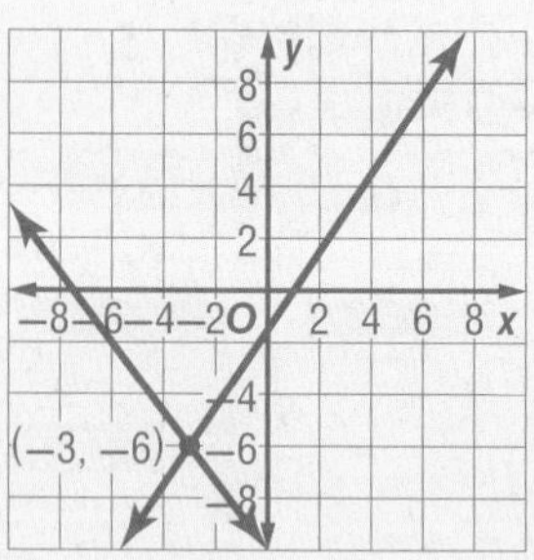

NGSSS PRACTICE 912.A.3.15, 912.A.3.6, 912.A.3.1

53. Flowering bushes need a mixture of 70% soil and 30% vermiculite. About how many buckets of vermiculite should you add to 20 buckets of soil? **B**

A. 6.0 C. 14.0
B. 8.0 D. 24.0

54. SAT/ACT The sum of the integers x and y is 495. The units digit of x is 0. If x is divided by 10, the result is equal to y. What is the value of x? **J**

F. 40 H. 250
G. 245 I. 450

55. What is the solution set of the inequality $|4x - 1| < 9$? **D**

A. $\{x \mid 2.5 < x \text{ or } x < -2\}$
B. $\{x \mid x < 2.5\}$
C. $\{x \mid x > -2\}$
D. $\{x \mid -2 < x < 2.5\}$

56. **SHORT RESPONSE** At your store, you buy wrenches for \$30.00 a dozen and sell them for \$3.50 each. What is the percent markup for the wrenches? **40%**

Spiral Review

63. minimum, $9\frac{1}{3}$ 64. maximum, $-17\frac{15}{16}$ 65. minimum, −12

Solve each equation by using the method of your choice. Find exact solutions. (Lesson 5-6)

57. $4x^2 + 15x = 21$ $\frac{-15 \pm \sqrt{561}}{8}$ **58.** $-3x^2 + 19 = 5x$ $\frac{-5 \pm \sqrt{253}}{6}$ **59.** $6x - 5x^2 + 9 = 3$ $\frac{3 \pm \sqrt{39}}{5}$

Find the value of c that makes each trinomial a perfect square. (Lesson 5-5)

60. $x^2 - 12x + c$ **36** **61.** $x^2 + 0.1x + c$ **0.0025** **62.** $x^2 - 0.45x + c$ **0.050625**

Determine whether each function has a maximum or minimum value, and find that value. (Lesson 5-1)

63. $f(x) = 6x^2 - 8x + 12$ **64.** $f(x) = -4x^2 + x - 18$ **65.** $f(x) = 3x^2 - 9 + 6x$

66. ARCHAEOLOGY A coordinate grid is laid over an archeology dig to identify the location of artifacts. Three corners of a building have been partially unearthed at (−1, 6), (4, 5), and (−1, −2). If each square on the grid measures one square foot, estimate the area of the floor of the building. (Lesson 4-5) **See margin.**

67. HOTELS Use the costs for an overnight stay at a hotel provided at the right. (Lesson 4-1) **a, b. See margin.**

a. Write a 3 × 2 matrix that represents the cost of each room.

b. Write a 2 × 3 matrix that represents the cost of each room.

HOTEL

	Weekday	Weekend
Single Room	\$60.00	\$79.00
Double Room	\$70.00	\$89.00
Suite	\$75.00	\$95.00

Solve each system of equations by graphing. (Lesson 3-1) **68–70. See margin.**

68. $y = 3x - 4$
$y = -2x + 16$

69. $2x + 5y = 1$
$6y - 5x = 16$

70. $4x + 3y = -30$
$3x - 2y = 3$

Evaluate each function. (Lesson 2-1)

71. $f(3)$ if $f(x) = x^2 - 4x + 12$ **9** **72.** $f(-2)$ if $f(x) = -4x^2 + x - 8$ **−26** **73.** $f(4)$ if $f(x) = 3x^2 + x$ **52**

Skills Review

Determine whether the given value satisfies the inequality. (Lesson 1-6)

74. $3x^2 - 5 > 6; x = 2$ **yes** **75.** $-2x^2 + x - 1 < 4; x = -2$ **yes** **76.** $4x^2 + x - 3 \leq 36; x = 3$ **yes**

Differentiated Instruction BL

Extension In this lesson on quadratic functions, only equations of parabolas that open up or down are analyzed and graphed. Ask students to explain why parabolas opening to the right or left are not included in this lesson. As an example, you can draw a graph of a parabola on the board with a vertex at (−2, 0), axis of symmetry through $y = 0$, and through (0, 2). Sample answer: This lesson is about quadratic functions. Parabolas opening right or left do not represent functions since 2 elements in the range are paired with one element of the domain, except at the vertex.

Algebra Lab
Quadratics and Rate of Change

You have learned that a linear function has a constant rate of change. You will investigate the rate of change for quadratic functions.

ACTIVITY Determine Rate of Change

Consider $f(x) = 0.1875x^2 - 3x + 12$. Steps 1–5. See Chapter 5 Answer Appendix.

Step 1 Make a table like the one below. Use values from 0 through 16 for x.

x	0	1	2	3	...	16
y	12	9.1875	6.75			
First Order Differences						
Second Order Differences						

Step 2 Find each y-value. For example, when $x = 1$, $y = 0.1875(1)^2 - 3(1) + 12$ or 9.1875.

Step 3 Graph the ordered pairs (x, y). Then connect the points with a smooth curve. Notice that the function *decreases* when $0 < x < 8$ and *increases* when $8 < x < 16$.

Step 4 The rate of change from one point to the next can be found by using the slope formula. From (0, 12) to (1, 9.1875), the slope is $\frac{9.1875 - 12}{1 - 0}$ or -2.8125. This is the first-order difference at $x = 1$. Complete the table for all the first-order differences. Describe any patterns in the differences.

Step 5 The second-order differences can be found by subtracting consecutive first-order differences. For example, the second-order difference at $x = 2$ is found by subtracting the first order difference at $x = 1$ from the first-order difference at $x = 2$. Describe any patterns in the differences.

Exercises

For each function make a table of values for the given x-values. Graph the function. Then determine the first-order and second-order differences. 1–3. See Chapter 5 Answer Appendix.

1. $y = -x^2 + 2x - 1$ for $x = -3, -2, -1, 0, 1, 2, 3$
2. $y = 0.5x^2 + 2x - 2$ for $x = -5, -4, -3, -2, -1, 0, 1$
3. $y = -3x^2 - 18x - 26$ for $x = -6, -5, -4, -3, -2, -1, 0$
4. **MAKE A CONJECTURE** Repeat the activity for a cubic function. At what order difference would you expect $g(x) = x^4$ to be constant? $h(x) = x^n$? fourth order; nth order

EXTEND 5-7 Lesson Notes

1 FOCUS

Objective Investigate the rate of change of quadratic functions by examining first- and second-order differences.

Teaching Tip

Each student's table should have a column for every integer value of x from 0 through 16.

2 TEACH

Working in Cooperative Groups

Have students work in pairs, mixing abilities. Then have the pairs complete the Activity.

Ask:

- Why is there no first difference written in the column labeled $x = 0$? Finding a difference requires two values of y.
- What is significant about the point where $x = 8$? (8, 0) is the vertex of the parabola.

Practice Have students complete Exercises 1–4.

3 ASSESS

Formative Assessment

Use Exercise 1 to assess whether students are evaluating both the function and the rate of change correctly when x is negative.

From Concrete to Abstract

Exercise 4 asks students to observe and then generalize a pattern as the order of differences increases.

5-8 Lesson Notes

1 FOCUS

Vertical Alignment

Before Lesson 5-8
Solve linear inequalities.

Lesson 5-8
Graph quadratic inequalities in two variables.
Solve quadratic inequalities in one variable.

After Lesson 5-8
Determine solutions of square root inequalities using graphs.

2 TEACH

Scaffolding Questions

Have students read the *Why* section of the lesson.

Ask:

- What is a slingshot and how is it used? Ask a student who is familiar with slingshots to explain.
- How else can you model this situation? Draw a graph of the given quadratic equation.
- Which way does the parabola for the given quadratic function open? How do you know? Downward; the *a* value is a negative number.

5-8 Quadratic Inequalities

Then
You solved linear inequalities. (Lesson 2-8)

Now
- Graph quadratic inequalities in two variables.
- Solve quadratic inequalities in one variable.

NGSSS
MA.912.A.4.11 Solve a polynomial inequality by examining the graph with and without the use of technology.
MA.912.A.10.3 Decide whether a given statement is always, sometimes, or never true (statements involving linear or quadratic expressions, equations, or inequalities rational or radical expressions or logarithmic or exponential functions).

New Vocabulary
quadratic inequality

FL Math Online
glencoe.com

Why?

A water balloon launched from a slingshot can be represented by several different quadratic equations and inequalities.

Suppose the height of a water balloon $h(t)$ in meters above the ground t seconds after being launched is modeled by the quadratic function $h(t) = -4.9t^2 + 32t + 1.2$. You can solve a quadratic inequality to determine how long the balloon will be a certain distance above the ground.

Graph Quadratic Inequalities You can graph **quadratic inequalities** in two variables by using the same techniques used to graph linear inequalities in two variables.

Step 1 Graph the related function.

Step 2 Test a point not on the parabola.

Step 3 Shade accordingly.

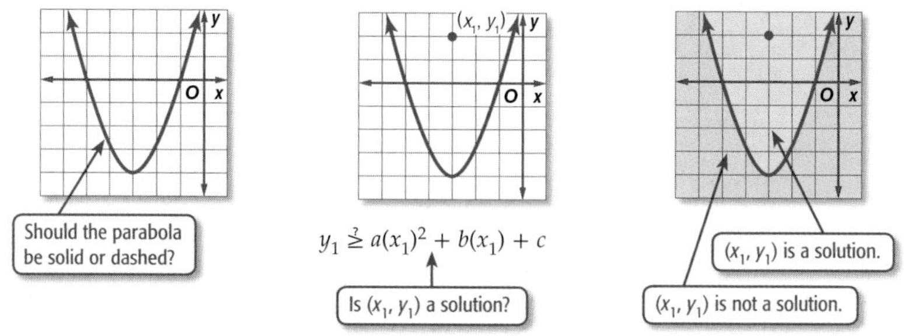

Should the parabola be solid or dashed?
(x_1, y_1)
$y_1 \overset{?}{\gtrless} a(x_1)^2 + b(x_1) + c$
Is (x_1, y_1) a solution?
(x_1, y_1) is a solution.
(x_1, y_1) is not a solution.
O
x
y

EXAMPLE 1 Graph a Quadratic Inequality

Graph $y > x^2 + 2x + 1$.

Step 1 Graph the related function, $y = x^2 + 2x + 1$. The parabola should be dashed.

Step 2 Test a point not on the graph of the parabola.

$y > x^2 + 2x + 1$

$-1 \overset{?}{>} 0^2 + 2(0) + 1$

$-1 \not> 1$ So, $(0, -1)$ is *not* a solution of the inequality.

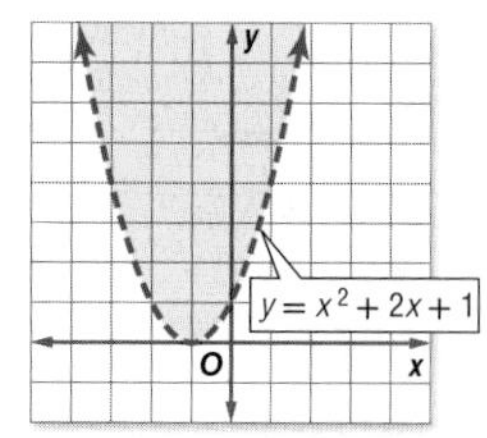

$y = x^2 + 2x + 1$
O
x
y

Step 3 Shade the region that does not contain the point $(0, -1)$.

Guided Practice

1. Graph each inequality. **1A, 1B. See margin.**
   A. $y \leq x^2 + 2x + 4$ **B.** $y < -2x^2 + 3x + 5$

Personal Tutor glencoe.com

Lesson 5-8 Resources

Resource	Approaching-Level	On-Level	Beyond-Level	English Learners
Teacher Edition	• Differentiated Instruction, p. 315	• Differentiated Instruction, pp. 315, 318	• Differentiated Instruction, p. 318	
Chapter Resource Masters	• Study Guide and Intervention, pp. 49–50 • Skills Practice, p. 51 • Practice, p. 52 • Word Problem Practice, p. 53	• Study Guide and Intervention, pp. 49–50 • Skills Practice, p. 51 • Practice, p. 52 • Word Problem Practice, p. 53 • Enrichment, p. 54	• Practice, p. 52 • Word Problem Practice, p. 53 • Enrichment, p. 54	• Study Guide and Intervention, pp. 49–50 • Skills Practice, p. 51 • Practice, p. 52 • Word Problem Practice, p. 53
Transparencies	• 5-Minute Check Transparency 5-8	• 5-Minute Check Transparency 5-8	• 5-Minute Check Transparency 5-8	• 5-Minute Check Transparency 5-8
Other	• Study Notebook	• Study Notebook	• Study Notebook	• Study Notebook

Solve Quadratic Inequalities Quadratic inequalities in one variable can be solved using the graphs of the related quadratic functions.

$ax^2 + bx + c < 0$

Graph $y = ax^2 + bx + c$ and identify the x-values for which the graph lies *below* the x-axis.

For $\leq$, include the x-intercepts in the solution.

$a > 0$

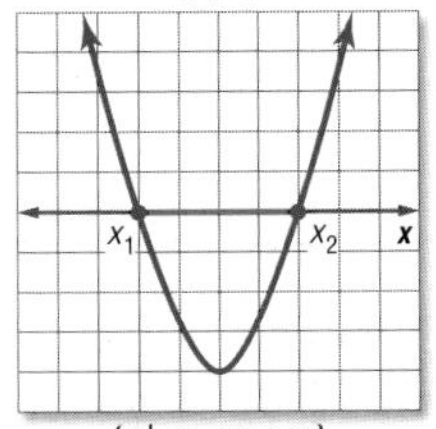

$\{x \mid x_1 < x < x_2\}$

$a < 0$

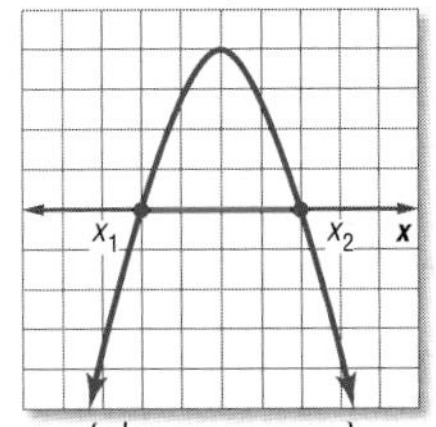

$\{x \mid x < x_1 \text{ or } x > x_2\}$

$ax^2 + bx + c > 0$

Graph $y = ax^2 + bx + c$ and identify the x-values for which the graph lies *above* the x-axis.

For $\geq$, include the x-intercepts in the solution.

$a > 0$

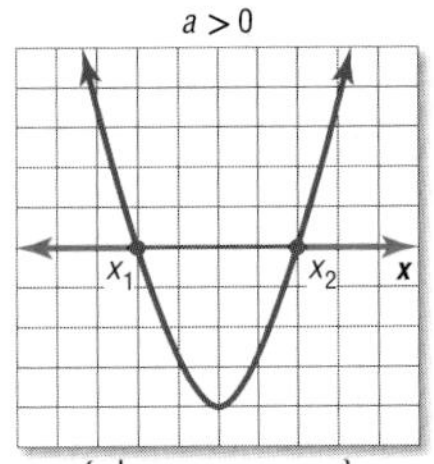

$\{x \mid x < x_1 \text{ or } x > x_2\}$

$a < 0$

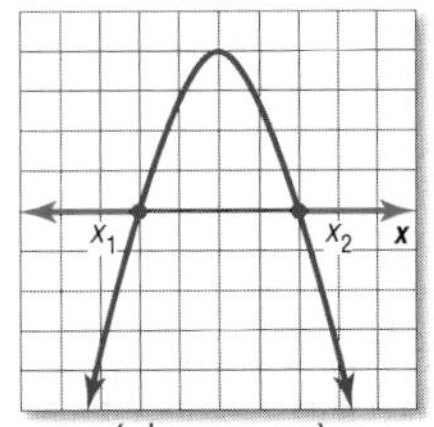

$\{x \mid x_1 < x < x_2\}$

StudyTip

Solving Quadratic Inequalities by Graphing A precise graph of the related quadratic function is not necessary since the zeros of the function were found algebraically.

EXAMPLE 2 **Solve $ax^2 + bx + c < 0$ by Graphing**

Solve $x^2 + 2x - 8 < 0$ by graphing.

The solution consists of x-values for which the graph of the related function lies *below* the x-axis. Begin by finding the roots of the related function.

$x^2 + 2x - 8 = 0$		**Related equation**
$(x - 2)(x + 4) = 0$		**Factor.**
$x - 2 = 0$	or $x + 4 = 0$	**Zero Product Property**
$x = 2$	$x = -4$	**Solve each equation.**

Sketch the graph of a parabola that has x-intercepts at -4 and 2. The graph should open up because $a > 0$.

The graph lies below the x-axis between $x = -4$ and $x = 2$. Thus, the solution set of the inequality is $\{x \mid -4 < x < 2\}$.

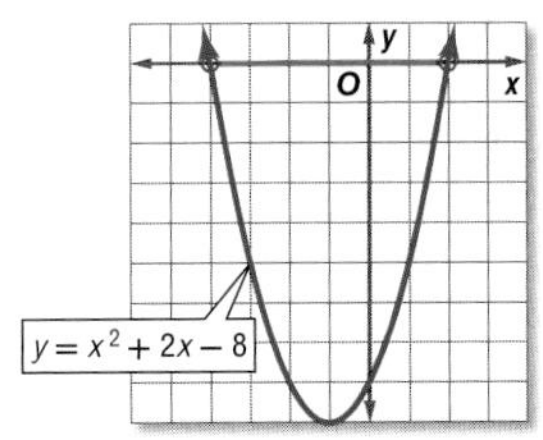

CHECK Test one value of x less than -4, one between -4 and 2, and one greater than 2 in the original inequality.

Test $x = -6$.	**Test $x = 0$.**	**Test $x = 5$.**
$x^2 + 2x - 8 < 0$	$x^2 + 2x - 8 < 0$	$x^2 + 2x - 8 < 0$
$(-6)^2 + 2(-6) - 8 \overset{?}{<} 0$	$0^2 + 2(0) - 8 \overset{?}{<} 0$	$5^2 + 2(5) - 8 \overset{?}{<} 0$
$16 < 0$ ✗	$-8 < 0$ ✓	$27 < 0$ ✗

Guided Practice

2. Solve each inequality by graphing.

A. $0 > x^2 + 5x - 6$ $\{x \mid -6 < x < 1\}$ **B.** $-x^2 + 3x + 10 \leq 0$ $\{x \mid x \leq -2 \text{ or } x \geq 5\}$

Personal Tutor glencoe.com

Graph Quadratic Inequalities

Example 1 shows how to graph a quadratic inequality by graphing the related quadratic function.

Formative Assessment

Use the Guided Practice exercises after each example to determine students' understanding of concepts.

Additional Example

1 Graph $y > x^2 - 3x + 2$.

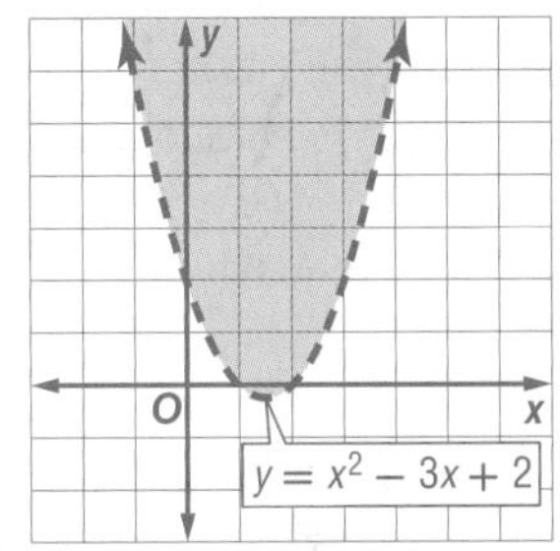

Additional Examples also in Interactive Classroom PowerPoint® Presentations

IWB INTERACTIVE WHITEBOARD READY

Solve Quadratic Inequalities

Example 2 shows how to solve a quadratic inequality of the form $ax^2 + bx + c < 0$ by graphing the related quadratic function.

Additional Example

2 Solve $x^2 - 4x + 3 < 0$ by graphing.

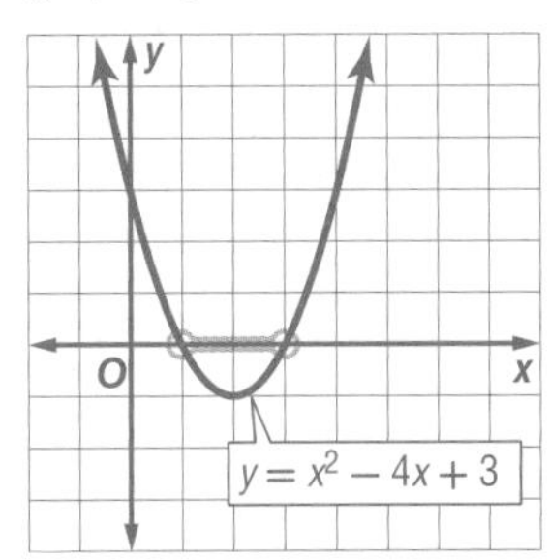

$\{x \mid 1 < x < 3\}$

Additional Answers (Guided Practice)

1A.

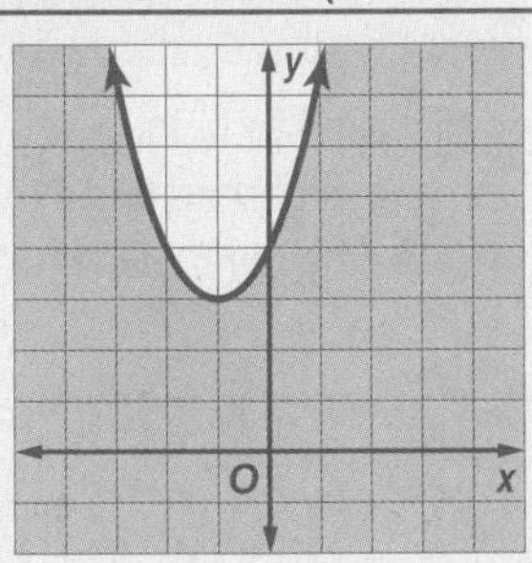

1B.

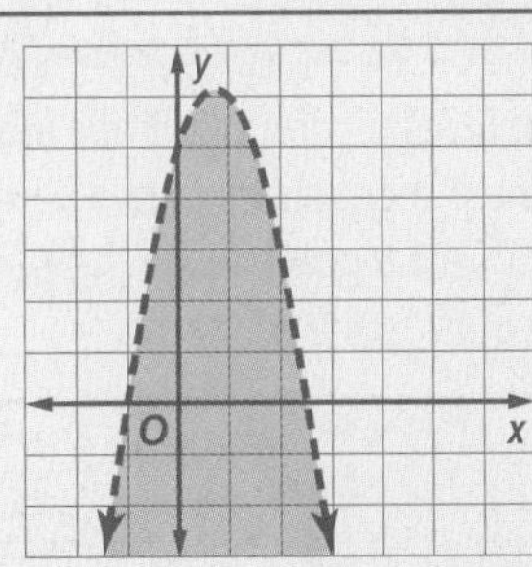

TEACH with TECH

BLOG Have students write a blog entry describing how graphing a quadratic inequality is similar to and different from graphing a linear inequality.

Solve Quadratic Inequalities continued

Example 3 shows how to solve a quadratic inequality of the form $ax^2 + bx + c \geq 0$ by graphing the related quadratic function. **Example 4** shows how to use the graph of a quadratic inequality to solve a real-world problem. **Example 5** shows how to solve a quadratic inequality algebraically.

Additional Examples

3 Solve $0 \leq -2x^2 - 6x + 1$ by graphing.

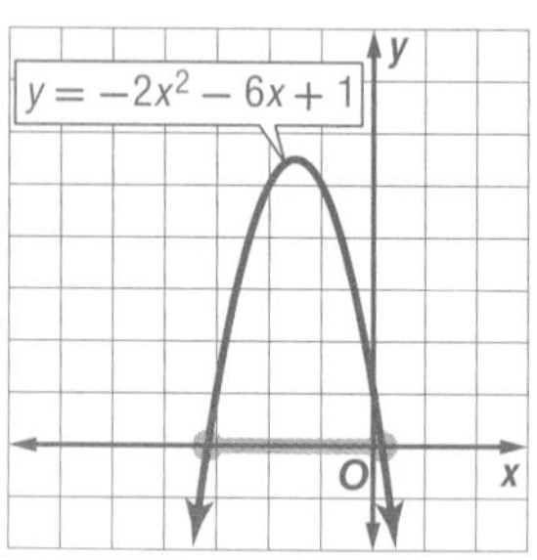

$\{x \mid -3.16 \leq x \leq 0.16\}$

4 **SPORTS** The height of a ball above the ground after it is thrown upwards at 40 feet per second can be modeled by the function $h(x) = 40x - 16x^2$, where the height $h(x)$ is given in feet and the time x is in seconds. At what time in its flight is the ball within 15 feet of the ground? The ball is within 15 feet of the ground for the first 0.46 second of its flight and again after 2.04 seconds until the ball hits the ground at 2.5 seconds.

5 Solve $x^2 + x \leq 2$ algebraically. $\{x \mid -2 \leq x \leq 1\}$

EXAMPLE 3 Solve $ax^2 + bx + c \geq 0$ by Graphing

Solve $2x^2 + 4x - 5 \geq 0$ by graphing.

The solution consists of x-values for which the graph of the related function lies *on and above* the x-axis. Begin by finding the roots of the related function.

$2x^2 + 4x - 5 = 0$ — **Related equation**

$x = \dfrac{-b \pm \sqrt{b^2 - 4ac}}{2a}$ — **Use the Quadratic Formula**

$x = \dfrac{-4 \pm \sqrt{4^2 - 4(2)(-5)}}{2(2)}$ — **Replace *a* with 4, *b* with 2, and *c* with −5.**

$x = \dfrac{-4 + \sqrt{56}}{4}$ or $x = \dfrac{-4 - \sqrt{56}}{4}$ — **Simplify and write as two equations.**

≈ 0.87 $\qquad \approx -2.87$ — **Simplify.**

Sketch the graph of a parabola with x-intercepts at -2.87 and 0.87. The graph opens up since $a > 0$. The graph lies on and above the x-axis at about $x \leq -2.87$ and $x \geq 0.87$. Therefore, the solution set of the inequality is approximately $\{x \mid x \leq -2.87 \text{ or } x \geq 0.87\}$.

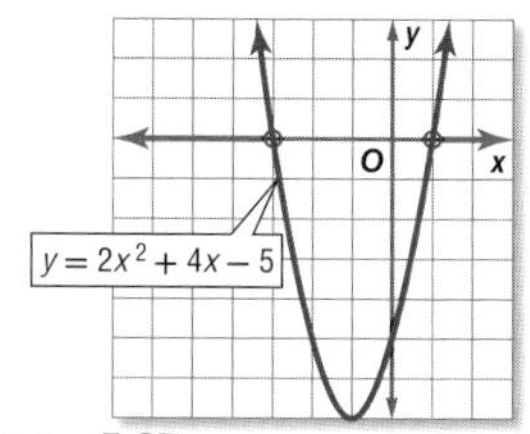

Guided Practice

3. Solve each inequality by graphing.

A. $x^2 - 6x + 2 > 0$ $\qquad$ **B.** $-4x^2 + 5x + 7 \geq 0$

3A. $\{x \mid x < 0.35 \text{ or } x > 5.65\}$
3B. $\{x \mid -0.84 \leq x \leq 2.09\}$

Personal Tutor glencoe.com

Real-world problems can be solved by graphing quadratic inequalities.

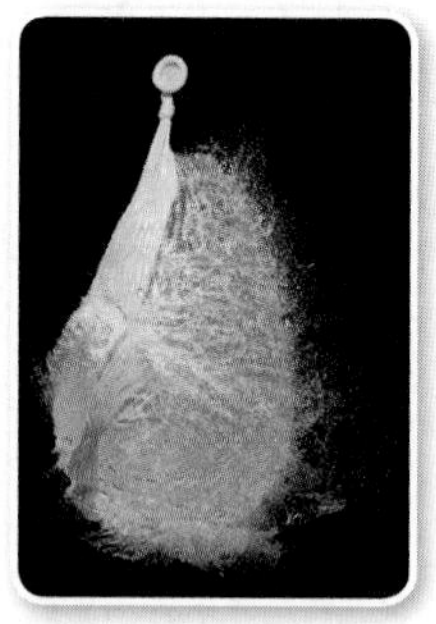

Real-World Link

It takes just milliseconds for a water balloon to break. A high-speed camera can capture the impact on the fluid before gravity makes it fall.

Source: NASA

Real-World EXAMPLE 4 Solve a Quadratic Inequality

WATER BALLOONS Refer to the application at the beginning of the lesson. At what time will a water balloon be within 3 meters of the ground after it has been launched?

The function $h(t) = -4.9t^2 + 32t + 1.2$ describes the height of the water balloon. Therefore, you want to find the values of t for which $h(t) \leq 3$.

$h(t) \leq 3$ — **Original inequality**

$-4.9t^2 + 32t + 1.2 \leq 3$ — **$h(t) = -4.9t^2 + 32t + 1.2$**

$-4.9t^2 + 32t - 1.8 \leq 0$ — **Subtract 3 from each side.**

Graph the related function $y = -4.9t^2 + 32x - 1.8$ using a graphing calculator. The zeros of the function are about 0.06 and 6.47, and the graph lies below the x-axis when $x < 0.06$ and $x > 6.47$.

So, the water balloon is within 3 meters of the ground during the first 0.06 second after being launched and again after about 6.47 seconds until it hits the ground.

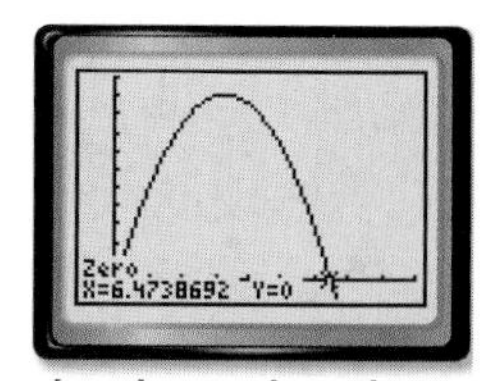

[−1, 9] scl: 1 by [−5, 55] scl: 5

Guided Practice

4. **ROCKETS** The height $h(t)$ of a model rocket in feet t seconds after its launch can be represented by the function $h(t) = -16t^2 + 82t + 0.25$. During what interval is the rocket at least 100 feet above the ground? $\{t \mid 1.99 \leq t \leq 3.14\}$

Personal Tutor glencoe.com

Focus on Mathematical Content

Quadratic Inequalities Graph quadratic inequalities in two variables using the same techniques as when graphing linear inequalities in two variables. Graph the related function. Use a dashed line if the symbol is $>$ or $<$. Test a point inside the parabola. If it is a solution, shade inside the parabola. If it is not a solution, shade outside the parabola.

StudyTip

Solving Quadratic Inequalities Algebraically The solution set of a quadratic inequality is all real numbers when all three test points satisfy the inequality. It is the empty set when none of the test points satisfy the inequality.

EXAMPLE 5 Solve a Quadratic Inequality Algebraically

Solve $x^2 - 3x \leq 18$ algebraically.

Step 1 Solve the related quadratic equation $x^2 - 3x = 18$.

$x^2 - 3x = 18$	**Related quadratic equation**
$x^2 - 3x - 18 = 0$	**Subtract 18 from each side.**
$(x + 3)(x - 6) = 0$	**Factor.**
$x + 3 = 0$ or $x - 6 = 0$	**Zero Product Property**
$x = -3$ $\quad$ $x = 6$	**Solve each equation.**

Step 2 Plot −3 and 6 on a number line. Use dots since these values are solutions of the original inequality. Notice that the number line is divided into three intervals.

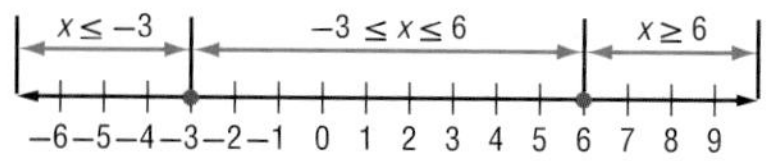

Step 3 Test a value from each interval to see if it satisfies the original inequality.

$x \leq -3$	$-3 \leq x \leq 6$	$x \geq 6$
Test $x = -5$.	Test $x = 0$.	Test $x = 8$.
$x^2 - 3x \leq 18$	$x^2 - 3x \leq 18$	$x^2 - 3x \leq 18$
$(-5)^2 - 3(-5) \overset{?}{\leq} 18$	$(0)^2 - 3(0) \overset{?}{\leq} 18$	$(8)^2 - 3(8) \overset{?}{\leq} 18$
$40 \nleq 18$	$0 \leq 18$	$40 \nleq 18$

The solution set is $\{x \mid -3 \leq x \leq 6\}$. This is shown on the number line below.

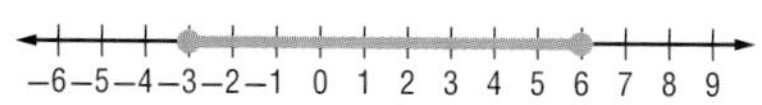

Guided Practice

5. Solve each inequality algebraically.

A. $x^2 + 5x < -6$ $\{x \mid -3 < x < -2\}$ **B.** $x^2 + 11x + 30 \geq 0$ $\{x \mid x \leq -6 \text{ or } x \geq -5\}$

Personal Tutor glencoe.com

Check Your Understanding

Example 1 p. 312 — **Graph each inequality.** 1–3. See margin.

1. $y \leq x^2 - 8x + 2$ 2. $y > x^2 + 6x - 2$ 3. $y \geq -x^2 + 4x + 1$

Examples 2 and 3 pp. 313–314 — **Solve each inequality by graphing.**

4. $0 < x^2 - 5x + 4$ $\{x \mid x < 1 \text{ or } x > 4\}$
5. $x^2 + 8x + 15 < 0$ $\{x \mid -5 < x < -3\}$
6. $-2x^2 - 2x + 12 \geq 0$ $\{x \mid -3 \leq x \leq 2\}$
7. $0 \geq 2x^2 - 4x + 1$ $\{x \mid 0.29 \leq x \leq 1.71\}$

Example 4 p. 314

8. **SOCCER** A midfielder kicks a ball toward the goal during a match. The height of the ball in feet above the ground $h(t)$ at time t can be represented by $h(t) = -0.1t^2 + 2.4t + 1.5$. If the height of the goal is 8 feet, at what time during the kick will the ball be able to enter the goal? $\{t \mid 0 < t < 3.11\}$ or $\{t \mid 20.89 < t \leq 24.61\}$

Example 5 p. 315 — **Solve each inequality algebraically.**

9. $x^2 + 6x - 16 < 0$ $\{x \mid -8 < x < 2\}$
10. $x^2 - 14x > -49$ $\{x \mid x < 7 \text{ or } x > 7\}$
11. $-x^2 + 12x \geq 28$ $\{x \mid 3.17 \leq x \leq 8.83\}$
12. $x^2 - 4x \leq 21$ $\{x \mid -3 \leq x \leq 7\}$

Tips for New Teachers

Alternative Method Another way to solve the inequality in Example 5 is first to subtract 18 from both sides of the inequality, obtaining $x^2 - 3x - 18 > 0$. After factoring the left side as $(x + 3)(x - 6)$, point out that either both binomials must be positive or both must be negative for $(x + 3)(x - 6)$ to be greater than 0. This fact can be used to test the three intervals of the number line.

3 PRACTICE

Formative Assessment

Use Exercises 1–12 to check for understanding.

Use the chart at the bottom of the next page to customize assignments for your students.

Additional Answers

1.

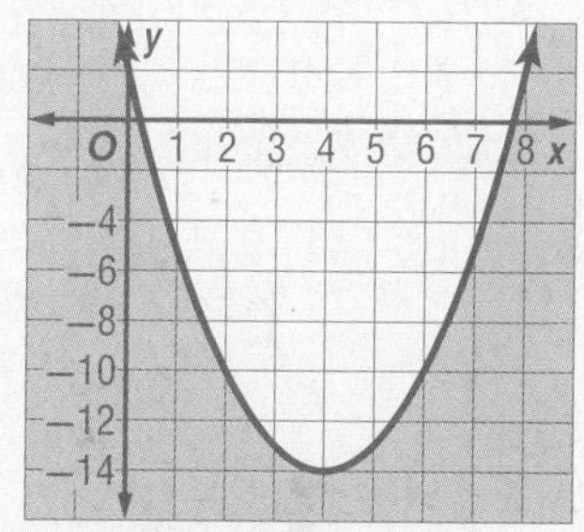

2.

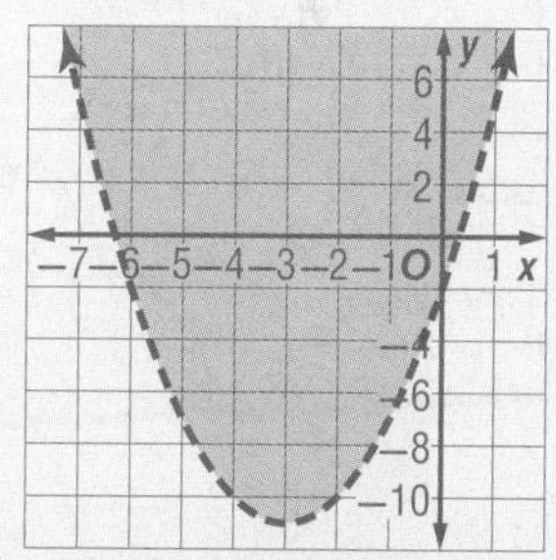

3.

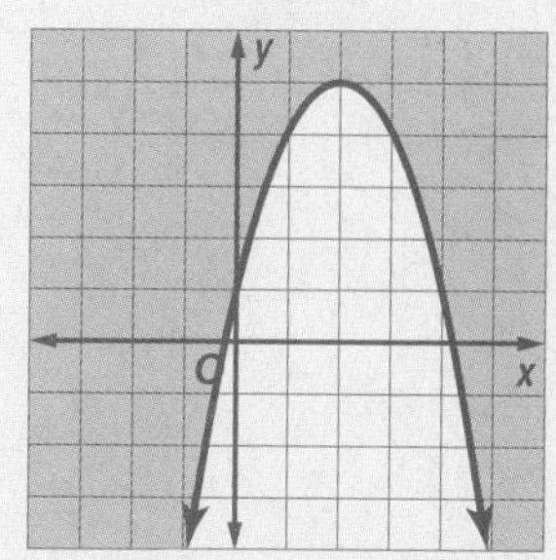

Differentiated Instruction AL OL

If students are having trouble making connections between the graph of a quadratic inequality and the inequality itself,

Then have students think about how the graph of a quadratic inequality helps them understand the meaning of the inequality. Ask them to explore whether the quadratic inequality itself or the graph of the inequality is more meaningful to them. Ask them to give explanations for their choices.

Additional Answers

13. 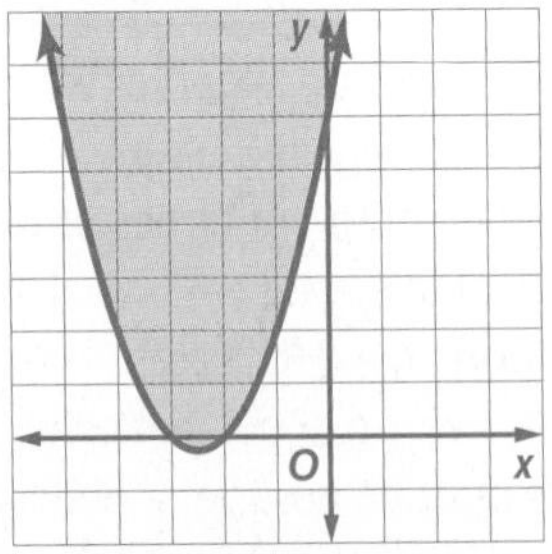

14. 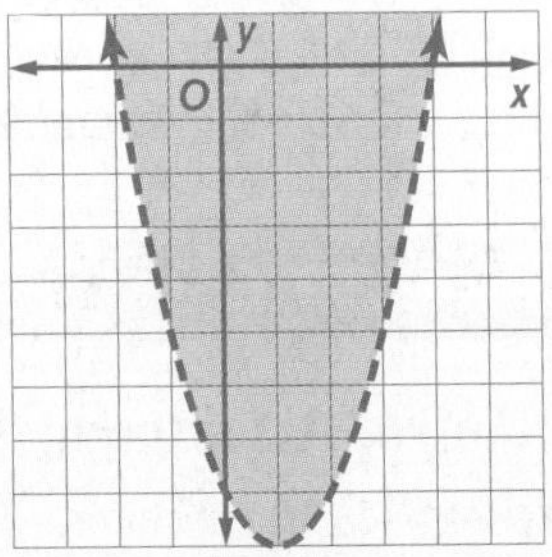

15. 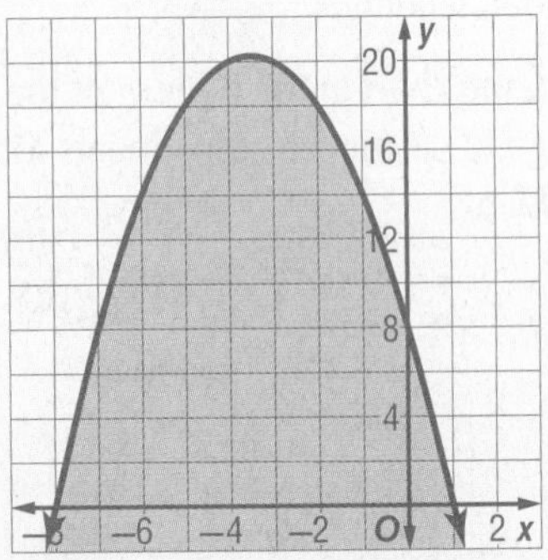

16. 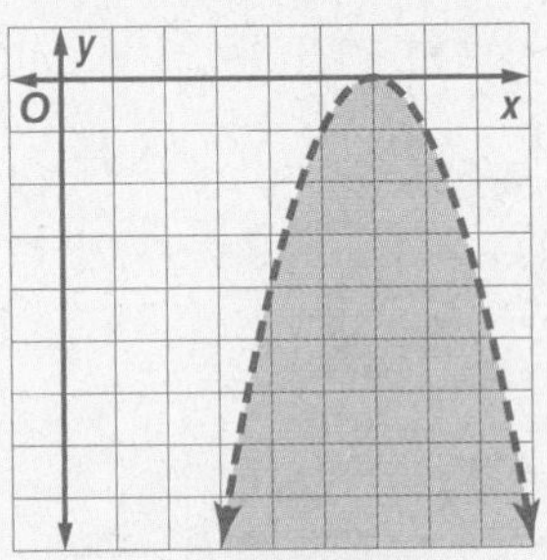

17. 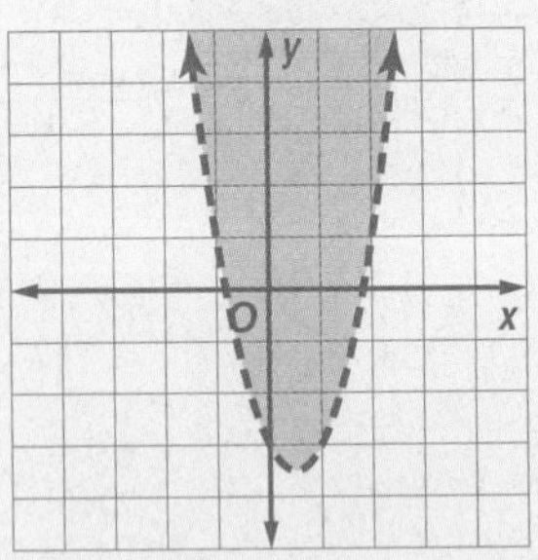

18. 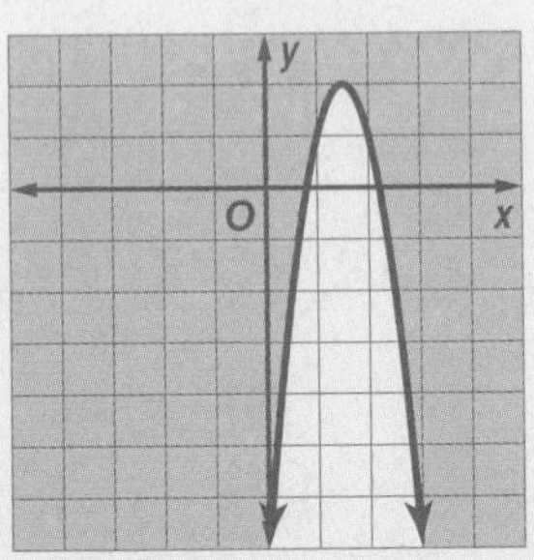

Practice and Problem Solving

● = **Step-by-Step Solutions** begin on page R20.
Extra Practice begins on page 947.

Example 1 p. 312

Graph each inequality. 13–18. See margin.

13. $y \geq x^2 + 5x + 6$
14. $x^2 - 2x - 8 < y$
15. $y \leq -x^2 - 7x + 8$
16. $-x^2 + 12x - 36 > y$
17. $y > 2x^2 - 2x - 3$
18. $y \geq -4x^2 + 12x - 7$

Examples 2 and 3 pp. 313–314

Solve each inequality by graphing.

19. $x^2 - 9x + 9 < 0$
20. $x^2 - 2x - 24 \leq 0$
21. $x^2 + 8x + 16 \geq 0$
22. $x^2 + 6x + 3 > 0$
23. $0 > -x^2 + 7x + 12$
24. $-x^2 + 2x - 15 < 0$
25. $4x^2 + 12x + 10 \leq 0$ ∅
26. $-3x^2 - 3x + 9 > 0$
27. $0 > -2x^2 + 4x + 4$
28. $3x^2 + 12x + 36 \leq 0$ ∅
29. $0 \leq -4x^2 + 8x + 5$ $\{x \mid -0.5 \leq x \leq 2.5\}$
30. $-2x^2 + 3x + 3 \leq 0$ $\{x \mid x \leq -0.69 \text{ or } x \geq 2.19\}$

19. $\{x \mid 1.1 < x < 7.9\}$
20. $\{x \mid -4 \leq x \leq 6\}$
21. $\{x \mid \text{all real numbers}\}$
22. $\{x \mid x < -5.45 \text{ or } x > -0.55\}$

Example 4 p. 314

31. **ARCHITECTURE** An arched entry of a room is shaped like a parabola that can be represented by the equation $f(x) = -x^2 + 6x + 1$. How far from the sides of the arch is its height at least 7 feet? about 1.26 ft to 4.73 ft

23. $\{x \mid x < -1.42 \text{ or } x > 8.42\}$
24. $\{x \mid \text{all real numbers}\}$
26. $\{x \mid -2.30 < x < 1.30\}$
27. $\{x \mid x < -0.73 \text{ or } x > 2.73\}$

32. **MANUFACTURING** A box is formed by cutting 4-inch by 4-inch squares from each corner of a square piece of cardboard and then folding the sides. If $V(x) = 4x^2 - 64x + 256$ represents the volume of the box, what should the dimensions of the original piece of cardboard be if the volume of the box cannot exceed 750 cubic inches? greater than 8 in. but no more than 21.69 in.

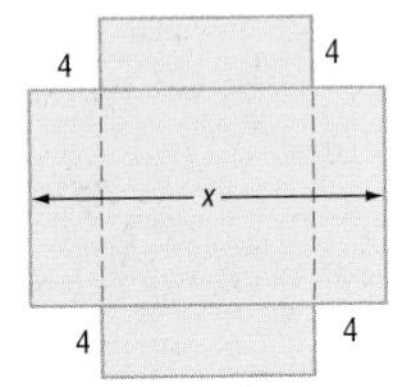

Example 5 p. 315

Solve each inequality algebraically. 33–44. See Chapter 5 Answer Appendix.

33. $x^2 - 9x < -20$
34. $x^2 + 7x \geq -10$
35. $2 > x^2 - x$
36. $-3 \leq -x^2 - 4x$
37. $-x^2 + 2x \leq -10$
38. $-6 > x^2 + 4x$
39. $2x^2 + 4 \geq 9$
40. $3x^2 + x \geq -3$
41. $-4x^2 + 2x < 3$
42. $-11 \geq -2x^2 - 5x$
43. $-12 < -5x^2 - 10x$
44. $-3x^2 - 10x > -1$

Real-World Link

As a rule of thumb, total poolside area should be at least equal to the surface area of a swimming pool.

Source: About

45. **SWIMMING POOLS** The Sanchez family is adding a deck along two sides of their swimming pool. The deck width will be the same on both sides and the total area of the pool and deck cannot exceed 750 square feet. a. See Chapter 5 Answer Appendix.
 a. Graph the quadratic inequality.
 b. Determine the possible widths of the deck. greater than 0 ft but no more than 10.04 ft

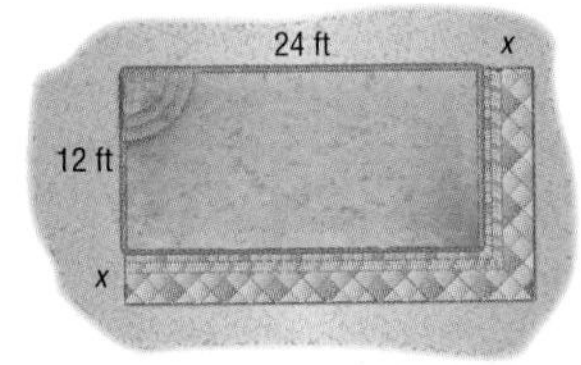

Write a quadratic inequality for each graph.

46. 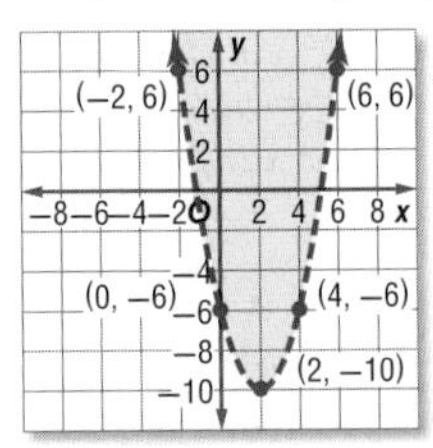

47. 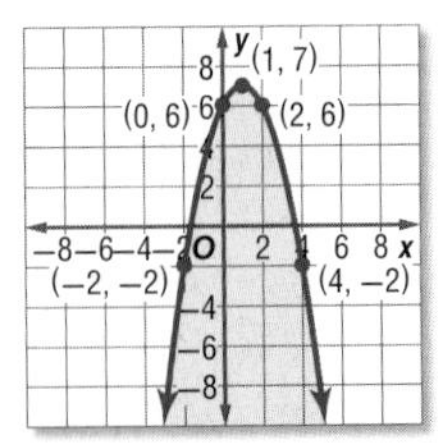

48. 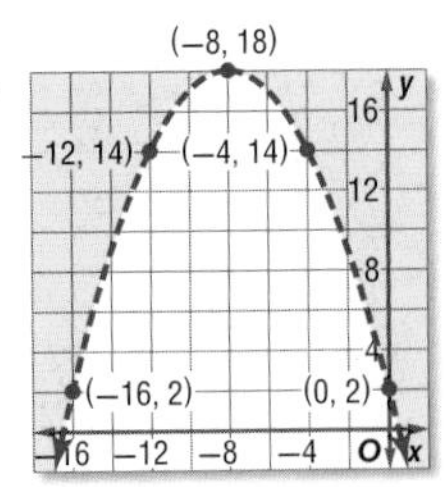

46. $y > x^2 - 4x - 6$
47. $y \leq -x^2 + 2x + 6$
48. $y > -0.25x^2 - 4x + 2$

Differentiated Homework Options

Level	Assignment	Two-Day Option	
AL Basic	13–44, 57–60, 62–82	13–43 odd, 63–66	14–44 even, 57–60, 62, 67–82
OL Core	13–55 odd, 56, 57–60, 62–82	13–44, 63–66	45–60, 62, 67–82
BL Advanced	45–76, (optional: 77–82)		

49. {x | x < −1.06 or x > 7.06}
50. {x | all real numbers}
51. {x | x ≤ −2.75 or x ≥ 1}
52. ∅
53. {x | x < 0.61 or x > 2.72}
54. {x | x ≤ −5.19 or x ≥ 0.19}
55c. The graph is shifted down 25,000 units. The manufacturer must sell from 47,000 to 81,000 digital audio players.

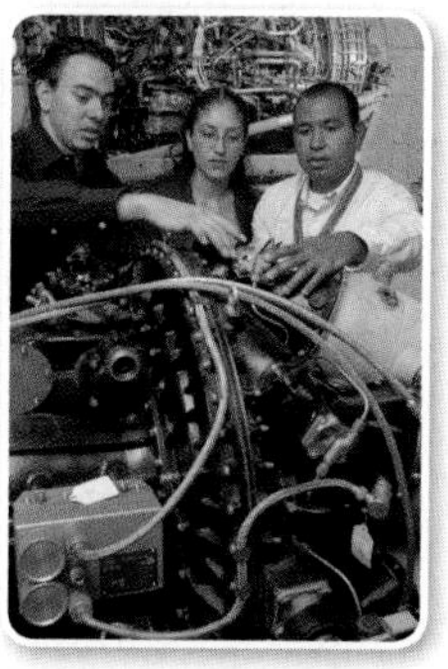

Real-World Career

Electrical Engineer
Electrical engineers design, develop, test, and supervise the making of electrical equipment such as digital music players, electric motors, lighting, and radar and navigation systems. A bachelor's degree in engineering is required for almost all entry-level engineering jobs.

58. Neither; Don graphed the inequality in two variables, and Diego graphed the wrong interval.
59–62. See Chapter 5 Answer Appendix.

Solve each quadratic inequality by using a graph, a table, or algebraically.

49. $-2x^2 + 12x < -15$ **50.** $5x^2 + x + 3 \geq 0$ **51.** $11 \leq 4x^2 + 7x$

52. $x^2 - 4x \leq -7$ **53.** $-3x^2 + 10x < 5$ **54.** $-1 \geq -x^2 - 5x$

55. BUSINESS An electronics manufacturer uses the function $P(x) = x(-27.5x + 3520) + 20{,}000$ to model their monthly profits when selling x thousand digital audio players.

a. Graph the quadratic inequality for a monthly profit of at least $100,000. **See margin.**

b. How many digital audio players must the manufacturer sell to earn a profit of at least $100,000 in a month? **from 30,000 to 98,000 digital audio players**

c. Suppose the manufacturer has an additional monthly expense of $25,000. Explain how this affects the graph of the profit function. Then determine how many digital audio players the manufacturer needs to sell to have at least $100,000 in profits.

56. UTILITIES A contractor is installing drain pipes for a shopping center's parking lot. The outer diameter of the pipe is to be 10 inches. The cross sectional area of the pipe must be at least 35 square inches and should not be more than 42 square inches.

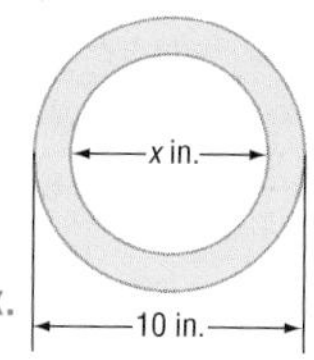

a. Graph the quadratic inequalities. **See Chapter 5 Answer Appendix.**

b. What thickness of drain pipe can the contractor use? **1.28 in. to 1.59 in.**

H.O.T. Problems
Use Higher-Order Thinking Skills

57. OPEN ENDED Write a quadratic inequality for each condition.

a. The solution set is all real numbers. **Sample answer: $x^2 + 2x + 1 \geq 0$**

b. The solution set is the empty set. **Sample answer: $x^2 - 4x + 6 < 0$**

58. ERROR ANALYSIS Don and Diego used a graph to solve the quadratic inequality $x^2 - 2x - 8 > 0$. Is either of them correct? Explain.

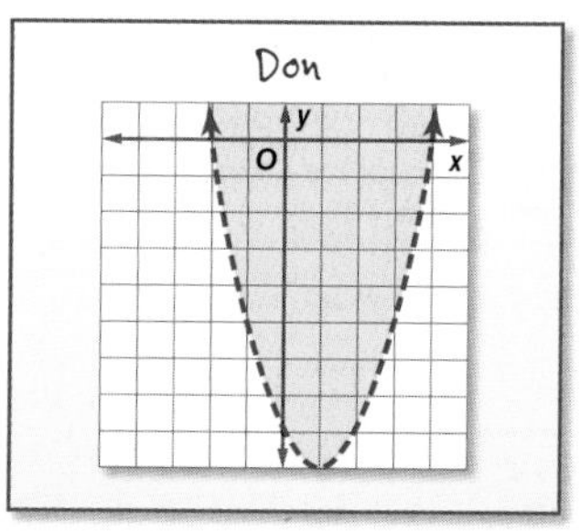

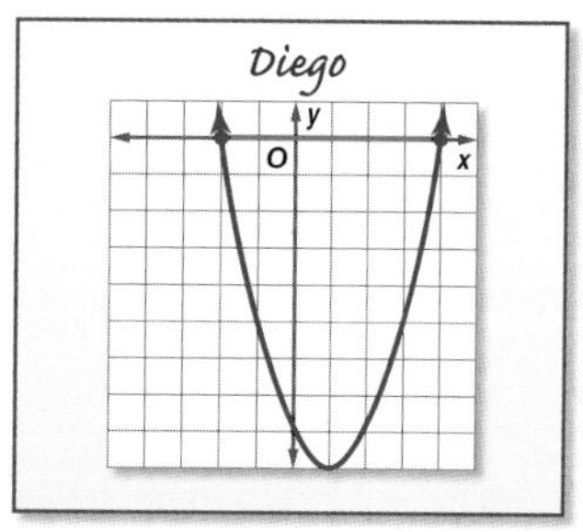

59. REASONING Are the boundaries of the solution set of $x^2 + 4x - 12 \leq 0$ twice the value of the boundaries of $\frac{1}{2}x^2 + 2x - 6 \leq 0$? Explain.

60. REASONING Determine if the following statement is *sometimes*, *always*, or *never* true. Explain your reasoning.

The intersection of $y \leq -ax^2 + c$ and $y \geq ax^2 - c$ is the empty set.

61. CHALLENGE Graph the intersection of the graphs of $y \leq -x^2 + 4$ and $y \geq x^2 - 4$.

62. WRITING IN MATH Compare and contrast graphing linear and quadratic inequalities.

Additional Answer

55a.

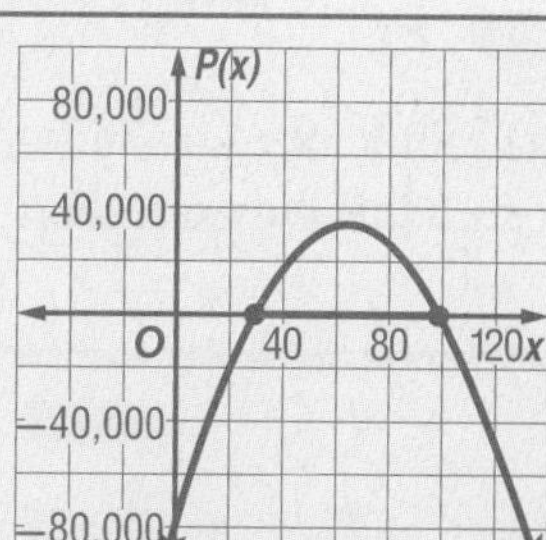

Study Guide and Intervention
CRM pp. 49–50 AL OL ELL

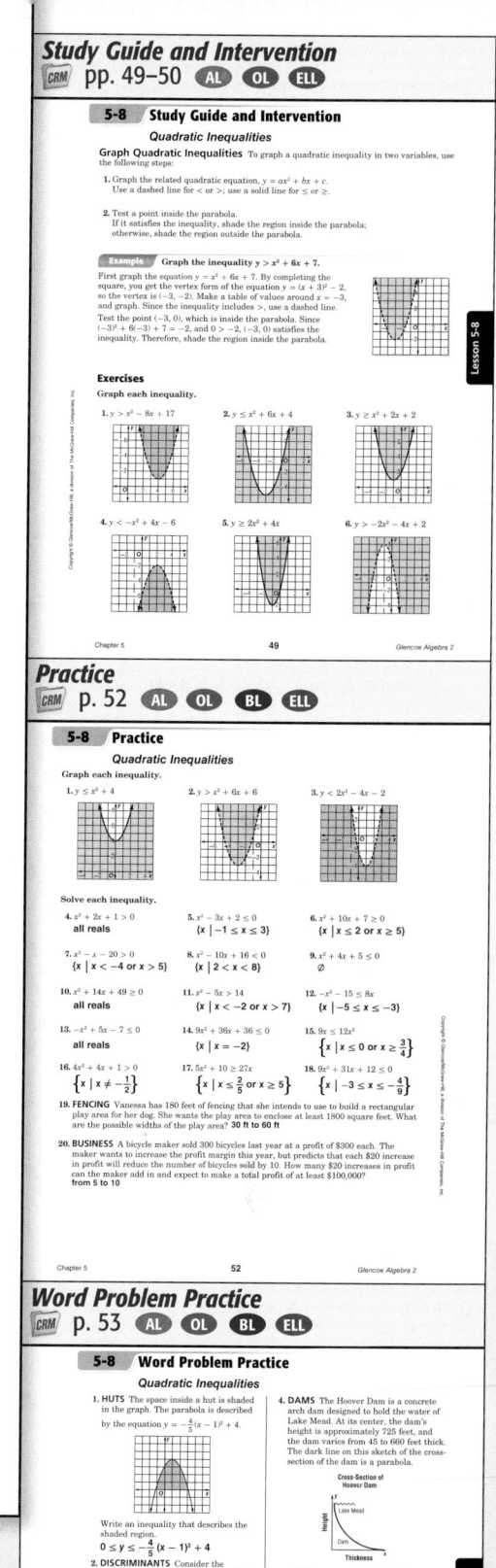

5-8 Study Guide and Intervention

Quadratic Inequalities

Graph Quadratic Inequalities To graph a quadratic inequality in two variables, use the following steps:

1. Graph the related quadratic equation, $y = ax^2 + bx + c$. Use a dashed line for < or >; use a solid line for ≤ or ≥.

2. Test a point inside the parabola. If it satisfies the inequality, shade the region inside the parabola; otherwise, shade the region outside the parabola.

Example Graph the inequality $y > x^2 + 6x + 7$.

First graph the equation $y = x^2 + 6x + 7$. By completing the square, you get the vertex form of the equation $y = (x + 3)^2 - 2$, so the vertex is (−3, −2). Make a table of values around $x = -3$, and graph. Since the inequality includes >, use a dashed line. Test the point (−3, 0), which is inside the parabola. Since $(-3)^2 + 6(-3) + 7 = -2$, and $0 > -2$, (−3, 0) satisfies the inequality. Therefore, shade the region inside the parabola.

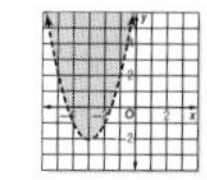

Exercises

Graph each inequality.

1. $y > x^2 - 8x + 17$

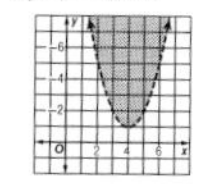

2. $y \leq x^2 + 6x + 4$

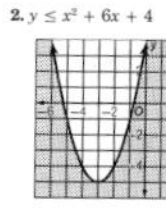

3. $y \geq x^2 + 2x + 2$

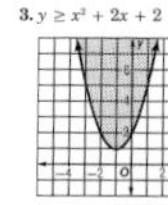

4. $y < -x^2 + 4x - 6$

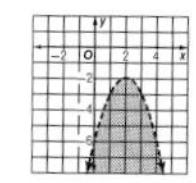

5. $y \geq 2x^2 + 4x$

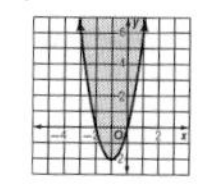

6. $y > -2x^2 - 4x + 2$

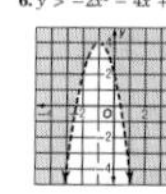

Lesson 5-8

Practice
CRM p. 52 AL OL BL ELL

5-8 Practice

Quadratic Inequalities

Graph each inequality.

1. $y \leq x^2 + 4$

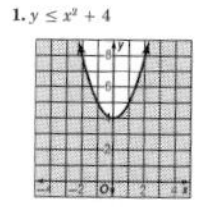

2. $y > x^2 + 6x + 6$

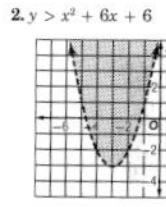

3. $y < 2x^2 - 4x - 2$

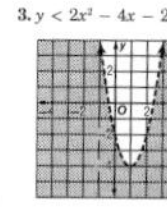

Solve each inequality.

4. $x^2 + 2x + 1 > 0$ **all reals**
5. $x^2 - 3x + 2 \leq 0$ **{x | −1 ≤ x ≤ 3}**
6. $x^2 + 10x + 7 \geq 0$ **{x | x ≤ 2 or x ≥ 5}**
7. $x^2 - x - 20 > 0$ **{x | x < −4 or x > 5}**
8. $x^2 - 10x + 16 < 0$ **{x | 2 < x < 8}**
9. $x^2 + 4x + 5 \leq 0$ **∅**
10. $x^2 + 14x + 49 \geq 0$ **all reals**
11. $x^2 - 5x > 14$ **{x | x < −2 or x > 7}**
12. $-x^2 - 15 \leq 8x$ **{x | −5 ≤ x ≤ −3}**
13. $-x^2 + 5x - 7 \leq 0$ **all reals**
14. $9x^2 + 36x + 36 \leq 0$ **{x | x = −2}**
15. $9x \leq 12x^2$ **$\left\{x \mid x \leq 0 \text{ or } x \geq \frac{3}{4}\right\}$**
16. $4x^2 + 4x + 1 > 0$ **$\left\{x \mid x \neq -\frac{1}{2}\right\}$**
17. $5x^2 + 10 \geq 27x$ **$\left\{x \mid x \leq \frac{2}{5} \text{ or } x \geq 5\right\}$**
18. $9x^2 + 31x + 12 \leq 0$ **$\left\{x \mid -3 \leq x \leq -\frac{4}{9}\right\}$**

19. **FENCING** Vanessa has 180 feet of fencing that she intends to use to build a rectangular play area for her dog. She wants the play area to enclose at least 1800 square feet. What are the possible widths of the play area? **30 ft to 60 ft**

20. **BUSINESS** A bicycle maker sold 300 bicycles last year at a profit of $300 each. The maker wants to increase the profit margin this year, but predicts that each $20 increase in profit will reduce the number of bicycles sold by 10. How many $20 increases in profit can the maker add in and expect to make a total profit of at least $100,000? **from 5 to 10**

Word Problem Practice
CRM p. 53 AL OL BL ELL

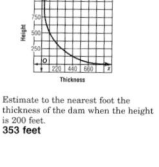

5-8 Word Problem Practice

Quadratic Inequalities

1. **HUTS** The space inside a hut is shaded in the graph. The parabola is described by the equation $y = -\frac{4}{5}(x - 1)^2 + 4$.

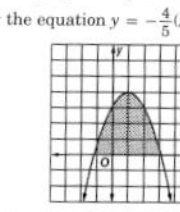

Write an inequality that describes the shaded region.
$0 \leq y \leq -\frac{4}{5}(x - 1)^2 + 4$

2. **DISCRIMINANTS** Consider the equation $ax^2 + bx + c = 0$. Assume that the discriminant is zero and that a is positive. What are the solutions of the inequality $ax^2 + bx + c \leq 0$?
$x = -\frac{b}{2a}$

3. **KIOSKS** Caleb is designing a kiosk by wrapping a piece of sheet metal with dimensions $x + 5$ inches by $4x + 8$ inches into a cylindrical shape. Ignoring cost, Caleb would like a kiosk that has a surface area of at least 4480 square inches. What values of x satisfy this condition?
x > 30 (Note that the values of x < −37 result in a higher product, but negative lengths do not make sense.)

4. **DAMS** The Hoover Dam is a concrete arch dam designed to hold the water of Lake Mead. At its center, the dam's height is approximately 725 feet, and the dam varies from 45 to 660 feet thick. The dark line on this sketch of the cross-section of the dam is a parabola.

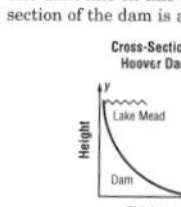

a. Write an equation for the Hoover Dam parabola. Let the height be the y-value of the parabola and the thickness be the x-value of the parabola. (Hint: the equation will be in the form: y = k (x − maximum thickness) + maximum height.)
$y = -0.00192(x - 660)^2 + 725$

b. Using your equation, graph the parabola of the Hoover Dam for $45 \leq x \leq 660$.

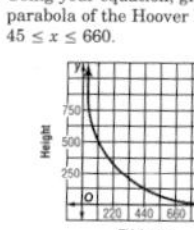

c. Estimate to the nearest foot the thickness of the dam when the height is 200 feet.
353 feet

Lesson 5-8

Enrichment
CRM p. 54 OL BL

5-8 Word Problem Practice

Quadratic Inequalities

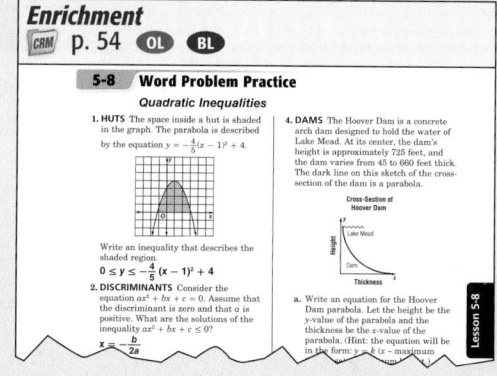

1. **HUTS** The space inside a hut is shaded in the graph. The parabola is described by the equation $y = -\frac{4}{5}(x - 1)^2 + 4$.

Write an inequality that describes the shaded region.
$0 \leq y \leq -\frac{4}{5}(x - 1)^2 + 4$

2. **DISCRIMINANTS** Consider the equation $ax^2 + bx + c = 0$. Assume that the discriminant is zero and that a is positive. What are the solutions of the inequality $ax^2 + bx + c \leq 0$?
$x = -\frac{b}{2a}$

4. **DAMS** The Hoover Dam is a concrete arch dam designed to hold the water of Lake Mead. At its center, the dam's height is approximately 725 feet, and the dam varies from 45 to 660 feet thick. The dark line on this sketch of the cross-section of the dam is a parabola.

a. Write an equation for the Hoover Dam parabola. Let the height be the y-value of the parabola and the thickness be the x-value of the parabola. (Hint: the equation will be in the form: y = k (x − maximum

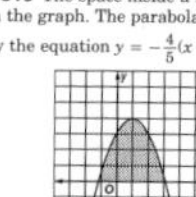

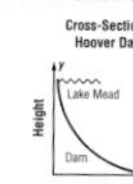

Lesson 5-8

Watch Out!

Error Analysis For an inequality containing x as the only variable, the solution set should refer only to values of x. Point out that in Exercise 58 Don has graphed an inequality in two variables.

4 ASSESS

Ticket Out the Door Write a quadratic inequality in one variable on the board. On an index card, have students solve the inequality graphically and algebraically.

Formative Assessment

Check for student understanding of concepts in Lessons 5-7 and 5-8.

CRM Quiz 4, p. 60

NGSSS PRACTICE 912.G.6.5, 912.A.7.5, 912.P.3.1, 912.A.1.6

63. **GRIDDED RESPONSE** You need to seed an area that is 80 feet by 40 feet. Each bag of seed can cover 25 square yards of land. How many bags of seed will you need? **15**

64. **SAT/ACT** The product of two integers is between 107 and 116. Which of the following *cannot* be one of the integers? **D**

A. 5   C. 12
B. 10   D. 15

65. **PROBABILITY** Five students are to be arranged side by side with the tallest student in the center and the two shortest students on the ends. If no two students are the same height, how many different arrangements are possible? **G**

F. 2   H. 5
G. 4   I. 6

66. **SHORT RESPONSE** Simplify $\frac{5+i}{6-3i}$. $\frac{3}{5}+\frac{7}{15}i$

Spiral Review

Write an equation in vertex form for each parabola. (Lesson 5-7)

67.

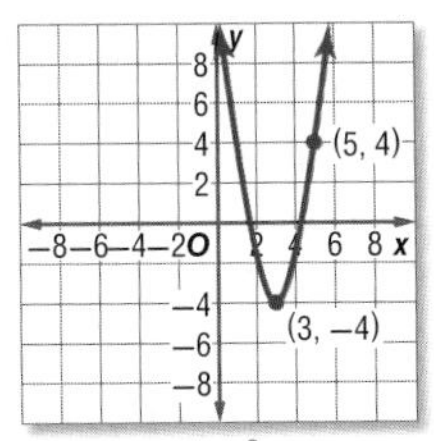

$y = 2(x-3)^2 - 4$

68.

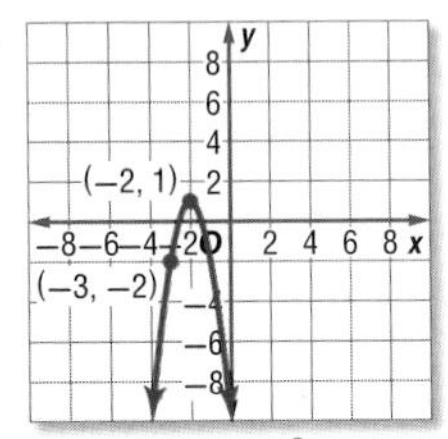

$y = -3(x+2)^2 + 1$

69.

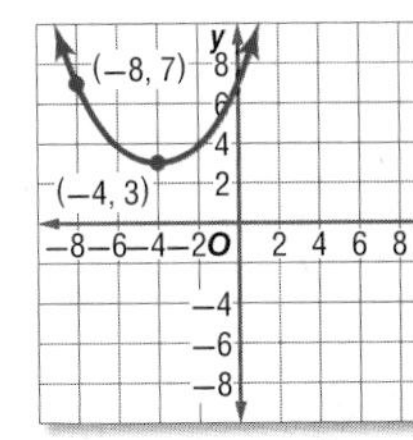

$y = 0.25(x+4)^2 + 3$

Complete parts a and b for each quadratic equation.

a. Find the value of the discriminant.

b. Describe the number and type of roots. (Lesson 5-6)

70. $4x^2 + 7x - 3 = 0$ **97; 2 irrational roots**

71. $-3x^2 + 2x - 4 = 9$ **−152; 2 complex roots**

72. $6x^2 + x - 4 = 12$ **385; 2 irrational roots**

73. **GYMNASTICS** Suppose the drawing is placed on a coordinate grid with the hand grips at $H(0, 0)$ and the toe of the figure in the upper right corner at $T(7, 8)$. Find the coordinates of the toes at the other three positions, if each successive position has been rotated 90° counterclockwise about the origin. (Lesson 4-4) **(−8, 7), (−7, −8), and (8, −7)**

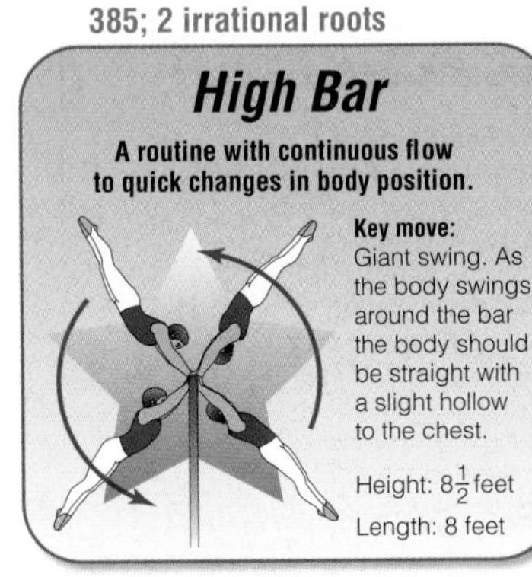

High Bar
A routine with continuous flow to quick changes in body position.
Key move:
Giant swing. As the body swings around the bar the body should be straight with a slight hollow to the chest.
Height: 8½ feet
Length: 8 feet

Perform the indicated operation. If the matrix does not exist, write *impossible*. (Lesson 4-2)

74. $4\begin{bmatrix}3 & -6\\ -5 & 2\end{bmatrix} - 3\begin{bmatrix}4 & -1\\ -2 & 8\end{bmatrix}$ $\begin{bmatrix}0 & -21\\ -14 & -16\end{bmatrix}$

75. $-2\begin{bmatrix}5 & -9\\ 5 & 11\end{bmatrix} - 6\begin{bmatrix}3 & -7\\ -5 & 8\end{bmatrix}$ $\begin{bmatrix}-28 & 60\\ 20 & -70\end{bmatrix}$

76. $\begin{bmatrix}2 & -6\\ -4 & 6\end{bmatrix} \cdot \begin{bmatrix}2 & -1 & 1\\ -1 & 6 & 4\end{bmatrix}$ $\begin{bmatrix}10 & -38 & -22\\ -14 & 40 & 20\end{bmatrix}$

Skills Review

Use the Distributive Property to find each product. (Lesson 1-2)

77. $-6(x - 4)$ **$-6x + 24$**

78. $8(w + 3x)$ **$8w + 24x$**

79. $-4(-2y + 3z)$ **$8y - 12z$**

80. $-1(c - d)$ **$d - c$**

81. $0.5(5x + 6y)$ **$2.5x + 3y$**

82. $-3(-6y - 4z)$ **$18y + 12z$**

Differentiated Instruction BL OL

Extension Write $\sqrt{x^2 - 2x - 3}$ on the board. Ask students to find the values for x for which this expression is a real number. Explain that the solution is all values of x such that the expression under the radical is greater than or equal to zero. $\{x \mid x \le -1 \text{ or } x \ge 3\}$

Modeling Motion

Set Up the Lab

- Place a board on a stack of books to create a ramp.
- Connect the data collection device to the graphing calculator. Place at the top of the ramp so that the data collection device can read the motion of the car on the ramp.
- Hold the car still about 6 inches up from the bottom of the ramp and zero the collection device.

ACTIVITY

Step 1 One group member should press the button to start collecting data.

Step 2 Another group member places the car at the bottom of the ramp. After data collection begins, gently but quickly push the car so it travels up the ramp toward the motion detector.

Step 3 Stop collecting data when the car returns to the bottom of the ramp. Save the data as Trial 1.

Step 4 Remove one book from the stack. Then repeat the experiment. Save the data as Trial 2. For Trial 3, create a steeper ramp and repeat the experiment.

1. Sample answer: The graph resembles a parabola, so a quadratic function could be used to model the data.
5. Sample answer: Trial 3 is widest and Trial 2 is most narrow. The car moved more quickly on the steeper ramps. The absolute value of a is least in the widest graph.

Analyze the Results 2–4. See students' work.

1. What type of function could be used to represent the data? Justify your answer.
2. Use the CALC menu to find the vertex of the graph. Record the coordinates in a table like the one at the right.
3. Use the TRACE feature of the calculator to find the coordinates of another point on the graph. Then use the coordinates of the vertex and the point to find an equation of the graph.
4. Find an equation for each of the graphs of Trials 2 and 3.
5. How do the equations for Trials 1, 2, and 3 compare? Which graph is widest and which is most narrow? Explain what this represents in the context of the situation. How is this represented in the equations?
6. What do the x-intercepts and vertex of each graph represent?
7. Why were the values of h and k different in each trial? The time at which the car stopped is different.

Trial	Vertex (h, k)	Point (x, y)	Equation
1			
2			
3			

6. the times at which the car passed the zero point; the time at which the car stopped its forward motion

EXTEND 5-8 Lesson Notes

1 FOCUS

Objective Use a data collection device to investigate the relationship between the time and the distance traveled by a car on a ramp.

Materials for Each Group

- long, flat, smooth-surface board
- stack of books
- data collection device (TI CBR Motion Detector)
- TI-83/84 Plus graphing calculator
- medium-size toy car (a 9-inch playground ball can also be used)

Teaching Tips

- Before starting the Activity, ask students to sketch prediction graphs of the distance vs. time as the car moves up and back down the ramp.
- You may want students to practice giving the car a quick but gentle push so it rolls halfway up the ramp. They must press **START** to begin collecting data as soon as they let go of the car. It is crucial that students get their hands out of the path of the data collection device quickly after releasing the car.
- The car should not come any closer than 1.5 feet (0.5 meters) to the collection device.

2 TEACH

Working in Cooperative Groups

Put students in groups of three or four, mixing abilities. Then have groups complete the Activity and Exercises 1–3.

- Ask students if the car covers more distance during the first two seconds of movement or the last two seconds.

Practice Have students complete Exercises 4–7.

3 ASSESS

Formative Assessment

Use Exercise 5 to assess whether students comprehend how changes in the car's movement affect the shape of the graph.

From Concrete to Abstract

Ask students what they think would happen to their graphs if the ramp got steeper and steeper. Then have them repeat the experiment to check their conjectures.

Extending the Concept

- Modify the activity by using a longer ramp.
- Modify the activity by adding weight to the car.

Formative Assessment

Key Vocabulary The page references after each word denote where that term was first introduced. If students have difficulty answering questions 1–8, remind them that they can use these page references to refresh their memories about the vocabulary.

Summative Assessment

CRM Vocabulary Test, p. 62

FL Math Online glencoe.com

Vocabulary PuzzleMaker improves students' mathematics vocabulary using four puzzle formats–crossword, scramble, word search using a word list, and word search using clues. Students can work online or from a printed worksheet.

Additional Answers

9a. y-int: 12; $x = \frac{-5}{2}; \frac{-5}{2}$

9b.

x	$f(x)$
−3	6
$\frac{-5}{2}$	$\frac{23}{4}$
−2	6
−1	8
0	12

9c.

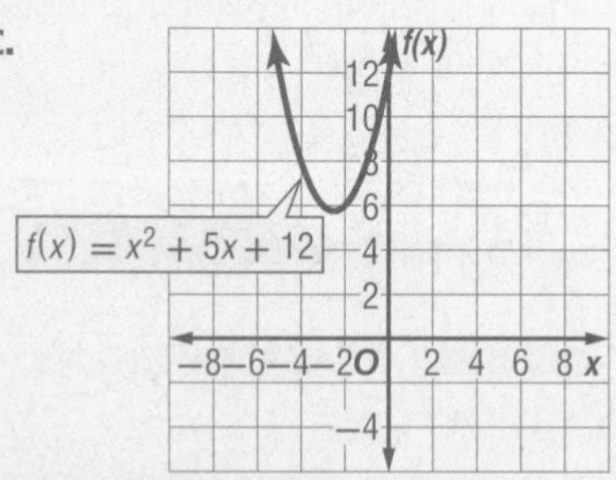

10a. y-int: 15; $x = \frac{7}{2}, \frac{7}{2}$

10b.

x	$f(x)$
2	5
3	3
$\frac{7}{2}$	$\frac{11}{4}$
4	3
5	5

CHAPTER 5 Study Guide and Review

FL Math Online glencoe.com
- STUDY TO GO
- Vocabulary Review

Chapter Summary

Key Concepts

Graphing Quadratic Functions (Lesson 5-1)

- The graph of $y = ax^2 + bx + c, a \neq 0$, opens up, and the function has a minimum value when $a > 0$. The graph opens down, and the function has a maximum value when $a < 0$.

Solving Quadratic Equations (Lessons 5-2 and 5-3)

- Roots of a quadratic equation are the zeros of the related quadratic function. You can find the zeros of a quadratic function by finding the x-intercepts of the graph.

Complex Numbers (Lesson 5-4)

- i is the imaginary unit; $i^2 = -1$ and $i = \sqrt{-1}$.

Solving Quadratic Equations (Lessons 5-5 and 5-6)

- Completing the square: **Step 1** Find one half of b, the coefficient of x. **Step 2** Square the result in Step 1. **Step 3** Add the result of Step 2 to $x^2 + bx$.
- Quadratic Formula: $x = \frac{-b \pm \sqrt{b^2 - 4ac}}{2a}$

Transformations with Quadratic Functions (Lesson 5-7)

- The graph of $y = (x - h)^2 + k$ is the graph of $y = x^2$ translated $|h|$ units left if h is negative or $|h|$ units right if h is positive and $|k|$ units up if k is positive or $|k|$ units down if k is negative.
- Consider $y = a(x - h)^2 + k, a \neq 0$. If $a > 0$, the graph opens up; if $a < 0$ the graph opens down. If $|a| > 1$, the graph is narrower than the graph of $y = x^2$. If $|a| < 1$, the graph is wider than the graph of $y = x^2$.

Quadratic Inequalities (Lesson 5-8)

- Graph the related function, test a point on the parabola and determine if it is a solution, and shade accordingly.

FOLDABLES® Study Organizer

Be sure the Key Concepts are noted in your Foldable.

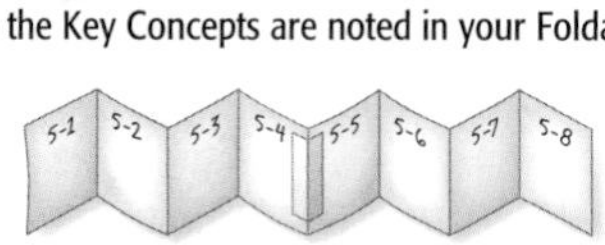

Key Vocabulary

- **axis of symmetry** (p. 250)
- **complex conjugates** (p. 279)
- **complex number** (p. 277)
- **completing the square** (p. 285)
- **constant term** (p. 249)
- **discriminant** (p. 295)
- **factored form** (p. 268)
- **FOIL method** (p. 268)
- **imaginary unit** (p. 276)
- **linear term** (p. 249)
- **maximum value** (p. 252)
- **minimum value** (p. 252)
- **parabola** (p. 249)
- **pure imaginary number** (p. 276)
- **quadratic equation** (p. 259)
- **Quadratic Formula** (p. 292)
- **quadratic function** (p. 249)
- **quadratic inequality** (p. 312)
- **quadratic term** (p. 249)
- **root** (p. 259)
- **Square Root Property** (p. 277)
- **standard form** (p. 259)
- **vertex** (p. 250)
- **vertex form** (p. 305)
- **zero** (p. 259)

5. false, completing the square

Vocabulary Check

State whether each sentence is *true* or *false*. If *false*, replace the underlined term to make a true sentence.

1. The factored form of a quadratic equation is $ax^2 + bx + c = 0$ where $a \neq 0$ and a, b, and c are integers. **false, standard form**
2. The graph of a quadratic function is called a parabola. **true**
3. The vertex form of a quadratic function is $y = a(x - p)(x - q)$. **false, factored form**
4. The axis of symmetry will intersect a parabola in one point called the vertex. **true**
5. A method called FOIL method is used to make a quadratic expression a perfect square in order to solve the related equation.
6. The equation $x = \frac{-b \pm \sqrt{b^2 - 4ac}}{2a}$ is known as the discriminant. **false, Quadratic Formula**
7. The number $6i$ is called a pure imaginary number. **true**
8. The two numbers $2 + 3i$ and $2 - 3i$ are called complex conjugates. **true**

FOLDABLES® Study Organizer

Dinah Zike's Foldables®

Have students look through the chapter to make sure they have included examples in their Foldables.

Suggest that students keep their Foldables handy while completing the Study Guide and Review pages. Point out that their Foldables can serve as a quick review tool when studying for the chapter test.

320 Chapter 5 Quadratic Functions and Relations

Lesson-by-Lesson Review

5-1 Graphing Quadratic Functions (pp. 249–257) 9–10. See margin.

912.A.2.6, 912.A.7.6

Complete parts a–c for each quadratic function.

a. Find the y-intercept, the equation of the axis of symmetry, and the x-coordinate of the vertex.

b. Make a table of values that includes the vertex.

c. Use this information to graph the function.

9. $f(x) = x^2 + 5x + 12$ **10.** $f(x) = x^2 - 7x + 15$

11. $f(x) = -2x^2 + 9x - 5$ **12.** $f(x) = -3x^2 + 12x - 1$

11, 12. See margin.

Determine whether each function has a maximum or minimum value and find the maximum or minimum value. Then state the domain and range of the function.

13. $f(x) = -x^2 + 3x - 1$ **14.** $f(x) = -3x^2 - 4x + 5$

15. **BUSINESS** Sal's Shirt Store sells 100 T-shirts per week at a rate of \$10 per shirt. Sal estimates that he will sell 5 less shirts for each \$1 increase in price. What price will maximize Sal's T-shirt income? 75 T-shirts at \$15 each

EXAMPLE 1

Consider the quadratic function $f(x) = x^2 - 4x + 11$. Find the y-intercept, the equation for the axis of symmetry, and the x-coordinate of the vertex.

In the function, $a = 1$, $b = -4$, and $c = 11$. The y-intercept is $c = 11$.

Use a and b to find the equation of the axis of symmetry.

$x = -\frac{b}{2a}$	Equation of the axis of symmetry.
$= -\frac{-4}{2(1)}$	$a = 1, b = -4$
$= 2$	Simplify.

The equation of the axis of symmetry is $x = 2$. Therefore, the x-coordinate of the vertex is 2.

13. max; 1.25; D = all real numbers; R = $\{f(x) \mid f(x) \leq 1.25\}$

14. max; $\frac{19}{3}$; D = all real numbers; R = $\left\{f(x) \middle| f(x) \leq \frac{19}{3}\right\}$

5-2 Solving Quadratic Functions by Graphing (pp. 259–266)

912.A.7.6, 912.A.7.10

Solve each equation by graphing. If exact roots cannot be found, state the consecutive integers between which the roots are located.

16. $x^2 - x - 20 = 0$ {−4, 5}

17. $2x^2 - x - 3 = 0$ $\left\{-1, \frac{3}{2}\right\}$

18. $4x^2 - 6x - 15 = 0$ between −1 and −2; between 2 and 3

19. **BASEBALL** A baseball is hit upward at 120 feet per second. Use the formula $h(t) = v_0 t - 16t^2$, where $h(t)$ is the height of an object in feet, v_0 is the object's initial velocity in feet per second, and t is the time in seconds. Ignoring the height of the ball when it was hit, how long does it take for the ball to hit the ground? 7.5 seconds

EXAMPLE 2

Solve $2x^2 - 7x + 3 = 0$ by graphing.

The equation of the axis of symmetry is $-\frac{-7}{2(2)}$ or $x = \frac{7}{4}$.

x	0	1	$\frac{7}{4}$	2	3
f(x)	3	−2	$-2\frac{5}{8}$	−3	0

The zeros of the related function are $\frac{1}{2}$ and 3. Therefore, the solutions of the equation are $\frac{1}{2}$ and 3.

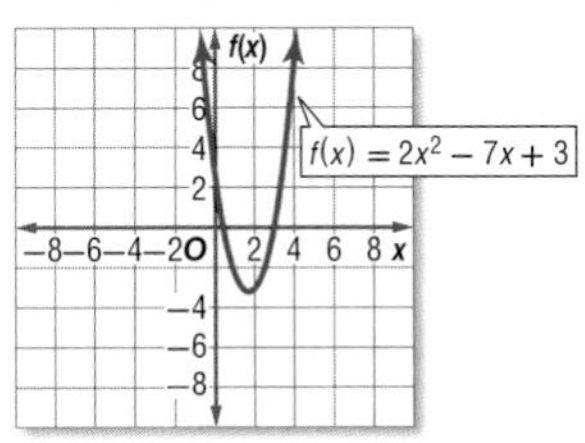

12a. y-int: −1; $x = 2$; 2

12b.

x	f(x)
0	−1
1	8
2	11
3	8
4	−1

12c.

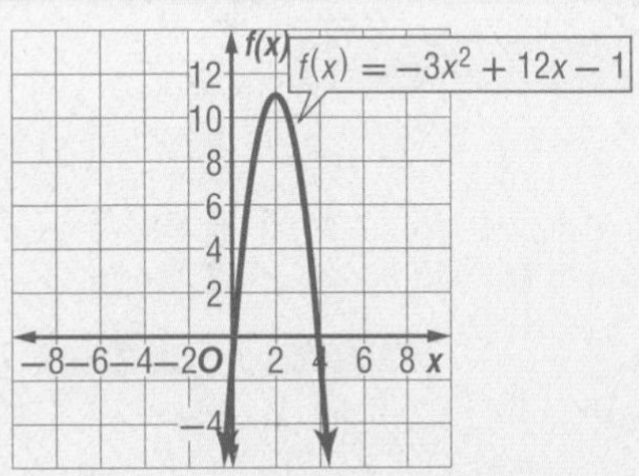

Lesson-by-Lesson Review

Intervention If the given examples are not sufficient to review the topics covered by the questions, remind students that the page references tell them where to review that topic in their textbook.

Two-Day Option Have students complete the Lesson-by-Lesson Review on pp. 321–324. Then you can use ExamView® Assessment Suite to customize another review worksheet that practices all the objectives of this chapter or only the objectives on which your students need more help.

Differentiated Instruction

Super DVD: Mindjogger Videoquizzes

Use this DVD as an alternative format of review for the test.

Additional Answers

10c.

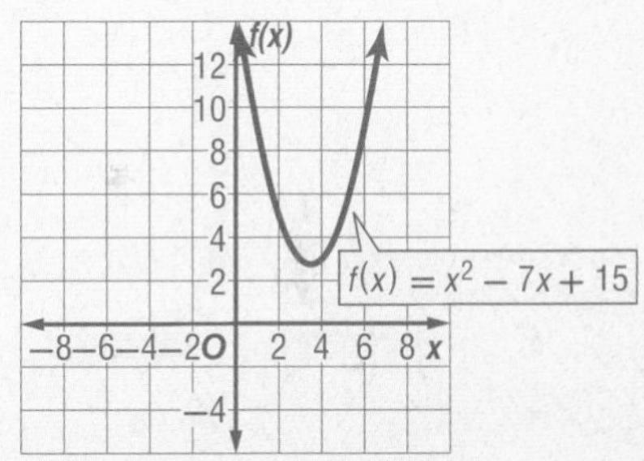

11a. y-int: −5; $x = \frac{9}{4}$; $\frac{9}{4}$

11b.

x	f(x)
1	2
2	5
$\frac{9}{4}$	$\frac{41}{8}$
3	4
4	−1

11c.

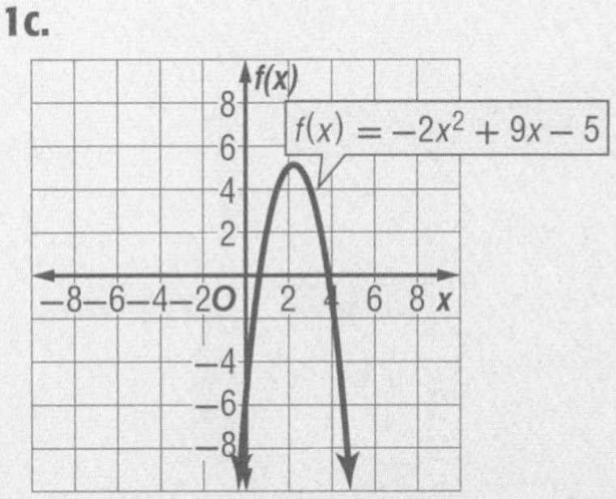

Additional Answers

20. $x^2 - 11x + 30 = 0$
21. $x^2 + 10x + 21 = 0$
22. $x^2 + 2x - 8 = 0$
23. $3x^2 - x - 2 = 0$
24. $6x^2 - 31x + 5 = 0$
25. $4x^2 + 5x + 1 = 0$

CHAPTER 5 Study Guide and Review

5-3 Solving Quadratic Equations by Factoring (pp. 268–275)

912.A.4.3, 912.A.10.3

Write a quadratic equation in standard form with the given roots. 20–25. See margin.

20. 5, 6
21. −3, −7
22. −4, 2
23. $-\frac{2}{3}, 1$
24. $\frac{1}{6}, 5$
25. $-\frac{1}{4}, -1$

Solve each equation by factoring.

26. $2x^2 - 2x - 24 = 0$ $\{-3, 4\}$
27. $2x^2 - 5x - 3 = 0$ $\left\{-\frac{1}{2}, 3\right\}$
28. $3x^2 - 16x + 5 = 0$ $\left\{\frac{1}{3}, 5\right\}$
29. Find x and the dimensions of the rectangle below. $x = 12$; 9 feet by 14 feet

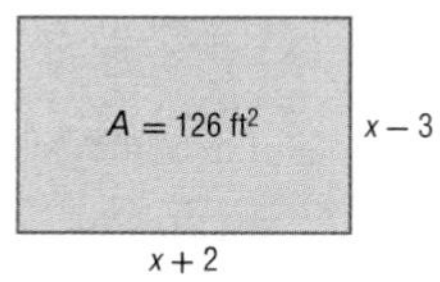

EXAMPLE 3

Write a quadratic equation in standard form with $-\frac{1}{2}$ and 4 as its roots.

$(x - p)(x - q) = 0$	**Write the pattern.**
$\left[x - \left(-\frac{1}{2}\right)\right](x - 4) = 0$	**Replace p with $-\frac{1}{2}$ and q with 4.**
$\left(x + \frac{1}{2}\right)(x - 4) = 0$	**Simplify.**
$x^2 - \frac{7}{2}x - 2 = 0$	**Multiply.**
$2x^2 - 7x - 4 = 0$	**Multiply each side by 2 so that b and c are integers.**

EXAMPLE 4

Solve $2x^2 - 3x - 5 = 0$ by factoring.

$2x^2 - 3x - 5 = 0$	**Original equation**
$(2x - 5)(x + 1) = 0$	**Factor the trinomial.**
$2x - 5 = 0$ or $x + 1 = 0$	**Zero Product Property**
$x = \frac{5}{2}$ or $x = -1$	

The solution set is $\left\{-1, \frac{5}{2}\right\}$.

5-4 Complex Numbers (pp. 276–282)

912.A.1.6

Simplify. 31. $15 + 3i$ 32. $2 + 5i$

30. $\sqrt{-8}$ $2i\sqrt{2}$
31. $(2 - i) + (13 + 4i)$
32. $(6 + 2i) - (4 - 3i)$
33. $(6 + 5i)(3 - 2i)$ $28 + 3i$
34. **ELECTRICITY** The impedance in one part of a series circuit is $3 + 2j$ ohms, and the impedance in the other part of the circuit is $4 - 3j$ ohms. Add these complex numbers to find the total impedance in the circuit. $7 - j$ ohms

Solve each equation.

35. $2x^2 + 50 = 0$ $\pm 5i$
36. $4x^2 + 16 = 0$ $\pm 2i$
37. $3x^2 + 15 = 0$ $\pm i\sqrt{5}$
38. $8x^2 + 16 = 0$ $\pm i\sqrt{2}$
39. $4x^2 + 1 = 0$ $\pm\frac{1}{2}i$

EXAMPLE 5

Simplify $(12 + 3i) - (-5 + 2i)$.

$(12 + 3i) - (-5 + 2i)$	
$= [12 - (-5)] + (3 - 2)i$	**Group the real and imaginary parts.**
$= 17 + i$	**Add.**

EXAMPLE 6

Solve $3x^2 + 12 = 0$.

$3x^2 + 12 = 0$	**Original equation**
$3x^2 = -12$	**Subtract 12 from each side.**
$x^2 = -4$	**Divide each side by 3.**
$x = \pm\sqrt{-4}$	**Square Root Property**
$x = \pm 2i$	$\sqrt{-4} = \sqrt{4} \cdot \sqrt{-1}$

MIXED PROBLEM SOLVING
For mixed problem-solving practice, see page 983.

5-5 Completing the Square (pp. 284–290)

912.A.7.3, 912.A.7.5

Find the value of c that makes each trinomial a perfect square. Then write the trinomial as a perfect square. **40–45. See margin.**

40. $x^2 + 18x + c$
41. $x^2 - 4x + c$
42. $x^2 - 7x + c$
43. $x^2 + 2.4x + c$
44. $x^2 - \frac{1}{2}x + c$
45. $x^2 + \frac{6}{5}x + c$

Solve each equation by completing the square.

46. $x^2 - 6x - 7 = 0$ **{−1, 7}**
47. $x^2 - 2x + 8 = 0$ $\{1 \pm i\sqrt{7}\}$
48. $2x^2 + 4x - 3 = 0$ $\left\{\frac{-2 \pm \sqrt{10}}{2}\right\}$
49. $2x^2 + 3x - 5 = 0$ $\left\{1, -\frac{5}{2}\right\}$

50. FLOOR PLAN Mario's living room has a length 6 feet wider than the width. The area of the living room is 280 square feet. What are the dimensions of his living room? **20 feet by 14 feet**

EXAMPLE 7

Find the value of c that makes $x^2 + 14x + c$ a perfect square. Then write the trinomial as a perfect square.

Step 1 Find one half of 14.

Step 2 Square the result of Step 1.

Step 3 Add the result of Step 2 to $x^2 + 14x$.

The trinomial $x^2 + 14x + 49$ can be written as $(x + 7)^2$.

EXAMPLE 8

Solve $x^2 + 12x - 13 = 0$ by completing the square.

$$x^2 + 12x - 13 = 0$$
$$x^2 + 12x = 13$$
$$x^2 + 12x + 36 = 13 + 36$$
$$(x + 6)^2 = 49$$
$$x + 6 = \pm 7$$

$x + 6 = 7$ or $x + 6 = -7$
$x = 1$ $\quad x = -13$

The solution set is $\{-13, 1\}$.

5-6 The Quadratic Formula and the Discriminant (pp. 292–300)

912.A.7.4, 912.A.7.5

Complete parts a–c for each quadratic equation.
a. Find the value of the discriminant.
b. Describe the number and type of roots.
c. Find the exact solutions by using the Quadratic Formula.

51. $x^2 - 10x + 25 = 0$ **51–57. See margin.**
52. $x^2 + 4x - 32 = 0$
53. $2x^2 + 3x - 18 = 0$
54. $2x^2 + 19x - 33 = 0$
55. $x^2 - 2x + 9 = 0$
56. $4x^2 - 4x + 1 = 0$
57. $2x^2 + 5x + 9 = 0$

58. PHYSICAL SCIENCE Lauren throws a ball with an initial velocity of 40 feet per second. The equation for the height of the ball is $h = -16t^2 + 40t + 5$, where h represents the height in feet and t represents the time in seconds. When will the ball hit the ground? **about 2.62 seconds**

EXAMPLE 9

Solve $x^2 - 4x - 45 = 0$ by using the Quadratic Formula.

In $x^2 - 4x - 45 = 0$, $a = 1$, $b = -4$, and $c = -45$.

$$x = \frac{-b \pm \sqrt{b^2 - 4ac}}{2a} \quad \text{Quadratic Formula}$$
$$= \frac{-(-4) \pm \sqrt{(-4)^2 - 4(1)(-45)}}{2(1)}$$
$$= \frac{4 \pm 14}{2}$$

Write as two equations.

$x = \frac{4 + 14}{2}$ or $x = \frac{4 - 14}{2}$
$= 9$ $\quad = -5$

The solution set is $\{-5, 9\}$.

Additional Answers

40. $81; (x + 9)^2$
41. $4; (x - 2)^2$
42. $\frac{49}{4}; \left(x - \frac{7}{2}\right)^2$
43. $1.44; (x + 1.2)^2$
44. $\frac{1}{16}; \left(x - \frac{1}{4}\right)^2$
45. $\frac{9}{25}; \left(x + \frac{3}{5}\right)^2$
51a. 0
51b. 1 real rational root
51c. $\{5\}$
52a. 144
52b. 2 rational real roots
52c. $\{-8, 4\}$
53a. 153
53b. 2 irrational real roots
53c. $\left\{\frac{-3 \pm 3\sqrt{17}}{4}\right\}$
54a. 625
54b. 2 real rational roots
54c. $\left\{-11, \frac{3}{2}\right\}$
55a. −32
55b. 2 complex roots
55c. $\{1 \pm 2i\sqrt{2}\}$
56a. 0
56b. 1 real rational root
56c. $\left\{\frac{1}{2}\right\}$
57a. −47
57b. 2 complex roots
57c. $\left\{\frac{-5 \pm i\sqrt{47}}{4}\right\}$

Problem Solving Review

For additional practice in problem solving for Chapter 5, see the Mixed Problem Solving Appendix, p. 984, in the Student Handbook section.

Anticipation Guide

Have students complete the Chapter 5 Anticipation Guide and discuss how their responses have changed now that they have completed Chapter 5.

Additional Answer

59. $y = -3(x - 1)^2 + 5$; $(1, 5)$; $x = 1$; opens down

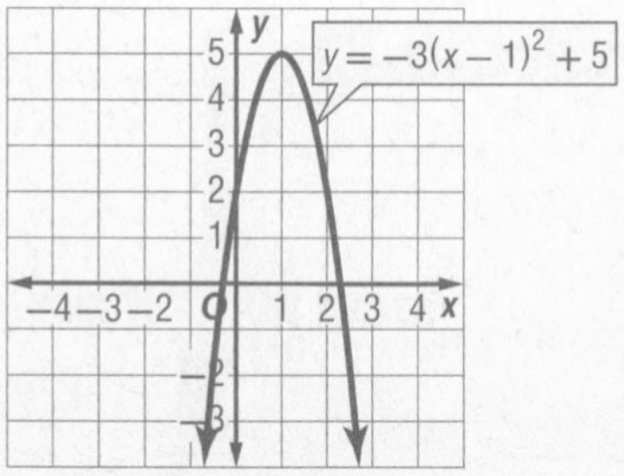

60. $y = 2(x + 3)^2 - 26$; $(-3, -26)$; $x = -3$; opens up

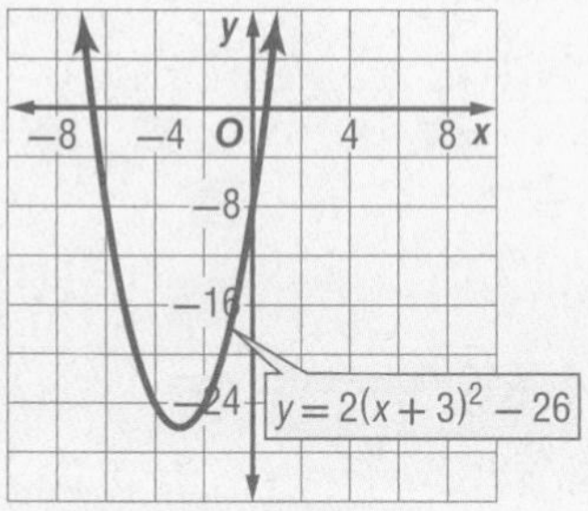

61. $y = -\frac{1}{2}(x + 2)^2 + 14$; $(-2, 14)$; $x = -2$; opens down

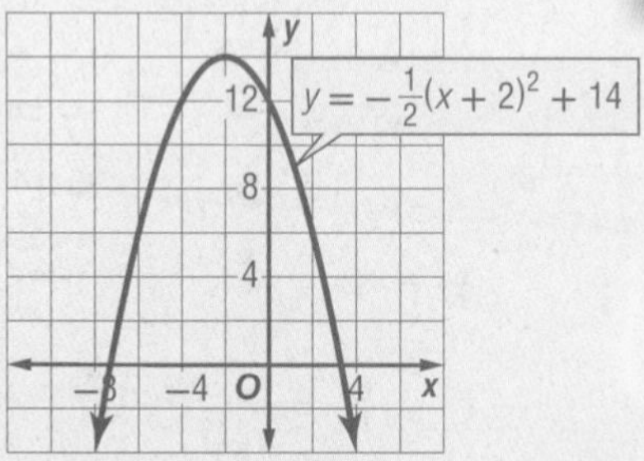

CHAPTER 5 Study Guide and Review

5-7 Transformations with Quadratic Functions (pp. 305–310)

912.A.2.10

Write each quadratic function in vertex form, if not already in that form. Then identify the vertex, axis of symmetry, and direction of opening. Then graph the function. **59–62. See margin.**

59. $y = -3(x - 1)^2 + 5$ **60.** $y = 2x^2 + 12x - 8$

61. $y = -\frac{1}{2}x^2 - 2x + 12$ **62.** $y = 3x^2 + 36x + 25$

63. The graph at the right shows a product of 2 numbers with a sum of 10. Find a function that models this product and use it to determine the two numbers that would give a maximum product. **$f(x) = -x^2 + 10x$; 5 and 5**

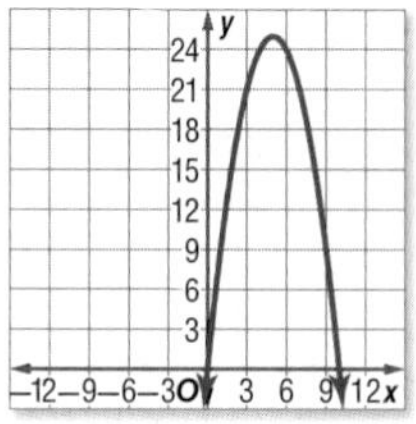

EXAMPLE 10

Write the quadratic function $y = 3x^2 + 24x + 15$ in vertex form. Then identify the vertex, axis of symmetry, and direction of opening.

$y = 3x^2 + 24x + 15$	**Original equation**
$y = 3(x^2 + 8x) + 15$	**Group and factor.**
$y = 3(x^2 + 8x + 16) + 15 - 3(16)$	**Complete the square.**
$y = 3(x + 4)^2 - 33$	**Rewrite $x^2 + 8x + 16$ as a perfect square.**

So, $a = 3$, $h = -4$, and $k = -33$. The vertex is at $(-4, -33)$ and the axis of symmetry is $x = -4$. Since a is positive, the graph opens up.

5-8 Quadratic Inequalities (pp. 312–318)

912.A.4.11, 912.A.10.3

Graph each quadratic inequality.

64. $y \geq x^2 + 5x + 4$ **65.** $y < -x^2 + 5x - 6$

66. $y > x^2 - 6x + 8$ **67.** $y \leq x^2 + 10x - 4$

64–67. See Chapter 5 Answer Appendix.

68. Solomon wants to put a deck along two sides of his garden. The deck width will be the same on both sides and the total area of the garden and deck cannot exceed 500 square feet. How wide can the deck be? **between 0 and 5 ft**

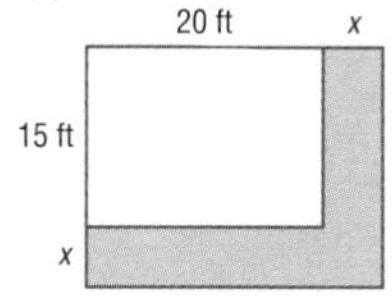

Solve each inequality using a graph or algebraically.

69. $x^2 + 8x + 12 > 0$ $\{x \mid x < -6 \text{ or } x > -2\}$

70. $6x + x^2 \geq -9$ {all real numbers}

71. $2x^2 + 3x - 20 > 0$ $\left\{x \,\middle|\, x < -4 \text{ or } x > \frac{5}{2}\right\}$

72. $4x^2 - 3 < -5x$ $\{x \mid -1.69 < x < 0.44\}$

73. $3x^2 + 4 > 8x$ $\left\{x \,\middle|\, x < \frac{2}{3} \text{ or } x > 2\right\}$

EXAMPLE 11

Graph $y > x^2 + 3x + 2$.

Step 1 Graph the related function, $y > x^2 + 3x + 2$. Because the inequality symbol $>$ is used, the parabola should be dashed.

Step 2 Test a point not on the graph of the parabola such as $(0, 0)$.

$y > x^2 + 3x + 2$

$(0) \overset{?}{>} 0^2 + 3(0) + 2$

$0 \not> 2$

So, $(0, 0)$ is not a solution of the inequality.

Step 3 Shade the region that does not contain the point $(0, 0)$.

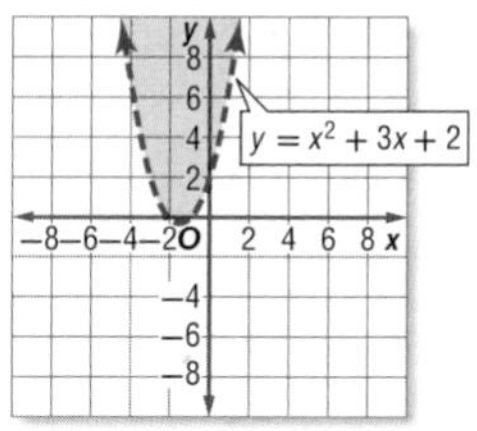

62. $y = 3(x + 6)^2 - 83$; $(-6, -83)$; $x = 6$; opens up

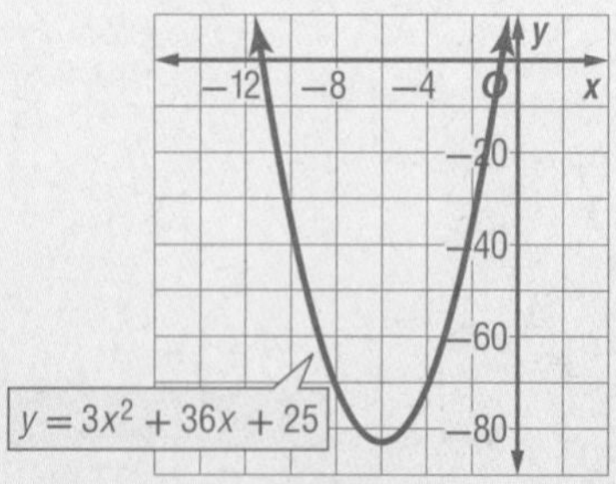

324 Chapter 5 Quadratic Functions and Relations

FL Math Online glencoe.com
Chapter Test

Complete parts a–c for each quadratic function.
a. Find the y-intercept, the equation of the axis of symmetry, and the x-coordinate of the vertex.
b. Make a table of values that includes the vertex.
c. Use this information to graph the function. **1–3. See Chapter 5 Answer Appendix.**

1. $f(x) = x^2 + 4x - 7$
2. $f(x) = -2x^2 + 5x$
3. $f(x) = -x^2 - 6x - 9$

Determine whether each function has a maximum or minimum value. State the maximum or minimum value of each function.

4. $f(x) = x^2 + 10x + 25$ **min.; 0**
5. $f(x) = -x^2 + 6x$ **max.; 9**

Solve each equation using the method of your choice. Find exact solutions.

6. $x^2 - 8x - 9 = 0$ **−1, 9**
7. $-4.8x^2 + 1.6x + 24 = 0$ $\frac{1 \pm \sqrt{181}}{6}$
8. $12x^2 + 15x - 4 = 0$ $\frac{-15 \pm \sqrt{417}}{24}$
9. $x^2 - 7x - \frac{17}{4} = 0$ $\frac{7 \pm \sqrt{66}}{2}$
10. $4x^2 + x = 3$ $-1, \frac{3}{4}$
11. $-9x^2 + 40x + 84 = 0$ $-\frac{14}{9}, 6$

12. **PHYSICAL SCIENCE** Parker throws a ball off the top of a building. The building is 350 feet high and the initial velocity of the ball is 30 feet per second. Find out how long it will take the ball to hit the ground by solving the equation $-16t^2 - 30t + 350 = 0$. **about 3.83 seconds**

13. **NGSSS PRACTICE** Which equation below has roots at −6 and $\frac{1}{5}$? **C**
 A. $0 = 5x^2 - 29x - 6$
 B. $0 = 5x^2 + 31x + 6$
 C. $0 = 5x^2 + 29x - 6$
 D. $0 = 5x^2 - 31x + 6$

14. **PHYSICS** A ball is thrown into the air vertically with a velocity of 112 feet per second. The ball was released 6 feet above the ground. The height above the ground t seconds after release is modeled by $h(t) = -16t^2 + 112t + 6$.
 a. When will the ball reach 130 feet? **at about 1.4 s and 5.6 s**
 b. Will the ball ever reach 250 feet? Explain. **See margin.**
 c. In how many seconds after its release will the ball hit the ground? **in about 7 s**

15. The rectangle below has an area of 104 square inches. Find the value of x and the dimensions of the rectangle. **x = 9; 8 inches by 13 inches**

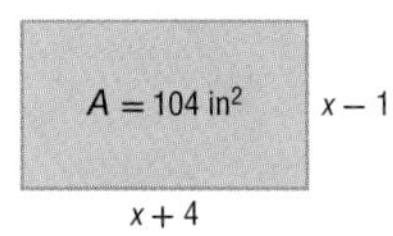

Simplify.

16. $(3 - 4i) - (9 - 5i)$ $-6 + i$
17. $\frac{4i}{4 - i}$ $-\frac{4}{17} + \frac{16}{17}i$

18. **NGSSS PRACTICE** Which value of c makes the trinomial $x^2 - 12x + c$ a perfect square trinomial? **H**
 F. 6
 G. 12
 H. 36
 I. 144

Complete parts a–c for each quadratic equation.
a. Find the value of the discriminant.
b. Describe the number and type of roots.
c. Find the exact solution by using the Quadratic Formula. **19–21. See margin.**

19. $6x^2 + 7x = 0$
20. $5x^2 = -6x + 1$
21. $2x^2 + 5x - 8 = -13$

Write each quadratic function in vertex form. Then identify the vertex, axis of symmetry, and direction of opening. **22, 23. See margin.**

22. $3x^2 + 6x = 2 + y$
23. $x^2 + 9x + \frac{81}{4} = y$

24. Graph the quadratic inequality $0 < -3x^2 + 4x + 10$. **See Chapter 5 Answer Appendix.**

Solve each inequality by using a graph or algebraically.

25. $x^2 + 6x > -5$ $\{x \mid x < -5 \text{ or } x > -1\}$
26. $4x^2 - 19x \leq -12$ $\left\{x \,\middle|\, \frac{3}{4} \leq x \leq 4\right\}$

CHAPTER 5 Practice Test

ExamView Assessment Suite — Customize and create multiple versions of your chapter test and their answer keys. All of the questions from the leveled chapter tests in the *Chapter 5 Resource Masters* are also available on ExamView® Assessment Suite.

Additional Answers

14b. No; if you graph the function, the vertex in 202 units above the horizontal axis. So, the height will never be 250.

19a. 49

19b. 2 rational roots

19c. $-\frac{7}{6}, 0$

20a. 56

20b. 2 irrational roots

20c. $\frac{-3 \pm \sqrt{14}}{5}$

21a. −15

21b. 2 complex roots

21c. $\frac{-5 \pm i\sqrt{15}}{4}$

22. $y = 3(x + 1)^2 - 5$; vertex: $(-1, -5)$; axis of symmetry: $x = -1$; opens up

23. $y = \left(x + \frac{9}{2}\right)^2$; vertex: $\left(-\frac{9}{2}, 0\right)$; axis of symmetry: $x = -\frac{9}{2}$; opens up

Intervention Planner

Tier 1 On Level		Tier 2 Strategic Intervention (Approaching grade level)		Tier 3 Intensive Intervention (2 or more grades below level)	
If	students miss about 25% of the exercises or less,	If	students miss about 50% of the exercises,	If	students miss about 75% of the exercises,
Then	choose a resource:	Then	choose a resource:	Then	use *Math Triumphs Alg. 2*, Chs. 1, 3, and 4
SE	Lessons 5-1, 5-2, 5-3, 5-4, 5-5, 5-6, and 5-8	CRM	Study Guide and Intervention, Chapter 5, pp. 5, 11, 17, 24, 30, 36, and 49		
CRM	Skills Practice, Chapter 5, pp. 7, 13, 19, 26, 32, 38, and 51				
TE	Chapter Project, p. 246				
FL Math Online	Self-Check Quiz	FL Math Online	Extra Examples, Personal Tutor, Homework Help	FL Math Online	Extra Examples, Personal Tutor, Homework Help, Review Vocabulary

1 FOCUS

Objective Use the strategy of use a graph to solve standardized test problems.

2 TEACH

Scaffolding Questions

Ask:

- What are some parts of a graph? Sample answers: title, vertical and horizontal axes, scale
- What type of equation does the graph of a parabola represent? quadratic equation
- What do you know about each and every point on the graph of a parabola? Each point is a solution to the equation or function representing the graph.

CHAPTER 5 Preparing for Standardized Tests

Use a Graph

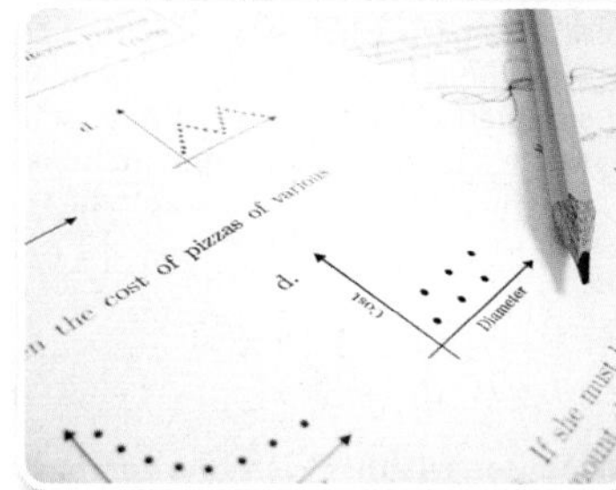

Using a graph can help you solve many different kinds of problems on standardized tests. Graphs can help you solve equations, evaluate functions, and interpret solutions to real-world problems.

Strategies for Using a Graph

Step 1

Read the problem statement carefully.

Ask yourself:

- What am I being asked to solve?
- What information is given in the problem?
- How could a graph help me solve the problem?

Step 2

Create your graph.

- Sketch your graph on scrap paper if appropriate.
- If allowed, you can also use a graphing calculator to create the graph.

Step 3

Solve the problem.

- Use your graph to help you model and solve the problem.
- Check to be sure your answer makes sense.

NGSSS PRACTICE EXAMPLE 7

Read the problem. Identify what you need to know. Then use the information in the problem to solve.

The students in Mr. Himebaugh's physics class built a model rocket. The rocket is launched in a large field with an initial upward velocity of 128 feet per second. The function $h(t) = -16t^2 + 128t$ models the height of the rocket above the ground (in feet) t seconds after it is launched. How long will it take for the rocket to reach its maximum height?

A. 4 seconds **C.** 6 seconds

B. 5 seconds **D.** 8 seconds

326 Chapter 5 Quadratic Functions and Relations

Graphing the quadratic function will allow you to determine the peak height of the rocket and when it occurs. A graphing calculator can help you quickly graph the function and analyze it.

KEYSTROKES: [Y=] [(–)] 16 [X,T,θ,n] [x^2] [+] 128 [X,T,θ,n] [Graph]

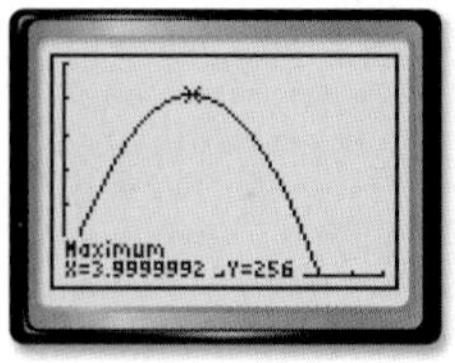

After graphing the equation, use maximum under the CALC menu.

Press [2nd] [CALC] 4. Then use [◀] to place the cursor to the left of the maximum point and press [ENTER]. Use [▶] to place the cursor to the right of the maximum point and press [ENTER] [ENTER].

The graph shows that the rocket takes 4 seconds to reach its maximum height of 256 feet. The correct answer is A.

Exercises

Read each problem. Identify what you need to know. Then use the information in the problem to solve.

1. What are the roots of $y = 2x^2 + 10x - 48$? **C**
   - A. $-5, 4$
   - B. $-6, 1$
   - C. $-8, 3$
   - D. $2, 3$

2. How many times does the graph of $f(x) = 2x^2 - 3x + 2$ cross the x-axis? **F**
   - F. 0
   - G. 1
   - H. 2
   - I. 3

3. Which statement best describes the graphs of the two equations? **C**

$$16x - 2y = 24$$
$$12x = 3y - 36$$

   - A. The lines are parallel.
   - B. The lines are the same.
   - C. The lines intersect in only one point.
   - D. The lines intersect in more than one point, but are not the same.

4. Adrian is using 120 feet of fencing to enclose a rectangular area for her puppy. One side of the enclosure will be her house.

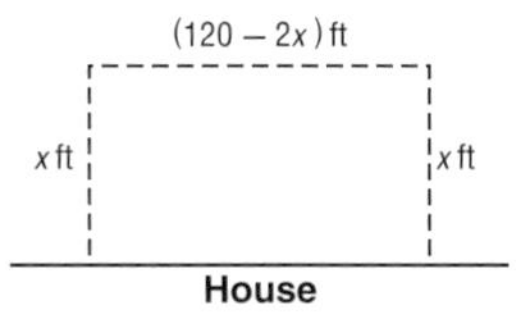

The function $f(x) = x(120 - 2x)$ represents the area of the enclosure. What is the greatest area Adrian can enclose with the fencing? **G**
   - F. 1,650 ft^2
   - G. 1,800 ft^2
   - H. 1,980 ft^2
   - I. 2,140 ft^2

5. For which equation is the x-coordinate of the vertex at 4? **A**
   - A. $f(x) = x^2 - 8x + 15$
   - B. $f(x) = -x^2 - 4x + 12$
   - C. $f(x) = x^2 + 6x + 8$
   - D. $f(x) = -x^2 - 2x + 2$

6. For what value of x does $f(x) = x^2 + 5x + 6$ reach its minimum value? **H**
   - F. -5
   - G. -3
   - H. $-\frac{5}{2}$
   - I. -2

Additional Example

STANDARDIZED TEST PRACTICE
Belinda throws a tennis ball upward at a velocity of 65 feet per second, releasing the ball when it is 4 feet above the ground. The height of the ball t seconds after being thrown is given by the formula $h(t) = -16t^2 + 65t + 4$. Find the time, to the nearest second, at which the tennis ball reaches its maximum height. **A**

- **A** 2 seconds
- **B** 4 seconds
- **C** 70 seconds
- **D** 140 seconds

3 ASSESS

Use Exercises 1–6 to assess students' understanding.

Chapter 5 Preparing for Standardized Tests 327

Diagnose Student Errors

Survey student responses for each item. Class trends may indicate common errors and misconceptions.

1. A. wrote an incorrect quadratic equation
B. wrote an incorrect quadratic equation
C. correct
D. wrote an incorrect quadratic equation

3. F. guess
G. correct
H. factored incorrectly
I. incorrectly used $8^2 = 16$ instead of $4^2 = 16$

4. A. guess
B. guess
C. correct
D. combined like terms incorrectly

6. F. added 5 instead of subtracting 5
G. correct
H. subtracted 5 from the x term instead of the constant term
I. added 5 to the x term instead of subtracting it from the constant term

7. A. correct
B. did not understand that in a dilation, all linear measures of the image change in the same ratio
C. did not understand that in a dilation, all linear measures of the image change in the same ratio
D. did not understand that in a dilation, all linear measures of the image change in the same ratio

10. F. correct
G. made $10.50 the constant term
H. did not represent a variable for the number of hours working
I. guess

CHAPTER 5 NGSSS Practice

Cumulative, Chapters 1 through 5

Read each question. Then fill in the correct answer on the answer document provided by your teacher or on a sheet of paper.

1. A rental store charges $30 per day to rent a bicycle. At this rate, the store rents about 200 bikes per month. The owner of the store estimates that they will rent 5 fewer bikes per month for each $2 increase in the rental price. What price will maximize the income of the store? **C**

A. $46

B. $51

C. $55

D. $57

2. THINK SOLVE EXPLAIN **SHORT RESPONSE** Use the quadratic function below to answer each question.

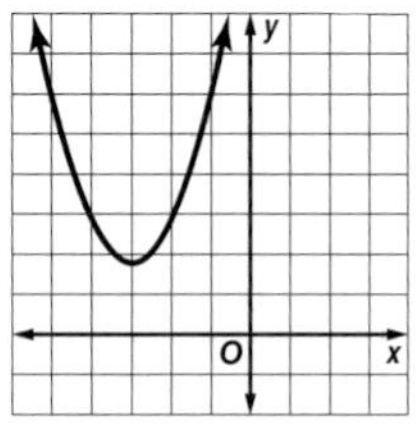

a. How many real roots does the quadratic function have? **0**

b. How many complex roots does the function have? **2**

c. What do you know about the discriminant of the quadratic equation? Explain.

3. Solve $x^2 - 2x = 15$ by completing the square. **G**

F. $-4, -1$

G. $-3, 5$

H. $-2, 3$

I. $5, 7$

2c. Sample answer: The discriminant is negative because the roots are complex.

Test-Taking Tip

Question 1 Multiply the expressions for the new price and new number of customers after x price increases to write a quadratic equation.

4. Leo sells T-shirts at a local swim meet. It costs him $250 to set up the stand and rent the machine. It costs him an additional $5 to make each T-shirt. If he sells each T-shirt for $15, how many T-shirts does he have to sell before he can make a profit? **C**

A. 10

B. 15

C. 25

D. 50

5. THINK SOLVE EXPLAIN **SHORT RESPONSE** Describe the translation of the graph of $y = (x + 5)^2 - 1$ to the graph of $y = (x - 1)^2 + 3$. **Sample answer: It is a translation 6 units right and 4 units up.**

6. The graph of $g(x) = \frac{2}{5}x^2 - 4x + 2$ is translated down 5 units to produce the graph of the function $h(x)$. Which of the following could be $h(x)$? **G**

F. $h(x) = \frac{2}{5}x^2 - 4x + 7$

G. $h(x) = \frac{2}{5}x^2 - 4x - 3$

H. $h(x) = \frac{2}{5}x^2 - 9x + 2$

I. $h(x) = \frac{2}{5}x^2 + x + 2$

7. Triangle ABC has vertices with coordinates $A(-4, 2)$, $B(-4, -3)$, and $C(3, -2)$. After a dilation, triangle $A'B'C'$ has coordinates $A'(-12, 6)$, $B'(-12, -9)$, and $C'(9, -6)$. How many times as great is the perimeter of $\triangle A'B'C'$ as that of $\triangle ABC$? **A**

A. 3

B. 6

C. 12

D. $\frac{1}{3}$

8. **GRIDDED RESPONSE** What is the y-coordinate of the solution of the system of equations below? **1**

$$y = 4x - 7$$
$$y = -\frac{1}{2}x + 2$$

328 **Chapter 5** Quadratic Functions and Relations

11. A. read the x-intercept values incorrectly
B. read the x-intercept values incorrectly
C. read the x-intercept values incorrectly
D. correct

14. F. guess
G. guess
H. misread the value of x on the graph when $P(t) = 200$
I. correct

9. **GRIDDED RESPONSE** Simplify $-2i \cdot 5i$. 10

10. Peyton works as a nanny. She charges at least \$10 to drive to a home and \$10.50 per hour. Which inequality best represents the relationship between the number of hours working n and the total charge c? F

F. $c \geq 10 + 10.50n$

G. $c \geq 10.50 + 10n$

H. $c \leq 10.50 + 10$

I. $c \leq 10n + 10.50n$

11. What are the solutions of the quadratic equation graphed below? D

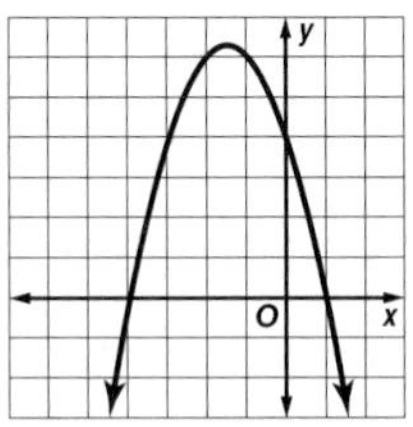

A. −4, −1　　C. −1, 4

B. 1, 4　　D. −4, 1

12. **SHORT RESPONSE** If one of the roots of $x^2 + kx - 12 = 0$ is 4, what is the value of k? −1

13. **EXTENDED RESPONSE** For a given quadratic equation $y = ax^2 + bx + c$, describe what the discriminant $b^2 - 4ac$ tells you about the roots of the equation. See margin.

14. The function $P(t) = -0.068t^2 + 7.85t + 56$ can be used to approximate the population, in thousands, of Clarksville between 1960 and 2000. The domain t of the function is the number of years since 1960. According to the model, in what year did the population of Clarksville reach 200,000 people? I

F. 1974　　H. 1981

G. 1977　　I. 1983

15a. $x + y = 40$; $200x + 500y = 11{,}600$

15. **EXTENDED RESPONSE** Craig is checking in a shipment of ink jet printers that cost \$200 each and laser printers that cost \$500 each. There are 40 boxes in the shipment, and the invoice total is \$11,600. b. See margin.

a. Write a system of equations to model the situation. Let x represent the number of ink jet printers, and let y represent the number of laser printers.

b. Write a matrix equation that can be used to solve the system of equations you wrote in part **a**.

c. Find the inverse of the coefficient matrix and solve the matrix equation. How many ink jet printers and laser printers were included in the shipment? 28 ink jet printers and 12 laser printers

16. **EXTENDED RESPONSE** If Robert kicks a football straight up into the air with an initial velocity of 100 feet per second, the function $h(t) = -16t^2 + 100t$ gives the height, in feet, of the ball after t seconds.

a. Graph the quadratic function on a coordinate grid. See margin.

b. What is the maximum height reached by the football? Round to the nearest foot. 156 ft

c. How long is the football in the air before it hits the ground? 6.25 seconds

Need Extra Help?

If you missed Question...	1	2	3	4	5	6	7	8	9	10	11	12	13	14	15	16
Go to Lesson or Page...	5-1	5-2	5-5	1-5	5-7	5-7	4-4	3-2	5-4	2-4	5-2	5-2	5-6	5-6	4-6	5-1
For help with NGSSS...	912.A.2.6	912.A.2.6	912.A.7.5	912.A.3.15	912.A.2.10	912.A.4.11	912.G.2.4	912.A.3.14	912.A.1.6	912.A.3.4	912.A.7.5	912.A.4.7	912.A.7.4	912.A.7.5	912.A.3.15	912.A.2.10

Formative Assessment

You can use these two pages to benchmark student progress.

CRM Chapter 5 Resource Masters

- Standardized Test Practice, pp. 76–78

ExamView Assessment Suite Create practice worksheets or tests that align to your state's standards as well as TIMSS and NAEP tests.

Homework Option

Get Ready for Chapter 6 Assign students the exercises on p. 331 as homework to assess whether they possess the prerequisite skills needed for the next chapter.

Additional Answers

13. Sample answer: If negative, there are 2 complex roots; if 0, there is 1 real, rational root; if positive and a perfect square, there are 2 real, rational roots; if positive but not a perfect square, there are 2 real, irrational roots.

15b. $$\begin{bmatrix} 1 & 1 \\ 200 & 500 \end{bmatrix} \begin{bmatrix} x \\ y \end{bmatrix} = \begin{bmatrix} 40 \\ 11{,}600 \end{bmatrix}$$

16a.

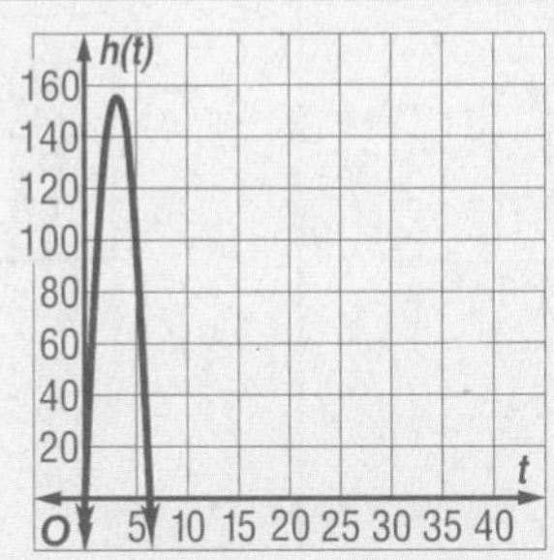

Pages 254–255, Lesson 5-1

1a. y-int = 0; axis of symmetry: $x = 0$; x-coordinate = 0

1b.

x	f(x)
−2	12
−1	3
0	0
1	3
2	12

1c.

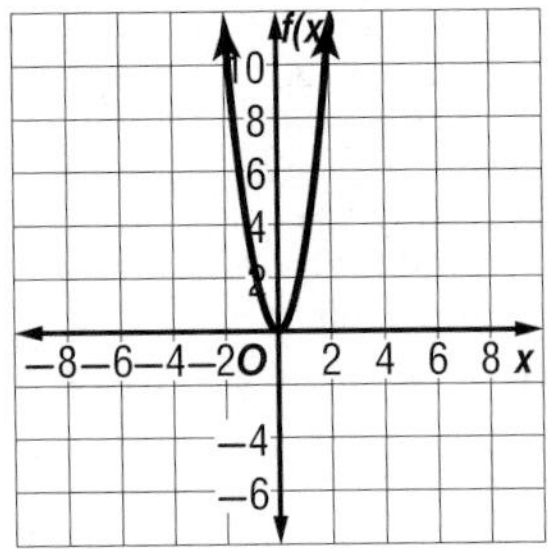

2a. y-int = 0; axis of symmetry: $x = 0$; x-coordinate = 0

2b.

x	f(x)
−2	−24
−1	−6
0	0
1	−6
2	−24

2c.

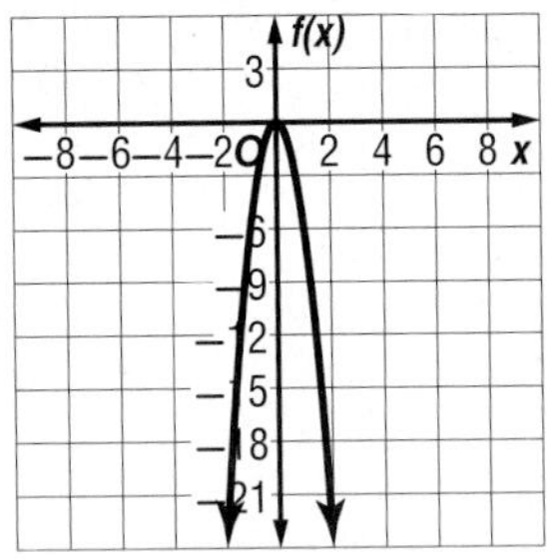

3a. y-int = 0; axis of symmetry: $x = 2$; x-coordinate = 2

3b.

x	f(x)
0	0
1	−3
2	−4
3	−3
4	0

3b.

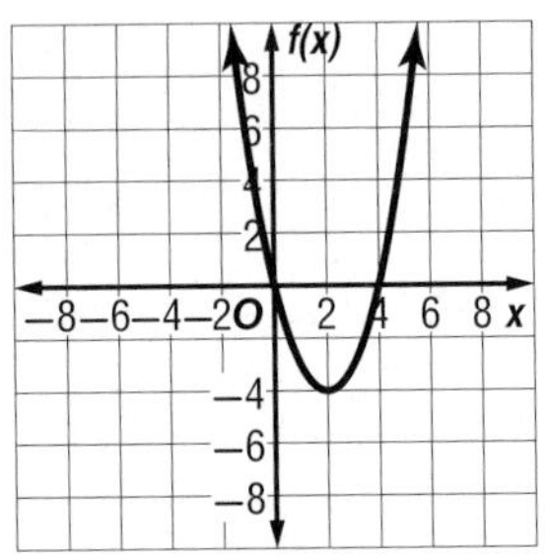

4a. y-int = 4; axis of symmetry: $x = -1.5$; x-coordinate = −1.5

4b.

x	f(x)
−3	4
−2	6
−1.5	6.25
−1	6
0	4

4c.

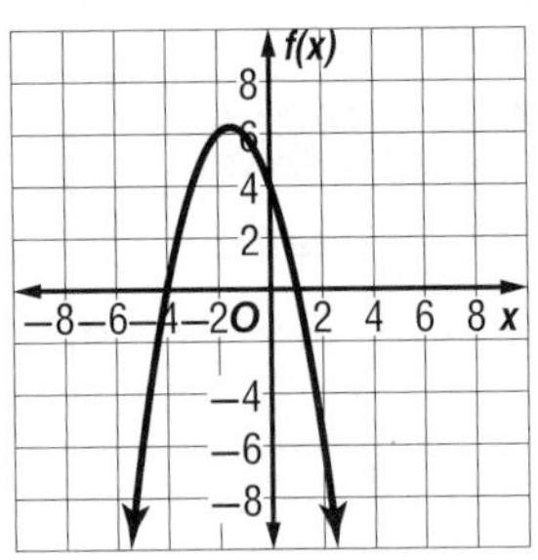

5a. y-int = −3; axis of symmetry: $x = 0.75$; x-coordinate = 0.75

5b.

x	f(x)
−1	7
0	−3
0.75	−5.25
1.5	−3
2.5	7

5c.

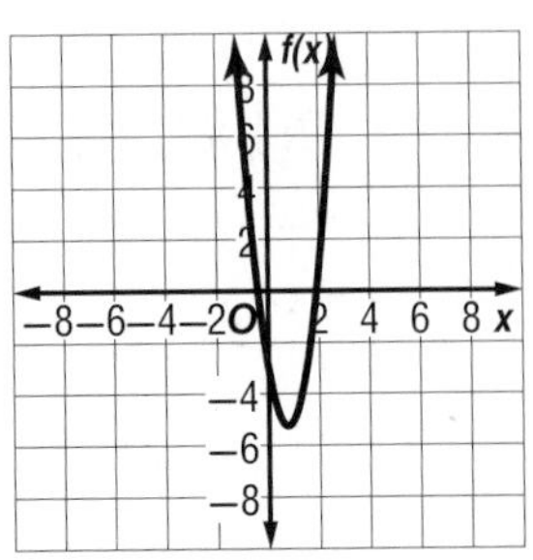

6a. y-int = 5; axis of symmetry: $x = 2$; x-coordinate = 2

6b.

x	f(x)
0	5
1	−1
2	−3
3	−1
4	5

6c.

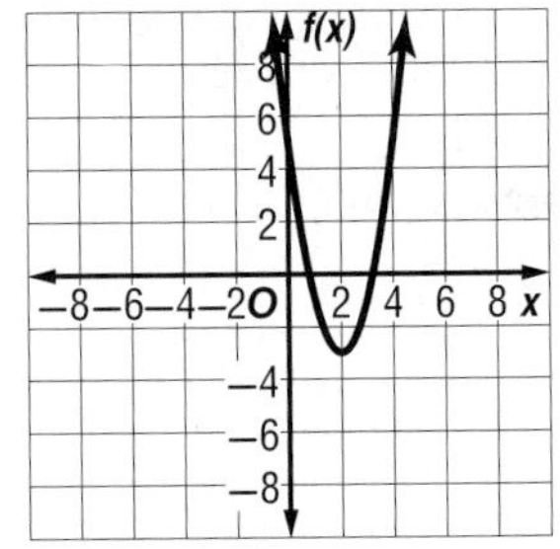

12a. y-int = 0; axis of symmetry: $x = 0$; x-coordinate = 0

12b.

x	f(x)
−2	16
−1	4
0	0
1	4
2	16

12c.

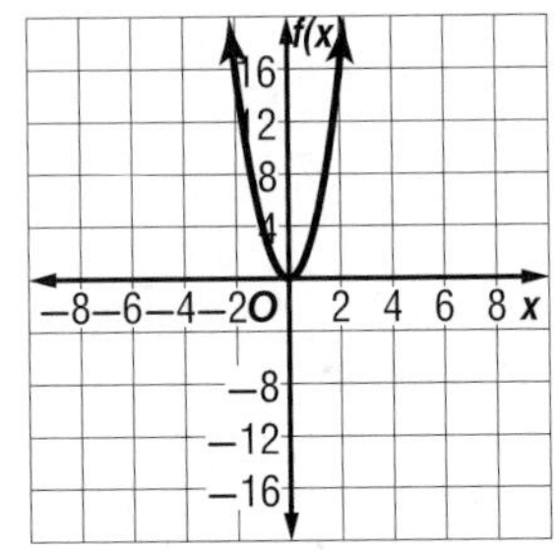

13a. y-int = 0; axis of symmetry: $x = 0$; x-coordinate = 0

13b.

x	f(x)
−2	−8
−1	−2
0	0
1	−2
2	−8

13c.

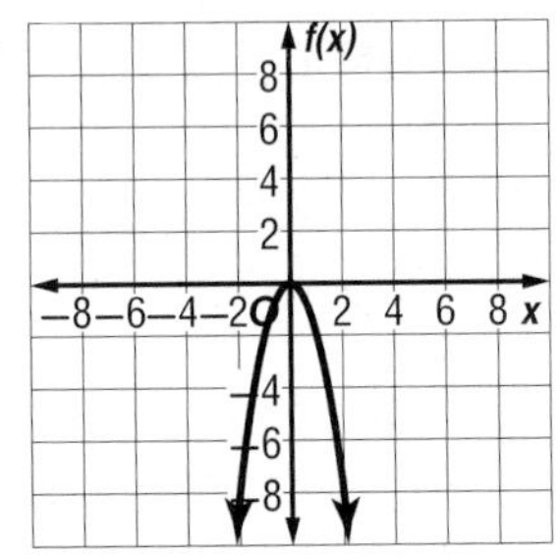

14a. y-int = −5; axis of symmetry: $x = 0$; x-coordinate = 0

14b.

x	f(x)
−2	−1
−1	−4
0	−5
1	−4
2	−1

14c.

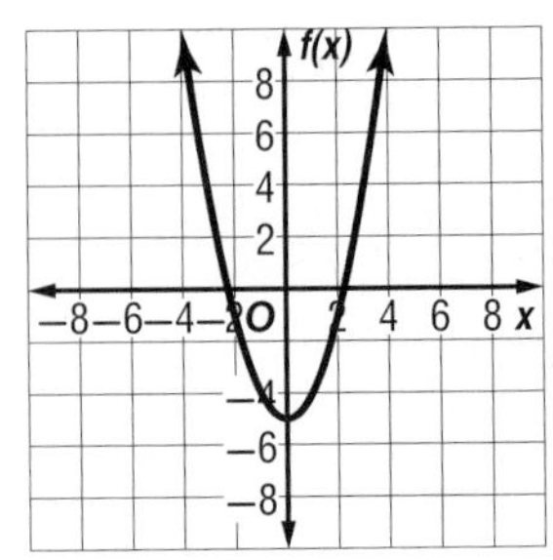

15a. y-int = 3; axis of symmetry: $x = 0$; x-coordinate = 0

15b.

x	f(x)
−2	7
−1	4
0	3
1	4
2	7

15c.

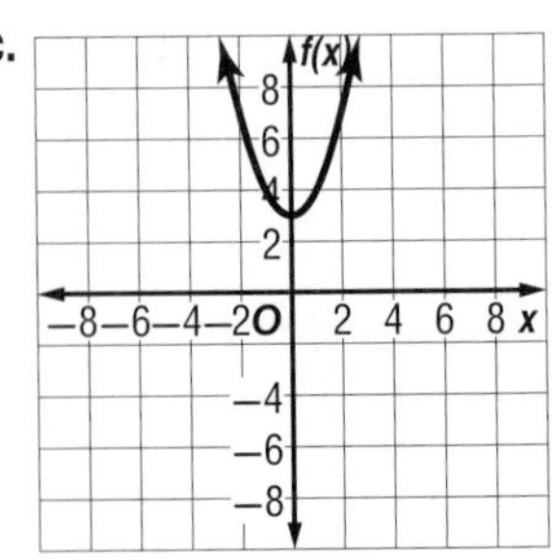

16a. y-int = –3; axis of symmetry: $x = 0$; x-coordinate = 0

16b.

x	$f(x)$
–2	13
–1	1
0	–3
1	1
2	13

16c.

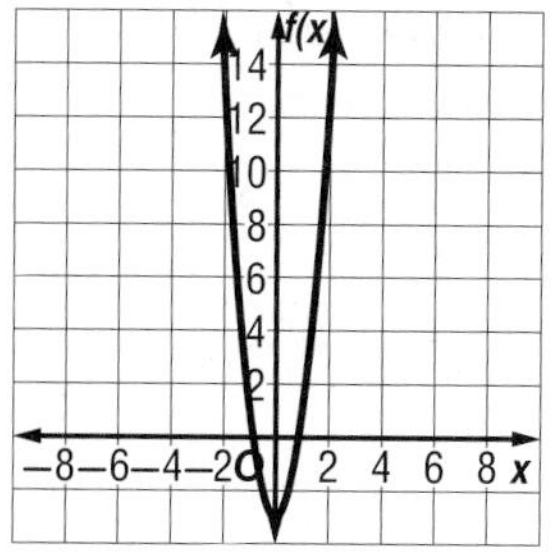

17a. y-int = 5; axis of symmetry: $x = 0$; x-coordinate = 0

17b.

x	$f(x)$
–2	–7
–1	2
0	5
1	2
2	–7

17c.

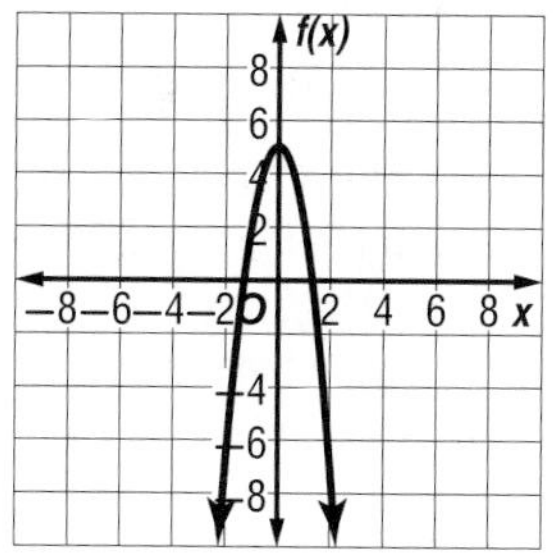

18a. y-int = 8; axis of symmetry: $x = 3$; x-coordinate = 3

18b.

x	$f(x)$
1	3
2	0
3	–1
4	0
5	3

18c.

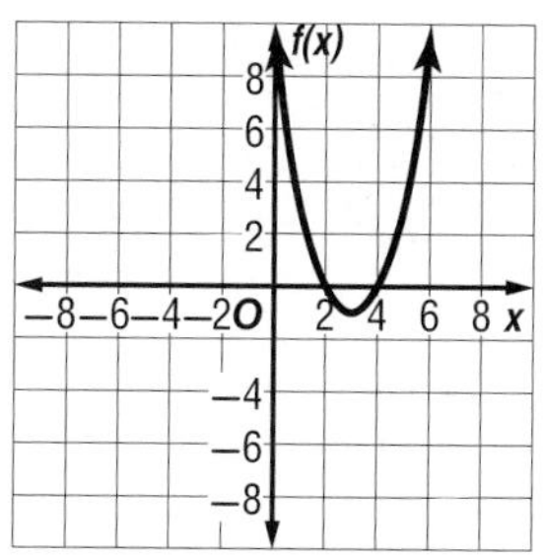

19a. y-int = –10; axis of symmetry: $x = 1.5$; x-coordinate =1.5

19b.

x	$f(x)$
0	–10
1	–12
1.5	–12.25
2	–12
3	–10

19c.

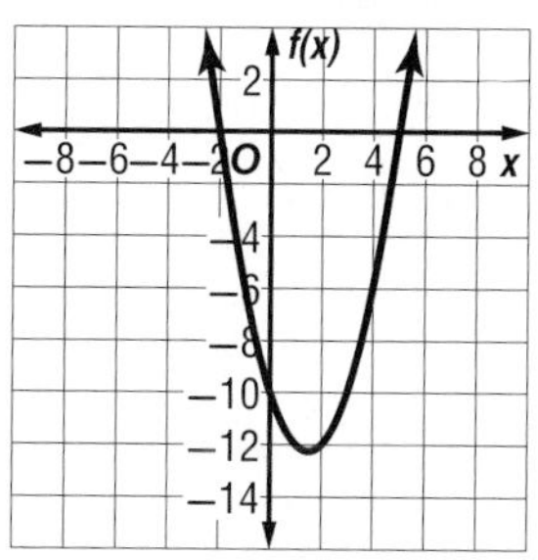

20a. y-int = –6; axis of symmetry: $x = 2$; x-coordinate = 2

20b.

x	$f(x)$
0	–6
1	–3
2	–2
3	–3
4	–6

20c.

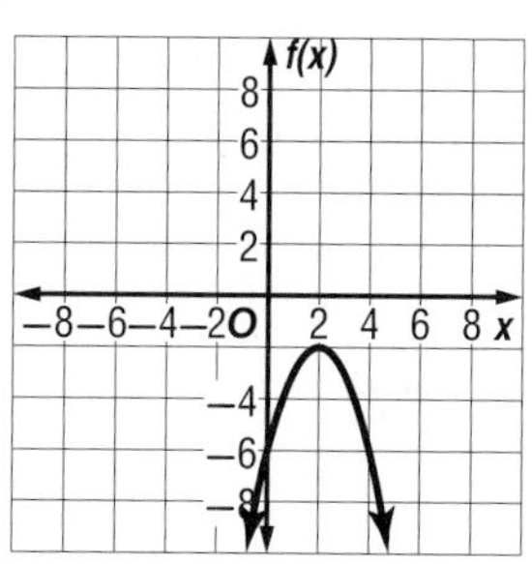

21a. y-int = 9; axis of symmetry: $x = 0.75$; x-coordinate = 0.75

21b.

x	$f(x)$
–1	4
0	9
0.75	10.125
1.5	9
2.5	4

21c.

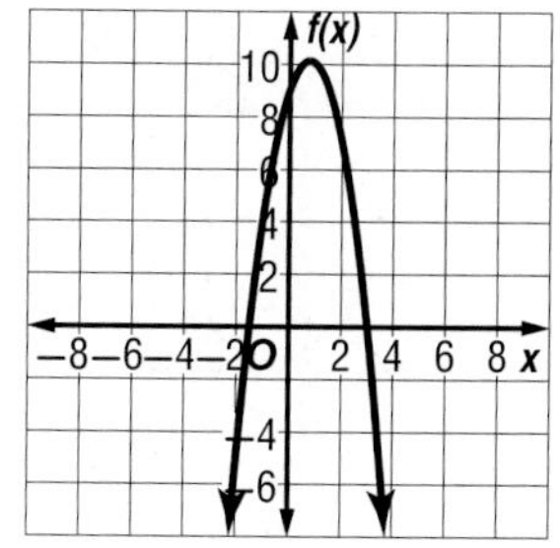

33a. y-int = –9; axis of symmetry: $x = 1.5$; x-coordinate of vertex = 1.5

33b.

x	$f(x)$
0	–9
1	–13
1.5	–13.5
2	–13
3	–9

33c.

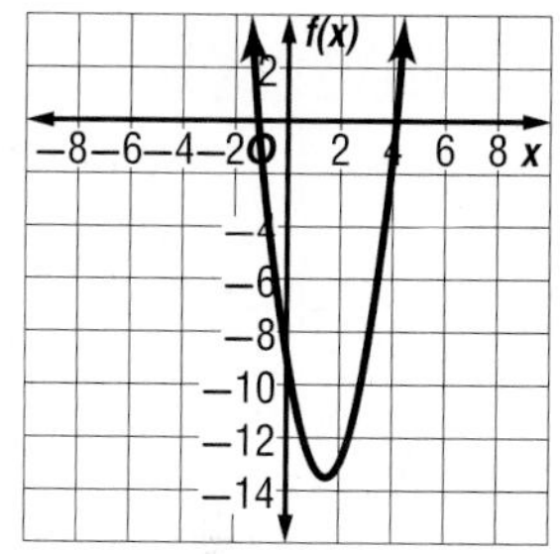

34a. y-int = 2; axis of symmetry: $x = -1.5$; x-coordinate of vertex = –1.5

34b.

x	$f(x)$
–3	2
–2	8
–1.5	8.75
–1	8
0	2

34c.

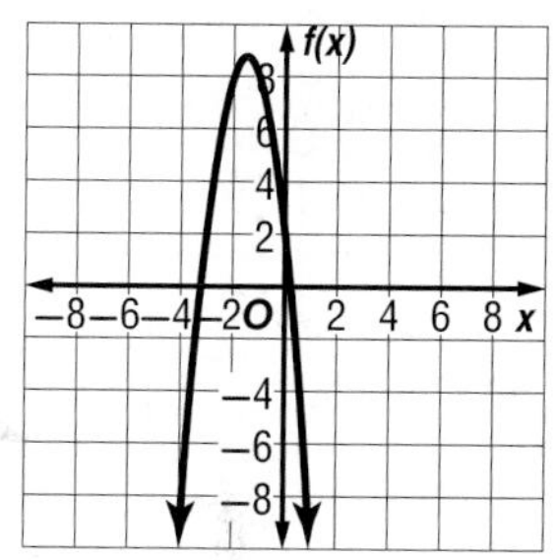

35a. y-int = 0; axis of symmetry: $x = \frac{5}{8}$; x-coordinate of vertex = $\frac{5}{8}$

35b.

x	$f(x)$
$-\frac{3}{4}$	–6
$\frac{1}{4}$	1
$\frac{5}{8}$	1.5625
1	1
2	–6

35c.

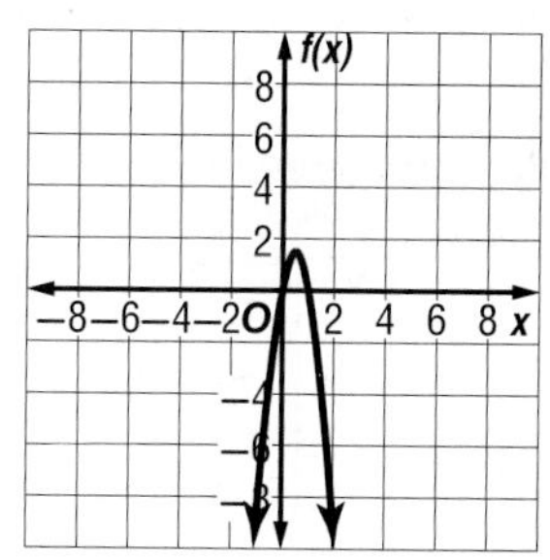

36a. y-int = 0; axis of symmetry: $x = -2.75$; x-coordinate of vertex = –2.75

36b.

x	$f(x)$
–4	–12
–3	–15
–2.75	–15.125
–2.5	–15
–1.5	–12

36c.

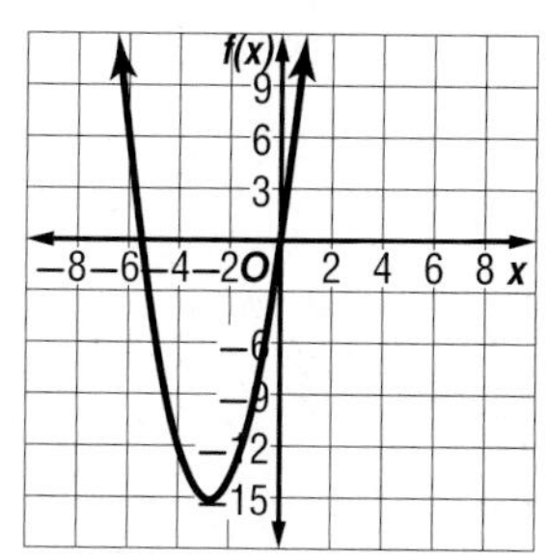

37a. y-int = 4; axis of symmetry: $x = -6$; x-coordinate of vertex = –6

37b.

x	$f(x)$
–10	–1
–8	–4
–6	–5
–4	–4
–2	–1

37c.

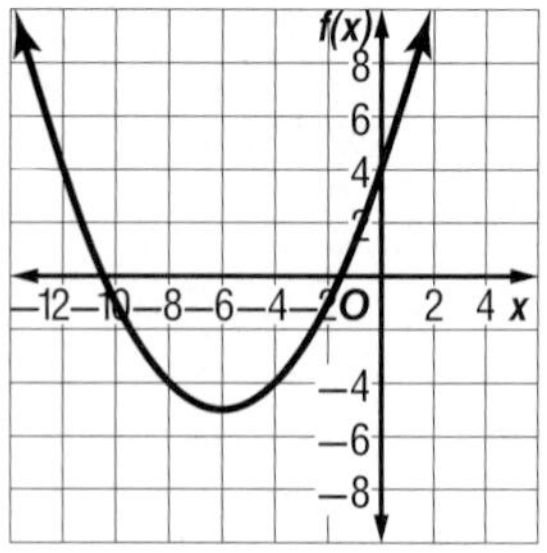

38a. y-int = 6; axis of symmetry: $x = \frac{8}{3}$; x-coordinate of vertex $= \frac{8}{3}$

38b.

x	$f(x)$
$\frac{4}{3}$	10
$\frac{7}{3}$	11.25
$\frac{8}{3}$	$11\frac{1}{3}$
3	11.25
4	10

38c.

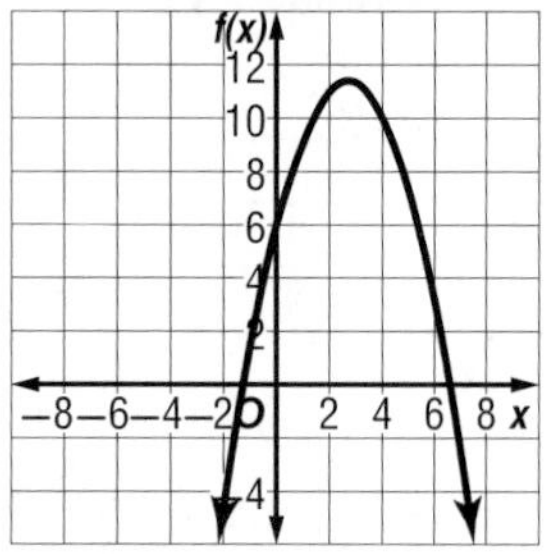

39a. y-int = –2.5; axis of symmetry: $x = -\frac{4}{3}$; x-coordinate of vertex $= -\frac{4}{3}$

39b.

x	$f(x)$
$-\frac{11}{3}$	3
$-\frac{8}{3}$	–2.5
$-\frac{4}{3}$	$-5\frac{1}{6}$
0	–2.5
1	3

39c.

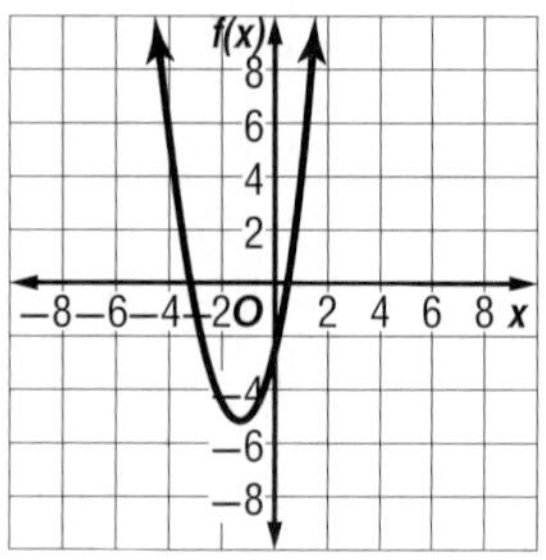

40a. y-int = 9; axis of symmetry: $x = 1.75$; x-coordinate of vertex = 1.75

40b.

x	$f(x)$
0.5	8
1.5	7
1.75	$6\frac{23}{24}$
2	7
3	8

40c.

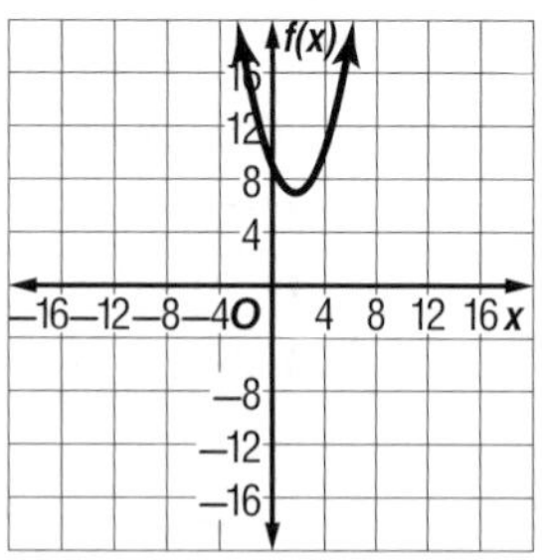

Page 258, Extend 5-1

1. Linear regression graph:

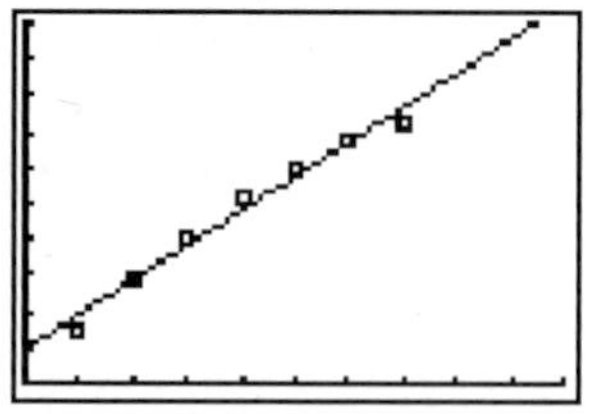

[0, 1] scl: 0.1 by [0, 20] scl: 2
linear equation:
$h(t) = 19.2t + 1.92$

Quadratic regression graph:

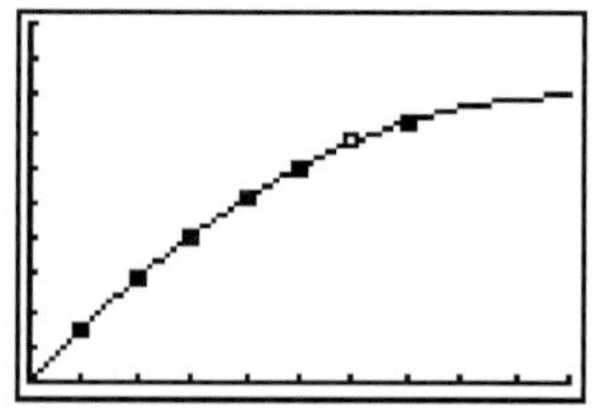

[0, 1] scl: 0.1 by [0, 20] scl: 2
quadratic equation:
$h(t) = -16t^2 + 32t$

The quadratic equation fits the data better.

3. The linear equation predicts that the basketball player will continue to rise indefinitely, and the quadratic equation shows that the player will reach the highest point of his jump and then return to the ground.

Page 260, Lesson 5-2 (Guided Practice)

2A.

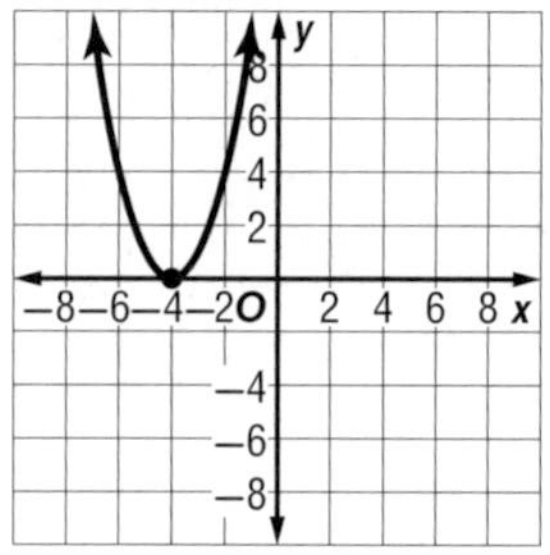

2B.

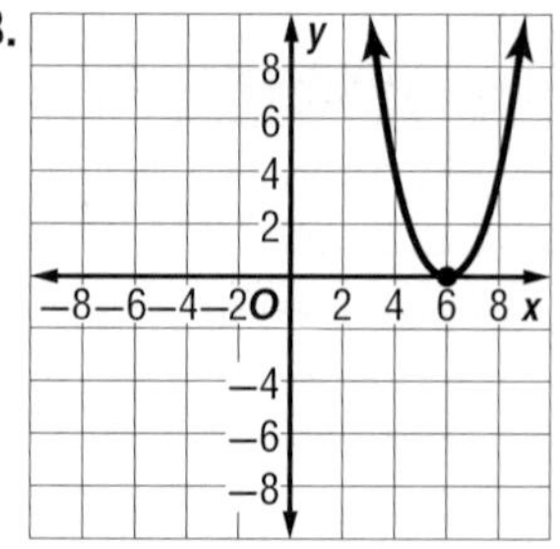

Pages 263–264, Lesson 5-2

4.

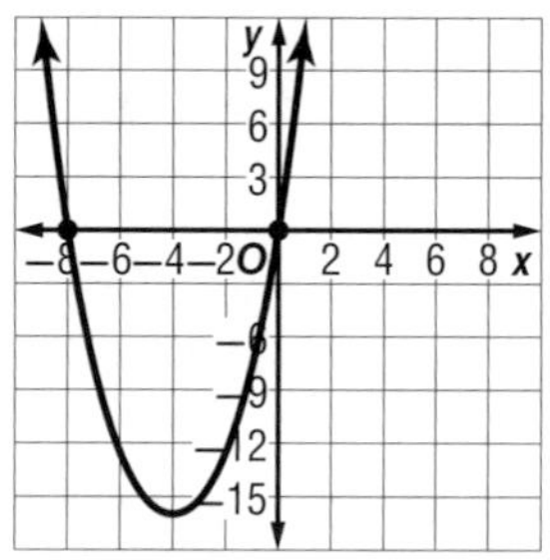

5.

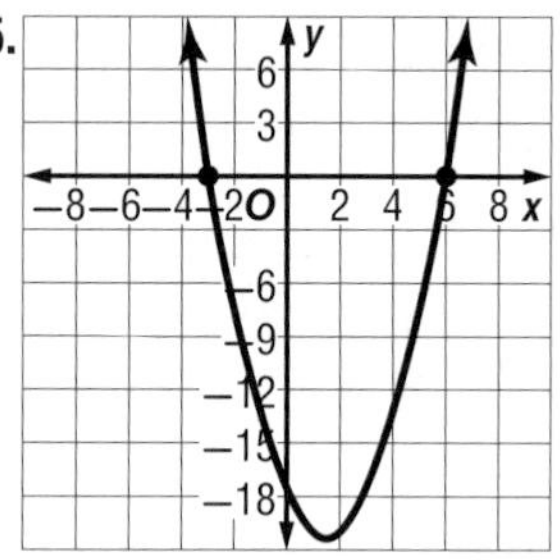

6.

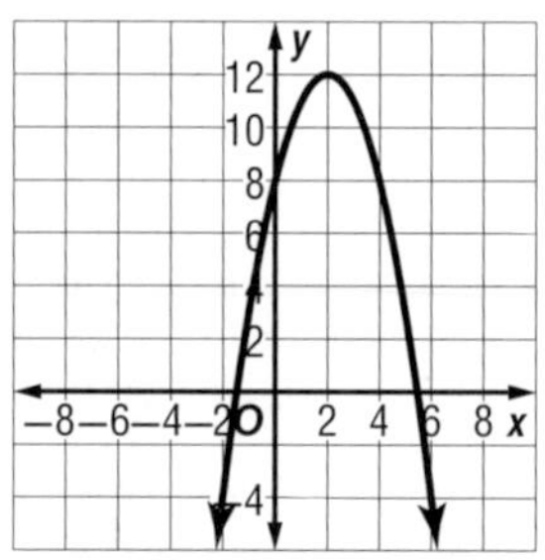

7.

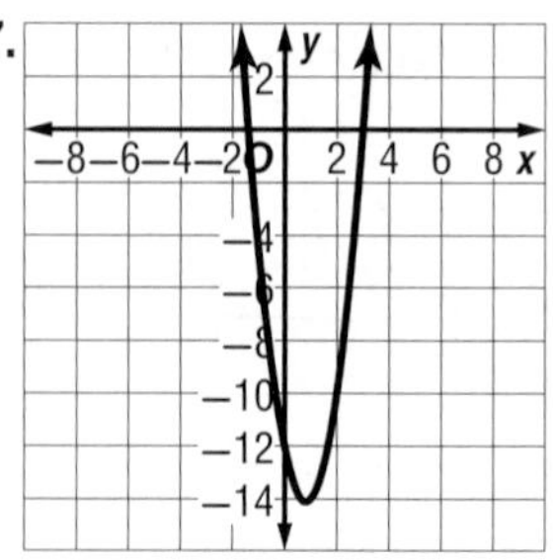

8.

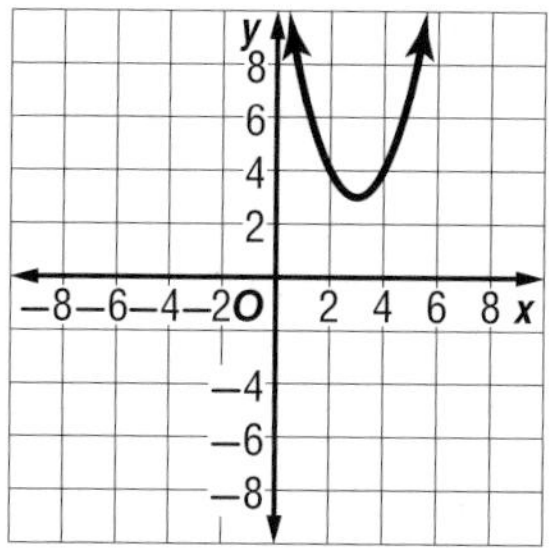

9.

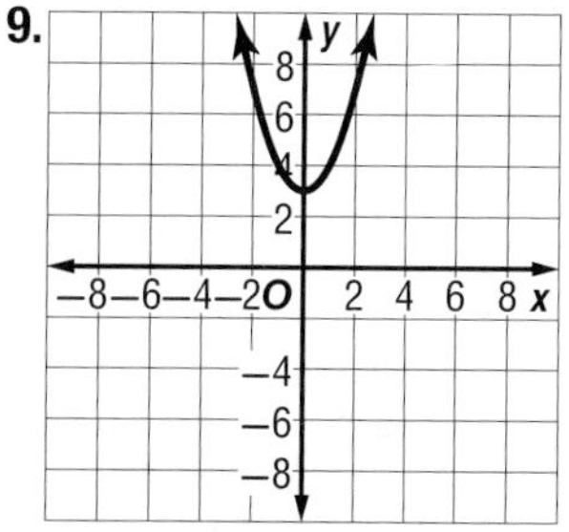

10.

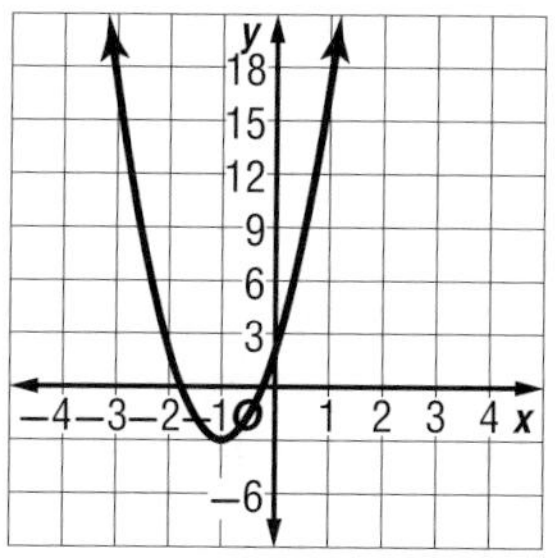

11.

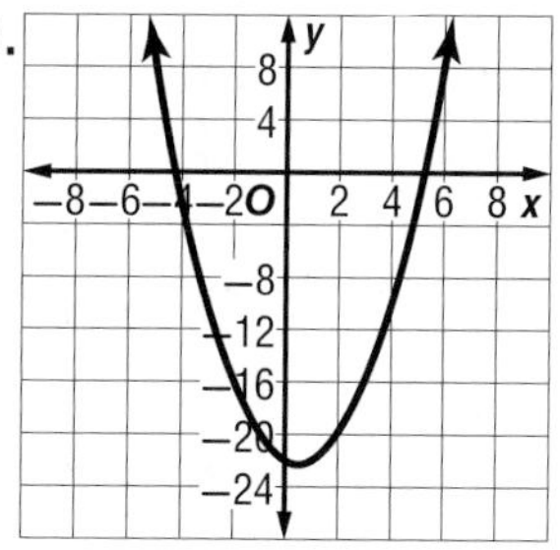

20.

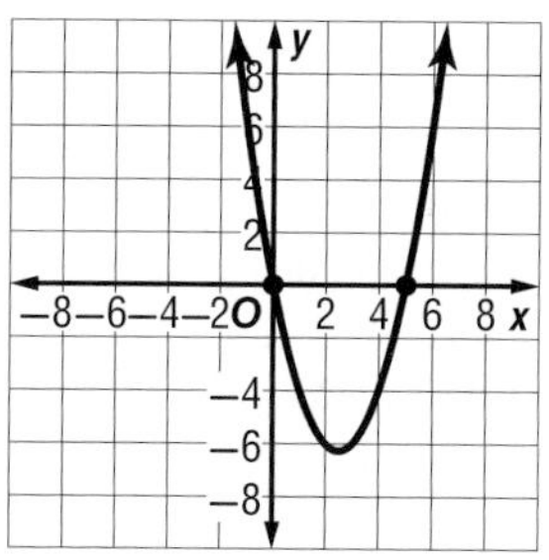

21.

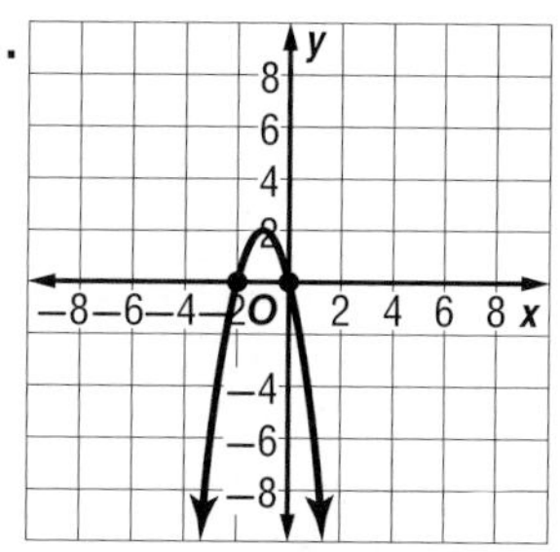

22.

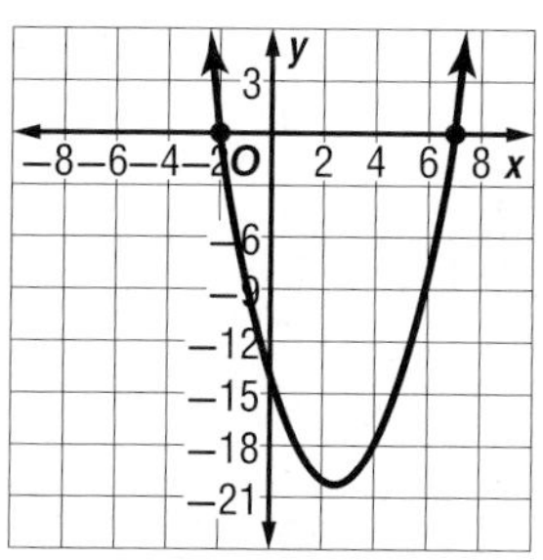

23.

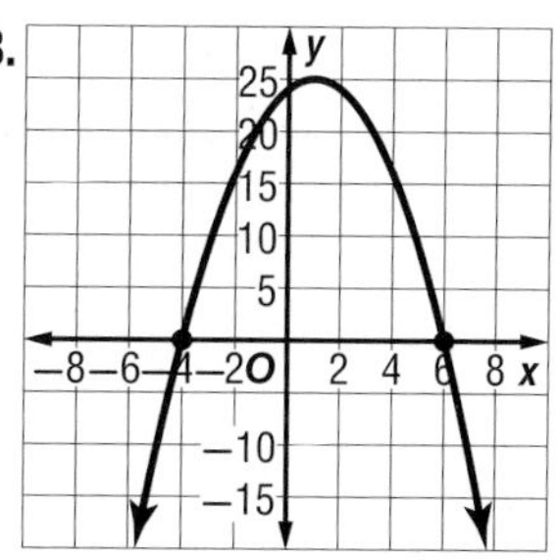

24.

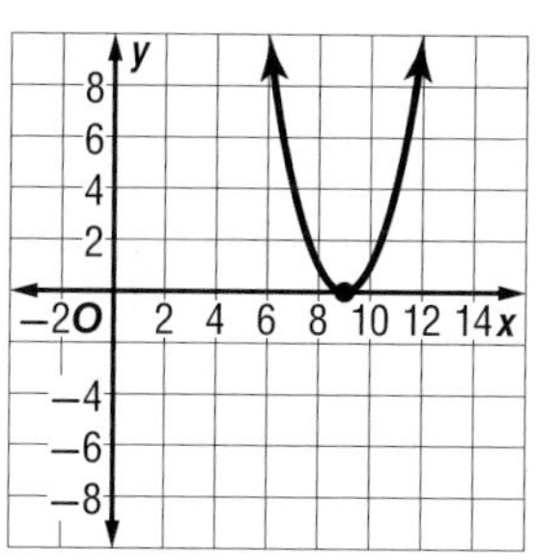

25.

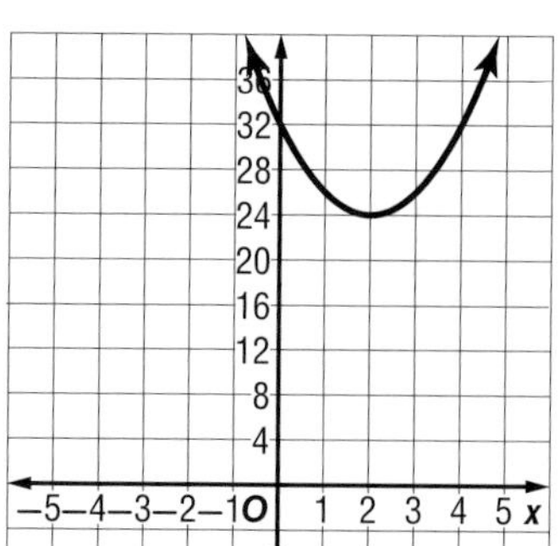

26.

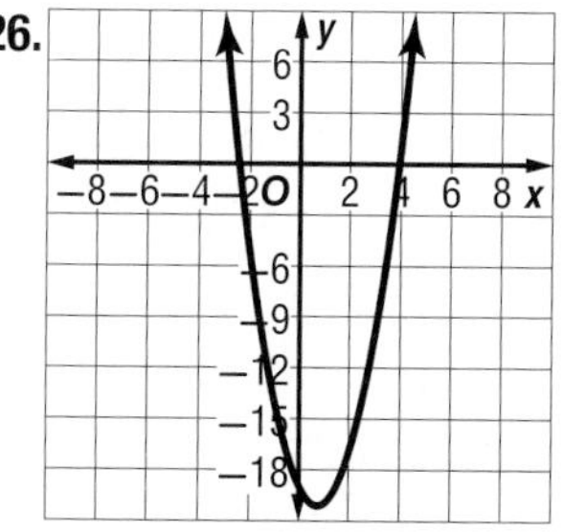

27.

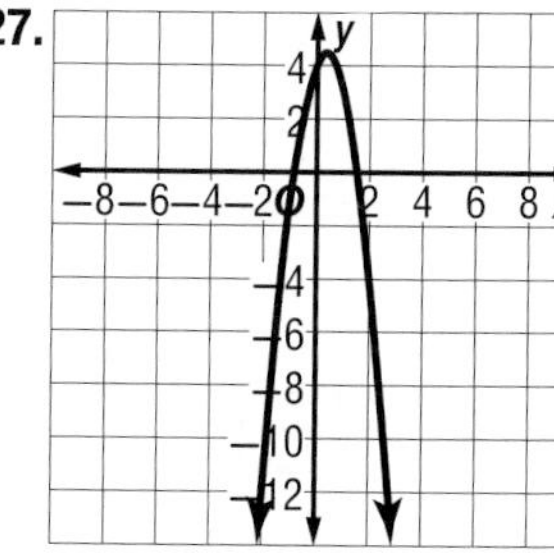

28.

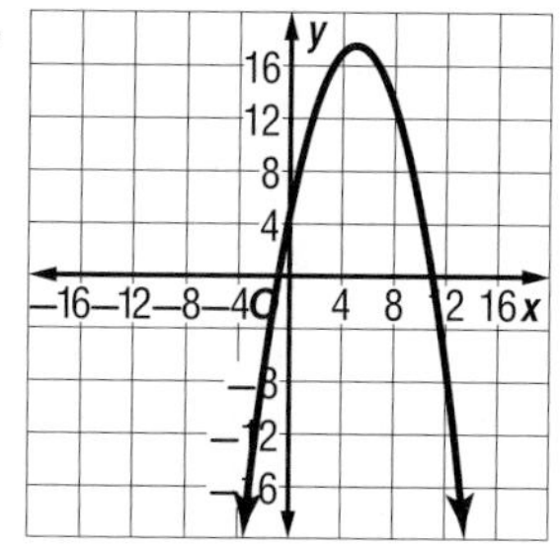

29.

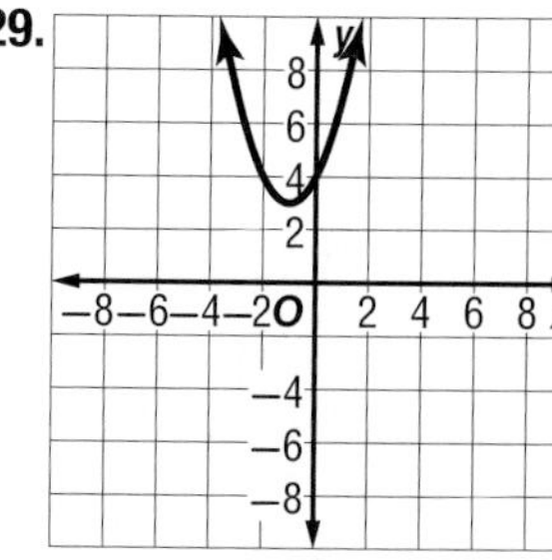

41.

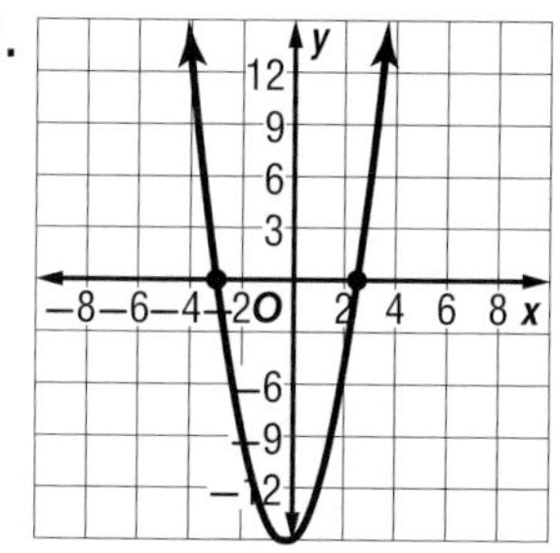

42.

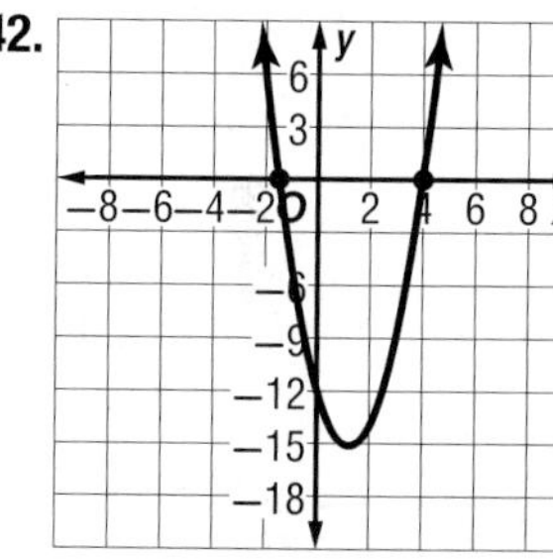

43.

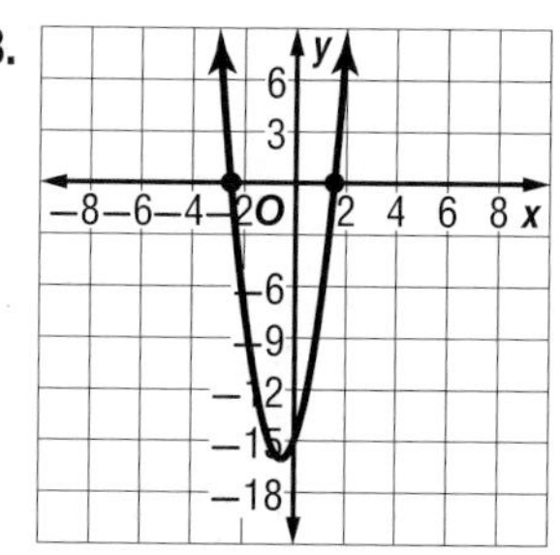

44.

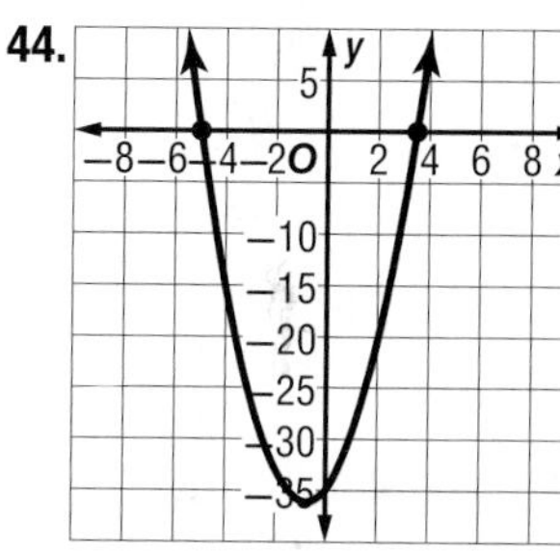

45.

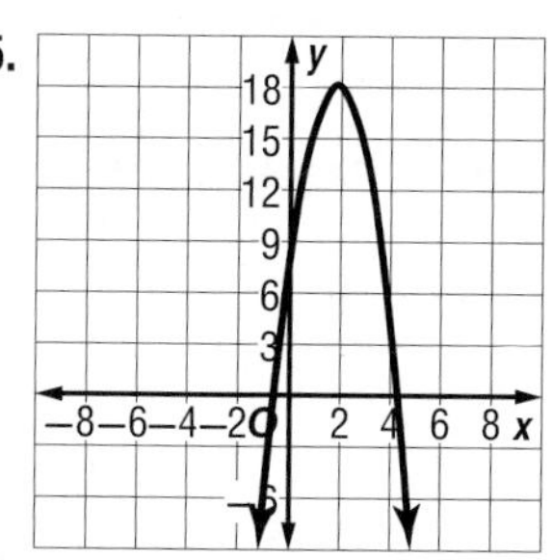

46.

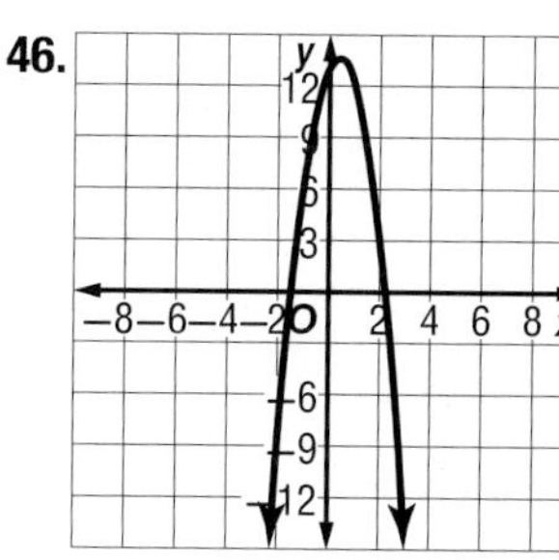

47.

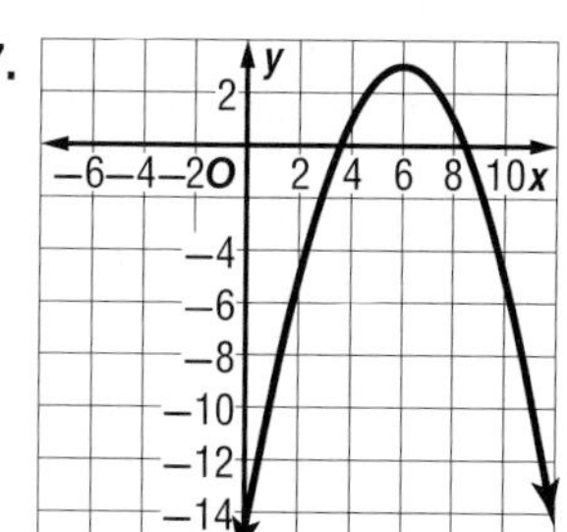

48.

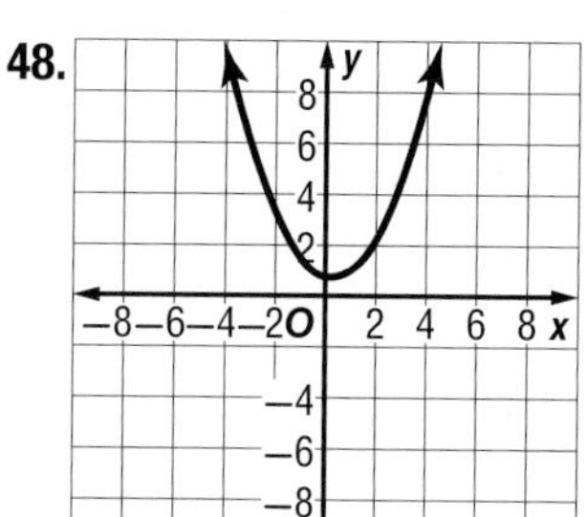

Page 299, Lesson 5-6

46a. 1 rational root

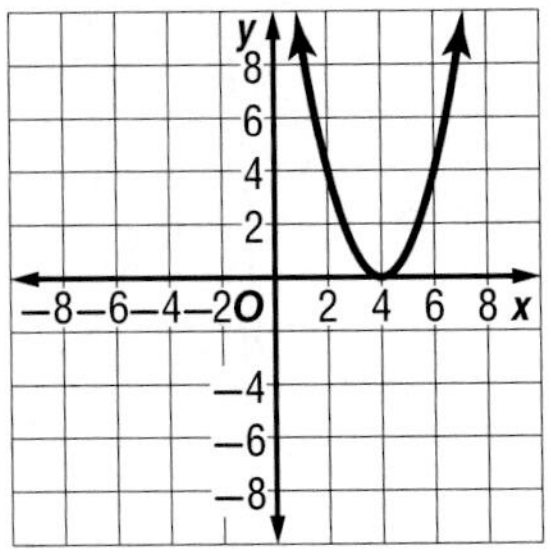

46b. 2 complex roots

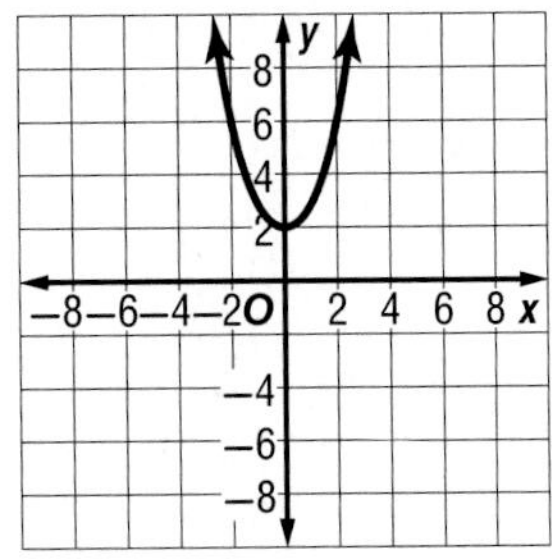

46c. 2 real roots

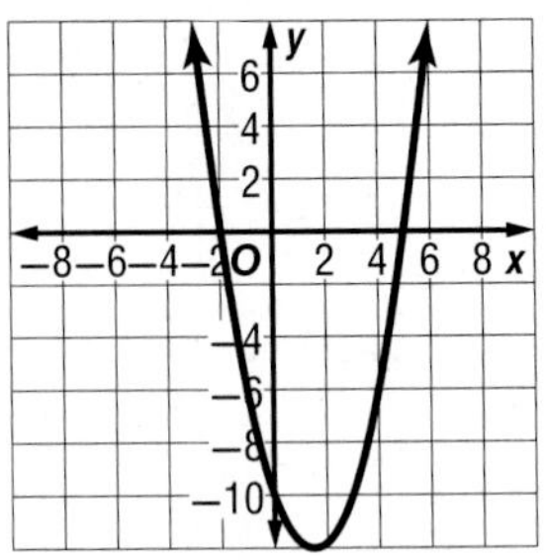

46d. 2 complex roots

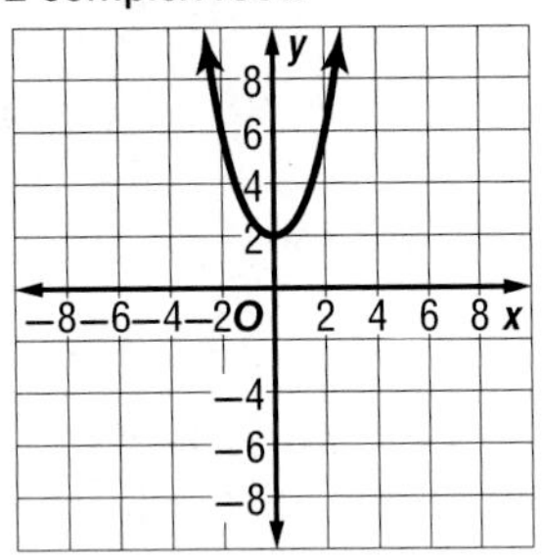

46e. 2 rational roots

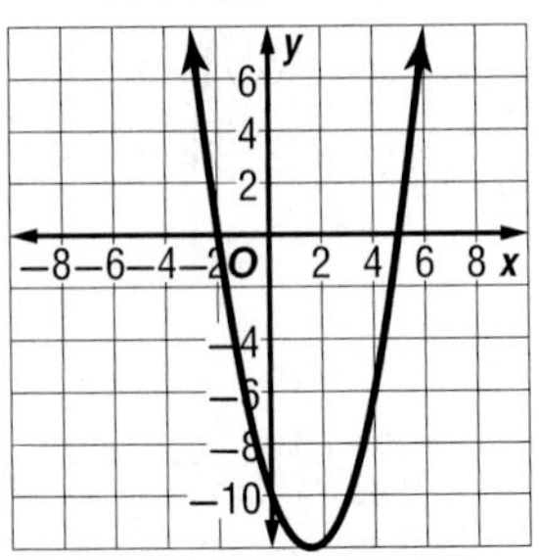

48. Sample answer: (1) Factor $x^2 - 2x - 15$ as $(x + 3)(x - 5)$. Then according to the Zero Product Property, either $x + 3 = 0$ or $x - 5 = 0$. Solving these equations, $x = -3$ or $x = 5$.
(2) Rewrite the equation as $x^2 - 2x = 15$. Then add 1 to each side of the equation to complete the square on the left side. Then $(x - 1)^2 = 16$. Taking the square root of each side, $x - 1 = \pm 4$. Therefore, $x = 1 \pm 4$ and $x = -3$ or $x = 5$.
(3) Use the Quadratic Formula. Thus, $x = \frac{2 \pm \sqrt{2^2 - 4(1)(-15)}}{2(1)}$ or $x = \frac{2 \pm \sqrt{64}}{2}$. Simplifying the expression, $x = -3$ or $x = 5$.
See students' preferences.

Page 304, Explore 5-7

4.

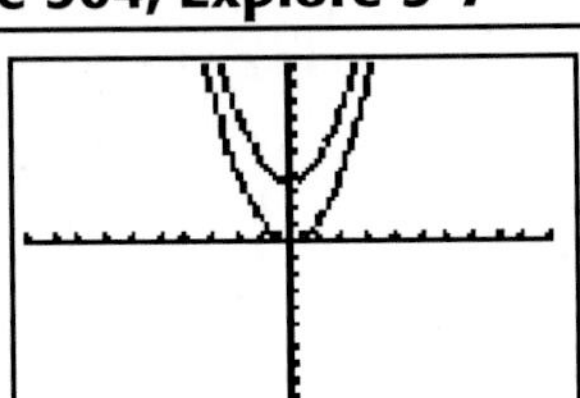

Both graphs have the same shape, but the graph of $y = x^2 + 3.5$ is 3.5 units above the graph of $y = x^2$.

5.

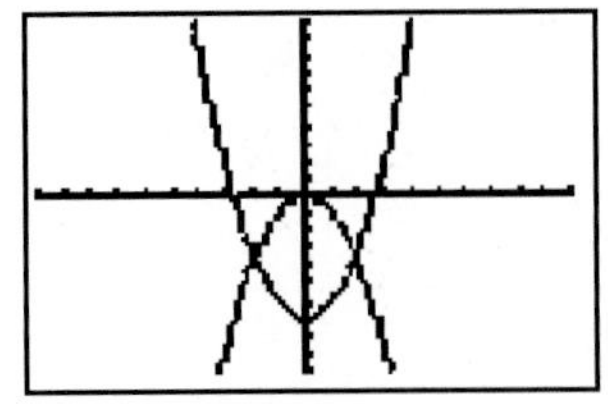

Both graphs have the same shape, but the graph of $y = -x^2$ opens downward while the graph of $y = x^2 - 7$ opens upward and is 7 units lower than the graph of $y = x^2$.

6.

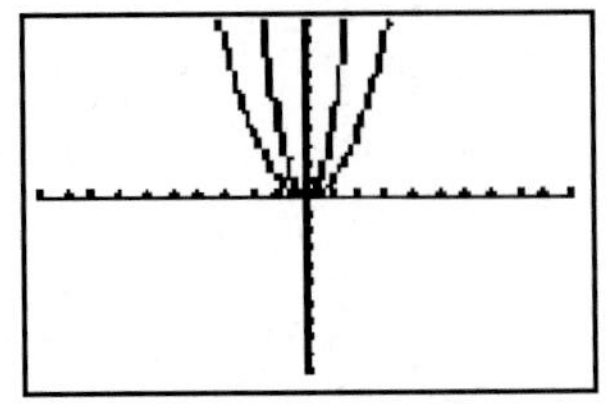

The graph of $y = 4x^2$ is narrower than the graph of $y = x^2$.

7.

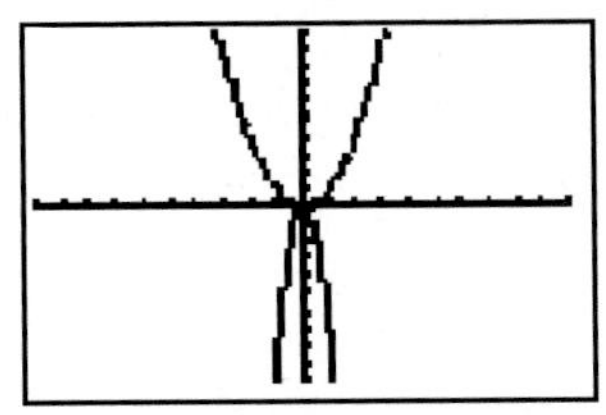

The graph of $y = -8x^2$ opens downwards and is narrower than the graph of $y = x^2$

8.

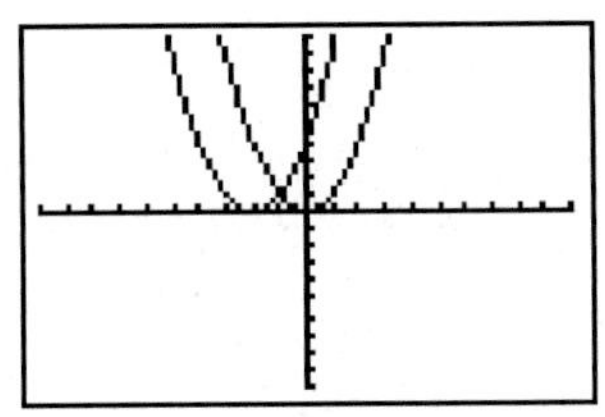

The graphs have the same shape and open upward, but the graph of $y = (x + 2)^2$ is two units to the left of the graph of $y = x^2$.

9.

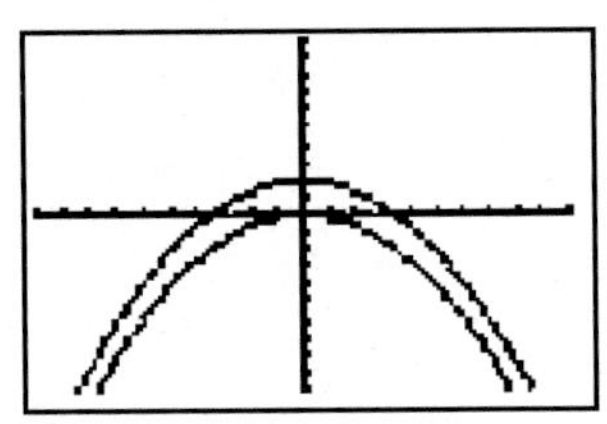

The graphs have the same shape and open downward, but the graph of $y = -\frac{1}{6}x^2 + 2$ is two units above the graph of $y = -\frac{1}{6}x^2$.

10.

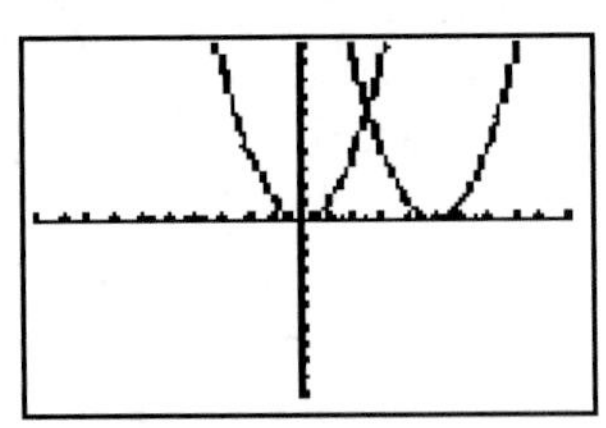

The graphs have the same shape, but the graph of $y = (x - 5)^2$ is 5 units to the right of the graph of $y = x^2$.

11.

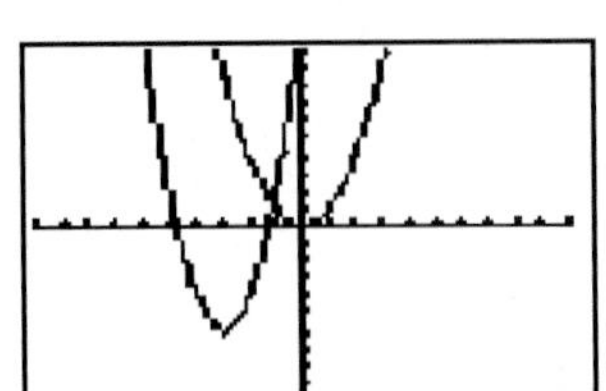

The graph of $y = 2(x + 3)^2 - 6$ is 3 units to the left, 6 units below, and narrower than the graph of $y = x^2$.

12.

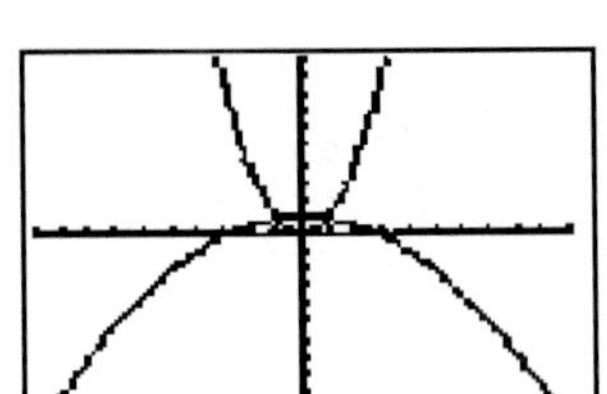

The graph of $y = -\frac{1}{8}x^2 + 1$ opens downward, is wider than and 1 unit above the graph of $y = x^2$.

13. 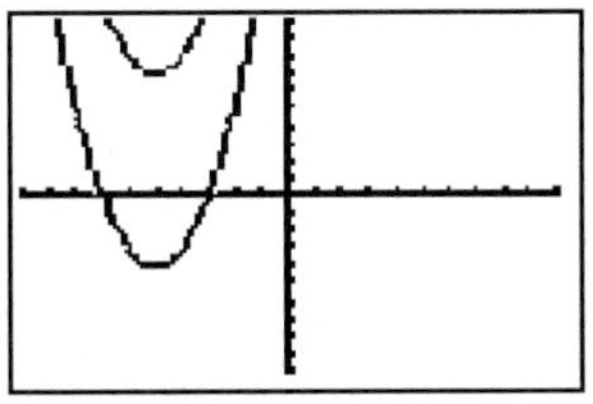

The graphs have the same shape, but the graph of $y = (x + 5)^2 + 7$ is 11 units above the graph of $y = (x + 5)^2 - 4$.

14. 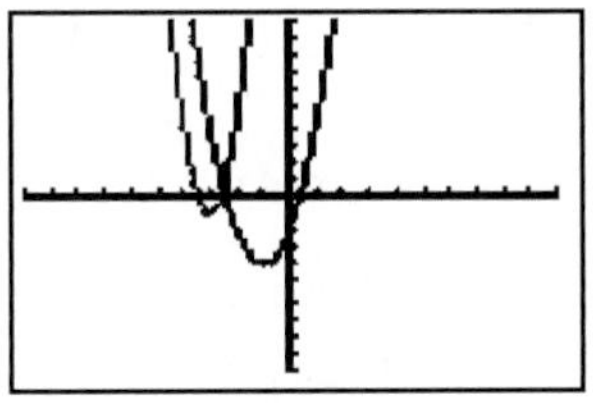

The graph of $y = 5(x + 3)^2 - 1$ is narrower than the graph of $y = 2(x + 1)^2 - 4$.

15. 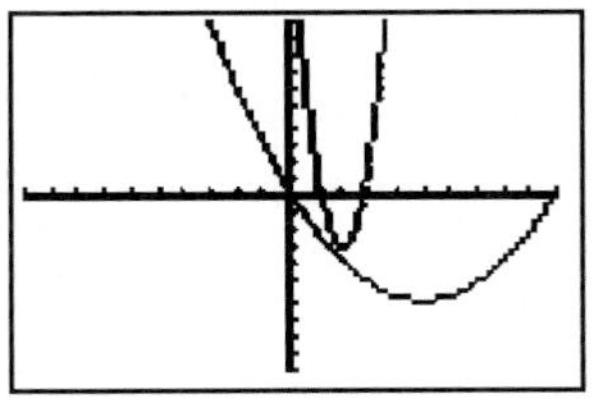

The graph of $y = \frac{1}{4}(x - 5)^2 - 6$ is wider than the graph of $y = 5(x - 2)^2 - 3$, and its vertex is 3 units below and 3 units right of the vertex of $y = 5(x - 2)^2 - 3$.

Page 307, Lesson 5-7 (Guided Practice)

3A. 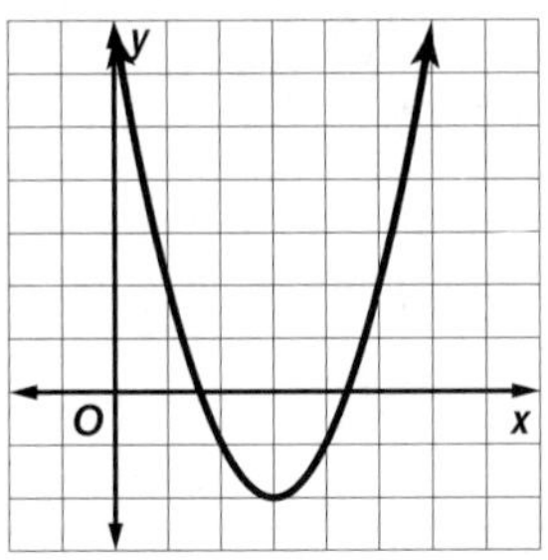

3B. 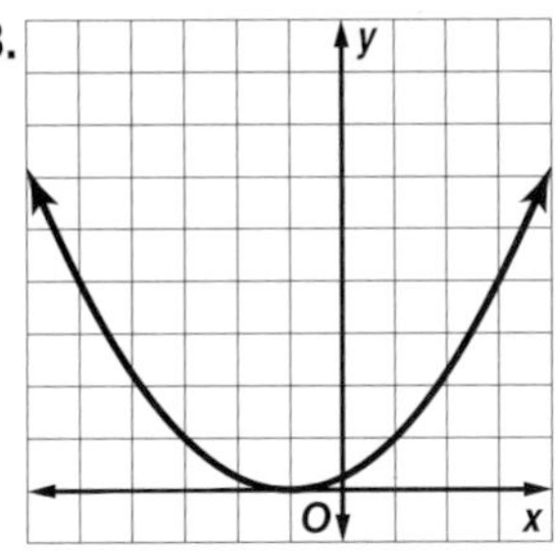

Pages 308–309, Lesson 5-7

21. 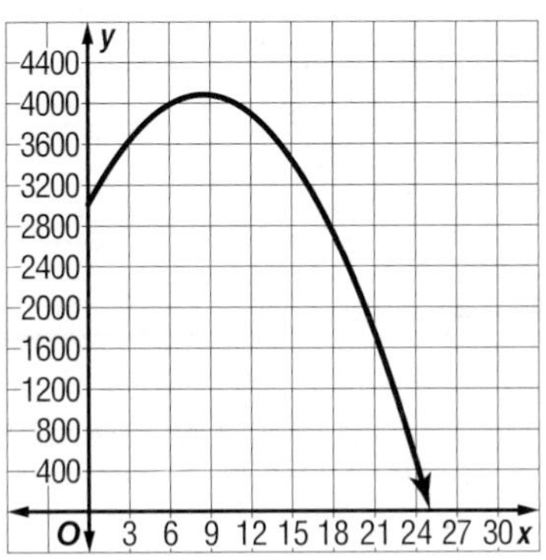

22. 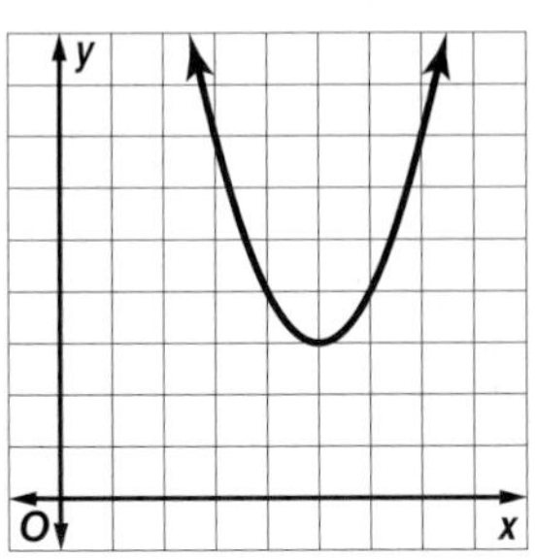

23. 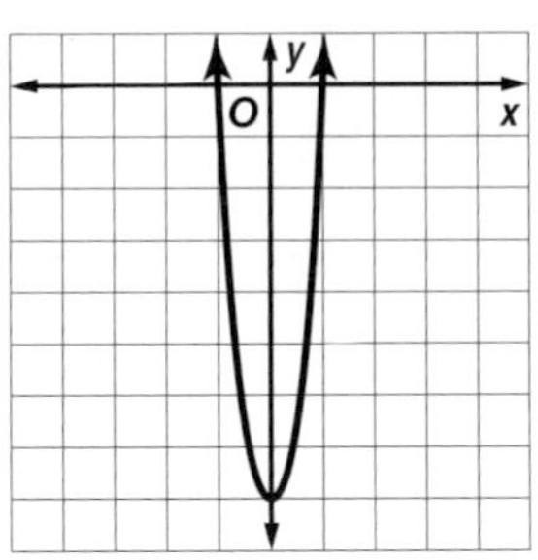

24. 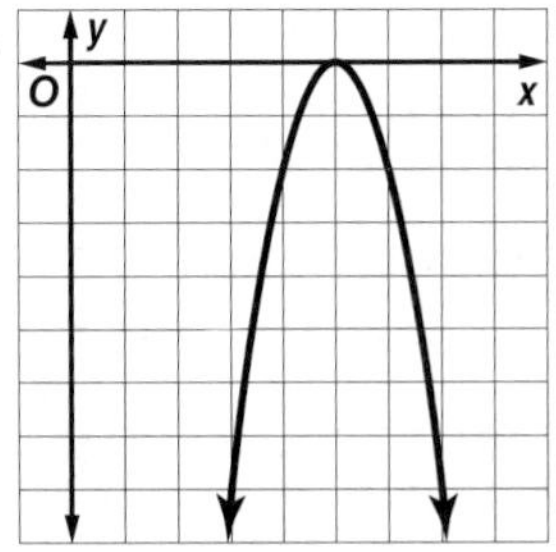

25. 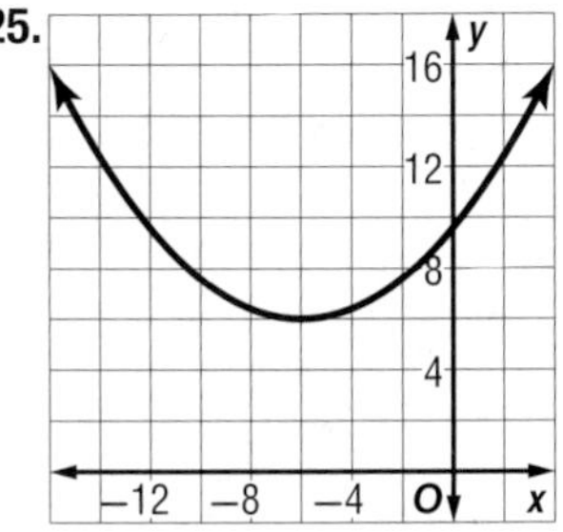

26. 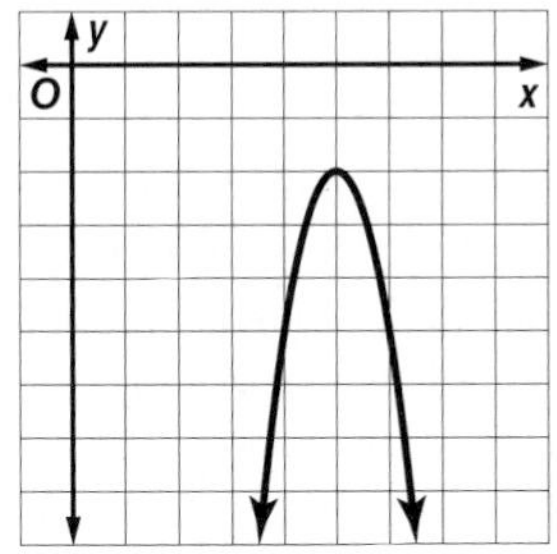

27. 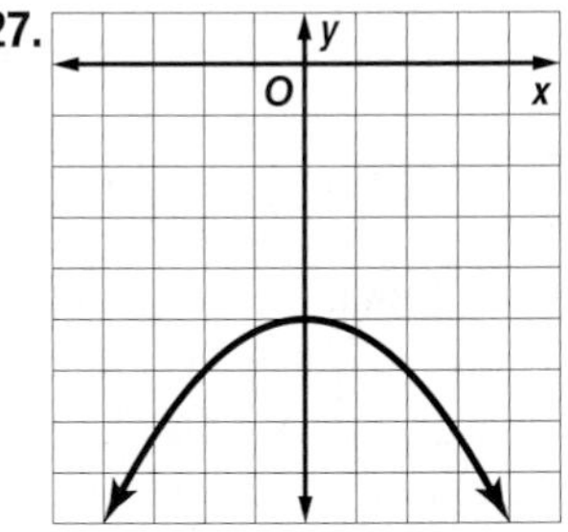

28. 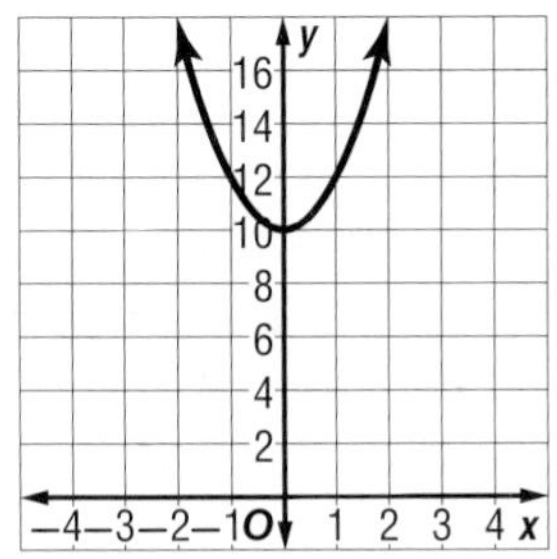

29. 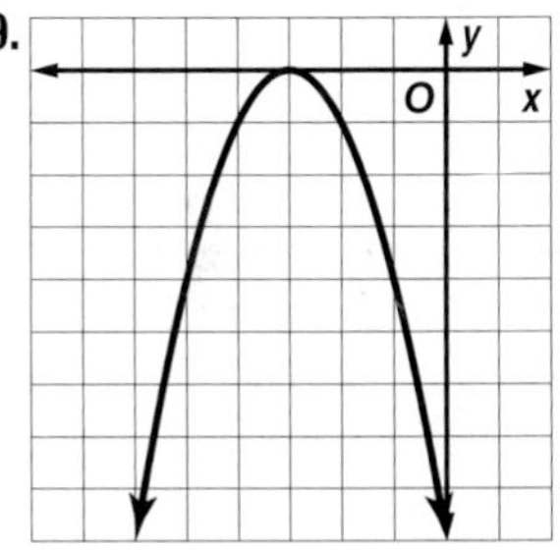

30. 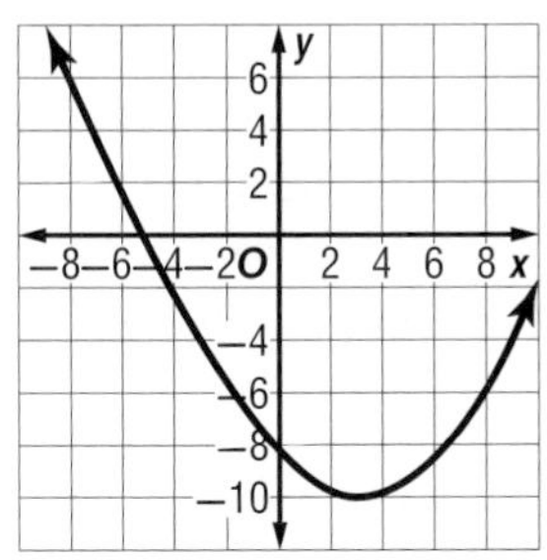

31. 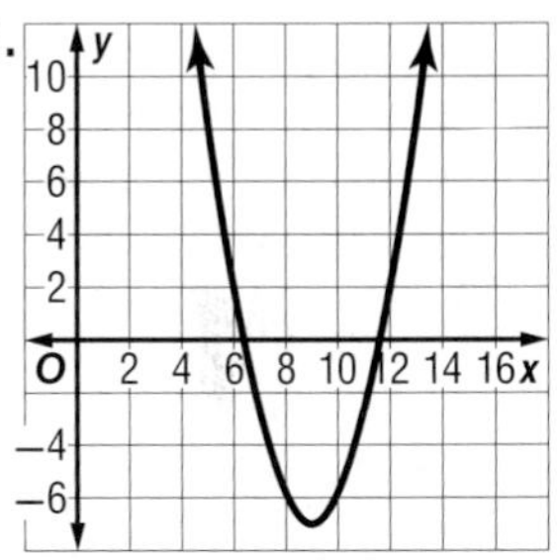

32. 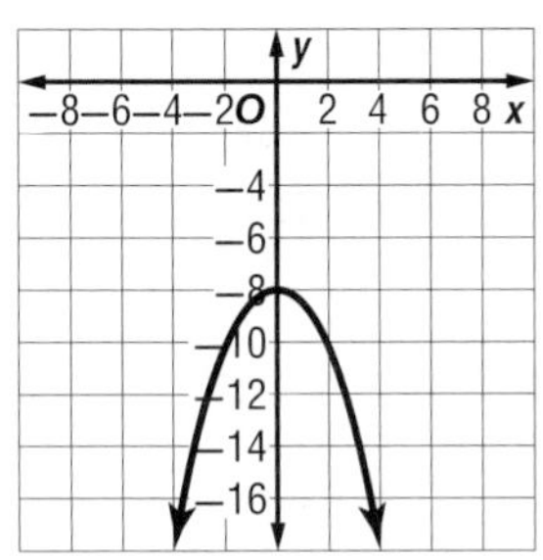

33. 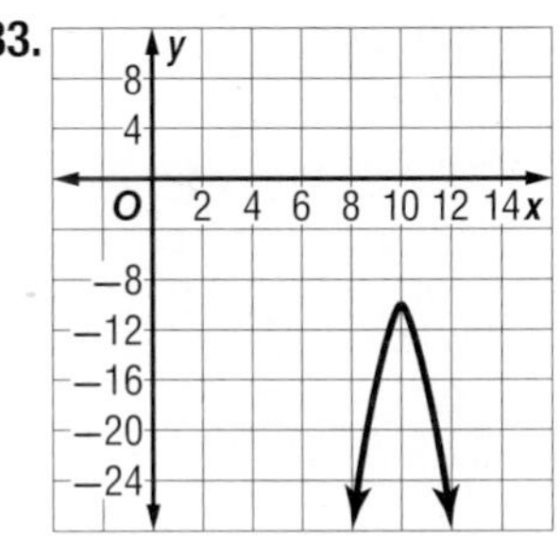

34a. $f(x) = \frac{1}{250}(x + 75)^2 - \frac{45}{2}$

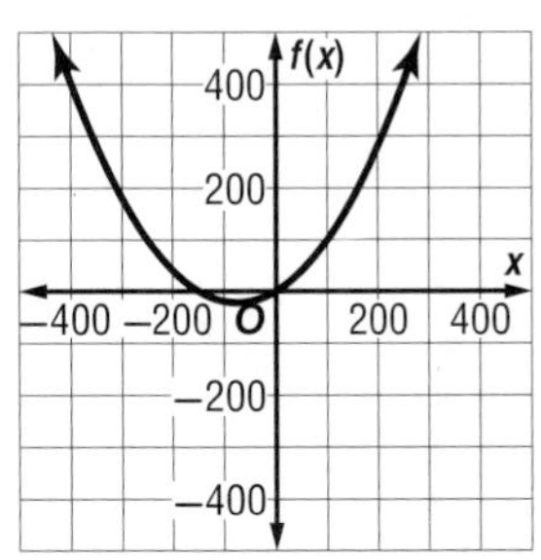

41. $y = 3\left(x - \frac{2}{3}\right)^2 - \frac{10}{3}; \left(\frac{2}{3}, -\frac{10}{3}\right), x = \frac{2}{3}$, opens up

42. $y = -2\left(x - \frac{7}{4}\right)^2 + \frac{145}{8}; \left(\frac{7}{4}, \frac{145}{8}\right), x = \frac{7}{4}$, opens down

43. $y = -(x + 2.35)^2 + 8.3225; (-2.35, 8.3225), x = -2.35$, opens down

44. $y = (x + 0.7)^2 - 1.69; (-0.7, -1.69), x = -0.7$, opens up

45. $y = \left(x - \frac{1}{3}\right)^2 - 3; \left(\frac{1}{3}, -3\right), x = \frac{1}{3}$, opens up

46. $y = (x + 3.5)^2; (-3.5, 0), x = -3.5$, opens up

49. The equation of a parabola can be written in the form $y = ax^2 + bx + c$ with $a \neq 0$. For each of the three points, substitute the value of the x-coordinate for x in the equation and substitute the value of the y-coordinate for y in the equation. This will produce three equations in three variables a, b, and c. Solve the system of equations to find the values of a, b, and c. These values determine the quadratic equation.

50. $a\left(x + \frac{b}{2a}\right)^2 + \left(c - \frac{b^2}{4a}\right) = 0; \left(\frac{-b}{2a}, c - \frac{b^2}{4a}\right); x = \frac{-b}{2a}$

51. Sample answer: The variable a represents different values for these functions, so making $a = 0$ will have a different effect on each function. For $f(x)$, when $a = 0$, the graph will be a horizontal line, $f(x) = k$. For $g(x)$, when $a = 0$, the graph will be linear, but not necessarily horizontal, $g(x) = bx + c$.

52. All quadratic functions are transformations of the parent graph $y = x^2$. By identifying these transformations when a quadratic function is written in vertex form, you can redraw the graph of $y = x^2$ with its vertex translated to (h, k), widened or narrowed as determined by a, opening downward if a is negative.

Page 311, Extend 5-7

Activity Steps 1 and 2

x	0	1	2	3	4	5
y	12	9.1875	6.75	4.6875	3	1.6875
First-Order Differences						
Second-Order Differences						

x	6	7	8	9	10	11
y	0.75	0.1875	0	0.1875	0.75	1.6875
First-Order Differences						
Second-Order Differences						

x	12	13	14	15	16
y	3	4.6875	6.75	9.1875	12
First-Order Differences					
Second-Order Differences					

Step 3

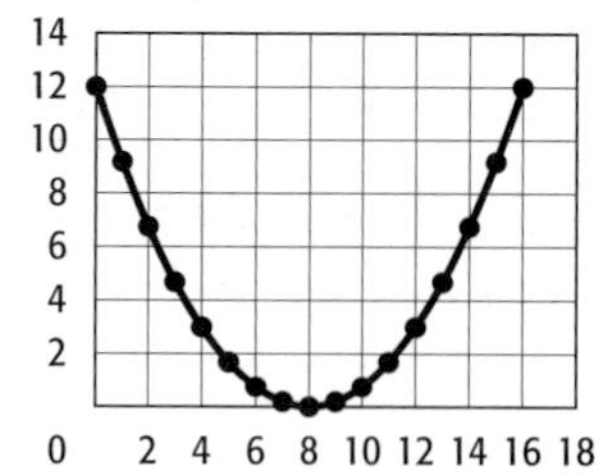

Step 4

x	0	1	2	3	4	5
y	12	9.1875	6.75	4.6875	3	1.6875
First-Order Differences		−2.8125	−2.4375	−2.0625	−1.6875	−1.3125
Second-Order Differences						

x	6	7	8	9	10	11
y	0.75	0.1875	0	0.1875	0.75	1.6875
First-Order Differences	−0.9375	−0.5625	−0.1875	0.1875	0.5625	0.9375
Second-Order Differences						

x	12	13	14	15	16
y	3	4.6875	6.75	9.1875	12
First-Order Differences	1.3125	1.6875	2.0625	2.4375	2.8125
Second-Order Differences					

The differences decrease until $x = 8$, and then the differences increase.

Step 5

x	0	1	2	3	4	5
y	12	9.1875	6.75	4.6875	3	1.6875
First-Order Differences		−2.8125	−2.4375	−2.0625	−1.6875	−1.3125
Second-Order Differences			0.375	0.375	0.375	0.375

x	6	7	8	9	10	11
y	0.75	0.1875	0	0.1875	0.75	1.6875
First-Order Differences	−0.9375	−0.5625	−0.1875	0.1875	0.5625	0.9375
Second-Order Differences	0.375	0.375	0.375	0.375	0.375	0.375

x	12	13	14	15	16
y	3	4.6875	6.75	9.1875	12
First-Order Differences	1.3125	1.6875	2.0625	2.4375	2.8125
Second-Order Differences	0.375	0.375	0.375	0.375	

The second-order differences are all 0.375.

1.

x	−3	−2	−1	0	1	2	3
y	−16	−9	−4	−1	0	−1	−4
First-Order Differences		7	5	3	1	−1	−3
Second-Order Differences			−2	−2	−2	−2	−2

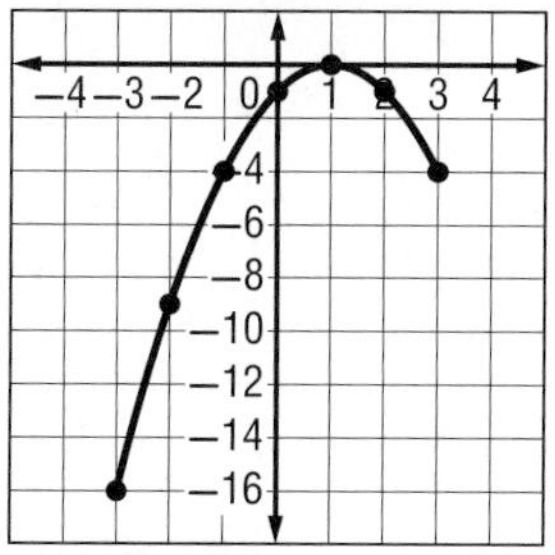

2.

x	−5	−4	−3	−2	−1	0	
y	0.5	−2	−3.5	−4	−3.5	−2	0.5
First-Order Differences		−2.5	−1.5	−0.5	0.5	1.5	2.5
Second-Order Differences			1	1	1	1	1

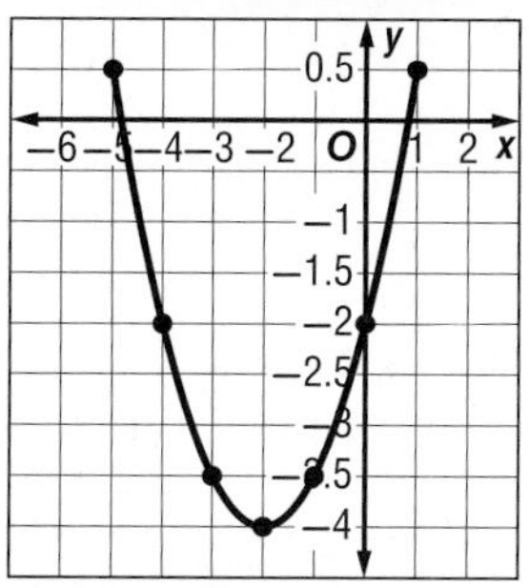

3.

x	−6	−5	−4	−3	−2	−1	0
y	−26	−11	−2	1	−2	−11	−26
First-Order Differences		15	9	3	−3	−9	−15
Second-Order Differences			−6	−6	−6	−6	−6

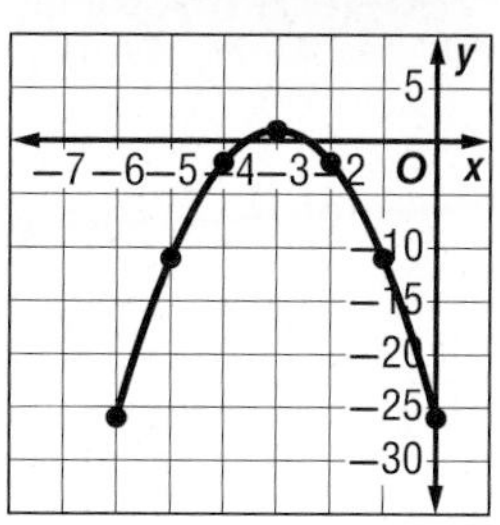

Pages 316–317, Lesson 5-8

33. $\{x \mid 4 < x < 5\}$

34. $\{x \mid x \leq -5 \text{ or } x \geq -2\}$

35. $\{x \mid -1 < x < 2\}$

36. $\{x \mid -4.65 \leq x \leq 0.65\}$

37. $\{x \mid x \leq -2.32 \text{ or } x \geq 4.32\}$

38. $\varnothing$

39. $\{x \mid x \leq -1.58 \text{ or } x \geq 1.58\}$

40. $\{x \mid \text{all real numbers}\}$

41. $\{x \mid \text{all real numbers}\}$

42. $\{x \mid x \leq -3.91 \text{ or } x \geq 1.41\}$

43. $\{x \mid -2.84 < x < 0.84\}$

44. $\{x \mid -3.43 < x < 0.10\}$

45a.

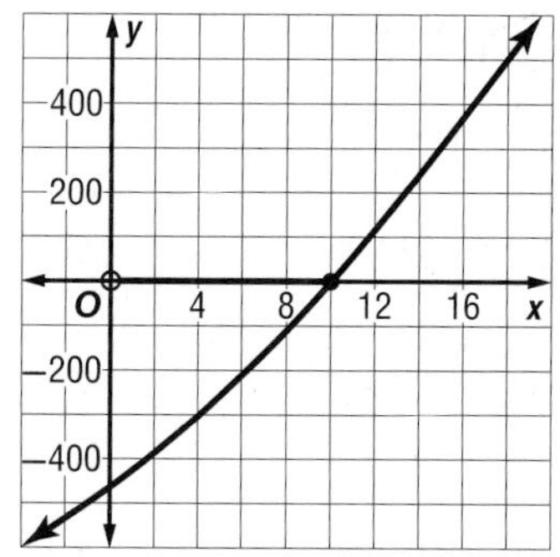

56a.

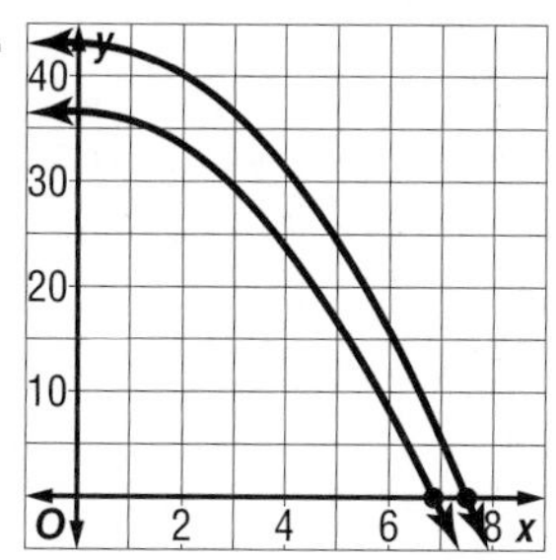

59. No; the graphs of the inequalities intersect the x-axis at the same points.

60. Sample answer: Sometimes; when a is positive and c is negative, there is no solution and when a is negative and c is positive there is a solution set.

61.

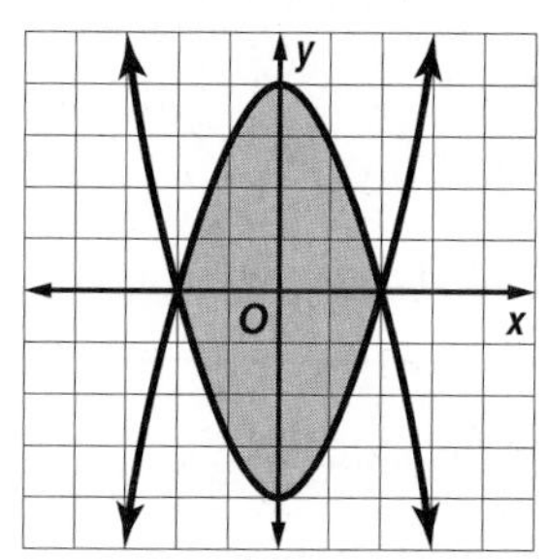

62. For both quadratic and linear inequalities, you must first graph the related equation. You use the inequality symbol to determine if the line is dashed or solid. Then you use test points to determine where to shade. One difference is that one is linear and the other is quadratic.

Page 324, Study Guide and Review

64.

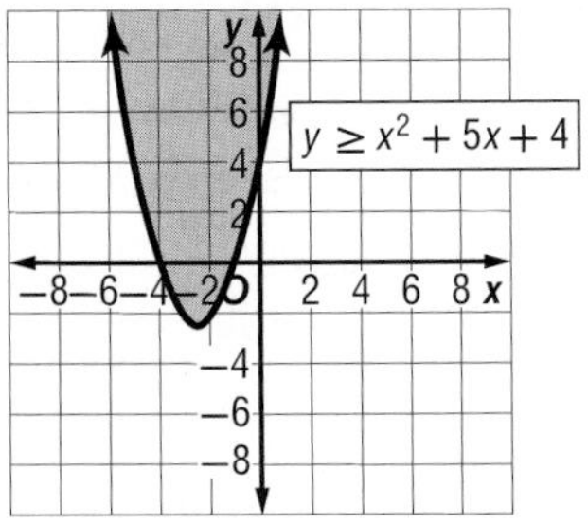

65.

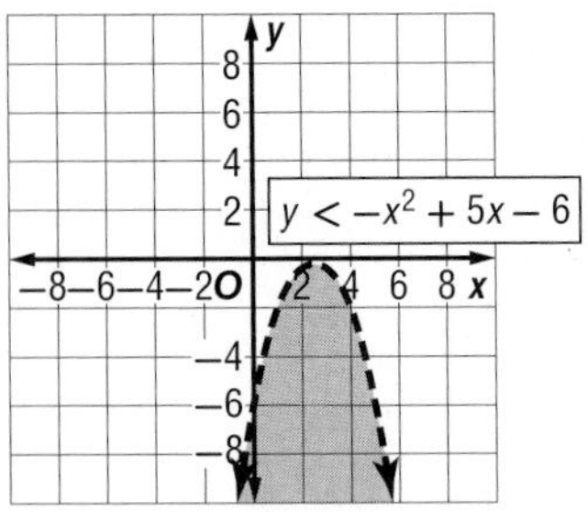

66.

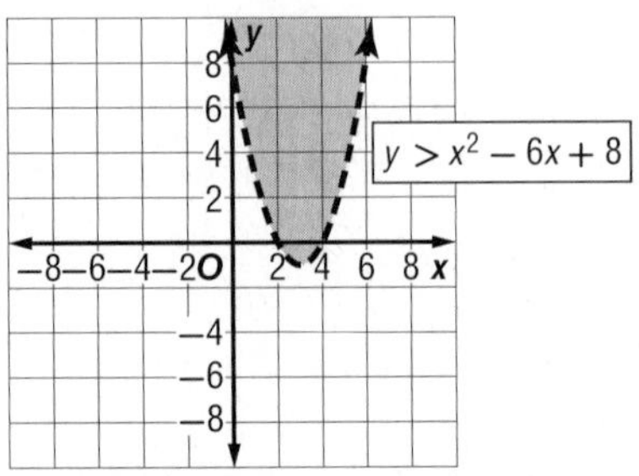

67.

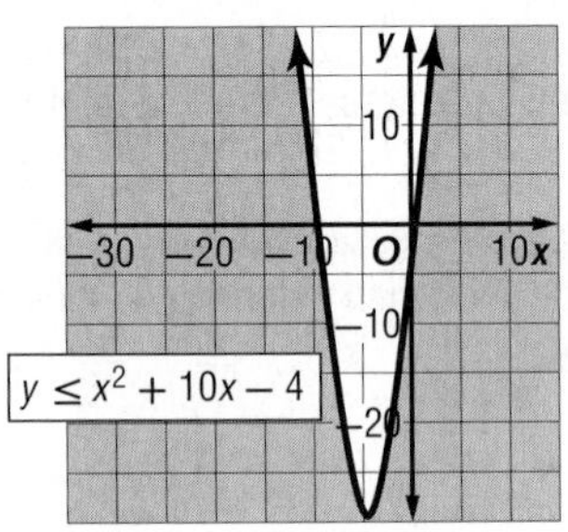

Page 325, Practice Test

1a. *y*-intercept : –7; axis of symmetry: $x = -2$; *x*-coordinate of vertex: –2

1b.

x	*f*(*x*)
–4	–7
–3	–10
–2	–11
–1	–10
0	–7

1c.

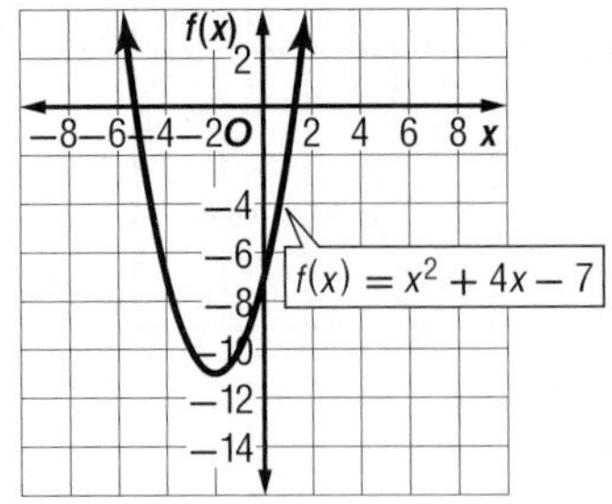

2a. *y*-intercept: 0; axis of symmetry: $x = \frac{5}{4}$; *x*-coordinate of vertex: $\frac{5}{4}$

2b.

x	*f*(*x*)
0	0
1	3
$\frac{5}{4}$	$\frac{25}{8}$
2	2
3	–3

2c.

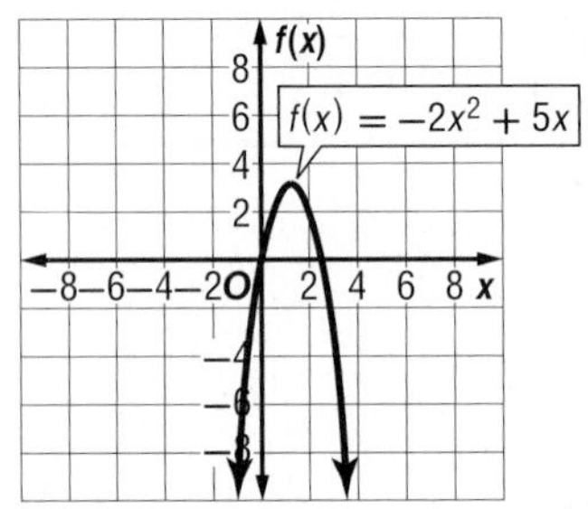

3a. *y*-intercept : –9; axis of symmetry: $x = -3$; *x*-coordinate of vertex: –3

3b.

x	*f*(*x*)
–5	–4
–4	–1
–3	0
–2	–1
–1	–4

3c.

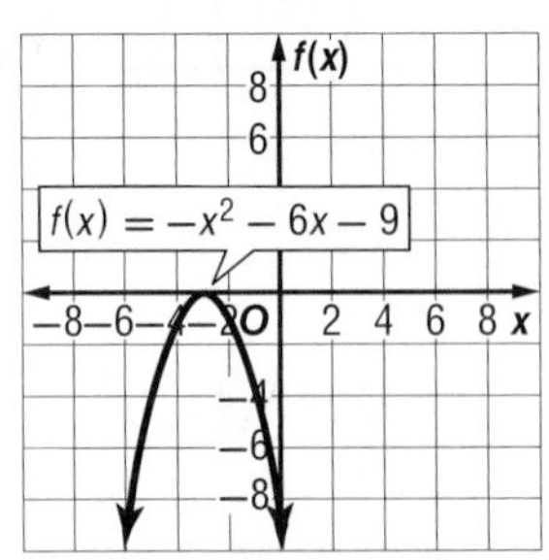

24.

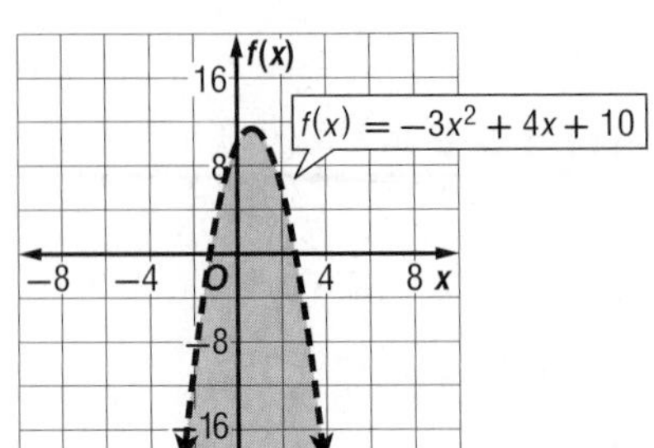

NOTES

CHAPTER 6

Chapter Planner

Diagnostic Assessment Quick Check, p. 331

	Lesson 6-1 Pacing: 1 day	Extend 6-1 Pacing: 0.5 day	Lesson 6-2 Pacing: 1 day	Lesson 6-3 Pacing: 1 day
Title	**Operations with Polynomials**	**Algebra Lab: Dimensional Analysis**	**Dividing Polynomials**	**Polynomial Functions**
Objectives	• Multiply, divide, and simplify monomials and expressions involving powers. • Add, subtract, and multiply polynomials.	• Use dimensional analysis to convert units and solve problems.	• Divide polynomials using long division. • Divide polynomials using synthetic division.	• Evaluate polynomial functions. • Identify general shapes of graphs of polynomial functions.
Key Vocabulary	simplify degree of a polynomial		synthetic division	polynomial in one variable leading coefficient polynomial function power function end behavior quartic function quintic function
NGSSS	MA.912.A.4.2	LA.910.1.6.1	MA.912.A.4.4	MA.912.A.4.5
Multiple Representations	p. 338		p. 346	p. 354
Lesson Resources	**Chapter 6 Resource Masters** • Study Guide and Intervention, pp. 5–6 AL OL ELL • Skills Practice, p. 7 AL OL ELL • Practice, p. 8 AL OL BL ELL • Word Problem Practice, p. 9 AL OL BL ELL • Enrichment, p. 10 OL BL **Transparencies** • 5-Minute Check Transparency 6-1 AL OL BL ELL **Additional Print Resources** • Study Notebook AL OL BL ELL	**Additional Print Resources** • *Teaching Algebra with Manipulatives,* p. 219 AL OL ELL	**Chapter 6 Resource Masters** • Study Guide and Intervention, pp. 11–12 AL OL ELL • Skills Practice, p. 13 AL OL ELL • Practice, p. 14 AL OL BL ELL • Word Problem Practice, p. 15 AL OL BL ELL • Enrichment, p. 16 OL BL • Quiz 1, p. 57 AL OL BL ELL **Transparencies** • 5-Minute Check Transparency 6-2 AL OL BL ELL **Additional Print Resources** • Study Notebook AL OL BL ELL	**Chapter 6 Resource Masters** • Study Guide and Intervention, pp. 17–18 AL OL ELL • Skills Practice, p. 19 AL OL ELL • Practice, p. 20 AL OL BL ELL • Word Problem Practice, p. 21 AL OL BL ELL • Enrichment, p. 22 OL BL **Transparencies** • 5-Minute Check Transparency 6-3 AL OL BL ELL **Additional Print Resources** • Study Notebook AL OL BL ELL
Technology for Every Lesson	FL Math Online glencoe.com • Extra Examples • Personal Tutor • Self-Check Quizzes • Homework Help	**CD/DVD Resources** IWB INTERACTIVE WHITEBOARD READY IWB StudentWorks Plus IWB Interactive Classroom IWB Diagnostic and Assessment Planner		• TeacherWorks Plus • eSolutions Manual Plus • ExamView Assessment Suite
Get Animated	Animation			Animation
Differentiated Instruction	pp. 334, 339		pp. 344, 347	pp. 350, 355

Suggested Pacing			
Time Periods	Instruction	Review & Assessment	Total
45-minute	11	2	13
90-minute	8	1	9

Extend 6-3 Pacing: 0.5 day	Lesson 6-4 Pacing: 1 day	Extend 6-4 Pacing: 0.5 day	Lesson 6-5 Pacing: 1 day	Extend 6-5 Pacing: 0.5 day
Algebra Lab: Polynomial Functions and Rate of Change	**Analyzing Graphs of Polynomial Functions**	**Graphing Technology Lab: Modeling Data Using Polynomial Functions**	**Solving Polynomial Equations**	**Graphing Technology Lab: Solving Polynomial Inequalities**
• Examine the differences for polynomial functions with degrees greater than 2.	• Graph polynomial functions and locate their zeros. • Find the relative maxima and minima of polynomial functions.	• Use a graphing calculator to model data whose curve of best fit is a polynomial function.	• Factor polynomials. • Solve polynomial equations by factoring.	• Use a graphing calculator to find approximate solutions for polynomial equations.
	relative maximum relative minimum extrema turning points		prime polynomials quadratic form	
MA.912.A.4.5	MA.912.A.2.6, MA.912.A.4.5	MA.912.A.4.5, MA.912.A.4.10	MA.912.A.4.3	MA.912.A.4.11
	p. 363			
Additional Print Resources • *Teaching Algebra with Manipulatives,* pp. 220–221 AL OL ELL	**Chapter 6 Resource Masters** • Study Guide and Intervention, pp. 23–24 AL OL ELL • Skills Practice, p. 25 AL OL ELL • Practice, p. 26 AL OL BL ELL • Word Problem Practice, p. 27 AL OL BL ELL • Enrichment, p. 28 OL BL • Quiz 2, p. 57 AL OL BL ELL **Transp.arencies** • 5-Minute Check Transparency 6-4 AL OL BL ELL **Additional Print Resources** • Study Notebook AL OL BL ELL	**Materials** • TI-83/84 Plus or other graphing calculator	**Chapter 6 Resource Masters** • Study Guide and Intervention, pp. 29–30 AL OL ELL • Skills Practice, p. 31 AL OL ELL • Practice, p. 32 AL OL BL ELL • Word Problem Practice, p. 33 AL OL BL ELL • Enrichment, p. 34 OL BL **Transparencies** • 5-Minute Check Transparency 6-5 AL OL BL ELL **Additional Print Resources** • Study Notebook AL OL BL ELL	**Materials** • TI-83/84 Plus or other graphing calculator

FL Math Online glencoe.com
- Extra Examples
- Self-Check Quizzes
- Personal Tutor
- Homework Help

CD/DVD Resources IWB INTERACTIVE WHITEBOARD READY
- IWB StudentWorks Plus
- IWB Interactive Classroom
- IWB Diagnostic and Assessment Planner
- TeacherWorks Plus
- eSolutions Manual Plus
- ExamView Assessment Suite

	Animation			
	pp. 360, 364	p. 365	pp. 370, 375	

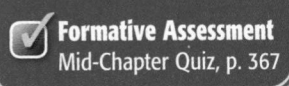

Formative Assessment
Mid-Chapter Quiz, p. 367

Chapter Planner

	Lesson 6-6 Pacing: 1 day	Lesson 6-7 Pacing: 1.5 days	Lesson 6-8 Pacing: 1.5 days
Title	**The Remainder and Factor Theorems**	**Roots and Zeros**	**Rational Zero Theorem**
Objectives	• Evaluate functions by using synthetic substitution. • Determine whether a binomial is a factor of a polynomial by using synthetic substitution.	• Determine the number and type of roots for a polynomial equation. • Find the zeros of a polynomial function.	• Identify possible rational zeros of a polynomial function. • Find all of the rational zeros of a polynomial function.
Key Vocabulary	synthetic substitution depressed polynomial		
NGSSS	MA.912.A.4.6, MA.912.A.4.8	MA.912.A.4.6, MA.912.A.4.8	MA.912.A.4.6, MA.912.A.4.8
Multiple Representations	p. 381		
Lesson Resources	**Chapter 6 Resource Masters** • Study Guide and Intervention, pp. 35–36 AL OL ELL • Skills Practice, p. 37 AL OL ELL • Practice, p. 38 AL OL BL ELL • Word Problem Practice, p. 39 AL OL BL ELL • Enrichment, p. 40 OL BL • Quiz 3, p. 58 AL OL BL ELL **Transparencies** • 5-Minute Check Transparency 6-6 AL OL BL ELL **Additional Print Resources** • Study Notebook AL OL BL ELL	**Chapter 6 Resource Masters** • Study Guide and Intervention, pp. 41–42 AL OL ELL • Skills Practice, p. 43 AL OL ELL • Practice, p. 44 AL OL BL ELL • Word Problem Practice, p. 45 AL OL BL ELL • Enrichment, p. 46 OL BL **Transparencies** • 5-Minute Check Transparency 6-7 AL OL BL ELL **Additional Print Resources** • Study Notebook AL OL BL ELL • Teaching Algebra with Manipulatives, p. 222 AL OL ELL	**Chapter 6 Resource Masters** • Study Guide and Intervention, pp. 47–48 AL OL ELL • Skills Practice, p. 49 AL OL ELL • Practice, p. 50 AL OL BL ELL • Word Problem Practice, p. 51 AL OL BL ELL • Enrichment, p. 52 OL BL • Graphing Calculator Activity, p. 53 OL • Quiz 4, p. 58 AL OL BL ELL **Transparencies** • 5-Minute Check Transparency 6-8 AL OL BL ELL **Additional Print Resources** • Study Notebook AL OL BL ELL
Technology for Every Lesson	FL Math Online **glencoe.com** • Extra Examples • Self-Check Quizzes • Personal Tutor • Homework Help	**CD/DVD Resources** IWB INTERACTIVE WHITEBOARD READY IWB StudentWorks Plus IWB Interactive Classroom IWB Diagnostic and Assessment Planner	• TeacherWorks Plus • eSolutions Manual Plus • ExamView Assessment Suite
Get Animated		Animation	
Differentiated Instruction	pp. 379, 382	pp. 386, 390	pp. 393, 396

Summative Assessment
- Study Guide and Review, pp. 397–400
- Practice Test, p. 401

KEY: AL Approaching Level, OL On Level, BL Beyond Level, ELL English Learners

What the Research Says...

Modeling provides an effective context for developing students' problem-solving skills. Moreover, it promises to highlight mathematical connections, address affective aspects of learning, and reinforce students' understanding of statistics. (Hodgson, 1995)

- In Lesson 6-4, polynomial functions are used to model movie attendance, prices, and sales trends over time.
- In Extend 6-4, students use a graphing calculator to find a polynomial model for seismic waves.
- In Lesson 6-5, polynomials are used to model geometric problem situations.

[Source: Hodgson, T. (1995). "Secondary Mathematical Modeling: Issues and Challenges," *School Science and Mathematics* 95(7), pp. 351–357.]

Teacher to Teacher

Christine Waddell
Albion Middle School
Sandy, UT

USE WITH LESSON 6-2

" To help students better understand the division algorithm for polynomials, I first work through a long division problem with large whole numbers, such as $3248 \div 24$, step by step. Then I work through Example 2 and point out the similarities in each process. "

NOTES:

CHAPTER 6

Assessment and Intervention

SE = Student Edition, **TE** = Teacher Edition, **CRM** = Chapter Resource Masters

	Diagnosis	Prescription
Diagnostic Assessment	**Beginning Chapter 6**	
	Get Ready for Chapter 6 **SE,** p. 331	Response to Intervention **TE,** p. 331
	Beginning Every Lesson	
	Then, Now, Why? **SE** 5-Minute Check Transparencies	Chapter 6 **SE,** p. 330 Concepts and Skills Bank **SE** pp. 996–997
Formative Assessment	**During/After Every Lesson**	
	Guided Practice **SE,** every example Check Your Understanding **SE** H.O.T. Problems **SE** Spiral Review **SE** Additional Examples **TE** Watch Out! **TE** Step 4, Assess **TE** Chapter 6 Quizzes **CRM,** pp. 57–58 Self-Check Quizzes glencoe.com	Tier 1 Intervention Concepts and Skills Bank **SE,** pp. 994–1007 Skills Practice **CRM,** Ch. 1–6 glencoe.com Tier 2 Intervention Differentiated Instruction **TE** Study Guide and Intervention Masters **CRM,** Ch. 1–6 Tier 3 Intervention *Math Triumphs, Alg. 2,* Chs. 1 and 4
	Mid-Chapter	
	Mid-Chapter Quiz **SE,** p. 367 Mid-Chapter Test **CRM,** p. 59 ExamView Assessment Suite	Tier 1 Intervention Concepts and Skills Bank **SE,** pp. 994–1007 Skills Practice **CRM,** Ch. 1–6 glencoe.com Tier 2 Intervention Study Guide and Intervention Masters **CRM,** Ch. 1–6 Tier 3 Intervention *Math Triumphs, Alg. 2,* Chs. 1 and 4
	Before Chapter Test	
	Chapter Study Guide and Review **SE,** pp. 397–400 Practice Test **SE,** p. 401 Standardized Test Practice **SE,** pp. 402–405 Chapter Test glencoe.com Standardized Test Practice glencoe.com Vocabulary Review glencoe.com ExamView Assessment Suite	Tier 1 Intervention Concepts and Skills Bank **SE,** pp. 994–1007 Skills Practice **CRM,** Ch. 1–6 glencoe.com Tier 2 Intervention Study Guide and Intervention Masters **CRM,** Ch. 1–6 Tier 3 Intervention *Math Triumphs, Alg. 2,* Chs. 1 and 4
Summative Assessment	**After Chapter 6**	
	Multiple-Choice Tests, Forms 1, 2A, 2B **CRM,** pp. 61–66 Free-Response Tests, Forms 2C, 2D, 3 **CRM,** pp. 67–72 Vocabulary Test **CRM,** p. 60 Extended Response Test **CRM,** p. 73 Standardized Test Practice **CRM,** pp. 74–76 ExamView Assessment Suite	Study Guide and Intervention Masters **CRM,** Ch. 1–6 glencoe.com

CHAPTER 6

Differentiated Instruction

Option 1 Reaching All Learners AL OL BL ELL

LOGICAL On the board, show the steps in the long division algorithm of a problem, such as 2930 ÷ 25. Then show the steps in the long division used to find $(x^2 + 2x - 29) \div (x - 4)$. Point out the similarities in the two divisions.

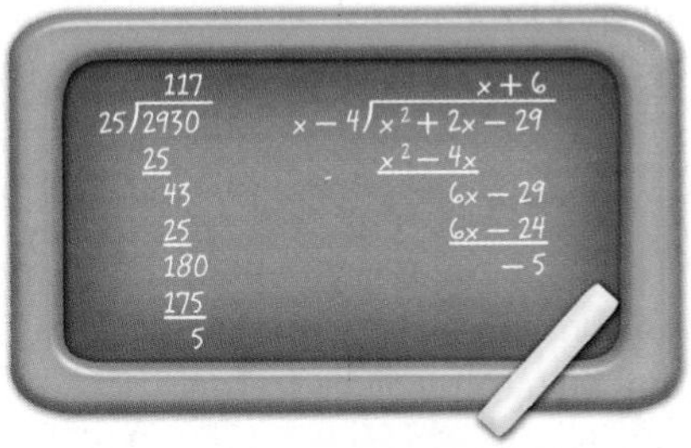

INTERPERSONAL Put students in groups of three or four. Have each student in a group write a polynomial function. As a group, students decide whether the polynomial functions are odd-degree or even-degree functions. Then have students predict the end behavior and the number of zeros of each function. Finally, have students check their predictions by graphing the function on a graphing calculator.

Option 2 Approaching Level AL

Put students into groups of three or four. Instruct students to take turns explaining how to make a table of values for a polynomial function, how to plot several points to begin a graph of the function, how to locate the zeros of the function, and how to estimate the x-coordinates at which the relative maxima and relative minima of the function occur.

Option 3 English Learners ELL

Ask students to explain how to find all the possible rational zeros of a polynomial function. Ask them to demonstrate the technique using a polynomial function of degree 3 or higher while explaining the process.

Option 4 Beyond Level BL

Ask students to make up their own "Find the Error" problems using concepts from this chapter. Have students write a problem, the incorrect steps used to "solve" it, and its incorrect solution on one side of an index card. On the flip side of the card, have students write the correct solution, the correct steps, and the correct solution to their problem. Then ask students to trade their cards with another student with the instructions to find the error in the problem, circle it in red, and then correct the error to find the correct solution.

FL Math Online Access Point Activities

CHAPTER 6
Focus on Mathematical Content

Vertical Alignment

Before Chapter 6

Related Topics before Algebra 1
- simplify numerical expressions involving exponents

Related Topics from Algebra 1
- use the Distributive Property to simplify algebraic expressions
- find specific function values
- solve quadratic equations using graphs

Previous Topics from Algebra 2
- use complex numbers to describe the solutions of quadratic equations

Chapter 6

Related Topics from Algebra 2
- use tools including factoring and properties of exponents to simplify expressions and to transform and solve equations
- identify the mathematical domains and ranges of functions
- determine the reasonable domain and range values for continuous situations

After Chapter 6

Preparation for Precalculus
- recognize and use connections among significant values of a function, points on the graph of a function, and the symbolic representation of a function
- investigate properties of polynomial functions
- use functions such as a polynomial to model real-life data

Lesson-by-Lesson Preview

6-1 Operations with Polynomials

To simplify an expression that contains powers means to rewrite the expression without parentheses or negative exponents. The rules for writing equivalent expressions include the *definition of negative exponents* and *properties of exponents.* The properties of exponents include finding the *product of powers, quotient of powers, power of a power, power of a product, power of a quotient,* and *zero power.*

- When adding (or subtracting) polynomials, rewrite the indicated sum (or difference) of polynomials as a sum of terms and then combine like terms.
- When multiplying a polynomial by a monomial, use the Distributive Property to rewrite the product as a single polynomial. When multiplying two binomials, use the Distributive Property and then combine like terms.

6-2 Dividing Polynomials

- To divide a polynomial by a monomial, use the Distributive Property. To divide a polynomial by a binomial (or by any polynomial), you can use a process and format analogous to the long division algorithm for whole numbers.
- An abbreviated form of the long division algorithm, called *synthetic division,* can be used when the divisor is a binomial of degree 1. If not, both the divisor and dividend must be rewritten so that it is.

6-3 Polynomial Functions

An expression made up of a sum of monomials that contains one variable is called a *polynomial in one variable.* The degree of a polynomial in one variable is the greatest exponent of its variable. The leading coefficient is the coefficient of the term with the highest degree. *A polynomial function* can be described by a polynomial equation in one variable.

If you know an element in the domain, x, of any polynomial function, you can find the corresponding value in the range, $f(x)$. Resulting sets of ordered pairs can be used to graph the functions. The maximum number of real zeros, where $f(x) = 0$, that a function will have is equal to the degree of the function. The degree and leading term of a polynomial function determine the graph's end behavior.

6-4 Analyzing Graphs of Polynomial Functions

Tables of values can be used to explore two types of changes in the values of a polynomial function.

- A change of signs in the value of $f(x)$ from one value of x to the next indicates that the graph of the function crosses the x-axis between the two x-values.
- A change between increasing values and decreasing values indicates that the graph is turning for that interval. A turning point on a graph is a relative maximum or minimum.

  For $f(x) = x^3 - 3x^2 + 5$, the table of values shown indicates the following graph.

x	$f(x)$	
−2	−15	zero between
−1	1	$x = -2$ and $x = -1$
0	5	← indicates a relative maximum
1	3	
2	1	← indicates a relative minimum
3	5	

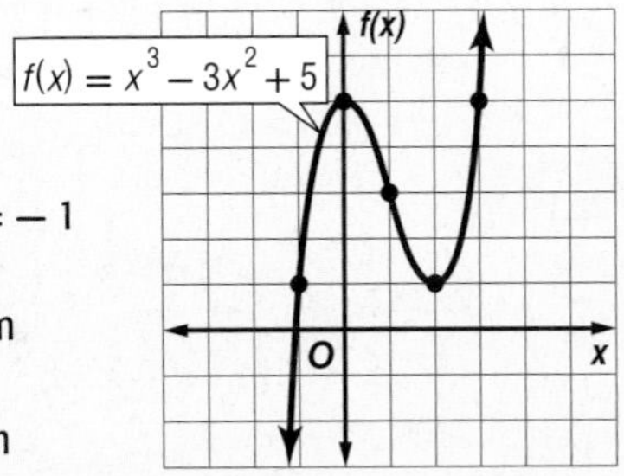

6-5 Solving Polynomial Equations

Some methods for factoring polynomials were taught in Lesson 5-3; others are taught in this lesson.

- Binomials in the form of the difference of two squares or as the sum or difference of two cubes can be rewritten as the product of two factors.
- A perfect square trinomial can be rewritten as the square of a binomial.
- Some other trinomials can be factored as the product of two binomials.
- Some polynomials with four or more terms can be regrouped to allow factoring.
- In some cases, higher-degree polynomials can be expressed in quadratic form and then factored.

A higher-degree polynomial equation can often be solved by writing the polynomial expression in quadratic form, factoring, and then using the Zero Product Property and/or the Quadratic Formula.

6-6 The Remainder and Factor Theorems

The *Remainder Theorem,* which says if a polynomial is divided by $x - a$, then the remainder k is equal to the value of the polynomial at a, or $f(a) = k$, allows for the use of synthetic division to evaluate a function. This method is called *synthetic substitution*.

The *Factor Theorem* states that $x - a$ is a factor of a polynomial if and only if $f(a) = 0$. This theorem can be used to help determine the factors of polynomials.

6-7 Roots and Zeros

According to the *Fundamental Theorem of Algebra,* every polynomial equation with a degree greater than 0 has at least one root in the set of complex numbers. And according to a corollary of that theorem, the number of complex roots of a polynomial equation is the same as the degree of the equation.

Descartes' Rule of Signs says that there is a relationship between the signs of the coefficients of a polynomial function and the number of positive and negative real zeros. By the *Complex Conjugates Theorem,* if an imaginary number is a zero of a function, its conjugate is also a zero.

6-8 Rational Zero Theorem

If a simplified fraction $\frac{p}{q}$ is a zero of a polynomial function with integral coefficients then the fraction's numerator, p, must be a factor of the constant term of the function, and the denominator, q, must be a factor of the leading coefficient. To use this property to find all the rational zeros of a polynomial function,

- first, find all the factors, p, of the constant term and all the factors, q, of the leading coefficient and then list all the possible fractions, $\frac{p}{q}$.
- Then, test whether particular values are zeros. Once you find a zero, you can use the depressed polynomial to find other zeros.

McGraw-Hill Professional Development

Targeted professional development has been articulated throughout *Algebra 2.* More quality, customized professional development is available from McGraw-Hill Professional Development. Visit glencoe.com for details on each product.

- **Online Lessons** emphasize the strategies and techniques used to teach Algebra 2. Includes streaming video, interactive pages, and online tools.
- **Video Workshops** allow mentors, coaches, or leadership personnel to facilitate on-site workshops on educational strategies in mathematics and mathematical concepts.
- **MHPD Online** (www.mhpdonline.com) offers online professional development with video clips of instructional strategies, links, student activities, and news and issues in education.
- **Teaching Today** (teachingtoday.glencoe.com) gives secondary teachers practical strategies and materials that inspire excellence and innovation in teaching.

CHAPTER 6 Notes

Chapter Project

Vehicles in Motion

Students use what they have learned about polynomials to investigate modes of transportation.

- Have students work in pairs. Ask students to consider what happens to the distance it takes to stop a car as the speed of the car increases.
- Have each group create a two-column table. Label the first column *Car Speed (in miles per hour).* Label the second column *Distance (in feet).* Have them fill in the first column with speeds of 10, 20, 30, 40, 50, 60, and 70 mph. In the second column, have students make guesses as to the corresponding stopping distances.
- Then have students add a third column to their table and label it: *Actual Stopping Distance (in feet).*
- Have students research mathematical models for stopping distance and use their model to complete the third column. For example, according to the U.S. Bureau of Public Roads, the distance d (in feet) required for a car to stop from a speed of v miles per hour is given approximately by the equation $d = 0.089v^2 - 1.96v + 49$.

Ask students to compare their guesses with the distances calculated from their model. Were their guesses consistently low? high? What does the model tell them about driving their own automobiles?

CHAPTER 6 Polynomials and Polynomial Functions

Then
In Chapter 5, you graphed quadratic functions and solved quadratic equations.

Now
In Chapter 6, you will:
- Add, subtract, multiply, divide, and factor polynomials.
- Analyze and graph polynomial functions.
- Evaluate polynomial functions and solve polynomial equations.
- Find factors and zeros of polynomial functions.

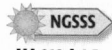

NGSSS
MA.912.A.4.5
MA.912.A.4.6

Why?
TRANSPORTATION
Polynomial functions can be used to determine bus schedules, highway capacity, traffic patterns, average fuel costs, and the prices of new and used cars.

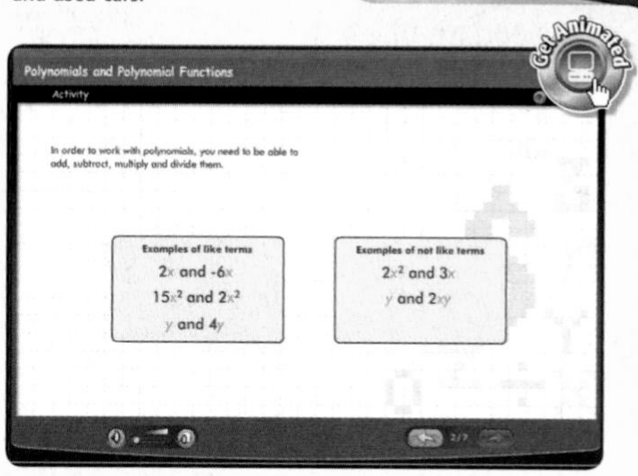

Key Vocabulary Introduce the key vocabulary in the chapter using the routine below.

Define: The degree of a given polynomial is the greatest degree of any term in the polynomial.

Example: The degree of the polynomial $\frac{2}{5}k^5 + 7m^3$ is 5.

Ask: What is the degree of the polynomial $9a^3 - 2b^8$? 8

Get Ready for Chapter 6

Diagnose Readiness You have two options for checking Prerequisite Skills.

Text Option Take the Quick Check below. Refer to the Quick Review for help.

*Quick*Check

(Used in Lesson 6-2)

Rewrite each difference as a sum. (Lesson 1-2)

1. $-5 - 13$
2. $5 - 3y$ $5 + (-3y)$
3. $5mr - 7mp$
4. $3x^2y - 14xy^2$
5. **PARTIES** Twenty people attended a going away party for Zach. The guests left in groups of 2. By 9:00, x groups had left. Rewrite the number of guests remaining at 9:00 as a sum.

(Used in Lesson 6-2)

Use the Distributive Property to rewrite each expression without parentheses. (Lesson 1-2)

6. $-4(a + 5)$ $-4a - 20$
7. $-1(3b^2 + 2b - 1)$
8. $-\frac{1}{2}(2m - 5)$ $-m + \frac{5}{2}$
9. $-\frac{3}{4}(3z + 5)$
10. **MONEY** Mr. Chávez is buying pizza and soda for the members of the science club. A slice of pizza costs \$2.25, and a soda costs \$1.25. Write an expression to represent the amount that Mr. Chávez will spend on 15 students. Evaluate the expression by using the Distributive Property.

(Used in Lesson 6-6)

Solve each equation. (Lesson 5-6)

11. $x^2 + 2x - 8 = 0$
12. $2x^2 + 7x + 3 = 0$
13. $6x^2 + 5x - 4 = 0$
14. $4x^2 - 2x - 1 = 0$
15. **PHYSICS** If an object is dropped from a height of 50 feet above the ground, then its height after t seconds is given by $h = -16t^2 + 50$. Use the equation $0 = -16t^2 + 50$ to find how long it will take until the ball reaches the ground. about 1.77 seconds

11. $-4, 2$ 12. $-3, -\frac{1}{2}$ 13. $-\frac{4}{3}, \frac{1}{2}$ 14. $\frac{1 \pm \sqrt{5}}{4}$

*Quick*Review

EXAMPLE 1

Rewrite $2xy - 3 - z$ as a sum.

$2xy - 3 - z$	Original expression
$= 2xy + (-3) + (-z)$	Rewrite using addition.

1. $-5 + (-13)$
3. $5mr + (-7mp)$ 4. $3x^2y + (-14xy^2)$
5. $20 + (-2x)$

EXAMPLE 2

Use the Distributive Property to rewrite $-3(a + b - c)$.

$-3(a + b - c)$	Original expression
$= -3(a) + (-3)(b) + (-3)(-c)$	Distributive Property
$= -3a - 3b + 3c$	Simplify.

7. $-3b^2 - 2b + 1$ 9. $-\frac{9}{4}z - \frac{15}{4}$
10. $15(2.25 + 1.25)$ or $15(2.25) + 15(1.25)$; \$52.50

EXAMPLE 3

Solve $2x^2 + 8x + 1 = 0$.

$x = \frac{-b \pm \sqrt{b^2 - 4ac}}{2a}$	Quadratic Formula
$= \frac{-8 \pm \sqrt{8^2 - 4(2)(1)}}{2(2)}$	$a = 2, b = 8, c = 1$
$= \frac{-8 \pm \sqrt{56}}{4}$	Simplify.
$= -2 \pm \frac{\sqrt{14}}{2}$	$\sqrt{56} = \sqrt{4 \cdot 14}$ or $2\sqrt{14}$

The exact solutions are $-2 + \frac{\sqrt{14}}{2}$ and $-2 - \frac{\sqrt{14}}{2}$.

The approximate solutions are -0.13 and -3.87.

Online Option FL Math Online Take a self-check Chapter Readiness Quiz at glencoe.com.

Get Ready for Chapter 6

Response to Intervention (RtI)

Use the *Quick Check* results and the Intervention Planner to help you determine your Response to Intervention. The If-Then statements in the chart below help you decide the appropriate tier of RtI and suggest intervention resources for each tier.

Intervention Planner

Tier 1 — On Level

If students miss about 25% of the exercises or less,

Then choose a resource:

- **SE** Concepts and Skills Bank, pp. 996–997 Lessons 6-2 and 6-6
- **CRM** Skills Practice, Chapter 6, pp. 13 and 37
- **TE** Chapter Project, p. 330

FL Math Online Self-Check Quiz

Tier 2 — Strategic Intervention approaching grade level

If students miss about 50% of the exercises,

Then choose a resource:

- **CRM** Study Guide and Intervention, Chapter 6, pp. 11 and 35

FL Math Online Extra Examples, Personal Tutor, Homework Help

Tier 3 — Intensive Intervention 2 or more years below grade level

If students miss about 75% of the exercises,

Then use *Math Triumphs, Alg. 2,* Chs. 1 and 4

FL Math Online Extra Examples, Personal Tutor, Homework Help, Review Vocabulary

CHAPTER 6 Notes

FOLDABLES® Study Organizer

Dinah Zike's Foldables®

Focus Students write notes as they explore polynomials and polynomial functions in this chapter.

Teach Have students make and label their Foldables as illustrated. As students work through the chapter, have them use index cards to write notes relating to the concepts on the tabs. Encourage students to write an example in their own words for each tab.

When to Use It Encourage students to add to their Foldables as they work through the chapter and to use them to review for the chapter test.

Differentiated Instruction

CRM Student-Built Glossary, pp. 1–2 Students should complete the chart by providing a definition of each term and an example as they progress through Chapter 6. This study tool can also be used to review for the chapter test.

Get Started on Chapter 6

You will learn several new concepts, skills, and vocabulary terms as you study Chapter 6. To get ready, identify important terms and organize your resources. You may wish to refer to **Chapter 0** to review prerequisite skills.

FOLDABLES® Study Organizer

Polynomials and Polynomial Functions Make this Foldable to help you organize your Chapter 6 notes about polynomials and polynomial functions. Begin with one sheet of $8\frac{1}{2}''$ by 14″ paper.

1. **Fold** a 2″ tab along the bottom of a long side.

2. **Fold** along the width into thirds.

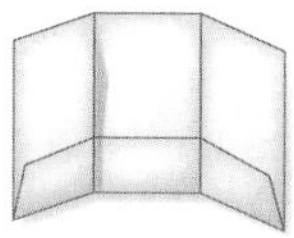

3. **Staple** the outer edges of the tab.

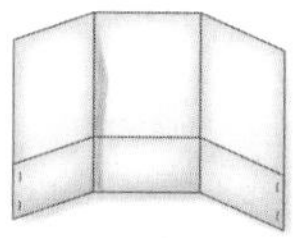

4. **Label** the tabs *Polynomials, Polynomial Functions and Graphs*, and *Solving Polynomial Equations.*

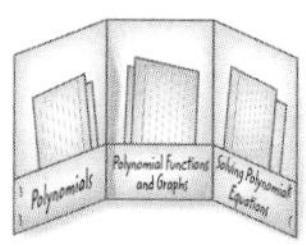

FL Math Online glencoe.com

- Study the chapter online
- Explore **Get Animated**
- Get extra help from your own **Personal Tutor**
- Use **Extra Examples** for additional help
- Take a **Self-Check Quiz**
- **Review Vocabulary** in fun ways

New Vocabulary

English		Español
simplify	p. 333	reducer
degree of a polynomial	p. 335	grado de un polinomio
synthetic division	p. 342	división sintética
polynomial in one variable	p. 348	polinomio de una variable
leading coefficient	p. 348	coeficiente líder
polynomial function	p. 349	functión polinomial
power function	p. 349	functión potencia
end behavior	p. 350	comportamiento final
relative maximum	p. 358	máximo relativo
relative minimum	p. 358	mínimo relativo
extrema	p. 358	extrema
turning points	p. 358	momentos cruciales
prime polynomials	p. 368	polinomios primeros
quadratic form	p. 371	forma de ecuación cuadrática
synthetic substitution	p. 377	sustitución sintética
depressed polynomial	p. 379	polinomio reducido

Review Vocabulary

factoring • p. 368 • factorización to express a polynomial as the product of monomials and polynomials

function • p. 348 • función a relation in which each element of the domain is paired with exactly one element in the range

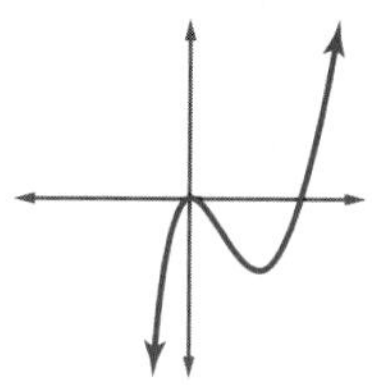

Function

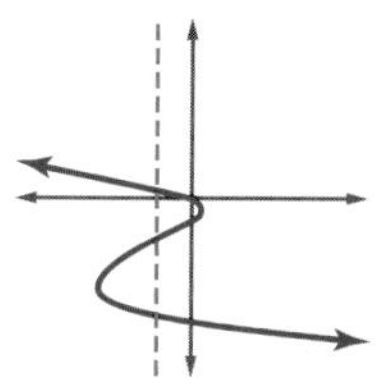

Not a Function

polynomial • p. 335 • polinomio a monomial or sum of monomials

Multilingual eGlossary glencoe.com

6-1 Operations with Polynomials

Why?

The light from the Sun takes approximately 8 minutes to reach Earth. So if you are outside right now you are basking in sunlight that the Sun emitted approximately 8 minutes ago.

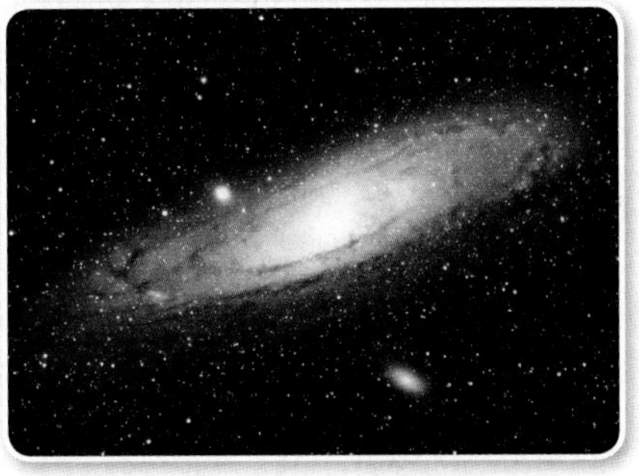

Light travels very fast, at a speed of about 3×10^8 meters per second. How long would it take light to get here from the Andromeda galaxy, which is approximately 2.367×10^{21} meters away?

Then
You evaluated powers. (Lesson 1-1)

Now
- Multiply, divide, and simplify monomials and expressions involving powers.
- Add, subtract, and multiply polynomials.

NGSSS
Reinforcement of MA.912.A.4.2 Add, subtract, and multiply polynomials.

New Vocabulary
simplify
degree of a polynomial

FL Math Online
glencoe.com

Multiply and Divide Monomials To **simplify** an expression containing powers means to rewrite the expression without parentheses or negative exponents. Negative exponents are a way of expressing the multiplicative inverse of a number. The following table summarizes the properties of exponents.

Concept Summary — Properties of Exponents

For any real numbers x and y, integers a and b:

Property	Definition	Examples
Product of Powers	$x^a \cdot x^b = x^{a+b}$	$3^2 \cdot 3^4 = 3^{2+4}$ or 3^6; $p^2 \cdot p^9 = p^{2+9}$ or p^{11}
Quotient of Powers	If $x \neq 0$, $\frac{x^a}{x^b} = x^{a-b}$.	$\frac{9^5}{9^2} = 9^{5-2}$ or 9^3; $\frac{b^6}{b^4} = b^{6-4}$ or b^2
Negative Exponent	$x^{-a} = \frac{1}{x^a}$ and $\frac{1}{x^{-a}} = x^a, x \neq 0$	$3^{-5} = \frac{1}{3^5}$; $\frac{1}{b^{-7}} = b^7$
Power of a Power	$(x^a)^b = x^{ab}$	$(3^3)^2 = 3^{3 \cdot 2}$ or 3^6; $(d^2)^4 = d^{2 \cdot 4}$ or d^8
Power of a Product	$(xy)^a = x^a y^a$	$(2k)^4 = 2^4k^4$ or $16k^4$; $(ab)^3 = a^3b^3$
Power of a Quotient	$\left(\frac{x}{y}\right)^a = \frac{x^a}{y^a}, y \neq 0$, and $\left(\frac{x}{y}\right)^{-a} = \left(\frac{y}{x}\right)^a$ or $\frac{y^a}{x^a}, x \neq 0, y \neq 0$	$\left(\frac{x}{y}\right)^2 = \frac{x^2}{y^2}$; $\left(\frac{a}{b}\right)^{-5} = \frac{b^5}{a^5}$
Zero Power	$x^0 = 1, x \neq 0$	$7^0 = 1$

Recall that a *monomial* is a number, a variable, or an expression that is the product of one or more variables with nonnegative integer exponents.

6-1 Lesson Notes

1 FOCUS

Vertical Alignment

Before Lesson 6-1
Evaluate powers.

Lesson 6-1
Multiply, divide, and simplify monomials and expressions involving powers.
Add, subtract, and multiply polynomials.

After Lesson 6-1
Use tools including factoring to transform and solve polynomial equations.

2 TEACH

Scaffolding Questions

Have students read the *Why?* section of the lesson.

Ask:
- How is 3×10^8 written without scientific notation? 300,000,000
- How many seconds are there in 8 minutes? 480
- Using the given information, about how far is Earth from the Sun? 1.44×10^{11} meters

Lesson 6-1 Resources

Resource	Approaching-Level	On-Level	Beyond-Level	English Learners
Teacher Edition	• Differentiated Instruction, p. 334	• Differentiated Instruction, pp. 334, 339	• Differentiated Instruction, p. 339	• Differentiated Instruction, p. 334
Chapter Resource Masters	• Study Guide and Intervention, pp. 5–6 • Skills Practice, p. 7 • Practice, p. 8 • Word Problem Practice, p. 9	• Study Guide and Intervention, pp. 5–6 • Skills Practice, p. 7 • Practice, p. 8 • Word Problem Practice, p. 9 • Enrichment, p. 10	• Practice, p. 8 • Word Problem Practice, p. 9 • Enrichment, p. 10	• Study Guide and Intervention, pp. 5–6 • Skills Practice, p. 7 • Practice, p. 8 • Word Problem Practice, p. 9
Transparencies	• 5-Minute Check Transparency 6-1	• 5-Minute Check Transparency 6-1	• 5-Minute Check Transparency 6-1	• 5-Minute Check Transparency 6-1
Other	• Study Notebook	• Study Notebook	• Study Notebook	• Study Notebook

Multiply and Divide Monomials

Example 1 shows how to use properties of exponents to simplify expressions involving multiplication and division of monomials.

Formative Assessment

Use the Guided Practice exercises after each Example to determine students' understanding of concepts.

Additional Example

1 Simplify each expression. Assume that no variable equals 0.

a. $(a^{-3})(a^2b^4)(c^{-1})$ $\frac{b^4}{ac}$

b. $\frac{n^2}{n^{10}}$ $\frac{1}{n^8}$

c. $\left(\frac{3a^3}{b^4}\right)^2$ $\frac{9a^6}{b^8}$

Additional Examples also in Interactive Classroom PowerPoint® Presentations

IWB INTERACTIVE WHITEBOARD READY

Focus on Mathematical Content

Properties of Exponents When multiplying or dividing powers of variables, be sure that the base is the same. Add the exponents if multiplying powers of the same variable, and subtract them if dividing powers.

Watch Out!

Common Errors When discussing Additional Example 1b, if any students get the incorrect answer $\frac{1}{n^5}$, lead them to understand that they divided the exponents instead of subtracting them.

When simplifying a monomial, check to be sure that it has been simplified fully.

Key Concept — Simplifying Monomials

A monomial expression is in simplified form when:

- there are no powers of powers,
- each base appears exactly once,
- all fractions are in simplest form, and
- there are no negative exponents.

Problem-Solving Tip

Check You can always check your answer using the definition of exponents.

$\frac{q^2}{q^7}$

$= \frac{q \cdot q}{q \cdot q \cdot q \cdot q \cdot q \cdot q \cdot q}$

$= \frac{1}{q^5}$

EXAMPLE 1 Simplify Expressions

Simplify each expression. Assume that no variable equals 0.

a. $(2a^{-2})(3a^3b^2)(c^{-2})$

$(2a^{-2})(3a^3b^2)(c^{-2})$	Original expression
$= 2\left(\frac{1}{a^2}\right)(3a^3b^2)\left(\frac{1}{c^2}\right)$	Definition of negative exponents
$= \left(\frac{2}{a \cdot a}\right)(3 \cdot a \cdot a \cdot a \cdot b \cdot b)\left(\frac{1}{c \cdot c}\right)$	Definition of exponents
$= \left(\frac{2}{\cancel{a} \cdot \cancel{a}}\right)(3 \cdot \cancel{a} \cdot \cancel{a} \cdot a \cdot b \cdot b)\left(\frac{1}{c \cdot c}\right)$	Divide out common factors.
$= \frac{6ab^2}{c^2}$	Simplify.

b. $\frac{q^2r^4}{q^7r^3}$

$\frac{q^2r^4}{q^7r^3} = q^{2-7} \cdot r^{4-3}$	Quotient of powers
$= q^{-5}r$	Subtract powers.
$= \frac{r}{q^5}$	Simplify.

c. $\left(\frac{-2a^4}{b^2}\right)^3$

$\left(\frac{-2a^4}{b^2}\right)^3 = \frac{(-2a^4)^3}{(b^2)^3}$	Power of a quotient
$= \frac{(-2)^3(a^4)^3}{(b^2)^3}$	Power of a product
$= \frac{-8a^{12}}{b^6}$	Power of a power

Guided Practice

1A. $(2x^{-3}y^3)(-7x^5y^{-6})$ $\frac{-14x^2}{y^3}$

1B. $\frac{15c^5d^3}{-3c^2d^7}$ $-\frac{5c^3}{d^4}$

1C. $\left(\frac{a}{4}\right)^{-3}$ $\frac{64}{a^3}$

1D. $(-2x^3y^2)^5$ $-32x^{15}y^{10}$

Personal Tutor glencoe.com

Differentiated Instruction AL OL ELL

If students have difficulty describing or using properties of exponents,

Then have them write their own summary of the properties of powers, such as "to multiply expressions with exponents, you add the exponents; to divide, you subtract the exponents."

StudyTip

Power of 1 Remember that a variable with no exponent indicated can be written as a power of 1.

Operations With Polynomials The **degree of a polynomial** is the degree of the monomial with the greatest degree. For example, the degree of the polynomial $x^2 + 4x + 58$ is 2.

EXAMPLE 2 Degree of a Polynomial

Determine whether each expression is a polynomial. If it is a polynomial, state the degree of the polynomial.

a. $\frac{1}{4}x^4y^3 - 8x^5$

This expression is a polynomial because each term is a monomial. The degree of the first term is 4 + 3 or 7, and the degree of the second term is 5. The degree of the polynomial is 7.

b. $\sqrt{x} + x + 4$

This expression is not a polynomial because $\sqrt{x}$ is not a monomial.

c. $x^{-3} + 2x^{-2} + 6$

This expression is not a polynomial because x^{-3} and x^{-2} are not monomials: $x^{-3} = \frac{1}{x^3}$ and $x^{-2} = \frac{1}{x^2}$. Monomials cannot contain variables in the denominator.

Guided Practice

2A. $\frac{x}{y} + 3x^2$ No; $\frac{x}{y}$ is not a monomial. **2B.** $x^5y + 9x^4y^3 - 2xy$ yes; 7

Personal Tutor glencoe.com

You can simplify a polynomial just like you simplify a monomial. Perform the operations indicated, and combine like terms.

StudyTip

Alternative Methods Notice that Example 3a uses a horizontal method, and Example 3b uses a vertical method to simplify. Either method will yield a correct solution.

EXAMPLE 3 Simplify Polynomial Expressions

Simplify each expression.

a. $(4x^2 - 5x + 6) - (2x^2 + 3x - 1)$

Remove parentheses, and group like terms together.

$(4x^2 - 5x + 6) - (2x^2 + 3x - 1)$

$= 4x^2 - 5x + 6 - 2x^2 - 3x + 1$ Distribute the −1.

$= (4x^2 - 2x^2) + (-5x - 3x) + (6 + 1)$ Group like terms.

$= 2x^2 - 8x + 7$ Combine like terms.

b. $(6x^2 - 7x + 8) + (-4x^2 + 9x - 5)$

Align like terms vertically and add.

$$\begin{array}{r} 6x^2 - 7x + 8 \\ (+)\ -4x^2 + 9x - 5 \\ \hline 2x^2 + 2x + 3 \end{array}$$

Guided Practice 3A. $-2x^2 - 5x - 1$

3A. $(-x^2 - 3x + 4) - (x^2 + 2x + 5)$ **3B.** $(3x^2 - 6) + (-x + 1)$ $3x^2 - x - 5$

Personal Tutor glencoe.com

Watch Out!

Preventing Errors Suggest that students return to the basic definitions for exponents rather than just memorizing rules. For example, they can derive the rule for multiplying quantities such as $x^2 \cdot x^3$ by rewriting the problem as $x \cdot x \cdot x \cdot x \cdot x$.

Operations with Polynomials

Example 2 shows how to determine whether an expression is a polynomial and if it is, state its degree. **Example 3** shows how to subtract and add polynomials. **Example 4** shows how to use the Distributive Property to multiply a polynomial by a monomial. **Example 5** shows how to represent a real-world situation using a polynomial. **Example 6** shows how to apply the Distributive Property two times to multiply a polynomial and a binomial.

Additional Examples

2 Determine whether each expression is a polynomial. If it is a polynomial, state the degree of the polynomial.

a. $c^4 - 4\sqrt{c} + 18$ no

b. $-16p^5 + \frac{3}{4}p^2t^7$ yes, 9

c. $x^2 - 3x^{-1} + 7$ no

3 Simplify each expression.

a. $(2a^3 + 5a - 7) - (a^3 - 3a + 2)$ $a^3 + 8a - 9$

b. $(4x^2 - 9x + 3) + (-2x^2 - 5x - 6)$ $2x^2 - 14x - 3$

TEACH with TECH

INTERACTIVE WHITEBOARD Write an expression on the board to add or subtract two polynomials. Drag the like terms to group them together. Then combine like terms and simplify the expression.

Additional Examples

4 Find $-y(4y^2 + 2y - 3)$.
$-4y^3 - 2y^2 + 3y$

5 **E-SALES** A small online retailer estimates that the cost, in dollars, associated with selling x units of a particular product is given by the expression $0.001x^2 + 5x + 500$. The revenue from selling x units is given by $10x$. Write a polynomial to represent the profits generated by the product if profit = revenue − cost.
$-0.001x^2 + 5x - 500$

6 Find $(a^2 + 3a - 4)(a + 2)$.
$a^3 + 5a^2 + 2a - 8$

You can use the Distributive Property to multiply polynomials.

EXAMPLE 4 Simplify by Using the Distributive Property

Find $3x(2x^2 - 4x + 6)$.

$3x(2x^2 - 4x + 6) = 3x(2x^2) + 3x(-4x) + 3x(6)$ **Distributive Property**
$= 6x^3 - 12x^2 + 18x$ **Multiply the monomials.**

Guided Practice 4B. $6a^3 + 22a^2 - 40a$

Find each product.

4A. $\frac{4}{3}x^2(6x^2 + 9x - 12)$ $8x^4 + 12x^3 - 16x^2$ **4B.** $-2a(-3a^2 - 11a + 20)$

Personal Tutor glencoe.com

Polynomials can be used to represent real-world situations.

Real-World EXAMPLE 5 Write a Polynomial Expression

DRIVING **The U.S. Department of Transportation limits the time a truck driver can work between periods of rest to ten hours. For the first part of his shift, Tom drives at a speed of 60 miles per hour, and for the second part of the shift, he drives at a speed of 70 miles per hour. Write a polynomial to represent the distance driven.**

Words	60 mph for some time, and 70 mph for the rest
Variable	Let x = the number of hours he drives at 60 miles per hour.
Expression	60 x + 70 $(10 - x)$

$60x + 70(10 - x)$ **Original expression**
$= 60x + 700 - 70x$ **Distributive Property**
$= 700 - 10x$ **Combine like terms.**

The polynomial is $700 - 10x$.

Guided Practice 5. $37.8 - 0.024x$

5. Paul has \$900 to invest in a savings account that has an annual interest rate of 1.8%, and a money market account that pays 4.2% per year. Write a polynomial for the interest he will earn in one year if he invests x dollars in the savings account.

Personal Tutor glencoe.com

Real-World Career

Truck Driver
Truck drivers are considered technical professionals because they are required to obtain specialized education and professional licensure. Although state motor vehicle departments administer the Commercial Driver's License program, federal law spells out the requirements to obtain one.

EXAMPLE 6 Multiply Polynomials

Find $(n^2 + 4n - 6)(n + 2)$.

$(n^2 + 4n - 6)(n + 2)$
$= n^2(n + 2) + 4n(n + 2) + (-6)(n + 2)$ **Distributive Property**
$= n^2 \cdot n + n^2 \cdot 2 + 4n \cdot n + 4n \cdot 2 + (-6) \cdot n + (-6) \cdot 2$ **Distributive Property**
$= n^3 + 2n^2 + 4n^2 + 8n - 6n - 12$ **Multiply monomials.**
$= n^3 + 6n^2 + 2n - 12$ **Combine like terms.**

Guided Practice 6B. $6x^3 - 14x^2 + 19x - 5$

Find each product.

6A. $(x^2 + 4x + 16)(x - 4)$ $x^3 - 64$ **6B.** $(2x^2 - 4x + 5)(3x - 1)$

Personal Tutor glencoe.com

Get Animated

336 Chapter 6 Polynomials and Polynomial Functions

Check Your Understanding

Example 1 p. 334

Simplify. Assume that no variable equals 0.

1. $(2a^3b^{-2})(-4a^2b^4)$ $-8a^5b^2$
2. $\frac{12x^4y^2}{2xy^5}$ $\frac{6x^3}{y^3}$
3. $\left(\frac{2a^2}{3b}\right)^3$ $\frac{8a^6}{27b^3}$
4. $(6g^5h^{-4})^3$ $\frac{216g^{15}}{h^{12}}$

Example 2 p. 335

Determine whether each expression is a polynomial. If it is a polynomial, state the degree of the polynomial.

5. $3x + 4y$ yes, 1
6. $\frac{1}{2}x^2 - 7y$ yes, 2
7. $x^2 + \sqrt{x}$ no
8. $\frac{ab^3 - 1}{az^4 + 3}$ no

Examples 3, 4, and 6 pp. 335–336

Simplify. 9. $-2x^2 - 6x + 3$ 12. $6x^3y - 9x^3y^2 + 12x^4y^3$

9. $(x^2 - 5x + 2) - (3x^2 + x - 1)$
10. $(3a + 4b) + (6a - 6b)$ $9a - 2b$
11. $2a(4b + 5)$ $8ab + 10a$
12. $3x^2(2xy - 3xy^2 + 4x^2y^3)$
13. $(n - 9)(n + 7)$ $n^2 - 2n - 63$
14. $(a + 4)(a - 6)$ $a^2 - 2a - 24$

Example 5 p. 336

15. **EXERCISE** Tara exercises 75 minutes a day. She does cardio, which burns an average of 10 Calories a minute, and weight training, which burns an average of 7.5 Calories a minute. Write a polynomial to represent the amount of Calories Tara burns in one day if she does x minutes of weight training. $750 - 2.5x$

Practice and Problem Solving

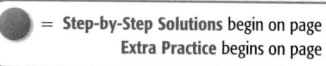

● = **Step-by-Step Solutions** begin on page R20.
Extra Practice begins on page 947.

Example 1 p. 334

Simplify. Assume that no variable equals 0. 17. $-8b^5c^3$

16. $\frac{20x^4}{y^2}$

16. $(5x^3y^{-5})(4xy^3)$
17. $(-2b^3c)(4b^2c^2)$
18. $\frac{a^3n^7}{an^4}$ a^2n^3
19. $\frac{-y^3z^5}{y^2z^3}$ $-yz^2$
20. $\frac{-7x^5y^5z^4}{21x^7y^5z^2}$ $\frac{z^2}{-3x^2}$
21. $\frac{9a^7b^5c^5}{18a^5b^9c^3}$ $\frac{a^2c^2}{2b^4}$
22. $(n^5)^4$ n^{20}
23. $(z^3)^6$ z^{18}

Example 2 p. 335

Determine whether each expression is a polynomial. If it is a polynomial, state the degree of the polynomial.

24. $2x^2 - 3x + 5$ yes; 2
25. $a^3 - 11$ yes; 3
26. $\frac{5np}{n^2} - \frac{2g}{h}$ no
27. $\sqrt{m - 7}$ no

Examples 3, 4, and 6 pp. 335–336

Simplify. 28. $2a^2 - a - 2$ 29. $3b^2 + 6b - 5$ 32. $x^3 + x^2y - xy^2 - y^3$

33. $a^4 + a^3b - 3a^2b - 4ab^2 - b^3$
34. $-6a^3 + 4a^2 + 8a - 9$
35. $10c^3 - c^2 + 4c$
36. $10x^2y - 5xy^2 + 6x^2y^2 + 36y^2$
37. $12a^2b + 8a^2b^2 - 15ab^2 + 4b^2$

28. $(6a^2 + 5a + 10) - (4a^2 + 6a + 12)$
29. $(7b^2 + 6b - 7) - (4b^2 - 2)$
30. $3p(np - z)$ $3np^2 - 3pz$
31. $4x(2x^2 + y)$ $8x^3 + 4xy$
32. $(x - y)(x^2 + 2xy + y^2)$
33. ● $(a + b)(a^3 - 3ab - b^2)$
34. $4(a^2 + 5a - 6) - 3(2a^3 + 4a - 5)$
35. $5c(2c^2 - 3c + 4) + 2c(7c - 8)$
36. $5xy(2x - y) + 6y^2(x^2 + 6)$
37. $3ab(4a - 5b) + 4b^2(2a^2 + 1)$
38. $(x - y)(x + y)(2x + y)$
39. $(a + b)(2a + 3b)(2x - y)$

Example 5 p. 336

38. $2x^3 + x^2y - 2xy^2 - y^3$
39. $4a^2x - 2a^2y + 10abx - 5aby + 6b^2x - 3b^2y$

40. **PAINTING** Connor has hired two painters to paint his house. The first painter charges \$12 an hour and the second painter charges \$11 an hour. It will take 15 hours to paint the house.
    a. Write a polynomial to represent the total cost of the job if Connor hires the first painter for x hours. $12x$
    b. Write a polynomial to represent the total cost of the job if Connor hires the second painter for y hours. $11y$

3 PRACTICE

Formative Assessment

Use Exercises 1–15 to check for understanding.

Use the chart at the bottom of this page to customize assignments for your students.

Differentiated Homework Options

Level	Assignment	Two-Day Option	
AL Basic	16–50, 65, 67–96	17–49 odd, 70–73	16–50 even, 65, 67–69, 74–96
OL Core	17–61 odd, 64, 65, 67–96	16–50, 70–73	51, 61, 64, 65, 67–69, 74–96
BL Advanced	51–90, (optional: 91–96)		

Study Guide and Intervention

CRM pp. 5–6 AL OL ELL

6-1 Study Guide and Intervention

Operations with Polynomials

Multiply and Divide Monomials **Negative exponents** are a way of expressing the multiplicative inverse of a number.

Negative Exponents	$a^{-n} = \frac{1}{a^n}$ and $\frac{1}{a^{-n}} = a^n$ for any real number $a \neq 0$ and any integer n.

When you **simplify an expression**, you rewrite it without powers of powers, parentheses, or negative exponents. Each base appears only once, and all fractions are in simplest form. The following properties are useful when simplifying expressions.

Product of Powers	$a^m \cdot a^n = a^{m+n}$ for any real number a and integers m and n.
Quotient of Powers	$\frac{a^m}{a^n} = a^{m-n}$ for any real number $a \neq 0$ and integers m and n.
Properties of Powers	For a, b real numbers and m, n integers: $(a^m)^n = a^{mn}$; $(ab)^m = a^m b^m$; $\left(\frac{a}{b}\right)^n = \frac{a^n}{b^n}, b \neq 0$; $\left(\frac{a}{b}\right)^{-n} = \left(\frac{b}{a}\right)^n$ or $\frac{b^n}{a^n}, a \neq 0, b \neq 0$

Example Simplify. Assume that no variable equals 0.

a. $(3m^4n^{-2})(-5mn)^2$

$(3m^4n^{-2})(-5mn)^2 = 3m^4n^{-2} \cdot 25m^2n^2$
$= 75m^4m^2n^{-2}n^2$
$= 75m^{4+2}n^{-2+2}$
$= 75m^6$

b. $\frac{(-m^4)^3}{(2m^2)^{-2}}$

$\frac{(-m^4)^3}{(2m^2)^{-2}} = \frac{-m^{12}}{\frac{1}{4m^4}}$
$= -m^{12} \cdot 4m^4$
$= -4m^{16}$

Exercises

Simplify. Assume that no variable equals 0.

1. $c^{12} \cdot c^{-4} \cdot c^6$ c^{14}
2. $\frac{b^8}{b^2}$ b^6
3. $(a^4)^5$ a^{20}
4. $\frac{x^{-2}y}{x^4y^{-1}}$ $\frac{y^2}{x^6}$
5. $\left(\frac{a^2b}{a^{-3}b^2}\right)^{-1}$ $\frac{b}{a^5}$
6. $\left(\frac{x^2y}{xy^3}\right)^2$ $\frac{x^2}{y^4}$
7. $\frac{1}{2}(-5a^2b^3)^2(abc)^2$ $5a^6b^8c^2$
8. $m^7 \cdot m^8$ m^{15}
9. $\frac{8m^3n^2}{4mn^3}$ $\frac{2m^2}{n}$
10. $\frac{2^3c^4t^2}{2^2c^4t^2}$ 2
11. $4j(-j^{-2}k^2)(3j^3k^{-7})$ $-\frac{12j^2}{k^5}$
12. $\frac{2mn^2(3m^2n)^2}{12m^3n^4}$ $\frac{3}{2}m^2$

Chapter 6 5 Glencoe Algebra 2

Practice

CRM p. 8 AL OL BL ELL

6-1 Practice

Operations with Polynomials

Simplify. Assume that no variable equals 0.

1. $n^5 \cdot n^2$ n^7
2. $y^7 \cdot y^3 \cdot y^2$ y^{12}
3. $t^9 \cdot t^{-8}$ t
4. $x^{-4} \cdot x^{-4} \cdot x^4$ $\frac{1}{x^4}$
5. $(2f^4)^6$ $64f^{24}$
6. $(-2b^{-2}c^3)^3$ $\frac{-8c^9}{b^6}$
7. $(4d^2t^5v^{-4})(-5dt^{-3}v^{-1})$ $-\frac{20d^3t^2}{v^5}$
8. $8u(2z)^3$ $64uz^3$
9. $\frac{12m^8y^6}{-9my^4}$ $-\frac{4m^7y^2}{3}$
10. $\frac{-6s^5x^3}{18sx^7}$ $-\frac{s^4}{3x^4}$
11. $\frac{-27x^3(-x^7)}{16x^4}$ $\frac{27x^6}{16}$
12. $\left(\frac{2}{3r^2s^3z^6}\right)^2$ $\frac{4}{9r^4s^6z^{12}}$
13. $-(4w^{-3}z^{-5})(8w)^2$ $-\frac{256}{wz^5}$
14. $(m^4n^6)^4(m^3n^2p^5)^6$ $m^{34}n^{36}p^{30}$
15. $\left(\frac{3}{2}d^{-}f^4\right)^4\left(-\frac{4}{3}d^5f\right)^3$ $-12d^{23}f^{19}$
16. $\left(\frac{2x^3y^2}{-x^2y^5}\right)^{-2}$ $\frac{y^6}{4x^2}$
17. $\frac{(3x^{-2}y^3)(5xy^{-8})}{(x^{-3})^4y^{-2}}$ $\frac{15x^{11}}{y^3}$
18. $\frac{-20(m^2v)(-v)^3}{5(-v)^2(-m^4)}$ $-\frac{4v^2}{m^2}$
19. $(3n^2 + 1) + (8n^2 - 8)$ $11n^2 - 7$
20. $(6w - 11w^2) - (4 + 7w^2)$ $-18w^2 + 6w - 4$
21. $(w + 2t)(w^2 - 2wt + 4t^2)$ $w^3 + 8t^3$
22. $(x + y)(x^2 - 3xy + 2y^2)$ $x^3 - 2x^2y - xy^2 + 2y^3$
23. **BANKING** Terry invests \$1500 in two mutual funds. The first year, one fund grows 3.8% and the other grows 6%. Write a polynomial to represent the amount Terry's \$1500 grows to in that year if x represents the amount he invested in the fund with the lesser growth rate. $-0.022x + 1590$
24. **GEOMETRY** The area of the base of a rectangular box measures $2x^2 + 4x - 3$ square units. The height of the box measures x units. Find a polynomial expression for the volume of the box. $2x^3 + 4x^2 - 3x$ units^3

Chapter 6 8 Glencoe Algebra 2

Word Problem Practice

CRM p. 9 AL OL BL ELL

6-1 Word Problem Practice

Operations with Polynomials

1. **THE EARTH** Earth's diameter is approximately 1.2756×10^4 kilometers. The surface area of a sphere can be found using the formula $SA = 4\pi r^2$.

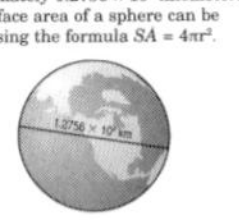

What is the approximate surface area of Earth?
5.112×10^8 km^2

2. **VOLUME** The volume of a rectangular prism is given by the product of its length, width, and height. Samantha has a rectangular prism that has a length of b^2 units, a width of a units, and a height of $ab + c$ units.

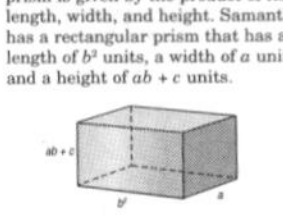

What is the volume of Samantha's rectangular prism? Express your answer in simplified form.
$a^2b^3 + ab^2c$

3. **CONSTRUCTION** A rectangular deck is built around a square pool. The pool has side length s. The length of the deck is 5 units longer than twice the side length of the pool. The width of the deck is 3 units longer than the side length of the pool. What is the area of the deck in terms of s?
$s^2 + 11s + 15$

4. **SAIL BOATS** Tamara requests a custom-made sail for her sailboat. The base of her triangular sail is $2x + 1$ and the height is $4x + 6$.

a. Find the area of the sail.
$4x^2 + 8x + 3$

b. If Tamara wants a different fabric on each side of her sail, write a polynomial to represent the total amount of fabric she will need to make the sail.
$8x^2 + 16x + 6$

c. Tamara decides she also wants a special trim for the hypotenuse of her triangular sail. Write an expression that describes the amount of trim she will need.
$\sqrt{20x^2 + 52x + 37}$

Chapter 6 9 Glencoe Algebra 2

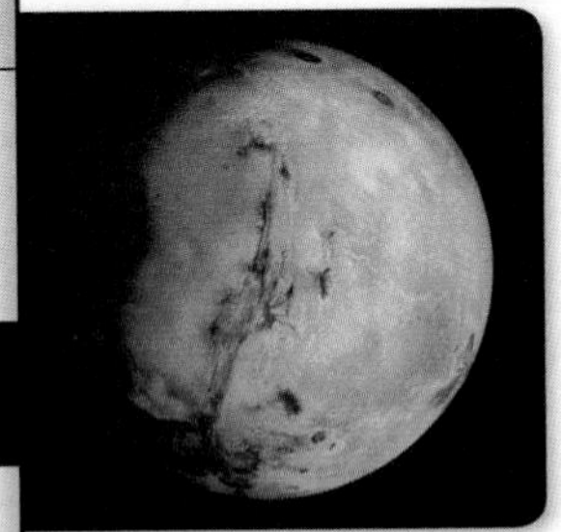

Real-World Link

The environment on Mars is very harsh. Mars has unpredictable weather patterns, as well as the deepest canyon and largest volcano in the solar system.

Source: NASA

Simplify. Assume that no variable equals 0.

41. $\left(\frac{8x^2y^3}{24x^3y^2}\right)^4$ $\frac{y^4}{81x^4}$
42. $\left(\frac{12a^3b^5}{4a^6b^3}\right)^3$ $\frac{27b^6}{a^9}$
43. $\left(\frac{4x^{-2}y^3}{xy^{-4}}\right)^{-2}$ $\frac{x^6}{16y^{14}}$
44. $\left(\frac{5a^{-7}b^2}{ab^{-6}}\right)^{-3}$ $\frac{a^{24}}{125b^{24}}$
45. $(a^2b^3)(ab)^{-2}$ b
46. $(-3x^3y)^2(4xy^2)$ $36x^7y^4$
47. $\frac{3c^2d(2c^3d^5)}{15c^4d^2}$ $\frac{2}{5}cd^4$
48. $\frac{-10g^6h^9(g^2h^3)}{30g^3h^3}$ $-\frac{1}{3}g^5h^9$
49. $\frac{5x^4y^2(2x^5y^6)}{20x^3y^5}$ $\frac{1}{2}x^6y^3$
50. $\frac{-12n^7p^5(n^2p^4)}{36n^6p^7}$ $-\frac{1}{3}n^3p^2$

51. **ASTRONOMY** Refer to the beginning of the lesson.
   a. How long does it take light from Andromeda to reach Earth? 7.89×10^{12} s or about 250,190.26 yr
   b. The average distance from the Sun to Mars is approximately 2.28×10^{11} meters. How long does it take light from the Sun to reach Mars? 760 seconds or about 12.67 min

Simplify.

52. $\frac{1}{4}g^2(8g + 12h - 16gh^2)$
53. $\frac{1}{3}n^3(6n - 9p + 18np^4)$
54. $x^{-2}(x^4 - 3x^3 + x^{-1})$
55. $a^{-3}b^2(ba^3 + b^{-1}a^2 + b^{-2}a)$
56. $(g^3 - h)(g^3 + h)$ $g^6 - h^2$
57. $(n^2 - 7)(2n^3 + 4)$
58. $(2x - 2y)^3$
59. $(4n - 5)^3$
60. $(3z - 2)^3$

52. $2g^3 + 3g^2h - 4g^3h^2$
53. $2n^4 - 3n^3p + 6n^4p^4$
54. $x^2 - 3x + \frac{1}{x^3}$
55. $b^3 + \frac{b}{a} + \frac{1}{a^2}$
57. $2n^5 - 14n^3 + 4n^2 - 28$
58. $8x^3 - 24x^2y + 24xy^2 - 8y^3$
59. $64n^3 - 240n^2 + 300n - 125$
60. $27z^3 - 54z^2 + 36z - 8$
64c. Each term is represented by one or more rectangles with an area that represents the variable and the power in the term.
66. Sample answer: It approaches 0.
67. Sample answer: We would have a 0 in the denominator, which makes the expression undefined.
68. Sample answer: $x^9 \cdot x^3, \frac{x^{14}}{x^2}, (x^6)^2$

61. **EDUCATION** The polynomials $0.108x^2 - 0.876x + 474.1$ and $0.047x^2 + 9.694x + 361.7$ approximate the number of bachelor's degrees, in thousands, earned by males and females, respectively, where x is the number of years after 1971.
   a. Find the polynomial that represents the total number of bachelor's degrees (in thousands) earned by both men and women. $0.155x^2 + 8.818x + 835.8$
   b. Find the polynomial that represents the difference between bachelor's degrees earned by men and by women. $0.061x^2 - 10.57x + 112.4$

62. If $5^{k+7} = 5^{2k-3}$, what is the value of k? 10

63. What value of k makes $q^{41} = q^{4k} \cdot q^5$ true? 9

64. **MULTIPLE REPRESENTATIONS** Use the model at the right that represents the product of $x + 3$ and $x + 4$.

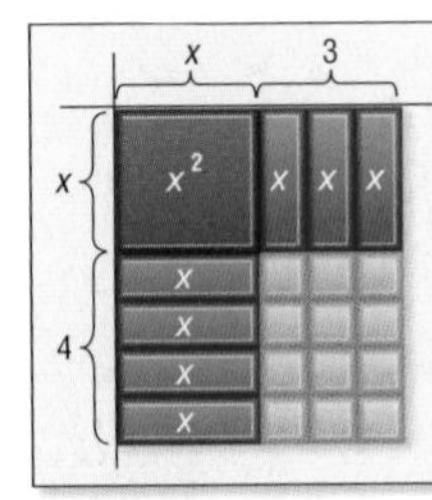

   a. **GEOMETRIC** The area of the each rectangle is the product of its length and width. Use the model to find the product of $x + 3$ and $x + 4$. $x^2 + 7x + 12$
   b. **ALGEBRAIC** Use FOIL to find the product of $x + 3$ and $x + 4$. $x^2 + 7x + 12$
   c. **VERBAL** Explain how each term of the product is represented in the model.

H.O.T. Problems Use Higher-Order Thinking Skills

65. **PROOF** Show how the property of negative exponents can be proven using the Quotient of Powers Property and the Zero Power Property. $\frac{1}{a^n} = \frac{a^0}{a^n} = a^{0-n} = a^{-n}$

66. **CHALLENGE** What happens to the quantity of x^{-y} as y increases, for $y > 0$ and $x > 1$?

67. **REASONING** Explain why the expression 0^{-2} is undefined.

68. **OPEN ENDED** Write three different expressions that are equivalent to x^{12}.

69. **WRITING IN MATH** Explain why properties of exponents are useful in astronomy. Include an explanation of how to find the amount of time it takes for light from a source to reach a planet. See margin.

Enrichment

CRM p. 10 OL BL

6-1 Enrichment

Polynomials with Fractional Coefficients

Polynomials may have fractional coefficients as long as there are no variables in the denominators. Computing with fractional coefficients is performed in the same way as computing with whole-number coefficients.

Simplify. Write all coefficients as fractions.

1. $\left(\frac{3}{5}m - \frac{2}{7}p - \frac{1}{3}n\right) - \left(\frac{7}{3}p - \frac{5}{2}m - \frac{3}{4}n\right)$ $\frac{31}{10}m + \frac{5}{12}n - \frac{55}{21}p$
2. $\left(\frac{3}{2}x - \frac{4}{3}y - \frac{5}{4}z\right) + \left(-\frac{1}{4}x + y + \frac{2}{5}z\right) + \left(-\frac{7}{8}x - \frac{6}{7}y + \frac{1}{2}z\right)$ $\frac{3}{8}x - \frac{25}{21}y - \frac{7}{20}z$
3. $\left(\frac{1}{2}a^2 - \frac{1}{3}ab + \frac{1}{4}b^2\right) + \left(\frac{5}{6}a^2 + \frac{2}{3}ab - \frac{3}{4}b^2\right)$ $\frac{4}{3}a^2 + \frac{1}{3}ab - \frac{1}{2}b^2$

Additional Answer

69. Sample answer: Astronomy deals with very large numbers that are sometimes difficult to work with because they contain so many digits. Properties of exponents make very large or very small numbers more manageable. As long as you know how far away a planet is from a light source you can divide that distance by the speed of light to obtain how long it will take light to reach that planet.

NGSSS PRACTICE 912.A.4.1, 912.A.3.15, 912.A.4.3, 912.A.1.6

70. **SHORT RESPONSE** Simplify $\frac{(2x^2)^3}{12x^4}$. $\frac{2x^2}{3}$

71. **STATISTICS** For the numbers a, b, and c, the average (arithmetic mean) is twice the median. If $a = 0$ and $a < b < c$, what is the value of $\frac{c}{b}$? **D**

A. 2 C. 4
B. 3 D. 5

72. Which is not a factor of $x^3 - x^2 - 2x$? **H**

F. x H. $x - 1$
G. $x + 1$ I. $x - 2$

73. **SAT/ACT** The expression $(-6 + i)^2$ is equivalent to which of the following expressions? **C**

A. $-12i$ C. $35 - 12i$
B. $-12 + i$ D. $37 - 12i$

Spiral Review

Solve each inequality algebraically. (Lesson 5-8)

74. $x^2 - 6x \leq 16$ $-2 \leq x \leq 8$
75. $x^2 + 3x > 40$ $x > 5$ or $x < -8$
76. $2x^2 - 12 \leq -5x$ $-4 \leq x \leq 1.5$

Graph each function. (Lesson 5-7) **77–79. See margin.**

77. $y = 3(x - 2)^2 - 4$
78. $y = -2(x + 4)^2 + 3$
79. $y = \frac{1}{3}(x + 1)^2 + 6$

80. **BASEBALL** A baseball player hits a high pop-up with an initial upward velocity of 30 meters per second, 1.4 meters above the ground. The height $h(t)$ of the ball in meters t seconds after being hit is modeled by $h(t) = -4.9t^2 + 30t + 1.4$. How long does an opposing player have to get under the ball if he catches it 1.7 meters above the ground? Does your answer seem reasonable? Explain. (Lesson 5-3) **See margin.**

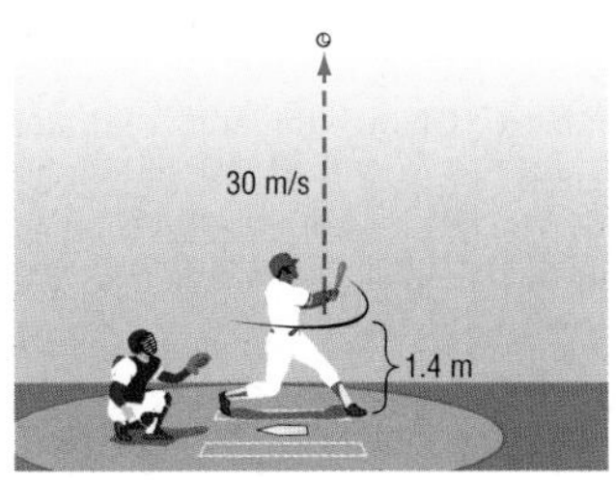

Evaluate each determinant. (Lesson 4-5)

81. $\begin{vmatrix} 3 & 0 & -2 \\ -1 & 4 & 3 \\ 5 & -2 & -1 \end{vmatrix}$ 42

82. $\begin{vmatrix} -2 & -4 & -6 \\ 0 & 6 & -5 \\ -1 & 3 & -1 \end{vmatrix}$ −74

83. $\begin{vmatrix} -3 & -1 & -2 \\ -2 & 3 & 4 \\ 6 & 1 & 0 \end{vmatrix}$ 28

84. **FINANCIAL LITERACY** A couple is planning to invest $15,000 in certificates of deposit (CDs). For tax purposes, they want their total interest the first year to be $800. They want to put $1000 more in a 2-year CD than in a 1-year CD and then invest the rest in a 3-year CD. How much should they invest in each type of CD? (Lesson 3-5) **$2500 in the 1-year; $3500 in the 2-year; $9000 in the 3-year**

Years	1	2	3
Rate	3.4%	5.0%	6.0%

Find the slope of the line that passes through each pair of points. (Lesson 2-3)

85. $(6, -2)$ and $(-2, -9)$ $\frac{7}{8}$
86. $(-4, -1)$ and $(3, 8)$ $\frac{9}{7}$
87. $(3, 0)$ and $(-7, -5)$ $\frac{1}{2}$
88. $\left(\frac{1}{2}, \frac{2}{3}\right)$ and $\left(\frac{1}{4}, \frac{1}{3}\right)$ $\frac{4}{3}$
89. $\left(\frac{2}{5}, \frac{1}{4}\right)$ and $\left(\frac{1}{10}, \frac{1}{12}\right)$ $\frac{5}{9}$
90. $(-4.5, 2.5)$ and $(-3, -1)$ $-\frac{7}{3}$

Skills Review

91. $4x(3ax^2 + 5bx + 8c)$ **93.** $(3y + 2)(4y + 3)$ **94.** $(m + x)(2y + 7)$
95. $(2x - 3)(4a - 3)$ **96.** $(2x - 3)(5x - 7y)$

Factor each polynomial. (Lesson 0-3)

91. $12ax^3 + 20bx^2 + 32cx$
92. $x^2 + 2x + 6 + 3x$ $(x + 3)(x + 2)$
93. $12y^2 + 9y + 8y + 6$
94. $2my + 7x + 7m + 2xy$
95. $8ax - 6x - 12a + 9$
96. $10x^2 - 14xy - 15x + 21y$

Differentiated Instruction

OL BL

Extension Write 3^0, $(4y^3x)^0$, 0^0, and $\left(\frac{x^5}{y^2}\right)^0$ on the board. Ask students to simplify each expression. They all equal 1 except 0^0. Then, prompt students to use 0^{m-m} to explain why 0^0 does not equal 1 like the other three expressions. $0^{m-m} = \frac{0^m}{0^m}$. $0^m = 0$, $\frac{0^m}{0^m}$ implies division by 0, which is not defined. Therefore, 0^0 is not defined.

Multiple Representations In Exercise 64, students use algebra tiles and algebraic operations to model multiplying binomials.

4 ASSESS

Crystal Ball Have students write how they think today's work with division of monomials will help them with dividing polynomials.

Additional Answers

77.

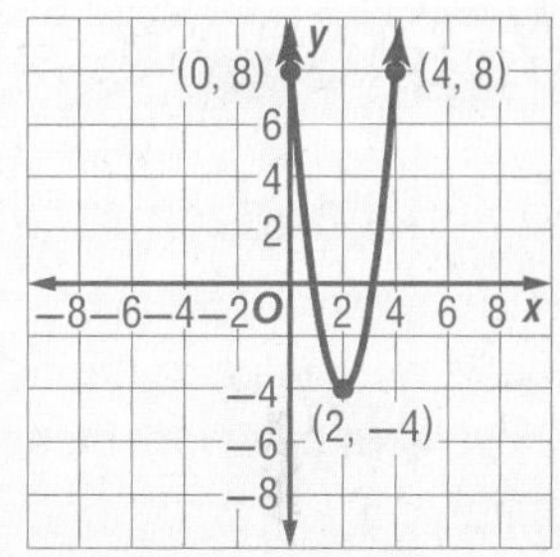

78.

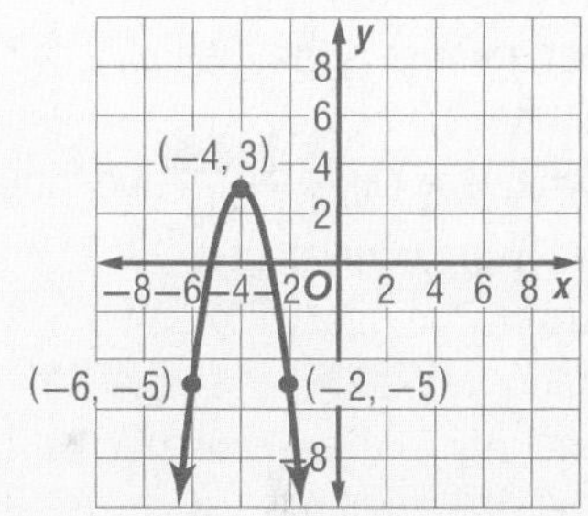

79.

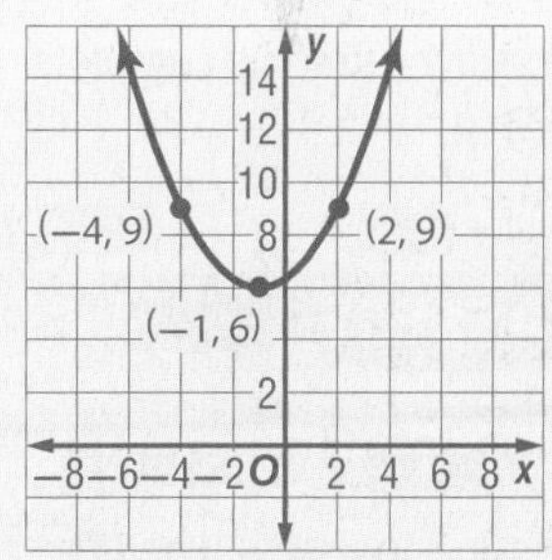

80. Sample answer: About 6.1 seconds; this answer seems reasonable. The equation has two solutions. The first solution, 0.01 second, is the time required for the ball to rise from 1.4 m to 1.7 m. 6.1 seconds is the time required for the ball to come back down to 1.7 m.

EXTEND 6-1

Lesson Notes

1 FOCUS

Objective Use dimensional analysis to convert units and solve problems.

Teaching Tip

Make sure that students have mastered multiplication of fractions before attempting this lesson.

2 TEACH

Working in Cooperative Groups

Have students work in pairs, mixing abilities. Have each pair work though the Example.

Ask:

- What number is the Multiplicative Identity? 1
- In what way can $\frac{5280 \text{ feet}}{1 \text{ mile}}$ be thought of as being equivalent to 1? Sample answer: One mile is the same distance as 5280 feet, so the numerator and denominator are equal size quantities.

Practice Have students complete Exercises 1–4.

3 ASSESS

Formative Assessment

Use Exercise 1 to assess whether students can set up a fraction that will change hours to minutes.

From Concrete to Abstract

In Exercise 5, ask students to give a specific example when they give their explanations.

EXTEND 6-1

Algebra Lab: Dimensional Analysis

NGSSS **LA.910.1.6.1** The student will use new vocabulary that is introduced and taught directly.

Real-world problems often involve units of measure. Performing operations with units is called **dimensional analysis** or **unit analysis**. You can use dimensional analysis to convert units or to perform calculations.

EXAMPLE

A car is traveling at 65 miles per hour. How fast is the car traveling in meters per second?

You want to find the speed in meters per second, so you need to change the unit of distance from miles to meters and the unit of time from hours to seconds. To make the conversion, use fractions that you can multiply.

Step 1 Change the units of length from miles to meters.
Use the relationships of miles to feet and feet to meters.

$$\frac{65 \text{ miles}}{1 \text{ hour}} \cdot \frac{5280 \text{ feet}}{1 \text{ mile}} \cdot \frac{1 \text{ meter}}{3.3 \text{ feet}}$$

Step 2 Change the units of time from hours to seconds.
Write fractions relating hours to minutes and minutes to seconds.

$$\frac{65 \text{ miles}}{1 \text{ hour}} \cdot \frac{5280 \text{ feet}}{1 \text{ mile}} \cdot \frac{1 \text{ meter}}{3.3 \text{ feet}} \cdot \frac{1 \text{ hour}}{60 \text{ minutes}} \cdot \frac{1 \text{ minute}}{60 \text{ seconds}}$$

Step 3 Simplify and check by canceling the units.

$$\frac{65 \cancel{\text{miles}}}{1 \cancel{\text{hour}}} \cdot \frac{5280 \cancel{\text{feet}}}{1 \cancel{\text{mile}}} \cdot \frac{1 \text{ meter}}{3.3 \cancel{\text{feet}}} \cdot \frac{1 \cancel{\text{hour}}}{60 \cancel{\text{minutes}}} \cdot \frac{1 \cancel{\text{minute}}}{60 \text{ seconds}}$$

$$= \frac{65 \cdot 5280}{3.3 \cdot 60 \cdot 60} \text{ m/s} \qquad \textbf{Simplify.}$$

$$\approx 28.9 \text{ m/s} \qquad \textbf{Use a calculator.}$$

So, 65 miles per hour is about 28.9 meters per second. This answer is reasonable because the final units are m/s, not m/hr, ft/s, or mi/hr.

Exercises

5. Sample answer: If the units in the final answer are not correct, then a mistake was made in solving the problem. Dimensional analysis helps you catch numerical errors as well as errors in setting up the problem.

Solve each problem by using dimensional analysis. Include the appropriate units with your answer.

1. A zebra can run 40 miles per hour. How far can a zebra run in 3 minutes? 2 mi
2. A cyclist traveled 43.2 miles at an average speed of 12 miles per hour. How long did the cyclist ride? 3.6 h
3. If you are going 50 miles per hour, how many feet per second are you traveling? 73.33 ft/s
4. The equation $d = \frac{1}{2}(9.8 \text{ m/s}^2)(3.5 \text{ s})^2$ represents the distance d that a ball falls 3.5 seconds after it is dropped from a tower. Find the distance. 60.025 m
5. **WRITING IN MATH** Explain how dimensional analysis can be useful in checking the reasonableness of your answer.

Dividing Polynomials

Then
You divided monomials. (Lesson 6-1)

Now
- Divide polynomials using long division.
- Divide polynomials using synthetic division.

NGSSS
MA.912.A.4.4 Divide polynomials by monomials and polynomials with various techniques, including synthetic division.

New Vocabulary
synthetic division

FL Math Online
glencoe.com

Why?

Arianna needed $140x^2 + 60x$ square inches of paper to make a book jacket $10x$ inches tall. In figuring the area, she allowed for a front and back flap. If the spine is $2x$ inches wide, and the front and back are $6x$ inches wide, how wide are the front and back flaps? You can use a quotient of polynomials to help you find the answer.

f = flap width

Long Division In Lesson 6-1, you learned to divide monomials. You can divide a polynomial by a monomial by using those same skills.

EXAMPLE 1 Divide a Polynomial by a Monomial

Simplify $\dfrac{6x^4y^3 + 12x^3y^2 - 18x^2y}{3xy}$.

$\dfrac{6x^4y^3 + 12x^3y^2 - 18x^2y}{3xy} = \dfrac{6x^4y^3}{3xy} + \dfrac{12x^3y^2}{3xy} - \dfrac{18x^2y}{3xy}$ **Sum of quotients**

$= \dfrac{6}{3} \cdot x^{4-1}y^{3-1} + \dfrac{12}{3} \cdot x^{3-1}y^{2-1} - \dfrac{18}{3} \cdot x^{2-1}y^{1-1}$ **Divide.**

$= 2x^3y^2 + 4x^2y - 6x$ **$y^{1-1} = y^0$ or 1**

Guided Practice **Simplify.** 1A. $5c^3d - 4f + 1$

1A. $(20c^4d^2f - 16cdf^2 + 4cdf) \div (4cdf)$ **1B.** $(18x^2y + 27x^3y^2z)(3xy)^{-1}$ $6x + 9x^2yz$

Personal Tutor glencoe.com

You can use a process similar to long division to divide a polynomial by a polynomial with more than one term. The process is known as the *division algorithm*.

EXAMPLE 2 Division Algorithm

Use long division to find $(x^2 + 3x - 40) \div (x - 5)$.

$$\begin{array}{r} x + 8 \\ x - 5 \overline{)x^2 + 3x - 40} \\ (-)\ x^2 - 5x \\ \hline 8x - 40 \\ (-)\ 8x - 40 \\ \hline 0 \end{array}$$

- $(-)\ x^2 - 5x$: **Multiply divisor by x since $\frac{x^2}{x} = x$.**
- $8x - 40$: **Subtract. Bring down next term.**
- $(-)\ 8x - 40$: **Multiply divisor by 8 since $\frac{8x}{x} = 8$.**
- 0: **Subtract.**

The quotient is $x + 8$. The remainder is 0.

Guided Practice **Use long division to find each quotient.**

2A. $(x^2 + 7x - 30) \div (x - 3)$ $x + 10$ **2B.** $(x^2 - 13x + 12) \div (x - 1)$ $x - 12$

Personal Tutor glencoe.com

1 FOCUS

Vertical Alignment

Before Lesson 6-2
Divide monomials.

Lesson 6-2
Divide polynomials using long division.
Divide polynomials using synthetic division.

After Lesson 6-2
Use tools including factoring to transform and solve polynomial equations.

2 TEACH

Scaffolding Questions

Have students read the *Why?* section of the lesson.

Ask:
- What is the height of the book jacket? $10x$ inches
- What is the total length of the book jacket? $14x + 2f$ inches
- If you know the height of the book jacket is $10x$ inches and the area is $140x^2 + 60x$ square inches, how can you find the length of the jacket? Divide the area of the jacket by its height.

Lesson 6-2 Resources

Resource	Approaching-Level	On-Level	Beyond-Level	English Learners
Teacher Edition	• Differentiated Instruction, p. 344	• Differentiated Instruction, p. 344	• Differentiated Instruction, p. 347	
Chapter Resource Masters	• Study Guide and Intervention, pp. 11–12 • Skills Practice, p. 13 • Practice, p. 14 • Word Problem Practice, p. 15	• Study Guide and Intervention, pp. 11–12 • Skills Practice, p. 13 • Practice, p. 14 • Word Problem Practice, p. 15 • Enrichment, p. 16	• Practice, p. 14 • Word Problem Practice, p. 15 • Enrichment, p. 16	• Study Guide and Intervention, pp. 11–12 • Skills Practice, p. 13 • Practice, p. 14 • Word Problem Practice, p. 15
Transparencies	• 5-Minute Check Transparency 6-2	• 5-Minute Check Transparency 6-2	• 5-Minute Check Transparency 6-2	• 5-Minute Check Transparency 6-2
Other	• Study Notebook	• Study Notebook	• Study Notebook	• Study Notebook

Long Division

Example 1 shows how to divide a polynomial by a monomial. **Example 2** shows how to divide a polynomial by a polynomial using the division algorithm. **Example 3** shows how to solve a multiple choice test item involving division of polynomials resulting in a quotient with a remainder.

Formative Assessment

Use the Guided Practice exercises after each example to determine students' understanding of concepts.

Additional Examples

1 Simplify $\frac{5a^2b - 15ab^3 + 10a^3b^4}{5ab}$.
$a - 3b^2 + 2a^2b^3$

2 Use long division to find $(x^2 - 2x - 15) \div (x - 5)$.
$x + 3$

3 **STANDARDIZED TEST PRACTICE** Which expression is equal to $(a^2 - 5a + 3)(2 - a)^{-1}$? D

A $a + 3$
B $-a + 3 + \frac{3}{2 - a}$
C $-a - 3 + \frac{3}{2 - a}$
D $-a + 3 - \frac{3}{2 - a}$

Additional Examples also in Interactive Classroom PowerPoint® Presentations

IWB INTERACTIVE WHITEBOARD READY

Tips for New Teachers

Test Taking Strategy Point out that $2 - a$ in Example 3 is rewritten as $-a + 2$ before starting the division in order to have both the numerator and denominator written in standard order. The first step in the long division eliminates choice A, and students also can eliminate choice B by multiplying $-a + 10$ by $-a + 3$ and noting that the product is not $a^2 + 7a - 11$.

Just as with the division of whole numbers, the division of two polynomials may result in a quotient with a remainder. Remember that $11 \div 3 = 3 + \text{R}2$, which is often written as $3\frac{2}{3}$. The result of a division of polynomials with a remainder can be written in a similar manner.

Test-Taking Tip

Multiple Choice You may be able to eliminate some of the answer choices by substituting the same value for a in the original expression and the answer choices, and then evaluating.

NGSSS PRACTICE EXAMPLE 3 912.A.4.4

Which expression is equal to $(a^2 + 7a - 11)(3 - a)^{-1}$?

A. $a + 10 - \frac{19}{3 - a}$ **C.** $-a - 10 + \frac{19}{3 - a}$

B. $-a + 10$ **D.** $-a - 10 - \frac{19}{3 - a}$

Read the Test Item

Since the second factor has an exponent of -1, this is a division problem.

$(a^2 + 7a - 11)(3 - a)^{-1} = \frac{a^2 + 7a - 11}{3 - a}$

Solve the Test Item

$$\begin{array}{r} -a - 10 \\ -a + 3\overline{)a^2 + 7a - 11} \\ \underline{(-)\ a^2 - 3a} \\ 10a - 11 \\ \underline{(-)\ 10a - 30} \\ 19 \end{array}$$

For ease in dividing, rewrite $3 - a$ as $-a + 3$.
$-a(-a + 3) = a^2 - 3a$
$7a - (-3a) = 10a$
$-10(-a + 3) = 10a - 30$
$-11 - (-30) = 19$

The quotient is $-a - 10$, and the remainder is 19.

Therefore, $(a^2 + 7a - 11)(3 - a)^{-1} = -a - 10 + \frac{19}{3 - a}$. The answer is **C**.

Guided Practice

3. Which expression is equal to $(r^2 + 5r + 7)(1 - r)^{-1}$? F

F. $-r - 6 + \frac{13}{1 - r}$ **H.** $r - 6 + \frac{13}{1 - r}$

G. $r + 6$ **I.** $r + 6 - \frac{13}{1 - r}$

Personal Tutor glencoe.com

Synthetic Division **Synthetic division** is a simpler process for dividing a polynomial by a binomial. Suppose you want to divide $2x^3 - 13x^2 + 26x - 24$ by $x - 4$ using long division. Compare the coefficients in this division with those in Example 4.

$$\begin{array}{r} 2x^2 - 5x + 6 \\ x - 4\overline{)2x^3 - 13x^2 + 26x - 24} \\ \underline{(-)\ 2x^3 - 8x^2} \\ -5x^2 + 26x \\ \underline{(-)\ -5x^2 + 20x} \\ 6x - 24 \\ \underline{(-)\ 6x - 24} \\ 0 \end{array}$$

When the polynomial in the dividend is missing a term, a zero must be used to represent the missing term. So, with a dividend of $2x^3 - 4x^2 + 6$, a 0 will be used as a placeholder for the x-term.

$$\overline{)2x^3 - 4x^2 + 0x + 6}$$

342 Chapter 6 Polynomials and Polynomial Functions

Key Concept — Synthetic Division

Step 1 Write the coefficients of the dividend so that the degrees of the terms are in descending order. Write the constant r of the divisor $x - r$ in the box. Bring the first coefficient down.

Step 2 Multiply the first coefficient by r, and write the product under the second coefficient.

Step 3 Add the product and the second coefficient.

Step 4 Repeat Steps 2 and 3 until you reach a sum in the last column. The numbers along the bottom row are the coefficients of the quotient. The power of the first term is one less than the degree of the dividend. The final number is the remainder.

EXAMPLE 4 Synthetic Division

Use synthetic division to find $(2x^3 - 13x^2 + 26x - 24) \div (x - 4)$.

Step 1 Write the coefficients of the dividend. Write the constant r in the box. In this case, $r = 4$. Bring the first coefficient, 2, down.

4	2	−13	26	−24
	↓			
	2			

Step 2 Multiply the first coefficient by r: $2 \cdot 4 = 8$. Write the product under the second coefficient.

4	2	−13	26	−24
		8		
	2 ↗			

Step 3 Add the product and the second coefficient: $-13 + 8 = -5$.

4	2	−13	26	−24
		8		
	2	−5		

Step 4 Multiply the sum, −5, by r: $-5 \times 4 = -20$. Write the product under the next coefficient, and add: $26 + (-20) = 6$. Multiply the sum, 6, by r: $6 \cdot 4 = 24$. Write the product under the next coefficient and add: $-24 + 24 = 0$.

4	2	−13	26	−24
		8	−20	24
	2	−5 ↗	6 ↗	0

CHECK Multiply the quotient by the divisor. The answer should be the dividend.

$$\begin{array}{r} 2x^2 - 5x + 6 \\ (\times) \qquad x - 4 \\ \hline -8x^2 + 20x - 24 \\ 2x^3 - 5x^2 + 6x \qquad \\ \hline 2x^3 - 13x^2 + 26x - 24 \end{array}$$

The quotient is $2x^2 - 5x + 6$. The remainder is 0.

Guided Practice 4A. $2x^2 - 3x + 5$ 4B. $3x^2 - 2x + 7$

Use synthetic division to find each quotient.

4A. $(2x^3 + 3x^2 - 4x + 15) \div (x + 3)$

4B. $(3x^3 - 8x^2 + 11x - 14) \div (x - 2)$

4C. $(4a^4 + 2a^2 - 4a + 12) \div (a + 2)$

4D. $(6b^4 - 8b^3 + 12b - 14) \div (b - 2)$

Personal Tutor glencoe.com

4C. $4a^3 - 8a^2 + 18a - 40 + \frac{92}{a + 2}$

4D. $6b^3 + 4b^2 + 8b + 28 + \frac{42}{b - 2}$

Watch Out!

Synthetic Division Remember to *add* terms when performing synthetic division.

Synthetic Division

Example 4 shows how to use synthetic division to divide a polynomial by a binomial. **Example 5** shows how to use synthetic division to divide a polynomial by a binomial when the coefficient of x in the divisor is not 1.

Additional Example

4 Use synthetic division to find $(x^3 - 4x^2 + 6x - 4) \div (x - 2)$. $x^2 - 2x + 2$

Watch Out!

Preventing Errors In the Guided Practice exercises, remind students to include a coefficient of 0 for any missing terms in the dividend.

Focus on Mathematical Content

Dividing Polynomials You can use synthetic division to divide a polynomial by a polynomial. The terms in both the divisor and dividend must be in descending order of powers. Include a coefficient of 0 for any term that is missing. If the divisor is not in the form $x - r$, divide every term in both the divisor and dividend by the coefficient of the first term of divisor and then use synthetic division.

TEACH with TECH

VIDEO RECORDING Have students work in groups, and assign a different polynomial division problem to each group. Have each group create a video showing how to use synthetic division to find the quotient. Post all of the videos to a video sharing Web site for students to view.

Additional Example

5 Use synthetic division to find $(4y^3 - 6y^2 + 4y - 1) \div (2y - 1)$.
$2y^2 - 2y + 1$

Tips for New Teachers

Reinforcing Concepts Ask students to discuss whether they would rather use long division or synthetic division, giving a reason for their choices.

To use synthetic division, the divisor must be of the form $x - r$. If the coefficient of x in a divisor is not 1, you can rewrite the division expression so that you can use synthetic division.

Watch Out!

Divide Throughout Remember to divide *all* terms in the numerator and denominator.

EXAMPLE 5 Divisor with First Coefficient Other than 1

Use synthetic division to find $(3x^4 - 5x^3 + x^2 + 7x) \div (3x + 1)$.

$$\frac{3x^4 - 5x^3 + x^2 + 7x}{3x + 1} = \frac{(3x^4 - 5x^3 + x^2 + 7x) \div 3}{(3x + 1) \div 3}$$ **Rewrite the divisor with a leading coeffient of 1. Then divide the numerator and denominator by 3.**

$$= \frac{x^4 - \frac{5}{3}x^3 + \frac{1}{3}x^2 + \frac{7}{3}x}{x + \frac{1}{3}}$$ **Simplify the numerator and the denominator.**

Since the numerator does not have a constant term, use a coefficient of 0 for the constant term.

$x - r = x + \frac{1}{3}$, so $r = -\frac{1}{3}$. →

$$\begin{array}{r|rrrrr} -\frac{1}{3} & 1 & -\frac{5}{3} & \frac{1}{3} & \frac{7}{3} & 0 \\ & & -\frac{1}{3} & \frac{2}{3} & -\frac{1}{3} & -\frac{2}{3} \\ \hline & 1 & -2 & 1 & 2 & \big| -\frac{2}{3} \end{array}$$

The result is $x^3 - 2x^2 + x + 2 - \frac{\frac{2}{3}}{x + \frac{1}{3}}$. Now simplify the fraction.

$$\frac{\frac{2}{3}}{x + \frac{1}{3}} = \frac{2}{3} \div \left(x + \frac{1}{3}\right)$$ **Rewrite as a division expression.**

$$= \frac{2}{3} \div \frac{3x + 1}{3}$$ **$x + \frac{1}{3} = \frac{3x}{3} + \frac{1}{3} = \frac{3x + 1}{3}$**

$$= \frac{2}{3} \cdot \frac{3}{3x + 1}$$ **Multiply by the reciprocal.**

$$= \frac{2}{3x + 1}$$ **Simplify.**

The solution is $x^3 - 2x^2 + x + 2 - \frac{2}{3x + 1}$.

CHECK Divide using long division.

$$\begin{array}{r} x^3 - 2x^2 + x + 2 \\ 3x + 1\overline{)3x^4 - 5x^3 + x^2 + 7x} \\ (-)\ 3x^4 + x^3 \quad\quad\quad\quad \\ \hline -6x^3 + x^2 \quad\quad \\ (-)\ -6x^3 - 2x^2 \quad\quad \\ \hline 3x^2 + 7x \\ (-)\ 3x^2 + x \\ \hline 6x + 0 \\ (-)\ 6x + 2 \\ \hline -2 \end{array}$$

The result is $x^3 - 2x^2 + x + 2 - \frac{2}{3x + 1}$. ✓

5A. $4x^3 - 2x^2 - x + 1 + \frac{3}{2x + 1}$ **5B.** $2y^4 - 4y - 1 + \frac{3}{4y - 1}$

5C. $3b^2 + 4b - 1 + \frac{2}{5b - 4}$ **5D.** $2c^2 - 3c - 2$

Guided Practice

Use synthetic division to find each quotient.

5A. $(8x^4 - 4x^2 + x + 4) \div (2x + 1)$

5B. $(8y^5 - 2y^4 - 16y^2 + 4) \div (4y - 1)$

5C. $(15b^3 + 8b^2 - 21b + 6) \div (5b - 4)$

5D. $(6c^3 - 17c^2 + 6c + 8) \div (3c - 4)$

Personal Tutor glencoe.com

Differentiated Instruction AL OL

If some students have trouble keeping their concentration throughout the sequence of steps required in long division,

Then encourage them to compare intermediate results with a partner so they can ask questions and catch errors before completing the entire problem.

Check Your Understanding

Examples 1, 2, and 4 pp. 341–343

Simplify.

1. $\frac{4xy^2 - 2xy + 2x^2y}{xy}$ $4y + 2x - 2$
2. $(3a^2b - 6ab + 5ab^2)(ab)^{-1}$ $3a + 5b - 6$
3. $(x^2 - 6x - 20) \div (x + 2)$ $x - 8 - \frac{4}{x+2}$
4. $(2a^2 - 4a - 8) \div (a + 1)$ $2a - 6 - \frac{2}{a+1}$
5. $(3z^4 - 6z^3 - 9z^2 + 3z - 6) \div (z + 3)$
6. $(y^5 - 3y^2 - 20) \div (y - 2)$

5. $3z^3 - 15z^2 + 36z - 105 + \frac{309}{z+3}$
6. $y^4 + 2y^3 + 4y^2 + 5y + 10$

Example 3 p. 342

7. **NGSSS PRACTICE** Which expression is equal to $(x^2 + 3x - 9)(4 - x)^{-1}$? A

A. $-x - 7 + \frac{19}{4-x}$ B. $-x - 7$ C. $x + 7 - \frac{19}{4-x}$ D. $-x - 7 - \frac{19}{4-x}$

Example 5 p. 344

Simplify. 8. $2x + 1 + \frac{3}{x+1}$ 9. $6a + 6 + \frac{21}{3a-2}$

8. $(10x^2 + 15x + 20) \div (5x + 5)$
9. $(18a^2 + 6a + 9) \div (3a - 2)$
10. $\frac{12b^2 + 23b + 15}{3b + 8}$ $4b - 3 + \frac{39}{3b+8}$
11. $\frac{27y^2 + 27y - 30}{9y - 6}$ $3y + 5$

Practice and Problem Solving

● = **Step-by-Step Solutions** begin on page R20. **Extra Practice** begins on page 947.

Example 1 p. 341

Simplify. 12. $3a^2b - 2ab^2$ 13. $x + 3y - 2$ 14. $7g^2h + 3g - 2h^2$

12. $\frac{24a^3b^2 - 16a^2b^3}{8ab}$
13. $\frac{5x^2y - 10xy + 15xy^2}{5xy}$
14. $\frac{7g^3h^2 + 3g^2h - 2gh^3}{gh}$
15. $\frac{4a^3b - 6ab + 2ab^2}{2ab}$ $2a^2 + b - 3$
16. $\frac{16c^4d^4 - 24c^2d^2}{4c^2d^2}$ $4c^2d^2 - 6$
17. $\frac{9n^3p^3 - 18n^2p^2 + 21n^2p^3}{3n^2p^2}$ $3np - 6 + 7p$
18. **ENERGY** Compact fluorescent light (CFL) bulbs reduce energy waste. The amount of energy waste that is reduced each day in a certain community can be estimated by $-b^2 + 8b$, where b is the number of bulbs. Divide by b to find the average amount of energy saved per CFL bulb. $-b + 8$
19. **BAKING** The number of cookies produced in a factory each day can be estimated by $-w^2 + 16w + 1000$, where w is the number of workers. Divide by w to find the average number of cookies produced per worker. $-w + 16 + \frac{1000}{w}$

Examples 2, 4, and 5 pp. 341–344

Simplify.

20. $(a^2 - 8a - 26) \div (a + 2)$ $a - 10 - \frac{6}{a+2}$
21. $(b^3 - 4b^2 + b - 2) \div (b + 1)$
22. $(z^4 - 3z^3 + 2z^2 - 4z + 4)(z - 1)^{-1}$
23. $(x^5 - 4x^3 + 4x^2) \div (x - 4)$
24. $\frac{y^3 + 11y^2 - 10y + 6}{y + 2}$
25. $(g^4 - 3g^2 - 18) \div (g - 2)$
26. $(6a^2 - 3a + 9) \div (3a - 2)$
27. $\frac{6x^5 + 5x^4 + x^3 - 3x^2 + x}{3x + 1}$
28. $\frac{4g^4 - 6g^3 + 3g^2 - g + 12}{4g - 4}$
29. $(2b^3 - 6b^2 + 8b) \div (2b + 2)$
30. $(6z^6 + 3z^4 - 9z^2)(3z - 6)^{-1}$
31. $(10y^6 + 5y^5 + 10y^3 - 20y - 15)(5y + 5)^{-1}$ $2y^5 - y^4 + y^3 + y^2 - y - 3$
32. **GEOMETRY** A rectangular box for a new product is designed in such a way that the three dimensions always have a particular relationship defined by the variable x. The volume of the box can be written as $6x^3 + 31x^2 + 53x + 30$, and the height is always $x + 2$. What are the width and length of the box? $2x + 3, 3x + 5$
33. **PHYSICS** The voltage V is related to current I and power P by the equation $V = \frac{P}{I}$. The power of a generator is modeled by $P(t) = t^3 + 9t^2 + 26t + 24$. If the current of the generator is $I = t + 4$, write an expression that represents the voltage. $V(t) = t^2 + 5t + 6$

21. $b^2 - 5b + 6 - \frac{8}{b+1}$
22. $z^3 - 2z^2 - 4$
23. $x^4 + 4x^3 + 12x^2 + 52x + 208 + \frac{832}{x-4}$
24. $y^2 + 9y - 28 + \frac{62}{y+2}$
25. $g^3 + 2g^2 + g + 2 - \frac{14}{g-2}$
26. $2a + \frac{1}{3} + \frac{29}{9a-6}$
27. $2x^4 + x^3 - x + \frac{2}{3} - \frac{2}{9x+3}$
28. $g^3 - \frac{1}{2}g^2 + \frac{1}{4}g + \frac{3}{g-1}$
29. $b^2 - 4b + 8 - \frac{8}{b+1}$
30. $2z^5 + 4z^4 + 9z^3 + 18z^2 + 33z + 66 + \frac{132}{z-2}$

3 PRACTICE

Formative Assessment

Use Exercises 1–11 to check for understanding.

Use the chart at the bottom of this page to customize assignments for your students.

Tips for New Teachers

Reasoning When solving problems using the division algorithm, advise students to do a simple numeric division example such as $8 \div 5$ to help them remember how to write the remainder as part of the quotient.

Differentiated Homework Options

Level	Assignment	Two-Day Option	
AL Basic	12–33, 43, 45–72	13–33 odd, 49–52	12–32 even, 43, 53–72
OL Core	13–33 odd, 34, 35, 37–41 odd, 42, 43, 45–72	12–33, 49–52	34–43, 45–48, 53–72
BL Advanced	34–66, (optional: 67–72)		

Study Guide and Intervention
CRM pp. 11–12 AL OL ELL

6-2 Study Guide and Intervention
Dividing Polynomials

Long Division To divide a polynomial by a monomial, use the skills learned in Lesson 6-1.

To divide a polynomial by a polynomial, use a long division pattern. Remember that only like terms can be added or subtracted.

Example 1 Simplify $\frac{12p^3t^2r - 21p^2qtr^2 - 9p^3tr}{3p^2tr}$.

$$\frac{12p^3t^2r - 21p^2qtr^2 - 9p^3tr}{3p^2tr} = \frac{12p^3t^2r}{3p^2tr} - \frac{21p^2qtr^2}{3p^2tr} - \frac{9p^3tr}{3p^2tr}$$
$$= \frac{12}{3}p^{(3-2)}t^{(2-1)}r^{(1-1)} - \frac{21}{3}p^{(2-2)}qt^{(1-1)}r^{(2-1)} - \frac{9}{3}p^{(3-2)}t^{(1-1)}r^{(1-1)}$$
$$= 4pt - 7qr - 3p$$

Example 2 Use long division to find $(x^3 - 8x^2 + 4x - 9) \div (x - 4)$.

$$\begin{array}{r} x^2 - 4x - 12 \\ x - 4\overline{)x^3 - 8x^2 + 4x - 9} \\ \underline{(-)x^3 - 4x^2} \\ -4x^2 + 4x \\ \underline{(-)-4x^2 + 16x} \\ -12x - 9 \\ \underline{(-)-12x + 48} \\ -57 \end{array}$$

The quotient is $x^2 - 4x - 12$, and the remainder is -57.

Therefore $\frac{x^3-8x^2-4x-9}{x-4} = x^2 - 4x - 12 - \frac{57}{x-4}$.

Exercises

Simplify.

1. $\frac{18a^3 + 30a^2}{3a}$ **$6a^2 + 10a$**
2. $\frac{24mn^6 - 40m^2n^3}{4m^2n^3}$ **$\frac{6n^3}{m} - 10$**
3. $\frac{60a^2b^3 - 48b^4 + 84a^5b^2}{12ab^2}$ **$5ab - \frac{4b^2}{a} + 7a^4$**
4. $(2x^2 - 5x - 3) \div (x - 3)$ **$2x + 1$**
5. $(m^2 - 3m - 7) \div (m + 2)$ **$m - 5 + \frac{3}{m+2}$**
6. $(p^3 - 6) \div (p - 1)$ **$p^2 + p + 1 - \frac{5}{p-1}$**
7. $(t^3 - 6t^2 + 1) \div (t + 2)$ **$t^2 - 8t + 16 - \frac{31}{t+2}$**
8. $(x^5 - 1) \div (x - 1)$ **$x^4 + x^3 + x^2 + x + 1$**
9. $(2x^3 - 5x^2 + 4x - 4) \div (x - 2)$ **$2x^2 - x + 2$**

Lesson 6-2

Chapter 6 11 Glencoe Algebra 2

Practice
CRM p. 14 AL OL BL ELL

6-2 Practice
Dividing Polynomials

Simplify.

1. $\frac{15r^{10} - 5r^8 + 40r^2}{5r^4}$ **$3r^6 - r^4 + \frac{8}{r^2}$**
2. $\frac{6k^2m - 12k^3m^2 + 9m^3}{2km^2}$ **$-6k^2 + \frac{9m}{2k}$**
3. $(-30x^3y + 12x^2y^2 - 18x^2y) \div (-6x^2y)$ **$5x - 2y + 3$**
4. $(-6w^3z^4 - 3w^2z^5 + 4w + 5z) \div (2w^2z)$ **$-3wz^3 - \frac{3z^4}{2} + \frac{2}{wz} + \frac{5}{2w^2}$**
5. $(4a^3 - 8a^2 + a^2)(4a)^{-1}$ **$a^2 - 2a + \frac{a}{4}$**
6. $(28d^3k^2 + d^2k^2 - 4dk^2)(4dk^2)^{-1}$ **$7d^2 + \frac{d}{4} - 1$**
7. $\frac{f^2 + 7f + 10}{f + 2}$ **$f + 5$**
8. $\frac{2x^2 + 3x - 14}{x - 2}$ **$2x + 7$**
9. $(a^3 - 64) \div (a - 4)$ **$a^2 + 4a + 16$**
10. $(b^3 + 27) \div (b + 3)$ **$b^2 - 3b + 9$**
11. $\frac{2x^3 + 6x + 152}{x + 4}$ **$2x^2 - 8x + 38$**
12. $\frac{2x^3 + 4x - 6}{x + 3}$ **$2x^2 - 6x + 22 - \frac{72}{x+3}$**
13. $(3w^3 + 7w^2 - 4w + 3) \div (w + 3)$ **$3w^2 - 2w + 2 - \frac{3}{w+3}$**
14. $(6y^4 + 15y^3 - 28y - 6) \div (y + 2)$ **$6y^3 + 3y^2 - 6y - 16 + \frac{26}{y+2}$**
15. $(x^4 - 3x^3 - 11x^2 + 3x + 10) \div (x - 5)$ **$x^3 + 2x^2 - x - 2$**
16. $(3m^5 + m - 1) \div (m + 1)$ **$3m^4 - 3m^3 + 3m^2 - 3m + 4 - \frac{5}{m+1}$**
17. $(x^4 - 3x^3 + 5x - 6)(x + 2)^{-1}$ **$x^3 - 5x^2 + 10x - 15 + \frac{24}{x+2}$**
18. $(6y^2 - 5y - 15)(2y + 3)^{-1}$ **$3y - 7 + \frac{6}{2y+3}$**
19. $\frac{4x^2 - 2x + 6}{2x - 3}$ **$2x + 2 + \frac{12}{2x-3}$**
20. $\frac{6x^2 - x - 7}{3x + 1}$ **$2x - 1 - \frac{6}{3x} + 1$**
21. $(2r^3 + 5r^2 - 2r - 15) \div (2r - 3)$ **$r^2 + 4r + 5$**
22. $(6t^3 + 5t^2 - 2t + 1) \div (3t + 1)$ **$2t^2 + t - 1 + \frac{2}{3t+1}$**
23. $\frac{4p^4 - 17p^2 + 14p - 3}{2p - 3}$ **$2p^3 + 3p^2 - 4p + 1$**
24. $\frac{2h^4 - h^3 + h^2 + h - 3}{h^2 - 1}$ **$2h^2 - h + 3$**
25. **GEOMETRY** The area of a rectangle is $2x^2 - 11x + 15$ square feet. The length of the rectangle is $2x - 5$ feet. What is the width of the rectangle? **$x - 3$ ft**
26. **GEOMETRY** The area of a triangle is $15x^4 + 3x^3 + 4x^2 - x - 3$ square meters. The length of the base of the triangle is $6x^2 - 2$ meters. What is the height of the triangle? **$5x^2 + x + 3$ m**

Chapter 6 14 Glencoe Algebra 2

Word Problem Practice
CRM p. 15 AL OL BL ELL

6-2 Word Problem Practice
Dividing Polynomials

1. **REMAINDERS** Jordan divided the polynomial $x^4 + x - 6$ into the polynomial $p(x)$ yesterday. Today his work is smudged and he cannot read $p(x)$ or most of his answer. The only part he could read was the remainder $x + 4$. His teacher wants him to find $p(-3)$. What is $p(-3)$?
1

2. **LONG DIVISION** Dana used long division to divide $x^4 + x^3 + x^2 + x + 1$ by $x + 2$. Her work is shown below with three numbers missing.

$$\begin{array}{r} x^3 - x^2 + 3x - 5 \\ x + 2\overline{)x^4 + x^3 + x^2 + x + 1} \\ \underline{(-)x^4 + 2x^3} \\ -x^3 + A \\ \underline{(-)-x^3 + 2x^2} \\ 3x^2 + x \\ \underline{(-)3x^2 + B} \\ -5x + 1 \\ \underline{(-)-5x - 10} \\ C \end{array}$$

What are A, B, and C?
***A* is x^2; *B* is 6x; C is 11.**

3. **AVERAGES** Shelby is a statistician. She has a list of $n + 1$ numbers and she needs to find their average. Two of the numbers are n^3 and 2. Each of the other $n - 1$ numbers are all equal to 1. What is the average of these numbers?
$n^2 - n + 2 - \frac{1}{n+1}$

4. **VOLUME** The volume of one column of the Lincoln Memorial is $\pi(x^3 - 32x^2 - 224x + 640)$. If the height of the column is $x + 40$ feet, find the area of the base of the column in terms of x and π.
$\pi(x^2 - 8x + 16)$

5. **NUMBER THEORY** Mr. Collins has his class working with bases and polynomials. He wrote on the board that the number 1111 in base B has the value $B^3 + B^2 + B + 1$. The class was then given the following questions to answer.

a. The number 11 in base B has the value $B + 1$. What is 1111 (in base B) divided by 11 (in base B)?
$B^2 + 1$

b. The number 111 in base B has the value $B^2 + B + 1$. What is 1111 (in base B) divided by 111 (in base B)?
$B + \frac{1}{B^2 + B + 1}$

Lesson 6-2

Chapter 6 15 Glencoe Algebra 2

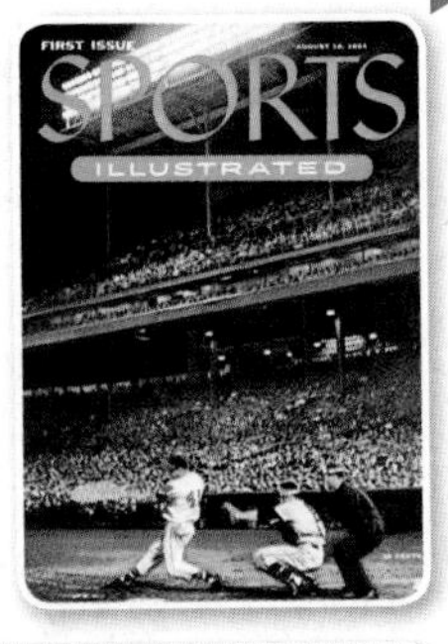

Real-World Link

Created in 1954, *Sports Illustrated* is read by over 23 million adults each week.

Source: *Sports Illustrated*

43. Sample answer: Sharon; Jamal actually divided by $x + 3$.
44. The binomial is a factor of the polynomial.
45. Sample answer: The degree of the quotient plus the degree of the divisor equals the degree of the dividend.
46. Sample answer: $\frac{x^2 + 5x + 9}{x + 2}$
47. $\frac{5}{x^2}$ does not belong with the other three. The other three expressions are polynomials. Since the denominator of $\frac{5}{x^2}$ contains a variable, it is not a polynomial.
48. Sample answer: By dividing $140x^2 + 60x$ by $10x$, the quotient of $14x + 6$ provides the length of the book jacket. Then subtracting $14x$, we are left with 6 inches. Half of this length is the width of each flap.

B

34. **ENTERTAINMENT** A magician gives these instructions to a volunteer.
- Choose a number and multiply it by 4.
- Then add the sum of your number and 15 to the product you found.
- Now divide by the sum of your number and 3.

a. What number will the volunteer always have at the end? **5**

b. Explain the process you used to discover the answer. **See margin.**

35. **BUSINESS** The number of magazine subscriptions sold can be estimated by $n = \frac{3500a^2}{a^2 + 100}$, where a is the amount of money the company spent on advertising in hundreds of dollars and n is the number of subscriptions sold.

a. Perform the division indicated by $\frac{3500a^2}{a^2 + 100}$. **$3500 - \frac{350{,}000}{a^2 + 100}$**

b. About how many subscriptions will be sold if \$1500 is spent on advertising? **about 2423 subscriptions**

C

Simplify. 36–41. See margin.

36. $(x^4 - y^4) \div (x - y)$
37. $(28c^3d^2 - 21cd^2) \div (14cd)$
38. $(a^3b^2 - a^2b + 2b)(-ab)^{-1}$
39. $\frac{n^3 + 3n^2 - 5n - 4}{n + 4}$
40. $\frac{p^3 + 2p^2 - 7p - 21}{p + 3}$
41. $\frac{3z^5 + 5z^4 + z + 5}{z + 2}$

42. **MULTIPLE REPRESENTATIONS** Consider a rectangle with area $2x^2 + 7x + 3$ and length $2x + 1$. **a–c. See margin.**

a. **CONCRETE** Use algebra tiles to represent this situation. Use the model to find the width.

b. **SYMBOLIC** Write an expression to represent the model.

c. **NUMERICAL** Solve this problem algebraically using synthetic or long division. Does your concrete model check with your algebraic model?

H.O.T. Problems
Use Higher-Order Thinking Skills

43. **ERROR ANALYSIS** Sharon and Jamal are dividing $2x^3 - 4x^2 + 3x - 1$ by $x - 3$. Sharon claims that the remainder is 26. Jamal argues that the remainder is -100. Is either of them correct? Explain your reasoning.

44. **CHALLENGE** If a polynomial is divided by a binomial and the remainder is 0, what does this tell you about the relationship between the binomial and the polynomial?

45. **REASONING** Review any of the division problems in this lesson. What is the relationship between the degrees of the dividend, the divisor, and the quotient?

46. **OPEN ENDED** Write a quotient of two polynomials for which the remainder is 3.

47. **WHICH ONE DOESN'T BELONG?** Identify the expression that does not belong with the other three. Explain your reasoning.

$3xy + 6x^2$	$\frac{5}{x^2}$	$x + 5$	$5b + 11c - 9ad^2$

48. **WRITING IN MATH** Use the information at the beginning of the lesson to write assembly instructions using the division of polynomials to make a paper cover for your textbook.

Enrichment
CRM p. 16 OL BL

6-2 Enrichment

Oblique Asymptotes

The graph of $y = ax + b$, where $a \neq 0$, is called an oblique asymptote of $y = f(x)$ if the graph of f comes closer and closer to the line as $x \to \infty$ or $x \to -\infty$. ∞ is the mathematical symbol for **infinity**, which means *endless*.

For $f(x) = 3x + 4 + \frac{2}{3}$, $y = 3x + 4$ is an oblique asymptote because $f(x) - 3x - 4 = \frac{2}{x}$, and $\frac{2}{x} \to 0$ as $x \to \infty$ or $-\infty$. In other words, as $|x|$ increases, the value of $\frac{2}{x}$ gets smaller and smaller approaching 0.

Example Find the oblique asymptote for $f(x) = \frac{x^2 + 8x + 15}{x + 2}$.

$$\begin{array}{r|rrr} -2 & 1 & 8 & 15 \\ & & -2 & -12 \\ \hline & 1 & 6 & 3 \end{array}$$ Use synthetic division.

$y = \frac{x^2 - 8x + 15}{x + 2} = x + 6 + \frac{3}{x + 2}$

As $|x|$ increases, the value of $\frac{3}{x+2}$ gets smaller. In other words, since $\frac{3}{x+2} \to 0$ as $x \to \infty$ or $x \to -\infty$, $y = x + 6$ is an oblique asymptote.

Multiple Representations In Exercise 42, students use algebra tiles and algebraic operations to divide polynomials.

Additional Answer

34b. Sample answer: Let x be the number. Multiply the x by 4 to get $4x$. Then add $x + 15$ to the product to get $5x + 15$. Divide the polynomial by $x + 3$. The quotient is 5.

NGSSS PRACTICE 912.A.4.4, 912.A.4.2, 912.G.2.2

49. An office employs x women and 3 men. What is the ratio of the total number of employees to the number of women? **A**

A. $\frac{x+3}{x}$ C. $\frac{3}{x}$

B. $\frac{x}{x+3}$ D. $\frac{x}{3}$

50. $(-4x^2 + 2x + 3) - 3(2x^2 - 5x + 1) =$ **H**

F. $2x^2$ H. $-10x^2 + 17x$

G. $-10x^2$ I. $2x^2 + 17x$

51. **GRIDDED RESPONSE** In the figure below, $m + n + p = ?$ **360**

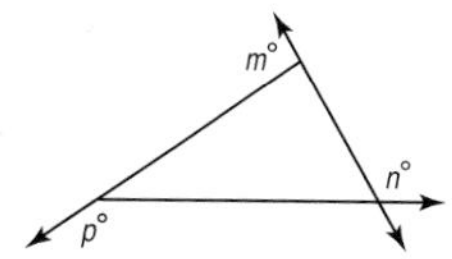

52. **SAT/ACT** Which polynomial has degree 3? **D**

A. $x^3 + x^2 - 2x^4$ C. $x^2 + x + 12^3$

B. $-2x^2 - 3x + 4$ D. $1 + x + x^3$

Spiral Review

53. $3x^3 + 2x^2 + x + 4$ 54. $2y^3 + 3y^2 - 9y + 8$
56. $2c^3 - 3c^2d - 2cd^2 + 3d^3$

Simplify. (Lesson 6-1)

53. $(5x^3 + 2x^2 - 3x + 4) - (2x^3 - 4x)$ **54.** $(2y^3 - 3y + 8) + (3y^2 - 6y)$ **55.** $4a(2a - 3) + 3a(5a - 4)$ $23a^2 - 24a$

56. $(c + d)(c - d)(2c - 3d)$ **57.** $(xy)^2(2xy^2z)^3$ $8x^5y^8z^3$ **58.** $(3ab^2)^{-2}(2a^2b)^2$ $\frac{4a^2}{9b^2}$

59. **LANDSCAPING** Amado wants to plant a garden and surround it with decorative stones. He has enough stones to enclose a rectangular garden with a perimeter of 68 feet, but he wants the garden to cover no more than 240 square feet. What could the width of his garden be? (Lesson 5-8) **0 to 10 ft or 24 to 34 ft**

Solve each equation by completing the square. (Lesson 5-5)

60. $x^2 + 6x + 2 = 0$ $-3 \pm \sqrt{7}$ **61.** $x^2 - 8x - 3 = 0$ $4 \pm \sqrt{19}$ **62.** $2x^2 + 6x + 5 = 0$ $-1.5 \pm \frac{i}{2}$

State the consecutive integers between which the zeros of each quadratic function are located. (Lesson 5-2)

63.

x	−7	−6	−5	−4	−3	−2	−1	0
f(x)	4	1	−3	−8	−1	2	8	16

between −6 and −5; between −3 and −2

64.

x	−2	−1	0	1	2	3	4	5
f(x)	−16	−7	−4	3	3	−4	−7	−16

between 0 and 1; between 2 and 3

65.

x	−2	−1	0	1	2	3	4	5
f(x)	6	1	−3	−5	−3	1	6	14

between −1 and 0; between 2 and 3

66. **BUSINESS** A landscaper can mow a lawn in 30 minutes and perform a small landscape job in 90 minutes. He works at most 10 hours per day, 5 days per week. He earns \$35 per lawn and \$125 per landscape job. He cannot do more than 3 landscape jobs per day. Find the combination of lawns mowed and completed landscape jobs per week that will maximize income. Then find the maximum income. (Lesson 3-4) **15 landscape jobs and 55 lawns; \$3800**

Skills Review

Find each value if $f(x) = 4x + 3$, $g(x) = -x^2$, and $h(x) = -2x^2 - 2x + 4$. (Lesson 2-1)

67. $f(-6)$ -21 **68.** $g(-8)$ -64 **69.** $h(3)$ -20

70. $f(c)$ $4c + 3$ **71.** $g(3d)$ $-9d^2$ **72.** $h(2b + 1)$ $-8b^2 - 12b$

Differentiated Instruction BL

Extension Dividing by polynomials that contain fractions or radicals requires attention to neatness and careful calculations. Ask students to divide $x^4 - 6x^2 + 8$ by $(x - \sqrt{2})$. $x^3 + \sqrt{2}x^2 - 4x - 4\sqrt{2}$

Exercise Alert!

Exercise 42 requires the use of algebra tiles.

Watch Out!

Error Analysis In Exercise 43, remind students that after each new term in the quotient is multiplied by the divisor, the result is subtracted from the dividend, not added.

4 ASSESS

Name the Math Ask students to explain how to use synthetic division to divide a polynomial by a binomial. Ask them to demonstrate the technique using the polynomial $3x^3 - 4x^2 + 5x^2 - 7$ and the binomial $x - 2$.

Formative Assessment

Check for understanding of concepts in Lessons 6-1 and 6-2.

CRM Quiz 1, p. 57

Additional Answers

36. $(x^2 + y^2)(x + y)$

37. $\frac{4c^2d - 3d}{2}$

38. $-a^2b + a - \frac{2}{a}$

39. $n^2 - n - 1$

40. $p^2 - p - 4 - \frac{9}{p+3}$

41. $3z^4 - z^3 + 2z^2 - 4z + 9 - \frac{13}{z+2}$

42a.

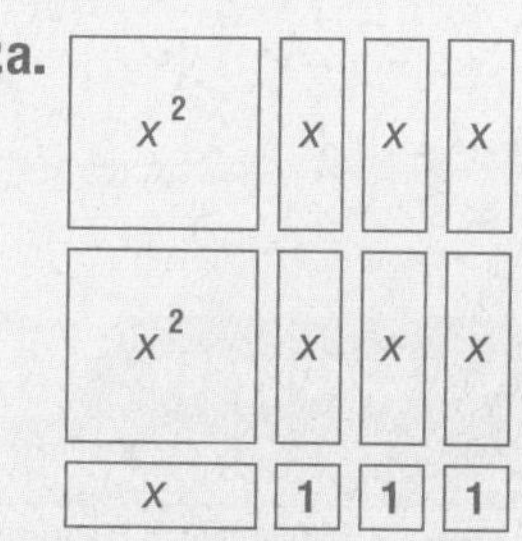

The width is $x + 3$.

42b. $2x^2 + 7x + 3 \div (2x + 1)$

42c.

$$\begin{array}{r|rrr} -\frac{1}{2} & 1 & \frac{7}{2} & \frac{3}{2} \\ & & -\frac{1}{2} & -\frac{3}{2} \\ \hline & 1 & 3 & 0 \end{array}$$

yes

6-3 Lesson Notes

1 FOCUS

Vertical Alignment

Before Lesson 6-3
Analyze graphs of quadratic functions.

Lesson 6-3
Evaluate polynomial functions.
Identify general shapes of graphs of polynomial functions.

After Lesson 6-3
Use tools including factoring to transform and solve polynomial equations.

2 TEACH

Scaffolding Questions

Have students read the *Why?* section of the lesson.

Ask:

- What is a respiratory cycle? Sample answer: a sequence consisting of one inhalation and one exhalation
- Using the formula, what is $v(1)$? 0.288 liter
- What is the largest value of t that makes sense for this model? 5

6-3 Polynomial Functions

Then
You analyzed graphs of quadratic functions. (Lesson 5-1)

Now
- Evaluate polynomial functions.
- Identify general shapes of graphs of polynomial functions.

NGSSS
MA.912.A.4.5 Graph polynomial functions with and without technology and describe end behavior.

New Vocabulary
polynomial in one variable
leading coefficient
polynomial function
power function
end behavior
quartic function
quintic function

FL Math Online
glencoe.com

Why?

The volume of air in the lungs during a 5-second respiratory cycle can be modeled by $v(t) = -0.037t^3 + 0.152t^2 + 0.173t$, where v is the volume in liters and t is the time in seconds. This model is an example of a polynomial function.

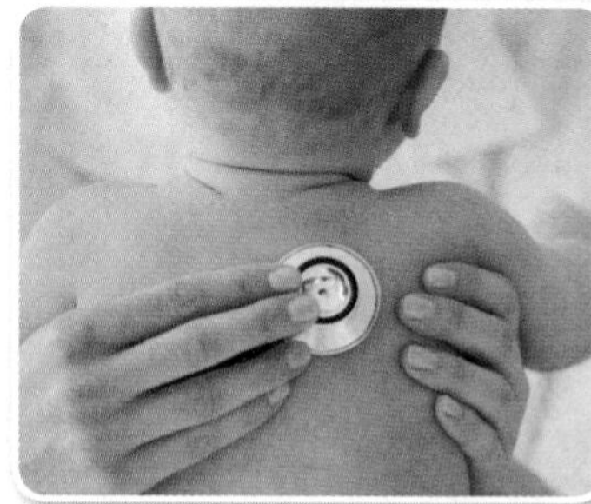

Polynomial Functions A **polynomial in one variable** is an expression of the form $a_nx^n + a_{n-1}x^{n-1} + \cdots + a_2x^2 + a_1x + a_0$, where $a_n \neq 0$, a_{n-1}, a_2, a_1, and a_0 are real numbers, and n is a nonnegative integer.

The polynomial is written in standard form when the values of the exponents are in descending order. The degree of the polynomial is the value of the greatest exponent. The coefficient of the first term of a polynomial in standard form is called the **leading coefficient**.

Polynomial	Expression	Degree	Leading Coefficient
Constant	12	0	12
Linear	$4x - 9$	1	4
Quadratic	$5x^2 - 6x - 9$	2	5
Cubic	$8x^3 + 12x^2 - 3x + 1$	3	8
General	$a_nx^n + a_{n-1}x^{n-1} + \cdots + a_1x + a_0$	n	a_n

EXAMPLE 1 Degrees and Leading Coefficients

State the degree and leading coefficient of each polynomial in one variable. If it is not a polynomial in one variable, explain why.

a. $8x^5 - 4x^3 + 2x^2 - x - 3$

This is a polynomial in one variable. The greatest exponent is 5, so the degree is 5 and the leading coefficient is 8.

b. $12x^2 - 3xy + 8x$

This is not a polynomial in one variable. There are two variables, x and y.

c. $3x^4 + 6x^3 - 4x^8 + 2x$

This is a polynomial in one variable. The greatest exponent is 8, so the degree is 8 and the leading coefficient is −4.

Guided Practice 1A–1C. See margin.

1A. $5x^3 - 4x^2 - 8x + \frac{4}{x}$ **1B.** $5x^6 - 3x^4 + 12x^3 - 14$ **1C.** $8x^4 - 2x^3 - x^6 + 3$

Personal Tutor glencoe.com

Lesson 6-3 Resources

Resource	Approaching-Level	On-Level	Beyond-Level	English Learners
Teacher Edition	• Differentiated Instruction, p. 350	• Differentiated Instruction, p. 350	• Differentiated Instruction, p. 355	
Chapter Resource Masters	• Study Guide and Intervention, pp. 17–18 • Skills Practice, p. 19 • Practice, p. 20 • Word Problem Practice, p. 21	• Study Guide and Intervention, pp. 17–18 • Skills Practice, p. 19 • Practice, p. 20 • Word Problem Practice, p. 21 • Enrichment, p. 22	• Practice, p. 20 • Word Problem Practice, p. 21 • Enrichment, p. 22	• Study Guide and Intervention, pp. 17–18 • Skills Practice, p. 19 • Practice, p. 20 • Word Problem Practice, p. 21
Transparencies	• 5-Minute Check Transparency 6-3	• 5-Minute Check Transparency 6-3	• 5-Minute Check Transparency 6-3	• 5-Minute Check Transparency 6-3
Other	• Study Notebook • Teaching Algebra with Manipulatives	• Study Notebook • Teaching Algebra with Manipulatives	• Study Notebook	• Study Notebook • Teaching Algebra with Manipulatives

A **polynomial function** is a continuous function that can be described by a polynomial equation in one variable. For example, $f(x) = 3x^3 - 4x + 6$ is a cubic polynomial function. The simplest polynomial functions of the form $f(x) = ax^b$ where a and b are real numbers are called **power functions**.

If you know an element in the domain of any polynomial function, you can find the corresponding value in the range.

Real-World Link

Total lung capacity is approximately 6 liters in a healthy young adult.

Source: *Family Practice Notebook*

Real-World EXAMPLE 2 Evaluate a Polynomial Function

RESPIRATION Refer to the beginning of the lesson. Find the volume of air in the lungs 2 seconds into the respiratory cycle.

By substituting 2 into the function we can find $v(2)$, the volume of air in the lungs 2 seconds into the respiration cycle.

$v(t) = -0.037t^3 + 0.152t^2 + 0.173t$	**Original function**
$v(2) = -0.037(2)^3 + 0.152(2)^2 + 0.173(2)$	**Replace t with 2.**
$= -0.296 + 0.608 + 0.346$	**Simplify.**
$= 0.658$ L	**Add.**

Guided Practice

2. Find the volume of air in the lungs 4 seconds into the respiratory cycle. **0.7332 L**

Personal Tutor glencoe.com

You can also evaluate functions for variables and algebraic expressions.

EXAMPLE 3 Function Values of Variables

Find $f(3c - 4) - 5f(c)$ if $f(x) = x^2 + 2x - 3$.

To evaluate $f(3c - 4)$, replace the x in $f(x)$ with $3c - 4$.

$f(x) = x^2 + 2x - 3$	**Original function**
$f(3c - 4) = (3c - 4)^2 + 2(3c - 4) - 3$	**Replace x with $3c - 4$.**
$= 9c^2 - 24c + 16 + 6c - 8 - 3$	**Multiply.**
$= 9c^2 - 18c + 5$	**Simplify.**

To evaluate $5f(c)$, replace x with c in $f(x)$, then multiply by 5.

$f(x) = x^2 + 2x - 3$	**Original function**
$5f(c) = 5(c^2 + 2c - 3)$	**Replace x with c.**
$= 5c^2 + 10c - 15$	**Distributive Property**

Now evaluate $f(3c - 4) - 5f(c)$.

$f(3c - 4) - 5f(c) = (9c^2 - 18c + 5) - (5c^2 + 10c - 15)$	
$= 9c^2 - 18c + 5 - 5c^2 - 10c + 15$	**Distribute.**
$= 4c^2 - 28c + 20$	**Simplify.**

Guided Practice

3A. Find $g(5a - 2) + 3g(2a)$ if $g(x) = x^2 - 5x + 8$. $37a^2 - 75a + 46$

3B. Find $h(-4d + 3) - 0.5h(d)$ if $h(x) = 2x^2 + 5x + 3$. $31d^2 - 70.5d + 34.5$

Personal Tutor glencoe.com

Polynomials Functions

Example 1 shows how to find the degree and leading coefficient of a polynomial in one variable. **Example 2** shows how to evaluate a polynomial function for a given value. **Example 3** shows how to evaluate a polynomial function for variables and algebraic expressions.

Formative Assessment

Use the Guided Practice exercises after each example to determine students' understanding of concepts.

Additional Examples

1 State the degree and leading coefficient of each polynomial in one variable. If it is not a polynomial in one variable, explain why.

a. $7z^3 - 4z^2 + z$ degree 3, leading coefficient 7

b. $6a^3 - 4a^2 + ab^2$ This is not a polynomial in one variable. It contains two variables, a and b.

c. $3x^5 + 2x^2 - 4 - 8x^6$ degree 6, leading coefficient –8

2 **RESPIRATION** Refer to the application at the beginning of the lesson. Find the volume of air in the lungs 1.5 seconds into the respiratory cycle. 0.4766 L

3 Find $b(2x - 1) - 3b(x)$ if $b(m) = 2m^2 + m - 1$. $2x^2 - 9x + 3$

Additional Examples also in Interactive Classroom PowerPoint® Presentations

IWB INTERACTIVE WHITEBOARD READY

Additional Answers (Guided Practice)

1A. Not a polynomial in one variable; $\frac{4}{x}$ has the variable with an exponent less than 0.

1B. degree = 6, leading coefficient = 5

1C. degree = 6, leading coefficient = –1

TEACH with TECH

DOCUMENT CAMERA Choose several students to show and explain to the class how to evaluate a polynomial function for a given value.

Watch Out!

Preventing Errors Point out that the leading coefficient is not always the coefficient of the first term of a polynomial.

Graphs of Polynomial Functions

Example 4 shows how to use the degree and leading coefficient of a polynomial function to describe the end behavior, determine whether it is an odd-degree or even-degree polynomial function, and determine the maximum number of times the graph of the function intersects the *x*-axis.

Tips for New Teachers

Extending the Concept Since the graphs on this page show the *maximum* number of times each type of graph may intersect the *x*-axis, some students may ask about the minimum number of times each graph type may intersect the *x*-axis. Have students work in pairs using the given graphs to discuss this issue. Lead students to see that, for functions of degree 1 the minimum is 1 (the same as the maximum), for functions of degree 2 the minimum is 0, for functions of degree 4 the minimum is 0, and for functions of degree 5 the minimum is 1. Some students may notice the pattern for functions with odd and even degrees.

Focus on Mathematical Content

Polynomial Function A polynomial function is a function whose rule is given by a polynomial in one variable. The leading term is the term with the variable that has the greatest exponent. The leading coefficient a_n is the coefficient of the leading term. The degree of the polynomial is the largest degree n of all of its terms.

Graphs of Polynomial Functions The general shapes of the graphs of several polynomial functions show the *maximum* number of times the graph of each function may intersect the *x*-axis. This is the same number as the degree of the polynomial.

Constant function
Degree 0

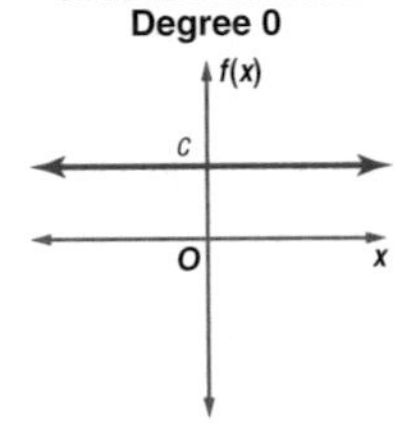

Linear function
Degree 1

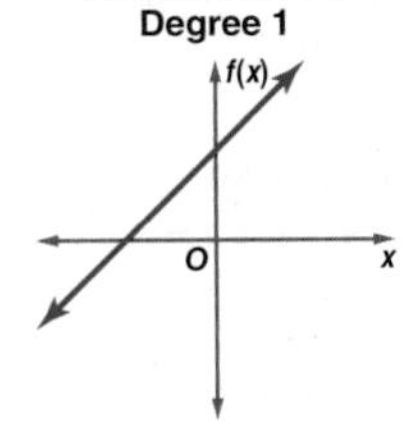

Quadratic function
Degree 2

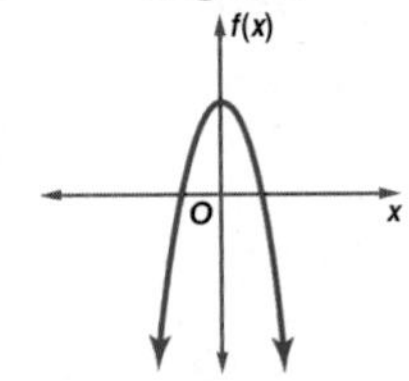

Cubic function
Degree 3

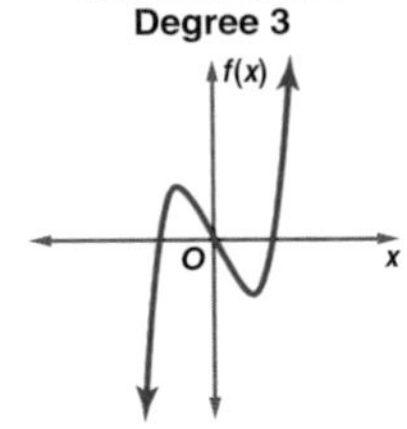

Quartic function
Degree 4

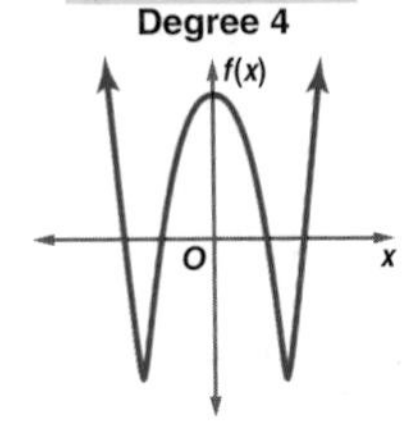

Quintic function
Degree 5

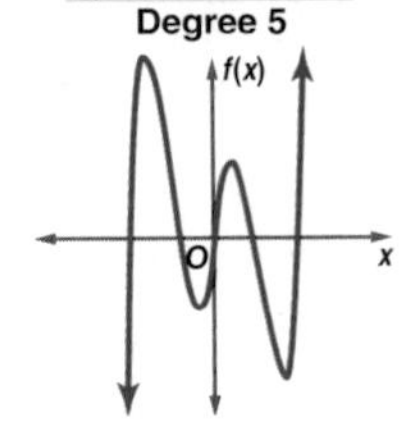

StudyTip

End behavior The leading coefficient and degree are the sole determining factors for the end behavior of a polynomial. With very large or very small numbers, the rest of the polynomial is insignificant in the appearance of the graph.

Review Vocabulary

infinity endless or boundless (Explore Lesson 1-6)

The domain of any polynomial function is all real numbers. The **end behavior** is the behavior of the graph of $f(x)$ as x approaches positive infinity ($x \to +\infty$) or negative infinity ($x \to -\infty$). The degree and leading coefficient of a polynomial function determine the end behavior of the graph and the range of the function.

Key Concept — End Behavior of a Polynomial Function

Degree: even
Leading Coefficient: positive
End Behavior:

$f(x) \to +\infty$
as $x \to -\infty$

$f(x) \to +\infty$
as $x \to +\infty$

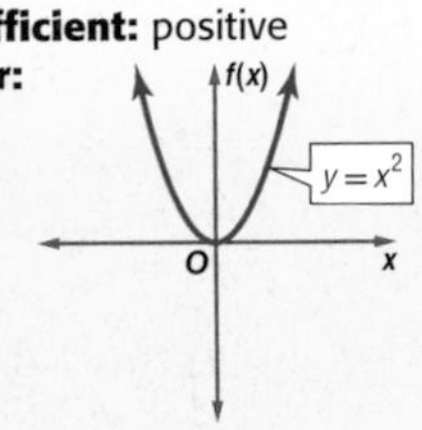

Domain: all reals
Range: all reals ≥ minimum

Degree: odd
Leading Coefficient: positive
End Behavior:

$f(x) \to -\infty$
as $x \to -\infty$

$f(x) \to +\infty$
as $x \to +\infty$

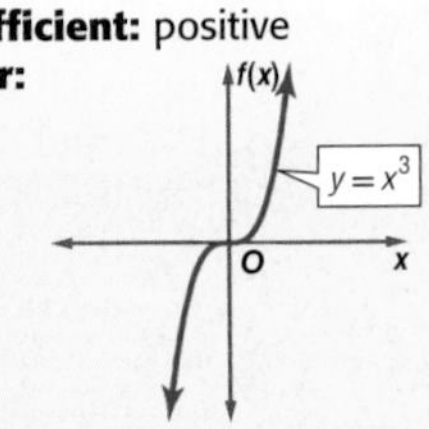

Domain: all reals
Range: all reals

Degree: even
Leading Coefficient: negative
End Behavior:

$f(x) \to -\infty$
as $x \to -\infty$

$f(x) \to -\infty$
as $x \to +\infty$

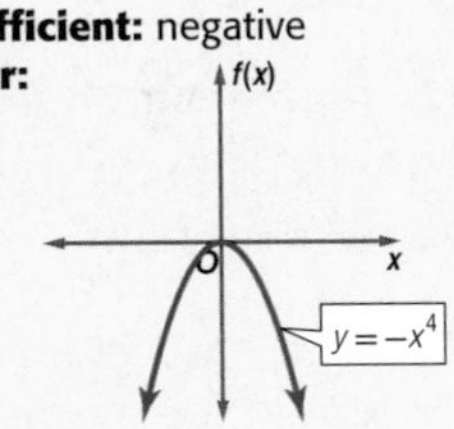

Domain: all reals
Range: all reals ≤ maximum

Degree: odd
Leading Coefficient: negative
End Behavior:

$f(x) \to +\infty$
as $x \to -\infty$

$f(x) \to -\infty$
as $x \to +\infty$

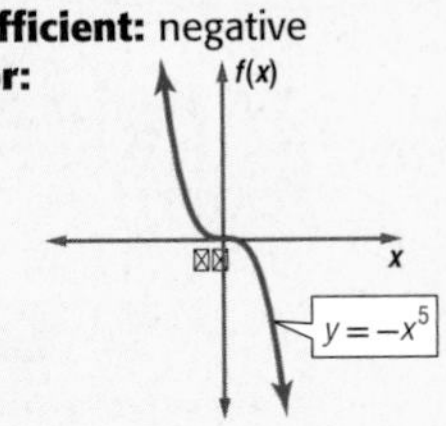

Domain: all reals
Range: all reals

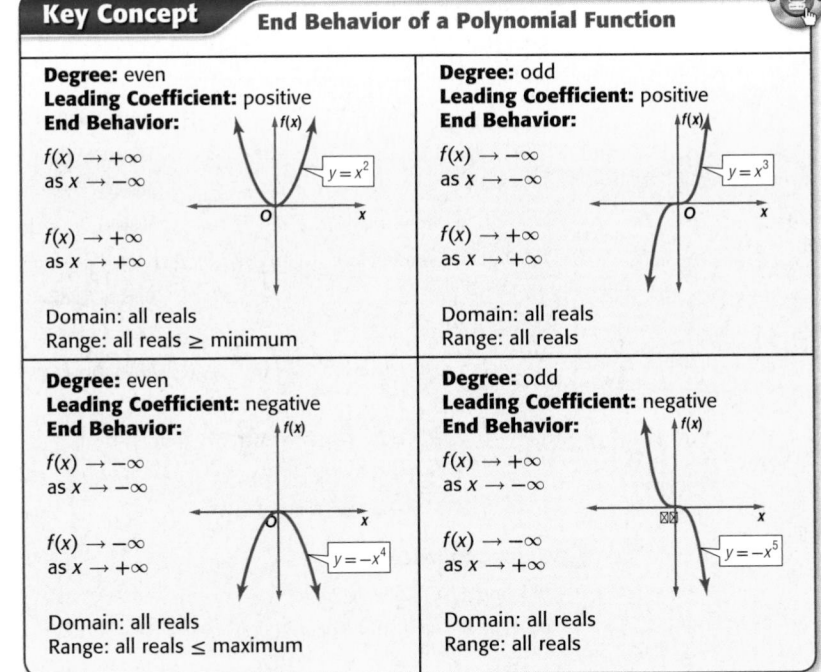

Differentiated Instruction AL OL

Logical Learners Power functions are single-term polynomials that can have any degree. Have students examine the graphs of a variety of power functions and describe their similarities and differences.

The number of real zeros of a polynomial equation can be determined from the graph of its related polynomial function. Recall that real zeros occur at x-intercepts, so the number of times a graph crosses the x-axis equals the number of real zeros.

StudyTip

Double roots When a graph is tangent to the x-axis, there is a *double root,* which represents two of the same root.

Key Concept — Zeros of Even- and Odd-Degree Functions

Odd-degree functions will always have an odd number of real zeros. Even-degree functions will always have an even number of real zeros or no real zeros at all.

Even-Degree Polynomials

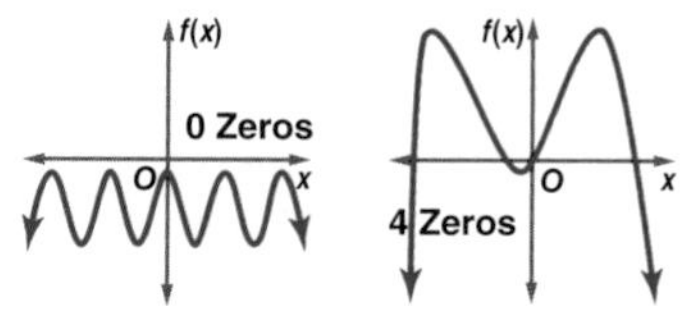

Odd-Degree Polynomials

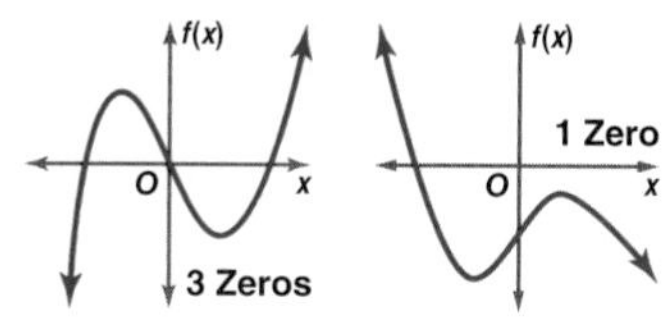

Review Vocabulary

zero the x-coordinate of the point at which a graph intersects the x-axis (Lesson 5-2)

EXAMPLE 4 Graphs of Polynomial Functions

For each graph,
- **describe the end behavior,**
- **determine whether it represents an odd-degree or an even-degree polynomial function, and**
- **state the number of real zeros.**

a.

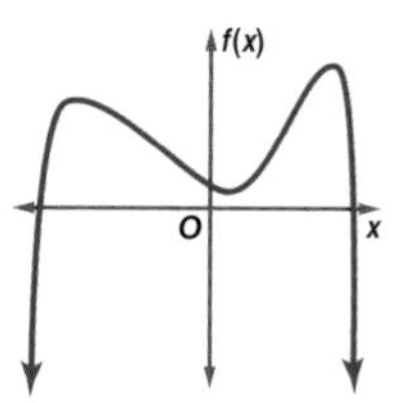

$f(x) \to -\infty$ as $x \to -\infty$.
$f(x) \to -\infty$ as $x \to +\infty$.

Since the end behavior is in the same direction, it is an even-degree function. The graph intersects the x-axis at two points, so there are two real zeros.

b.

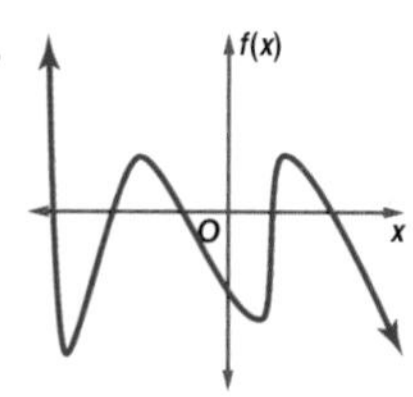

$f(x) \to +\infty$ as $x \to -\infty$.
$f(x) \to -\infty$ as $x \to +\infty$.

Since the end behavior is in opposite directions, it is an odd-degree function. The graph intersects the x-axis at five points, so there are five real zeros.

Guided Practice 4A, 4B. See margin.

4A.

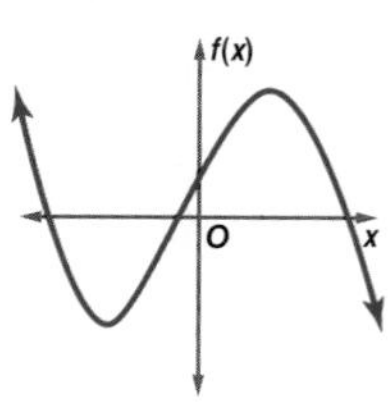

4B.

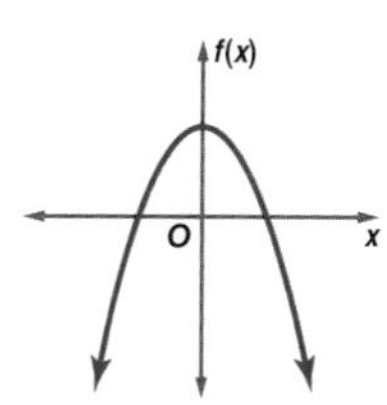

Personal Tutor glencoe.com

Additional Example

4 For each graph,
- describe the end behavior,
- determine whether it represents an odd-degree or an even-degree polynomial function, and
- state the number of real zeros.

a.

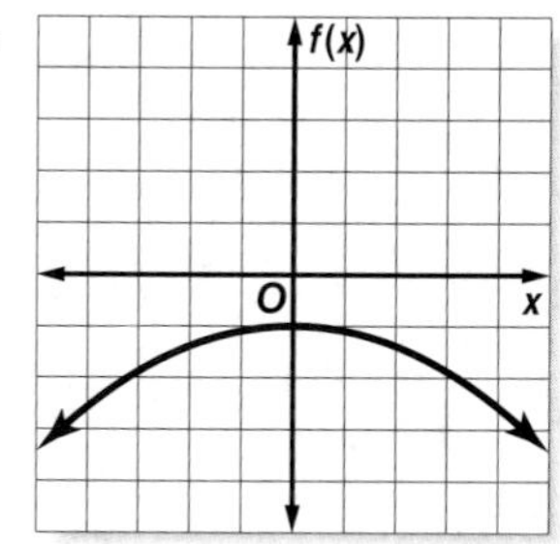

- $f(x) \to -\infty$ as $x \to +\infty$. $f(x) \to -\infty$ as $x \to -\infty$.
- It is an even-degree polynomial function.
- The graph does not intersect the x-axis, so the function has no real zeros.

b.

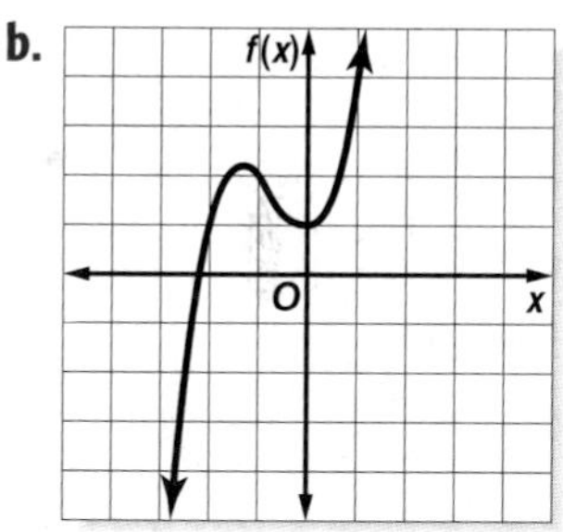

- $f(x) \to +\infty$ as $x \to +\infty$. $f(x) \to -\infty$ as $x \to -\infty$.
- It is an odd-degree polynomial function.
- The graph intersects the x-axis at one point, so the function has one real zero.

Additional Answers (Guided Practice)

4A. $f(x) \to +\infty$ as $x \to -\infty$. $f(x) \to -\infty$ as $x \to +\infty$. Since the end behavior is in opposite directions, it is an odd-degree function. The graph intersects the x-axis at three points, so there are three real zeros.

4B. $f(x) \to -\infty$ as $x \to -\infty$. $f(x) \to -\infty$ as $x \to +\infty$. Since the end behavior is in the same direction, it is an even-degree function. The graph intersects the x-axis at two points, so there are two real zeros.

3 PRACTICE

Formative Assessment

Use Exercises 1–12 to check for understanding.

Use the chart at the bottom of this page to customize assignments for your students.

Additional Answers

11a. $f(x) \to -\infty$ as $x \to -\infty$. $f(x) \to +\infty$ as $x \to +\infty$.

11b. Since the end behavior is in opposite directions, it is an odd-degree function.

11c. The graph intersects the x-axis at three points, so there are three real zeros.

12a. $f(x) \to -\infty$ as $x \to -\infty$. $f(x) \to -\infty$ as $x \to +\infty$.

12b. Since the end behavior is in the same direction, it is an even-degree function.

12c. The graph intersects the x-axis at zero points, so there are no real zeros.

13. not in one variable because there are two variables, x and y

14. not a polynomial because there is a negative exponent

15. degree = 6, leading coefficient = –12

16. degree = 7, leading coefficient = –21

17. degree = 4, leading coefficient = –5

18. degree = 5, leading coefficient = 3

19. degree = 2, leading coefficient = 3

20. degree = 2, leading coefficient = –6

21. degree = 9, leading coefficient = 2

22. degree = 8, leading coefficient = –2

23. $p(-6) = 1227$; $p(3) = 66$

24. $p(-6) = 546$; $p(3) = -93$

25. $p(-6) = -156$; $p(3) = 78$

26. $p(-6) = 2322$; $p(3) = 9$

27. $p(-6) = 319$; $p(3) = -5$

28. $p(-6) = 2232$; $p(3) = 153$

Check Your Understanding

Example 1 p. 348

State the degree and leading coefficient of each polynomial in one variable. If it is not a polynomial in one variable, explain why. 2. degree = 7, leading coefficient = –10

1. degree = 6, leading coefficient = 11

1. $11x^6 - 5x^5 + 4x^2$

2. $-10x^7 - 5x^3 + 4x - 22$

3. $14x^4 - 9x^3 + 3x - 4y$ not in one variable because there are two variables, x and y

4. $8x^5 - 3x^2 + 4xy - 5$ not in one variable because there are two variables, x and y

Example 2 p. 349

Find $w(5)$ and $w(-4)$ for each function.

5. $w(x) = -2x^3 + 3x - 12$ $w(5) = -247$; $w(-4) = 104$

6. $w(x) = 2x^4 - 5x^3 + 3x^2 - 2x + 8$ $w(5) = 698$; $w(-4) = 896$

Example 3 p. 349

If $c(x) = 4x^3 - 5x^2 + 2$ and $d(x) = 3x^2 + 6x - 10$, find each value.

7. $c(y^3)$ $4y^9 - 5y^6 + 2$

8. $-4[d(3z)]$ $-108z^2 - 72z + 40$

9. $6c(4a) + 2d(3a - 5)$ $1536a^3 - 426a^2 - 144a + 82$

10. $-3c(2b) + 6d(4b - 3)$ $-96b^3 + 348b^2 - 288b - 12$

Example 4 p. 351

For each graph,

a. describe the end behavior,

b. determine whether it represents an odd-degree or an even-degree function, and

c. state the number of real zeros. 11, 12. See margin.

11.

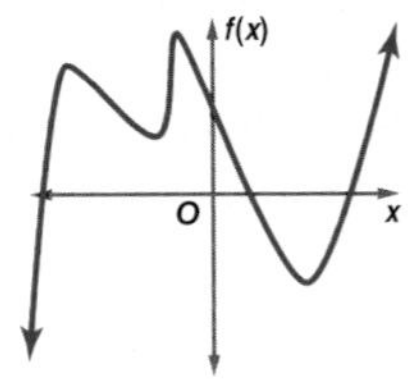

12.

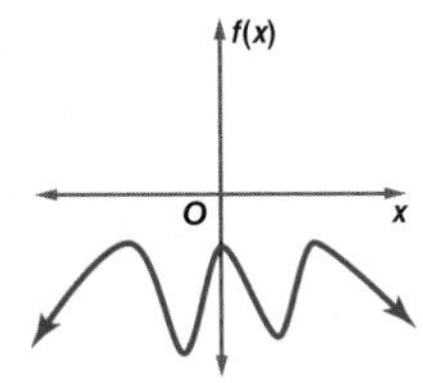

Practice and Problem Solving

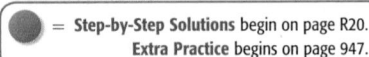

● = Step-by-Step Solutions begin on page R20. Extra Practice begins on page 947.

Example 1 p. 348

State the degree and leading coefficient of each polynomial in one variable. If it is not a polynomial in one variable, explain why. 13–22. See margin.

13. $-6x^6 - 4x^5 + 13xy$

14. $3a^7 - 4a^4 + \frac{3}{a}$

15. $8x^5 - 12x^6 + 14x^3 - 9$

16. $-12 - 8x^2 + 5x - 21x^7$

17. $15x - 4x^3 + 3x^2 - 5x^4$

18. $13b^3 - 9b + 3b^5 - 18$

19. $(d + 5)(3d - 4)$

20. $(5 - 2y)(4 + 3y)$

21. $6x^5 - 5x^4 + 2x^9 - 3x^2$

22. $7x^4 + 3x^7 - 2x^8 + 7$

Example 2 p. 349

Find $p(-6)$ and $p(3)$ for each function. 23–28. See margin.

23. $p(x) = x^4 - 2x^2 + 3$

24. $p(x) = -3x^3 - 2x^2 + 4x - 6$

25. $p(x) = 2x^3 + 6x^2 - 10x$

26. $p(x) = x^4 - 4x^3 + 3x^2 - 5x + 24$

27. $p(x) = -x^3 + 3x^2 - 5$

28. $p(x) = 2x^4 + x^3 - 4x^2$

Example 3 p. 349

If $c(x) = 2x^2 - 4x + 3$ and $d(x) = -x^3 + x + 1$, find each value.

29. $c(3a)$ $18a^2 - 12a + 3$

30. $5d(2a)$ $-40a^3 + 10a + 5$

31. $c(b^2)$ $2b^4 - 4b^2 + 3$

32. $d(4a^2)$ $-64a^6 + 4a^2 + 1$

33. $d(4y - 3)$ $-64y^3 + 144y^2 - 104y + 25$

34. $c(y^2 - 1)$ $2y^4 - 8y^2 + 9$

Differentiated Homework Options

Level	Assignment	Two-Day Option	
AL Basic	13–42, 63, 66–85	13–41 odd, 69–72	14–42 even, 63, 66–68, 73–85
OL Core	13–41 odd, 43–55 odd, 56–63, 66–85	13–42, 69–72	55, 56, 63, 66–68, 73–85
BL Advanced	43–82, (optional: 83–85)		

352 Chapter 6 Polynomials and Polynomial Functions

Example 4
p. 351

For each graph,

a. describe the end behavior,

b. determine whether it represents an odd-degree or an even-degree function, and

c. state the number of real zeros. **35–40. See Chapter 6 Answer Appendix.**

35.
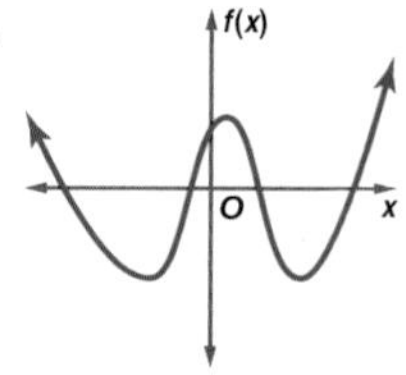

36.
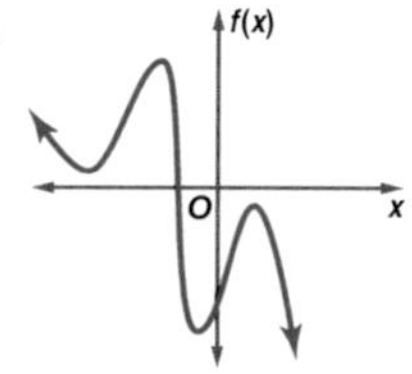

37.
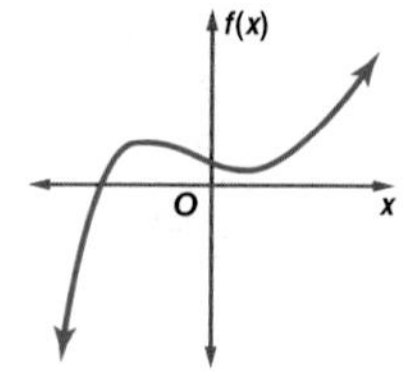

38.
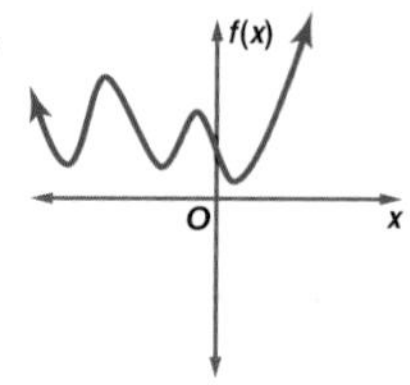

39.
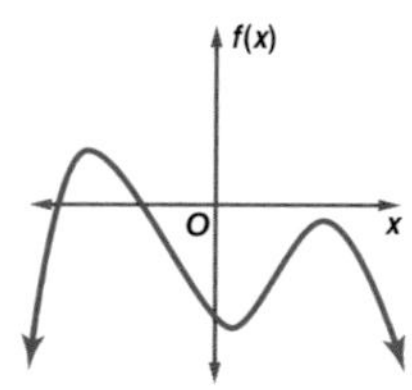

40.
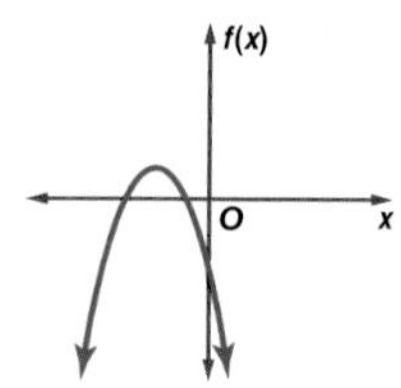

Real-World Link

In 1947, the first commercial microwave oven hit the market. These early units were gigantic and enormously expensive, standing $5\frac{1}{2}$ feet tall, weighing over 750 pounds, and costing about $5000 each.

Source: Microtech

41. **PHYSICS** For a moving object with mass m in kilograms, the kinetic energy KE in joules is given by the function $KE(v) = 0.5mv^2$, where v represents the speed of the object in meters per second. Find the kinetic energy of an all-terrain vehicle with a mass of 171 kilograms moving at a speed of 11 meters/second. **10,345.5 joules**

42. **BUSINESS** A microwave manufacturing firm has determined that their profit function is $P(x) = -0.0014x^3 + 0.3x^2 + 6x - 355$, where x is the number of microwaves sold annually.

a. Graph the profit function using a calculator. **See margin.**

b. Determine a reasonable viewing window for the function.

c. Approximate all of the zeros of the function using the CALC menu.

d. What must be the range of microwaves sold in order for the firm to have a profit?

42b. Sample answer: [−500, 500], scl: 50 by [−10,000, 10,000], scl: 1000

42c. −41.0, 27.1, 228.2

42d. 28 to 228 microwaves

44. $p(-2) = -28$; $p(8) = -178$

45. $p(-2) = -0.5$; $p(8) = 3112$

46. $p(-2) = 1.5$; $p(8) = 304$

B Find $p(-2)$ and $p(8)$ for each function. **43. $p(-2) = -16$; $p(8) = 1024$**

43. $p(x) = \frac{1}{4}x^4 + \frac{1}{2}x^3 - 4x^2$

44. $p(x) = \frac{1}{8}x^4 - \frac{3}{2}x^3 + 12x - 18$

45. $p(x) = \frac{3}{4}x^4 - \frac{1}{8}x^2 + 6x$

46. $p(x) = \frac{5}{8}x^3 - \frac{1}{2}x^2 + \frac{3}{4}x + 10$

Use the degree and end behavior to match each polynomial to its graph.

A
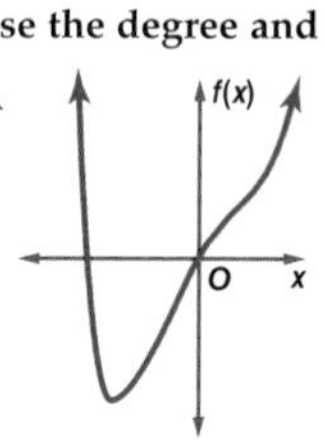

B
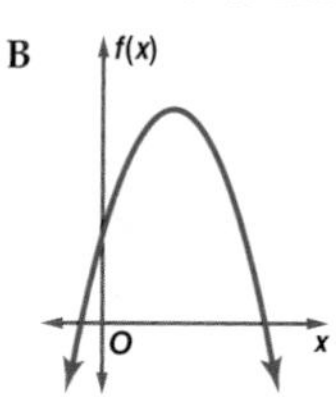

C
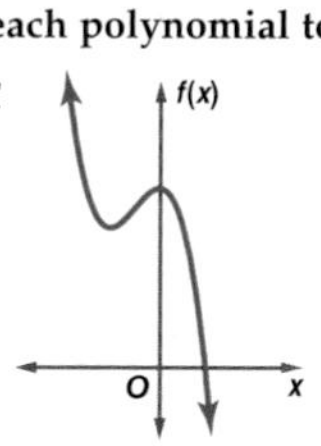

D
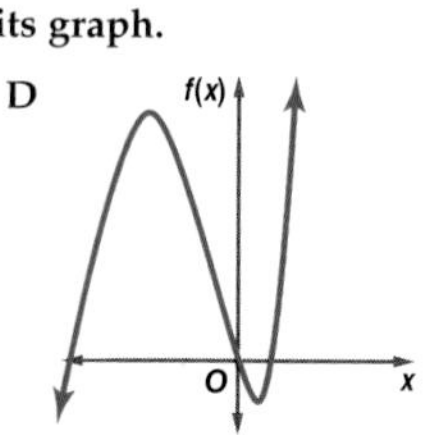

47. $f(x) = x^3 + 3x^2 - 4x$ **D**

48. $f(x) = -2x^2 + 8x + 5$ **B**

49. $f(x) = x^4 - 3x^2 + 6x$ **A**

50. $f(x) = -4x^3 - 4x^2 + 8$ **C**

If $c(x) = x^3 - 2x$ and $d(x) = 4x^2 - 6x + 8$, find each value.

51. $3a^3 - 24a^2 + 240a + 66$

52. $-4a^6 - 12a^4 - 36a^2 - 72a - 48$

51. $3c(a - 4) + 3d(a + 5)$

52. $-2d(2a + 3) - 4c(a^2 + 1)$

53. $5c(a^2) - 8d(6 - 3a)$
$5a^6 - 298a^2 + 1008a - 928$

54. $-7d(a^3) + 6c(a^4 + 1)$
$6a^{12} + 18a^8 - 28a^6 + 6a^4 + 42a^3 - 62$

Additional Answers

42a.

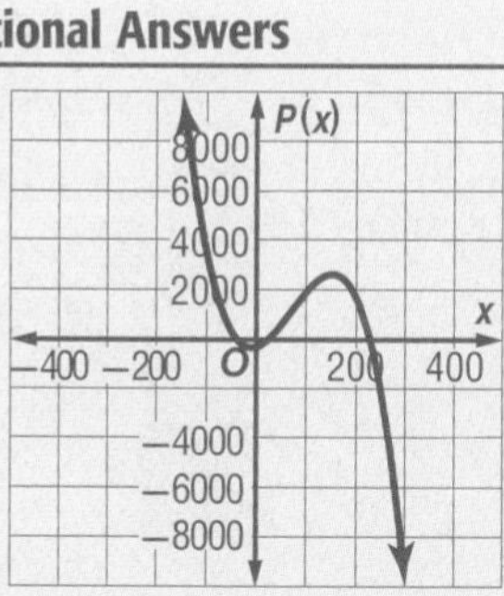

Enrichment
CRM p. 22 OL BL

6-3 Enrichment

Approximation by Means of Polynomials

Many scientific experiments produce pairs of numbers $[x, f(x)]$ that can be related by a formula. If the pairs form a function, you can fit a polynomial to the pairs in exactly one way. Consider the pairs given by the following table.

x	1	2	4	7
f(x)	6	11	39	−54

We will assume the polynomial is of degree three. Substitute the given values into this expression.

$f(x) = A + B(x - x_0) + C(x - x_0)(x - x_1) + D(x - x_0)(x - x_1)(x - x_2)$

You will get the system of equations shown below. You can solve this system and use the values for A, B, C, and D to find the desired polynomial.

$6 = A$
$11 = A + B(2 - 1) = A + B$
$39 = A + B(4 - 1) + C(4 - 1)(4 - 2) = A + 3B + 6C$
$-54 = A + B(7 - 1) + C(7 - 1)(7 - 2) + D(7 - 1)(7 - 2)(7 - 4) = A + 6B + 30C + 90D$

Solve.

Study Guide and Intervention
CRM pp. 17–18 AL OL BL

6-3 Study Guide and Intervention

Polynomial Functions

Polynomial Functions

Polynomial in One Variable	A polynomial of degree n in one variable x is an expression of the form $a_nx^n + a_{n-1}x^{n-1} + \ldots + a_2x^2 + a_1x + a_0$, where the coefficients $a_{n-1}, a_{n-2}, a_{n-3}, \ldots, a_0$ represent real numbers, a_n is not zero, and n represents a nonnegative integer.

The **degree of a polynomial** in one variable is the greatest exponent of its variable. The **leading coefficient** is the coefficient of the term with the highest degree.

Polynomial Function	A polynomial function of degree n can be described by an equation of the form $P(x) = a_nx^n + a_{n-1}x^{n-1} + \ldots + a_2x^2 + a_1x + a_0$, where the coefficients $a_{n-1}, a_{n-2}, a_{n-3}, \ldots, a_0$ represent real numbers, a_n is not zero, and n represents a nonnegative integer.

Example 1 What are the degree and leading coefficient of $3x^2 - 2x^4 - 7 + x^3$?

Rewrite the expression so the powers of x are in decreasing order.

$-2x^4 + x^3 + 3x^2 - 7$

This is a polynomial in one variable. The degree is 4, and the leading coefficient is −2.

Example 2 Find $f(-5)$ if $f(x) = x^3 + 2x^2 - 10x + 20$.

$f(x) = x^3 + 2x^2 - 10x + 20$ Original function
$f(-5) = (-5)^3 + 2(-5)^2 - 10(-5) + 20$ Replace x with −5.
$= -125 + 50 + 50 + 20$ Evaluate.
$= -5$ Simplify.

Example 3 Find $g(a^2 - 1)$ if $g(x) = x^2 + 3x - 4$.

$g(x) = x^2 + 3x - 4$ Original function
$g(a^2 - 1) = (a^2 - 1)^2 + 3(a^2 - 1) - 4$ Replace x with $a^2 - 1$.
$= a^4 - 2a^2 + 1 + 3a^2 - 3 - 4$ Evaluate.
$= a^4 + a^2 - 6$ Simplify.

Exercises

State the degree and leading coefficient of each polynomial in one variable. If it is not a polynomial in one variable, explain why.

1. $3x^4 + 6x^3 - x^2 + 12$ **4; 3**
2. $100 - 5x^3 + 10x^7$ **7; 10**
3. $4x^6 + 6x^4 + 8x^8 - 10x^2 + 20$ **8; 8**
4. $4x^2 - 3xy + 16y^2$ **not a polynomial in one variable; contains two variables**
5. $8x^3 - 9x^5 + 4x^2 - 36$ **5; −9**
6. $\frac{x^2}{18} - \frac{x^6}{25} + \frac{x^3}{36} - \frac{1}{72}$ **6; $-\frac{1}{25}$**

Find $f(2)$ and $f(-5)$ for each function.

7. $f(x) = x^2 - 9$ **−5; 16**
8. $f(x) = 4x^3 - 3x^2 + 2x - 1$ **23; −586**
9. $f(x) = 9x^3 - 4x^2 + 5x + 7$ **73; −1243**

Chapter 6 17 Glencoe Algebra 2

Lesson 6-3

Practice
CRM p. 20 AL OL BL ELL

6-3 Practice

Polynomial Functions

State the degree and leading coefficient of each polynomial in one variable. If it is not a polynomial in one variable, explain why.

1. $(3x^2 + 1)(2x^2 - 9)$ **4; 6**
2. $\frac{1}{5}a^3 - \frac{3}{5}a^2 + \frac{4}{5}a$ **3; $\frac{1}{5}$**
3. $\frac{2}{m^2} + 3m - 12$ **Not a polynomial; $\frac{2}{m^2}$ cannot be written in the form m^n for a nonnegative integer n.**
4. $27 + 3xy^3 - 12x^2y^2 - 10y$ **No, this polynomial contains two variables, x and y.**

Find $p(-2)$ and $p(3)$ for each function.

5. $p(x) = x^3 - x^5$ **24; −216**
6. $p(x) = -7x^2 + 5x + 9$ **−29; −39**
7. $p(x) = -x^5 + 4x^3$ **0; −135**
8. $p(x) = 3x^3 - x^2 + 2x - 5$ **−37; 73**
9. $p(x) = x^4 + \frac{1}{2}x^3 - \frac{1}{2}x$ **13; 93**
10. $p(x) = \frac{1}{3x^3} + \frac{2}{3x^2} + 3x$ **−6; 24**

If $p(x) = 3x^2 - 4$ and $r(x) = 2x^2 - 5x + 1$, find each value.

11. $p(8a)$ **$192a^2 - 4$**
12. $r(a^2)$ **$2a^4 - 5a^2 + 1$**
13. $-5r(2a)$ **$-40a^2 + 50a - 5$**
14. $r(x + 2)$ **$2x^2 + 3x - 1$**
15. $p(x^2 - 1)$ **$3x^4 - 6x^2 - 1$**
16. $5[p(x + 2)]$ **$15x^2 + 60x + 40$**

For each graph,
a. describe the end behavior,
b. determine whether it represents an odd-degree or an even-degree function, and
c. state the number of real zeroes.

17.
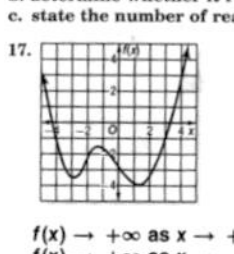

$f(x) \to +\infty$ as $x \to +\infty$, $f(x) \to +\infty$ as $x \to -\infty$; even; 2

18.
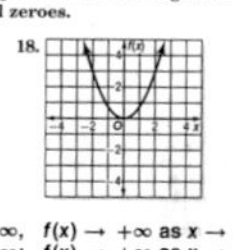

$f(x) \to +\infty$ as $x \to +\infty$, $f(x) \to +\infty$ as $x \to -\infty$; even; 1

19.
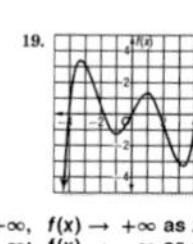

$f(x) \to +\infty$ as $x \to +\infty$, $f(x) \to -\infty$ as $x \to -\infty$; odd; 5

20. **WIND CHILL** The function $C(w) = 0.013w^2 - w - 7$ estimates the wind chill temperature $C(w)$ at 0°F for wind speeds w from 5 to 30 miles per hour. Estimate the wind chill temperature at 0°F if the wind speed is 20 miles per hour. **about −22°F**

Chapter 6 20 Glencoe Algebra 2

Word Problem Practice
CRM p. 21 AL OL BL ELL

6-3 Word Problem Practice

Polynomial Functions

1. **MANUFACTURING** A metal sheet is curved according to the shape of the graph of $f(x) = x^4 - 9x^2$. What is the degree of this polynomial?
4

2. **GRAPHS** Kendra graphed the polynomial $f(x)$ shown below.

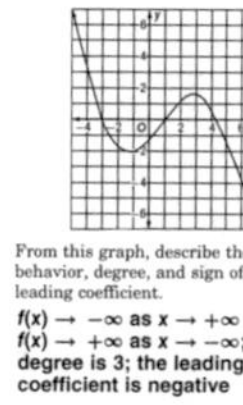

From this graph, describe the end behavior, degree, and sign of the leading coefficient.
$f(x) \to -\infty$ as $x \to +\infty$ and $f(x) \to +\infty$ as $x \to -\infty$; the degree is 3; the leading coefficient is negative

3. **PENTAGONAL NUMBERS** The nth pentagonal number is given by the expression

$$\frac{n(3n - 1)}{2}.$$

What is the degree of this polynomial? What is the seventh pentagonal number?
2; 70

4. **DRILLING** The volume of a drill bit can be estimated by the formula for a cone, $V = \frac{1}{3}\pi hr^2$, where h is the height of the bit and r is its radius. Substituting $\frac{\sqrt{3}}{3}r$ for h, the volume of the drill bit is estimated as $\frac{\sqrt{3}}{9}\pi r^3$. Graph the function of drill bit volume. Describe the end behavior, degree, and sign of the leading coefficient.

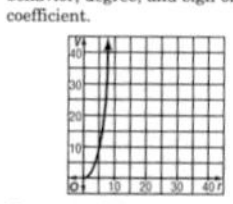

V approaches $+\infty$ as r approaches $+\infty$; degree = 3; sign of the leading coefficient is positive

5. **TRIANGLES** Dylan drew n dots on a piece of paper making sure that no line contained 3 of the dots. The number of triangles that can be made using the dots as vertices is equal to $f(n) = \frac{1}{6}(n^3 - 3n^2 + 2n)$.

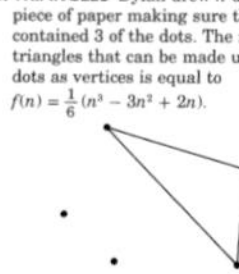

a. What is the degree of f?
3

b. If Dylan drew 15 dots, how many triangles can be made?
455

Chapter 6 21 Glencoe Algebra 2

Lesson 6-3

Multiple Representations In Exercise 56, students use analysis, algebra, a table of values, and a graph to represent a higher-order function.

Watch Out!

Error Analysis In Exercise 63, point out that "double root" does not mean there are two different solutions to an equation, only that there are two identical factors in the solution process.

Additional Answers

55a.

x	$p(x)$
−7	−585
−6	0
−4	240
−3	135
−2	0
0	−144
1	−105
2	0
4	240
6	0
7	−585

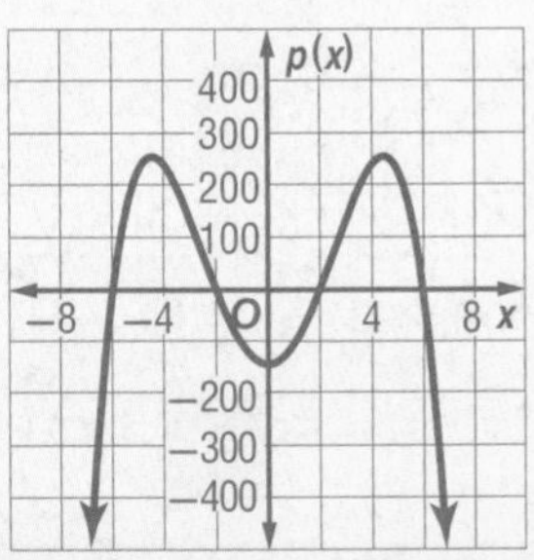

55d. Sample answer: The negative values should not be considered because the company will not produce negative items.

66.

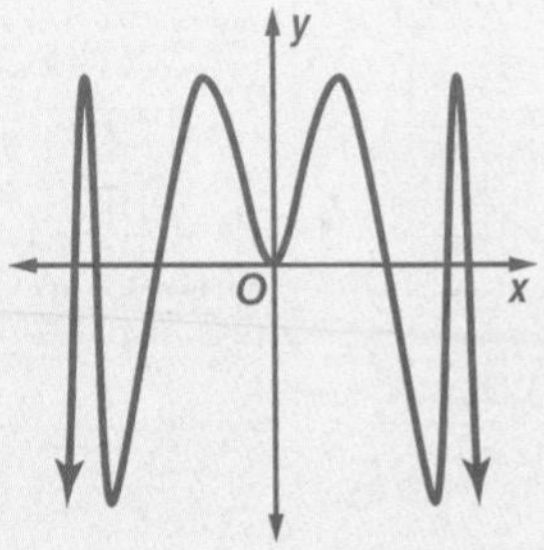

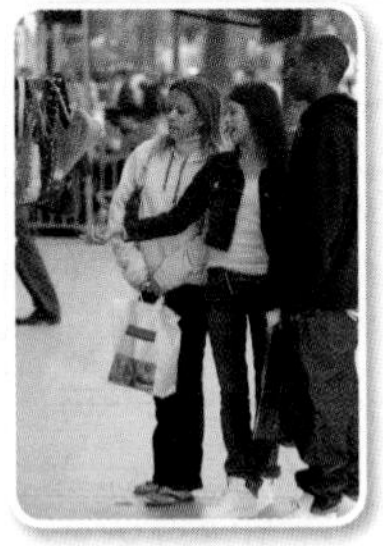

Real-World Link

Teens are important customers to clothing makers. Clothing tops the lists of both what teens plan to buy and what they actually purchase.

Source: NOPWorld

57. $f(x) \to -\infty$ as $x \to -\infty$; $f(x) \to -\infty$ as $x \to +\infty$
58. $g(x) \to -\infty$ as $x \to -\infty$; $g(x) \to +\infty$ as $x \to +\infty$
59. $h(x) \to +\infty$ as $x \to -\infty$; $h(x) \to -\infty$ as $x \to +\infty$
60. $f(x) \to -\infty$ as $x \to -\infty$; $f(x) \to -\infty$ as $x \to +\infty$
61. $g(x) \to -\infty$ as $x \to -\infty$; $g(x) \to +\infty$ as $x \to +\infty$
62. $h(x) \to +\infty$ as $x \to -\infty$; $h(x) \to -\infty$ as $x \to +\infty$
63. Sample answer: Virginia is correct; an even function will have an even number of zeros and the double root represents 2 zeros.
65. Sample answer: $f(x) \to +\infty$ as $x \to -\infty$; $f(x) \to +\infty$ as $x \to +\infty$; $\frac{f(x)}{g(x)}$ will become a 2-degree function with a positive leading coefficient.

55. BUSINESS A clothing manufacturer's profitability can be modeled by $p(x) = -x^4 + 40x^2 - 144$, where x is the number of items sold in thousands and $p(x)$ is the company's profit in thousands of dollars. **c. 2000 and 6000 items**

a. Use a table of values to sketch the function. **See margin.**

b. Determine the zeros of the function. **−6, −2, 2, 6**

c. Between what two values should the company sell in order to be profitable?

d. Explain why only two of the zeros are considered in part c. **See margin.**

56. MULTIPLE REPRESENTATIONS Consider $g(x) = (x - 2)(x + 1)(x - 3)(x + 4)$.

a. **ANALYTICAL** Determine the x- and y-intercepts, roots, degree, and end behavior of $g(x)$. **See Chapter 6 Answer Appendix.**

b. **ALGEBRAIC** Write the function in standard form **$g(x) = x^4 - 15x^2 + 10x + 24$**

c. **TABULAR** Make a table of values for the function. **See Chapter 6 Answer Appendix.**

d. **GRAPHICAL** Sketch a graph of the function by plotting points and connecting them with a smooth curve. **See Chapter 6 Answer Appendix.**

Describe the end behavior of the graph of each function.

57. $f(x) = -5x^4 + 3x^2$ **58.** $g(x) = 2x^5 + 6x^4$ **59.** $h(x) = -4x^7 + 8x^6 - 4x$

60. $f(x) = 6x - 7x^2$ **61.** $g(x) = 8x^4 + 5x^5$ **62.** $h(x) = 9x^6 - 5x^7 + 3x^2$

H.O.T. Problems Use Higher-Order Thinking Skills

63. ERROR ANALYSIS Shenequa and Virginia are determining the number of zeros of the graph at the right. Is either of them correct? Explain your reasoning.

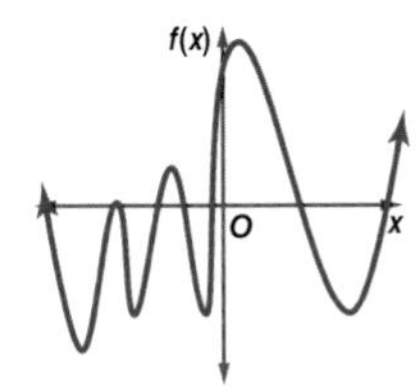

Shenequa	Virginia
There are 7 zeros because the graph crosses the x-axis 7 times.	There are 8 zeros because the graph crosses the x-axis 7 times, and there is a double root.

64. CHALLENGE Use the table to determine the minimum number of real roots and the minimum degree of the polynomial function $f(x)$. **5 roots and degree of 5**

x	−24	−18	−12	−6	0	6	12	18	24
$f(x)$	−8	−1	3	−2	4	7	−1	−8	5

65. CHALLENGE If $f(x)$ has a degree of 5 and a positive leading coefficient and $g(x)$ has a degree of 3 and a positive leading coefficient, determine the end behavior of $\frac{f(x)}{g(x)}$. Explain your reasoning.

66. OPEN ENDED Sketch the graph of an even-degree polynomial with 8 real roots, one of them a double root. **See margin.**

67. REASONING Determine whether the following statement is *always*, *sometimes*, or *never* true. Explain. **See margin.**

A polynomial function that has four real roots is a fourth-degree polynomial.

68. WRITING IN MATH Describe what the end behavior of a polynomial function is and how to determine it. **See margin.**

67. Sometimes; a polynomial function with four real roots may be a sixth-degree polynomial function with two imaginary roots. A polynomial function that has four real roots is at least a fourth-degree polynomial.

68. Sample answer: The end behavior of a polynomial function is what the graph does as the input value approaches negative and positive infinity. It can be determined by the leading coefficient and the degree of the polynomial.

NGSSS PRACTICE 912.A.4.1, 912.A.4.4, 912.A.3.15, 912.A.1.6

69. THINK SOLVE EXPLAIN **SHORT RESPONSE** Four students solved the same math problem. Each student's work is shown below. Who is correct? **Student A**

Student A	Student C
$x^2x^{-5} = \frac{x^2}{x^5}$	$x^2x^{-5} = \frac{x^2}{x^{-5}}$
$= \frac{1}{x^3}, x \neq 0$	$= x^7, x \neq 0$

Student B	Student D
$x^2x^{-5} = \frac{x^2}{x^{-5}}$	$x^2x^{-5} = \frac{x^2}{x^5}$
$= x^{-7}, x \neq 0$	$= x^3, x \neq 0$

70. SAT/ACT What is the remainder when $x^3 - 7x + 5$ is divided by $x + 3$? **B**

A. −11
B. −1
C. 1
D. 11

71. THINK SOLVE EXPLAIN **EXTENDED RESPONSE** A company manufactures tables and chairs. It costs $40 to make each table and $25 to make each chair. There is $1440 available to spend on manufacturing each week. Let t = the number of tables produced and c = the number of chairs produced. **See margin.**

a. The manufacturing equation is $40t + 25c = 1500$. Construct a graph of this equation.
b. The company always produces two chairs with each table. Write and graph an equation to represent this situation on the same graph as the one in part **a**.
c. Determine the number of tables and chairs that the company can produce each week.
d. Explain how to determine this answer using the graph.

72. If $i = \sqrt{-1}$, then $5i(7i) =$ **H**

F. 70
G. 35
H. −35
I. −70

Spiral Review

Simplify. (Lesson 6-2) **73.** $2x^2y^2 + 4x^4y^4z^2$ **74.** $3b^3c^3 - 5a^3b^2 + 2a^4c$ **75.** $6c^3 - 1 + 4a^5cd^2$

73. $\frac{16x^4y^3 + 32x^6y^5z^2}{8x^2y}$ **74.** $\frac{18ab^4c^5 - 30a^4b^3c^2 + 12a^5bc^3}{6abc^2}$ **75.** $\frac{18c^5d^2 - 3c^2d^2 + 12a^5c^3d^4}{3c^2d^2}$

Determine whether each expression is a polynomial. If it is a polynomial, state the degree of the polynomial. (Lesson 6-1)

76. $8x^2 + 5xy^3 - 6x + 4$ **yes; 4** **77.** $9x^4 + 12x^6 - 16$ **yes; 6** **78.** $3x^4 + 2x^2 - x^{-1}$ **not a polynomial**

79. FOUNTAINS The height of a fountain's water stream can be modeled by a quadratic function. Suppose the water from a jet reaches a maximum height of 8 feet at a distance 1 foot away from the jet. (Lesson 5-7) **a, b. See margin.**

a. If the water lands 3 feet away from the jet, find a quadratic function that models the height $h(d)$ of the water at any given distance d feet from the jet. Then compare the graph of the function to the parent function.
b. Suppose a worker increases the water pressure so that the stream reaches a maximum height of 12.5 feet at a distance of 15 inches from the jet. The water now lands 3.75 feet from the jet. Write a new quadratic function for $h(d)$. How do the changes in h and k affect the shape of the graph?

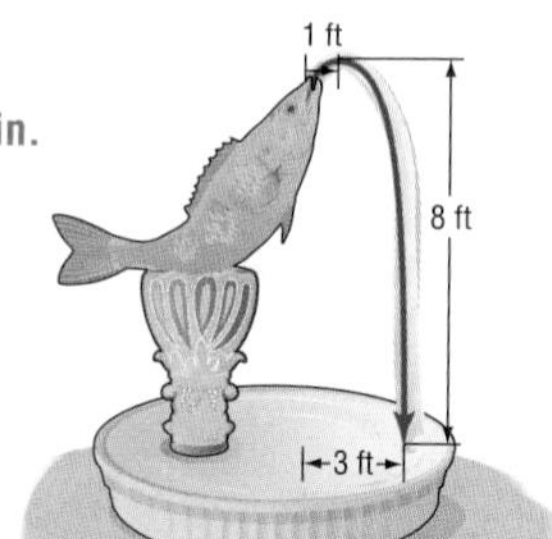

Solve each inequality. (Lesson 1-6)

80. $|2x + 4| \leq 8$ $-6 \leq x \leq 2$ **81.** $|-3x + 2| \geq 4$ $x \leq -\frac{2}{3}$ or $x \geq 2$ **82.** $|2x - 8| - 4 \leq -6$ **no solution**

Skills Review

83. minimum; $-\frac{4}{3}$

Determine whether each function has a maximum or minimum value, and find that value. (Lesson 5-1)

83. $f(x) = 3x^2 - 8x + 4$ **84.** $f(x) = -4x^2 + 2x - 10$ **maximum; −0.75** **85.** $f(x) = -0.25x^2 + 4x - 5$ **maximum; 11**

Differentiated Instruction BL

Extension Explain to students that functions can have symmetry with respect to the origin or to the y-axis. An even function is a function for which $f(x) = f(-x)$. Even functions are symmetrical with respect to the y-axis. An example of an even function is $f(x) = x^2$. An odd function is a function for which $f(x) = -f(-x)$. Odd functions are symmetrical with respect to the origin. An example of an odd function is $f(x) = x$. Ask students to determine if $f(x) = x^3 - 5x$ and $f(x) = x^4 - 3x^2$ are even or odd functions. odd, even Ask students if it is possible for a function to have symmetry across the x-axis. No. Except for the equation $y = 0$, equations that produce such graphs are not functions.

4 ASSESS

Ticket Out the Door Make several copies of five different polynomial functions. Give one function to each student. As students leave the room, ask them to tell you the values of the functions for a given numerical value, variable, or algebraic expression.

Additional Answers

71a.

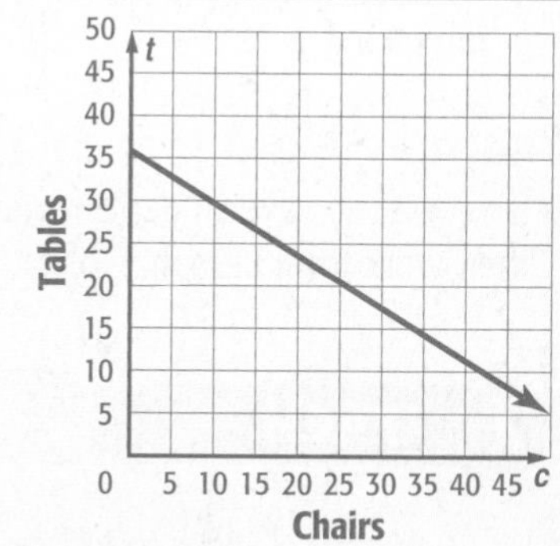

71b. $t = 0.5c$;

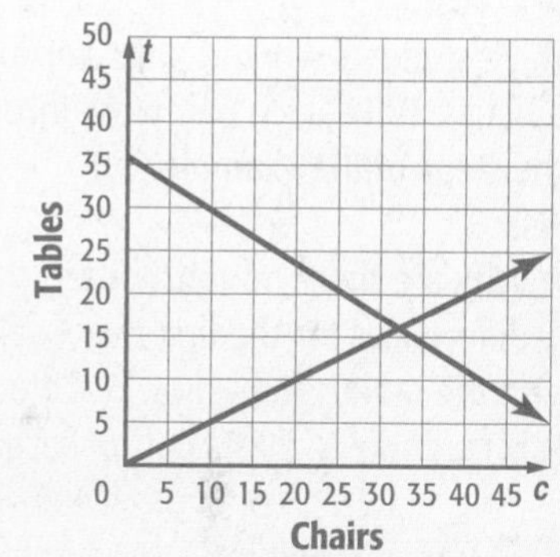

71c. 16 tables and 32 chairs

71d. Sample answer: This can be determined by the intersection of the graphs. This point of intersection is the optimal amount of tables and chairs manufactured.

79a. $h(d) = -2d^2 + 4d + 6$; The graph opens downward and is narrower than the parent graph, and the vertex is at (1, 8).

79b. $h(d) = -2(d - 1.25)^2 + 12.5$; It shifted the graph to the right 4.5 ft and up 3 in.

EXTEND 6-3 Lesson Notes

1 FOCUS

Objective Examine the differences for polynomial functions with degree greater than 2.

Materials for Each Student

- graph paper

Teaching Tip

- If necessary, have students review their work from Lesson 5-7B.

2 TEACH

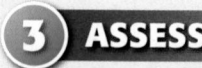

Working in Cooperative Groups

Have students work in pairs, mixing abilities. Have each pair work through the steps of the example.

Ask:

- Why are there no third-order differences for the first two x-values in the table? A third-order difference is computed from a pair of second-order differences, which is not available in the first two columns.
- What does the sign of a second-order difference tell you about the graph of a function? Sample answer: Whether the slope is increasing or decreasing.

Practice Have students complete Exercises 1–3.

3 ASSESS

Formative Assessment

Use Exercise 1 to assess whether students can identify the degree of a polynomial function by noticing where nth-order differences become constant.

EXTEND 6-3 Algebra Lab: Polynomial Functions and Rate of Change

NGSSS **MA.912.A.4.5** Graph polynomial functions with and without technology and describe end behavior.

In Chapter 2, you learned that linear functions have a constant first-order difference. Then in Chapter 5, you learned that quadratic functions have a constant second-order difference. Now, you will examine the differences for polynomial functions with degree greater than 2.

ACTIVITY

Consider $f(x) = -2x^3$. Steps 1–5. See Chapter 6 Answer Appendix.

Step 1 Copy the table and complete row 2 for x-values from -4 through 4.

x	-4	-3	-2	-1	...	4
y						
First-order Differences						
Second-order Differences						
Third-order Differences						

Step 2 Graph the ordered pairs (x, y) and connect the points with a smooth curve.

Step 3 Find the first-order differences and complete row 3. Describe any patterns in the differences.

Step 4 Complete rows 4 and 5 by finding the second- and third-order differences. Describe any patterns in the differences. Make a conjecture about the differences for a third-degree polynomial function.

Step 5 Repeat Steps 1 through 4 using a fourth-degree polynomial function. Make a conjecture about the differences for an nth-degree polynomial function.

Exercises

State the degree of each polynomial function described.

1. constant second-order difference of -3 2
2. constant fifth-order difference of 12 5
3. constant first-order difference of -1.25 1
4. **CHALLENGE** Write an equation for a polynomial function with real-number coefficients for the ordered pairs and differences in the table. Make sure your equation is satisfied for all of the ordered pairs (x, y). $y = x^3 + 2$

x	-3	-2	-1	0	1	2	3
y	-25	?	?	?	?	?	?
First-order Differences		19	7	1	1	7	19
Second-order Differences			-12	-6	0	6	12

From Concrete to Abstract

Use Exercise 4 to see if students can construct a function from its first- and second-order differences.

Extending the Concept

Ask:

- What can you say about second-order differences near a maximum point on the graph of a function? They are negative.

Analyzing Graphs of Polynomial Functions

Then

You used maxima and minima and graphs of polynomials. (Lessons 5-1 and 6-3)

Now

- Graph polynomial functions and locate their zeros.
- Find the relative maxima and minima of polynomial functions.

NGSSS

MA.912.A.2.6 Identify and graph common functions (including but not limited to linear, rational, **quadratic**, cubic, radical, absolute value).
MA.912.A.4.5 Graph polynomial functions with and without technology and describe end behavior.

New Vocabulary

relative maximum
relative minimum
extrema
turning points

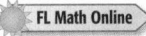

FL Math Online

glencoe.com

Why?

Annual attendance at the movies has fluctuated since the first movie theater, the Nickelodeon, opened in Pittsburgh in 1906. Overall attendance peaked during the 1920s, and it was at its lowest during the 1970s. A graph of the annual attendance to the movies can be represented by a polynomial function.

Graphs of Polynomial Functions To graph a polynomial function, make a table of values to find several points and then connect them to make a smooth continuous curve. Knowing the end behavior of the graph will assist you in completing the graph.

EXAMPLE 1 Graph of a Polynomial Function

Graph $f(x) = -x^4 + x^3 + 3x^2 + 2x$ by making a table of values.

x	$f(x)$	x	$f(x)$
−2.5	≈−41	0.5	≈1.8
−2.0	−16	1.0	5.0
−1.5	≈−4.7	1.5	≈8.1
−1.0	−1.0	2.0	8.0
−0.5	≈−0.4	2.5	≈0.3
0.0	0.0	3.0	−21

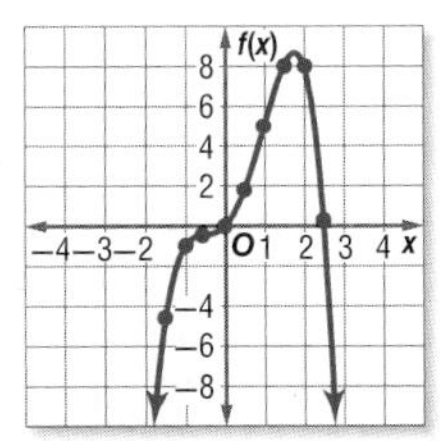

This is an even-degree polynomial with a negative leading coefficient, so $f(x) \to -\infty$ as $x \to -\infty$ and $f(x) \to -\infty$ as $x \to +\infty$. Notice that the graph intersects the x-axis at two points, indicating there are two zeros for this function.

Guided Practice 1. See Chapter 6 Answer Appendix.

1. Graph $f(x) = x^4 - x^3 - 2x^2 + 4x - 6$ by making a table of values.

Personal Tutor glencoe.com

In Example 1, one of the zeros occurred at $x = 0$. Another zero occurred between $x = 2.5$ and $x = 3.0$. Because $f(x)$ is positive for $x = 2.5$ and negative for $x = 3.0$ and all polynomial functions are continuous, we know there is a zero between these two values.

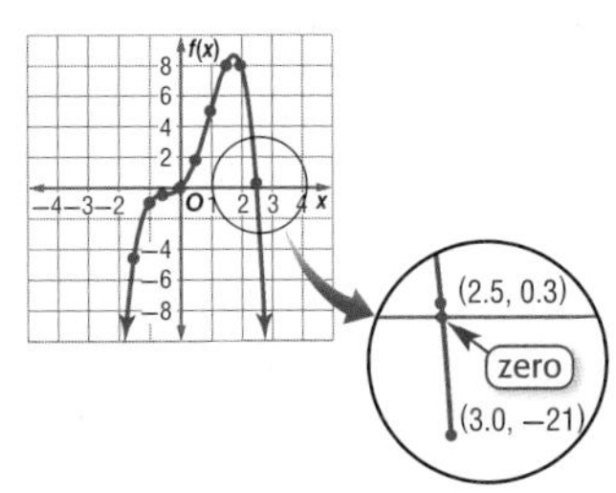

So, if the value of $f(x)$ *changed signs* from one value of x to the next, then there is a zero between those two x-values. This idea is called the **Location Principle**.

6-4 Lesson Notes

1 FOCUS

Vertical Alignment

Before Lesson 6-4
Use maxima and minima and graphs of polynomials.

Lesson 6-4
Graph polynomial functions and locate their zeros.
Find the relative maxima and minima of polynomial functions.

After Lesson 6-4
Use tools including factoring to transform and solve polynomial equations.

2 TEACH

Scaffolding Questions

Have students read the *Why?* section of the lesson.

Ask:

- If you drew a graph with years on the x-axis and attendance on the y-axis, where would the x-intercept be? in the year 1906
- If the graph sloped upward to the right, what would that show about movie attendance? that attendance was increasing
- What can you say about the average slope of the graph from the 1920s to the 1970s? It is negative.

Lesson 6-4 Resources

Resource	Approaching-Level	On-Level	Beyond-Level	English Learners
Teacher Edition	• Differentiated Instruction, p. 360	• Differentiated Instruction, pp. 360, 364	• Differentiated Instruction, pp. 360, 364	• Differentiated Instruction, p. 360
Chapter Resource Masters	• Study Guide and Intervention, pp. 23–24 • Skills Practice, p. 25 • Practice, p. 26 • Word Problem Practice, p. 27	• Study Guide and Intervention, pp. 23–24 • Skills Practice, p. 25 • Practice, p. 26 • Word Problem Practice, p. 27 • Enrichment, p. 28	• Practice, p. 26 • Word Problem Practice, p. 27 • Enrichment, p. 28	• Study Guide and Intervention, pp. 23–24 • Skills Practice, p. 25 • Practice, p. 26 • Word Problem Practice, p. 27
Transparencies	• 5-Minute Check Transparency 6-4	• 5-Minute Check Transparency 6-4	• 5-Minute Check Transparency 6-4	• 5-Minute Check Transparency 6-4
Other	• Study Notebook	• Study Notebook	• Study Notebook	• Study Notebook

Graphs of Polynomial Functions

Example 1 shows how to graph a polynomial function by making a table of values. **Example 2** shows how to graph a polynomial function by determining consecutive values of x between which each real zero of the function is located.

Formative Assessment

Use the Guided Practice exercises after each example to determine students' understanding of concepts.

Additional Examples

1 Graph $f(x) = -x^3 - 4x^2 + 5$ by making a table of values.

x	$f(x)$
−4	5
−3	−4
−2	−3
−1	2
0	5
1	0
2	−19

See bottom margin for graph.

2 Determine consecutive integer values of x between which each real zero of the function $f(x) = x^4 - x^3 - 4x^2 + 1$ is located. Then draw the graph.

x	$f(x)$	
−2	9	
−1	−1	} change in signs
0	1	} change in signs
1	−3	} change in signs
2	−7	
3	19	} change in signs

There are zeros between $x = -2$ and $x = -1$, between $x = -1$ and $x = 0$, between $x = 0$ and $x = 1$, and between $x = 2$ and $x = 3$. See bottom margin for graph.

Additional Examples also in Interactive Classroom PowerPoint® Presentations

IWB INTERACTIVE WHITEBOARD READY

StudyTip

Degree Recall that the degree of the function is also the maximum number of zeros the function can have.

Key Concept — Location Principle

Words Suppose $y = f(x)$ represents a polynomial function and a and b are two real numbers such that $f(a) < 0$ and $f(b) > 0$. Then the function has at least one real zero between a and b.

Model

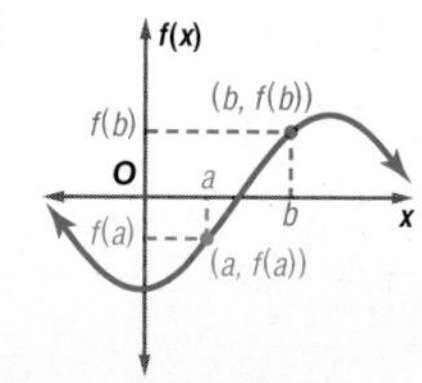

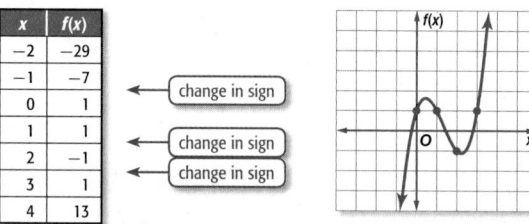

EXAMPLE 2 Locate Zeros of a Function

Determine consecutive integer values of x between which each real zero of $f(x) = x^3 - 4x^2 + 3x + 1$ is located. Then draw the graph.

Make a table of values. Since $f(x)$ is a third-degree polynomial function, it will have either 3 or 1 real zeros. Look at the values of $f(x)$ to locate the zeros. Then use the points to sketch a graph of the function.

x	$f(x)$	
−2	−29	
−1	−7	← change in sign
0	1	
1	1	← change in sign
2	−1	← change in sign
3	1	
4	13	

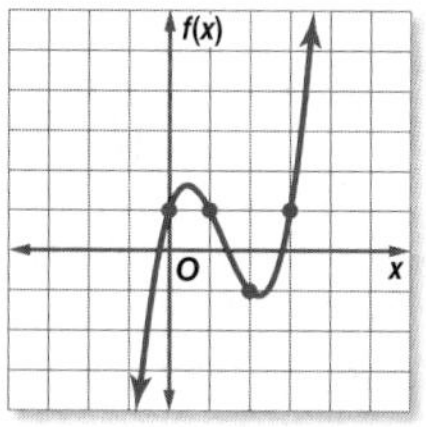

The changes in sign indicate that there are zeros between $x = -1$ and $x = 0$, between $x = 1$ and $x = 2$, and between $x = 2$ and $x = 3$.

Guided Practice 2. between 0 and 1 and between 3 and 4 See margin for graph.

2. Determine consecutive integer values of x between which each real zero of the function $f(x) = x^4 - 3x^3 - 2x^2 + x + 1$ is located. Then draw the graph.

Personal Tutor glencoe.com

StudyTip

Odd Functions Some odd functions, like $f(x) = x^3$, have no turning points.

Maximum and Minimum Points The graph below shows the general shape of a third-degree polynomial function.

Point A on the graph is a **relative maximum** of the function since no other nearby points have a greater y-coordinate. The graph is increasing as it approaches A and decreasing as it moves from A.

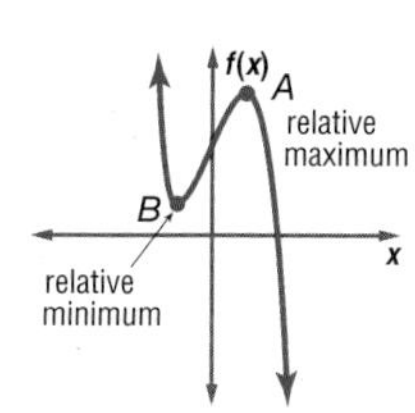

Likewise, point B is a **relative minimum** since no other nearby points have a lesser y-coordinate. The graph is decreasing as it approaches B and increasing as it moves from B. The maximum and minimum values of a function are called the **extrema**.

These points are often referred to as **turning points**. The graph of a polynomial function of degree n has at most $n - 1$ turning points.

Additional Answers (Additional Examples)

1.

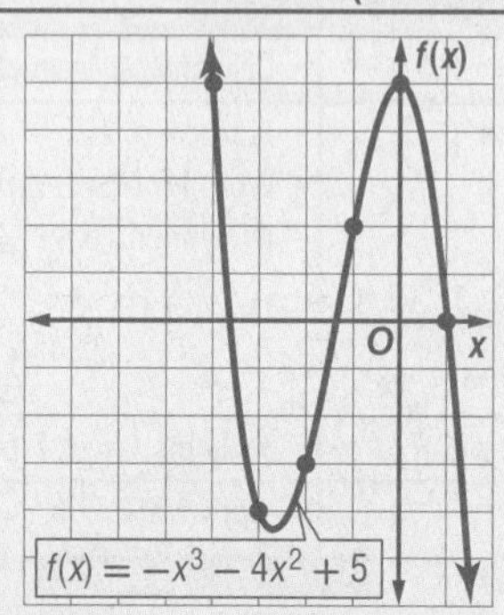

2.

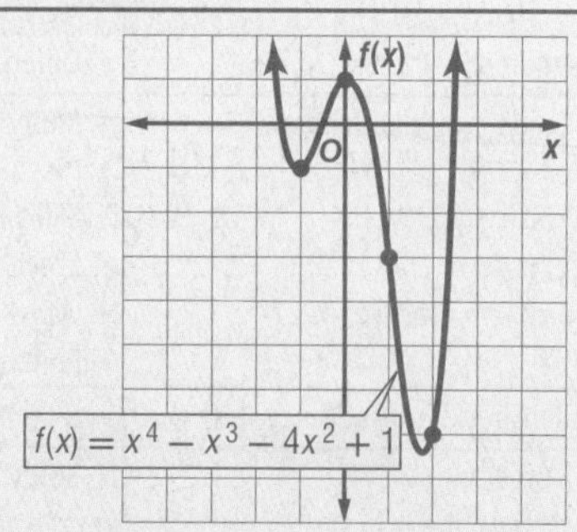

StudyTip

Maximum and Minimum A polynomial with a degree greater than 3 may have more than one relative maximum or relative minimum.

EXAMPLE 3 Maximum and Minimum Points

Graph $f(x) = x^3 - 4x^2 - 2x + 3$. Estimate the x-coordinates at which the relative maxima and relative minima occur.

Make a table of values and graph the function.

x	$f(x)$	
−2	−17	
−1	0	zero
0	3	indicates a relative maximum
1	−2	
2	−9	
3	−12	indicates a relative minimum
4	−4	zero between 4 and 5
5	18	

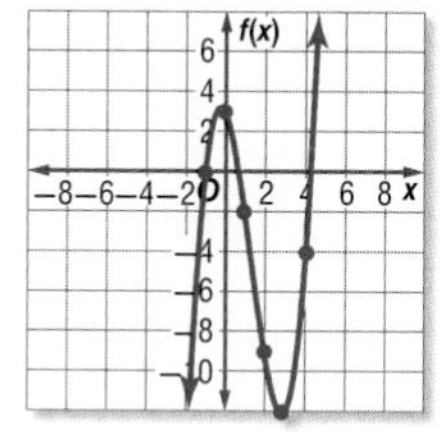

Look at the table of values and the graph.

The value of $f(x)$ changes signs between $x = 4$ and $x = 5$, indicating a zero of the function.

The value of $f(x)$ at $x = 0$ is greater than the surrounding points, so there must be a relative maximum *near* $x = 0$.

The value of $f(x)$ at $x = 3$ is less than the surrounding points, so there must be a relative minimum *near* $x = 3$.

CHECK You can use a graphing calculator to find the relative maximum and relative minimum of a function and confirm your estimates.

Enter $y = x^3 - 4x^2 - 2x + 3$ in the **Y=** list and graph the function.

Use the **CALC** menu to find each maximum and minimum.

When selecting the left bound, move the cursor to the left of the maximum or minimum. When selecting the right bound, move the cursor to the right of the maximum or minimum.

Press ENTER twice.

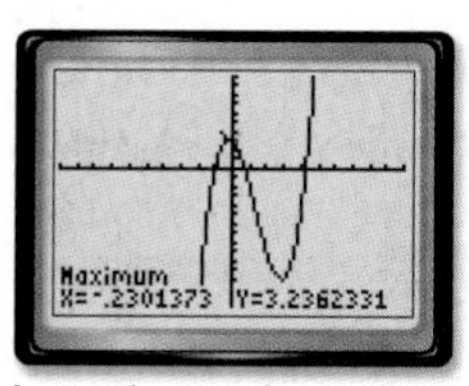

[−10, 10] scl: 1 by [−15, 10] scl: 1

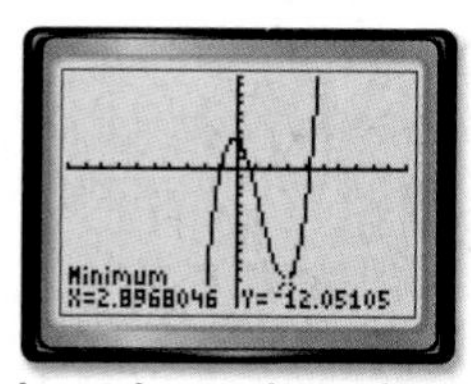

[−10, 10] scl: 1 by [−15, 10] scl: 1

The estimates for a relative maximum near $x = 0$ and a relative minimum near $x = 3$ are accurate.

Guided Practice

3. Graph $f(x) = 2x^3 + x^2 - 4x - 2$. Estimate the x-coordinates at which the relative maxima and relative minima occur. **See margin.**

Personal Tutor glencoe.com

StudyTip

Rational Values Zeros and turning points will not always occur at integral values of x.

Maximum and Minimum Points

Example 3 shows how to graph a polynomial function and estimate the x-coordinates at which the relative maxima and relative minima occur.

Example 4 shows how to use the graph of a polynomial function to reveal trends in real-world data.

Additional Example

3 Graph $f(x) = x^3 - 3x^2 + 5$. Estimate the x-coordinates at which the relative maxima and relative minima occur.

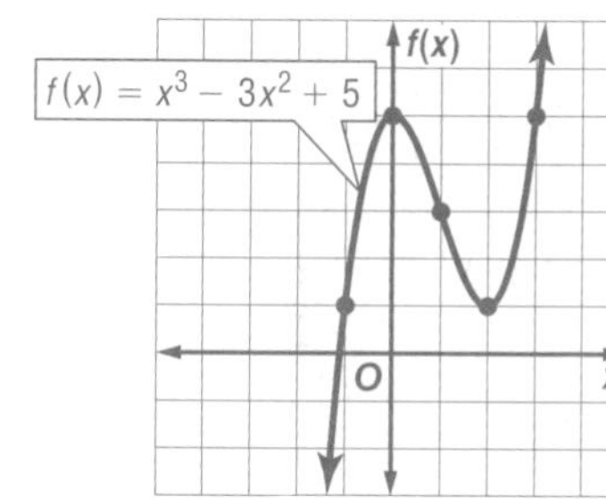

The value of $f(x)$ at $x = 0$ is greater than the surrounding points, so it is a relative maximum.

The value of $f(x)$ at $x = 2$ is less than the surrounding points, so it is a relative minimum.

TEACH with TECH

STUDENT RESPONSE SYSTEM Show a slideshow to students showing different graphs of polynomial functions. For each, ask students if this graph shows a polynomial with an even or an odd degree. Have students reply with A for even and B for odd.

Additional Answers (Guided Practice)

2.

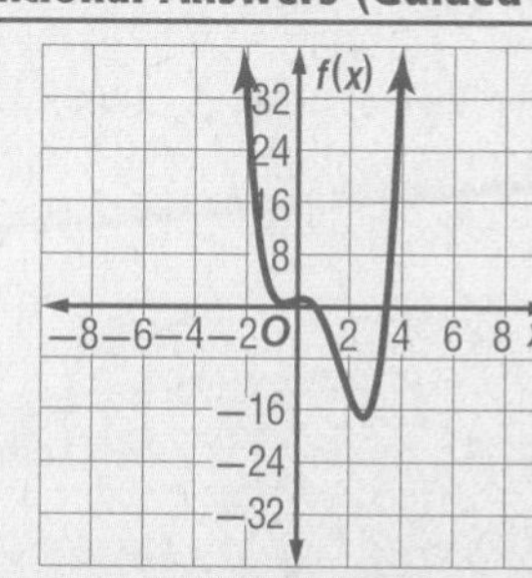

3.

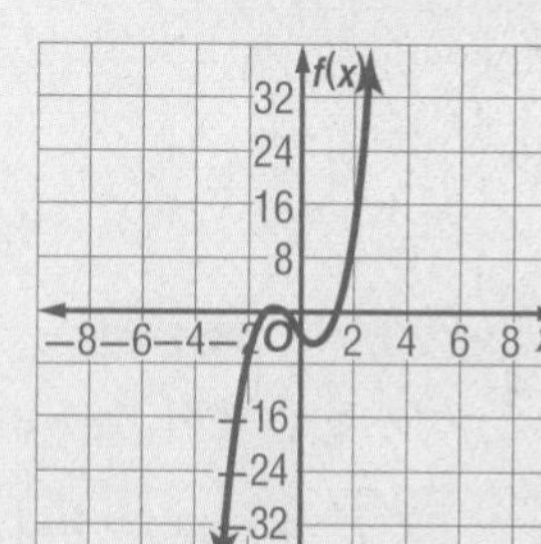

relative maximum near $x = -1$, relative minimum near $x = 1$

Lesson 6-4 Analyzing Graphs of Polynomial Functions 359

Additional Example

4 **HEALTH** The weight w, in pounds, of a patient during a 7-week illness is modeled by the cubic equation $w(n) = 0.1n^3 - 0.6n^2 + 110$, where n is the number of weeks since the patient became ill.

a. Graph the equation.

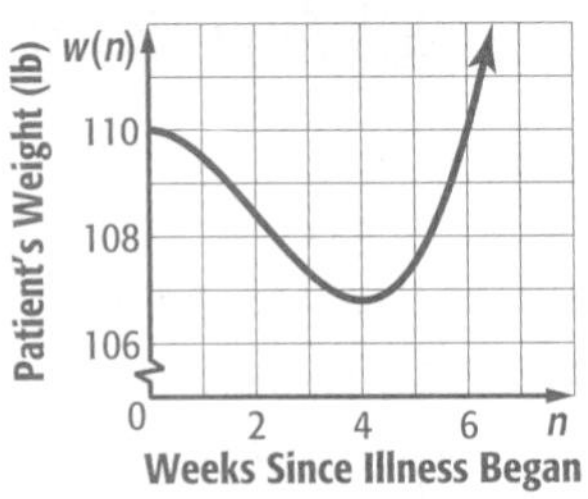

b. Describe the turning points of the graph and its end behavior. There is a relative minimum point at week 4. For the end behavior, $w(n)$ increases as n increases.

c. What trends in the patient's weight does the graph suggest? The patient lost weight for each of 4 weeks after becoming ill. After 4 weeks, the patient gained weight and continued to gain weight.

d. Is it reasonable to assume the trend will continue indefinitely? The trend may continue for a few weeks, but it is unlikely that the patient's weight will rise indefinitely.

Additional Answer (Guided Practice)

4A.

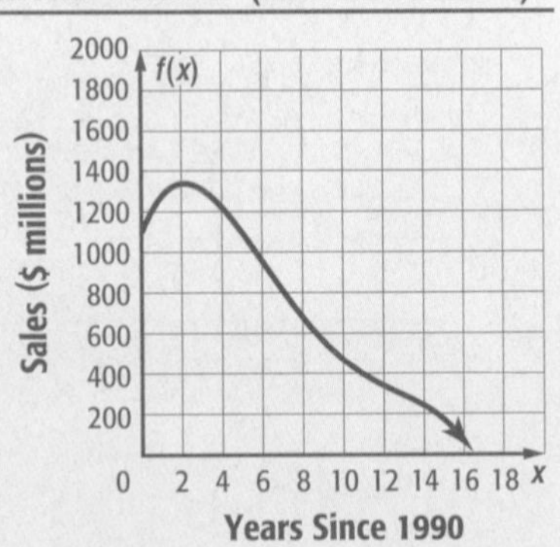

Real-World Link

Over 1.4 billion movie tickets were sold in the United States in 2006.

Source: CNN

The graph of a polynomial function can reveal trends in real-world data. It is often helpful to note when the graph is increasing or decreasing.

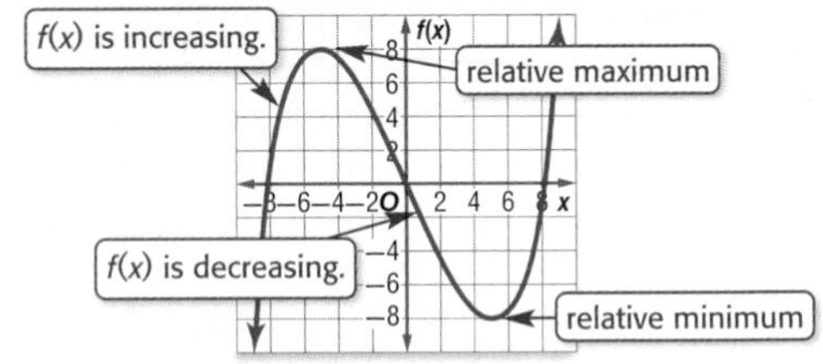

Real-World EXAMPLE 4 Graph a Polynomial Model

MOVIES Refer to the beginning of the lesson. Annual admissions to movies in the United States can be modeled by the function $f(x) = -0.0017x^4 + 0.31x^3 - 17.66x^2 + 277x + 3005$, where x is the number of years since 1926 and $f(x)$ is the annual admissions in millions.

a. Graph the function.

Make a table of values for the years 1926–2006. Plot the points and connect with a smooth curve. Finding and plotting the points for every tenth year gives a good approximation of the graph.

x	$f(x)$
0	3005
10	4302
20	3689
30	2414
40	1317
50	830
60	977
70	1374
80	1229

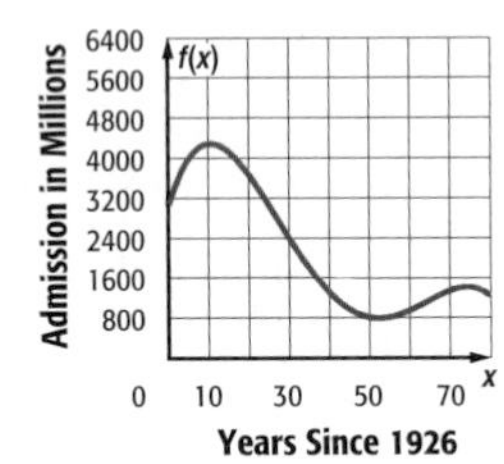

b. Describe the turning points of the graph and its end behavior.

There are relative maxima near 1936 and 2000 and a relative minimum between 1976 and 1981. $f(x) \to -\infty$ as $x \to -\infty$ and $f(x) \to -\infty$ as $x \to \infty$.

c. What trends in movie admissions does the graph suggest? Is it reasonable that the trend will continue indefinitely?

Movie attendance peaked around 1936 and declined until about 1978. It then increased until 2000 and began a decline.

d. Is it reasonable that the trend will continue indefinitely?

This trend may continue for a couple of years, but the graph will soon become unreasonable as it predicts negative attendance for the future.

Guided Practice

4. FAX MACHINES The annual sales of fax machines for home use can be modeled by $f(x) = -0.17x^4 + 6.29x^3 - 77.65x^2 + 251x + 1100$, where x is the number of years after 1990 and $f(x)$ is the annual sales in millions of dollars.

A. Graph the function. See margin.

B. Describe the turning points of the graph and its end behavior.

C. What trends in fax machine sales does the graph suggest?

D. Is it reasonable that the trend will continue indefinitely?

4B. The graph peaks around $x = 2$, then steadily decreases as the x increases.
4C. Fax machine sales peaked in 1992 and have decreased ever since. By 2006, fax machine sales hit zero.
4D. Sample answer: The graph is reasonable to suggest a sharp decline in sales, but not reasonable in suggesting 0 sales in 2006.

Personal Tutor glencoe.com

Differentiated Instruction

AL OL BL ELL

If students ask how math functions can describe real-world situations,

Then have them discuss the appropriateness of describing real-world situations with mathematical functions. Help them to understand that a function is usually just an approximation of the real-world data, and is often only a reasonable model of a limited domain of values.

360 Chapter 6 Polynomials and Polynomial Functions

Check Your Understanding

Example 1 p. 357

Graph each polynomial equation by making a table of values. 1–4. See margin.

1. $f(x) = 2x^4 - 5x^3 + x^2 - 2x + 4$

2. $f(x) = -2x^4 + 4x^3 + 2x^2 + x - 3$

3. $f(x) = 3x^4 - 4x^3 - 2x^2 + x - 4$

4. $f(x) = -4x^4 + 5x^3 + 2x^2 + 3x + 1$

Example 2 p. 358

Determine the consecutive integer values of x between which each real zero of each function is located. Then draw the graph. 5–8. See Chapter 6 Answer Appendix.

5. $f(x) = x^3 - 2x^2 + 5$

6. $f(x) = -x^4 + x^3 + 2x^2 + x + 1$

7. $f(x) = -3x^4 + 5x^3 + 4x^2 + 4x - 8$

8. $f(x) = 2x^4 - x^3 - 3x^2 + 2x - 4$

Example 3 p. 359

Graph each polynomial function. Estimate the x-coordinates at which the relative maxima and relative minima occur. State the domain and range for each function.

9–12. See Chapter 6 Answer Appendix.

9. $f(x) = x^3 + x^2 - 6x - 3$

10. $f(x) = 3x^3 - 6x^2 - 2x + 2$

11. $f(x) = -x^3 + 4x^2 - 2x - 1$

12. $f(x) = -x^3 + 2x^2 - 3x + 4$

Example 4 p. 360

13. MUSIC SALES Annual compact disc sales can be modeled by the quartic function $f(x) = 0.48x^4 - 9.6x^3 + 53x^2 - 49x + 599$, where x is the number of years after 1995 and $f(x)$ is annual sales in millions.

a. Graph the function for $0 \le x \le 10$. See Chapter 6 Answer Appendix.

b. Describe the turning points of the graph and its end behavior.

c. Continue the graph for $x = 11$ and $x = 12$. What trends in compact disc sales does the graph suggest? See Chapter 6 Answer Appendix.

d. Is it reasonable that the trend will continue indefinitely? Explain. See Chapter 6 Answer Appendix.

13b. Sample answer: The graph (music sales) increases until $x = 5$ (year 2000), then decreases until $x \approx 9.5$ (year 2004), and then increases indefinitely.

Practice and Problem Solving

● = **Step-by-Step Solutions** begin on page R20. **Extra Practice** begins on page 947.

Examples 1–3 pp. 357–359

Complete each of the following. 14–21. See Chapter 6 Answer Appendix.

a. Graph each function by making a table of values.

b. Determine the consecutive integer values of x between which each real zero is located.

c. Estimate the x-coordinates at which the relative maxima and minima occur.

14. $f(x) = x^3 + 3x^2$

15. $f(x) = -x^3 + 2x^2 - 4$

16. $f(x) = x^3 + 4x^2 - 5x$

17. $f(x) = x^3 - 5x^2 + 3x + 1$

18. $f(x) = -2x^3 + 12x^2 - 8x$

19. $f(x) = 2x^3 - 4x^2 - 3x + 4$

20. $f(x) = x^4 + 2x - 1$

21. $f(x) = x^4 + 8x^2 - 12$

22b. Sample answer: The graph has a relative minimum at $x = 10$ and then increases as x increases.

Example 4 p. 360

22. FINANCIAL LITERACY The average annual price of gasoline can be modeled by the cubic function $f(x) = 0.0007x^3 - 0.014x^2 + 0.08x + 0.96$, where x is the number of years after 1987 and $f(x)$ is the price in dollars. a, d. See Chapter 6 Answer Appendix.

a. Graph the function for $0 \le x \le 30$.

b. Describe the turning points of the graph and its end behavior.

c. What trends in gasoline prices does the graph suggest?

d. Is it reasonable that the trend will continue indefinitely? Explain.

22c. The graph suggests a fairly steep continuous increase and gas prices at \$5 per gallon by 2012, which could be possible.

Use a graphing calculator to estimate the x-coordinates at which the maxima and minima of each function occur. Round to the nearest hundredth.

23. $f(x) = x^3 + 3x^2 - 6x - 6$

24. $f(x) = -2x^3 + 4x^2 - 5x + 8$

25. $f(x) = -2x^4 + 5x^3 - 4x^2 + 3x - 7$ rel. max: $x = 1.34$; no rel. min

26. $f(x) = x^5 - 4x^3 + 3x^2 - 8x - 6$ rel. max: $x = -1.87$; rel. min: $x = 1.52$

23. rel. max: $x = -2.73$; rel. min: $x = 0.73$

24. no relative max or min

3 PRACTICE

Formative Assessment

Use Exercises 1–13 to check for understanding.

Use the chart at the bottom of this page to customize assignments for your students.

Additional Answers

1.

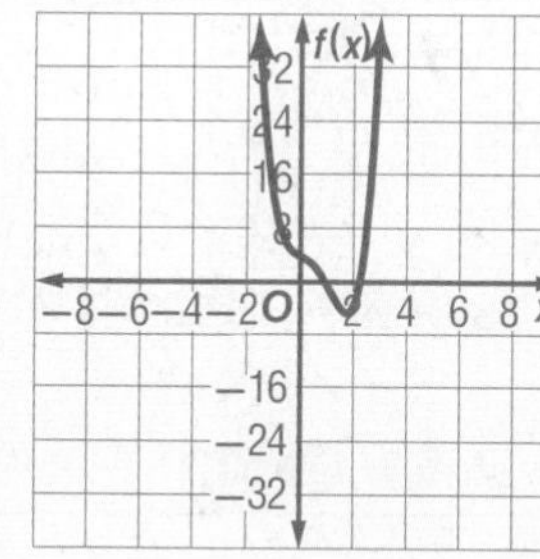

2.

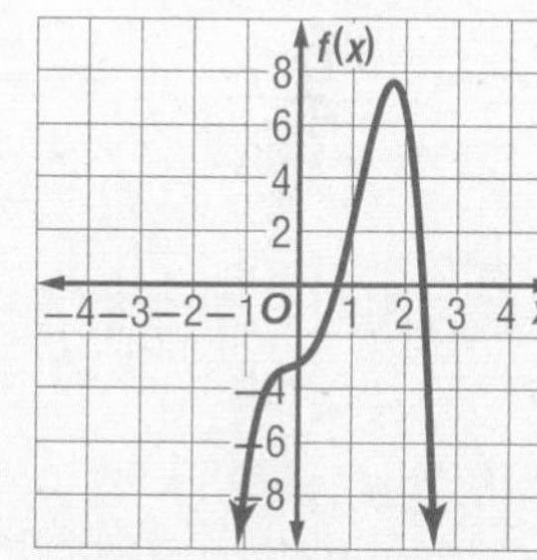

3.

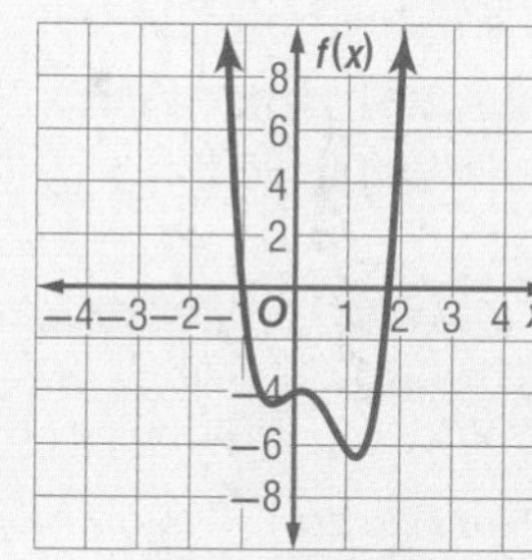

4.

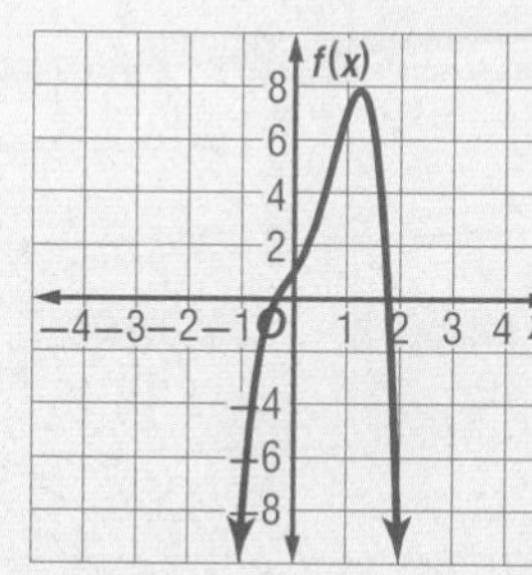

Differentiated Homework Options

Level	Assignment	Two-Day Option	
AL Basic	14–32, 47–70	15–31 odd, 54–57	14–32 even, 47–53, 58–70
OL Core	15–31 odd, 33, 40, 43, 45, 46–70	14–32, 54–57	33, 40, 41, 46–53, 58–70
BL Advanced	33–64, (optional: 65–70)		

Study Guide and Intervention
CRM pp. 23–24 AL OL ELL

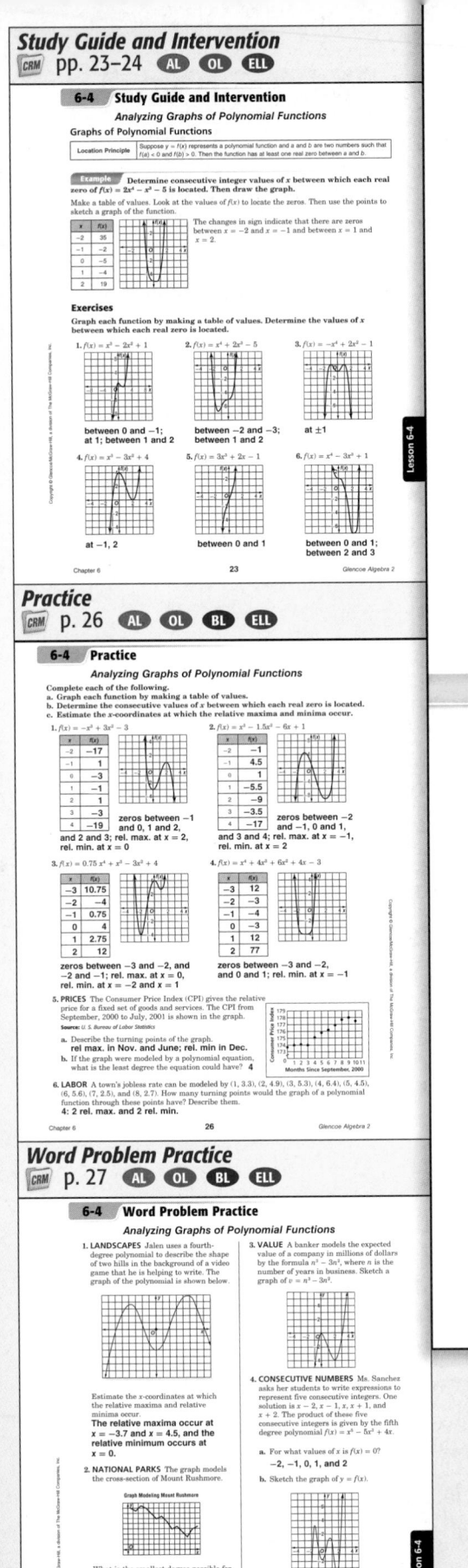

6-4 Study Guide and Intervention

Analyzing Graphs of Polynomial Functions

Graphs of Polynomial Functions

Location Principle	Suppose $y = f(x)$ represents a polynomial function and a and b are two numbers such that $f(a) < 0$ and $f(b) > 0$. Then the function has at least one real zero between a and b.

Example **Determine consecutive integer values of x between which each real zero of $f(x) = 2x^4 - x^3 - 5$ is located. Then draw the graph.**

Make a table of values. Look at the values of $f(x)$ to locate the zeros. Then use the points to sketch a graph of the function.

x	$f(x)$
−2	35
−1	−2
0	−5
1	−4
2	19

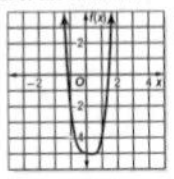

The changes in sign indicate that there are zeros between $x = -2$ and $x = -1$ and between $x = 1$ and $x = 2$.

Exercises

Graph each function by making a table of values. Determine the values of x between which each real zero is located.

1. $f(x) = x^3 - 2x^2 + 1$

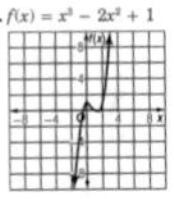

between 0 and −1; at 1; between 1 and 2

2. $f(x) = x^4 + 2x^3 - 5$

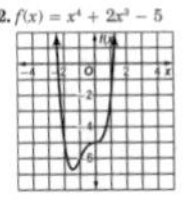

between −2 and −3; between 1 and 2

3. $f(x) = -x^4 + 2x^2 - 1$

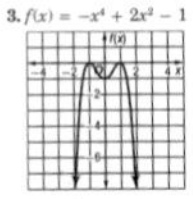

at ±1

4. $f(x) = x^3 - 3x^2 + 4$

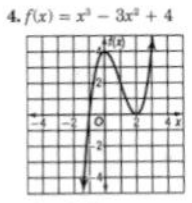

at −1, 2

5. $f(x) = 3x^3 + 2x - 1$

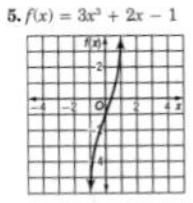

between 0 and 1

6. $f(x) = x^4 - 3x^3 + 1$

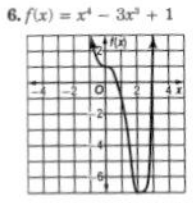

between 0 and 1; between 2 and 3

Chapter 6 23 Glencoe Algebra 2

Lesson 6-4

Practice
CRM p. 26 AL OL BL ELL

6-4 Practice

Analyzing Graphs of Polynomial Functions

Complete each of the following.
a. Graph each function by making a table of values.
b. Determine the consecutive values of x between which each real zero is located.
c. Estimate the x-coordinates at which the relative maxima and minima occur.

1. $f(x) = -x^3 + 3x^2 - 3$

x	$f(x)$
−2	−17
−1	1
0	−3
1	−1
2	1
3	−3
4	−19

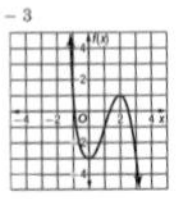

zeros between −1 and 0, 1 and 2, and 2 and 3; rel. max. at x = 2, rel. min. at x = 0

2. $f(x) = x^3 - 1.5x^2 - 6x + 1$

x	$f(x)$
−2	−1
−1	4.5
0	1
1	−5.5
2	−9
3	−3.5
4	−17

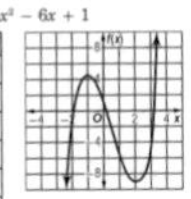

zeros between −2 and −1, 0 and 1, and 3 and 4; rel. max. at x = −1, rel. min. at x = 2

3. $f(x) = 0.75x^4 + x^3 - 3x^2 + 4$

x	$f(x)$
−3	10.75
−2	−4
−1	0.75
0	4
1	2.75
2	12

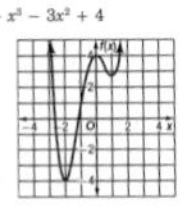

zeros between −3 and −2, and −2 and −1; rel. max. at x = 0, rel. min. at x = −2 and x = 1

4. $f(x) = x^4 + 4x^3 + 6x^2 + 4x - 3$

x	$f(x)$
−3	12
−2	−3
−1	−4
0	−3
1	12
2	77

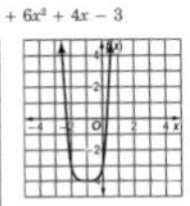

zeros between −3 and −2, and 0 and 1; rel. min. at x = −1

5. **PRICES** The Consumer Price Index (CPI) gives the relative price for a fixed set of goods and services. The CPI from September, 2000 to July, 2001 is shown in the graph.

Source: U. S. Bureau of Labor Statistics

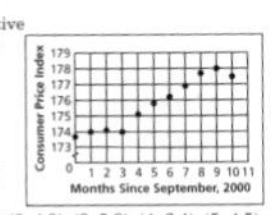

a. Describe the turning points of the graph. **rel max. in Nov. and June; rel. min in Dec.**

b. If the graph were modeled by a polynomial equation, what is the least degree the equation could have? **4**

6. **LABOR** A town's jobless rate can be modeled by (1, 3.3), (2, 4.9), (3, 5.3), (4, 6.4), (5, 4.5), (6, 5.6), (7, 2.5), and (8, 2.7). How many turning points would the graph of a polynomial function through these points have? Describe them.
4: 2 rel. max. and 2 rel. min.

Chapter 6 26 Glencoe Algebra 2

Word Problem Practice
CRM p. 27 AL OL BL ELL

6-4 Word Problem Practice

Analyzing Graphs of Polynomial Functions

1. **LANDSCAPES** Jalen uses a fourth-degree polynomial to describe the shape of two hills in the background of a video game that he is helping to write. The graph of the polynomial is shown below.

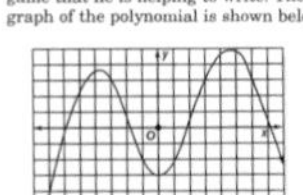

Estimate the x-coordinates at which the relative maxima and relative minima occur.
The relative maxima occur at x = −3.7 and x = 4.5, and the relative minimum occurs at x = 0.

2. **NATIONAL PARKS** The graph models the cross-section of Mount Rushmore.

Graph Modeling Mount Rushmore

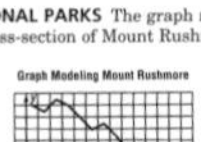

What is the smallest degree possible for the equation that corresponds with this graph?

8

3. **VALUE** A banker models the expected value of a company in millions of dollars by the formula $n^3 - 3n^2$, where n is the number of years in business. Sketch a graph of $v = n^3 - 3n^2$.

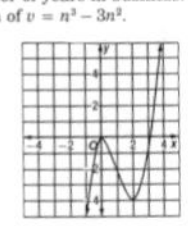

4. **CONSECUTIVE NUMBERS** Ms. Sanchez asks her students to write expressions to represent five consecutive integers. One solution is $x - 2$, $x - 1$, x, $x + 1$, and $x + 2$. The product of these five consecutive integers is given by the fifth degree polynomial $f(x) = x^5 - 5x^3 + 4x$.

a. For what values of x is $f(x) = 0$?
−2, −1, 0, 1, and 2

b. Sketch the graph of $y = f(x)$.

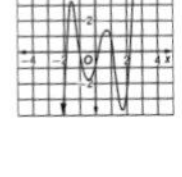

Chapter 6 27 Glencoe Algebra 2

Lesson 6-4

Sketch the graph of polynomial functions with the following characteristics. 27–32. See Chapter 6 Answer Appendix.

27. an odd function with zeros at −5, −3, 0, 2 and 4
28. an even function with zeros at −2, 1, 3, and 5
29. a 4-degree function with a zero at −3, maximum at $x = 2$, and minimum at $x = -1$
30. a 5-degree function with zeros at −4, −1, and 3, maximum at $x = -2$
31. an odd function with zeros at −1, 2, and 5 and a negative leading coefficient
32. an even function with a minimum at $x = 3$ and a positive leading coefficient

33d. Sample answer: no; x cannot be greater than 10

B

33. **DIVING** The deflection d of a 10-foot-long diving board can be calculated using the function $d(x) = 0.015x^2 - 0.0005x^3$, where x is the distance between the diver and the stationary end of the board in feet.

a. Make a table of values of the function for $0 \le x \le 10$. See Chapter 6 Answer Appendix.
b. Graph the function. See Chapter 6 Answer Appendix.
c. What does the end behavior of the graph suggest as x increases? $d(x)$ increases.
d. Will this trend continue indefinitely? Explain your reasoning.

Real-World Link

There are about 250,000 swimmers and divers on high school teams nationwide. The sport ranks 8th in popularity for girls and 10th for boys.

Source: National Federation of State High School Associations

Complete each of the following. 34–39. See Chapter 6 Answer Appendix.

a. Estimate the x-coordinate of every turning point and determine if those coordinates are relative maxima or relative minima.
b. Estimate the x-coordinate of every zero.
c. Determine the smallest possible degree of the function.
d. Determine the domain and range of the function.

34.

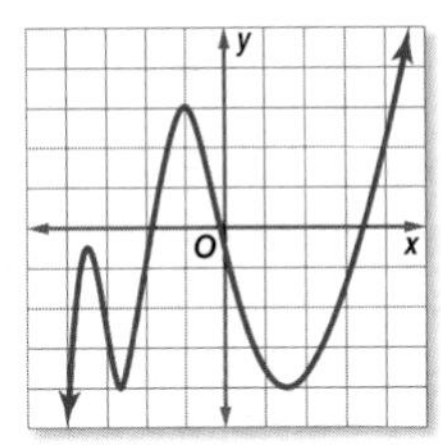

35.

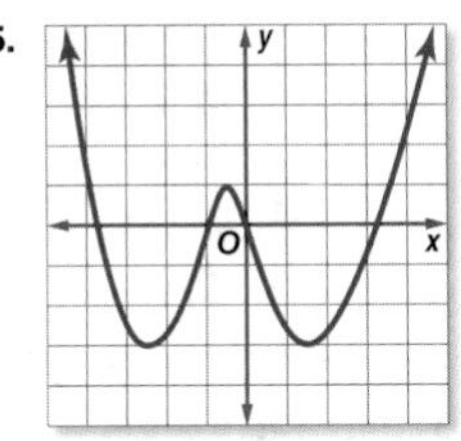

36.

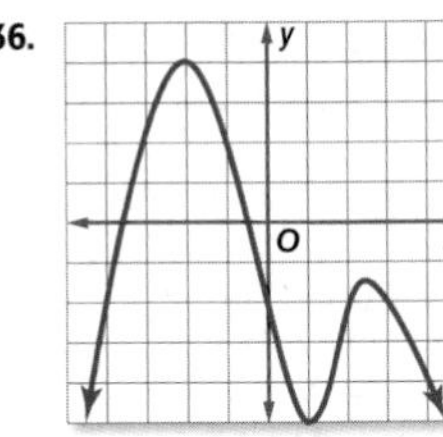

37.

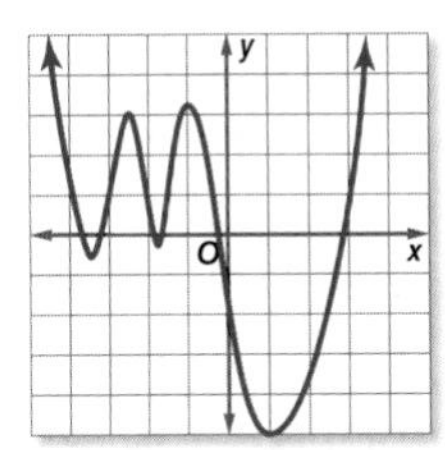

38.

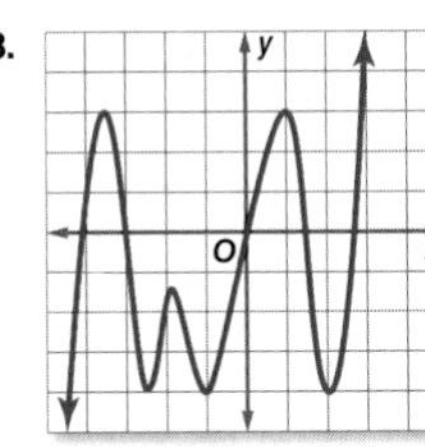

39.

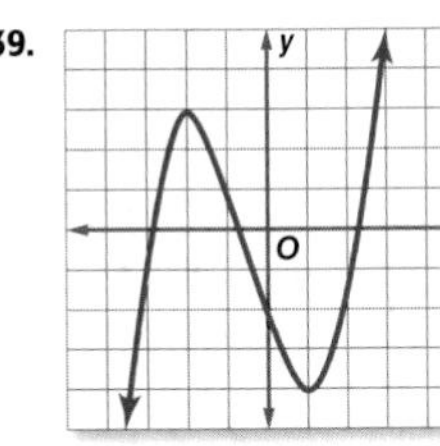

40c. Sample answer: The graph suggests that the number of pager subscribers will increase dramatically and continue to increase.

40d. Sample answer: The graph is unreasonable for $x \ge 15$ since pager use is currently decreasing rapidly and pagers have been replaced by more efficient products.

40. **PAGERS** The number of subscribers using pagers in the United States can be modeled by $f(x) = 0.015x^4 - 0.44x^3 + 3.46x^2 - 2.7x + 9.68$, where x is the number of years after 1990 and $f(x)$ is the number of subscribers in millions.

a. Graph the function. See margin.
b. Describe the end behavior of the graph. As x increases, $f(x)$ increases.
c. What does the end behavior suggest about the number of pager subscribers?
d. Will this trend continue indefinitely? Explain your reasoning.

Enrichment
CRM p. 28 OL BL

6-4 Enrichment

Golden Rectangles

Use a straightedge, a compass, and the instructions below to construct a golden rectangle.

1. Construct square $ABCD$ with sides of 2 centimeters.
2. Construct the midpoint of $\overline{AB}$. Call the midpoint M.
3. Using M as the center, set your compass opening at MC. Construct an arc with center M that intersects $\overline{AB}$. Call the point of intersection P.
4. Construct a line through P that is perpendicular to $\overline{AB}$.
5. Extend DC so that it intersects the perpendicular. Call the intersection point Q. $APQD$ is a golden rectangle. Check this

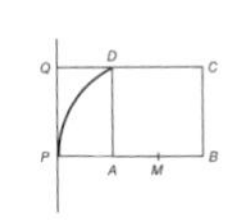

Additional Answer

40a.

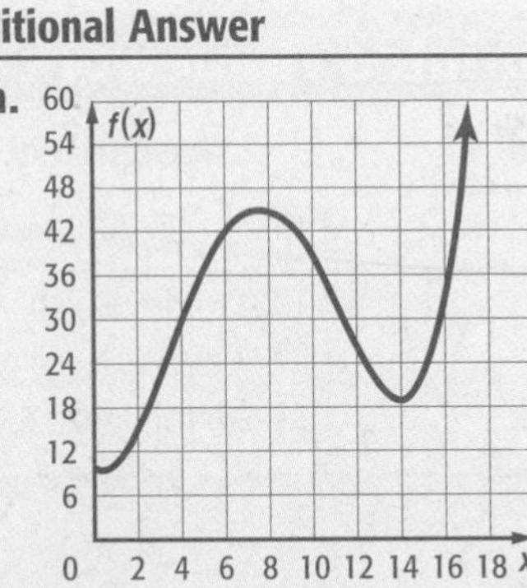

Real-World Link

Recent innovations in vending machines include telephone numbers that allow customers to call a machine and have the cost of the snack billed directly to their mobile phones.

Source: Reuters

41. **PRICING** Jin's vending machines currently sell an average of 3500 beverages per week at a rate of \$0.75 per can. She is considering increasing the price. Her weekly earnings can be represented by $f(x) = -5x^2 + 100x + 2625$, where x is the number of \$0.05 increases. Graph the function and determine the most profitable price for Jin. See margin.

For each function, 42–45. See margin.

a. **determine the zeros, x- and y-intercepts, and turning points,**

b. **determine the axis of symmetry, and**

c. **determine the intervals for which it is increasing, decreasing, or constant.**

42. $y = x^4 - 8x^2 + 16$

43. $y = x^5 - 3x^3 + 2x - 4$

44. $y = -2x^4 + 4x^3 - 5x$

45. $y = \begin{cases} x^2 \text{ if } x \leq -4 \\ 5 \text{ if } -4 < x \leq 0 \\ x^3 \text{ if } x > 0 \end{cases}$

46. **MULTIPLE REPRESENTATIONS** Consider the following function. a–d. See Chapter 6 Answer Appendix.

$$f(x) = x^4 - 8.65x^3 + 27.34x^2 - 37.2285x + 18.27$$

a. **ANALYTICAL** What are the degree, leading coefficient, and end behavior?

b. **TABULAR** Make a table of integer values $f(x)$ if $-4 \leq x \leq 4$. How many zeros does the function appear to have from the table?

c. **GRAPHICAL** Graph the function by using a graphing calculator.

d. **GRAPHICAL** Change the viewing window to [0, 4] scl: 1 by [−0.4, 0.4] scl: 0.2. What conclusions can you make from this new view of the graph?

H.O.T. Problems

Use Higher-Order Thinking Skills

47. **REASONING** Explain why the leading coefficient and the degree are the only determining factors in the end behavior of a polynomial function.

48. **REASONING** The table below shows the values of $g(x)$, a cubic function. Could there be a zero between $x = 2$ and $x = 3$? Explain your reasoning.

x	−2	−1	0	1	2	3
$g(x)$	4	−2	−1	1	−2	−2

49. **OPEN ENDED** Sketch the graph of an odd polynomial function with 6 turning points and 2 double roots. See margin.

50. **REASONING** Determine whether the following statement is *sometimes*, *always*, or *never* true. Explain your reasoning.

For any continuous polynomial function, the y-coordinate of a turning point is also either a relative maximum or relative minimum.

51. **REASONING** A function is said to be even if for every x in the domain of f, $f(x) = f(-x)$. Is every even-degree polynomial function also an even function? Explain.

52. **REASONING** A function is said to be *odd* if for every x in the domain, $-f(x) = f(-x)$. Is every odd-degree polynomial function also an odd function? Explain.

53. **WRITING IN MATH** Describe the process of sketching the graph of a polynomial function using its degree, leading coefficient, zeros, and turning points. See margin.

47. As the x-values approach large positive or negative numbers, the term with the largest degree becomes more and more dominant in determining the value of $f(x)$.

48. Sample answer: No; the cubic function is of degree 3 and cannot have any more than three zeros. Those zeros are located between −2 and −1, 0 and 1, and 1 and 2.

50. Sample answer: Always; the definition of a turning point of a graph is a point in which the graph stops increasing and begins to decrease, causing a maximum, or stops decreasing and begins to increase, causing a minimum.

51. Sample answer: No; $f(x) = x^2 + x$ is an even degree, but $f(1) \neq f(-1)$.

52. Sample answer: No; $f(x) = x^3 + 2x^2$ is an odd degree, but $-f(1) \neq f(-1)$.

Multiple Representations In Exercise 46, students use a table of values, analysis, and a graphing calculator to investigate the properties of a higher-order function.

Additional Answers

41.

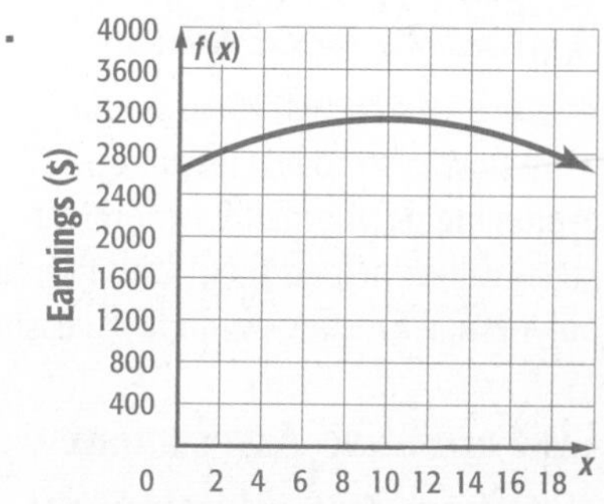

\$1.25

42a. zeros: $x = \pm 2$; x-intercepts: ± 2; y-intercept: 16; turning points: $x = -2, 0, 2$

42b. $x = 0$

42c. decreasing: $x < -2$ and $0 < x < 2$; increasing: $-2 < x < 0$ and $2 < x$

43a. zeros: $x \approx 1.75$; x-intercept: ≈ 1.75; y-intercept: −4; turning points: $x \approx -1.25, -0.5, 0.5, 1.25$

43b. no axis of symmetry

43c. decreasing: $-1.25 \leq x \leq -0.5$ and $0.5 \leq x \leq 1.25$; increasing: $x \leq -1.25$, $-0.5 \leq x \leq 0.5$, and $x \geq 1.25$

44a. zeros: $x \approx -1$ and 0; x-intercept: ≈ -1 and 0; y-intercept: 0; turning point: $x \approx -0.5$

44b. no axis of symmetry

44c. decreasing: $x \geq -0.5$; increasing: $x \leq -0.5$

45a. no zeros, no x-intercepts, y-intercept: 5; no turning points

45b. no axis of symmetry

45c. decreasing: $x \leq -4$; constant: $-4 < x \leq 0$; increasing $x > 0$

49. Sample answer:

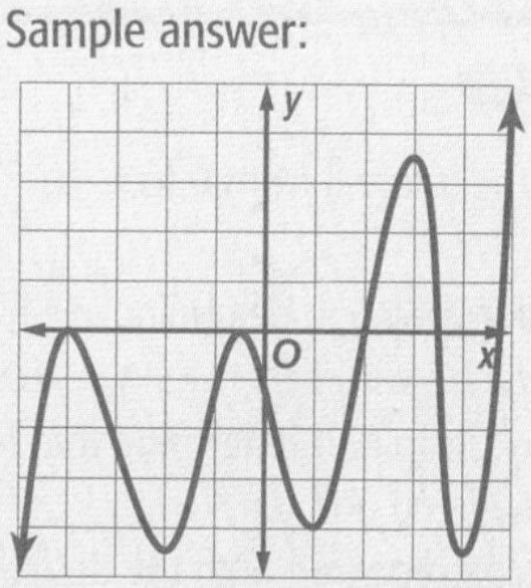

53. Sample answer: The degree will help determine whether the graph is even or odd and the maximum number of zeros and turning points for the graph. The leading coefficient determines the end behavior of the graph, and, along with the degree, builds the shape of the graph. The zeros and turning points allow for the plotting of specific points in the center of the graph. All of these things combine for an accurate sketch of the graph of a polynomial function.

Tips for New Teachers

Vocabulary In Exercise 64, the percent concentration of an acid solution refers to the volume of pure acid as a percent of total solution volume.

4 ASSESS

Yesterday's News Have students write how yesterday's lesson on evaluating polynomial functions for given values helped them with graphing polynomial functions in today's lesson.

Formative Assessment

Check for student understanding of concepts from Lessons 6-3 and 6-4.

CRM Quiz 2, p. 57

Additional Answers

58. $f(x) \rightarrow +\infty$ as $x \rightarrow -\infty$. $f(x) \rightarrow +\infty$ as $x \rightarrow +\infty$. Since the end behavior is in the same direction, it is an even-degree function. The graph intersects the *x*-axis at two points, so there are two real zeros.

59. $f(x) \rightarrow -\infty$ as $x \rightarrow -\infty$. $f(x) \rightarrow -\infty$ as $x \rightarrow +\infty$. Since the end behavior is in the same direction, it is an even-degree function. The graph intersects the *x*-axis at six points, so there are six real zeros.

60. $f(x) \rightarrow +\infty$ as $x \rightarrow -\infty$. $f(x) \rightarrow +\infty$ as $x \rightarrow +\infty$. Since the end behavior is in the same direction, it is an even-degree function. The graph intersects the *x*-axis at four points, so there are four real zeros.

NGSSS PRACTICE 912.A.4.3, 912.G.2.2, 912.A.4.2

54. Which of the following is the factorization of $2x - 15 + x^2$? **B**

A. $(x - 3)(x - 5)$
B. $(x - 3)(x + 5)$
C. $(x + 3)(x - 5)$
D. $(x + 3)(x + 5)$

55. **SHORT RESPONSE** In the figure below, if $x = 35$ and $z = 50$, what is the value of y? **95**

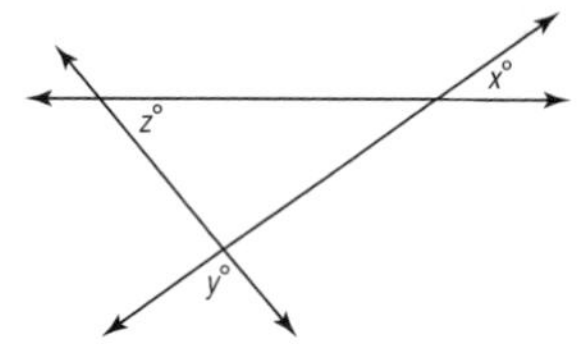

56. Which polynomial represents $(4x^2 + 5x - 3)(2x - 7)$? **H**

F. $8x^3 - 18x^2 - 41x - 21$
G. $8x^3 + 18x^2 + 29x - 21$
H. $8x^3 - 18x^2 - 41x + 21$
I. $8x^3 + 18x^2 - 29x + 21$

57. **SAT/ACT** The figure at the right shows the graph of a polynomial function f(x). Which of the following could be the degree of f(x)? **C**

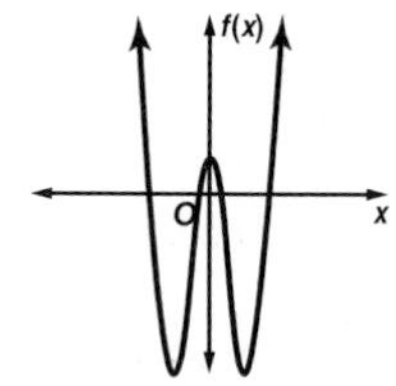

A. 2 C. 4
B. 3 D. 5

Spiral Review

For each graph,
a. describe the end behavior,
b. determine whether it represents an odd-degree or an even-degree function, and
c. state the number of real zeros. (Lesson 6-3) **58–60. See margin.**

58.

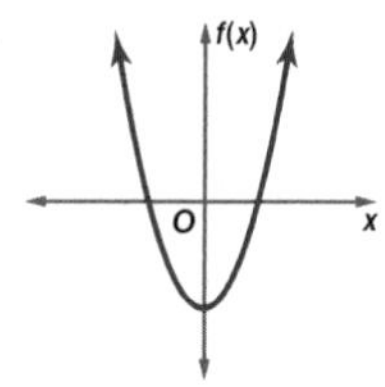

59.

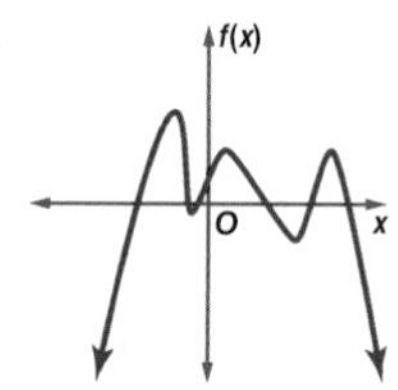

60.

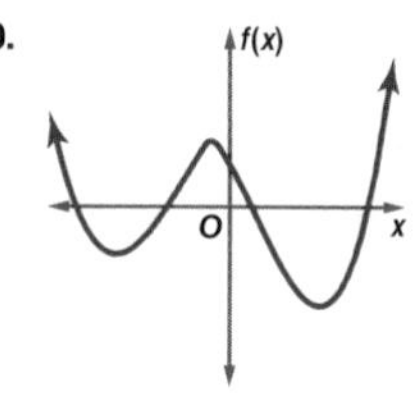

Simplify. (Lesson 6-2)

61. $(x^3 + 2x^2 - 5x - 6) \div (x + 1)$ **$(x - 2)(x + 3)$**

62. $(4y^3 + 18y^2 + 5y - 12) \div (y + 4)$ **$4y^2 + 2y - 3$**

63. $(2a^3 - a^2 - 4a) \div (a - 1)$ **$2a^2 + a - 3 - \frac{3}{a - 1}$**

64. **CHEMISTRY** Tanisha needs 200 milliliters of a 48% concentration acid solution. She has 60% and 40% concentration solutions in her lab. How many milliliters of 40% acid solution should be mixed with 60% acid solution to make the required amount of 48% acid solution? (Lesson 4-6) **80 mL of the 60% solution and 120 mL of the 40% solution**

Skills Review

Factor. (Lesson 5-3)

65. $x^2 + 6x + 3x + 18$ **$(x + 6)(x + 3)$**

66. $y^2 - 5y - 8y + 40$ **$(y - 5)(y - 8)$**

67. $a^2 + 6a - 16$ **$(a + 8)(a - 2)$**

68. $b^2 - 4b - 21$ **$(b - 7)(b + 3)$**

69. $6x^2 - 5x - 4$ **$(3x - 4)(2x + 1)$**

70. $4x^2 - 7x - 15$ **$(4x + 5)(x - 3)$**

Differentiated Instruction OL BL

Extension Real zeros of a function such as $f(x) = 4x^3 - x^2 - 11x + 3$ can be approximated using a method known as the *bisection method.* Confirm that this function has real zeros between –2 and –1, 0 and 1, and 1 and 2. $f(-2) = -11$, $f(-1) = 9$; $f(0) = 3$, $f(1) = -5$, $f(2) = 9$ Next, explain the following steps to students to approximate the zero between 0 and 1.

- Average (bisect) the interval from 0 to 1. $\frac{0 + 1}{2} = 0.5$
- Evaluate the function for 0.5 to determine in which half of the interval the zero lies. $f(0.5) = -2.25$
- Use the Location Principle to determine that the zero must lie between 0 and 0.5.

This procedure can be repeated until the desired accuracy of the zero is obtained.

364 Chapter 6 Polynomials and Polynomial Functions

EXTEND 6-4

Graphing Technology Lab: Modeling Data Using Polynomial Functions

FL Math Online glencoe.com
- Other Calculator Keystrokes
- Graphing Technology Personal Tutor

NGSSS **MA.912.A.4.5** Graph polynomial functions with and without technology and describe end behavior.
MA.912.A.4.10 Use polynomial equations to solve real-world problems.

You can use a TI-83/84 Plus graphing calculator to model data points when a curve of best fit is a polynomial function.

EXAMPLE

The table shows the distance a seismic wave produced by an earthquake travels from the epicenter. Draw a scatter plot and a curve of best fit to show how the distance is related to time. Then determine approximately how far away from the epicenter a seismic wave will be felt 8.5 minutes after an earthquake occurs.

Travel Time (min)	1	2	5	7	10	12	13
Distance (km)	400	800	2500	3900	6250	8400	10,000

Source: University of Arizona

Step 1 Enter time in L1 and distance in L2.

KEYSTROKES: [STAT] 1 1 [ENTER] 2 [ENTER] 5 [ENTER] 7 [ENTER] 10 [ENTER] 12 [ENTER] 13 [ENTER] [▶] 400 [ENTER] 800 [ENTER] 2500 [ENTER] 3900 [ENTER] 6250 [ENTER] 8400 [ENTER] 10000 [ENTER]

Step 2 Graph the scatter plot.

KEYSTROKES: [2nd] [STAT PLOT] 1 [ENTER] [▼] [ENTER] [ZOOM] 9

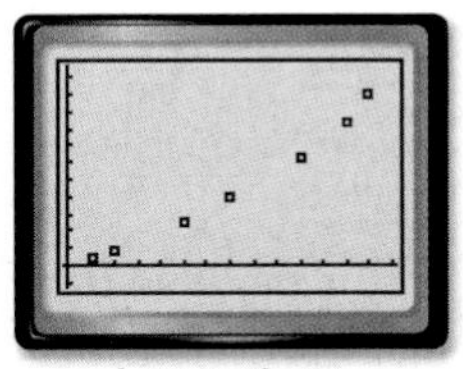

[−0.2, 14.2] scl: 1 by [−1232, 11632] scl: 1000

Step 3 Determine and graph the equation for a curve of best fit. Use a quartic regression for the data.

KEYSTROKES: [STAT] [▶] 7 [ENTER] [Y=] [VARS] 5 [▶] [▶] 1 [GRAPH]

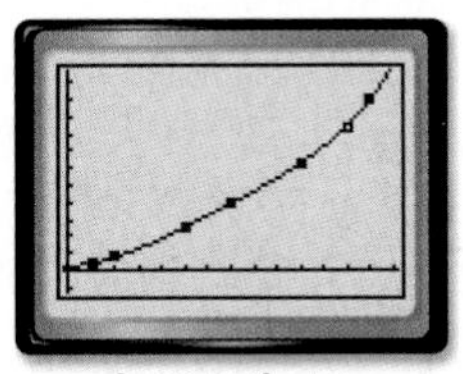

[−0.2, 14.2] scl: 1 by [−1232, 11632] scl: 1000

Step 4 Use the [CALC] feature to find the value of the function for $x = 8.5$.

KEYSTROKES: [2nd] [CALC] 1 8.5 [ENTER]

After 8.5 minutes, the wave could be expected to be felt approximately 4980 kilometers from the epicenter.

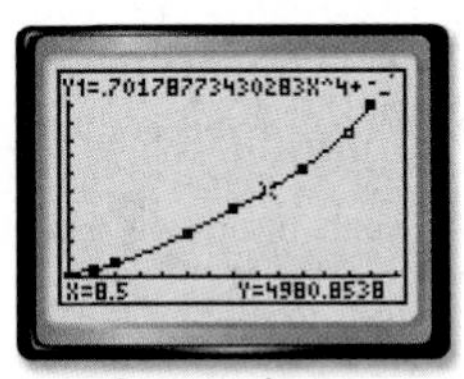

[−0.2, 14.2] scl: 1 by [−1232, 11632] scl: 1000

Differentiated Instruction

OL BL

Extension The nature of polynomial functions makes them perfect for inventing funny stories about how things change over time. Challenge students to create stories about something that is growing or shrinking (or both) and display the growth graphically. Extend the problem by having them create scales for the graphs that match the context of their stories.

EXTEND 6-4

Lesson Notes

1 FOCUS

Objective Use a graphing calculator to model data whose curve of best fit is a polynomial function.

Materials

- TI-83/84 Plus or other graphing calculator

Teaching Tip

Students should clear lists L1 and L2 before entering the data from the table in Step 1. This is a more reliable approach than simply "overwriting" old data with new data.

2 TEACH

Working in Cooperative Groups

Put students in pairs, mixing abilities. Then have pairs complete all steps in the Example.

- In Step 3, a quartic curve will fit the data best. An easy way to verify this is to find quadratic and cubic regression equations and then copy them to the Y = list along with the quartic regression equation. Change the window settings for the *x*-axis to [−0.2, 18.6]. Turn off the scatter plot and graph all three regression equations on the same screen. Then use TRACE to go to each *x* value in the first row of the table. While at each *x* value, use the up/down arrow keys to move between the curves, comparing the *y* values for each regression curve with the *y* value given in the table.

Practice Have students complete Exercises 1–3.

3 ASSESS

Formative Assessment

Use Exercises 4–10 to make sure students understand how to decide which of the several curves they graphed best fits the data. Ask students to justify their final choice.

In Exercises 3, 6, and 9, students' answers may vary slightly depending on their best-fit curves.

From Concrete to Abstract

Ask:

Given the description and command, what is the formula for each of the following?

Description	Command	Formula
Linear Regression	LinReg ($ax + b$)	$y = ax + b$
Quadratic Regression	QuadReg	$y = ax^2 + bx + c$
Cubic Regression	CubicReg	$y = ax^3 + bx^2 + cx + d$

Additional Answer

1. Sample graphs:

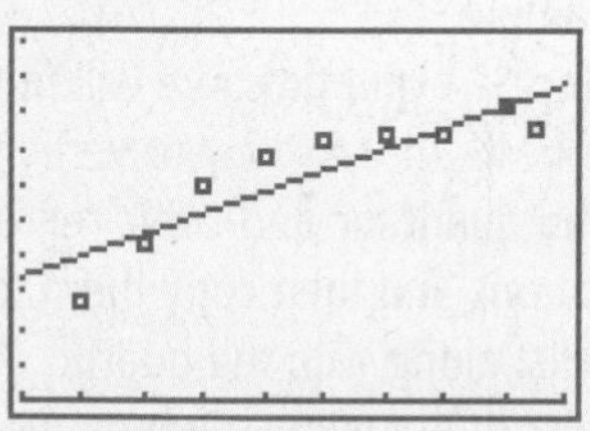

[1920, 2010] scl: 10 by [0, 200] scl: 20

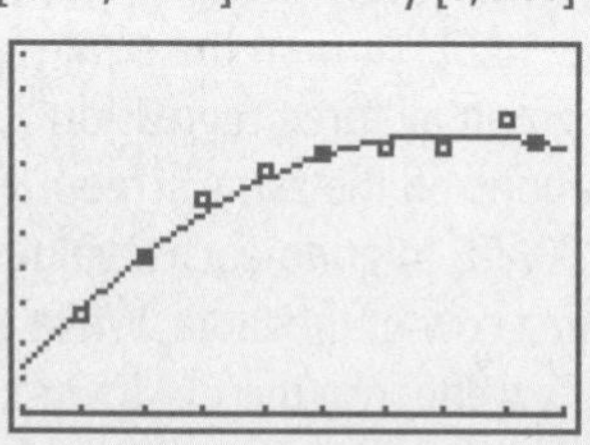

[1920, 2010] scl: 10 by [0, 200] scl: 20

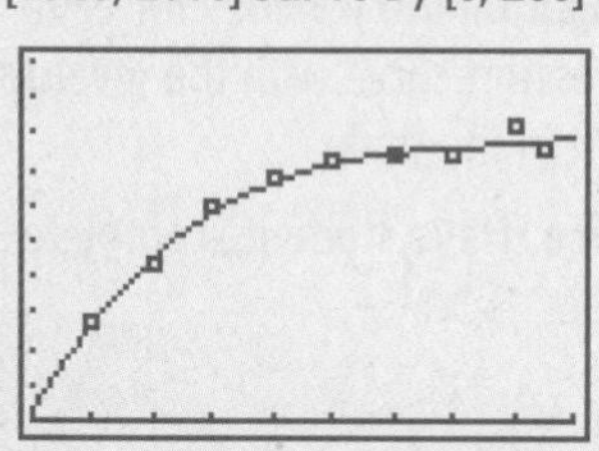

[1920, 2010] scl: 10 by [0, 200] scl: 20

Exercises

The table shows how many minutes out of each eight-hour work day are used to pay one day's worth of taxes.

Year	Minutes
1930	56
1940	86
1950	119
1960	134
1970	144
1980	147
1990	148
2000	163
2005	151

Source: Tax Foundation

1. Draw a scatter plot of the data. Then graph several curves of best fit that relate the number of minutes to the number of years. Try LinReg, QuadReg, and CubicReg. **See margin.**
2. Write the equation for the curve that best fits the data.
3. Based on this equation, how many minutes should you expect to work each day in the year 2020 to pay one day's taxes? **about 164 min**

2. Sample answer: $y = (3.24 + 10^{-4})x^3 - 1.94x^2 + 3861.99x - 2{,}566{,}944.04$

The table shows the estimated number of alternative-fueled vehicles in use in the United States per year. **4–6. See Chapter 6 Answer Appendix.**

Year	Number of Vehicles	Year	Number of Vehicles
1995	246,855	2000	394,664
1996	265,006	2001	425,457
1997	280,205	2002	471,098
1998	295,030	2003	510,805
1999	322,302	2004	547,904

Source: U.S. Department of Energy

4. Draw a scatter plot of the data. Then graph several curves of best fit that relate the distance to the month.
5. Which curve best fits the data? Is that curve best for predicting future values?
6. Use the best-fit equation you think will give the most accurate prediction for how many alternative-fuel vehicles will be in use in the year 2012.

The table shows the average distance from the Sun to Earth during each month of the year.

Month	Distance (astronomical units)
January	0.9840
February	0.9888
March	0.9962
April	1.0050
May	1.0122
June	1.0163
July	1.0161
August	1.0116
September	1.0039
October	0.9954
November	0.9878
December	0.9837

Source: The Astronomy Cafe

7. Draw a scatter plot of the data. Then graph several curves of best fit that relate the distance to the month. **See Chapter 6 Answer Appendix.**
8. Write the equation for the curve that best fits the data. **See margin.**
9. Based on your regression equation, what is the distance from the Sun to Earth halfway through September? **about 1.003**
10. Would you use this model to find the distance from the Sun to Earth in subsequent years? Explain your reasoning. **Sample answer: No; the distances should be cyclical, repeating from one year to the next.**

Extension **11–13. See students' work.**

11. Write a question that could be answered by examining data. For example, you might estimate the number of people living in your town 5 years from now or predict the future cost of a car.
12. Collect and organize the data you need to answer the question you wrote. You may need to research your topic on the Internet or conduct a survey to collect the data you need.
13. Make a scatter plot and find a regression equation for your data. Then use the regression equation to answer the question.

5. Sample answer: The cubic curve is the best fit for the data based on the r^2 value. However, it shows the number of alternative-fueled vehicles going down in future years. This decrease is probably not realistic considering the situation. The quadratic model is probably better for making realistic predictions.

6. Using the quadratic model, 1,121,418 alternative fueled vehicles will be in use in 2012.

8. [0, 13] scl: 1 by [0.8, 1.1] scl: 0.05
Sample answer: $y = 0.0000065x^3 - 0.0012x^2 + 0.0147x + 0.967$

NGSSS 912.A.4.1, 912.A.4.2, 912.A.4.4

Simplify. Assume that no variable equals 0. (Lesson 6-1)

1. $(3x^2y^{-3})(-2x^3y^5)$ $-6x^5y^2$
2. $4t(3rt - r)$ $12rt^2 - 4rt$
3. $\frac{3a^4b^3c}{6a^2b^5c^3}$ $\frac{a^2}{2b^2c^2}$
4. $\left(\frac{p^2r^3}{pr^4}\right)^2$ $\frac{p^2}{r^2}$
5. $(4m^2 - 6m + 5) - (6m^2 + 3m - 1)$ $-2m^2 - 9m + 6$
6. $(x + y)(x^2 + 2xy - y^2)$ $x^3 + 3x^2y + xy^2 - y^3$

7. **NGSSS PRACTICE** The volume of the rectangular prism is $6x^3 + 19x^2 + 2x - 3$. Which polynomial expression represents the area of the base? (Lesson 6-1) C

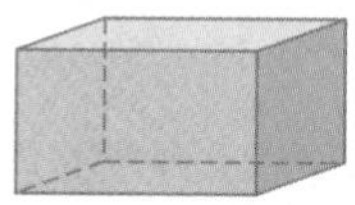

A. $6x^4 + 37x^3 + 59x^2 + 3x - 9$
B. $6x^2 + x + 1$
C. $6x^2 + x - 1$
D. $6x + 1$

Simplify. (Lesson 6-2)

8. $(4r^3 - 8r^2 - 13r + 20) \div (2r - 5)$ $2r^2 + r - 4$
9. $\frac{3x^3 - 16x^2 + 9x - 24}{x - 5}$ $3x^2 - x + 4 - \frac{4}{x - 5}$

10. Describe the end behavior of the graph. Then determine whether it represents an odd-degree or an even-degree polynomial function and state the number of real zeros. (Lesson 6-3)
end behavior: $f(x) \to \infty$ as $x \to -\infty$ and $f(x) \to -\infty$ as $x \to \infty$; odd-degree function; 3 real zeros

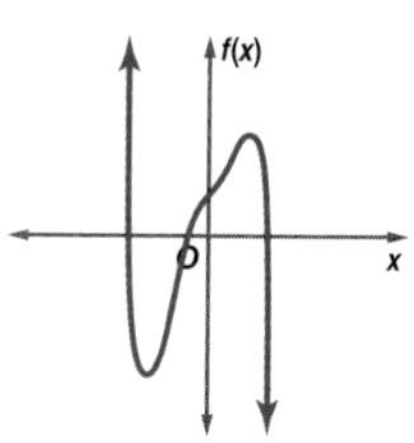

11. **NGSSS PRACTICE** Find $p(-3)$ if $p(x) = \frac{2}{3}x^3 + \frac{1}{3}x^2 - 5x$. (Lesson 6-3) F

F. 0
G. 11
H. 30
I. 36

12. **PENDULUMS** The formula $L(t) = \frac{8t^2}{\pi^2}$ can be used to find the length of a pendulum in feet when it swings back and forth in t seconds. Find the length of a pendulum that makes one complete swing in 4 seconds. (Lesson 6-3) about 12.97 ft

13. **NGSSS PRACTICE** Find $3f(a - 4) - 2h(a)$ if $f(x) = x^2 + 3x$ and $h(x) = 2x^2 - 3x + 5$. (Lesson 6-3) D

A. $-a^2 + 15a - 74$
B. $-a^2 - 2a - 1$
C. $a^2 + 9a - 2$
D. $-a^2 - 9a + 2$

14. **ENERGY** The power generated by a windmill is a function of the speed of the wind. The approximate power is given by the function $P(s) = \frac{s^3}{1000}$, where s represents the speed of the wind in kilometers per hour. Find the units of power $P(s)$ generated by a windmill when the wind speed is 18 kilometers per hour. (Lesson 6-3) 5.832 units

Use $f(x) = x^3 - 2x^2 - 3x$ for Exercises 15–17. (Lesson 6-4)

15. Graph the function. See margin.
16. Estimate the x-coordinates at which the relative maxima and relative minima occur. $x = -0.5$ and 2
17. State the domain and range of the function. D = {all real numbers}, R = {all real numbers}
18. Determine the consecutive integer values of x between which each real zero is located for $f(x) = 3x^2 - 3x - 1$. (Lesson 6-4) between −1 and 0 and between 1 and 2

Refer to the graph. (Lesson 6-4)

19. maximum at $x \approx 1$; minima at $x \approx -1.5$ and $x \approx 4$
20. −2, −0.5, 2.5, 5

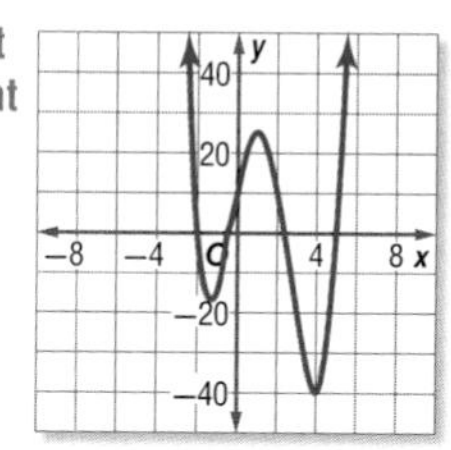

19. Estimate the x-coordinate of every turning point, and determine if those coordinates are relative maxima or relative minima.
20. Estimate the x-coordinate of every zero.
21. What is the least possible degree of the function? 4

CHAPTER 6 Mid-Chapter Quiz

Formative Assessment

Use the Mid-Chapter Quiz to assess students' progress in the first half of the chapter.

For problems answered incorrectly, have students review the lessons indicated in parentheses.

ExamView Assessment Suite Customize and create multiple versions of your Mid-Chapter Quiz and their answer keys.

FOLDABLES Follow-Up

Before students complete the Mid-Chapter Quiz, encourage them to review the information for Lessons 6-1 through 6-4 in their Foldables.

Additional Answer

15.

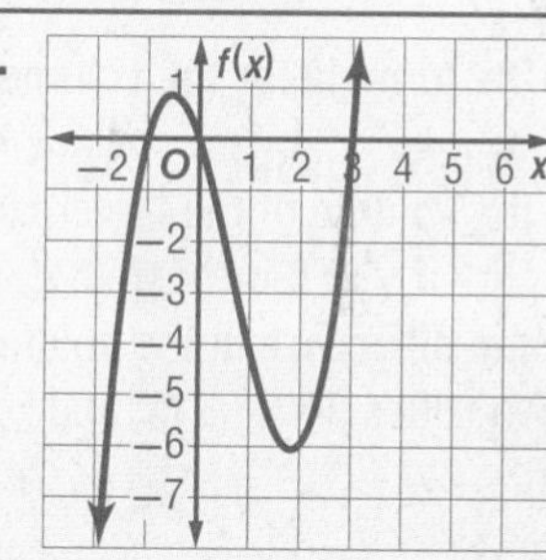

Intervention Planner

Tier 1 On Level	Tier 2 Strategic Intervention approaching grade level	Tier 3 Intensive Intervention 2 or more grades below level
If students miss about 25% of the exercises or less,	**If** students miss about 50% of the exercises or less,	**If** students miss about 75% of the exercises or less,
Then choose a resource: **SE** Lessons 6-1, 6-2, 6–3, 6-4 **CRM** Skills Practice, pp. 7, 13, 19, and 25 **TE** Chapter Project, p. 330	**Then** choose a resource: **CRM** Study Guide and Intervention, pp. 5, 11, 17, and 23	**Then** use *Math Triumphs, Alg. 2,* Chs. 1 and 4
FL Math Online Self-Check Quiz	FL Math Online Extra Examples, Personal Tutor, Homework Help	FL Math Online Extra Examples, Personal Tutor, Homework Help, Review Vocabulary

6-5 Lesson Notes

1 FOCUS

Vertical Alignment

Before Lesson 6-5
Solve quadratic equations by factoring.

Lesson 6-5
Factor polynomials.
Solve polynomial equations by factoring.

After Lesson 6-5
Use tools including factoring to transform and solve polynomial equations.

2 TEACH

Scaffolding Questions

Have students read the *Why?* section of the lesson.

Ask:

- What is the formula for the volume of a cube? $V = e^3$
- What is the volume of the larger cube in the figure if $x = 5$ inches? 125 in^3
- What is the difference in the volume of the two cubes if $x = 5$ in. and $y = 2$ in.? 117 in^3

6-5 Solving Polynomial Equations

Then
You solved quadratic functions by factoring. (Lesson 5-3)

Now
- Factor polynomials.
- Solve polynomial equations by factoring.

NGSSS
MA.912.A.4.3 Factor polynomial expressions.

New Vocabulary
prime polynomials
quadratic form

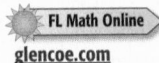

FL Math Online
glencoe.com

Why?

A small cube is cut out of a larger cube. The volume of the remaining figure is given and the dimensions of each cube need to be determined.

This can be accomplished by factoring the cubic polynomial $x^3 - y^3$.

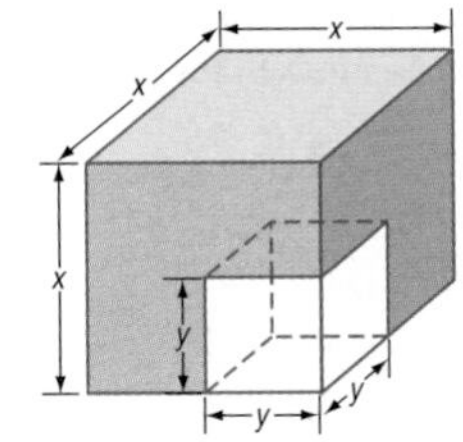

Factor Polynomials In Lesson 5-3, you learned that quadratics can be factored just like whole numbers. Their factors, however, are other polynomials. Like quadratics, some cubic polynomials can also be factored with special rules.

Key Concept Sum and Difference of Cubes

Factoring Technique	General Case
Sum of Two Cubes	$a^3 + b^3 = (a + b)(a^2 - ab + b^2)$
Difference of Two Cubes	$a^3 - b^3 = (a - b)(a^2 + ab + b^2)$

Polynomials that cannot be factored are called **prime polynomials**.

EXAMPLE 1 Sum and Difference of Cubes

Factor each polynomial. If the polynomial cannot be factored, write *prime*.

a. $16x^4 + 54xy^3$

$16x^4 + 54xy^3 = 2x(8x^3 + 27y^3)$ **Factor out the GCF.**

$8x^3$ and $27y^3$ are both perfect cubes, so we can factor the sum of two cubes.

$8x^3 + 27y^3 = (2x)^3 + (3y)^3$ **$(2x)^3 = 8x^3$; $(3y)^3 = 27y^3$**

$= (2x + 3y)[(2x)^2 - (2x)(3y) + (3y)^2]$ **Sum of two cubes**

$= (2x + 3y)(4x^2 - 6xy + 9y^2)$ **Simplify.**

$16x^4 + 54xy^3 = 2x(2x + 3y)(4x^2 - 6xy + 9y^2)$ **Replace the GCF.**

b. $9y^3 + 5x^3$

The first term is a perfect cube, but the second term is not. So, the polynomial cannot be factored using the sum of two cubes pattern. The polynomial also cannot be factored using quadratic methods or the GCF. Therefore, it is a prime polynomial.

Guided Practice

1A. $5y^4 - 320yz^3$ 1A. $5y(y - 4z)(y^2 + 4yz + 16z^2)$

1B. $-54w^4 - 250wz^3$ 1B. $-2w(3w + 5z)(9w^2 - 15wz + 25z^2)$

Personal Tutor glencoe.com

Lesson 6-5 Resources

Resource	Approaching-Level	On-Level	Beyond-Level	English Learners
Teacher Edition	• Differentiated Instruction, p. 370	• Differentiated Instruction, p. 370	• Differentiated Instruction, p. 375	• Differentiated Instruction, p. 370
Chapter Resource Masters	• Study Guide and Intervention, pp. 29–30 • Skills Practice, p. 31 • Practice, p. 32 • Word Problem Practice, p. 33	• Study Guide and Intervention, pp. 29–30 • Skills Practice, p. 31 • Practice, p. 32 • Word Problem Practice, p. 33 • Enrichment, p. 34	• Practice, p. 32 • Word Problem Practice, p. 33 • Enrichment, p. 34	• Study Guide and Intervention, pp. 29–30 • Skills Practice, p. 31 • Practice, p. 32 • Word Problem Practice, p. 33
Transparencies	• 5-Minute Check Transparency 6-5	• 5-Minute Check Transparency 6-5	• 5-Minute Check Transparency 6-5	• 5-Minute Check Transparency 6-5
Other	• Study Notebook	• Study Notebook	• Study Notebook	• Study Notebook

Math History Link

Sophie Germain (1776–1831)
Sophie Germain taught herself mathematics with books from her father's library during the French Revolution, when she was confined for safety. Germain discovered the identity $x^4 + 4y^4 = (x^2 + 2y^2 + 2xy)(x^2 + 2y^2 - 2xy)$, which is named for her.

The table below summarizes the most common factoring techniques used with polynomials. Whenever you factor a polynomial, always look for a common factor first. Then determine whether the resulting polynomial factors can be factored again using one or more of the methods below.

Concept Summary **Factoring Techniques**

Number of Terms	Factoring Technique	General Case
any number	Greatest Common Factor (GCF)	$4a^3b^2 - 8ab = 4ab(a^2b - 2)$
two	Difference of Two Squares Sum of Two Cubes Difference of Two Cubes	$a^2 - b^2 = (a + b)(a - b)$ $a^3 + b^3 = (a + b)(a^2 - ab + b^2)$ $a^3 - b^3 = (a - b)(a^2 + ab + b^2)$
three	Perfect Square Trinomials	$a^2 + 2ab + b^2 = (a + b)^2$ $a^2 - 2ab + b^2 = (a - b)^2$
	General Trinomials	$acx^2 + (ad + bc)x + bd$ $= (ax + b)(cx + d)$
four or more	Grouping	$ax + bx + ay + by$ $= x(a + b) + y(a + b)$ $= (a + b)(x + y)$

EXAMPLE 2 **Factoring by Grouping**

Factor each polynomial. If the polynomial cannot be factored, write *prime*.

a. $8ax + 4bx + 4cx + 6ay + 3by + 3cy$

$8ax + 4bx + 4cx + 6ay + 3by + 3cy$ — Original expression
$= (8ax + 4bx + 4cx) + (6ay + 3by + 3cy)$ — Group to find a GCF.
$= 4x(2a + b + c) + 3y(2a + b + c)$ — Factor the GCF.
$= (4x + 3y)(2a + b + c)$ — Distributive Property

b. $20fy - 16fz + 15gy + 8hz - 10hy - 12gz$

$20fy - 16fz + 15gy + 8hz - 10hy - 12gz$ — Original expression
$= (20fy + 15gy - 10hy) + (-16fz - 12gz + 8hz)$ — Group to find a GCF.
$= 5y(4f + 3g - 2h) - 4z(4f + 3g - 2h)$ — Factor the GCF.
$= (5y - 4z)(4f + 3g - 2h)$ — Distributive Property

StudyTip

Answer Checks Multiply the factors to check your answer.

Guided Practice

2A. $30ax - 24bx + 6cx - 5ay^2 + 4by^2 - cy^2$ $(6x - y^2)(5a - 4b + c)$

2B. $13ax + 18bz - 15by - 14az - 32bx + 9ay$ prime

Personal Tutor glencoe.com

Factoring by grouping is the only method that can be used to factor polynomials with four or more terms. For polynomials with two or three terms, it may be possible to factor according to one of the patterns listed above.

When factoring two terms in which the exponents are 6 or greater, look to factor perfect squares before factoring perfect cubes.

Factor Polynomials

Example 1 shows how to factor the sum or difference of two cubes. **Example 2** shows how to use grouping to factor a polynomial. **Example 3** shows how to factor combinations of cubes and squares.

Formative Assessment

Use the Guided Practice exercises after each example to determine students' understanding of concepts.

Additional Examples

1 Factor each polynomial. If the polynomial cannot be factored, write *prime*.

a. $x^3 - 400$ The first term is a perfect cube, but the second term is not. It is a prime polynomial.

b. $24x^5 + 3x^2y^3$
$3x^2(2x + y)(4x^2 - 2xy + y^2)$

2 **a.** $x^3 + 5x^2 - 2x - 10$
$(x + 5)(x^2 - 2)$

b. $a^2 + 3ay + 2ay^2 + 6y^3$
$(a + 3y)(a + 2y^2)$

Additional Examples also in Interactive Classroom PowerPoint® Presentations

IWB INTERACTIVE WHITEBOARD READY

Watch Out!

Preventing Errors Point out to students that it is often difficult to recognize that grouping can be used to factor a polynomial. Stress that this technique should only be considered when trying to factor a polynomial with four or more terms.

Preventing Errors Emphasize the importance of checking each factor to make sure it is prime before deciding the final group of factors has been found.

Additional Example

3 Factor each polynomial. If the polynomial cannot be factored, write *prime.*

a. $x^2y^3 - 3xy^3 + 2y^3 + x^2z^3 - 3xz^3 + 2z^3$ $(x - 2)(x - 1)(y + z)(y^2 - yz + z^2)$

b. $64x^6 - y^6$ $(2x - y)(4x^2 + 2xy + y^2)(2x + y)(4x^2 - 2xy + y^2)$

Solve Polynomial Equations

Example 4 shows how to solve a polynomial equation by factoring. **Example 5** shows how some expressions can be written in quadratic form. **Example 6** shows how to rewrite higher-degree polynomial equations in order to solve the equation using the Zero Product Property.

Additional Example

4 **GEOMETRY** Refer to Example 4. Determine the dimensions of the cubes if the length of the smaller cube is one half the length of the larger cube, and the volume of the object is 23,625 cubic centimeters. larger cube: 30 cm; smaller cube: 15 cm

Focus on Mathematical Content

Solving Polynomial Equations If a polynomial can be written as a product of linear and quadratic factors, its zeros can be found. Set each of the factors equal to 0 and solve the resulting equations.

EXAMPLE 3 Combine Cubes and Squares

Factor each polynomial. If the polynomial cannot be factored, write *prime*.

a. $x^6 - y^6$

This polynomial could be considered the difference of two squares or the difference of two cubes. The difference of two squares should always be done before the difference of two cubes for easier factoring.

$x^6 - y^6 = (x^3 + y^3)(x^3 - y^3)$	**Difference of two squares**
$= (x + y)(x^2 - xy + y^2)(x - y)(x^2 + xy + y^2)$	**Sum and difference of two cubes**

b. $a^3x^2 - 6a^3x + 9a^3 - b^3x^2 + 6b^3x - 9b^3$

With six terms, factor by grouping first.

StudyTip

Grouping 6 or more terms Group the terms that have the *most* common values.

$a^3x^2 - 6a^3x + 9a^3 - b^3x^2 + 6b^3x - 9b^3$	
$= (a^3x^2 - 6a^3x + 9a^3) + (-b^3x^2 + 6b^3x - 9b^3)$	**Group to find a GCF.**
$= a^3(x^2 - 6x + 9) - b^3(x^2 - 6x + 9)$	**Factor the GCF.**
$= (a^3 - b^3)(x^2 - 6x + 9)$	**Distributive Property**
$= (a - b)(a^2 + ab + b^2)(x^2 - 6x + 9)$	**Difference of cubes**
$= (a - b)(a^2 + ab + b^2)(x - 3)^2$	**Perfect squares**

Guided Practice 3B. $(x + y)(x^2 - xy + y^2)(x + 2)^2$

3A. $a^6 + b^6$ $(a^2 + b^2)(a^4 - a^2b^2 + b^4)$ **3B.** $x^5 + 4x^4 + 4x^3 + x^2y^3 + 4xy^3 + 4y^3$

Personal Tutor glencoe.com

Solve Polynomial Equations In Chapter 5, you learned to solve quadratic equations by factoring and using the Zero Product Property. You can extend these techniques to solve higher-degree polynomial equations.

Real-World EXAMPLE 4 Solve Polynomial Functions by Factoring

GEOMETRY Refer to the beginning of the lesson. If the small cube is half the length of the larger cube and the figure is 7000 cubic centimeters, what should be the dimensions of the cubes?

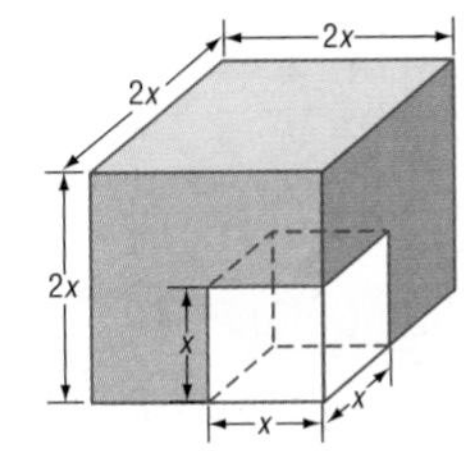

Since the length of the smaller cube is half the length of the larger cube, then their lengths can be represented by x and $2x$, respectively. The volume of the object equals the volume of the larger cube minus the volume of the smaller cube.

$(2x)^3 - x^3 = 7000$	**Volume of object**
$8x^3 - x^3 = 7000$	$(2x)^3 = 8x^3$
$7x^3 = 7000$	**Subtract.**
$x^3 = 1000$	**Divide.**
$x^3 - 1000 = 0$	**Subtract 1000 from each side.**
$(x - 10)(x^2 + 10x + 100) = 0$	**Difference of cubes**
$x - 10 = 0$ or $x^2 + 10x + 100 = 0$	**Zero Product Property**
$x = 10$ $\quad x = -5 \pm 5i\sqrt{3}$	

Since 10 is the only real solution, the lengths of the cubes are 10 cm and 20 cm.

Guided Practice

4. Determine the dimensions of the cubes if the length of the smaller cube is one third of the length of the larger cube, and the volume of the object is 3250 cubic centimeters. 5 cm and 15 cm

Personal Tutor glencoe.com

Differentiated Instruction

AL OL ELL

If some students need a visual to help them solve problems like Example 4 and Additional Example 4,

Then it may help them to construct cardboard models of the figures.

370 Chapter 6 Polynomials and Polynomial Functions

In some cases, you can rewrite a polynomial in x in the form $au^2 + bu + c$. For example, by letting $u = x^2$, the expression $x^4 + 12x^2 + 32$ can be written as $(x^2)^2 + 12(x^2) + 32$ or $u^2 + 12u + 32$. This new, but equivalent, expression is said to be in **quadratic form**.

Key Concept — Quadratic Form

Words An expression that is in quadratic form can be written as $au^2 + bu + c$ for any numbers a, b, and c, $a \neq 0$, where u is some expression in x. The expression $au^2 + bu + c$ is called the quadratic form of the original expression.

Example $12x^6 + 8x^6 + 1 = 3(2x^3)^2 + 2(2x^3)^2 + 1$

StudyTip

Quadratic Form When writing a polynomial in quadratic form, choose the expression equal to u by examining the terms with variables. Pay special attention to the exponents in those terms. Not every polynomial can be written in quadratic form.

EXAMPLE 5 Quadratic Form

Write each expression in quadratic form, if possible.

a. $150n^8 + 40n^4 - 15$

$150n^8 + 40n^4 - 15 = 6(5n^4)^2 + 8(5n^4) - 15$ — $(5n^4)^2 = 25n^8$

b. $y^8 + 12y^3 + 8$

This cannot be written in quadratic form since $y^8 \neq (y^3)^2$.

Guided Practice

5A. $x^4 + 5x + 6$ cannot be written in quadratic form

5B. $8x^4 + 12x^2 + 18$ $2(2x^2)^2 + 6(2x^2) + 18$

Personal Tutor glencoe.com

You can use quadratic form to solve equations with larger degrees.

EXAMPLE 6 Solve Equations in Quadratic Form

Solve $18x^4 - 21x^2 + 3 = 0$.

$18x^4 - 21x^2 + 3 = 0$		**Original equation**
$2(3x^2)^2 - 7(3x^2) + 3 = 0$		**$2(3x^2)^2 = 18x^4$**
$2u^2 - 7u + 3 = 0$		**Let $u = 3x^2$.**
$(2u - 1)(u - 3) = 0$		**Factor.**
$u = \frac{1}{2}$ or	$u = 3$	**Zero Product Property**
$3x^2 = \frac{1}{2}$	$3x^2 = 3$	**Replace u with $3x^2$.**
$x^2 = \frac{1}{6}$	$x^2 = 1$	**Divide by 3.**
$x = \pm\frac{\sqrt{6}}{6}$	$x = \pm 1$	**Take the square root.**

The solutions of the equation are $1, -1, \frac{\sqrt{6}}{6}$, and $-\frac{\sqrt{6}}{6}$.

Guided Practice 6A. $-\frac{\sqrt{2}}{2}, \frac{\sqrt{2}}{2}, -\frac{\sqrt{6}}{2}, \frac{\sqrt{6}}{2}$ 6B. $-\frac{\sqrt{3}}{2}, \frac{\sqrt{3}}{2}, \sqrt{2}i, -\sqrt{2}i$

6A. $4x^4 - 8x^2 + 3 = 0$

6B. $8x^4 + 10x^2 - 12 = 0$

Personal Tutor glencoe.com

TEACH with TECH

VIDEO RECORDING Record yourself as you work through an example showing how to solve a polynomial equation by first writing it in quadratic form. Post the video to a class Web site for students to use as a reference outside of class.

Additional Examples

5 Write each expression in quadratic form, if possible.

a. $2x^6 - x^3 + 9$
$2(x^3)^2 - (x^3) + 9$

b. $x^4 - 2x^3 - 1$ This cannot be written in quadratic form since $x^4 \neq (x^3)^2$.

6 Solve $x^4 - 29x^2 + 100 = 0$
$-5, -2, 2, 5$

Watch Out!

Common Misconceptions In Example 5, students may mistakenly conclude that variables must have even powers in order for the expression to be written in quadratic form. Clarify that the relationship between powers of two terms indicates whether an expression can be written in quadratic form. For example, $x - 9x^{\frac{1}{2}} + 3$ can be rewritten as $\left(x^{\frac{1}{2}}\right)^2 - 9\left(x^{\frac{1}{2}}\right) + 3$ since the power of the x term is twice the power of the $x^{\frac{1}{2}}$ term.

3 PRACTICE

Formative Assessment

Use Exercises 1–19 to check for understanding.

Use the chart at the bottom of this page to customize assignments for your students.

Additional Answers

36. $(x^2)^2 + 12(x^2) - 8$

37. $-15(x^2)^2 + 18(x^2) - 4$

38. $2(2x^3)^2 + 3(2x^3) + 7$

39. not possible

40. $(3x^4)^2 - 7(3x^4) + 12$

41. $4(2x^5)^2 + 1(2x^5) + 6$

42. $\pm i\sqrt{5}, \pm i$

43. $\pm\sqrt{5}, \pm i\sqrt{2}$

44. $\pm\sqrt{2}, \pm\frac{\sqrt{6}}{2}$

45. $\pm\frac{2\sqrt{3}}{3}, \pm\frac{\sqrt{15}}{3}$

46. $\pm\sqrt{2}, \pm i\frac{\sqrt{3}}{2}$

47. $\pm\frac{\sqrt{6}}{6}, \pm i\frac{\sqrt{3}}{2}$

49. $(x^2 + 25)(x + 5)(x - 5)$

50. $(x + 2)(x^2 - 2x + 4)(x - 2)(x^2 + 2x + 4)$

51. $x(x + 2)(x - 2)(x^2 + 4)$

52. $x^2y^2(2x - 3y)(4x^2 + 6xy + 9y^2)$

53. $(5x + 4y + 5z)(3a - 2b + c)$

54. $(6x^2 - 5y^3 + 2z^2)(a^2 - 4b^2 + 3c^2)$

55. $x(x + 3)(x - 3)(3x + 2)(2x - 5)$

56. $x^2(x + 5)(x - 5)(4x - 3)(5x + 2)$

58. $\pm\frac{1}{2}, \pm i\frac{\sqrt{6}}{2}$

59. $\pm\frac{2\sqrt{3}}{3}, \pm i\frac{\sqrt{2}}{2}$

60. $\pm\frac{3}{2}, \pm\frac{\sqrt{10}}{5}$

61. $\pm\frac{1}{3}, \pm i\frac{\sqrt{10}}{2}$

62. $\pm\frac{1}{2}, \pm\sqrt{2}$

63. $3, -3, \pm i\frac{\sqrt{15}}{3}$

64. $1, -2, \frac{-1 \pm i\sqrt{3}}{2}, 1 \pm i\sqrt{3}$

65. $-1, 3, \frac{-3 \pm 3i\sqrt{3}}{2}, \frac{1 \pm i\sqrt{3}}{2}$

Check Your Understanding

Examples 1–3 pp. 368–370

1. $(a + b)(3x + 2y - z)$
2. $(2x - 3y)(k + 2m - n)$
5. $12q(w - q)(w^2 + qw + q^2)$
7. $x^2(a + b)(a - b)(a^4 + a^2b^2 + b^4)$
8. $(x + y)(x^2 - xy + y^2)(y - 4)^2$
9. $(2c - 5d)(4c^2 + 10cd + 25d^2)$

Factor completely. If the polynomial is not factorable, write *prime.*

1. $3ax + 2ay - az + 3bx + 2by - bz$

2. $2kx + 4mx - 2nx - 3ky - 6my + 3ny$

3. $2x^3 + 5y^3$ prime

4. $16g^3 + 2h^3$ $2(2g + h)(4g^2 - 2gh + h^2)$

5. $12qw^3 - 12q^4$

6. $3w^2 + 5x^2 - 6y^2 + 2z^2 + 7a^2 - 9b^2$ prime

7. $a^6x^2 - b^6x^2$

8. $x^3y^2 - 8x^3y + 16x^3 + y^5 - 8y^4 + 16y^3$

9. $8c^3 - 125d^3$

10. $6bx + 12cx + 18dx - by - 2cy - 3dy$ $(6x - y)(b + 2c + 3d)$

Example 4 p. 370

Solve each equation.

11. $x^4 - 19x^2 + 48 = 0$ $4, -4, \pm\sqrt{3}$

12. $x^3 - 64 = 0$ $4, -2 \pm 2i\sqrt{3}$

13. $x^3 + 27 = 0$ $-3, \frac{3 \pm 3i\sqrt{3}}{2}$

14. $x^4 - 33x^2 + 200 = 0$ $5, -5, \pm 2\sqrt{2}$

15. LANDSCAPING A boardwalk that is x feet wide is built around a rectangular pond. The pond is 30 feet wide and 40 feet long. The combined area of the pond and the boardwalk is 2000 square feet. What is the width of the boardwalk? 5 ft

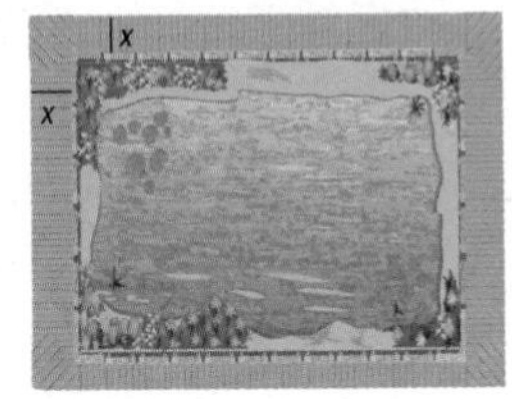

Example 5 p. 371

Write each expression in quadratic form, if possible.

16. $4x^6 - 2x^3 + 8$ $(2x^3)^2 - 1(2x^3) + 8$

17. $25y^6 - 5y^2 + 20$ not possible

Example 6 p. 371

Solve each equation.

18. $x^4 - 6x^2 + 8 = 0$ $2, -2, \sqrt{2}, -\sqrt{2}$

19. $y^4 - 18y^2 + 72 = 0$ $\sqrt{6}, -\sqrt{6}, 2\sqrt{3}, -2\sqrt{3}$

Practice and Problem Solving

● = Step-by-Step Solutions begin on page R20. Extra Practice begins on page 947.

Examples 1–3 pp. 368–370

20. $(2c - 3d)(4c^2 + 6cd + 9d^2)$
21. $x(4x + y)(16x^2 - 4xy + y^2)$
22. $a^2(a + b)(a - b)(a^4 + a^2b^2 + b^4)$
23. $y^3(x^2 + y^2)(x^4 - x^2y^2 + y^4)$

Factor completely. If the polynomial is not factorable, write *prime.*

20. $8c^3 - 27d^3$

21. $64x^4 + xy^3$

22. $a^8 - a^2b^6$

23. $x^6y^3 + y^9$

24. $18x^6 + 5y^6$ prime

25. $w^3 - 2y^3$ prime

26. $gx^2 - 3hx^2 - 6fy^2 - gy^2 + 6fx^2 + 3hy^2$ $(x + y)(x - y)(6f + g - 3h)$

27. $12ax^2 - 20cy^2 - 18bx^2 - 10ay^2 + 15by^2 + 24cx^2$ $(6x^2 - 5y^2)(2a - 3b + 4c)$

28. $a^3x^2 - 16a^3x + 64a^3 - b^3x^2 + 16b^3x - 64b^3$ $(a - b)(a^2 + ab + b^2)(x - 8)^2$

29. $8x^5 - 25y^3 + 80x^4 - x^2y^3 + 200x^3 - 10xy^3$ $(2x - y)(4x^2 + 2xy + y^2)(x + 5)^2$

Example 4 p. 370

33. $\pm\sqrt{7}, \pm i\sqrt{13}$
34. $-6, 3 \pm 3i\sqrt{3}$

Solve each equation. 30. $3, -3, \pm i\sqrt{10}$ 31. $6, -6, \pm 2i\sqrt{5}$ 32. $\pm\sqrt{11}, \pm 2i$

30. $x^4 + x^2 - 90 = 0$

31. $x^4 - 16x^2 - 720 = 0$

32. $x^4 - 7x^2 - 44 = 0$

33. $x^4 + 6x^2 - 91 = 0$

34. $x^3 + 216 = 0$

35. $64x^3 + 1 = 0$ $-\frac{1}{4}, \frac{1 \pm i\sqrt{3}}{8}$

Example 5 p. 371

Write each expression in quadratic form, if possible. 36–41. See margin.

36. $x^4 + 12x^2 - 8$

37. $-15x^4 + 18x^2 - 4$

38. $8x^6 + 6x^3 + 7$

39. $5x^6 - 2x^2 + 8$

40. $9x^8 - 21x^4 + 12$

41. $16x^{10} + 2x^5 + 6$

Example 6 p. 371

Solve each equation. 42–47. See margin.

42. $x^4 + 6x^2 + 5 = 0$

43. $x^4 - 3x^2 - 10 = 0$

44. $4x^4 - 14x^2 + 12 = 0$

45. $9x^4 - 27x^2 + 20 = 0$

46. $4x^4 - 5x^2 - 6 = 0$

47. $24x^4 + 14x^2 - 3 = 0$

Differentiated Homework Options

Level	Assignment	Two-Day Option	
AL Basic	20–47, 81–99	21–47 odd, 84–87	20–46 even, 81–83, 88–99
OL Core	21–69 odd, 70–75, 77, 78, 81–99	20–47, 84–87	48, 57, 70–74, 78, 81–83, 88–99
BL Advanced	48–96, (optional: 97–99)		

Real-World Link

Brought by Spanish explorers in the 16th century, the modern horse is one of the most important species ever introduced to North America. Closely related horse ancestors had become extinct on the continent some 10,000 years before.

Source: Buffalo Bill Historical Center

48. ZOOLOGY A species of animal is introduced to a small island. Suppose the population of the species is represented by $P(t) = -t^4 + 9t^2 + 400$, where t is the time in years. Determine when the population becomes zero. **5 yr**

Factor completely. If the polynomial is not factorable, write *prime*. **49–56. See margin.**

49. $x^4 - 625$ **50.** $x^6 - 64$ **51.** $x^5 - 16x$ **52.** $8x^5y^2 - 27x^2y^5$

53. $15ax - 10bx + 5cx + 12ay - 8by + 4cy + 15az - 10bz + 5cz$

54. $6a^2x^2 - 24b^2x^2 + 18c^2x^2 - 5a^2y^3 + 20b^2y^3 - 15c^2y^3 + 2a^2z^2 - 8b^2z^2 + 6c^2z^2$

55. $6x^5 - 11x^4 - 10x^3 - 54x^3 + 99x^2 + 90x$

56. $20x^6 - 7x^5 - 6x^4 - 500x^4 + 175x^3 + 150x^2$

57. GEOMETRY The volume of the figure at the right is 440 cubic centimeters. Find the value of x and the length, height, and width. **$x = 8$; 5, 8, 11**

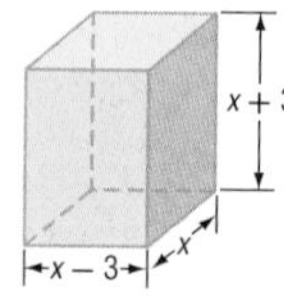

Solve each equation. **58–65. See margin.**

58. $8x^4 + 10x^2 - 3 = 0$ **59.** $6x^4 - 5x^2 - 4 = 0$

60. $20x^4 - 53x^2 + 18 = 0$ **61.** $18x^4 + 43x^2 - 5 = 0$

62. $8x^4 - 18x^2 + 4 = 0$ **63.** $3x^4 - 22x^2 - 45 = 0$

64. $x^6 + 7x^3 - 8 = 0$ **65.** $x^6 - 26x^3 - 27 = 0$

66. $8x^6 + 999x^3 = 125$ **$-5, \frac{1}{2}$** **67.** $4x^4 - 4x^2 - x^2 + 1 = 0$ **$-1, 1, \pm\frac{1}{2}$**

68. $x^6 - 9x^4 - x^2 + 9 = 0$ **$\pm 3, \pm 1, \pm i$** **69.** $x^4 + 8x^2 + 15 = 0$ **$\pm i\sqrt{5}, \pm i\sqrt{3}$**

66. $-5, \frac{1}{2}, \frac{-1 \pm i\sqrt{3}}{2}, \frac{5 \pm 5i\sqrt{3}}{2}$

70. GEOMETRY A rectangular prism with dimensions $x - 2$, $x - 4$, and $x - 6$ has a volume equal to $40x$ cubic units. **a. $x^3 - 12x^2 + 44x - 48 = 40x$**

a. Write out a polynomial equation using the formula for volume.

b. Use factoring to solve for x. **12, $\pm 2i$**

c. Are any values for x unreasonable? Explain.

d. What are the dimensions of the prism? **6, 8, and 10**

70c. Sample answer: $\pm 2i$ because they are imaginary numbers

71. POOL DESIGN Andrea wants to build a pool following the diagram at the right. The pool will be surrounded by a sidewalk of a constant width.

a. If the total area of the pool itself is to be 336 ft², what is x? **2 ft**

b. If the value of x were doubled, what would be the new area of the pool? **176 ft²**

c. If the value of x were halved, what would be the new area of the pool? **428 ft²**

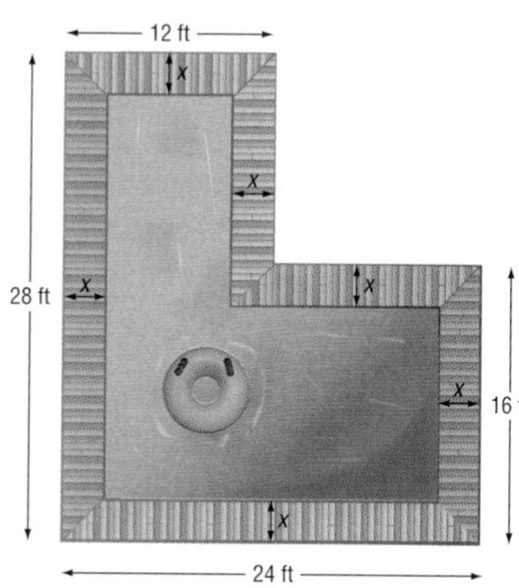

Study Guide and Intervention

CRM pp. 29–30 AL OL ELL

6-5 Study Guide and Intervention

Solving Polynomial Equations

Factor Polynomials

Techniques for Factoring Polynomials	For any number of terms, check for: greatest common factor
	For two terms, check for: Difference of two squares $a^2 - b^2 = (a + b)(a - b)$; Sum of two cubes $a^3 + b^3 = (a + b)(a^2 - ab + b^2)$; Difference of two cubes $a^3 - b^3 = (a - b)(a^2 + ab + b^2)$
	For three terms, check for: Perfect square trinomials $a^2 + 2ab + b^2 = (a + b)^2$, $a^2 - 2ab + b^2 = (a - b)^2$; General trinomials $acx^2 + (ad + bc)x + bd = (ax + b)(cx + d)$
	For four or more terms, check for: Grouping $ax + bx + ay + by = x(a + b) + y(a + b) = (a + b)(x + y)$

Example **Factor $24x^2 - 42x - 45$.**

First factor out the GCF to get $24x^2 - 42x - 45 = 3(8x^2 - 14x - 15)$. To find the coefficients of the x terms, you must find two numbers whose product is $8 \cdot (-15) = -120$ and whose sum is -14. The two coefficients must be -20 and 6. Rewrite the expression using $-20x$ and $6x$ and factor by grouping.

$8x^2 - 14x - 15 = 8x^2 - 20x + 6x - 15$ Group to find a GCF.

$= 4x(2x - 5) + 3(2x - 5)$ Factor the GCF of each binomial.

$= (4x + 3)(2x - 5)$ Distributive Property

Thus, $24x^2 - 42x - 45 = 3(4x + 3)(2x - 5)$.

Exercises

Factor completely. If the polynomial is not factorable, write *prime*.

1. $14x^2y^2 + 42xy^3$ **$14xy^2(x + 3y)$**
2. $6mn + 18m - n - 3$ **$(6m - 1)(n + 3)$**
3. $2x^2 + 18x + 16$ **$2(x + 8)(x + 1)$**
4. $x^4 - 1$ **$(x^2 + 1)(x + 1)(x - 1)$**
5. $35x^3y^4 - 60x^4y$ **$5x^3y(7y^3 - 12x)$**
6. $2r^3 + 250$ **$2(r + 5)(r^2 - 5r + 25)$**
7. $100m^8 - 9$ **$(10m^4 - 3)(10m^4 + 3)$**
8. $x^2 + x + 1$ **prime**
9. $c^4 + c^3 - c^2 - c$ **$c(c + 1)^2(c - 1)$**

Lesson 6-5

Practice

CRM p. 32 AL OL BL ELL

6-5 Practice

Solving Polynomial Equations

Factor completely. If the polynomial is not factorable, write *prime*.

1. $15a^2b - 10ab^2$ **$5ab(3a - 2b)$**
2. $3st^2 - 9s^3t + 6s^2t^2$ **$3st(t - 3s^2 + 2st)$**
3. $3x^3y^2 - 2x^2y + 5xy$ **$xy(3x^2y - 2x + 5)$**
4. $2x^3y - x^2y + 5xy^2 + xy^3$ **$xy(2x^2 - x + 5y + y^2)$**
5. $21 - 7t + 3r - rt$ **$(7 + r)(3 - t)$**
6. $x^2 - xy + 2x - 2y$ **$(x + 2)(x - y)$**
7. $y^2 + 20y + 96$ **$(y + 8)(y + 12)$**
8. $4ab + 2a + 6b + 3$ **$(2a + 3)(2b + 1)$**
9. $6n^2 - 11n - 2$ **$(6n + 1)(n - 2)$**
10. $6x^2 + 7x - 3$ **$(3x - 1)(2x + 3)$**
11. $x^2 - 8x - 8$ **prime**
12. $6p^2 - 17p - 45$ **$(2p - 9)(3p + 5)$**

Write each expression in quadratic form, if possible.

13. $10b^4 + 3b^2 - 11$ **$10(b^2)^2 + 3(b^2) - 11$**
14. $-5x^8 + x^2 + 6$ **not possible**
15. $28d^6 + 25d^3$ **$28(d^3)^2 + 25(d^3)$**
16. $4s^8 + 4s^4 + 7$ **$4(s^4)^2 + 4(s^4) + 7$**
17. $500x^4 - x^2$ **$500(x^2)^2 - x^2$**
18. $8b^5 - 8b^3 - 1$ **not possible**

Solve each equation.

19. $y^4 - 7y^3 - 18y^2 = 0$ **$-2, 0, 9$**
20. $s^5 + 4s^4 - 32s^3 = 0$ **$-8, 0, 4$**
21. $m^4 - 625 = 0$ **$-5, 5, -5i, 5i$**
22. $n^4 - 49n^2 = 0$ **$0, -7, 7$**
23. $x^4 - 50x^2 + 49 = 0$ **$-1, 1, -7, 7$**
24. $t^4 - 21t^2 + 80 = 0$ **$-4, 4, \sqrt{5}, -\sqrt{5}$**

25. **PHYSICS** A proton in a magnetic field follows a path on a coordinate grid modeled by the function $f(x) = x^4 - 2x^2 - 15$. What are the x-coordinates of the points on the grid where the proton crosses the x-axis? **$-\sqrt{5}, \sqrt{5}$**

26. **SURVEYING** Vista county is setting aside a large parcel of land to preserve it as open space. The county has hired Meghan's surveying firm to survey the parcel, which is in the shape of a right triangle. The longer leg of the triangle measures 5 miles less than the square of the shorter leg, and the hypotenuse of the triangle measures 13 miles less than twice the square of the shorter leg. The length of each boundary is a whole number. Find the length of each boundary. **3 mi, 4 mi, 5 mi**

Word Problem Practice

CRM p. 33 AL OL BL ELL

6-5 Word Problem Practice

Solving Polynomial Equations

1. **CODES** Marisa has been trying to discover the secret code for a lock. After a long investigation, she discovers that the numbers in the secret code are solutions of the polynomial equation $x^4 - 68x^3 + 1557x^2 - 13770x + 37800 = 0$. After more work, Marisa found that $x^4 - 68x^3 + 1557x^2 - 13770x + 37800 = (x - 5)(x - 12)(x - 21)(x - 30)$. What are the numbers in the secret code? **5, 12, 21, and 30**

2. **OUTPUT** Eduardo is a mechanical engineer. For one of his projects, he had to solve the polynomial equation

$$m^6 + 5m^3 - 10 = 0.$$

Write the polynomial $m^6 + 5m^3 - 10$ in quadratic form. **$(m^3)^2 + 5(m^3) - 10$**

3. **VOLUME** A standard shipping box measures x inches high. The width is 3.5 inches more than the height, and the length is 3 inches less than the height. The volume of the box is 561 cubic inches.

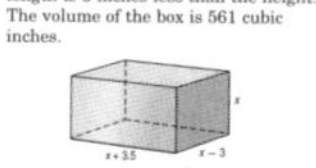

What is x? **8.5**

4. **ROBOTS** A robot explorer's distance from its starting location is given by the polynomial $t^5 - 29t^3 + 100t$, where t is time measured in hours.

Factor this polynomial. **$t(t - 2)(t - 5)(t + 2)(t + 5)$**

5. **PACKAGING** A small box is placed inside a larger box. The dimensions of the small box are $x + 1$ by $x + 2$ by $x - 1$. The dimensions of the larger box are $2x$ by $x + 4$ by $x + 2$.

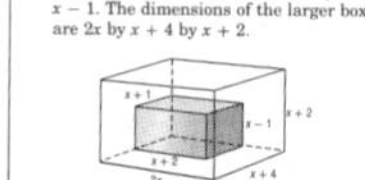

a. Write an expression for the volume of the space inside the larger box but outside the smaller box. **$x^3 + 10x^2 + 17x + 2$**

b. If the volume of the space inside the larger box but outside the smaller box is equal to $33x + 162$ cubic units, what is x? **4**

c. What is the volume of the smaller box? **90 units³**

d. What is the volume of the larger box? **384 units³**

Lesson 6-5

Enrichment

CRM p. 34 OL BL

6-5 Enrichment

History of Quadratic Equations

The ancient Babylonians are believed to be the first to solve quadratic equations, around 400 B.C. Euclid, who devised a geometrical approach in 300 B.C., followed them. Around 598–665 A.D., a Hindu mathematician named Brahmagupta created an almost modern method for solving equations. Finally, around 800 A.D., an Arab mathematician named al-Khwarizmi created a classification of quadratic equations. He classified them into six different categories and devoted a chapter to each type. His equations are made up of three different types of expressions: roots (x), squares of roots (x^2) and numbers.

For example, his first classification was squares equal to roots. A sample of this type of equations is: $x^2 = 2x$.

Now solve this quadratic equation.

$x^2 = 2x$

$x^2 - 2x = 0$ Subtract $2x$ from each side.

$x(x - 2) = 0$ Factor.

$x = 0$ or $x - 2 = 0$ Set both factors equal to 0.

So, $x = 0$ or 2. Solve.

and … a sample problem … the remai… 5 classification…

Additional Answers

72b. Sample answer: Subtract 8000 from each side. Then multiply each side by 1000 to eliminate the decimals. Factor out $-12t$, then factor the remaining trinomial.

72c. Sample answer: 15 and 0 are reasonable, and -35 is unreasonable because time cannot be negative.

72d.

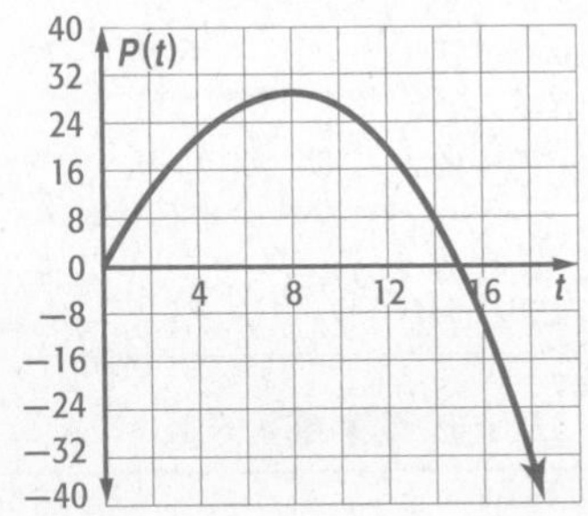

78a.

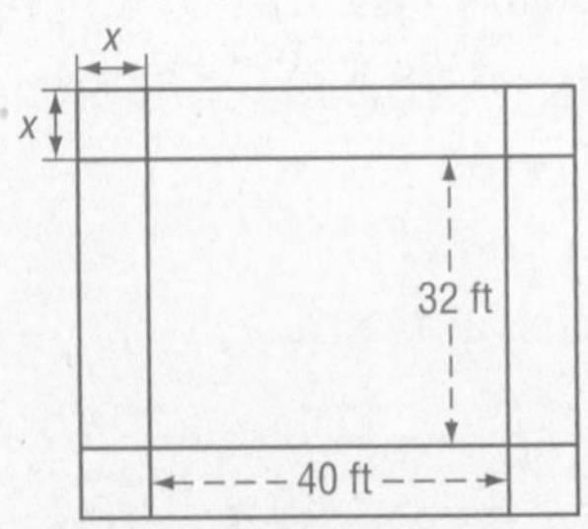

78c.

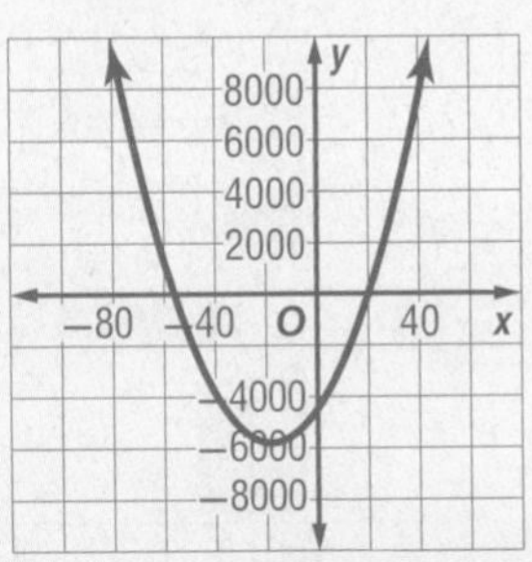

Tips for New Teachers

Sense-Making Ask students why the statement in Exercise 81, $a^2 + b^2 = (a + b)^2$, is not true. Show students that when you expand the expression $(a + b)^2$ the statement becomes $a^2 + 2ab + b^2 = a^2 + b^2$, which is not true.

C

72. **BIOLOGY** During an experiment, the number of cells of a virus can be modeled by $P(t) = -0.012t^3 - 0.24t^2 + 6.3t + 8000$, where t is the time in hours and P is the number of cells. Jack wants to determine the times at which there are 8000 cells.

a. Solve for t by factoring. **15, 0, −35**

b. What method did you use to factor? **b, c, d. See margin.**

c. Which values for t are reasonable and which are unreasonable? Explain.

d. Graph the function for $0 \le t \le 20$ using your calculator.

Real-World Link

Americans have tripled their spending on home theater systems to nearly \$1 billion a year. An estimated one fourth of U.S. households have some kind of home theater.

Source: *USA TODAY*

73 **HOME BUILDING** Alicia's parents want their basement home theater designed according to the diagram at the right.

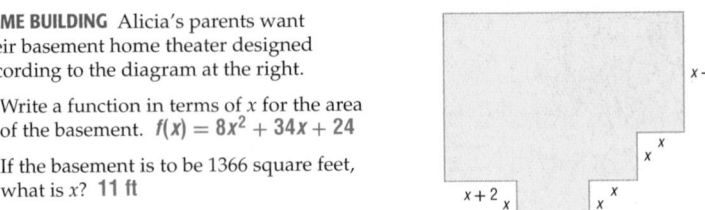

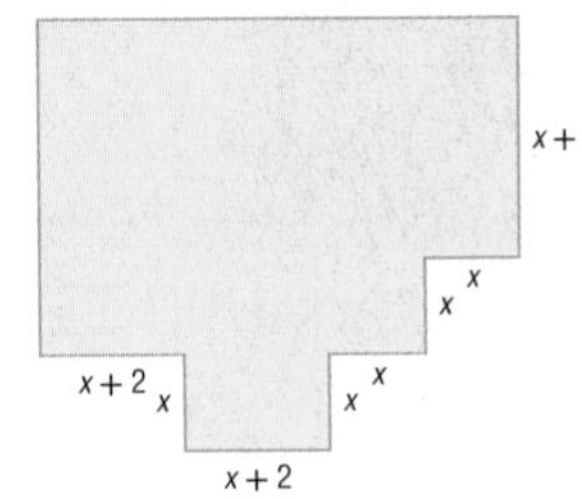

a. Write a function in terms of x for the area of the basement. **$f(x) = 8x^2 + 34x + 24$**

b. If the basement is to be 1366 square feet, what is x? **11 ft**

74. **BIOLOGY** A population of parasites in an experiment can be modeled by $f(t) = t^3 + 5t^2 - 4t - 20$, where t is the time in days. **a. 2, −2, −5**

a. Use factoring by grouping to determine the values of t for which $f(t) = 0$.

b. At what times does the population reach zero? **2 days, −2 days, and −5 days**

c. Are any of the values of t unreasonable? Explain.

74c. Sample answer: −2 and −5 are unreasonable because time cannot be negative.

Factor completely. If the polynomial is not factorable, write *prime*.

75. $x^6 - 4x^4 - 8x^4 + 32x^2 + 16x^2 - 64$ **$(x + 2)^3(x - 2)^3$**

76. $y^9 - y^6 - 2y^6 + 2y^3 + y^3 - 1$ **$(y - 1)^3(y^2 + y + 1)^3$**

77. $x^6 - 3x^4y^2 + 3x^2y^4 - y^6$ **$(x + y)^3(x - y)^3$**

78. **CORRALS** Fredo's corral, an enclosure for livestock, is currently 32 feet by 40 feet. He wants to enlarge the area to 4.5 times its current area by increasing the length and width by the same amount. **a, c. See margin.**

a. Draw a diagram to represent the situation.

b. Write a polynomial equation for the area of the new corral. Then solve the equation by factoring. **$4x^2 + 144x + 1280 = 5760$; $x = -56$ or 20**

c. Graph the function.

d. Which solution is irrelevant? Explain.

78d. Sample answer: −56 is irrelevant because length cannot be negative.

H.O.T. Problems Use Higher-Order Thinking Skills

79. **CHALLENGE** Factor $36x^{2n} + 12x^n + 1$. **$(6x^n + 1)^2$**

80. **CHALLENGE** Solve $6x - 11\sqrt{3x} + 12 = 0$. **$\frac{16}{3}, \frac{3}{4}$**

81. **REASONING** Find a counterexample to the statement $a^2 + b^2 = (a + b)^2$.

82. **OPEN ENDED** The cubic form of an equation is $ax^3 + bx^2 + cx + d = 0$. Write an equation with degree 6 that can be written in *cubic* form.

83. **WRITING IN MATH** Explain how the graph of a polynomial function can help you factor the polynomial.

81. Sample answer: $a = 1$, $b = -1$

82. Sample answer: $12x^6 + 6x^4 + 8x^2 + 4 = 12(x^2)^3 + 6(x^2)^2 + 8(x^2) + 4$

83. Sample answer: The factors can be determined by the x-intercepts of the graph. An x-intercept of 5 represents a factor of $(x - 5)$.

NGSSS PRACTICE 912.P.3.1, 912.A.3.11, 912.A.2.10, 912.A.3.15

84. THINK SOLVE EXPLAIN **SHORT RESPONSE** Tiles numbered from 1 to 6 are placed in a bag and are drawn to determine which of six tasks will be assigned to six people. What is the probability that the tiles numbered 5 and 6 are the last two drawn? $\frac{1}{15}$

85. STATISTICS Which of the following represents a negative correlation? D

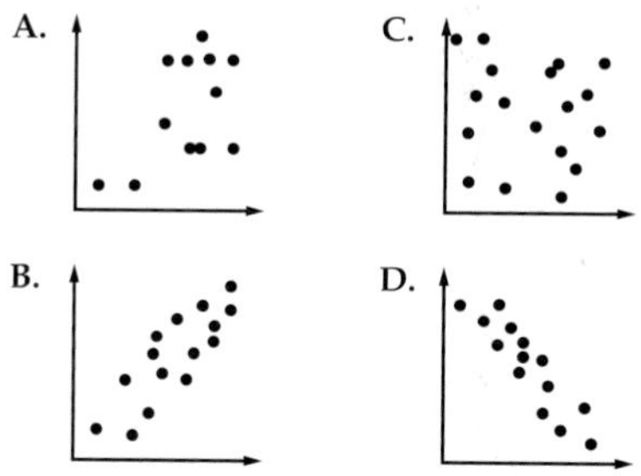

86. Which of the following most accurately describes the translation of the graph $y = (x + 4)^2 - 3$ to the graph of $y = (x - 1)^2 + 3$? I

F. down 1 and to the right 3
G. down 6 and to the left 5
H. up 1 and to the left 3
I. up 6 and to the right 5

87. SAT/ACT The positive difference between k and $\frac{1}{12}$ is the same as the positive difference between $\frac{1}{3}$ and $\frac{1}{5}$. Which of the following is the value of k? D

A. $\frac{1}{60}$
B. $\frac{1}{20}$
C. $\frac{1}{15}$
D. $\frac{13}{60}$

Spiral Review

Graph each polynomial function. Estimate the x-coordinates at which the relative maxima and relative minima occur. (Lesson 6-4) 88–90. See margin.

88. $f(x) = 2x^3 - 4x^2 + x + 8$

89. $f(x) = -3x^3 + 6x^2 + 2x - 1$

90. $f(x) = -x^3 + 3x^2 + 4x - 6$

State the degree and leading coefficient of each polynomial in one variable. If it is not a polynomial in one variable, explain why. (Lesson 6-3) 91–93. See margin.

91. $f(x) = 4x^3 - 6x^2 + 5x^4 - 8x$

92. $f(x) = -2x^5 + 5x^4 + 3x^2 + 9$

93. $f(x) = -x^4 - 3x^3 + 2x^6 - x^7$

94. ELECTRICITY The impedance in one part of a series circuit is $3 + 4j$ ohms, and the impedance in another part of the circuit is $2 - 6j$ ohms. Add these complex numbers to find the total impedance of the circuit. (Lesson 5-4) $5 - 2j$ ohms

95. SKIING All 28 members of a ski club went on a trip. The club paid a total of \$478 for the equipment. How many skis and snowboards did they rent? (Lesson 3-2) 18 skis and 10 snowboards

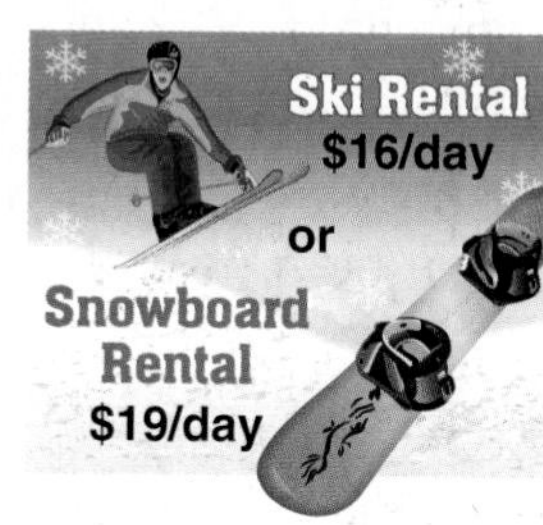

96. GEOMETRY The sides of an angle are parts of two lines whose equations are $2y + 3x = -7$ and $3y - 2x = 9$. The angle's vertex is the point where the two sides meet. Find the coordinates of the vertex of the angle. (Lesson 3-1) $(-3, 1)$

Skills Review

97. $x + 2 - \frac{10}{x + 4}$ 98. $x + 3.5 - \frac{13.5}{2x + 1}$ 99. $8x^2 - 12x + 24 - \frac{42}{x + 2}$

Divide. (Lesson 6-2)

97. $(x^2 + 6x - 2) \div (x + 4)$

98. $(2x^2 + 8x - 10) \div (2x + 1)$

99. $(8x^3 + 4x^2 + 6) \div (x + 2)$

Differentiated Instruction BL

Extension Draw a right triangle on the board. Under the triangle write "Area: $6x^2 + zy + 2xz + 3xy$." Ask students to find binomials with whole number coefficients for the base and height of this triangle. (*Hint:* The formula for the area of a triangle is $A = \frac{1}{2}bh$.) There are two possible answers: base: $(6x + 2z)$, height: $(2x + y)$; or base: $(3x + z)$, height: $(4x + 2y)$.

4 ASSESS

Name the Math Prepare two paper bags containing small pieces of paper: one containing polynomial equations that can be solved by factoring, and the other containing polynomial equations that are in quadratic form. Have each student select one equation from each bag and solve both equations.

Additional Answers

88. rel. maximum at $x \approx 0.1$; rel. minimum at $x \approx 1.2$;

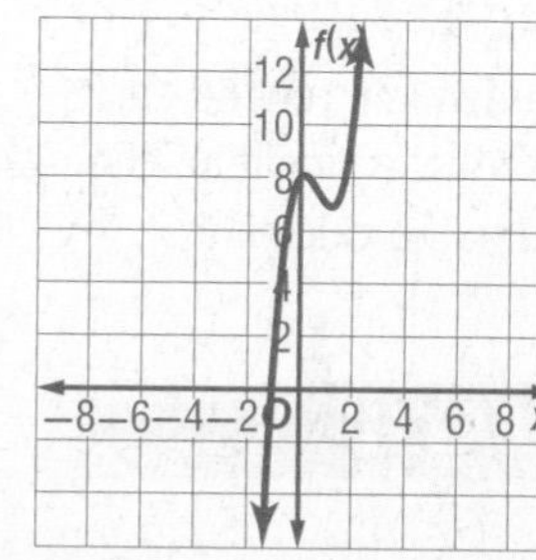

89. rel. maximum at $x \approx 1.5$, rel. minimum at $x \approx 0.1$;

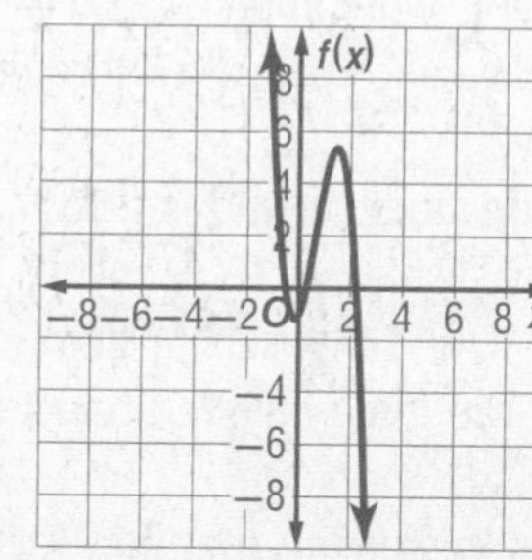

90. rel. maximum at $x \approx 2.5$, rel. minimum at $x \approx -0.5$;

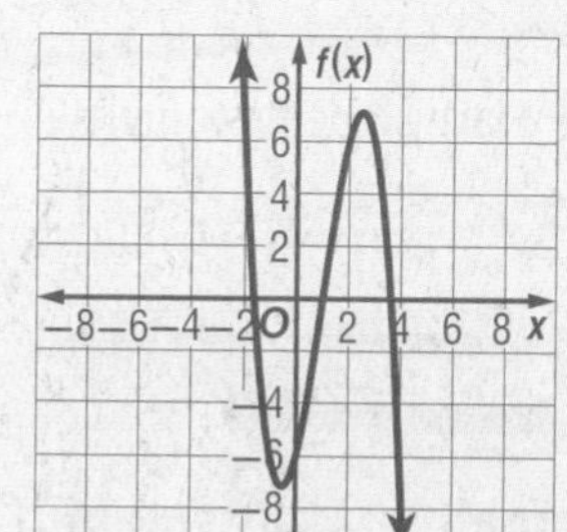

91. degree = 4; leading coefficient = 5

92. degree = 5; leading coefficient = −2

93. degree = 7; leading coefficient = −1

EXTEND **6-5** Lesson Notes

1 FOCUS

Objective Use a graphing calculator to find approximate solutions for polynomial equations.

Materials for Each Student

- TI-83/84 Plus or other graphing calculator

Teaching Tip

Remind students to rewrite each equation so that a single function can be entered in the calculator.

2 TEACH

Working in Cooperative Groups

Have students work in pairs, mixing abilities. Have each pair work through the Activity.

- Make sure students understand that a calculator display of 1E-12 means 1×10^{-12}, and that such a small number can often be interpreted as essentially 0.
- Point out to students that they may have to experiment to find appropriate window settings in the Exercises.

Practice Have students complete Exercises 1–9.

3 ASSESS

Formative Assessment

Use Exercise 1 to assess whether students are locating x-intercepts correctly.

From Concrete to Abstract

What is the maximum number of x-intercepts that the graph of a polynomial function can have? a number equal to the degree of the polynomial

EXTEND **6-5** Graphing Technology Lab

Solving Polynomial Equations

FL Math Online glencoe.com
- Other Calculator Keystrokes
- Graphing Technology Personal Tutor

NGSSS **MA.912.A.4.11 Solve a polynomial inequality by examining the graph with and without the use of technology.**

You can use a TI-83/84 Plus graphing calculator to approximate solutions of polynomial equations.

ACTIVITY

Solve $x^4 + 2x^3 \leq 7$.

Method 1

Step 1 Graph each side of the related equation separately.

KEYSTROKES: [Y=] [X,T,θ,n] [^] 4 [+] 2 [X,T,θ,n] [^] 3 [ENTER] 7 [ZOOM] 6

Step 2 Find the points of intersection.

KEYSTROKES: [2nd] [CALC] 5

Use [◀] or [▶] to position the cursor on Y1, near the first point of intersection. Press [ENTER] [ENTER] [ENTER].

Then use [▶] to position the cursor near the second intersection point. Press [ENTER] [ENTER] [ENTER].

Step 3 Examine the graphs. Determine where the graph of $y = x^4 + 2x^3$ intersects $y = 7$.

The solutions are approximately −2.47 and 1.29.

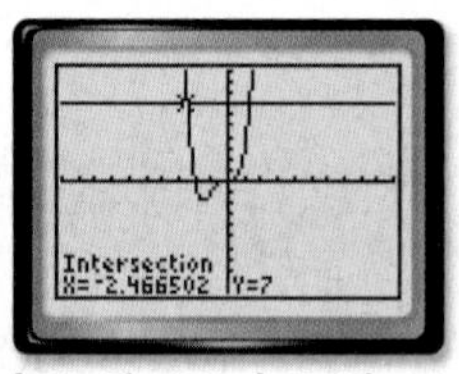

[−10, 10] scl: 1 by [−10, 10] scl: 1

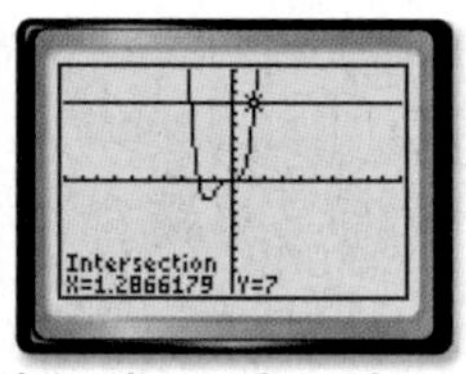

[−10, 10] scl: 1 by [−10, 10] scl: 1

Method 2

Step 1 Rewrite the equation so that one side equals 0. Then graph.

$$x^4 + 2x^3 = 7$$
$$x^4 + 2x^3 - 7 = 0$$

KEYSTROKES: [Y=] [X,T,θ,n] [^] 4 [+] 2 [X,T,θ,n] [^] 3 [−] 7 [ZOOM] 6

Step 2 Find the x-intercepts.

KEYSTROKES: [2nd] [CALC] 2

Use [◀] or [▶] to position the cursor to the left of the first x-intercept. Press [ENTER]. Then use [▶] to position the cursor to the right of the first x-intercept. Press [ENTER] [ENTER] to display the x-intercept. Then, repeat the procedure for any remaining x-intercepts.

Step 3 Examine the graphs. Determine where the graph of $y = x^4 + 2x^3 - 7$ crosses the x-axis.

The solutions are approximately −2.47 and 1.29.

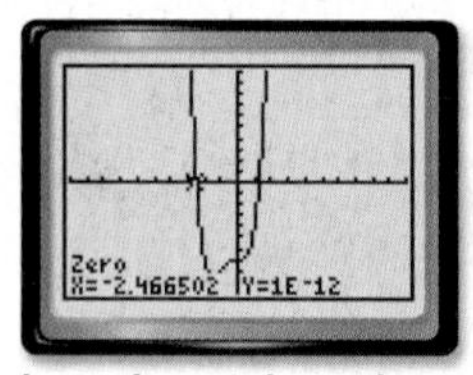

[−10, 10] scl: 1 by [−10, 10] scl: 1

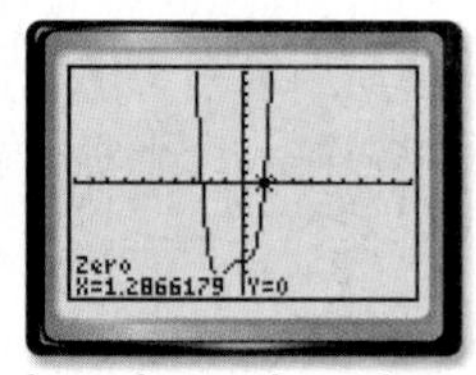

[−10, 10] scl: 1 by [−10, 10] scl: 1

Exercises 4. −2.31, 2.31 7. −3.63, −1.35, 1.35, 3.63 8. −0.69, 1.75, 4.95

Approximate the solutions of each inequality. Round to the nearest hundredth.

1. $\frac{2}{3}x^3 + x^2 - 5x = -9$ −4.11
2. $x^3 - 9x^2 + 27x = 20$ 1.09
3. $x^3 + 1 = 4x^2$ −0.47, 0.54, 3.94
4. $x^6 - 15 = 5x^4 - x^2$
5. $\frac{1}{2}x^5 = \frac{1}{5}x^2 - 2$ −1.27
6. $x^8 = -x^7 + 3$ −1.36, 1.06
7. $x^4 - 15x^2 = -24$
8. $x^3 - 6x^2 + 4x = -6$
9. $x^4 - 15x^2 + x + 65 = 0$ no solution

6-6 The Remainder and Factor Theorems

Why?

The number of college students from the United States who study abroad can be modeled by the function $S(x) = 0.02x^4 - 0.52x^3 + 4.03x^2 + 0.09x + 77.54$, where x is the number of years since 1993 and $S(x)$ is the number of students in thousands.

You can use this function to estimate the number of U.S. college students studying abroad in 2013 by evaluating the function for $x = 20$. Another method you can use is *synthetic substitution*.

Then
You used the Distributive Property and factoring to simplify algebraic expressions. (Lesson 5-3)

Now
- Evaluate functions by using synthetic substitution.
- Determine whether a binomial is a factor of a polynomial by using synthetic substitution.

NGSSS
MA.912.A.4.6 Use theorems of polynomial behavior to find the zeros of a polynomial function.
MA.912.A.4.8 Describe the relationships among the solutions of an equation, the zeros of a function, the x-intercepts of a graph, and the factors of a polynomial expression, with and without technology. *Also addresses MA.912.A.4.3.*

New Vocabulary
synthetic substitution
depressed polynomial

FL Math Online
glencoe.com

Synthetic Substitution Synthetic division can be used to find the value of a function. Consider the polynomial function $f(x) = -3x^2 + 5x + 4$. Divide the polynomial by $x - 3$.

Method 1 Long Division

$$\begin{array}{r} -3x - 4 \\ x - 3\overline{)-3x^2 + 5x + 4} \\ \underline{-3x^2 + 9x} \\ -4x + 4 \\ \underline{-4x + 12} \\ -8 \end{array}$$

Method 2 Synthetic Division

$$\begin{array}{r|rrr} 3 & -3 & 5 & 4 \\ & & -9 & -12 \\ \hline & -3 & -4 & -8 \end{array}$$

Compare the remainder of -8 to $f(3)$.

$f(3) = -3(3)^2 + 5(3) + 4$ **Replace x with 3.**

$= -27 + 15 + 4$ **Multiply.**

$= -8$ **Simplify.**

Notice that the value of $f(3)$ is the same as the remainder when the polynomial is divided by $x - 3$. This illustrates the **Remainder Theorem**.

Key Concept: Remainder Theorem

Words If a polynomial $P(x)$ is divided by $x - r$, the remainder is a constant $P(r)$, and

Dividend	equals	quotient	times	divisor	plus	remainder.
$P(x)$	$=$	$Q(x)$	$\cdot$	$(x - r)$	$+$	$P(r)$,

where $Q(x)$ is a polynomial with degree one less than $P(x)$.

Example $x^2 + 6x + 2 = (x - 4) \cdot (x + 10) + 42$

Applying the Remainder Theorem using synthetic division to evaluate a function is called **synthetic substitution**. It is a convenient way to find the value of a function, especially when the degree of the polynomial is greater than 2.

6-6 Lesson Notes

1 FOCUS

Vertical Alignment

Before Lesson 6-6
Use the Distributive Property and factoring to simplify algebraic expressions.

Lesson 6-6
Evaluate functions by using synthetic substitution.
Determine whether a binomial is a factor of a polynomial by using synthetic substitution.

After Lesson 6-6
Use tools including factoring to transform and solve equations.

2 TEACH

Scaffolding Questions

Have students read the *Why?* section of the lesson.

Ask:
- What would be the value of x if you wanted to estimate the number of students in 1994? 1
- Would you expect the actual number in 2013 to match the number predicted by the function? Explain. No. Sample answer: The equation is a model based on available data.

Lesson 6-6 Resources

Resource	Approaching-Level	On-Level	Beyond-Level	English Learners
Teacher Edition	• Differentiated Instruction, p. 379	• Differentiated Instruction, p. 379	• Differentiated Instruction, pp. 379, 382	• Differentiated Instruction, p. 379
Chapter Resource Masters	• Study Guide and Intervention, pp. 35–36 • Skills Practice, p. 37 • Practice, p. 38 • Word Problem Practice, p. 39	• Study Guide and Intervention, pp. 35–36 • Skills Practice, p. 37 • Practice, p. 38 • Word Problem Practice, p. 39 • Enrichment, p. 40	• Practice, p. 38 • Word Problem Practice, p. 39 • Enrichment, p. 40	• Study Guide and Intervention, pp. 35–36 • Skills Practice, p. 37 • Practice, p. 38 • Word Problem Practice, p. 39
Transparencies	• 5-Minute Check Transparency 6-6	• 5-Minute Check Transparency 6-6	• 5-Minute Check Transparency 6-6	• 5-Minute Check Transparency 6-6
Other	• Study Notebook	• Study Notebook	• Study Notebook	• Study Notebook

- Is the model more accurate for the years immediately following 1993 or for later years? Explain. Sample answer: The model closely matches actual data for the years immediately following 1993.

Synthetic Substitution

Example 1 shows how to use synthetic substitution to evaluate a function. **Example 2** shows how to use synthetic substitution to solve a real-world problem.

Formative Assessment

Use the Guided Practice exercises after each example to determine students' understanding of concepts.

Tips for New Teachers

Building on Prior Knowledge In Lesson 6-2, students learned synthetic division. In this lesson, students will use synthetic division to evaluate a function and to find factors of polynomials.

Additional Examples

1. If $f(x) = 2x^4 - 5x^2 + 8x - 7$, find $f(6)$. 2453
2. **COLLEGE** Refer to the application at the beginning of the lesson. How many U.S. college students will study abroad in 2011? about 451,760

Additional Examples also in Interactive Classroom PowerPoint® Presentations

IWB INTERACTIVE WHITEBOARD READY

EXAMPLE 1 Synthetic Substitution

If $f(x) = 3x^4 - 2x^3 + 5x + 2$, find $f(4)$.

Method 1 Synthetic Substitution

By the Remainder Theorem, $f(4)$ should be the remainder when the polynomial is divided by $x - 4$.

4	3	−2	0	5	2
		12	40	160	660
	3	10	40	165	662

Because there is no x^2 term, a zero is placed in this position as a placeholder.

The remainder is 662. Therefore, by using synthetic substitution, $f(4) = 662$.

Method 2 Direct Substitution

Replace x with 4.

$f(x) = 3x^4 - 2x^3 + 5x + 2$ **Original function**

$f(4) = 3(4)^4 - 2(4)^3 + 5(4) + 2$ **Replace x with 4.**

$= 768 - 128 + 20 + 2$ or 662 **Simplify.**

By using direct substitution, $f(4) = 662$. Both methods give the same result.

Guided Practice

1A. If $f(x) = 3x^3 - 6x^2 + x - 11$, find $f(3)$. 19

1B. If $g(x) = 4x^5 + 2x^3 + x^2 - 1$, find $f(-1)$. −6

Personal Tutor glencoe.com

Real-World Link

Some benefits of studying abroad include learning a new language, becoming more independent, and improving communication skills. Studying abroad also gives students a chance to experience different cultures and customs as well as try new foods.

Source: StudyAbroad

Synthetic substitution can be used in situations in which direct substitution would involve cumbersome calculations.

Real-World EXAMPLE 2 Find Function Values

COLLEGE Refer to the beginning of the lesson. How many U.S. college students will study abroad in 2013?

Use synthetic substitution to divide $0.02x^4 - 0.52x^3 + 4.03x^2 + 0.09x + 77.54$ by $x - 20$.

20	0.02	−0.52	4.03	0.09	77.54
		0.4	−2.4	32.6	653.8
	0.02	−0.12	1.63	32.69	731.34

In 2013, there will be about 731,340 U.S. college students studying abroad.

Guided Practice

2. COLLEGE The function $C(x) = 2.46x^3 - 22.37x^2 + 53.81x + 548.24$ can be used to approximate the number, in thousands, of international college students studying in the United States x years since 2000. How many international college students can be expected to study in the U.S. in 2012? **2,223,560**

Personal Tutor glencoe.com

Tips for New Teachers

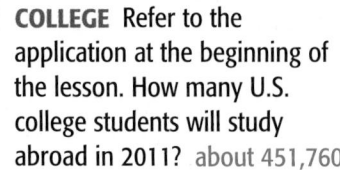

Pacing Most of this lesson relies heavily on synthetic substitution. Before finishing your discussion of Example 1, be certain that students understand the method. Ask a student volunteer to demonstrate the steps of synthetic substitution shown in Method 1 of Example 1, and invite students to discuss any problems they have with the technique.

Additional Answer (Guided Practice)

3.

2	1	−7	4	12
		2	−10	−12
	1	−5	−6	0

$(x - 2)(x - 6)(x + 1)$

378 Chapter 6 Polynomials and Polynomial Functions

Factors of Polynomials The synthetic division below shows that the quotient of $2x^3 - 3x^2 - 17x + 30$ and $x + 3$ is $2x^2 - 9x + 10$.

$$\begin{array}{r|rrrr} -3 & 2 & -3 & -17 & 30 \\ & & -6 & 27 & -30 \\ \hline & 2 & -9 & 10 & 0 \end{array}$$

When you divide a polynomial by one of its binomial factors, the quotient is called a depressed polynomial. A **depressed polynomial** has a degree that is one less than the original polynomial. From the results of the division, and by using the Remainder Theorem, we can make the following statement.

Dividend	equals	quotient	times	divisor	plus	remainder.
$2x^3 - 3x^2 - 17x + 30$	$=$	$(2x^2 - 9x + 10)$	$\cdot$	$(x + 3)$	$+$	0

Since the remainder is 0, $f(-3) = 0$. This means that $x + 3$ is a factor of $2x^3 - 3x^2 - 17x + 30$. This illustrates the **Factor Theorem**, which is a special case of the Remainder Theorem.

Key Concept **Factor Theorem**

The binomial $x - r$ is a factor of the polynomial $P(x)$ if and only if $P(r) = 0$.

The Factor Theorem can be used to determine whether a binomial is a factor of a polynomial. It can also be used to determine all of the factors of a polynomial.

EXAMPLE 3 Use the Factor Theorem

Determine whether $x - 5$ is a factor of $x^3 - 7x^2 + 7x + 15$. Then find the remaining factors of the polynomial.

The binomial $x - 5$ is a factor of the polynomial if 5 is a zero of the related polynomial function. Use the Factor Theorem and synthetic division.

$$\begin{array}{r|rrrr} 5 & 1 & -7 & 7 & 15 \\ & & 5 & -10 & -15 \\ \hline & 1 & -2 & -3 & 0 \end{array}$$

Because the remainder is 0, $x - 5$ is a factor of the polynomial. The polynomial $x^3 - 7x^2 + 7x + 15$ can be factored as $(x - 5)(x^2 - 2x - 3)$. The polynomial $x^2 - 2x - 3$ is the depressed polynomial. Check to see if this polynomial can be factored.

$x^2 - 2x - 3 = (x + 1)(x - 3)$ **Factor the trinomial.**

So, $x^3 - 7x^2 + 7x + 15 = (x - 5)(x + 1)(x - 3)$.

You can check your answer by multiplying out the factors and seeing if you come up with the initial polynomial.

StudyTip

Factoring The factors of a polynomial do not have to be binomials. For example, the factors of $x^3 + x^2 - x + 15$ are $x + 3$ and $x^2 - 2x + 5$.

Guided Practice

3. Show that $x - 2$ is a factor of $x^3 - 7x^2 + 4x + 12$. Then find the remaining factors of the polynomial. **See margin.**

Personal Tutor glencoe.com

Factors of Polynomials

Example 3 shows how to use the Factor Theorem to show that a binomial is a factor of a polynomial and then to find the remaining factors of the polynomial.

Additional Example

3 Determine whether $x - 3$ is a factor of $x^3 + 4x^2 - 15x - 18$. Then find the remaining factors of the polynomial

$$\begin{array}{r|rrrr} 3 & 1 & 4 & -15 & -18 \\ & & 3 & 21 & 18 \\ \hline & 1 & 7 & 6 & 0 \end{array}$$

So, $x^3 + 4x^2 - 15x - 18 = (x - 3)(x^2 + 7x + 6)$. Since $x^2 + 7x + 6 = (x + 1)(x + 6)$, $x^3 + 4x^2 - 15x - 18 = (x - 3)(x + 1)(x + 6)$.

Focus on Mathematical Content

Factor Theorem The Remainder Theorem says that the value of $f(a)$ is the same as the remainder when the polynomial is divided by $x - a$. The Factor Theorem is a special case of the Remainder Theorem. It says: If $f(a)$ has a value of 0, then $x - a$ is a factor of the polynomial.

Watch Out!

Preventing Errors Point out that the Factor Theorem does not say anything about which numbers to try. Techniques for identifying potential factors will be introduced later in the chapter.

Differentiated Instruction

AL OL BL ELL

If students can describe two or three things about this lesson that they found difficult to understand,

Then have them address each item by writing explanations that will help them review the material later.

TEACH with TECH

BLOG Have students write a blog entry explaining how the Remainder and Factor Theorems are related – specifically, have students describe how the Factor Theorem is a special case of the Remainder Theorem.

3 PRACTICE

Formative Assessment

Use Exercises 1–7 to check for understanding.

Use the chart at the bottom of this page to customize assignments for your students.

Watch Out!

Common Misconceptions Remind students that not all polynomials can be factored. Emphasize that the factors indicate where the graph of the function crosses the *x*-axis. If the graph of a polynomial function has no *x*-intercepts, then the polynomial cannot be factored. To see an example of a polynomial that cannot be factored, students can graph the function $f(x) = x^4 - x^3 - x^2 + 2$.

Additional Answers

28b. Sample answer: No; the graph of the function has a relative maximum at about $x = 8$ or the year 2008 and then the values for sales decrease. It is not likely that the sales would continually decrease.

36. $f(x) = 0.1(x - 1)^2(x + 5)^2$

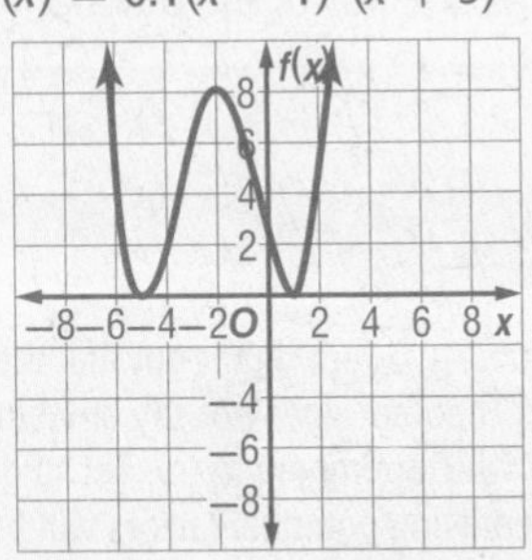

42. Sample answer: When $x = 1$, $f(1)$ is the sum of all of the coefficients and constants in $f(x)$, in this case, *a, b, c, d,* and *e*. The sum of *a, b, c, d,* and *e* is 0, so however the coefficients are arranged, $f(1)$ will always equal 0, and $f(x)$ will have a rational root.

Check Your Understanding

Example 1 p. 378 — **Use synthetic substitution to find $f(4)$ and $f(-2)$ for each function.**

1. $f(x) = 2x^3 - 5x^2 - x + 14$ **58; −20**
2. $f(x) = x^4 + 8x^3 + x^2 - 4x - 10$ **758; −46**

Example 2 p. 378

3. **NATURE** The approximate number of bald eagle nesting pairs in the United States can be modeled by the function $P(x) = -0.16x^3 + 15.83x^2 - 154.15x + 1147.97$, where x is the number of years since 1970. About how many nesting pairs of bald eagles can be expected in 2018? **12,526**

Example 3 p. 379 — **Given a polynomial and one of its factors, find the remaining factors of the polynomial.**

4. $x^3 - 6x^2 + 11x - 6;\ x - 1$ **$x - 2,\ x - 3$**
5. $x^3 + x^2 - 16x - 16;\ x + 1$ **$x + 4,\ x - 4$**
6. $3x^3 + 10x^2 - x - 12;\ x - 1$ **$x + 3,\ 3x + 4$**
7. $2x^3 - 5x^2 - 28x + 15;\ x + 3$ **$x - 5,\ 2x - 1$**

Practice and Problem Solving

= Step-by-Step Solutions begin on page R20.
Extra Practice begins on page 947.

Example 1 p. 378 — **Use synthetic substitution to find $f(-5)$ and $f(2)$ for each function.**

8. $f(x) = x^3 + 2x^2 - 3x + 1$ **−59; 11**
9. $f(x) = x^2 - 8x + 6$ **71; −6**
10. $f(x) = 3x^4 + x^3 - 2x^2 + x + 12$ **1707; 62**
11. $f(x) = 2x^3 - 8x^2 - 2x + 5$ **−435; −15**
12. $f(x) = x^3 - 5x + 2$ **−98; 0**
13. $f(x) = x^5 + 8x^3 + 2x - 15$ **−4150; 85**
14. $f(x) = x^6 - 4x^4 + 3x^2 - 10$ **13,190; 2**
15. $f(x) = x^4 - 6x - 8$ **647; −4**

Example 2 p. 378

16. **FINANCIAL LITERACY** A specific car's fuel economy in miles per gallon can be approximated by $f(x) = 0.00000056x^4 - 0.000018x^3 - 0.016x^2 + 1.38x - 0.38$, where x represents the car's speed in miles per hour. Determine the fuel economy when the car is traveling 40, 50 and 60 miles per hour. **29.5 mpg; 29.87 mpg; 28.19 mpg**

Example 3 p. 379 — **Given a polynomial and one of its factors, find the remaining factors of the polynomial.** **18. $x - 2,\ x^2 + 2x + 4$ 21. $x + 6,\ 2x + 7$ 23. $x + 1,\ x^2 + 2x + 3$**

17. $x^3 - 3x + 2;\ x + 2$ **$(x - 1)^2$**
18. $x^4 + 2x^3 - 8x - 16;\ x + 2$
19. $x^3 - x^2 - 10x - 8;\ x + 2$ **$x - 4,\ x + 1$**
20. $x^3 - x^2 - 5x - 3;\ x - 3$ **$(x + 1)^2$**
21. $2x^3 + 17x^2 + 23x - 42;\ x - 1$
22. $2x^3 + 7x^2 - 53x - 28;\ x - 4$ **$x + 7,\ 2x + 1$**
23. $x^4 + 2x^3 + 2x^2 - 2x - 3;\ x - 1$
24. $x^3 + 2x^2 - x - 2;\ x + 2$ **$x - 1,\ x + 1$**
25. $6x^3 - 25x^2 + 2x + 8;\ 2x + 1$ **$x - 4,\ 3x - 2$**
26. $16x^5 - 32x^4 - 81x + 162;\ 2x - 3$ **$x - 2,\ 2x + 3,\ 4x^2 + 9$**

Real-World Link

The average American spends about $8500 annually on consumer electronics.

Source: IT Facts

27. **BOATING** A motor boat traveling against waves accelerates from a resting position. Suppose the speed of the boat in feet per second is given by the function $f(t) = -0.04t^4 + 0.8t^3 + 0.5t^2 - t$, where t is the time in seconds.
    a. Find the speed of the boat at 1, 2, and 3 seconds. **0.26 ft/s, 5.76 ft/s, 19.86 ft/s**
    b. It takes 6 seconds for the boat to travel between two buoys while it is accelerating. Use synthetic substitution to find $f(6)$ and explain what this means. **132.96 ft/s; This means the boat is traveling at 132.96 ft/s when it passes the second buoy.**
28. **SALES** A company's sales, in millions of dollars, of consumer electronics can be modeled by $S(x) = -1.7x^3 + 18x^2 + 26.4x + 678$, where x is the number of years since 2005. **a. $1047.5 million; $1042 million**
    a. Use synthetic substitution to estimate the sales for 2010 and 2015.
    b. Do you think this model is useful in estimating future sales? Explain. **See margin.**

Differentiated Homework Options

Level	Assignment	Two-Day Option	
AL Basic	8–26, 36, 39, 41, 43, 44–63	8–26 odd, 44–47	8–26 even, 36, 39, 41, 43, 48–63
OL Core	9–35 odd, 36, 39, 41, 43, 44–63	8–26, 44–47	27–35, 36, 39, 41, 43, 48–63
BL Advanced	27–57, (optional: 58–63)		

Use the graph to find all of the factors for each polynomial function.

29.

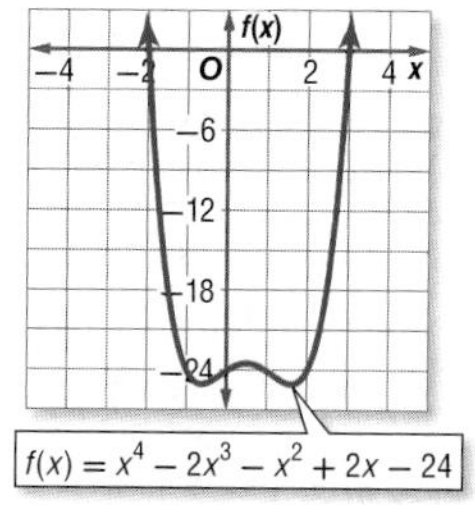

$x + 2$, $x - 3$, $x^2 - x + 4$

30.

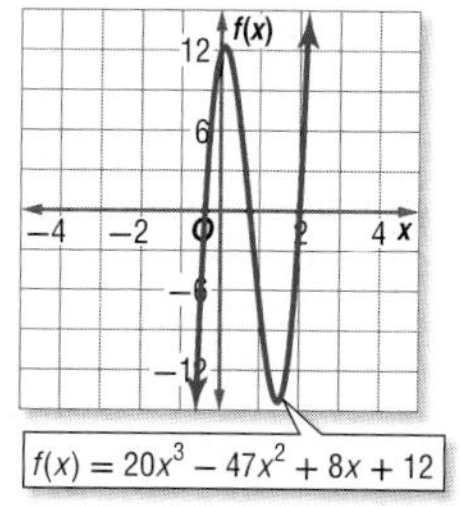

$x - 2$, $4x - 3$, $5x + 2$

31a–d. See Chapter 6 Answer Appendix.

31. **MULTIPLE REPRESENTATIONS** In this problem, you will consider the function $f(x) = -9x^5 + 104x^4 - 249x^3 - 456x^2 + 828x + 432$.

a. **ALGEBRAIC** If $x - 6$ is a factor of the function, find the depressed polynomial.

b. **TABULAR** Make a table of values for $-5 \leq x \leq 6$ for the depressed polynomial.

c. **ANALYTICAL** What conclusions can you make about the locations of the other zeros based on the table? Explain your reasoning.

d. **GRAPHICAL** Graph the original function to confirm your conclusions.

Find values of k so that each remainder is 3.

32. $(x^2 - x + k) \div (x - 1)$ **3**

33. $(x^2 + kx - 17) \div (x - 2)$ **8**

34. $(x^2 + 5x + 7) \div (x - k)$ **1, 4**

35. $(x^3 + 4x^2 + x + k) \div (x + 2)$ **−3**

Watch Out!

Synthetic Substitution Remember that synthetic substitution is used to divide a polynomial by $(x - a)$. If the binomial is $(x - a)$, use a. If the binomial is $(x + a)$, use $-a$.

H.O.T. Problems

Use Higher-Order Thinking Skills

36. **OPEN ENDED** Write a polynomial function that has a double root of 1 and a double root of −5. Graph the function. **See margin.**

CHALLENGE Find the solutions of each polynomial function. **37. $\pm\sqrt{6}$, $\pm\sqrt{3}$**

37. $(x^2 - 4)^2 - (x^2 - 4) - 2 = 0$

38. $(x^2 + 3)^2 - 7(x^2 + 3) + 12 = 0$ **−1, 0, 1**

39. **REASONING** Polynomial $f(x)$ is divided by $x - c$. What can you conclude if:

a. the remainder is 0? **$x - c$ is a factor of $f(x)$.**

b. the remainder is 1? **$x - c$ is not a factor of $f(x)$.**

c. the quotient is 1, and the remainder is 0? **$f(x) = x - c$**

40. **CHALLENGE** Review the definition for the Factor Theorem. Provide a proof of the theorem.

40. If $x - a$ is a factor of $f(x)$, then $f(a)$ has a factor of $(a - a)$ or 0. Since a factor of $f(a)$ is 0, $f(a) = 0$. Now assume that $f(a) = 0$. If $f(a) = 0$, then the Remainder Theorem states that the remainder is 0 when $f(x)$ is divided by $x - a$. This means that $x - a$ is a factor of $f(x)$. This proves the Factor Theorem.

41. **OPEN ENDED** Write a cubic function that has a remainder of 8 for $f(2)$ and a remainder of −5 for $f(3)$. **Sample answer: $f(x) = -x^3 + x^2 + x + 10$**

42. **CHALLENGE** Show that the quartic function $f(x) = ax^4 + bx^3 + cx^2 + dx + e$ will always have a rational zero when the numbers 1, −2, 3, 4, and −6 are randomly assigned to replace a through e, and all of the numbers are used. **See margin.**

43. **WRITING IN MATH** Explain how the zeros of a function can be located by using the Remainder Theorem and making a table of values for different input values and then comparing the remainders.

43. Sample answer: A zero can be located using the Remainder Theorem and a table of values by determining when the output, or remainder, is equal to zero. For instance, if $f(6)$ leaves a remainder of 2 and $f(7)$ leaves a remainder of −1, then you know that there is a zero between $x = 6$ and $x = 7$.

Multiple Representations In Exercise 31, students use analysis, a table of values, and a graph to investigate the properties of a higher-order function.

Study Guide and Intervention

CRM pp. 35–36 AL OL ELL

6-6 Study Guide and Intervention

The Remainder and Factor Theorems

Synthetic Substitution

Remainder Theorem	The remainder, when you divide the polynomial $f(x)$ by $(x - a)$, is the constant $f(a)$. $f(x) = q(x) \cdot (x - a) + f(a)$, where $q(x)$ is a polynomial with degree one less than the degree of $f(x)$.

Example 1 If $f(x) = 3x^4 + 2x^3 - 5x^2 + x - 2$, find $f(-2)$.

Method 1 Synthetic Substitution

By the Remainder Theorem, $f(-2)$ should be the remainder when you divide the polynomial by $x + 2$.

−2	3	2	−5	1	−2
		−6	8	−6	10
	3	−4	3	−5	8

The remainder is 8, so $f(-2) = 8$.

Method 2 Direct Substitution

Replace x with −2.

$f(x) = 3x^4 + 2x^3 - 5x^2 + x - 2$

$f(-2) = 3(-2)^4 + 2(-2)^3 - 5(-2)^2 + (-2) - 2$

$= 48 - 16 - 20 - 2 - 2$ or 8

So $f(-2) = 8$.

Example 2 If $f(x) = 5x^3 + 2x - 1$, find $f(3)$.

Again, by the Remainder Theorem, $f(3)$ should be the remainder when you divide the polynomial by $x - 3$.

3	5	0	2	−1
		15	45	141
	5	15	47	140

The remainder is 140, so $f(3) = 140$.

Exercises

Use synthetic substitution to find $f(-5)$ and $f(\frac{1}{2})$ for each function.

1. $f(x) = -3x^2 + 5x - 1$ **$-101; \frac{3}{4}$**
2. $f(x) = 4x^2 + 6x - 7$ **63; −3**
3. $f(x) = -x^3 + 3x^2 - 5$ **$195; -\frac{35}{8}$**
4. $f(x) = x^4 + 11x^2 - 1$ **$899; \frac{29}{16}$**

Use synthetic substitution to find $f(4)$ and $f(-3)$ for each function.

5. $f(x) = 2x^3 + x^2 - 5x + 3$ **127; −27**
6. $f(x) = 3x^3 - 4x + 2$ **178; −67**
7. $f(x) = 5x^3 - 4x^2 + 2$ **258; −169**
8. $f(x) = 2x^4 - 4x^3 + 3x^2 + x - 6$ **302; 288**
9. $f(x) = 5x^4 + 3x^3 - 4x^2 - 2x + 4$ **1404; 298**
10. $f(x) = 3x^4 - 2x^3 - x^2 + 2x - 5$ **627; 277**
11. $f(x) = 2x^4 - 4x^3 - x^2 - 6x + 3$ **219; 282**
12. $f(x) = 4x^4 - 4x^3 + 3x^2 - 2x - 3$ **805; 462**

Chapter 6 35 Glencoe Algebra 2

Practice

CRM p. 38 AL OL BL ELL

6-6 Practice

The Remainder and Factor Theorems

Use synthetic substitution to find $f(-3)$ and $f(4)$ for each function.

1. $f(x) = x^2 + 2x + 3$ **6, 27**
2. $f(x) = x^2 - 5x + 10$ **34, 6**
3. $f(x) = x^2 - 5x - 4$ **20, −8**
4. $f(x) = x^3 - x^2 - 2x + 3$ **−27, 43**
5. $f(x) = x^3 + 2x^2 + 5$ **−4, 101**
6. $f(x) = x^3 - 6x^2 + 2x$ **−87, −24**
7. $f(x) = x^3 - 2x^2 - 2x + 8$ **−31, 32**
8. $f(x) = x^3 - x^2 + 4x - 4$ **−52, 60**
9. $f(x) = x^3 + 3x^2 + 2x - 50$ **−56, 70**
10. $f(x) = x^4 + x^3 - 3x^2 - x + 12$ **42, 280**
11. $f(x) = x^4 - 2x^2 - x + 7$ **73, 227**
12. $f(x) = 2x^4 - 3x^3 + 4x^2 - 2x + 1$ **286, 377**
13. $f(x) = 2x^4 - x^3 + 2x^2 - 26$ **181, 454**
14. $f(x) = 3x^4 - 4x^3 + 3x^2 - 5x - 3$ **390, 537**
15. $f(x) = x^5 + 7x^3 - 4x - 10$ **−430, 1446**
16. $f(x) = x^6 + 2x^5 - x^4 + x^3 - 9x^2 + 20$ **74, 5828**

Given a polynomial and one of its factors, find the remaining factors of the polynomial.

17. $x^3 + 3x^2 - 6x - 8; x - 2$ **$x + 1, x + 4$**
18. $x^3 + 7x^2 + 7x - 15; x - 1$ **$x + 3, x + 5$**
19. $x^3 - 9x^2 + 27x - 27; x - 3$ **$x - 3, x - 3$**
20. $x^3 - x^2 - 8x + 12; x + 3$ **$x - 2, x - 2$**
21. $x^3 + 5x^2 - 2x - 24; x - 2$ **$x + 3, x + 4$**
22. $x^3 - x^2 - 14x + 24; x + 4$ **$x - 3, x - 2$**
23. $3x^3 - 4x^2 - 17x + 6; x + 2$ **$x - 3, 3x - 1$**
24. $4x^3 - 12x^2 - x + 3; x - 3$ **$2x - 1, 2x + 1$**
25. $18x^3 + 9x^2 - 2x - 1; 2x + 1$ **$3x + 1, 3x - 1$**
26. $6x^3 + 5x^2 - 3x - 2; 3x - 2$ **$2x + 1, x + 1$**
27. $x^5 + x^4 - 5x^3 - 5x^2 + 4x + 4; x + 1$ **$x - 1, x + 1, x - 2, x + 2$**
28. $x^5 - 2x^4 + 4x^3 - 8x^2 - 5x + 10; x - 2$ **$x - 1, x + 1, x^2 + 5$**

29. **POPULATION** The projected population in thousands for a city over the next several years can be estimated by the function $P(x) = x^3 + 2x^2 - 8x + 520$, where x is the number of years since 2005. Use synthetic substitution to estimate the population for 2010. **655,000**

30. **VOLUME** The volume of water in a rectangular swimming pool can be modeled by the polynomial $2x^3 - 9x^2 + 7x + 6$. If the depth of the pool is given by the polynomial $2x + 1$, what polynomials express the length and width of the pool? **$x - 3$ and $x - 2$**

Chapter 6 38 Glencoe Algebra 2

Word Problem Practice

CRM p. 39 AL OL BL ELL

6-6 Word Problem Practice

The Remainder and Factor Theorems

1. **HEIGHT** A ball tossed into the air follows a parabolic trajectory. Its height after t seconds is given by a polynomial of degree two with leading coefficient −16. Using synthetic substitution, Norman found that the polynomial evaluates to 0 for the values $t = 0$ and $t = 4$. What is the polynomial that describes the ball's height as a function of t?
$-16t^2 + 64t$

2. **SYNTHETIC SUBSTITUTION** Branford evaluates the polynomial $p(x) = x^3 - 5x^2 + 3x + 5$ for a factor using synthetic substitution. Some of his work is shown below. Unfortunately, the factor and the solution have ink spots over it.

[illegible]	1	−5	3	5
		11	66	759
	1	6	69	[illegible]

What is the factor he solved for? What is the hidden solution?
11; 764

3. **PROFIT** The profits of Clyde's Corporation can be modeled by the polynomial $P(y) = y^4 - 4y^3 + 2y^2 + 10y - 200$, where y is the number of years after the business was started. The chief financial officer wants to know the value of $P(10)$. Use synthetic substitution to determine $P(10)$. Show your work.

10	1	−4	2	10	−200
		10	60	620	6300
	1	6	62	630	6100

$P(10) = 6100$

4. **EXPONENTIALS** The exponential function $t = e^x$ is a special function that you will learn about later. It is not a polynomial function. However, for small values of x, the value of e^x is very closely approximated by the polynomial function

$e(x) = \frac{1}{6}x^3 + \frac{1}{2}x^2 + x + 1.$

Use synthetic substitution to determine $e(0.1)$. Show your work.

0.1	$\frac{1}{6}$	$\frac{1}{2}$	1	1
		$\frac{1}{60}$	$\frac{31}{600}$	$\frac{631}{6000}$
	$\frac{1}{6}$	$\frac{31}{60}$	$\frac{631}{600}$	$\frac{6631}{6000}$

$1\frac{631}{6000}$

5. **VOLUME** The volume in cubic feet of one popular size of above-ground pool is given by the polynomial

$v(x) = \pi(x^3 - 5x^2 - 80x + 360).$

a. Use synthetic division to show that $x - 4$ is a factor of $v(x)$. Show your work.
See students' work.

b. Factor $v(x)$ completely.
$\pi(x - 4)(x + 9)(x - 10)$

c. What is the value of $v(10)$?
0

Chapter 6 39 Glencoe Algebra 2

Enrichment

CRM p. 40 OL BL

6-6 Enrichment

Radical Notation

In 1494, the first Edition of *Summa de arithmetica geometrica proprtioni et proportionalita*, now known as the *Suma*, was printed in Italy. The author, Luca Pacioli, wrote the book as a summary of the mathematical knowledge at the time. However, the notation used in the book is quite similar to the notation used today. For example, to represent radicals, the following was used:

6 . p . R . 10

In our notation, the p represents "plus" and the R represents "radical." So, 6 . p . R . 10 means $6 + \sqrt{10}$.

1. What letter would you expect to represent subtraction?
m

2. Translate the following notations into modern notation.

a. 18 . m . R . 90
$18 - \sqrt{90}$

b. 108 . m . R . 3240 . p . R . 3240 . m . R . 900
$108 - \sqrt{3240} + \sqrt{3240} - \sqrt{900}$

Lesson 6-6 The Remainder and Factor Theorems 381

4 ASSESS

Ticket out the Door Ask students to explain how synthetic substitution is related to synthetic division.

Formative Assessment

Check for student understanding of concepts in Lessons 6-5 and 6-6.

CRM Quiz 3, p. 58

Additional Answers

51a. −1.5(max), 0.5(min), 2.5(max)

51b. −3.5, 3.75 **51c.** 4

51d. D = {all real numbers}; R = {y | y ≤ 4.5}

52a. −2(max), 0(min), 3(max), 3.5(min)

52b. −3.75, −1, 1.5, 3.25, 3.75 **52c.** 5

52d. D = {all real numbers}; R = {all real numbers}

53a. −3(min), −1(max), 1(min)

53b. −0.25, 3 **53c.** 4

53d. D = {all real numbers}; R = {y | y ≥ −4.5}

55.

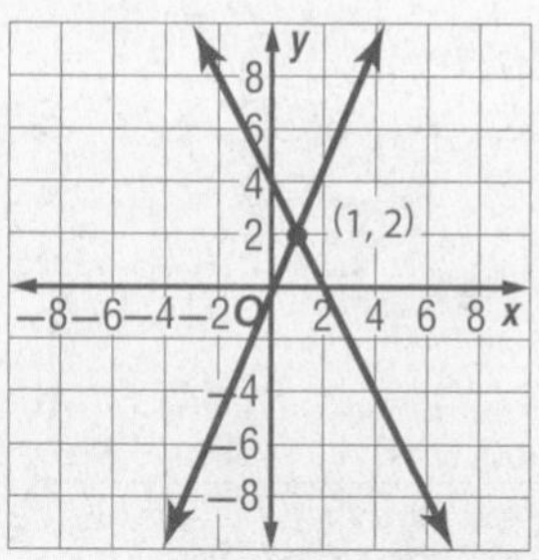

56.

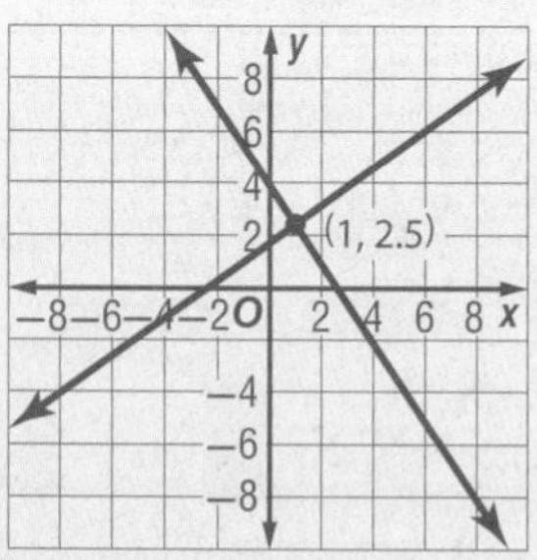

57.

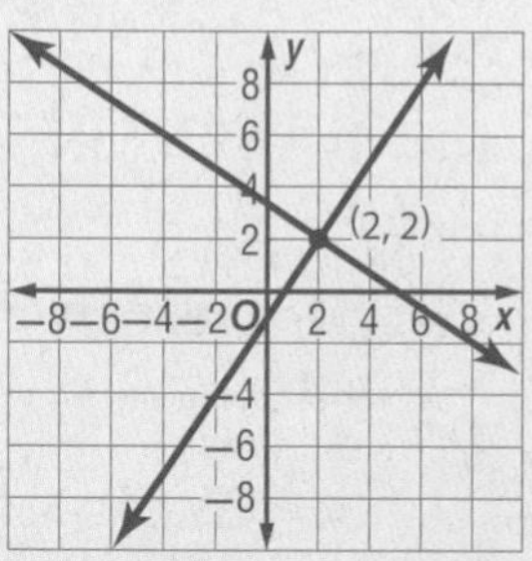

NGSSS PRACTICE 912.A.4.3, 912.G.6.5, 912.A.1.6, 912.A.3.15

44. $27x^3 + y^3 =$ **B**

A. $(3x + y)(3x + y)(3x + y)$
B. $(3x + y)(9x^2 - 3xy + y^2)$
C. $(3x - y)(9x^2 + 3xy + y^2)$
D. $(3x - y)(9x^2 + 9xy + y^2)$

45. **GRIDDED RESPONSE** In the figure, a square with side length $2\sqrt{2}$ is inscribed in a circle. The area of the circle is $k\pi$. What is the exact value of k? **4**

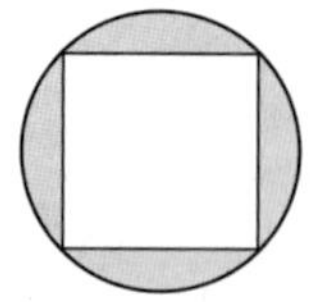

46. What is the product of the complex numbers $(4 + i)(4 - i)$? **H**

F. 15 H. 17
G. $16 - i$ I. $17 - 8i$

47. **SAT/ACT** The measure of the largest angle of a triangle is 14 less than twice the measure of the smallest angle. The third angle measure is 2 more than the measure of the smallest angle. What is the measure of the smallest angle? **B**

A. 46 C. 50
B. 48 D. 82

Spiral Review

Solve each equation. (Lesson 6-5)

48. $x^4 - 4x^2 - 21 = 0$ $\pm\sqrt{7}, \pm i\sqrt{3}$ **49.** $x^4 - 6x^2 = 27$ $\pm 3, \pm i\sqrt{3}$ **50.** $4x^4 - 8x^2 - 96 = 0$ $\pm\sqrt{6}, \pm 2i$

Complete each of the following. (Lesson 6-4)

a. Estimate the x-coordinate of every turning point and determine if those coordinates are relative maxima or relative minima.
b. Estimate the x-coordinate of every zero.
c. Determine the smallest possible degree of the function.
d. Determine the domain and range of the function. **51–53. See margin.**

51.

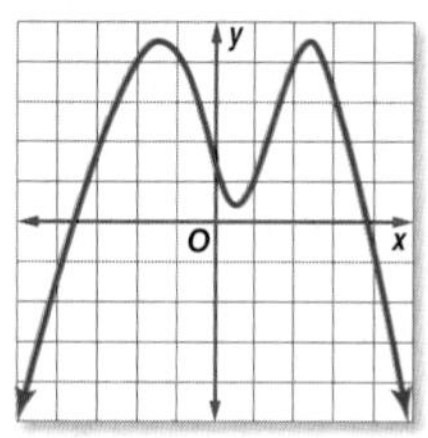

52.

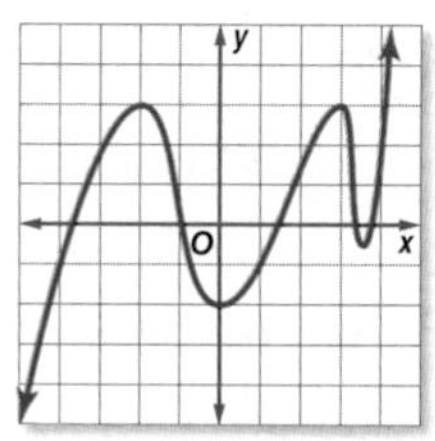

53.

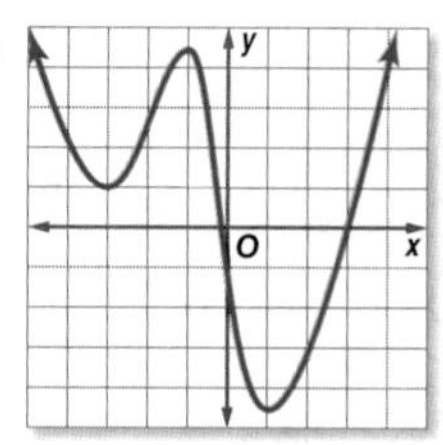

54. **HIGHWAY SAFETY** Engineers can use the formula $d = 0.05v^2 + 1.1v$ to estimate the minimum stopping distance d in feet for a vehicle traveling v miles per hour. If a car is able to stop after 125 feet, what is the fastest it could have been traveling when the driver first applied the brakes? (Lesson 5-6) **about 40.2 mph**

Solve by graphing. (Lesson 3-1) **55–57. See margin.**

55. $y = 3x - 1$, $y = -2x + 4$ **56.** $3x + 2y = 8$, $-4x + 6y = 11$ **57.** $5x - 2y = 6$, $3x - 2y = 2$

Skills Review

If $c(x) = x^2 - 2x$ and $d(x) = 3x^2 - 6x + 4$, find each value. (Lesson 6-3) **58.** $-2a^2 + 32a - 76$

58. $c(a + 2) - d(a - 4)$ **59.** $c(a - 3) + d(a + 1)$ $4a^2 - 8a + 16$ **60.** $c(-3a) + d(a + 4)$ $12a^2 + 24a + 28$

61. $3d(3a) - 2c(-a)$ $79a^2 - 58a + 12$ **62.** $c(a) + 5d(2a)$ $61a^2 - 62a + 20$ **63.** $-2d(2a + 3) - 4c(a^2 + 1)$ $-4a^4 - 24a^2 - 48a - 22$

Differentiated Instruction OL BL

Extension Explain to students that they already know how to use substitution to find $f(4)$ when $f(x) = x^3 - 6x^2 + 9x - 7$; $f(4) = 4^3 - 6(4)^2 + 9(4) - 7 = 64 - 96 + 36 - 7 = -3$. This method often requires a calculator. Tell students you will show them a method of evaluating a polynomial in which you do not have to compute powers using what is known as a recursive form of the polynomial. In this case, rewrite $x^3 - 6x^2 + 9x - 7$ as $[(x - 6)x + 9]x - 7$.
So $f(4) = [(4 - 6) \cdot 4 + 9] \cdot 4 - 7 = (-2 \cdot 4 + 9) \cdot 4 - 7 = 1 \cdot 4 - 7 = -3$.

6-7 Roots and Zeros

Why?

The function $g(x) = 1.384x^4 - 0.003x^3 + 0.28x^2 - 0.078x + 1.365$ can be used to model the average price of a gallon of gasoline in a given year if x is the number of years since 1990. To find the average price of gasoline in a specific year, you can use the roots of the related polynomial equation.

Then
You used complex numbers to describe solutions of quadratic equations. (Lesson 5-4)

Now
- Determine the number and type of roots for a polynomial equation.
- Find the zeros of a polynomial function.

NGSSS
MA.912.A.4.6 Use theorems of polynomial behavior to find the zeros of a polynomial function.
MA.912.A.4.8 Describe the relationships among the solutions of an equation, the zeros of a function, the x-intercepts of a graph, and the factors of a polynomial expression, with and without technology. *Also addresses MA.912.A.4.3 and MA.912.A.4.7.*

FL Math Online
glencoe.com

Synthetic Types of Roots Previously, you learned that a zero of a function $f(x)$ is any value c such that $f(c) = 0$. When the function is graphed, the real zeros of the function are the x-intercepts of the graph.

Concept Summary

Zeros, Factors, Roots, and Intercepts

Words Let $P(x) = a_nx^n + \cdots + a_1x + a_0$ be a polynomial function. Then the following statements are equivalent.

- c is a zero of $P(x)$.
- c is a root or solution of $P(x) = 0$.
- $x - c$ is a factor of $a_nx^n + \cdots + a_1x + a_0$.
- If c is a real number, then $(c, 0)$ is an x-intercept of the graph of $P(x)$.

Example Consider the polynomial function $P(x) = x^4 + 2x^3 - 7x^2 - 8x + 12$.

The zeros of $P(x) = x^4 + 2x^3 - 7x^2 - 8x + 12$ are $-3, -2, 1$, and 2.

The roots of $x^4 + 2x^3 - 7x^2 - 8x + 12 = 0$ are $-3, -2, 1$, and 2.

The factors of $x^4 + 2x^3 - 7x^2 - 8x + 12$ are $(x + 3), (x + 2), (x - 1)$, and $(x - 2)$.

The x-intercepts of the graph of $P(x) = x^4 + 2x^3 - 7x^2 - 8x + 12$ are $(-3, 0), (-2, 0), (1, 0)$, and $(2, 0)$.

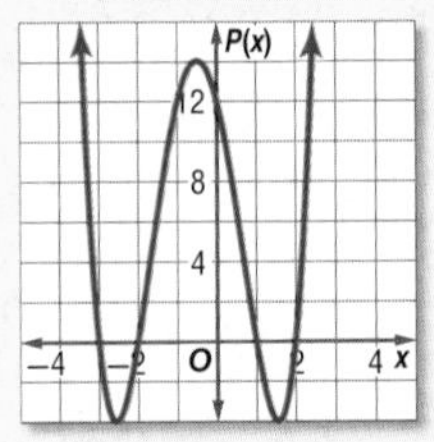

When solving a polynomial equation with degree greater than zero, there may be one or more real roots or no real roots (the roots are imaginary numbers). Since real numbers and imaginary numbers both belong to the set of complex numbers, all polynomial equations with degree greater than zero will have at least one root in the set of complex numbers. This is the **Fundamental Theorem of Algebra**.

Key Concept — Fundamental Theorem of Algebra

Every polynomial equation with degree greater than zero has at least one root in the set of complex numbers.

6-7 Lesson Notes

1 FOCUS

Vertical Alignment

Before Lesson 6-7
Use complex numbers to describe the solutions of quadratic equations.

Lesson 6-7
Determine the number and type of roots for a polynomial equation.
Find the zeros of a polynomial function.

After Lesson 6-7
Use tools including factoring to transform and solve equations.

2 TEACH

Scaffolding Questions

Have students read the *Why?* section of the lesson.

Ask:
- According to the equation, what was the average price of a gallon of gas in 1990? about $1.37
- Would the given equation be valid for negative values of x? Possibly; negative x would correspond to years *before* 1990.

Lesson 6-7 Resources

Resource	Approaching-Level	On-Level	Beyond-Level	English Learners
Teacher Edition	• Differentiated Instruction, p. 386	• Differentiated Instruction, pp. 386, 390	• Differentiated Instruction, pp. 386, 390	• Differentiated Instruction, p. 386
Chapter Resource Masters	• Study Guide and Intervention, pp. 41–42 • Skills Practice, p. 43 • Practice, p. 44 • Word Problem Practice, p. 45	• Study Guide and Intervention, pp. 41–42 • Skills Practice, p. 43 • Practice, p. 44 • Word Problem Practice, p. 45 • Enrichment, p. 46	• Practice, p. 44 • Word Problem Practice, p. 45 • Enrichment, p. 46	• Study Guide and Intervention, pp. 41–42 • Skills Practice, p. 43 • Practice, p. 44 • Word Problem Practice, p. 45
Transparencies	• 5-Minute Check Transparency 6-7	• 5-Minute Check Transparency 6-7	• 5-Minute Check Transparency 6-7	• 5-Minute Check Transparency 6-7
Other	• Study Notebook • Teaching Algebra with Manipulatives	• Study Notebook • Teaching Algebra with Manipulatives	• Study Notebook	• Study Notebook • Teaching Algebra with Manipulatives

Synthetic Types of Roots

Example 1 shows how to determine the number and type of roots of a polynomial equation. **Example 2** shows how to determine the possible number of positive real zeros, negative real zeros, and imaginary zeros of a polynomial function.

Formative Assessment

Use the Guided Practice exercises after each example to determine students' understanding of concepts.

Additional Example

1 Solve each equation. State the number and type of roots.

a. $x^2 + 2x - 48 = 0$ This equation has two real roots, 6 and –8.

b. $y^4 - 256 = 0$ This equation has two real roots, 4 and –4, and two imaginary roots, $4i$ and $-4i$.

Additional Examples also in Interactive Classroom PowerPoint® Presentations

IWB INTERACTIVE WHITEBOARD READY

Focus on Mathematical Content

Zeros The real zeros of a polynomial function f are the x-intercepts of the graph of f. They are also the real solutions of the polynomial equation $f(x) = 0$. A polynomial function cannot have more zeros than its degree.

ReadingMath

Repeated Roots Polynomial equations can have double roots, triple roots, quadruple roots, and so on. In general, these are referred to as *multiple roots*.

1B. $2, -2, 2i, -2i$; 2 real, 2 imaginary
1C. $-1, 2, -5$; 3 real
1D. $\frac{1}{3}, i\sqrt{3}, -i\sqrt{3}$; 1 real, 2 imaginary

EXAMPLE 1 Determine Number and Type of Roots

Solve each equation. State the number and type of roots.

a. $x^2 + 6x + 9 = 0$

$x^2 + 6x + 9 = 0$	**Original equation**
$(x + 3)^2 = 0$	**Factor.**
$x + 3 = 0$	**Take the root of each side.**
$x = -3$	**Solve for *x*.**

Because $(x + 3)$ is twice a factor of $x^2 + 6x + 9$, -3 is a double root. Thus, the equation has one real repeated root, -3.

CHECK The graph of the equation touches the x-axis at $x = -3$. Since -3 is a double root, the graph does not cross the axis. ✓

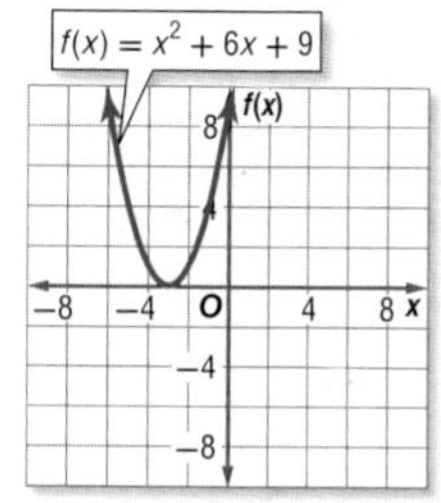

b. $x^3 + 25x = 0$

$x^3 + 25x = 0$	**Original equation**
$x(x^2 + 25) = 0$	**Factor.**
$x = 0$ or $x^2 + 25 = 0$	
$x^2 = -25$	
$x = \pm\sqrt{-25}$ or $\pm 5i$	

This equation has one real root, 0, and two imaginary roots, $5i$ and $-5i$.

CHECK The graph of this equation crosses the x-axis at only one place, $x = 0$. ✓

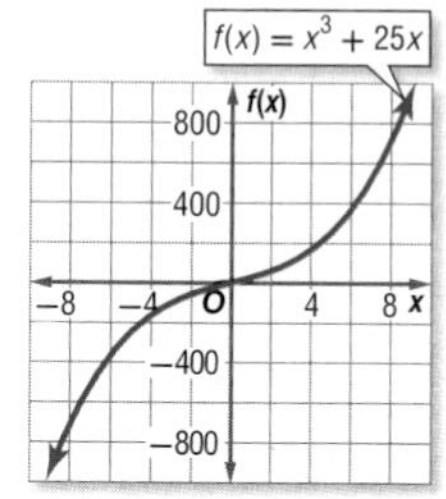

Guided Practice 1A. $0, i\sqrt{2}, -i\sqrt{2}$; 1 real, 2 imaginary

1A. $x^3 + 2x = 0$

1B. $x^4 - 16 = 0$

1C. $x^3 + 4x^2 - 7x - 10 = 0$

1D. $3x^3 - x^2 + 9x - 3 = 0$

Personal Tutor glencoe.com

Examine the solutions for each equation in Example 1. Notice that the number of solutions for each equation is the same as the degree of each polynomial. The following corollary to the Fundamental Theorem of Algebra describes this relationship between the degree and the number of roots of a polynomial equation.

Key Concept

Corollary to the Fundamental Theorem of Algebra

Words A polynomial equation of degree n has exactly n roots in the set of complex numbers, including repeated roots.

Example

$x^3 + 2x^2 + 6$	$4x^4 - 3x^3 + 5x - 6$	$-2x^5 - 3x^2 + 8$
3 roots	4 roots	5 roots

Similarly, an *n*th degree polynomial function has exactly *n* zeros.

Additionally, French mathematician René Descartes discovered a relationship between the signs of the coefficients of a polynomial function and the number of positive and negative real zeros.

StudyTip

Zero at the Origin If a zero of a function is at the origin, the sum of the number of positive real zeros, negative real zeros, and imaginary zeros is reduced by how many times 0 is a zero of the function.

Key Concept — Descartes' Rule of Signs

Let $P(x) = a_n x^n + \cdots + a_1 x + a_0$ be a polynomial function with real coefficients. Then

- the number of positive real zeros of $P(x)$ is the same as the number of changes in sign of the coefficients of the terms, or is less than this by an even number, and
- the number of negative real zeros of $P(x)$ is the same as the number of changes in sign of the coefficients of the terms of $P(-x)$, or is less than this by an even number.

EXAMPLE 2 Find Numbers of Positive and Negative Zeros

State the possible number of positive real zeros, negative real zeros, and imaginary zeros of $f(x) = x^6 + 3x^5 - 4x^4 - 6x^3 + x^2 - 8x + 5$.

Because $f(x)$ has degree 6, it has six zeros, either real or imaginary. Use Descartes' Rule of Signs to determine the possible number and type of *real* zeros.

Count the number of changes in sign for the coefficients of $f(x)$.

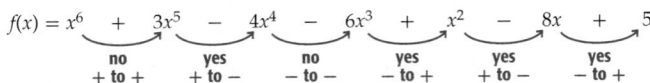

$f(x) = x^6 \; + \; 3x^5 \; - \; 4x^4 \; - \; 6x^3 \; + \; x^2 \; - \; 8x \; + \; 5$

no	yes	no	yes	yes	yes
+ to +	+ to −	− to −	− to +	+ to −	− to +

There are 4 sign changes, so there are 4, 2, or 0 positive real zeros.

Count the number of changes in sign for the coefficients of $f(-x)$.

$f(-x) = (-x)^6 + 3(-x)^5 - 4(-x)^4 - 6(-x)^3 + (-x)^2 - 8(-x) + 5$

$= x^6 - 3x^5 - 4x^4 + 6x^3 + x^2 + 8x + 5$

yes	no	yes	no	no	no
+ to −	− to −	− to +	+ to +	+ to +	+ to +

There are 2 sign changes, so there are 2, or 0 negative real zeros.
Make a chart of the possible combinations of real and imaginary zeros.

Number of Positive Real Zeros	Number of Negative Real Zeros	Number of Imaginary Zeros	Total Number of Zeros
4	2	0	$4 + 2 + 0 = 6$
4	0	2	$4 + 0 + 2 = 6$
2	2	2	$2 + 2 + 2 = 6$
2	0	4	$2 + 0 + 4 = 6$
0	2	4	$0 + 2 + 4 = 6$
0	0	6	$0 + 0 + 6 = 6$

Guided Practice

2. State the possible number of positive real zeros, negative real zeros, and imaginary zeros of $h(x) = 2x^5 + x^4 + 3x^3 - 4x^2 - x + 9$. 2 or 0; 3 or 1; 4, 2, or 0

Personal Tutor glencoe.com

Find Zeros You can use the various strategies and theorems you have learned to find all of the zeros of a function.

TEACH with TECH

INTERACTIVE WHITEBOARD
Write a polynomial function on the board. Show students how to apply Descartes' Rule of Signs by highlighting each change in signs in the coefficients.

Additional Example

2 State the possible number of positive real zeros, negative real zeros, and imaginary zeros of $p(x) = -x^6 + 4x^3 - 2x^2 - x - 1$. The function has either 2 or 0 positive zeros, 2 or 0 negative zeros, and 6, 4, or 2 imaginary zeros.

Watch Out!

Common Misconceptions Point out to students the method for determining the number of imaginary zeros for a polynomial function. In Example 2, the polynomial has degree 6, so it has a maximum of 6 real zeros. You find the numbers of positive and negative real zeros, and subtract the sum of these two numbers from 6 to find the number of imaginary zeros. Remind students that imaginary zeros come in conjugate pairs, so the number of imaginary zeros must be an even number.

Find Zeros

Example 3 shows how to find the zeros of a polynomial function using synthetic substitution. **Example 4** shows how to use zeros to write a polynomial function.

Additional Example

3 Find all of the zeros of $f(x) = x^3 - x^2 + 2x + 4$.
The function has one real zero at $x = -1$, and two imaginary zeros at $x = 1 + i\sqrt{3}$ and $x = 1 - i\sqrt{3}$.

EXAMPLE 3 Use Synthetic Substitution to Find Zeros

Find all of the zeros of $f(x) = x^4 - 18x^2 + 12x + 80$.

Step 1 Determine the total number of zeros.
Since $f(x)$ has degree 4, the function has 4 zeros.

Step 2 Determine the type of zeros.
Examine the number of sign changes for $f(x)$ and $f(-x)$.

$f(x) = x^4 - 18x^2 + 12x + 80$ — yes, yes, no

$f(-x) = x^4 - 18x^2 - 12x + 80$ — yes, no, yes

Because there are 2 sign changes for the coefficients of $f(x)$, the function has 2 or 0 positive real zeros. Because there are 2 sign changes for the coefficients of $f(-x)$, $f(x)$ has 2 or 0 negative real zeros. Thus, $f(x)$ has 4 real zeros, 2 real zeros and 2 imaginary zeros, or 4 imaginary zeros.

StudyTip
Testing for Zeros If a value is not a zero for a polynomial, then it will not be a zero for the depressed polynomial either, so it does not need to be checked again.

Step 3 Determine the real zeros.
List some possible values, and then use synthetic substitution to evaluate $f(x)$ for real values of x.

x	1	0	−18	12	80
−3	1	−3	−9	39	−37
−2	1	−2	−14	40	0
−1	1	−1	−17	29	51
0	1	0	−18	12	80
1	1	1	−17	−5	75
2	1	2	−14	−2	76

Each row shows the coefficients of the depressed polynomial and the remainder.

From the table, we can see that one zero occurs at $x = -2$. Since there are 2 negative real zeros, use synthetic substitution with the depressed polynomial function $f(x) = x^3 - 2x^2 - 14x + 40$ to find a second negative zero.

A second negative zero is at $x = -4$. Since the depressed polynomial $x^2 - 6x + 10$ is quadratic, use the Quadratic Formula to find the remaining zeros of $f(x) = x^2 - 6x + 10$.

x	1	−2	−14	40
−4	1	−6	10	0
−5	1	−7	21	−65
−6	1	−8	34	−164

$x = \frac{-b \pm \sqrt{b^2 - 4ac}}{2a}$ **Quadratic Formula**

$= \frac{-(-6) \pm \sqrt{(-6)^2 - 4(1)(10)}}{2(1)}$ **Replace *a* with 1, *b* with −6, and *c* with 10.**

$= 3 \pm i$ **Simplify.**

The function has zeros at -4, -2, $3 + i$, and $3 - i$.

CHECK Graph the function on a graphing calculator. The graph crosses the x-axis two times, so there are two real zeros. Use the **zero** function under the **CALC** menu to locate each zero. The two real zeros are −4 and −2.

StudyTip
Locating Zeros Refer to Lesson 5-2 on how to use the CALC menu to locate a zero on your calculator.

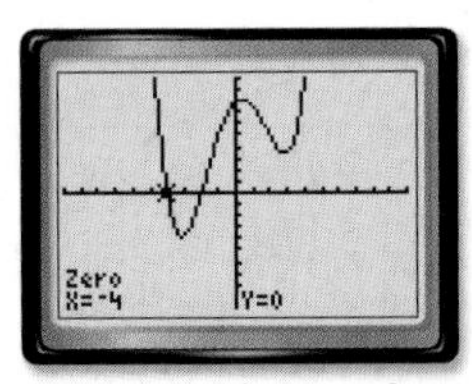

[−10, 10] scl: 1 by [−100, 100] scl: 10

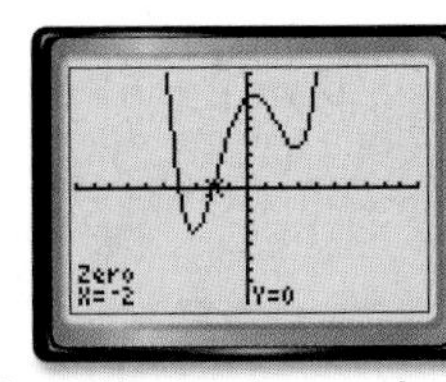

[−10, 10] scl: 1 by [−100, 100] scl: 10

Guided Practice

3. Find all of the zeros of $h(x) = x^3 + 2x^2 + 9x + 18$.
−2, 3*i*, −3*i*

Personal Tutor glencoe.com

Differentiated Instruction

AL OL BL ELL

If students sometimes make mistakes in mathematics exercises because they cannot read their own handwriting,

Then stress that throughout this course, students must work using neat and careful handwriting. It is extremely easy to misread coefficients and exponents, or misread ***i*** as the number 1.

Review Vocabulary

complex conjugates two complex numbers of the form $a + bi$ and $a - bi$ (Lesson 5-4)

In Chapter 5, you learned that the product of complex conjugates is always a real number and that complex roots always come in conjugate pairs. For example, if one root of $x^2 - 8x + 52 = 0$ is $4 + 6i$, then the other root is $4 - 6i$.

This applies to the zeros of polynomial functions as well. For any polynomial function with real coefficients, if an imaginary number is a zero of that function, its conjugate is also a zero. This is called the **Complex Conjugates Theorem**.

Key Concept — **Complex Conjugates Theorem**

Words Let a and b be real numbers, and $b \neq 0$. If $a + bi$ is a zero of a polynomial function with real coefficients, then $a - bi$ is also a zero of the function.

Example If $3 + 4i$ is a zero of $f(x) = x^3 - 4x^2 + 13x + 50$, then $3 - 4i$ is also a zero of the function.

When you are given all of the zeros of a polynomial function and are asked to determine the function, convert the zeros to factors and then multiply all of the factors together. The result is the polynomial function.

EXAMPLE 4 **Use Zeros to Write a Polynomial Function**

Write a polynomial function of least degree with integral coefficients, the zeros of which include −1 and $5 - i$.

Understand If $5 - i$ is a zero, then $5 + i$ is also a zero according to the Complex Conjugates Theorem. So, $x + 1$, $x - (5 - i)$, and $x - (5 + i)$ are factors of the polynomial.

Plan Write the polynomial function as a product of its factors.

$P(x) = (x + 1)[x - (5 - i)][x - (5 + i)]$

Solve Multiply the factors to find the polynomial function.

$P(x) = (x + 1)\,[x - (5 - i)][x - (5 + i)]$	**Write the equation.**
$= (x + 1)\,[(x - 5) + i][(x - 5) - i]$	**Regroup terms.**
$= (x + 1)\,[(x - 5)^2 - i^2]$	**Difference of squares**
$= (x + 1)\,[(x^2 - 10x + 25 - (-1)]$	**Square terms.**
$= (x + 1)\,(x^2 - 10x + 26)$	**Simplify.**
$= x^3 - 10x^2 + 26x + x^2 - 10x + 26$	**Multiply.**
$= x^3 - 9x^2 + 16x + 26$	**Combine like terms.**

Check Because there are 3 zeros, the degree of the polynomial function must be 3, so $P(x) = x^3 - 9x^2 + 16x + 26$ is a polynomial function of least degree with integral coefficients and zeros of -1, $5 - i$, and $5 + i$.

Guided Practice

4. Write a polynomial function of least degree with integral coefficients having zeros that include −1 and $1 + 2i$. $x^3 - x^2 + 3x + 5$

Personal Tutor glencoe.com

Additional Example

4 Write a polynomial function of least degree with integral coefficients, the zeros of which include 4 and $4 - i$.
$f(x) = x^3 - 12x^2 + 49x - 68$

3 PRACTICE

Formative Assessment

Use Exercises 1–16 to check for understanding.

Use the chart at the bottom of this page to customize assignments for your students.

Additional Answers

17. $-2, \frac{3}{2}$; 2 real

18. $-\frac{1}{2}i, \frac{1}{2}i$; 2 imaginary

19. $-1, \frac{1 \pm i\sqrt{3}}{2}$; 1 real, 2 imaginary

20. $\frac{5 \pm i\sqrt{87}}{4}$; 2 imaginary

21. $-\frac{8}{3}, 1$; 2 real

22. $\frac{3}{2}, \frac{-3 \pm 3i\sqrt{3}}{4}$; 1 real, 2 imaginary

23. $-\frac{5}{2}, \frac{5}{2}, -\frac{5}{2}i, \frac{5}{2}i$; 2 real, 2 imaginary

24. $0, 3 + \sqrt{2}, 3 - \sqrt{2}$; 3 real

25. $-2, -2, 0, 2, 2$; 5 real

26. $0, -i, -i, i, i$; 1 real, 4 imaginary

43. $y = x^3 - 2x^2 - 13x - 10$

44. $y = x^3 + 2x^2 - 23x - 60$

45. $y = x^4 + 2x^3 + 5x^2 + 8x + 4$

46. $y = x^4 + 2x^3 + 6x^2 + 18x - 27$

47. $y = x^4 - x^3 - 20x^2 + 50x$

48. $y = x^4 - 3x^3 - 9x^2 + 77x + 150$

53b.

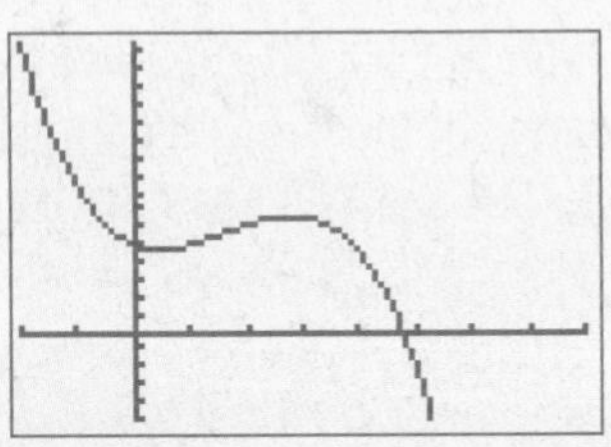

[–10, 40] scl: 5 by [–4000, 13,200] scl: 100

57. Sample answer: $f(x) = (x + 2i)(x - 2i)(3x + 5)(x + \sqrt{5})(x - \sqrt{5})$ Use conjugates for the imaginary and irrational values.

58. $r^4 + 1 = 0$; Sample answer: The equation has imaginary solutions and all of the others have real solutions.

Check Your Understanding

Example 1 p. 384

Solve each equation. State the number and type of roots.

1. $x^2 - 3x - 10 = 0$ $-2, 5$; 2 real

2. $x^3 + 12x^2 + 32x = 0$ $-8, -4, 0$; 3 real

3. $16x^4 - 81 = 0$

3. $-\frac{3}{2}, \frac{3}{2}, -\frac{3}{2}i, \frac{3}{2}i$; 2 real, 2 imaginary

4. $0 = x^3 - 8$ $2, -1 + i\sqrt{3}, -1 - i\sqrt{3}$; 1 real, 2 imaginary

Example 2 p. 385

State the possible number of positive real zeros, negative real zeros, and imaginary zeros of each function. 6. 1; 1 or 3; 0 or 2

5. $f(x) = x^3 - 2x^2 + 2x - 6$ 3 or 1; 0; 0 or 2

6. $f(x) = 6x^4 + 4x^3 - x^2 - 5x - 7$

7. $f(x) = 3x^5 - 8x^3 + 2x - 4$ 1 or 3; 0 or 2; 0, 2, or 4

8. $f(x) = -2x^4 - 3x^3 - 2x - 5$ 0; 0 or 2; 2 or 4

Example 3 p. 386

Find all of the zeros of each function.

9. $f(x) = x^3 + 9x^2 + 6x - 16$ $-8, -2, 1$

10. $f(x) = x^3 + 7x^2 + 4x + 28$ $-7, -2i, 2i$

11. $f(x) = x^4 - 2x^3 - 8x^2 - 32x - 384$ $-4, 6, -4i, 4i$

12. $f(x) = x^4 - 6x^3 + 9x^2 + 6x - 10$ $-1, 1, 3 - i, 3 + i$

Example 4 p. 387

Write a polynomial function of least degree with integral coefficients that have the given zeros.

13. 4, −1, 6 $x^3 - 9x^2 + 14x + 24$

14. 3, −1, 1, 2 $x^4 - 5x^3 + 5x^2 + 5x - 6$

15. −2, 5, −3i $x^4 - 3x^3 - x^2 - 27x - 90$

16. −4, 4 + i $x^3 - 4x^2 - 15x + 68$

Practice and Problem Solving

= **Step-by-Step Solutions** begin on page R20. **Extra Practice** begins on page 947.

Example 1 p. 384

Solve each equation. State the number and type of roots. 17–26. See margin.

17. $2x^2 + x - 6 = 0$

18. $4x^2 + 1 = 0$

19. $x^3 + 1 = 0$

20. $2x^2 - 5x + 14 = 0$

21. $-3x^2 - 5x + 8 = 0$

22. $8x^3 - 27 = 0$

23. $16x^4 - 625 = 0$

24. $x^3 - 6x^2 + 7x = 0$

25. $x^5 - 8x^3 + 16x = 0$

26. $x^5 + 2x^3 + x = 0$

Example 2 p. 385

State the possible number of positive real zeros, negative real zeros, and imaginary zeros of each function.

27. $f(x) = x^4 - 5x^3 + 2x^2 + 5x + 7$

28. $f(x) = 2x^3 - 7x^2 - 2x + 12$ 0 or 2; 1; 0 or 2

29. $f(x) = -3x^5 + 5x^4 + 4x^2 - 8$

30. $f(x) = x^4 - 2x^2 - 5x + 19$

31. $f(x) = 4x^6 - 5x^4 - x^2 + 24$

32. $f(x) = -x^5 + 14x^3 + 18x - 36$

27. 0 or 2; 0 or 2; 0, 2, or 4
29. 0 or 2; 1; 2 or 4
30. 0 or 2; 0 or 2; 0, 2, or 4
31. 0 or 2; 0 or 2; 2, 4, or 6
32. 0 or 2; 1; 2 or 4

Example 3 p. 386

Find all of the zeros of each function.

33. $f(x) = x^3 + 7x^2 + 4x - 12$ $-6, -2, 1$

34. $f(x) = x^3 + x^2 - 17x + 15$ $-5, 1, 3$

35. $f(x) = x^4 - 3x^3 - 3x^2 - 75x - 700$

36. $f(x) = x^4 + 6x^3 + 73x^2 + 384x + 576$

37. $f(x) = x^4 - 8x^3 + 20x^2 - 32x + 64$

38. $f(x) = x^5 - 8x^3 - 9x$ $-3, 0, 3, -i, i$

39. $f(x) = x^3 - 5x^2 + 17x - 85$

40. $f(x) = x^3 + 2x$ $0, \pm i\sqrt{2}$

41. $f(x) = 4x^4 + 15x^2 - 4$ $-\frac{1}{2}, \frac{1}{2}, -2i, 2i$

42. $f(x) = 9x^4 + 9x^3 + 4x^2 + 4x$

35. $-4, 7, -5i, 5i$
36. $-3, -3, -8i, 8i$
37. $4, 4, -2i, 2i$
39. $5, \pm i\sqrt{17}$
42. $-1, 0, -\frac{2}{3}i, \frac{2}{3}i$

Example 4 p. 387

Write a polynomial function of least degree with integral coefficients that have the given zeros. 43–48. See margin.

43. 5, −2, −1

44. −4, −3, 5

45. −1, −1, 2i

46. −3, 1, −3i

47. 0, −5, 3 + i

48. −2, −3, 4 − 3i

388 Chapter 6 Polynomials and Polynomial Functions

Differentiated Homework Options

Level	Assignment	Two-Day Option	
AL Basic	17–48, 56, 58–76	17–47 odd, 61–64	18–48 even, 56, 58–60, 65–76
OL Core	17–49 odd, 53, 56, 58–76	17–48, 61–64	49–56, 58–60, 65–76
BL Advanced	49–73, (optional: 74–76)		

49b. Nonnegative roots represent numbers of computers produced per day which lead to no profit for the manufacturer.

Real-World Link

On average, 3500 people attend a concert in the U.S. each night.

Source: *Billboard Magazine*

53c. 23.8; Sample answer: According to the model, the music hall will not earn any money after 2026.

54. 0 positive, 1 negative, 2 imaginary; Sample answer: The graph does not cross the positive x-axis, and crosses the negative x-axis once. Because the degree of the polynomial is 3, there are 3 − 1 or 2 imaginary zeros.

55. 1 positive, 2 negative, 2 imaginary; Sample answer: The graph crosses the positive x-axis once, and crosses the negative x-axis twice. Because the degree of the polynomial is 5, there are 5 − 3 or 2 imaginary zeros.

49. BUSINESS A computer manufacturer determines that for each employee, the profit for producing x computers per day is $P(x) = -0.006x^4 + 0.15x^3 - 0.05x^2 - 1.8x$.

B

a. How many positive real zeros, negative real zeros, and imaginary zeros exist? **2 or 0; 1; 1 or 3**

b. What is the meaning of the zeros in this situation?

Match each graph to the given zeros.

a. $-3, 4, i, -i$ b. $-4, 3$ c. $-4, 3, i, -i$

50. 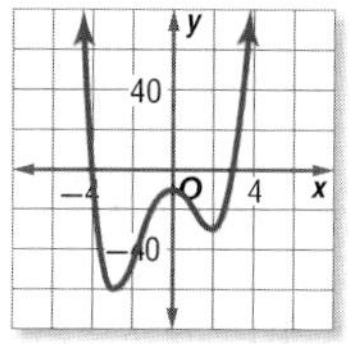 c

51. 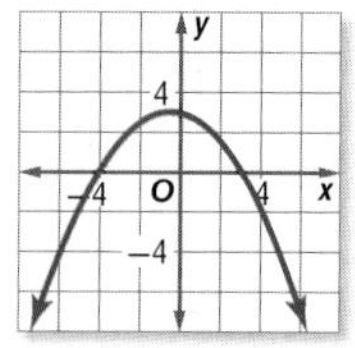 b

52. 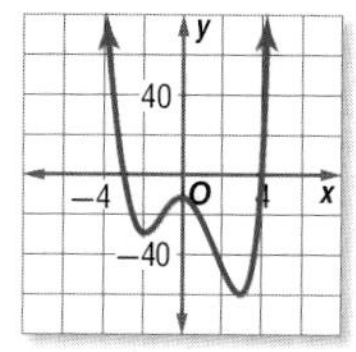 a

53. CONCERTS The amount of money Hoshi's Music Hall took in from 2003 to 2010 can be modeled by $M(x) = -2.03x^3 + 50.1x^2 - 214x + 4020$, where x is the years since 2003.

a. How many positive real zeros, negative real zeros, and imaginary zeros exist? **3 or 1; 0; 2 or 0**

b. Graph the function using your calculator. **See margin.**

c. Approximate all real zeros to the nearest tenth. What is the significance of each zero in the context of the situation?

C **Determine the number of positive real zeros, negative real zeros, and imaginary zeros for each function. Explain your reasoning.**

54. 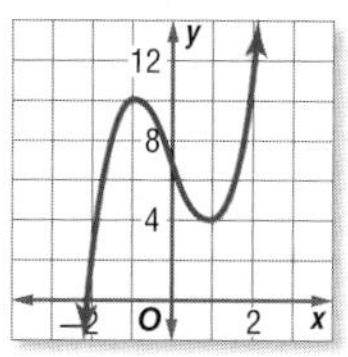

degree: 3

55. 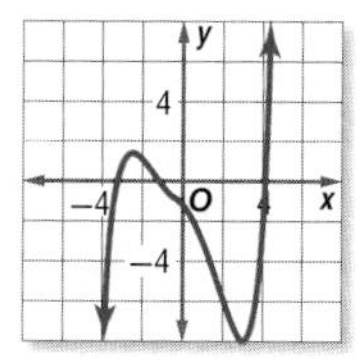

degree: 5

H.O.T. Problems Use Higher-Order Thinking Skills

56. OPEN ENDED Sketch the graph of a polynomial function with: **a–c. See Chapter 6 Answer Appendix.**

a. 3 real, 2 imaginary zeros b. 4 real zeros c. 2 imaginary zeros

57. CHALLENGE Write an equation in factored form of a polynomial function of degree 5 with 2 imaginary zeros, 1 nonintegral zero, and 2 irrational zeros. Explain. **See margin.**

58. WHICH ONE DOESN'T BELONG Determine which equation is not like the others. Explain. **See margin.**

$r^4 + 1 = 0$ $r^3 + 1 = 0$ $r^2 - 1 = 0$ $r^3 - 8 = 0$

59. REASONING Provide a counterexample for each statement.

a. All polynomial functions of degree greater than 2 have at least 1 negative real root. **Sample answer: $f(x) = x^4 + 4x^2 + 4$**

b. All polynomial functions of degree greater than 2 have at least 1 positive real root. **Sample answer: $f(x) = x^3 + 6x^2 + 9x$**

60. WRITING IN MATH Explain to a friend how you would use Descartes' Rule of Signs to determine the number of possible positive real roots and the number of possible negative roots of the polynomial function $f(x) = x^4 - 2x^3 + 6x^2 + 5x - 12$. **See Chapter 6 Answer Appendix.**

Study Guide and Intervention

CRM pp. 41–42 AL OL ELL

6-7 Study Guide and Intervention

Roots and Zeros

Synthetic Types of Roots The following statements are equivalent for any polynomial function $f(x)$.

- c is a zero of the polynomial function $f(x)$.
- c is a root or solution of the polynomial equation $f(x) = 0$.
- $(x - c)$ is a factor of the polynomial $f(x)$.
- If c is real, then $(c, 0)$ is an intercept of the graph of $f(x)$.

Fundamental Theorem of Algebra	Every polynomial equation with degree greater than zero has at least one root in the set of complex numbers.
Corollary to the Fundamental Theorem of Algebras	A polynomial equation of the form $P(x) = 0$ of degree n with complex coefficients has exactly n roots in the set of complex numbers, including repeated roots.
Descartes' Rule of Signs	If $P(x)$ is a polynomial with real coefficients whose terms are arranged in descending powers of the variable, • the number of positive real zeros of $y = P(x)$ is the same as the number of changes in sign of the coefficients of the terms, or is less than this by an even number, and • the number of negative real zeros of $y = P(x)$ is the same as the number of changes in sign of the coefficients of the terms of $P(-x)$, or is less than this number by an even number.

Example 1 **Solve the equation $6x^3 + 3x = 0$. State the number and type of roots.**

$6x^3 + 3x = 0$

$3x(2x^2 + 1) = 0$

Use the Zero Product Property.

$3x = 0$ or $2x^2 + 1 = 0$

$x = 0$ or $2x^2 = -1$

$x = \pm \frac{i\sqrt{2}}{2}$

The equation has one real root, 0, and two imaginary roots, $\pm \frac{i\sqrt{2}}{2}$.

Example 2 **State the number of positive real zeros, negative real zeros, and imaginary zeros for $p(x) = 4x^4 - 3x^3 - x^2 + 2x - 5$.**

Since $p(x)$ has degree 4, it has 4 zeros.

Since there are three sign changes, there are 3 or 1 positive real zeros.

Find $p(-x)$ and count the number of changes in sign for its coefficients.

$p(-x) = 4(-x)^4 - 3(-x)^3 + (-x)^2 + 2(-x) - 5$

$= 4x^4 + 3x^3 + x^2 - 2x - 5$

Since there is one sign change, there is exactly 1 negative real zero.

Thus, there are 3 positive and 1 negative real zero or 1 positive and 1 negative real zeros and 2 imaginary zeros.

Exercises

Solve each equation. State the number and type of roots.

1. $x^2 + 4x - 21 = 0$ **3, −7; 2 real**
2. $2x^3 - 50x = 0$ **0, ±5; 3 real**
3. $12x^3 + 100x = 0$ **$0, \pm\frac{5i\sqrt{3}}{3}$; 1 real, 2 imaginary**

State the possible number of positive real zeros, negative real zeros, and imaginary zeros for each function.

4. $f(x) = 3x^3 + x^2 - 8x - 12$ **1; 2 or 0; 0 or 2**
5. $f(x) = 3x^5 - x^4 - x^3 + 6x^2 - 5$ **3 or 1; 2 or 0; 0, 2, or 4**

Chapter 6 41 *Glencoe Algebra 2*

Lesson 6-7

Practice

CRM p. 44 AL OL BL ELL

6-7 Practice

Roots and Zeros

Solve each equation. State the number and type of roots.

1. $-9x - 15 = 0$ **$-\frac{5}{3}$; 1 real**
2. $x^4 - 5x^2 + 4 = 0$ **−1, 1, −2, 2; 4 real**
3. $x^5 - 81x = 0$ **0, −3, 3, −3i, 3i; 3 real, 2 imaginary**
4. $x^3 + x^2 - 3x - 3 = 0$ **$-1, -\sqrt{3}, \sqrt{3}$; 3 real**
5. $x^3 + 6x + 20 = 0$ **$-2, 1 \pm 3i$; 1 real, 2 imaginary**
6. $x^4 - x^3 - x^2 - x - 2 = 0$ **2, −1, −i, i; 2 real, 2 imaginary**

State the possible number of positive real zeros, negative real zeros, and imaginary zeros of each function.

7. $f(x) = 4x^3 - 2x^2 + x + 3$ **2 or 0; 1; 2 or 0**
8. $p(x) = 2x^4 - 2x^3 + 2x^2 - x - 1$ **3 or 1; 1; 2 or 0**
9. $q(x) = 3x^4 + x^3 - 3x^2 + 7x + 5$ **2 or 0; 2 or 0; 4, 2, or 0**
10. $h(x) = 7x^4 + 3x^3 - 2x^2 - x + 1$ **2 or 0; 2 or 0; 4, 2, or 0**

Find all zeros of each function.

11. $h(x) = 2x^3 + 3x^2 - 65x + 84$ **$-7, \frac{3}{2}, 4$**
12. $p(x) = x^3 - 3x^2 + 9x - 7$ **$1, 1 + i\sqrt{6}, 1 - i\sqrt{6}$**
13. $h(x) = x^3 - 7x^2 + 17x - +5$ **3, 2 + i, 2 − i**
14. $q(x) = x^4 + 50x^2 + 49$ **−i, i, −7i, 7i**
15. $g(x) = x^4 + 4x^3 - 3x^2 - 14x - 8$ **−1, −1, 2, −4**
16. $f(x) = x^4 - 6x^3 + 6x^2 + 24x - 40$ **−2, 2, 3 − i, 3 + i**

Write a polynomial function of least degree with integral coefficients that has the given zeros.

17. −5, 3i **$f(x) = x^3 + 5x^2 + 9x + 45$**
18. −2, 3 + i **$f(x) = x^3 - 4x^2 - 2x + 20$**
19. −1, 4, 3i **$f(x) = x^4 - 3x^3 + 5x^2 - 27x - 36$**
20. 2, 5, 1 + i **$f(x) = x^4 - 9x^3 + 26x^2 - 34x + 20$**

21. **CRAFTS** Stephan has a set of plans to build a wooden box. He wants to reduce the volume of the box to 105 cubic inches. He would like to reduce the length of each dimension in the plan by the same amount. The plans call for the box to be 10 inches by 8 inches by 6 inches. Write and solve a polynomial equation to find out how much Stephan should take from each dimension. **$(10 - x)(8 - x)(6 - x) = 105$; 3 in.**

Chapter 6 44 *Glencoe Algebra 2*

Word Problem Practice

CRM p. 45 AL OL BL ELL

6-7 Word Problem Practice

Roots and Zeros

1. **TABLES** Li Pang made a table of values for the polynomial $p(x)$. Her table is shown below.

x	$p(x)$
−4	−3
−3	−1
−2	0
−1	2
0	0
1	4
2	0
3	2
4	5

Name three roots of $p(x)$.

−2, 0, and 2

2. **ROOTS** Ryan is an electrical engineer. He often solves polynomial equations to work out various properties of the circuits he builds. For one circuit, he must find the roots of a polynomial $p(x)$. He finds that $p(2 - 3i) = 0$. Give two different roots of $p(x)$.

2 − 3i and 2 + 3i

3. **REAL ROOTS** There are more than a thousand roller coasters around the world. Roller coaster designers can use polynomial functions to model the shapes of possible roller coasters. Madison is studying a roller coaster modeled by the polynomial $f(x) = x^6 - 14x^4 + 49x^2 - 36$. She knows that all of the roots of $f(x)$ are real. How many positive and how many negative roots are there? How are the set of positive roots and negative roots related to each other? Explain.

There are 3 positive and 3 negative roots. The set of positive roots is the mirror image of the set of negative roots because the polynomial is even.

4. **COMPLEX ROOTS** Eric is a statistician. During the course of his work, he had to find something called the "eigenvalues of a matrix," which was basically the same as finding the roots of a polynomial. The polynomial was $x^4 + 6x^2 + 25$. One of the roots of this polynomial is $1 + 2i$. What are the other 3 roots? Explain.

The other 3 roots are −1 − 2i, 1 − 2i, and −1 + 2i. Sample answer: Since $f(x) = f(-x)$, if r is a root, so is $-r$; hence −1 − 2i is a root. Because the coefficients are real, if r is a root, its complex conjugate must also be a root; therefore, 1 − 2i and −1 + 2i are also roots.

5. **QUADRILATERALS** Shayna plotted the four vertices of a quadrilateral in the complex plane and then encoded the points in a polynomial $p(x)$ by making them the roots of $p(x)$. The polynomial $p(x)$ is $x^4 - 9x^3 + 27x^2 + 23x - 150$.

a. The polynomial $p(x)$ has one positive real root, and it is an integer. Find the integer.

3

b. Find the negative real root(s) of $p(x)$.

−2

c. Find the complex roots of $p(x)$.

4 + 3i and 4 − 3i

Chapter 6 45 *Glencoe Algebra 2*

Lesson 6-7

Enrichment

CRM p. 46 OL BL

6-7 Enrichment

The Bisection Method for Approximating Real Zeros

The **bisection method** can be used to approximate zeros of polynomial functions like $f(x) = x^3 + x^2 - 3x - 3$.

Since $f(1) = -4$ and $f(2) = 3$, there is at least one real zero between 1 and 2. The midpoint of this interval $\frac{1+2}{2} = 1.5$. Since $f(1.5) = -1.875$, the zero is between 1.5 and 2. The midpoint of this interval is $\frac{1.5+2}{2} = 1.75$. Since $f(1.75)$ is about 0.172, the zero is between 1.5 and 1.75. The midpoint of this interval is $\frac{1.5+1.75}{2} = 1.625$ and $f(1.625)$ is about −0.94. The zero is between 1.625 and 1.75. The midpoint of this interval is $\frac{1.625+1.75}{2} = 1.6875$. Since $f(1.6875)$ is about −0.41, the zero is between 1.6875 and 1.75. Therefore, the zero is 1.7 to the nearest tenth.

The diagram below summarizes the results obtained by the bisection method.

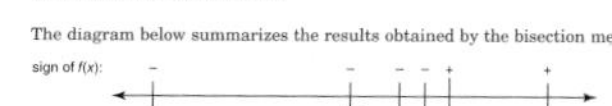

4 ASSESS

Crystal Ball Have students write how what they learned today about the Fundamental Theorem of Algebra and Descartes' Rule of Signs will help them with identifying all the rational zeros of a polynomial function in tomorrow's lesson.

Additional Answers

65. $f(-8) = -1638$; $f(4) = 342$

66. $f(-8) = 21{,}808$; $f(4) = 1192$

67. $f(-8) = -63{,}940$; $f(4) = 1868$

72a. 0.98, 4.81; The owner will break even if he charges \$0.98 or \$4.81 per square foot.

72b. $0.98 < r < 4.81$; The owner will make a profit if the rent per square foot is between \$0.98 and \$4.81.

72c. $1.34 < r < 4.45$; If rent is set between \$1.34 and \$4.45 per sq ft, the profit will be greater than \$10,000.

72d. $r < 1.34$ or $r > 4.45$; If rent is set between \$0 and \$1.34 or above \$4.45 per sq ft, the profit will be less than \$10,000.

74. $\pm1, \pm2, \pm3, \pm6, \pm\frac{1}{2}, \pm\frac{3}{2}, \pm\frac{1}{4}, \pm\frac{3}{4}$

75. $\pm1, \pm2, \pm4, \pm8, \pm\frac{1}{5}, \pm\frac{2}{5}, \pm\frac{4}{5}, \pm\frac{8}{5}$

76. $\pm1, \pm7, \pm\frac{1}{2}, \pm\frac{7}{2}, \pm\frac{1}{3}, \pm\frac{7}{3}, \pm\frac{1}{6}, \pm\frac{7}{6}$

NGSSS PRACTICE 912.A.4.5, 912.G.5.3, 912.A.4.3

61. SAT/ACT Use the graph of the polynomial function below. Which is not a factor of the polynomial $x^5 + x^4 - 3x^3 - 3x^2 - 4x - 4$? **C**

A. $x - 2$
B. $x + 2$
C. $x - 1$
D. $x + 1$

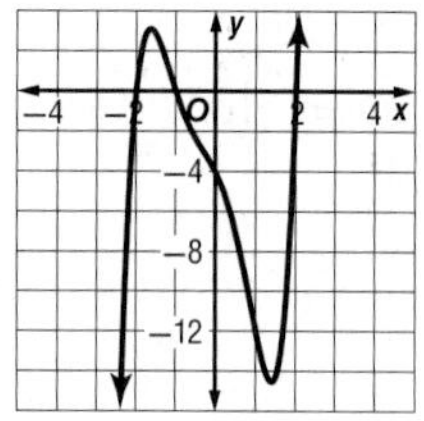

62. SHORT RESPONSE A window is in the shape of an equilateral triangle. Each side of the triangle is 8 feet long. The window is divided in half by a support from one vertex to the midpoint of the side of the triangle opposite the vertex. Approximately how long is the support? **6.9 feet**

63. GEOMETRY In rectangle $ABCD$, $\overline{AD}$ is 8 units long. What is the length of $\overline{AB}$? **H**

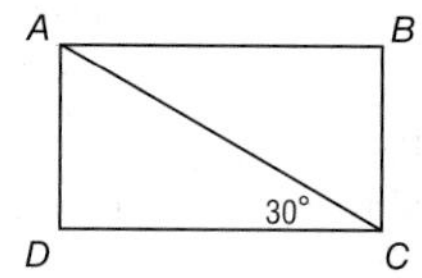

F. 4 units
G. 8 units
H. $8\sqrt{3}$ units
I. 16 units

64. The total area of a rectangle is $25a^4 - 16b^2$ square units. Which factors could represent the length and width? **B**

A. $(5a^2 + 4b)$ units and $(5a^2 + 4b)$ units
B. $(5a^2 + 4b)$ units and $(5a^2 - 4b)$ units
C. $(5a - 4b)$ units and $(5a - 4b)$ units
D. $(5a + 4b)$ units and $(5a - 4b)$ units

Spiral Review

70. $(x^2 + 2x + 4)(4y - 3z)$ **71.** $(a - 4)(a - 2)(5a + 2b)$

Use synthetic substitution to find $f(-8)$ and $f(4)$ for each function. (Lesson 6-6) **65–67. See margin.**

65. $f(x) = 4x^3 + 6x^2 - 3x + 2$
66. $f(x) = 5x^4 - 2x^3 + 4x^2 - 6x$
67. $f(x) = 2x^5 - 3x^3 + x^2 - 4$

Factor completely. If the polynomial is not factorable, write *prime*. (Lesson 6-5)

68. $x^6 - y^6$ $(x + y)(x - y)(x^4 + x^2y^2 + y^4)$
69. $a^6 + b^6$ $(a^2 + b^2)(a^4 - a^2b^2 + b^4)$
70. $4x^2y + 8xy + 16y - 3x^2z - 6xz - 12z$
71. $5a^3 - 30a^2 + 40a + 2a^2b - 12ab + 16b$

72. BUSINESS A mall owner has determined that the relationship between monthly rent charged for store space r (in dollars per square foot) and monthly profit $P(r)$ (in thousands of dollars) can be approximated by $P(r) = -8.1r^2 + 46.9r - 38.2$. Solve each quadratic equation or inequality. Explain what each answer tells about the relationship between monthly rent and profit for this mall. (Lesson 5-8) **a–d. See margin.**

a. $-8.1r^2 + 46.9r - 38.2 = 0$
b. $-8.1r^2 + 46.9r - 38.2 > 0$
c. $-8.1r^2 + 46.9r - 38.2 > 10$
d. $-8.1r^2 + 46.9r - 38.2 < 10$

73. DIVING To avoid hitting any rocks below, a cliff diver jumps up and out. The equation $h = -16t^2 + 4t + 26$ describes her height h in feet t seconds after jumping. Find the time at which she returns to a height of 26 feet. (Lesson 5-3) **0.25 s**

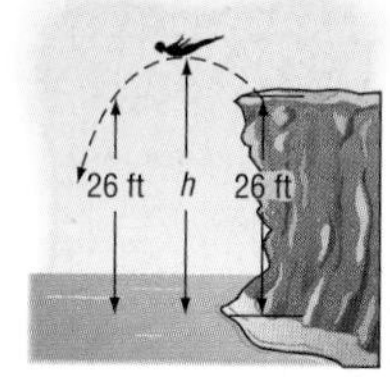

Skills Review

Find all of the possible values of $\pm\frac{b}{a}$ for each replacement set. **74–76. See margin.**

74. $a = \{1, 2, 4\}$; $b = \{1, 2, 3, 6\}$
75. $a = \{1, 5\}$; $b = \{1, 2, 4, 8\}$
76. $a = \{1, 2, 3, 6\}$; $b = \{1, 7\}$

Differentiated Instruction OL BL

Extension Explain to students that if $(x - r)^k$ is a factor of a polynomial $f(x)$, then r is a zero of the polynomial function $f(x)$ and k is the degree of the factor that produced r. From this, it is said that r has a *multiplicity of k.* When $k = 1$, we say that the zero has a multiplicity of 1 and is often called a *simple zero.* Use the following example to explain multiplicity and simple zeros: $f(x) = x^7 - 5x^6 + 6x^5 + 4x^4 - 8x^3$. When factored, $f(x) = x^3(x - 2)^3(x + 1)$. This polynomial function has 3 zeros: $x = -1$ (a simple zero), $x = 0$ with a multiplicity of 3, and $x = 2$ with multiplicity of 3. Challenge students to find the zeros and their multiplicities for the polynomial $f(x) = (x^6 - x^4)(x + 1)$. This polynomial has 3 zeros: $x = 1$, which is a simple zero, $x = 0$ with a multiplicity of 4, and $x = -1$ with multiplicity of 2.

390 Chapter 6 Polynomials and Polynomial Functions

6-8 Rational Zero Theorem

Then

You found zeros of quadratic functions of the form $f(x) = ax^2 + bx + c$. (Lesson 5-3)

Now

- Identify possible rational zeros of a polynomial function.
- Find all of the rational zeros of a polynomial function.

NGSSS

MA.912.A.4.6 Use theorems of polynomial behavior to find the zeros of a polynomial function.
MA.912.A.4.8 Describe the relationships among the solutions of an equation, the zeros of a function, the x-intercepts of a graph, and the factors of a polynomial expression, with and without technology. *Also addresses MA.912.A.4.3.*

FL Math Online
glencoe.com

Why?

Annual sales of recorded music in the United States can be approximated by $d(t) = 30t^3 - 478t^2 + 1758t + 12{,}392$, where $d(t)$ is the total sales in millions of dollars and t is the number of years since 1997. You can use this function to estimate when music sales will be \$20 billion.

Identify Rational Zeros Usually it is not practical to test all possible zeros of a polynomial function using synthetic substitution. The **Rational Zero Theorem** can help you choose some possible zeros to test. **If the leading coefficient is 1, the corollary applies.**

Key Concept — Rational Zero Theorem

Words If $P(x)$ is a polynomial function with integral coefficients, then every rational zero of $P(x) = 0$ is of the form $\frac{p}{q}$, a rational number in simplest form, where p is a factor of the constant term and q is a factor of the leading coefficient

Example Let $f(x) = 6x^4 + 22x^3 + 11x^2 - 80x - 40$. If $\frac{4}{3}$ is a zero of $f(x)$, then 4 is a factor of -40, and 3 is a factor of 6.

Corollary to the Rational Zero Theorem

If $P(x)$ is a polynomial function with integral coefficients, a leading coefficient of 1, and a nonzero constant term, then any rational zeros of $P(x)$ must be factors of the constant term.

EXAMPLE 1 Identify Possible Zeros

List all of the possible rational zeros of each function.

a. $f(x) = 4x^5 + x^4 - 2x^3 - 5x^2 + 8x + 16$

If $\frac{p}{q}$ is a rational zero, then p is a factor of 16 and q is a factor of 4.

p: $\pm1, \pm2, \pm4, \pm8, \pm16$ $\quad$ q: $\pm1, \pm2, \pm4$

Write the possible values of $\frac{p}{q}$ in simplest form.

$\frac{p}{q} = \pm1, \pm2, \pm4, \pm8, \pm16, \pm\frac{1}{2}, \pm\frac{1}{4}$

b. $f(x) = x^3 - 2x^2 + 5x + 12$

If $\frac{p}{q}$ is a rational zero, then p is a factor of 12 and q is a factor of 1.

p: $\pm1, \pm2, \pm3, \pm4, \pm6, \pm12$ $\quad$ q: ±1

So, $\frac{p}{q} = \pm1, \pm2, \pm3, \pm4, \pm6$, and ±12

Guided Practice 1A, 1B. See margin.

1A. $g(x) = 3x^3 - 4x + 10$ $\quad$ **1B.** $h(x) = x^3 + 11x^2 + 24$

Personal Tutor glencoe.com

6-8 Lesson Notes

1 FOCUS

Vertical Alignment

Before Lesson 6-8
Find zeros of quadratic functions of the form $f(x) = ax^2 + bx + c$.

Lesson 6-8
Identify possible rational zeros of a polynomial function.
Find all of the rational zeros of a polynomial function.

After Lesson 6-8
Use quotients of polynomials to describe the graphs of rational functions.

2 TEACH

Scaffolding Questions

Have students read the *Why?* section of the lesson.

Ask:

- In what year was the total annual sales of recorded music about \$12.392 billion? 1997
- What value of x would you use to approximate the total annual sales of recorded music for the year 2010? 13

Additional Answers (Guided Practice)

1A. $\pm\frac{10}{3}, \pm10, \pm\frac{5}{3}, \pm5, \pm\frac{2}{3}, \pm2, \pm\frac{1}{3}, \pm1$

1B. $\pm24, \pm12, \pm8, \pm6, \pm4, \pm3, \pm2, \pm1$

Lesson 6-8 Resources

Resource	Approaching-Level	On-Level	Beyond-Level	English Learners
Teacher Edition	• Differentiated Instruction, p. 393	• Differentiated Instruction, pp. 393, 396	• Differentiated Instruction, pp. 393, 396	
Chapter Resource Masters	• Study Guide and Intervention, pp. 47–48 • Skills Practice, p. 49 • Practice, p. 50 • Word Problem Practice, p. 51	• Study Guide and Intervention, pp. 47–48 • Skills Practice, p. 49 • Practice, p. 50 • Word Problem Practice, p. 51 • Enrichment, p. 52 • Graphing Calculator Activity, p. 53	• Practice, p. 50 • Word Problem Practice, p. 51 • Enrichment, p. 52	• Study Guide and Intervention, pp. 47–48 • Skills Practice, p. 49 • Practice, p. 50 • Word Problem Practice, p. 51
Transparencies	• 5-Minute Check Transparency 6-8	• 5-Minute Check Transparency 6-8	• 5-Minute Check Transparency 6-8	• 5-Minute Check Transparency 6-8
Other	• Study Notebook	• Study Notebook	• Study Notebook	• Study Notebook

Identify Rational Zeros

Example 1 shows how to use the Rational Zero Theorem to identify all of the possible rational zeros of a polynomial function with integral coefficients.

Formative Assessment

Use the Guided Practice exercises after each example to determine students' understanding of concepts.

Additional Example

1 List all the possible rational zeros of each function.

a. $f(x) = 3x^4 - x^3 + 4$

$\pm 1, \pm 2, \pm 4, \pm \frac{1}{3}, \pm \frac{2}{3}, \pm \frac{4}{3}$

b. $f(x) = x^4 + 7x^3 - 15$

$\pm 1, \pm 3, \pm 5, \pm 15$

Additional Examples also in Interactive Classroom PowerPoint® Presentations

IWB INTERACTIVE WHITEBOARD READY

Watch Out!

Common Misconceptions While discussing Example 1, point out that ± 1 will always be possible rational zeros. Also make sure students clearly understand that these are just *possible* zeros. Until each potential zero has been tested by synthetic substitution, it should not be called a zero.

Find Rational Zeros

Example 2 shows how to identify the zeros once you have listed the possible zeros for a real-world problem. **Example 3** shows how to use one identified zero of a polynomial function to factor and find any other zeros.

Find Rational Zeros Once you have written the possible rational zeros, you can test each number using synthetic substitution and use the other tools you have learned to determine the zeros of a function.

Real-World EXAMPLE 2 Find Rational Zeros

WOODWORKING Adam is building a computer desk with a separate compartment for the computer. The compartment for the computer is a rectangular prism and will be 8019 cubic inches. Find the dimensions of the computer compartment.

Let x = width, $x + 24$ = length, and $x + 18$ = height.

Write an equation for the volume.

$\ell wh = V$	**Formula for volume**
$(x + 24)(x)(x + 18) = 8019$	**Substitute.**
$x^3 + 42x^2 + 432x = 8019$	**Multiply.**
$x^3 + 42x^2 + 432x - 8019 = 0$	**Subtract 8019 from each side.**

The leading coefficient is 1, so the possible rational zeros are factors of 8019.

$\pm 1, \pm 3, \pm 9, \pm 11, \pm 27, \pm 33, \pm 81, \pm 99, \pm 243, \pm 297, \pm 729, \pm 891, \pm 2673$, and ± 8019

Since length can only be positive, we only need to check positive values.

There is one change of sign of the coefficients, so by Descartes' Rule of Signs, there is only one positive real zero. Make a table for synthetic division and test possible values.

StudyTip

Descartes' Rule of Signs Examine the signs of the coefficients of the equation. In this case, there is only one change of sign, so there is only one positive real zero.

p	1	42	432	−8019
1	1	43	475	−7544
3	1	45	567	−6318
9	1	51	891	0

One zero is 9. Since there is only one positive real zero, we do not have to test the other numbers. The other dimensions are 9 + 24 or 33 inches, and 9 + 18 or 27 inches.

CHECK Multiply the dimensions and see if they equal the volume of 8019 cubic inches.
$9 \times 33 \times 27 = 8019$ ✓

Guided Practice

2. GEOMETRY The volume of a rectangular prism is 1056 cubic centimeters. The length is 1 centimeter more than the width, and the height is 3 centimeters less than the width. Find the dimensions of the prism. **8 cm × 11 cm × 12 cm**

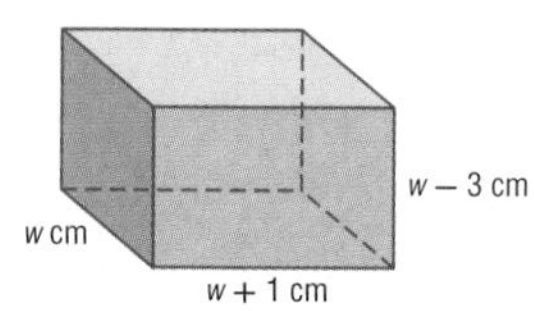

Personal Tutor glencoe.com

You usually do not need to test all of the possible zeros. Once you find a zero, you can try to factor the depressed polynomial to find any other zeros.

TEACH with TECH

DOCUMENT CAMERA Choose several students to show and explain to the class how to find the rational zeros of a polynomial function. Have one student list the possible rational zeros, and have a second student create a table to test these values.

392 Chapter 6 Polynomials and Polynomial Functions

EXAMPLE 3 Find All Zeros

Find all of the zeros of $f(x) = 5x^4 - 8x^3 + 41x^2 - 72x - 36$.

From the corollary to the Fundamental Theorem of Algebra, there are exactly 4 complex zeros. According to Descartes' Rule of Signs, there are 3 or 1 positive real zeros and exactly 1 negative real zero. The possible rational zeros are $\pm1, \pm2, \pm3, \pm4, \pm6, \pm9, \pm12, \pm18, \pm36, \pm\frac{1}{5}, \pm\frac{2}{5}, \pm\frac{3}{5}, \pm\frac{4}{5}, \pm\frac{6}{5}, \pm\frac{9}{5}, \pm\frac{12}{5}, \pm\frac{18}{5}$, and $\pm\frac{36}{5}$.

Make a table and test some possible rational zeros.

$\frac{p}{q}$	5	−8	41	−72	−36
−1	5	−13	54	−126	90
1	5	−3	38	−34	−70
2	5	2	45	18	0

Because $f(2) = 0$, there is a zero at $x = 2$. Factor the depressed polynomial $5x^3 + 2x^2 + 45x + 18$.

$5x^3 + 2x^2 + 45x + 18 = 0$ **Write the depressed polynomial.**

$(5x^3 + 2x^2) + (45x + 18) = 0$ **Group terms.**

$x^2(5x + 2) + 9(5x + 2) = 0$ **Factor.**

$(x^2 + 9)(5x + 2) = 0$ **Distributive Property**

$x^2 + 9 = 0$ or $5x + 2 = 0$ **Zero Product Property**

$x^2 = -9$ $\quad 5x = -2$

$x = \pm 3i$ $\quad x = -\frac{2}{5}$

There is another real zero at $x = -\frac{2}{5}$ and two imaginary zeros at $x = 3i$ and $x = -3i$.

The zeros of the function are $-\frac{2}{5}$, 2, $3i$, and $-3i$.

Guided Practice 3B. $2, -\frac{1}{2}, \pm3i$

Find all of the zeros of each function.

3A. $h(x) = 9x^4 + 5x^2 - 4$ $\pm\frac{2}{3}, \pm i$

3B. $k(x) = 2x^4 - 5x^3 + 20x^2 - 45x + 18$

Personal Tutor glencoe.com

1. $\pm1, \pm2, \pm3, \pm4, \pm6, \pm8, \pm12, \pm24$

Check Your Understanding

Example 1 p. 391

List all of the possible rational zeros of each function.

1. $f(x) = x^3 - 6x^2 - 8x + 24$

2. $f(x) = 2x^4 + 3x^2 - x + 15$

Example 2 p. 392

2. $\pm1, \pm3, \pm5, \pm15, \pm\frac{1}{2}, \pm\frac{3}{2}, \pm\frac{5}{2}, \pm\frac{15}{2}$

3. **GEOMETRY** The volume of the triangular pyramid is 210 cubic inches. Find the dimensions of the solid. 5 in. × 9 in. × 28 in.

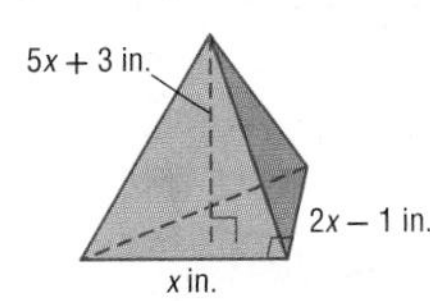

Find all of the rational zeros of each function.

4. $f(x) = x^3 - 6x^2 - 13x + 42$ $-3, 2, 7$

5. $f(x) = 2x^4 + 11x^3 + 26x^2 + 29x + 12$ $-\frac{3}{2}, -1$

Example 3 p. 393

Find all of the zeros of each function.

6. $f(x) = 3x^3 - 2x^2 - 8x + 5$

7. $f(x) = 8x^3 + 14x^2 + 11x + 3$

8. $f(x) = 4x^4 + 13x^3 - 8x^2 + 13x - 12$ $-4, \frac{3}{4}, -i, i$

9. $f(x) = 4x^4 - 12x^3 + 25x^2 - 14x - 15$

6. $\frac{5}{3}, \frac{-1 \pm \sqrt{5}}{2}$

7. $-\frac{1}{2}, \frac{-5 \pm i\sqrt{23}}{8}$

9. $-\frac{1}{2}, \frac{3}{2}, 1 + 2i, 1 - 2i$

Additional Examples

2 **GEOMETRY** The volume of a rectangular solid is 1120 cubic feet. The width is 2 feet less than the height, and the length is 4 feet more than the height. Find the dimensions of the solid.

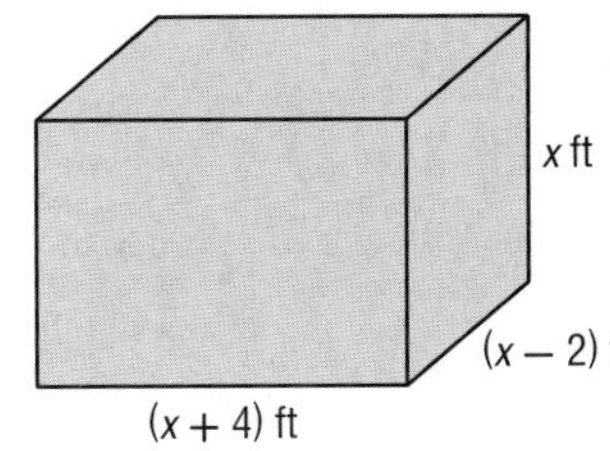

length: 14 ft, width: 8 ft, height: 10 ft

3 Find all of the zeros of $f(x) = x^4 + x^3 - 19x^2 + 11x + 30$.
$-5, -1, 2, 3$

Focus on Mathematical Content

The Rational Zero Theorem The Rational Zero Theorem provides information about the rational zeros of polynomial functions with *integral coefficients.* It says that if there is a rational zero, then it is one of the possible zeros. It is possible for there to be no rational zeros.

3 PRACTICE

Formative Assessment

Use Exercises 1–9 to check for understanding.

Use the chart at the bottom of the next page to customize assignments for your students.

Differentiated Instruction AL OL BL

Logical Learners Organize the students in groups of four or five. Have the students in each group split the work shown in Example 3 into four or five steps. The students should give explanations to the group about their parts of the Example. In particular, students should explain any mathematical processes, the results of their steps, and how the results relate to the next step in the process.

Watch Out!

Error Analysis For Exercise 46, remind students that the leading coefficient is the coefficient of the term with highest degree, not necessarily the coefficient of the term given first.

Additional Answers

10. $\pm1, \pm2, \pm4, \pm8, \pm16, \pm32$

11. $\pm1, \pm2, \pm4, \pm7, \pm8, \pm14, \pm28, \pm56$

12. $\pm1, \pm2, \pm5, \pm10, \pm\frac{1}{2}, \pm\frac{5}{2}$

13. $\pm1, \pm5, \pm7, \pm35, \pm\frac{1}{3}, \pm\frac{5}{3}, \pm\frac{7}{3}, \pm\frac{35}{3}$

14. $\pm1, \pm2, \pm3, \pm6, \pm9, \pm18, \pm\frac{1}{2}, \pm\frac{3}{2}, \pm\frac{9}{2}, \pm\frac{1}{3}, \pm\frac{2}{3}, \pm\frac{1}{6}$

15. $\pm1, \pm2, \pm3, \pm6, \pm7, \pm14, \pm21, \pm42, \pm\frac{1}{2}, \pm\frac{3}{2}, \pm\frac{7}{2}, \pm\frac{21}{2}, \pm\frac{1}{4}, \pm\frac{3}{4}, \pm\frac{7}{4}, \pm\frac{21}{4}, \pm\frac{1}{8}, \pm\frac{3}{8}, \pm\frac{7}{8}, \pm\frac{21}{8}$

16. $\pm1, \pm2, \pm3, \pm5, \pm6, \pm9, \pm10, \pm15, \pm18, \pm30, \pm45, \pm90, \pm\frac{1}{3}, \pm\frac{2}{3}, \pm\frac{5}{3}, \pm\frac{10}{3}, \pm\frac{1}{5}, \pm\frac{2}{5}, \pm\frac{3}{5}, \pm\frac{6}{5}, \pm\frac{9}{5}, \pm\frac{18}{5}, \pm\frac{1}{15}, \pm\frac{2}{15}$

17. $\pm1, \pm2, \pm4, \pm8, \pm16, \pm32, \pm64, \pm128, \pm\frac{1}{2}, \pm\frac{1}{4}, \pm\frac{1}{8}, \pm\frac{1}{16}$

18a. $V(x) = (28 - 2x)(28 - 2x)x = 4x^3 - 112x^2 + 784x$

Practice and Problem Solving

● = **Step-by-Step Solutions** begin on page R20.
Extra Practice begins on page 947.

Example 1 p. 391

List all of the possible rational zeros of each function. 10–17. See margin.

10. $f(x) = x^4 + 8x - 32$

11. $f(x) = x^3 + x^2 - x - 56$

12. $f(x) = 2x^3 + 5x^2 - 8x - 10$

13. $f(x) = 3x^6 - 4x^4 - x^2 - 35$

14. $f(x) = 6x^5 - x^4 + 2x^3 - 3x^2 + 2x - 18$

15. $f(x) = 8x^4 - 4x^3 - 4x^2 + x + 42$

16. $f(x) = 15x^3 + 6x^2 + x + 90$

17. $f(x) = 16x^4 - 5x^2 + 128$

Example 2 p. 392

18. MANUFACTURING A box is to be constructed by cutting out equal squares from the corners of a square piece of cardboard and turning up the sides. a. See margin.

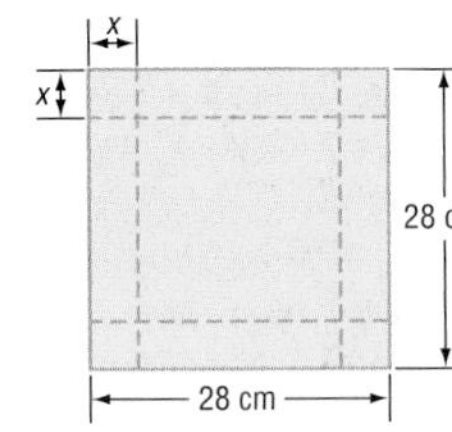

a. Write a function $V(x)$ for the volume of the box.

b. For what value of x will the volume of the box equal 1152 cubic centimeters? 2 or 8

c. What will be the volume of the box if $x = 6$ centimeters? 1536 cm^3

22. $-\frac{5}{2}, -2, \frac{1}{2}, 1$

30. $-\frac{1}{2}, \frac{1}{5}, 2$

33. $-2, \frac{4}{3}, \frac{-3 \pm i}{2}$

35. $3, \frac{2}{3}, -\frac{2}{3}, \frac{-3 \pm \sqrt{13}}{2}$

36. $-1, -2, 5, i, -i$

37. $-\frac{1}{2}, \frac{1}{3}, \frac{1}{2}, \frac{3}{4}$

38. $\frac{4}{5}, 0, \frac{5 \pm i\sqrt{3}}{2}$

Find all of the rational zeros of each function.

19. $f(x) = x^3 + 10x^2 + 31x + 30$ $-5, -3, -2$

20. $f(x) = x^3 - 2x^2 - 56x + 192$ $-8, 4, 6$

21. $f(x) = 4x^3 - 3x^2 - 100x + 75$ $-5, \frac{3}{4}, 5$

22. $f(x) = 4x^4 + 12x^3 - 5x^2 - 21x + 10$

23. $f(x) = x^4 + x^3 - 8x - 8$ $-1, 2$

24. $f(x) = 2x^4 - 3x^3 - 24x^2 + 4x + 48$ $-2, 4, \frac{3}{2}$

25. $f(x) = 4x^3 + x^2 + 16x + 4$ $-\frac{1}{4}$

26. $f(x) = 81x^4 - 256$ $-\frac{4}{3}, \frac{4}{3}$

Example 3 p. 393

Find all of the zeros of each function.

27. $f(x) = x^3 + 3x^2 - 25x + 21$ $-7, 1, 3$

28. $f(x) = 6x^3 + 5x^2 - 9x + 2$ $\frac{2}{3}, \frac{-3 \pm \sqrt{17}}{4}$

29. $f(x) = x^4 - x^3 - x^2 - x - 2$ $2, -1, i, -i$

30. $f(x) = 10x^3 - 17x^2 - 7x + 2$

31 $f(x) = x^4 - 3x^3 + x^2 - 3x$ $0, 3, -i, i$

32. $f(x) = 6x^3 + 11x^2 - 3x - 2$ $\frac{1}{2}, -\frac{1}{3}, -2$

33. $f(x) = 6x^4 + 22x^3 + 11x^2 - 38x - 40$

34. $f(x) = 2x^3 - 7x^2 - 8x + 28$ $-2, 2, \frac{7}{2}$

35. $f(x) = 9x^5 - 94x^3 + 27x^2 + 40x - 12$

36. $f(x) = x^5 - 2x^4 - 12x^3 - 12x^2 - 13x - 10$

37. $f(x) = 48x^4 - 52x^3 + 13x - 3$

38. $f(x) = 5x^4 - 29x^3 + 55x^2 - 28x$

Real-World Link

The world's largest swimming pool is along the coastline in San Alfonso del Mar, Chile. It is 1 kilometer long, about 6000 times as large as an average pool.

Source: OhGizmo!

39. SWIMMING POOLS A diagram of the swimming pool at the Midtown Community Center is shown below. The pool can hold 9175 cubic feet of water.

a. $V(x) = 324x^3 + 54x^2 - 19x - 2$

b. $\frac{-57 \pm i\sqrt{8987}}{36}$, 3; 3 is the only reasonable value for x. The other two values are imaginary.

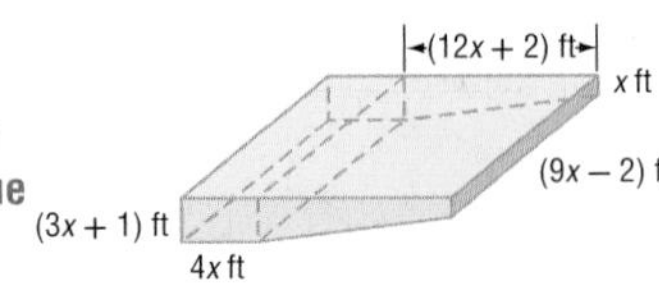

B **a.** Write a polynomial function that represents the volume of the swimming pool.

b. What are the possible values of x? Which of these values are reasonable?

40. ROLLER COASTERS A portion of the path of a certain roller coaster can be modeled by $f(t) = t^4 - 31t^3 + 308t^2 - 1100t + 1200$ where t represents the time in seconds and $f(t)$ represents the height of the roller coaster. Use the Rational Zero Theorem to determine the four times at which the roller coaster is at ground level.

Differentiated Homework Options

Level	Assignment	Two-Day Option	
AL Basic	10–38, 46, 48, 49, 51–69	11–37 odd, 52–55	10–38 even, 46, 48, 49, 51, 56–69
OL Core	11–43 odd, 46, 48, 49, 51–69	10–38, 52–55	39–46, 48, 49, 51, 56–69
BL Advanced	39–63, (optional: 64–69)		

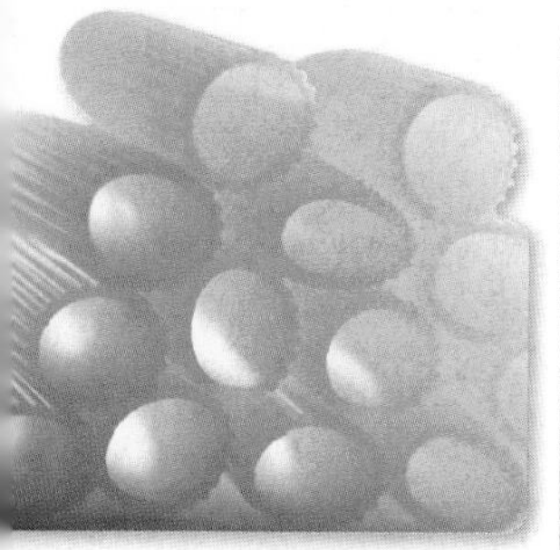

Real-World Link

Thomas Jefferson is credited with introducing macaroni to the United States after serving as the U.S. Ambassador to France.

Source: National Pasta Association

41. FOOD A restaurant orders spaghetti sauce in cylindrical metal cans. The volume of each can is about 160π cubic inches, and the height of the can is 6 inches more than the radius.

a. Write a polynomial equation that represents the volume of a can. Use the formula for the volume of a cylinder, $V = \pi r^2 h$. **$V = \pi r^3 + 6\pi r^2$**

b. What are the possible values of r? Which of these values are reasonable for this situation? **$4, -5 \pm i\sqrt{15}$; 4**

c. Find the dimensions of the can. **$r = 4$ in., $h = 10$ in.**

42. Refer to the graph at the right.

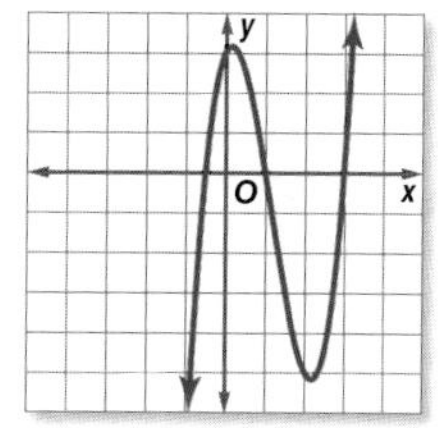

a. Find all of the zeros of $f(x) = 2x^3 + 7x^2 + 2x - 3$ and $g(x) = 2x^3 - 7x^2 + 2x + 3$. **$-1, \frac{1}{2}, -3; -\frac{1}{2}, 1, 3$**

b. Determine which function, f or g, is shown in the graph at the right. **g**

43. MUSIC SALES Refer to the beginning of the lesson.

a. Write a polynomial equation that could be used to determine the year in which music sales would be about \$20,000,000,000. **$30x^3 - 478x^2 + 1758x - 7608 = 0$**

b. List the possible whole number solutions for your equation in part a.

c. Determine the approximate year in which music sales will reach \$20,000,000,000.

d. Does the model represent a realistic estimate for all future music sales? Explain your reasoning.

Find all of the zeros of each function.

44. $f(x) = x^5 + 3x^4 - 19x^3 - 43x^2 + 18x + 40$ **1, −1, −2, 4, −5**

45. $f(x) = x^5 - x^4 - 23x^3 + 33x^2 + 126x - 216$ **2, 3, 3, −3, −4**

H.O.T. Problems

Use Higher-Order Thinking Skills

46. ERROR ANALYSIS Doug and Mika are listing all of the possible rational zeros for $f(x) = 4x^4 + 8x^5 + 10x^2 + 3x + 16$. Is either of them correct? Explain your reasoning.

Doug	Mika
$\pm1, \pm2, \pm4, \pm8, \pm16, \pm\frac{1}{2}, \pm\frac{1}{4}$	$\pm1, \pm2, \pm4, \pm8, \pm16, \pm\frac{1}{2}, \pm\frac{1}{4}, \pm\frac{1}{8}$

47. CHALLENGE Give a polynomial function that has zeros at $1 + \sqrt{3}$ and $5 + 2i$.

48. REASONING Determine if the following statement is *sometimes*, *always*, or *never* true. Explain your reasoning.

If all of the possible zeros of a polynomial function are integers, then the leading coefficient of the function is 1 or −1.

49. OPEN ENDED Write a function that has possible zeros of $\pm18, \pm9, \pm6, \pm3, \pm2, \pm1, \pm\frac{9}{4}, \pm\frac{9}{2}, \pm\frac{3}{2}, \pm\frac{3}{4}, \pm\frac{1}{2}$, and $\pm\frac{1}{4}$. **Sample answer: $f(x) = 4x^5 + 3x^3 + 8x + 18$**

50. CHALLENGE The roots of $x^2 + bx + c = 0$ are M and N. If $|M - N| = 1$, express c in terms of b. **$c = \frac{b^2 - 1}{4}$**

51. WRITING IN MATH Explain the process of using the Rational Zero Theorem to determine the number of possible rational zeros of a function. **See margin.**

43b. 1, 2, 3, 4, 6, 8, 12, 24, 317, 634, 951, 1268, 1902, 2536, 3804, 7608
43c. 2010
43d. No; Sample answer: Music sales decline from 1997 to 2005, then increase indefinitely. It is not reasonable to expect sales to increase forever.
46. Sample answer: Doug; the value of q is the leading coefficient, which is 4, not 8.
47. Sample answer: $f(x) = x^4 - 12x^3 + 47x^2 - 38x - 58$
48. Sample answer: Always; in order for the possible zeros of a polynomial function to be integers, the value of q must be 1 or −1. Otherwise, the possible zeros could be a fraction. In order for q to be 1 or −1, the leading coefficient of the polynomial must also be 1 or −1.

Additional Answer

51. Sample answer: For any polynomial function, the constant term represents p and the leading coefficient represents q. The possible zeros of the function can be found with $\pm\frac{p}{q}$ where the fraction is every combination of factors of p and q. For example, if p is 4 and q is 3, then $\pm4, \pm2, \pm1, \pm\frac{4}{3}, \pm\frac{2}{3}$, and $\pm\frac{1}{3}$ are all possible zeros.

Enrichment

CRM p. 52 OL BL

6-8 Enrichment

Irrational Numbers

Philosopher Hippasus of Metapontum was believed to have discovered that $\sqrt{2}$ was irrational. Mathematicians of the time denied the existence of irrational numbers and killed Hippasus, not wishing to believe this fundamental number could fail to be a ratio of integers.

The typical way to prove that $\sqrt{2}$ is irrational is by contradiction and relies on a few other common facts that are easily proven. That is, the proof assumes that it is rational and deduces a contradiction.

Theorem: $\sqrt{2}$ is irrational

Proof: Suppose $\sqrt{2}$ is a rational number. Then $\sqrt{2} = \frac{a}{b}$, where a and b are relatively prime integers. Relatively prime integers are integers that have no common factor other than one, therefore $\frac{a}{b}$ is a fraction written in lowest terms. It is also this condition that provides the contradiction. If we square both sides of the equation, $\sqrt{2} = \frac{a}{b}$, we have $2 = \frac{a^2}{b^2}$. This is equivalent to $a^2 = 2b^2$. However, this says that a^2 is an even number, thus a is an even number. If a is even and $\frac{a^2}{2} = b^2$, b is also even. Thus a and b have a factor in common other than one, namely two, and are not relatively prime. Hence $\sqrt{2}$ is irrational.

The Rational Zero Theorem provides a direct proof method.

...rcises

Study Guide and Intervention

CRM pp. 47–48 AL OL ELL

6-8 Study Guide and Intervention

Rational Zero Theorem

Identify Rational Zeros

Rational Zero Theorem	Let $f(x) = a_n x^n + a_{n-1}x^{n-1} + \ldots + a_2x^2 + a_1x + a_0$ represent a polynomial function with integral coefficients. If $\frac{p}{q}$ is a rational number in simplest form and is a zero of $y = f(x)$, then p is a factor of a_0 and q is a factor of a_n.
Corollary (Integral Zero Theorem)	If the coefficients of a polynomial are integers such that $a_n = 1$ and $a_0 \neq 0$, any rational zeros of the function must be factors of a_0.

Example List all of the possible rational zeros of each function.

a. $f(x) = 3x^4 - 2x^2 + 6x - 10$

If $\frac{p}{q}$ is a rational root, then p is a factor of −10 and q is a factor of 3. The possible values for p are ±1, ±2, ±5, and ±10. The possible values for q are 61 and 63. So all of the possible rational zeros are $\frac{p}{q} = \pm1, \pm2, \pm5, \pm10, \pm\frac{1}{3}, \pm\frac{2}{3}, \pm\frac{5}{3}$, and $\pm\frac{10}{3}$.

b. $q(x) = x^3 - 10x^2 + 14x - 36$

Since the coefficient of x^3 is 1, the possible rational zeros must be the factors of the constant term −36. So the possible rational zeros are ±1, ±2, ±3, ±4, ±6, ±9, ±12, ±18, and ±36.

Exercises

List all of the possible rational zeros of each function.

1. $f(x) = x^3 + 3x^2 - x + 8$ **±1, ±2, ±4, ±8**
2. $g(x) = x^5 - 7x^4 + 3x^2 + x - 20$ **±1, ±2, ±4, ±5, ±10, ±20**
3. $h(x) = x^4 - 7x^3 - 4x^2 + x - 49$ **±1, ±7, ±49**
4. $p(x) = 2x^4 - 5x^3 + 8x^2 + 3x - 5$ **$\pm1, \pm5, \pm\frac{1}{2}, \pm\frac{5}{2}$**
5. $q(x) = 3x^4 - 5x^3 + 10x + 12$ **$\pm1, \pm2, \pm3, \pm4, \pm6, \pm12, \pm\frac{1}{3}, \pm\frac{2}{3}, \pm\frac{4}{3}$**
6. $r(x) = 4x^5 - 2x + 18$ **$\pm1, \pm2, \pm3, \pm6, \pm9, \pm18, \pm\frac{1}{2}, \pm\frac{3}{2}, \pm\frac{9}{2}, \pm\frac{1}{4}, \pm\frac{3}{4}, \pm\frac{9}{4}$**
7. $f(x) = x^7 - 6x^5 - 3x^4 + x^3 + 4x^2 - 120$ **±1, ±2, ±3, ±4, ±5, ±6, ±8, ±10, ±12, ±15, ±20, ±24, ±30, ±40, ±60, ±120**
8. $g(x) = 5x^6 - 3x^4 + 5x^3 + 2x^2 - 15$ **$\pm1, \pm3, \pm5, \pm15, \pm\frac{1}{5}, \pm\frac{3}{5}$**
9. $h(x) = 6x^5 - 3x^4 + 12x^3 + 18x^2 - 9x + 21$ **$\pm1, \pm3, \pm7, \pm21, \pm\frac{1}{2}, \pm\frac{3}{2}, \pm\frac{7}{2}, \pm\frac{21}{2}, \pm\frac{1}{3}, \pm\frac{7}{3}, \pm\frac{1}{6}, \pm\frac{7}{6}$**
10. $p(x) = 2x^7 - 3x^6 + 11x^5 - 20x^2 + 11$ **$\pm1, \pm11, \pm\frac{1}{2}, \pm\frac{11}{2}$**

Lesson 6-8

Chapter 6 47 Glencoe Algebra 2

Practice

CRM p. 50 AL OL BL ELL

6-8 Practice

Rational Zero Theorem

List all of the possible rational zeros of each function.

1. $h(x) = x^3 - 5x^2 + 2x + 12$ **±1, ±2, ±3, ±4, ±6, ±12**
2. $s(x) = x^4 - 8x^3 + 7x - 14$ **±1, ±2, ±7, ±14**
3. $f(x) = 3x^5 - 5x^2 + x + 6$ **$\frac{1}{3}, \pm\frac{2}{3}, \pm1, \pm2, \pm3, \pm6$**
4. $p(x) = 3x^2 + x + 7$ **$\pm\frac{1}{3}, \pm\frac{7}{3}, \pm1, \pm7$**
5. $g(x) = 5x^3 + x^2 - x + 8$ **$\pm\frac{1}{5}, \pm\frac{2}{5}, \pm\frac{4}{5}, \pm\frac{8}{5}, \pm1, \pm2, \pm4, \pm8$**
6. $q(x) = 6x^5 + x^3 - 3$ **$\pm\frac{1}{6}, \pm\frac{1}{3}, \pm\frac{1}{2}, \pm\frac{3}{2}, \pm1, \pm3$**

Find all of the rational zeros of each function.

7. $q(x) = x^3 + 3x^2 - 6x - 8$ **−4, −1, 2**
8. $v(x) = x^3 - 9x^2 + 27x - 27$ **3**
9. $c(x) = x^3 - x^2 - 8x + 12$ **−3, 2**
10. $f(x) = x^4 - 49x^2$ **0, −7, 7**
11. $h(x) = x^3 - 7x^2 + 17x - 15$ **3**
12. $b(x) = x^3 + 6x + 20$ **−2**
13. $f(x) = x^3 - 6x^2 + 4x - 24$ **6**
14. $g(x) = 2x^3 + 3x^2 - 4x - 4$ **−2**
15. $h(x) = 2x^3 - 7x^2 - 21x + 54$ **$-3, 2, \frac{9}{2}$**
16. $z(x) = x^4 - 3x^3 + 5x^2 - 27x - 36$ **−1, 4**
17. $d(x) = x^4 + x^3 + 16$ **no rational zeros**
18. $n(x) = x^4 - 2x^3 - 3$ **−1**
19. $p(x) = 2x^4 - 7x^3 + 4x^2 + 7x - 6$ **$-1, 1, \frac{3}{2}, 2$**
20. $q(x) = 6x^4 + -9x^3 + 40x^2 + 7x - 12$ **$-\frac{3}{2}, -\frac{4}{3}$**

Find all of the zeros of each function.

21. $f(x) = 2x^4 + 7x^3 - 2x^2 - 19x - 12$ **$-1, -3, \frac{1+\sqrt{33}}{4}, \frac{1-\sqrt{33}}{4}$**
22. $q(x) = x^4 - 4x^3 + x^2 + 16x - 20$ **$-2, 2, 2 + i, 2 - i$**
23. $h(x) = x^6 - 8x^3$ **$0, 2, -1 + i\sqrt{3}, -1 - i\sqrt{3}$**
24. $g(x) = x^6 - 1$ **$-1, 1, \frac{-1 + i\sqrt{3}}{2}, \frac{-1 - i\sqrt{3}}{2}, \frac{1 + i\sqrt{3}}{2}, \frac{1 - i\sqrt{3}}{2}$**
25. **TRAVEL** The height of a box that Joan is shipping is 3 inches less than the width of the box. The length is 2 inches more than twice the width. The volume of the box is 1540 in^3. What are the dimensions of the box? **22 in. by 10 in. by 7 in.**
26. **GEOMETRY** The height of a square pyramid is 3 meters shorter than the side of its base. If the volume of the pyramid is 432 m^3, how tall is it? Use the formula $V = \frac{1}{3}Bh$. **9 m**

Chapter 6 50 Glencoe Algebra 2

Word Problem Practice

CRM p. 51 AL OL BL ELL

6-8 Word Problem Practice

Rational Zero Theorem

1. **ROOTS** Paul was examining an old algebra book. He came upon a page about polynomial equations and saw the polynomial below.

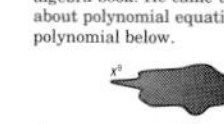

As you can see, all the middle terms were blotted out by an ink spill. What are all the possible rational roots of this polynomial?

−8, −4, −2, −1, 1, 2, 4, 8

2. **IRRATIONAL CONSTANTS** Cherie was given a polynomial whose constant term was $\sqrt{2}$. Is it possible for this polynomial to have a rational root? If it is not, explain why not. If it is possible, give an example of such a polynomial with a rational root.

Yes, it is possible. For example, the polynomial $x^2 - (1 + \sqrt{2})x + \sqrt{2}$ has 1 as a root.

3. **MARKOV CHAINS** Tara is a mathematician who specializes in probability. In the course of her work, she needed to find the roots of the polynomial $p(x) = 288x^4 - 288x^3 + 106x^2 - 17x + 1$. What are the roots of $p(x)$?

$\frac{1}{3}, \frac{1}{4}, \frac{1}{4}$ and $\frac{1}{6}$

4. **PYRAMIDS** The Great Pyramid in Giza, Egypt has a square base with side lengths of $5x$ yards and a height of $4x - 50$ yards. The volume of the Great Pyramid is 3,125,000 cubic yards. Use a calculator to find the value of x and the dimensions of the pyramid.

$x = 50$; length= 250 yards; height= 150 yards

5. **BOXES** Devon made a box with length $x + 1$, width $x + 3$, and height $x - 3$.

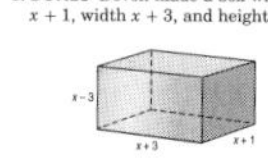

a. What is the volume of Devon's box as a function of x? **$V(x) = x^3 + x^2 - 9x - 9$**

b. What is x if the volume of the box is equal to 1001 cubic inches? **10**

c. What is x if the volume of the box is equal to $14\frac{5}{8}$ cubic inches? **3.5**

Lesson 6-8

Chapter 6 51 Glencoe Algebra 2

4 ASSESS

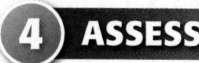

Name the Math Ask students:

- What must be true about the coefficients of a polynomial function in order to apply the Rational Zero Theorem?
- How can they identify the possible zeros of such a polynomial function?

Formative Assessment

Check for student understanding of concepts in Lessons 6-7 and 6-8.

CRM Quiz 4, p. 58

NGSSS PRACTICE 912.A.4.3, 912.A.3.9

52. ALGEBRA Which of the following is a zero of the function $f(x) = 12x^5 - 5x^3 + 2x - 9$? **D**

A. -6 C. $\frac{3}{8}$
B. $-\frac{2}{3}$ D. 1

53. SAT/ACT How many negative real zeros does $f(x) = x^5 - 2x^4 - 4x^3 + 4x^2 - 5x + 6$ have? **H**

F. 3 H. 1
G. 2 I. 0

54. ALGEBRA For all nonnegative numbers n, let $\boxed{n}$ be defined by $\boxed{n} = \frac{\sqrt{n}}{2}$. If $\boxed{n} = 4$, what is the value of n? **D**

A. 2 C. 16
B. 4 D. 64

55. GRIDDED RESPONSE What is the y-intercept of a line that contains the point $(-1, 4)$ and has the same x-intercept as $x + 2y = -3$? **6**

Spiral Review

Write a polynomial function of least degree with integral coefficients that has the given zeros. (Lesson 6-7)

56. $6, -3, \sqrt{2}$ **$f(x) = x^4 - 3x^3 - 20x^2 + 6x + 36$**

57. $5, -1, 4i$ **$f(x) = x^4 - 4x^3 + 11x^2 - 64x - 80$**

58. $-4, -2, i\sqrt{2}$ **$f(x) = x^4 + 6x^3 + 10x^2 + 12x + 16$**

Given a polynomial and one of its factors, find the remaining factors of the polynomial. (Lesson 6-6)

59. $x^4 + 5x^3 + 5x^2 - 5x - 6; x + 3$ **$(x - 1)(x + 2)(x + 1)$**

60. $a^4 - 2a^3 - 17a^2 + 18a + 72; a - 3$ **$(a + 3)(a - 4)(a + 2)$**

61. $x^4 + x^3 - 11x^2 + x - 12; x + i$ **$(x - 3)(x + 4)(x - i)$**

62. BRIDGES The supporting cables of the Golden Gate Bridge approximate the shape of a parabola. The parabola can be modeled by the quadratic function $y = 0.00012x^2 + 6$, where x represents the distance from the axis of symmetry and y represents the height of the cables. The related quadratic equation is $0.00012x^2 + 6 = 0$. (Lesson 5-6)

a. Calculate the value of the discriminant. **-0.00288**

b. What does the discriminant tell you about the supporting cables of the Golden Gate Bridge? **Sample answer: This means that the cables do not touch the floor of the bridge, since the graph does not intersect the x-axis and the roots are imaginary.**

63. RIDES An amusement park ride carries riders to the top of a 225-foot tower. The riders then free-fall in their seats until they reach 30 feet above the ground. (Lesson 5-2)

a. Use the formula $h(t) = -16t^2 + h_0$, where the time t is in seconds and the initial height h_0 is in feet, to find how long the riders are in free-fall. **about 3.5 s**

b. Suppose the designer of the ride wants the riders to experience free-fall for 5 seconds before stopping 30 feet above the ground. What should be the height of the tower? **430 ft**

Skills Review

Simplify. (Lesson 6-1)

64. $(x - 4)(x + 3)$ **$x^2 - x - 12$**

65. $3x(x^2 + 4)$ **$3x^3 + 12x$**

66. $x^2(x - 2)(x + 1)$ **$x^4 - x^3 - 2x^2$**

Find each value if $f(x) = 6x + 2$ and $g(x) = -4x^2$. (Lesson 2-1)

67. $f(5)$ **32**

68. $g(-3)$ **-36**

69. $f(3c)$ **$18c + 2$**

Differentiated Instruction OL BL

Extension Ask students to factor $x^4 - 2x^2 - 3$ as the product of factors that are irreducible over rational numbers. $(x^2 - 3)(x^2 + 1)$

Then have students factor as the product of factors that are irreducible over real numbers. $(x - \sqrt{3})(x + \sqrt{3})(x^2 + 1)$

Finally, have students factor completely, including complex numbers. $(x - \sqrt{3})(x + \sqrt{3})(x + i)(x - i)$

FL Math Online glencoe.com
- STUDY TO GO
- Vocabulary Review

Chapter Summary

Key Concepts

Operations with Polynomials (Lessons 6-1 and 6-2)

- To add or subtract: Combine like terms.
- To multiply: Use the Distributive Property.
- To divide: Use long division or synthetic division.

Polynomial Functions and Graphs (Lessons 6-3 and 6-4)

- Turning points of a function are called *relative maxima* and *relative minima*.

Solving Polynomial Equations (Lesson 6-5)

- You can factor polynomials by using the GCF, grouping, or quadratic techniques.

The Remainder and Factor Theorems (Lesson 6-6)

- Factor Theorem: The binomial $x - a$ is a factor of the polynomial $f(x)$ if and only if $f(a) = 0$.

Roots, Zeros, and the Rational Zero Theorem (Lessons 6-7 and 6-8)

- Complex Conjugates Theorem: If $a + bi$ is a zero of a function, then $a - bi$ is also a zero.
- Integral Zero Theorem: If the coefficients of a polynomial function are integers such that $a_0 = 1$ and $a_n = 0$, any rational zeros of the function must be factors of a_n.
- Rational Zero Theorem: If $P(x)$ is a polynomial function with integral coefficients, then every rational zero of $P(x) = 0$ is of the form $\frac{p}{q}$, a rational number in simplest form, where p is a factor of the constant term and q is a factor of the leading coefficient.

FOLDABLES® Study Organizer

Be sure the Key Concepts are noted in your Foldable.

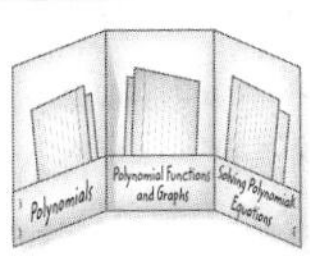

Key Vocabulary

degree of a polynomial (p. 335)
depressed polynomial (p. 379)
end behavior (p. 350)
extrema (p. 358)
leading coefficient (p. 348)
location priciple (p. 357)
polynomial function (p. 349)
polynomial in one variable (p. 348)
power function (p. 349)
prime polynomials (p. 368)
quadratic form (p. 371)
relative maximum (p. 358)
relative minimum (p. 358)
simplify (p. 333)
synthetic division (p. 342)
synthetic substitution (p. 377)
turning points (p. 358)

2. false; prime polynomials
3. false; depressed polynomial
8. false; turning points

Vocabulary Check

State whether each sentence is *true* or *false*. If *false*, replace the underlined term to make a true sentence.

1. The coefficient of the first term of a polynomial in standard form is called the <u>leading coefficient</u>. true
2. Polynomials that cannot be factored are called <u>polynomials in one variable</u>.
3. A <u>prime polynomial</u> has a degree that is one less than the original polynomial.
4. A point on the graph of a function where no other nearby point has a greater y-coordinate is called a <u>relative maximum</u>. true
5. A <u>polynomial function</u> is a continuous function that can be described by a polynomial equation in one variable. true
6. To <u>simplify</u> an expression containing powers means to rewrite the expression without parentheses or negative exponents. true
7. <u>Synthetic division</u> is a shortcut method for dividing a polynomial by a binomial. true
8. The relative maximum and relative minimum of a function are often referred to as <u>end behavior</u>.
9. When a polynomial is divided by one of its binomial factors, the quotient is called a <u>depressed polynomial</u>. true
10. $(x^3)^2 + 3x^3 - 8 = 0$ is a <u>power function</u>. false; written in quadratic form

CHAPTER 6 Study Guide and Review

Formative Assessment

Key Vocabulary The page references after each word denote where that term was first introduced. If students have difficulty answering questions 1–10, remind them that they can use these page references to refresh their memories about the vocabulary.

Summative Assessment

CRM Vocabulary Test, p. 60

FL Math Online glencoe.com

Vocabulary PuzzleMaker improves students' mathematics vocabulary using four puzzle formats– crossword, scramble, word search using a word list, and word search using clues. Students can work online or from a printed worksheet.

FOLDABLES® Study Organizer

Dinah Zike's Foldables®

Have students look through the chapter to make sure they have included examples in their Foldables.

Suggest that students keep their Foldables handy while completing the Study Guide and Review pages. Point out that their Foldables can serve as a quick review tool when studying for the Chapter Test.

Lesson-by-Lesson Review

Intervention If the given examples are not sufficient to review the topics covered by the questions, remind students that the page references tell them where to review that topic in their textbook.

Two-Day Option Have students complete the Lesson-by-Lesson Review on pp. 398–400. Then you can use ExamView® Assessment Suite to customize another review worksheet that practices all the objectives of this chapter or only the objectives on which your students need more help.

Differentiated Instruction

Super DVD: Mindjogger Videoquizzes Use this DVD as an alternative format of review for the test.

Additional Answers

22. degree: 6; leading coefficient: 5

23. This is not a polynomial in one variable. It has two variables, x and y.

24. degree: 8; leading coefficient: 6

25. $p(-2) = -3$; $p(x + h) = x^2 + 2xh + h^2 + 2x + 2h - 3$

26. $p(-2) = 14$; $p(x + h) = 3x^2 + 6xh + 3h^2 - x - h$

27. $p(-2) = -25$; $p(x + h) = 3 - 5x^2 - 10xh - 5h^2 + x^3 + 3hx^2 + 3h^2x + h^3$

CHAPTER 6 Study Guide and Review

Lesson-by-Lesson Review

6-1 Operations with Polynomials (pp. 333–339)

912.A.4.2

Simplify. Assume that no variable equals 0.

11. $\frac{14x^4y}{2x^3y^5}$ $\frac{7x}{y^4}$

12. $3t(tn - 5)$ $3t^2n - 15t$

13. $(4r^2 + 3r - 1) - (3r^2 - 5r + 4)$ $r^2 + 8r - 5$

14. $(x^4)^3$ x^{12}

15. $(m + p)(m^2 - 2mp + p^2)$ $m^3 - m^2p - mp^2 + p^3$

16. $3b(2b - 1) + 2b(b + 3)$ $8b^2 + 3b$

EXAMPLE 1

Simplify each expression.

a. $(-4a^3b^5)(5ab^3)$

$(-4a^3b^5)(5ab^3) = (-4)(5)a^{3+1}b^{5+3}$ — Product of Powers

$= -20a^4b^8$ — Simplify.

b. $(2x^2 + 3x - 8) + (3x^2 - 5x - 7)$

$(2x^2 + 3x - 8) + (3x^2 - 5x - 7)$
$= (2x^2 + 3x^2) + (3x - 5x) + [-8 + (-7)]$
$= 5x^2 - 2x - 15$

6-2 Dividing Polynomials (pp. 341–347)

20. $2a^5 - a^4 - 2a^3 + a^2 + a - 1 + \frac{1}{2a + 1}$

912.A.4.4

Simplify.

17. $\frac{12x^4y^5 + 8x^3y^7 - 16x^2y^6}{4xy^5}$ $3x^3 + 2x^2y^2 - 4xy$

18. $(6y^3 + 13y^2 - 10y - 24) \div (y + 2)$ $6y^2 + y - 12$

19. $(a^4 + 5a^3 + 2a^2 - 6a + 4)(a + 2)^{-1}$

20. $(4a^6 - 5a^4 + 3a^2 - a) \div (2a + 1)$

21. **GEOMETRY** The volume of the rectangular prism is $3x^3 + 11x^2 - 114x - 80$ cubic units. What is the area of the base? $x^2 + 3x - 40$ units^2

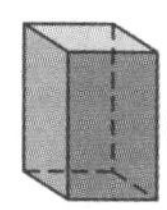

$3x + 2$

19. $a^3 + 3a^2 - 4a + 2$

EXAMPLE 2

Simplify $(6x^3 - 31x^2 - 34x + 22) \div (2x - 1)$.

$$\begin{array}{r}
3x^2 - 14x - 24 \\
2x - 1\overline{)6x^3 - 31x^2 - 34x + 22} \\
\underline{(-)\ 6x^3 - 3x^2} \\
-28x^2 - 34x \\
\underline{(-)\ -28x^2 + 14x} \\
-48x + 22 \\
\underline{(-)\ -48x + 24} \\
-2
\end{array}$$

The result is $3x^2 - 14x - 24 - \frac{2}{2x - 1}$.

6-3 Polynomial Functions (pp. 348–355)

912.A.4.5

State the degree and leading coefficient of each polynomial in one variable. If it is not a polynomial in one variable, explain why.

22. $5x^6 - 3x^4 + x^3 - 9x^2 + 1$ 22–24. See margin.

23. $6xy^2 - xy + y^2$

24. $12x^3 - 5x^4 + 6x^8 - 3x - 3$

Find $p(-2)$ and $p(x + h)$ for each function.

25. $p(x) = x^2 + 2x - 3$ 25–27. See margin.

26. $p(x) = 3x^2 - x$

27. $p(x) = 3 - 5x^2 + x^3$

EXAMPLE 3

What are the degree and leading coefficient of $4x^3 + 3x^2 - 7x^7 + 4x - 1$?

The greatest exponent is 7, so the degree is 7. The leading coefficient is -7.

EXAMPLE 4

Find $p(a - 2)$ if $p(x) = 3x + 2x^2 - x^3$.

$p(a - 2) = 3(a - 2) + 2(a - 2)^2 - (a - 2)^3$
$= 3a - 6 + 2a^2 - 8a + 8 - (a^3 - 6a^2 + 12a - 8)$
$= -a^3 + 8a^2 - 17a + 10$

398 Chapter 6 Polynomials and Polynomial Functions

MIXED PROBLEM SOLVING
For mixed problem-solving practice, see page 984.

6-4 Analyzing Graphs of Polynomial Functions (pp. 357–364)

912.A.2.6, 912.A.4.5

Complete each of the following.

a. **Graph each function by making a table of values.**

b. **Determine the consecutive integer values of x between which each real zero is located.**

c. **Estimate the x-coordinates at which the relative maxima and minima occur.**

28. $h(x) = x^3 - 4x^2 - 7x + 10$ **28–32. See margin.**

29. $g(x) = 4x^4 - 21x^2 + 5$

30. $f(x) = x^3 - 3x^2 - 4x + 12$

31. $h(x) = 4x^3 - 6x^2 + 1$

32. $p(x) = x^5 - x^4 + 1$

33. **BUSINESS** Milo tracked the monthly profits for his sports store business for the first six months of the year. They can be modeled by using the following six points: (1, 675), (2, 950), (3, 550), (4, 250), (5, 600), and (6, 400). How many turning points would the graph of a polynomial function through these points have? Describe them. **2 relative maxima and 1 relative minima**

EXAMPLE 5

Graph $f(x) = x^3 + 3x^2 - 4$ by making a table of values.

Make a table of values for several values of x.

x	−3	−2	−1	0	1	2
$f(x)$	−4	0	−2	−4	0	16

Plot the points and connect the points with a smooth curve.

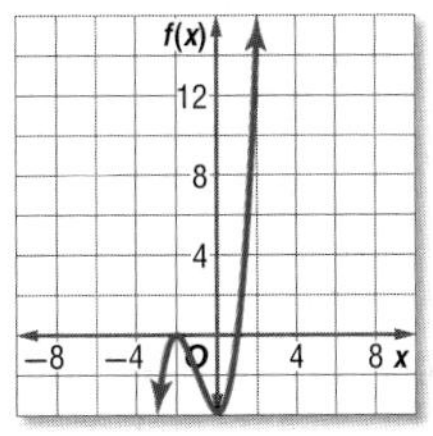

6-5 Solving Polynomial Equations by Factoring (pp. 368–375)

912.A.4.3

Factor completely. If the polynomial is not factorable, write *prime*.

34. $a^4 - 16$ **$(a - 2)(a + 2)(a^2 + 4)$**

35. $x^3 + 6y^3$ **prime**

36. $54x^3y - 16y^4$ **$2y(3x - 2y)(9x^2 + 6xy + 4y^2)$**

37. $6ay + 4by - 2cy + 3az + 2bz - cz$ **$(2y + z)(3a + 2b - c)$**

Solve each equation.

38. $x^3 + 2x^2 - 35x = 0$ **−7, 0, 5**

39. $8x^4 - 10x^2 + 3 = 0$ **$\pm\frac{\sqrt{3}}{2}, \pm\frac{\sqrt{2}}{2}$**

40. **GEOMETRY** The volume of the prism is 315 cubic inches. Find the value of x and the length, height, and width.

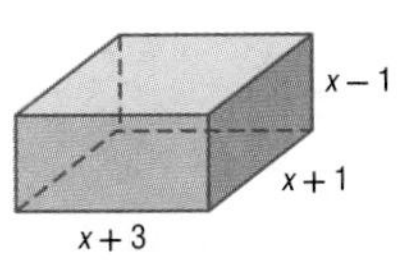

EXAMPLE 6

Factor $r^7 + 64r$.

$r^7 + 64r = r(r^6 + 64)$ **Factor by GCF.**

$= r[(r^2)^3 + 4^3]$ **Write as cubes.**

$= r(r^2 + 4)(r^4 - 4r^2 + 16)$

EXAMPLE 7

Solve $4x^4 - 25x^2 + 36 = 0$.

$(x^2 - 4)(4x^2 - 9) = 0$

$x^2 - 4 = 0$ or $4x^2 - 9 = 0$

$x^2 = 4$ $\quad x^2 = \frac{9}{4}$

$x = \pm 2$ $\quad x = \pm\frac{3}{2}$

The solutions are −2, 2, $-\frac{3}{2}$, and $\frac{3}{2}$.

40. $x = 6$, length = 9 in., height = 5 in., width = 7 in.

Additional Answers

28a.

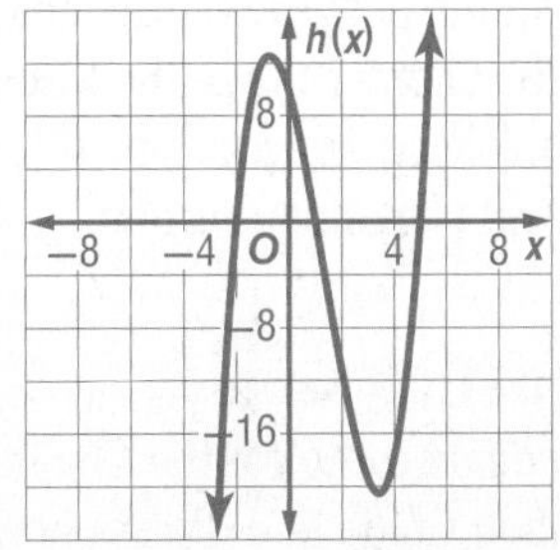

28b. The zeros are at −2, 1, and 5.

28c. rel. max: $x \approx -0.69$; rel. min: $x \approx 3.36$

29a.

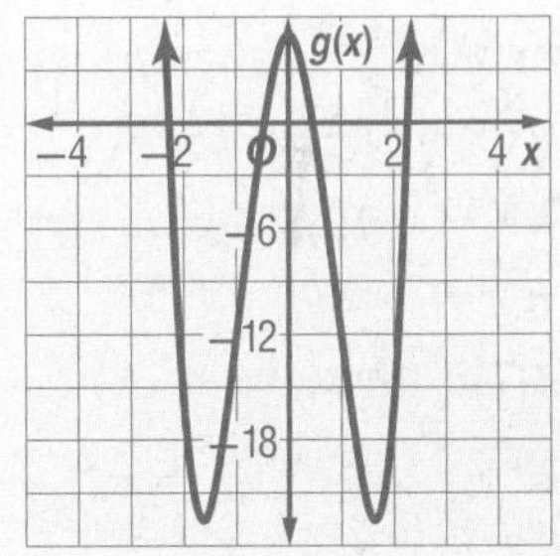

29b. between −3 and −2, between −1 and 0, between 0 and 1, between 2 and 3

29c. rel. max: $x \approx 0$; rel. min: $x \approx 1.62$ and $x \approx -1.62$

30a.

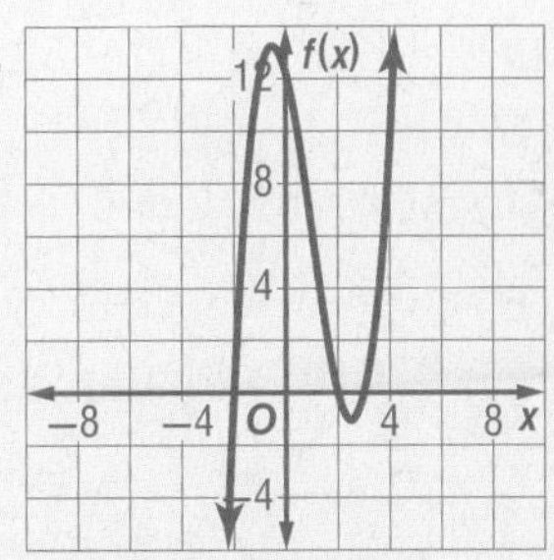

30b. zeros at −2, 2, and 3

30c. rel. max: $x \approx -0.53$; rel. min: $x \approx 2.53$

31a.

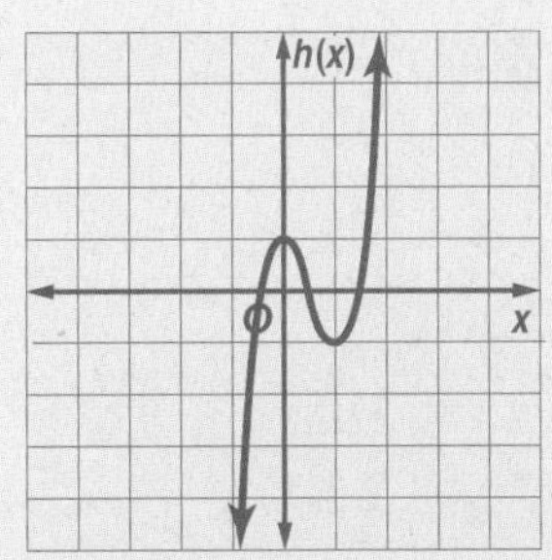

31b. between −1 and 0, between 0 and 1, and between 1 and 2

31c. rel. max: $x \approx 0$; rel. min: $x \approx 1$

32a.

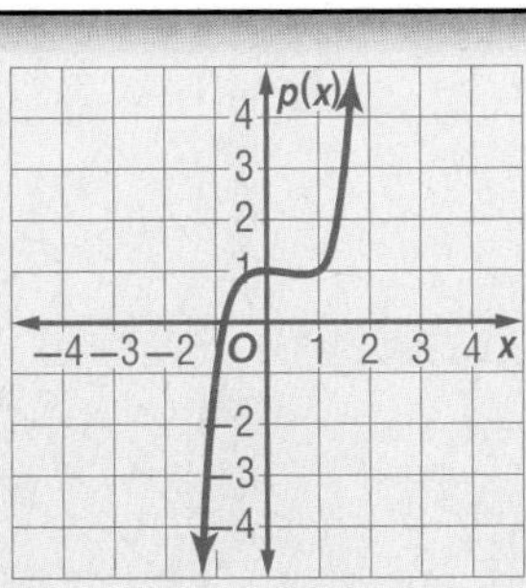

32b. between −1 and 0

32c. rel. max: $x \approx 0$; rel. min: $x \approx 0.80$

Problem Solving Review

For additional practice in problem solving for Chapter 6, see the Mixed Problem Solving Appendix, p. 985, in the Student Handbook section.

Anticipation Guide

Have students complete the Chapter 6 Anticipation Guide and discuss how their responses have changed now that they have completed Chapter 6.

Additional Answers

48. positive real zeros: 3 or 1
negative real zeros: 0
imaginary zeros: 2 or 0

49. positive real zeros: 0
negative real zeros: 4, 2, or 0
imaginary zeros: 4, 2, or 0

50. positive real zeros: 3 or 1
negative real zeros: 1
imaginary zeros: 4 or 2

51. positive real zeros: 2 or 0
negative real zeros: 1
imaginary zeros: 4 or 2

52. positive real zeros: 2 or 0
negative real zeros: 2 or 0
imaginary zeros: 6, 4, or 2

CHAPTER 6 Study Guide and Review

6-6 The Remainder and Factor Theorems (pp. 377–382)

912.A.4.6, 912.A.4.8

Use synthetic substitution to find $f(-2)$ and $f(4)$ for each function.

41. $f(x) = x^2 - 3$ $f(-2) = 1$; $f(4) = 13$

42. $f(x) = x^2 - 5x + 4$ $f(-2) = 18$; $f(4) = 0$

43. $f(x) = x^3 + 4x^2 - 3x + 2$ $f(-2) = 16$; $f(4) = 118$

44. $f(x) = 2x^4 - 3x^3 + 1$ $f(-2) = 57$; $f(4) = 321$

Given a polynomial and one of its factors, find the remaining factors of the polynomial.

45. $3x^3 + 20x^2 + 23x - 10$; $x + 5$ $x + 2$ and $3x - 1$

46. $2x^3 + 11x^2 + 17x + 5$; $2x + 5$ $x^2 + 3x + 1$

47. $x^3 + 2x^2 - 23x - 60$; $x - 5$ $x + 3$, $x + 4$

EXAMPLE 8

Determine whether $x - 6$ is a factor of $x^3 - 2x^2 - 21x - 18$.

$$\begin{array}{c|cccc} 6 & 1 & -2 & -21 & -18 \\ & & 6 & 24 & 18 \\ \hline & 1 & 4 & 3 & 0 \end{array}$$

$x - 6$ is a factor because $r = 0$.

$x^3 - 2x^2 - 21x - 18 = (x - 6)(x^2 + 4x + 3)$

6-7 Roots and Zeros (pp. 383–390)

912.A.4.6, 912.A.4.8

State the possible number of positive real zeros, negative real zeros, and imaginary zeros of each function. 48–52. See margin.

48. $f(x) = -2x^3 + 11x^2 - 3x + 2$

49. $f(x) = -4x^4 - 2x^3 - 12x^2 - x - 23$

50. $f(x) = x^6 - 5x^3 + x^2 + x - 6$

51. $f(x) = -2x^5 + 4x^4 + x^2 - 3$

52. $f(x) = -2x^6 + 4x^4 + x^2 - 3x - 3$

EXAMPLE 9

State the possible number of positive real zeros, negative real zeros, and imaginary zeros of $f(x) = 3x^4 + 2x^3 - 2x^2 - 26x - 48$.

$f(x)$ has one sign change, so there is 1 positive real zero.

$f(-x)$ has 3 sign changes, so there are 3 or 1 negative real zeros.

There are 0 or 2 imaginary zeros.

6-8 Rational Zero Theorem (pp. 391–396)

912.A.4.6, 912.A.4.8

Find all of the zeros of each function.

53. $f(x) = x^3 + 4x^2 + 3x - 2$ $-2, -1 \pm \sqrt{2}$

54. $f(x) = 4x^3 + 4x^2 - x - 1$ $-1, -\frac{1}{2}, \frac{1}{2}$

55. $f(x) = x^3 + 2x^2 + 4x + 8$ $-2, \pm 2i$

56. STORAGE Melissa is building a storage box that is shaped like a rectangular prism. It will have a volume of 96 cubic feet. Using the diagram below, find the dimensions of the box.

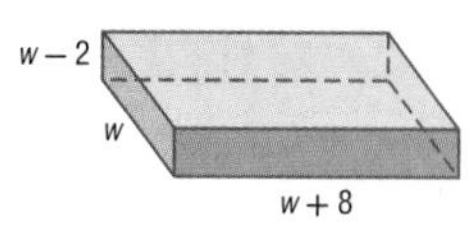

width = 4 ft, length = 12 ft, height = 2 ft

EXAMPLE 10

Find all of the zeros of $f(x) = x^3 + 4x^2 - 11x - 30$.

There are exactly 3 zeros.

There are 1 positive real zero and 2 negative real zeros. The possible rational zeros are $\pm 1, \pm 2, \pm 3, \pm 5, \pm 6, \pm 10, \pm 15, \pm 30$.

$$\begin{array}{c|cccc} 3 & 1 & 4 & -11 & -30 \\ & & 3 & 21 & 30 \\ \hline & 1 & 7 & 10 & 0 \end{array}$$

$$\begin{aligned} x^3 + 4x^2 - 11x - 30 &= (x - 3)(x^2 + 7x + 10) \\ &= (x - 3)(x + 2)(x + 5) \end{aligned}$$

Thus, the zeros are 3, −2, and −5.

400 Chapter 6 Polynomials and Polynomial Functions

FL Math Online > glencoe.com
Chaper Test

Simplify.

1. $(3a)^2(7b)^4$ **$21{,}609a^2b^4$**
2. $(7x-2)(2x+5)$ **$14x^2+31x-10$**
3. $(2x^2+3x-4)-(4x^2-7x+1)$ **$-2x^2+10x-5$**
4. $(4x^3-x^2+5x-4)+(5x-10)$ **$4x^3-x^2+10x-14$**
5. $(x^4+5x^3+3x^2-8x+3)\div(x+3)$ **x^3+2x^2-3x+1**
6. $(3x^3-5x^2-23x+24)\div(x-3)$ **$3x^2+4x-11-\frac{9}{x-3}$**
7. **NGSSS PRACTICE** How many unique real zeros does the graph have? **C**

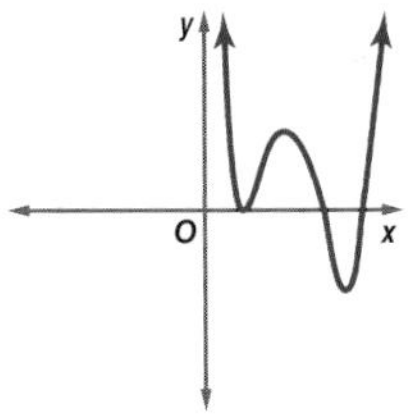

A. 0   C. 3

B. 2   D. 5

8. If $c(x)=3x^3+5x^2-4$, what is the value of $4c(3b)$? **$324b^3+180b^2-16$**

Complete each of the following.

a. Graph each function by making a table of values.
b. Determine consecutive integer values of x between which each real zero is located.
c. Estimate the x-coordinates at which the relative maxima and relative minima occur.

9. $g(x)=x^3+4x^2-3x+1$ **9, 10. See margin.**
10. $h(x)=x^4-4x^3-3x^2+6x+2$

Factor completely. If the polynomial is not factorable, write *prime*.

11. $8y^4+x^3y$ **$y(2y+x)(4y^2-2xy+x^2)$**
12. $2x^2+2x+1$ **prime**
13. $a^2x+3ax+2x-a^2y-3ay-2y$ **$(x-y)(a+2)(a+1)$**

Solve each equation.

14. $8x^3+1=0$ **$-\frac{1}{2}, \frac{1\pm i\sqrt{3}}{4}$**
15. $x^4-11x^2+28=0$ **$\pm\sqrt{7}, \pm 2$**
16. **FRAMING** The area of the picture and frame shown below is 168 square inches. What is the width of the frame? **2 in.**

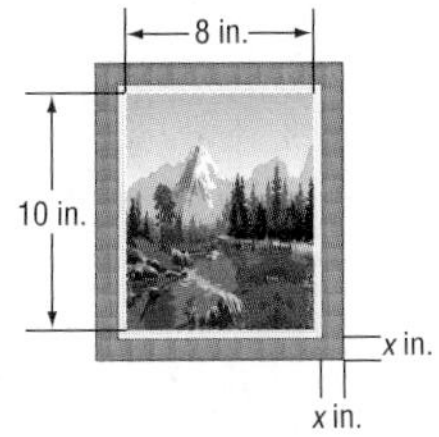

17. **NGSSS PRACTICE** Let $f(x)=x^4-3x^3+5x-3$. Use synthetic substitution to find $f(-2)$. **G**

F. 37   H. −33

G. 27   I. −21

Given a polynomial and one of its factors, find the remaining factors of the polynomial.

18. $2x^3+15x^2+22x-15$; $x+5$ **$2x-1, x+3$**
19. $x^3-4x^2+10x-12$; $x-2$ **x^2-2x+6**

State the possible number of positive real zeros, negative real zeros, and imaginary zeros of each function.

20. $p(x)=x^3-x^2-x-3$ **1 positive, 2 or 0 negative, 2 or 0 imaginary**
21. $p(x)=2x^6+5x^4-x^3-5x-1$ **1 positive, 1 negative, 4 imaginary**

Find all zeros of each function.

22. $p(x)=x^3-4x^2+x+6$ **−1, 2, 3**
23. $p(x)=x^3+2x^2+4x+8$ **$-2, \pm 2i$**
24. **GEOMETRY** The volume of the rectangular prism shown is 612 cubic centimeters. Find the dimensions of the prism. **9 cm by 17 cm by 4 cm**

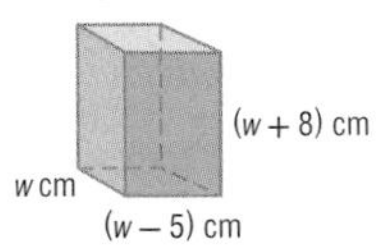

25. List all possible rational zeros of $f(x)=2x^4+3x^2-12x+8$. **$\pm\frac{1}{2}, \pm1, \pm2, \pm4, \pm8$**

CHAPTER 6 Practice Test

ExamView Assessment Suite Customize and create multiple versions of your chapter test and their answer keys. All of the questions from the leveled chapter tests in the Chapter 6 *Resource Masters* are also available on ExamView® Assessment Suite.

Additional Answers

6. $3x^2+4x-11-\frac{9}{x-3}$

9a.

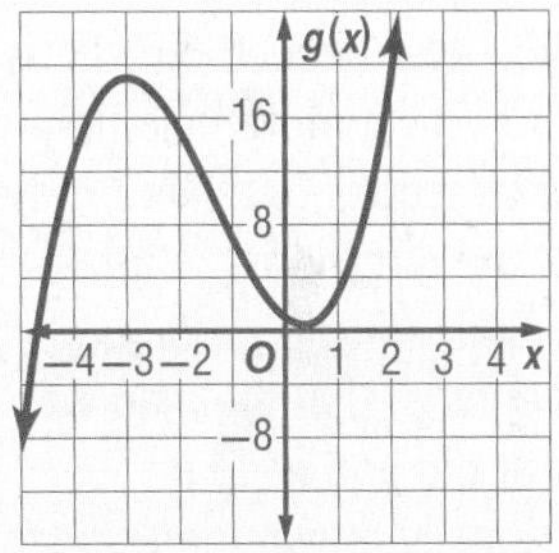

9b. between −5 and −4

9c. rel. max: $x=-3$; rel. min: $x\approx0.3$

10a.

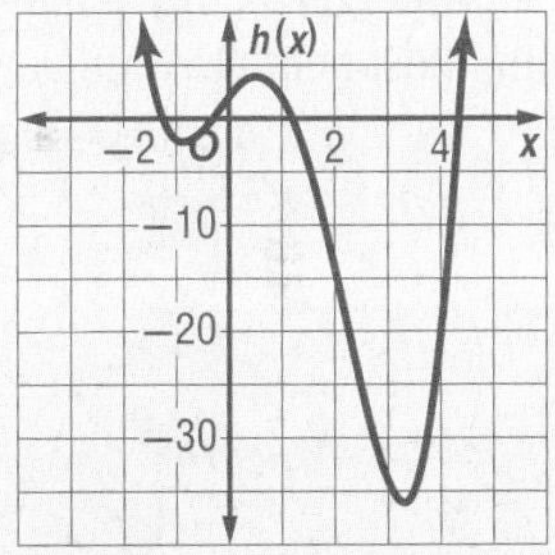

10b. between −2 and −1, between −1 and 0, between 1 and 2, between 4 and 5

10c. rel max: $x\approx0.5$; rel min: $x\approx-0.8$, $x\approx3.3$

Intervention Planner

Tier 1 On Level	Tier 2 Strategic Intervention approaching grade level	Tier 3 Intensive Intervention 2 or more grades below level
If students miss about 25% of the exercises or less,	**If** students miss about 50% of the exercises,	**If** students miss about 75% of the exercises,
Then choose a resource: **SE** Lessons 6-1 through 6-8 **CRM** Skills Practice, pp. 7, 13, 19, 25, 31, 37, 43, and 49 **TE** Chapter Project, p. 330 FL Math Online > Self-Check Quiz	**Then** choose a resource: **CRM** Study Guide and Intervention, pp. 5, 11, 17, 23, 29, 35, 41, and 47 FL Math Online > Extra Examples, Personal Tutor, Homework Help	**Then** use *Math Triumphs, Alg. 2*, Chs. 1 and 4 FL Math Online > Extra Examples, Personal Tutor, Homework Help, Review Vocabulary

1 FOCUS

Objective Use the strategy of drawing a picture to solve standardized test problems.

2 TEACH

Scaffolding Questions

Ask:

- Have you ever needed directions to a location? Was it more helpful to get written directions or a hand-drawn map of the directions? Answers will vary.
- Was it enough that the map was hand drawn or did you need a professionally drawn map? Answers will vary.
- What information is necessary to make a drawing, whether a map or a diagram, most helpful? Sample answers: distances, lengths, points of interest, landmarks, starting point

CHAPTER 6 Preparing for Standardized Tests

Draw a Picture

Drawing a picture can be a helpful way for you to visualize how to solve a problem. Sketch your picture on scrap paper or in your test booklet (if allowed). Do not make any marks on your answer sheet other than your answers.

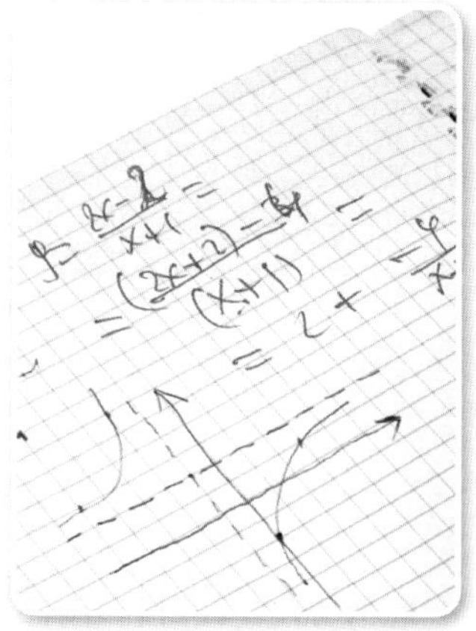

Strategies for Drawing a Picture

Step 1

Read the problem statement carefully.

Ask yourself:

- What am I being asked to solve?
- What information is given in the problem?
- What are the unknowns that I need to model and solve for?

Step 2

Sketch and label your picture.

- Draw your picture as clearly and accurately as possible.
- Label the picture carefully. Be sure to include all of the information given in the problem statement.

Step 3

Solve the problem.

- Use your picture to help you model the problem situation with an equation. Solve the equation.
- Check to be sure your answer makes sense.

NGSSS PRACTICE EXAMPLE

Read the problem. Identify what you need to know. Then use the information in the problem to solve.

Mr. Nolan has a rectangular swimming pool that measures 25 feet by 14 feet. He wants to have a cement walkway installed around the perimeter of the pool. The combined area of the pool and walkway will be 672 square feet. What will be the width of the walkway?

A. 2.75 ft　　**C.** 3.25 ft

B. 3 ft　　**D.** 3.5 ft

402 Chapter 6 Polynomials and Polynomial Functions

Draw a picture to help you visualize the problem situation. Let x represent the unknown width of the cement walkway.

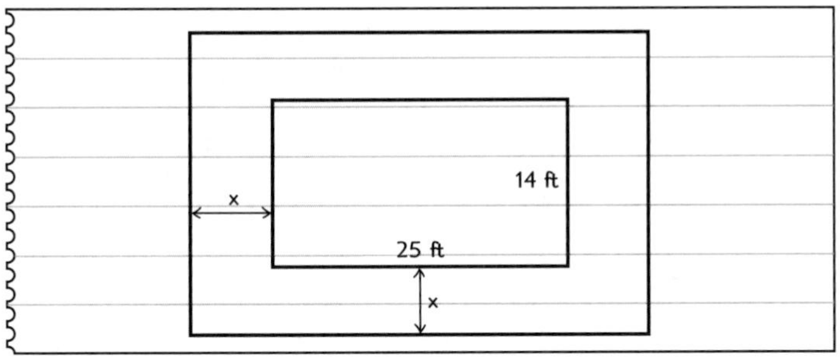

The width of the pool and walkway is $14 + 2x$, and the length is $25 + 2x$. Multiply these polynomial expressions and set the result equal to the combined area, 672 square feet. Then solve for x.

$$(14 + 2x)(25 + 2x) = 672$$
$$350 + 78x + 4x^2 = 672$$
$$4x^2 + 78x - 322 = 0$$
$$x = -23 \text{ or } 3.5$$

Since the width cannot be negative, the width of the walkway will be 3.5 feet. The correct answer is D.

Exercises

Read each problem. Identify what you need to know. Then use the information in the problem to solve.

1. A farmer has 240 feet of fencing that he wants to use to enclose a rectangular area for his chickens. He plans to build the enclosure using the wall of his barn as one of the walls. What is the maximum amount of area he can enclose? **A**

   A. 7200 ft^2

   B. 4960 ft^2

   C. 3600 ft^2

   D. 3280 ft^2

2. Metal washers are made by cutting a hole in a circular piece of metal. Suppose a washer is made by removing the center of a piece of metal with a 1.8-inch diameter. What is the radius of the hole if the washer has an area of 0.65π square inches? **H**

   F. 0.35 in.

   G. 0.38 in.

   H. 0.40 in.

   I. 0.42 in.

Additional Example

STANDARDIZED TEST PRACTICE
Robin has glued a 3″ by 5″ index card to a sheet of red paper. She trims the red paper so that it creates an equal-width border around the index card. The index card and the red paper border have a combined area of 168 square inches. What is the width of the border? **A**

A 4.5 inches

B 8.5 inches

C 9 inches

D 14 inches

3 ASSESS

Use Exercises 1 and 2 to assess students' understanding.

Chapter 6 Preparing for Standardized Tests 403

Diagnose Student Errors

Survey student responses for each item. Class trends may indicate common errors and misconceptions.

1. A. −1 was not distributed to the −5
   B. correct
   C. −1 was not distributed correctly
   D. $2n^2$ was added to $5n^2$ instead of subtracted from it

3. F. did not square $2x + 1$
   G. correct
   H. confused the sign of the numbers
   I. added the value of $(2x + 1)^2$ to 3

7. A. correct
   B. did not understand that *between* means *not included*
   C. did not add $100 to the low estimate
   D. did not understand that *between* means *not included*

9. F. incorrectly made a negative divided by a negative be a negative
   G. made errors when combining like terms
   H. made errors when combining like terms
   I. correct

10. A. simplified incorrectly
    B. did not square 20 in the x^2 term
    C. simplified incorrectly
    D. correct

12. F. correct
    G. counted the x-and y-intercepts
    H. guess
    I. guess

13. A. found a solution to the equation
    B. found a solution to the equation
    C. correct
    D. found a solution to the equation

14. F. guess
    G. did not understand that the coefficient of squared term affects the width of the graph
    H. correct
    I. did not understand that the value of h in $y = (x - h)^2 + k$ causes a shift left or right

17. A. did not understand the key words indicating the operation to use
    B. guess
    C. correct
    D. guess

Read each question. Then fill in the correct answer on the answer document provided by your teacher or on a sheet of paper.

1. Simplify the following expression.
   $(5n^2 + 11n - 6) - (2n^2 - 5)$ **B**

   A. $3n^2 + 11n - 11$
   B. $3n^2 + 11n - 1$
   C. $7n^2 + 11n - 11$
   D. $7n^2 + 11n - 1$

2. **SHORT RESPONSE** What are the slope and y-intercept of the equation of the line graphed at the right? $m = \frac{1}{2}$; $b = 3$

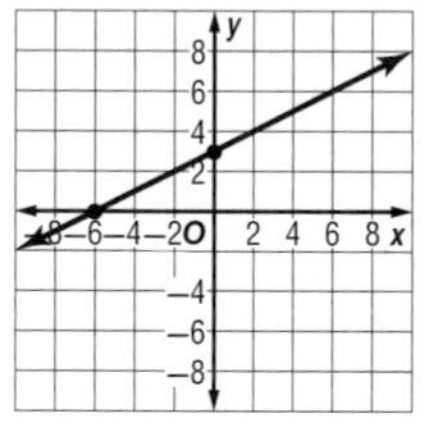

3. What is the solution set for the equation $3(2x + 1)^2 = 27$? **G**

   F. {−5, 4}
   G. {−2, 1}
   H. {2, −1}
   I. {−3, 3}

4. **GRIDDED RESPONSE** Matt has a cubic aquarium as shown below. He plans to fill it by emptying cans of water with the dimensions as shown.

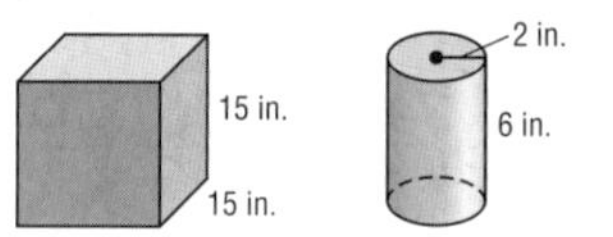

   About how many cylindrical cans will it take to fill the aquarium? **45**

5. **SHORT RESPONSE** Factor $64a^4 + ab^3$ completely. Show your work. $a(4a + b)(16a^2 - 4ab + b^2)$

Test-TakingTip

Question 3 You can use substitution to check each possible solution and identify the one that does not result in a true number sentence.

6a. See margin.

6. **EXTENDED RESPONSE** Scott launches a model rocket from ground level. The rocket's height h in meters is given by the equation $h = -4.9t^2 + 56t$, where t is the time in seconds after the launch.

   a. What is the maximum height the rocket will reach? Round to the nearest tenth of a meter. Show each step and explain your method.

   b. How long after it is launched will the rocket reach its maximum height? Round to the nearest tenth of a second. **5.7 s**

7. For Marla's vacation, it will cost $100 to drive her car, plus between $0.50 and $0.75 per mile. If she will drive her car 400 miles, what is a reasonable conclusion about c, the total cost to drive her car on the vacation? **A**

   A. $300 < c < 400$
   B. $200 < c \leq 400$
   C. $100 < c < 400$
   D. $200 \leq c \leq 300$

8. **SHORT RESPONSE** A stone path that is x feet wide is built around a rectangular flower garden. The garden is 12 feet wide and 25 feet long as shown below.

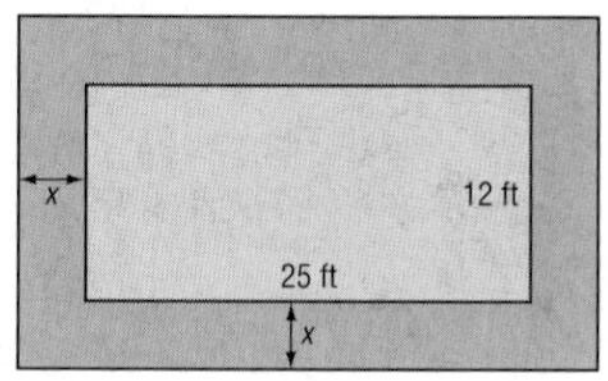

   If the combined area of the garden and the stone path is 558 square feet, what is the width of the walkway? Express your answer in feet. **3 ft**

9. Solve $4x - 5 = 2x + 5 - 3x$ for x. **I**

   F. −2
   G. −1
   H. 1
   I. 2

10. The function $P(x) = -0.000047x^2 + 0.027x + 3$ can be used to approximate the population of Ling's home country between 1960 and 2000. The domain of the function x represents the number of years since 1960, and P is given in millions of people. Evaluate $P(20)$ to estimate the population of the country in 1980. **D**

A. about 2 million people

B. about 2.5 million people

C. about 3 million people

D. about 3.5 million people

11. **GRIDDED RESPONSE** What is the value of a in the matrix equation below? **7.5**

$$\begin{bmatrix} 4 & 3 \\ 2 & 2 \end{bmatrix} \cdot \begin{bmatrix} a \\ b \end{bmatrix} = \begin{bmatrix} 21 \\ 9 \end{bmatrix}$$

12. How many real zeros does the polynomial function graphed below have? **F**

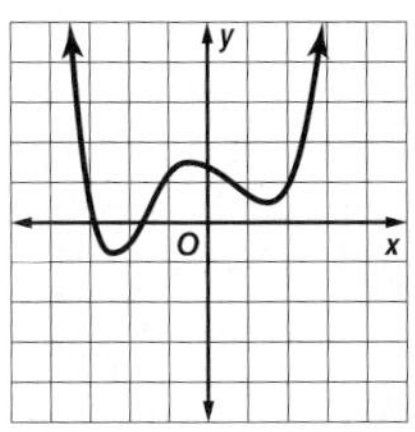

F. 2 H. 4

G. 3 I. 5

13. Which of the following is *not* a solution to the cubic equation below? **C**

$$x^3 - 37x - 84 = 0$$

A. −4 C. 6

B. −3 D. 7

14. What is the effect on the graph of the equation $y = x^2 + 4$ when it is changed to $y = x^2 - 3$? **H**

F. The slope of the graph changes.

G. The graph widens.

H. The graph is the same shape, and the vertex of the graph is moved down.

I. The graph is the same shape, and the vertex of the graph is shifted to the left.

15a. $h^3 + 2h^2 - 3h = 864$

15. **EXTENDED RESPONSE** The volume of a rectangular prism is 864 cubic centimeters. The length is 1 centimeter less than the height, and the width is 3 centimeters more than the height.

a. Write a polynomial equation that can be used to solve for the height of the prism h.

b. How many possible roots are there for h in the polynomial equation you wrote? Explain.

c. Solve the equation from part **a** for all real roots h. What are the dimensions of the prism?

b, c. See margin.

16. **SHORT RESPONSE** Simplify $\frac{3x^3 - 4x^2 - 28x - 16}{x + 2}$. Give your answer in factored form. Show your work. **$(3x + 2)(x - 4)$**

17. Let p represent the price that Ella charges for a necklace. Let $f(x)$ represent the total amount of money that Ella makes for selling x necklaces. The function $f(x)$ is best represented by **C**

A. $f(x) = x + p$ C. $f(x) = px$

B. $f(x) = xp^2$ D. $f(x) = x^2 + p$

Need Extra Help?

If you missed Question...	1	2	3	4	5	6	7	8	9	10	11	12	13	14	15	16	17
Go to Lesson or Page...	6-2	2-3	5-5	6-7	6-5	5-7	3-3	6-5	1-3	6-3	4-6	6-7	6-5	5-7	6-8	6-2	2-4
For help with NGSSS...	912.A.4.2	912.G.3.10	912.A.3.1	912.G.7.5	912.A.4.3	912.A.7.5	912.A.3.14	912.A.4.10	912.A.3.1	912.A.4.5	912.D.8.2	912.A.4.6	912.A.4.3	912.A.2.10	912.A.4.8	912.A.4.4	912.A.2.12

Formative Assessment

You can use these two pages to benchmark student progress.

Chapter 6 Resource Masters

- Standardized Test Practice, pp. 74–76

ExamView Assessment Suite Create practice worksheets or tests that align to your state's standards as well as TIMSS and NAEP tests.

Homework Option

Get Ready for Chapter 7 Assign students the exercises on p. 407 as homework to assess whether they possess the prerequisite skills needed for the next chapter.

Additional Answers

6a. 160 m; Sample answer: the vertex form of the equation is $h = -4.9\left(t - \frac{40}{7}\right)^2 + 160$, so the vertex is at $\left(\frac{40}{7}, 160\right)$.

15b. Sample answer: The order of the equation is 3, so there are up to 3 possible solutions to the equation.

15c. $h = 9$, the prism is 9 centimeters tall, 8 centimeters long, and 12 centimeters wide.

Pages 353–354, Lesson 6-3

35a. $f(x) \to +\infty$ as $x \to -\infty$. $f(x) \to +\infty$ as $x \to +\infty$.

35b. Since the end behavior is in the same direction, it is an even-degree function.

35c. The graph intersects the x-axis at four points, so there are four real zeros.

36a. $f(x) \to +\infty$ as $x \to -\infty$. $f(x) \to -\infty$ as $x \to +\infty$.

36b. Since the end behavior is in opposite directions, it is an odd-degree function.

36c. The graph intersects the x-axis at one point, so there is one real zero.

37a. $f(x) \to -\infty$ as $x \to -\infty$. $f(x) \to +\infty$ as $x \to +\infty$.

37b. Since the end behavior is in opposite directions, it is an odd-degree function.

37c. The graph intersects the x-axis at one point, so there is one real zero.

38a. $f(x) \to +\infty$ as $x \to -\infty$. $f(x) \to +\infty$ as $x \to +\infty$.

38b. Since the end behavior is in the same direction, it is an even-degree function.

38c. The graph intersects the x-axis at no points, so there are no real zeros.

39a. $f(x) \to -\infty$ as $x \to -\infty$. $f(x) \to -\infty$ as $x \to +\infty$.

39b. Since the end behavior is in the same direction, it is an even-degree function.

39c. The graph intersects the x-axis at two points, so there are two real zeros.

40a. $f(x) \to -\infty$ as $x \to -\infty$. $f(x) \to -\infty$ as $x \to +\infty$.

40b. Since the end behavior is in the same direction, it is an even-degree function.

40c. The graph intersects the x-axis at two points, so there are two real zeros.

56a. degree: 4; x-intercepts: 2, –1, 3, –4; g-intercept: 24; roots: 2, –1, 3, –4, end behavior: as $x \to -\infty$, $g(x) \to +\infty$; as $x \to +\infty$, $g(x) \to +\infty$

56c.

x	$g(x)$
–5	224
–4	0
–3	–60
–2	–40
–1	0
0	24
1	20
2	0
3	0
4	80
5	324

56d.

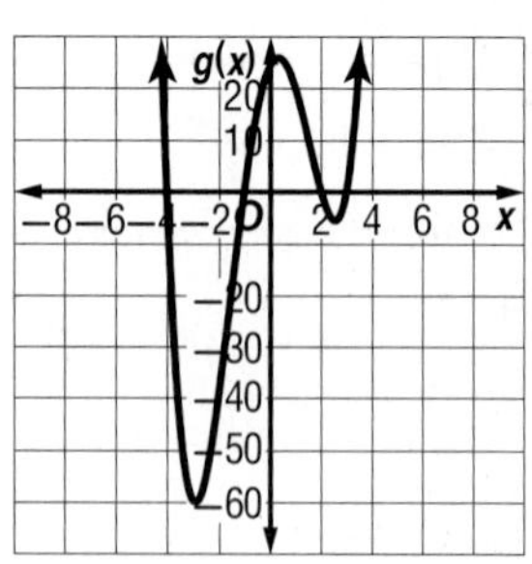

Page 356, Extend 6-3

Step 1

x	–4	–3	–2	–1	0
y	128	54	16	2	0
First-Order Differences					
Second-Order Differences					
Third-Order Differences					

x	1	2	3	4
y	–2	–16	–54	–128
First-Order Differences				
Second-Order Differences				
Third-Order Differences				

Step 2

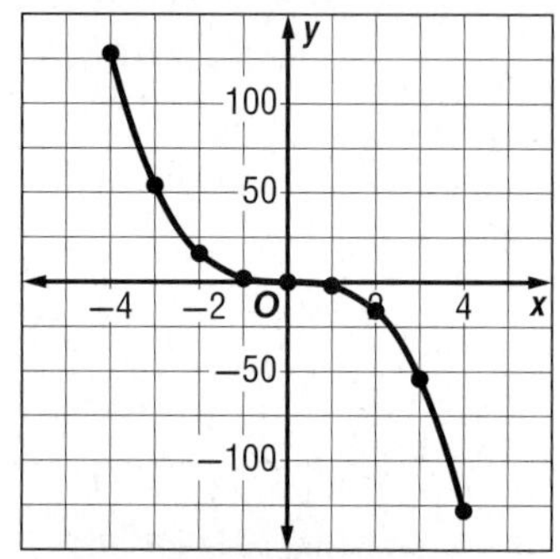

Step 3

x	–4	–3	–2	–1	0
y	128	54	16	2	0
First-Order Differences		–74	–38	–14	–2
Second-Order Differences					
Third-Order Differences					

x	1	2	3	4
y	–2	–16	–54	–128
First-Order Differences	–2	–14	–38	–74
Second-Order Differences				
Third-Order Differences				

Sample answer: The first-order differences become greater until reaching –2, then –2 is repeated and so are the other values.

Step 4

x	–4	–3	–2	–1	0
y	128	54	16	2	0
First-Order Differences		–74	–38	–14	–2
Second-Order Differences			36	24	12
Third-Order Differences				–12	–12

x	1	2	3	4
y	–2	–16	–54	–128
First-Order Differences	–2	–14	–38	–74
Second-Order Differences	0	–12	–24	–36
Third-Order Differences	–12	–12	–12	–12

Sample answer: The second-order differences decrease by 12 each time and have positive values and negative values with the same absolute values. The third-order differences are constant at –12. A conjecture about the differences for a third degree polynomial function is that the third-order differences are always constant.

Step 5 Sample function: $y = -0.5x^4$.

x	–4	–3	–2	–1	0
y	–128	–40.5	–8	–0.5	0
First-Order Differences		87.5	32.5	7.5	0.5
Second-Order Differences			–55	–25	–7
Third-Order Differences				30	18
Fourth-Order Differences					–12

x	1	2	3	4
y	–0.5	–8	–40.5	–128
First-Order Differences	–0.5	–7.5	–32.5	–87.5
Second-Order Differences	–1	–7	–25	–55
Third-Order Differences	6	–6	–18	–30
Fourth-Order Differences	–12	–12	–12	–12

An *n*th degree polynomial function will have a constant difference at the *n*th order of difference.

Page 357, Lesson 6-4 (Guided Practice)

1.

x	$f(x)$
–2.5	≈26
–2.0	2.0
–1.5	≈–8.1
–1.0	–10
–0.5	≈–8.3

x	$f(x)$
0.0	–6.0
0.5	≈–4.6
1.0	–4.0
1.5	≈–2.8
2.0	2.0

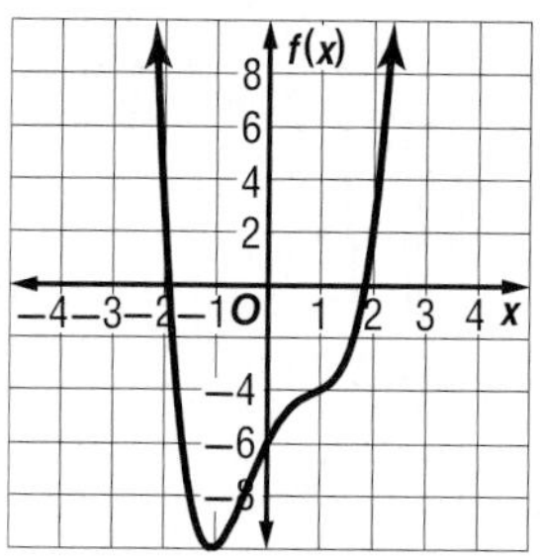

Pages 361–363, Lesson 6-4

5. between –2 and –1

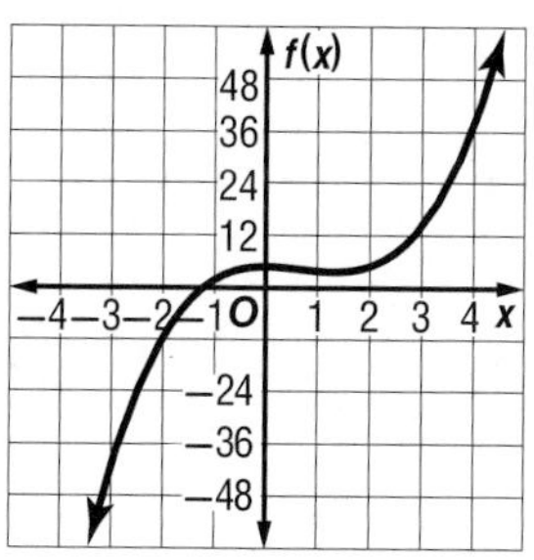

6. at –1 and between 2 and 3

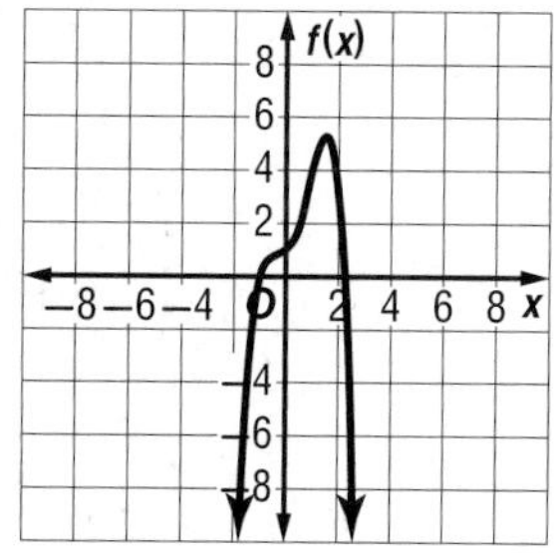

7. between 0 and 1 and between 2 and 3

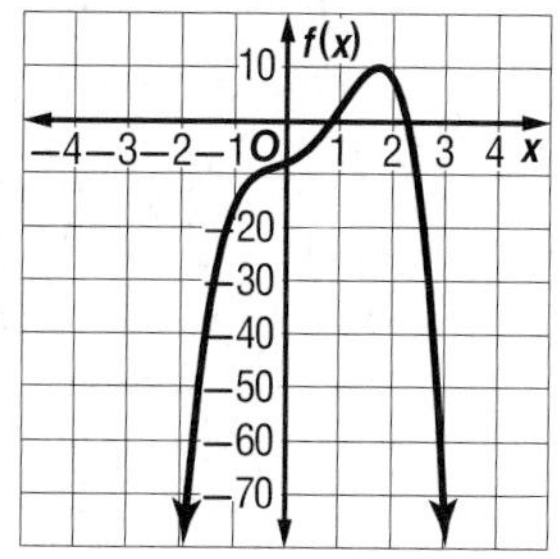

8. between –2 and –1 and between 1 and 2

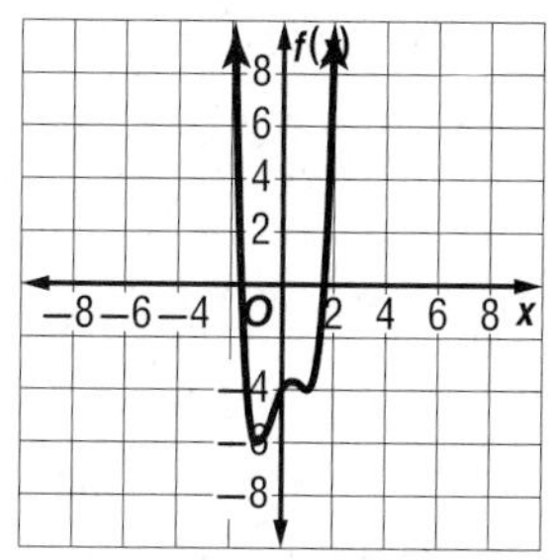

9. rel. max at $x \approx -1.8$; rel. min at $x \approx 1.1$;
D = {all real numbers}, R = {all real numbers}

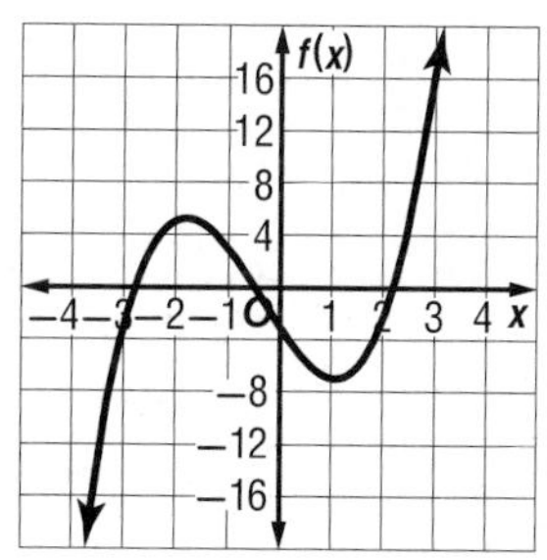

10. rel. max at $x \approx -0.1$; rel. min at $x \approx 1.5$;
D = {all real numbers}, R = {all reals numbers}

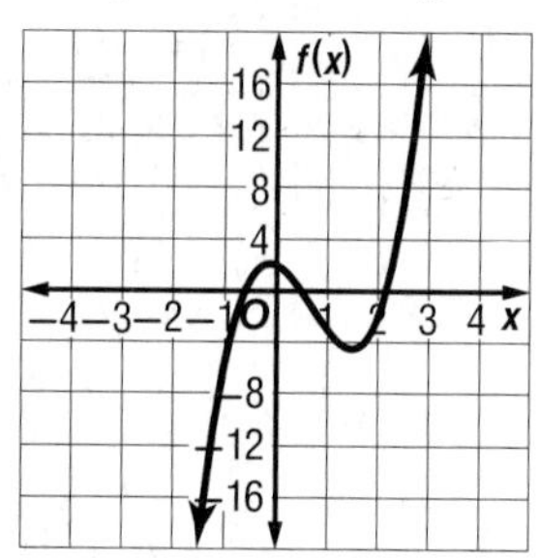

11. rel. max at $x \approx 2.4$; rel. min at $x \approx 0.3$; D = {all real numbers}, R = {all real numbers}

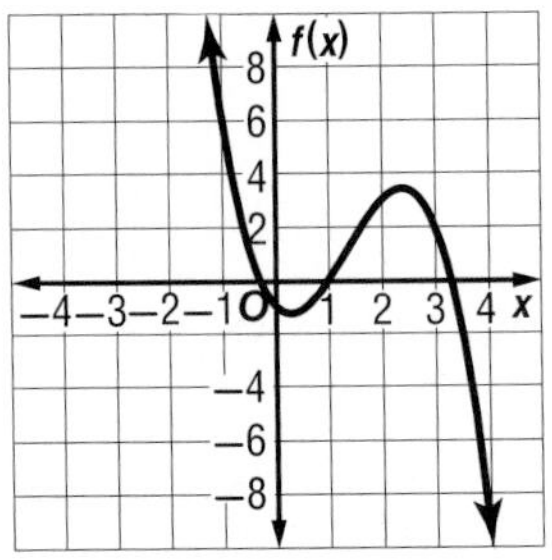

12. no relative max or min; D = {all real numbers}, R = {all real numbers}

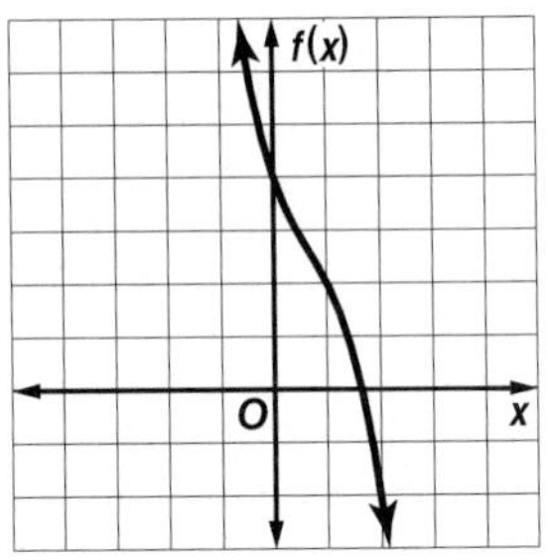

13a.

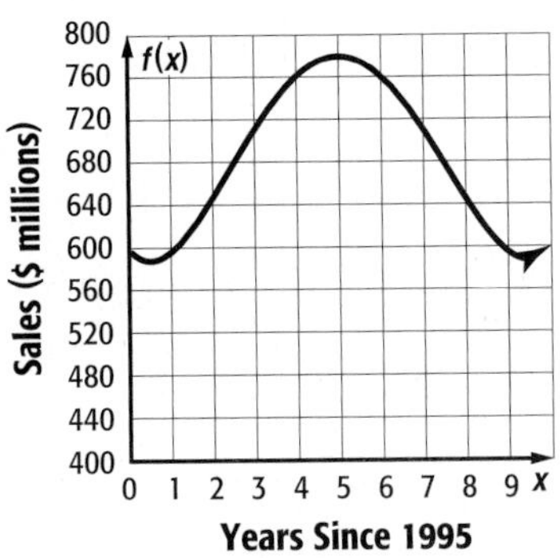

13c.

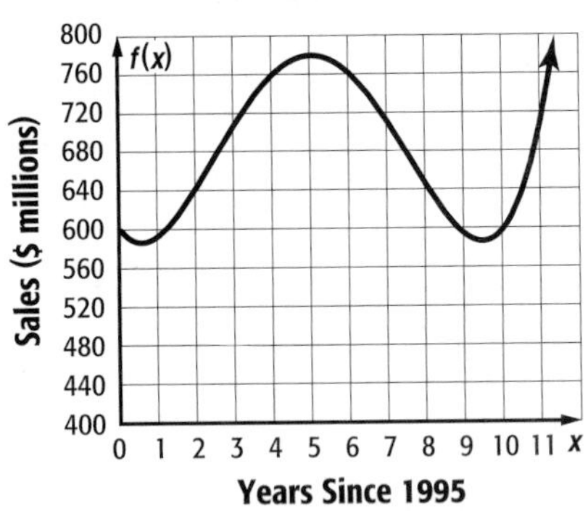

Sample answer: This suggests a dramatic increase in sales.

13d. Sample answer: No; with so many other forms of media on the market today, CD sales will not increase dramatically. In fact, the sales will probably decrease. The function appears to be accurate only until about 2005.

14a.

x	$f(x)$
–4	–16
–3	0
–2	4
–1	2
0	0
1	4
2	20
3	54
4	112

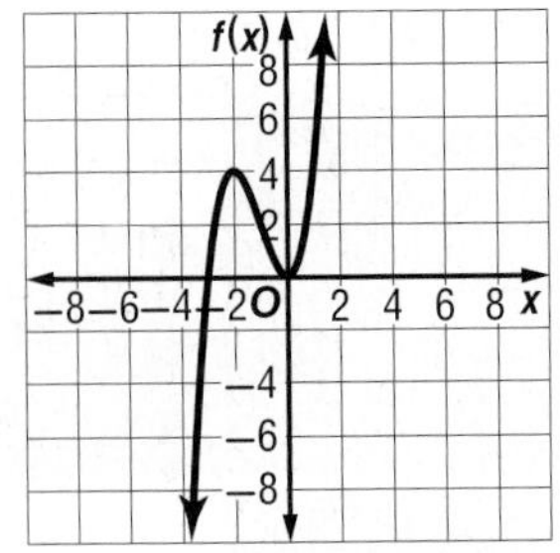

14b. at 0 and at –3

14c. rel. max: $x = -2$; rel. min: $x = 0$

15a.

x	$f(x)$
–4	92
–3	41
–2	12
–1	–1
0	–4
1	–3
2	–4
3	–13
4	–36

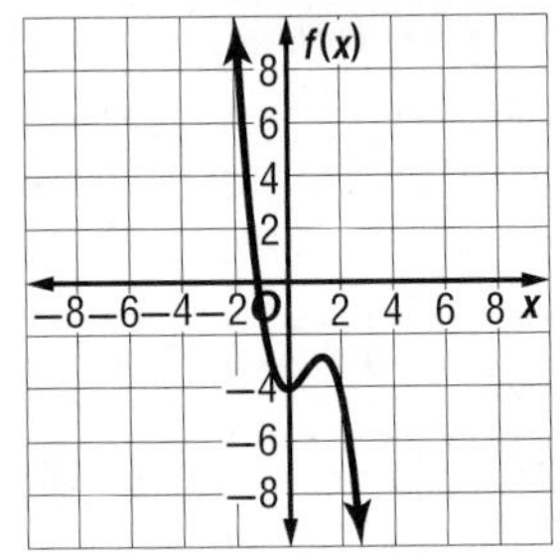

15b. between –2 and –1

15c. rel. min: $x = 0$; rel. max: $x = 1$

16a.

x	$f(x)$
–6	–42
–5	0
–4	20
–3	24
–2	18
–1	8
0	0
1	0
2	14
3	48

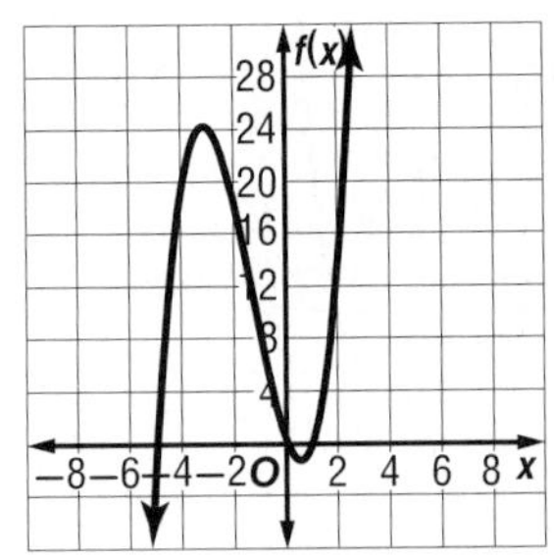

16b. –5, 0, and 1

16c. rel. max: $x = -3$; rel. min: between $x = 0$ and $x = 1$

17a.

x	$f(x)$
–4	–155
–3	–80
–2	–33
–1	–8
0	1
1	0
2	–5
3	–8
4	–3
5	16

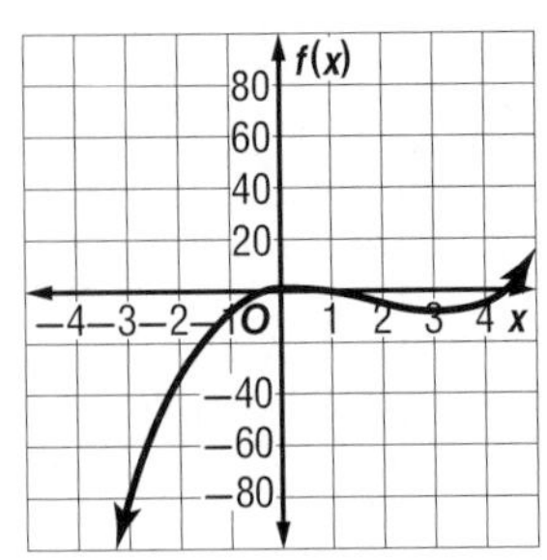

17b. at $x = 1$, between –1 and 0, and between $x = 4$ and $x = 5$

17c. rel. max: $x \approx \frac{1}{3}$, rel. min: $x \approx 3$

18a.

x	$f(x)$
–1	22
0	0
1	2
2	16
3	30
4	32
5	10
6	–48
7	–154

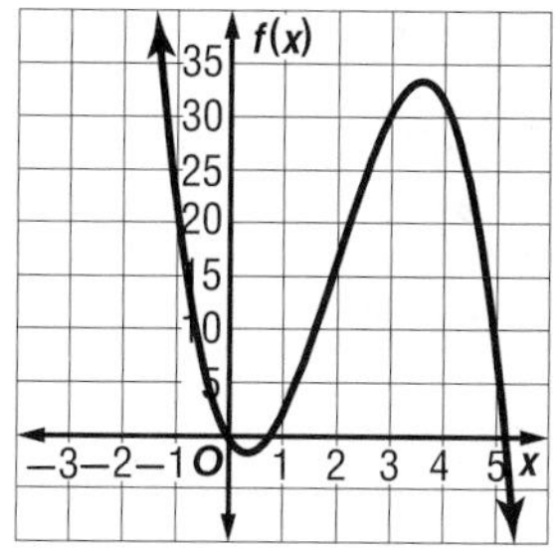

18b. at 0, between 0 and 1, and between 5 and 6

18c. rel. min: between $x = 0$ and $x = 1$; rel. max: near $x = 4$

19a.

x	$f(x)$
–4	–176
–3	–77
–2	–22
–1	1
0	4
1	–1
2	–2
3	13
4	56

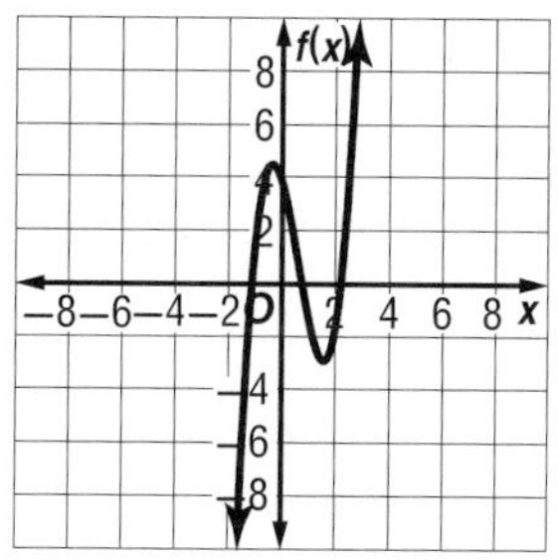

19b. between $x = -2$ and $x = -1$, between $x = 0$ and $x = 1$, and between $x = 2$ and $x = 3$

19c. rel. max: near $x = -0.3$; rel. min: near $x = 1.6$

20a.

x	$f(x)$
–4	247
–3	74
–2	11
–1	–2
0	–1
1	2
2	19
3	86
4	263

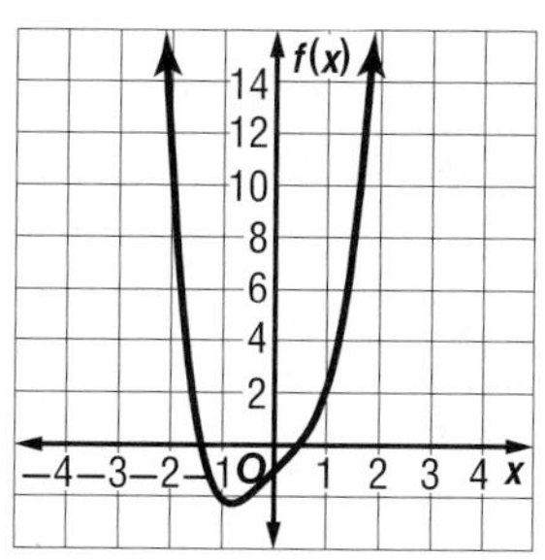

20b. between $x = -2$ and $x = -1$ and between $x = 0$ and $x = 1$

20c. rel. min: near $x = -1$; no rel. max

21a.

x	$f(x)$
–4	372
–3	141
–2	36
–1	–3
0	–12
1	–3
2	36
3	141
4	372

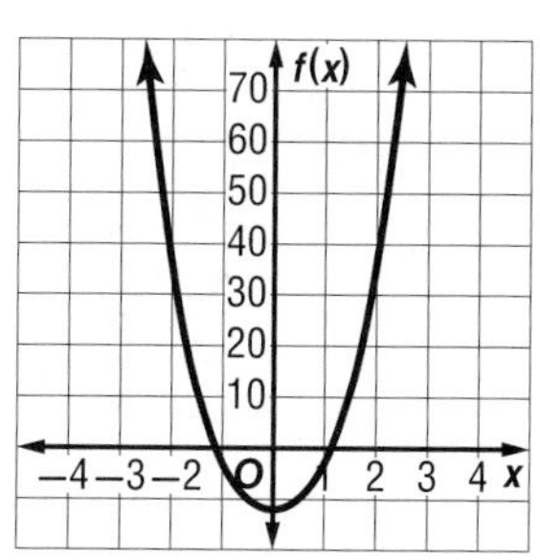

21b. between $x = -2$ and $x = -1$ and between $x = 1$ and $x = 2$

21c. min: near $x = 0$

22a.

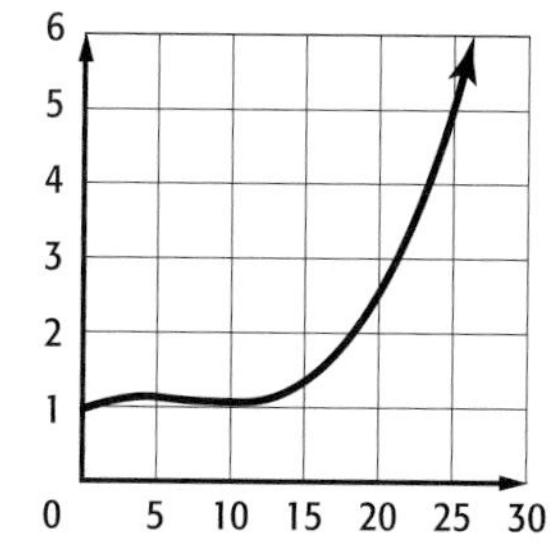

22d. Sample answer: While it is possible for gasoline prices to continue to soar at this rate, it is likely that alternate forms of transportation and fuel will slow down this rapid increase.

27.

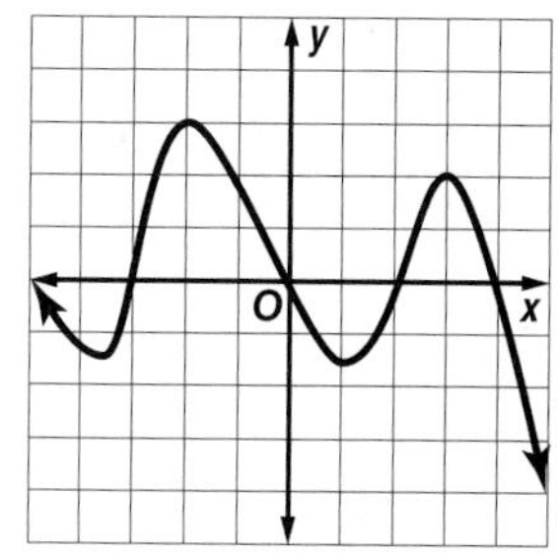

28.

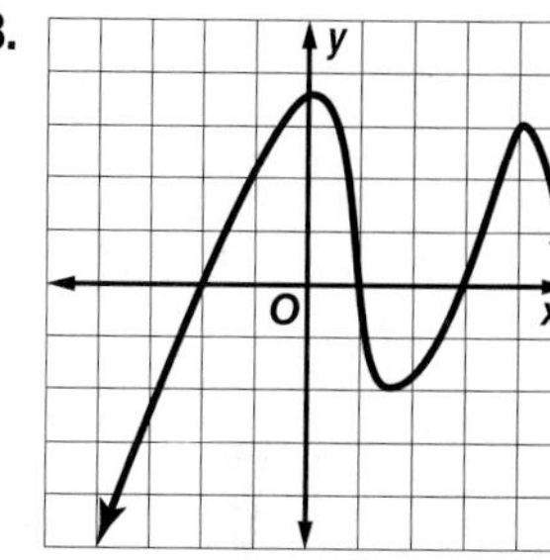

29.

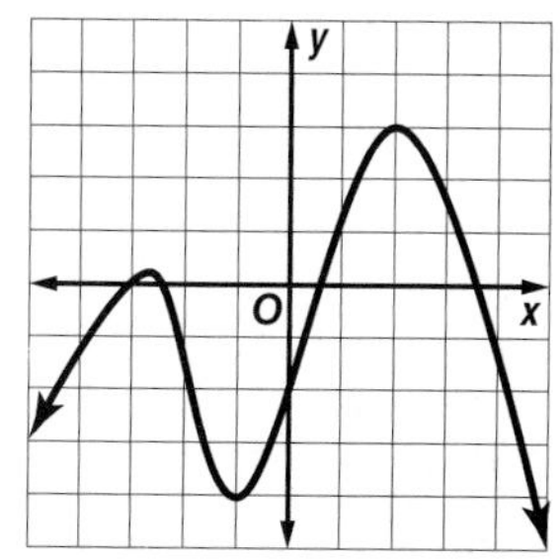

30.

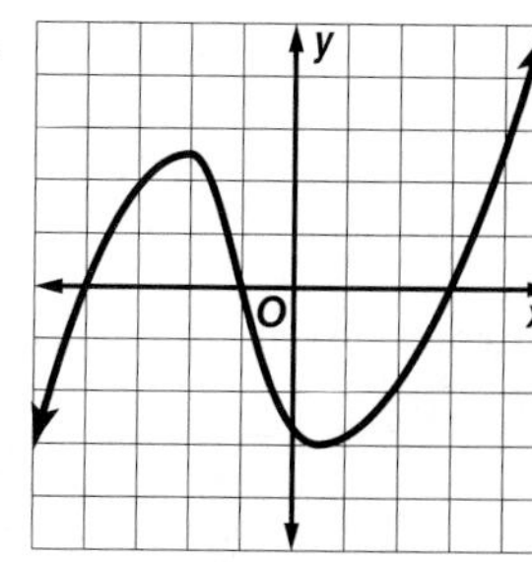

31.

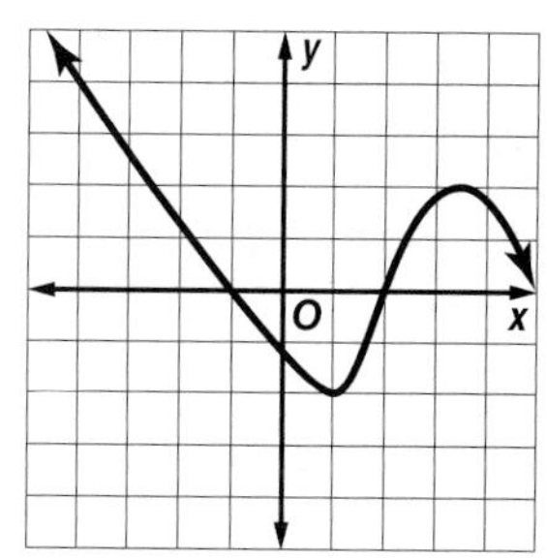

32.

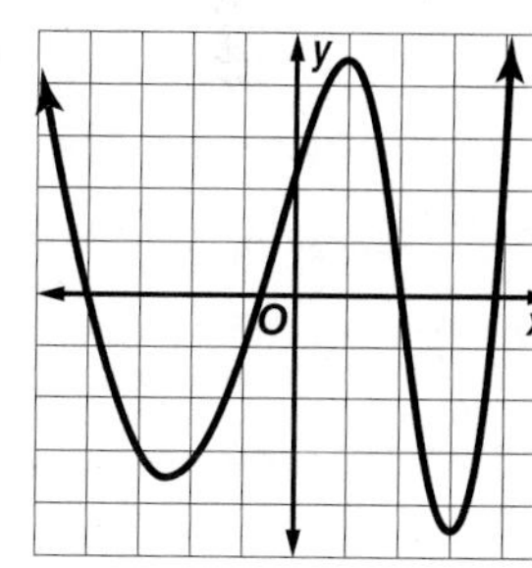

33a.

x	$d(x)$
0	0
1	0.0145
2	0.056
3	0.1215
4	0.208
5	0.3125
6	0.432
7	0.5635
8	0.704
9	0.8505
10	1

33b.

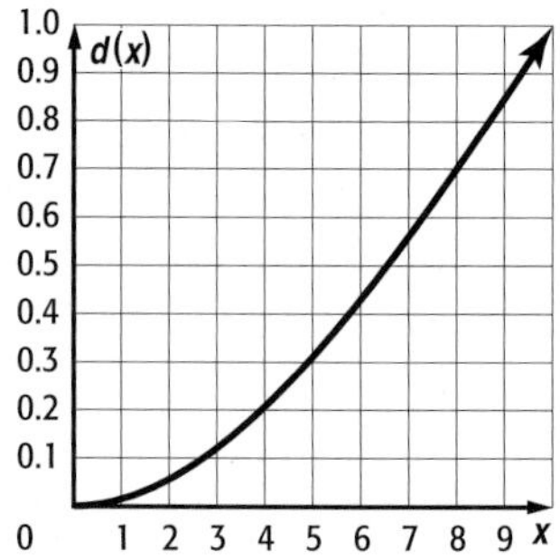

34a. –3.5(max), –2.5(min), –1(max), 2(min)

34b. –1.75, –0.25, 3.5

34c. 5

34d. D = {all real numbers}; R = {all real numbers}

35a. –2.5(min), –0.5(max), 1.5(min)

35b. –3.5, –1, 0, 3

35c. 4

35d. D = {all real numbers}; R = $\{y \mid y \geq -3.1\}$

36a. –2(max), 1(min), 2.5(max)

36b. –3.5, –0.5

36c. 4

36d. D = {all real numbers}; R = $\{y \mid y \leq 4.1\}$

37a. –3.5(min), –2.5(max), –2(min), –1(max), 1(min)

37b. –3.75, –3.25, –2, –1.75, –0.25, 2.9

37c. 6

37d. D = {all real numbers}; R = $\{y \mid y \geq -5\}$

38a. –3.5(max), –2.5(min), –1.75(max), –1(min), 1(max), 2(min)

38b. –4, –3, 0, 1.5, 2.75

38c. 7

38d. D = {all real numbers}; R = {all real numbers}

39a. –2(max), 1(min)

39b. –3, –0.5, 2

39c. 3

39d. D = {all real numbers}; R = {all real numbers}

46a. degree: 4; leading coefficient: 1; end behavior: as $x \to -\infty$, $f(x) \to +\infty$, as $x \to +\infty$, $f(x) \to +\infty$,

46b.

x	$f(x)$
–4	1414
–3	690
–2	287
–1	92
0	18
1	0.7
2	–0.03
3	0.09
4	9.2

2 zeros

46c.

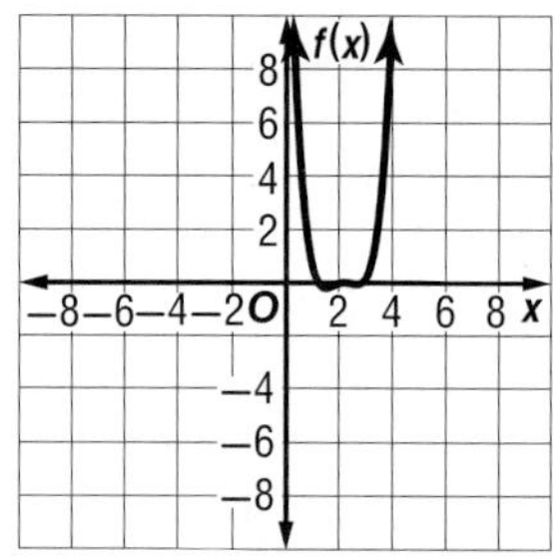

46d.

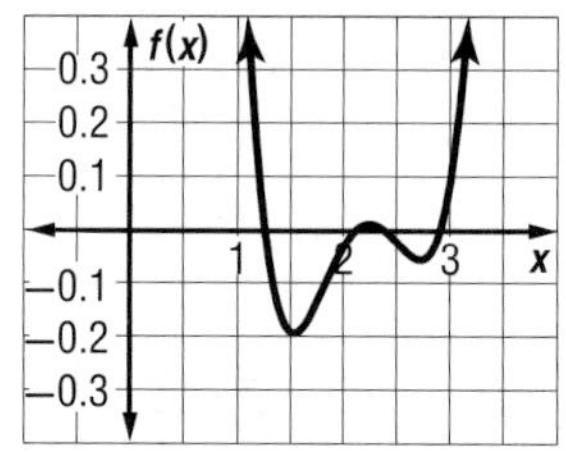

Sample answer: Sometimes it is necessary to have a more accurate viewing window or to change the interval values of the table function in order to assess the graph more accurately.

Page 366, Extend 6-4

4. Sample graphs:

linear

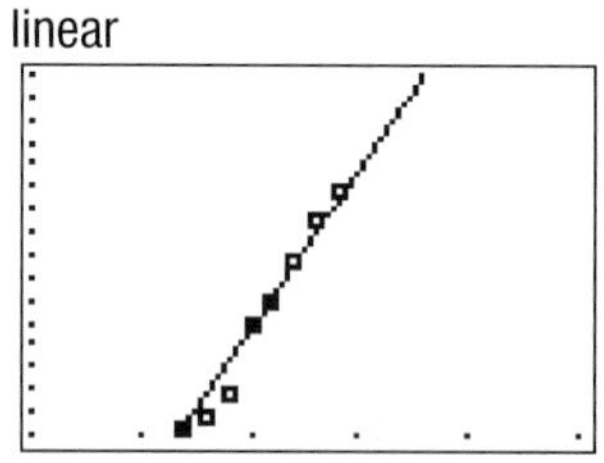

[1990, 2015] scl: 5 by [275,000, 675,000] scl: 25,000

quadratic

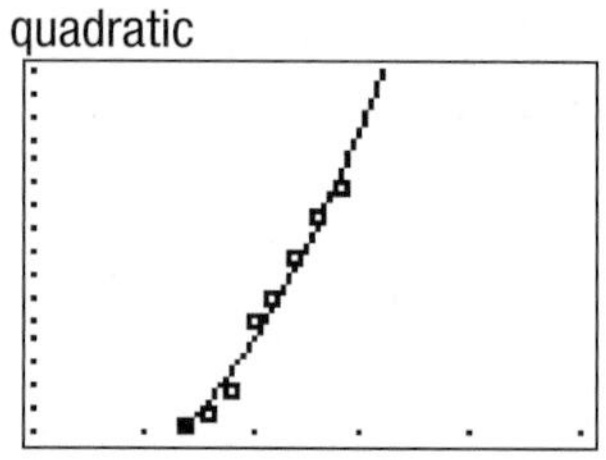

[1990, 2015] scl: 5 by [275,000, 675,000] scl: 25,000

cubic

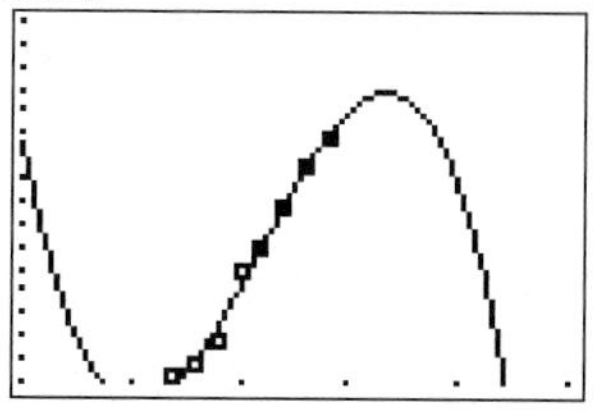

[1990, 2015] scl: 5 by [275,000, 675,000] scl: 25,000

7. Sample graphs:

linear

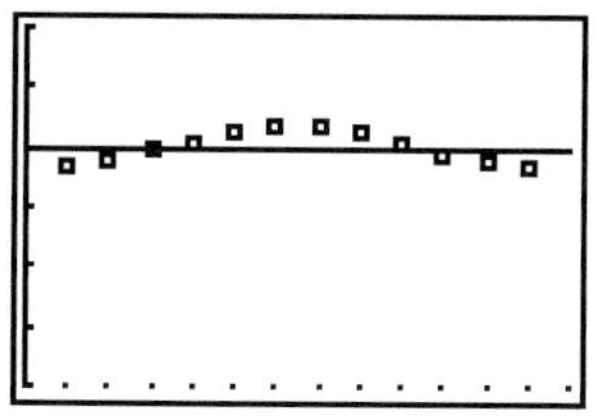

[0, 13] scl: 1 by [0.8, 1.1] scl: 0.05

quadratic

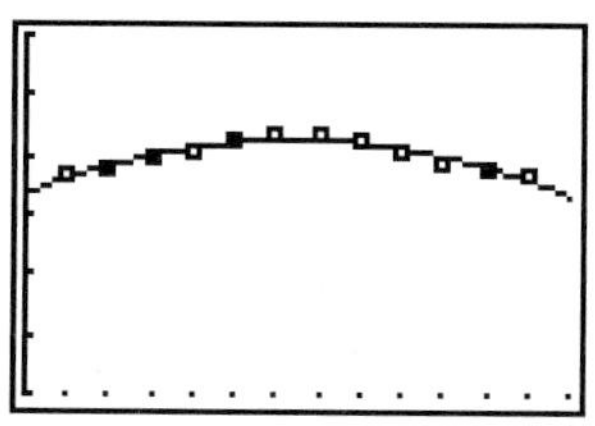

[0, 13] scl: 1 by [0.8, 1.1] scl: 0.05

cubic

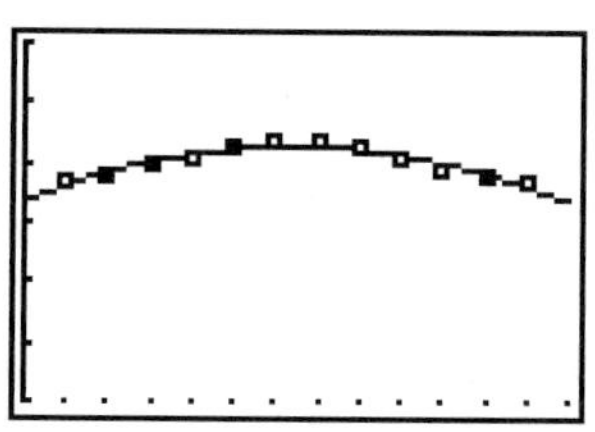

[0, 13] scl: 1 by [0.8, 1.1] scl: 0.05

Page 381, Lesson 6-6

31a. $g(x) = -9x^4 + 50x^3 + 51x^2 - 150x - 72$

31b.

x	$g(x)$
–5	–9922
–4	–4160
–3	–1242
–2	–112
–1	70
0	–72
1	–130
2	88
3	558
4	1040
5	1078
6	0

31c. There is a zero between $x = -2$ and $x = -1$ because $f(x)$ changes sign between the two values. There are also zeros between $x = -1$ and 0 and between $x = 1$ and $x = 2$ because $f(x)$ changes sign between the two values. There is also a zero at $x = 6$.

31d.

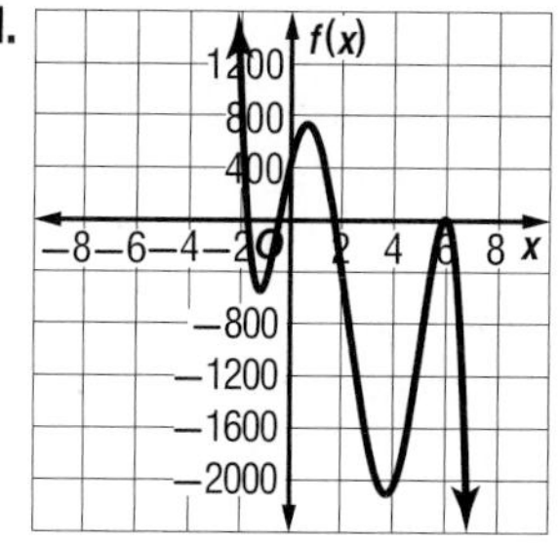

Page 389, Lesson 6-7

56a.

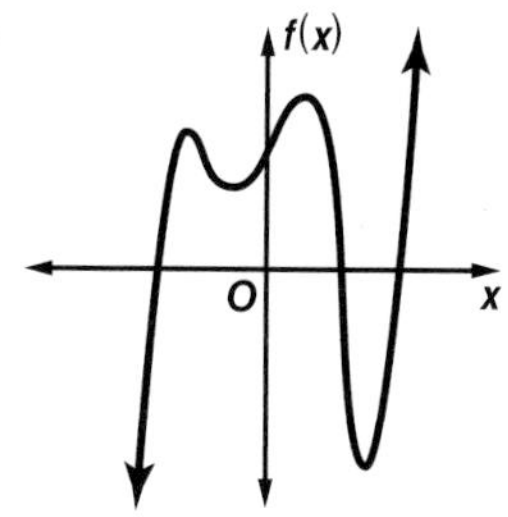

56b.

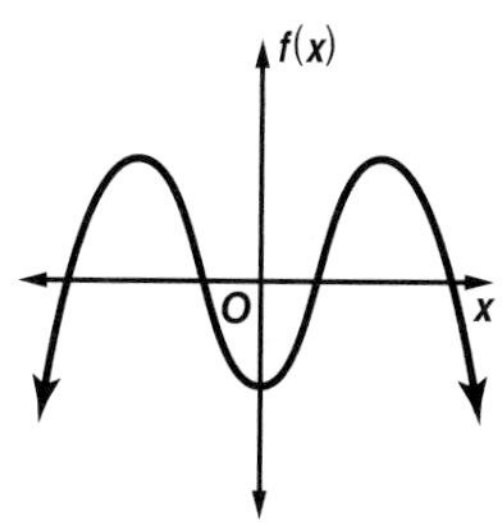

56c.

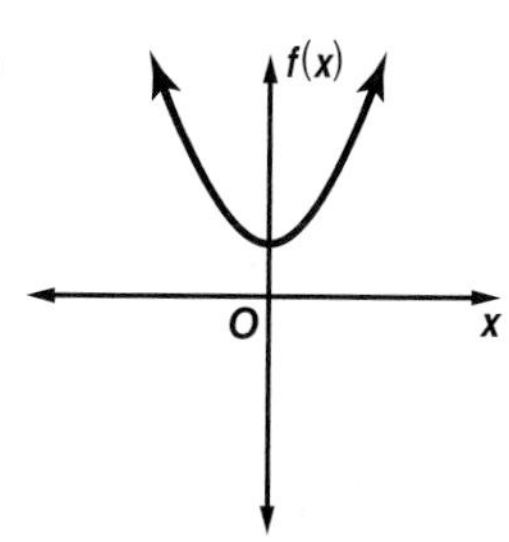

60. Sample answer: To determine the number of positive real roots, determine how many time the signs change in the polynomial as you move from left to right. In this function there are 3 changes in sign. Therefore, there may be 3 or 1 positive real roots. To determine the number of negative real roots, I would first evaluate the polynomial for $-x$. All of the terms with an odd-degree variable would change signs. Then I would again count the number of sign changes as I move from left to right. There would be only one change. Therefore there may be 1 negative root.

Chapter Planner

Diagnostic Assessment
Quick Check, p. 407

	Lesson 7-1 Pacing: 1 day	Lesson 7-2 Pacing: 1 day	Extend 7-2 Pacing: 0.5 day
Title	**Operations on Functions**	**Inverse Functions and Relations**	**Graphing Technology Lab: Inverse Functions and Relations**
Objectives	• Find the sum, difference, product, and quotient of functions. • Find the composition of functions.	• Find the inverse of a function or relation. • Determine whether two functions or relations are inverses.	• Compare a function and its inverse using a graphing calculator.
Key Vocabulary	composition of functions	inverse relation inverse function	
NGSSS	MA.912.A.2.7, MA.912.A.2.8	MA.912.A.2.11	MA.912.A.2.11
Multiple Representations	pp. 414, 415	p. 421	
Lesson Resources	**Chapter 7 Resource Masters** • Study Guide and Intervention, pp. 5–6 AL OL ELL • Skills Practice, p. 7 AL OL ELL • Practice, p. 8 AL OL BL ELL • Word Problem Practice, p. 9 AL OL BL ELL • Enrichment, p. 10 OL BL • Spreadsheet Activity, p. 11 OL **Transparencies** • 5-Minute Check Transparency 7-1 AL OL BL ELL **Additional Print Resources** • Study Notebook AL OL BL ELL • Teaching Algebra with Manipulatives, pp. 226–228 AL OL ELL	**Chapter 7 Resource Masters** • Study Guide and Intervention, pp. 12–13 AL OL ELL • Skills Practice, p. 14 AL OL ELL • Practice, p. 15 AL OL BL ELL • Word Problem Practice, p. 16 AL OL BL ELL • Enrichment, p. 17 OL BL • TI-Nspire Calculator Activity, p. 18 OL • Quiz 1, p. 53 AL OL BL ELL **Transparencies** • 5-Minute Check Transparency 7-2 AL OL BL ELL **Additional Print Resources** • Study Notebook AL OL BL ELL • Teaching Algebra with Manipulatives, pp. 229–230 AL OL ELL	**Materials** • TI-83/84 Plus or other graphing calculator
Technology for Every Lesson	FL Math Online glencoe.com • Extra Examples • Self-Check Quizzes • Personal Tutor • Homework Help	**CD/DVD Resources** IWB INTERACTIVE WHITEBOARD READY IWB StudentWorks Plus IWB Interactive Classroom IWB Diagnostic and Assessment Planner	• TeacherWorks Plus • eSolutions Manual Plus • ExamView Assessment Suite
Get Animated	Animation		
Differentiated Instruction	pp. 411, 412	pp. 419, 422	

KEY: AL Approaching Level OL On Level BL Beyond Level ELL English Learners

Inverses and Radical Functions and Relations

Suggested Pacing			
Time Periods	Instruction	Review & Assessment	Total
45-minute	9	2	11
90-minute	5	1	6

Lesson 7-3 Pacing: 1 day	Lesson 7-4 Pacing: 1 day	Extend 7-4 Pacing: 0.5 day	Lesson 7-5 Pacing: 1 day
Square Root Functions and Inequalities	***n*th Roots**	**Graphing Technology Lab: Graphing *n*th Root Functions**	**Operations with Radical Expressions**
• Graph and analyze square root functions. • Graph square root inequalities.	• Simplify radicals. • Use a calculator to approximate radicals.	• Use a graphing calculator to graph *n*th root functions.	• Simplify radical expressions. • Add, subtract, multiply, and divide radical expressions.
square root function radical function square root inequality	*n*th root radical sign index radicand principal root		rationalizing the denominator like radical expressions conjugate
MA.912.A.2.6	MA.912.A.10.3	MA.912.A.2.6	MA.912.A.6.2
p. 428	p. 435		p. 444
Chapter 7 Resource Masters • Study Guide and Intervention, pp. 19–20 AL OL ELL • Skills Practice, p. 21 AL OL ELL • Practice, p. 22 AL OL BL ELL • Word Problem Practice, p. 23 AL OL BL ELL • Enrichment, p. 24 OL BL **Transparencies** • 5-Minute Check Transparency 7-3 AL OL BL ELL **Additional Print Resources** • Study Notebook AL OL BL ELL	**Chapter 7 Resource Masters** • Study Guide and Intervention, pp. 25–26 AL OL ELL • Skills Practice, p. 27 AL OL ELL • Practice, p. 28 AL OL BL ELL • Word Problem Practice, p. 29 AL OL BL ELL • Enrichment, p. 30 OL BL • Quiz 2, p. 53 AL OL BL ELL **Transparencies** • 5-Minute Check Transparency 7-4 AL OL BL ELL **Additional Print Resources** • Study Notebook AL OL BL ELL • Teaching Algebra with Manipulatives, pp. 231–232 AL OL ELL	**Materials** • TI-83/84 Plus or other graphing calculator	**Chapter 7 Resource Masters** • Study Guide and Intervention, pp. 31–32 AL OL ELL • Skills Practice, p. 33 AL OL ELL • Practice, p. 34 AL OL BL ELL • Word Problem Practice, p. 35 AL OL BL ELL • Enrichment, p. 36 OL BL • Graphing Calculator Activity, p. 37 OL **Transparencies** • 5-Minute Check Transparency 7-5 AL OL BL ELL **Additional Print Resources** • Study Notebook AL OL BL ELL

FL Math Online glencoe.com
- Extra Examples
- Self-Check Quizzes
- Personal Tutor
- Homework Help

CD/DVD Resources IWB INTERACTIVE WHITEBOARD READY
- IWB StudentWorks Plus
- IWB Interactive Classroom
- IWB Diagnostic and Assessment Planner
- TeacherWorks Plus
- eSolutions Manual Plus
- ExamView Assessment Suite

			Animation
pp. 428, 430	pp. 433, 436		pp. 442, 445

Formative Assessment
Mid-Chapter Quiz, p. 438

CHAPTER 7

Chapter Planner

	Lesson 7-6 Pacing: 1 day	Lesson 7-7 Pacing: 1 day	Extend 7-7 Pacing: 1 day
Title	**Rational Exponents**	**Solving Radical Equations and Inequalities**	**Graphing Technology Lab: Solving Radical Equations and Inequalities**
Objectives	• Write expressions with rational exponents in radical form and vice versa. • Simplify expressions in exponential or radical form.	• Solve equations containing radicals. • Solve inequalities containing radicals.	• Use a graphing calculator to solve radical equations and inequalities.
Key Vocabulary		radical equation extraneous solution radical inequality	
NGSSS	MA.912.A.6.3, MA.912.A.6.4	MA.912.A.6.5,, MA.912.A.10.3	MA.912.A.6.5
Multiple Representations	p. 451		
Lesson Resources	**Chapter 7 Resource Masters** • Study Guide and Intervention, pp. 38–39 AL OL ELL • Skills Practice, p. 40 AL OL ELL • Practice, p. 41 AL OL BL ELL • Word Problem Practice, p. 42 AL OL BL ELL • Enrichment, p. 43 OL BL • Spreadsheet Activity, p. 44 OL • Quiz 3, p. 54 AL OL BL ELL **Transparencies** • 5-Minute Check Transparency 7-6 AL OL BL ELL **Additional Print Resources** • Study Notebook AL OL BL ELL	**Chapter 7 Resource Masters** • Study Guide and Intervention, pp. 45–46 AL OL ELL • Skills Practice, p. 47 AL OL ELL • Practice, p. 48 AL OL BL ELL • Word Problem Practice, p. 49 AL OL BL ELL • Enrichment, p. 50 OL BL • Quiz 4, p. 54 AL OL BL ELL **Transparencies** • 5-Minute Check Transparency 7-7 AL OL BL ELL **Additional Print Resources** • Study Notebook AL OL BL ELL	**Materials** • TI-83/84 Plus or other graphing calculator
Technology for Every Lesson	FL Math Online glencoe.com • Extra Examples • Self-Check Quizzes • Personal Tutor • Homework Help	**CD/DVD Resources** IWB INTERACTIVE WHITEBOARD READY IWB StudentWorks Plus IWB Interactive Classroom IWB Diagnostic and Assessment Planner	• TeacherWorks Plus • eSolutions Manual Plus • ExamView Assessment Suite
Get Animated			
Differentiated Instruction	pp. 447, 448	pp. 455, 459	

KEY: AL Approaching Level OL On Level BL Beyond Level ELL English Learners

Summative Assessment
- Study Guide and Review, pp. 462–466
- Practice Test, p. 467

What the Research Says...

Jitendra et al. (1999) found that each lesson should provide an adequate number of practice exercises on the new skill.

- After composition of functions is introduced for the first time in Lesson 7-1, a large number of exercises (both contextual and noncontextual) allow students to practice this new concept.
- Numerous practice exercises on properties and operations with radicals are provided in Lessons 7-4 through 7-7.

[Source: Jitendra, A.K., Salmento, M.M., and Haydt, L.A. (1999). "Adherence to Important Instructional Design Criteria," *Learning Disabilities Research & Practice*, 14(2), pp. 69–79.]

Teacher to Teacher

Melissa Williamson
Mathematics Department Head
Klein Collins High School
Spring, Texas

USE BEFORE LESSON 7-5

" When multiplying radical expressions, my students like the 'box method' best. For example, to multiply $(2\sqrt{3} + 5)\,(3\sqrt{3} - 2)$, they start with a 2×2 grid and write the terms along the top and left side. Then they fill in the grid, one row at a time. Simplify and combine like terms along the diagonal.

	$2\sqrt{3}$	$+5$
$3\sqrt{3}$	$6\sqrt{9}$	$15\sqrt{3}$
-2	$-4\sqrt{3}$	-10

→

	$2\sqrt{3}$	$+5$
$3\sqrt{3}$	18	$15\sqrt{3}$
-2	$-4\sqrt{3}$	-10

$+\,11\sqrt{3}$ $\quad 8$

The product is $8 + 11\sqrt{3}$. Students prefer this method because it is a good organizer. "

NOTES:

CHAPTER 7 Assessment and Intervention

SE = Student Edition, **TE** = Teacher Edition, **CRM** = Chapter Resource Masters

	Diagnosis	Prescription
Diagnostic Assessment	**Beginning Chapter 7**	
	Get Ready for Chapter 7 **SE,** p. 407	Respnse to Intervention **TE,** p. 407
	Beginning Every Lesson	
	Then, Now, Why? **SE** 5-Minute Check Transparencies	Chapter 7 **SE,** p. 406 Concepts and Skills Bank **SE** pp. 994–1007
Formative Assessment	**During/After Every Lesson**	
	Guided Practice **SE,** every example Check Your Understanding **SE** H.O.T. Problems **SE** Spiral Review **SE** Additional Examples **TE** Watch Out! **TE** Step 4, Assess **TE** Chapter 7 Quizzes **CRM,** pp. 53–54 Self-Check Quizzes glencoe.com	**Tier 1 Intervention** Concepts and Skills Bank **SE,** pp. 994–1007 Skills Practice **CRM,** Ch. 1–7 glencoe.com **Tier 2 Intervention** Differentiated Instruction **TE** Study Guide and Intervention Masters **CRM,** Ch. 1–7 **Tier 3 Intervention** *Math Triumphs, Alg. 2,* Ch. 1
	Mid-Chapter	
	Mid-Chapter Quiz **SE,** p. 438 Mid-Chapter Test **CRM,** p. 55 ExamView Assessment Suite	**Tier 1 Intervention** Concepts and Skills Bank **SE,** pp. 994–1007 Skills Practice **CRM,** Ch. 1–7 glencoe.com **Tier 2 Intervention** Study Guide and Intervention Masters **CRM,** Ch. 1–7 **Tier 3 Intervention** *Math Triumphs, Alg. 2,* Ch. 1
	Before Chapter Test	
	Chapter Study Guide and Review **SE,** pp. 462–466 Practice Test **SE,** p. 467 Standardized Test Practice **SE,** pp. 470–471 Chapter Test glencoe.com Standardized Test Practice glencoe.com Vocabulary Review glencoe.com ExamView Assessment Suite	**Tier 1 Intervention** Concepts and Skills Bank **SE,** pp. 994–1007 Skills Practice **CRM,** Ch. 1–7 glencoe.com **Tier 2 Intervention** Study Guide and Intervention Masters **CRM,** Ch. 1–7 **Tier 3 Intervention** *Math Triumphs, Alg. 2,* Ch. 1
Summative Assessment	**After Chapter 7**	
	Multiple-Choice Tests, Forms 1, 2A, 2B **CRM,** pp. 57–62 Free-Response Tests, Forms 2C, 2D, 3 **CRM,** pp. 63–68 Vocabulary Test **CRM,** p. 56 Extended Response Test **CRM,** p. 69 Standardized Test Practice **CRM,** pp. 70–72 ExamView Assessment Suite	Study Guide and Intervention Masters **CRM,** Ch. 45–46 glencoe.com

CHAPTER 7

Differentiated Instruction

Option 1 Reaching All Learners AL OL BL ELL

AUDITORY/MUSICAL Divide the class into groups of three or four students. Challenge each group to give themselves a group name based on the vocabulary in a lesson, such as "The Radical Inequalities." Have students write a musical verse about one of the Key Concepts in the chapter. Have students share their verses with the entire class.

VISUAL/SPATIAL Have students use grid paper to draw rectangles of various sizes, and then cut them out. Then have them use the formula $d = \sqrt{\ell^2 + w^2}$ to find the length of the diagonal of each rectangle.

Option 2 Approaching Level AL

Have students read math expressions and equations using correct mathematical language. For example, an exponent should be read in a way that distinguishes it from a coefficient or multiplier. Have students practice reading math expressions and equations aloud. For example, they should read x^3 aloud as "x to the third power" or "x cubed."

Option 3 English Learners ELL

Whenever possible, write vocabulary words on the board, using diagrams that indicate the meaning of the words. For example, write the following diagram for *n*th roots on the board.

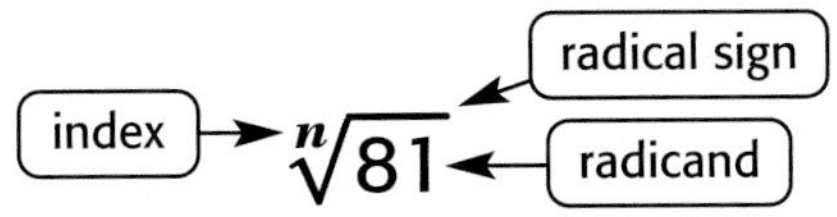

Ask students to explain each term in their own words.

Option 4 Beyond Level BL

After discussing how to determine if $f(x) = 5x + 10$ and $g(x) = \frac{1}{5}x - 2$ are inverses, challenge students to find two functions f and g such that $f(g(x)) \neq g(f(x))$, with one of the two compositions having a value of x. Allow students to work in groups to brainstorm as they attempt this puzzler.

FL Math Online Access Point Activities

CHAPTER 7

Focus on Mathematical Content

Vertical Alignment

Before Chapter 7

Related Topics from Algebra 1

- simplify polynomial expressions
- transform and solve equations
- graph equations of lines
- use the Distributive Property to simplify algebraic expressions

Previous Topics from Algebra 2

- use the properties of exponents to simplify expressions

Chapter 7

Related Topics from Algebra 2

- relate representations of square root functions
- connect inverses of square root functions with quadratic functions
- determine solutions of square root equations and inequalities using graphs, tables, and algebraic methods
- determine the reasonable domain and range values of square root functions, and interpret and determine the reasonableness of solutions to square root equations and inequalities
- use the parent function to investigate, describe, and predict the effects of parameter changes on graphs of square root functions and describe limitations on the domains and ranges

After Chapter 7

Preparation for Precalculus

- define functions, describe characteristics of functions, and translate among verbal, numerical, graphical, and symbolic representations of functions, including power functions
- perform operations including composition on functions, finding inverses, and describing these procedures and results verbally, numerically, symbolically, and graphically

Lesson-by-Lesson Preview

7-1 Operations on Functions

Any two functions, $f(x)$ and $g(x)$, can be added, subtracted, multiplied, and divided. If f and g are functions,

- their *sum* is the function defined by $(f + g)(x) = f(x) + g(x)$,
- their *difference* is the function defined by $(f - g)(x) = f(x) - g(x)$,
- their *product* is the function defined by $(f \cdot g)(x) = f(x) \cdot g(x)$, and
- their *quotient* is the function defined by $\left(\frac{f}{g}\right)(x) = \frac{f(x)}{g(x)}$, such that $g(x) \neq 0$.

The *composition of functions* provides another way of combining functions. Given two functions f and g, the composition, $f \circ g$, is described by $[f \circ g](x) = f[g(x)]$.

In most cases, $f \circ g \neq g \circ f$. Therefore, the order in which you compose functions is very important. It is also important to identify relationships between and restrictions on ranges and domains when composing functions.

7-2 Inverse Functions and Relations

The inverse of a function can be found by exchanging the domain and the range of the function. To find the inverse of $f(x)$:

- Rewrite $f(x)$ as an equation using x and y.
- Exchange x and y in the equation.
- Solve for y and then replace y with $f^{-1}(x)$.

To test whether two functions $f(x)$ and $g(x)$ are inverses, check that each of the two compositions $[f \circ g](x)$ and $[g \circ f](x)$ has the value x. When the inverse of a function is a function, then the original function is said to be *one-to-one*.

7-3 Square Root Functions and Inequalities

A function that contains a variable inside a square root symbol is called a *square root function.* The domains and ranges of these functions are limited to values for which the function is defined.

As with other functions, square root functions can be transformed.

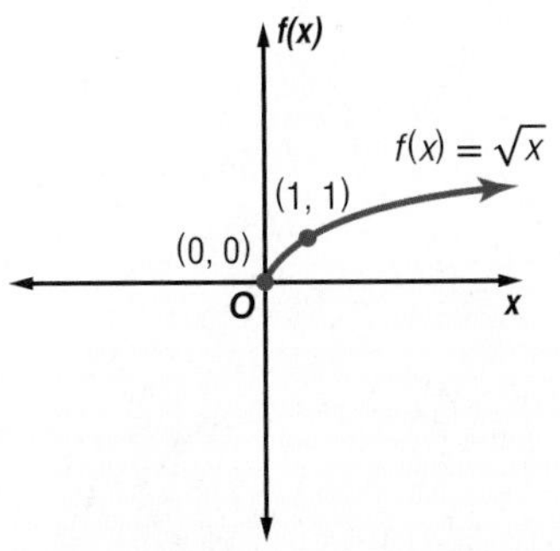

The parent function of the square root function is $f(x) = \sqrt{x}$, where the domain is $\{x \mid x \geq 0\}$ and the range is $\{f(x) \mid f(x) \geq 0\}$.

A *square root inequality* is an inequality involving square roots. To graph a square root inequality, first graph the related square root equation, forming two regions. Then select a point in one of the regions. If the point is a solution of the inequality, shade that region. If not, shade the other region.

7-4 *n*th Roots

A common definition of a square root, that a is a square root of b if $a^2 = b$, can be used to help students understand that a is an nth root of b if $a^n = b$. The symbol $\sqrt[n]{}$ indicates an nth root. In the symbol $\sqrt[n]{x}$, n is called the *index,* x is the *radicand,* and the symbol $\sqrt{}$ is called the *radical sign.*

The *principal root* of a number is always a nonnegative number. The value of a principal nth root depends on whether the *radicand* is positive or negative and whether its index is even or odd. When you find the nth root of an even power and the result is an odd power, you must use absolute value symbols around the result to ensure that the answer is nonnegative.

7-5 Operations with Radical Expressions

Radical expressions can be simplified using the *Product Property of Radicals* and the *Quotient Property of Radicals* as defined in this lesson. These properties are also used when multiplying or dividing radical expressions. In order to add or subtract radical expressions, the two radical expressions must be *like radical expressions;* that is, both the index and radicand are identical.

A process called *rationalizing the denominator* is used to eliminate radicals from a denominator or fractions from a radicand. To rationalize a denominator, multiply the numerator and denominator by a quantity so that the radicand has an exact root. A *conjugate* can be used to rationalize a denominator of the form $a\sqrt{b} \pm c\sqrt{d}$.

7-6 Rational Exponents

Exponents can be fractions. The rules for writing equivalent expressions for rational exponents include properties that describe how to translate between radical form and exponential form.

- For any real number b and for any positive integer n, $b^{\frac{1}{n}} = \sqrt[n]{b}$ except when $b < 0$ and n is even.
- For any non-zero real number b, and for any integers m and n, with $n > 1$, $b^{\frac{m}{n}} = \sqrt[n]{b^m} = \left(\sqrt[n]{b}\right)^m$, except when $b < 0$ and n is even.

An expression with rational exponents is in simplest form when all the exponents are positive and no fractional exponents are in the denominator. Also, the index used should be as small as possible.

7-7 Solving Radical Equations and Inequalities

Radical equations and radical inequalities are equations and inequalities that contain variables in the radicands. When solving a radical equation,

- first isolate the radical.
- Then raise each side of the equation to a power equal to the index of the radical. That is, to undo an nth root, you must raise each side of the equation to the nth power. This will eliminate the radical.
- Finally, solve the resulting equation.

Sometimes the process of raising both sides of a radical equation to a power does not produce an equivalent statement. For example, it is clear that $\sqrt{x} = -5$ has no real number solution. Squaring both sides results in $x = 25$. But $x = 25$ is not a solution to the original equation. Therefore, it is important to check solutions for *extraneous solutions.* When checking a solution to an inequality, test three numbers, one found within the solution interval, one less than, and one greater than the interval.

McGraw Hill Professional Development

Targeted professional development has been articulated throughout *Algebra 2.* More quality, customized professional development is available from McGraw-Hill Professional Development. Visit glencoe.com for details on each product.

- **Online Lessons** emphasize the strategies and techniques used to teach Algebra 2. Includes streaming video, interactive pages, and online tools.
- **Video Workshops** allow mentors, coaches, or leadership personnel to facilitate on-site workshops on educational strategies in mathematics and mathematical concepts.
- **MHPD Online** (www.mhpdonline.com) offers online professional development with video clips of instructional strategies, links, student activities, and news and issues in education.
- **Teaching Today** (teachingtoday.glencoe.com) gives secondary teachers practical strategies and materials that inspire excellence and innovation in teaching.

CHAPTER 7

Notes

Chapter Project

Saving for College

Students use what they have learned about inverse functions and roots to determine how long it will take to save a given amount of money.

- When interest on a deposit P is compounded, the amount A after n compounding periods is given by $A = P(1 + i)^n$, where i is the interest rate *per period.*
- Ask students to assume that $10,000 was put into a savings account for college expenses for a time of 2 years. If compounding were done yearly, ask them to find a function giving the required interest rate i as a function of the amount A needed at the end of the 2 years. Have them graph this function and estimate the interest rate needed for the amount in the account to grow to $12,000. Then have them calculate the exact rate needed.
- Then ask them to find the needed interest rate if the $10,000 were left in the account for 5 years instead of 2 years.
- Finally, have them repeat the entire exercise for a situation in which interest is compounded monthly instead of yearly.

CHAPTER 7

Inverses and Radical Functions and Relations

Then

In Chapter 6, you simplified polynomial expressions.

Now

In Chapter 7, you will:

- Find compositions and inverses of functions.
- Graph and analyze square root functions and inequalities.
- Simplify and solve equations involving roots, radicals, and rational exponents.

NGSSS

MA.912.A.2.6
MA.912.A.6.5

Why?

FINANCE Connecting finances to mathematics is a skill that, once mastered, you will use your entire life. Learning to manage your finances entails creating a budget and living within that budget. In this chapter, you will explore financial topics such as saving for college, income, profit, inflation, and converting money when traveling.

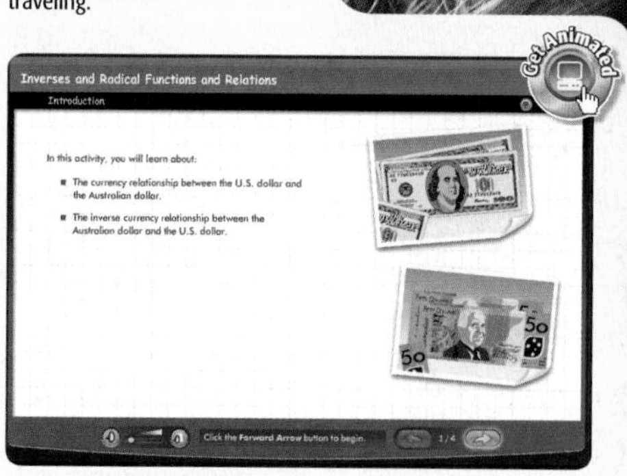

Key Vocabulary Introduce the key vocabulary in the chapter using the routine below.

Define: A radical inequality is an inequality that has a variable in the radicand.

Example: $\sqrt{4x + 8} - 1 \leq 15$

Ask: Is the following inequality a radical inequality? Explain. $7x - 11 > \sqrt{9}$ No, because there is no variable in the radicand.

Get Ready for Chapter 7

Diagnose Readiness You have two options for checking Prerequisite Skills.

Text Option Take the Quick Check below. Refer to the Quick Review for help.

*Quick*Check

(Used in Lesson 7-2)

Use the related graph of each equation to determine its roots. If exact roots cannot be found, state the consecutive integers between which the roots are located. (Lesson 5-2)

1. $x^2 - 4x + 1 = 0$
2. $2x^2 + x - 6 = 0$ $\frac{3}{2}$ and -2
3. **PHYSICS** Allie drops a ball from the top of a 30-foot building. How long does it take for the ball to reach the ground, assuming there is no air resistance? Use the formula $h(t) = -16t^2 + h_0$, where t is the time in seconds and the initial height h_0 is in feet. between 1 and 2 seconds

1. between 0 and 1, and between 3 and 4

(Used in Lessons 7-4 through 7-6)

Simplify each expression by using synthetic division. (Lesson 6-2)

4. $(5x^2 - 22x - 15) \div (x - 5)$ $5x + 3$
5. $(3x^2 + 14x - 12) \div (x + 4)$ $3x + 2 - \frac{20}{x + 4}$
6. $(2x^3 - 7x^2 - 36x + 36) \div (x - 6)$ $2x^2 + 5x - 6$
7. $(3x^4 - 13x^3 + 17x^2 - 18x + 15) \div (x - 3)$
8. **FINANCE** The number of specialty coffee mugs sold at a coffee shop can be estimated by $n = \frac{4000x^2}{x^2 + 50}$, where x is the amount of money spent on advertising in hundreds of dollars and n is the number of mugs sold.
   a. Perform the division indicated by $\frac{4000x^2}{x^2 + 50}$.
   b. About how many mugs will be sold if $1000 is spent on advertising?

*Quick*Review

EXAMPLE 1

Use the related graph of $0 = 3x^2 - 4x + 1$ to determine its roots. If exact roots cannot be found, state the consecutive integers between which the roots are located.

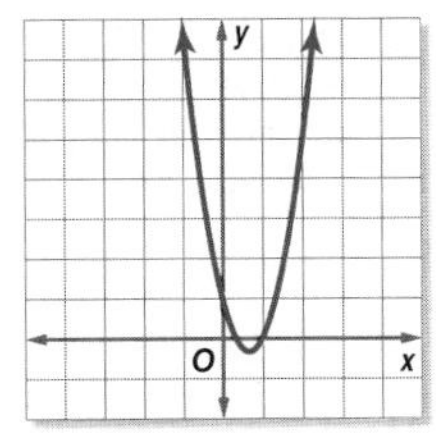

The roots are the x-coordinates where the graph crosses the x-axis.

The graph crosses the x-axis between 0 and 1 and at 1.

EXAMPLE 2

Simplify $(3x^4 + 4x^3 + x^2 + 9x - 6) \div (x + 2)$ by using synthetic division.

$x - r = x + 2$, so $r = -2$.

−2	3	4	1	9	−6
	↓	−6	4	−10	2
	3	−2	5	−1	−4

The result is $3x^3 - 2x^2 + 5x - 1 - \frac{4}{x + 2}$.

7. $3x^3 - 4x^2 + 5x - 3 + \frac{6}{x - 3}$

8a. $4000 - \frac{200,000}{x^2 + 50}$

8b. about 2667

Online Option FL Math Online Take a self-check Chapter Readiness Quiz at glencoe.com.

Response to Intervention (RtI)

Use the *Quick Check* results and the Intervention Planner to help you determine your Response to Intervention. The If-Then statements in the chart below help you decide the appropriate tier of RtI and suggest intervention resources for each tier.

Intervention Planner

Tier 1 On Level

If students miss about 25% of the exercises or less,

Then choose a resource:

SE Concepts and Skills Bank, p. 996; Lessons 5-2 and 6-2

CRM Skills Practice, Chapter 5, p. 13, Chapter 6, p. 13

TE Chapter Project, p. 406

FL Math Online Self-Check Quiz

Tier 2 Strategic Intervention approaching grade level

If students miss about 50% of the exercises,

Then choose a resource:

CRM Study Guide and Intervention, Chapter 5, p. 11, Chapter 6, p. 11

FL Math Online Extra Examples, Personal Tutor, Homework Help

Tier 3 Intensive Intervention 2 or more years below grade level

If students miss about 75% of the exercises,

Then use *Math Triumphs, Alg. 2*, Ch. 1

FL Math Online Extra Examples, Personal Tutor, Homework Help, Review Vocabulary

FOLDABLES® Study Organizer

Dinah Zike's Foldables®

Focus Students write notes as they study inverses and radical functions and relations in the lessons of this chapter.

Teach Have students make and label their Foldables as illustrated. Have students use the appropriate tab as they cover each lesson in this chapter. Encourage them to apply what they have learned by writing examples as well.

When to Use It Encourage students to add to their Foldables as they work through the chapter and to use them to review for the chapter test.

Differentiated Instruction

CRM Student-Built Glossary, p. 1
Students should complete the chart by providing a definition of each term and an example as they progress through Chapter 7. This study tool can also be used to review for the chapter test.

Get Started on Chapter 7

You will learn several new concepts, skills, and vocabulary terms as you study Chapter 7. To get ready, identify important terms and organize your resources. You may wish to refer to **Chapter 0** to review prerequisite skills.

FOLDABLES® Study Organizer

Inverses and Radical Functions Make this Foldable to help you organize your Chapter 7 notes about radical equations and inequalities. Begin with four sheets of notebook paper.

1. **Stack** three sheets of notebook paper so that each sheet is one inch higher than the sheet in front of it.

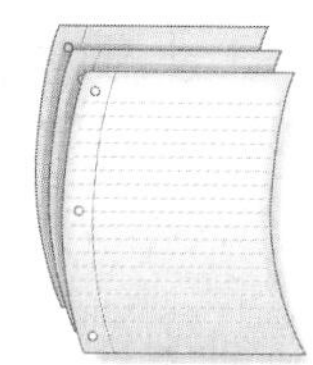

2. **Bring** the bottom of all the sheets upward and align the edges so that all of the layers or tabs are the same distance apart.

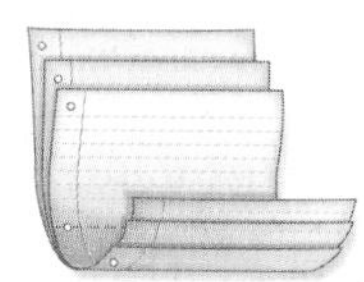

3. **When** all the tabs are an equal distance apart, fold the papers and crease well. Open the papers and staple them together along the valley or inner center fold. Label the pages with lesson titles.

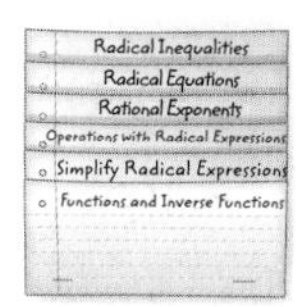

FL Math Online glencoe.com

- Study the chapter online
- Explore **Get Animated**
- Get extra help from your own **Personal Tutor**
- Use **Extra Examples** for additional help
- Take a **Self-Check Quiz**
- **Review Vocabulary** in fun ways

New Vocabulary

English		Español
composition of functions	• p. 411 •	composición de funciones
inverse relations	• p. 418 •	relaciones inversas
inverse function	• p. 418 •	función inversa
square root function	• p. 424 •	función raíz cuadrada
radical function	• p. 424 •	función radical
square root inequality	• p. 426 •	desigualdad raíz cuadrada
*n*th root	• p. 431 •	raíz enésima
principal root	• p. 431 •	raíz principal
radical sign	• p. 431 •	signo radical
radicand	• p. 431 •	radicando
index	• p. 431 •	índice
rationalizing the denominator	• p. 440 •	racionalizar el denominador
conjugates	• p. 442 •	conjugados
radical equation	• p. 453 •	ecuación radical
extraneous solution	• p. 453 •	solución extraña
radical inequality	• p. 455 •	desigualdad radical

Review Vocabulary

absolute value • p. 432 • valor absoluto a number's distance from zero on the number line, represented by $|x|$

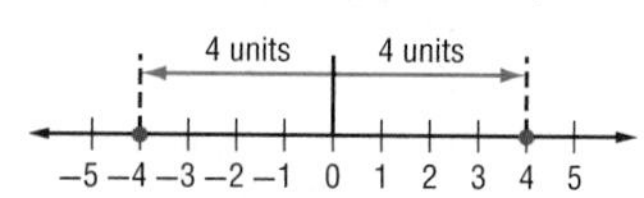

rational number • p. 11 • número racional Any number $\frac{m}{n}$, where m and n are integers and n is not zero; the decimal form is either a terminating or repeating decimal.

relation • p. 418 • relación a set of ordered pairs

Multilingual eGlossary glencoe.com

7-1 Operations on Functions

Why?

The graphs model the income for the Brooks family since 2000, where $m(x)$ represents Mr. Brooks' income and $f(x)$ represents Mrs. Brooks' income.

The total household income for the Brooks household can be represented by $f(x) + m(x)$.

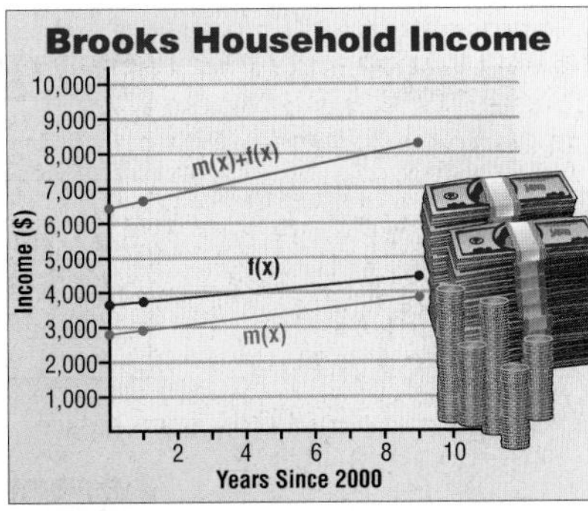

Then
You performed operations on polynomials. (Lesson 6-1)

Now
- Find the sum, difference, product, and quotient of functions.
- Find the composition of functions.

NGSSS
MA.912.A.2.7 Perform operations of functions algebraically, numerically, and graphically.
MA.912.A.2.8 Determine the composition of functions.

New Vocabulary
composition of functions

FL Math Online
glencoe.com

Arithmetic Operations In Chapter 6, you performed arithmetic operations with polynomials. You can also use addition, subtraction, multiplication, and division with functions.

You can perform arithmetic operations according to the following rules.

Key Concept: Operations on Functions

Operation	Definition	Example Let $f(x) = 2x$ and $g(x) = -x + 5$.
Addition	$(f + g)(x) = f(x) + g(x)$	$2x + (-x + 5) = x + 5$
Subtraction	$(f - g)(x) = f(x) - g(x)$	$2x - (-x + 5) = 3x - 5$
Multiplication	$(f \cdot g)(x) = f(x) \cdot g(x)$	$2x(-x + 5) = -2x^2 + 10x$
Division	$\left(\frac{f}{g}\right)(x) = \frac{f(x)}{g(x)}, g(x) \neq 0$	$\frac{2x}{-x + 5}, x \neq 5$

EXAMPLE 1 Add and Subtract Functions

Given $f(x) = x^2 - 4$ and $g(x) = 2x + 1$, find each function.

a. $(f + g)(x)$

$(f + g)(x) = f(x) + g(x)$ — **Addition of functions**
$= (x^2 - 4) + (2x + 1)$ — **$f(x) = x^2 - 4$ and $g(x) = 2x + 1$**
$= x^2 + 2x - 3$ — **Simplify.**

b. $(f - g)(x)$

$(f - g)(x) = f(x) - g(x)$ — **Subtraction of functions**
$= (x^2 - 4) - (2x + 1)$ — **$f(x) = x^2 - 4$ and $g(x) = 2x + 1$**
$= x^2 - 2x - 5$ — **Simplify.**

Guided Practice

Given $f(x) = x^2 + 5x - 2$ and $g(x) = 3x - 2$, find each function.

1A. $(f + g)(x)$ $(f + g)(x) = x^2 + 8x - 4$ **1B.** $(f - g)(x)$ $(f - g)(x) = x^2 + 2x$

Personal Tutor glencoe.com

7-1 Lesson Notes

1 FOCUS

Vertical Alignment

Before Lesson 7-1
Perform operations on polynomials.

Lesson 7-1
Find the sum, difference, product, and quotient of functions.
Find the composition of functions.

After Lesson 7-1
Describe and analyze the relationship between a function and its inverse.

2 TEACH

Scaffolding Questions

Have students read the *Why?* section of the lesson.

Ask:
- What years are represented by $x = 0$, $x = 4$, and $x = 10$? 2000, 2004, 2010
- What are the approximate values of $f(0)$, $m(0)$, and $f(0) + m(0)$? $f(0) \approx 3{,}700$, $m(0) \approx 2{,}900$, $f(0) + m(0) \approx 6{,}600$
- Which graph, $m(x)$, $f(x)$, or $f(x) + m(x)$, has the greatest slope? Explain your answer. $f(x) + m(x)$; all three slopes are positive, and the slope of $f(x) + m(x)$ is the sum of the slopes of $f(x)$ and $m(x)$.

Lesson 7-1 Resources

Resource	Approaching-Level	On-Level	Beyond-Level	English Learners
Teacher Edition	• Differentiated Instruction, p. 412	• Differentiated Instruction, pp. 411, 412	• Differentiated Instruction, p. 411	• Differentiated Instruction, p. 412
Chapter Resource Masters	• Study Guide and Intervention, pp. 5–6 • Skills Practice, p. 7 • Practice, p. 8 • Word Problem Practice, p. 9	• Study Guide and Intervention, pp. 5–6 • Skills Practice, p. 7 • Practice, p. 8 • Word Problem Practice, p. 9 • Enrichment, p. 10 • Spreadsheet Activity, p. 11	• Practice, p. 8 • Word Problem Practice, p. 9 • Enrichment, p. 10	• Study Guide and Intervention, pp. 5–6 • Skills Practice, p. 7 • Practice, p. 8 • Word Problem Practice, p. 9
Transparencies	• 5-Minute Check Transparency 7-1	• 5-Minute Check Transparency 7-1	• 5-Minute Check Transparency 7-1	• 5-Minute Check Transparency 7-1
Other	• Study Notebook • Teaching Algebra with Manipulatives	• Study Notebook • Teaching Algebra with Manipulatives	• Study Notebook	• Study Notebook • Teaching Algebra with Manipulatives

Arithmetic Operations

Example 1 shows how to add and subtract functions. **Example 2** shows how to multiply and divide functions.

Formative Assessment

Use the Guided Practice exercises after each example to determine students' understanding of concepts.

Additional Examples

1 Given $f(x) = 3x^2 + 7x$ and $g(x) = 2x^2 - x - 1$, find each function.

a. $(f + g)(x)$
$(f + g)(x) = 5x^2 + 6x - 1$

b. $(f - g)(x)$
$(f - g)(x) = x^2 + 8x + 1$

2 Given $f(x) = 3x^2 - 2x + 1$ and $g(x) = x - 4$, find each function.

a. $(f \cdot g)(x)$
$(f \cdot g)(x) = 3x^3 - 14x^2 + 9x - 4$

b. $\left(\frac{f}{g}\right)(x)$
$\left(\frac{f}{g}\right)(x) = \frac{3x^2 - 2x + 1}{x - 4}, x \neq 4$

Additional Examples also in Interactive Classroom PowerPoint® Presentations

IWB INTERACTIVE WHITEBOARD READY

Focus on Mathematical Content

Combining Functions Addition, subtraction, multiplication, and division can be used to combine functions. Composition of functions is a method of combining functions, and is fundamentally different from arithmetic operations on functions. In the composition $(g \circ f)$, the output $f(x)$ is used as input for g.

Review Vocabulary

intersection the intersection of two sets is the set of elements common to both

You can graph sum and difference functions by graphing each function involved separately, then adding their corresponding functional values. Let $f(x) = x^2$ and $g(x) = x$. Examine the graphs of $f(x)$, $g(x)$, and their sum and difference.

Find $(f + g)(x)$.

x	$f(x) = x^2$	$g(x) = x$	$(f + g)(x) = x^2 + x$
−3	9	−3	9 + (−3) = 6
−2	4	−2	4 + (−2) = 2
−1	1	−1	1 + (−1) = 0
0	0	0	0 + 0 = 0
1	1	1	1 + 1 = 2
2	4	2	4 + 2 = 6
3	9	3	9 + 3 = 12

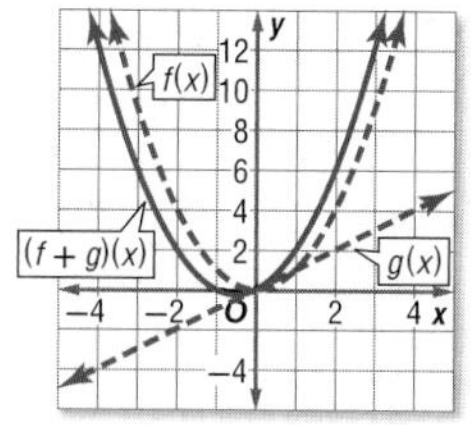

Find $(f - g)(x)$.

x	$f(x) = x^2$	$g(x) = x$	$(f - g)(x) = x^2 + x$
−3	9	−3	9 − (−3) = 12
−2	4	−2	4 − (−2) = 6
−1	1	−1	1 − (−1) = 2
0	0	0	0 − 0 = 0
1	1	1	1 − 1 = 0
2	4	2	4 − 2 = 2
3	9	3	9 − 3 = 6

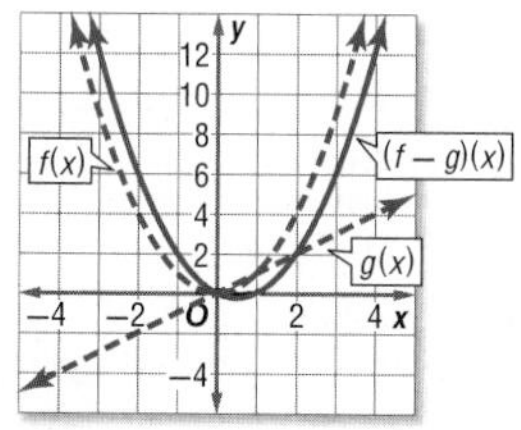

In Example 1, the functions $f(x)$ and $g(x)$ have the same domain of all real numbers. The functions $(f + g)(x)$ and $(f - g)(x)$ also have domains that include all real numbers. For each new function, the domain consists of the intersection of the domains of $f(x)$ and $g(x)$. Under division, the domain of the new function is restricted by excluded values that cause the denominator to equal zero.

EXAMPLE 2 Multiply and Divide Functions

Given $f(x) = x^2 + 7x + 12$ and $g(x) = 3x - 4$, find each function.

a. $(f \cdot g)(x)$

$(f \cdot g)(x) = f(x) \cdot g(x)$ — **Multiplication of functions**
$= (x^2 + 7x + 12)(3x - 4)$ — **Substitution**
$= 3x^3 + 21x^2 + 36x - 4x^2 - 28x - 48$ — **Distributive Property**
$= 3x^3 + 17x^2 + 8x - 48$ — **Simplify.**

b. $\left(\frac{f}{g}\right)(x)$

$\left(\frac{f}{g}\right)(x) = \frac{f(x)}{g(x)}$ — **Division of functions**
$= \frac{x^2 + 7x + 12}{-3x - 4}, x \neq -\frac{4}{3}$ — **Substitution**

Because $x = -\frac{4}{3}$ makes the denominator $-3x - 4 = 0$, $-\frac{4}{3}$ is excluded from the domain of $\left(\frac{f}{g}\right)(x)$.

Guided Practice

Given $f(x) = x^2 - 7x + 2$ and $g(x) = x + 4$, find each function.

2A. $(f \cdot g)(x)$ $(f \cdot g)(x) = x^3 - 3x^2 - 26x + 8$ **2B.** $\left(\frac{f}{g}\right)(x)$ $\left(\frac{f}{g}\right)(x) = \frac{x^2 - 7x + 2}{x + 4}, x \neq -4$

Personal Tutor glencoe.com

Watch Out!

Student Misconceptions Some students may read $f \circ g$ as the word *fog*. Listen for students making this verbal error. Stress that the correct wording may help them understand the meaning. Lead students to understand the similarity in meaning between $f(x)$ (read "f of x") and $[f \circ g](x)$ (read "f of g of x"). Show how $f \circ g$ can also be written as $f[g(x)]$. You can also relate $f[g(x)]$ to an expression containing nested parentheses, such as $(1 + (3 \cdot 5(4)))$, in which the expressions in parentheses are evaluated from the innermost parentheses to the outermost.

Composition of Functions Another method used to combine functions is a composition of functions. In a **composition of functions**, the results of one function are used to evaluate a second function.

ReadingMath

Composite Functions The composition of f and g, denoted by $f \circ g$ or $f[g(x)]$, is read f of g.

Key Concept — Composition of Functions

Words Suppose f and g are functions such that the range of g is a subset of the domain of f. Then the composition function $f \circ g$ can be described by

$$[f \circ g](x) = f[g(x)].$$

Model

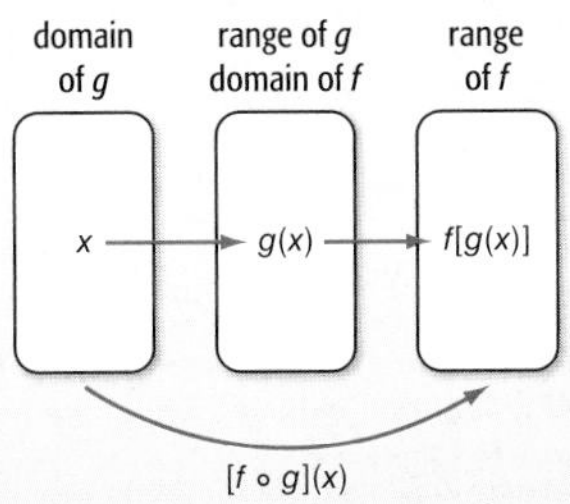

The composition of two functions may not exist. Given two functions f and g, $[f \circ g](x)$ is defined only if the range of $g(x)$ is a subset of the domain of f. Likewise, $[g \circ f](x)$ is defined only if the range of $f(x)$ is a subset of the domain of g.

EXAMPLE 3 Compose Functions

For each pair of functions, find $[f \circ g](x)$ and $[g \circ f](x)$, if they exist.

a. $f = \{(1, 8), (0, 13), (15, 11), (14, 9)\}$, $g = \{(8, 15), (5, 1), (10, 14), (9, 0)\}$

To find $f \circ g$, evaluate $g(x)$ first. Then use the range as the domain of f and evaluate $f(x)$.

$f[g(8)] = f(15)$ or 11   **$g(8) = 15$** $f[g(10)] = f(14)$ or 9   **$g(10) = 14$**

$f[g(5)] = f(1)$ or 8   **$g(5) = 1$** $f[g(9)] = f(0)$ or 13   **$g(9) = 0$**

$f \circ g = \{(8, 11), (5, 8), (10, 9), (9, 13)\}$

To find $g \circ f$, evaluate $f(x)$ first. Then use the range as the domain of g and evaluate $g(x)$.

$g[f(1)] = g(8)$ or 15   **$f(1) = 8$** $g[f(15)] = g(11)$ **$g(11)$ is undefined.**

$g[f(0)] = g(13)$ **$g(13)$ is undefined.** $g[f(14)] = g(9)$ or 0   **$f(14) = 0$**

Because 11 and 13 are not in the domain of g, $g \circ f$ is undefined for $x = 11$ and $x = 13$. However, $g[f(1)] = 15$ and $g[f(14)] = 0$, so $g \circ f = \{(1, 15), (14, 0)\}$.

b. $f(x) = 2a - 5$, $g(x) = 4a$

$[f \circ g](x) = f[g(x)]$	**Composition of functions**	$[g \circ f](x) = g[f(x)]$
$= f(4a)$	**Substitute.**	$= g(2a - 5)$
$= 2(4a) - 5$	**Substitute again.**	$= 4(2a - 5)$
$= 8a - 5$	**Simplify.**	$= 8a - 20$

StudyTip

Composition Be careful not to confuse a composition $f[g(x)]$ with multiplication of functions $(f \cdot g)(x)$.

Guided Practice

3A. $f(x) = \{(3, -2), (-1, -5), (4, 7), (10, 8)\}$, $g(x) = \{(4, 3), (2, -1), (9, 4), (3, 10)\}$

3B. $f(x) = x^2 + 2$ and $g(x) = x - 6$

3A. $f \circ g = \{(4, -2), (2, -5), (9, 7), (3, 8)\}$; $g \circ f$ is undefined.
3B. $[f \circ g](x) = x^2 - 12x + 38$; $[g \circ f](x) = x^2 - 4$

Personal Tutor glencoe.com

Composition of Functions

Example 3 shows how to evaluate composition of functions. **Example 4** shows how to use composition of functions to solve a real-world problem.

Additional Example

3 For each pair of functions, find $[f \circ g](x)$ and $[g \circ f](x)$, if they exist.

a. $f = \{(2, 6), (9, 4), (7, 7), (0, -1)\}$ and $g = \{(7, 0), (-1, 7), (4, 9), (8, 2)\}$
$[f \circ g](x) = \{(7, -1), (-1, 7), (4, 4), (8, 6)\}$;
$[g \circ f](x) = \{(9, 9), (7, 0), (0, 7)\}$

b. $f(x) = 3x^2 - x + 4$ and $g(x) = 2x - 1$
$[f \circ g](x) = 12x^2 - 14x + 8$;
$[g \circ f](x) = 6x^2 - 2x + 7$

TEACH with TECH

INTERACTIVE WHITEBOARD Write two functions $f(x)$ and $g(x)$ on the board. To show students how to write $f(g(x))$, drag the expression for $g(x)$ and replace each x in $f(x)$. Repeat for $g(f(x))$.

Differentiated Instruction OL BL

Extension In some courses, a function $f(x)$ is modeled by a "machine" that accepts values for x as inputs and then outputs values for $f(x)$. Using this model, ask students to explain how the composition of two functions could be modeled by two such "machines" linked together. Also ask them to use the model to explain how the composition of two functions could be undefined for some initial input values.

Additional Example

4 **TAXES** Hector has \$100 deducted from every paycheck for retirement. He can have this deduction taken before state taxes are applied, which reduces his taxable income. His state income tax rate is 4%. If Hector earns \$1500 every pay period, find the difference in his net income if he has the retirement deduction taken before or after state taxes. His net pay is \$4 more by having his retirement deduction taken before state taxes.

Additional Answers

1. $(f+g)(x) = 4x + 1$; $(f-g)(x) = -2x + 3$; $(f \cdot g)(x) = 3x^2 + 5x - 2$; $\left(\frac{f}{g}\right)(x) = \frac{x+2}{3x-1}, x \neq \frac{1}{3}$
2. $(f+g)(x) = x^2 - x + 3$; $(f-g)(x) = x^2 + x - 13$; $(f \cdot g)(x) = -x^3 + 8x^2 + 5x - 40$; $\left(\frac{f}{g}\right)(x) = \frac{x^2-5}{-x+8}, x \neq 8$
3. $f \circ g$ is undefined; $g \circ f = \{(2, 8), (6, 13), (12, 11), (7, 15)\}$.
4. $f \circ g$ is undefined; $g \circ f = \{(0, 2)\}$.
5. $[f \circ g](x) = -15x + 18$; $[g \circ f](x) = -15x - 6$
6. $[f \circ g](x) = x^2 + 3x - 6$; $[g \circ f](x) = x^2 + 11x + 18$
7. Either way, she will have \$228.95 taken from her paycheck. If she takes the college savings plan deduction before taxes, \$76 will go to her college plan and \$152.95 will go to taxes. If she takes the college savings plan deduction after taxes, only \$62.70 will go to her college plan and \$166.25 will go to taxes.
8. $(f+g)(x) = -2x + 5$; $(f-g)(x) = 6x - 5$; $(f \cdot g)(x) = -8x^2 + 10x$; $\left(\frac{f}{g}\right)(x) = \frac{2x}{-4x+5}, x \neq \frac{5}{4}$

Real-World Link

Adjusted for inflation, the average price of a new car declined from \$23,014 in 1995 to \$22,013 in 2005.

Source: U.S. Department of Commerce

Notice that in most cases, $f \circ g \neq g \circ f$. Therefore, the order in which two functions are composed is important.

Real-World EXAMPLE 4 Use Composition of Functions

SHOPPING A new car dealer is discounting all new cars by 12%. At the same time, the manufacturer is offering a \$1500 rebate on all new cars. Mr. Navarro is buying a car that is priced \$24,500. Will the final price be lower if the discount is applied before the rebate or if the rebate is applied before the discount?

Understand Let x represent the original price of a new car, $d(x)$ represent the price of a car after the discount, and $r(x)$ the price of the car after the rebate.

Plan Write equations for $d(x)$ and $r(x)$.

The original price is discounted by 12%.
$d(x) = x - 0.12x$

There is a \$1500 rebate on all new cars.
$r(x) = x - 1500$

Solve If the discount is applied *before* the rebate, then the final price of Mr. Navarro's new car is represented by $[r \circ d](24{,}500)$.

$[r \circ d](x) = r[d(x)]$

$$\begin{aligned}[r \circ d](24{,}500) &= r[24{,}500 - 0.12(24{,}500)] \\ &= r(24{,}500 - 2940) \\ &= r(21{,}560) \\ &= 21{,}560 - 1500 \\ &= 20{,}060\end{aligned}$$

If the rebate is given *before* the discount is applied, then the final price of Mr. Navarro's car is represented by $[d \circ r](24{,}500)$.

$[d \circ r](x) = d[r(x)]$

$$\begin{aligned}[d \circ r](24{,}500) &= d(24{,}500 - 1500) \\ &= d(23{,}000) \\ &= 23{,}000 - 0.12(23{,}000) \\ &= 23{,}000 - 2760 \\ &= 20{,}240\end{aligned}$$

$[r \circ d](24{,}500) = 20{,}060$ and $[d \circ r](24{,}500) = 20{,}240$. So, the final price of the car is less when the discount is applied before the rebate.

Check The answer seems reasonable because the 12% discount is being applied to a greater amount. Thus, the dollar amount of the discount is greater.

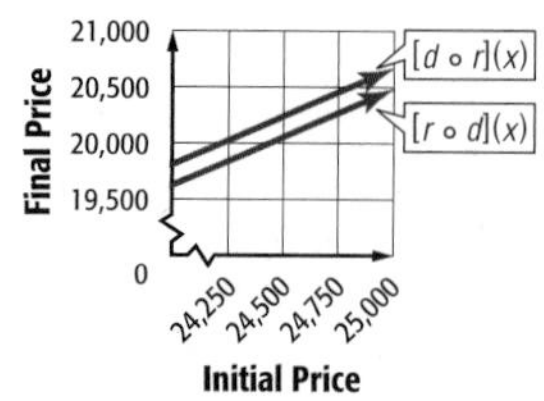

Guided Practice

4. **SHOPPING** Sounds-to-Go offers both an in-store \$35 rebate and a 15% discount on a digital audio player that normally sells for \$300. Which provides the better price: taking the discount before the rebate or taking the discount after the rebate?
It is better, by a difference of \$5.25, to take the discount before the rebate.

Personal Tutor glencoe.com

Differentiated Instruction

AL OL ELL

Intrapersonal Learners Have students write expressions that involve compositions of functions and then annotate the expressions with notes to themselves such as, "$(f \circ g(x))$ is pronounced "f of g of x" and, "Start by finding the value $g(x)$; then use that value as the input for f."

Check Your Understanding

Examples 1 and 2 pp. 409–410

Find $(f + g)(x)$, $(f - g)(x)$, $(f \cdot g)(x)$, and $\left(\frac{f}{g}\right)(x)$ for each $f(x)$ and $g(x)$. **1, 2. See margin.**

1. $f(x) = x + 2$
   $g(x) = 3x - 1$
2. $f(x) = x^2 - 5$
   $g(x) = -x + 8$

Example 3 p. 411

For each pair of functions, find $f \circ g$ and $g \circ f$, if they exist. **3, 4. See margin.**

3. $f = \{(2, 5), (6, 10), (12, 9), (7, 6)\}$
   $g = \{(9, 11), (6, 15), (10, 13), (5, 8)\}$
4. $f = \{(-5, 4), (14, 8), (12, 1), (0, -3)\}$
   $g = \{(-2, -4), (-3, 2), (-1, 4), (5, -6)\}$

Find $[f \circ g](x)$ and $[g \circ f](x)$, if they exist. **5, 6. See margin.**

5. $f(x) = -3x$
   $g(x) = 5x - 6$
6. $f(x) = x + 4$
   $g(x) = x^2 + 3x - 10$

Example 4 p. 412

7. **FINANCIAL LITERACY** Dora has 8% of her earnings deducted from her paycheck for a college savings plan. She can choose to take the deduction either before taxes are withheld, which reduces her taxable income, or after taxes are withheld. Dora's tax rate is 17.5%. If her pay before taxes and deductions is \$950, will she save more money if the deductions are taken before or after taxes are withheld? Explain. **See margin.**

Practice and Problem Solving

● = **Step-by-Step Solutions** begin on page R20.
Extra Practice begins on page 947.

Examples 1 and 2 pp. 409–410

Find $(f + g)(x)$, $(f - g)(x)$, $(f \cdot g)(x)$, and $\left(\frac{f}{g}\right)(x)$ for each $f(x)$ and $g(x)$. **8–15. See margin.**

8. $f(x) = 2x$
   $g(x) = -4x + 5$
9. $f(x) = x - 1$
   $g(x) = 5x - 2$
10. $f(x) = x^2$
    $g(x) = -x + 1$
11. $f(x) = 3x$
    $g(x) = -2x + 6$
12. $f(x) = x - 2$
    $g(x) = 2x - 7$
13. $f(x) = x^2$
    $g(x) = x - 5$
14. $f(x) = -x^2 + 6$
    $g(x) = 2x^2 + 3x - 5$
15. $f(x) = 3x^2 - 4$
    $g(x) = x^2 - 8x + 4$

16. **WALKING** Isaac is walking on a moving walkway. His speed is given by the function $I(x) = 3x - 4$, and the speed of the walkway is $W(x) = 4x + 7$, where x is time in seconds. **a. $(W + I)(x) = 7x + 3$**
    a. What is his total speed as he walks along the moving walkway?
    b. Isaac turned around because he left his cell phone at a restaurant. What was his speed as he walked against the moving walkway? **$(I - W)(x) = -x - 11$**

Example 3 p. 411

For each pair of functions, find $f \circ g$ and $g \circ f$, if they exist. **17–20. See margin.**

17. $f = \{(-8, -4), (0, 4), (2, 6), (-6, -2)\}$
    $g = \{(4, -4), (-2, -1), (-4, 0), (6, -5)\}$
18. $f = \{(-7, 0), (4, 5), (8, 12), (-3, 6)\}$
    $g = \{(6, 8), (-12, -5), (0, 5), (5, 1)\}$
19. $f = \{(5, 13), (-4, -2), (-8, -11), (3, 1)\}$
    $g = \{(-8, 2), (-4, 1), (3, -3), (5, 7)\}$
20. $f = \{(-4, -14), (0, -6), (-6, -18), (2, -2)\}$
    $g = \{(-6, 1), (-18, 13), (-14, 9), (-2, -3)\}$

3 PRACTICE

Formative Assessment

Use Exercises 1–7 to check for understanding.

Use the chart at the bottom of this page to customize assignments for your students.

Additional Answers

9. $(f + g)(x) = 6x - 3$; $(f - g)(x) = -4x + 1$; $(f \cdot g)(x) = 5x^2 - 7x + 2$; $\left(\frac{f}{g}\right)(x) = \frac{x - 1}{5x - 2}, x \neq \frac{2}{5}$
10. $(f + g)(x) = x^2 - x + 1$; $(f - g)(x) = x^2 + x - 1$; $(f \cdot g)(x) = -x^3 + x^2$; $\left(\frac{f}{g}\right)(x) = \frac{x^2}{-x + 1}, x \neq 1$
11. $(f + g)(x) = x + 6$; $(f - g)(x) = 5x - 6$; $(f \cdot g)(x) = -6x^2 + 18x$; $\left(\frac{f}{g}\right)(x) = \frac{3x}{-2x + 6}, x \neq 3$
12. $(f + g)(x) = 3x - 9$; $(f - g)(x) = -x + 5$; $(f \cdot g)(x) = 2x^2 - 11x + 14$; $\left(\frac{f}{g}\right)(x) = \frac{x - 2}{2x - 7}, x \neq \frac{7}{2}$
13. $(f + g)(x) = x^2 + x - 5$; $(f - g)(x) = x^2 - x + 5$; $(f \cdot g)(x) = x^3 - 5x^2$; $\left(\frac{f}{g}\right)(x) = \frac{x^2}{x - 5}, x \neq 5$
14. $(f + g)(x) = x^2 + 3x + 1$; $(f - g)(x) = -3x^2 - 3x + 11$; $(f \cdot g)(x) = -2x^4 - 3x^3 + 17x^2 + 18x - 30$; $\left(\frac{f}{g}\right)(x) = \frac{-x^2 + 6}{2x^2 + 3x - 5}, x \neq 1$ or $-\frac{5}{2}$
15. $(f + g)(x) = 4x^2 - 8x$; $(f - g)(x) = 2x^2 + 8x - 8$; $(f \cdot g)(x) = 3x^4 - 24x^3 + 8x^2 + 32x - 16$; $\left(\frac{f}{g}\right)(x) = \frac{3x^2 - 4}{x^2 - 8x + 4}, x \neq 4 \pm 2\sqrt{3}$
17. $f \circ g = \{(-4, 4)\}$; $g \circ f = \{(-8, 0), (0, -4), (2, -5), (-6, -1)\}$
18. $f \circ g = \{(6, 12)\}$; $g \circ f = \{(-7, 5), (4, 1), (-3, 8)\}$
19. $f \circ g$ is undefined; $g \circ f$ is undefined.
20. $f \circ g$ is undefined; $g \circ f = \{(-4, 9), (0, 1), (-6, 13), (2, -3)\}$.

Differentiated Homework Options

Level	Assignment	Two-Day Option	
AL Basic	8–37, 59–60, 62–86	9–37 odd, 64–67	8–36 even, 59, 60, 62–63, 68–86
OL Core	9–49 odd, 50–51, 53–57 odd, 58–60, 62–86	8–37, 64–67	38–60, 62–63, 68–86
BL Advanced	38–80, (optional: 81–86)		

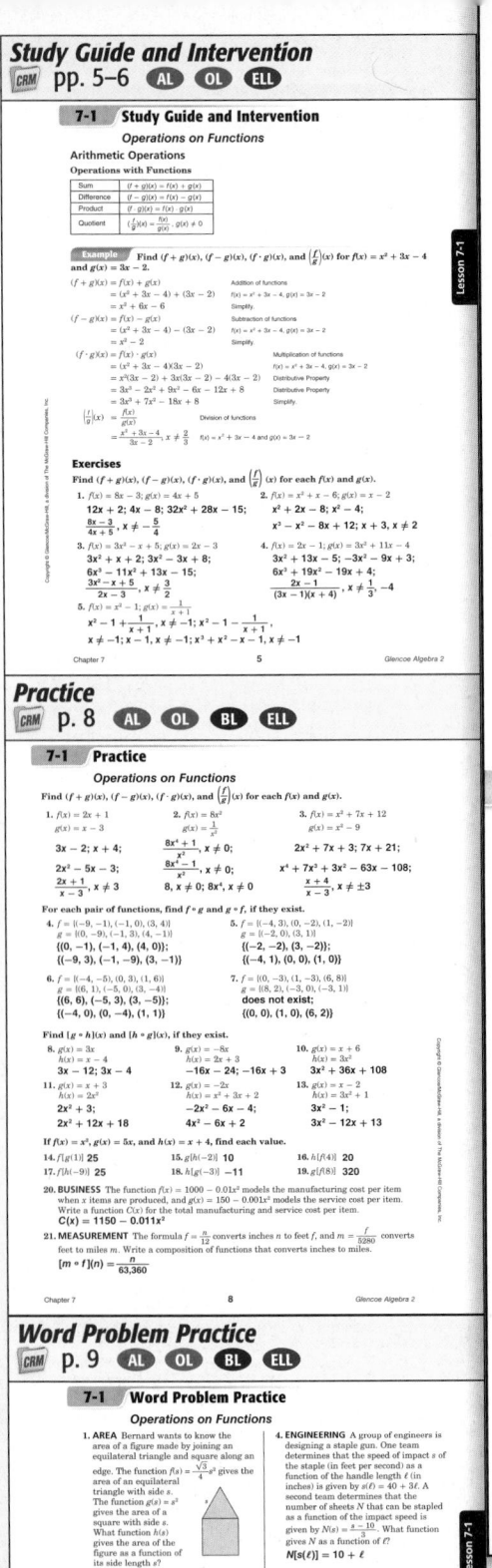

Study Guide and Intervention
CRM pp. 5–6 AL OL ELL

7-1 Study Guide and Intervention
Operations on Functions

Arithmetic Operations

Operations with Functions

Sum	$(f+g)(x) = f(x) + g(x)$
Difference	$(f-g)(x) = f(x) - g(x)$
Product	$(f \cdot g)(x) = f(x) \cdot g(x)$
Quotient	$\left(\frac{f}{g}\right)(x) = \frac{f(x)}{g(x)},\ g(x) \neq 0$

Example Find $(f+g)(x)$, $(f-g)(x)$, $(f \cdot g)(x)$, and $\left(\frac{f}{g}\right)(x)$ for $f(x) = x^2 + 3x - 4$ and $g(x) = 3x - 2$.

$(f+g)(x) = f(x) + g(x)$ — Addition of functions
$= (x^2 + 3x - 4) + (3x - 2)$ — $f(x) = x^2 + 3x - 4,\ g(x) = 3x - 2$
$= x^2 + 6x - 6$ — Simplify.

$(f-g)(x) = f(x) - g(x)$ — Subtraction of functions
$= (x^2 + 3x - 4) - (3x - 2)$ — $f(x) = x^2 + 3x - 4,\ g(x) = 3x - 2$
$= x^2 - 2$ — Simplify.

$(f \cdot g)(x) = f(x) \cdot g(x)$ — Multiplication of functions
$= (x^2 + 3x - 4)(3x - 2)$ — $f(x) = x^2 + 3x - 4,\ g(x) = 3x - 2$
$= x^2(3x - 2) + 3x(3x - 2) - 4(3x - 2)$ — Distributive Property
$= 3x^3 - 2x^2 + 9x^2 - 6x - 12x + 8$ — Distributive Property
$= 3x^3 + 7x^2 - 18x + 8$ — Simplify.

$\left(\frac{f}{g}\right)(x) = \frac{f(x)}{g(x)}$ — Division of functions
$= \frac{x^2 + 3x - 4}{3x - 2},\ x \neq \frac{2}{3}$ — $f(x) = x^2 + 3x - 4$ and $g(x) = 3x - 2$

Exercises

Find $(f+g)(x)$, $(f-g)(x)$, $(f \cdot g)(x)$, and $\left(\frac{f}{g}\right)(x)$ for each $f(x)$ and $g(x)$.

1. $f(x) = 8x - 3$; $g(x) = 4x + 5$
$12x + 2$; $4x - 8$; $32x^2 + 28x - 15$; $\frac{8x-3}{4x+5}, x \neq -\frac{5}{4}$

2. $f(x) = x^2 + x - 6$; $g(x) = x - 2$
$x^2 + 2x - 8$; $x^2 - 4$; $x^3 - x^2 - 8x + 12$; $x + 3, x \neq 2$

3. $f(x) = 3x^2 - x + 5$; $g(x) = 2x - 3$
$3x^2 + x + 2$; $3x^2 - 3x + 8$; $6x^3 - 11x^2 + 13x - 15$; $\frac{3x^2 - x + 5}{2x - 3}, x \neq \frac{3}{2}$

4. $f(x) = 2x - 1$; $g(x) = 3x^2 + 11x - 4$
$3x^2 + 13x - 5$; $-3x^2 - 9x + 3$; $6x^3 + 19x^2 - 19x + 4$; $\frac{2x - 1}{(3x - 1)(x + 4)}, x \neq \frac{1}{3}, -4$

5. $f(x) = x^2 - 1$; $g(x) = \frac{1}{x+1}$
$x^2 - 1 + \frac{1}{x+1}, x \neq -1$; $x^2 - 1 - \frac{1}{x+1}, x \neq -1$; $x - 1, x \neq -1$; $x^3 + x^2 - x - 1, x \neq -1$

Chapter 7 — 5 — Glencoe Algebra 2

Lesson 7-1

Practice
CRM p. 8 AL OL BL ELL

7-1 Practice
Operations on Functions

Find $(f+g)(x)$, $(f-g)(x)$, $(f \cdot g)(x)$, and $\left(\frac{f}{g}\right)(x)$ for each $f(x)$ and $g(x)$.

1. $f(x) = 2x + 1$, $g(x) = x - 3$
$3x - 2$; $x + 4$; $2x^2 - 5x - 3$; $\frac{2x+1}{x-3}, x \neq 3$

2. $f(x) = 8x^2$, $g(x) = \frac{1}{x^2}$
$\frac{8x^4 + 1}{x^2}, x \neq 0$; $\frac{8x^4 - 1}{x^2}, x \neq 0$; $8, x \neq 0$; $8x^4, x \neq 0$

3. $f(x) = x^2 + 7x + 12$, $g(x) = x^2 - 9$
$2x^2 + 7x + 3$; $7x + 21$; $x^4 + 7x^3 + 3x^2 - 63x - 108$; $\frac{x+4}{x-3}, x \neq \pm 3$

For each pair of functions, find $f \circ g$ and $g \circ f$, if they exist.

4. $f = \{(-9, -1), (-1, 0), (3, 4)\}$
$g = \{(0, -9), (-1, 3), (4, -1)\}$
$\{(0, -1), (-1, 4), (4, 0)\}$; $\{(-9, 3), (-1, -9), (3, -1)\}$

5. $f = \{(-4, 3), (0, -2), (1, -2)\}$
$g = \{(-2, 0), (3, 1)\}$
$\{(-2, -2), (3, -2)\}$; $\{(-4, 1), (0, 0), (1, 0)\}$

6. $f = \{(-4, -5), (0, 3), (1, 6)\}$
$g = \{(6, 1), (-5, 0), (3, -4)\}$
$\{(6, 6), (-5, 3), (3, -5)\}$; $\{(-4, 0), (0, -4), (1, 1)\}$

7. $f = \{(0, -3), (1, -3), (6, 8)\}$
$g = \{(8, 2), (-3, 0), (-3, 1)\}$
does not exist; $\{(0, 0), (1, 0), (6, 2)\}$

Find $[g \circ h](x)$ and $[h \circ g](x)$, if they exist.

8. $g(x) = 3x$, $h(x) = x - 4$ **$3x - 12$; $3x - 4$**

9. $g(x) = -8x$, $h(x) = 2x + 3$ **$-16x - 24$; $-16x + 3$**

10. $g(x) = x + 6$, $h(x) = 3x^2$ **$3x^2 + 36x + 108$**

11. $g(x) = x + 3$, $h(x) = 2x^2$ **$2x^2 + 3$; $2x^2 + 12x + 18$**

12. $g(x) = -2x$, $h(x) = x^2 + 3x + 2$ **$-2x^2 - 6x - 4$; $4x^2 - 6x + 2$**

13. $g(x) = x - 2$, $h(x) = 3x^2 + 1$ **$3x^2 - 1$; $3x^2 - 12x + 13$**

If $f(x) = x^2$, $g(x) = 5x$, and $h(x) = x + 4$, find each value.

14. $f[g(1)]$ **25**
15. $g[h(-2)]$ **10**
16. $h[f(4)]$ **20**
17. $f[h(-9)]$ **25**
18. $h[g(-3)]$ **−11**
19. $g[f(8)]$ **320**

20. **BUSINESS** The function $f(x) = 1000 - 0.01x^2$ models the manufacturing cost per item when x items are produced, and $g(x) = 150 - 0.001x^2$ models the service cost per item. Write a function $C(x)$ for the total manufacturing and service cost per item. **$C(x) = 1150 - 0.011x^2$**

21. **MEASUREMENT** The formula $f = \frac{n}{12}$ converts inches n to feet f, and $m = \frac{f}{5280}$ converts feet to miles m. Write a composition of functions that converts inches to miles. **$[m \circ f](n) = \frac{n}{63{,}360}$**

Chapter 7 — 8 — Glencoe Algebra 2

Word Problem Practice
CRM p. 9 AL OL BL ELL

7-1 Word Problem Practice
Operations on Functions

1. **AREA** Bernard wants to know the area of a figure made by joining an equilateral triangle and square along an edge. The function $f(s) = \frac{\sqrt{3}}{4}s^2$ gives the area of an equilateral triangle with side s. The function $g(s) = s^2$ gives the area of a square with side s. What function $h(s)$ gives the area of the figure as a function of its side length s?

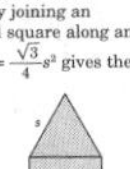

$h(s) = (f + g)(s) = \left(\frac{\sqrt{3}}{4} + 1\right)s^2$

2. **PRICING** A computer company decides to continuously adjust the pricing of and discounts to its products in an effort to remain competitive. The function $P(t)$ gives the sale price of its Super2000 computer as a function of time. The function $D(t)$ gives the value of a special discount it offers to valued customers. How much would valued customers have to pay for one Super2000 computer? **$(P - D)(t)$**

3. **LAVA** The temperature of lava has been measured at up to 2000°F. A freshly ejected lava rock immediately begins to cool down. The temperature of the lava rock in degrees Fahrenheit as a function of time is given by $T(t)$. Let $C(F)$ be the function that gives degrees Celsius as a function of degrees Fahrenheit. What function gives the temperature of the lava rock in degrees Celsius as a function of time? **$C[T(t)]$**

4. **ENGINEERING** A group of engineers is designing a staple gun. One team determines that the speed of impact s of the staple (in feet per second) as a function of the handle length ℓ (in inches) is given by $s(\ell) = 40 + 3\ell$. A second team determines that the number of sheets N that can be stapled as a function of the impact speed is given by $N(s) = \frac{s - 10}{3}$. What function gives N as a function of ℓ? **$N[s(\ell)] = 10 + \ell$**

5. **HOT AIR BALLOONS** Hannah and Terry went on a one-hour hot air balloon ride. Let $T(A)$ be the outside air temperature as a function of altitude and let $A(t)$ be the altitude of the balloon as a function of time.

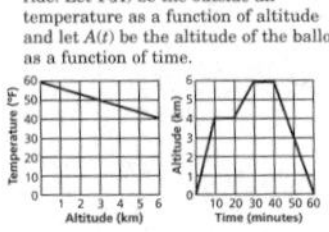

a. What function describes the air temperature Hannah and Terry felt at different times during their trip? **$T[A(t)]$**

b. Sketch a graph of the function you wrote for part **a** based on the graphs for $T(A)$ and $A(t)$ that are given.

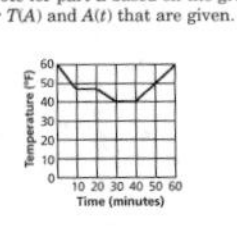

Chapter 7 — 9 — Glencoe Algebra 2

Lesson 7-1

For each pair of functions, find $f \circ g$ and $g \circ f$, if they exist. **21–26. See margin.**

21. $f = \{(-15, -5), (-4, 12), (1, 7), (3, 9)\}$
$g = \{(3, -9), (7, 2), (8, -6), (12, 0)\}$

22. $f = \{(-1, 11), (2, -2), (5, -7), (4, -4)\}$
$g = \{(5, -4), (4, -3), (-1, 2), (2, 3)\}$

23. $f = \{(7, -3), (-10, -3), (-7, -8), (-3, 6)\}$
$g = \{(4, -3), (3, -7), (9, 8), (-4, -4)\}$

24. $f = \{(1, -1), (2, -2), (3, -3), (4, -4)\}$
$g = \{(1, -4), (2, -3), (3, -2), (4, -1)\}$

25. $f = \{(-4, -1), (-2, 6), (-1, 10), (4, 11)\}$
$g = \{(-1, 5), (3, -4), (6, 4), (10, 8)\}$

26. $f = \{(12, -3), (9, -2), (8, -1), (6, 3)\}$
$g = \{(-1, 5), (-2, 6), (-3, -1), (-4, 8)\}$

Find $[f \circ g](x)$ and $[g \circ f](x)$, if they exist. **27–35. See margin.**

27. $f(x) = 2x$, $g(x) = x + 5$

28. $f(x) = -3x$, $g(x) = -x + 8$

29. $f(x) = x + 5$, $g(x) = 3x - 7$

30. $f(x) = x - 4$, $g(x) = x^2 - 10$

31. $f(x) = x^2 + 6x - 2$, $g(x) = x - 6$

32. $f(x) = 2x^2 - x + 1$, $g(x) = 4x + 3$

33. $f(x) = 4x - 1$, $g(x) = x^3 + 2$

34. $f(x) = x^2 + 3x + 1$, $g(x) = x^2$

35. $f(x) = 2x^2$, $g(x) = 8x^2 + 3x$

Real-World Link

The main distinguishing characteristic of HDTV is the exclusive use of the 16:9 aspect ratio to deliver a widescreen viewing experience that more closely resembles the human field of vision.

Source: TV Authority

36. **FINANCE** A ceramics store manufactures and sells coffee mugs. The revenue $r(x)$ from the sale of x coffee mugs is given by $r(x) = 6.5x$. Suppose the function for the cost of manufacturing x coffee mugs is $c(x) = 0.75x + 1850$.
a. Write the profit function. **$P(x) = 5.75x - 1850$**
b. Find the profit on 500, 1000, and 5000 coffee mugs. **$P(500) = \$1025$; $P(1000) = \$3900$; $P(5000) = \$26{,}900$**

37. **SHOPPING** Ms. Smith wants to buy an HDTV, which is on sale for 35% off the original price of \$2299. The sales tax is 6.25%.
a. Write two functions representing the price after the discount $p(x)$ and the price after sales tax $t(x)$. **$p(x) = 0.65x$; $t(x) = 1.0625x$**
b. Which composition of functions represents the price of the HDTV, $[p \circ t](x)$ or $[t \circ p](x)$? Explain your reasoning.
c. How much will Ms. Smith pay for the HDTV? **\$1587.75**
37b. Since $[p \circ t](x) = [t \circ p](x)$, either function represents the price.

B

Perform each operation if $f(x) = x^2 + x - 12$ and $g(x) = x - 3$. State the domain of the resulting function.

38. $(f - g)(x)$

39. $2(g \cdot f)(x)$

40. $\left(\frac{f}{g}\right)(x)$

38. $(f - g)(x) = x^2 - 9$; D = {all real numbers}
39. $2(g \cdot f)(x) = 2x^3 - 4x^2 - 30x + 72$; D = {all real numbers}
40. $\left(\frac{f}{g}\right)(x) = x + 4$; D = $\{x \mid x \neq 3\}$

If $f(x) = 5x$, $g(x) = -2x + 1$, and $h(x) = x^2 + 6x + 8$, find each value.

41. $f[g(-2)]$ **25**

42. $g[h(3)]$ **−69**

43. $h[f(-5)]$ **483**

44. $h[g(2)]$ **−1**

45. $f[h(-3)]$ **−5**

46. $h[f(9)]$ **2303**

47. $f[g(3a)]$ **$-30a + 5$**

48. $f[h(a + 4)]$ **$5a^2 + 70a + 240$**

49. $g[f(a^2 - a)]$ **$-10a^2 + 10a + 1$**

50. **MULTIPLE REPRESENTATIONS** Let $f(x) = x^2$ and $g(x) = x$.
a. **TABULAR** Make a table showing values for $f(x)$, $g(x)$, $(f + g)(x)$, and $(f - g)(x)$.
b. **GRAPHICAL** Graph $f(x)$, $g(x)$, and $(f + g)(x)$ on the same coordinate grid.
c. **GRAPHICAL** Graph $f(x)$, $g(x)$, and $(f - g)(x)$ on the same coordinate grid.
d. **VERBAL** Describe the relationship among the graphs of $f(x)$, $g(x)$, $(f + g)(x)$, and $(f - g)(x)$.

50a–d. See Chapter 7 Answer Appendix.

Enrichment
CRM p. 10 OL BL

7-1 Enrichment

Relative Maximum Values

The graph of $f(x) = x^3 - 6x - 9$ shows a relative maximum value somewhere between $f(-2)$ and $f(-1)$. You can obtain a closer approximation by comparing values such as those shown in the table.

To the nearest tenth a relative maximum value for $f(x)$ is −3.3.

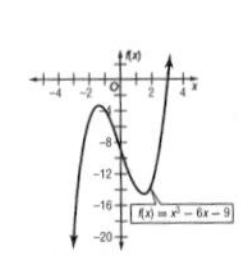

x	f(x)
−2	−5
−1.5	−3.375
−1.4	−3.344
−1.3	−3.397
−1	−4

Using a calculator to find points, graph each function. To the nearest tenth, find a relative maximum value of the function.

1. $f(x) = x(x^2 - 3)$ **rel. max. of 2.0**

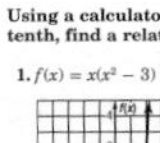

2. $f(x) = x^3 - 3x - 3$ **rel. max. of −1.0**

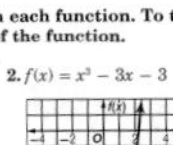

Additional Answers

21. $f \circ g$ is undefined; $g \circ f = \{(-4, 0), (1, 2)\}$.

22. $f \circ g = \{(-1, -2)\}$; $g \circ f$ is undefined.

23. $f \circ g = \{(4, 6), (3, -8)\}$; $g \circ f$ is undefined.

Real-World Link

Recently, 21.7 million, or about 58% of the 16- to 24-year-olds, were employed in the United States.

Source: U.S. Bureau of Labor and Statistics

51b. The function represents the difference in the number of men and women employed in the U.S.

59. Sample answer: $f(x) = x - 9$, $g(x) = x + 5$

60. Tobias; Chris did not substitute $g(x)$ for every x in $f(x)$.

63. Compositions of functions are used when the value of a function is determined by another function. For example, the product of a manufacturing plant may have to go through several processes in a particular order, in which each process is described by a function.

51. **EMPLOYMENT** The number of women and men age 16 and over employed each year in the United States can be modeled by the following equations, where x is the number of years since 1994 and y is the number of people in thousands.
women: $y = 1086.4x + 56{,}610$
men: $y = 999.2x + 66{,}450$

a. Write a function that models the total number of men and women employed in the United States during this time. **$y = 2085.6x + 123{,}060$**

b. If f is the function for the number of men, and g is the function for the number of women, what does $(f - g)(x)$ represent?

C

If $f(x) = x + 2$, $g(x) = -4x + 3$, and $h(x) = x^2 - 2x + 1$, find each value.

52. $(f \cdot g \cdot h)(3)$ **-180**

53. $[(f + g) \cdot h](1)$ **0**

54. $\left(\frac{h}{fg}\right)(-6)$ **$-\frac{49}{108}$**

55. $[f \circ (g \circ h)](2)$ **1**

56. $[g \circ (h \circ f)](-4)$ **-33**

57. $[h \circ (f \circ g)](5)$ **256**

58. **MULTIPLE REPRESENTATIONS** You will explore $(f \cdot g)$ and $\left(\frac{f}{g}\right)$ if $f(x) = x^2 + 1$ and $g(x) = x - 3$.

a. **TABULAR** Copy and complete the table.

x	$(f \cdot g)(x)$	$\left(\frac{f}{g}\right)(x)$
1	−4	−1
2	−5	−5
3	0	undef.
4	17	17
5	52	13

b. **GRAPHICAL** Graph $(f \cdot g)$ and $\left(\frac{f}{g}\right)$ on the same coordinate grid. **See margin.**

c. **VERBAL** Explain the relationship between $(f \cdot g)$ and $\left(\frac{f}{g}\right)$. **Sample answer: When x is 2 or 4 the functions are equal.**

H.O.T. Problems

Use Higher-Order Thinking Skills

59. **OPEN ENDED** Write two functions $f(x)$ and $g(x)$ such that $(f \circ g)(4) = 0$.

60. **ERROR ANALYSIS** Chris and Tobias are finding the composition $(f \circ g)(x)$, where $f(x) = x^2 + 2x - 8$ and $g(x) = x^2 + 8$. Is either of them correct? Explain your reasoning.

Chris	Tobias
$(f \circ g)(x) = f[g(x)]$	$(f \circ g)(x) = f[g(x)]$
$= (x^2 + 8)^2 + 2x - 8$	$= (x^2 + 8)^2 + 2(x^2 + 8) - 8$
$= x^4 + 16x^2 + 64 + 2x - 8$	$= x^4 + 16x^2 + 64 + 2x^2 + 16 - 8$
$= x^4 + 16x^2 + 2x + 58$	$= x^4 + 18x^2 + 72$

61. **CHALLENGE** Given $f(x) = \sqrt{x^3}$ and $g(x) = \sqrt{x^6}$, determine the restrictions on the domain for the following.

a. $g(x) \cdot g(x)$ **D = {all real numbers}**

b. $f(x) \cdot f(x)$ **$D = \{x \mid x \geq 0\}$**

62. **REASONING** State whether each statement is *sometimes*, *always*, or *never* true. Explain your reasoning.

a. The domain of two functions $f(x)$ and $g(x)$ that are composed $g[f(x)]$ is restricted by the domain of $f(x)$. **always**

b. The domain of two functions $f(x)$ and $g(x)$ that are composed $g[f(x)]$ is restricted by the domain of $g(x)$. **sometimes**

63. **WRITING IN MATH** Explain why a person would perform a composition of functions. Include a real-world example that you could solve by using composition of functions.

Watch Out!

Error Analysis For Exercise 60, remind students that they will be finding $f(x^2 + 8)$. So every x in $x^2 + 2x - 8$ will be replaced with $x^2 + 8$.

Multiple Representations In Exercise 58, students use a table of values, a graph, and analysis to compare and contrast the product and the quotient of two functions.

Additional Answers

24. $f \circ g$ is undefined; $g \circ f$ is undefined.

25. $f \circ g = \{(3, -1), (6, 11)\}$; $g \circ f = \{(-4, 5), (-2, 4), (-1, 8)\}$

26. $f \circ g = \{(-2, 3), (-4, -1)\}$; $g \circ f = \{(12, -1), (9, 6), (8, 5)\}$

27. $[f \circ g](x) = 2x + 10$; $[g \circ f](x) = 2x + 5$

28. $[f \circ g](x) = 3x - 24$; $[g \circ f](x) = 3x + 8$

29. $[f \circ g](x) = 3x - 2$; $[g \circ f](x) = 3x + 8$

30. $[f \circ g](x) = x^2 - 14$; $[g \circ f](x) = x^2 - 8x + 6$

31. $[f \circ g](x) = x^2 - 6x - 2$; $[g \circ f](x) = x^2 + 6x - 8$

32. $[f \circ g](x) = 32x^2 + 44x + 16$; $[g \circ f](x) = 8x^2 - 4x + 7$

33. $[f \circ g](x) = 4x^3 + 7$; $[g \circ f](x) = 64x^3 - 48x^2 + 12x + 1$

34. $[f \circ g](x) = x^4 + 3x^2 + 1$; $[g \circ f](x) = x^4 + 6x^3 + 11x^2 + 6x + 1$

35. $[f \circ g](x) = 128x^4 + 96x^3 + 18x^2$; $[g \circ f](x) = 32x^4 + 6x^2$

58b.

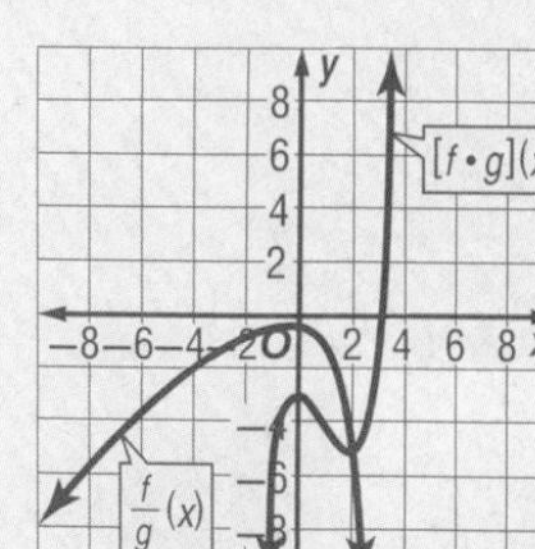

Differentiated Instruction

OL BL

Extension Many states use function compositions to calculate speeding ticket amounts. They do this be calculating the nuber of miles over the speed limit a driver is traveling, multiplying this number by a per mile charge, and adding a flat rate. Ask students to create a composition of three different functions, substituting made-up or reserarched values for the posted speed limit, the per mile charge, and the flat rate. The function composition should be of the form $(f \circ g \circ h)(x)$ where x is the speed of the driver in miles per hour.

4 ASSESS

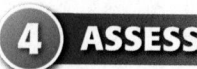

Name the Math Have students tell a partner or write on a piece of paper the mathematical procedure they would use to determine their tax savings by having medical expenses deducted before they receive their pay. Some medical expenses can be paid from a special medical savings account that is not taxed. composition of functions

NGSSS PRACTICE 912.A.3.1, 912.A.2.7, 912.A.2.8

64. What is the value of x in the equation $7(x - 4) = 44 - 11x$? **D**

A. 1
B. 2
C. 3
D. 4

65. If $g(x) = x^2 + 9x + 21$ and $h(x) = 2(x + 5)^2$, which is an equivalent form of $h(x) - g(x)$? **G**

F. $k(x) = -x^2 - 11x - 29$
G. $k(x) = x^2 + 11x + 29$
H. $k(x) = x + 4$
I. $k(x) = x^2 + 7x + 11$

66. **GRIDDED RESPONSE** In his first three years of coaching basketball at North High School, Coach Lucas' team won 8 games the first year, 17 games the second year, and 6 games the third year. How many games does the team need to win in the fourth year so the coach's average will be 10 wins per year? **9**

67. **ACT/SAT** What is the value of $f[g(6)]$ if $f(x) = 2x + 4$ and $g(x) = x^2 + 5$? **C**

A. 38
B. 43
C. 86
D. 261

Spiral Review

Find all of the rational zeros of each function. (Lesson 6-8)

68. $f(x) = 2x^3 - 13x^2 + 17x + 12$ $-\frac{1}{2}, 3, 4$

69. $f(x) = x^3 - 3x^2 - 10x + 24$ $-3, 2, 4$

70. $f(x) = x^4 - 4x^3 - 7x^2 + 34x - 24$ $1, 2, 4, -3$

71. $f(x) = 2x^3 - 5x^2 - 28x + 15$ $-3, 5, \frac{1}{2}$

State the possible number of positive real zeros, negative real zeros, and imaginary zeros of each function. (Lesson 6-7)

72. $f(x) = 2x^4 - x^3 + 5x^2 + 3x - 9$ 3 or 1; 1; 2 or 0

73. $f(x) = -4x^4 - x^2 - x + 1$ 1; 1; 2

74. $f(x) = 3x^4 - x^3 + 8x^2 + x - 7$ 3 or 1; 1; 0 or 2

75. $f(x) = 2x^4 - 3x^3 - 2x^2 + 3$ 2 or 0; 2 or 0; 4, 2, or 0

76. **MANUFACTURING** A box measures 12 inches by 16 inches by 18 inches. The manufacturer will increase each dimension of the box by the same number of inches and have a new volume of 5985 cubic inches. How much should be added to each dimension? (Lesson 6-7) **3 in.**

Solve each system of equations. (Lesson 3-5)

77. $x + 4y - z = 6$ $(1, 2, 3)$
$3x + 2y + 3z = 16$
$2x - y + z = 3$

78. $2a + b - c = 5$ $(4, -2, 1)$
$a - b + 3c = 9$
$3a - 6c = 6$

79. $y + z = 4$ $(3, -1, 5)$
$2x + 4y - z = -3$
$3y = -3$

80. **INTERNET** A webmaster estimates that the time, in seconds, to connect to the server when n people are connecting is given by $t(n) = 0.005n + 0.3$. Estimate the time to connect when 50 people are connecting. (Lesson 2-2) **0.55 second**

Skills Review

81. $x = \frac{12 + 7y}{5}$ 82. $y = \frac{1 - x^2}{-2x}$ 83. $x = \frac{15 - 8yz}{4}$

Solve each equation or formula for the specified variable. (Lesson 1-3)

81. $5x - 7y = 12$, for x

82. $3x^2 - 6xy + 1 = 4$, for y

83. $4x + 8yz = 15$, for x

84. $D = mv$, for m $m = \frac{D}{v}$

85. $A = k^2 + b$, for k $k = \pm\sqrt{A - b}$

86. $(x + 2)^2 - (y + 5)^2 = 4$, for y $y = \pm\sqrt{(x + 2)^2 - 4} - 5$

7-2 Inverse Functions and Relations

Why?

The table shows the value of $1 (U.S.) compared to Canadian dollars and Mexican pesos.

The equation $p = 10.75d$ represents the number of pesos p you can receive for every U.S. dollar d. To determine how many U.S. dollars you can receive for one Mexican peso, solve the equation $p = 10.75d$ for d. The result, $d \approx 0.09p$, is the inverse function.

	U.S.	Canada	Mexico
U.S.		1.05	10.75
Canada	0.95		10.26
Mexico	0.09	0.10	

Then
You transformed and solved equations for a specific variable. (Lesson 1-3)

Now
- Find the inverse of a function or relation.
- Determine whether two functions or relations are inverses.

NGSSS
MA.912.A.2.11 Solve problems involving functions and their inverses.

New Vocabulary
inverse relation
inverse function

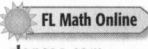

FL Math Online
glencoe.com

Find Inverses Recall that a relation is a set of ordered pairs. The **inverse relation** is the set of ordered pairs obtained by exchanging the coordinates of each ordered pair. The domain of a relation becomes the range of its inverse, and the range of the relation becomes the domain of its inverse.

Key Concept — Inverse Relations

Words Two relations are inverse relations if and only if whenever one relation contains the element (a, b), the other relation contains the element (b, a).

Example A and B are inverse relations.

$A = \{(1, 5), (2, 6), (3, 7)\}$ $B = \{(5, 1), (6, 2), (7, 3)\}$

EXAMPLE 1 Find an Inverse Relation

GEOMETRY The vertices of $\triangle ABC$ can be represented by the relation $\{(1, -2), (2, 5), (4, -1)\}$. Find the inverse of this relation. Describe the graph of the inverse.

Graph the relation. To find the inverse, exchange the coordinates of the ordered pairs. The inverse of the relation is $\{(-2, 1), (5, 2), (-1, 4)\}$.

Plotting these points shows that the ordered pairs describe the vertices of $\triangle A'B'C'$ after a reflection in the line $y = x$.

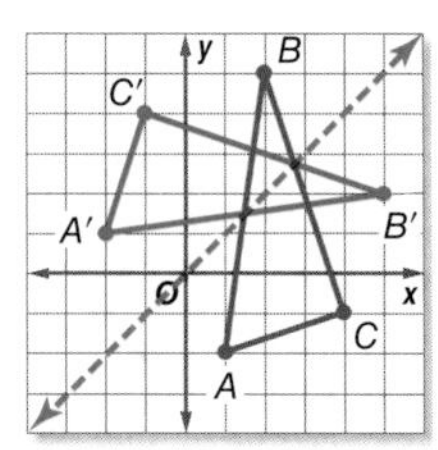

Guided Practice

1. **GEOMETRY** The ordered pairs of the relation $\{(-8, -3), (-8, -6), (-3, -6)\}$ are the coordinates of the vertices of a right triangle. Find the inverse of this relation. Describe the graph of the inverse. $\{(-3, -8), (-6, -8), (-6, -3)\}$; It is a reflection in the line $y - x$.

Personal Tutor glencoe.com

As with relations, the ordered pairs of **inverse functions** are also related. We can write the inverse of the function $f(x)$ as $f^{-1}(x)$.

7-2 Lesson Notes

1 FOCUS

Vertical Alignment

Before Lesson 7-2
Transform and solve equations for a specific variable.

Lesson 7-2
Find the inverse of a function or relation.
Determine whether two functions or relations are inverses.

After Lesson 7-2
Develop the definition of logarithm by exploring the relationship between exponential functions and their inverses.

2 TEACH

Scaffolding Questions

Have students read the *Why?* section of the lesson.

Ask:

- According to the table, how many Canadian dollars can you get for 5 U.S. dollars? for 10 U.S. dollars? 5.25, 10.50
- How many U.S. dollars can you get for 1 Canadian dollar? for 5 Canadian dollars? $0.95; $4.75
- What are the reciprocals of 1.05 and 10.75? Do the reciprocals appear in the table? $\frac{1}{1.05} \approx 0.95$; $\frac{1}{10.75} \approx 0.09$; the values 0.95 and 0.09 do appear in the table.

Lesson 7-2 Resources

Resource	Approaching-Level	On-Level	Beyond-Level	English Learners
Teacher Edition	• Differentiated Instruction, p. 419	• Differentiated Instruction, pp. 419, 422	• Differentiated Instruction, p. 422	
Chapter Resource Masters	• Study Guide and Intervention, pp. 12–13 • Skills Practice, p. 14 • Practice, p. 15 • Word Problem Practice, p. 16	• Study Guide and Intervention, pp. 12–13 • Skills Practice, p. 14 • Practice, p. 15 • Word Problem Practice, p. 16 • Enrichment, p. 17 • Graphing Calculator Activity, p. 18	• Practice, p. 15 • Word Problem Practice, p. 16 • Enrichment, p. 17	• Study Guide and Intervention, pp. 12–13 • Skills Practice, p.14 • Practice, p. 15 • Word Problem Practice, p. 16
Transparencies	• 5-Minute Check Transparency 7-2	• 5-Minute Check Transparency 7-2	• 5-Minute Check Transparency 7-2	• 5-Minute Check Transparency 7-2
Other	• Study Notebook • Teaching Algebra with Manipulatives	• Study Notebook • Teaching Algebra with Manipulatives	• Study Notebook	• Study Notebook • Teaching Algebra with Manipulatives

Find Inverses

Example 1 shows how to find the inverse relation for a set of ordered pairs. **Example 2** shows how to find the inverse of a function and graph it.

Formative Assessment

Use the Guided Practice exercises after each example to determine students' understanding of concepts.

Additional Examples

1 **GEOMETRY** The ordered pairs of the relation {(1, 3), (6, 3), (6, 0), (1, 0)} are the coordinates of the vertices of a rectangle. Find the inverse of this relation. Describe the graph of the inverse. The inverse of the relation is {(3, 1), (3, 6), (0, 6), (0, 1)}. The ordered pairs are the vertices of a rectangle; the vertices are the original vertices reflected across the line $y = x$.

2 Find the inverse of $f(x) = -\frac{1}{2}x + 1$. Then graph the function and its inverse. $f^{-1}(x) = -2x + 2$

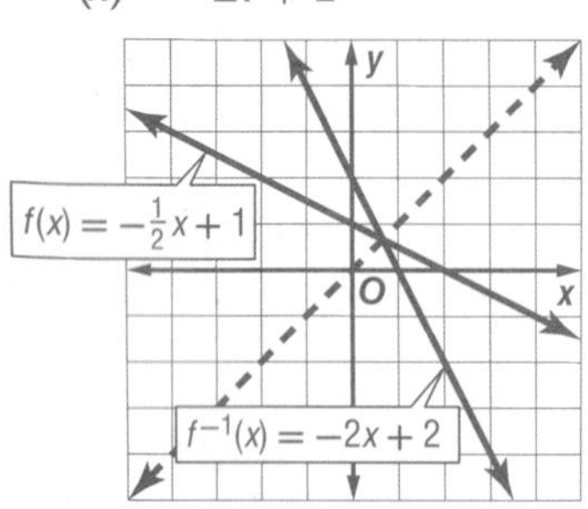

Additional Examples also in Interactive Classroom PowerPoint® Presentations

IWB INTERACTIVE WHITEBOARD READY

ReadingMath

Inverse Functions f^{-1} is read *f inverse* or *the inverse of f.* Note that -1 is *not* an exponent.

Key Concept Property of Inverses

Words If f and f^{-1} are inverses, then $f(a) = b$ if and only if $f^{-1}(b) = a$.

Example Let $f(x) = x - 4$ and represent its inverse as $f^{-1}(x) = x + 4$.

Evaluate $f(6)$.	Evaluate $f^{-1}(2)$.
$f(x) = x - 4$	$f^{-1}(x) = x + 4$
$f(6) = 6 - 4$ or 2	$f^{-1}(2) = 2 + 4$ or 6

Because $f(x)$ and $f^{-1}(x)$ are inverses, $f(6) = 2$ and $f^{-1}(2) = 6$.

When the inverse of a function is a function, the original function is one-to-one. Recall that the vertical line test can be used to determine whether a relation is a function. Similarly, the *horizontal line test* can be used to determine whether the inverse of a function is also a function.

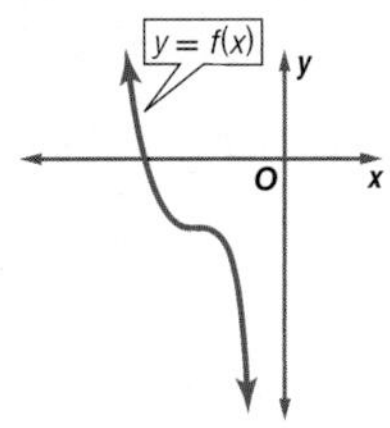

No horizontal line can be drawn so that it passes through more than one point. The inverse of $y = f(x)$ is a function.

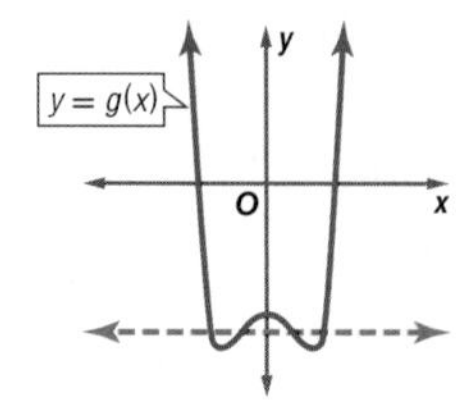

A horizontal line can be drawn that passes through more than one point. The inverse of $y = g(x)$ is not a function.

The inverse of a function can be found by exchanging the domain and the range.

EXAMPLE 2 Find and Graph an Inverse

Find the inverse of each function. Then graph the function and its inverse.

a. $f(x) = 2x - 5$

Step 1 Rewrite the function as an equation relating x and y.
$f(x) = 2x - 5 \rightarrow y = 2x - 5$

Step 2 Exchange x and y in the equation. $x = 2y - 5$

Step 3 Solve the equation for y.

$x = 2y - 5$ **Inverse of $y = 2x - 5$**

$x + 5 = 2y$ **Add 5 to each side.**

$\frac{x + 5}{2} = y$ **Divide each side by 2.**

Step 4 Replace y with $f^{-1}(x)$.

$y = \frac{x + 5}{2} \rightarrow f^{-1}(x) = \frac{x + 5}{2}$

The inverse of $f(x) = 2x - 5$ is $f^{-1}(x) = \frac{x + 5}{2}$. The graph of $f^{-1}(x) = \frac{x + 5}{2}$ is the reflection of the graph of $f(x) = 2x - 5$ in the line $y = x$.

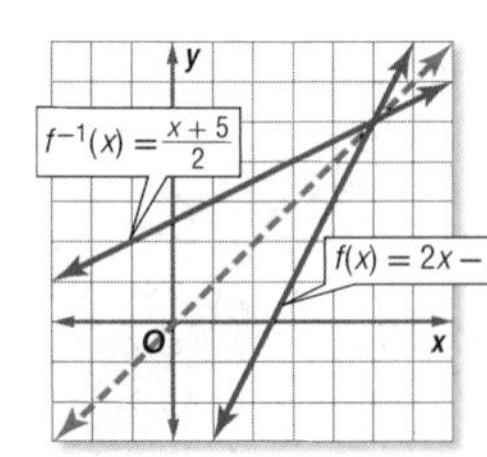

TEACH with TECH

AUDIO RECORDING Have students create audio recordings explaining how to find the inverse of a function. Also have students explain how they can check if two given functions are inverses of each other.

StudyTip

Functions The inverse of the function in part **b** is not a function since it does not pass the vertical line test.

b. $f(x) = x^2 + 1$

Step 1 $f(x) = x^2 + 1 \rightarrow y = x^2 + 1$

Step 2 $x = y^2 + 1$

Step 3
$$x = y^2 + 1$$
$$x - 1 = y^2$$
$$\pm\sqrt{x - 1} = y$$
Take the square root of each side.

Step 4 $y = \pm\sqrt{x - 1}$

Graph $y = \pm\sqrt{x - 1}$ by reflecting the graph of $f(x) = x^2 + 1$ in the line $y = x$.

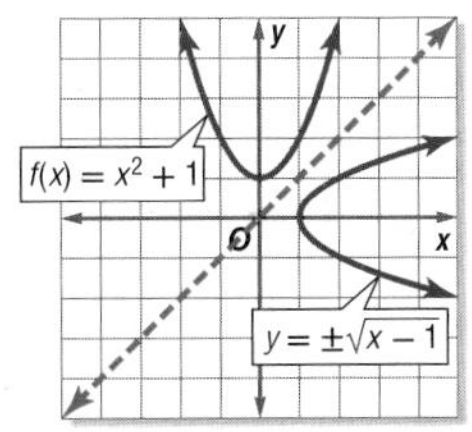

Guided Practice 2A, 2B. See margin.

Find the inverse of each function. Then graph the function and its inverse.

2A. $f(x) = \frac{x - 3}{5}$

2B. $f(x) = 3x^2$

Personal Tutor glencoe.com

Review Vocabulary

identity function the function $f(x) = x$ (Lesson 2-7)

Verifying Inverses You can determine whether two functions are inverses by finding both of their compositions. If both compositions equal the identity function $I(x) = x$, then the functions are inverse functions.

Key Concept Inverse Functions

Words	Two functions f and g are inverse functions if and only if both of their compositions are the identity function.
Symbols	$f(x)$ and $g(x)$ are inverses if and only if $[f \circ g](x) = x$ and $[g \circ f](x) = x$.

EXAMPLE 3 Verify that Two Functions are Inverses

Determine whether each pair of functions are inverse functions. Explain your reasoning.

a. $f(x) = 3x + 9$ **and** $g(x) = \frac{1}{3}x - 3$

Verify that the compositions of $f(x)$ and $g(x)$ are identity functions.

$$[f \circ g](x) = f[g(x)] \qquad [g \circ f](x) = g[f(x)]$$
$$= f\left(\tfrac{1}{3}x - 3\right) \qquad = g(3x + 9)$$
$$= 3\left(\tfrac{1}{3}x - 3\right) + 9 \qquad = \tfrac{1}{3}(3x + 9) - 3$$
$$= x - 9 + 9 \text{ or } x \qquad = x + 3 - 3 \text{ or } x$$

The functions are inverses because $[f \circ g](x) = [g \circ f](x) = x$.

b. $f(x) = 4x^2$ **and** $g(x) = 2\sqrt{x}$

$$[f \circ g](x) = f\left(2\sqrt{x}\right)$$
$$= 4\left(2\sqrt{x}\right)^2$$
$$= 4(4x) \text{ or } 16x$$

Because $[f \circ g](x) \neq x$, $f(x)$ and $g(x)$ are not inverses.

Watch Out!

Inverse Functions Be sure to check both $[f \circ g](x)$ and $[g \circ f](x)$ to verify that functions are inverses. By definition, both compositions must be the identity function.

Guided Practice

3A. $f(x) = 3x - 3$, $g(x) = \frac{1}{3}x + 4$

3B. $f(x) = 2x^2 - 1$, $g(x) = \sqrt{\frac{x + 1}{2}}$

Personal Tutor glencoe.com

3A. No; they are not inverse functions because $[f \circ g](x) = x + 9$ and $[g \circ f](x) = x + 3$.

3B. Yes; they are inverse functions because $[f \circ g](x) = x$ and $[g \circ f](x) = x$.

Tips for New Teachers

Sense-Making Some students may confuse the symbols f^{-1} and $\frac{1}{f}$ for a function f. Tell students that generally, the notation f^{-1} refers to the inverse of f, while $\frac{1}{f}$ refers to the reciprocal of f.

Verifying Inverses

Example 3 shows how to verify that two functions are inverses.

Additional Example

3 Determine whether $f(x) = \frac{3}{4}x - 6$ and $g(x) = \frac{4}{3}x + 8$ are inverse functions. Explain your reasoning. The functions are inverses since both $[f \circ g](x)$ and $[g \circ f](x)$ equal x.

Additional Answers (Guided Practice)

2A. $f^{-1}(x) = 5x + 3$

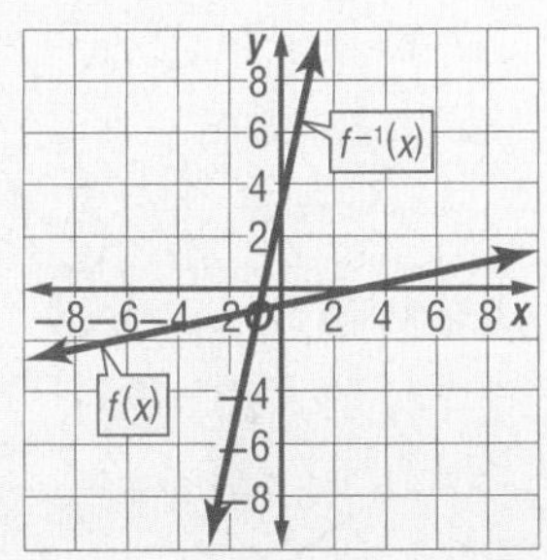

2B. $y = \pm\sqrt{\frac{1}{3}x}$

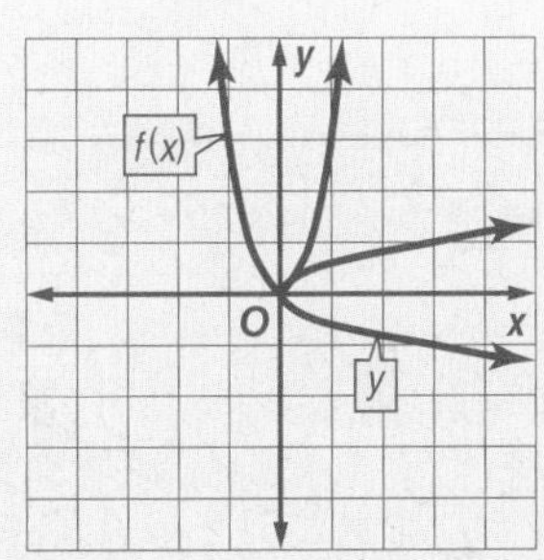

Differentiated Instruction AL OL

Kinesthetic Learners On a large coordinate grid, students model the graph of the identity function $f(x) = x$ using a length of string, a piece of uncooked spaghetti, or something similar. Then place a second length of string to model the graph of $f(x) = 2x - 5$ from Example 2. Have students model the graph of the inverse of this function and relate the graphs of the function, and its inverse, to the graph of $f(x) = x$.

3 PRACTICE

Formative Assessment

Use Exercises 1–8 to check for understanding.

Use the chart at the bottom of this page to customize assignments for your students.

Additional Answers

3. $f^{-1}(x) = -\frac{1}{3}x$

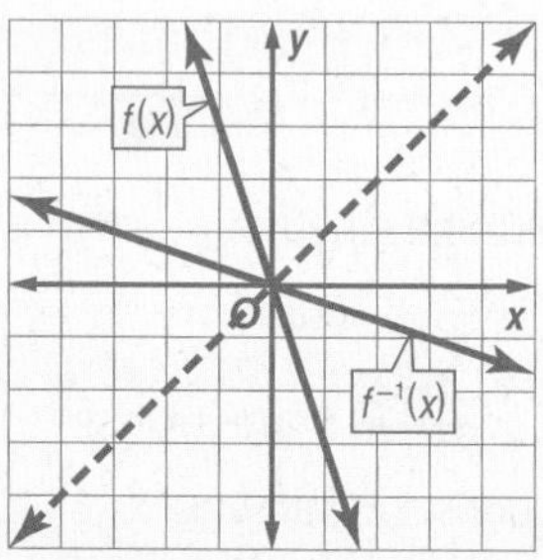

4. $g^{-1}(x) = \frac{x+6}{4}$

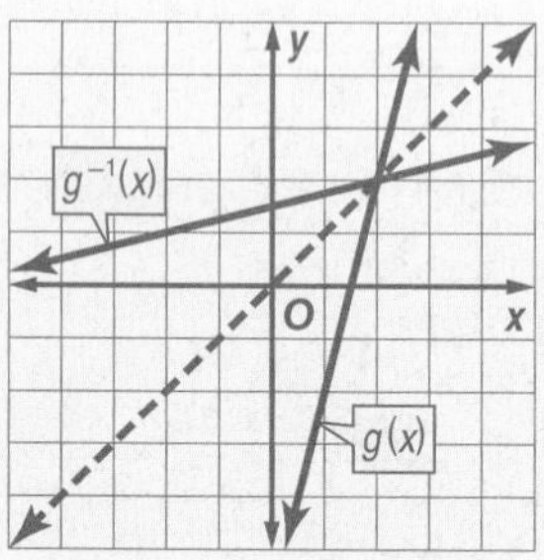

5. $y = \pm\sqrt{x+3}$

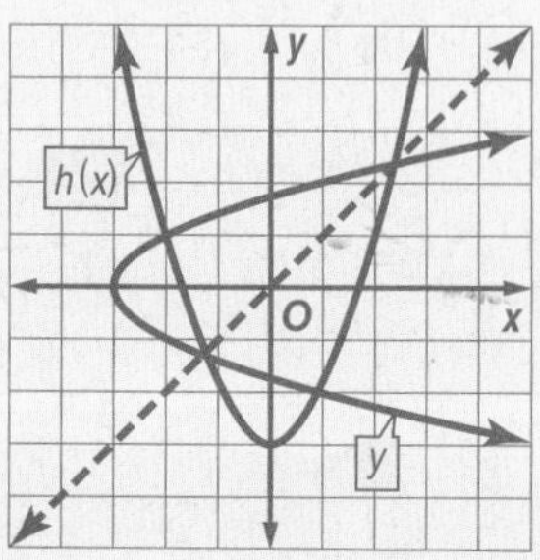

Check Your Understanding

Example 1 p. 417

Find the inverse of each relation.

1. $\{(-9, 10), (1, -3), (8, -5)\}$ **{(10, −9), (−3, 1), (−5, 8)}**
2. $\{(-2, 9), (4, -1), (-7, 9), (7, 0)\}$ **{(9, −2), (−1, 4), (9, −7), (0, 7)}**

Example 2 pp. 418–419

Find the inverse of each function. Then graph the function and its inverse. **3–5. See margin.**

3. $f(x) = -3x$
4. $g(x) = 4x - 6$
5. $h(x) = x^2 - 3$

Example 3 p. 419

Determine whether each pair of functions are inverse functions. Write *yes* or *no*.

6. $f(x) = x - 7$; $g(x) = x + 7$ **yes**
7. $f(x) = \frac{1}{2}x + \frac{3}{4}$; $g(x) = 2x - \frac{4}{3}$ **no**
8. $f(x) = 2x^3$; $g(x) = \frac{1}{3}\sqrt{x}$ **no**

Practice and Problem Solving

= **Step-by-Step Solutions** begin on page R20. **Extra Practice** begins on page 947.

Example 1 p. 417

Find the inverse of each relation.

9. $\{(-8, 6), (6, -2), (7, -3)\}$ **{(6, −8), (−2, 6), (−3, 7)}**
10. $\{(7, 7), (4, 9), (3, -7)\}$ **{(7, 7), (9, 4), (−7, 3)}**
11. $\{(8, -1), (-8, -1), (-2, -8), (2, 8)\}$ **{(−1, 8), (−1, −8), (−8, −2), (8, 2)}**
12. $\{(4, 3), (-4, -4), (-3, -5), (5, 2)\}$ **{(3, 4), (−4, −4), (−5, −3), (2, 5)}**
13. $\{(1, -5), (2, 6), (3, -7), (4, 8), (5, -9)\}$ **{(−5, 1), (6, 2), (−7, 3), (8, 4), (−9, 5)}**
14. $\{(3, 0), (5, 4), (7, -8), (9, 12), (11, 16)\}$ **{(0, 3), (4, 5), (−8, 7), (12, 9), (16, 11)}**

Example 2 pp. 418–419

Find the inverse of each function. Then graph the function and its inverse. **15–26. See Chapter 7 Answer Appendix.**

15. $f(x) = x + 2$
16. $g(x) = 5x$
17. $y = -2x + 1$
18. $h(x) = \frac{x-4}{3}$
19. $y = -\frac{5}{3}x - 8$
20. $g(x) = x + 4$
21. $f(x) = 4x$
22. $y = -8x + 9$
23. $f(x) = 5x^2$
24. $h(x) = x^2 + 4$
25. $f(x) = \frac{1}{2}x^2 - 1$
26. $y = (x + 1)^2 + 3$

Example 3 p. 419

Determine whether each pair of functions are inverse functions. Write *yes* or *no*.

27. $f(x) = 2x + 3$; $g(x) = 2x - 3$ **no**
28. $f(x) = 4x + 6$; $g(x) = \frac{x-6}{4}$ **yes**
29. $f(x) = -\frac{1}{3}x + 3$; $g(x) = -3x + 9$ **yes**
30. $f(x) = -6x$; $g(x) = \frac{1}{6}x$ **no**
31. $f(x) = \frac{1}{2}x + 5$; $g(x) = 2x - 10$ **yes**
32. $f(x) = \frac{x+10}{8}$; $g(x) = 8x - 10$ **yes**
33. $f(x) = 4x^2$; $g(x) = \frac{1}{2}\sqrt{x}$ **yes**
34. $f(x) = \frac{1}{3}x^2 + 1$; $g(x) = \sqrt{3x - 3}$ **yes**
35. $f(x) = x^2 - 9$; $g(x) = x + 3$ **no**
36. $f(x) = \frac{2}{3}x^3$; $g(x) = \sqrt{\frac{2}{3}x}$ **no**
37. $f(x) = (x + 6)^2$; $g(x) = \sqrt{x} - 6$ **yes**
38. $f(x) = 2\sqrt{x - 5}$; $g(x) = \frac{1}{4}x^2 - 5$ **no**

39. **FUEL** The average miles traveled for every gallon g of gas consumed by Leroy's car is represented by the function $m(g) = 28g$.
    a. Find a function $c(g)$ to represent the cost per gallon of gasoline. **$c(g) = 2.95g$**
    b. Use inverses to determine the function used to represent the cost per mile traveled in Leroy's car. **$c(m) \approx 0.105m$**

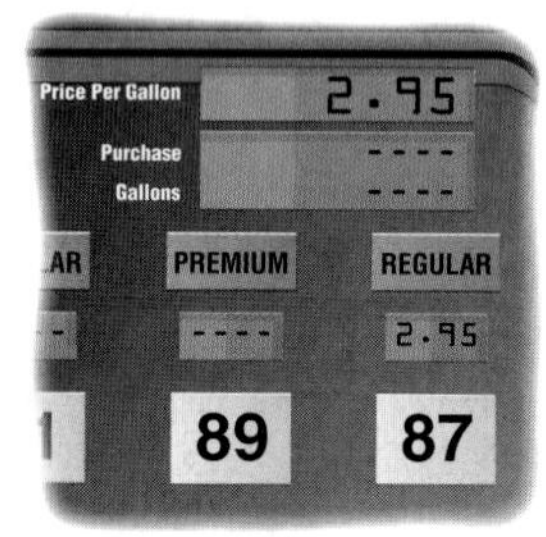

Differentiated Homework Options

Level	Assignment	Two-Day Option	
AL Basic	9–39, 52–53, 55–76	9–39 odd, 57–60	10–38 even, 52–53, 55–56, 61–76
OL Core	9–39 odd, 41–47 odd, 48–53, 55–76	9–39, 57–60	40–53, 55–56, 61–76
BL Advanced	40–73, (optional: 74–76)		

B

40. **SHOES** The shoe size for the average U.S. teen or adult male can be determined using the formula $M(x) = 3x - 22$, where x is length of a foot in measured inches. The shoe size for the average U.S. teen or adult female can be found by using the formula $F(x) = 3x - 21$.

   a. Find the inverse of each function. $M^{-1}(x) = \frac{x + 22}{3}$; $F^{-1}(x) = \frac{x + 21}{3}$

   b. If Lucy wears a size $7\frac{1}{2}$ shoe, how long are her feet? $9\frac{1}{2}$ in.

Real-World Link

Until the nineteenth century, there was no distinction between right and left shoes. The first right and left shoes were made in Philadelphia, Pennsylvania.

Source: Fact Monster

41. **GEOMETRY** The formula for the area of a circle is $A = \pi r^2$. b. ≈ 3.39 cm

   a. Find the inverse of the function. $r = \sqrt{\frac{A}{\pi}}$

   b. Use the inverse to find the radius of a circle with an area of 36 square centimeters.

Use the horizontal line test to determine whether the inverse of each function is also a function.

42. $f(x) = 2x^2$ no
43. $f(x) = x^3 - 8$ yes
44. $g(x) = x^4 - 6x^2 + 1$ no
45. $h(x) = -2x^4 - x - 2$ no
46. $g(x) = x^5 + x^2 - 4x$ no
47. $h(x) = x^3 + x^2 - 6x + 12$ no

48. **SHOPPING** Felipe bought a used car. The sales tax rate was 7.25% of the selling price, and he paid \$350 in processing and registration fees. Find the selling price if Felipe paid a total of \$8395.75. **\$7501.86**

C

49. **TEMPERATURE** A formula for converting degrees Celsius to Fahrenheit is $F(x) = \frac{9}{5}x + 32$.

   a. Find the inverse $F^{-1}(x)$. Show that $F(x)$ and $F^{-1}(x)$ are inverses. See Chapter 7 Answer Appendix.

   b. Explain what purpose $F^{-1}(x)$ serves. It can be used to convert Fahrenheit to Celsius.

50. **MEASUREMENT** There are approximately 1.852 kilometers in a nautical mile.

   a. Write a function that converts nautical miles to kilometers. $K(m) = 1.852m$

   b. Find the inverse of the function that converts kilometers back to nautical miles.

   c. Using composition of functions, verify that these two functions are inverses.

51. **MULTIPLE REPRESENTATIONS** Consider the functions $y = x^n$ for $n = 0, 1, 2, \ldots$.

   a. **GRAPHING** Use a graphing calculator to graph $y = x^n$ for $n = 0, 1, 2, 3$, and 4.

   b. **TABULAR** For which values of n is the inverse a function? Record your results in a table. See Chapter 7 Answer Appendix.

   c. **ANALYTICAL** Make a conjecture about the values of n for which the inverse of $f(x) = x^n$ is a function. Assume that n is a whole number. n is odd.

50b. $K^{-1}(m) = \frac{1}{1.852}m$

50c. $K[K^{-1}(m)] = m$ and $K^{-1}[K(m)] = m$, so the two functions are inverses of each other.

51a. See Chapter 7 Answer Appendix.

52. Sample answer: Sometimes; $y = \pm\sqrt{x}$ is an example of a relation that is not a function, with an inverse being a function. A circle is an example of a relation that is not a function with an inverse not being a function.

54. Sample answer: $f(x) = x$ and $f^{-1}(x) = x$ or $f(x) = -x$ and $f^{-1}(x) = -x$

56. Sample answer: One of the functions carries out an operation on 5. Then the second function that is an inverse of the first function reverses the operation on 5. Thus, the result is 5.

H.O.T. Problems

Use Higher-Order Thinking Skills

52. **REASONING** If a relation is *not* a function, then its inverse is *sometimes*, *always*, or *never* a function. Explain your reasoning.

53. **OPEN ENDED** Give an example of a function and its inverse. Verify that the two functions are inverses. Sample answer: $f(x) = 2x$, $f^{-1}(x) = 0.5x$; $f[f^{-1}(x)] = f^{-1}[f(x)] = x$

54. **CHALLENGE** Give an example of a function that is its own inverse.

55. **PROOF** Show that the inverse of a linear function $y = mx + b$, where $m \neq 0$ and $x \neq b$, is also a linear function. $y^{-1} = \frac{x - b}{m}$

56. **WRITING IN MATH** Suppose you have a composition of two functions that are inverses. When you put in a value of 5 for x, why is the result always 5?

Study Guide and Intervention

CRM pp. 12–13 AL OL ELL

7-2 Study Guide and Intervention

Inverse Functions and Relations

Find Inverses

Inverse Relations	Two relations are inverse relations if and only if whenever one relation contains the element (a, b), the other relation contains the element (b, a).
Property of Inverse Functions	Suppose f and f^{-1} are inverse functions. Then $f(a) = b$ if and only if $f^{-1}(b) = a$.

Example Find the inverse of the function $f(x) = \frac{2}{5}x - \frac{1}{5}$. Then graph the function and its inverse.

Step 1 Replace $f(x)$ with y in the original equation.

$f(x) = \frac{2}{5}x - \frac{1}{5} \rightarrow y = \frac{2}{5}x - \frac{1}{5}$

Step 2 Interchange x and y.

$x = \frac{2}{5}y - \frac{1}{5}$

Step 3 Solve for y.

$x = \frac{2}{5}y - \frac{1}{5}$ Inverse of $y = \frac{2}{5}x - \frac{1}{5}$

$5x = 2y - 1$ Multiply each side by 5.

$5x + 1 = 2y$ Add 1 to each side.

$\frac{1}{2}(5x + 1) = y$ Divide each side by 2.

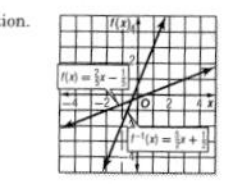

The inverse of $f(x) = \frac{2}{5}x - \frac{1}{5}$ is $f^{-1}(x) = \frac{1}{2}(5x + 1)$.

Exercises

Find the inverse of each function. Then graph the function and its inverse.

1. $f(x) = \frac{2}{3}x - 1$ $f^{-1}(x) = \frac{3}{2}x + \frac{3}{2}$
2. $f(x) = 2x - 3$ $f^{-1}(x) = \frac{1}{2}x + \frac{3}{2}$
3. $f(x) = \frac{1}{4}x - 2$ $f^{-1}(x) = 4x + 8$

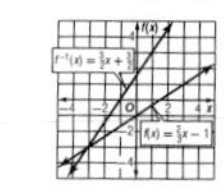
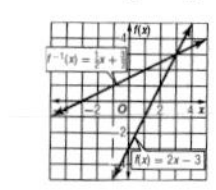
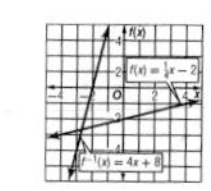

Practice

CRM p. 15 AL OL BL ELL

7-2 Practice

Inverse Functions and Relations

Find the inverse of each relation.

1. {(0, 3), (4, 2), (5, −6)} {(3, 0), (2, 4), (−6, 5)}
2. {(−5, 1), (−5, −1), (−5, 8)} {(1, −5), (−1, −5), (8, −5)}
3. {(−3, −7), (0, −1), (5, 9), (7, 13)} {(−7, −3), (−1, 0), (9, 5), (13, 7)}
4. {(8, −2), (10, 5), (12, 6), (14, 7)} {(−2, 8), (5, 10), (6, 12), (7, 14)}
5. {(−5, −4), (1, 2), (3, 4), (7, 8)} {(−4, −5), (2, 1), (4, 3), (8, 7)}
6. {(−3, 9), (−2, 4), (0, 0), (1, 1)} {(9, −3), (4, −2), (0, 0), (1, 1)}

Find the inverse of each function. Then graph the function and its inverse.

7. $f(x) = \frac{3}{4}x$ $f^{-1}(x) = \frac{4}{3}x$
8. $g(x) = 3 + x$ $g^{-1}(x) = x - 3$
9. $y = 3x - 2$ $y = \frac{x + 2}{3}$

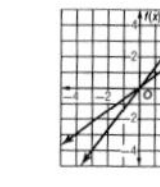
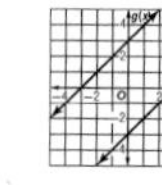
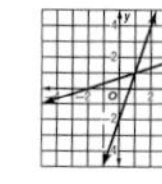

Determine whether each pair of functions are inverse functions. Write *yes* or *no*.

10. $f(x) = x + 6$, $g(x) = x - 6$ yes
11. $f(x) = -4x + 1$, $g(x) = \frac{1}{4}(1 - x)$ yes
12. $g(x) = 13x - 13$, $h(x) = \frac{1}{13}x - 1$ no
13. $f(x) = 2x$, $g(x) = -2x$ no
14. $f(x) = \frac{6}{7}x$, $g(x) = \frac{7}{6}x$ yes
15. $g(x) = 2x - 8$, $h(x) = \frac{1}{2}x + 4$ yes

16. **MEASUREMENT** The points (63, 121), (71, 180), (67, 140), (65, 108), and (72, 165) give the weight in pounds as a function of height in inches for 5 students in a class. Give the points for these students that represent height as a function of weight. (121, 63), (180, 71), (140, 67), (108, 65), (165, 72)

17. **REMODELING** The Clearys are replacing the flooring in their 15 foot by 18 foot kitchen. The new flooring costs \$17.99 per square yard. The formula $f(x) = 9x$ converts square yards to square feet.

   a. Find the inverse $f^{-1}(x)$. What is the significance of $f^{-1}(x)$ for the Clearys? $f^{-1}(x) = \frac{x}{9}$; It will allow them to convert the square footage of their kitchen floor to square yards, so they can then calculate the cost of the new flooring.

   b. What will the new flooring cost the Clearys? \$539.70

Lesson 7-2

Word Problem Practice

CRM p. 16 AL OL BL ELL

7-2 Word Problem Practice

Inverse Functions and Relations

1. **VOLUME** Jason wants to make a spherical water cooler that can hold half a cubic meter of water. He knows that $V = \frac{4}{3}\pi r^3$, but he needs to know how to find r given V. Find this inverse function. $r = \sqrt[3]{\frac{3V}{4\pi}}$

2. **EXERCISE** Alex began a new exercise routine. To gain the maximum benefit from his exercise, Alex calculated his maximum target heart rate using the function $f(x) = 0.85(220 - x)$, where x represents his age. Find the inverse of this function. $f^{-1}(x) = 220 - \frac{x}{0.85}$

3. **ROCKETS** The altitude of a rocket in feet as a function of time is given by $f(t) = 49t^2$, where $t \geq 0$. Find the inverse of this function and determine the times when the rocket will be 10, 100, and 1000 feet high. Round your answers to the nearest hundredth of a second. $f^{-1}(t) = \frac{\sqrt{t}}{7}$; 10 ft at 0.45 s, 100 ft at 1.43 s, 1000 ft at 4.52 s

4. **SELF-INVERTIBLE** Karen finds the incomplete graph of a function in the back of her engineering handbook. The function is graphed in the figure below.

   Karen knows that this function is its own inverse. Armed with this knowledge, extend the graph for values of x between −7 and 2.

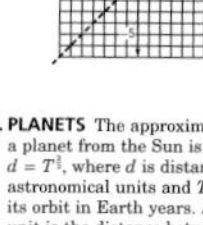

5. **PLANETS** The approximate distance of a planet from the Sun is given by $d = T^{\frac{2}{3}}$, where d is distance in astronomical units and T is the period of its orbit in Earth years. An astronomical unit is the distance between the Earth and the Sun.

   a. Solve for T in terms of d. $T = d^{1.5}$

   b. Pluto is about 39.44 times as far from the Sun as the Earth. About how many years does it take Pluto to orbit the Sun? 248 yr

Multiple Representations

In Exercise 51, students use graphing calculator, a table of values, and analysis to investigate the properties of inverse functions.

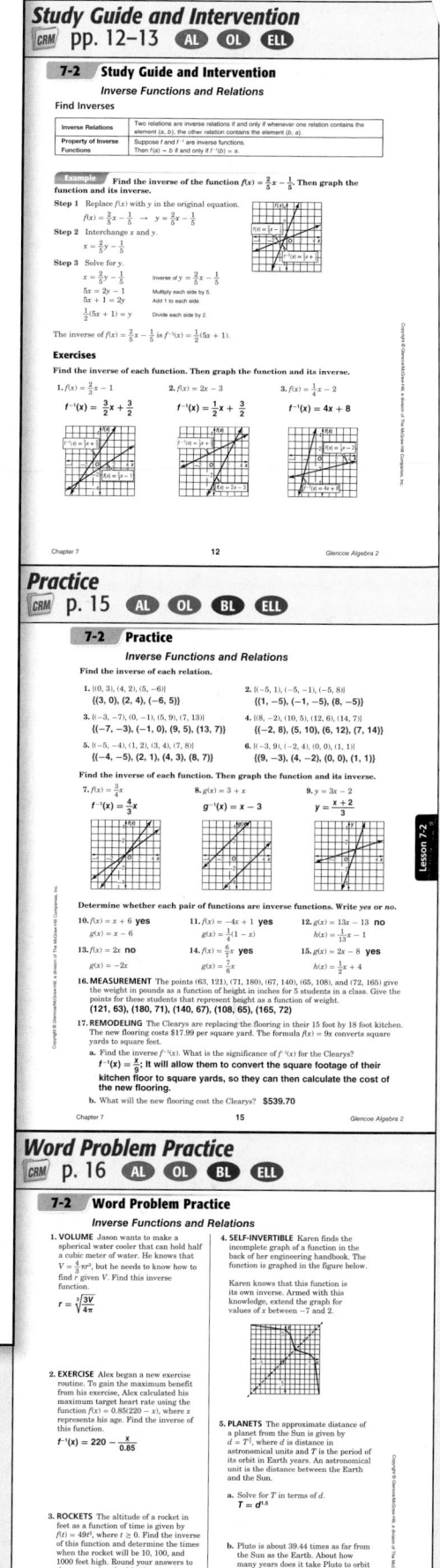

Enrichment

CRM p. 17 AL OL

7-2 Enrichment

Reading Algebra

In mathematics, the term *group* has a special meaning. The following numbered sentences discuss the idea of group and one interesting example of a group.

01 To be a group, a set of elements and a binary operation must satisfy four conditions: the set must be closed under the operation, the operation must be associative, there must be an identity element, and every element must have an inverse.

02 The following six functions form a group under the operation of composition of functions: $f_1(x) = x$, $f_2(x) = \frac{1}{x}$, $f_3(x) = 1 - x$, $f_4(x) = \frac{(x-1)}{x}$, $f_5(x) = \frac{x}{(x-1)}$, and $f_6(x) = \frac{1}{(1-x)}$.

03 This group is an example of a noncommutative group. For example, $f_3 \circ f_2 = f_4$, but $f_2 \circ f_3 = f_6$.

04 Some experimentation with this group will show that the identity element is f_1.

05 Every element is its own inverse except for f_4 and f_6, each of which is the inverse of the other.

Use the paragraph to answer these questions.

Lesson 7-2

4 ASSESS

Yesterday's News Have students write how yesterday's concept of composition of functions helped them verify that two functions were inverses.

Formative Assessment

Check for student understanding of concepts in Lessons 7-1 and 7-2.

CRM Quiz 1, p. 53

Additional Answers

72.

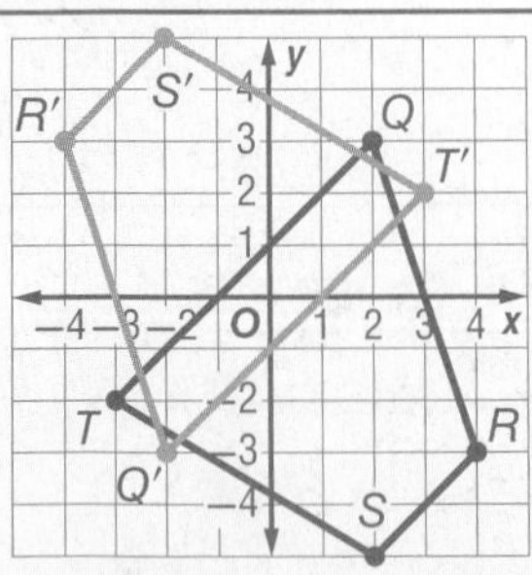

74.

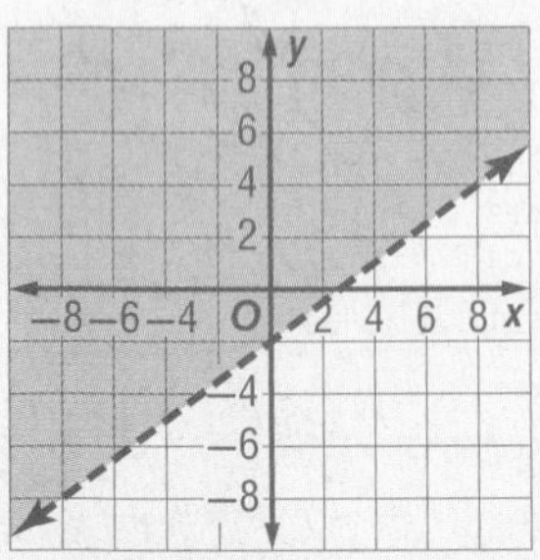

75.

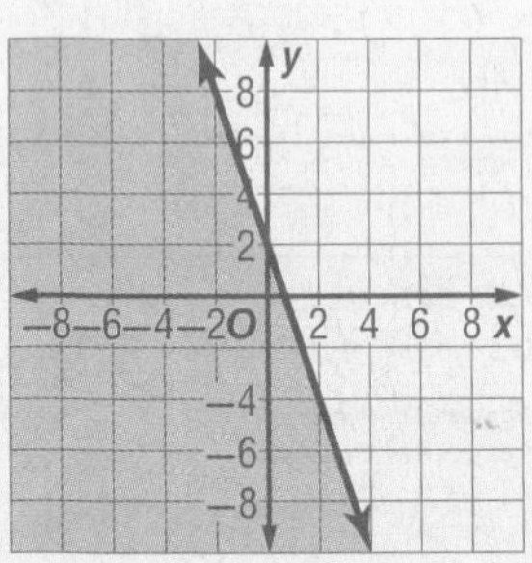

76.

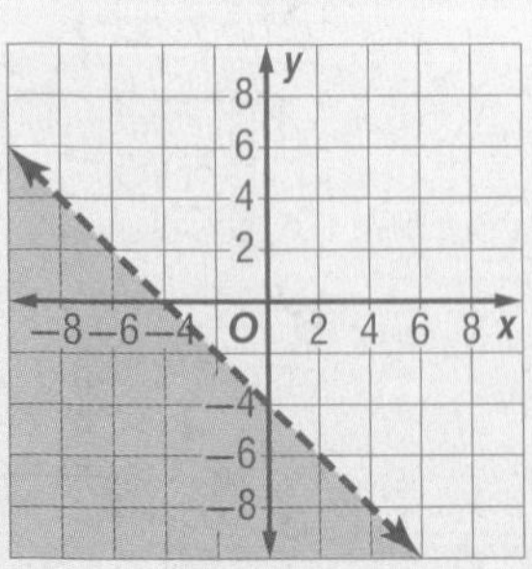

NGSSS PRACTICE 912.G.1.1, 912.G.2.5, 912.A.2.8, 912.A.2.11

57. THINK SOLVE EXPLAIN **SHORT RESPONSE** If the length of a rectangular television screen is 24 inches and its height is 18 inches, what is the length of its diagonal in inches? **30 in.**

58. GEOMETRY If the base of a triangle is represented by $2x + 5$ and the height is represented by $4x$, which expression represents the area of the triangle? **D**

A. $(2x + 5) + (4x)$

B. $(2x + 5)(4x)$

C. $\frac{1}{2}(2x + 5) + (4x)$

D. $\frac{1}{2}(2x + 5)(4x)$

59. Which expression represents $f[g(x)]$ if $f(x) = x^2 + 3$ and $g(x) = -x + 1$? **J**

F. $x^2 - x + 2$

G. $-x^2 - 2$

H. $-x^3 + x^2 - 3x + 3$

I. $x^2 - 2x + 4$

60. ACT/SAT Which of the following is the inverse of $f(x) = \frac{3x - 5}{2}$? **C**

A. $g(x) = \frac{2x + 5}{3}$

B. $g(x) = \frac{3x + 5}{2}$

C. $g(x) = 2x + 5$

D. $g(x) = \frac{2x - 5}{3}$

Spiral Review

If $f(x) = 3x + 5$, $g(x) = x - 2$, and $h(x) = x^2 - 1$, find each value. (Lesson 7-1)

61. $g[f(3)]$ **12**

62. $f[h(-2)]$ **14**

63. $h[g(1)]$ **0**

64. CONSTRUCTION A picnic area has the shape of a trapezoid. The longer base is 8 more than 3 times the length of the shorter base, and the height is 1 more than 3 times the shorter base. What are the dimensions if the area is 4104 square feet? (Lesson 6-8) $b_1 = 25$ **ft**, $b_2 = 83$ **ft**, $h = 76$ **ft**

Find the value of c that makes each trinomial a perfect square. Then write the trinomial as a perfect square. (Lesson 5-5)

65. $x^2 + 34x + c$ **289; $(x + 17)^2$**

66. $x^2 - 11x + c$ $\frac{121}{4}$; $\left(x - \frac{11}{2}\right)^2$

Simplify. (Lesson 5-4)

67. $(3 + 4i)(5 - 2i)$ **$23 + 14i$**

68. $(\sqrt{6} + i)(\sqrt{6} - i)$ **7**

69. $\frac{1 + i}{1 - i}$ i

70. $\frac{4 - 3i}{1 + 2i}$ $-\frac{2}{5} - \frac{11}{5}i$

Refer to quadrilateral $QRST$ shown at the right. (Lesson 4-4)

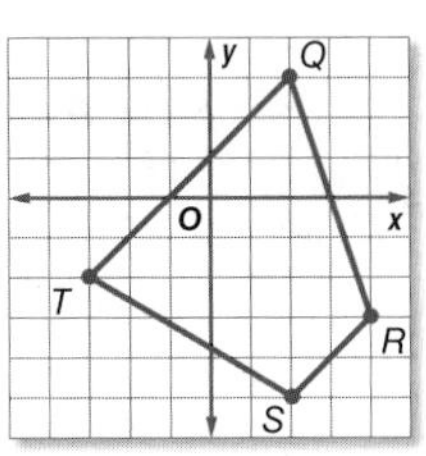

71. Write the vertex matrix. Multiply the vertex matrix by -1.

72. Graph the preimage and image. **See margin.**

73. What type of transformation does the graph represent? **180° rotation**

71. $\begin{bmatrix} 2 & 4 & 2 & -3 \\ 3 & -3 & -5 & -2 \end{bmatrix}$; $\begin{bmatrix} -2 & -4 & -2 & 3 \\ -3 & 3 & 5 & 2 \end{bmatrix}$

Skills Review

Graph each inequality. (Lesson 2-7) **74–76. See margin.**

74. $y > \frac{3}{4}x - 2$

75. $y \leq -3x + 2$

76. $y < -x - 4$

Differentiated Instruction OL BL

Extension The equation $f(x) = 2.3x + 61$ can be used to approximate height in centimeters when the length of a person's femur (thighbone) is known. Find $f^{-1}(x)$ and explain what it computes. $f^{-1}(x) = \frac{x - 61}{2.3}$; it is used to find the approximate length of the femur when a person's height is known.

422 Chapter 7 Inverses and Radical Functions and Relations

Graphing Technology Lab
Inverse Functions and Relations

FL Math Online glencoe.com
- Other Calculator Keystrokes
- Graphing Technology Personal Tutor

NGSSS MA.912.A.2.11 Solve problems involving functions and their inverses.

You can use a TI-83/84 Plus graphing calculator to compare a function and its inverse using tables and graphs. Note that before you enter any values in the calculator, you should clear all lists.

ACTIVITY 1 Graph Inverses with Ordered Pairs

Graph $f(x) = \{(1, 2), (2, 4), (3, 6), (4, 8), (5, 10), (6, 12)\}$ and its inverse.

Step 1 Enter the x-values in L1 and the y-values in L2. Then graph the function.

KEYSTROKES: STAT ENTER 1 ENTER 2 ENTER 3 ENTER 4 ENTER 5 ENTER 6 ENTER ▶ 2 ENTER 4 ENTER 6 ENTER 8 ENTER 10 ENTER 12 ENTER 2nd [STAT PLOT] ENTER ENTER GRAPH

Adjust the window to reflect the domain and range.

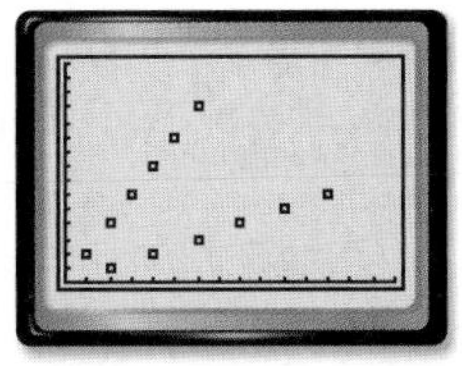

Step 2 Define the inverse function by setting Xlist to L2 and Ylist to L1. Then graph the inverse function.

KEYSTROKES: 2nd [STAT PLOT] ▼ ENTER ENTER ▼ ▼ 2nd [L2] ▼ 2nd [L1] GRAPH

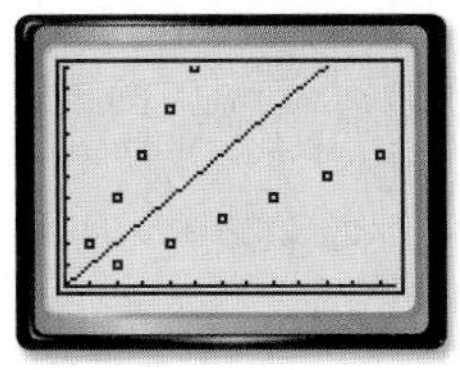

Step 3 Graph the line $y = x$.

KEYSTROKES: Y= X,T,θ,n GRAPH

ACTIVITY 2 Graph Inverses with Function Notation

Graph $f(x) = 3x$ and its inverse $g(x) = \frac{x}{3}$.

Step 1 Clear the data from Activity 1.

KEYSTROKES: 2nd [STAT PLOT] ENTER ▶ ENTER ▲ ▶ ENTER ▶ ENTER 2nd [QUIT]

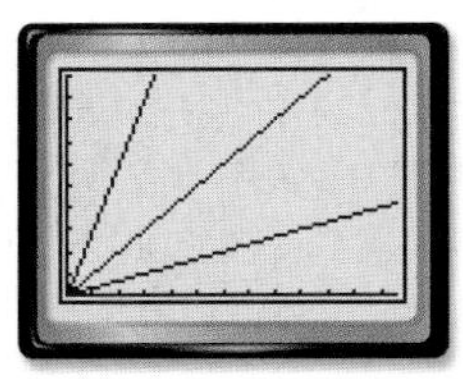

Step 2 Enter $f(x)$ as Y1, $g(x)$ as Y2, and $y = x$ as Y3. Then graph.

KEYSTROKES: Y= 3 X,T,θ,n ENTER X,T,θ,n ÷ 3 ENTER X,T,θ,n ZOOM 6

1–6. See Chapter 7 Answer Appendix. 7. The graph of a function and its inverse are reflections in the line $y = x$.

Exercises

Graph each function $f(x)$ and its inverse $g(x)$. Then graph $f \circ g(x)$.

1. $f(x) = 5x$
2. $f(x) = x - 3$
3. $f(x) = 2x + 1$
4. $f(x) = \frac{1}{2}x + 3$
5. $f(x) = x^2$
6. $f(x) = x^2 - 3$
7. What is the relationship between the graphs of a function and its inverse?
8. **MAKE A CONJECTURE** For any function $f(x)$ and its inverse $g(x)$, what is $(f \circ g)(x)$? $(f \circ g)(x) = x$

1 FOCUS

Objective Compare a function and its inverse using a graphing calculator.

Materials for Each Student

- TI-83/84 Plus or other graphing calculator

Teaching Tip

Be sure students know how to enter data lists and switch between lists in their calculators.

2 TEACH

Working in Cooperative Groups

Have students work in pairs, mixing abilities, to complete Activities 1 and 2. Students should confirm that their screens are identical at each step.

Ask:

- What is the difference between Activity 1 and Activity 2? Activity 1 compares discrete ordered pairs, while Activity 2 compares two continuous linear functions.
- How are the graphs of the function and its inverse related? They are reflections of each other across the line $y = x$.

Practice Have students complete Exercises 1–8.

3 ASSESS

Formative Assessment

Use Exercises 1, 2, and 5 to assess whether students can compare a function and its inverse using a graphing calculator.

From Concrete to Abstract

For each exercise, ask students to predict whether the graph passes through the origin. Then ask them to predict whether the graph of the inverse will pass through the origin. A function of the form $f(x) = ax^n$ contains the origin; if the graph of a function contains the origin, its inverse will also contain the origin.

Extending the Concept

Ask:

- If you have a set of ordered pairs that is a function, how can you generate the inverse of the function? Switch the values of x and y in each ordered pair.

7-3 Lesson Notes

1 FOCUS

Vertical Alignment

Before Lesson 7-3
Simplify expressions with square roots.

Lesson 7-3
Graph and analyze square root functions.
Graph square root inequalities.

After Lesson 7-3
Determine solutions of square root equations using algebraic methods.

2 TEACH

Scaffolding Questions

Have students read the *Why?* section of the lesson.

Ask:

- If a shorter and a longer string produce the same pitch, which one has more tension? the longer string
- If a string and a heavier string produce the same pitch, which one has less tension? the less heavy string
- In the expression for *f*, which quantity is expressed as a function of which other quantities? Pitch is expressed as a function of length, tension, and mass.

7-3 Square Root Functions and Inequalities

Then
You simplified expressions with square roots. (Lesson 5-4)

Now
- Graph and analyze square root functions.
- Graph square root inequalities.

NGSSS
MA.912.A.2.6 Identify and graph common functions (including but not limited to linear, rational, quadratic, cubic, **radical**, absolute value).

New Vocabulary
square root function
radical function
square root inequality

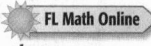

FL Math Online
glencoe.com

Why?

With guitars, pitch is dependent on string length and string tension. The longer the string, the higher the tension needed to produce a desired pitch. Likewise, the heavier the string, the higher the tension needed to reach a desired pitch.

This can be represented by the square root function $f = \frac{1}{2L}\sqrt{\frac{T}{P}}$, where T is the tension, P is the mass of the string, L is the length of the string, and f is the pitch.

Square Root Functions If a function contains the square root of a variable, it is called a **square root function**. The square root function is a type of **radical function**.

Key Concept Parent Function of Square Root Functions

Parent function:	$f(x) = \sqrt{x}$
Domain:	$\{x \mid x \geq 0\}$
Range:	$\{f(x) \mid f(x) \geq 0\}$
Intercepts:	$x = 0, f(x) = 0$
Not defined:	$x < 0$
End behavior:	$x \to 0, f(x) \to 0$ $x \to +\infty, f(x) \to +\infty$

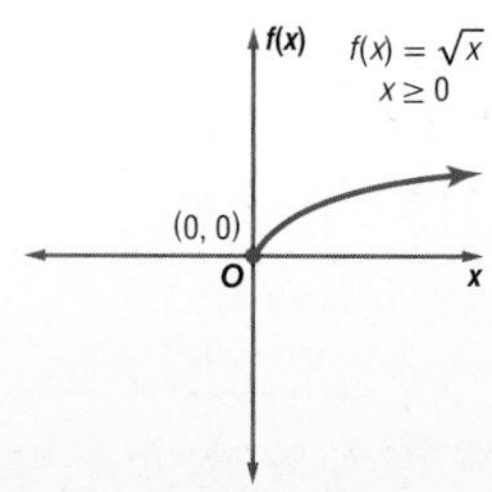

The domain of a square root function is limited to values for which the function is defined.

EXAMPLE 1 Identify Domain and Range

Identify the domain and range of $f(x) = \sqrt{x + 4}$.

The domain only includes values for which the radicand is nonnegative.

$x + 4 \geq 0$ **Write an inequality.**
$x \geq -4$ **Subtract 4 from each side.**

Thus, the domain is $\{x \mid x \geq -4\}$.

Find $f(-4)$ to determine the lower limit of the range.

$f(-4) = \sqrt{-4 + 4}$ or 0

So, the range is $\{f(x) \mid f(x) \geq 0\}$.

Guided Practice

1A. $D = \{x \mid x \geq 3\}$; $R = \{f(x) \mid f(x) \geq 0\}$
1B. $D = \{x \mid x \geq -6\}$; $R = \{f(x) \mid f(x) \geq 2\}$

Identify the domain and range of each function.

1A. $f(x) = \sqrt{x - 3}$ **1B.** $f(x) = \sqrt{x + 6} + 2$

Personal Tutor glencoe.com

Lesson 7-3 Resources

Resource	Approaching-Level	On-Level	Beyond-Level	English Learners
Teacher Edition	• Differentiated Instruction, p. 428	• Differentiated Instruction, pp. 428, 430	• Differentiated Instruction, p. 430	• Differentiated Instruction, p. 428
Chapter Resource Masters	• Study Guide and Intervention, pp. 19–20 • Skills Practice, p. 21 • Practice, p. 22 • Word Problem Practice, p. 23	• Study Guide and Intervention, pp. 19–20 • Skills Practice, p. 21 • Practice, p. 22 • Word Problem Practice, p. 23 • Enrichment, p. 24	• Practice, p. 22 • Word Problem Practice, p. 23 • Enrichment, p. 24	• Study Guide and Intervention, pp. 19–20 • Skills Practice, p. 21 • Practice, p. 22 • Word Problem Practice, p. 23
Transparencies	• 5-Minute Check Transparency 7-3	• 5-Minute Check Transparency 7-3	• 5-Minute Check Transparency 7-3	• 5-Minute Check Transparency 7-3
Other	• Study Notebook	• Study Notebook	• Study Notebook	• Study Notebook

The same techniques used to transform the graph of other functions you have studied can be applied to the graphs of square root functions.

Key Concept — Transformations of Square Root Functions

$f(x) = a\sqrt{x - h} + k$

***h*—Horizontal Translation**	***k*—Vertical Translation**
$\lvert h \rvert$ units right if h is positive $\lvert h \rvert$ units left if h is negative	$\lvert k \rvert$ units up if k is positive $\lvert k \rvert$ units down if k is negative
The domain is $\{x \mid x \geq h\}$.	The range is $\{f(x) \mid f(x) \geq k\}$.

***a*—Orientation and Shape**

- If $a < 0$, the graph is reflected across the x-axis.
- If $\lvert a \rvert > 1$, the graph is vertically expanded.
- If $0 < \lvert a \rvert < 1$, the graph is vertically compressed.

EXAMPLE 2 Graph Square Root Functions

Graph each function. State the domain and range.

a. $y = \sqrt{x - 2} + 5$

The minimum point is at $(h, k) = (2, 5)$. Make a table of values for $x \geq 2$, and graph the function. The graph is the same shape as $f(x) = \sqrt{x}$, but is translated 2 units right and 5 units up. Notice the end behavior. As x increases, y increases.

The domain is $\{x \mid x \geq 2\}$ and the range is $\{y \mid y \geq 5\}$.

x	y
2	5
3	6
4	6.4
5	6.7
6	7
7	7.2
8	7.4

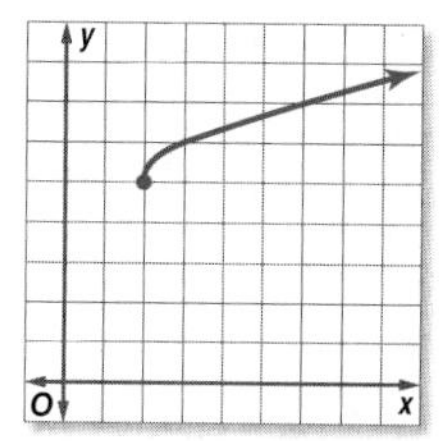

b. $y = -2\sqrt{x + 3} - 1$

The minimum domain value is at h or -3. Make a table of values for $x \geq -3$, and graph the function. Because a is negative, the graph is similar to $f(x) = \sqrt{x}$, but is reflected in the line $f(x) = -1$. Because $\lvert a \rvert > 1$, the graph is vertically compressed. It is also translated 3 units left and 1 unit down.

x	y
−3	−1
−2	−3
−1	−3.8
0	−4.5
1	−5
2	−5.5
3	−5.9

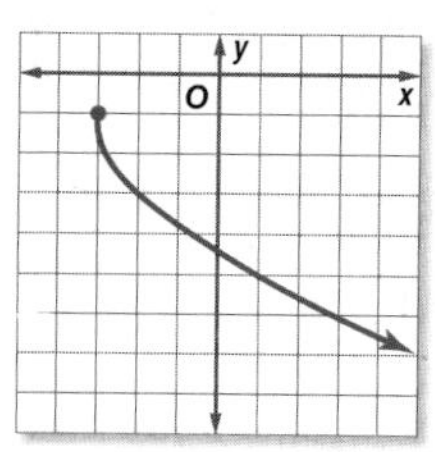

The domain is $\{x \mid x \geq -3\}$ and the range is $\{y \mid y \leq -1\}$.

Guided Practice 2A, 2B. See margin.

2A. $f(x) = 2\sqrt{x + 4}$

2B. $f(x) = \frac{1}{4}\sqrt{x - 5} + 3$

Personal Tutor glencoe.com

StudyTip

Domain and Range The limits on the domain and range also represent the initial point of the graph of a square root function.

ReadingMath

Power Functions Square root functions are also *power functions* when the exponent is a fraction. In the case of square roots, the exponent is $\frac{1}{2}$.

Square Root Functions

Example 1 shows how to find the domain and range of a square root function. **Example 2** shows how to graph square root functions. **Example 3** shows how to solve a real-world problem by graphing and solving a square root function.

Formative Assessment

Use the Guided Practice exercises after each example to determine students' understanding of concepts.

Additional Examples

1 Identify the domain and range of $f(x) = \sqrt{x - 2}$ $D = \{x \mid x \geq 2\}$; $R = \{f(x) \mid f(x) \geq 0\}$

2 Graph each function. State the domain and range.

a. $y = 3\sqrt{x - 4} + 2$

b. $y = -\sqrt{x + 5} - 6$

a. The domain is $\{x \mid x \geq 4\}$; the range is $\{y \mid y \geq 2\}$.

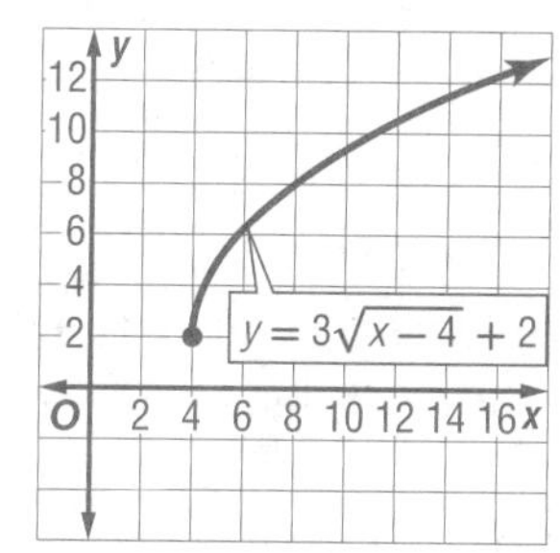

b. The domain is $\{x \mid x \geq -5\}$; the range is $\{y \mid y \leq -6\}$.

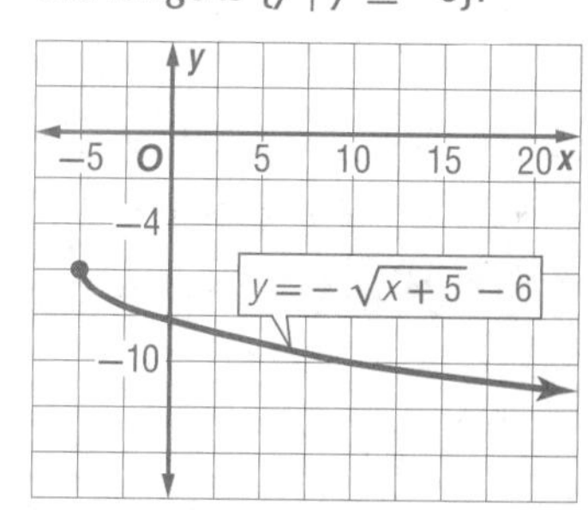

Additional Examples also in Interactive Classroom PowerPoint® Presentations

IWB INTERACTIVE WHITEBOARD READY

Additional Answers (Guided Practice)

2A.

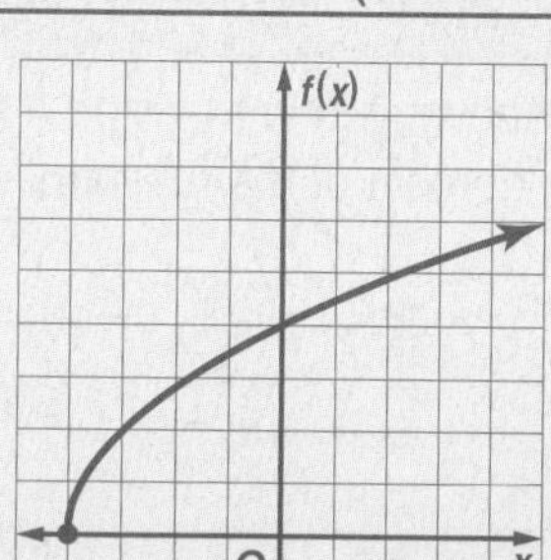

$D = \{x \mid x \geq -4\}$; $R = \{f(x) \mid f(x) \geq 0\}$

2B.

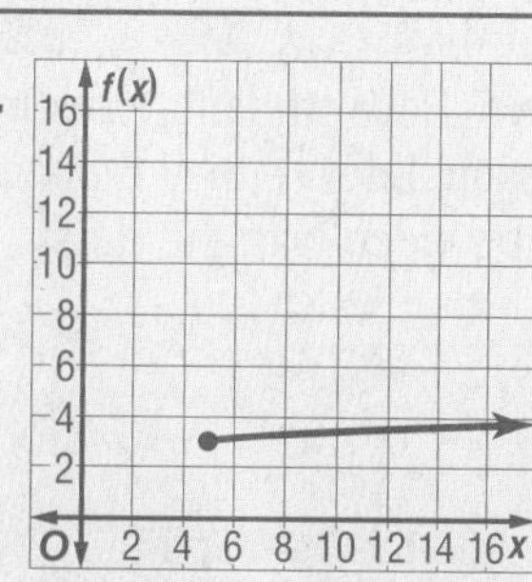

$D = \{x \mid x \geq 5\}$; $R = \{f(x) \mid f(x) \geq 3\}$

Additional Example

3 **PHYSICS** When an object is spinning in a circular path of radius 2 meters with velocity v, in meters per second, the centripetal acceleration a, in meters per second squared, is directed toward the center of the circle. The velocity v and acceleration a of the object are related by the function $v = \sqrt{2a}$.

a. Graph the function in the domain $\{a \mid a \geq 0\}$.

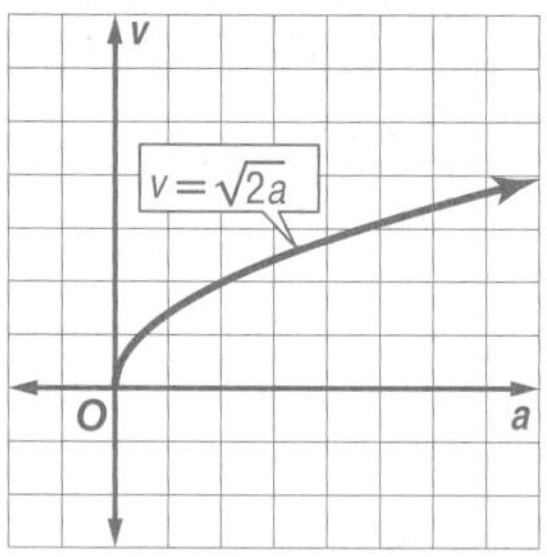

b. What would be the centripetal acceleration of an object spinning along the circular path with a velocity of 4 meters per second? 8 m/s^2

Square Root Inequalities

Example 4 shows how to graph a square root inequality.

Additional Example

4 Graph $y > \sqrt{3x + 5}$.

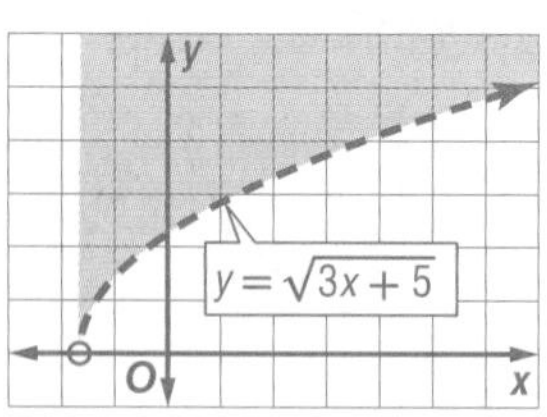

Real-World Link

On every string, the guitar player has an option of decreasing the length of the string in about 24 different ways. This will produce 24 different frequencies on each string.

Source: *Guitar World*

Problem-Solving Tip

Make a Table Making a table is a good way to organize ordered pairs in order to see the general behavior of a graph.

Real-World EXAMPLE 3 Use Graphs to Analyze Square Root Functions

MUSIC Refer to the application at the beginning of the lesson. The pitch, or frequency, measured in hertz (Hz) of a certain string can be determined by $f(T) = \frac{1}{1.28}\sqrt{\frac{T}{0.0000708}}$, where T is tension in kilograms.

a. Graph the function for tension in the domain $\{T \mid 0 \leq T \leq 10\}$.

Make a table of values for $0 \leq T \leq 10$ and graph.

T	$f(T)$
0	0
1	92.8
2	131.3
3	160.8
4	185.7
5	207.6

T	$f(T)$
6	227.4
7	245.7
8	262.6
9	278.5
10	293.6

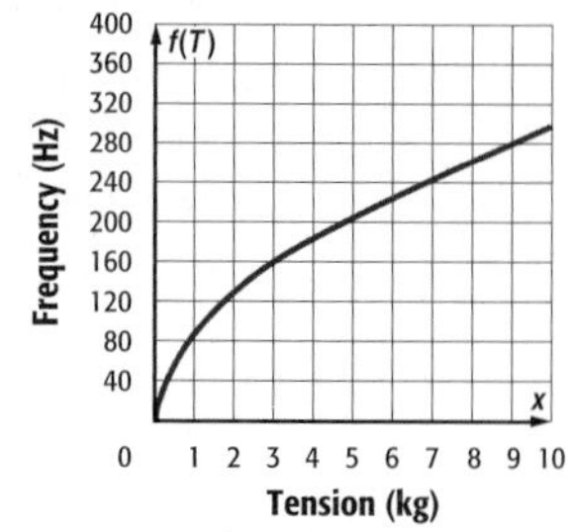

b. How much tension is needed for a pitch of over 200 Hz?

According to the graph and the table, more than 4.5 kilograms of tension is needed for a pitch of more than 200 hertz.

Guided Practice

3. MUSIC The frequency of vibrations for a certain guitar string when it is plucked can be determined by $F = 200\sqrt{T}$, where F is the number of vibrations per second and T is the tension measured in pounds. Graph the function for $0 \leq T \leq 10$. Then determine the frequency for $T = 3$, 6, and 9 pounds. **See Chapter 7 Answer Appendix.**

Personal Tutor glencoe.com

Square Root Inequalities A **square root inequality** is an inequality involving square roots. They are graphed using the same method as other inequalities.

EXAMPLE 4 Graph a Square Root Inequality

Graph $y < \sqrt{x - 4} - 6$.

Graph the boundary $y = \sqrt{x - 4} - 6$.

The domain is $\{x \mid x \geq 4\}$. Because y is *less than*, the shaded region should be *below* the boundary and within the domain.

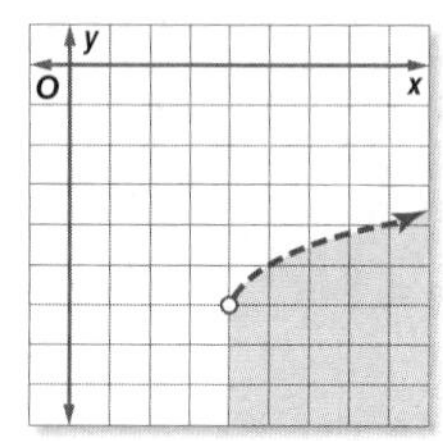

CHECK Select a point in the shaded region, and verify that it is a solution of the inequality.

Test (7, −5): $-5 \stackrel{?}{<} \sqrt{7 - 4} - 6$

$-5 \stackrel{?}{<} \sqrt{3} - 6$

$-5 < -4.27$ ✓

Guided Practice **4A, 4B. See Chapter 7 Answer Appendix.**

Graph each inequality.

4A. $f(x) \geq \sqrt{2x + 1}$

4B. $f(x) < -\sqrt{x + 2} - 4$

Personal Tutor glencoe.com

TEACH with TECH

VIDEO RECORDING Have students work in groups to create a video showing how to graph a square root function. Be sure they explain how they determined the domain of the function. Share each group's video with the class.

426 **Chapter 7** Inverses and Radical Functions and Relations

Check Your Understanding

1. D = {x | x ≥ 0}; R = {f(x) | f(x) ≥ 0}

Example 1 p. 424

Identify the domain and range of each function.

1. $f(x) = \sqrt{4x}$ **2.** $f(x) = \sqrt{x - 5}$ **3.** $f(x) = \sqrt{x + 8} - 2$

2. D = {x | x ≥ 5}; R = {f(x) | f(x) ≥ 0}

3. D = {x | x ≥ −8}; R = {f(x) | f(x) ≥ −2}

Example 2 p. 425

Graph each function. State the domain and range. 4–7. See margin.

4. $f(x) = \sqrt{x} - 2$ **5.** $f(x) = 3\sqrt{x - 1}$

6. $f(x) = \frac{1}{2}\sqrt{x + 4} - 1$ **7.** $f(x) = -\sqrt{3x - 5} + 5$

Example 3 p. 426

8. OCEAN The speed that a tsunami, or tidal wave, can travel is modeled by the equation $v = 356\sqrt{d}$, where v is the speed in kilometers per hour and d is the average depth of the water in kilometers. A tsunami is found to be traveling at 145 kilometers per hour. What is the average depth of the water? Round to the nearest hundredth of a kilometer. 0.17 km

Example 4 p. 426

Graph each inequality. 9–12. See Chapter 7 Answer Appendix.

9. $f(x) \geq \sqrt{x} + 4$ **10.** $f(x) \leq \sqrt{x - 6} + 2$

11. $f(x) < -2\sqrt{x + 3}$ **12.** $f(x) > \sqrt{2x - 1} - 3$

Practice and Problem Solving

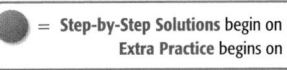

= **Step-by-Step Solutions** begin on page R20. **Extra Practice** begins on page 947.

Example 1 p. 424

Identify the domain and range of each function.

13. $f(x) = -\sqrt{2x} + 2$ **14.** $f(x) = \sqrt{x} - 6$ **15** $f(x) = 4\sqrt{x - 2} - 8$

16. $f(x) = \sqrt{x + 2} + 5$ **17.** $f(x) = \sqrt{x - 4} - 6$ **18.** $f(x) = -\sqrt{x - 6} + 5$

13. D = {x | x ≥ 0}; R = {f(x) | f(x) ≤ 2}
14. D = {x | x ≥ 0}; R = {f(x) | f(x) ≥ −6}
15. D = {x | x ≥ 2}; R = {f(x) | f(x) ≥ −8}
16. D = {x | x ≥ −2}; R = {f(x) | f(x) ≥ 5}
17. D = {x | x ≥ 4}; R = {f(x) | f(x) ≥ −6}
18. D = {x | x ≥ 6}; R = {f(x) | f(x) ≤ 5}

Example 2 p. 425

Graph each function. State the domain and range. 19–28. See Chapter 7 Answer Appendix.

19. $f(x) = \sqrt{6x}$ **20.** $f(x) = -\sqrt{5x}$

21. $f(x) = \sqrt{x - 8}$ **22.** $f(x) = \sqrt{x + 1}$

23. $f(x) = \sqrt{x + 3} + 2$ **24.** $f(x) = \sqrt{x - 4} - 10$

25. $f(x) = 2\sqrt{x - 5} - 6$ **26.** $f(x) = \frac{3}{4}\sqrt{x + 12} + 3$

27. $f(x) = -\frac{1}{5}\sqrt{x - 1} - 4$ **28.** $f(x) = -3\sqrt{x + 7} + 9$

Example 3 p. 426

29. SKYDIVING The approximate time t in seconds that it takes an object to fall a distance of d feet is given by $t = \sqrt{\frac{d}{16}}$. Suppose a parachutist falls 11 seconds before the parachute opens. How far does the parachutist fall during this time? 1936 ft

30. ROLLER COASTERS The velocity of a roller coaster as it moves down a hill is $V = \sqrt{v^2 + 64h}$, where v is the initial velocity in feet per second and h is the vertical drop in feet. The designer wants the coaster to have a velocity of 90 feet per second when it reaches the bottom of the hill.

a. If the initial velocity of the coaster at the top of the hill is 10 feet per second, write an equation that models the situation. $90 = \sqrt{100 + 64h}$

b. How high should the designer make the hill? 125 ft

Differentiated Homework Options

Level	Assignment	Two-Day Option	
AL Basic	13–38, 48–66	13–37 odd, 54–57	14–38 even, 48–53, 58–66
OL Core	13–37 odd, 39–46, 48–66	13–38, 54–57	39–53, 58–66
BL Advanced	39–62, (optional: 63–66)		

3 PRACTICE

Formative Assessment

Use Exercises 1–12 to check for understanding.

Use the chart at the bottom of this page to customize assignments for your students.

Additional Answers

4. D = {x | x ≥ 0}; R = {f(x) | f(x) ≥ −2}

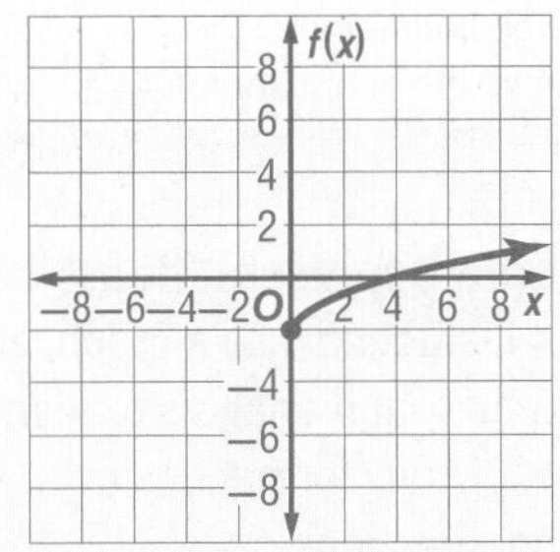

5. D = {x | x ≥ 1}; R = {f(x) | f(x) ≥ 0}

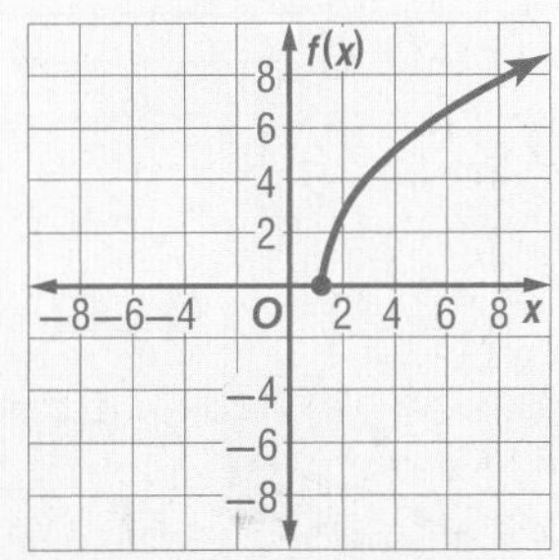

6. D = {x | x ≥ −4}; R = {f(x) | f(x) ≥ −1}

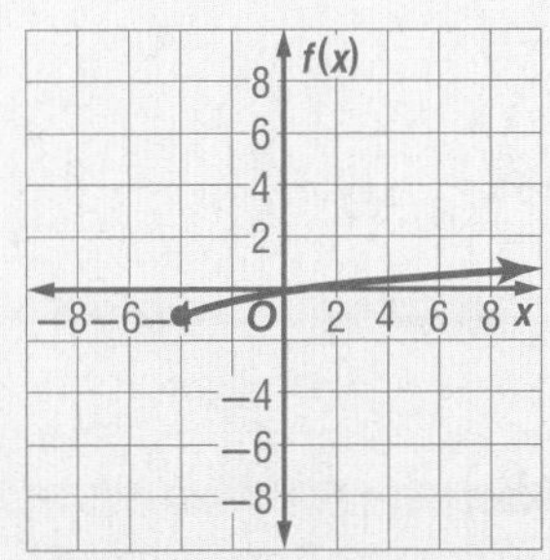

7. D = $\left\{x \mid x \geq \frac{5}{3}\right\}$; R = {f(x) | f(x) ≤ 5}

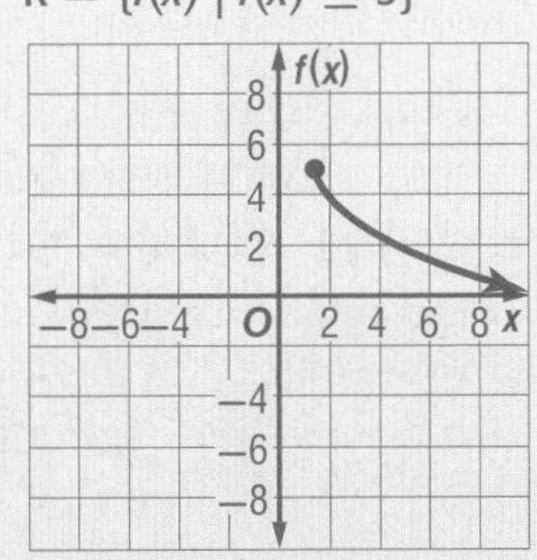

Watch Out!

Error Analysis For Exercise 51, students should see that Cleveland's graph is incorrect because the shaded region is above the boundary represented by $y = \sqrt{5x + 15}$, so that shaded region (together with the boundary itself) represents $y \geq \sqrt{5x + 15}$. Explain to students that the inequality sign determines whether the boundary line is solid or dashed; the value inside the square root symbol, which must be nonnegative, determines the domain; and the shading should be on and below the boundary for "$y \leq \ldots$" or on and above the boundary for "$y \geq \ldots$"

Multiple Representations In Exercise 44, students use a graph, a table of values, and analysis to identify the effects of transformations on square-root functions.

Additional Answers

45a.

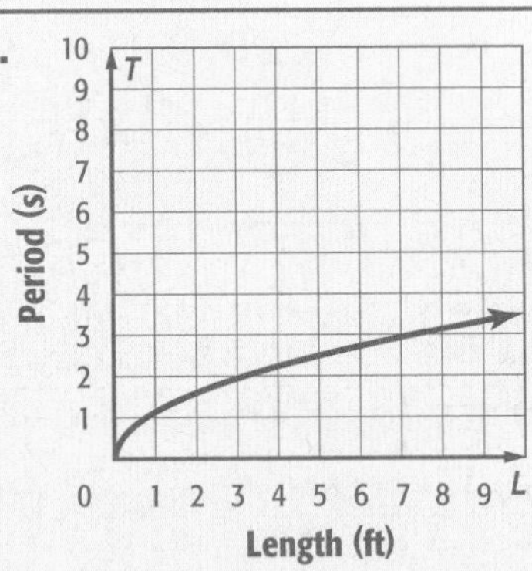

45b. 1.57 s, 2.48 s, 3.14 s

46a.

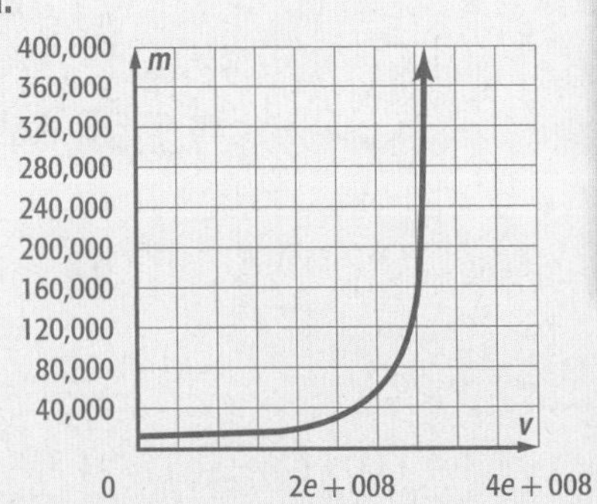

52. To be a function, for every x-value there must be exactly one y-value. For every x in this equation there are two y-values, one that is negative and one that is positive. Also, the graph of $y = \pm\sqrt{x}$ does not pass the vertical line test.

Example 4 p. 426

Graph each inequality. 31–38. See Chapter 7 Answer Appendix.

31. $y < \sqrt{x - 5}$

32. $y > \sqrt{x + 6}$

33. $y \geq -4\sqrt{x + 3}$

34. $y \leq -2\sqrt{x - 6}$

35. $y > 2\sqrt{x + 7} - 5$

36. $y \geq 4\sqrt{x - 2} - 12$

37. $y \leq 6 - 3\sqrt{x - 4}$

38. $y < \sqrt{4x - 12} + 8$

B

39. PHYSICS The kinetic energy of an object is the energy produced due to its motion and mass. The formula for kinetic energy, measured in joules j, is $E = 0.5mv^2$, where m is the mass in kilograms and v is the velocity of the object in meters per second.

a. Solve the above formula for v. $v = \sqrt{\frac{2E}{m}}$

b. If a 1500-kilogram vehicle is generating 1 million joules of kinetic energy, how fast is it traveling? about 36.5 m/s

c. *Escape velocity* is the minimum velocity at which an object must travel to escape the gravitational field of a planet or other object. Suppose a 100,000-kilogram ship must have a kinetic energy of 3.624×10^{14} joules to escape the gravitational field of Jupiter. Estimate the escape velocity of Jupiter. about 85,135 m/s

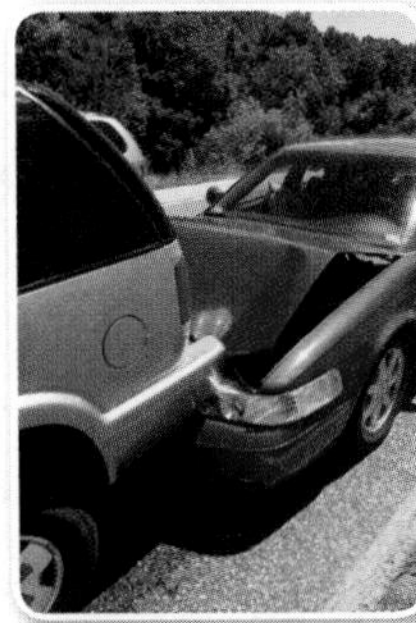

Real-World Link

The leading cause of driving accidents among teenagers is distractions. Thirteen percent of teens admit to text messaging while driving.

Source: Allstate Foundation

40c. No; it is not a linear function. The skid will be 4 times as long.

41. $y = \sqrt{x - 4} - 6$

42. $y = \sqrt{x + 2} + 4$

43. $y = -\sqrt{x + 6} - 6$

44a–e. See Chapter 7 Answer Appendix.

40. DRIVING After an accident, police can determine how fast a car was traveling before the driver put on his or her brakes by using the equation $v = \sqrt{30fd}$. In this equation, v represents the speed in miles per hour, f represents the coefficient of friction, and d represents the length of the skid marks in feet. The coefficient of friction varies depending on road conditions. Assume that $f = 0.6$. b. about 68 ft

a. Find the speed of a car that skids 25 feet. about 21.2 mph

b. If your car is going 35 miles per hour, how many feet would it take you to stop?

c. If the speed of a car is doubled, will the skid be twice as long? Explain.

Write the square root function represented by each graph.

41.

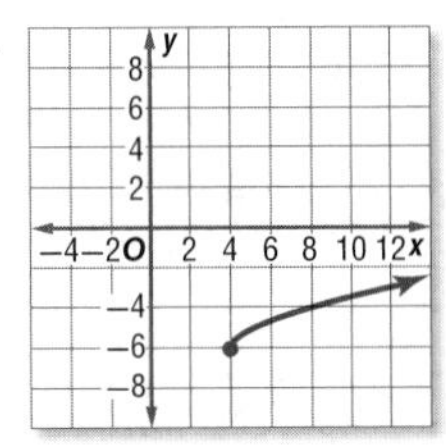

42.

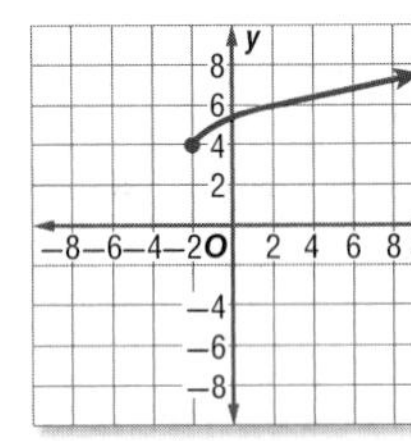

43.

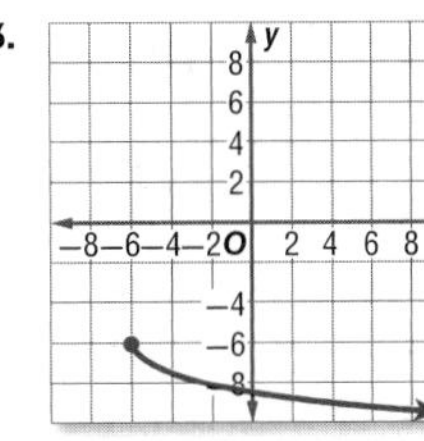

C

44. MULTIPLE REPRESENTATIONS In this problem, you will use the following functions to investigate transformations of square root functions.

$f(x) = 4\sqrt{x - 6} + 3$ $g(x) = \sqrt{16x + 1} - 6$ $h(x) = \sqrt{x + 3} + 2$

a. GRAPHICAL Graph each function on the same set of axes.

b. ANALYTICAL Identify the transformation on the graph of the parent function. What values caused each transformation?

c. ANALYTICAL Which functions appear to be stretched or compressed vertically? Explain your reasoning.

d. VERBAL The two functions that are stretched appear to be stretched by the same magnitude. How is this possible?

e. TABULAR Make a table of the rate of change for all three functions between 8 and 12 as compared to 12 and 16. What generalization about rate of change in square root functions can be made as a result of your findings?

Differentiated Instruction

AL OL ELL

If students continue to struggle with graphing square root functions,

Then have students work in pairs or small groups to discuss how to graph square root inequalities such as those in Exercises 31–38. Students should discuss how to determine the domain and range of an inequality, how to determine whether the boundary is solid or dashed, and how to determine where to shade the inequality.

Real-World Link

Pendulum clocks have been used to keep time since 1656, and they have not changed dramatically since then. These were the first clocks made that kept time accurately.

Source: HowStuffWorks, Inc.

45. PENDULUMS The period of a pendulum can be represented by $T = 2\pi\sqrt{\frac{L}{g}}$, where T is the time in seconds, L is the length in feet, and g is gravity, 32 feet per second squared. **a, b. See margin.**

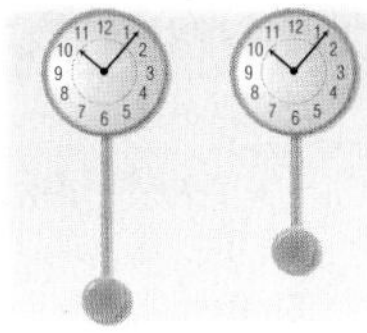

a. Graph the function for $0 \leq L \leq 10$.

b. What is the period for lengths of 2, 5, and 8 feet?

46. PHYSICS Using the function $m = \frac{m_0}{\sqrt{1 - \left(\frac{v^2}{c^2}\right)}}$, Einstein's theory of relativity states that the apparent mass m of a particle depends on its velocity v. An object that is traveling extremely fast, close to the speed of light c, will *appear* to have more mass compared to its mass at rest, m_0.

a. Use a graphing calculator to graph the function for a 10,000-kilogram ship for the domain $0 \leq v \leq 300{,}000{,}000$. Use 300 million meters per second for the speed of light. **See margin.**

b. What viewing window did you use to view the graph?

c. Determine the apparent mass m of the ship for speeds of 100 million, 200 million, and 299 million meters per second.
(100 million, 10,607)(200 million, 13,416)(299 million, 122,577)

46b. [0, 400,000,000] scl: 40,000,000 by [0, 400,000] scl: 40,000

H.O.T. Problems

Use **H**igher-**O**rder **T**hinking Skills

47. CHALLENGE Write an equation for a square root function with a domain of $\{x \mid x \geq -4\}$, a range of $\{y \mid y \leq 6\}$, and that passes through (5, 3).

48. REASONING For what positive values of a are the domain and range of $f(x) = \sqrt[a]{x}$ the set of real numbers? **all positive odd numbers**

49. OPEN ENDED Write a square root function for which the domain is $\{x \mid x \geq 8\}$ and the range is $\{y \mid y \leq 14\}$. **Sample answer: $y = -\sqrt{x - 8} + 14$**

50. WRITING IN MATH Explain why there are limitations on the domain and range of square root functions.

51. ERROR ANALYSIS Molly and Cleveland are graphing $y \leq \sqrt{5x + 15}$. Is either of them correct? Explain your reasoning.

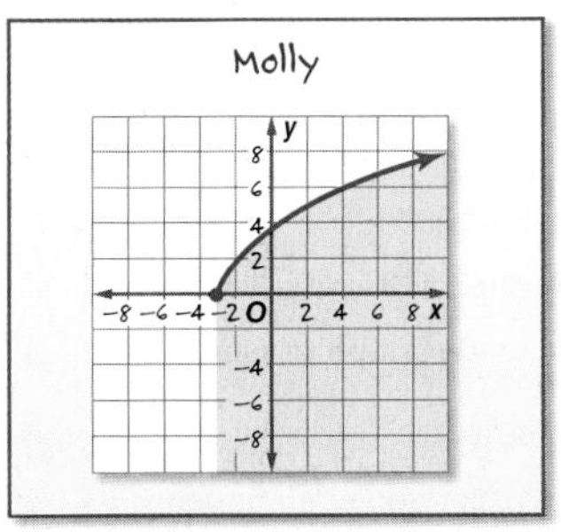

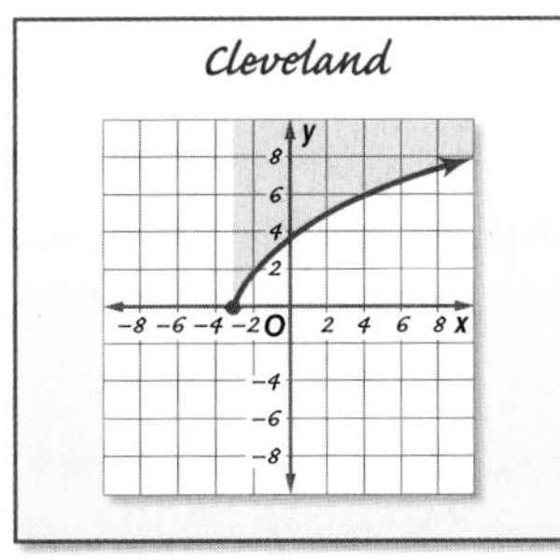

52. WRITING IN MATH Explain why $y = \pm\sqrt{x}$ is not a function. **See margin.**

53. OPEN ENDED Write an equation of a relation that contains a radical and its inverse such that:

a. the original relation is a function, and its inverse is not a function.

b. the original relation is not a function, and its inverse is a function.

47. Sample answer: $y = -\sqrt{x + 4} + 6$

50. Sample answer: The domain is limited because square roots of negative numbers are imaginary. The range is limited due to the limitation of the domain.

51. Molly is correct; Cleveland shaded incorrectly. He shaded above the graph when he should have shaded below.

53a. Sample answer: The original is $y = x^2 + 2$ and inverse is $y = \pm\sqrt{x - 2}$.

53b. Sample answer: The original is $y = \pm\sqrt{x} + 4$ and inverse is $y = (x - 4)^2$.

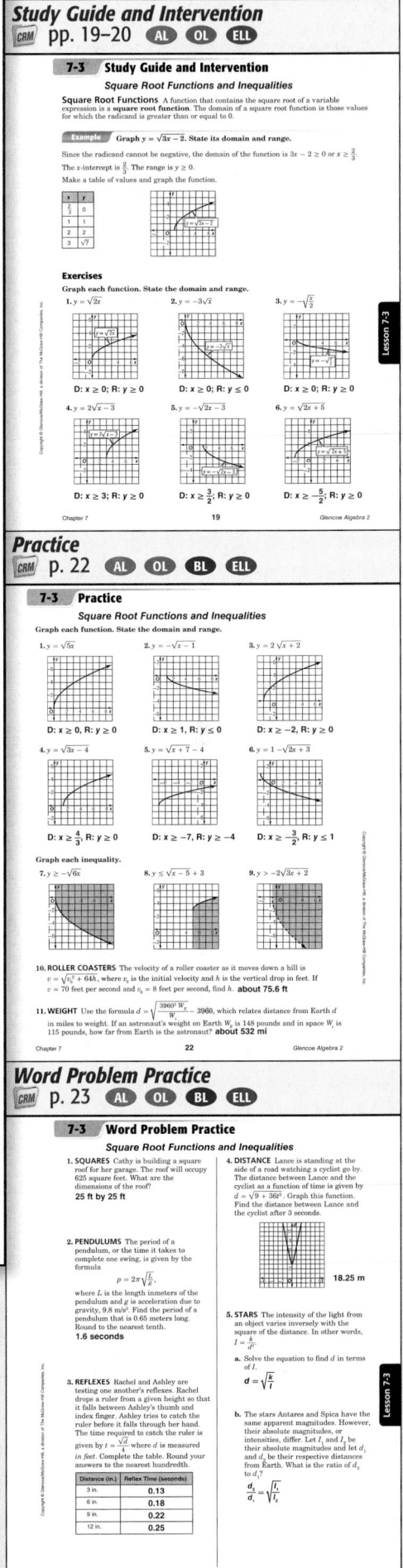

Study Guide and Intervention

CRM pp. 19–20 AL OL ELL

7-3 Study Guide and Intervention

Square Root Functions and Inequalities

Square Root Functions A function that contains the square root of a variable expression is a **square root function**. The domain of a square root function is those values for which the radicand is greater than or equal to 0.

Example Graph $y = \sqrt{3x - 2}$. State its domain and range.

Since the radicand cannot be negative, the domain of the function is $3x - 2 \geq 0$ or $x \geq \frac{2}{3}$. The x-intercept is $\frac{2}{3}$. The range is $y \geq 0$.

Make a table of values and graph the function.

x	y
$\frac{2}{3}$	0
1	1
2	2
3	$\sqrt{7}$

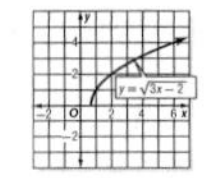

Exercises

Graph each function. State the domain and range.

1. $y = \sqrt{2x}$
2. $y = -3\sqrt{x}$
3. $y = -\sqrt{\frac{x}{2}}$

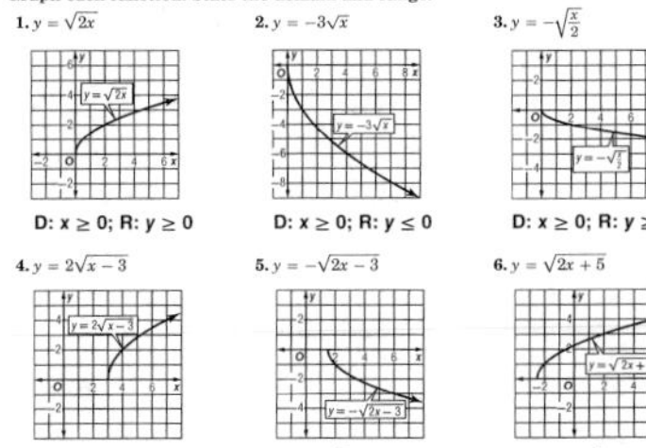

D: $x \geq 0$; R: $y \geq 0$ | D: $x \geq 0$; R: $y \leq 0$ | D: $x \geq 0$; R: $y \geq 0$

4. $y = 2\sqrt{x - 3}$
5. $y = -\sqrt{2x - 3}$
6. $y = \sqrt{2x + 5}$

D: $x \geq 3$; R: $y \geq 0$ | D: $x \geq \frac{3}{2}$; R: $y \geq 0$ | D: $x \geq -\frac{5}{2}$; R: $y \geq 0$

Lesson 7-3

Chapter 7 19 Glencoe Algebra 2

Practice

CRM p. 22 AL OL BL ELL

7-3 Practice

Square Root Functions and Inequalities

Graph each function. State the domain and range.

1. $y = \sqrt{5x}$
2. $y = -\sqrt{x - 1}$
3. $y = 2\sqrt{x + 2}$

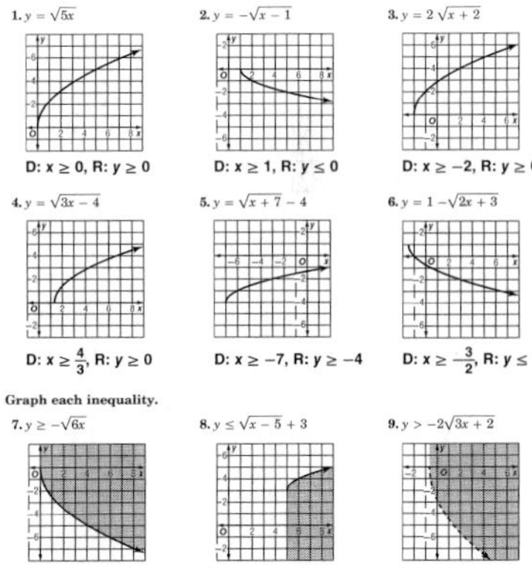

D: $x \geq 0$, R: $y \geq 0$ | D: $x \geq 1$, R: $y \leq 0$ | D: $x \geq -2$, R: $y \geq 0$

4. $y = \sqrt{3x - 4}$
5. $y = \sqrt{x + 7} - 4$
6. $y = 1 - \sqrt{2x + 3}$

D: $x \geq \frac{4}{3}$, R: $y \geq 0$ | D: $x \geq -7$, R: $y \geq -4$ | D: $x \geq -\frac{3}{2}$, R: $y \leq 1$

Graph each inequality.

7. $y \geq -\sqrt{6x}$
8. $y \leq \sqrt{x - 5} + 3$
9. $y > -2\sqrt{3x + 2}$

10. **ROLLER COASTERS** The velocity of a roller coaster as it moves down a hill is $v = \sqrt{v_0^2 + 64h}$, where v_0 is the initial velocity and h is the vertical drop in feet. If $v = 70$ feet per second and $v_0 = 8$ feet per second, find h. **about 75.6 ft**

11. **WEIGHT** Use the formula $d = \sqrt{\frac{3960^2 W_E}{W_s}} - 3960$, which relates distance from Earth d in miles to weight. If an astronaut's weight on Earth W_E is 148 pounds and in space W_s is 115 pounds, how far from Earth is the astronaut? **about 532 mi**

Chapter 7 22 Glencoe Algebra 2

Word Problem Practice

CRM p. 23 AL OL BL ELL

7-3 Word Problem Practice

Square Root Functions and Inequalities

1. **SQUARES** Cathy is building a square roof for her garage. The roof will occupy 625 square feet. What are the dimensions of the roof?
25 ft by 25 ft

2. **PENDULUMS** The period of a pendulum, or the time it takes to complete one swing, is given by the formula
$$p = 2\pi\sqrt{\frac{L}{g}},$$
where L is the length inmeters of the pendulum and g is acceleration due to gravity, 9.8 m/s². Find the period of a pendulum that is 0.65 meters long. Round to the nearest tenth.
1.6 seconds

3. **REFLEXES** Rachel and Ashley are testing one another's reflexes. Rachel drops a ruler from a given height so that it falls between Ashley's thumb and index finger. Ashley tries to catch the ruler before it falls through her hand. The time required to catch the ruler is given by $t = \frac{\sqrt{d}}{4}$ where d is measured *in feet*. Complete the table. Round your answers to the nearest hundredth.

Distance (in.)	Reflex Time (seconds)
3 in.	0.13
6 in.	0.18
9 in.	0.22
12 in.	0.25

4. **DISTANCE** Lance is standing at the side of a road watching a cyclist go by. The distance between Lance and the cyclist as a function of time is given by $d = \sqrt{9 + 36t^2}$. Graph this function. Find the distance between Lance and the cyclist after 3 seconds.

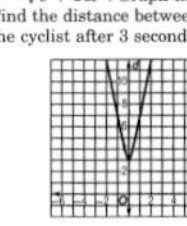

18.25 m

5. **STARS** The intensity of the light from an object varies inversely with the square of the distance. In other words, $I = \frac{k}{d^2}$.

a. Solve the equation to find d in terms of I.
$d = \sqrt{\frac{k}{I}}$

b. The stars Antares and Spica have the same apparent magnitudes. However, their absolute magnitudes, or intensities, differ. Let I_1 and I_2 be their absolute magnitudes and let d_1 and d_2 be their respective distances from Earth. What is the ratio of d_2 to d_1?
$\frac{d_2}{d_1} = \sqrt{\frac{I_1}{I_2}}$

Lesson 7-3

Chapter 7 23 Glencoe Algebra 2

Enrichment

CRM p. 24 OL BL

7-3 Enrichment

Reading Algebra

If two mathematical problems have basic structural similarities, they are said to be **analogous.** Using analogies is one way of discovering and proving new theorems.

The following numbered sentences discuss a three-dimensional analogy to the Pythagorean theorem.

01 Consider a tetrahedron with three perpendicular faces that meet at vertex O.
02 Suppose you want to know how the areas A, B, and C of the three faces that meet at vertex O are related to the area D of the face opposite vertex O.
03 It is natural to expect a formula analogous to the Pythagorean theorem $z^2 = x^2 + y^2$, which is true for a similar situation in two dimensions.
04 To explore the three-dimensional case, you might guess a formula and then try to prove it.
05 Two reasonable guesses are $D^3 = A^3 + B^3 + C^3$ and $D^2 = A^2 + B^2 + C^2$.

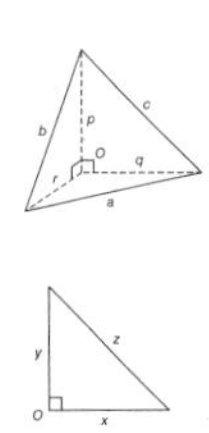

…er to the …umbered sentences t… …nswer the q…stions.

4 ASSESS

Crystal Ball In tomorrow's lesson, students will be simplifying radicals and using the calculator to approximate radicals. Have students write about how they think today's topic will connect with tomorrow's theme.

Additional Answers

62a.

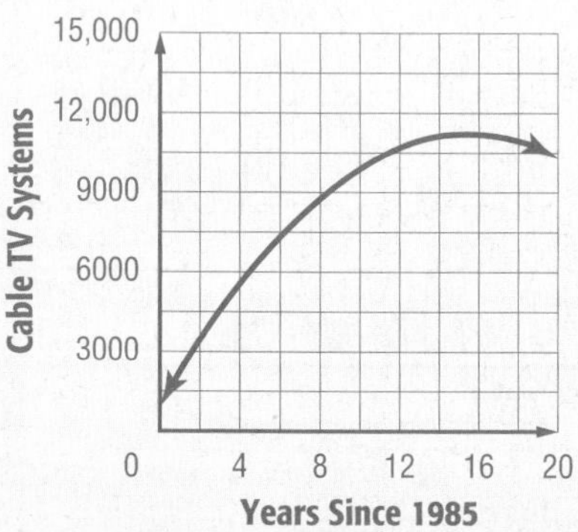

62d. The number of cable TV systems rose steadily from 1985 to 2000. Then the number began to decline. The trend may continue for some years, but the number of cable TV systems cannot decline at this rate indefinitely. The number cannot fall below 0. It is not likely that the number would come close to 0 for the foreseeable future; there is no reason to believe that cable TV systems will not be in use.

NGSSS PRACTICE 912.A.4.1, 912.P.3.1, 912.A.4.2

54. The expression $\frac{-64x^6}{8x^3}$, $x \neq 0$, is equivalent to **D**

A. $8x^2$
B. $8x^3$
C. $-8x^2$
D. $-8x^3$

55. PROBABILITY For a game, Patricia must roll a standard die and draw a card from a deck of 26 cards, each card having a letter of the alphabet on it. What is the probability that Patricia will roll an odd number and draw a letter in her name? **G**

F. $\frac{2}{3}$
G. $\frac{3}{26}$
H. $\frac{1}{13}$
I. $\frac{1}{26}$

56. THINK SOLVE EXPLAIN **SHORT RESPONSE** What is the product of $(d + 6)$ and $(d - 3)$? $d^2 + 3d - 18$

57. ACT/SAT Given the graph of the square root function below, which must be true? **D**

I. The domain is all real numbers.
II. The function is $y = \sqrt{x} + 3.5$.
III. The range is about $\{y \mid y \geq 3.5\}$.

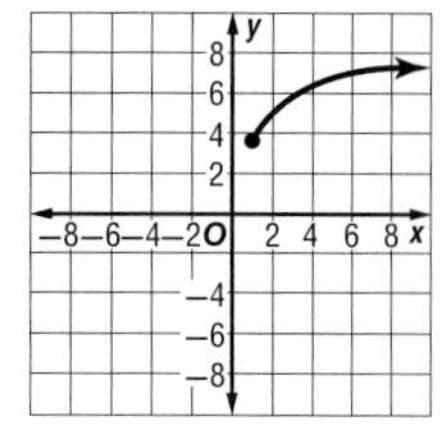

A. I only
B. I, II, and III
C. II and III only
D. III only

Spiral Review

Determine whether each pair of functions are inverse functions. Write *yes* or *no*. (Lesson 7-2)

58. $f(x) = 2x$ **yes**
$g(x) = \frac{1}{2}x$

59. $f(x) = 3x - 7$ **no**
$g(x) = \frac{1}{3}x - \frac{7}{16}$

60. $f(x) = \frac{3x + 2}{5}$ **yes**
$g(x) = \frac{5x - 2}{3}$

61. TIME The formula $h = \frac{m}{60}$ converts minutes m to hours h, and $d = \frac{h}{24}$ converts hours h to days d. Write a function that converts minutes to days. (Lesson 7-1) $[d \circ h](m) = \frac{m}{1440}$

62. CABLE TV The number of households in the United States with cable TV after 1985 can be modeled by the function $C(t) = -43.2t^2 + 1343t + 790$, where t represents the number of years since 1985. (Lesson 6-4) **a, d. See margin.** **b. rel. max. between $t = 15$ and $t = 16$, and no rel. min.; $C(t) \to -\infty$ as $t \to -\infty$, $C(t) \to -\infty$ as $t \to +\infty$**

a. Graph this equation for the years 1985 to 2005.
b. Describe the turning points of the graph and its end behavior.
c. What is the domain of the function? Use the graph to estimate the range for the function. **D = {all real numbers}; R = $\{C(t) \mid C(t) \leq 11{,}225\}$**
d. What trends in households with cable TV does the graph suggest? Is it reasonable to assume that the trend will continue indefinitely?

Skills Review

Determine whether each number is *rational* or *irrational*. (Lesson 1-2)

63. 6.34 **rational** **64.** 3.787887888... **irrational** **65.** 5.333... **rational** **66.** 1.25 **rational**

Differentiated Instruction OL BL

Extension How is the graph of $y = \sqrt{x - 3} - 5$ related to the graph of $y = \sqrt{x}$? It is translated 3 units right and 5 units down.

*n*th Roots

Why?

According to a world-wide injury prevention study, the number of collisions between bicycles and automobiles increased as the number of bicycles per intersection increased. The relationship can be expressed using the equation $c = \sqrt[5]{b^2}$, where b is the number of bicycles and c is the number of collisions.

Then
You worked with square root functions. (Lesson 7-3)

Now
- Simplify radicals.
- Use a calculator to approximate radicals.

NGSSS
MA.912.A.10.3 Decide whether a given statement is always, sometimes, or never true (statements involving linear or quadratic expressions, equations, or inequalities rational or radical expressions or logarithmic or exponential functions).

New Vocabulary
*n*th root
radical sign
index
radicand
principal root

FL Math Online
glencoe.com

Simplify Radicals Finding the square root of a number and squaring a number are inverse operations. To find the square root of a number a, you must find a number with a square of a. Similarly, the inverse of raising a number to the nth power is finding the ***n*th root** of a number.

Powers	Factors	Words	Roots
$x^3 = 64$	$4 \cdot 4 \cdot 4 = 64$	4 is a cube root of 64.	$\sqrt[3]{64} = 4$
$x^4 = 625$	$5 \cdot 5 \cdot 5 \cdot 5 = 625$	5 is a fourth root of 625.	$\sqrt[4]{625} = 5$
$x^5 = 32$	$2 \cdot 2 \cdot 2 \cdot 2 \cdot 2 = 32$	2 is a fifth root of 32.	$\sqrt[5]{32} = 2$
$a^n = b$	$\underbrace{a \cdot a \cdot a \cdot \cdots \cdot a}_{n \text{ factors of } a} = b$	a is an nth root of b.	$\sqrt[n]{b} = a$

This pattern suggests the following formal definition of an nth root.

Key Concept — **Definition of *n*th Root**

Words For any real numbers a and b, and any positive integer n, if $a^n = b$, then a is an nth root of b.

Example Because $(-3)^4 = 81$, -3 is a fourth root of 81 and 3 is a principal root.

The symbol $\sqrt[n]{}$ indicates an nth root.

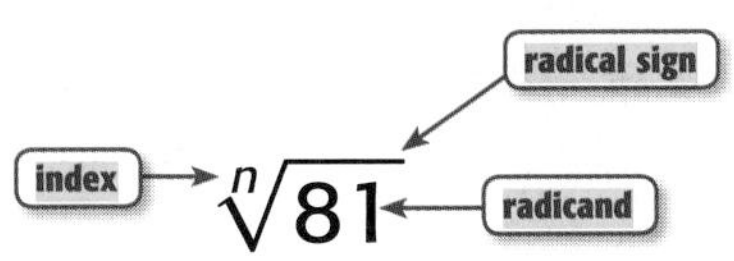

Some numbers have more than one real nth root. For example, 64 has two square roots, 8 and -8, since 8^2 and $(-8)^2$ both equal 64. When there is more than one real root and n is even, the nonnegative root is called the **principal root**.

Some examples of nth roots are listed below.

$\sqrt{25} = 5$ — $\sqrt{25}$ indicates the principal square root of 25.

$-\sqrt{25} = -5$ — $-\sqrt{25}$ indicates the opposite of the principal square root of 25.

$\pm\sqrt{25} = \pm 5$ — $\pm\sqrt{25}$ indicates both square roots of 25.

1 FOCUS

Vertical Alignment

Before Lesson 7-4
Work with square root functions.

Lesson 7-4
Simplify radicals.
Use a calculator to approximate radicals.

After Lesson 7-4
Determine solutions of square root equations using algebraic methods.

2 TEACH

Scaffolding Questions

Have students read the *Why?* section of the lesson.

Ask:
- What is the independent variable that is measured? number of bicycles
- What is the dependent variable that is calculated? number of collisions
- Do you think the number of collisions will increase or decrease as the number of bicycles increases? increase

Lesson 7-4 Resources

Resource	Approaching-Level	On-Level	Beyond-Level	English Learners
Teacher Edition	• Differentiated Instruction, p. 433	• Differentiated Instruction, pp. 433, 436	• Differentiated Instruction, p. 436	
Chapter Resource Masters	• Study Guide and Intervention, pp. 25–26 • Skills Practice, p. 27 • Practice, p. 28 • Word Problem Practice, p. 29	• Study Guide and Intervention, pp. 25–26 • Skills Practice, p. 27 • Practice, p. 28 • Word Problem Practice, p. 29 • Enrichment, p. 30	• Practice, p. 28 • Word Problem Practice, p. 29 • Enrichment, p. 30	• Study Guide and Intervention, pp. 25–26 • Skills Practice, p. 27 • Practice, p. 28 • Word Problem Practice, p. 29
Transparencies	• 5-Minute Check Transparency 7-4	• 5-Minute Check Transparency 7-4	• 5-Minute Check Transparency 7-4	• 5-Minute Check Transparency 7-4
Other	• Study Notebook • Teaching Algebra with Manipulatives	• Study Notebook • Teaching Algebra with Manipulatives	• Study Notebook	• Study Notebook • Teaching Algebra with Manipulatives

Simplify Radicals

Example 1 shows how to simplify nth root expressions. **Example 2** shows how to use the absolute value of the result to simplify the nth roots of expressions with even powers.

Formative Assessment

Use the Guided Practice exercises after each example to determine students' understanding of concepts.

Additional Example

1 Simplify.

a. $\pm\sqrt{16x^8}$ $\pm 4x^4$

b. $-\sqrt{(q^3+5)^4}$ $-(q^3+5)^2$

c. $\sqrt[5]{243a^{10}b^{15}}$ $3a^2b^3$

d. $\sqrt{-4}$ $2i$

Additional Examples also in Interactive Classroom PowerPoint® Presentations

IWB INTERACTIVE WHITEBOARD READY

Watch Out!

Common Error Be sure students understand that since $3^2 = 9$ and $(-3)^2 = 9$, the number 9 has two square roots, 3 and –3. However, the value of $\sqrt{9}$ is 3 only. To indicate both square roots and not just the principal root, the expression must be given as $\pm\sqrt{9}$.

Focus on Mathematical Content

Use of Absolute Value In general, if n is an integer greater than or equal to 2 and a is a real number, then $\sqrt[n]{a^n} = a$ if n is odd and $\sqrt[n]{a^n} = |a|$ if n is even.

Key Concept — Real *n*th Roots

Suppose n is an integer greater than 1, and a is a real number.

a	n is even.	n is odd.
$a > 0$	1 unique positive and 1 unique negative real root: $\pm\sqrt[n]{a}$; positive root is principal root	1 unique positive and 0 negative real root: $\sqrt[n]{a}$
$a < 0$	0 real roots	0 positive and 1 negative real root: $\sqrt[n]{a}$
$a = 0$	1 real root: $\sqrt[n]{0} = 0$	1 real root: $\sqrt[n]{0} = 0$

EXAMPLE 1 Find Roots

Simplify.

a. $\pm\sqrt{16y^4}$

$\pm\sqrt{16y^4} = \pm\sqrt{(4y^2)^2}$

$= \pm 4y^2$

The square roots of $16y^4$ are $\pm 4y^2$.

b. $-\sqrt{(x^2-6)^8}$

$-\sqrt{(x^2-6)^8} = -\sqrt{[(x^2-6)^4]^2}$

$= -(x^2-6)^4$

The opposite of the principal square root of $(x^2-6)^8$ is $-(x^2-6)^4$.

c. $\sqrt[5]{243a^{20}b^{25}}$

$\sqrt[5]{243a^{20}b^{25}} = \sqrt[5]{(3a^4b^5)^5}$

$= 3a^4b^5$

The fifth root of $243a^{20}b^{25}$ is $3a^4b^5$.

d. $\sqrt{-16x^4y^8}$

$\sqrt[2]{-16x^4y^8}$ ← b is negative. ← n is even.

There are no real roots since $\sqrt{-16}$ is not a real number. However, there are two imaginary roots, $4ix^2y^4$ and $-4ix^2y^4$.

Review Vocabulary

pure imaginary numbers Square roots of negative real numbers; for any positive real number b, $\sqrt{-b^2} = \sqrt{b^2} \cdot \sqrt{-1}$, or bi, where i is the imaginary unit. (Lesson 5-4)

Guided Practice

1A. $\pm\sqrt{36x^{10}}$ $\pm 6x^5$

1B. $-\sqrt{(y+7)^{16}}$ $-(y+7)^8$

Personal Tutor glencoe.com

When you find an even root of an even power and the result is an odd power, you must use the absolute value of the result to ensure that the answer is nonnegative.

StudyTip

Odd Index If n is odd, there is only one real root. Therefore, there is no principal root when n is odd, and absolute value symbols are never needed.

EXAMPLE 2 Simplify Using Absolute Value

Simplify.

a. $\sqrt[4]{y^4}$

$\sqrt[4]{y^4} = |y|$

Since y could be negative, you must take the absolute value of y to identify the principal root.

b. $\sqrt[6]{64(x^2-3)^{18}}$

$\sqrt[6]{64(x^2-3)^{18}} = 2|(x^2-3)^3|$

Since the index 6 is even and the exponent 3 is odd, you must use absolute value.

Guided Practice

2A. $\sqrt{36y^6}$ $6|y^3|$

2B. $\sqrt[4]{16(x-3)^{12}}$ $2|(x-3)^3|$

Personal Tutor glencoe.com

Watch Out!

Preventing Errors When discussing the information following Example 1, suggest that another way to simplify radicals that involve only numbers and no variables is to simplify the expression under the radical sign first. For example, $\sqrt{(-5)^2}$ could be rewritten by *first* simplifying under the radical sign to get $\sqrt{25}$, and then taking the principal root to get 5. Similarly, $\sqrt{(-2)^6}$ simplifies to $\sqrt{64}$, so the principal square root is 8.

Approximate Radicals with a Calculator Recall that real numbers that cannot be expressed as terminating or repeating decimals are irrational numbers. Approximations for irrational numbers are often used in real-world problems.

Real-World EXAMPLE 3 Approximate Radicals

INJURY PREVENTION Refer to the beginning of the lesson.

a. If $c = \sqrt[5]{b^2}$ represents the number of collisions and b represents the number of bicycle riders per intersection, estimate the number of collisions at an intersection that has 1000 bicycle riders per week.

Understand You want to find out how many collisions there were.

Plan Let b be the number of bicycles. The number of collisions c is 1000.

Solve

$c = \sqrt[5]{b^2}$	Original formula
$= \sqrt[5]{1000^2}$	$b = 1000$
≈ 15.85	Use a calculator.

There are about 16 collisions per week at the intersection.

Check

$15.85 \stackrel{?}{=} \sqrt[5]{b^2}$	$c = 15.85$
$15.85^5 \stackrel{?}{=} b^2$	Raise each side to the fifth power.
$1{,}000{,}337 \stackrel{?}{=} b^2$	Simplify.
$1000 \approx b$ ✓	Take the square root of each side.

Real-World Link

77% of the employees in China commute by bicycle.

Source: International Bicycle Fund

b. If the total number of collisions reported in one week is 21, estimate the number of bicycle riders that passed through that intersection.

$c = \sqrt[5]{b^2}$	Original formula
$21 = \sqrt[5]{b^2}$	$c = 27$
$21^5 = b^2$	Raise each side to the fifth power.
$4{,}084{,}101 = b^2$	Simplify.
$2021 \approx b$	Take the square root of each side.

Guided Practice

3A. The surface area of a sphere can be determined from the volume of the sphere using the formula $S = \sqrt[3]{36\pi V^2}$, where V is the volume. Determine the surface area of a sphere with a volume of 200 cubic inches. about 165 in^2

3B. If the surface area of a sphere is about 214.5 square inches, determine the volume. 295.4 in^2

Personal Tutor glencoe.com

Check Your Understanding

Examples 1 and 2 p. 432 Simplify.

1. $\pm\sqrt{100y^8}$ $\pm 10y^4$
2. $-\sqrt{49u^8v^{12}}$ $-7u^4v^6$
3. $\sqrt{(y-6)^8}$ $(y-6)^4$
4. $\sqrt[4]{16g^{16}h^{24}}$ $2g^4h^6$
5. $\sqrt{-16y^4}$ $\pm 4iy^2$
6. $\sqrt[6]{64(2y+1)^{18}}$ $2|(2y+1)^3|$

Example 3 p. 433 Use a calculator to approximate each value to three decimal places.

7. $\sqrt{58}$ 7.616
8. $-\sqrt{76}$ -8.718
9. $\sqrt[5]{-43}$ -2.122
10. $\sqrt[4]{71}$ 2.903

11. **TELEVISION** The radius r of the orbit of a television satellite is given by $\sqrt[3]{\frac{GMt^2}{4\pi^2}}$, where G is the universal gravitational constant, M is the mass of Earth, and t is the time it takes the satellite to complete one orbit. Find the radius of the satellite's orbit if G is $6.67 \times 10^{-11} N \cdot m^2/kg^2$, M is 5.98×10^{24} kg, and t is 2.6×10^6 seconds. about 4.088×10^8 m

TEACH with TECH

BLOG Have students write a blog entry explaining how to find the number of roots (and their signs) before performing any calculations.

Additional Example

2 Simplify.

a. $\sqrt[6]{t^6}$ $|t|$

b. $\sqrt[5]{243(x+2)^{15}}$ $3(x+2)^3$

Approximate Radicals With a Calculator

Example 3 shows students how to use a calculator to approximate the solution to a real-world situation.

Additional Example

3 **FISH** The relationship between the length and mass of Pacific halibut can be approximated by the equation $L = 0.46\sqrt[3]{M}$, where L is the length of the fish in meters and M is the mass in kilograms. Use a calculator to approximate the length of a 30-kilogram Pacific halibut. about 1.43 m

Differentiated Instruction AL OL

Logical Learners Some students tend to think that x must represent a positive number and $-x$ must represent a negative number. Reading $-x$ as "the opposite of x" should help them understand that $-x$ is 9 if $x = -9$. Also, explain that -9 has no square root that is a real number. That is, no real number can be squared to give -9. Remind students that $\sqrt{-9}$ is $3i$, an imaginary number.

3 PRACTICE

Formative Assessment

Use Exercises 1–11 to check for understanding.

Use the chart at the bottom of this page to customize assignments for your students.

Multiple Representations In Exercise 58, students use a table of values, a graph, and logical analysis to explore inverse functions.

Watch Out!

Error Analysis For Exercise 59, students should see that $\sqrt[4]{16x^4y^8} = \sqrt[4]{16} \cdot \sqrt[4]{x^4} \cdot \sqrt[4]{y^8}$ $= 2y^2|x|$, so Kimi is correct. Explain to students that $\sqrt[n]{b^{2n}}$ is b^2, with no absolute value symbol, while $\sqrt[n]{b^n}$ is $|b|$.

Additional Answers

57. bald eagle: ≈ 226.5 Cal/d; golden retriever: ≈ 939.6 Cal/d; komodo dragon: ≈ 1811.8 Cal/d; bottlenose dolphin: ≈ 3235.5 Cal/d; Asian elephant: ≈ 24,344.4 Cal/d

64. Sample answer: They are needed to ensure that the answer is not a negative number. When we take any odd root of a number, we find that there is just one answer. If the number is positive, the root is positive. If the number is negative, the root is negative. Every positive real number has two *nth* roots when *n* is even; one of these roots is positive and one is negative. Negative real numbers do not have *nth* roots when *n* is even. Absolute value signs are never needed when finding odd roots. When finding even *nth* roots, absolute value signs are sometimes necessary, as with square roots.

Practice and Problem Solving

● = **Step-by-Step Solutions** begins on page R20.
Extra Practice begins on page 947.

Examples 1 and 2 p. 432

Simplify.

12. $\pm\sqrt{121x^4y^16}$ $\pm 11x^2y^8$
13. $\pm\sqrt{225a^{16}b^{36}}$ $\pm 15a^8b^{18}$
14. $\pm\sqrt{49x^4}$ $\pm 7x^2$
15. $-\sqrt{16c^4d^2}$ $-4c^2|d|$
16. $-\sqrt{81a^{16}b^{20}c^{12}}$
17. $-\sqrt{400x^{32}y^{40}}$ $-20x^{16}y^{20}$
18. $\sqrt{(x+15)^4}$ $(x+15)^2$
19. $\sqrt{(x^2+6)^{16}}$ $(x^2+6)^8$
20. $\sqrt{(a^2+4a)^{12}}$ $(a^2+4a)^6$
21. $\sqrt[3]{8a^6b^{12}}$ $2a^2b^4$
22. $\sqrt[6]{d^{24}x^{36}}$ d^4x^6
23. $\sqrt[3]{27b^{18}c^{12}}$ $3b^6c^4$
24. $-\sqrt{(2x+1)^6}$
25. $\sqrt{-(x+2)^8}$ $\pm i(x+2)^4$
26. $\sqrt[3]{-(y-9)^9}$ $-(y-9)^3$
27. $\sqrt[6]{x^{18}}$ $|x^3|$
28. $\sqrt[4]{a^{12}}$ $|a^3|$
29. $\sqrt[3]{a^{12}}$ a^4
30. $\sqrt[4]{81(x+4)^4}$ $3|(x+4)|$
31. $\sqrt[3]{(4x-7)^{24}}$ $(4x-7)^8$
32. $\sqrt[3]{(y^3+5)^{18}}$ $(y^3+5)^6$
33. $\sqrt[4]{256(5x-2)^{12}}$
34. $\sqrt[8]{x^{16}y^8}$ $x^2|y|$
35. $\sqrt[5]{32a^{15}b^{10}}$ $2a^3b^2$

16. $-9a^8b^{10}c^6$
24. $-|(2x+1)^3|$
33. $4|(5x-2)^3|$

Example 3 p. 433

36. **SHIPPING** An online book store wants to increase the size of the boxes it uses to ship orders. The new volume N is equal to the old volume V times the scale factor F cubed, or $N = V \cdot F^3$. What is the scale factor if the old volume was 0.8 cubic feet and the new volume is 21.6 cubic feet? 3

37. **GEOMETRY** The side length of a cube is determined by $r = \sqrt[3]{V}$, where V is the volume in cubic units. Determine the side length of a cube with a volume of 512 cm^3. 8 cm

Use a calculator to approximate each value to three decimal places.

38. $\sqrt{92}$ 9.592
39. $-\sqrt{150}$ −12.247
40. $\sqrt{0.43}$ 0.656
41. $\sqrt{0.62}$ 0.787
42. $\sqrt[3]{168}$ 5.518
43. $\sqrt[5]{-4382}$ −5.350
44. $\sqrt[6]{(8912)^2}$ 20.733
45. $\sqrt[5]{(4756)^2}$ 29.573

B

46. **GEOMETRY** The radius r of a sphere with volume V can be found using the formula $r = \sqrt[3]{\frac{3V}{4\pi}}$.

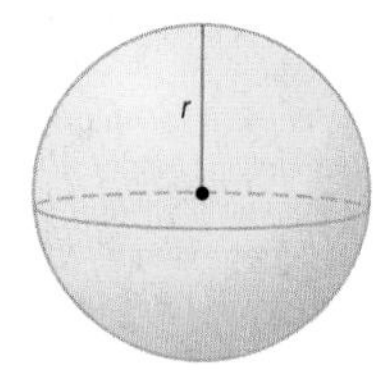

a. Determine the radius for volumes of 1000 cm^3, 8000 cm^3, and 64,000 cm^3. (1000, 6.2), (8000, 12.4), (64,000, 24.8)

b. How does the volume of the sphere change if the radius is doubled? Explain.

46b. Sample answer: As *r* doubles, the volume increases by a factor of 2^3 or 8.

Simplify. 47. $14|c^3|d^2$ 48. $\pm 8iy^4z^6$ 49. $-3a^5b^3$ 50. $\pm 2ix^4y^2$ 51. $20x^8|y^3|$

47. $\sqrt{196c^6d^4}$
48. $\sqrt{-64y^8z^6}$
49. $\sqrt[3]{-27a^{15}b^9}$
50. $\sqrt[4]{-16x^{16}y^8}$
51. $\sqrt{400x^{16}y^6}$
52. $\sqrt[3]{8c^3d^{12}}$ $2cd^4$
53. $\sqrt[3]{64(x+y)^6}$
54. $\sqrt[5]{-(y-z)^{15}}$

53. $4(x+y)^2$
54. $-(y-z)^3$

55. **PHYSICS** Johannes Kepler developed the formula $d = \sqrt[3]{6t^2}$, where d is the distance of a planet from the Sun in millions of miles and t is the number of Earth-days that it takes for the planet to orbit the Sun. If the length of a year on Mars is 687 Earth-days, how far from the Sun is Mars? about 141 million mi

56. **CHEMISTRY** All matter is composed of atoms. The nucleus of an atom is the center portion of the atom that contains most of the mass of the atom. A theoretical formula for the radius r of the nucleus of an atom is $r = (1.3 \times 10^{-15})\sqrt[3]{A}$ meters, where A is the mass number of the nucleus. Find the radius of the nucleus for each atom in the table.

Atom	Mass Number
carbon	6
oxygen	8
sodium	11
aluminum	13
chlorine	17

56. carbon: $\approx 2.36 \times 10^{-15}$; oxygen: $= 2.6 \times 10^{-15}$; sodium: $\approx 2.9 \times 10^{-15}$; aluminum: $\approx 3.1 \times 10^{-15}$; chlorine: $\approx 3.34 \times 10^{-15}$

Differentiated Homework Options

Level	Assignment	Two-Day Option	
AL Basic	12–45, 59, 61, 63–64, 70–92	13–45 odd, 70–73	12–44 even, 59, 61, 63–64, 74–92
OL Core	13–45 odd, 46, 47–53 odd, 55–59 61, 63–64, 70–92	12–45, 70–73	46–59, 61, 63–64, 74–92
BL Advanced	46–86, (optional: 87–92)		

434 Chapter 7 Inverses and Radical Functions and Relations

Real-World Link

The komodo dragon is the largest lizard in the world, spanning up to over 10 feet in length. A large male can weigh over 500 pounds after a large meal.

Source: The Circle of the Dragon

57. **BIOLOGY** Kleiber's Law, $P = 73.3\sqrt[4]{m^3}$, shows the relationship between the mass m in kilograms of an organism and its metabolism P in Calories per day. Determine the metabolism for each of the animals listed at the right. **See margin.**

Animal	Mass (kg)
bald eagle	4.5
golden retriever	30
komodo dragon	72
bottlenose dolphin	156
Asian elephant	2300

58. **MULTIPLE REPRESENTATIONS** In this problem, you will use $f(x) = x^n$ and $g(x) = \sqrt[n]{x}$ to explore inverses. **a, b. See Chapter 7 Answer Appendix.**

a. **TABULAR** Make tables for $f(x)$ and $g(x)$ using $n = 3$ and $n = 4$.

b. **GRAPHICAL** Graph the equations.

c. **ANALYTICAL** Which equations are functions? Which functions are one-to-one?

d. **ANALYTICAL** For what values of n are $g(x)$ and $f(x)$ inverses of each other?

e. **VERBAL** What conclusions can you make about $g(x) = \sqrt[n]{x}$ and $f(x) = x^n$ for all positive even values of n? for odd values of n?

H.O.T. Problems Use Higher-Order Thinking Skills

59. **ERROR ANALYSIS** Ashley and Kimi are simplifying $\sqrt[4]{16x^4y^8}$. Is either of them correct? Explain your reasoning.

Ashley	Kimi
$\sqrt[4]{16x^4y^8} = \sqrt[4]{(2xy^2)^4}$ $= 2\lvert xy^2 \rvert$	$\sqrt[4]{16x^4y^8} = \sqrt[4]{(2xy^2)^4}$ $= 2y^2\lvert x \rvert$

60. **CHALLENGE** Under what conditions is $\sqrt{x^2 + y^2} = x + y$ true? **when x or y or both are 0**

61. **REASONING** Determine whether the statement $\sqrt[4]{(-x)^4} = x$ is *sometimes*, *always*, or *never* true.

62. **CHALLENGE** For what real values of x is $\sqrt[3]{x} > x$? **$0 < x < 1$, $x < -1$**

63. **OPEN ENDED** Write a number for which the principal square root and cube root are both integers. **Sample answers: 1, 64**

64. **WRITING IN MATH** Explain when and why absolute value symbols are needed when taking an nth root. **See margin.**

65. **CHALLENGE** Write an equivalent expression for $\sqrt[3]{2x} \cdot \sqrt[3]{8y}$. Simplify the radical. **$2\sqrt[3]{2xy}$**

CHALLENGE Simplify each expression.

66. $\sqrt[4]{0.0016}$ **0.2**

67. $\sqrt[7]{-0.0000001}$ **−0.1**

68. $\dfrac{\sqrt[5]{-0.00032}}{\sqrt[3]{-0.027}}$ **$\frac{2}{3}$**

69. **CHALLENGE** Solve $-\dfrac{5}{\sqrt{a}} = -125$ for a. **$\frac{1}{625}$**

58c. $f(x) = x^3$; $f(x) = x^4$; $g(x) = \sqrt[3]{x}$; $f(x) = x^3$ and $g(x) = \sqrt[3]{x}$

58d. positive odd values

58e. Sample answer: For all positive odd values of n, $f(x)$ and $g(x)$ are inverse functions. For all positive even values of n, $f(x)$ and $g(x)$ are inverse functions only if the range of $f(x)$ and the domain of $g(x)$ are restricted to positive values.

59. Kimi; Ashley's error was keeping the y^2 inside the absolute value symbol.

61. Sample answer: Sometimes; when $x = -3$, $\sqrt[4]{(-x)^4} = \lvert(-x)\rvert$ or 3. When $x = 3$, $\sqrt[4]{(-x)^4} = \lvert 3 \rvert$ or 3.

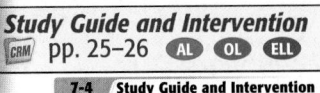

Study Guide and Intervention
CRM pp. 25–26 AL OL ELL

7-4 Study Guide and Intervention
nth Roots

Simplify Radicals

Square Root	For any real numbers a and b, if $a^2 = b$, then a is a square root of b.
nth Root	For any real numbers a and b, and any positive integer n, if $a^n = b$, then a is an nth root of b.
Real nth Roots of b, $\sqrt[n]{b}$, $-\sqrt[n]{b}$	1. If n is even and $b > 0$, then b has one positive real root and one real negative root. 2. If n is odd and $b > 0$, then b has one positive real root. 3. If n is even and $b < 0$, then b has no real roots. 4. If n is odd and $b < 0$, then b has one negative real root.

Example 1 Simplify $\sqrt{49z^8}$.

$\sqrt{49z^8} = \sqrt{(7z^4)^2} = 7z^4$

z^4 must be positive, so there is no need to take the absolute value.

Example 2 Simplify $-\sqrt[3]{(2a-1)^6}$

$-\sqrt[3]{(2a-1)^6} = -\sqrt[3]{[(2a-1)^2]^3} = -(2a-1)^2$

Exercises

Simplify.

1. $\sqrt{81}$ **9**
2. $\sqrt[3]{-343}$ **−7**
3. $\sqrt{144p^6}$ **$12\lvert p^3\rvert$**
4. $\pm\sqrt{4a^{10}}$ **$\pm 2a^5$**
5. $\sqrt[5]{243p^{10}}$ **$3p^2$**
6. $-\sqrt[3]{m^6n^9}$ **$-m^2n^3$**
7. $\sqrt[3]{-b^{12}}$ **$-b^4$**
8. $\sqrt{16a^{10}b^8}$ **$4\lvert a^5\rvert b^4$**
9. $\sqrt{121x^6}$ **$11\lvert x^3\rvert$**
10. $\sqrt{(4k)^4}$ **$16k^2$**
11. $\pm\sqrt{169r^4}$ **$\pm 13r^2$**
12. $-\sqrt[3]{-27p^6}$ **$3p^2$**
13. $-\sqrt{625y^2z^4}$ **$-25\lvert y\rvert z^2$**
14. $\sqrt{36q^{34}}$ **$6\lvert q^{17}\rvert$**
15. $\sqrt{100x^2y^4z^6}$ **$10\lvert x\rvert y^2\lvert z^3\rvert$**
16. $\sqrt[3]{-0.027}$ **−0.3**
17. $-\sqrt{-0.36}$ **not a real number**
18. $\sqrt{0.64p^{10}}$ **$0.8\lvert p^5\rvert$**
19. $\sqrt[4]{(2x)^8}$ **$4x^2$**
20. $\sqrt{(11y^2)^4}$ **$121y^4$**
21. $\sqrt[3]{(5a^2b)^6}$ **$25a^4b^2$**
22. $\sqrt{(3x-1)^2}$ **$\lvert 3x-1\rvert$**
23. $\sqrt[3]{(m-5)^6}$ **$(m-5)^2$**
24. $\sqrt{36x^2-12x+1}$ **$\lvert 6x-1\rvert$**

Chapter 7 25 Glencoe Algebra 2

Lesson 7-4

Practice
CRM p. 28 AL OL BL ELL

7-4 Practice
nth Roots

Simplify.

1. $\sqrt{0.81}$ **0.9**
2. $-\sqrt{324}$ **−18**
3. $-\sqrt[4]{256}$ **−4**
4. $\sqrt[6]{64}$ **2**
5. $\sqrt[3]{-64}$ **−4**
6. $\sqrt[3]{0.512}$ **0.8**
7. $\sqrt[5]{-243}$ **−3**
8. $-\sqrt[4]{1296}$ **−6**
9. $\sqrt[5]{\frac{-1024}{243}}$ **$-\frac{4}{3}$**
10. $\sqrt[5]{243x^{10}}$ **$3x^2$**
11. $\sqrt{14a^2}$ **$14\lvert a\rvert$**
12. $\sqrt{-(14a)^2}$ **not a real number**
13. $\sqrt{49m^2t^8}$ **$7\lvert m\rvert t^4$**
14. $\sqrt{\frac{16m^2}{25}}$ **$\frac{4\lvert m\rvert}{5}$**
15. $\sqrt[3]{-64r^2w^{15}}$ **$-4r^2w^5$**
16. $\sqrt{(2x)^8}$ **$16x^4$**
17. $-\sqrt[4]{625s^8}$ **$-5s^2$**
18. $\sqrt[3]{216p^3q^9}$ **$6pq^3$**
19. $\sqrt{676x^4y^6}$ **$26x^2\lvert y^3\rvert$**
20. $\sqrt[3]{-27x^9y^{12}}$ **$-3x^3y^4$**
21. $-\sqrt{144m^8n^6}$ **$-12m^4\lvert n^3\rvert$**
22. $\sqrt[5]{-32x^5y^{10}}$ **$-2xy^2$**
23. $\sqrt[6]{(m+4)^6}$ **$\lvert m+4\rvert$**
24. $\sqrt[3]{(2x+1)^3}$ **$2x+1$**
25. $-\sqrt{49a^{10}b^{16}}$ **$-7\lvert a^5\rvert b^8$**
26. $\sqrt[4]{(x-5)^8}$ **$(x-5)^2$**
27. $\sqrt[3]{343d^6}$ **$7d^2$**
28. $\sqrt{x^2+10x+25}$ **$\lvert x+5\rvert$**

Use a calculator to approximate each value to three decimal places.

29. $\sqrt{7.8}$ **2.793**
30. $-\sqrt{89}$ **−9.434**
31. $\sqrt[3]{25}$ **2.924**
32. $\sqrt[3]{-4}$ **−1.587**
33. $\sqrt[4]{1.1}$ **1.024**
34. $\sqrt[5]{-0.1}$ **−0.631**
35. $\sqrt[6]{5555}$ **4.208**
36. $\sqrt[4]{(0.94)^2}$ **0.970**

37. **RADIANT TEMPERATURE** Thermal sensors measure an object's *radiant* temperature, which is the amount of energy radiated by the object. The *internal* temperature of an object is called its *kinetic* temperature. The formula $T_r = T_k\sqrt[4]{e}$ relates an object's radiant temperature T_r to its kinetic temperature T_k. The variable e in the formula is a measure of how well the object radiates energy. If an object's kinetic temperature is 30°C and $e = 0.94$, what is the object's radiant temperature to the nearest tenth of a degree? **29.5°C**

38. **HERO'S FORMULA** Salvatore is buying fertilizer for his triangular garden. He knows the lengths of all three sides, so he is using Hero's formula to find the area. Hero's formula states that the area of a triangle is $\sqrt{s(s-a)(s-b)(s-c)}$, where a, b, and c are the lengths of the sides of the triangle and s is half the perimeter of the triangle. If the lengths of the sides of Salvatore's garden are 15 feet, 17 feet, and 20 feet, what is the area of the garden? Round your answer to the nearest whole number. **124 ft²**

Chapter 7 28 Glencoe Algebra 2

Word Problem Practice
CRM p. 29 AL OL BL ELL

7-4 Word Problem Practice
nth Roots

1. **CUBES** Cathy is building a cubic storage room. She wants the volume of the space to be 1728 cubic feet. What should the dimensions of the cube be?

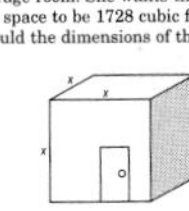

12 ft by 12 ft by 12 ft

2. **ASTRONOMY** A special form of Kepler's Third Law of Planetary Motion is given by $a = \sqrt[3]{P^2}$, where a is the average distance of an object from the Sun in AU (astronomical units) and P is the period of the orbit in years. The period of Jupiter's orbit is 12 years. What is its distance from the Sun in AU? **5.24 AU**

3. **TUNING** Two notes are an octave apart if the frequency of the higher note is twice the frequency of the lower note. Casey is experimenting with an instrument that has 6 notes tuned so that the frequency of each successive note increases by the same factor and the first and last note are an octave apart. By what factor does the frequency increase from note to note? **$\sqrt[5]{2}$ or approximately 1.15**

4. **MARKUPS** A wholesaler manufactures a part for D dollars. The wholesaler sells the part to a dealer for a P percent markup. The dealer sells the part to a retailer at an additional P percent markup. The retailer in turn sells the part to its customers marking up the price yet another P percent. What is the price that customers see? If the customer buys the part for \$80 and the original cost to make the part was \$29.15, what is the markup? **$D(1+P)^3$; 40%**

5. **PENDULUMS** Mr. Topalian's physics class is experimenting with pendulums. The class learned the formula $T = 2\pi\sqrt{\frac{L}{g}}$ which relates the time T that it takes for a pendulum to swing back and forth based on gravity g, equal to 32 feet per second squared, and the length of the pendulum L in feet.

a. One group in the class made a 2-foot long pendulum. Use the formula to determine how long it will take for their pendulum to swing back and forth. **1.57 seconds**

b. Another group decided they wanted to make a pendulum that took about 1.76 seconds to go back and forth. Approximately how long should their pendulum be? **2.5 feet**

Chapter 7 29 Glencoe Algebra 2

Lesson 7-4

Enrichment
CRM p. 30 OL BL

7-4 Enrichment

Approximating Square Roots

Consider the following expansion.

$$\left(a + \frac{b}{2a}\right)^2 = a^2 + \frac{2ab}{2a} + \frac{b^2}{4a^2} = a^2 + b + \frac{b^2}{4a^2}$$

Think what happens if a is very great in comparison to b. The term $\frac{b^2}{4a^2}$ is very small and can be disregarded in an approximation.

$$\left(a + \frac{b^2}{2a^2}\right)^2 \approx a^2 + b$$

$$a + \frac{b}{2a} \approx \sqrt{a^2 + b}$$

Suppose a number can be expressed as $a^2 + b$, $a > b$. Then an approximate value of the square root is $a + \frac{b}{2a}$. You should also see that $a - \frac{b}{2a} \approx \sqrt{a^2 - b}$.

Example Use the formula $\sqrt{a^2 \pm b} \approx a \pm \frac{b}{2a}$ to approximate $\sqrt{101}$ and $\sqrt{622}$.

a. $\sqrt{101} = \sqrt{100 + 1} = \sqrt{10^2 + 1}$

b. $\sqrt{622} = \sqrt{625 - 3} = \sqrt{25^2 - 3}$

4 ASSESS

Ticket Out the Door Make several copies of five different radicals similar to those in Example 1. Give one expression to each student. Have students simplify their radicals and, as the students leave the room, ask them to tell you the simplified expression.

Formative Assessment

Check for student understanding of concepts in Lessons 7-3 and 7-4.

CRM Quiz 2, p. 53

Additional Answers

74.

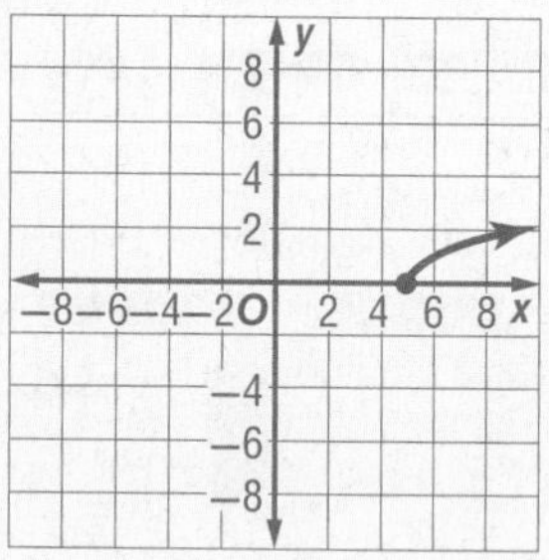

75.

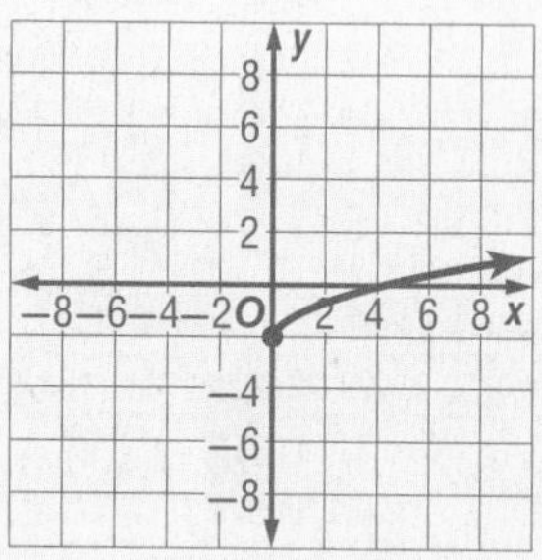

76.

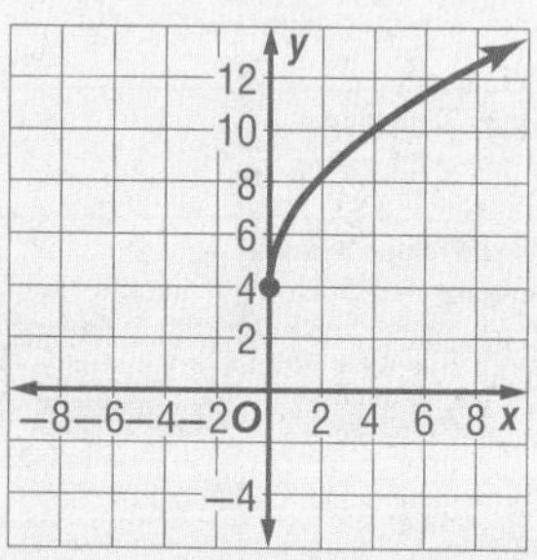

NGSSS PRACTICE 912.A.3.1, 912.A.1.6, 912.G.7.5

70. What is the value of w in the equation $\frac{1}{2}(4w + 36) = 3(4w - 3)$? **B**

A. 2
B. 2.7
C. 27
D. 36

71. What is the product of the complex numbers $(5 + i)$ and $(5 - i)$? **G**

F. 24
G. 26
H. $25 - i$
I. $26 - 10i$

72. THINK SOLVE EXPLAIN **EXTENDED RESPONSE** A cylindrical cooler has a diameter of 9 inches and a height of 11 inches. Tate plans to use it for soda cans that have a diameter of 2.5 inches and a height of 4.75 inches.

a. Tate plans to place two layers consisting of 9 cans each into the cooler. What is the volume of the space that will not be filled with the cans? **280.1 in^3**

b. Find the ratio of the volume of the cooler to the volume of the cans in part **a.** **about 1.7**

73. ACT/SAT Which of the following is closest to $\sqrt[3]{7.32}$? **B**

A. 1.8
B. 1.9
C. 2.0
D. 2.1

Spiral Review

Graph each function. (Lesson 7-3) **74–76. See margin.**

74. $y = \sqrt{x - 5}$

75. $y = \sqrt{x} - 2$

76. $y = 3\sqrt{x} + 4$

77. HEALTH The average weight of a baby born at a certain hospital is $7\frac{1}{2}$ pounds and the average length is 19.5 inches. One kilogram is about 2.2 pounds and 1 centimeter is about 0.3937 inches. Find the average weight in kilograms and the length in centimeters. (Lesson 7-2) **3.41 kg and 49.53 cm**

Simplify. (Lesson 6-1) **79.** $4x^2 + 22x - 34$

78. $(4c - 5) - (c + 11) + (-6c + 17)$ $-3c + 1$

79. $(11x^2 + 13x - 15) - (7x^2 - 9x + 19)$

80. $(d - 5)(d + 3)$ $d^2 - 2d - 15$

81. $(2a^2 + 6)^2$ $4a^4 + 24a^2 + 36$

82. GAS MILEAGE The gas mileage y in miles per gallon for a certain vehicle is given by the equation $y = 10 + 0.9x - 0.01x^2$, where x is the speed of the vehicle between 10 and 75 miles per hour. Find the range of speeds that would give a gas mileage of at least 25 miles per gallon. (Lesson 5-8) **$22.087 \leq x \leq 67.91$ mph**

Write each equation in vertex form, if not already in that form. Identify the vertex, axis of symmetry, and direction of opening. Then graph the function. (Lesson 5-7) **83–86. See Chapter 7 Answer Appendix.**

83. $y = -6(x + 2)^2 + 3$

84. $y = -\frac{1}{3}x^2 + 8x$

85. $y = (x - 2)^2 - 2$

86. $y = 2x^2 + 8x + 10$

Skills Review

Find each product. (Lesson 6-1)

87. $(x + 4)(x + 5)$ $x^2 + 9x + 20$

88. $(y - 3)(y + 4)$ $y^2 + y - 12$

89. $(a + 2)(a - 9)$ $a^2 - 7a - 18$

90. $(a - b)(a - 3b)$ $a^2 - 4ab + 3b^2$

91. $(x + 2y)(x - y)$ $x^2 + xy - 2y^2$

92. $2(w + z)(w - 4z)$ $2w^2 - 6wz - 8z^2$

Differentiated Instruction

OL BL

Extension Under what conditions is it true that $\frac{\sqrt[n]{a}}{\sqrt[n]{b}} = \sqrt[n]{\frac{a}{b}}$? n must be a positive integer; if n is even then $a \geq 0$ and $b > 0$; if n is odd then $b \neq 0$.

EXTEND 7-4

Graphing Technology Lab
Graphing *n*th Root Functions

FL Math Online glencoe.com
- Other Calculator Keystrokes
- Graphing Technology Personal Tutor

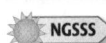

NGSSS **MA.912.A.2.6 Identify and graph common functions** (including but not limited to linear, rational, quadratic, cubic, **radical,** absolute value).

You can use a graphing calculator to graph *n*th root functions.

EXAMPLE 1 Graph an *n*th Root Function

Graph $y = \sqrt[5]{x}$.

Enter the equation as Y1 and graph.

KEYSTROKES: [Y=] 5 [MATH] 5 [X,T,θ,*n*] [GRAPH]

Another way to enter the equation is to use $y = x^{\frac{1}{5}}$**. You will learn about this later in Chapter 7.**

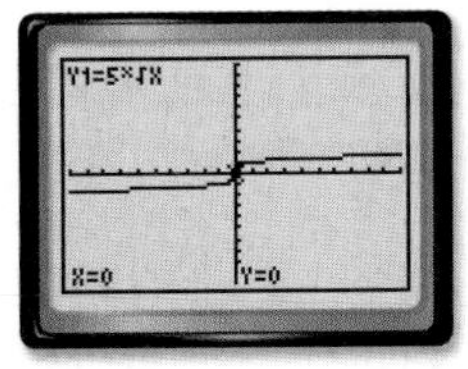

EXAMPLE 2 *n*th Root Functions with Different Roots

Graph and compare $y = \sqrt{x}$ **and** $y = \sqrt[4]{x}$.

Enter $y = \sqrt{x}$ as Y1 and $y = \sqrt[4]{x}$ as Y2. Then graph.

KEYSTROKES: [Y=] [CLEAR] [2nd] [√] [X,T,θ,*n*] [ENTER] 4 [MATH] 5 [X,T,θ,*n*] [GRAPH]

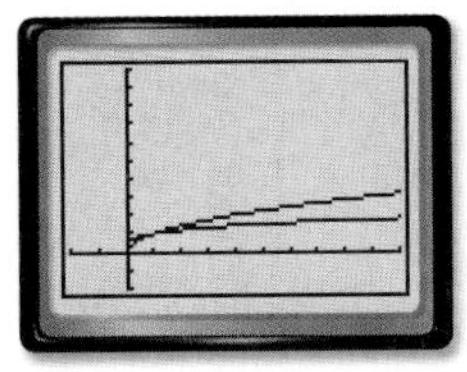

EXAMPLE 3 *n*th Root Functions with Different Radicands

Graph and compare $y = \sqrt[3]{x}$, $y = \sqrt[3]{x + 4}$, **and** $y = \sqrt[3]{x} + 4$.

Enter $y = \sqrt[3]{x}$ as Y1, $y = \sqrt[3]{x + 4}$ as Y2, and $y = \sqrt[3]{x} + 4$ as Y3. Then graph.

KEYSTROKES: [Y=] [CLEAR] 3 [MATH] 5 [X,T,θ,*n*] [ENTER] [CLEAR] 3 [MATH] 5 [(] [X,T,θ,*n*] [+] 4 [)] [ENTER] 3 [MATH] 5 [X,T,θ,*n*] [)] [+] 4 [ENTER] [ZOOM] 6

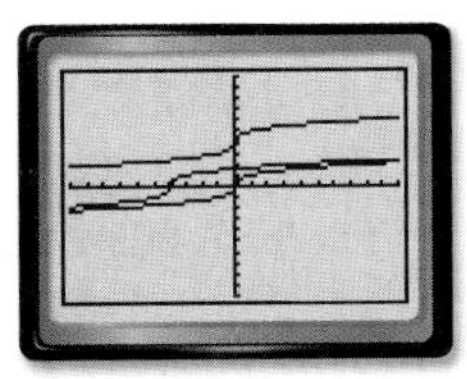

Exercises

Graph each function. 1–6. See Chapter 7 Answer Appendix.

1. $y = \sqrt[4]{x}$
2. $y = \sqrt[4]{x + 2}$
3. $y = \sqrt[4]{x} + 2$
4. $y = \sqrt[5]{x}$
5. $y = \sqrt[5]{x - 5}$
6. $y = \sqrt[5]{x} - 5$
7. What is the effect of adding or subtracting a constant under the radical sign? The graph shifts to the right or left.
8. What is the effect of adding or subtracting a constant outside the radical sign? The graph shifts up or down.

EXTEND 7-4

Lesson Notes

1 FOCUS

Objective Use a graphing calculator to graph *n*th root functions.

Materials for Each Student

- TI-83/84 Plus or other graphing calculator

Teaching Tip

There is more than one way to enter the square root function into the Y =list. The function can be entered as $\sqrt{x}$ using the square root key, as $x \wedge (1/2)$ or as $x \wedge (0.5)$.

2 TEACH

Working in Cooperative Groups

Have students work in pairs, mixing abilities, to complete the activity.

Ask:

- What values of *n* allow negative domain values for $\sqrt[n]{x}$? odd values of *n*
- Why is the domain restricted to nonnegative values for $\sqrt[n]{x}$ if *n* is even? An even root of a negative number is not a real number.

Practice Have students complete Exercises 1–8.

3 ASSESS

Formative Assessment

Use Exercises 1–3 to assess whether students can use a graphing calculator to graph *n*th root functions.

From Concrete to Abstract

Ask students to describe how to find the ordered pairs for the intersection of a graph and the *y*-axis, and the ordered pairs for the intersection of the graph and the *x*-axis. Let $x = 0$, then solve for *y*; let $y = 0$, then solve for *x*.

Formative Assessment

Use the Mid-Chapter Quiz to assess students' progress in the first half of the chapter.

For problems answered incorrectly, have students review the lessons indicated in parentheses.

ExamView Assessment Suite: Customize and create multiple versions of your Mid-Chapter Quiz and their answer keys.

FOLDABLES Follow-Up

Before students complete the Mid-Chapter Quiz, encourage them to review the information for Lessons 7-1 through 7-4 in their Foldables.

Additional Answers

12. $h^{-1}(x) = \frac{5}{2}(x - 8)$

13. $f^{-1}(x) = \frac{9}{4}x + 3$

14. $h^{-1}(x) = -\frac{3}{10}x - 5$

15. $f^{-1}(x) = 7x - 12$

16a. $f^{-1}(h) = \frac{1}{15}h - \frac{5}{3}$; $f^{-1}(h)$ represents the number of hours worked

CHAPTER 7 Mid-Chapter Quiz

Lessons 7-1 through 7-4

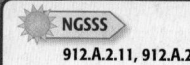

NGSSS 912.A.2.11, 912.A.2.6

Given $f(x) = 2x^2 + 4x - 3$ and $g(x) = 5x - 2$, find each function. (Lesson 7-1) 3. $(f \cdot g)(x) = 10x^3 + 16x^2 - 23x + 6$

4. $\left(\frac{f}{g}\right)(x) = \frac{2x^2 + 4x - 3}{5x - 2}$, $x \neq \frac{2}{5}$

1. $(f + g)(x)$ $(f + g)(x) = 2x^2 + 9x - 5$
2. $(f - g)(x)$ $(f - g)(x) = 2x^2 - x - 1$
3. $(f \cdot g)(x)$
4. $\left(\frac{f}{g}\right)(x)$
5. $[f \circ g](x)$ $(f \circ g)(x) = 50x^2 - 20x - 3$
6. $[g \circ f](x)$ $(g \circ f)(x) = 10x^2 + 20x - 17$

7a. $p(x) = 0.75x$, $g(x) = 1.06x$

7. **SHOPPING** Mrs. Ross is shopping for her children's school clothes. She has a coupon for 25% off her total. The sales tax of 6% is added to the total after the coupon is applied. (Lesson 7-1)
   a. Express the total price after the discount and the total price after the tax using function notation. Let x represent the price of the clothing, $p(x)$ represent the price after the 25% discount, and $g(x)$ represent the price after the tax is added.
   b. Which composition of functions represents the final price, $p[g(x)]$ or $g[p(x)]$? Explain your reasoning. Since $p[g(x)] = g[p(x)]$, either function represents the price.

Determine whether each pair of functions are inverse functions. Write *yes* or *no*. (Lesson 7-2)

8. $f(x) = 2x + 16$, $g(x) = \frac{1}{2}x - 8$ yes
9. $g(x) = 4x + 15$, $h(x) = \frac{1}{4}x - 15$ no
10. $f(x) = x^2 - 5$, $g(x) = 5 + x^{-2}$ no
11. $g(x) = -6x + 8$, $h(x) = \frac{8 - x}{6}$ yes

Find the inverse of each function, if it exists. (Lesson 7-2)

12. $h(x) = \frac{2}{5}x + 8$
13. $f(x) = \frac{4}{9}(x - 3)$
14. $h(x) = -\frac{10}{3}(x + 5)$
15. $f(x) = \frac{x + 12}{7}$

12–15. See margin.

16. **JOBS** Louise runs a lawn care service. She charges \$25 for supplies plus \$15 per hour. The function $f(h) = 15h + 25$ gives the cost $f(h)$ for h hours of work. (Lesson 7-2) a. See margin.
   a. Find $f^{-1}(h)$. What is the significance of $f^{-1}(h)$?
   b. If Louise charges a customer \$85, how many hours did she work? 4 hours

17–20. See Chapter 7 Answer Appendix.

Graph each inequality. (Lesson 7-3)

17. $y < \sqrt{x - 5}$
18. $y \leq -2\sqrt{x}$
19. $y > \sqrt{x + 9} + 3$
20. $y \geq \sqrt{x + 4} - 5$

21, 22. See Chapter 7 Answer Appendix.

Graph each function. State the domain and range of each function. (Lesson 7-3)

21. $y = 2 + \sqrt{x}$
22. $y = \sqrt{x + 4} - 1$

23. **NGSSS PRACTICE** What is the domain of $f(x) = \sqrt{2x + 5}$? (Lesson 7-3) D
   A. $\left\{x \mid x > \frac{5}{2}\right\}$
   B. $\left\{x \mid x > -\frac{5}{2}\right\}$
   C. $\left\{x \mid x \geq \frac{5}{2}\right\}$
   D. $\left\{x \mid x \geq -\frac{5}{2}\right\}$

24. $\pm 11a^2|b^9|$ 25. $(x^4 + 3)^6$

Simplify. (Lesson 7-4) 26. $3(2x - 5)^5$ 27. $-(y - 6)^4$

24. $\pm\sqrt{121a^4b^{18}}$
25. $\sqrt{(x^4 + 3)^{12}}$
26. $\sqrt[3]{27(2x - 5)^{15}}$
27. $\sqrt[5]{-(y - 6)^{20}}$
28. $\sqrt[3]{8(x + 4)^6}$ $2(x + 4)^2$
29. $\sqrt[4]{16(y + x)^8}$ $2(y + x)^2$

30. **NGSSS PRACTICE** The radius of the cylinder below is equal to the height of the cylinder. The radius r can be found using the formula $r = \sqrt[3]{\frac{V}{\pi}}$. Find the radius of the cylinder if the volume is 500 cubic inches. (Lesson 7-4) G

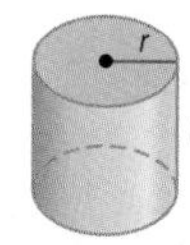

   F. 2.53 inches
   G. 5.42 inches
   H. 7.94 inches
   I. 24.92 inches

31a. $C[P(h)] = 200h + 60$

31. **PRODUCTION** The cost in dollars of producing x cell phones in a factory is represented by $C(p) = 5p + 60$. The number of cell phones produced in h hours is represented by $P(h) = 40h$. (Lesson 7-1)
   a. Find the composition function.
   b. Determine the cost of producing cell phones for 8 hours. \$1660

Intervention Planner

Tier 1 On Level	Tier 2 Strategic Intervention approaching grade level	Tier 3 Intensive Intervention 2 or more grades below level
If students miss about 25% of the exercises or less,	**If** students miss about 50% of the exercises,	**If** students miss about 75% of the exercises,
Then choose a resource: SE Lessons 7-1, 7-2, 7-3, and 7-4 CRM Skills Practice, pp. 7, 14, 21, and 27 TE Chapter Project, p. 406 FL Math Online Self-Check Quiz	**Then** choose a resource: CRM Study Guide and Intervention, pp. 5, 12, 19 and 25 *Quick Review Math Handbook* FL Math Online Extra Examples, Personal Tutor, Homework Help	**Then** use *Math Triumphs, Alg. 2*, Ch. 1 FL Math Online Extra Examples, Personal Tutor, Homework Help, Review Vocabulary

7-5 Operations with Radical Expressions

Why?

Golden rectangles have been used by artists and architects to create beautiful designs. Many golden rectangles appear in the Parthenon in Athens, Greece. The ratio of the lengths of the sides of a golden rectangle is $\frac{2}{\sqrt{5}-1}$.

In this lesson, you will learn to simplify radical expressions like $\frac{2}{\sqrt{5}-1}$.

Then
You simplified expressions with nth roots. (Lesson 7-4)

Now
- Simplify radical expressions.
- Add, subtract, multiply, and divide radical expressions.

NGSSS
MA.912.A.6.2 Add, subtract, multiply and divide radical expressions (square roots and higher).

New Vocabulary
rationalizing the denominator
like radical expressions
conjugate

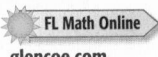

FL Math Online
glencoe.com

Simplify Radicals The properties you have used to simplify radical expressions involving square roots also hold true for expressions involving nth roots.

Key Concept — Product Property of Radicals

Words For any real numbers a and b and any integer $n > 1$,
$\sqrt[n]{ab} = \sqrt[n]{a} \cdot \sqrt[n]{b}$, if n is even and a and b are both nonnegative or if n is odd.

Examples $\sqrt{2} \cdot \sqrt{8} = \sqrt{16}$ or 4 and $\sqrt[3]{3} \cdot \sqrt[3]{9} = \sqrt[3]{27}$ or 3

In order for a radical to be in simplest form, the radicand must contain no factors that are nth powers of an integer or polynomial.

EXAMPLE 1 Simplify Expressions with the Product Property

Simplify.

a. $\sqrt{32x^8}$

$\sqrt{32x^8} = \sqrt{4^2 \cdot 2 \cdot (x^4)^2}$ — Factor into squares.

$= \sqrt{4^2} \cdot \sqrt{(x^4)^2} \cdot \sqrt{2}$ — Product Property of Radicals

$= 4x^4\sqrt{2}$ — Simplify.

b. $\sqrt[4]{16a^{24}b^{13}}$

$\sqrt[4]{16a^{24}b^{13}} = \sqrt[4]{2^4 \cdot (a^6)^4(b^3)^4 \cdot b}$ — Factor into squares.

$= \sqrt[4]{2^4} \cdot \sqrt[4]{(a^6)^4} \cdot \sqrt[4]{(b^3)^4} \cdot \sqrt[4]{b}$ — Product Property of Radicals

$= 2a^6|b^3|\sqrt[4]{b}$ — Simplify.

In this case, the absolute value symbols are not necessary because in order for $\sqrt[4]{16a^{24}b^{13}}$ to be defined, b must be nonnegative.

Thus, $\sqrt[4]{16a^{24}b^{13}} = 2a^6b^3\sqrt[4]{b}$.

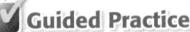

Guided Practice

1A. $\sqrt{12c^6d^3}$ $2c^3d\sqrt{3d}$

1B. $\sqrt[3]{27y^{12}z^7}$ $3y^4z^2\sqrt[3]{z}$

Personal Tutor glencoe.com

7-5 Lesson Notes

1 FOCUS

Vertical Alignment

Before Lesson 7-5
Simplify expressions with nth roots.

Lesson 7-5
Simplify radical expressions.
Add, subtract, multiply, and divide radical expressions.

After Lesson 7-5
Determine solutions of square root equations using algebraic methods.

2 TEACH

Scaffolding Questions

Have students read the *Why?* section of the lesson.

Ask:
- Is the denominator, $\sqrt{5}-1$, greater than 2 or less than 2? less than 2
- Is the ratio $\frac{2}{\sqrt{5}-1}$ greater than 1 or less than 1? greater than 1

Lesson 7-5 Resources

Resource	Approaching-Level	On-Level	Beyond-Level	English Learners
Teacher Edition	• Differentiated Instruction, p. 442	• Differentiated Instruction, p. 442	• Differentiated Instruction, p. 445	
Chapter Resource Masters	• Study Guide and Intervention, pp. 31–32 • Skills Practice, p. 33 • Practice, p. 34 • Word Problem Practice, p. 35	• Study Guide and Intervention, pp. 31–32 • Skills Practice, p. 33 • Practice, p. 34 • Word Problem Practice, p. 35 • Enrichment, p. 36 • Graphing Calculator Activity, p. 37	• Practice, p. 34 • Word Problem Practice, p. 35 • Enrichment, p. 36	• Study Guide and Intervention, pp. 31–32 • Skills Practice, p. 33 • Practice, p. 34 • Word Problem Practice, p. 35
Transparencies	• 5-Minute Check Transparency 7-5	• 5-Minute Check Transparency 7-5	• 5-Minute Check Transparency 7-5	• 5-Minute Check Transparency 7-5
Other	• Study Notebook	• Study Notebook	• Study Notebook	• Study Notebook

Simplify Radicals

Example 1 shows how to use the Product Property of Radicals to simplify a radical expression. **Example 2** shows how to use the Quotient Property of Radicals to simplify a radical expression.

Formative Assessment

Use the Guided Practice exercises after each example to determine students' understanding of concepts.

Additional Examples

1 Simplify.

a. $\sqrt{25a^4b^9}$ $5a^2b^4\sqrt{b}$

b. $\sqrt[3]{125m^{30}p^{20}}$ $5m^{10}p^6\sqrt[3]{p^2}$

2 Simplify.

a. $\sqrt{\frac{y^8}{x^7}}$ $\frac{y^4\sqrt{x}}{x^4}$

b. $\sqrt[3]{\frac{2}{9x}}$ $\frac{\sqrt[3]{6x^2}}{3x}$

Additional Examples also in Interactive Classroom PowerPoint® Presentations

IWB INTERACTIVE WHITEBOARD READY

Focus on Mathematical Content

Product Property of Radicals The Product Property of Radicals states that $\sqrt[n]{ab} = \sqrt[n]{a} \cdot \sqrt[n]{b}$. This statement is true for all real numbers a and b when n is an odd integer greater than 1. If n is even, then a and b must be nonnegative real numbers.

The Quotient Property of Radicals is another property used to simplify radicals.

Key Concept — Quotient Property of Radicals

Words For any real numbers a and $b \neq 0$ and any integer $n > 1$, $\sqrt[n]{\frac{a}{b}} = \frac{\sqrt[n]{a}}{\sqrt[n]{b}}$, if all roots are defined.

Examples $\frac{\sqrt{27}}{\sqrt{3}} = \sqrt{9}$ or 3 $\quad \sqrt[3]{\frac{x^6}{8}} = \frac{\sqrt[3]{x^6}}{\sqrt[3]{8}} = \frac{x^2}{2}$ or $\frac{1}{2}x^2$

StudyTip

Exact Roots Exact roots occur when the powers of the constants and variables are all identical to or multiples of the index. For example, $\sqrt[3]{2} \cdot \sqrt[3]{2^2} = \sqrt[3]{2^3}$ or 2.

To eliminate radicals from a denominator or fractions from a radicand, you can use a process called **rationalizing the denominator**. To rationalize a denominator, multiply the numerator and denominator by a quantity so that the radicand has an exact root.

If the denominator is:	Multiply the numerator and denominator by:	Examples
$\sqrt{b}$	$\sqrt{b}$	$\frac{2}{\sqrt{3}} = \frac{2}{\sqrt{3}} \cdot \frac{\sqrt{3}}{\sqrt{3}}$ or $\frac{2\sqrt{3}}{3}$
$\sqrt[n]{b^x}$	$\sqrt[n]{b^{n-x}}$	$\frac{5}{\sqrt[3]{2}} = \frac{5}{\sqrt[3]{2}} \cdot \frac{\sqrt[3]{2^2}}{\sqrt[3]{2^2}}$ or $\frac{5\sqrt[3]{4}}{2}$

EXAMPLE 2 Simplify Expressions with the Quotient Property

Simplify.

a. $\sqrt{\frac{x^6}{y^7}}$

$\sqrt{\frac{x^6}{y^7}} = \frac{\sqrt{x^6}}{\sqrt{y^7}}$ Quotient Property

$= \frac{\sqrt{(x^3)^2}}{\sqrt{(y^3)^2 \cdot y}}$ Factor into squares.

$= \frac{\sqrt{(x^3)^2}}{\sqrt{(y^3)^2} \cdot \sqrt{y}}$ Product Property

$= \frac{x^3}{y^3\sqrt{y}}$ Simplify.

$= \frac{x^3}{y^3\sqrt{y}} \cdot \frac{\sqrt{y}}{\sqrt{y}}$ Rationalize the denominator.

$= \frac{x^3\sqrt{y}}{y^4}$ $\sqrt{y} \cdot \sqrt{y} = y$

b. $\sqrt[4]{\frac{6}{5x}}$

$\sqrt[4]{\frac{6}{5x}} = \frac{\sqrt[4]{6}}{\sqrt[4]{5x}}$ Quotient Property

$= \frac{\sqrt[4]{6}}{\sqrt[4]{5x}} \cdot \frac{\sqrt[4]{5^3x^3}}{\sqrt[4]{5^3x^3}}$ Rationalize the denominator.

$= \frac{\sqrt[4]{6 \cdot 5^3x^3}}{\sqrt[4]{5x \cdot 5^3x^3}}$ Product Property

$= \frac{\sqrt[4]{750x^3}}{\sqrt[4]{5^4x^4}}$ Multiply.

$= \frac{\sqrt[4]{750x^3}}{5x}$ $\sqrt[4]{5^4x^4} = 5x$

Guided Practice

2A. $\frac{\sqrt{a^9}}{\sqrt{b^5}}$ $\frac{a^4\sqrt{ab}}{b^3}$

2B. $\sqrt[5]{\frac{3}{4y}}$ $\frac{\sqrt[5]{24y^4}}{2y}$

Personal Tutor glencoe.com

Tips for New Teachers

Product Property of Radicals When discussing the Product Property of Radicals, stress that a and b must both be nonnegative if n is even. This means that $\sqrt{-2}$ times $\sqrt{-8}$ may *not* be written as $\sqrt{16}$. This condition is necessary because $\sqrt{-2}$ and $\sqrt{-8}$ are *not* real numbers.

Here is a summary of the rules used to simplify radicals.

Concept Summary — **Simplifying Radical Expressions**

A radical expression is in simplified form when the following conditions are met.

- The index n is as small as possible.
- The radicand contains no factors (other than 1) that are nth powers of an integer or polynomial.
- The radicand contains no fractions.
- No radicals appear in a denominator.

Operations with Radicals You can use the Product and Quotient Properties to multiply and divide some radicals.

EXAMPLE 3 Multiply Radicals

Simplify $5\sqrt[3]{-12ab^4} \cdot 3\sqrt[3]{18a^2b^2}$.

$5\sqrt[3]{-12ab^4} \cdot 3\sqrt[3]{18a^2b^2} = 5 \cdot 3 \cdot \sqrt[3]{-12ab^4 \cdot 18a^2b^2}$	**Product Property of Radicals**
$= 15 \cdot \sqrt[3]{-2^2 \cdot 3 \cdot ab^4 \cdot 2 \cdot 3^2 \cdot a^2b^2}$	**Factor constants.**
$= 15 \cdot \sqrt[3]{-2^3 \cdot 3^3 \cdot a^3b^6}$	**Group into cubes if possible.**
$= 15 \cdot \sqrt[3]{-2^3} \cdot \sqrt[3]{3^3} \cdot \sqrt[3]{a^3} \cdot \sqrt[3]{b^6}$	**Product Property of Radicals**
$= 15 \cdot (-2) \cdot 3 \cdot a \cdot b^2$	**Simplify.**
$= -90ab^2$	**Multiply.**

Guided Practice

Simplify.

3A. $6\sqrt{8c^3d^5} \cdot 4\sqrt{2cd^3}$ $96c^2d^4$

3B. $2\sqrt[4]{8x^3y^2} \cdot 3\sqrt[4]{2x^5y^2}$ $12x^2|y|$

Personal Tutor glencoe.com

Radicals can be added and subtracted in the same manner as monomials. In order to add or subtract, the radicals must be like terms. Radicals are **like radical expressions** if *both* the index and the radicand are identical.

Like: $\sqrt{3b}$ and $4\sqrt{3b}$ **Unlike: $\sqrt{3b}$ and $\sqrt[3]{3b}$** **Unlike: $\sqrt{2b}$ and $\sqrt{3b}$**

StudyTip

Adding and Subtracting Radicals Simplify the individual radicals before attempting to combine like terms.

EXAMPLE 4 Add and Subtract Radicals

Simplify $\sqrt{98} - 2\sqrt{32}$.

$\sqrt{98} - 2\sqrt{32} = \sqrt{2 \cdot 7^2} - 2\sqrt{4^2 \cdot 2}$	**Factor using squares.**
$= \sqrt{7^2} \cdot \sqrt{2} - 2 \cdot \sqrt{4^2} \cdot \sqrt{2}$	**Product Property**
$= 7\sqrt{2} - 2 \cdot 4 \cdot \sqrt{2}$	**Simplify radicals.**
$= 7\sqrt{2} - 8\sqrt{2}$	**Multiply.**
$= -\sqrt{2}$	$(7 - 8)\sqrt{2} = (-1)(\sqrt{2})$

Guided Practice

4A. $4\sqrt{8} + 3\sqrt{50}$ $23\sqrt{2}$

4B. $5\sqrt{12} + 2\sqrt{27} - \sqrt{128}$ $16\sqrt{3} - 8\sqrt{2}$

Personal Tutor glencoe.com

Operations With Radicals

Example 3 shows how to use the Product Property of Radicals to multiply radicals. **Example 4** shows how to add or subtract radicals. **Example 5** shows how to multiply binomials that contain radicals. **Example 6** shows how to use a conjugate to rationalize the denominator of a radical expression.

Additional Examples

3 Simplify $5\sqrt[3]{100a^2} \cdot \sqrt[3]{10a}$. $50a$

4 Simplify $3\sqrt{45} - 5\sqrt{80} + 4\sqrt{20}$. $-3\sqrt{5}$

Watch Out!

Preventing Errors Urge students to verify that each of their final answers is in simplified form by testing it against the four conditions listed in the Concept Summary for simplifying radical expressions.

TEACH with TECH

INTERACTIVE WHITEBOARD Write an expression on the board to add or subtract radical expressions. As you simplify the expression, drag the like terms to group them together. Then, combine like terms and simplify the expression.

Lesson 7-5 Operations with Radical Expressions 441

Additional Examples

5 Simplify.
$(2\sqrt{3} + 3\sqrt{5})(3 - \sqrt{3})$
$6\sqrt{3} - 6 + 9\sqrt{5} - 3\sqrt{15}$

6 **GEOMETRY** In a square with side a, the ratio of a side to the difference between the diagonal and a side is $\frac{a}{a\sqrt{2} - a}$. Use a conjugate to rationalize the denominator and simplify $\frac{a}{a\sqrt{2} - a}$.

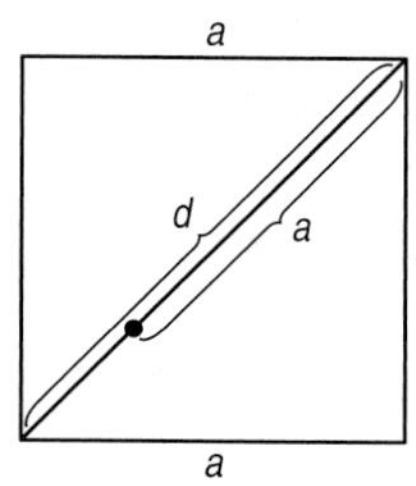

$\frac{\sqrt{2} + 1}{1}$ or $\sqrt{2} + 1$

Just as you can add and subtract radicals like monomials, you can multiply radicals using the FOIL method as you do when multiplying binomials.

EXAMPLE 5 Multiply Radicals

Simplify $(4\sqrt{3} + 5\sqrt{2})(3\sqrt{2} - 6)$.

$$(4\sqrt{3} + 5\sqrt{2})(3\sqrt{2} - 6) = \overset{F}{4\sqrt{3} \cdot 3\sqrt{2}} + \overset{O}{4\sqrt{3} \cdot (-6)} + \overset{I}{5\sqrt{2} \cdot 3\sqrt{2}} + \overset{L}{5\sqrt{2} \cdot (-6)}$$

$$= 12\sqrt{3 \cdot 2} - 24\sqrt{3} + 15\sqrt{2^2} - 30\sqrt{2} \quad \text{Product Property}$$

$$= 12\sqrt{6} - 24\sqrt{3} + 30 - 30\sqrt{2} \quad \text{Simplify.}$$

StudyTip

Conjugates The product of conjugates is always a rational number.

Guided Practice **5A.** $12\sqrt{15} - 10\sqrt{5} + 24\sqrt{6} - 20\sqrt{2}$

Simplify.

5A. $(6\sqrt{3} - 5)(2\sqrt{5} + 4\sqrt{2})$

5B. $(7\sqrt{2} - 3\sqrt{3})(7\sqrt{2} + 3\sqrt{3})$ **71**

Personal Tutor glencoe.com

Binomials of the form $a\sqrt{b} + c\sqrt{d}$ and $a\sqrt{b} - c\sqrt{d}$, where a, b, c, and d are rational numbers, are called **conjugates** of each other. You can use conjugates to rationalize denominators.

Real-World EXAMPLE 6 Use a Conjugate to Rationalize a Denominator

ARCHITECTURE **Refer to the beginning of the lesson. Use a conjugate to rationalize the denominator and simplify $\frac{2}{\sqrt{5} - 1}$.**

$$\frac{2}{\sqrt{5} - 1} = \frac{2}{\sqrt{5} - 1} \cdot \frac{\sqrt{5} + 1}{\sqrt{5} + 1} \quad \sqrt{5} + 1 \text{ is the conjugate of } \sqrt{5} - 1.$$

$$= \frac{2\sqrt{5} + 2(1)}{(\sqrt{5})^2 + 1(\sqrt{5}) - 1(\sqrt{5}) - 1(1)} \quad \text{Multiply.}$$

$$= \frac{2\sqrt{5} + 2}{5 + \sqrt{5} - \sqrt{5} - 1} \quad \text{Simplify.}$$

$$= \frac{2\sqrt{5} + 2}{4} \quad \text{Subtract.}$$

$$= \frac{\sqrt{5} + 1}{2} \quad \text{Simplify.}$$

The Granger Collection, New York

Math History Link

Theano (c. 5th century B.C.) Theano is believed to have been the wife of Pythagoras. It is also believed that she directed a famous mathematics academy and carried on the work of Pythagoras after his death. Her most important work was on the idea of the golden mean, which is the irrational number $\frac{1 + \sqrt{5}}{2}$.

Guided Practice

6. **GEOMETRY** The area of the rectangle at the right is 900 ft². Write and simplify an equation for L in terms of x. $\frac{10{,}800\sqrt{3} - 900x}{432 - x^2}$

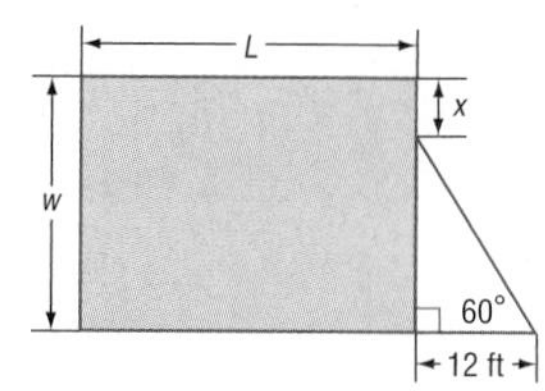

Personal Tutor glencoe.com

Differentiated Instruction

AL OL

If when presented with a radical expression such as $11 + 6\sqrt{3}$, some students persist in trying to add the 11 and the 6,

Then to help them understand why this cannot be done, compare the radical expression $11 + 6\sqrt{3}$ to the expression $11 + 6x$. Stress that the radical $6\sqrt{3}$ is a multiplication expression just like $6x$. Remind students that the order of operations requires that multiplication be performed before addition. Students may find it helpful to rewrite $11 + 6\sqrt{3}$, as $11 + 6 \cdot \sqrt{3}$.

Check Your Understanding

1. $6b^2c^2\sqrt{ac}$ 2. $12x^3y^2\sqrt{xy}$

Examples 1–5 pp. 439–442

Simplify.

1. $\sqrt{36ab^4c^5}$

2. $\sqrt{144x^7y^5}$

3. $\dfrac{\sqrt{c^5}}{\sqrt{d^9}}$ $\dfrac{c^2\sqrt{cd}}{d^5}$

4. $\sqrt[4]{\dfrac{5x}{8y}}$ $\dfrac{\sqrt[4]{10xy^3}}{2y}$

5. $5\sqrt{2x} \cdot 3\sqrt{8x}$ $60x$

6. $4\sqrt{5a^5} \cdot \sqrt{125a^3}$ $100a^4$

7. $3\sqrt[3]{36xy} \cdot 2\sqrt[3]{6x^2y^2}$ $36xy$

8. $\sqrt[4]{3x^3y^2} \cdot \sqrt[4]{27xy^2}$ $3xy$

9. $5\sqrt{32} + \sqrt{27} + 2\sqrt{75}$ $20\sqrt{2} + 13\sqrt{3}$

10. $4\sqrt{40} + 3\sqrt{28} - \sqrt{200}$

11. $(4 + 2\sqrt{5})(3\sqrt{3} + 4\sqrt{5})$

12. $(8\sqrt{3} - 2\sqrt{2})(8\sqrt{3} + 2\sqrt{2})$ 184

13. $\dfrac{5}{\sqrt{2} + 3}$ $\dfrac{15 - 5\sqrt{2}}{7}$

14. $\dfrac{8}{\sqrt{6} - 5}$ $\dfrac{-40 - 8\sqrt{6}}{19}$

15. $\dfrac{4 + \sqrt{2}}{\sqrt{2} - 3}$ $-2 - \sqrt{2}$

16. $\dfrac{6 - \sqrt{3}}{\sqrt{3} + 4}$ $\dfrac{27 - 10\sqrt{3}}{13}$

10. $8\sqrt{10} + 6\sqrt{7} - 10\sqrt{2}$

11. $12\sqrt{3} + 16\sqrt{5} + 40 + 6\sqrt{15}$

Example 6 p. 442

17. **GEOMETRY** Find the altitude of the triangle if the area is $189 + 4\sqrt{3}$ square centimeters.
$32 - 2\sqrt{3}$ cm

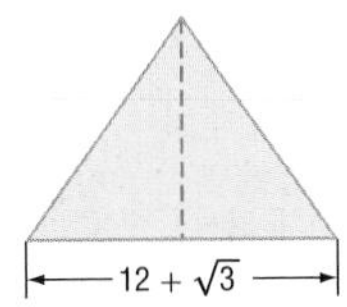

Practice and Problem Solving

● = **Step-by-Step Solutions** begin on page R20.
Extra Practice begins on page 947.

Examples 1–4 pp. 439–441

Simplify. 18. $6a^4b^2\sqrt{2b}$ 19. $3a^7b\sqrt{ab}$ 20. $2a^8b^4\sqrt{6c}$

18. $\sqrt{72a^8b^5}$

19. $\sqrt{9a^{15}b^3}$

20. $\sqrt{24a^{16}b^8c}$

21. $\sqrt{18a^6b^3c^5}$

22. $\dfrac{\sqrt{5a^5}}{\sqrt{b^{13}}}$ $\dfrac{a^2\sqrt{5ab}}{b^7}$

23. $\sqrt{\dfrac{7x}{10y^3}}$ $\dfrac{\sqrt{70xy}}{10y^2}$

24. $\dfrac{\sqrt[3]{6x^2}}{\sqrt[3]{5y}}$ $\dfrac{\sqrt[3]{150x^2y^2}}{5y}$

25. $\sqrt[4]{\dfrac{7x^3}{4b^2}}$ $\dfrac{\sqrt[4]{28b^2x^3}}{2|b|}$

21. $3|a^3|bc^2\sqrt{2bc}$

26. $3\sqrt{5y} \cdot 8\sqrt{10yz}$

27. $2\sqrt{32a^3b^5} \cdot \sqrt{8a^7b^2}$

28. $6\sqrt{3ab} \cdot 4\sqrt{24ab^3}$

29. $5\sqrt{x^8y^3} \cdot 5\sqrt{2x^5y^4}$

30. $3\sqrt{90} + 4\sqrt{20} + \sqrt{162}$

31. $9\sqrt{12} + 5\sqrt{32} - \sqrt{72}$

32. $4\sqrt{28} - 8\sqrt{810} + \sqrt{44}$
$8\sqrt{7} - 72\sqrt{10} + 2\sqrt{11}$

33. $3\sqrt{54} + 6\sqrt{288} - \sqrt{147}$
$9\sqrt{6} + 72\sqrt{2} - 7\sqrt{3}$

26. $120y\sqrt{2z}$
27. $32a^5b^3\sqrt{b}$
28. $144ab^2\sqrt{2}$
29. $25x^6y^3\sqrt{2xy}$
30. $9\sqrt{10} + 8\sqrt{5} + 9\sqrt{2}$
31. $18\sqrt{3} + 14\sqrt{2}$

34. **GEOMETRY** Find the perimeter of the rectangle.
$16 + 2\sqrt{3} + 2\sqrt{6}$ ft

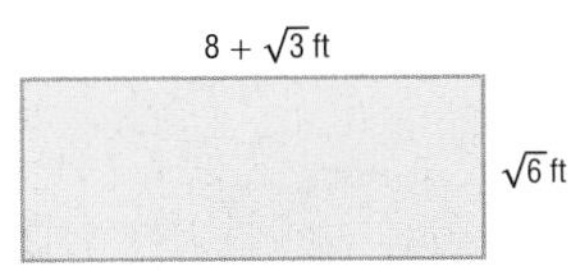

35 **GEOMETRY** Find the area of the rectangle.
$8\sqrt{6} + 3\sqrt{2}$ ft^2

36. **GEOMETRY** Find the exact surface area of a sphere with radius of $4 + \sqrt{5}$ inches.
$(84 + 32\sqrt{5})\pi$ in^2

Examples 5 and 6 p. 442

Simplify. 37. $56\sqrt{3} + 42\sqrt{6} - 36\sqrt{2} - 54$ 40. $36\sqrt{2} + 36\sqrt{6} + 20\sqrt{3} + 60$

37. $(7\sqrt{2} - 3\sqrt{3})(4\sqrt{6} + 3\sqrt{12})$

38. $(8\sqrt{5} - 6\sqrt{3})(8\sqrt{5} + 6\sqrt{3})$ 212

39. $(12\sqrt{10} - 6\sqrt{5})(12\sqrt{10} + 6\sqrt{5})$ 1260

40. $(6\sqrt{3} + 5\sqrt{2})(2\sqrt{6} + 3\sqrt{8})$

41. $\dfrac{6}{\sqrt{3} - \sqrt{2}}$
$6\sqrt{3} + 6\sqrt{2}$

42. $\dfrac{\sqrt{2}}{\sqrt{5} - \sqrt{3}}$

43. $\dfrac{9 - 2\sqrt{3}}{\sqrt{3} + 6}$

44. $\dfrac{2\sqrt{2} + 2\sqrt{5}}{\sqrt{5} + \sqrt{2}}$ 2

42. $\dfrac{\sqrt{10} + \sqrt{6}}{2}$

43. $\dfrac{20 - 7\sqrt{3}}{11}$

3 PRACTICE

Formative Assessment

Use Exercises 1–17 to check for understanding.

Use the chart at the bottom of this page to customize assignments for your students.

Differentiated Homework Options

Level	Assignment	Two-Day Option	
AL Basic	18–44, 60, 62, 64–88	19–43 odd, 66–69	18–44 even, 60, 62, 64–65, 70–88
OL Core	19–53 odd, 54, 55, 57, 59, 60, 62, 64–88	18–44, 66–69	45–60, 62, 64–65, 70–82
BL Advanced	45–82, (optional: 83–88)		

Lesson 7-5 Operations with Radical Expressions **443**

Study Guide and Intervention
CRM pp. 31–32 AL OL ELL

7-5 Study Guide and Intervention
Operations with Radical Expressions

Simplify Radicals

Product Property of Radicals	For any real numbers a and b, and any integer $n > 1$: 1. if n is even and a and b are both nonnegative, then $\sqrt[n]{ab} = \sqrt[n]{a} \cdot \sqrt[n]{b}$. 2. if n is odd, then $\sqrt[n]{ab} = \sqrt[n]{a} \cdot \sqrt[n]{b}$.

To simplify a square root, follow these steps:
1. Factor the radicand into as many squares as possible.
2. Use the Product Property to isolate the perfect squares.
3. Simplify each radical.

Quotient Property of Radicals	For any real numbers a and $b \neq 0$, and any integer $n > 1$, $\sqrt[n]{\frac{a}{b}} = \frac{\sqrt[n]{a}}{\sqrt[n]{b}}$, if all roots are defined.

To eliminate radicals from a denominator or fractions from a radicand, multiply the numerator and denominator by a quantity so that the radicand has an exact root.

Example 1 Simplify $\sqrt[3]{-6a^5b^7}$.

$\sqrt[3]{-16a^5b^7} = \sqrt[3]{(-2)^3 \cdot 2 \cdot a^3 \cdot a^2 \cdot (b^2)^3 \cdot b}$
$= -2ab^2\sqrt[3]{2a^2b}$

Example 2 Simplify $\sqrt{\frac{8x^3}{45y^5}}$.

$\sqrt{\frac{8x^3}{45y^5}} = \frac{\sqrt{8x^3}}{\sqrt{45y^5}}$ Quotient Property

$= \frac{\sqrt{(2x)^2 \cdot 2x}}{\sqrt{(3y^2)^2 \cdot 5y}}$ Factor into squares.

$= \frac{\sqrt{(2x)^2} \cdot \sqrt{2x}}{\sqrt{(3y^2)^2} \cdot \sqrt{5y}}$ Product Property

$= \frac{2|x|\sqrt{2x}}{3y^2\sqrt{5y}}$ Simplify.

$= \frac{2|x|\sqrt{2x}}{3y^2\sqrt{5y}} \cdot \frac{\sqrt{5y}}{\sqrt{5y}}$ Rationalize the denominator.

$= \frac{2|x|\sqrt{10xy}}{15y^3}$ Simplify.

Exercises

Simplify.

1. $5\sqrt{54}$ **$15\sqrt{6}$**
2. $\sqrt[4]{32a^9b^{20}}$ **$2a^2|b^5|\sqrt[4]{2a}$**
3. $\sqrt{75x^4y^7}$ **$5x^2y^3\sqrt{3y}$**
4. $\sqrt{\frac{36}{125}}$ **$\frac{6\sqrt{5}}{25}$**
5. $\sqrt{\frac{a^6b^3}{98}}$ **$\frac{|a^3|b\sqrt{2b}}{14}$**
6. $\sqrt[3]{\frac{p^5q^3}{40}}$ **$\frac{pq\sqrt[3]{25p^2}}{10}$**

Lesson 7-5

Chapter 7 31 Glencoe Algebra 2

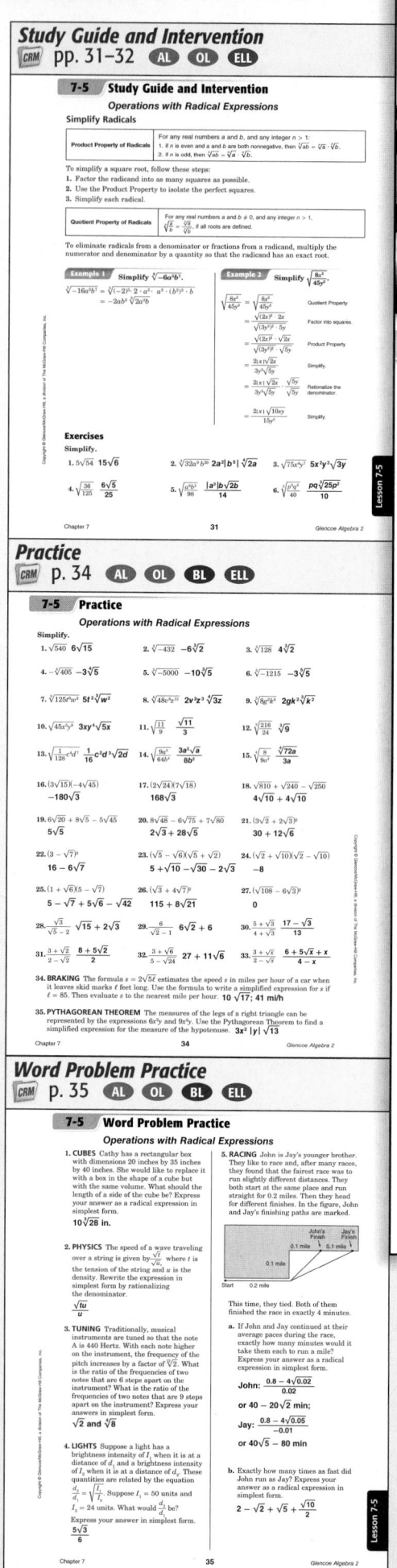

Practice
CRM p. 34 AL OL BL ELL

7-5 Practice
Operations with Radical Expressions

Simplify.

1. $\sqrt{540}$ **$6\sqrt{15}$**
2. $\sqrt[3]{-432}$ **$-6\sqrt[3]{2}$**
3. $\sqrt[3]{128}$ **$4\sqrt[3]{2}$**
4. $-\sqrt[4]{405}$ **$-3\sqrt[4]{5}$**
5. $\sqrt[3]{-5000}$ **$-10\sqrt[3]{5}$**
6. $\sqrt[5]{-1215}$ **$-3\sqrt[5]{5}$**
7. $\sqrt[3]{125t^6w^2}$ **$5t^2\sqrt[3]{w^2}$**
8. $\sqrt[4]{48v^8z^{13}}$ **$2v^2z^3\sqrt[4]{3z}$**
9. $\sqrt[3]{8g^3k^8}$ **$2gk^2\sqrt[3]{k^2}$**
10. $\sqrt{45x^3y^8}$ **$3xy^4\sqrt{5x}$**
11. $\sqrt{\frac{11}{9}}$ **$\frac{\sqrt{11}}{3}$**
12. $\sqrt[3]{\frac{216}{24}}$ **$\sqrt[3]{9}$**
13. $\sqrt{\frac{1}{128}c^4d^7}$ **$\frac{1}{16}c^2d^3\sqrt{2d}$**
14. $\sqrt{\frac{9a^5}{64b^4}}$ **$\frac{3a^2\sqrt{a}}{8b^2}$**
15. $\sqrt[4]{\frac{8}{9a^3}}$ **$\frac{\sqrt[4]{72a}}{3a}$**
16. $(3\sqrt{15})(-4\sqrt{45})$ **$-180\sqrt{3}$**
17. $(2\sqrt{24})(7\sqrt{18})$ **$168\sqrt{3}$**
18. $\sqrt{810} + \sqrt{240} - \sqrt{250}$ **$4\sqrt{10} + 4\sqrt{10}$**
19. $6\sqrt{20} + 8\sqrt{5} - 5\sqrt{45}$ **$5\sqrt{5}$**
20. $8\sqrt{48} - 6\sqrt{75} + 7\sqrt{80}$ **$2\sqrt{3} + 28\sqrt{5}$**
21. $(3\sqrt{2} + 2\sqrt{3})^2$ **$30 + 12\sqrt{6}$**
22. $(3 - \sqrt{7})^2$ **$16 - 6\sqrt{7}$**
23. $(\sqrt{5} - \sqrt{6})(\sqrt{5} + \sqrt{2})$ **$5 + \sqrt{10} - \sqrt{30} - 2\sqrt{3}$**
24. $(\sqrt{2} + \sqrt{10})(\sqrt{2} - \sqrt{10})$ **-8**
25. $(1 + \sqrt{6})(5 - \sqrt{7})$ **$5 - \sqrt{7} + 5\sqrt{6} - \sqrt{42}$**
26. $(\sqrt{3} + 4\sqrt{7})^2$ **$115 + 8\sqrt{21}$**
27. $(\sqrt{108} - 6\sqrt{3})^2$ **0**
28. $\frac{\sqrt{3}}{\sqrt{5} - 2}$ **$\sqrt{15} + 2\sqrt{3}$**
29. $\frac{6}{\sqrt{2} - 1}$ **$6\sqrt{2} + 6$**
30. $\frac{5 + \sqrt{3}}{4 + \sqrt{3}}$ **$\frac{17 - \sqrt{3}}{13}$**
31. $\frac{3 + \sqrt{2}}{2 - \sqrt{2}}$ **$\frac{8 + 5\sqrt{2}}{2}$**
32. $\frac{3 + \sqrt{6}}{5 - \sqrt{24}}$ **$27 + 11\sqrt{6}$**
33. $\frac{3 + \sqrt{x}}{2 - \sqrt{x}}$ **$\frac{6 + 5\sqrt{x} + x}{4 - x}$**

34. **BRAKING** The formula $s = 2\sqrt{5\ell}$ estimates the speed s in miles per hour of a car when it leaves skid marks ℓ feet long. Use the formula to write a simplified expression for s if $\ell = 85$. Then evaluate s to the nearest mile per hour. **$10\sqrt{17}$; 41 mi/h**

35. **PYTHAGOREAN THEOREM** The measures of the legs of a right triangle can be represented by the expressions $6x^2y$ and $9x^2y$. Use the Pythagorean Theorem to find a simplified expression for the measure of the hypotenuse. **$3x^2|y|\sqrt{13}$**

Chapter 7 34 Glencoe Algebra 2

Word Problem Practice
CRM p. 35 AL OL BL ELL

7-5 Word Problem Practice
Operations with Radical Expressions

1. **CUBES** Cathy has a rectangular box with dimensions 20 inches by 35 inches by 40 inches. She would like to replace it with a box in the shape of a cube but with the same volume. What should the length of a side of the cube be? Express your answer as a radical expression in simplest form.
$10\sqrt[3]{28}$ in.

2. **PHYSICS** The speed of a wave traveling over a string is given by $\frac{\sqrt{t}}{\sqrt{u}}$, where t is the tension of the string and u is the density. Rewrite the expression in simplest form by rationalizing the denominator.
$\frac{\sqrt{tu}}{u}$

3. **TUNING** Traditionally, musical instruments are tuned so that the note A is 440 Hertz. With each note higher on the instrument, the frequency of the pitch increases by a factor of $\sqrt[12]{2}$. What is the ratio of the frequencies of two notes that are 6 steps apart on the instrument? What is the ratio of the frequencies of two notes that are 9 steps apart on the instrument? Express your answers in simplest form.
$\sqrt{2}$ and $\sqrt[4]{8}$

4. **LIGHTS** Suppose a light has a brightness intensity of I_1 when it is at a distance of d_1 and a brightness intensity of I_2 when it is at a distance of d_2. These quantities are related by the equation $\frac{d_2}{d_1} = \sqrt{\frac{I_1}{I_2}}$. Suppose $I_1 = 50$ units and $I_2 = 24$ units. What would $\frac{d_2}{d_1}$ be? Express your answer in simplest form.
$\frac{5\sqrt{3}}{6}$

5. **RACING** John is Jay's younger brother. They like to race and, after many races, they found that the fairest race was to run slightly different distances. They both start at the same place and run straight for 0.2 miles. Then they head for different finishes. In the figure, John and Jay's finishing paths are marked.

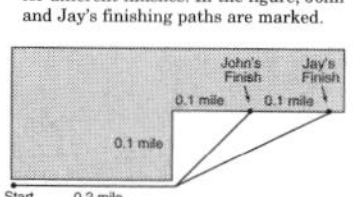

This time, they tied. Both of them finished the race in exactly 4 minutes.

a. If John and Jay continued at their average paces during the race, exactly how many minutes would it take them each to run a mile? Express your answer as a radical expression in simplest form.
John: $\frac{0.8 - 4\sqrt{0.02}}{0.02}$ or $40 - 20\sqrt{2}$ min; Jay: $\frac{0.8 - 4\sqrt{0.05}}{-0.01}$ or $40\sqrt{5} - 80$ min

b. Exactly how many times as fast did John run as Jay? Express your answer as a radical expression in simplest form.
$2 - \sqrt{2} + \sqrt{5} + \frac{\sqrt{10}}{2}$

Lesson 7-5

Chapter 7 35 Glencoe Algebra 2

Real-World Link

Fresh apples float because 25% of their volume is air.

49. $\frac{\sqrt[4]{1500a^2b^3x^3y^2}}{5|a|b}$

51. $\frac{(x+1)(\sqrt{x}+1)}{x-1}$ or $\frac{x\sqrt{x} + \sqrt{x} + x + 1}{x-1}$

60. Twyla; Ben's mistakes were multiplying the 4 by 16 instead of 4 and multiplying the 6 by 9 instead of 3.

62. Sample answer: 0 is the only possible value for a since $\sqrt{a}$ is defined for $a \geq 0$, and $\sqrt{-a}$ is defined for $a \leq 0$.

63. $\sqrt[1]{256} = 256$; $\sqrt[2]{256} = 16$; $\sqrt[4]{256} = 4$; $\sqrt[8]{256} = 2$

65. Sample answer: It is only necessary to use absolute values when it is possible that n could be odd or even and still be defined. It is when the radicand must be nonnegative in order for the root to be defined that the absolute values are not necessary.

B Simplify. **47. $3|a|b^3\sqrt[4]{2a^2bc}$**

45. $\sqrt[3]{16y^4z^{12}}$ **$2yz^4\sqrt[3]{2y}$**

46. $\sqrt[3]{-54x^6y^{11}}$ **$-3x^2y^3\sqrt[3]{2y^2}$**

47. $\sqrt[4]{162a^6b^{13}c}$

48. $\sqrt[4]{48a^9b^3c^{16}}$ **$2a^2c^4\sqrt[4]{3ab^3}$**

49. $\sqrt[4]{\frac{12x^3y^2}{5a^2b}}$

50. $\frac{\sqrt[3]{36xy^2}}{\sqrt[3]{10xz}}$ **$\frac{\sqrt[3]{450y^2z^2}}{5z}$**

51. $\frac{x+1}{\sqrt{x}-1}$

52. $\frac{x-2}{\sqrt{x^2-4}}$ **$\frac{\sqrt{x^2-4}}{x+2}$**

53. $\frac{\sqrt{x}}{\sqrt{x^2-1}}$ **$\frac{\sqrt{x^3-x}}{x^2-1}$**

54. **APPLES** The diameter of an apple is related to its weight and can be modeled by the formula $d = \sqrt[3]{3w}$, where d is the diameter in inches and w is the weight in ounces. Find the diameter of an apple that weighs 6.47 ounces. **2.69 in.**

Simplify each expression if b is an even number.

55. $\sqrt[b]{a^b}$ **$|a|$**

56. $\sqrt[b]{a^{4b}}$ **a^4**

57. $\sqrt[b]{a^{2b}}$ **a^2**

58. $\sqrt[b]{a^{3b}}$ **$|a^3|$**

C

59. **MULTIPLE REPRESENTATIONS** In this problem, you will explore operations with like radicals. **a–e. See Chapter 7 Answer Appendix.**

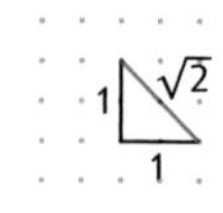

a. **NUMERICAL** Copy the diagram at the right on dot paper. Use the Pythagorean Theorem to prove that the length of the red segment is $\sqrt{2}$ units.

b. **GRAPHICAL** Extend the segment to represent $\sqrt{2} + \sqrt{2}$.

c. **ANALYTICAL** Use your drawing to show that $\sqrt{2} + \sqrt{2} \neq \sqrt{2+2}$ or 2.

d. **GRAPHICAL** Use the dot paper to draw a square with side lengths $\sqrt{2}$ units.

e. **NUMERICAL** Prove that the area of the square is $\sqrt{2} \cdot \sqrt{2} = 2$ square units.

H.O.T. Problems
Use Higher-Order Thinking Skills

60. **ERROR ANALYSIS** Twyla and Ben are simplifying $4\sqrt{32} + 6\sqrt{18}$. Is either of them correct? Explain your reasoning.

Twyla	Ben
$4\sqrt{32} + 6\sqrt{18}$	$4\sqrt{32} + 6\sqrt{18}$
$= 4\sqrt{4^2 \cdot 2} + 6\sqrt{3^2 \cdot 2}$	$= 4\sqrt{16 \cdot 2} + 6\sqrt{9 \cdot 2}$
$= 16\sqrt{2} + 18\sqrt{2}$	$= 64\sqrt{2} + 54\sqrt{2}$
$= 34\sqrt{2}$	$= 118\sqrt{2}$

61. **CHALLENGE** Show that $\frac{-1 - i\sqrt{3}}{2}$ is a cube root of 1. **See Chapter 7 Answer Appendix.**

62. **REASONING** For what values of a is $\sqrt{a} \cdot \sqrt{-a}$ a real number? Explain.

63. **CHALLENGE** Find four combinations of whole numbers that satisfy $\sqrt[a]{256} = b$.

64. **OPEN ENDED** Find a number other than 1 that has a positive whole number for a square root, cube root, and fourth root. **Sample answer: 4096**

65. **WRITING IN MATH** Explain why absolute values may be unnecessary when an nth root of an even power results in an odd power.

Enrichment
CRM p. 36 AL OL

7-5 Enrichment

Special Products with Radicals

Notice that $(\sqrt{3})(\sqrt{3}) = 3$, or $(\sqrt{3})^2 = 3$. In general, $(\sqrt{x})^2 = x$ when $x \geq 0$.

Also, notice that $(\sqrt{9})(\sqrt{4}) = \sqrt{36}$. In general, $(\sqrt{x})(\sqrt{y}) = \sqrt{xy}$ when x and y are not negative.

You can use these ideas to find the special products below.

$(\sqrt{a} + \sqrt{b})(\sqrt{a} - \sqrt{b}) = (\sqrt{a})^2 - (\sqrt{b})^2 = a - b$
$(\sqrt{a} + \sqrt{b})^2 = (\sqrt{a})^2 + 2\sqrt{ab} + (\sqrt{b})^2 = a + 2\sqrt{ab} + b$
$(\sqrt{a} - \sqrt{b})^2 = (\sqrt{a})^2 - 2\sqrt{ab} + (\sqrt{b})^2 = a - 2\sqrt{ab} + b$

Example 1 Find the product: $(\sqrt{2} + \sqrt{5})(\sqrt{2} - \sqrt{5})$.

$(\sqrt{2} + \sqrt{5})(\sqrt{2} - \sqrt{5}) = (\sqrt{2})^2 - (\sqrt{5})^2 = 2 - 5 = -3$

Example 2 Evaluate $(\sqrt{2} + \sqrt{8})^2$.

$(\sqrt{2} + \sqrt{8})^2 = (\sqrt{2})^2 + 2\sqrt{2}\sqrt{8} + (\sqrt{8})^2$
$= 2 + 2\sqrt{16} + 8 = 2 + 2(4) + 8 = 2 + 8 + 8 = 18$

Multiple Representations In Exercise 59, students use dot paper and the Pythagorean Theorem to explore operations with like radicals.

NGSSS PRACTICE 912.P.3.1, 912.A.3.2

66. **PROBABILITY** A six-sided number cube has faces with the numbers 1 though 6 marked on it. What is the probability that a number less than 4 will occur on one toss of the number cube? **A**

A. $\frac{1}{2}$ C. $\frac{1}{4}$

B. $\frac{1}{3}$ D. $\frac{1}{5}$

67. When the number of a year is divisible by 4, the year is a leap year. However, when the year is divisible by 100, the year is not a leap year, unless the year is divisible by 400. Which is *not* a leap year? **G**

F. 1884 H. 1904

G. 1900 I. 1940

68. **SHORT RESPONSE** Which property is illustrated by $4x + 0 = 4x$? **Additive Identity Property**

69. **ACT/SAT** The expression $\sqrt{180a^2b^8}$ is equivalent to which of the following? **B**

A. $5\sqrt{6}\,|a|\,b^4$

B. $6\sqrt{5}\,|a|\,b^4$

C. $3\sqrt{10}\,|a|\,b^4$

D. $36\sqrt{5}\,|a|\,b^4$

Spiral Review

Simplify. (Lesson 7-4)

70. $\sqrt{81x^6}$ **$9|x^3|$** 71. $\sqrt[3]{729a^3b^9}$ **$9ab^3$** 72. $\sqrt{(g+5)^2}$ **$|g+5|$**

73. Graph $y \leq \sqrt{x-2}$. (Lesson 7-3) **See margin.**

Solve each equation. (Lesson 6-5) **76. $-\sqrt{3}, \sqrt{3}, -3i, 3i$ 77. $-4, 2+2i\sqrt{3}, 2-2i\sqrt{3}$ 78, 79. See margin.**

74. $x^4 - 34x^2 + 225 = 0$ **$-5, -3, 3, 5$** 75. $x^4 - 15x^2 - 16 = 0$ **$-4, 4, -i, i$** 76. $x^4 + 6x^2 - 27 = 0$

77. $x^3 + 64 = 0$ 78. $27x^3 + 1 = 0$ 79. $8x^3 - 27 = 0$

80. **MODELS** A model car builder is building a display table for model cars. He wants the perimeter of the table to be 26 feet, but he wants the area of the table to be no more than 30 square feet. What could be the width of the table? (Lesson 5-8) **between 0 and 3 ft or between 10 and 13 ft**

81. **CONSTRUCTION** Cho charges $1500 to build a small deck and $2500 to build a large deck. During the spring and summer, she built 5 more small decks than large decks. If she earned $23,500 how many of each type of deck did she build? (Lesson 4-6) **9 small, 4 large**

82. **FOOD** The Hot Dog Grille offers the lunch combinations shown. Assume that the price of a combo meal is the same price as purchasing each item separately. Find the prices for a hot dog, a soda, and a bag of potato chips. (Lesson 3-5) **hot dog, $1.95; soda, $1.50; potato chips, $0.90**

Lunch Combo Meals	
1. Two hot dogs, one soda	$5.40
2. One hot dog, potato chips, one soda	$4.35
3. Two hot dogs, two bags of chips	$5.70

Skills Review

Evaluate each expression.

83. $2\left(\frac{1}{6}\right)$ **$\frac{1}{3}$** 84. $3\left(\frac{1}{8}\right)$ **$\frac{3}{8}$** 85. $\frac{1}{4} + \frac{1}{3}$ **$\frac{7}{12}$**

86. $\frac{1}{2} + \frac{3}{8}$ **$\frac{7}{8}$** 87. $\frac{2}{3} - \frac{1}{4}$ **$\frac{5}{12}$** 88. $\frac{5}{6} - \frac{2}{5}$ **$\frac{13}{30}$**

Differentiated Instruction

BL

Extension Solve for a and b.

$\sqrt{\frac{3^a}{7^b}} = \frac{3^2\sqrt{7}}{7^2}$ $a = 4, b = 3$

Exercise Alert

Dot Paper Exercise 59 requires the use of dot paper.

Watch Out!

Error Analysis In Exercise 60, students should see that Ben made an error each time he "took out" a factor from the square root symbol. Explain to students that $4\sqrt{16 \cdot 2} = 4 \cdot 4\sqrt{2} = 16\sqrt{2}$ and $6\sqrt{9 \cdot 2} = 6 \cdot 3\sqrt{2} = 18\sqrt{2}$, as shown in Twyla's solution.

4 ASSESS

Name the Math Ask students to describe how combining radicals is the same as and different from combining expressions with variables.

Watch Out!

Common Misconceptions Students will need to simplify expressions involving radicals in much of their future work in algebra. Take time to help students uncover and correct their misconceptions by analyzing the errors they make.

Additional Answers

73.

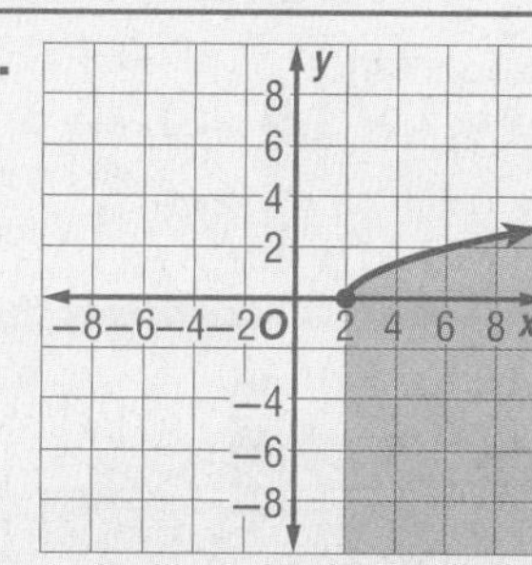

78. $-\frac{1}{3}, \frac{1+i\sqrt{3}}{6}, \frac{1-i\sqrt{3}}{6}$

79. $\frac{3}{2}, \frac{-3+3i\sqrt{3}}{4}, \frac{-3-3i\sqrt{3}}{4}$

Lesson 7-5 Operations with Radical Expressions 445

7-6 Lesson Notes

1 FOCUS

Vertical Alignment

Before Lesson 7-6
Use properties of exponents.

Lesson 7-6
Write expressions with rational exponents in radical form, and vice versa.
Simplify expressions in exponential or radical form.

After Lesson 7-6
Determine solutions of square root equations using algebraic methods.

2 TEACH

Scaffolding Questions

Have students read the *Why?* section of the lesson.

Ask:

- In the formula $C = c(1 + r)^n$, what is the exponent of c? The exponent of c is 1.
- Which expression is raised to the exponent n? n is the exponent of the quantity $(1 + r)$.
- Why does $\frac{1}{2}$ appear as an exponent in the last sentence? n represents a number of years, and 6 months is half of a year.

7-6 Rational Exponents

Then
You used properties of exponents. (Lesson 6-1)

Now
- Write expressions with rational exponents in radical form and vice versa.
- Simplify expressions in exponential or radical form.

NGSSS
MA.912.A.6.3 Simplify expressions using properties of rational exponents.
MA.912.A.6.4 Convert between rational exponent and radical forms of expressions. *Also addresses MA.912.A.6.5.*

FL Math Online
glencoe.com

Why?

The formula $C = c(1 + r)^n$ can be used to estimate the future cost of an item due to inflation. C represents the future cost, c represents the current cost, r is the rate of inflation, and n is the number of years for the projection.

For example, $C = c(1 + r)^{\frac{1}{2}}$ can be used to estimate the cost of a video game system in six months.

Rational Exponents and Radicals You know that squaring a number and taking the square root of a number are inverse operations. But how would you evaluate an expression that contains a fractional exponent such as the one above? You can investigate such an expression by assuming that fractional exponents behave as integral exponents.

$\left(b^{\frac{1}{2}}\right)^2 = b^{\frac{1}{2}} \cdot b^{\frac{1}{2}}$ **Write as a multiplication expression.**

$= b^{\frac{1}{2}+\frac{1}{2}}$ **Add the exponents.**

$= b^1$ or b **Simplify.**

Thus, $b^{\frac{1}{2}}$ is a number with a square equal to b. So $b^{\frac{1}{2}} = \sqrt{b}$.

Key Concept $b^{\frac{1}{n}}$

Words For any real number b and any positive integer n, $b^{\frac{1}{n}} = \sqrt[n]{b}$, except when $b < 0$ and n is even. When $b < 0$ and n is even, a complex root may exist.

Examples $27^{\frac{1}{3}} = \sqrt[3]{27}$ or 3 $\quad (-16)^{\frac{1}{2}} = \sqrt{-16}$ or $4i$

EXAMPLE 1 Radical and Exponential Forms

Simplify.

a. Write $x^{\frac{1}{6}}$ in radical form.

$x^{\frac{1}{6}} = \sqrt[6]{x}$ **Definition of $b^{\frac{1}{n}}$**

b. Write $\sqrt[4]{z}$ in exponential form.

$\sqrt[4]{z} = z^{\frac{1}{4}}$ **Definition of $b^{\frac{1}{n}}$**

Guided Practice

1A. Write $a^{\frac{1}{5}}$ in radical form. $\sqrt[5]{a}$

1B. Write $\sqrt[8]{c}$ in exponential form. $c^{\frac{1}{8}}$

1C. Write $d^{\frac{7}{4}}$ in radical form. $\sqrt[4]{d^7}$

1D. Write $\sqrt[3]{c^{-5}}$ in exponential form. $c^{-\frac{5}{3}}$

Personal Tutor glencoe.com

Lesson 7-6 Resources

Resource	Approaching-Level	On-Level	Beyond-Level	English Learners
Teacher Edition	• Differentiated Instruction, p. 447	• Differentiated Instruction, p. 447, 448	• Differentiated Instruction, p. 448	• Differentiated Instruction, p. 447
Chapter Resource Masters	• Study Guide and Intervention, pp. 38–39 • Skills Practice, p. 40 • Practice, p. 41 • Word Problem Practice, p. 42	• Study Guide and Intervention, pp. 38–39 • Skills Practice, p. 40 • Practice, p. 41 • Word Problem Practice, p. 42 • Enrichment, p. 43 • Spreadsheet Activity, p. 44	• Practice, p. 41 • Word Problem Practice, p. 42 • Enrichment, p. 43	• Study Guide and Intervention, pp. 38–39 • Skills Practice, p. 40 • Practice, p. 41 • Word Problem Practice, p. 42
Transparencies	• 5-Minute Check Transparency 7-6	• 5-Minute Check Transparency 7-6	• 5-Minute Check Transparency 7-6	• 5-Minute Check Transparency 7-6
Other	• Study Notebook	• Study Notebook	• Study Notebook	• Study Notebook

The rules for negative exponents also apply to negative rational exponents.

EXAMPLE 2 **Evaluate Expressions with Rational Exponents**

Evaluate each expression.

a. $81^{-\frac{1}{4}}$

$81^{-\frac{1}{4}} = \frac{1}{81^{\frac{1}{4}}}$ $\quad$ $b^{-n} = \frac{1}{b^n}$

$= \frac{1}{\sqrt[4]{81}}$ $\quad$ $81^{\frac{1}{4}} = \sqrt[4]{81}$

$= \frac{1}{\sqrt[4]{3^4}}$ $\quad$ $81 = 3^4$

$= \frac{1}{3}$ $\quad$ Simplify.

b. $216^{\frac{2}{3}}$

$216^{\frac{2}{3}} = (6^3)^{\frac{2}{3}}$ $\quad$ $216 = 6^3$

$= 6^{3 \cdot \frac{2}{3}}$ $\quad$ Power of a Power

$= 6^2$ $\quad$ Multiply exponents.

$= 36$ $\quad$ Simplify.

Guided Practice

2A. $-3125^{-\frac{1}{5}}$ $\;-\frac{1}{5}$

2B. $256^{\frac{3}{8}}$ $\;8$

Personal Tutor glencoe.com

Real-World Career

Economist
Economists are employed in banking, finance, accounting, commerce, marketing, and business administration. Politicians often consult economists before enacting policy. Economists use shopping as one way of judging the economy. A bachelor's or master's degree in economics is required.

Examples 2a and 2b use the definition of $b^{\frac{1}{n}}$ and the properties of powers to evaluate an expression. Both methods suggest the following general definition of rational exponents.

Key Concept **Rational Exponents**

Words For any real nonzero number b, and any integers x and y, with $y > 1$, $b^{\frac{x}{y}} = \sqrt[y]{b^x} = \left(\sqrt[y]{b}\right)^x$, except when $b < 0$ and y is even. When $b < 0$ and y is even, a complex root may exist.

Examples $27^{\frac{2}{3}} = \left(\sqrt[3]{27}\right)^2 = 3^2$ or 9 $\qquad (-16)^{\frac{3}{2}} = \left(\sqrt{-16}\right)^3 = (4i)^3$ or $-64i$

Real-World EXAMPLE 3 **Solve Equations with Rational Exponents**

FINANCIAL LITERACY **Refer to the beginning of the lesson. Suppose a video game system costs \$390 now. How much would the price increase in six months with an annual inflation rate of 5.3%?**

$C = c(1 + r)^n$ $\quad$ Original formula

$= 390(1 + 0.053)^{\frac{1}{2}}$ $\quad$ $c = 390$, $r = 0.053$, and $n = \frac{6 \text{ months}}{12 \text{ months}}$ or $\frac{1}{2}$

≈ 400.20 $\quad$ Use a calculator.

In six months the price of the video game system will be \$400.20 − \$390.00 or \$10.20 more than its current price.

Guided Practice

3. Suppose a gallon of milk costs \$2.99 now. How much would the price increase in 9 months with an inflation rate of 5.3%? **\$0.12**

Personal Tutor glencoe.com

Differentiated Instruction

AL OL ELL

If students are not reading the exponent,

Then encourage students to read an exponent aloud in a way that distinguishes it from a coefficient or multiplier. Ask them to practice reading the exponent correctly, for example, reading x^3 as "x to the third power" or "x cubed." Also ask students to practice reading radical expressions correctly, for example, reading $\sqrt{y^3}$ as "the square root of y cubed" or "the square root of the third power of y."

TEACH with TECH

INTERACTIVE WHITEBOARD
Write an expression with a rational exponent on the board. Display a template such as $a^{\frac{\square}{\square}} = \sqrt[\square]{a^{\square}}$ and drag the numerator and denominator of the exponent to rewrite the expression as a radical.

Rational Exponents and Radicals

Example 1 shows how to write expressions in radical and exponential form. **Example 2** shows how to evaluate expressions with rational exponents. **Example 3** is a real-world example with a rational exponent.

Formative Assessment

Use the Guided Practice exercises after each example to determine students' understanding of concepts.

Additional Examples

1 **a.** Write $a^{\frac{1}{7}}$ in radical form. $\sqrt[7]{a}$

b. Write $\sqrt{w}$ in exponential form. $w^{\frac{1}{2}}$

2 Evaluate each expression.

a. $49^{-\frac{1}{2}}$ $\;\frac{1}{7}$ $\qquad$ **b.** $32^{\frac{2}{5}}$ $\;4$

3 **WEIGHTLIFTING** The formula $M = 512 - 146{,}230B^{-\frac{8}{5}}$ can be used to estimate the maximum total mass that a weightlifter of mass B kilograms can lift using the snatch and the clean and jerk. According to the formula, what is the maximum that a weightlifter weighing 168 kilograms can lift? The formula predicts that he can lift at most 472 kilograms.

Additional Examples also in Interactive Classroom PowerPoint® Presentations

IWB INTERACTIVE WHITEBOARD READY

Focus on Mathematical Content

Rational Exponents In the general definition of rational exponents, $b^{\frac{m}{n}} = \sqrt[n]{b^m} = \left(\sqrt[n]{b}\right)^m$, there are restrictions on the variables b, m, and n. The variable b must be a nonzero real number except when n is even, and then b must be a positive real number. The variable m must be an integer, and n must be a natural number. These restrictions on m and n do not decrease the generality of the definition since any rational number can be expressed as a quotient of an integer and a natural number.

Simplify Expressions

Example 4 shows how to simplify expressions with rational exponents. **Example 5** shows how to simplify radical expressions.

Additional Example

4 Evaluate each expression.

a. $y^{\frac{1}{7}} \cdot y^{\frac{4}{7}}$ $y^{\frac{5}{7}}$

b. $x^{-\frac{2}{3}}$ $\frac{x^{\frac{1}{3}}}{x}$

Watch Out!

Preventing Errors If students are having difficulty remembering which part of the fractional exponent is the index, suggest that they recall the basic definition $b^{\frac{1}{2}} = \sqrt{b}$.

Simplify Expressions All of the properties of powers you learned in Lesson 6-1 apply to rational exponents. Write each expression with all positive exponents. Also, any exponents in the denominator of a fraction must be positive *integers*. So, it may be necessary to rationalize a denominator.

EXAMPLE 4 Simplify Expressions with Rational Exponents

Evaluate each expression.

a. $a^{\frac{2}{7}} \cdot a^{\frac{4}{7}}$

$a^{\frac{2}{7}} \cdot a^{\frac{4}{7}} = a^{\frac{2}{7}+\frac{4}{7}}$ — **Add powers.**

$= a^{\frac{6}{7}}$ — **Add exponents.**

b. $b^{-\frac{5}{6}}$

$b^{-\frac{5}{6}} = \frac{1}{b^{\frac{5}{6}}}$ — $b^{-n} = \frac{1}{b^n}$

$= \frac{1}{b^{\frac{5}{6}}} \cdot \frac{b^{\frac{1}{6}}}{b^{\frac{1}{6}}}$ — **Why use** $\frac{b^{\frac{1}{6}}}{b^{\frac{1}{6}}}$**?**

$= \frac{b^{\frac{1}{6}}}{b^{\frac{6}{6}}}$ — $b^{\frac{5}{6}} \cdot b^{\frac{1}{6}} = b^{\frac{5}{6}+\frac{1}{6}}$

$= \frac{b^{\frac{1}{6}}}{b}$ — $b^{\frac{6}{6}} = b^1$ **or** b

StudyTip

Simplifying Expressions When simplifying expressions containing rational exponents, leave the exponent in rational form rather than writing the expression as a radical.

Guided Practice

4A. $p^{\frac{1}{4}} \cdot p^{\frac{9}{4}}$ $p^{\frac{5}{2}}$

4B. $r^{-\frac{4}{5}}$ $\frac{r^{\frac{1}{5}}}{r}$

Personal Tutor glencoe.com

When simplifying a radical expression, always use the least index possible. Using rational exponents makes this process easier, but the answer should be written in radical form.

EXAMPLE 5 Simplify Radical Expressions

Simplify each expression.

a. $\frac{\sqrt[4]{27}}{\sqrt{3}}$

$\frac{\sqrt[4]{27}}{\sqrt{3}} = \frac{27^{\frac{1}{4}}}{3^{\frac{1}{2}}}$ — **Rational exponents**

$= \frac{(3^3)^{\frac{1}{4}}}{3^{\frac{1}{2}}}$ — $27 = 3^3$

$= \frac{3^{\frac{3}{4}}}{3^{\frac{1}{2}}}$ — **Power of a Power**

$= 3^{\frac{3}{4}-\frac{1}{2}}$ — **Quotient of Powers**

$= 3^{\frac{1}{4}}$ — **Simplify.**

$= \sqrt[4]{3}$ — **Rewrite in radical form.**

b. $\sqrt[3]{64z^6}$

$\sqrt[3]{64z^6} = (64z^6)^{\frac{1}{3}}$ — **Rational exponents**

$= (8^2 \cdot z^6)^{\frac{1}{3}}$ — $64 = 8^2$

$= 8^{\frac{2}{3}} \cdot z^{\frac{6}{3}}$ — **Power of a Power**

$= 4z^2$ — $8^{\frac{2}{3}} = 4$

Differentiated Instruction OL BL

Extension Assume that x and y are nonnegative real numbers. Multiply $\left(x^{\frac{1}{2}} + y^{\frac{1}{2}}\right)\left(x^{\frac{1}{2}} - y^{\frac{1}{2}}\right)$. $x - y$

c. $\dfrac{x^{\frac{1}{2}} - 2}{3x^{\frac{1}{2}} + 2}$

$\dfrac{x^{\frac{1}{2}} - 2}{3x^{\frac{1}{2}} + 2} = \dfrac{x^{\frac{1}{2}} - 2}{3x^{\frac{1}{2}} + 2} \cdot \dfrac{3x^{\frac{1}{2}} - 2}{3x^{\frac{1}{2}} - 2}$ — **$3x^{\frac{1}{2}} - 2$ is the conjugate of $3x^{\frac{1}{2}} + 2$.**

$= \dfrac{3x^{\frac{2}{2}} - 8x^{\frac{1}{2}} + 4}{9x^{\frac{2}{2}} - 4}$ — **Multiply.**

$= \dfrac{3x - 8x^{\frac{1}{2}} + 4}{9x - 4}$ — **Simplify.**

StudyTip

Radical Expressions Write the simplified expression in the same form as the beginning expression. When you start with a radical expression, end with a radical expression. When you start with an expression with rational exponents, end with an expression with rational exponents.

Guided Practice

5A. $\dfrac{\sqrt[4]{32}}{\sqrt[3]{2}}$ $\sqrt[12]{2^{11}}$ **5B.** $\sqrt[3]{16x^4}$ $2x\sqrt[3]{2x}$ **5C.** $\dfrac{y^{\frac{1}{2}} + 2}{y^{\frac{1}{2}} - 2}$ $\dfrac{y + 4y^{\frac{1}{2}} + 4}{y - 4}$

Personal Tutor glencoe.com

Concept Summary

Expressions with Rational Exponents

An expression with rational exponents is simplified when all of the following conditions are met.

- It has no negative exponents.
- It has no exponents that are not positive integers in the denominator.
- It is not a complex fraction.
- The index of any remaining radical is the least number possible.

Check Your Understanding

Example 1 p. 446

Write each expression in radical form, or write each radical in exponential form.

1. $10^{\frac{1}{4}}$ $\sqrt[4]{10}$ **2.** $x^{\frac{3}{5}}$ $\sqrt[5]{x^3}$ **3.** $\sqrt[3]{15}$ $15^{\frac{1}{3}}$ **4.** $\sqrt[4]{7x^6y^9}$ $7^{\frac{1}{4}}x^{\frac{3}{2}}y^{\frac{9}{4}}$

Example 2 p. 447

Evaluate each expression.

5. $343^{\frac{1}{3}}$ 7 **6.** $32^{-\frac{1}{5}}$ $\frac{1}{2}$ **7.** $125^{\frac{2}{3}}$ 25 **8.** $\dfrac{24}{4^{\frac{3}{2}}}$ 3

Example 3 p. 447

9 **GARDENING** If the area A of a square is known, then the lengths of its sides ℓ can be computed using $\ell = A^{\frac{1}{2}}$. You have purchased a 169 ft^2 share in a community garden for the season. What is the length of one side of your square garden? 13 ft

Examples 4 and 5 p. 448

Simplify each expression.

10. $a^{\frac{3}{4}} \cdot a^{\frac{1}{2}}$ $a^{\frac{5}{4}}$ **11.** $\dfrac{x^{\frac{4}{5}}}{x^{\frac{1}{5}}}$ $x^{\frac{3}{5}}$ **12.** $\dfrac{b^3}{c^{\frac{1}{2}}} \cdot \dfrac{c}{b^{\frac{1}{3}}}$ $b^{\frac{8}{3}}c^{\frac{1}{2}}$

13. $\sqrt[4]{9g^2}$ $\sqrt{3g}$ **14.** $\dfrac{\sqrt[5]{64}}{\sqrt[5]{4}}$ $2^{\frac{4}{5}}$ or $\sqrt[5]{16}$ **15.** $\dfrac{g^{\frac{1}{2}} - 1}{g^{\frac{1}{2}} + 1}$ $\dfrac{g - 2g^{\frac{1}{2}} + 1}{g - 1}$

Additional Example

5 Simplify each expression.

a. $\dfrac{\sqrt[6]{16}}{\sqrt[3]{2}}$ $2^{\frac{1}{3}}$ or $\sqrt[3]{2}$

b. $\sqrt[6]{4x^4}$ $\sqrt[3]{2x^2}$

c. $\dfrac{y^{\frac{1}{2}} + 1}{y^{\frac{1}{2}} - 1}$ $\dfrac{y + 2y^{\frac{1}{2}} + 1}{y - 1}$

Tips for New Teachers

Checking answers Encourage students to substitute values in both the original expression and their simplified expression. If the values of the expressions are equal, their answer is likely to be correct.

3 PRACTICE

Formative Assessment

Use Exercises 1–15 to check for understanding.

Use the chart at the bottom of the next page to customize assignments for your students.

Additional Answers

52a. about 475

52b.

Year	0	1	2	3	4	5
Deer	100	141	200	282	400	565

52c.

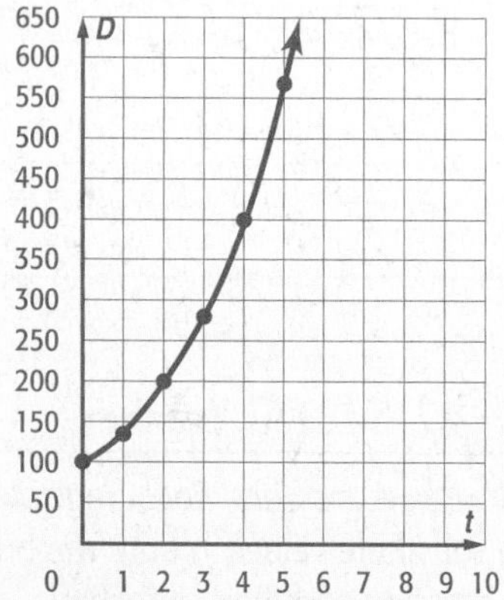

52d. Sample answer: No; it is not reasonable to think that the population will continue to grow without bounds. This does not take into account the death rate of the deer.

65b.

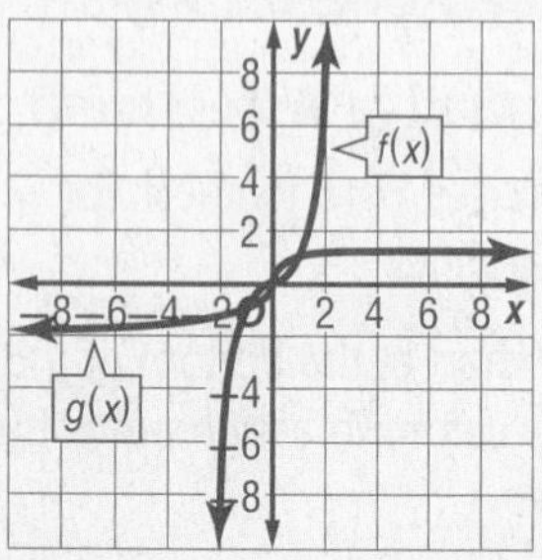

67a. Sample answer: $\sqrt[4]{(-16)^3} = \sqrt[4]{-4096}$; there is no real number that when raised to the forth power results in a negative number.

69. Sample answer: It may be easier to simplify an expression when it has rational exponents because all the properties of exponents apply. We do not have as many properties dealing directly with radicals. However, we can convert all radicals to rational exponents, and then use the properties of exponents to simplify.

Practice and Problem Solving

● = Step-by-Step Solutions begin on page R20. Extra Practice begins on page 947.

Example 1 p. 446

Write each expression in radical form, or write each radical in exponential form.

16. $8^{\frac{1}{5}}$ $\sqrt[5]{8}$
17. $4^{\frac{2}{7}}$ $\sqrt[7]{16}$
18. $a^{\frac{3}{4}}$ $\sqrt[4]{a^3}$
19. $(x^3)^{\frac{3}{2}}$ $\sqrt{x^9}$

20. $\sqrt{17}$ $17^{\frac{1}{2}}$
21. $\sqrt[4]{63}$ $63^{\frac{1}{4}}$
22. $\sqrt[3]{5xy^2}$ $5^{\frac{1}{3}}x^{\frac{1}{3}}y^{\frac{2}{3}}$
23. $\sqrt[4]{625x^2}$ $5x^{\frac{1}{2}}$

Example 2 p. 447

Evaluate each expression.

24. $27^{\frac{1}{3}}$ 3
25. $256^{\frac{1}{4}}$ 4
26. $16^{-\frac{1}{2}}$ $\frac{1}{4}$
27. $81^{-\frac{1}{4}}$ $\frac{1}{3}$

Example 3 p. 447

28. BASKETBALL A women's regulation-sized basketball is slightly smaller than a men's basketball. The radius r of the ball that holds V cubic units of air is $\left(\frac{3V}{4\pi}\right)^{\frac{1}{3}}$.

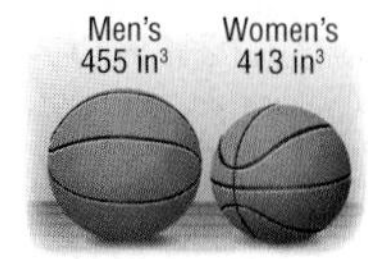

a. Find the radius of a women's basketball. about 4.62 in.

b. Find the radius of a men's basketball. about 4.77 in.

29. GEOMETRY The radius r of a sphere with volume V is given by $r = \left(\frac{3V}{4\pi}\right)^{\frac{1}{3}}$. Find the radius of a ball with a volume of 77 cm^3. about 2.64 cm

Examples 4 and 5 p. 448

Simplify each expression. 37. $\sqrt[3]{9} \cdot \sqrt{g}$

30. $x^{\frac{1}{3}} \cdot x^{\frac{2}{5}}$ $x^{\frac{11}{15}}$
31. $a^{\frac{4}{9}} \cdot a^{\frac{1}{4}}$ $a^{\frac{25}{36}}$
32. $b^{-\frac{3}{4}}$ $\frac{b^{\frac{1}{4}}}{b}$
33. $y^{-\frac{4}{5}}$ $\frac{y^{\frac{1}{5}}}{y}$
34. $\frac{\sqrt[8]{81}}{\sqrt[6]{3}}$ $\sqrt[3]{3}$

35 $\frac{\sqrt[4]{27}}{\sqrt[4]{3}}$ $\sqrt{3}$
36. $\sqrt[4]{25x^2}$ $\sqrt{5x}$
37. $\sqrt[6]{81g^3}$
38. $\frac{h^{\frac{1}{2}}+1}{h^{\frac{1}{2}}-1}$
39. $\frac{x^{\frac{1}{4}}+2}{x^{\frac{1}{4}}-2}$

38. $\frac{h + 2h^{\frac{1}{2}} + 1}{h - 1}$ 39. $\frac{x + 4x^{\frac{3}{4}} + 8x^{\frac{1}{2}} + 16x^{\frac{1}{4}} + 16}{x - 16}$

B **GEOMETRY** Find the area of each figure.

40. $6r^{\frac{3}{4}}w^{\frac{3}{4}}$ units^2

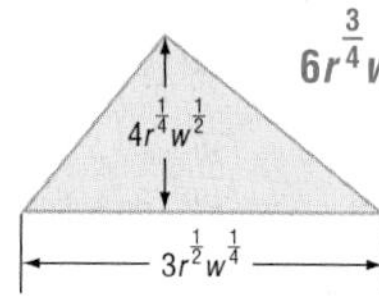

41. $28.27x^{\frac{4}{3}}y^{\frac{2}{5}}z^4$ units^2

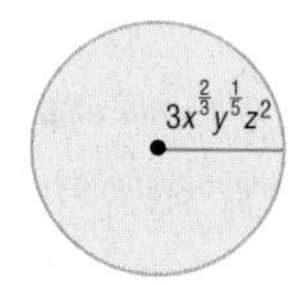

42. Find the simplified form of $18^{\frac{1}{2}} + 2^{\frac{1}{2}} - 32^{\frac{1}{2}}$. 0

43. What is the simplified form of $64^{\frac{1}{3}} - 32^{\frac{1}{3}} + 8^{\frac{1}{3}}$? $6 - 2 \cdot 4^{\frac{1}{3}}$

Simplify each expression.

44. $a^{\frac{7}{4}} \cdot a^{\frac{5}{4}}$ a^3
45. $x^{\frac{2}{3}} \cdot x^{\frac{8}{3}}$ $x^{\frac{10}{3}}$
46. $\left(b^{\frac{3}{4}}\right)^{\frac{1}{3}}$ $b^{\frac{1}{4}}$
47. $\left(y^{-\frac{3}{5}}\right)^{-\frac{1}{4}}$ $y^{\frac{3}{20}}$

48. $\sqrt[4]{64}$ $2\sqrt{2}$
49. $\sqrt[6]{216}$ $\sqrt{6}$
50. $d^{-\frac{5}{6}}$ $\frac{d^{\frac{1}{6}}}{d}$
51. $w^{-\frac{7}{8}}$ $\frac{w^{\frac{1}{8}}}{w}$

Differentiated Homework Options

Level	Assignment	Two-Day Option	
AL Basic	16–39, 66, 68–97	17–39 odd, 71–74	16–38 even, 66, 68–70, 75–97
OL Core	17–51 odd, 52, 53–65 odd, 66, 68–97	16–39, 71–74	40–66, 68–70, 75–97
BL Advanced	40–91, (optional: 92–97)		

52. **WILDLIFE** A population of 100 deer is reintroduced to a wildlife preserve. Suppose the population does extremely well and the deer population doubles in two years. Then the number D of deer after t years is given by $D = 100 \cdot 2^{\frac{t}{2}}$. **a–d. See margin.**

a. How many deer will there be after $4\frac{1}{2}$ years?

b. Make a table that charts the population of deer every year for the next five years.

c. Make a graph using your table.

d. Using your table and graph, decide whether this is a reasonable trend over the long term. Explain.

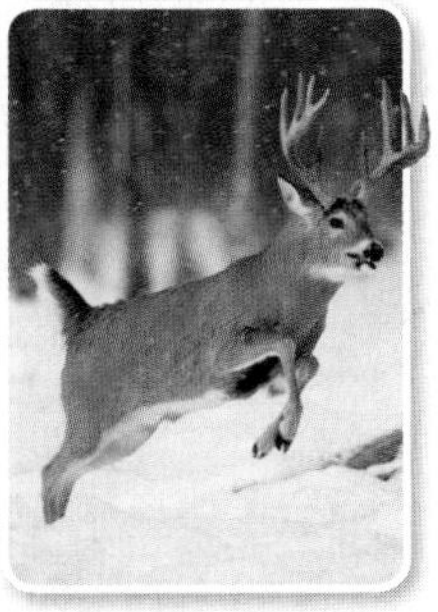

Real-World Link

The most accurate method of determining the age of a deer is to look at a cross-section of a tooth. Each winter, deer develop a layer of cementum on the teeth, creating a ring, so each ring represents a year, just like the rings of a tree trunk.

Source: Wildlife Analytical Laboratories

Simplify each expression. **57.** $23\sqrt[6]{23}$ **63.** $2\sqrt{6} - 5$ **64.** $x - x^{\frac{1}{3}}z^{\frac{2}{3}}$

53. $\dfrac{f^{-\frac{1}{4}}}{4f^{\frac{1}{2}} \cdot f^{-\frac{1}{3}}}$ $\dfrac{f^{\frac{7}{12}}}{4f}$

54. $\dfrac{g^{\frac{5}{2}}}{g^{\frac{1}{2}} + 2}$ $\dfrac{g^3 - 2g^{\frac{5}{2}}}{g - 4}$

55. $\dfrac{c^{\frac{2}{3}}}{c^{\frac{1}{6}}}$ $c^{\frac{1}{2}}$

56. $\dfrac{z^{\frac{4}{5}}}{z^{\frac{1}{2}}}$ $z^{\frac{3}{10}}$

57. $\sqrt{23} \cdot \sqrt[3]{23^2}$

58. $\sqrt[8]{36h^4j^4}$ $6^{\frac{1}{4}}h^{\frac{1}{2}}j^{\frac{1}{2}}$

59. $\sqrt{\sqrt{81}}$ 3

60. $\sqrt[4]{\sqrt{256}}$ 2

61. $\dfrac{ab}{\sqrt{c}}$ $\dfrac{ab\sqrt{c}}{c}$

62. $\dfrac{xy}{\sqrt[3]{z}}$ $\dfrac{xy\sqrt[3]{z^2}}{z}$

63. $\dfrac{8^{\frac{1}{6}} - 9^{\frac{1}{4}}}{\sqrt{3} + \sqrt{2}}$

64. $\dfrac{x^{\frac{5}{3}} - x^{\frac{1}{3}}z^{\frac{4}{3}}}{x^{\frac{2}{3}} + z^{\frac{2}{3}}}$

65. **MULTIPLE REPRESENTATIONS** In this problem, you will explore the functions $f(x) = x^3$ and $g(x) = x^{\frac{1}{3}}$.

a. **TABULAR** Copy and complete the table to the right.

b. **GRAPHICAL** Graph $f(x)$ and $g(x)$. **See margin.**

c. **VERBAL** Explain the transformation between $f(x)$ and $g(x)$. **It is a reflection of the line $y = x$.**

x	$f(x)$	$g(x)$
−2	−8	−1.26
−1	−1	−1
0	0	0
1	1	1
2	8	1.26

H.O.T. Problems

Use Higher-Order Thinking Skills

66. **REASONING** Determine whether $-x^{-2} = (-x)^{-2}$ is *always*, *sometimes*, or *never* true. Explain your reasoning.

67. **CHALLENGE** Consider $\sqrt[4]{(-16)^3}$.

a. Explain why the expression is not a real number. **See margin.**

b. Find n such that $n\sqrt[4]{(-16)^3}$ is a real number. **Sample answer: $\sqrt[4]{-1}$**

68. **OPEN ENDED** Find two different expressions that equal 2 in the form $x^{\frac{1}{a}}$.

69. **WRITING IN MATH** Explain how it might be easier to simplify an expression using rational exponents rather than using radicals. **See margin.**

70. **ERROR ANALYSIS** Ayana and Kenji are simplifying $\dfrac{x^{\frac{3}{4}}}{x^{\frac{1}{2}}}$. Is either of them correct? Explain your reasoning.

Ayana

$\dfrac{x^{\frac{3}{4}}}{x^{\frac{1}{2}}} = x^{\frac{3}{4} + \frac{1}{2}}$

$= x^{\frac{3}{4} + \frac{2}{4}}$

$= x^{\frac{5}{4}}$

Kenji

$\dfrac{x^{\frac{3}{4}}}{x^{\frac{1}{2}}} = x^{\frac{3}{4} \div \frac{1}{2}}$

$= x^{\frac{3}{4} \cdot \frac{2}{1}}$

$= x^{\frac{3}{2}}$

66. Never; the quantities are not the same. When the negative is enclosed inside of the parentheses and the base is raised to an even power, the answer is positive. When the negative is not enclosed inside of the parentheses and the base is raised to an even power, the answer is negative.

68. Sample answer: $4^{\frac{1}{2}}$ and $16^{\frac{1}{4}}$

70. No; Ayana added the exponents and Kenji divided the exponents. The exponents should have been subtracted.

Multiple Representations In Exercise 65, students use a table of values and a graph to compare and contrast a cubic and a radical equation.

Study Guide and Intervention

CRM pp. 38–39 AL OL ELL

7-6 Study Guide and Intervention

Rational Exponents

Rational Exponents and Radicals

Definition of $b^{\frac{1}{n}}$	For any real number b and any positive integer n, $b^{\frac{1}{n}} = \sqrt[n]{b}$, except when $b < 0$ and n is even.
Definition of $b^{\frac{m}{n}}$	For any nonzero real number b, and any integers m and n, with $n > 1$, $b^{\frac{m}{n}} = \sqrt[n]{b^m} = (\sqrt[n]{b})^m$, except when $b < 0$ and n is even.

Example 1 Write $28^{\frac{1}{2}}$ in radical form.

Notice that $28 > 0$.

$28^{\frac{1}{2}} = \sqrt{28}$
$= \sqrt{2^2 \cdot 7}$
$= \sqrt{2^2} \cdot \sqrt{7}$
$= 2\sqrt{7}$

Example 2 Evaluate $\left(\frac{-8}{-125}\right)^{\frac{1}{3}}$.

Notice that $-8 < 0$, $-125 < 0$, and 3 is odd.

$\left(\frac{-8}{-125}\right)^{\frac{1}{3}} = \frac{\sqrt[3]{-8}}{\sqrt[3]{-125}}$
$= \frac{-2}{-5}$
$= \frac{2}{5}$

Exercises

Write each expression in radical form, or write each radical in exponential form.

1. $11^{\frac{1}{7}}$ $\sqrt[7]{11}$
2. $15^{\frac{1}{3}}$ $\sqrt[3]{15}$
3. $300^{\frac{3}{2}}$ $3000\sqrt{3}$
4. $\sqrt{47}$ $47^{\frac{1}{2}}$
5. $\sqrt[3]{3a^5b^2}$ $3^{\frac{1}{3}}a^{\frac{5}{3}}b^{\frac{2}{3}}$
6. $\sqrt[4]{162p^5}$ $3 \cdot 2^{\frac{1}{4}} \cdot p^{\frac{5}{4}}$

Evaluate each expression.

7. $-27^{\frac{2}{3}}$ 9
8. $216^{\frac{1}{3}}$ 6
9. $(0.0004)^{\frac{1}{2}}$ 0.02

Chapter 7 38 Glencoe Algebra 2

Practice

CRM p. 41 AL OL BL ELL

7-6 Practice

Rational Exponents

Write each expression in radical form, or write each radical in exponential form.

1. $5^{\frac{1}{3}}$ $\sqrt[3]{5}$
2. $6^{\frac{2}{5}}$ $\sqrt[5]{6^2}$ or $(\sqrt[5]{6})^2$
3. $m^{\frac{4}{7}}$ $\sqrt[7]{m^4}$ or $(\sqrt[7]{m})^4$
4. $(n^3)^{\frac{2}{5}}$ $n\sqrt[5]{n}$
5. $\sqrt{79}$ $79^{\frac{1}{2}}$
6. $\sqrt[4]{153}$ $153^{\frac{1}{4}}$
7. $\sqrt[3]{27m^6n^4}$ $3m^2n^{\frac{4}{3}}$
8. $\sqrt[5]{2a^{10}b}$ $5 \cdot 2^{\frac{1}{2}}|a^5|b^{\frac{1}{2}}$

Evaluate each expression.

9. $81^{\frac{1}{4}}$ 3
10. $1024^{-\frac{1}{5}}$ $\frac{1}{4}$
11. $8^{-\frac{5}{3}}$ $\frac{1}{32}$
12. $-256^{-\frac{3}{4}}$ $-\frac{1}{64}$
13. $(-64)^{-\frac{2}{3}}$ $\frac{1}{16}$
14. $27^{\frac{1}{3}} \cdot 27^{\frac{4}{3}}$ 243
15. $\left(\frac{125}{216}\right)^{\frac{2}{3}}$ $\frac{25}{36}$
16. $\frac{64^{\frac{2}{3}}}{343^{\frac{2}{3}}}$ $\frac{16}{49}$
17. $(25^{\frac{1}{2}})(-64^{\frac{1}{3}})$ $-\frac{5}{4}$

Simplify each expression.

18. $g^{\frac{4}{7}} \cdot g^{\frac{3}{7}}$ g
19. $s^{\frac{3}{4}} \cdot s^{\frac{13}{4}}$ s^4
20. $(u^{\frac{1}{3}})^{\frac{4}{5}}$ $u^{\frac{4}{15}}$
21. $y^{-\frac{1}{2}}$ $\frac{1}{y^{\frac{1}{2}}}$ or $\frac{y^{\frac{1}{2}}}{y}$
22. $b^{-\frac{3}{5}}$ $\frac{1}{b^{\frac{3}{5}}}$ or $\frac{b^{\frac{2}{5}}}{b}$
23. $\frac{q^{\frac{3}{5}}}{q^{\frac{2}{5}}}$ $q^{\frac{1}{5}}$
24. $\frac{t^{\frac{2}{3}}}{5t^{\frac{1}{2}} \cdot t^{-\frac{3}{4}}}$ $\frac{t^{\frac{11}{12}}}{5}$
25. $\frac{2z^{\frac{1}{2}}}{z^{\frac{1}{2}} - 1}$ $\frac{2z + 2z^{\frac{1}{2}}}{z - 1}$
26. $\sqrt[10]{8^5}$ $2\sqrt{2}$
27. $\sqrt{12} \cdot \sqrt[5]{12^3}$ $12\sqrt[10]{12}$
28. $\sqrt[4]{6} \cdot 3\sqrt[4]{6}$ $3\sqrt{6}$
29. $\frac{a}{\sqrt{3b}}$ $\frac{a\sqrt{3b}}{3b}$

30. **ELECTRICITY** The amount of current in amps I that an appliance uses can be calculated using the formula $I = \left(\frac{P}{R}\right)^{\frac{1}{2}}$, where P is the power in watts and R is the resistance in ohms. How much current does an appliance use if $P = 500$ watts and $R = 10$ ohms? Round your answer to the nearest tenth. **7.1 amps**

31. **BUSINESS** A company that produces DVDs uses the formula $C = 88n^{\frac{1}{3}} + 330$ to calculate the cost C in dollars of producing n DVDs per day. What is the company's cost to produce 150 DVDs per day? Round your answer to the nearest dollar. **$798**

Chapter 7 41 Glencoe Algebra 2

Word Problem Practice

CRM p. 42 AL OL BL ELL

7-6 Word Problem Practice

Rational Exponents

1. **SQUARING THE CUBE** A cube has side length s. What side length of the square will cause its area to have the same numerical value as the volume of the cube? Write your answer using rational exponents.
$s^{\frac{3}{2}}$

2. **WATER TOWER** Typically, drinking water for towns is stored in water towers. A water tower in Edmond, Oklahoma is 218 feet high and holds half a million gallons. One town is replacing its water tower. Residents of the town insist that their new tower be a sphere. If the new tank will hold 10 times as much water as the old tank, how many times longer should the radius of the new tank be compared to the old tank? Write your answer using rational exponents.

$10^{\frac{1}{3}}$

3. **BALLOONS** A spherical balloon is being inflated faster and faster. The volume of the balloon as a function of time is $9\pi t^2$. What is the radius of the balloon as a function of time? Write your answer using rational exponents.
$3\left(\frac{t}{2}\right)^{\frac{2}{3}}$

4. **INTEREST** Rita opened a bank account that accumulated interest at the rate of 1% compounded annually. Her money accumulated interest in that account for 8 years. She then took all of her money out of that account and placed it into another account that paid 5% interest compounded annually. After 4 years, she took all of her money out of that account. What single interest rate when compounded annually would give her the same outcome for those 12 years? Round your answer to the nearest hundredth of a percent.
2.32%

5. **CELLS** The number of cells in a cell culture grows exponentially. The number of cells in the culture as a function of time is given by the expression $N\left(\frac{6}{5}\right)^t$, where t is measured in hours and N is the initial size of the culture.

a. After 3 hours, there were 1728 cells in the culture. What is N?
1000

b. How many cells were in the culture after 20 minutes? Express your answer in simplest form.
$200 \cdot 150^{\frac{1}{3}}$

c. How many cells were in the culture after 2.5 hours? Express your answer in simplest form.
$288 \cdot 30^{\frac{1}{2}}$

Chapter 7 42 Glencoe Algebra 2

Enrichment

CRM p. 43 OL BL

7-6 Enrichment

Lesser-Known Geometric Formulas

Many geometric formulas involve radical expressions.

Make a drawing to illustrate each of the formulas given on this page. Then evaluate the formula for the given value of the variable. Round answers to the nearest hundredth.

1. The area of an isosceles triangle. Two sides have length a; the other side has length c. Find A when $a = 6$ and $c = 7$.
$A = \frac{c}{4}\sqrt{4a^2 - c^2}$
$A \approx 17.06$ units²

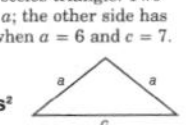

2. The area of an equilateral triangle with a side of length a. Find A when $a = 8$.
$A = \frac{a^2}{4}\sqrt{3}$
$A \approx 27.71$ units²

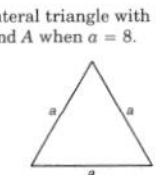

3. The area of a regular pentagon with a side of length a. Find A when $a = 4$.
$A = \frac{a^2}{4}\sqrt{25 + 10\sqrt{5}}$
$A \approx 27.53$ units²

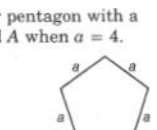

4. The area of a regular hexagon with a side of length a. Find A when $a = 9$.
$A = \frac{3a^2}{2}\sqrt{3}$
$A \approx 210.44$ units²

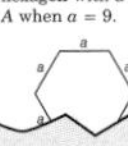

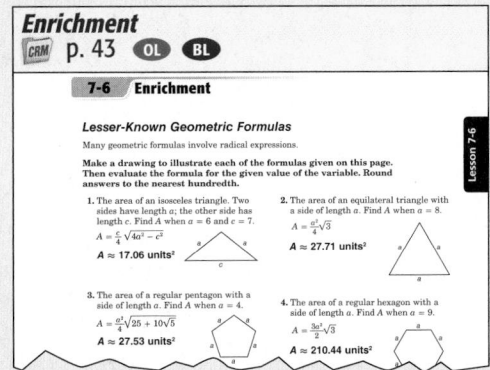

4 ASSESS

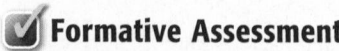

Yesterday's News Have students write how yesterday's lesson on radical expressions helped them with writing and simplifying expressions with rational exponents in today's lesson.

Formative Assessment

Check for student understanding of concepts in Lessons 7-5 and 7-6.

CRM Quiz 3, p. 54

Additional Answers

83. 20; $x^2 + 2xh + h^2 - x - h$

84. −129; $2x^3 + 6x^2h + 6xh^2 + 2h^3 - 1$

NGSSS PRACTICE 912.A.4.5, 912.A.8.5

71. The expression $\sqrt{56 - c}$ is equivalent to a positive integer when c is equal to **B**

A. 8
B. −8
C. 56
D. 36

72. ACT/SAT Which of the following sentences is true about the graphs of $y = 2(x - 3)^2 + 1$ and $y = 2(x + 3)^2 + 1$? **G**

F. Their vertices are maximums.
G. The graphs have the same shape with different vertices.
H. The graphs have different shapes with different vertices.
I. One graph has a vertex that is a maximum while the other graph has a vertex that is a minimum.

73. GEOMETRY What is the converse of the statement? *If it is summer, then it is hot outside.* **C**

A. If it is not hot outside, then it is not summer.
B. If it is not summer, then it is not hot outside.
C. If it is hot outside, then it is summer.
D. If it is hot outside, it is not summer.

74. THINK SOLVE EXPLAIN **SHORT RESPONSE** If $3^5 \cdot p = 3^3$, then find p. **3^{-2}**

Spiral Review

Simplify. (Lesson 7-5)

75. $\sqrt{243}$ **$9\sqrt{3}$**
76. $\sqrt[3]{16y^3}$ **$2y\sqrt[3]{2}$**
77. $3\sqrt[3]{56y^6z^3}$ **$6y^2z\sqrt[3]{7}$**

78. PHYSICS The speed of sound in a liquid is $s = \sqrt{\frac{B}{d}}$, where B is the bulk modulus of the liquid and d is its density. For water, $B = 2.1 \times 10^9$ N/m^2 and $d = 10^3$ kg/m^3. Find the speed of sound in water to the nearest meter per second. (Lesson 7-4) **1449 m/s**

Find $p(-4)$ and $p(x + h)$ for each function. (Lesson 6-3) **82. 21; $x^2 + 2xh + h^2 + 5$**

79. $p(x) = x - 2$ **−6; $x + h - 2$**
80. $p(x) = -x + 4$ **8; $-x - h + 4$**
81. $p(x) = 6x + 3$ **−21; $6x + 6h + 3$**
82. $p(x) = x^2 + 5$
83. $p(x) = x^2 - x$ **See margin.**
84. $p(x) = 2x^3 - 1$ **See margin.**

Solve each equation by factoring. (Lesson 5-3)

85. $x^2 - 11x = 0$ **{0, 11}**
86. $x^2 + 6x - 16 = 0$ **{−8, 2}**
87. $4x^2 - 13x = 12$ **$\left\{-\frac{3}{4}, 4\right\}$**
88. $x^2 - 14x = -49$ **{7}**
89. $x^2 + 9 = 6x$ **{3}**
90. $x^2 - 3x = -\frac{9}{4}$ **$\left\{\frac{3}{2}\right\}$**

91. GEOMETRY A rectangle is inscribed in an isosceles triangle as shown. Find the dimensions of the inscribed rectangle with maximum area. (*Hint*: Use similar triangles.) (Lesson 5-1) **5 in. by 4 in.**

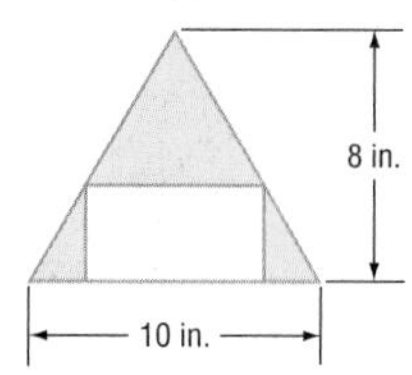

Skills Review

Find each power. (Lesson 7-5)

92. $(\sqrt{x - 3})^2$ **$x - 3$**
93. $(\sqrt[3]{3x - 4})^3$ **$3x - 4$**
94. $(\sqrt[4]{7x - 1})^4$ **$7x - 1$**
95. $(\sqrt{x} - 4)^2$ **$x - 8\sqrt{x} + 16$**
96. $(2\sqrt{x} - 5)^2$ **$4x - 20\sqrt{x} + 25$**
97. $(3\sqrt{x} + 1)^2$ **$9x + 6\sqrt{x} + 1$**

452 Chapter 7 Inverses and Radical Functions and Relations

Solving Radical Equations and Inequalities

Then

You solved polynomial equations. (Lesson 6-5)

Now

- Solve equations containing radicals.
- Solve inequalities containing radicals.

NGSSS

MA.912.A.6.5 Solve equations that contain radical expressions.
MA.912.A.10.3 Decide whether a given statement is always, sometimes, or never true (statements involving linear or quadratic expressions, equations, or inequalities rational or radical expressions or logarithmic or exponential functions).

New Vocabulary

radical equation
extraneous solution
radical inequality

FL Math Online

glencoe.com

Why?

When you jump, the time that you are in the air is your hang time. Hang time can be calculated in seconds t if you know the height h of the jump in feet. The formula for hang time is $t = 0.5\sqrt{h}$.

Michael Jordan had a hang time of about 0.98 second. How would you calculate the height of Jordan's jump?

Solve Radical Equations **Radical equations** include radical expressions. You can solve a radical equation by raising each side of the equation to a power.

Key Concept **Solving Radical Equations**

Step 1 Isolate the radical on one side of the equation.

Step 2 Raise each side of the equation to a power equal to the index of the radical to eliminate the radical.

Step 3 Solve the resulting polynomial equation. Check your results.

When solving radical equations, the result may be a number that does not satisfy the original equation. Such a number is called an **extraneous solution**.

EXAMPLE 1 **Solve Radical Equations**

Solve each equation.

a. $\sqrt{x+2} + 4 = 7$

$\sqrt{x+2} + 4 = 7$	Original equation
$\sqrt{x+2} = 3$	Subtract 4 from each side to isolate the radical.
$(\sqrt{x+2})^2 = 3^2$	Square each side to eliminate the radical.
$x + 2 = 9$	Find the squares.
$x = 7$	Subtract 2 from each side.

CHECK	$\sqrt{x+2} + 4 = 7$	Original equation
	$\sqrt{7+2} + 4 \stackrel{?}{=} 7$	Replace x with 7.
	$7 = 7$ ✓	Simplify.

b. $\sqrt{x-12} = 2 - \sqrt{x}$

$\sqrt{x-12} = 2 - \sqrt{x}$	Original equation
$(\sqrt{x-12})^2 = (2 - \sqrt{x})^2$	Square each side.
$x - 12 = 4 - 4\sqrt{x} + x$	Find the squares.
$-16 = -4\sqrt{x}$	Isolate the radical.
$4 = \sqrt{x}$	Divide each side by -4.
$16 = x$	Evaluate the squares.

1 FOCUS

Vertical Alignment

Before Lesson 7-7
Solve polynomial equations.

Lesson 7-7
Solve equations containing radicals.
Solve inequalities containing radicals.

After Lesson 7-7
Identify a conic section from a given equation.

2 TEACH

Scaffolding Questions

Have students read the *Why?* section of the lesson.

Ask:

- In the formula $t = 0.5\sqrt{h}$, which variable appears in the radical? *h*, the height of the jump in feet
- What is the value of t if $h = 4$? Describe your results. If $h = 4$, then $t = 1$; a jump of height 4 feet results in a hang time of 1 second.
- Looking at your answer to the previous question, how is t affected if h is multiplied by 4? t is doubled

Lesson 7-7 Resources

Resource	Approaching-Level	On-Level	Beyond-Level	English Learners
Teacher Edition	• Differentiated Instruction, p. 455	• Differentiated Instruction, pp. 455, 459	• Differentiated Instruction, pp. 455, 459	• Differentiated Instruction, p. 455
Chapter Resource Masters	• Study Guide and Intervention, pp. 45–46 • Skills Practice, p. 47 • Practice, p. 48 • Word Problem Practice, p. 49	• Study Guide and Intervention, pp. 45–46 • Skills Practice, p. 47 • Practice, p. 48 • Word Problem Practice, p. 49 • Enrichment, p. 50	• Practice, p. 48 • Word Problem Practice, p. 49 • Enrichment, p. 50	• Study Guide and Intervention, pp. 45–46 • Skills Practice, p. 47 • Practice, p. 48 • Word Problem Practice, p. 49
Transparencies	• 5-Minute Check Transparency 7-7	• 5-Minute Check Transparency 7-7	• 5-Minute Check Transparency 7-7	• 5-Minute Check Transparency 7-7
Other	• Study Notebook	• Study Notebook	• Study Notebook	• Study Notebook

Solve Radical Equations

Example 1 shows how to solve two radical equations, one with a solution and the other with an extraneous solution. **Example 2** shows how to solve a cube root equation. **Example 3** shows how to answer test questions involving radical equations.

Formative Assessment

Use the Guided Practice exercises after each example to determine students' understanding of concepts.

Additional Examples

1 Solve each equation.

a. $\sqrt{y-2} - 1 = 5$ 38

b. $\sqrt{x-12} = 2 - \sqrt{x}$ no solution

2 Solve $(3y+1)^{\frac{1}{3}} + 5 = 0$. −42

Additional Examples also in Interactive Classroom PowerPoint® Presentations

IWB INTERACTIVE WHITEBOARD READY

Focus on Mathematical Content

Extraneous Roots It is always important to check the solution to an equation or inequality in the *original* equation, but it is especially important when both sides of an equation are raised to a power. If a solution is an approximation, it is sometimes difficult to determine whether a discrepancy is due to rounding or if it is an incorrect solution. Students should check exact solutions whenever possible.

StudyTip

Solution Check You can use a graphing calculator to check solutions of equations. Graph each side of the original equation, and examine the intersection.

CHECK
$$\sqrt{x-12} = 2 - \sqrt{x}$$
$$\sqrt{16-12} \stackrel{?}{=} 2 - \sqrt{16}$$
$$\sqrt{4} \stackrel{?}{=} 2 - 4$$
$$2 \neq -2 \ ✗$$

The solution does not check, so the equation has an extraneous solution. The graphs of $y = \sqrt{x-12}$ and $y = 2 - \sqrt{x}$ do not intersect, which confirms that there is no real solution.

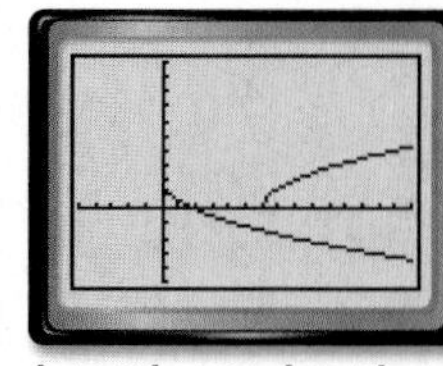

[−10, 30] scl: 2 by [−5, 10] scl: 1

Guided Practice

1A. $5 = \sqrt{x-2} - 1$ 38

1B. $\sqrt{x+15} = 5 + \sqrt{x}$ no real solution

Personal Tutor glencoe.com

To undo a square root, you square the expression. To undo a cube root, you must raise the expression to the third power.

EXAMPLE 2 Solve a Cube Root Equation

Solve $2(6x-3)^{\frac{1}{3}} - 4 = 0$.

In order to remove the $\frac{1}{3}$ power, or cube root, you must first isolate it and then raise each side of the equation to the third power.

$2(6x-3)^{\frac{1}{3}} - 4 = 0$	**Original equation**
$2(6x-3)^{\frac{1}{3}} = 4$	**Add 4 to each side.**
$(6x-3)^{\frac{1}{3}} = 2$	**Divide each side by 2.**
$\left[(6x-3)^{\frac{1}{3}}\right]^3 = 2^3$	**Cube each side.**
$6x - 3 = 8$	**Evaluate the cubes.**
$6x = 11$	**Add 3 to each side.**
$x = \frac{11}{6}$	**Divide each side by 6.**

CHECK

$2(6x-3)^{\frac{1}{3}} - 4 = 0$	**Original equation**
$2\left(6 \cdot \frac{11}{6} - 3\right)^{\frac{1}{3}} - 4 \stackrel{?}{=} 0$	**Replace x with $\frac{11}{6}$.**
$2(8)^{\frac{1}{3}} - 4 \stackrel{?}{=} 0$	**Simplify.**
$2(2) - 4 \stackrel{?}{=} 0$	**The cube root of 8 is 2.**
$0 = 0$ ✓	**Subtract.**

Guided Practice

Solve each equation.

2A. $(3n+2)^{\frac{1}{3}} + 1 = 0$ −1

2B. $3(5y-1)^{\frac{1}{3}} - 2 = 0$ $\frac{7}{27}$

Personal Tutor glencoe.com

Watch Out!

Preventing Errors Have a discussion with students about which operations may introduce extraneous solutions when solving an equation that contains a radical. Remind students that the square root sign in an equation means the principal root.

TEACH with TECH

BLOG Have students write a blog entry about extraneous solutions. Have them explain what extraneous solutions are and how they can check their solutions graphically and algebraically.

454 Chapter 7 Inverses and Radical Functions and Relations

You can apply the methods used to solve square and cube root equations to solving equations with roots of any index. To undo an nth root, raise to the nth power.

Test-Taking Tip

Substitute Values You could also solve the test question by substituting each answer for n in the equation to see if the solution is correct.

NGSSS PRACTICE EXAMPLE 3 — 912.A.6.5

What is the solution of $3(\sqrt[4]{2n+6}) - 6 = 0$?

A. −1 **B.** 1 **C.** 5 **D.** 11

$3(\sqrt[4]{2n+6}) - 6 = 0$ **Original equation**

$3(\sqrt[4]{2n+6}) = 6$ **Add 6 to each side.**

$\sqrt[4]{2n+6} = 2$ **Divide each side by 3.**

$(\sqrt[4]{2n+6})^4 = 2^4$ **Raise each side to the fourth power.**

$2n + 6 = 16$ **Evaluate each side.**

$2n = 10$ **Subtract 6 from each side.**

$n = 5$ The answer is C.

Guided Practice

3. What is the solution of $4(3x+6)^{\frac{1}{4}} - 12 = 0$? G

F. $x = 7$ **G.** $x = 25$ **H.** $x = 29$ **I.** $x = 37$

Personal Tutor glencoe.com

Solve Radical Inequalities A **radical inequality** has a variable in the radicand. To solve radical inequalities, complete the following steps.

Key Concept — Solving Radical Inequalities

Step 1 If the index of the root is even, identify the values of the variable for which the radicand is nonnegative.

Step 2 Solve the inequality algebraically.

Step 3 Test values to check your solution.

StudyTip

Radical Inequalities Since a principal square root is never negative, inequalities that simplify to the form $\sqrt{ax+b} \le c$, where c is a negative number, have no solutions.

EXAMPLE 4 Solve a Radical Inequality

Solve $3 + \sqrt{5x-10} \le 8$.

Step 1 Since the radicand of a square root must be greater than or equal to zero, first solve $5x - 10 \ge 0$ to identify the values of x for which the left side of the inequality is defined.

$5x - 10 \ge 0$ **Set the radicand ≥ 0.**

$5x \ge 10$ **Add 10 to each side.**

$x \ge 2$ **Divide each side by 5.**

Step 2 Solve $3 + \sqrt{5x-10} \le 8$.

$3 + \sqrt{5x-10} \le 8$ **Original inequality**

$\sqrt{5x-10} \le 5$ **Isolate the radical.**

$5x - 10 \le 25$ **Eliminate the radical.**

$5x \le 35$ **Add 10 to each side.**

$x \le 7$ **Divide each side by 5.**

Additional Example

3 STANDARDIZED TEST EXAMPLE What is the solution of $7(\sqrt[6]{5m+4}) - 4 = 10$? C

A $m = -2$ **C** $m = 12$

B $m = 0$ **D** $m = 14$

Solve Radical Inequalities

Example 4 shows how to solve a radical inequality and confirm the solution.

Additional Example

4 Solve $\sqrt{3x-6} + 4 \le 7$. $2 \le x \le 5$

Differentiated Instruction

AL OL BL ELL

Interpersonal Learners Ask students to work in groups as they compare solving radical equations and inequalities to solving other types of equations and inequalities. Have them write or give a short presentation about the similarities and differences between the procedures used in the solution process.

Watch Out!

Preventing Errors Emphasize the importance of checking key test values in the appropriate ranges.

3 PRACTICE

Formative Assessment

Use Exercises 1–22 to check for understanding.

Use the chart at the bottom of the next page to customize assignments for your students.

Watch Out!

Preventing Errors Make sure that students know the constraints on the values of the variables in a radical equation so that the solutions are real numbers.

Step 3 It appears that $2 \leq x \leq 7$. You can test some x-values to confirm the solution. Use three test values: one less than 2, one between 2 and 7, and one greater than 7. Organize the test values in a table.

$x = 0$	$x = 4$	$x = 9$
$3 + \sqrt{5(0) - 10} \overset{?}{\leq} 8$ $3 + \sqrt{-5} \leq 8$ ✗ Since $\sqrt{-5}$ is not a real number, the inequality is not satisfied.	$3 + \sqrt{5(4) - 10} \overset{?}{\leq} 8$ $6.16 \leq 8$ ✓ Since $6.16 \leq 8$, the inequality is satisfied.	$3 + \sqrt{5(9) - 10} \overset{?}{\leq} 8$ $8.92 \leq 8$ ✗ Since $8.92 \nleq 8$, the inequality is not satisfied.

The solution checks. Only values in the interval $2 \leq x \leq 7$ satisfy the inequality. You can summarize the solution with a number line.

Guided Practice

Solve each inequality.

4A. $\sqrt{2x + 2} + 1 \geq 5$ $x \geq 7$

4B. $\sqrt{4x - 4} - 2 < 4$ $1 \leq x < 10$

Personal Tutor glencoe.com

Check Your Understanding

Examples 1 and 2 pp. 453–454

Solve each equation.

1. $\sqrt{x - 4} + 6 = 10$ 20

2. $\sqrt{x + 13} - 8 = -2$ 23

3. $8 - \sqrt{x + 12} = 3$ 13

4. $\sqrt{x - 8} + 5 = 7$ 12

5. $\sqrt[3]{x - 2} = 3$ 29

6. $(x - 5)^{\frac{1}{3}} - 4 = -2$ 13

7. $(4y)^{\frac{1}{3}} + 3 = 5$ 2

8. $\sqrt[3]{n + 8} - 6 = -3$ 19

9. $\sqrt{y} - 7 = 0$ 49

10. $2 + 4z^{\frac{1}{2}} = 0$ no solution

11. $5 + \sqrt{4y - 5} = 12$ $\frac{27}{2}$

12. $\sqrt{2t - 7} = \sqrt{t + 2}$ 9

13. **PHYSICS** The time T in seconds that it takes a pendulum to make a complete swing back and forth is given by the formula $T = 2\pi\sqrt{\frac{L}{g}}$, where L is the length of the pendulum in feet and g is the acceleration due to gravity, 32 feet per second squared.

a. In Tokyo, Japan, a huge pendulum in the Shinjuku building measures 73 feet 9.75 inches. How long does it take for the pendulum to make a complete swing?

13a. about 9.5 seconds

b. A clockmaker wants to build a pendulum that takes 20 seconds to swing back and forth. How long should the pendulum be? about 324 ft

Example 3 p. 455

14. **NGSSS PRACTICE** Solve $(2y + 6)^{\frac{1}{4}} - 2 = 0$. B

A. $y = 1$ **B.** $y = 5$ **C.** $y = 11$ **D.** $y = 15$

Example 4 p. 455

Solve each inequality.

15. $\sqrt{3x + 4} - 5 \leq 4$ $-\frac{4}{3} \leq x \leq \frac{77}{3}$

16. $\sqrt{b - 7} + 6 \leq 12$ $7 \leq b \leq 43$

17. $2 + \sqrt{4y - 4} \leq 6$ $1 \leq y \leq 5$

18. $\sqrt{3a + 3} - 1 \leq 2$ $-1 \leq a < 2$

19. $1 + \sqrt{7x - 3} > 3$ $x > 1$

20. $\sqrt{3x + 6} + 2 \leq 5$ $-2 \leq x \leq 1$

21. $-2 + \sqrt{9 - 5x} \geq 6$ $x \leq -11$

22. $6 - \sqrt{2y + 1} < 3$ $y > 4$

456 Chapter 7 Inverses and Radical Functions and Relations

Practice and Problem Solving

● = **Step-by-Step Solutions** begin on page R20.
Extra Practice begins on page 947.

Example 1 p. 453

Solve each equation.

23. $\sqrt{2x+5} - 4 = 3$ 22
24. $6 + \sqrt{3x+1} = 11$ 8
25. $\sqrt{x+6} = 5 - \sqrt{x+1}$ 3
26. $\sqrt{x-3} = \sqrt{x+4} - 1$ 12
27. $\sqrt{x-15} = 3 - \sqrt{x}$ no real solution
28. $\sqrt{x-10} = 1 - \sqrt{x}$ no real solution
29. $6 + \sqrt{4x+8} = 9$ $\frac{1}{4}$
30. $2 + \sqrt{3y-5} = 10$ 23
31. $\sqrt{x-4} = \sqrt{2x-13}$ 9
32. $\sqrt{7a-2} = \sqrt{a+3}$ $\frac{5}{6}$
33. $\sqrt{x-5} - \sqrt{x} = -2$ $\frac{81}{16}$
34. $\sqrt{b-6} + \sqrt{b} = 3$ $\frac{25}{4}$
35. **GRAVITY** Isabel accidentally dropped her keys from the top of a Ferris wheel. The formula $t = \frac{1}{4}\sqrt{d-h}$ describes the time t in seconds at which the keys are h meters above the ground and Isabel is d meters above the ground. If Isabel was 65 meters high when she dropped the keys, how many meters above the ground will the keys be after 2 seconds? 1 m

Example 2 p. 454

Solve each equation.

36. $(5n-6)^{\frac{1}{3}} + 3 = 4$ $\frac{7}{5}$
37. $(5p-7)^{\frac{1}{3}} + 3 = 5$ 3
38. $(6q+1)^{\frac{1}{4}} + 2 = 5$ $\frac{40}{3}$
39. $(3x+7)^{\frac{1}{4}} - 3 = 1$ 83
40. $(3y-2)^{\frac{1}{5}} + 5 = 6$ 1
41. $(4z-1)^{\frac{1}{5}} - 1 = 2$ 61
42. $2(x-10)^{\frac{1}{3}} + 4 = 0$ 2
43. $3(x+5)^{\frac{1}{3}} - 6 = 0$ 3
44. $\sqrt[3]{5x+10} - 5 = 0$ 23
45. $\sqrt[3]{4n-8} - 4 = 0$ 18
46. $\frac{1}{7}(14a)^{\frac{1}{3}} = 1$ 24.5
47. $\frac{1}{4}(32b)^{\frac{1}{3}} = 1$ 2

Example 3 p. 455

48. **MULTIPLE CHOICE** Solve $\sqrt[4]{y+2} + 9 = 14$. D

A 23 B 53 C 123 D 623

49. **MULTIPLE CHOICE** Solve $(2x-1)^{\frac{1}{4}} - 2 = 1$. F

F 41 G 28 H 13 J 1

Example 4 p. 455

Solve each inequality. 53. no real solution 54. $x > 4$ 55. $d > -\frac{3}{4}$

50. $1 + \sqrt{5x-2} > 4$ $x > \frac{11}{5}$
51. $\sqrt{2x+14} - 6 \geq 4$ $x \geq 43$
52. $10 - \sqrt{2x+7} \leq 3$ $x \geq 21$
53. $6 + \sqrt{3y+4} < 6$
54. $\sqrt{2x+5} - \sqrt{9+x} > 0$
55. ● $\sqrt{d+3} + \sqrt{d+7} > 4$
56. $\sqrt{3x+9} - 2 < 7$
57. $\sqrt{2y+5} + 3 \leq 6$
58. $-2 + \sqrt{8-4z} \geq 8$
59. $-3 + \sqrt{6a+1} > 4$ $a > 8$
60. $\sqrt{2} - \sqrt{b+6} \leq -\sqrt{b}$
61. $\sqrt{c+9} - \sqrt{c} > \sqrt{3}$

56. $-3 \leq x < 24$
57. $-\frac{5}{2} \leq y \leq 2$
58. $z \leq -23$
60. $0 \leq b \leq 2$
61. $0 \leq c < 3$

B

62. **PENDULUMS** The formula $s = 2\pi\sqrt{\frac{\ell}{32}}$ represents the swing of a pendulum, where s is the time in seconds to swing back and forth, and ℓ is the length of the pendulum in feet. Find the length of a pendulum that makes one swing in 1.5 seconds. about 1.82 ft

63. **FISH** The relationship between the length and mass of certain fish can be approximated by the equation $L = 0.46\sqrt[3]{M}$, where L is the length in meters and M is the mass in kilograms. Solve this equation for M.

63. $M = \left(\frac{L}{0.46}\right)^3$

Tips for New Teachers

Reasoning Advise students that they cannot use the Distributive Property in Exercises 46 and 47. Ask them why this is the case, reminding them that the order of operations requires operations with exponents to be performed before those involving multiplication.

Differentiated Homework Options

Level	Assignment	Two-Day Option	
AL Basic	23–61, 67, 69–72, 74–98	23–61 odd, 76–79	24–60 even, 64–75, 80–98
OL Core	23–61 odd, 62–67, 69–72, 74–98	23–61, 76–79	62–67, 69–72, 74–75, 80–98
BL Advanced	62–90, (optional: 91–98)		

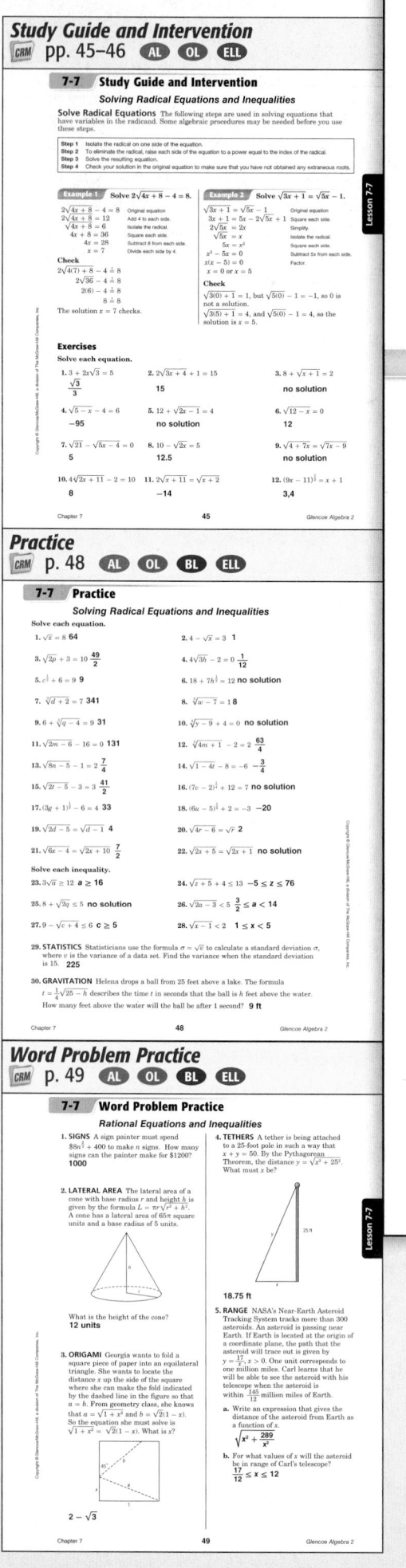

Study Guide and Intervention
CRM pp. 45–46 AL OL ELL

7-7 Study Guide and Intervention
Solving Radical Equations and Inequalities

Solve Radical Equations The following steps are used in solving equations that have variables in the radicand. Some algebraic procedures may be needed before you use these steps.

Step 1	Isolate the radical on one side of the equation.
Step 2	To eliminate the radical, raise each side of the equation to a power equal to the index of the radical.
Step 3	Solve the resulting equation.
Step 4	Check your solution in the original equation to make sure that you have not obtained any extraneous roots.

Example 1 Solve $2\sqrt{4x+8} - 4 = 8$.

$2\sqrt{4x+8} - 4 = 8$ Original equation
$2\sqrt{4x+8} = 12$ Add 4 to each side.
$\sqrt{4x+8} = 6$ Isolate the radical.
$4x + 8 = 36$ Square each side.
$4x = 28$ Subtract 8 from each side.
$x = 7$ Divide each side by 4.

Check
$2\sqrt{4(7)+8} - 4 \stackrel{?}{=} 8$
$2\sqrt{36} - 4 \stackrel{?}{=} 8$
$2(6) - 4 \stackrel{?}{=} 8$
$8 \stackrel{?}{=} 8$
The solution $x = 7$ checks.

Example 2 Solve $\sqrt{3x+1} = \sqrt{5x} - 1$.

$\sqrt{3x+1} = \sqrt{5x} - 1$ Original equation
$3x + 1 = 5x - 2\sqrt{5x} + 1$ Square each side.
$2\sqrt{5x} = 2x$ Simplify.
$\sqrt{5x} = x$ Isolate the radical.
$5x = x^2$ Square each side.
$x^2 - 5x = 0$ Subtract 5x from each side.
$x(x - 5) = 0$ Factor.
$x = 0$ or $x = 5$

Check
$\sqrt{3(0)+1} = 1$, but $\sqrt{5(0)} - 1 = -1$, so 0 is not a solution.
$\sqrt{3(5)+1} = 4$, and $\sqrt{5(0)} - 1 = 4$, so the solution is $x = 5$.

Exercises

Solve each equation.

1. $3 + 2x\sqrt{3} = 5$ **$\frac{\sqrt{3}}{3}$**
2. $2\sqrt{3x+4} + 1 = 15$ **15**
3. $8 + \sqrt{x+1} = 2$ **no solution**
4. $\sqrt{5-x} - 4 = 6$ **−95**
5. $12 + \sqrt{2x-1} = 4$ **no solution**
6. $\sqrt{12-x} = 0$ **12**
7. $\sqrt{21} - \sqrt{5x-4} = 0$ **5**
8. $10 - \sqrt{2x} = 5$ **12.5**
9. $\sqrt{4+7x} = \sqrt{7x-9}$ **no solution**
10. $4\sqrt[3]{2x+11} - 2 = 10$ **8**
11. $2\sqrt{x+11} = \sqrt{x+2}$ **−14**
12. $(9x-11)^{\frac{1}{2}} = x + 1$ **3,4**

Chapter 7 45 Glencoe Algebra 2

Lesson 7-7

Practice
CRM p. 48 AL OL BL ELL

7-7 Practice
Solving Radical Equations and Inequalities

Solve each equation.

1. $\sqrt{x} = 8$ **64**
2. $4 - \sqrt{x} = 3$ **1**
3. $\sqrt{2p} + 3 = 10$ **$\frac{49}{2}$**
4. $4\sqrt{3h} - 2 = 0$ **$\frac{1}{12}$**
5. $c^{\frac{1}{2}} + 6 = 9$ **9**
6. $18 + 7h^{\frac{1}{2}} = 12$ **no solution**
7. $\sqrt[3]{d+2} = 7$ **341**
8. $\sqrt[5]{w-7} = 1$ **8**
9. $6 + \sqrt[3]{q-4} = 9$ **31**
10. $\sqrt[4]{y-9} + 4 = 0$ **no solution**
11. $\sqrt{2m-6} - 16 = 0$ **131**
12. $\sqrt[3]{4m+1} - 2 = 2$ **$\frac{63}{4}$**
13. $\sqrt{8n-5} - 1 = 2$ **$\frac{7}{4}$**
14. $\sqrt{1-4t} - 8 = -6$ **$-\frac{3}{4}$**
15. $\sqrt{2t-5} - 3 = 3$ **$\frac{41}{2}$**
16. $(7v-2)^{\frac{1}{4}} + 12 = 7$ **no solution**
17. $(3g+1)^{\frac{1}{2}} - 6 = 4$ **33**
18. $(6u-5)^{\frac{1}{3}} + 2 = -3$ **−20**
19. $\sqrt{2d-5} = \sqrt{d-1}$ **4**
20. $\sqrt{4r-6} = \sqrt{r}$ **2**
21. $\sqrt{6x-4} = \sqrt{2x+10}$ **$\frac{7}{2}$**
22. $\sqrt{2x+5} = \sqrt{2x+1}$ **no solution**

Solve each inequality.

23. $3\sqrt{a} \geq 12$ **$a \geq 16$**
24. $\sqrt{z+5} + 4 \leq 13$ **$-5 \leq z \leq 76$**
25. $8 + \sqrt{2q} \leq 5$ **no solution**
26. $\sqrt{2a-3} < 5$ **$\frac{3}{2} \leq a < 14$**
27. $9 - \sqrt{c+4} \leq 6$ **$c \geq 5$**
28. $\sqrt{x-1} < 2$ **$1 \leq x < 5$**

29. **STATISTICS** Statisticians use the formula $\sigma = \sqrt{v}$ to calculate a standard deviation σ, where v is the variance of a data set. Find the variance when the standard deviation is 15. **225**

30. **GRAVITATION** Helena drops a ball from 25 feet above a lake. The formula $t = \frac{1}{4}\sqrt{25 - h}$ describes the time t in seconds that the ball is h feet above the water. How many feet above the water will the ball be after 1 second? **9 ft**

Chapter 7 48 Glencoe Algebra 2

Word Problem Practice
CRM p. 49 AL OL BL ELL

7-7 Word Problem Practice
Rational Equations and Inequalities

1. **SIGNS** A sign painter must spend $\$8n^{\frac{2}{3}} + 400$ to make n signs. How many signs can the painter make for \$1200? **1000**

2. **LATERAL AREA** The lateral area of a cone with base radius r and height h is given by the formula $L = \pi r\sqrt{r^2 + h^2}$. A cone has a lateral area of 65π square units and a base radius of 5 units.

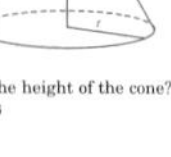

What is the height of the cone? **12 units**

3. **ORIGAMI** Georgia wants to fold a square piece of paper into an equilateral triangle. She wants to locate the distance x up the side of the square where she can make the fold indicated by the dashed line in the figure so that $a = b$. From geometry class, she knows that $a = \sqrt{1 + x^2}$ and $b = \sqrt{2}(1 - x)$. So the equation she must solve is $\sqrt{1 + x^2} = \sqrt{2}(1 - x)$. What is x?

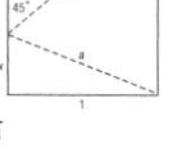

$2 - \sqrt{3}$

4. **TETHERS** A tether is being attached to a 25-foot pole in such a way that $x + y = 50$. By the Pythagorean Theorem, the distance $y = \sqrt{x^2 + 25^2}$. What must x be?

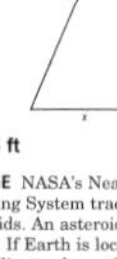

18.75 ft

5. **RANGE** NASA's Near-Earth Asteroid Tracking System tracks more than 300 asteroids. An asteroid is passing near Earth. If Earth is located at the origin of a coordinate plane, the path that the asteroid will trace out is given by $y = \frac{17}{x}$, $x > 0$. One unit corresponds to one million miles. Carl learns that he will be able to see the asteroid with his telescope when the asteroid is within $\frac{145}{12}$ million miles of Earth.

   a. Write an expression that gives the distance of the asteroid from Earth as a function of x. **$\sqrt{x^2 + \frac{289}{x^2}}$**

   b. For what values of x will the asteroid be in range of Carl's telescope? **$\frac{17}{12} \leq x \leq 12$**

Chapter 7 49 Glencoe Algebra 2

Lesson 7-7

C

64. **HANG TIME** Refer to the information at the beginning of the lesson regarding hang time. Describe how the height of a jump is related to the amount of time in the air. Write a step-by-step explanation of how to determine the height of Jordan's 0.98-second jump. **See margin.**

65. **CONCERTS** The organizers of a concert are preparing for the arrival of 50,000 people in the open field where the concert will take place. Each person is allotted 5 square feet of space, so the organizers rope off a circular area of 250,000 square feet. Using the formula $A = \pi r^2$, where A represents the area of the circular region and r represents the radius of the region, find the radius of this region. **about 282 ft**

Real-World Link

The Florida High School Athletic Association sanctioned girls' weightlifting as a high school sport in 1997. To date, they are the only state to support the sport for girls.

Source: *The New York Times*

66. **WEIGHTLIFTING** The formula $M = 512 - 146{,}230B^{-\frac{8}{5}}$ can be used to estimate the maximum total mass that a weightlifter of mass B kilograms can lift using the snatch and the clean and jerk. According to the formula, how much does a person weigh who can lift at most 470 kilograms? **163 kg**

H.O.T. Problems
Use **H**igher-**O**rder **T**hinking Skills

67. **WHICH ONE DOESN'T BELONG?** Which equation does not have a solution?

$\sqrt{x-1} + 3 = 4$	$\sqrt{x+1} + 3 = 4$
$\sqrt{x-2} + 7 = 10$	$\sqrt{x+2} - 7 = -10$

$\sqrt{x+2} - 7 = -10$

68. **CHALLENGE** Lola is working to solve $(x + 5)^{\frac{1}{4}} = -4$. She said that she could tell there was no real solution without even working the problem. Is Lola correct? Explain your reasoning.

68. Yes; since $\sqrt[4]{x+5} \geq 0$, the left side of the equation is nonnegative. Therefore, the left side of the equation cannot equal −4. Thus the equation has no solution.

69. **REASONING** Determine whether $\frac{\sqrt{(x^2)^2}}{-x} = x$ is *sometimes*, *always*, or *never* true when x is a real number. Explain your reasoning. **See margin.**

70. **OPEN ENDED** Select a whole number. Now work backward to write two radical equations that have that whole number as solutions. Write one square root equation and one cube root equation. You may need to experiment until you find a whole number you can easily use.

70. Sample answer using 6: $\sqrt{x-2} = 2$, $(x + 21)^{\frac{1}{3}} = 3$

71. **WRITING IN MATH** Explain the relationship between the index of the root of a variable in an equation and the power to which you raise each side of the equation to solve the equation. **They are reciprocals of each other.**

72. **OPEN ENDED** Write an equation that can be solved by raising each side of the equation to the given power.

   a. $\frac{3}{2}$ power **b.** $\frac{5}{4}$ power **c.** $\frac{7}{8}$ power

72a. Sample answer: $y = 6x^{\frac{2}{3}} - 5$
72b. Sample answer: $4y = x^{\frac{4}{5}} - 9$
72c. Sample answer: $10x^{\frac{8}{7}} - 2y = -1$

73. **CHALLENGE** Solve $7^{3x-1} = 49^{x+1}$ for x. (*Hint*: $b^x = b^y$ if and only if $x = y$.) **3**

REASONING Determine whether the following statements are *sometimes*, *always*, or *never* true for $x^{\frac{1}{n}} = a$. Explain your reasoning.

74. If n is odd, there will be extraneous solutions.

74. Never; sample answer: The radicand can be negative.

75. If n is even, there will be extraneous solutions. **Sometimes; sample answer: when the radicand is negative, then there will be extraneous roots.**

Enrichment
CRM p. 50 OL BL

7-7 Enrichment

Truth Tables

In mathematics, the basic operations are addition, subtraction, multiplication, division, finding a root, and raising to a power. In logic, the basic operations are the following: *not* (~), *and* (∧), *or* (∨), and *implies* (→).

If p and q are statements, then $\sim p$ means not p; $\sim q$ means not q; $p \wedge q$ means p and q; $p \vee q$ means p or q; and $p \rightarrow q$ means p implies q. The operations are defined by truth tables. On the left below is the truth table for the statement $\sim p$. Notice that there are two possible conditions for p, true (T) or false (F). If p is true, $\sim p$ is false; if p is false, $\sim p$ is true. Also shown are the truth tables for $p \wedge q$, $p \vee q$, and $p \rightarrow q$.

p	$\sim p$
T	F
F	T

p	q	$p \wedge q$
T	T	T
T	F	F
F	T	F
F	F	F

p	q	$p \vee q$
T	T	T
T	F	T
F	T	T
F	F	F

p	q	$p \rightarrow q$
T	T	T
T	F	F
F	T	T
F	F	T

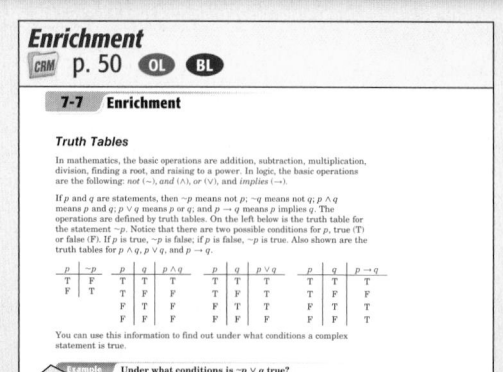

You can use this information to find out under what conditions a complex statement is true.

Example Under what conditions is $\sim p \vee q$ true?

Additional Answer

64. If the height of a person's jump and the amount of time he or she is in the air are related by an equation involving radicals, then the hang time associated with a given height can be found by solving a radical equation.

NGSSS PRACTICE 912.A.6.3, 912.A.2.6, 912.A.3.1, 912.A.6.5

76. What is an equivalent form of $\frac{4}{5+i}$? **A**

A. $\frac{10-2i}{13}$ C. $\frac{6-i}{6}$

B. $\frac{5-i}{6}$ D. $\frac{6-i}{13}$

77. Which set of points describes a function? **G**

F. {(3, 0), (−2, 5), (2, −1), (2, 9)}
G. {(−3, 5), (−2, 3), (−1, 5), (0, 7)}
H. {(2, 5), (2, 4), (2, 3), (2, 2)}
I. {(3, 1), (−3, 2), (3, 3), (−3, 4)}

78. THINK SOLVE EXPLAIN **SHORT RESPONSE** The perimeter of an isosceles triangle is 56 inches. If one leg is 20 inches long, what is the measure of the base of the triangle?

79. ACT/SAT If $\sqrt{x+5}+1=4$, what is the value of x? **A**

A. 4
B. 10
C. 11
D 20

Spiral Review

Evaluate. (Lesson 7-6)

80. $27^{-\frac{2}{3}}$ $\frac{1}{9}$ **81.** $9^{\frac{1}{3}} \cdot 9^{\frac{5}{3}}$ 81 **82.** $\left(\frac{8}{27}\right)^{-\frac{2}{3}}$ $\frac{9}{4}$

83. GEOMETRY The measures of the legs of a right triangle can be represented by the expressions $4x^2y^2$ and $8x^2y^2$. Use the Pythagorean Theorem to find a simplified expression for the measure of the hypotenuse. (Lesson 7-5) $4x^2y^2\sqrt{5}$

Find the inverse of each function. (Lesson 7-2) 84. $y=\frac{x+4}{3}$

84. $y = 3x - 4$ **85.** $y = -2x - 3$ $y=\frac{-x-3}{2}$ **86.** $y = x^2$ $y=\pm\sqrt{x}$ **87.** $y = (2x + 3)^2$ $y=\pm\frac{1}{2}\sqrt{x}-\frac{3}{2}$

For each graph,

a. **describe the end behavior,**

b. **determine whether it represents an odd-degree or an even-degree polynomial function, and**

c. **state the number of real zeros.** (Lesson 6-3) **88–90. See margin.**

88.

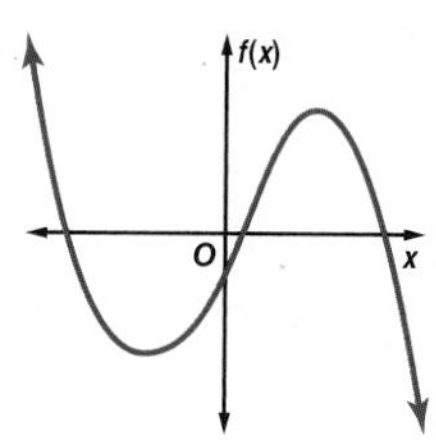

89.

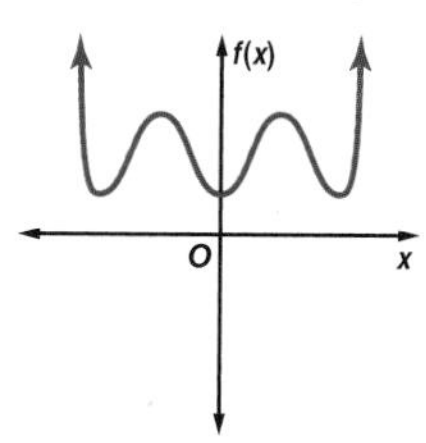

90.

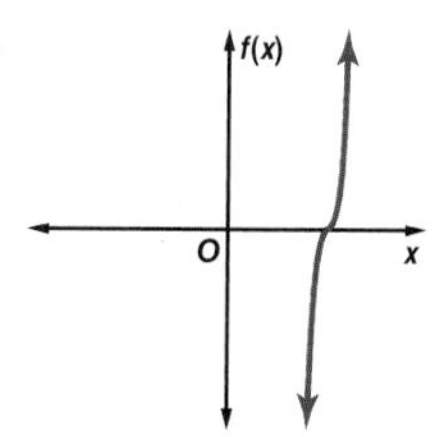

Skills Review

Solve each equation. Write in simplest form. (Lesson 1-3)

91. $\frac{8}{5}x = \frac{4}{15}$ $\frac{1}{6}$ **92.** $\frac{27}{14}y = \frac{6}{7}$ $\frac{4}{9}$ **93.** $\frac{3}{10} = \frac{12}{25}a$ $\frac{5}{8}$ **94.** $\frac{6}{7} = 9m$ $\frac{2}{21}$

95. $\frac{9}{8}b = 18$ 16 **96.** $\frac{6}{7}n = \frac{3}{4}$ $\frac{7}{8}$ **97.** $\frac{1}{3}p = \frac{5}{6}$ $2\frac{1}{2}$ **98.** $\frac{2}{3}q = 7$ $10\frac{1}{2}$

4 ASSESS

Ticket Out the Door Make several copies each of five different radical equations or inequalities. Give one equation or inequality to each student. Have students solve their equations (or inequalities) and hand them to you as they leave the room.

Formative Assessment

Check for student understanding of concepts in Lesson 7-7.

CRM Quiz 4, p. 54

Additional Answers

69. never;

$$\frac{\sqrt{(x^2)^2}}{-x} = x$$

$$\frac{\sqrt{(x^2)^2}}{-x} = x$$

$$\frac{x^2}{-x} = x$$

$$x^2 = (x)(-x)$$

$$x^2 \neq -x^2$$

88a. $f(x) \to -\infty$ as $x \to +\infty$, $f(x) \to +\infty$ as $x \to -\infty$;

88b. odd;

88c. 3

89a. $f(x) \to +\infty$ as $x \to +\infty$, $f(x) \to +\infty$ as $x \to -\infty$;

89b. even;

89c. 0

90a. $f(x) \to +\infty$ as $x \to +\infty$, $f(x) \to -\infty$ as $x \to -\infty$;

90b. odd;

90c. 1

Differentiated Instruction OL BL

Extension Present the following problem to students: The radius r of the orbit of a satellite is given by the formula $r=\sqrt[3]{\frac{GMt^2}{4\pi^4}}$, where G is the universal gravitational constant, M is the mass of the central object, and t is the time it takes the satellite to complete one orbit. Solve this formula for t.

$t = 2\pi^2 r\sqrt{\frac{r}{GM}}$

EXTEND 7-7 Lesson Notes

1 FOCUS

Objective Use a graphing calculator to solve radical equations and inequalities.

Materials for Each Student

- TI-83/84 Plus or other graphing calculator

Teaching Tips

Explain to students the following information about their calculators.

- The TI-83/84 Plus automatically supplies a left parenthesis after each radical sign. When functions are entered on the Y= list, it is important to supply right parentheses as needed to ensure correct graphs and correct numerical results.
- To display the table in Step 2 on this page, students should check to be sure that the **AUTO** option has been selected on each of the last two lines of the **TABLE SETUP** screen.
- To determine exact solutions for repeating decimals, as in the approximate zero displayed on the screen shown in Step 4, go to the home screen immediately after Step 4 and use the keystrokes [X,T,θ,n] [MATH] 1 [ENTER]. The calculator will display a fraction for the exact solution, $\frac{49}{36}$. The calculator can be used to verify that this is indeed the exact solution of the equation.

EXTEND 7-7 Graphing Technology Lab

Solving Radical Equations and Inequalities

FL Math Online glencoe.com
- Other Calculator Keystrokes
- Graphing Technology Personal Tutor

NGSSS **MA.912.A.6.5** Solve equations that contain radical expressions.

You can use a TI-83/84 Plus graphing calculator to solve radical equations and inequalities. One way to do this is to rewrite the equation or inequality so that one side is 0. Then use the **zero** feature on the calculator.

EXAMPLE 1 Radical Equation

Solve $\sqrt{x} + \sqrt{x+2} = 3$.

Step 1 Rewrite the equation.

- Subtract 3 from each side of the equation to get $\sqrt{x} + \sqrt{x+2} - 3 = 0$.
- Enter the function $y = \sqrt{x} + \sqrt{x+2} - 3$ in the Y= list.

KEYSTROKES: [Y=] [2nd] [x^2] [X,T,θ,n] [)] [+] [2nd] [x^2] [X,T,θ,n] [+] 2 [)] [−] 3 [ENTER]

Step 2 Use a table.

- You can use the TABLE function to locate intervals where the solution(s) lie. First, enter the starting value and the interval for the table.

KEYSTROKES: [2nd] [TBLSET] 0 [ENTER] 1 [ENTER]

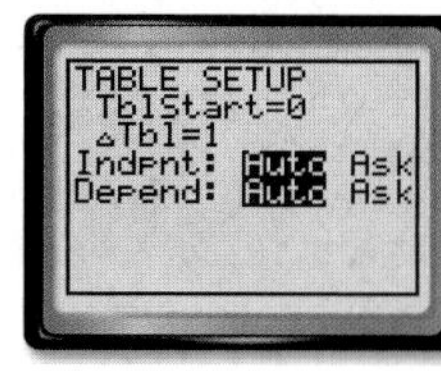

Step 3 Estimate the solution.

- Complete the table and estimate the solution(s).

KEYSTROKES: [2nd] [TABLE]

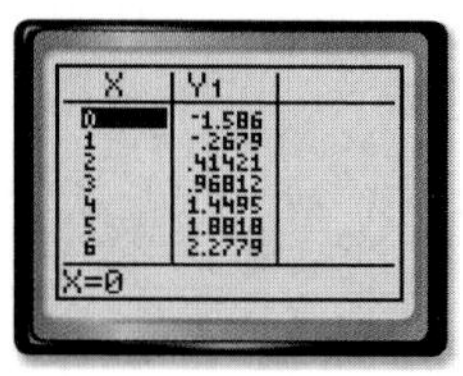

Since the function changes sign from negative to positive between $x = 1$ and $x = 2$, there is a solution between 1 and 2.

Step 4 Use the **zero** feature.

- Graph the function; then select ZERO from the CALC menu.

KEYSTROKES: [2nd] [CALC] 2

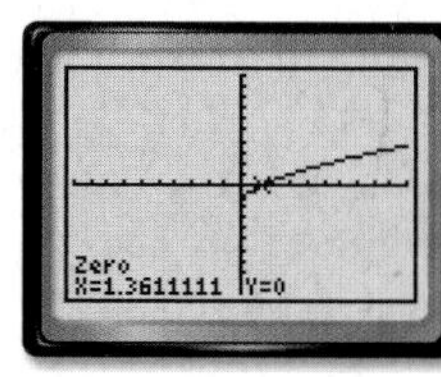

Place the cursor on a point at which $y < 0$ and press [ENTER] for the LEFT BOUND. Then place the cursor on a point at which $y > 0$ and press [ENTER] for the RIGHT BOUND. You can use the same point for the GUESS as for the RIGHT BOUND.

The solution is about 1.36. This is consistent with the estimate made by using the TABLE.

EXAMPLE 2 Radical Inequality

Solve $2\sqrt{x} > \sqrt{x+2} + 1$.

Step 1 Graph each side of the inequality and use the **trace** feature.

- In the Y= list, enter $y_1 = 2\sqrt{x}$ and $y_2 = \sqrt{x+2} + 1$. Then press GRAPH.

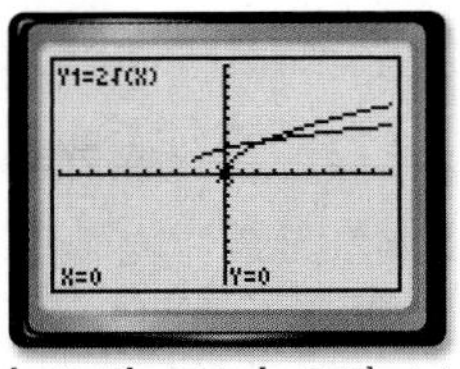

[−10, 10] scl: 1 by [−10, 10] scl: 1

- Press TRACE. You can use ▲ or ▼ to switch the cursor between the two curves.

The calculator screen above shows that, for points to the left of where the curves cross, Y1 < Y2 or $2\sqrt{x} < \sqrt{x+2} + 1$. To solve the original inequality, you must find points for which Y1 > Y2. These are the points to the right of where the curves cross.

Step 2 Use the **intersect** feature.

- You can use the intersect feature on the CALC menu to approximate the x-coordinate of the point at which the curves cross.

KEYSTROKES: 2nd [CALC] 5

- Press ENTER for each of FIRST CURVE?, SECOND CURVE?, and GUESS?.

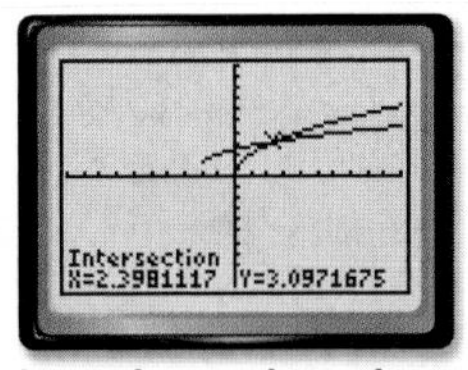

[−10, 10] scl: 1 by [−10, 10] scl: 1

The calculator screen shows that the x-coordinate of the point at which the curves cross is about 2.40. Therefore, the solution of the inequality is about $x > 2.40$. *Use the symbol > in the solution because the symbol in the original inequality is >.*

Step 3 Use the **table** feature to check your solution.

- Start the table at 2 and show x-values in increments of 0.1. Scroll through the table.

KEYSTROKES: 2nd [TBLSET] 2 ENTER .1 ENTER 2nd [TABLE]

Notice that when x is less than or equal to 2.4, Y1 < Y2. This verifies the solution $\{x \mid x > 2.40\}$.

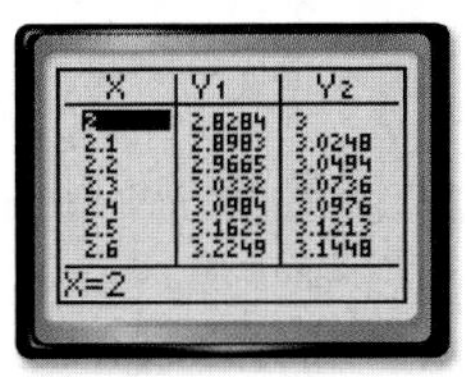

Exercises

Use a graphical method to solve each equation or inequality. **8. $0 \le x < 1$** **9. about $1 \le x < 4.52$**

1. $\sqrt{x+4} = 3$ **5**
2. $\sqrt{3x-5} = 1$ **2**
3. $\sqrt{x+5} = \sqrt{3x+4}$ **0.5**
4. $\sqrt{x+3} + \sqrt{x-2} = 4$ **about 3.89**
5. $\sqrt{3x-7} = \sqrt{2x-2} - 1$ **about 2.52**
6. $\sqrt{x+8} - 1 = \sqrt{x+2}$ **4.25**
7. $\sqrt{x-3} \ge 2$ **$x \ge 7$**
8. $\sqrt{x+3} > 2\sqrt{x}$
9. $\sqrt{x} + \sqrt{x-1} < 4$
10. **WRITING IN MATH** Explain how you could apply the technique in the first example to solving an inequality. **See margin.**

2 TEACH

Working in Cooperative Groups

Put students in pairs, mixing abilities. Then have pairs complete both Activities and Exercises 1–3 and 7.

Activity 1

- Have students solve this radical equation again by treating each side as a separate function. Point out that the right side will simply be graphed as the function $y = 3$.

Activity 2

- Instead of treating each side of the inequality in Activity 2 as a separate function, have students solve it again by first subtracting $2\sqrt{x}$ from both sides and then graphing the function $y = \sqrt{x+2} + 1 - 2\sqrt{x}$. Point out that the portion of the graph below the x-axis shows the solution.

Practice Have students complete Exercises 4–6 and 8–9.

3 ASSESS

Formative Assessment

Use Exercises 5 and 9 to assess whether students comprehend how to solve a radical equation or inequality.

From Concrete to Abstract

Ask:

- When examining the table of values of the equation in Activity 1, how do you know a solution lies between the two x-values where the graphed function changes signs? Sample answer: Since the original equation was solved so that one side was zero, the function representing the other side has a value of 0 when the value of y is 0. That must occur for a value of x somewhere between two values of x whose corresponding values of y have different signs (because 0 lies between the positive numbers and negative numbers).

Additional Answer

10. Rewrite the inequality so that one side is 0. Then graph the other side and find the x-values for which the graph is above or below the x-axis, according to the inequality symbol. Use the zero feature to approximate the x-coordinate of the point at which the graph crosses the x-axis.

Formative Assessment

Key Vocabulary The page references after each word denote where that term was first introduced. If students have difficulty answering questions 1–9, remind them that they can use these page references to refresh their memories about the vocabulary.

Summative Assessment

CRM Vocabulary Test, p. 56

FL Math Online glencoe.com

Vocabulary PuzzleMaker improves students' mathematics vocabulary using four puzzle formats–crossword, scramble, word search using a word list, and word search using clues. Students can work online or from a printed worksheet.

Additional Answers

10. $[f \circ g](x) = 8x - 9$
$[g \circ f](x) = 8x - 1$

11. $[f \circ g](x) = x^2 - 14x + 50$
$[g \circ f](x) = x^2 - 6$

12. $[f \circ g](x) = 4x^2 - 4x + 5$
$[g \circ f](x) = -2x^2 - 7$

13. $[f \circ g](x) = 20x - 4$
$[g \circ f](x) = 20x - 1$

14. $[f \circ g](x) = x - 3x^2 + 3x - 1$
$[g \circ f](x) = x^3 - 1$

15. $[f \circ g](x) = x^2 + 4x$
$[g \circ f](x) = x^2 + 2x - 2$

17. $f^{-1}(x) = \dfrac{x + 6}{5}$

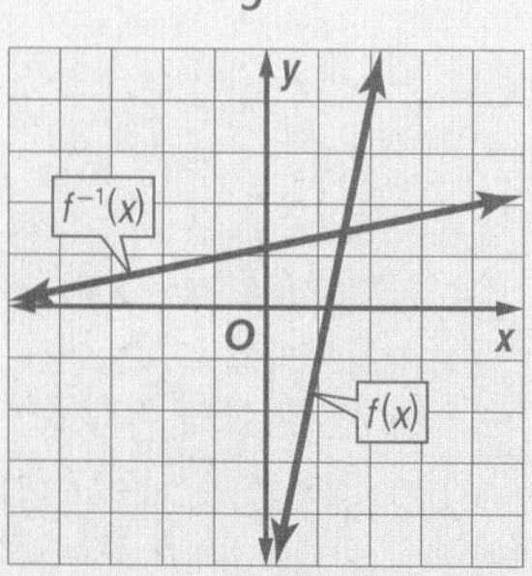

FL Math Online glencoe.com
- STUDY TO GO
- Vocabulary Review

Chapter Summary

Key Concepts

Operations on Functions (Lesson 7-1)

Operation	Definition
Sum	$(f + g)(x) = f(x) + g(x)$
Difference	$(f - g)(x) = f(x) - g(x)$
Product	$(f \cdot g)(x) = f(x) \cdot g(x)$
Quotient	$\left(\frac{f}{g}\right)(x) = \frac{f(x)}{g(x)}, g(x) \neq 0$
Composition	$[f \circ g](x) = f[g(x)]$

Inverse and Square Root Functions (Lessons 7-2 and 7-3)

- Reverse the coordinates of ordered pairs to find the inverse of a relation.
- Two functions are inverses if and only if both their compositions are the identity function.

Roots of Real Numbers (Lesson 7-4)

Real *n*th roots of *b*, $\sqrt[n]{b}$, or $-\sqrt[n]{b}$			
n	$\sqrt[n]{b}$ if $b > 0$	$\sqrt[n]{b}$ if $b < 0$	$\sqrt[n]{b}$ if $b = 0$
even	one positive root one negative root	no real roots	one real root, 0
odd	one positive root no negative roots	no positive roots one negative root	one real root, 0

Radicals (Lessons 7-5 through 7-7)

For any real numbers *a* and *b* and any integers *n*, *x*, and *y*, with $b \neq 0$, $n > 1$, and $y > 1$, the following are true.

- Product Property: $\sqrt[n]{ab} = \sqrt[n]{a} \cdot \sqrt[n]{b}$
- Quotient Property: $\sqrt[n]{\frac{a}{b}} = \frac{\sqrt[n]{a}}{\sqrt[n]{b}}$
- Rational Exponents: $b^{\frac{x}{y}} = \sqrt[y]{b^x} = \left(\sqrt[y]{b}\right)^x, b \geq 0$

FOLDABLES® Study Organizer

Be sure the Key Concepts are noted in your Foldable.

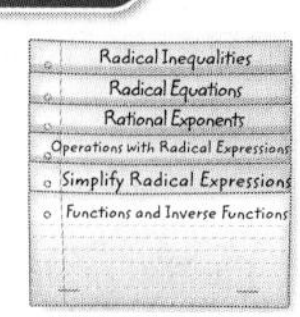

Key Vocabulary

composition of functions (p. 411)
conjugates (p. 442)
extraneous solution (p. 453)
index (p. 431)
inverse function (p. 417)
inverse relation (p. 417)
like radical expressions (p. 441)
***n*th root** (p. 431)
principal root (p. 431)
radical equation (p. 453)
radical function (p. 424)
radical inequality (p. 455)
radical sign (p. 431)
radicand (p. 431)
rationalizing the denominator (p. 440)
square root function (p. 424)
square root inequality (p. 426)

Vocabulary Check

Choose a word or term that best completes each statement. 1. identity function

1. If both compositions result in the __________, then the functions are inverse functions.
2. Radicals are __________ if *both* the index and the radicand are identical. like radical expressions
3. In a(n) __________, the results of one function are used to evaluate a second function. composition of functions
4. When there is more than one real root, the nonnegative root is called the __________. principal root
5. To eliminate radicals from a denominator or fractions from a radicand, you use a process called __________. rationalizing the denominator
6. Equations with radicals that have variables in the radicands are called __________. radical equations
7. Two relations are __________ if and only if one relation contains the element (*b*, *a*) when the other relation contains the element (*a*, *b*). inverse relations
8. When solving a radical equation, sometimes you will obtain a number that does not satisfy the original equation. Such a number is called a(n) __________. extraneous solution
9. The square root function is a type of __________. radical function

FOLDABLES® Study Organizer

Dinah Zike's Foldables®
Have students look through the chapter to make sure they have included examples in their Foldables.

Suggest that students keep their Foldables handy while completing the Study Guide and Review pages. Point out that their Foldables can serve as a quick review tool when studying for the chapter test.

Lesson-by-Lesson Review

7-1 Operations on Functions (pp. 409–416)

912.A.2.7, 912.A.2.8

Find $[f \circ g](x)$ and $[g \circ f](x)$. **10–15. See margin.**

10. $f(x) = 2x + 1$, $g(x) = 4x - 5$

11. $f(x) = x^2 + 1$, $g(x) = x - 7$

12. $f(x) = x^2 + 4$, $g(x) = -2x + 1$

13. $f(x) = 4x$, $g(x) = 5x - 1$

14. $f(x) = x^3$, $g(x) = x - 1$

15. $f(x) = x^2 + 2x - 3$, $g(x) = x + 1$

16. **MEASUREMENT** The formula $f = 3y$ converts yards y to feet f and $f = \frac{n}{12}$ converts inches n to feet f. Write a composition of functions that converts yards to inches. **$n = 36y$**

EXAMPLE 1

If $f(x) = x^2 + 3$ and $g(x) = 3x - 2$, find $g[f(x)]$ and $f[g(x)]$.

$g[f(x)] = 3(x^2 + 3) - 2$	Replace $f(x)$ with $x^2 + 3$.
$= 3x^2 + 9 - 2$	Multiply.
$= 3x^2 + 7$	Simplify.
$f[g(x)] = (3x - 2)^2 + 3$	Replace $g(x)$ with $3x - 2$.
$= 9x^2 - 12x + 4 + 3$	Multiply.
$= 9x^2 - 12x + 7$	Simplify.

7-2 Inverse Functions and Relations (pp. 417–422)

912.A.2.11

Find the inverse of each function. Then graph the function and its inverse. **17–22. See margin.**

17. $f(x) = 5x - 6$

18. $f(x) = -3x - 5$

19. $f(x) = \frac{1}{2}x + 3$

20. $f(x) = \frac{4x + 1}{5}$

21. $f(x) = x^2$

22. $f(x) = (2x + 1)^2$

23. **SHOPPING** Samuel bought a computer. The sales tax rate was 6% of the sale price, and he paid \$50 for shipping. Find the sale price if Samuel paid a total of \$1322. **\$1200**

Use the horizontal line test to determine whether the inverse of each function is also a function. **26, 28. no**

24. $f(x) = 3x^2$ **no**

25. $h(x) = x^3 - 3$ **yes**

26. $g(x) = -3x^4 + 2x - 1$

27. $g(x) = 4x^3 - 5x$ **no**

28. $f(x) = -3x^5 + x^2 - 3$

29. $h(x) = 4x^4 + 7x$ **no**

30. **FINANCIAL LITERACY** During the last month, Jonathan has made two deposits of \$45, made a deposit of double his original balance, and has withdrawn \$35 five times. His balance is now \$189. Write an equation that models this problem. How much money did Jonathan have in his account at the beginning of the month? **$x + 2(45) + 2x - 5(35) = 189$; about \$91.33**

EXAMPLE 2

Find the inverse of $f(x) = -2x + 7$.

Rewrite $f(x)$ as $y = -2x + 7$. Then interchange the variables and solve for y.

$x = -2y + 7$	Interchange the variables.
$2y = -x + 7$	Solve for y.
$y = \frac{-x + 7}{2}$	Divide each side by 2.
$f^{-1}(x) = \frac{-x + 7}{2}$	Rewrite using function notation.

EXAMPLE 3

Use the horizontal line test to determine whether the inverse of $f(x) = 2x^3 + 1$ is also a function.

Graph the function.

No horizontal line can be drawn so that it passes through more than one point. The inverse of this function is a function.

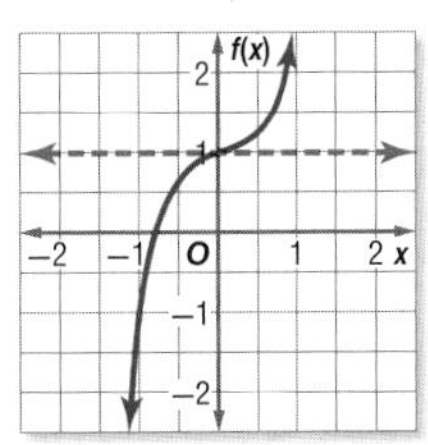

Lesson-by-Lesson Review

Intervention If the given examples are not sufficient to review the topics covered by the questions, remind students that the page references tell them where to review that topic in their textbook.

Two-Day Option Have students complete the Lesson-by-Lesson Review on pp. 463–466. Then you can use ExamView® Assessment Suite to customize another review worksheet that practices all the objectives of this chapter or only the objectives on which your students need more help.

Differentiated Instruction

Super DVD: MindJogger Videoquizzes Use this DVD as an alternative format of review for the test.

Additional Answers

18. $f^{-1}(x) = \frac{x + 5}{-3}$

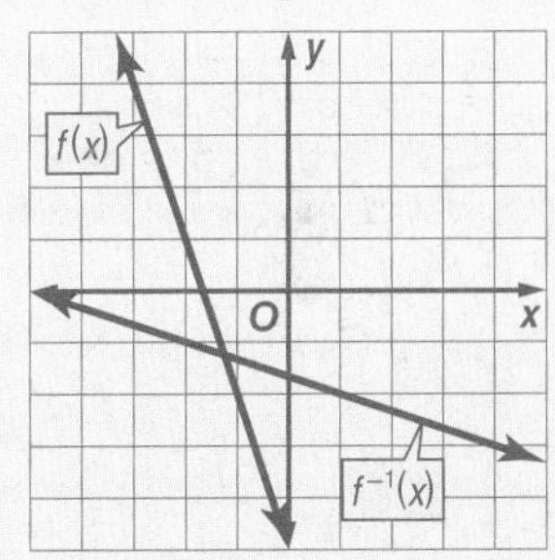

19. $f^{-1}(x) = 2x - 6$

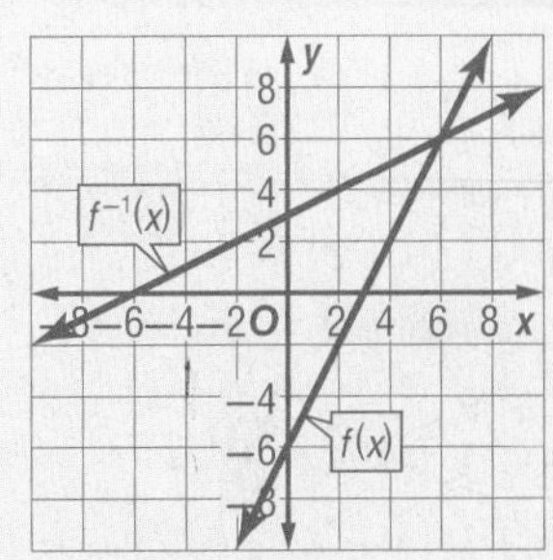

20. $f^{-1}(x) = \frac{5x - 1}{4}$

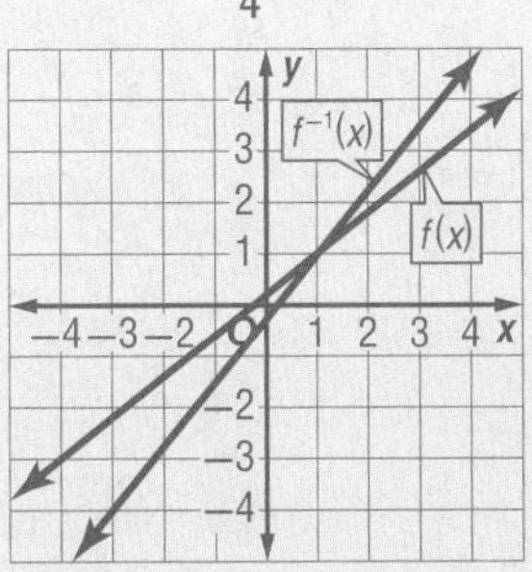

21. $y = \pm\sqrt{x}$

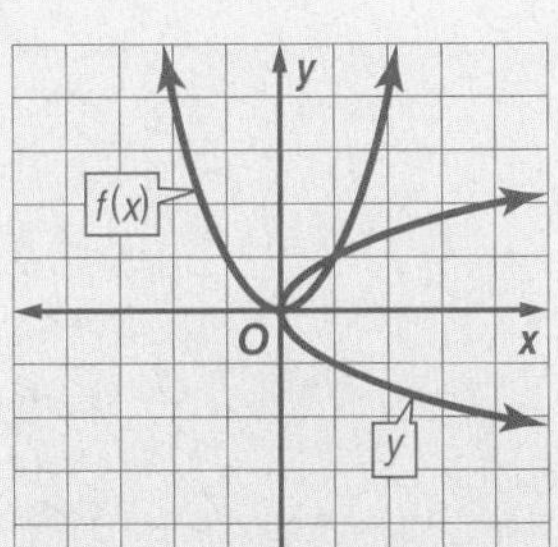

22. $y = \frac{-1 \pm \sqrt{x}}{2}$

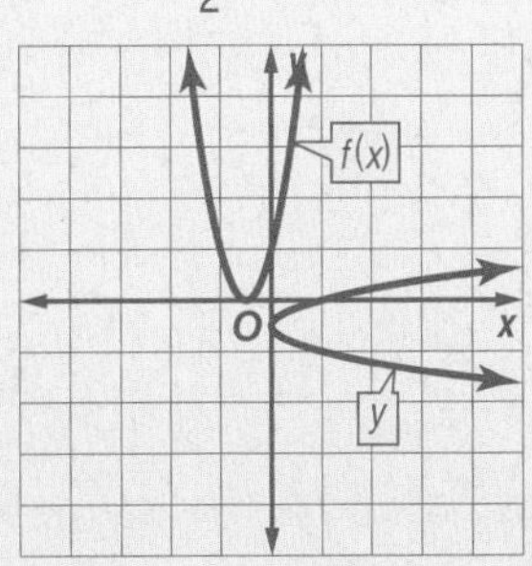

Additional Answers

31.

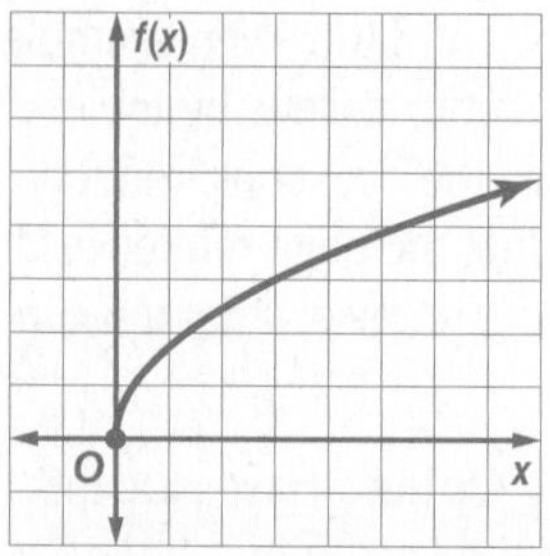

$D = \{x \mid x \geq 0\}$; $R = \{f(x) \mid f(x) \geq 0\}$

32.

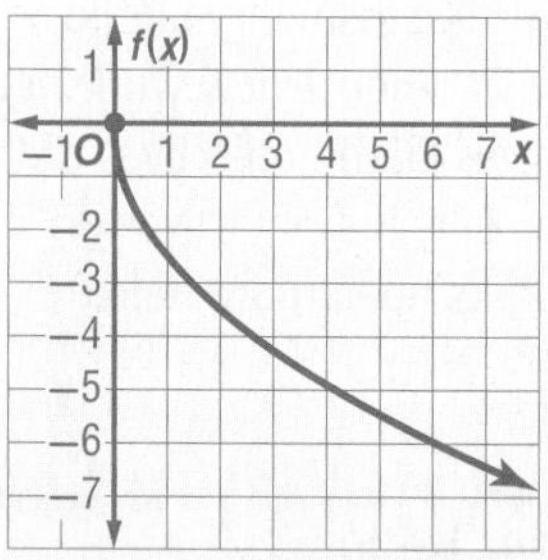

$D = \{x \mid x \geq 0\}$; $R = \{f(x) \mid f(x) \leq 0\}$

33.

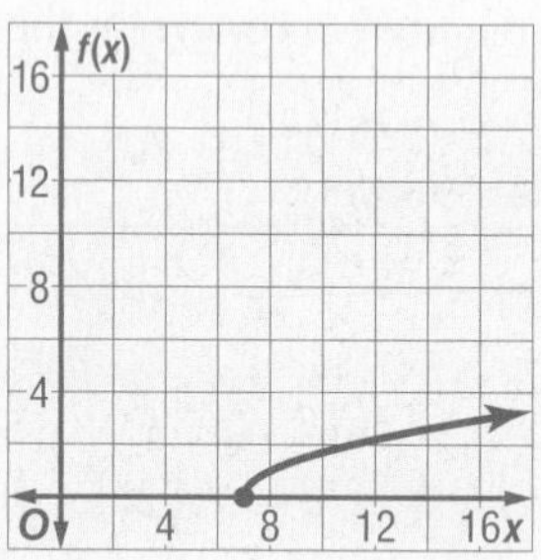

$D = \{x \mid x \geq 7\}$; $R = \{f(x) \mid f(x) \geq 0\}$

34.

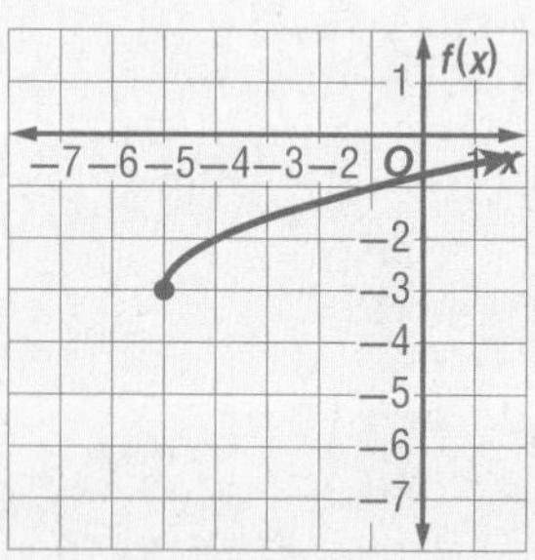

$D = \{x \mid x \geq -5\}$; $R = \{f(x) \mid f(x) \geq -3\}$

35.

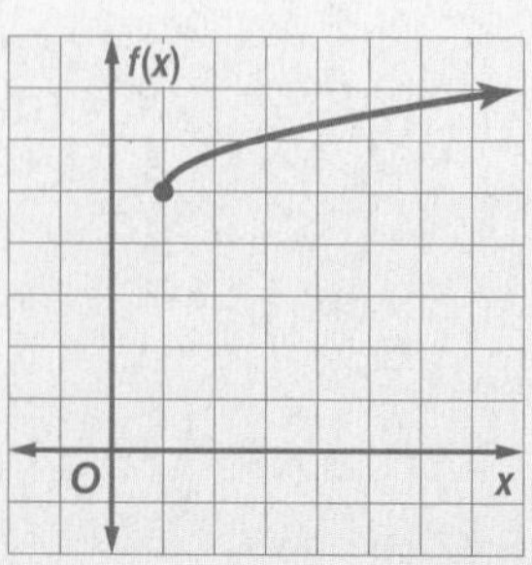

$D = \{x \mid x \geq 1\}$; $R = \{f(x) \mid f(x) \geq 5\}$

36.

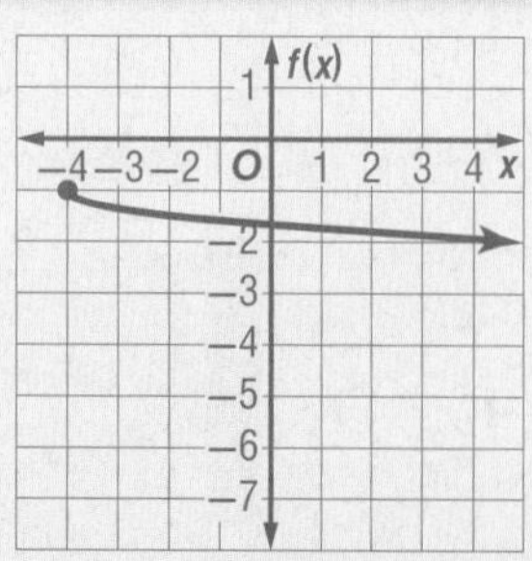

$D = \{x \mid x \geq -4\}$; $R = \{f(x) \mid f(x) \leq -1\}$

CHAPTER 7 Study Guide and Review

7-3 Square Root Functions and Inequalities (pp. 424–430)

912.A.2.6

Graph each function. State the domain and range.

31. $f(x) = \sqrt{3x}$ **31–36. See margin.**

32. $f(x) = -\sqrt{6x}$

33. $f(x) = \sqrt{x - 7}$

34. $f(x) = \sqrt{x + 5} - 3$

35. $f(x) = \frac{3}{4}\sqrt{x - 1} + 5$

36. $f(x) = -\frac{1}{3}\sqrt{x + 4} - 1$

37. **GEOMETRY** The area of a circle is given by the formula $A = \pi r^2$. What is the radius of a circle with an area of 300 square inches? **about 9.8 in.**

Graph each inequality. **38–40. See margin.**

38. $y \geq \sqrt{x} + 3$

39. $y < 2\sqrt{x - 5}$

40. $y > -\sqrt{x - 1} + 2$

EXAMPLE 4

Graph $f(x) = \sqrt{x + 1} - 2$. State the domain and range.

Identify the domain.

$x + 1 \geq 0$ **Write the radicand as greater than or equal to 0.**

$x \geq -1$ **Subtract 1 from each side.**

Make a table of values for $x \geq -1$ and graph the function.

x	f(x)
−1	−2
0	−1
1	−0.59
2	−0.27
3	0
4	0.24
5	0.45

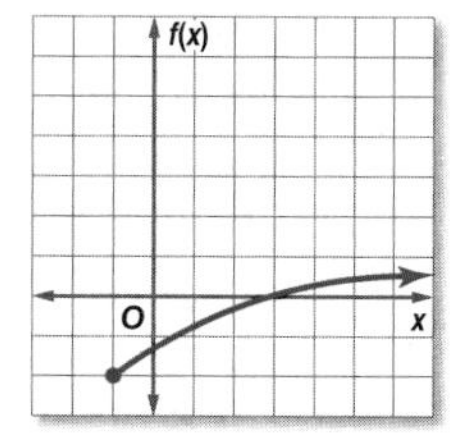

The domain is $\{x \mid x \geq -1\}$, and the range is $\{f(x) \mid f(x) \geq -2\}$.

7-4 nth Roots (pp. 431–436)

912.A.10.3

Simplify.

41. $\pm\sqrt{121}$ **± 11**

42. $\sqrt[3]{-125}$ **-5**

43. $\sqrt{(-6)^2}$ **6**

44. $\sqrt{-(x + 3)^4}$ **undefined**

45. $\sqrt[3]{(x^2 + 2)^{18}}$ **$(x^2 + 2)^6$**

46. $\sqrt[3]{27(x + 3)^3}$ **$3(x + 3)$**

47. $\sqrt[4]{a^8b^{12}}$ **$a^2|b^3|$**

48. $\sqrt[5]{243x^{10}y^{25}}$ **$3x^2y^5$**

49. **PHYSICS** The velocity v of an object can be defined as $v = \sqrt{\frac{2K}{m}}$, where m is the mass of an object and K is the kinetic energy in joules. Find the velocity in meters per second of an object with a mass of 17 grams and a kinetic energy of 850 joules. **10 m/s**

EXAMPLE 5

Simplify $\sqrt{64x^6}$.

$\sqrt{64x^6} = \sqrt{(8x^3)^2}$ **$64x^6 = (8x^3)^2$**

$= 8|x^3|$ **Simplify.**

Use absolute value symbols because x could be negative.

EXAMPLE 6

Simplify $\sqrt[6]{4096x^{12}y^{24}}$.

$\sqrt[6]{4096x^{12}y^{24}} = \sqrt[6]{(4x^2y^4)^6}$ **$4096x^{12}y^{24} = (4x^2y^4)^6$**

$= 4x^2y^4$ **Simplify.**

MIXED PROBLEM SOLVING
For mixed problem-solving practice, see page 985.

7-5 Operations with Radical Expressions (pp. 439–445)

912.A.6.2

Simplify.

50. $\sqrt[3]{54}$ $3\sqrt[3]{2}$

51. $\sqrt{144a^3b^5}$ $12ab^2\sqrt{ab}$

52. $4\sqrt{6y} \cdot 3\sqrt{7x^2y}$ $12|x|y\sqrt{42}$

53. $6\sqrt{72} + 7\sqrt{98} - \sqrt{50}$ $80\sqrt{2}$

54. $(6\sqrt{5} - 2\sqrt{2})(3\sqrt{5} + 4\sqrt{2})$ $74 + 18\sqrt{10}$

55. $\dfrac{\sqrt{6m^5}}{\sqrt{p^{11}}}$ $\dfrac{m^2\sqrt{6mp}}{p^6}$

56. $\dfrac{3}{5 + \sqrt{2}}$ $\dfrac{15 - 3\sqrt{2}}{23}$

57. $\dfrac{\sqrt{3}}{\sqrt{5} - \sqrt{6}}$ $-\sqrt{15} - 3\sqrt{2}$

58. **GEOMETRY** What are the perimeter and the area of the rectangle?

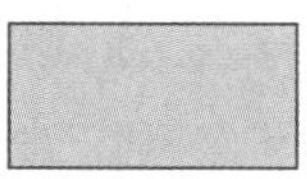

$6 - \sqrt{2}$

$8 + \sqrt{3}$

perimeter $= 28 + 2\sqrt{3} - 2\sqrt{2}$ units;
area $= 48 + 6\sqrt{3} - 8\sqrt{2} - \sqrt{6}$ units^2

EXAMPLE 7

Simplify $2\sqrt[3]{18a^2b} \cdot 3\sqrt[3]{12ab^5}$.

$2\sqrt[3]{18a^2b} \cdot 3\sqrt[3]{12ab^5}$	
$= (2 \cdot 3)\sqrt[3]{18a^2b \cdot 12ab^5}$	**Product Property**
$= 6\sqrt[3]{2^3 3^3 a^3 b^6}$	**Factor.**
$= 6 \cdot \sqrt[3]{2^3} \cdot \sqrt[3]{3^3} \cdot \sqrt[3]{a^3} \cdot \sqrt[3]{b^6}$	**Product Property**
$= 6 \cdot 2 \cdot 3 \cdot a \cdot b^2$	**Find cube roots.**
$= 36ab^2$	**Simplify.**

EXAMPLE 8

Simplify $\sqrt{\dfrac{x^4}{y^5}}$.

$\sqrt{\dfrac{x^4}{y^5}} = \dfrac{\sqrt{x^4}}{\sqrt{y^5}}$	**Quotient Property**
$= \dfrac{\sqrt{(x^2)^2}}{\sqrt{(y^2)^2} \cdot \sqrt{y}}$	**Factor into squares.**
$= \dfrac{x^2}{y^2\sqrt{y}} \cdot \dfrac{\sqrt{y}}{\sqrt{y}}$	**Rationalize the denominator.**
$= \dfrac{x^2\sqrt{y}}{y^3}$	$\sqrt{y} \cdot \sqrt{y} = y$

7-6 Rational Exponents (pp. 446–452)

912.A.6.3, 912.A.6.4

Simplify each expression.

59. $x^{\frac{1}{2}} \cdot x^{\frac{2}{3}}$ $x^{\frac{7}{6}}$

60. $m^{-\frac{3}{4}}$ $\dfrac{m^{\frac{1}{4}}}{m}$

61. $\dfrac{d^{\frac{1}{6}}}{d^{\frac{3}{4}}}$ $\dfrac{d^{\frac{5}{12}}}{d}$

Simplify each expression.

62. $\dfrac{1}{y^{\frac{1}{4}}}$ $\dfrac{y^{\frac{3}{4}}}{y}$

63. $\sqrt[3]{\sqrt{729}}$ 3

64. $\dfrac{x^{\frac{2}{3}} - x^{\frac{1}{3}}y^{\frac{2}{3}}}{x^{\frac{1}{3}}}$ $x^{\frac{1}{3}} - y^{\frac{2}{3}}$

65. **GEOMETRY** What is the area of the circle?

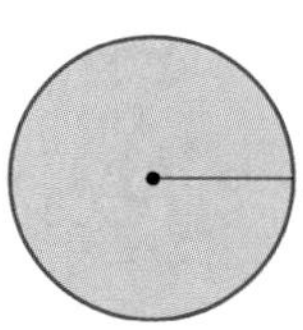

$r = 2a^{\frac{1}{3}}b^{\frac{2}{5}}c$

65. $4a^{\frac{2}{3}}b^{\frac{4}{5}}c^2\pi$ units^2

EXAMPLE 9

Simplify $a^{\frac{2}{3}} \cdot a^{\frac{1}{5}}$.

$a^{\frac{2}{3}} \cdot a^{\frac{1}{5}} = a^{\frac{2}{3} + \frac{1}{5}}$	**Product of Powers**
$= a^{\frac{13}{15}}$	**Add.**

EXAMPLE 10

Simplify $\dfrac{2a}{\sqrt[3]{b}}$.

$\dfrac{2a}{\sqrt[3]{b}} = \dfrac{2a}{b^{\frac{1}{3}}}$	**Rational exponents**
$= \dfrac{2a}{b^{\frac{1}{3}}} \cdot \dfrac{b^{\frac{2}{3}}}{b^{\frac{2}{3}}}$	**Rationalize the denominator.**
$= \dfrac{2ab^{\frac{2}{3}}}{b}$ or $\dfrac{2a\sqrt[3]{b^2}}{b}$	**Rewrite in radical form.**

Additional Answers

38.

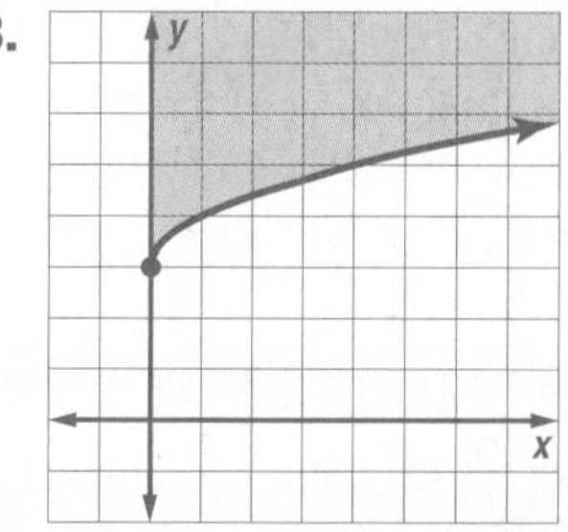

39.

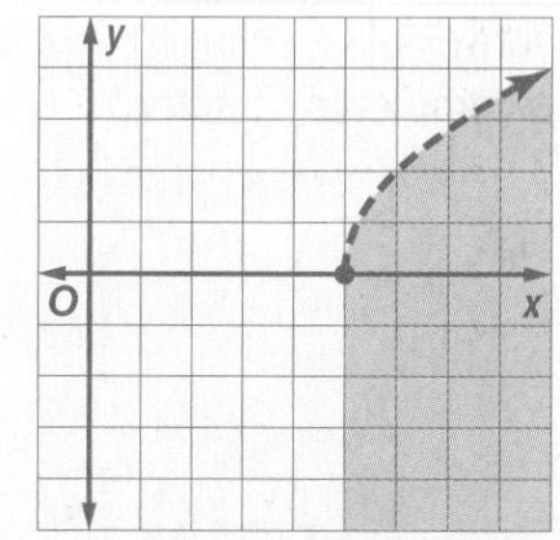

40.

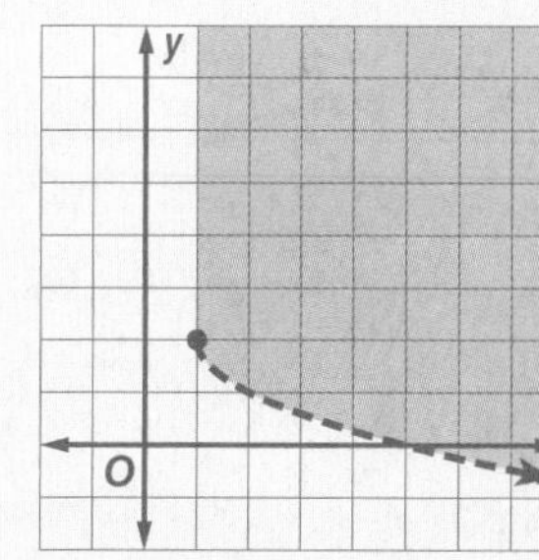

Chapter 7 Study Guide and Review 465

Problem Solving Review

For additional practice in problem solving for Chapter 7, see the Mixed Problem Solving Appendix, p. 986, in the Student Handbook section.

Anticipation Guide

Have students complete the Chapter 7 Anticipation Guide and discuss how their responses have changed now that they have completed Chapter 7.

CHAPTER 7 Study Guide and Review

7-7 Solving Radical Equations and Inequalities (pp. 453–459)

912.A.6.5, 912.A.10.3

Solve each equation. 67. $\frac{100}{9}$ 71. no solution

66. $\sqrt{x-3}+5=15$ 103 **67.** $-\sqrt{x-11}=3-\sqrt{x}$

68. $4+\sqrt{3x-1}=8$ $\frac{17}{3}$ **69.** $\sqrt{m+3}=\sqrt{2m+1}$ 2

70. $\sqrt{2x+3}=3$ 3 **71.** $(x+1)^{\frac{1}{4}}=-3$

72. $a^{\frac{1}{3}}-4=0$ 64 **73.** $3(3x-1)^{\frac{1}{3}}-6=0$ 3

74. PHYSICS The formula $t=2\pi\sqrt{\frac{\ell}{32}}$ represents the swing of a pendulum, where t is the time in seconds for the pendulum to swing back and forth and ℓ is the length of the pendulum in feet. Find the length of a pendulum that makes one swing in 2.75 seconds. about 6.13 ft

Solve each inequality.

75. $2+\sqrt{3x-1}<5$ **76.** $\sqrt{3x+13}-5\geq 5$

77. $6-\sqrt{3x+5}\leq 3$ **78.** $\sqrt{-3x+4}-5\geq 3$

79. $5+\sqrt{2y-7}<5$ **80.** $3+\sqrt{2x-3}\geq 3$

81. $\sqrt{3x+1}-\sqrt{6+x}>0$ $x>\frac{5}{2}$

75. $\frac{1}{3}\leq x<\frac{10}{3}$
76. $x\geq 29$
77. $x\geq\frac{4}{3}$
78. $x\leq -20$
79. no solution
80. $x\geq\frac{3}{2}$

EXAMPLE 11

Solve $\sqrt{2x+9}-2=5$.

$\sqrt{2x+9}-2=5$	**Original equation**
$\sqrt{2x+9}=7$	**Add 2 to each side.**
$(\sqrt{2x+9})^2=7^2$	**Square each side.**
$2x+9=49$	**Evaluate the squares.**
$2x=40$	**Subtract 9 from each side.**
$x=20$	**Divide each side by 2.**

EXAMPLE 12

Solve $\sqrt{2x-5}+2>5$.

$\sqrt{2x-5}\geq 0$	**Radicand must be ≥ 0.**
$2x-5\geq 0$	**Square each side.**
$2x\geq 5$	**Add 5 to each side.**
$x\geq 2.5$	**Divide each side by 2.**

The solution must be greater than or equal to 2.5 to satisfy the domain restriction.

$\sqrt{2x-5}+2>5$	**Original inequality**
$\sqrt{2x-5}>3$	**Subtract 2 from each side.**
$(\sqrt{2x-5})^2>3^2$	**Square each side.**
$2x-5>9$	**Evaluate the squares.**
$2x>14$	**Add 5 to each side.**
$x>7$	**Divide each side by 2.**

Since $x\geq 2.5$ contains $x>7$, the solution of the inequality is $x>7$.

466 Chapter 7 Inverses and Radical Functions and Relations

FL Math Online glencoe.com
Chapter Test

Determine whether each pair of functions are inverse functions. Write *yes* or *no*. Explain your reasoning.

1. $f(x) = 3x + 8$, $g(x) = \frac{x-8}{3}$ yes
2. $f(x) = \frac{1}{3}x + 5$, $g(x) = 3x - 15$ yes
3. $f(x) = x + 7$, $g(x) = x - 7$ yes
4. $g(x) = 3x - 2$, $f(x) = \frac{x-2}{3}$ no

5. **NGSSS PRACTICE** Which inequality represents the graph below? B

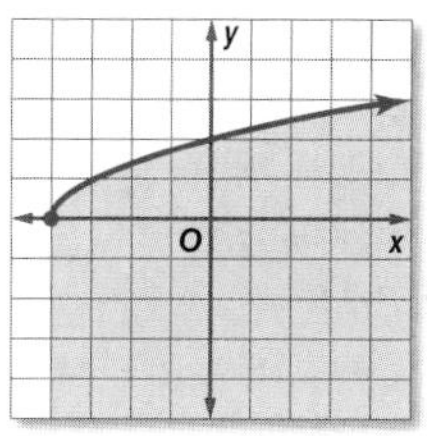

A. $y \geq \sqrt{x+4}$ C. $y \geq \sqrt{x-4}$
B. $y \leq \sqrt{x+4}$ D. $y \leq \sqrt{x-4}$

If $f(x) = 3x + 2$ and $g(x) = x^2 - 2x + 1$, find each function. 7. $(f \cdot g)(x) = 3x^3 - 4x^2 - x + 2$

6. $(f + g)(x)$ $(f + g)(x) = x^2 + x + 3$
7. $(f \cdot g)(x)$
8. $(f - g)(x)$ $(f - g)(x) = -x^2 + 5x + 1$
9. $\left(\frac{f}{g}\right)(x)$ $\left(\frac{f}{g}\right)(x) = \frac{3x+2}{x^2-2x+1}; x \neq 1$

Solve each equation.

10. $\sqrt{a+12} = \sqrt{5a-4}$ 4
11. $\sqrt{3x} = \sqrt{x-2}$ no solution
12. $4(\sqrt[4]{3x+1}) - 8 = 0$ 5
13. $\sqrt[3]{5m+6} + 15 = 21$ 42
14. $\sqrt{3x+21} = \sqrt{5x+27}$ −3
15. $1 + \sqrt{x+11} = \sqrt{2x+15}$ 5
16. $\sqrt{x-5} = \sqrt{2x-4}$ no solution
17. $\sqrt{x-6} - \sqrt{x} = 3$ no solution

18. **NGSSS PRACTICE** Which expression is equivalent to $125^{-\frac{1}{3}}$? H

F. −5 H. $\frac{1}{5}$
G. $-\frac{1}{5}$ I. 5

Simplify. 20. $17\sqrt{2} - 25$

19. $(2 + \sqrt{5})(6 - 3\sqrt{5})$ −3
20. $(3 - 2\sqrt{2})(-7 + \sqrt{2})$
21. $\frac{12}{2 - \sqrt{3}}$ $12\sqrt{3} + 24$
22. $\frac{m^{\frac{1}{2}} - 1}{2m^{\frac{1}{2}} + 1}$ $\frac{2m - 3m^{\frac{1}{2}} + 1}{4m - 1}$
23. $4\sqrt{3} - 8\sqrt{48}$ $-28\sqrt{3}$
24. $5^{\frac{2}{3}} \cdot 5^{\frac{1}{2}} \cdot 5^{\frac{5}{6}}$ 5^2 or 25
25. $\sqrt[6]{729a^9b^{24}}$ $3ab^4\sqrt{a}$
26. $\sqrt[5]{32x^{15}y^{10}}$ $2x^3y^2$
27. $w^{-\frac{4}{5}}$ $\frac{w^{\frac{1}{5}}}{w}$
28. $\frac{r^{\frac{2}{3}}}{r^{\frac{1}{6}}}$ $r^{\frac{1}{2}}$
29. $\frac{a^{-\frac{1}{2}}}{6a^{\frac{1}{3}} \cdot a^{-\frac{1}{4}}}$ $\frac{a^{\frac{5}{12}}}{6a}$
30. $\frac{y^{\frac{3}{2}}}{y^{\frac{1}{2}} + 2}$ $\frac{y^2 - 2y^{\frac{3}{2}}}{y - 4}$

31. **NGSSS PRACTICE** What is the area of the rectangle? A

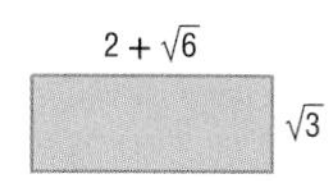

A. $2\sqrt{3} + 3\sqrt{2}$ units²
B. $4 + 2\sqrt{6} + 2\sqrt{3}$ units²
C. $2\sqrt{3} + \sqrt{6}$ units²
D. $2\sqrt{3} + 3$ units²

33. $\frac{1}{3} \leq m < \frac{37}{3}$
34. $1 \leq x \leq 5$
35. $-\frac{3}{2} \leq x \leq 39$
36. $0 \leq b < 4$

Solve each inequality.

32. $\sqrt{4x-3} < 5$ $\frac{3}{4} \leq x < 7$
33. $-2 + \sqrt{3m-1} < 4$
34. $2 + \sqrt{4x-4} \leq 6$
35. $\sqrt{2x+3} - 4 \leq 5$
36. $\sqrt{b+12} - \sqrt{b} > 2$
37. $\sqrt{y-7} + 5 \geq 10$ $y \geq 32$
38. $\sqrt{a-5} - \sqrt{a+7} \leq 4$ $a \geq 5$
39. $\sqrt{c+5} + \sqrt{c+10} > 2$ $c > -5$

40. **GEOMETRY** The area of a triangle with sides of length a, b, and c is given by $A = \sqrt{s(s-a)(s-b)(s-c)}$, where $s = \frac{1}{2}(a + b + c)$. What is the area of the triangle expressed in radical form? $2\sqrt{66}$ ft²

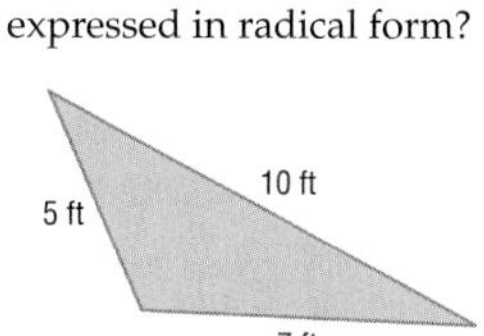

CHAPTER 7 Practice Test

ExamView Assessment Suite Customize and create multiple versions of your chapter test and their answer keys. All of the questions from the leveled chapter tests in the *Chapter 7 Resource Masters* are also available on ExamView® Assessment Suite.

Intervention Planner

Tier 1 On Level	Tier 2 Strategic Intervention approaching grade level	Tier 3 Intensive Intervention 2 or more grades below level
If students miss about 25% of the exercises or less,	**If** students miss about 50% of the exercises,	**If** students miss about 75% of the exercises,
Then choose a resource: **SE** Lessons 7-1, 7-2, 7-3, 7-4, 7-5, 7-6, and 7-7 **CRM** Skills Practice, pp. 7, 14, 21, 27, 33, 40, and 47 **TE** Chapter Project, p. 406 FL Math Online Self-Check Quiz	**Then** choose a resource: **CRM** Study Guide and Intervention, pp. 5, 12, 19, 25, 31, 38, and 45 *Quick Review Math Handbook* FL Math Online Extra Examples, Personal Tutor, Homework Help	**Then** use *Math Triumphs, Alg. 2*, Ch. 1 FL Math Online Extra Examples, Personal Tutor, Homework Help, Review Vocabulary

1 FOCUS

Objective Use the strategy of working backward to solve standardized test problems.

2 TEACH

Scaffolding Questions

Ask:

- Have you ever lost something and retraced your steps in order to find it? Answers will vary.
- Did you retrace your steps in reverse order or in any random order? Answers will vary.
- What is the reverse of adding? multiplying? subtracting; dividing

CHAPTER 7 Preparing for Standardized Tests

Work Backward

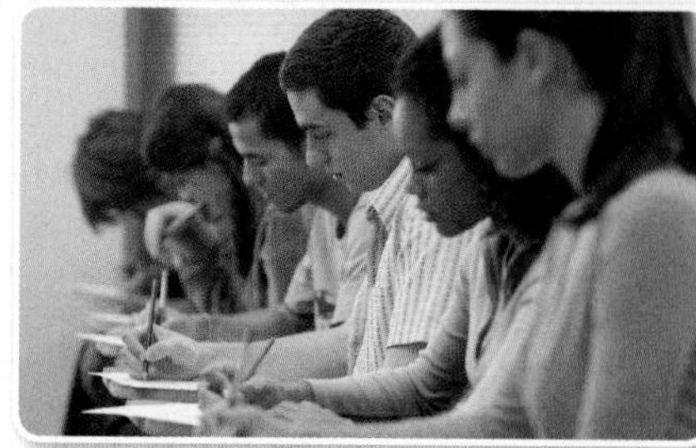

In certain math problems, you are given information about an end result, but you need to find out something that happened earlier. You can work backward to solve problems like this.

Strategies for Working Backward

Step 1

Read the problem statement carefully.

Ask yourself:

- What information am I given?
- What am I being asked to solve?
- Does any of the information given relate to an end result?
- Am I being asked to solve for a quantity that occurred "earlier" in the problem statement?
- What operations are being used in the problem?

Step 2

Model the problem situation with an equation, an inequality, or a graph as appropriate. Then work backward to solve the problem.

- If needed, sketch a flow of events to show the sequence described in the problem statement.
- Use inverse operations to undo any operations while working backward until you arrive at your answer.

Step 3

Check by beginning with your answer and seeing if you arrive at the same result given in the problem statement.

NGSSS PRACTICE EXAMPLE

Read the problem. Identify what you need to know. Then use the information in the problem to solve.

> Maria bought a used car. The sales tax rate was 6.75% of the selling price, and she had to pay $450 in processing, title, and registration fees. If Maria paid a total of $15,768.63, what was the sale price of the car? Show your work.

Read the problem carefully. You know the total amount that Maria paid for the car after sales tax was applied and after she paid all of the other fees. You need to find the sale price of the car before taxes and fees.

Let x represent the sale price of the car and set up an equation. Use the work backward strategy to solve the problem.

Words	The sale price of the car plus the sales tax and other fees is equal to the final price.
Variable	Let x = sale price.
Equation	$1.0675x + 450 = 15{,}768.63$

Using the work backward strategy results in a simple equation. Use inverse operations to solve for x.

$$1.0675x + 450 = 15{,}768.63$$
$$1.0675x = 15{,}318.63$$
$$x \approx 14{,}350$$

Check your answer by working the problem forward. Begin with your answer and see if you get the same result as in the problem statement.

$14{,}350(1.0675) \approx 15{,}318.63$ **Compute the sales tax.**
$15{,}318.63 + 450 = 15{,}768.63$ **Add the other fees.**
$15{,}768.63 = 15{,}768.63$ **The result is the same.**

So, the sale price of the car was $14,350.

Exercises

Read the problem. Identify what you need to know. Then use the information in the problem to solve.

1. The equation $d = \frac{s^2}{30f}$ can be used to model the length of the skid marks left by a car when a driver applies the brakes to come to a sudden stop. In the equation, d is the length (in feet) of the skid marks left on the road, s is the speed of the car in miles per hour, and f is a coefficient of friction that describes the condition of the road. Suppose a car left skid marks that are 120 feet long. **a. $s = \sqrt{30df}$**

   a. Solve the equation for s, the speed of the car.

   b. If the coefficient of friction for the road is 0.75, about how fast was the car traveling? **about 52 mph**

   c. How fast was the car traveling if the coefficient of friction for the road is 1.1? **about 63 mph**

2. An object is shot straight upward into the air with an initial speed of 800 feet per second. The height h that the object will be after t seconds is given by the equation $h = -16t^2 + 800t$. When will the object reach a height of 10,000 feet? **B**

   A. 10 seconds

   B. 25 seconds

   C. 100 seconds

   D. 625 seconds

3. Pedro is creating a scale drawing of a car. He finds that the height of the car in the drawing is $\frac{1}{32}$ of the actual height of the car x. Which equation best represents this relationship? **H**

   F. $y = x - \frac{1}{32}$

   G. $y = -\frac{1}{32}x$

   H. $y = \frac{1}{32}x$

   I. $y = x + \frac{1}{32}$

Additional Examples

STANDARDIZED TEST PRACTICE Nate used a $15 gift card to partially pay for a dinner for two at his favorite restaurant. After a sales tax of 6.5% was added, a $5.25 tip was left, and he used the gift card, Nate paid a total of $18.21 for the cost of the dinners. What was the price of the two dinners before taxes? C

A $16.94

B $26.21

C $26.25

D $31.50

3 ASSESS

Use Exercises 1–3 to assess students' understanding.

Diagnose Student Errors

Survey student responses for each item. Class trends may indicate common errors and misconceptions.

1. A. added the coupon to the original cost then multiplied by the percent to be paid
B. correct
C. subtracted the coupon from the original cost and then multiplied by the percent of discount
D. subtracted the coupon from the original cost and then multiplied by the percent to be paid

3. F. used a tax rate of 9.6%
G. used a tax rate of 7.5%
H. correct
I. used a tax rate of 3.59%

4. A. did not follow the correct order of operations
B. correct
C. did not multiply correctly
D. did not multiply correctly

8. F. correct
G. multiplied instead of adding
H. divided instead of adding
I. multiplied by −1 instead of exchanging variables and solving

9. A. solved for values for the first equation only
B. guess
C. correct
D. simplified the system of equations incorrectly

10. F. guess
G. added the area of a circle to the area of the rectangle
H. did not find the correct value for the radius
I. correct

13. A. did not find the cube root of an exponent correctly
B. correct
C. did not find the cube root of −27 correctly
D. guess

Read each question. Then fill in the correct answer on the answer document provided by your teacher or on a sheet of paper.

1. A sporting goods store is discounting all camping equipment by 20% during the off-season. Charles also has a coupon good for $5.00 off his next purchase from the store. If the coupon is applied *after* the store discount, which of the following functions can be used to find the final price of a tent that originally cost d dollars? **B**

A. $P(d) = 0.8 \times (d + 5)$

B. $P(d) = (0.8 \times d) - 5$

C. $P(d) = 0.2 \times (d - 5)$

D. $P(d) = 0.8 \times (d - 5)$

2. **EXTENDED RESPONSE** Suppose $f(x)$ and $g(x)$ are inverse functions.

a. Describe how the graphs of $f(x)$ and $g(x)$ would appear on a coordinate grid. **a, b. See margin.**

b. What is the value of the composition $f[g(2)]$? Explain.

3. Kay bought a used car. The sales tax rate was 6.5% of the selling price, and she also had to pay $325 in registration fees. Find the selling price if Kay spent a total of $15,501.25. **H**

F. $13,850 H. $14,250

G. $14,120 I. $14,650

4. Which expression is equivalent to $3a(2a + 1) - (2a - 2)(a + 3)$? **B**

A. $2a^2 + 6a + 7$

B. $4a^2 - a + 6$

C. $4a^2 + 6a - 6$

D. $4a^2 - 3a + 7$

Test-TakingTip

Question 3 You know the final price but need to know the sale price. Work backward to find the solution.

5. **GRIDDED RESPONSE** The perimeter of the quadrilateral below is 160. What is the value of m? **4**

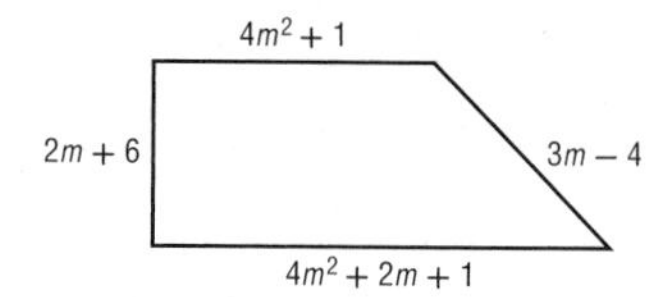

6. **SHORT RESPONSE** Suppose a projectile is launched into the air from a platform. The formula $h = -16t^2 + 40t + 70$ relates the height h of the object (in feet) and the time t since it was launched (in seconds). What is the maximum height the object reaches? **95 ft**

7. **EXTENDED RESPONSE** The amount that a retailer charges for shipping an electronics purchase is determined by the weight of the package. The charges for several different weights are given in the table.

Electronics Shipping Charges

Weight (lb)	Shipping ($)
1	5.58
3	6.76
4	7.35
7	9.12
10	10.89
13	12.66
15	13.84

a. Find the rate of change of the shipping charge per pound. **$0.59**

b. Write an equation that could be used to find the shipping charge y for a package that weighs x pounds. $y = 0.59x + 4.99$

c. Find the shipping charge for a package that weighs 19 pounds. **$16.20**

8. Find the inverse of $f(x) = x - 5$. **F**

F. $f(x) = x + 5$

G. $f(x) = 5x$

H. $f(x) = \frac{x}{5}$

I. $f(x) = 5 - x$

14. F. confused the constants that cause a shift up and down with those that shift the graph right and left
G. did not understand that the constant under the radical shifts the graph right or left
H. guess
I. correct

15. A. did not find the least value for $\left|\frac{1}{a}\right|$
B. did not find the least value for $\left|\frac{1}{a}\right|$
C. correct
D. did not find the least value for $\left|\frac{1}{a}\right|$

9. The equations of two lines are $2x - y = 6$ and $4x - y = -2$. Which of the following describes their point of intersection? **C**

A. $(2, -2)$ C. $(-4, -14)$

B. $(-8, -38)$ D. no intersection

10. Find the equation that can be used to determine the total area of the composite figure below. **I**

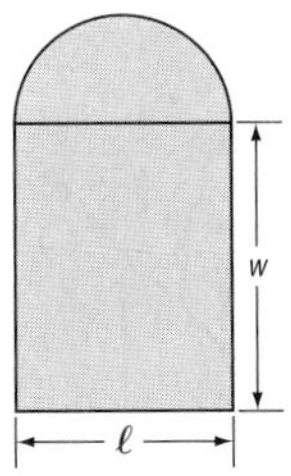

F. $A = \ell w + \frac{1}{2}\ell w$

G. $A = \ell w + \pi\left(\frac{1}{2}\ell\right)^2$

H. $A = \ell w + \frac{1}{2}\pi\ell^2$

I. $A = \ell w + \pi\left(\frac{1}{2}\ell\right)^2\left(\frac{1}{2}\right)$

11. THINK SOLVE EXPLAIN **SHORT RESPONSE** Which pair of polygons is congruent? **Polygon A and Polygon B**

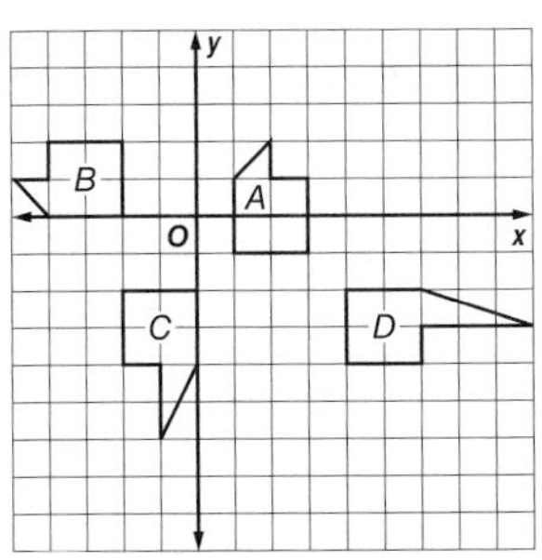

12. THINK SOLVE EXPLAIN **SHORT RESPONSE** The radius of a sphere with volume V can be found using the formula $r = \sqrt[3]{\frac{3V}{4\pi}}$.

V = 8580 cu. in.

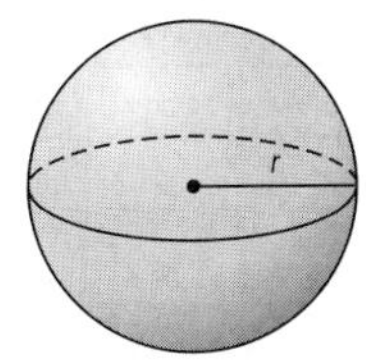

a. What is the radius of the sphere at the right? Round to the nearest tenth. **12.7 in.**

b. Solve the formula for V to find the formula for the volume of a sphere, given its radius. $V = \frac{4}{3}\pi r^3$

c. What is the volume of a basketball that has a diameter of 9 inches? Round to the nearest tenth. **381.7 in^3**

13. Simplify $\sqrt[3]{-27b^6c^{12}}$. **B**

A. $-3b^3c^6$ C. $3b^2c^4$

B. $-3b^2c^4$ D. $3b^3c^6$

14. What is the equation of the square root function graphed at the right? **I**

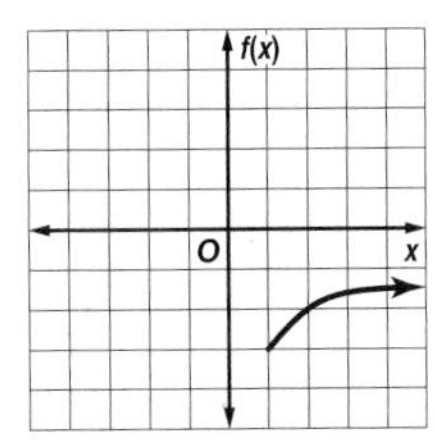

F. $f(x) = \sqrt{x - 3} - 1$

G. $f(x) = \sqrt{x + 1} - 3$

H. $f(x) = \sqrt{x + 3} + 1$

I. $f(x) = \sqrt{x - 1} - 3$

15. Which equation will produce the narrowest parabola when graphed? **C**

A. $y = 3x^2$ C. $y = -6x^2$

B. $y = \frac{3}{4}x^2$ D. $y = -\frac{3}{4}x^2$

Need Extra Help?

If you missed Question...	1	2	3	4	5	6	7	8	9	10	11	12	13	14	15
Go to Lesson or Page...	7-1	7-2	7-2	7-3	4-4	7-7	2-4	7-2	3-1	1-1	6-1	7-4	7-4	6-1	5-7
For help with NGSSS...	912. A.2.13	912. A.2.11	912. A.2.11	912. A.2.6	912. G.2.4	912. A.6.5	912. A.3.1	912. A.2.11	912. A.3.14	912. A.2.7	912. A.4.2	912. A.6.5	912. A.6.3	912. A.3.1	912. A.4.5

Formative Assessment

You can use these two pages to benchmark student progress.

CRM *Chapter 7 Resource Masters*

- Standardized Test Practice, pp. 70–72

ExamView Assessment Suite Create practice worksheets or tests that align to your state's standards as well as TIMSS and NAEP tests.

Homework Option

Get Ready for Chapter 8 Assign students the exercises on p. 473 as homework to assess whether they possess the prerequisite skills needed for the next chapter.

Additional Answers

2a. Sample answer: They would be reflections of each other across the line $y = x$.

2b. Sample answer: The value is 2 because f and g are inverses. Whatever g does to 2, g undoes, so the ouput is the same as the input.

Page 415, Lesson 7-1

50a.

x	$f(x) = x^2$	$g(x) = x$	$(f + g)(x) = x^2 + x$	$(f - g)(x) = x^2 - x$
–3	9	–3	6	12
–2	4	–2	2	6
–1	1	–1	0	2
0	0	0	0	0
1	1	1	2	0
2	4	2	6	2
3	9	3	12	6

50b.

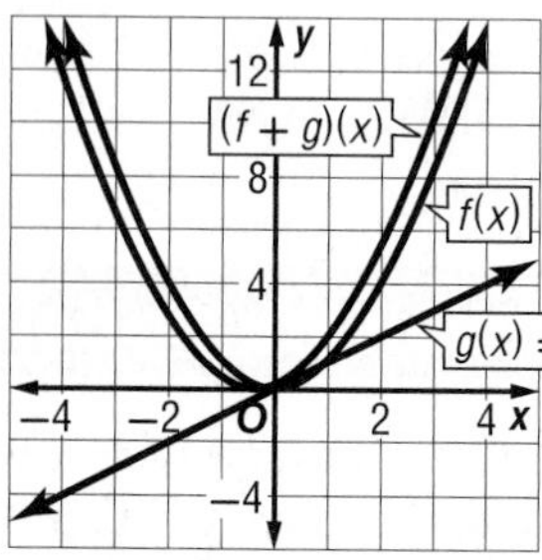

50c.

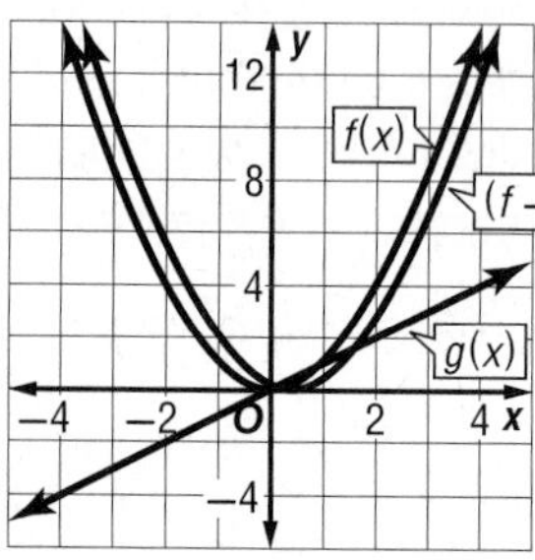

50d. Sample answer: For each value of x, the vertical distance between the graph of $g(x)$ and the x-axis is the same as the vertical distance between the graphs of $f(x)$ and $(f + g)(x)$ and between $f(x)$ and $(f - g)(x)$.

Pages 420–421, Lesson 7-2

15. $f^{-1}(x) = x - 2$

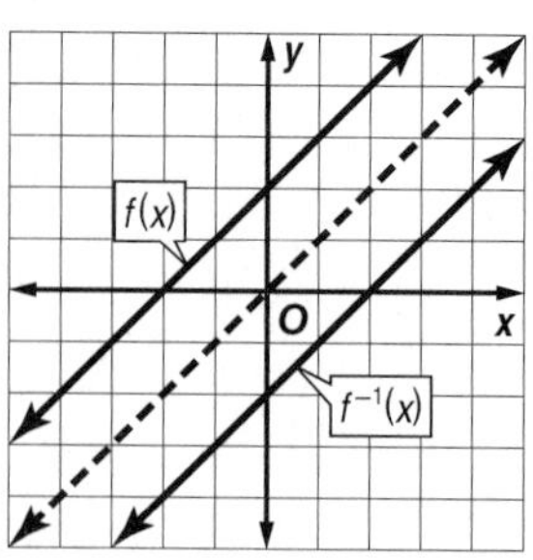

16. $g^{-1}(x) = \frac{1}{5}x$

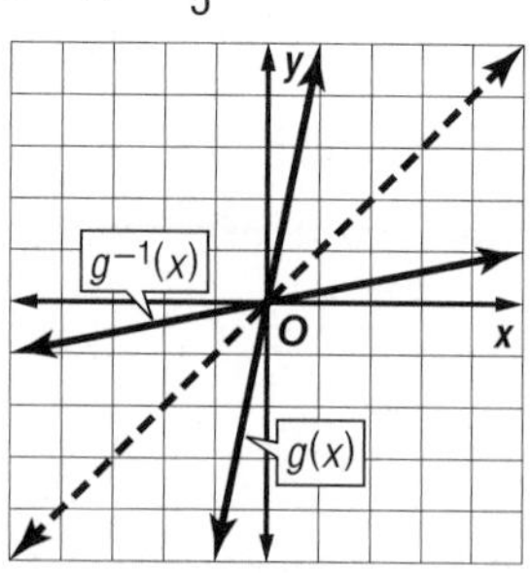

17. $y^{-1} = \frac{x - 1}{-2}$

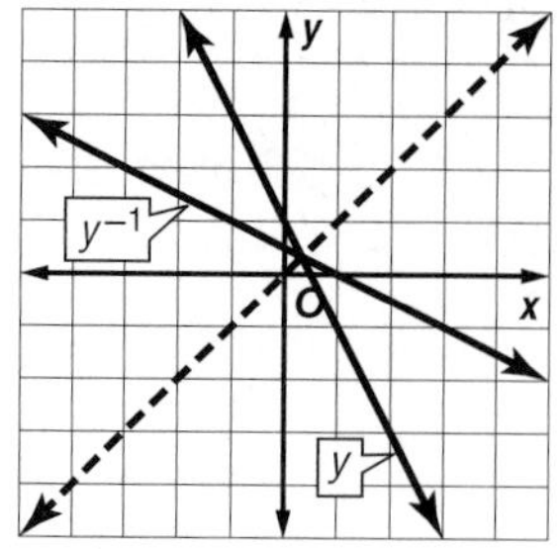

18. $h^{-1}(x) = 3x + 4$

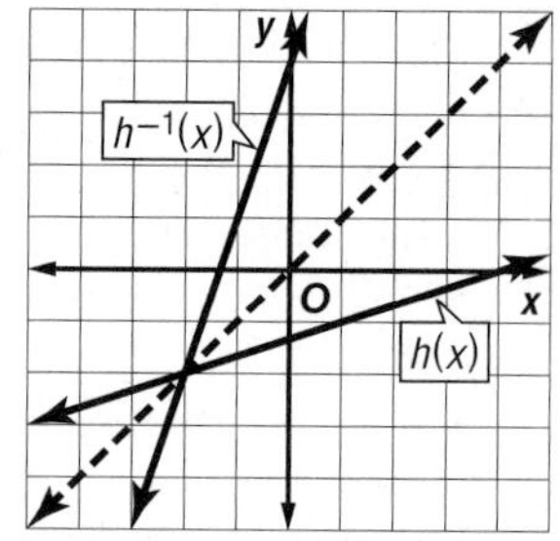

19. $y^{-1} = -\frac{3}{5}(x + 8)$

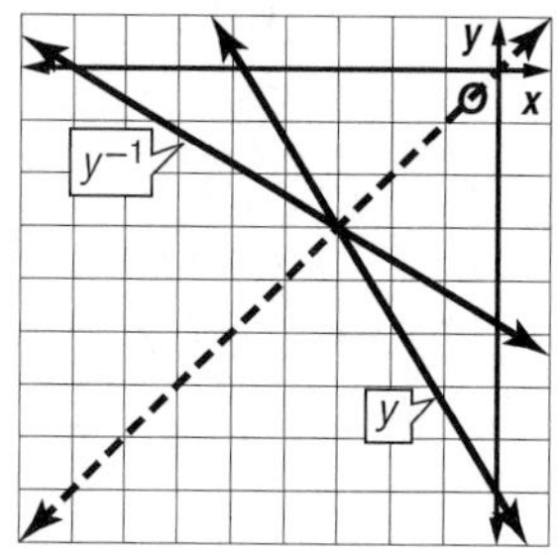

20. $g^{-1}(x) = x - 4$

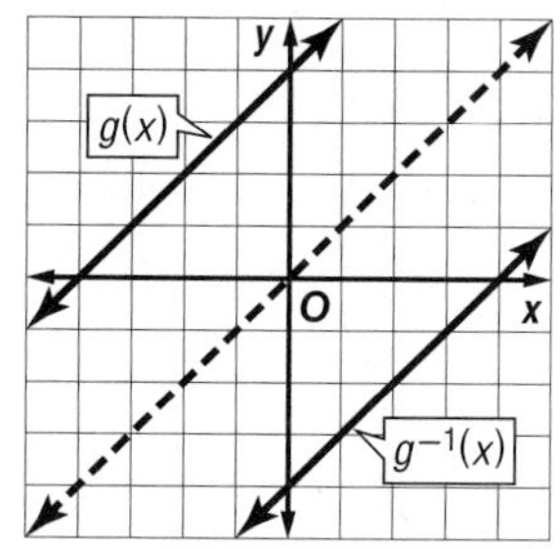

21. $f^{-1}(x) = \frac{1}{4}x$

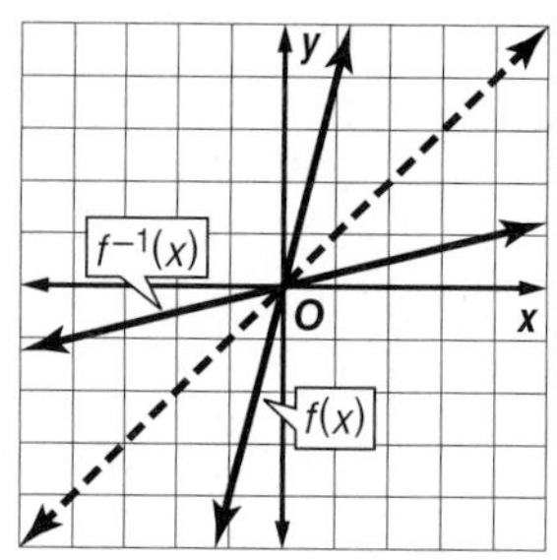

22. $y^{-1} = \frac{x - 9}{-8}$

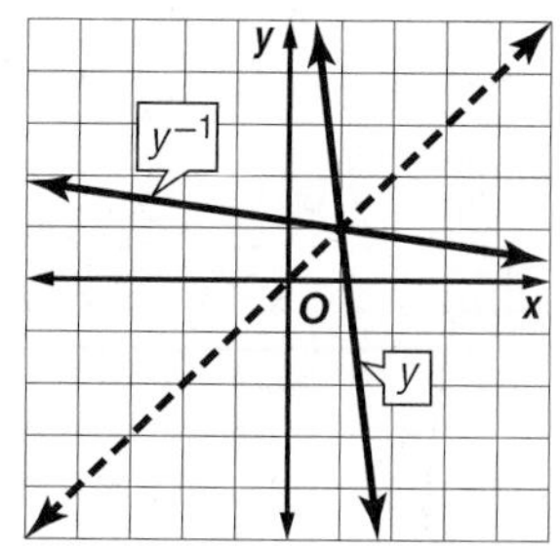

23. $y = \pm\sqrt{\frac{1}{5}x}$

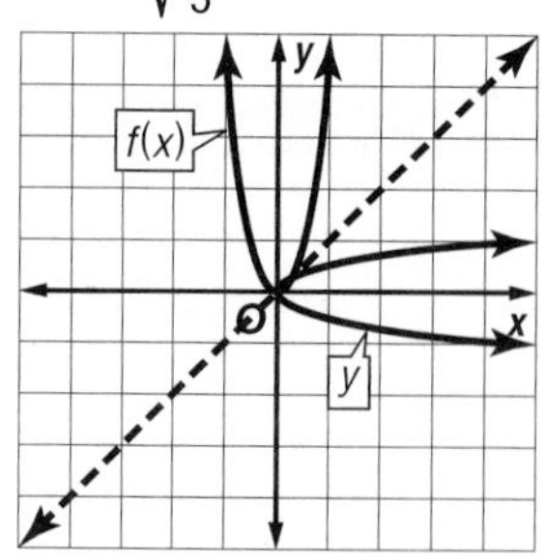

24. $y = \pm\sqrt{x - 4}$

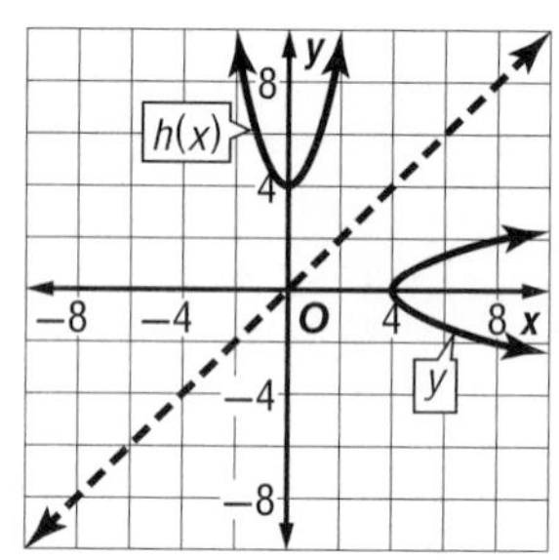

25. $y = \pm\sqrt{2x + 2}$

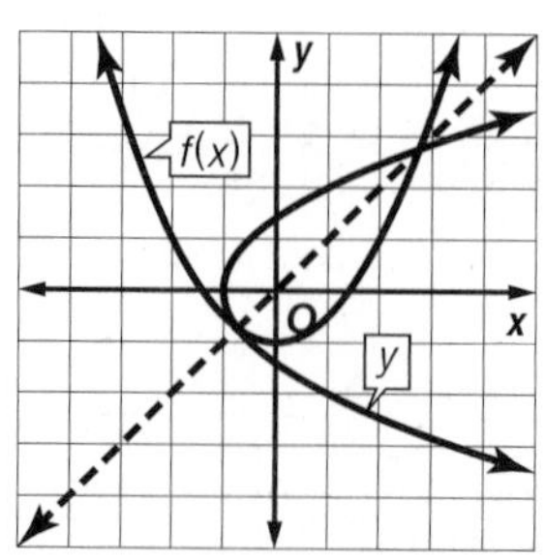

26. $y^{-1} = \pm\sqrt{x - 3} - 1$

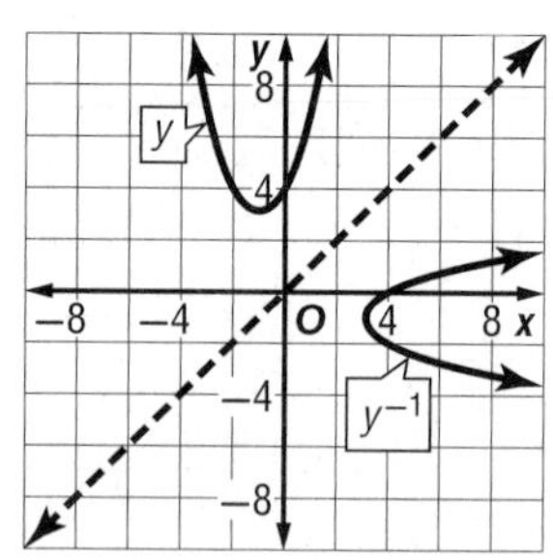

49a. $F^{-1}(x) = \frac{5}{9}(x - 32)$;

$$F[F^{-1}(x)] = \frac{9}{5}\left[\frac{5}{9}(x - 32)\right] + 32$$
$$= x - 32 + 32$$
$$= x$$

$$F^{-1}[F(x)] = \frac{5}{9}\left(\frac{9}{5}x + 32 - 32\right)$$
$$= \frac{5}{9}\left(\frac{9}{5}x + 0\right)$$
$$= x$$

51a.

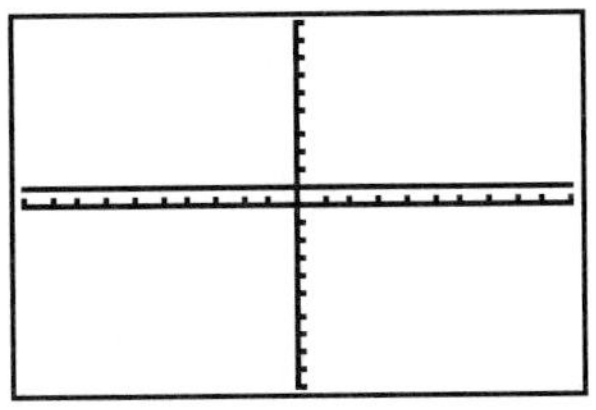

[−10, 10] scl: 1 by [−10, 10] scl: 1

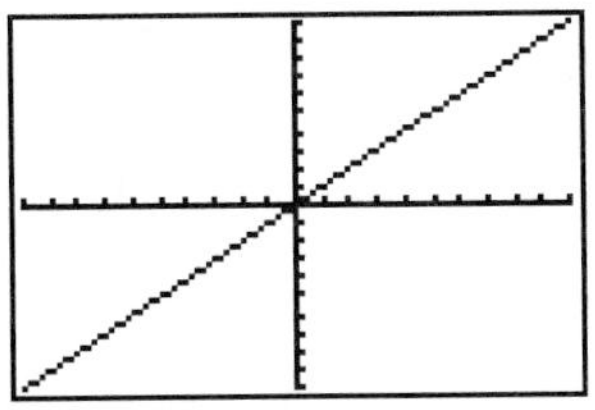

[−10, 10] scl: 1 by [−10, 10] scl: 1

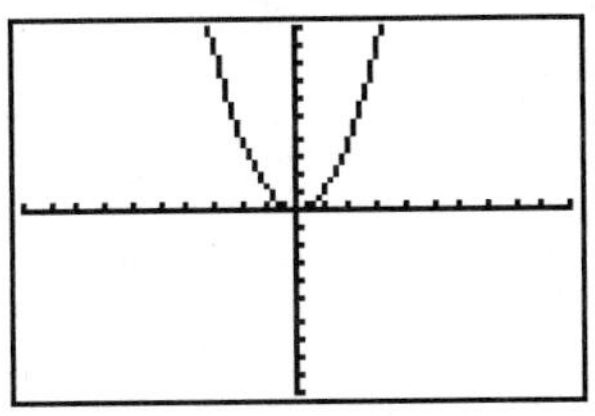

[−10, 10] scl: 1 by [−10, 10] scl: 1

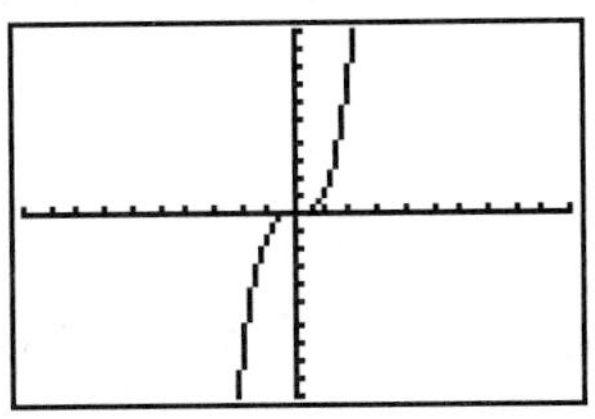

[−10, 10] scl: 1 by [−10, 10] scl: 1

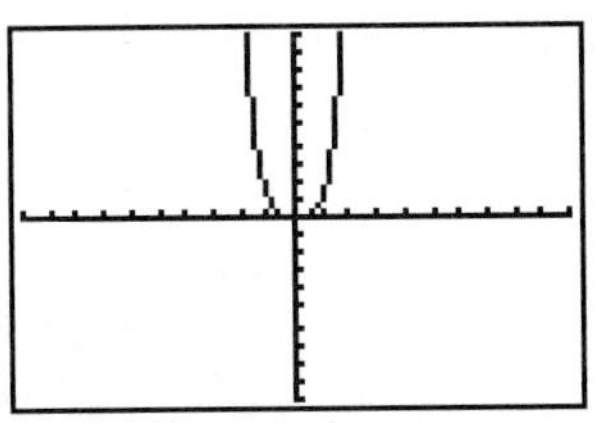

[−10, 10] scl: 1 by [−10, 10] scl: 1

51b.

Function	Inverse a function?
$y = x^0$ or $y = 1$	no
$y = x^1$ or $y = x$	yes
$y = x^2$	no
$y = x^3$	yes
$y = x^4$	no

Page 423, Lesson Extend 7-2

1.

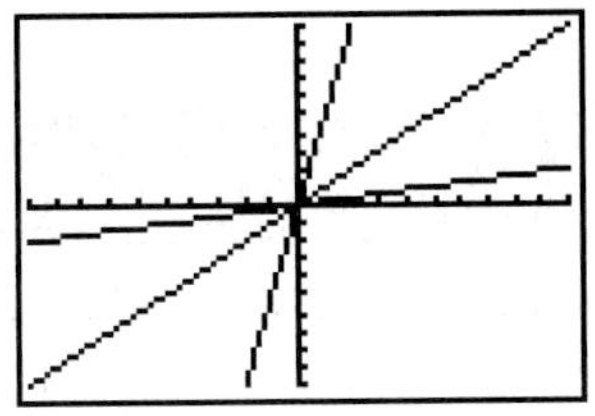

[−10, 10] scl: 1 by [−10, 10] scl: 1

2.

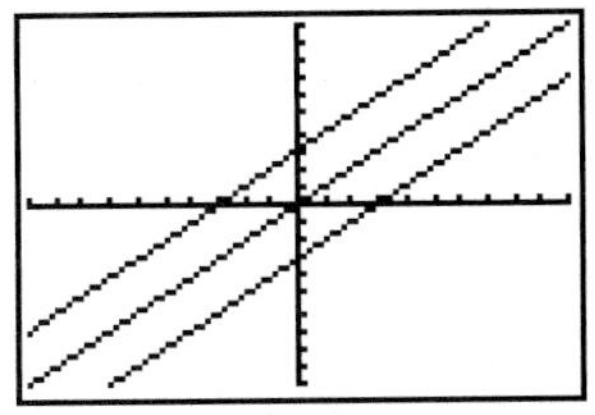

[−10, 10] scl: 1 by [−10, 10] scl: 1

3.

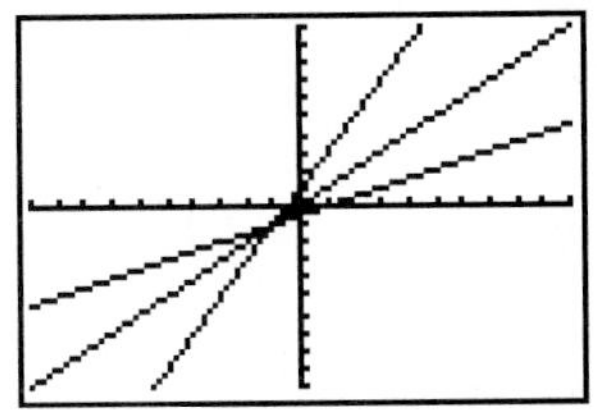

[−10, 10] scl: 1 by [−10, 10] scl: 1

4.

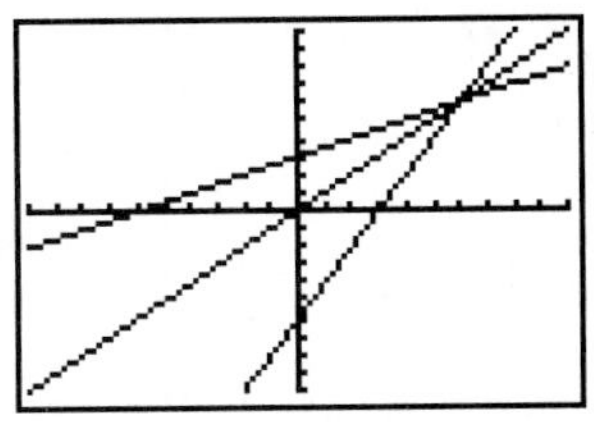

[−10, 10] scl: 1 by [−10, 10] scl: 1

5.

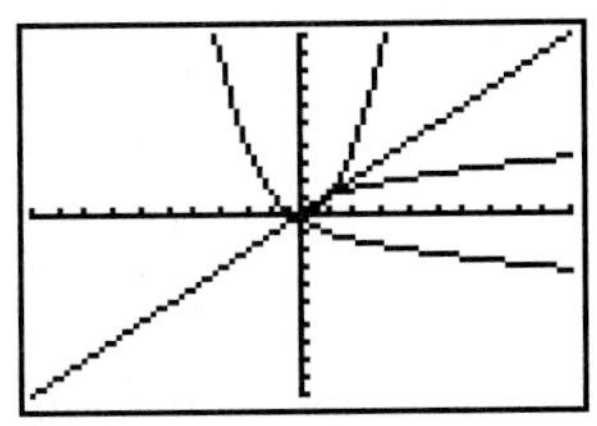

[−10, 10] scl: 1 by [−10, 10] scl: 1

6.

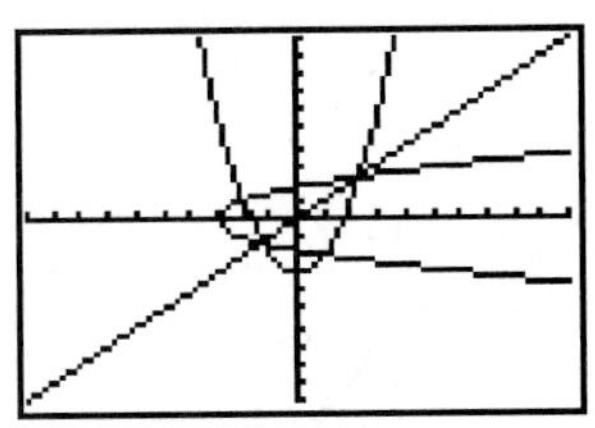

[−10, 10] scl: 1 by [−10, 10] scl: 1

Pages 426-428, Lesson 7-3 (Guided Practice)

3.

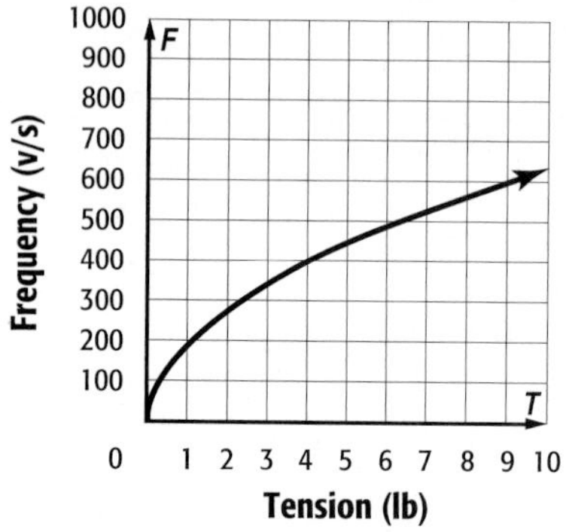

(3, 346.4); (6, 489.9); (9, 600)

4A.

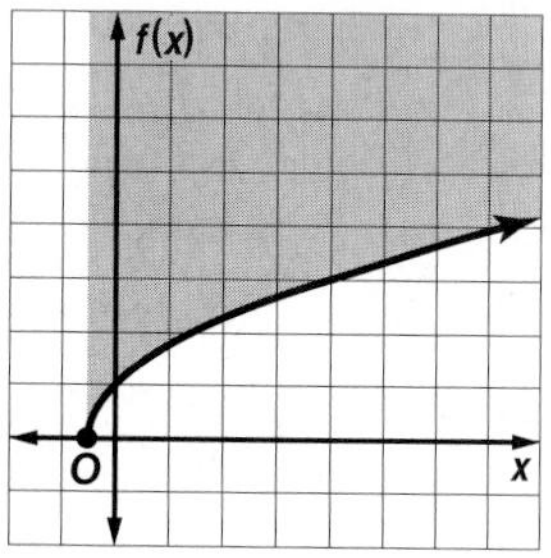

4B.

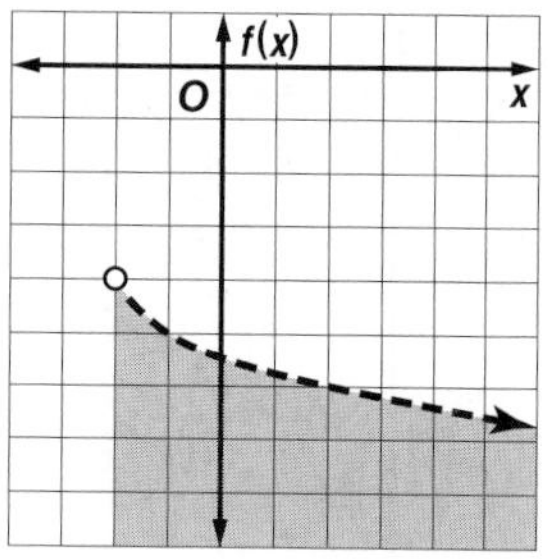

Pages 427–429, Lesson 7-3

9.

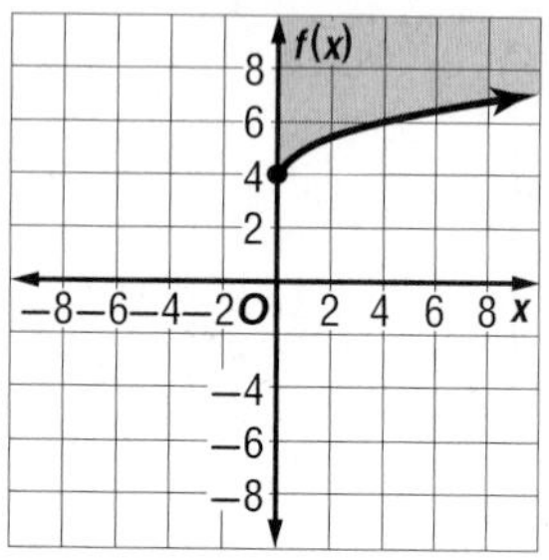

10.

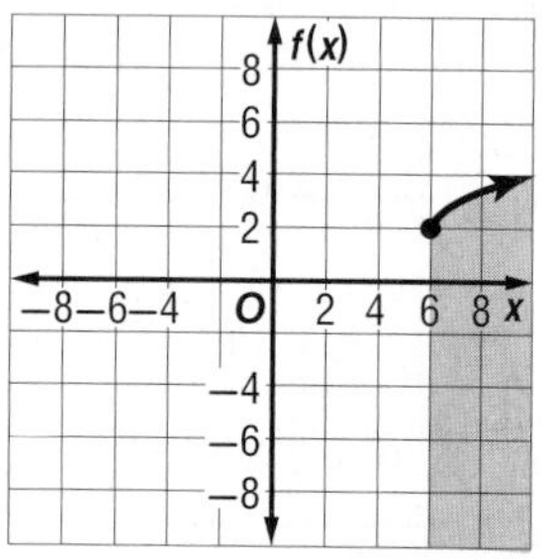

11.

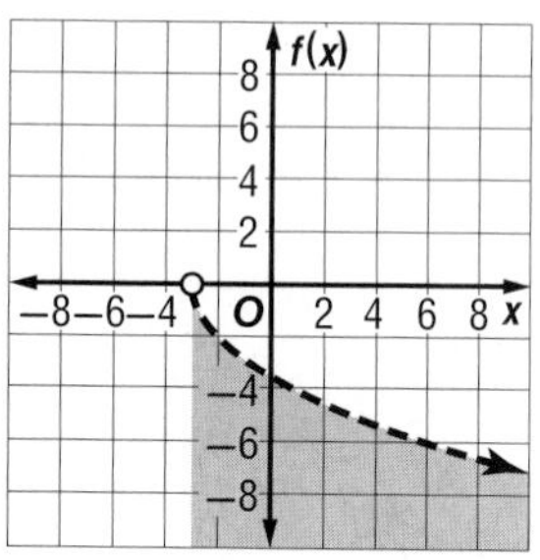

12.

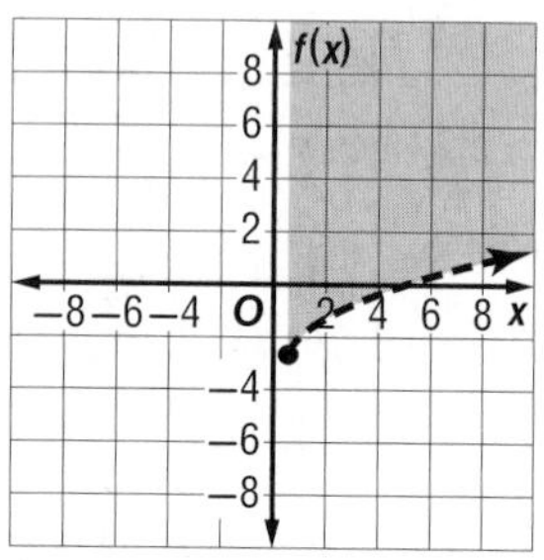

19.

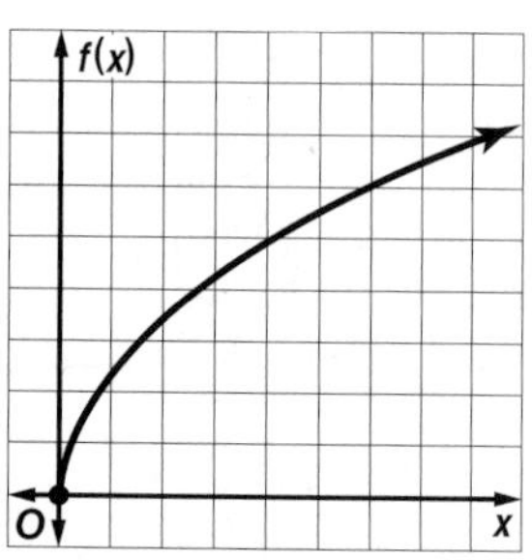

D = {x | $x \geq 0$};
R = {$f(x)$ | $f(x) \geq 0$}

20.

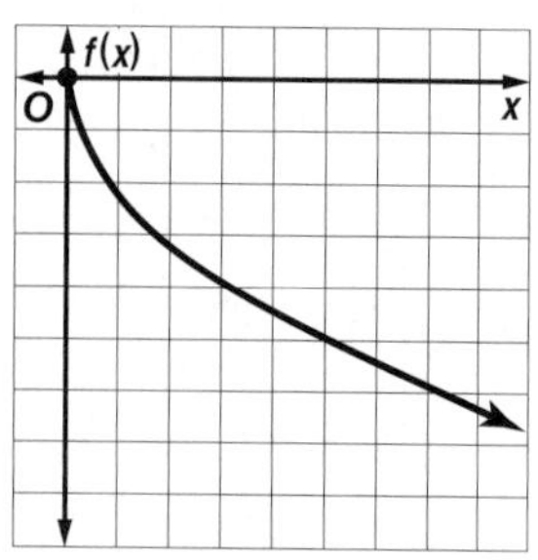

D = {x | $x \geq 0$};
R = {$f(x)$ | $f(x) \leq 0$}

21.

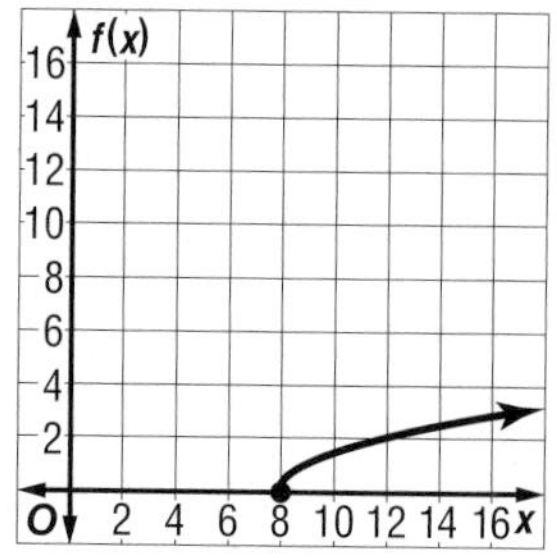

D = {x | $x \geq 8$};
R = {$f(x)$ | $f(x) \geq 0$}

22.

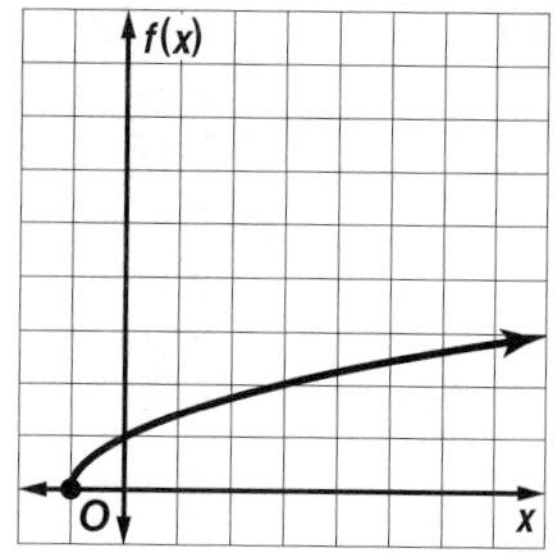

D = {x | $x \geq -1$};
R = {$f(x)$ | $f(x) \geq 0$}

23.

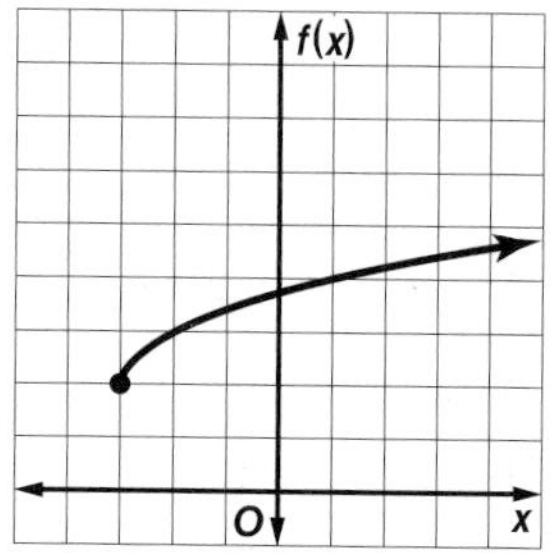

D = {x | $x \geq -3$};
R = {$f(x)$ | $f(x) \geq 2$}

24.

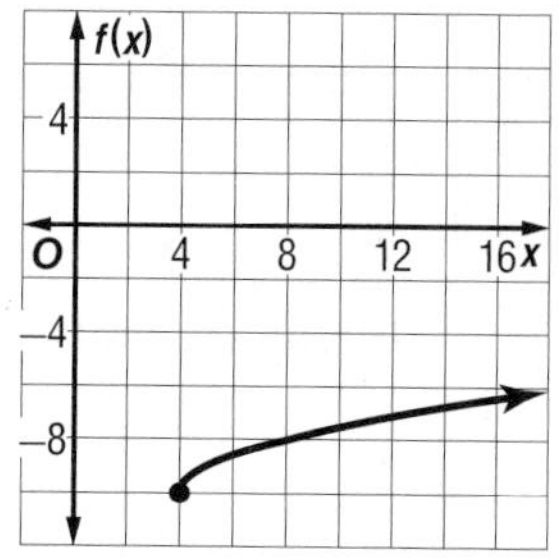

D = {x | $x \geq 4$};
R = {$f(x)$ | $f(x) \geq -10$}

25.

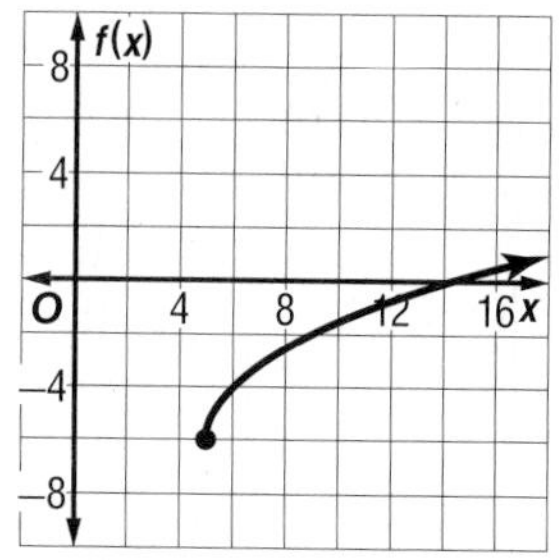

D = {x | $x \geq 5$};
R = {$f(x)$ | $f(x) \geq -6$}

26.

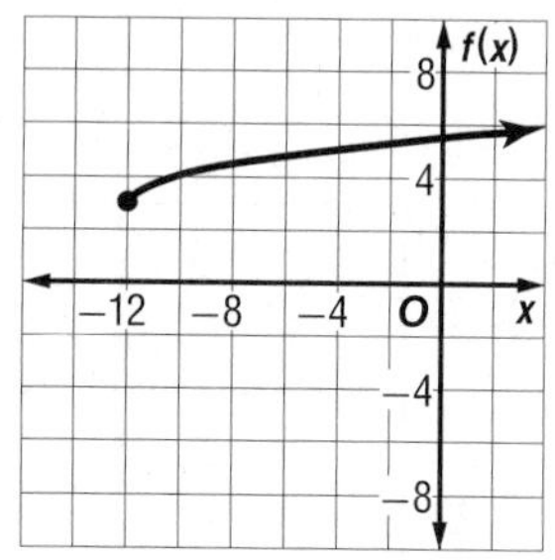

D = {x | $x \geq -12$};
R = {$f(x)$ | $f(x) \geq 3$}

27.

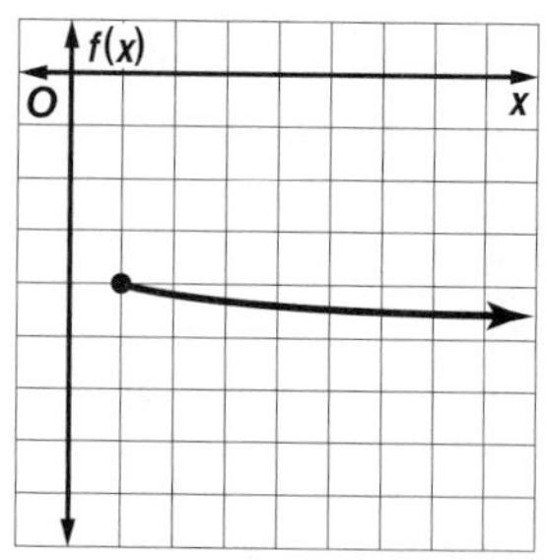

D = {x | $x \geq 1$};
R = {$f(x)$ | $f(x) \leq -4$}

28.

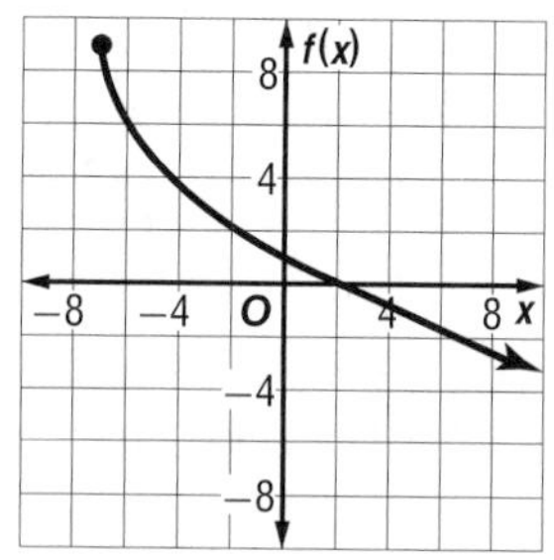

D = {x | $x \geq -7$};
R = {$f(x)$ | $f(x) \leq 9$}

31.

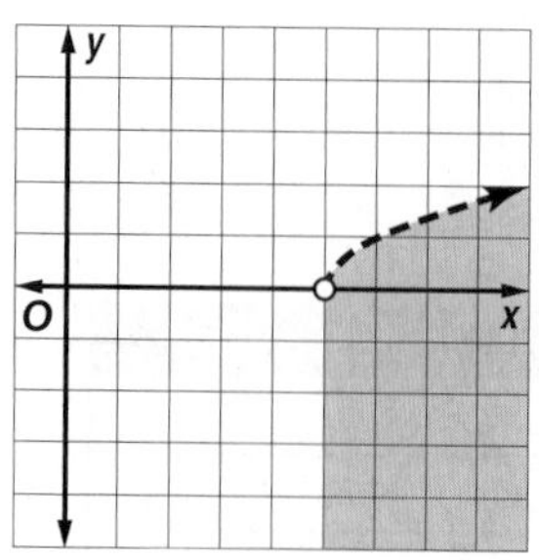

32.

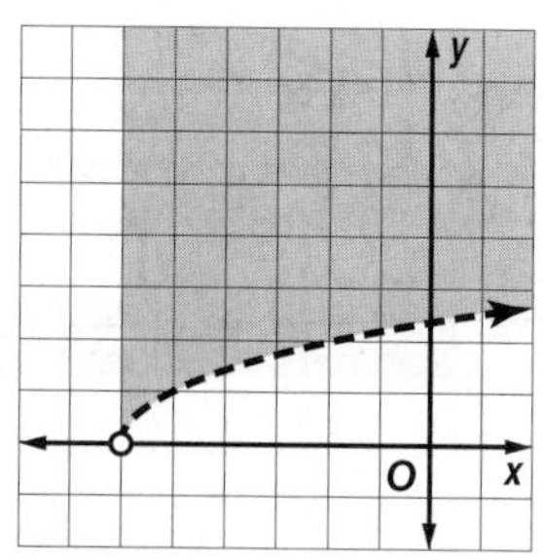

33.

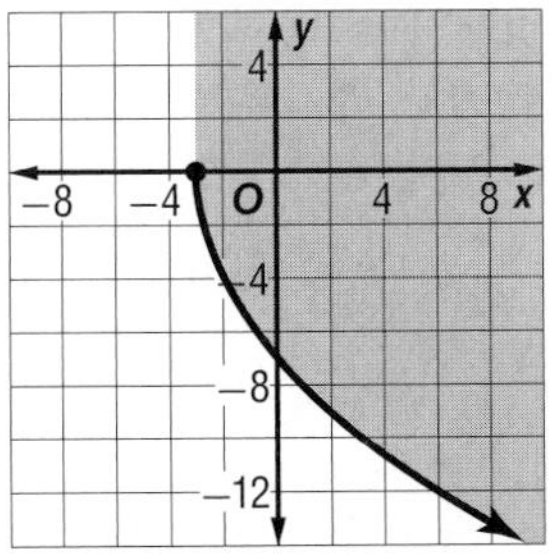

34.

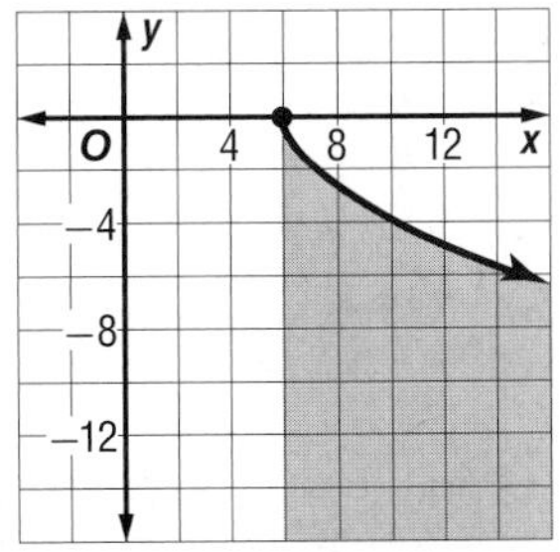

35.

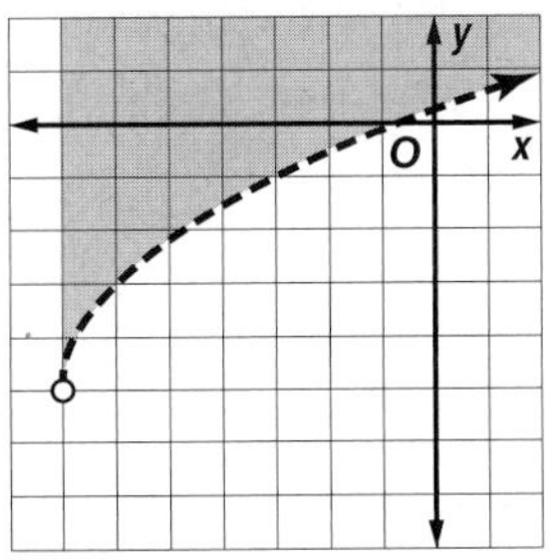

36.

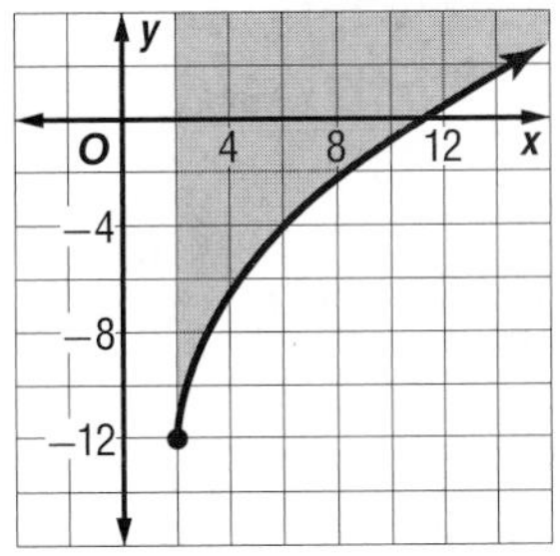

37.

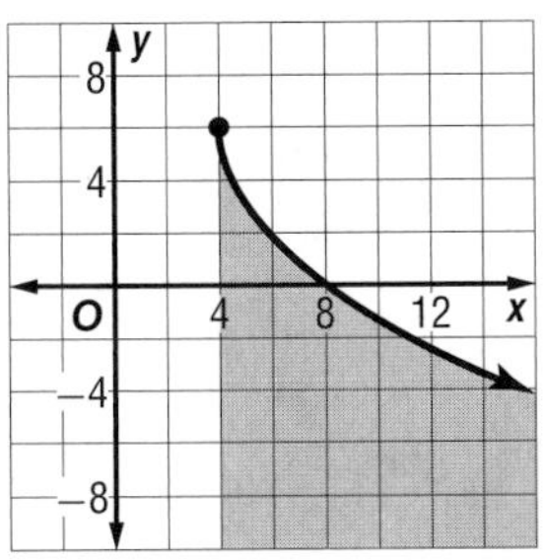

38.

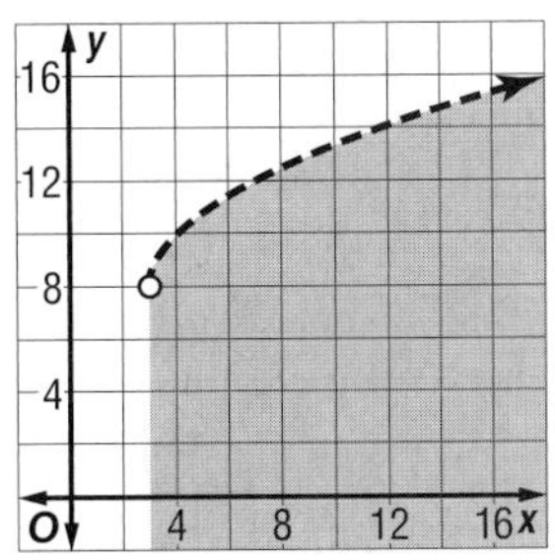

44a.

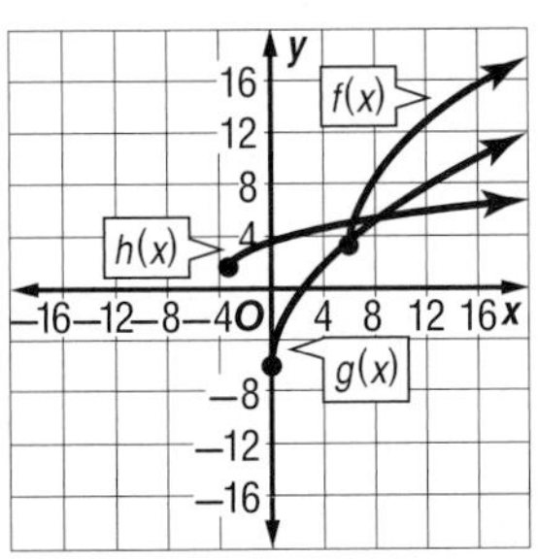

44b. $f(x)$: 6 units to the right, 3 units up; $g(x)$: $\frac{1}{16}$ to the left, 6 units down; $h(x)$: 3 units to the left, 2 units up

44c. Sample answer: $f(x)$ and $g(x)$ appear to be stretched because the graph increases much more quickly than the parent graph.

44d. Sample answer: They are stretched by the same magnitude because $4 = \sqrt{16}$.

44e.

$x = 8$	$x = 12$	$x = 16$	Rate of Change between 8 and 12	Rate of Change between 12 and 16
$f(8) = 8.66$	$f(12) = 12.798$	$f(16) = 15.65$	1.0345	0.713
$g(8) = 5.36$	$g(12) = 7.89$	$g(16) = 10.03$	0.6325	0.535
$h(8) = 5.317$	$h(12) = 5.873$	$h(16) = 6.359$	0.139	0.1215

The rate of change decreases as the x-values increase for square root functions of the form $a\sqrt{x - b} + c$, where $a > 0$.

Pages 435–436, Lesson 7-4

58a. $n = 3$

x	–5	–4	–3	–2	–1	0
$f(x)$	–125	–64	–27	–8	–1	0
x	1	2	3	4	5	
$f(x)$	1	8	27	64	125	

$n = 4$

x	–5	–4	–3	–2	–1	0
$f(x)$	625	256	81	16	1	0
x	1	2	3	4	5	
$f(x)$	1	16	81	256	625	

$n = 3$

x	–125	–64	–27	–8	–1	0
$g(x)$	–5	–4	–3	–2	–1	0
x	1	8	27	64	125	
$g(x)$	1	2	3	4	5	

$n = 4$

x	625	256	81	16	1	0
$g(x)$	imaginary	imaginary	imaginary	imaginary	imaginary	0
x	1	16	18	256	625	
$g(x)$	1	2	3	4	5	

58b. $n = 3$

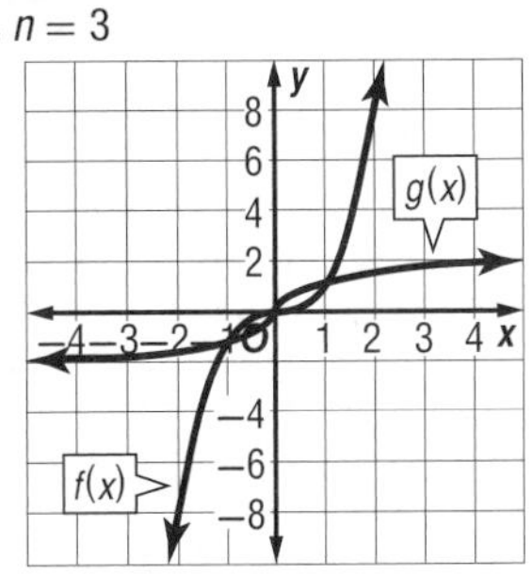

$n = 4$

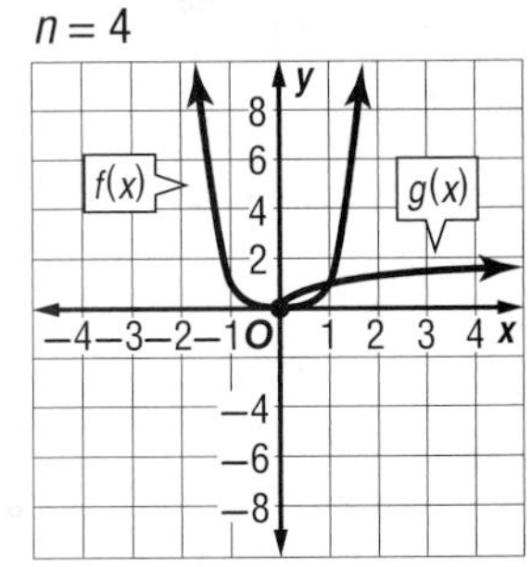

83. (–2, 3); $x = -2$; down

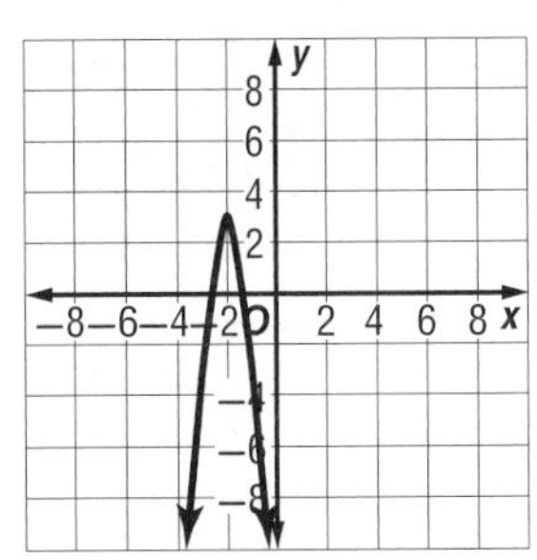

84. $y = -\frac{1}{3}(x - 12)^2 + 48$; (12, 48); $x = 12$; down

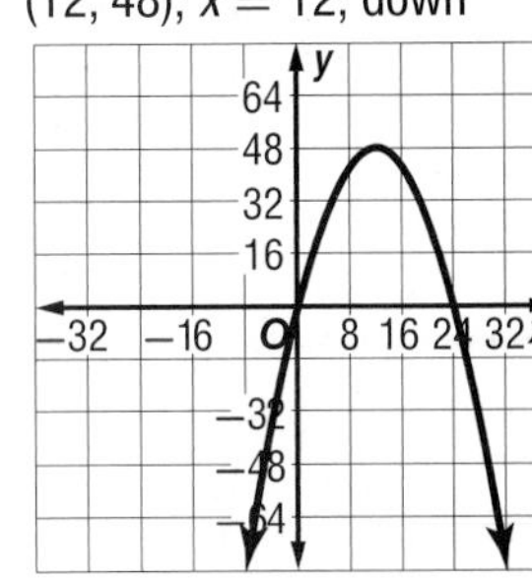

85. (2, –2); $x = 2$; up

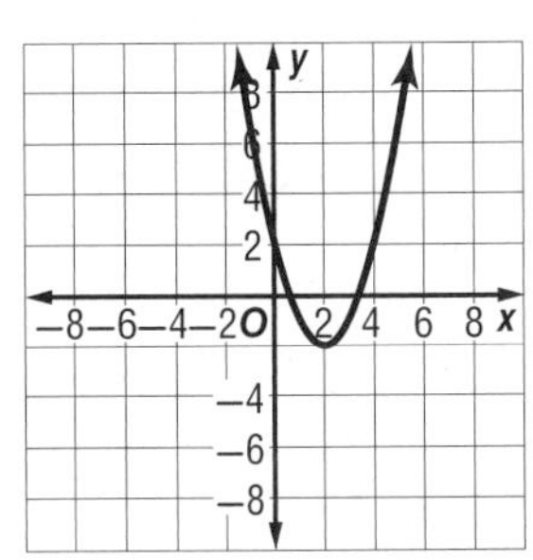

86. $y = 2(x + 2)^2 + 2$; (–2, 2); $x = -2$; up

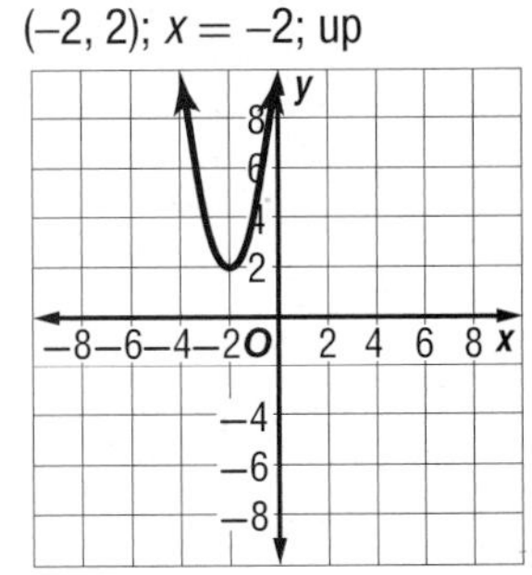

Page 437, Extend 7-4

1. 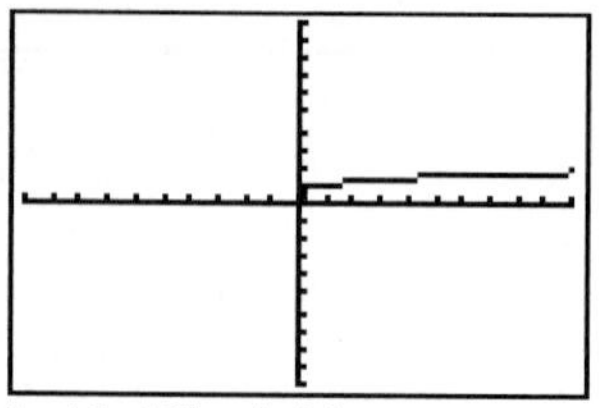

[−10, 10] scl: 1 by [−10, 10] scl: 1

2. 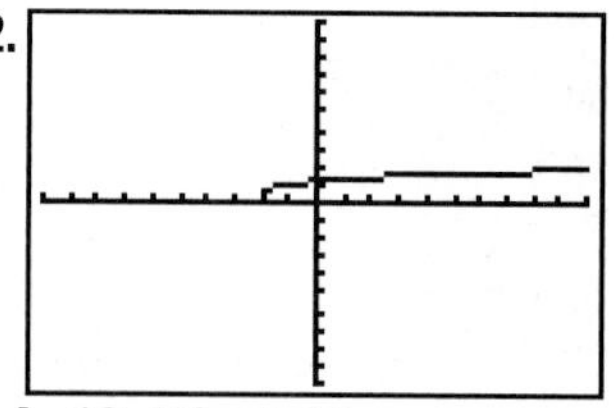

[−10, 10] scl: 1 by [−10, 10] scl: 1

3. 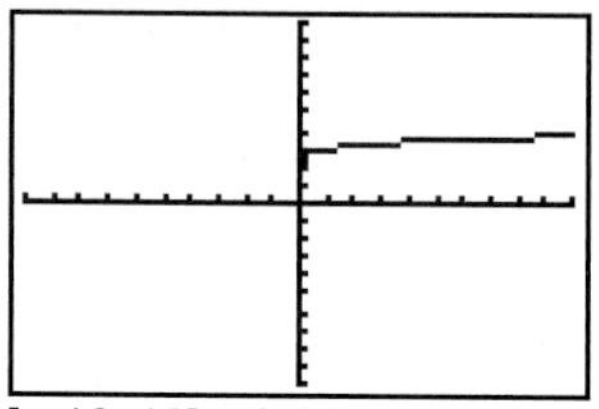

[−10, 10] scl: 1 by [−10, 10] scl: 1

4. 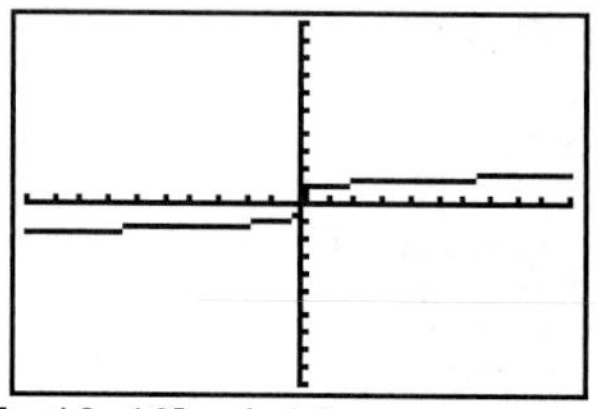

[−10, 10] scl: 1 by [−10, 10] scl: 1

5. 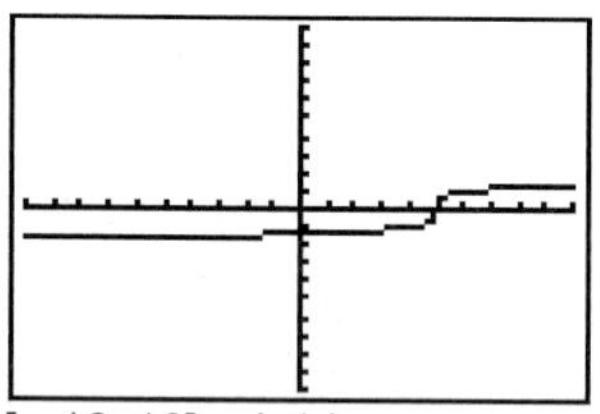

[−10, 10] scl: 1 by [−10, 10] scl: 1

6. 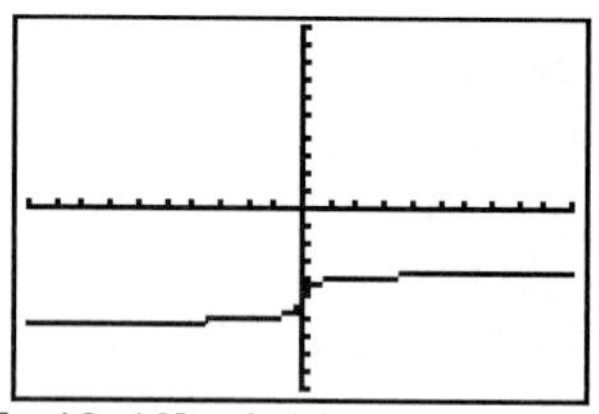

[−10, 10] scl: 1 by [−10, 10] scl: 1

Page 438, Mid-Chapter Quiz

17. 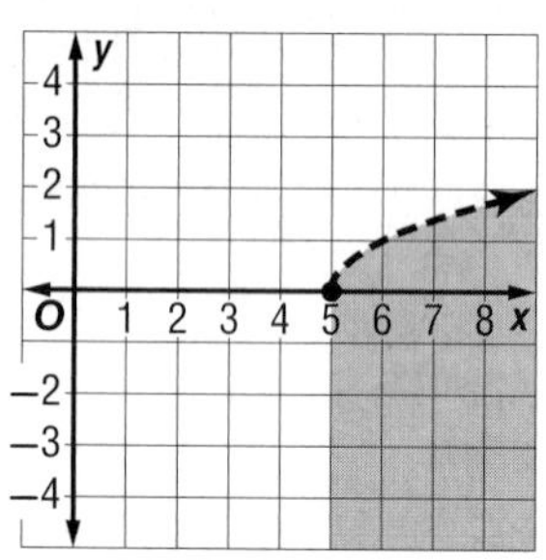

18. 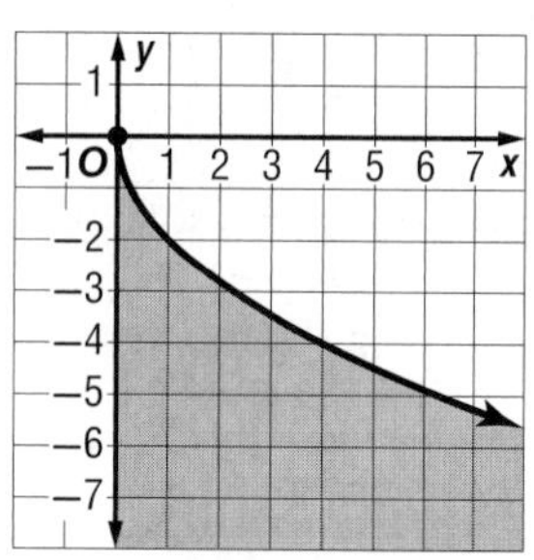

19. 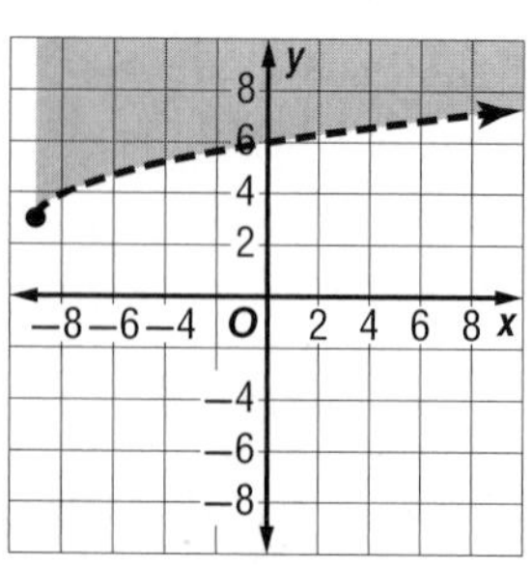

20. 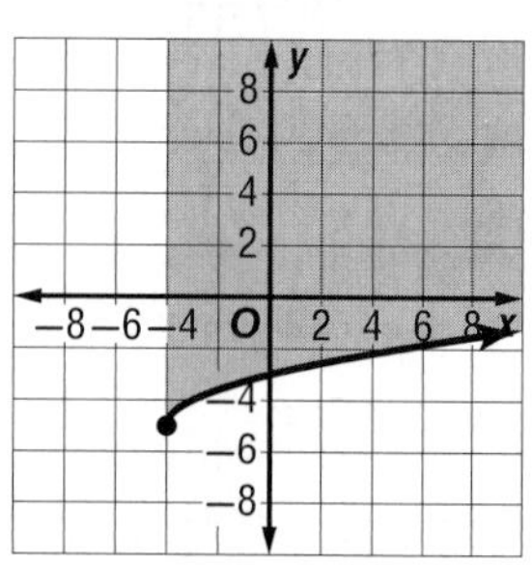

21. 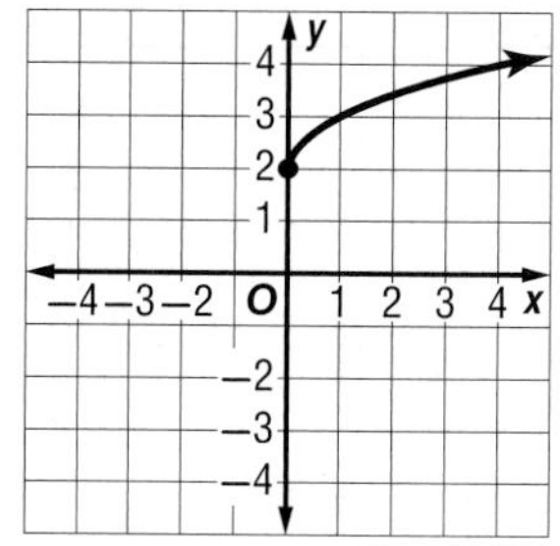

$D = \{x \mid x \geq 0\}$; $R = \{y \mid y \geq 2\}$

22. 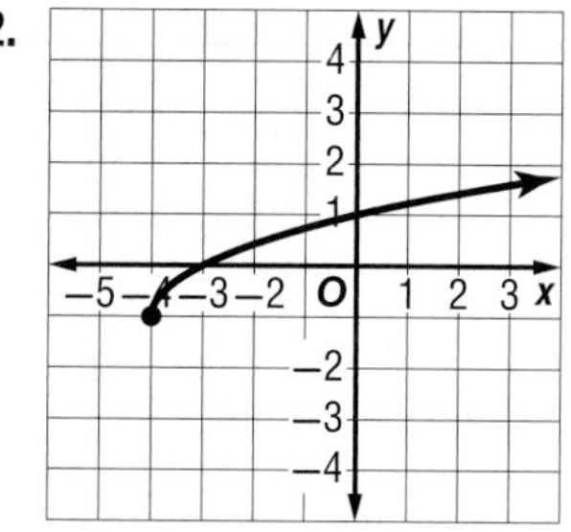

$D = \{x \mid x \geq -4\}$; $R = \{y \mid y \geq -1\}$

Page 444, Lesson 7-5

59a. $a^2 + b^2 = c^2$

$1^2 + 1^2 = c^2$

$2 = c^2$

$c = \sqrt{2}$

59b. 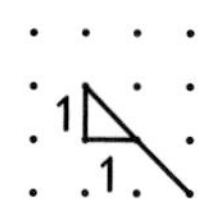

59c. $\sqrt{2} + \sqrt{2}$ units is the length of the hypotenuse of an isosceles right triangle with legs of length 2 units.

Therefore, $\sqrt{2} + \sqrt{2} > 2$.

59d. 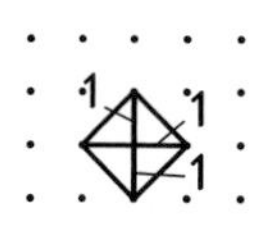

59e. The square creates 4 triangles with a base of 1 and a height of 1. Therefore the area of each triangle is $\frac{1}{2}bh = \frac{1}{2}(1)(1)$ or $\frac{1}{2} \cdot 4\left(\frac{1}{2}\right) = 2$. The area of the square is 2, so $\sqrt{2} \cdot \sqrt{2} = 2$.

61.
$$\left(\frac{-1 - i\sqrt{3}}{2}\right)^3 = \left(\frac{-1 - i\sqrt{3}}{2}\right) \cdot \left(\frac{-1 - i\sqrt{3}}{2}\right) \cdot \left(\frac{-1 - i\sqrt{3}}{2}\right)$$
$$= \frac{(-1 - i\sqrt{3})(-1 - i\sqrt{3})(-1 - i\sqrt{3})}{8}$$
$$= \frac{(1 + i\sqrt{3} + i\sqrt{3} + 3i^2)(-1 - i\sqrt{3})}{8}$$
$$= \frac{(2i\sqrt{3} - 2)(-1 - i\sqrt{3})}{8}$$
$$= \frac{-2i\sqrt{3} - 6i^2 + 2 + 2i\sqrt{3}}{8}$$
$$= \frac{-6i^2 + 2}{8} = \frac{8}{8} \text{ or } 1$$

NOTES

CHAPTER 8

Chapter Planner

Diagnostic Assessment
Quick Check, p. 473

	Lesson 8-1 Pacing: 1 day	Explore 8-2 Pacing: 0.5 day	Lesson 8-2 Pacing: 1.5 days
Title	**Graphing Exponential Functions**	**Graphing Technology Lab: Solving Exponential Equations and Inequalities**	**Solving Exponential Equations and Inequalities**
Objectives	• Graph exponential growth functions. • Graph exponential decay functions.	• Use a graphing calculator to solve exponential equations by graphing or by using the table feature.	• Solve exponential equations. • Solve exponential inequalities.
Key Vocabulary	exponential function exponential growth asymptote growth factor exponential decay decay factor		exponential equation compound interest exponential inequality
NGSSS	MA.912.A.8.3, MA.912.A.8.7	MA.912.A.8.5	MA.912.A.8.5, MA.912.A.10.3
Multiple Representations	p. 481		p. 490
Lesson Resources	**Chapter 8 Resource Masters** • Study Guide and Intervention, pp. 5–6 AL OL ELL • Skills Practice, p. 7 AL OL ELL • Practice, p. 8 AL OL BL ELL • Word Problem Practice, p. 9 AL OL BL ELL • Enrichment, p. 10 OL BL • Graphing Calculator Activity, p. 11 OL **Transparencies** • 5-Minute Check Transparency 8-1 AL OL BL ELL **Additional Print Resources** • Study Notebook AL OL BL ELL • Teaching Algebra with Manipulatives, p. 234 AL OL ELL	**Materials** • TI-83/84 Plus or other graphing calculator	**Chapter 8 Resource Masters** • Study Guide and Intervention, pp. 12–13 AL OL ELL • Skills Practice, p. 14 AL OL ELL • Practice, p. 15 AL OL BL ELL • Word Problem Practice, p. 16 AL OL BL ELL • Enrichment, p. 17 OL BL • Graphing Calculator Activity, p. 18 OL • Quiz 1, p. 63 AL OL BL ELL **Transparencies** • 5-Minute Check Transparency 8-2 AL OL BL ELL **Additional Print Resources** • Study Notebook AL OL BL ELL
Technology for Every Lesson	FL Math Online glencoe.com • Extra Examples • Self-Check Quizzes • Personal Tutor • Homework Help	**CD/DVD Resources** IWB INTERACTIVE WHITEBOARD READY IWB StudentWorks Plus IWB Interactive Classroom IWB Diagnostic and Assessment Planner	• TeacherWorks Plus • eSolutions Manual Plus • ExamView Assessment Suite
Get Animated	Animation		
Differentiated Instruction	pp. 477, 482		pp. 487, 489, 491

KEY: AL Approaching Level OL On Level BL Beyond Level ELL English Learners

Exponential and Logarithmic Functions and Relations

Suggested Pacing			
Time Periods	Instruction	Review & Assessment	Total
45-minute	12	2	14
90-minute	9	1	10

Lesson 8-3 Pacing: 1.5 days	Extend 8-3 Pacing: 0.5 day	Lesson 8-4 Pacing: 1 day	Lesson 8-5 Pacing: 1 day
Logarithms and Logarithmic Functions	**Graphing Technology Lab: Choosing the Best Model**	**Solving Logarithmic Equations and Inequalities**	**Properties of Logarithms**
• Evaluate logarithmic expressions. • Graph logarithmic functions.	• Use a graphing calculator to find an equation of best fit for exponential and logarithmic functions.	• Solve logarithmic equations. • Solve logarithmic inequalities.	• Simplify and evaluate expressions using the properties of logarithms. • Solve logarithmic equations using the properties of logarithms.
logarithm logarithmic function		logarithmic equation logarithmic inequality	
MA.912.A.8.1, MA.912.A.8.2		MA.912.A.8.2, MA.912.A.8.5	MA.912.A.8.2
		p. 505	
Chapter 8 Resource Masters • Study Guide and Intervention, pp. 19–20 AL OL ELL • Skills Practice, p. 21 AL OL ELL • Practice, p. 22 AL OL BL ELL • Word Problem Practice, p. 23 AL OL BL ELL • Enrichment, p. 24 OL BL • TI-Nspire Practice, p. 25 OL **Transparencies** • 5-Minute Check Transparency 8-3 AL OL BL ELL **Additional Print Resources** • Study Notebook AL OL BL ELL	**Materials** • TI-83/84 Plus or other graphing calculator	**Chapter 8 Resource Masters** • Study Guide and Intervention, pp. 26–27 AL OL ELL • Skills Practice, p. 28 AL OL ELL • Practice, p. 29 AL OL BL ELL • Word Problem Practice, p. 30 AL OL BL ELL • Enrichment, p. 31 OL BL • Graphing Calculator Activity, p. 32 OL • Quiz 2, p. 63 AL OL BL ELL **Transparencies** • 5-Minute Check Transparency 8-4 AL OL BL ELL **Additional Print Resources** • Study Notebook AL OL BL ELL	**Chapter 8 Resource Masters** • Study Guide and Intervention, pp. 33–34 AL OL ELL • Skills Practice, p. 35 AL OL ELL • Practice, p. 36 AL OL BL ELL • Word Problem Practice, p. 37 AL OL BL ELL • Enrichment, p. 38 OL BL • TI-Nspire Practice, p. 39 OL **Transparencies** • 5-Minute Check Transparency 8-5 AL OL BL ELL **Additional Print Resources** • Study Notebook AL OL BL ELL

FL Math Online glencoe.com
- Extra Examples
- Self-Check Quizzes
- Personal Tutor
- Homework Help

CD/DVD Resources IWB INTERACTIVE WHITEBOARD READY
- IWB StudentWorks Plus
- IWB Interactive Classroom
- IWB Diagnostic and Assessment Planner
- TeacherWorks Plus
- eSolutions Manual Plus
- ExamView Assessment Suite

Animation			
pp. 493, 499		pp. 503, 507	pp. 511, 515

Formative Assessment
Mid-Chapter Quiz, p. 508

CHAPTER 8

Chapter Planner

	Lesson 8-6 Pacing: 1.5 days	Extend 8-6 Pacing: 0.5 day	Lesson 8-7 Pacing: 1 day
Title	**Common Logarithms**	**Graphing Technology Lab: Solving Logarithmic Equations and Inequalities**	**Base *e* and Natural Logarithms**
Objectives	• Solve exponential equations and inequalities using common logarithms. • Evaluate logarithmic expressions using the Change of Base Formula.	• Use a graphing calculator to solve exponential and logarithmic equations and inequalities.	• Evaluate expressions involving the natural base and natural logarithm. • Solve exponential equations and inequalities using natural logarithms.
Key Vocabulary	common logarithm Change of Base Formula		natural base, *e* natural base exponential function natural logarithm
NGSSS	MA.912.A.8.2, MA.912.A.8.6	MA.912.A.8.5	MA.912.A.8.2, MA.912.A.8.7
Multiple Representations	p. 521		p. 530
Lesson Resources	**Chapter 8 Resource Masters** • Study Guide and Intervention, pp. 40–41 AL OL ELL • Skills Practice, p. 42 AL OL ELL • Practice, p. 43 AL OL BL ELL • Word Problem Practice, p. 44 AL OL BL ELL • Enrichment, p. 45 OL BL • Graphing Calculator Activity, p. 46 OL • Quiz 3, p. 64 AL OL BL ELL **Transparencies** • 5-Minute Check Transparency 8-6 AL OL BL ELL **Additional Print Resources** • Study Notebook AL OL BL ELL	**Materials** • TI-83/84 Plus or other graphing calculator	**Chapter 8 Resource Masters** • Study Guide and Intervention, pp. 47–48 AL OL ELL • Skills Practice, p. 49 AL OL ELL • Practice, p. 50 AL OL BL ELL • Word Problem Practice, p. 51 AL OL BL ELL • Enrichment, p. 52 OL BL **Transparencies** • 5-Minute Check Transparency 8-7 AL OL BL ELL **Additional Print Resources** • Study Notebook AL OL BL ELL
Technology for Every Lesson	FL Math Online glencoe.com • Extra Examples • Self-Check Quizzes • Personal Tutor • Homework Help	**CD/DVD Resources** IWB INTERACTIVE WHITEBOARD READY IWB StudentWorks Plus IWB Interactive Classroom IWB Diagnostic and Assessment Planner	• TeacherWorks Plus • eSolutions Manual Plus • ExamView Assessment Suite
Get Animated	Interactive Lab		
Differentiated Instruction	pp. 518, 522		pp. 527, 531

KEY: AL Approaching Level OL On Level BL Beyond Level ELL English Learners

Explore 8-8 Pacing: 0.5 day	Lesson 8-8 Pacing: 1 day	Extend 8-8 Pacing: 0.5 day
Spreadsheet Lab: Compound Interest	**Using Exponential and Logarithmic Functions**	**Graphing Technology Lab: Cooling**
• Use a spreadsheet to display the growth of an investment over time.	• Use logarithms to solve problems involving exponential growth and decay. • Use logarithms to solve problems involving logistic growth.	• Use a data collection device to investigate the differences between types of insulated cups and cooling time.
	rate of continuous growth rate of continuous decay logistic growth model	
	MA.912.A.8.5, MA.912.A.8.7	
	p. 538	
Materials • spreadsheet program	**Chapter 8 Resource Masters** • Study Guide and Intervention, pp. 53–54 AL OL ELL • Skills Practice, p. 55 AL OL ELL • Practice, p. 56 AL OL BL ELL • Word Problem Practice, p. 57 AL OL BL ELL • Enrichment, p. 58 OL BL • Spreadsheet Activity, p. 59 OL • Quiz 4, p. 64 AL OL BL ELL **Transparencies** • 5-Minute Check Transparency 8-8 AL OL BL ELL **Additional Print Resources** • Study Notebook AL OL BL ELL	**Materials** • TI-83/84 Plus or other graphing calculator • data collection device and compatible temperature probe • variety of containers • very hot water

FL Math Online glencoe.com
- Extra Examples
- Self-Check Quizzes
- Personal Tutor
- Homework Help

CD/DVD Resources IWB INTERACTIVE WHITEBOARD READY
- IWB StudentWorks Plus
- IWB Interactive Classroom
- IWB Diagnostic and Assessment Planner
- TeacherWorks Plus
- eSolutions Manual Plus
- ExamView Assessment Suite

	pp. 534, 535, 539	

Summative Assessment
- Study Guide and Review, pp. 541–544
- Practice Test, p. 545

Chapter 8 Assessment and Intervention

SE = Student Edition, TE = Teacher Edition, CRM = Chapter Resource Masters

	Diagnosis	Prescription
Diagnostic Assessment	**Beginning Chapter 8**	
	Get Ready for Chapter 8 **SE,** p. 473	Response to Intervention **TE,** p. 473
	Beginning Every Lesson	
	Then, Now, Why? **SE** 5-Minute Check Transparencies	Chapter 0 **SE,** pp. P1–P19 Concepts and Skills Bank **SE,** pp. 994–1007
Formative Assessment	**During/After Every Lesson**	
	Guided Practice **SE,** every example Check Your Understanding **SE** H.O.T. Problems **SE** Spiral Review **SE** Additional Examples **TE** Watch Out! **TE** Step 4, Assess **TE** Chapter 8 Quizzes **CRM,** pp. 63–64 Self-Check Quizzes glencoe.com	**Tier 1 Intervention** Concepts and Skills Bank **SE,** pp. 994–1007 Skills Practice **CRM,** Ch. 1–8 glencoe.com **Tier 2 Intervention** Differentiated Instruction **TE** Study Guide and Intervention Masters **CRM,** Ch. 1–8 **Tier 3 Intervention** *Math Triumphs, Alg. 2*
	Mid-Chapter	
	Mid-Chapter Quiz **SE,** p. 508 Mid-Chapter Test **CRM,** p. 65 ExamView Assessment Suite	Concepts and Skills Bank **SE,** pp. 994–1007 Skills Practice **CRM,** Ch. 1–8 glencoe.com **Tier 1 Intervention** Study Guide and Intervention Masters **CRM,** Ch. 1–8 **Tier 2 Intervention** *Math Triumphs, Alg. 2*
	Before Chapter Test	
	Chapter Study Guide and Review **SE,** pp. 541–544 Practice Test **SE,** p. 545 Standardized Test Practice **SE,** pp. 546–549 Chapter Test glencoe.com Standardized Test Practice glencoe.com Vocabulary Review glencoe.com ExamView Assessment Suite	**Tier 1 Intervention** Concepts and Skills Bank **SE,** pp. 994–1007 Skills Practice **CRM,** Ch. 1–8 glencoe.com **Tier 2 Intervention** Study Guide and Intervention Masters **CRM,** Ch. 1–8 **Tier 3 Intervention** *Math Triumphs, Alg. 2*
Summative Assessment	**After Chapter 8**	
	Multiple-Choice Tests, Forms 1, 2A, 2B **CRM,** pp. 67–72 Free-Response Tests, Forms 2C, 2D, 3 **CRM,** pp. 73–78 Vocabulary Test **CRM,** p. 66 Extended Response Test **CRM,** p. 79 Standardized Test Practice **CRM,** pp. 80–82 ExamView Assessment Suite	Study Guide and Intervention Masters **CRM,** Ch. 1–8 glencoe.com

Differentiated Instruction

Option 1 Reaching All Learners AL OL BL ELL

VISUAL Because there are so many new properties taught in this chapter, suggest that students make up properties posters. Encourage students to be as abbreviated as possible and to use color to help them see at a glance how the property works.

Properties of Logarithms

$\log_a(M \cdot N) = \log_a M + \log_a N$

$\log_a(M/N) = \log_a M - \log_a N$

$\log_a(M^p) = p \log_a M$

LOGICAL Have pairs of students begin with $10, choose an interest rate that will be compounded continuously, and calculate how much they will have after 5, 10, 15, and 20 years. After each calculation, have students model the amount of money they have on a bar graph.

Option 2 Approaching Level AL

As a class, make a Venn diagram for the set of real numbers. Once the diagram is made, review with students what it means for a number to be a rational, integer, whole, natural, or an irrational number. Write an example of each type of real number on the diagram. Then discuss *e* as an irrational number.

Real Numbers

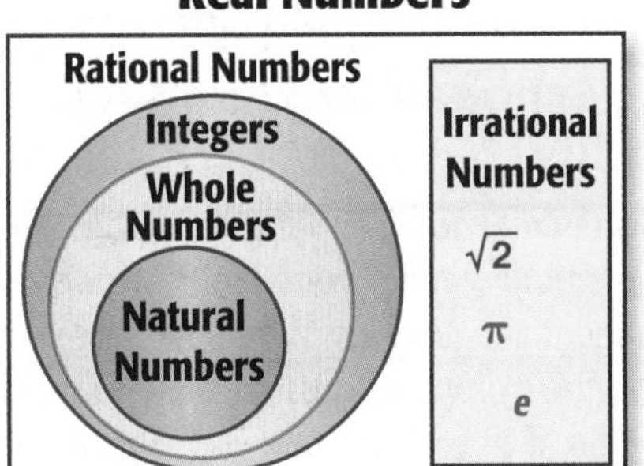

Option 3 English Learners ELL

Write several exponential functions and their related logarithmic functions on the board. Ask students to read aloud each expression. For example, have students say *two to the third power is equal to eight* for $2^3 = 8$. Then have students say *the logarithm of eight with base two is equal to three* for $\log_2 8 = 3$.

Option 4 Beyond Level BL

Ask student to do a search for the tables of common logarithms of numbers either in the appendices of older algebra texts or online. As a class, learn to read and use these tables. Then ask students to use the tables to evaluate several common logarithms, such as $\log_{10}125$. Then have students compare their results with what they get when they evaluate the same logarithms using their calculator.

FL Math Online Access Point Activities

Focus on Mathematical Content

Vertical Alignment

Before Chapter 8

Related Topics from Algebra 2

- use tools including the properties of exponents to simplify expressions

Chapter 8

- analyze a situation modeled by an exponential function, formulate an equation or inequality, and solve the problem
- develop the definition of logarithms by exploring and describing the relationships between exponential functions and their inverses
- use parent functions to investigate, describe, and predict the effects of parameter changes on the graphs of exponential and logarithmic functions, describe limitations on the domains and ranges, and examine asymptotic behavior
- determine solutions of exponential and logarithmic equations using graphs, tables, and algebraic methods
- interpret and determine the reasonableness of solutions to exponential and logarithmic equations and inequalities

After Chapter 8

Preparation for Precalculus

- describe parent functions symbolically and graphically, including $f(x) = \log_a x$ and $f(x) = \ln x$
- investigate the concepts of continuity, end behavior, and asymptotes, and connect these characteristics to functions represented graphically and numerically
- investigate logarithmic and exponential properties

Lesson-by-Lesson Preview

8-1 Graphing Exponential Functions

An equation of the form $y = b^x$, where $b > 0$, and $b \neq 1$ is called an exponential function. The domain of an exponential function is the set of *all real numbers.* There are two types of exponential functions:

- *exponential growth*, where $b > 1$, and
- *exponential decay*, where $0 < b < 1$.

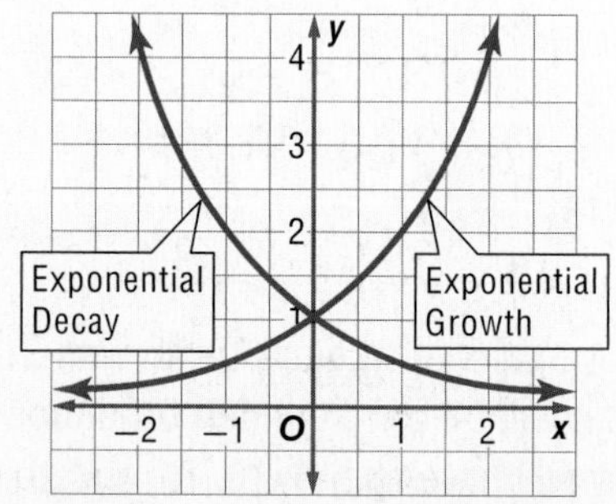

- *continuous,* that is, the graph can be traced without lifting your pencil; and
- *one-to-one,* that is, a horizontal line passing through any graph will intersect no more than one point on the graph.

The graph of an exponential function has a horizontal asymptote. This characteristic means that the graph approaches a horizontal line. For the parent function $f(x) = b^x$, the horizontal asymptote is the x-axis.

The same transformations that have been performed on previously studied parent functions can be applied to the graphs of exponential functions.

8-2 Solving Exponential Equations and Inequalities

In an *exponential equation,* variables occur as exponents. The *Property of Equality for Exponential Functions* can be used to solve exponential equations. When the bases are the same, as in $3^x = 3^7$, the exponents must also be equal for the equation to be true. So, if $3^x = 3^7$, then $x = 7$. When the bases are not equal, as in $3^x = 9^4$, the expressions must be rewritten so the bases are equal. In this case, 9 can be rewritten as 3^2, so that $9^4 = (3^2)^4 = 3^8$. Therefore $3^x = 3^8$, so $x = 8$.

In an *exponential inequality,* variables also occur as exponents. *The Property of Inequality for Exponential Functions* can be used to solve exponential inequalities. This property says that $b^x > b^y$ if and only if $x > y$, and $b^x < b^y$ if and only if $x < y$, for values of b greater than 1. This property also holds true for $\leq$ and $\geq$.

8-3 Logarithms and Logarithmic Functions

In general, the inverse of $y = b^x$ is $x = b^y$. In the equation $x = b^y$, b is the base and y is referred to as the *logarithm* of x. This relationship is usually written as $y = \log_b x$, where $b > 0$ and $b \neq 1$. It is read *y equals log base b of x*, and is called a *logarithmic function*.

The graph of $f(x) = \log_b x$ is continuous, one-to-one, and has a domain of all positive real numbers. The y-axis is a vertical asymptote of the graph. The same transformations that have been performed on previously studied parent functions can be applied to the graphs of logarithmic functions.

8-4 Solving Logarithmic Equations and Inequalities

When solving logarithmic equations and inequalities, it is important to remember that a defining characteristic of a logarithmic function is that its domain is the set of all *positive* numbers. This means that the logarithm of 0 or of a negative number for any base is undefined. It is very important to check possible solutions to logarithmic equations in the original equation to be sure that they do not result in taking the logarithm of 0 or a negative number. For logarithmic inequalities, this fact will exclude not just one value from the solution set, but a range of values.

8-5 Properties of Logarithms

Logarithms were invented to make computation easier. In fact, the word logarithm is a contraction of "logical arithmetic." According to the *Product and Quotient Properties of Logarithms*, when using logarithms, multiplication changes to addition and division changes to subtraction. For example, $\log_3 (5 \cdot 7)$ is equivalent to $\log_3 5 + \log_3 7$. The *Power Property of Logarithms* states that the logarithm of a power is the product of the logarithm and the exponent. For example, $\log_5 3^7 = 7 \log_5 3$. Using these properties of logarithms helps solve equations that involve logarithms.

8-6 Common Logarithms

Logarithms with a base of 10 are called *common logarithms.* The 10 is usually not written, that is, $\log_{10} x$ is written as $\log x$. Most calculators have a [LOG] key for evaluating common logarithms.

Logarithms can be used to solve exponential equations and inequalities that cannot be easily written as powers of the same base. To find a solution to an equation such as $5^x = 41$, take the logarithm of both sides of the equation and then solve for x.

The *Change of Base Formula* makes it possible to evaluate alogarithmic expression of any base by translating the expression into one that involves common logarithms.

8-7 Base *e* and Natural Logarithms

An exponential function with base e is called a *natural base exponential function.* The number e is an irrational number with a value of 2.71828....

The logarithm with base e is called the *natural logarithm,* and is denoted by either $\log_e x$ or $\ln x$. It is the inverse function of the natural base exponential function. All the properties of logarithms from previous lessons apply to natural logarithms as well. Most calculators have an e^x function for evaluating natural base expressions and an [LN] key for finding the natural logarithm of a real number.

8-8 Using Exponential and Logarithmic Functions

The functions $f(x) = ae^{kt}$ and $f(x) = ae^{-kt}$, where a is the initial value, t is time in years, and k is a constant, that can be used to model exponential growth and decay, respectively. The constant k represents the rate of continuous growth in the growth model and the rate of continuous decay in the decay model.

When growth has a limiting factor, a logistic growth model such as the logistic growth function $f(t) = \dfrac{c}{1 + ae^{-kt}}$ where t represents time, can be used.

Professional Development

Targeted professional development has been articulated throughout *Algebra 2.* More quality, customized professional development is available from McGraw-Hill Professional Development. Visit glencoe.com for details on each product.

- **Online Lessons** emphasize the strategies and techniques used to teach Algebra 2. Includes streaming video, interactive pages, and online tools.
- **Video Workshops** allow mentors, coaches, or leadership personnel to facilitate on-site workshops on educational strategies in mathematics and mathematical concepts.
- **MHPD Online** (www.mhpdonline.com) offers online professional development with video clips of instructional strategies, links, student activities, and news and issues in education.
- **Teaching Today** (teachingtoday.glencoe.com) gives secondary teachers practical strategies and materials that inspire excellence and innovation in teaching.

Chapter 8 Notes

Chapter Project

Measuring Sound

Students use what they have learned about exponential and logarithmic functions to explain observations of sound intensity level.

- Borrow a sound level meter (decibel meter) from a physics lab. Also find two identical sound-producing objects, like portable fans or alarm clocks.
- Place students in groups of three or four. Have them take sound measurements in a quiet room. Ask them to place the decibel meter a few feet in front of, and facing, one of the objects and record the sound level in decibels. Then place both objects where the original object was and record the sound level again. Repeat with a pair of different objects if available.
- Point out that regardless of the objects used, the sound level of two objects should be about 3 decibels louder than for just one object. Ask groups to use their knowledge of logarithms to show why this must be true.
- Finally, ask students to predict the sound level that would result if 3, 4, 5, or more identical objects were used.

Chapter 8 Exponential and Logarithmic Functions and Relations

Then

In Chapter 2, you graphed functions and transformations of functions.

Now

In Chapter 8, you will:

- Graph exponential and logarithmic functions.
- Solve exponential and logarithmic equations and inequalities.
- Solve problems involving exponential growth and decay.

NGSSS

MA.912.A.8.3
MA.912.A.8.5

Why?

SCIENCE Mathematics and science go hand in hand. Whether it is chemistry, biology, paleontology, zoology, or anthropology, you will need strong math skills. In this chapter, you will learn mathematical aspects of science such as computer viruses, populations of insects,bacteria growth, cell division, astronomy, tornados, and earthquakes.

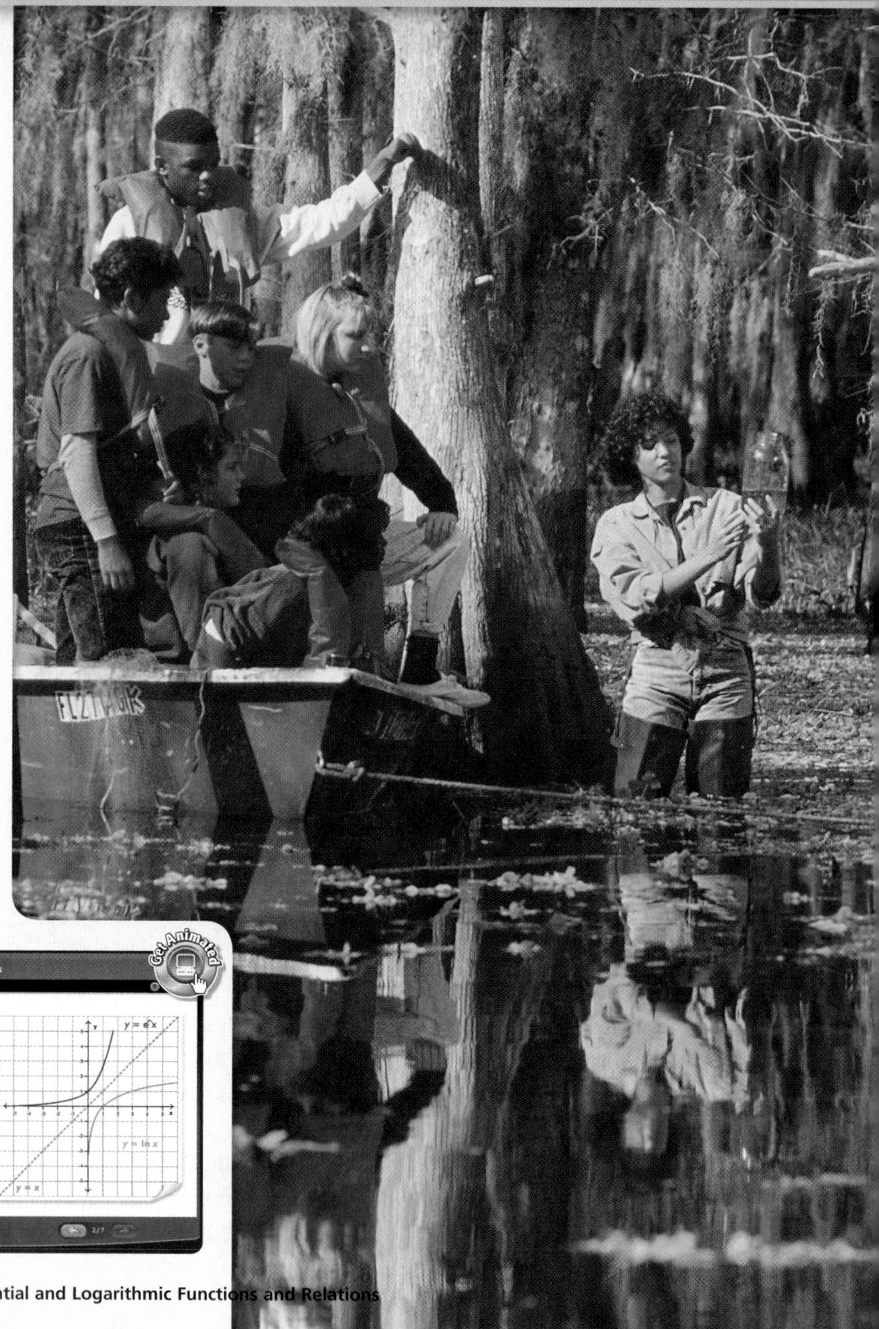

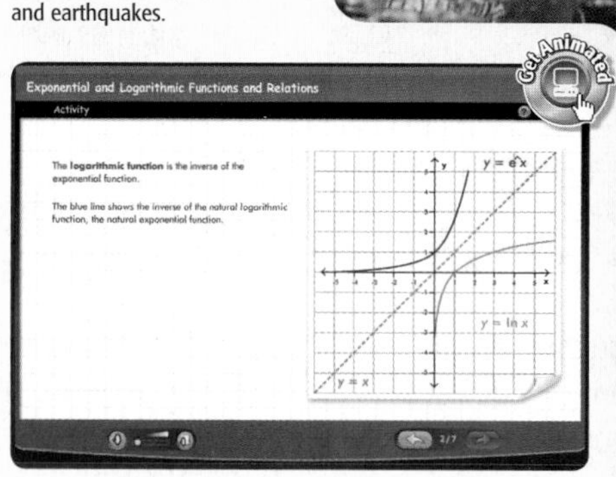

Key Vocabulary Introduce the key vocabulary in the chapter using the routine below.

Define: In the function $x = b^y$, y is called the logarithm, base b, of x. Usually it is written as $y = \log_b x$ and is read "y equals log base b of x."

Example: $3 = \log_2 8$

Ask: How would you write the following in logarithmic form? $3^5 = 243$ $\log_3 243 = 5$

Get Ready for Chapter 8

Diagnose Readiness You have two options for checking Prerequisite Skills.

Text Option Take the Quick Check below. Refer to the Quick Review for help.

QuickCheck

(Used in Lessons 8-1 through 8-3)

Simplify. Assume that no variable equals zero. (Lesson 6-1)

1. $a^4a^3a^5$ a^{12}
2. $(2xy^3z^2)^3$ $8x^3y^9z^6$
3. $\frac{-24x^8y^5z}{16x^2y^8z^6}$ $\frac{-3x^6}{2y^3z^5}$
4. $\left(\frac{-8r^2n}{36n^3t}\right)^2$ $\frac{4r^4}{81n^4t^2}$
5. **DENSITY** The density of an object is equal to the mass divided by the volume. An object has a mass of 7.5×10^3 grams and a volume of 1.5×10^3 cubic centimeters. What is the density of the object? $5\ g/cm^3$

(Used in Lessons 8-2 and 8-3)

Find the inverse of each function. Then graph the function and its inverse. (Lesson 7-2)

6. $f(x) = 2x + 5$
7. $f(x) = x - 3$
8. $f(x) = -4x$
9. $f(x) = \frac{1}{4}x - 3$
10. $f(x) = \frac{x-1}{2}$
11. $y = \frac{1}{3}x + 4$

6–11. See Chapter 8 Answer Appendix.

Determine whether each pair of functions are inverse functions.

12. $f(x) = x - 6$, $g(x) = x + 6$ yes
13. $f(x) = 2x + 5$, $g(x) = 2x - 5$ no
14. **FOOD** A pizzeria charges \$12 for a medium cheese pizza and \$2 for each additional topping. If $f(x) = 2x + 12$ represents the cost of a medium pizza with x toppings, find $f^{-1}(x)$ and explain its meaning. See margin.

QuickReview

EXAMPLE 1

Simplify $\frac{(a^3bc^2)^2}{a^4a^2b^2bc^5c^3}$. Assume that no variable equals zero.

$\frac{(a^3bc^2)^2}{a^4a^2b^2bc^5c^3}$

$= \frac{a^6b^2c^4}{a^6b^3c^8}$ — Simplify the numerator by using the Power of a Power Rule and the denominator by using the Product of Powers Rule.

$= \frac{1}{bc^4}$ or $b^{-1}c^{-4}$ — Simplify by using the Quotient of Powers Rule.

EXAMPLE 2

Find the inverse of $f(x) = 3x - 1$.

Step 1 Replace $f(x)$ with y in the original equation: $f(x) = 3x - 1 \rightarrow y = 3x - 1$.

Step 2 Interchange x and y: $x = 3y - 1$.

Step 3 Solve for y.

$x = 3y - 1$ — Inverse

$x + 1 = 3y$ — Add 1 to each side.

$\frac{x+1}{3} = y$ — Divide each side by 3.

$\frac{1}{3}x + \frac{1}{3} = y$ — Simplify.

Step 4 Replace y with $f^{-1}(x)$.

$y = \frac{1}{3}x + \frac{1}{3} \rightarrow f^{-1}(x) = \frac{1}{3}x + \frac{1}{3}$

Online Option FL Math Online Take a self-check Chapter Readiness Quiz at glencoe.com.

Additional Answer

14. $f^{-1}(x) = \frac{1}{2}x - 6$, this gives $f^{-1}(x)$ as the number of toppings someone can have if they spend x dollars.

Response to Intervention (RtI)

Use the *Quick Check* results and the Intervention Planner to help you determine your Response to Intervention. The If-Then statements in the chart below help you decide the appropriate tier of RtI and suggest intervention resources for each tier

Intervention Planner

Tier 1 On Level

If students miss about 25% of the exercises or less,

Then choose a resource:

- **SE** Concepts and Skills Bank, p. 996; Lessons 6-1 and 7-2
- **CRM** Skills Practice, Chapter 6, p. 7, Chapter 7, p. 14
- **TE** Chapter Project, p. 472
- FL Math Online Self-Check Quiz

Tier 2 Strategic Intervention approaching grade level

If students miss about 50% of the exercises,

Then choose a resource:

- **CRM** Study Guide and Intervention, Chapter 6, p. 5, Chapter 7, p. 12
- FL Math Online Extra Examples, Personal Tutor, Homework Help

Tier 3 Intensive Intervention 2 or more years below grade level

If students miss about 75% of the exercises,

Then use *Math Triumphs, Alg. 2*

- FL Math Online Extra Examples, Personal Tutor, Homework Help, Review Vocabulary

CHAPTER 8 Notes

FOLDABLES® Study Organizer

Dinah Zike's Foldables®

Focus As students work through the lessons in this chapter, they write notes about exponential and logarithmic functions and relations.

Teach Have students make and label their Foldables as illustrated. Have students label one page of their Foldables for every two lessons in the chapter and use the appropriate pages as they cover the material. Have students list the Key Concepts and the vocabulary terms and their definitions in their Foldables. Point out that the Foldables can also be used to record positive and negative experiences during learning.

When to Use It Encourage students to add to their Foldables as they work through the chapter and to use them to review for the chapter test.

Differentiated Instruction

Student-Built Glossary, pp. 1–2
Students should complete the chart by providing a definition of each term and an example as they progress through Chapter 8. This study tool can also be used to review for the chapter test.

Get Started on Chapter 8

You will learn several new concepts, skills, and vocabulary terms as you study Chapter 8. To get ready, identify important terms and organize your resources. You may wish to refer to **Chapter 0** to review prerequisite skills.

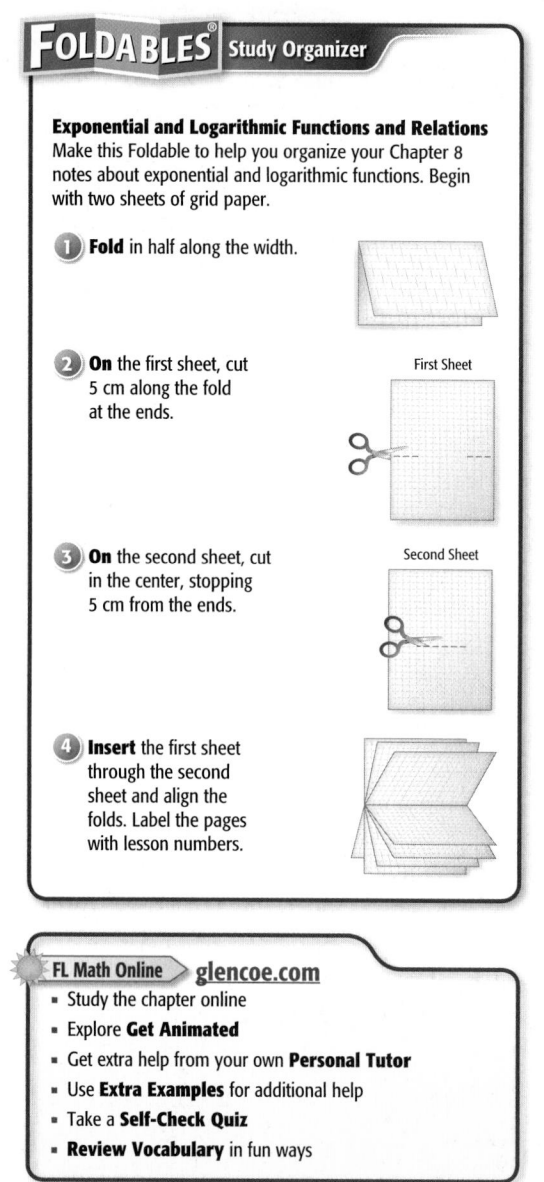

FOLDABLES® Study Organizer

Exponential and Logarithmic Functions and Relations
Make this Foldable to help you organize your Chapter 8 notes about exponential and logarithmic functions. Begin with two sheets of grid paper.

1. **Fold** in half along the width.

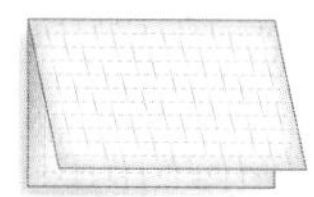

2. **On** the first sheet, cut 5 cm along the fold at the ends.

First Sheet

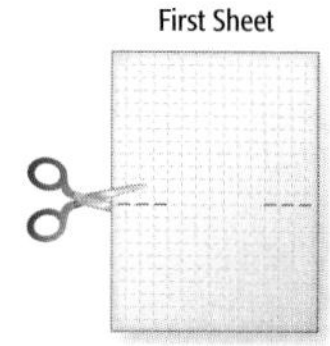

3. **On** the second sheet, cut in the center, stopping 5 cm from the ends.

Second Sheet

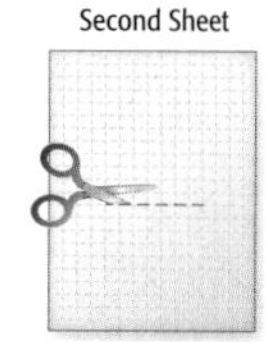

4. **Insert** the first sheet through the second sheet and align the folds. Label the pages with lesson numbers.

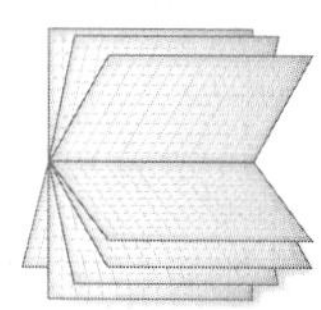

FL Math Online glencoe.com

- Study the chapter online
- Explore **Get Animated**
- Get extra help from your own **Personal Tutor**
- Use **Extra Examples** for additional help
- Take a **Self-Check Quiz**
- **Review Vocabulary** in fun ways

New Vocabulary

English		Español
exponential function	• p. 475 •	función exponencial
exponential growth	• p. 475 •	crecimiento exponencial
asymptote	• p. 475 •	asíntota
growth factor	• p. 477 •	factor de crecimiento
exponential decay	• p. 477 •	desintegración exponencial
decay factor	• p. 478 •	factor de desintegración
exponential equation	• p. 485 •	ecuación exponencial
compound interest	• p. 486 •	interés compuesto
exponential inequality	• p. 487 •	desigualdad exponencial
logarithm	• p. 492 •	logaritmo
logarithmic function	• p. 493 •	función logarítmica
logarithmic equation	• p. 502 •	ecuación logarítmica
logarithmic inequality	• p. 503 •	desigualdad logarítmica
common logarithm	• p. 516 •	logaritmos communes
Change of Base Formula	• p. 518 •	fórmula del cambio de base
natural base, *e*	• p. 525 •	*e* base natural
natural base exponential function	• p. 525 •	base natural función exponencial
natural logarithm	• p. 525 •	logaritmo natural

Review Vocabulary

domain • p. P7 • dominio the set of all *x*-coordinates of the ordered pairs of a relation

function • p. P7 • función a relation in which each element of the domain is paired with exactly one element in the range

range • p. P7 • rango the set of all *y*-coordinates of the ordered pairs of a relation

$\{(-3,1), (0, 2), (2, 4)\}$

Domain Range

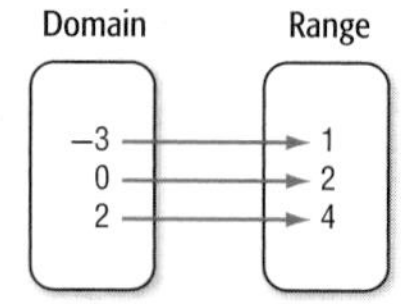

Multilingual eGlossary glencoe.com

474 Chapter 8 Exponential and Logarithmic Functions and Relations

8-1 Graphing Exponential Functions

Why?

Have you ever received an e-mail that tells you to forward it to 5 friends? If each of those 5 friends then forwards it to 5 of their friends, who each forward it to 5 of their friends, the number of people receiving the e-mail is growing exponentially.

The equation $y = 5^x$ can be used to represent this situation, where x is the number of rounds that the e-mail has been forwarded.

Then
You graphed polynomial functions. (Lesson 6-4)

Now
- Graph exponential growth functions.
- Graph exponential decay functions.

NGSSS
MA.912.A.8.3 Graph exponential and logarithmic **functions.**
MA.912.A.8.7 Solve applications of exponential growth and decay. *Also addresses MA.912.A.2.10 and MA.912.A.10.3.*

New Vocabulary
exponential function
exponential growth
asymptote
growth factor
exponential decay
decay factor

FL Math Online
glencoe.com

Exponential Growth A function like $y = 5^x$, where the base is a constant and the exponent is the independent variable, is an **exponential function**. One type of exponential function is exponential growth. An **exponential growth** function is a function of the form $f(x) = b^x$, where $b > 1$. The graph of an exponential function has an **asymptote**, which is a line that the graph of the function approaches.

Key Concept

Parent Function of Exponential Growth Functions

Parent function:	$f(x) = b^x, b > 1$
Type of graph:	continuous, one-to-one, and increasing
Domain:	all real numbers
Range:	all positive real numbers
Asymptote:	x-axis
Intercept:	(0, 1)

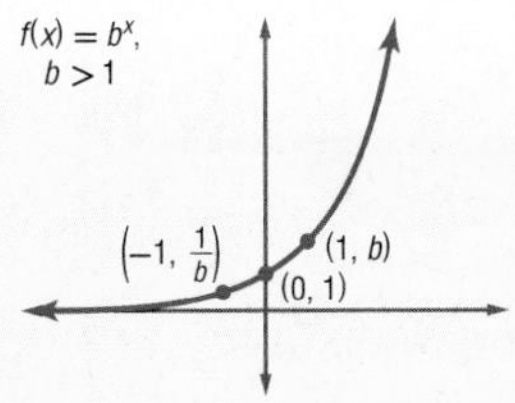

EXAMPLE 1 Graph Exponential Growth Functions

Graph $y = 3^x$. State the domain and range.

Make a table of values. Then plot the points and sketch the graph.

x	-3	-2	$-\frac{1}{2}$	0
$y = 3^x$	$3^{-3} = \frac{1}{27}$	$3^{-2} = \frac{1}{9}$	$3^{-\frac{1}{2}} = \frac{\sqrt{3}}{3}$	$3^0 = 1$
x	1	$\frac{3}{2}$	2	
$y = 3^x$	$3^1 = 3$	$3^{\frac{3}{2}} = \sqrt{27}$	$3^2 = 9$	

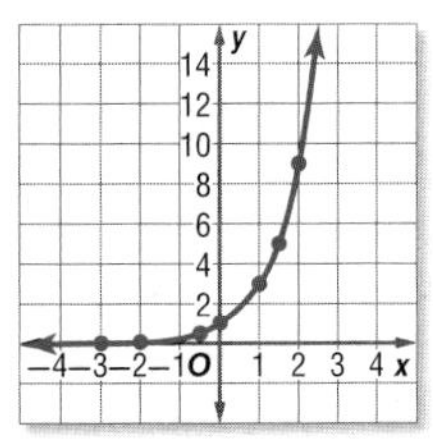

The domain is all real numbers, and the range is all positive real numbers.

Guided Practice

1. Graph $y = 4^x$. State the domain and range. **See Chapter 8 Answer Appendix.**

Personal Tutor glencoe.com

1 FOCUS

Vertical Alignment

Before Lesson 8-1
Graph polynomial functions.

Lesson 8-1
Graph exponential growth functions.
Graph exponential decay functions.

After Lesson 8-1
Solve exponential equations and inequalities.

2 TEACH

Scaffolding Questions

Have students read the *Why?* section of the lesson.

Ask:
- How many people will receive the e-mail in the second round? 25
- How many people will receive the e-mail in the fourth round? 625
- Suppose the same scenario as in the *Why?* section, only this e-mail tells you to forward it on to 8 friends. Write an equation to represent this situation. $y = 8^x$

Lesson 8-1 Resources

Resource	Approaching-Level	On-Level	Beyond-Level	English Learners
Teacher Edition	• Differentiated Instruction, p. 477	• Differentiated Instruction, p. 477	• Differentiated Instruction, p. 482	• Differentiated Instruction, p. 477
Chapter Resource Masters	• Study Guide and Intervention, pp. 5–6 • Skills Practice, p. 7 • Practice, p. 8 • Word Problem Practice, p. 9	• Study Guide and Intervention, pp. 5–6 • Skills Practice, p. 7 • Practice, p. 8 • Word Problem Practice, p. 9 • Enrichment, p. 10 • Graphing Calculator Activity, p. 11	• Practice, p. 8 • Word Problem Practice, p. 9 • Enrichment, p. 10	• Study Guide and Intervention, pp. 5–6 • Skills Practice, p. 7 • Practice, p. 8 • Word Problem Practice, p. 9
Transparencies	• 5-Minute Check Transparency 8-1	• 5-Minute Check Transparency 8-1	• 5-Minute Check Transparency 8-1	• 5-Minute Check Transparency 8-1
Other	• Study Notebook • Teaching Algebra with Manipulatives	• Study Notebook • Teaching Algebra with Manipulatives	• Study Notebook	• Study Notebook • Teaching Algebra with Manipulatives

Exponential Growth

Example 1 shows how to graph an exponential growth function. **Example 2** shows how to graph transformations of exponential growth functions. **Example 3** shows how to graph an exponential function to model real-world growth.

Formative Assessment

Use the Guided Practice exercises after each example to determine students' understanding of concepts.

Additional Examples

1 Graph $y = 4^x$. State the domain and range.

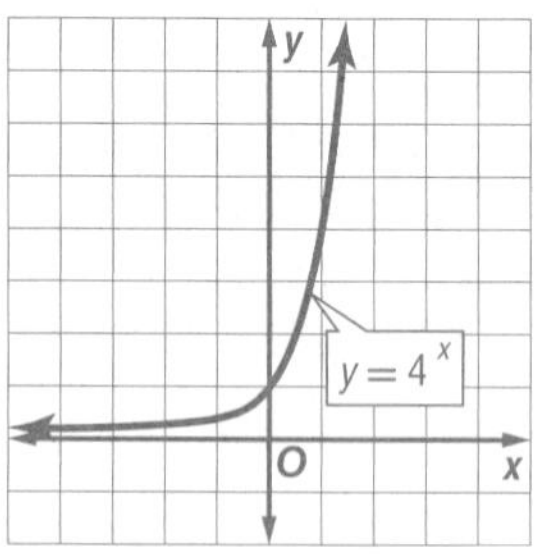

The domain is all real numbers. The range is all positive numbers.

2 Graph each function. State the domain and range.

a. $y = 3^x - 2$

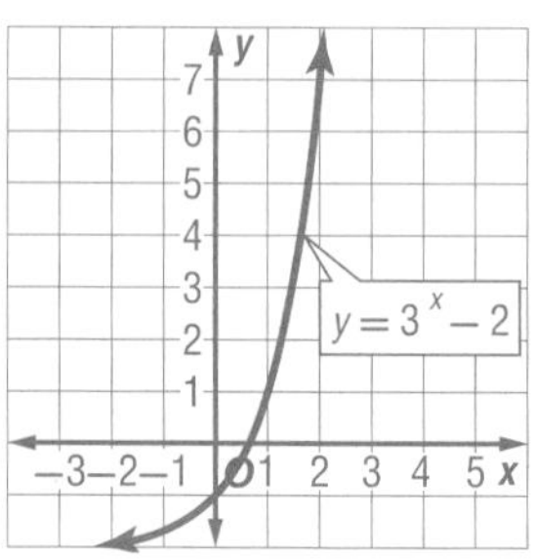

Domain = {all real numbers}
Range = $\{y \mid y > -2\}$

b. $y = 2^{x-1}$

Additional Examples also in Interactive Classroom PowerPoint® Presentations

IWB INTERACTIVE WHITEBOARD READY

The graph of $f(x) = b^x$ represents a parent graph of the exponential functions. The same techniques used to transform the graphs of other functions you have studied can be applied to the graphs of exponential functions.

StudyTip

Look Back To review **transformations of parent functions**, see Lesson 2-7.

Key Concept — Transformations of Exponential Functions

$$f(x) = ab^{x-h} + k$$

h – Horizontal Translation	*k* – Vertical Translation
$\lvert h \rvert$ units right if *h* is positive $\lvert h \rvert$ units left if *h* is negative	$\lvert k \rvert$ units up if *k* is positive $\lvert k \rvert$ units down if *k* is negative

a – Orientation and Shape

If $a < 0$, the graph is reflected in the *x*-axis.

If $\lvert a \rvert > 1$, the graph is stretched vertically.
If $0 < \lvert a \rvert < 1$, the graph is compressed vertically.

EXAMPLE 2 Graph Transformations

Graph each function. State the domain and range.

a. $y = 2^x + 1$

The equation represents a translation of the graph of $y = 2^x$ one unit up.

x	$y = 2^x + 1$
−3	$2^{-3} + 1 = 1.125$
−2	$2^{-2} + 1 = 1.25$
−1	$2^{-1} + 1 = 1.5$
0	$2^0 + 1 = 2$
1	$2^1 + 1 = 3$
2	$2^2 + 1 = 5$
3	$2^3 + 1 = 9$

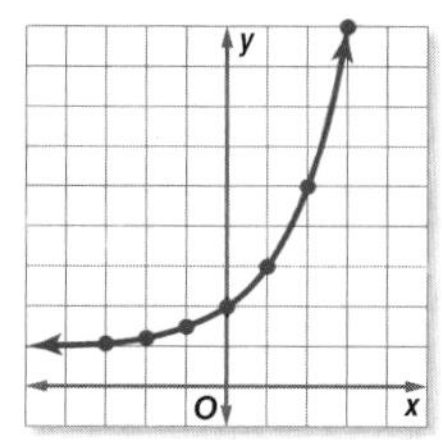

Domain = {all real numbers}; Range = $\{y \mid y > 1\}$

StudyTip

End Behavior Remember that end behavior is the action of the graph as *x* approaches positive infinity or negative infinity. In Example 2a, as *x* approaches infinity, *y* approaches infinity. In Example 2b, as *x* approaches infinity, *y* approaches negative infinity.

b. $y = -\frac{1}{2} \cdot 5^{x-2}$

The equation represents a transformation of the graph of $y = 5^x$. Graph $y = 5^x$ and transform the graph.

- $a = -\frac{1}{2}$: The graph is reflected in the *x*-axis and compressed vertically.
- $h = 2$: The graph is translated 2 units right.
- $k = 0$: The graph is not translated vertically.

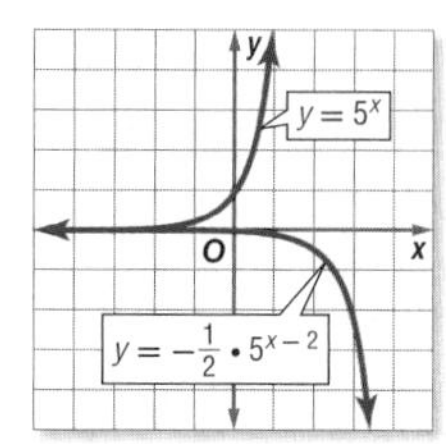

Domain = {all real numbers}

Range = $\{y \mid y < 0\}$

Guided Practice 2A, 2B. See Chapter 8 Answer Appendix.

2A. $y = 2^{x+3} - 5$

2B. $y = 0.1(6)^x - 3$

Personal Tutor glencoe.com

Additional Answer (Additional Example)

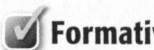

2b.

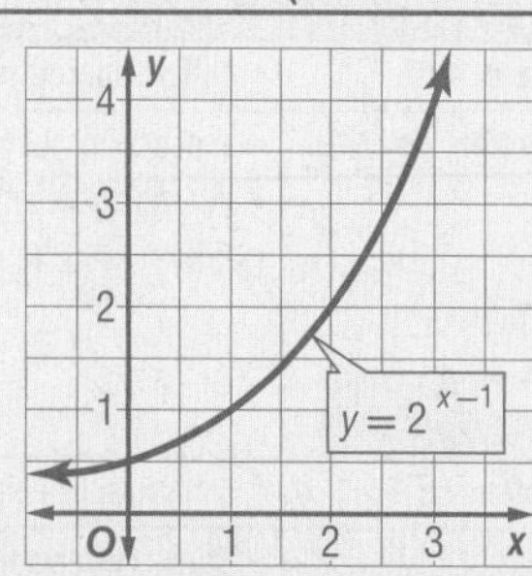

Domain = {all real numbers} Range = $\{y \mid y > 0\}$

TEACH with TECH

DOCUMENT CAMERA Select a student to work through an example in front of the class. Have the student create a table of values for the function and show how to draw the graph of the function.

476 Chapter 8 Exponential and Logarithmic Functions and Relations

You can model exponential growth with a constant percent increase over specific time periods using the following function.

$$A(t) = a(1 + r)^t$$

The function can be used to find the amount $A(t)$ after t time periods, where a is the initial amount and r is the percent of increase per time period. Note that the base of the exponential expression, $1 + r$, is called the **growth factor**.

The exponential growth function is often used to model population growth.

Real-World Link

The U.S. Census Bureau's American Community Survey is mailed to approximately 1 out of every 480 households.

Source: Census Bureau

Real-World EXAMPLE 3 Graph Exponential Growth Functions

CENSUS The first U.S. Census was conducted in 1790. At that time, the population was 3,929,214. Since then, the U.S. population has grown by approximately 2.03% annually. Draw a graph showing the population growth of the U.S. since 1790.

First, write an equation using $a = 3{,}929{,}214$, and $r = 0.0203$.

$y = 3{,}929{,}214(1.0203)^t$

Then graph the equation.

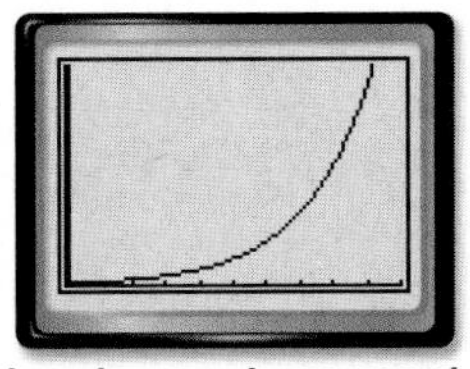

[0, 250] scl: 25 by [0, 400,000,000] scl: 40,000,000

Guided Practice 3. See Chapter 8 Answer Appendix.

3. **FINANCIAL LITERACY** Teen spending is expected to grow 3.5% annually from \$79.7 billion in 2006. Draw a graph to show the spending growth.

Personal Tutor glencoe.com

StudyTip

Interest The formula for simple interest, $i = prt$, illustrates linear growth over time. However, the formula for compound interest, $A(t) = a(1 + r)^t$, illustrates exponential growth over time. This is why investments with compound interest make more money.

Exponential Decay The second type of exponential function is **exponential decay**.

Key Concept

Parent Function of Exponential Decay Functions

Parent function: $f(x) = b^x$, $0 < b < 1$

Type of graph: continuous, one-to-one, and decreasing

Domain: all real numbers

Range: positive real numbers

Asymptote: x-axis

Intercept: (0, 1)

Model

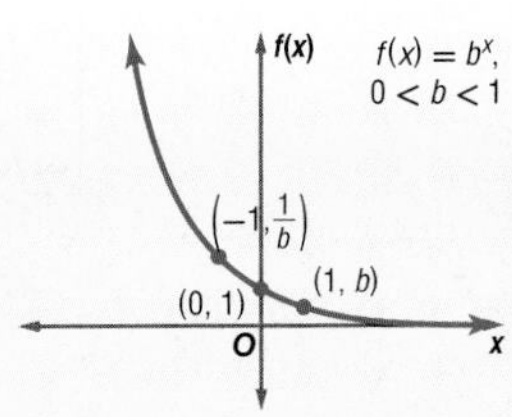

The graphs of exponential decay functions can be transformed in the same manner as those of exponential growth.

Additional Example

3 **INTERNET** In 2006, there were 1,020,000,000 people worldwide using the Internet. At that time, the number of users was growing by 19.5% annually. Draw a graph showing how the number of users would grow from 2006 to 2016 if that rate continued.

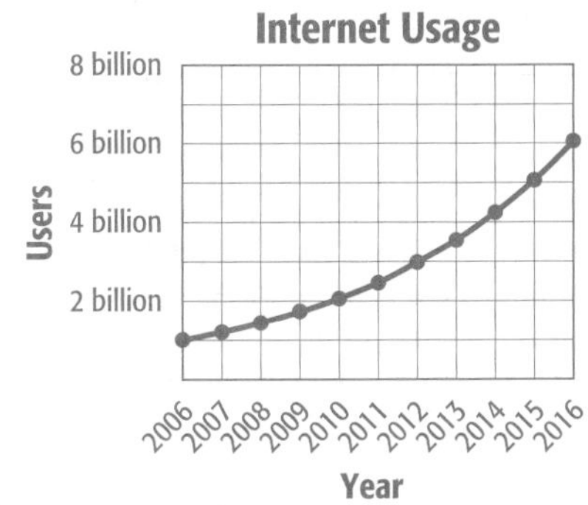

Watch Out!

Common Misconceptions Be sure students do not confuse polynomial functions and exponential functions. While $y = x^2$ and $y = 2^x$ each have an exponent, $y = x^2$ is a polynomial, and $y = 2^x$ is an exponential function.

Focus on Mathematical Content

Exponential Functions The function $f(x) = b^x$, where b is a positive real number and $b \neq 1$, is an exponential function. When $b > 1$, the function has no x-intercepts and one y-intercept. It is an increasing function with a horizontal asymptote (the x-axis). When $0 < b < 1$, the function has no x-intercepts and one y-intercept. It is a decreasing function with a horizontal asymptote (the x-axis).

Differentiated Instruction

AL OL ELL

Linguistic Learners Ask students where they have heard the term *exponential* before and what they think it might mean. Students may have heard terms like *exponential growth* on a television news program and they might think that exponential means "enormous." Use students' answers to introduce the concept of exponential functions.

Exponential Decay

Examples 4 and 5 show how to graph exponential decay functions.

Additional Example

4 Graph each function. State the domain and range.

a. $y = \left(\frac{1}{5}\right)^x$

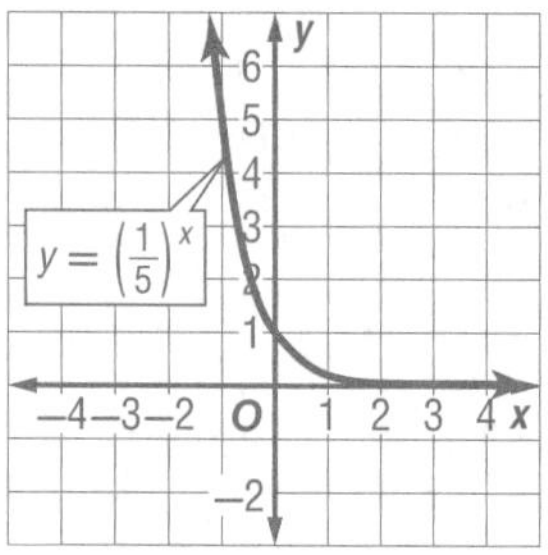

Domain = {all real numbers}
Range = $\{y \mid y > 0\}$

b. $y = -4\left(\frac{1}{2}\right)^{x-1} + 2$

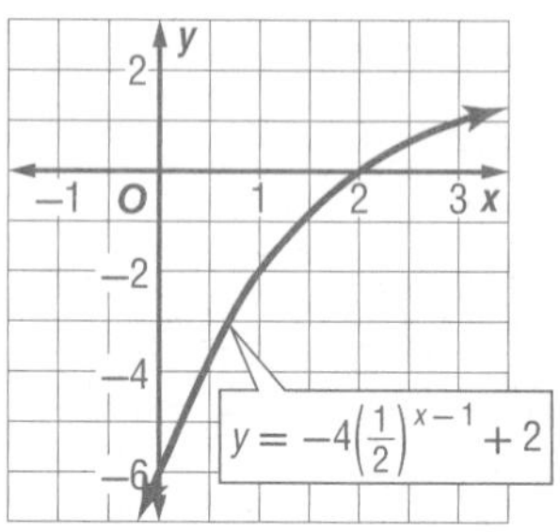

Domain = {all real numbers}
Range = $\{y \mid y < 2\}$

EXAMPLE 4 Graph Exponential Decay Functions

Graph each function. State the domain and range.

a. $y = \left(\frac{1}{3}\right)^x$

x	$y = \left(\frac{1}{3}\right)^x$
-3	$\left(\frac{1}{3}\right)^{-3} = 27$
-2	$\left(\frac{1}{3}\right)^{-2} = 9$
$-\frac{1}{2}$	$\left(\frac{1}{3}\right)^{-\frac{1}{2}} = \sqrt{3}$
0	$\left(\frac{1}{3}\right)^{0} = 1$
1	$\left(\frac{1}{3}\right)^{1} = \frac{1}{3}$
$\frac{3}{2}$	$\left(\frac{1}{3}\right)^{\frac{3}{2}} = \sqrt{\frac{1}{27}}$
2	$\left(\frac{1}{3}\right)^{2} = \frac{1}{9}$

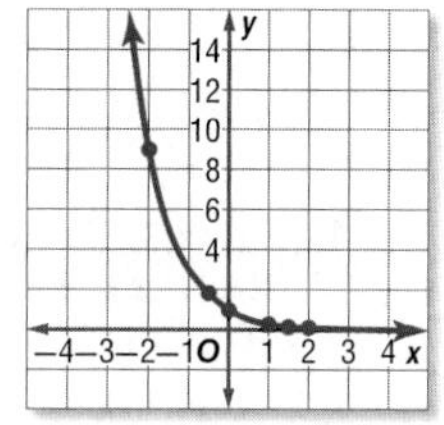

The domain is all real numbers, and the range is all positive real numbers.

b. $y = 2\left(\frac{1}{4}\right)^{x+2} - 3$

The equation represents a transformation of the graph of $y = \left(\frac{1}{4}\right)^x$.

Examine each parameter.

- $a = 2$: The graph is stretched vertically.
- $h = -2$: The graph is translated 2 units left.
- $k = -3$: The graph is translated 3 units down.

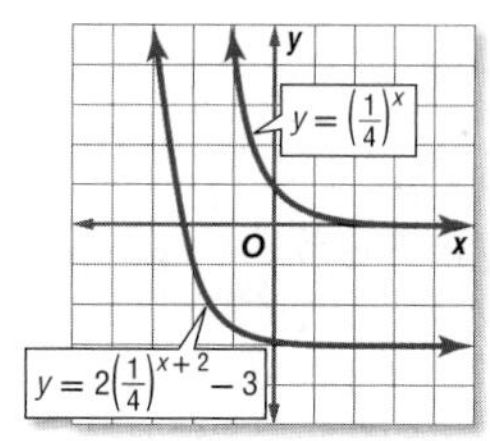

The domain is all real numbers, and the range is all real numbers greater than -3.

StudyTip

Exponential Decay Be sure not to confuse a dilation in which $|a| < 1$ with exponential decay in which $0 < b < 1$.

Guided Practice 4A, 4B. See margin.

4A. $y = -3\left(\frac{2}{5}\right)^{x-4} + 2$ **4B.** $y = \frac{3}{8}\left(\frac{5}{6}\right)^{x-1} + 1$

Personal Tutor glencoe.com

Similar to exponential growth, you can model exponential decay with a constant percent increase over specific time periods using the following function.

$$A(t) = a(1 - r)^t$$

The base of the exponential expression, $1 - r$, is called the **decay factor**.

Additional Answers (Guided Practice)

4A.

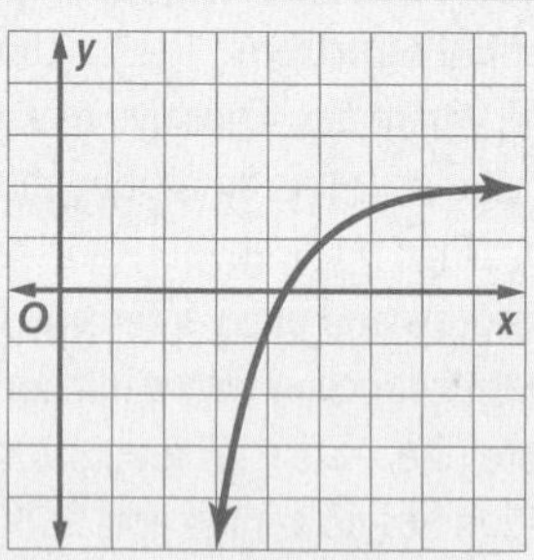

D = {all reals numbers};
R = $\{y \mid y < 2\}$

4B.

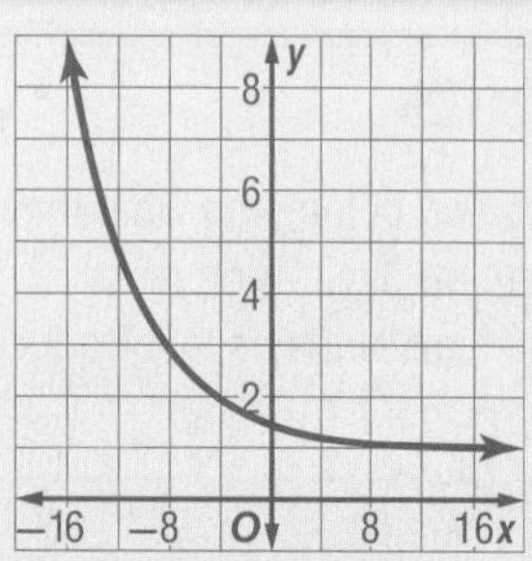

D = {all reals numbers}; R = $\{y \mid y > 1\}$

Real-World EXAMPLE 5 Graph Exponential Decay Functions

TEA A cup of green tea contains 35 milligrams of caffeine. The average teen can eliminate approximately 12.5% of the caffeine from their system per hour.

a. Draw a graph to represent the amount of caffeine remaining after drinking a cup of green tea.

$y = a(1 - r)^t$
$= 35(1 - 0.125)^t$
$= 35(0.875)^t$

Graph the equation.

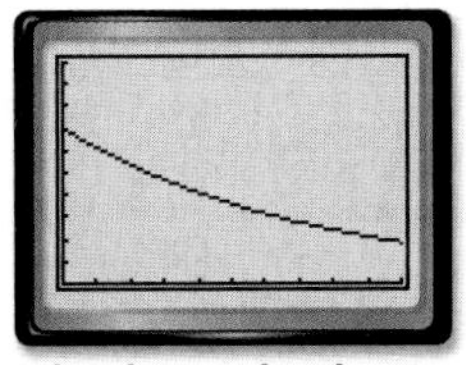

[0, 10] scl: 1 by [0, 50] scl: 5

b. Estimate the amount of caffeine in a teenager's body 3 hours after drinking a cup of green tea.

$y = 35(0.875)^t$	**Equation from part a**
$= 35(0.875)^3$	**Replace *t* with 3.**
≈ 23.45	**Use a calculator.**

The caffeine in a teenager will be about 23.45 milligrams after 3 hours.

Guided Practice

5. A cup of black tea contains about 68 milligrams of caffeine. Draw a graph to represent the amount of caffeine remaining in the body of an average teen after drinking a cup of black tea. Estimate the amount of caffeine in the body 2 hours after drinking a cup of black tea. See margin for graph; 52.06 mg

Personal Tutor glencoe.com

Real-World Link

After water, tea is the most consumed beverage in the U.S. It can be found in over 80% of American households. Just over half the American population drinks tea daily.

Source: The Tea Association of the USA

Check Your Understanding

Examples 1 and 2 pp. 475–476

Graph each function. State the domain and range. 1–6. See Chapter 8 Answer Appendix.

1. $f(x) = 2^x$ **2.** $f(x) = 5^x$ **3.** $f(x) = 3^{x-2} + 4$

4. $f(x) = 2^{x+1} + 3$ **5.** $f(x) = 0.25(4)^x - 6$ **6.** $f(x) = 3(2)^x + 8$

Example 3 p. 477

7. SCIENCE A virus spreads through a network of computers such that each minute, 25% more computers are infected. If the virus began at only one computer, graph the function for the first hour of the spread of the virus. See margin.

Example 4 p. 478

Graph each function. State the domain and range. 8–11. See Chapter 8 Answer Appendix.

8. $f(x) = 2\left(\frac{2}{3}\right)^{x-3} - 4$ **9.** $f(x) = -\frac{1}{2}\left(\frac{3}{4}\right)^{x+1} + 5$

10. $f(x) = -\frac{1}{3}\left(\frac{4}{5}\right)^{x-4} + 3$ **11.** $f(x) = \frac{1}{8}\left(\frac{1}{4}\right)^{x+6} + 7$

Example 5 p. 479

12. FINANCIAL LITERACY A new SUV depreciates in value each year by a factor of 15%. Draw a graph of the SUV's value for the first 20 years after the initial purchase. See margin.

Additional Example

5 AIR PRESSURE The pressure of the atmosphere is 14.7 lb/in² at Earth's surface. It decreases by about 20% for each mile of altitude up to about 50 miles.

a. Draw a graph to represent atmospheric pressure for altitude from 0 to 50 miles.

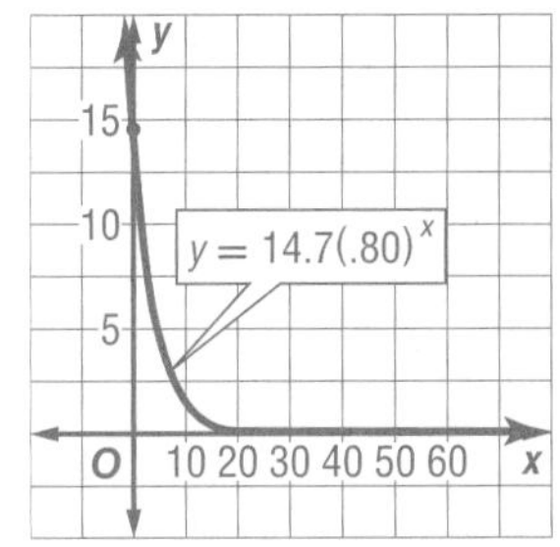

b. Estimate the atmospheric pressure at an altitude of 10 miles. 1.6 lb/in²

3 PRACTICE

Formative Assessment

Use Exercises 1–12 to check for understanding.

Use the chart at the bottom of the next page to customize assignments for your students.

Additional Answer (Guided Practice)

5.

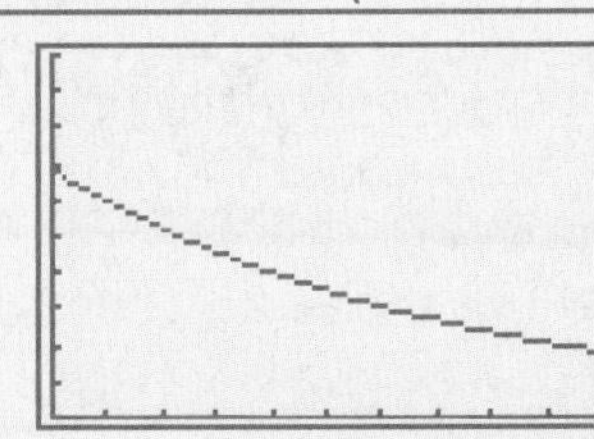

[0, 10] scl: 1 by [0, 100] scl: 10

Additional Answers

7.

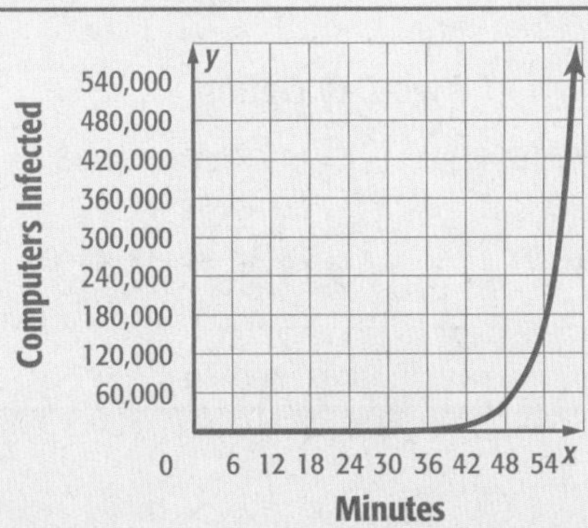

12.

Multiple Representations In Exercise 33, students use tables of values, graphs, and analysis to investigate exponential functions and distinguish growth models from decay models.

Watch Out!

Error Analysis In Exercise 35, remind students that multiplying any function by a negative number reflects the graph of the function across the x-axis.

Additional Answers

26.

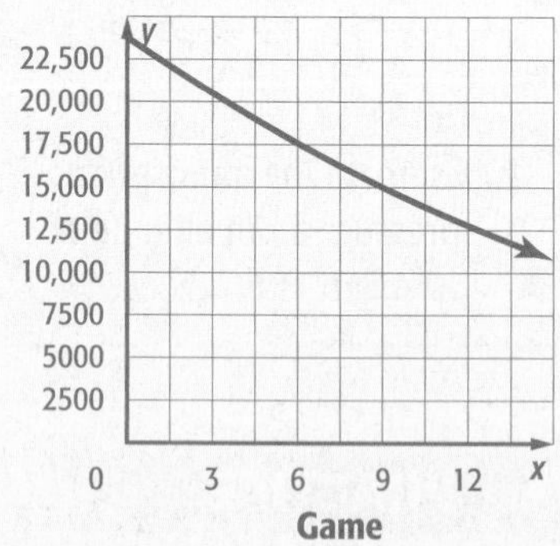

27a.

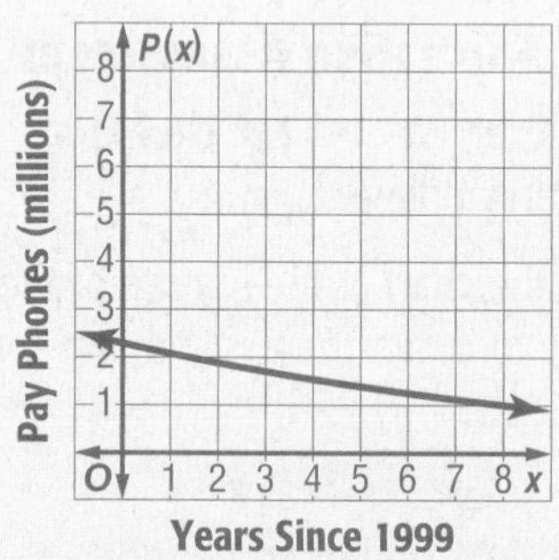

27b. The $P(x)$-intercept represents the number of pay phones in 1999. The asymptote is the x-axis. The number of pay phones can approach 0, but will never equal 0. This makes sense as there will probably always be a need for some pay phones.

28a.

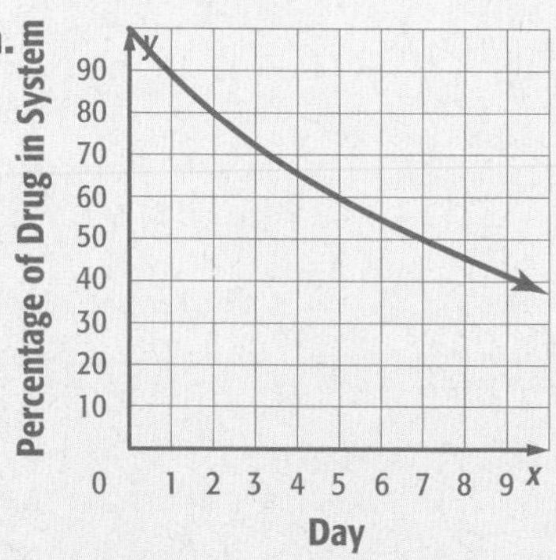

Practice and Problem Solving

● = **Step-by-Step Solutions** begin on page R20. **Extra Practice** begins on page 947.

Examples 1 and 2 pp. 475–476

Graph each function. State the domain and range. **13–18. See Chapter 8 Answer Appendix.**

13. $f(x) = 2(3)^x$ **14.** $f(x) = -2(4)^x$ **15.** $f(x) = 4^{x+1} - 5$

16. $f(x) = 3^{2x} + 1$ **17.** $f(x) = -0.4(3)^{x+2} + 4$ **18.** $f(x) = 1.5(2)^x + 6$

Example 3 p. 477

19 **SCIENCE** The population of a colony of beetles grows 30% each week for 10 weeks. If the initial population is 65 beetles, graph the function that represents the situation. **See Chapter 8 Answer Appendix.**

Example 4 p. 478

Graph each function. State the domain and range. **20–25. See Chapter 8 Answer Appendix.**

20. $f(x) = -4\left(\frac{3}{5}\right)^{x+4} + 3$ **21.** $f(x) = 3\left(\frac{2}{5}\right)^{x-3} - 6$ **22.** $f(x) = \frac{1}{2}\left(\frac{1}{5}\right)^{x+5} + 8$

23. $f(x) = \frac{3}{4}\left(\frac{2}{3}\right)^{x+4} - 2$ **24.** $f(x) = -\frac{1}{2}\left(\frac{3}{8}\right)^{x+2} + 9$ **25.** $f(x) = -\frac{5}{4}\left(\frac{4}{5}\right)^{x+4} + 2$

Example 5 p. 479

26. **ATTENDANCE** The attendance for a basketball team declined at a rate of 5% per game throughout a losing season. Graph the function modeling the attendance if 15 home games were played and 23,500 people were at the first game. **See margin.**

B

27. **PHONES** The number of pay phones in use in the United States has been declining due, in large part, to increased usage of cell phones. The function $P(x) = 2.28(0.9^x)$ can be used to model the number of pay phones in millions x years since 1999.

a. Graph the function. **See margin.**

b. Explain what the $P(x)$-intercept and the asymptote represent in this situation. **See margin.**

Real-World Link

Inventor William Gray installed the first coin-operated phone in 1889 at a bank in Hartford, Connecticut.

28. **HEALTH** A certain drug is taken once every ten days. Each day, 10% of the drug dissipates from the system.

a. Graph the function representing this situation. **See margin.**

b. At what point is 50% of the original amount still in the system? **after the 6th day**

c. How much of the original amount remains in the system after 9 days? **a little less than 40%**

29. **NUMBER THEORY** A sequence of numbers follows a pattern in which the next number is 125% of the previous number. The first number in the pattern is 18.

a. Write the function that represents the situation. $f(x) = 18(1.25)^{x-1}$

b. Graph the function for the first 10 numbers. **See margin.**

c. What is the value of the tenth number? Round to the nearest whole number. **134**

C

For each graph, $f(x)$ is the parent function and $g(x)$ is a transformation of $f(x)$. Use the graph to determine the equation of $g(x)$.

30. $g(x) = 3^{x-4} + 5$
31. $g(x) = 4(2)^{x-3}$ or $g(x) = \frac{1}{2}(2^x)$
32. $g(x) = -2(4)^{x+1} + 3$

30. $f(x) = 3^x$

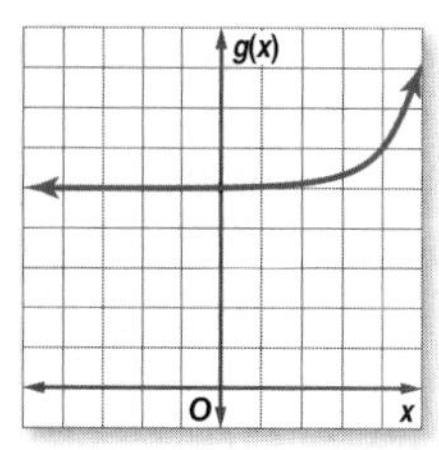

31. $f(x) = 2^x$

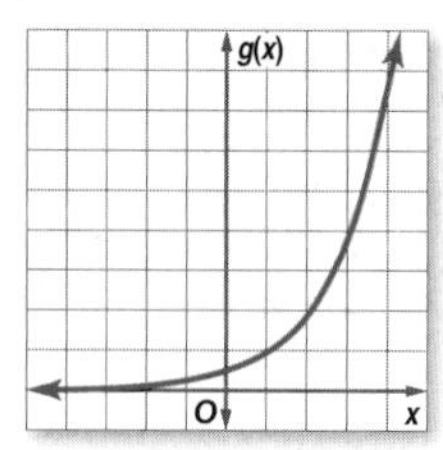

32. $f(x) = 4^x$

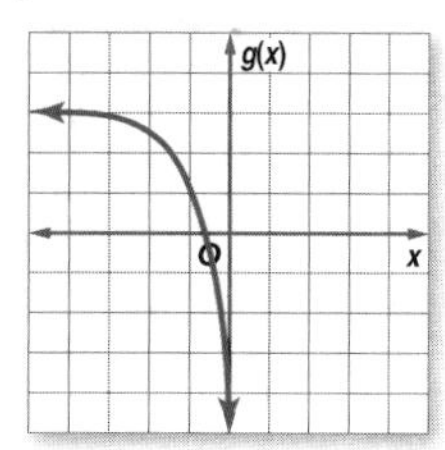

Differentiated Homework Options

Level	Assignment	Two-Day Option	
AL Basic	13–25, 34–35, 37–60	13–25 odd, 39–42	14–24 even, 34–35, 37–38, 43–60
OL Core	13–25 odd, 26–29, 31, 33, 34–35, 37–60	13–25, 39–42	26–35, 37–38, 43–60
BL Advanced	26–56, (optional: 57–60)		

StudyTip

Parent Function For Exercise 33, it may be helpful to remember that the graph of any parent function $y = b^x$ passes through (0, 1).

33. **MULTIPLE REPRESENTATIONS** In this problem, you will use the tables below for exponential functions $f(x)$, $g(x)$, and $h(x)$. **a, b. See Chapter 8 Answer Appendix.**

x	−1	0	1	2	3	4	5
$f(x)$	2.5	2	1	−1	−5	−13	−29

x	−1	0	1	2	3	4	5
$g(x)$	5	11	23	47	95	191	383

x	−1	0	1	2	3	4	5
$h(x)$	3	2.5	2.25	2.125	2.0625	2.0313	2.0156

a. **GRAPHICAL** Graph the functions for $-1 \le x \le 5$ on separate graphs.

b. **VERBAL** Which function(s) has a negative coefficient, a? Explain your reasoning.

c. **ANALYTICAL** Which function(s) is translated to the left? **$g(x)$ and $h(x)$**

d. **ANALYTICAL** Determine which functions are growth models and which are decay models. **See Chapter 8 Answer Appendix.**

H.O.T. Problems Use Higher-Order Thinking Skills

34. **REASONING** Determine whether each statement is *sometimes*, *always*, or *never* true. Explain your reasoning.

a. An exponential function of the form $y = ab^{x-h} + k$ has a y-intercept.

b. An exponential function of the form $y = ab^{x-h} + k$ has an x-intercept.

c. The function $f(x) = |b|^x$ is an exponential growth function if b is an integer.

35. **ERROR ANALYSIS** Vince and Grady were asked to graph $f(x) = -\frac{2}{3}\left(\frac{3}{4}\right)^{x-1}$. Is either of them correct? Explain your reasoning.

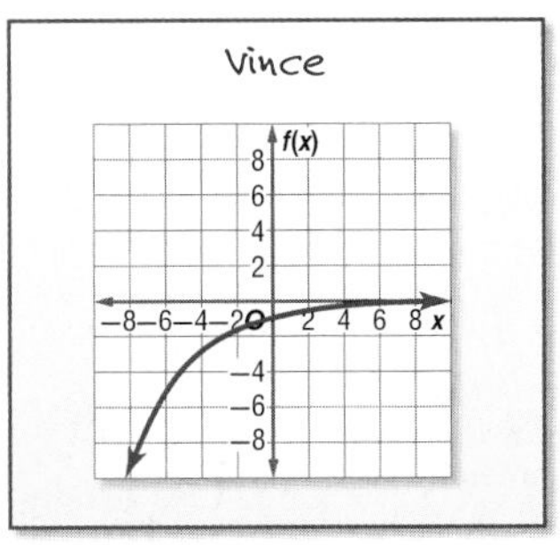

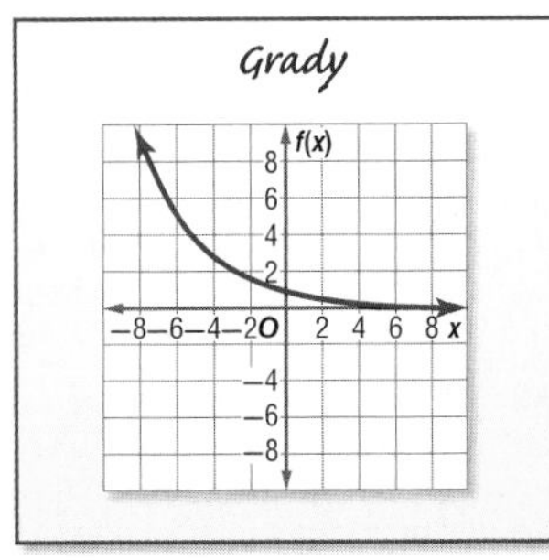

36. **CHALLENGE** A substance decays 35% each day. After 8 days, there are 8 milligrams of the substance remaining. How many milligrams were there initially? **about 251 mg**

37. **OPEN ENDED** Give an example of a value of b for which $f(x) = \left(\frac{8}{b}\right)^x$ represents exponential decay. **Sample answer: 10**

38. **WRITING IN MATH** Write the procedure for transforming the graph of $g(x) = b^x$ to the graph of $f(x) = ab^{x-h} + k$.

34a. Always; sample answer: The domain of exponential functions is all real numbers, so (0, y) always exists.
34b. Sometimes; sample answer: The graph of an exponential function crosses the x-axis when $k < 0$.
34c. Sometimes; Sample answer: The function is not exponential if $b = 1$ or -1.
35. Vince; Grady neglected to multiply by the negative sign.
38. Sample answer: The parent function, $g(x) = b^x$, is stretched if a is greater than 1 or compressed if a is less than 1. The parent function is translated up k units if k is positive and down $|k|$ units if k is negative. The parent function is translated h units to the right if h is positive and $|h|$ units to the left if h is negative.

Study Guide and Intervention

CRM pp. 5–6 AL OL ELL

8-1 Study Guide and Intervention

Graphing Exponential Functions

Exponential Growth An **exponential growth function** has the form $y = b^x$, where $b > 1$. The graphs of exponential equations can be transformed by changing the value of the constants a, h, and k in the exponential equation: $f(x) = ab^{x-h} + k$.

Parent Function of Exponential Growth Functions, $f(x) = b^x$, $b > 1$	1. The function is continuous, one-to-one, and increasing. 2. The domain is the set of all real numbers. 3. The x-axis is the asymptote of the graph. 4. The range is the set of all non-zero real numbers. 5. The graph contains the point (0, 1).

Example Graph $y = 4^x + 2$. State the domain and range.

Make a table of values. Connect the points to form a smooth curve.

x	−1	0	1	2	3
y	2.25	3	6	18	66

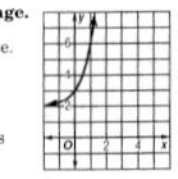

The domain of the function is all real numbers, while the range is the set of all positive real numbers greater than 2.

Exercises

Graph each function. State the domain and range.

1. $y = 3(2)^x$ 2. $y = \frac{1}{3}(3)^x$ 3. $y = 0.25(5)^x$

4. $y = 2(3)^x$ 5. $y = 4^x - 2$ 6. $y = 2^{x+3}$

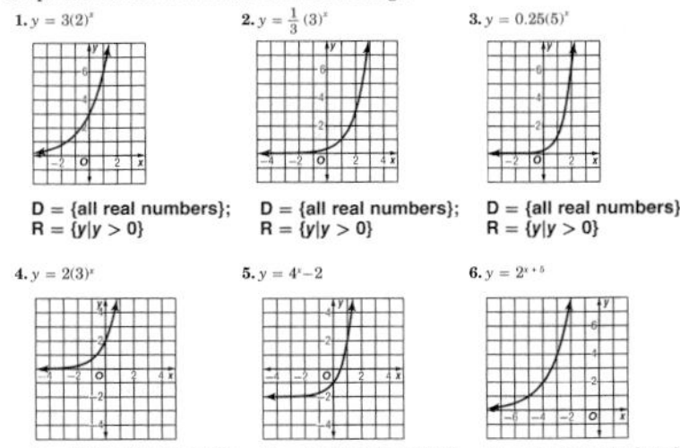

1. D = {all real numbers}; R = {y|y > 0}
2. D = {all real numbers}; R = {y|y > 0}
3. D = {all real numbers}; R = {y|y > 0}
4. D = {all real numbers}; R = {y|y > 0}
5. D = {all real numbers}; R = {y|y > −2}
6. D = {all real numbers}; R = {y|y > 0}

Chapter 8 5 Glencoe Algebra 2

Practice

CRM p. 8 AL OL BL ELL

8-1 Practice

Graphing Exponential Functions

Graph each function. State the domain and range.

1. $y = 1.5(2)^x$ 2. $y = 4(3)^x$ 3. $y = 3(0.5)^x$

4. $y = 5\left(\frac{1}{2}\right)^x - 8$ 5. $y = -2\left(\frac{1}{4}\right)^{x-3}$ 6. $y = \frac{1}{2}(3)^{x+4} - 5$

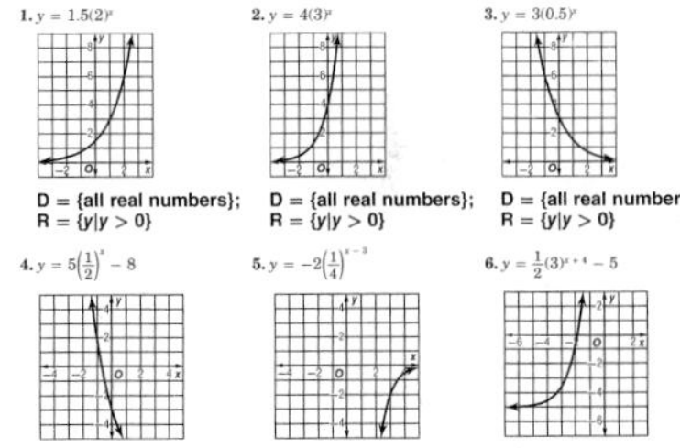

1. D = {all real numbers}; R = {y|y > 0}
2. D = {all real numbers}; R = {y|y > 0}
3. D = {all real numbers}; R = {y|y > 0}
4. D = {all real numbers}; R = {y|y > −8}
5. D = {all real numbers}; R = {y|y < 0}
6. D = {all real numbers}; R = {y|y > −5}

7. **BIOLOGY** The initial number of bacteria in a culture is 12,000. The culture doubles each day.
a. Write an exponential function to model the population y of bacteria after x days. **$y = 12{,}000(2)^x$**
b. How many bacteria are there after 6 days? **768,000**

8. **EDUCATION** A college with a graduating class of 4000 students in the year 2008 predicts that its graduating class will grow 5% per year. Write an exponential function to model the number of students y in the graduating class t years after 2008. **$y = 4000(1.05)^t$**

Chapter 8 8 Glencoe Algebra 2

Word Problem Practice

CRM p. 9 AL OL BL ELL

8-1 Word Problem Practice

Graphing Exponential Functions

1. **GOLF BALLS** A golf ball manufacturer packs 3 golf balls into a single package. Three of these packages make a gift box. Three gift boxes make a value pack. The display shelf is high enough to stack 3 value packs one on top of the other. Three such columns of value packs make up a display front. Three display fronts can be packed in a single shipping box and shipped to various retail stores. How many golf balls are in a single shipping box? **729**

2. **FOLDING** Paper thickness ranges from 0.0032 inch to 0.0175 inch. Kay folds a piece of paper 0.01 inch thick in half over and over until it is at least 25 layers thick. How many times does she fold the paper in half and how many layers are there? How thick is the folded paper? **5 folds; 32 layers; 0.32 in.**

3. **SUBSCRIPTIONS** Subscriptions to an online arts and crafts club have been increasing by 20% every year. The club began with 40 members.

Year	0	1	2	3	4
Subscriptions	40	48			

Make a graph of the number of subscribers over the first 5 years of the club's existence.

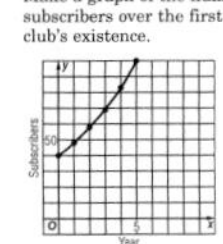

4. **TENNIS SHOES** The cost of a pair of tennis shoes increases about 5.1% every year. About how much would a $50 pair of tennis shoes cost 25 years from now? **$173.40**

5. **MONEY** Sam opened a savings account that compounds interest at a rate of 3% annually. Let P be the initial amount Sam deposited and let t be the number of years the account has been open.
a. Write an equation to find A, the amount of money in the account after t years. Assume that Sam made more additional deposits and no withdrawals. **$A = P(1.03)^t$**
b. If Sam opened the account with $500 and made no deposits or withdrawals, how much is in the account 10 years later? **$671.96**
c. What is the least number of years it would take for such an account to double in value? **24 yr**

Chapter 8 9 Glencoe Algebra 2

Additional Answer

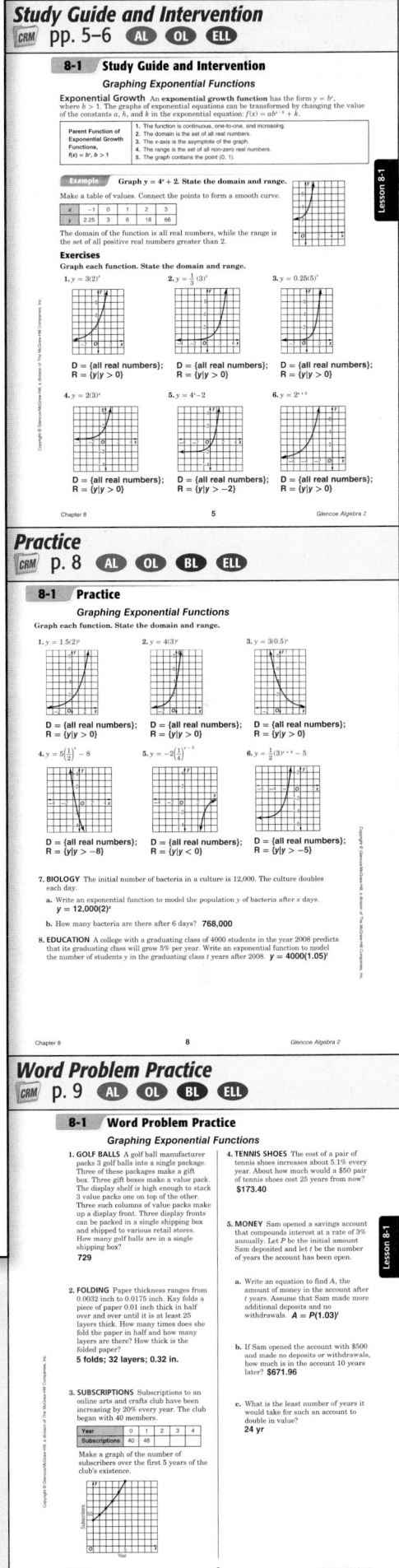

29b.

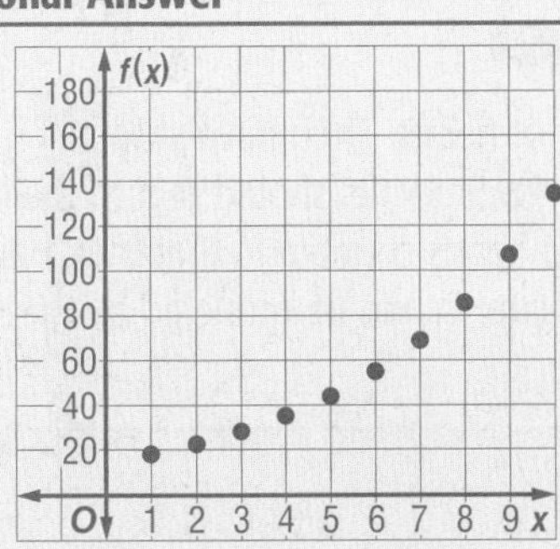

Enrichment

CRM p. 10 OL BL

8-1 Enrichment

Families of Curves

Use these graphs for the problems below.

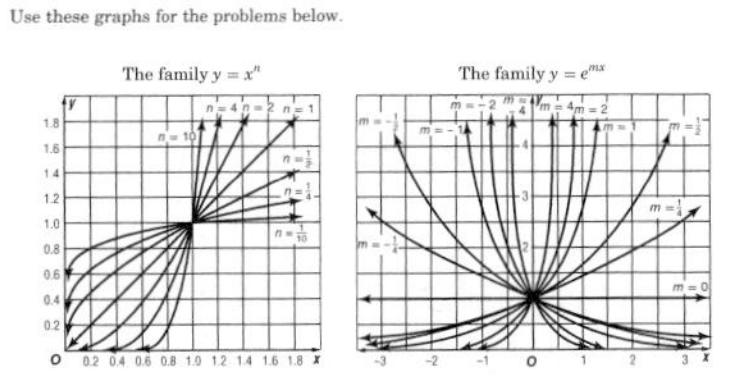

1. Use the graph on the left to describe the relationship among the curves $y = x^{\frac{1}{2}}$, $y = x^1$, and $y = x^2$. For $n = \frac{1}{2}$ and $n = 2$ the graphs are …

4 ASSESS

Ticket Out the Door Make several copies each of five exponential functions. Give one function to each student. As the students leave the room, ask them to tell you whether their functions represent exponential growths or decays.

NGSSS PRACTICE 912.G.2.1, 912.A.3.15, 912.A.6.5

39. **GRIDDED RESPONSE** In the figure, $\overline{PO} \parallel \overline{RN}$, $ON = 12$, $MN = 6$, and $RN = 4$. What is the length of $\overline{PO}$? **12**

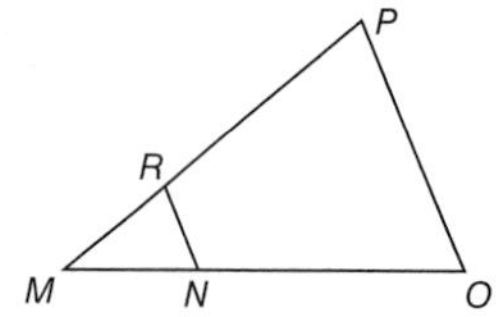

40. Ivan has enough money to buy 12 used CDs. If the cost of each CD was \$0.20 less, Ivan could buy 2 more CDs. How much money does Ivan have to spend on CDs? **A**

A. \$16.80
B. \$16.40
C. \$15.80
D. \$15.40

41. One hundred students will attend the fall dance if tickets cost \$30 each. For each \$5 increase in price, 10 fewer students will attend. What price will deliver the maximum dollar sales? **H**

F. \$30
G. \$35
H. \$40
I. \$45

42. **ACT/SAT** Javier mows a lawn in 2 hours. Tonya mows the same lawn in 1.5 hours. About how many minutes will it take to mow the lawn if Javier and Tonya work together? **C**

A. 28 minutes
B. 42 minutes
C. 51 minutes
D. 1.2 hours

Spiral Review

Solve each equation or inequality. (Lesson 7-7)

43. $\sqrt{y+5} = \sqrt{2y-3}$ **8**

44. $\sqrt{y+1} + \sqrt{y-4} = 5$ **8**

45. $10 - \sqrt{2x+7} \leq 3$ $x \geq 21$

46. $6 + \sqrt{3y+4} < 6$ **no solution**

47. $\sqrt{d+3} + \sqrt{d+7} > 4$ $d > -\frac{3}{4}$

48. $\sqrt{2x+5} - \sqrt{9+x} > 0$ $x > 4$

Simplify. (Lesson 7-6)

49. $\frac{1}{y^{\frac{2}{5}}}$ $\frac{y^{\frac{3}{5}}}{y}$

50. $\frac{xy}{\sqrt[3]{z}}$ $\frac{xyz^{\frac{2}{3}}}{z}$

51. $\frac{3x+4x^2}{x^{-\frac{2}{3}}}$ $3x^{\frac{5}{3}} + 4x^{\frac{8}{3}}$

52. $\sqrt[6]{27x^3}$ $\sqrt{3x}$

53. $\frac{\sqrt[4]{27}}{\sqrt[4]{3}}$ $\sqrt{3}$

54. $\frac{a^{-\frac{1}{2}}}{6a^{\frac{1}{3}} \cdot a^{-\frac{1}{4}}}$ $\frac{a^{\frac{5}{12}}}{6a}$

55. **FOOTBALL** The path of a football thrown across a field is given by the equation $y = -0.005x^2 + x + 5$, where x represents the distance, in feet, the ball has traveled horizontally and y represents the height, in feet, of the ball above ground level. About how far has the ball traveled horizontally when it returns to ground level? (Lesson 5-6) **about 204.88 ft**

56. **COMMUNITY SERVICE** A drug awareness program is being presented at a theater that seats 300 people. Proceeds will be donated to a local drug information center. If every two adults must bring at least one student, what is the maximum amount of money that can be raised? (Lesson 3-4) **\$500**

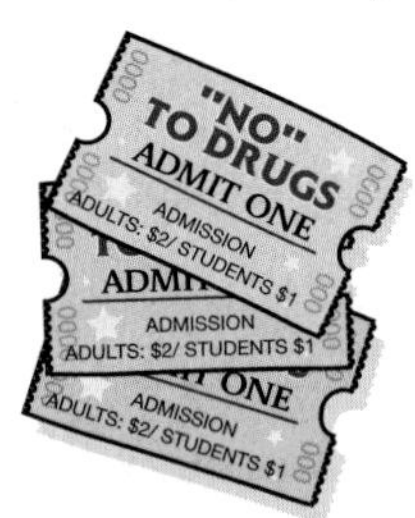

Skills Review

Simplify. Assume that no variable equals 0. (Lesson 6-1)

57. $f^{-7} \cdot f^4$ $\frac{1}{f^3}$

58. $(3x^2)^3$ $27x^6$

59. $(2y)(4xy^3)$ $8xy^4$

60. $\left(\frac{3}{5}c^2f\right)\left(\frac{4}{3}cd\right)^2$ $\frac{16}{15}c^4d^2f$

Differentiated Instruction

BL

Extension Have students flip 50 pennies and count the number of heads. Then have students remove those pennies that landed on heads and repeat the activity. Students should record their results and make a plot of the trial number versus the number of heads counted in that trial. Have students graph their data and then explain why, in theory, their data should be modeled by the equation $y = \left(\frac{1}{2}\right)^x$.

482 Chapter 8 Exponential and Logarithmic Functions and Relations

EXPLORE 8-2 Graphing Technology Lab
Solving Exponential Equations and Inequalities

FL Math Online glencoe.com
- Other Calculator Keystrokes
- Graphing Technology Personal Tutor

NGSSS MA.912.A.8.5 **Solve** logarithmic and **exponential equations.**

You can use a TI-83/84 Plus graphing calculator to solve exponential equations by graphing or by using the table feature. To do this, you will write the equations as systems of equations.

ACTIVITY 1

Solve $3^{x-4} = \frac{1}{9}$.

Step 1 Graph each side of the equation as a separate function. Enter 3^{x-4} as Y1. Enter $\frac{1}{9}$ as Y2. Be sure to include parentheses around each exponent. Then graph the two equations.

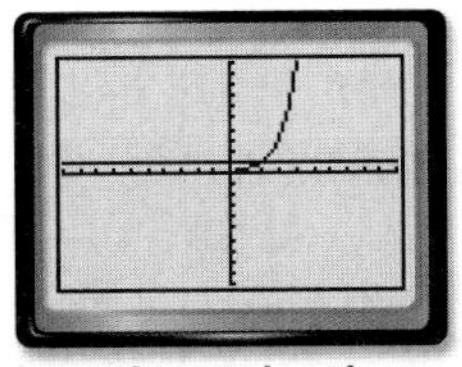

[−10, 10] scl: 1 by [−1, 1] scl: 0.1

Step 2 Use the intersect feature.

You can use the intersect feature on the CALC menu to approximate the ordered pair of the point at which the graphs cross.

The calculator screen shows that the x-coordinate of the point at which the curves cross is 2. Therefore, the solution of the equation is 2.

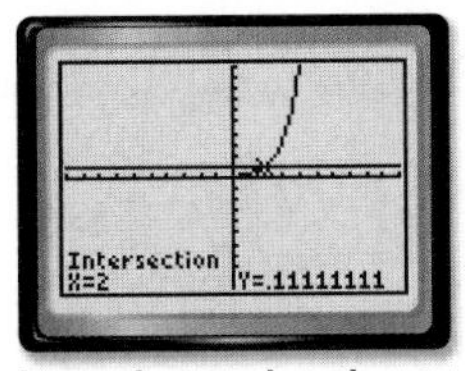

[−10, 10] scl: 1 by [−1, 1] scl: 0.1

Step 3 Use the TABLE feature.

You can also use the table feature to locate the point at which the curves intersect.

The table displays x-values and corresponding y-values for each graph. Examine the table to find the x-value for which the y-values of the graphs are equal.

At $x = 2$, both functions have a y-value of $0.\overline{1}$ or $\frac{1}{9}$. Thus, the solution of the equation is 2.

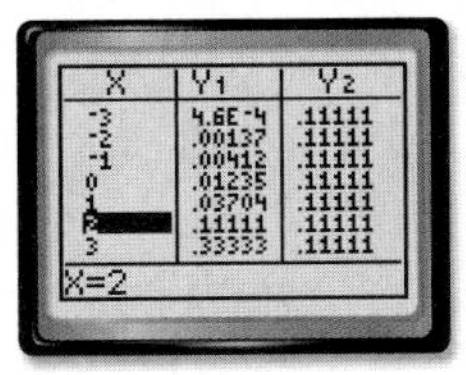

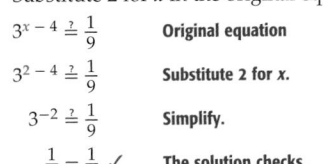

CHECK Substitute 2 for x in the original equation.

$3^{x-4} \stackrel{?}{=} \frac{1}{9}$	**Original equation**
$3^{2-4} \stackrel{?}{=} \frac{1}{9}$	**Substitute 2 for x.**
$3^{-2} \stackrel{?}{=} \frac{1}{9}$	**Simplify.**
$\frac{1}{9} = \frac{1}{9}$ ✓	**The solution checks.**

A similar procedure can be used to solve exponential inequalities using a graphing calculator.

EXPLORE 8-2 Lesson Notes

1 FOCUS

Objective Use a graphing calculator to solve exponential equations by graphing or by using the table feature.

Materials

- TI-83/84 Plus or other graphing calculator

Teaching Tip

In Step 1 of Activity 1, remind students to include parentheses around the exponent.

2 TEACH

Working in Cooperative Groups

Put students in groups of two or three, mixing abilities. Then have groups complete Activities 1 and 2 and Exercises 1 and 9.

Activity 1

- Before discussing Activity 1, use a simple equation such as $2x = 6$ to remind students how the equation can be solved by graphing. Graph the equations $y = 2x$ and $y = 6$ and then identify the point of intersection of the graphs.
- Ask students why it is necessary in Step 1 to enter the equation using parentheses around the exponent.
- Have students substitute the solution to Activity 1 into the original equation to verify that it is correct.

Activity 2

- In Activity 2, make sure students understand why the inequality needs to be rewritten as a system of inequalities.

Practice Have students complete Exercises 2–9.

3 ASSESS

Formative Assessment

Use Exercises 4 and 9 to assess whether students comprehend how to use a graphing calculator to solve exponential equations and inequalities.

From Concrete to Abstract

Have students explain how the solution set for Activity 2 would change if the inequality were $2^{x-2} \leq 0.5^{x-3}$.

ACTIVITY 2

Solve $2^{x-2} \geq 0.5^{x-3}$.

Step 1 Enter the related inequalities.

Rewrite the problem as a system of inequalities.

The first inequality is $2^{x-2} \geq y$ or $y \leq 2^{x-2}$. Since this inequality includes the *less than or equal to* symbol, shade below the curve.

First enter the boundary, and then use the arrow and [ENTER] keys to choose the shade below icon.

The second inequality is $y \geq 0.5^{x-3}$. Shade above the curve since this inequality contains *greater than or equal to.*

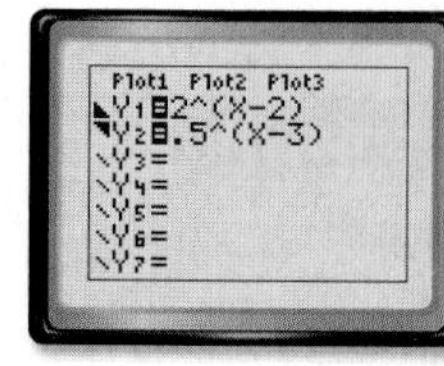

KEYSTROKES: [Y=] [◄] [◄] [ENTER] [ENTER] [ENTER] [►] [►] 2 [^] [(] [X,T,θ,n] [−] 2 [)] [ENTER] [◄] [◄] [ENTER] [ENTER] [►] [►] .5 [^] [(] [X,T,θ,n] [−] 3 [)]

Step 2 Graph the system.

KEYSTROKES: [GRAPH]

The x-values of the points in the region where the shadings overlap is the solution set of the original inequality. Using the **intersect** feature, you can conclude that the solution set is $\{x \mid x \geq 2.5\}$.

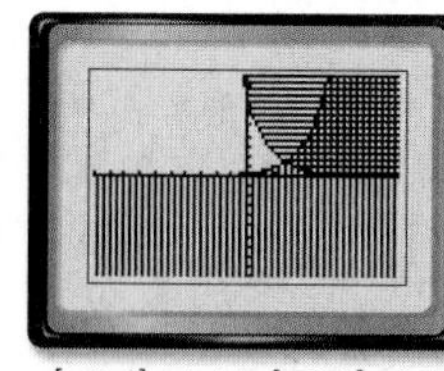

[−2, 8] scl: 1 by [−2, 8] scl: 1

Step 3 Use the TABLE feature.

Verify using the TABLE feature. Set up the table to show x-values in increments of 0.5.

KEYSTROKES: [2nd] [TBLSET] 0 [ENTER] .5 [ENTER] [2nd] [TABLE]

Notice that for x-values greater than $x = 2.5$, Y1 > Y2. This confirms that the solution of the inequality is $\{x \mid x \geq 2.5\}$.

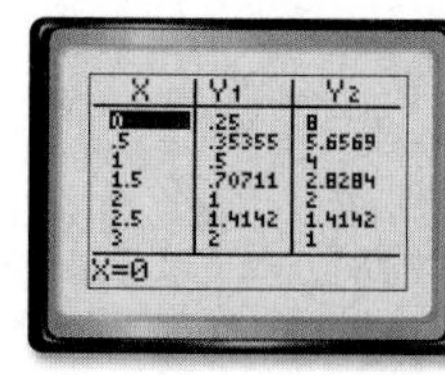

Exercises

10. Because the system consists of the expressions on both sides of the original equation or inequality, whatever values are solutions of the system will satisfy the original equation or inequality.

Solve each equation or inequality.

1. $9^{x-1} = \frac{1}{81}$ **−1**
2. $4^{x+3} = 2^{5x}$ **2**
3. $5^{x-1} = 2^x$ **1.76**
4. $3.5^{x+2} = 1.75^{x+3}$ **−1.2**
5. $-3^{x+4} = -0.5^{2x+3}$ **−2.6**
6. $6^{2-x} - 4 < -0.25^{x-2.5}$ **$\{x \mid x > 1.8\}$**
7. $16^{x-1} > 2^{2x+2}$ **$\{x \mid x > 3\}$**
8. $3^x - 4 \leq 5^{\frac{x}{2}}$ **$\{x \mid x < 2\}$**
9. $5^{x+3} \leq 2^{x+4}$ **$\{x \mid x \leq -2.2\}$**

10. **WRITING IN MATH** Explain why this technique of graphing a system of equations or inequalities works to solve exponential equations and inequalities.

484 Chapter 8 Exponential and Logarithmic Functions and Relations

Solving Exponential Equations and Inequalities

Then
You graphed exponential functions. (Lesson 8-1)

Now
- Solve exponential equations.
- Solve exponential inequalities.

NGSSS
MA.912.A.8.5 Solve logarithmic and **exponential equations.**
MA.912.A.10.3 Decide whether a given statement is always, sometimes, or never true (statements involving linear or quadratic expressions, equations, or inequalities rational or radical expressions or logarithmic or exponential functions).

New Vocabulary
exponential equation
compound interest
exponential inequality

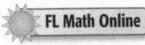

FL Math Online
glencoe.com

Why?

Membership on Internet social networking sites tends to increase exponentially. The membership growth of one Web site can be modeled by the equation $y = 2.2(1.37)^x$, where x is the number of years since 2004 and y is the number of members in millions.

You can use $y = 2.2(1.37)^x$ to determine how many members there will be in a given year, or to determine the year in which membership was at a certain level.

Solve Exponential Equations In an **exponential equation**, variables occur as exponents.

Key Concept

Property of Equality for Exponential Functions

Words Let $b > 0$ and $b \neq 1$. Then $b^x = b^y$ if and only if $x = y$.

Example If $3^x = 3^5$, then $x = 5$. If $x = 5$, then $3^x = 3^5$.

The Equality Property can be used to solve exponential equations.

EXAMPLE 1 Solve Exponential Equations

Solve each equation.

a. $2^x = 8^3$

$2^x = 8^3$	Original equation
$2^x = (2^3)^3$	Rewrite 8 as 2^3.
$2^x = 2^9$	Power of a Power
$x = 9$	Property of Equality for Exponential Functions

b. $9^{2x-1} = 3^{6x}$

$9^{2x-1} = 3^{6x}$	Original equation
$(3^2)^{2x-1} = 3^{6x}$	Rewrite 9 as 3^2.
$3^{4x-2} = 3^{6x}$	Power of a Power
$4x - 2 = 6x$	Property of Equality for Exponential Functions
$-2 = 2x$	Subtract $4x$ from each side.
$-1 = x$	Divide each side by 2.

Guided Practice

1A. $4^{2n-1} = 64$ 2 **1B.** $5^{5x} = 125^{x+2}$ 3

Personal Tutor glencoe.com

8-2 Lesson Notes

1 FOCUS

Vertical Alignment

Before Lesson 8-2
Graph exponential functions.

Lesson 8-2
Solve exponential equations.
Solve exponential inequalities.

After Lesson 8-2
Develop the definition of logarithms by exploring and describing the relationship between exponential functions and their inverses.

2 TEACH

Scaffolding Questions

Have students read the *Why?* section of the lesson.

Ask:
- What value of x represents the year 2010? 6
- How many members are represented by $y = 5.2$? 5,200,000
- How many members will there be in 2012? about 27,300,000

Lesson 8-2 Resources

Resource	Approaching-Level	On-Level	Beyond-Level	English Learners
Teacher Edition	• Differentiated Instruction, p. 487	• Differentiated Instruction, pp. 487, 489, 491	• Differentiated Instruction, pp. 489, 491	
Chapter Resource Masters	• Study Guide and Intervention, pp. 12–13 • Skills Practice, p. 14 • Practice, p. 15 • Word Problem Practice, p. 16	• Study Guide and Intervention, pp. 12–13 • Skills Practice, p. 14 • Practice, p. 15 • Word Problem Practice, p. 16 • Enrichment, p. 17 • Graphing Calculator Activity, p. 18	• Practice, p. 15 • Word Problem Practice, p. 16 • Enrichment, p. 17	• Study Guide and Intervention, pp. 12–13 • Skills Practice, p. 14 • Practice, p. 15 • Word Problem Practice, p. 16
Transparencies	• 5-Minute Check Transparency 8-2	• 5-Minute Check Transparency 8-2	• 5-Minute Check Transparency 8-2	• 5-Minute Check Transparency 8-2
Other	• Study Notebook	• Study Notebook	• Study Notebook	• Study Notebook

Solve Exponential Equations

Example 1 shows how to solve an exponential equation. **Example 2** shows how to write an exponential function to model a real-world situation. **Example 3** shows how to determine compound interest using an exponential function.

Formative Assessment

Use the Guided Practice exercises after each example to determine students' understanding of concepts.

Additional Examples

1 Solve each equation.

a. $3^x = 9^4$ 8

b. $2^{5x} = 4^{2x-1}$ −2

2 **POPULATION** In 2000, the population of Phoenix was 1,321,045. By 2007, it was estimated at 1,512,986.

a. Write an exponential function that could be used to model the population of Phoenix. Write *x* in terms of the number of years since 2000. $y = 1{,}321{,}045(1.0196)^x$

b. Predict the population of Phoenix in 2013. 1,700,221

Additional Examples also in Interactive Classroom PowerPoint® Presentations

IWB INTERACTIVE WHITEBOARD READY

You can use information about growth or decay to write the equation of an exponential function.

Real-World Link

In 2005, the U.S. recycling rate of 32% percent prevented the release of approximately 49 million metric tons of carbon into the air—roughly the amount emitted annually by 39 million cars.

Source: Environmental Protection Agency

Real-World EXAMPLE 2 Write an Exponential Function

SCIENCE Kristin starts an experiment with 7500 bacteria cells. After 4 hours, there are 23,000 cells.

a. Write an exponential function that could be used to model the number of bacteria after *x* hours if the number of bacteria changes at the same rate.

At the beginning of the experiment, the time is 0 hours and there are 7500 bacteria cells. Thus, the *y*-intercept, and the value of *a*, is 7500.

When $x = 4$, the number of bacteria cells is 23,000. Substitute these values into an exponential function to determine the value of *b*.

$y = ab^x$	Exponential function
$23{,}000 = 7500 \cdot b^4$	Replace *x* with 4, *y* with 23,000, and *a* with 7500.
$3.067 \approx b^4$	Divide each side by 7500.
$\sqrt[4]{3.067} \approx b$	Take the 4th root of each side.
$1.323 \approx b$	Use a calculator.

An equation that models the number of bacteria is $y \approx 7500(1.323)^x$.

b. How many bacteria cells can be expected in the sample after 12 hours?

$y \approx 7500(1.323)^x$	Modeling equation
$\approx 7500(1.323)^{12}$	Replace *x* with 12.
$\approx 215{,}665$	Use a calculator.

There will be approximately 215,665 bacteria cells after 12 hours.

Guided Practice

2. RECYCLING A manufacturer distributed 3.2 million aluminum cans in 2005.

A. In 2010, the manufacturer distributed 420,000 cans made from the recycled cans it had previously distributed. Assuming that the recycling rate continues, write an equation to model the distribution each year of cans that are made from recycled aluminum. $y = 3.2(0.67)^x$

B. How many cans made from recycled aluminum can be expected in the year 2050? none

Personal Tutor glencoe.com

Exponential functions are used in situations involving compound interest. **Compound interest** is interest paid on the principal of an investment and any previously earned interest.

Key Concept Compound Interest

You can calculate compound interest using the following formula.

$$A = P\left(1 + \frac{r}{n}\right)^{nt},$$

where *A* is the amount in the account after *t* years, *P* is the principal amount invested, *r* is the annual interest rate, and *n* is the number of compounding periods each year.

Focus on Mathematical Content

Solving Exponential Equations Simple exponential equations can be solved by rewriting one or both sides of the equation so that the bases are the same. Once that has been achieved, the Property of Equality for Exponential Functions can be used to solve for the variable.

486 Chapter 8 Exponential and Logarithmic Functions and Relations

EXAMPLE 3 Compound Interest

An investment account pays 4.2% annual interest compounded monthly. If $2500 is invested in this account, what will be the balance after 15 years?

Understand Find the total amount in the account after 15 years.

Plan Use the compound interest formula.

$P = 2500$, $r = 0.042$, $n = 12$, and $t = 15$

Solve $A = P\left(1 + \frac{r}{n}\right)^{nt}$ **Compound Interest Formula**

$= 2500\left(1 + \frac{0.042}{12}\right)^{12 \cdot 15}$ **$P = 2500, r = 0.042, n = 12, t = 15$**

≈ 4688.87 **Use a calculator.**

Check Graph the corresponding equation $y = 2500(1.0035)^{12t}$. Use CALC: value to find y when $x = 15$.

The y-value 4688.8662 is very close to 4688.87, so the answer is reasonable.

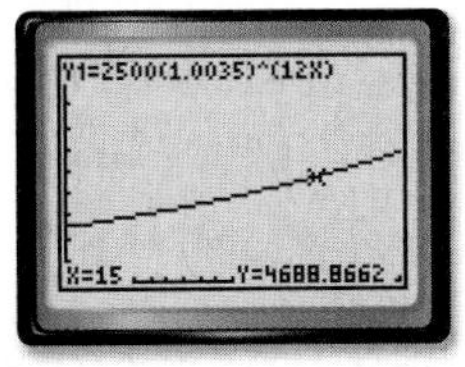

Guided Practice

3. Find the account balance after 20 years if $100 is placed in an account that pays 1.2% interest compounded twice a month. $127.12

Personal Tutor glencoe.com

Watch Out!

Percents Remember to convert all percents to decimal form; 4.2% is 0.042.

Solve Exponential Inequalities An **exponential inequality** is an inequality involving exponential functions.

Key Concept

Property of Inequality for Exponential Functions

Words Let $b > 1$. Then $b^x > b^y$ if and only if $x > y$, and $b^x < b^y$ if and only if $x < y$.

Example If $2^x > 2^6$, then $x > 6$. If $x > 6$, then $2^x > 2^6$.

This property also holds true for $\leq$ and $\geq$.

EXAMPLE 4 Solve Exponential Inequalities

Solve $16^{2x-3} < 8$.

$16^{2x-3} < 8$	**Original inequality**
$(2^4)^{2x-3} < 2^3$	**Rewrite 16 as 2^4 and 8 as 2^3.**
$2^{8x-12} < 2^3$	**Power of a Power**
$8x - 12 < 3$	**Property of Inequality for Exponential Functions**
$8x < 15$	**Add 12 to each side.**
$x < \frac{15}{8}$	**Divide each side by 8.**

Guided Practice

Solve each inequality.

4A. $3^{2x-1} \geq \frac{1}{243}$ $x \geq -2$

4B. $2^{x+2} > \frac{1}{32}$ $x > -7$

Personal Tutor glencoe.com

Additional Example

3 An investment account pays 5.4% annual interest compounded quarterly. If $4000 is placed in this account, find the balance after 8 years. $6143.56

Solve Exponential Inequalities

Example 4 shows how to solve an exponential inequality.

Additional Example

4 Solve $5^{3-2x} > \frac{1}{625}$. $x < \frac{7}{2}$

TEACH with TECH

BLOG Have students write a blog entry explaining the properties of equality and inequality for exponential functions.

Differentiated Instruction AL OL

If you want students to check to see if their answer is correct,

Then remind students to choose any value in the solution interval and see if it satisfies the original inequality.

Lesson 8-2 Solving Exponential Equations and Inequalities 487

3 PRACTICE

Formative Assessment

Use Exercises 1–8 to check for understanding.

Use the chart at the bottom of this page to customize assignments for your students.

Check Your Understanding

Example 1 p. 485

Solve each equation.

1. $3^{5x} = 27^{2x-4}$ **12**
2. $16^{2y-3} = 4^{y+1}$ $\frac{7}{3}$
3. $2^{6x} = 32^{x-2}$ **−10**
4. $49^{x+5} = 7^{8x-6}$ $\frac{8}{3}$

Example 2 p. 486

5. **SCIENCE** Mitosis is a process in which one cell divides into two. The *Escherichia coli* is one of the fastest growing bacteria. It can reproduce itself in 15 minutes.
   a. Write an exponential function to represent the number of cells c after t minutes.
   b. If you begin with one *Escherichia coli* cell, how many cells will there be in one hour?

5a. $c = 2^{\frac{t}{15}}$
5b. 16 cells

Example 3 p. 487

6. A certificate of deposit (CD) pays 2.25% annual interest compounded biweekly. If you deposit $500 into this CD, what will the balance be after 6 years? **$572.23**

Example 4 p. 487

Solve each inequality.

7. $4^{2x+6} \leq 64^{2x-4}$ $x \geq 4.5$
8. $25^{y-3} \leq \left(\frac{1}{125}\right)^{y+2}$ $y \leq 0$

Practice and Problem Solving

● = **Step-by-Step Solutions** begin on page R20.
Extra Practice begins on page 947.

Example 1 p. 485

Solve each equation.

9. $8^{4x+2} = 64$ **0**
10. $5^{x-6} = 125$ **9**
11. $81^{a+2} = 3^{3a+1}$ **−7**
12. $256^{b+2} = 4^{2-2b}$ **−1**
13. $9^{3c+1} = 27^{3c-1}$ $\frac{5}{3}$
14. $8^{2y+4} = 16^{y+1}$ **−4**

Example 2 p. 486

15. **MONEY** In 2003, My-Lien received $10,000 from her grandmother. Her parents invested all of the money, and by 2015, the amount will have grown to $16,960.
    a. Write an exponential function that could be used to model the money y. Write the function in terms of x, the number of years since 2003. $y = 10{,}000(1.045)^x$
    b. Assume that the amount of money continues to grow at the same rate. What would be the balance in the account in 2025? **about $26,336.52**

Write an exponential function for the graph that passes through the given points.

16. (0, 6.4) and (3, 100) $y = 6.4(2.5)^x$
17. (0, 256) and (4, 81) $y = 256(0.75)^x$
18. (0, 128) and (5, 371,293) $y = 128(4.926)^x$
19. (0, 144), and (4, 21,609) $y = 144(3.5)^x$

Example 3 p. 487

20. Find the balance of an account after 7 years if $700 is deposited into an account paying 4.3% interest compounded monthly. **$945.34**
21. Determine how much is in a retirement account after 20 years if $5000 was invested at 6.05% interest compounded weekly. **$16,755.63**
22. A savings account offers 0.7% interest compounded bimonthly. If $110 is deposited in this account, what will the balance be after 15 years? **$122.17**
23. A college savings account pays 13.2% annual interest compounded semiannually. What is the balance of an account after 12 years if $21,000 was initially deposited? **$97,362.61**

Example 4 p. 487

Solve each inequality.

24. $625 \geq 5^{a+8}$ $a \leq -4$
25. $10^{5b+2} > 1000$ $b > \frac{1}{5}$
26. $\left(\frac{1}{64}\right)^{c-2} < 32^{2c}$ $c > \frac{3}{4}$
27. $\left(\frac{1}{27}\right)^{2d-2} \leq 81^{d+4}$ $d \geq -1$
28. $\left(\frac{1}{9}\right)^{3t+5} \geq \left(\frac{1}{243}\right)^{t-6}$ $t \leq -40$
29. $\left(\frac{1}{36}\right)^{w+2} < \left(\frac{1}{216}\right)^{4w}$ $w < \frac{2}{5}$

Differentiated Homework Options

Level	Assignment	Two-Day Option	
AL Basic	9–29, 42–43, 45–73	9–29 odd, 50–53	10–28 even, 42–43, 45–49, 54–73
OL Core	9–29 odd, 30–31, 33–37 odd, 38–43, 45–73	9–29, 50–53	30–43, 45–49, 54–73
BL Advanced	30–67, (optional: 68–73)		

30. **SCIENCE** A mug of hot chocolate is 90°C at time $t = 0$. It is surrounded by air at a constant temperature of 20°C. If stirred steadily, its temperature in Celsius after t minutes will be $y(t) = 20 + 70(1.071)^{-t}$.

a. Find the temperature of the hot chocolate after 15 minutes. **45.02° C**

b. Find the temperature of the hot chocolate after 30 minutes. **28.94° C**

c. The optimum drinking temperature is 60°C. Will the mug of hot chocolate be at or below this temperature after 10 minutes? **below**

31. **ANIMALS** Studies show that an animal will defend a territory, with area in square yards, that is directly proportional to the 1.31 power of the animal's weight in pounds.

a. If a 45-pound beaver will defend 170 square yards, write an equation for the area a defended by a beaver weighing w pounds. $a = 1.16w^{1.31}$

b. Scientists believe that thousands of years ago, the beaver's ancestors were 11 feet long and weighed 430 pounds. Use your equation to determine the area defended by these animals. **about 3268 yd²**

Solve each equation.

32. $\left(\frac{1}{2}\right)^{4x+1} = 8^{2x+1}$ $-\frac{2}{5}$

33. $\left(\frac{1}{5}\right)^{x-5} = 25^{3x+2}$ $\frac{1}{7}$

34. $216 = \left(\frac{1}{6}\right)^{x+3}$ -6

35. $\left(\frac{1}{8}\right)^{3x+4} = \left(\frac{1}{4}\right)^{-2x+4}$ $-\frac{4}{13}$

36. $\left(\frac{2}{3}\right)^{5x+1} = \left(\frac{27}{8}\right)^{x-4}$ $\frac{11}{8}$

37. $\left(\frac{25}{81}\right)^{2x+1} = \left(\frac{729}{125}\right)^{-3x+1}$ 1

38. **POPULATION** In 1950, the world population was about 2.556 billion. By 1980, it had increased to about 4.458 billion. **d. See margin.**

a. Write an exponential function of the form $y = abx$ that could be used to model the world population y in billions for 1950 to 1980. Write the equation in terms of x, the number of years since 1950. (Round the value of b to the nearest ten-thousandth.) $y = 2.556(1.0187)^x$

b. Suppose the population continued to grow at that rate. Estimate the population in 2000. **6.455 billion**

c. In 2000, the population of the world was about 6.08 billion. Compare your estimate to the actual population.

d. Use the equation you wrote in Part **a** to estimate the world population in the year 2020. How accurate do you think the estimate is? Explain your reasoning.

39. **TREES** The diameter of the base of a tree trunk in centimeters varies directly with the $\frac{3}{2}$ power of its height in meters.

a. A young sequoia tree is 6 meters tall, and the diameter of its base is 19.1 centimeters. Use this information to write an equation for the diameter d of the base of a sequoia tree if its height is h meters high. $d = 1.30h^{\frac{3}{2}}$

b. Refer to the information at the left. Find the diameter of the General Sherman Tree at its base. **about 1001 cm**

40. **FINANCIAL LITERACY** Mrs. Jackson has two different retirement investment plans from which to choose.

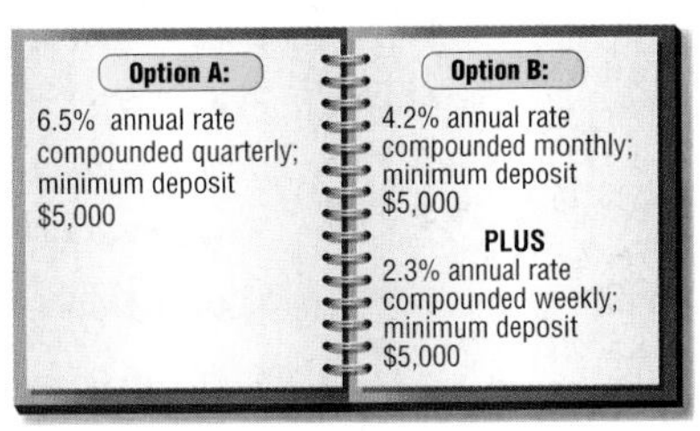

a. Write equations for Option A and Option B given the minimum deposits.

b. Draw a graph to show the balances for each investment option after t years. **See margin.**

c. Explain whether Option A or Option B is the better investment choice.

Real-World Link

One of the oldest living organisms on Earth, the General Sherman Tree in Sequoia National Park, California, is between 2100 and 2500 years old. It is the tallest of the giant sequoias, measuring approximately 84 meters.

Source: National Park Service

38c. The prediction was about 375 million greater than the actual.

40a. $A = 5000\left(\frac{4.065}{4}\right)^{4t}$; $A = 5000\left[\left(\frac{12.042}{12}\right)^{12t} + \left(\frac{52.023}{52}\right)^{52t}\right]$

40c. Sample answer: During the first 22 years, Option B is the better choice because the total is greater than that of Option A. However, after about 22 years, the balance of Option A exceeds that of Option B, so Option A is the better choice.

Additional Answers

38d. About 9.3498 billion; because the prediction for 2000 was greater than the actual population, this prediction is probably even higher than the actual population will be at the time.

40b.

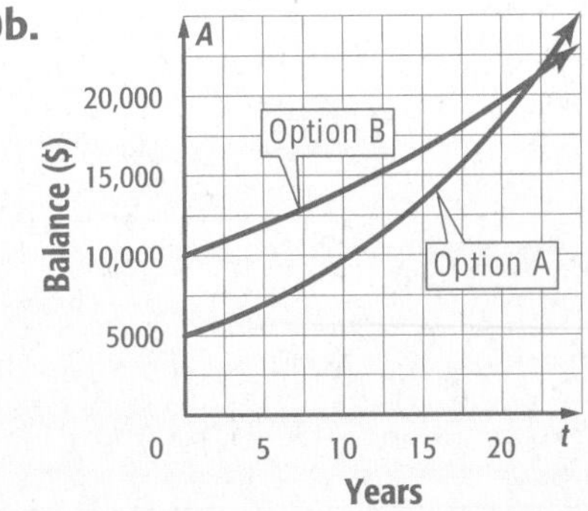

Differentiated Instruction

OL BL

Extension Allow students to develop their sense of consumerism by providing them with an initial deposit amount and having them shop around for the best interest rates. Students should record relevant information including bank name, account type, interest rate, how often interest is compounded, and restrictions on the account. Ask students to graph the growth of their initial deposit over time.

41. **MULTIPLE REPRESENTATIONS** In this problem, you will explore the rapid increase of an exponential function. A large sheet of paper is cut in half, and one of the resulting pieces is placed on top of the other. Then the pieces in the stack are cut in half and placed on top of each other. Suppose this procedure is repeated several times.

a. **CONCRETE** Perform this activity and count the number of sheets in the stack after the first cut. How many pieces will there be after the second cut? How many pieces after the third cut? How many pieces after the fourth cut? **2, 4, 8, 16**

b. **TABULAR** Record your results in a table. **See Chapter 8 Answer Appendix.**

c. **SYMBOLIC** Use the pattern in the table to write an equation for the number of pieces in the stack after x cuts. $y = 2^x$

d. **ANALYTICAL** The thickness of ordinary paper is about 0.003 inch. Write an equation for the thickness of the stack of paper after x cuts. $y = 0.003(2)^x$

e. **ANALYTICAL** How thick will the stack of paper be after 30 cuts? **about 3,221,225.47 in.**

Real-World Link

In theory, if you repeated the process of cutting and stacking paper 42 times your stack of paper would reach the Moon.

43. Sample answer: Beth; Liz added the exponents instead of multiplying them when taking the power of a power.

45. Reducing the term will be more beneficial. The multiplier is 1.3756 for the 4-year and 1.3828 for the 6.5%.

46a. Always; 2^x will always be positive, and -8^{20x} will always be negative.

46b. Always; by definition the graph will always be increasing even if it is a small increase.

46c. Never; by definition the graph will always be decreasing even if it is a small decrease.

49. Sample answer: Divide the final amount by the initial amount. If n is the number of time intervals that pass, take the nth root of the answer.

H.O.T. Problems

Use Higher-Order Thinking Skills

42. **WRITING IN MATH** In a problem about compound interest, describe what happens as the compounding period becomes more frequent while the principal and overall time remain the same. **See Chapter 8 Answer Appendix.**

43. **ERROR ANALYSIS** Beth and Liz are solving $6^{x-3} > 36^{-x-1}$. Is either of them correct? Explain your reasoning.

Beth	Liz
$6^{x-3} > 36^{-x-1}$	$6^{x-3} > 36^{-x-1}$
$6^{x-3} > (6^2)^{-x-1}$	$6^{x-3} > (6^2)^{-x-1}$
$6^{x-3} > 6^{-2x-2}$	$6^{x-3} > 6^{-x+1}$
$x-3 > -2x-2$	$x-3 > -x+1$
$3x > 1$	$2x > 4$
$x > \frac{1}{3}$	$x > 2$

44. **CHALLENGE** Solve for x: $16^{18} + 16^{18} + 16^{18} + 16^{18} + 16^{18} = 4^x$. **37.1610**

45. **OPEN ENDED** What would be a more beneficial change to a 5-year loan at 8% interest compounded monthly: reducing the term to 4 years or reducing the interest rate to 6.5%?

46. **REASONING** Determine whether the following statements are *sometimes*, *always*, or *never* true. Explain your reasoning.

a. $2^x > -8^{20x}$ for all values of x.

b. The graph of an exponential growth equation is increasing.

c. The graph of an exponential decay equation is increasing.

47. **OPEN ENDED** Write an exponential inequality with a solution of $x \le 2$. **Sample answer: $4^x \le 4^2$**

48. **PROOF** Show that $27^{2x} \cdot 81^{x+1} = 3^{2x+2} \cdot 9^{4x+1}$. **See Chapter 8 Answer Appendix.**

49. **WRITING IN MATH** If you were given the initial and final amounts of a radioactive substance and the amount of time that passes, how would you determine the rate at which the amount was increasing or decreasing in order to write an equation?

Study Guide and Intervention

CRM pp. 12–13 AL OL ELL

8-2 Study Guide and Intervention

Solving Exponential Equations and Inequalities

Solve Exponential Equations All the properties of rational exponents that you know also apply to real exponents. Remember that $a^m \cdot a^n = a^{m+n}$, $(a^m)^n = a^{mn}$, and $a^m \div a^n = a^{m-n}$.

Property of Equality for Exponential Functions	If b is a positive number other than 1, then $b^x = b^y$ if and only if $x = y$.

Example 1 Solve $4^{x-1} = 2^{x+5}$.

$4^{x-1} = 2^{x+5}$	Original equation
$(2^2)^{x-1} = 2^{x+5}$	Rewrite 4 as 2^2.
$2(x-1) = x+5$	Prop. of Inequality for Exponential Functions
$2x - 2 = x + 5$	Distributive Property
$x = 7$	Subtract x and add 2 to each side.

Example 2 Write an exponential function whose graph passes through the points (0, 3) and (4, 81).

The y-intercept is (0, 3), so $a = 3$. Since the other point is (4, 81), $b = \sqrt[4]{\frac{81}{3}}$.

Simplifying $\sqrt[4]{\frac{81}{3}} = \sqrt[4]{27} \approx 2.280$, the equation is $y = 3(2.280)^x$.

Exercises

Solve each equation.

1. $3^{2x-1} = 3^{x+2}$ **3**
2. $2^{3x} = 4^{x+2}$ **4**
3. $3^{2x-1} = \frac{1}{9}$ $-\frac{1}{2}$
4. $4^{x+1} = 8^{2x+3}$ $-\frac{7}{4}$
5. $8^{x-2} = \frac{1}{16}$ $\frac{2}{3}$
6. $25^{2x} = 125^{x+2}$ **6**
7. $9^{x+1} = 27^{x+4}$ **−10**
8. $36^{2x+4} = 216^{x+5}$ **7**
9. $\left(\frac{1}{64}\right)^{x-2} = 16^{3x+1}$ $\frac{4}{9}$

Write an exponential function for the graph that passes through the given points.

10. (0, 4) and (2, 36) $y = 4(3)^x$
11. (0, 6) and (1, 81) $y = 6(13.5)^x$
12. (0, 5) and (6, 320) $y = 5(2)^x$
13. (0, 2) and (5, 486) $y = 2(3)^x$
14. (0, 8) and $\left(3, \frac{27}{8}\right)$ $y = 8\left(\frac{3}{4}\right)^x$
15. (0, 1) and (4, 625) $y = (5)^x$
16. (0, 3) and (3, 24) $y = 3(2)^x$
17. (0, 12) and (4, 144) $y = 12(1.861)^x$
18. (0, 9) and (2, 49) $y = 9(2.333)^x$

Chapter 8 12 Glencoe Algebra 2

Practice

CRM p. 15 AL OL BL ELL

8-2 Practice

Solving Exponential Equations and Inequalities

Solve each equation.

1. $4^{x+35} = 64^{x-3}$ $x = 22$
2. $\left(\frac{1}{64}\right)^{0.5x-3} = 8^{9x-2}$ $x = 0.8$
3. $3^{x-4} = 9^{x+28}$ $x = -60$
4. $\left(\frac{1}{4}\right)^{2x+2} = 64^{x-1}$ $x = \frac{1}{5}$
5. $\left(\frac{1}{2}\right)^{x-3} = 16^{3x+1}$ $x = \frac{-1}{13}$
6. $3^{6x-2} = \left(\frac{1}{9}\right)^{x+1}$ $x = 0$

Write an exponential function for the graph that passes through the given points.

7. (0, 5) and (4, 3125) $y = 5(5)^x$
8. (0, 8) and (4, 2048) $y = 8(4)^x$
9. $(0, \frac{3}{4})$ and (2, 36.75) $y = .75(7)^x$
10. (0, −0.2) and (−3, −3.125) $y = -0.2(0.4)^x$
11. (0, 15) and $\left(2, \frac{15}{16}\right)$ $y = 15(\frac{1}{4})^x$
12. (0, 0.7) and $\left(\frac{1}{2}, 3.5\right)$ $y = 0.7(25)^x$

Solve each inequality.

13. $400 > \left(\frac{1}{20}\right)^{7x+8}$ $x > -\frac{10}{7}$
14. $10^{2x+7} \ge 1000^x$ $x \le 7$
15. $\left(\frac{1}{16}\right)^{3x-4} \le 64^{x-1}$ $x \ge \frac{11}{9}$
16. $\left(\frac{1}{8}\right)^{x-6} < 4^{4x+5}$ $x > \frac{8}{11}$
17. $\left(\frac{1}{36}\right)^{x+8} \le 216^{x-3}$ $x \ge -\frac{7}{5}$
18. $128^{x+3} < \left(\frac{1}{1024}\right)^{2x}$ $x < \frac{7}{9}$

19. At time t, there are 216^{t+18} bacteria of type A and 36^{2t+8} bacteria of type b organisms in a sample. When will the number of each type of bacteria be equal? $t = 38$

Chapter 8 15 Glencoe Algebra 2

Lesson 8-2

Word Problem Practice

CRM p. 16 AL OL BL ELL

8-2 Word Problem Practice

Solving Exponential Equations and Inequalities

1. **BANKING** The certificate of deposit that Siobhan bought on her birthday pays interest according to the formula $A = 1200\left(1 + \frac{0.052}{12}\right)^{48}$. What is the annual interest rate? **5.2%**

2. **INTEREST** Marty invested $2000 in an account that pays at least 4% annual interest. He wants to see how much money he will have over the next few years. Graph the inequality $y \ge 2000(1 + 0.04)^x$ to show his potential earnings.

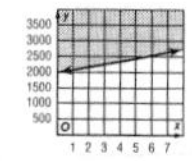

3. **BUSINESS** Ahmed's consulting firm began with 23 clients. After 7 years, he now has 393 clients. Write an exponential equation describing the firm's growth. $y = 23(1.5)^x$

4. **POPULATION** In 2000, the world population was calculated to be 6,071,675,206. In 2008, it was 6,679,493,893. Write an exponential equation to model the growth of the world population over these 8 years. Round the base to the nearest thousandth.
Source: U.S. Census Bureau
$y = 6{,}071{,}675{,}206(1.012)^x$

5. **BUSINESS** Ingrid and Alberto each opened a business in 2000. Ingrid started with 2 employees and in 2003 she had 50 employees. Alberto began with 32 employees and in 2007 he had 310 employees. Since 2000, each company has experienced exponential growth.

a. Write an exponential equation representing the growth for each business. **Ingrid: $y = 2(2.924)^x$; Alberto: $y = 32(1.383)^x$**

b. Calculate the number of employees each company had in 2005. **Ingrid: 427; Alberto: 162**

c. Is it reasonable to expect that a business can experience exponential growth? Explain your answer. **Sample answer: No; a business cannot grow exponentially indefinitely.**

Chapter 8 16 Glencoe Algebra 2

Enrichment

CRM p. 17 OL BL

8-2 Enrichment

Richter Scale

In 1935, Charles Richter and Beno Gutenberg working in California recognized that seismic waves that are radiated by earthquakes could be a way to estimate the magnitude or strength of an earthquake. Using a piece of equipment known as a Wood-Anderson seismograph, they developed the Richter scale. They discovered that the magnitude of an earthquake is equal to the base-10 logarithm of the amplitude of the wave recorded by the seismograph plus a correction factor based on the location of the seismograph or $M = \log_{10} A + CF$. With the magnitude, the amount of seismic energy in erg of the earthquake can be calculated using the formula $E_s = 10^{11.8 + 1.5M}$

1. The largest earthquake ever recorded was in Chile in 1960. It released about $1.995 + 10^{25}$ erg.

a. On the Richter scale what was the magnitude of this earthquake? Round to the nearest tenth. **9**

b. Assume that the seismograph that records this has a correction factor of 6.2, what would be the amplitude of wave recorded by the seismograph? Round to the nearest tenth. **630.95**

2. The amount of seismic energy released divided by 6.4×10^8 would give the number of ounces of TNT (dynamite) needed for a comparable destructive force.

Lesson 8-2

Multiple Representations In Exercise 41, students use a concrete model, a table of values, an equation, and analysis to describe an exponential function.

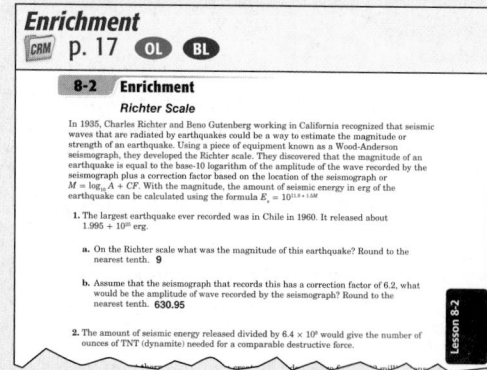

NGSSS PRACTICE 912.A.3.4, 912.A.4.1, 912.A.8.1

50. $3 \times 10^{-4} =$ **B**

A. $-30{,}000$ C. -120
B. 0.0003 D 0.00003

51. Which of the following could *not* be a solution to $5 - 3x < -3$? **F**

F. 2.5 H. 3.5
G. 3 I. 4

52. **GRIDDED RESPONSE** The three angles of a triangle are $3x$, $x + 10$, and $2x - 40$. Find the measure of the smallest angle in the triangle. **30**

53. **ACT/SAT** Which of the following is equivalent to $(x)(x)(x)(x)$ for all x? **B**

A. $4x$ C. $x + 4$
B. x^4 D. $2x^2$

Spiral Review

Graph each function. (Lesson 8-1) **54–56. See margin.**

54. $y = 2(3)^x$ **55.** $y = 5(2)^x$ **56.** $y = 4\left(\frac{1}{3}\right)^x$

Solve each equation. (Lesson 7-7)

57. $\sqrt{x+5} - 3 = 0$ **4**
58. $\sqrt{3t-5} - 3 = 4$ **18**
59. $\sqrt[4]{2x-1} = 2$ **8.5**
60. $\sqrt{x-6} - \sqrt{x} = 3$ **no solution**
61. $\sqrt[3]{5m+2} = 3$ **5**
62. $(6n-5)^{\frac{1}{3}} + 3 = -2$ **−20**
63. $(5x+7)^{\frac{1}{5}} + 3 = 5$ **5**
64. $(3x-2)^{\frac{1}{5}} + 6 = 5$ $\frac{1}{3}$
65. $(7x-1)^{\frac{1}{3}} + 4 = 2$ **−1**

66. **SALES** A salesperson earns \$10 an hour plus a 10% commission on sales. Write a function to describe the salesperson's income. If the salesperson wants to earn \$1000 in a 40-hour week, what should his sales be? (Lesson 7-2) $I(m) = 400 + 0.1m$; **\$6000**

67. **STATE FAIR** A dairy makes three types of cheese—cheddar, Monterey Jack, and Swiss—and sells the cheese in three booths at the state fair. At the beginning of one day, the first booth received x pounds of each type of cheese. The second booth received y pounds of each type of cheese, and the third booth received z pounds of each type of cheese. By the end of the day, the dairy had sold 131 pounds of cheddar, 291 pounds of Monterey Jack, and 232 pounds of Swiss. The table below shows the percent of the cheese delivered in the morning that was sold at each booth. How many pounds of cheddar cheese did each booth receive in the morning? (Lesson 3-5) **booth 1, 190 lb; booth 2, 150 lb; booth 3, 100 lb**

Type	Booth 1	Booth 2	Booth 3
Cheddar	40%	30%	10%
Monterey Jack	40%	90%	80%
Swiss	30%	70%	70%

Skills Review

69. $x^2 - 1$; $x^2 - 6x + 11$ **70.** $-2x^2 - 1$; $4x^2 - 4x + 2$
71. $-15x - 5$; $-15x + 25$ **72.** $x^3 - 2$; $x^3 - 6x^2 + 12x - 8$

Find $[g \circ h](x)$ and $[h \circ g](x)$. (Lesson 7-1)

68. $h(x) = 2x - 1$, $g(x) = 3x + 4$ **$6x + 1$; $6x + 7$**
69. $h(x) = x^2 + 2$, $g(x) = x - 3$
70. $h(x) = x^2 + 1$, $g(x) = -2x + 1$
71. $h(x) = -5x$, $g(x) = 3x - 5$
72. $h(x) = x^3$, $g(x) = x - 2$
73. $h(x) = x + 4$, $g(x) = |x|$ **$|x + 4|$; $|x| + 4$**

Differentiated Instruction OL BL

Extension Have students extend the solution to Example 3 for an increasing number of compounding periods. Try daily compounding ($n = 365$), and then explore what happens if n is varied up to tens of thousands of times per year. The final amount approaches an upper limit, which in this case is about \$4694.03.

Watch Out!

Error Analysis In Exercise 43, students may fail to recognize the use of basic exponent rules when variables are involved. Remind them that $(a^m)^n = a^{mn}$.

4 ASSESS

Name the Math Have students describe the set of values for b that are possible in an exponential function of the form $y = b^x$.

Formative Assessment

Check for student understanding of the concepts in Lessons 8-1 and 8-2.

CRM Quiz 1, p. 63

Additional Answers

54.

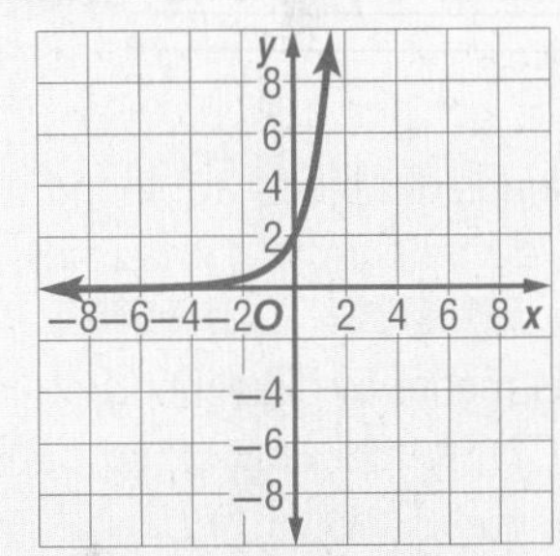

55.

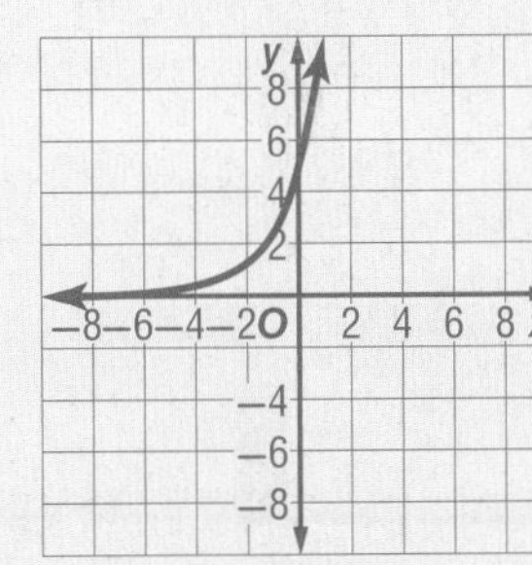

56.

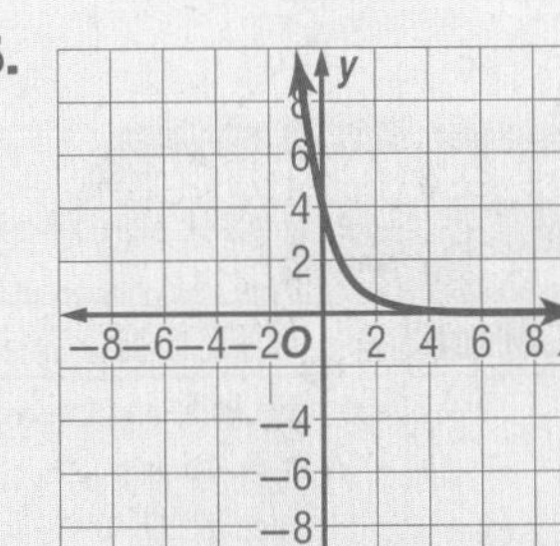

1 FOCUS

Vertical Alignment

Before Lesson 8-3
Find the inverse of a function.

Lesson 8-3
Evaluate logarithmic expressions.
Graph logarithmic functions.

After Lesson 8-3
Determine the solutions of logarithmic equations using algebraic methods.

2 TEACH

Scaffolding Questions

Have students read the *Why?* section of the lesson.

Ask:

- What kinds of objects are found near Earth? Sample answer: asteroids, meteors, comets
- What is meant by "likelihood of impact"? Sample answer: probability that an object hits Earth

8-3 Logarithms and Logarithmic Functions

Then
You found the inverse of a function. (Lesson 7-2)

Now
- Evaluate logarithmic expressions.
- Graph logarithmic functions.

NGSSS
MA.912.A.8.1 Define exponential and **logarithmic functions** and determine their relationship.
MA.912.A.8.2 Define and use the properties of logarithms to simplify logarithmic expressions and to find their approximate values. *Also addresses MA.912.A.2.10 and MA.912.A.8.3.*

New Vocabulary
logarithm
logarithmic function

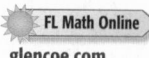

FL Math Online
glencoe.com

Why?

Many scientists believe the extinction of the dinosaurs was caused by an asteroid striking Earth. Astronomers use the Palermo scale to classify objects near Earth based on the likelihood of impact. To make comparing several objects easier, the scale was developed using *logarithms*. The Palermo scale value of any object can be found using the equation $PS = \log_{10} R$, where R is the relative risk posed by the object.

Logarithmic Functions and Expressions Consider the exponential function $f(x) = 2^x$ and its inverse. Recall that you can graph an inverse function by interchanging the x- and y-values in the ordered pairs of the function.

$y = 2^x$	
x	y
-3	$\frac{1}{8}$
-2	$\frac{1}{4}$
-1	$\frac{1}{2}$
0	1
1	2
2	4
3	8

$x = 2^y$	
x	y
$\frac{1}{8}$	-3
$\frac{1}{4}$	-2
$\frac{1}{2}$	-1
1	0
2	1
4	2
8	3

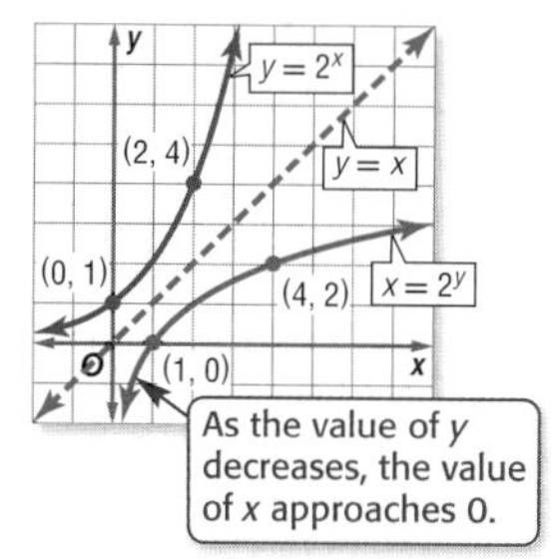

The inverse of $y = 2^x$ can be defined as $x = 2^y$. In general, the inverse of $y = b^x$ is $x = b^y$. In $x = b^y$, the variable y is called the **logarithm** of x. This is usually written as $y = \log_b x$, which is read *y equals log base b of x*.

Key Concept: Logarithm with Base b

Words Let b and x be positive numbers, $b \neq 1$. The *logarithm of x with base b* is denoted $\log_b x$ and is defined as the exponent y that makes the equation $b^y = x$ true.

Symbols Suppose $b > 0$ and $b \neq 1$. For $x > 0$, there is a number y such that

$$\log_b x = y \text{ if and only if } b^y = x.$$

Example If $\log_3 27 = y$, then $3^y = 27$.

The definition of logarithms can be used to express logarithms in exponential form.

EXAMPLE 1 Logarithmic to Exponential Form

Write each equation in exponential form.

a. $\log_2 8 = 3$

$\log_2 8 = 3 \rightarrow 8 = 2^3$

b. $\log_4 \frac{1}{256} = -4$

$\log_4 \frac{1}{256} = -4 \rightarrow \frac{1}{256} = 4^{-4}$

Guided Practice

1A. $\log_4 16 = 2$ $16 = 4^2$

1B. $\log_3 729 = 6$ $729 = 3^6$

Personal Tutor glencoe.com

Lesson 8-3 Resources

Resource	Approaching-Level	On-Level	Beyond-Level	English Learners
Teacher Edition		• Differentiated Instruction, pp. 493, 499	• Differentiated Instruction, pp. 493, 499	
Chapter Resource Masters	• Study Guide and Intervention, pp. 19–20 • Skills Practice, p. 21 • Practice, p. 22 • Word Problem Practice, p. 23	• Study Guide and Intervention, pp. 19–20 • Skills Practice, p. 21 • Practice, p. 22 • Word Problem Practice, p. 23 • Enrichment, p. 24 • TI-Nspire Activity, p. 25	• Practice, p. 22 • Word Problem Practice, p. 23 • Enrichment, p. 24	• Study Guide and Intervention, pp. 19–20 • Skills Practice, p. 21 • Practice, p. 22 • Word Problem Practice, p. 23
Transparencies	• 5-Minute Check Transparency 8-3	• 5-Minute Check Transparency 8-3	• 5-Minute Check Transparency 8-3	• 5-Minute Check Transparency 8-3
Other	• Study Notebook	• Study Notebook	• Study Notebook	• Study Notebook

The definition of logarithms can also be used to write exponential equations in logarithmic form.

EXAMPLE 2 Exponential to Logarithmic Form

Write each equation in logarithmic form.

a. $15^3 = 3375$

$15^3 = 3375 \rightarrow \log_{15} 3375 = 3$

b. $4^{\frac{1}{2}} = 2$

$4^{\frac{1}{2}} = 2 \rightarrow \log_4 2 = \frac{1}{2}$

Guided Practice

2A. $4^3 = 64$ $\log_4 64 = 3$

2B. $125^{\frac{1}{3}} = 5$ $\log_{125} 5 = \frac{1}{3}$

Personal Tutor glencoe.com

You can use the definition of a logarithm to evaluate a logarithmic expression.

Watch Out!

Logarithmic Base It is easy to get confused about which number is the base and which is the exponent in logarithmic equations. Consider highlighting each number as you solve to help organize your calculations.

EXAMPLE 3 Evaluate Logarithmic Expressions

Evaluate $\log_{16} 4$.

$\log_{16} 4 = y$	**Let the logarithm equal y.**
$4 = 16^y$	**Definition of logarithm**
$4^1 = 4^{2y}$	**$16 = 4^2$**
$1 = 2y$	**Property of Equality for Exponential Functions**
$\frac{1}{2} = y$	**Divide each side by 2.**

Thus, $\log_{16} 4 = \frac{1}{2}$.

Guided Practice

Evaluate each expression.

3A. $\log_3 81$ 4

3B. $\log_{\frac{1}{2}} 256$ -8

Personal Tutor glencoe.com

Graphing Logarithmic Functions The function $y = \log_b x$, where $b \neq 1$, is called a **logarithmic function**. The graph of $f(x) = \log_b x$ represents a parent graph of the logarithmic functions.

Key Concept Parent Function of Logarithmic Functions

Parent function:	$f(x) = \log_b x$	**Type of graph:**	continuous, one-to-one
Domain:	all positive real numbers	**Range:**	all real numbers
Asymptote:	$f(x)$-axis	**Intercept:**	(1, 0)

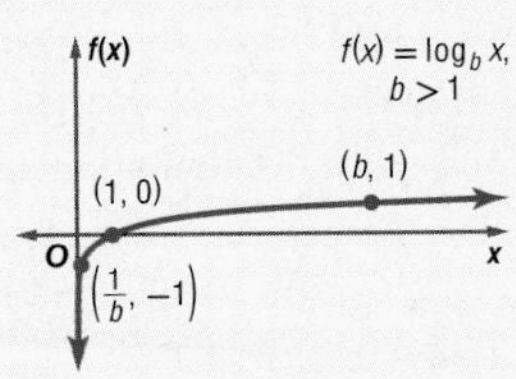

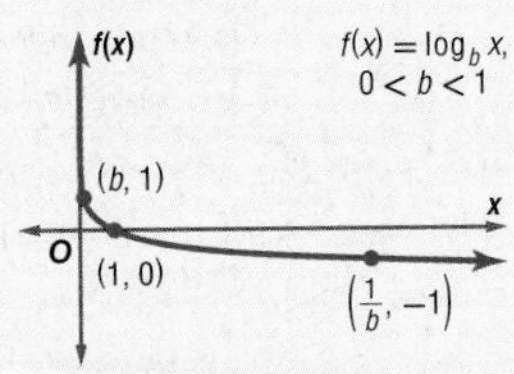

TEACH with TECH

INTERACTIVE WHITEBOARD As you introduce logarithms to your class, use a color code for each part of corresponding exponential and logarithmic functions. For example, use different colors for x, y, and b when showing that $\log_b x = y$ corresponds to $x = b^y$.

Logarithmic Functions and Expressions

Example 1 shows how to write logarithmic equations in exponential form. **Example 2** shows how to write exponential equations in logarithmic form. **Example 3** shows how to use the definition of a logarithm to evaluate a logarithmic expression.

Formative Assessment

Use the Guided Practice exercises after each example to determine students' understanding of concepts.

Additional Examples

1 Write each equation in exponential form.

a. $\log_3 9 = 2$ $9 = 3^2$

b. $\log_{10} \frac{1}{100} = -2$ $\frac{1}{100} = 10^{-2}$

2 Write each equation in logarithmic form.

a. $5^3 = 125$ $\log_5 125 = 3$

b. $27^{\frac{1}{3}} = 3$ $\log_{27} 3 = \frac{1}{3}$

3 Evaluate $\log_3 243$. 5

Additional Examples also in Interactive Classroom PowerPoint® Presentations

IWB INTERACTIVE WHITEBOARD READY

Graphing Logarithmic Functions

Example 4 shows how to graph a logarithmic function. **Example 5** shows how to use transformations to graph logarithmic functions. **Example 6** shows how to find the inverse of an exponential function to solve a real world example.

Differentiated Instruction OL BL

Logical Learners After discussing the definition of logarithm, write $y = 2x$ on the board and ask students to rewrite the equation with x in terms of y. $x = \frac{1}{2}y$ Repeat for $y = x^2$. $x = \pm\sqrt{y}$ Now write $y = 2^x$ on the board and ask students to rewrite this equation with x in terms of y. This will likely have students baffled. Explain that the rewritten equation is $x = \log_2 y$. Stress that a logarithm is defined as the inverse of an exponential function.

Additional Example

4 Graph each function.

a. $f(x) = \log_3 x$

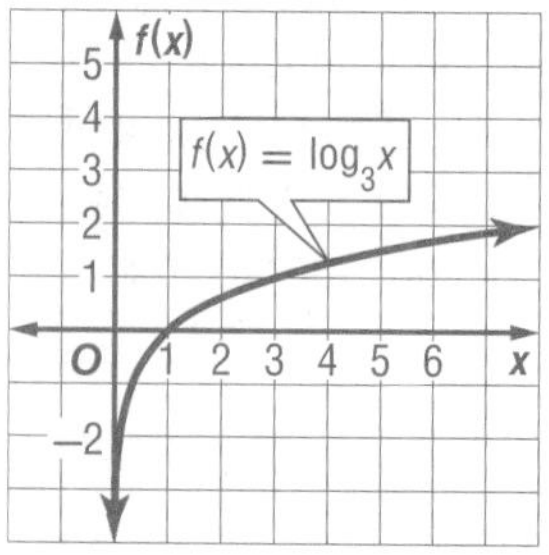

b. $f(x) = \log_{\frac{1}{4}} x$

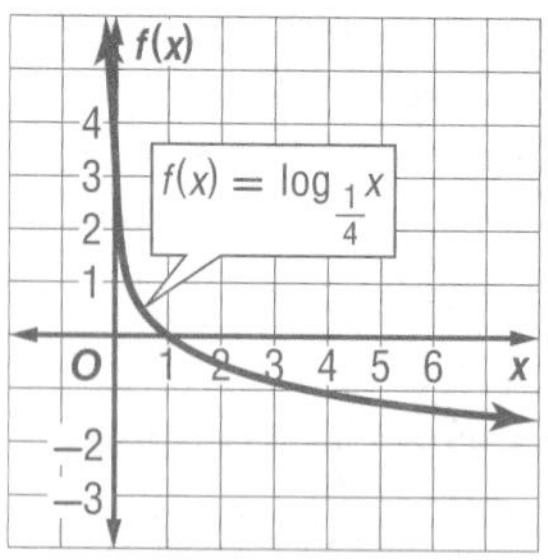

Tips for New Teachers

Pacing Students have not covered logarithmic functions before and are likely to find them confusing. Expect students to need extra time to absorb the material in this lesson before continuing with the rest of the chapter.

Additional Answers (Guided Practice)

4A.

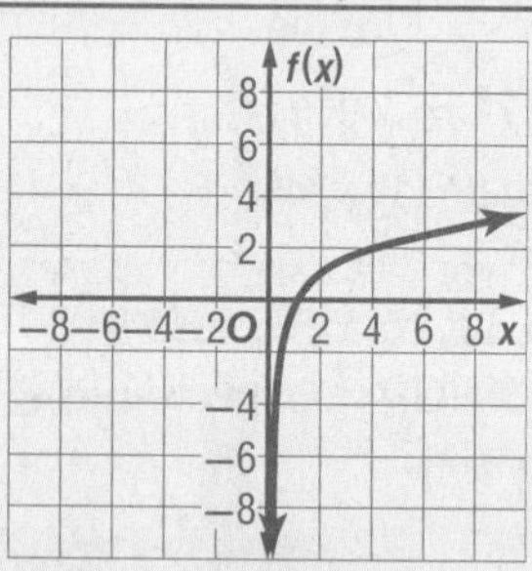

4B.

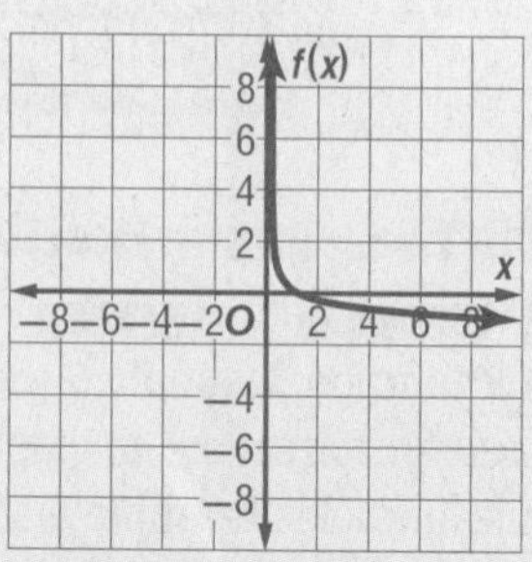

StudyTip

Zero Exponent Recall that for any $b \neq 0$, $b^0 = 1$. Therefore, $\log_2 0$ is undefined because $2^x \neq 0$ for any x value.

EXAMPLE 4 Graph Logarithmic Functions

Graph each function.

a. $f(x) = \log_5 x$

Step 1 Identify the base.
$b = 5$

Step 2 Determine points on the graph.
Because $5 > 1$, use the points $\left(\frac{1}{b}, -1\right)$, $(1, 0)$, and $(b, 1)$.

Step 3 Plot the points and sketch the graph.
$\left(\frac{1}{b}, -1\right) \rightarrow \left(\frac{1}{5}, -1\right)$
$(1, 0)$
$(b, 1) \rightarrow (5, 1)$

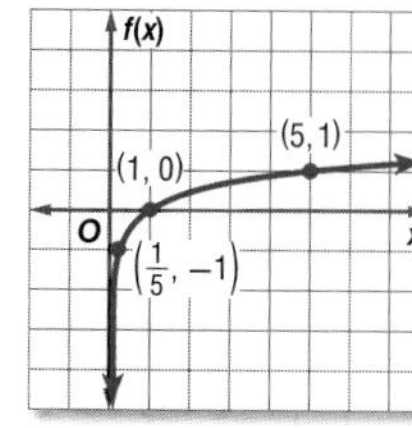

StudyTip

Continuity Most exponential and logarithmic functions are continuous. In Example 2a, $f(x)$ is increasing from 0 to infinity.

b. $f(x) = \log_{\frac{1}{3}} x$

Step 1 $b = \frac{1}{3}$

Step 2 $0 < \frac{1}{3} < 1$,

so use the points $\left(\frac{1}{3}, 1\right)$, $(1, 0)$ and $(3, -1)$.

Step 3 Sketch the graph.

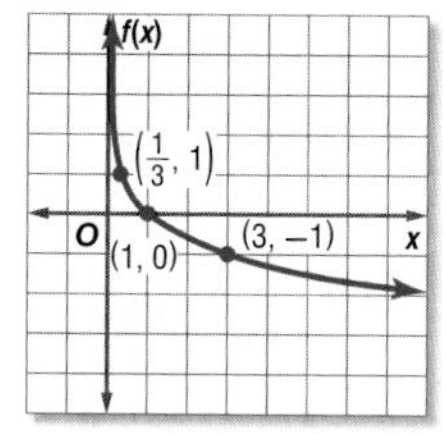

Guided Practice 4A, 4B. See margin.

4A. $f(x) = \log_2 x$

4B. $f(x) = \log_{\frac{1}{8}} x$

Personal Tutor glencoe.com

The same techniques used to transform the graphs of other functions you have studied can be applied to the graphs of logarithmic functions.

Key Concept Transformations of Logarithmic Functions

$f(x) = a \log_b (x - h) + k$

h – Horizontal Translation	*k* – Vertical Translation
$\lvert h \rvert$ units right if h is positive $\lvert h \rvert$ units left if h is negative	$\lvert k \rvert$ units up if k is positive $\lvert k \rvert$ units down if k is negative

***a* – Orientation and Shape**

If $a < 0$, the graph is reflected across the x-axis.	If $\lvert a \rvert > 1$, the graph is expanded vertically. If $0 < \lvert a \rvert < 1$, the graph is compressed vertically.

Focus on Mathematical Content

Logarithms The equation $y = \log_b x$ is read "y equals the logarithm to the base b of the number x." The base b is always positive and $b \neq 1$. And since the equation $y = \log_b x$ is equivalent to the exponential equation $x = b^y$, a logarithm is an exponent. It is the exponent that the base b requires in order to equal the number x.

494 Chapter 8 Exponential and Logarithmic Functions and Relations

StudyTip

End Behavior In Example 5a, as x approaches infinity, $f(x)$ approaches infinity.

EXAMPLE 5 Graph Logarithmic Functions

Graph each function.

a. $f(x) = 3 \log_{10} x + 1$

This represents a transformation of the graph of $f(x) = \log_{10} x$.

- $|a| = 3$: The graph expands vertically.
- $h = 0$: There is no horizontal shift.
- $k = 1$: The graph is translated 1 unit up.

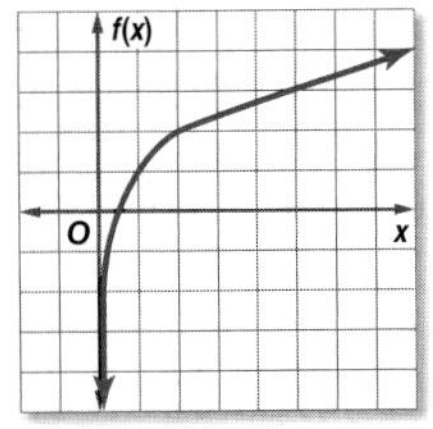

b. $f(x) = \frac{1}{2} \log_{\frac{1}{4}} (x - 3)$

This is a transformation of the graph of $f(x) = \log_{\frac{1}{4}} x$.

- $|a| = \frac{1}{2}$: The graph is compressed vertically.
- $h = 3$: The graph is translated 3 units to the right.
- $k = 0$: There is no vertical shift.

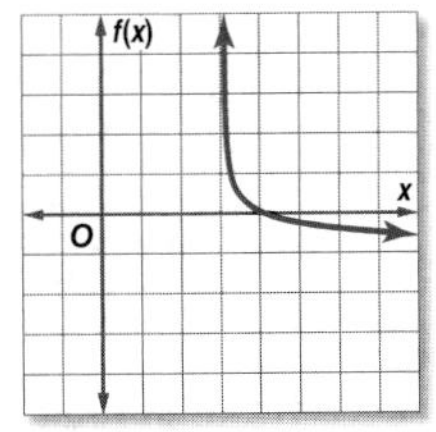

Guided Practice 5A, 5B. See margin.

Graph each function.

5A. $f(x) = 2 \log_3 (x - 2)$

5B. $f(x) = \frac{1}{4} \log_{\frac{1}{2}} (x + 1) - 5$

Personal Tutor glencoe.com

Real-World EXAMPLE 6 Find Inverses of Exponential Functions

Real-World Link

The largest recorded earthquake in the United States was a magnitude 9.2 that struck Prince William Sound, Alaska, on Good Friday, March 28, 1964.

Source: United States Geological Survey

EARTHQUAKES The Richter scale measures earthquake intensity. The increase in intensity between each number is 10 times. For example, an earthquake with a rating of 7 is 10 times more intense than one measuring 6. The intensity of an earthquake can be modeled by $y = 10^{x-1}$, where x is the Richter scale rating.

a. Use the information at the left to find the intensity of the strongest recorded earthquake in the United States.

$y = 10^{x-1}$	Original equation
$= 10^{9.2-1}$	Substitute 9.2 for x.
$= 10^{8.2}$	Simplify.
$= 158{,}489{,}319.2$	Use a calculator.

b. Write an equation of the form $y = \log_{10} x + c$ for the inverse of the function.

$y = 10^{x-1}$	Original equation
$x = 10^{y-1}$	Replace x with y, replace y with x, and solve for y.
$y - 1 = \log_{10} x$	Definition of logarithm
$y = \log_{10} x + 1$	Add 1 to each side.

Guided Practice

6. Write an equation for the inverse of the function $y = 0.5^x$. $y = \log_{0.5} x$

Personal Tutor glencoe.com

Additional Examples

5 Graph each function.

a. $f(x) = \frac{1}{3} \log_6 x - 1$

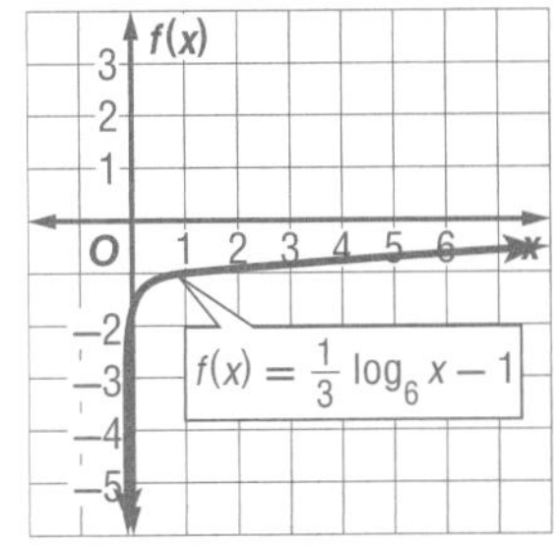

b. $f(x) = 4 \log_{\frac{1}{3}} (x + 2)$

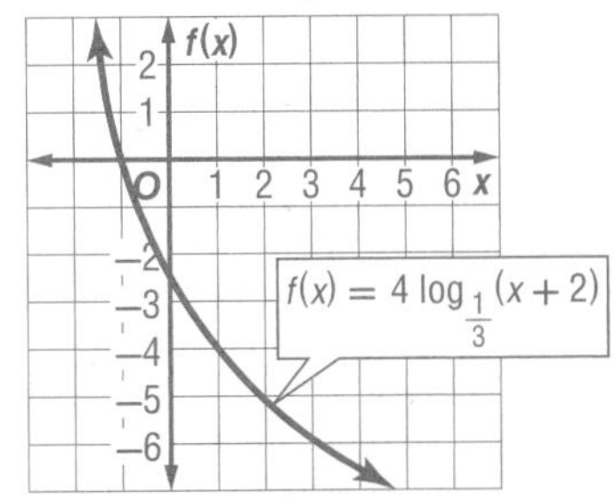

6 **AIR PRESSURE** At Earth's surface, the air pressure is defined as 1 atmosphere. Pressure decreases by about 20% for each mile of altitude. Atmospheric pressure can be modeled by $P = 0.8^x$, where x measures altitude in miles.

a. Find the atmospheric pressure in atmospheres at an altitude of 8 miles. 0.168 atmospheres

b. Write an equation for the inverse of the function. $P = \log_{0.8} x$

Additional Answers (Guided Practice)

5A.

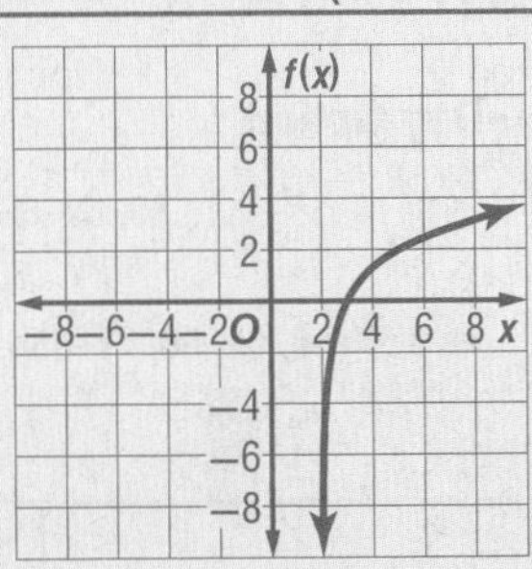

5B.

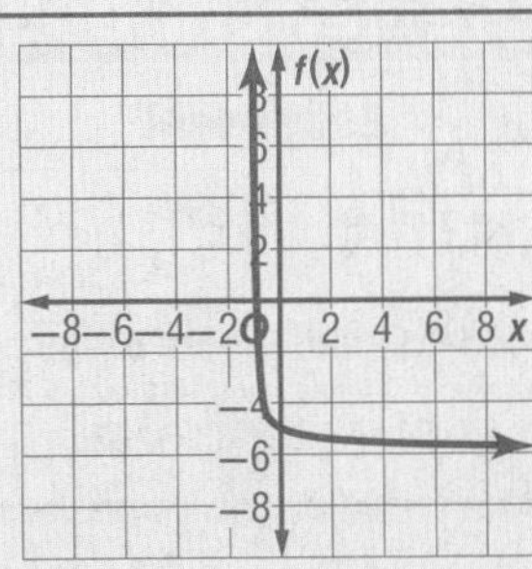

3 PRACTICE

Formative Assessment

Use Exercises 1–12 to check for understanding.

Use the chart at the bottom of this page to customize assignments for your students.

Additional Answers

8.
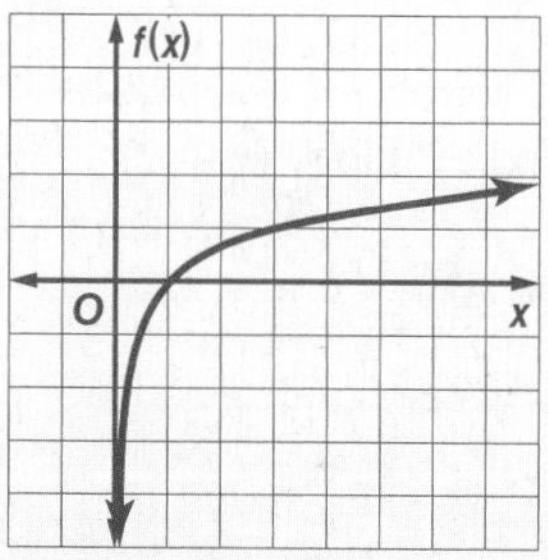

9.
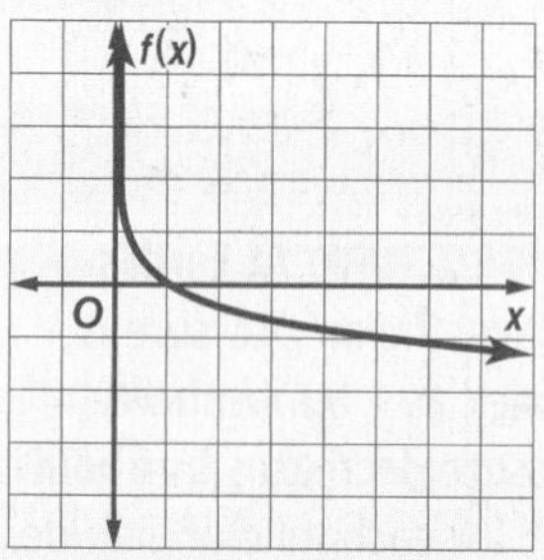

10.
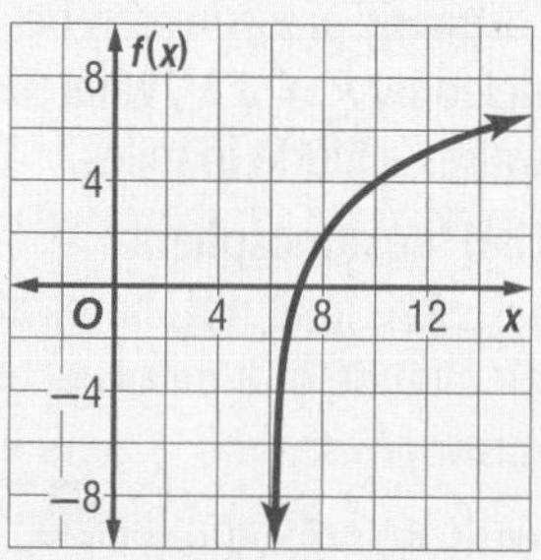

11.
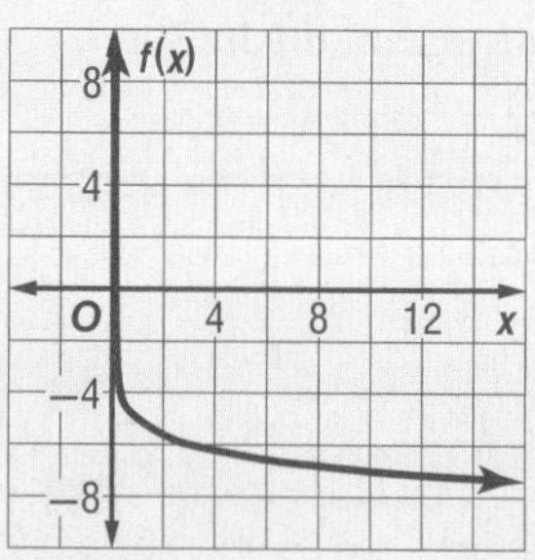

Check Your Understanding

Example 1 p. 492

Write each equation in exponential form.

1. $\log_8 512 = 3$ $8^3 = 512$
2. $\log_5 625 = 4$ $5^4 = 625$

Example 2 p. 493

Write each equation in logarithmic form.

3. $11^3 = 1331$ $\log_{11} 1331 = 3$
4. $16^{\frac{3}{4}} = 8$ $\log_{16} 8 = \frac{3}{4}$

Example 3 p. 493

Evaluate each expression.

5. $\log_{13} 169$ 2
6. $\log_2 \frac{1}{128}$ -7
7. $\log_6 1$ 0

Examples 4 and 5 pp. 494–495

Graph each function. **8–11. See margin.**

8. $f(x) = \log_3 x$
9. $f(x) = \log_{\frac{1}{6}} x$
10. $f(x) = 4\log_4 (x - 6)$
11. $f(x) = 2\log_{\frac{1}{10}} x - 5$

Example 6 p. 495

12. **SCIENCE** Use the information at the beginning of the lesson. The Palermo scale value of any object can be found using the equation $PS = \log_{10} R$, where R is the relative risk posed by the object. Write an equation in exponential form for the inverse of the function. $PS = 10^R$

Practice and Problem Solving

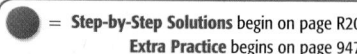

● = **Step-by-Step Solutions** begin on page R20.
Extra Practice begins on page 947.

Example 1 p. 492

Write each equation in exponential form.

13. $\log_2 16 = 4$ $2^4 = 16$
14. $\log_7 343 = 3$ $7^3 = 343$
15. $\log_9 \frac{1}{81} = -2$ $9^{-2} = \frac{1}{81}$
16. $\log_3 \frac{1}{27} = -3$ $3^{-3} = \frac{1}{27}$
17. $\log_{12} 144 = 2$ $12^2 = 144$
18. $\log_9 1 = 0$ $9^0 = 1$

Example 2 p. 493

Write each equation in logarithmic form.

19. $9^{-1} = \frac{1}{9}$ $\log_9 \frac{1}{9} = -1$
20. $6^{-3} = \frac{1}{216}$ $\log_6 \frac{1}{216} = -3$
21. $2^8 = 256$ $\log_2 256 = 8$
22. $4^6 = 4096$ $\log_4 4096 = 6$
23. $27^{\frac{2}{3}} = 9$ $\log_{27} 9 = \frac{2}{3}$
24. $25^{\frac{3}{2}} = 125$ $\log_{25} 125 = \frac{3}{2}$

Example 3 p. 493

Evaluate each expression.

25. $\log_3 \frac{1}{9}$ -2
26. $\log_4 \frac{1}{64}$ -3
27. $\log_8 512$ 3
28. $\log_6 216$ 3
29. $\log_{27} 3$ $\frac{1}{3}$
30. $\log_{32} 2$ $\frac{1}{5}$
31. $\log_9 3$ $\frac{1}{2}$
32. $\log_{121} 11$ $\frac{1}{2}$
33. $\log_{\frac{1}{5}} 3125$ -5
34. $\log_{\frac{1}{8}} 512$ -3
35. $\log_{\frac{1}{3}} \frac{1}{81}$ 4
36. $\log_{\frac{1}{6}} \frac{1}{216}$ 3

Examples 4 and 5 pp. 494–495

Graph each function. **37–48. See Chapter 8 Answer Appendix.**

37. $f(x) = \log_6 x$
38. $f(x) = \log_{\frac{1}{5}} x$
39. $f(x) = 4\log_2 x + 6$
40. $f(x) = \log_{\frac{1}{9}} x$
41. $f(x) = \log_{10} x$
42. $f(x) = -3\log_{\frac{1}{12}} x + 2$
43. $f(x) = 6\log_{\frac{1}{8}} (x + 2)$
44. $f(x) = -8\log_3 (x - 4)$
45. $f(x) = \log_{\frac{1}{4}} (x + 1) - 9$
46. $f(x) = \log_5 (x - 4) - 5$
47. $f(x) = -\frac{1}{6}\log_8 (x - 3) + 4$
48. $f(x) = -\frac{1}{3}\log_{\frac{1}{6}} (x + 2) - 5$

Differentiated Homework Options

Level	Assignment	Two-Day Option	
AL Basic	13–56, 60, 62–85	13–55 odd, 67–70	14–56 even, 60, 62–66, 71–85
OL Core	13–55 odd, 57–60, 62–85	13–56, 67–70	57–60, 62–66, 71–85
BL Advanced	57–81, (optional: 82–85)		

Example 6 p. 495

Real-World Link

The aperture setting, or f-stop, of a camera controls the amount of light exposure on film. Each step up in f-stop setting allows twice as much light exposure as the previous setting.

49. PHOTOGRAPHY The formula $n = \log_2 \frac{1}{p}$ represents the change in the f-stop setting n to use in less light where p is the fraction of sunlight.

a. Benito's camera is set up to take pictures in direct sunlight, but it is a cloudy day. If the amount of sunlight on a cloudy day is $\frac{1}{4}$ as bright as direct sunlight, how many f-stop settings should he move to accommodate less light? **2**

b. Graph the function. **See margin.**

c. Use the graph in part b to predict what fraction of daylight Benito is accommodating if he moves down 3 f-stop settings. Is he allowing more or less light into the camera? **less light; $\frac{1}{8}$**

50. EDUCATION To measure a student's retention of knowledge, the student is tested after a given amount of time. A student's score on an Algebra 2 test t months after the school year is over can be approximated by $y(t) = 85 - 6 \log_2 (t + 1)$, where $y(t)$ is the student's score as a percent.

a. What was the student's score at the time the school year ended ($t = 0$)? **85**

b. What was the student's score after 3 months? **73**

c. What was the student's score after 15 months? **61**

Graph each function. **51–56. See Chapter 8 Answer Appendix.**

51. $f(x) = 4 \log_2 (2x - 4) + 6$ **52.** $f(x) = -3 \log_{12} (4x + 3) + 2$

53. $f(x) = 15 \log_{14} (x + 1) - 9$ **54.** $f(x) = 10 \log_5 (x - 4) - 5$

55. $f(x) = -\frac{1}{6} \log_8 (x - 3) + 4$ **56.** $f(x) = -\frac{1}{3} \log_6 (6x + 2) - 5$

57a. $S(3) = 30$, $S(15) = 50$, $S(63) = 70$

57b. If \$3000 is spent on advertising, \$30,000 is returned in sales. If \$15,000 is spent on advertising, \$50,000 is returned in sales. If \$63,000 is spent on advertising, \$70,000 is returned in sales.

57d. Because eventually the graph plateaus, and no matter how much money you spend you are still returning about the same in sales.

B **57. ADVERTISING** In general, the more money a company spends on advertising, the higher the sales. The amount of money in sales for a company, in thousands, can be modeled by the equation $S(a) = 10 + 20 \log_4(a + 1)$, where a is the amount of money spent on advertising in thousands, when $a \geq 0$.

a. The value of $S(0) \approx 10$, which means that if \$10 is spent on advertising, \$10,000 is returned in sales. Find the values of $S(3)$, $S(15)$, and $S(63)$.

b. Interpret the meaning of each function value in the context of the problem.

c. Graph the function. **See Chapter 8 Answer Appendix.**

d. Use the graph in part c and your answers from part a to explain why the money spent in advertising becomes less "efficient" as it is used in larger amounts.

58. BIOLOGY The generation time for bacteria is the time that it takes for the population to double. The generation time G for a specific type of bacteria can be found using experimental data and the formula $G = \frac{t}{3.3 \log_b f}$, where t is the time period, b is the number of bacteria at the beginning of the experiment, and f is the number of bacteria at the end of the experiment.

a. The generation time for mycobacterium tuberculosis is 16 hours. How long will it take four of these bacteria to multiply into 1024 bacteria? **264 h or 11 days**

b. An experiment involving rats that had been exposed to salmonella showed that the generation time for the salmonella was 5 hours. After how long would 20 of these bacteria multiply into 8000? **49.5 h or 2 days 1.5 h**

c. *E. coli* are fast growing bacteria. If 6 *E. coli* can grow to 1296 in 4.4 hours, what is the generation time of *E. coli*? **$\frac{1}{3}$ h or 20 min**

Additional Answer

49b.

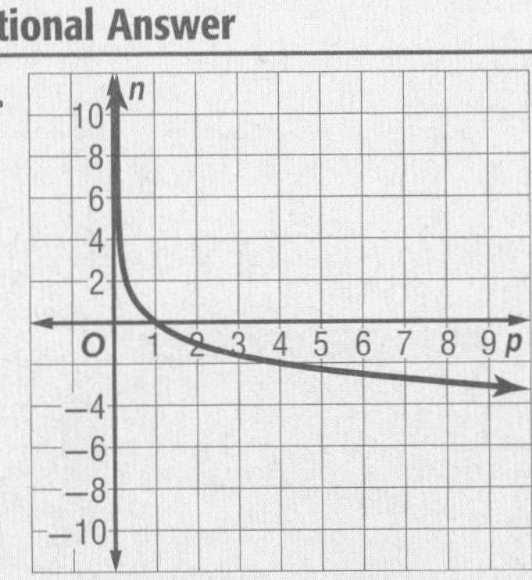

Study Guide and Intervention
CRM pp. 19–20 AL OL ELL

8-3 Study Guide and Intervention

Logarithms and Logarithmic Functions

Logarithmic Functions and Expressions

Definition of Logarithm with Base b	Let b and x be positive numbers, b ≠ 1. The logarithm of x with base b is denoted $\log_b x$ and is defined as the exponent y that makes the equation $b^y = x$ true.

The inverse of the exponential function $y = b^x$ is the **logarithmic function** $x = b^y$. This function is usually written as $y = \log_b x$.

Example 1 Write an exponential equation equivalent to $\log_3 243 = 5$.
$3^5 = 243$

Example 2 Write a logarithmic equation equivalent to $6^{-3} = \frac{1}{216}$.
$\log_6 \frac{1}{216} = -3$

Example 3 Evaluate $\log_8 16$.
$8^{\frac{4}{3}} = 16$, so $\log_8 16 = \frac{4}{3}$.

Exercises

Write each equation in exponential form.
1. $\log_{15} 225 = 2$ $15^2 = 225$ 2. $\log_3 \frac{1}{27} = -3$ $3^{-3} = \frac{1}{27}$ 3. $\log_4 32 = \frac{5}{2}$ $4^{\frac{5}{2}} = 32$

Write each equation in logarithmic form.
4. $2^7 = 128$ $\log_2 128 = 7$ 5. $3^{-4} = \frac{1}{81}$ $\log_3 \frac{1}{81} = -4$ 6. $\left(\frac{1}{7}\right)^3 = \frac{1}{343}$ $\log_{\frac{1}{7}} \frac{1}{343} = 3$
7. $7^{-2} = \frac{1}{49}$ $\log_7 \frac{1}{49} = -2$ 8. $2^9 = 512$ $\log_2 512 = 9$ 9. $64^{\frac{2}{3}} = 16$ $\log_{64} 16 = \frac{2}{3}$

Evaluate each expression.
10. $\log_4 64$ 3 11. $\log_2 64$ 6 12. $\log_{100} 100{,}000$ 2.5
13. $\log_5 625$ 4 14. $\log_{27} 81$ $\frac{4}{3}$ 15. $\log_{25} 5$ $\frac{1}{2}$
16. $\log_2 \frac{1}{128}$ −7 17. $\log_{10} 0.00001$ −5 18. $\log_4 \frac{1}{32}$ −2.5

Chapter 8 19 Glencoe Algebra 2

Practice
CRM p. 22 AL OL BL ELL

8-3 Practice

Logarithms and Logarithmic Functions

Write each equation in exponential form.
1. $\log_6 216 = 3$ $6^3 = 216$ 2. $\log_2 64 = 6$ $2^6 = 64$ 3. $\log_3 \frac{1}{81} = -4$ $3^{-4} = \frac{1}{81}$
4. $\log_{10} 0.00001 = -5$ $10^{-5} = 0.00001$ 5. $\log_{25} 5 = \frac{1}{2}$ $25^{\frac{1}{2}} = 5$ 6. $\log_{32} 8 = \frac{3}{5}$ $32^{\frac{3}{5}} = 8$

Write each equation in logarithmic form.
7. $5^3 = 125$ $\log_5 125 = 3$ 8. $7^0 = 1$ $\log_7 1 = 0$ 9. $3^4 = 81$ $\log_3 81 = 4$
10. $3^{-4} = \frac{1}{81}$ $\log_3 \frac{1}{81} = -4$ 11. $\left(\frac{1}{4}\right)^3 = \frac{1}{64}$ $\log_{\frac{1}{4}} \frac{1}{64} = 3$ 12. $7776^{\frac{1}{5}} = 6$ $\log_{7776} 6 = \frac{1}{5}$

Evaluate each expression.
13. $\log_3 81$ 4 14. $\log_{10} 0.0001$ −4 15. $\log_2 \frac{1}{16}$ −4 16. $\log_{\frac{1}{3}} 27$ −3
17. $\log_9 1$ 0 18. $\log_8 4$ $\frac{2}{3}$ 19. $\log_7 \frac{1}{49}$ −2 20. $\log_6 6^4$ 4

Graph each function.
21. $f(x) = \log_3 (x - 2)$ 22. $f(x) = -2 \log_4 x$

23. SOUND An equation for loudness, in decibels, is $L = 10 \log_{10} R$, where R is the relative intensity of the sound. Sounds that reach levels of 120 decibels or more are painful to humans. What is the relative intensity of 120 decibels? 10^{12}

24. INVESTING Maria invests \$1000 in a savings account that pays 4% interest compounded annually. The value of the account A at the end of five years can be determined from the equation $\log_{10} A = \log_{10}[1000(1 + 0.04)^5]$. Write this equation in exponential form.
$A = 1000(1 + 0.04)^5$

Chapter 8 22 Glencoe Algebra 2

Word Problem Practice
CRM p. 23 AL OL BL ELL

8-3 Word Problem Practice

Logarithms and Logarithmic Functions

1. CHEMISTRY The pH of a solution is found by the formula pH = −log H, where H stands for the hydrogen ion concentration in the formula. What is the pH of a solution to the nearest hundredth when H is 1356?
−3.13

2. FIND THE ERROR Michio wanted to find the value of x in the equation $2(3)^x = 34$. He first converted the equation to $\log_3 2x = 17$. Next he wrote $2x = 3^{17}$ and used a calculator to find x = 64,570,081. Was his answer correct? If not, what was his mistake and what is the right answer?
He should have converted to $x = \log_3(17)$; x = 2.58

3. SOUND The decibel level L of a sound is determined by the formula $L = 10 \log_{10} \frac{I}{M}$. Find I in terms of M for a noise with a decibel level of 120.
I = 1,000,000,000,000 M or 10^{12} M

4. EARTHQUAKES The intensity of an earthquake can be measured on the Richter scale using the formula $y = 10^{R-1}$, where y is the absolute intensity of the earthquake and R is its Richter scale measurement.

Richter Scale Number	Absolute Intensity
1	1
2	10
3	100
4	1000
5	10,000

An earthquake in San Francisco in 1906 had an absolute intensity of 6,000,000. What was that earthquake's measurement on the Richter scale?
7.8

5. GAMES Julio and Natalia decided to play a game in which they each selected a logarithmic function and compare their functions to see which gave larger values. Julio selected the function $f(x) = 10 \log_2 x$ and Natalia selected the function $2 \log_{10} x$.

a. Which of the functions has a larger value when x = 7?
Julio's; Julio's is 28.07 and Natalia's is 1.69

b. Which of their functions has a larger value when x = 1?
Neither; both equal 0.

c. Do you think the base or the multiplier is more important in determining the value of a logarithmic function?
Answers will vary.

Chapter 8 23 Glencoe Algebra 2

Enrichment
CRM p. 24 OL BL

8-3 Enrichment

Comparing Logarithmic Graphs

Solve the problems below to relate the graphs of $y = \log_n ax$.

1. Graph the functions $y = \log_2 x$, $y = \log_3 x$, $y = \log_4 x$.
What can you conclude about the graph of $y = \log_n ax$ as the value of n increases and a is constant?
As the value of n increases the dilation of the graph changes.

2. Graph the functions $y = \log_2 x$, $y = \log_2 2x$, $y = \log_2 4x$.
What can you conclude about the graph of $y = \log_n ax$ as the value of a increases and n is constant?
The intersection along the x-axis moves to the left and the intersection along the y-axis moves up.

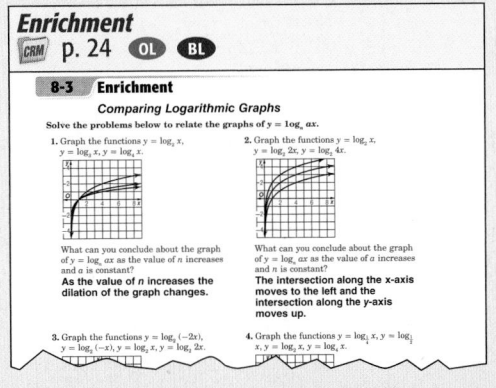

3. Graph the functions $y = \log_2 (-2x)$, $y = \log_2 (-x)$, $y = \log_2 x$, $y = \log_2 2x$.

4. Graph the functions $y = \log_{\frac{1}{2}} x$, $y = \log_{\frac{1}{3}} x$, $y = \log_2 x$, $y = \log_3 x$.

Watch Out!

Error Analysis For Exercise 62, point out that Betsy is thinking only of logarithmic functions of the form $f(x) = a\log_b x$.

Error Analysis For Exercise 65, point out that in the expression $a\log_b x$, b is the base of a power. Remind students that finding the logarithm of x with base b means finding what power of b equals x.

Additional Answers

59a.

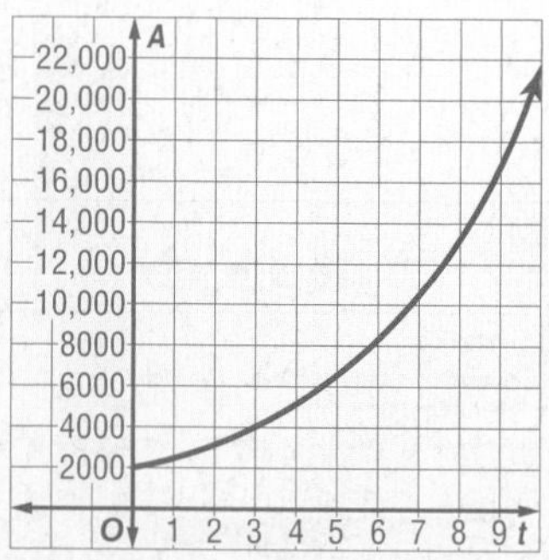

64a–e. Sample answers given.

64a. $\log_2 33554432 = 25$

64b. $\log_4 \frac{1}{64} = -3$

64c. $\log_2 \sqrt{2} = \frac{1}{2}$

64d. $\log_7 1 = 0$

64e. There is no possible solution; this is the empty set.

65. No; Elisa was closer. She should have $-y = 2$ or $y = -2$ instead of $y = 2$. Matthew used the definition of logarithms incorrectly.

66. Sample answer: In $g(x) = a\log_{10}(x - h) + k$, the value of k is a vertical translation and the graph will shift up k units if k is positive and down $|k|$ units if k is negative. The value of h is a horizontal translation and the graph will shift h units to the right if h is positive and $|h|$ units to the left if h is negative. If $a < 0$, the graph will be reflected across the x-axis. if $|a| > 1$, the graph will be expanded and if $0 < |a| < 1$, then the graph will be compressed.

Real-World Link

Approximately half of all credit card holders pay only their minimum monthly requirements. The average American household is solicited seven times a year by credit card companies.

Source: American Consumer Credit Counseling

59 **FINANCIAL LITERACY** Jacy has spent \$2000 on a credit card. The credit card company charges 24% interest, compounded monthly. The credit card company uses $\log_{\left(1 + \frac{0.24}{12}\right)} \frac{A}{2000} = 12t$ to determine how much time it will be until Jacy's debt reaches a certain amount, if A is the amount of debt after a period of time, and t is time in years.

a. Graph the function for Jacy's debt. **See margin.**

b. Approximately how long will it take Jacy's debt to double? **≈ 3 years**

c. Approximately how long will it be until Jacy's debt triples? **≈ 4.5 years**

H.O.T. Problems

Use Higher-Order Thinking Skills

60. WHICH ONE DOESN'T BELONG? Find the expression that does not belong. Explain.

$\log_4 16$	$\log_2 16$	$\log_2 4$	$\log_3 9$

61. CHALLENGE Consider $y = \log_b x$ in which b, x, and y are real numbers. Zero can be in the domain *sometimes*, *always* or *never*. Justify your answer.

62. ERROR ANALYSIS Betsy says that the graphs of all logarithmic functions cross the y-axis at (0, 1) because any number to the zero power equals 1. Tyrone disagrees. Is either of them correct? Explain your reasoning.

63. REASONING Without using a calculator, compare $\log_7 51$, $\log_8 61$, and $\log_9 71$. Which of these is the greatest? Explain your reasoning.

64. OPEN ENDED Write a logarithmic expression of the form $y = \log_b x$ for each of the following conditions. **a–e. See margin.**

a. y is equal to 25.

b. y is negative.

c. y is between 0 and 1.

d. x is 1.

e. x is 0.

65. ERROR ANALYSIS Elisa and Matthew are evaluating $\log_{\frac{1}{7}} 49$. Is either of them correct? Explain your reasoning. **See margin.**

Elisa	Matthew
$\log_{\frac{1}{7}} 49 = y$	$\log_{\frac{1}{7}} 49 = y$
$\left(\frac{1}{7}\right)^y = 49$	$49^y = \frac{1}{7}$
$(7^{-1})^y = 7^2$	$(7^2)^y = (7)^{-1}$
$(7)^{-y} = 7^2$	$7^{2y} = (7)^{-1}$
$y = 2$	$2y = -1$
	$y = -\frac{1}{2}$

66. WRITING IN MATH A transformation of $\log_{10} x$ is $g(x) = a\log_{10}(x - h) + k$. Explain the process of graphing this transformation. **See margin.**

60. $\log_2 16 = 4$; all other choices are equal to 2.

61. Never; if zero were in the domain, the equation would be $y = \log_b 0$. Then $b^y = 0$. However, for any real number b, there is no real power that would let $b^y = 0$.

62. Tyrone; sample answer: The graphs of logarithmic functions pass through (1, 0), not (0, 1).

63. $\log_7 51$; sample answer: $\log_7 51$ equals a little more than 2. $\log_8 61$ equals a little less than 2. $\log_9 71$ equals a little less than 2. Therefore, $\log_7 51$ is the greatest.

NGSSS PRACTICE 912.A.3.14, 912.A.3.15

67. A rectangle is twice as long as it is wide. If the width of the rectangle is 3 inches, what is the area of the rectangle in square inches? **D**

- **A.** 9
- **B.** 12
- **C.** 15
- **D.** 18

68. ACT/SAT Ichiro has some pizza. He sold 40% more slices than he ate. If he sold 70 slices of pizza, how many did he eat? **G**

- **F.** 25
- **G.** 50
- **H.** 75
- **I.** 100

69. THINK SOLVE EXPLAIN **SHORT RESPONSE** In the figure $AB = BC$, $CD = BD$, and angle $CAD = 70°$. What is the measure of angle ADC? **80**

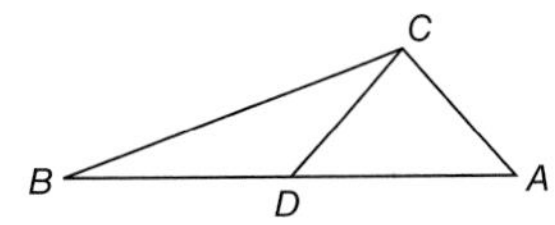

70. If $6x - 3y = 30$ and $4x = 2 - y$ then find $x + y$. **A**

- **A.** −4
- **B.** −2
- **C.** 2
- **D.** 4

Spiral Review

Solve each inequality. Check your solution. (Lesson 8-2)

71. $3^{n-2} > 27$ $n > 5$

72. $2^{2n} \leq \frac{1}{16}$ $n \leq -2$

73. $16^n < 8^{n+1}$ $n < 3$

74. $32^{5p+2} \geq 16^{5p}$ $p \geq -2$

Graph each function. (Lesson 8-1) **75–78. See margin.**

75. $y = -\left(\frac{1}{5}\right)^x$

76. $y = -2.5(5)^x$

77. $y = 30^{-x}$

78. $y = 0.2(5)^{-x}$

79. GEOMETRY The area of a triangle with sides of length a, b, and c is given by $\sqrt{s(s-a)(s-b)(s-c)}$, where $s = \frac{1}{2}(a + b + c)$. If the lengths of the sides of a triangle are 6, 9, and 12 feet, what is the area of the triangle expressed in radical form? (Lesson 7-5) $\frac{27\sqrt{15}}{4}$ **ft²**

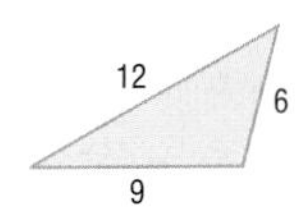

80. GEOMETRY The volume of a rectangular box can be written as $6x^3 + 31x^2 + 53x + 30$ when the height is $x + 2$. (Lesson 6-5)

a. What are the width and length of the box? $2x + 3$ **and** $3x + 5$

b. Will the ratio of the dimensions of the box always be the same regardless of the value of x? Explain.

80b. No; for example, if $x = 1$, the ratio is 3:5:8, but if $x = 2$, the ratio is 4:7:11. The ratios are not equivalent.

81. AUTO MECHANICS Shandra is inventory manager for a local repair shop. She orders 6 batteries, 5 cases of spark plugs, and two dozen pairs of wiper blades and pays \$830. She orders 3 batteries, 7 cases of spark plugs, and four dozen pairs of wiper blades and pays \$820. The batteries are \$22 less than twice the price of a dozen wiper blades. Use augmented matrices to determine what the cost of each item on her order is. (Lesson 4-6) **batteries, \$74; spark plugs, \$58; wiper blades, \$48**

Skills Review

Solve each equation or inequality. Check your solution. (Lesson 8-2)

82. $9^x = \frac{1}{81}$ -2

83. $2^{6x} = 4^{5x+2}$ -1

84. $49^{3p+1} = 7^{2p-5}$ $-\frac{7}{4}$

85. $9^{x^2} \leq 27^{x^2-2}$ $x \leq -\sqrt{6}$ or $x \geq \sqrt{6}$

4 ASSESS

Crystal Ball Ask students to discuss how they think today's work on logarithms will help them solve logarithmic equations in tomorrow's lesson.

Additional Answers

75.

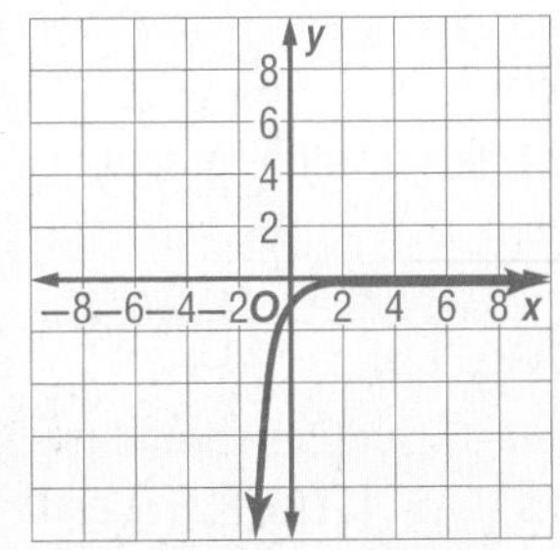

76.

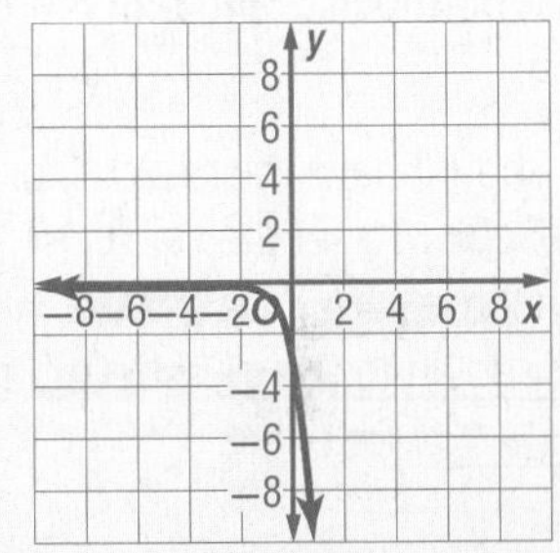

77.

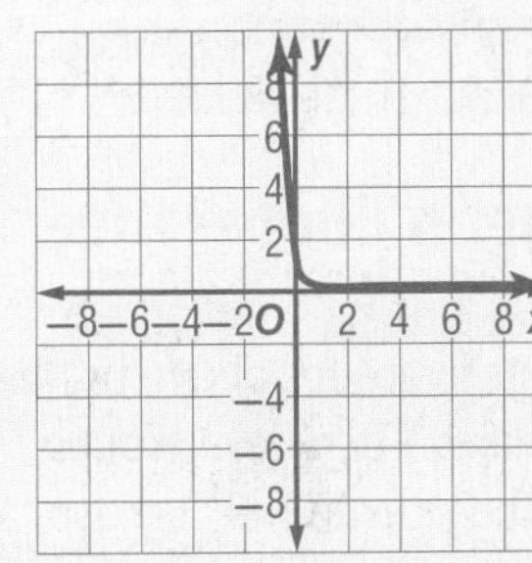

78.

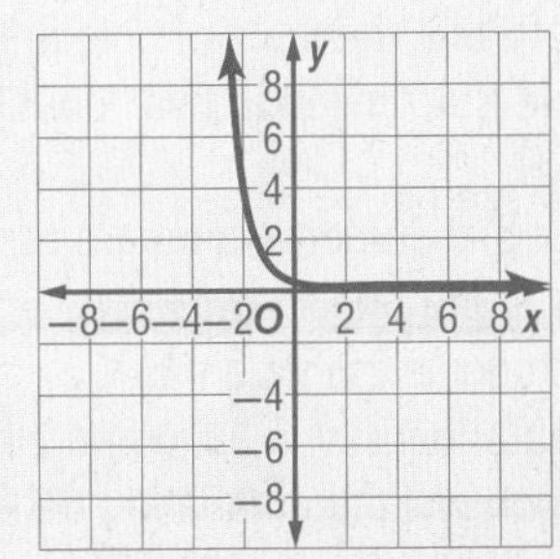

Differentiated Instruction OL BL

Extension Point out that the division problem $\frac{32}{4} = 8$ can be written as $\frac{2^5}{2^2} = 2^3$. Ask students to identify the base 2 logarithm in the dividend, the divisor, and the resulting quotient. Then have them write an equation that relates the logarithms. $\log_2 32 = 5$; $\log_2 4 = 2$; $\log_2 8 = 3$; $\log_2 32 - \log_2 4 = \log_2 8$

1 FOCUS

Objective Use a graphing calculator to find an equation of best fit for exponential and logarithmic functions.

Materials

- TI-83/84 Plus or other graphing calculator

Teaching Tip

Before Step 1, students should use the keystrokes 2nd [STAT PLOT] and check that both plot 2 and plot 3 are turned off.

Students should have their calculator set **DiagnosticOn.** To set the calculator for diagnostics, use 2nd **CATALOG,** move the cursor down to **DiagnosticOn,** and press ENTER twice.

2 TEACH

Working in Cooperative Groups

Put students in groups of two or three, mixing abilities. Then have groups complete the Activity and Exercises 1–3.

- Point out that the table of data in the example is arranged in two "double" columns.
- Suggest that students compare their graphs to the one shown.
- Have students estimate the population density in 2020 and 2050. How soon will the population density be twice what it was in 2000? about 2085
- When students begin the exercises, they should clear lists L_1 and L_2. They should also enter appropriate settings for the graphing window.

Graphing Technology Lab

Choosing the Best Model

FL Math Online glencoe.com
- Other Calculator Keystrokes
- Graphing Technology Personal Tutor

We can find exponential and logarithmic functions of best fit using a TI-83/84 Plus graphing calculator.

ACTIVITY

The population per square mile in the United States has changed dramatically over a period of years. The table shows the number of people per square mile for several years.

U.S. Population Density

Year	People per square mile	Year	People per square mile
1790	4.5	1900	21.5
1800	6.1	1910	26.0
1810	4.3	1920	29.9
1820	5.5	1930	34.7
1830	7.4	1940	37.2
1840	9.8	1950	42.6
1850	7.9	1960	50.6
1860	10.6	1970	57.5
1870	10.9	1980	64.0
1880	14.2	1990	70.3
1890	17.8	2000	80.0

Source: Northeast-Midwest Institute

a. Use a graphing calculator to enter the data. Then draw a scatter plot that shows how the number of people per square mile is related to the year.

Step 1 Enter the year into L1 and the people per square mile into L2.

KEYSTROKES: *See pages 94 and 95 to review how to enter lists.*

Be sure to clear the Y= list. Use the ▶ key to move the cursor from L1 to L2.

Step 2 Draw the scatter plot.

KEYSTROKES: *See pages 94 and 95 to review how to graph a scatter plot.*

Make sure that Plot 1 is on, the scatter plot is chosen, Xlist is L1, and Ylist is L2.

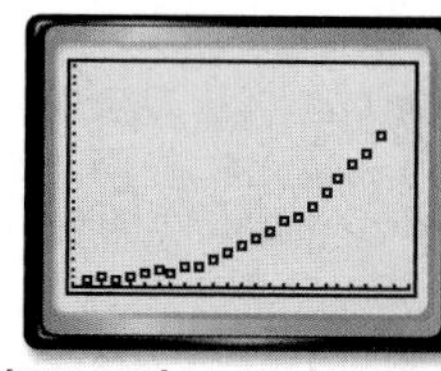

[1790, 2000] scl: 10 by [0, 115] scl: 5

Step 3 Find a regression equation.

To find an equation that best fits the data, use the regression feature of the calculator. Examine various regressions to determine the best model.

Recall that the calculator returns the correlation coefficient r, which is used to indicate how well the model fits the data. The closer r is to 1 or -1, the better the fit.

Linear regression

KEYSTROKES: STAT ▶ 4 ENTER

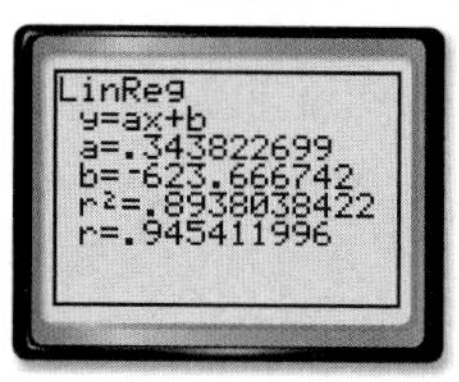

Quadratic regression

KEYSTROKES: STAT ▶ 5 ENTER

$r^2 = 0.9974003374$

$r = \sqrt{0.9974003374}$

$r \approx 0.9986993228$

Exponential regression

KEYSTROKES: STAT ▶ 0 ENTER

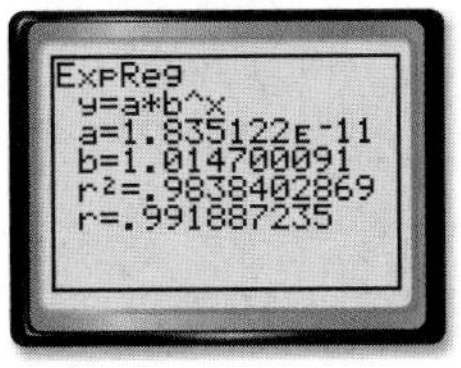

Power regression

KEYSTROKES: STAT ▶ ALPHA [A] ENTER

Compare the r-values.
Linear: 0.945411996
Exponential: 0.991887235
Quadratic: 0.9986993228
Power: 0.9917543535

The r-value of the quadratic regression is closest to 1, so it appears best models the data. You can examine the equation visually by graphing the regression equation with the scatter plot.

KEYSTROKES: STAT ▶ 5 ENTER Y= VARS 5 ▶ ▶ 1 GRAPH

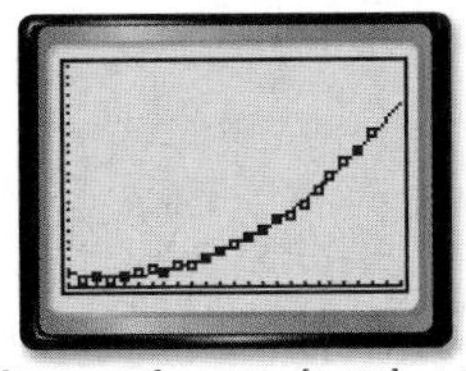

[1790, 2000] scl: 10 by [0, 115] scl: 5

b. If this trend continues, what will be the population per square mile in 2020?

To determine the population per square mile in 2020, find the value of y when $x = 2020$.

KEYSTROKES: 2nd [CALC] 2020 ENTER

If this trend continues, there will be approximately 94.9 people per square mile.

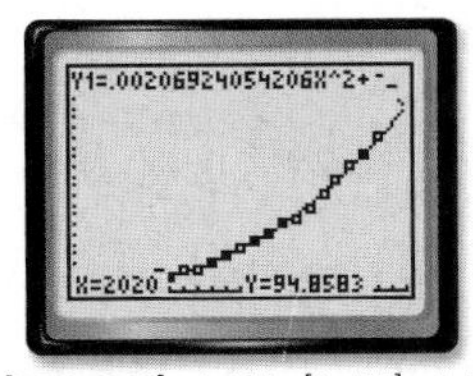

[1790, 2000] scl: 10 by [0, 115] scl: 5

Exercises

Jewel received $50 from her grandparents on her tenth birthday. Her mother deposited it into a new bank account for her. Both Jewel and her mother forgot about the account and made no further deposits or withdrawals. The table shows the account balance for several years. **1, 2. See margin.**

Elapsed Time (years)	Balance
0	$50.00
2	$55.80
4	$64.80
6	$83.09
8	$101.40
10	$123.14
12	$162.67

1. Use a graphing calculator to draw a scatter plot of the data.
2. Calculate and graph a curve of fit for the data using an exponential regression.
3. Write the equation of best fit. **Sample answer: $y = 46.47(1.10^x)$**
4. Based on the model, what will the account balance be after 25 years? **$558.58**
5. Is an exponential model the best fit for the data? Explain. **No; sample answer: The r-value of the exponential regression is 0.9936096203. The r-value of a quadratic regression is 0.9980751795, which is closer to 1.**

Practice Have students complete Exercises 4–5.

3 ASSESS

Formative Assessment

Use Exercise 2 to assess whether students can explain why their equations of best fit are good choices.

From Concrete to Abstract

When you discuss Exercise 5, you may want to ask for any ideas that students have about how to use the calculator to judge the relative merits of various models (quadratic, cubic, quartic, and exponential).

Additional Answers

1.

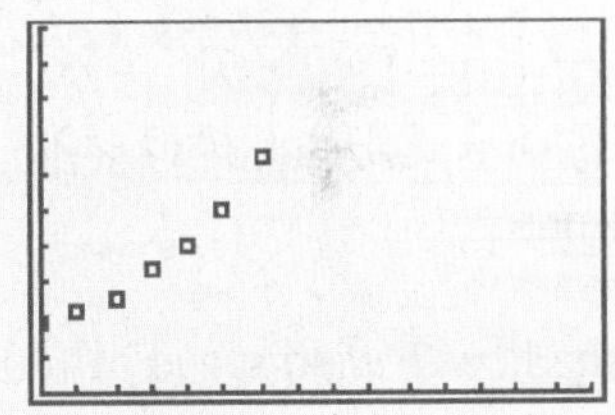

[0, 30] scl: 2 by [0, 250] scl: 25

2.

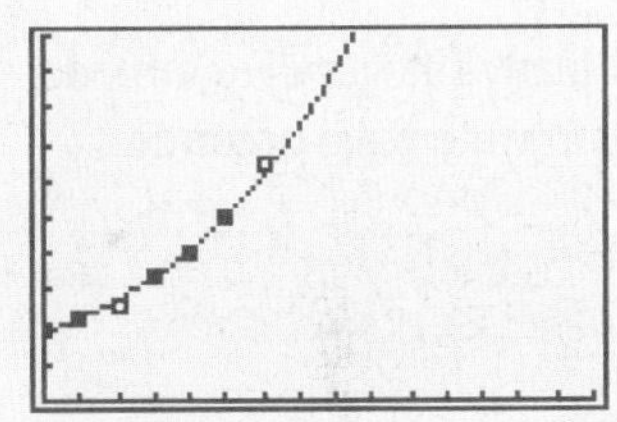

[0, 30] scl: 2 by [0, 250] scl: 25

Extend 8-3 Graphing Technology Lab: Choosing the Best Model 501

8-4 Lesson Notes

1 FOCUS

Vertical Alignment

Before Lesson 8-4
Evaluate logarithmic expressions.

Lesson 8-4
Solve logarithmic equations.
Solve logarithmic inequalities.

After Lesson 8-4
Determine the solutions of logarithmic equations using algebraic methods.

2 TEACH

Scaffolding Questions

Have students read the *Why?* section of the lesson.

Ask:

- A tornado with wind speed of 100 miles per hour is in which category? F-1
- How many category F-6 tornadoes are known to have occurred? 0

8-4 Solving Logarithmic Equations and Inequalities

Then
You evaluated logarithmic expressions. (Lesson 8-3)

Now
- Solve logarithmic equations.
- Solve logarithmic inequalities.

NGSSS
MA.912.A.8.2 Define and use the properties of logarithms to simplify logarithmic expressions and to find their approximate values.
MA.912.A.8.5 Solve logarithmic and exponential **equations.**

New Vocabulary
logarithmic equation
logarithmic inequality

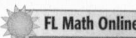

FL Math Online
glencoe.com

Why?

Each year the National Weather Service documents about 1000 tornado touchdowns in the United States. The intensity of a tornado is measured on the Fujita scale. Tornados are divided into six categories according to their wind speed, path length, path width, and damage caused. Category F6 is the most destructive type of tornado.

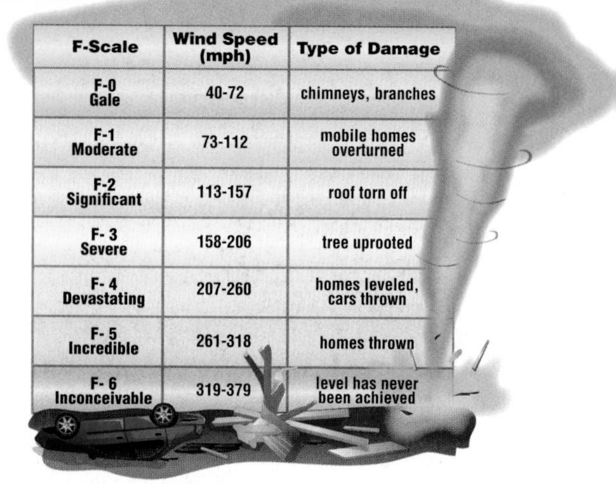

F-Scale	Wind Speed (mph)	Type of Damage
F-0 Gale	40-72	chimneys, branches
F-1 Moderate	73-112	mobile homes overturned
F-2 Significant	113-157	roof torn off
F- 3 Severe	158-206	tree uprooted
F- 4 Devastating	207-260	homes leveled, cars thrown
F- 5 Incredible	261-318	homes thrown
F- 6 Inconceivable	319-379	level has never been achieved

Solve Logarithmic Equations A **logarithmic equation** contains one or more logarithms. You can use the definition of a logarithm to help you solve logarithmic equations.

EXAMPLE 1 Solve a Logarithmic Equation

Solve $\log_{36} x = \frac{3}{2}$.

$\log_{36} x = \frac{3}{2}$	**Original equation**
$x = 36^{\frac{3}{2}}$	**Definition of logarithm**
$x = (6^2)^{\frac{3}{2}}$	**$36 = 6^2$**
$x = 6^3$ or 216	**Power of a Power**

Guided Practice

Solve each equation.

1A. $\log_9 x = \frac{3}{2}$ 27

1B. $\log_{16} x = \frac{5}{2}$ 1024

Personal Tutor glencoe.com

Use the following property to solve logarithmic equations that have logarithms with the same base on each side.

Key Concept

Property of Equality for Logarithmic Functions

Symbols If b is a positive number other than 1, then $\log_b x = \log_b y$ if and only if $x = y$.

Example If $\log_5 x = \log_5 8$, then $x = 8$. If $x = 8$, then $\log_5 x = \log_5 8$.

Lesson 8-4 Resources

Resource	Approaching-Level	On-Level	Beyond-Level	English Learners
Teacher Edition	• Differentiated Instruction, p. 503	• Differentiated Instruction, pp. 503, 507	• Differentiated Instruction, p. 507	
Chapter Resource Masters	• Study Guide and Intervention, pp. 26–27 • Skills Practice, p. 28 • Practice, p. 29 • Word Problem Practice, p. 30	• Study Guide and Intervention, pp. 26–27 • Skills Practice, p. 28 • Practice, p. 29 • Word Problem Practice, p. 30 • Enrichment, p. 31 • Graphing Calculator Activity, p. 32	• Practice, p. 29 • Word Problem Practice, p. 30 • Enrichment, p. 31	• Study Guide and Intervention, pp. 26–27 • Skills Practice, p. 28 • Practice, p. 29 • Word Problem Practice, p. 30
Transparencies	• 5-Minute Check Transparency 8-4	• 5-Minute Check Transparency 8-4	• 5-Minute Check Transparency 8-4	• 5-Minute Check Transparency 8-4
Other	• Study Notebook	• Study Notebook	• Study Notebook	• Study Notebook

NGSSS PRACTICE EXAMPLE 2 912.A.8.5

Solve $\log_2 (x^2 - 4) = \log_2 3x$.

A. -2 B. -1 C. 2 D. 4

Read the Test Item

You need to find x for the logarithmic equation.

Solve the Test Item

$\log_2 (x^2 - 4) = \log_2 3x$	**Original equation**
$x^2 - 4 = 3x$	**Property of Equality for Logarithmic Functions**
$x^2 - 3x - 4 = 0$	**Subtract 3x from each side.**
$(x - 4)(x + 1) = 0$	**Factor.**
$x - 4 = 0$ or $x + 1 = 0$	**Zero Product Property**
$x = 4$ $x = -1$	**Solve each equation.**

CHECK Substitute each value into the original equation.

$x = 4$: $\log_2 (4^2 - 4) \stackrel{?}{=} \log_2 3(4)$; $\log_2 12 = \log_2 12$ ✓

$x = -1$: $\log_2 [(-1)^2 - 4] \stackrel{?}{=} \log_2 3(-1)$; $\log_2 (-3) \stackrel{?}{=} \log_2 (-3)$ ✗

The domain of a logarithmic function cannot be 0, so $\log_2 (-3)$ is undefined and -1 is an extraneous solution. The answer is D.

Guided Practice

2. Solve $\log_3 (x^2 - 15) = \log_3 2x$. H

F. -3 G. -1 H. 5 I. 15

Personal Tutor glencoe.com

Test-TakingTip

Substitution To save time, you can substitute each answer choice in the original equation to find the one that results in a true statement.

Solve Logarithmic Inequalities A **logarithmic inequality** is an inequality that involves logarithms. The following property can be used to solve logarithmic inequalities.

Key Concept

Property of Inequality for Logarithmic Functions

If $b > 1$, $x > 0$, and $\log_b x > y$, then $x > b^y$.

If $b > 1$, $x > 0$, and $\log_b x < y$, then $0 < x < b^y$.

This property also holds true for $\leq$ and $\geq$.

EXAMPLE 3 Solve a Logarithmic Inequality

Solve $\log_3 x > 4$.

$\log_3 x > 4$	**Original inequality**
$x > 3^4$	**Property of Inequality for Logarithmic Functions**
$x > 81$	**Simplify.**

Guided Practice Solve each inequality.

3A. $\log_4 x \geq 3$ $\{x \mid x \geq 64\}$ **3B.** $\log_2 x < 4$ $\{x \mid 0 < x < 16\}$

Differentiated Instruction AL OL

If student need help visualizing the relative locations of the digits in equivalent logarithmic and exponential equations,

Then have students create colorful posters showing several equivalent exponential and logarithmic equations, such as $2^3 = 8$ and $3 = \log_2 8$. Suggest that students use a different color for each of the digits 2, 3, and 8.

Solve Logarithmic Equations

Example 1 shows how to solve logarithmic equations involving a single logarithm. **Example 2** shows how to solve an equation with logarithms on each side.

Formative Assessment

Use the Guided Practice exercises after each example to determine students' understanding of concepts.

Additional Examples

1 Solve $\log_8 x = \frac{4}{3}$. 16

2 **STANDARDIZED TEST EXAMPLE** Solve $\log_4 x^2 = \log_4(-6x - 8)$. C

A 4 **C** -4 and -2

B 2 **D** no solutions

Additional Examples also in Interactive Classroom PowerPoint® Presentations

IWB INTERACTIVE WHITEBOARD READY

Solve Logarithmic Inequalties

Example 3 shows how to solve a logarithmic inequality. **Example 4** shows how to solve an inequality with logarithms on each side of the symbol.

TEACH with TECH

VIDEO RECORDING Have students work in pairs to create a video showing how to solve a logarithmic inequality. Be sure they explain each step of their work, specifically how to rewrite the logarithmic inequality as an exponential inequality.

Additional Example

3 Solve $\log_6 x > 3$. $\{x \mid x > 216\}$

Additional Example

4 Solve $\log_7(2x + 8) > \log_7(x + 5)$. $\{x \mid x > -3\}$

3 PRACTICE

Formative Assessment

Use Exercises 1–7 to check for understanding.

Use the chart at the bottom of this page to customize assignments for your students.

Additional Answers

36b. The graphs are reflections of each other over the x-axis.

36c 1. The second graph is the same as the first, except it is shifted vertically up 2 units.

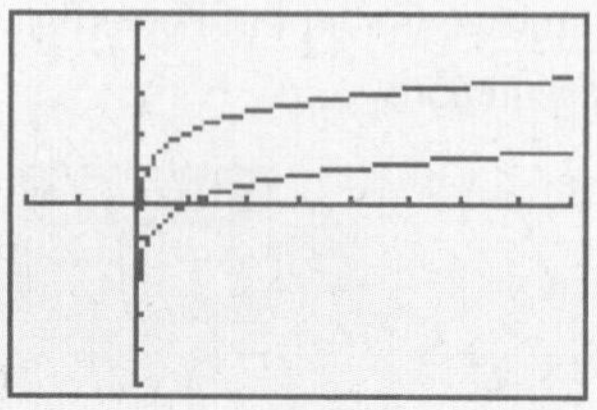

[−2, 8] scl: 1 by [−5, 5] scl: 1

2. The second graph is the same as the first, except it is shifted horizontally to the left 2 units.

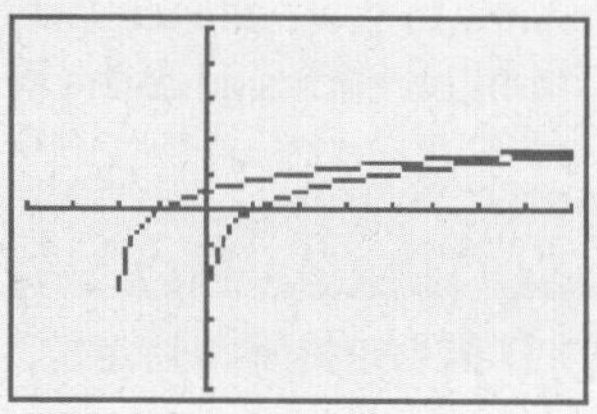

[−4, 8] scl: 1 by [−5, 5] scl: 1

3. Each point on the second graph has a y-coordinate 3 times that of the corresponding point on the first graph.

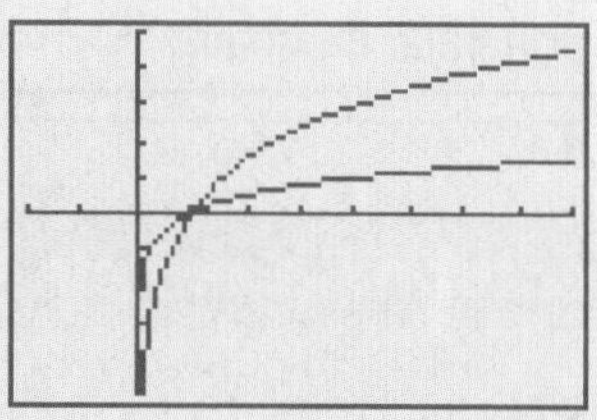

[−2, 8] scl: 1 by [−5, 5] scl: 1

The following property can be used to solve logarithmic inequalities that have logarithms with the same base on each side. Exclude from your solution set values that would result in taking the logarithm of a number less than or equal to zero in the original inequality.

Key Concept

Property of Inequality for Logarithmic Functions

Symbols If $b > 1$, then $\log_b x > \log_b y$ if and only if $x > y$, and $\log_b x < \log_b y$ if and only if $x < y$.

Example If $\log_6 x > \log_6 35$, then $x > 35$.

This property also holds true for $\leq$ and $\geq$.

EXAMPLE 4 Solve Inequalities with Logarithms on Each Side

Solve $\log_4 (x + 3) > \log_4 (2x + 1)$.

$\log_4 (x + 3) > \log_4 (2x + 1)$	**Original inequality**
$x + 3 > 2x + 1$	**Property of Inequality for Logarithmic Functions**
$2 > x$	**Subtract $x + 1$ from each side.**

Exclude all values of x for which $x + 3 \leq 0$ or $2x + 1 \leq 0$. So, $x > -3$, $x > -\frac{1}{2}$, and $x < 2$. The solution set is $\left\{x \mid -\frac{1}{2} < x < 2\right\}$.

Guided Practice

4. Solve $\log_5 (2x + 1) \leq \log_5 (x + 4)$. Check your solution. $\left\{x \mid -\frac{1}{2} < x \leq 3\right\}$

Personal Tutor glencoe.com

Check Your Understanding

Example 1 p. 502

Solve each equation.

1. $\log_8 x = \frac{4}{3}$ 16

2. $\log_{16} x = \frac{3}{4}$ 8

Example 2 p. 503

3. NGSSS PRACTICE Solve $\log_5 (x^2 - 10) = \log_5 3x$. C

A. 10 B. 2 C. 5 D. 2, 5

Examples 3 and 4 pp. 503–504

Solve each inequality.

4. $\log_5 x > 3$ $\{x \mid x > 125\}$

5. $\log_8 x \leq -2$ $\left\{x \mid 0 < x \leq \frac{1}{64}\right\}$

6. $\log_4 (2x + 5) \leq \log_4 (4x - 3)$ $\{x \mid x \geq 4\}$

7. $\log_8 (2x) > \log_8 (6x - 8)$ $\left\{x \mid 2 > x > \frac{4}{3}\right\}$

Practice and Problem Solving

● = **Step-by-Step Solutions** begin on page R20. **Extra Practice** begins on page 947.

Examples 1 and 2 pp. 502–503

Solve each equation.

8. $\log_{81} x = \frac{3}{4}$ 27

9. $\log_{25} x = \frac{5}{2}$ 3125

10. $\log_8 \frac{1}{2} = x$ $-\frac{1}{3}$

11. $\log_6 \frac{1}{36} = x$ −2

12. $\log_x 32 = \frac{5}{2}$ 4

13. $\log_x 27 = \frac{3}{2}$ 9

14. $\log_3 (3x + 8) = \log_3 (x^2 + x)$ −2 or 4

15 $\log_{12} (x^2 - 7) = \log_{12} (x + 5)$ 4 or −3

16. $\log_6 (x^2 - 6x) = \log_6 (-8)$ no solution

17. $\log_9 (x^2 - 4x) = \log_9 (3x - 10)$ 5

18. $\log_4 (2x^2 + 1) = \log_4 (10x - 7)$ 1 or 4

19. $\log_7 (x^2 - 4) = \log_7 (-x + 2)$ −3

Differentiated Homework Options

Level	Assignment	Two-Day Option	
AL Basic	8–33, 38, 40–68	9–33 odd, 45–48	8–32 even, 38, 40–44, 49–68
OL Core	9–33 odd, 34–38, 40–68	9–33, 45–48	34–38, 40–44, 49–68
BL Advanced	34–62, (optional: 63–68)		

504 Chapter 8 Exponential and Logarithmic Functions and Relations

24. $\left\{x \mid x \geq \frac{1}{81}\right\}$

25. $\left\{x \mid 0 < x \leq \frac{1}{4}\right\}$

29. $\left\{x \mid \frac{1}{2} < x \leq 1\right\}$

Examples 3 and 4
pp. 503–504

30. $\left\{x \mid \frac{6}{7} < x < 5\right\}$

31. $\left\{x \mid -\frac{5}{12} < x \leq 1\right\}$

34a. 10^3 or 1000 times as great
34b. $10^{0.3}$ or about 2 times as great

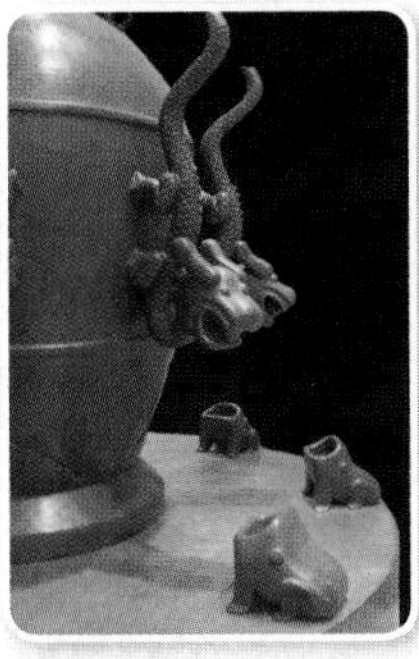

Math History Link

Zhang Heng (A.D. 78–139) The earliest known seismograph was invented by Zhang Heng in China in 132 B.C. It was a large brass vessel with a heavy pendulum and several arms that tripped when an earthquake tremor was felt. This helped determine the direction of the quake.

36a. The shapes of the graphs are the same. The asymptote for each graph is the y-axis and the x-intercept for each graph is 1.
36d. The graphs are reflections of each other over the x-axis. D = $\{x \mid x > 0\}$; R = {all real numbers}

SCIENCE The equation for wind speed w, in miles per hour, near the center of a tornado is $w = 93 \log_{10} d + 65$, where d is the distance in miles that the tornado travels.

20. Write this equation in exponential form. $d = 10^{\frac{w-65}{93}}$

21. In May of 1999, a tornado devastated Oklahoma City with the fastest wind speed ever recorded. If the tornado traveled 525 miles, estimate the wind speed near the center of the tornado. **318 mph**

Solve each inequality.

22. $\log_6 x < -3$ $\left\{x \mid 0 < x < \frac{1}{216}\right\}$
23. $\log_4 x \geq 4$ $\{x \mid x \geq 256\}$
24. $\log_3 x \geq -4$
25. $\log_2 x \leq -2$
26. $\log_5 x > 2$ $\{x \mid x > 25\}$
27. $\log_7 x < -1$ $\left\{x \mid 0 < x < \frac{1}{7}\right\}$
28. $\log_2 (4x - 6) > \log_2 (2x + 8)$ $\{x \mid x > 7\}$
29. $\log_7 (x + 2) \geq \log_7 (6x - 3)$
30. $\log_3 (7x - 6) < \log_3 (4x + 9)$
31. $\log_5 (12x + 5) \leq \log_5 (8x + 9)$
32. $\log_{11} (3x - 24) \geq \log_{11} (-5x - 8)$ $\{x \mid x \geq 2\}$
33. $\log_9 (9x + 4) \leq \log_9 (11x - 12)$ $\{x \mid x \geq 8\}$

34. B **SCIENCE** The magnitude of an earthquake is measured on a logarithmic scale called the Richter scale. The magnitude M is given by $M = \log_{10} x$, where x represents the amplitude of the seismic wave causing ground motion.
   - **a.** How many times as great is the amplitude caused by an earthquake with a Richter scale rating of 8 as an aftershock with a Richter scale rating of 5?
   - **b.** In 1906, San Francisco was almost completely destroyed by a 7.8 magnitude earthquake. In 1911, an earthquake estimated at magnitude 8.1 occurred along the New Madrid fault in the Mississippi River Valley. How many times greater was the New Madrid earthquake than the San Francisco earthquake?

35. **MUSIC** The first key on a piano keyboard corresponds to a pitch with a frequency of 27.5 cycles per second. With every successive key, going up the black and white keys, the pitch multiplies by a constant. The formula for the frequency of the pitch sounded when the nth note up the keyboard is played is given by $n = 1 + 12 \log_2 \frac{f}{27.5}$.
   - **a.** A note has a frequency of 220 cycles per second. How many notes up the piano keyboard is this? **37**
   - **b.** Another pitch on the keyboard has a frequency of 880 cycles per second. After how many notes up the keyboard will this be found? **61**

36. **MULTIPLE REPRESENTATIONS** In this problem, you will explore the graphs shown: $y = \log_4 x$ and $y = \log_{\frac{1}{4}} x$.

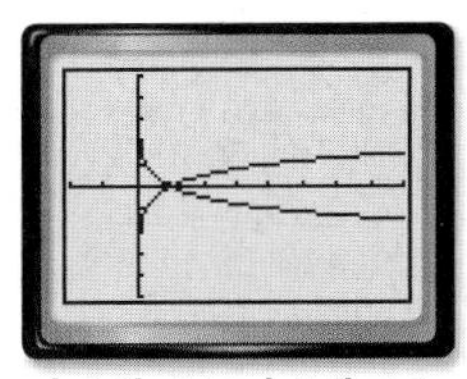

[−2, 8] scl: 1 by [−5, 5] scl: 1

   - **a. ANALYTICAL** How do the shapes of the graphs compare? How do the asymptotes and the x-intercepts of the graphs compare?
   - **b. VERBAL** Describe the relationship between the graphs. **See margin.**
   - **c. GRAPHICAL** Use what you know about transformations of graphs to compare and contrast the graph of each function and the graph of $y = \log_4 x$. **See margin.**
     1. $y = \log_4 x + 2$ 2. $y = \log_4 (x + 2)$ 3. $y = 3 \log_4 x$
   - **d. ANALYTICAL** Describe the relationship between $y = \log_4 x$ and $y = -1(\log_4 x)$. What are a reasonable domain and range for each function?
   - **e. ANALYTICAL** Write an equation for a function for which the graph is the graph of $y = \log_3 x$ translated 4 units left and 1 unit up. $y = \log_3 (x + 4) + 1$

Study Guide and Intervention
CRM pp. 26–27 AL OL ELL

8-4 Study Guide and Intervention
Solving Logarithmic Equations and Inequalities

Solving Logarithmic Equations

Property of Equality for Logarithmic Functions	If b is a positive number other than 1, then $\log_b x = \log_b y$ if and only if $x = y$.

Example 1 Solve $\log_2 2x = 3$.
$\log_2 2x = 3$ Original equation
$2x = 2^3$ Definition of logarithm
$2x = 8$ Simplify.
$x = 4$ Simplify.
The solution is $x = 4$.

Example 2 Solve the equation $\log_2 (x + 17) = \log_2 (3 + 23)$.
Since the bases of the logarithms are equal, $(x + 17)$ must equal $(3x + 23)$.
$(x + 17) = (3x + 23)$
$-6 = 2x$
$x = -3$.

Exercises

Solve each equation.

1. $\log_2 32 = 3x$ $\frac{5}{3}$
2. $\log_3 2c = -2$ $\frac{1}{18}$
3. $\log_{2x} 16 = -2$ $\frac{1}{8}$
4. $\log_{25} \left(\frac{x}{2}\right) = \frac{1}{2}$ 10
5. $\log_4 (5x + 1) = 2$ 3
6. $\log_8 (x - 5) = \frac{2}{3}$ 9
7. $\log_4 (3x - 1) = \log_4 (2x + 3)$ 4
8. $\log_2 (x^2 - 6) = \log_2 (2x + 2)$ 4
9. $\log_{x+4} 27 = 3$ −1
10. $\log_2 (x + 3) = 4$ 13
11. $\log_x 1000 = 3$ 10
12. $\log_8 (4x + 4) = 2$ 15
13. $\log_2 x = \log_2 12$ x = 12
14. $\log_3 (x - 5) = \log_3 13$ x = 18
15. $\log_{10} x = \log_{10} (5x - 20)$ x = 5
16. $\log_5 x = \log_5 (2x - 1)$ x = 1
17. $\log_4 (x + 12) = \log_4 4x$ x = 4
18. $\log_6 (x - 3) = \log_6 2x$ no solution

Chapter 8 26 Glencoe Algebra 2

Practice
CRM p. 29 AL OL BL ELL

8-4 Practice
Solving Logarithmic Equations and Inequalities

Solve each equation.

1. $x + 5 = \log_4 256$ x = −1
2. $3x - 5 = \log_2 1024$ x = 5
3. $\log_3 (4x - 17) = 5$ x = 65
4. $\log_5 (3 - x) = 5$ x = −3122
5. $\log_{13} (x^2 - 4) = \log_{13} 3x$ x = 4
6. $\log_3 (x - 5) = \log_3 (3x - 25)$ x = 10

Solve each inequality

7. $\log_8 (-6x) < 1$ $\left\{x \mid 0 > x > -\frac{4}{3}\right\}$
8. $\log_9 (x + 2) > \log_9 (6 - 3x)$ $\{x \mid -2 > x > 1\}$
9. $\log_{11} (x + 7) < 1$ $\{x \mid -7 < x < 4\}$
10. $\log_{81} x \leq 0.75$ $\{x \mid 27 \geq x > 0\}$
11. $\log_2 (x + 6) < \log_2 17$ $\{x \mid 11 > x > -6\}$
12. $\log_{12} (2x - 1) > \log_{12} (5x - 16)$ $\left\{x \mid 3\frac{1}{5} < x < 5\right\}$
13. $\log_9 (2x - 1) < 0.5$ $\{x \mid 0.5 < x < 2\}$
14. $\log_{10} (x - 5) > \log_{10} 2x$ no solution
15. $\log_3 (x + 12) > \log_3 2x$ $\{x \mid 12 > x > 0\}$
16. $\log_3 (0.3x + 5) > \log_3 (x - 2)$ $\{x \mid 2 < x < 10\}$
17. $\log_2 (x + 3) < \log_2 (1 - 3x)$ no solution
18. $\log_6 (3 - x) \leq \log_6 (x - 1)$ $\{x \mid 3 > x \geq 2\}$

19. **WILDLIFE** An ecologist discovered that the population of a certain endangered species has been doubling every 12 years. When the population reaches 20 times the current level, it may no longer be endangered. Write the logarithmic expression that gives the number of years it will take for the population to reach that level.
$12 \log_2 20$

Chapter 8 29 Glencoe Algebra 2

Lesson 8-4

Word Problem Practice
CRM p. 30 AL OL BL ELL

8-4 Word Problem Practice
Solving Logarithmic Equations and Inequalities

1. **FISH** The population of silver carp has been growing in the Mississippi River. About every 3 years, the population doubles. Write logarithmic expression that gives the number of years it will take for the population to increase by a factor of ten.
$3 \log_2 10$

2. **POWERS** Haley tries to solve the equation $\log_4 2x = 5$. She got the wrong answer. What was her mistake? What should the correct answer be?

1.	$\log_4 2x = 5$
2.	$2x = 4^5$
3.	$x = 2^5$
4.	$x = 32$

From step 2 to step 3, Haley divided the equation by 2 incorrectly. The correct answer is 512.

3. **DIGITS** A computer programmer wants to write a formula that tells how many digits there are in a number n, where n is a positive integer. For example, if $n = 343$, the formula should evaluate to 3 and if $n = 10{,}000$, the formula should evaluate to 5. Suppose $8 \leq \log_{10} n < 9$. How many digits does n have?
9

4. **LOGARITHMS** Pauline knows that $\log_b x = 3$ and $\log_b y = 5$. She knows that this is the same as knowing that $b^3 = x$ and $b^5 = y$. Multiply these two equations together and rewrite it as an equation involving logarithms. What is $\log_b xy$?
$b^3b^5 = xy$, or $b^8 = xy$; in other words, $\log_b xy = 8$

5. **MUSIC** The first note on a piano keyboard corresponds to a pitch with a frequency of 27.5 cycles per second.

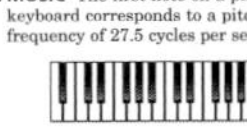

With every successive note you go up the white and black keys of a piano, the pitch multiplies by a factor of $\sqrt[12]{2}$. The formula for the frequency of the pitch sounded when the nth note up the keyboard is played is given by
$$n = 1 + 12 \log_2 \frac{f}{27.5}.$$
   - **a.** The pitch that orchestras tune to is the A above middle C. It has a frequency of 440 cycles per second. How many notes up the piano keyboard is this A?
49
   - **b.** Another pitch on the keyboard has a frequency of 1760 cycles per second. How many notes up the keyboard will this be found?
73

Chapter 8 30 Glencoe Algebra 2

Multiple Representations In Exercise 36, students use a graphing calculator, logic, and analysis to compare and contrast logarithmic functions.

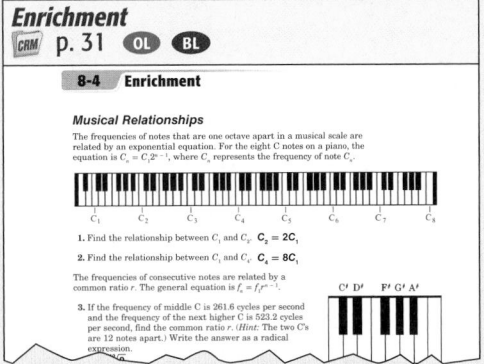

Enrichment
CRM p. 31 OL BL

8-4 Enrichment

Musical Relationships

The frequencies of notes that are one octave apart in a musical scale are related by an exponential equation. For the eight C notes on a piano, the equation is $C_n = C_1 2^{n-1}$, where C_n represents the frequency of note C_n.

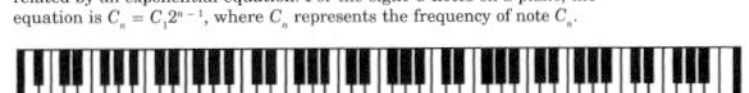

1. Find the relationship between C_1 and C_2. $C_2 = 2C_1$
2. Find the relationship between C_1 and C_4. $C_4 = 8C_1$

The frequencies of consecutive notes are related by a common ratio r. The general equation is $f_n = f_1 r^{n-1}$.

3. If the frequency of middle C is 261.6 cycles per second and the frequency of the next higher C is 523.2 cycles per second, find the common ratio r. (*Hint:* The two C's are 12 notes apart.) Write the answer as a radical expression.

Watch Out!

Error Analysis For Exercise 38, remind students that raising a number to a negative power is not the same as multiplying by −1.

Additional Answers

37c. Sample answer: The power of the logarithm only changes by 2. The power is the answer to the logarithm. That 2 is multiplied by the 10 before the logarithm. So we expect the decibels to change by 20.

44. The y-intercept of the exponential function $y = b^x$ is (0, 1). When the x and y coordinates are switched, the y-intercept is transformed to the x-intercept of (1, 0). There was no x-intercept (1, 0) in the exponential function of the form $y = b^x$. So when the x- and y-coordinates are switched there would be no point on the inverse of (0, 1), and there is no y-intercept.

Real-World Link

The maximum exposure time before your hearing is endangered at 85 decibels is 8 hours.

Source: National Institute for Occupational Safety and Health

37 **SOUND** The relationship between the intensity of sound I and the number of decibels β is $\beta = 10 \log_{10}\left(\frac{I}{10^{-12}}\right)$, where I is the intensity of sound in watts per square meter.

Sound	Intensity	Decibels
pin drop	10^0	0
normal breathing	10^1	1
clothes dryer	10^6	6
subway train	10^{10}	10
firecracker	10^{12}	12

a. Find the number of decibels of a sound with an intensity of 1 watt per square meter. **120**

b. Find the number of decibels of sound with an intensity of 10^{-2} watts per square meter. **100**

c. The intensity of the sound of 1 watt per square meter is 100 times as much as the intensity of 10^{-2} watts per square meter. Why are the decibels of sound not 100 times as great? **See margin.**

38. Sample answer: Ryan; Heather did not need to switch the inequality symbol when raising to a negative power.

H.O.T. Problems

Use Higher-Order Thinking Skills

38. ERROR ANALYSIS Ryan and Heather are solving $\log_3 x \geq -3$. Is either of them correct? Explain your reasoning.

Ryan	Heather
$\log_3 x \geq -3$	$\log_3 x \geq -3$
$x \geq 3^{-3}$	$\log_3 x \geq 3^{-3}$
$x \geq \frac{1}{27}$	$0 < x \leq \frac{1}{27}$

39. CHALLENGE Find $\log_3 27 + \log_9 27 + \log_{27} 27 + \log_{81} 27 + \log_{243} 27$. $6\frac{17}{20}$

40. REASONING The Property of Inequality for Logarithmic Functions states that when $b > 1$, $\log_b x > \log_b y$ if and only if $x > y$. What is the case for when $0 < b < 1$? Explain your reasoning.

41. WRITING IN MATH Explain how the domain and range of logarithmic functions are related to the domain and range of exponential functions.

42. OPEN ENDED Give an example of a logarithmic equation that has no solution.

43. REASONING Choose the appropriate term. Explain your reasoning. All logarithmic equations are of the form $y = \log_b x$.

a. If the base of a logarithmic equation is greater than 1 and the value of x is between 0 and 1, then the value for y is (*less than*, *greater than*, *equal to*) 0.

b. If the base of a logarithmic equation is between 0 and 1 and the value of x is greater than 1, then the value of y is (*less than*, *greater than*, *equal to*) 0.

c. There is/are (*no*, *one*, *infinitely many*) solution(s) for b in the equation $y = \log_b 0$.

d. There is/are (*no*, *one*, *infinitely many*) solution(s) for b in the equation $y = \log_b 1$.

44. WRITING IN MATH Explain why any logarithmic function of the form $y = \log_b x$ has an x-intercept of (1, 0) and no y-intercept. **See margin.**

40. Sample answer: When $0 < b < 1$, $\log_b x > \log_b y$ if and only if $x < y$. The inequality symbol is switched because a fraction that is less than 1 becomes smaller when it is taken to a greater power.

41. The logarithmic function of the form $y = \log_b x$ is the inverse of the exponential function of the form $y = b^x$. The domain of one of the two inverse functions is the range of the other. The range of one of the two inverse functions is the domain of the other.

42. Sample answer: $\log_3 (x + 4) = \log_3 (2x + 12)$

NGSSS PRACTICE 912.A.5.5, 912.S.3.3, 912.A.2.11, 912.P.3.1

45. Find x if $\frac{6.4}{x} = \frac{4}{7}$. C

A. 3.4
B. 9.4
C. 11.2
D. 44.8

46. The monthly precipitation in Houston for part of a year is shown. H

Month	Precipitation (in.)
April	3.60
May	5.15
June	5.35
July	3.18
August	3.83

Find the median precipitation.

F. 3.60 in.
G. 4.22 in.
H. 3.83 in.
I. 4.25 in.

47. Clara received a 10% raise each year for 3 consecutive years. What was her salary after the three raises if her starting salary was $12,000 per year? B

A. $14,520
B. $15,972
C. $16,248
D. $16,410

48. **ACT/SAT** A vendor has 14 helium balloons for sale: 9 are yellow, 3 are red, and 2 are green. A balloon is selected at random and sold. If the balloon sold is yellow, what is the probability that the next balloon, selected at random, is also yellow? $\frac{8}{13}$

Spiral Review

Evaluate each expression. (Lesson 8-3)

49. $\log_4 256$ 4
50. $\log_2 \frac{1}{8}$ -3
51. $\log_6 216$ 3
52. $\log_3 27$ 3
53. $\log_5 \frac{1}{125}$ -3
54. $\log_7 2401$ 4

Solve each equation or inequality. Check your solution. (Lesson 8-2)

55. $5^{2x+3} \leq 125$ $x \leq 0$
56. $3^{3x-2} > 81$ $x > 2$
57. $4^{4a+6} \leq 16^a$ $a \leq -3$
58. $11^{2x+1} = 121^{3x}$ $x = 0.25$
59. $3^{4x-7} = 27^{2x+3}$ $x = -8$
60. $8^{x-4} \leq 2^{4-x}$ $x \leq 4$

61. **SHIPPING** The height of a shipping cylinder is 4 feet more than the radius. If the volume of the cylinder is 5π cubic feet, how tall is it? Use the formula $V = \pi \cdot r^2 \cdot h$. (Lesson 6-8) 5 ft

62. **NUMBER THEORY** Two complex conjugate numbers have a sum of 12 and a product of 40. Find the two numbers. (Lesson 5-4) $6 + 2i, 6 - 2i$

Skills Review

Simplify. Assume that no variable equals zero. (Lesson 6-1)

63. $x^5 \cdot x^3$ x^8
64. $a^2 \cdot a^6$ a^8
65. $(2p^2n)^3$ $8p^6n^3$
66. $(3b^3c^2)^2$ $9b^6c^4$
67. $\frac{x^4y^6}{xy^2}$ x^3y^4
68. $\left(\frac{c^9}{d^7}\right)^0$ 1

4 ASSESS

Name the Math Have students write a step-by-step explanation of the procedure for solving a logarithmic equation such as $\log_8 n = \frac{7}{3}$.

Formative Assessment

Check for student understanding of Lessons 8-3 and 8-4.

CRM Quiz 2, p. 63

Differentiated Instruction OL BL

Extension Ask students to evaluate $\log_3 9$ and $\log_3 27$. 2, 3 Then ask them to predict the value of $\log_3 (9 \cdot 27)$. After they have made their predictions, ask them to check to see if 3 raised to their predicted values is equal to $9 \cdot 27$, or 243. Have them predict the value of $\log_3(mn)$. $\log_3 m + \log_3 n$

CHAPTER 8 Mid-Chapter Quiz

Formative Assessment

Use the Mid-Chapter Quiz to assess students' progress in the first half of the chapter.

For problems answered incorrectly, have students review the lessons indicated in parentheses.

ExamView Assessment Suite Customize and create multiple versions of your Mid-Chapter Quiz and their answer keys.

FOLDABLES Follow-Up

Before students complete the Mid-Chapter Quiz, encourage them to review the information for Lessons 8-1 through 8-4 in their Foldables.

CHAPTER 8 Mid-Chapter Quiz

Lessons 8-1 through 8-4

NGSSS 912.A.8.3, 912.A.8.1, 912.A.8.2

Graph each function. State the domain and range. (Lesson 8-1)

1. $f(x) = 3(4)^x$ **1–4. See Chapter 8 Answer Appendix.**

2. $f(x) = -(2)^x + 5$

3. $f(x) = -0.5(3)^{x+2} + 4$

4. $f(x) = -3\left(\frac{2}{3}\right)^{x-1} + 8$

5. SCIENCE You are studying a bacteria population. The population originally started with 6000 bacteria cells. After 2 hours, there were 28,000 bacteria cells. (Lesson 8-1)

a. Write an exponential function that could be used to model the number of bacteria after x hours if the number of bacteria changes at the same rate. **$f(x) = 6000(2.16025)^x$**

b. How many bacteria cells can be expected after 4 hours? **about 130,667**

6. NGSSS **PRACTICE** Which exponential function has a graph that passes through the points at (0, 125) and (3, 1000)? (Lesson 8-1) **D**

A. $f(x) = 125(3)^x$

B. $f(x) = 1000(3)^x$

C. $f(x) = 125(1000)^x$

D. $f(x) = 125(2)^x$

7. POPULATION In 1995, a certain city had a population of 45,000. It increased to 68,000 by 2007. (Lesson 8-2)

a. What is an exponential function that could be used to model the population of this city x years after 1995? **$f(x) = 45{,}000(1.0350)^x$**

b. Use your model to estimate the population in 2015. **89,541**

8. NGSSS **PRACTICE** Find the value of x for $\log_3 (x^2 + 2x) = \log_3 (x + 2)$. (Lesson 8-3) **H**

F. $x = -2, 1$

G. $x = -2$

H. $x = 1$

I. no solution

Graph each function. (Lesson 8-3) **9, 10. See Chapter 8 Answer Appendix.**

9. $f(x) = 3 \log_2 (x - 1)$

10. $f(x) = -4 \log_3 (x - 2) + 5$

11. NGSSS **PRACTICE** Which graph below is the graph of the function $f(x) = \log_3 (x + 5) + 3$? (Lesson 8-3) **A**

A.

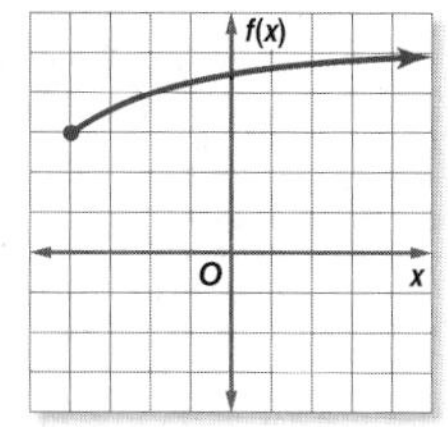

C.

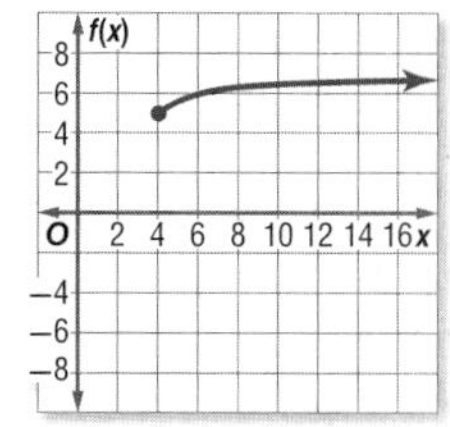

B.

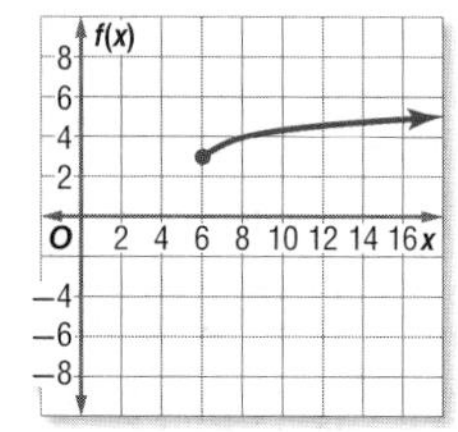

D.

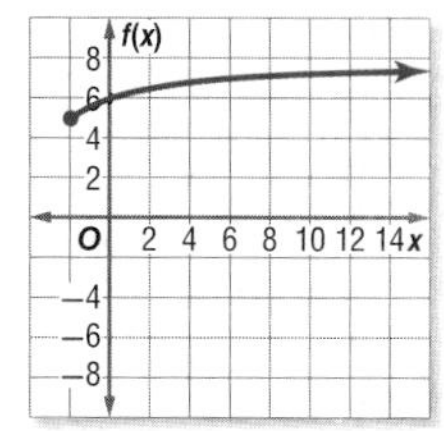

Evaluate each expression. (Lesson 8-3)

12. $\log_4 32$ **$\frac{5}{2}$**

13. $\log_5 5^{12}$ **12**

14. $\log_{16} 4$ **$\frac{1}{2}$**

15. Write $\log_9 729 = 3$ in exponential form. (Lesson 8-3) **$9^3 = 729$**

Solve each equation or inequality. Check your solution. (Lessons 8-2 and 8-4)

16. $3^x = 27^2$ **6**

17. $4^{3x-1} = 16^x$ **1**

18. $\frac{1}{9} = 243^{2x+1}$ **$-\frac{7}{10}$**

19. $16^{2x+3} < 64$ **$x < -\frac{3}{4}$**

20. $\left(\frac{1}{32}\right)^{x+3} \geq 16^{3x}$ **$x \leq -\frac{15}{17}$**

21. $\log_4 x = \frac{3}{2}$ **8**

22. $\log_7 (-x + 3) = \log_7 (6x + 5)$ **$-\frac{2}{7}$**

23. $\log_2 x < -3$ **$\left\{x \middle| 0 < x < \frac{1}{8}\right\}$**

24. $\log_8 (3x + 7) = \log_8 (2x - 5)$ **no solution**

Intervention Planner

Tier 1 On Level	Tier 2 Strategic Intervention approaching grade level	Tier 3 Intensive Intervention 2 or more grades below level
If students miss about 25% of the exercises or less,	**If** students miss about 50% of the exercises,	**If** students miss about 75% of the exercises,
Then choose a resource: **SE** Lessons 8-1, 8-2, 8-3, and 8-4 **CRM** Skills Practice, pp. 7, 14, 21, and 28 **TE** Chapter Project, p. 472 FL Math Online Self-Check Quiz	**Then** choose a resource: **CRM** Study Guide and Intervention, Chapter 8, pp. 5, 12, 19, and 26 FL Math Online Extra Examples, Personal Tutor, Homework Help	**Then** use *Math Triumphs, Alg. 2* FL Math Online Extra Examples, Personal Tutor, Homework Help, Review Vocabulary

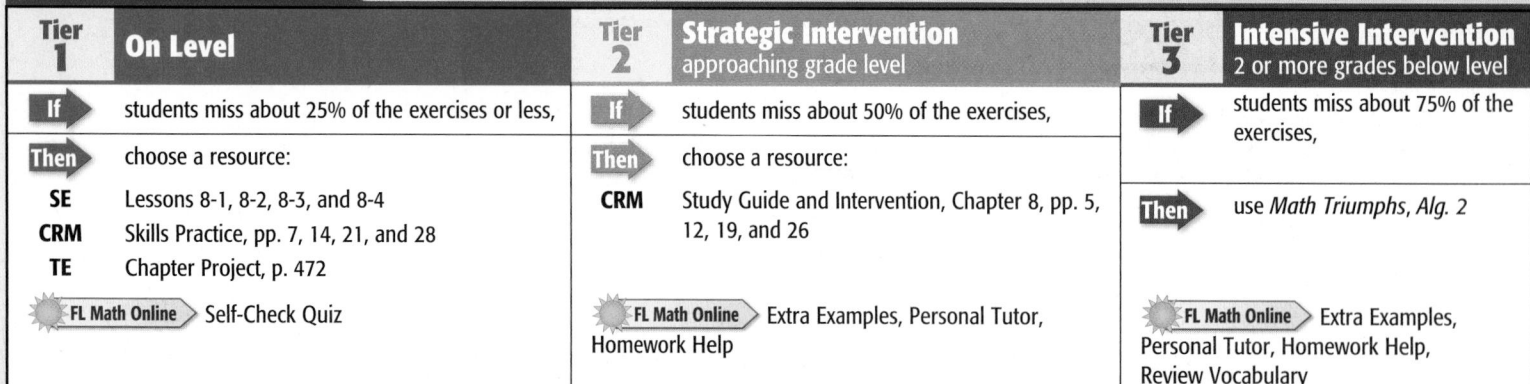

8-5 Properties of Logarithms

Why?

The level of acidity in food is important to some consumers with sensitive stomachs. Most of the foods that we consume are more acidic than basic. The pH scale measures acidity; a low pH indicates an acidic solution, and a high pH indicates a basic solution. It is another example of a logarithmic scale based on powers of ten. Black coffee has a pH of 5, while neutral water has a pH of 7. Black coffee is one hundred times as acidic as neutral water, because $10^{7-5} = 10^2$ or 100.

Product	pH Level
Lemon Juice	2.1
Sauerkraut	3.5
Tomatoes	4.2
Black Coffee	5.0
Milk	6.4
Pure Water	7.0
Eggs	7.8
Milk of Magnesia	10.0

Then
You evaluated logarithmic expressions and solved logarithmic equations. (Lesson 8-4)

Now
- Simplify and evaluate expressions using the properties of logarithms.
- Solve logarithmic equations using the properties of logarithms.

NGSSS
MA.912.A.8.2 Define and use the properties of logarithms to simplify logarithmic expressions and to find their approximate values.

FL Math Online
glencoe.com

Properties of Logarithms Since logarithms are exponents, the properties of logarithms can be derived from the properties of exponents. The Product Property of Logarithms can be derived from the Product of Powers Property of Exponents.

Key Concept — **Product Property of Logarithms**

Words The logarithm of a product is the sum of the logarithms of its factors.

Symbols For all positive numbers a, b, and x, where $x \neq 1$, $\log_x ab = \log_x a + \log_x b$.

Example $\log_2 [(5)(6)] = \log_2 5 + \log_2 6$

To show that this property is true, let $b^x = a$ and $b^y = c$. Then, using the definition of logarithm, $x = \log_b a$ and $y = \log_b c$.

$b^x b^y = ac$	**Substitution**
$b^{x+y} = ac$	**Product of Powers**
$\log_b b^{x+y} = \log_b ac$	**Property of Equality for Logarithmic Functions**
$x + y = \log_b ac$	**Inverse Property of Exponents and Logarithms**
$\log_b a + \log_b c = \log_b ac$	**Replace x with $\log_b a$ and y with $\log_b c$.**

You can use the Product Property of Logarithms to approximate logarithmic expressions.

EXAMPLE 1 **Use the Product Property**

Use $\log_4 3 \approx 0.7925$ to approximate the value of $\log_4 192$.

$\log_4 192 = \log_4 (4^3 \cdot 3)$	**Replace 192 with $64 \cdot 3$ or $4^3 \cdot 3$.**
$= \log_4 4^3 + \log_4 3$	**Product Property**
$= 3 + \log_4 3$	**Inverse Property of Exponents and Logarithms**
$= 3 + 0.7925$ or 3.7925	**Replace $\log_4 3$ with 0.7925.**

Guided Practice

1. Use $\log_4 2 = 0.5$ to approximate the value of $\log_4 32$. 2.5

Personal Tutor glencoe.com

8-5 Lesson Notes

1 FOCUS

Vertical Alignment

Before Lesson 8-5
Evaluate logarithmic expressions and solve logarithmic equations.

Lesson 8-5
Simplify and evaluate expressions using the properties of logarithms. Solve logarithmic equations using the properties of logarithms.

After Lesson 8-5
Determine solutions of exponential equations using algebraic methods.

2 TEACH

Scaffolding Questions

Have students read the *Why?* section of the lesson.

Ask:
- Is lemon juice acidic or basic? acidic
- Is milk of magnesia acidic or basic? basic
- Milk of magnesia is how many times as basic as neutral water? $10^{10-7} = 10^3 = 1000$

Lesson 8-5 Resources

Resource	Approaching-Level	On-Level	Beyond-Level	English Learners
Teacher Edition	• Differentiated Instruction, p. 511	• Differentiated Instruction, p. 511	• Differentiated Instruction, pp. 511, 515	• Differentiated Instruction, p. 511
Chapter Resource Masters	• Study Guide and Intervention, pp. 33–34 • Skills Practice, p. 35 • Practice, p. 36 • Word Problem Practice, p. 37	• Study Guide and Intervention, pp. 33–34 • Skills Practice, p. 35 • Practice, p. 36 • Word Problem Practice, p. 37 • Enrichment, p. 38 • TI-Nspire Activity, p. 39	• Practice, p. 36 • Word Problem Practice, p. 37 • Enrichment, p. 38	• Study Guide and Intervention, pp. 33–34 • Skills Practice, p. 35 • Practice, p. 36 • Word Problem Practice, p. 37
Transparencies	• 5-Minute Check Transparency 8-5	• 5-Minute Check Transparency 8-5	• 5-Minute Check Transparency 8-5	• 5-Minute Check Transparency 8-5
Other	• Study Notebook	• Study Notebook	• Study Notebook	• Study Notebook

Properties of Logarithms

Example 1 shows how to use the Product Property to approximate the value of a logarithmic expression. **Example 2** shows how to use the Quotient Property to solve a real-world problem. **Example 3** shows how to use the Power Property of Logarithms to approximate the value of a logarithmic expression.

Additional Examples

1 Use $\log_5 2 \approx 0.4307$ to approximate the value of $\log_5 250$. 3.4307

2 **SCIENCE** Find the amount of hydrogen in a liter of acid rain that has a pH of 5.5. $10^{-5.5}$, or 0.0000032 moles

Additional Examples also in Interactive Classroom PowerPoint® Presentations

IWB INTERACTIVE WHITEBOARD READY

Focus on Mathematical Content

Properties of Logarithms In addition to the Product, Quotient, and Power Properties of Logarithms, there are other properties such as the four listed below that can be helpful.

$$\log_b 1 = 0$$
$$\log_b b = 1$$
$$\log_b b^x = x$$
$$b^{\log_b x} = x$$

The first two of these properties become clear when the equations are written in exponential form. The third and fourth properties result from the fact that logarithmic and exponential functions are inverse functions.

Recall that the quotient of powers is found by subtracting exponents. The property for the logarithm of a quotient is similar. Let $b^x = a$ and $b^y = c$. Then $\log_b a = x$ and $\log_b c = y$

$\frac{b^x}{b^y} = \frac{a}{c}$	
$b^{x-y} = \frac{a}{c}$	**Quotient Property**
$\log_b b^{x-y} = \log_b \frac{a}{c}$	**Property of Equality for Logarithmic Equations**
$x - y = \log_b \frac{a}{c}$	**Inverse Property of Exponents and Logarithms**
$\log_b a - \log_b c = \log_b \frac{a}{c}$	**Replace x with $\log_b a$ and y with $\log_b c$.**

Key Concept — Quotient Property of Logarithms

Words The logarithm of a quotient is the difference of the logarithms of the numerator and the denominator.

Symbols For all positive numbers a, b, and x, where $x \neq 1$,
$\log_x \frac{a}{b} = \log_x a - \log_x b$.

Example $\log_2 \frac{5}{6} = \log_2 5 - \log_2 6$

Real-World Link

Acid rain is more acidic than normal rain. Smoke and fumes from burning fossil fuels rise into the atmosphere and combine with the moisture in the air to form acid rain. Acid rain can be responsible for the erosion of statues, as in the photo above.

Real-World EXAMPLE 2 — Quotient Property

SCIENCE The pH of a substance is defined as the concentration of hydrogen ions $[H^+]$ in moles. It is given by the formula $\text{pH} = \log_{10} \frac{1}{H^+}$. Find the amount of hydrogen in a liter of acid rain that has a pH of 4.2.

Understand The formula for finding pH and the pH of the rain is given. You want to find the amount of hydrogen in a liter of this rain.

Plan Write the equation. Then, solve for $[H^+]$.

Solve

$\text{pH} = \log_{10} \frac{1}{H^+}$	**Original equation**
$4.2 = \log_{10} \frac{1}{H^+}$	**Substitute 4.2 for pH.**
$4.2 = \log_{10} 1 - \log_{10} H^+$	**Quotient Property**
$4.2 = 0 - \log_{10} H^+$	**$\log_{10} 1 = 0$**
$4.2 = -\log_{10} H^+$	**Simplify.**
$-4.2 = \log_{10} H^+$	**Multiply each side by −1.**
$10^{-4.2} = H^+$	**Definition of logarithm**

There are $10^{-4.2}$, or about 0.000063, mole of hydrogen in a liter of this rain.

Check

$4.2 = \log_{10} \frac{1}{H^+}$	**pH = 4.2**
$4.2 \stackrel{?}{=} \log_{10} \frac{1}{10^{-4.2}}$	**$H^+ = 10^{-4.2}$**
$4.2 \stackrel{?}{=} \log_{10} 1 - \log_{10} 10^{-4.2}$	**Quotient Property**
$4.2 \stackrel{?}{=} 0 - (-4.2)$	**Simplify.**
$4.2 = 4.2$ ✓	

Guided Practice

2. SOUND The loudness L of a sound, measured in decibels, is given by $L = 10 \log_{10} R$, where R is the sound's relative intensity. Suppose one person talks with a relative intensity of 10^6 or 60 decibels. How much louder would 100 people be, talking at the same intensity? **20 decibels louder**

Personal Tutor glencoe.com

Tips for New Teachers

Problem Solving When discussing the Product Property of Logarithms, point out that the logarithms used in the example show that the property applies to all logarithms, not just those that can be simplified.

TEACH with TECH

INTERACTIVE WHITEBOARD On the board, work through several examples that use the different properties of logarithms. Save each example as a notes page, and clearly label it with which property was used. Post your notes to a class Web page so students can use them as an additional reference outside of class.

510 Chapter 8 Exponential and Logarithmic Functions and Relations

Recall that the power of a power is found by multiplying exponents. The property for the logarithm of a power is similar.

Key Concept **Power Property of Logarithms**

Words The logarithm of a power is the product of the logarithm and the exponent.

Symbols For any real number p, and positive numbers m and b, where $b \neq 1$, $\log_b m^p = p \log_b m$.

Example $\log_2 6^5 = 5 \log_2 6$

StudyTip

Answer Check You can check this answer by evaluating $2^{4.6438}$ on a calculator. The calculator should give a result of about 25, since $\log_2 25 \approx 4.6438$ means $2^{4.6438} \approx 25$.

EXAMPLE 3 **Power Property of Logarithms**

Given $\log_2 5 \approx 2.3219$, approximate the value of $\log_2 25$.

$\log_2 25 = \log_2 5^2$ — **Replace 25 with 5^2.**

$= 2 \log_2 5$ — **Power Property**

$\approx 2(2.3219)$ or 4.6438 — **Replace $\log_2 5$ with 2.3219.**

Guided Practice

3. Given $\log_3 7 \approx 1.7712$, approximate the value of $\log_3 49$. $\approx$**3.5424**

Personal Tutor glencoe.com

Solve Logarithmic Equations You can use the properties of logarithms to solve equations involving logarithms.

EXAMPLE 4 **Solve Equations Using Properties of Logarithms**

Solve $\log_6 x + \log_6 (x - 9) = 2$.

$\log_6 x + \log_6 (x - 9) = 2$ — **Original equation**

$\log_6 x(x - 9) = 2$ — **Product Property**

$x(x - 9) = 6^2$ — **Definition of logarithm**

$x^2 - 9x - 36 = 0$ — **Subtract 36 from each side.**

$(x - 12)(x + 3) = 0$ — **Factor.**

$x - 12 = 0$ or $x + 3 = 0$ — **Zero Product Property**

$x = 12$ $\quad$ $x = -3$ — **Solve each equation.**

CHECK

$\log_6 x + \log_6 (x - 9) = 2$

$\log_6 12 + \log_6 (12 - 9) \stackrel{?}{=} 2$

$\log_6 12 + \log_6 3 \stackrel{?}{=} 2$

$\log_6 (12 \cdot 3) \stackrel{?}{=} 2$

$\log_6 36 \stackrel{?}{=} 2$

$2 = 2$ ✓

$\log_6 x + \log_6 (x - 9) = 2$

$\log_6 (-3) + \log_6 (-3 - 9) \stackrel{?}{=} 2$

$\log_6 (-3) + \log_6 (-12) \stackrel{?}{=} 2$

Because $\log_6 (-3)$ and $\log_6 (-12)$ are undefined, -3 is an extraneous solution.

The solution is $x = 12$.

Guided Practice

4A. $2 \log_7 x = \log_7 27 + \log_7 3$ 9

4B. $\log_6 x + \log_6 (x + 5) = 2$ 4

Personal Tutor glencoe.com

Additional Example

3 Given $\log_5 6 \approx 1.1133$, approximate the value of $\log_5 216$. 3.3399

Solve Logarithmic Equations

Example 4 shows how to solve logarithmic equations using properties of logarithms.

Additional Example

4 Solve the equation.

$4 \log_2 x - \log_2 5 = \log_2 125$ 5

Tips for New Teachers

Sense-Making Encourage students to check their answers by estimating. For instance, in Example 3, $2^4 = 16$ and $2^5 = 32$. So, it is reasonable for $\log_2 25$ to be between 4 and 5.

Differentiated Instruction

AL OL BL ELL

Interpersonal Learners Immediately after discussing Example 4, have pairs of students rework the Example together without looking at the solution in the text. Have the partners take turns explaining the solution steps to each other. Have them also discuss the reasonableness of their solutions.

3 PRACTICE

Formative Assessment

Use Exercises 1–11 to check for understanding.

Use the chart at the bottom of this page to customize assignments for your students.

Check Your Understanding

Examples 1 and 2 (pp. 509–510)

Use $\log_4 3 \approx 0.7925$ and $\log_4 5 \approx 1.1610$ to approximate the value of each expression.

1. $\log_4 18$ 2.085

2. $\log_4 15$ 1.9535

3. $\log_4 \frac{5}{3}$ 0.3685

4. $\log_4 \frac{3}{4}$ −0.2075

Example 2 (p. 510)

5. **MOUNTAIN CLIMBING** As elevation increases, the atmospheric air pressure decreases. The formula for pressure based on elevation is $a = 15{,}500(5 - \log_{10} P)$, where a is the altitude in meters and P is the pressure in pascals (1 psi ≈ 6900 pascals). What is the air pressure at the summit in pascals for each mountain listed in the table at the right?

Mountain	Country	Height (m)
Everest	Nepal/Tibet	8850
Trisuli	India	7074
Bonete	Argentina/Chile	6872
McKinley	United States	6194
Logan	Canada	5959

5. Mt. Everest: 26,855.44 pascals; Mt. Trisuli: 34,963.34 pascals; Mt. Bonete: 36,028.42 pascals; Mt. McKinley: 39,846.22 pascals; Mt. Logan: 41,261.82 pascals

Example 3 (p. 511)

Given $\log_3 5 \approx 1.465$ and $\log_5 7 \approx 1.2091$, approximate the value of each expression.

6. $\log_3 25$ 2.93

7. $\log_5 49$ 2.4182

Example 4 (p. 511)

Solve each equation. Check your solutions.

8. $\log_4 48 - \log_4 n = \log_4 6$ 8

9. $\log_3 2x + \log_3 7 = \log_3 28$ 2

10. $3 \log_2 x = \log_2 8$ 2

11. $\log_{10} a + \log_{10} (a - 6) = 2$ 13.4403

Practice and Problem Solving

● = **Step-by-Step Solutions** begin on page R20.
Extra Practice begins on page 947.

Examples 1 and 2 (pp. 509–510)

Use $\log_4 2 = 0.5$, $\log_4 3 \approx 0.7925$, and $\log_4 5 \approx 1.1610$ to approximate the value of each expression.

12. $\log_4 30$ 2.4535

13. $\log_4 20$ 2.1610

14. $\log_4 \frac{2}{3}$ −0.2925

15. $\log_4 \frac{4}{3}$ 0.2075

16. $\log_4 9$ 1.5850

17. $\log_4 8$ 1.5

Example 2 (p. 510)

18. **SCIENCE** In 1979, an earthquake near San Francisco registered approximately 5.9 on the Richter scale. The famous San Francisco earthquake of 1906 measured 8.3 in magnitude.

a. How much more intense was the 1906 earthquake than the 1979 earthquake?

b. Richter himself classified the 1906 earthquake as having a magnitude of 8.3. More recent research indicates it was most likely a 7.9. What is the difference in intensities?

Year	Location	Magnitude
1906	San Francisco	8.3
1923	Tokyo, Japan	8.3
1932	Gansu, China	7.6
1960	Chile	9.5
1964	Alaska	9.2
1979	San Francisco	5.9

Source: TLC

18a. $10^{2.4}$ or about 250 times as great
18b. Richter thought the earthquake was $10^{0.4}$ or about $2\frac{1}{2}$ times greater than it actually was.

Example 3 (p. 511)

Given $\log_6 8 \approx 1.1606$ and $\log_7 9 \approx 1.1292$, approximate the value of each expression.

19. $\log_6 48$ 2.1606

20. $\log_7 81$ 2.2584

21. $\log_6 512$ 3.4818

22. $\log_7 729$ 3.3876

Example 4 (p. 511)

Solve each equation. Check your solutions.

23. $\log_3 56 - \log_3 n = \log_3 7$ 8

24. $\log_2 (4x) + \log_2 5 = \log_2 40$ 2

25. $5 \log_2 x = \log_2 32$ 2

26. $\log_{10} a + \log_{10} (a + 21) = 2$ 4

Differentiated Homework Options

Level	Assignment	Two-Day Option	
AL Basic	12–26, 61–63, 65–88	13–25 odd, 69–72	12–26 even, 61–63, 73–88
OL Core	13–57 odd, 59–63, 65–88	13–25, 69–72	27–63, 65–68, 73–88
BL Advanced	27–82, (optional: 83–88)		

B

27. **PROBABILITY** In the 1930s, Dr. Frank Benford demonstrated a way to determine whether a set of numbers has been randomly chosen or manually chosen. If the sets of numbers were not randomly chosen, then the Benford formula, $P = \log_{10}\left(1 + \frac{1}{d}\right)$, predicts the probability of a digit d being the first digit of the set. For example, there is a 4.6% probability that the first digit is 9.

   a. Rewrite the formula to solve for the digit if given the probability. $d = \frac{1}{10^P - 1}$

   b. Find the digit that has a 9.7% probability of being selected. 4

   c. Find the probability that the first digit is 1 ($\log_{10} 2 \approx 0.30103$). 30.1%

Use $\log_5 3 \approx 0.6826$ and $\log_5 4 \approx 0.8614$ to approximate the value of each expression.

28. $\log_5 40$ 2.2921
29. $\log_5 30$ 2.1133
30. $\log_5 \frac{3}{4}$ -0.1788
31. $\log_5 \frac{4}{3}$ 0.1788
32. $\log_5 9$ 1.3652
33. $\log_5 16$ 1.7228
34. $\log_5 12$ 1.5440
35. $\log_5 27$ 2.0478

Solve each equation. Check your solutions.

36. $\log_3 6 + \log_3 x = \log_3 12$ 2
37. $\log_4 a + \log_4 8 = \log_4 24$ 3
38. $\log_{10} 18 - \log_{10} 3x = \log_{10} 2$ 3
39. $\log_7 100 - \log_7 (y + 5) = \log_7 10$ 5
40. $\log_2 n = \frac{1}{3}\log_2 27 + \log_2 36$ 108
41. $3\log_{10} 8 - \frac{1}{2}\log_{10} 36 = \log_{10} x$ $85\frac{1}{3}$

Real-World Link

Humpback whales are known for their songs. Scientists are studying these sounds to decipher their meaning, but they still do not know why whales sing. It is most likely that humpbacks sing to communicate with others.

Solve for *n*. 43. $\left(\frac{x-2}{256}\right)^{\frac{1}{6}}$

42. $\log_a 6n - 3\log_a x = \log_a x$ $\frac{x^4}{6}$
43. $2\log_b 16 + 6\log_b n = \log_b (x - 2)$

Solve each equation. Check your solutions. 46. no real solution

44. $\log_{10} z + \log_{10} (z + 9) = 1$ 1
45. $\log_3 (a^2 + 3) + \log_3 3 = 3$ $\sqrt{6}, -\sqrt{6}$
46. $\log_2 (15b - 15) - \log_2 (-b^2 + 1) = 1$
47. $\log_4 (2y + 2) - \log_4 (y - 2) = 1$ 5
48. $\log_6 0.1 + 2\log_6 x = \log_6 2 + \log_6 5$ 10
49. $\log_7 64 - \log_7 \frac{8}{3} + \log_7 2 = \log_7 4p$ 12

50. **ENVIRONMENT** The humpback whale is an endangered species. Suppose there are 5000 humpback whales in existence today, and the population decreases at a rate of 4% per year.

   a. Write a logarithmic function for the time in years based upon population.

   b. After how long will the population drop below 1000? Round your answer to the nearest year. 40 yr

50a. $t = \log_{0.96}\left(\frac{p}{5000}\right)$

State whether each equation is *true* or *false*.

51. $\log_8 (x - 3) = \log_8 x - \log_8 3$ false
52. $\log_5 22x = \log_5 22 + \log_5 x$ true
53. $\log_{10} 19k = 19\log_{10} k$ false
54. $\log_2 y^5 = 5\log_2 y$ true
55. $\log_7 \frac{x}{3} = \log_7 x - \log_7 3$ true
56. $\log_4 (z + 2) = \log_4 z + \log_4 2$ false
57. $\log_8 p^4 = (\log_8 p)^4$ false
58. $\log_9 \frac{x^2y^3}{z^4} = 2\log_9 x + 3\log_9 y - 4\log_9 z$ true

59. **PARADE** An equation for loudness L, in decibels, is $L = 10\log_{10} R$, where R is the relative intensity of the sound.

   a. Solve $120 = 10\log_{10} R$ to find the relative intensity of the Macy's Thanksgiving Day Parade with a loudness of 120 decibels depending on how close you are. 10^{12}

   b. Some parents with young children want the decibel level lowered to 80. How many times less intense would this be? In other words, find the ratio of their intensities. 10^4 or about 10,000 times

Lesson 8-5 Properties of Logarithms 513

Study Guide and Intervention
CRM pp. 33–34 AL OL ELL

8-5 Study Guide and Intervention
Properties of Logarithms

Properties of Logarithms Properties of exponents can be used to develop the following properties of logarithms.

Product Property of Logarithms	For all positive numbers a, b, and x, where $x \neq 1$, $\log_x ab = \log_x a + \log_x b$.
Quotient Property of Logarithms	For all positive numbers a, b, and x, where $x \neq 1$, $\log_x \frac{a}{b} = \log_x a - \log_x b$.
Power Property of Logarithms	For any real number p and positive numbers m and b, where $b \neq 1$, $\log_b m^p = p \log_b m$.

Example Use $\log_3 28 \approx 3.0331$ and $\log_3 4 \approx 1.2619$ to approximate the value of each expression.

a. $\log_3 36$

$\log_3 36 = \log_3 (3^2 \cdot 4) = \log_3 3^2 + \log_3 4 = 2 + \log_3 4 \approx 2 + 1.2619 \approx 3.2619$

b. $\log_3 7$

$\log_3 7 = \log_3 \left(\frac{28}{4}\right) = \log_3 28 - \log_3 4 \approx 3.0331 - 1.2619 \approx 1.7712$

c. $\log_3 256$

$\log_3 256 = \log_3 (4^4) = 4 \cdot \log_3 4 \approx 4(1.2619) \approx 5.0476$

Exercises

Use $\log_{12} 3 \approx 0.4421$ and $\log_{12} 7 \approx 0.7831$ to approximate the value of each expression.

1. $\log_{12} 21$ **1.2252**
2. $\log_{12} \frac{7}{3}$ **0.3410**
3. $\log_{12} 49$ **1.5662**
4. $\log_{12} 36$ **1.4421**
5. $\log_{12} 63$ **1.6673**
6. $\log_{12} \frac{27}{49}$ **−0.2399**
7. $\log_{12} \frac{81}{49}$ **0.2022**
8. $\log_{12} 16{,}807$ **3.9155**
9. $\log_{12} 441$ **2.4504**

Use $\log_5 3 \approx 0.6826$ and $\log_5 4 \approx 0.8614$ to approximate the value of each expression.

10. $\log_5 12$ **1.5440**
11. $\log_5 100$ **2.8614**
12. $\log_5 0.75$ **−0.1788**
13. $\log_5 144$ **3.0880**
14. $\log_5 \frac{27}{16}$ **0.3250**
15. $\log_5 375$ **3.6826**
16. $\log_5 1.\overline{3}$ **0.1788**
17. $\log_5 \frac{9}{16}$ **−0.3576**
18. $\log_5 \frac{81}{5}$ **1.7304**

Lesson 8-5

Practice
CRM p. 36 AL OL BL ELL

8-5 Practice
Properties of Logarithms

Use $\log_{10} 5 \approx 0.6990$ and $\log_{10} 7 \approx 0.8451$ to approximate the value of each expression.

1. $\log_{10} 35$ **1.5441**
2. $\log_{10} 25$ **1.3980**
3. $\log_{10} \frac{7}{5}$ **0.1461**
4. $\log_{10} \frac{5}{7}$ **−0.1461**
5. $\log_{10} 245$ **2.3892**
6. $\log_{10} 175$ **2.2431**
7. $\log_{10} 0.2$ **−0.6990**
8. $\log_{10} \frac{25}{7}$ **0.5529**

Solve each equation. Check your solutions.

9. $\log_7 n = \frac{2}{3} \log_7 8$ **4**
10. $\log_{10} u = \frac{3}{2} \log_{10} 4$ **8**
11. $\log_6 x + \log_6 9 = \log_6 54$ **6**
12. $\log_8 48 - \log_8 w = \log_8 4$ **12**
13. $\log_9 (3u + 14) - \log_9 5 = \log_9 2u$ **2**
14. $4 \log_2 x + \log_2 5 = \log_2 405$ **3**
15. $\log_3 y = -\log_3 16 + \frac{1}{3} \log_3 64$ **$\frac{1}{4}$**
16. $\log_2 d = 5 \log_2 2 - \log_2 8$ **4**
17. $\log_{10} (3m - 5) + \log_{10} m = \log_{10} 2$ **2**
18. $\log_{10} (b + 3) + \log_{10} b = \log_{10} 4$ **1**
19. $\log_8 (t + 10) - \log_8 (t - 1) = \log_8 12$ **2**
20. $\log_3 (a + 3) + \log_3 (a + 2) = \log_3 6$ **0**
21. $\log_{10} (r + 4) - \log_{10} r = \log_{10} (r + 1)$ **2**
22. $\log_4 (x^2 - 4) - \log_4 (x + 2) = \log_4 1$ **3**
23. $\log_{10} 4 + \log_{10} w = 2$ **25**
24. $\log_8 (n - 3) + \log_8 (n + 4) = 1$ **4**
25. $3 \log_5 (x^2 + 9) - 6 = 0$ **±4**
26. $\log_{16} (9x + 5) - \log_{16} (x^2 - 1) = \frac{1}{2}$ **3**
27. $\log_6 (2x - 5) + 1 = \log_6 (7x + 10)$ **8**
28. $\log_2 (5y + 2) - 1 = \log_2 (1 - 2y)$ **0**
29. $\log_{10} (c^2 - 1) - 2 = \log_{10} (c + 1)$ **101**
30. $\log_7 x + 2 \log_7 x - \log_7 3 = \log_7 72$ **6**
31. **SOUND** Recall that the loudness L of a sound in decibels is given by $L = 10 \log_{10} R$, where R is the sound's relative intensity. If the intensity of a certain sound is tripled, by how many decibels does the sound increase? **about 4.8 dB**
32. **EARTHQUAKES** An earthquake rated at 3.5 on the Richter scale is felt by many people, and an earthquake rated at 4.5 may cause local damage. The Richter scale magnitude reading m is given by $m = \log_{10} x$, where x represents the amplitude of the seismic wave causing ground motion. How many times greater is the amplitude of an earthquake that measures 4.5 on the Richter scale than one that measures 3.5? **10 times**

Word Problem Practice
CRM p. 37 AL OL BL ELL

8-5 Word Problem Practice
Properties of Logarithms

1. **MENTAL COMPUTATION** Jessica has memorized $\log_5 2 \approx 0.4307$ and $\log_5 3 \approx 0.6826$. Using this information, to the nearest thousandth, what power of 5 is equal to 6?
1.113

2. **POWERS** A chemist is testing a soft drink. The pH of a solution is given by
$$-\log_{10} C,$$
where C is the concentration of hydrogen ions. The pH of a popular soft drink is 2.5. If the concentration of hydrogen ions is increased by a factor of 100, what is the new pH of the solution?
4.5

3. **LUCKY MATH** Frank is solving a problem involving logarithms. He does everything correctly except for one thing. He mistakenly writes
$$\log_2 a + \log_2 b = \log_2 (a + b).$$
However, after substituting the values for a and b in his problem, he amazingly still gets the right answer! The value of a was 11. What must the value of b have been?
1.1

4. **LENGTHS** Charles has two poles. One pole has length equal to $\log_7 21$ and the other has length equal to $\log_7 25$. Express the length of both poles joined end to end as the logarithm of a single number.
$\log_7 525$

5. **SIZE** Alicia wanted to try to quantify the terms *tiny, small, medium, large, big, huge,* and *humongous*. She picked a number of objects and classified them with these adjectives of size. She noticed that the scale seemed exponential. Therefore, she came up with the following definition. Define S to be $\frac{1}{3}\log_3 V$, where V is volume in cubic feet. Then use the following table to find the appropriate adjective.

S satisfies	Adjective
$-2 \le S < -1$	tiny
$-1 \le S < 0$	small
$0 \le S < 1$	medium
$1 \le S < 2$	large
$2 \le S < 3$	big
$3 \le S < 4$	huge
$4 \le S < 5$	humongous

a. Derive an expression for S applied to a cube in terms of ℓ where ℓ is the side length of a cube.
$\log_3 \ell$

b. How many cubes, each one foot on a side, would have to be put together to get an object that Alicia would call "big"?
729

c. How likely is it that a large object attached to a big object would result in a huge object, according to Alicia's scale?
Not very likely; most likely the result will be big, not huge.

Lesson 8-5

Real-World Link

According to the Jump Start Coalition, an advocate for financial literacy, one in every three high school seniors uses credit cards.

60. FINANCIAL LITERACY The average American carries a credit card debt of approximately \$8600 with an annual percentage rate (APR) of 18.3%. The formula $m = \frac{b\left(\frac{r}{n}\right)}{1 - \left(1 + \frac{r}{n}\right)^{-nt}}$ can be used to compute the monthly payment m that is necessary to pay off a credit card balance b in a given number of years t, where r is the annual percentage rate and n is the number of payments per year.

a. What monthly payment should be made in order to pay off the debt in exactly three years? What is the total amount paid? **\$312.21; \$11,239.56**

b. The equation $t = \frac{\log\left(1 - \frac{br}{mn}\right)}{-n \log\left(1 + \frac{r}{n}\right)}$ can be used to calculate the number of years necessary for a given payment schedule. Copy and complete the table.

Payment (m)	Years (t)
\$50	**non-real**
\$100	**non-real**
\$150	**11.42**
\$200	**5.87**
\$250	**4.09**
\$300	**3.16**

c. Graph the information in the table from part c.

d. If you could only afford to pay \$100 a month, will you be able to pay off the debt? If so, how long will it take? If not, why not?

e. What is the minimum monthly payment that will work toward paying off the debt? **\$131.16**

60c. See margin.
60d. No; the monthly interest is \$131.15, so the payments do not even cover the interest.

61c. Sample answer: $\log_b \frac{j^8k}{h^5} = 8 \log_b j + \log_b k - 5 \log_b h$

H.O.T. Problems
Use Higher-Order Thinking Skills

61. OPEN ENDED Write a logarithmic expression for each condition. Then write the expanded expression.

a. a product and a quotient **Sample answer: $\log_b \frac{xz}{5}; = \log_b x + \log_b z - \log_b 5$**

b. a product and a power **Sample answer: $\log_b m^4p^6 = 4 \log_b m + 6 \log_b p$**

c. a product, a quotient, and a power

62. PROOF Use the properties of exponents to prove the Power Property of Logarithms.

62. See margin.

63. WRITING IN MATH Explain why the following are true.

a. $\log_b 1 = 0$ **b.** $\log_b b = 1$ **c.** $\log_b b^x = x$

63a. $\log_b 1 = 0$, because $b^0 = 1$.
63b. $\log_b b = 1$, because $b^1 = b$.
63c. $\log_b b^x = x$, because $b^x = b^x$.

64. CHALLENGE Simplify $\log_{\sqrt{a}} (a^2)$ to find an exact numerical value. **See margin.**

65. WHICH ONE DOESN'T BELONG? Find the expression that does not belong. Explain.

$\log_b 24 = \log_b 2 + \log_b 12$	$\log_b 24 = \log_b 20 + \log_b 4$
$\log_b 24 = \log_b 8 + \log_b 3$	$\log_b 24 = \log_b 4 + \log_b 6$

$\log_b 24 \neq \log_b 20 + \log_b 4$; all other choices are equal to $\log_b 24$.

66. REASONING Use the properties of logarithms to prove that $\log_a \frac{1}{x} = -\log_a x$. **See Chapter 8 Answer Appendix.**

67. CHALLENGE Simplify $x^{3 \log_x 2 - \log_x 5}$ to find an exact numerical value.

67. See Chapter 8 Answer Appendix.

68. WRITING IN MATH Explain how the properties of exponents and logarithms are related. Include examples like the one shown at the beginning of the lesson illustrating the Product Property, but with the Quotient Property and Power Property of Logarithms. **See Chapter 8 Answer Appendix.**

Enrichment
CRM p. 38 OL BL

8-5 Enrichment

Spirals

Consider an angle in standard position with its vertex at a point O called the pole. Its initial side is on a coordinatized axis called the *polar axis*. A point P on the terminal side of the angle is named by the *polar coordinates* (r, θ), where r is the directed distance of the point from O and θ is the measure of the angle. Graphs in this system may be drawn on polar coordinate paper such as the kind shown below.

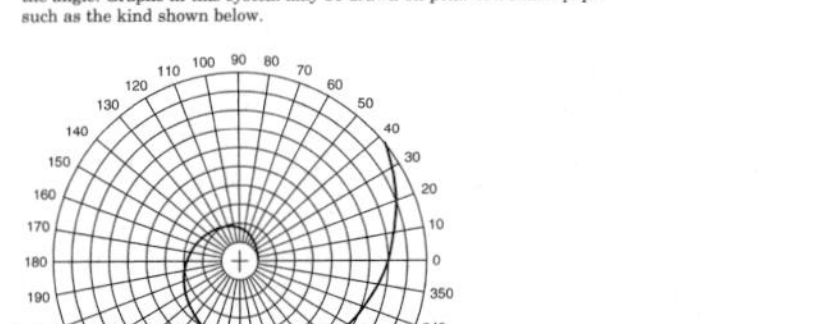

514 Chapter 8 Exponential and Logarithmic Functions and Relations

NGSSS PRACTICE 912.A.3.3, 912.A.8.5, 912.A.7.5

69. Find the mode of the data.

22, 11, 12, 23, 7, 6, 17, 15, 21, 19 **D**

A. 11 C. 16
B. 15 D. There is no mode.

70. ACT/SAT What is the effect on the graph of $y = 4x^2$ when the equation is changed to $y = 2x^2$? **H**

F. The graph is rotated 90 degrees about the origin.
G. The graph is narrower.
H. The graph is wider.
I. The graph of $y = 2x^2$ is a reflection of the graph $y = 4x^2$ across the x-axis.

71. THINK SOLVE EXPLAIN **SHORT RESPONSE** In $y = 6.5(1.07)^x$, x represents the number of years since 2000, and y represents the approximate number of millions of Americans 7 years of age and older who went camping two or more times that year. Describe how the number of millions of Americans who go camping is changing over time.
growing exponentially

72. What are the x-intercepts of the graph of $y = 4x^2 - 3x - 1$? **D**

A. $-\frac{1}{4}$ and $\frac{1}{4}$ C. -1 and 1
B. -1 and $\frac{1}{4}$ D. 1 and $-\frac{1}{4}$

Spiral Review

Solve each equation. Check your solutions. (Lesson 8-4)

73. $\log_5(3x - 1) = \log_5(2x^2)$ **$\frac{1}{2}$, 1**
74. $\log_{10}(x^2 + 1) = 1$ **± 3**
75. $\log_{10}(x^2 - 10x) = \log_{10}(-21)$ **no solution**

Evaluate each expression. (Lesson 8-3)

76. $\log_{10} 0.001$ **-3**
77. $\log_4 16^x$ **$2x$**
78. $\log_3 27^x$ **$3x$**

79. ELECTRICITY The amount of current in amperes I that an appliance uses can be calculated using the formula $I = \left(\frac{P}{R}\right)^{\frac{1}{2}}$, where P is the power in watts and R is the resistance in ohms. How much current does an appliance use if $P = 120$ watts and $R = 3$ ohms? Round to the nearest tenth. (Lesson 7-6) **6.3**

Determine whether each pair of functions are inverse functions. Write *yes* or *no*. (Lesson 7-2)

80. $f(x) = x + 73$
$g(x) = x - 73$ **yes**

81. $g(x) = 7x - 11$
$h(x) = \frac{1}{7}x + 11$ **no**

82. SCULPTING Antonio is preparing to make an ice sculpture. He has a block of ice that he wants to reduce in size by shaving off the same amount from the length, width, and height. He wants to reduce the volume of the ice block to 24 cubic feet. (Lesson 6-7) **a. $(3 - x)(4 - x)(5 - x) = 24$**

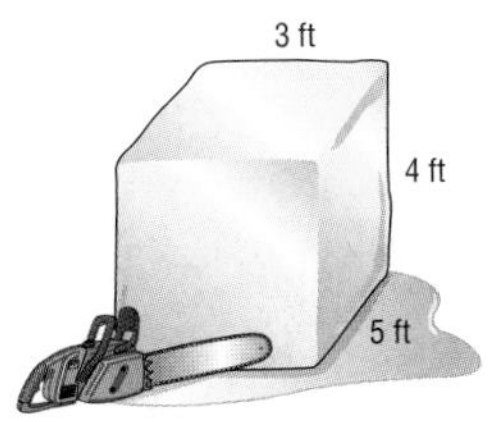

a. Write a polynomial equation to model this situation.
b. How much should he take from each dimension? **1 ft**

Skills Review

Solve each equation or inequality. Check your solution. (Lessons 9-1 through 9-4)

83. $3^{4x} = 3^{3-x}$ **$\frac{3}{5}$**
84. $3^{2n} \leq \frac{1}{9}$ **$n \leq -1$**
85. $3^{5x} \cdot 81^{1-x} = 9^{x-3}$ **10**
86. $49^x = 7^{x^2 - 15}$ **$-3, 5$**
87. $\log_2(x + 6) > 5$ **$x > 26$**
88. $\log_5(4x - 1) = \log_5(3x + 2)$ **3**

4 ASSESS

Crystal Ball Tell students that in the next lesson they will learn to solve equations using common (base 10) logarithms. Ask them to write how they think what they learned today will connect with the next lesson they will study.

Additional Answers

60c.

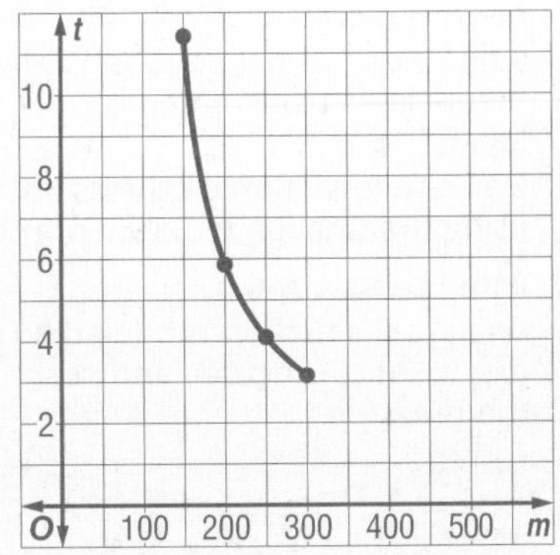

62.
$$m^p = m^p$$
$$\left(b^{\log_b m}\right)^p = b^{\log_b (m^p)}$$
$$b^{\log_b mp} = b^{\log_b (m^p)}$$
$$\log_b mp = \log_b (m^p)$$
$$p \log_b m = \log_b (m^p)$$

64.
$$\log_{\sqrt{a}} (a^2) = x$$
$$(\sqrt{a})^x = a^2$$
$$\left(a^{\frac{1}{2}}\right)^x = a^2$$
$$a^{\frac{x}{2}} = a^2$$
$$\frac{x}{2} = 2$$
$$x = 4$$

Differentiated Instruction BL

Extension Show students the following:

$\log_{10} 3 \approx 0.4771$
$\log_{10} 30 \approx 1.4771$
$\log_{10} 300 \approx 2.4771$
$\log_{10} 3000 \approx 3.4771$

Ask students to predict $\log_{10} 30{,}000$. 4.4771

Have students use properties of logarithms to explain this pattern. Sample explanation: 3, 30, 300, and 3000 can be written as 3×10^0, 3×10^1, 3×10^2, and 3×10^3 respectively. Then the base 10 logarithms of each can be rewritten as a sum of two logarithms. For example, $\log_{10} 3000$ can be written as $\log_{10}(3 \cdot 10^3)$. Then it follows that $\log_{10}(3 \cdot 10^3) = \log_{10} 3 + \log_{10} 10^3 = \log_{10}(3) + 3 = 3.4771$

8-6 Lesson Notes

1 FOCUS

Vertical Alignment

Before Lesson 8-6
Simplify expressions and solve equations using properties of logarithms.

Lesson 8-6
Solve exponential equations and inequalities using common logarithms.
Evaluate logarithmic expressions using the Change of Base Formula.

After Lesson 8-6
Analyze a situation modeled by an exponential function, and solve the problem.

2 TEACH

Scaffolding Questions

Have students read the *Why?* section of the lesson.

Ask:

- How does the Richter number of a "Great" earthquake compare with the number for a "Light" earthquake? It is twice as large.
- How does the intensity of a "Great" earthquake compare to the intensity of a "Light" earthquake? It is 10,000 times as large.
- Where would an earthquake with an intensity half as large as 10^8 appear on the diagram? between "Major" and "Great"

8-6 Common Logarithms

Then
You simplified expressions and solved equations using properties of logarithms. (Lesson 8-4)

Now
- Solve exponential equations and inequalities using common logarithms.
- Evaluate logarithmic expressions using the Change of Base Formula.

NGSSS
MA.912.A.8.2 Define and use the properties of logarithms to simplify logarithmic expressions and to find their approximate values.
MA.912.A.8.6 Use the change of base formula.

New Vocabulary
common logarithm
Change of Base Formula

FL Math Online
glencoe.com

Why?

Seismologists use the Richter scale to measure the strength or magnitude of earthquakes. The magnitude of an earthquake is determined using the logarithm of the amplitude of waves recorded by seismographs.

Richter Number	1	2	3	4	5	6	7	8
Intensity	10^1 Micro	10^2 Minor	10^3 Minor	10^4 Light	10^5 Moderate	10^6 Strong	10^7 Major	10^8 Great
Effect in Populated Areas	not felt, but recorded	generally not felt, loose hanging items sway	often felt, little to no damage	noticeable shaking, minor damage	slight damage to buildings over small regions	damage over regions up to 100 miles across	severe destruction over large areas	catastrophic destruction to areas several hundred miles across

The logarithmic scale used by the Richter scale is based on the powers of 10. For example, a magnitude 6.4 earthquake can be represented by $6.4 = \log_{10} x$.

Common Logarithms You have seen that the base 10 logarithm function, $y = \log_{10} x$, is used in many applications. Base 10 logarithms are called **common logarithms**. Common logarithms are usually written without the subscript 10.

$$\log_{10} x = \log x, x > 0$$

Most scientific calculators have a LOG key for evaluating common logarithms.

EXAMPLE 1 Find Common Logarithms

Use a calculator to evaluate each expression to the nearest ten-thousandth.

a. log 5

KEYSTROKES: LOG 5 ENTER .6989700043

$\log 5 \approx 0.6990$

b. log 0.3

KEYSTROKES: LOG 0.3 ENTER −.5228787453

$\log 0.3 \approx -0.5229$

Guided Practice

1A. log 7 **0.8451** **1B.** log 0.5 **−0.3010**

Personal Tutor glencoe.com

The common logarithms of numbers that differ by integral powers of ten are closely related. Remember that a logarithm is an exponent. For example, in the equation $y = \log x$, y is the power to which 10 is raised to obtain the value of x.

$\log x = y$	→ means →	$10^y = x$
$\log 1 = 0$	since	$10^0 = 1$
$\log 10 = 1$	since	$10^1 = 10$
$\log 10^m = m$	since	$10^m = 10^m$

Lesson 8-6 Resources

Resource	Approaching-Level	On-Level	Beyond-Level	English Learners
Teacher Edition		• Differentiated Instruction, p. 518, 522	• Differentiated Instruction, pp. 518, 522	
Chapter Resource Masters	• Study Guide and Intervention, pp. 40–41 • Skills Practice, p. 42 • Practice, p. 43 • Word Problem Practice, p. 44	• Study Guide and Intervention, pp. 40–41 • Skills Practice, p. 42 • Practice, p. 43 • Word Problem Practice, p. 44 • Enrichment, p. 45 • Graphing Calculator Activity, p. 46	• Practice, p. 43 • Word Problem Practice, p. 44 • Enrichment, p. 45	• Study Guide and Intervention, pp. 40–41 • Skills Practice, p. 42 • Practice, p. 43 • Word Problem Practice, p. 44
Transparencies	• 5-Minute Check Transparency 8-6	• 5-Minute Check Transparency 8-6	• 5-Minute Check Transparency 8-6	• 5-Minute Check Transparency 8-6
Other	• Study Notebook	• Study Notebook	• Study Notebook	• Study Notebook

Real-World Career

Acoustical Engineer
Acoustical engineers are concerned with reducing unwanted sounds, noise control, and making useful sounds. Examples of useful sounds are ultrasound, sonar, and sound reproduction. Employment in this field requires a minimum of a bachelor's degree.

Common logarithms are used in the measure of sound. Soft recorded music is about 36 decibels (dB).

Real-World EXAMPLE 2 Solve Logarithmic Equations

ROCK CONCERT The loudness L, in decibels, of a sound is $L = 10 \log \frac{I}{m}$, where I is the intensity of the sound and m is the minimum intensity of sound detectable by the human ear. Residents living several miles from a concert venue can hear the music at an intensity of 66.6 decibels. How many times the minimum intensity of sound detectable by the human ear was this sound, if m is defined to be 1?

$L = 10 \log \frac{I}{m}$	**Original equation**
$66.6 = 10 \log \frac{I}{1}$	**Replace L with 66.6 and m with 1.**
$6.66 = \log I$	**Divide each side by 10 and simplify.**
$I = 10^{6.66}$	**Exponential form**
$I = 4{,}570{,}882$	**Use a calculator.**

The sound heard by the residents was approximately 4,570,000 times the minimum intensity of sound detectable by the human ear.

Guided Practice

2. **EARTHQUAKES** The amount of energy E in ergs that an earthquake releases is related to its Richter scale magnitude M by the equation $\log E = 11.8 + 1.5M$. Use the equation to find the amount of energy released by the 2004 Sumatran earthquake, which measured 9.0 on the Richter scale and led to a tsunami. about 2×10^{25} ergs

Personal Tutor glencoe.com

If both sides of an exponential equation cannot easily be written as powers of the same base, you can solve by taking the logarithm of each side.

EXAMPLE 3 Solve Exponential Equations Using Logarithms

Solve $4^x = 19$. Round to the nearest ten-thousandth.

$4^x = 19$	**Original equation**
$\log 4^x = \log 19$	**Property of Equality for Logarithmic Functions**
$x \log 4 = \log 19$	**Power Property of Logarithms**
$x = \frac{\log 19}{\log 4}$	**Divide each side by log 4.**
$x \approx 2.1240$	**Use a calculator.**

The solution is approximately 2.1240.

CHECK You can check this answer graphically by using a graphing calculator. Graph the line $y = 4^x$ and the line $y = 19$. Then use the CALC menu to find the intersection of the two graphs. The intersection is very close to the answer that was obtained algebraically. ✓

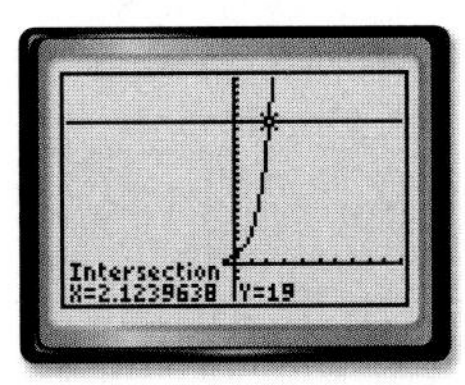

Guided Practice

3A. $3^x = 15$ ≈ 2.4650

3B. $6^x = 42$ ≈ 2.0860

Personal Tutor glencoe.com

Common Logarithms

Example 1 shows how to use a calculator to evaluate a common logarithm. **Example 2** shows how to use the inverse of logarithms, or exponentiation, to solve a logarithmic equation that models a real-world application. **Example 3** shows how to solve exponential equations using logarithms. **Example 4** shows how to use logarithms to solve exponential inequalities.

Formative Assessment

Use the Guided Practice Exercises after each example to determine students' understanding of concepts.

Additional Examples

1. Use a calculator to evaluate each expression to the nearest ten-thousandth.
   a. log 6 about 0.7782
   b. log 0.35 about −0.4559
2. **JET ENGINES** Refer to Example 2. The sound of a jet engine can reach a loudness of 125 decibels. How many times the minimum intensity of audible sound is this? $10^{12.5}$, or about 3×10^{12}, which is 3 trillion
3. Solve $5^x = 62$. about 2.5643

Additional Examples also in Interactive Classroom PowerPoint® Presentations

IWB INTERACTIVE WHITEBOARD READY

Additional Example

4 Solve $3^{7x} > 2^{5x-3}$. Round to the nearest ten thousandth.

$\{x \mid x > -0.4922\}$

Focus on Mathematical Content

Common Logarithms Base 10 logarithms are called *common logarithms.* When the base of a logarithm is not shown, the base is assumed to be 10. When you have a logarithmic expression of any base, you can evaluate it using the Change of Base Formula to translate the expression into one that involves common logarithms.

Change of Base Formula

Example 5 shows how to express a logarithmic expression of any base in terms of common logarithms.

Tips for New Teachers

Reasoning As you discuss the Change of Base Formula, point out that the base b that students are changing to does not have to be 10. Any base could be used; however, 10 is the most common because this allows for the logarithms to be evaluated with a calculator. When the base of a logarithm is not shown, the base is assumed to be 10.

TEACH with TECH

INTERACTIVE WHITEBOARD Display a template such as $\log_{\square}\square = \dfrac{\log_b \square}{\log_b \square}$. Drag the values from the original logarithm to demonstrate the change of base formula.

The same strategies that are used to solve exponential equations can be used to solve exponential inequalities.

StudyTip

Solving Inequalities Remember that the direction of an inequality must be switched if each side is multiplied or divided by a negative number. Since $5 \log 3 - \log 7 > 0$, the inequality does not change.

EXAMPLE 4 Solve Exponential Inequalities Using Logarithms

Solve $3^{5y} < 7^{y-2}$. Round to the nearest ten-thousandth.

$3^{5y} < 7^{y-2}$	**Original inequality**
$\log 3^{5y} < \log 7^{y-2}$	**Property of Inequality for Logarithmic Functions**
$5y \log 3 < (y-2) \log 7$	**Power Property of Logarithms**
$5y \log 3 < y \log 7 - 2 \log 7$	**Distributive Property**
$5y \log 3 - y \log 7 < -2 \log 7$	**Subtract $y \log 7$ from each side.**
$y(5 \log 3 - \log 7) < -2 \log 7$	**Distributive Property**
$y < \dfrac{-2 \log 7}{5 \log 3 - \log 7}$	**Divide each side by $5 \log 3 - \log 7$.**
$\{y \mid y < -1.0972\}$	**Use a calculator.**

CHECK Test $y = -2$.

$3^{5y} < 7^{y-2}$	**Original inequality**
$3^{5(-2)} \overset{?}{<} 7^{(-2)-2}$	**Replace y with -2.**
$3^{-10} \overset{?}{<} 7^{-4}$	**Simplify.**
$\dfrac{1}{59{,}049} < \dfrac{1}{2401}$ ✓	**Negative Exponent Property**

Guided Practice

Solve each inequality. Round to the nearest ten-thousandth.

4A. $3^{2x} \geq 6^{x+1}$ $\{x \mid x \geq 4.4190\}$

4B. $4^{y} < 5^{2y+1}$ $\{y \mid y > -0.8782\}$

Personal Tutor glencoe.com

Change of Base Formula The **Change of Base Formula** allows you to write equivalent logarithmic expressions that have different bases.

Key Concept Change of Base Formula

Symbols For all positive numbers a, b, and n, where $a \neq 1$ and $b \neq 1$,

$$\log_a n = \frac{\log_b n}{\log_b a}.$$

← **log base b of original number**
← **log base b of old base**

Example $\log_3 11 = \dfrac{\log_{10} 11}{\log_{10} 3}$

To prove this formula, let $\log_a n = x$.

$a^x = n$	**Definition of logarithm**
$\log_b a^x = \log_b n$	**Property of Equality for Logarithmic Functions**
$x \log_b a = \log_b n$	**Power Property of Logarithms**
$x = \dfrac{\log_b n}{\log_b a}$	**Divide each side by $\log_b a$.**
$\log_a n = \dfrac{\log_b n}{\log_b a}$	**Replace x with $\log_a n$.**

The Granger Collection, New York

Math History Link

John Napier (1550–1617) John Napier was a Scottish mathematician and theologian who began the use of logarithms to aid in calculations. He is also known for popularizing the use of the decimal point.

Differentiated Instruction OL BL

Logical Learners Ask students to recall that an equation like $4^x = 19$ from Example 3 could be written in logarithmic form as $\log_4 19 = x$. Although this logarithm cannot be directly evaluated, the Change of Base Formula can be used to give the correct result of $x \approx 2.1234$.

The Change of Base Formula makes it possible to evaluate a logarithmic expression of any base by translating the expression into one that involves common logarithms.

EXAMPLE 5 **Change of Base Formula**

Express $\log_3 20$ in terms of common logarithms. Then round to the nearest ten-thousandth.

$\log_3 20 = \frac{\log_{10} 20}{\log_{10} 3}$ **Change of Base Formula**

≈ 2.7268 **Use a calculator.**

Guided Practice 5. $\frac{\log_{10} 8}{\log_{10} 6} \approx 1.1606$

5. Express $\log_6 8$ in terms of common logarithms. Then round to the nearest ten-thousandth.

Personal Tutor glencoe.com

Check Your Understanding

Example 1 p. 516 — **Use a calculator to evaluate each expression to the nearest ten-thousandth.**

1. log 5 0.6990 **2.** log 21 1.3222 **3.** log 0.4 −0.3979 **4.** log 0.7 −0.1549

Example 2 p. 517

5. SCIENCE The amount of energy E in ergs that an earthquake releases is related to its Richter scale magnitude M by the equation $\log E = 11.8 + 1.5M$. Use the equation to find the amount of energy released by the 1960 Chilean earthquake, which measured 8.5 on the Richter scale. 3.55×10^{24} ergs

Example 3 p. 517 — **Solve each equation. Round to the nearest ten-thousandth.** 7. 0.8442 8. ±1.2451

6. $6^x = 40$ 2.0588 **7.** $2.1^{a+2} = 8.25$ **8.** $7^{x^2} = 20.42$ **9.** $11^{b-3} = 5^b$ 9.1237

Example 4 p. 518 — **Solve each inequality. Round to the nearest ten-thousandth.**

10. $5^{4n} > 33$ $\{n \mid n > 0.5431\}$ **11.** $6^{p-1} \leq 4^p$ $\{p \mid p \leq 4.4190\}$

Example 5 p. 519 — **Express each logarithm in terms of common logarithms. Then approximate its value to the nearest ten-thousandth.** 12–15. See margin.

12. $\log_3 7$ **13.** $\log_4 23$ **14.** $\log_9 13$ **15.** $\log_2 5$

Practice and Problem Solving

● = **Step-by-Step Solutions** begin on page R20. **Extra Practice** begins on page 947.

Example 1 p. 516 — **Use a calculator to evaluate each expression to the nearest ten-thousandth.**

16. log 3 0.4771 **17.** log 11 1.0414 **18.** log 3.2 0.5051

19. log 8.2 0.9138 **20.** log 0.9 −0.0458 **21.** log 0.04 −1.3979

Example 2 p. 517

22. AUTO REPAIR Loretta had a new muffler installed on her car. The noise level of the engine dropped from 85 decibels to 73 decibels.

a. How many times the minimum intensity of sound detectable by the human ear was the car with the old muffler, if m is defined to be 1? about 316,227,766 times

b. How many times the minimum intensity of sound detectable by the human ear was the car with the new muffler? Find the percent of decrease of the intensity of the sound with the new muffler. about 19,952,623 times; about 93.7%

Additional Example

5 Express $\log_5 140$ in terms of common logarithms. Then round to the nearest ten-thousandth.

$\log_5 140 = \frac{\log_{10} 140}{\log_{10} 5}$; $\log_5 140 \approx 3.0704$

3 PRACTICE

Formative Assessment

Use Exercises 1–15 to check for understanding.

Use the chart at the bottom of this page to customize assignments for your students.

Additional Answers

12. $\frac{\log 7}{\log 3} \approx 1.7712$

13. $\frac{\log 23}{\log 4} \approx 2.2618$

14. $\frac{\log 13}{\log 9} \approx 1.1674$

15. $\frac{\log 5}{\log 2} \approx 2.3219$

Differentiated Homework Options

Level	Assignment	Two-Day Option	
AL Basic	16–38, 68, 70–92	17–37 odd, 73–76	16–38 even, 68, 70–72, 77–92
OL Core	17–39 odd, 40, 41–65 odd, 66–68, 70–92	16–38, 73–76	39–68, 70–72, 77–92
BL Advanced	39–86, (optional: 87–92)		

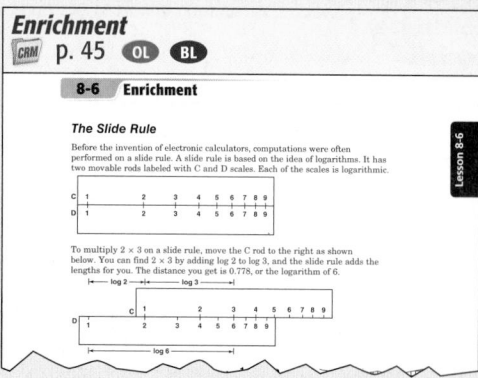

Example 3 p. 517

Solve each equation. Round to the nearest ten-thousandth.

23. $8^x = 40$ **1.7740**
24. $5^x = 55$ **2.4899**
25. $2.9^{a-4} = 8.1$ **5.9647**
26. $9^{b-1} = 7^b$ **8.7429**
27. $13^{x^2} = 33.3$ **±1.1691**
28. $15^{x^2} = 110$ **±1.3175**

Example 4 p. 518

Solve each inequality. Round to the nearest ten-thousandth.

29. $6^{3n} > 36$ **$\{n \mid n > 0.6667\}$**
30. $2^{4x} \leq 20$ **$\{x \mid x \leq 1.0805\}$**
31. $3^{y-1} \leq 4^y$ **$\{y \mid y \geq -3.8188\}$**
32. $5^{p-2} \geq 2^p$ **$\{p \mid p \geq 3.5129\}$**

Example 5 p. 519

Express each logarithm in terms of common logarithms. Then approximate its value to the nearest ten-thousandth.

33. $\log_7 18$ **$\frac{\log 18}{\log 7} \approx 1.4854$**
34. $\log_5 31$ **$\frac{\log 31}{\log 5} \approx 2.1337$**
35. $\log_2 16$ **$\frac{\log 16}{\log 2} = 4$**
36. $\log_4 9$ **$\frac{\log 9}{\log 4} \approx 1.5850$**
37. $\log_3 11$ **$\frac{\log 11}{\log 3} \approx 2.1827$**
38. $\log_6 33$ **$\frac{\log 33}{\log 6} \approx 1.9514$**

B

39. **PETS** The number n of pet owners in thousands after t years can be modeled by $n = 35[\log_4 (t + 2)]$. Let $t = 0$ represent 2000. Use the Change of Base Formula to solve the following questions.
    a. How many pet owners were there in 2010? **62,737 owners**
    b. How long until there are 80,000 pet owners? When will this occur? **2022**

Real-World Link

The grizzly bear is a North American subspecies of the brown bear. Grizzlies are typically 800 pounds; however, they are quite fast and have been clocked at 30 miles an hour.

40. **GRIZZLY BEARS** Five years ago the grizzly bear population in a certain national park was 325. Today it is 450. Studies show that the park can support a population of 750.
    a. What is the average annual rate of growth in the population if the grizzly bears reproduce once a year? **0.067 or 6.7%**
    b. How many years will it take to reach the maximum population if the population growth continues at the same average rate? **8 yr**

Solve each equation or inequality. Round to the nearest ten-thousandth.

41. $3^x = 40$ **3.3578**
42. $5^{3p} = 15$ **0.5609**
43. $4^{n+2} = 14.5$ **−0.0710**
44. $8^{z-4} = 6.3$ **4.8851**
45. $7.4^{n-3} = 32.5$ **4.7393**
46. $3.1^{y-5} = 9.2$ **6.9615**
47. $5^x \geq 42$ **$\{x \mid x \geq 2.3223\}$**
48. $9^{2a} < 120$ **$\{a \mid a < 1.0894\}$**
49. $3^{4x} \leq 72$ **$\{x \mid x \leq 0.9732\}$**
50. $7^{2n} > 52^{4n+3}$ **$\{n \mid n < -0.9950\}$**
51. $6^p \leq 13^{5-p}$ **$\{p \mid p \leq 2.9437\}$**
52. $2^{y+3} \geq 8^{3y}$ **$\{y \mid y \leq 0.3750\}$**

Express each logarithm in terms of common logarithms. Then approximate its value to the nearest ten-thousandth.

53. $\log_4 12$ **$\frac{\log 12}{\log 4} \approx 1.7925$**
54. $\log_3 21$ **$\frac{\log 21}{\log 3} \approx 2.7712$**
55. $\log_8 2$ **$\frac{\log 2}{\log 8} = 0.3333$**
56. $\log_6 7$ **$\frac{\log 7}{\log 6} \approx 1.0860$**
57. $\log_5 (2.7)^2$ **$\frac{\log 7.29}{\log 5} \approx 1.2343$**
58. $\log_7 \sqrt{5}$ **$\frac{\log \sqrt{5}}{\log 7} \approx 0.4135$**

59. **MUSIC** A musical cent is a unit in a logarithmic scale of relative pitch or intervals. One octave is equal to 1200 cents. The formula $n = 1200\left(\log_2 \frac{a}{b}\right)$ can be used to determine the difference in cents between two notes with frequencies a and b.
    a. Find the interval in cents when the frequency changes from 443 Hertz (Hz) to 415 Hz. **113.03 cents**
    b. If the interval is 55 cents and the beginning frequency is 225 Hz, find the final frequency. **about 218 Hz**

Study Guide and Intervention
CRM pp. 40–41 AL OL ELL

8-6 Study Guide and Intervention

Common Logarithms

Common Logarithms Base 10 logarithms are called **common logarithms**. The expression $\log_{10} x$ is usually written without the subscript as $\log x$. Use the LOG key on your calculator to evaluate common logarithms.

The relation between exponents and logarithms gives the following identity.

Inverse Property of Logarithms and Exponents	$10^{\log x} = x$

Example 1 **Evaluate log 50 to the nearest ten-thousandth.**

Use the LOG key on your calculator. To four decimal places, log 50 = 1.6990.

Example 2 **Solve $3^{2x+1} = 12$.**

$3^{2x+1} = 12$ Original equation
$\log 3^{2x+1} = \log 12$ Property of Equality for Logarithmic Functions.
$(2x + 1) \log 3 = \log 12$ Power Property of Logarithms
$2x + 1 = \frac{\log 12}{\log 3}$ Divide each side by log 3.
$2x = \frac{\log 12}{\log 3} - 1$ Subtract 1 from each side.
$x = \frac{1}{2}\left(\frac{\log 12}{\log 3} - 1\right)$ Multiply each side by $\frac{1}{2}$.
$x = \frac{1}{2}\left(\frac{1.0792}{0.4771} - 1\right)$ Use a calculator.
$x \approx 0.6309$

Exercises

Use a calculator to evaluate each expression to the nearest ten-thousandth.

1. log 18 **1.2553**
2. log 39 **1.5911**
3. log 120 **2.0792**
4. log 5.8 **0.7634**
5. log 42.3 **1.6263**
6. log 0.003 **−2.5229**

Solve each equation or inequality. Round to the nearest ten-thousandth.

7. $4^{3x} = 12$ **0.5975**
8. $6^{x+2} = 18$ **−0.3869**
9. $5^{4x-2} = 120$ **1.2437**
10. $7^{3x-1} \geq 21$ **$\{x \mid x \geq 0.8549\}$**
11. $2.4^{x+4} = 30$ **−0.1150**
12. $6.5^{2x} \geq 200$ **$\{x \mid x \geq 1.4153\}$**
13. $3.6^{4x-1} = 85.4$ **1.1180**
14. $2^{x+5} = 3^{x-2}$ **13.9666**
15. $9^{3x} = 4^{5x+2}$ **−8.1595**
16. $6^{x-5} = 2^{7x+3}$ **−3.6069**

Chapter 8 40 Glencoe Algebra 2

Practice
CRM p. 43 AL OL BL ELL

8-6 Practice

Common Logarithms

Use a calculator to evaluate each expression to the nearest ten-thousandth.

1. log 101 **2.0043**
2. log 2.2 **0.3424**
3. log 0.05 **−1.3010**

Use the formula pH = −log[H+] to find the pH of each substance given its concentration of hydrogen ions.

4. milk: [H+] = 2.51×10^{-7} mole per liter **6.6**
5. acid rain: [H+] = 2.51×10^{-6} mole per liter **5.6**
6. black coffee: [H+] = 1.0×10^{-5} mole per liter **5.0**
7. milk of magnesia: [H+] = 3.16×10^{-11} mole per liter **10.5**

Solve each equation or inequality. Round to the nearest ten-thousandth.

8. $2^x < 25$ **$\{x \mid x < 4.6439\}$**
9. $5^a = 120$ **2.9746**
10. $6^z = 45.6$ **2.1319**
11. $9^m \geq 100$ **$\{m \mid m \geq 2.0959\}$**
12. $3.5^x = 47.9$ **3.0885**
13. $8.2^y = 64.5$ **1.9802**
14. $2^{b+1} \leq 7.31$ **$\{b \mid b \leq 1.8699\}$**
15. $4^{2x} = 27$ **1.1887**
16. $2^{a-4} = 82.1$ **10.3593**
17. $9^{z-2} > 38$ **$\{z \mid z > 3.6555\}$**
18. $5^{w+3} = 17$ **−1.2396**
19. $30^{x^2} = 50$ **±1.0725**
20. $5^{x^2-3} = 72$ **±2.3785**
21. $4^{2x} = 9^{x+1}$ **3.8188**
22. $2^{n+1} = 5^{2n-1}$ **0.9117**

Express each logarithm in terms of common logarithms. Then approximate its value to the nearest ten-thousandth.

23. $\log_5 12$ **$\frac{\log 12}{\log 5}$; 1.5440**
24. $\log_8 32$ **$\frac{\log 32}{\log 8}$; 1.6667**
25. $\log_{11} 9$ **$\frac{\log 9}{\log 11}$; 0.9163**
26. $\log_2 18$ **$\frac{\log 18}{\log 2}$; 4.1699**
27. $\log_9 6$ **$\frac{\log 6}{\log 9}$; 0.8155**
28. $\log_7 \sqrt{8}$ **$\frac{\log 8}{2 \log 7}$; 0.5343**

29. **HORTICULTURE** Siberian irises flourish when the concentration of hydrogen ions [H+] in the soil is not less than 1.58×10^{-8} mole per liter. What is the pH of the soil in which these irises will flourish? **7.8 or less**

30. **ACIDITY** The pH of vinegar is 2.9 and the pH of milk is 6.6. Approximately how many times greater is the hydrogen ion concentration of vinegar than of milk? **about 5000**

31. **BIOLOGY** There are initially 1000 bacteria in a culture. The number of bacteria doubles each hour. The number of bacteria N present after t hours is $N = 1000(2)^t$. How long will it take the culture to increase to 50,000 bacteria? **about 5.6 h**

32. **SOUND** An equation for loudness L in decibels is given by $L = 10 \log R$, where R is the sound's relative intensity. An air-raid siren can reach 150 decibels and jet engine noise can reach 120 decibels. How many times greater is the relative intensity of the air-raid siren than that of the jet engine noise? **1000**

Chapter 8 43 Glencoe Algebra 2

Word Problem Practice
CRM p. 44 AL OL BL ELL

8-6 Word Problem Practice

Common Logarithms

1. **OTHER BASES** Jamie needs to figure out what $\log_2 3$ is, but she only has a table of common logarithms. In the table, she finds that $\log_{10} 2 \approx 0.3010$ and $\log_{10} 3 \approx 0.4771$. Using this information, to the nearest thousandth, what is $\log_2 3$?
1.585

2. **pH** The pH of a solution is given by
$-\log_{10} C$,
where C is the concentration of hydrogen ions in moles per liter. A solution of baking soda creates a hydrogen ion concentration 5×10^{-9} of mole per liter. What is the pH of a solution of baking soda? Round your answer to the nearest tenth.
8.3

3. **GRAPHING** The graph of $y = \log_{10} x$ is shown below. Use the fact that $\frac{1}{\log_{10} 2} \approx 3.32$ to sketch a graph of $y = \log_2 x$ on the same graph.

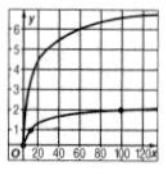

4. **SCIENTIFIC NOTATION** When a number n is written in scientific notation, it has the form $n = s \times 10^p$, where s is a number greater than or equal to 1 and less than 10 and p is an integer. Show that $p \leq \log_{10} n < p + 1$.
$n = s \times 10^p$
$\log n = \log (s \times 10^p)$
$= \log s + \log 10^p$
$= \log s + p$
Because $1 \leq s < 10$,
$0 \leq \log s < 1$.
Therefore, $p \leq \log n < p + 1$.

5. **LOG TABLE** Marjorie is looking through some old science books owned by her grandfather. At the back of one of them, there is a table of logarithms base 10. However, the book is worn out and some of the entries are unreadable.

Table of Common Logarithms (4 decimal places of accuracy)	
x	$\log_{10} x$
2	0.3010
3	0.4771
4	?
5	0.6989
6	?

a. Approximately what are the missing entries in the table? Round off your answers to the nearest thousandth.
log 4 ≈ 0.602
log 6 ≈ 0.778

b. How can you use this table to determine $\log_{10} 1.5$?
Sample answer: log 1.5
= log 3 + log 5 − log 10
≈ 0.4771 + 0.6989 − 1
≈ 0.1760

Chapter 8 44 Glencoe Algebra 2

Enrichment
CRM p. 45 OL BL

8-6 Enrichment

The Slide Rule

Before the invention of electronic calculators, computations were often performed on a slide rule. A slide rule is based on the idea of logarithms. It has two movable rods labeled with C and D scales. Each of the scales is logarithmic.

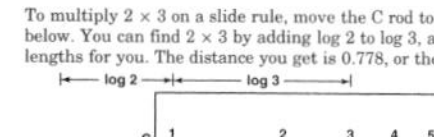

To multiply 2 × 3 on a slide rule, move the C rod to the right as shown below. You can find 2 × 3 by adding log 2 to log 3, and the slide rule adds the lengths for you. The distance you get is 0.778, or the logarithm of 6.

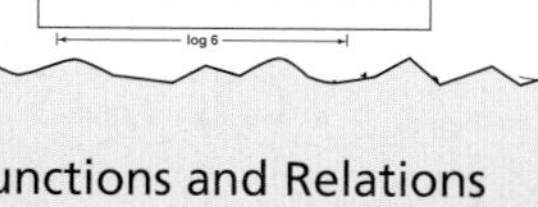

Lesson 8-6

Solve each equation. Round to the nearest ten-thousandth. $61.\ \pm\sqrt{5} \approx \pm 2.2361$

60. $10^{x^2} = 60$ ± 1.3335 **61** $4^{x^2-3} = 16$ **62.** $9^{6y-2} = 3^{3y+1}$ 0.5556

63. $8^{2x-4} = 4^{x+1}$ 3.5 **64.** $16^x = \sqrt{4^{x+3}}$ 1 **65.** $2^y = \sqrt{3^{y-1}}$ -3.8188

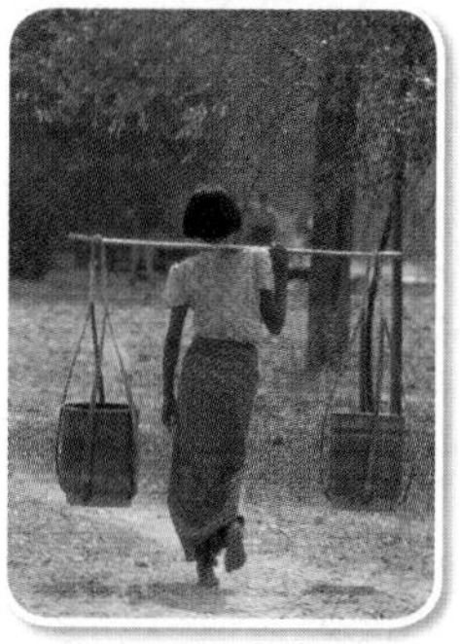

Real-World Link

Worldwide, over 1.1 billion people lack access to safe drinking water because of industrial pollution, poor sanitation, and environmental factors.

Source: United Nations

66. ENVIRONMENTAL SCIENCE An environmental engineer is testing drinking water wells in coastal communities for pollution, specifically unsafe levels of arsenic. The safe standard for arsenic is 0.025 parts per million (ppm). Also, the pH of the arsenic level should be less than 9.5. The formula for hydrogen ion concentration is pH = $-\log H$. (*Hint*: 1 kilogram of water occupies approximately 1 liter. 1 ppm = 1 mg/kg.) **a. yes; $10.9 > 9.5$**

a. Suppose the hydrogen ion concentration of a well is 1.25×10^{-11}. Should the environmental engineer be worried about too high an arsenic content?

b. The environmental engineer finds 1 milligram of arsenic in a 3 liter sample, is the well safe? **no**

c. What is the hydrogen ion concentration that meets the troublesome pH level of 9.5? **3.16×10^{-10}**

67. MULTIPLE REPRESENTATIONS In this problem, you will solve the exponential equation $4^x = 13$. **a. The solution is between 1.8 and 1.9.**

a. TABULAR Enter the function $y = 4^x$ into a graphing calculator, create a table of values for the function, and scroll through the table to find x when $y = 13$.

b. GRAPHICAL Graph $y = 4^x$ and $y = 13$ on the same screen. Use the **intersect** feature to find the point of intersection. **(1.85, 13)**

c. NUMERICAL Solve the equation algebraically. Do all of the methods produce the same result? Explain why or why not.

H.O.T. Problems

Use Higher-Order Thinking Skills

68. ERROR ANALYSIS Sam and Rosamaria are solving $4^{3p} = 10$. Is either of them correct? Explain your reasoning.

Sam	Rosamaria
$4^{3p} = 10$	$4^{3p} = 10$
$\log 4^{3p} = \log 10$	$\log 4^{3p} = \log 10$
$p \log 4 = \log 10$	$3p \log 4 = \log 10$
$p = \dfrac{\log 10}{\log 4}$	$p = \dfrac{\log 10}{3 \log 4}$

69. CHALLENGE Solve $\log_{\sqrt{a}} 3 = \log_a x$ for x and explain each step. **See margin.**

70. REASONING Write $\dfrac{\log_5 9}{\log_5 3}$ as a single logarithm. $\dfrac{\log_5 9}{\log_5 3} = \log_3 9$

71. PROOF Find the values of $\log_3 27$ and $\log_{27} 3$. Make and prove a conjecture about the relationship between $\log_a b$ and $\log_b a$. **See margin.**

72. WRITING IN MATH Explain how exponents and logarithms are related. Include examples like how to solve a logarithmic equation using exponents and how to solve an exponential equation using logarithms.

67c. Yes; all methods produce the solution of 1.85. They all should produce the same result because you are starting with the same equation. If they do not, then an error was made.

68. Rosamaria; Sam forgot to bring the 3 down from the exponent when he took the log of each side.

72. Logarithms are exponents. To solve logarithmic equations, write each side of the equation using exponents and solve by using the Inverse Property of Exponents and Logarithms. To solve exponential equations, use the Property of Equality for Logarithmic Functions and the Power Property of Logarithms.

Multiple Representations In Exercise 67, students use a graphing calculator and algebra to solve a higher-level equation algebraically and graphically and compare the results.

Watch Out!

Error Analysis For Exercise 68, point out to students that in the Power Property of Logarithms, $\log_b m^p = p \log_b m$, the p represents the entire exponent of m.

Additional Answers

69. $\log_{\sqrt{a}} 3 = \log_a x$ Original equation

$\dfrac{\log_a 3}{\log_a \sqrt{a}} = \log_a x$ Change of Base Formula

$\dfrac{\log_a 3}{\frac{1}{2}} = \log_a x$ $\sqrt{a} = a^{\frac{1}{2}}$

$2 \log_a 3 = \log_a x$ Multiply numerator and denominator by 2.

$\log_a 3^2 = \log_a x$ Power Property of Logarithms

$3^2 = x$ Property of Equality for Logarithms Functions

$9 = x$ Simplify

71. $\log_3 27 = 3$ and $\log_{27} 3 = \frac{1}{3}$;

Conjecture: $\log_a b = \dfrac{1}{\log_b a}$

Proof: $\log_a b \stackrel{?}{=} \dfrac{1}{\log_b a}$ Original statement

$\dfrac{\log_b b}{\log_b a} \stackrel{?}{=} \dfrac{1}{\log_b a}$ Change of Base Formula

$\dfrac{1}{\log_b a} = \dfrac{1}{\log_b a}$ Inverse Property of Exponents and Logarithms

4 ASSESS

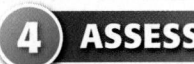

Yesterday's News Have students write how knowing the properties of logarithms has helped them with solving the exponential equations and inequalities in today's lesson.

Formative Assessment

Check for student understanding of Lessons 8-5 and 8-6.

CRM Quiz 3, p. 64

Additional Answers

74a. $3d + 2v + 2m = 16.29$, $d + 3v + 4m = 19.84$, $2d + v + m = 9.14$

74b. documentaries: $1.99, video games: $2.79, movies: $2.37

NGSSS PRACTICE 912.A.2.8, 912.A.3.15, 912.G.2.6, 912.G.2.4

73. Which expression represents $f[g(x)]$ if $f(x) = x^2 + 4x + 3$ and $g(x) = x - 5$? **B**

A. $x^2 + 4x - 2$
B. $x^2 - 6x + 8$
C. $x^2 - 9x + 23$
D. $x^2 - 14x + 6$

74. THINK SOLVE EXPLAIN **EXTENDED RESPONSE** Colleen rented 3 documentaries, 2 video games, and 2 movies. The charge was $16.29. The next week, she rented 1 documentary, 3 video games, and 4 movies for a total charge of $19.84. The third week she rented 2 documentaries, 1 video game, and 1 movie for a total charge of $9.14.

a. Write a system of equations to determine the cost to rent each item. **a, b. See margin.**

b. What is the cost to rent each item?

75. GEOMETRY If the surface area of a cube is increased by a factor of 9, what is the change in the length of the sides if the cube? **G**

F. The length is 2 times the original length.
G. The length is 3 times the original length.
H. The length is 6 times the original length.
I. The length is 9 times the original length.

76. ACT/SAT Which of the following *most* accurately describes the translation of the graph $y = (x + 4)^2 - 3$ to the graph of $y = (x - 1)^2 + 3$? **D**

A. down 1 and to the right 3
B. down 6 and to the left 5
C. up 1 and to the left 3
D. up 6 and to the right 5

Spiral Review

Solve each equation. Check your solutions. (Lesson 8-5)

77. $\log_5 7 + \frac{1}{2}\log_5 4 = \log_5 x$ **14**

78. $2 \log_2 x - \log_2 (x + 3) = 2$ **6**

79. $\log_6 48 - \log_6 \frac{16}{5} + \log_6 5 = \log_6 5x$ **15**

80. $\log_{10} a + \log_{10} (a + 21) = 2$ **4**

Solve each equation or inequality. (Lesson 8-4)

81. $\log_4 x = \frac{1}{2}$ **2**

82. $\log_{81} 729 = x$ $\frac{3}{2}$

83. $\log_8 (x^2 + x) = \log_8 12$ **−4, 3**

84. $\log_8 (3y - 1) < \log_8 (y + 5)$ $\frac{1}{3} < y < 3$

85. SAILING The area of a triangular sail is $16x^4 - 60x^3 - 28x^2 + 56x - 32$ square meters. The base of the triangle is $x - 4$ meters. What is the height of the sail? (Lesson 6-2) $32x^3 + 8x^2 - 24x + 16$

86. HOME REPAIR Mr. Turner is getting new locks installed. The locksmith charges $85 for the service call, $25 for each door, and each lock costs $30. (Lesson 2-4)

a. Write an equation that represents the cost for x number of doors. $y = 85 + 55x$

b. Mr. Turner wants the front, side, back, and garage door locks changed. How much will this cost? **$305**

Skills Review

Write an equivalent exponential equation. (Lesson 8-3)

87. $\log_2 5 = x$ $2^x = 5$

88. $\log_4 x = 3$ $4^3 = x$

89. $\log_5 25 = 2$ $5^2 = 25$

90. $\log_7 10 = x$ $7^x = 10$

91. $\log_6 x = 4$ $6^4 = x$

92. $\log_4 64 = 3$ $4^3 = 64$

Differentiated Instruction OL BL

Extension Remind students that the formula $A = P\left(1 + \frac{r}{n}\right)^{nt}$ can be used to find the final amount of an investment using compound interest. Have them use logarithms to find the number of years t that it will take for an investment of $5000 to grow to $8000 at an interest rate of 5% compounded monthly. about 9.4 years

EXTEND 8-6

Graphing Technology Lab: Solving Logarithmic Equations and Inequalities

FL Math Online glencoe.com
- Other Calculator Keystrokes
- Graphing Technology Personal Tutor

NGSSS MA.912.A.8.5 **Solve logarithmic** and exponential **equations.**

You have solved logarithmic equations algebraically. You can also solve logarithmic equations by graphing or by using a table. The TI-83/84 Plus has $y = \log_{10} x$ as a built-in function. Enter [Y=] [LOG] [X,T,θ,n] [GRAPH] to view this graph. To graph logarithmic functions with bases other than 10, you must use the Change of Base Formula, $\log_a n = \frac{\log_b n}{\log_b a}$.

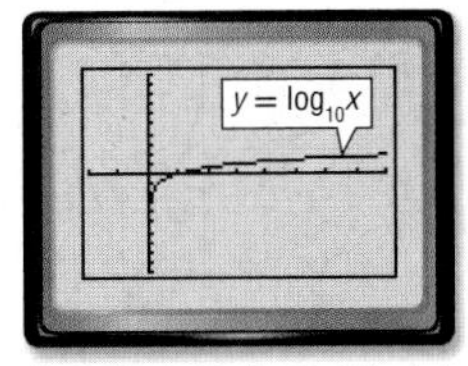

[−2, 8] scl: 1 by [−10, 10] scl: 1

ACTIVITY 1

Solve $\log_2 (6x - 8) = \log_3 (20x + 1)$.

Step 1 Graph each side of the equation.

Graph each side of the equation as a separate function. Enter $\log_2 (6x - 8)$ as **Y1** and $\log_3 (20x + 1)$ as **Y2**. Then graph the two equations.

KEYSTROKES: [Y=] [LOG] 6 [X,T,θ,n] [−] 8 [)] [÷] [LOG] 2 [)] [ENTER] [LOG] 20 [X,T,θ,n] [+] 1 [)] [÷] [LOG] 3 [)] [GRAPH]

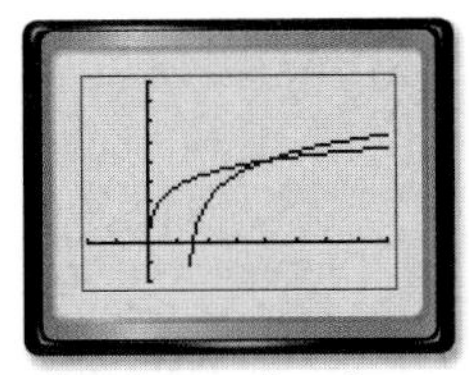

[−2, 8] scl: 1 by [−2, 8] scl: 1

Step 2 Use the **intersect** feature.

Use the **intersect** feature on the **CALC** menu to approximate the ordered pair of the point at which the curves intersect.

The calculator screen shows that the x-coordinate of the point at which the curves intersect is 4. Therefore, the solution of the equation is 4.

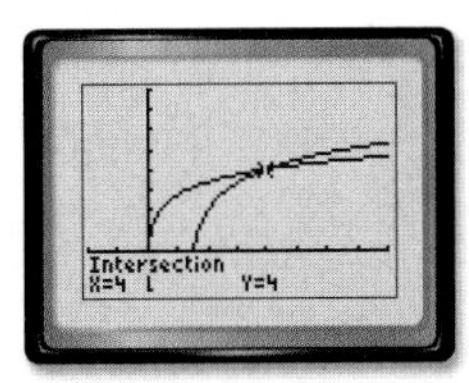

[−2, 8] scl: 1 by [−2, 8] scl: 1

Step 3 Use the **TABLE** feature.

Examine the table to find the x-value for which the y-values for the graphs are equal. At $x = 4$, both functions have a y-value of 4. Thus, the solution of the equation is 4.

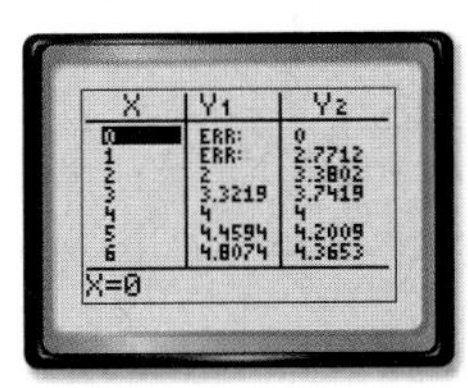

You can use a similar procedure to solve logarithmic inequalities using a graphing calculator.

EXTEND 8-6

Lesson Notes

1 FOCUS

Objective Use a graphing calculator to solve exponential and logarithmic equations and inequalities.

Materials for Each Student

- TI-83/84 Plus or other graphing calculator

Teaching Tip

Point out that the operation **log (** can be used with numbers or expressions. Remind students that it is always a good idea to use closing parentheses at the end of the expression.

2 TEACH

Working in Cooperative Groups

Put students in groups of two or three, mixing abilities. Then have groups complete Activities 1 and 2 and Exercises 1–4.

Activity 1

- Before discussing the Activity, have students use the Change of Base Formula to express each side of the equation in terms of common logarithms.
- Be sure students understand how to read the table feature to find the x-value for which the y-values are equal.
- Have students substitute the solution into the original equation to verify that it is correct.

Activity 2

- Before discussing Activity 2, have students use the Change of Base Formula to express each side of the inequality in terms of common logarithms.
- Make sure students understand why the inequality needs to be rewritten as a system of inequalities.
- Be sure students understand how to read the table feature to find the *x*-value for which the *y*-values are undefined as well as the *x*-value for which the *y*-values are equal.

Practice Have students complete Exercises 5–8.

3 ASSESS

Formative Assessment

In Exercise 8, check that students record the inequalities in the solution set correctly. In particular, students must include the fact that *x* must be greater than 0.

From Concrete to Abstract

Have students explain how the solution set for Activity 2 would change if the inequality were $\log_4 (10x + 1) > \log_5 (16 + 6x)$.

ACTIVITY 2

Solve $\log_4 (10x + 1) < \log_5 (16 + 6x)$.

Step 1 Enter the inequalities.

Rewrite the problem as a system of inequalities.

The first inequality is $\log_4 (10x + 1) < y$ or $y > \log_4 (10x + 1)$. Since this inequality includes the *greater than* symbol, shade above the curve.

First enter the boundary and then use the arrow and [ENTER] keys to choose the shade above icon, ◥.

The second inequality is $y < \log_5 (16 + 6x)$. Shade below the curve since this inequality contains *less than*.

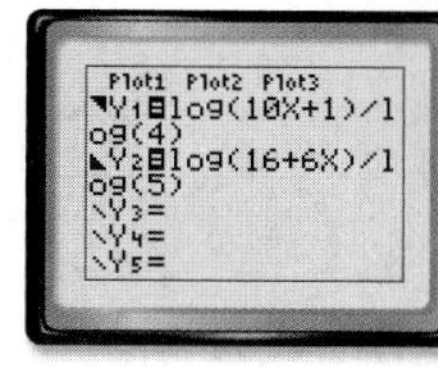

KEYSTROKES: [Y=] [◄] [◄] [ENTER] [ENTER] [►] [►] [LOG] 10 [X,T,θ,n] [+] 1 [)] [÷] [LOG] 4 [)] [ENTER] [◄] [◄] [ENTER] [ENTER] [ENTER] [►] [►] [LOG] 16 [+] 6 [X,T,θ,n] [)] [÷] [LOG] 5 [)]

Step 2 Graph the system.

KEYSTROKES: [GRAPH]

The left boundary of the solution set is where the first inequality is undefined. It is undefined for $10x + 1 \le 0$.

$$10x + 1 \le 0$$
$$10x \le -1$$
$$x \le -\frac{1}{10}$$

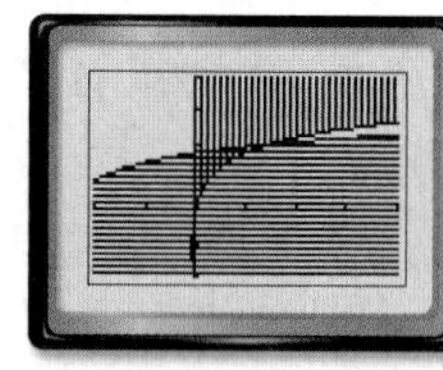

[−2, 4] scl: 1 by [−2, 4] scl: 1

Use the calculator's **intersect** feature to find the right boundary. You can conclude that the solution set is $\{x \mid -0.1 < x < 1.5\}$.

Step 3 Use the **TABLE** feature to check your solution.

Start the table at −0.1 and show *x*-values in increments of 0.1. Scroll through the table.

KEYSTROKES: [2nd] [TBLSET] −0.1 [ENTER] .5 [ENTER] [2nd] [TBLSET]

The table confirms the solution of the inequality is $\{x \mid -0.1 < x < 1.5\}$.

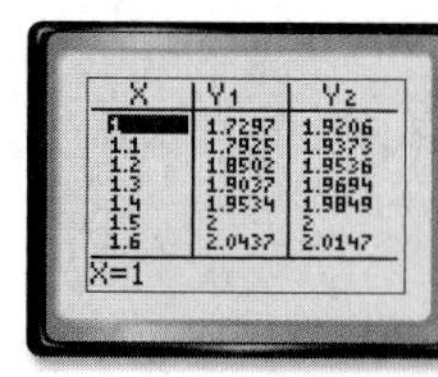

Exercises

Solve each equation or inequality. Check your solution.

1. $\log_2 (3x + 2) = \log_3 (12x + 3)$ **0, 2**
2. $\log_6 (7x + 1) = \log_4 (4x - 4)$ **5**
3. $\log_2 3x = \log_3 (2x + 2)$ **about 0.7**
4. $\log_{10} (1 - x) = \log_5 (2x + 5)$ **about −1.5**
5. $\log_4 (9x + 1) > \log_3 (18x - 1)$ **$\{x \mid 0.06 < x < 0.17\}$**
6. $\log_3 (3x - 5) \ge \log_3 (x + 7)$ **$\{x \mid x \ge 6\}$**
7. $\log_5 (2x + 1) < \log_4 (3x - 2)$ **$\{x \mid x > 2\}$**
8. $\log_2 2x \le \log_4 (x + 3)$ **$\{x \mid 0 < x \le 1\}$**

8-7 Base *e* and Natural Logarithms

Then
You worked with common logarithms. (Lesson 8-6)

Now
- Evaluate expressions involving the natural base and natural logarithm.
- Solve exponential equations and inequalities using natural logarithms.

NGSSS
MA.912.A.8.2 Define and use the properties of logarithms to simplify logarithmic expressions and to find their approximate values.
MA.912.A.8.7 Solve applications of exponential growth and decay. *Also addresses MA.912.A.10.3.*

New Vocabulary
natural base, *e*
natural base exponential function
natural logarithm

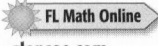

FL Math Online
glencoe.com

Why?

The St. Louis Gateway Arch in Missouri is in the form of an inverted catenary curve. A catenary curve directs the force of its weight along itself, so that:

- if a rope or chain is hanging, it is pulled into that shape, and,
- if a catenary is standing upright, it can support itself.

The equation for the catenary curve involves e, a special number that appears throughout mathematics and science.

Base *e* and Natural Logarithms Like π and $\sqrt{2}$, the number e is an irrational number. The value of e is 2.71828… . It is referred to as the **natural base, *e***. An exponential function with base e is called a **natural base exponential function**.

Key Concept Natural Base Functions

The function $f(x) = e^x$ is used to model continuous exponential growth.
The function $f(x) = e^{-x}$ is used to model continuous exponential decay.

The inverse of a natural base exponential function is called the **natural logarithm**. This logarithm can be written as $\log_e x$, but is more often abbreviated as $\ln x$.

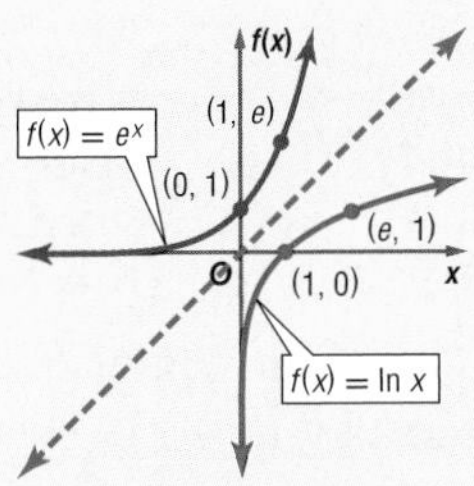

Exponential Growth

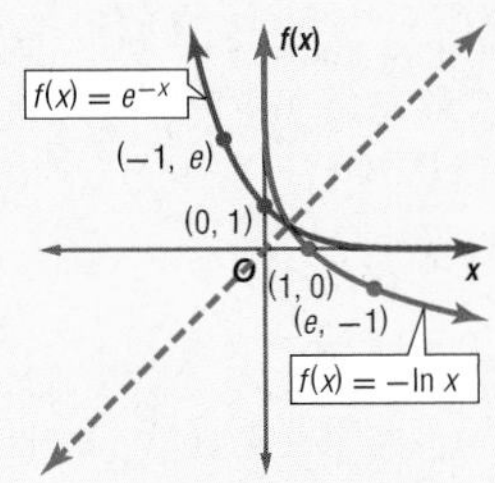

Exponential Decay

You can write an equivalent base e exponential equation for a natural logarithmic equation by using the fact that $\ln x = \log_e x$.

$$\ln 4 = x \rightarrow \log_e 4 = x \rightarrow e^x = 4$$

EXAMPLE 1 Write Equivalent Expressions

Write each exponential equation in logarithmic form.

a. $e^x = 8$

$e^x = 8 \rightarrow \log_e 8 = x$
$\ln 8 = x$

b. $e^5 = x$

$e^5 = x \rightarrow \log_e x = 5$
$\ln x = 5$

Guided Practice

1A. $e^x = 9$ $\ln 9 = x$

1B. $e^7 = x$ $\ln x = 7$

Personal Tutor glencoe.com

1 FOCUS

Vertical Alignment

Before Lesson 8-7
Work with common logarithms.

Lesson 8-7
Evaluate expressions involving the natural base and natural logarithm.
Solve exponential equations and inequalities using natural logarithms.

After Lesson 8-7
Analyze a situation modeled by an exponential function, and solve the problem.

2 TEACH

Scaffolding Questions

Have students read the *Why?* section of the lesson.

Ask:

- What other arch-shaped structures have you seen? Sample answers: McDonald's arches, arch bridges
- What other special numbers have you studied? π

Lesson 8-7 Resources

Resource	Approaching-Level	On-Level	Beyond-Level	English Learners
Teacher Edition	• Differentiated Instruction, p. 527	• Differentiated Instruction, p. 531	• Differentiated Instruction, p. 531	
Chapter Resource Masters	• Study Guide and Intervention, pp. 47–48 • Skills Practice, p. 49 • Practice, p. 50 • Word Problem Practice, p. 51	• Study Guide and Intervention, pp. 47–48 • Skills Practice, p. 49 • Practice, p. 50 • Word Problem Practice, p. 51 • Enrichment, p. 52	• Practice, p. 50 • Word Problem Practice, p. 51 • Enrichment, p. 52	• Study Guide and Intervention, pp. 47–48 • Skills Practice, p. 49 • Practice, p. 50 • Word Problem Practice, p. 51
Transparencies	• 5-Minute Check Transparency 8-7	• 5-Minute Check Transparency 8-7	• 5-Minute Check Transparency 8-7	• 5-Minute Check Transparency 8-7
Other	• Study Notebook	• Study Notebook	• Study Notebook	• Study Notebook

Base *e* and Natural Logarithms

Example 1 shows how to write an equivalent natural logarithmic equation for an exponential equation. **Example 2** shows how to write an equivalent exponential equation for a natural logarithmic equation. **Example 3** shows how to simplify expressions containing natural logarithms.

Formative Assessment

Use the Guided Practice exercises after each example to determine students' understanding of concepts.

Additional Examples

1 Write each exponential equation in logarithmic form.

a. $e^x = 23$ $\ln 23 = x$

b. $e^4 = x$ $\ln x = 4$

2 Write each logarithmic equation in exponential form.

a. $\ln x \approx 1.2528$ $x \approx e^{1.2528}$

b. $\ln 25 = x$ $25 = e^x$

3 Write each expression as a single logarithm.

a. $4 \ln 3 + \ln 6$ $\ln 486$

b. $2 \ln 3 + \ln 4 + \ln y$ $\ln 36y$

Additional Examples also in Interactive Classroom PowerPoint® Presentations

IWB INTERACTIVE WHITEBOARD READY

Watch Out!

Common Misconceptions Stress that *e* is a constant like π and not a variable like *x* or *y*.

You can also write an equivalent natural logarithm equation for a natural base *e* exponential equation.

$$e^x = 12 \rightarrow \log_e 12 = x \rightarrow \ln 12 = x$$

EXAMPLE 2 Write Equivalent Expressions

Write each logarithmic equation in exponential form.

a. $\ln x \approx 0.7741$

$\ln x \approx 0.7741 \rightarrow \log_e x = 0.7741$

$x \approx e^{0.7741}$

b. $\ln 10 = x$

$\ln 10 = x \rightarrow \log_e 10 = x$

$10 = e^x$

Guided Practice

2A. $\ln x \approx 2.1438$ $x = e^{2.1438}$

2B. $\ln 18 = x$ $18 = e^x$

Personal Tutor glencoe.com

The properties of logarithms you learned in Lesson 8-5 also apply to the natural logarithms. The logarithmic expressions below can be simplified into a single logarithmic term.

StudyTip

Simplifying When you simplify logarithmic expressions, verify that the logarithm contains no operations and no powers.

EXAMPLE 3 Simplify Expressions with *e* and the Natural Log

Write each expression as a single logarithm.

a. $3 \ln 10 - \ln 8$

$3 \ln 10 - \ln 8 = \ln 10^3 - \ln 8$ **Power Property of Logarithms**

$= \ln \frac{10^3}{8}$ **Quotient Property of Logarithms**

$= \ln 125$ **Simplify.**

$= \ln 5^3$ **$5^3 = 125$**

$= 3 \ln 5$ **Power Property of Logarithms**

CHECK Use a calculator to verify the solution.

KEYSTROKES: 3 [LN] 10 [)] [−] [LN] 8 [)] [ENTER]

KEYSTROKES: 3 [LN] 5 [)] [ENTER] 4.828313737 ✓

b. $\ln 40 + 2 \ln \frac{1}{2} + \ln x$

$\ln 40 + 2 \ln \frac{1}{2} + \ln x = \ln 40 + \ln \frac{1}{4} + \ln x$ **Power Property of Logarithms**

$= \ln \left(40 \cdot \frac{1}{4} \cdot x\right)$ **Product Property of Logarithms**

$= \ln 10x$ **Simplify.**

Guided Practice

3A. $6 \ln 8 - 2 \ln 4$ $14 \ln 2$

3B. $2 \ln 5 + 4 \ln 2 + \ln 5y$ $\ln 2000y$

Personal Tutor glencoe.com

StudyTip

Look Back Refer to Lesson 7-2 to review **inverse functions**.

Because the natural base and natural log are inverse functions, they can be used to *undo* or eliminate each other.

$$e^{\ln x} = x \qquad \ln e^x = x$$

TEACH with TECH

BLOG Have students write a blog entry describing how natural logarithms and common logarithms are similar and different.

Equations and Inequalities with *e* and ln Equations and inequalities involving base e are easier to solve by using natural logarithms rather than by using common logarithms, because $\ln e = 1$.

EXAMPLE 4 Solve Base *e* Equations

Solve $4e^{-2x} - 5 = 3$. Round to the nearest ten-thousandth.

$4e^{-2x} - 5 = 3$	**Original equation**
$4e^{-2x} = 8$	**Add 5 to each side.**
$e^{-2x} = 2$	**Divide each side by 4.**
$\ln e^{-2x} = \ln 2$	**Property of Equality for Logarithms**
$-2x = \ln 2$	**$\ln e^x = x$**
$x = \frac{\ln 2}{-2}$	**Divide each side by −2.**
$x \approx -0.3466$	**Use a calculator.**

KEYSTROKES: [LN] 2 [)] [÷] −2 [ENTER] −.34657359

StudyTip

Calculators Most calculators have an e^x and LN key for evaluating natural base and natural log expressions.

Guided Practice

Solve each equation. Round to the nearest ten-thousandth.

4A. $3e^{4x} - 12 = 15$ **0.5493** **4B.** $4e^{-x} + 8 = 17$ **−0.8109**

Personal Tutor glencoe.com

Just like the natural logarithm can be used to eliminate e^x, the natural base exponential function can eliminate $\ln x$.

EXAMPLE 5 Solve Natural Log Equations and Inequalities

Solve each equation or inequality. Round to the nearest ten-thousandth.

a. $3 \ln 4x = 24$

$3 \ln 4x = 24$	**Original equation**
$\ln 4x = 8$	**Divide each side by 3.**
$e^{\ln 4x} = e^8$	**Property of Equality for Exponential Functions**
$4x = e^8$	**$e^{\ln x} = x$**
$x = \frac{e^8}{4}$	**Divide each side by 4.**
$x \approx 745.2395$	**Use a calculator.**

b. $\ln (x - 8)^4 < 4$

$\ln (x - 8)^4 < 4$	**Original equation**
$e^{\ln (x-8)^4} < e^4$	**Write each side using exponents and base *e*.**
$(x - 8)^4 < e^4$	**$e^{\ln x} = x$**
$x - 8 < e$	**Property of Equality for Exponential Functions**
$x < e + 8$	**Add 8 to each side.**
$x < 10.7183$	**Use a calculator.**

Guided Practice

Solve each equation or inequality. Round to four decimal places.

5A. $5 \ln 6x = 8$ **$x = 0.8255$** **5B.** $\ln (2x - 3)^3 > 6$ **$\{x \mid x > 5.1945\}$**

Personal Tutor glencoe.com

Focus on Mathematical Content

Base *e* A logarithm with base e is called a natural logarithm, written as $\log_e x$ or $\ln x$. The natural logarithmic function, $y = \ln x$, is the inverse of the natural base exponential function $y = e^x$.

Equations and Inequalities With *e* and ln

Example 4 shows how to use natural logarithms to solve an equation involving base *e*. **Example 5** shows how to solve natural logarithmic equations and inequalities. **Example 6** shows how to use the formula $A = Pe^{rt}$ to solve a real-world problem involving interest that is compounded continuously.

Additional Examples

4 Solve $3e^{-2x} + 4 = 10$. Round to four decimal places. $x \approx -0.3466$

5 Solve each equation or inequality. Round to the nearest ten-thousandth.

a. $2 \ln 5x = 6$ 4.0171

b. $\ln (3x + 1)^2 > 8$ $x > 17.8661$

Differentiated Instruction

AL

If some students mistakenly think that an equation like $4e^{-2x} - 5 = 3$ contains two variables,

Then point out that the letter *e* represents a constant, just as π does. Both *e* and π are irrational numbers, which cannot be expressed exactly with numerals. To help students avoid this confusion, have them highlight the variables in the equation with a marker.

Additional Example

6 **SAVINGS** Suppose you deposit \$700 into an account paying 3% annual interest, compounded continuously.

a. What is the balance after 8 years? \$889.87

b. How long will it take for the balance in your account to reach at least \$1200? about 18 years

c. How much would have to be deposited in order to reach a balance of \$1500 after 12 years? \$1046.51

Watch Out!

Preventing Errors Remind students that the value of $\ln x$ is defined only for positive values of x. Sometimes the least possible value for x must be determined to eliminate any values of x for which the logarithm function would be undefined.

Real-World Link

The average cost of tuition at four-year public colleges is about \$6000 per year.

Source: CNN

StudyTip

Rounding Not rounding until the very end will provide a more accurate answer.

Interest compounded continuously can be found using e.

Key Concept **Continuously Compounded Interest**

Calculate continuously compounded interest using the following formula.

$$A = Pe^{rt},$$

where A is the amount in the account after t years, P is the principal amount invested, and r is the annual interest rate.

Real-World EXAMPLE 6 Solve Base e Inequalities

FINANCIAL LITERACY When Angelina was born, her grandparents deposited \$3000 into a college savings account paying 4% interest compounded continuously.

a. Assuming there are no deposits or withdrawals from the account, what will the balance be after 10 years?

$A = Pe^{rt}$	**Continuous Compounding Formula**
$= 3000e^{(0.04)(10)}$	**$P = 3000$, $r = 0.04$, and $t = 10$**
$= 3000e^{0.4}$	**Simplify.**
≈ 4475.47	**Use a calculator.**

The balance will be \$4475.47.

b. How long will it take the balance to reach at least \$10,000?

$A < Pe^{rt}$	**Continuous Compounding Formula**
$10{,}000 < 3000e^{(0.04)t}$	**$P = 3000$, $r = 0.04$, and $A = 10{,}000$**
$\frac{10}{3} < e^{0.04t}$	**Divide each side by 3000.**
$\ln \frac{10}{3} < \ln e^{0.04t}$	**Property of Equality of Logarithms**
$\ln \frac{10}{3} < 0.04t$	**$\ln e^x = x$**
$\frac{\ln \frac{10}{3}}{0.04} < t$	**Divide each side by 0.04.**
$30.099 < t$	**Use a calculator.**

It will take about 30 years to reach at least \$10,000.

c. If her grandparents want Angelina to have \$10,000 after 18 years, how much would they need to invest?

$10{,}000 = Pe^{(0.04)18}$	**$A = 10{,}000$, $r = 0.04$, and $t = 18$**
$\frac{10{,}000}{e^{0.72}} = P$	**Divide each side by $e^{0.72}$.**
$4867.52 \approx P$	**Use a calculator.**

They need to invest \$4867.52.

Guided Practice

6. Use the information in Example 6 to answer the following.

A. If they invested \$8000 at 3.75% interest compounded continuously, how much money would be in the account in 30 years? **\$24,641.73**

B. If they could only deposit \$10,000 in the account above, at what rate would the account need to grow in order for Angelina to have \$30,000 in 18 years? **about 6.1%**

C. If Angelina's grandparents found an account that paid 5% compounded continuously and wanted her to have \$30,000 after 18 years, how much would they need to deposit? **\$12,197.09**

Personal Tutor glencoe.com

528 Chapter 8 Exponential and Logarithmic Functions and Relations

Check Your Understanding

Examples 1 and 2 pp. 525–526

Write an equivalent exponential or logarithmic function.

1. $e^x = 30$ $\ln 30 = x$
2. $\ln x = 42$ $e^{42} = x$
3. $e^3 = x$ $\ln x = 3$
4. $\ln 18 = x$ $e^x = 18$

Example 3 p. 526

Write each as a single logarithm.

5. $3 \ln 2 + 2 \ln 4$ $7 \ln 2$
6. $5 \ln 3 - 2 \ln 9$ $\ln 3$
7. $3 \ln 6 + 2 \ln 9$ $\ln 17496$
8. $3 \ln 5 + 4 \ln x$ $\ln 125x^4$

Example 4 p. 527

Solve each equation. Round to the nearest ten-thousandth.

9. $5e^x - 24 = 16$ 2.0794
10. $-3e^x + 9 = 4$ 0.5108
11. $3e^{-3x} + 4 = 6$ 0.1352
12. $2e^{-x} - 3 = 8$ -1.7047

Example 5 p. 527

Solve each equation or inequality. Round to the nearest ten-thousandth.

13. $\ln 3x = 8$ 993.6527
14. $-4 \ln 2x = -26$ 332.5708
15. $\ln (x + 5)^2 < 6$
16. $\ln (x - 2)^3 > 15$ $\{x \mid x > 150.4132\}$
17. $e^x > 29$ $\{x \mid x > 3.3673\}$
18. $5 + e^{-x} > 14$ $\{x \mid x < -2.1972\}$

15. $\{x \mid -25.0855 < x < 15.0855, x \neq -5\}$

Example 6 p. 528

19. **SCIENCE** A virus is spreading through a computer network according to the formula $v(t) = 30e^{0.1t}$, where v is the number of computers infected and t is the time in minutes. How long will it take the virus to infect 10,000 computers? about 58 min

$\{x \mid -25.0855 < x < 15.0855, x \neq -55\}$

Practice and Problem Solving

● = **Step-by-Step Solutions** begin on page R20. **Extra Practice** begins on page 947.

Examples 1 and 2 pp. 525–526

Write an equivalent exponential or logarithmic function. 22. $0.25 = e^x$ 23. $5.4 = e^x$

20. $e^{-x} = 8$
21. $e^{-5x} = 0.1$
22. $\ln 0.25 = x$
23. $\ln 5.4 = x$
24. $e^{x-3} = 2$ $\ln 2 = x - 3$
25. $\ln (x + 4) = 36$ $e^{36} = x + 4$
26. $e^{-2} = x^6$ $-2 = 6 \ln x$
27. $\ln e^x = 7$ $e^7 = e^x$

20. $\ln 8 = -x$
21. $\ln 0.1 = -5x$

Example 3 p. 526

Write each as a single logarithm.

28. $\ln 125 - 2 \ln 5$ $\ln 5$
29. $3 \ln 10 + 2 \ln 100$ $7 \ln 10$
30. $4 \ln \frac{1}{3} - 6 \ln \frac{1}{9}$ $-8 \ln \frac{1}{3}$
31. ● $7 \ln \frac{1}{2} + 5 \ln 2$ $-2 \ln 2$
32. $8 \ln x - 4 \ln 5$ $\ln \frac{x^8}{625}$
33. $3 \ln x^2 + 4 \ln 3$ $\ln 81x^6$

Example 4 p. 527

Solve each equation. Round to the nearest ten-thousandth.

34. $6e^x - 3 = 35$ 1.8458
35. $4e^x + 2 = 180$ 3.7955
36. $3e^{2x} - 5 = -4$ -0.5493
37. $-2e^{3x} + 19 = 3$ 0.6931
38. $6e^{4x} + 7 = 4$ no solution
39. $-4e^{-x} + 9 = 2$ -0.5596

Examples 5 and 6 pp. 527–528

40. **FINANCIAL LITERACY** The value of a certain car depreciates according to $v(t) = 18500e^{-0.186t}$, where t is the number of years after the car is purchased new.
    a. What will the car be worth in 18 months? \$13,996 $\{x \mid x < 8103.0839\}$
    b. When will the car be worth half of its original value? about 3.73 yr
    c. When will the car be worth less than \$1000? about 15.69 yr

Solve each inequality. Round to the nearest ten-thousandth. 43. $\{x \mid x > 8.0105\}$

41. $e^x \leq 8.7$ $\{x \mid x \leq 2.1633\}$
42. $e^x \geq 42.1$ $\{x \mid x \geq 3.7400\}$
43. $\ln (3x + 4)^3 > 10$
44. $4 \ln x^2 < 72$
45. $\ln (8x^4) > 24$
46. $-2 [\ln (x - 6)^{-1}] \leq 6$ $\{x \mid 6 < x \leq 26.0855\}$

44. $\{x \mid -8103.0839 < x < 8103.0839, x \neq 0\}$
45. $\{x \mid x < -239.8802 \text{ or } x > 239.8802\}$

3 PRACTICE

Formative Assessment

Use Exercises 1–19 to check for understanding.

Use the chart at the bottom of this page to customize assignments for your students.

Tips for New Teachers

Reasonableness Encourage students to evaluate each solution to logarithmic equations and inequalities for reasonableness.

Differentiated Homework Options

Level	Assignment	Two-Day Option	
AL Basic	20–46, 59–82	21–45 odd, 63–66	20–46 even, 59–62, 67–82
OL Core	21–55 odd, 56–57, 59–82	20–46, 63–66	47–57, 59–62, 67–82
BL Advanced	47–76, (optional: 77–82)		

47. FINANCIAL LITERACY Use the formula for continuously compounded interest. **c. about 7.7%**

a. If you deposited \$800 in an account paying 4.5% interest compounded continuously, how much money would be in the account in 5 years? **\$1001.86**

b. How long would it take you to double your money? **about 15.4 yr**

c. If you want to double your money in 9 years, what rate would you need?

d. If you want to open an account that pays 4.75% interest compounded continuously and have \$10,000 in the account 12 years after your deposit, how much would you need to deposit? **about \$5655.25**

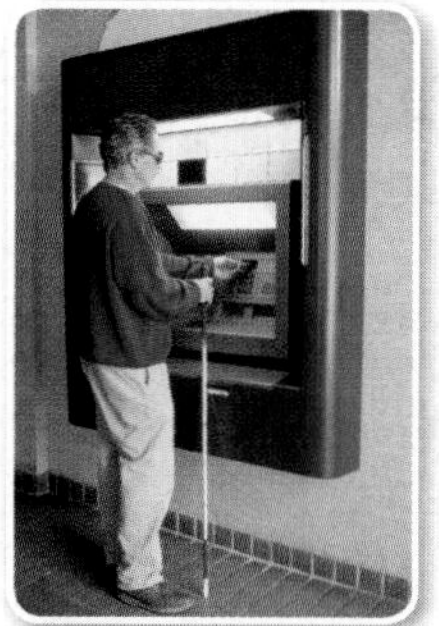

Real-World Link

Recently, the U.S. personal average saving rate was −1%. This means that Americans withdrew more money than they deposited.

Source: *Business Week*

Write the expression as a sum or difference of logarithms or multiples of logarithms.

48. $\ln 12x^2$ **$\ln 12 + 2 \ln x$**

49. $\ln \frac{16}{125}$ **$4 \ln 2 - 3 \ln 5$**

50. $\ln \sqrt[5]{x^3}$ **$\frac{3}{5} \ln x$**

51. $\ln xy^4z^{-3}$ **$\ln x + 4 \ln y - 3 \ln z$**

Use the natural logarithm to solve each equation.

52. $8^x = 24$ **1.5283**

53. $3^x = 0.4$ **−0.8340**

54. $2^{3x} = 18$ **1.3900**

55. $5^{2x} = 38$ **1.1301**

56. SCIENCE Newton's Law of Cooling, which can be used to determine how fast an object will cool in given surroundings, is represented by $T(t) = T_s + (T_0 - T_s)e^{-kt}$, where T_0 is the initial temperature of the object, T_s is the temperature of the surroundings, t is the time in minutes, and k is a constant value that depends on the type of object.

a. If a cup of coffee with an initial temperature of 180° is placed in a room with a temperature of 70°, then the coffee cools to 140° after 10 minutes, find the value of k. **0.045**

b. Use this value of k to determine the temperature of the coffee after 20 minutes.

c. When will the temperature of the coffee reach 75°? **about 68 min**

56b. about 114.7°

57. MULTIPLE REPRESENTATIONS In this problem, you will use $f(x) = e^x$ and $g(x) = \ln x$.

a. **GRAPHICAL** Graph both functions and their axis of symmetry, $y = x$, for $-5 \le x \le 5$. Then graph $a(x) = e^{-x}$ on the same graph. **See margin.**

b. **ANALYTICAL** The graphs of $a(x)$ and $f(x)$ are reflections along which axis? What function would be a reflection of $f(x)$ along the other axis? **y-axis; $a(x) = -e^x$**

c. **GRAPHICAL** Determine the two functions that are reflections of $g(x)$. Graph these new functions.

d. **VERBAL** We know that $f(x)$ and $g(x)$ are inverses. Are any of the other functions that we have graphed inverses as well? Explain your reasoning.

57c. $\ln(-x)$ is a reflection across the y-axis. $-\ln x$ is a reflection across the x-axis.

57d. Sample answer: no; These functions are reflections along $y = -x$, which indicates that they are not inverses.

60. Sample answer: Always; the graph of $y = x$ is always greater than the graph of $y = \ln x$ and the graphs never intersect.

62. Sample answer: The natural log and natural base are inverse functions, so taking the natural log of a natural base will *undo* the natural base and make the problem easier to solve.

H.O.T. Problems

Use **H**igher-**O**rder **T**hinking Skills

58. CHALLENGE Solve $4^x - 2^{x+1} = 15$ for x. **2.3219**

59. PROOF Prove $\ln ab = \ln a + \ln b$ for natural logarithms. **See margin.**

60. REASONING Determine whether $x > \ln x$ is *sometimes*, *always*, or *never* true. Explain your reasoning.

61. OPEN ENDED Express the value 3 using e^x and the natural log. **Sample answer: $e^{\ln 3}$**

62. WRITING IN MATH Explain how the natural log can be used to solve a natural base exponential function.

Study Guide and Intervention

CRM pp. 47–48 AL OL ELL

8-7 Study Guide and Intervention

Base e and Natural Logarithms

Base e and Natural Logarithms The irrational number $e \approx 2.71828...$ often occurs as the base for exponential and logarithmic functions that describe real-world phenomena.

Natural Base e	As n increases, $\left(1+\frac{1}{n}\right)^n$ approaches $e \approx 2.71828....$ $\ln x = \log_e x$

The functions $f(x) = e^x$ and $f(x) = \ln x$ are inverse functions.

Inverse Property of Base e and Natural Logarithms	$e^{\ln x} = x$ $\ln e^x = x$

Natural base expressions can be evaluated using the e^x and ln keys on your calculator.

Example 1 Write a logarithmic equation equivalent to $e^{2x} = 7$.

$e^{2x} = 7 \rightarrow \log_e 7 = 2x$

$2x = \ln 7$

Example 2 Write each logarithmic equation in exponential form.

a. $\ln x \approx 0.3345$

$\ln x \approx 0.3345 \rightarrow \log_e x \approx 0.3345$

$x \approx e^{0.3345}$

b. $\ln 42 = x$

$\ln 42 = x \rightarrow \log_e 10 = x$

$10 = e^x$

Exercises

Write an equivalent exponential or logarithmic equation.

1. $e^{15} = x$ **$\ln x = 15$**
2. $e^{3x} = 45$ **$3x = \ln 45$**
3. $\ln 20 = x$ **$e^x = 20$**
4. $\ln x = 8$ **$x = e^8$**
5. $e^{-5x} = 0.2$ **$-5x = \ln 0.2$**
6. $\ln(4x) = 9.6$ **$4x = e^{9.6}$**
7. $e^{8.2} = 10x$ **$\ln 10x = 8.2$**
8. $\ln 0.0002 = x$ **$e^x = 0.0002$**

Evaluate each logarithm to the nearest ten-thousandth.

9. ln 12,492 **9.4328**
10. ln 50.69 **3.9257**
11. ln 9275 **9.1351**
12. ln 0.835 **−0.1803**
13. ln 943 − ln 181 **1.6506**
14. ln 67 + ln 103 **8.8394**
15. ln 931 · ln 32 **23.6927**
16. ln (139 − 45) **4.5433**

Chapter 8 47 Glencoe Algebra 2

Lesson 8-7

Practice

CRM p. 50 AL OL BL ELL

8-7 Practice

Base e and Natural Logarithms

Write an equivalent exponential or logarithmic equation.

1. $\ln 50 = x$ **$e^x = 50$**
2. $\ln 36 = 2x$ **$e^{2x} = 36$**
3. $\ln 6 \approx 1.7918$ **$e^{1.7918} \approx 6$**
4. $\ln 9.3 \approx 2.2300$ **$e^{2.2300} \approx 9.3$**
5. $e^x = 8$ **$x = \ln 8$**
6. $e^5 = 10x$ **$5 = \ln 10x$**
7. $e^{-x} = 4$ **$x = -\ln 4$**
8. $e^2 = x + 1$ **$2 = \ln(x + 1)$**

Solve each equation or inequality. Round to four decimal places.

9. $e^x < 9$ **$\{x \mid x < 2.1972\}$**
10. $e^{-x} = 31$ **−3.4340**
11. $e^x = 1.1$ **0.0953**
12. $e^x = 5.8$ **1.7579**
13. $2e^x - 3 = 1$ **0.6931**
14. $5e^x + 1 \ge 7$ **$\{x \mid x \ge 0.1823\}$**
15. $4 + e^x = 19$ **2.7081**
16. $-3e^x + 10 < 8$ **$\{x \mid x > -0.4055\}$**
17. $e^{3x} = 8$ **0.6931**
18. $e^{-4x} = 5$ **−0.4024**
19. $e^{0.5x} = 6$ **3.5835**
20. $2e^{5x} = 24$ **0.4970**
21. $e^{2x} + 1 = 55$ **1.9945**
22. $e^{3x} - 5 = 32$ **1.2036**
23. $9 + e^{2x} = 10$ **0**
24. $e^{-3x} + 7 \ge 15$ **$\{x \mid x \le -0.6931\}$**
25. $\ln 4x = 3$ **5.0214**
26. $\ln(-2x) = 7$ **−548.3166**
27. $\ln 2.5x = 10$ **8810.5863**
28. $\ln(x - 6) = 1$ **8.7183**
29. $\ln(x + 2) = 3$ **18.0855**
30. $\ln(x + 3) = 5$ **145.4132**
31. $\ln 3x + \ln 2x = 9$ **36.7493**
32. $\ln 5x + \ln x = 7$ **14.8097**

33. **INVESTING** Sarita deposits \$1000 in an account paying 3.4% annual interest compounded continuously. Use the formula for continuously compounded interest, $A = Pe^{rt}$, where P is the principal, r is the annual interest rate, and t is the time in years.

a. What is the balance in Sarita's account after 5 years? **\$1185.30**

b. How long will it take the balance in Sarita's account to reach \$2000? **about 20.4 yr**

34. **RADIOACTIVE DECAY** The amount of a radioactive substance y that remains after t years is given by the equation $y = ae^{kt}$, where a is the initial amount present and k is the decay constant for the radioactive substance. If $a = 100$, $y = 50$, and $k = -0.035$, find t. **about 19.8 yr**

Chapter 8 50 Glencoe Algebra 2

Word Problem Practice

CRM p. 51 AL OL BL ELL

8-7 Word Problem Practice

Base e and Natural Logarithms

1. **INTEREST** Horatio opens a bank account that pays 2.3% annual interest compounded continuously. He makes an initial deposit of 10,000. What will be the balance of the account in 10 years? Assume that he makes no additional deposits and no withdrawals. **\$12,586**

2. **INTEREST** Janie's bank pays 2.8% annual interest compounded continuously on savings accounts. She placed \$2000 in the account. How long will it take for her initial deposit to double in value? Assume that she makes no additional deposits and no withdrawals. Round your answer to the nearest quarter year. **24.75 yr**

3. **BACTERIA** A bacterial population grows exponentially, doubling every 72 hours.

bacteria	x	2x	4x	8x
time	0	72	144	216

Let P be the initial population size and let t be time in hours. Write a formula using the natural base exponential function that gives the size of the population as a function of P and t. **$P = e^{\frac{\ln 2}{72}t}$**

4. **POPULATION** The equation $A = A_0e^{rt}$ describes the growth of the world's population where A is the population at time t, A_0 is the population at $t = 0$, and r is the annual growth rate. The world's population at the start of 2008 was estimated at 6,641,000,000. If the annual growth rate is 1.2%, when will the world population reach 9 billion? **2033**

5. **MONEY MANAGEMENT** Linda wants to invest \$20,000. She is looking at two possible accounts. Account A is a standard savings account that pays 3.4% annual interest compounded continuously. Account B would pay her a fixed amount of \$200 every quarter.

a. If Linda can invest the money for 5 years only, which account would give her the higher return on her investment? How much more money would she make by choosing the higher paying account? **Account B; she'll make \$24000 − \$23706.10 = \$293.90 more**

b. If Linda can invest the money for 10 years only, which account would give her the higher return on her investment? How much more money would she make by choosing the higher paying account? **Account A; she'll make \$28098.95 − \$28000 = \$98.95 more**

c. If Linda can invest the money for 20 years only, which account would give her the higher return on her investment? How much more money would she make by choosing the higher paying account? **Account A; she'll make \$39477.55 − \$36000 = \$3477.55 more**

Chapter 8 51 Glencoe Algebra 2

Lesson 8-7

Enrichment

CRM p. 52 OL BL

8-7 Enrichment

Approximations for π and e

The following expression can be used to approximate e. If greater and greater values of n are used, the value of the expression approximates e more and more closely.

$$\left(1 + \frac{1}{n}\right)^n$$

Another way to approximate e is to use this infinite sum. The greater the value of n, the closer the approximation.

$$e = 1 + 1 + \frac{1}{2} + \frac{1}{2 \cdot 3} + \frac{1}{2 \cdot 3 \cdot 4} + \ldots + \frac{1}{2 \cdot 3 \cdot 4 \cdot \ldots \cdot n} + \ldots$$

In a similar manner, π can be approximated using an infinite product discovered by the English mathematician John Wallis (1616–1703).

$$\frac{\pi}{2} = \frac{2}{1} \cdot \frac{2}{3} \cdot \frac{4}{3} \cdot \frac{4}{5} \cdot \frac{6}{5} \cdot \frac{6}{7} \cdot \ldots \cdot \frac{2n}{2n-1} \cdot \frac{2n}{2n+1} \cdots$$

Solve each problem.

1. Use a calculator with an e^x key to find e to 7 decimal places. **2.7182818**

2. Use the expression $\left(1 + \frac{1}{n}\right)^n$ to approximate e to 3 decimal places. Use 5, 100, 500, and 7000 as values of n. **2.488, 2.705, 2.716, 2.718**

Multiple Representations In Exercise 57, students use a graphing calculator and analysis to explore natural logarithmic functions.

530 Chapter 8 Exponential and Logarithmic Functions and Relations

NGSSS PRACTICE 912.A.3.15, 912.A.3.6

63. Given the function $y = 2.34x + 11.33$, which statement best describes the effect of moving the graph down two units? **B**

A. The x-intercept decreases.
B. The y-intercept decreases.
C. The x-intercept remains the same.
D. The y-intercept remains the same.

64. **GRIDDED RESPONSE** Aidan sells wooden picture frames over the Internet. He purchases materials for \$85 and pays \$19.95 for his website. If he charges \$15 each, how many frames will he need to sell in order to make a profit of at least \$270? **25**

65. Solve $|2x - 5| = 17$. **G**

F. $-6, -11$
G. $-6, 11$
H. $6, -11$
I. $6, 11$

66. A local pet store sells rabbit food. The cost of two 5-pound bags is \$7.99. The total cost c of purchasing n bags can be found by— **C**

A. multiplying n by c.
B. multiplying n by 5.
C. multiplying n by the cost of 1 bag.
D. dividing n by c.

Spiral Review

Solve each equation or inequality. Round to the nearest ten-thousandth. (Lesson 8-6)

67. $2^x = 53$ **5.7279**
68. $2.3^{x^2} = 66.6$ **± 2.2452**
69. $3^{4x-7} < 4^{2x+3}$ **$x < 7.3059$**
70. $6^{3y} = 8^{y-1}$ **-0.6309**
71. $12^{x-5} \geq 9.32$ **$x \geq 5.8983$**
72. $2.1^{x-5} = 9.32$ **8.0086**

73. SOUND Use the formula $L = 10 \log_{10} R$, where L is the loudness of a sound and R is the sound's relative intensity. Suppose the sound of one alarm clock is 80 decibels. Find out how much louder 10 alarm clocks would be than one alarm clock. (Lesson 8-5) **10 decibels**

Given a polynomial and one of its factors, find the remaining factors of the polynomial. Some factors may not be binomials. (Lesson 6-6)

74. $x^3 + 5x^2 + 8x + 4; x + 1$ **$x + 2, x + 2$**
75. $x^3 + 4x^2 + 7x + 6; x + 2$ **$x^2 + 2x + 3$**

76. CRAFTS Mrs. Hall is selling crocheted items. She sells large afghans for \$60, baby blankets for \$40, doilies for \$25, and pot holders for \$5. She takes the following number of items to the fair: 12 afghans, 25 baby blankets, 45 doilies, and 50 pot holders. (Lesson 4-3)

a. Write an inventory matrix for the number of each item and a cost matrix for the price of each item.

b. Suppose Mrs. Hall sells all of the items. Find her total income as a matrix. **[3095]**

76a. $\begin{bmatrix} 12 & 25 & 45 & 50 \end{bmatrix}$ $\begin{bmatrix} 60 \\ 40 \\ 25 \\ 5 \end{bmatrix}$

Skills Review

Solve each equation. (Lesson 9-2)

77. $2^{3x+5} = 128$ **$\frac{2}{3}$**
78. $5^{n-3} = \frac{1}{25}$ **1**
79. $\left(\frac{1}{9}\right)^m = 81^{m+4}$ **$-\frac{8}{3}$**
80. $\left(\frac{1}{7}\right)^{y-3} = 343$ **0**
81. $10^{x-1} = 100^{2x-3}$ **$\frac{5}{3}$**
82. $36^{2p} = 216^{p-1}$ **-3**

4 ASSESS

Name the Math Have each student write a natural logarithmic equation and a natural logarithmic inequality. Then have students write out all the steps for solving their problems.

Additional Answers

57a.

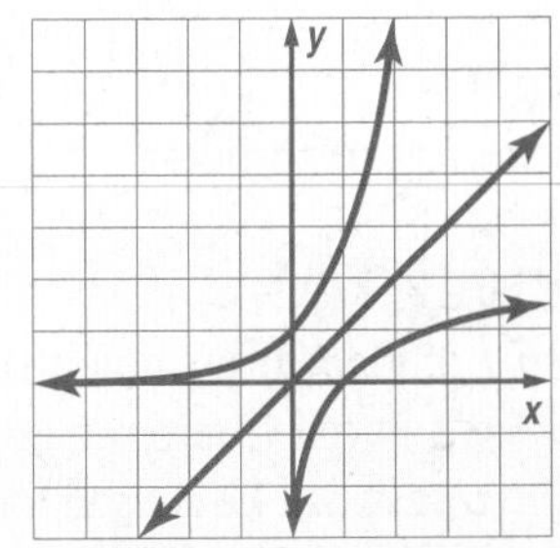

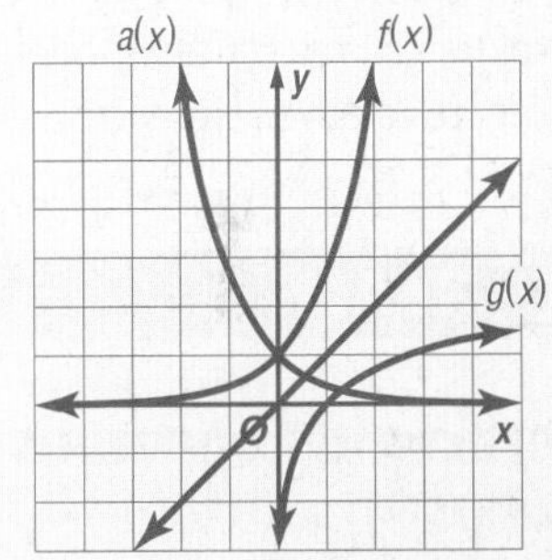

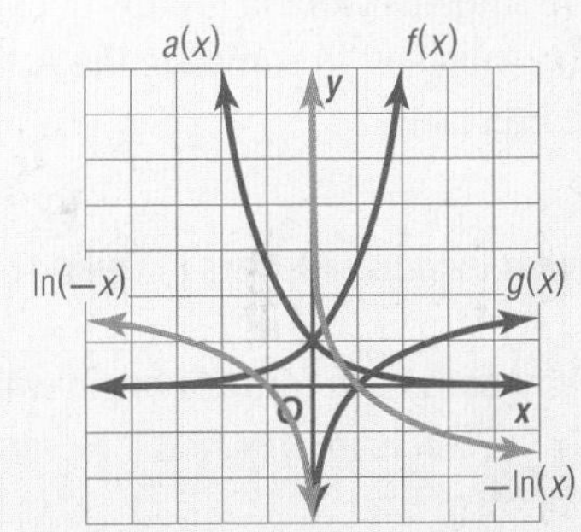

59. Let $p = \ln a$ and $q = \ln b$. That means that $e^p = a$ and $e^q = b$.

$ab = e^p \times e^q$
$ab = e^{p+q}$
$\ln(ab) = (p + q)$
$\ln(ab) = \ln a + \ln b$

Differentiated Instruction OL BL

Extension Explain to students that 2! means 2×1, 3! means $3 \times 2 \times 1$, 4! means $4 \times 3 \times 2 \times 1$, and so on. Ask students to use a calculator to find the value of the following series, for as many terms as they want:

$$1 + \frac{1}{1!} + \frac{1}{2!} + \frac{1}{3!} + \frac{1}{4!} + \ldots.$$

Discuss with students how the value of this series approaches the value of e. Point out that the series expressed to about 20 terms will give the accuracy for e that Euler gave. Euler, a Swiss mathematician, studied the number e in the 1720s.

1 FOCUS

Objective Use a spreadsheet to display the growth of an investment over time.

Materials for Each Student

- electronic spreadsheet

Teaching Tip

In Step 2 of the Activity, note that the dollar signs in cell C3 are required so that the rate in cell E2 is used for all cells in column C. This is called an "absolute cell reference," whereas all others are relative references.

2 TEACH

Working in Cooperative Groups

Have students work in groups of two, mixing abilities, to complete the Activity and Exercise 1.

Ask:

- What formula appears in cell A4? = A3 + 1
- Why does each formula begin with "="? Cell entries without "=" are not calculated.

Practice Have students complete Exercises 2–6.

3 ASSESS

Formative Assessment

Use Exercise 4 to assess whether students understand how to find yearly balances after annual compounding with different starting values and interest rates.

Compound Interest

FL Math Online glencoe.com
Other Calculator Keystrokes

You can use a spreadsheet to organize and display data. A spreadsheet is an easy way to track the amount of interest earned over a period of time.

Compound interest is earned not only on the original amount, but also on any interest that has been added to the principal.

ACTIVITY

Find the total amount of money after 5 years if you deposit $100 at 7% compounded annually.

Step 1 Label your columns as shown. The period is one year. Enter the starting values and the rate.

Step 2 Each row will be generated using formulas. Enter the formulas as shown.

Savings Account

	A	B	C	D	E
1	End of Period	Principal	Interest	Balance	Rate per Period
2	0			$100.00	7%
3	=A2+1	=D2	=B3*E2	=C3+D2	

Sheet 1 / Sheet 2 / Sheet 3

Step 3 Use the FILL DOWN function to fill 4 additional rows.

Savings Account

	A	B	C	D	E
1	End of Period	Principal	Interest	Balance	Rate per Period
2	0			$100.00	7%
3	1	$100.00	$7.00	$107.00	
4	2	$107.00	$7.49	$114.49	
5	3	$114.49	$8.01	$122.50	
6	4	$122.50	$8.58	$131.08	
7	5	$131.08	$9.18	$140.26	

Sheet 1 / Sheet 2 / Sheet 3

If you deposit $100 at 7% annual interest for 5 years, you will have $140.26 at the end of the 5 years.

Exercises

Find the total balance for each situation.

1. deposit $500 for 7 years at 5% **$703.55**
2. deposit $1000 for 5 years at 6% **$1338.23**
3. deposit $200 for 2 years at 10% **$242.00**
4. deposit $800 for 3 years at 8% **$1007.77**
5. borrow $10,000 for 5 years at 5.05% **$12,793.23**
6. borrow $25,000 for 30 years at 8% **$251,566.42**

From Concrete to Abstract

Use Exercise 5 to see if students recognize that borrowed amounts will increase the same as deposits if allowed to accumulate.

Extending the Concept

Ask:

- How could the spreadsheet be changed to reflect monthly compounding? Divide the amount in cell E2 by 12.
- How would the yearly balances compare to those in the original spreadsheet? greater

8-8 Using Exponential and Logarithmic Functions

Then
You used exponential growth and decay formulas. (Lesson 8-1)

Now
- Use logarithms to solve problems involving exponential growth and decay.
- Use logarithms to solve problems involving logistic growth.

NGSSS
MA.912.A.8.5 Solve logarithmic and exponential equations.
MA.912.A.8.7 Solve applications of exponential growth and decay.

New Vocabulary
rate of continuous growth
rate of continuous decay
logistic growth model

FL Math Online
glencoe.com

Why?

The ancient footprints of Acahualinca, discovered in Managua, Nicaragua, are believed to be the oldest human footprints in the world. Using carbon dating, scientists estimate that these footprints are 6000 years old.

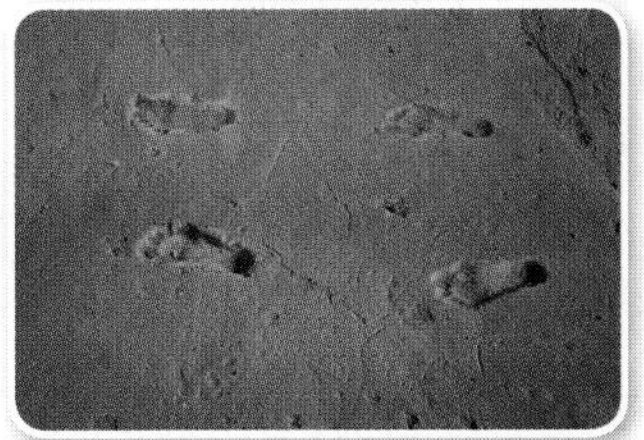

Exponential Growth and Decay Scientists and researchers frequently use alternate forms of the growth and decay formulas that you learned in Lesson 8-1.

Key Concept Exponential Growth and Decay

Exponential Growth	Exponential Decay
Exponential growth can be modeled by the function $f(x) = ae^{kt}$, where a is the initial value, t is time in years, and k is a constant representing the **rate of continuous growth**.	Exponential decay can be modeled by the function $f(x) = ae^{-kt}$, where a is the initial value, t is time in years, and k is a constant representing the **rate of continuous decay**.

Real-World EXAMPLE 1 Exponential Decay

SCIENCE The half-life of a radioactive substance is the time it takes for half of the atoms of the substance to disintegrate. The half-life of Carbon-14 is 5730 years. Determine the value of k and the equation of decay for Carbon-14.

If a is the initial amount of the substance, then the amount y that remains after 5730 years can be represented by $\frac{1}{2}a$ or $0.5a$.

$y = ae^{-kt}$	Exponential Decay Formula
$0.5a = ae^{-k(5730)}$	$y = 0.5a$ and $t = 5730$
$0.5 = e^{-5730k}$	Divide each side by a.
$\ln 0.5 = \ln e^{-5730k}$	Property of Equality for Logarithmic Functions
$\ln 0.5 = -5730k$	$\ln e^x = x$
$\frac{\ln 0.5}{-5730} = k$	Divide each side by -5730.
$0.00012 \approx k$	Use a calculator.

Thus, the equation for the decay of Carbon-14 is $y = ae^{-0.00012t}$.

Guided Practice 1. $k \approx 2.888 \cdot 10^{-5}$

1. The half-life of Plutonium-239 is 24,000 years. Determine the value of k.

Personal Tutor glencoe.com

8-8 Lesson Notes

1 FOCUS

Vertical Alignment

Before Lesson 8-8
Use exponential growth and decay formulas.

Lesson 8-8
Use logarithms to solve problems involving exponential growth and decay.
Use logarithms to solve problems involving logistic growth.

After Lesson 8-8
Simplify rational expressions.

2 TEACH

Scaffolding Questions

Have students read the *Why?* section of the lesson.

Ask:
- In what region is Nicaragua located? Central America
- Why can carbon be used for dating purposes? It decays over time in a measurable pattern.

Lesson 8-8 Resources

Resource	Approaching-Level	On-Level	Beyond-Level	English Learners
Teacher Edition	• Differentiated Instruction, p. 534	• Differentiated Instruction, pp. 534, 535, 539	• Differentiated Instruction, pp. 534, 535, 539	• Differentiated Instruction, p. 534
Chapter Resource Masters	• Study Guide and Intervention, pp. 53–54 • Skills Practice, p. 55 • Practice, p. 56 • Word Problem Practice, p. 57	• Study Guide and Intervention, pp. 53–54 • Skills Practice, p. 55 • Practice, p. 56 • Word Problem Practice, p. 57 • Enrichment, p. 58 • Spreadsheet Activity, p. 59	• Practice, p. 56 • Word Problem Practice, p. 57 • Enrichment, p. 58	• Study Guide and Intervention, pp. 53–54 • Skills Practice, p. 55 • Practice, p. 56 • Word Problem Practice, p. 57
Transparencies	• 5-Minute Check Transparency 8-8	• 5-Minute Check Transparency 8-8	• 5-Minute Check Transparency 8-8	• 5-Minute Check Transparency 8-8
Other	• Study Notebook	• Study Notebook	• Study Notebook	• Study Notebook

Exponential Growth and Decay

Examples 1 and 2 show how to use the algebraic model $y = ae^{-kt}$ to solve a problem involving exponential decay. **Example 3** shows how to use the algebraic model $y = ae^{kt}$ to solve a real-world problem involving exponential growth.

Formative Assessment

Use the Guided Practice exercises after each example to determine students' understanding of concepts.

Additional Examples

1 **GEOLOGY** The half-life of Sodium-22 is 2.6 years. Determine the value of k and the equation of decay for Sodium-22. $k \approx 0.2666$; $y = ae^{-0.2666t}$, where t is given in years

2 **GEOLOGY** A geologist examining a meteorite estimates that it contains only about 10% as much Sodium-22 as it would have contained when it reached Earth's surface. How long ago did the meteorite reach the surface of Earth? about 9 years ago

Additional Examples also in Interactive Classroom PowerPoint® Presentations

IWB INTERACTIVE WHITEBOARD READY

TEACH with TECH

WEB SEARCH Have students search the Web to find the half-life of different radioactive elements. Have them choose three elements and ask them to calculate the amount of a 500-gram sample that remains after 10 years.

Now that the value of k for Carbon-14 is known, it can be used to date fossils.

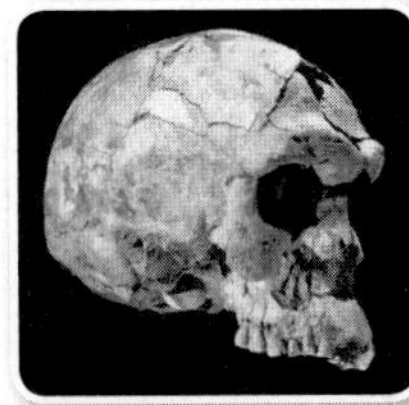

Real-World Link

The oldest modern human fossil, found in Ethiopia, is approximately 160,000 years old.

Source: National Public Radio

StudyTip

Carbon Dating When given a percent or fraction of decay, use an original amount of a or 1.

Real-World EXAMPLE 2 Carbon Dating

SCIENCE A paleontologist examining the bones of a prehistoric animal estimates that they contain 2% as much Carbon-14 as they would have contained when the animal was alive.

a. How long ago did the animal live?

Understand The formula for the decay of Carbon-14 is $y = ae^{-0.00012t}$. You want to find out how long ago the animal lived.

Plan Let a be the initial amount of Carbon-14 in the animal's body. The amount y that remains after t years is 2% of a or $0.02a$.

Solve

$y = ae^{-0.00012t}$	Formula for the decay of Carbon-14
$0.02a = ae^{-0.00012t}$	$y = 0.02a$
$0.02 = e^{-0.00012t}$	Divide each side by a.
$\ln 0.02 = \ln e^{-0.00012t}$	Property of Equality for Logarithmic Functions
$\ln 0.02 = -0.00012t$	$\ln e^x = x$
$\frac{\ln 0.02}{-0.00012} = t$	Divide each side by -0.00012.
$32{,}600 \approx t$	Use a calculator.

The animal lived about 32,600 years ago.

Check Use the formula to find the amount of a sample remaining after 32,600 years. Use an original amount of 1.

$y = ae^{-0.00012t}$	Original equation
$= 1e^{-0.00012(32{,}600)}$	$a = 1$ and $t = 32{,}600$
≈ 0.02 or 2% ✓	Use a calculator.

b. If prior research points to the animal being around 20,000 years old, how much Carbon-14 should be in the animal?

$y = ae^{-0.00012t}$	Formula for the decay of Carbon-14
$= 1e^{-0.00012(20{,}000)}$	$a = 1$ and $t = 20{,}000$
$= e^{-2.4}$	Simplify.
$= 0.09$ or 9%	Use a calculator.

Guided Practice

2. Use the information in Example 2 to answer the following.

A. A specimen that originally contained 42 milligrams of Carbon-14 now contains 8 milligrams. How old is the fossil? **about 13,819 yr**

B. A wooly mammoth specimen was thought to be about 12,000 years old. How much Carbon-14 should be in the animal? **about 23.7%**

Personal Tutor glencoe.com

The exponential growth equation $y = ae^{kt}$ is identical to the continuously compounded interest formula you learned in Lesson 8-7.

Continuous Compounding	Population Growth
$A = Pe^{rt}$	$y = ae^{kt}$
P = initial amount	a = initial population
A = amount at time t	y = population at time t
r = interest rate	k = rate of continuous growth

Differentiated Instruction

AL OL BL ELL

Logical Learners Have students work in pairs or small groups. Ask them to examine the growth and decay formulas used in Examples 1–3 and to discuss how the equations are related. In particular, ask them to discuss how they can identify which equations are used for exponential decay situations (minus/negative sign) and which are used for exponential growth.

534 Chapter 8 Exponential and Logarithmic Functions and Relations

Problem-SolvingTip

Use a Formula When dealing with population, it is almost always necessary to use an exponential growth or decay formula.

Real-World EXAMPLE 3 Continuous Exponential Growth

POPULATION In 2007, the population of Georgia was 9.36 million people. In 2000, it was 8.18 million.

a. Determine the value of k, Georgia's relative rate of growth.

$y = ae^{kt}$	**Formula for continuous exponential growth**
$9.36 = 8.18e^{k(7)}$	**$y = 9.36$, $a = 8.18$, and $t = 2007 - 2000$ or 7**
$\frac{9.36}{8.18} = e^{7k}$	**Divide each side by 8.18.**
$\ln \frac{9.36}{8.18} = \ln e^{7k}$	**Property of Equality for Logarithmic Functions**
$\ln \frac{9.36}{8.18} = 7k$	**$\ln e^x = x$**
$\frac{\ln \frac{9.36}{8.18}}{7} = k$	**Divide each side by 7.**
$0.01925 = k$	**Use a calculator.**

Georgia's relative rate of growth is about 0.01925 or about 2%.

b. When will Georgia's population reach 10 million people?

$y = ae^{kt}$	**Formula for continuous exponential growth**
$10 = 8.18e^{0.01925t}$	**$y = 10$, $a = 8.18$, and $k = 0.01925$**
$1.2225 = e^{0.01925t}$	**Divide each side by 8.18.**
$\ln 1.2225 = \ln e^{0.01925t}$	**Property of Equality for Logarithmic Functions**
$\ln 1.2225 = 0.01925t$	**$\ln e^x = x$**
$\frac{\ln 1.2225}{0.01925} = t$	**Divide each side by 0.01925.**
$10.436 \approx t$	**Use a calculator.**

Georgia's population will reach 10 million people by 2010.

StudyTip

Rounding Error In order to avoid any errors due to rounding, do not round until the very end of your calculations.

c. Michigan's population in 2000 was 9.9 million and can be modeled by $y = 9.9e^{0.0028t}$. Determine when Georgia's population will surpass Michigan's.

$8.18e^{0.01925t} > 9.9e^{0.0028t}$	**Formula for exponential growth**
$\ln 8.18e^{0.01925t} > \ln 9.9e^{0.0028t}$	**Property of Inequality for Logarithms**
$\ln 8.18 + \ln e^{0.01925t} > \ln 9.9 + \ln e^{0.0028t}$	**Product Property of Logarithms**
$\ln 8.18 + 0.01925t > \ln 9.9 + 0.0028t$	**$\ln e^x = x$**
$0.01645t > \ln 9.9 - \ln 8.18$	**Subtract $(0.0028t + \ln 8.18)$ from each side.**
$t > \frac{\ln 9.9 - \ln 8.18}{0.01645}$	**Divide each side by 0.01645.**
$t > 11.6$	**Use a calculator.**

Georgia's population will surpass Michigan's by the year 2012.

Guided Practice

3. BIOLOGY A type of bacteria is growing exponentially according to the model $y = 1000e^{kt}$, where t is the time in minutes.

A. If there are 1000 cells initially and 1650 cells after 40 minutes, find the value of k for the bacteria. $k \approx 0.0125$

B. Suppose a second type of bacteria is growing exponentially according to the model $y = 50e^{0.0432t}$. Determine how long it will be before the number of cells of this bacteria exceed the number of cells in the other bacteria. about 97.58 min

Personal Tutor glencoe.com

Focus on Mathematical Content

Exponential Growth and Decay The exponential decay formulas are of the form $y = a(1 - r)^t$, or $y = ae^{-kt}$. The exponential growth formulas are of the form $y = a(1 + r)^t$, or $y = ae^{kt}$. Logarithms can be used to solve problems involving exponential growth and decay.

Additional Example

3 **POPULATION** In 2007, the population of China was 1.32 billion. In 2000, it was 1.26 billion.

a. Determine the value of k, China's relative rate of growth. 0.0066

b. When will China's population reach 1.5 billion? in 2026

c. India's population in 2007 was 1.13 billion, and can be modeled by $1.13e^{0.015t}$. Determine when India's population will surpass China's. (Note: t represents years after 2007.) after 18.5 years, or midway through the year 2025

Differentiated Instruction OL BL

Extension Mathematically and scientifically talented students can research the growth rates of different bacteria types. Students can explore how these growth rates are determined, environmental factors that cause them to thrive or inhibit their prosperity, and graph the growth of different types for comparison purposes.

Logistic Growth

Example 4 shows how to use a logistic growth function to model growth with a limiting factor.

Additional Example

4 A city's population in millions is modeled by $f(t) = \dfrac{1.432}{1 + 1.05e^{-0.32t}}$, where t is the number of years since 2000.

a. Graph the function.

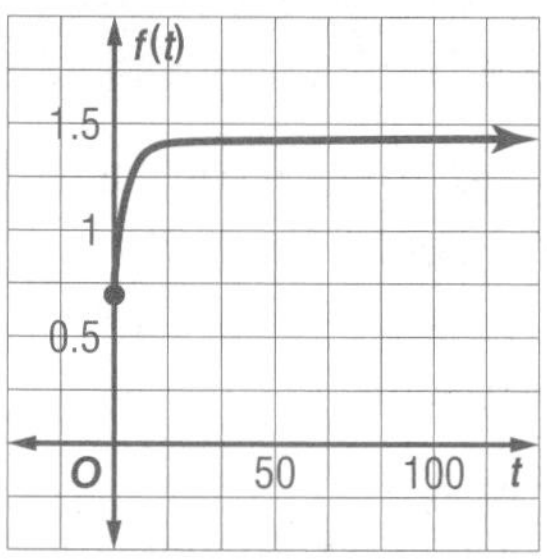

b. What is the horizontal asymptote? $f(t) = 1.432$

c. What will be the maximum population? 1,432,000.

d. According to the function, when will the city's population reach 1 million? 2003

Additional Answer (Guided Practice)

4A.

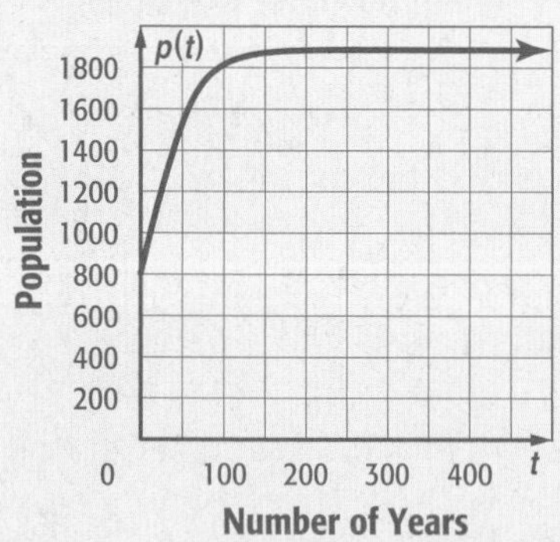

Logistic Growth Refer to the equation representing Georgia's population in Example 3. According to the graph at the right, Georgia's population will be about one billion by the year 2130. Does this seem logical?

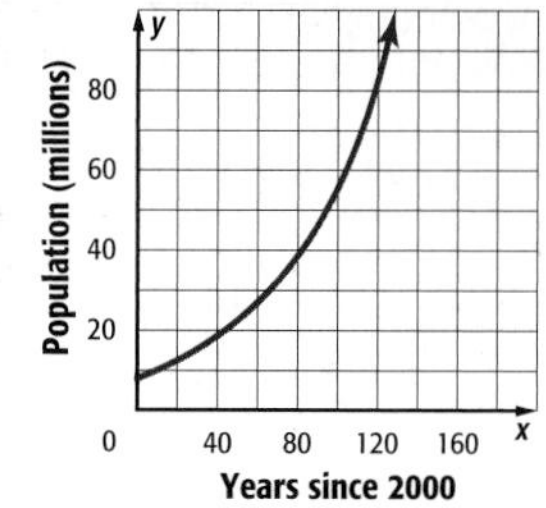

Populations cannot grow infinitely large. There are limitations, such as food supplies, war, living space, diseases, available resources, and so on.

Exponential growth is unrestricted, meaning it will increase without bound. A **logistic growth model**, however, represents growth that has a limiting factor. Logistic models are the most accurate models for representing population growth.

Key Concept — Logistic Growth Function

Let a, b, and c be positive constants where $b < 1$. The logistic growth function is represented by $f(t) = \dfrac{c}{1 + ae^{-bt}}$, where t represents time.

Real-World Link

Phoenix is the fifth largest city in the country and has a population of 1.5 million.

EXAMPLE 4 Logistic Growth

The population of Phoenix, Arizona, in millions can be modeled by the logistic function $f(t) = \dfrac{2.0666}{1 + 1.66e^{-0.048t}}$, where t is the number of years after 1980.

a. Graph the function for $0 \le t \le 500$.

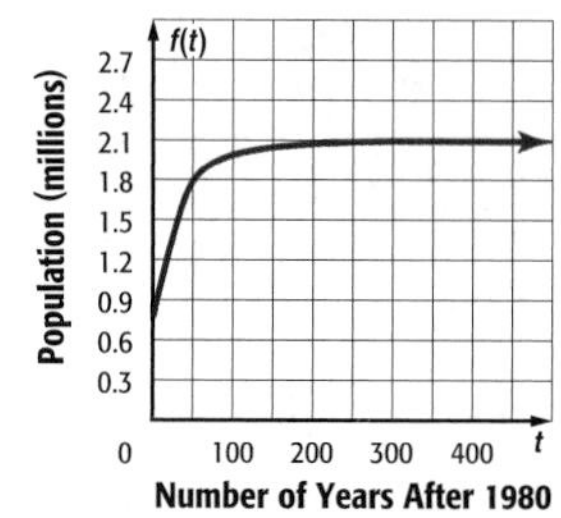

b. What is the horizontal asymptote?

The horizontal asymptote is at $y = 2.0666$.

c. Will the population of Phoenix increase indefinitely? If not, what will be their maximum population?

No. The population will reach a maximum of a little less than 2.0666 million people.

d. According to the function, when will the population of Phoenix reach 1.8 million people?

The graph indicates the population will reach 1.8 million people at $t \approx 50$. Replacing $f(t)$ with 1.8 and solving for t in the equation yields $t = 50.35$ years. So, the population of Phoenix will reach 1.8 million people by 2031.

StudyTip

Intersections To determine where the graph intersects 1.8 on the calculator, graph $y = 1.8$ on the same graph and select *intersection* in the CALC menu.

Guided Practice

4. The population of a certain species of fish in a lake after t years can be modeled by the function $P(t) = \dfrac{1880}{1 + 1.42e^{-0.037t}}$, where $t \ge 0$.

A. Graph the function for $0 \le t \le 500$. **See margin.**

B. What is the horizontal asymptote? **$y = 1880$**

C. What is the maximum population of the fish in the lake? **1880**

D. When will the population reach 1875? **about 170 yr**

Personal Tutor glencoe.com

Check Your Understanding

Examples 1 and 2 pp. 533–534

1. **PALEONTOLOGY** The half-life of Potassium-40 is about 1.25 billion years.
   a. Determine the value of k and the equation of decay for Potassium-40. **5.545×10^{-10}**
   b. A specimen currently contains 36 milligrams of Potassium-40. How long will it take the specimen to decay to only 15 milligrams of Potassium-40? **1,578,843,530 yr**
   c. How many milligrams of Potassium-40 will be left after 300 million years?
   d. How long will it take Potassium-40 to decay to one eighth of its original amount?

1c. about 30.48 mg
1d. 3,750,120,003 yr

Example 3 p. 535

2. **SCIENCE** A certain food is dropped on the floor and is growing bacteria exponentially according to the model $y = 2e^{kt}$, where t is the time in seconds. **b. about 2.828 cells**
   a. If there are 2 cells initially and 8 cells after 20 seconds, find the value of k for the bacteria. **$k \approx 0.0693$**
   b. The "5-second rule" says that if a person who drops food on the floor eats it within 5 seconds, there will be no harm. How much bacteria is on the food after 5 seconds?
   c. Would you eat food that had been on the floor for 5 seconds? Why or why not? Do you think that the information you obtained in this exercise is reasonable? Explain.

2c. Sample answer: Yes; it has not even grown 1 cell in 5 seconds. There are many factors that affect this equation, such as how clean the floor is and what type of food was dropped.

Example 4 p. 536

3. **ZOOLOGY** Suppose the red fox population in a restricted habitat follows the function $P(t) = \frac{16{,}500}{1 + 18e^{-0.085t}}$, where t represents the time in years.
   a. Graph the function for $0 \le t \le 200$. **See margin.**
   b. What is the horizontal asymptote? **$P(t) = 16{,}500$**
   c. What is the maximum population? **16,500**
   d. When does the population reach 16,450? **about 102 years**

Practice and Problem Solving

= Step-by-Step Solutions begin on page R20.
Extra Practice begins on page 947.

Examples 1 and 2 pp. 533–534

4. **SCIENCE** The half-life of Rubidium-87 is about 48.8 billion years.
   a. Determine the value of k and the equation of decay for Rubidium-87. **$k \approx 1.42 \times 10^{-11}$**
   b. A specimen currently contains 50 milligrams of Rubidium-87. How long will it take the specimen to decay to only 18 milligrams of Rubidium-87? **71,947,270,950 yr**
   c. How many milligrams of Rubidium-87 will be left after 800 million years?
   d. How long will it take Rubidium-87 to decay to one-sixteenth its original amount?

4c. about 49.4 mg
4d. 195.3 billion yr

Example 3 p. 535

5. **BIOLOGY** A certain bacteria is growing exponentially according to the model $y = 80e^{kt}$, where t is the time in minutes.
   a. If there are 80 cells initially and 675 cells after 30 minutes, find the value of k for the bacteria. **$k \approx 0.071$**
   b. When will the bacteria reach a population of 6000 cells? **about 60.8 min**
   c. If a second type of bacteria is growing exponentially according to the model $y = 35e^{0.0978t}$, determine how long it will be before the number of cells of this bacteria exceed the number of cells in the other bacteria. **about 30.85 min**

Example 4 p. 536

6. **FORESTRY** The population of trees in a certain forest follows the function $f(t) = \frac{18000}{1 + 16e^{-0.084t}}$, where t is the time in years.
   a. Graph the function for $0 \le t \le 100$. **See margin.**
   b. When does the population reach 17500 trees? **about 75.33 yr**

3 PRACTICE

Formative Assessment

Use Exercises 1–3 to check for understanding.

Use the chart at the bottom of this page to customize assignments for your students.

Additional Answers

3a.

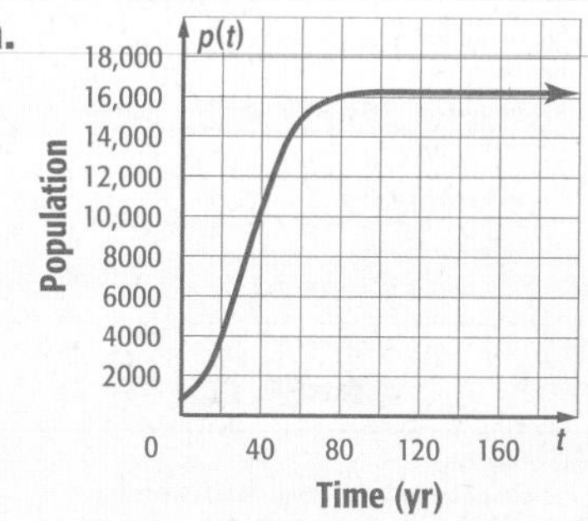

6a.

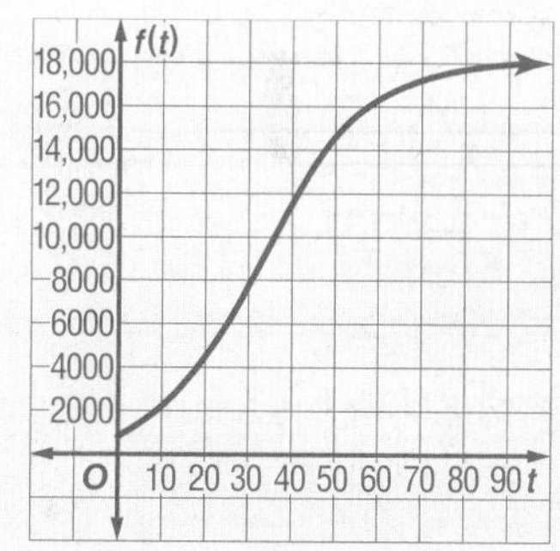

Differentiated Homework Options

Level	Assignment	Two-Day Option	
AL Basic	4–6, 14, 16–34	5, 19–22	4, 6, 14, 16–18, 23–34
OL Core	5, 7–14, 16–34	4–6, 19–22	7–14, 16–18, 23–34
BL Advanced	7–26, (optional: 27–34)		

Study Guide and Intervention
CRM pp. 53–54 AL OL ELL

8-8 Study Guide and Intervention
Using Exponential and Logarithmic Functions

Exponential Growth and Decay

Exponential Growth	$f(x) = ae^{kt}$ where a is the initial value of y, t is time in years, and k is a constant representing the **rate of continuous growth**.
Exponential Decay	$f(x) = ae^{-kt}$ where a is the initial value of y, t is time in years, and k is a constant representing **the rate of continuous decay**.

Example POPULATION **In 2000, the world population was estimated to be 6.124 billion people. In 2005, it was 6.515 billion.**

a. Determine the value of k, the world's relative rate of growth

$y = ae^{kt}$ — Formula for continuous growth.

$6.515 = 6.124e^{k(5)}$ — $y = 6.515$, $a = 6.124$, and $t = 2005 - 2000$ or 5

$\frac{6.515}{6.124} = e^{5k}$ — Divide each side by 6.124.

$\ln \frac{6.515}{6.124} = \ln e^{5k}$ — Property of Equality for Logarithmic Functions.

$\ln \frac{6.515}{6.124} = 5k$ — $\ln e^x = x$

$0.01238 = k$ — Divide each side by 5 and use a calculator.

The world's relative rate of growth is about 0.01238 or 1.2%

b. When will the world's population reach 7.5 billion people?

$7.5 = 6.124e^{0.01238t}$ — $y = 7.5$, $a = 6.124$, and $k = 0.01238$

$\frac{7.5}{6.124} = e^{0.01238t}$ — Divide each side by 6.124.

$\ln \frac{7.5}{6.124} = e^{0.01238t}$ — Property of Equality for Logarithmic Functions.

$\ln \frac{7.5}{6.124} = 0.01238t$ — $\ln e^x = x$

$16.3722 = t$ — Divide each side by 0.01238 and use a calculator.

The world's population will reach 7.5 billion in 2016

Exercises

1. **CARBON DATING** Use the formula $y = ae^{-0.00012t}$, where a is the initial amount of carbon 14, t is the number of years ago the animal lived, and y is the remaining amount after t years.
   a. How old is a fossil remain that has lost 95% of its Carbon-14? **about 25,000 years old**
   b. How old is a skeleton that has 95% of its Carbon-14 remaining? **about 427 years old**

Lesson 8-8

Practice
CRM p. 56 AL OL BL ELL

8-8 Practice
Using Exponential and Logarithmic Functions

1. **BACTERIA** How many hours will it take a culture of bacteria to increase from 20 to 2000? Use $k = 0.614$. **about 7.5 hr**
2. **RADIOACTIVE DECAY** A radioactive substance has a half-life of 32 years. Find the constant k in the decay formula for the substance. **about 0.02166**
3. **RADIOACTIVE DECAY** Cobalt, an element used to make alloys, has several isotopes. One of these, cobalt 60, is radioactive and has a half-life of 5.7 years. Cobalt 60 is used to trace the path of nonradioactive substances in a system. What is the value of k for cobalt 60? **about 0.1216**
4. **WHALES** Modern whales appeared 5–10 million years ago. The vertebrae of a whale discovered by paleontologists contain roughly 0.25% as much carbon-14 as they would have contained when the whale was alive. How long ago did the whale die? Use $k = 0.00012$. **about 50,000 yr**
5. **POPULATION** The population of rabbits in an area is modeled by the growth equation $P(t) = 8e^{0.26t}$, where P is in thousands and t is in years. How long will it take for the population to reach 25,000? **about 4.4 yr**
6. **RADIOACTIVE DECAY** A radioactive element decays exponentially. The decay model is given by the formula $A = A_0e^{-0.04463t}$. A is the amount present after t days and A_0 is the amount present initially. Assume you are starting with 50g. How much of the element remains after 10 days? 30 days? **about 32 g; about 13.1 g**
7. **POPULATION** A population is growing continuously at a rate of 3%. If the population is now 5 million, what will it be in 17 years' time? **about 8,326,455**
8. **BACTERIA** A certain bacteria is growing exponentially according to the model $y = 80e^{kt}$. Using $k = 0.071$, find how many hours it will take for the bacteria reach a population of 10,000 cells? **about 68 hr**
9. **LOGISTIC GROWTH** The population of a certain habitat follows the function:
   $P(t) = \frac{16{,}300}{(1 + 17.5e^{-0.065t})}$
   a. What is the maximum population? **16,300**
   b. When does the population reach 16,200? **$t = 122.3$**

Word Problem Practice
CRM p. 57 AL OL BL ELL

8-8 Word Problem Practice
Using Exponential and Logarithmic Functions

1. **PROGRAMMING** For reasons having to do with speed, a computer programmer wishes to model population size using a natural base exponential function. However, the programmer is told that the users of the program will be thinking in terms of the annual percentage increase. Let r be the percentage that the population increases each year. Find the value for k in terms of r so that
   $e^k = 1 + r.$
   $k = \ln(1 + r)$
2. **CARBON DATING** Archeologists uncover an ancient wooden tool. They analyze the tool and find that it has 22% as much carbon 14 compared to the likely amount that it contained when it was made. Given that the half-life of carbon 14 is about 5730 years, about how old is the artifact? Round your answer to the nearest 100 years.
   12,500 yr
3. **POPULATION** The doubling time of a population is d years. The population size can be modeled by an exponential equation of the form Pe^{kt}, where P is the initial population size and t is time. What is k in terms of d?
   $k = \frac{1}{d}\ln 2$
4. **POPULATION** Louisa read that the population of her town has increased steadily at a rate of 2% each year. Today, the population of her town has grown to 68,735.

Population	68,735	67,387	66,066	64,770
Year	Today	−1	−2	−3

   Based on this information, what was the population of her town 100 years ago?
   About 9,488 people.

5. **CONSUMER AWARENESS** Jason wants to buy a brand new high-definition (HD) television. He could buy one now because he has \$7000 to spend, but he thinks that if he waits, the quality of HD televisions will improve. His \$7000 earns 2.5% interest annually compounded continuously. The television he wants to buy costs \$5000 now, but the cost increases each year by 7%.
   a. Write a natural base exponential function that gives the value of Jason's account as a function of time t.
   $7000e^{0.025t}$
   b. Write a natural base exponential function that gives the cost of the television Jason wants as a function of time t.
   $5000e^{(\ln 1.07)t}$
   c. In how many years will the cost of the television exceed the value of the money in Jason's account? In other words, how much time does Jason have to decide whether he wants to buy the television? Round your answer to the nearest tenth of a year.
   7.9 yr
6. **LOGISTIC GROWTH** The population of a bacteria, in thousands, can be modeled by $P(t) = \frac{22{,}000}{(1 + 1.2e^{-kt})}$ where t is time in hours and k is a constant.
   a. After 1 hour the bacteria population is 10,532, what is the value of k?
   0.0971
   b. When does the population reach 21,900?
   $t = 57.3$ hr

Lesson 8-8

B 7. **PALEONTOLOGY** A paleontologist finds a human bone and determines that the Carbon-14 found in the bone is 85% of that found in living bone tissue. How old is the bone? **about 1354 yr old**

8. **ANTHROPOLOGY** An anthropologist has determined that a newly discovered human bone is 8000 years old. How much of the original amount of Carbon-14 is in the bone? **about 38%**

9. **RADIOACTIVE DECAY** 100 milligrams of Uranium-238 are stored in a container. If Uranium-238 has a half-life of about 4.47 billion years, after how many years will only 10 milligrams be present? **about 14.85 billion yr**

10. **POPULATION GROWTH** The population of the state of Oregon has grown from 3.4 million in 2000 to 3.7 million in 2006.
    a. Write an exponential growth equation of the form $y = ae^{kt}$ for Oregon, where t is the number of years after 2000. **$y = 3.4e^{0.014t}$**
    b. Use your equation to predict the population of Oregon in 2020. **4.5 million**
    c. According to the equation, when will Oregon reach 6 million people? **about 2041**

11. **HALF-LIFE** A substance decays 99.9% of its total mass after 200 years. Determine the half-life of the substance. **about 20.1 yr**

C 12. **LOGISTIC GROWTH** The population in millions of the state of Ohio after 1900 can be modeled by $P(t) = \frac{12.95}{1 + 2.4e^{-kt}}$, where t is the number of years after 1900 and k is a constant.
    a. If Ohio had a population of 10 million in 1970, find the value of k. **$k \approx 0.0299464$**
    b. According to the equation, when will the population of Ohio reach 12 million? **2014**

13. **MULTIPLE REPRESENTATIONS** In this problem, you will explore population growth. The population growth of a country follows the exponential function $f(t) = 8e^{0.075t}$ or the logistic function $g(t) = \frac{400}{1 + 16e^{-0.025t}}$. The population is measured in millions and t is time in years.
    a. **GRAPHICAL** Graph both functions for $0 \le t \le 100$. **See margin.**
    b. **ANALYTICAL** Determine the intersection of the graphs. What is the significance of this intersection?
    c. **ANALYTICAL** Which function is a more accurate estimate of the country's population 100 years from now? Explain your reasoning.

14. Sample answer: money in a bank; See students' work.

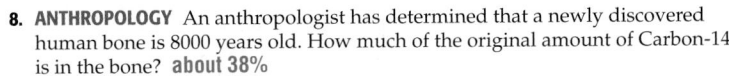

Real-World Link

Oregon is known as "The Beaver State," and has a beaver pictured on the reverse side of its state flag. Oregon is the only state in the union that has a different pattern on the reverse side of its flag.

Source: *Oregon Blue Book*

13b. The graphs intersect at $t = 20.79$. Sample answer: This intersection indicates the point at which both functions determine the same population at the same time.

13c. Sample answer: The logistic function $g(t)$ is a more accurate estimate of the country's population since $f(t)$ will continue to grow exponentially and $g(t)$ considers limitations on population growth such as food supply.

16. Sample answer: As $t \to +\infty$, $e^{-t} \to 0$. So, the denominator approaches $1 + 0$ or 1. As the denominator approaches 1, $f(r) \to \frac{c}{1}$ or c. However, since e^{-t} never reaches 0, $f(t)$ can never reach c.

H.O.T. Problems
Use **H**igher-**O**rder **T**hinking Skills

14. **OPEN ENDED** Give an example of a quantity that grows or decays at a fixed rate. Write a real-world problem involving the rate and solve by using logarithms.

15. **CHALLENGE** Solve $\frac{120{,}000}{1 + 48e^{-0.015t}} = 24e^{0.055t}$ for t. **$t \approx 113.45$**

16. **REASONING** Explain mathematically why $f(t) = \frac{c}{1 + 60e^{-0.5t}}$ approaches, but never reaches the value of c as $t \to +\infty$.

17. **OPEN ENDED** Give an example of a quantity that grows logistically and has limitations to growth. Explain why the quantity grows in this manner. **See margin.**

18. **WRITING IN MATH** Summarize the differences between exponential, continuous exponential, and logistic growth. **See margin.**

Enrichment
CRM p. 58 OL BL

8-8 Enrichment

Effective Annual Yield

When interest is compounded more than once per year, the effective annual yield is higher than the annual interest rate. The effective annual yield, E, is the interest rate that would give the same amount of interest if the interest were compounded once per year. If P dollars are invested for one year, the value of the investment at the end of the year is $A = P(1 + E)$. If P dollars are invested for one year at a nominal rate r compounded n times per year, the value of the investment at the end of the year is $A = P\left(1 + \frac{r}{n}\right)^n$. Setting the amounts equal and solving for E will produce a formula for the effective annual yield.

$P(1 + E) = P\left(1 + \frac{r}{n}\right)^n$

$1 + E = \left(1 + \frac{r}{n}\right)^n$

$E = \left(1 + \frac{r}{n}\right)^n - 1$

If compounding is continuous, the value of the investment at the end of one year is $A = Pe^r$. Again set the amounts equal and solve for E. A formula for the effective annual yield under continuous compounding is obtained.

$P(1 + E) = Pe^r$

$1 + E = e^r$

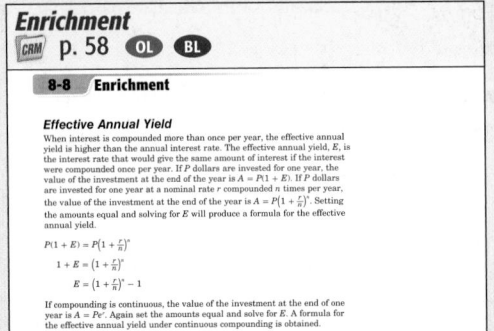

Multiple Representations In Exercise 13, students use a graphing, calculator and algebra to solve a higher-level equation algebraically and graphically and compare the results.

NGSSS PRACTICE 912.G.6.4, 912.P.3.1

19. Kareem is making a circle graph showing the favorite ice cream flavors of customers at his store. The table summarizes the data. What central angle should Kareem use for the section representing chocolate? C

Flavor	Customers
chocolate	35
vanilla	42
strawberry	7
mint chip	12
butter pecan	4

A. 35° C. 126°
B. 63° D. 150°

20. PROBABILITY Lydia has 6 books on her bookshelf. Two are literature books, one is a science book, two are math books, and one is a dictionary. What is the probability that she randomly chooses a science book and the dictionary? I

F. $\frac{1}{3}$ H. $\frac{1}{12}$
G. $\frac{1}{4}$ I. $\frac{1}{15}$

21. ACT/SAT Peter has made a game for his daughter's birthday party. The playing board is a circle divided evenly into 8 sectors. If the circle has a radius of 18 inches, what is the approximate area of one of the sectors? C

A. 4 in^2 C. 127 in^2
B. 32 in^2 D. 254 in^2

22. STATISTICS In a survey of 90 physical trainers, 15 said they went for a run at least 5 times per week. Of that group, 5 said they also swim during the week, and at least 25% of all trainers run and swim every week. Which conclusion is valid based on the information given? H

F. The report is accurate because 15 out of 90 is 25%.
G. The report is accurate because 5 out of 15 is 33%, which is at least 25%.
H. The report is inaccurate because 5 out of 90 is only 5.6%.
I. The report is inaccurate because no one knows if swimming is really exercising.

Spiral Review

Write an equivalent exponential or logarithmic equation. (Lesson 8-7)

23. $e^7 = y$ $\ln y = 7$
24. $e^{2n-4} = 36$ $\ln 36 = 2n - 4$
25. $\ln 5 + 4 \ln x = 9$ $5x^4 = e^9$

26a. Armenia and Yugoslavia, or Turkey and Armenia; Turkey and Yugoslavia

26. EARTHQUAKES The table shows the magnitude of some major earthquakes. (Lessons 8-5 and 8-6)

Year	Location	Magnitude
1939	Turkey	8.0
1963	Yugoslavia	6.0
1970	Peru	7.8
1988	Armenia	7.0
2004	Morocco	6.4

a. For which two earthquakes was the intensity of one 10 times that of the other? For which two was the intensity of one 100 times that of the other?

b. What would be the magnitude of an earthquake that is 1000 times as intense as the 1963 earthquake in Yugoslavia? 9.0

c. Suppose you know that $\log_7 2 \approx 0.3562$ and $\log_7 3 \approx 0.5646$. Describe two different methods that you could use to approximate $\log_7 2.5$. (You may use a calculator, of course.) Then describe how you can check your result. See margin.

Skills Review

Solve each equation. Write in simplest form. (Lesson 1-3)

27. $\frac{8}{5}x = \frac{4}{15}$ $\frac{1}{6}$
28. $\frac{27}{14}n = \frac{6}{7}$ $\frac{4}{9}$
29. $\frac{3}{10} = \frac{12}{25}a$ $\frac{5}{8}$
30. $\frac{6}{7} = 9p$ $\frac{2}{21}$
31. $\frac{9}{8}b = 18$ 16
32. $\frac{6}{7}y = \frac{3}{4}$ $\frac{7}{8}$
33. $\frac{1}{3}z = \frac{5}{6}$ $2\frac{1}{2}$
34. $\frac{2}{3}q = 7$ $10\frac{1}{2}$

4 ASSESS

Ticket Out the Door Ask students to write questions that can be solved using $y = ae^{kt}$ on one side of an index card. Then have students solve their problems on the reverse sides of the cards.

Formative Assessment

Check for student understanding of concepts in Lessons 8-7 and 8-8.

CRM Quiz 4, p. 64

Additional Answers

13a.

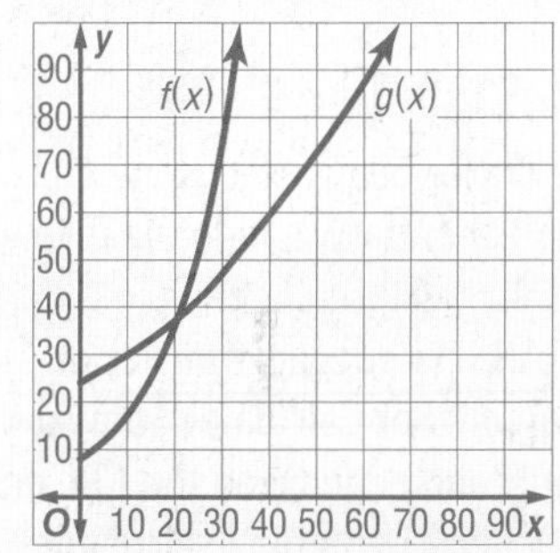

17. Sample answer: The spread of the flu throughout a small town. The growth of this is limited to the population of the town itself.

18. Sample answer: Exponential growth incorporates a percentage of growth per year. Continuous exponential growth incorporates the fact that population grows *continuously*. Logistic growth is the most accurate long-term measurement of population growth since it incorporates limitations on growth.

26c. Sample answer: Method 1: Use the Change of Base Formula and find that the value is about 0.4709. Method 2: Use the values $\log_7 2 \approx 0.3562$ and $\log_7 3 \approx 0.5646$. First, average the values and then guess and check by raising 7 to the various powers. Continue until you get the desired closeness to 2.5. To check find $7^{0.4709}$ which is very close to 2.5.

Differentiated Instruction OL BL

Extension *Catenary curves* are curves similar to those formed by a chain hanging between two hooks. Every segment of chain pulls on every other segment of chain, giving the hanging chain its curved shape. The Gateway Arch in St. Louis, Missouri is an example of an inverted catenary curve. Ask students to use graphing calculators to graph $y = \frac{e^x + e^{-x}}{2}$ to see a model of a catenary curve.

EXTEND 8-8 Lesson Notes

1 FOCUS

Objective Use a data collection device to investigate the differences between types of insulated cups and cooling time.

Materials

- TI-83/84 Plus graphing calculator
- data collection device and compatible temperature probe
- variety of containers
- very hot water

Teaching Tip

If the device being used is the Calculator-Based Laboratory 2, note the following: The CBL has three keys:

- [TRANSFER] begins transfer of programs of Calculator Software Applications between the CBL and an attached TI graphing calculator.
- [QUICK SET-UP] clears any data stored in CBLs memory.
- [START/STOP] begins sampling for Quick Set-Up. Sampling continues until the number of samples is collected or you press [START/STOP].

2 TEACH

Working in Cooperative Groups

Put students in groups of three or four, mixing abilities. Then have groups complete the Activity and Exercises 1–4.

- To set up the calculator and CBL for data collection, select **Collect Data** from the Main Menu. Select **Time Graph** from the **Data Collection** menu. Enter 60 as the time between samples in seconds. Then enter 20 as the number of samples (the CBL will collect data for a total of 1200 seconds). Press ENTER, then select **Use Time Setup** to continue.
- Discuss with students the **Ymin** and the **Ymax** and the **Yscl** that are appropriate for this lab.

EXTEND 8-8 Graphing Technology Lab: Cooling

In this lab, you will explore the type of equation that models the change in the temperature of water as it cools under various conditions.

Set Up the Lab

- Collect a variety of containers, such as a foam cup, a ceramic coffee mug, and an insulated cup.
- Boil water or collect hot water from a tap.
- Choose a container to test and fill with hot water. Place the temperature probe in the cup.
- Connect the temperature probe to your data collection device.

ACTIVITY Description

Step 1 Program the device to collect 20 or more samples in 1 minute intervals.

Step 2 Wait a few seconds for the probe to warm to the temperature of the water.

Step 3 Press the button to begin collecting data.

Analyze the Results

3. Sample answer: No; the temperature will approach the temperature of the room but it will not drop below it.

1. When the data collection is complete, graph the data in a scatter plot. Use time as the independent variable and temperature as the dependent variable. Write a sentence that describes the points on the graph. **Sample answer: It's an exponential pattern.**
2. Use the **STAT** menu to find an equation to model the data you collected. Try linear, quadratic, and exponential models. Which model appears to fit the data best? Explain. **Sample answer: The exponential model fits best. Its correlation coefficient is closest to 1.**
3. Would you expect the temperature of the water to drop below the temperature of the room? Explain your reasoning.
4. Use the data collection device to find the temperature of the air in the room. Graph the function $y = t$, where t is the temperature of the room, along with the scatter plot and the model equation. Describe the relationship among the graphs. What is the meaning of the relationship in the context of the experiment?

4. Sample answer: The linear graph of the room temperature is the asymptote for the exponential graph. The temperature of the water will approach the temperature of the room, but it will not go below that temperature.

Make a Conjecture

5. Sample answer: Yes; the thermal container will slow the rate of cooling.

5. Do you think the results of the experiment would change if you used an insulated container for the water? Repeat the experiment to verify your conjecture.
6. How might the results of the experiment change if you added ice to the water? Repeat the experiment to verify your conjecture. **Sample answer: The ice will speed the rate of cooling.**

Practice Have groups complete Exercises 5–6.

3 ASSESS

Formative Assessment

In Exercise 5, check that students have used different containers, but the same initial water temperature. Ask students why it is necessary to begin the second experiment with water at the same temperature as the first experiment.

From Concrete to Abstract

Have students describe the containers that make the best insulators.

540 Chapter 8 Exponential and Logarithmic Functions and Relations

FL Math Online glencoe.com
• STUDY TO GO
• Vocabulary Review

CHAPTER 8 Study Guide and Review

Chapter Summary

Key Concepts

Exponential Functions (Lessons 8-1 and 8-2)

- An exponential function is in the form $y = ab^x$, where $a \neq 0$, $b > 0$ and $b \neq 1$.
- Property of Equality for Exponential Functions: If b is a positive number other than 1, then $b^x = b^y$ if and only if $x = y$.
- Property of Inequality for Exponential Functions: If $b > 1$, then $b^x > b^y$ if and only if $x > y$, and $b^x < b^y$ if and only if $x < y$.

Logarithms and Logarithmic Functions (Lessons 8-3 through 8-6)

- Suppose $b > 0$ and $b \neq 1$. For $x > 0$, there is a number y such that $\log_b x = y$ if and only if $b^y = x$.
- The logarithm of a product is the sum of the logarithms of its factors.
- The logarithm of a quotient is the difference of the logarithms of the numerator and the denominator.
- The logarithm of a power is the product of the logarithm and the exponent.
- The Change of Base Formula: $\log_a n = \frac{\log_b n}{\log_b a}$

Natural Logarithms (Lesson 8-7)

- Since the natural base function and the natural logarithmic function are inverses, these two can be used to "undo" each other.

Using Exponential and Logarithmic Functions (Lesson 8-8)

- Exponential growth can be modeled by the function $f(x) = ae^{kt}$, where k is a constant representing the rate of continuous growth.
- Exponential decay can be modeled by the function $f(x) = ae^{-kt}$, where k is a constant representing the rate of continuous decay.

FOLDABLES® Study Organizer

Be sure the Key Concepts are noted in your Foldable.

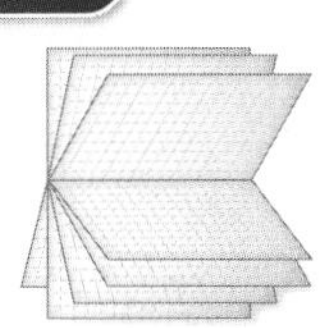

Key Vocabulary

- **asymptote** (p. 475)
- **Change of Base Formula** (p. 518)
- **common logarithm** (p. 516)
- **compound interest** (p. 486)
- **decay factor** (p. 478)
- **exponential decay** (p. 477)
- **exponential equation** (p. 485)
- **exponential function** (p. 475)
- **exponential growth** (p. 475)
- **exponential inequality** (p. 487)
- **growth factor** (p. 477)
- **logarithmic equation** (p. 502)
- **logarithmic function** (p. 493)
- **logarithmic inequality** (p. 503)
- **logarithm** (p. 492)
- **logistic growth model** (p. 536)
- **natural base, e** (p. 525)
- **natural base exponential function** (p. 525)
- **natural logarithm** (p. 525)
- **rate of continuous decay** (p. 533)
- **rate of continuous growth** (p. 533)

5. change of base formula
6. decay factor
9. natural logarithm

Vocabulary Check

Choose a word or term from the list above that best completes each statement or phrase.

1. A function of the form $f(x) = b^x$ where $b > 1$ is a(n) ________ function. exponential growth
2. In $x = b^y$, the variable y is called the ________ of x. logarithm
3. Base 10 logarithms are called ________. common logarithms
4. A(n) ________ is an equation in which variables occur as exponents. exponential equation
5. The ________ allows you to write equivalent logarithmic expressions that have different bases.
6. The base of the exponential function, $A(t) = a(1 - r)^t$, $1 - r$ is called the ________.
7. The function $y = \log_b x$, where $b > 0$ and $b \neq 1$, is called a(n) ________. logarithmic function
8. An exponential function with base e is called the ________. natural base exponential function
9. The logarithm with base e is called the ________.
10. The number e is referred to as the ________. natural base

Formative Assessment

Key Vocabulary The page references after each word denote where that term was first introduced. If students have difficulty answering questions 1–10, remind them that they can use these page references to refresh their memories about the vocabulary.

Summative Assessment

CRM Vocabulary Test, p. 66

FL Math Online glencoe.com

Vocabulary PuzzleMaker improves students' mathematics vocabulary using four puzzle formats—crossword, scramble, word search using a word list, and word search using clues. Students can work online or from a printed worksheet.

FOLDABLES® Study Organizer

Dinah Zike's Foldables®

Have students look through the chapter to make sure they have included examples in their Foldables.

Suggest that students keep their Foldables handy while completing the Study Guide and Review pages. Point out that their Foldables can serve as a quick review tool when studying for the chapter test.

Lesson-by-Lesson Review

Intervention If the given examples are not sufficient to review the topics covered by the questions, remind students that the page references tell them where to review that topic in their textbook.

Two-Day Option Have students complete the Lesson-by-Lesson Review on pp. 542–544. Then you can use ExamView® Assessment Suite to customize another review worksheet that practices all the objectives of this chapter or only the objectives on which your students need more help.

Differentiated Instruction

Super DVD: MindJogger Videoquizzes Use this DVD as an alternative format of review for the test.

Additional Answers

11.
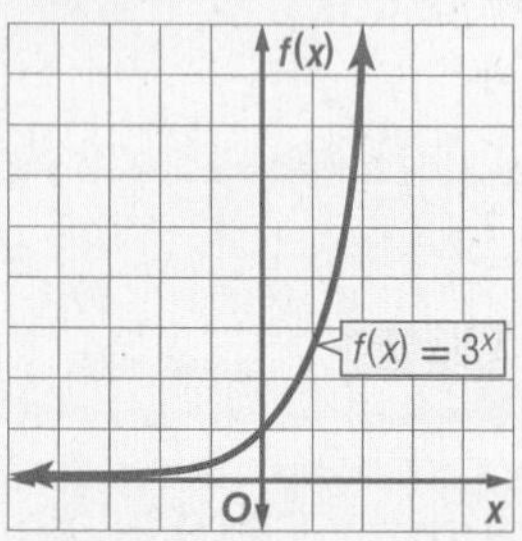

D = {all real numbers}
R = {$f(x)$ | $f(x) > 0$}

12.
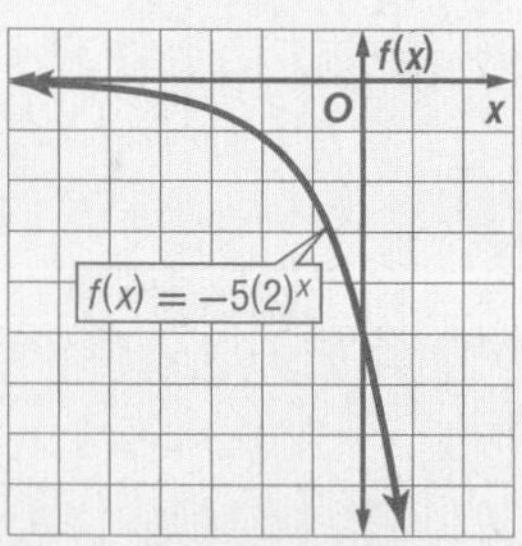

D = {all real numbers}
R = {$f(x)$ | $f(x) < 0$}

13.
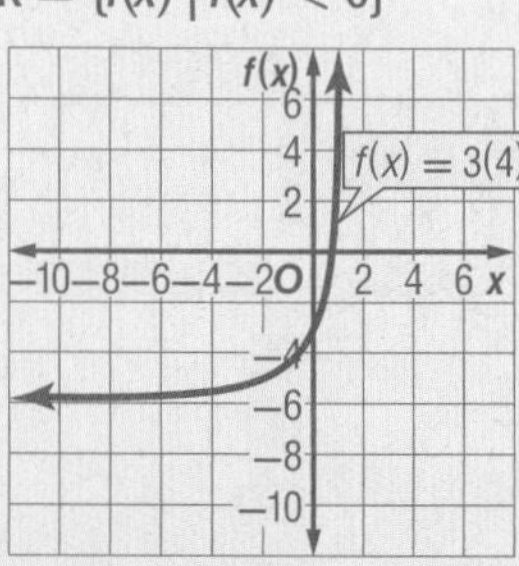

D = {all real numbers}
R = {$f(x)$ | $f(x) > -6$}

Lesson-by-Lesson Review

8-1 Graphing Exponential Functions (pp. 475–482)

912.A.8.3, 912.A.8.7

Graph each function. State the domain and range.

11. $f(x) = 3^x$
12. $f(x) = -5(2)^x$
13. $f(x) = 3(4)^x - 6$
14. $f(x) = 3^{2x} + 5$
15. $f(x) = 3\left(\frac{1}{4}\right)^{x+3} - 1$
16. $f(x) = \frac{3}{5}\left(\frac{2}{3}\right)^{x-2} + 3$

11–16. See margin.

17. **POPULATION** A city with a population of 120,000 decreases at a rate of 3% annually.
    a. Write the function that represents this situation. **$f(x) = 120{,}000(0.97)^x$**
    b. What will the population be in 10 years? **about 88,491**

EXAMPLE 1

Graph $f(x) = -2(3)^x + 1$. State the domain and range.

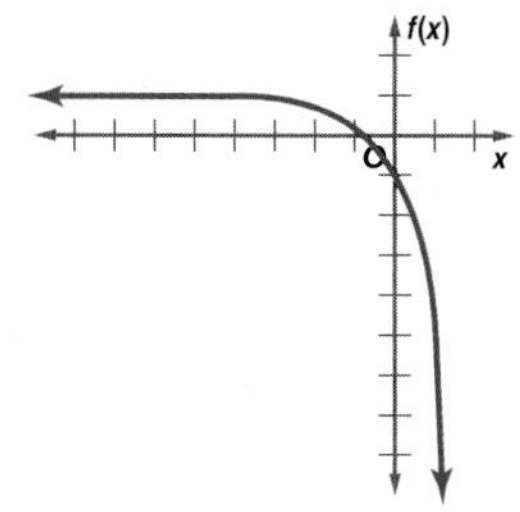

The domain is all real numbers, and the range is all real numbers less than 1.

8-2 Solving Exponential Equations and Inequalities (pp. 485–491)

912.A.8.5, 912.A.10.3

Solve each equation or inequality. **20. $-\frac{3}{4}$**

18. $16^x = \frac{1}{64}$ **$-\frac{3}{2}$**
19. $3^{4x} = 9^{3x+7}$ **−7**
20. $64^{3n} = 8^{2n-3}$
21. $8^{3-3y} = 256^{4y}$ **$\frac{9}{41}$**
22. $9^{x-2} > \left(\frac{1}{81}\right)^{x+2}$
23. $27^{3x} \leq 9^{2x-1}$

24. **BACTERIA** A bacteria population started with 5000 bacteria. After 8 hours there were 28,000 in the sample.
    a. Write an exponential function that could be used to model the number of bacteria after x hours if the number of bacteria changes at the same rate. **$y = 5000(1.240)^x$**
    b. How many bacteria can be expected in the sample after 32 hours? **about 4,880,496**

EXAMPLE 2

Solve $4^{3x} = 32^{x-1}$ for x.

$4^{3x} = 32^{x-1}$	Original equation
$(2^2)^{3x} = (2^5)^{x-1}$	Rewrite so each side has the same base.
$2^{6x} = 2^{5x-5}$	Simplify.
$6x = 5x - 5$	Property of Equality for Exponential Functions
$x = -5$	Simplify.

The solution is −5.

22. $x > -\frac{2}{3}$

23. $x \leq -\frac{2}{5}$

8-3 Logarithms and Logarithmic Functions (pp. 492–499)

912.A.8.1, 912.A.8.2

25. Write $\log_2 \frac{1}{16} = -4$ in exponential form.
26. Write $10^2 = 100$ in logarithmic form. **$\log_{10} 100 = 2$**

Evaluate each expression.

27. $\log_4 256$ **4**
28. $\log_2 \frac{1}{8}$ **−3**

Graph each function. **29, 30. See margin.**

29. $f(x) = 2\log_{10} x + 4$
30. $f(x) = \frac{1}{6}\log_{\frac{1}{3}}(x - 2)$

EXAMPLE 3

Evaluate $\log_2 64$.

$\log_2 64 = y$	Let the logarithm equal y.
$64 = 2^y$	Definition of logarithm
$2^6 = 2^y$	$64 = 2^6$
$6 = y$	Property of Equality for Exponential Functions

25. $2^{-4} = \frac{1}{16}$

14.
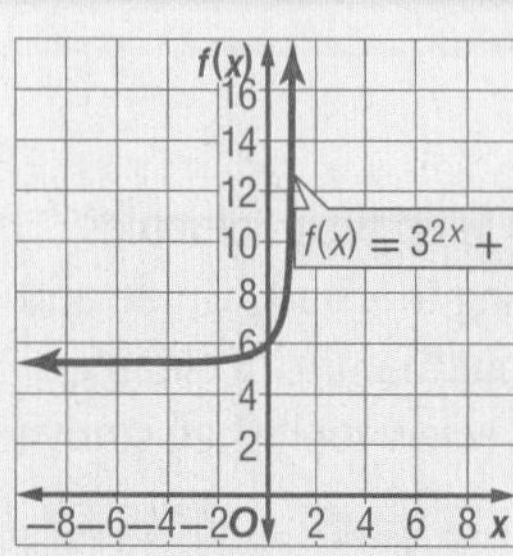

D = {all real numbers}
R = {$f(x)$ | $f(x) > 5$}

15.
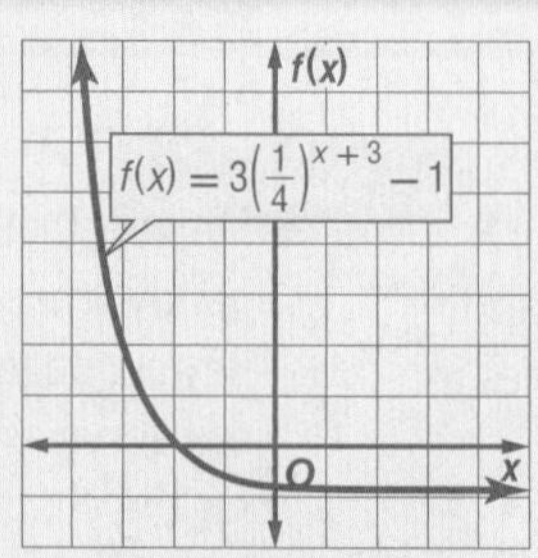

D = {all real numbers}
R = {$f(x)$ | $f(x) > -1$}

16.
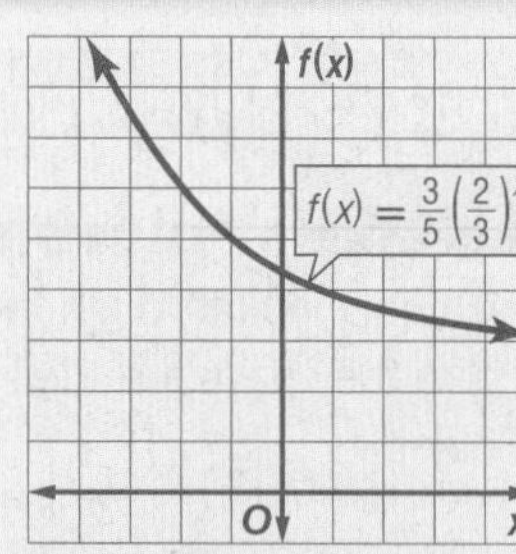

D = {all real numbers}
R = {$f(x)$ | $f(x) > 3$}

MIXED PROBLEM SOLVING
For mixed problem-solving practice, see page 986.

8-4 Solving Logarithmic Equations and Inequalities (pp. 502–507)

912.A.8.2, 912.A.8.5

Solve each equation or inequality. 33. $0 < x < 64$

31. $\log_{16} x = \frac{3}{2}$ 64
32. $\log_2 \frac{1}{64} = x$ −6
33. $\log_4 x < 3$
34. $\log_5 x < -3$ $0 < x < \frac{1}{125}$
35. $\log_9 (3x - 1) = \log_9 (4x)$ no solution
36. $\log_2 (x^2 - 18) = \log_2 (-3x)$ −6
37. $\log_3 (3x + 4) \leq \log_3 (x - 2)$ no solution
38. **EARTHQUAKE** The magnitude of an earthquake is measured on a logarithmic scale called the Richter scale. The magnitude M is given by $M = \log_{10} x$, where x represents the amplitude of the seismic wave causing ground motion. How many times as great is the amplitude caused by an earthquake with a Richter scale rating of 10 as an aftershock with a Richter scale rating of 7? 1000

EXAMPLE 4

Solve $\log_{27} x < \frac{2}{3}$.

$\log_{27} x < \frac{2}{3}$	**Original inequality**
$x < 27^{\frac{2}{3}}$	**Logarithmic to Exponential Inequality**
$x < 9$	**Simplify.**

EXAMPLE 5

Solve $\log_5 (p^2 - 2) = \log_5 p$.

$\log_5 (p^2 - 2) = \log_5 p$	**Original equation**
$p^2 - 2 = p$	**Property of Equality**
$p^2 - p - 2 = 0$	**Subtract p from each side.**
$(p - 2)(p + 1) = 0$	**Factor.**
$p - 2 = 0$ or $p + 1 = 0$	**Zero Product Property**
$p = 2$ $\quad p = -1$	**Solve each equation.**

The solution is $p = 2$, since $\log_5 p$ is undefined for $p = -1$.

8-5 Properties of Logarithms (pp. 509–515)

48. 361.6 times

912.A.8.2

Use $\log_5 16 \approx 1.7227$ and $\log_5 2 \approx 0.4307$ to approximate the value of each expression.

39. $\log_5 8$ 1.2920
40. $\log_5 64$ 2.5841
41. $\log_5 4$ 0.8614
42. $\log_5 \frac{1}{8}$ −1.2921
43. $\log_5 \frac{1}{2}$ −0.4307

Solve each equation. Check your solution.

44. $\log_5 x - \log_5 2 = \log_5 15$ 30
45. $3 \log_4 a = \log_4 27$ 3
46. $2 \log_3 x + \log_3 3 = \log_3 36$ $2\sqrt{3}$
47. $\log_4 n + \log_4 (n - 4) = \log_4 5$ 5
48. **SOUND** Use the formula $L = 10 \log_{10} R$, where L is the loudness of a sound and R is the sound's relative intensity, to find out how much louder 20 people talking would be than one person talking. Suppose the sound of one person talking has a relative intensity of 80 decibels.

EXAMPLE 6

Use $\log_5 16 \approx 1.7227$ and $\log_5 2 \approx 0.4307$ to approximate $\log_5 32$.

$\log_5 32 = \log_5 16 \cdot 2$	**Replace 32 with 16.**
$= \log_5 16 + \log_5 2$	**Product Property**
$\approx 1.7227 + 0.4307$	**Use a calculator.**
≈ 2.1534	

EXAMPLE 7

Solve $\log_3 3x + \log_3 4 = \log_3 36$.

$\log_3 3x + \log_3 4 = \log_3 36$	**Original equation**
$\log_3 3x(4) = \log_3 36$	**Product Property**
$3x(4) = 36$	**Definition of logarithm**
$12x = 36$	**Multiply.**
$x = 3$	**Divide each side by 12.**

Additional Answers

29.

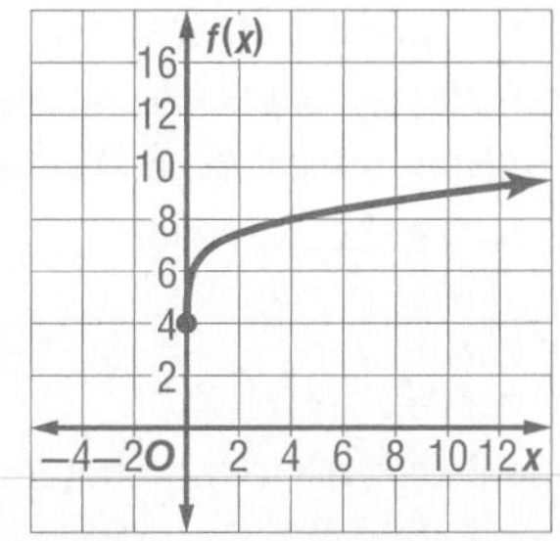

30.

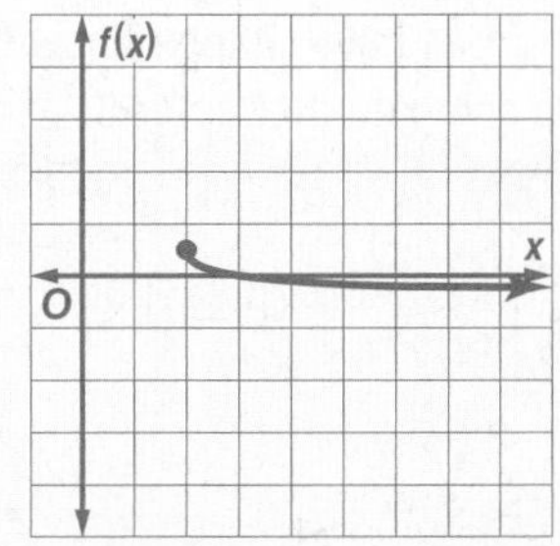

CHAPTER 8 Study Guide and Review

Problem Solving Review

For additional practice in problem solving for Chapter 8, see the Mixed Problem Solving Appendix, p. 987, in the Student Handbook section.

Anticipation Guide

Have students complete the Chapter 8 Anticipation Guide and discuss how their responses have changed now that they have completed Chapter 8.

Additional Answers

56. $x \approx 1.9459$
57. $x \approx -1.9459$
58. $x \approx 201.7144$
59. $x > 1.9459$
60. $-3 < x < -0.2817$
61. $x < -2.8904$

CHAPTER 8 Study Guide and Review

8-6 Common Logarithms (pp. 516–522)

912.A.8.2, 912.A.8.6

Solve each equation or inequality. Round to the nearest ten-thousandth. 51. $m \approx 0.6356$

49. $3^x = 15$ $x \approx 2.4650$
50. $6^{x^2} = 28$ $x \approx \pm 1.3637$
51. $8^{m+1} = 30$
52. $12^{r-1} = 7^r$ $r \approx 4.6102$
53. $3^{5n} > 24$ $n > 0.5786$
54. $5^{x+2} \leq 3^x$ $x \leq -6.3013$
55. **SAVINGS** You deposited $1000 into an account that pays an annual interest rate r of 5% compounded quarterly. Use $A = P\left(1 + \frac{r}{n}\right)^{nt}$.
    a. How long will it take until you have $1500 in your account? about 8.2 years
    b. How long it will take for your money to double? about 13.9 years

EXAMPLE 8

Solve $5^{3x} > 7^{x+1}$.

$5^{3x} > 7^{x+1}$	Original inequality
$\log 5^{3x} > \log 7x + 1$	Property of Inequality
$3x \log 5 > (x + 1) \log 7$	Power Property
$3x \log 5 > x \log 7 + \log 7$	Distributive Property
$3x \log 5 - x \log 7 > \log 7$	Subtract $x \log 7$.
$x(3 \log 5 - \log 7) > \log 7$	Distributive Property
$x > \dfrac{\log 7}{3 \log 5 - \log 7}$	Divide by $3 \log 5 - \log 7$.
$x > 0.6751$	Use a calculator.

The solution set is $\{x \mid x > 0.6751\}$.

8-7 Base e and Natural Logarithms (pp. 525–531)

912.A.8.2, 912.A.8.7

Solve each equation or inequality. Round to the nearest ten-thousandth. 56–61. See margin.

56. $4e^x - 11 = 17$
57. $2e^{-x} + 1 = 15$
58. $\ln 2x = 6$
59. $2 + e^x > 9$
60. $\ln (x + 3)^5 < 5$
61. $e^{-x} > 18$
62. **SAVINGS** If you deposit $2000 in an account paying 6.4% interest compounded continuously, how long will it take for your money to triple? Use $A = Pe^{rt}$. about 17.2 years

EXAMPLE 9

Solve $3e^{5x} + 1 = 10$. Round to the nearest ten-thousandth.

$3e^{5x} + 1 = 10$	Original equation
$3e^{5x} = 9$	Subtract 1 from each side.
$e^{5x} = 3$	Divide each side by 3.
$\ln e^{5x} = \ln 3$	Property of Equality
$5x = \ln 3$	$\ln e^x = x$
$x = \dfrac{\ln 3}{5}$	Divide each side by 5.
$x \approx 0.2197$	Use a calculator.

8-8 Using Exponential and Logarithmic Functions (pp. 533–539)

912.A.8.5, 912.A.8.7

63. **CARS** Abe bought a used car for $2500. It is expected to depreciate at a rate of 25% per year. What will be the value of the car in 3 years?
64. **BIOLOGY** For a certain strain of bacteria, k is 0.728 when t is measured in days. Using the formula $y = ae^{kt}$, how long will it take 10 bacteria to increase to 675 bacteria? ≈5.8 days
65. **POPULATION** The population of a city 20 years ago was 24,330. Since then, the population has increased at a steady rate each year. If the population is currently 55,250, find the annual rate of growth for this city. about 4.2%

63. $1054.69

EXAMPLE 10

A certain culture of bacteria will grow from 250 to 2000 bacteria in 1.5 hours. Find the constant k for the growth formula. Use $y = ae^{kt}$.

$y = ae^{kt}$	Exponential Growth Formula
$2000 = 250e^{k(1.5)}$	Replace y with 2000, a with 250, and t with 1.5.
$8 = e^{1.5k}$	Divide each side by 250.
$\ln 8 = \ln e^{1.5k}$	Property of Equality
$\ln 8 = 1.5k$	Inverse Property
$\dfrac{\ln 8}{1.5} = k$	Divide each side by 1.5.
$1.3863 \approx k$	Use a calculator.

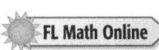

FL Math Online glencoe.com
Chapter Test

Graph each function. State the domain and range.

1. $f(x) = 3^{x-3} + 2$ **1, 2. See margin.**
2. $f(x) = 2\left(\frac{3}{4}\right)^{x+1} - 3$

Solve each equation or inequality. Round to four decimal places if necessary.

3. $8^{c+1} = 16^{2c+3}$ $c = -\frac{9}{5}$
4. $9^{x-2} > \left(\frac{1}{27}\right)^x$ $x > \frac{4}{5}$
5. $2^{a+3} = 3^{2a-1}$ $a \approx 2.1130$
6. $\log_2 (x^2 - 7) = \log_2 6x$ $x = 7$
7. $\log_5 x > 2$ $x > 25$
8. $\log_3 x + \log_3 (x - 3) = \log_3 4$ $x = 4$
9. $6^{n-1} \le 11^n$ $n \le -2.9560$
10. $4e^{2x} - 1 = 5$ $x \approx 0.2027$
11. $\ln (x + 2)^2 > 2$ $\{x \mid x < -4.7183 \text{ or } x > 0.7183, x \ne -2\}$

Use $\log_5 11 \approx 1.4899$ and $\log_5 2 \approx 0.4307$ to approximate the value of each expression.

12. $\log_5 44$ 2.3513
13. $\log_5 \frac{11}{2}$ 1.0592

14. **POPULATION** The population of a city 10 years ago was 150,000. Since then, the population has increased at a steady rate each year. The population is currently 185,000. **a.** $y = 150{,}000(1.0212)^x$
    a. Write an exponential function that could be used to model the population after x years if the population changes at the same rate.
    b. What will the population be in 25 years? about 253,432

15. Write $\log_9 27 = \frac{3}{2}$ in exponential form. $9^{\frac{3}{2}} = 27$

16. **AGRICULTURE** An equation that models the decline in the number of U.S. farms is $y = 3{,}962{,}520(0.98)^x$, where x is the number of years since 1960 and y is the number of farms. **a.** $b < 1$
    a. How can you tell that the number is declining?
    b. By what annual rate is the number declining? 2%
    c. Predict when the number of farms will be less than 1 million. in about 2028

17. NGSSS PRACTICE What is the value of $\log_4 \frac{1}{64}$? A
    A. -3
    B. $-\frac{1}{3}$
    C. $\frac{1}{3}$
    D. 3

18. **SAVINGS** You put $7500 in a savings account paying 3% interest compounded continuously.
    a. Assuming there are no deposits or withdrawals from the account, what is the balance after 5 years? $8713.76 **b.** ≈23.1 years
    b. How long will it take your savings to double?
    c. In how many years will you have $10,000 in your account? about 9.6 years

19. NGSSS PRACTICE What is the solution of $\log_4 16 - \log_4 x = \log_4 8$? G
    F. $\frac{1}{2}$
    G. 2
    H. 4
    I. 8

20. NGSSS PRACTICE Which function is graphed below? C

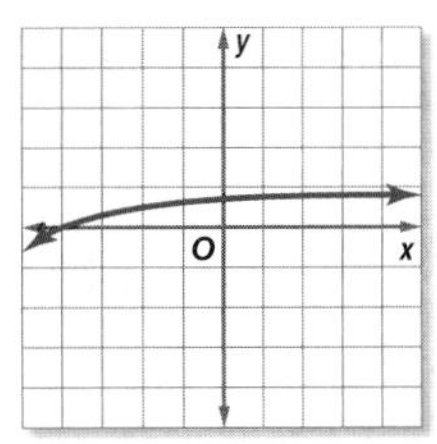

    A. $y = \log_{10} (x - 5)$
    B. $y = 5 \log_{10} x$
    C. $y = \log_{10} (x + 5)$
    D. $y = -5 \log_{10} x$

21. Write $2 \ln 6 + 3 \ln 4 - 5 \ln \left(\frac{1}{3}\right)$ as a single logarithm. **21.** $\ln \frac{(6^2)(4^3)}{\left(\frac{1}{3}\right)^5}$ or ln 559,872

CHAPTER 8 Practice Test

ExamView Assessment Suite: Customize and create multiple versions of your chapter test and their answer keys. All of the questions from the leveled chapter tests in the *Chapter 8 Resource Masters* are also available on ExamView® Assessment Suite.

Additional Answers

1.

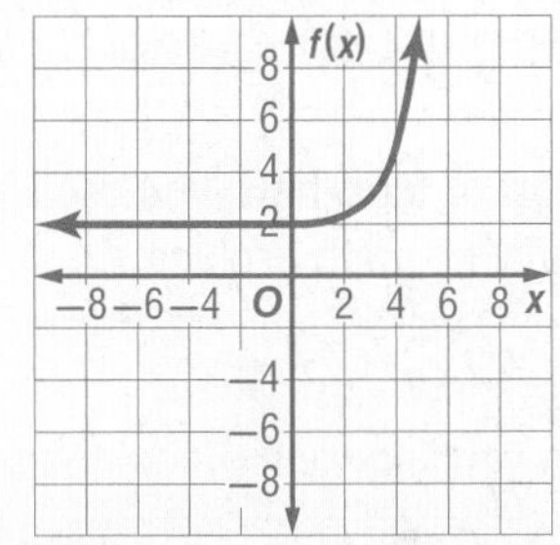

D = {all real numbers}
R = {f(x) | f(x) > 2}

2.

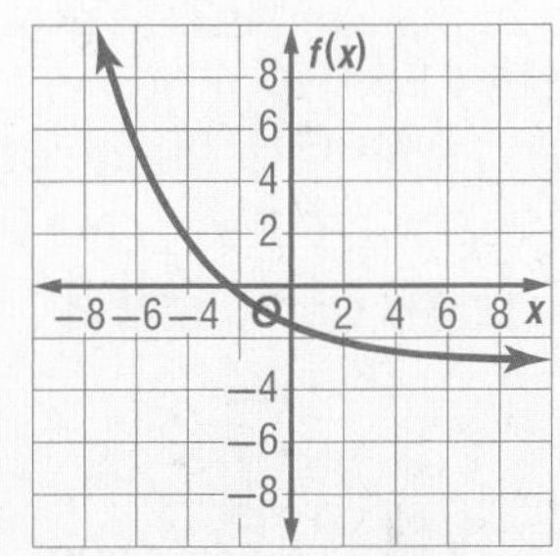

D = {all real numbers}
R = {f(x) | f(x) > −3}

Intervention Planner

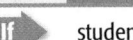

Tier 1 On Level	Tier 2 Strategic Intervention approaching grade level	Tier 3 Intensive Intervention 2 or more grades below level
If students miss about 25% of the exercises or less,	**If** students miss about 50% of the exercises,	**If** students miss about 75% of the exercises,
Then choose a resource: **SE** Lessons 8-1, 8-2, 8-3, 8-4, 8-5, 8-6, 8-7, and 8-8 **CRM** Skills Practice, pp. 7, 14, 21, 28, 35, 42, 49, and 55 **TE** Chapter Project, p. 472	**Then** choose a resource: **CRM** Study Guide and Intervention, Chapter 8, pp. 5, 12, 19, 26, 33, 40, 47, and 53	**Then** use *Math Triumphs, Alg. 2*
FL Math Online Self-Check Quiz	FL Math Online Extra Examples, Personal Tutor, Homework Help	FL Math Online Extra Examples, Personal Tutor, Homework Help, Review Vocabulary

1 FOCUS

Objective Use the strategy of using technology to solve standardized test problems.

2 TEACH

Scaffolding Questions

Ask:

- What sort of tools have you used when solving math problems? Sample answer: calculator, protractor, compass, ruler, pencil, paper
- How do you know which tool to use? Sample answers: Use a calculator when graphing functions; use a protractor when measuring angles; use a compass when constructing angles; use a ruler when measuring; use pencil and paper when you do not have a calculator handy or when you cannot perform mental math.

CHAPTER 8 Preparing for Standardized Tests

Using Technology

Your calculator can be a useful tool in taking standardized tests. Some problems that you encounter might have steps or computations that require the use of a calculator. A calculator may also help you solve a problem more quickly.

Strategies for Using Technology

Step 1

A calculator is a useful tool, but typically it should be used sparingly. Standardized tests are designed to measure your ability to reason and solve problems, not to measure your ability to punch keys on a calculator.

Before using a calculator, ask yourself:

- How would I normally solve this type of problem?
- Are there any steps that I cannot perform mentally or by using paper and pencil?
- Is a calculator absolutely necessary to solve this problem?
- Would a calculator help me solve this problem more quickly or efficiently?

Step 2

When might a calculator come in handy?

- solving problems that involve large, complex computations
- solving certain problems that involve graphing functions, evaluating functions, solving equations, and so on
- checking solutions of problems

NGSSS PRACTICE EXAMPLE

Read the problem. Identify what you need to know. Then use the information in the problem to solve.

A certain can of soda contains 60 milligrams of caffeine. The caffeine is eliminated from the body at a rate of 15% per hour. What is the *half-life* of the caffeine? That is, how many hours does it take for half of the caffeine to be eliminated from the body?

A. 4 hours

B. 4.25 hours

C. 4.5 hours

D. 4.75 hours

Read the problem carefully. The problem can be solved using an exponential function. Use the exponential decay formula to model the problem and solve for the half-life of caffeine.

$$y = a(1 - r)^t$$
$$y = 60(1 - 0.15)^t$$

Half of 60 milligrams is 30. So, let $y = 30$ and solve for t.

$$30 = 60(1 - 0.15)^t$$
$$0.5 = (0.85)^t$$

Take the log of each side and use the power property.

$$\log 0.5 = \log (0.85)^t$$
$$\log 0.5 = t \log 0.85$$
$$\frac{\log 0.5}{\log 0.85} = t$$

At this point, it is necessary to use a calculator to evaluate the logarithms and solve the problem. Doing so shows that $t \approx 4.265$. So, the half-life of caffeine is about 4.25 hours. The correct answer is B.

Exercises

Read each problem. Identify what you need to know. Then use the information in the problem to solve.

1. Jason recently purchased a new truck for $34,750. The value of the truck decreases by 12% each year. What will the approximate value of the truck be 7 years after Jason purchased it? **D**

   A. $13,775

   B. $13,890

   C. $14,125

   D. $14,200

2. A baseball is thrown upward at a velocity of 105 feet per second, releasing the baseball when it is 5 feet above the ground. The height of the baseball t seconds after being thrown is given by the formula $h(t) = -16t^2 + 105t + 5$. Find the time at which the baseball reaches its maximum height. **G**

   F. 1.0 s　　H. 6.6 s

   G. 3.3 s　　I. 177.3 s

3. Lucinda deposited $2500 in a CD with the terms described below.

   Super CD!
   Earn 4.25% interest compounded daily!
   (Minimum deposit of $1,000 over a period of at least 12 months.)

   Use the formula below to solve for t, the number of years needed to earn $250 in interest with the CD.

   $$2750 = 2500\left(1 + \frac{0.0425}{365}\right)^{365t}$$ **B**

   A. about 2.15 years

   B. about 2.24 years

   C. about 2.35 years

   D. about 2.46 years

Additional Example

STANDARDIZED TEST PRACTICE
A certain city had a population of 4590 in 1800. Since then, the population has grown by approximately 1.05% annually. In what year was the population of this city 37,075? **D**

A 1808

B 1820

C 1997

D 2000

3 ASSESS

Use Exercises 1–3 to assess students' understanding.

Chapter 8 Preparing for Standardized Tests 547

Diagnose Student Errors

Survey student responses for each item. Class trends may indicate common errors and misconceptions.

1. A. correct
B. incorrectly simplified $\log 1 \div \log 4$
C. guess
D. incorrectly let $4^0 = 4$ instead of $4^0 = 1$

2. F. incorrectly inputted values in the calculator
G. correct
H. incorrectly used the properties of logarithms
I. incorrectly used the properties of logarithms

8. A. did not use a rate of 100%
B. used an incorrect formula for growth
C. incorrectly let $t = 5$ instead of 6
D. correct

9. F. multiplied wrong quantities
G. incorrectly assumed the cost of 1 book is $5
H. correct
I. guess

10. A. did not understand that no values for x can be ≤ 0
B. did not understand that no values for x can be ≤ 0
C. correct
D. did not understand that no values for x can be ≤ 0

13. F. guess
G. guess
H. correct
I. did not understand that parallel lines have the same slope

14. A. only double once
B. multiplied by 6 instead of finding 2^6
C. found 2^5 instead of 2^6
D. correct

CHAPTER 8 NGSSS Practice

Cumulative, Chapters 1 through 8

Read each question. Then fill in the correct answer on the answer document provided by your teacher or on a sheet of paper.

1. What is the y-intercept of the exponential function below? **A**

$$y = 4^x - 1$$

A. 0 B. 1 C. 2 D. 3

2. Suppose there are only 3500 birds of a particular endangered species left on an island and the population decreases at a rate of about 5% each year. The logarithmic function $t = \log_{0.95} \frac{p}{3500}$ predicts how many years t it will be for the population to decease to a number p. About how long will it take for the population to reach 3000 birds? **G**

F. 2 years H. 5 years
G. 3 years I. 8 years

3. **SHORT RESPONSE** Figure $QRST$ is shown on the coordinate plane.

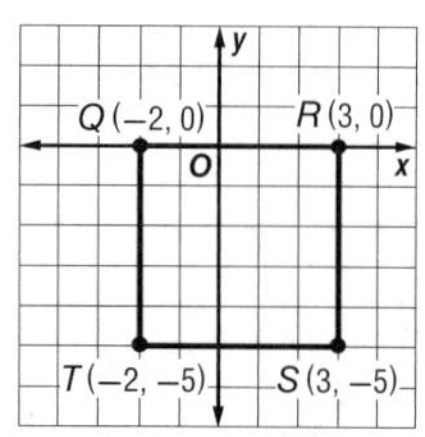

What transformation creates an image with a vertex at the origin? **Sample answer: Translate figure *QRST* to the left 3 units and up 5 units.**

4. **GRIDDED RESPONSE** If $f(x) = 3x$ and $g(x) = x^2 - 1$, what is the value of $f(g(-3))$? **24**

Test-TakingTip

Question 2 Use technology and the properties of logarithms to find t when $p = 3000$.

5. **GRIDDED RESPONSE** For what value of x would the rectangle below have an area of 48 square units? **12**

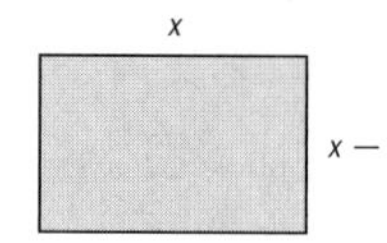

6. **SHORT RESPONSE** The function $y = \left(\frac{1}{2}\right)^x$ is graphed below. What is the domain of the function? **all real numbers**

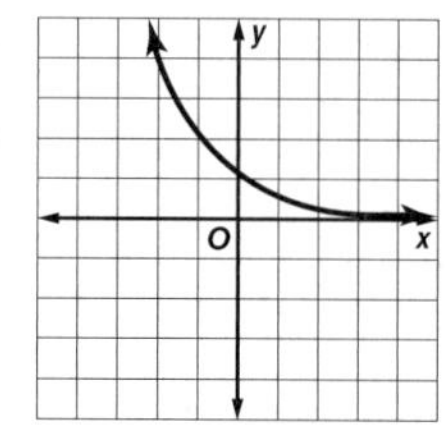

7. **EXTENDED RESPONSE** Suppose the number of whitetail deer in a particular region has increased at an annual rate of about 10% since 1995. There were 135,000 deer in 1995.

a. Write a function to model the number of whitetail deer after t years. **See margin.**

b. About how many whitetail deer inhabited the region in 2000? Round your answer to the nearest hundred deer. **about 217,400 deer**

8. Suppose a certain bacteria duplicates to reproduce itself every 20 minutes. If you begin with one cell of the bacteria, how many will there be after 2 hours? **D**

A. 2 B. 6 C. 32 D. 64

9. Ray's Book Store sells two used books for $7.99. The total cost c of purchasing n books can be found by— **H**

F. multiplying n by c.
G. multiplying n by 5.
H. multiplying n by the cost of 1 book.
I. dividing n by c.

548 Chapter 8 Exponential and Logarithmic Functions and Relations

10. Graph $y = \log_5 x$. **C**

A.

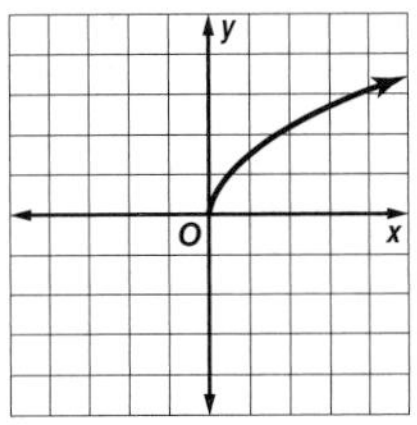

B.

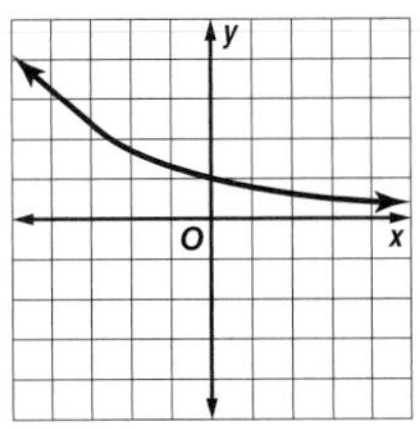

C.

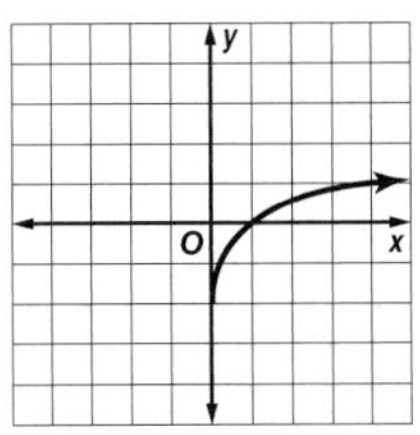

D.

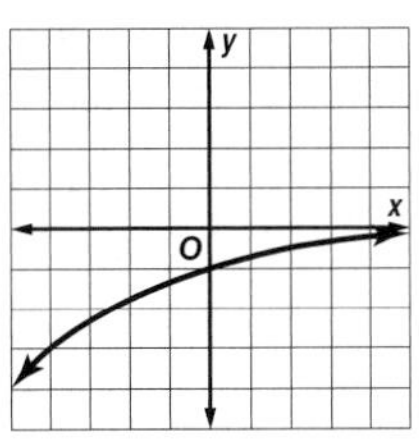

11. THINK SOLVE EXPLAIN **SHORT RESPONSE** Simplify $(-2a^{-2}b^{-6})(-3a^{-1}b^{8})$. $\frac{6b^2}{a^3}$

12. THINK SOLVE EXPLAIN **SHORT RESPONSE** Suzanne bought a new car this year for $33,750. The value of the car is expected to decrease by 10.5% per year. What will be the **approximate** value of the car 6 years after Suzanne purchased it? Show your work. **about $17,347**

13. Which of the following best describes the graph of $3y = 4x - 3$ and $8y = -6x - 5$? **H**

F. The lines have the same y-intercept.
G. The lines have the same x-intercept.
H. The lines are perpendicular.
I. The lines are parallel.

14. Lucas determined that the total cost C to rent a car could be represented by the equation $C = 0.35m + 125$, where m is the number of miles that he drives. If the total cost to rent the car was $363, how many miles did he drive? **D**

A. 125
B. 238
C. 520
D. 680

15. THINK SOLVE EXPLAIN **EXTENDED RESPONSE** Sandy inherited $250,000 from her aunt in 1992. She invested the money and increased it as shown in the table below.

Year	Amount
1992	$250,000
2000	$329,202
2005	$390,989

a. Write an exponential function that could be used to predict the amount of money A after investing for t years. $A(t) = 250{,}000(1.035)^t$

b. If the money continues to grow at the same rate, in what year will it be worth $500,000? **2012**

Need Extra Help?

If you missed Question...	1	2	3	4	5	6	7	8	9	10	11	12	13	14	15
Go to Lesson or Page...	8-1	8-4	4-4	7-1	5-3	8-1	8-6	8-2	2-4	8-3	6-1	8-6	3-1	1-3	8-2
For help with NGSSS...	912.A.8.3	912.A.8.2	912.G.2.4	912.A.2.8	912.A.7.5	912.A.2.4	912.A.6.5	912.A.8.5	912.A.3.10	912.A.8.3	912.A.4.2	912.A.8.5	912.A.3.14	912.A.3.1	912.A.8.5

Formative Assessment

You can use these two pages to benchmark student progress.

CRM Chapter 8 Resource Masters

- Standardized Test Practice, pp. 80–82

ExamView Assessment Suite Create practice worksheets or tests that align to your state's standards as well as TIMSS and NAEP tests.

Homework Option

Get Ready for Chapter 9 Assign students the exercises on p. 551 as homework to assess whether they possess the prerequisite skills needed for the next chapter.

Additional Answer

7a. $N = 135{,}000(1.1)^t$, where N is the number of deer and t is the number of years since 1995.

Page 473, Get Ready for Chapter 8

6. $f^{-1}(x) = \frac{1}{2}x - \frac{5}{2}$

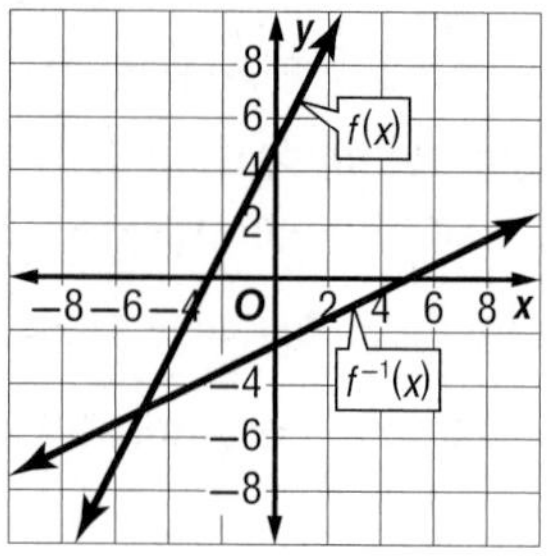

7. $f^{-1}(x) = x + 3$

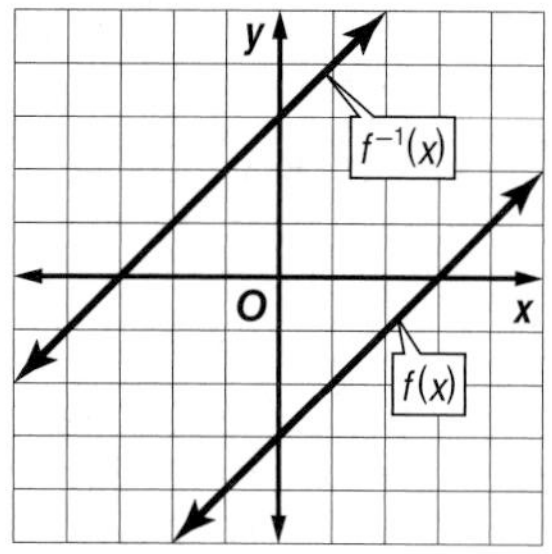

8. $f^{-1}(x) = -\frac{1}{4}x$

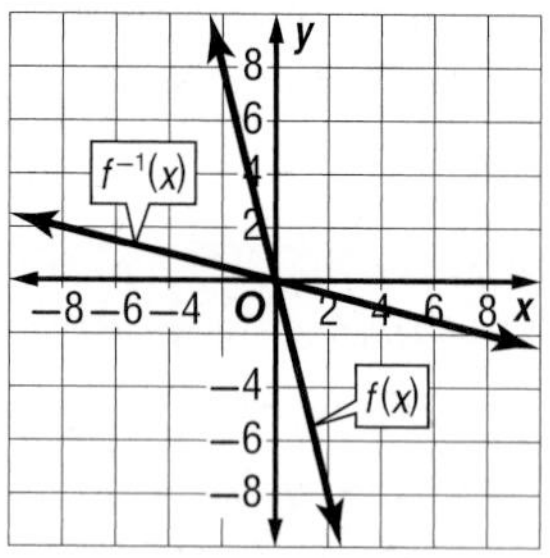

9. $f^{-1}(x) = 4x + 12$

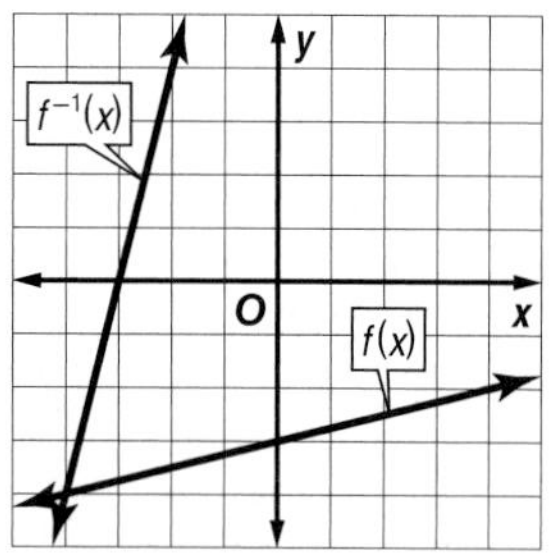

10. $f^{-1}(x) = 2x + 1$

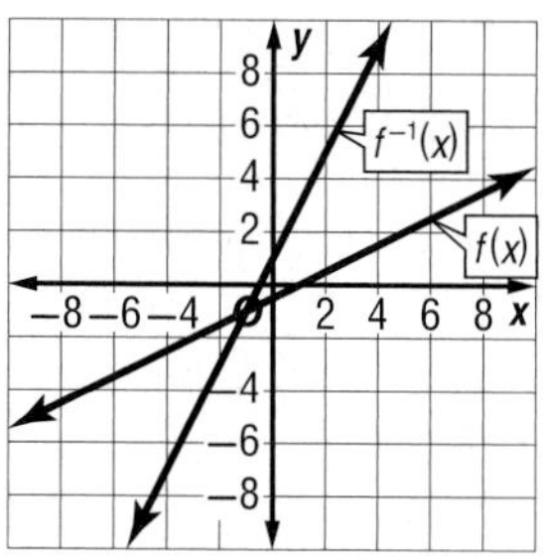

11. $f^{-1}(x) = 3x - 12$

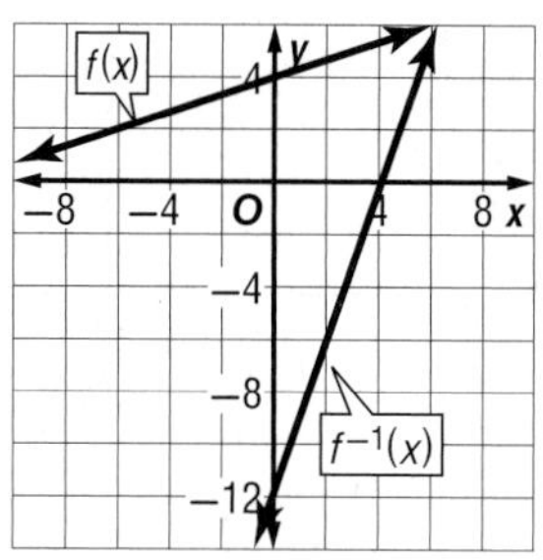

Pages 475–477, Lesson 8-1, (Guided Practice)

1.

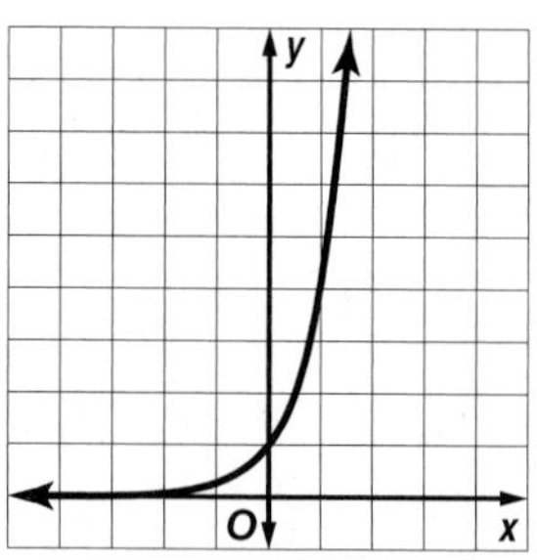

D = {all real numbers}; R = $\{y \mid y > 0\}$

2A.

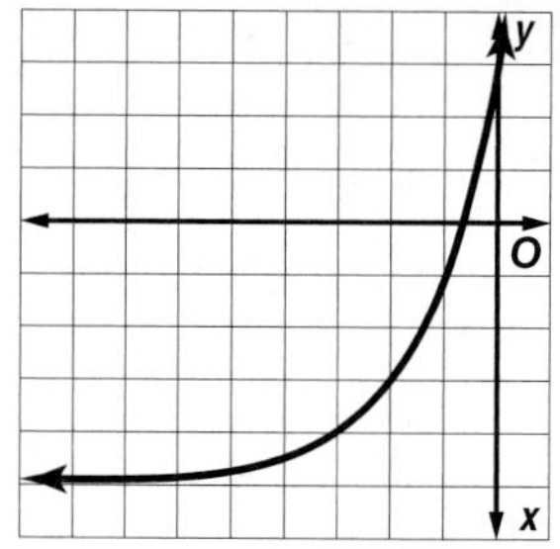

D = {all real numbers};
R = $\{y \mid y > -5\}$

2B.

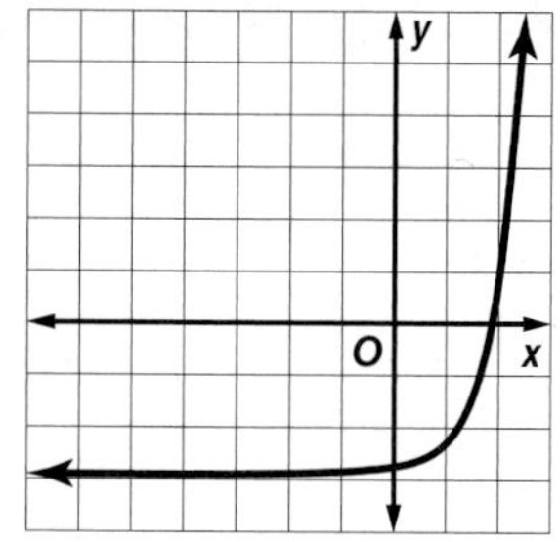

D = {all real numbers};
R = $\{y \mid y > -3\}$

3.

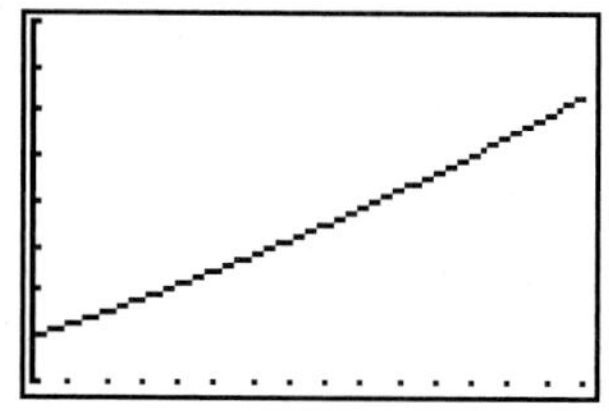

[0, 15] scl: 1 by [70, 150] scl: 10

Pages 479–481, Lesson 8-1

1.

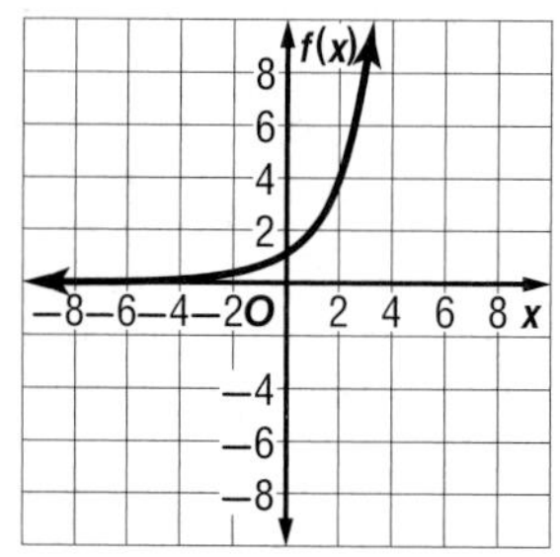

D = {all real numbers};
R = $\{f(x) \mid f(x) > 0\}$

2.

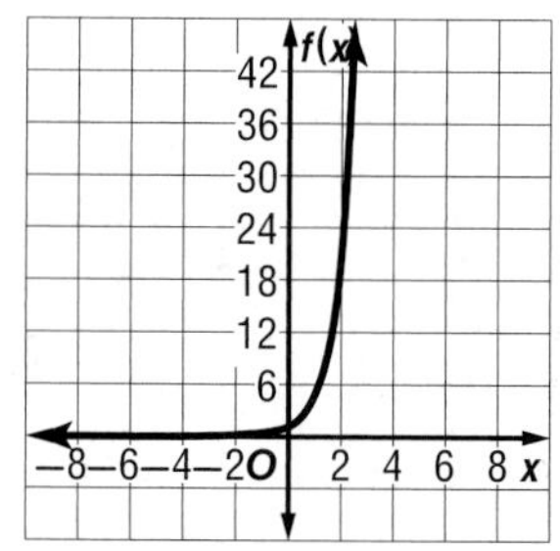

D = {all real numbers};
R = $\{f(x) \mid f(x) > 0\}$

3.

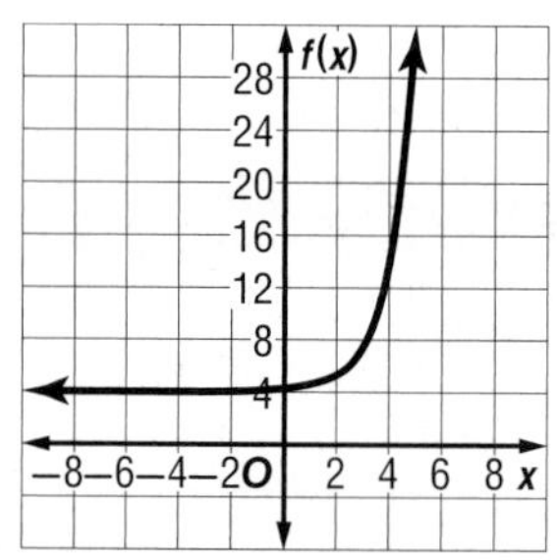

D = {all real numbers};
R = $\{f(x) \mid f(x) > 4\}$

4.

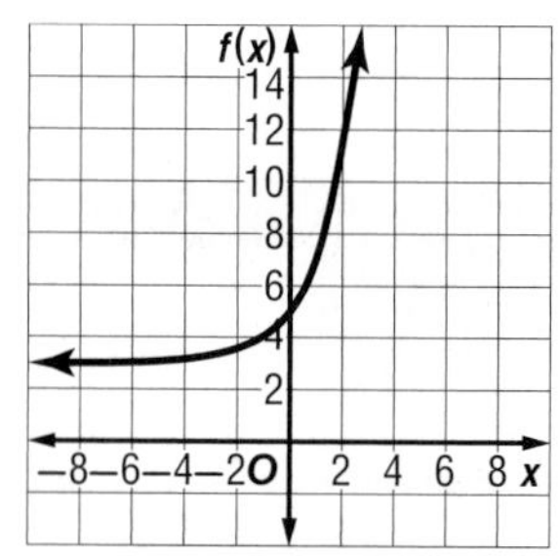

D = {all real numbers};
R = $\{f(x) \mid f(x) > 3\}$

5.

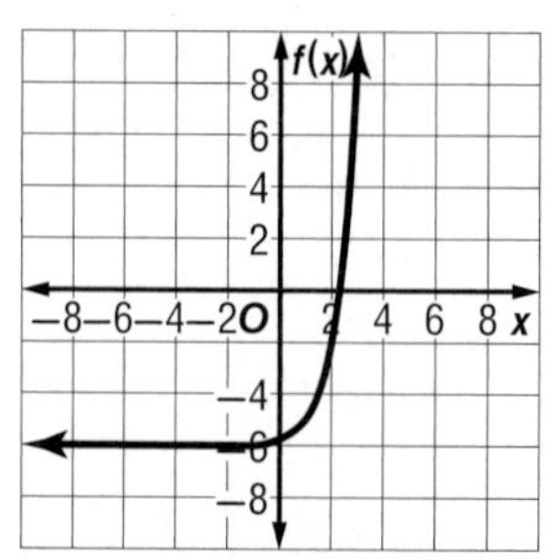

D = {all real numbers};
R = $\{f(x) \mid f(x) > -6\}$

6.

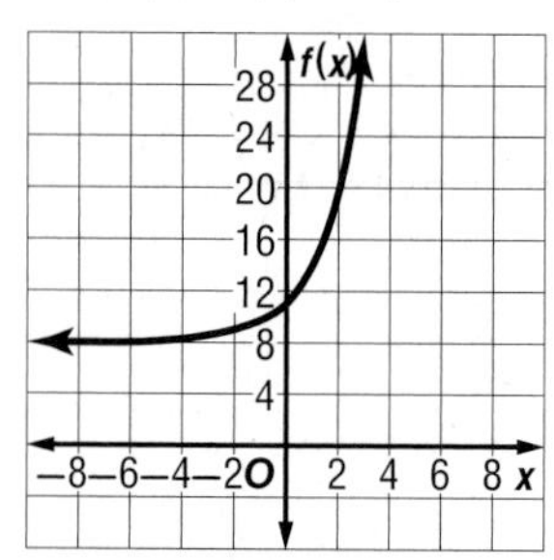

D = {all real numbers};
R = $\{f(x) \mid f(x) > 8\}$

8.

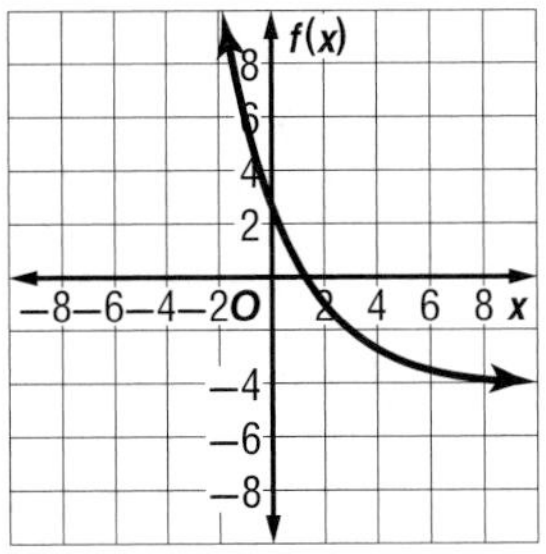

D = {all real numbers};
R = {$f(x) \mid f(x) > -4$}

9.

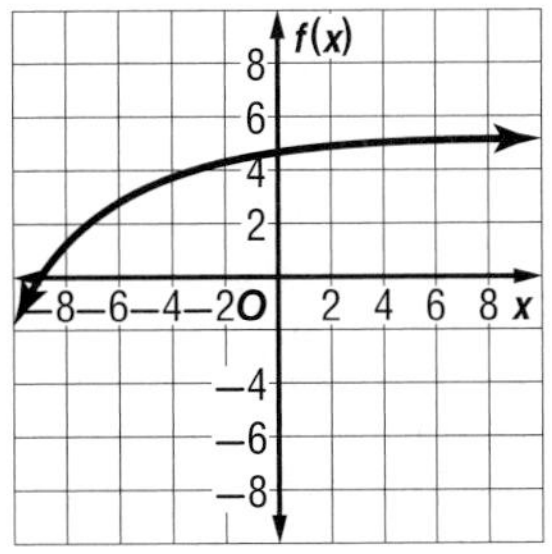

D = {all real numbers};
R = {$f(x) \mid f(x) < 5$}

10.

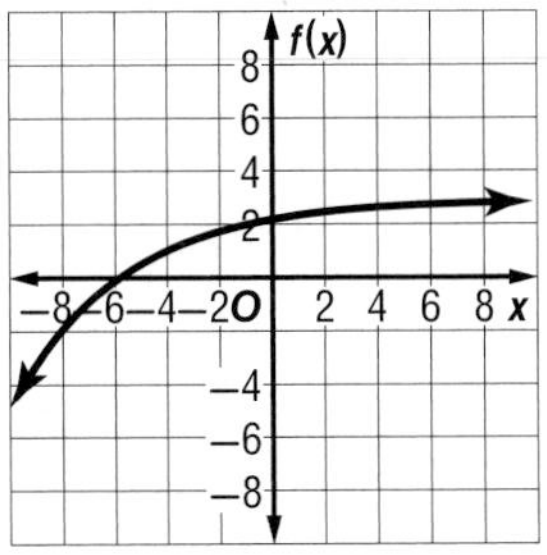

D = {all real numbers};
R = {$f(x) \mid f(x) < 3$}

11.

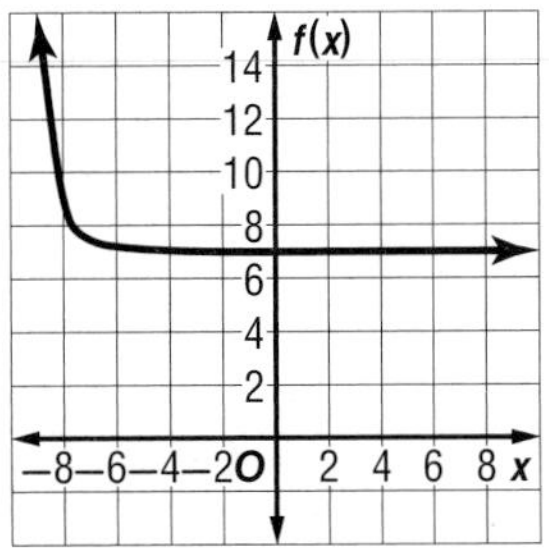

D = {all real numbers};
R = {$f(x) \mid f(x) > 7$}

13.

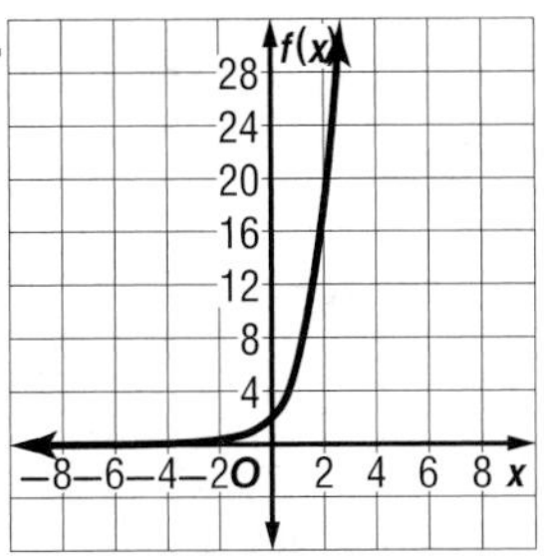

D = {all real numbers};
R = {$f(x) \mid f(x) > 0$}

14.

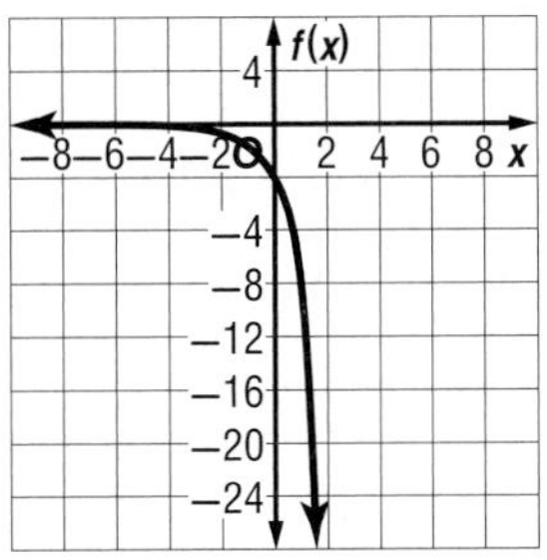

D = {all real numbers};
R = {$f(x) \mid f(x) < 0$}

15.

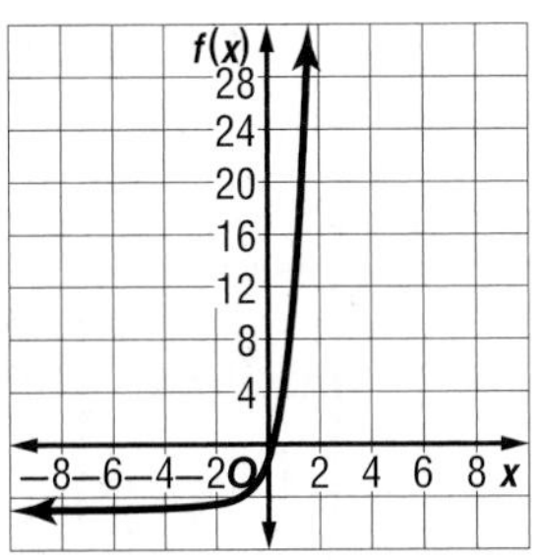

D = {all real numbers};
R = {$f(x) \mid f(x) > -5$}

16.

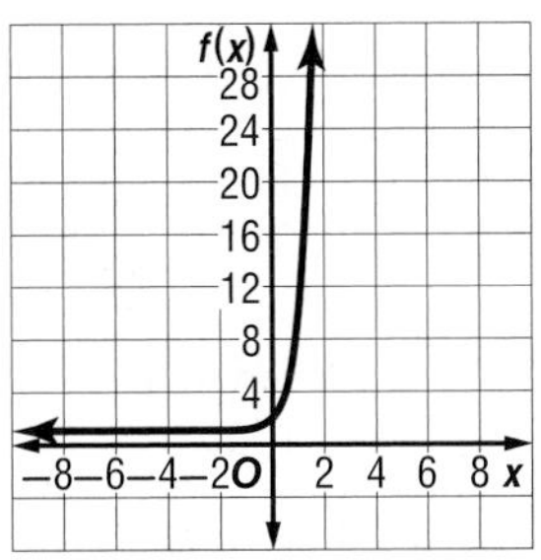

D = {all real numbers};
R = {$f(x) \mid f(x) > 1$}

17.

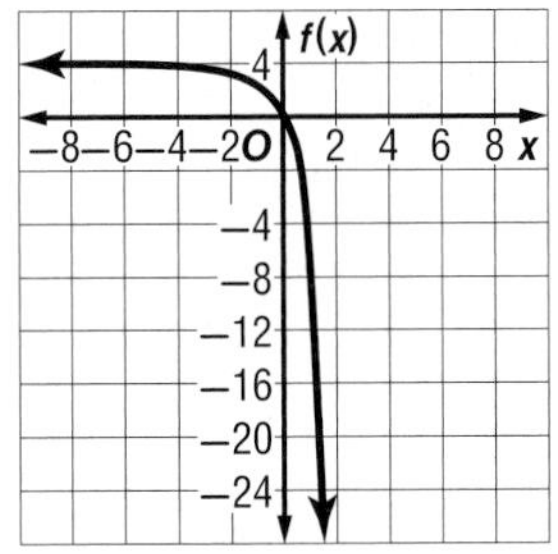

D = {all real numbers};
R = {$f(x) \mid f(x) < 4$}

18.

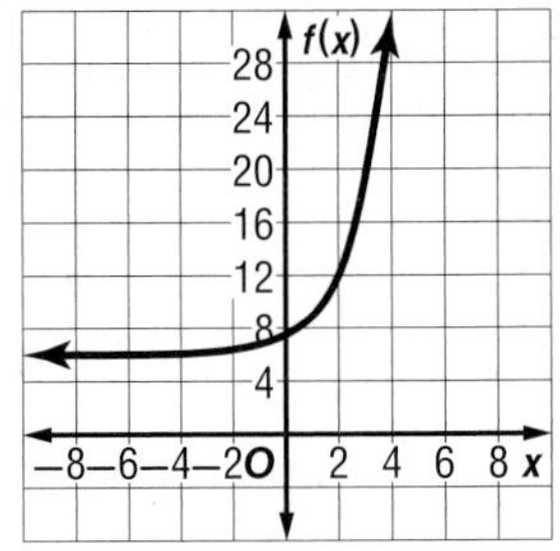

D = {all real numbers};
R = {$f(x) \mid f(x) > 6$}

19.

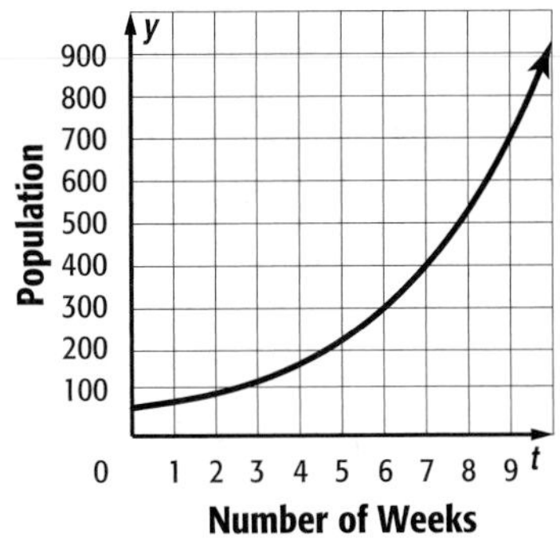

20.

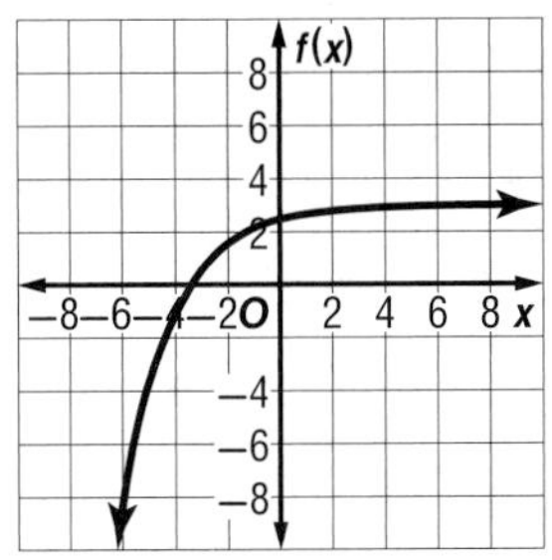

D = {all real numbers};
R = {$f(x) \mid f(x) < 3$}

21.

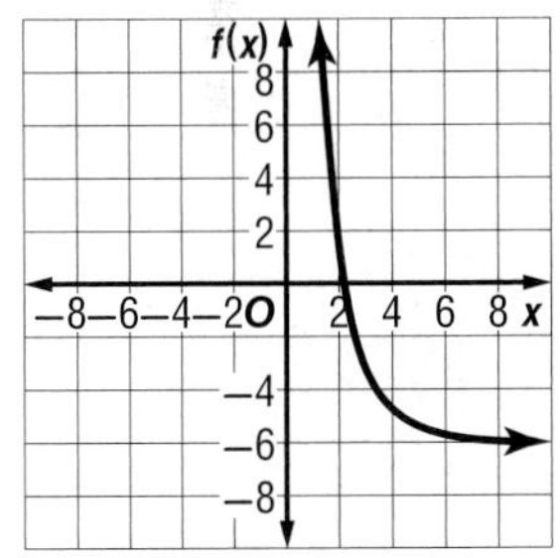

D = {all real numbers};
R = {$f(x) \mid f(x) > -6$}

22.

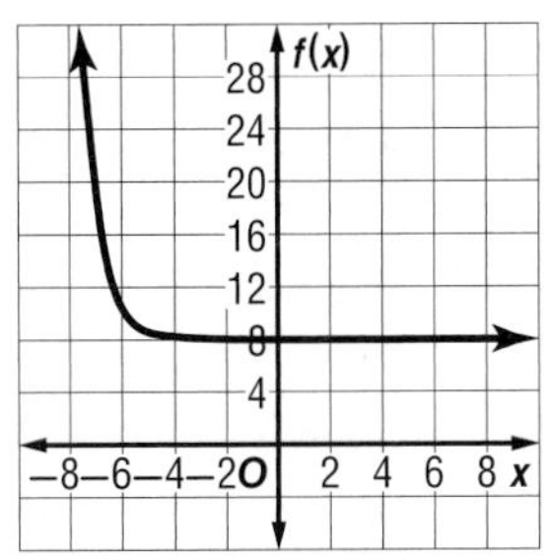

D = {all real numbers};
R = {$f(x) \mid f(x) > 8$}

23.

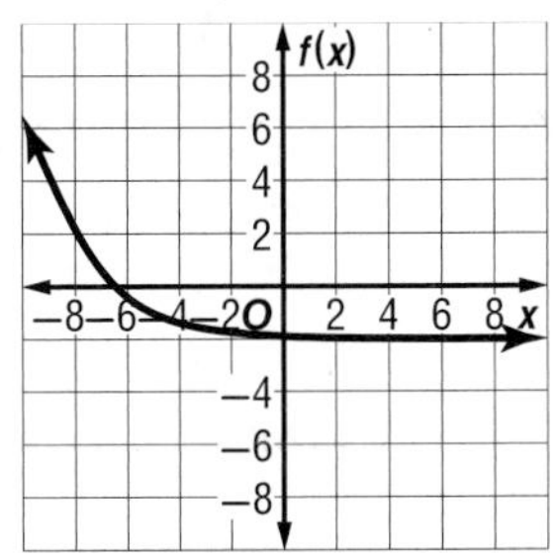

D = {all real numbers};
R = {$f(x) \mid f(x) > -2$}

24.

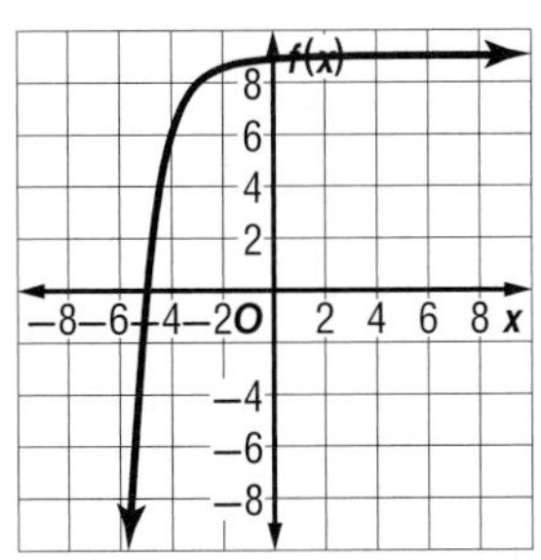

D = {all real numbers};
R = {$f(x) \mid f(x) < 9$}

25.

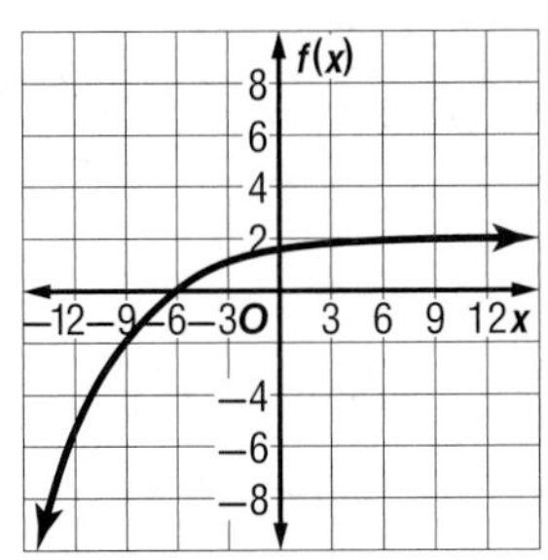

D = {all real numbers};
R = {$f(x) \mid f(x) < 2$}

33a.

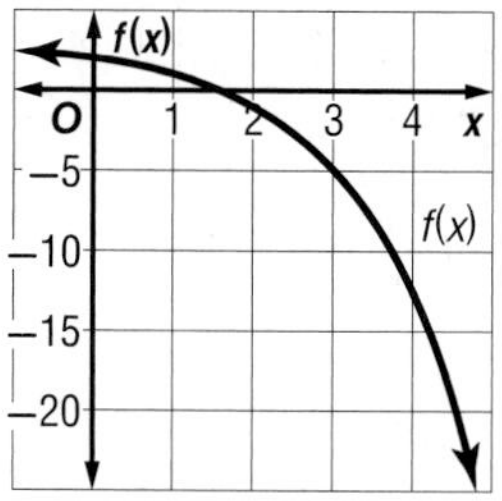

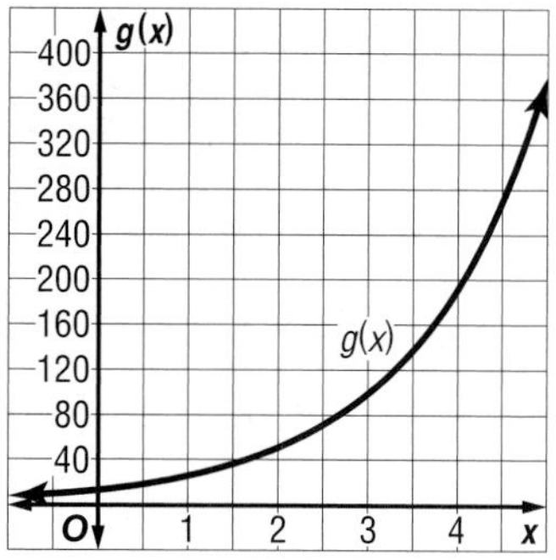

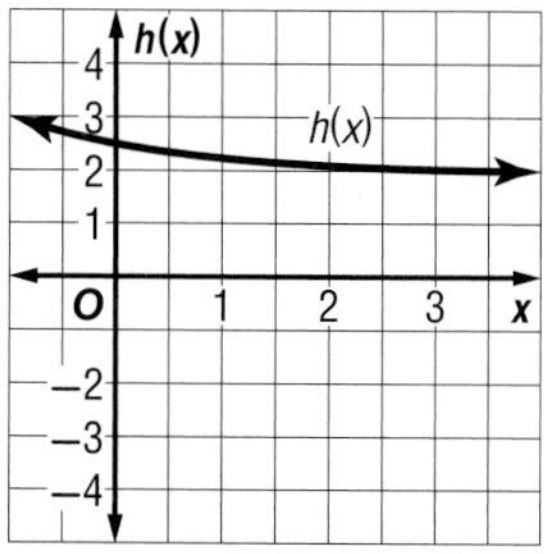

33b. Sample answer = $f(x)$; the graph of $f(x)$ is a reflection along the x-axis and the output values in the table are negative.

33d. Sample answer = $f(x)$ and $g(x)$ are growth and $h(x)$ is decay; The absolute value of the output is increasing for the growth functions and decreasing for the decay function.

Page 490, Lesson 8-2

41b.

Cuts	Pieces
1	2
2	4
3	8
4	16

42. Sample answer: The more frequently interest is compounded, the higher the account balance becomes.

48.

$27^{2x} \cdot 81^{x+1} = 3^{2x+2} \cdot 9^{4x+1}$	Original equation
$(3^3)^{2x} \cdot (3^4)^{x+1} = 3^{2x+2} \cdot (3^2)^{4x+1}$	$3^2 = 9, 3^3 = 27$, and $3^4 = 81$
$3^{6x} \cdot 3^{4x+4} = 3^{2x+2} \cdot 3^{8x+2}$	Power of a Power
$3^{10x+4} = 3^{10x+4}$	Product of Powers
$10x + 4 = 10x + 4$	Property of Equality for Exponential Functions
$10x = 10x$	Subtract 4 from each side.
$x = x$	Divide each side by 10.

Pages 496–497, Lesson 8-3

37.

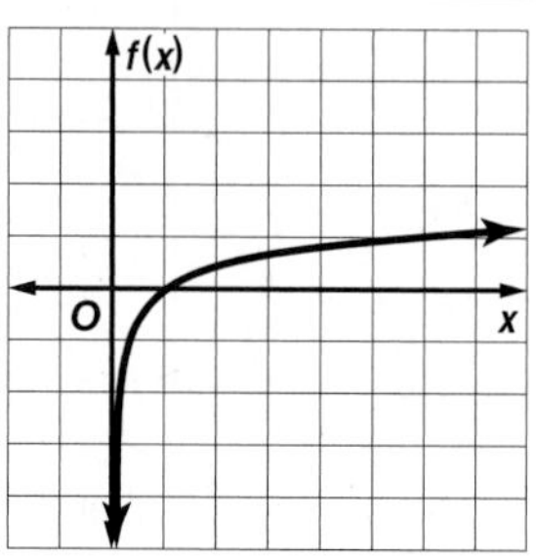

38.

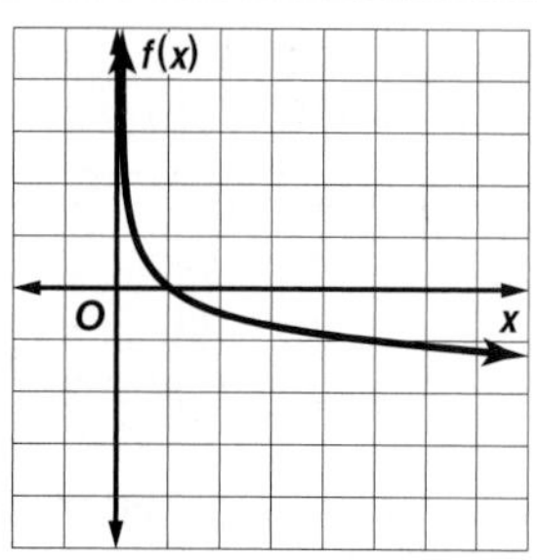

39.

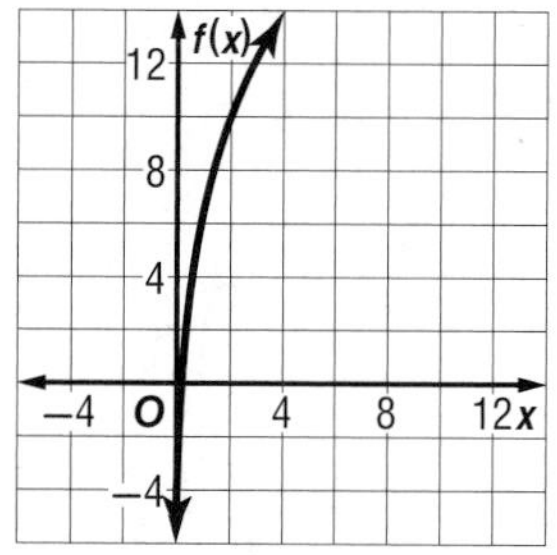

40.

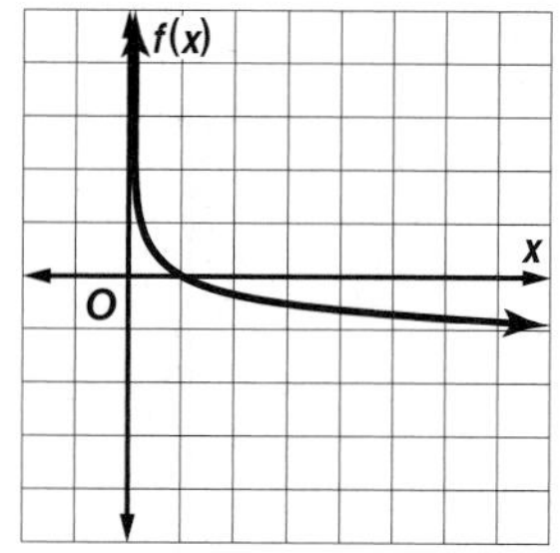

41.

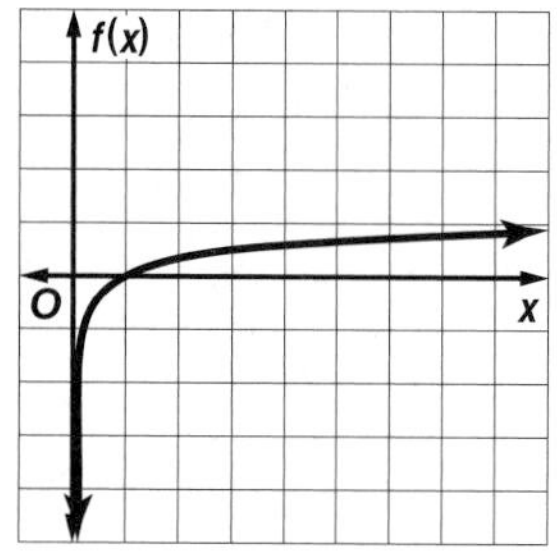

42.

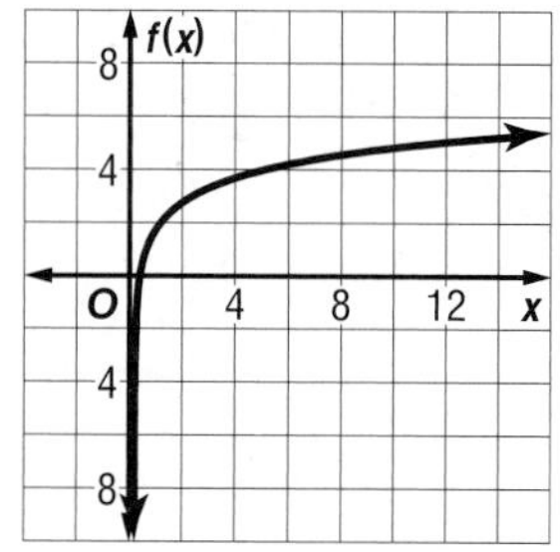

43.

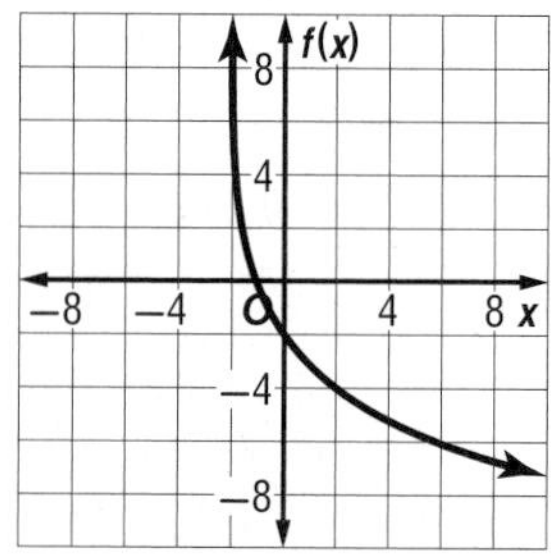

44.

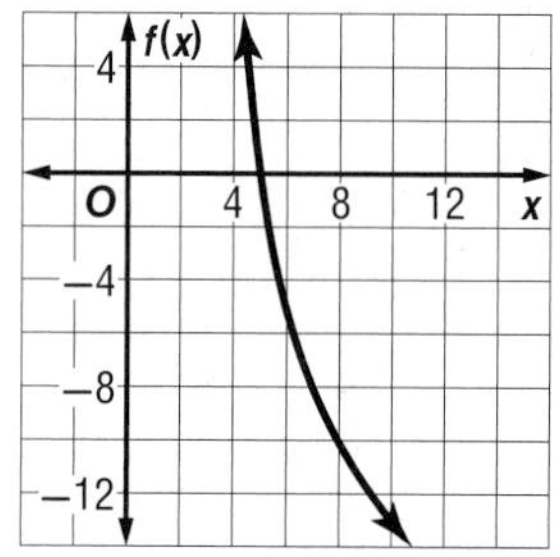

45.

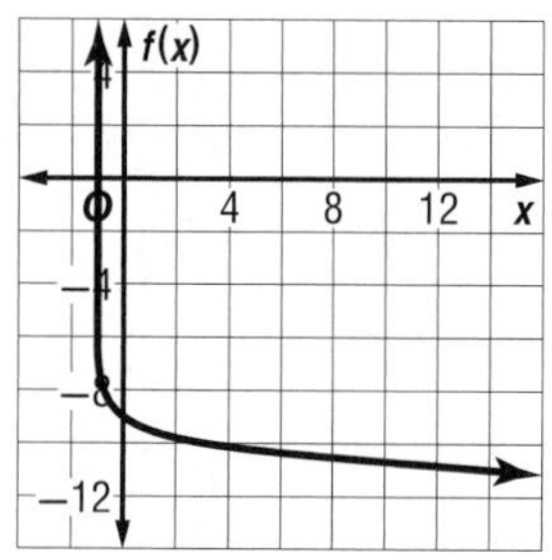

46.

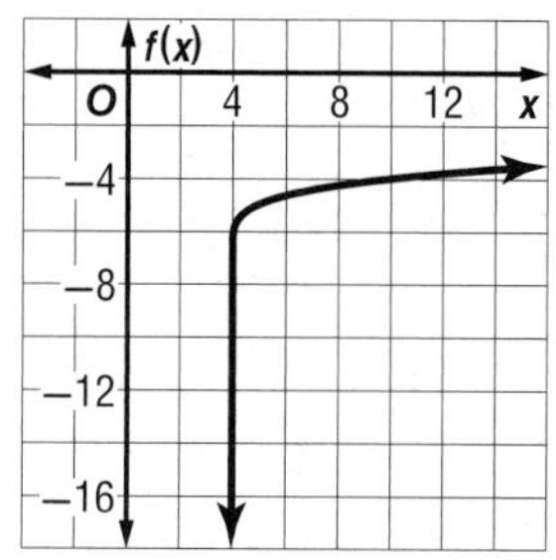

47.

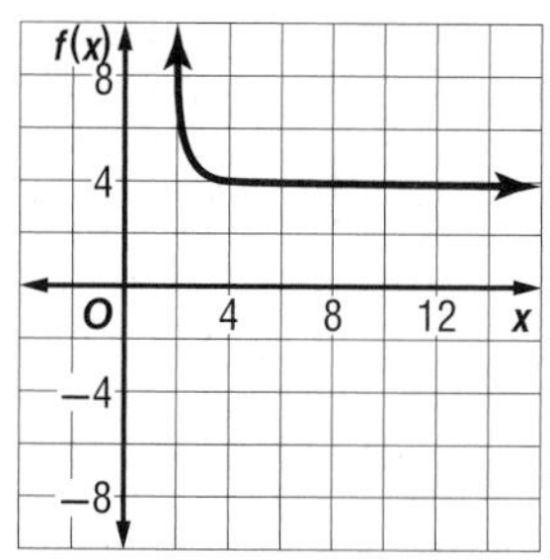

48.

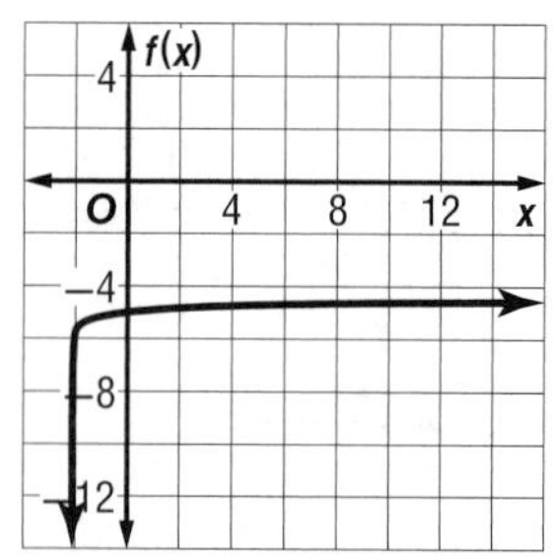

51.

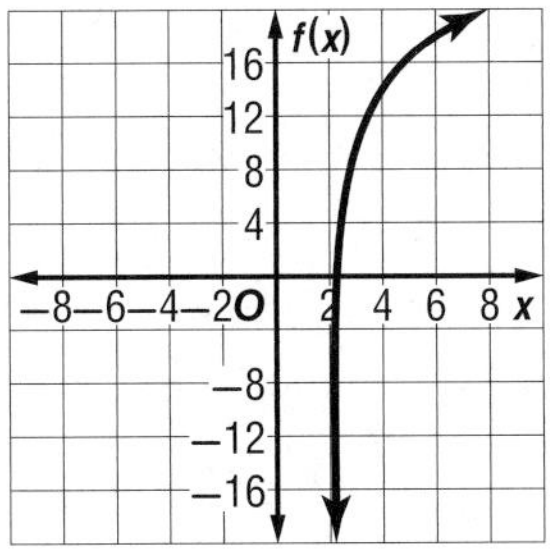

52.

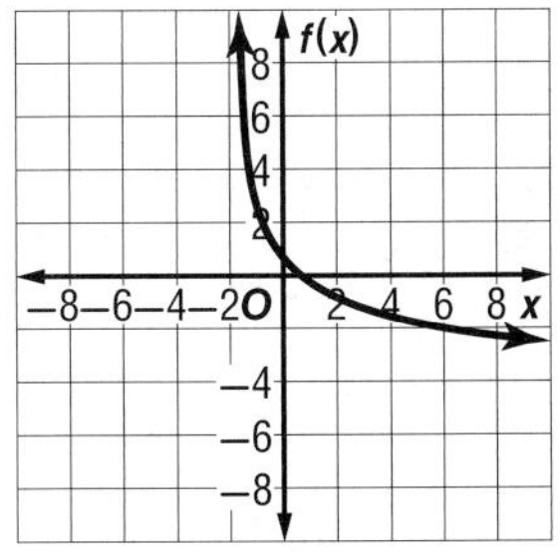

53.

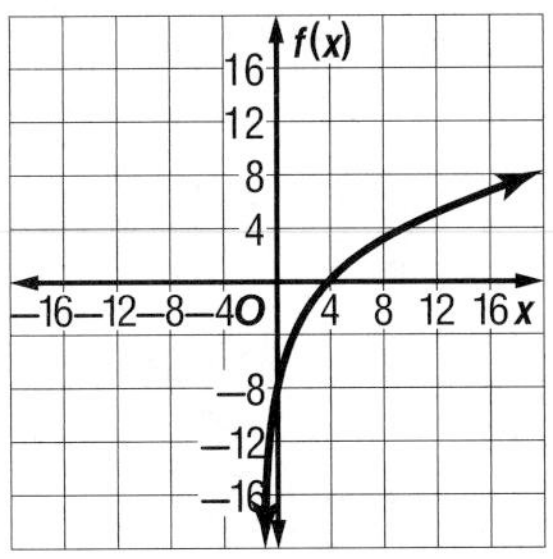

54.

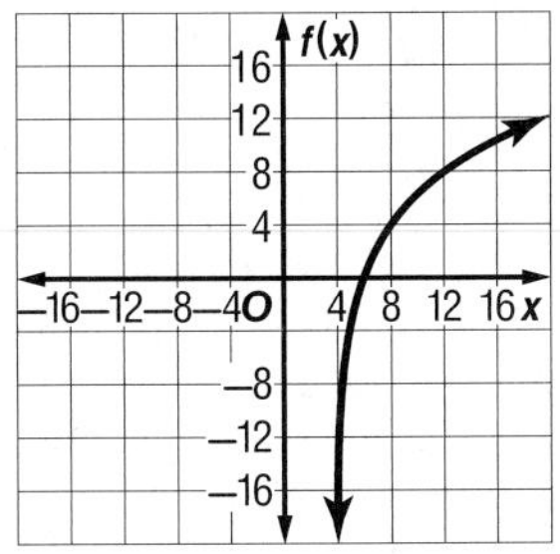

55.

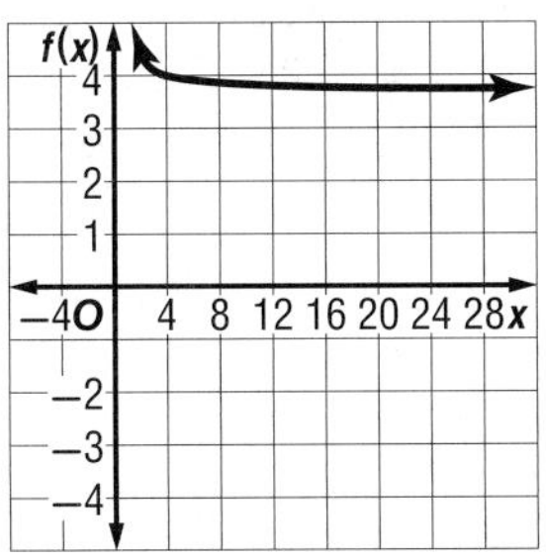

56.

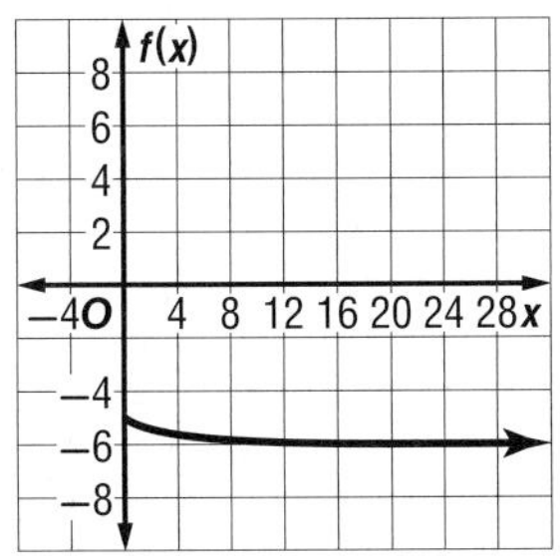

57c.

Sales versus Money Spent on Advertising

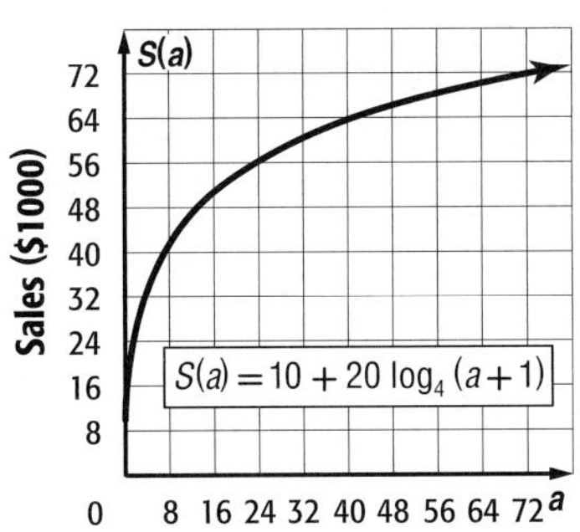

Page 508, Mid-Chapter Quiz

1.

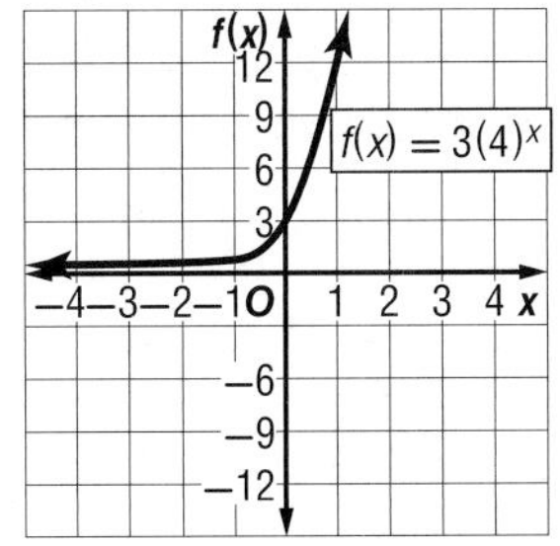

D = {all real numbers}; R = {$f(x)$ | $f(x) > 0$}

2.

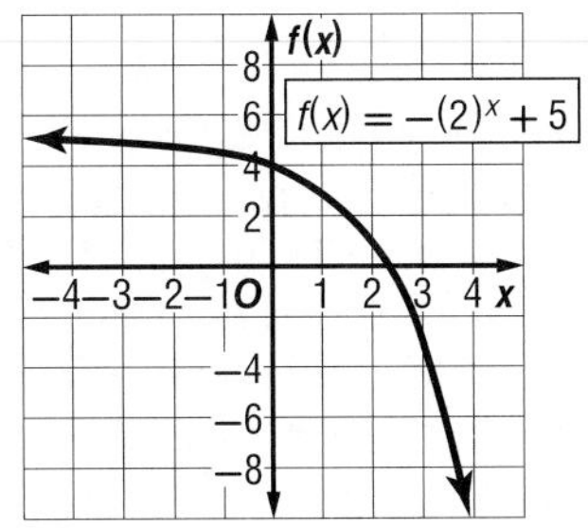

D = {all real numbers}; R = {$f(x)$ | $f(x) < 5$}

3.

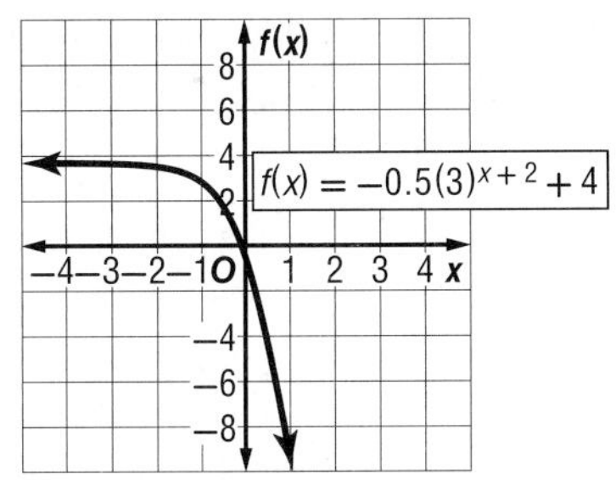

D = {all real numbers}; R = {$f(x)$ | $f(x) < 4$}

4.

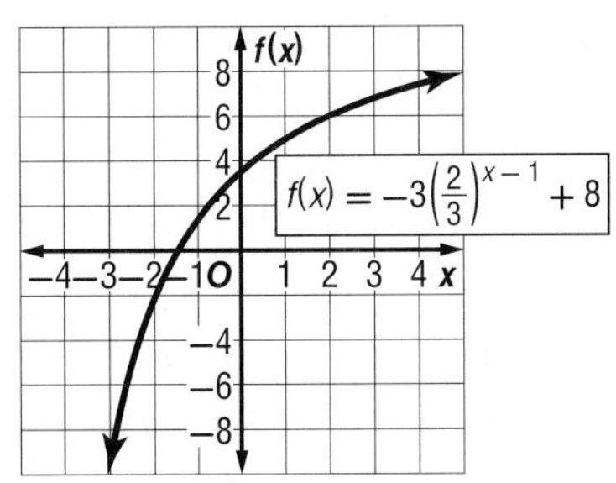

D = {all real numbers}; R = {$f(x)$ | $f(x) < 8$}

9.

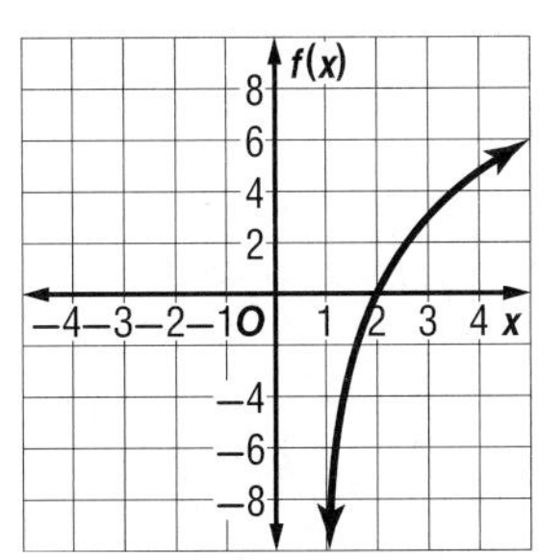

10.

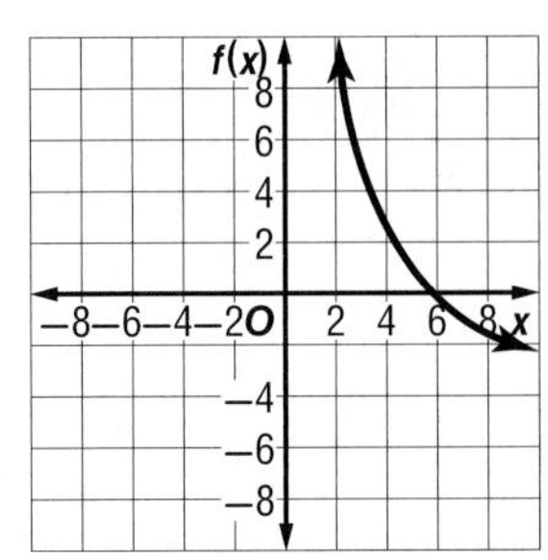

Page 514, Lesson 8-5

66. $\log_a \frac{1}{x} = -\log_a x$ Original equation

$\log_a x^{-1} = -\log_a x$ Definition of negative exponents

$\log_a x^{-1} = (-1)\log_a x$ Power Property of Logarithms

$\log_a \frac{1}{x} = -\log_a x$ Simplify.

67. $x^{3\log_x 2 - \log_x 5} = x^{3\log_x 2\ -\ \log_x 5}$

$= x^{\log_x 2^3\ -\ \log_x 5}$

$= x^{\log_x 8\ -\ \log_x 5}$

$= x^{\log_x \frac{8}{5}}$

$= \frac{8}{5}$

68. Since logarithms are exponents, the properties of logarithms are similar to the properties of exponents. The Product Property states that to multiply two powers that have the same base, add the exponents. Similarly, the logarithm of a product is the sum of the logarithms of its factors. The Quotient Property states that to divide two powers that have the same base, subtract their exponents. Similarly the logarithm of a quotient is the difference of the logarithms of the numerator and the denominator. The Power Property states that to find the power of a power, multiply the exponents. Similarly, the logarithm of a power is the product of the logarithm and the exponent. Answers should include the following.

- Quotient Property: $\log_2\left(\frac{32}{8}\right) = \log_2\left(\frac{2^5}{2^3}\right)$ Replace 32 with 2^5 and 8 with 2^8.

  $= \log_2 2^{(5\ -\ 3)}$ Quotient of Powers

  $= 5 - 3$ or 2 Inverse Property of Exponents and Logarithms

  $\log_2 32 - \log_2 8 = \log_2 2^5 - \log_2 2^3$ Replace 32 with 2^5 and 8 with 2^3.

  $= 5 - 3$ or 2 Inverse Property of Exponents and Logarithms

  So, $\log_2\left(\frac{32}{8}\right) = \log_2 32 - \log_2 8$.

  Power Property: $\log_3 9^4 = \log_3 (3^2)^4$ Replace 9 with 3^2.

  $= \log_3 3^{(2\cdot 4)}$ Power of a Power

  $= 2 \cdot 4$ or 8 Inverse Property of Exponents and Logarithms

  $4 \log_3 9 = (\log_3 9) \cdot 4$ Commutative Property ($\times$)

  $= (\log_3 3^2) \cdot 4$ Replace 9 with 3^2.

  $= 2 \cdot 4$ or 8 Inverse Property of Exponents and Logarithms

  So, $\log_3 9^4 = 4 \log_3 9$.

- The Product of Powers Property and Product Property of Logarithms both involve the addition of exponents, since logarithms are exponents.

NOTES

CHAPTER 9 Chapter Planner

Diagnostic Assessment
Quick Check, p. 551

	Lesson 9-1 Pacing: 1.5 days	Lesson 9-2 Pacing: 1.5 days	Lesson 9-3 Pacing: 1 day	Lesson 9-4 Pacing: 1.5 days
Title	**Multiplying and Dividing Rational Expressions**	**Adding and Subtracting Rational Expressions**	**Graphing Reciprocal Functions**	**Graphing Rational Functions**
Objectives	• Simplify rational expressions. • Simplify complex fractions.	• Determine the LCM of polynomials. • Add and subtract rational expressions.	• Determine properties of reciprocal functions. • Graph transformations of reciprocal functions.	• Graph rational functions with vertical and horizontal asymptotes. • Graph rational functions with oblique asymptotes and point discontinuity.
Key Vocabulary	rational expression, complex fraction		reciprocal function, hyperbola, asymptote	rational function, point discontinuity
NGSSS	MA.912.A.5.2	MA.912.A.5.2	LA.910.1.6.1, MA.912.A.5.6	MA.912.A.2.10, MA.912.A.5.6
Multiple Representations	p. 560		p. 574	
Lesson Resources	**Chapter 9 Resource Masters** • Study Guide and Intervention, pp. 5–6 AL OL ELL • Skills Practice, p. 7 AL OL ELL • Practice, p. 8 AL OL BL ELL • Word Problem Practice, p. 9 AL OL BL ELL • Enrichment, p. 10 OL BL **Transparencies** • 5-Minute Check Transparency 9-1 AL OL BL ELL **Additional Print Resources** • Study Notebook AL OL BL ELL • Teaching Algebra with Manipulatives, p. 237 AL OL ELL	**Chapter 9 Resource Masters** • Study Guide and Intervention, pp. 11–12 AL OL ELL • Skills Practice, p. 13 AL OL ELL • Practice, p. 14 AL OL BL ELL • Word Problem Practice, p. 15 AL OL BL ELL • Enrichment, p. 16 OL BL • TI-Nspire Activity, p. 17 OL • Quiz 1, p. 48 AL OL BL ELL **Transparencies** • 5-Minute Check Transparency 9-2 AL OL BL ELL **Additional Print Resources** • Study Notebook AL OL BL ELL	**Chapter 9 Resource Masters** • Study Guide and Intervention, pp. 18–19 AL OL ELL • Skills Practice, p. 20 AL OL ELL • Practice, p. 21 AL OL BL ELL • Word Problem Practice, p. 22 AL OL BL ELL • Enrichment, p. 23 OL BL • Graphing Calculator Activity, p. 24 OL • Quiz 2, p. 48 AL OL BL ELL **Transparencies** • 5-Minute Check Transparency 9-3 AL OL BL ELL **Additional Print Resources** • Study Notebook AL OL BL ELL	**Chapter 9 Resource Masters** • Study Guide and Intervention, pp. 25–26 AL OL ELL • Skills Practice, p. 27 AL OL ELL • Practice, p. 28 AL OL BL ELL • Word Problem Practice, p. 29 AL OL BL ELL • Enrichment, p. 30 BL • Graphing Calculator Activity, p. 31 OL **Transparencies** • 5-Minute Check Transparency 9-4 AL OL BL ELL **Additional Print Resources** • Study Notebook AL OL BL ELL
Technology for Every Lesson	FL Math Online glencoe.com • Extra Examples • Self-Check Quizzes • Personal Tutor • Homework Help	**CD/DVD Resources** IWB INTERACTIVE WHITEBOARD READY IWB StudentWorks Plus IWB Interactive Classroom IWB Diagnostic and Assessment Planner		• TeacherWorks Plus • eSolutions Manual Plus • ExamView Assessment Suite
Get Animated	Animation			Interactive Lab
Differentiated Instruction	pp. 556, 561	pp. 564, 566	pp. 570, 572	pp. 580, 584

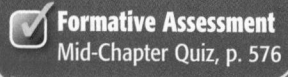

Formative Assessment
Mid-Chapter Quiz, p. 576

KEY: AL Approaching Level OL On Level BL Beyond Level ELL English Learners

Suggested Pacing			
Time Periods	Instruction	Review& Assessment	Total
45-minute	9	2	11
90-minute	4	1	5

Rational Functions and Relations

Extend 9-4 Pacing: 0.5 day	Lesson 9-5 Pacing: 1 day	Lesson 9-6 Pacing: 1.5 days	Extend 9-6 Pacing: 0.5 day
Graphing Technology Lab: Graphing Rational Functions	**Variation Functions**	**Solving Rational Equations and Inequalities**	**Graphing Technology Lab: Solving Rational Equations and Inequalities**
• Use a graphing calculator to explore the graphs of rational functions.	• Recognize and solve direct and joint variation problems. • Recognize and solve inverse and combined variation problems.	• Solve rational equations. • Solve rational inequalities.	• Use a graphing calculator to solve rational equations by graphing or by using the table feature.
	direct variation, constant of variation	rational equations, rational inequalities, weighted average	
MA.912.A.5.6	MA.912.A.2.12	MA.912.A.5.5, MA.912.A.5.7	MA.912.A.5.5
		p. 601	
Materials • TI-83/84 Plus or other graphing calculator	**Chapter 9 Resource Masters** • Study Guide and Intervention, pp. 32–33 AL OL ELL • Skills Practice, p. 34 AL OL ELL • Practice, p. 35 AL OL BL ELL • Word Problem Practice, p. 36 AL OL BL ELL • Enrichment, p. 37 OL BL • Spreadsheet Activity, p. 38 OL • Quiz 3, p. 49 AL OL BL ELL **Transparencies** • 5-Minute Check Transparency 9-5 AL OL BL ELL **Additional Print Resources** • Study Notebook AL OL BL ELL	**Chapter 9 Resource Masters** • Study Guide and Intervention, pp. 39–40 AL OL ELL • Skills Practice, p. 41 AL OL ELL • Practice, p. 42 AL OL BL ELL • Word Problem Practice, p. 43 AL OL BL ELL • Enrichment, p. 44 OL BL • Quiz 4, p. 49 AL OL BL ELL **Transparencies** • 5-Minute Check Transparency 9-5 AL OL BL ELL **Additional Print Resources** • Study Notebook AL OL BL ELL	**Materials** • TI-83/84 Plus or other graphing calculator

FL Math Online glencoe.com
- Extra Examples
- Self-Check Quizzes
- Personal Tutor
- Homework Help

CD/DVD Resources IWB INTERACTIVE WHITEBOARD READY
- IWB StudentWorks Plus
- IWB Interactive Classroom
- IWB Diagnostic and Assessment Planner
- TeacherWorks Plus
- eSolutions Manual Plus
- ExamView Assessment Suite

		Interactive Lab	
	pp. 591, 593	pp. 598, 602	

Summative Assessment
- Study Guide and Review, pp. 605–608
- Practice Test, p. 609

CHAPTER 9

Assessment and Intervention

SE = Student Edition, **TE** = Teacher Edition, **CRM** = Chapter Resource Masters

	Diagnosis	Prescription
Diagnostic Assessment	**Beginning Chapter 9**	
	Get Ready for Chapter 9 **SE,** p. 551	Response to Intervention **TE,** p. 551
	Beginning Every Lesson	
	Then, Now, Why? **SE** 5-Minute Check Transparencies	Chapter 0 **SE,** pp. P1–P19 through P1–P19 Concepts and Skills Bank **SE** pp. 994–1007
Formative Assessment	**During/After Every Lesson**	
	Guided Practice **SE,** every example Check Your Understanding **SE** H.O.T. Problems **SE** Spiral Review **SE** Additional Examples **TE** Watch Out! **TE** Step 4, Assess **TE** Chapter 9 Quizzes **CRM,** pp. 48–49 Self-Check Quizzes glencoe.com	**Tier 1 Intervention** Concepts and Skills Bank **SE,** pp. 994–1007 Skills Practice **CRM,** Ch. 1–9 glencoe.com **Tier 2 Intervention** Differentiated Instruction **TE** Study Guide and Intervention Masters **CRM,** Ch. 1–9 **Tier 3 Intervention** *Math Triumphs, Alg. 2,* Ch. 2
	Mid-Chapter	
	Mid-Chapter Quiz **SE,** p. 576 Mid-Chapter Test **CRM,** p. 50 ExamView Assessment Suite	**Tier 1 Intervention** Concepts and Skills Bank **SE,** pp. 994–1007 Skills Practice **CRM,** Ch. 1–9 glencoe.com **Tier 2 Intervention** Study Guide and Intervention Masters **CRM,** Ch. 1–9 **Tier 3 Intervention** *Math Triumphs, Alg. 2,* Ch. 2
	Before Chapter Test	
	Chapter Study Guide and Review **SE,** pp. 605–608 Practice Test **SE,** p. 609 Standardized Test Practice **SE,** pp. 610–613 Chapter Test glencoe.com Standardized Test Practice glencoe.com Vocabulary Review glencoe.com ExamView Assessment Suite	**Tier 1 Intervention** Concepts and Skills Bank **SE,** pp. 994–1007 Skills Practice **CRM,** Ch. 1–9 glencoe.com **Tier 2 Intervention** Study Guide and Intervention Masters **CRM,** Ch. 1–9 **Tier 3 Intervention** *Math Triumphs, Alg. 2,* Ch. 2
Summative Assessment	**After Chapter 9**	
	Multiple-Choice Tests, Forms 1, 2A, 2B, **CRM,** pp. 52–57 Free-Response Tests, Forms 2C, 2D, 3, **CRM,** pp. 58–63 Vocabulary Test **CRM,** p. 51 Extended Response Test **CRM,** p. 64 Standardized Test Practice **CRM,** pp. 65–67 ExamView Assessment Suite	Study Guide and Intervention Masters **CRM,** Ch. 1–9 glencoe.com

Differentiated Instruction

Option 1 Reaching All Learners AL OL BL ELL

INTERPERSONAL Place students in groups of four. Since there are several tasks involved in graphing reciprocal functions of the form $f(x) = \frac{a}{x - h} + k$, have the group members decide which tasks they should each complete in order to graph a given function. For example, one member can be responsible for finding the a, h, and k values, another can identify the asymptotes, another can substitute values in order to determine points on the graph, and a fourth member can graph the points and draw the curve of the function.

LOGICAL As you explain the various types of variation functions, have students copy and complete the following table to help them organize all the types studied.

Variation	Equation	Graph
Direct		
Joint		
Inverse		
Combined		

Option 2 Approaching Level AL

Write the following fraction and rational expression on the board.

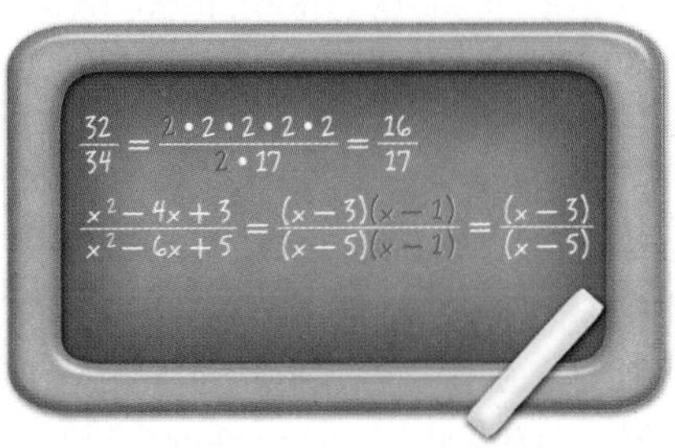

$\frac{32}{34} = \frac{2 \cdot 2 \cdot 2 \cdot 2 \cdot 2}{2 \cdot 17} = \frac{16}{17}$
$\frac{x^2 - 4x + 3}{x^2 - 6x + 5} = \frac{(x-3)(x-1)}{(x-5)(x-1)} = \frac{(x-3)}{(x-5)}$

Review how to simplify fractions. Emphasize that you can only divide the numerator and denominator by common factors–common terms are not "fair game." Explain that the 3 in 32 and the 3 in 34 cannot be factored out because 3 is NOT a factor. As a class, simplify the rational expression. Explain that even though the x^2 term appears in both the numerator and the denominator, it cannot be factored out, since x^2 is a term in this expression and NOT a factor. Use colors to highlight the common factors.

Option 3 English Learners ELL

Have students think about the aspects of multiplying and dividing rational expressions they find challenging. Then, have them write about or tell the procedures and cautions for multiplying and dividing rational expressions, demonstrating with examples.

Option 4 Beyond Level BL

Write a fraction and a rational expression on the board. Ask students to find two fractions whose sum is equal to the fraction you wrote. Then ask students to use similar thinking to find two rational expressions whose sum is equal to the expression you wrote.
To make it a little more challenging, ask students to write two fractions whose denominators are different from the one you wrote, yet whose sum is equal to the fraction you wrote. Finally, challenge students do the same with the rational expression you wrote.

FL Math Online Access Point Activities

CHAPTER 9

Focus on Mathematical Content

Vertical Alignment

Before Chapter 9

Related Topics from Algebra 1

- use Commutative, Associative, and Distributive Properties to simplify algebraic expressions
- identify mathematical domains and ranges and determine reasonable domain and range values for given situations
- solve problems involving proportional change

Previous Topics from Algebra 2

- sketch graphs of parent functions, including linear functions
- use tools including factoring to transform and solve equations

Chapter 9

Topics from Algebra 2

- determine properties of reciprocal functions and graph their transformations
- use quotients of polynomials to describe the graphs of rational functions, describe limitations on the domains and ranges, and examine asymptotic behavior
- determine the reasonable domain and range values of rational functions and determine the reasonableness of solutions to rational equations and inequalities
- analyze a situation modeled by a rational function, formulate an equation composed of a linear or quadratic function, and solve the problem
- use functions to model and make predictions in problem situations involving direct and inverse variation

After Chapter 9

Preparation for Precalculus

- determine the domain and range of functions using graphs, tables, and symbols
- investigate the concepts of continuity, end behavior, and asymptotes and connect these characteristics to functions represented graphically and numerically

Lesson-by-Lesson Preview

9-1 Multiplying and Dividing Rational Expressions

In this lesson, students apply their prior knowledge of fractions to rational expressions (a ratio of two polynomial expressions).

- *A fraction is undefined if the denominator is zero.* Students examine polynomials in the denominators of rational expressions and identify values of variables for which the denominators are zero.
- *A fraction can be simplified by replacing a quotient of common factors in the numerator and denominator with 1.* In rational expressions, the common factors may be polynomials. Students should also recognize that the quotient of factors of the form $b - a$ and $a - b$ can be replaced with -1.
- *To multiply fractions, divide the product of the numerators by the product of the denominators.* Rational expressions are multiplied in the same way.
- *To divide by a fraction, multiply by its reciprocal.* Do the same to divide by a rational expression.
- *To simplify a complex fraction, rewrite it and treat it as a division expression.* The same is true when the complex fraction involves rational expressions.

9-2 Adding and Subtracting Rational Expressions

Adding and subtracting rational expressions is similar to adding and subtracting fractions. Least common multiples can be found by comparing prime factorizations. If two or more polynomials are factored, their least common multiple will include each factor with an exponent indicating the maximum number of times that factor appears in one of the polynomials.

To add and subtract rational expressions:

- Make sure the expressions have common denominators. If not, find the LCM of the given denominators and rewrite each rational expression as an equivalent expression having the LCM as its denominator.
- The sum (or difference) of rational expressions with common denominators is equal to an expression in which the denominator is the common denominator and the numerator is the sum (or difference) of the numerators.

9-3 Graphing Reciprocal Functions

A reciprocal function has an equation of the form $f(x) = \frac{1}{a(x)}$, where $a(x)$ is a linear function and $a(x) \neq 0$.

Reciprocal functions may have breaks in continuity for values that are excluded from the domain, and some may have an *asymptote,* a line that the graph of the function approaches.

- A *vertical asymptote* shows where a function is undefined. A reciprocal function is undefined for values of x that make $a(x) = 0$.
- A *horizontal asymptote* shows the end behavior of a graph.

The parent function of reciprocal functions is $f(x) = \frac{1}{x}$. The same techniques used to transform the graphs of other functions can be applied to the graphs of reciprocal functions.

9-4 Graphing Rational Functions

A rational function has an equation of the form $f(x) = \frac{a(x)}{b(x)}$, where $a(x)$ and $b(x)$ are polynomial functions and $b(x) \neq 0$. Some graphs of rational functions have breaks in continuity. A break in continuity may appear as:

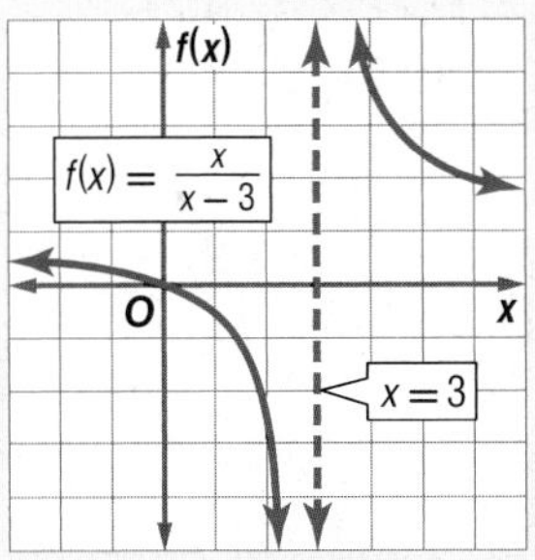

- a *vertical asymptote* whenever $b(x) = 0$.

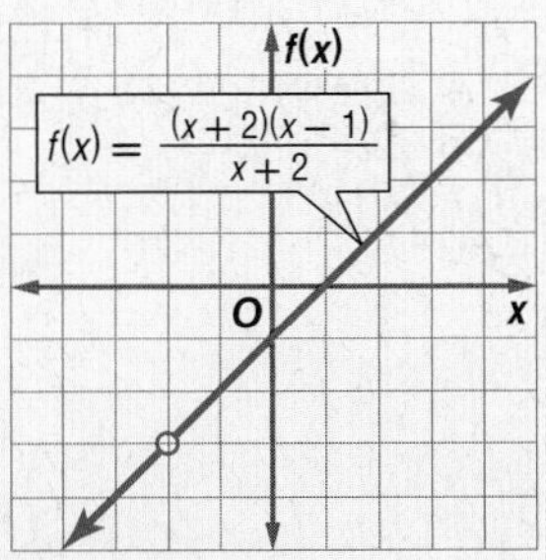

- *point discontinuity,* a hole in a graph. This type of discontinuity appears at $x = c$ whenever $x - c$ is a factor of both $a(x)$ and $b(x)$.

A rational function has at most one *horizontal asymptote.* It is:

- the line $y = 0$, whenever the degree of $a(x)$ is less than the degree of $b(x)$.
- the line $y = \frac{\text{leading coefficient of } a(x)}{\text{leading coefficient of } b(x)}$, whenever the degree of $a(x)$ equals the degree of $b(x)$.
- If the degree of $a(x)$ is greater than the degree of $b(x)$, there is no horizontal axis.

An *oblique asymptote,* also called a slant asymptote, occurs for rational functions that have a numerator polynomial that is one degree higher than the denominator polynomial.

Students can identify the asymptotes of a function and use them along with a table of values to graph the function.

9-5 Variation Functions

- A *direct variation* function is denoted by $y = kx$ $\left(\text{also written } \frac{y}{x} = k\right)$, when k is a constant. Its graph is a *line* that passes through the origin and has slope k.
- A *joint variation* function occurs when y varies jointly as x and z and there is some nonzero constant k such that $y = kxz$.
- An *inverse variation* function is denoted by $y = \frac{k}{x}$ (or $xy = k$). Its graph is a *hyperbola.*
- A *combined variation* function occurs when one quantity varies directly and/or inversely as two or more other quantities.

9-6 Solving Rational Equations and Inequalities

Equations that contain one or more rational expressions are called *rational equations.* The same concepts and skills used to solve linear equations can be used to solve rational equations once the fractions are eliminated using the LCD. All solutions found should be checked in the original equation to identify extraneous solutions.

Rational equations can be written to solve *weighted average* problems. The weighted average of a set of data is the sum of the product of the number of units and the value per unit divided by the sum of the number of units. These types of problems include *mixture, work, distance,* and *interest* problems.

Mc Graw Hill Professional Development

Targeted professional development has been articulated throughout *Algebra 2.* More quality, customized professional development is available from McGraw-Hill Professional Development. Visit glencoe.com for details on each product.

- **Online Lessons** emphasize the strategies and techniques used to teach Algebra 2. Includes streaming video, interactive pages, and online tools.
- **Video Workshops** allow mentors, coaches, or leadership personnel to facilitate on-site workshops on educational strategies in mathematics and mathematical concepts.
- **MHPD Online** (www.mhpdonline.com) offers online professional development with video clips of instructional strategies, links, student activities, and news and issues in education.
- **Teaching Today** (teachingtoday.glencoe.com) gives secondary teachers practical strategies and materials that inspire excellence and innovation in teaching.

Chapter 9 Notes

Chapter Project

A Plane Trip

Students use what they have learned about rational functions and variation to investigate airplane travel.

- Working in pairs, ask students to find an average speed for an airplane traveling coast-to-coast. Then have them use the equation $v = \frac{d}{t}$, where v is the average speed, d is distance, and t is time, to calculate the time that it would take for an airplane trip of 3476 kilometers.
- Another way to look at average speed is to include time spent at the airport (check-in, security check, etc.). If non-travel time at the airport is 2 hours, then a revised equation for average speed would be $v = \frac{d}{t + 2}$. Find the revised average speed for the same 3476-kilometer trip.
- What would the average speed *in the air* have to be to make up for the time spent at the airport (that is, so the total time is the same as in the first calculation)?

Chapter 9 Rational Functions and Relations

Then

In Chapter 5, you used factoring to solve quadratic equations and you graphed quadratic equations.

Now

In Chapter 9, you will:

- Simplify rational expressions.
- Graph rational functions.
- Solve direct, joint, and inverse variation problems.
- Solve rational equations and inequalities.

NGSSS

MA.912.A.2.12
MA.912.A.5.6

Why?

TRAVEL Whether you travel by boat, car, bicycle, or airplane, rational functions can be used to find distance traveled, time spent traveling, and speed. If you want to arrive at a destination on time, rational relations can tell you at what speed you need to travel to reach your goal. When graphing rational functions you see clearly how the speed at which you travel affects the time it takes to get there.

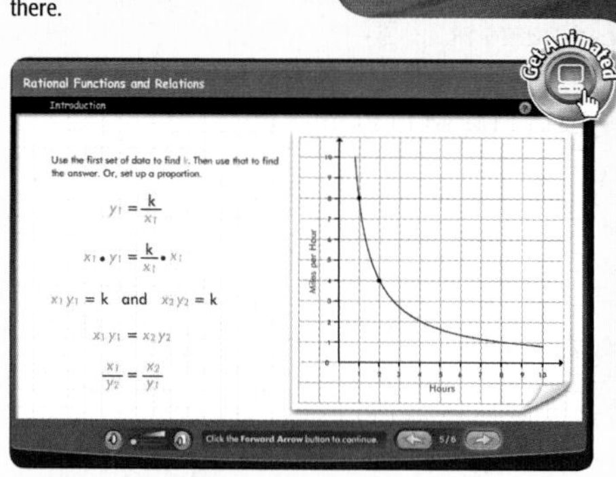

Key Vocabulary Introduce the key vocabulary in the chapter using the routine below.

Define: An asymptote is a line that a graph approaches.

Example:

The graph shows asymptotes at $x = -3$ and $f(x) = 2$.

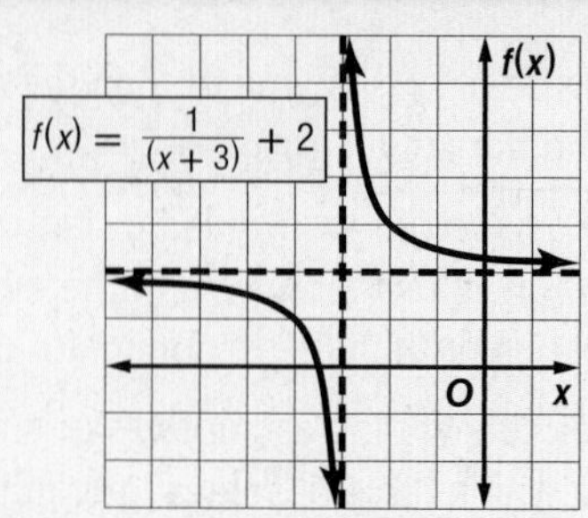

Ask: What does a vertical asymptote show? where a function is undefined

Get Ready for Chapter 9

Diagnose Readiness You have two options for checking Prerequisite Skills.

Text Option

Take the Quick Check below. Refer to the Quick Review for help.

QuickCheck

(Used in Lesson 9-1)

Solve each equation. Write in simplest form. (Lesson 1-3)

1. $\frac{5}{14} = \frac{1}{3}x$ $x = \frac{15}{14}$
2. $\frac{1}{8}m = \frac{7}{3}$ $m = \frac{56}{3}$
3. $\frac{8}{5} = \frac{1}{4}k$ $k = \frac{32}{5}$
4. $\frac{10}{9}p = 7$ $p = \frac{63}{10}$
5. **TRUCKS** Martin used $\frac{1}{3}$ of a tank of gas in his truck to get to work. He began with a full tank of gas. If he had 18 gallons of gas left, how many gallons does his tank hold? 27 gal

(Used in Lesson 9-2)

Simplify each expression.

6. $\frac{3}{4} - \frac{7}{8}$ $-\frac{1}{8}$
7. $\frac{8}{9} - \frac{7}{6} + \frac{1}{3}$ $1\frac{1}{18}$
8. $\frac{9}{10} - \frac{4}{15} + \frac{1}{3}$ $1\frac{29}{30}$
9. $\frac{10}{3} + \frac{5}{6} + 3$ $\frac{43}{6}$
10. **BAKING** Annie baked cookies for a bake sale. She used $\frac{2}{3}$ cups of flour for one recipe and $4\frac{1}{2}$ cups of flour for the other recipe. How many cups total did she use? $5\frac{1}{6}$ c

(Used in Lesson 9-4)

Solve each proportion. (Concepts and Skills Bank 1)

11. $\frac{9}{12} = \frac{p}{36}$ $p = 27$
12. $\frac{9}{18} = \frac{6}{m}$ $m = 12$
13. $\frac{2}{7} = \frac{5}{k}$ $k = 17.5$
14. **SALES TAX** Kirsten pays \$4.40 tax on \$55 worth of clothes. What amount of tax will she pay on \$35 worth of clothes? \$2.80

QuickReview

EXAMPLE 1

Solve $\frac{9}{11} = \frac{7}{8}r$. Write in simplest form.

$\frac{9}{11} = \frac{7}{8}r$	
$\frac{72}{11} = 7r$	Multiply each side by 8.
$\frac{72}{77} = r$	Divide each side by 7.

Since the GCF of 72 and 77 is 1, the solution is in simplest form.

EXAMPLE 2

Simplify $\frac{1}{3} + \frac{3}{4} - \frac{5}{6}$.

$\frac{1}{3} + \frac{3}{4} - \frac{5}{6}$	
$= \frac{1}{3}\left(\frac{4}{4}\right) + \frac{3}{4}\left(\frac{3}{3}\right) - \frac{5}{6}\left(\frac{2}{2}\right)$	The GCF of 3, 4, and 6 is 12.
$= \frac{4}{12} + \frac{9}{12} - \frac{10}{12}$	Simplify.
$= \frac{3}{12}$	Add and subtract.
$= \frac{3 \div 3}{12 \div 3}$ or $\frac{1}{4}$	Simplify.

EXAMPLE 3

Solve $\frac{5}{8} = \frac{u}{11}$.

$\frac{5}{8} = \frac{u}{11}$	Write the equation.
$5(11) = 8u$	Find the cross products.
$55 = 8u$	Simplify.
$\frac{55}{8} = u$	Divide each side by 8.

Since the GCF of 55 and 8 is 1, the answer is in simplified form. $u = \frac{55}{8}$ or $6\frac{7}{8}$.

Online Option

FL Math Online Take a self-check Chapter Readiness Quiz at glencoe.com.

Response to Intervention (RtI)

Use the *Quick Check* results and the Intervention Planner to help you determine your Response to Intervention. The If-Then statements in the chart below help you decide the appropriate tier of RtI and suggest intervention resources for each tier.

Intervention Planner

Tier 1 — On Level

If students miss about 25% of the exercises or less,

Then choose a resource:

- **SE** Concepts and Skills Bank, p. 993 Lesson 1-3
- **CRM** Skills Practice, Chapter 1, p. 19
- **TE** Chapter Project, p. 550
- FL Math Online Self-Check Quiz

Tier 2 — Strategic Intervention approaching grade level

If students miss about 50% of the exercises,

Then choose a resource:

- **CRM** Study Guide and Intervention, Chapter 1, p. 17
- FL Math Online Extra Examples, Personal Tutor, Homework Help

Tier 3 — Intensive Intervention 2 or more years below grade level

If students miss about 75% of the exercises,

Then use *Math Triumphs, Alg. 2,* Ch. 2

FL Math Online Extra Examples, Personal Tutor, Homework Help, Review Vocabulary

FOLDABLES® Study Organizer

Dinah Zike's Foldables®

Focus Students write notes about rational functions and relations in this chapter.

Teach Have students make and label their Foldables as illustrated. Students should use the appropriate tab to record their notes and examples for the concepts in each lesson of this chapter.

When to Use It Encourage students to add to their Foldables as they work through the chapter and to use them to review for the chapter test.

Differentiated Instruction

CRM Student-Built Glossary, pp. 1–2 Students should complete the chart by providing a definition of each term and an example as they progress through Chapter 9. This study tool can also be used to review for the chapter test.

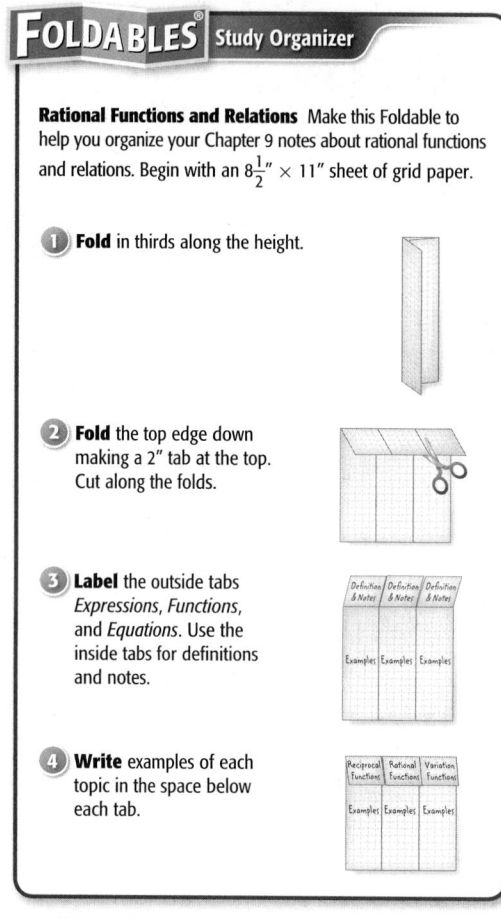

Get Started on Chapter 9

You will learn several new concepts, skills, and vocabulary terms as you study Chapter 9. To get ready, identify important terms and organize your resources. You may wish to refer to **Chapter 0** to review prerequisite skills.

FOLDABLES® Study Organizer

Rational Functions and Relations Make this Foldable to help you organize your Chapter 9 notes about rational functions and relations. Begin with an $8\frac{1}{2}'' \times 11''$ sheet of grid paper.

1. **Fold** in thirds along the height.

2. **Fold** the top edge down making a 2″ tab at the top. Cut along the folds.

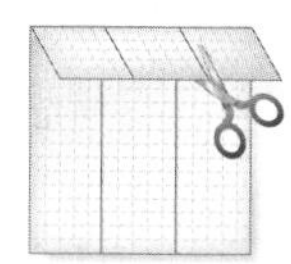

3. **Label** the outside tabs *Expressions*, *Functions*, and *Equations*. Use the inside tabs for definitions and notes.

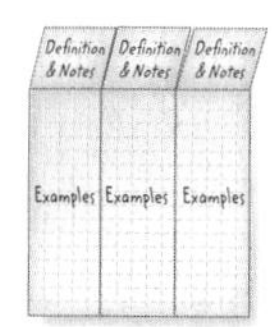

4. **Write** examples of each topic in the space below each tab.

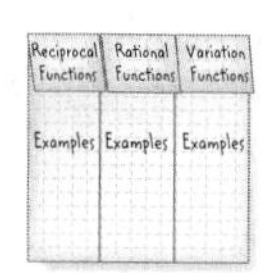

FL Math Online glencoe.com

- Study the chapter online
- Explore **Get Animated**
- Get extra help from your own **Personal Tutor**
- Use **Extra Examples** for additional help
- Take a **Self-Check Quiz**
- **Review Vocabulary** in fun ways

New Vocabulary

English		Español
rational expression	• p. 553 •	expresión racional
complex fraction	• p. 556 •	fracción compleja
reciprocal function	• p. 569 •	función recíproco
hyperbola	• p. 569 •	hipérbola
asymptote	• p. 569 •	asíntota
rational function	• p. 577 •	función racional
vertical asymptote	• p. 577 •	asíntota vertical
horizontal asymptote	• p. 577 •	asíntota horizontal
oblique asymptote	• p. 579 •	asíntota oblicua
point discontinuity	• p. 580 •	discontinuidad evitable
direct variation	• p. 586 •	variación directa
constant of variation	• p. 586 •	constante de variación
joint variation	• p. 587 •	variación conjunta
inverse variation	• p. 588 •	variación inversa
combined variation	• p. 589 •	variación combinada
rational equation	• p. 594 •	ecuación racional
weighted average	• p. 596 •	media ponderada
rational inequality	• p. 599 •	desigualdad racional

Review Vocabulary

function • p. P4 • función a relation in which each element of the domain is paired with exactly one element of the range

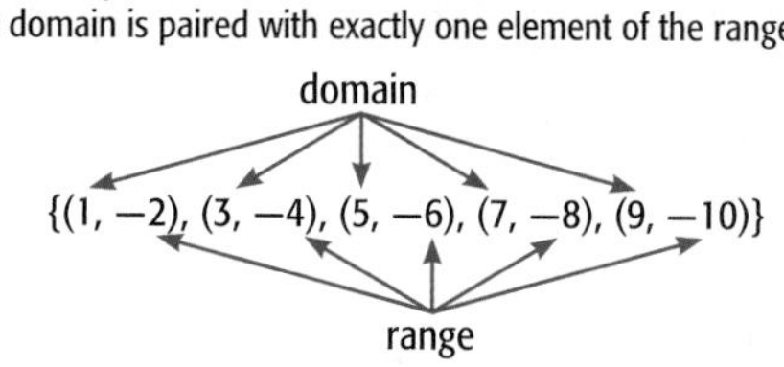

least common multiple • mínimo común múltiplo the least number that is a common multiple of two or more numbers

rational number • p. 11 • número racional a number expressed in the form $\frac{a}{b}$, where a and b are integers and $b \neq 0$

Multilingual eGlossary glencoe.com

9-1 Multiplying and Dividing Rational Expressions

Then
You factored polynomials. (Lesson 5-3)

Now
- Simplify rational expressions.
- Simplify complex fractions.

NGSSS
MA.912.A.5.2 Add, subtract, **multiply, and divide rational expressions.**
MA.912.A.5.3 simplify complex fractions. *Also addresses MA.912.A.10.3.*

New Vocabulary
rational expression
complex fraction

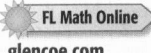

FL Math Online
glencoe.com

Why?

If a scuba diver goes to depths greater than 33 feet, the rational function $T(d) = \frac{1700}{d - 33}$ gives the maximum time a diver can remain at those depths and still surface at a steady rate with no stops. $T(d)$ represents the dive time in minutes, and d represents the depth in feet.

Simplify Rational Expressions A ratio of two polynomial expressions such as $\frac{1700}{d - 33}$ is called a **rational expression**.

Because variables in algebra often represent real numbers, operations with rational numbers and rational expressions are similar. Just as with reducing fractions, to simplify a rational expression, you divide the numerator and denominator by their greatest common factor (GCF).

$$\frac{8}{12} = \frac{2 \cdot \cancel{4}^{1}}{3 \cdot \cancel{4}_{1}} = \frac{2}{3} \quad \text{GCF} = 4$$

$$\frac{x^2 - 4x + 3}{x^2 - 6x + 5} = \frac{(x - 3)\cancel{(x - 1)}^{1}}{(x - 5)\cancel{(x - 1)}_{1}} = \frac{(x - 3)}{(x - 5)} \quad \text{GCF} = (x - 1)$$

EXAMPLE 1 Simplify a Rational Expression

a. Simplify $\frac{5x(x^2 + 4x + 3)}{(x - 6)(x^2 - 9)}$.

$$\frac{5x(x^2 + 4x + 3)}{(x - 6)(x^2 - 9)} = \frac{5x(x + 3)(x + 1)}{(x - 6)(x + 3)(x - 3)} \qquad \textbf{Factor numerator and denominator.}$$

$$= \frac{5x(x + 1)}{(x - 6)\ (x - 3)} \cdot \frac{\cancel{(x + 3)}^{1}}{\cancel{(x + 3)}_{1}} \qquad \textbf{Eliminate common factors.}$$

$$= \frac{5x(x + 1)}{(x - 6)(x - 3)} \qquad \textbf{Simplify.}$$

b. Under what conditions is this expression undefined?

The original factored denominator is $(x - 6)(x + 3)(x - 3)$.
Determine the values that would make the denominator equal to 0.
These values are 6, −3, or 3, so the expression is undefined when $x = 6, 3$ or -3.

Guided Practice 1A. $\frac{4(y + 4)}{(y + 2)}$; $y \neq 0, -2$, or 3 1B. $\frac{2z(z + 4)}{(z - 1)}$; $z \neq 1, 2$, or -5

Simplify each expression. Under what conditions is the expression undefined?

1A. $\frac{4y(y - 3)(y + 4)}{y(y^2 - y - 6)}$ **1B.** $\frac{2z(z + 5)(z^2 + 2z - 8)}{(z - 1)(z + 5)(z - 2)}$

Personal Tutor glencoe.com

9-1 Lesson Notes

1 FOCUS

Vertical Alignment

Before Lesson 9-1
Factor polynomials.

Lesson 9-1
Simplify rational expressions.
Simplify complex fractions.

After Lesson 9-1
Solve rational equations.

2 TEACH

Scaffolding Questions

Have students read the *Why?* section of the lesson.

Ask:

- How can the term *rational expression* help you identify what it means? "Rational" contains the word "ratio."
- What ratio is in the function $T(d) = \frac{1700}{d - 33}$? $\frac{1700}{d - 33}$
- What does it mean to say that 6 is the GCF of 12 and 30? It is the greatest integer that divides both 12 and 30 without a remainder.

Lesson 9-1 Resources

Resource	Approaching-Level	On-Level	Beyond-Level	English Learners
Teacher Edition	• Differentiated Instruction, p. 556	• Differentiated Instruction, pp. 556, 561	• Differentiated Instruction, p. 561	
Chapter Resource Masters	• Study Guide and Intervention, pp. 5–6 • Skills Practice, p. 7 • Practice, p. 8 • Word Problem Practice, p. 9	• Study Guide and Intervention, pp. 5–6 • Skills Practice, p. 7 • Practice, p. 8 • Word Problem Practice, p. 9 • Enrichment, p. 10	• Practice, p. 8 • Word Problem Practice, p. 9 • Enrichment, p. 10	• Study Guide and Intervention, pp. 5–6 • Skills Practice, p. 7 • Practice, p. 8 • Word Problem Practice, p. 9
Transparencies	• 5-Minute Check Transparency 9-1	• 5-Minute Check Transparency 9-1	• 5-Minute Check Transparency 9-1	• 5-Minute Check Transparency 9-1
Other	• Study Notebook • Teaching Algebra with Manipulatives	• Study Notebook • Teaching Algebra with Manipulatives	• Study Notebook	• Study Notebook • Teaching Algebra with Manipulatives

Simplify Rational Expressions

Example 1 shows how to simplify a rational expression and determine the excluded values. **Example 2** shows how to use elimination to answer a test item. **Example 3** shows how to factor out –1 in order to simplify a rational expression. **Example 4** shows how to multiply and divide rational expressions. **Example 5** shows how to simplify a rational expression containing polynomials.

Formative Assessment

Use the Guided Practice exercises after each example to determine students' understanding of concepts.

Additional Examples

1 **a.** Simplify $\dfrac{3y(y+7)}{(y+7)(y^2-9)}$. $\dfrac{3y}{y^2-9}$

b. Under what conditions is this expression undefined? when $y = -7$, $y = -3$, or $y = 3$

2 **STANDARDIZED TEST EXAMPLE**

For what value(s) is $\dfrac{p^2+2p-3}{p^2-2p-15}$ undefined? B

A 5 **C** 3, –5

B –3, 5 **D** 5, 1, –3

3 Simplify $\dfrac{a^4b-2a^4}{2a^3-a^3b}$. $-a$

Additional Examples also in
Interactive Classroom PowerPoint® Presentations

IWB INTERACTIVE WHITEBOARD READY

NGSSS PRACTICE EXAMPLE 2 912.A.5.2

For what value(s) is $\dfrac{x^2(x^2-5x-14)}{4x(x^2+6x+8)}$ undefined?

A. –2, –4
B. –2, 7
C. 0, –2, –4
D. 0, –2, –4, 7

Read the Test Item

You want to determine which values of x make the denominator equal to 0.

Solve the Test Item

With $4x$ in the denominator, x cannot equal 0. So, choices A and B can be eliminated. Next, factor the denominator.

$x^2 + 6x + 8 = (x + 2)(x + 4)$, so the denominator is $4x(x + 2)(x + 4)$.

Because the denominator equals 0 when $x = 0, -2$, and -4, the answer is C.

Test-Taking Tip

Eliminating Choices Sometimes you can save time by looking at the possible answers and eliminating choices.

Guided Practice

2. For what value(s) of x is $\dfrac{x(x^2+8x+12)}{-6(x^2-3x-10)}$ undefined? G

F. 0, 5, –2 **G.** 5, –2 **H.** 0, –2, –6 **I.** 5, –2, –6

Personal Tutor glencoe.com

Sometimes you can factor out –1 in the numerator or denominator to help simplify a rational expression.

EXAMPLE 3 Simplify Using –1

Simplify $\dfrac{(4w^2-3wy)(w+y)}{(3y-4w)(5w+y)}$.

$\dfrac{(4w^2-3wy)(w+y)}{(3y-4w)(5w+y)} = \dfrac{w(4w-3y)(w+y)}{(3y-4w)(5w+y)}$ **Factor.**

$= \dfrac{w(-1)\overset{1}{\cancel{(3y-4w)}}(w+y)}{\underset{1}{\cancel{(3y-4w)}}(5w+y)}$ **$4w - 3y = -1(3y - 4w)$**

$= \dfrac{(-w)(w+y)}{5w+y}$ **Simplify.**

Guided Practice

Simplify each expression.

3A. $\dfrac{(xz-4z)}{z^2(4-x)}$ $-\dfrac{1}{z}$

3B. $\dfrac{ab^2-5ab}{(5+b)(5-b)}$ $-\dfrac{ab}{(5+b)}$

Personal Tutor glencoe.com

The method for multiplying and dividing fractions also works with rational expressions. Remember that to multiply two fractions, you multiply the numerators and multiply the denominators. To divide two fractions, you multiply by the multiplicative inverse, or the reciprocal, of the divisor.

Multiplication

$$\frac{2}{9} \cdot \frac{15}{4} = \frac{\overset{1}{\cancel{2}} \cdot \overset{1}{\cancel{3}} \cdot 5}{\underset{1}{\cancel{3}} \cdot 3 \cdot \underset{1}{\cancel{2}} \cdot 2} = \frac{5}{3 \cdot 2} = \frac{5}{6}$$

Division

$$\frac{3}{5} \div \frac{6}{35} = \frac{3}{5} \cdot \frac{35}{6} = \frac{\overset{1}{\cancel{3}} \cdot \overset{1}{\cancel{5}} \cdot 7}{\underset{1}{\cancel{5}} \cdot 2 \cdot \underset{1}{\cancel{3}}} = \frac{7}{2}$$

Watch Out!

Common Misconceptions Point out that rational expressions are usually used without specifically excluding those values that make the expression undefined. It is understood that only those values for which the expression has meaning are included.

TEACH with TECH

INTERACTIVE WHITEBOARD Use the board to help demonstrate canceling out common factors. Cross out the common factors as you simplify the expression, and drag the remaining factors to create the simplified expression.

554 Chapter 9 Rational Functions and Relations

The following table summarizes the rules for multiplying and dividing rational expressions.

Key Concept

Multiplying Rational Expressions

Words To multiply rational expressions, multiply the numerators and multiply the denominators.

Symbols For all rational expressions $\frac{a}{b}$ and $\frac{c}{d}$ with $b \neq 0$ and $d \neq 0$, $\frac{a}{b} \cdot \frac{c}{d} = \frac{ac}{bd}$.

Dividing Rational Expressions

Words To divide rational expressions, multiply by the reciprocal of the divisor.

Symbols For all rational expressions $\frac{a}{b}$ and $\frac{c}{d}$ with $b \neq 0$, $c \neq 0$, and $d \neq 0$, $\frac{a}{b} \div \frac{c}{d} = \frac{a}{b} \cdot \frac{d}{c} = \frac{ad}{bc}$.

StudyTip

Eliminating Common Factors Be sure to eliminate factors from both the numerator and denominator.

EXAMPLE 4 Multiply and Divide Rational Expressions

Simplify each expression.

a. $\frac{6c}{5d} \cdot \frac{15cd^2}{8a}$

$\frac{6c}{5d} \cdot \frac{15cd^2}{8a} = \frac{2 \cdot 3 \cdot c \cdot 5 \cdot 3 \cdot c \cdot d \cdot d}{5 \cdot d \cdot 2 \cdot 2 \cdot 2 \cdot a}$ Factor.

$= \frac{\overset{1}{\cancel{2}} \cdot 3 \cdot c \cdot \overset{1}{\cancel{5}} \cdot 3 \cdot c \cdot \overset{1}{\cancel{d}} \cdot d}{\underset{1}{\cancel{5}} \cdot \underset{1}{\cancel{d}} \cdot \underset{1}{\cancel{2}} \cdot 2 \cdot 2 \cdot a}$ Eliminate common factors.

$= \frac{3 \cdot 3 \cdot c \cdot c \cdot d}{2 \cdot 2 \cdot a}$ Simplify.

$= \frac{9c^2d}{4a}$ Simplify.

b. $\frac{18xy^3}{7a^2b^2} \div \frac{12x^2y}{35a^2b}$

$\frac{18xy^3}{7a^2b^2} \div \frac{12x^2y}{35a^2b} = \frac{18xy^3}{7a^2b^2} \cdot \frac{35a^2b}{12x^2y}$ Multiply by reciprocal of the divisor.

$= \frac{2 \cdot 3 \cdot 3 \cdot x \cdot y \cdot y \cdot y \cdot 5 \cdot 7 \cdot a \cdot a \cdot b}{7 \cdot a \cdot a \cdot b \cdot b \cdot 2 \cdot 2 \cdot 3 \cdot x \cdot x \cdot y}$ Factor.

$= \frac{\overset{1}{\cancel{2}} \cdot \overset{1}{\cancel{3}} \cdot 3 \cdot \overset{1}{\cancel{x}} \cdot \overset{1}{\cancel{y}} \cdot y \cdot y \cdot 5 \cdot \overset{1}{\cancel{7}} \cdot \overset{1}{\cancel{a}} \cdot \overset{1}{\cancel{a}} \cdot \overset{1}{\cancel{b}}}{\underset{1}{\cancel{7}} \cdot \underset{1}{\cancel{a}} \cdot \underset{1}{\cancel{a}} \cdot \underset{1}{\cancel{b}} \cdot b \cdot \underset{1}{\cancel{2}} \cdot 2 \cdot \underset{1}{\cancel{3}} \cdot \underset{1}{\cancel{x}} \cdot x \cdot \underset{1}{\cancel{y}}}$ Eliminate common factors.

$= \frac{3 \cdot 5 \cdot y \cdot y}{2 \cdot b \cdot x}$ Simplify.

$= \frac{15y^2}{2bx}$ Simplify.

Guided Practice

4A. $\frac{12c^3d^2}{21ab} \cdot \frac{14a^2b}{8c^2d}$ acd

4B. $\frac{6xy}{15ab^2} \cdot \frac{21a^3}{18x^4y}$ $\frac{7a^2}{15b^2x^3}$

4C. $\frac{16mt^2}{21a^4b^3} \div \frac{24m^3}{7a^2b^2}$ $\frac{2t^2}{9a^2bm^2}$

4D. $\frac{12x^4y^2}{40a^4b^4} \div \frac{6x^2y^4}{16a^2x}$ $\frac{4x^3}{5a^2b^4y^2}$

Personal Tutor glencoe.com

Focus on Mathematical Content

Simplifying Rational Expressions The primary skill needed to multiply and divide rational expressions is simplifying. After division is changed to multiplication by the reciprocal of the divisor, and numerators and denominators are multiplied, complete the problem by dividing by the common factors.

Additional Example

4 Simplify each expression.

a. $\frac{8x}{21y^3} \cdot \frac{7y^2}{16x^3}$ $\frac{1}{6x^2y}$

b. $\frac{10mk^2}{3c^2d} \div \frac{5m^5}{6c^2d^2}$ $\frac{4dk^2}{m^4}$

Tips for New Teachers

Building on Prior Knowledge To help students understand why division is equivalent to multiplying by the reciprocal, discuss simple examples such as this: dividing 18 marbles between two people means that each person gets one-half, or 9, of the marbles.

Focus on Mathematical Content

Division by Zero By definition, $\frac{a}{b} = c$ if $a = bc$. If students think $\frac{6}{0} = 0$, use the definition to show $\frac{6}{0} = 0$ if $6 = 0 \cdot 0$, which is false.

Additional Example

5 Simplify each expression.

a. $\frac{k-3}{k+1} \cdot \frac{1-k^2}{k^2-4k+3}$ -1

b. $\frac{2d+6}{d^2+d-2} \div \frac{d+3}{d^2+3d+2}$ $\frac{2(d+1)}{d-1}$

Watch Out!

Avoiding Errors Have students replace the variables with small whole numbers. Then evaluate both the original expression and the simplified answer. The values should be the same.

Simplify Complex Fractions

Example 6 shows how to simplify a complex fraction by rewriting it as a division expression.

Sometimes you must factor the numerator and/or the denominator first before you can simplify a product or a quotient of rational expressions.

EXAMPLE 5 Polynomials in the Numerator and Denominator

Simplify each expression.

a. $\frac{x^2-6x-16}{x^2-16x+64} \cdot \frac{x-8}{x^2+5x+6}$

$\frac{x^2-6x-16}{x^2-16x+64} \cdot \frac{x-8}{x^2+5x+6} = \frac{(x-8)(x+2)}{(x-8)(x-8)} \cdot \frac{x-8}{(x+3)(x+2)}$ **Factor.**

$= \frac{\overset{1}{\cancel{(x-8)}}\overset{1}{\cancel{(x+2)}}}{\underset{1}{\cancel{(x-8)}}\underset{1}{\cancel{(x-8)}}} \cdot \frac{\overset{1}{\cancel{x-8}}}{(x+3)\underset{1}{\cancel{(x+2)}}}$ **Eliminate common factors.**

$= \frac{1}{x+3}$ **Simplify.**

b. $\frac{x^2-16}{12y+36} \div \frac{x^2-12x+32}{y^2-3y-18}$

$\frac{x^2-16}{12y+36} \div \frac{x^2-12x+32}{y^2-3y-18} = \frac{x^2-16}{12y+36} \cdot \frac{y^2-3y-18}{x^2-12x+32}$ **Multiply by reciprocal.**

$= \frac{(x+4)(x-4)}{12(y+3)} \cdot \frac{(y-6)(y+3)}{(x-4)(x-8)}$ **Factor.**

$= \frac{(x+4)\overset{1}{\cancel{(x-4)}}}{12\underset{1}{\cancel{(y+3)}}} \cdot \frac{(y-6)\overset{1}{\cancel{(y+3)}}}{\underset{1}{\cancel{(x-4)}}(x-8)}$ **Eliminate common factors.**

$= \frac{(x+4)(y-6)}{12(x-8)}$ **Simplify.**

StudyTip

Factoring Polynomials When simplifying rational expressions, factors in one polynomial will often reappear in other polynomials. In Example 5a, $x-8$ appears four times. Use this as a guide when factoring challenging polynomials.

Guided Practice

5A. $\frac{8x-20}{x^2+2x-35} \cdot \frac{x^2-7x+10}{4x^2-16}$ $\frac{2x-5}{(x+2)(x+7)}$

5B. $\frac{x^2-9x+20}{x^2+10x+21} \div \frac{x^2-x-12}{6x+42}$ $\frac{6x-30}{(x+3)^2}$

Personal Tutor glencoe.com

Simplify Complex Fractions A **complex fraction** is a rational expression with a numerator and/or denominator that is also a rational expression. The following expressions are complex fractions.

$\frac{\frac{c}{6}}{5d}$ $\frac{\frac{8}{x}}{x-2}$ $\frac{\frac{x-3}{8}}{\frac{x-2}{x+4}}$ $\frac{\frac{4}{a}+6}{\frac{12}{a}-3}$

To simplify a complex fraction, first rewrite it as a division expression.

EXAMPLE 6 Simplify Complex Fractions

Simplify each expression.

a. $\frac{\frac{a+b}{4}}{\frac{a^2+b^2}{4}}$

$\frac{\frac{a+b}{4}}{\frac{a^2+b^2}{4}} = \frac{a+b}{4} \div \frac{a^2+b^2}{4}$ **Express as a division expression.**

$= \frac{a+b}{4} \cdot \frac{4}{a^2+b^2}$ **Multiply by the reciprocal.**

$= \frac{a+b}{\underset{1}{\cancel{4}}} \cdot \frac{\overset{1}{\cancel{4}}}{a^2+b^2}$ or $\frac{a+b}{a^2+b^2}$ **Simplify.**

Differentiated Instruction AL OL

If students are having difficulty with these problems,

Then encourage them to use several steps, writing each one below the previous and keeping each line equivalent to the one above. Caution them to make only one change per step.

b. $\dfrac{\frac{x^2}{x^2-y^2}}{\frac{4x}{y-x}}$

$$\dfrac{\frac{x^2}{x^2-y^2}}{\frac{4x}{y-x}} = \frac{x^2}{x^2-y^2} \div \frac{4x}{y-x}$$ **Express as a division expression.**

$$= \frac{x^2}{x^2-y^2} \cdot \frac{y-x}{4x}$$ **Multiply by the reciprocal.**

$$= \frac{x \cdot x}{(x+y)(x-y)} \cdot \frac{(-1)(x-y)}{4x}$$ **Factor.**

$$= \frac{x \cdot \overset{1}{\cancel{x}}}{(x+y)\underset{1}{\cancel{(x-y)}}} \cdot \frac{(-1)\overset{1}{\cancel{(x-y)}}}{\underset{1}{4\cancel{x}}}$$ **Eliminate Factors.**

$$= \frac{-x}{4(x+y)}$$ **Simplify.**

Guided Practice

Simplify each expression.

6A. $\dfrac{\frac{(x-2)^2}{2(x^2-5x+4)}}{\frac{x^2-4}{4x-10}}$ $\dfrac{(2x-5)(x-2)}{(x+2)(x-4)(x-1)}$

6B. $\dfrac{\frac{x^2-y^2}{y^2-49}}{\frac{y-x}{y+7}}$ $\dfrac{-x-y}{y-7}$

Personal Tutor glencoe.com

Check Your Understanding

Example 1 p. 553

Simplify each expression.

1. $\dfrac{x^2-5x-24}{x^2-64}$ $\dfrac{x+3}{x+8}$

2. $\dfrac{c+d}{3c^2-3d^2}$ $\dfrac{1}{3(c-d)}$

Example 2 p. 554

3. **NGSSS PRACTICE** Identify all values of x for which $\dfrac{x+7}{x^2-3x-28}$ is undefined. D

A. −7, 4 B. 7, 4 C. 4, −7, 7 D. −4, 7

Examples 3–6 pp. 554–557

Simplify each expression.

4. $\dfrac{y^2+3y-40}{25-y^2}$ $-\dfrac{y+8}{y+5}$

5 $\dfrac{a^2x-b^2x}{by-ay}$ $\dfrac{-x(a+b)}{y}$

6. $\dfrac{27x^2y^4}{16yz^3} \cdot \dfrac{8z}{9xy^3}$ $\dfrac{3x}{2z^2}$

7. $\dfrac{12x^3y}{13ab^2} \div \dfrac{36xy^3}{26b}$ $\dfrac{2x^2}{3aby^2}$

8. $\dfrac{x^2-4x-21}{x^2-6x+8} \cdot \dfrac{x-4}{x^2-2x-35}$ $\dfrac{x+3}{(x-2)(x+5)}$

9. $\dfrac{a^2-b^2}{3a^2-6a+3} \div \dfrac{4a+4b}{a^2-1}$ $\dfrac{(a-b)(a+1)}{12(a-1)}$

10. $\dfrac{\frac{a^3b^3}{xy^4}}{\frac{a^2b}{x^2y}}$ $\dfrac{ab^2x}{y^3}$

11. $\dfrac{\frac{4x}{x+6}}{\frac{x^2-3x}{x^2+3x-18}}$ 4

12. **MANUFACTURING** The volume of a shipping container in the shape of a rectangular prism can be represented by the polynomial $6x^3 + 11x^2 + 4x$, where the height is x. a. $2x + 1$, $3x + 4$

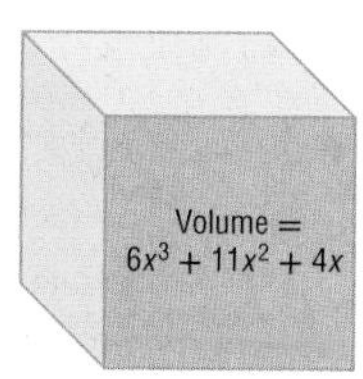

a. Find the length and width of the container.

b. Find the ratio of of the three dimensions of the container when $x = 2$. 2 : 5 : 10

c. Will the ratio of the three dimensions be the same for all values of x? no

Additional Example

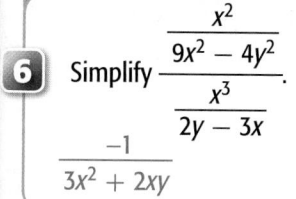

6 Simplify $\dfrac{\frac{x^2}{9x^2-4y^2}}{\frac{x^3}{2y-3x}}$. $\dfrac{-1}{3x^2+2xy}$

Tips for New Teachers

Reasoning Help students understand why the quotient of $(x - y)$ and $(y - x)$ is −1 by pointing out that these two expressions are opposites (or additive inverses), just like 2 and −2.

3 PRACTICE

Formative Assessment

Use Exercises 1–12 to check for understanding.

Use the chart at the bottom of the next page to customize assignments for your students.

Lesson 9-1 Multiplying and Dividing Rational Expressions 557

Practice and Problem Solving

● = **Step-by-Step Solutions** begin on page R20. **Extra Practice** begins on page 947.

Example 1 p. 553

Simplify each expression.

13. $\frac{x(x-3)(x+6)}{x^2+x-12}$ $\frac{x(x+6)}{x+4}$

14. $\frac{y^2(y^2+3y+2)}{2y(y-4)(y+2)}$ $\frac{y(y+1)}{2(y-4)}$

15. $\frac{(x^2-9)(x^2-z^2)}{4(x+z)(x-3)}$ $\frac{(x+3)(x-z)}{4}$

16. $\frac{(x^2-16x+64)(x+2)}{(x^2-64)(x^2-6x-16)}$ $\frac{1}{x+8}$

17. $\frac{x^2(x+2)(x-4)}{6x(x^2+x-20)}$ $\frac{x(x+2)}{6(x+5)}$

18. $\frac{3y(y-8)(y^2+2y-24)}{15y^2(y^2-12y+32)}$ $\frac{(y+6)}{5y}$

Example 2 p. 554

19. **NGSSS PRACTICE** Identify all values of x for which $\frac{(x-3)(x+6)}{(x^2-7x+12)(x^2-36)}$ is undefined. I

F. 3, −6 G. 4, 6 H. −6, 6 I. −6, 3, 4, 6

Example 3 p. 554

Simplify each expression.

20. $\frac{x^2-5x-14}{28+3x-x^2}$ $-\frac{x+2}{x+4}$

21. $\frac{x^3-9x^2}{x^2-3x-54}$ $\frac{x^2}{x+6}$

22. $\frac{(x-4)(x^2+2x-48)}{(36-x^2)(x^2+4x-32)}$ $-\frac{1}{x+6}$

23. $\frac{16-c^2}{c^2+c-20}$ $-\frac{c+4}{c+5}$

24. **GEOMETRY** The cylinder at the right has a volume of $(x+3)(x^2-3x-18)\pi$ cubic centimeters. Find the height of the cylinder. $x-6$ cm

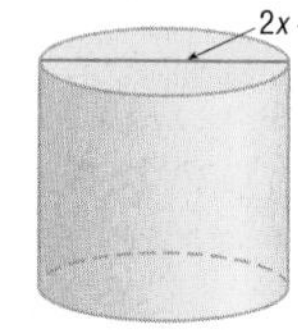

Examples 4–6 pp. 555–557

Simplify each expression.

25. $\frac{3ac^3f^3}{8a^2bcf^4}\cdot\frac{12ab^2c}{18ab^3c^2f}$ $\frac{c}{4ab^2f^2}$

26. $\frac{14xy^2z^3}{21w^4x^2yz}\cdot\frac{7wxyz}{12w^2y^3z}$ $\frac{7z^2}{18w^5y}$

27. $\frac{64a^2b^5}{35b^2c^3f^4}\div\frac{12a^4b^3c}{70abcf^2}$ $\frac{32b}{3ac^3f^2}$

28. $\frac{9x^2yz}{5z^4}\div\frac{12x^4y^2}{50xy^4z^2}$ $\frac{15y^3}{2xz}$

29. $\frac{15a^2b^2}{21ac}\cdot\frac{14a^4c^2}{6ab^3}$ $\frac{5a^4c}{3b}$

30. $\frac{14c^2f^5}{9a^2}\div\frac{35cf^4}{18ab^3}$ $\frac{4b^3cf}{5a}$

31. $\frac{y^2+8y+15}{y-6}\cdot\frac{y^2-9y+18}{y^2-9}$ $y+5$

32. $\frac{c^2-6c-16}{c^2-d^2}\div\frac{c^2-8c}{c+d}$ $\frac{c+2}{c(c-d)}$

33. $\frac{x^2+9x+20}{8x+16}\cdot\frac{4x^2+16x+16}{x^2-25}$

33. $\frac{(x+4)(x+2)}{2(x-5)}$

34. $\frac{3a^2+6a+3}{a^2-3a-10}\div\frac{12a^2-12}{a^2-4}$ $\frac{(a+1)(a-2)}{4(a-5)(a-1)}$

35. $\frac{\frac{x^2-9}{6x-12}}{\frac{x^2+10x+21}{x^2-x-2}}$ $\frac{(x-3)(x+1)}{6(x+7)}$

36. $\frac{\frac{y-x}{z^3}}{\frac{x-y}{6z^2}}$ $-\frac{6}{z}$

37. $\frac{\frac{a^2-b^2}{b^3}}{\frac{b^2-ab}{a^2}}$ $\frac{-a^2(a+b)}{b^4}$

38. $\frac{\frac{x-y}{a+b}}{\frac{x^2-y^2}{b^2-a^2}}$ $\frac{b-a}{x+y}$

39. **SOCCER** At the end of her high school soccer career, Ashley had made 33 goals out of 121 attempts.

a. Write a ratio to represent the ratio of the number of goals made to goals attempted by Ashley at the end of her high school career. $\frac{33}{121}$

b. Suppose Ashley attempted a goals and made m goals during her first year at college. Write a rational expression to represent the ratio of the number of career goals made to the number of career goals attempted at the end of her first year in college. $\frac{33+m}{121+a}$

Differentiated Homework Options

Level	Assignment	Two-Day Option	
AL Basic	13–39, 59–60, 62–86	13–39 odd, 66–69	14–38 even, 59–60, 62–86
OL Core	13–39 odd, 40, 41–55 odd, 56–60, 62–86	13–39, 66–69	40–60, 62–65, 70–86
BL Advanced	40–80, (optional: 81–86)		

558 Chapter 9 Rational Functions and Relations

B **40. GEOMETRY** Parallelogram F has an area of $8x^2 + 10x - 3$ square meters and a height of $2x + 3$ meters. Parallelogram G has an area of $6x^2 + 13x - 5$ square meters and a height of $3x - 1$ meters. Find the area of right triangle H. $\frac{1}{2}(8x^2 + 18x - 5)$ m²

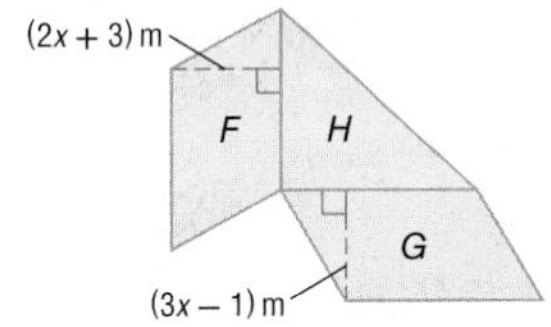

Real-World Link

In 1989, the Exxon Valdez spilled an estimated 11 million gallons of crude oil near the gulf coast of Alaska.

Source: Environmental Protection Agency

41. POLLUTION The thickness of an oil spill from a ruptured pipe on a rig is modeled by the function $T(x) = \frac{0.4(x^2 - 2x)}{x^3 + x^2 - 6x}$, where T is the thickness of the oil slick in meters and x is the distance from the rupture in meters.

a. Simplify the function. $T(x) = \frac{0.4}{x + 3}$

b. How thick is the slick 100 meters from the rupture? about 3.9 mm thick

Simplify each expression.

42. $\frac{x^2 - 16}{3x^3 + 18x^2 + 24x} \cdot \frac{x^3 - 4x}{2x^2 - 7x - 4}$ $\frac{x - 2}{3(2x + 1)}$

43. $\frac{3x^2 - 17x - 6}{4x^2 - 20x - 24} \div \frac{6x^2 - 7x - 3}{2x^2 - x - 3}$ $\frac{1}{4}$

44. $\frac{9 - x^2}{x^2 - 4x - 21} \cdot \left(\frac{2x^2 + 7x + 3}{2x^2 - 15x + 7}\right)^{-1}$

45. $\left(\frac{2x^2 + 2x - 12}{x^2 + 4x - 5}\right)^{-1} \cdot \frac{2x^3 - 8x}{x^2 - 2x - 35}$

46. $\left(\frac{3xy^3z}{2a^2bc^2}\right)^3 \cdot \frac{16a^4b^3c^5}{15x^7yz^3}$ $\frac{18y^8}{5a^2cx^4}$

47. $\frac{20x^2y^6z^{-2}}{3a^3c^2} \cdot \left(\frac{16x^3y^3}{9acz}\right)^{-1}$

48. $\left(\frac{2xy^3}{3abc}\right)^{-2} \div \frac{6a^2b}{x^2y^4}$ $\frac{3bc^2}{8y^2}$

49. $\dfrac{\frac{8x^2 - 10x - 3}{10x^2 + 35x - 20}}{\frac{2x^2 + x - 6}{4x^2 + 18x + 8}}$

50. $\dfrac{\frac{2x^2 + 7x - 30}{-6x^2 + 13x + 5}}{\frac{4x^2 + 12x - 72}{3x^2 - 11x - 4}}$ $\frac{x - 4}{-4(x - 3)}$

51. $\dfrac{\frac{4x^2 - 1}{3x^3 - 6x^2 - 24x}}{\frac{12x^2 + 12x - 9}{-2x^2 + 5x + 12}}$ $\frac{2x + 1}{-9x(x + 2)}$

44. $\frac{(3 - x)(2x - 1)}{(x + 3)(2x + 1)}$

45. $\frac{x(x + 2)(x - 1)}{(x + 3)(x - 7)}$

47. $\frac{15y^3}{4a^2cxz}$

49. $\frac{2(4x + 1)(2x + 1)}{5(2x - 1)(x + 2)}$

52. GEOMETRY The area of the base of the rectangular prism at the right is 20 square centimeters.

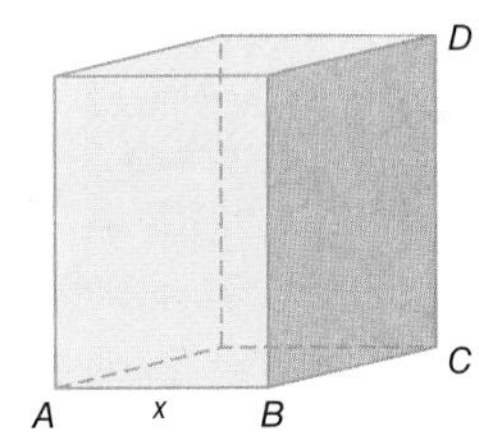

a. Find the length of $\overline{BC}$ in terms of x. $\frac{20}{x}$

b. If $DC = 3BC$, determine the area of the shaded region in terms of x. $\frac{1200}{x^2}$

c. Determine the volume of the prism in terms of x. $\frac{1200}{x}$

C **Simplify each expression.**

53. $\frac{x^2 + 4x - 32}{2x^2 + 9x - 5} \cdot \frac{3x^2 - 75}{3x^2 - 11x - 4} \div \frac{6x^2 - 18x - 60}{x^3 - 4x}$ $\frac{x(x - 2)(x + 8)}{2(2x - 1)(3x + 1)}$

54. $\frac{8x^2 + 10x - 3}{3x^2 - 12x - 36} \div \frac{2x^2 - 5x - 12}{3x^2 - 17x - 6} \cdot \frac{4x^2 + 3x - 1}{4x^2 - 40x + 24}$ $\frac{(4x - 1)^2(3x + 1)(x + 1)}{12(x + 2)(x - 4)(x^2 - 10x + 6)}$

55. $\frac{4x^2 - 9x - 9}{3x^2 + 6x - 18} \div \frac{-2x^2 + 5x + 3}{x^2 - 4x - 32} \div \frac{8x^2 + 10x + 3}{6x^2 - 6x - 12}$ $\frac{-2(x - 8)(x + 4)(x - 2)(x + 1)}{(2x + 1)^2(x^2 + 2x - 6)}$

56. AIRPLANES Use the formula $d = rt$ and the following information. An airplane is traveling at a rate r of 500 miles per hour for a time t of $(6 + x)$ hours. A second airplane travels at the rate of $(540 + 90x)$ miles per hour for a time t of 6 hours.

a. Write a rational expression to represent the ratio of the distance d traveled by the first airplane to the distance d traveled by the second airplane. $\frac{(500)(6 + x)}{(540 + 90x)(6)}$

b. Simplify the rational expression. What does this expression tell you about the distances traveled by the two airplanes?

c. Under what condition is the rational expression undefined? Describe what this condition would tell you about the two airplanes.

56b. $\frac{25}{27}$; Sample answer: The second airplane travels a bit farther than the first airplane.

56c. $x = -6$; Sample answer: When $x = -6$, the first airplane would travel for 0 hours and the second airplane would travel at a rate of 0 miles per hour.

Exercise Alert

Formula For Exercise 52, students will need to know the formula for the volume of a rectangular prism, $V = Bh$, where B is the area of the base. For Exercise 80, students will need to know the formula for the volume of a rectangular prism, $V = \ell wh$, where ℓ is the length, w is the width, and h is the height.

Study Guide and Intervention
CRM pp. 5–6 AL OL ELL

9-1 Study Guide and Intervention

Multiplying and Dividing Rational Expressions

Simplify Rational Expressions A ratio of two polynomial expressions is a **rational expression**. To simplify a rational expression, divide both the numerator and the denominator by their greatest common factor (GCF).

Multiplying Rational Expressions	For all rational expressions $\frac{a}{b}$ and $\frac{c}{d}$, $\frac{a}{b}\cdot\frac{c}{d}=\frac{ac}{bd}$, if $b\neq 0$ and $d\neq 0$.
Dividing Rational Expressions	For all rational expressions $\frac{a}{b}$ and $\frac{c}{d}$, $\frac{a}{b}\div\frac{c}{d}=\frac{ad}{bc}$, if $b\neq 0$, $c\neq 0$, and $d\neq 0$.

Example Simplify each expression.

a. $\frac{24a^5b^2}{(2ab)^4}$

b. $\frac{3r^2s^3}{5t^4}\cdot\frac{20t^2}{9r^4s}$

c. $\frac{x^2+8x+16}{2x-2}\div\frac{x^2+2x-8}{x-1}$

$=\frac{x+4}{2(x-2)}$

Exercises

Simplify each expression.

1. $\frac{(-2ab^2)^3}{20ab^4}$ $-\frac{2a^2b^2}{5}$
2. $\frac{4x-12x+9}{9-6x}$ $\frac{3-2x}{3}$
3. $\frac{x^2+x-6}{x^2-6x-27}$ $\frac{x-2}{x-9}$
4. $\frac{3m^3-3m}{6m^4}\cdot\frac{4m^5}{m+1}$ $2m^2(m-1)$
5. $\frac{c^2-3c}{c^2-25}\cdot\frac{c^2+4c-5}{c^2-4c+3}$ $\frac{c}{c-5}$
6. $\frac{(m-3)^2}{m^2-6m+9}\cdot\frac{m^3-9m}{m^2-9}$ m
7. $\frac{6xy^4}{25z^2}\div\frac{18xz^2}{5y}$ $\frac{y^5}{15z^4}$
8. $\frac{16p^2-8p+1}{14p^4}\div\frac{4p^2+7p-2}{7p^5}$ $\frac{p(4p-1)}{2(p+2)}$
9. $\frac{2m-1}{m^2-3m-10}\div\frac{4m^2-1}{4m+8}$ $\frac{4}{(2m+1)(m-5)}$

Chapter 9 5 Glencoe Algebra 2

Practice
CRM p. 8 AL OL BL ELL

9-1 Practice

Multiplying and Dividing Rational Expressions

Simplify each expression.

1. $\frac{9a^2b^3}{27a^4b^4c}$ $\frac{1}{3a^2bc}$
2. $\frac{(2m^3n^2)^2}{-18m^5n^4}$ $-\frac{4m^4n^2}{9}$
3. $\frac{10y^2+15y}{35y^2-5y}$ $\frac{2y+3}{7y-1}$
4. $\frac{2k^2-k-15}{k^2-9}$ $\frac{2k+5}{k+3}$
5. $\frac{25-v^2}{3v^2-13v-10}$ $-\frac{v+5}{3v+2}$
6. $\frac{x^3+x^2-2x^2}{x^2-x}$ $\frac{x+2}{x}$
7. $\frac{-2u^2y}{15xz^5}\cdot\frac{25z^2}{14u^3y^2}$ $-\frac{5ux^2}{21yz^3}$
8. $\frac{a+y}{6}\cdot\frac{4}{y+a}$ $\frac{2}{3}$
9. $\frac{n^2}{n-6}\cdot\frac{n^2-6n}{n^4}$ $\frac{1}{n^2}$
10. $\frac{a-y}{w+n}\cdot\frac{w^2-n^2}{y-a}$ $n-w$
11. $\frac{x^2-5x-24}{6x+2x^2}\cdot\frac{5x^2}{8-x}$ $-\frac{5x}{2}$
12. $\frac{x-5}{10x-2}\div\frac{25x^2-1}{x^2-10x+25}$ $\frac{5x+1}{2(x-5)}$
13. $\frac{a^3y^2}{wy^3}\div\frac{a^2w^3}{w^2y^3}$ $\frac{a^3w^2}{y^2}$
14. $\left(\frac{2xy}{w^2}\right)^3\div\frac{24x^2}{w^5}$ $\frac{xy^3}{3w}$
15. $\frac{x+y}{6}\div\frac{x^2-y^2}{3}$ $\frac{1}{2(x-y)}$
16. $\frac{3x+6}{x^2-9}\div\frac{6x^2+12x}{4x+12}$ $\frac{2}{x(x-3)}$
17. $\frac{2s^2-7s-15}{(s+4)^2}\div\frac{s^2-10s+25}{s+4}$ $\frac{2s+3}{(s+4)(s-5)}$
18. $\frac{9-a^2}{a^2+5a+6}\div\frac{2a-6}{5a+10}$ $-\frac{5}{2}$
19. $\frac{\frac{2x+1}{x}}{\frac{4-x}{x}}$ $\frac{2x+1}{4-x}$
20. $\frac{\frac{x^2-9}{4}}{\frac{3-x}{8}}$ $-2(x+3)$
21. $\frac{\frac{x^2+2x}{x^2-2x}}{\frac{(x+2)^2}{x^2+4x+4}}$ $\frac{x^2-2x+4}{x(x-2)}$

22. GEOMETRY A right triangle with an area of x^2-4 square units has a leg that measures $2x+4$ units. Determine the length of the other leg of the triangle. $x-2$ units

23. GEOMETRY A rectangular pyramid has a base area of $\frac{x^2+3x-10}{2x}$ square centimeters and a height of $\frac{x^2-3x}{x^2-5x+6}$ centimeters. Write a rational expression to describe the volume of the rectangular pyramid. $\frac{x+5}{6}$ cm³

Chapter 9 8 Glencoe Algebra 2

Word Problem Practice
CRM p. 9 AL OL BL ELL

9-1 Word Problem Practice

Multiplying and Dividing Rational Expressions

1. JELLY BEANS A large vat contains G green jelly beans and R red jelly beans. A bag of 100 red and 100 green jelly beans is added to the vat. What is the new ratio of red to green jelly beans in the vat? $\frac{R+100}{G+100}$

2. MILEAGE Beth drives a hybrid car that gets 48 miles per gallon in the city and 45 miles per gallon on the highway. Beth uses C gallons of gas in the city and H gallons of gas on the highway. Write an expression for the average number of miles per gallon that Beth gets with her car in terms of C and H. $\frac{48C+45H}{C+H}$

3. HEIGHT The front face of a Nordic house is triangular. The surface area of the face is $x^2+3x+10$ where x is the base of the triangle.

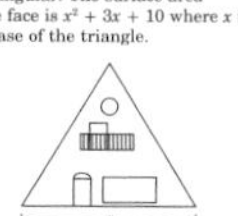

What is the height of the triangle in terms of x? $h=\frac{2x^2+6x+20}{x}$

4. OIL SLICKS David was moving a drum of oil around his circular outdoor pool when the drum cracked, and oil spilled into the pool. The oil spread itself evenly over the surface of the pool. Let V denote the volume of oil spilled and let r be the radius of the pool. Write an equation for the thickness of the oil layer. $h=\frac{V}{\pi r^2}$

5. RUNNING Harold runs to the local food mart to buy a gallon of soy milk. Because he is weighed down on his return trip, he runs slower on the way back. He travels S_1 feet per second on the way to the food mart and S_2 feet per second on the way back. Let d be the distance he has to run to get to the food mart. Remember: distance = rate × time.

a. Write an equation that gives the total time Harold spent running for this errand. $t=\frac{d}{S_1}+\frac{d}{S_2}$

b. What speed would Harold have to run if he wanted to maintain a constant speed for the entire trip yet take the same amount of time running? $\frac{2S_1S_2}{S_1+S_2}$

Chapter 9 9 Glencoe Algebra 2

Real-World Link

The fastest train in the world is Japan's Shin Kansen line that travels at a top speed of 186 miles per hour.

Source: Yahoo

57a. 5 tracks $\cdot\frac{2\text{ miles}}{1\text{ track}}\cdot\frac{5280\text{ feet}}{1\text{ mile}}\cdot\frac{1\text{ car}}{75\text{ feet}}$

58c. $f(4)$ results in an error because the function is undefined at $x=4$. $g(4)=3$

58e. The expressions and functions are equivalent except for $x=4$.

59. Sample answer: The two expressions are equivalent, except that the rational expression is undefined at $x=3$.

60. Sample answer: Beverly; Troy's mistake was multiplying by the reciprocal of the dividend instead of the divisor.

64. Sample answer: $\frac{x^2-1}{x^2+5x+4}$

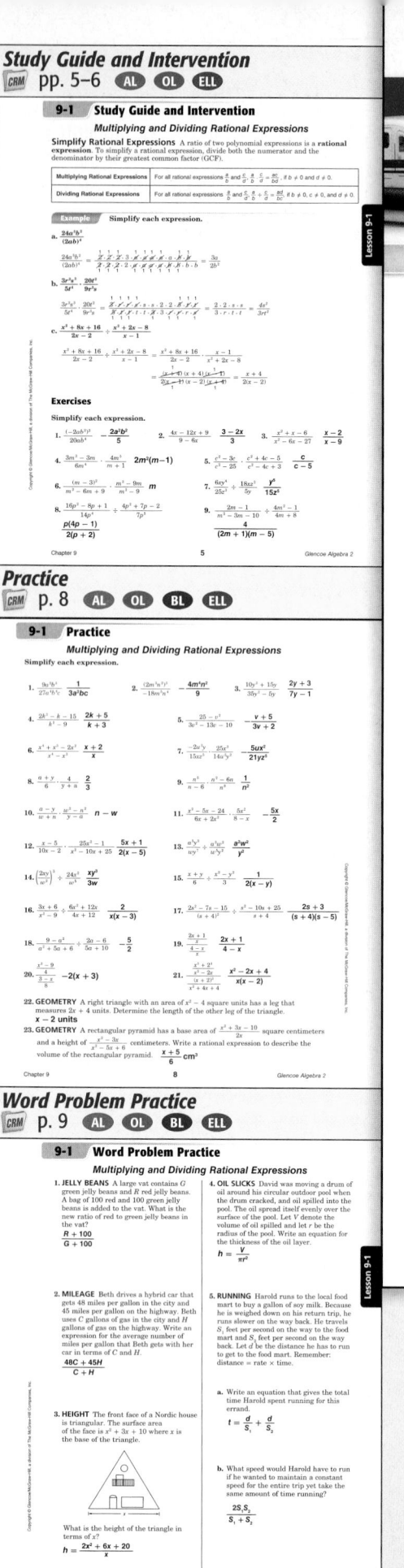

57. TRAINS Trying to get into a train yard one evening, all of the trains are backed up for 2 miles along a system of tracks. Assume that each car occupies an average of 75 feet of space on a track and that the train yard has 5 tracks.

a. Write an expression that could be used to determine the number of train cars involved in the backup.

b. How many train cars are involved in the backup? **704**

c. Suppose that there are 8 attendants doing safety checks on each car, and it takes each vehicle an average of 45 seconds for each check. Approximately how many hours will it take for all the vehicles in the backup to exit? **70.4 h**

58. **MULTIPLE REPRESENTATIONS** In this problem, you will investigate the graph of a rational function. **b, d. See margin.**

a. **ALGEBRAIC** Simplify $\frac{x^2-5x+4}{x-4}$. **$x-1$**

b. **TABULAR** Let $f(x)=\frac{x^2-5x+4}{x-4}$. Use the expression you wrote in part **a** to write the related function $g(x)$. Use a graphing calculator to make a table for both functions for $0\le x\le 10$.

c. **ANALYTICAL** What are $f(4)$ and $g(4)$? Explain the significance of these values.

d. **GRAPHICAL** Graph the functions on the graphing calculator. Use the **TRACE** function to investigate each graph, using the ▲ and ▼ keys to switch from one graph to the other. Compare and contrast the graphs.

e. **VERBAL** What conclusions can you draw about the expressions and the functions?

H.O.T. Problems
Use Higher-Order Thinking Skills

59. REASONING Compare and contrast $\frac{(x-6)(x+2)(x+3)}{x+3}$ and $(x-6)(x+2)$.

60. ERROR ANALYSIS Troy and Beverly are simplifying $\frac{x+y}{x-y}\div\frac{4}{y-x}$. Is either of them correct? Explain your reasoning.

Troy	Beverly
$\frac{x+y}{x-y}\div\frac{4}{y-x}=\frac{x-y}{x+y}\cdot\frac{4}{y-x}$ $=\frac{-4}{x+y}$	$\frac{x+y}{x-y}\div\frac{4}{y-x}=\frac{x+y}{x-y}\cdot\frac{y-x}{4}$ $=-\frac{x+y}{4}$

61. CHALLENGE Find the value that makes the following statement true. **x^2+x-6**

$$\frac{x-6}{x+3}\cdot\frac{?}{x-6}=x-2$$

62. WHICH ONE DOESN'T BELONG? Identify the expression that does not belong with the other three. Explain your reasoning. **See margin.**

$\frac{1}{x-1}$	$\frac{x^2+3x+2}{x-5}$	$\frac{x+1}{\sqrt{x+3}}$	$\frac{x^2+1}{3}$

63. REASONING Determine whether the following statement is *sometimes*, *always*, or *never* true. Explain your reasoning. **See margin.**

A rational function that has a variable in the denominator is defined for all real values of x.

64. OPEN ENDED Write a rational expression that simplifies to $\frac{x-1}{x+4}$.

65. WRITING IN MATH The rational expression $\frac{x^2+3x}{4x}$ is simplified to $\frac{x+3}{4}$. Explain why this new expression is not defined for all values of x. **See margin.**

560 Chapter 9 Rational Functions and Relations

Enrichment
CRM p. 10 OL BL

9-1 Enrichment

Dimensional Analysis

Scientists always express the units of measurement in their solution. It is insufficient and ambiguous to state a solution regarding distance as 17; Seventeen what, feet, miles, meters? Often it is helpful to analyze the units of the quantities in a formula to determine the desired units of an output. For example, it is known that torque is the product of force and distance, but what are the units of force?

The units also depend on the measuring system. The two most commonly used systems are the British system and the international system of units (SI). Some common units of the British system are inches, feet, miles, and pounds. Common SI units include meters, kilometers, Newtons, and grams. Frequently conversion from one system to another is necessary and accomplished by multiplication by conversion factors.

Consider changing units from miles per hour to kilometers per hour. What is 60 miles per hour in kilometers per hour? Use the conversion 1 ft = 30.5 cm.

$60\,\frac{mi}{h}=60\,\frac{mi}{h}\times\frac{5280\text{ ft}}{1\text{ mi}}\times\frac{30.5\text{ cm}}{1\text{ ft}}\times\frac{1\text{ m}}{100\text{ cm}}\times\frac{1\text{ km}}{1000\text{ m}}=96.62\,\frac{km}{h}$

1. The SI unit for force is a Newton (N) and the SI unit for distance is meters or centimeters. The British unit for force is pounds and the British unit for distance is feet or inches. Using the formula for torque (torque = force times distance), determine the SI unit and the British

Watch Out!

Error Analysis For Exercise 60, ask students to copy the problem that Troy and Beverly were solving. Then have students circle the divisor and rewrite the problem as a multiplication problem.

NGSSS PRACTICE 912.A.3.1

66. **SAT/ACT** The Mason family wants to drive an average of 250 miles per day on their vacation. On the first five days, they travel 220 miles, 300 miles, 210 miles, 275 miles, and 240 miles. How many miles must they travel on the sixth day to meet their goal? **B**

A. 235 miles C. 275 miles
B. 255 miles D. 315 miles

67. Which of the following equations gives the relationship between N and T in the table? **I**

N	1	2	3	4	5	6
T	1	4	7	10	13	16

F. $T = 2 - N$ H. $T = 3N + 1$
G. $T = 4 - 3N$ I. $T = 3N - 2$

68. Cell phone calls cost 15 cents per minute for the first 12 minutes and 9 cents per minute thereafter. Which of the following represents the amount of money needed (in dollars) to talk for x minutes? **B**

A. $1.80 + 0.09(12 - x)$
B. $1.80 + 0.09(x - 12)$
C. $1.80 + 0.09x$
D. $1.80 + 0.12x$

69. THINK SOLVE EXPLAIN **SHORT RESPONSE** The area of a circle 6 meters in diameter exceeds the combined areas of a circle 4 meters in diameter and a circle 2 meters in diameter by how many square meters? **4π**

Spiral Review

70. **ANTHROPOLOGY** An anthropologist studying the bones of a prehistoric person finds there is so little remaining Carbon-14 in the bones that instruments cannot measure it. This means that there is less than 0.5% of the amount of Carbon-14 the bones would have contained when the person was alive. The half-life of Carbon-14 is 5760 years. How long ago did the person die? (Lesson 8-8) **more than 44,000 years ago**

Solve each equation. Round to the nearest ten thousandth. (Lesson 8-7)

71. $3e^x + 1 = 5$ **0.2877** **72.** $2e^x - 1 = 0$ **−0.6931** **73.** $-3e^{4x} + 11 = 2$ **0.2747** **74.** $8 + 3e^{3x} = 26$ **0.5973**

75. **NOISE ORDINANCE** A proposed city ordinance will make it illegal in a residential area to create sound that exceeds 72 decibels during the day and 55 decibels during the night. How many times as intense is the noise level allowed during the day as at night? (Lesson 8-3) **$10^{1.7}$ or about 50 times**

Simplify. (Lesson 7-5)

76. $\sqrt{50x^4}$ **$5x^2\sqrt{2}$** **77.** $\sqrt[3]{16y^3}$ **$2y\sqrt[3]{2}$** **78.** $\sqrt{18x^2y^3}$ **$3|x|y\sqrt{2y}$** **79.** $\sqrt{40a^3b^4}$ **$2ab^2\sqrt{10a}$**

80. **AUTOMOBILES** The length of the cargo space in a sport-utility vehicle is 4 inches greater than the height of the space. The width is 16 inches less than twice the height. The cargo space has a total volume of 55,296 cubic inches. (Lesson 6-8) **a. $V = 2h^3 - 8h^2 - 64h$**

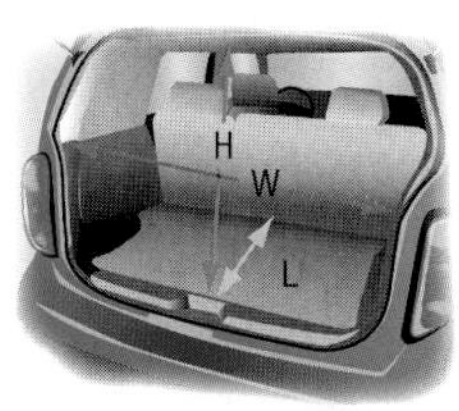

a. Write a polynomial function that represents the volume of the cargo space.

b. Will a package 34 inches long, 44 inches wide, and 34 inches tall fit in the cargo space? Explain. **No; the dimensions of the space are $\ell = 36$ in., $w = 48$ in., $h = 32$ in., so the package is too tall to fit.**

Skills Review

82. $-3x^2 - 7x + 8$
86. $x^3 - x^2 + x + 3$

Simplify. (Lesson 6-1)

81. $(2a + 3b) + (8a - 5b)$ **$10a - 2b$** **82.** $(x^2 - 4x + 3) - (4x^2 + 3x - 5)$ **83.** $(5y + 3y^2) + (-8y - 6y^2)$ **$-3y - 3y^2$**

84. $2x(3y + 9)$ **$6xy + 18x$** **85.** $(x + 6)(x + 3)$ **$x^2 + 9x + 18$** **86.** $(x + 1)(x^2 - 2x + 3)$

Differentiated Instruction OL BL

Extension To prepare students for the next lesson and to build a strong base for future work with rational expressions, give them an expression like $\frac{5x^2(x^2 + 3)}{5x(x + 3)}$. Ask them to explain in detail, citing fundamentals from arithmetic, why the fives can be divided out but not the threes. Also explain why the first x^2 and x can be divided by x to simplify, but not those within parentheses. Students' explanations should mention that common factors of both the numerator and denominator can be divided out, but not terms that are parts of polynomials. Substitution of a number, like 2, for x may help some students reach this realization.

4 ASSESS

Crystal Ball Ask students to describe how they think their practice with multiplying and simplifying rational expressions will help them when they add or subtract rational expressions.

Additional Answers

58b.

x	0	1	2	3
$f(x)$	−1	0	1	2
$g(x)$	−1	0	1	2

x	4	5	6	7
$f(x)$	ERR	4	5	6
$g(x)$	3	4	5	6

x	8	9	10
$f(x)$	7	8	9
$g(x)$	7	8	9

58d.

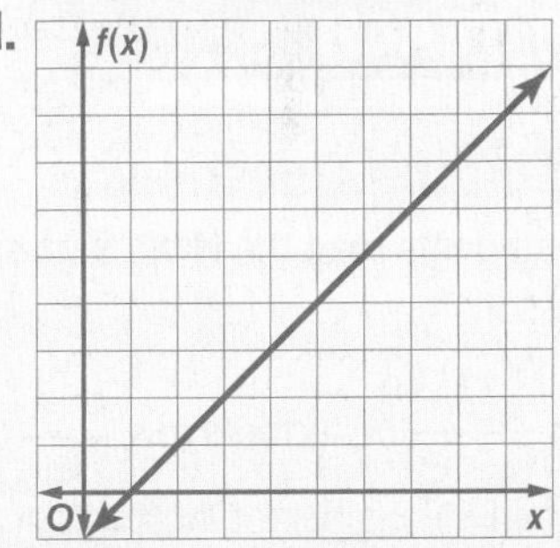

The graphs appear to be the same on the graphing calculator. But $f(x)$ is undefined for $f(4)$ and $g(4) = 3$.

62. $\frac{x + 1}{\sqrt{x + 3}}$ does not belong with the other three. The other three expressions are rational expressions. Since the denominator of $\frac{x + 1}{\sqrt{x + 3}}$ is not a polynomial, $\frac{x + 1}{\sqrt{x + 3}}$ is not a rational expression.

63. Sample answer: Sometimes; with a denominator like $x^2 + 2$, in which the denominator cannot equal 0, the rational expression can be defined for all values of x.

65. Sample answer: When the original expression was simplified, a factor of x was taken out of the denominator. If x were to equal 0, then this expression would be undefined. So, the simplified expression is also undefined for x.

9-2 Lesson Notes

1 FOCUS

Vertical Alignment

Before Lesson 9-2
Add and subtract polynomial expressions.

Lesson 9-2
Determine the LCM of polynomials. Add and subtract rational expressions.

After Lesson 9-2
Solve rational equations and inequalities.

2 TEACH

Scaffolding Questions

Have students read the *Why?* section of the lesson.

Ask:

- Can $\frac{s_0}{s_0 - v}$ be factored to $s_0\left(\frac{1}{1-v}\right)$? Explain. No; s_0 is not a common factor.
- To multiply P_0 times $\frac{s_0}{s_0 - v}$, do you need a common denominator? no

LCM of Polynomials

Example 1 shows how to find the least common multiple of a set of polynomials.

9-2 Adding and Subtracting Rational Expressions

Then
You added and subtracted polynomial expressions. (Lesson 6-2)

Now
- Determine the LCM of polynomials.
- Add and subtract rational expressions.

NGSSS
MA.912.A.5.2 Add, subtract, multiply, and divide **rational expressions.**

FL Math Online
glencoe.com

Why?

As a fire engine moves toward a person, the pitch of the siren sounds higher to that person than it would if the fire engine were at rest. This is because the sound waves are compressed closer together, referred to as the *Doppler effect*. The Doppler effect can be represented by the rational expression $P_0\left(\frac{s_0}{s_0 - v}\right)$, where P_0 is the actual pitch of the siren, v is the speed of the fire truck, and s_0 is the speed of sound in air.

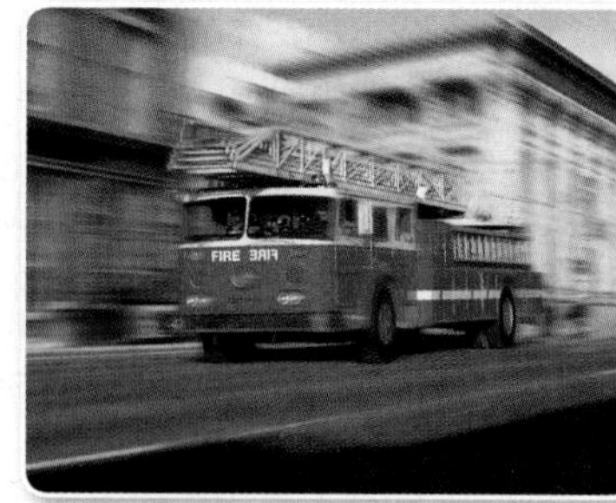

LCM of Polynomials Just as with rational numbers in fractional form, to add or subtract two rational expressions that have unlike denominators, you must first find the least common denominator (LCD). The LCD is the least common multiple (LCM) of the denominators.

To find the LCM of two or more numbers or polynomials, factor them. The LCM contains each factor the greatest number of times it appears as a factor.

Numbers	Polynomials
$\frac{5}{6} + \frac{4}{9}$	$\frac{3}{x^2 - 3x + 2} + \frac{5}{2x^2 - 2}$
LCM of 6 and 9	**LCM of $x^2 - 3x + 2$ and $2x^2 - 2$**
$6 = 2 \cdot 3$	$x^2 - 3x + 2 = (x-1)(x-2)$
$9 = 3 \cdot 3$	$2x^2 - 2 = 2 \cdot (x-1)(x+1)$
$\text{LCM} = 2 \cdot 3 \cdot 3$ or 18	$\text{LCM} = 2(x-1)(x-2)(x+1)$

EXAMPLE 1 LCM of Monomials and Polynomials

Find the LCM of each set of polynomials.

a. $6xy$, $15x^2$, and $9xy^4$

$6xy = 2 \cdot 3 \cdot x \cdot y$ — **Factor the first monomial.**
$15x^2 = 3 \cdot 5 \cdot x^2$ — **Factor the second monomial.**
$9xy^4 = 3 \cdot 3 \cdot x \cdot y^4$ — **Factor the third monomial.**
$\text{LCM} = 2 \cdot 3 \cdot 3 \cdot 5 \cdot x^2 \cdot y^4$ — **Use each factor the greatest number of times it appears.**
$= 90x^2y^4$ — **Then simplify.**

b. $y^4 + 8y^3 + 15y^2$ and $y^2 - 3y - 40$

$y^4 + 8y^3 + 15y^2 = y^2(y+5)(y+3)$ — **Factor the first polynomial.**
$y^2 - 3y - 40 = (y+5)(y-8)$ — **Factor the second polynomial.**
$\text{LCM} = y^2(y+5)(y+3)(y-8)$ — **Use each factor the greatest number of times it appears as a factor.**

Guided Practice 1B. $4a(a-4)(a-5)(a+1)$

1A. $12a^2b$, $15abc$, $8b^3c^4$ $120a^2b^3c^4$ **1B.** $4a^2 - 12a - 16$ and $a^3 - 9a^2 + 20a$

Personal Tutor glencoe.com

Lesson 9-2 Resources

Resource	Approaching-Level	On-Level	Beyond-Level	English Learners
Teacher Edition	• Differentiated Instruction, p. 564	• Differentiated Instruction, p. 564	• Differentiated Instruction, p. 566	• Differentiated Instruction, p. 564
Chapter Resource Masters	• Study Guide and Intervention, pp. 11–12 • Skills Practice, p. 13 • Practice, p. 14 • Word Problem Practice, p. 15	• Study Guide and Intervention, pp. 11–12 • Skills Practice, p. 13 • Practice, p. 14 • Word Problem Practice, p. 15 • Enrichment, p. 16 • TI-Nspire Activity, p. 17	• Practice, p. 14 • Word Problem Practice, p. 15 • Enrichment, p. 16	• Study Guide and Intervention, pp. 11–12 • Skills Practice, p. 13 • Practice, p. 14 • Word Problem Practice, p. 15
Transparencies	• 5-Minute Check Transparency 9-2	• 5-Minute Check Transparency 9-2	• 5-Minute Check Transparency 9-2	• 5-Minute Check Transparency 9-2
Other	• Study Notebook	• Study Notebook	• Study Notebook	• Study Notebook

Add and Subtract Rational Expressions As with fractions, rational expressions must have common denominators in order to be added or subtracted.

Key Concept

Adding Rational Expressions

Words To add rational expressions, find the least common denominator (LCD). Rewrite each expression with the LCD. Then add.

Symbols For all $\frac{a}{b}$ and $\frac{c}{d}$, with $b \neq 0$ and $d \neq 0$, $\frac{a}{b} + \frac{c}{d} = \frac{ad}{bd} + \frac{bc}{bd} = \frac{ad + bc}{bd}$.

Subtracting Rational Expressions

Words To subtract rational expressions, find the least common denominator (LCD). Rewrite each expression with the LCD. Then subtract.

Symbols For all $\frac{a}{b}$ and $\frac{c}{d}$, with $b \neq 0$ and $d \neq 0$, $\frac{a}{b} - \frac{c}{d} = \frac{ad}{bd} - \frac{bc}{bd} = \frac{ad - bc}{bd}$.

EXAMPLE 2 Monomial Denominators

Simplify $\frac{3y}{2x^3} + \frac{5z}{8xy^2}$.

$\frac{3y}{2x^3} + \frac{5z}{8xy^2} = \frac{3y}{2x^3} \cdot \frac{4y^2}{4y^2} + \frac{5z}{8xy^2} \cdot \frac{x^2}{x^2}$ The LCD is $8x^3y^2$.

$= \frac{12y^3}{8x^3y^2} + \frac{5x^2z}{8x^3y^2}$ Multiply fractions.

$= \frac{12y^3 + 5x^2z}{8x^3y^2}$ Add the numerators.

Guided Practice Simplify each expression.

2A. $\frac{4}{5a^3b^2} + \frac{9c}{10ab}$ $\frac{8 + 9a^2bc}{10a^3b^2}$

2B. $\frac{3a^2}{16b^2} - \frac{8x}{5a^3b}$ $\frac{15a^5 - 128bx}{80a^3b^2}$

Personal Tutor glencoe.com

StudyTip

Simplifying Rational Expressions After you add or subtract rational expressions, it is possible that the resulting expression can be further simplified.

The LCD is also used to combine rational expressions with polynomial denominators.

EXAMPLE 3 Polynomial Denominators

Simplify $\frac{5}{6x - 18} - \frac{x - 1}{4x^2 - 14x + 6}$.

$\frac{5}{6x - 18} - \frac{x - 1}{4x^2 - 14x + 6} = \frac{5}{6(x - 3)} - \frac{x - 1}{2(2x - 1)(x - 3)}$ Factor denominators.

$= \frac{5(2x - 1)}{6(x - 3)(2x - 1)} - \frac{(x - 1)(3)}{2(2x - 1)(x - 3)(3)}$ Multiply by missing factors.

$= \frac{10x - 5 - 3x + 3}{6(x - 3)(2x - 1)}$ Subtract numerators.

$= \frac{7x - 2}{6(x - 3)(2x - 1)}$ Simplify.

Guided Practice Simplify each expression.

3A. $\frac{x - 1}{x^2 - x - 6} - \frac{4}{5x + 10}$ $\frac{x + 7}{5(x + 2)(x - 3)}$

3B. $\frac{x - 8}{4x^2 + 21x + 5} + \frac{6}{12x + 3}$ $\frac{3x + 2}{(4x + 1)(x + 5)}$

Personal Tutor glencoe.com

Formative Assessment

Use the Guided Practice exercises after each example to determine students' understanding of concepts.

Additional Example

1 Find the LCM of each set of polynomials.

a. $15a^2bc^3$, $16b^5c^2$, and $20a^3c^6$ $240a^3b^5c^6$

b. $x^3 - x^2 - 2x$ and $x^2 - 4x + 4$ $x(x + 1)(x - 2)^2$

Additional Examples also in Interactive Classroom PowerPoint® Presentations

IWB INTERACTIVE WHITEBOARD READY

Add and Subtract Rational Expressions

Example 2 shows how to add two rational expressions with monomial denominators. **Example 3** shows how to subtract two rational expressions with polynomial denominators. **Examples 4 and 5** show how to simplify complex fractions.

Additional Examples

2 Simplify $\frac{5a^2}{6b} + \frac{9}{14a^2b^2}$. $\frac{35a^4b + 27}{42a^2b^2}$

3 Simplify $\frac{x + 10}{3x - 15} - \frac{3x + 15}{6x - 30}$. $-\frac{1}{6}$

TEACH with TECH

DOCUMENT CAMERA Choose several students to work through examples in front of the class. Be sure they clearly explain how to find the LCD.

Watch Out!

Preventing Errors Have students discuss the differences between procedures for adding and multiplying fractions. It is important that they see why common denominators are required for addition but not for multiplication.

Additional Examples

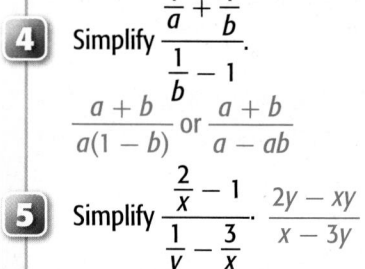

4 Simplify $\dfrac{\frac{1}{a} + \frac{1}{b}}{\frac{1}{b} - 1}$. $\dfrac{a + b}{a(1 - b)}$ or $\dfrac{a + b}{a - ab}$

5 Simplify $\dfrac{\frac{2}{x} - 1}{\frac{1}{y} - \frac{3}{x}}$. $\dfrac{2y - xy}{x - 3y}$

Focus on Mathematical Content

Equivalent Expressions When rational expressions are given the same denominators in preparation for addition or subtraction, they are equivalent to the original expressions. Multiplying a rational expression by a form of 1 such as $\frac{6x}{6x}$ or $\frac{y - 3}{y - 3}$ does not change the value of the expression.

StudyTip

Undefined Terms Remember that there are restrictions on variables in the denominator.

One way to simplify a complex fraction is to simplify the numerator and the denominator separately, and then simplify the resulting expressions.

EXAMPLE 4 Complex Fractions with Different LCDs

Simplify $\dfrac{1 + \frac{1}{x}}{1 - \frac{x}{y}}$.

$\dfrac{1 + \frac{1}{x}}{1 - \frac{x}{y}} = \dfrac{\frac{x}{x} + \frac{1}{x}}{\frac{y}{y} - \frac{x}{y}}$ — **The LCD of the numerator is x. The LCD of the denominator is y.**

$= \dfrac{\frac{x + 1}{x}}{\frac{y - x}{y}}$ — **Simplify the numerator and denominator.**

$= \dfrac{x + 1}{x} \div \dfrac{y - x}{y}$ — **Write as a division expression.**

$= \dfrac{x + 1}{x} \cdot \dfrac{y}{y - x}$ — **Multiply by the reciprocal of the divisor.**

$= \dfrac{xy + y}{xy - x^2}$ — **Simplify.**

Guided Practice

Simplify each expression.

4A. $\dfrac{1 - \frac{y}{x}}{\frac{1}{y} + \frac{1}{x}}$ $\dfrac{xy - y^2}{x + y}$

4B. $\dfrac{\frac{c}{d} - \frac{d}{c}}{\frac{d}{c} + 2}$ $\dfrac{c^2 - d^2}{d^2 + 2cd}$

Personal Tutor glencoe.com

Another method of simplifying complex fractions is to find the LCD of all of the denominators. Then, the denominators are all eliminated by multiplying by the LCD.

EXAMPLE 5 Complex Fractions with Same LCD

Simplify $\dfrac{1 + \frac{1}{x}}{1 - \frac{x}{y}}$.

$\dfrac{1 + \frac{1}{x}}{1 - \frac{x}{y}} = \dfrac{\left(1 + \frac{1}{x}\right)}{\left(1 - \frac{x}{y}\right)} \cdot \dfrac{xy}{xy}$ — **The LCD of all of the denominators is xy. Multiply by $\frac{xy}{xy}$.**

$= \dfrac{xy + y}{xy - x^2}$ — **Distribute xy.**

Notice that the same problem is solved in Examples 4 and 5 using different methods, but both produce the same answer. So, how you solve problems similar to these is left up to your own discretion.

Guided Practice

Simplify each expression.

5A. $\dfrac{1 + \frac{2}{x}}{\frac{3}{y} - \frac{4}{x}}$ $\dfrac{xy + 2y}{3x - 4y}$

5B. $\dfrac{\frac{1}{d} - \frac{d}{c}}{\frac{1}{c} + 6}$ $\dfrac{c - d^2}{d + 6cd}$

5C. $\dfrac{\frac{1}{y} + \frac{1}{x}}{\frac{1}{y} - \frac{1}{x}}$ $\dfrac{x + y}{x - y}$

5D. $\dfrac{\frac{a}{b} + 1}{1 - \frac{b}{a}}$ $\dfrac{a(a + b)}{b(a - b)}$

Personal Tutor glencoe.com

Differentiated Instruction

AL OL ELL

If students have difficulty adding and subtracting rational expressions,

Then have students work with a partner, one in the role of a coach, the other in the role of an athlete. The athlete works a problem, using steps and explaining the thinking while the coach listens and watches for errors, correcting as necessary. Then the partners exchange roles.

564 Chapter 9 Rational Functions and Relations

Check Your Understanding

Example 1 p. 562

Find the LCM of each set of polynomials.

1. $16x, 8x^2y^3, 5x^3y$ $\mathbf{80x^3y^3}$
2. $7a^2, 9ab^3, 21abc^4$ $\mathbf{63a^2b^3c^4}$
3. $3y^2 - 9y, y^2 - 8y + 15$ $\mathbf{3y(y-3)(y-5)}$
4. $x^3 - 6x^2 - 16x, x^2 - 4$ $\mathbf{x(x+2)(x-2)(x-8)}$

Examples 2 and 3 p. 563

Simplify each expression.

5. $\frac{12y}{5x} + \frac{5x}{4y^3}$ $\mathbf{\frac{48y^4 + 25x^2}{20xy^3}}$
6. $\frac{5}{6ab} + \frac{3b^2}{14a^3}$ $\mathbf{\frac{35a^2 + 9b^3}{42a^3b}}$
7. $\frac{7b}{12a} - \frac{1}{18ab^3}$ $\mathbf{\frac{21b^4 - 2}{36ab^3}}$
8. $\frac{y^2}{8c^2d^2} - \frac{3x}{14c^4d}$ $\mathbf{\frac{7c^2y^2 - 12dx}{56c^4d^2}}$
9. $\frac{4x}{x^2 + 9x + 18} + \frac{5}{x+6}$ $\mathbf{\frac{9x + 15}{(x+3)(x+6)}}$
10. $\frac{8}{y-3} + \frac{2y-5}{y^2 - 12y + 27}$ $\mathbf{\frac{10y - 77}{(y-3)(y-9)}}$
11. $\frac{4}{3x+6} - \frac{x+1}{x^2 - 4}$ $\mathbf{\frac{x - 11}{3(x+2)(x-2)}}$
12. $\frac{3a+2}{a^2 - 16} - \frac{7}{6a + 24}$ $\mathbf{\frac{11a + 40}{6(a+4)(a-4)}}$

13. **GEOMETRY** Find the perimeter of the rectangle. $\mathbf{\frac{14x - 10}{(x+1)(x-2)}}$

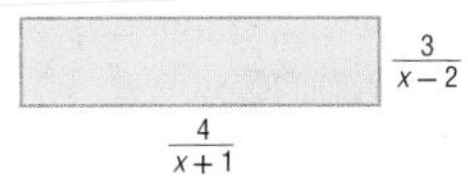

Examples 4 and 5 p. 564

Simplify each expression.

14. $\frac{4 + \frac{2}{x}}{3 - \frac{2}{x}}$ $\mathbf{\frac{4x+2}{3x-2}}$
15. $\frac{6 + \frac{4}{y}}{2 + \frac{6}{y}}$ $\mathbf{\frac{3y+2}{y+3}}$
16. $\frac{\frac{3}{x} + \frac{2}{y}}{1 + \frac{4}{y}}$ $\mathbf{\frac{3y + 2x}{xy + 4x}}$
17. $\frac{\frac{2}{b} + \frac{5}{a}}{\frac{3}{a} - \frac{8}{b}}$ $\mathbf{\frac{2a + 5b}{3b - 8a}}$

Practice and Problem Solving

= **Step-by-Step Solutions** begin on page R20.
Extra Practice begins on page 947.

Example 1 p. 562

Find the LCM of each set of polynomials.

18. $24cd, 40a^2c^3d^4, 15abd^3$ $\mathbf{120a^2bc^3d^4}$
19. $4x^2y^3, 18xy^4, 10xz^2$ $\mathbf{180x^2y^4z^2}$
20. $x^2 - 9x + 20, x^2 + x - 30$ **20.** $\mathbf{(x-4)(x-5)(x+6)}$
21. $6x^2 + 21x - 12, 4x^2 + 22x + 24$ **21.** $\mathbf{6(x+4)(2x-1)(2x+3)}$

Examples 2 and 3 p. 563

Simplify each expression.

22. $\frac{5a}{24cf^4} + \frac{a}{36bc^4f^3}$ $\mathbf{\frac{15abc^3 + 2af}{72bc^4f^4}}$
23. $\frac{4b}{15x^3y^2} - \frac{3b}{35x^2y^4z}$ $\mathbf{\frac{28by^2z - 9bx}{105x^3y^4z}}$
24. $\frac{5b}{6a} + \frac{3b}{10a^2} + \frac{2}{ab^2}$ $\mathbf{\frac{25ab^3 + 9b^3 + 60a}{30a^2b^2}}$
25. $\frac{4}{3x} + \frac{8}{x^3} + \frac{2}{5xy}$ $\mathbf{\frac{20x^2y + 120y + 6x^2}{15x^3y}}$
26. $\frac{8}{3y} + \frac{2}{9} - \frac{3}{10y^2}$ $\mathbf{\frac{240y + 20y^2 - 27}{90y^2}}$
27. $\frac{1}{16a} + \frac{5}{12b} - \frac{9}{10b^3}$ $\mathbf{\frac{15b^3 + 100ab^2 - 216a}{240ab^3}}$
28. $\frac{8}{x^2 - 6x - 16} + \frac{9}{x^2 - 3x - 40}$ **28.** $\mathbf{\frac{17x + 58}{(x-8)(x+2)(x+5)}}$
29. $\frac{6}{y^2 - 2y - 35} + \frac{4}{y^2 + 9y + 20}$ **29.** $\mathbf{\frac{10y - 4}{(y-7)(y+5)(y+4)}}$
30. $\frac{12}{3y^2 - 10y - 8} - \frac{3}{y^2 - 6y + 8}$ **30.** $\mathbf{\frac{3y - 30}{(3y+2)(y-4)(y-2)}}$
31. $\frac{6}{2x^2 + 11x - 6} - \frac{8}{x^2 + 3x - 18}$ **31.** $\mathbf{\frac{-10x - 10}{(2x-1)(x+6)(x-3)}}$
32. $\frac{2x}{4x^2 + 9x + 2} + \frac{3}{2x^2 - 8x - 24}$ **32.** $\mathbf{\frac{4x^2 - 12x + 3}{2(x-6)(4x+1)(x+2)}}$
33. $\frac{4x}{3x^2 + 3x - 18} - \frac{2x}{2x^2 + 11x + 15}$ **33.** $\mathbf{\frac{2x^2 + 32x}{3(x-2)(x+3)(2x+5)}}$

34. **BIOLOGY** After a person eats something, the pH or acid level A of his or her mouth can be determined by the formula $A = \frac{20.4t}{t^2 + 36} + 6.5$, where t is the number of minutes that have elapsed since the food was eaten.
    a. Simplify the equation. $\mathbf{A = \frac{6.5t^2 + 20.4t + 234}{t^2 + 36}}$
    b. What would the acid level be after 30 minutes? $\mathbf{\approx 7.2}$

3 PRACTICE

Formative Assessment

Use Exercises 1–17 to check for understanding.

Use the chart at the bottom of this page to customize assignments for your students.

Differentiated Homework Options

Level	Assignment	Two-Day Option	
AL Basic	18–39, 64–90	19–39 odd, 67–70	18–38 even, 64–66, 71–90
OL Core	19–39 odd, 40–57 odd, 59–62, 64–90	18–39, 67–70	40–62, 64–66, 71–90
BL Advanced	40–84, (optional: 85–90)		

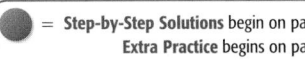

Exercise Alerts

Formulas For Exercise 35, students will need to know the formula for the area of a triangle, $A = \frac{1}{2}bh$.

Grid Paper For Exercises 75–80, and 85–90, students will need grid paper.

Tips for New Teachers

Pacing The skills for combining and simplifying that are developed in this lesson are used extensively in algebra. Take time to clear up student errors and misconceptions before proceeding.

Additional Answers

62b.

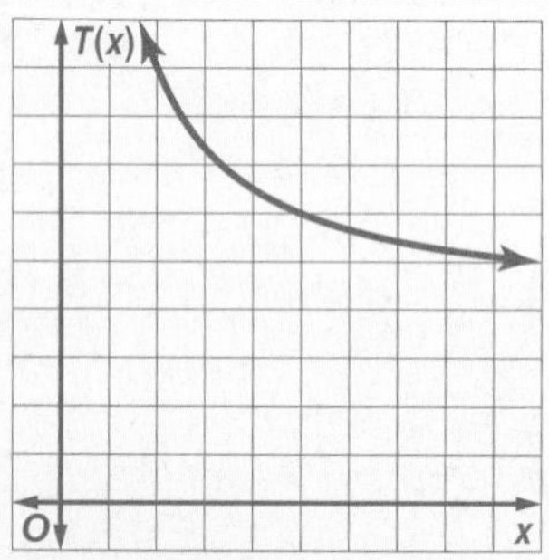

62c.

x	T(x)
20	4.5
50	4.2
100	4.1
200	4.05
400	4.025

35. GEOMETRY Both triangles in the figure at the right are equilateral. If the area of the smaller triangle is 200 square centimeters and the area of the larger triangle is 300 square centimeters, find the minimum distance from A to B in terms of x and y and simplify. $\frac{1000x + 800y}{x(x + 2y)}$

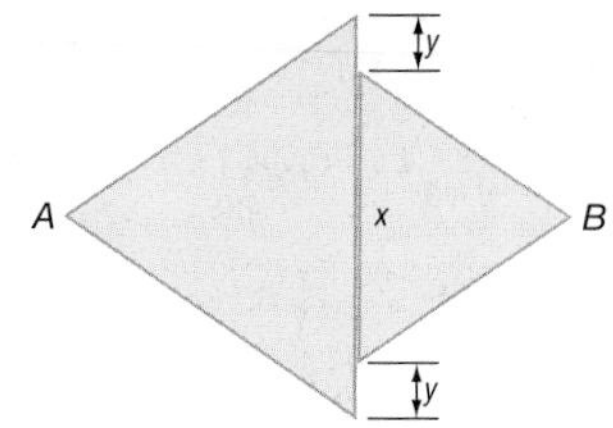

Examples 4 and 5 p. 564

Simplify each expression.

36. $\dfrac{\frac{2}{x-3} + \frac{3x}{x^2-9}}{\frac{3}{x+3} - \frac{4x}{x^2-9}}$ $\frac{5x + 6}{-x - 9}$

37. $\dfrac{\frac{4}{x+5} + \frac{9}{x-6}}{\frac{5}{x-6} - \frac{8}{x+5}}$ $\frac{13x + 21}{-3x + 73}$

38. $\dfrac{\frac{5}{x+6} - \frac{2x}{2x-1}}{\frac{x}{2x-1} + \frac{4}{x+6}}$ $\frac{-2x^2 - 2x - 5}{x^2 + 14x - 4}$

39. $\dfrac{\frac{8}{x-9} - \frac{x}{3x+2}}{\frac{3}{3x+2} + \frac{4x}{x-9}}$ $\frac{-x^2 + 33x + 16}{12x^2 + 11x - 27}$

B

40. OIL PRODUCTION Managers of an oil company have estimated that oil will be pumped from a certain well at a rate based on the function $R(x) = \frac{20}{x} + \frac{200x}{3x^2 + 20}$, where $R(x)$ is the rate of production in thousands of barrels per year x years after pumping begins.

a. Simplify $R(x)$. $R(x) = \frac{260x^2 + 400}{3x^3 + 20x}$

b. At what rate will oil be pumping from the well in 50 years? **about 1730 barrels/yr**

Real-World Link

Prudhoe Bay, Alaska, is home to the largest oil field in the United States with cumulative production and reserves of over 13 billion barrels.

Source: Energy Information Administration

Find the LCM of each set of polynomials.

41. $12xy^4$, $14x^4y^2$, $5xyz^3$, $15x^5y^3$ $420x^5y^4z^3$

42. $-6abc^2$, $18a^2b^2$, $15a^4c$, $8b^3$ $-360a^4b^3c^2$

43. $x^2 - 3x - 28$, $2x^2 + 9x + 4$, $x^2 - 16$

44. $x^2 - 5x - 24$, $x^2 - 9$, $3x^2 + 8x - 3$

Simplify each expression.

45. $\frac{1}{12a} + 6 - \frac{3}{5a^2}$ $\frac{360a^2 + 5a - 36}{60a^2}$

46. $\frac{5}{16y^2} - 4 - \frac{8}{3x^2y}$ $\frac{15x^2 - 192x^2y^2 - 128y}{48x^2y^2}$

47. $\frac{5}{6x^2 + 46x - 16} + \frac{2}{6x^2 + 57x + 72}$

48. $\frac{1}{8x^2 - 20x - 12} + \frac{4}{6x^2 + 27x + 12}$

49. $\frac{x^2 + y^2}{x^2 - y^2} + \frac{y}{x + y} - \frac{x}{x - y}$ 0

50. $\frac{x^2 + x}{x^2 - 9x + 8} + \frac{4}{x - 1} - \frac{3}{x - 8}$ $\frac{x^2 + 2x - 29}{x^2 - 9x + 8}$

51. $\dfrac{\frac{2}{a-1} + \frac{3}{a-4}}{\frac{6}{a^2 - 5a + 4}}$ $\frac{5a - 11}{6}$

52. $\dfrac{\frac{1}{x} + \frac{1}{y}}{\left(\frac{1}{x} - \frac{1}{y}\right)(x + y)}$ $\frac{1}{y - x}$

43. $(x + 4)(x - 4)(2x + 1)(x - 7)$
44. $(x + 3)(x - 3)(x - 8)(3x - 1)$
47. $\frac{42x + 41}{6(3x - 1)(x + 8)(2x + 3)}$
48. $\frac{19x - 36}{12(2x + 1)(x - 3)(x + 4)}$
54c. $\frac{20(x - 1)}{x(x - 2)}$

53. GEOMETRY An expression for the length of one rectangle is $\frac{x^2 - 9}{x - 2}$. The length of a similar rectangle is expressed as $\frac{x + 3}{x^2 - 4}$. What is the scale factor of the two rectangles? Write in simplest form. $(x - 3)(x + 2)$ **to 1**

54. KAYAKING Cameron is taking a 20-mile kayaking trip. He travels half the distance at one rate. The rest of the distance he travels 2 miles per hour slower.

a. If x represents the faster pace in miles per hour, write an expression that represents the time spent at that pace. $\frac{10}{x}$

b. Write an expression for the amount of time spent at the slower pace. $\frac{10}{x - 2}$

c. Write an expression for the amount of time Cameron needed to complete the trip.

Find the slope of the line that passes through each pair of points.

55. $A\left(\frac{2}{p}, \frac{1}{2}\right)$ and $B\left(\frac{1}{3}, \frac{3}{p}\right)$ $-\frac{3}{2}$

56. $C\left(\frac{1}{4}, \frac{4}{q}\right)$ and $D\left(\frac{5}{q}, \frac{1}{5}\right)$ $-\frac{4}{5}$

57. $E\left(\frac{7}{w}, \frac{1}{7}\right)$ and $F\left(\frac{1}{7}, \frac{7}{w}\right)$ -1

58. $G\left(\frac{6}{n}, \frac{1}{6}\right)$ and $H\left(\frac{1}{6}, \frac{6}{n}\right)$ -1

Differentiated Instruction

BL

Extension *Partial fraction decomposition* is a useful algebraic skill in more advanced mathematics courses, including calculus. Give students a rational expression like $\frac{5x + 3}{x(x + 1)}$, and ask what kinds of simpler fractions might be added to yield this expression. If they can identify x and $x + 1$ as denominators for such "partial fractions," ask them to try and find values of A and B that will make the equation $\frac{A}{x} + \frac{B}{x + 1} = \frac{5x + 3}{x(x + 1)}$ a true statement for any value of x. $A = 3$ and $B = 2$

Real-World Link

Macro photography is commonly described as being able to focus on a subject closely so that when a regular 4" × 6" print is made, the image is life-size or larger.

59. PHOTOGRAPHY The focal length of a lens establishes the field of view of the camera. The shorter the focal length is, the larger the field of view. For a camera with a fixed focal length of 70 mm to focus on an object x mm from the lens, the film must be placed a distance y from the lens. This is represented by $\frac{1}{x} + \frac{1}{y} = \frac{1}{70}$.

a. Express y as a function of x. $y = \frac{70x}{x - 70}$

b. What happens to the focusing distance when the object is 70 mm away?

60. PHARMACOLOGY Two drugs are administered to a patient. The concentrations in the bloodstream of each are given by $f(t) = \frac{2t}{3t^2 + 9t + 6}$ and $g(t) = \frac{3t}{2t^2 + 6t + 4}$ where t is the time, in hours, after the drugs are administered.

a. Add the two functions together to determine a function for the total concentration of drugs in the patient's bloodstream. $h(t) = \frac{13t}{6t^2 + 18t + 12}$

b. What is the concentration of drugs after 8 hours? about 0.19

61. DOPPLER EFFECT Refer to the application at the beginning of the lesson. George is equidistant from two fire engines traveling toward him from opposite directions.

a. Let x be the speed of the faster fire engine and y be the speed of the slower fire engine. Write and simplify a rational expression representing the difference in pitch between the two sirens according to George.

b. If one is traveling at 45 meters per second and the other is traveling at 70 meters per second, what is the difference in their pitches according to George? The speed of sound in air is 332 meters per second, and both engines have a siren with a pitch of 500 Hz. about 55.2 Hz

62. RESEARCH A student studying learning behavior performed an experiment in which a rat was repeatedly sent through a maze. It was determined that the time it took the rat to complete the maze followed the rational function $T(x) = 4 + \frac{10}{x}$, where x represented the number of trials. b, c. See margin.

a. What is the domain of the function? $x \neq 0$

b. Graph the function for $0 \leq x \leq 10$.

c. Make a table of the function for $x = 20, 50, 100, 200$, and 400.

d. If it were possible to have an infinite number of trials, what do you think would be the rat's best time? Explain your reasoning. Sample answer: 4; The fraction approaches 0 as x approaches infinity; $4 + 0 = 4$.

59b. Sample answer: When the object is 70 mm away, y needs to be 0, which is impossible.

61a. $\frac{P_0 s_0 x - P_0 s_0 y}{(s_0 - x)(s_0 - y)}$

H.O.T. Problems

Use Higher-Order Thinking Skills

63. CHALLENGE Simplify $\dfrac{5x^{-2} - \frac{x+1}{x}}{\frac{4}{3 - x^{-1}} + 6x^{-1}}$. $\dfrac{-3x^3 - 2x^2 + 16x - 5}{4x^3 + 18x^2 - 6x}$

64. REASONING Determine whether the following statement is *true* or *false*. Explain your reasoning.

$$\frac{6}{x+2} + \frac{4}{x-3} = \frac{10x - 10}{(x+2)(x-3)} \textit{ for all values of } x.$$

65. OPEN ENDED Write three monomials with an LCM of $180a^4b^6c$. Sample answer: $20a^4b^2c$, $15ab^6$, $9abc$

66. WRITING IN MATH Write a how-to manual for adding rational expressions that have unlike denominators.

64. Sample answer: False; it is true for all values of x except -2 and 3.

66. Sample answer: First, factor the denominators of all of the expressions. Find the LCD of the denominators. Convert each expression so they all have the LCD. Add or subtract the numerators. Then simplify.

Study Guide and Intervention
CRM pp. 11–12 AL OL ELL

9-2 Study Guide and Intervention
Adding and Subtracting Rational Expressions

LCM of Polynomials To find the least common multiple of two or more polynomials, factor each expression. The LCM contains each factor the greatest number of times it appears as a factor.

Example 1 Find the LCM of $16p^2q^3r$, $40pq^4r^2$, and $15p^3r^4$.

$16p^2q^3r = 2^4 \cdot p^2 \cdot q^3 \cdot r$
$40pq^4r^2 = 2^3 \cdot 5 \cdot p \cdot q^4 \cdot r^2$
$15p^3r^4 = 3 \cdot 5 \cdot p^3 \cdot r^4$
LCM $= 2^4 \cdot 3 \cdot 5 \cdot p^3 \cdot q^4 \cdot r^4$
$= 240p^3q^4r^4$

Example 2 Find the LCM of $3m^2 - 3m - 6$ and $4m^2 + 12m - 40$.

$3m^2 - 3m - 6 = 3(m + 1)(m - 2)$
$4m^2 + 12m - 40 = 4(m - 2)(m + 5)$
LCM $= 12(m + 1)(m - 2)(m + 5)$

Exercises

Find the LCM of each set of polynomials.

1. $14ab^2, 42bc^3, 18a^2c$ — $126a^2b^2c^3$
2. $8cdf^3, 28c^2f, 35d^4f^2$ — $280c^2d^4f^3$
3. $65x^4y, 10x^2y^2, 26y^4$ — $130x^4y^4$
4. $11mn^5, 18m^2n^3, 20mn^4$ — $1980m^2n^5$
5. $15a^4b, 50a^2b^2, 40b^8$ — $600a^4b^8$
6. $24p^7q, 30p^2q^2, 45pq^3$ — $360p^7q^3$
7. $39b^2c^2, 52b^4c, 12c^3$ — $156b^4c^3$
8. $12xy^4, 42x^2y, 30x^2y^3$ — $420x^2y^4$
9. $56stv^2, 24s^2v^2, 70t^3v^3$ — $840s^2t^3v^3$
10. $x^2 + 3x, 10x^2 + 25x - 15$ — $5x(x + 3)(2x - 1)$
11. $9x^2 - 12x + 4, 3x^2 + 10x - 8$ — $(3x - 2)^2(x + 4)$
12. $22x^2 + 66x - 220, 4x^2 - 16$ — $44(x - 2)(x + 2)(x + 5)$
13. $8x^2 - 36x - 20, 2x^2 + 2x - 60$ — $4(x - 5)(x + 6)(2x + 1)$
14. $5x^2 - 125, 5x^2 + 24x - 5$ — $5(x - 5)(x + 5)(5x - 1)$
15. $3x^2 - 18x + 27, 2x^3 - 4x^2 - 6x$ — $6x(x - 3)^2(x + 1)$
16. $45x^2 - 6x - 3, 45x^2 - 5$ — $15(5x + 1)(3x - 1)(3x + 1)$
17. $x^3 + 4x^2 - x - 4, x^2 + 2x - 3$ — $(x - 1)(x + 1)(x + 3)(x + 4)$
18. $54x^3 - 24x, 12x^2 - 26x + 12$ — $6x(3x + 2)(3x - 2)(2x - 3)$

Chapter 9 11 Glencoe Algebra 2

Lesson 9-2

Practice
CRM p. 14 AL OL BL ELL

9-2 Practice
Adding and Subtracting Rational Expressions

Find the LCM of each set of polynomials.

1. x^2y, xy^3 — x^2y^3
2. a^2b^3c, abc^4 — $a^2b^3c^4$
3. $x + 1, x + 3$ — $(x + 1)(x + 3)$
4. $g - 1, g^2 + 3g - 4$ — $(g - 1)(g + 4)$
5. $2r + 2, r^2 + r, r + 1$ — $2r(r + 1)$
6. $3, 4w + 2, 4w^2 - 1$ — $6(2w + 1)(2w - 1)$
7. $x^2 + 2x - 8, x + 4$ — $(x + 4)(x - 2)$
8. $x^2 - x - 6, x^2 + 6x + 8$ — $(x + 2)(x + 4)(x - 3)$
9. $d^2 + 6d + 9, 2(d^2 - 9)$ — $2(d - 3)(d + 3)^2$

Simplify each expression.

10. $\frac{5}{6ab} - \frac{7}{8a}$ — $\frac{20 - 21b}{24ab}$
11. $\frac{5}{12x^4y} - \frac{1}{5x^2y^3}$ — $\frac{25y^2 - 12x^2}{60x^4y^3}$
12. $\frac{1}{6c^2d} + \frac{3}{4cd^3}$ — $\frac{2d^2 + 9c}{12c^2d^3}$
13. $\frac{4m}{3mn} + 2$ — $\frac{2(2 + 3n)}{3n}$
14. $2x - 5 - \frac{x - 8}{x + 4}$ — $\frac{2(x + 3)(x - 2)}{x + 4}$
15. $\frac{4}{a - 3} + \frac{9}{a - 5}$ — $\frac{13a - 47}{(a - 3)(a - 5)}$
16. $\frac{16}{x^2 - 16} + \frac{2}{x + 4}$ — $\frac{2}{x - 4}$
17. $\frac{2 - 5m}{m - 9} + \frac{4m - 5}{9 - m}$ — $\frac{7 - 9m}{m - 9}$
18. $\frac{y - 5}{y^2 - 3y - 10} + \frac{y}{y^2 + y - 2}$ — $\frac{2y - 1}{(y + 2)(y - 1)}$
19. $\frac{5}{2x - 12} - \frac{20}{x^2 - 4x - 12}$ — $\frac{5}{2(x + 2)}$
20. $\frac{2p - 3}{p^2 - 5p + 6} - \frac{5}{p^2 - 9}$ — $\frac{2p^2 - 2p + 1}{(p - 2)(p + 3)(p - 3)}$
21. $\frac{1}{5n} - \frac{3}{4} + \frac{7}{10n}$ — $\frac{3(6 - 5n)}{20n}$
22. $\frac{2a}{a - 3} - \frac{2a}{a + 3} + \frac{36}{a^2 - 9}$ — $\frac{12}{a - 3}$
23. $\dfrac{\frac{2}{x - y} + \frac{1}{x + y}}{\frac{1}{x - y}}$ — $\frac{3x + y}{x + y}$
24. $\dfrac{\frac{r + 6}{r} - \frac{1}{r + 2}}{\frac{r^2 + 4r + 3}{r^2 + 2r}}$ — $\frac{r + 4}{r + 1}$

25. **GEOMETRY** The expressions $\frac{5x}{2}$, $\frac{20}{x + 4}$, and $\frac{10}{x - 4}$ represent the lengths of the sides of a triangle. Write a simplified expression for the perimeter of the triangle. $\frac{5(x^3 - 4x - 16)}{2(x - 4)(x + 4)}$

26. **KAYAKING** Mai is kayaking on a river that has a current of 2 miles per hour. If r represents her rate in calm water, then $r + 2$ represents her rate with the current, and $r - 2$ represents her rate against the current. Mai kayaks 2 miles downstream and then back to her starting point. Use the formula for time, $t = \frac{d}{r}$, where d is the distance, to write a simplified expression for the total time it takes Mai to complete the trip. $\frac{4r}{(r + 2)(r - 2)}$ hrs

Chapter 9 14 Glencoe Algebra 2

Word Problem Practice
CRM p. 15 AL OL BL ELL

9-2 Word Problem Practice
Adding and Subtracting Rational Expressions

1. **SQUARES** Susan's favorite perfect square is s^2 and Travis' is t^2, where s and t are whole numbers. What perfect square is guaranteed to be divisible by both Susan's and Travis' favorite perfect squares regardless of their specific value? s^2t^2

2. **ELECTRIC POTENTIAL** The electrical potential function between two electrons is given by a formula that has the form $\frac{1}{r} + \frac{1}{1 - r}$. Simplify this expression. $\frac{1}{r(1 - r)}$

3. **TRAPEZOIDS** The cross section of a stand consists of two trapezoids stacked one on top of the other.

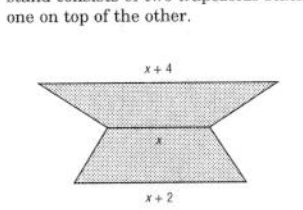

The total area of the cross section is x^2 square units. Assuming the trapezoids have the same height, write an expression for the height of the stand in terms of x. Put your answer in simplest form. (Recall that the area of a trapezoid with height h and bases b_1 and b_2 is given by $\frac{1}{2}h(b_1 + b_2)$.) $\frac{x^2}{2x + 3}$

4. **FRACTIONS** In the seventeenth century, Lord Brouncker wrote down a most peculiar mathematical equation:

$$\frac{4}{\pi} = 1 + \cfrac{1^2}{2 + \cfrac{3^2}{2 + \cfrac{5^2}{2 + \cfrac{7^2}{\ddots}}}}$$

This is an example of a continued fraction. Simplify the continued fraction $n + \frac{1}{n + \frac{1}{n}}$. $\frac{n^3 + 2n}{n^3 + 1}$

5. **RELAY RACE** Mark, Connell, Zack, and Moses run the 400 meter relay together. Each of them runs 100 meters. Their average speeds were s, $s + 0.5$, $s - 0.5$, and $s - 1$ meters per second, respectively.

a. What were their individual times for their own legs of the race? $\frac{100}{s}, \frac{100}{s + \frac{1}{2}}, \frac{100}{s - \frac{1}{2}}, \frac{100}{s - 1}$

b. Write an expression for their time as a team. Write your answer as a ratio of two polynomials. $100\frac{16s^3 + 12s^2 - 2s - 1}{4s^4 + 4s^3 - s^2 - s}$

c. The world record for the 100 meter relay is 37.4 seconds. What will s equal if the team ties the world record? 37.65 s

Chapter 9 15 Glencoe Algebra 2

Lesson 9-2

Enrichment
CRM p. 16 OL BL

9-2 Enrichment
Zeno's Paradox

The Greek philosopher Zeno of Elea (born sometime between 495 and 480 B.C.) proposed four paradoxes to challenge the notions of space and time. Zeno's first paradox works like this:

Suppose you are on your way to school. Assume you are able to cover half of the remaining distance each minute that you walk. You leave your house at 7:45 A.M. After the first minute, you are half of the way to school. In the next minute you cover half of the remaining distance to school, and at 7:47 A.M. you are three-quarters of the way to school. This pattern continues each minute. At what time will you arrive at school? Before 8:00 A.M.? Before lunch?

Since space is infinitely divisible, we can repeat this pattern forever. Thus, on the way to school you must reach an infinite number of 'midpoints' in a finite time. This is impossible, so you can never reach your goal. In general, according to Zeno anyone who wants to move from one point to another must meet these requirements, and motion is impossible. Therefore, what we perceive as motion is merely an illusion.

Addition of fractions can be defined by $\frac{a}{b} + \frac{c}{d} = \frac{ad + bc}{bd}$, similarly for subtraction.

Assume your house is one mile from school. At 7:46 A.M., you have walked half of a mile, so you have left $1 - \frac{1}{2}$, or $\frac{1}{2}$ a mile. At 7:47 A.M. you only have $\frac{1}{2} - \frac{1}{4} = \frac{1}{4}$ of a mile to go.

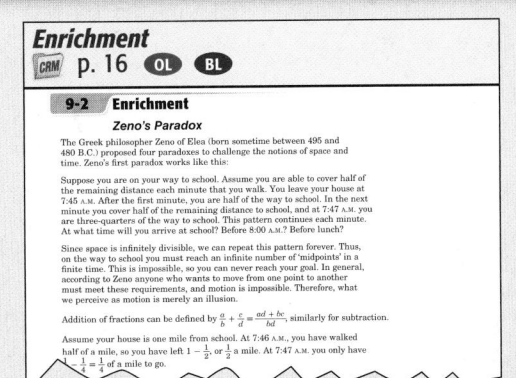

4 ASSESS

Yesterday's News Ask students to describe how yesterday's lesson on multiplication and division of rational expressions helped prepare them for today's lesson on addition and subtraction of rational expressions.

Formative Assessment

Check for student understanding of concepts in Lessons 9-1 and 9-2.

CRM Quiz 1, p. 48

Additional Answers

75. $D = \{x \mid x \geq -0.5\}$, $R = \{y \mid y \leq 0\}$

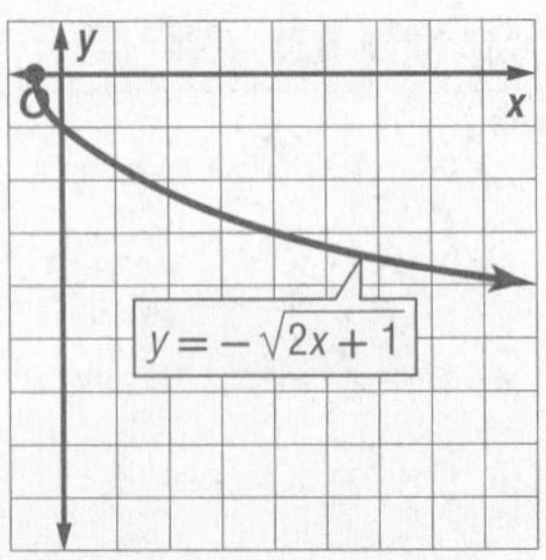

76. $D = \{x \mid x \geq 0.6\}$, $R = \{y \mid y \geq 0\}$

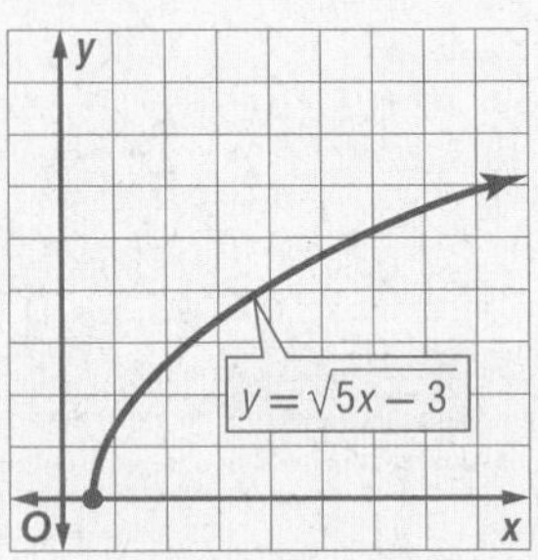

77. $D = \{x \mid x \geq -6\}$, $R = \{y \mid y \geq -3\}$

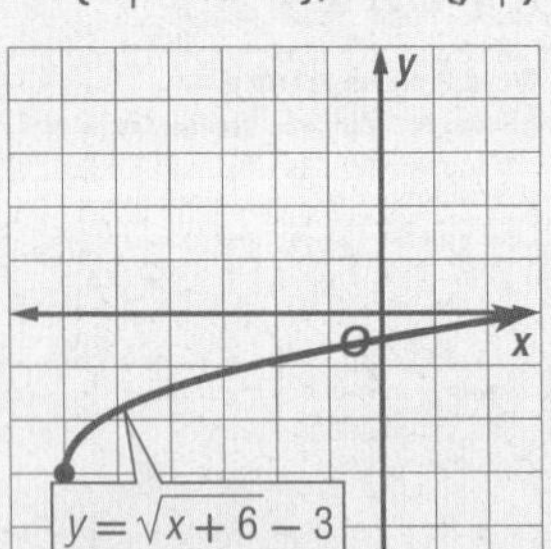

78. $D = \{x \mid x \geq -4\}$, $R = \{y \mid y \leq 5\}$

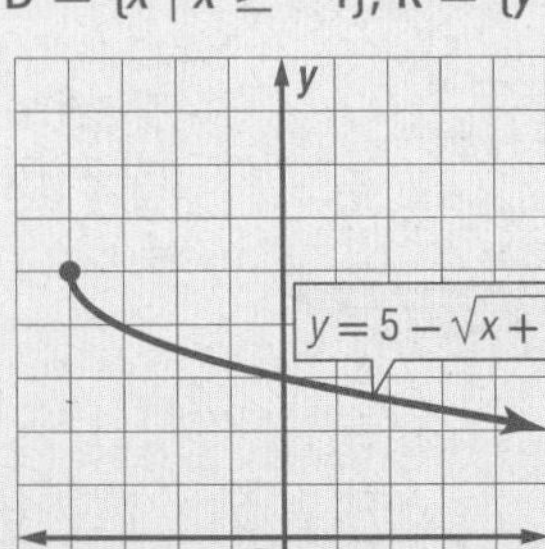

NGSSS PRACTICE 912.P.3.1, 912.G.2.5, 912.A.5.2

67. PROBABILITY A drawing is to be held to select the winner of a new bike. There are 100 seniors, 150 juniors, and 200 sophomores who had correct entries. The drawing will contain 3 tickets for each senior name, 2 for each junior, and 1 for each sophomore. What is the probability that a senior's ticket will be chosen? **D**

A. $\frac{1}{8}$ C. $\frac{2}{7}$

B. $\frac{2}{9}$ D. $\frac{3}{8}$

68. THINK SOLVE EXPLAIN **SHORT RESPONSE** Find the area of the figure. **$24 + 12.5\pi$ cm^2**

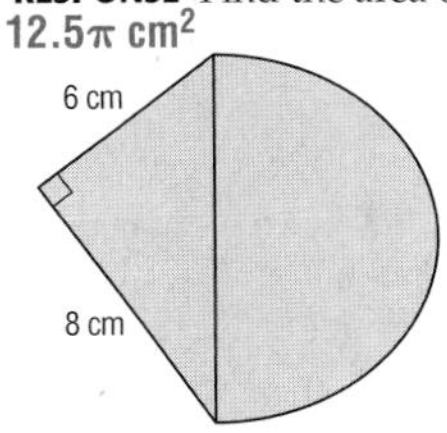

69. SAT/ACT If Mauricio receives b books in addition to the number of books he had, he will have t times as many as he had originally. In terms of b and t, how many books did Mauricio have at the beginning? **F**

F. $\frac{b}{t-1}$ H. $\frac{t+1}{b}$

G. $\frac{b}{t+1}$ I. $\frac{b}{t}$

70. If $\frac{2a}{a} + \frac{1}{a} = 4$, then $a =$ ____. **B**

A. $-\frac{1}{8}$ C. $\frac{1}{8}$

B. $\frac{1}{2}$ D. 2

Spiral Review

Simplify each expression. (Lesson 9-1)

71. $\frac{-4ab}{21c} \cdot \frac{14c^2}{22a^2}$ $-\frac{4bc}{33a}$

72. $\frac{x^2 - y^2}{6y} \div \frac{x+y}{36y^2}$ $6y(x - y)$

73. $\frac{n^2 - n - 12}{n+2} \div \frac{n-4}{n^2 - 4n - 12}$ $(n + 3)(n - 6)$

74. BIOLOGY Bacteria usually reproduce by a process known as *binary fission*. In this type of reproduction, one bacterium divides, forming two bacteria. Under ideal conditions, some bacteria reproduce every 20 minutes. (Lesson 8-8)

a. Find the constant k for this type of bacteria under ideal conditions. **about 0.0347**

b. Write the equation for modeling the exponential growth of this bacterium. $y = ae^{0.0347t}$

Graph each function. State the domain and range of each function. (Lesson 7-3) **75–80. See margin.**

75. $y = -\sqrt{2x+1}$ **76.** $y = \sqrt{5x-3}$ **77.** $y = \sqrt{x+6} - 3$

78. $y = 5 - \sqrt{x+4}$ **79.** $y = \sqrt{3x-6} + 4$ **80.** $y = 2\sqrt{3-4x} + 3$

Solve each equation. State the number and type of roots. (Lesson 6-7) **82. $\frac{5 \pm i\sqrt{71}}{4}$; 2 imaginary**

81. $3x + 8 = 0$ $-\frac{8}{3}$; **1 real**   **82.** $2x^2 - 5x + 12 = 0$ **83.** $x^3 + 9x = 0$ **84.** $x^4 - 81 = 0$

83. 0, $3i$, $-3i$; 1 real, 2 imaginary 84. 3, −3, $3i$, and $-3i$; 2 real, 2 imaginary

Skills Review

Graph each function. (Lesson 5-7) **85–90. See Chapter 9 Answer Appendix.**

85. $y = 4(x+3)^2 + 1$ **86.** $y = -(x-5)^2 - 3$ **87.** $y = \frac{1}{4}(x-2)^2 + 4$

88. $y = \frac{1}{2}(x-3)^2 - 5$ **89.** $y = x^2 + 6x + 2$ **90.** $y = x^2 - 8x + 18$

79. $D = \{x \mid x \geq 2\}$, $R = \{y \mid y \geq 4\}$

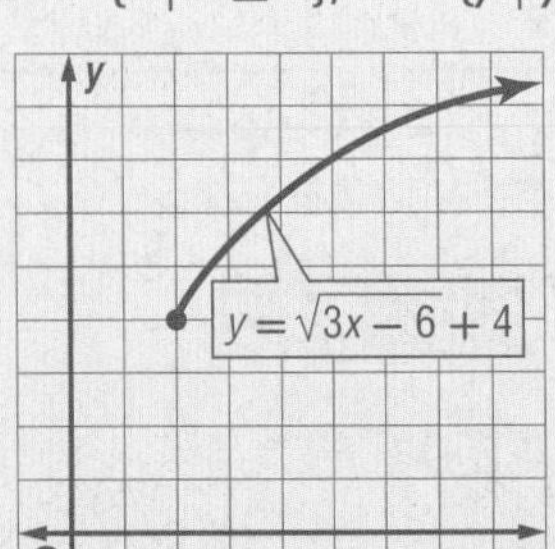

80. $D = \{x \mid x \leq 0.75\}$, $R = \{y \mid y \geq 3\}$

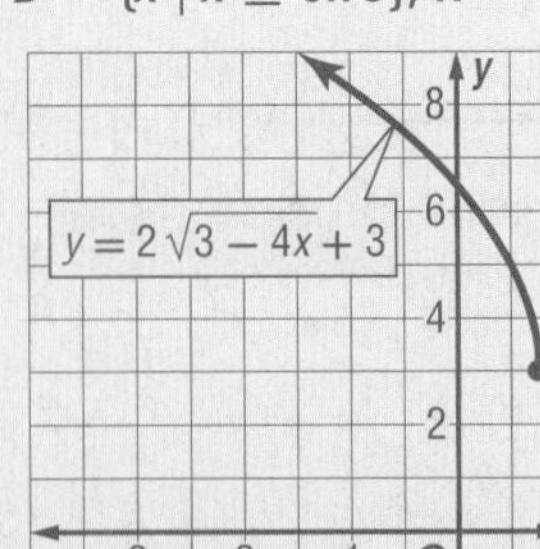

568 Chapter 9 Rational Functions and Relations

9-3 Graphing Reciprocal Functions

Then

You graphed polynomial functions. (Lesson 6-5)

Now

- Determine properties of reciprocal functions.
- Graph transformations of reciprocal functions.

NGSSS

LA.910.1.6.1 The student will use new vocabulary that is introduced and taught directly.
MA.912.A.5.6 Identify removable and non-removable discontinuities, and vertical, horizontal, and oblique asymptotes of a graph of a rational function, find the zeros, and graph the function.

New Vocabulary

reciprocal function
hyperbola
asymptote

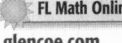

FL Math Online
glencoe.com

Why?

The East High School Chorale wants to raise $5000 to fund a trip to a national competition in Tampa. They have decided to sell candy bars. They will make a $1 profit on each candy bar they sell, so they need to sell 5000 candy bars.

If c represents the number of candy bars each student has to sell and n represents the number of students, then $c = \frac{5000}{n}$.

Vertical and Horizontal Asymptotes The function $c = \frac{5000}{n}$ is a reciprocal function. A **reciprocal function** has an equation of the form $f(x) = \frac{1}{a(x)}$, where $a(x)$ is a linear function and $a(x) \neq 0$.

Key Concept — Parent Function of Reciprocal Functions

Parent function:	$f(x) = \frac{1}{x}$
Type of graph:	**hyperbola**
Domain and range:	all nonzero real numbers
Axes of symmetry:	$x = 0$ and $f(x) = 0$
Intercepts:	none
Not defined:	$x = 0$ and $f(x) = 0$

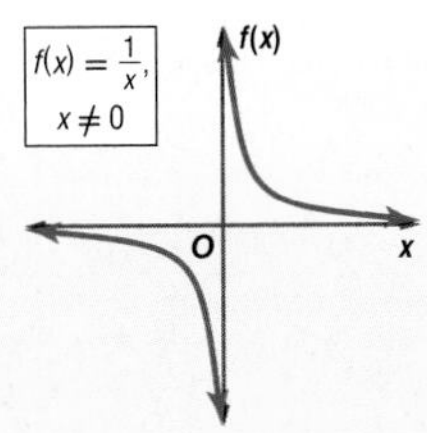

The domain of a reciprocal function is limited to values for which the function is defined.

Functions:	$f(x) = \frac{-3}{x+2}$	$g(x) = \frac{4}{x-5}$	$h(x) = \frac{3}{x}$
Not defined at:	$x = -2$	$x = 5$	$x = 0$

EXAMPLE 1 Limitations on Domain

Determine the value of x for which $f(x) = \frac{3}{2x+5}$ is not defined.

Find the value for which the denominator of the expression equals 0.

$\frac{3}{2x+5} \rightarrow 2x + 5 = 0$

$x = -\frac{5}{2}$ The function is undefined for $x = -\frac{5}{2}$.

Guided Practice

Determine the value of x for which each function is not defined.

1A. $f(x) = \frac{2}{x-1}$ $x = 1$

1B. $f(x) = \frac{7}{3x+2}$ $x = -\frac{2}{3}$

Personal Tutor glencoe.com

9-3 Lesson Notes

1 FOCUS

Vertical Alignment

Before Lesson 9-3
Graph polynomial functions.

Lesson 9-3
Determine properties of reciprocal functions.
Graph transformations of reciprocal functions.

After Lesson 9-3
Graph rational functions using asymptotes.

2 TEACH

Scaffolding Questions

Have students read the *Why?* section of the lesson.

Ask:

- On what does the number of candy bars each student has to sell depend? the number of students participating
- What happens to the value of c as the value of n increases? It decreases.
- The variable n must be greater than or equal to what whole number? 1
- The variable n must be less than or equal to what number? the number of students in the chorale

Lesson 9-3 Resources

Resource	Approaching-Level	On-Level	Beyond-Level	English Learners
Teacher Edition	• Differentiated Instruction, p. 572	• Differentiated Instruction, pp. 570, 572	• Differentiated Instruction, p. 570	• Differentiated Instruction, p. 572
Chapter Resource Masters	• Study Guide and Intervention, pp. 18–19 • Skills Practice, p. 20 • Practice, p. 21 • Word Problem Practice, p. 22	• Study Guide and Intervention, pp. 18–19 • Skills Practice, p. 20 • Practice, p. 21 • Word Problem Practice, p. 22 • Graphing Calculator, p. 24	• Practice, p. 21 • Word Problem Practice, p. 22	• Study Guide and Intervention, pp. 18–19 • Skills Practice, p. 20 • Practice, p. 21 • Word Problem Practice, p. 22
Transparencies	• 5-Minute Check Transparency 9-3	• 5-Minute Check Transparency 9-3	• 5-Minute Check Transparency 9-3	• 5-Minute Check Transparency 9-3
Other	• Study Notebook	• Study Notebook	• Study Notebook	• Study Notebook

Vertical and Horizontal Asymptotes

Example 1 shows how to find the limitations on the domain of a rational function. **Example 2** shows how to determine the properties of reciprocal functions.

Formative Assessment

Use the Guided Practice exercises after each example to determine students' understanding of concepts.

Additional Examples

1 Determine the values of x for which $f(x) = \frac{2}{x^2 + 5x - 24}$ is not defined. $x = -8$ and $x = 3$

2 Identify the asymptotes, domain, and range at each function.

a.

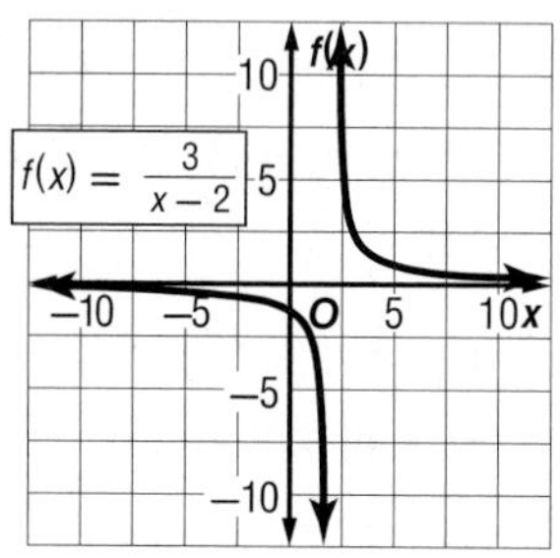

asymptotes: $x = 2$, $y = 0$; domain: all real numbers not equal to 2; range: all real numbers not equal to 0

b.

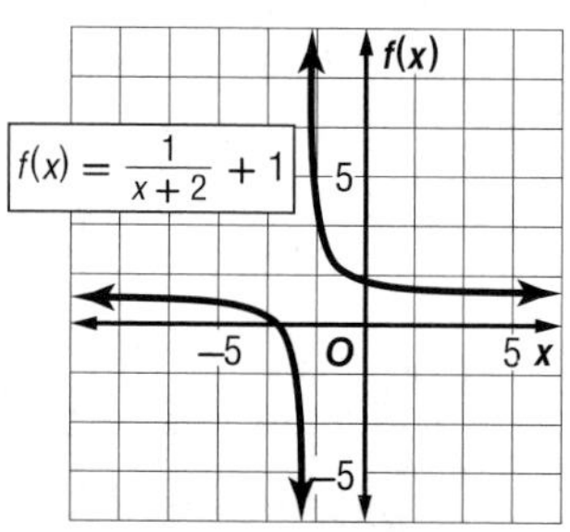

asymptotes: $x = -2$, $f(x) = 1$; domain: all real numbers not equal to –2; range: all real numbers not equal to 1

Additional Examples also in Interactive Classroom PowerPoint® Presentations

IWB INTERACTIVE WHITEBOARD READY

The graphs of reciprocal functions may have breaks in continuity for excluded values. Some may have an **asymptote**, which is a line that the graph of the function approaches.

EXAMPLE 2 Determine Properties of Reciprocal Functions

Identify the asymptotes, domain, and range of each function.

a.

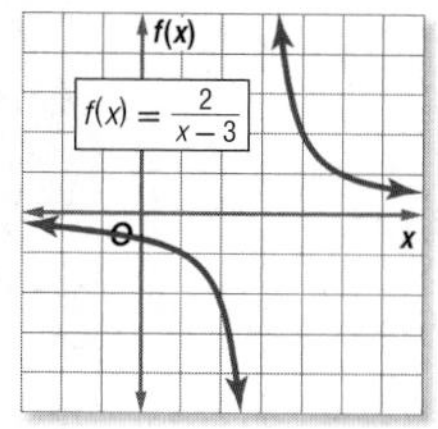

Identify x-values for which $f(x)$ is undefined.

$x - 3 = 0$

$x = 3$

$f(x)$ is not defined when $x = 3$. So there is an asymptote at $x = 3$.

From $x = 3$, as x-values decrease, $f(x)$-values approach 0, and as x-values increase, $f(x)$-values approach 0. So there is an asymptote at $f(x) = 0$.

The domain is all real numbers not equal to 3 and the range is all real numbers not equal to 0.

b.

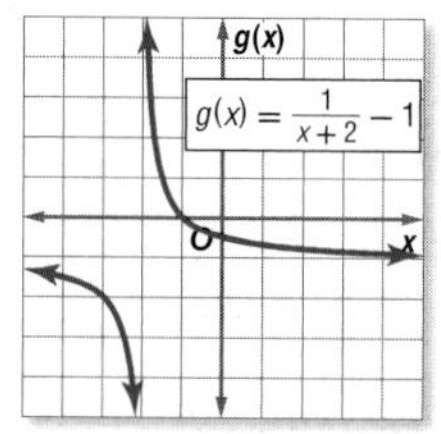

Identify x-values for which $g(x)$ is undefined.

$x + 2 = 0$

$x = -2$

$g(x)$ is not defined when $x = -2$. So there is an asymptote at $x = -2$.

From $x = -2$, as x-values decrease, $g(x)$-values approach -1, and as x-values increase, $g(x)$-values approach -1. So there is an asymptote at $g(x) = -1$.

The domain is all real numbers not equal to -2 and the range is all real numbers not equal to -1.

StudyTip

Asymptotes and Rational Functions Vertical asymptotes show where a function is undefined, while horizontal asymptotes show the end behavior of a graph.

Guided Practice

2A.

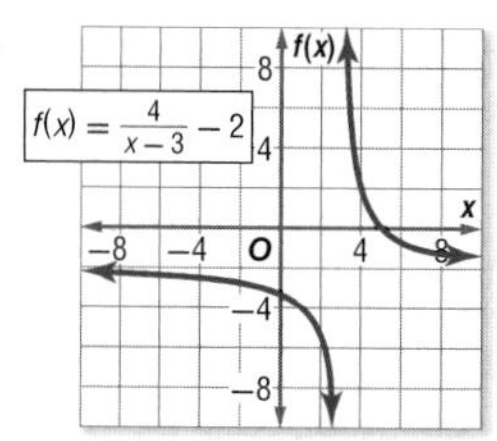

2B.

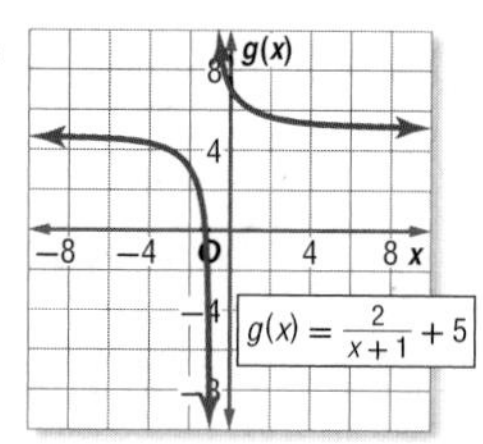

2A. $x = 3$, $f(x) = -2$; $D = \{x \mid x \neq 3\}$; $R = \{f(x) \mid f(x) \neq -2\}$
2B. $x = -1$, $g(x) = 5$; $D = \{x \mid x \neq -1\}$; $R = \{g(x) \mid g(x) \neq 5\}$

Personal Tutor glencoe.com

Differentiated Instruction OL BL

Extension Tell students the following:

- A function is called an **even** function if $f(-x) = f(x)$ for all values of x in its domain. The graph of an even function is *symmetric* with respect to the y-axis.
- A function is called an **odd** function if $f(-x) = -f(x)$ for all values of x in its domain. The graph of an odd function is *symmetric* with respect to the origin.

Ask students whether $f(x) = \frac{1}{x}$ is an odd or even function. odd

Transformations of Reciprocal Functions The same techniques used to transform the graphs of other functions you have studied can be applied to the graphs of reciprocal functions. In Example 2, note that the asymptotes have been moved along with the graphs of the functions.

StudyTip

Asymptotes The asymptotes of a reciprocal function move with the graph of the function and intersect at (h, k).

Key Concept Transformations of Reciprocal Functions

$$f(x) = \frac{a}{x - h} + k$$

h – Horizontal Translation	*k* – Vertical Translation
$\lvert h \rvert$ units right if h is positive $\lvert h \rvert$ units left if h is negative The *vertical* asymptote is at $x = h$.	$\lvert k \rvert$ units up if k is positive $\lvert k \rvert$ units down if k is negative The *horizontal* asymptote is at $f(x) = k$.

***a* – Orientation and Shape**

If $a < 0$, the graph is reflected across the *x*-axis.	If $\lvert a \rvert > 1$, the graph is stretched vertically. If $0 < \lvert a \rvert < 1$, the graph is compressed vertically.

EXAMPLE 3 Graph Transformations

Graph each function. State the domain and range.

a. $f(x) = \frac{2}{x - 4} + 2$

This represents a transformation of the graph of $f(x) = \frac{1}{x}$.

$a = 2$: The graph is expanded.

$h = 4$: The graph is translated 4 units right. There is an asymptote at $x = 4$.

$k = 2$: The graph is translated 2 units up. There is an asymptote at $f(x) = 2$.

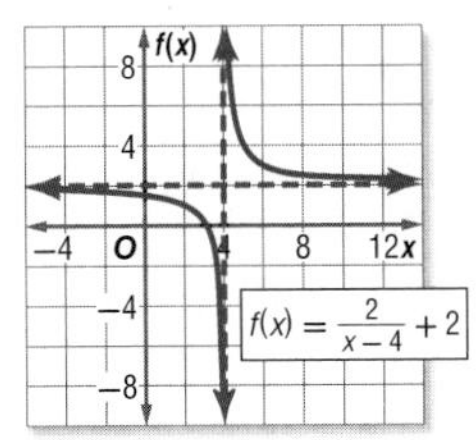

Domain: $\{x \mid x \neq 4\}$ Range: $\{f(x) \mid f(x) \neq 2\}$

b. $f(x) = \frac{-3}{x + 1} - 4$

This represents a transformation of the graph of $f(x) = \frac{1}{x}$.

$a = -3$: The graph is expanded and reflected across the *x*-axis.

$h = -1$: The graph is translated 1 unit left. There is an asymptote at $x = -1$.

$k = -4$: The graph is translated 4 units down. There is an asymptote at $y = -4$.

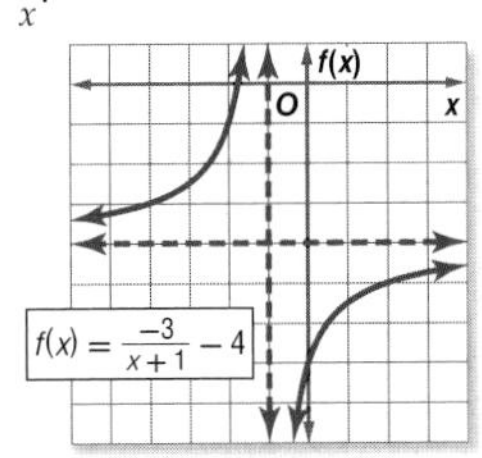

Domain: $\{x \mid x \neq -1\}$ Range: $\{f(x) \mid f(x) \neq -4\}$

Guided Practice 3A, 3B. See Chapter 9 Answer Appendix.

3A. $f(x) = \frac{-2}{x + 4} + 1$ **3B.** $g(x) = \frac{1}{3(x - 1)} - 2$

Personal Tutor glencoe.com

Reciprocal functions can be used to solve many real-world situations.

Focus on Mathematical Content

Asymptotes The presence of an asymptote indicates a missing value for one of the variables. Just as a vertical asymptote indicates that a value of x is excluded from the function's domain, a horizontal asymptote indicates that a value of y is absent from the function's range.

Transformations of Reciprocal Functions

Example 3 illustrates graph transformations. **Example 4** is a real-world problem that shows that when a function is used to model a real situation, its meaningful domain may be smaller than its mathematical domain.

Additional Example

3 Graph each function. State the domain and range.

a. $f(x) = -\frac{1}{x + 1} + 3$

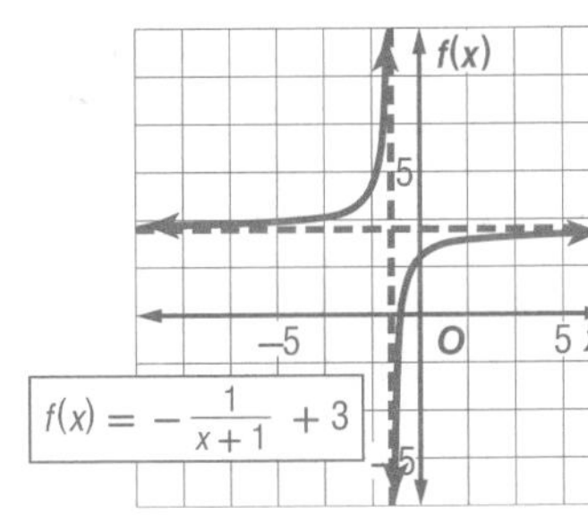

$D = \{x \mid x \neq -1\}$;
$R = \{f(x) \mid f(x) \neq 3\}$

b. $f(x) = \frac{-4}{x - 2} - 1$

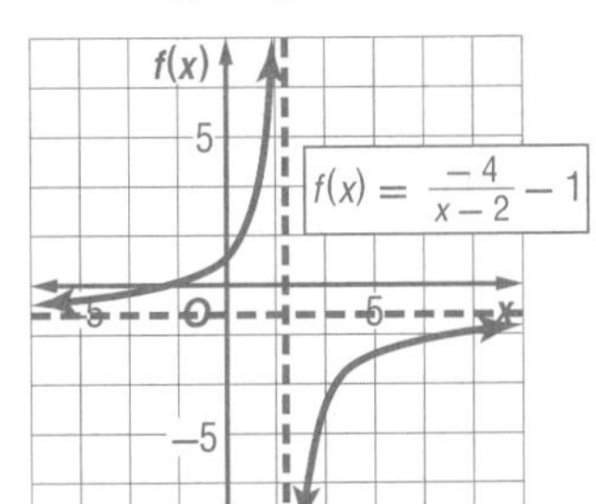

$D = \{x \mid x \neq 2\}$;
$R = \{f(x) \mid f(x) \neq -1\}$

TEACH with TECH

INTERACTIVE WHITEBOARD Use a graphing program to display a coordinate grid and the graph of a function $f(x)$. Choose several students to come to the board and draw what they think would be the graph of $\frac{1}{f(x)}$. Then use the graphing program to show the graph of $\frac{1}{f(x)}$, and compare it to students' graphs.

Watch Out!

Preventing Errors Suggest that students choose a large unit on their grid paper and estimate point coordinates to the nearest tenth. Point out that they may not be able to see the shape of the graph as a whole unless they use a graphing calculator or computer program.

Additional Example

4 **COMMUTING** A commuter train has a nonstop service from one city to another, a distance of about 25 miles.

a. Write an equation to represent the travel time between these two cities as a function of rail speed. Then graph the equation. $t = \frac{25}{r}$

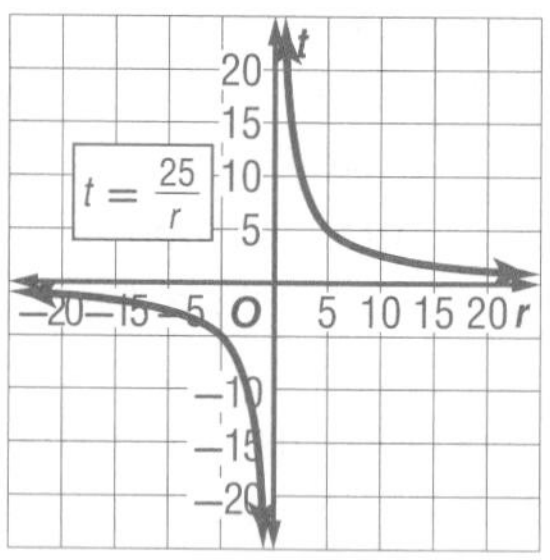

b. Explain any limitations to the range and domain in this situation. The range and domain are limited to all real numbers greater than 0 because negative values do not make sense. There will be further restrictions to the domain because the train has minimum and maximum speeds at which it can travel.

3 PRACTICE

Formative Assessment

Use Exercises 1–6 to check for understanding.

Use the chart at the bottom of the next page to customize assignments for your students.

Real-World Career

Travel Agent
Travel agents assess individual and business needs to help make the best possible travel arrangements. They may specialize by type of travel, such as leisure or business, or by destination, such as Europe or Africa. A high school diploma is required, and vocational training is preferred.

Real-World EXAMPLE 4 Write Equations

TRAVEL **An airline has a daily nonstop flight between Los Angeles, California, and Sydney, Australia. A one-way trip is about 7500 miles.**

a. Write an equation to represent the travel time from Los Angeles to Sydney as a function of flight speed. Then graph the equation.

Solve the formula $rt = d$ for t.

$rt = d$	**Original formula**
$t = \frac{d}{r}$	**Divide each side by r.**
$t = \frac{7500}{r}$	**$d = 7500$**

Graph the equation $t = \frac{7500}{r}$.

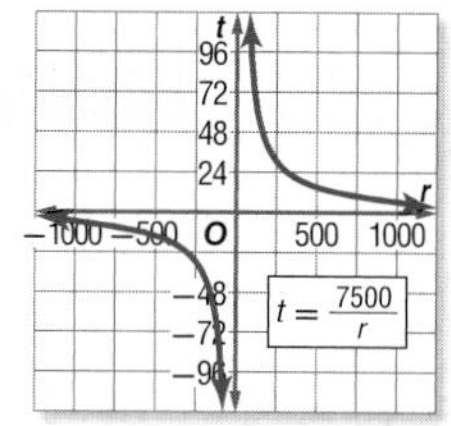

b. Explain any limitations to the range or domain in this situation.

In this situation, the range and domain are limited to all real numbers greater than zero because negative values do not make sense. There will be further restrictions to the domain because the aircraft has minimum and maximum speeds at which it can travel.

Guided Practice 4. See Chapter 9 Answer Appendix.

4. **HOMECOMING DANCE** The junior and senior class officers are sponsoring a homecoming dance. The total cost for the facilities and catering is \$45 per person plus a \$2500 deposit. Write and graph an equation to represent the average cost per person. Then explain any limitations to the domain and range.

Personal Tutor glencoe.com

Check Your Understanding

Examples 1 and 2 pp. 569–570

1. $x = 1$, $f(x) = 0$; $D = \{x \mid x \neq 1\}$; $R = \{f(x) \mid f(x) \neq 0\}$
2. $x = -2$, $f(x) = 1$; $D = \{x \mid x \neq -2\}$; $R = \{f(x) \mid f(x) \neq 1\}$

Identify the asymptotes, domain, and range of each function.

1.

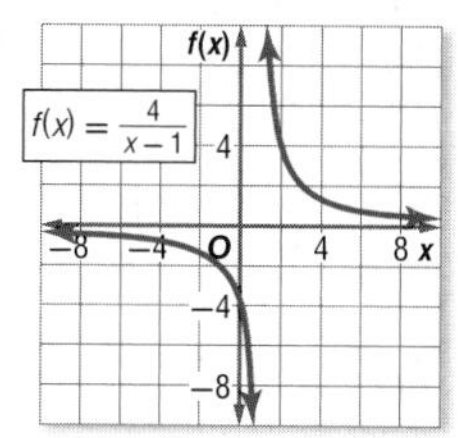

2.

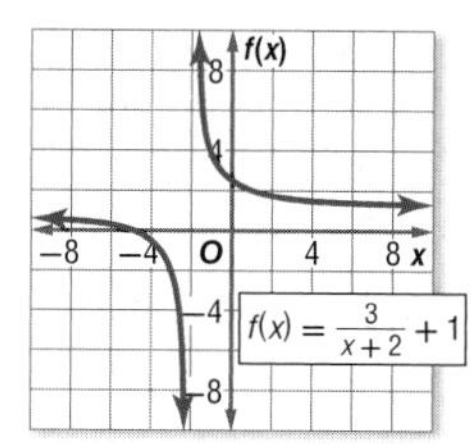

Example 3 p. 571

Graph each function. State the domain and range. 3–5. See margin.

3. $f(x) = \frac{5}{x}$ **4.** $f(x) = \frac{2}{x+3}$ **5.** $f(x) = \frac{-1}{x-2} + 4$

Example 4 p. 572

6c. In this situation, the range and domain are limited to all real numbers greater than zero because negative values do not make sense.

6. **GROUP GIFT** A group of friends plans to get their youth group leader a gift certificate for a day at a spa. The certificate costs \$150.

a. If c represents the cost for each friend and f represents the number of friends, write an equation to represent the cost to each friend as a function of how many friends give. $c = \frac{150}{f}$

b. Graph the function. See margin.

c. Explain any limitations to the range or domain in this situation.

Differentiated Instruction

AL OL ELL

Visual/Spatial Learners Have students graph one of the functions from the lesson on a large sheet of poster board to clearly show how the graph approaches but never reaches an asymptote. Encourage students to use a variety of colored markers.

Practice and Problem Solving

= **Step-by-Step Solutions** begin on page R20.
Extra Practice begins on page 947.

Examples 1 and 2
pp. 569–570

7. $x = -4$, $f(x) = 0$; $D = \{x \mid x \neq -4\}$; $R = \{f(x) \mid f(x) \neq 0\}$
8. $x = 0$, $f(x) = -3$; $D = \{x \mid x \neq 0\}$; $R = \{f(x) \mid f(x) \neq -3\}$
9. $x = -6$, $f(x) = -2$; $D = \{x \mid x \neq -6\}$; $R = \{f(x) \mid f(x) \neq -2\}$
10. $x = 1$, $f(x) = 5$; $D = \{x \mid x \neq 1\}$; $R = \{f(x) \mid f(x) \neq 5\}$

Identify the asymptotes, domain, and range of each function.

7.
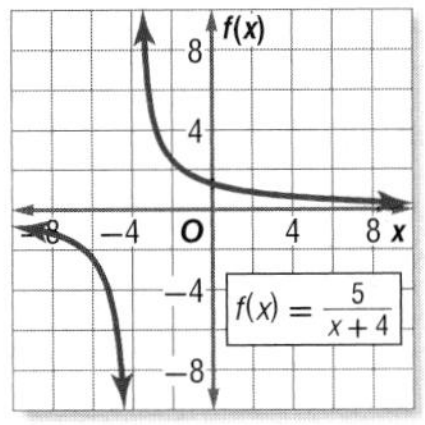

8.
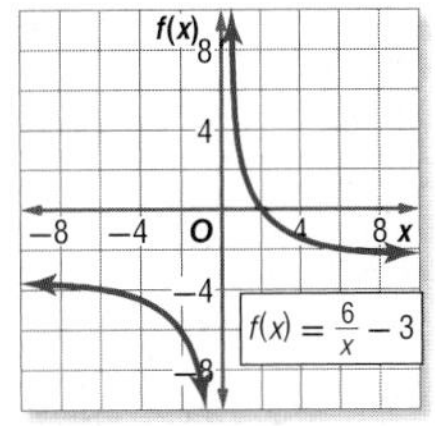

9.
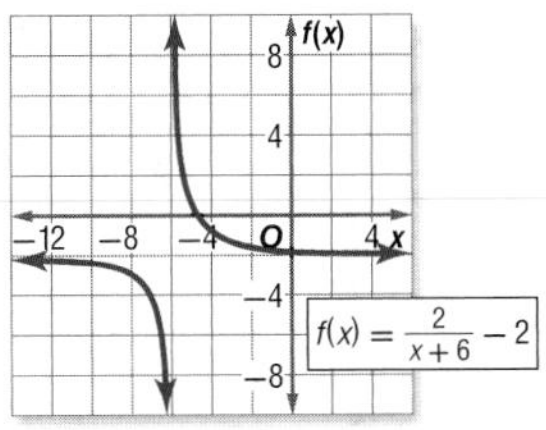

10.
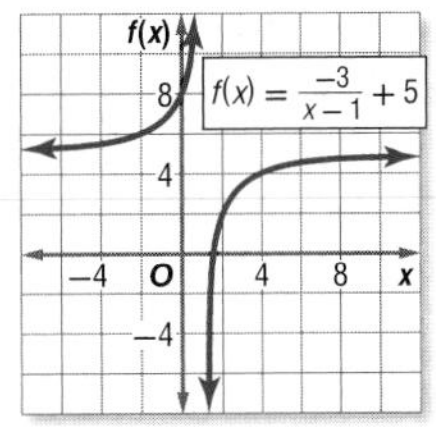

Example 3
p. 571

Graph each function. State the domain and range. 11–22. See Chapter 9 Answer Appendix.

11. $f(x) = \frac{3}{x}$ **12.** $f(x) = \frac{-4}{x+2}$ **13.** $f(x) = \frac{2}{x-6}$

14. $f(x) = \frac{6}{x} - 5$ **15.** $f(x) = \frac{2}{x} + 3$ **16.** $f(x) = \frac{8}{x}$

17. $f(x) = \frac{-2}{x-5}$ **18.** $f(x) = \frac{3}{x-7} - 8$ **19.** $f(x) = \frac{9}{x+3} + 6$

20. $f(x) = \frac{8}{x+3}$ **21.** $f(x) = \frac{-6}{x+4} - 2$ **22.** $f(x) = \frac{-5}{x-2} + 2$

Example 4
p. 572

23. CYCLING Marina's New Year's resolution is to ride her bike 5000 miles.

a. If m represents the mileage Marina rides each day and d represents the number of days, write an equation to represent the mileage each day as a function of the number of days that she rides. $m = \frac{5000}{d}$

b. Graph the function. See Chapter 9 Answer Appendix.

c. If she rides her bike every day of the year, how many miles should she ride each day to meet her goal? 13.7 mi

24c. $v = 0$, $d = 0$; $D = \{v \mid v \neq 0\}$; $R = \{d \mid d \neq 0\}$

24. CHEMISTRY Parker has 200 grams of an unknown liquid. Knowing the density will help him discover what type of liquid this is.

a. Density of a liquid is found by dividing the mass by the volume. Write an equation to represent the density of this unknown as a function of volume. $d = \frac{200}{v}$

b. Graph the function. See Chapter 9 Answer Appendix.

c. From the graph, identify the asymptotes, domain, and range of the function.

B **Graph each function. State the domain and range.** 25–28. See Chapter 9 Answer Appendix.

25. $f(x) = \frac{3}{2x-4}$ **26.** $f(x) = \frac{5}{3x}$ **27.** $f(x) = \frac{2}{4x+1}$ **28.** $f(x) = \frac{1}{2x+3}$

Differentiated Homework Options

Level	Assignment	Two-Day Option	
AL Basic	7–24, 38–40, 42–61	7–23 odd, 43–47	8–24 even, 38–40, 42, 48–61
OL Core	7–35 odd, 36–40, 42–61	7–24, 43–47	25–40, 42, 48–61
BL Advanced	25–59, (optional: 60–61)		

Exercise Alert

Grid Paper For Exercises 3–6, 11–39, 41, 52–55, and 60–61, students will need grid paper.

Additional Answers

3.
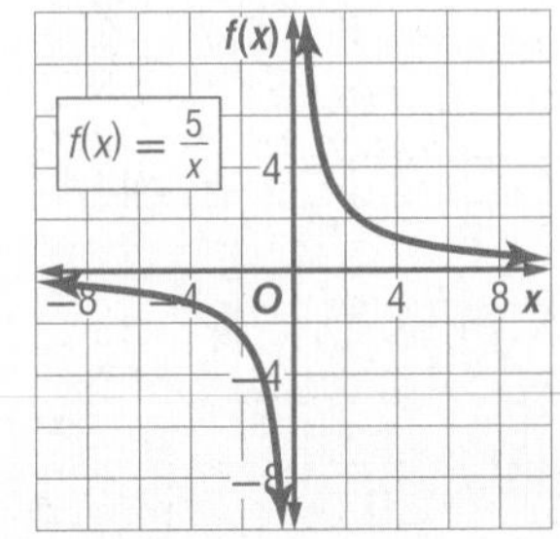

$D = \{x \mid x \neq 0\}$;
$R = \{f(x) \mid f(x) \neq 0\}$

4.
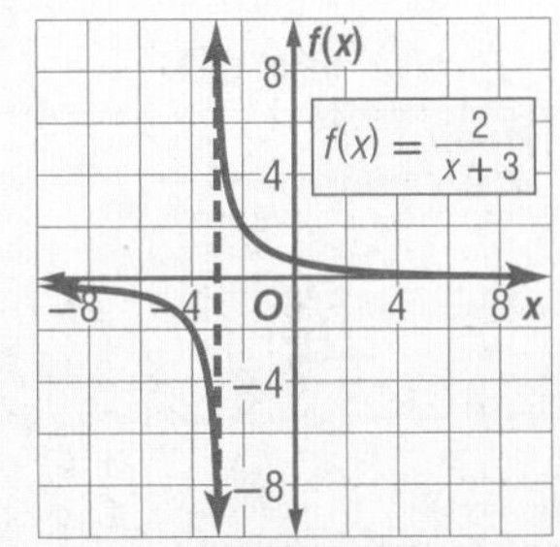

$D = \{x \mid x \neq -3\}$;
$R = \{f(x) \mid f(x) \neq 0\}$

5.
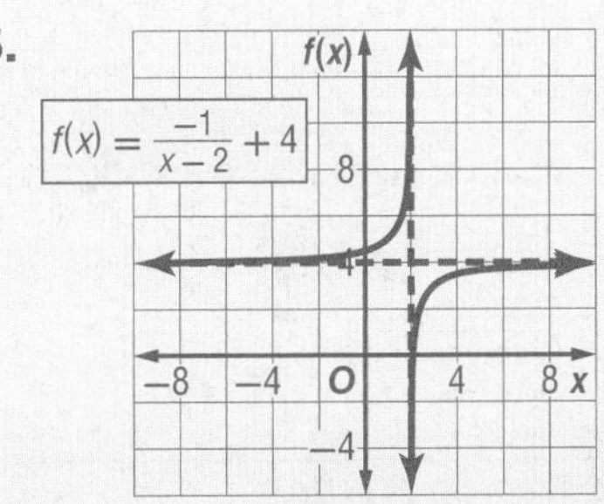

$D = \{x \mid x \neq 2\}$;
$R = \{f(x) \mid f(x) \neq 4\}$

6b.
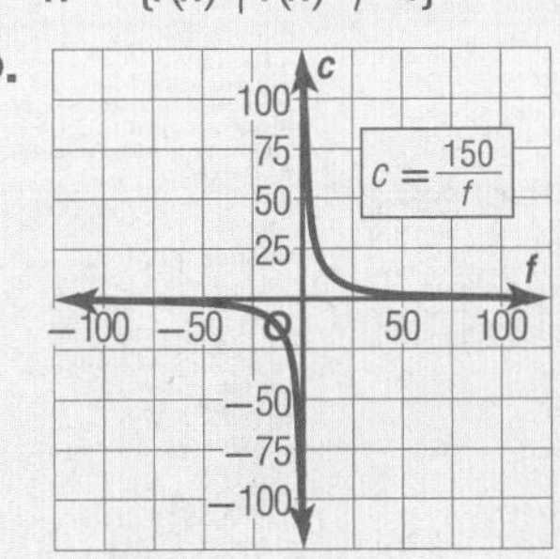

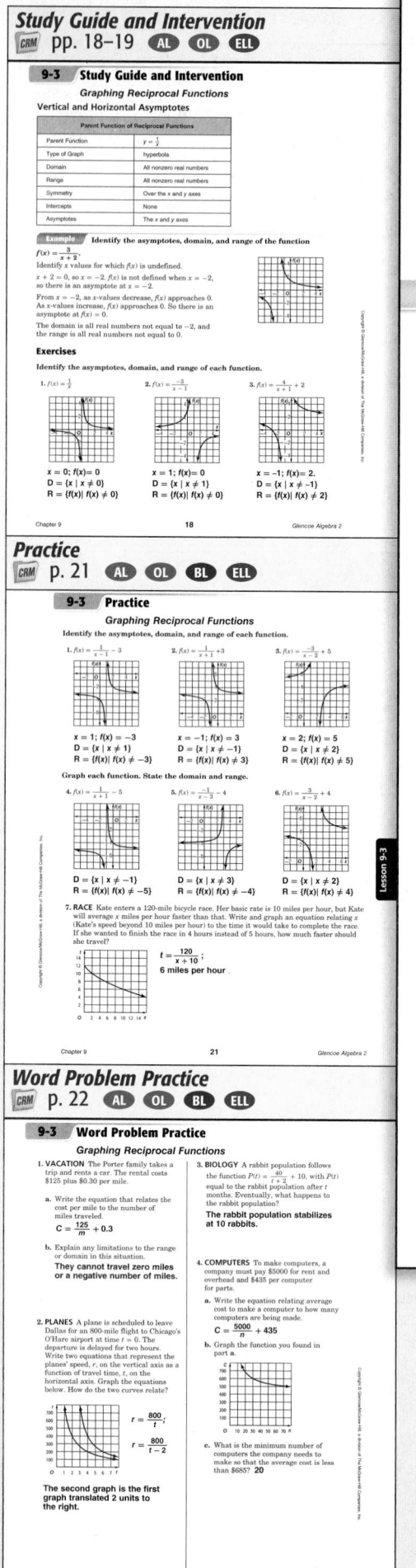

29. BASEBALL The distance from the pitcher's mound to home plate is 60.5 feet.

a. If r represents the speed of the pitch and t represents the time it takes the ball to get to the plate, write an equation to represent the speed as a function of time. $r = \frac{60.5}{t}$

b. Graph the function. **See Chapter 9 Answer Appendix.**

c. If a two-seam fastball reaches the plate in 0.48 second, what was its speed? **126 ft/s**

30–35. See Chapter 9 Answer Appendix.

Graph each function. State the domain and range, and identify the asymptotes.

30. $f(x) = \frac{-3}{x+7} - 1$ **31.** $f(x) = \frac{-4}{x+2} - 5$ **32.** $f(x) = \frac{6}{x-1} + 2$

33. $f(x) = \frac{2}{x-4} + 3$ **34.** $f(x) = \frac{-7}{x-8} - 9$ **35.** $f(x) = \frac{-6}{x-7} - 8$

Real-World Link

Breaking the color barrier in 1947, Larry Doby became the first African-American player in the American League when he joined the Cleveland Indians. That same year, Doby also became the first African-American to play in the American Basketball League.

36. FINANCIAL LITERACY Lawanda's car went 440 miles on one tank of gas.

a. If g represents the number of miles to the gallon that the car gets and t represents the size of the gas tank, write an equation to represent the miles to the gallon as a function of tank size. $g = \frac{440}{t}$

b. Graph the function. **See Chapter 9 Answer Appendix.**

c. How many miles does the car get per gallon if it has a 15-gallon tank? **$29\frac{1}{3}$ mi/gal**

37. MULTIPLE REPRESENTATIONS Consider the functions $f(x) = \frac{1}{x}$ and $g(x) = \frac{1}{x^2}$.

a. **TABULAR** Make a table of values comparing the two functions. **a–d. See Chapter 9 Answer Appendix.**

b. **GRAPHICAL** Use the table of values to graph both functions.

c. **VERBAL** Compare and contrast the two graphs.

d. **ANALYTICAL** Make a conjecture about the difference between the graphs of functions of the form $f(x) = \frac{1}{x^n}$ with an even exponent in the denominator and those with an odd exponent in the denominator.

H.O.T. Problems Use Higher-Order Thinking Skills

38. OPEN ENDED Write a reciprocal function for which the graph has a vertical asymptote at $x = -4$ and a horizontal asymptote at $f(x) = 6$. **Sample answer: $f(x) = \frac{1}{x+4} + 6$**

39. REASONING Compare and contrast the graphs of each pair of equations.

a. $y = \frac{1}{x}$ and $y - 7 = \frac{1}{x}$ b. $y = \frac{1}{x}$ and $y = 4\left(\frac{1}{x}\right)$ c. $y = \frac{1}{x}$ and $y = \frac{1}{x+5}$

d. Without making a table of values, use what you observed in parts **a–c** to sketch a graph of $y - 7 = 4\left(\frac{1}{x+5}\right)$. **See Chapter 9 Answer Appendix.**

39a. The first graph has a vertical asymptote at $x = 0$ and a horizontal asymptote at $y = 0$. The second graph is translated 7 units up and has a vertical asymptote at $x = 0$ and a horizontal asymptote at $y = 7$.
39b. Both graphs have a vertical asymptote at $x = 0$ and a horizontal asymptote at $y = 0$. The second graph is stretched by a factor of 4.
39c. The first graph has a vertical asymptote at $x = 0$ and a horizontal asymptote at $y = 0$. The second graph is translated 5 units to the left and has a vertical asymptote at $x = -5$ and a horizontal asymptote at $y = 0$.
40. Sample answer: $g(x)$, all other choices have unknowns only in the denominator.

40. WHICH ONE DOESN'T BELONG? Find the function that does not belong. Explain.

$f(x) = \frac{3}{x+1}$	$g(x) = \frac{x+2}{x^2+1}$	$h(x) = \frac{5}{x^2+2x+1}$	$j(x) = \frac{20}{x-7}$

41. CHALLENGE Write two different reciprocal functions with graphs having the same vertical and horizontal asymptotes. Then graph the functions. **See Chapter 9 Answer Appendix.**

42. WRITING IN MATH Refer to the beginning of the lesson. Explain how rational functions can be used in fundraising. Explain why only part of the graph is meaningful in the context of the problem. **See Chapter 9 Answer Appendix.**

Study Guide and Intervention
CRM pp. 18–19 AL OL ELL

9-3 Study Guide and Intervention

Graphing Reciprocal Functions

Vertical and Horizontal Asymptotes

Parent Function of Reciprocal Functions	
Parent Function	$y = \frac{1}{x}$
Type of Graph	hyperbola
Domain	All nonzero real numbers
Range	All nonzero real numbers
Symmetry	Over the x and y axes
Intercepts	None
Asymptotes	The x and y axes

Example Identify the asymptotes, domain, and range of the function $f(x) = \frac{3}{x+2}$.

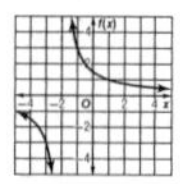

Identify x values for which $f(x)$ is undefined.

$x + 2 = 0$, so $x = -2$. $f(x)$ is not defined when $x = -2$, so there is an asymptote at $x = -2$.

From $x = -2$, as x-values decrease, $f(x)$ approaches 0. As x-values increase, $f(x)$ approaches 0. So there is an asymptote at $f(x) = 0$.

The domain is all real numbers not equal to -2, and the range is all real numbers not equal to 0.

Exercises

Identify the asymptotes, domain, and range of each function.

1. $f(x) = \frac{1}{x}$

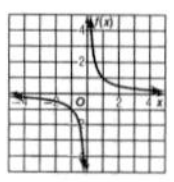

$x = 0$; $f(x) = 0$
$D = \{x \mid x \neq 0\}$
$R = \{f(x) \mid f(x) \neq 0\}$

2. $f(x) = \frac{-3}{x-1}$

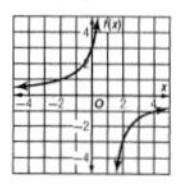

$x = 1$; $f(x) = 0$
$D = \{x \mid x \neq 1\}$
$R = \{f(x) \mid f(x) \neq 0\}$

3. $f(x) = \frac{4}{x+1} + 2$

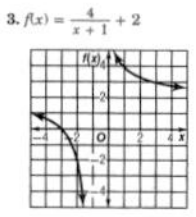

$x = -1$; $f(x) = 2$.
$D = \{x \mid x \neq -1\}$
$R = \{f(x) \mid f(x) \neq 2\}$

Chapter 9 18 Glencoe Algebra 2

Practice
CRM p. 21 AL OL BL ELL

9-3 Practice

Graphing Reciprocal Functions

Identify the asymptotes, domain, and range of each function.

1. $f(x) = \frac{1}{x-1} - 3$

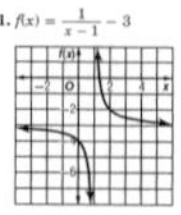

$x = 1$; $f(x) = -3$
$D = \{x \mid x \neq 1\}$
$R = \{f(x) \mid f(x) \neq -3\}$

2. $f(x) = \frac{1}{x+1} + 3$

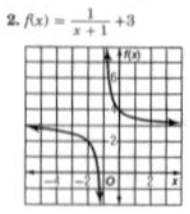

$x = -1$; $f(x) = 3$
$D = \{x \mid x \neq -1\}$
$R = \{f(x) \mid f(x) \neq 3\}$

3. $f(x) = \frac{-3}{x-2} + 5$

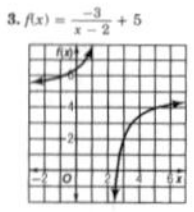

$x = 2$; $f(x) = 5$
$D = \{x \mid x \neq 2\}$
$R = \{f(x) \mid f(x) \neq 5\}$

Graph each function. State the domain and range.

4. $f(x) = \frac{1}{x+1} - 5$

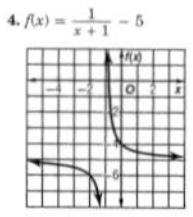

$D = \{x \mid x \neq -1\}$
$R = \{f(x) \mid f(x) \neq -5\}$

5. $f(x) = \frac{-1}{x-3} - 4$

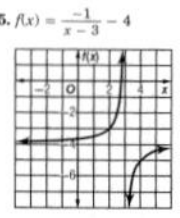

$D = \{x \mid x \neq 3\}$
$R = \{f(x) \mid f(x) \neq -4\}$

6. $f(x) = \frac{3}{x-2} + 4$

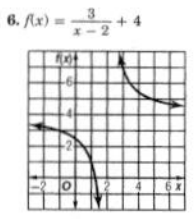

$D = \{x \mid x \neq 2\}$
$R = \{f(x) \mid f(x) \neq 4\}$

7. **RACE** Kate enters a 120-mile bicycle race. Her basic rate is 10 miles per hour, but Kate will average x miles per hour faster than that. Write and graph an equation relating x (Kate's speed beyond 10 miles per hour) to the time it would take to complete the race. If she wanted to finish the race in 4 hours instead of 5 hours, how much faster should she travel?

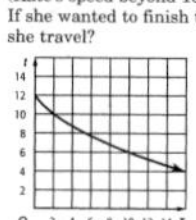

$t = \frac{120}{x+10}$;
6 miles per hour

Chapter 9 21 Glencoe Algebra 2

Lesson 9-3

Word Problem Practice
CRM p. 22 AL OL BL ELL

9-3 Word Problem Practice

Graphing Reciprocal Functions

1. **VACATION** The Porter family takes a trip and rents a car. The rental costs \$125 plus \$0.30 per mile.

a. Write the equation that relates the cost per mile to the number of miles traveled.
$C = \frac{125}{m} + 0.3$

b. Explain any limitations to the range or domain in this situation.
They cannot travel zero miles or a negative number of miles.

2. **PLANES** A plane is scheduled to leave Dallas for an 800-mile flight to Chicago's O'Hare airport at time $t = 0$. The departure is delayed for two hours. Write two equations that represent the planes' speed, r, on the vertical axis as a function of travel time, t, on the horizontal axis. Graph the equations below. How do the two curves relate?

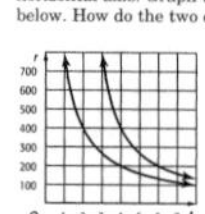

$r = \frac{800}{t}$;
$r = \frac{800}{t-2}$

The second graph is the first graph translated 2 units to the right.

3. **BIOLOGY** A rabbit population follows the function $P(t) = \frac{40}{t+2} + 10$, with $P(t)$ equal to the rabbit population after t months. Eventually, what happens to the rabbit population?
The rabbit population stabilizes at 10 rabbits.

4. **COMPUTERS** To make computers, a company must pay \$5000 for rent and overhead and \$435 per computer for parts.

a. Write the equation relating average cost to make a computer to how many computers are being made.
$C = \frac{5000}{n} + 435$

b. Graph the function you found in part **a**.

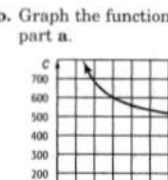

c. What is the minimum number of computers the company needs to make so that the average cost is less than \$685? **20**

Chapter 9 22 Glencoe Algebra 2

Enrichment
CRM p. 23 OL BL

9-3 Enrichment

Group Theory

In mathematics, the term *group* has a special meaning. The following paragraph discusses the idea of group and one interesting example of a group.

- To be a group, a set of elements and a binary operation must satisfy four conditions: the set must be closed under the operation, the operation must be associative, there must be an identity element, and every element must have an inverse.
- The following six functions form a group under the operation of composition of functions: $f_1(x) = x$, $f_2(x) = \frac{1}{x}$, $f_3(x) = 1 - x$, $f_4(x) = \frac{(x-1)}{x}$, $f_5(x) = \frac{x}{(x-1)}$, and $f_6(x) = \frac{1}{(1-x)}$.
- This group is an example of a noncommutative group. For example, $f_3 \cdot f_2 = f_4$, but $f_2 \cdot f_3 = f_6$.
- Some experimentation with this group will show that the identity element is f_1.
- Every element is its own inverse except for f_4 and f_6, each of which is the inverse of the other.

Use the paragraph to answer these questions.

1. Explain what it means to say that a set is *closed* under an operation. Is the set of positive integers closed under subtraction? **Performing the operation on any two elements of the set results in an element of the same set; no, 3 and 4 are [illegible]itive integers but [illegible]4 is not.**

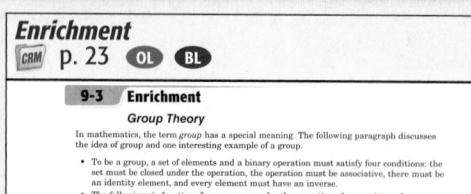

Multiple Representations In Exercise 37, students use a table of values, a graph, and verbal analysis to compare and contrast two reciprocal functions.

NGSSS PRACTICE 912.A.8.5, 912.A.5.5

43. **SHORT RESPONSE** What is the value of $(x + y)(x + y)$ if $xy = -3$ and $x^2 + y^2 = 10$? **4**

44. **GRIDDED RESPONSE** If $x = 2y$, $y = 4z$, $2z = w$, and $w \neq 0$, then $\frac{x}{w} =$ ___. **4**

45. If $c = 1 + \frac{1}{d}$ and $d > 1$, then c could equal ___. **B**

A. $\frac{5}{7}$ C. $\frac{15}{7}$

B. $\frac{9}{7}$ D. $\frac{19}{7}$

46. **SAT/ACT** A car travels m miles at the rate of t miles per hour. How many hours does the trip take? **F**

F. $\frac{m}{t}$ H. $\frac{t}{m}$

G. $m - t$ I. $t - m$

47. If $-1 < a < b < 0$, then which of the following has the greatest value? **B**

A. $a - b$ C. $a + b$

B. $b - a$ D. $2b - a$

Spiral Review

48a. $\frac{0.5(0.08p)}{6} + \frac{0.5(0.08p)}{4}$

48. **BUSINESS** A small corporation decides that 8% of its profits will be divided among its six managers. There are two sales managers and four nonsales managers. Fifty percent will be split equally among all six managers. The other 50% will be split among the four nonsales managers. Let p represent the profits. (Lesson 9-2)

a. Write an expression to represent the share of the profits each nonsales manager will receive.

b. Simplify this expression. $\frac{0.05p}{3}$

c. Write an expression in simplest form to represent the share of the profits each sales manager will receive. $\frac{0.5(0.08p)}{6}$

Simplify each expression. (Lesson 9-1)

49. $\dfrac{\frac{p^3}{2n}}{-\frac{p^2}{4n}}$ $-2p$

50. $\dfrac{\frac{m+q}{5}}{\frac{m^2+q^2}{5}}$ $\frac{m+q}{m^2+q^2}$

51. $\dfrac{\frac{x+y}{2x-y}}{\frac{x+y}{2x+y}}$ $\frac{2x+y}{2x-y}$

Graph each function. State the domain and range. (Lesson 8-1) **52–55. See margin.**

52. $y = 2(3)^x$ **53.** $y = 5(2)^x$ **54.** $y = 0.5(4)^x$ **55.** $y = 4\left(\frac{1}{3}\right)^x$

Find $(f + g)(x)$, $(f - g)(x)$, $(f \cdot g)(x)$, and $\left(\frac{f}{g}\right)(x)$ for each $f(x)$ and $g(x)$. (Lesson 7-1) **56–58. See margin.**

56. $f(x) = x + 9$, $g(x) = x - 9$

57. $f(x) = 2x - 3$, $g(x) = 4x + 9$

58. $f(x) = 2x^2$, $g(x) = 8 - x$

59. **GEOMETRY** The width of a rectangular prism is w centimeters. The height is 2 centimeters less than the width. The length is 4 centimeters more than the width. If the volume of the prism is 8 times the measure of the length, find the dimensions of the prism. (Lesson 6-5) $w = 4$ cm, $\ell = 8$ cm, $h = 2$ cm

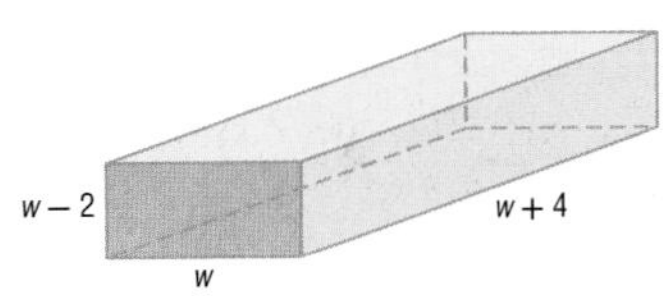

Skills Review

Graph each polynomial function. Estimate the x-coordinates at which the relative maxima and relative minima occur. State the domain and range for each function. (Lesson 6-4) **60, 61. See Chapter 9 Answer Appendix.**

60. $f(x) = x^3 + 2x^2 - 3x - 5$

61. $f(x) = x^4 - 8x^2 + 10$

4 ASSESS

Crystal Ball Ask students to tell how they think their practice with graphing reciprocal functions will help them when they graph rational functions.

Formative Assessment

Check for student understanding of concepts in Lesson 9-3.

CRM Quiz 2, p. 48

Additional Answers

52. D = {all real numbers}, R = $\{y \mid y > 0\}$

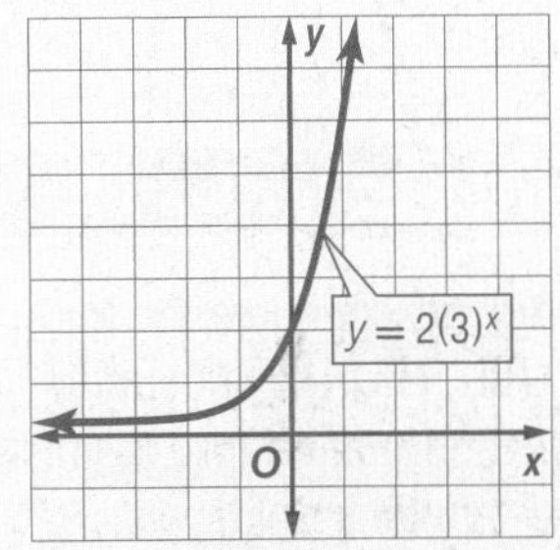

53. D = {all real numbers}, R = $\{y \mid y > 0\}$

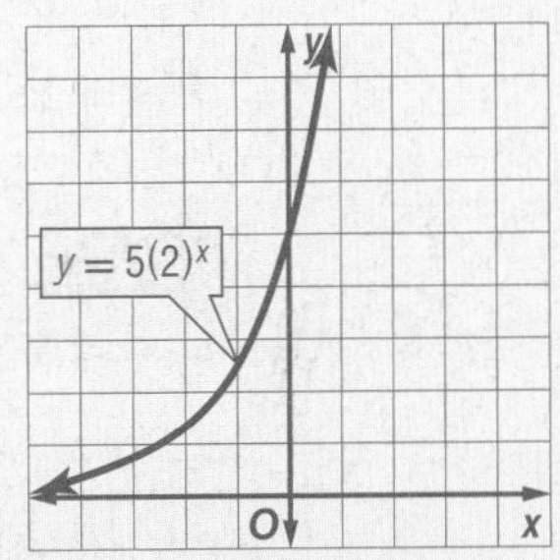

54. D = {all real numbers}, R = $\{y \mid y > 0\}$

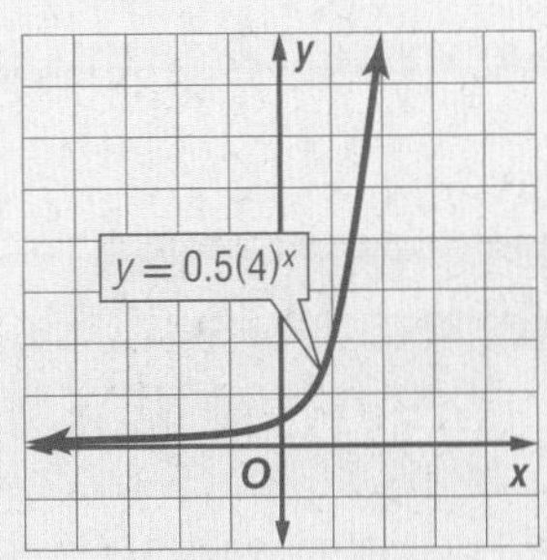

55. D = {all real numbers}, R = $\{y \mid y > 0\}$

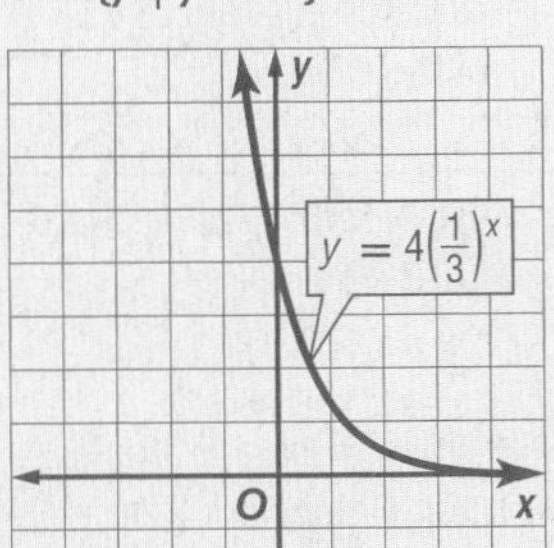

56. $(f + g)(x) = 2x$; $(f - g)(x) = 18$; $(f \cdot g)(x) = x^2 - 81$; $\left(\frac{f}{g}\right)(x) = \frac{x+9}{x-9}, x \neq 9$

57. $(f + g)(x) = 6x + 6$; $(f - g)(x) = -2x - 12$; $(f \cdot g)(x) = 8x^2 + 6x - 27$; $\left(\frac{f}{g}\right)(x) = \frac{2x-3}{4x+9}, x \neq -\frac{9}{4}$

58. $(f + g)(x) = 2x^2 - x + 8$; $(f - g)(x) = 2x^2 + x - 8$; $(f \cdot g)(x) = -2x^3 + 16x^2$; $\left(\frac{f}{g}\right)(x) = \frac{2x^2}{8-x}, x \neq 8$

Formative Assessment

Use the Mid-Chapter Quiz to assess students' progress in the first half of the chapter.

For problems answered incorrectly, have students review the lessons indicated in parentheses.

ExamView Assessment Suite Customize and create multiple versions of your Mid-Chapter Quiz and their answer keys.

FOLDABLES Follow-Up

Before students complete the Mid-Chapter Quiz, encourage them to review the information for Lessons 9-1 through 9-3 in their Foldables.

Additional Answer

25b.

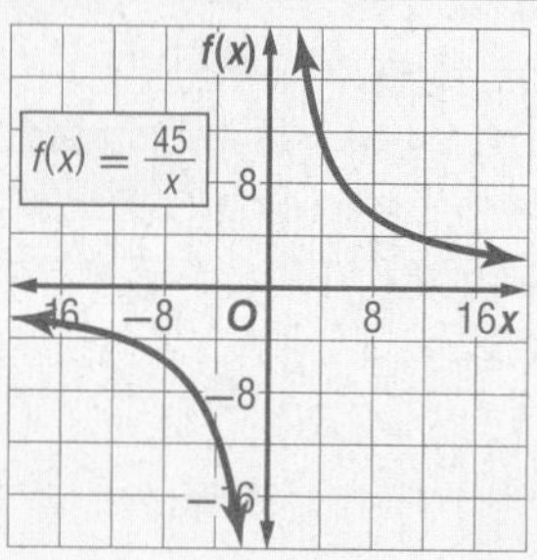

CHAPTER 9 Mid-Chapter Quiz

Lessons 9-1 through 9-3

NGSSS 912.A.2.4, 912.A.5.2, 912.A.5.6

Simplify each expression. (Lesson 9-1)

1. $\frac{2x^2y^5}{7x^3yz} \cdot \frac{14xyz^2}{18x^4y}$ **$\frac{2y^4z}{9x^4}$**

2. $\frac{24a^4b^6}{35ab^3} \div \frac{12abc}{7a^2c}$ **$\frac{2a^4b^2}{5}$**

3. $\frac{3x-3}{x^2+x-2} \cdot \frac{4x+8}{6x+18}$ **$\frac{2}{x+3}$**

4. $\frac{m^2+3m+2}{9} \div \frac{m+1}{3m+15}$ **4. $\frac{(m+2)(m+5)}{3}$**

5. $\dfrac{\frac{r^2+3r}{r+1}}{\frac{3r}{3r+3}}$ **$r+3$**

6. $\dfrac{\frac{2y}{y^2-4}}{\frac{3}{y^2-4y+4}}$ **$\frac{2y(y-2)}{3(y+2)}$**

7. NGSSS **PRACTICE** For all $r \neq 0$, $\frac{r^2+6r+8}{r^2-4} =$ ____. (Lesson 9-1) **B**

A. $\frac{r-2}{r+4}$ C. $\frac{r+2}{r-4}$

B. $\frac{r+4}{r-2}$ D. $\frac{r+4}{r+2}$

8. NGSSS **PRACTICE** Identify all values of x for which $\frac{x^2-16}{(x^2-6x-27)(x+1)}$ is undefined. (Lesson 9-1) **H**

F. −3, −1 H. −3, −1, 9

G. 3, 1, −9 I. −1

9. What is the LCM of $x^2 - x$ and $3 - 3x$? (Lesson 9-2) **$-3x(x-1)$**

Simplify each expression. (Lesson 9-2)

10. $\frac{2x}{4x^2y} + \frac{x}{3xy^3}$ **$\frac{6xy^2+4x^2}{12x^2y^3}$**

11. $\frac{3}{4m} + \frac{2}{3mn^2} - \frac{4}{n}$ **$\frac{9n^2+8-48mn}{12mn^2}$**

12. $\frac{6}{r^2-3r-18} - \frac{1}{r^2+r-6}$ **$\frac{5r-6}{(r-6)(r+3)(r-2)}$**

13. $\frac{3x+6}{x+y} + \frac{6}{-x-y}$ **$\frac{3x}{x+y}$**

14. $\frac{x-4}{x^2-3x-4} + \frac{x+1}{2x-8}$ **$\frac{x^2+4x-7}{2(x-4)(x+1)}$**

15. Determine the perimeter of the rectangle. (Lesson 9-2) **$\frac{18x-6}{(x-3)(x+1)}$**

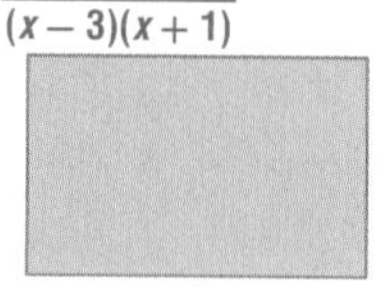

$\frac{3}{x+1}$

$\frac{6}{x-3}$

16. **TRAVEL** Lucita is going to a beach 100 miles away. She travels half the distance at one rate. The rest of the distance, she travels 15 miles per hour slower. (Lesson 9-2)

a. If x represents the faster pace in miles per hour, write an expression that represents the time spent at that pace. **$\frac{50}{x}h$**

b. Write an expression for the amount of time spent at the slower pace. **$\frac{50}{x-15}h$**

c. Write an expression for the amount of time Lucita needed to complete the trip. **$\frac{100(x-7.5)}{x(x-15)}$**

Identify the asymptotes, domain, and range of each function. (Lesson 9-3)

17.

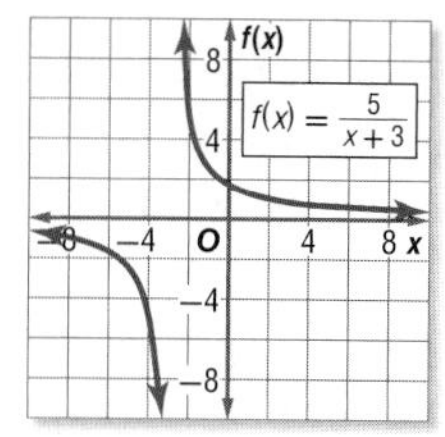

$x = -3$; $f(x) = 0$; $D = \{x \mid x \neq -3\}$, $R = \{f(x) \mid f(x) \neq 0\}$

18.

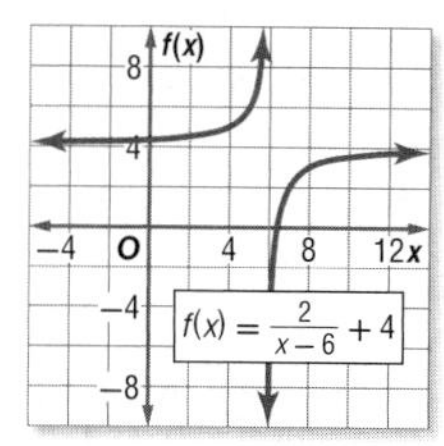

$x = 6$; $f(x) = 4$; $D = \{x \mid x \neq 6\}$, $R = \{f(x) \mid f(x) \neq 4\}$

Graph each reciprocal function. State the domain and range. (Lesson 9-3) **19–24. See Chapter 9 Answer Appendix.**

19. $f(x) = \frac{4}{x}$

20. $f(x) = \frac{1}{3x}$

21. $f(x) = \frac{6}{x-1}$

22. $f(x) = \frac{-2}{x} + 4$

23. $f(x) = \frac{3}{x+2} - 5$

24. $f(x) = -\frac{1}{x-3} + 2$

25. **SANDWICHES** A group makes 45 sandwiches to take on a picnic. The number of sandwiches a person can eat depends on how many people go on the trip. (Lesson 9-3) **a. $f(x) = \frac{45}{x}$**

a. Write a function to represent this situation.

b. Graph the function. **See margin.**

Intervention Planner

Tier 1 On Level	Tier 2 Strategic Intervention approaching grade level	Tier 3 Intensive Intervention 2 or more grades below level
If students miss about 25% of the exercises or less,	**If** students miss about 50% of the exercises,	**If** students miss about 75% of the exercises,
Then choose a resource: **SE** Lessons 9-1, 9-2, and 9-3 **CRM** Skills Practice, pp. 7, 13, and 20 **TE** Chapter Project, p. 550 FL Math Online Self-Check Quiz	**Then** choose a resource: **CRM** Study Guide and Intervention, Chapter 9, pp. 5, 11, and 18 FL Math Online Extra Examples, Personal Tutor, Homework Help	**Then** use *Math Triumphs, Alg. 2*, Ch. 2 FL Math Online Extra Examples, Personal Tutor, Homework Help, Review Vocabulary

9-4 Graphing Rational Functions

Why?

Regina bought a digital camera and a photo printer for \$350. The manufacturer claims that ink and photo paper cost \$0.47 per photo. The rational function $C(p) = \frac{0.47p + 350}{p}$ can be used to determine the average cost $C(p)$ for printing p photos.

Then
You graphed reciprocal functions. (Lesson 9-3)

Now
- Graph rational functions with vertical and horizontal asymptotes.
- Graph rational functions with oblique asymptotes and point discontinuity.

NGSSS
MA.912.A.2.10 Describe and graph transformations of functions.
MA.912.A.5.6 Identify removable and non-removable discontinuities, and vertical, horizontal, and oblique asymptotes of a graph of a rational function, find the zeros, and graph the function.

New Vocabulary
rational function
vertical asymptote
horizontal asymptote
oblique asymptote
point discontinuity

FL Math Online
glencoe.com

Vertical and Horizontal Asymptotes A **rational function** has an equation of the form $f(x) = \frac{a(x)}{b(x)}$, where $a(x)$ and $b(x)$ are polynomial functions and $b(x) \neq 0$.

In order to graph a rational function, it is helpful to locate the zeros and asymptotes. A zero of a rational function $f(x) = \frac{a(x)}{b(x)}$ occurs at every value of x for which $a(x) = 0$.

Key Concept: Vertical and Horizontal Asymptotes

Words If $f(x) = \frac{a(x)}{b(x)}$, $a(x)$ and $b(x)$ are polynomial functions with no common factors other than 1, and $b(x) \neq 0$, then:
- $f(x)$ has a **vertical asymptote** whenever $b(x) = 0$.
- $f(x)$ has at most one **horizontal asymptote**.
  - If the degree of $a(x)$ is greater than the degree of $b(x)$, there is no horizontal asymptote.
  - If the degree of $a(x)$ is less than the degree of $b(x)$, the horizontal asymptote is the line $y = 0$.
  - If the degree of $a(x)$ equals the degree of $b(x)$, the horizontal asymptote is the line $y = \frac{\text{leading coefficient of } a(x)}{\text{leading coefficient of } b(x)}$.

Examples

No horizontal asymptote

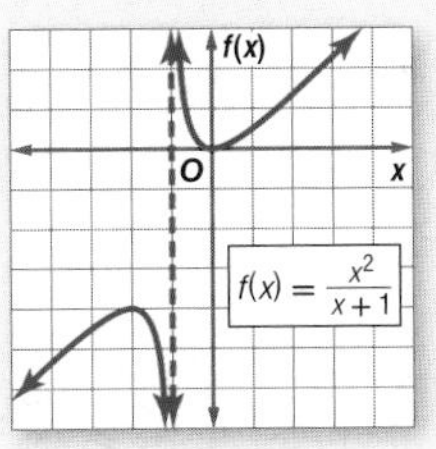

Vertical asymptote: $x = -1$

One horizontal asymptote

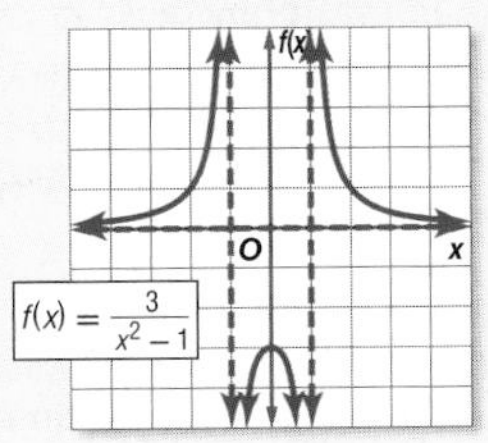

Vertical asymptotes: $x = -1, x = 1$
Horizontal asymptote: $f(x) = 0$

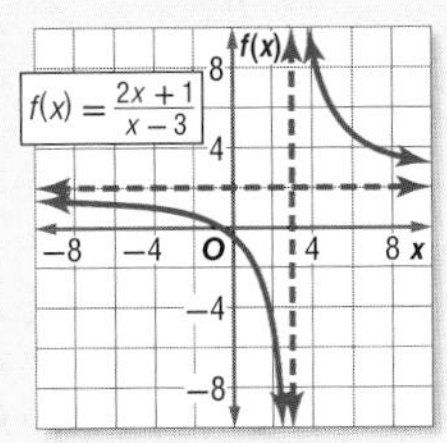

Vertical asymptote: $x = 3$
Horizontal asymptote: $f(x) = 2$

1 FOCUS

Vertical Alignment

Before Lesson 9-4
Graph reciprocal functions.

Lesson 9-4
Graph rational functions with vertical and horizontal asymptotes.
Graph rational functions with oblique asymptotes and point discontinuity.

After Lesson 9-4
Solve rational equations by graphing.

2 TEACH

Scaffolding Questions

Have students read the *Why?* section of the lesson.
- On what does the average cost for printing photos depend? the number of photos printed
- What happens to the value of $C(p)$ as the value of p increases? It decreases.
- Can $p = 0$? no
- Can $C(p)$ ever equal 0? Yes, the function has a zero at $p = -\frac{350}{0.47}$, or about −744.68. However, negative values are not realistic to the context of the situation.

Lesson 9-4 Resources

Resource	Approaching-Level	On-Level	Beyond-Level	English Learners
Teacher Edition		• Differentiated Instruction, pp. 580, 584	• Differentiated Instruction, pp. 579, 584	• Differentiated Instruction, p. 580
Chapter Resource Masters	• Study Guide and Intervention, pp. 25–26 • Skills Practice, p. 27 • Practice, p. 28 • Word Problem Practice, p. 29	• Study Guide and Intervention, pp. 25–26 • Skills Practice, p. 27 • Practice, p. 28 • Word Problem Practice, p. 29 • Enrichment, p. 30 • Graphing Calculator Activity, p. 31	• Practice, p. 28 • Word Problem Practice, p. 29 • Enrichment, p. 30	• Study Guide and Intervention, pp. 25–26 • Skills Practice, p. 27 • Practice, p. 28 • Word Problem Practice, p. 29
Transparencies	• 5-Minute Check Transparency 9-4	• 5-Minute Check Transparency 9-4	• 5-Minute Check Transparency 9-4	• 5-Minute Check Transparency 9-4
Other	• Study Notebook	• Study Notebook	• Study Notebook	• Study Notebook

Vertical and Horizontal Asymptotes

Example 1 shows how to identify and graph rational functions with no horizontal asymptotes. **Example 2** is a real-world problem that shows that when a function is used to model a real situation, its meaningful domain may be smaller than its mathematical domain.

Formative Assessment

Use the Guided Practice exercises after each example to determine students' understanding of concepts.

Additional Example

1 Graph $f(x) = \frac{x^3}{x+1}$.

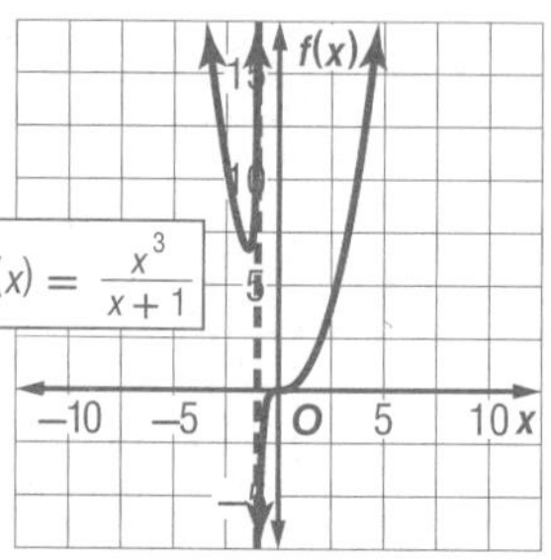

Additional Examples also in Interactive Classroom PowerPoint® Presentations

IWB INTERACTIVE WHITEBOARD READY

Additional Answer (Guided Practice)

1A.

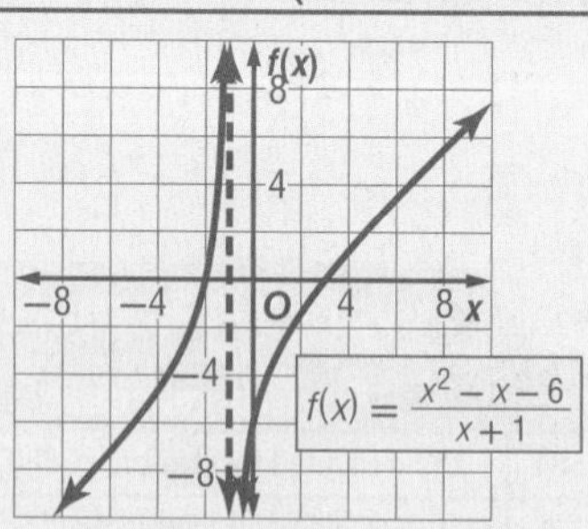

1B.

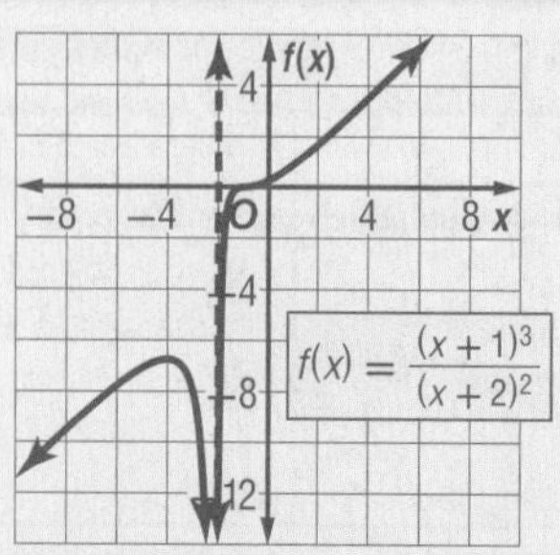

The asymptotes of a rational function can be used to draw the graph of the function. Additionally, the asymptotes can be used to divide a graph into regions to find ordered pairs on the graph.

EXAMPLE 1 Graph with no Horizontal Asymptote

Graph $f(x) = \frac{x^3}{x - 1}$.

Step 1 Find the zeros.

$x^3 = 0$ **Set $a(x) = 0$.**

$x = 0$ **Take the cube root of each side.**

There is a zero at $x = 0$.

Step 2 Draw the asymptotes.

Find the vertical asymptote.

$x - 1 = 0$ **Set $b(x) = 0$.**

$x = 1$ **Add 1 to each side.**

There is a vertical asymptote at $x = 1$.

The degree of the numerator is greater than the degree of the denominator. So, there is no horizontal asymptote.

Step 3 Draw the graph.

Use a table to find ordered pairs on the graph. Then connect the points.

x	f(x)
−3	6.75
−2	2.67
−1	0.5
0	0
0.5	−0.25
1.5	6.75
2	8
3	13.5

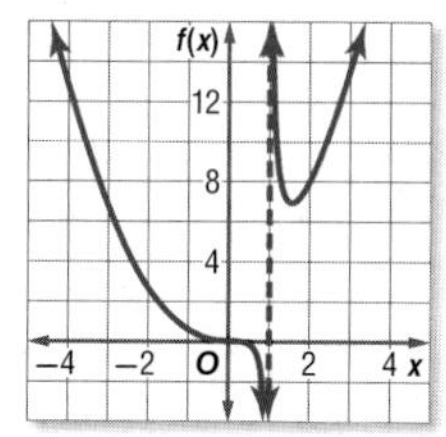

StudyTip

Graphing Calculator The TABLE feature of a graphing calculator can be used to calculate decimal values for x and y.

Guided Practice 1A, 1B. See margin.

Graph each function.

1A. $f(x) = \frac{x^2 - x - 6}{x + 1}$ **1B.** $f(x) = \frac{(x + 1)^3}{(x + 2)^2}$

Personal Tutor glencoe.com

In the real world, sometimes values on the graph of a rational function are not meaningful. In the graph at the right, x-values such as time, distance, and number of people cannot be negative in the context of the problem. So, you do not even need to consider that portion of the graph.

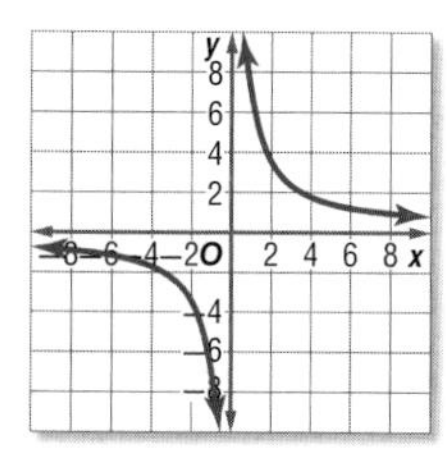

TEACH with TECH

VIDEO RECORDING Have students create video recordings showing how to graph a rational function. Have students first describe how to find the horizontal and vertical asymptotes, and then use a table of values to draw the graph.

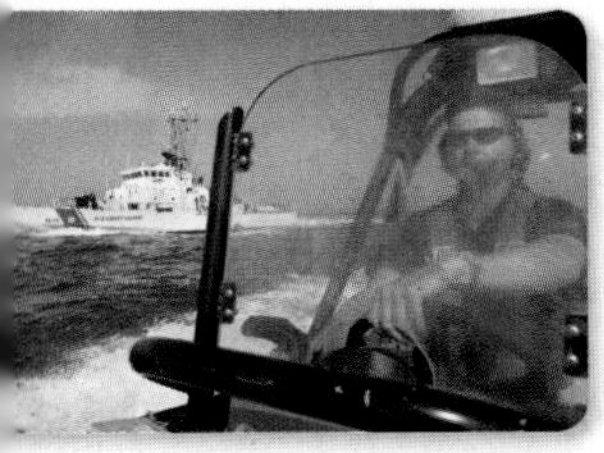

Real-World Career

U.S. Coast Guard Boatswain's Mate The most versatile member of the U.S. Coast Guard's operational team is the boatswain's mate. BMs are capable of performing almost any task. Training for BMs is accomplished through 12 weeks of intensive training.

Real-World EXAMPLE 2 Use Graphs of Rational Functions

AVERAGE SPEED A boat traveled upstream at r_1 miles per hour. During the return trip to its original starting point, the boat traveled at r_2 miles per hour. The average speed for the entire trip R is given by the formula $R = \frac{2r_1r_2}{r_1 + r_2}$.

a. Let r_1 be the independent variable, and let R be the dependent variable. Draw the graph if $r_2 = 10$ miles per hour.

The function is $R = \frac{2r_1(10)}{r_1 + (10)}$ or $R = \frac{20r_1}{r_1 + 10}$.

The vertical asymptote is $r_1 = -10$.
Graph the vertical asymptote and the function.
Notice that the horizontal asymptote is $R = 20$.

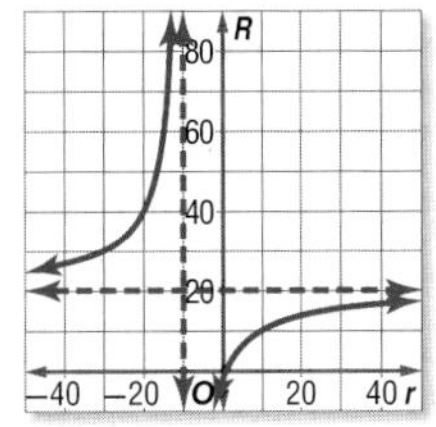

b. What is the R-intercept of the graph?

The R-intercept is 0.

c. What domain and range values are meaningful in the context of the problem?

In the problem context, speeds are nonnegative values. Therefore, only values of r_1 greater than or equal to 0 and values of R between 0 and 20 are meaningful.

Guided Practice

2. SALARIES A company uses the formula $S(x) = \frac{45x + 25}{x + 1}$ to determine the salary in thousands of dollars of an employee during his xth year. Graph $S(x)$. What domain and range values are meaningful in the context of the problem? What is the meaning of the horizontal asymptote for the graph? **See margin.**

Personal Tutor glencoe.com

Oblique Asymptotes and Point Discontinuity An **oblique asymptote**, sometimes called a *slant asymptote*, is an asymptote that is neither horizontal nor vertical.

Key Concept Oblique Asymptotes

Words If $f(x) = \frac{a(x)}{b(x)}$, $a(x)$ and $b(x)$ are polynomial functions with no common factors other than 1 and $b(x) \neq 0$, then $f(x)$ has an oblique asymptote if the degree of $a(x)$ minus the degree of $b(x)$ equals 1. The equation of the asymptote is $f(x) = \frac{a(x)}{b(x)}$ with no remainder.

Example $f(x) = \frac{x^4 + 3x^3}{x^3 - 1}$

Vertical asymptote: $x = 1$
Oblique asymptote: $f(x) = x + 3$

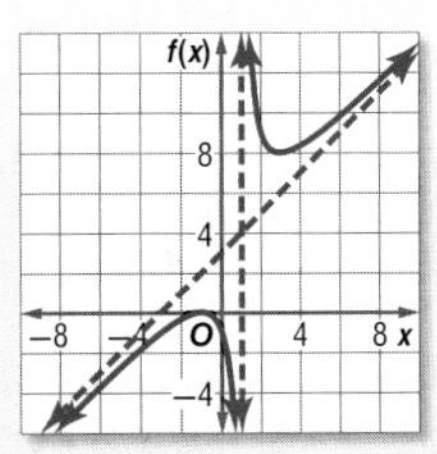

Additional Example

2 **AVERAGE SPEED** Use the situation and formula given in Example 2.

a. Draw the graph if $r_2 = 15$ miles per hour.

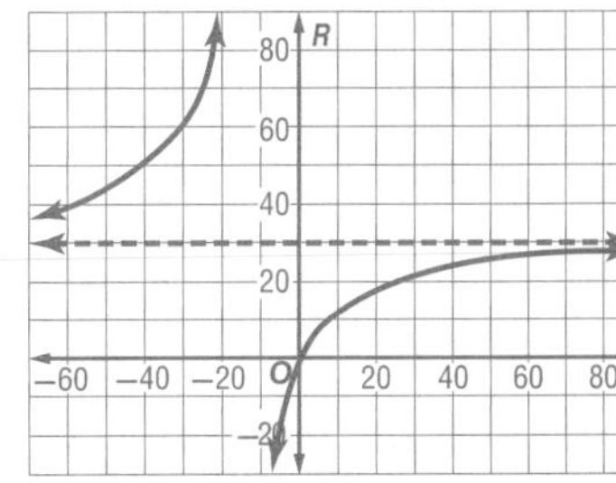

b. What is the R-intercept of the graph? The R-intercept is 0.

c. What domain and range values are meaningful in the context of the problem? Values of r_1 greater than or equal to 0 and values of R between 0 and 30 are meaningful.

Oblique Asymptotes and Point Discontinuity

Example 3 shows how to graph a function with oblique asymptotes.
Example 4 shows a graph with point discontinuity.

Additional Answer (Guided Practice)

2. The number of years worked must be greater than or equal to 0, and salary values must be between 25 and 45. The asymptote represents a salary cap of $45,000.

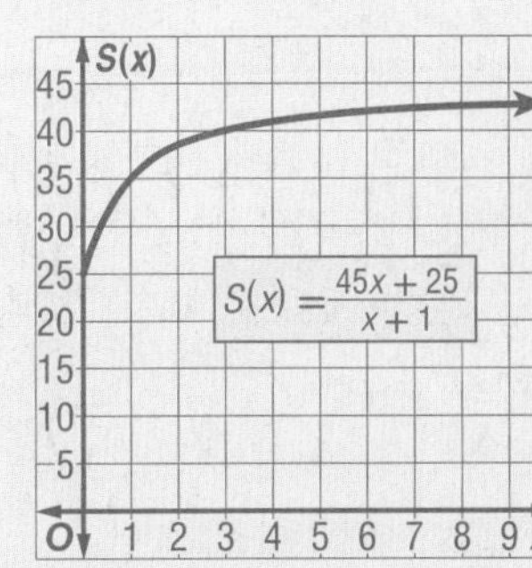

Differentiated Instruction BL

Extension Challenge students to explain the rules for finding horizontal and oblique asymptotes. While the chapter shows students how to find them, the explanation of why the rules work can be left to high ability students. Scaffold the task by having students examine graphs of varying degrees in the numerator and denominator and look for general patterns in the asymptotes.

Additional Example

3 Graph $f(x) = \dfrac{x^2}{x+1}$.

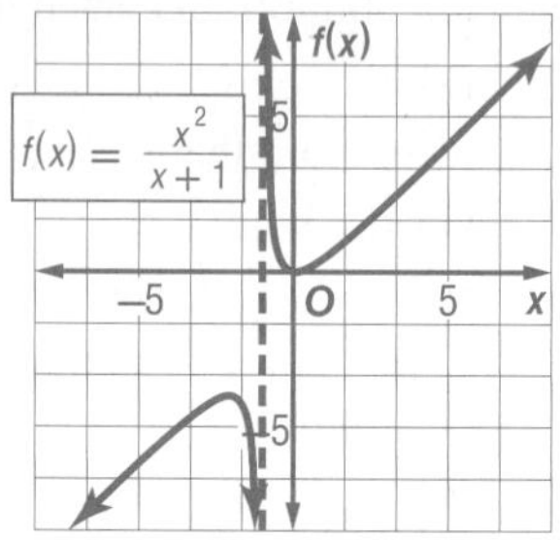

Additional Answer (Guided Practice)

3A.

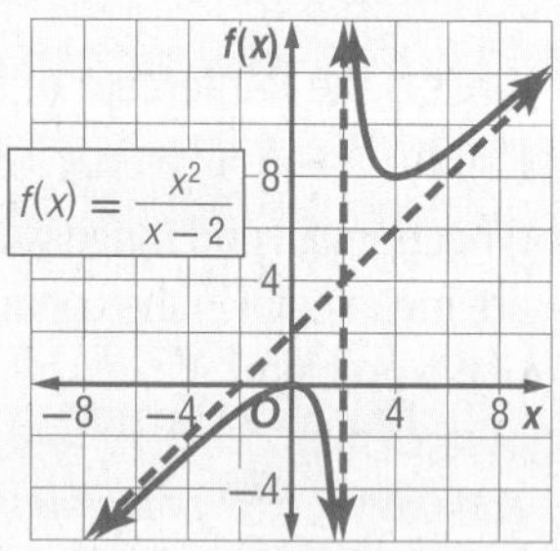

3B.

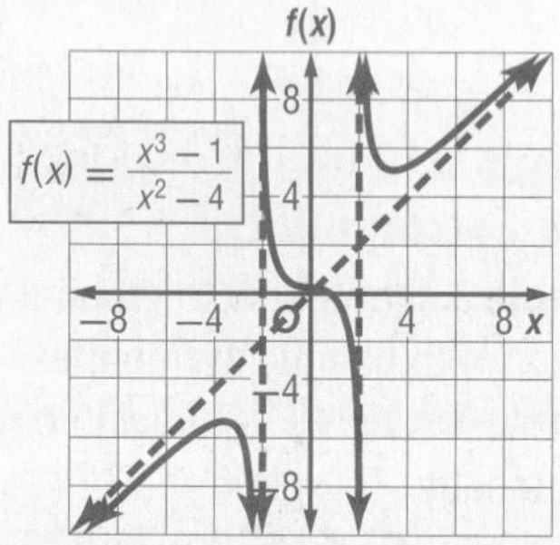

StudyTip

Oblique Asymptotes Oblique asymptotes occur for rational functions that have a numerator polynomial that is one degree higher than the denominator polynomial.

EXAMPLE 3 Determine Oblique Asymptotes

Graph $f(x) = \dfrac{x^2 + 4x + 4}{2x - 1}$.

Step 1 Find the zeros.

$x^2 + 4x + 4 = 0$	**Set $a(x) = 0$.**
$(x+2)^2 = 0$	**Factor.**
$x + 2 = 0$	**Take the square root of each side.**
$x = -2$	**Subtract 2 from each side.**

There is a zero at $x = -2$.

Step 2 Find the asymptotes.

$2x - 1 = 0$	**Set $b(x) = 0$.**
$2x = 1$	**Add 1 to each side.**
$x = \frac{1}{2}$	**Divide each side by 2.**

There is a vertical asymptote at $x = \frac{1}{2}$.

The degree of the numerator is greater than the degree of the denominator, so there is no horizontal asymptote.

The difference between the degree of the numerator and the degree of the denominator is 1, so there is an oblique asymptote.

Divide the numerator by the denominator to determine the equation of the oblique asymptote.

The equation of the asymptote is the quotient excluding any remainder.

Thus, the oblique asymptote is the line $f(x) = \frac{1}{2}x + \frac{9}{4}$.

$$\begin{array}{r} \frac{1}{2}x + \frac{9}{4} \\ 2x - 1\overline{)x^2 + 4x + 4} \\ \underline{(-)x^2 - \frac{1}{2}x} \\ \frac{9}{2}x + 4 \\ \underline{(-)\frac{9}{2}x - \frac{9}{4}} \\ \frac{25}{4} \end{array}$$

Step 3 Draw the asymptotes, and then use a table of values to graph the function.

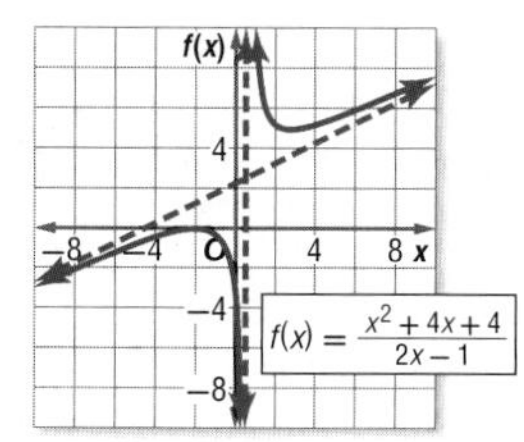

Guided Practice 3A, 3B. See margin.

Graph each function.

3A. $f(x) = \dfrac{x^2}{x-2}$ **3B.** $f(x) = \dfrac{x^3 - 1}{x^2 - 4}$

Personal Tutor glencoe.com

In some cases, graphs of rational functions may have **point discontinuity**, which looks like a hole in the graph. This is because the function is undefined at that point.

Differentiated Instruction OL ELL

Verbal/Linguistic Learners Have students write a list of tips to help someone draw the graphs of rational functions.

Key Concept — Point Discontinuity

Words If $f(x) = \frac{a(x)}{b(x)}$, $b(x) \neq 0$, and $x - c$ is a factor of both $a(x)$ and $b(x)$, then there is a point discontinuity at $x = c$.

Example $f(x) = \frac{(x + 2)(x + 1)}{x + 1}$
$= x + 2; x \neq -1$

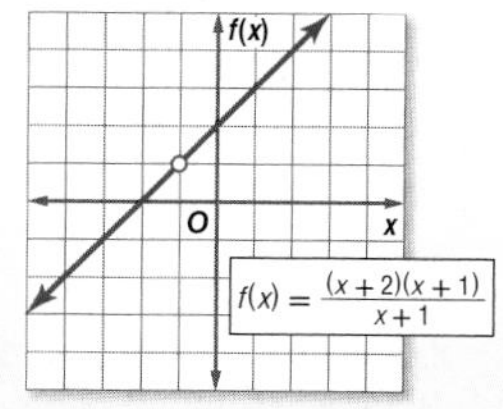

Focus on Mathematical Content

Point Discontinuity Since the discontinuity consists of only one point (and a mathematical point has no dimensions) circles are drawn on the graphs to indicate the discontinuity.

EXAMPLE 4 Graph with Point Discontinuity

Graph $f(x) = \frac{x^2 - 16}{x - 4}$.

Notice that $\frac{x^2 - 16}{x - 4} = \frac{(x + 4)\cancel{(x - 4)}^{1}}{\cancel{x - 4}_{1}}$ or $x + 4$.

Therefore, the graph of $f(x) = \frac{x^2 - 16}{x - 4}$ is the graph of $f(x) = x + 4$ with a hole at $x = 4$.

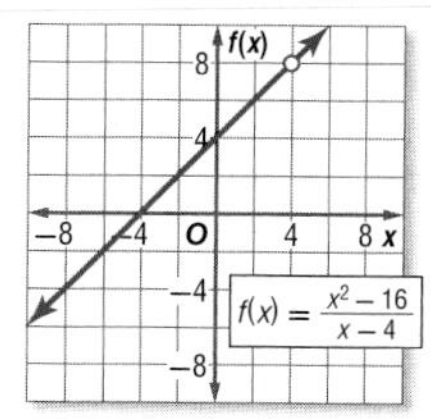

Watch Out!

Holes Remember that a common factor in the numerator and denominator can signal a hole.

Guided Practice 4A, 4B. See margin.

Graph each function.

4A. $f(x) = \frac{x^2 + 4x - 5}{x + 5}$

4B. $f(x) = \frac{x^3 + 2x^2 - 9x - 18}{x^2 - 9}$

Personal Tutor glencoe.com

Additional Example

4 Graph $f(x) = \frac{x^2 - 4}{x - 2}$.

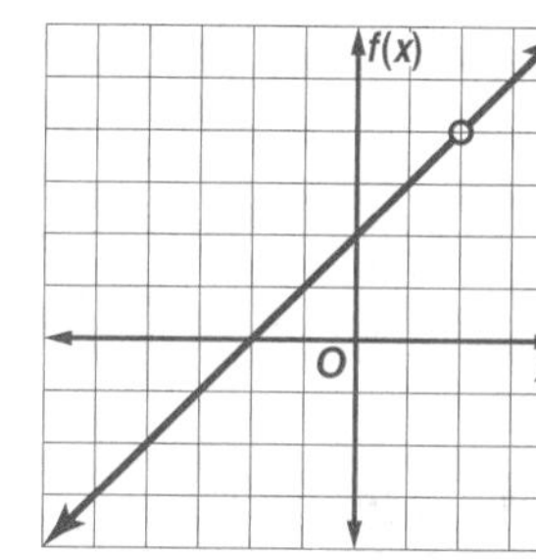

Check Your Understanding

Example 1 p. 578

Graph each function. 1, 2. See Chapter 9 Answer Appendix.

1. $f(x) = \frac{x^4 - 2}{x^2 - 1}$

2. $f(x) = \frac{x^3}{x + 2}$

Example 2 p. 579

3. FOOTBALL Eduardo plays football for his high school. So far this season, he has made 7 out of 11 field goals. He would like to improve his field goal percentage. If he can make x consecutive field goals, his field goal percentage can be determined using the function $P(x) = \frac{7 + x}{11 + x}$.

a. Graph the function. See Chapter 9 Answer Appendix.

b. What part of the graph is meaningful in the context of this problem? the part in the first quadrant

c. Describe the meaning of the intercept of the vertical axis.

d. What is the equation of the horizontal asymptote? Explain its meaning with respect to Eduardo's field goal percentage.

3c. It represents his original field goal percentage of 63.6%.
3d. $y = 1$; this represents 100% which he cannot achieve because he has already missed 4 field goals.

Examples 3 and 4 pp. 580–581

Graph each function. 4–7. See Chapter 9 Answer Appendix.

4. $f(x) = \frac{6x^2 - 3x + 2}{x}$

5. $f(x) = \frac{x^2 + 8x + 20}{x + 2}$

6. $f(x) = \frac{x^2 - 4x - 5}{x + 1}$

7. $f(x) = \frac{x^2 + x - 12}{x + 4}$

3 PRACTICE

Formative Assessment

Use Exercises 1–7 to check for understanding.

Use the chart at the bottom of the next page to customize assignments for your students.

Exercise Alert

Grid Paper For Exercises 1–42 and 51–53, students will need grid paper.

Additional Answers (Guided Practice)

4A.

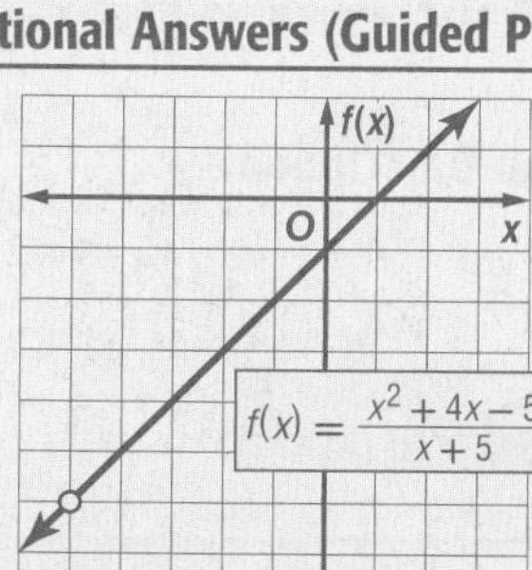

4B.

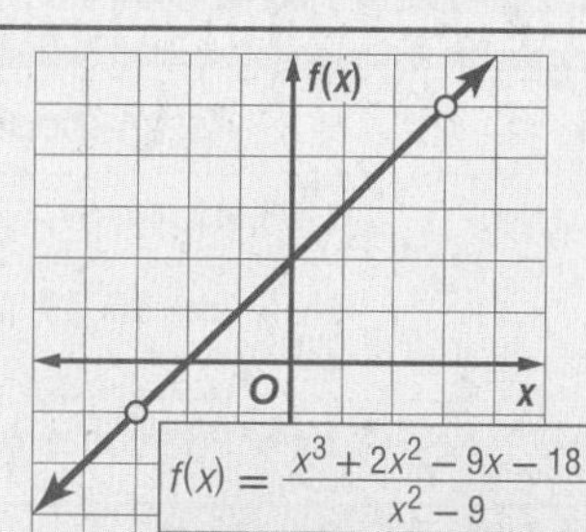

Lesson 9-4 Graphing Rational Functions 581

Additional Answers

8.

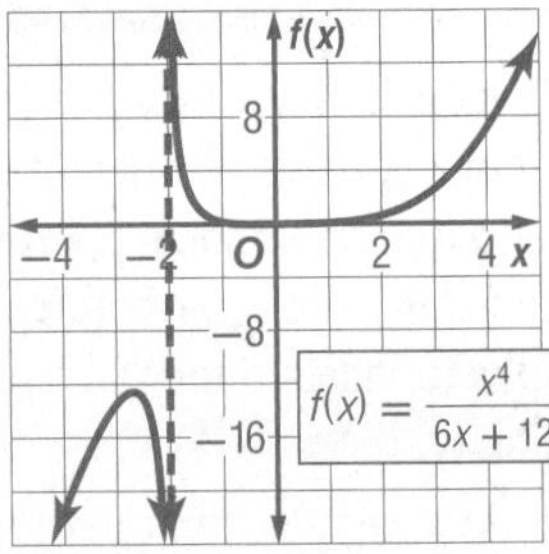

9.

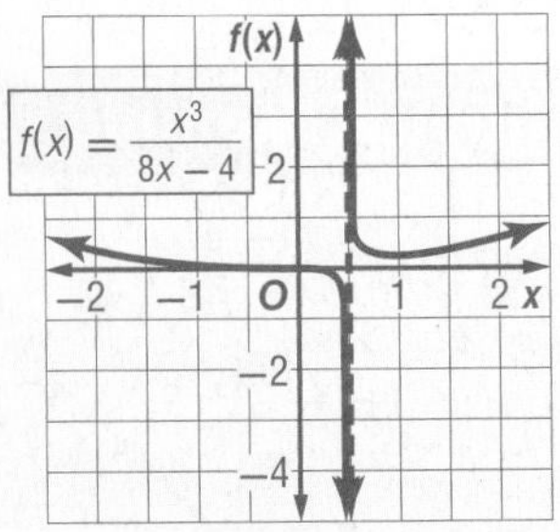

10.

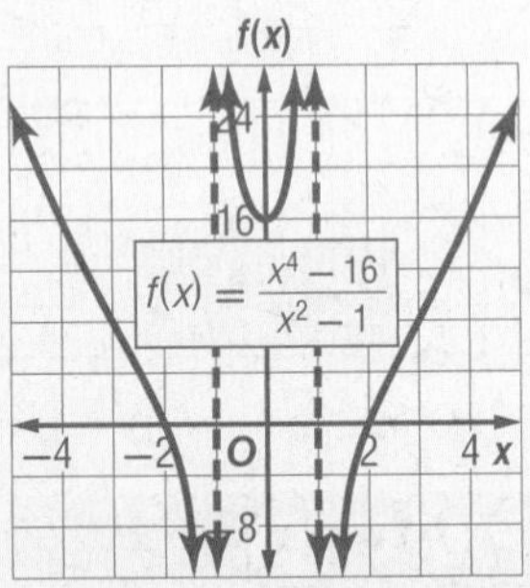

11.

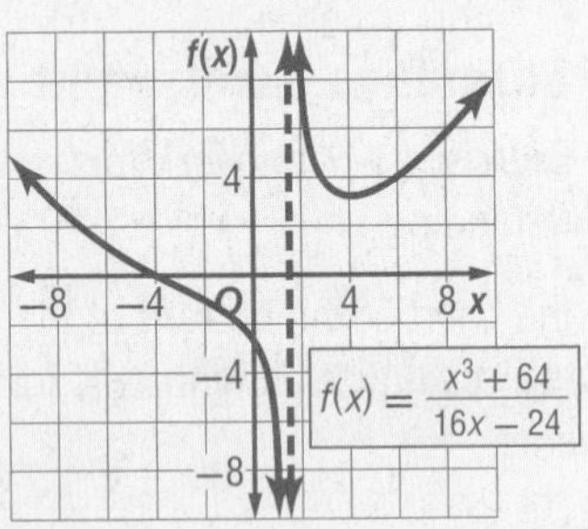

12a.

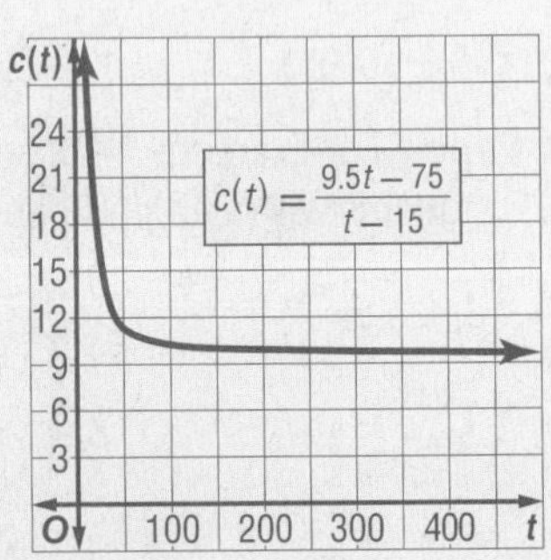

Practice and Problem Solving

= Step-by-Step Solutions begin on page R20.
Extra Practice begins on page 947.

Example 1 p. 578

Graph each function. 8–11. See margin.

8. $f(x) = \frac{x^4}{6x + 12}$

9. $f(x) = \frac{x^3}{8x - 4}$

10. $f(x) = \frac{x^4 - 16}{x^2 - 1}$

11. $f(x) = \frac{x^3 + 64}{16x - 24}$

Example 2 p. 579

12. **SCHOOL SPIRIT** As president of Student Council, Brandy is getting T-shirts made for a pep rally. Each T-shirt costs \$9.50, and there is a set-up fee of \$75. The student council plans to sell the shirts, but each of the 15 council members will get one for free.

a. Write a function for the average cost of a T-shirt to be sold. Graph the function.

b. What is the average cost if 200 shirts are ordered? if 500 shirts are ordered?

c. How many T-shirts must be ordered to bring the average cost under \$9.75? more than 885

12a. $c(t) = \frac{9.5t - 75}{t - 15}$; See margin for graph.
12b. \$10.68; \$9.95

Examples 2 and 3 pp. 579–580

Graph each function. 13–26. See Chapter 9 Answer Appendix.

13. $f(x) = \frac{x}{x + 2}$

14. $f(x) = \frac{5}{(x - 1)(x + 4)}$

15. $f(x) = \frac{4}{(x - 2)^2}$

16. $f(x) = \frac{x - 3}{x + 1}$

17. $f(x) = \frac{1}{(x + 4)^2}$

18. $f(x) = \frac{2x}{(x + 2)(x - 5)}$

19. $f(x) = \frac{(x - 4)^2}{x + 2}$

20. $f(x) = \frac{(x + 3)^2}{x - 5}$

21. $f(x) = \frac{x^3 + 1}{x^2 - 4}$

22. $f(x) = \frac{4x^3}{2x^2 + x - 1}$

23. $f(x) = \frac{3x^2 + 8}{2x - 1}$

24. $f(x) = \frac{2x^2 + 5}{3x + 4}$

25. $f(x) = \frac{x^4 - 2x^2 + 1}{x^3 + 2}$

26. $f(x) = \frac{x^4 - x^2 - 12}{x^3 - 6}$

27. **ELECTRICITY** The current in amperes in an electrical circuit with three resistors in a series is given by the equation $I = \frac{V}{R_1 + R_2 + R_3}$, where V is the voltage in volts in a the circuit and R_1, R_2, and R_3 are the resistances in ohms of the three resistors.

a. Let R_1 be the independent variable, and let I be the dependent variable. Graph the function if $V = 120$ volts, $R_2 = 25$ ohms, and $R_3 = 75$ ohms. See Chapter 9 Answer Appendix.

b. Give the equation of the vertical asymptote and the R_1- and I-intercepts of the graph. $R_1 = -100$; no R_1-intercept; 1.2

c. Find the value of I when the value of R_1 is 140 ohms. 0.5 amperes

d. What domain and range values are meaningful in the context of the problem? $R_1 \geq 0$ and $0 < I \leq 1.2$

Example 4 p. 581

Graph each function. 28–35. See Chapter 9 Answer Appendix.

28. $f(x) = \frac{x^2 - 2x - 8}{x - 4}$

29. $f(x) = \frac{x^2 + 4x - 12}{x - 2}$

30. $f(x) = \frac{x^2 - 25}{x + 5}$

31. $f(x) = \frac{x^2 - 64}{x - 8}$

32. $f(x) = \frac{(x - 4)(x^2 - 4)}{x^2 - 6x + 8}$

33. $f(x) = \frac{(x + 5)(x^2 + 2x - 3)}{x^2 + 8x + 15}$

34. $f(x) = \frac{3x^4 + 6x^3 + 3x^2}{x^2 + 2x + 1}$

35. $f(x) = \frac{2x^4 + 10x^3 + 12x^2}{x^2 + 5x + 6}$

Differentiated Homework Options

Level	Assignment	Two-Day Option	
AL Basic	8–35, 42, 44–61, 62	9–35 odd, 47–50	8–34 even, 42, 44–62
OL Core	9–35 odd, 36–39, 41–42, 44–62	8–35, 47–50	36–42, 44–46, 51–62
BL Advanced	36–61, (optional: 62)		

36. BUSINESS Liam purchased a snow plow for \$4500 and plows the parking lots of local businesses. Each time he plows a parking lot, he incurs a cost of \$50 for gas and maintenance.

a. Write and graph the rational function representing his average cost per customer as a function of the number of parking lots. **See Chapter 9 Answer Appendix.**

b. What are the asymptotes of the graph? **$x = 0$ and $f(x) = 50$**

c. Why is the first quadrant in the graph the only relevant quadrant?

d. How many total parking lots does Liam need to plow for his average cost per parking lot to be less than \$80? **150**

Real-World Link

The primary snow belt along the eastern Great Lakes gets anywhere from 60 to more than 110 inches of snow per year.

Source: Weathernet5

37. FINANCIAL LITERACY Kristina bought a new cell phone with Internet access. The phone cost \$150, and her monthly usage charge is \$30 plus \$10 for the Internet access.

a. Write and graph the rational function representing her average monthly cost as a function of the number of months Kristina uses the phone. **See Chapter 9 Answer Appendix.**

b. What are the asymptotes of the graph? **$x = 0$ and $f(x) = 40$**

c. Why is the first quadrant in the graph the only relevant quadrant?

d. After how many months will the average monthly charge be \$45? **30**

38. SOFTBALL Alana plays softball for Centerville High School. So far this season she has gotten a hit 4 out of 12 times at bat. She is determined to improve her batting average. If she can get x consecutive hits, her batting average can be determined using $B(x) = \frac{4 + x}{12 + x}$. **c. It represents her original batting average of .333.**

a. Graph the function. **See Chapter 9 Answer Appendix.**

b. What part of the graph is meaningful in the context of the problem? **the part in the first quadrant**

c. Describe the meaning of the intercept of the vertical axis.

d. What is the equation of the horizontal asymptote? Explain its meaning with respect to Alana's batting average.

36c. Sample answer: The number of parking lots and the average cost cannot be negative.
37c. Sample answer: The number of months and the average cost cannot have negative values.
38d. $y = 1$; This represents 100%, which she can never achieve because she has already missed getting a hit 8 times.

Graph each function. 39–41. See Chapter 9 Answer Appendix.

39. $f(x) = \frac{x + 1}{x^2 + 6x + 5}$ **40.** $f(x) = \frac{x^2 - 10x - 24}{x + 2}$ **41.** $f(x) = \frac{6x^2 + 4x + 2}{x + 2}$

H.O.T. Problems

Use Higher-Order Thinking Skills

42. OPEN ENDED Sketch the graph of a rational function with a horizontal asymptote $y = 1$ and a vertical asymptote $x = -2$. **See Chapter 9 Answer Appendix.**

43. CHALLENGE Write a rational function for the graph at the right. **$f(x) = \frac{x^2 - 1}{x(x^2 - 1)}$**

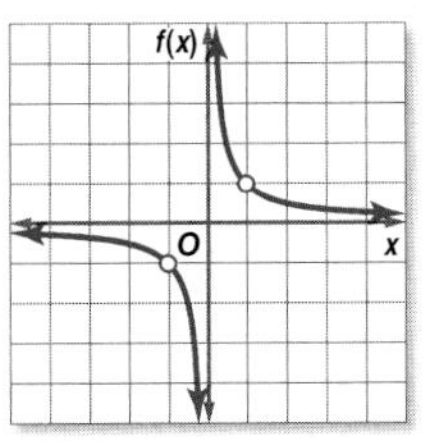

44. REASONING What is the difference between the graphs of $f(x) = x - 2$ and $g(x) = \frac{(x + 3)(x - 2)}{x + 3}$? **The graph of $g(x)$ has a hole in it at -3.**

45. PROOF A rational function has an equation of the form $f(x) = \frac{a(x)}{b(x)}$, where $a(x)$ and $b(x)$ are polynomial functions and $b(x) \neq 0$. Show that $f(x) = \frac{x}{a - b} + c$ is a rational function.

45. $f(x) = \frac{x}{a - b} + \frac{c(a - b)}{(a - b)} \rightarrow \frac{x + ca - cb}{a - b}$

46. WRITING IN MATH Explain how factoring can be used to determine the vertical asymptotes or point discontinuity of a rational function. **See margin.**

Study Guide and Intervention

CRM pp. 25–26 AL OL ELL

9-4 Study Guide and Intervention

Graphing Rational Functions

Vertical and Horizontal Asymptotes

Rational Function	an equation of the form $f(x) = \frac{p(x)}{q(x)}$, where $p(x)$ and $q(x)$ are polynomial expressions and $q(x) \neq 0$
Domain	The domain of a rational function is limited to values for which the function is defined.
Vertical Asymptote	An asymptote is a line that the graph of a function approaches. If the simplified form of the related rational expression is undefined for $x = a$, then $x = a$ is a vertical asymptote.
Horizontal Asymptote	Often a horizontal asymptote occurs in the graph of a rational function where a value is excluded from the range.

Example Graph $f(x) = \frac{x^2 + x - 6}{x + 1}$.

$\frac{x^2 + x - 6}{x + 1} = \frac{(x + 3)(x - 2)}{x + 1}$

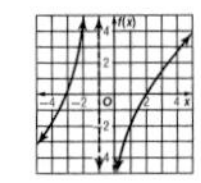

Therefore the graph of $f(x)$ has zeroes at $x = -3$ and $x = 2$ and a vertical asymptote at $x = -1$. Because the degree of $x^2 + x - 6$ is greater than $x + 1$, there is no horizontal asymptote. Make a table of values. Plot the points and draw the graph.

x	−5	−4	−3	−2	0	1	2	3	4
$f(x)$	−3.5	−2	0	4	−6	−2	0	1.5	2.8

Exercises

Graph each function.

1. $f(x) = \frac{4}{x^2 + 3x - 10}$ 2. $f(x) = \frac{x^2 - 2x + 1}{x^2 + 2x + 1}$ 3. $f(x) = \frac{x + 3}{x^2 - x - 2}$

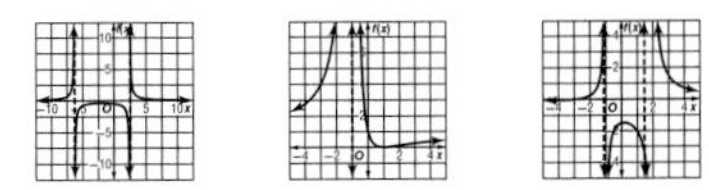

Lesson 9-4

Practice

CRM p. 28 AL OL BL ELL

9-4 Practice

Graphing Rational Functions

Graph each function.

1. $f(x) = \frac{-4}{x - 2}$ 2. $f(x) = \frac{x - 3}{x - 2}$ 3. $f(x) = \frac{3x}{(x + 3)^2}$

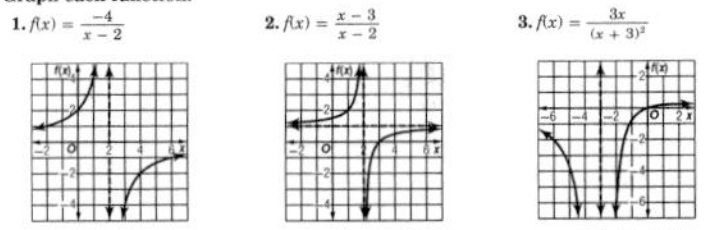

4. $f(x) = \frac{2x^2 + 5}{6x - 4}$ 5. $f(x) = \frac{x^2 + 2x - 8}{x - 2}$ 6. $f(x) = \frac{x^2 - 7x + 12}{x - 3}$

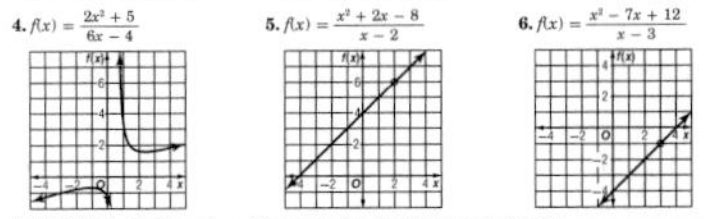

7. **PAINTING** Working alone, Tawa can give the shed a coat of paint in 6 hours. It takes her father x hours working alone to give the shed a coat of paint. The equation $f(x) = \frac{6 + x}{6x}$ describes the portion of the job Tawa and her father working together can complete in 1 hour. Graph $f(x) = \frac{6 + x}{6x}$ for $x > 0$, $y > 0$. If Tawa's father can complete the job in 4 hours alone, what portion of the job can they complete together in 1 hour? What domain and range values are meaningful in the context of the problem?

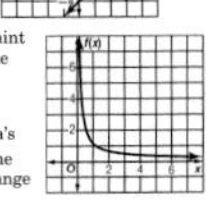

$\frac{5}{12}$; Sample answer: The number of hours it takes her father to give the shed a coat of paint should be positive. Therefore, only values of x greater than 0 and values of f(x) greater than $\frac{1}{16}$ are meaningful.

8. **LIGHT** The relationship between the illumination an object receives from a light source of I foot-candles and the square of the distance d in feet of the object from the source can be modeled by $I(d) = \frac{4500}{d^2}$. Graph the function $I(d) = \frac{4500}{d^2}$ for $0 < I \leq 80$ and $0 < d \leq 80$. What is the illumination in foot-candles that the object receives at a distance of 20 feet from the light source? What domain and range values are meaningful in the context of the problem? **11.25 foot-candles; Sample answer: The distance of the object from the source should be positive. Therefore, only values of d greater than 0 and values of I(d) greater than 0 are meaningful.**

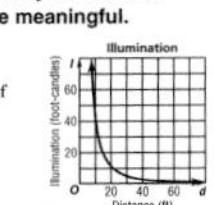

Word Problem Practice

CRM p. 29 AL OL BL ELL

9-4 Word Problem Practice

Graphing Rational Expressions

1. **ROAD TRIP** Robert and Sarah start off on a road trip from the same house. During the trip, Robert's and Sarah's cars remain separated by a constant distance. The graph shows the ratio of the distance Sarah has traveled to the distance Robert has traveled. The dotted line shows how this graph would be extended to hypothetical negative values of x. What does the x-coordinate of the vertical asymptote represent?

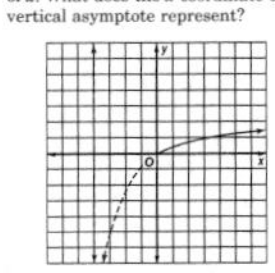

the distance by which Sarah trails Robert

2. **GRAPHS** Alma graphed the function $f(x) = \frac{x^2 - 4x}{x - 4}$ below.

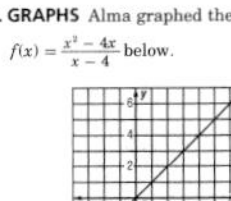

There is a problem with her graph. Explain how to correct it.

The point (4, 4) needs to be erased and a small circle put around it.

3. **NEWTON** Sir Isaac Newton studied the rational function $f(x) = \frac{ax^3 + bx^2 + cx + d}{x}$.

Assuming that $d \neq 0$, where will there be a vertical asymptote to the graph of this function?

$x = 0$

4. **BATTING AVERAGES** Alex Rodriguez had a lifetime batting average of .305 at the begining of the 2007 season. He had 2067 hits out of 6767 at bats. During the 2007 season, he had 183 hits.

a. Write an equation describing Rodriguez's batting average at the end of the 2007 season using x for the number of at bats he had during the season.

$y = \frac{2067 + 183}{6767 + x}$

b. Determine where the horizontal and vertical asymptotes for the graph of the equation would be.

vertical asymptote at $x = -6767$; horizontal asymptote at $y = 0$

c. What is the meaning of the horizontal asymptote for the graph of this equation?

As the number of at bats increases towards infinity, the ratio grows closer and closer to zero, since the number of hits remains constant.

Lesson 9-4

Additional Answer

46. Sample answer: By factoring the denominator of a rational function and determining the values that cause each factor to equal zero you can determine the asymptotes of a rational function. After factoring the numerator and denominator of a rational function, if there is a common factor $x - c$, then there is point discontinuity at $x = c$.

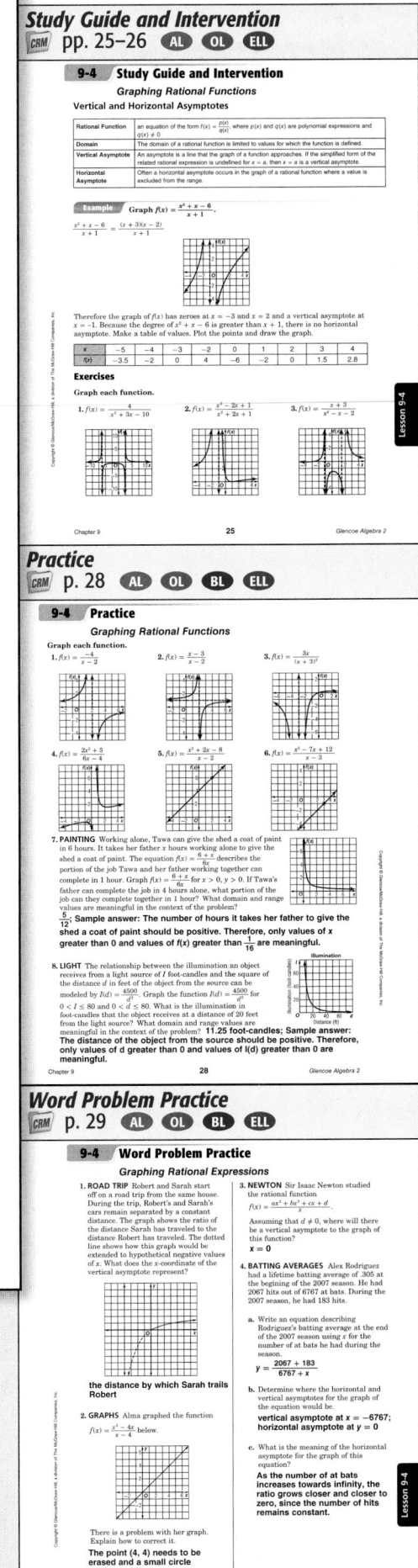

Enrichment

CRM p. 30 OL BL

9-4 Enrichment

Characteristics of Rational Function Graphs

The table summarizes some of the information used to graph rational functions.

CHARACTERISTIC	MEANING	HOW TO FIND IT
Vertical asymptotes	A vertical line at an x value where the rational function is undefined	Set the denominator equal to zero and solve for x.
Horizontal asymptotes	A horizontal line at a y value that the graph approaches at large values of x	Study the end-behaviors.
Right end-behavior	How the graph behaves at large positive values of x	Evaluate the rational expression at increasing positive values of x.
Left end-behavior	How the graph behaves at large negative values of x	Evaluate the rational expression at increasing negative values of x.
Roots, zeros, or x-intercepts	Point(s) where the graph crosses the x-axis	Set the numerator equal to zero and solve for x.
y-intercepts	Point where the graph crosses the y-axis	Set $x = 0$ to determine the y-intercept.

A useful tool for graphing functions is the sign chart.

Example A **sign chart** uses an x value from the left and right of each critical value to determine if the graph is positive or negative on that interval. A sign chart for $y = \frac{x - 1}{x^2 - x - 6}$ is shown below.

4 ASSESS

Name the Math Have students write their own examples of rational functions and graph them, showing any asymptotes or discontinuities.

Additional Answers

51.

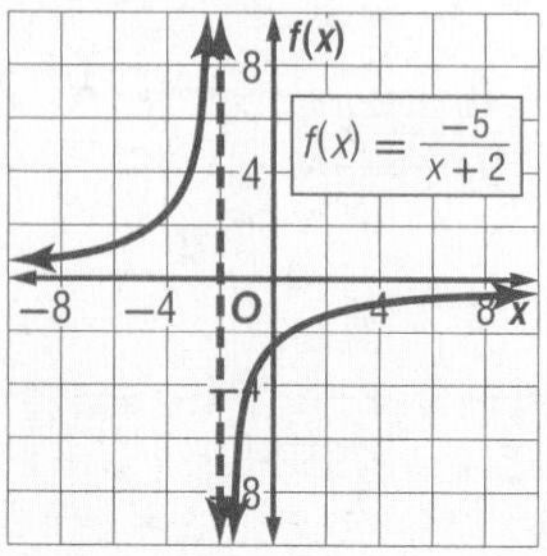

$D = \{x \mid x \neq -2\}$,
$R = \{f(x) \mid f(x) \neq 0\}$

52.

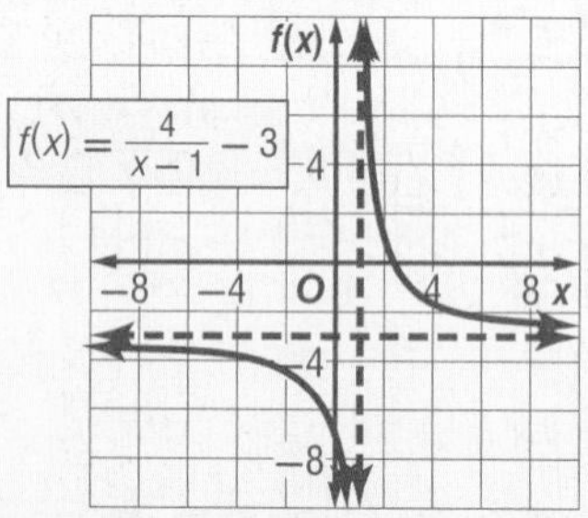

$D = \{x \mid x \neq 1\}$,
$R = \{f(x) \mid f(x) \neq -3\}$

53.

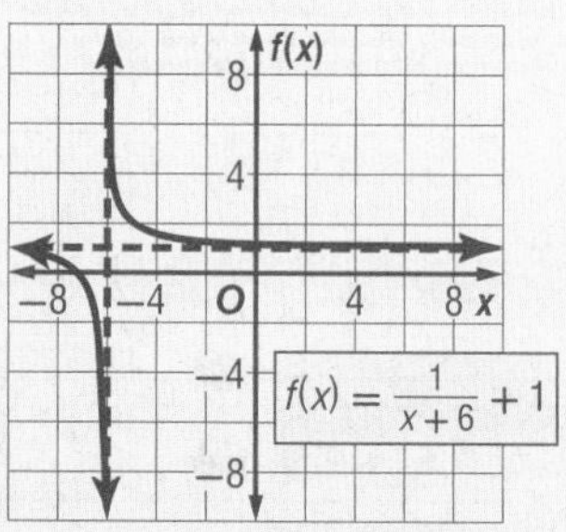

$D = \{x \mid x \neq -6\}$,
$R = \{f(x) \mid f(x) \neq 1\}$

NGSSS PRACTICE 912.P.3.1, 912.A.8.5, 912.A.1.2, 912.A.3.15

47. PROBABILITY Of the 6 courses offered by the music department at her school, Kaila must choose exactly 2 of them. How many different combinations of 2 courses are possible for Kaila if there are no restrictions on which 2 courses she can choose? **C**

A. 48 C. 15
B. 18 D. 12

48. The projected sales of a game cartridge is given by the function $S(p) = \frac{3000}{2p + a}$, where $S(p)$ is the number of cartridges sold, in thousands, p is the price per cartridge, in dollars, and a is a constant.

If 100,000 cartridges are sold at \$10 per cartridge, how many cartridges will be sold at \$20 per cartridge? **H**

F. 20,000 H. 60,000
G. 50,000 I. 150,000

49. GRIDDED RESPONSE Five distinct points lie in a plane such that 3 of the points are on line ℓ and 3 of the points are on a different line m. What is the total number of lines that can be drawn so that each line passes through exactly 2 of these 5 points? **4**

50. GEOMETRY In the figure below, what is the value of $w + x + y + z$? **B**

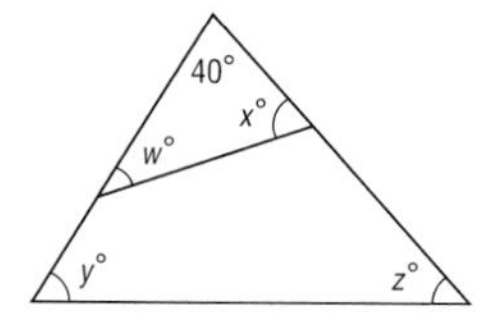

A. 140 C. 320
B. 280 D. 360

Spiral Review

Graph each function. State the domain and range. (Lesson 9-3) **51–53. See margin.**

51. $f(x) = \frac{-5}{x+2}$
52. $f(x) = \frac{4}{x-1} - 3$
53. $f(x) = \frac{1}{x+6} + 1$

Simplify each expression. (Lesson 9-2)

54. $\frac{m}{m^2 - 4} + \frac{2}{3m + 6}$ **$\frac{5m - 4}{3(m+2)(m-2)}$**

55. $\frac{y}{y+3} - \frac{6y}{y^2 - 9}$ **$\frac{y(y-9)}{(y+3)(y-3)}$**

56. $\frac{5}{x^2 - 3x - 28} + \frac{7}{2x - 14}$ **$\frac{7x + 38}{2(x-7)(x+4)}$**

57. $\frac{d-4}{d^2 + 2d - 8} - \frac{d+2}{d^2 - 16}$ **$\frac{-8d + 20}{(d-4)(d+4)(d-2)}$**

Simplify each expression. (Lesson 7-6)

58. $y^{\frac{5}{3}} \cdot y^{\frac{7}{3}}$ **y^4**

59. $x^{\frac{3}{4}} \cdot x^{\frac{9}{4}}$ **x^3**

60. $\left(b^{\frac{1}{3}}\right)^{\frac{3}{5}}$ **$b^{\frac{1}{5}}$**

61. $\left(a^{-\frac{2}{3}}\right)^{-\frac{1}{6}}$ **$a^{\frac{1}{9}}$**

Skills Review

62. TRAVEL Mr. and Mrs. Wells are taking their daughter to college. The table shows their distances from home after various amounts of time. (Lesson 2-3)

a. Find the average rate of change in their distances from home between 1 and 3 hours after leaving home. **55 mph**

b. Find the average rate of change in their distances from home between 0 and 5 hours after leaving home. **45 mph**

Time (h)	Distance (mi)
0	0
1	55
2	110
3	165
4	165
5	225

Differentiated Instruction OL BL

Extension Draw a straight line on the board, but leave a hole in the line for some integral value of x. For example, draw the line representing $y = x - 2$, but leave a hole at the point $(1, -1)$. Ask students to write possible rational functions that could be described by the graph. Many answers are possible, as long as $x = 1$ is an excluded value and the simplified form of the function is $f(x) = x - 2$. Sample answer: $f(x) = \frac{(x-1)(x-2)}{x-1}$ or $f(x) = \frac{x^2 - 3x + 2}{x - 1}$.

EXTEND 9-4

Graphing Technology Lab
Graphing Rational Functions

FL Math Online glencoe.com
- Other Calculator Keystrokes
- Graphing Technology Personal Tutor

NGSSS **MA.912.A.5.6 Identify removable and non-removable discontinuities, and vertical, horizontal, and oblique asymptotes of a graph of a rational function,** find the zeros, and graph the function.

A TI-83/84 Plus graphing calculator can be used to explore graphs of rational functions. These graphs have some features that never appear in the graphs of polynomial functions.

ACTIVITY 1 Graph with Asymptotes

Graph $y = \frac{8x - 5}{2x}$ in the standard viewing window. Find the equations of any asymptotes.

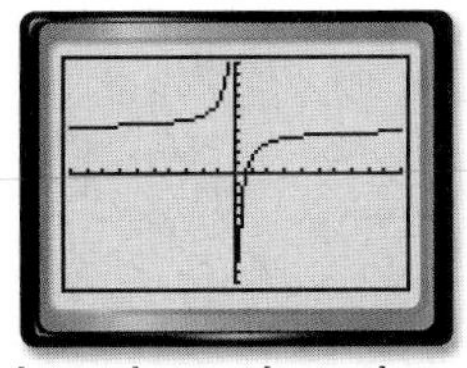

[−10, 10] scl: 1 by [−10, 10] scl: 1

Step 1 Enter the equation in the Y= list, and then graph.

KEYSTROKES: [Y=] [(] 8 [X,T,θ,n] [−] 5 [)] [÷] [(] 2 [X,T,θ,n] [)] [ZOOM] 6

Step 2 Examine the graph.

By looking at the equation, we can determine that if $x = 0$, the function is undefined. The equation of the vertical asymptote is $x = 0$. Notice what happens to the y-values as x grows larger and as x gets smaller. The y-values approach 4. So, the equation for the horizontal asymptote is $y = 4$.

ACTIVITY 2 Graph with Point Discontinuity

Graph $y = \frac{x^2 - 16}{x + 4}$ in the window [−5, 4.4] by [−10, 2] with scale factors of 1.

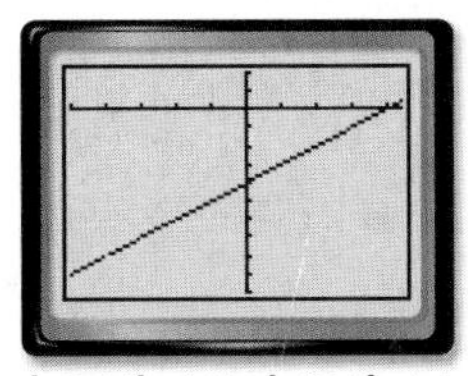

[−5, 4.4] scl: 1 by [−20, 2] scl: 1

Step 1 Because the function is not continuous, put the calculator in dot mode.

KEYSTROKES: [MODE] [▼] [▼] [▼] [▼] [▶] [ENTER]

Step 2 Examine the graph.

This graph looks like a line with a break in continuity at $x = -4$. This happens because the denominator is 0 when $x = -4$. Therefore, the function is undefined when $x = -4$.

If you TRACE along the graph, when you come to $x = -4$, you will see that there is no corresponding y-value.

Exercises

Use a graphing calculator to graph each function. Write the x-coordinates of any points of discontinuity and/or the equations of any asymptotes.

1. $f(x) = \frac{1}{x}$ $x = 0, y = 0$

2. $f(x) = \frac{x}{x + 2}$ $x = -2, y = 1$

3. $f(x) = \frac{2}{x - 4}$ $x = 4, y = 0$

4. $f(x) = \frac{2x}{3x - 6}$ $x = 2, y = \frac{2}{3}$

5. $f(x) = \frac{4x + 2}{x - 1}$ $x = 1, y = 4$

6. $f(x) = \frac{x^2 - 9}{x + 3}$ point discontinuity at $x = -3$

EXTEND 9-4 Lesson Notes

1 FOCUS

Objective Use a graphing calculator to explore the graphs of rational functions.

Materials for Each Group

- TI-83/84 Plus or other graphing calculator

Teaching Tip

Students may find it instructive to experiment with the graph style feature found to the left of the equation in the function editor (**Y** = list). They can begin by using the usual line style, indicated by a backslash icon. The path style slows down the graphing so students can follow it more easily. Its icon is calculator font, minus sign touching a zero.

2 TEACH

Working in Cooperative Groups

Have students work in pairs to complete Activities 1 and 2.

- Students may need to trace a graph beyond the current window in order to identify asymptotes precisely.
- A calculator graphing in Connected mode may seem to graph a vertical asymptote when it is merely connecting two sequential pixels on a graph. Switching to Dot mode will eliminate this possibility.

Practice Have students complete Exercises 1–6.

3 ASSESS

Formative Assessment

Use Exercises 1–3 to assess whether students can use a graphing calculator to explore the graphs of rational functions.

From Concrete to Abstract

Exercise 5 asks students to apply their findings to sketching the graph of a general rational function.

Extending the Concept

In preparation for study of inverse variation, ask students to graph $y = \frac{1}{x}$, $y = \frac{2}{x}$, $y = \frac{3}{x}$, and $y = \frac{4}{x}$ on the same screen and describe their similarities. The coordinate axes are asymptotes for the graphs of all four functions.

9-5 Lesson Notes

1 FOCUS

Vertical Alignment

Before Lesson 9-5
Write and graph linear equations.

Lesson 9-5
Recognize and solve direct and joint variation problems.
Recognize and solve inverse and combined variation problems.

After Lesson 9-5
Graph hyperbolic functions.

2 TEACH

Scaffolding Questions

Have students read the *Why?* section of the lesson.

Ask:

- If the height of the ramp increases, what happens to the length of the top of the ramp? It increases.
- If h decreases, what happens to ℓ? It decreases.
- Which value remains constant? the ratio $\frac{\ell}{h}$, which equals 1.5

9-5 Variation Functions

Then
You wrote and graphed linear equations. (Lesson 2-4)

Now
- Recognize and solve direct and joint variation problems.
- Recognize and solve inverse and combined variation problems.

NGSSS
MA.912.A.2.12 Solve problems using direct, inverse, and joint variations.

New Vocabulary
direct variation
constant of variation
joint variation
inverse variation
combined variation

FL Math Online
glencoe.com

Why?

While building skateboard ramps, Yu determined that the best ramps were the ones in which the length of the top of the ramp was 1.5 times as long as the height of the ramp.

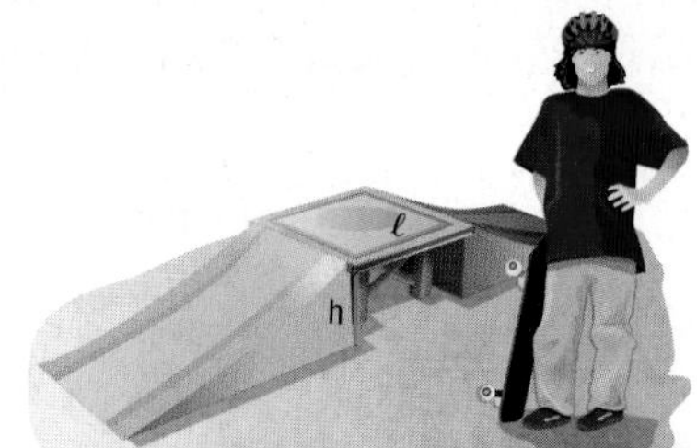

As shown in the table, the length of the top of the ramp depends on the height of a ramp. The length increases as the height increases, but the ratio remains the same, or is *constant*.

Length (ℓ)	Height (h)	Ratio $\frac{\ell}{h}$
3	2	1.5
6	4	1.5
9	6	1.5
12	8	1.5

The equation $\frac{\ell}{h} = 1.5$ can be written as $\ell = 1.5h$.

The length *varies directly* with the height of the ramp.

Direct Variation and Joint Variation The relationship given by $\ell = 1.5h$ is an example of direct variation. A **direct variation** can be expressed in the form $y = kx$. In this equation, k is called the **constant of variation**.

Notice that the graph of $\ell = 1.5h$ is a straight line through the origin. A direct variation is a special case of an equation written in slope-intercept form, $y = mx + b$. When $m = k$ and $b = 0$, $y = mx + b$ becomes $y = kx$. So the slope of a direct variation equation is its constant of variation.

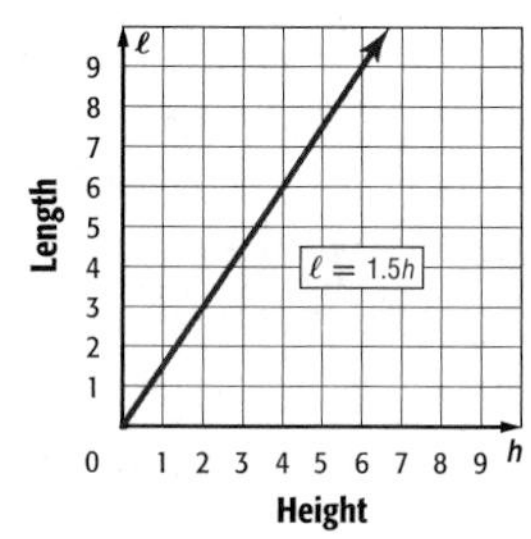

To express a direct variation, we say that y varies directly as x. In other words, as x increases, y increases or decreases at a constant rate.

Key Concept Direct Variation

Words y varies directly as x if there is some nonzero constant k such that $y = kx$. k is called the *constant of variation*.

Example If $y = 3x$ and $x = 7$, then $y = 3(7)$ or 21.

If you know that y varies directly as x and one set of values, you can use a proportion to find the other set of corresponding values.

$$y_1 = kx_1 \quad \text{and} \quad y_2 = kx_2$$

$$\frac{y_1}{x_1} = k \qquad \frac{y_2}{x_2} = k \qquad \text{Therefore, } \frac{y_1}{x_1} = \frac{y_2}{x_2}.$$

Using the properties of equality, you can find many other proportions that relate these same x- and y-values.

Lesson 9-5 Resources

Resource	Approaching-Level	On-Level	Beyond-Level	English Learners
Teacher Edition	• Differentiated Instruction, p. 591	• Differentiated Instruction, pp. 591, 593	• Differentiated Instruction, p. 593	
Chapter Resource Masters	• Study Guide and Intervention, pp. 32–33 • Skills Practice, p. 34 • Practice, p. 35 • Word Problem Practice, p. 36	• Study Guide and Intervention, pp. 32–33 • Skills Practice, p. 34 • Practice, p. 35 • Word Problem Practice, p. 36 • Enrichment, p. 37 • Spreadsheet Activity, p. 37	• Practice, p. 35 • Word Problem Practice, p. 36 • Enrichment, p. 37	• Study Guide and Intervention, pp. 32–33 • Skills Practice, p. 34 • Practice, p. 35 • Word Problem Practice, p. 36
Transparencies	• 5-Minute Check Transparency 9-5	• 5-Minute Check Transparency 9-5	• 5-Minute Check Transparency 9-5	• 5-Minute Check Transparency 9-5
Other	• Study Notebook	• Study Notebook	• Study Notebook	• Study Notebook

586 Chapter 9 Rational Functions and Relations

EXAMPLE 1 Direct Variation

If y varies directly as x and $y = 15$ when $x = -5$, find y when $x = 7$.

Use a proportion that relates the values.

$\frac{y_1}{x_1} = \frac{y_2}{x_2}$	**Direct variation**
$\frac{15}{-5} = \frac{y_2}{7}$	**$y_1 = 15$, $x_1 = -5$, and $x_2 = 7$**
$15(7) = -5(y_2)$	**Cross multiply.**
$105 = -5y_2$	**Simplify.**
$-21 = y_2$	**Divide each side by -5.**

Guided Practice

1. If r varies directly as t and $r = -20$ when $t = 4$, find r when $t = -6$. **30**

Personal Tutor glencoe.com

Another type of variation is joint variation. **Joint variation** occurs when one quantity varies directly as the product of two or more other quantities.

Key Concept Joint Variation

Words y varies jointly as x and z if there is some nonzero constant k such that $y = kxz$.

Example If $y = 5xz$, $x = 6$ and $z = -2$, then $y = 5(6)(-2)$ or -60.

StudyTip

Joint Variation Some mathematicians consider joint variation a special type of combined variation.

If you know that y varies jointly as x and z and one set of values, you can use a proportion to find the other set of corresponding values.

$$y_1 = kx_1z_1 \quad \text{and} \quad y_2 = kx_2z_2$$

$$\frac{y_1}{x_1z_1} = k \qquad \frac{y_2}{x_2z_2} = k \qquad \text{Therefore, } \frac{y_1}{x_1z_1} = \frac{y_2}{x_2z_2}.$$

EXAMPLE 2 Joint Variation

Suppose y varies jointly as x and z. Find y when $x = 9$ and $z = 2$, if $y = 20$ when $z = 3$ and $x = 5$.

Use a proportion that relates the values.

$\frac{y_1}{x_1z_1} = \frac{y_2}{x_2z_2}$	**Joint variation**
$\frac{20}{5(3)} = \frac{y_2}{9(2)}$	**$y_1 = 20$, $x_1 = 5$, $z_1 = 3$, $x_2 = 9$, and $z_2 = 2$**
$20(9)(2) = 5(3)(y_2)$	**Cross multiply.**
$360 = 15y_2$	**Simplify.**
$24 = y_2$	**Divide each side by 15.**

Guided Practice

2. Suppose r varies jointly as v and t. Find r when $v = 2$ and $t = 8$, if $r = 70$ when $v = 10$ and $t = 4$. **28**

Personal Tutor glencoe.com

Direct Variation and Joint Variation

Example 1 shows how to use a proportion to analyze a simple direct variation. **Example 2** shows how to solve a joint variation problem.

Formative Assessment

Use the Guided Practice exercises after each example to determine students' understanding of concepts.

Additional Examples

1 If y varies directly as x and $y = -15$ when $x = 5$, find y when $x = 3$. -9

2 Suppose y varies jointly as x and z. Find y when $x = 10$ and $z = 5$, if $y = 12$ when $z = 8$ and $x = 3$. 25

Additional Examples also in Interactive Classroom PowerPoint® Presentations

IWB INTERACTIVE WHITEBOARD READY

Watch Out!

Preventing Errors Discuss with students how to write variation equations that include a constant of variation.

Focus on Mathematical Content

Direct and Inverse Variation The type of variation present can sometimes be identified from a table of values for x and y. If the quotient $\frac{y}{x}$ has a constant value, y varies directly as x. If the product xy has a constant value, y varies inversely as x.

Inverse Variation and Combined Variation

Example 3 shows how to use a proportion to solve an inverse variation problem. **Example 4** provides an example of a contextual application of inverse variation. **Example 5** shows how to solve a combined variation problem.

Additional Example

3 If r varies inversely as t and $r = -6$ when $t = 2$, find r when $t = -7$. $\frac{12}{7}$

Tips for New Teachers

Alternate Method In Example 3, students may wish to solve the problem by using the equation $a_1b_1 = a_2b_2$.

Tips for New Teachers

Sense-Making Help students understand the difference between the two types of variation by using the example of speed, distance, and driving time. When driving at a given rate, the distance increases as driving time increases (direct). However, for a given distance, the time needed decreases as speed increases (inverse).

Inverse Variation and Combined Variation Another type of variation is inverse variation. If two quantities x and y show **inverse variation**, their product is equal to a constant k.

Inverse variation is often described as one quantity increasing while the other quantity is decreasing. For example, speed and time for a fixed distance vary inversely with each other; the faster you go, the less time it takes you to get there.

Key Concept — Inverse Variation

Words y varies inversely as x if there is some nonzero constant k such that $xy = k$ or $y = \frac{k}{x}$, where $x \neq 0$ and $y \neq 0$.

Example If $xy = 2$, and $x = 6$, then $y = \frac{2}{6}$ or $\frac{1}{3}$.

StudyTip

Direct and Inverse Variation You can identify the type of variation by looking at a table of values for x and y. If the quotient $\frac{y}{x}$ has a constant value, y varies directly as x. If the product xy has a constant value, y varies inversely as x.

Suppose y varies inversely as x such that $xy = 6$ or $y = \frac{6}{x}$. The graph of this equation is shown at the right. Since k is a positive value, as the values of x increase, the values of y decrease.

Notice that the graph of an inverse variation is a reciprocal function.

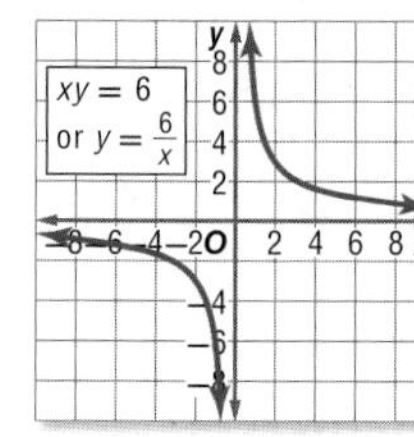

A proportion can be used with inverse variation to solve problems in which some quantities are known. The following proportion is only one of several that can be formed.

$$x_1y_1 = k \text{ and } x_2y_2 = k$$

$$x_1y_1 = x_2y_2 \quad \text{Substitution Property of Equality}$$

$$\frac{x_1}{y_2} = \frac{x_2}{y_1} \quad \text{Divide each side by } y_1y_2.$$

EXAMPLE 3 Inverse Variation

If a varies inversely as b and $a = 28$ when $b = -2$, find a when $b = -10$.

Use a proportion that relates the values.

$\frac{a_1}{b_2} = \frac{a_2}{b_1}$	**Inverse Variation**
$\frac{28}{-10} = \frac{a_2}{-2}$	**$a_1 = 28$, $b_1 = -2$, and $b_2 = -10$**
$28(-2) = -10(a_2)$	**Cross multiply.**
$-56 = -10(a_2)$	**Simplify.**
$5\frac{3}{5} = a_2$	**Divide each side by -10.**

Guided Practice

3. If x varies inversely as y and $x = 24$ when $y = 4$, find x when $y = 12$. 8

Personal Tutor glencoe.com

Inverse variation is often used in real-world situations.

588 Chapter 9 Rational Functions and Relations

Real-World Link

When you pluck a string, it vibrates back and forth. This causes mechanical energy to travel through the air in waves. The number of times per second these waves hit our ear is called the *frequency*. The more waves per second, the higher the pitch.

Real-World EXAMPLE 4 Write and Solve an Inverse Variation

MUSIC The length of a violin string varies inversely as the frequency of its vibrations. A violin string 10 inches long vibrates at a frequency of 512 cycles per second. Find the frequency of an 8-inch violin string.

Let $v_1 = 10, f_1 = 512$, and $v_2 = 8$. Solve for f_2.

$v_1 f_1 = v_2 f_2$	**Original equation**
$10 \cdot 512 = 8 \cdot f_2$	**$v_1 = 10, f_1 = 512$, and $v_2 = 8$**
$\frac{5120}{8} = f_2$	**Divide each side by 8.**
$640 = f_2$	**Simplify.**

The 8-inch violin string vibrates at a frequency of 640 cycles per second.

Guided Practice

4. The apparent length of an object is inversely proportional to one's distance from the object. Earth is about 93 million miles from the Sun. Jupiter is about 483.6 million miles from the Sun. Find how many times as large the diameter of the Sun would appear on Earth as on Jupiter. **5.2 times as large**

Personal Tutor glencoe.com

Another type of variation is combined variation. **Combined variation** occurs when one quantity varies directly and/or inversely as two or more other quantities.

If you know that y varies directly as x, y varies inversely as z and one set of values, you can use a proportion to find the other set of corresponding values.

$$y_1 = \frac{kx_1}{z_1} \quad \text{and} \quad y_2 = \frac{kx_2}{z_2}$$

$$\frac{y_1 z_1}{x_1} = k \qquad \frac{y_2 z_2}{x_2} = k \qquad \text{Therefore, } \frac{y_1 z_1}{x_1} = \frac{y_2 z_2}{x_2}.$$

EXAMPLE 5 Combined Variation

Suppose f varies directly as g, and f varies inversely as h. Find g when $f = 18$ and $h = -3$, if $g = 24$ when $h = 2$ and $f = 6$.

First set up a correct proportion for the information given.

$f_1 = \frac{kg_1}{h_1}$ and $f_2 = \frac{kg_2}{h_2}$	***g* varies directly as *f*, so *g* goes in the numerator. *h* varies inversely as *f*, so *h* goes in the denominator.**
$k = \frac{f_1 h_1}{g_1}$ and $k = \frac{f_2 h_2}{g_2}$	**Solve for *k*.**
$\frac{f_1 h_1}{g_1} = \frac{f_2 h_2}{g_2}$	**Set the two proportions equal to each other.**
$\frac{6(2)}{24} = \frac{18(-3)}{g_2}$	**$f_1 = 6, g_1 = 24, h_1 = 2, f_2 = 18$, and $h_2 = -3$**
$24(18)(-3) = 6(2)(g_2)$	**Cross multiply.**
$-1296 = 12g_2$	**Simplify.**
$-108 = g_2$	**Divide each side by 12.**

When $f = 18$ and $h = -3$, the value of g is -108.

Guided Practice

5. Suppose p varies directly as r, and p varies inversely as t. Find t when $r = 10$ and $p = -5$, if $t = 20$ when $p = 4$ and $r = 2$. **−80**

Personal Tutor glencoe.com

StudyTip

Combined Variation Quantities that vary directly appear in the numerator. Quantities that vary inversely appear in the denominator.

Additional Examples

4 **SPACE** Use the information from *Guided Practice* and the fact that Venus is about 67 million miles away from the Sun. How much larger would the diameter of the Sun appear on Venus than on Earth? about 1.39 times as large

5 Suppose f varies directly as g, and f varies inversely as h. Find g when $f = 6$ and $h = -5$, if $g = 18$ when $h = 3$ and $f = 5$. -36

TEACH with TECH

AUDIO RECORDING Create a recording of several variation examples read out loud. Play the recordings for the class (or load them onto students' portable media players), and have students write and solve the variation problem.

3 PRACTICE

Formative Assessment

Use Exercises 1–6 to check for understanding.

Then use the chart on the bottom of this page to customize assignments for your students.

Check Your Understanding

Examples 1–3 pp. 587–588

1. If y varies directly as x and $y = 12$ when $x = 8$, find y when $x = 14$. **21**
2. Suppose y varies jointly as x and z. Find y when $x = 9$ and $z = -3$, if $y = -50$ when z is 5 and x is -10. **−27**
3. If y varies inversely as x and $y = -18$ when $x = 16$, find x when $y = 9$. **−32**

Example 4 p. 589

4. **TRAVEL** A map of Illinois is scaled so that 2 inches represents 15 miles. How far apart are Chicago and Rockford if they are 12 inches apart on the map? **90 mi**

Example 5 p. 589

5. Suppose a varies directly as b, and a varies inversely as c. Find b when $a = 8$ and $c = -3$, if $b = 16$ when $c = 2$ and $a = 4$. **−48**
6. Suppose d varies directly as f, and d varies inversely as g. Find g when $d = 6$ and $f = -7$, if $g = 12$ when $d = 9$ and $f = 3$. **−42**

Practice and Problem Solving

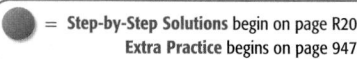

● = **Step-by-Step Solutions** begin on page R20. **Extra Practice** begins on page 947.

Example 1 p. 587

If x varies directly as y, find x when $y = 8$.

7. $x = 6$ when $y = 32$ **1.5**
8. $x = 11$ when $y = -3$ $-\frac{88}{3}$
9. $x = 14$ when $y = -2$ **−56**
10. $x = -4$ when $y = 10$ **−3.2**

11. **MOON** Astronaut Neil Armstrong, the first man on the Moon, weighed 360 pounds on Earth with all his equipment on, but weighed only 60 pounds on the Moon. Write an equation that relates weight on the Moon m with weight on Earth w. $m = \frac{1}{6}w$

Example 2 p. 587

If a varies jointly as b and c, find a when $b = 4$ and $c = -3$.

12. $a = -96$ when $b = 3$ and $c = -8$ **−48**
13. ● $a = -60$ when $b = -5$ and $c = 4$ **−36**
14. $a = -108$ when $b = 2$ and $c = 9$ **72**
15. $a = 24$ when $b = 8$ and $c = 12$ **−3**

16. **TELEVISION** According to the A.C. Nielsen Company, the average American watches 4 hours of television a day.
    a. Write an equation to represent the average number of hours spent watching television by m household members during a period of d days. $t = 4md$
    b. Assume that members of your household watch the same amount of television each day as the average American. How many hours of television would the members of your household watch in a week? **Sample answer for four household members: 112 hours**

Example 3 p. 588

If f varies inversely as g, find f when $g = -6$.

17. $f = 15$ when $g = 9$ **−22.5**
18. $f = 4$ when $g = 28$ $-\frac{56}{3}$
19. $f = -12$ when $g = 19$ **38**
20. $f = 0.6$ when $g = -21$ **2.1**

21. **COMMUNITY SERVICE** Every year students at West High School collect canned goods for a local food pantry. They plan to distribute flyers to homes in the community asking for donations. Last year, 12 students were able to distribute 1000 flyers in four hours.
    a. Write an equation that relates the number of students s to the amount of time t it takes to distribute 1000 flyers. $s = \frac{48}{t}$
    b. How long would it take 15 students to hand out the same number of flyers this year? **3.2 hours**

Differentiated Homework Options

Level	Assignment	Two-Day Option	
AL Basic	7–24, 48, 50–72	7–23 odd, 53–56	8–24 even, 48, 50–52, 57–72
OL Core	7–43 odd, 44–48, 50–72	7–24, 53–56	25–48, 50–52, 57–72
BL Advanced	25–66, (optional: 67–72)		

Example 4 p. 589

22. **BIRDS** When a group of snow geese migrate, the distance that they fly varies directly with the amount of time they are in the air.

   a. A group of snow geese migrated 375 miles in 7.5 hours. Write a direct variation equation that represents this situation. $d = 50t$

   b. Every year, geese migrate 3000 miles from their winter home in the southwest United States to their summer home in the Canadian Arctic. Estimate the number of hours of flying time that it takes for the geese to migrate. **60 hours**

Example 5 p. 589

23. Suppose a varies directly as b, and a varies inversely as c. Find b when $a = 5$ and $c = -4$, if $b = 12$ when $c = 3$ and $a = 8$. **−10**

24. Suppose x varies directly as y, and x varies inversely as z. Find z when $x = 10$ and $y = -7$, if $z = 20$ when $x = 6$ and $y = 14$. **−6**

B **Determine whether each relation shows *direct* or *inverse* variation, or *neither*.**

25. **direct**

x	y
4	12
8	24
16	48
32	96

26. **inverse**

x	y
8	2
4	4
−2	−8
−8	−2

27. **neither**

x	y
2	4
3	9
4	16
5	25

28. If y varies inversely as x and $y = 6$ when $x = 19$, find y when $x = 2$. **57**

29. If x varies inversely as y and $x = 16$ when $y = 5$, find x when $y = 20$. **4**

30. Suppose a varies directly as b, and a varies inversely as c. Find b when $a = 7$ and $c = -8$, if $b = 15$ when $c = 2$ and $a = 4$. **−105**

31. Suppose x varies directly as y, and x varies inversely as z. Find z when $x = 8$ and $y = -6$, if $z = 26$ when $x = 8$ and $y = 13$. **−12**

32. direct; 2.75
33. inverse; −2
34. joint; 3
35. combined; 10
36. direct; −11
37. direct; 4
38. combined; 9
39. direct; −2

State whether each equation represents a *direct*, *joint*, *inverse*, or *combined* variation. Then name the constant of variation.

32. $\frac{x}{y} = 2.75$
33. $fg = -2$
34. $a = 3bc$
35. $10 = \frac{xy^2}{z}$
36. $y = -11x$
37. $\frac{n}{p} = 4$
38. $9n = pr$
39. $-2y = z$
40. $a = 27b$ **direct; 27**
41. $c = \frac{7}{d}$ **inverse; 7**
42. $-10 = gh$ **inverse; −10**
43. $m = 20cd$ **joint; 20**

Real-World Link

Lake Tahoe is fed by 63 streams and 2 hot springs. According to research, with a volume of 39 trillion gallons of water, if the lake was ever drained it would take around 700 years to fill it again entirely.

Source: Lake Tahoe Visitor's Bureau

44. **CHEMISTRY** The volume of a gas v varies inversely as the pressure p and directly as the temperature t.

   a. Write an equation to represent the volume of a gas in terms of pressure and temperature. $v = \frac{kt}{p}$

   b. Is your equation a *direct*, *joint*, *inverse*, or *combined* variation? **combined**

   c. A certain gas has a volume of 8 liters, a temperature of 275 Kelvin, and a pressure of 1.25 atmospheres. If the gas is compressed to a volume of 6 liters and is heated to 300 Kelvin, what will the new pressure be? **approximately 1.82 atmospheres or $\frac{20}{11}$ atm**

45. **VACATION** The time it takes the Levensteins to reach Lake Tahoe varies inversely with their average rate of speed.

   a. If they are 800 miles away, write and graph an equation relating their travel time to their average rate of speed. **See margin.**

   b. Their goal is to arrive within 18 hours. What minimum average speed will accomplish this goal? **44.4 mph**

Additional Answer

45a.

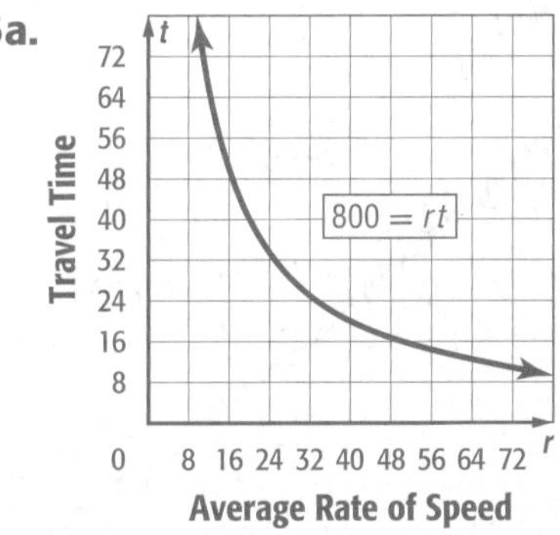

Differentiated Instruction

AL OL

If students have difficulty keeping the formulas for the different variation functions straight,

Then have students write the formulas using different colors for each variable and another color for k. For example: direct variation: $y = kx$; joint variation: $y = kxz$; and inverse variation: $y = \frac{k}{x}$.

Study Guide and Intervention

CRM pp. 32–33 AL OL ELL

9-5 Study Guide and Intervention

Variation Functions

Direct Variation and Joint Variation

Direct Variation	y varies directly as x if there is some nonzero constant k such that $y = kx$. k is called the constant of variation.
Joint Variation	y varies jointly as x and z if there is some number k such that $y = kxz$, where $k \neq 0$.

Example 1 If y varies directly as x and $y = 16$ when $x = 4$, find x when $y = 20$.

$\frac{y_1}{x_1} = \frac{y_2}{x_2}$ Direct proportion

$\frac{16}{4} = \frac{20}{x_2}$ $y_1 = 16$, $x_1 = 4$, and $y_2 = 20$

$16x_2 = (20)(4)$ Cross multiply.

$x_2 = 5$ Simplify.

The value of x is 5 when y is 20.

Example 2 If y varies jointly as x and z and $y = 10$ when $x = 2$ and $z = 4$, find y when $x = 4$ and $z = 3$.

$\frac{y_1}{x_1z_1} = \frac{y_2}{x_2z_2}$ Joint variation

$\frac{10}{2 \cdot 4} = \frac{y_2}{4 \cdot 3}$ $y_1 = 10$, $x_1 = 2$, $z_1 = 4$, $x_2 = 4$, and $z_2 = 3$

$120 = 8y_2$ Simplify.

$y_2 = 15$ Divide each side by 8.

The value of y is 15 when $x = 4$ and $z = 3$.

Exercises

1. If y varies directly as x and $y = 9$ when $x = 6$, find y when $x = 8$. **12**
2. If y varies directly as x and $y = 16$ when $x = 36$, find y when $x = 54$. **24**
3. If y varies directly as x and $x = 15$ when $y = 5$, find x when $y = 9$. **27**
4. If y varies directly as x and $x = 33$ when $y = 22$, find x when $y = 32$. **48**
5. Suppose y varies jointly as x and z. Find y when $x = 5$ and $z = 3$, if $y = 18$ when x is 3 and z is 2. **45**
6. Suppose y varies jointly as x and z. Find y when $x = 6$ and $z = 8$, if $y = 6$ when x is 4 and z is 2. **36**
7. Suppose y varies jointly as x and z. Find y when $x = 4$ and $z = 11$, if $y = 60$ when x is 3 and z is 5. **176**
8. Suppose y varies jointly as x and z. Find y when $x = 5$ and $z = 2$, if $y = 84$ when x is 4 and z is 7. **30**
9. If y varies directly as x and $y = 39$ when $x = 52$, find y when $x = 22$. **16.5**
10. If y varies directly as x and $x = 60$ when $y = 75$, find x when $y = 42$. **33.6**
11. Suppose y varies jointly as x and z. Find y when $x = 7$ and $z = 18$, if $y = 351$ when x is 6 and z is 13. **567**
12. Suppose y varies jointly as x and z. Find y when $x = 5$ and $z = 27$, if $y = 480$ when x is 9 and z is 20. **360**

Chapter 9 32 *Glencoe Algebra 2*

Practice

CRM p. 35 AL OL BL ELL

9-5 Practice

Variation Functions

State whether each equation represents a *direct*, *joint*, *inverse*, or *combined* variation. Then name the constant of variation.

1. $u = 8wz$ **joint; 8**
2. $p = 4s$ **direct; 4**
3. $L = \frac{5}{k}$ **inverse; 5**
4. $xy = 4.5$ **inverse; 4.5**
5. $\frac{C}{d} = \pi$ **direct; π**
6. $2d = mn$ **joint; $\frac{1}{2}$**
7. $\frac{1.25}{g} = h$ **inverse; 1.25**
8. $y = \frac{3}{4x}$ **inverse; $\frac{3}{4}$**
9. If y varies directly as x and $y = 8$ when $x = 2$, find y when $x = 6$. **24**
10. If y varies directly as x and $y = -16$ when $x = 6$, find x when $y = -4$. **1.5**
11. If y varies directly as x and $y = 132$ when $x = 11$, find y when $x = 33$. **396**
12. If y varies directly as x and $y = 7$ when $x = 1.5$, find y when $x = 4$. **$\frac{56}{3}$**
13. If y varies jointly as x and z and $y = 24$ when $x = 2$ and $z = 1$, find y when x is 12 and z is 2. **288**
14. If y varies jointly as x and z and $y = 60$ when $x = 3$ and $z = 4$, find y when x is 6 and z is 8. **240**
15. If y varies jointly as x and z and $y = 12$ when $x = -2$ and $z = 3$, find y when x is 4 and z is -1. **8**
16. If y varies inversely as x and $y = 16$ when $x = 4$, find y when $x = 3$. **$\frac{64}{3}$**
17. If y varies inversely as x and $y = 3$ when $x = 5$, find x when $y = 2.5$. **6**
18. If y varies directly as z and inversely as x and $y = -18$ and $z = 3$ when $x = 6$, find y when $x = 5$ and $z = -5$. **−21.6**
19. If y varies directly as z and directly as x and $y = 5$ and $z = 5$ when $x = 0.4$, find x when $y = 37.5$ and $z = 2$. **3**
20. **GASES** The volume V of a gas varies inversely as its pressure P. If $V = 80$ cubic centimeters when $P = 2000$ millimeters of mercury, find V when $P = 320$ millimeters of mercury. **500 cm^3**
21. **SPRINGS** The length S that a spring will stretch varies directly with the weight F that is attached to the spring. If a spring stretches 20 inches with 25 pounds attached, how far will it stretch with 15 pounds attached? **12 in.**
22. **GEOMETRY** The area A of a trapezoid varies jointly as its height and the sum of its bases. If the area is 480 square meters when the height is 20 meters and the bases are 28 meters and 20 meters, what is the area of a trapezoid when its height is 8 meters and its bases are 10 meters and 15 meters? **100 m^2**

Lesson 9-5

Chapter 9 35 *Glencoe Algebra 2*

Word Problem Practice

CRM p. 36 AL OL BL ELL

9-5 Word Problem Practice

Variation Functions

1. **DIVING** The height that a diver leaps above a diving board varies directly with the amount that the tip of the diving board dips below its normal level. If a diver leaps 44 inches above the diving board when the diving board tip dips 12 inches, how high will the diver leap above the diving board if the tip dips 18 inches?

   66 inches

2. **PARKING LOT DESIGN** As a general rule, the number of parking spaces in a parking lot for a movie theater complex varies directly with the number of theaters in the complex. A typical complex has 30 parking spaces for each theater. A businessman wants to build a new cinema complex on a lot that has enough space for 210 parking spaces. How many theaters should the businessman build in his complex?

   7

3. **RENT** An apartment rents for m dollars per month. If n students share the rent equally, how much would each student have to pay? How does the cost per student vary with the number of students? If 2 students have to pay $700 each, how much money would each student have to pay if there were 5 students sharing the rent?

   Each student pays $\frac{m}{n}$ dollars.

   The cost per student varies inversely with the number of students, so each student would pay $280.

4. **PAINTING** The cost of painting a wall varies directly with the area of the wall. Write a formula for the cost of painting a rectangular wall with dimensions ℓ by w. With respect to ℓ and w, does the cost vary directly, jointly, or inversely?

   $C = k\ell w$, where C is the cost and k is a constant. C varies jointly with ℓ and w.

5. **HYDROGEN** The cost of a hydrogen storage tank varies directly with the volume of the tank. A laboratory wants to purchase a storage tank shaped like a block with dimensions L by W by H.

   a. Fill in the missing spaces in the following table from a brochure of various tank sizes.

Hydrogen Tank Dimensions (inches)			Cost
L	W	H	
36	36	36	**$900**
18	**18**	24	$150
24	24	24	$800

   b. The hydrogen tank must fit in a shelf that has a fixed height and depth. How does the cost of the hydrogen storage tank vary with the width of tank with fixed depth and height?

   The cost varies directly with the width.

   c. How much would a spherical tank of radius 24 inches cost? (Recall that the volume of a sphere is given by $\frac{4}{3}\pi r^3$, where r is the radius.)

   $1,117.01

Chapter 9 36 *Glencoe Algebra 2*

Real-World Link

As of 2007, digital audio players could hold up to 23,000 songs.

Source: *Consumer Reports*

47a. about 2 × 10^{20} newtons

48. Jamil; Savannah multiplied when she should have divided and divided when she should have multiplied.

50. Sample answer: Every joint variation is a combined variation because there are two *combined* direct variations. However, a combined variation can have a combination of a direct and an inverse variation, so it cannot be considered as a joint variation.

51. Sample answer: The force of an object varies jointly as its mass and acceleration.

52. Sample answer: Inverse and some types of combined variation functions cannot have a value of 0 in the domain because division by zero is undefined.

46. **MUSIC** The maximum number of songs that a digital audio player can hold depends on the lengths and the quality of the songs that are recorded. A song will take up more space on the player if it is recorded at a higher quality, like from a CD, than at a lower quality, like from the Internet.
    a. If a certain player has 5400 megabytes of storage space, write a function that represents the number of songs the player can hold as a function of the average size of the songs. **$f(x) = \frac{5400}{x}$**
    b. Is your function a *direct*, *joint*, *inverse*, or *combined* variation? **inverse**
    c. Suppose the average file size for a high-quality song is 8 megabytes and the average size for a low-quality song is 5 megabytes. Determine how many more songs the player can hold if they are low quality than if they are high quality. **405**

47. **GRAVITY** According to the Law of Universal Gravitation, the attractive force F in newtons between any two bodies in the universe is directly proportional to the product of the masses m_1 and m_2 in kilograms of the two bodies and inversely proportional to the square of the distance d in meters between the bodies. That is, $F = \frac{Gm_1m_2}{d^2}$. G is the universal gravitational constant. Its value is 6.67×10^{-11} Nm^2/kg^2.
    a. The distance between Earth and the Moon is about 3.84×10^8 meters. The mass of the Moon is 7.36×10^{22} kilograms. The mass of Earth is 5.97×10^{24} kilograms. What is the gravitational force that the Moon and Earth exert upon each other?
    b. The distance between Earth and the Sun is about 1.5×10^{11} meters. The mass of the Sun is about 1.99×10^{30} kilograms. What is the gravitational force that the Sun and Earth exert upon each other? **about 3.5 × 10^{22} newtons**
    c. Find the gravitational force exerted on each other by two 1000-kilogram iron balls at a distance of 0.1 meter apart. **6.67 × 10^{-3} newtons**

H.O.T. Problems

Use Higher-Order Thinking Skills

48. **ERROR ANALYSIS** Jamil and Savannah are setting up a proportion to begin solving the combined variation in which z varies directly as x and z varies inversely as y. Who has set up the correct proportion? Explain your reasoning.

Jamil

$z_1 = \frac{kx_1}{y_1}$ and $z_2 = \frac{kx_2}{y_2}$

$k = \frac{z_1y_1}{x_1}$ and $k = \frac{z_2y_2}{x_2}$

$\frac{z_1y_1}{x_1} = \frac{z_2y_2}{x_2}$

Savannah

$z_1 = \frac{kx_1}{y_1}$ and $z_2 = \frac{kx_2}{y_2}$

$k = \frac{z_1x_1}{y_1}$ and $k = \frac{z_2x_2}{y_2}$

$\frac{z_1x_1}{y_1} = \frac{z_2x_2}{y_2}$

49. **CHALLENGE** If a varies inversely as b, c varies jointly as b and f, and f varies directly as g, how are a and g related? **a and g are directly related.**

50. **REASONING** Explain why some mathematicians consider every joint variation a combined variation, but not every combined variation a joint variation.

51. **OPEN ENDED** Describe three real-life quantities that vary jointly with each other.

52. **WRITING IN MATH** Determine the type(s) of variation(s) for which 0 cannot be one of the values. Explain your reasoning.

Enrichment

CRM p. 37 OL BL

9-5 Enrichment

Geosynchronous Satellites

Satellites circling the Earth are almost as common as the cell phones that depend on them. A geosynchronous satellite is one that maintains the same position above the Earth at all times. Geosynchronous satellites are used in cell phone communications, transmitting signals from towers on Earth and to each other.

The speed at which they travel is very important. If the speed is too low, the satellite will be forced back down to Earth due to the Earth's gravity. However, if it is too fast, it will overcome gravity's force and escape into space, never to return. Newton's second law of motion says that force on an object is equal to mass times acceleration or $F = ma$. It is also well known that the net gravitational force between two objects is inversely proportional to the square of the distance between them. Therefore, there are two variables on which the force depends: speed and height above the Earth.

In particular, Newton's second law, $F = ma$, shows that force varies directly with acceleration, where m is the constant taking the place of "k."

Exercises

1. Show that the net gravitational force providing a satellite with acceleration [illegible]

Watch Out!

Error Analysis For Exercise 48, suggest students write the problem as $\frac{z_1}{1} = \frac{kx_1}{y_1}$ and $\frac{z_2}{1} = \frac{kx_2}{y_2}$, then cross multiply toget $z_1y_1 = kx_1$ and $z_2y_2 = kx_2$. With the combined variations written this way, they can be simplified to the $k =$ form with fewer errors.

NGSSS PRACTICE 912.A.8.5, 912.A.2.12, 912.A.3.1, 912.A.7.5

53. SAT/ACT Rafael left the dorm and drove toward the cabin at an average speed of 40 km/h. Monica left some time later driving in the same direction at an average speed of 48 km/h. After driving for five hours, Monica caught up with Rafael. How long did Rafael drive before Monica caught up? **C**

A. 2 hours
B. 4 hours
C. 6 hours
D. 8 hours

54. 75% of 88 is the same as 60% of what number? **I**

F. 100
G. 105
H. 108
I. 110

55. EXTENDED RESPONSE Audrey's hair is 7 inches long and is expected to grow at an average rate of 3 inches per year.

a. Make a table that shows the expected length of Audrey's hair after each of the first 4 years.

b. Write a function that can be used to determine the length of her hair after each year. $f(x) = 3x + 7$

c. If she does not get a haircut, determine the length of her hair after 9 years. **34 in.**

a. See margin.

56. Which of the following is equal to the sum of two consecutive even integers? **B**

A. 144
B. 146
C. 147
D. 148

Spiral Review

Determine any vertical asymptotes and holes in the graph of each rational function. (Lesson 9-4)

57. $f(x) = \frac{1}{x^2 + 5x + 6}$ asymptotes: $x = -2, x = -3$

58. $f(x) = \frac{x + 2}{x^2 + 3x - 4}$ asymptotes: $x = -4, x = 1$

59. $f(x) = \frac{x^2 + 4x + 3}{x + 3}$ hole: $x = -3$

60. PHOTOGRAPHY The formula $\frac{1}{q} = \frac{1}{f} - \frac{1}{p}$ can be used to determine how far the film should be placed from the lens of a camera to create a perfect photograph. The variable q represents the distance from the lens to the film, f represents the focal length of the lens, and p represents the distance from the object to the lens. (Lesson 9-3)

a. Solve the formula for $\frac{1}{p}$. $\frac{1}{p} = \frac{1}{f} - \frac{1}{q}$

b. Write the expression containing f and q as a single rational expression. $\frac{q - f}{fq}$

c. If a camera has a focal length of 8 centimeters and the lens is 10 centimeters from the film, how far should an object be from the lens so that the picture will be in focus? **40 cm**

Solve each equation. Check your solutions. (Lesson 8-5)

61. $\log_3 42 - \log_3 n = \log_3 7$ **6**

62. $\log_2(3x) + \log_2 5 = \log_2 30$ **2**

63. $2 \log_5 x = \log_5 9$ **3**

64. $\log_{10} a + \log_{10}(a + 21) = 2$ **4**

Given a polynomial and one of its factors, find the remaining factors of the polynomial. Some factors may not be binomials. (Lesson 6-6)

65. $2x^3 - 5x^2 - 28x + 15; x - 5$ $x + 3, x - \frac{1}{2}$, or $2x - 1$

66. $3x^3 + 10x^2 - x - 12; x + 3$ $x - 1, x + \frac{4}{3}$, or $3x + 4$

Skills Review

Find the LCM of each set of polynomials. (Lesson 5-3)

67. $a, 2a, a + 1$ $2a(a + 1)$

68. $x, 4y, x - y$ $4xy(x - y)$

69. $8, 24x, 12$ $24x$

70. $x^4, 3x^2, 2xy$ $6x^4y$

71. $12a, 15, 4b^2$ $60ab^2$

72. $x + 2, x - 3, x^2 - x - 6$ $x^2 - x - 6$

Watch Out!

Preventing Misconceptions Make sure that students understand the essential differences between direct and inverse variation. For example, ask them if the number of candles on a birthday cake varies directly or indirectly with the age of the birthday person. Then ask how the time the candle has burned varies with the length of the candle remaining.

4 ASSESS

Ticket Out the Door On a small slip of paper, have each student write an equation for some variation in daily life (time spent studying, hours of sleep, etc.). When leaving the classroom, have each student tell what kind of variation the equation exhibits.

Formative Assessment

Check for student understanding of concepts in Lessons 9-4 and 9-5.

CRM Quiz 3, p. 49

Additional Answer

55a.

Year	Length
1	10
2	13
3	16
4	19

Differentiated Instruction OL BL

Extension Write the equation $y = kx^3$ on the board. Ask students to describe the kind of variation modeled by this equation. Have them describe what happens to the value of y when the value of x is doubled, tripled, halved, etc. For this equation, y varies directly as the cube of x. When x is doubled, y is multiplied by 8. When x is tripled, y is multiplied by 27. When x is halved, y is divided by 8.

9-6 Lesson Notes

1 FOCUS

Vertical Alignment

Before Lesson 9-6
Simplify rational expressions.

Lesson 9-6
Solve rational equations.
Solve rational inequalities.

After Lesson 9-6
Solve equations with rational exponents.

2 TEACH

Scaffolding Questions

Have students read the *Why?* section of the lesson.

Ask:

- What is the cost per visit if a member visits 10 times in a given month? \$7
- If a member visits the club 10 times in a given month, how much does the monthly membership fee add to the cost of each visit? The fee adds \$2 for each visit.
- If a member visits x times in a given month, how much does the monthly membership fee add to the cost of each visit? The fee adds $\frac{20}{x}$ dollars for each visit.

9-6 Solving Rational Equations and Inequalities

Then
You simplified rational expressions. (Lesson 9-2)

Now
- Solve rational equations.
- Solve rational inequalities.

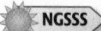

NGSSS
MA.912.A.5.5 Solve rational equations. Reinforcement of MA.912.A.5.7 Solve real-world problems involving rational equations.

New Vocabulary
rational equation
weighted average
rational inequality

FL Math Online
glencoe.com

Why?

A gaming club charges \$20 per month for membership. Members also have to pay \$5 each time they visit the club. If a member visits the club x times in one month, then the charge for that month will be $20 + 5x$. The actual cost per visit will be $\frac{20 + 5x}{x}$.

To determine how many visits are needed for the cost per visit to be \$6, you would need to solve the equation $\frac{20 + 5x}{x} = 6$.

Solve Rational Equations Equations that contain one or more rational expressions are called **rational equations**. These equations are often easier to solve once the fractions are eliminated. You can eliminate the fractions by multiplying each side by the least common denominator (LCD).

EXAMPLE 1 Solve a Rational Equation

Solve $\frac{4}{x+3} + \frac{5}{6} = \frac{23}{18}$. Check your solution.

The LCD for the terms is $18(x + 3)$.

$$\frac{4}{x+3} + \frac{5}{6} = \frac{23}{18} \quad \text{Original equation}$$

$$18(x+3)\left(\frac{4}{x+3}\right) + 18(x+3)\left(\frac{5}{6}\right) = 18(x+3)\left(\frac{23}{18}\right) \quad \text{Multiply by LCD.}$$

$$\overset{}{18}\cancel{(x+3)}_1\left(\frac{4}{\cancel{x+3}_1}\right) + \cancel{18}_3(x+3)\left(\frac{5}{\cancel{6}_1}\right) = \cancel{18}_1(x+3)\left(\frac{23}{\cancel{18}_1}\right) \quad \text{Divide common factors.}$$

$$72 + 15x + 45 = 23x + 69 \quad \text{Multiply.}$$

$$15x + 117 = 23x + 69 \quad \text{Simplify.}$$

$$48 = 8x \quad \text{Subtract } 15x \text{ and } 69.$$

$$6 = x \quad \text{Divide.}$$

CHECK

$$\frac{4}{x+3} + \frac{5}{6} = \frac{23}{18} \quad \text{Original equation}$$

$$\frac{4}{6+3} + \frac{5}{6} \stackrel{?}{=} \frac{23}{18} \quad x = 6$$

$$\frac{4}{9} + \frac{5}{6} \stackrel{?}{=} \frac{23}{18} \quad \text{Simplify.}$$

$$\frac{8}{18} + \frac{15}{18} \stackrel{?}{=} \frac{23}{18} \quad \text{Simplify.}$$

$$\frac{23}{18} = \frac{23}{18} \checkmark \quad \text{Add.}$$

Guided Practice

Solve each equation. Check your solution.

1A. $\frac{2}{x+3} + \frac{3}{2} = \frac{19}{10}$ 2

1B. $\frac{7}{12} + \frac{9}{x-4} = \frac{55}{48}$ 20

Personal Tutor glencoe.com

Lesson 9-6 Resources

Resource	Approaching-Level	On-Level	Beyond-Level	English Learners
Teacher Edition		• Differentiated Instruction, pp. 598, 602	• Differentiated Instruction, pp. 598, 602	• Differentiated Instruction, p. 598
Chapter Resource Masters	• Study Guide and Intervention, pp. 39–40 • Skills Practice, p. 41 • Practice, p. 42 • Word Problem Practice, p. 43	• Study Guide and Intervention, pp. 39–40 • Skills Practice, p. 41 • Practice, p. 42 • Word Problem Practice, p. 43 • Enrichment, p. 44	• Practice, p. 42 • Word Problem Practice, p. 43 • Enrichment, p. 44	• Study Guide and Intervention, pp. 39–40 • Skills Practice, p. 41 • Practice, p. 42 • Word Problem Practice, p. 43
Transparencies	• 5-Minute Check Transparency 9-6	• 5-Minute Check Transparency 9-6	• 5-Minute Check Transparency 9-6	• 5-Minute Check Transparency 9-6
Other	• Study Notebook	• Study Notebook	• Study Notebook	• Study Notebook

Multiplying each side of an equation by the LCD of rational expressions can yield results that are not solutions of the original equation. These are extraneous solutions.

EXAMPLE 2 Solve a Rational Equation

Solve $\frac{2x}{x+5} - \frac{x^2 - x - 10}{x^2 + 8x + 15} = \frac{3}{x+3}$. Check your solution.

The LCD for the terms is $(x + 3)(x + 5)$.

$$\frac{2x}{x+5} - \frac{x^2 - x - 10}{x^2 + 8x + 15} = \frac{3}{x+3}$$ **Original equation**

$$\frac{(x+3)(x+5)(2x)}{x+5} - \frac{(x+3)(x+5)(x^2 - x - 10)}{x^2 + 8x + 15} = \frac{(x+3)(x+5)3}{x+3}$$ **Multiply by LCD.**

$$\frac{(x+3)\overset{1}{\cancel{(x+5)}}(2x)}{\underset{1}{\cancel{x+5}}} - \frac{\overset{1}{\cancel{(x+3)}}\overset{1}{\cancel{(x+5)}}(x^2 - x - 10)}{\underset{1}{\cancel{x^2 + 8x + 15}}} = \frac{(x+5)\overset{1}{\cancel{(x+3)}}3}{\underset{1}{\cancel{x+3}}}$$ **Divide common factors.**

$$(x + 3)(2x) - (x^2 - x - 10) = 3(x + 5)$$ **Simplify.**

$$2x^2 + 6x - x^2 + x + 10 = 3x + 15$$ **Distribute.**

$$x^2 + 7x + 10 = 3x + 15$$ **Simplify.**

$$x^2 + 4x - 5 = 0$$ **Subtract $3x + 15$.**

$$(x + 5)(x - 1) = 0$$ **Factor.**

$$x + 5 = 0 \quad \text{or} \quad x - 1 = 0$$ **Zero Product Property**

$$x = -5 \qquad\qquad x = 1$$

CHECK Try $x = -5$.

$$\frac{2x}{x+5} - \frac{x^2 - x - 10}{x^2 + 8x + 15} = \frac{3}{x+3}$$

$$\frac{2(-5)}{-5+5} - \frac{(-5)^2 - (-5) - 10}{(-5)^2 + 8(-5) + 15} \stackrel{?}{=} \frac{3}{-5+3}$$

$$\frac{-10}{0} - \frac{25 + 5 - 10}{25 - 40 + 15} \neq -\frac{3}{2} \ \text{✗}$$

Try $x = 1$.

$$\frac{2x}{x+5} - \frac{x^2 - x - 10}{x^2 + 8x + 15} = \frac{3}{x+3}$$

$$\frac{2(1)}{1+5} - \frac{1^2 - 1 - 10}{1^2 + 8(1) + 15} \stackrel{?}{=} \frac{3}{1+3}$$

$$\frac{2}{6} - \frac{-10}{24} \stackrel{?}{=} \frac{3}{4}$$

$$\frac{8}{24} + \frac{10}{24} \stackrel{?}{=} \frac{3}{4}$$

$$\frac{3}{4} = \frac{3}{4} \ \checkmark$$

When solving a rational equation, any possible solution that results in a zero in the denominator must be excluded from your list of solutions.

Since $x = -5$ results in a zero in the denominator, it is extraneous. Eliminate -5 from the list of solutions. The solution is 1.

Guided Practice

2A. $\frac{5}{y-2} + 2 = \frac{17}{6}$ **8**

2B. $\frac{2}{z+1} - \frac{1}{z-1} = \frac{-2}{z^2-1}$ **no solutions**

2C. $\frac{7n}{3n+3} - \frac{5}{4n-4} = \frac{3n}{2n+2}$ **$-\frac{1}{2}$, 3**

2D. $\frac{1}{p-2} = \frac{2p+1}{p^2+2p-8} + \frac{2}{p+4}$ **$\frac{7}{3}$**

Personal Tutor glencoe.com

Math History Link

Brook Taylor (1685–1731) English mathematician Taylor developed a theorem used in calculus known as Taylor's Theorem that relies on the remainders after computations with rational expressions.

Review Vocabulary

extraneous solutions solutions that do not satisfy the original equation (Lesson 7-7)

Solve Rational Equations

Example 1 shows how to solve a rational equation. **Example 2** shows how to solve a rational equation and eliminate any extraneous solutions. **Examples 3–5** show how to use rational equations to solve mixture, distance, and work problems.

Formative Assessment

Use the Guided Practice exercises after each example to determine students' understanding of concepts.

Additional Examples

1 Solve $\frac{5}{24} + \frac{2}{3-x} = \frac{1}{4}$. Check your solution. $x = -45$

2 Solve $\frac{p^2 - p - 5}{p+1} = \frac{p^2 - 7}{p-1} + p$. Check your solution. $p = -3, -2, 2$

Additional Examples also in Interactive Classroom PowerPoint® Presentations

IWB INTERACTIVE WHITEBOARD READY

Focus on Mathematical Content

Solving Rational Equations During the solution process, a rational equation is usually transformed into another type of equation. Solving a rational equation may require solving a related linear, quadratic, or other type of equation.

Watch Out!

Preventing Misconceptions Remind students that a possible solution must always be checked in the original equation, rather than in any of the steps of the solution. However, it is not permissible simply to substitute the solution for the variable and then multiply both sides of the equation by the LCD, because the truth of the equation is being tested.

Additional Example

3 **BRINE** Aaron adds an 80% brine (salt and water) solution to 16 ounces of solution that is 10% brine. How much of the solution should be added to create a solution that is 50% brine? $21\frac{1}{3}$ ounces

The **weighted average** is a method for finding the mean of a set of numbers in which some elements of the set carry more importance, or weight, than others. Many real-world problems involving mixtures, work, distance, and interest can be solved by using rational equations.

StudyTip

Tables Tables like the one in Example 3 are useful in organizing and solving mixture, work, weighted average, and distance problems.

Real-World EXAMPLE 3 Mixture Problem

CHEMISTRY Mia adds a 70% acid solution to 12 milliliters of a solution that is 15% acid. How much of the 70% acid solution should be added to create a solution that is 60% acid?

Understand Mia needs to know how much of a solution needs to be added to an original solution to create a new solution.

Plan Each solution has a certain percentage that is acid. The percentage of acid in the final solution must equal the amount of acid divided by the total solution.

	Original	Added	New
Amount of Acid	0.15(12)	0.7(x)	0.15(12) + 0.7x
Total Solution	12	x	12 + x

$$\text{Percentage of acid in solution} = \frac{\text{amount of acid}}{\text{total solution}}$$

Solve

$$\frac{\text{percent}}{100} = \frac{\text{amount of acid}}{\text{total solution}}$$ **Write a proportion.**

$$\frac{60}{100} = \frac{0.15(12) + 0.7x}{12 + x}$$ **Substitute.**

$$\frac{60}{100} = \frac{1.8 + 0.7x}{12 + x}$$ **Simplify numerator.**

$$100(12 + x)\frac{60}{100} = 100(12 + x)\frac{1.8 + 0.7x}{12 + x}$$ **LCD is 100(12 + x). Multiply by LCD.**

$$\overset{1}{\cancel{100}}(12 + x)\frac{60}{\underset{1}{\cancel{100}}} = 100(\underset{1}{\cancel{12 + x}})\frac{1.8 + 0.7x}{\underset{1}{\cancel{12 + x}}}$$ **Divide common factors.**

$$(12 + x)60 = 100(1.8 + 0.7x)$$ **Simplify.**

$$720 + 60x = 180 + 70x$$ **Distribute.**

$$540 = 10x$$ **Subtract 60x and 180.**

$$54 = x$$ **Divide by 10.**

Check

$$\frac{60}{100} = \frac{0.15(12) + 0.7x}{12 + x}$$ **Original equation**

$$\frac{60}{100} \stackrel{?}{=} \frac{0.15(12) + 0.7(54)}{12 + 54}$$ **x = 54**

$$\frac{60}{100} \stackrel{?}{=} \frac{37.8}{66}$$ **Simplify.**

$$0.6 = 0.6 \checkmark$$ **Simplify.**

Mia needs to add 54 milliliters of the 70% acid solution.

Real-World Link

Training future politicians in chemistry and science will assure their ability to write science policy bills from an intelligent point of view, and will guarantee future funding for science.

Source: *Chemical Education Journal*

Guided Practice

3. Jimmy adds a 65% fruit juice solution to 15 milliliters of a drink that is 10% fruit juice. How much of the 65% fruit juice solution must be added to create a fruit punch that is 35% fruit juice? 12.5 mL

Personal Tutor glencoe.com

596 Chapter 9 Rational Functions and Relations

The formula relating distance, rate, and time can also be used to solve rational equations. The most common use is $d = rt$. However, it can also be represented by $r = \frac{d}{t}$ and $t = \frac{d}{r}$.

Real-World EXAMPLE 4 Distance Problem

ROWING Sandra is rowing a canoe on Stanhope Lake. Her rate in still water is 6 miles per hour. It takes Sandra 3 hours to travel 10 miles round trip. Assuming that Sandra rowed at a constant rate of speed, determine the rate of the current.

Understand We are given her speed in still water and the time it takes her to travel with the current and against it. We need to determine the speed of the current.

Plan She traveled 5 miles with the current and 5 miles against it. The formula that relates distance, rate, and time is $d = rt$, or $t = \frac{d}{r}$.

Time with the Current	Time Against the Current	Total Time
$\frac{5}{6+r}$	$\frac{5}{6-r}$	3 hours

Solve

$$\frac{5}{6+r} + \frac{5}{6-r} = 3$$ **Write the equation.**

$$(6+r)(6-r)\frac{5}{6+r} + (6+r)(6-r)\frac{5}{6-r} = (6+r)(6-r)3$$ **LCD = (6 + r)(6 − r) Multiply by LCD.**

$$\overset{}{\underset{1}{\cancel{(6+r)}}}(6-r)\frac{5}{\underset{1}{\cancel{6+r}}} + (6+r)\underset{1}{\cancel{(6-r)}}\frac{5}{\underset{1}{\cancel{6-r}}} = (6+r)(6-r)3$$ **Divide common factors.**

$$(6-r)5 + (6+r)5 = (36-r^2)3$$ **Simplify.**

$$30 - 5r + 30 + 5r = 108 - 3r^2$$ **Distribute.**

$$60 = 108 - 3r^2$$ **Simplify.**

$$0 = -3r^2 + 48$$ **Subtract 10r.**

$$0 = -3(r+4)(r-4)$$ **Factor.**

$$0 = (r+4)(r-4)$$ **Divide each side by −3.**

$$r = 4 \text{ or } -4$$ **Zero Product Property**

Check

$$\frac{5}{6+r} + \frac{5}{6-r} = 3$$ **Original equation**

$$\frac{5}{6+4} + \frac{5}{6-4} \stackrel{?}{=} 3$$ **$r = 4$**

$$\frac{5}{10} + \frac{5}{2} \stackrel{?}{=} 3$$ **Simplify.**

$$\frac{1}{2} + \frac{5}{2} = \frac{6}{2} \checkmark$$ **Simplify.**

Since speed cannot be negative, the speed of the current is 4 miles per hour.

Guided Practice

4. FLYING The speed of the wind is 20 miles per hour. If it takes a plane 7 hours to fly 2368 miles round trip, determine the plane's speed in still air. **339.5 mph**

Personal Tutor glencoe.com

StudyTip

Distance Problems When distances involve round trips, the distance in one direction usually equals the distance in the other direction.

Additional Example

4 SWIMMING Lilia swims for 5 hours in a stream that has a current of 1 mile per hour. She leaves her dock, swims upstream for 2 miles and then swims back to her dock. What is her swimming speed in still water? about 1.5 mi/h

Watch Out!

Avoiding Misconceptions In Example 4, make sure that students understand the difference between the solutions of the quadratic equation (of which there are two) and the solution of the problem (of which there is only one).

Preventing Errors When solving rational equations, students often forget that *all* terms in the equation must be multiplied by the LCD. Remind them to do so in order to obtain equivalent equations.

Lesson 9-6 Solving Rational Equations and Inequalities 597

Watch Out!

Preventing Errors Suggest that when a problem involves completing part of a job while working together, students think about what part of the work gets done in one day, or one year, or one unit of the time.

Additional Example

5 **MOWING LAWNS** Wuyi and Uima mow lawns together. Wuyi working alone could complete a particular job in 4.5 hours, and Uima could complete it alone in 3.7 hours. How long does it take to complete the job when they work together? about 2 hours

Tips for New Teachers

Alternative Method The equation in Example 5 could also be solved by first subtracting $\frac{1}{24}$ from each side. Then find the cross products and solve.

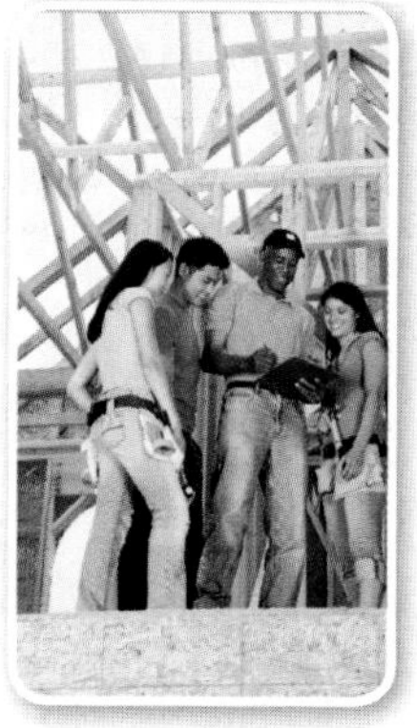

Real-World Link

Since 1997, students from Rock Point School in Burlington, Vermont, spend a week servicing communities throughout the world. While working with Habitat for Humanity, the students spent the time in rural Tennessee, starting and completing the roof of a Habitat home in one week.

Source: Vermont Community Work

Real-world problems that involve work can often be solved using rational equations.

Real-World EXAMPLE 5 Work Problems

COMMUNITY SERVICE **Every year, the junior and senior classes at Hillcrest High School build a house for the community. If it takes the senior class 24 days to complete a house and 18 days if they work with the junior class, how long would it take the junior class to complete a house if they worked alone?**

Understand We are given how long it takes the senior class working alone and when the classes work together. We need to determine how long it would take the junior class by themselves.

Plan The senior class can complete 1 house in 24 days, so their rate is $\frac{1}{24}$ of a house per day.

The rate for the junior class is $\frac{1}{j}$.

The combined rate for both classes is $\frac{1}{18}$.

Senior Rate	Junior Rate	Combined Rate
$\frac{1}{24}$	$\frac{1}{j}$	$\frac{1}{18}$

Solve

$\frac{1}{24} + \frac{1}{j} = \frac{1}{18}$ — **Write the equation.**

$72j\,\frac{1}{24} + 72j\,\frac{1}{j} = 72j\,\frac{1}{18}$ — **LCD = 72*j*** **Multiply by LCD.**

$\overset{3}{\cancel{72}}j\,\frac{1}{\underset{1}{\cancel{24}}} + 72\overset{1}{\cancel{j}}\,\frac{1}{\underset{1}{\cancel{j}}} = \overset{4}{\cancel{72}}j\,\frac{1}{\underset{1}{\cancel{18}}}$ — **Divide common factors.**

$3j + 72 = 4j$ — **Distribute.**

$72 = j$ — **Subtract 3*j*.**

Check Two methods are possible.

Method 1 Substitute values.

$\frac{1}{24} + \frac{1}{j} = \frac{1}{18}$ — **Original equation**

$\frac{1}{24} + \frac{1}{72} \stackrel{?}{=} \frac{1}{18}$ — ***j* = 72**

$\frac{3}{72} + \frac{1}{72} \stackrel{?}{=} \frac{4}{72}$ — **LCD = 72**

$\frac{4}{72} = \frac{4}{72}$ ✓ — **Simplify.**

Method 2 Use a calculator.

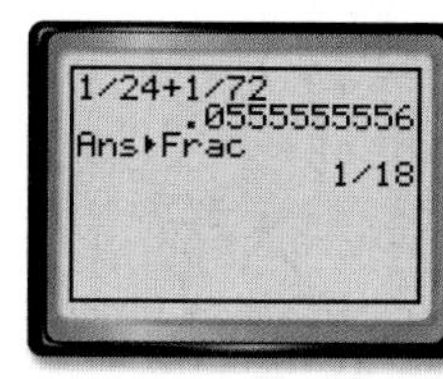

It would take the junior class 72 days to complete the house by themselves.

Guided Practice

5A. It took Anthony and Travis 6 hours to rake the leaves together last year. The previous year it took Travis 10 hours to do it alone. How long will it take Anthony if he rakes them by himself this year? 15 hours

5B. Noah and Owen paint houses together. If Noah can paint a particular house in 6 days and Owen can paint the same house in 5 days, how long would it take the two of them if they work together? $2\frac{8}{11}$ days

Personal Tutor glencoe.com

Differentiated Instruction

OL BL ELL

Logical Learners Have students think about the difference between "pure" mathematics, such as solving an equation, and "applied" mathematics, such as solving a real-world problem. Ask them to list some ways in which these two are alike and some ways in which they are different.

598 Chapter 9 Rational Functions and Relations

Solve Rational Inequalities To solve **rational inequalities**, which are inequalities that contain one or more rational expressions, follow these steps.

Key Concept — Solving Rational Inequalities

Step 1 State the excluded values. These are the values for which the denominator is 0.

Step 2 Solve the related equation.

Step 3 Use the values determined from the previous steps to divide a number line into intervals.

Step 4 Test a value in each interval to determine which intervals contain values that satisfy the inequality.

EXAMPLE 6 Solve a Rational Inequality

Solve $\frac{x}{3} - \frac{1}{x-2} < \frac{x+1}{4}$.

Step 1 The excluded value for this inequality is 2.

Step 2 Solve the related equation.

$\frac{x}{3} - \frac{1}{x-2} = \frac{x+1}{4}$	**Related equation**
$\overset{4}{\cancel{12}}(x-2)\frac{x}{\underset{1}{\cancel{3}}} - \overset{1}{12(\cancel{x-2})}\frac{1}{\underset{1}{\cancel{x-2}}} = \overset{3}{\cancel{12}}(x-2)\frac{x+1}{\underset{1}{\cancel{4}}}$	**LCD is 12(x − 2). Multiply by LCD.**
$4x^2 - 8x - 12 = 3x^2 - 3x - 6$	**Distribute.**
$x^2 - 5x - 6 = 0$	**Subtract $3x^2 - 3x - 6$.**
$(x-6)(x+1) = 0$	**Factor.**
$x = 6$ or -1	**Zero Product Property**

Step 3 Draw vertical lines at the excluded value and at the solutions to separate the number line into intervals.

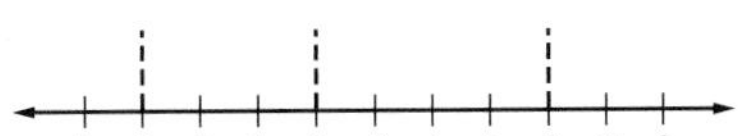

Step 4 Now test a sample value in each interval to determine whether the values in the interval satisfy the inequality.

Test $x = -3$.

$\frac{-3}{3} - \frac{1}{-3-2} \overset{?}{<} \frac{-3+1}{4}$

$-1 + \frac{1}{5} \overset{?}{<} -\frac{2}{4}$

$-\frac{4}{5} < -\frac{1}{2}$ ✓

Test $x = 0$.

$\frac{0}{3} - \frac{1}{0-2} \overset{?}{<} \frac{0+1}{4}$

$0 + \frac{1}{2} \overset{?}{<} \frac{1}{4}$

$\frac{1}{2} \not< \frac{1}{4}$

Test $x = 4$.

$\frac{4}{3} - \frac{1}{4-2} \overset{?}{<} \frac{4+1}{4}$

$\frac{4}{3} - \frac{1}{2} \overset{?}{<} \frac{5}{4}$

$\frac{5}{6} < \frac{5}{4}$

Test $x = 8$.

$\frac{8}{3} - \frac{1}{8-2} \overset{?}{<} \frac{8+1}{4}$

$\frac{32}{12} - \frac{2}{12} \overset{?}{<} \frac{27}{12}$

$\frac{30}{12} \not< \frac{27}{12}$

The statement is true for $x = -3$ and $x = 4$. Therefore, the solution is $x < -1$ or $2 < x < 6$.

StudyTip

Rational Inequalities It is possible that none or all of the intervals will produce a true statement.

Guided Practice Solve each inequality.

6A. $\frac{5}{x} + \frac{6}{5x} > \frac{2}{3}$ $0 < x < 9.3$

6B. $\frac{4}{3x} + \frac{7}{x} < \frac{5}{9}$ $x < 0$ or $x > 15$

Personal Tutor glencoe.com

Solve Rational Inequalities

Example 6 shows how to solve a rational inequality.

Additional Example

6 Solve $\frac{1}{3k} + \frac{2}{9k} < \frac{2}{3}$. $k < 0$ or $k > \frac{5}{6}$

Watch Out!

Preventing Errors Suggest that students also verify whether the boundary indicated by the solution of the equation is or is not in the solution set of the inequality.

TEACH with TECH

DOCUMENT CAMERA Choose a student to show and explain how to solve a rational inequality. Be sure the student shows how to use test points and a sign chart to find the solution set.

Lesson 9-6 Solving Rational Equations and Inequalities 599

3 PRACTICE

Formative Assessment

Use Exercises 1–15 to check for understanding.

Use the chart at the bottom of this page to customize assignments for your students.

Exercise Alert

Grid Paper For Exercises 33 and 47–49, students will need grid paper.

Check Your Understanding

Examples 1 and 2 pp. 594–595

Solve each equation. Check your solution.

1. $\frac{4}{7}+\frac{3}{x-3}=\frac{53}{56}$ 11
2. $\frac{7}{3}-\frac{3}{x-5}=\frac{19}{12}$ 9
3. $\frac{10}{2x+1}+\frac{4}{3}=2$ 7
4. $\frac{11}{4}-\frac{5}{y+3}=\frac{23}{12}$ 3
5. $\frac{8}{x-5}-\frac{9}{x-4}=\frac{5}{x^2-9x+20}$ 8
6. $\frac{14}{x+3}+\frac{10}{x-2}=\frac{122}{x^2+x-6}$ 5
7. $\frac{14}{x-8}-\frac{5}{x-6}=\frac{82}{x^2-14x+48}$ 14
8. $\frac{5}{x+2}-\frac{3}{x-2}=\frac{12}{x^2-4}$ 14

Example 3 p. 596

9. **MIXTURES** Sara has 10 pounds of dried fruit selling for \$6.25 per pound. She wants to know how many pounds of mixed nuts selling for \$4.50 per pound she needs to make a trail mix selling for \$5 per pound.

   a. Let m = the number of pounds of mixed nuts. Complete the following table.

	Pounds	Price per Pound	Total Price
Dried Fruit	10	\$6.25	6.25(10)
Mixed Nuts	m	\$4.50	$4.5m$
Trail Mix	$10 + m$	\$5.00	$5(10 + m)$

   b. Write a rational equation using the last column of the table. $62.5 + 4.5m = 50 + 5m$

   c. Solve the equation to determine how many pounds of mixed nuts are needed. 25

Example 4 p. 597

10. **DISTANCE** Alicia's average speed riding her bike is 11.5 miles per hour. She takes a round trip of 40 miles. It takes her 1 hour and 20 minutes with the wind and 2 hours and 30 minutes against the wind.

    a. Write an expression for Alicia's time with the wind. $\frac{20}{11.5+x}$

    b. Write an expression for Alicia's time against the wind. $\frac{20}{11.5-x}$

    c. How long does it take to complete the trip? 3 h and 50 min

    d. Write and solve the rational equation to determine the speed of the wind.

10d. $\frac{20}{11.5+x}+\frac{20}{11.5-x}=\frac{23}{6}$; 3.5 mph

Example 5 p. 598

11. **WORK** Kendal and Chandi wax cars. Kendal can wax a particular car in 60 minutes and Chandi can wax the same car in 80 minutes. They plan on waxing the same car together and want to know how long it will take.

    a. How much will Kendal complete in 1 minute? $\frac{1}{60}$

    b. How much will Kendal complete in x minutes? $\frac{x}{60}$

    c. How much will Chandi complete in 1 minute? $\frac{1}{80}$

    d. How much will Chandi complete in x minutes? $\frac{x}{80}$

    e. Write a rational equation representing Kendal and Chandi working together on the car. $\frac{x}{60}+\frac{x}{80}=1$

    f. Solve the equation to determine how long it will take them to finish the car. about 34.3 min

Example 6 p. 599

Solve each inequality. Check your solutions.

12. $\frac{3}{5x}+\frac{1}{6x}>\frac{2}{3}$ $0 < x < 1.15$
13. $\frac{1}{4c}+\frac{1}{9c}<\frac{1}{2}$ $c < 0$, or $\frac{13}{18} < c$
14. $\frac{4}{3y}+\frac{2}{5y}<\frac{3}{2}$ $y > \frac{52}{45}$, or $y < 0$
15. $\frac{1}{3b}+\frac{1}{4b}<\frac{1}{5}$ $b < 0$, or $\frac{35}{12} < b$

Differentiated Homework Options

Level	Assignment	Two-Day Option	
AL Basic	16–30, 36, 38–54	17–29 odd, 40–43	16–30 even, 36, 38–40, 44–54
OL Core	17–29 odd, 31–36, 38–54	16–30, 40–43	31–36, 38–39, 44–54
BL Advanced	31–51, (optional: 52–54)		

600 Chapter 9 Rational Functions and Relations

Practice and Problem Solving

● = Step-by-Step Solutions begin on page R20.
Extra Practice begins on page 947.

Examples 1 and 2 pp. 594–595

Solve each equation. Check your solutions.

16. $\frac{9}{x-7} - \frac{7}{x-6} = \frac{13}{x^2 - 13x + 42}$ **9**

17. $\frac{13}{y+3} - \frac{12}{y+4} = \frac{18}{y^2 + 7y + 12}$ **2**

18. $\frac{14}{x-2} - \frac{18}{x+1} = \frac{22}{x^2 - x - 2}$ **7**

19. $\frac{11}{a+2} - \frac{10}{a+5} = \frac{36}{a^2 + 7a + 10}$ **1**

20. $\frac{x}{2x-1} + \frac{3}{x+4} = \frac{-21}{2x^2 + 7x - 4}$ **−2.35, −7.65**

21. $\frac{2}{y-5} + \frac{y-1}{2y+1} = \frac{2}{2y^2 - 9y - 5}$ **∅**

Examples 3–5 pp. 596–598

22. **CHEMISTRY** How many milliliters of a 20% acid solution must be added to 40 milliliters of a 75% acid solution to create a 30% acid solution? **180 mL**

23. **GROCERIES** Ellen bought 3 pounds of bananas for \$0.90 per pound. How many pounds of apples costing \$1.25 per pound must she purchase so that the total cost for fruit is \$1 per pound? **1.2 lb**

24. **BUILDING** Bryan's volunteer group can build a garage in 12 hours. Sequoia's group can build it in 16 hours. How long would it take them if they worked together?

Example 6 p. 599

Solve each inequality. Check your solutions.

25. $3 - \frac{4}{x} > \frac{5}{4x}$

26. $\frac{5}{3a} - \frac{3}{4a} > \frac{5}{6}$ **$0 < a < 1.1$**

27. $\frac{x-2}{x+2} + \frac{1}{x-2} > \frac{x-4}{x-2}$

28. $\frac{3}{4} - \frac{1}{x-3} > \frac{x}{x+4}$

29. $\frac{x}{5} + \frac{2}{3} < \frac{3}{x-4}$

30. $\frac{x}{x+2} + \frac{1}{x-1} < \frac{3}{2}$

31. **AIR TRAVEL** It takes a plane 20 hours to fly to its destination against the wind. The return trip takes 16 hours. If the plane's average speed in still air is 500 miles per hour, what is the average speed of the wind during the flight? **55.56 mph**

32. **FINANCIAL LITERACY** Judie wants to invest \$10,000 in two different accounts. The risky account could earn 9% interest, while the other account earns 5% interest. She wants to earn \$750 interest for the year. Of tables, graphs, or equations, choose the best representation needed and determine how much should be invested in each account.

33. **MULTIPLE REPRESENTATIONS** Consider $\frac{2}{x-3} + \frac{1}{x} = \frac{x-1}{x-3}$. **b. See margin.**

a. **ALGEBRAIC** Solve the equation for x. Were any values of x extraneous? **1; yes; 3**

b. **GRAPHICAL** Graph $y_1 = \frac{2}{x-3} + \frac{1}{x}$ and $y_2 = \frac{x-1}{x-3}$ on the same graph for $0 < x < 5$.

c. **ANALYTICAL** For what value(s) of x do they intersect? Do they intersect where x is extraneous for the original equation? **1; no**

d. **VERBAL** Use this knowledge to describe how you can use a graph to determine whether an apparent solution of a rational equation is extraneous.

Solve each equation. Check your solutions.

34. $\frac{2}{y+3} - \frac{3}{4-y} = \frac{2y-2}{y^2 - y - 12}$ **−1**

35. $\frac{2}{y+2} - \frac{y}{2-y} = \frac{y^2+4}{y^2-4}$ **∅**

H.O.T. Problems

Use Higher-Order Thinking Skills

36. **OPEN ENDED** Give an example of a rational equation that can be solved by multiplying each side of the equation by $4(x+3)(x-4)$.

37. **CHALLENGE** Solve $\frac{1 + \frac{9}{x} + \frac{20}{x^2}}{1 - \frac{25}{x^2}} = \frac{x+4}{x-5}$. **all real numbers except 5, −5, 0**

38. **WRITING IN MATH** While using the table feature on the graphing calculator to explore $f(x) = \frac{1}{x^2 - x - 6}$, the values −2 and 3 say "ERROR." Explain its meaning.

39. **REASONING** Explain why solutions of rational inequalities need to be checked.

24. about 6.86 hours

25. $x < 0$ or $x > 1.75$

27. $x < -2$, or $2 < x < 14$

28. $-4 < x < 3$

29. $x < -5$ or $4 < x < \frac{17}{3}$

30. $2 < x$, $-2 < x < 1$, $x < -5$

32. \$6250 at 9% and \$3750 at 5%

33d. Graph both sides of the equation. Where the graphs intersect, there is a solution. If they do not, then the possible solution is extraneous.

36. Sample answer: $\frac{4}{x+3} = \frac{x}{x-4} + \frac{7}{4}$

38. Sample answer: The values −3 and 2 are undefined values. On the graph of $f(x)$ these values would be vertical asymptotes.

39. Sample answer: Multiplying both sides of a rational inequality can produce extraneous solutions.

Additional Answer

33b.

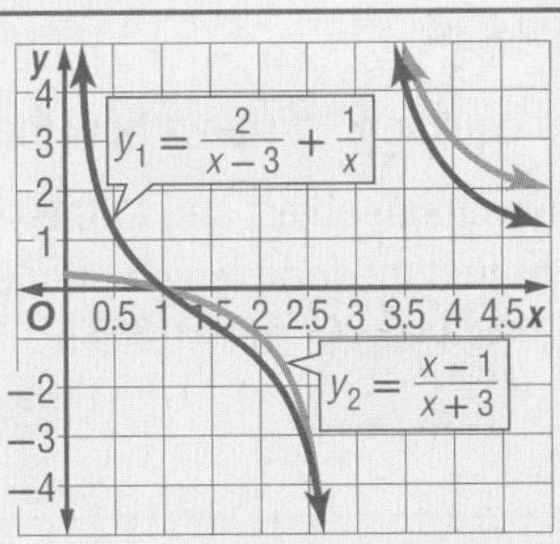

Enrichment

CRM p. 44 OL BL

9-6 Enrichment

Asymptotes in Three-Dimensions

In the same way that lines can be asymptotes to a graph in two-dimensions, a plane can be an asymptote to a three-dimensional graph. The curve graphed by $z = x + y$ has no asymptotes. The value of z approaches negative infinity as x and y approach negative infinity; the value of z approaches positive infinity as x and y approach positive infinity. On the other hand, the curve $z = \frac{1}{x} + \frac{1}{y}$ does have an asymptote and hole. The curve is undefined for the planes $x = 0$ and for $y = 0$. The plane $z = 0$ is an asymptote because the curve approaches this plane as x and y grow infinitely positive or as x and y grow infinitely negative.

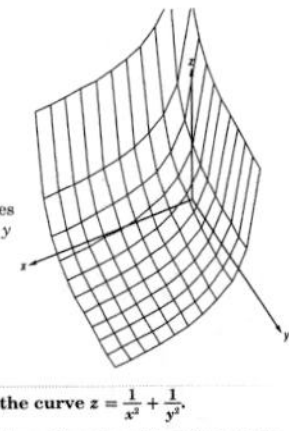

Example Identify holes and asymptotes for the curve $z = \frac{1}{x^2} + \frac{1}{y^2}$.

Because x^2 and y^2 are the denominators of fractions, the three-dimensional function must be undefined where undefined for the planes $x = 0$ and for $y = 0$. In addition, as x and y grow infinitely positive or as x and y grow infinitely negative, z approaches but does not reach 0.

Study Guide and Intervention

CRM pp. 39–40 AL OL ELL

9-6 Study Guide and Intervention

Solving Rational Equations and Inequalities

Lesson 9-6

Solve Rational Equations A **rational equation** contains one or more rational expressions. To solve a rational equation, first multiply each side by the least common denominator of all of the denominators. Be sure to exclude any solution that would produce a denominator of zero.

Example Solve $\frac{9}{10} + \frac{2}{x+1} = \frac{2}{5}$. Check your solution.

$\frac{9}{10} + \frac{2}{x+1} = \frac{2}{5}$ Original equation

$10(x+1)\left(\frac{9}{10} + \frac{2}{x+1}\right) = 10(x+1)\left(\frac{2}{5}\right)$ Multiply each side by $10(x+1)$.

$9(x+1) + 2(10) = 4(x+1)$ Multiply.

$9x + 9 + 20 = 4x + 4$ Distribute.

$5x = -25$ Subtract $4x$ and 29 from each side.

$x = -5$ Divide each side by 5.

Check $\frac{9}{10} + \frac{2}{x+1} = \frac{2}{5}$ Original equation

$\frac{9}{10} + \frac{2}{-5+1} \stackrel{?}{=} \frac{2}{5}$ $x = -5$

$\frac{18}{20} - \frac{10}{20} \stackrel{?}{=} \frac{2}{5}$ Simplify.

$\frac{2}{5} = \frac{2}{5}$

Exercises

Solve each equation. Check your solution.

1. $\frac{2y}{3} - \frac{y+3}{6} = 2$ **5**
2. $\frac{4t-3}{5} - \frac{4-2t}{3} = 1$ **2**
3. $\frac{2x+1}{3} - \frac{x-5}{4} = \frac{1}{2}$ **$-\frac{13}{5}$**
4. $\frac{3m+2}{5m} + \frac{2m-1}{2m} = 4$ **$-\frac{1}{24}$**
5. $\frac{4}{x-1} = \frac{x+1}{12}$ **±7**
6. $\frac{x}{x-2} + \frac{4}{x-2} = 10$ **$\frac{8}{3}$**

7. **NAVIGATION** The current in a river is 6 miles per hour. In her motorboat Marissa can travel 12 miles upstream or 16 miles downstream in the same amount of time. What is the speed of her motorboat in still water? Is this a reasonable answer? Explain.
42 mph; Sample answer: The answer is reasonable. The boat will travel 48 mph one way and 36 mph the other way. Therefore it will take $\frac{1}{3}$ of an hour to travel 16 miles and 12 miles, respectively.

8. **WORK** Adam, Bethany, and Carlos own a painting company. To paint a particular house alone, Adam estimates that it would take him 4 days, Bethany estimates $5\frac{1}{2}$ days, and Carlos 6 days. If these estimates are accurate, how long should it take the three of them to paint the house if they work together? Is this a reasonable answer?
about $1\frac{2}{3}$ days; Sample answer: The answer is reasonable. It will take each person about 5 days to paint the house alone, so it should take about $\frac{1}{3}$ of the time to paint the house together.

Chapter 9 39 Glencoe Algebra 2

Practice

CRM p. 42 AL OL BL ELL

9-6 Practice

Solving Rational Equations and Inequalities

Solve each equation or inequality. Check your solutions.

1. $\frac{12}{x} + \frac{3}{4} = \frac{3}{2}$ **16**
2. $\frac{x}{x-1} - 1 = \frac{x}{2}$ **−1, 2**
3. $\frac{p+10}{p^2-2} = \frac{4}{p}$ **$-\frac{2}{3}$, 4**
4. $\frac{s}{s+2} + s = \frac{5s+8}{s+2}$ **4**
5. $\frac{5}{y-5} = \frac{y}{y-5} - 1$ **all reals except 5**
6. $\frac{1}{3x-2} + \frac{5}{x} = 0$ **$\frac{5}{8}$**
7. $\frac{5}{t} < \frac{9}{2t+1}$ **$t < -5$ or $-\frac{1}{2} < t < 0$**
8. $\frac{1}{2h} + \frac{5}{h} = \frac{3}{h-1}$ **$\frac{11}{5}$**
9. $\frac{4}{w-2} = \frac{-1}{w+3}$ **−2**
10. $5 - \frac{3}{a} < \frac{7}{a}$ **$0 < a < 2$**
11. $\frac{4}{5x} + \frac{1}{10} < \frac{3}{2x}$ **$0 < x < 7$**
12. $8 + \frac{3}{y} > \frac{19}{y}$ **$y < 0$ or $y > 2$**
13. $\frac{4}{p} + \frac{1}{3p} < \frac{1}{5}$ **$p < 0$ or $p > \frac{65}{3}$**
14. $\frac{6}{x-1} = \frac{4}{x-2} + \frac{2}{x+1}$ **∅**
15. $g + \frac{g}{g-2} = \frac{2}{g-2}$ **−1**
16. $b + \frac{2b}{b-1} = 1 - \frac{b-3}{b-1}$ **−2**
17. $\frac{1}{n+2} + \frac{1}{n-2} = \frac{3}{n^2-4}$ **$\frac{3}{2}$**
18. $\frac{c+1}{c-3} = 4 - \frac{12}{c^2-2c-3}$ **$-\frac{5}{3}$, 5**
19. $\frac{3}{k-3} + \frac{4}{k-4} = \frac{25}{k^2-7k+12}$ **7**
20. $\frac{4v}{v-1} - \frac{5v}{v-2} = \frac{2}{v^2-3v+2}$ **−1, −2**
21. $\frac{y}{y+2} + \frac{7}{y-5} = \frac{14}{y^2-3y-10}$ **0**
22. $\frac{x^2+4}{x^2-4} + \frac{x}{2-x} = \frac{2}{x+2}$ **∅**
23. $\frac{r}{r+4} + \frac{4}{r-4} = \frac{r^2+16}{r^2-16}$ **all reals except −4 and 4**
24. $3 = \frac{6a-1}{2a+7} + \frac{22}{a+5}$ **−2**

27. **BASKETBALL** Kiana has made 9 of 19 free throws so far this season. Her goal is to make 60% of her free throws. If Kiana makes her next x free throws in a row, the function $f(x) = \frac{9+x}{19+x}$ represents Kiana's new ratio of free throws made. How many successful free throws in a row will raise Kiana's percent made to 60%? Is this a reasonable answer? Explain.
6; Sample answer: It is a reasonable answer. She will have made 15 out of 25 free throws, which is equivalent to 60%.

28. **OPTICS** The lens equation $\frac{1}{p} + \frac{1}{q} = \frac{1}{f}$ relates the distance p of an object from a lens, the distance q of the image of the object from the lens, and the focal length f of the lens. What is the distance of an object from a lens if the image of the object is 5 centimeters from the lens and the focal length of the lens is 4 centimeters? Is this a reasonable answer? Explain.
20 cm; Sample answer: It is a reasonable answer, since $\frac{1}{20} + \frac{1}{5} = \frac{1}{4}$.

Chapter 9 42 Glencoe Algebra 2

Word Problem Practice

CRM p. 43 AL OL BL ELL

9-6 Word Problem Practice

Solving Rational Equations and Inequalities

Lesson 9-6

1. **HEIGHT** Serena can be described as being 8 inches shorter than her sister Malia, or as being 12.5% shorter than Malia. In other words, $\frac{8}{H+8} = \frac{1}{8}$, where H is Serena's height in inches. How tall is Serena?
56 inches

2. **CRANES** For a wedding, Paula wants to fold 1000 origami cranes.

She does not want to make anyone fold more than 15 cranes. In other words, if N is the number of people enlisted to fold cranes, Paula wants $\frac{1000}{N} \le 15$. What is the minimum number of people that will satisfy this inequality?
67

3. **RENTAL** Carlos and his friends rent a car. They split the \$200 rental fee evenly. Carlos, together with just two of his friends, decide to rent a portable DVD player as well, and split the \$30 rental fee for the DVD player evenly among themselves. Carlos ends up spending \$50 for these rentals. Write an equation involving N, the number of friends Carlos has, using this information. Solve the equation for N.
$\frac{200}{N+1} + \frac{30}{3} = 50$; $N = 4$

4. **PROJECTILES** A projectile target is launched into the air. A rocket interceptor is fired at the target. The ratio of the altitude of the rocket to the altitude of the projectile t seconds after the launch of the rocket is given by the formula $\frac{333t}{-32t^2 + 420t + 27}$. At what time are the target and interceptor at the same altitude?
at $t = 3$ seconds

5. **FLIGHT TIME** The distance between John F. Kennedy International Airport and Los Angeles International Airport is about 2500 miles. Let S be the airspeed of a jet. The wind speed is 100 miles per hour. Because of the wind, it takes longer to fly one way than the other.

a. Write an equation for S if it takes 2 hours and 5 minutes longer to fly between New York and Los Angeles against the wind versus flying with the wind.
$\frac{2500}{S-100} - \frac{2500}{S+100} = 2\frac{1}{12}$

b. Solve the equation you wrote in part **a** for S.
500 mph

c. Write an equation and find how much longer to fly between New York and Los Angeles if the wind speed increases to 150 miles per hour and the airspeed of the jet is 525 miles per hour.
$\frac{2500}{525-150} - \frac{2500}{525+150} = x$; $x = \frac{400}{135} = 2.96$ h

Chapter 9 43 Glencoe Algebra 2

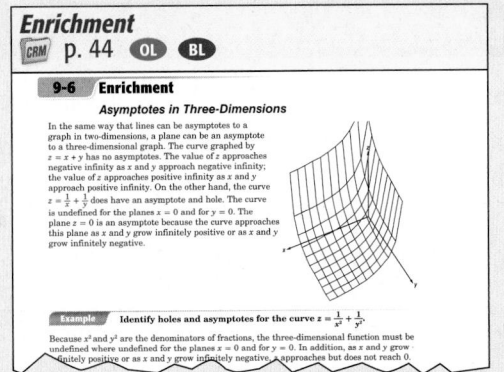

4 ASSESS

Name the Math Have students write their own real-world problems similar to those they have seen in this lesson but using their own data. Have students solve the problems.

Formative Assessment

Check for student understanding of concepts in Lesson 9-6.

CRM Quiz 4, p. 49

Additional Answers

47.

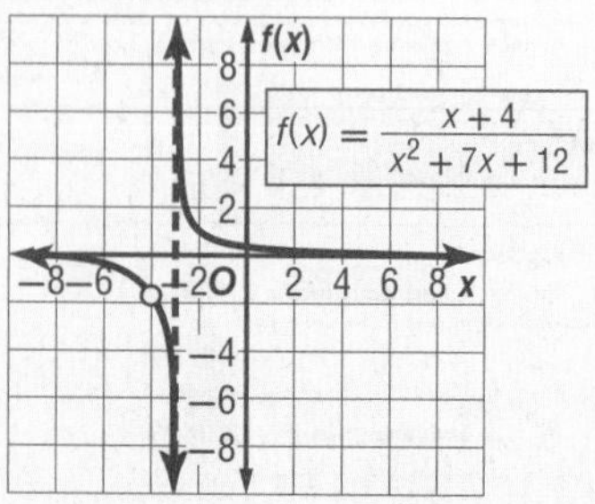

48.

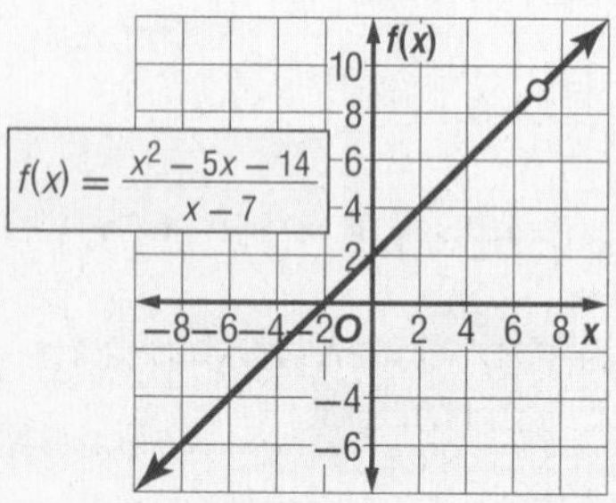

49.

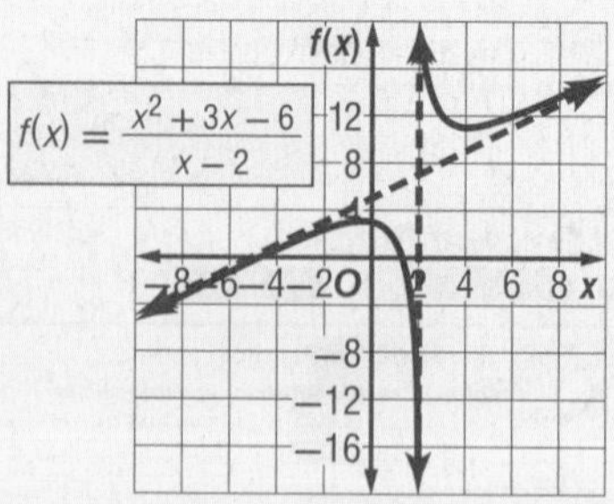

NGSSS PRACTICE 912.A.3.1, 912.A.6.5, 912.A.2.13

40. Nine pounds of mixed nuts containing 55% peanuts were mixed with 6 pounds of another kind of mixed nuts that contain 40% peanuts. What percent of the new mixture is peanuts? **C**

A. 58% B. 51% C. 49% D. 47%

41. Working alone, Dato can dig a 10-foot by 10-foot hole in five hours. Pedro can dig the same hole in six hours. How long would it take them if they worked together? **I**

F. 1.5 hours H. 2.52 hours
G. 2.34 hours I. 2.73 hours

42. An aircraft carrier made a trip to Guam and back. The trip there took three hours and the trip back took four hours. It averaged 6 kilometers per hour on the return trip. Find the average speed of the trip to Guam. **B**

A. 6 km/h C. 10 km/h
B. 8 km/h D. 12 km/h

43. **SHORT RESPONSE** If a line ℓ is perpendicular to a segment CD at point F and $CF = FD$, how many points on line ℓ are the same distance from point C as from point D? **all of the points**

Spiral Review

Determine whether each relation shows *direct* or *inverse* variation, or *neither*. (Lesson 9-5)

44. **inverse**

x	y
14	3
28	1.5
56	0.75
112	0.375

45. **direct**

x	y
0.2	24
0.6	72
1.8	216
5.4	648

46. **neither**

x	y
12	18
24	36
36	18
72	9

Graph each function. (Lesson 9-4) **47–49. See margin.**

47. $f(x) = \frac{x + 4}{x^2 + 7x + 12}$ **48.** $f(x) = \frac{x^2 - 5x - 14}{x - 7}$ **49.** $f(x) = \frac{x^2 + 3x - 6}{x - 2}$

50. WEATHER The atmospheric pressure P, in bars, of a given height on Earth is given by using the formula $P = a \cdot e^{-\frac{k}{H}}$. In the formula, a is the surface pressure on Earth, which is approximately 1 bar, k is the altitude for which you want to find the pressure in kilometers, and H is always 7 kilometers. (Lesson 8-7)

a. Find the pressure for 2, 4, and 7 kilometers. **0.75 bars; 0.56 bars; 0.37 bars**

b. What do you notice about the pressure as altitude increases? **The pressure decreases as the altitude increases.**

51. COMPUTERS Since computers have been invented, computational speed has multiplied by a factor of 4 about every three years. (Lesson 8-1)

a. If a typical computer operates with a computational speed s today, write an expression for the speed at which you can expect an equivalent computer to operate after x three-year periods. $\mathbf{s \cdot 4^x}$

b. Suppose your computer operates with a processor speed of 2.8 gigahertz and you want a computer that can operate at 5.6 gigahertz. If a computer with that speed is currently unavailable for home use, how long can you expect to wait until you can buy such a computer? **0.5 three-yr periods or 1.5 yr**

Skills Review

Determine whether the following are possible lengths of the sides of a right triangle. (Lesson 0-7)

52. 5, 12, 13 **yes** **53.** 60, 80, 100 **yes** **54.** 7, 24, 25 **yes**

Differentiated Instruction OL BL

Extension The equation $\frac{1}{f} = \frac{1}{d} + \frac{1}{i}$ is sometimes called the "lens equation." It shows how the focal length f of a lens is related to the distances d and i from the lens to an object and to the object's image as seen through the lens, respectively. Ask students to find the focal length of a lens if, for a particular object, d is measured to be 20 cm and i is 12 cm. Ask them to solve the lens equation for f in terms of d and i. 7.5 cm; $f = \frac{di}{d + i}$

Graphing Technology Lab
Solving Rational Equations and Inequalities

FL Math Online glencoe.com
- Other Calculator Keystrokes
- Graphing Technology Personal Tutor

NGSSS MA.912.A.5.5 Solve rational equations.

You can use a TI-83/84 Plus graphing calculator to solve rational equations by graphing or by using the table feature. Graph both sides of the equation, and locate the point(s) of intersection.

ACTIVITY 1 Rational Equation

Solve $\frac{4}{x+1} = \frac{3}{2}$.

Step 1 Graph each side of the equation.

Graph each side of the equation as a separate function. Enter $\frac{4}{x+1}$ as **Y1** and $\frac{3}{2}$ as **Y2**. Then graph the two equations.

KEYSTROKES: [Y=] 4 [÷] [(] [X,T,θ,n] [+] 1 [)] [ENTER] 3 [÷] 2 [ZOOM] 6

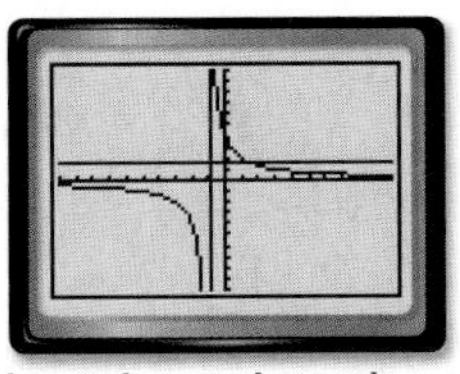

[−10, 10] scl: 1 by [−10, 10] scl: 1

Because the calculator is in connected mode, a vertical line may appear connecting the two branches of the hyperbola. This line is not part of the graph.

Step 2 Use the **intersect** feature.

The **intersect** feature on the **CALC** menu allows you to approximate the ordered pair of the point at which the graphs cross.

KEYSTROKES: [2nd] [CALC] 5

Select one graph and press [ENTER]. Select the other graph, press [ENTER], and press [ENTER] again.

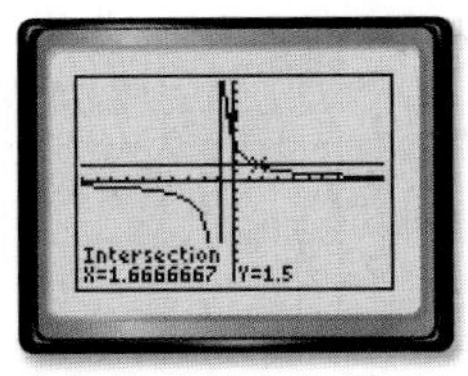

[−10, 10] scl: 1 by [−10, 10] scl: 1

The solution is $1\frac{2}{3}$.

Step 3 Use the **table** feature.

Verify the solution using the table feature. Set up the table to show x-values in increments of $\frac{1}{3}$.

KEYSTROKES: [2nd] [TblSet] 0 [ENTER] 1 [÷] 3 [ENTER] [2nd] [TABLE]

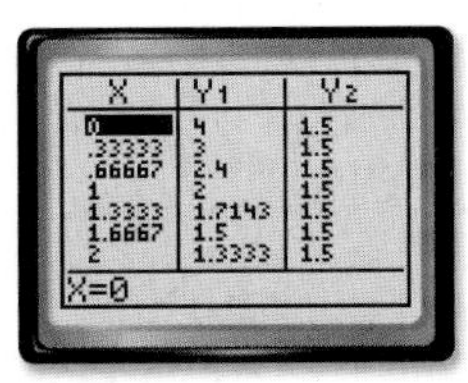

The table displays x-values and corresponding y-values for each graph. At $x = 1\frac{2}{3}$, both functions have a y-value of 1.5. Thus, the solution of the equation is $1\frac{2}{3}$.

1 FOCUS

Objective Use a graphing calculator to solve rational equations by graphing or by using the table feature.

Materials for Each Group

- TI-83/84 Plus or other graphing calculator

Teaching Tip

When students enter functions in the function editor, (Y = list), they should use parentheses around any numerator or denominator that is not a single number or variable.

2 TEACH

Working in Cooperative Groups

Have students work in pairs so they can help each other correct keystroke errors. Have pairs complete Activities 1 and 2 and Exercises 1 and 6.

Activity 1

- When using the intersect feature in Step 2, students should press to select the graph of each function. They will then be prompted for a **Guess?**. They should move the cursor close to an estimated point of intersection before pressing a third time.
- As an alternative to using the table feature in Step 3, students can verify the solution for each function directly on the home screen. Entering $Y_1 = (5/3)$ and $Y_2 = (5/3)$ will both produce results of 1.5.

Activity 2

- In Activity 2, since the graph of the inequality $y > 9$ begins at the top of the standard window screen, students may want to change the window for y to $[-10, 20]$.

Practice Have students complete Exercises 2–5 and 7–9.

3 ASSESS

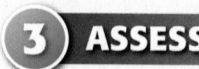

Formative Assessment

Use Exercise 2 to assess whether students comprehend how to find the intersection of the graphs of the left and right sides of a rational equation.

From Concrete to Abstract

Ask students to solve the equation $\frac{x}{2} = \frac{8}{x}$. They will find that the graphs of $y = \frac{x}{2}$ and $y = \frac{8}{x}$ intersect in two places. It is especially important in a case like this that they use the **intersect** feature correctly. In response to **Guess?,** they must first select one of the points of intersection, then repeat the **intersect** process and select the other point of intersection. The two solutions are $x = 4$ and $x = -4$.

You can use a similar procedure to solve rational inequalities using a graphing calculator.

ACTIVITY 2 Rational Inequality

Solve $\frac{3}{x} + \frac{7}{x} > 9$.

Step 1 Enter the inequalities.

Rewrite the problem as a system of inequalities.

The first inequality is $\frac{3}{x} + \frac{7}{x} > y$ or $y < \frac{3}{x} + \frac{7}{x}$. Since this inequality includes the *less than* symbol, shade below the curve. First enter the boundary and then use the arrow and [ENTER] keys to choose the shade below icon, ◣.

The second inequality is $y > 9$. Shade above the curve since this inequality contains *less than.*

KEYSTROKES: [◀] [◀] [ENTER] [ENTER] [ENTER] [▶] [▶] 3 [÷] [X,T,θ,n] [+] 7 [÷] [X,T,θ,n] [ENTER] [◀] [◀] [ENTER] [ENTER] [▶] [▶] 9 [GRAPH]

Step 2 Graph the system.

KEYSTROKES: [GRAPH]

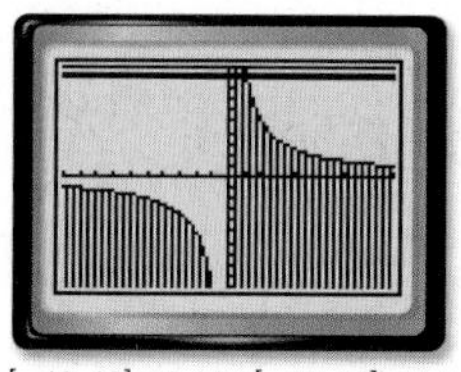

[−10, 10] scl: 1 by [−10, 10] scl: 1

The solution set of the original inequality is the set of x-values of the points in the region where the shadings overlap. Using the calculator's intersect feature, you can conclude that the solution set is $\left\{x \middle| 0 < x < 1\frac{1}{9}\right\}$.

Step 3 Use the TABLE feature.

Verify using the **table** feature. Set up the table to show x-values in increments of $\frac{1}{9}$.

KEYSTROKES: [2nd] [TblSet] 0 [ENTER] 1 [÷] 9 [ENTER] [2nd] [TABLE]

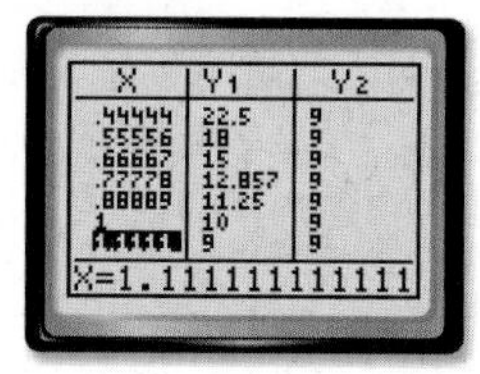

Scroll through the table. Notice that for x-values greater than 0 and less than $1\frac{1}{9}$, Y1 > Y2. This confirms that the solution of the inequality is $\left\{x \middle| 0 < x < 1\frac{1}{9}\right\}$.

Exercises

7. $\left\{x \middle| x < 0 \text{ or } \frac{2}{3} < x < 1\right\}$

Solve each equation or inequality. 4. all real numbers except 1 5. no real solution

1. $\frac{1}{x} + \frac{1}{2} = \frac{2}{x}$ 2
2. $\frac{1}{x-4} = \frac{2}{x-2}$ 6
3. $\frac{4}{x} = \frac{6}{x^2}$ 1.5
4. $\frac{1}{1-x} = 1 - \frac{x}{x-1}$
5. $\frac{1}{x+4} = \frac{2}{x^2+3x-4} - \frac{1}{1-x}$
6. $\frac{1}{x} + \frac{1}{2x} > 5$ $\{x | 0 < x < 0.3\}$
7. $\frac{1}{x-1} + \frac{2}{x} < 0$
8. $1 + \frac{5}{x-1} \leq 0$ $\{x | -4 \leq x < 1\}$
9. $2 + \frac{1}{x-1} \geq 0$ $\{x | x \leq 0.5 \text{ or } x > 1\}$

FL Math Online glencoe.com
- STUDY TO GO
- Vocabulary Review

CHAPTER 9 Study Guide and Review

Chapter Summary

Key Concepts

Rational Expressions (Lessons 9-1 and 9-2)

- Multiplying and dividing rational expressions is similar to multiplying and dividing fractions.
- To simplify complex fractions, simplify the numerator and the denominator separately, and then simplify the resulting expression.

Reciprocal and Rational Functions (Lessons 9-3 and 9-4)

- A reciprocal function is of the form $f(x) = \frac{1}{a(x)}$, where $a(x)$ is a linear function and $a(x) \neq 0$.
- A rational function is of the form $\frac{a(x)}{b(x)}$, where $a(x)$ and $b(x)$ are polynomial functions and $b(x) \neq 0$.

Direct, Joint, and Inverse Variation (Lesson 9-5)

- Direct Variation: There is a nonzero constant k such that $y = kx$.
- Joint Variation: There is a number k such that $y = kxz$, where $x \neq 0$ and $z \neq 0$.
- Inverse Variation: There is a nonzero constant k such that $xy = k$ or $y = \frac{k}{x}$.

Rational Equations and Inequalities (Lesson 9-6)

- Eliminate fractions in rational equations by multiplying each side of the equation by the LCD.
- Possible solutions of a rational equation must exclude values that result in zero in the denominator.

FOLDABLES® Study Organizer

Be sure the Key Concepts are noted in your Foldable.

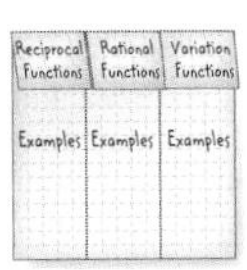

Key Vocabulary

asymptote (p. 570)
combined variation (p. 589)
complex fraction (p. 556)
constant of variation (p. 586)
direct variation (p. 586)
horizontal asymptote (p. 577)
inverse variation (p. 588)
joint variation (p. 587)
oblique asymptote (p. 579)
point discontinuity (p. 580)
rational equation (p. 594)
rational expression (p. 553)
rational function (p. 577)
rational inequality (p. 599)
reciprocal function (p. 569)
vertical asymptote (p. 577)
weighted average (p. 596)

Vocabulary Check

Choose a term from the list above that best completes each statement or phrase.

1. A(n) ________ is a rational expression whose numerator and/or denominator contains a rational expression. **complex fraction**
2. If two quantities show ________, their product is equal to a constant k. **inverse variation**
3. A(n) ________ asymptote is a linear asymptote that is neither horizontal nor vertical. **oblique**
4. A(n) ________ can be expressed in the form $y = kx$. **direct variation**
5. Equations that contain one or more rational expressions are called ________. **rational equations**
6. The graph of $y = \frac{x}{x+2}$ has a(n) ________ at $x = -2$. **asymptote**
7. ________ occurs when one quantity varies directly as the product of two or more other quantities. **Joint variation**
8. A ratio of two polynomial expressions is called a(n) ________. **rational expression**
9. ________ looks like a hole in a graph because the graph is undefined at that point. **Point discontinuity**
10. ________ occurs when one quantity varies directly and/or inversely as two or more other quantities. **Combined variation**

Formative Assessment

Key Vocabulary The page references after each word denote where that term was first introduced. If students have difficulty answering questions 1–10, remind them that they can use these page references to refresh their memories about the vocabulary.

Summative Assessment

CRM Vocabulary Test, p. 51

FL Math Online glencoe.com

Vocabulary PuzzleMaker improves students' mathematics vocabulary using four puzzle formats–crossword, scramble, word search using a word list, and word search using clues. Students can work online or from a printed worksheet.

FOLDABLES® Study Organizer

Dinah Zike's Foldables®

Have students look through the chapter to make sure they have included examples in their Foldables.

Suggest that students keep their Foldables handy while completing the Study Guide and Review pages. Point out that their Foldables can serve as a quick review tool when studying for the chapter test.

Lesson-by-Lesson Review

Intervention If the given examples are not sufficient to review the topics covered by the questions, remind students that the page references tell them where to review that topic in their textbook.

Two-Day Option Have students complete the Lesson-by-Lesson Review on pp. 606–608. Then you can use ExamView® Assessment Suite to customize another review worksheet that practices all the objectives of this chapter or only the objectives on which your students need more help.

Differentiated Instruction

Super DVD: MindJogger Videoquizzes Use this DVD as an alternative format of review for the test.

Additional Answers

24.

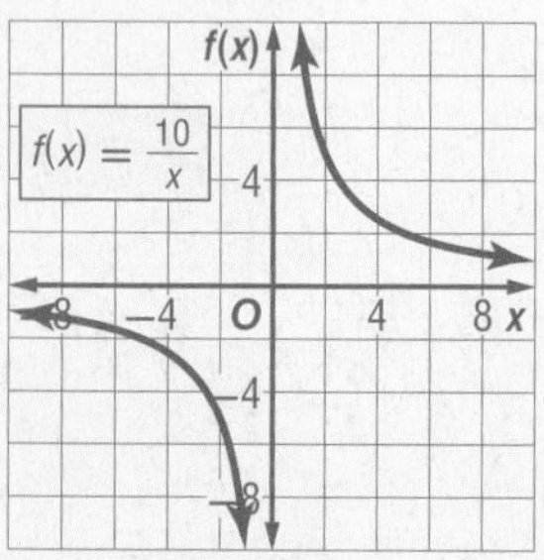

D = {x | x ≠ 0},
R = {f(x) | f(x) ≠ 0}

25.

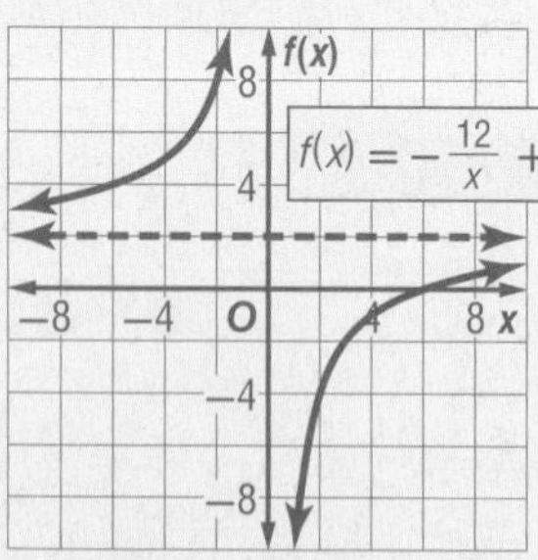

D = {x | x ≠ 0},
R = {f(x) | f(x) ≠ 2}

Lesson-by-Lesson Review

9-1 Multiplying and Dividing Rational Expressions (pp. 553–561)

912.A.5.2, 912.A.5.3

Simplify each expression.

11. $\frac{-16xy}{27z} \cdot \frac{15z^3}{8x^2}$ $\frac{10yz^2}{9x}$

12. $\frac{x^2 - 2x - 8}{x^2 + x - 12} \cdot \frac{x^2 + 2x - 15}{x^2 + 7x + 10}$ $\frac{x-4}{x+4}$

13. $\frac{x^2 - 1}{x^2 - 4} \cdot \frac{x^2 - 5x - 14}{x^2 - 6x - 7}$ $\frac{x-1}{x-2}$

14. $\frac{x + y}{15x} \div \frac{x^2 - y^2}{3x^2}$ $\frac{x}{5(x-y)}$

15. $\dfrac{\frac{x^2 + 3x - 18}{x + 4}}{\frac{x^2 + 7x + 6}{x + 4}}$ $\frac{x-3}{x+1}$

16. **GEOMETRY** A triangle has an area of $3x^2 + 9x - 54$ square centimeters. If the height of the triangle is $x + 6$ centimeters, find the length of the base. $6x - 18$ cm

EXAMPLE 1

Simplify $\frac{4a}{3b} \cdot \frac{9b^4}{2a^2}$.

$\frac{4a}{3b} \cdot \frac{9b^4}{2a^2} = \frac{\cancel{2} \cdot 2 \cdot \cancel{a} \cdot \cancel{3} \cdot 3 \cdot \cancel{b} \cdot b \cdot b \cdot b}{\cancel{3} \cdot \cancel{b} \cdot \cancel{2} \cdot \cancel{a} \cdot a}$

$= \frac{6b^3}{a}$

EXAMPLE 2

Simplify $\frac{r^2 + 5r}{2r} \div \frac{r^2 - 25}{6r - 12}$.

$\frac{r^2 + 5r}{2r} \div \frac{r^2 - 25}{6r - 12} = \frac{r^2 + 5r}{2r} \cdot \frac{6r - 12}{r^2 - 25}$

$= \frac{r(r + 5)}{2r} \cdot \frac{6(r - 2)}{(r + 5)(r - 5)}$

$= \frac{3(r - 2)}{r - 5}$

9-2 Adding and Subtracting Rational Expressions (pp. 562–568)

912.A.5.2

Simplify each expression.

17. $\frac{9}{4ab} + \frac{5a}{6b^2}$ $\frac{27b + 10a^2}{12ab^2}$

18. $\frac{3}{4x - 8} - \frac{x - 1}{x^2 - 4}$ $\frac{-x + 10}{4(x-2)(x+2)}$

19. $\frac{y}{2x} + \frac{4y}{3x^2} - \frac{5}{6xy^2}$ $\frac{3xy^3 + 8y^3 - 5x}{6x^2y^2}$

20. $\frac{2}{x^2 - 3x - 10} - \frac{6}{x^2 - 8x + 15}$ $\frac{-4x - 18}{(x-5)(x+2)(x-3)}$

21. $\frac{3}{3x^2 + 2x - 8} + \frac{4x}{2x^2 + 6x + 4}$ $\frac{12x^2 - 10x + 6}{2(x+2)(3x-4)(x+1)}$

22. $\dfrac{\frac{3}{2x + 3} - \frac{x}{x + 1}}{\frac{2x}{x + 1} + \frac{5}{2x + 3}}$ $\frac{-2x^2 + 3}{4x^2 + 11x + 5}$

23. **GEOMETRY** What is the perimeter of the rectangle? $\frac{10x + 20}{(x+6)(x+1)}$

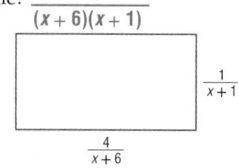

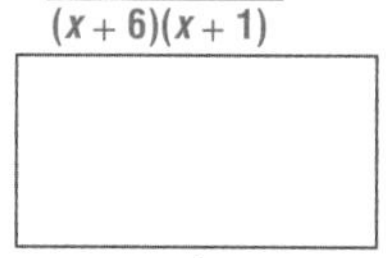

EXAMPLE 3

Simplify $\frac{3a}{a^2 - 4} - \frac{2}{a - 2}$.

$\frac{3a}{a^2 - 4} - \frac{2}{a - 2} = \frac{3a}{(a - 2)(a + 2)} - \frac{2}{a - 2}$

$= \frac{3a}{(a - 2)(a + 2)} - \frac{2\cancel{(a + 2)}}{(a - 2)\cancel{(a + 2)}}$

$= \frac{3a - 2(a + 2)}{(a - 2)(a + 2)}$ **Subtract numerators.**

$= \frac{3a - 2a - 4}{(a - 2)(a + 2)}$ **Distributive Property**

$= \frac{a - 4}{(a - 2)(a + 2)}$ **Simplify.**

26.

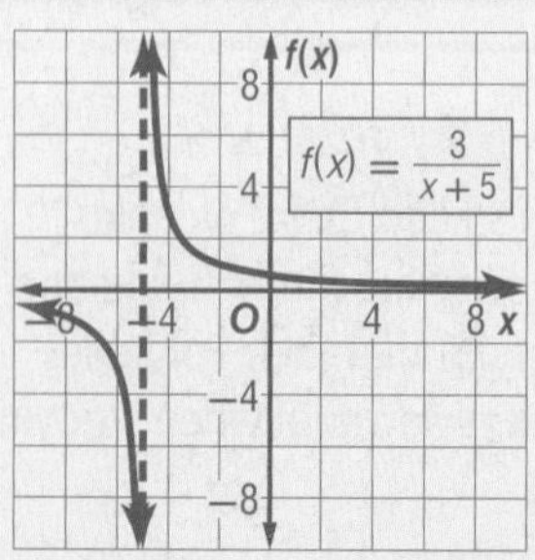

D = {x | x ≠ −5}, R = {f(x) | f(x) ≠ 0}

27.

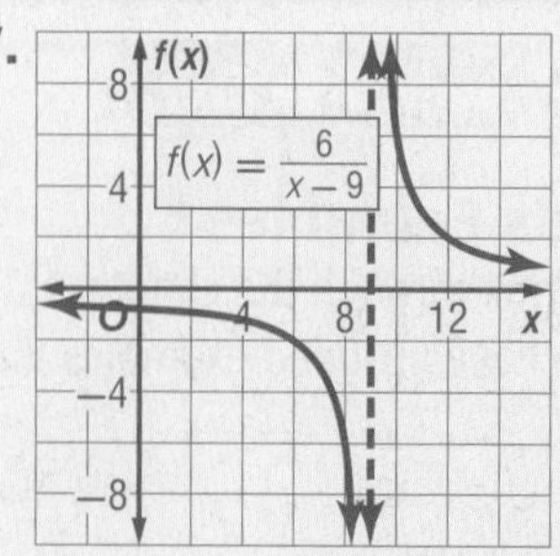

D = {x | x ≠ 9}, R = {f(x) | f(x) ≠ 0}

9-3 Graphing Reciprocal Functions (pp. 569–575) 24–29. See margin.

912.A.5.6

Graph each function. State the domain and range.

24. $f(x) = \frac{10}{x}$ **25.** $f(x) = -\frac{12}{x} + 2$

26. $f(x) = \frac{3}{x+5}$ **27.** $f(x) = \frac{6}{x-9}$

28. $f(x) = \frac{7}{x-2} + 3$ **29.** $f(x) = -\frac{4}{x+4} - 8$

30. CONSERVATION The student council is planting 28 trees for a service project. The number of trees each person plants depends on the number of student council members. a. $f(x) = \frac{28}{x}$

a. Write a function to represent this situation.

b. Graph the function. See margin.

EXAMPLE 4

Graph $f(x) = \frac{3}{x+2} - 1$. State the domain and range.

$a = 3$: The graph is stretched vertically.
$h = -2$: The graph is translated 2 units left. There is an asymptote at $x = -2$.
$k: = -1$: The graph is translated 1 unit down. There is an asymptote is at $f(x) = -1$.

Domain: $\{x \mid x \neq -2\}$,
Range: $\{f(x) \mid f(x) \neq -1\}$

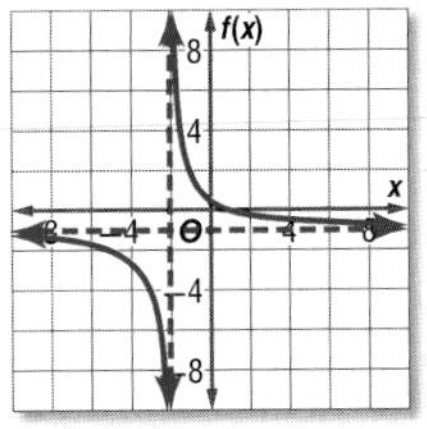

9-4 Graphing Rational Functions (pp. 577–584)

912.A.2.10, 912.A.5.6

Determine the equations of any vertical asymptotes and the values of x for any holes in the graph of each rational function.

31. $f(x) = \frac{3}{x^2 + 4x}$ $x = -4$, $x = 0$

32. $f(x) = \frac{x+2}{x^2 + 6x + 8}$ $x = -4$; hole: $x = -2$

33. $f(x) = \frac{x^2 - 9}{x^2 - 5x - 24}$ $x = 8$; hole: $x = -3$

Graph each rational function. 34–37. See margin.

34. $f(x) = \frac{x+2}{(x+5)^2}$ **35.** $f(x) = \frac{x}{x+1}$

36. $f(x) = \frac{x^2 + 4x + 4}{x+2}$ **37.** $f(x) = \frac{x-1}{x^2 + 5x + 6}$

38. SALES Aliyah is selling magazine subscriptions. Out of the first 15 houses, she sold subscriptions to 10 of them. Suppose Aliyah goes to x more houses and sells subscriptions to all of them. The percentage of houses that she sold to out of the total houses can be determined using $P(x) = \frac{10 + x}{15 + x}$.

a. Graph the function. See p. 608 margin.

b. What domain and range values are meaningful in the context of the problem? $D = \{x \geq 0\}$, $R = \{0 \leq P(x) \leq 1.0\}$

EXAMPLE 5

Determine the equation of any vertical asymptotes and the values of x for any holes in the graph of $f(x) = \frac{x^2 - 1}{x^2 + 2x - 3}$.

$$\frac{x^2 - 1}{x^2 + 2x - 3} = \frac{(x-1)(x+1)}{(x-1)(x+3)}$$

The function is undefined for $x = 1$ and $x = -3$.

Since $\frac{(x-1)(x+1)}{(x-1)(x+3)} = \frac{x+1}{x+3}$, $x = -3$ is a vertical asymptote, and $x = 1$ represents a hole in the graph.

EXAMPLE 6

Graph $f(x) = \frac{1}{6x(x-1)}$.

The function is undefined for $x = 0$ and $x = 1$. Because $\frac{1}{6x(x-1)}$ is in simplest form, $x = 0$ and $x = 1$ are vertical asymptotes. Draw the two asymptotes and sketch the graph.

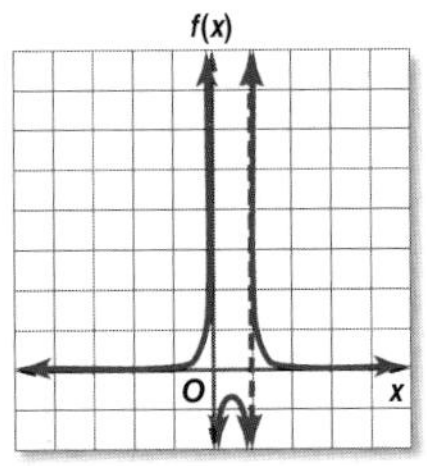

Additional Answers

28.

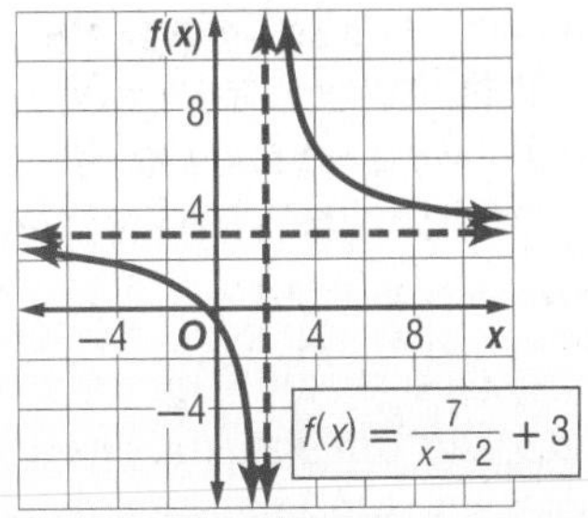

$D = \{x \mid x \neq 2\}$,
$R = \{f(x) \mid f(x) \neq 3\}$

29.

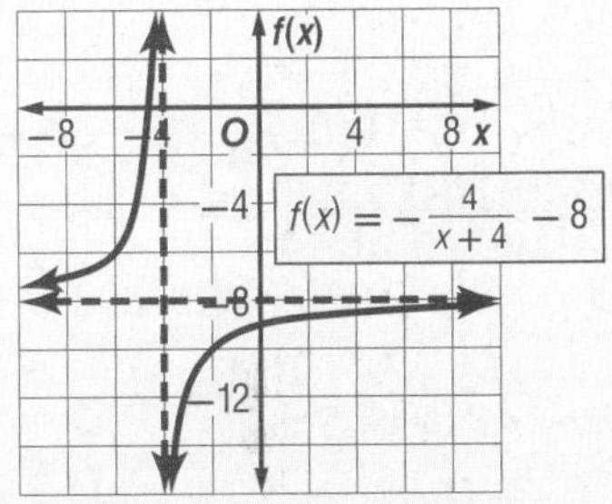

$D = \{x \mid x \neq -4\}$,
$R = \{f(x) \mid f(x) \neq -8\}$

30b.

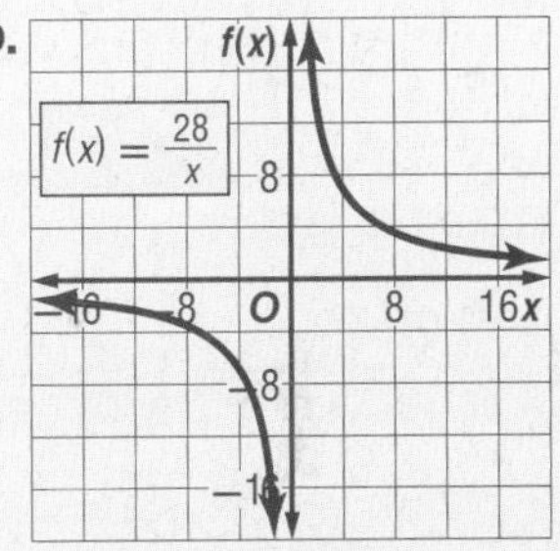

34.

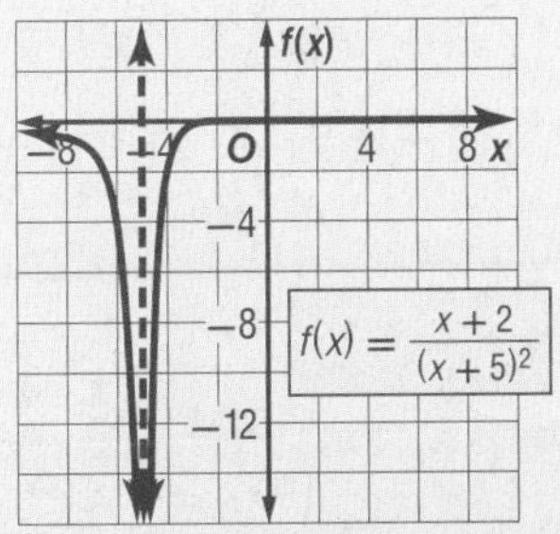

36.

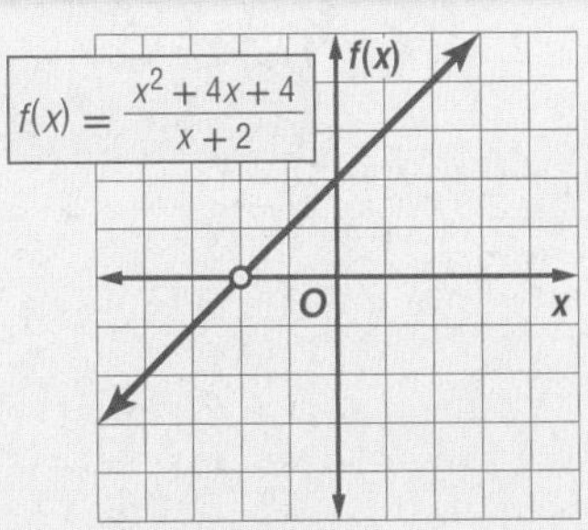

37.

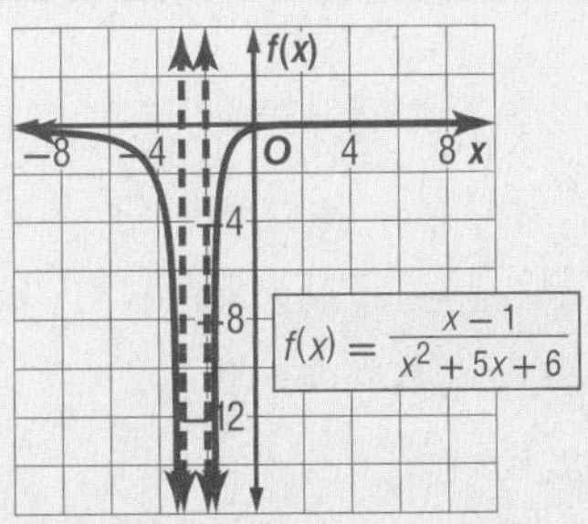

35.

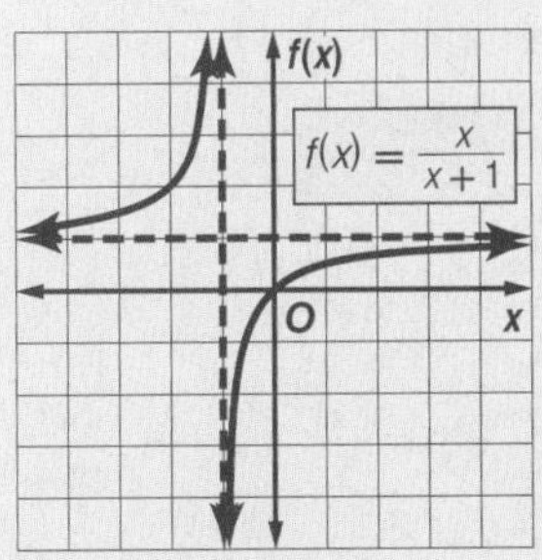

Problem Solving Review

For additional practice in problem solving for Chapter 9, see the Mixed Problem Solving Appendix, p. 988, in the Student Handbook section.

Anticipation Guide

Have students complete the Chapter 9 Anticipation Guide and discuss how their responses have changed now that they have completed Chapter 9.

Additional Answer (p. 607)

38a.

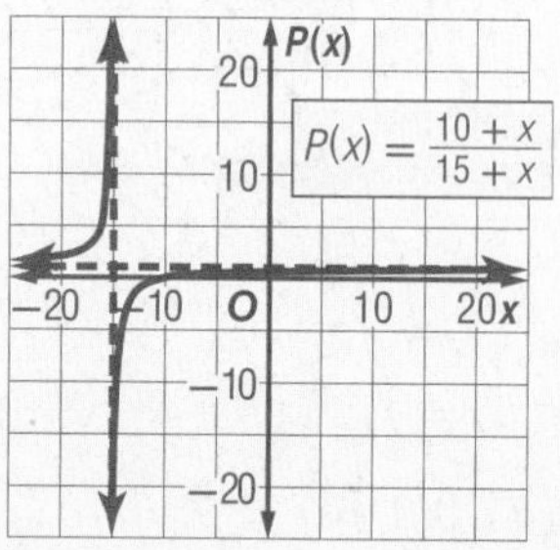

CHAPTER 9 Study Guide and Review

9-5 Variation Functions (pp. 586–593)

912.A.2.12

39. If a varies directly as b and $b = 18$ when $a = 27$, find a when $b = 10$. **$a = 15$**

40. If y varies inversely as x and $y = 15$ when $x = 3.5$, find y when $x = -5$. **$y = -10.5$**

41. If y varies inversely as x and $y = -3$ when $x = 9$, find y when $x = 81$. **$y = -\frac{1}{3}$**

42. If y varies jointly as x and z, and $x = 8$ and $z = 3$ when $y = 72$, find y when $x = -2$ and $z = -5$. **$y = 30$**

43. If y varies jointly as x and z, and $y = 18$ when $x = 6$ and $z = 15$, find y when $x = 12$ and $z = 4$. **$y = \frac{48}{5}$**

44. JOBS Lisa's earnings vary directly with how many hours she babysits. If she earns $68 for 8 hours of babysitting, find her earnings after 5 hours of babysitting. **$42.50**

EXAMPLE 7

If y varies inversely as x and $x = 24$ when $y = -8$, find x when $y = 15$.

$\frac{x_1}{y_2} = \frac{x_2}{y_1}$	**Inverse variation**
$\frac{24}{15} = \frac{x_2}{-8}$	**$x_1 = 24$, $y_1 = -8$, $y_2 = 15$**
$24(-8) = 15(x_2)$	**Cross multiply.**
$-192 = 15x_2$	**Simplify.**
$-12\frac{4}{5} = x_2$	**Divide each side by 15.**

When $y = 15$, the value of x is $-12\frac{4}{5}$.

9-6 Solving Rational Equations and Inequalities (pp. 594–602)

912.A.5.5, 912.A.5.7

Solve each equation or inequality. Check your solutions.

45. $\frac{1}{3} + \frac{4}{x-2} = 6$ **$x = \frac{46}{17}$**

46. $\frac{6}{x+5} - \frac{3}{x-3} = \frac{6}{x^2+2x-15}$ **$x = 13$**

47. $\frac{2}{x^2-9} = \frac{3}{x^2-2x-3}$ **$x = -7$**

48. $\frac{4}{2x-3} + \frac{x}{x+1} = \frac{-8x}{2x^2-x-3}$ **$x = -\frac{1}{2}, -4$**

49. $\frac{x}{x+4} - \frac{28}{x^2+x-12} = \frac{1}{x-3}$ **$x = 8$**

50. $\frac{x}{2} + \frac{1}{x-1} < \frac{x}{4}$ **$x < 1$**

51. $\frac{1}{2x} - \frac{4}{5x} > \frac{1}{3}$ **$-\frac{9}{10} < x < 0$**

52. YARD WORK Lana can plant a garden in 3 hours. Milo can plant the same garden in 4 hours. How long will it take them if they work together? **$1\frac{5}{7}$ h**

EXAMPLE 8

Solve $\frac{3}{x+2} + \frac{1}{x} = 0$.

The LCD is $x(x + 2)$.

$$\frac{3}{x+2} + \frac{1}{x} = 0$$

$$x(x+2)\left(\frac{3}{x+2} + \frac{1}{x}\right) = x(x+2)(0)$$

$$x(x+2)\left(\frac{3}{x+2}\right) + x(x+2)\left(\frac{1}{x}\right) = 0$$

$$3(x) + 1(x+2) = 0$$

$$3x + x + 2 = 0$$

$$4x + 2 = 0$$

$$4x = -2$$

$$x = -\frac{1}{2}$$

FL Math Online glencoe.com Chapter Test

Simplify each expression.

3. $\frac{m+3}{n-3}$ 5–7. See margin.

1. $\frac{r^2+rt}{2r} \div \frac{r+t}{16r^2}$ $8r^2$

2. $\frac{m^2-4}{3m^2} \cdot \frac{6m}{2-m}$ $\frac{2(m+2)}{m}$

3. $\frac{m^2+m-6}{n^2-9} \div \frac{m-2}{n+3}$

4. $\frac{\frac{x^2+4x+3}{x^2-2x-15}}{\frac{x^2-1}{x^2-x-20}}$ $\frac{x+4}{x-1}$

5. $\frac{x+4}{6x+3} + \frac{1}{2x+1}$

6. $\frac{x}{x^2-1} - \frac{3}{2x+2}$

7. $\frac{1}{y} + \frac{2}{7} - \frac{3}{2y^2}$

8. $\frac{2+\frac{1}{x}}{5-\frac{1}{x}}$ $\frac{2x+1}{5x-1}$

9. Identify the asymptotes, domain, and range of the function graphed. See margin.

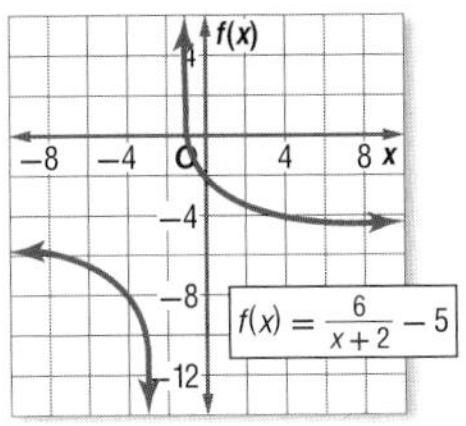

10. NGSSS PRACTICE What is the equation for the vertical asymptote of the rational function $f(x) = \frac{x+1}{x^2+3x+2}$? A

A. $x = -2$

B. $x = -1$

C. $x = 1$

D. $x = 2$

Graph each function.

11–16. See Chapter 9 Answer Appendix.

11. $f(x) = -\frac{8}{x} - 9$

12. $f(x) = \frac{2}{x+4}$

13. $f(x) = \frac{3}{x-1} + 8$

14. $f(x) = \frac{5x}{x+1}$

15. $f(x) = \frac{x}{x-5}$

16. $f(x) = \frac{x^2+5x-6}{x-1}$

17. Determine the equations of any vertical asymptotes and the values of x for any holes in the graph of the function $f(x) = \frac{x+5}{x^2-2x-35}$. vertical asymptote: $x = 7$; hole: $x = -5$

18. Determine the equations of any oblique asymptotes in the graph of the function $f(x) = \frac{x^2+x-5}{x+3}$. $f(x) = x - 2$

Solve each equation or inequality.

19. $\frac{-1}{x+4} = 6 - \frac{x}{x+4}$ $x = -5$

20. $\frac{1}{3} = \frac{5}{m+3} + \frac{8}{21}$ $m = -108$

21. $7 + \frac{2}{x} < -\frac{5}{x}$ $-1 < x < 0$

22. $r + \frac{6}{r} - 5 = 0$ $r = 2, 3$

23. $\frac{6}{7} - \frac{3m}{2m-1} = \frac{11}{7}$ $m = \frac{5}{31}$

24. $\frac{r+2}{3r} = \frac{r+4}{r-2} - \frac{2}{3}$ $r = -\frac{1}{4}$

25. If y varies inversely as x and $y = 18$ when $x = -\frac{1}{2}$, find x when $y = -10$. $\frac{9}{10}$

26. If m varies directly as n and $m = 24$ when $n = -3$, find n when $m = 30$. $-\frac{15}{4}$

27. Suppose r varies jointly as s and t. If $s = 20$ when $r = 140$ and $t = -5$, find s when $r = 7$ and $t = 2.5$. -2

28. **BICYCLING** When Susan rides her bike, the distance that she travels varies directly with the amount of time she is biking. Suppose she bikes 50 miles in 2.5 hours. At this rate, how many hours would it take her to bike 80 miles? 4 hours

29. **PAINTING** Peter can paint a house in 10 hours. Melanie can paint the same house in 9 hours. How long would it take if they worked together? about 4.7 hours

30. NGSSS PRACTICE How many liters of a 25% acid solution must be added to 30 liters of an 80% acid solution to create a 50% acid solution? H

F. 18

G. 30

H. 36

I. 66

31. What is the volume of the rectangular prism?

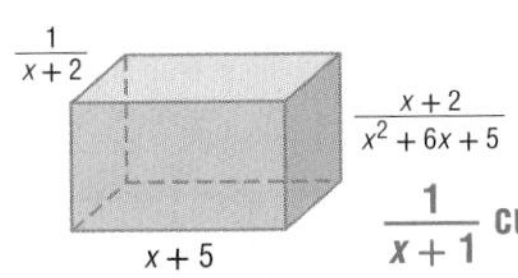

$\frac{1}{x+1}$ cubic units

CHAPTER 9 Practice Test

ExamView Assessment Suite Customize and create multiple versions of your chapter test and their answer keys. All of the questions from the leveled chapter tests in the *Chapter 9 Resource Masters* are also available on ExamView® Assessment Suite.

Additional Answers

5. $\frac{x+7}{3(2x+1)}$

6. $\frac{-x+3}{2(x-1)(x+1)}$

7. $\frac{4y^2+14y-21}{14y^2}$

9. $x = -2$; $f(x) = -5$; $D = \{x \mid x \neq -2\}$, $R = \{f(x) \mid f(x) \neq -5\}$

Intervention Planner

Tier 1 On Level	Tier 2 Strategic Intervention approaching grade level	Tier 3 Intensive Intervention 2 or more grades below level
If students miss about 25% of the exercises or less,	**If** students miss about 50% of the exercises,	**If** students miss about 75% of the exercises,
Then choose a resource:	**Then** choose a resource:	**Then** use *Math Triumphs, Alg. 2*, Ch. 2
SE Lessons 9-1, 9-2, 9-3, 9-4, 9-5, and 9-6	**CRM** Study Guide and Intervention, Chapter 9, pp. 5, 11, 18, 25, 32, and 39	
CRM Skills Practice, pp. 7, 13, 20, 27, 34, and 41		
TE Chapter Project, p. 550		
FL Math Online Self-Check Quiz	FL Math Online Extra Examples, Personal Tutor, Homework Help	FL Math Online Extra Examples, Personal Tutor, Homework Help, Review Vocabulary

1 FOCUS

Objective Use the strategy of guess and check to solve standardized test problems.

2 TEACH

Scaffolding Questions

Ask:

- Why is guess and check a good strategy to use in standardized tests? Sample answer: You know that the correct answer is among the choices you are given. Once you make a reasonable guess, you can check it against the information in the problem to determine if it is correct or if you should go on to the next reasonable guess. Then you can be confident in your answer.
- When should you use guess and check strategy? Sample answer: You can use guess and check at any time in a standardized test. It is most helpful when the answer choices can replace information given in a problem, for example, when choices are values that can replace a variable in an expression or an equation.

Guess and Check

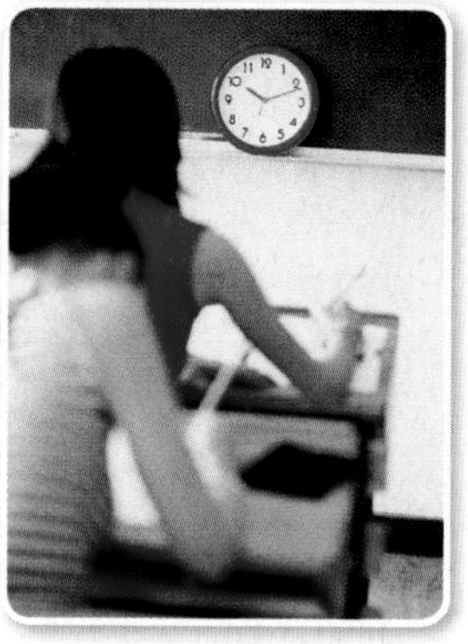

It is very important to pace yourself and keep track of how much time you have when taking a standardized test. If time is running short, or if you are unsure how to solve a problem, the guess-and-check strategy may help you determine the correct answer quickly.

Strategies for Guessing and Checking

Step 1

Carefully look over each possible answer choice and evaluate for reasonableness. Eliminate unreasonable answers.

Ask yourself:

- Are there any answer choices that are clearly incorrect?
- Are there any answer choices that are not in the proper format?
- Are there any answer choices that do not have the proper units for the correct answer?

Step 2

For the remaining answer choices, use the guess-and-check method.

- **Equations:** If you are solving an equation, substitute the answer choice for the variable and see if this results in a true number sentence.
- **System of Equations:** For a system of equations, substitute the answer choice for all variables and make sure all equations result in a true number sentence.

Step 3

Choose an answer choice and see if it satisfies the constraints of the problem statement. Identify the correct answer.

- If the answer choice you are testing does not satisfy the problem, move on to the next reasonable guess and check it.
- When you find the correct answer choice, stop.

NGSSS PRACTICE EXAMPLE

Read the problem. Identify what you need to know. Then use the information in the problem to solve.

Solve: $\frac{2}{x-3} - \frac{4}{x+3} = \frac{8}{x^2-9}$.

A. -1

B. 1

C. 5

D. 7

The solution of the rational equation will be a real number. Since all four answer choices are real numbers, they are all possible correct answers and must be checked. Begin with the first answer choice and check it in the rational equation. Continue until you find the answer choice that results in a true number sentence.

	Check:
Guess: −1	$\frac{2}{(-1)-3} - \frac{4}{(-1)+3} = \frac{8}{(-1)^2-9}$ $-\frac{5}{2} \neq -1$ ✗
Guess: 1	$\frac{2}{1-3} - \frac{4}{1+3} = \frac{8}{(1)^2-9}$ $-2 \neq -1$ ✗
Guess: 5	$\frac{2}{5-3} - \frac{4}{5+3} = \frac{8}{(5)^2-9}$ $\frac{1}{2} = \frac{1}{2}$ ✓

If $x = 5$, the result is a true number sentence. So, the correct answer is C.

Exercises

Read each problem. Identify what you need to know. Then use the information in the problem to solve.

1. Solve: $\frac{2}{5x} - \frac{1}{2x} = -\frac{1}{2}$. B

A. $\frac{1}{10}$

B. $\frac{1}{5}$

C. $\frac{1}{4}$

D. $\frac{1}{2}$

2. The sum of Kevin's, Anna's, and Tia's ages is 40. Anna is 1 year more than twice as old as Tia. Kevin is 3 years older than Anna. How old is Anna? H

F. 7 H. 15

G. 14 I. 18

3. Determine the point(s) where the following rational function crosses the x-axis. D

$$f(x) = \frac{2}{x-1} - \frac{x+4}{3}$$

A. −5

B. 4

C. 2 or 3

D. −5 or 2

4. Rafael's Theatre Company sells tickets for $10. At this price, they sell 400 tickets. Rafael estimates that they would sell 40 fewer tickets for each $2 price increase. What charge would give the most income? H

F. 10 H. 15

G. 13 I. 20

Additional Example

STANDARDIZED TEST PRACTICE

Suppose y varies jointly as x and z. Find y when $x = 12$ and $z = 7$, if $y = 40$ when $z = 15$ and $x = 28$. A

A 8

B 20

C 80

D 200

3 ASSESS

Use Exercises 1–4 to assess students' understanding.

Diagnose Student Errors

Survey student responses for each item. Class trends may indicate common errors and misconceptions.

2. A. incorrectly wrote 1 hour 45 minutes as 1.45
B. mistakenly added denominators
C. correct
D. guess

3. F. found the correct difference but added it when should have multiplied by it
G. correct
H. divided by the correct difference instead of multiplying by it
I. used multiplication but not the correct difference

10. A. misinterpreted the graph
B. correct
C. misinterpreted the graph
D. misinterpreted the graph

12. F. did not factor $x^2 - 16$ correctly
G. correct
H. simplified the fraction incorrectly
I. mistakenly inverted the simplified fraction

13. A. correct
B. incorrectly interpreted 2 as an x-intercept
C. did not use + sign for direction of shift
D. incorrectly interpreted 2 as an x-intercept

14. F. ignored the word *not* in the question
G. ignored the word *not* in the question
H. ignored the word *not* in the question
I. correct

15. A. correct
B. in this function when x is negative, y is negative
C. in this function when x is negative, y is undefined
D. in this function when x is negative, y is negative

Read each question. Then fill in the correct answer on the answer document provided by your teacher or on a sheet of paper.

1. **GRIDDED RESPONSE** Suppose y varies inversely as x and $y = 4$ when $x = 12$. What is y when x is 5? Round to the nearest tenth. **9.6**

2. Greg's father can mow the lawn on his riding mower in 45 minutes. It takes Greg 1 hour 45 minutes to mow the lawn with a push mower. Which of the following rational equations can be solved for the number of minutes t it would take them to mow the lawn working together? **C**

A. $\frac{t}{45} + \frac{t}{1.45} = 1$

B. $\frac{t}{150} = 1$

C. $\frac{t}{45} + \frac{t}{105} = 1$

D. $\frac{t + 45}{t + 105} = 1$

3. The total cost of reserving a campsite varies directly as the number of nights the site is rented, as shown in the table.

Days	Total Cost
1	$24
2	$48
3	$72
4	$96

Which equation represents the direct variation? **G**

F. $y = x + 24$

G. $y = 24x$

H. $y = \frac{24}{x}$

I. $y = 96x$

4. **SHORT RESPONSE** What is the area of the shaded region of the rectangle expressed as a polynomial in simplest form? **$3x^2 - 14x + 8$**

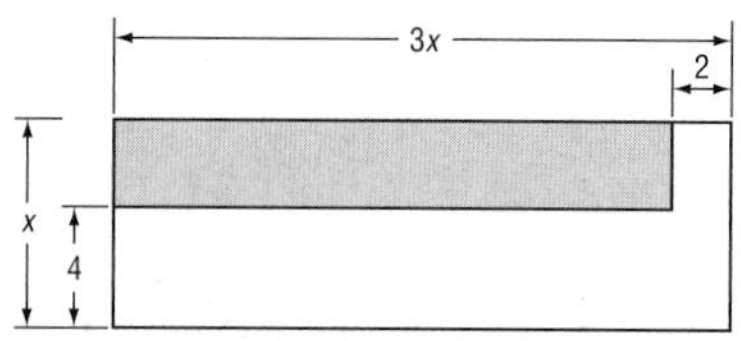

Test-Taking Tip

Question 3 Check your answer by substituting 1, 2, 3, and 4 for x and making sure the values in the table are produced.

5. **EXTENDED RESPONSE** Use the graph of the rational function at the right to answer each question.

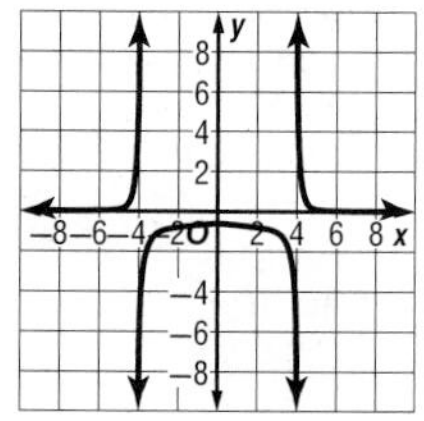

a. Describe the vertical and horizontal asymptotes of the graph.

b. Write the equation of the rational function. Explain how you found your answer.
5a, b. See margin.

6. **GRIDDED RESPONSE** Elaine had some money saved for a week-long vacation. The first day of the vacation she spent $125 on food and a hotel. On the second day, she was given $80 from her sister for expenses. Elaine then had $635 left for the rest of the vacation. How much money, in dollars, did she begin the vacation with? **680**

7. **SHORT RESPONSE** Carlos wants to print 800 one-page flyers for his landscaping business. He has a printer that is capable of printing 8 pages per minute. His business partner has another printer that prints 10 pages per minute.

a. How long would it take Carlos' printer to print all the flyers? How long would it take his partner's printer? **100 min; 80 min**

b. Set up a rational equation that can be used to find the number of minutes t it would take to print all 800 flyers if both printers are used simultaneously.

c. Solve the equation you wrote in part **b**. How long would it take both printers to print all the flyers if they print simultaneously? Round to the nearest minute. **about 44 min**

7b. $\frac{t}{100} + \frac{t}{80} = 1$

8. **EXTENDED RESPONSE** Consider the polynomial function

$$f(x) = 3x^4 + 19x^3 + 7x^2 - 11x - 2.$$

a. What is the degree of the function? **4**

b. What is the leading coefficient of the function? **3**

c. Evaluate $f(1)$, $f(-2)$, and $f(2a)$. Show your work.
16; −56; $48a^4 + 152a^3 + 28a^2 - 22a - 2$

9. **SHORT RESPONSE** Martha is putting a stone walkway around the garden pictured at the right. About how many feet of stone are needed? **56.8 ft**

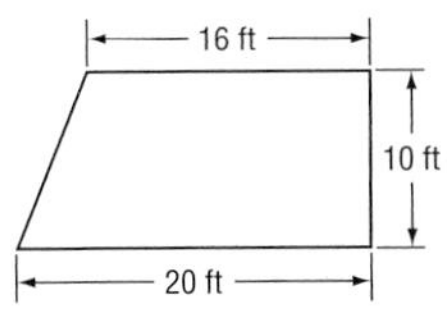

10. A ball was thrown upward with an initial velocity of 16 feet per second from the top of a building 128 feet high. Its height h in feet above the ground t seconds later will be $h = 128 + 16t - 16t^2$.

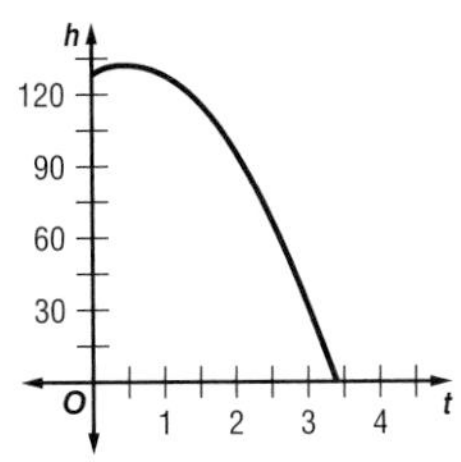

Which is the best conclusion about the ball's action? **B**

A. The ball stayed above 128 feet for more than 3 seconds.

B. The ball returned to the ground in less than 4 seconds.

C. The ball traveled more slowly going up than it did going down.

D. The ball traveled less than 128 feet in 3.4 seconds.

11. **GRIDDED RESPONSE** The population of a country can be modeled by the equation $P(t) = 40e^{0.02t}$, where P is the population in millions and t is the number of years since 2000. When will the population be 400 million? **2115**

12. Simplify the complex fraction. **G**

$$\frac{\frac{(x+3)^2}{x^2-16}}{\frac{x+3}{x+4}}$$

F. $\frac{1}{x-4}$

G. $\frac{x+3}{x-4}$

H. $\frac{x-4}{x+3}$

I. $\frac{x+3}{x+4}$

13. In which direction must the graph of $y = \frac{1}{x}$ be shifted to produce the graph of $y = \frac{1}{x} + 2$? **A**

A. up

B. down

C. right

D. left

14. Which of the following is a **not** an asymptote of the rational function $f(x) = \frac{1}{x^2 - 49}$? **I**

F. $f(x) = 0$

G. $x = -7$

H. $x = 7$

I. $f(x) = 1$

15. Which of these equations describes a relationship in which every negative real number x corresponds to a nonnegative real number y? **A**

A. $y = -x$

B. $y = x$

C. $y = \sqrt{x}$

D. $y = x^3$

Need Extra Help?

If you missed Question...	1	2	3	4	5	6	7	8	9	10	11	12	13	14	15
Go to Lesson or Page...	9-5	9-5	9-4	6-1	9-3	3-2	9-5	7-1	1-4	5-7	8-8	9-1	9-3	9-3	2-4
For help with NGSSS...	912.A.2.12	912.A.2.12	912.A.2.12	912.A.4.2	912.A.5.6	912.A.3.15	912.A.2.12	912.A.2.7	912.A.3.1	912.A.7.5	912.A.8.7	912.A.5.2	912.A.2.10	912.A.5.6	912.A.2.12

Formative Assessment

You can use these two pages to benchmark student progress.

Standardized Test Practice, pp. 65–67

ExamView Assessment Suite — Create practice worksheets or tests that align to your state's standards as well as TIMSS and NAEP tests.

Homework Option

Get Ready for Chapter 10 Assign students the exercises on p. 615 as homework to assess whether they possess the prerequisite skills needed for the next chapter.

Additional Answers

5a. Sample answer: vertical asymptotes at $x = -4$ and $x = 4$; horizontal asymptote at $y = 0$

5b. $y = \frac{1}{x^2 - 16}$

Page 568, Lesson 9-2

85.

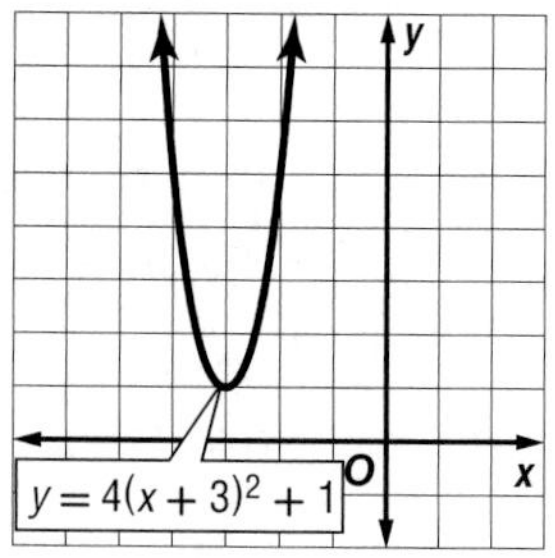

86.

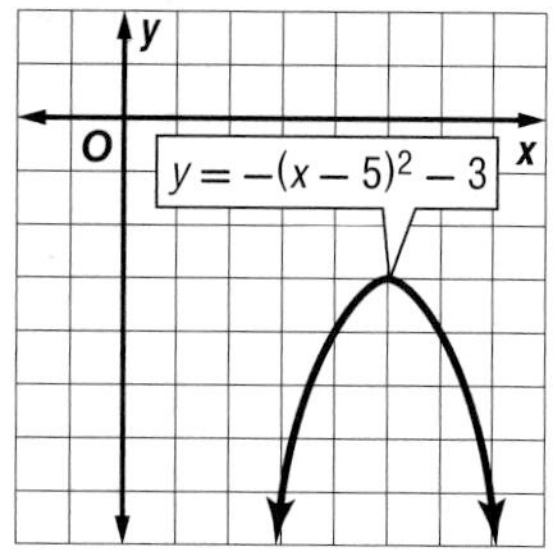

87.

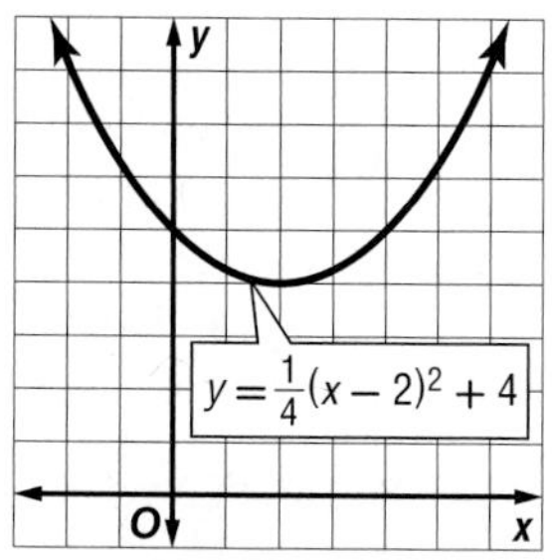

88.

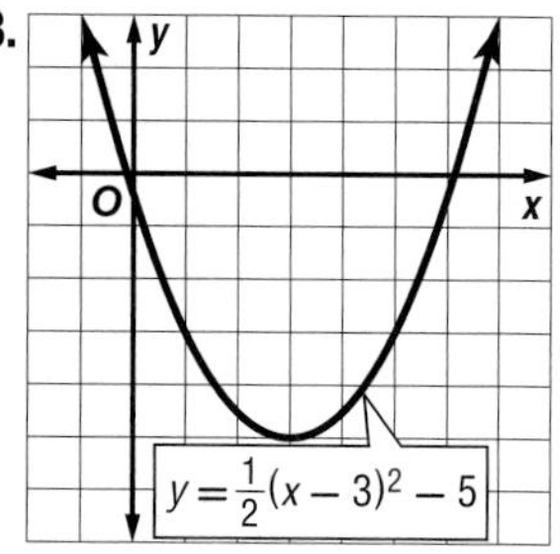

89.

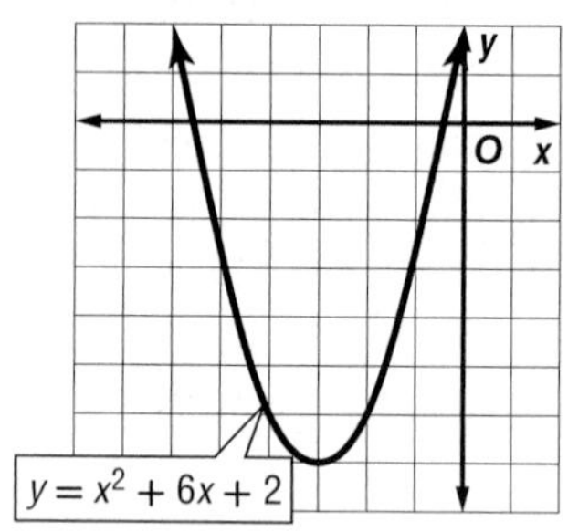

90.

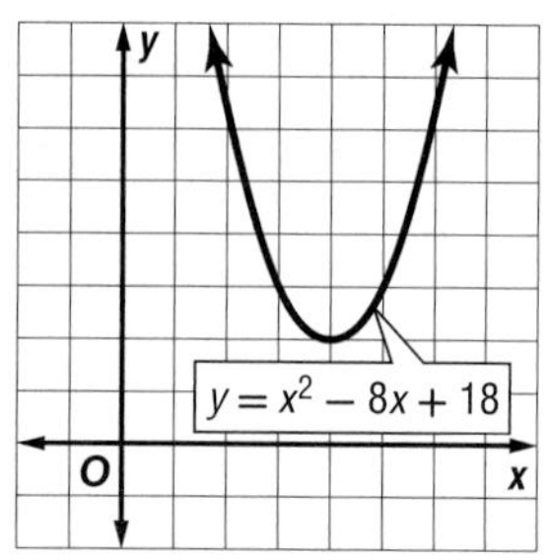

Pages 571-572, Lesson 9-3 (Guided Practice)

3A.

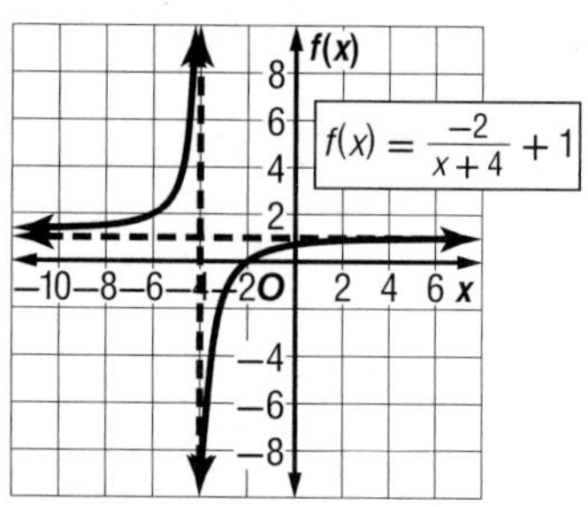

$D = \{x \mid x \neq -4\}$; $R = \{f(x) \mid f(x) \neq 1\}$

3B.

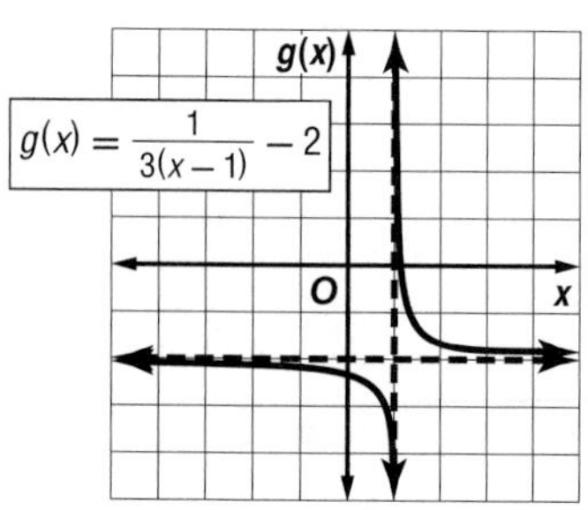

$D = \{x \mid x \neq 1\}$; $R = \{g(x) \mid g(x) \neq -2\}$

4. $T = \dfrac{2500 + 45p}{p}$

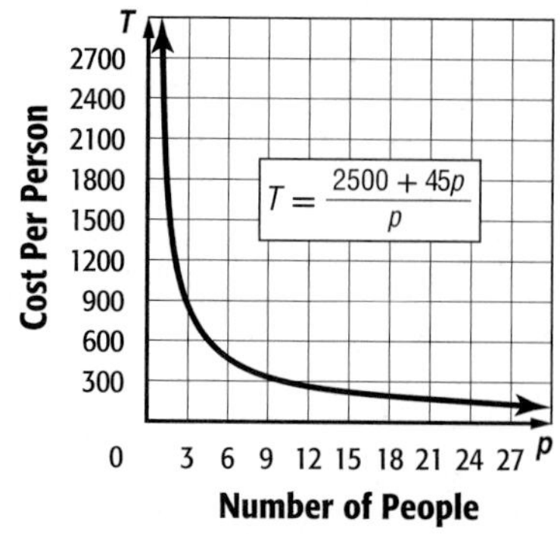

The domain will never reach zero because someone has to be at the dance. The range will never reach zero because, even if there are thousands of people there, they will incur some cost. Neither value is negative because there cannot be a negative cost or a negative number of people.

Pages 573–575, Lesson 9-3

11.

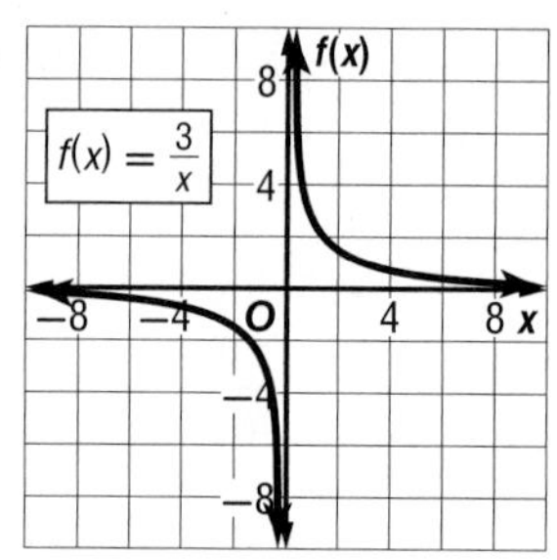

$D = \{x \mid x \neq 0\}$;
$R = \{f(x) \mid f(x) \neq 0\}$

12.

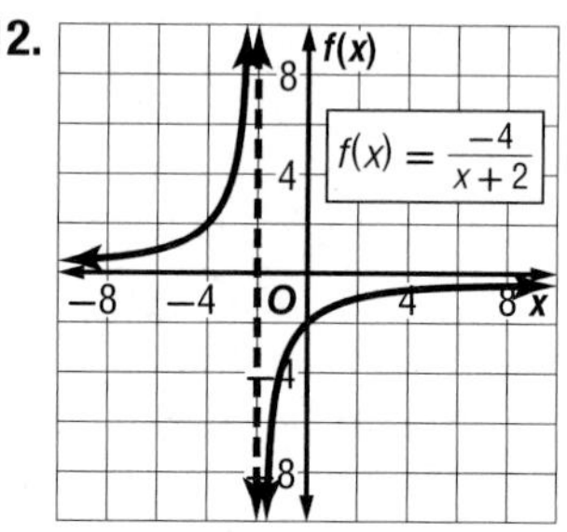

$D = \{x \mid x \neq -2\}$;
$R = \{f(x) \mid f(x) \neq 0\}$

13.

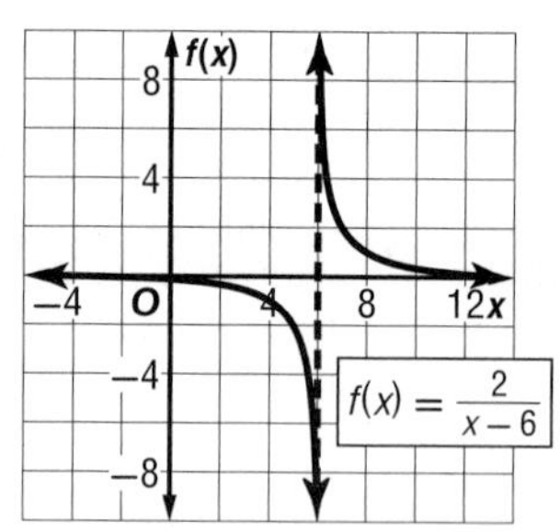

$D = \{x \mid x \neq 6\}$;
$R = \{f(x) \mid f(x) \neq 0\}$

14.

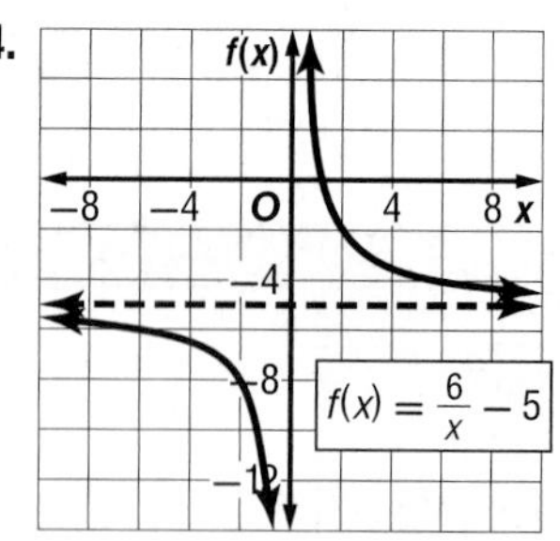

$D = \{x \mid x \neq 0\}$;
$R = \{f(x) \mid f(x) \neq -5\}$

15.

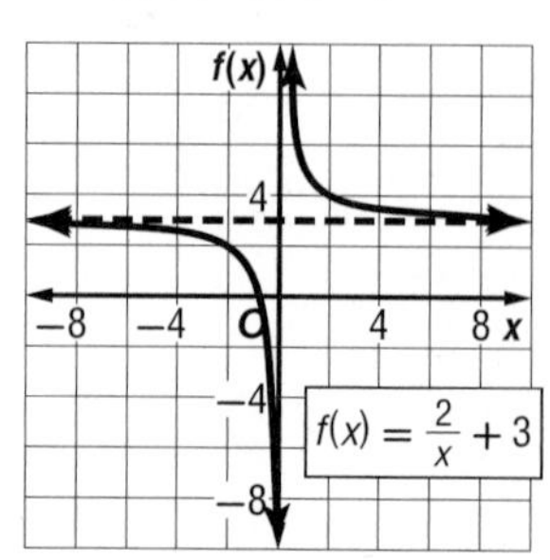

$D = \{x \mid x \neq 0\}$;
$R = \{f(x) \mid f(x) \neq 3\}$

16.

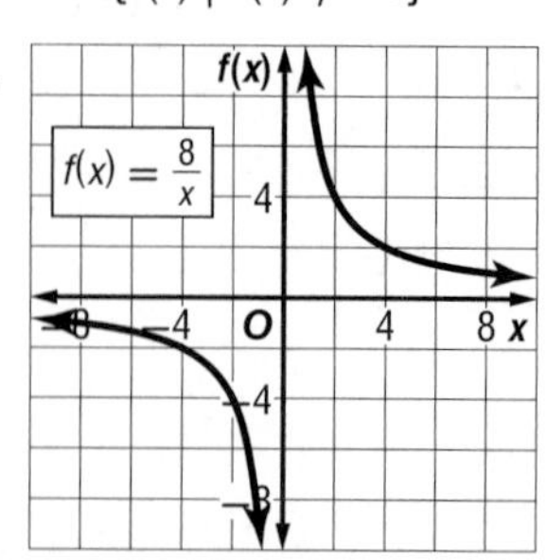

$D = \{x \mid x \neq 0\}$;
$R = \{f(x) \mid f(x) \neq 0\}$

17.

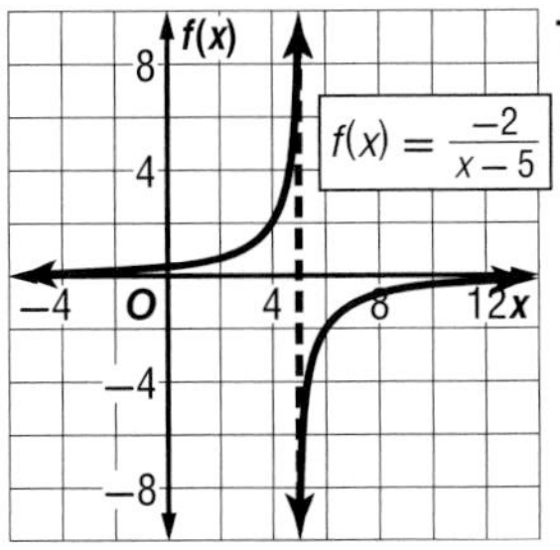

D = {x | x ≠ 5};
R = {f(x) | f(x) ≠ 0}

18.

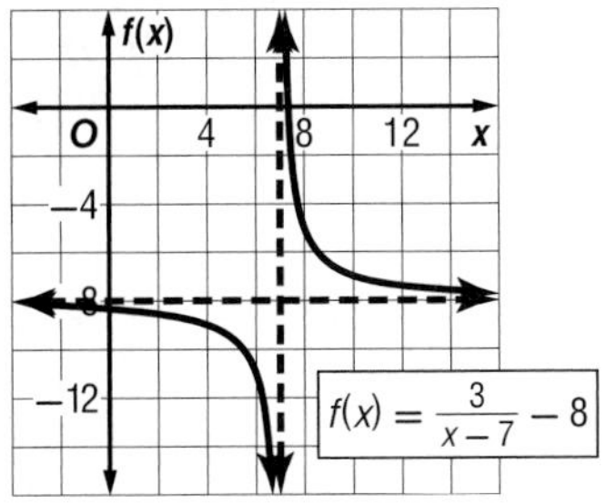

D = {x | x ≠ 7};
R = {f(x) | f(x) ≠ –8}

19.

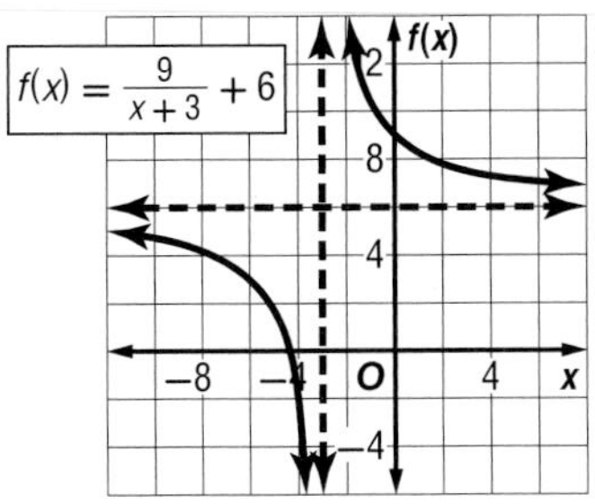

D = {x | x ≠ –3};
R = {f(x) | f(x) ≠ 6}

20.

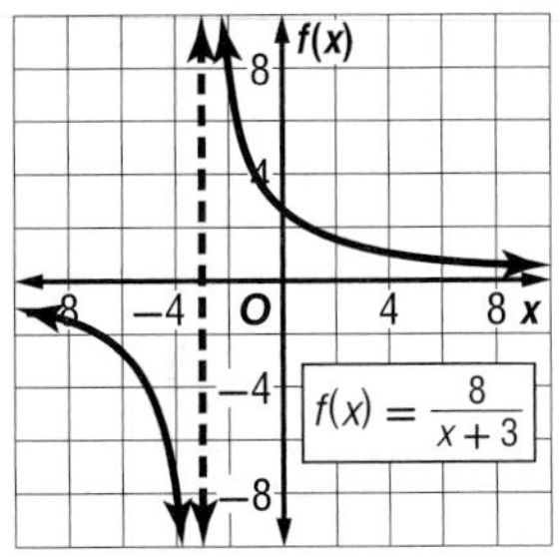

D = {x | x ≠ –3};
R = {f(x) | f(x) ≠ 0}

21.

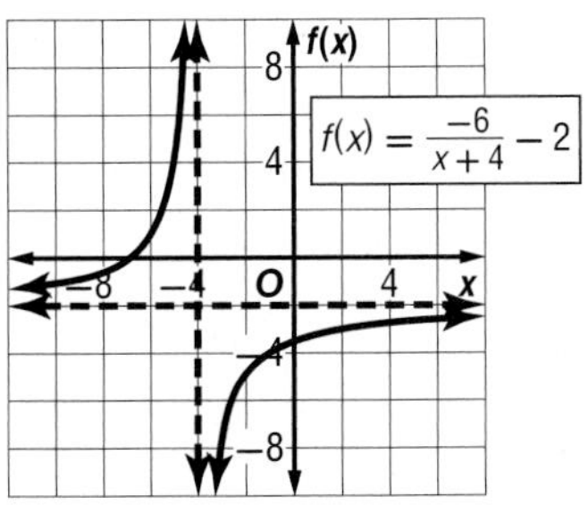

D = {x | x ≠ –4}; R = {f(x) | f(x) ≠ –2}

22.

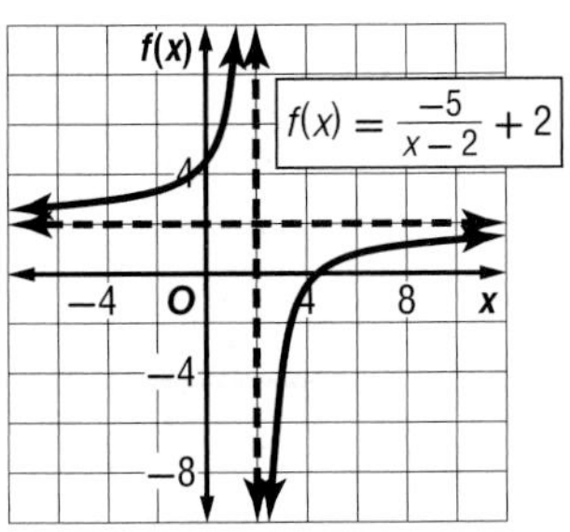

D = {x | x ≠ 2}; R = {f(x) | f(x) ≠ 2}

23b.

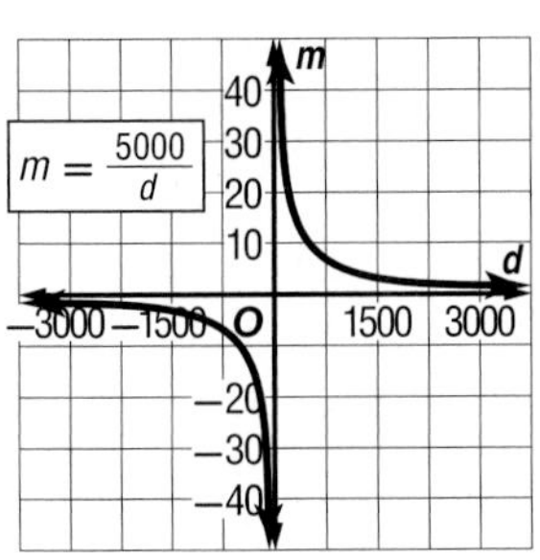

24b.

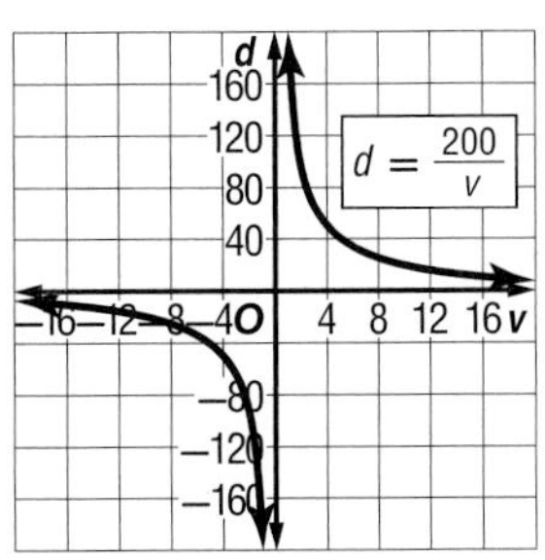

25.

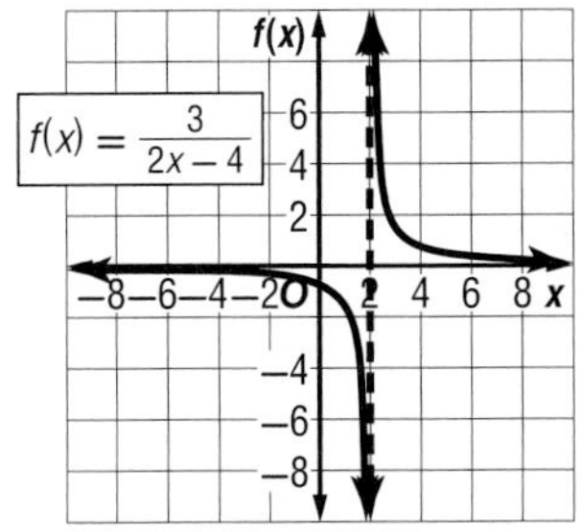

D = {x | x ≠ 2};
R = {f(x) | f(x) ≠ 0}

26.

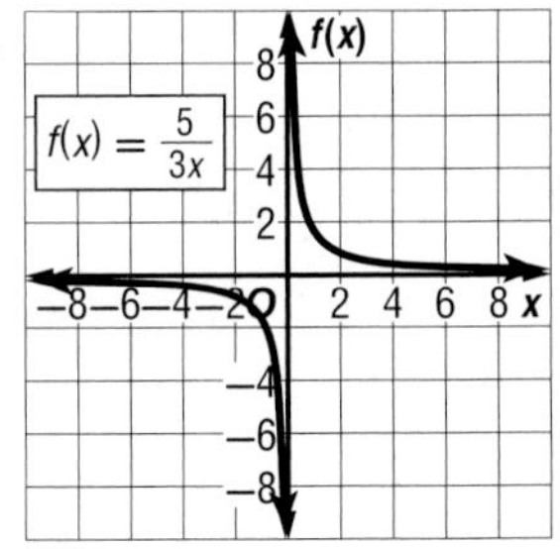

D = {x | x ≠ 0};
R = {f(x) | f(x) ≠ 0}

27.

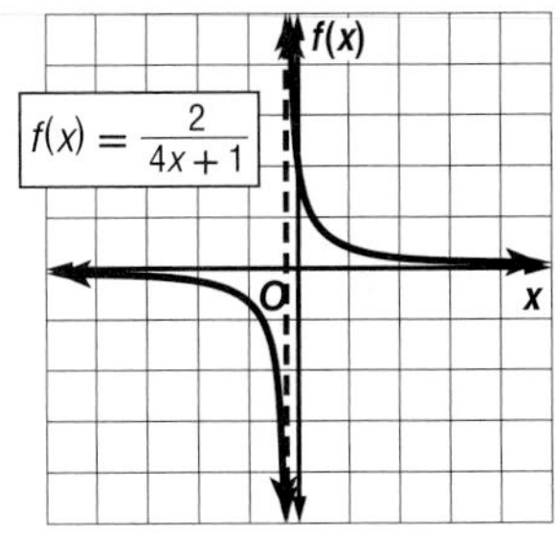

$D = \left\{x \middle| x \neq -\frac{1}{4}\right\}$;
R = {f(x) | f(x) ≠ 0}

28.

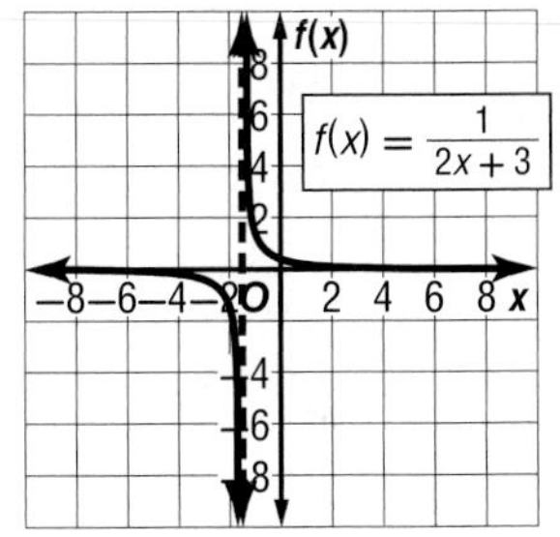

$D = \left\{x \middle| x \neq -\frac{3}{2}\right\}$;
R = {f(x) | f(x) ≠ 0}

29b.

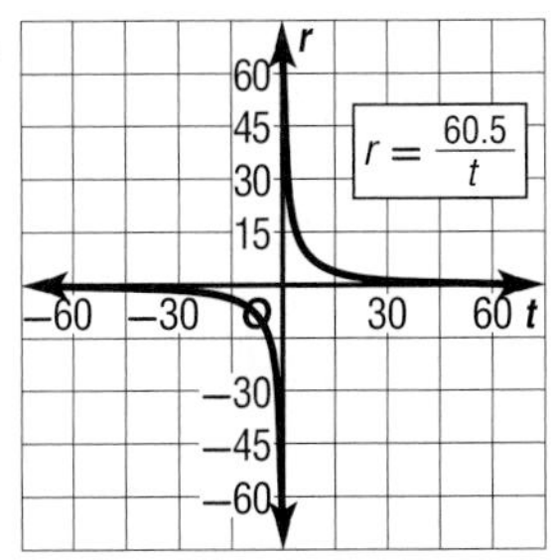

30.

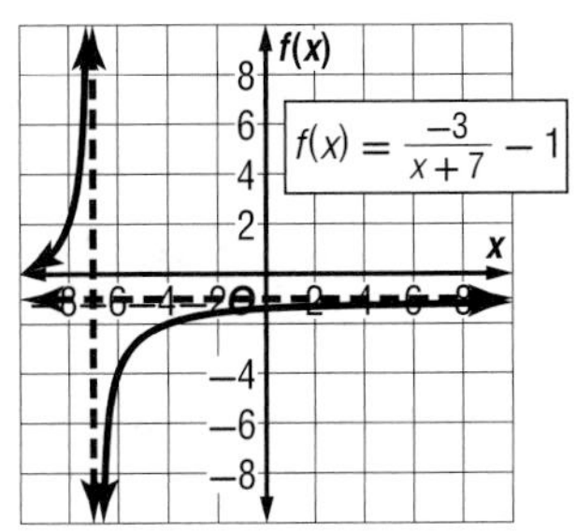

D = {x | x ≠ –7}; R = {f(x) | f(x) ≠ –1}; x = –7, f(x) = –1

31.

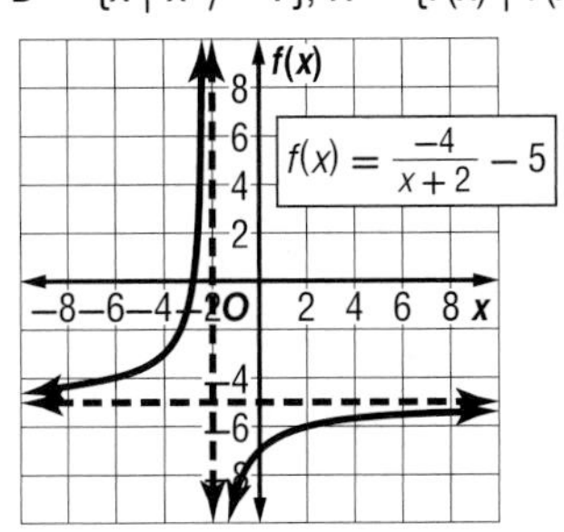

D = {x | x ≠ –2}; R = {f(x) | f(x) ≠ –5}; x = –2, f(x) = –5

32.

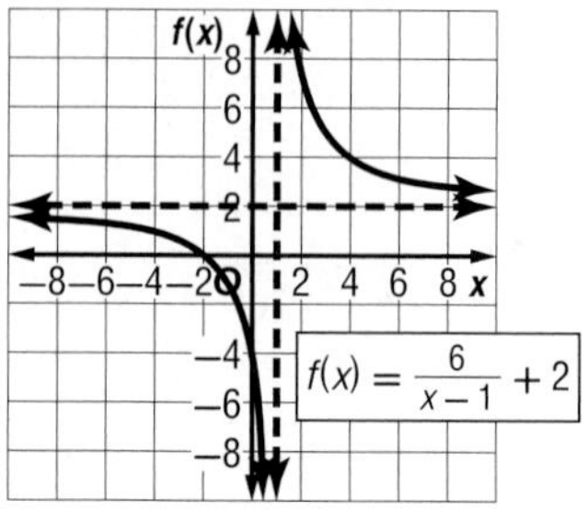

$D = \{x \mid x \neq 1\}$; $R = \{f(x) \mid f(x) \neq 2\}$; $x = 1$, $f(x) = 2$

33.

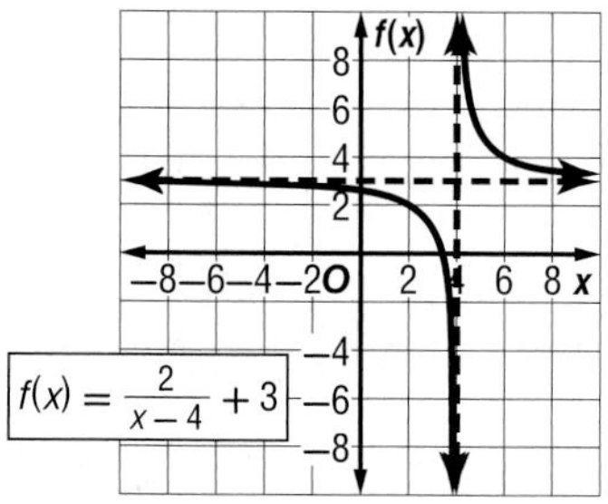

$D = \{x \mid x \neq 4\}$; $R = \{f(x) \mid f(x) \neq 3\}$; $x = 4$, $f(x) = 3$

34.

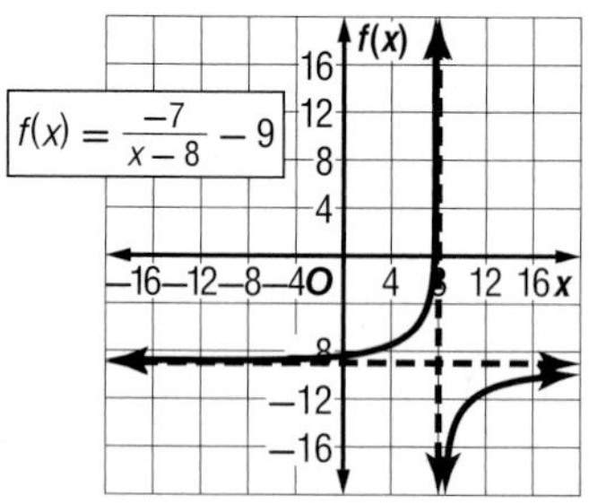

$D = \{x \mid x \neq 8\}$; $R = \{f(x) \mid f(x) \neq -9\}$; $x = 8$, $f(x) = -9$

35.

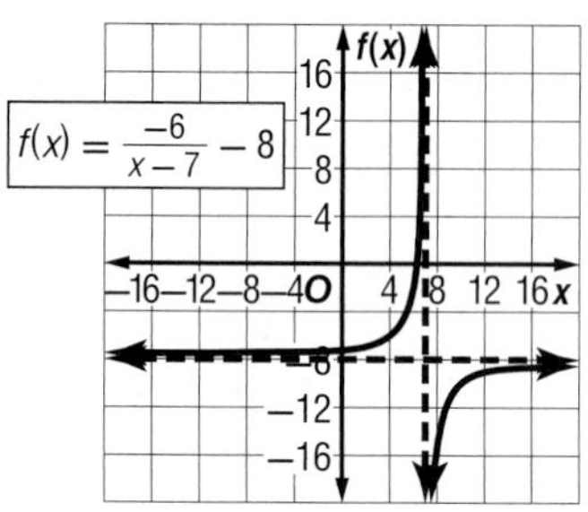

$D = \{x \mid x \neq 7\}$; $R = \{f(x) \mid f(x) \neq -8\}$; $x = 7$, $f(x) = -8$

36b.

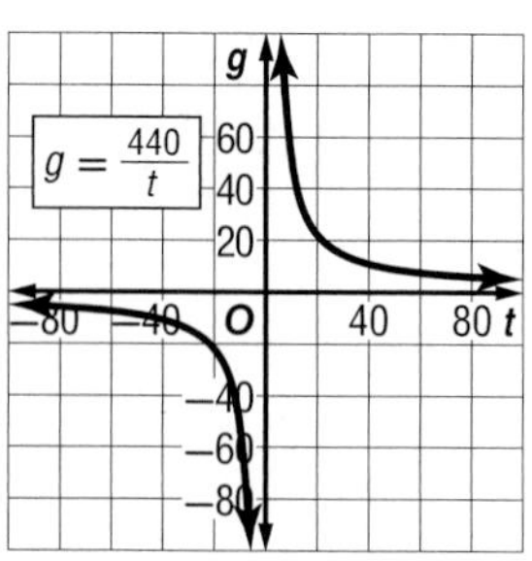

37a.

$f(x) = \frac{1}{x}$		$f(x) = \frac{1}{x^2}$	
x	$f(x)$	x	$f(x)$
−3	$-\frac{1}{3}$	−3	$\frac{1}{9}$
−2	$-\frac{1}{2}$	−2	$\frac{1}{4}$
−1	−1	−1	1
0	undefined	0	undefined
1	1	1	1
2	$\frac{1}{2}$	2	$\frac{1}{4}$
3	$\frac{1}{3}$	3	$\frac{1}{9}$

37b.

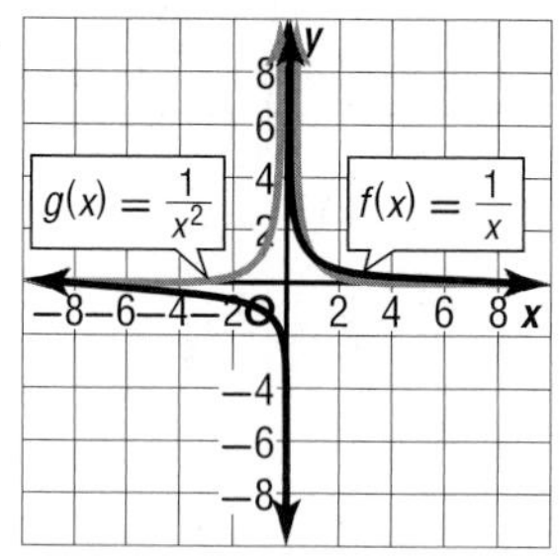

37c. The positive portion of $g(x) = \frac{1}{x^2}$ is similar to the graph of $f(x) = \frac{1}{x}$. Positive values of x produce positive values of $f(x)$. The negative portion of $g(x) = \frac{1}{x^2}$ appears to be a reflection of $f(x) = \frac{1}{x}$ over the x-axis. Negative values of x produce positive values of $g(x)$.

37d. Sample answer: When n is even, the graph will show symmetry with respect to the y-axis. When n is odd, the graph will show symmetry with respect to the origin.

39d.

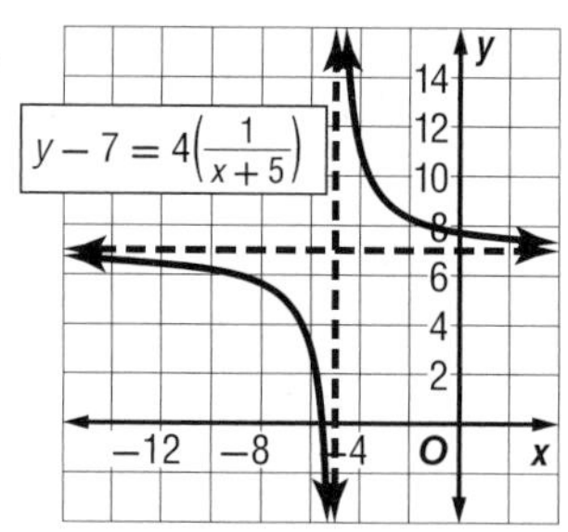

41. Sample answer = $f(x) = \frac{2}{x-3} + 4$ and $g(x) = \frac{5}{x-3} + 4$

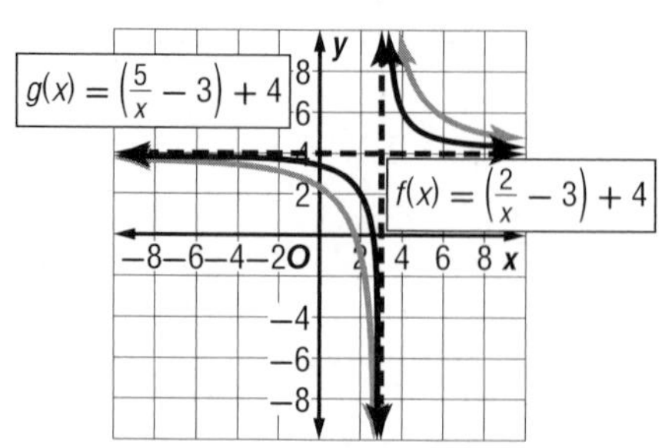

42. A rational function can be used to determine how much each person needs to sell if the cost of the trip and the number of people going on the trip and selling the candy is *s*. The number of people selling and the number of bars sold per person must both be non-negative they also must both be integers. So only the first quadrant part of the graph is meaningful in the context of the problem.

60.

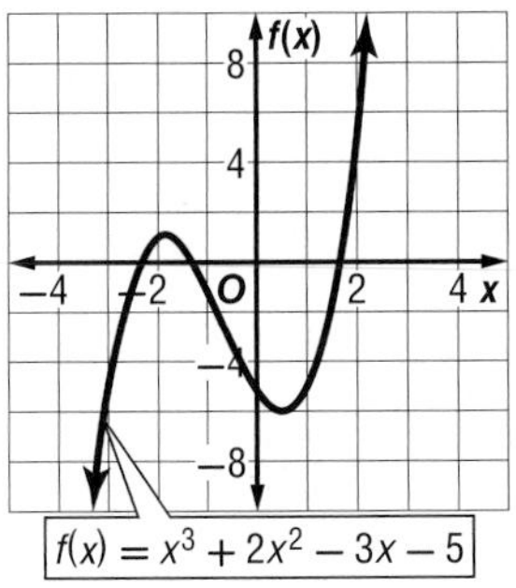

rel. max. at $x = -2$, rel. min. at $x = 0.5$; D = {all real numbers}, R = {all real numbers}

61.

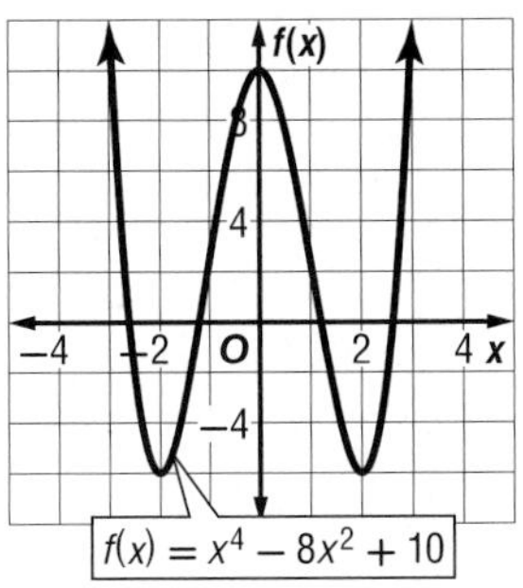

rel. max. at $x = 0$, rel. min. at $x = -2$ and at $x = 2$; D = {all real numbers}, R = $\{f(x) \mid f(x) \geq -6\}$

Page 576, Mid-Chapter Quiz

19.

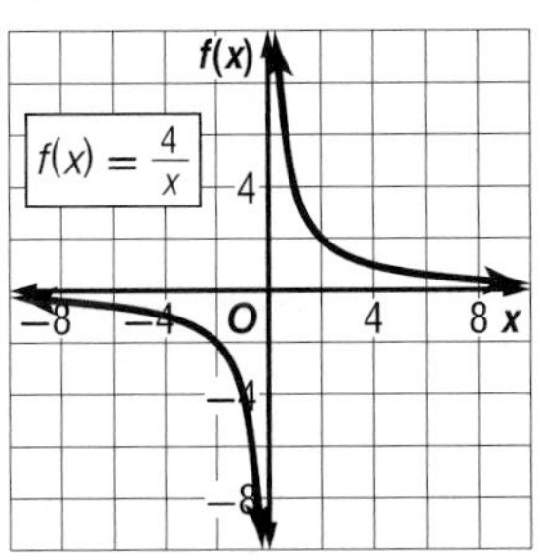

$D = \{x \mid x \neq 0\}$, $R = \{f(x) \mid f(x) \neq 0\}$

20.

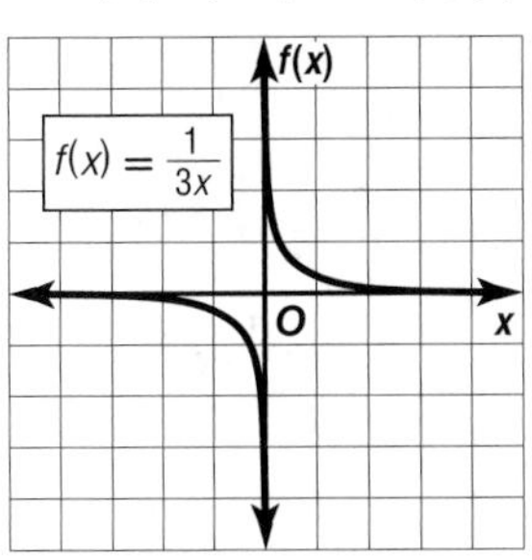

$D = \{x \mid x \neq 0\}$, $R = \{f(x) \mid f(x) \neq 0\}$

21.

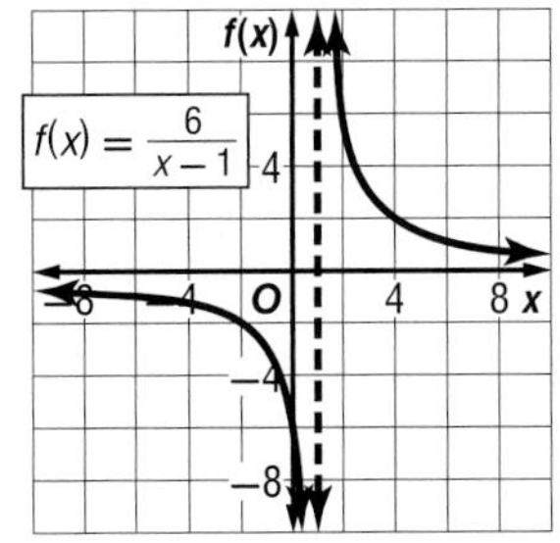

$D = \{x \mid x \neq 1\}$, $R = \{f(x) \mid f(x) \neq 0\}$

22.

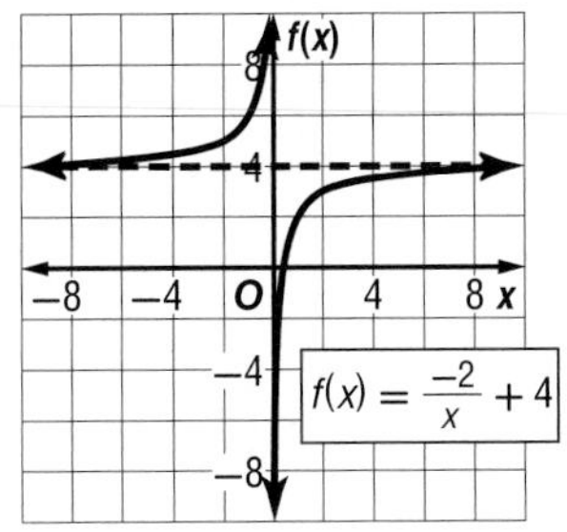

$D = \{x \mid x \neq 0\}$, $R = \{f(x) \mid f(x) \neq 4\}$

23.

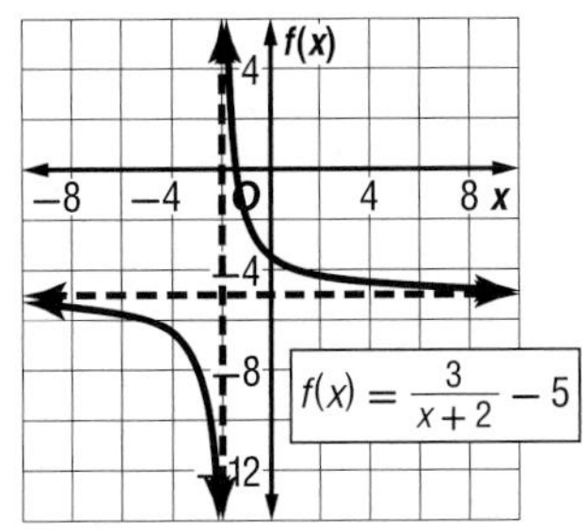

$D = \{x \mid x \neq -2\}$, $R = \{f(x) \mid f(x) \neq -5\}$

24.

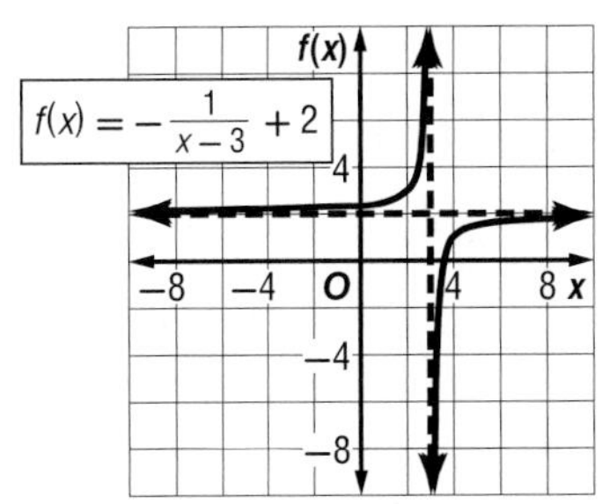

$D = \{x \mid x \neq 3\}$, $R = \{f(x) \mid f(x) \neq 2\}$

Pages 581–583, Lesson 9-4

1.

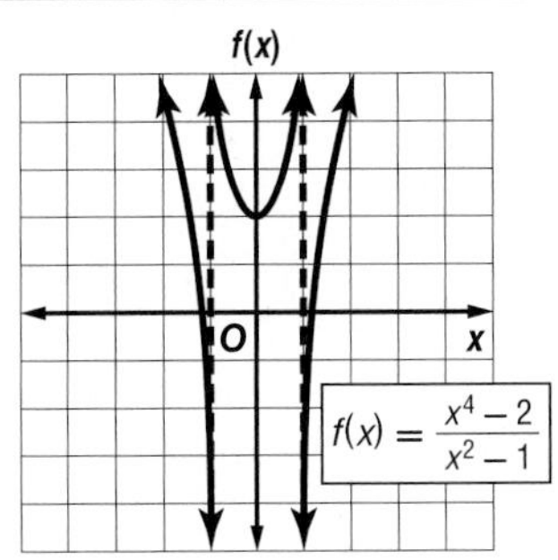

2.

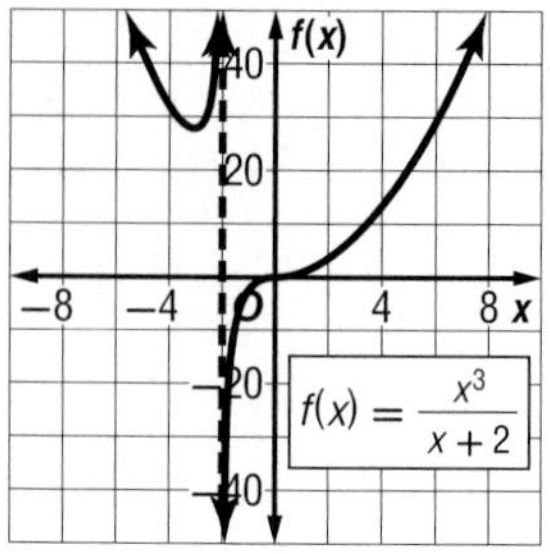

3a.

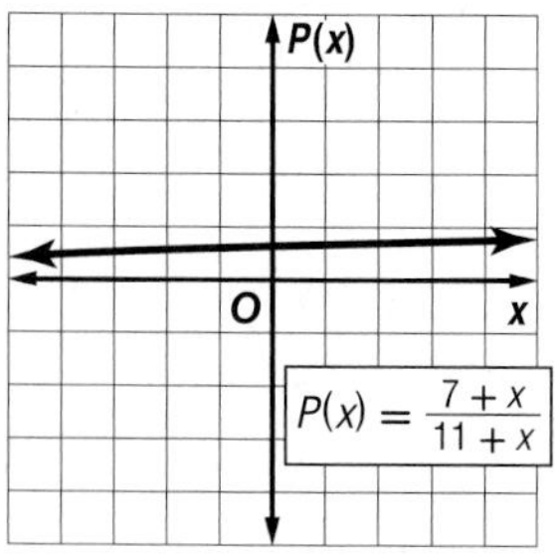

4.

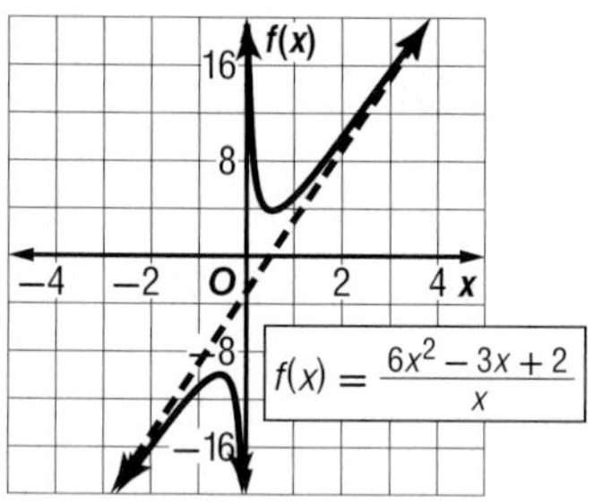

5.

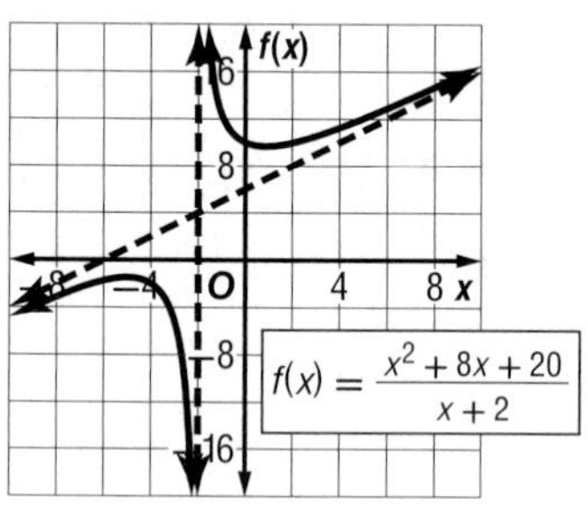

6.

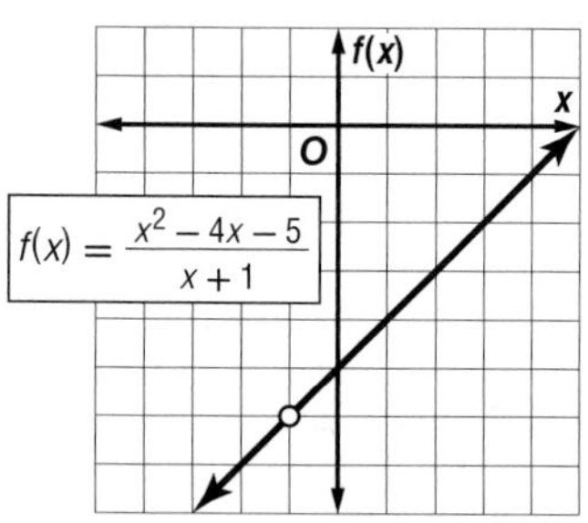

7.

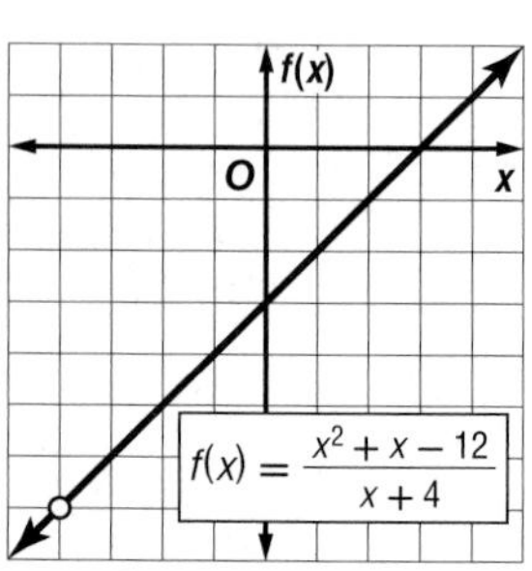

13.

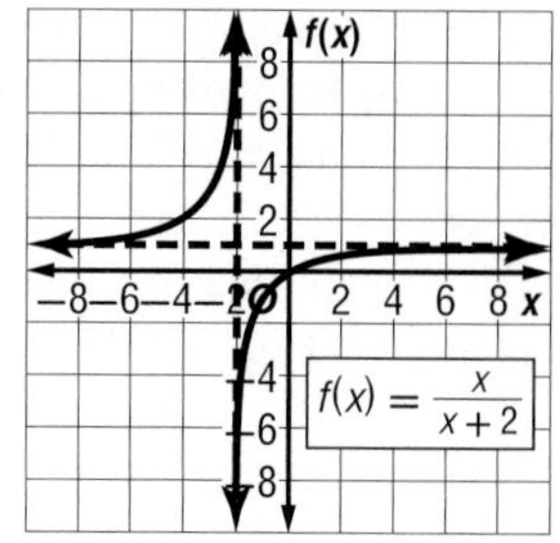

14.

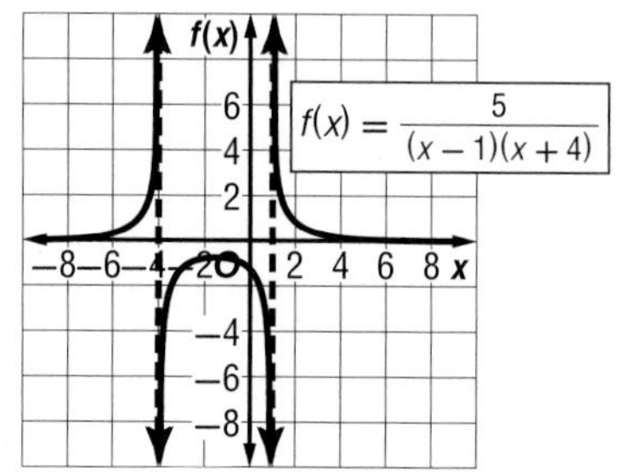

15.

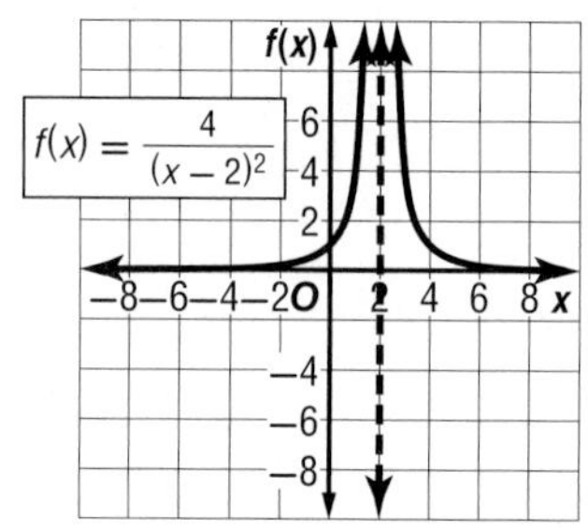

16.

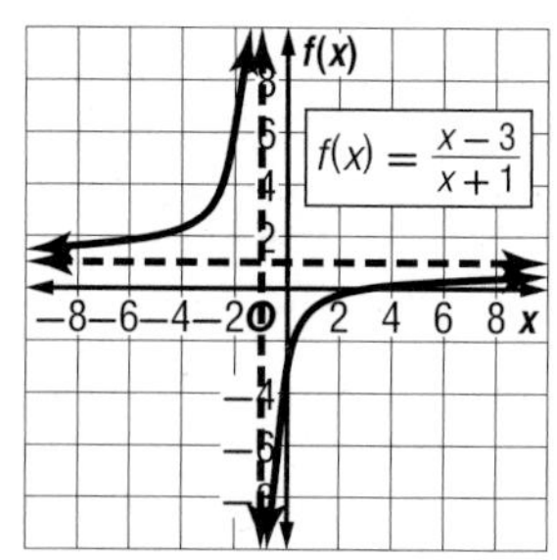

17.

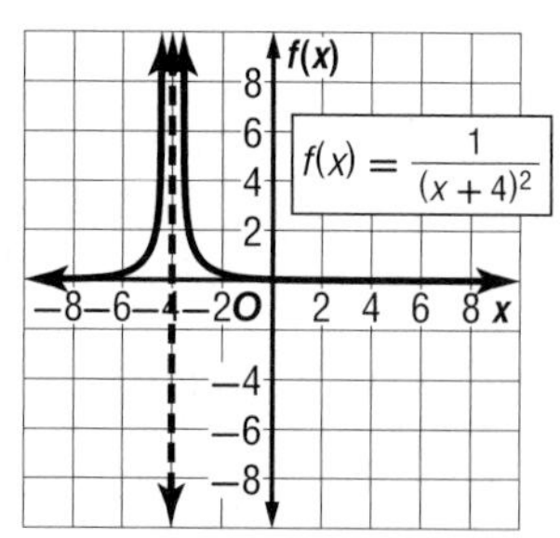

18.

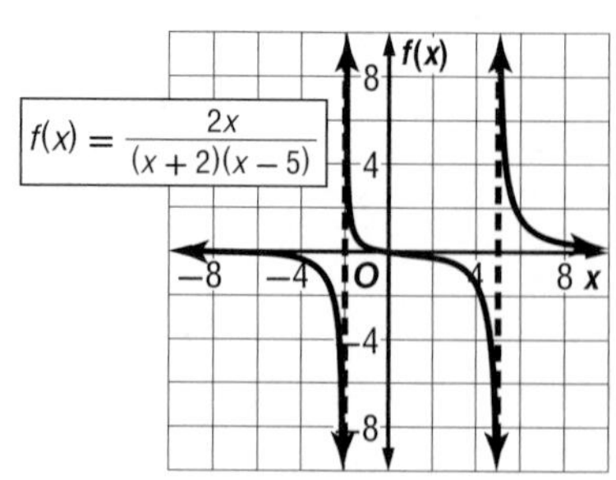

19.

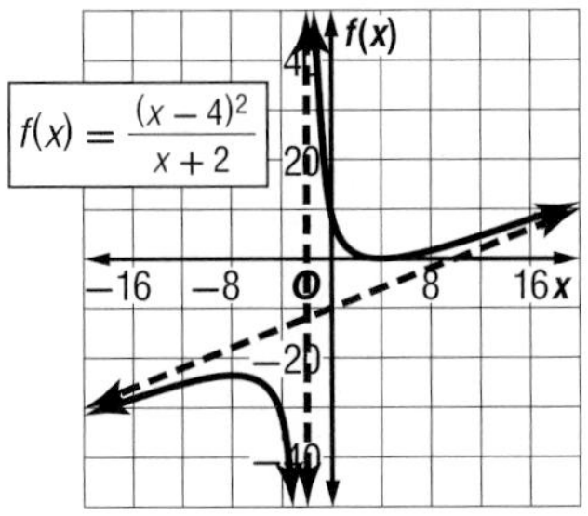

20.

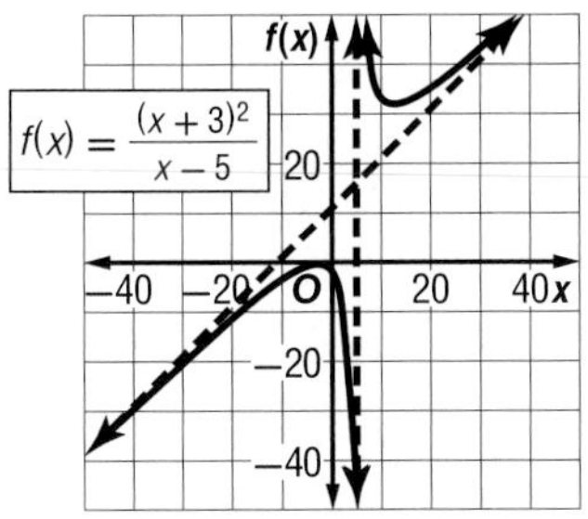

21.

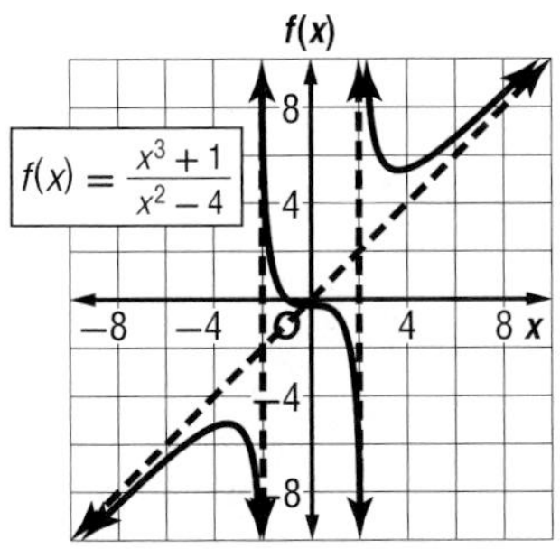

22.

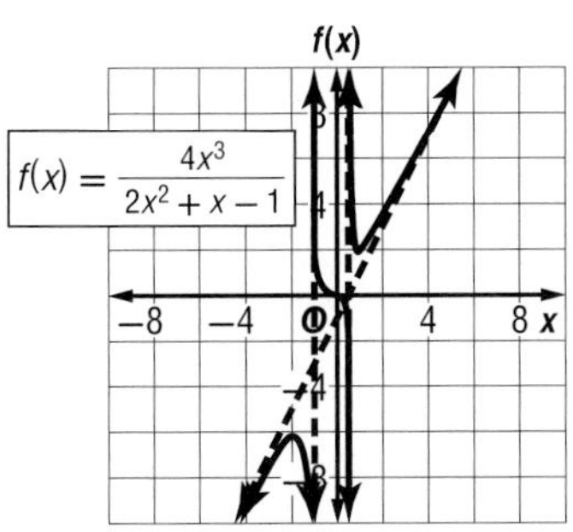

23.

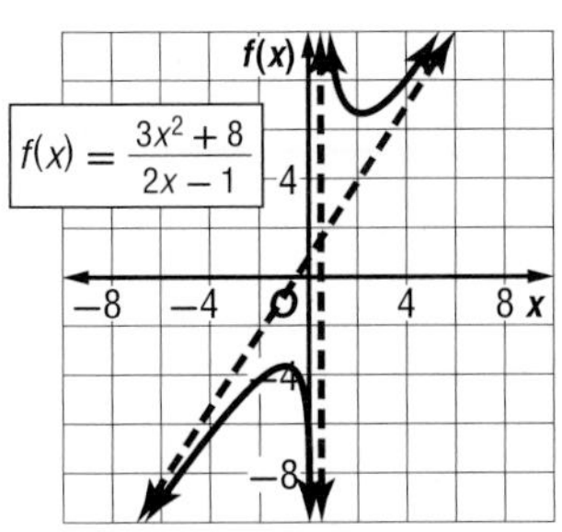

24.

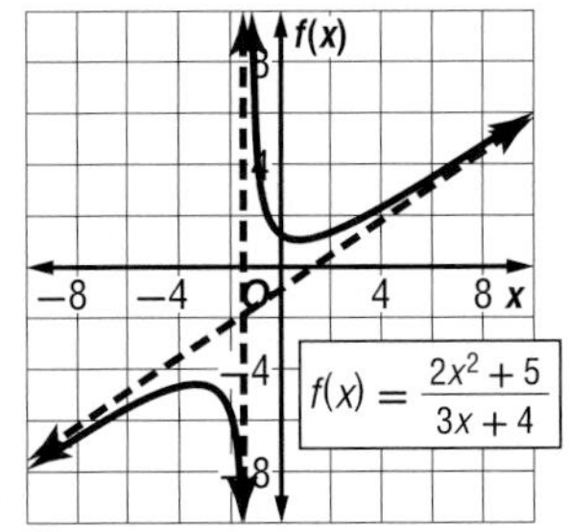

25.

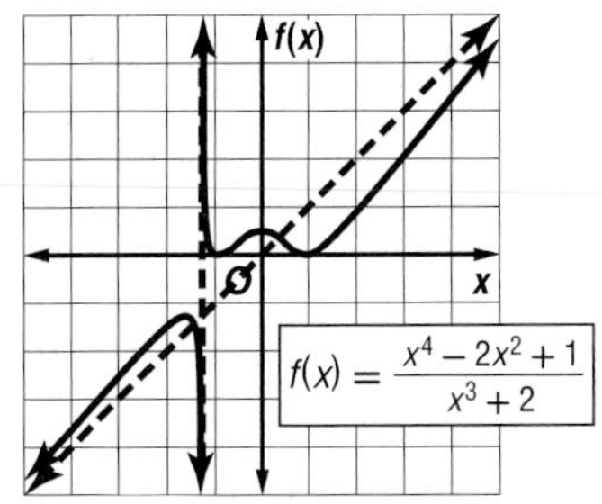

26.

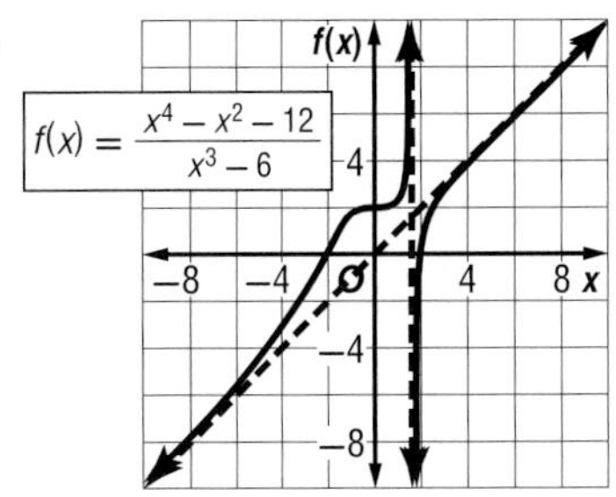

27a.

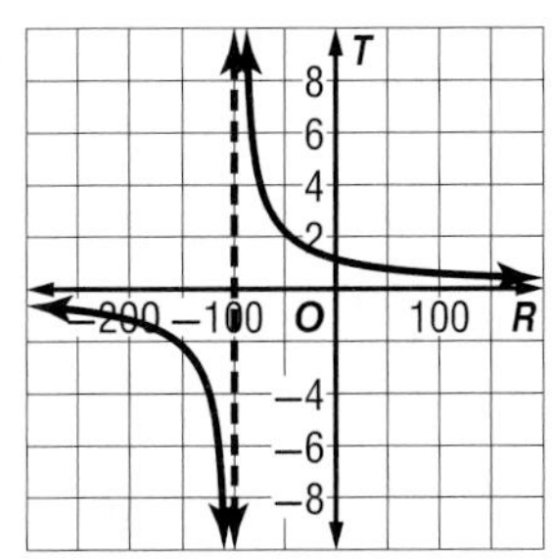

28.

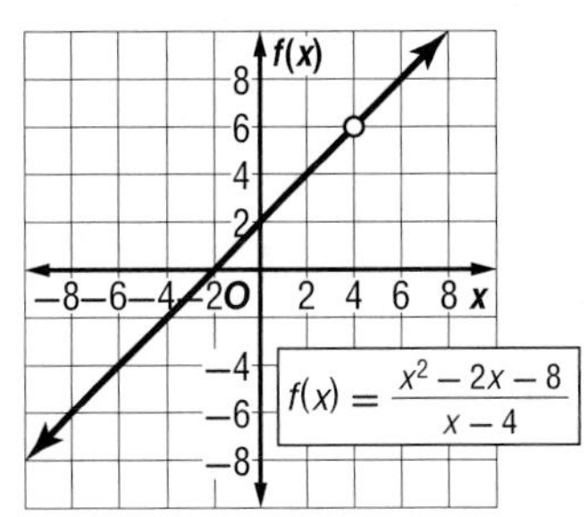

29.

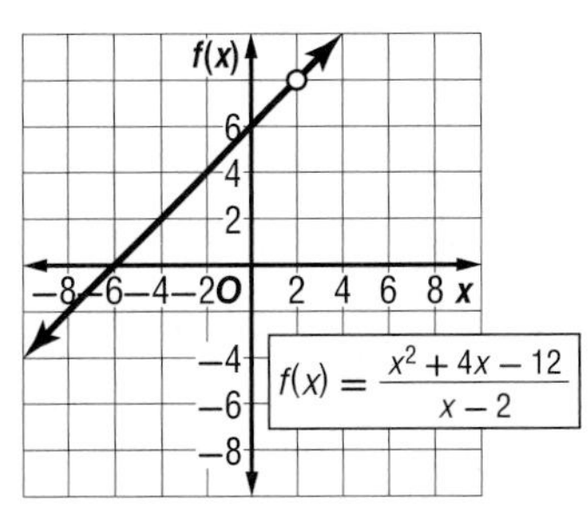

30.

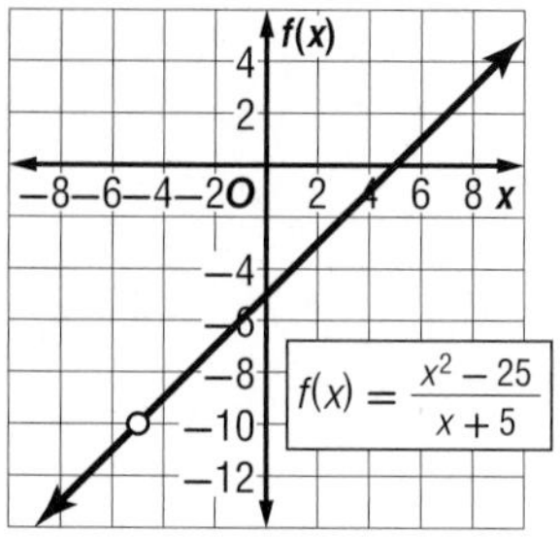

31.

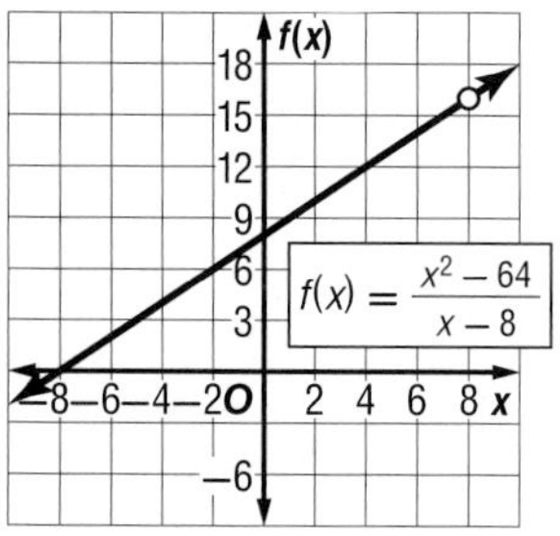

32.

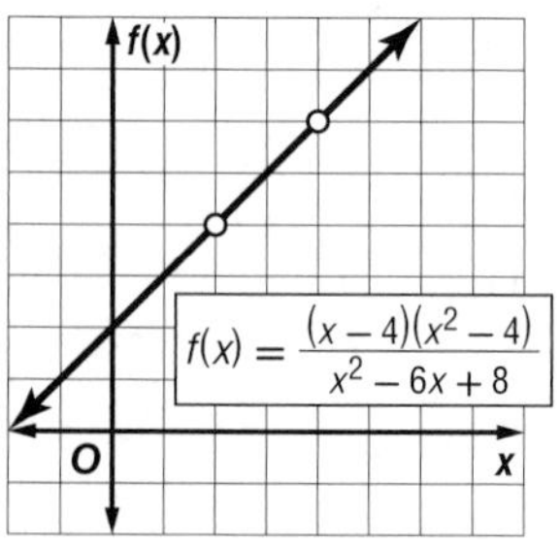

33.

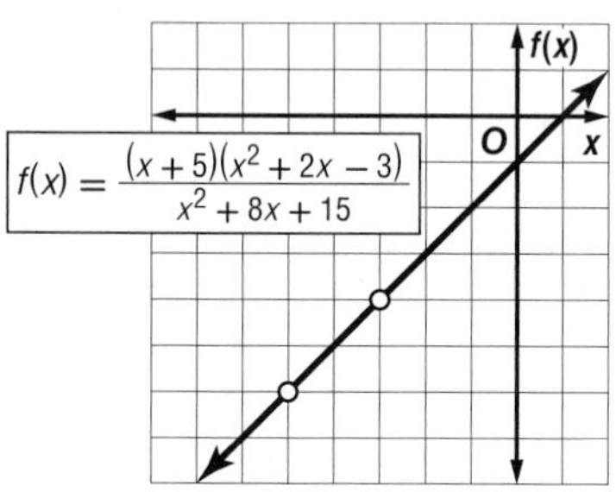

34.

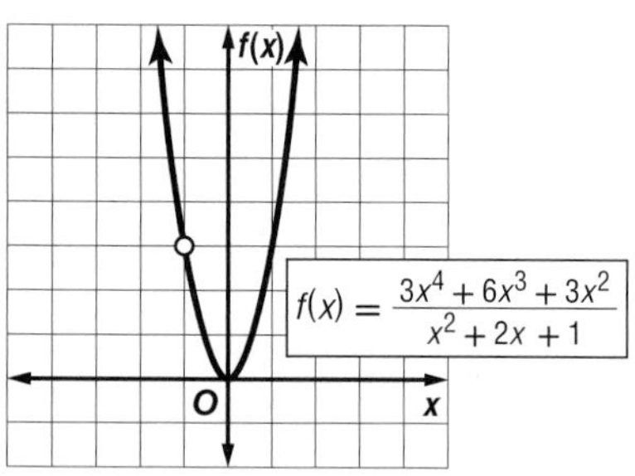

35.

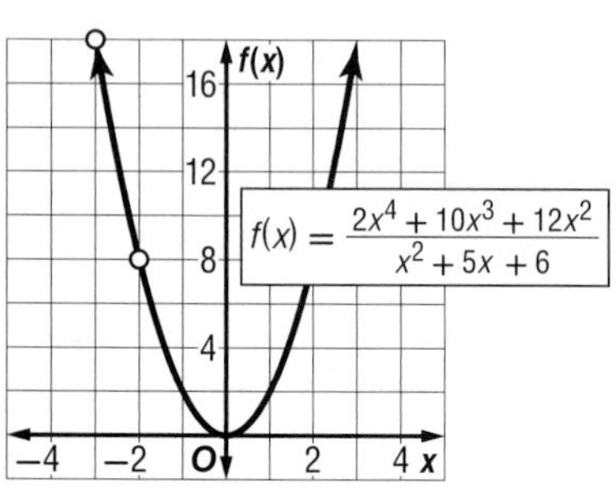

36a. $f(x) = \dfrac{4500 + 50x}{x}$

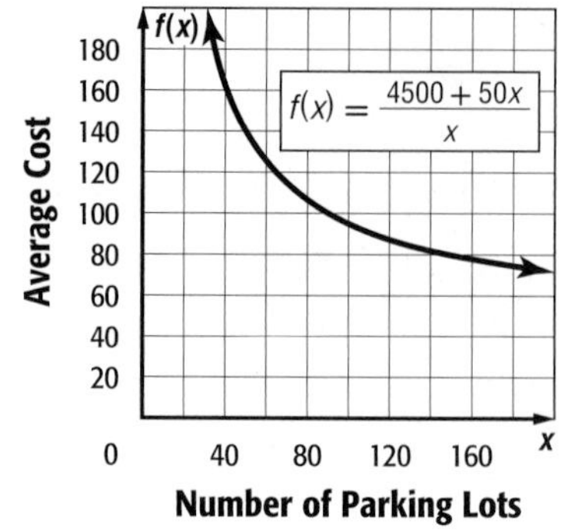

37a. $f(x) = \dfrac{150 + 40x}{x}$

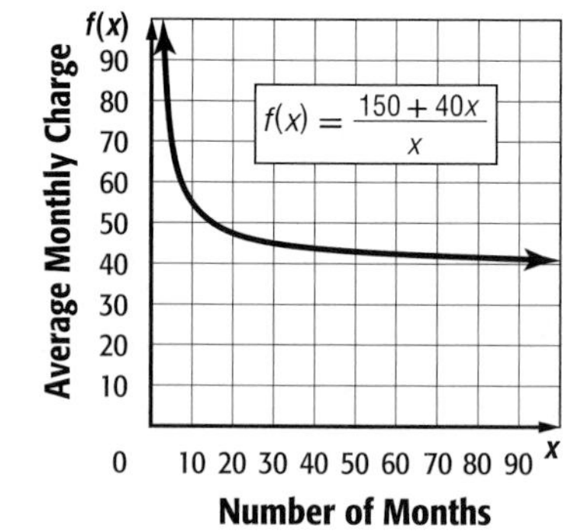

38a.

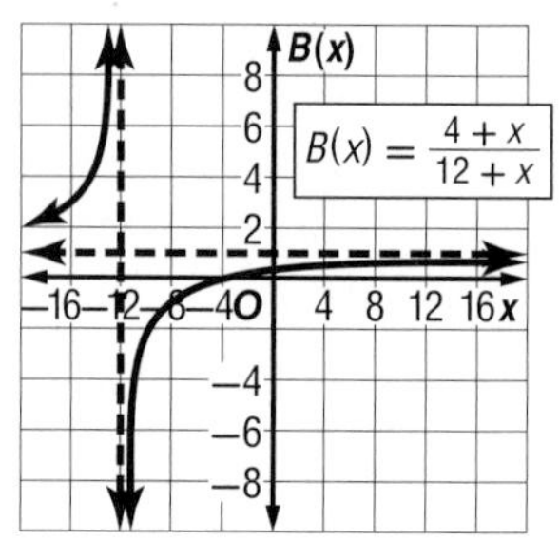

39.

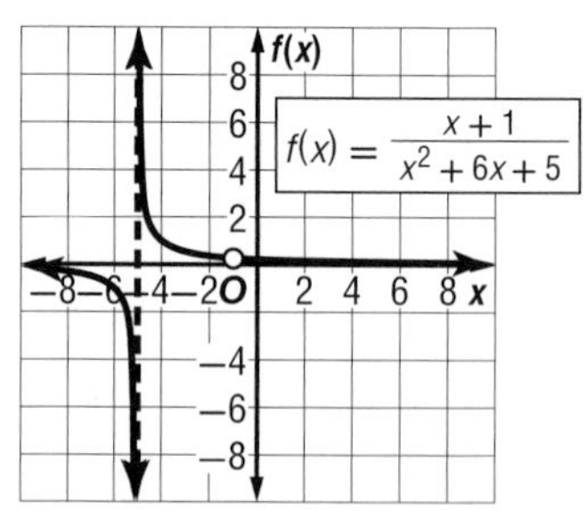

40.

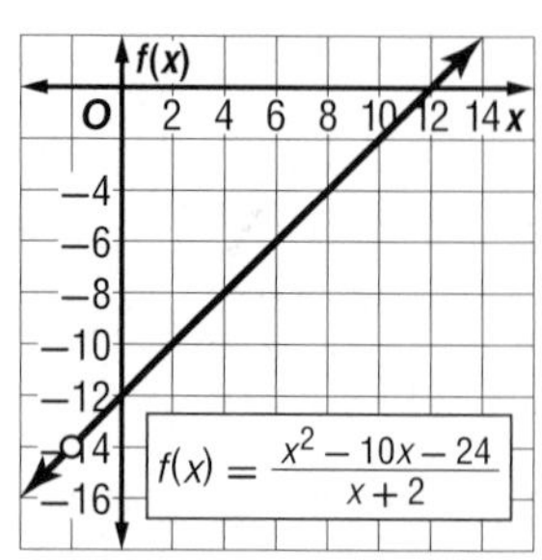

Chapter 9 Answer Appendix

41. 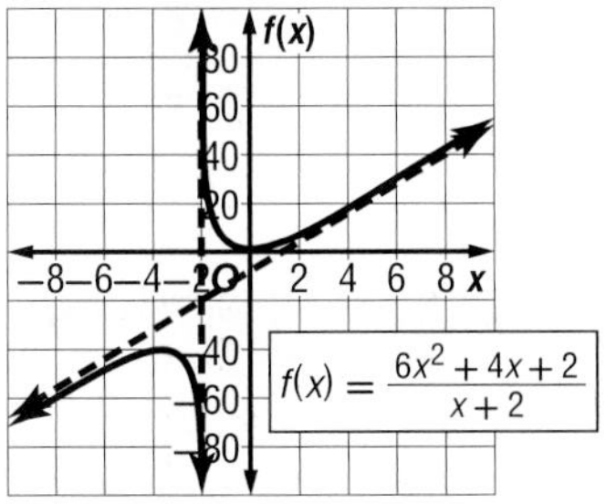

42. Sample graph:

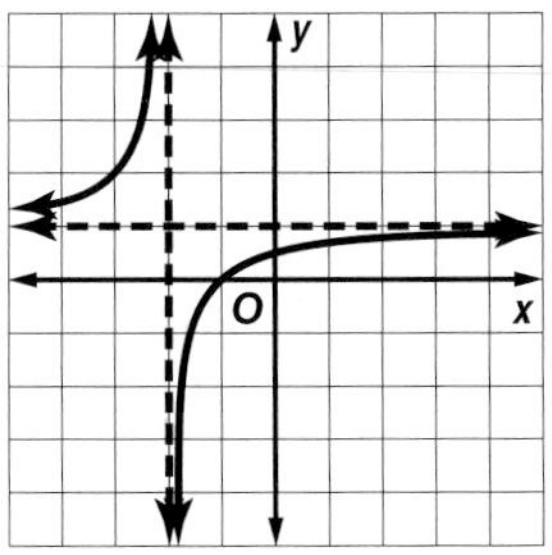

Page 609, Practice Test

11. 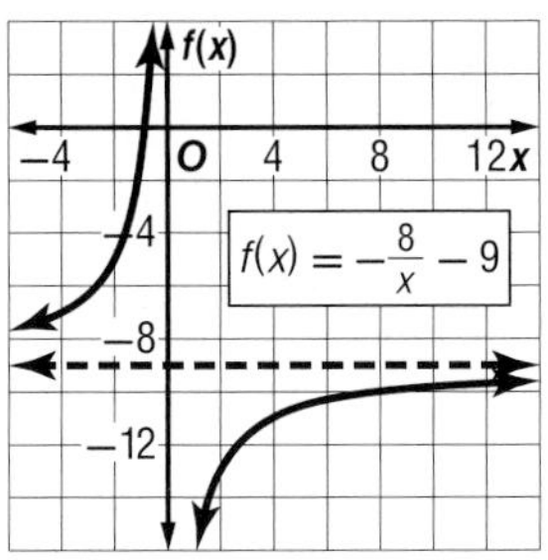

12. 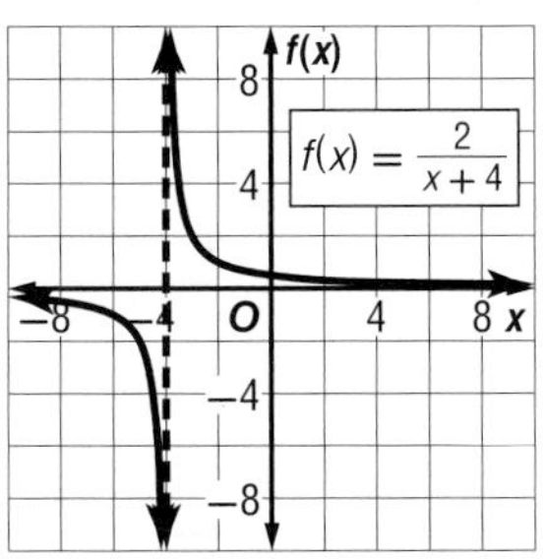

13. 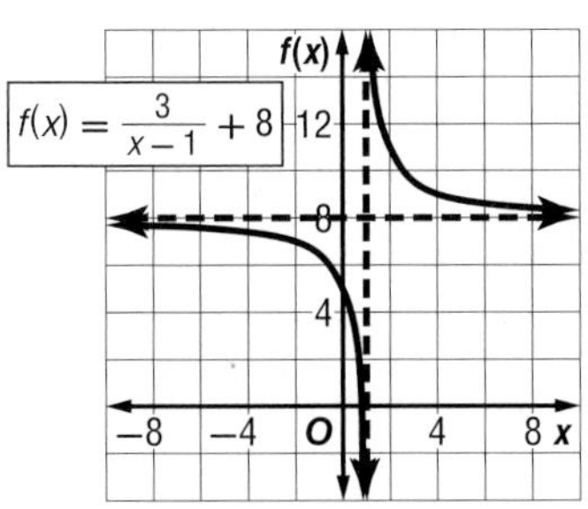

14. 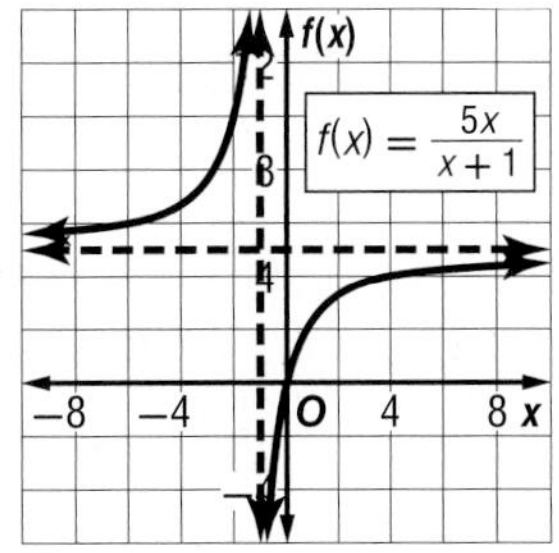

15. 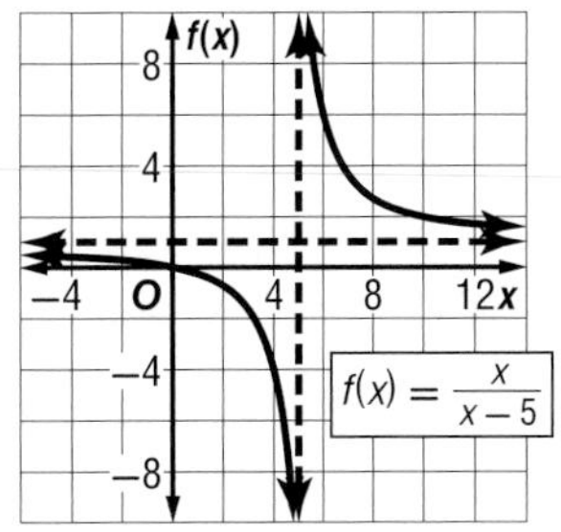

16. 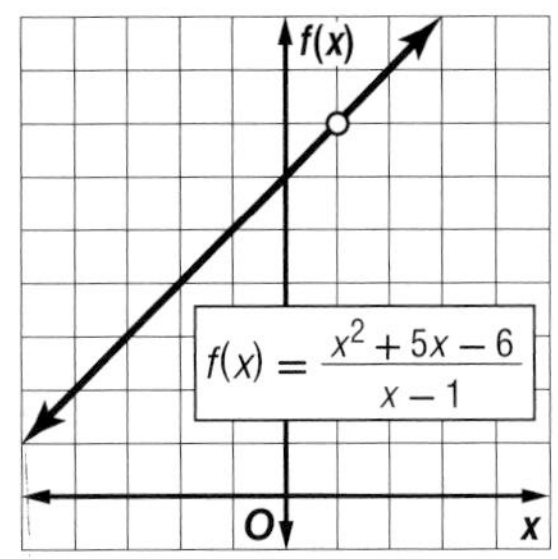

Chapter 9 Answer Appendix

CHAPTER 10 Chapter Planner

Diagnostic Assessment
Quick Check, p. 615

	Lesson 10-1 Pacing: 1 day	Lesson 10-2 Pacing: 1 day	Explore 10-3 Pacing: 0.5 day
Title	**Midpoint and Distance Formulas**	**Parabolas**	**Graphing Technology Lab: Equations of Circles**
Objectives	• Find the midpoint of a segment on the coordinate plane. • Find the distance between two points on the coordinate plane.	• Write equations of parabolas in standard form. • Graph parabolas.	• Use a graphing calculator to examine the characteristics of a circle and its equation.
Key Vocabulary		parabola focus directrix latus rectum standard form general form	
NGSSS	MA.912.G.1.1	MA.912.A.9.1, MA.912.A.9.2	MA.912.A.9.2
Multiple Representations	p. 621	p. 628	
Lesson Resources	**Chapter 10 Resource Masters** • Study Guide and Intervention, pp. 5–6 AL OL ELL • Skills Practice, p. 7 AL OL ELL • Practice, p. 8 AL OL BL ELL • Word Problem Practice, p. 9 AL OL BL ELL • Enrichment, p. 10 OL BL • Quiz 1, p. 53 AL OL BL ELL **Transparencies** • 5-Minute Check Transparency 10-1 AL OL BL ELL **Additional Print Resources** • Study Notebook AL OL BL ELL	**Chapter 10 Resource Masters** • Study Guide and Intervention, pp. 11–12 AL OL ELL • Skills Practice, p. 13 AL OL ELL • Practice, p. 14 AL OL BL ELL • Word Problem Practice, p. 15 AL OL BL ELL • Enrichment, p. 16 OL BL • Spreadsheet Activity, p. 17 OL • Quiz 1, p. 53 AL OL BL ELL **Transparencies** • 5-Minute Check Transparency 10-2 AL OL BL ELL **Additional Print Resources** • Study Notebook AL OL BL ELL • Teaching Algebra with Manipulatives, p. 241 AL OL ELL	**Materials** • TI-Nspire or TI-Nspire CAS graphing calculator
Technology for Every Lesson	FL Math Online glencoe.com • Extra Examples • Self-Check Quizzes • Personal Tutor • Homework Help	**CD/DVD Resources** IWB INTERACTIVE WHITEBOARD READY IWB StudentWorks Plus IWB Interactive Classroom IWB Diagnostic and Assessment Planner	• TeacherWorks Plus • eSolutions Manual Plus • ExamView Assessment Suite
Get Animated			
Differentiated Instruction	pp. 618, 622	pp. 624, 629	

KEY: AL Approaching Level OL On Level BL Beyond Level ELL English Learners

Suggested Pacing			
Time Periods	Instruction	Review & Assessment	Total
45-minute	10	2	12
90-minute	6	1	7

Lesson 10-3 Pacing: 1 day	Explore 10-4 Pacing: 0.5 day	Lesson 10-4 Pacing: 1.5 days	Lesson 10-5 Pacing: 1.5 days
Circles	**Algebra Lab: Investigating Ellipses**	**Ellipses**	**Hyperbolas**
• Write equations of circles. • Graph circles.	• Determine how the graph of an ellipsis is affected by changing the location of the foci.	• Write equations of ellipses. • Graph ellipses.	• Write equations of hyperbolas. • Graph hyperbolas.
circle center radius		ellipse foci major axis minor axis constant sum	hyperbola transverse axis conjugate axis vertices co-vertices constant difference
MA.912.G.6.6, MA.912.G.6.7	MA.912.A.9.2	MA.912.A.9.1, MA.912.A.9.2	MA.912.A.9.1, MA.912.A.9.2
p. 636		p. 645	p. 653
Chapter 10 Resource Masters • Study Guide and Intervention, pp. 18–19 AL OL ELL • Skills Practice, p. 20 AL OL ELL • Practice, p. 21 AL OL BL ELL • Word Problem Practice, p. 22 AL OL BL ELL • Enrichment, p. 23 OL BL • Graphing Calculator Activity, p. 24 OL • Quiz 2, p. 53 AL OL BL ELL **Transparencies** • 5-Minute Check Transparency 10-3 AL OL BL ELL **Additional Print Resources** • Study Notebook AL OL BL ELL	**Additional Print Resources** • Teaching Algebra with Manipulatives, pp. 242–243 AL OL ELL	**Chapter 10 Resource Masters** • Study Guide and Intervention, pp. 25–26 AL OL ELL • Skills Practice, p. 27 AL OL ELL • Practice, p. 28 AL OL BL ELL • Word Problem Practice, p. 29 AL OL BL ELL • Enrichment, p. 30 OL BL • Graphing Calculator Activity, p. 31 OL • Quiz 2, p. 53 AL OL BL ELL **Transparencies** • 5-Minute Check Transparency 10-4 AL OL BL ELL **Additional Print Resources** • Study Notebook AL OL BL ELL	**Chapter 10 Resource Masters** • Study Guide and Intervention, pp. 32–33 AL OL ELL • Skills Practice, p. 34 AL OL ELL • Practice, p. 35 AL OL BL ELL • Word Problem Practice, p. 36 AL OL BL ELL • Enrichment, p. 37 OL BL • Graphing Calculator Activity, p. 38 OL • Quiz 3, p. 54 AL OL BL ELL **Transparencies** • 5-Minute Check Transparency 10-5 AL OL BL ELL **Additional Print Resources** • Study Notebook AL OL BL ELL
FL Math Online glencoe.com • Extra Examples • Self-Check Quizzes • Personal Tutor • Homework Help	**CD/DVD Resources** IWB INTERACTIVE WHITEBOARD READY IWB StudentWorks Plus IWB Interactive Classroom IWB Diagnostic and Assessment Planner	• TeacherWorks Plus • eSolutions Manual Plus • ExamView Assessment Suite	
pp. 632, 634, 637		pp. 641, 642, 646	pp. 649, 655

Formative Assessment
Mid-Chapter Quiz, p. 647

CHAPTER 10

Chapter Planner

	Lesson 10-6 Pacing: 1.5 days	Extend 10-6 Pacing: 0.5 day	Lesson 10-7 Pacing: 1 day
Title	**Identifying Conic Sections**	**Graphing Technology Lab: Identifying and Graphing conic sections.**	**Solving Linear-Nonlinear Systems**
Objectives	• Write equations of conic sections in standard form. • Identify conic sections from their equations.	• Graph conic sections using a graphing calculator.	• Solve systems of linear and nonlinear equations algebraically and graphically. • Solve systems of linear and nonlinear inequalities graphically.
Key Vocabulary			
NGSSS	MA.912.A.9.1, MA.912.A.9.2	MA.912.A.9.2	MA.912.A.7.7
Multiple Representations	p. 659		p. 666
Lesson Resources	**Chapter 10 Resource Masters** • Study Guide and Intervention, pp. 39–40 AL OL ELL • Skills Practice, p. 41 AL OL ELL • Practice, p. 42 AL OL BL ELL • Word Problem Practice, p. 43 AL OL BL ELL • Enrichment, p. 44 OL BL • Quiz 3, p. 54 AL OL BL ELL **Transparencies** • 5-Minute Check Transparency 10-6 AL OL BL ELL **Additional Print Resources** • Study Notebook AL OL BL ELL • Teaching Algebra with Manipulatives, pp. 244–245 AL OL ELL	**Materials** • TI-83/84 Plus graphing calculator	**Chapter 10 Resource Masters** • Study Guide and Intervention, pp. 45–46 AL OL ELL • Skills Practice, p. 47 AL OL ELL • Practice, p. 48 AL OL BL ELL • Word Problem Practice, p. 49 AL OL BL ELL • Enrichment, p. 50 OL BL • Quiz 4, p. 55 AL OL BL ELL **Transparencies** • 5-Minute Check Transparency 10-7 AL OL BL ELL **Additional Print Resources** • Study Notebook AL OL BL ELL
Technology for Every Lesson	FL Math Online glencoe.com • Extra Examples • Self-Check Quizzes • Personal Tutor • Homework Help	**CD/DVD Resources** IWB INTERACTIVE WHITEBOARD READY IWB StudentWorks Plus IWB Interactive Classroom IWB Diagnostic and Assessment Planner	• TeacherWorks Plus • eSolutions Manual Plus • ExamView Assessment Suite
Get Animated			Interactive Lab
Differentiated Instruction	pp. 657, 660		pp. 663, 667

KEY: AL Approaching Level OL On Level BL Beyond Level ELL English Learners

Summative Assessment
- Study Guide and Review, pp. 668–672
- Practice Test, p. 673

What the Research Says . . .

Students retain what they learn from their own efforts to address challenging problems that arise from situations that resonate with their own interests. (Steen and Forman, 1995)

- Examples in Chapter 10 include interesting contexts such as solar energy (Lesson 10-2) and astronomy (Lesson 10-5).
- Student-centered contexts such as baseball trajectories (Lesson 10-2), basketball free-throws (Lesson 10-5), and cell phones (Lesson 10-7).

Teacher To Teacher

Judie Campbell
Derry Area High School
Derry, PA

USE BEFORE LESSON 10-6

“ As a final project, I have students make a poster with 6 different types of graphs, explaining how each was derived, and then have them label each part of the graph. An explanation of each graph is required. ”

NOTES:

CHAPTER 10 Assessment and Intervention

SE = Student Edition, **TE** = Teacher Edition, **CRM** = Chapter Resource Masters

	Diagnosis	Prescription
Diagnostic Assessment	**Beginning Chapter 10**	
	Get Ready for Chapter 10 **SE,** p. 615	Response to Intervention **TE,** p. 615
	Beginning Every Lesson	
	Then, Now, Why? **SE** 5-Minute Check Transparencies	Chapter 0 **SE,** pp. P1 through P19 Concepts and Skills Bank **SE** pp. 994–1007
Formative Assessment	**During/After Every Lesson**	
	Guided Practice **SE,** every example Check Your Understanding **SE** H.O.T. Problems **SE** Spiral Review **SE** Additional Examples **TE** Watch Out! **TE** Step 4, Assess **TE** Chapter 10 Quizzes **CRM,** pp. 53–54 Self-Check Quizzes glencoe.com	**Tier 1 Intervention** Concepts and Skills Bank **SE,** pp. 994–1007 Skills Practice **CRM,** Ch. 1–10 glencoe.com **Tier 2 Intervention** Differentiated Instruction **TE** Study Guide and Intervention Masters **CRM,** Ch. 1–10 **Tier 3 Intervention** *Math Triumphs, Alg. 2*
	Mid-Chapter	
	Mid-Chapter Quiz **SE,** 647 Mid-Chapter Test **CRM,** p. 55 ExamView Assessment Suite	**Tier 1 Intervention** Concepts and Skills Bank **SE,** pp. 994–1007 Skills Practice **CRM,** Ch. 1–10 glencoe.com **Tier 2 Intervention** Study Guide and Intervention Masters **CRM,** Ch. 1–10 **Tier 3 Intervention** *Math Triumphs, Alg. 2*
	Before Chapter Test	
	Chapter Study Guide and Review **SE,** pp. 668–672 Practice Test **SE,** p. 673 Standardized Test Practice **SE,** pp. 674–677 Chapter Test glencoe.com Standardized Test Practice glencoe.com Vocabulary Review glencoe.com ExamView Assessment Suite	**Tier 1 Intervention** Concepts and Skills Bank **SE,** pp. 994–1007 Skills Practice **CRM,** Ch. 1–10 glencoe.com **Tier 2 Intervention** Study Guide and Intervention Masters **CRM,** Ch. 1–10 **Tier 3 Intervention** *Math Triumphs, Alg. 2*
Summative Assessment	**After Chapter 10**	
	Multiple-Choice Tests, Forms 1, 2a, 2b, **CRM,** pp. 57–62 Free-Response Tests, Forms 2c, 2d, 3 **CRM,** pp. 63–68 Vocabulary Test **CRM,** p. 56 Extended Response Test **CRM,** p. 69 Standardized Test Practice **CRM,** pp. 70–72 ExamView Assessment Suite	Study Guide and Intervention Masters **CRM,** Ch. 1–10 glencoe.com

Differentiated Instruction

Option 1 Reaching All Learners AL OL BL ELL

NATURALIST Ask each student to find a picture or photograph of an object in nature that is related to circles. Although circles in nature may not be mathematically perfect, they are seen often, as in the shape of a flower, the designs on an insect, or in the ripples on a pond after a stone hits the water. Have students draw a coordinate grid on the picture, find the ordered pair for the center point, a point on the graph, and write an equation for the graph.

KINESTHETIC Write an equation of a parabola on the board. Have your class create a table of values and then graph this parabola using the tiles on the classroom floor as a coordinate grid. Masking tape can be used to mark the focus point and the directrix line. Mark the set of points on the graph with colored masking tape. Connect these points with a heavy rope to create a parabola.

Option 2 Approaching Level AL

As a class, make a set of double paper cone conic section models. Demonstrate that no matter where a cone is sliced horizontally, the result is a circle, as shown below. Demonstrate the other conic sections in a similar manner.

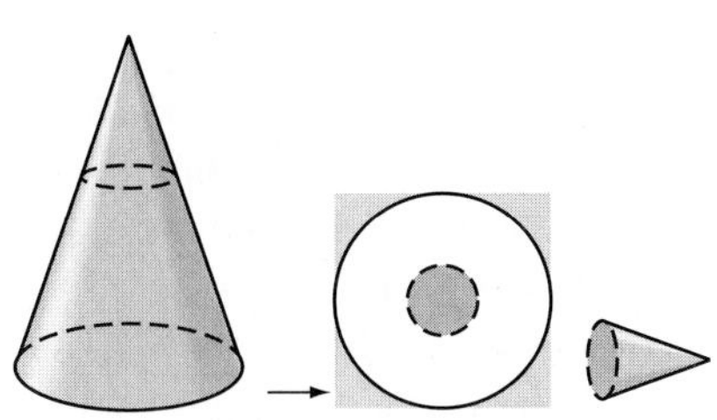

FL Math Online Access Point Activities

Option 3 English Learners ELL

Have students work in pairs. One student gives the other student two ordered pairs to graph on a coordinate grid. Then one student explains how to find the distance between them and the coordinates of the midpoint of the segment joining them. Then pairs switch roles and repeat the activity.

Option 4 Beyond Level BL

Have students research methods of drawing each conic section using only pushpins, string, and a pencil. For example, if the string is attached to the pushpins–representing the foci–an ellipse can be drawn.

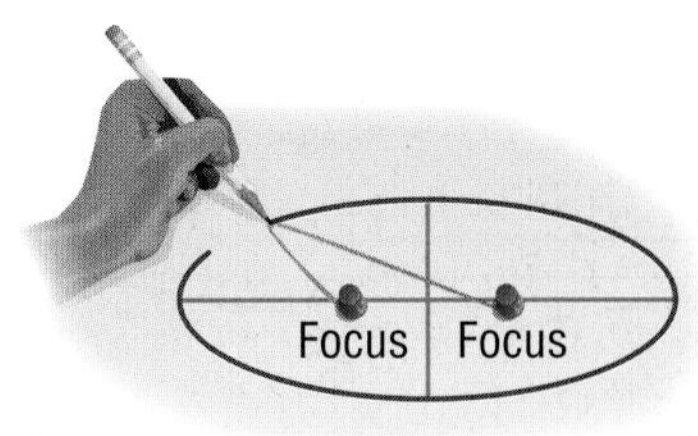

Challenge students to develop three-dimensional models depicting the different types of conic sections or have them explore computer technology with the capacity to perform this task.

CHAPTER 10

Focus on Mathematical Content

Vertical Alignment

Before Chapter 10

Related Topics from Algebra 1

- use tools including factoring and properties of exponents to simplify expressions
- graph equations of lines
- solve systems of linear equations using algebraic methods

Previous Topics from Algebra 2

- solve quadratic equations using algebraic methods
- determine solutions of square root equations using algebraic methods

Chapter 10

Related Topics from Algebra 2

- sketch graphs of conic sections to relate simple parameter changes in the equation to corresponding changes in the graph
- describe a conic section as the intersection of a plane and a cone
- identify symmetries from graphs of conic sections
- identify the conic section from a given equation
- use algebraic methods and graphs to solve systems of linear and nonlinear equations or inequalities

After Chapter 10

Preparation for Precalculus

- use conic sections to model motion, such as motion of the planets
- use conic sections to describe physical phenomena such as the reflective properties of light and sound

Lesson-by-Lesson Preview

10-1 Midpoint and Distance Formulas

A *line segment* on a coordinate plane has two endpoints. The coordinates of these endpoints can be used to find the *midpoint* of the segment (Midpoint Formula) and the *length* of the segment (Distance Formula). The coordinates of the midpoint of a line segment are the arithmetic means of the corresponding coordinates of the endpoints. The Distance Formula can be derived from the Pythagorean Theorem.

10-2 Parabolas

A *parabola* is the set of all points in a plane that are the same distance from a given point called the *focus* and a given line called the *directrix.* This definition combined with the Distance Formula can be used to derive the equation $y = a(x - h)^2 + k$, which is the *standard form* of the equation of a parabola with vertex (h, k) and axis of symmetry $x = h$. The graph of $y = a(x - h)^2 + k$ is a transformation of the parent graph of $y = x^2$.

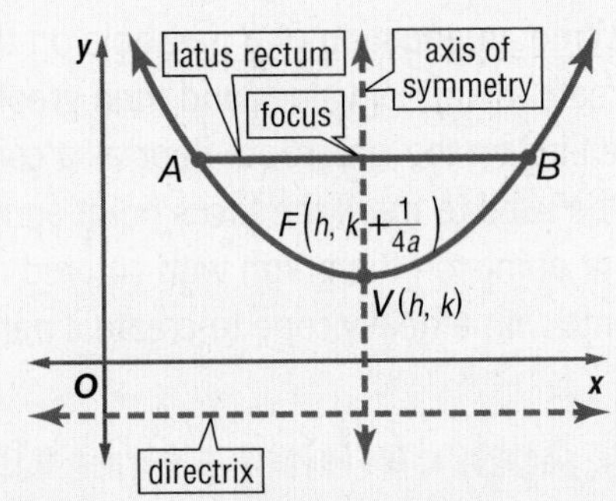

If a parabola has a vertical axis of symmetry, it is a function. If it has a horizontal axis of symmetry, its equation is of the form $x = a(y - k)^2 + h$, and it is not a function.

10-3 Circles

A *circle* is the set of all points in a plane that are a given distance (the radius) from a given point (the center) in the plane. Using (h, k) as the given point and r as the given radius, the equation of a circle is $\sqrt{(x - h)^2 + (y - k)^2} = r$. Squaring the equation, $(x - h)^2 + (y - k)^2 = r^2$. An equation for a circle that is not in standard form can be rewritten in standard form by completing the square (Lesson 5-5) of both the variables.

10-4 Ellipses

An *ellipse* is the set of all points in a plane such that the sum of the distances from two fixed points is constant. The two fixed points are called the *foci* of the ellipse. If the orientation of an ellipse is horizontal and its center is the origin, the standard form of its equation is $\frac{x^2}{a^2} + \frac{y^2}{b^2} = 1$. If the orientation is vertical, the standard form of its equation is $\frac{y^2}{a^2} + \frac{x^2}{b^2} = 1$. Every ellipse has two axes of symmetry as shown below.

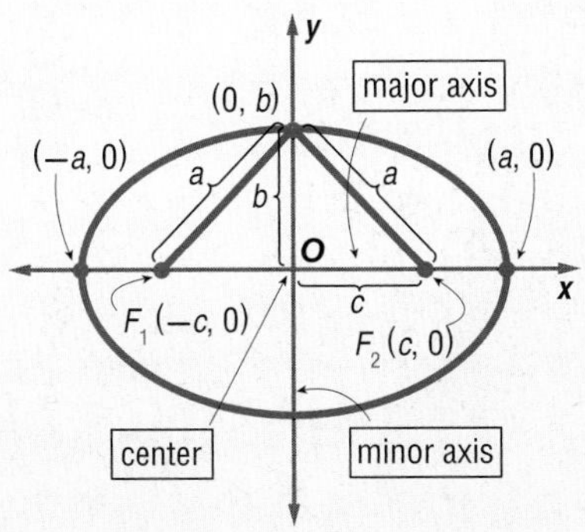

The values a and b determine the length of the major and minor axes and whether the major axis of the ellipse is horizontal or vertical. The equations $\frac{(x-h)^2}{a^2} + \frac{(y-k)^2}{b^2} = 1$ and $\frac{(y-k)^2}{a^2} + \frac{(x-h)^2}{b^2} = 1$ represent ellipses with centers translated to the point (h, k).

10-5 Hyperbolas

A *hyperbola* is the set of all points in a plane such that the absolute value of the difference of the distances from two fixed points (foci) is constant. The standard form of the equation for a hyperbola centered at the origin with a horizontal orientation is $\frac{x^2}{a^2} - \frac{y^2}{b^2} = 1$. If the orientation is vertical, the standard form of the equation is $\frac{y^2}{a^2} - \frac{x^2}{b^2} = 1$. A hyperbola has two axes of symmetry, the *transverse axis* and the *conjugate axis.* A hyperbola centered at the origin and having foci on the x-axis has asymptotes with the equations $y = \pm\frac{b}{a}x$. If the foci are on the y-axis, the equations of the asymptotes are $y = \pm\frac{a}{b}x$.

The equations $\frac{(x-h)^2}{a^2} - \frac{(y-k)^2}{b^2} = 1$ and $\frac{(y-k)^2}{a^2} - \frac{(x-h)^2}{b^2} = 1$ represent hyperbolas with centers translated to the point (h, k).

10-6 Identifying Conic Sections

The four curves (parabola, circle, ellipse, or hyperbola) are called *conic sections* because they are the cross-sections formed when a double cone is sliced by a plane.

The general equation for any conic section is $Ax^2 + Bxy + Cy^2 + Dx + Ey + F = 0$, where A, B, and C are not all zero. This equation is related to the standard forms of the equations of the four conic sections. If A, B, and C are not equal to zero, the expression $B^2 - 4AC$ (the discriminant) can be used to identify the conic.

10-7 Solving Linear-Nonlinear Systems

A system of a linear and a nonlinear equation can be solved algebraically or graphically.

- For a *linear-quadratic system,* a graph indicates whether the conic section and the line intersect in 0, 1, or 2 points. Substitution can be used as the first step in solving the system algebraically.
- For a *quadratic-quadratic system,* a graph indicates the number of solutions (0, 1, 2, 3, or 4). Elimination can be used to solve the system algebraically.

The solutions to systems of linear and nonlinear inequalities can be illustrated graphically and described algebraically.

Professional Development

Targeted professional development has been articulated throughout *Algebra 2.* More quality, customized professional development is available from McGraw-Hill Professional Development. Visit glencoe.com for details on each product.

- **Online Lessons** emphasize the strategies and techniques used to teach Algebra 2. Includes streaming video, interactive pages, and online tools.
- **Video Workshops** allow mentors, coaches, or leadership personnel to facilitate on-site workshops on educational strategies in mathematics and mathematical concepts.
- **MHPD Online** (www.mhpdonline.com) offers online professional development with video clips of instructional strategies, links, student activities, and news and issues in education.
- **Teaching Today** (teachingtoday.glencoe.com) gives secondary teachers practical strategies and materials that inspire excellence and innovation in teaching.

Chapter 10 Notes

Chapter Project

Celestial Orbits

Students use what they have learned about conic sections to examine paths of objects in space.

- Working in groups of three or four, students choose their favorite planet and research facts about its elliptical orbit around the sun. In particular, ask them to find the planet's *perihelion,* or closest distance to the sun, and the *eccentricity* of the orbit.
- From these two numbers $\left(\text{perihelion} = a - c \text{ and eccentricity} = \frac{c}{a}\right)$, have them find the parameters a, b, and c for the planet's orbit, with the sun at one focus of the ellipse.
- Ask them to determine an equation for the elliptical orbit. Then have them find the distance of the planet from the sun at *aphelion* (furthest distance to the sun) and when it is halfway between perihelion and aphelion in its orbit.
- Every conic has an eccentricity associated with it. Have students research the role of the eccentricity for ellipses, circles, parabolas, and hyperbolas.

Key Vocabulary Introduce the key vocabulary in the chapter using the routine below.

Define: A parabola is the set of all points in a plane that are the same distance from a given point, called the focus, and a given line, called the directrix.

Example: The diagram shows a parabola.

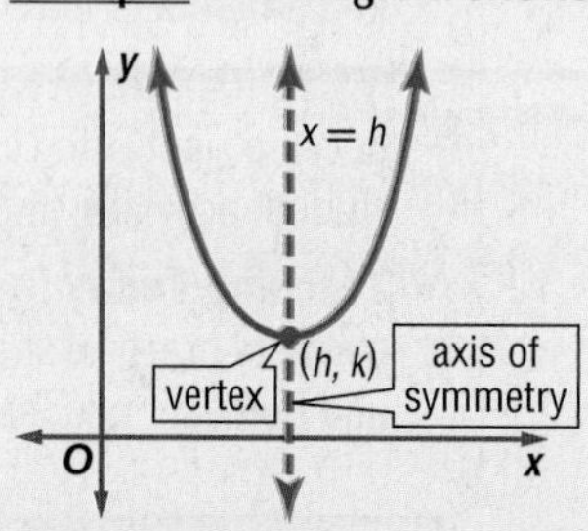

Ask: What are the coordinates of the vertex of the parabola? *(h, k)*

Additional Answer (Get Ready for Chapter 10)

9. $A'(-2, -5)$, $B'(-1, -1)$, $C'(5, -1)$, $D'(4, -5)$

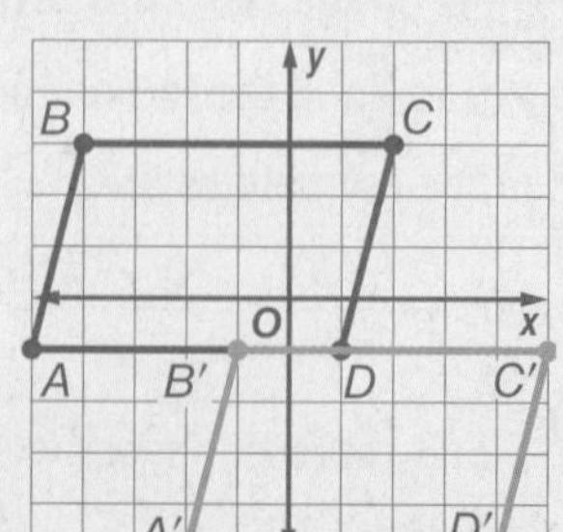

Chapter 10 Conic Sections

Then
In Chapter 3, you solved systems of linear equations algebraically and graphically.

Now
In Chapter 10, you will:

- Use the Midpoint and Distance Formulas.
- Write and graph equations of parabolas, circles, ellipses, and hyperbolas.
- Identify conic sections.
- Solve systems of quadratic equations and inequalities.

NGSSS
MA.912.A.9.1
MA.912.A.9.2

Why?
SPACE Conic sections are evident in many aspects of space. Equations of circles are used to pilot spacecraft and satellites in circular orbits around Earth and the Moon. Planets travel in elliptical paths, not circular ones as previously thought. Comets travel along one branch of a hyperbola, which can help us to predict when they will appear again.

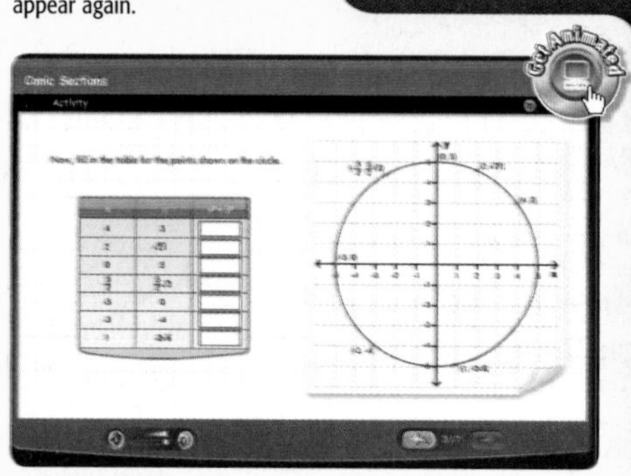

Get Ready for Chapter 10

Diagnose Readiness You have two options for checking Prerequisite Skills.

Text Option

Take the Quick Check below. Refer to the Quick Review for help.

QuickCheck

(Used in Lessons 10-2 through 10-6)

Solve each equation by completing the square. (Lesson 5-5)

1. $x^2 + 8x + 7 = 0$ {−7, −1}
2. $x^2 + 5x - 6 = 0$ {−6, 1}
3. $x^2 - 8x + 15 = 0$ {3, 5}
4. $x^2 + 2x - 120 = 0$ {−12, 10}
5. $2x^2 + 7x - 15 = 0$
6. $2x^2 + 3x - 5 = 0$
7. $x^2 - \frac{3}{2}x - \frac{23}{16} = 0$
8. $3x^2 - 4x = 2$

5. $\left\{-5, \frac{3}{2}\right\}$ 6. $\left\{-\frac{5}{2}, 1\right\}$ 7. $\left\{\frac{3}{4} \pm \sqrt{2}\right\}$ 8. $\left\{\frac{2 \pm \sqrt{10}}{3}\right\}$

(Used in Lessons 10-2 through 10-5)

Find the coordinates of the vertices of the image for each figure after the given translation. Then graph the preimage and image. (Lesson 4-4) 9–12. See margin.

9. quadrilateral $ABCD$ with vertices $A(-5, -1)$, $B(-4, 3)$, $C(2, 3)$, and $D(1, -1)$, translated 3 units right and 4 units down
10. triangle EFG with vertices $E(-2, 0)$, $F(5, 2)$, and $G(4, -3)$, translated 1 unit left and 2 units up
11. triangle JKL with vertices $J(1, 4)$, $K(2, -5)$, and $L(-6, -6)$, translated 4 units left and 2 units up
12. Triangle XYZ with vertices $X(-2, 2)$, $Y(3, 5)$, and $Z(5, -2)$ is translated so that X' is at $(1, -5)$. Find the coordinates of Y' and Z'.
13. **LANDSCAPING** Laura plots her shed plans on a grid with each unit equal to 1 foot. She places the corners at (100, 50), (110, 50), (110, 40), and (100, 40). She decides to move the shed up 10 feet and to the right 15 feet. What will be the new coordinates of the shed? (115, 60), (125, 60), (125, 50), and (115, 50)

QuickReview

EXAMPLE 1

Solve $x^2 + 6x - 16 = 0$ by completing the square.

$$x^2 + 6x = 16$$
$$x^2 + 6x + 9 = 16 + 9$$
$$(x + 3)^2 = 25$$
$$x + 3 = \pm 5$$

$x + 3 = 5$ or $x + 3 = -5$

$x = 2$ $\quad$ $x = -8$

EXAMPLE 2

Find the coordinates of the vertices of the image of triangle RST with $R(1, 4)$, $S(4, 2)$, and $T(2, 0)$ if it is moved 2 units to the left and 1 unit up. Then graph $\triangle RST$ and its image $\triangle R'S'T'$.

Write the vertex matrix for $\triangle RST$.

$$\begin{bmatrix} 1 & 4 & 2 \\ 4 & 2 & 0 \end{bmatrix}$$

Add the translation matrix $\begin{bmatrix} -2 & -2 & -2 \\ 1 & 1 & 1 \end{bmatrix}$ to the vertex matrix.

$$\begin{bmatrix} 1 & 4 & 2 \\ 4 & 2 & 0 \end{bmatrix} + \begin{bmatrix} -2 & -2 & -2 \\ 1 & 1 & 1 \end{bmatrix} =$$

$$\begin{bmatrix} -1 & 2 & 0 \\ 5 & 3 & 1 \end{bmatrix}$$

The vertices of $\triangle R'S'T'$ are $R'(-1, 5)$, $S'(2, 3)$, and $T'(0, 1)$.

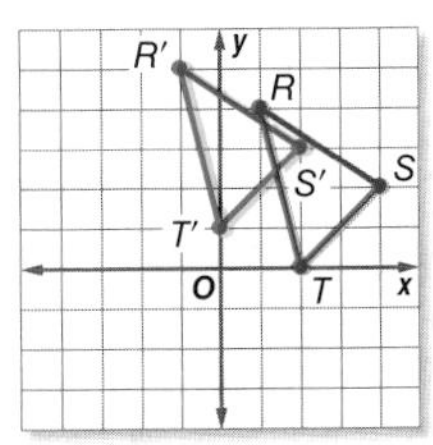

Online Option

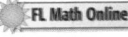

FL Math Online Take a self-check Chapter Readiness Quiz at glencoe.com.

Get Ready for Chapter 10

Response to Intervention (RtI)

Use the *Quick Check* results and the Intervention Planner to help you determine your Response to Intervention. The If-Then statements in the chart below help you decide the appropriate tier of RtI and suggest intervention resources for each tier.

Intervention Planner

Tier 1 On Level

If students miss about 25% of the exercises or less,

Then choose a resource:

- **SE** Lessons 4-4 and 4-5
- **CRM** Skills Practice, Chapter 4, p. 29, 37
- **TE** Chapter Project, p. 614
- FL Math Online Self-Check Quiz

Tier 2 Strategic Intervention approaching grade level

If students miss about 50% of the exercises,

Then choose a resource:

- **CRM** Study Guide and Intervention, Chapter 4, p. 27, 35
- FL Math Online Extra Examples, Personal Tutor, Homework Help

Tier 3 Intensive Intervention 2 or more years below grade level

If students miss about 75% of the exercises,

Then use *Math Triumphs, Alg. 2*

FL Math Online Extra Examples, Personal Tutor, Homework Help, Review Vocabulary

Additional Answers

10. $E'(-3, 2)$, $F'(4, 4)$, $G'(3, -1)$

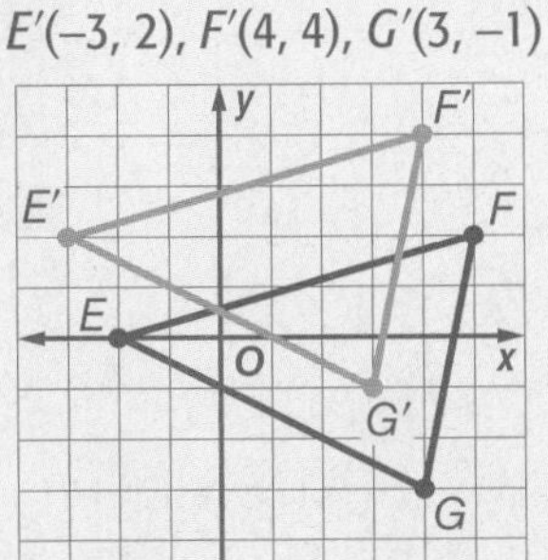

11. $J'(-3, 6)$, $K'(-2, -3)$, $L'(-10, -4)$

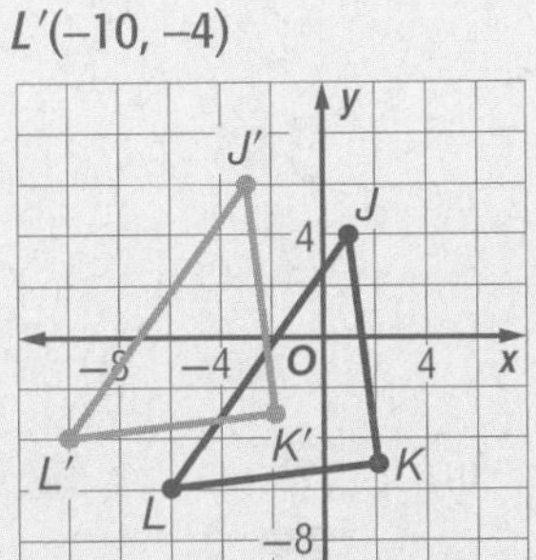

12. $Y'(6, -2)$, $Z'(8, -9)$

CHAPTER 10 Notes

FOLDABLES® Study Organizer

Dinah Zike's Foldables®

Focus Students write notes on what they learn about conic sections throughout this chapter.

Teach Have students make and label their Foldables as illustrated. Students should use the appropriate lines to record their notes and examples of the concepts in each lesson of this chapter.

When to Use It Encourage students to add to their Foldables as they work through the chapter and to use them to review conic sections for the chapter test.

Differentiated Instruction

CRM Student-Built Glossary, pp. 1–2 Students should complete the chart by providing a definition of each term and an example as they progress through Chapter 10. This study tool can also be used to review for the chapter test.

Get Started on Chapter 10

You will learn several new concepts, skills, and vocabulary terms as you study Chapter 10. To get ready, identify important terms and organize your resources. You may wish to refer to **Chapter 0** to review prerequisite skills.

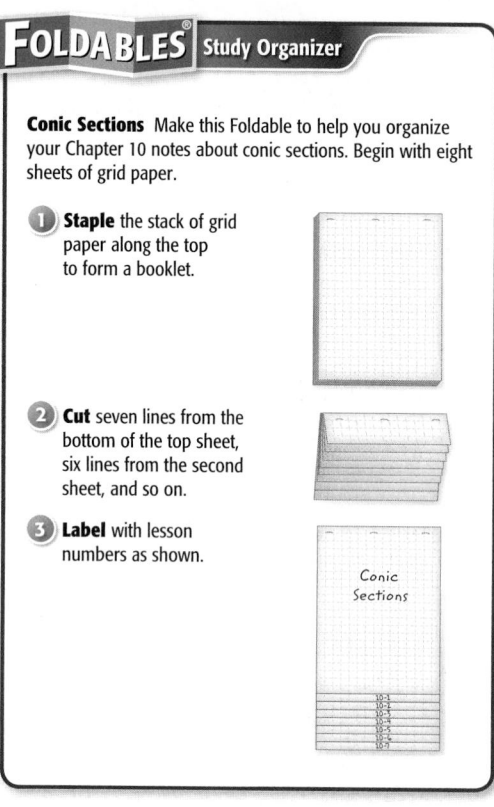

FOLDABLES® Study Organizer

Conic Sections Make this Foldable to help you organize your Chapter 10 notes about conic sections. Begin with eight sheets of grid paper.

1. **Staple** the stack of grid paper along the top to form a booklet.

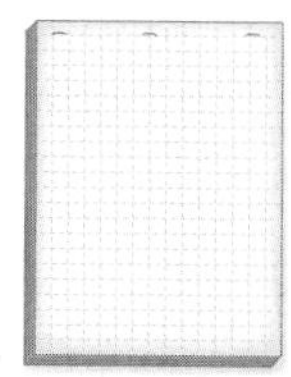

2. **Cut** seven lines from the bottom of the top sheet, six lines from the second sheet, and so on.

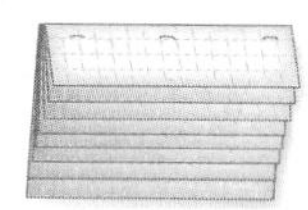

3. **Label** with lesson numbers as shown.

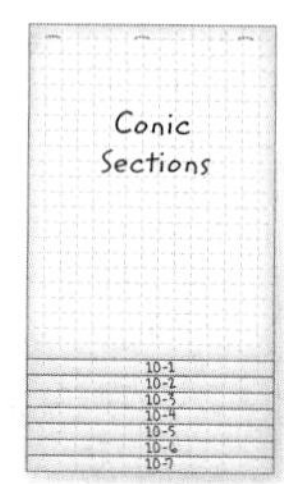

New Vocabulary

English		Español
parabola	p. 623	parábola
focus	p. 623	foco
directrix	p. 623	directriz
latus rectum	p. 623	latus rectum
circle	p. 631	círculo
center of a circle	p. 631	centro de un círculo
radius	p. 631	radio
ellipse	p. 639	elipse
foci	p. 639	focos
major axis	p. 639	eje mayor
minor axis	p. 639	eje menor
center of an ellipse	p. 639	centro de una elipse
vertices	p. 639	vértices
co-vertices	p. 639	co-vértices
constant sum	p. 640	suma constante
hyperbola	p. 648	hipérbola
transverse axis	p. 648	eje transversal
conjugate axis	p. 648	eje conjugado
constant difference	p. 651	diferencia constante

Review Vocabulary

quadratic equation • p. 259 • ecuación cuadrática a quadratic function in the form $ax^2 + bx + c = 0$, where $a \neq 0$

system of equations • p. 135 • sistema de ecuaciones a set of equations with the same variables

x- and *y*-intercepts • p. 71 • intersecciónes *x* e *y* the *x*- or *y*-coordinate of the point at which a graph crosses the *x*- or *y*-axis

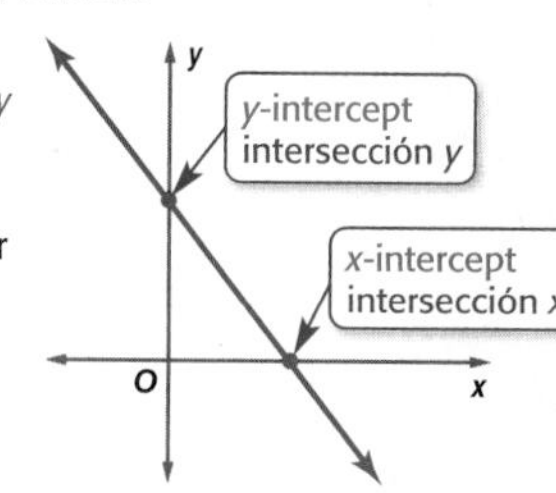

Multilingual eGlossary glencoe.com

FL Math Online glencoe.com

- Study the chapter online
- Explore **Get Animated**
- Get extra help from your own **Personal Tutor**
- Use **Extra Examples** for additional help
- Take a **Self-Check Quiz**
- **Review Vocabulary** in fun ways

10-1 Midpoint and Distance Formulas

Why?

Then
You found the slope of a line passing through two points. (Lesson 2-3)

Now
- Find the midpoint of a segment on the coordinate plane.
- Find the distance between two points on the coordinate plane.

NGSSS
Reinforcement of MA.912.G.1.1 Find the lengths and midpoints of line segments in two-dimensional coordinate systems.

FL Math Online
glencoe.com

The Zero Milestone in Washington, D.C., was established in 1919. It was intended to serve as the origin for all highway measures with highway markers across the United States displaying the distances from the Zero Milestone.

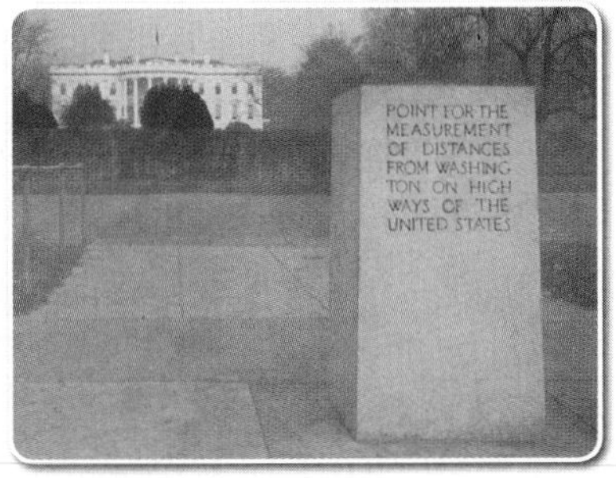

The Midpoint Formula Recall that point M is the midpoint of segment PQ if M is between P and Q and $PM = MQ$. There is a formula for the coordinates of the midpoint of a segment in terms of the coordinates of the endpoints.

Key Concept — Midpoint Formula

Words If a line segment has endpoints $P(x_1, y_1)$ and $Q(x_2, y_2)$, then the midpoint of the segment has coordinates $M\left(\frac{x_1 + x_2}{2}, \frac{y_1 + y_2}{2}\right)$.

Model

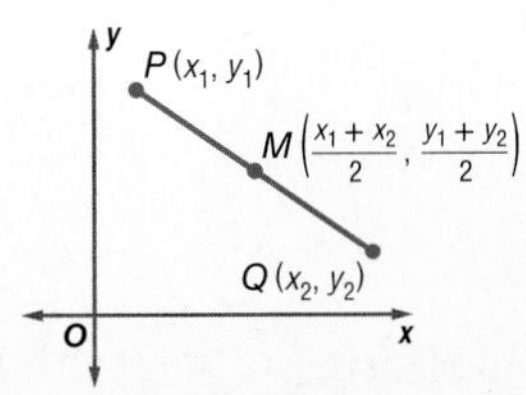

EXAMPLE 1 Find a Midpoint

Find the coordinates of M, the midpoint of $\overline{JK}$, for $J(-1, 2)$ and $K(6, 1)$.

Let J be (x_1, y_1) and K be (x_2, y_2).

$M\left(\frac{x_1 + x_2}{2}, \frac{y_1 + y_2}{2}\right)$ **Midpoint Formula**

$= M\left(\frac{-1 + 6}{2}, \frac{2 + 1}{2}\right)$ $(x_1, y_1) = (-1, 2), (x_2, y_2) = (6, 1)$

$= M\left(\frac{5}{2}, \frac{3}{2}\right)$ or $M\left(2\frac{1}{2}, 1\frac{1}{2}\right)$ **Simplify.**

Guided Practice

1A. Find the coordinates of the midpoint of $\overline{AB}$ for $A(5, 12)$ and $B(-4, 8)$. $\left(\frac{1}{2}, 10\right)$

1B. Find the coordinates of the midpoint of $\overline{CD}$ for $C(4, 5)$ and $D(14, 13)$. $(9, 9)$

Personal Tutor glencoe.com

The Distance Formula The distance between two points, a and b, on a number line is $|a - b|$ or $|b - a|$. You can use this fact and the Pythagorean Theorem to derive a formula for the distance between two points on a coordinate plane.

10-1 Lesson Notes

1 FOCUS

Vertical Alignment

Before Lesson 10-1
Find the slope of a line passing through two points.

Lesson 10-1
Find the midpoint of a segment on the coordinate plane.
Find the distance between two points on the coordinate plane.

After Lesson 10-1
Describe a conic section as the intersection of a plane and a cone.

2 TEACH

Scaffolding Questions

Have students read the *Why?* section of the lesson.

Ask:
- What does the word "origin" mean? Sample answer: the start or beginning
- If the Zero Milestone were graphed on a coordinate plane, what would its coordinates be? (0, 0)
- If a fountain were graphed on the same coordinate plane, at (0, 8), how far from the Zero Milestone would it be? 8 units

Lesson 10-1 Resources

Resource	Approaching-Level	On-Level	Beyond-Level	English Learners
Teacher Edition	• Differentiated Instruction, p. 618	• Differentiated Instruction, pp. 618, 622	• Differentiated Instruction, p. 622	
Chapter Resource Masters	• Study Guide and Intervention, pp. 5–6 • Skills Practice, p. 7 • Practice, p. 8 • Word Problem Practice, p. 9	• Study Guide and Intervention, pp. 5–6 • Skills Practice, p. 7 • Practice, p. 8 • Word Problem Practice, p. 9 • Enrichment, p. 10	• Practice, p. 8 • Word Problem Practice, p. 9 • Enrichment, p. 10	• Study Guide and Intervention, pp. 5–6 • Skills Practice, p. 7 • Practice, p. 8 • Word Problem Practice, p. 9
Transparencies	• 5-Minute Check Transparency 10-1	• 5-Minute Check Transparency 10-1	• 5-Minute Check Transparency 10-1	• 5-Minute Check Transparency 10-1
Other	• Study Notebook	• Study Notebook	• Study Notebook	• Study Notebook

The Midpoint Formula

Example 1 shows how to use the Midpoint Formula to find the coordinates of the midpoint of a segment given the coordinates of its endpoints.

Formative Assessment

Use the Guided Practice exercises after each example to determine students' understanding of concepts.

Additional Example

1 Find the coordinates of B, the midpoint of $\overline{AC}$, for $A(5, 2)$ and $C(7, 8)$. (6, 5)

Additional Examples also in Interactive Classroom PowerPoint® Presentations

IWB INTERACTIVE WHITEBOARD READY

The Distance Formula

Example 2 shows how to use the Distance Formula to find the distance between two points. **Example 3** shows how to use both the Midpoint Formula and the Distance Formula to solve a real-world problem.

Additional Example

2 **DISC GOLF** Matt's disc is 3 feet short and 2 feet to the right of the basket. On his first putt the disc lands 4 feet beyond the basket and 1 foot to the left. If the disc went in a straight line, how far did it go? $\sqrt{58}$ feet or about 7.6 feet

StudyTip

Distance In mathematics, just as in real-world situations, distances are always nonnegative.

Let d represent the distance between (x_1, y_1) and (x_2, y_2).

$c^2 = a^2 + b^2$	**Pythagorean Theorem**
$d^2 = \lvert x_2 - x_1\rvert^2 + \lvert y_2 - y_1\rvert^2$	**Substitute.**
$d^2 = (x_2 - x_1)^2 + (y_2 - y_1)^2$	$\lvert x_2 - x_1\rvert^2 = (x_2 - x_1)^2$, $\lvert y_2 - y_1\rvert^2 = (y_2 - y_1)^2$
$d = \sqrt{(x_2 - x_1)^2 + (y_2 - y_1)^2}$	**Find the nonnegative square root of each side.**

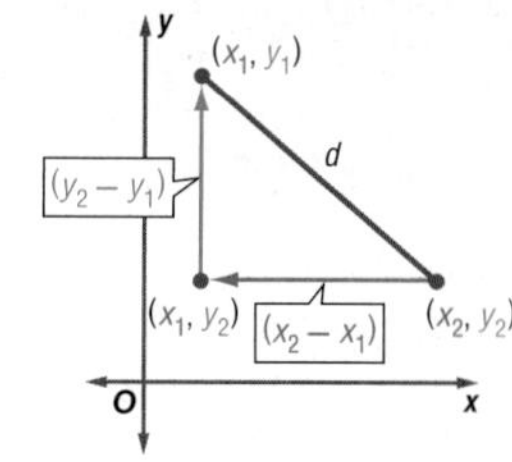

Key Concept — Distance Formula

Words The distance between two points with coordinates (x_1, y_1) and (x_2, y_2) is given by $\sqrt{(x_2 - x_1)^2 + (y_2 - y_1)^2}$.

Model

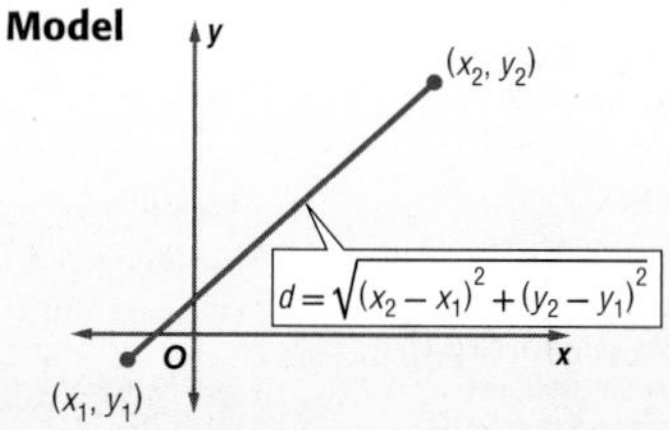

Real-World Link

There are more than 700 disc golf courses in the U.S. These courses are permanent installations, usually located in public parks, where players actually "drive" and "putt" with specially-styled discs.

Real-World EXAMPLE 2 Find the Distance Between Two Points

DISC GOLF Troy's disc is 20 feet short and 8 feet to the right of the basket. On his first putt, the disc lands 2 feet to the left and 3 feet beyond the basket. If the disc went in a straight line, how far did it go?

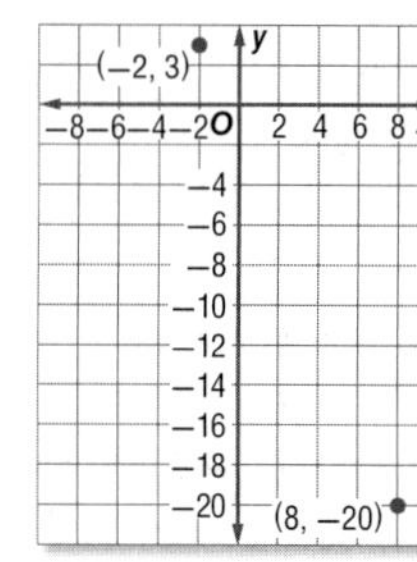

Model the situation. If the basket is at (0, 0), then the location of the disc is (8, −20). The location after the first putt is (−2, 3).

$d = \sqrt{(x_2 - x_1)^2 + (y_2 - y_1)^2}$	**Distance Formula**
$= \sqrt{(-2 - 8)^2 + [3 - (-20)]^2}$	$(x_1, y_1) = (8, -20)$ **and** $(x_2, y_2) = (-2, 3)$
$= \sqrt{(-10)^2 + 23^2}$	**Simplify.**
$= \sqrt{629}$ or about 25	

The disc traveled about 25 feet on his first putt.

Guided Practice

2. Sharon hits a golf ball 12 feet above the hole and 3 feet to the left. Her first putt traveled to 2 feet above the cup and 1 foot to the right. How far did the ball travel on her first putt? $2\sqrt{29}$ or about 10.77 ft

Personal Tutor glencoe.com

Differentiated Instruction AL OL

Visual/Spatial Learners After finding the midpoints of line segments, suggest that students draw graphs to check the coordinates.

618 Chapter 10 Conic Sections

StudyTip

Midpoints The coordinates of the midpoint are the means of the coordinates of the endpoints.

There most likely will be problems involving the Midpoint and Distance Formulas on standardized tests you will have to take.

NGSSS PRACTICE EXAMPLE 3 — 912.G.1.1

A coordinate grid is placed over a Florida map. St. Augustine is located at (3, 13), and Rockledge is located at (8, −1). If Port Orange is halfway between St. Augustine and Rockledge, which is closest to the distance in coordinate units from St. Augustine to Port Orange?

A. 4.75 **B.** 7.45 **C.** 14.9 **D.** 19

Read the Test Item

The question asks you to find the distance between one city and the midpoint. Find the midpoint, and then use the Distance Formula.

Solve the Test Item

Use the Midpoint Formula to find the coordinates of Port Orange.

$\text{midpoint} = \left(\frac{3+8}{2}, \frac{13+(-1)}{2}\right)$ **Midpoint Formula**

$= (5.5, 6)$ **Simplify.**

Use the Distance Formula to find the distance between St. Augustine (3, 13) and Port Orange (5.5, 6).

$\text{distance} = \sqrt{(3-5.5)^2 + (13-6)^2}$ **Distance Formula**

$= \sqrt{(-2.5)^2 + 7^2}$ **Evaluate exponents and add.**

$= \sqrt{55.25}$ or about 7.43 **Simplify.**

The answer is B.

Test-TakingTip

Answer Check To check your answer, find the distance between Port Orange and Rockledge. Since Port Orange is at the midpoint, these distances should be equal.

Guided Practice

3. The coordinates for points A and B are (−4, −5) and (10, −7), respectively. Find the distance between the midpoint of A and B and point B. H

F. $\sqrt{10}$ units G. $5\sqrt{10}$ units H. $\sqrt{50}$ units I. $10\sqrt{5}$ units

Personal Tutor glencoe.com

Check Your Understanding

Example 1 p. 617 — **Find the midpoint of the line segment with endpoints at the given coordinates.**

1. (−4, 7), (3, 9) $\left(-\frac{1}{2}, 8\right)$
2. (8, 2), (−1, −5) (3.5, −1.5)
3. (11, 6), (18, 13.5) (14.5, 9.75)
4. (−12, −2), (−10.5, −6) (−11.25, −4)

Example 2 p. 618 — **Find the distance between each pair of points with the given coordinates.**

5. (3, −5), (13, −11) 11.662 units
6. (8, 1), (−2, 9) 12.806 units
7. (0.25, 1.75), (3.5, 2.5) 3.335 units
8. (−4.5, 10.75), (−6.25, −7) 17.836 units

Example 3 p. 619

9. **NGSSS PRACTICE** The map of a mall is overlaid with a numeric grid. The kiosk for the cell phone store is halfway between The Ice Creamery and the See Clearly eyeglass store. If the ice cream store is at (2, 4) and the eyeglass store is at (78, 46), find the distance the kiosk is from the eyeglass store. A

A. 43.4 units B. 47.2 units C. 62.4 units D. 94.3 units

TEACH with TECH

INTERACTIVE WHITEBOARD Display a coordinate plane on the board. Plot two points on the plane and have students find the midpoint and the distance of the segment that connects these two points. Then drag the points to other locations on the board and repeat.

Tips for New Teachers

Meaningful Solutions Have students refer to Example 3. Tell students that in radical form, $\sqrt{53.25}$ is an exact mathematical representation of the value of the distance between St. Augustine and Port Orange. However, since this value is being used to describe a distance, it is more useful to express the distance in decimal form by using a calculator to find an approximate value. For example, $\sqrt{53.25} \approx 7.43$. Also point out that writing the steps helps to prevent careless errors in calculations.

Additional Example

3 **STANDARDIZED TEST EXAMPLE** A coordinate grid is placed over a scale drawing of Nita's patio. A grill is located at (2, −3). A flowerpot is located at (−6, −1). If a picnic table is halfway between the grill and the flowerpot. In coordinate units, about how far is it from the grill to the picnic table? C

A 0.2 **C** 4.1
B 2.24 **D** 5

3 PRACTICE

Formative Assessment

Use Exercises 1–9 to check for understanding.

Use the chart at the bottom of the next page to customize assignments for your students.

Focus on Mathematical Content

The Distance Formula You can use the Distance Formula, $d = \sqrt{(x_2 - x_1)^2 + (y_2 - y_1)^2}$ to find the distance between two points, (x_1, y_1) and (x_2, y_2), on a coordinate plane. Since distance is always nonnegative, the equation must be solved for the nonnegative square root.

Additional Answers

41a.

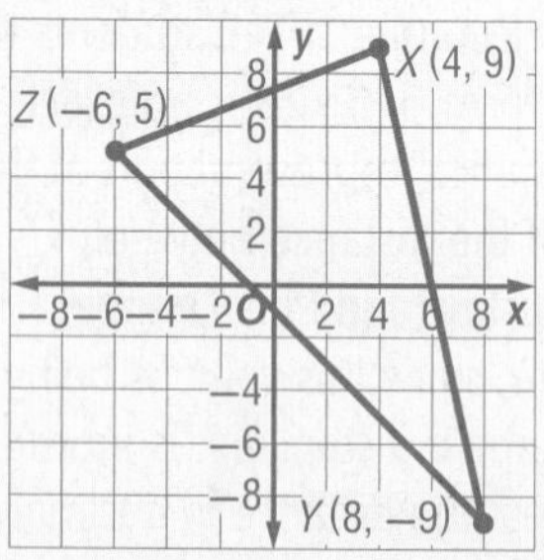

45. See students' graphs; the distance from *A* to *B* equals the distance from *B* to *A*. Using the Distance Formula, the solution is the same no matter which ordered pair is used first.

46. Most maps have a superimposed grid. Think of the grid as a coordinate system and assign approximate coordinates to the two locations. Then use the Midpoint Formula to find the midpoint between the points with those coordinates.

Practice and Problem Solving

= Step-by-Step Solutions begin on page R20.
Extra Practice begins on page 947.

11. (−4, −1)
12. (5.3, 2.7)

Example 1 p. 617

Find the midpoint of the line segment with endpoints at the given coordinates.

10. (20, 3), (15, 5) **(17.5, 4)**
11. (−27, 4), (19, −6)
12. (−0.4, 7), (11, −1.6)
13. (5.4, −8), (9.2, 10) **(7.3, 1)**
14. (−5.3, −8.6), (−18.7, 1) **(−12, −3.8)**
15. (−6.4, −8.2), (−9.1, −0.8) **(−7.75, −4.5)**

Example 2 p. 618

Find the distance between each pair of points with the given coordinates.

16. (1, 2), (6, 3) **5.099 units**
17. (3, −4), (0, 12) **16.279 units**
18. (−6, −7), (11, −12) **17.720 units**
19. (−10, 8), (−8, −8) **16.125 units**
20. (4, 0), (5, −6) **6.083 units**
21. (7, 9), (−2, −10) **21.024 units**
22. (−4, −5), (15, 17) **29.069 units**
23. (14, −20), (−18, 25) **55.218 units**

Example 3 p. 619

24. TRACK AND FIELD A shot put is thrown from the inside of a circle. A coordinate grid is placed over the shot put circle. The toe board is located at the front of the circle at (−4, 1), and the back of the circle is at (5, 2). If the center of the circle is halfway between these two points, what is the distance from the toe board to the center of the circle? $\sqrt{20.5} \approx 4.528$ **units**

25. (−1.5, 0); 185.443 units
26. (17.5, 22); 88.549 units
27. (−5.5, −50.5); 148.223 uits
28. (−87.5, 39.5); 62.626 units
29. (8, 15); 136.953 units
30. (43.5, 29); 111.772 units
31. (−0.43, −2.25); 9.624 units
32. (−1.75, 1.755); 12.342 units
33. (−4.458, −1); 8.193 units
34. (−1.292, −3.667); 5.667 units
35. (−4.719, 0.028); 17.97 units
36. (−0.289, −0.401); $\sqrt{3}$ units
38c. Triangle *EFG* is also isosceles with two sides of measure $2\sqrt{5}$.
38d. The side lengths of $\triangle EFG$ are one half the side lengths of the sides of $\triangle ABC$.

B Find the midpoint of the line segment with endpoints at the given coordinates. Then find the distance between the points.

25. (−93, 15), (90, −15)
26. (−22, 42), (57, 2)
27. (−70, −87), (59, −14)
28. (−98, 5), (−77, 64)
29. (41, −45), (−25, 75)
30. (90, 60), (−3, −2)
31. (−1.2, 2.5), (0.34, −7)
32. (−7.54, 3.89), (4.04, −0.38)
33. $\left(-\frac{5}{12}, -\frac{1}{3}\right), \left(-\frac{17}{2}, -\frac{5}{3}\right)$
34. $\left(-\frac{5}{4}, -\frac{13}{2}\right), \left(-\frac{4}{3}, -\frac{5}{6}\right)$
35. $\left(-3\sqrt{2}, -4\sqrt{5}\right), \left(-3\sqrt{3}, 9\right)$
36. $\left(\frac{\sqrt{3}}{3}, \frac{\sqrt{2}}{4}\right), \left(\frac{-2\sqrt{3}}{3}, \frac{\sqrt{2}}{4}\right)$

37. SPACE Use the labeled points on the outline of the circular crater on Mars to estimate its diameter in kilometers. Assume each unit on the coordinate system is 1 kilometer. **14.53 km**

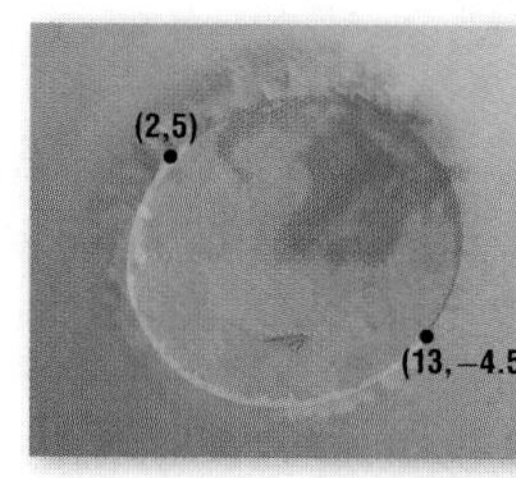

38. GEOMETRY Triangle *ABC* has vertices *A*(2, 1), *B*(−6, 5), and *C*(−2, −3).

a. An isosceles triangle has two sides with equal length. Is triangle *ABC* isosceles? Explain. **Yes;** $AB = BC = 4\sqrt{5}$.

b. An equilateral triangle has three sides of equal length. Is triangle *ABC* equilateral? Explain. **No;** $AC = 4\sqrt{2}$.

c. Triangle *EFG* is formed by joining the midpoints of the sides of triangle *ABC*. What type of triangle is *EFG*? Explain.

d. Describe any relationship between the lengths of the sides of the two triangles.

Differentiated Homework Options

Level	Assignment	Two-Day Option	
AL Basic	10–24, 43–66	11–23 odd, 47–50	10–24 even, 43–46, 51–66
OL Core	11–37 odd, 38–41, 43–66	10–24, 47–50	25–41, 43–46, 51–66
BL Advanced	25–63, (optional: 64–66)		

Real-World Link

U.S. Postal Service carriers travel over 1.2 billion miles every year delivering the mail.

Source: U.S. Postal Service

39. **PACKAGE DELIVERY** To determine the mileage between cities for their overnight delivery service, a package delivery service superimposes a coordinate grid over the United States. Each side of a grid unit is equal to 0.316 mile. Suppose the locations of two distribution centers are at (132, 428) and (254, 105). Find the actual distance between these locations to the nearest mile. **109 mi**

40. **HIKING** Orlando wants to hike from his camp to a waterfall. The waterfall is 5 miles south and 8 miles east of his campsite.
    a. Use the Distance Formula to determine how far the waterfall is from the campsite. $\sqrt{89} \approx 9.4$ **mi**
    b. Verify your answer in part a by using the Pythagorean Theorem to determine the distance between the campsite and the waterfall.
    c. Orlando wants to stop for lunch halfway to the waterfall. If the camp is at the origin, where should he stop? $\left(4, -\frac{5}{2}\right)$

41. **MULTIPLE REPRESENTATIONS** Triangle XYZ has vertices $X(4, 9)$, $Y(8, -9)$, and $Z(-6, 5)$.
    a. **CONCRETE** Draw $\triangle XYZ$ on a coordinate plane. **See margin.**
    b. **NUMERICAL** Find the coordinates of the midpoint of each side of the triangle.
    c. **GEOMETRIC** Find the perimeter of $\triangle XYZ$ and the perimeter of the triangle with vertices at the points found in part **b**.
    d. **ANALYTICAL** How do the perimeters in part **c** compare? **The perimeter of $\triangle XYZ$ is twice the perimeter of the smaller triangle.**

H.O.T. Problems
Use Higher-Order Thinking Skills

42. **CHALLENGE** Find the coordinates of the point that is three fourths of the way from $P(-1, 12)$ to $Q(5, -10)$. $\left(\frac{7}{2}, -\frac{9}{2}\right)$

43. **REASONING** Identify all the points in a plane that are 3 units or less from the point (5, 6). What figure does this make? **a circle and its interior with center at (5, 6) and radius 3 units**

44. **REASONING** Triangle ABC is a right triangle.
    a. Find the midpoint of the hypotenuse. Call it point Q.
    b. Classify $\triangle BQC$ according to the lengths of its sides. Include sufficient evidence to support your conclusion.
    c. Classify $\triangle BQA$ according to its angles. **obtuse**

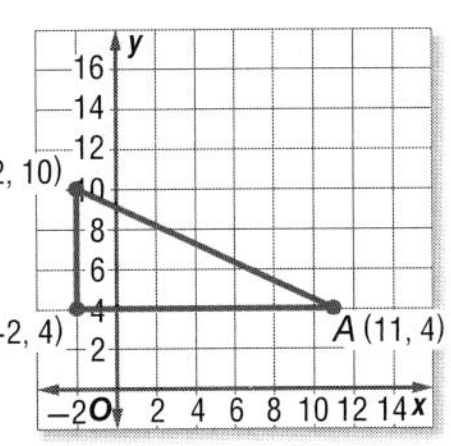

45. **OPEN ENDED** Plot two points, and find the distance between them. Does it matter which ordered pair is first when using the Distance Formula? Explain. **See margin.**

46. **WRITING IN MATH** Explain how the Midpoint Formula can be used to approximate the halfway point between two locations on a map. **See margin.**

40b. $8^2 + 5^2 = c^2$
$64 + 25 = c^2$
$89 = c^2$
$c = \sqrt{89}$ or about 9.4 mi

41b. midpoint of $\overline{XY} = (6, 0)$; midpoint of $\overline{YZ} = (1, -2)$; midpoint of $\overline{XZ} = (-1, 7)$

41c. The perimeter of $\triangle XYZ$ is $2\sqrt{29} + 14\sqrt{2} + 2\sqrt{85}$ units. perimeter $= \sqrt{29} + 7\sqrt{2} + \sqrt{85}$

44a. $Q\left(\frac{9}{2}, 7\right)$

44b. $BC = 6$, $QC = \frac{\sqrt{205}}{2}$, $BQ = \frac{\sqrt{205}}{2}$; $\overline{QC}$ and $\overline{BQ}$ are the same length; therefore, $\triangle BQC$ is isosceles.

Multiple Representations In Exercise 41, students use a graph in the coordinate plane and geometry to compare the perimeters of two triangles drawn from the coordinates of their vertices.

Study Guide and Intervention
CRM pp. 5–6 AL OL ELL

10-1 Study Guide and Intervention
Midpoint and Distance Formulas

The Midpoint Formula

Midpoint Formula	The midpoint M of a segment with endpoints (x_1, y_1) and (x_2, y_2) is $\left(\frac{x_1 + x_2}{2}, \frac{y_1 + y_2}{2}\right)$.

Example 1 Find the coordinates of M, the midpoint of $\overline{JK}$, for $J(4, -7)$ and $K(-2, 3)$.

$\left(\frac{x_1 + x_2}{2}, \frac{y_1 + y_2}{2}\right) = \left(\frac{4 + (-2)}{2}, \frac{-7 + 3}{2}\right) = \left(\frac{2}{2}, \frac{-4}{2}\right)$ or $(1, -2)$

The midpoint of $\overline{JK}$ is $(1, -2)$.

Example 2 A diameter $\overline{AB}$ of a circle has endpoints $A(5, -11)$ and $B(-7, 6)$. What are the coordinates of the center of the circle?

The center of the circle is the midpoint of all of its diameters.

$\left(\frac{x_1 + x_2}{2}, \frac{y_1 + y_2}{2}\right) = \left(\frac{5 + (-7)}{2}, \frac{-11 + 6}{2}\right) = \left(\frac{-2}{2}, \frac{-5}{2}\right)$ or $\left(-1, -2\frac{1}{2}\right)$

The circle has center $\left(-1, -2\frac{1}{2}\right)$.

Lesson 10-1

Exercises

Find the midpoint of the line segment with endpoints at the given coordinates.

1. (12, 7) and (−2, 11) **(5, 9)**
2. (−8, −3) and (10, 9) **(1, 3)**
3. (4, 15) and (10, 1) **(7, 8)**
4. (−3, −3) and (3, 3) **(0, 0)**
5. (15, 6) and (12, 14) $\left(\frac{27}{2}, 10\right)$
6. (22, −8) and (−10, 6) **(6, −1)**
7. (3, 5) and (−6, 11) $\left(-\frac{3}{2}, 8\right)$
8. (8, −15) and (−7, 13) $\left(\frac{1}{2}, -1\right)$
9. (2.5, −6.1) and (7.9, 13.7) **(5.2, 3.8)**
10. (−7, −6) and (−1, 24) **(−4, 9)**
11. (3, −10) and (30, −20) $\left(\frac{33}{2}, -15\right)$
12. (−9, 1.7) and (−11, 1.3) **(−10, 1.5)**
13. **GEOMETRY** Segment $\overline{MN}$ has midpoint P. If M has coordinates (14, −3) and P has coordinates (−8, 6), what are the coordinates of N? **(−30, 15)**
14. **GEOMETRY** Circle R has a diameter $\overline{ST}$. If R has coordinates (−4, −8) and S has coordinates (1, 4), what are the coordinates of T? **(−9, −20)**
15. **GEOMETRY** Segment $\overline{AD}$ has midpoint B, and $\overline{BD}$ has midpoint C. If A has coordinates (−5, 4) and C has coordinates (10, 11), what are the coordinates of B and D? **B is $\left(5, \frac{26}{3}\right)$, D is $\left(15, \frac{40}{3}\right)$.**

Chapter 10 5 Glencoe Algebra 2

Practice
CRM p. 8 AL OL AL ELL

10-1 Practice
Midpoint and Distance Formulas

Find the midpoint of the line segment with endpoints at the given coordinates.

1. (8, −3), (−6, −11) **(1, −7)**
2. (−14, 5), (10, 6) $\left(-2, \frac{11}{2}\right)$
3. (−7, −6), (1, −2) **(−3, −4)**
4. (8, −2), (8, −8) **(8, −5)**
5. (9, −4), (1, −1) $\left(5, -\frac{5}{2}\right)$
6. (3, 3), (4, 9) $\left(\frac{7}{2}, 6\right)$
7. (4, −2), (3, −7) $\left(\frac{7}{2}, -\frac{9}{2}\right)$
8. (6, 7), (4, 4) $\left(5, \frac{11}{2}\right)$
9. (−4, −2), (−8, 2) **(−6, 0)**
10. (5, −2), (3, 7) $\left(4, \frac{5}{2}\right)$
11. (−6, 3), (−5, −7) $\left(-\frac{11}{2}, -2\right)$
12. (−9, −8), (8, 3) $\left(-\frac{1}{2}, -\frac{5}{2}\right)$
13. (2.6, −4.7), (8.4, 2.5) **(5.5, −1.1)**
14. $\left(-\frac{1}{3}, 6\right), \left(\frac{2}{3}, 4\right)$ $\left(\frac{1}{6}, 5\right)$
15. (−2.5, −4.2), (8.1, 4.2) **(2.8, 0)**
16. $\left(\frac{1}{8}, \frac{1}{2}\right), \left(-\frac{5}{8}, -\frac{1}{2}\right)$ $\left(-\frac{1}{4}, 0\right)$

Find the distance between each pair of points with the given coordinates.

17. (5, 2), (2, −2) **5 units**
18. (−2, −4), (4, 4) **10 units**
19. (−3, 8), (−1, −5) $\sqrt{173}$ **units**
20. (0, 1), (9, −6) $\sqrt{130}$ **units**
21. (−5, 6), (−6, 6) **1 unit**
22. (−3, 5), (12, −3) **17 units**
23. (−2, −3), (9, 3) $\sqrt{157}$ **units**
24. (−9, −8), (−7, 8) $2\sqrt{65}$ **units**
25. (9, 3), (9, −2) **5 units**
26. (−1, −7), (0, 6) $\sqrt{170}$ **units**
27. (10, −3), (−2, −8) **13 units**
28. (−0.5, −6), (1.5, 0) $2\sqrt{10}$ **units**
29. $\left(\frac{2}{5}, \frac{3}{5}\right), \left(1, \frac{7}{5}\right)$ **1 unit**
30. $(-4\sqrt{2}, -\sqrt{5}), (-5\sqrt{2}, 4\sqrt{5})$ $\sqrt{127}$ **units**
31. **GEOMETRY** Circle O has a diameter $\overline{AB}$. If A is at (−6, −2) and B is at (−3, 4), find the center of the circle and the length of its diameter. $\left(-\frac{9}{2}, 1\right)$; $3\sqrt{5}$ **units**
32. **GEOMETRY** Find the perimeter of a triangle with vertices at (1, −3), (−4, 9), and (−2, 1). $18 + 2\sqrt{17}$ **units**

Chapter 10 8 Glencoe Algebra 2

Word Problem Practice
CRM p. 9 AL OL BL ELL

10-1 Word Problem Practice
Midpoint and Distance Formulas

1. **EXHIBITS** Museum planners want to place a statue directly in the center of their Special Exhibits Room. Suppose the room is placed on a coordinate plane as shown. What are the coordinates of the center of this room?

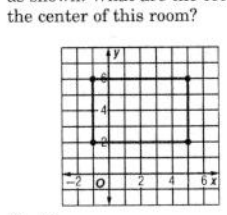

(2, 4)

2. **WALKING** Laura starts at the origin. She walks 8 units to the right and then 12 units up. How far away from the origin is she? Round your answer to the nearest tenth.
14.4 units

3. **SURVEILLANCE** A grid is superimposed on a map of the area directly surrounding the home of a suspect. Detectives want to position themselves on opposite sides of the suspect's house. Coordinates are assigned to the suspect's home. Unit A is positioned at (−1, 6) on the coordinate plane. Where should Unit B be located so that the suspect's home is centered between the two units?

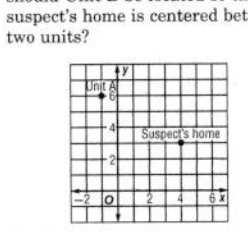

(9, 0)

4. **AIRPLANES** A grid is superimposed on a map of Texas. Dallas has coordinates (200, 5) and Amarillo has coordinates (−100, 208). If each unit represents 1 mile, how long will it take a plane flying at an average speed of 410 miles per hour to fly directly from Dallas to Amarillo? Round your answer to the nearest tenth of an hour.
0.9 hour

5. **TRAVEL** The Martinez family is planning a trip from their home in Fort Lauderdale to Tallahassee. They plan to stop overnight at a location about halfway between the two cities.

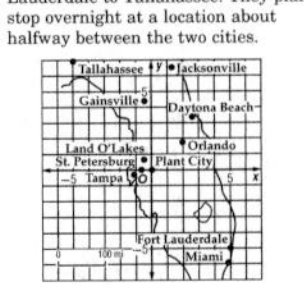

a. What are the coordinates of the point halfway between Tallahassee and Fort Lauderdale? Which of the cities on the map is closest to this point?
(0, 1); Land O'Lakes

b. How many miles is it from Fort Lauderdale to Tallahassee? Round your answer to the nearest mile.
521 mi

Lesson 10-1

Chapter 10 9 Glencoe Algebra 2

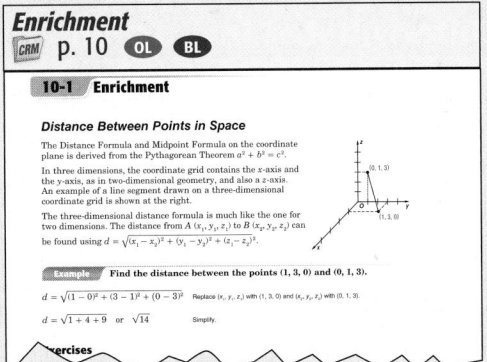

Enrichment
CRM p. 10 OL BL

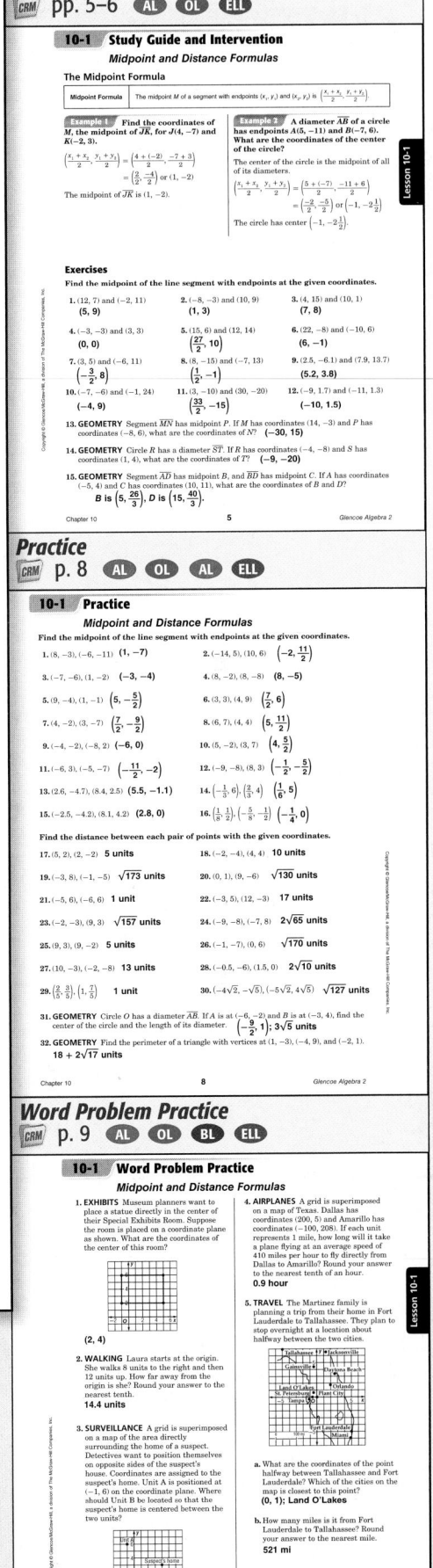

10-1 Enrichment

Distance Between Points in Space

The Distance Formula and Midpoint Formula on the coordinate plane is derived from the Pythagorean Theorem $a^2 + b^2 = c^2$.

In three dimensions, the coordinate grid contains the x-axis and the y-axis, as in two-dimensional geometry, and also a z-axis. An example of a line segment drawn on a three-dimensional coordinate grid is shown at the right.

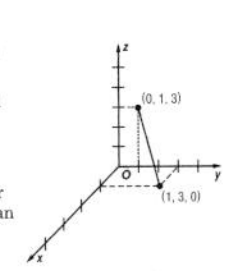

The three-dimensional distance formula is much like the one for two dimensions. The distance from $A(x_1, y_1, z_1)$ to $B(x_2, y_2, z_2)$ can be found using $d = \sqrt{(x_1 - x_2)^2 + (y_1 - y_2)^2 + (z_1 - z_2)^2}$.

Example Find the distance between the points (1, 3, 0) and (0, 1, 3).

$d = \sqrt{(1-0)^2 + (3-1)^2 + (0-3)^2}$ Replace (x_1, y_1, z_1) with (1, 3, 0) and (x_2, y_2, z_2) with (0, 1, 3).

$d = \sqrt{1 + 4 + 9}$ or $\sqrt{14}$ Simplify.

Exercises

4 ASSESS

Name the Math Have students plot two points on a coordinate grid and explain how to find the distance between them and the coordinates of the midpoint of the segment joining them.

Additional Answer

54d.

Depth (ft)	Pressure (psi)
0	0
1	0.43
2	0.86
3	1.29
4	1.72

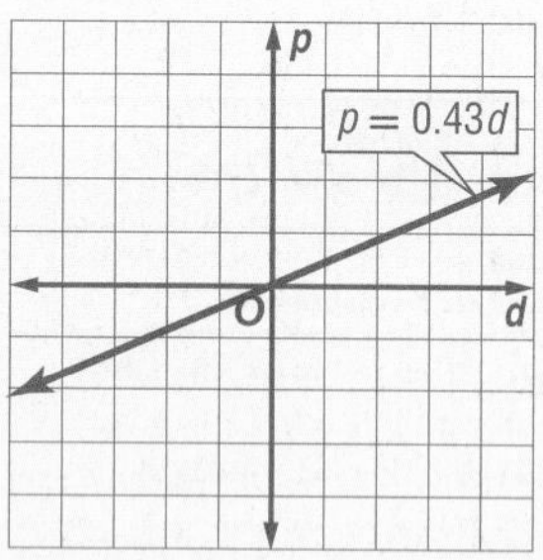

NGSSS PRACTICE 912.G.7.5, 912.A.3.15, 912.A.3.1

47. THINK SOLVE EXPLAIN **SHORT RESPONSE** You currently earn \$8.10 per hour and your boss gives you a 10% raise. What is your new hourly wage? **\$8.91**

48. **ACT/SAT** A right circular cylinder has a radius of 3 and a height of 5. Which of the following dimensions of a rectangular solid will have a volume closest to that of the cylinder? **A**

A. 5, 5, 6
B. 5, 6, 6
C. 5, 5, 5
D. 4, 5, 6

49. **GEOMETRY** If the sum of the lengths of the two legs of a right triangle is 49 inches and the hypotenuse is 41 inches, find the longer of the two legs. **G**

F. 9 in. H. 42 in.
G. 40 in. I. 49 in.

50. Five more than 3 times a number is 17. Find the number. **B**

A. 3 C. 5
B. 4 D. 6

Spiral Review

Solve each equation. Check your solutions. (Lesson 9-6)

51. $\frac{12}{v^2-16} - \frac{24}{v-4} = 3$ **−6, −2**

52. $\frac{w}{w-1} + w = \frac{4w-3}{w-1}$ **3**

53. $\frac{4n^2}{n^2-9} - \frac{2n}{n+3} = \frac{3}{n-3}$ $\mathbf{\frac{3}{2}}$

54. **SWIMMING** When a person swims underwater, the pressure in his or her ears varies directly with the depth at which he or she is swimming. (Lesson 9-5)

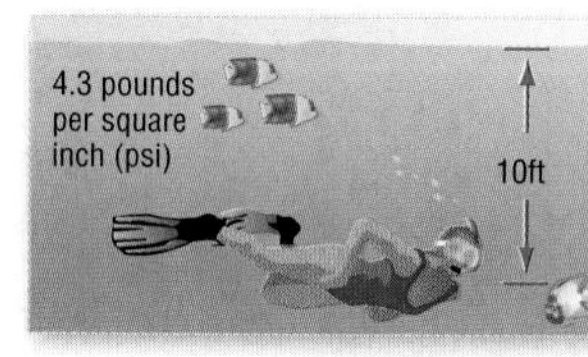

a. Write a direct variation equation that represents this situation. $P = 0.43d$

b. Find the pressure at 60 feet. **25.8 psi**

c. It is unsafe for amateur divers to swim where the water pressure is more than 65 pounds per square inch. How deep can an amateur diver safely swim? **about 151 ft**

d. Make a table showing the number of pounds of pressure at various depths of water. Use the data to draw a graph of pressure versus depth. **See margin.**

Solve each equation or inequality. Round to the nearest ten-thousandth. (Lesson 8-6)

55. $9^{z-4} = 6.28$ **4.8362**

56. $8.2^{n-3} = 42.5$ **4.7820**

57. $2.1^{t-5} = 9.32$ **8.0086**

58. $8^{2n} > 52^{4n+3}$ $\{n \mid n < -1.0178\}$

59. $7^{p+2} \leq 13^{5-p}$ $\{p \mid p \leq 1.9803\}$

60. $3^{y+2} \geq 8^{3y}$ $\{y \mid y \leq 0.4275\}$

Solve each equation. (Lesson 7-7)

61. $(6n-5)^{\frac{1}{3}} + 3 = -2$ **−20**

62. $(5x+7)^{\frac{1}{5}} + 3 = 5$ **5**

63. $(3x-2)^{\frac{1}{5}} + 6 = 5$ $\mathbf{\frac{1}{3}}$

64. $y = -(x+2)^2 + 12$; $(-2, 12)$; $x = -2$; down **65.** $y = (x-3)^2 - 8$; $(3, -8)$; $x = 3$; up

Skills Review

66. $y = -2(x-5)^2 + 15$; $(5, 15)$; $x = 5$; down

Write each quadratic equation in vertex form. Then identify the vertex, axis of symmetry, and direction of opening. (Lesson 5-7)

64. $y = -x^2 - 4x + 8$

65. $y = x^2 - 6x + 1$

66. $y = -2x^2 + 20x - 35$

Differentiated Instruction OL BL

Extension Ask students how they would go about finding the coordinates of a point three-fourths of the distance from $A(1, -5)$ to $B(-4, -7)$. Then have students find the point. Sample answer: First find the midpoint of A and B, and call it C. Then find D, the midpoint of C and B. Point D is three-fourths of the distance from A to B. Since the midpoint is at $C\left(-\frac{3}{2}, -6\right)$, the point three-fourths of the distance is at $D\left(-2\frac{3}{4}, -6\frac{1}{2}\right)$.

622 Chapter 10 Conic Sections

10-2 Parabolas

Why?

Instead of expensive polished metal, glass, or an array of large mirrors to view images from space, frugal astronomers have begun using spinning basins of mercury.

While spinning, the surface of the mercury becomes *parabolic*, the perfect shape for a telescope's mirror.

Then

You graphed quadratic functions. (Lessons 5-1 and 5-7)

Now

- Write equations of parabolas in standard form.
- Graph parabolas.

NGSSS

MA.912.A.9.1 Write the equations of conic sections in standard form and general form, in order to identify the conic section and to find its geometric properties (foci, asymptotes, eccentricity, etc.).
MA.912.A.9.2 Graph conic sections with and without using graphing technology.

New Vocabulary

parabola
focus
directrix
latus rectum
standard form
general form

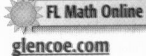

FL Math Online

glencoe.com

Equations of Parabolas A **parabola** can be defined as the set of all points in a plane that are the same distance from a given point called the **focus** and a given line called the **directrix**.

The line segment through the focus of a parabola and perpendicular to the axis of symmetry is called the **latus rectum**. The endpoints of the latus rectum lie on the parabola.

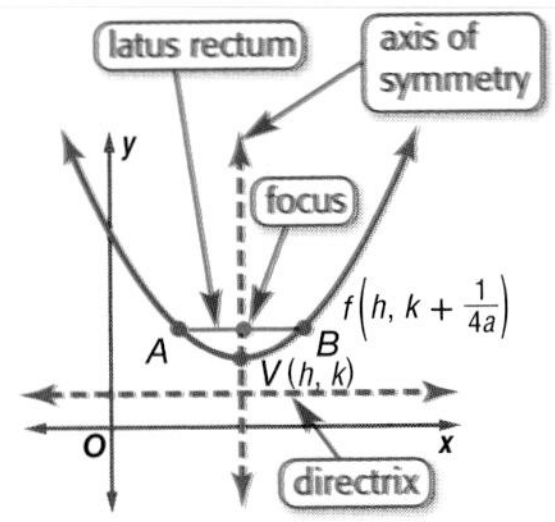

Key Concept Equations of Parabolas

Form of Equation	$y = a(x - h)^2 + k$	$x = a(y - k)^2 + h$
Direction of Opening	upward if $a > 0$, downward if $a < 0$	right if $a > 0$, left if $a < 0$
Vertex	(h, k)	(h, k)
Axis of Symmetry	$x = h$	$y = k$
Focus	$\left(h, k + \frac{1}{4a}\right)$	$\left(h + \frac{1}{4a}, k\right)$
Directrix	$y = k - \frac{1}{4a}$	$x = h - \frac{1}{4a}$
Length of Latus Rectum	$\left\lvert\frac{1}{a}\right\rvert$ units	$\left\lvert\frac{1}{a}\right\rvert$ units

The **standard form** of the equation of a parabola with vertex (h, k) and axis of symmetry $x = h$ is $y = a(x - h)^2 + k$.

- If $a > 0$, k is the minimum value of the related function and the parabola opens upward.
- If $a < 0$, k is the maximum value of the related function and the parabola opens downward.

An equation of a parabola in the form $y = ax^2 + bx + c$ is the **general form**. Any equation in general form can be written in standard form. The shape of a parabola and the distance between the focus and directrix depend on the value of a in the equation.

10-2 Lesson Notes

1 FOCUS

Vertical Alignment

Before Lesson 10-2
Graph quadratic functions.

Lesson 10-2
Write equations of parabolas in standard form.
Graph parabolas.

After Lesson 10-2
Identify the conic section from a given equation.

2 TEACH

Scaffolding Questions

Have students read the *Why?* section of the lesson.

Ask:

- What color is mercury? silver
- Why would mercury be a good substitute for a mirror or polished metal? It is reflective.
- Why is a parabola the perfect shape for a telescope's mirror? The parabola reflects all parallel incoming rays to the same point.

Lesson 10-2 Resources

Resource	Approaching-Level	On-Level	Beyond-Level	English Learners
Teacher Edition	• Differentiated Instruction, p. 624	• Differentiated Instruction, pp. 624, 629	• Differentiated Instruction, p. 629	
Chapter Resource Masters	• Study Guide and Intervention, pp. 11–12 • Skills Practice, p. 13 • Practice, p. 14 • Word Problem Practice, p. 15	• Study Guide and Intervention, pp. 11–12 • Skills Practice, p. 13 • Practice, p. 14 • Word Problem Practice, p. 15 • Enrichment, p. 16 • Spreadsheet Activity, p. 17	• Practice, p. 14 • Word Problem Practice, p. 15 • Enrichment, p. 16	• Study Guide and Intervention, pp. 11–12 • Skills Practice, p. 13 • Practice, p. 14 • Word Problem Practice, p. 15
Transparencies	• 5-Minute Check Transparency 10-2	• 5-Minute Check Transparency 10-2	• 5-Minute Check Transparency 10-2	• 5-Minute Check Transparency 10-2
Other	• Study Notebook • Teaching Algebra with Manipulatives	• Study Notebook • Teaching Algebra with Manipulatives	• Study Notebook	• Study Notebook • Teaching Algebra with Manipulatives

Equations of Parabolas

Example 1 shows how to write an equation of a parabola in standard form and then analyze the equation to identify the vertex, axis of symmetry, and direction of opening of the parabola.

Formative Assessment

Use the Guided Practice exercises after each example to determine students' understanding of concepts.

Additional Example

1 Write $y = -x^2 - 2x + 3$ in standard form. Identify the vertex, axis of symmetry, and direction of opening of the parabola. $y = -(x + 1)^2 + 4$; vertex: $(-1, 4)$; axis of symmetry: $x = -1$; opens downward

Additional Examples also in Interactive Classroom PowerPoint® Presentations

IWB INTERACTIVE WHITEBOARD READY

Graph Parabolas

Example 2 shows how to use the parent function, $y = ax^2$, symmetry, and translations to graph the equation of a parabola with a vertical axis of symmetry. **Example 3** shows how to graph the equation of a parabola that is not in standard form and has a horizontal axis of symmetry. **Example 4** shows how to write and graph the equation of a parabola given the vertex and directrix. **Example 5** shows how to write and graph the equation of a parabola to solve a real-world problem.

Tips for New Teachers

Reasoning Point out that students have studied parabolas before. In this lesson, the study is extended to include new terms and characteristics of parabolas. In Lesson 10-6, students will learn how all the conic sections are related.

Review Vocabulary

completing the square rewriting a quadratic expression as a perfect square trinomial (Lesson 5-5)

EXAMPLE 1 Analyze the Equation of a Parabola

Write $y = 2x^2 - 12x + 6$ in standard form. Identify the vertex, axis of symmetry, and direction of opening of the parabola.

$y = 2x^2 - 12x + 6$	**Original equation**
$= 2(x^2 - 6x) + 6$	**Factor 2 from the x- and x^2-terms.**
$= 2(x^2 - 6x + \blacksquare) + 6 - 2(\blacksquare)$	**Complete the square on the right side.**
$= 2(x^2 - 6x + 9) + 6 - 2(9)$	**The 9 added when you complete the square is multiplied by 2.**
$= 2(x - 3)^2 - 12$	**Factor.**

The vertex of this parabola is located at $(3, -12)$, and the equation of the axis of symmetry is $x = 3$. The parabola opens upward.

Guided Practice

1. Write $y = 4x^2 + 16x + 34$ in standard form. Identify the vertex, axis of symmetry, and direction of opening of the parabola.

1. $y = 4(x + 2)^2 + 18$; vertex: $(h, k) = (-2, 18)$; axis of symmetry: $x = -2$; opens upward

Personal Tutor glencoe.com

Graph Parabolas In Chapter 5, you learned that the graph of the quadratic equation $y = a(x - h)^2 + k$ is a transformation of the parent graph of $y = x^2$ translated h units horizontally and k units vertically, and reflected and/or dilated depending on the value of a.

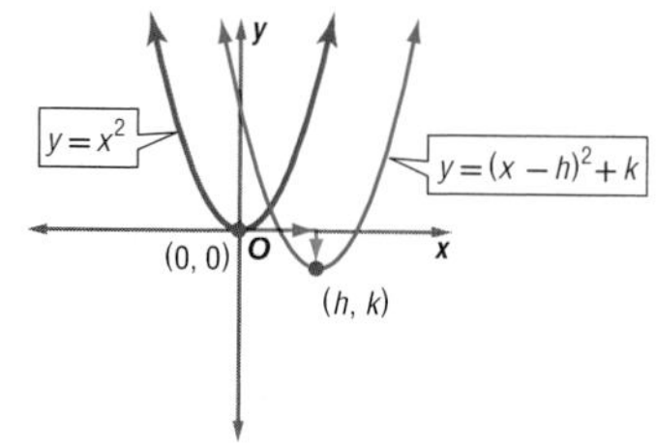

EXAMPLE 2 Graph Parabolas

Graph each equation.

a. $y = -3x^2$

For this equation, $h = 0$ and $k = 0$. The vertex is at the origin. Since the equation of the axis of symmetry is $x = 0$, substitute some small positive integers for x and find the corresponding y-values.

x	y
1	−3
2	−12
3	−27

Since the graph is symmetric about the y-axis, the points at $(-1, -3)$, $(-2, -12)$, and $(-3, -27)$ are also on the parabola. Use all of these points to draw the graph.

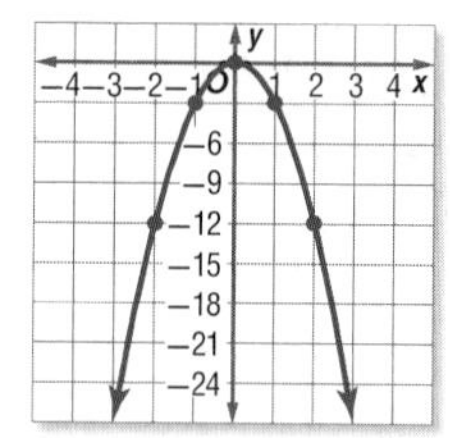

b. $y = -3(x - 4)^2 + 5$

The equation is of the form $y = a(x - h)^2 + k$, where $h = 4$ and $k = 5$. The graph of this equation is the graph of $y = -3x^2$ in part **a** translated 4 units to the right and up 5 units. The vertex is now at $(4, 5)$.

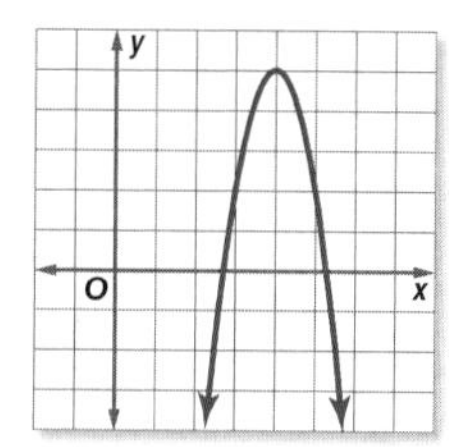

Watch Out!

Translations It is easy to confuse the effect of a translation.

- If h is positive, translate the graph h units to the right.
- If h is negative, translate the graph h units to the left.
- If k is positive, translate the graph k units up.
- If k is negative, translate the graph k units down.

Guided Practice

2A. $y = 2x^2$ **2B.** $y = 2(x - 1)^2 - 4$

2A, 2B. See Chapter 10 Answer Appendix.

Personal Tutor glencoe.com

Differentiated Instruction

AL OL

If some students think that any curve can be called a parabola,

Then explain that only curves with a certain well-defined shape meet the definition of a parabola. Have students use the Internet to research objects in the real world that are parabolas. Ask them to make a poster to display their findings.

StudyTip

Graphing When graphing these functions, it may be helpful to sketch the graph of the parent function.

Equations of parabolas with vertical axes of symmetry have the parent function $y = x^2$ and are of the form $y = a(x - h)^2 + k$. These are functions. Equations of parabolas with horizontal axes of symmetry are of the form $x = a(y - k)^2 + h$ and are not functions. The parent graph for these equations is $x = y^2$.

EXAMPLE 3 Graph an Equation in General Form

Graph each equation.

a. $2x - y^2 = 4y + 10$

Step 1 Write the equation in the form $x = a(y - k)^2 + h$.

$2x - y^2 = 4y + 10$	**Original equation**
$2x = y^2 + 4y + 10$	**Add y^2 to each side to isolate the x-term.**
$2x = (y^2 + 4y + \blacksquare) + 10 - \blacksquare$	**Complete the square.**
$2x = (y^2 + 4y + 4) + 10 - 4$	**Add and subtract 4, since $\left(\frac{4}{2}\right)^2 = 4$.**
$2x = (y + 2)^2 + 6$	**Factor and subtract.**
$x = \frac{1}{2}(y + 2)^2 + 3$	**$(h, k) = (3, -2)$**

Step 2 Use the equation to find information about the graph. Then draw the graph based on the parent graph, $x = y^2$.

vertex: $(3, -2)$

axis of symmetry: $y = -2$

focus: $\left(3 + \frac{1}{4\left(\frac{1}{2}\right)}, -2\right)$ or $(3.5, -2)$

directrix: $x = 3 - \frac{1}{4\left(\frac{1}{2}\right)}$ or 2.5

direction of opening: right, since $a > 0$

length of latus rectum: $\left|\frac{1}{\left(\frac{1}{2}\right)}\right|$ or 2 units

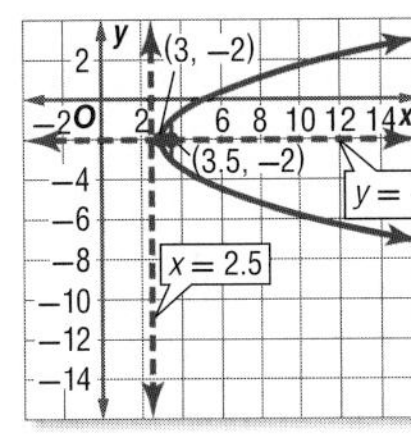

ReadingMath

latus rectum from the Latin *latus*, meaning side, and *rectum*, meaning straight

b. $y + 2x^2 + 32 = -16x - 1$

Step 1	$y + 2x^2 + 32 = -16x - 1$	**Original equation**
	$y = -2x^2 - 16x - 33$	**Solve for y.**
	$y = -2(x^2 + 8x + \blacksquare) - 33 - \blacksquare$	**Complete the square.**
	$y = -2(x^2 + 8x + 16) - 33 - (-32)$	**Add and subtract −32.**
	$y = -2(x + 4)^2 - 1$	**Factor and simplify.**

Step 2 vertex: $(-4, -1)$

axis of symmetry: $x = -4$

focus: $\left(-4, -\frac{9}{8}\right)$

directrix: $y = -\frac{7}{8}$

length of latus rectum: $\frac{1}{2}$ unit

opens down

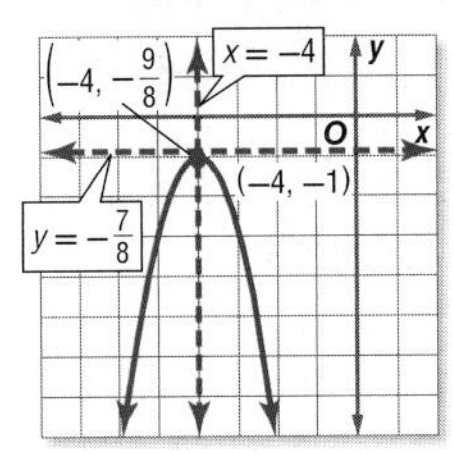

Guided Practice 3A, 3B. See Chapter 10 Answer Appendix.

3A. $3x - y^2 = 4x + 25$ **3B.** $y = x^2 + 6x - 4$

▷ Personal Tutor glencoe.com

Additional Examples

2 Graph each equation.

a. $y = 2x^2$

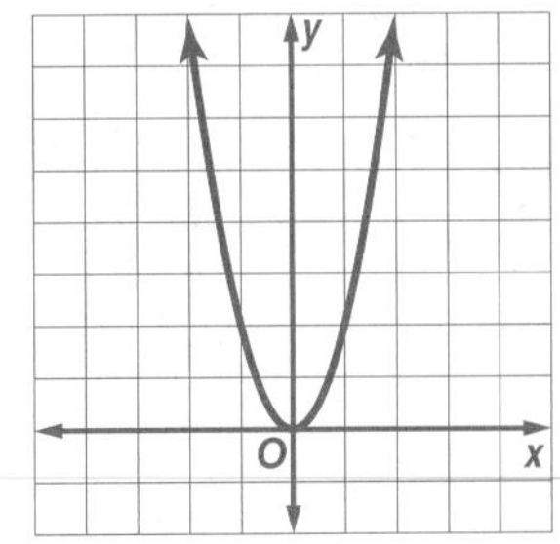

b. $y = 2(x - 1)^2 - 5$

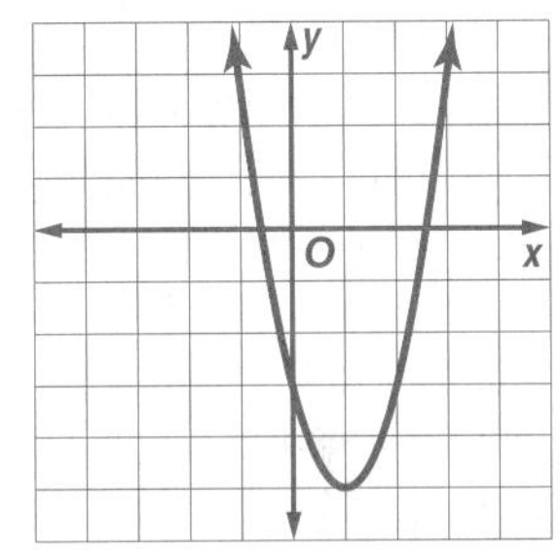

3 Graph each equation.

a. $x + y^2 = 4y - 1$

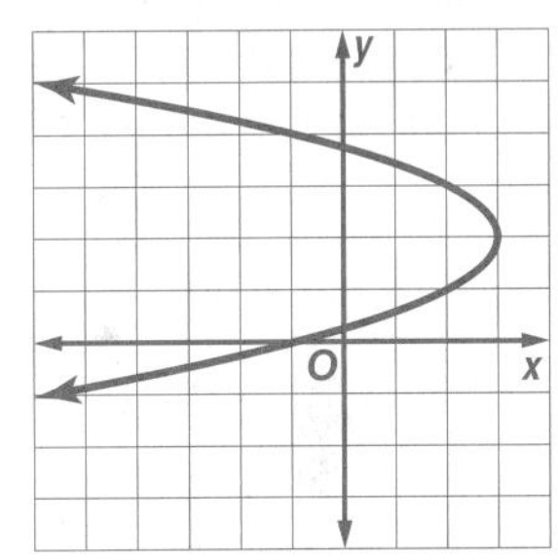

b. $y + 2x^2 + 10 = 8x + 5$

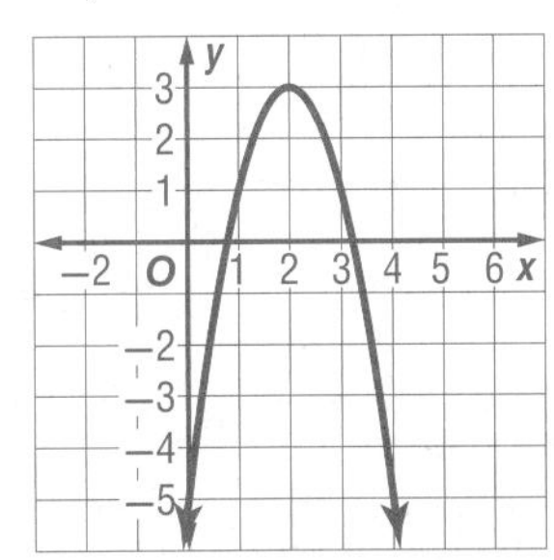

TEACH with TECH

VIDEO RECORDING Break the class into groups, and give each group an equation of a different parabola. Have the group create a video showing how to find all of the properties and information about the parabola. Share each group's video with the entire class.

Tips for New Teachers

Building on Prior Knowledge Remind students that the distance from a point to a line is measured on the perpendicular from the point to the line.

Additional Examples

4 Write an equation for a parabola with a vertex (8, 6) and focus (2, 6). Then graph the equation.

$x = -\frac{1}{24}(y - 6)^2 + 8$

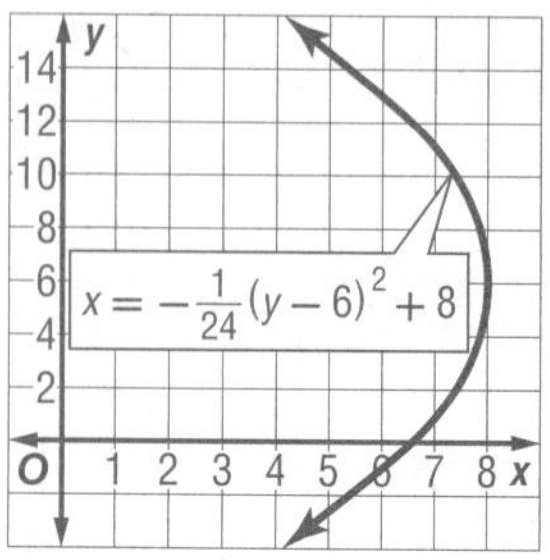

5 **BRIDGES** The Hulme Arch Bridge in Manchester, England, is supported by cables suspended from a parabolic steel arch. The highest point of the arch is 25 meters above the bridge, and the focus of the arch is 18 meters above the bridge.

a. Let the bridge be the *x*–axis, and let the *y*-axis pass through the vertex of the arch. Write an equation that models the arch. $y = -\frac{1}{28}x^2 + 25$

b. Graph the equation.

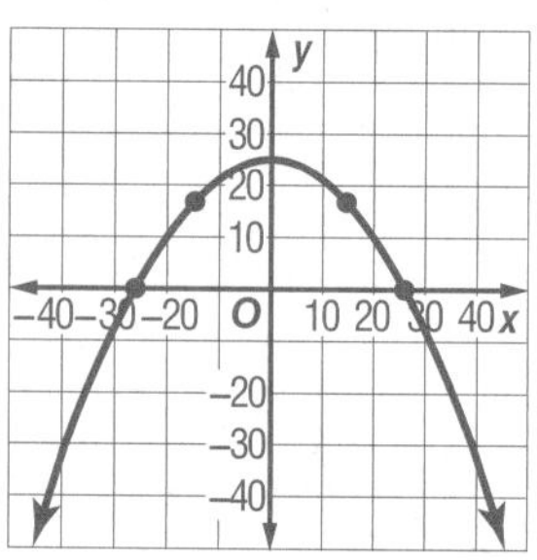

You can use specific information about a parabola to write an equation and draw a graph.

EXAMPLE 4 Write an Equation of a Parabola

Write an equation for a parabola with a vertex (−2, −4) and directrix $y = 1$. Then graph the equation.

The directrix is a horizontal line, so the equation of the parabola is of the form $y = a(x - h)^2 + k$. Find a, h, and k.

- The vertex is at (−2, −4), so $h = -2$ and $k = -4$.
- Use the equation of the directrix to find a.

$y = k - \frac{1}{4a}$	**Equation of directrix**
$1 = -4 - \frac{1}{4a}$	**Replace *y* with 1 and *k* with −4.**
$5 = -\frac{1}{4a}$	**Add 4 to each side.**
$20a = -1$	**Multiply each side by 4*a*.**
$a = -\frac{1}{20}$	**Divide each side by 20.**

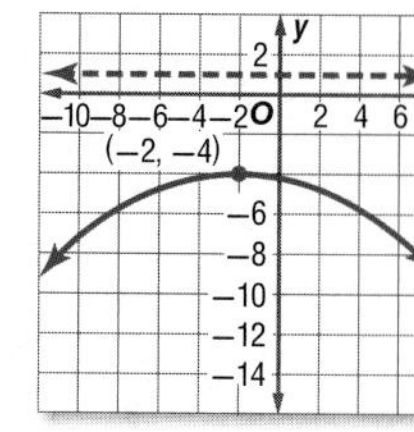

So, the equation of the parabola is $y = -\frac{1}{20}(x + 2)^2 - 4$.

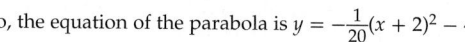

Guided Practice 4A, 4B. See margin.

Write an equation for each parabola described below. Then graph the equation.

4A. vertex (1, 3), focus (1, 5)

4B. focus (5, 6), directrix $x = -2$

Personal Tutor glencoe.com

Parabolas are often used in the real world.

Real-World EXAMPLE 5 Write an Equation for a Parabola

ENVIRONMENT **Solar energy may be harnessed by using parabolic mirrors. The mirrors reflect the rays from the Sun to the focus of the parabola. The focus of each parabolic mirror at the facility described at the left is 6.25 feet above the vertex. The latus rectum is 25 feet long.**

Real-World Link

In California's Mojave Desert, parabolic mirrors are used to heat oil that flows through tubes placed at the focus. The heated oil is used to produce electricity.

Source: Solel

a. Assume that the focus is at the origin. Write an equation for the parabola formed by each mirror.

In order for the mirrors to collect the Sun's energy, the parabola must open upward. Therefore, the vertex must be below the focus.

focus: (0, 0) vertex: (0, −6.25)

The measure of the latus rectum is 25. So $25 = \left|\frac{1}{a}\right|$, and $a = \frac{1}{25}$.

Using the form $y = a(x - h)^2 + k$, an equation for the parabola formed by each mirror is $y = \frac{1}{25}x^2 - 6.25$.

b. Graph the equation.

Now use all of the information to draw a graph.

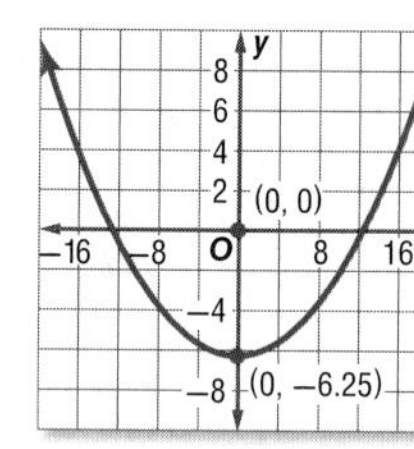

Guided Practice 5. See margin.

5. Write and graph an equation for a parabolic mirror that has a focus 4.5 feet above the vertex and a latus rectum that is 18 feet long, when the focus is at the origin.

Personal Tutor glencoe.com

Additional Answers (Guided Practice)

4A. $y = \frac{1}{8}(x - 1)^2 + 3$

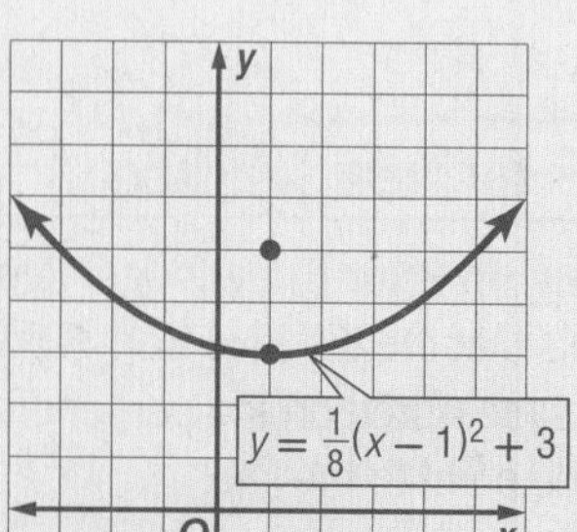

4B. $x = \frac{1}{14}(y - 6)^2 + 1.5$

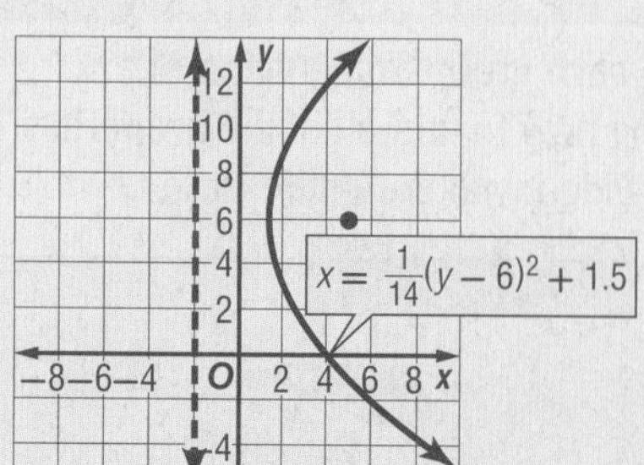

5. $y = \frac{1}{18}x^2 - 4.5$

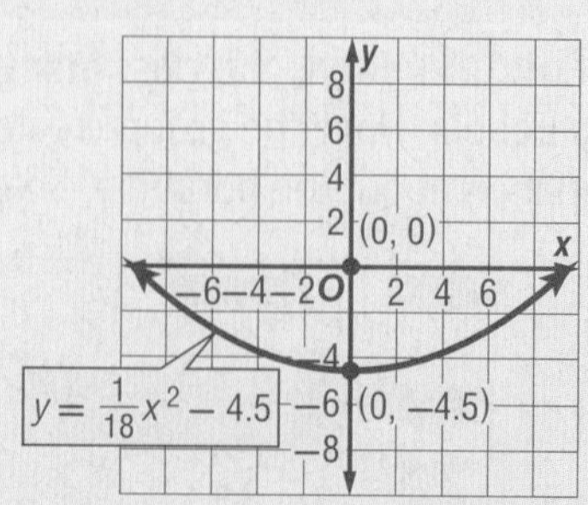

Check Your Understanding

Example 1 p. 624

Write each equation in standard form. Identify the vertex, axis of symmetry, and direction of opening of the parabola. 1–4. See margin.

1. $y = 2x^2 - 24x + 40$
2. $y = 3x^2 - 6x - 4$
3. $x = y^2 - 8y - 11$
4. $x + 3y^2 + 12y = 18$

Examples 2 and 3 pp. 624–625

Graph each equation. 5–8. See Chapter 10 Answer Appendix.

5. $y = (x - 4)^2 - 6$
6. $y = 4(x + 5)^2 + 3$
7. $y = -3x^2 - 4x - 8$
8. $x = 3y^2 - 6y + 9$

Example 4 p. 626

Write an equation for each parabola described below. Then graph the equation.

9–12. See Chapter 10 Answer Appendix.

9. vertex (0, 2), focus (0, 4)
10. vertex (−2, 4), directrix $x = -1$
11. focus (3, 2), directrix $y = 8$
12. vertex (−1, −5), focus (−5, −5)

Example 5 p. 626

13. **ASTRONOMY** Consider a parabolic mercury mirror like the one described at the beginning of the lesson. The focus is 6 feet above the vertex and the latus rectum is 24 feet long.
    a. Assume that the focus is at the origin. Write an equation for the parabola formed by the parabolic microphone. $y = \frac{1}{24}x^2 - 6$
    b. Graph the equation. See margin.

Practice and Problem Solving

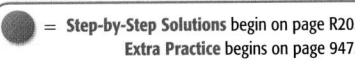

● = **Step-by-Step Solutions** begin on page R20. **Extra Practice** begins on page 947.

Example 1 p. 624

Write each equation in standard form. Identify the vertex, axis of symmetry, and direction of opening of the parabola. 14–19. See margin.

14. $y = x^2 - 8x + 13$
15. $y = 3x^2 + 42x + 149$
16. $y = -6x^2 - 36x - 8$
17. $y = -3x^2 - 9x - 6$
18. $x = \frac{1}{3}y^2 - 3y + 4$
19. $x = \frac{2}{3}y^2 - 4y + 12$

Examples 2 and 3 pp. 624–625

Graph each equation. 20–25. See Chapter 10 Answer Appendix.

20. $y = \frac{1}{3}x^2$
21. $y = -2x^2$
22. $y = -2(x - 2)^2 + 3$
23. $y = 3(x - 3)^2 - 5$
24. $x = \frac{1}{2}y^2$
25. $4x - y^2 = 2y + 13$

Example 4 p. 626

Write an equation for each parabola described below. Then graph the equation.

26–31. See Chapter 10 Answer Appendix.

26. vertex (0, 1), focus (0, 4)
27. vertex (1, 8), directrix $y = 3$
28. focus (−2, −4), directrix $x = -6$
29. focus (2, 4), directrix $x = 10$
30. vertex (−6, 0), directrix $x = 2$
31. vertex (9, 6), focus (9, 5)

Example 5 p. 626

32. **BASEBALL** When a ball is thrown, the path it travels is a parabola. Suppose a baseball is thrown from ground level, reaches a maximum height of 50 feet, and hits the ground 200 feet from where it was thrown. Assuming this situation could be modeled on a coordinate plane with the focus of the parabola at the origin, find the equation of the parabolic path of the ball. Assume the focus is on ground level.

32. $y = -\frac{1}{200}x^2 + 50$

33. **SPACE** Ground antennas and satellites are used to relay signals between the NASA Mission Operations Center and the spacecraft it controls. One such dish is 146 feet in diameter. Its focus is 48 feet from the vertex. a. See Chapter 10 Answer Appendix.
    a. Sketch two options for the dish, one that opens up and one that opens left.
    b. Write two equations that model the sketches in part **a**. $y = \frac{x^2}{192}$ and $x = \frac{y^2}{-192}$
    c. If you wanted to find the depth of the dish, does it matter which equation you use? Why or why not? Sample answer: No; except for the direction in which they open, the graphs are identical.

Differentiated Homework Options

Level	Assignment	Two-Day Option	
AL Basic	14–33, 37–61	15–33 odd, 41–44	14–32 even, 37–40, 45–61
OL Core	15–30 odd, 32–61	14–33, 41–44	34–40, 45–61
BL Advanced	34–57, (optional: 58–61)		

3 PRACTICE

Formative Assessment

Use Exercises 1–13 to check for understanding.

Use the chart at the bottom of this page to customize assignments for your students.

Additional Answers

1. $y = 2(x - 6)^2 - 32$; vertex (6, −32); axis of symmetry: $x = 6$; opens upward
2. $y = 3(x - 1)^2 - 7$; vertex (1, −7); axis of symmetry: $x = 1$; opens upward
3. $x = (y - 4)^2 - 27$; vertex (−27, 4); axis of symmetry: $y = 4$; opens right
4. $x = -3(y + 2)^2 + 30$; vertex (30, −2); axis of symmetry: $y = -2$; opens left

13b.

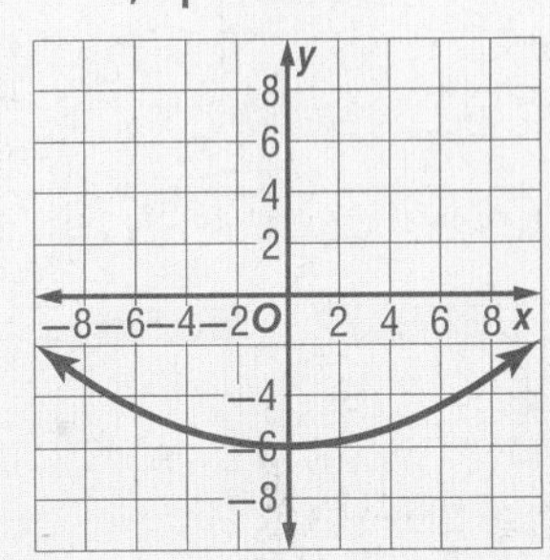

14. $y = (x - 4)^2 - 3$; vertex = (4, −3); axis of symmetry: $x = 4$; opens upward
15. $y = 3(x + 7)^2 + 2$; vertex = (−7, 2); axis of symmetry: $x = -7$; opens upward
16. $y = -6(x + 3)^2 + 46$; vertex = (−3, 46); axis of symmetry: $x = -3$; opens downward
17. $y = -3\left(x + \frac{3}{2}\right)^2 + \frac{3}{4}$; vertex = $\left(-\frac{3}{2}, \frac{3}{4}\right)$; axis of symmetry: $x = -\frac{3}{2}$; opens downward
18. $x = \frac{1}{3}(y - 4.5)^2 - 2.75$; vertex = (−2.75, 4.5); axis of symmetry: $y = 4.5$; opens right
19. $x = \frac{2}{3}(y - 3)^2 + 6$; vertex = (6, 3); axis of symmetry: $y = 3$; opens right

Study Guide and Intervention
CRM pp. 11–12 AL OL ELL

10-2 Study Guide and Intervention

Parabolas

Equations of Parabolas A parabola is a curve consisting of all points in the coordinate plane that are the same distance from a given point (the **focus**) and a given line (the **directrix**). The following chart summarizes important information about parabolas.

Standard Form of Equation	$y = a(x - h)^2 + k$	$x = a(y - k)^2 + h$
Axis of Symmetry	$x = h$	$y = k$
Vertex	(h, k)	(h, k)
Focus	$\left(h, k + \frac{1}{4a}\right)$	$\left(h + \frac{1}{4a}, k\right)$
Directrix	$y = k - \frac{1}{4a}$	$x = h - \frac{1}{4a}$
Direction of Opening	upward if $a > 0$, downward if $a < 0$	right if $a > 0$, left if $a < 0$
Length of Latus Rectum	$\left\|\frac{1}{a}\right\|$ units	$\left\|\frac{1}{a}\right\|$ units

Example Write $y = 2x^2 - 12x - 25$ in standard form. Identify the vertex, axis of symmetry, and direction of opening of the parabola.

$y = 2x^2 - 12x - 25$ Original equation
$y = 2(x^2 - 6x) - 25$ Factor 2 from the x-terms.
$y = 2(x^2 - 6x + ■) - 25 - 2(■)$ Complete the square on the right side.
$y = 2(x^2 - 6x + 9) - 25 - 2(9)$ The 9 added to complete the square is multiplied by 2.
$y = 2(x - 3)^2 - 43$ Write in standard form.

The vertex of this parabola is located at (3, −43), the equation of the axis of symmetry is $x = 3$, and the parabola opens upward.

Exercises

Write each equation in standard form. Identify the vertex, axis of symmetry, and direction of opening of the parabola.

1. $y = x^2 + 2x + 1$ — $y = (x + 1)^2$, (−1, 0) $x = -1$, opens upward
2. $y = -x^2$ — $y = -1(x + 0)^2$, (0, 0) $x = 0$, opens downward
3. $y = x^2 + 4x - 15$ — $y = (x + 2)^2 - 19$, (−2, −19), $x = -2$, opens upward
4. $y = x^2 + 6x - 4$ — $y = (x + 3)^2 - 13$, $\left(-3, -12\frac{3}{4}\right)$, $x = -3$, opens upward
5. $y = 8x - 2x^2 + 10$ — $y = -2(x - 2)^2 + 18$, $\left(2, 17\frac{1}{8}\right)$, $x = 2$, opens downward
6. $x = y^2 - 8y + 6$ — $x = (y - 4)^2 - 10$, $\left(-9\frac{3}{4}, 4\right)$, $y = 4$, opens right

Chapter 10 11 Glencoe Algebra 2

Practice
CRM p. 14 AL OL BL ELL

10-2 Practice

Parabolas

Write each equation in standard form. Identify the vertex, axis of symmetry, and direction of opening of the parabola.

1. $y = 2x^2 - 12x + 19$ — $y = 2(x - 3)^2 + 1$, (3, 1), $x = 3$, opens upward
2. $y = \frac{1}{2}x^2 + 3x + \frac{1}{2}$ — $y = \frac{1}{2}(x + 3)^2 - 4$, (−3, −4), $x = -3$, opens upward
3. $y = -3x^2 - 12x - 7$ — $y = -3(x + 2)^2 + 5$, (−2, 5), $x = -2$, opens downward

Graph each equation.

4. $y = (x - 4)^2 + 3$
5. $x = -\frac{1}{3}y^2 + 1$
6. $x = 3(y + 1)^2 - 3$

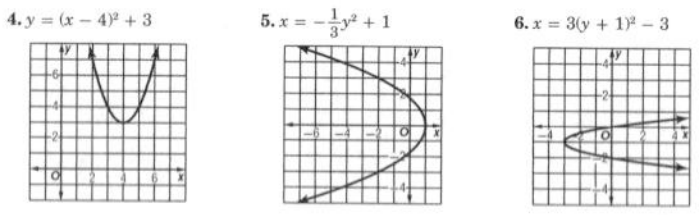

Write an equation for each parabola described below. Then graph the equation.

7. vertex (0, −4), focus $\left(0, -3\frac{7}{8}\right)$
8. vertex (−2, 1), directrix $x = -3$
9. vertex (1, 3), latus rectum: 2 units, $a < 0$

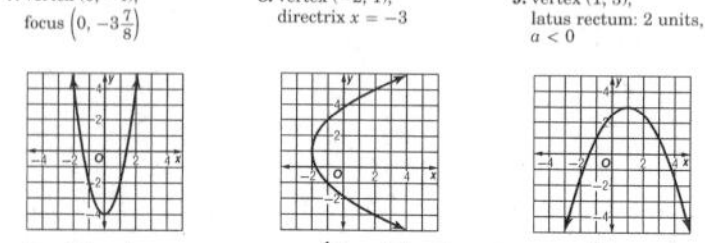

$y = 2x^2 - 4$ $x = \frac{1}{4}(y - 1)^2 - 2$ $y = -\frac{1}{2}(x - 1)^2 + 3$

10. TELEVISION Write the equation in the form $y = ax^2$ for a satellite dish. Assume that the bottom of the upward-facing dish passes through (0, 0) and that the distance from the bottom to the focus point is 8 inches. $y = \frac{1}{32}x^2$

Chapter 10 14 Glencoe Algebra 2

Word Problem Practice
CRM p. 15 AL OL BL ELL

10-2 Word Problem Practice

Parabolas

1. PROJECTILE A projectile follows the graph of the parabola $y = -\frac{3}{2}x^2 + 6x$. Sketch the path of the projectile by graphing the parabola.

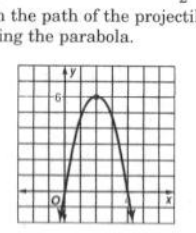

2. COMMUNICATION David has just made a large parabolic dish whose cross section is based on the graph of the parabola $y = 0.25x^2$. Each unit represents one foot and the diameter of his dish is 4 feet. He wants to make a listening device by placing a microphone at the focus of the parabola. Where should the microphone be placed? **1 foot away from the vertex along the axis (at the point (0, 1) with respect to the graph)**

3. BRIDGES A bridge is in the shape of a parabola that opens downward. The equation of the parabola to model the arch of the bridge is given by $y = -\frac{x^2}{24} + \frac{5}{6}x + \frac{11}{6}$, where each unit is equivalent to 1 yard. The x-axis is the ground level. What is the maximum height of the bridge above the ground? **6 yd**

4. TELESCOPES An astronomer is working with a large reflecting telescope. The reflecting mirror in the telescope has the parabolic cross section shown in the graph whose equation is given by $y = \frac{1}{8}(x - 4)^2 + 2$. Each unit represents 1 meter. The astronomer is standing at the origin. How far from the focus of the parabola is the point on the mirror directly over the astronomer's head?

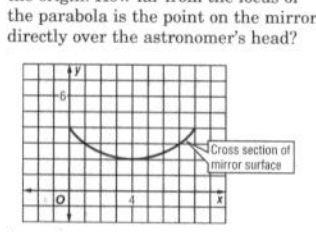

4 m

5. BRIDGES Part of the Sydney Harbor Bridge in Sydney, Australia, can be modeled by a parabolic arch. If each unit corresponds to 10 meters, the arch would pass through the points at (−25, 5), (0, 10), and (25, 5).

a. Write the equation of the parabola to model the arch. $y = -\frac{1}{125}x^2 + 10$

b. Identify the coordinates of the focus of this parabola. **(0, −21.25)**

Chapter 10 15 Glencoe Algebra 2

Real-World Link

Parabolic headlights use a special bulb with two filaments to produce high beams and low beams. The filament placed at the focus produces high beams, and the filament placed off the focus produces low beams.

Source: General Motors

Lesson 10-2

34. **UMBRELLAS** A beach umbrella has an arch in the shape of a parabola that opens downward. The umbrella spans 6 feet across and is $1\frac{1}{2}$ feet high. Write an equation of a parabola to model the arch, assuming that the origin is at the point where the pole and umbrella meet, beneath the vertex of the arch. $y = -\frac{1}{6}x^2$

35. **AUTOMOBILES** An automobile headlight contains a parabolic reflector. The light coming from the source bounces off the parabolic reflector and shines out the front of the headlight. The equation of the cross section of the reflector is $y = \frac{1}{12}x^2$. How far from the vertex should the filament for the high beams be placed? **3 units**

36. **MULTIPLE REPRESENTATIONS** Start with a sheet of wax paper that is about 15 inches long and 12 inches wide. **a–c. See students' work.**

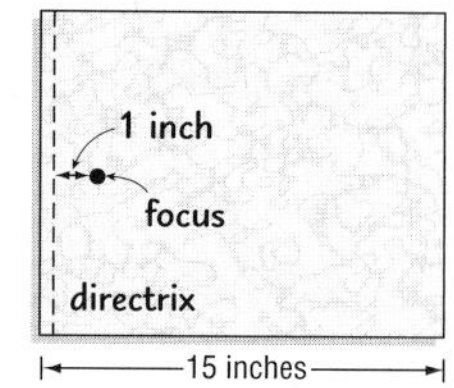

a. **CONCRETE** Make a line that is perpendicular to the sides of the sheet by folding the sheet near one end. Open up the paper again. This line is the directrix. Mark a point about midway between the sides of the sheet so that the distance from the directrix is about 1 inch. This is the focus.

b. **CONCRETE** Start with a new sheet of wax paper. Form another outline of a parabola with a focus that is about 3 inches from the directrix.

c. **CONCRETE** On a new sheet of a wax paper, form a third outline of a parabola with a focus that is about 5 inches from the directrix.

d. **VERBAL** Compare the shapes of the three parabolas. How does the distance between the focus and the directrix affect the shape of a parabola?

36d. As the distance between the directrix and the focus increases, the parabola becomes wider.

38. Sample answers: $y = -\frac{1}{4}(x + 3)^2 + 1$ and $x = 2(y - 1)^2 - 3$

39. Russell; the parabola should open to the left rather than to the right.

40. A parabolic microphone can be used to make capturing sound more effective, because reflected sound waves are focused at the particular point where the microphone is. A standard microphone would not be able to capture sounds from all directions. With a parabolic microphone most of the noise from the game can be directed toward the microphone resulting in better sound quality.

H.O.T. Problems
Use Higher-Order Thinking Skills

37. **REASONING** How do you change the equation of the parent function $y = x^2$ to shift the graph to the right? **Rewrite it as $y = (x - h)^2$, where $h > 0$.**

38. **OPEN ENDED** Two different parabolas have their vertex at (−3, 1) and contain the point with coordinates (−1, 0). Write two possible equations for these parabolas.

39. **ERROR ANALYSIS** Brianna and Russell are graphing $\frac{1}{4}y^2 + x = 0$. Is either of them correct? Explain your reasoning.

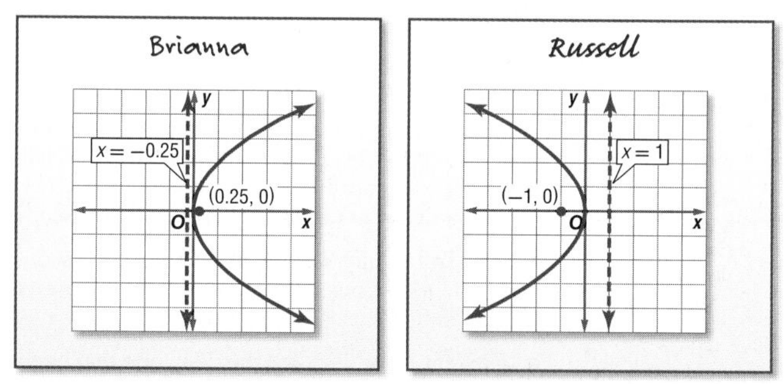

40. **WRITING IN MATH** How are parabolas used in televising sporting events? Explain why a televised sporting event filmed with a parabolic microphone is better than a televised sporting event filmed with a standard microphone.

Enrichment
CRM p. 16 OL BL

10-2 Enrichment

Limits

Sequences of numbers with a rational expression for the general term often approach some number as a finite limit. For example, the reciprocals of the positive integers approach 0 as n gets larger and larger. This is written using the notation shown below. The symbol ∞ stands for infinity and $n \to \infty$ means that n is getting larger and larger, or "n goes to infinity."

$1, \frac{1}{2}, \frac{1}{3}, \frac{1}{4}, \ldots, \frac{1}{n}, \ldots$ $\lim_{n \to \infty} \frac{1}{n} = 0$

Example Find $\lim_{n \to \infty} \frac{n^2}{(n + 1)^2}$

It is not immediately apparent whether the sequence approaches a limit or not. But notice what happens if we divide the numerator and denominator of the general term by n^2.

$\frac{n^2}{(n + 1)^2} = \frac{n^2}{n^2 + 2n + 1}$

$= \frac{\frac{n^2}{n^2}}{\frac{n^2}{n^2} + \frac{2n}{n^2} + \frac{1}{n^2}}$

Multiple Representations In Exercise 36, students use a concrete model and verbal analysis to investigate how the shape of a parabola is determined by its directrix and focus.

NGSSS PRACTICE 912.A.3.15, 912.A.3.1, 912.G.2.5

41. A gardener is placing a fence around a 1320-square-foot rectangular garden. He ordered 148 feet of fencing. If he uses all the fencing, what is the length of the longer side of the garden? **C**

A. 30 ft C. 44 ft
B. 34 ft D. 46 ft

42. ACT/SAT When a number is divided by 5, the result is 7 more than the number. Find the number. **G**

F. $\frac{35}{4}$

G. $-\frac{35}{4}$

H. $\frac{28}{7}$

I. $\frac{28}{4}$

43. GEOMETRY What is the area of the following square, if the length of $\overline{BD}$ is $2\sqrt{2}$? **D**

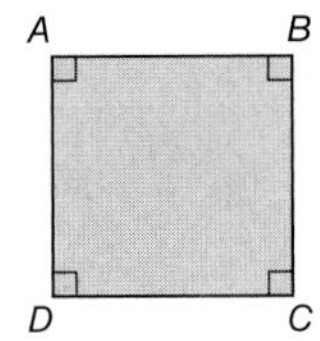

A. 1
B. 2
C. 3
D. 4

44. **SHORT RESPONSE** The measure of the smallest angle of a triangle is two thirds the measure of the middle angle. The measure of the middle angle is three sevenths of the measure of the largest angle. Find the largest angle's measure. **105°**

Spiral Review

45. GEOMETRY Find the perimeter of a triangle with vertices at (2, 4), (−1, 3), and (1, −3). (Lesson 10-1) $5\sqrt{2} + 3\sqrt{10}$ **units**

46. WORK A worker can powerwash a wall of a certain size in 5 hours. Another worker can do the same job in 4 hours. If the workers work together, how long would it take to do the job? Determine whether your answer is reasonable. (Lesson 9-6)

46. $2\frac{2}{9}$ h; The answer is reasonable. The time to complete the job when working together must be less than the time it would take either person working alone.

Solve each equation or inequality. Round to the nearest ten-thousandth. (Lesson 8-7)

47. $\ln(x + 1) = 1$ **1.7183**

48. $\ln(x - 7) = 2$ **14.3891**

49. $e^x > 1.6$ $x > 0.4700$

50. $e^{5x} \geq 25$ $x \geq 0.6438$

Simplify. (Lesson 7-4)

51. $\sqrt{0.25}$ **0.5**

52. $\sqrt[3]{-0.064}$ **−0.4**

53. $\sqrt[4]{z^8}$ z^2

54. $-\sqrt[6]{x^6}$ $-|x|$

List all of the possible rational zeros of each function. (Lesson 6-8)

55. $h(x) = x^3 + 8x + 6$ $\pm1, \pm2, \pm3, \pm6$

56. $p(x) = 3x^3 - 5x^2 - 11x + 3$ $\pm1, \pm\frac{1}{3}, \pm3$

57. $h(x) = 9x^6 - 5x^3 + 27$ $\pm1, \pm\frac{1}{3}, \pm\frac{1}{9}, \pm3, \pm9, \pm27$

Skills Review

Simplify each expression. (Concepts and Skills Bank 2)

58. $\sqrt{24}$ $2\sqrt{6}$

59. $\sqrt{45}$ $3\sqrt{5}$

60. $\sqrt{252}$ $6\sqrt{7}$

61. $\sqrt{512}$ $16\sqrt{2}$

Exercise Alert

Wax paper For Exercise 36, Students will need three 15″ by 12″ sheets of wax paper.

Watch Out!

Error Analysis In Exercise 39, remind students that they must rewrite the equation in standard form before graphing.

4 ASSESS

Yesterday's News Have students write how understanding how to complete the square helped them in today's lesson with graphing equations of a parabola.

Formative Assessment

Check for student understanding of concepts in Lessons 10-1 and 10-2.

CRM Quiz 1, p. 53

Differentiated Instruction OL BL

Extension Remind students that if they know two points on a line, they can write the equation of the line. Tell students that to write the equation of a parabola, they need three points on the graph. Ask students to write the equation for a parabola through (0, 3), (1, 4), and (−2, 7). Using the standard quadratic equation $y = ax^2 + bx + c$, substitute each of the given values for x and y. Solve the system of three equations in a, b, and c. Substituting (0, 3): $c = 3$; (1, 4): $a + b + c = 4$; (−2, 7): $4a - 2b + c = 7$. Solving simultaneously, $a = 1$, $b = 0$, and $c = 3$; the equation is $y = x^2 + 3$.

EXPLORE 10-3 Lesson Notes

1 FOCUS

Objective Use a graphing calculator to examine the characteristics of a circle and its equation.

Materials for Each Student

- TI-Nspire or TI-Nspire CAS graphing calculator

Teaching Tip

The calculator opens on the same screen as when it was turned off. Have students press the Home key to begin the lab.

2 TEACH

Working in Cooperative Groups

Have students of mixed abilities work in pairs to complete the Activity.

Ask:

- What do you know about all of the points on a circle? They are the same distance from a given point called the center.
- Is the center of a circle a part of the circle? no
- If the radius of a circle is increased, what happens to the circle? It becomes larger.

Practice Have students complete the Exercises 1–4.

3 ASSESS

Formative Assessment

Use Exercise 3 to assess whether students can use a graphing calculator to examine the characteristics of a circle and its equation.

EXPLORE 10-3 Graphing Technology Lab: Equations of Circles

FL Math Online glencoe.com
- Other Calculator Keystrokes
- Graphing Technology Personal Tutor

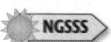

NGSSS **MA.912.A.9.2 Graph conic sections with and without using graphing technology.**
Also addresses MA.912.A.9.1 and MA.912.G.6.6.

You can use TI-Nspire™ or TI-Nspire CAS™ technology to examine characteristics of circles and the relationship with an equation of the circle.

ACTIVITY

Step 1 Draw a circle.

- From the Home screen, select New Document. Select Add Graphs & Geometry. Then press (menu) and select Shapes, and then select Circle. Place the pointer at the origin and press (enter) to set the center of the circle. Move the pointer out, creating a circle like the one shown.
- From (menu), select Points & Lines, and then Point On to place a point on the circle.
- Then, draw a radius by selecting (menu), Points & Lines, and then Segment.

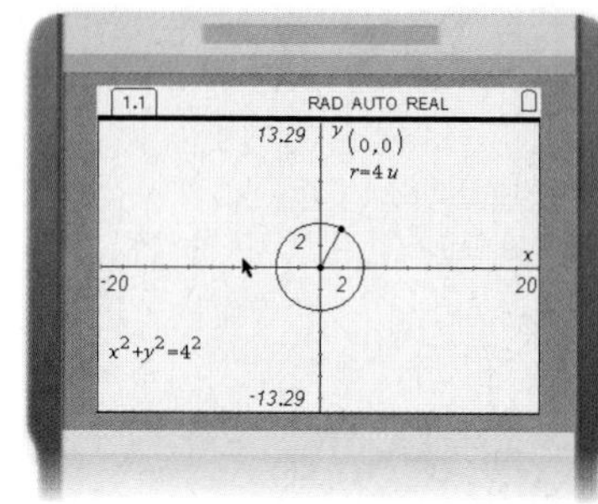

Step 2 Add labels.

- Under (menu), select Actions, then Coordinates and Equations. Use the pointer to select the center of the circle and display its coordinates. Move the coordinates out of the way.
- Display the length of the radius using (menu), then Measurement, and then Length.
- Use (menu), Actions, and Coordinates and Equations to display an equation of the circle.

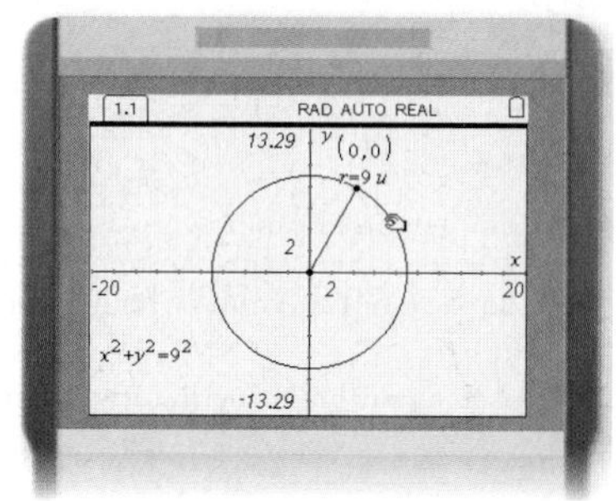

Step 3 Change the radius.

Move the pointer so that a point on the circle is highlighted, then press and hold (grab) until it is selected. Examine the equation of the circle. Then move the edge of the circle in. Make note of changes in the equation.

Step 4 Move the center of the circle.

Move the pointer so that the center of the circle is highlighted, then press and hold (grab) until it is selected. Move the center of the circle. Again, examine the equation of the circle.

Analyze the Results

3. Sample answer: The equation is affected the same as when it was drawn centered at the origin.

1. How does moving the edge of the circle in or out affect the equation of the circle? See margin.
2. What effect does moving the center of the circle have on the equation? See margin.
3. Repeat the activity by placing the center of a circle in Quadrant I. Move the center to each of the other three quadrants. How does the equation change?
4. **MAKE A CONJECTURE** Without graphing, write an equation of each circle.
   a. center: (4, 2), radius: 3 **b.** center: (−1, 1), radius: 8
   c. center: (−6, −5), radius: 2.5 **d.** center: (h, k), radius: r

4a. $(x-4)^2+(y-2)^2=3^2$
4b. $(x+1)^2+(y-1)^2=8^2$
4c. $(x+6)^2+(y+5)^2=2.5^2$
4d. $(x-h)^2+(y-k)^2=r^2$

From Concrete to Abstract

Write the equation $x^2+y^2=100$ on the board. Ask students to identify the center of the circle and the length of the radius without graphing. center: (0, 0), radius: 10

Additional Answers

1. Sample answer: The squared constant term on the right side of the equation is the same as the length of the radius. It increases as the radius increases and decreases as the radius decreases.
2. Sample answer: The x-coordinate of the center is subtracted from x on the left side of the equation, and the y-coordinate of the center is subtracted from y in the equation.

10-3 Circles

Why?

When a rock is thrown into water, ripples move out from the center forming concentric circles. If the point where the rock entered the water is assigned coordinates, each ripple can be modeled by an equation of a circle.

Then
You graphed and wrote equations of parabolas. (Lesson 10-2)

Now
- Write equations of circles.
- Graph circles.

NGSSS
MA.912.G.6.6 Given the center and the radius, find the equation of a circle in the coordinate plane or given the equation of a circle in center-radius form, state the center and the radius of the circle. MA.912.G.6.7 Given the equation of a circle in center-radius form or given the center and the radius of a circle, sketch the graph of the circle. *Also addresses MA.912.A.9.1 and MA.912.A.9.2.*

New Vocabulary
circle
center
radius

FL Math Online
glencoe.com

Equations of Circles A **circle** is the set of all points in a plane that are equidistant from a given point in the plane, called the **center**. Any segment with endpoints at the center and a point on the circle is a **radius** of the circle.

Assume that (x, y) are the coordinates of a point on the circle at the right. The center is at (h, k), and the radius is r. You can find an equation of the circle by using the Distance Formula.

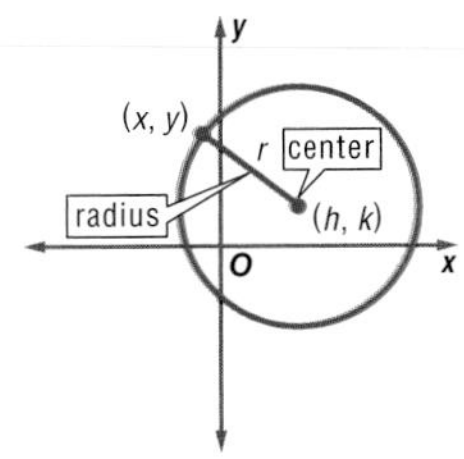

$$\sqrt{(x_2 - x_1)^2 + (y_2 - y_1)^2} = d \quad \textbf{Distance Formula}$$
$$\sqrt{(x - h)^2 + (y - k)^2} = r \quad (x_1, y_1) = (h, k),\ (x_2, y_2) = (x, y),\ d = r$$
$$(x - h)^2 + (y - k)^2 = r^2 \quad \textbf{Square each side.}$$

Key Concept — Equations of Circles

Standard Form of Equation	$x^2 + y^2 = r^2$	$(x - h)^2 + (y - k)^2 = r^2$
Center	$(0, 0)$	(h, k)
Radius	r	r

You can use the standard form of the equation of a circle to write an equation for a circle given the center and the radius or diameter.

Real-World EXAMPLE 1 Write an Equation Given the Radius

DELIVERY Appliances + More offers free delivery within 35 miles of the store. The Jacksonville store is located 100 miles north and 45 miles east of the corporate office. Write an equation to represent the delivery boundary of the Jacksonville store if the origin of the coordinate system is the corporate office.

Since the corporate office is at (0, 0), the Jacksonville store is at (45, 100). The boundary of the delivery region is the circle centered at (45, 100) with radius 35 miles.

$$(x - h)^2 + (y - k)^2 = r^2 \quad \textbf{Equation of a circle}$$
$$(x - 45)^2 + (y - 100)^2 = 35^2 \quad (h, k) = (45, 100) \text{ and } r = 35$$
$$(x - 45)^2 + (y - 100)^2 = 1225 \quad \textbf{Simplify.}$$

Guided Practice 1. $(x + 3)^2 + (y + 4)^2 = 900$

1. WI-FI A certain Wi-Fi phone has a range of 30 miles in any direction. If the phone is 4 miles south and 3 miles west of headquarters, write an equation to represent the area within which the phone can operate via the Wi-Fi system.

Personal Tutor glencoe.com

10-3 Lesson Notes

1 FOCUS

Vertical Alignment

Before Lesson 10-3
Graph and write equations of parabolas.

Lesson 10-3
Write equations of circles.
Graph circles.

After Lesson 10-3
Write and graph equations of ellipses.

2 TEACH

Scaffolding Questions

Have students read the *Why?* section of the lesson.

Ask:
- What are concentric circles? circles with a common center
- What part of a circle is the point where the rock hits the water? center
- Are all the circles similar? Explain. Yes; they are the same shape, but different sizes.

Lesson 10-3 Resources

Resource	Approaching-Level	On-Level	Beyond-Level	English Learners
Teacher Edition	• Differentiated Instruction, p. 632	• Differentiated Instruction, pp. 632, 637	• Differentiated Instruction, pp. 634, 637	
Chapter Resource Masters	• Study Guide and Intervention, pp. 18–19 • Skills Practice, p. 20 • Practice, p. 21 • Word Problem Practice, p. 22	• Study Guide and Intervention, pp. 18–19 • Skills Practice, p. 20 • Practice, p. 21 • Word Problem Practice, p. 22 • Enrichment, p. 23 • Graphing Calculator Activity, p. 24	• Practice, p. 21 • Word Problem Practice, p. 22 • Enrichment, p. 23	• Study Guide and Intervention, pp. 18–19 • Skills Practice, p. 20 • Practice, p. 21 • Word Problem Practice, p. 22
Transparencies	• 5-Minute Check Transparency 10-3	• 5-Minute Check Transparency 10-3	• 5-Minute Check Transparency 10-3	• 5-Minute Check Transparency 10-3
Other	• Study Notebook	• Study Notebook	• Study Notebook	• Study Notebook

Equations of Circles

Example 1 shows how to write an equation for a circle for a real-world problem given the center and radius. **Example 2** shows how to write an equation for a circle given the graph of the circle. **Example 3** shows how to write an equation for a circle given the endpoints of a diameter.

Formative Assessment

Use the Guided Practice exercises after each example to determine students' understanding of concepts.

Additional Examples

1 **LANDSCAPING** The plan for a park puts the center of a circular pond of radius 0.6 miles at 2.5 miles east and 3.8 miles south of the park headquarters. Write an equation to represent the border of the pond, using the headquarters as the origin.
$(x - 2.5)^2 + (y + 3.8)^2 = 0.36$

2 Write an equation for the graph. $x^2 + (y - 3)^2 = 49$

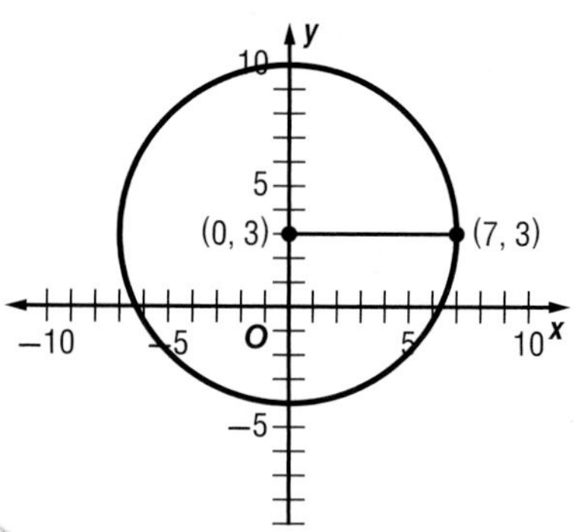

3 Write an equation for a circle if the endpoints of the diameter are at (2, 8) and (2, −2).
$(x - 2)^2 + (y - 3)^2 = 25$

Additional Examples also in Interactive Classroom PowerPoint® Presentations

IWB INTERACTIVE WHITEBOARD READY

You can write the equation of a circle when you know the location of the center and a point on the circle.

StudyTip

Center-Radius Form Standard form is sometimes referred to as *center-radius form* because the center and radius of the circle are apparent in the equation.

EXAMPLE 2 Write an Equation from a Graph

Write an equation for the graph.

$(x - h)^2 + (y - k)^2 = r^2$	**Standard form**
$(2 + 3)^2 + (-1 - 1)^2 = r^2$	$x = 2, y = -1, h = -3, k = 1$
$(5)^2 + (-2)^2 = r^2$	**Simplify.**
$25 + 4 = r^2$	**Evaluate the exponents.**
$29 = r^2$	**Add.**

So, the equation of the circle is $(x + 3)^2 + (y - 1)^2 = 29$.

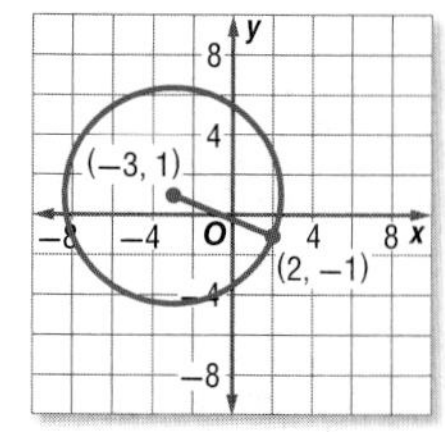

Guided Practice

Write an equation for each graph. 2B. $(x + 1)^2 + (y - 4)^2 = 13$

2A.

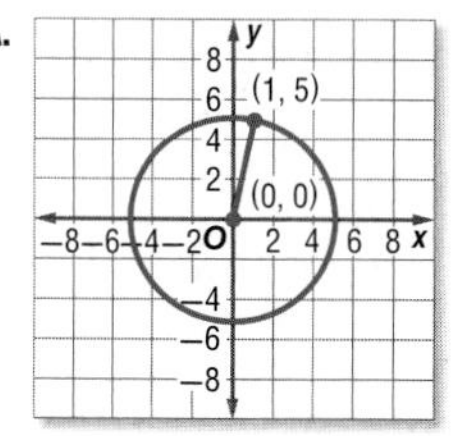

$x^2 + y^2 = 26$

2B.

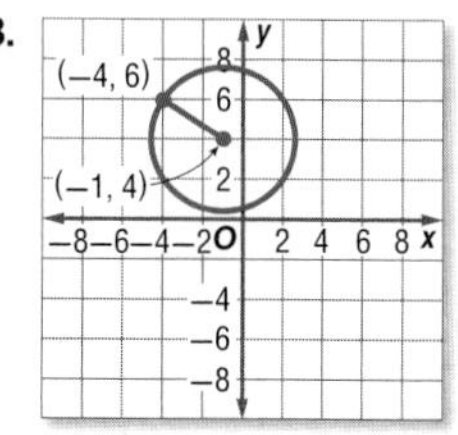

Personal Tutor glencoe.com

You can use the Midpoint and Distance Formulas when you know the endpoints of the radius or diameter of a circle.

EXAMPLE 3 Write an Equation Given a Diameter

Write an equation for a circle if the endpoints of a diameter are at (7, 6) and (−1, −8).

Step 1 Find the center.

$(h, k) = \left(\frac{x_1 + x_2}{2}, \frac{y_1 + y_2}{2}\right)$	**Midpoint Formula**
$= \left(\frac{7 + (-1)}{2}, \frac{6 + (-8)}{2}\right)$	$(x_1, y_1) = (7, 6), (x_2, y_2) = (-1, -8)$
$= \left(\frac{6}{2}, \frac{-2}{2}\right)$	**Add.**
$= (3, -1)$	**Simplify.**

Step 2 Find the radius.

$r = \sqrt{(x_2 - x_1)^2 + (y_2 - y_1)^2}$	**Distance Formula**
$= \sqrt{(3 - 7)^2 + (-1 - 6)^2}$	$(x_1, y_1) = (7, 6), (x_2, y_2) = (3, -1)$
$= \sqrt{(-4)^2 + (-7)^2}$	**Subtract.**
$= \sqrt{65}$	**Simplify.**

The radius of the circle is $\sqrt{65}$ units, so $r^2 = 65$. Substitute h, k, and r^2 into the standard form of the equation of a circle. An equation of the circle is $(x - 3)^2 + (y + 1)^2 = 65$.

Guided Practice 3. $(x - 2)^2 + (y - 1)^2 = 17$

3. Write an equation for a circle if the endpoints of a diameter are at (3, −3) and (1, 5).

Personal Tutor glencoe.com

632 **Chapter 10** Conic Sections

Differentiated Instruction

AL OL

If students need study tools,

Then have students write the Key Concepts for each conic section on a notecard.

StudyTip

Axis of Symmetry Every diameter in a circle is an axis of symmetry. There are infinitely many axes of symmetry in a circle.

Graph Circles You can use symmetry to help you graph circles.

EXAMPLE 4 **Graph an Equation in Standard Form**

Find the center and radius of the circle with equation $x^2 + y^2 = 100$. Then graph the circle.

- The center of the circle is at (0, 0), and the radius is 10.
- The table lists some integer values for x and y that satisfy the equation.
- Because the circle is centered at the origin, it is symmetric about the y-axis. Therefore, the points at (−6, 8), (−8, 6), and (−10, 0) lie on the graph.
- The circle is also symmetric about the x-axis, so the points (−6, −8), (−8, −6), (0, −10), (6, −8), and (8, −6) lie on the graph.
- Plot all of these points and draw the circle that passes through them.

x	y
0	10
6	8
8	6
10	0

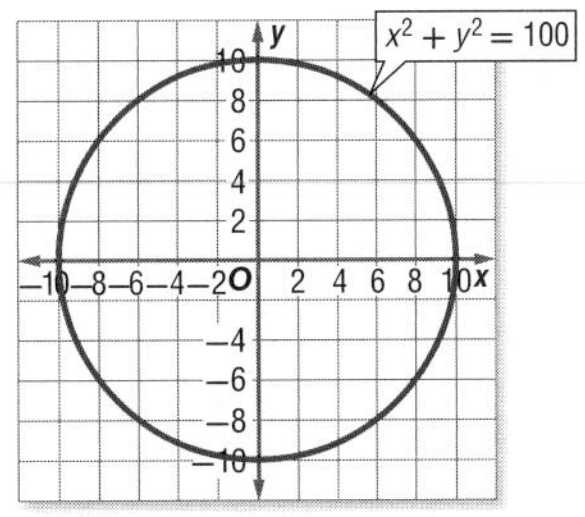

Guided Practice

4. Find the center and radius of the circle with equation $x^2 + y^2 = 81$. Then graph the circle. **See margin.**

Personal Tutor glencoe.com

Circles with centers that are not (0, 0) can be graphed by using translations. The graph of $(x - h)^2 + (y - k)^2 = r^2$ is the graph of $x^2 + y^2 = r^2$ translated h units horizontally and k units vertically.

EXAMPLE 5 **Graph an Equation Not in Standard Form**

Find the center and radius of the circle with equation $x^2 + y^2 - 8x + 12y - 12 = 0$. Then graph the circle.

Complete the squares.

$$x^2 + y^2 - 8x + 12y - 12 = 0$$
$$x^2 - 8x + \blacksquare + y^2 + 12y + \blacksquare = 12 + \blacksquare + \blacksquare$$
$$x^2 - 8x + 16 + y^2 + 12y + 36 = 12 + 16 + 36$$
$$(x - 4)^2 + (y + 6)^2 = 64$$

The center of the circle is at (4, −6) and the radius is 8. The graph of $(x - 4)^2 + (y + 6)^2 = 64$ is the same as $x^2 + y^2 = 64$ translated 4 units to the right and down 6 units.

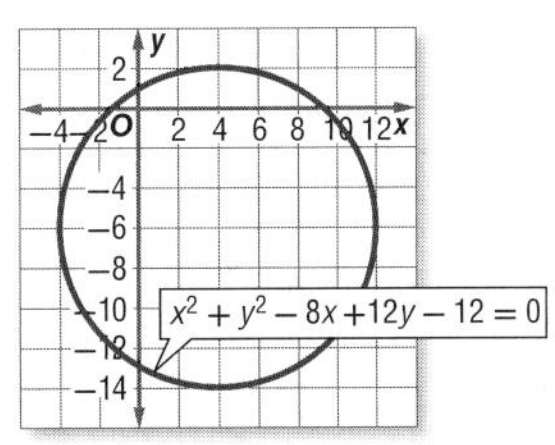

Guided Practice

5. Find the center and radius of the circle with equation $x^2 + y^2 + 4x - 10y - 7 = 0$. Then graph the circle. **See margin.**

Personal Tutor glencoe.com

TEACH with TECH

BLOG Divide the class into two groups. Have the first group write blog entries containing the coordinates of the center of a circle and its radius. Have the second group of students reply to the postings with the equation of the circle. Have students check each others' answers.

Watch Out!

Preventing Errors Suggest that students draw sketches showing the circle and the endpoints of the diameter to check their work.

Graph Circles

Example 4 shows how to find the center and radius of a circle and how to graph the circle given its equation in standard form. **Example 5** shows how to use translations to graph a circle with an equation not in standard form.

Additional Examples

4 Find the center and radius of the circle with equation $x^2 + y^2 = 16$. Then graph the circle. (0, 0); 4

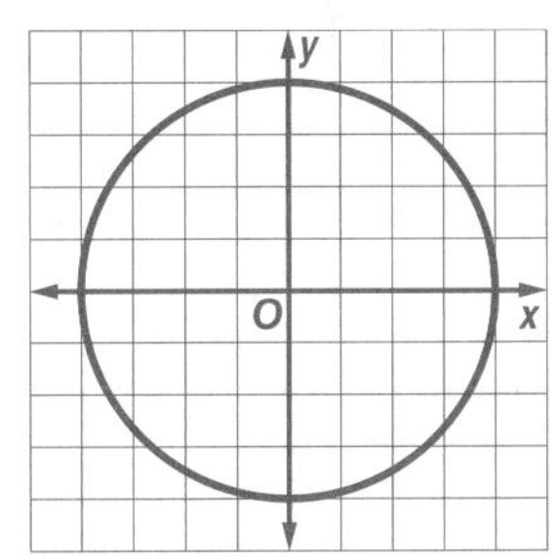

5 Find the center and radius of the circle with equation $x^2 + y^2 + 6x - 7 = 0$. Then graph the circle. (−3, 0); 4

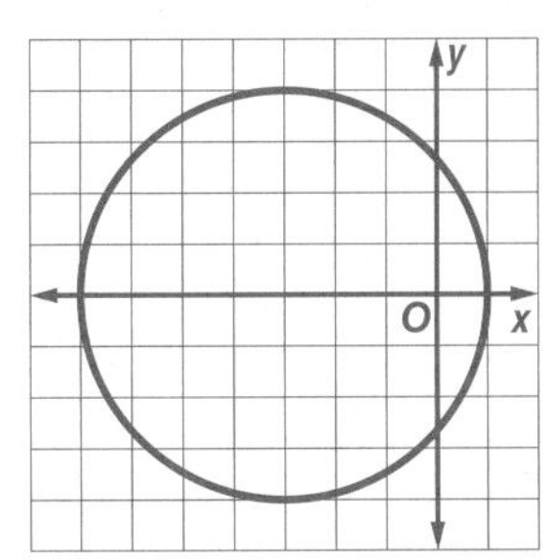

Additional Answers (Guided Practice)

4. center: (0, 0); radius 9

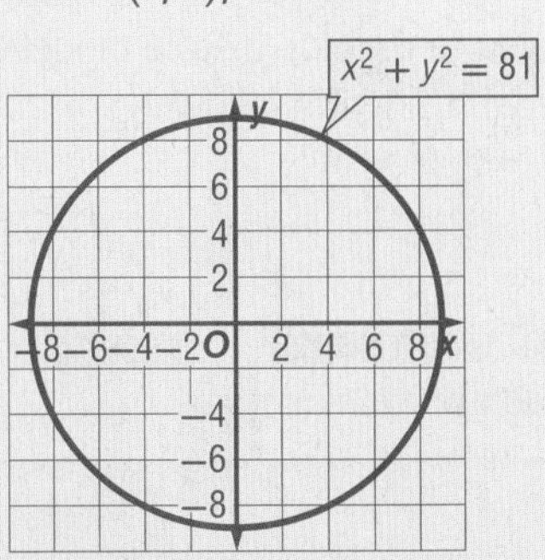

5. center: (−2, 5); radius: 6

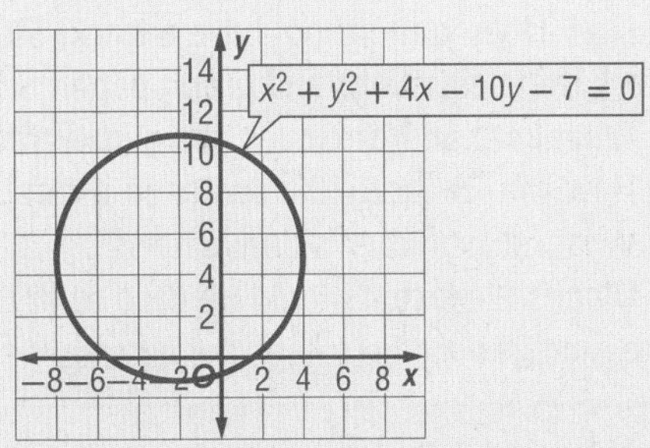

3 PRACTICE

Formative Assessment

Use Exercises 1–11 to check for understanding.

Use the chart at the bottom of the next page to customize assignments for your students.

Additional Answers

8. center: (0, 0); radius: 4

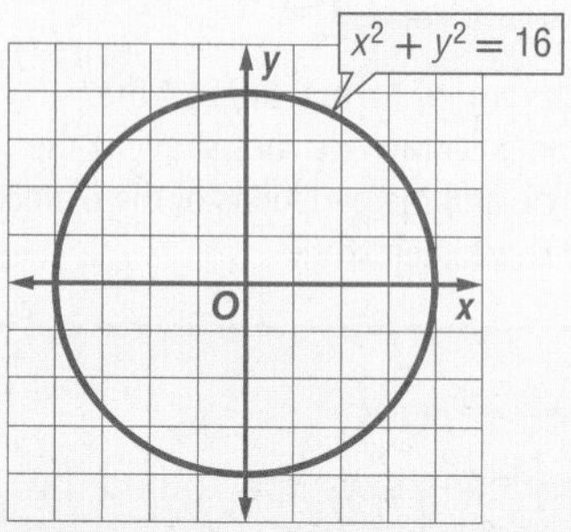

9. center: (0, 7); radius: 3

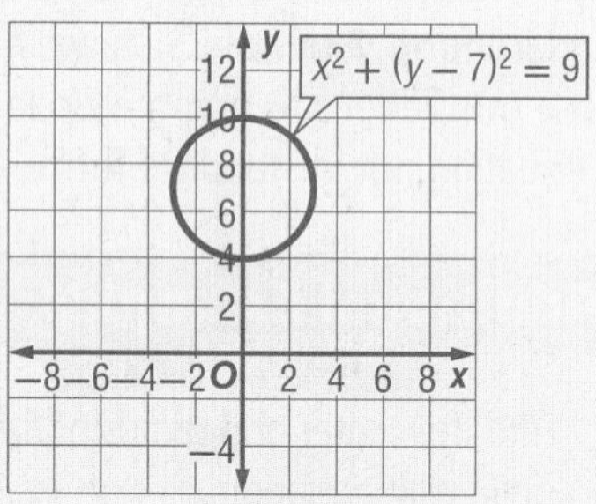

10. center: (4, 4); radius: 5

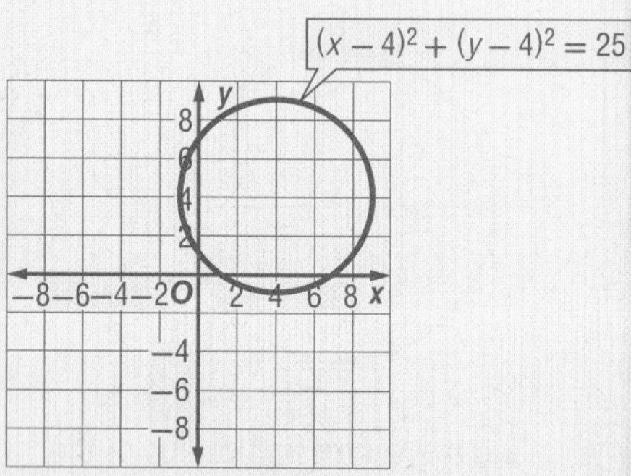

11. center: (2, −4); radius: 5

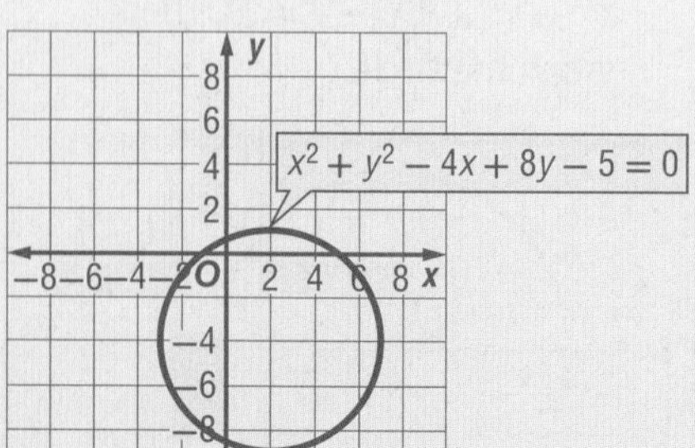

Check Your Understanding

Example 1 p. 631

1. $(x - 72)^2 + (y - 39)^2 = 10{,}000$
2. $(x + 2)^2 + (y + 6)^2 = 16$

Example 2 p. 632

3. $(x - 1)^2 + (y + 5)^2 = 9$

6. $\left(x + \frac{1}{2}\right)^2 + \left(y + \frac{7}{2}\right)^2 = \frac{25}{2}$

1. WEATHER On average, the eye of a tornado is about 200 feet across. Suppose the center of the eye is at the point (72, 39). Write an equation to represent the boundary of the eye.

Write an equation for each circle given the center and radius.

2. center: (−2, −6), $r = 4$ units

3. center: (1, −5), $r = 3$ units

Write an equation for each graph.

4.

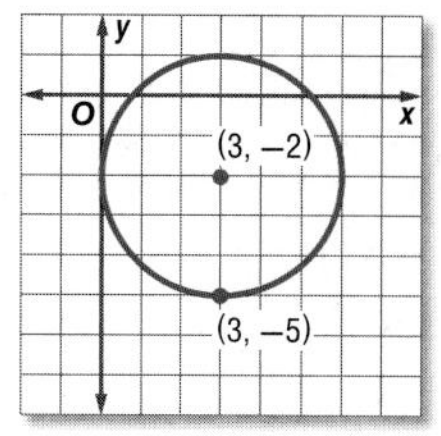

$(x - 3)^2 + (y + 2)^2 = 9$

5.

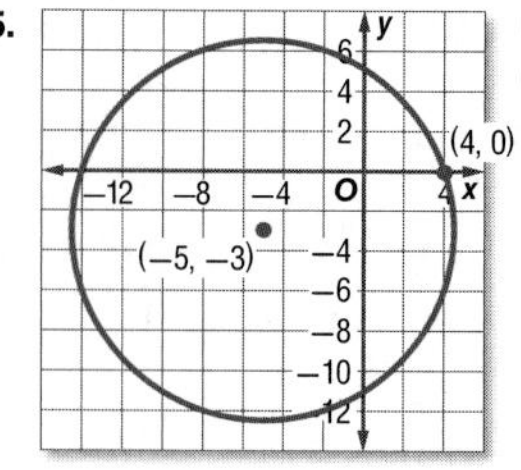

$(x + 5)^2 + (y + 3)^2 = 90$

Example 3 p. 632

Write an equation for each circle given the endpoints of a diameter.

6. (−1, −7) and (0, 0)

7. (4, −2) and (−4, −6) $x^2 + (y + 4)^2 = 20$

Examples 4 and 5 p. 633

Find the center and radius of each circle. Then graph the circle. 8–11. See margin.

8. $x^2 + y^2 = 16$

9. $x^2 + (y - 7)^2 = 9$

10. $(x - 4)^2 + (y - 4)^2 = 25$

11. $x^2 + y^2 - 4x + 8y - 5 = 0$

Practice and Problem Solving

● = **Step-by-Step Solutions** begin on page R20.
Extra Practice begins on page 947.

Example 1 p. 631

12. $(x - 4)^2 + (y - 9)^2 = 36$
13. $(x + 3)^2 + (y - 1)^2 = 16$
14. $(x + 7)^2 + (y + 3)^2 = 169$

Example 2 p. 632

15. $(x + 2)^2 + (y + 1)^2 = 81$
16. $(x - 1)^2 + y^2 = 15$
17. $x^2 + (y + 6)^2 = 35$

Write an equation for each circle given the center and radius.

12. center: (4, 9), $r = 6$

13. center: (−3, 1), $r = 4$

14. center: (−7, −3), $r = 13$

15. center: (−2, −1), $r = 9$

16. center: (1, 0), $r = \sqrt{15}$

17. center: (0, −6), $r = \sqrt{35}$

18. AIR TRAFFIC CONTROL The radar for a county airport control tower is located at (5, 10) on a map. It can detect a plane up to 20 miles away. Write an equation for the outer limits of the detection area. $(x - 5)^2 + (y - 10)^2 = 400$

Write an equation for each graph.

19.

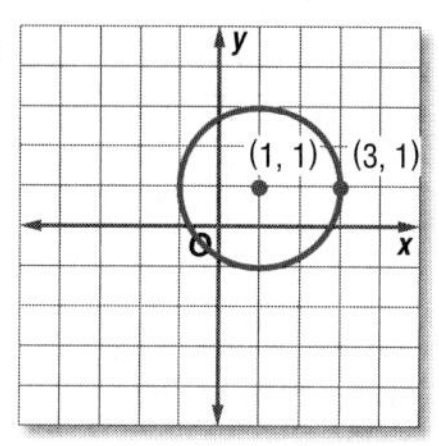

$(x - 1)^2 + (y - 1)^2 = 4$

20.

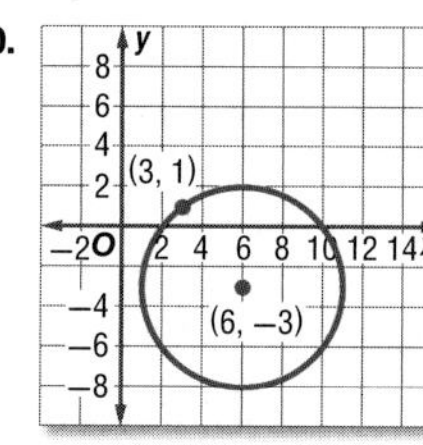

$(x - 6)^2 + (y + 3)^2 = 25$

21.

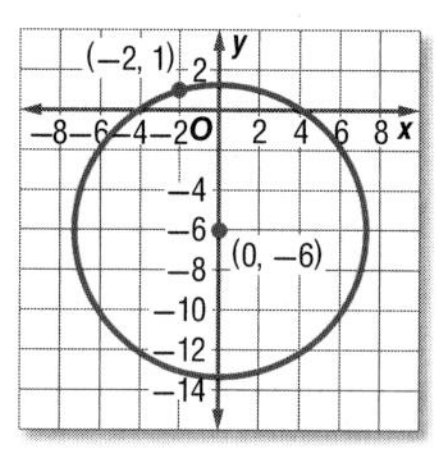

$x^2 + (y + 6)^2 = 53$

22.

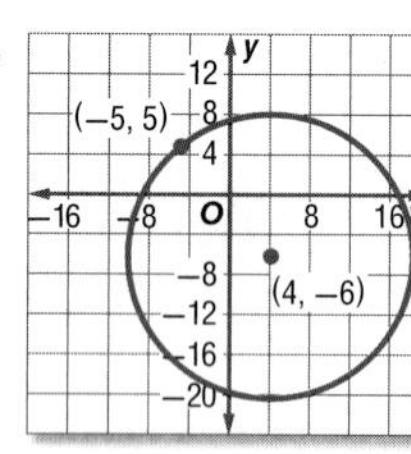

$(x - 4)^2 + (y + 6)^2 = 202$

Differentiated Instruction

BL

Extension Does your school have a track? Students can be challenged to develop a scale model of the track using equations and graph paper. Scaffold the task as needed using the following:

- What lines and/or curves make up a track?
- How can we locate the center so it can be placed at (0, 0)?
- What measurements do we need?
- What scale factor should be used to fit the model on a sheet of graph paper?

If there is no track at the school, the necessary information can be found using the Internet.

Example 3 p. 632

23. $(x-2)^2 + \left(y+\frac{3}{2}\right)^2 = \frac{25}{4}$
24. $x^2 + (y+10)^2 = 64$
25. $\left(x-\frac{3}{2}\right)^2 + (y+8)^2 = \frac{53}{4}$
26. $(x+1)^2 + (y-6)^2 = 29$
27. $(x-4)^2 + (y+1)^2 = 20$

Write an equation for each circle given the endpoints of a diameter.

23. (2, 1) and (2, −4) **24.** (−4, −10) and (4, −10) **25.** (5, −7) and (−2, −9)

26. (−6, 4) and (4, 8) **27.** (2, −5) and (6, 3) **28.** (18, 11) and (−19, −13)

29 **LAWN CARE** A sprinkler waters a circular section of lawn.

a. Write an equation to represent the boundary of the sprinkler area if the endpoints of a diameter are at (−12, 16) and (12, −16). $x^2 + y^2 = 400$

b. What is the area of the lawn that the sprinkler waters? approximately 1256.64 units^2

30. **SPACE** Apollo 8 was the first manned spacecraft to orbit the Moon at an average altitude of 185 kilometers above the Moon's surface. Write an equation to model a single circular orbit of the command module if the endpoints of a diameter of the Moon are at (1740, 0) and (−1740, 0). Let the center of the Moon be at the origin of the coordinate system measured in kilometers. $x^2 + y^2 = 3{,}705{,}625$

Examples 4 and 5 p. 633

28. $\left(x+\frac{1}{2}\right)^2 + (y+1)^2 = 486\frac{1}{4}$

Find the center and radius of each circle. Then graph the circle. 31–46. See Chapter 10 Answer Appendix.

31. $x^2 + y^2 = 75$ **32.** $(x-3)^2 + y^2 = 4$

33. $(x-1)^2 + (y-4)^2 = 34$ **34.** $x^2 + (y-14)^2 = 144$

35. $(x-5)^2 + (y+2)^2 = 16$ **36.** $x^2 + y^2 = 256$

37. $(x-4)^2 + y^2 = \frac{8}{9}$ **38.** $\left(x+\frac{2}{3}\right)^2 + \left(y-\frac{1}{2}\right)^2 = \frac{16}{25}$

39. $x^2 + y^2 + 4x = 9$ **40.** $x^2 + y^2 - 6y + 8x = 0$

41. $x^2 + y^2 + 2x + 4y = 9$ **42.** $x^2 + y^2 - 3x + 8y = 20$

43. $x^2 + y^2 + 6y = -50 - 14x$ **44.** $x^2 - 18x + 53 = 18y - y^2$

45. $2x^2 + 2y^2 - 4x + 8y = 32$ **46.** $3x^2 + 3y^2 - 6y + 12x = 24$

Real-World Link

There are more than 2500 satellites in orbit around Earth. There are also more than 10,000 human-made objects orbiting around Earth. These include a variety of pieces of satellite debris ranging from panels to old equipment.

49a. $(x+1)^2 + (y-4)^2 = 36 + 16\sqrt{5}$
49b. $(x+1)^2 + (y-4)^2 = 24 - 8\sqrt{5}$

47. **SPACE** A satellite is in a circular orbit 25,000 miles above Earth.

B **a.** Write an equation for the orbit of this satellite if the origin is at the center of Earth. Use 8000 miles as the diameter of Earth. $x^2 + y^2 = 841{,}000{,}000$

b. Draw a sketch of Earth and the orbit to scale. Label your sketch. See margin.

48. **COMMUNICATIONS** Suppose an unobstructed radio station broadcast could travel 120 miles. Assume the station is centered at the origin.

a. Write an equation to represent the boundary of the broadcast area with the origin as the center. $x^2 + y^2 = 14{,}400$

b. If the transmission tower is relocated 40 miles east and 10 miles south of the current location, and an increased signal will transmit signals an additional 80 miles, what is an equation to represent the new broadcast area? $(x-40)^2 + (y+10)^2 = 40{,}000$

49. **GEOMETRY** Concentric circles are circles with the same center but different radii. Refer to the graph at the right where $\overline{AB}$ is a diameter of the circle.

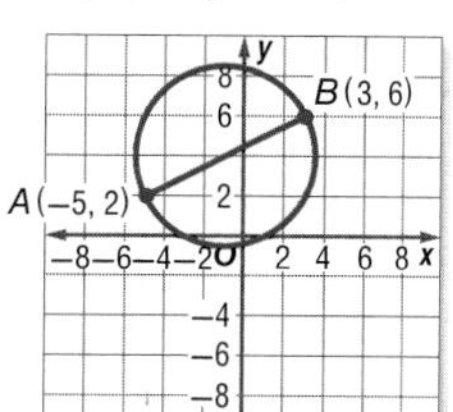

a. Write an equation of the circle concentric with the circle at the right, with radius 4 units greater.

b. Write an equation of the circle concentric with the circle at the right, with radius 2 units less.

c. Graph the circles from parts a and b on the same coordinate plane. See margin.

50. **EARTHQUAKES** The Rose Bowl is located about 35 miles west and 40 miles north of downtown Los Angeles. Suppose an earthquake occurs with its epicenter about 55 miles from the stadium. Assume that the origin of a coordinate plane is located at the center of downtown Los Angeles. Write an equation for the set of points that could be the epicenter of the earthquake. $(y+35)^2 + (x-40)^2 = 3025$

4 ASSESS

Ticket Out the Door Write five different equations for circles on separate sheets of paper. Make several copies of each. Give one equation to each student. As students leave the room, ask them to tell you either the center or the radius of the circles formed by the equations.

Additional Answers

47b.

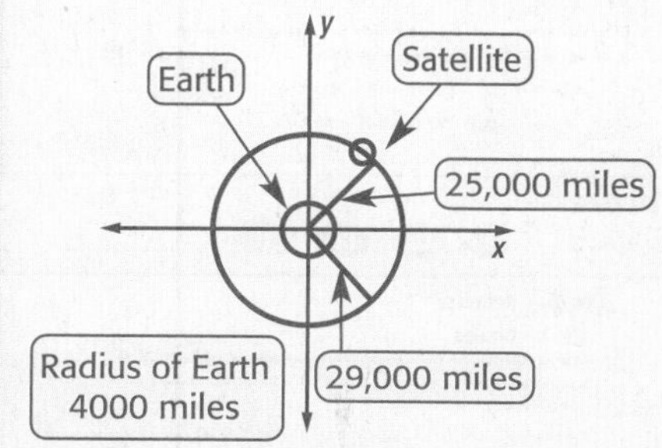

49c.

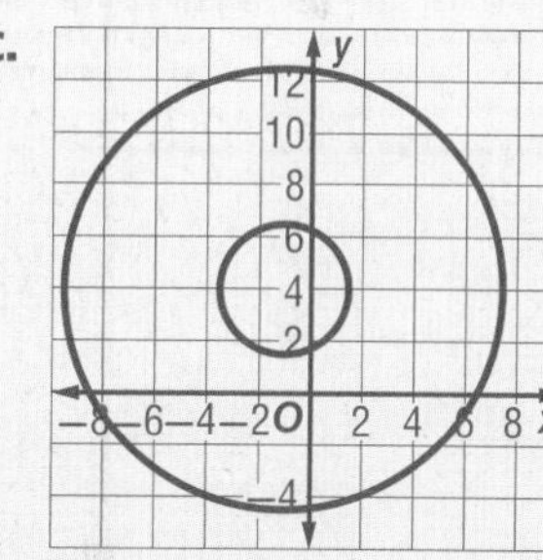

Differentiated Homework Options

Level	Assignment	Two-Day Option	
AL Basic	12–46, 62–88	13–45 odd, 68–71	12–46 even, 62–67, 72–88
OL Core	13–45 odd, 47–50, 51–61 odd, 62–88	12–46, 68–71	47–88
BL Advanced	47–85, (optional: 86–88)		

C Write an equation for the circle that satisfies each set of conditions.

51. center (9, −8), passes through (19, 22) $(x-9)^2+(y+8)^2=1000$
52. center $(-\sqrt{15}, 30)$, passes through the origin $(x+\sqrt{15})^2+(y-30)^2=915$
53. center at (8, −9), tangent to y-axis $(x-8)^2+(y+9)^2=64$
54. center at (2, 4), tangent to x-axis $(x-2)^2+(y-4)^2=16$
55. center in the first quadrant; tangent to $x=5$, the x-axis, and the y-axis
56. center in the second quadrant; tangent to $y=1$, $y=5$, and the y-axis

57. **MULTIPLE REPRESENTATIONS** Graph $y=\sqrt{9-x^2}$ and $y=-\sqrt{9-x^2}$ on the same graphing calculator screen.

a. **VERBAL** Describe the graph formed by the union of these two graphs. **circle**

b. **ALGEBRAIC** Write an equation for the union of the two graphs. $x^2+y^2=9$

c. **VERBAL** Most graphing calculators cannot graph the equation $x^2+y^2=49$ directly. Describe a way to use a graphing calculator to graph the equation. Then graph the equation. **See margin.**

d. **ANALYTICAL** Solve $(x-2)^2+(y+1)^2=4$ for y. Why do you need two equations to graph a circle on a graphing calculator?

e. **VERBAL** Do you think that it is easier to graph the equation in part **d** using graph paper and a pencil or using a graphing calculator? Explain. **See students' work.**

Review Vocabulary

tangent a line in the plane of a circle that intersects the circle in exactly one point

55. $(x-2.5)^2+(y-2.5)^2=6.25$
56. $(x+2)^2+(y-3)^2=4$
57d. $y=\pm\sqrt{4-(x-2)^2}-1$; When you solve for y you must take the square root resulting in both a positive and negative answer, so you have to enter the positive equation as Y1 and the negative equation as Y2.

58–61. See Chapter 10 Answer Appendix.

Find the center and radius of each circle. Then graph the circle.

58. $x^2-12x+84=-y^2+16y$
59. $4x^2+4y^2+36y+5=0$
60. $(x+\sqrt{5})^2+y^2-8y=9$
61. $x^2+2\sqrt{7}x+7+(y-\sqrt{11})^2=11$

H.O.T. Problems Use Higher-Order Thinking Skills

62. **ERROR ANALYSIS** Heather says that $(x-2)^2+(y+3)^2=36$ and $(x-2)+(y+3)=6$ are equivalent equations. Carlota says that the equations are *not* equivalent. Is either of them correct? Explain your reasoning.

63. **OPEN ENDED** Consider graphs with equations of the form $(x-3)^2+(y-a)^2=64$. Assign three different values for a, and graph each equation. Describe all graphs with equations of this form.

64. **REASONING** Explain why the phrase "in a plane" is included in the definition of a circle. What would be defined if the phrase were *not* included?

65. **OPEN ENDED** Concentric circles have the same center, but most often, not the same radius. Write equations of two concentric circles. Then graph the circles. **See margin.**

66. **REASONING** Assume that (x, y) are the coordinates of a point on a circle. The center is at (h, k), and the radius is r. Find an equation of the circle by using the Distance Formula. **See margin.**

67. **WRITING IN MATH** The circle with equation $(x-a)^2+(y-b)^2=r^2$ lies in the first quadrant and is tangent to both the x-axis and the y-axis. Sketch the circle. Describe the possible values of a, b, and r. Do the same for a circle in Quadrants II, III, and IV. Discuss the similarities among the circles. **See Chapter 10 Answer Appendix.**

62. Carlota; the square root of $(x-2)^2+(y+3)^2$ is not $(x-2)+(y+3)$.
63. See students' work; circles with a radius of 8 and centers on the graph of $x=3$.
64. If the phrase is not included, the figure would be a sphere.

Study Guide and Intervention
CRM pp. 18–19 AL OL ELL

10-3 Study Guide and Intervention

Circles

Equations of Circles The equation of a circle with center (h, k) and radius r units is $(x-h)^2+(y-k)^2=r^2$.

A line is tangent to a circle when it touches the circle at only one point.

Example Write an equation for a circle if the endpoints of a diameter are at (−4, 5) and (6, −3).

Use the midpoint formula to find the center of the circle.

$$(h,k)=\left(\frac{x_1+x_2}{2},\frac{y_1+y_2}{2}\right)$$ Midpoint formula

$$=\left(\frac{-4+6}{2},\frac{5+(-3)}{2}\right)$$ $(x_1, y_1)=(-4, 5), (x_2, y_2)=(6, -3)$

$$=\left(\frac{2}{2},\frac{2}{2}\right) \text{ or } (1, 1)$$ Simplify.

Use the coordinates of the center and one endpoint of the diameter to find the radius.

$$r=\sqrt{(x_2-x_1)^2+(y_2-y_1)^2}$$ Distance formula

$$=\sqrt{(-4-1)^2+(5-1)^2}$$ $(x_1, y_1)=(1, 1), (x_2, y_2)=(-4, 5)$

$$=\sqrt{(-5)^2+4^2}=\sqrt{41}$$ Simplify.

The radius of the circle is $\sqrt{41}$, so $r^2=41$.

An equation of the circle is $(x-1)^2+(y-1)^2=41$.

Exercises

Write an equation for the circle that satisfies each set of conditions.

1. center (8, −3), radius 6 $(x-8)^2+(y+3)^2=36$
2. center (5, −6), radius 4 $(x-5)^2+(y+6)^2=16$
3. center (−5, 2), passes through (−9, 6) $(x+5)^2+(y-2)^2=32$
4. center (3, 6), tangent to the x-axis $(x-3)^2+(y-6)^2=36$
5. center (−4, −7), tangent to $x=2$ $(x+4)^2+(y+7)^2=36$
6. center (−2, 8), tangent to $y=-4$ $(x+2)^2+(y-8)^2=144$
7. center (7, 7), passes through (12, 9) $(x-7)^2+(y-7)^2=29$

Write an equation for each circle given the end points of a diameter.

8. (6, 6) and (10, 12) $(x-8)^2+(y-9)^2=13$
9. (−4, −2) and (8, 4) $(x-2)^2+(y-1)^2=45$
10. (−4, 3) and (6, −8) $(x-1)^2+(y+2.5)^2=55.25$

Chapter 10 18 Glencoe Algebra 2

Practice
CRM p. 21 AL OL BL ELL

10-3 Practice

Circles

Write an equation for the circle that satisfies each set of conditions.

1. center (−4, 2), radius 8 units $(x+4)^2+(y-2)^2=64$
2. center (0, 0), radius 4 units $x^2+y^2=16$
3. center $\left(-\frac{1}{4}, -\sqrt{3}\right)$, radius $5\sqrt{2}$ units $\left(x+\frac{1}{4}\right)^2+(y+\sqrt{3})^2=50$
4. center (2.5, 4.2), radius 0.9 units $(x-2.5)^2+(y-4.2)^2=0.81$
5. endpoints of a diameter at (−2, −9) and (0, −5) $(x+1)^2+(y+7)^2=5$
6. center at (−9, −12), passes through (−4, −5) $(x+9)^2+(y+12)^2=74$
7. center at (−6, 5), tangent to x-axis $(x+6)^2+(y-5)^2=25$

Find the center and radius of each circle. Then graph the circle.

8. $(x+3)^2+y^2=16$ $(-3, 0), r=4$

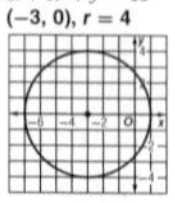

9. $3x^2+3y^2=12$ $(0, 0), r=2$

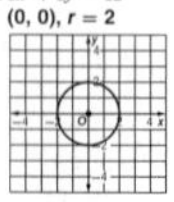

10. $x^2+y^2+2x+6y=26$ $(-1, -3), r=6$

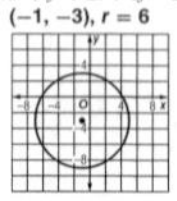

11. $(x-1)^2+y^2+4y=12$ $(1, -2), r=4$

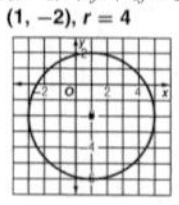

12. $x^2-6x+y^2=0$ $(3, 0), r=3$

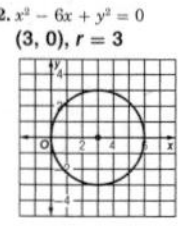

13. $x^2+y^2+2x+6y=-1$ $(-1, -3), r=3$

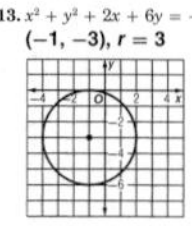

14. **WEATHER** On average, the circular eye of a hurricane is about 15 miles in diameter. Gale winds can affect an area up to 300 miles from the storm's center. A satellite photo of a hurricane's landfall showed the center of its eye on one coordinate system could be approximated by the point (80, 26).

a. Write an equation to represent a possible boundary of the hurricane's eye. $(x-80)^2+(y-26)^2=56.25$

b. Write an equation to represent a possible boundary of the area affected by gale winds. $(x-80)^2+(y-26)^2=90{,}000$

Chapter 10 21 Glencoe Algebra 2

Lesson 10-3

Word Problem Practice
CRM p. 22 AL OL BL ELL

10-3 Word Problem Practice

Circles

1. **RADAR** A scout plane is equipped with radar. The boundary of the radar's range is given by the circle $(x-4)^2+(y-6)^2=4900$. Each unit corresponds to one mile. What is the maximum distance that an object can be from the plane and still be detected by its radar?

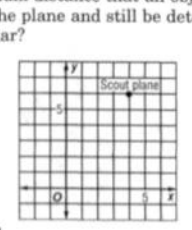

70 mi

2. **STORAGE** An engineer uses a coordinate plane to show the layout of a side view of a storage building. The y-axis represents a wall and the x-axis represents the floor. A 10-meter diameter cylinder rests on its side flush against the wall. On the side view, the cylinder is represented by a circle in the first quadrant that is tangent to both axes. Each unit represents 1 meter. What is the equation of this circle? $(x-5)^2+(y-5)^2=25$

3. **FERRIS WHEEL** The Texas Star, the largest Ferris wheel in North America, is located in Dallas, Texas. It weighs 678,554 pounds and can hold 264 riders in its 44 gondolas. The Texas Star has a diameter of 212 feet. Use the rectangular coordinate system with the origin on the ground directly below the center of the wheel and write the equation of the circle that models the Texas Star. $x^2+(y-106)^2=11{,}236$

4. **POOLS** The pool on an architectural blueprint is given by the equation $x^2+6x+y^2+8y=0$. What point on the edge of the pool is farthest from the origin? $(-6, -8)$

5. **TREASURE** A mathematically inclined pirate decided to hide the location of a treasure by marking it as the center of a circle given by an equation in non-standard form.

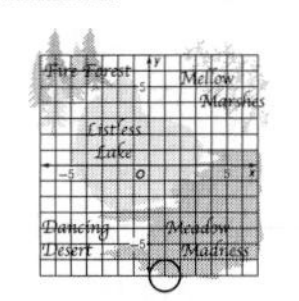

The circle can be represented by: $x^2+y^2-2x+14y+49=0$.

a. Rewrite the equation of the circle in standard form. $(x-1)^2+(y+7)^2=1$

b. Draw the circle on the map. Where is the treasure? **See circle on map at (1, −7); the southwest corner of Meadow Madness.**

Chapter 10 22 Glencoe Algebra 2

636 Chapter 10 Conic Sections

Enrichment
CRM p. 23 OL BL

10-3 Enrichment

Tangents to Circles

A line that intersects a circle in exactly one point is a **tangent** to the circle. In the diagram, line ℓ is tangent to the circle with equation $x^2+y^2=25$ at the point whose coordinates are (3, 4).

A line is tangent to a circle at a point P on the circle if and only if the line is perpendicular to the radius from the center of the circle to point P. This fact enables you to find an equation of the tangent to a circle at a point P if you know an equation for the circle and the coordinates of P.

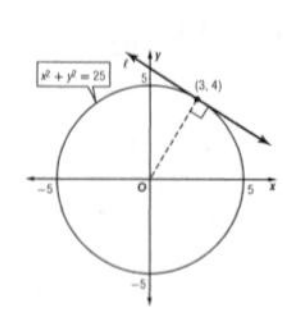

Exercises

Use the diagram above to solve each problem.

1. What is the slope of the radius to the point with coordinates (3, 4)? What is the slope of the tangent to that point? $\frac{4}{3}, -\frac{3}{4}$

Multiple Representations
In Exercise 57, students compare the results of graphing a circle using graph paper with the results using a graphing calculator.

NGSSS PRACTICE 912.A.2.12, 912.A.8.5, 912.S.3.3

68. **GRIDDED RESPONSE** Two circles, both with radii 6, have exactly one point in common. If A is a point on one circle and B is a point on the other circle, what is the maximum possible length for the line segment $\overline{AB}$? **24**

69. In the senior class, there are 20% more girls than boys. If there are 180 girls, how many more girls than boys are there among the seniors? **A**

A. 30
B. 36
C. 90
D. 144

70. A \$1000 deposit is made at a bank that pays 2% compounded weekly. How much will you have in your account at the end of 10 years? **H**

F. \$1200.00
G. \$1218.99
H. \$1221.36
I. \$1224.54

71. The mean of six numbers is 20. If one of the numbers is removed, the average of the remaining numbers is 15. What is the number that was removed? **C**

A. 42
B. 43
C. 45
D. 48

75. $\left(1, \frac{7}{22}\right)$; $\sqrt{65}$ **units** **76.** $\left(-\frac{\sqrt{3}}{2}, 2\right)$; $\sqrt{271}$ **units**

Spiral Review

Graph each equation. (Lesson 10-2) **72–74. See Chapter 10 Answer Appendix.**

72. $y = -\frac{1}{2}(x - 1)^2 + 4$ **73.** $4(x - 2) = (y + 3)^2$ **74.** $(y - 8)^2 = -4(x - 4)$

Find the midpoint of the line segment with endpoints at the given coordinates. Then find the distance between the points. (Lesson 10-1)

75. $\left(-3, -\frac{2}{11}\right), \left(5, \frac{9}{11}\right)$ **76.** $(2\sqrt{3}, -5), (-3\sqrt{3}, 9)$ **77.** $(2.5, 4), (-2.5, 2)$ **(0, 3); $\sqrt{29}$ units**

78. If y varies directly as x and $y = 8$ when $x = 6$, find y when $x = 15$. (Lesson 9-5) **20**

79. If y varies jointly as x and z and $y = 80$ when $x = 5$ and $z = 8$, find y when $x = 16$ and $z = 2$. (Lesson 9-5) **64**

80. If y varies inversely as x and $y = 16$ when $x = 5$, find y when $x = 20$. (Lesson 9-5) **4**

Evaluate each expression. (Lesson 8-3)

81. $\log_9 243$ $\frac{5}{2}$ **82.** $\log_2 \frac{1}{32}$ **−5** **83.** $\log_3 \frac{1}{81}$ **−4** **84.** $\log_{10} 0.001$ **−3**

85. **AMUSEMENT PARKS** The velocity v in feet per second of a roller coaster at the bottom of a hill is related to the vertical drop h in feet and the velocity v_0 in feet per second of the coaster at the top of the hill by the formula $v_0 = \sqrt{v^2 - 64h}$. (Lesson 7-5)

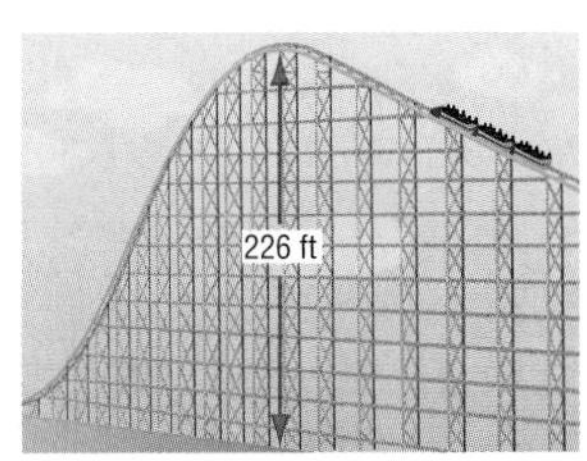

a. Explain why $v_0 = v - 8\sqrt{h}$ is not equivalent to the given formula.

b. What velocity must the coaster have at the top of the hill to achieve a velocity of 125 feet per second at the bottom? **34.1 ft/s**

85a. The square root of a difference is not the difference of the square roots.

Skills Review

Solve each equation by completing the square. (Lesson 5-5)

86. $x^2 + 3x - 18 = 0$ **{−6, 3}** **87.** $2x^2 - 3x - 3 = 0$ $\left\{\frac{3 \pm \sqrt{33}}{4}\right\}$ **88.** $x^2 + 2x + 6 = 0$ $\{-1 \pm i\sqrt{5}\}$

Watch Out!

Error Analysis In Exercise 62, ask students if the square root of $(x - 2)^2 + (y + 3)^2$ is $(x - 2) + (y + 3)$. If they think it is, ask them to check to see if the square root of $4^2 + 3^2$ is equal to $4 + 3$.

Additional Answers

57c. Solve the equation for y: $y = \pm\sqrt{49 - x^2}$. Then graph the positive and negative answers.

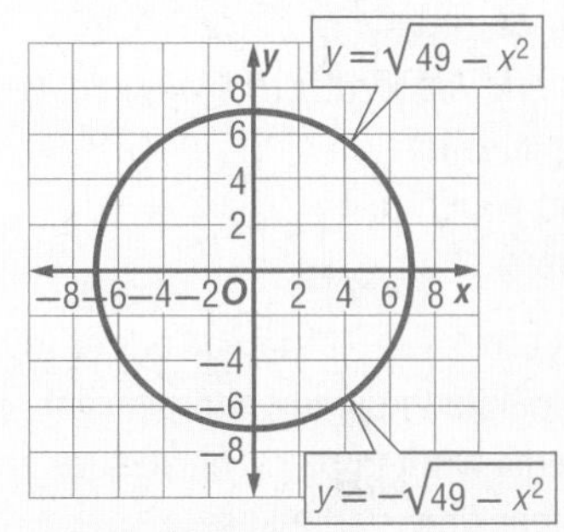

65. Sample answer: $(x - 2)^2 + (y - 3)^2 = 25$ and $(x - 2)^2 + (y - 3)^2 = 36$

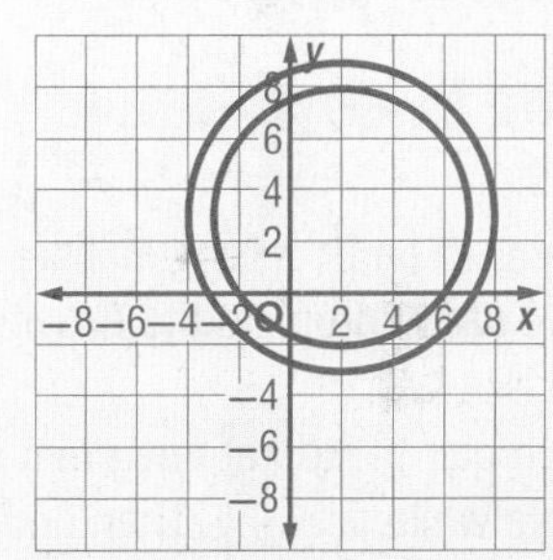

66. $\sqrt{(x_2 - x_1)^2 + (y_2 - y_1)^2} = d$ Distance Formula

$\sqrt{(x - h)^2 + (y - k)^2} = r$

$(x_1, y_1) = (h, k)$,
$(x_2, y_2) = (x, y)$, $d = r$

$(x - h)^2 + (y - k)^2 = r^2$

Square each side.

This is the standard form of the equation of a circle.

Differentiated Instruction OL BL

Extension Write $x + 2y = 2$ and $x^2 + y^2 = 25$ on the board. Ask students to determine how many points the graphs of these two equations have in common. Then ask students to explain whether all lines intersect a circle in two points. There are two points that the graphs of the equations have in common: (–4, 3) and (4.8, –1.4). Not all lines intersect a circle in two points. A tangent line intersects a circle at one point. Some lines do not intersect a circle at all. Hence, a line can intersect a circle in 0, 1, or 2 points.

EXPLORE 10-4 Algebra Lab
Investigating Ellipses

NGSSS **MA.912.A.9.2 Graph conic sections with and without using graphing technology.**

Follow the steps below to construct a type of conic section.

ACTIVITY **Make an Ellipse**

Step 1 Place two thumbtacks in a piece of cardboard, about 1 foot apart.

Step 2 Tie a knot in a piece of string and loop it around the thumbtacks. Place your pencil in the string.

Step 3 Keep the string tight and draw a curve. Continue drawing until you return to your starting point.

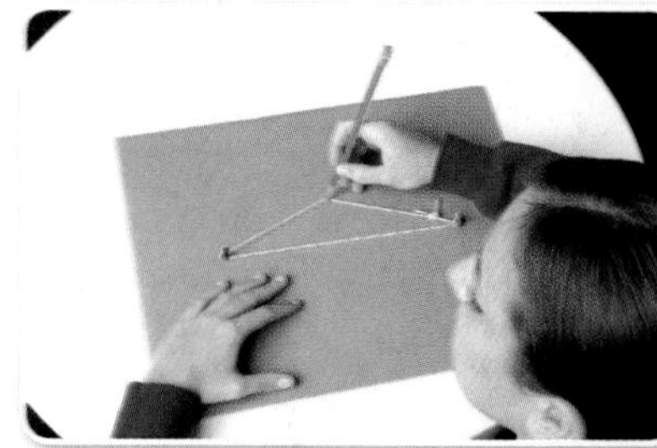

The curve you have drawn is called an **ellipse**. The points where the thumbtacks are located are called the **foci** of the ellipse. *Foci* is the plural of *focus*.

Model and Analyze

Place a large piece of grid paper on a piece of cardboard.

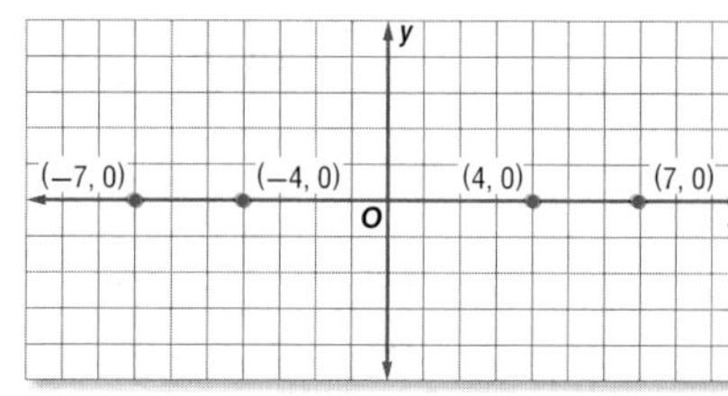

1. Place the thumbtacks at (7, 0) and (−7, 0). Choose a string long enough to loop around both thumbtacks. Draw an ellipse. See students's work.

2. Repeat Exercise 1, but place the thumbtacks at (4, 0) and (−4, 0). Use the same loop of string and draw an ellipse. How does this ellipse compare to the one in Exercise 1? See students' work; the ellipse is more circular.

Place the thumbtacks at each set of points and draw an ellipse. You may change the length of the loop of string if you like. 3–5. See students' work.

3. (11, 0), (−11, 0) **4.** (3, 0), (−3, 0) **5.** (13, 3), (−9, 3)

Make a Conjecture

Describe what happens to the shape of an ellipse when each change is made.

6. The thumbtacks are moved closer together. The ellipse becomes more circular.

7. The thumbtacks are moved farther apart. The ellipse becomes more elongated.

8. The length of the loop of string is increased. The ellipse becomes larger.

9. The thumbtacks are arranged vertically. The ellipse is longer in the vertical direction than in the horizontal direction.

10. One thumbtack is removed, and the string is looped around the remaining thumbtack. The ellipse is a circle.

11. Pick a point on one of the ellipses you have drawn. Use a ruler to measure the distances from that point to the points where the thumbtacks were located. Add the distances. Repeat for other points on the same ellipse. What relationship do you notice? The sum of the distances is constant.

12. Could this activity be done with a rubber band instead of a piece of string? Explain. No; a rubber band might stretch so that the sum of the distances to the thumbtacks would not be constant.

EXPLORE 10-4 Lesson Notes

1 FOCUS

Objective Determine how the graph of an ellipse is affected by changing the location of the foci.

Materials for Each Student

- two thumbtacks
- cardboard
- string
- ruler
- grid paper

Easy to Make Manipulatives

Teaching Algebra with Manipulatives, Templates for:

- grid paper, p. 1
- rulers, p. 24

Teaching Tip It may be easier to manipulate the string and pencil if students work in pairs. Make sure each member draws an ellipse.

2 TEACH

Working in Cooperative Groups

Put students in pairs, mixing abilities. Then have pairs complete the Activity and Exercises 1–5.

- Ask each pair to stop at one point in the curve while drawing. Then find the total distance from the point to one thumbtack plus the distance from the same point to the other thumbtack. the length of the string minus the distance between the thumbtacks
- Ask students what the total distance to the tacks is for any point on the ellipse. the length of the string minus the distance between the thumbtacks

Practice Have students complete Exercises 6–12.

3 ASSESS

Formative Assessment

Use Exercise 8 to assess whether students comprehend the changes that result from varying the positions of the thumbtacks and the length of the string.

From Concrete to Abstract Ask students to describe the set of points they studied in Lesson 10-3. Ask students to use what they have learned to describe the set of points called an ellipse. A circle is the set of points in a plane a constant distance from a given point in the plane, called the *center.* An ellipse is the set of all points in a plane such that the sum of the distances from two fixed points, the *foci,* is constant.

Extending the Concept

Ask:

As the coordinates of the foci of an ellipse come closer and closer together, what happens to the shape of the ellipse? It becomes more circular.

10-4 Ellipses

Why?

Mercury, like all of the planets of our solar system, does not orbit the Sun in a perfect circular path. At its farthest point, Mercury is about 43 million miles from the Sun. At its closest point, it is only about 28.5 million miles from the Sun. This orbit is in the shape of an ellipse with the Sun at a focus.

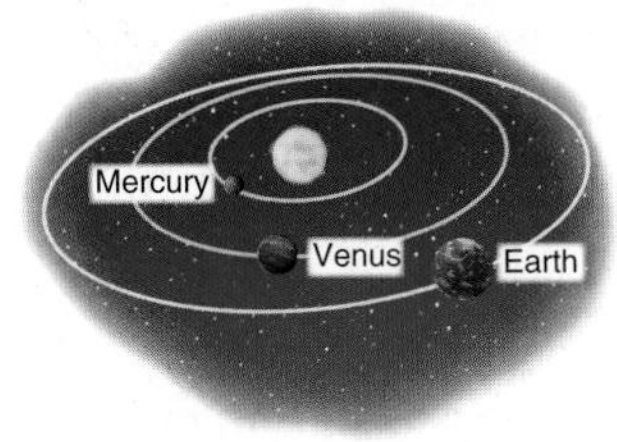

Then
You graphed and wrote equations for circles. (Lesson 10-3)

Now
- Write equations of ellipses.
- Graph ellipses.

NGSSS
MA.912.A.9.1 Write the equations of conic sections in standard form and general form, in order to identify the conic section and to find its geometric properties (foci, asymptotes, eccentricity, etc.).
MA.912.A.9.2 Graph conic sections with and without using graphing technology.

New Vocabulary
ellipse
foci
major axis
minor axis
center
vertices
co-vertices
constant sum

FL Math Online
glencoe.com

Equations of Ellipses An **ellipse** is the set of all points in a plane such that the sum of the distances from two fixed points is constant. These two points are called the **foci** of the ellipse.

Every ellipse has two axes of symmetry, the **major axis** and the **minor axis**. The axes are perpendicular at the **center** of the ellipse.

The foci of an ellipse always lie on the major axis. The endpoints of the major axis are the **vertices** of the ellipse and the endpoints of the minor axis are the **co-vertices** of the ellipse.

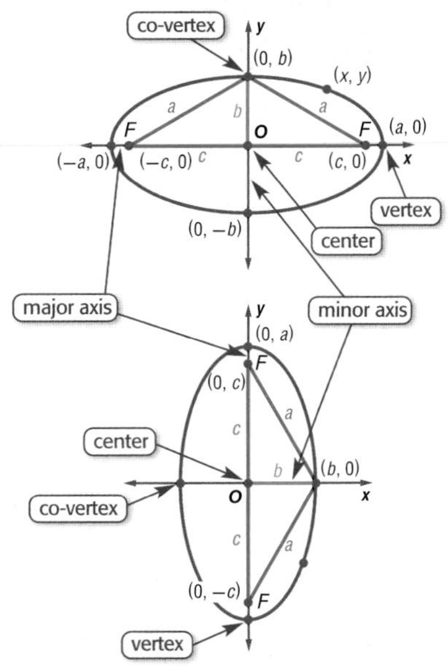

Key Concept

Equations of Ellipses Centered at the Origin

Standard Form	$\frac{x^2}{a^2} + \frac{y^2}{b^2} = 1$	$\frac{y^2}{a^2} + \frac{x^2}{b^2} = 1$
Orientation	horizontal	vertical
Foci	$(c, 0), (-c, 0)$	$(0, c), (0, -c)$
Length of Major Axis	$2a$ units	$2a$ units
Length of Minor Axis	$2b$ units	$2b$ units

There are several important relationships among the many parts of an ellipse.

- The length of the major axis, $2a$ units, equals the sum of the distances from the foci to any point on the ellipse.
- The values of a, b, and c are related by the equation $c^2 = a^2 - b^2$.
- The distance from a focus to either co-vertex is a units.

10-4 Lesson Notes

1 FOCUS

Vertical Alignment

Before Lesson 10-4
Graph and write equations for circles.

Lesson 10-4
Write equations of ellipses.
Graph ellipses.

After Lesson 10-4
Write and graph equations of hyperbolas.

2 TEACH

Scaffolding Questions

Have students read the *Why?* section of the lesson.

Ask:
- What makes up our solar system? The Sun and the group of objects orbiting around the Sun.
- Is Earth always the same distance from the Sun? No; it is closest in January and farthest in July.
- What does it mean when it says that the Sun is at a focus? The Sun is not the center of the ellipse. It is at a point off to one side.

Lesson 10-4 Resources

Resource	Approaching-Level	On-Level	Beyond-Level	English Learners
Teacher Edition		• Differentiated Instruction, pp. 641, 642, 646	• Differentiated Instruction, pp. 641, 642, 646	• Differentiated Instruction, p. 642
Chapter Resource Masters	• Study Guide and Intervention, pp. 25–26 • Skills Practice, p. 27 • Practice, p. 28 • Word Problem Practice, p. 29	• Study Guide and Intervention, pp. 25–26 • Skills Practice, p. 27 • Practice, p. 28 • Word Problem Practice, p. 29 • Enrichment, p. 30 • Graphing Calculator Activity, p. 31	• Practice, p. 28 • Word Problem Practice, p. 29 • Enrichment, p. 30	• Study Guide and Intervention, pp. 25–26 • Skills Practice, p. 27 • Practice, p. 28 • Word Problem Practice, p. 29
Transparencies	• 5-Minute Check Transparency 10-4	• 5-Minute Check Transparency 10-4	• 5-Minute Check Transparency 10-4	• 5-Minute Check Transparency 10-4
Other	• Study Notebook	• Study Notebook	• Study Notebook	• Study Notebook

TEACH with TECH

DOCUMENT CAMERA Work on the document camera to show students how to construct an ellipse using two pins, string, and a pencil. Repeat several times to show how the shape of the ellipse changes when the foci are closer and farther away from each other.

Equation of Ellipses

Example 1 shows how to write an equation for an ellipse shown on a graph. **Example 2** shows how to write an equation for an ellipse when all four vertices are given. **Example 3** shows how to write the equation of an ellipse that models a real-world situation.

Formative Assessment

Use the Guided Practice exercises after each example to determine students' understanding of concepts.

Additional Example

1 Write an equation for the ellipse.

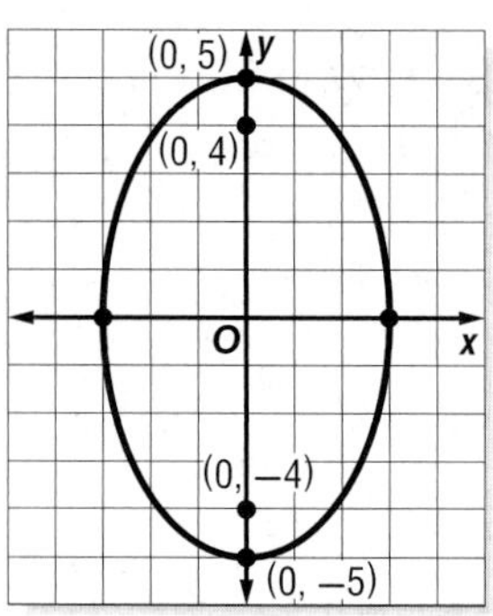

$\frac{y^2}{25} + \frac{x^2}{9} = 1$

Additional Examples also in Interactive Classroom PowerPoint® Presentations

IWB INTERACTIVE WHITEBOARD READY

The sum of the distances from the foci to any point on the ellipse, or the **constant sum**, must be greater than the distance between the foci.

StudyTip

Major Axis In standard form, if the x^2-term has the greater denominator, then the major axis is horizontal. If the y^2-term has the greater denominator, then it is vertical.

EXAMPLE 1 Write an Equation Given Vertices and Foci

Write an equation for the ellipse.

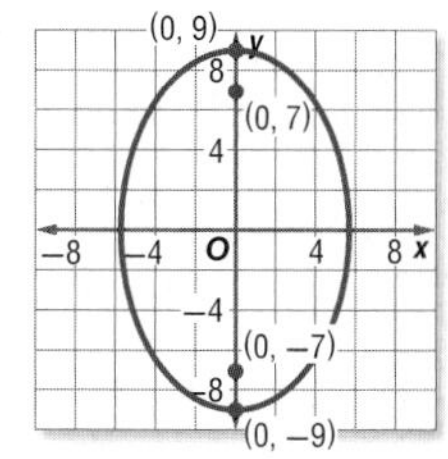

Step 1 Find the center.
The foci are equidistant from the center.
The center is at (0, 0).

Step 2 Find the value of a.
The vertices are (0, 9) and (0, −9), so the length of the major axis is 18.
The value of a is 18 ÷ 2 or 9, and $a^2 = 81$.

Step 3 Find the value of b.
We can use $c^2 = a^2 - b^2$ to find b.
The foci are 7 units from the center, so $c = 7$.

$c^2 = a^2 - b^2$	**Equation relating a, b, and c**
$49 = 81 - b^2$	**$a = 9$ and $c = 7$**
$b^2 = 32$	**Solve for b^2.**

Step 4 Write the equation.
Because the major axis is vertical, a^2 goes with y and b^2 goes with x.
The equation for the ellipse is $\frac{y^2}{81} + \frac{x^2}{32} = 1$.

Guided Practice

1. Write an equation for an ellipse with vertices at (−4, 0) and (4, 0) and foci at (2, 0) and (−2, 0). $\frac{x^2}{16} + \frac{y^2}{12} = 1$

Personal Tutor glencoe.com

Like other graphs, the graph of an ellipse can be translated. When the graph is translated h units right and k units up, the center of the translation is (h, k). This is equivalent to replacing x with $x - h$ and replacing y with $y - k$ in the parent function.

Key Concept Equations of Ellipses Centered at (h, k)

Standard Form	$\frac{(x-h)^2}{a^2} + \frac{(y-k)^2}{b^2} = 1$	$\frac{(y-k)^2}{a^2} + \frac{(x-h)^2}{b^2} = 1$
Orientation	horizontal	vertical
Foci	$(h \pm c, k)$	$(h, k \pm c)$
Vertices	$(h \pm a, k)$	$(h, k \pm a)$
Co-vertices	$(h, k \pm b)$	$(h \pm b, k)$

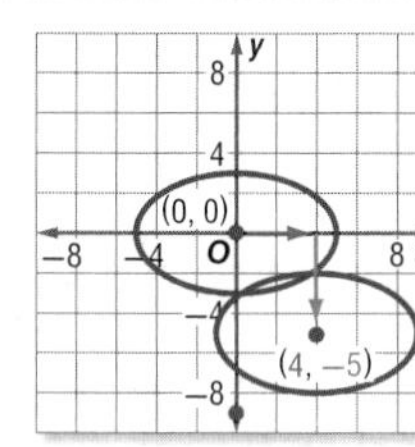

We can use this information to determine the equations for ellipses. The original ellipse at the right is horizontal and has a major axis of 10 units, so $a = 5$.

The length of the minor axis is 6 units, so $b = 3$.

The ellipse is translated 4 units right and 5 units down. So, the value of h is 4 and the value of k is −5.

The equation for the original ellipse is $\frac{x^2}{25} + \frac{y^2}{9} = 1$.

The equation for the translation is $\frac{(x-4)^2}{25} + \frac{(y+5)^2}{9} = 1$.

Watch Out!

Common Misconceptions Point out to students that when the Pythagorean Theorem is used to derive the standard form of the equation of an ellipse with its center at the origin and a horizontal major axis, it is a, not c, that is used to represent the length of the hypotenuse.

Focus on Mathematical Content

Ellipses Every ellipse has two axes of symmetry. The points at which the ellipse intersects its axes of symmetry determine two segments with endpoints on the ellipse. These segments are called the *major axis* and the *minor axis*. The intersection of the axes is the center of the ellipse.

You can also determine the equation for an ellipse if you are given all four vertices.

EXAMPLE 2 Write an Equation Given the Lengths of the Axes

Write an equation for the ellipse with vertices at (6, −8) and (6, 4) and co-vertices at (3, −2) and (9, −2).

The x-coordinate is the same for both vertices, so the ellipse is vertical.

The center of the ellipse is at $\left(\frac{6+6}{2}, \frac{-8+4}{2}\right)$ or (6, −2).

The length of the major axis is 4 − (−8) or 12 units, so $a = 6$.

The length of the minor axis is 9 − 3 or 6 units, so $b = 3$.

The equation for the ellipse is $\frac{(y+2)^2}{36} + \frac{(x-6)^2}{9} = 1$. $a^2 = 36, b^2 = 9$

Guided Practice

2. Write an equation for the ellipse with vertices at (−3, 8) and (9, 8) and co-vertices at (3, 12) and (3, 4). $\frac{(x-3)^2}{36} + \frac{(y-8)^2}{16} = 1$

Personal Tutor glencoe.com

Many real-world phenomena can be represented by ellipses.

Real-World EXAMPLE 3 Write an Equation for an Ellipse

SPACE Refer to the application at the beginning of the lesson. Mercury's greatest distance from the Sun, or *aphelion*, is about 43 million miles. Mercury's closest distance, or *perihelion*, is about 28.5 million miles. The diameter of the Sun is about 870,000 miles. Use this information to determine an equation relating Mercury's elliptical orbit around the Sun in millions of miles.

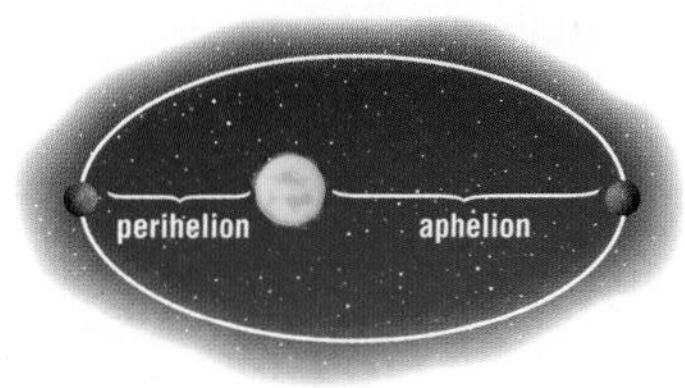

Understand We need to determine an equation representing Mercury's orbit around the Sun.

Plan Including the diameter of the Sun, the sum of the perihelion and aphelion equals the length on the major axis of the ellipse. We can use this information to determine the values of a, b, and c.

Solve Find the value of a.
The value of a is one half the length of the major axis.
$a = 0.5(43 + 28.5 + 0.87)$ or 36.185

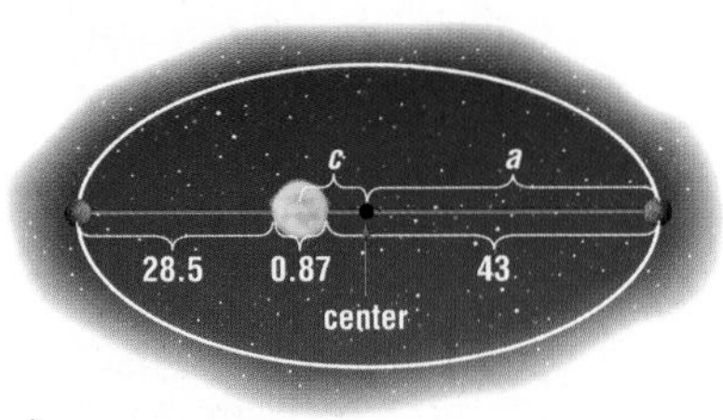

Find the value of c.
The value of c is the distance from the center of the ellipse to the focus.
This distance is equal to a minus the perihelion and the radius of the Sun.
$c = 36.185 - 28.5 - 0.435$ or 7.25

(continued on the next page)

Real-World Career

Aerospace Technician Aerospace technicians work for NASA, helping engineers research and develop virtual reality and verbal communication between humans and computer systems. Although a bachelor's degree is desired, on-the-job training is available.

Source: NASA

Problem-Solving Tip

Draw a Diagram Draw a diagram when the problem situation involves spatial reasoning or geometric figures.

Additional Examples

2 Write an equation for the ellipse with vertices at (−6, −2) and (4, −2) and co-vertices at (−1, −4) and (−1, 0). $\frac{(x+1)^2}{25} + \frac{(y+2)^2}{4} = 1$

3 **SOUND** A listener is standing in an elliptical room 150 feet wide and 320 feet long. When a speaker stands at one focus and whispers, the best place for the listener to stand is at the other focus. Write an equation to model this ellipse, assuming the major axis is horizontal and the center is at the origin. $\frac{x^2}{25{,}600} + \frac{y^2}{5625} = 1$

Watch Out!

Preventing Errors Suggest that students make rough sketches of situations like the one in Example 3.

Tips for New Teachers

Sense-Making Make sure students understand that an ellipse has two axes of symmetry, the major axis and the minor axis. Point out that the major axis is the longer of the two axes.

Differentiated Instruction OL BL

Extension Ask students to create a town on graph paper. The town should include the following components:

- An elliptical border (give equation)
- Two police headquarters located at the foci of the ellipse (give coordinates)
- Five other locations of your choice (give coordinates)
- Create a series of problems about police responding to calls at various locations. Which police headquarters should respond to the call? What other factors must be considered?

Graph Ellipses

Example 4 shows how to graph an equation for an ellipse that is not in standard form.

Additional Example

4 Find the coordinates of the center and foci and the lengths of the major and minor axes of an ellipse with equation $x^2 + 4y^2 - 6x - 16y - 11 = 0$. Then graph the ellipse. center: (3, 2); foci: $(3\sqrt{3} + 3, 2)$, $(-3\sqrt{3} + 3, 2)$: major axis 12; minor axis: 6

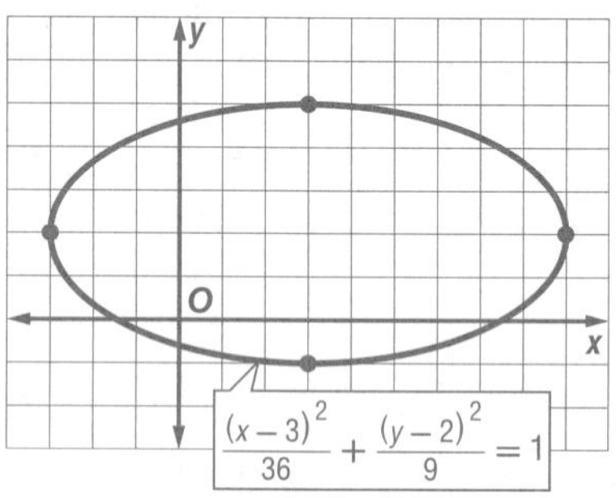

Focus on Mathematical Content

Graphing Ellipses The parent graph of an ellipse is of the form $\frac{x^2}{a^2} + \frac{y^2}{b^2} = 1$ or $\frac{y^2}{a^2} + \frac{x^2}{b^2} = 1$, depending on the direction of the major axis. When the parent graph of an ellipse is translated h units to the right (or left) and k units up (or down), the equations would then have the form $\frac{(x-h)^2}{a^2} + \frac{(y-k)^2}{b^2} = 1$ or $\frac{(y-k)^2}{a^2} + \frac{(x-h)^2}{b^2} = 1$, depending on the direction of the major axis.

Find the value of b.

$c^2 = a^2 - b^2$	**Equation relating a, b, and c**
$(7.25)^2 = (36.185)^2 - b^2$	**$c = 7.25$ and $a = 36.185$**
$52.5625 = 1309.3542 - b^2$	**Simplify.**
$b^2 = 1256.828$	**Solve for b^2.**
$b = 35.4518$	**Take the square root of each side.**

So, with the center of the orbit at the origin, the equation relating Mercury's orbit around the Sun can be modeled by $\frac{x^2}{1309.3542} + \frac{y^2}{1256.792} = 1$.

Check Use your answer to recalculate a, b, and c. Then determine the aphelion and perihelion based on your answer. Compare to the actual values.

Real-World Link

Earth's orbit around the Sun is nearly circular, with only about a 3% difference between perihelion and aphelion.

Source: *The Astronomer*

Guided Practice 3. $\frac{x^2}{13.47} + \frac{y^2}{12.42} = 1$

3. SPACE Pluto's distance from the Sun is 2.757 billion miles at perihelion and about 4.583 billion miles at aphelion. Determine an equation relating Pluto's orbit around the Sun in billions of miles with the center of the horizontal ellipse at the origin.

Personal Tutor glencoe.com

Graph Ellipses When you are given an equation for an ellipse that is not in standard form, you can write it in standard form by completing the square for both x and y. Once the equation is in standard form, you can use it to graph the ellipse.

EXAMPLE 4 Graph an Ellipse

Find the coordinates of the center and foci, and the lengths of the major and minor axes of an ellipse with equation $25x^2 + 9y^2 + 250x - 36y + 436 = 0$. Then graph the ellipse.

Step 1 Write in standard form. Complete the square for each variable to write this equation in standard form.

$25x^2 + 9y^2 + 250x - 36y + 436 = 0$	**Original equation**
$25x^2 + 250x + 9y^2 - 36y = -436$	**Associative Property**
$25(x^2 + 10x) + 9(y^2 - 4y) = -436$	**Distributive Property**
$25(x^2 + 10x + ■) + 9(y^2 - 4y + ■) = -436 + 25(■) + 9(■)$	**Complete the squares.**
$25(x^2 + 10x + 25) + 9(y^2 - 4y + 4) = -436 + 25(25) + 9(4)$	**$5^2 = 25$ and $(-2)^2 = 4$**
$25(x + 5)^2 + 9(y - 2)^2 = 225$	**Write as perfect squares.**
$\frac{(x+5)^2}{9} + \frac{(y-2)^2}{25} = 1$	**Divide each side by 225.**

Step 2 Find the center.
$h = -5$ and $k = 2$, so the center of the ellipse is at $(-5, 2)$.

Step 3 Find the lengths of the axes and graph.
The ellipse is vertical.
$a^2 = 25$, so $a = 5$. $b^2 = 9$, so $b = 3$.
The length of the major axis is $2 \cdot 5$ or 10.
The length of the minor axis is $2 \cdot 3$ or 6.
The vertices are at $(-5, 7)$ and $(-5, -3)$.
The co-vertices are at $(-2, 2)$ and $(-8, 2)$.

Differentiated Instruction

OL BL ELL

Linguistic Learners Remind students that the Moon travels around Earth in an elliptical orbit. The distance the Moon is from Earth varies from about 364,000 kilometers to about 405,000 kilometers. Ask students to research what shape the orbits are for other planets and their moons.

Step 4 Find the foci.
$c^2 = 25 - 9$ or 16, so $c = 4$.
The foci are at $(-5, 6)$ and $(-5, -2)$.

Step 5 Graph the ellipse.
Draw the ellipse that passes through the vertices and co-vertices.

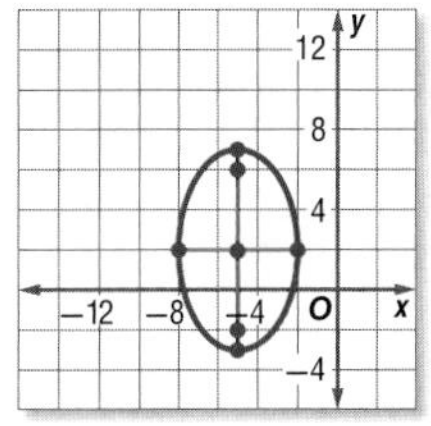

Guided Practice

4. Find the coordinates of the center and foci and the lengths of the major and minor axes of the ellipse with equation $x^2 + 4y^2 - 2x + 24y + 21 = 0$. Then graph the ellipse. **See margin.**

Personal Tutor glencoe.com

Check Your Understanding

Example 1 p. 640

Write an equation for each ellipse.

2. $\frac{(x-4)^2}{49} + \frac{(y+6)^2}{33} = 1$

1.

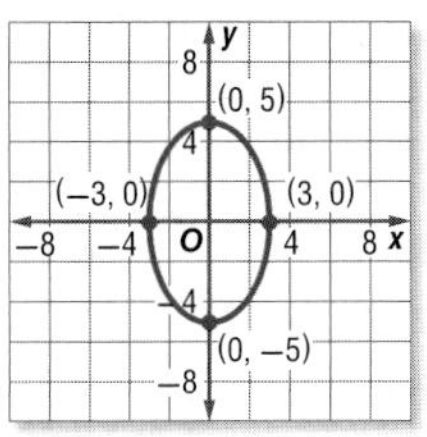

$\frac{y^2}{25} + \frac{x^2}{9} = 1$

2.

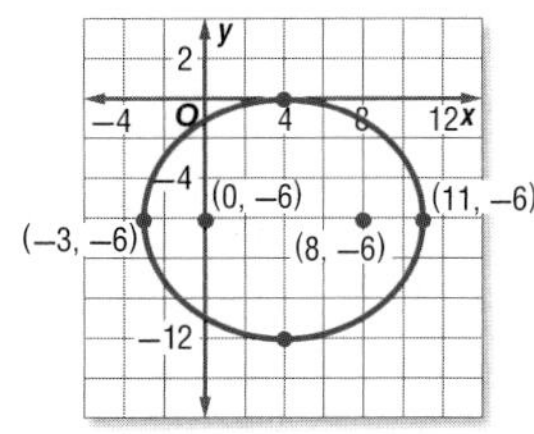

Example 2 p. 641

Write an equation for an ellipse that satisfies each set of conditions.

3. $\frac{(y+1)^2}{25} + \frac{(x+2)^2}{9} = 1$

3. vertices at $(-2, -6)$ and $(-2, 4)$, co-vertices at $(-5, -1)$ and $(1, -1)$

4. vertices at $(-2, 5)$ and $(14, 5)$, co-vertices at $(6, 1)$ and $(6, 9)$ $\frac{(x-6)^2}{64} + \frac{(y-5)^2}{16} = 1$

Example 3 pp. 641–642

5. ARCHITECTURE An architectural firm sent a proposal to a city for building a coliseum, shown at the right.

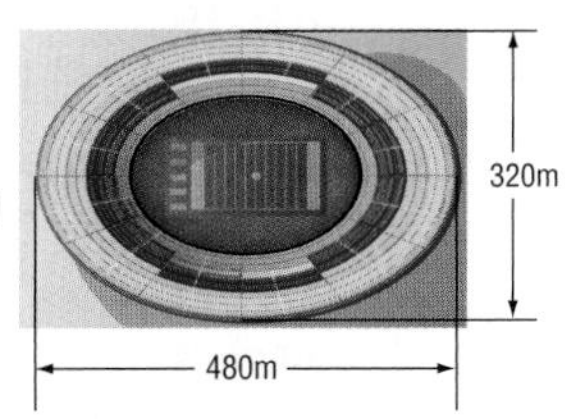

a. Determine the values of a and b. $a = 240$, $b = 160$

5b. $\frac{x^2}{57{,}600} + \frac{y^2}{25{,}600} = 1$

b. Assuming that the center is at the origin, write an equation to represent the ellipse.

c. Determine the coordinates of the foci. **about (179, 0) and (−179, 0)**

6. $\frac{x^2}{8720.8} + \frac{y^2}{8718.4} = 1$

6. SPACE Earth's orbit is about 91.4 million miles at perihelion and about 94.5 million miles at aphelion. Determine an equation relating Earth's orbit around the Sun in millions of miles with the center of the horizontal ellipse at the origin.

Example 4 pp. 642–643

Find the coordinates of the center and foci and the lengths of the major and minor axes for the ellipse with the given equation. Then graph the ellipse. **7–10. See margin.**

7. $\frac{(y+1)^2}{64} + \frac{(x-5)^2}{28} = 1$

8. $\frac{(x+2)^2}{48} + \frac{(y-1)^2}{20} = 1$

9. $4x^2 + y^2 - 32x - 4y + 52 = 0$

10. $9x^2 + 25y^2 + 72x - 150y + 144 = 0$

3 PRACTICE

Formative Assessment

Use Exercises 1–10 to check for understanding.

Use the chart at the bottom of the next page to customize assignments for your students.

Additional Answer (Guided Practice)

4. center (1, −3); foci (4.46, −3) and (−2.46, −3); major axis: 8; minor axis: 4

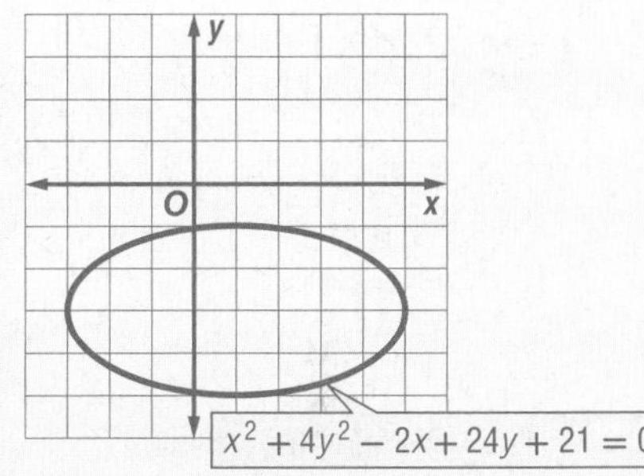

Additional Answers

7. center (5, −1); foci (5, 5) and (5, −7); major axis: 16; minor axis: ≈10.58

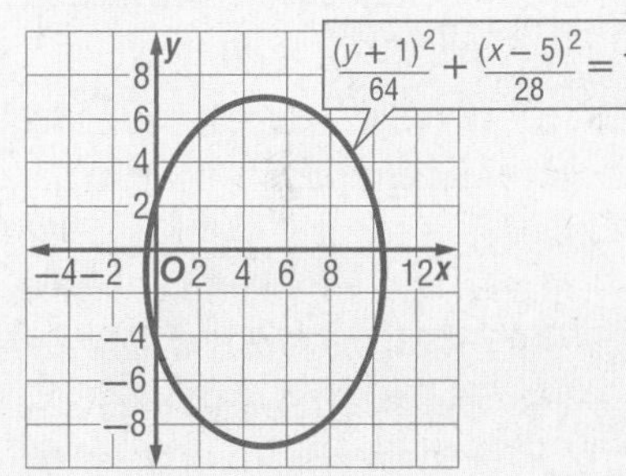

8. center (−2, 1); foci (3.29, 1) and (−7.29, 1); major axis: ≈13.86; minor axis: ≈8.94

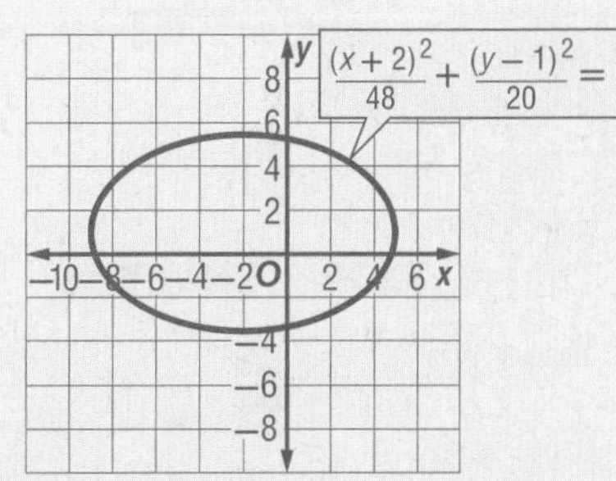

9. center (4, 2); foci (4, 5.46) and (4, −1.46); major axis: 8; minor axis: 4

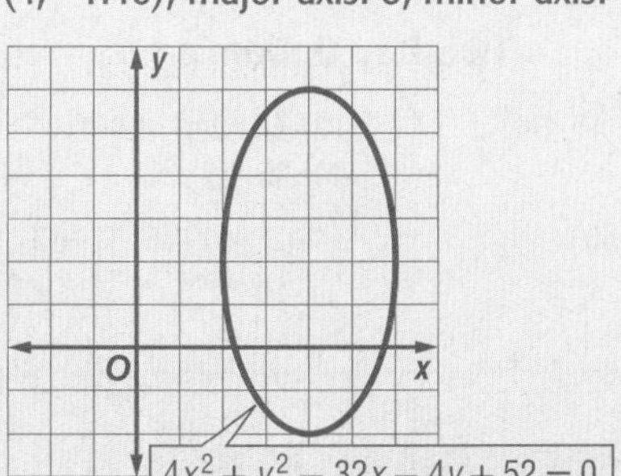

10. center (−4, 3); foci (0, 3) and (−8, 3); major axis: 10; minor axis: 6

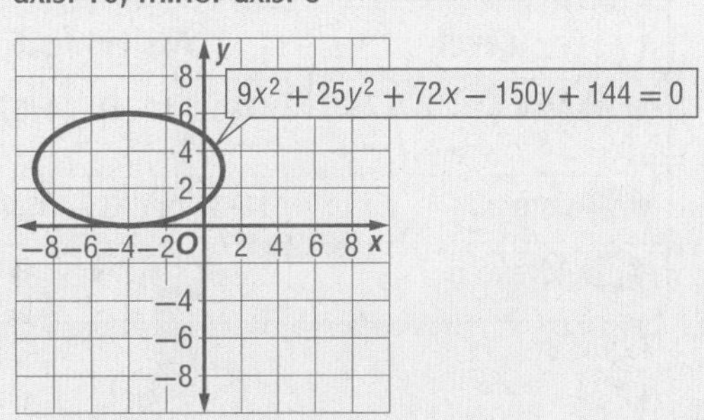

Multiple Representations In Exercise 39, students use a graph and algebraic analysis to examine the relationship between the shape of an ellipse and the value of its eccentricity.

Tips for New Teachers

Graphing Allow students to use grid paper when graphing ellipses. Remind them to keep their work neat.

Additional Answers

39a.

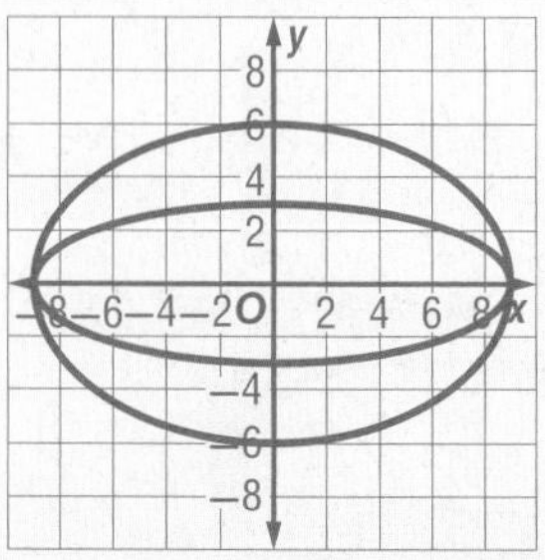

44. Sample answer: As an ellipse becomes more circular, the difference between a and b becomes smaller. This causes the value of c to become smaller since $c^2 = a^2 - b^2$. The value of $2c$ is the distance between the foci, so the foci get closer together.

45. For any point on an ellipse, the sum of the distances from that point to the foci is constant by the definition of an ellipse. So, if (2, 14) is on the ellipse, then the sum of the distances from it to the foci will be a certain value consistent with every other point on the ellipse. The distance between (–7, 2) and (2, 14) is $\sqrt{(-7-2)^2 + (2-14)^2}$ or 15. The distance between (18, 2) and (2, 14) is $\sqrt{(18-2)^2 + (2-14)^2}$ or 20. The sum of these two distances is 35.

The distance between (–7, 2) and (2, –10) is $\sqrt{(-7-2)^2 + [2-(-10)]^2}$ or 15. The distance between (18, 2) and (2, –10) is $\sqrt{(18-2)^2 + [2-(-10)]^2}$ or 20. The sum of these distances is also 35. Thus, (2, –10) also lies on the ellipse.

Practice and Problem Solving

= Step-by-Step Solutions begin on page R20.
Extra Practice begins on page 947.

Example 1 p. 640

Write an equation for each ellipse.

11.

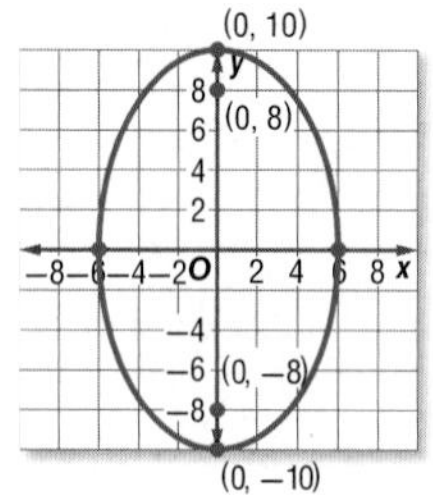

12.

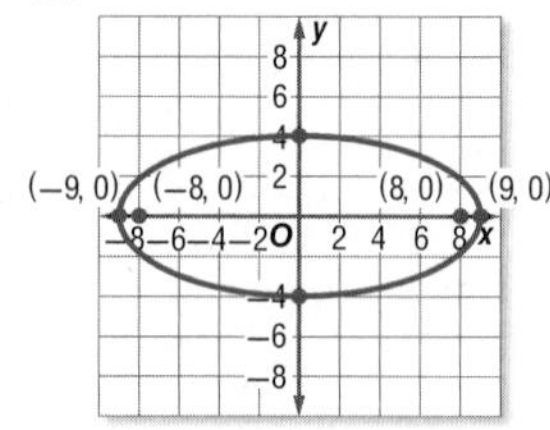

13.

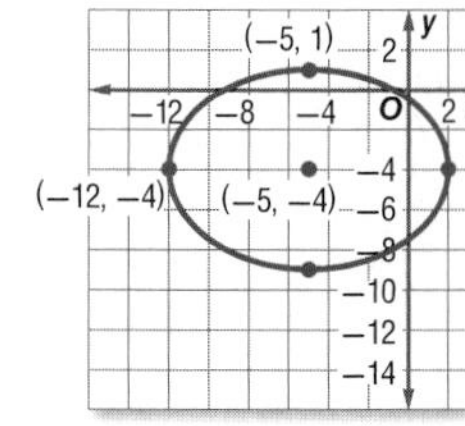

14.

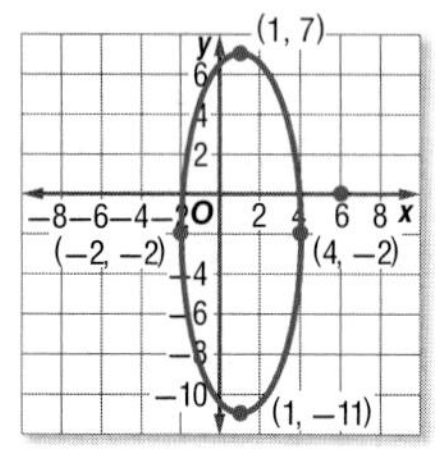

15.

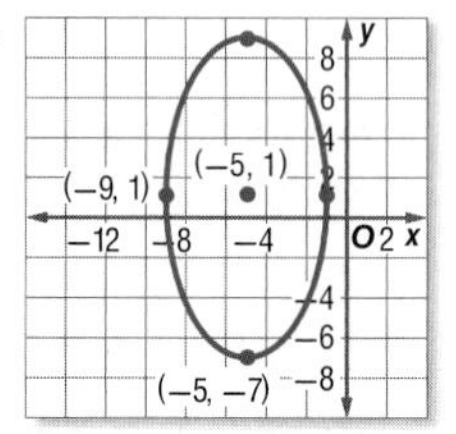

16.

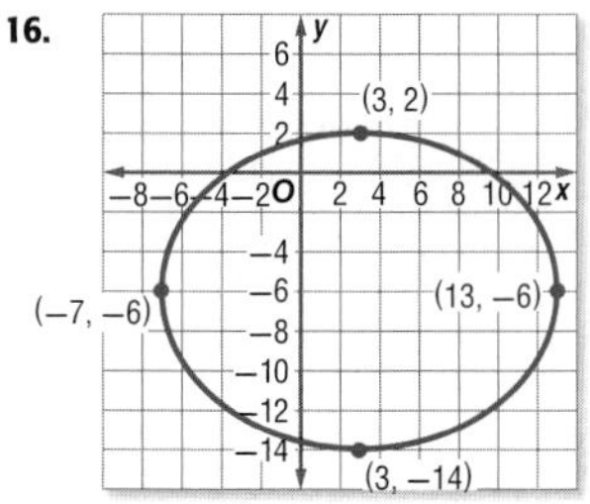

11. $\frac{y^2}{100} + \frac{x^2}{36} = 1$
12. $\frac{x^2}{81} + \frac{y^2}{17} = 1$
13. $\frac{(x+5)^2}{49} + \frac{(y+4)^2}{25} = 1$
14. $\frac{(y+2)^2}{81} + \frac{(x-1)^2}{9} = 1$
15. $\frac{(y-1)^2}{64} + \frac{(x+5)^2}{16} = 1$
16. $\frac{(x-3)^2}{100} + \frac{(y+6)^2}{64} = 1$

Example 2 p. 641

Write an equation for an ellipse that satisfies each set of conditions.

17. vertices at (–6, 4) and (12, 4), co-vertices at (3, 12) and (3, –4) $\frac{(x-3)^2}{81} + \frac{(y-4)^2}{64} = 1$

18. vertices at (–1, 11) and (–1, 1), co-vertices at (–4, 6) and (2, 6) $\frac{(y-6)^2}{25} + \frac{(x+1)^2}{9} = 1$

19. center at (–2, 6), vertex at (–2, 16), co-vertex at (1, 6) $\frac{(y-6)^2}{100} + \frac{(x+2)^2}{9} = 1$

Example 3 pp. 641–642

20. center at (3, –4), vertex at (8, –4), co-vertex at (3, –2) $\frac{(x-3)^2}{25} + \frac{(y+4)^2}{4} = 1$

21. vertices at (4, 12) and (4, –4), co-vertices at (1, 4) and (7, 4) $\frac{(y-4)^2}{64} + \frac{(x-4)^2}{9} = 1$

22. vertices at (–11, 2) and (–1, 2), co-vertices at (–6, 0) and (–6, 4) $\frac{(x+6)^2}{25} + \frac{(y-2)^2}{4} = 1$

23. TUNNELS The opening of a tunnel in the mountains can be modeled by semiellipses, or halves of ellipses. If the opening is 14.6 meters wide and 8.6 meters high, determine an equation to represent the opening with the center at the origin. $\frac{y^2}{73.96} + \frac{x^2}{53.29} = 1$

Example 4 pp. 642–643

Find the coordinates of the center and foci and the lengths of the major and minor axes for the ellipse with the given equation. Then graph the ellipse. 24–31. See Chapter 10 Answer Appendix.

24. $\frac{(x-3)^2}{36} + \frac{(y-2)^2}{128} = 1$

25. $\frac{(x+6)^2}{50} + \frac{(y-3)^2}{72} = 1$

26. $\frac{x^2}{27} + \frac{(y-5)^2}{64} = 1$

27. $\frac{(x+4)^2}{16} + \frac{y^2}{75} = 1$

28. $3x^2 + y^2 - 6x - 8y - 5 = 0$

29. $3x^2 + 4y^2 - 18x + 24y + 3 = 0$

30. $7x^2 + y^2 - 56x + 6y + 93 = 0$

31. $3x^2 + 2y^2 + 12x - 20y + 14 = 0$

32. SPACE Like the planets, Halley's Comet travels around the Sun in an elliptical orbit. The aphelion is 3282.9 million miles and the perihelion is 54.87 million miles. Determine an equation relating the comet's orbit around the Sun in millions of miles with the center of the horizontal ellipse at the origin. $\frac{x^2}{2{,}786{,}629.3} + \frac{y^2}{181{,}584.8} = 1$

Differentiated Homework Options

Level	Assignment	Two-Day Option	
AL Basic	11–32, 40–41, 44–67	11–31 odd, 47–50	12–32 even, 40–41, 44–46, 51–67
OL Core	11–31 odd, 33–41, 44–67	11–32, 47–50	33–41, 44–46, 51–67
BL Advanced	33–64, (optional: 65–67)		

B Write an equation for an ellipse that satisfies each set of conditions.

33. center at $(-5, -2)$, focus at $(-5, 2)$, co-vertex at $(-8, -2)$ $\frac{(y+2)^2}{25} + \frac{(x+5)^2}{9} = 1$

34. center at $(4, -3)$, focus at $(9, -3)$, co-vertex at $(4, -5)$

35. foci at $(-2, 8)$ and $(6, 8)$, co-vertex at $(2, 10)$ $\frac{(x-2)^2}{20} + \frac{(y-8)^2}{4} = 1$

36. foci at $(4, 4)$ and $(4, 14)$, co-vertex at $(0, 9)$

37. **GOVERNMENT** The Oval Office is located in the West Wing of the White House. It is an elliptical shaped room used as the main office by the President of the United States. The long axis is 10.9 meters long and the short axis is 8.8 meters long. Write an equation to represent the outer walls of the Oval Office. Assume that the center of the room is at the origin.

Real-World Link

President Taft established the first Oval Office in 1909. The room changed locations and was modified several times. Since 1934, though, the Oval Office has changed very little.

Source: The White House

38. **SOUND** A whispering gallery is an elliptical room in which a faint whisper at one focus that cannot be heard by other people in the room, can easily be heard by someone at the other focus. Suppose an ellipse is 400 feet long and 120 feet wide. What is the distance between the foci? **about 381.58 ft**

39. **MULTIPLE REPRESENTATIONS** The *eccentricity* of an ellipse measures how circular the ellipse is.

a. **GRAPHICAL** Graph $\frac{x^2}{81} + \frac{y^2}{36} = 1$ and $\frac{x^2}{81} + \frac{y^2}{9} = 1$ on the same graph. **See margin.**

b. **VERBAL** Describe the difference between the two graphs.

c. **ALGEBRAIC** The eccentricity of an ellipse is $\frac{c}{a}$. Find the eccentricity for each.

d. **ANALYTICAL** Make a conjecture about the relationship between the value of an ellipse's eccentricity and the shape of the ellipse as compared to a circle.

H.O.T. Problems Use Higher-Order Thinking Skills

40. **C** **ERROR ANALYSIS** Serena and Karissa are determining the equation for an ellipse with foci at $(-4, -11)$ and $(-4, 5)$ and co-vertices at $(2, -3)$ and $(-10, -3)$. Is either of them correct? Explain your reasoning.

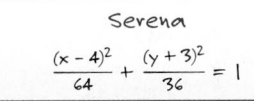

Serena	Karissa
$\frac{(x-4)^2}{64} + \frac{(y+3)^2}{36} = 1$	$\frac{(x+4)^2}{100} + \frac{(y+3)^2}{36} = 1$

41. **OPEN ENDED** Write an equation for an ellipse with a focus at the origin.

42. **CHALLENGE** When the values of a and b are equal, an ellipse is a circle. Use this information and your knowledge of ellipses to determine the formula for the area of an ellipse in terms of a and b. $A = \pi ab$

43. **CHALLENGE** Determine an equation for an ellipse with foci at $(2, \sqrt{6})$ and $(2, -\sqrt{6})$ that passes through $(3, \sqrt{6})$. $\frac{y^2}{9} + \frac{(x-2)^2}{3} = 1$

44. **REASONING** What happens to the location of the foci as an ellipse becomes more circular? Explain your reasoning. **See margin.**

45. **REASONING** An ellipse has foci at $(-7, 2)$ and $(18, 2)$. If $(2, 14)$ is a point on the ellipse, show that $(2, -10)$ is also a point on the ellipse. **See margin.**

46. **WRITING IN MATH** Explain why the domain is $\{x \mid -a \le x \le a\}$ and the range is $\{y \mid -b \le y \le b\}$ for an ellipse with equation $\frac{x^2}{a^2} + \frac{y^2}{b^2} = 1$. **See Chapter 10 Answer Appendix.**

34. $\frac{(x-4)^2}{29} + \frac{(y+3)^2}{4} = 1$

36. $\frac{(y-9)^2}{41} + \frac{(x-4)^2}{16} = 1$

37. $\frac{x^2}{29.7025} + \frac{y^2}{19.36} = 1$ or $\frac{y^2}{29.7025} + \frac{x^2}{19.36} = 1$

39b. Sample answer: The first graph is more circular than the second graph.

39c. first graph: 0.745; second graph: 0.943

39d. Sample answer: The closer the eccentricity is to 0, the more circular the ellipse.

40. Sample answer: Neither; both are showing horizontal ellipses and answer is vertical.

41. Sample answer: $\frac{(x+4)^2}{40} + \frac{y^2}{24} = 1$

Watch Out!

Error Analysis In Exercise 40, remind students that the foci are used to determine the value of c.

Enrichment CRM p. 30 OL BL

10-4 Enrichment

Eccentricity

In an ellipse, the ratio $\frac{c}{a}$ is called the **eccentricity** and is denoted by the letter e. Eccentricity measures the elongation of an ellipse. The closer e is to 0, the more an ellipse looks like a circle. The closer e is to 1, the more elongated it is. Recall that the equation of an ellipse is $\frac{x^2}{a^2} + \frac{y^2}{b^2} = 1$ or $\frac{x^2}{b^2} + \frac{y^2}{a^2} = 1$ where a is the length of the major axis, and that $c = \sqrt{a^2 - b^2}$.

Find the eccentricity of each ellipse rounded to the nearest hundredth.

1. $\frac{x^2}{9} + \frac{y^2}{36} = 1$ **0.87**
2. $\frac{x^2}{81} + \frac{y^2}{9} = 1$ **0.94**
3. $\frac{x^2}{4} + \frac{y^2}{9} = 1$ **0.75**
4. $\frac{x^2}{16} + \frac{y^2}{9} = 1$ **0.66**
5. $\frac{x^2}{36} + \frac{y^2}{16} = 1$ **0.75**
6. $\frac{x^2}{4} + \frac{y^2}{36} = 1$ **0.94**

Study Guide and Intervention CRM pp. 25–26 AL OL ELL

10-4 Study Guide and Intervention

Ellipses

Equations of Ellipses An **ellipse** is the set of all points in a plane such that the *sum* of the distances from two given points in the plane, called the foci, is constant. An ellipse has two axes of symmetry which contain the **major** and **minor axes**. In the table, the lengths a, b, and c are related by the formula $c^2 = a^2 - b^2$.

Standard Form of Equation	$\frac{(x-h)^2}{a^2} + \frac{(y-k)^2}{b^2} = 1$	$\frac{(y-k)^2}{a^2} + \frac{(x-h)^2}{b^2} = 1$
Center	(h, k)	(h, k)
Orientation	Horizontal	Vertical
Foci	$(h + c, k), (h - c, k)$	$(h, k - c), (h, k + c)$
Vertices	$(h + a, k), (h - a, k)$	$(h, k + a), (h, k - a)$
Length of Major Axis	$2a$ units	$2a$ units
Length of Minor Axis	$2b$ units	$2b$ units

Example **Write an equation for the ellipse.**

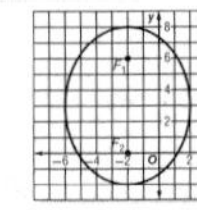

The length of the major axis is the distance between $(-2, -2)$ and $(-2, 8)$. This distance is 10 units.

$2a = 10$, so $a = 5$

The foci are located at $(-2, 6)$ and $(-2, 0)$, so $c = 3$.

$b^2 = a^2 - c^2$
$= 25 - 9$
$= 16$

The center of the ellipse is at $(-2, 3)$, so $h = -2$, $k = 3$, $a^2 = 25$, and $b^2 = 16$. The major axis is vertical.

An equation of the ellipse is $\frac{(y-3)^2}{25} + \frac{(x+2)^2}{16} = 1$.

Exercises

Write an equation for an ellipse that satisfies each set of conditions.

1. vertices at $(-7, 2)$ and $(5, 2)$, co-vertices at $(-1, 0)$ and $(-1, 4)$ $\frac{(x+1)^2}{36} + \frac{(y-2)^2}{4} = 1$
2. major axis 8 units long and parallel to the x-axis, minor axis 2 units long, center at $(-2, -5)$ $\frac{(x+2)^2}{16} + (y+5)^2 = 1$
3. vertices at $(-8, 4)$ and $(4, 4)$, foci at $(-3, 4)$ and $(-1, 4)$ $\frac{(x+2)^2}{36} + \frac{(y-4)^2}{35} = 1$
4. vertices at $(3, 2)$ and $(3, -14)$, co-vertices at $(-1, -6)$ and $(7, -6)$ $\frac{(y+6)^2}{64} + \frac{(x-3)^2}{16} = 1$
5. minor axis 6 units long and parallel to the x-axis, major axis 12 units long, center at $(6, 1)$ $\frac{(y-1)^2}{36} + \frac{(x-6)^2}{9} = 1$

Chapter 10 25 Glencoe Algebra 2

Practice CRM p. 28 AL OL BL ELL

10-4 Practice

Ellipses

Write an equation for each ellipse.

1. 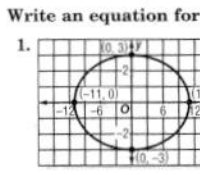 $\frac{x^2}{121} + \frac{y^2}{9} = 1$
2. 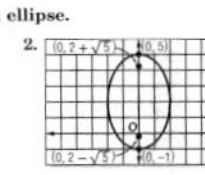 $\frac{(y-2)^2}{9} + \frac{x^2}{4} = 1$
3. 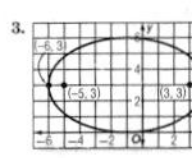 $\frac{(x+1)^2}{25} + \frac{(y-3)^2}{9} = 1$

Write an equation for an ellipse that satisfies each set of conditions.

4. endpoints of major axis at $(-9, 0)$ and $(9, 0)$, endpoints of minor axis at $(0, 3)$ and $(0, -3)$ $\frac{x^2}{81} + \frac{y^2}{9} = 1$
5. endpoints of major axis at $(4, 2)$ and $(4, -8)$, endpoints of minor axis at $(1, -3)$ and $(7, -3)$ $\frac{(y+3)^2}{25} + \frac{(x-4)^2}{9} = 1$
6. major axis 20 units long and parallel to x-axis, minor axis 10 units long, center at $(2, 1)$ $\frac{(x-2)^2}{100} + \frac{(y-1)^2}{25} = 1$
7. major axis 10 units long, minor axis 6 units long and parallel to x-axis, center at $(2, -4)$ $\frac{(y+4)^2}{25} + \frac{(x-2)^2}{9} = 1$
8. major axis 16 units long, center at $(0, 0)$, foci at $(0, 2\sqrt{15})$ and $(0, -2\sqrt{15})$ $\frac{y^2}{64} + \frac{x^2}{4} = 1$
9. endpoints of minor axis at $(0, 2)$ and $(0, -2)$, foci at $(-4, 0)$ and $(4, 0)$ $\frac{x^2}{20} + \frac{y^2}{4} = 1$

Find the coordinates of the center and foci and the lengths of the major and minor axes for the ellipse with the given equation. Then graph the ellipse.

10. $\frac{y^2}{16} + \frac{x^2}{9} = 1$ **$(0, 0)$; $(0, \pm\sqrt{7})$; 8; 6**

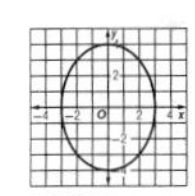

11. $\frac{(y-1)^2}{36} + \frac{(x-3)^2}{1} = 1$ **$(3, 1)$; $(3, 1 \pm \sqrt{35})$; 12; 2**

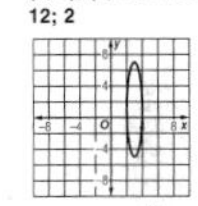

12. $\frac{(x+4)^2}{49} + \frac{(y+3)^2}{25} = 1$ **$(-4, -3)$; $(-4 \pm 2\sqrt{6}\ -3)$; 14; 10**

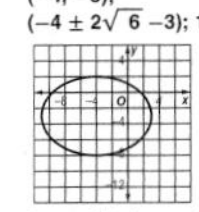

13. **SPORTS** An ice skater traces two congruent ellipses to form a figure eight. Assume that the center of the first loop is at the origin, with the second loop to its right. Write an equation to model the first loop if its major axis (along the x-axis) is 12 feet long and its minor axis is 6 feet long. Write another equation to model the second loop. $\frac{x^2}{36} + \frac{y^2}{9} = 1$; $\frac{(x-12)^2}{36} + \frac{y^2}{9} = 1$

Chapter 10 28 Glencoe Algebra 2

Word Problem Practice CRM p. 29 AL OL BL ELL

10-4 Word Problem Practice

Ellipses

1. **PERSPECTIVE** A graphic designer uses an ellipse to draw a circle from the horizontal perspective. The equation used is $\frac{x^2}{25} + y^2 = 1$. Graph this ellipse.

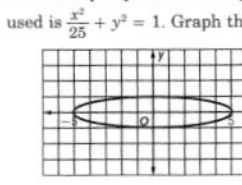

2. **ECHOES** Some rooms like the Oval Office in the White House are shaped as ellipses. The walls of one elliptical room are given by the equation $\frac{x^2}{25} + \frac{y^2}{16} = 1$. Two people want to stand at the foci of the ellipse so that they can whisper to each other without anybody else hearing. What are the coordinates of the foci? **$(3, 0)$ and $(-3, 0)$**

3. **FLASHLIGHTS** Daniella ended up doing her math homework late at night. To avoid disturbing others, she worked in bed with a pen light. One problem asked her to draw an ellipse. She noticed that her pen light created an elliptical patch of light on her paper, so she simply traced the outline of the patch of light. The outline of the ellipse is shown below. What is the equation of this ellipse in standard form?

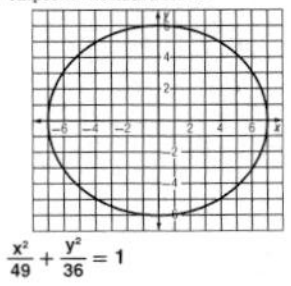

$\frac{x^2}{49} + \frac{y^2}{36} = 1$

4. **ASTRONOMY** The orbit of an asteroid is given by the equation $\frac{x^2}{400} + \frac{y^2}{441} = 1$, where each unit represents one astronomical unit (i.e. the distance from Sun to Earth). What are the lengths of the major and minor axes of the orbit? **Major axis: 42 astronomical units, Minor axis: 40 astronomical units**

5. **MODELING** James wants to try to make an ellipse using a piece of string 26 inches long. He tacks the two ends down 10 inches apart. He then takes a pen and pulls the string taut. He keeps the string taut and pulls the pen around the tacks. By doing this, he creates an ellipse.

a. Determine the lengths of the major and minor axes of the ellipse that James drew. **Major axis has length 26, minor axis has length 24.**

b. If a coordinate grid is overlaid on the ellipse so that the tacks are located at $(5, 0)$ and $(-5, 0)$, what is the equation of the ellipse in standard form? $\frac{x^2}{169} + \frac{y^2}{144} = 1$

Chapter 10 29 Glencoe Algebra 2

Lesson 10-4

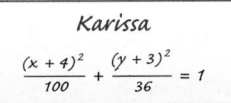

4 ASSESS

Yesterday's News Have students write how yesterday's lesson helped them with writing and graphing equations for ellipses in today's lesson.

Formative Assessment

Check for student understanding of concepts in Lessons 10-3 and 10-4.

CRM Quiz 2, p. 53

Additional Answers

54c.

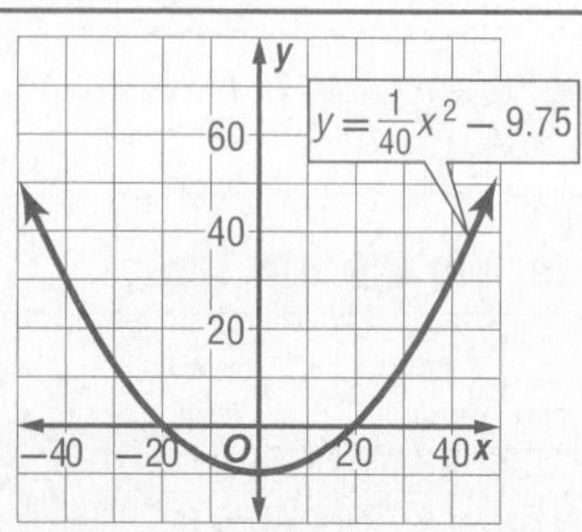

54d. Sample answer: The equation in feet is easier to graph because the numbers have fewer decimal places.

NGSSS PRACTICE 912.A.6.1, 912.A.3.9, 912.A.3.1, 912.A.4.2

47. Multiply. B

$$(2 + 3i)(4 + 7i)$$

A. $8 + 21i$
B. $-13 + 26i$
C. $-6 + 10i$
D. $13 + 12i$

48. The average lifespan of American women has been tracked, and the model for the data is $y = 0.2t + 73$, where $t = 0$ corresponds to 1960. What is the meaning of the y-intercept? H

F. In 2007, the average lifespan was 60.
G. In 1960, the average lifespan was 58.
H. In 1960, the average lifespan was 73.
I. The lifespan is increasing 0.2 years every year.

49. **GRIDDED RESPONSE** If we decrease a number by 6 and then double the result, we get 5 less than the number. What is the number? 7

50. **ACT/SAT** The length of a rectangular prism is one inch greater than its width. The height is three times the length. Find the volume of the prism. C

A. $3x^3 + x^2 + 3x$
B. $x^3 + x^2 + x$
C. $3x^3 + 6x^2 + 3x$
D. $3x^3 + 3x^2 + 3x$

Spiral Review

Write an equation for the circle that satisfies each set of conditions. (Lesson 10-3)

51. center (8, −9), passes through (21, 22) $(x - 8)^2 + (y + 9)^2 = 1130$

52. center at (4, 2), tangent to x-axis $(x - 4)^2 + (y - 2)^2 = 4$

53. center in the second quadrant; tangent to $y = -1$, $y = 9$, and the y-axis $(x + 5)^2 + (y - 4)^2 = 25$

54. **ENERGY** A parabolic mirror is used to collect solar energy. The mirrors reflect the rays from the Sun to the focus of the parabola. The focus of a particular mirror is 9.75 feet above the vertex, and the latus rectum is 39 feet long. (Lesson 10-2)

a. Assume that the focus is at the origin. Write an equation for the parabola formed by the mirror. $y = \frac{1}{39}x^2 - 9.75$

b. One foot is exactly 0.3048 meter. Rewrite the equation for the mirror in meters. $y = \frac{1}{11.8872}x^2 - 2.9718$

c. Graph one of the equations for the mirror. See margin.

d. Which equation did you choose to graph? Explain why. See margin.

Simplify each expression. (Lesson 9-2)

55. $\frac{6}{d^2 + 4d + 4} + \frac{5}{d + 2}$ $\frac{5d + 16}{(d + 2)^2}$

56. $\frac{a}{a^2 - a - 20} + \frac{2}{a + 4}$ $\frac{3a - 10}{(a - 5)(a + 4)}$

57. $\frac{x}{x + 1} + \frac{3}{x^2 - 4x - 5}$ $\frac{x^2 - 5x + 3}{(x - 5)(x + 1)}$

Solve each equation. (Lesson 8-4)

58. $\log_{10}(x^2 + 1) = 1$ ± 3

59. $\log_b 64 = 3$ 4

60. $\log_b 121 = 2$ 11

Simplify. (Lesson 6-1) 61. $15a^3b^3 - 30a^4b^3 + 15a^5b^6$

61. $-5ab^2(-3a^2b + 6a^3b - 3a^4b^4)$

62. $2xy(3xy^3 - 4xy + 2y^4)$ $6x^2y^4 - 8x^2y^2 + 4xy^5$

63. $(4x^2 - 3y^2 + 5xy) - (8xy + 3y^2)$ $4x^2 - 3xy - 6y^2$

64. $(10x^2 - 3xy + 4y^2) - (3x^2 + 5xy)$ $7x^2 - 8xy + 4y^2$

Skills Review

65. $y = -\frac{4}{5}x + \frac{17}{5}$ 67. $y = -\frac{3}{5}x + \frac{16}{5}$

Write an equation of the line passing through each pair of points. (Lesson 2-4)

65. (−2, 5) and (3, 1)

66. (7, 1) and (7, 8) $x = 7$

67. (−3, 5) and (2, 2)

Differentiated Instruction OL BL

Extension Tell students that the area of an ellipse can be found using the formula $A = \pi ab$. Have students find the approximate area of the first ellipse on page 640 by counting the number of squares on the grid inside the ellipse and multiplying by 4 since each square equals 4 square units. Next, have students find the area of the same ellipse to the nearest tenth using the formula. Discuss with students how this formula is similar to the formula for the area of a circle. Sample answer: A = about 160 square units; answer: A = 159.9 square units

CHAPTER 10 Mid-Chapter Quiz
Lessons 10-1 through 10-4

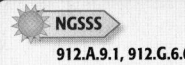

NGSSS 912.A.9.1, 912.G.6.6

Find the midpoint of the line segment with endpoints at the given coordinates. (Lesson 10-1)

1. (7, 4), (−1, −5) $\left(3, -\frac{1}{2}\right)$ **2.** (−2, −9), (−6, 0) $\left(-4, -\frac{9}{2}\right)$

Find the distance between each pair of points with the given coordinates. (Lesson 10-1)

3. (0, 6), (−2, 5) $\sqrt{5}$ units **4.** (10, 1), (0, −4) $5\sqrt{5}$ units

5. HIKING Carla and Lance left their campsite and hiked 6 miles directly north and then turned and hiked 7 miles east to view a waterfall. (Lesson 10-1) a. $\sqrt{85}$ or about 9.22 miles

a. How far is the waterfall from their campsite?

b. Let the campsite be located at the origin on a coordinate grid. At the waterfall they decide to head directly back to the campsite. If they stop halfway between the waterfall and the campsite for lunch, at what coordinate will they stop for lunch? (3.5, 3)

Write each equation in standard form. Identify the vertex, axis of symmetry, and direction of opening of the parabola. (Lesson 10-2) 6–9. See margin.

6. $y = 3x^2 - 12x + 21$ **7.** $x - 2y^2 = 4y + 6$

8. $y = \frac{1}{2}x^2 + 12x - 8$ **9.** $x = 3y^2 + 5y - 9$

10. BRIDGES Write an equation of a parabola to model the shape of the suspension cable of the bridge shown. Assume that the origin is at the lowest point of the cables. (Lesson 10-2) $y = \frac{2}{625}x^2$

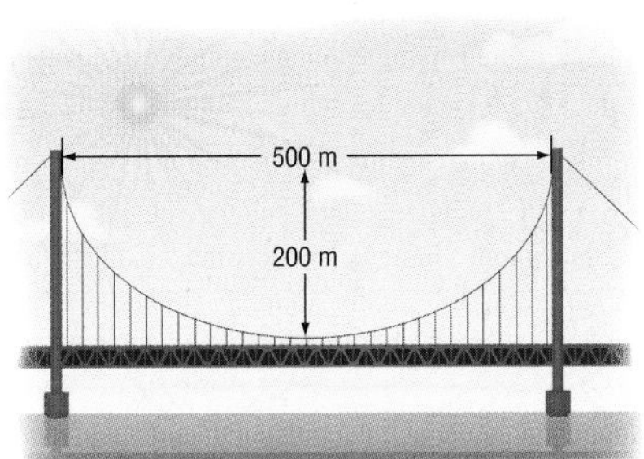

Identify the coordinates of the vertex and focus, the equation of the axis of symmetry and directrix, and the direction of opening of the parabola with the given equation. Then find the length of the latus rectum. (Lesson 10-2) 11, 12. See Chapter 10 Answer Appendix.

11. $y = x^2 + 6x + 5$

12. $x = -2y^2 + 4y + 1$

13. Find the center and radius of the circle with equation $(x - 1)^2 + y^2 = 9$. Then graph the circle. (Lesson 10-3) See Chapter 10 Answer Appendix.

14. Write an equation for a circle that has center at (3, −2) and passes through (3, 4). (Lesson 10-3) $(x - 3)^2 + (y + 2)^2 = 36$

15. Write an equation for a circle if the endpoints of a diameter are at (8, 31) and (32, 49). (Lesson 10-3) $(x - 20)^2 + (y - 40)^2 = 225$

16. NGSSS **PRACTICE** What is the radius of the circle with equation $x^2 + 2x + y^2 + 14y + 34 = 0$? (Lesson 10-3) B

A. 2 C. 8

B. 4 D. 16

Find the coordinates of the center and foci and the lengths of the major and minor axes of the ellipse with the given equation. Then graph the ellipse. (Lesson 10-4) 17–19. See Chapter 10 Answer Appendix.

17. $\frac{(x + 4)^2}{16} + \frac{(y - 2)^2}{9} = 1$

18. $\frac{(x - 1)^2}{20} + \frac{(y + 2)^2}{4} = 1$

19. $4y^2 + 9x^2 + 16y - 90x + 205 = 0$

20. NGSSS **PRACTICE** Which equation represents an ellipse with endpoints of the major axis at (−4, 10) and (−4, −6) and foci at about (−4, 7.3) and (−4, −3.3)? (Lesson 10-4) H

F. $\frac{(x - 2)^2}{36} + \frac{(y + 4)^2}{64} = 1$

G. $\frac{(x + 4)^2}{64} + \frac{(y - 2)^2}{36} = 1$

H. $\frac{(y - 2)^2}{64} + \frac{(x + 4)^2}{36} = 1$

I. $\frac{(x - 2)^2}{64} + \frac{(y + 4)^2}{36} = 1$

CHAPTER 10 Mid-Chapter Quiz

Formative Assessment

Use the Mid-Chapter Quiz to assess students' progress in the first half of the chapter.

For problems answered incorrectly, have students review the lessons indicated in parentheses.

ExamView Assessment Suite Customize and create multiple versions of your Mid-Chapter Quiz and their answer keys.

FOLDABLES® Follow-Up

Before students complete the Mid-Chapter Quiz, encourage them to review the information for Lessons 10-1 through 10-4 in their Foldables.

Additional Answers

6. $y = 3(x - 2)^2 + 9$; (2, 9); $x = 2$; opens up

7. $x = 2(y + 1)^2 + 4$; (4, −1); $y = -1$; opens to the right

8. $y = \frac{1}{2}(x + 12)^2 - 80$; (−12, −80); $x = -12$; opens up

9. $x = 3\left(y + \frac{5}{6}\right)^2 - 11\frac{1}{12}$; $\left(-\frac{133}{12}, -\frac{5}{6}\right)$; $y = -\frac{5}{6}$; opens to the right

Intervention Planner

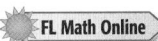

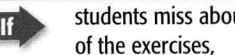

Tier 1 On Level	Tier 2 Strategic Intervention approaching grade level	Tier 3 Intensive Intervention 2 or more grades below level
If students miss about 25% of the exercises or less,	**If** students miss about 50% of the exercises,	**If** students miss about 75% of the exercises,
Then choose a resource:	**Then** choose a resource:	**Then** use *Math Triumphs, Alg. 2*
SE Lessons 10-1, 10-2, 10-3, and 10-4 **CRM** Skills Practice, pp. 7, 13, 20, 27 **TE** Chapter Project, p. 614	**CRM** Study Guide and Intervention, Chapter 10, pp. 5, 11, 18, 25	
FL Math Online Self-Check Quiz	FL Math Online Extra Examples, Personal Tutor, Homework Help	FL Math Online Extra Examples, Personal Tutor, Homework Help, Review Vocabulary

10-5 Lesson Notes

1 FOCUS

Vertical Alignment

Before Lesson 10-5
Graph and analyze equations of ellipses.

Lesson 10-5
Write equations of hyperbolas. Graph hyperbolas.

After Lesson 10-5
Identify the conic section from a given equation.

2 TEACH

Scaffolding Questions

Have students read the *Why?* section of the lesson.

Ask:

- It takes about 76 years for Halley's comet to orbit the sun, and it was last seen in 1986. Approximately when will it appear again? 2062
- How is a hyperbola unlike other conic sections? A hyperbola has two branches.
- Of the conic sections studied so far, which is the only one that could be a function? a parabola whose parent function is $y = x^2$ and has a vertical axis of symmetry.
- Could the graph of a hyperbola ever be a function? No.

10-5 Hyperbolas

Then
You graphed and analyzed equations of ellipses. (Lesson 10-4)

Now
- Write equations of hyperbolas.
- Graph hyperbolas.

NGSSS
MA.912.A.9.1 Write the equations of conic sections in standard form and general form, **in order to identify the conic section and to find its geometric properties** (foci, asymptotes, eccentricity, etc.).
MA.912.A.9.2 Graph conic sections with and without using graphing technology.

New Vocabulary
hyperbola
transverse axis
conjugate axis
foci
vertices
co-vertices
constant difference

FL Math Online
glencoe.com

Why?

Because Halley's Comet travels around the Sun in an elliptical path, it reappears in our sky. Other comets pass through our sky only once. Many of these comets travel in paths that resemble hyperbolas.

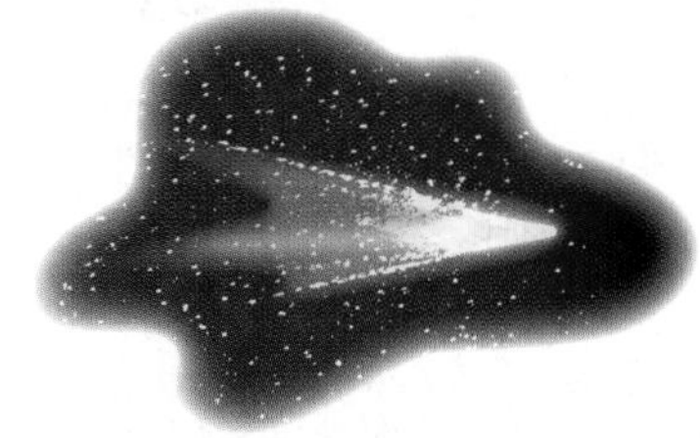

Equations of Hyperbolas

Similar to an ellipse, a **hyperbola** is the set of all points in a plane such that the absolute value of the differences of the distances from the foci is constant.

Every hyperbola has two axes of symmetry, the **transverse axis** and the **conjugate axis**. The axes are perpendicular at the center of the hyperbola.

The **foci** of a hyperbola always lie on the transverse axis. The **vertices** are the endpoints of the transverse axis. The **co-vertices** are the endpoints of the conjugate axis.

As a hyperbola recedes from the center, both halves approach asymptotes.

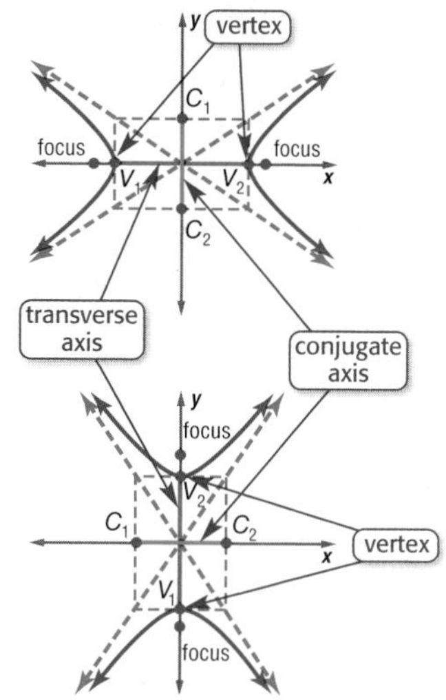

Key Concept

Equations of Hyperbolas Centered at the Origin

Standard Form	$\frac{x^2}{a^2} - \frac{y^2}{b^2} = 1$	$\frac{y^2}{a^2} - \frac{x^2}{b^2} = 1$
Orientation	horizontal	vertical
Foci	$(\pm c, 0)$	$(0, \pm c)$
Length of Transverse Axis	$2a$ units	$2a$ units
Length of Conjugate Axis	$2b$ units	$2b$ units
Equations of Asymptotes	$y = \pm\frac{b}{a}x$	$y = \pm\frac{a}{b}x$

As with ellipses, there are several important relationships among the parts of hyperbolas.

- There are two axes of symmetry.
- The values of a, b, and c are related by the equation $c^2 = a^2 + b^2$.

Lesson 10-5 Resources

Resource	Approaching-Level	On-Level	Beyond-Level	English Learners
Teacher Edition	• Differentiated Instruction, p. 649	• Differentiated Instruction, pp. 649, 655	• Differentiated Instruction, p. 655	
Chapter Resource Masters	• Study Guide and Intervention, pp. 32–33 • Skills Practice, p. 34 • Practice, p. 35 • Word Problem Practice, p. 36	• Study Guide and Intervention, pp. 32–33 • Skills Practice, p. 34 • Practice, p. 35 • Word Problem Practice, p. 36 • Enrichment, p. 37 • Graphing Calculator Activity, p. 38	• Practice, p. 35 • Word Problem Practice, p. 36 • Enrichment, p. 37	• Study Guide and Intervention, pp. 32–33 • Skills Practice, p. 34 • Practice, p. 35 • Word Problem Practice, p. 36
Transparencies	• 5-Minute Check Transparency 10-5	• 5-Minute Check Transparency 10-5	• 5-Minute Check Transparency 10-5	• 5-Minute Check Transparency 10-5
Other	• Study Notebook • Teaching Algebra with Manipulatives	• Study Notebook • Teaching Algebra with Manipulatives	• Study Notebook	• Study Notebook • Teaching Algebra with Manipulatives

EXAMPLE 1 Write an Equation Given Vertices and Foci

Write an equation for the hyperbola shown in the graph.

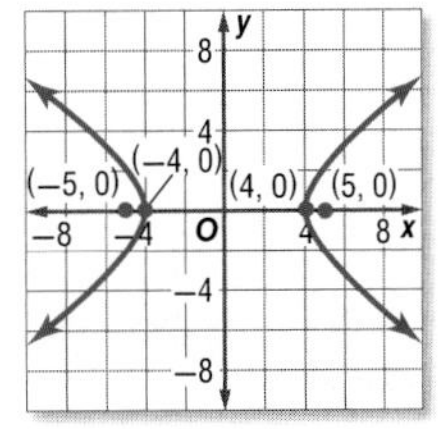

Step 1 Find the center.

The vertices are equidistant from the center.

The center is at (0, 0).

Step 2 Find the values of a, b, and c.

The value of a is the distance between a vertex and the center, or 4 units.

The value of c is the distance between a focus and the center, or 5 units.

$c^2 = a^2 + b^2$	**Equation relating *a*, *b*, and *c* for a hyperbola**
$5^2 = 4^2 + b^2$	**$c = 5$ and $a = 3$**
$9 = b^2$	**Subtract 4^2 from each side.**

Step 3 Write the equation.

The transverse axis is horizontal, so the equation is $\frac{x^2}{16} - \frac{y^2}{9} = 1$.

Guided Practice

1. Write an equation for a hyperbola with vertices at (6, 0) and (−6, 0) and foci at (8, 0) and (−8, 0). $\frac{x^2}{36} - \frac{y^2}{28} = 1$

Personal Tutor glencoe.com

ReadingMath

Standard Form In the standard form of a hyperbola, the squared terms are subtracted. For an ellipse, they are added.

Hyperbolas can also be determined using the equations of their asymptotes.

EXAMPLE 2 Write an Equation Given Asymptotes

The asymptotes for a vertical hyperbola are $y = \frac{5}{3}x$ and $y = -\frac{5}{3}x$ and the vertices are at (0, 5) and (0, −5). Write the equation for the hyperbola.

Step 1 Find the center.

The vertices are equidistant from the center.

The center of the hyperbola is at (0, 0).

Step 2 Find the values of a and b.

The hyperbola is vertical, so $a = 5$.

From the asymptotes, $b = 3$.

The value of c is not needed.

Step 3 Write the equation.

The equation for the hyperbola is $\frac{y^2}{25} - \frac{x^2}{9} = 1$.

Guided Practice

2. $\frac{x^2}{81} - \frac{y^2}{49} = 1$

2. The asymptotes for a horizontal hyperbola are $y = \frac{7}{9}x$ and $y = -\frac{7}{9}x$. The vertices are (9, 0) and (−9, 0). Write an equation for the hyperbola.

Personal Tutor glencoe.com

Equations of Hyperbolas

Example 1 shows how to write an equation for a hyperbola given the graph of the hyperbola. **Example 2** shows how to write an equation for a hyperbola given the asymptotes and vertices.

Formative Assessment

Use the Guided Practice exercises after each example to determine students' understanding of concepts.

Additional Examples

1 Write an equation for the hyperbola shown in the graph.

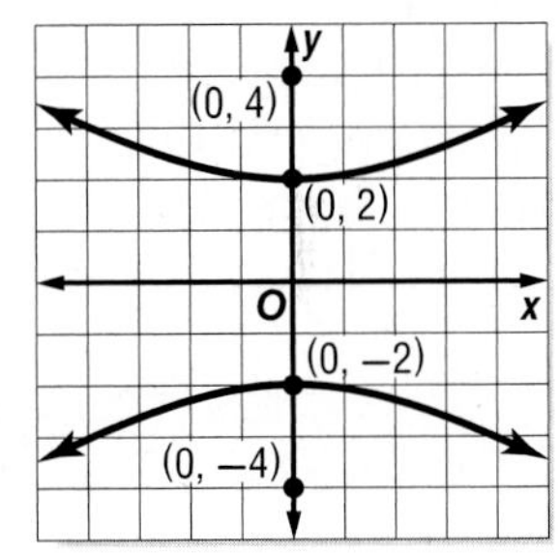

$\frac{y^2}{4} - \frac{x^2}{12} = 1$

2 The asymptotes for a vertical hyperbola are $y = 3x$ and $y = -3x$ and the vertices are at $(0, 2\sqrt{10})$ and $(0, -2\sqrt{10})$. Write the equation for the hyperbola.

$\frac{y^2}{36} - \frac{x^2}{4} = 1$

Additional Examples also in Interactive Classroom PowerPoint® Presentations

IWB INTERACTIVE WHITEBOARD READY

Differentiated Instruction

AL OL

If some students think that a hyperbola has the shape of two parabolas,

Then explain that this is not true, and encourage students to draw parabolas on transparent paper and place them over hyperbolas to see that the shapes of the curves are different.

Focus on Mathematical Content

Hyperbolas Every hyperbola has *asymptotes*, or lines which the hyperbola branches approach. Every hyperbola has two axes of symmetry. The endpoints of the *transverse axis*, length $2a$, are the vertices of the hyperbola. The *conjugate axis* of length $2b$ is perpendicular to the transverse axis and passes through the midpoint of the transverse axis (the center). The distance from the center to a focus is c. For a hyperbola, $a^2 + b^2 = c^2$.

Graphs of Hyperbolas

Example 3 shows how to use the asymptotes to graph a hyperbola from an equation in standard form. **Example 4** shows how to graph a hyperbola that models a real-world situation.

Additional Example

3 Graph $\frac{(x-3)^2}{4} - \frac{(y+5)^2}{9} = 1$. Identify the vertices, foci, and asymptotes. vertices: (5, –5), (1, –5); foci: $(3 + \sqrt{13}, -5)$, $(3 - \sqrt{13}, -5)$; asymptotes: $y + 5 = \frac{3}{2}(x - 3)$, $y + 5 = -\frac{3}{2}(x - 3)$

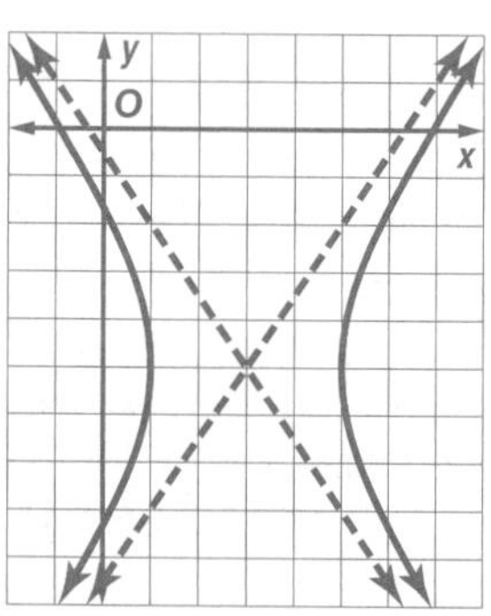

Graphs of Hyperbolas Hyperbolas can be translated in the same manner as the other conic sections.

Key Concept — Equations of Hyperbolas Centered at (*h*, *k*)

Standard Form	$\frac{(x-h)^2}{a^2} - \frac{(y-k)^2}{b^2} = 1$	$\frac{(y-k)^2}{a^2} - \frac{(x-h)^2}{b^2} = 1$
Orientation	horizontal	vertical
Foci	$(h \pm c, k)$	$(h, k \pm c)$
Vertices	$(h \pm a, k)$	$(h, k \pm a)$
Co-vertices	$(h, k \pm b)$	$(h \pm b, k)$
Equations of Asymptotes	$y - k = \pm\frac{b}{a}(x - h)$	$y - k = \pm\frac{a}{b}(x - h)$

StudyTip

Calculator You can graph a hyperbola on a graphing calculator by solving for y then graphing the two equations on the same screen.

EXAMPLE 3 Graph a Hyperbola

Graph $\frac{(x-3)^2}{4} - \frac{(y+2)^2}{16} = 1$. Identify the vertices, foci, and asymptotes.

Step 1 Find the center. The center is at (3, –2).

Step 2 Find a, b, and c. From the equation, $a^2 = 4$ and $b^2 = 16$, so $a = 2$ and $b = 4$.

$c^2 = a^2 + b^2$ — **Equation relating *a*, *b*, and *c* for a hyperbola**

$c^2 = 2^2 + 4^2$ — **$a = 2, b = 4$**

$c^2 = 20$ — **Simplify.**

$c = \sqrt{20}$ or about 4.47 — **Take the square root of each side.**

Step 3 Identify the vertices and foci. The hyperbola is horizontal and the vertices are 2 units from the center, so the vertices are at (1, –2) and (5, –2).
The foci are about 4.47 units from the center.
The foci are at (–1.47, –2) and (7.47, –2).

Step 4 Identify the asymptotes.

$y - k = \pm\frac{b}{a}(x - h)$ — **Equation for asymptotes of a horizontal hyperbola**

$y - (-2) = \pm\frac{4}{2}(x - 3)$ — **$a = 2, b = 4, h = 3$, and $k = -2$**

The equations for the asymptotes are $y = 2x - 8$ and $y = -2x + 4$.

Step 5 Graph the hyperbola. The hyperbola is symmetric about the transverse and conjugate axes. Use this symmetry to plot additional points for the hyperbola.

Use the asymptotes as a guide to draw the hyperbola that passes through the vertices and the other points.

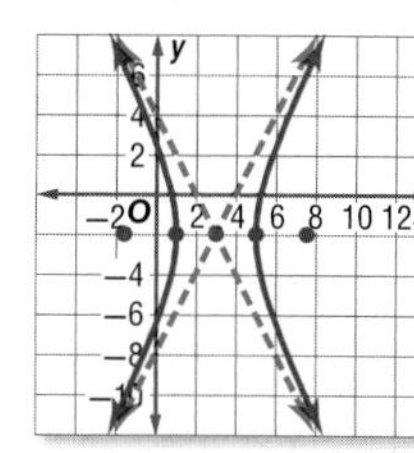

Guided Practice **3. See margin.**

3. Graph $\frac{(y-4)^2}{9} - \frac{(x+3)^2}{25} = 1$. Identify the vertices, foci, and asymptotes.

Personal Tutor glencoe.com

Additional Answer (Guided Practice)

3.

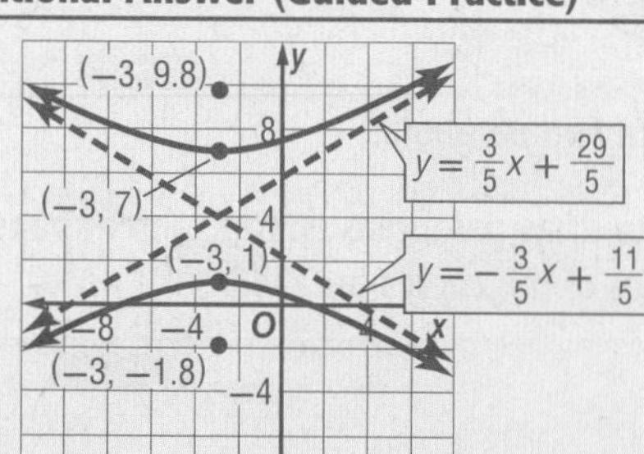

In the equation for any hyperbola, the value of $2a$ represents the **constant difference**. This is the absolute value of the difference between the distances from any point on the hyperbola to the foci of the hyperbola.

Any point on the hyperbola at the right will have the same constant difference, $|y - x|$ or $2a$.

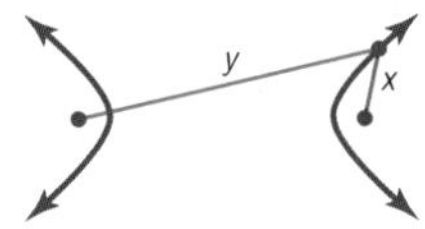

Real-World Link

Halley's Comet becomes visible to the unaided eye about every 76 years as it nears the Sun.

Source: NASA

Real-World EXAMPLE 4 Write an Equation of a Hyperbola

SPACE Earth and the Sun are 146 million kilometers apart. A comet follows a path that is one branch of a hyperbola. Suppose the comet is 30 million miles farther from the Sun than from Earth. Determine the equation of the hyperbola centered at the origin for the path of the comet.

Understand We need to determine the equation for the hyperbola.

Plan Find the center and the values of a and b. Once we have this information, we can determine the equation.

Solve The foci are Earth and the Sun, with the origin between them.

The value of c is $146 \div 2$ or 73.

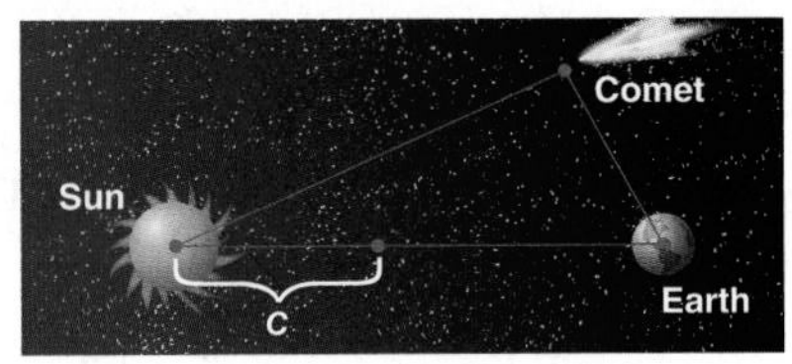

The difference of the distances from the comet to each body is 30. Therefore, a is $30 \div 2$ or 15 million miles.

$c^2 = a^2 + b^2$ **Equation relating a, b, and c for a hyperbola**

$73^2 = 15^2 + b^2$ **$a = 15$ and $c = 73$**

$5104 = b^2$ **Simplify.**

The equation of the hyperbola is $\frac{x^2}{225} - \frac{y^2}{5104} = 1$.

Since the comet is farther from the Sun, it is located on the branch of the hyperbola near Earth.

Check (21, 70) is a point that satisfies the equation.

The distance between this point and the Sun (−73, 0) is $\sqrt{[21 - (-73)]^2 + (70 - 0)^2}$ or 117.2 million kilometers.

The distance between this point and Earth (73, 0) is $\sqrt{(21 - 73)^2 + (70 - 0)^2}$ or 87.2 million kilometers.

The difference between these distances is 30. ✓

StudyTip

Exact Locations A third receiving station is necessary to determine the plane's exact location.

Guided Practice

4. SEARCH AND RESCUE Two receiving stations that are 150 miles apart receive a signal from a downed airplane. They determine that the airplane is 80 miles farther from station A than from station B. Determine the equation of the hyperbola centered at the origin on which the plane is located. $\frac{x^2}{1600} - \frac{y^2}{4025} = 1$

Personal Tutor glencoe.com

Watch Out!

Preventing Errors Tell students to make rough sketches for the situations in problems such as those in Example 4.

Additional Example

4 NAVIGATION The LORAN navigational system is based on hyperbolas. Two stations send out signals at the same time. A ship notes the difference in the times at which it receives the signals. The ship is on a hyperbola with the stations at the foci. Suppose a ship determines that the difference of its distances from two stations is 50 nautical miles. Write an equation for a hyperbola on which the ship lies if the stations are at (−50, 0) and (50, 0).

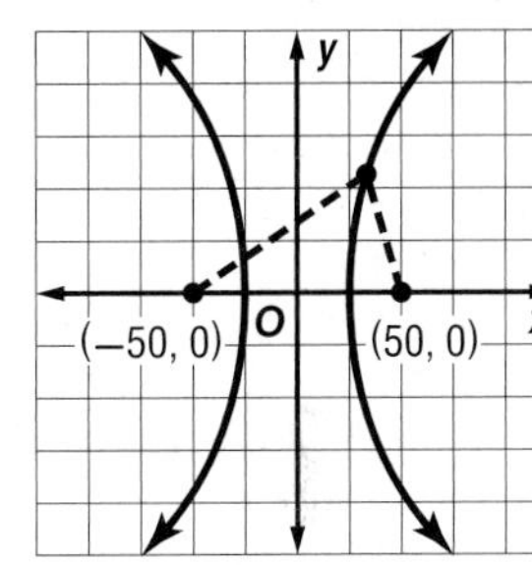

$\frac{x^2}{625} - \frac{y^2}{1875} = 1$

Watch Out!

Preventing Errors Suggest that students make lists of the values of a, b, c, h, and k. This will help avoid confusion about the signs of h and k.

TEACH with TECH

WEB PAGE Have students search the Web to find applications and real-world situations involving hyperbolas. Have students create links on their social networking Web sites for pages with specific examples they find interesting.

3 PRACTICE

Formative Assessment

Use Exercises 1–9 to check for understanding.

Use the chart at the bottom of this page to customize assignments for your students.

Additional Answers

5.

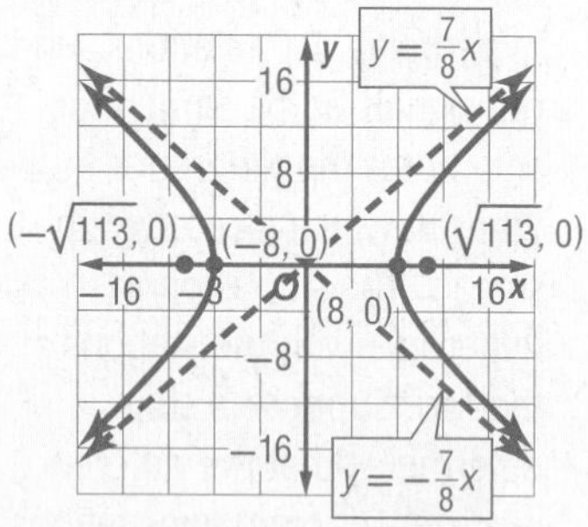

6.

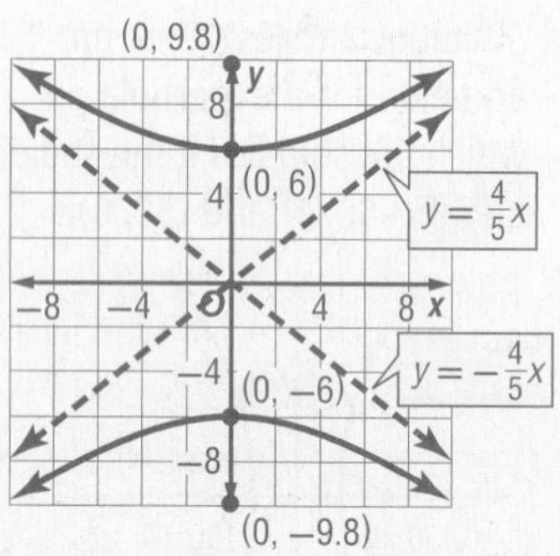

7.

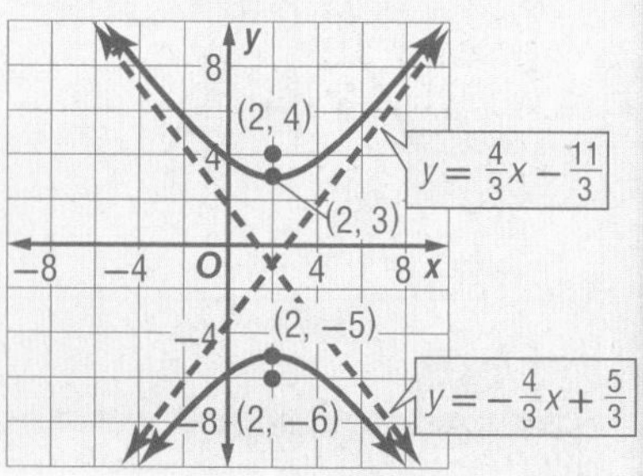

8.

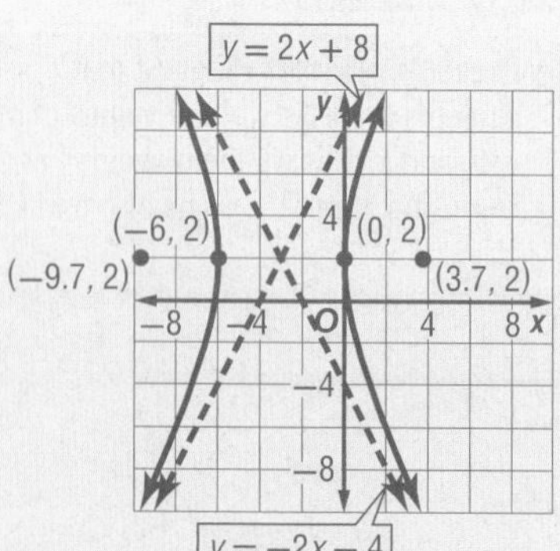

Check Your Understanding

Examples 1 and 2 p. 649

Write an equation for each hyperbola.

1.

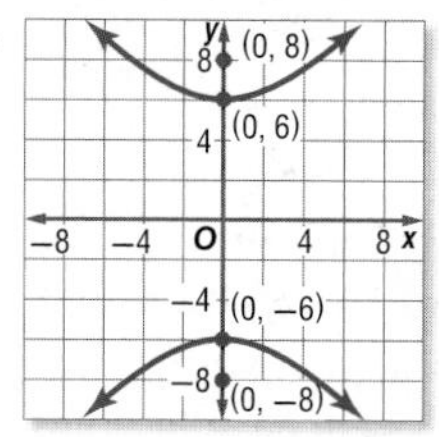

$\frac{y^2}{36} - \frac{x^2}{28} = 1$

2.

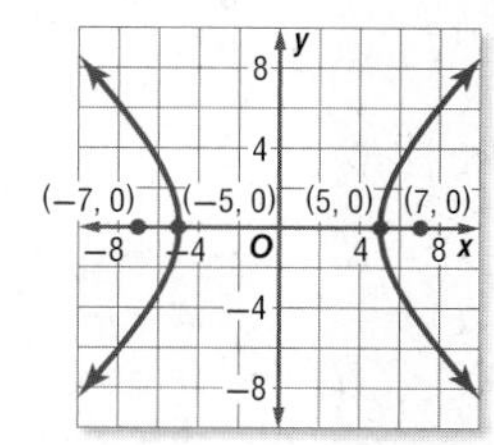

$\frac{x^2}{25} - \frac{y^2}{24} = 1$

3.

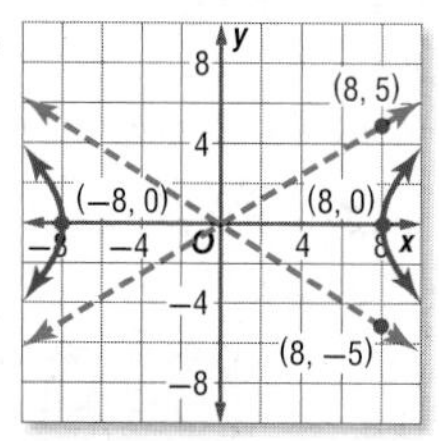

$\frac{x^2}{64} - \frac{y^2}{25} = 1$

4.

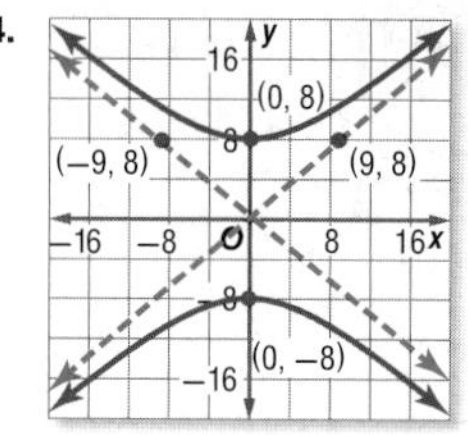

$\frac{y^2}{64} - \frac{x^2}{81} = 1$

Example 3 p. 650

Graph each hyperbola. Identify the vertices, foci, and asymptotes. **5–8. See margin.**

5. $\frac{x^2}{64} - \frac{y^2}{49} = 1$

6. $\frac{y^2}{36} - \frac{x^2}{60} = 1$

7. $9y^2 + 18y - 16x^2 + 64x - 199 = 0$

8. $4x^2 + 24x - y^2 + 4y - 4 = 0$

Example 4 p. 651

9. NAVIGATION A ship determines that the difference of its distances from two stations is 60 nautical miles. Write an equation for a hyperbola on which the ship lies if the stations are at (–80, 0) and (80, 0). $\frac{x^2}{900} - \frac{y^2}{5500} = 1$

Practice and Problem Solving

● = **Step-by-Step Solutions** begin on page R20. **Extra Practice** begins on page 947.

Examples 1 and 2 p. 649

Write an equation for each hyperbola.

10. $\frac{(x-3)^2}{25} - \frac{(y+6)^2}{11} = 1$

11. $\frac{(y-4)^2}{16} - \frac{(x+8)^2}{48} = 1$

10.

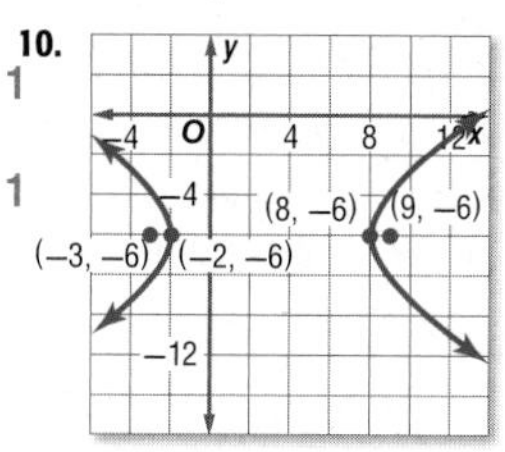

11

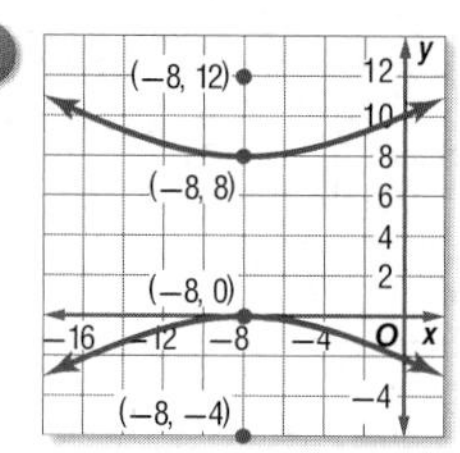

12. $\frac{(y+5)^2}{16} - \frac{(x+4)^2}{36} = 1$

13. $\frac{(x+1)^2}{9} - \frac{(y-6)^2}{49} = 1$

12.

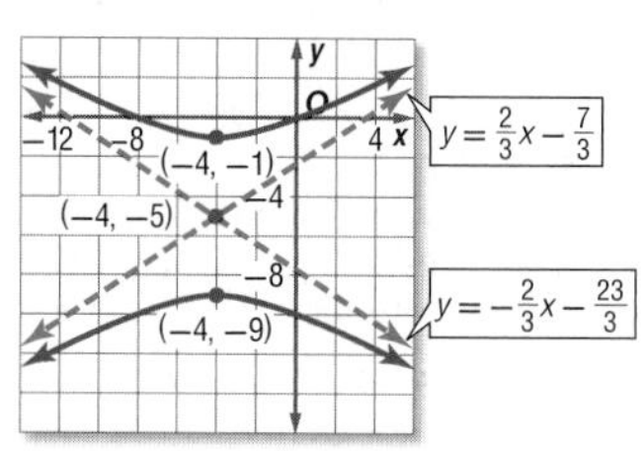

13.

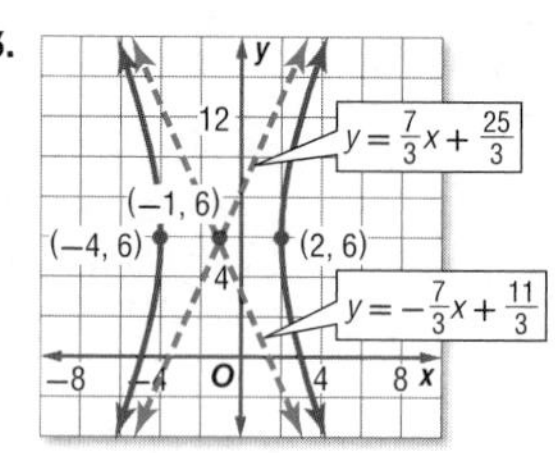

Differentiated Homework Options

Level	Assignment	Two-Day Option	
AL Basic	10–24, 44, 46–67	11–23 odd, 50–53	10–24 even, 44, 46–49, 54–67
OL Core	11–31 odd, 32–44, 46–67	10–24, 50–53	25–44, 46–49, 54–67
BL Advanced	25–65, (optional: 66, 67)		

652 Chapter 10 Conic Sections

Example 3 p. 650

Graph each hyperbola. Identify the vertices, foci, and asymptotes. **14–23. See Chapter 10 Answer Appendix.**

14. $\frac{x^2}{36} - \frac{y^2}{4} = 1$

15. $\frac{y^2}{9} - \frac{x^2}{49} = 1$

16. $\frac{y^2}{36} - \frac{x^2}{25} = 1$

17. $\frac{x^2}{16} - \frac{y^2}{16} = 1$

18. $\frac{(x-3)^2}{16} - \frac{(y+1)^2}{4} = 1$

19. $\frac{(y+5)^2}{16} - \frac{(x+2)^2}{36} = 1$

20. $9y^2 - 4x^2 - 54y + 32x - 19 = 0$

21. $16x^2 - 9y^2 + 128x + 36y + 76 = 0$

22. $25x^2 - 4y^2 - 100x + 48y - 144 = 0$

23. $81y^2 - 16x^2 - 810y + 96x + 585 = 0$

Example 4 p. 651

24. **NAVIGATION** A ship determines that the difference of its distances from two stations is 80 nautical miles. Write an equation for a hyperbola on which the ship lies if the stations are at (−100, 0) and (100, 0). $\frac{x^2}{1600} - \frac{y^2}{8400} = 1$

B Determine whether the following equations represent ellipses or hyperbolas.

25. $4x^2 = 5y^2 + 6$ **hyperbola**

26. $8x^2 - 2x = 8y - 3y^2$ **ellipse**

27. $-5x^2 + 4x = 6y + 3y^2$ **ellipse**

28. $7y - 2x^2 = 6x - 2y^2$ **hyperbola**

29. $6x - 7x^2 - 5y^2 = 2y$ **ellipse**

30. $4x + 6y + 2x^2 = -3y^2$ **ellipse**

33d. They are perpendicular.
33e. For $xy = 25$, the vertices will be at (5, 5) and (−5, −5), and for $xy = 36$, they will be at (−6, −6) and (6, 6).

31. **SPACE** Refer to the application at the beginning of the lesson. With the Sun as a focus and the center at the origin, a certain comet's path follows a branch of a hyperbola. If two of the coordinates of the path are (10, 0) and (30, 100) where the units are in millions of miles, determine the equation of the path. $\frac{x^2}{100} - \frac{y^2}{1250} = 1$

32. **COOLING** Natural draft cooling towers are shaped like hyperbolas for more efficient cooling of power plants. The hyperbola in the tower at the right can be modeled by $\frac{x^2}{16} - \frac{y^2}{225} = 1$, where the units are in meters. Find the width of the tower at the top and at its narrowest point in the middle. **8 m in the middle and 40.8 m at the top**

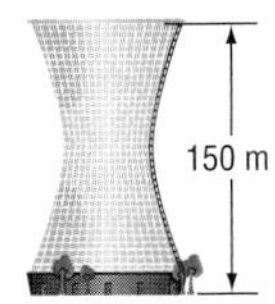

33. **MULTIPLE REPRESENTATIONS** Consider $xy = 16$. **a–c. See Chapter 10 Answer Appendix.**

a. **TABULAR** Make a table of values for the equation for $-12 \le x \le 12$.

b. **GRAPHICAL** Graph the hyperbola represented by the equation.

c. **LOGICAL** Determine and graph the asymptotes for the hyperbola.

d. **ANALYTICAL** What special property do you notice about the asymptotes? Hyperbolas that represent this property are called *rectangular hyperbolas*.

e. **ANALYTICAL** Without any calculations, what do you think will be the coordinates of the vertices for $xy = 25$? for $xy = 36$?

Real-World Link

Lightning strikes somewhere on the surface of Earth about 100 times every second.

Source: *National Geographic*

34. **SEARCH AND RESCUE** Two receiving stations that are 250 miles apart receive a signal from a downed airplane. They determine that the airplane is 70 miles farther from station *B* than from station *A*. Determine the equation of the horizontal hyperbola centered at the origin on which the plane is located. $\frac{x^2}{1225} - \frac{y^2}{14400} = 1$

35. **WEATHER** Luisa and Karl live exactly 4000 feet apart. While on the phone at their homes, Luisa hears thunder out of her window and Karl hears it 3 seconds later out of his. If sound travels 1100 feet per second, determine the equation for the horizontal hyperbola on which the lightning is located. $\frac{x^2}{2{,}722{,}500} - \frac{y^2}{1{,}277{,}500} = 1$

Multiple Representations

In Exercise 33, students use a table of values, a graph, and logical analysis to classify hyperbolas and predict their properties.

Enrichment

CRM p. 37 OL BL

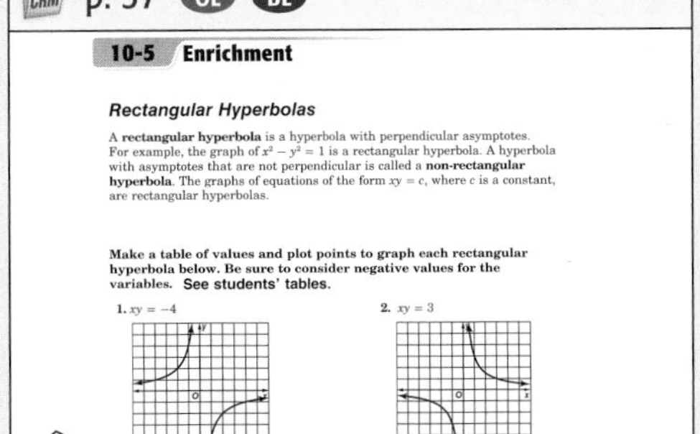

10-5 Enrichment

Rectangular Hyperbolas

A **rectangular hyperbola** is a hyperbola with perpendicular asymptotes. For example, the graph of $x^2 - y^2 = 1$ is a rectangular hyperbola. A hyperbola with asymptotes that are not perpendicular is called a **non-rectangular hyperbola**. The graphs of equations of the form $xy = c$, where c is a constant, are rectangular hyperbolas.

Make a table of values and plot points to graph each rectangular hyperbola below. Be sure to consider negative values for the variables. See students' tables.

1. $xy = -4$

2. $xy = 3$

Study Guide and Intervention

CRM pp. 32–33 AL OL ELL

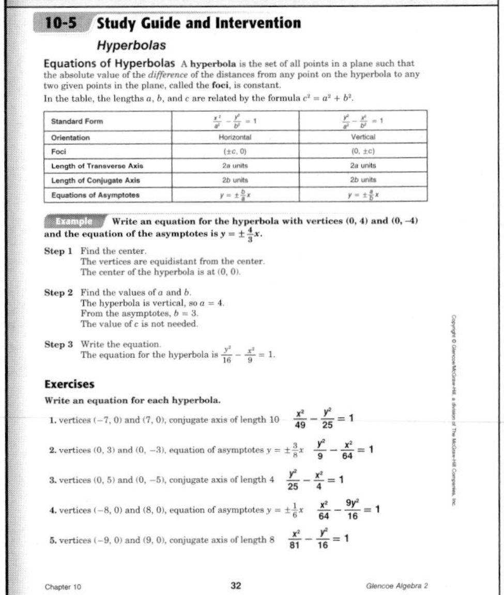

10-5 Study Guide and Intervention

Hyperbolas

Equations of Hyperbolas A **hyperbola** is the set of all points in a plane such that the absolute value of the *difference* of the distances from any point on the hyperbola to two given points in the plane, called the **foci**, is constant.

In the table, the lengths a, b, and c are related by the formula $c^2 = a^2 + b^2$.

Standard Form	$\frac{x^2}{a^2} - \frac{y^2}{b^2} = 1$	$\frac{y^2}{a^2} - \frac{x^2}{b^2} = 1$
Orientation	Horizontal	Vertical
Foci	$(\pm c, 0)$	$(0, \pm c)$
Length of Transverse Axis	2a units	2a units
Length of Conjugate Axis	2b units	2b units
Equations of Asymptotes	$y = \pm\frac{b}{a}x$	$y = \pm\frac{a}{b}x$

Example Write an equation for the hyperbola with vertices (0, 4) and (0, −4) and the equation of the asymptotes is $y = \pm\frac{4}{3}x$.

Step 1 Find the center. The vertices are equidistant from the center. The center of the hyperbola is at (0, 0).

Step 2 Find the values of a and b. The hyperbola is vertical, so $a = 4$. From the asymptotes, $b = 3$. The value of c is not needed.

Step 3 Write the equation. The equation for the hyperbola is $\frac{y^2}{16} - \frac{x^2}{9} = 1$.

Exercises

Write an equation for each hyperbola.

1. vertices (−7, 0) and (7, 0), conjugate axis of length 10 $\frac{x^2}{49} - \frac{y^2}{25} = 1$

2. vertices (0, 3) and (0, −3), equation of asymptotes $y = \pm\frac{3}{8}x$ $\frac{y^2}{9} - \frac{x^2}{64} = 1$

3. vertices (0, 5) and (0, −5), conjugate axis of length 4 $\frac{y^2}{25} - \frac{x^2}{4} = 1$

4. vertices (−8, 0) and (8, 0), equation of asymptotes $y = \pm\frac{1}{6}x$ $\frac{x^2}{64} - \frac{9y^2}{16} = 1$

5. vertices (−9, 0) and (9, 0), conjugate axis of length 8 $\frac{x^2}{81} - \frac{y^2}{16} = 1$

Chapter 10 32 Glencoe Algebra 2

Practice

CRM p. 35 AL OL BL ELL

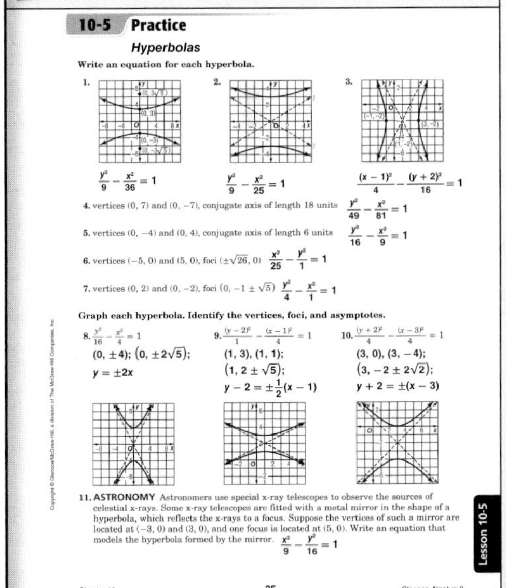

10-5 Practice

Hyperbolas

Write an equation for each hyperbola.

1. $\frac{y^2}{9} - \frac{x^2}{36} = 1$

2. $\frac{y^2}{9} - \frac{x^2}{25} = 1$

3. $\frac{(x-1)^2}{4} - \frac{(y+2)^2}{16} = 1$

4. vertices (0, 7) and (0, −7), conjugate axis of length 18 units $\frac{y^2}{49} - \frac{x^2}{81} = 1$

5. vertices (0, −4) and (0, 4), conjugate axis of length 6 units $\frac{y^2}{16} - \frac{x^2}{9} = 1$

6. vertices (−5, 0) and (5, 0), foci $(\pm\sqrt{26}, 0)$ $\frac{x^2}{25} - \frac{y^2}{1} = 1$

7. vertices (0, 2) and (0, −2), foci $(0, -1 \pm \sqrt{5})$ $\frac{y^2}{4} - \frac{x^2}{1} = 1$

Graph each hyperbola. Identify the vertices, foci, and asymptotes.

8. $\frac{y^2}{16} - \frac{x^2}{4} = 1$ $(0, \pm 4)$; $(0, \pm 2\sqrt{5})$; $y = \pm 2x$

9. $\frac{(y-2)^2}{1} - \frac{(x-1)^2}{4} = 1$ (1, 3), (1, 1); $(1, 2 \pm \sqrt{5})$; $y - 2 = \pm\frac{1}{2}(x - 1)$

10. $\frac{(y+2)^2}{4} - \frac{(x-3)^2}{4} = 1$ (3, 0), (3, −4); $(3, -2 \pm 2\sqrt{2})$; $y + 2 = \pm(x - 3)$

11. **ASTRONOMY** Astronomers use special x-ray telescopes to observe the sources of celestial x-rays. Some x-ray telescopes are fitted with a metal mirror in the shape of a hyperbola, which reflects the x-rays to a focus. Suppose the vertices of such a mirror are located at (−3, 0) and (3, 0), and one focus is located at (5, 0). Write an equation that models the hyperbola formed by the mirror. $\frac{x^2}{9} - \frac{y^2}{16} = 1$

Chapter 10 35 Glencoe Algebra 2

Lesson 10-5

Word Problem Practice

CRM p. 36 AL OL BL ELL

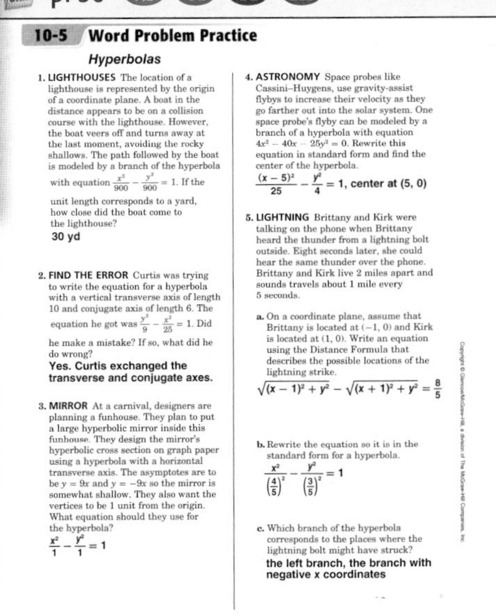

10-5 Word Problem Practice

Hyperbolas

1. **LIGHTHOUSES** The location of a lighthouse is represented by the origin of a coordinate plane. A boat in the distance appears to be on a collision course with the lighthouse. However, the boat veers off and turns away at the last moment, avoiding the rocky shallows. The path followed by the boat is modeled by a branch of the hyperbola with equation $\frac{x^2}{900} - \frac{y^2}{900} = 1$. If the unit length corresponds to a yard, how close did the boat come to the lighthouse? **30 yd**

2. **FIND THE ERROR** Curtis was trying to write the equation for a hyperbola with a vertical transverse axis of length 10 and conjugate axis of length 6. The equation he got was $\frac{y^2}{9} - \frac{x^2}{25} = 1$. Did he make a mistake? If so, what did he do wrong? **Yes. Curtis exchanged the transverse and conjugate axes.**

3. **MIRROR** At a carnival, designers are planning a funhouse. They plan to put a large hyperbolic mirror inside this funhouse. They design the mirror's hyperbolic cross section on graph paper using a hyperbola with a horizontal transverse axis. The asymptotes are to be $y = 9x$ and $y = -9x$ so the mirror is somewhat shallow. They also want the vertices to be 1 unit from the origin. What equation should they use for the hyperbola? $\frac{x^2}{1} - \frac{y^2}{1} = 1$

4. **ASTRONOMY** Space probes like Cassini–Huygens, use gravity-assist flybys to increase their velocity as they go farther out into the solar system. One space probe's flyby can be modeled by a branch of a hyperbola with equation $4x^2 - 40x - 25y^2 = 0$. Rewrite this equation in standard form and find the center of the hyperbola. $\frac{(x-5)^2}{25} - \frac{y^2}{4} = 1$, **center at (5, 0)**

5. **LIGHTNING** Brittany and Kirk were talking on the phone when Brittany heard the thunder from a lightning bolt outside. Eight seconds later, she could hear the same thunder over the phone. Brittany and Kirk live 2 miles apart and sounds travels about 1 mile every 5 seconds.

a. On a coordinate plane, assume that Brittany is located at (−1, 0) and Kirk is located at (1, 0). Write an equation using the Distance Formula that describes the possible locations of the lightning strike. $\sqrt{(x-1)^2 + y^2} - \sqrt{(x+1)^2 + y^2} = \frac{8}{5}$

b. Rewrite the equation so it is in the standard form for a hyperbola. $\frac{x^2}{\left(\frac{4}{5}\right)^2} - \frac{y^2}{\left(\frac{3}{5}\right)^2} = 1$

c. Which branch of the hyperbola corresponds to the places where the lightning bolt might have struck? **the left branch, the branch with negative x coordinates**

Chapter 10 36 Glencoe Algebra 2

Watch Out!

Error Analysis For Exercise 44, remind students that they must use the standard form of the equation to determine the orientation of the hyperbola.

Additional Answers

44. Sample answer: Simon; The equation indicates a hyperbola that opens up and down. Gabriel drew a horizontal hyperbola.

46. Sample answer: The foci move farther away from the vertices. When a is only slightly smaller than b, the value of c is only fairly larger than a. However, as b becomes much larger than a, by way of $c^2 = a^2 + b^2$, c becomes much larger than a. When this happens, the distance between the foci c becomes much greater than the distance between the vertices a. Therefore, the foci are much farther away from the vertices.

49. Sample answer: The graphs of ellipses are closed in while the branches of the hyperbolas extend without bound. There is always an upper and lower limit to the values of the coordinates of an ellipse, while maximum x- and y-values for the coordinates of hyperbolas are infinite. When both of the x^2 and y^2 terms are on the same side of the equation, the equation is for an ellipse if the signs of their coefficients are the same. Otherwise it is a hyperbola. (This is true only for conics that are not rotated.)

56. (3, 0), 4 units

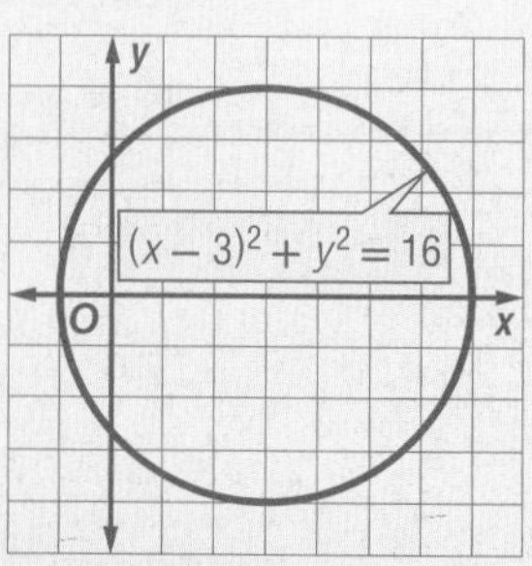

57. (0, 3), 5 units

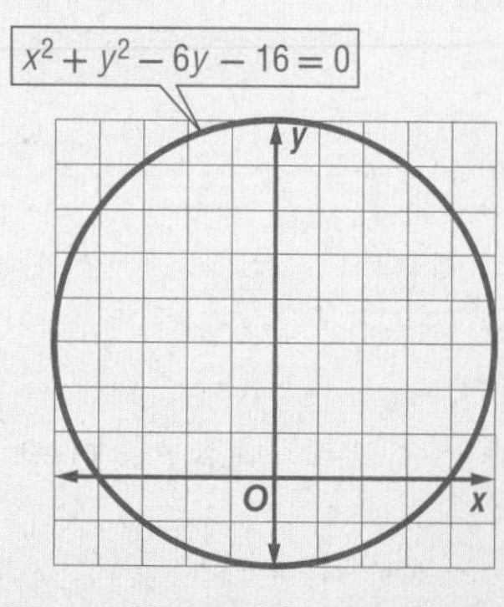

58. $\left(-\frac{9}{2}, 4\right), \frac{\sqrt{129}}{2}$ units

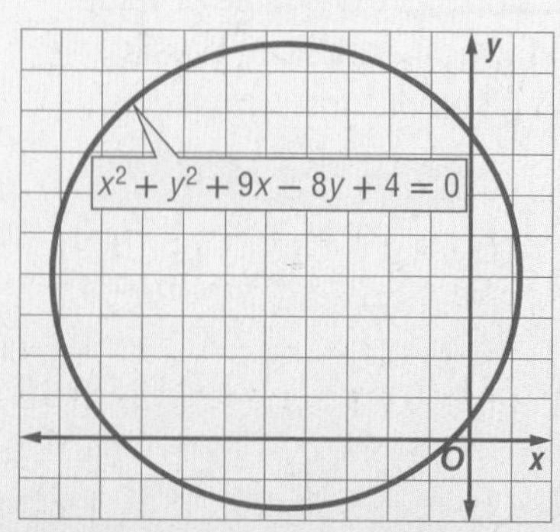

Math History Link

Hypatia (415–370 B.C.) Hypatia was a mathematician, scientist, and philosopher in Alexandria, Egypt. She is considered the first woman to write on mathematical topics. Hypatia edited the book *On the Conics of Apollonius*, adding her own problems and examples to clarify the topic for her students. This book developed the ideas of hyperbolas, parabolas, and ellipses.

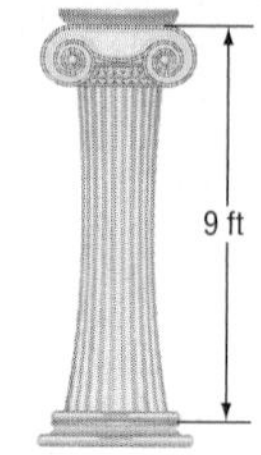

36. ARCHITECTURE Large pillars with cross sections in the shape of hyperbolas were popular in ancient Greece. The curves can be modeled by the equation $\frac{x^2}{0.16} - \frac{y^2}{4} = 1$, where the units are in feet. If the pillars are 9 feet tall, find the width of the top of each pillar and the width of each pillar at the narrowest point in the middle. Round to the nearest hundredth of a foot. **≈1.96 ft, 0.8 ft**

Write an equation for the hyperbola that satisfies each set of conditions.

37. vertices (−8, 0) and (8, 0), conjugate axis of length 20 units $\frac{x^2}{64} - \frac{y^2}{100} = 1$

38. vertices (0, −6) and (0, 6), conjugate axis of length 24 units

39. vertices (6, −2) and (−2, −2), foci (10, −2) and (−6, −2) $\frac{(x-2)^2}{16} - \frac{(y+2)^2}{48} = 1$

40. vertices (−3, 4) and (−3, −8), foci (−3, 9) and (−3, −13)

41. centered at the origin with a horizontal transverse axis of length 10 units and a conjugate axis of length 4 units $\frac{x^2}{25} - \frac{y^2}{4} = 1$

42. centered at the origin with a vertical transverse axis of length 16 units and a conjugate axis of length 12 units $\frac{y^2}{64} - \frac{x^2}{36} = 1$

43. TRIANGULATION While looking for their lost dog in the woods, Lae, Meg, and Cesar hear a bark. Meg hears it 2 seconds after Lae and Cesar hears it 3 seconds after Lae. With Lae at the origin, determine the exact location of their dog if sound travels 1100 feet per second. **(2308, 826)**

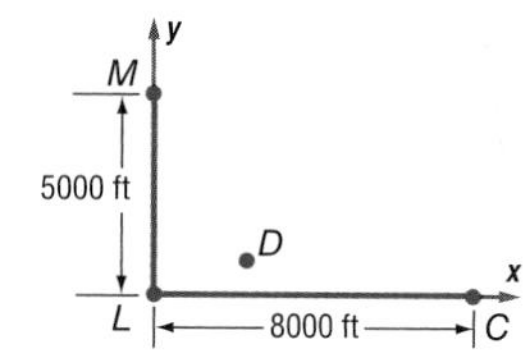

38. $\frac{y^2}{36} - \frac{x^2}{144} = 1$
40. $\frac{(y+2)^2}{36} - \frac{(x+3)^2}{85} = 1$
45. $\frac{(x-3)^2}{5} - \frac{(y+2)^2}{5} = 1$

46. See margin.
47. Sample answer: When 36 changes to 9, the vertical hyperbola widens (splits out from the y-axis faster). This is due to a smaller value of y being needed to produce the same value of x. The vertices are moved closer together due to the value of a decreasing from 6 to 3. The foci move farther from the vertices because the difference between c and a increased.
48. Sample answer: $\frac{(x-5)^2}{9} - \frac{y^2}{16} = 1$

H.O.T. Problems

Use Higher-Order Thinking Skills

44. ERROR ANALYSIS Simon and Gabriel are graphing $\frac{y^2}{25} - \frac{x^2}{4} = 1$. Is either of them correct? Explain your reasoning. **See margin.**

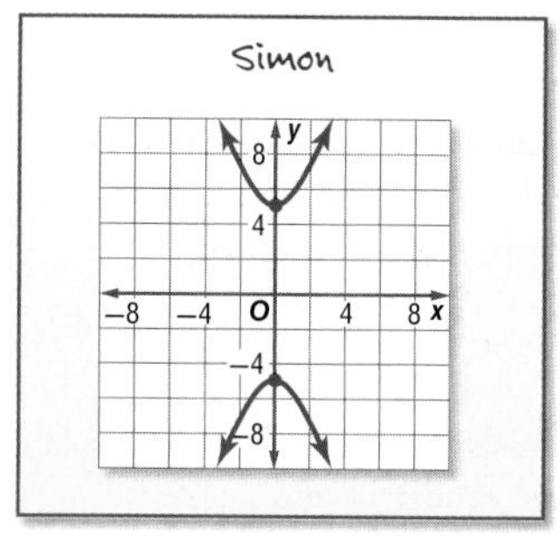

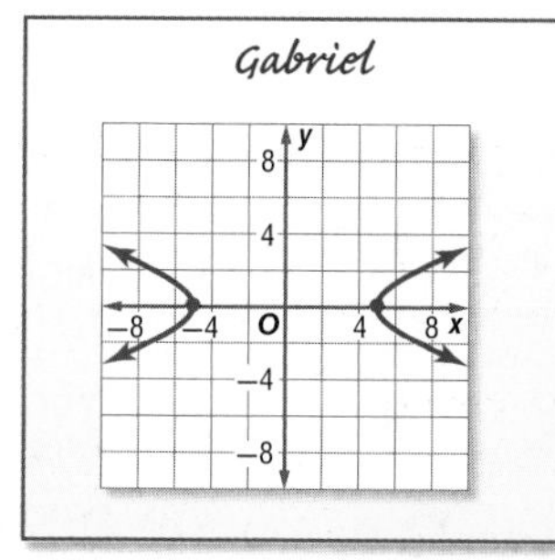

45. CHALLENGE The origin lies on a horizontal hyperbola. The asymptotes for the hyperbola are $y = -x + 1$ and $y = x - 5$. Find the equation for the hyperbola.

46. REASONING What happens to the location of the foci of a hyperbola as the value of a becomes increasingly smaller than the value of b? Explain your reasoning.

47. REASONING Consider $\frac{y^2}{36} - \frac{x^2}{16} = 1$. Describe the change in the shape of the hyperbola and the locations of the vertices and foci if 36 is changed to 9. Explain why this happens.

48. OPEN ENDED Write an equation for a hyperbola with a focus at the origin.

49. WRITING IN MATH Compare and contrast the characteristics of the equations and graphs of ellipses and hyperbolas. **See margin.**

NGSSS PRACTICE 912.A.3.1, 912.A.3.15, 912.A.9.2

50. You have 6 more dimes than quarters. You have a total of $5.15. How many dimes do you have? C

A. 13 C. 19
B. 16 D. 25

51. How tall is a tree that is 15 feet shorter than a pole three times as tall as the tree? I

F. 24.5 ft
G. 22.5 ft
H. 21.5 ft
I. 7.5 ft

52. **SHORT RESPONSE** A rectangle is 8 feet long and 6 feet wide. If each dimension is increased by the same number of feet, the area of the new rectangle formed is 32 square feet more than the area of the original rectangle. By how many feet was each dimension increased? 2

53. **ACT/SAT** When the equation $y = 4x^2 - 5$ is graphed in the coordinate plane, the graph is which of the following? D

A. circle C. hyperbola
B. ellipse D. parabola

Spiral Review

Write an equation for an ellipse that satisfies each set of conditions. (Lesson 10-4)

54. endpoints of major axis at (2, 2) and (2, −10), endpoints of minor axis at (0, −4) and (4, −4) $\frac{(y+4)^2}{36} + \frac{(x-2)^2}{4} = 1$

55. endpoints of major axis at (0, 10) and (0, −10), foci at (0, 8) and (0, −8) $\frac{y^2}{100} + \frac{x^2}{36} = 1$

Find the center and radius of the circle with the given equation. Then graph the circle. (Lesson 10-3) 56–58. See margin.

56. $(x-3)^2 + y^2 = 16$

57. $x^2 + y^2 - 6y - 16 = 0$

58. $x^2 + y^2 + 9x - 8y + 4 = 0$

59. **BASKETBALL** Zonta plays basketball for Centerville High School. So far this season, she has made 6 out of 10 free-throws. She is determined to improve her free-throw percentage. If she can make x consecutive free throws, her free-throw percentage can be determined using $P(x) = \frac{6+x}{10+x}$. (Lesson 9-4)

a. Graph the function. See margin.

b. What part of the graph is meaningful in the context of the problem? the part in the first quadrant

c. Describe the meaning of the y-intercept. It represents her original free-throw percentage of 60%.

d. What is the equation of the horizontal asymptote? Explain its meaning with respect to Zonta's shooting percentage. $P(x) = 1$; this represents 100%, which she cannot achieve because she has already missed 4 free throws.

Solve each equation. (Lesson 8-2)

60. $\left(\frac{1}{7}\right)^{y-3} = 343$ 0

61. $10^{x-1} = 100^{2x-3}$ $\frac{5}{3}$

62. $36^{2p} = 216^{p-1}$ −3

Graph each inequality. (Lesson 7-3) 63–65. See margin.

63. $y \geq \sqrt{5x-8}$

64. $y \geq \sqrt{x-3} + 4$

65. $y < \sqrt{6x-2} + 1$

Skills Review

66. Write an equation for a parabola with vertex at the origin that passes through (2, −8). (Lesson 5-7) $y = -2x^2$

67. Write an equation for a parabola with vertex at (−3, −4) that opens up and has y-intercept 8. (Lesson 5-7) $y = \frac{4}{3}(x+3)^2 - 4$

Differentiated Instruction OL BL

Extension

- Use a compass to draw a circle on a piece of paper. Be sure not to take up the entire page.
- Use the sharp end of your compass to poke a small hole anywhere outside of your circle. Label the point where the hole is F.
- Fold the paper so that point F lands somewhere on the circumference of the circle.
- Repeat the last step using point F and several other points on the circumference of the circle. Predict what kind of curve these creases are forming. The fixed point F is the focus of a hyperbola.
- Discuss with students how the shape of the curve would change if they varied the location of point F. As point F moves farther from the center of the circle, the branches of the hyperbola become wider.

4 ASSESS

Name the Math Prepare two bags: one containing an ordered pair for the center of a hyperbola on each paper, the other with values for a and b on each paper. Have each student select both an ordered pair and values for a and b. Have students write the equations for the hyperbolas and tell as much about them as possible given the values they chose.

Additional Answers

59a.

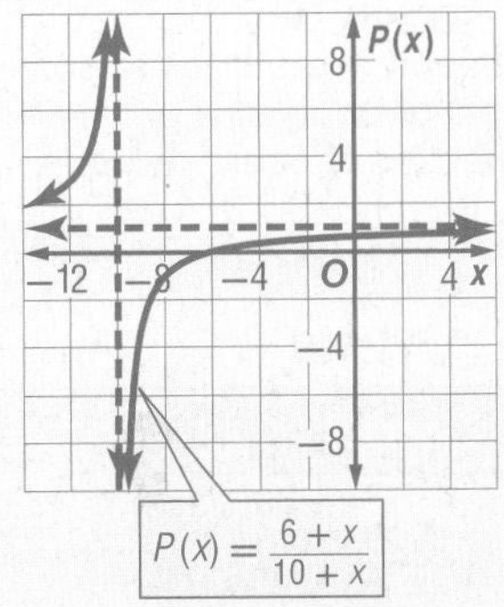

63.

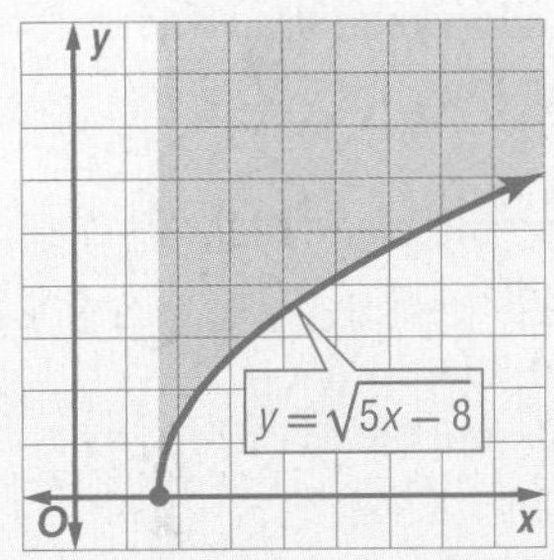

64.

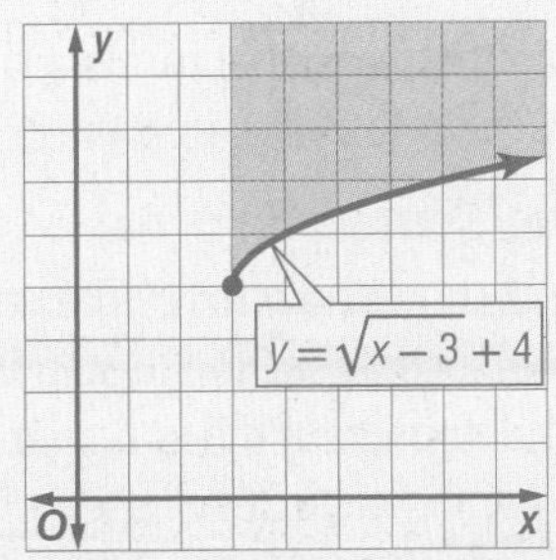

65.

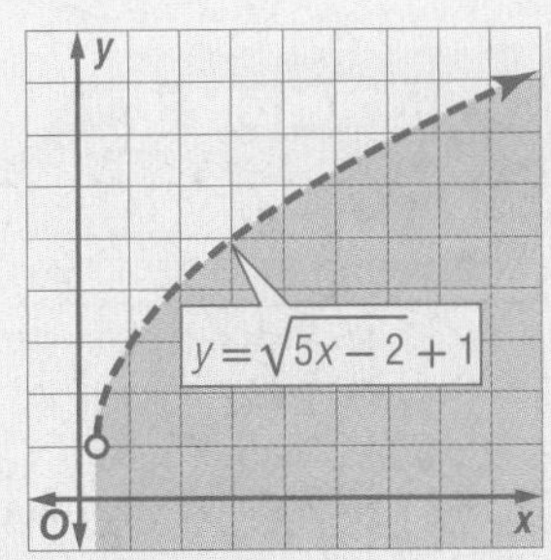

10-6 Identifying Conic Sections

1 FOCUS

Vertical Alignment

Before Lesson 10-6
Analyze different conic sections.

Lesson 10-6
Write equations of conic sections in standard form.
Identify conic sections from their equations.

After Lesson 10-6
Use algebraic methods to solve systems of equations or inequalities of conic sections.

2 TEACH

Scaffolding Questions

Have students read the *Why?* section of the lesson.

Ask:

- Describe the plane that forms a hyperbola. perpendicular to the base of the double cone
- Describe the plane that forms a parabola. parallel to the slant height of a cone
- Describe the plane that forms a circle. parallel to the base of a cone

Conics in Standard Form

Example 1 shows how to rewrite an equation of a conic section in standard form and determine if the equation is that of a parabola, circle, ellipse, or hyperbola.

Then
You analyzed different conic sections. (Lessons 10-2 through 10-5)

Now
- Write equations of conic sections in standard form.
- Identify conic sections from their equations.

NGSSS
MA.912.A.9.1 Write the equations of conic sections in standard form and general form, in order to identify the conic section and to find its geometric properties (foci, asymptotes, eccentricity, etc.).
MA.912.A.9.2 Graph conic sections with and without using graphing technology.

FL Math Online
glencoe.com

Why?

Parabolas, circles, ellipses, and hyperbolas are called conic sections because they are the cross sections formed when a double cone is sliced by a plane.

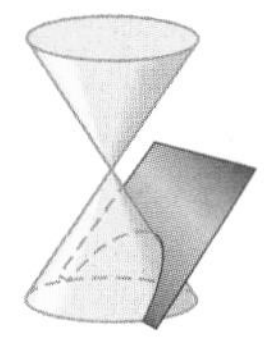
Parabola

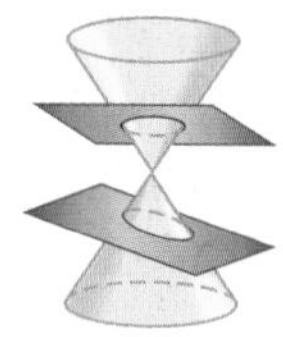
Circle and Ellipse

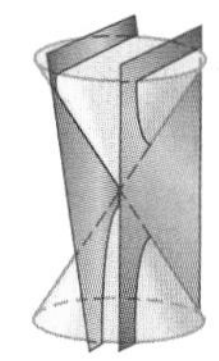
Hyperbola

Conics in Standard Form The equation for any conic section can be written in the form $Ax^2 + Bxy + Cy^2 + Dx + Ey + F = 0$, where A, B, and C are not all zero. This general form can be converted to the standard forms below by completing the square.

Concept Summary — Standard Forms of Conic Sections

Conic Section	Standard Form of Equation	
Circle	$(x-h)^2 + (y-k)^2 = r^2$	
	Horizontal Axis	Vertical Axis
Parabola	$y = a(x-h)^2 + k$	$x = a(y-k)^2 + h$
Ellipse	$\frac{(x-h)^2}{a^2} + \frac{(y-k)^2}{b^2} = 1$	$\frac{(y-k)^2}{a^2} + \frac{(x-h)^2}{b^2} = 1$
Hyperbola	$\frac{(x-h)^2}{a^2} - \frac{(y-k)^2}{b^2} = 1$	$\frac{(y-k)^2}{a^2} - \frac{(x-h)^2}{b^2} = 1$

EXAMPLE 1 Rewrite an Equation of a Conic Section

Write $16x^2 - 25y^2 - 128x - 144 = 0$ in standard form. State whether the graph of the equation is a *parabola, circle, ellipse,* or *hyperbola*. Then graph the equation.

$16x^2 - 25y^2 - 128x - 144 = 0$	**Original equation**
$16(x^2 - 8x + ■) - 25y^2 = 144 + 16(■)$	**Isolate terms.**
$16(x^2 - 8x + 16) - 25y^2 = 144 + 16(16)$	**Complete the square.**
$16(x-4)^2 - 25y^2 = 400$	**Perfect square**
$\frac{(x-4)^2}{25} - \frac{y^2}{16} = 1$	**Divide each side by 400.**

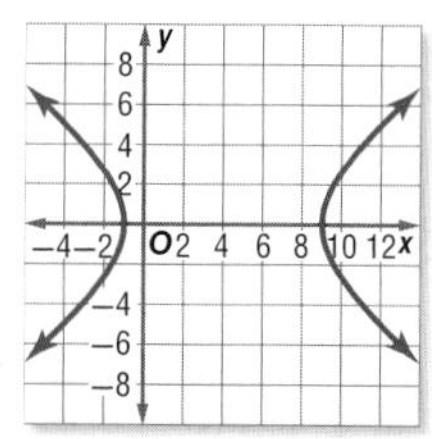

The graph is a hyperbola with its center at (4, 0).

Guided Practice 1. See Chapter 10 Answer Appendix.

1. Write $4x^2 + y^2 - 16x + 8y - 4 = 0$ in standard form. State whether the graph of the equation is a *parabola, circle, ellipse,* or *hyperbola*. Then graph the equation.

Personal Tutor glencoe.com

Lesson 10-6 Resources

Resource	Approaching-Level	On-Level	Beyond-Level	English Learners
Teacher Edition	• Differentiated Instruction, p. 657	• Differentiated Instruction, p. 657, 660	• Differentiated Instruction, p. 660	
Chapter Resource Masters	• Study Guide and Intervention, pp. 39–40 • Skills Practice, p. 41 • Practice, p. 42 • Word Problem Practice, p. 43	• Study Guide and Intervention, pp. 39–40 • Skills Practice, p. 41 • Practice, p. 42 • Word Problem Practice, p. 43 • Enrichment, p. 44	• Practice, p. 42 • Word Problem Practice, p. 43 • Enrichment, p. 44	• Study Guide and Intervention, pp. 39–40 • Skills Practice, p. 41 • Practice, p. 42 • Word Problem Practice, p. 43
Transparencies	• 5-Minute Check Transparency 10-6	• 5-Minute Check Transparency 10-6	• 5-Minute Check Transparency 10-6	• 5-Minute Check Transparency 10-6
Other	• Study Notebook • Teaching Algebra with Manipulatives	• Study Notebook • Teaching Algebra with Manipulatives	• Study Notebook	• Study Notebook • Teaching Algebra with Manipulatives

Review Vocabulary

discriminant the expression $b^2 - 4ac$ from the Quadratic Formula (Lesson 5-6)

Identify Conic Sections You can determine the type of conic without having to write $Ax^2 + Bxy + Cy^2 + Dx + Ey + F = 0$ in standard form. When there is an xy-term ($B \neq 0$), you can use the discriminant to identify the conic. $B^2 - 4AC$ is the discriminant of $Ax^2 + Bxy + Cy^2 + Dx + Ey + F = 0$.

Key Concept Classify Conics with the Discriminant

Discriminant	Conic Section
$B^2 - 4AC < 0$; $B = 0$ and $A = C$	circle
$B^2 - 4AC < 0$; either $B \neq 0$ or $A \neq C$	ellipse
$B^2 - 4AC = 0$	parabola
$B^2 - 4AC > 0$	hyperbola

StudyTip

Identifying Conics When there is no xy-term ($B = 0$), use A and C.
Parabola: A or $C = 0$ but not both.
Circle: $A = C$
Ellipse: A and C have the same sign but are not equal.
Hyperbola: A and C have opposite signs.

When $B = 0$, the conic will be either vertical or horizontal. When $B \neq 0$, the conic will be neither vertical nor horizontal.

Horizontal Ellipse: $B = 0$

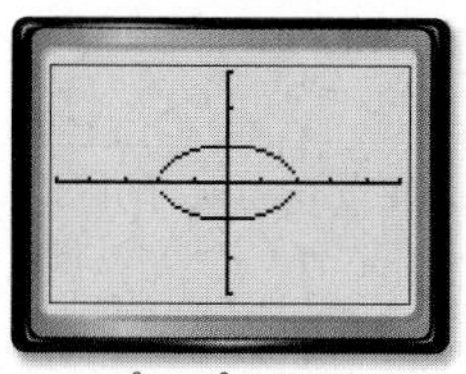

$x^2 + 4y^2 - 4 = 0$

Rotated Ellipse: $B \neq 0$

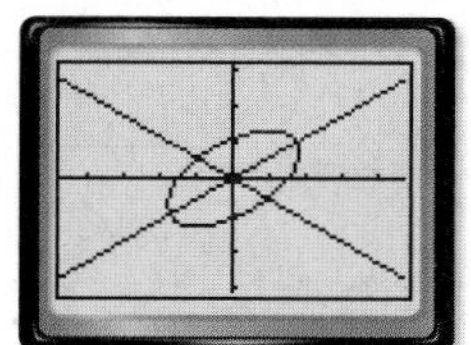

$7x^2 - 6\sqrt{3}xy + 13y^2 - 16 = 0$

EXAMPLE 2 Analyze an Equation of a Conic Section

Without writing in standard form, state whether the graph of each equation is a *parabola*, *circle*, *ellipse*, or *hyperbola*.

a. $y^2 + 4x^2 - 3xy + 4x - 5y - 8 = 0$

$A = 4$, $B = -3$, and $C = 1$
The discriminant is $(-3)^2 - 4(4)(1)$ or -7.
Because the discriminant is less than 0 and $B \neq 0$, the conic is an ellipse.

b. $3x^2 - 6x + 4y - 5y^2 + 2xy - 4 = 0$

$A = 3$, $B = 2$, and $C = -5$
The discriminant is $2^2 - 4(3)(-5)$ or 64.
Because the discriminant is greater than 0, the conic is a hyperbola.

c. $4y^2 - 8x + 6y - 14 = 0$

$A = 0$, $B = 0$, and $C = 4$
The discriminant is $0^2 - 4(0)(4)$ or 0.
Because the discriminant equals 0, the conic is a parabola.

Guided Practice

2A. $8y^2 - 6x^2 + 4xy - 6x + 2y - 4 = 0$ **hyperbola**

2B. $3xy + 4x^2 - 2y + 9x - 3 = 0$ **hyperbola**

2C. $3x^2 + 16x - 12y + 2y^2 - 6 = 0$ **ellipse**

Personal Tutor glencoe.com

Differentiated Instruction

AL OL

If students need a visual aid in identifying conic sections,

Then divide students into groups of two or three. Assign each group a different conic section and have them make a poster describing how to identify the conic section from an equation in standard form and from an equation not in standard form.

Formative Assessment

Use the Guided Practice exercises after each example to determine students' understanding of concepts.

Additional Example

1 Write $y^2 = 18 - 2x^2$ in standard form. State whether the graph of the equation is a *parabola, circle, ellipse,* or *hyperbola.* Then graph the equation.
$\frac{x^2}{9} + \frac{y^2}{18} = 1$; ellipse

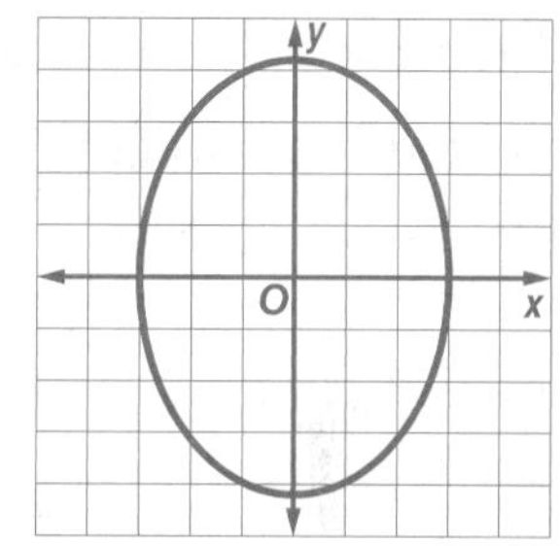

Additional Examples are also in Interactive Classroom PowerPoint® Presentations

IWB INTERACTIVE WHITEBOARD READY

Identify Conic Sections

Example 2 shows how to determine if an equation is that of a parabola, circle, ellipse, or hyperbola without writing the equation in standard form.

Additional Example

2 Without writing the equation in standard form, state whether the graph of the equation is a *parabola, circle, ellipse,* or *hyperbola.*

a. $3y^2 - x^2 - 9 = 0$ hyperbola

b. $2x^2 + 2y^2 + 16x - 20y = -32$ circle

c. $y^2 - 2x - 4y + 10 = 0$ parabola

Check Your Understanding

1–4. See Chapter 10 Answer Appendix.

Example 1 p. 656

Write each equation in standard form. State whether the graph of the equation is a *parabola, circle, ellipse,* or *hyperbola.* Then graph the equation.

1. $x^2 + 4y^2 - 6x + 16y - 11 = 0$
2. $x^2 + y^2 + 12x - 8y + 36 = 0$
3. $9y^2 - 16x^2 - 18y - 64x - 199 = 0$
4. $6y^2 - 24y + 28 - x = 0$

Example 2 p. 657

Without writing in standard form, state whether the graph of each equation is a *parabola, circle, ellipse,* or *hyperbola.* 9. hyperbola

5. $4x^2 + 6y^2 - 3x - 2y = 12$ ellipse
6. $5y^2 = 2x + 6y - 8 + 3x^2$ hyperbola
7. $8x^2 + 8y^2 + 16x + 24 = 0$ circle
8. $4x^2 - 6y = 8x + 2$ parabola
9. $4x^2 - 3y^2 + 8xy - 12 = 2x + 4y$
10. $5xy - 3x^2 + 6y^2 + 12y = 18$ hyperbola
11. $8x^2 + 12xy + 16y^2 + 4y - 3x = 12$ ellipse
12. $16xy + 8x^2 + 8y^2 - 18x + 8y = 13$ parabola
13. **AVIATION** A military jet performs for an air show. The path of the plane during one maneuver can be modeled by a conic section with equation $24x^2 + 1000y - 31{,}680x - 45{,}600 = 0$, where distances are represented in feet.
    a. Identify the shape of the curved path of the jet. Write the equation in standard form. parabola; $y = -0.024(x - 660)^2 + 10{,}500$
    b. If the jet begins its path upward, or ascent, at $x = 0$, what is the horizontal distance traveled by the jet from the beginning of the ascent to the end of the descent?
    c. What is the maximum height of the jet? 10,500 ft

13b. about 1321 ft

Practice and Problem Solving

● = Step-by-Step Solutions begin on page R20. Extra Practice begins on page 947.

Example 1 p. 656

Write each equation in standard form. State whether the graph of the equation is a *parabola, circle, ellipse,* or *hyperbola.* Then graph the equation.

14–23. See Chapter 10 Answer Appendix.

14. $3x^2 - 2y^2 + 18x + 8y - 35 = 0$
15. $3x^2 + 24x + 4y^2 - 40y + 52 = 0$
16. $x^2 + y^2 = 16 + 6y$
17. $32x + 28 = y - 8x^2$
18. $7x^2 - 8y = 84x - 2y^2 - 176$
19. $x^2 + 8y = 11 + 6x - y^2$
20. $4y^2 = 24y - x - 31$
21. $112y + 64x = 488 + 7y^2 - 8x^2$
22. $28x^2 + 9y^2 - 188 = 56x - 36y$
23. $25x^2 + 384y - 64y^2 + 200x = 1776$

Example 2 p. 657

Without writing in standard form, state whether the graph of each equation is a *parabola, circle, ellipse,* or *hyperbola.* 29. hyperbola 31. hyperbola

24. $4x^2 - 5y = 9x - 12$ parabola
25. $4x^2 - 12x = 18y - 4y^2$ circle
26. $9x^2 + 12y = 9y^2 + 18y - 16$ hyperbola
27. $18x^2 - 16y = 12x - 4y^2 + 19$ ellipse
28. $12y^2 - 4xy + 9x^2 = 18x - 124$ ellipse
29. $5xy + 12x^2 - 16x = 5y + 3y^2 + 18$
30. $19x^2 + 14y = 6x - 19y^2 - 88$ circle
31. $8x^2 + 20xy + 18 = 4y^2 - 12 + 9x$
32. $5x - 12xy + 6x^2 = 8y^2 - 24y - 9$ hyperbola
33. $18x - 24y + 324xy = 27x^2 + 3y^2 - 5$ hyperbola
34. **LIGHT** A lamp standing near a wall throws an arc of light in the shape of a conic section. Suppose the edge of the light can be represented by the equation $3y^2 - 2y - 4x^2 + 2x - 8 = 0$. Identify the shape of the edge of the light and graph the equation. See margin.

TEACH with TECH

STUDENT RESPONSE SYSTEM Show several equations of conics in general form on the board. For each, ask students to identify what type of conic section the equation represents. Have students reply with A for parabola, B for circle, C for ellipse, and D for hyperbola. Discuss student results for each equation.

3 PRACTICE

Formative Assessment

Use Exercises 1–13 to check for understanding.

Use the chart at the bottom of this page to customize assignments for your students.

Additional Answers

34. hyperbola

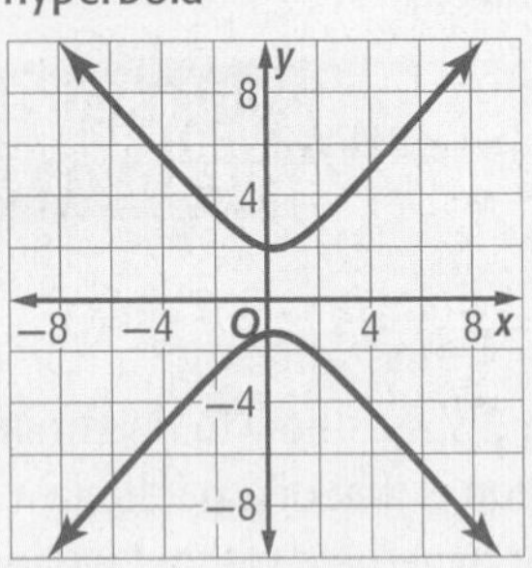

43c.

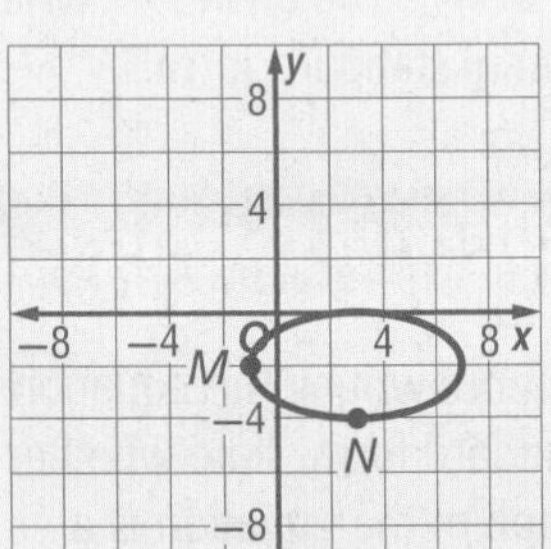

44b.

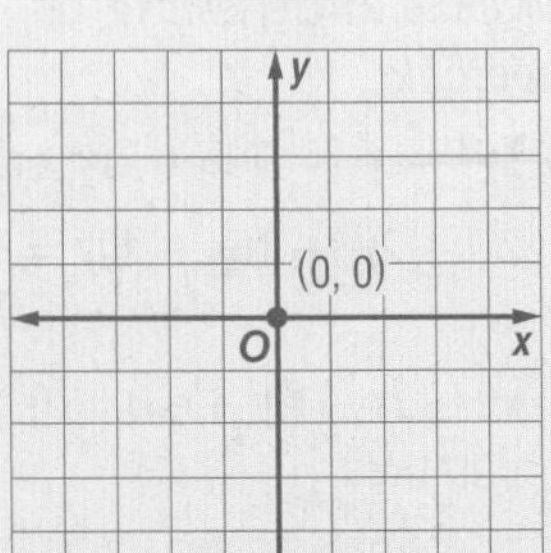

Differentiated Homework Options

Level	Assignment	Two-Day Option	
AL Basic	14–34, 45–62	15–33 odd, 48–51	14–34 even, 45–47, 52–62
OL Core	15–33 odd, 35–43, 45–62	14–34, 48–51	35–43, 45–47, 52–62
BL Advanced	35–59, (optional: 60–62)		

658 Chapter 10 Conic Sections

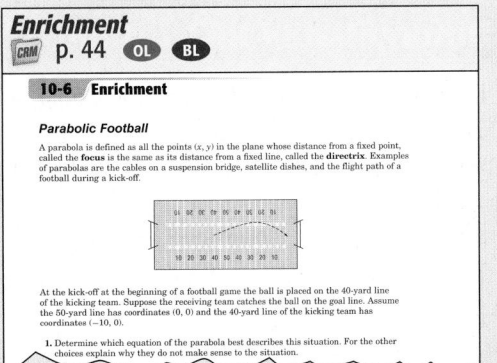

B Match each graph with its corresponding equation.

35. c

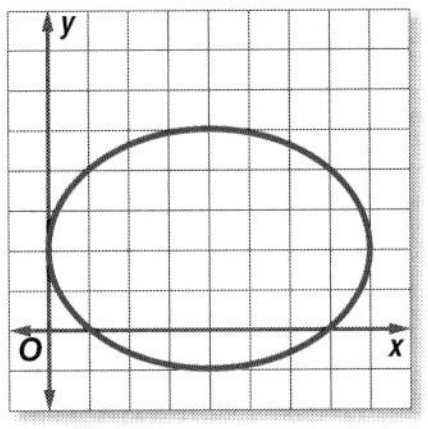

36. a

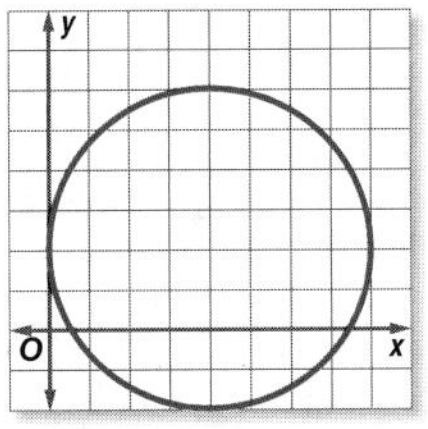

37. b

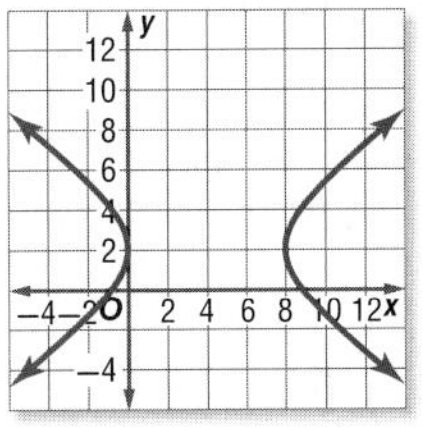

a. $x^2 + y^2 - 8x - 4y = -4$ b. $9x^2 - 16y^2 - 72x + 64y = 64$ c. $9x^2 + 16y^2 = 72x + 64y - 64$

C For Exercises 38–41, match each situation with an equation that could be used to represent it.

a. $47.25x^2 - 9y^2 + 18y + 33.525 = 0$

b. $25x^2 + 100y^2 - 1900x - 2200y + 45{,}700 = 0$

c. $16x^2 - 90x + y - 0.25 = 0$

d. $x^2 + y^2 - 18x - 30y - 14{,}094 = 0$

38. **COMPUTERS** the boundary of a wireless network with a range of 120 feet **d**

39. **FITNESS** the oval path of your foot on an exercise machine **b**

40. **COMMUNICATIONS** the position of a cell phone between two cell towers **a**

41. **SPORTS** the height of a football above the ground after being kicked **c**

42. **ENGINEERING** The shape of the cables in a suspension bridge is approximately parabolic. If the towers for a planned bridge are 1000 meters apart and the lowest point of the suspension cables is 200 meters below the top of the towers, write the equation in standard form with the origin at the vertex. $y = 0.0008x^2$

Real-World Link

The Golden Gate Bridge is an example of a suspension bridge. It took more than four years to complete and opened in 1937.

Source: Golden Gate Bridge Highway and Transportation District

43. **MULTIPLE REPRESENTATIONS** Consider an ellipse with center $(3, -2)$, vertex $M(-1, -2)$, and co-vertex $N(3, -4)$.

a. **ANALYTICAL** Determine the standard form of the equation of the ellipse.

b. **ALGEBRAIC** Convert part **a** to $Ax^2 + Bxy + Cy^2 + Dx + Ey + F = 0$ form. $x^2 + 4y^2 - 6x + 16y + 9 = 0$

c. **GRAPHICAL** Graph the ellipse. **See margin.**

d. **ANALYTICAL** If the ellipse is rotated such that M is moved to $(3, -6)$, determine the location of N and the angle of rotation. $N(5, -2)$; **90° counterclockwise**

H.O.T. Problems

Use Higher-Order Thinking Skills

44. **CHALLENGE** When a plane passes through the vertex of a cone, a *degenerate* conic is formed.

a. Determine the type of conic represented by $4x^2 + 8y^2 = 0$. **ellipse**

b. Graph the conic. **See margin.**

c. Describe the difference between this degenerate conic and a standard conic.

45. **REASONING** Determine whether the following statement is *sometimes*, *always*, or *never* true. Explain your reasoning.

When a conic is vertical and A = C, it is a circle.

46. **OPEN ENDED** Write an equation of the form $Ax^2 + Bxy + Cy^2 + Dx + Ey + F = 0$, where $A = 9C$, that represents a parabola.

47. **WRITING IN MATH** Compare and contrast the graphs of the four types of conics and their corresponding equations. **See Chapter 10 Answer Appendix.**

43a. $\frac{(x-3)^2}{16} + \frac{(y+2)^2}{4} = 1$

44c. A degenerate ellipse is the graph of a single point.

45. Sample answer: Always; when a conic is vertical, $B = 0$. When this is true and $A = C$, the conic is a circle.

46. Sample answer: $9x^2 + 6xy + y^2 + 2x + 2y + 8 = 0$

Multiple Representations In Exercise 43, students use a graph and algebraic analysis to draw an ellipse on the basis of its specified dimensions and redraw it after a transformation.

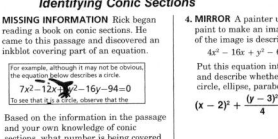

Study Guide and Intervention

CRM pp. 39–40 AL OL ELL

10-6 Study Guide and Intervention

Identifying Conic Sections

Conics in Standard Form Any conic section in the coordinate plane can be described by an equation of the form

$Ax^2 + Bxy + Cy^2 + Dx + Ey + F = 0$, where A, B, and C are not all zero.

One way to tell what kind of conic section an equation represents is to rearrange terms and complete the square, if necessary, to get one of the standard forms from an earlier lesson. This method is especially useful if you are going to graph the equation.

Example Write the equation $3x^2 - 4y^2 - 30x - 8y + 59 = 0$ in standard form. State whether the graph of the equation is a *parabola*, *circle*, *ellipse*, or *hyperbola*.

$3x^2 - 4y^2 - 30x - 8y + 59 = 0$ Original equation

$3x^2 - 30x - 4y^2 - 8y = -59$ Isolate terms.

$3(x^2 - 10x + ■) - 4(y^2 + 2y + ■) = -59 + ■ + ■$ Factor out common multiples.

$3(x^2 - 10x + 25) - 4(y^2 + 2y + 1) = -59 + 3(25) + (-4)(1)$ Complete the squares.

$3(x - 5)^2 - 4(y + 1)^2 = 12$ Simplify.

$\frac{(x-5)^2}{4} - \frac{(y+1)^2}{3} = 1$ Divide each side by 12.

The graph of the equation is a hyperbola with its center at $(5, -1)$. The length of the transverse axis is 4 units and the length of the conjugate axis is $2\sqrt{3}$ units.

Exercises

Write each equation in standard form. State whether the graph of the equation is a *parabola*, *circle*, *ellipse*, or *hyperbola*. Then graph the equation.

1. $4x^2 + 48x + y + 158 = 0$
$y = -4(x + 6)^2 - 14$; parabola

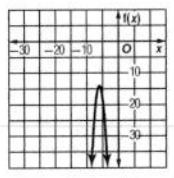

2. $3x^2 + y^2 - 48x - 4y + 184 = 0$
$\frac{(x-8)^2}{4} + \frac{(y-2)^2}{12} = 1$; ellipse

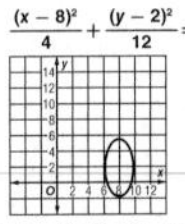

3. $-3x^2 + 2y^2 - 18x + 20y + 5 = 0$
$\frac{(y+5)^2}{9} - \frac{(x+3)^2}{6} = 1$; hyperbola

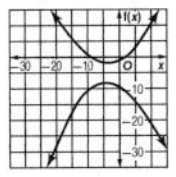

4. $x^2 + y^2 + 8x + 2y + 8 = 0$
$(x + 4)^2 + (y + 1)^2 = 9$; circle

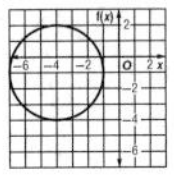

Chapter 10 39 Glencoe Algebra 2

Practice

CRM p. 42 AL OL BL ELL

10-6 Practice

Identifying Conic Sections

Write each equation in standard form. State whether the graph of the equation is a *parabola*, *circle*, *ellipse*, or *hyperbola*. Then graph the equation.

1. $y^2 = -3x$
$x = -\frac{1}{3}y^2$
parabola

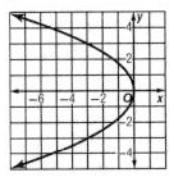

2. $x^2 + y^2 + 6x = 7$
$(x + 3)^2 + y^2 = 16$
circle

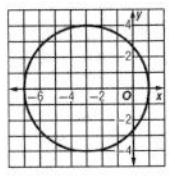

3. $5x^2 - 6y^2 - 30x - 12y = -9$
$\frac{(x-3)^2}{6} - \frac{(y+1)^2}{5} = 1$
hyperbola

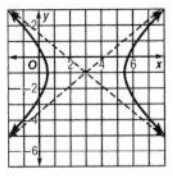

4. $196y^2 = 1225 - 100x^2$
$\frac{x^2}{12.25} + \frac{y^2}{6.25} = 1$
ellipse

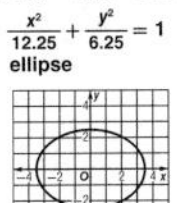

5. $3x^2 = 9 - 3y^2 - 6y$
$x^2 + (y + 1)^2 = 4$
circle

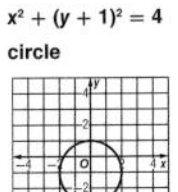

6. $9x^2 + y^2 + 54x - 6y = -81$
$\frac{(x+3)^2}{1} - \frac{(y-3)^2}{9} = 1$
ellipse

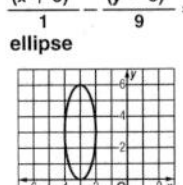

Without writing the equation in standard form, state whether the graph of each equation is a *parabola*, *circle*, *ellipse*, or *hyperbola*.

7. $6x^2 + 6y^2 = 36$ **circle**

8. $4x^2 + 6xy - y^2 = 16$ **hyperbola**

9. $9x^2 + 16y^2 - 10xy - 64y - 80 = 0$ **ellipse**

10. $5x^2 + 5y^2 - 45 = 0$ **circle**

11. $x^2 + 2x = y$ **parabola**

12. $4y^2 - 12xy - 36x^2 + 4x - 144 = 0$ **hyperbola**

13. **ASTRONOMY** A space probe flies by a planet in an hyperbolic orbit. It reaches the vertex of its orbit at $(5, 0)$ and then travels along a path that gets closer and closer to the line $y = \frac{2}{5}x$. Write an equation that describes the path of the space probe if the center of its hyperbolic orbit is at $(0, 0)$.
$\frac{x^2}{25} - \frac{y^2}{4} = 1$

Chapter 10 42 Glencoe Algebra 2

Word Problem Practice

CRM p. 43 AL OL BL ELL

10-6 Word Problem Practice

Identifying Conic Sections

1. **MISSING INFORMATION** Rick began reading a book on conic sections. He came to this passage and discovered an inkblot covering part of an equation.

> For example, although it may not be obvious, the equation below describes a circle.
> $7x^2 - 12x + ■y^2 - 16y - 94 = 0$
> To see that it is a circle, observe that the

Based on the information in the passage and your own knowledge of conic sections, what number is being covered by the inkblot?
7

2. **HEADLIGHTS** The light from the headlight of a car is in the shape of a cone. The axis of the cone is parallel to the ground. What shape does the edge of the lit region form on the road, assuming that the road is flat and level?
hyperbola

3. **GEOGRAPHY** Earth is shaped approximately like a sphere with a radius of 4,000 miles. This means any straight path on Earth's surface is actually a conic section. Which types of conic sections cannot trace straight paths on Earth's surface?
parabolas, hyperbolas, ellipses

4. **MIRROR** A painter used a can of spray paint to make an image. The boundary of the image is described by the equation
$4x^2 - 16x + y^2 - 6y + 21 = 0$.
Put this equation into standard form and describe whether the curve is a circle, ellipse, parabola, or hyperbola.
$(x - 2)^2 + \frac{(y-3)^2}{4} = 1$, ellipse

5. **NONSTANDARD EQUATIONS** Consider the equation $xy = 1$.

a. Are there any solutions of this equation that lie on the x- or y-axis?
no

b. Sketch a graph of the solutions of the equation.

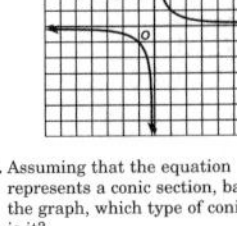

c. Assuming that the equation represents a conic section, based on the graph, which type of conic section is it?
a hyperbola

Chapter 10 43 Glencoe Algebra 2

Enrichment

CRM p. 44 OL BL

10-6 Enrichment

Parabolic Football

A parabola is defined as all the points (x, y) in the plane whose distance from a fixed point, called the **focus** is the same as its distance from a fixed line, called the **directrix**. Examples of parabolas are the cables on a suspension bridge, satellite dishes, and the flight path of a football during a kick-off.

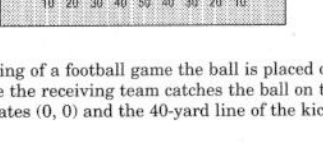

At the kick-off at the beginning of a football game the ball is placed on the 40-yard line of the kicking team. Suppose the receiving team catches the ball on the goal line. Assume the 50-yard line has coordinates $(0, 0)$ and the 40-yard line of the kicking team has coordinates $(-10, 0)$.

1. Determine which equation of the parabola best describes this situation. For the other choices explain why they do not make sense to the situation.

4 ASSESS

Crystal Ball Ask students to write how today's lesson will connect with solving linear-nonlinear systems.

Formative Assessment

Check for student understanding of concepts in Lessons 10-5 and 10-6.

CRM Quiz 3, p. 54

Additional Answers

52. (0, ±15); (0, ±25); $y = \pm\frac{3}{4}x$

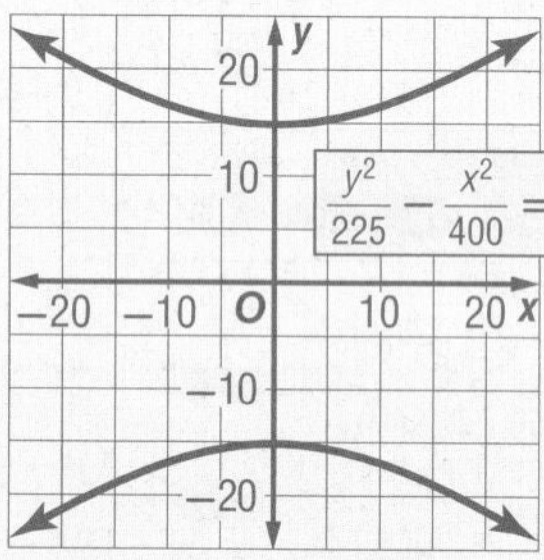

53. (0, 0); (0, ±3); $6\sqrt{2}$; 6

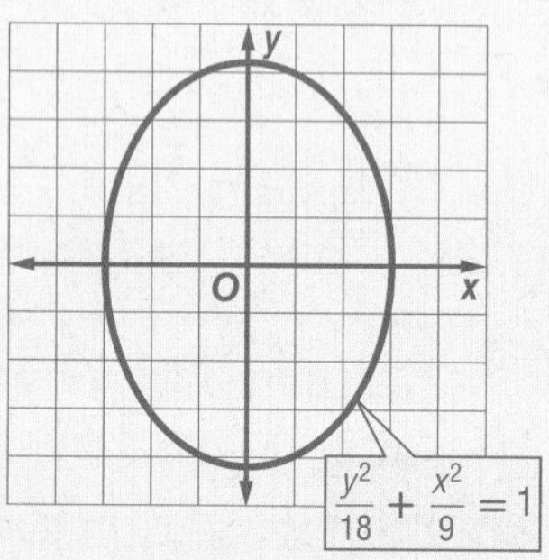

54. (0, 0); (±2, 0); $4\sqrt{2}$; 4

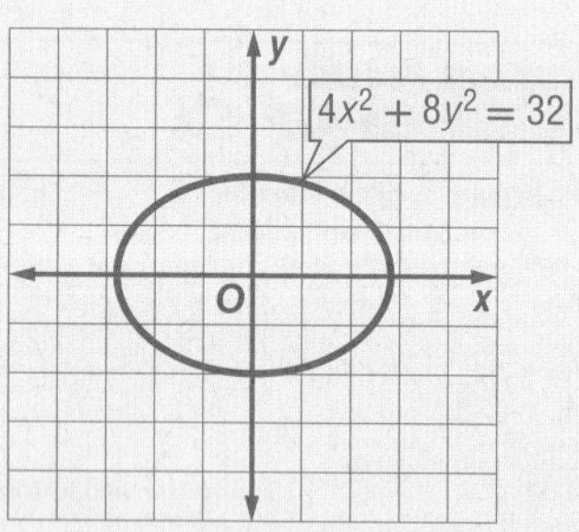

55. (4, −2); ($4 \pm 2\sqrt{6}$, −2); 10; 2

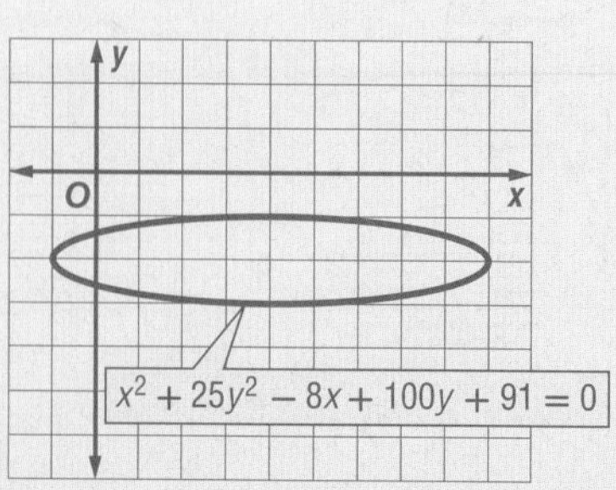

NGSSS PRACTICE 912.S.3.3, 912.A.3.1, 912.A.7.5, 912.G.7.5

48. ACT/SAT A class of 25 students took a science test. Ten students had a mean score of 80. The other students had an average score of 60. What is the average score of the whole class? **B**

A. 66
B. 68
C. 70
D. 72

49. Six times a number minus 11 is 43. What is the number? **I**

F. 12
G. 11
H. 10
I. 9

50. 130 L; 4.6 min

50. THINK SOLVE EXPLAIN **EXTENDED RESPONSE** The amount of water remaining in a storage tank as it is drained can be represented by the equation $L = -4t^2 - 10t + 130$, where L represents the number of liters of water remaining and t represents the number of minutes since the drain was opened. How many liters of water were in the tank initially? Determine to the nearest tenth of a minute how long it will take for the tank to drain completely.

51. Ruben has a square piece of paper with sides 4 inches long. He rolled up the paper to form a cylinder. What is the volume of the cylinder? **B**

A. $\frac{4}{\pi}$ **C.** 4π
B. $\frac{16}{\pi}$ **D.** 16π

Spiral Review

52. ASTRONOMY Suppose a comet's path can be modeled by a branch of the hyperbola with equation $\frac{y^2}{225} - \frac{x^2}{400} = 1$. Find the coordinates of the vertices and foci and the equations of the asymptotes for the hyperbola. Then graph the hyperbola. (Lesson 10-5) **See margin.**

Find the coordinates of the center and foci and the lengths of the major and minor axes for the ellipse with the given equation. Then graph the ellipse. (Lesson 10-4) **53–55. See margin.**

53. $\frac{y^2}{18} + \frac{x^2}{9} = 1$ **54.** $4x^2 + 8y^2 = 32$ **55.** $x^2 + 25y^2 - 8x + 100y + 91 = 0$

Graph each function. (Lesson 9-3) **56–58. See Chapter 10 Answer Appendix.**

56. $f(x) = \frac{3}{x}$ **57.** $f(x) = \frac{-2}{x+5}$ **58.** $f(x) = \frac{6}{x-2} - 4$

59. SPACE A radioisotope is used as a power source for a satellite. The power output P (in watts) is given by $P = 50e^{-\frac{t}{250}}$, where t is the time in days. (Lesson 8-8)

a. Is the formula for power output an example of exponential *growth* or *decay*? Explain your reasoning. **Decay; the exponent is negative.**

b. Find the power available after 100 days. **about 33.5 watts**

c. Ten watts of power are required to operate the equipment in the satellite. How long can the satellite continue to operate? **about 402 days**

Skills Review

Solve each system of equations. (Lesson 3-2)

60. $6g - 8h = 50$ **(7, −1)**
$6h = 22 - 4g$

61. $3u + 5v = 6$ $\left(-\frac{1}{2}, \frac{3}{2}\right)$
$2u - 4v = -7$

62. $10m - 9n = 15$ **(6, 5)**
$5m - 4n = 10$

Differentiated Instruction

OL BL

Extension Students have learned that a quadratic equation of the form $Ax^2 + Bxy + Cy^2 + Dx + Ey + F = 0$, where $B = 0$, is either a *parabola, circle, ellipse,* or a *hyperbola* when graphed. Ask students to determine the shape of the graph of the equations $x^2 + y^2 + 1 = 0$, $x^2 + y^2 = 0$ and $x^2 = 0$. empty set; single point (0, 0); the line $x = 0$

Graphing Technology Lab
Identifying and Graphing Conic Sections

FL Math Online glencoe.com
- Other Calculator Keystrokes
- Graphing Technology Personal Tutor

Objective
Graph conic sections using a graphing calculator.

NGSSS
MA.912.A.9.2 Graph conic sections with and without using graphing technology. *Also addresses MA.912.A.9.1.*

You can use a TI-83/84 Plus application to make graphing conics on your graphing calculator without having to solve for y.

EXAMPLE Identify and Graph a Conic

Write $x^2 + y^2 + 4x - 6y = -4$ in standard form. State whether the graph of the equation is a *parabola, circle, ellipse,* or *hyperbola.* Then graph the equation.

Step 1 Write in standard form.

$x^2 + y^2 + 4x - 6y = -4$	**Original equation**
$(x^2 + 4x + \blacksquare) + (y^2 - 6y + \blacksquare) = -4$	**Isolate terms.**
$(x^2 + 4x + 4) + (y^2 - 6y + 9) = -4 + 4 + 9$	**Complete the square.**
$(x + 2)^2 + (y - 3)^2 = 9$	**Write as perfect squares.**

Step 2 Identify the conic.

The equation is in the form $(x - h)^2 + (y - k)^2 = r^2$, so the conic is a circle.

Step 3 Graph the equation.

Use the Conics application to graph the circle.

KEYSTROKES: Press [APPS]. Then use [▼] to select Conics and press [ENTER]. Press 1 to graph a circle, then press 1 to graph an equation of the form $(x - h)^2 + (y - k)^2 = r^2$.

Enter the values for H, K, and R: press [(–)] 2 [ENTER] 3 [ENTER] 3 [ENTER] [GRAPH].

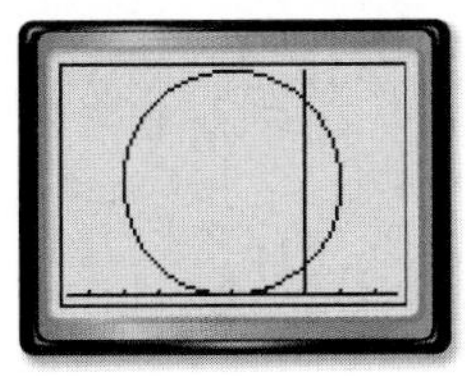

Exercises

Write each equation in standard form. State whether the graph of the equation is a *parabola, circle, ellipse,* or *hyperbola.* Then graph the equation. **1–10. See Chapter 10 Answer Appendix.**

1. $x^2 - y^2 + 8x = 16$
2. $y^2 - 2x^2 - 16 = 0$
3. $x^2 + 2y^2 = 2x + 8$
4. $x^2 - 8y + y^2 + 11 = 0$
5. $9y^2 + 18y = 25x^2 + 216$
6. $x^2 + 4y^2 + 2x - 24y + 33 = 0$
7. $3x^2 + 4y^2 + 8y = 8$
8. $x^2 + 4y^2 - 11 = 2(4y - x)$
9. $6x^2 - 24x - 5y^2 - 10y - 11 = 0$
10. $25y^2 + 9x^2 - 50y - 54x = 119$

EXTEND 10-6 Lesson Notes

1 FOCUS

Objective Graph conic sections using a graphing calculator.

Materials for Each Group
- TI-83/84 Plus graphing calculator

Teaching Tip
Remind students that to activate the INFO feature on their screens, allowing them to scroll back to the conics application screen or to get information, they should press the [Y=] key. To activate the QUIT feature on the conics application screen, press the [GRAPH] key.

2 TEACH

Working in Cooperative Groups
Pair students with different abilities. Have students work through the Activity Steps 1–3 and then answer Exercises 1–5.

Before students begin the activity, have students investigate the choices of equations for each conic. Each conic has a choice of two equation formats. Caution students to note the similarities between the *H* and *K* on their screens.

Ask:
- How do the equations for the parabola differ from the equations for the parabola that we have studied? The calculator uses 4*P* instead of *a*.
- What does 4*P* equal? $4P = a$
- What does *P* equal? $P = \frac{a}{4}$

Practice Have students complete Exercises 6–10.

3 ASSESS

Formative Assessment
Use Exercise 5 to assess whether students are able to graph a conic section without solving for *y*, using a graphing calculator.

From Concrete to Abstract Ask students to choose one of the equations in the exercises and explain how they chose which conics application to use to graph it.

10-7 Lesson Notes

1 FOCUS

Vertical Alignment

Before Lesson 10-7
Solve systems of linear equations.

Lesson 10-7
Solve systems of linear and nonlinear equations algebraically and graphically.
Solve systems of linear and nonlinear inequalities graphically.

2 TEACH

Scaffolding Questions

Have students read the *Why?* section of the lesson.

Ask:

- Can a person be easily located using one cellular tower? Why or why not? No; the person could be anywhere in a circular path around the tower.
- If law enforcement only knew the distance a caller was from 2 cellular towers, what is the maximum number of locations they would have to search to find the caller? two

10-7 Solving Linear-Nonlinear Systems

Then
You solved systems of linear equations. (Lessons 3-1 and 3-2)

Now
- Solve systems of linear and nonlinear equations algebraically and graphically.
- Solve systems of linear and nonlinear inequalities graphically.

NGSSS
MA.912.A.7.7 Solve nonlinear systems of equations with and without using technology.

FL Math Online
glencoe.com

Why?

Ever wonder how law enforcement agencies can track a cell phone user's location? A person using a cell phone can be located in respect to three cellular towers. The respective coordinates and distances each tower is from the caller are used to pinpoint the caller's location. This is accomplished using a system of quadratic equations.

Systems of Equations When a system of equations consists of a linear and a nonlinear equation, the system may have zero, one, or two solutions. Some of the possible solutions are shown below.

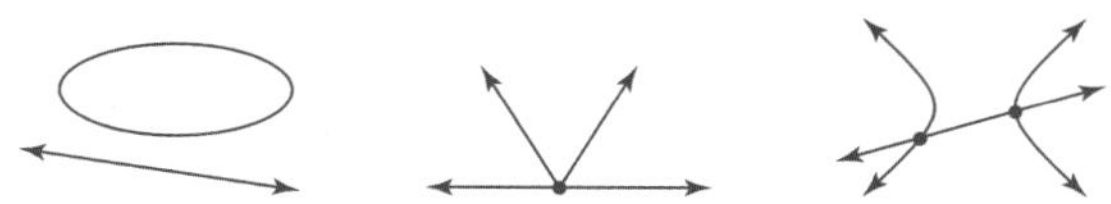

You can solve linear-quadratic systems by using graphical or algebraic methods. One way is to first solve for a variable in the linear equation and then substitute into the quadratic equation.

EXAMPLE 1 Linear-Quadratic System

Solve the system of equations.

$9x^2 + 25y^2 = 225$ (1)

$10y + 6x = 6$ (2)

Step 1 Solve the linear equation for y.

$10y + 6x = 6$	**Equation (2)**
$y = -0.6x + 0.6$	**Solve for *y*.**

Step 2 Substitute into the quadratic equation and solve for x.

$9x^2 + 25y^2 = 225$	**Quadratic equation**
$9x^2 + 25(-0.6x + 0.6)^2 = 225$	**Substitute $-0.6x + 0.6$ for *y*.**
$9x^2 + 25(0.36x^2 - 0.72x + 0.36) = 225$	**Simplify.**
$9x^2 + 9x^2 - 18x + 9 = 225$	**Distribute.**
$18x^2 - 18x - 216 = 0$	**Simplify.**
$x^2 - x - 12 = 0$	**Divide each side by 18.**
$(x - 4)(x + 3) = 0$	**Factor.**
$x = 4$ or -3	**Zero Product Property**

Step 3 Substitute x-values into the linear equation and solve for y.

$y = -0.6x + 0.6$	**Equation (2)**	$y = -0.6x + 0.6$
$= -0.6(4) + 0.6$	**Substitute the *x*-values.**	$= -0.6(-3) + 0.6$
$= -1.8$	**Simplify.**	$= 2.4$

The solutions of the system are $(4, -1.8)$ and $(-3, 2.4)$.

Guided Practice 1A. $\left(-11, -49\frac{1}{3}\right)$ and $(5, 4)$

Solve each system of equations.

1A. $3y + x^2 - 4x - 17 = 0$
$3y - 10x + 38 = 0$

1B. $3(y - 4) - 2(x - 3) = -6$
$5x^2 + 2y^2 - 53 = 0$ $(3, 2)$ and $(-3, -2)$

Personal Tutor glencoe.com

Lesson 10-7 Resources

Resource	Approaching-Level	On-Level	Beyond-Level	English Learners
Teacher Edition		• Differentiated Instruction, pp. 663, 667	• Differentiated Instruction, pp. 663, 667	
Chapter Resource Masters	• Study Guide and Intervention, pp. 45–46 • Skills Practice, p. 47 • Practice, p. 48 • Word Problem Practice, p. 49	• Study Guide and Intervention, pp. 45–46 • Skills Practice, p. 47 • Practice, p. 48 • Word Problem Practice, p. 49 • Enrichment, p. 50	• Practice, p. 48 • Word Problem Practice, p. 49 • Enrichment, p. 50	• Study Guide and Intervention, pp. 45–46 • Skills Practice, p. 47 • Practice, p. 48 • Word Problem Practice, p. 49
Transparencies	• 5-Minute Check Transparency 10-7	• 5-Minute Check Transparency 10-7	• 5-Minute Check Transparency 10-7	• 5-Minute Check Transparency 10-7
Other	• Study Notebook	• Study Notebook	• Study Notebook	• Study Notebook

If a quadratic system contains two conic sections, the system may have anywhere from zero to four solutions. Some graphical representations are shown below.

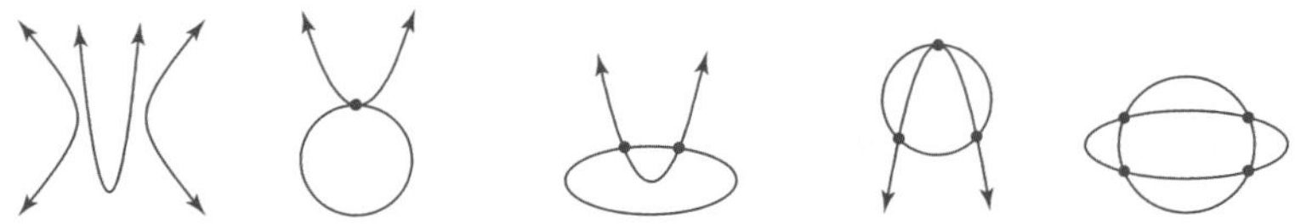

You can use elimination to solve quadratic-quadratic systems.

EXAMPLE 2 **Quadratic-Quadratic System**

Solve the system of equations.

$x^2 + y^2 = 45$ (1)

$y^2 - x^2 = 27$ (2)

$y^2 + x^2 = 45$	**Equation (1), Commutative Property**
$(+)\ y^2 - x^2 = 27$	**Equation (2)**
$2y^2 = 72$	**Add.**
$y^2 = 36$	**Divide each side by 2.**
$y = \pm 6$	**Take the square root of each side.**

Substitute 6 and −6 into one of the original equations and solve for x.

$x^2 + y^2 = 45$	**Equation (1)**	$x^2 + y^2 = 45$
$x^2 + 6^2 = 45$	**Substitute for y.**	$x^2 + (-6)^2 = 45$
$x^2 = 9$	**Subtract 36 from each side.**	$x^2 = 9$
$x = \pm 3$	**Take the square root of each side.**	$x = \pm 3$

The solutions are (−3, −6), (−3, 6), (3, −6), and (3, 6).

Guided Practice **Solve each system of equations.**

2A. $x^2 + y^2 = 8$
$x^2 + 3y = 10$
(−2, 2), (2, 2), $(-\sqrt{7}, 1)$, $(\sqrt{7}, 1)$

2B. $3x^2 + 4y^2 = 48$
$2x^2 - y^2 = -1$
(−2, −3), (−2, 3), (2, −3), (2, 3)

Personal Tutor glencoe.com

StudyTip

Graphing Calculators If you use ZSquare on the ZOOM menu, the graph of the first equation will look like a circle.

Systems of Inequalities Systems of quadratic inequalities can be solved by graphing.

EXAMPLE 3 **Quadratic Inequalities**

Solve the system of inequalities by graphing.

$x^2 + y^2 \leq 49$

$x^2 - 4y^2 > 16$

The intersection of the graphs, shaded green, represents the solution of the system.

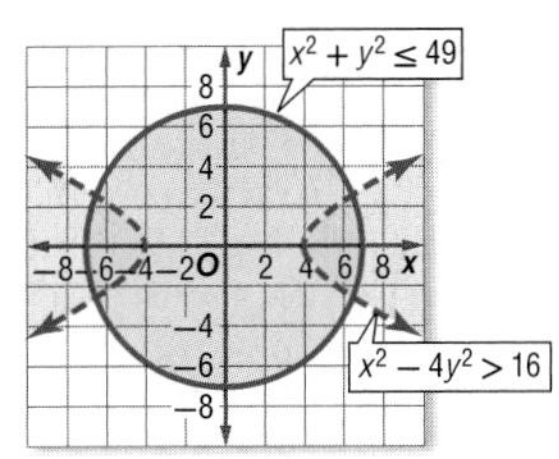

CHECK (6, 0) is in the shaded area. Use this point to check your solution.

$x^2 + y^2 \leq 49$	$x^2 - 4y^2 > 16$
$6^2 + 0^2 \overset{?}{\leq} 49$	$62 - 4(0)^2 \overset{?}{>} 16$
$36 \leq 49$ ✓	$36 > 16$ ✓

Guided Practice

Solve each system of inequalities by graphing.

3A. $5x^2 + 2y^2 \leq 10$
$y \geq x^2 - 2x + 1$

3B. $x^2 - y^2 \leq 8$
$x^2 + y^2 \geq 120$

3A, 3B. See Chapter 10 Answer Appendix.

Personal Tutor glencoe.com

Systems of Equations

Example 1 shows how to solve a linear-quadratic system using substitution. **Example 2** shows how to solve a quadratic-quadratic system using elimination.

Formative Assessment

Use the Guided Practice exercises after each example to determine students' understanding of concepts.

Additional Examples

1 Solve the system of equations.
$4x^2 - 16y^2 = 25$
$2y + x = 2$
$\left(\frac{41}{16}, -\frac{9}{32}\right)$

2 Solve the system of equations.
$x^2 + y^2 = 16$
$4x^2 + y^2 = 23$
$\left(\frac{\sqrt{21}}{3}, \frac{\sqrt{123}}{3}\right)$, $\left(-\frac{\sqrt{21}}{3}, \frac{\sqrt{123}}{3}\right)$, $\left(\frac{\sqrt{21}}{3}, -\frac{\sqrt{123}}{3}\right)$, $\left(-\frac{\sqrt{21}}{3}, -\frac{\sqrt{123}}{3}\right)$

Additional Examples also in Interactive Classroom PowerPoint® Presentations

IWB INTERACTIVE WHITEBOARD READY

TEACH with TECH

BLOG Have students write a blog entry describing how solving a quadratic system is similar to and different from solving a linear system. Be sure students explain how both the concepts and the methods of solving the systems are similar and different.

Differentiated Instruction

OL BL

Social Learners Point out that there are combinations of graphs other than those shown on page 663 just before Example 2, that are possible for each number of solutions. As a class, challenge students to sketch as many different possibilities as they can to add to the figures shown.

Systems of Inequalities

Example 3 shows how to solve a system of inequalities by graphing. **Example 4** shows how to solve a system of inequalities involving absolute value by graphing.

Additional Examples

3 Solve the system of inequalities by graphing.
$y > x^2 + 1$
$x^2 + y^2 \leq 9$

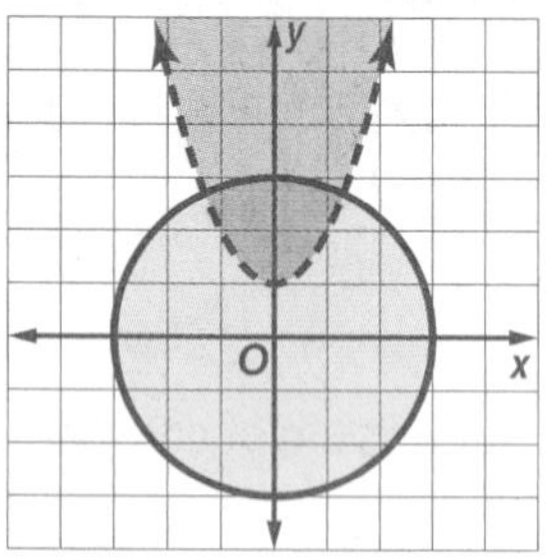

4 Solve the system of inequalities by graphing.
$x^2 + y^2 > 16$
$y > |x + 4|$

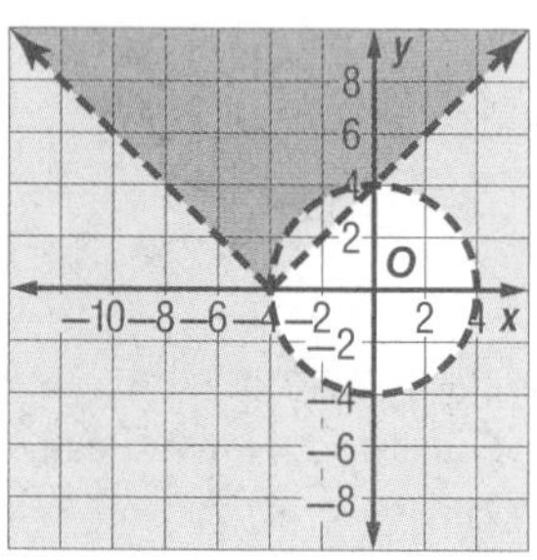

3 PRACTICE

Formative Assessment

Use Exercises 1–13 to check for understanding.

Use the chart at the bottom of the next page to customize assignments for your students.

Systems involving absolute value can also be solved by graphing.

StudyTip

Graphing Calculator Like linear inequalities, systems of quadratic and absolute value inequalities can be checked with a graphing calculator.

EXAMPLE 4 Quadratics with Absolute Value

Solve the system of inequalities by graphing.
$y \geq |2x - 4|$
$y \leq -x^2 + 4x + 2$

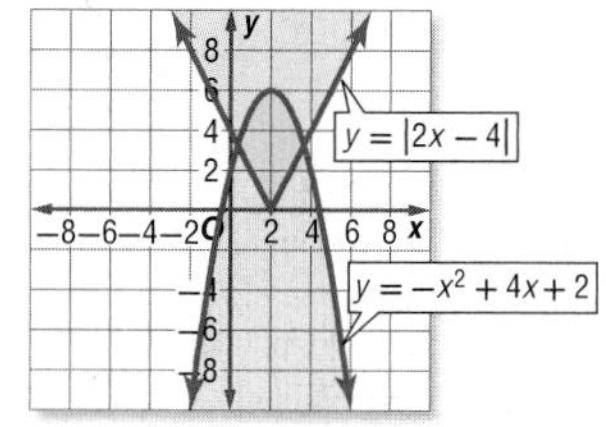

Graph the boundary equations. Then shade appropriately.

The intersection of the graphs, shaded green, represents the solution to the system.

CHECK (2, 4) is in the shaded area. Use the point to check your solution.

$y \geq \|2x - 4\|$	$y \leq -x^2 + 4x + 2$
$4 \overset{?}{\geq} \|2(2) - 4\|$	$4 \overset{?}{\leq} -(2)^2 + 4(2) + 2$
$4 \geq 0$ ✓	$4 \leq 6$ ✓

Guided Practice

Solve each system of inequalities by graphing. 4A, 4B. See Chapter 10 Answer Appendix.

4A. $y > |-0.5x + 2|$
$\frac{x^2}{16} + \frac{y^2}{36} \leq 1$

4B. $x^2 + y^2 \leq 49$
$y \geq |x^2 + 1|$

Personal Tutor glencoe.com

Check Your Understanding

Examples 1 and 2 pp. 662–663

Solve each system of equations.

1. $8y = -10x$
$y^2 = 2x^2 - 7$ (4, −5), (−4, 5)

2. $x^2 + y^2 = 68$
$5y = -3x + 34$ (−2, 8), (8, 2)

3. $y = 12x - 30$
$4x^2 - 3y = 18$ (3, 6), (6, 42)

4. $6y^2 - 27 = 3x$
$6y - x = 13$ (−7, 1), (−1, 2)

5. $x^2 + y^2 = 16$
$x^2 - y^2 = 20$ no solution

6. $y^2 - 2x^2 = 8$
$3y^2 + x^2 = 52$

7 $x^2 + 2y = 7$
$y^2 - x^2 = 8$

8. $4y^2 - 3x^2 = 11$
$3y^2 + 2x^2 = 21$

6. (2, 4), (−2, 4), (−2, −4), (2, −4)
7. (−1, 3), (1, 3), $(-\sqrt{17}, -5)$, $(\sqrt{17}, -5)$
8. $(-\sqrt{3}, -\sqrt{5})$, $(-\sqrt{3}, \sqrt{5})$, $(\sqrt{3}, -\sqrt{5})$, $(\sqrt{3}, \sqrt{5})$

9. CELL PHONES Refer to the beginning of the lesson. A person using a cell phone can be located in respect to three cellular towers. In a coordinate system where one unit represents one mile, the location of the caller is determined to be 50 miles from the tower at the origin. The person is also 40 miles from a tower at (0, 30) and 13 miles from a tower at (35, 18). Where is the caller? (40, 30)

Examples 3 and 4 pp. 663–664

Solve each system of inequalities by graphing. 10–13. See Chapter 10 Answer Appendix.

10. $6x^2 + 9(y - 2)^2 \leq 36$
$x^2 + (y + 3)^2 \leq 25$

11. $16x^2 + 4y^2 \leq 64$
$y \geq -x^2 + 2$

12. $4x^2 - 8y^2 \geq 32$
$y \geq |1.5x| - 8$

13. $x^2 + 8y^2 < 32$
$y < -|x - 2| + 2$

Focus on Mathematical Content

Systems of Quadratic Inequalities The graph of an inequality that uses < or > involving a parabola, circle, or ellipse is either the interior or the exterior of the conic section. The graph of an inequality involving a hyperbola is either the region between the branches or the two regions inside the branches. If the inequality symbol is ≤ or ≥, then the boundary will be included. The solution of a system of quadratic inequalities is the region where the shading of the graphs overlaps.

Practice and Problem Solving

● = **Step-by-Step Solutions** begin on page R20.
Extra Practice begins on page 947.

Examples 1 and 2
pp. 662–663

Solve each system of equations. 16–23, 25. See margin.

14. $3x^2 - 2y^2 = -24$, $2y = -3x$ (−4, 6), (4, −6)

15. $5x^2 + 4y^2 = 20$, $5y = 7x + 35$ no solution

16. $x^2 + 3x = -4y - 2$, $y = -2x + 1$

17. $y = 2x$, $4x^2 - 2y^2 = -36$

18. $2y = x + 10$, $y^2 - 4y = 5x + 10$

19. $9y = 8x - 19$, $8x + 11 = 2y^2 + 5y$

20. $2y^2 + 5x^2 = 26$, $2x^2 - y^2 = 5$

21. $x^2 + y^2 = 16$, $x^2 - 4x + y^2 = 12$

22. $x^2 + y^2 = 8$, $5y^2 = 3x^2$

23. $y^2 - x^2 + 3y = 26$, $x^2 + 2y^2 = 34$

24. $x^2 - y^2 = 25$, $x^2 + y^2 + 7 = 0$ no solution

25. $x^2 - 10x + 2y^2 = 47$, $y^2 - 2x^2 = -14$

39a. $y = \pm 900\sqrt{1 - \frac{x^2}{(300)^2}}$; $y = \pm 690\sqrt{1 - \frac{x^2}{(600)^2}}$

39b. Sample answer: (209, 647), (−209, 647), (−209, −647), (209, −647)

26. FIREWORKS Two fireworks are set off simultaneously but from different altitudes. The height y in feet of one is represented by $y = -16t^2 + 120t + 10$, where t is the time in seconds. The height of the other is represented by $y = -16t^2 + 60t + 310$.

a. After how many seconds are the fireworks the same height? 5 seconds

b. What is that height? 210 ft

Examples 3 and 4
pp. 663–664

Solve each system of inequalities by graphing. 27–36. See Chapter 10 Answer Appendix.

27. $x^2 + y^2 \geq 36$, $x^2 + 9(y + 6)^2 \leq 36$

28. $-x > y^2$, $4x^2 + 14y^2 \leq 56$

29. $12x^2 - 4y^2 \geq 48$, $16(x - 4)^2 + 25y^2 < 400$

30. $8y^2 - 3x^2 \leq 24$, $2y > x^2 - 8x + 14$

31. $y > x^2 - 6x + 8$, $x \geq y^2 - 6y + 8$

32. $x^2 + y^2 \geq 9$, $25x^2 + 64y^2 \leq 1600$

33. $16(x - 3)^2 + 4y^2 \leq 64$, $y \leq -|x - 2| + 2$

34. $x^2 - 4x + y^2 + 6y \leq 23$, $y > |x - 2| - 6$

35. $2y - 4 \geq |x + 4|$, $12 - 2y > x^2 + 12x + 36$

36. $18y^2 - 3x^2 \leq 54$, $y \geq |2x| - 6$

37. $x^2 + y^2 < 16$, $y \geq |x - 2| + 6$ no solution

38. $x^2 < y - 2$, $y \leq |x + 8| - 7$ no solution

39c. Sample answer: The orbit of the satellite modeled by the second equation is closer to a circle than the other orbit. The distance on the x-axis is twice as great for one satellite as the other.

39. SPACE Two satellites are placed in orbit about Earth. The equations of the two orbits are $\frac{x^2}{(300)^2} + \frac{y^2}{(900)^2} = 1$ and $\frac{x^2}{(600)^2} + \frac{y^2}{(690)^2} = 1$, where distances are in kilometers and Earth is the center of each curve.

a. Solve each equation for y.

b. Use a graphing calculator to estimate the intersection points of the two orbits.

c. Compare the orbits of the two satellites.

Real-World Link

The first electronic monitoring device was introduced in 1983.

Source: Federal Probation

40. PETS Taci's dog was missing one day. Fortunately, he was wearing an electronic monitoring device. If the dog is 10 units from the tree, 13 units from the tower, and 20 units from the house, determine the coordinates of his location. (4, 5)

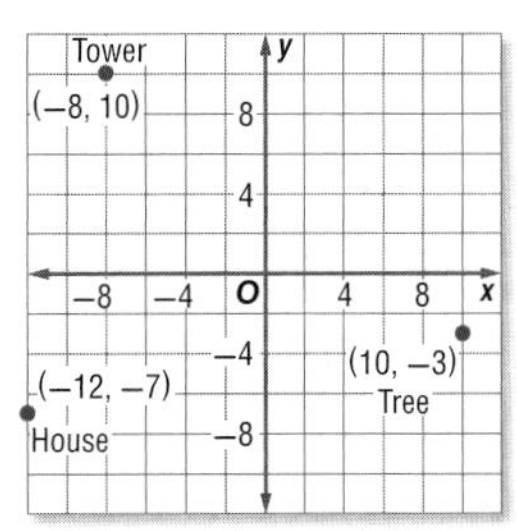

41. BASEBALL In 1997, after Mark McGuire hit a home run, the claim was made that the ball would have traveled 538 feet if it had not landed in the stands. The path of the baseball can be modeled by $y = -0.0037x^2 + 1.77x - 1.72$ and the stands can be modeled by $y = \frac{3}{7}x - 128.6$. How far vertically and horizontally from home plate did the ball land in the stands? 440 ft from home plate, 60 ft above the playing surface

Watch Out!

Preventing Errors Remind students that it is always a good idea to check a point inside the solution region as well as one outside that region.

Additional Answers

16. (3, −5), (2, −3)

17. (−3, −6), (3, 6)

18. (−2, 4), (10, 10)

19. (−1, −3), (8, 5)

20. $(-2, -\sqrt{3})$, $(-2, \sqrt{3})$, $(2, -\sqrt{3})$, $(2, \sqrt{3})$

21. $(1, -\sqrt{15})$, $(1, \sqrt{15})$

22. $(-\sqrt{5}, -\sqrt{3})$, $(-\sqrt{5}, \sqrt{3})$, $(\sqrt{5}, -\sqrt{3})$, $(\sqrt{5}, \sqrt{3})$

23. $(-\sqrt{2}, 4)$, $(\sqrt{2}, 4)$

25. (5, −6), (5, (6), (−3, −2), (−3, 2)

Differentiated Homework Options

Level	Assignment	Two-Day Option	
AL Basic	14–41, 52–74	15–41 odd, 55–58	14–40 even, 52–54, 59–74
OL Core	15–41 odd, 42–50, 52–74	14–41, 55–58	42–50, 52–54, 59–74
BL Advanced	42–70, (optional: 71–74)		

Study Guide and Intervention
CRM pp. 45–46 AL OL ELL

10-7 Study Guide and Intervention
Solving Linear-Nonlinear Systems

Systems of Equations Like systems of linear equations, systems of linear-nonlinear equations can be solved by substitution and elimination. If the graphs are a conic section and a line, the system will have 0, 1, or 2 solutions. If the graphs are two conic sections, the system will have 0, 1, 2, 3, or 4 solutions.

Example Solve the system of equations. $y = x^2 - 2x - 15$
$x + y = -3$

Rewrite the second equation as $y = -x - 3$ and substitute into the first equation.

$-x - 3 = x^2 - 2x - 15$
$0 = x^2 - x - 12$ Add $x + 3$ to each side.
$0 = (x - 4)(x + 3)$ Factor.

Use the Zero Product property to get
$x = 4$ or $x = -3$.

Substitute these values for x in $x + y = -3$:
$4 + y = -3$ or $-3 + y = -3$
$y = -7$ $y = 0$

The solutions are $(4, -7)$ and $(-3, 0)$.

Exercises

Solve each system of equations.

1. $y = x^2 - 5$, $y = x - 3$ **(2, −1), (−1, −4)**
2. $x^2 + (y - 5)^2 = 25$, $y = -x^2$ **(0, 0)**
3. $x^2 + (y - 5)^2 = 25$, $y = x^2$ **(0, 0), (3, 9), (−3, 9)**
4. $x^2 + y^2 = 9$, $x^2 + y = 3$ **$(0, 3), (\sqrt{5}, -2), (-\sqrt{5}, -2)$**
5. $x^2 - y^2 = 1$, $x^2 + y^2 = 16$ **$\left(\frac{\sqrt{34}}{2}, \frac{\sqrt{30}}{2}\right), \left(\frac{\sqrt{34}}{2}, -\frac{\sqrt{30}}{2}\right), \left(-\frac{\sqrt{34}}{2}, \frac{\sqrt{30}}{2}\right), \left(-\frac{\sqrt{34}}{2}, -\frac{\sqrt{30}}{2}\right)$**
6. $y = x - 3$, $x = y^2 - 4$ **$\left(\frac{7 + \sqrt{29}}{2}, \frac{1 + \sqrt{29}}{2}\right), \left(\frac{7 - \sqrt{29}}{2}, \frac{1 - \sqrt{29}}{2}\right)$**

Lesson 10-7

Chapter 10 45 Glencoe Algebra 2

Practice
CRM p. 48 AL OL BL ELL

10-7 Practice
Solving Linear-Nonlinear Systems

Solve each system of equations.

1. $(x - 2)^2 + y^2 = 5$, $x - y = 1$ **(0, −1), (3, 2)**
2. $x = 2(y + 1)^2 - 6$, $x + y = 3$ **(2, 1), (6.5, −3.5)**
3. $y^2 - 3x^2 = 6$, $y = 2x - 1$ **(−1, −3), (5, 9)**
4. $x^2 + 2y^2 = 1$, $y = -x + 1$ **$(1, 0), \left(\frac{1}{3}, \frac{2}{3}\right)$**
5. $4y^2 - 9x^2 = 36$, $4x^2 - 9y^2 = 36$ **no solution**
6. $y = x^2 - 3$, $x^2 + y^2 = 9$ **$(0, -3), (\pm\sqrt{5}, 2)$**
7. $x^2 + y^2 = 25$, $4y = 3x$ **(4, 3), (−4, −3)**
8. $y^2 = 10 - 6x^2$, $4y^2 = 40 - 2x^2$ **$(0, \pm\sqrt{10})$**
9. $x^2 + y^2 = 25$, $x = 3y - 5$ **(−5, 0), (4, 3)**
10. $4x^2 + 9y^2 = 36$, $2x^2 - 9y^2 = 18$ **(±3, 0)**
11. $x = -(y - 3)^2 + 2$, $x = (y - 3)^2 + 3$ **no solution**
12. $\frac{x^2}{9} - \frac{y^2}{16} = 1$, $x^2 + y^2 = 9$ **(±3, 0)**
13. $25x^2 + 4y^2 = 100$, $x = -\frac{5}{2}$ **no solution**
14. $x^2 + y^2 = 4$, $\frac{x^2}{4} + \frac{y^2}{8} = 1$ **(±2, 0)**
15. $x^2 - y^2 = 3$, $y^2 - x^2 = 3$ **no solution**
16. $\frac{x^2}{7} + \frac{y^2}{7} = 1$, $3x^2 - y^2 = 9$ **$(\pm 2, \pm\sqrt{3})$**
17. $x + 2y = 3$, $x^2 + y^2 = 9$ **$(3, 0), \left(-\frac{9}{5}, \frac{12}{5}\right)$**
18. $x^2 + y^2 = 64$, $x^2 - y^2 = 8$ **$(\pm 6, \pm 2\sqrt{7})$**

Solve each system of inequalities by graphing.

19. $y \geq x^2$, $y > -x + 2$
20. $x^2 + y^2 < 36$, $x^2 + y^2 \geq 16$
21. $\frac{(y - 3)^2}{16} + \frac{(x - 2)^2}{4} \leq 1$, $(x + 1)^2 + (y - 2)^2 \leq 4$

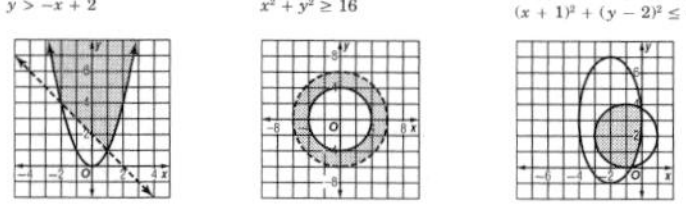

22. **GEOMETRY** The top of an iron gate is shaped like half an ellipse with two congruent segments from the center of the ellipse to the ellipse as shown. Assume that the center of the ellipse is at (0, 0). If the ellipse can be modeled by the equation $x^2 + 4y^2 = 4$ for $y \geq 0$ and the two congruent segments can be modeled by $y = \frac{\sqrt{3}}{2}x$ and $y = -\frac{\sqrt{3}}{2}x$, what are the coordinates of points A and B? **$\left(-1, \frac{\sqrt{3}}{2}\right)$ and $\left(1, \frac{\sqrt{3}}{2}\right)$**

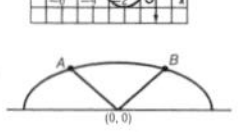

Chapter 10 48 Glencoe Algebra 2

Word Problem Practice
CRM p. 49 AL OL BL ELL

10-7 Word Problem Practice
Solving Linear-Nonlinear Systems

1. **GRAPHIC DESIGN** A graphic designer is drawing an ellipse and a line. The ellipse is drawn so that it appears on top of the line. In order to determine if the line is partially covered by the ellipse, the program solves for simultaneous solutions of the equations of the line and the ellipse. Complete the following table.

No. of Intersections	Covered? Y/N
0	N
1	Y
2	Y

2. **ORBITS** Objects in the solar system travel in elliptical orbits where the Sun is one focal point. Earth's orbit is an ellipse. What is the maximum number of times per orbit that an asteroid also in an elliptical orbit can cross Earth's orbit? **4**

3. **CIRCLES** An artist is commissioned to complete a painting of only circles. She wants to include all possible ways circles can relate. What are the possible numbers of intersection points between two circles? For each case, sketch two distinct circles that intersect with the corresponding number of points. Explain why more intersections are not possible.

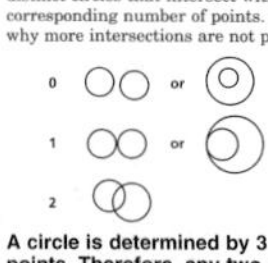

A circle is determined by 3 points. Therefore, any two circles that share 3 or more points must be identical and not distinct.

4. **COLLISION AVOIDANCE** An object is traveling along a hyperbola given by the equation $\frac{x^2}{9} - \frac{y^2}{36} = 1$. A probe is launched from the origin along a straight-line path. Mission planners want the probe to get closer and closer to the object, but never hit it. There are two straight lines that meet their criteria. What are they? **$y = 2x$ and $y = -2x$**

5. **TANGENTS** An architect wants a straight path to run from the origin of a coordinate plane to the edge of an elliptically shaped patio so that the pathway forms a tangent to the ellipse. The ellipse is given by the equation
$$\frac{(x - 6)^2}{12} + \frac{y^2}{96} = 1$$
a. Using the equation $y = mx$ to describe the path, substitute into the equation for the ellipse to get a quadratic equation in x. **$\left(1 + \frac{m^2}{8}\right)x^2 - 12x + 24 = 0$**
b. Solve for m in the equation you found for part a. **$m = 2$ or -2**

Lesson 10-7

Chapter 10 49 Glencoe Algebra 2

Real-World Link

With over 10.3 million participants, paintball is one of America's most popular extreme sports.

Source: *World and Regional Paintball Information Guide*

42. Sample answer: $x^2 + y^2 = 45$, $y = 3|x - 3| - 6$, $y = 3|x + 3| - 6$

Review Vocabulary

quartic equation a fourth-degree polynomial equation (Lesson 6-3)

49. See Chapter 10 Answer Appendix.

53. Sample answer: $\frac{y^2}{128} + \frac{x^2}{32} = 1$ and $\frac{x^2}{8} - \frac{y^2}{64} = 1$

54. Sample answer: By sketching a quick graph of a quadratic system, you can determine how many real solutions there are as well as estimate the values of the solutions. This can help you when confirming the answers that you get algebraically.

42. ADVERTISING The corporate logo for an automobile manufacturer is shown at the right. Write a system of three equations to model this logo.

B

Write a system of equations that satisfies each condition.

43. a circle and an ellipse that intersect at one point

44. a parabola and an ellipse that intersect at two points

45. a hyperbola and a circle that do not intersect

46. an ellipse and a parabola that intersect at three points

47. an ellipse and a hyperbola that intersect at four points

43–47. See Chapter 10 Answer Appendix.

48. FINANCIAL LITERACY Prices are often set on an equilibrium curve, where the supply of a certain product equals its corresponding demand by consumers. An economist represents the supply of a product with $y = p^2 + 10p$ and the corresponding demand with $y = -p^2 + 40p$, where p is the price. Determine the equilibrium price. **$15**

49. PAINTBALL The shape of a paintball field is modeled by $x^2 + 4y^2 = 10{,}000$ in yards where the center is at the origin. The teams are provided with short-range walkie-talkies with a maximum range of 80 yards. Are the teams capable of hearing each other anywhere on the field? Explain your reasoning graphically.

C

50. MULTIPLE REPRESENTATIONS **a, c. See Chapter 10 Answer Appendix.**

a. **GRAPHICAL** Sketch separate graphs of linear, quadratic, cubic, and quartic equations. Draw a straight line through each graph to maximize the number of intersections (solutions).

b. **ANALYTICAL** Use your graphs to fill in the first column of the table below.

50e. Sample answer: The greatest number of solutions to a system of equations equals the product of the degrees of each individual equation.

Maximum Number of Solutions for each System

Type	linear	quadratic	cubic
linear	1	2	3
quadratic	2	4	6
cubic	3	6	9
quartic	4	8	12

c. **GRAPHICAL** Use a parabola and the original four graphs in part **a** to maximize the number of intersections with a quadratic.

d. **ANALYTICAL** Complete the table.

e. **VERBAL** What can you conclude about the relationship between a system of two equations and the greatest number of finite solutions for the system?

H.O.T. Problems
Use Higher-Order Thinking Skills

51. CHALLENGE Find all values of k for which the following system of equations has two solutions. **$k = a$ or $k = b$**

$$\frac{x^2}{a^2} + \frac{y^2}{b^2} = 1 \qquad x^2 + y^2 = k^2$$

52. REASONING When the vertex of a parabola lies on an ellipse, how many solutions can the quadratic system represented by the two graphs have? Explain your reasoning using graphs. **See Chapter 10 Answer Appendix.**

53. OPEN ENDED Write a system of equations, one a hyperbola and the other an ellipse, for which a solution is $(-4, 8)$.

54. WRITING IN MATH Explain how sketching the graph of a quadratic system can help you solve it.

Enrichment
CRM p. 50 OL BL

10-7 Enrichment

Graphing Quadratic Equations with xy-Terms

You can use a graphing calculator to examine graphs of quadratic equations that contain xy-terms.

Example Use a graphing calculator to display the graph of $x^2 + xy + y^2 = 4$.

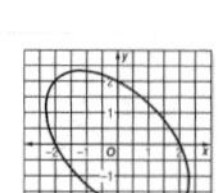

Solve the equation for y in terms of x by using the quadratic formula.

$y^2 + xy + (x^2 - 4) = 0$

To use the formula, let $a = 1$, $b = x$, and $c = (x^2 - 4)$.

$y = \frac{-x \pm \sqrt{x^2 - 4(1)(x^2 - 4)}}{2}$

$y = \frac{-x \pm \sqrt{16 - 3x^2}}{2}$

To graph the equation on the graphing calculator, enter the two equations:

$y = \frac{-x + \sqrt{16 - 3x^2}}{2}$ and $y = \frac{-x - \sqrt{16 - 3x^2}}{2}$

Multiple Representations In Exercise 50, students use graphs, information organized in a table, and analysis to show the relationship between the graphic intersections of two equations and the solutions of systems of two equations.

666 Chapter 10 Conic Sections

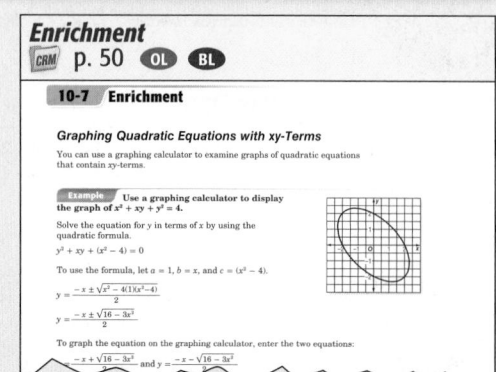

NGSSS PRACTICE 912.A.3.14, 912.A.3.15, 912.A.3.1

55. **SHORT RESPONSE** Solve.

$$4x - 3y = 0$$
$$x^2 + y^2 = 25 \quad (-3, -4), (3, 4)$$

56. You have 16 stamps. Some are postcard stamps that cost \$0.23, and the rest cost \$0.41. If you spent a total of \$5.30 on the stamps, how many postcard stamps do you have? **A**

A. 7
B. 8
C. 9
D. 10

57. Ms. Talbot received a promotion and a 7.2% raise. Her new salary is \$53,600 a year. What was her salary before the raise? **F**

F. \$50,000
G. \$53,600
H. \$55,000
I. \$57,500

58. **ACT/SAT** When a number is multiplied by $\frac{2}{3}$, the result is 188. Find the number. **B**

A. 292
B. 282
C. 272
D. 262

Spiral Review

Match each equation with the situation that it could represent. (Lesson 10-6)

a. $9x^2 + 4y^2 - 36 = 0$
b. $0.004x^2 - x + y - 3 = 0$
c. $x^2 + y^2 - 20x + 30y - 75 = 0$

59. **SPORTS** the flight of a baseball **b**

60. **PHOTOGRAPHY** the oval opening in a picture frame **a**

61. **GEOGRAPHY** the set of all points 20 miles from a landmark **c**

Find the coordinates of the vertices and foci and the equations of the asymptotes for the hyperbola with the given equation. Then graph the hyperbola. (Lesson 10-5) **62–64. See margin.**

62. $\frac{y^2}{16} - \frac{x^2}{25} = 1$ **63.** $\frac{(y-3)^2}{25} - \frac{(x-2)^2}{16} = 1$ **64.** $6y^2 = 2x^2 + 12$

Simplify each expression. (Lesson 9-1)

65. $\frac{12p^2 + 6p - 6}{4(p+1)^2} \div \frac{6p - 3}{2p + 10}$ $\frac{p+5}{p+1}$

66. $\frac{x^2 + 6x + 9}{x^2 + 7x + 6} \div \frac{4x + 12}{3x + 3}$ $\frac{3x+9}{4x+24}$

67. $\frac{r^2 + 2r - 8}{r^2 + 4r + 3} \div \frac{r - 2}{3r + 3}$ $\frac{3(r+4)}{r+3}$

Graph each function. State the domain and range. (Lesson 8-1) **68–70. See Chapter 10 Answer Appendix.**

68. $f(x) = -\left(\frac{1}{5}\right)^x$ **69.** $y = -2.5(5)^x$ **70.** $f(x) = 2\left(\frac{1}{3}\right)^x$

Skills Review

Solve each equation or formula for the specified variable. (Lesson 1-3) 73. $\frac{3V}{\pi r^2} = h$ 74. $\frac{2A}{h} - a = b$

71. $d = rt$, for r $\frac{d}{t} = r$ **72.** $x = \frac{-b}{2a}$, for a $a = \frac{-b}{2x}$ **73.** $V = \frac{1}{3}\pi r^2 h$, for h **74.** $A = \frac{1}{2}h(a + b)$, for b

4 ASSESS

Yesterday's News Ask students to write how yesterday's lesson on conic equations helped them with today's lesson.

Formative Assessment

Check for student understanding of concepts in Lesson 10-7.

CRM Quiz 4, p. 55

Additional Answers

62. $(0, \pm 4)$; $(0, \pm\sqrt{41})$; $y = \pm\frac{4}{5}x$

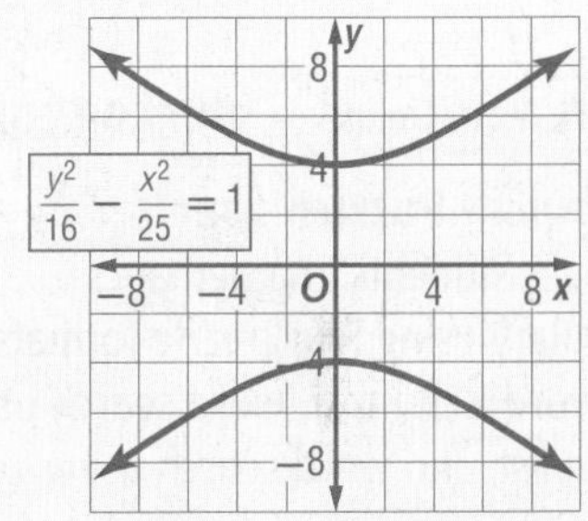

63. $(2, -2), (2, 8)$; $(2, 3 \pm \sqrt{41})$; $y - 3 = \pm\frac{5}{4}(x - 2)$

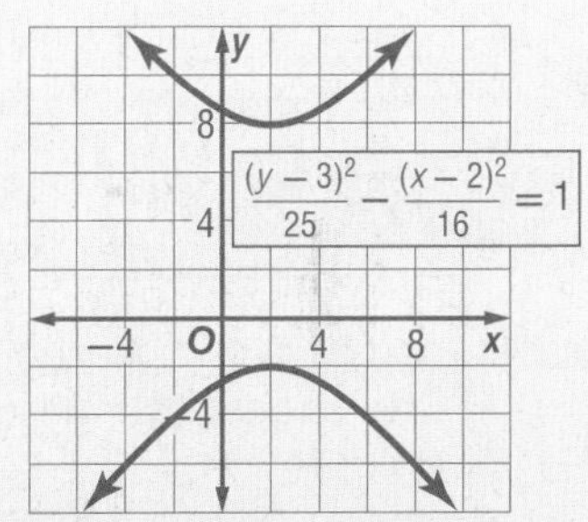

64. $(0, \pm\sqrt{2})$; $(0, \pm 2\sqrt{2})$; $y = \pm\frac{\sqrt{3}}{3}x$;

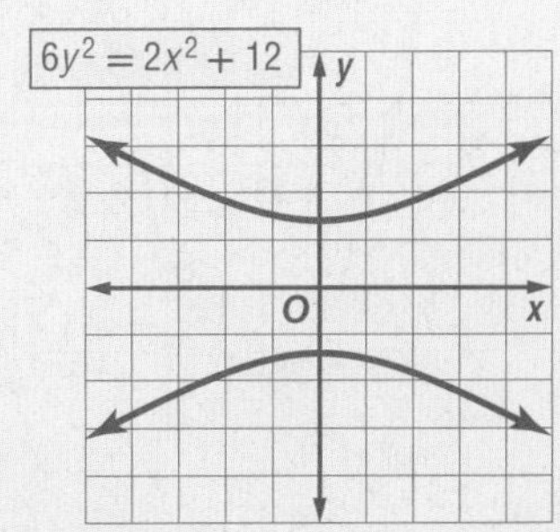

Differentiated Instruction

OL BL

Extension Ask students to solve this system of inequalities by graphing.

$y \geq x^2$
$x^2 + (y - 3)^2 \leq 4$
$y > -x + 2$

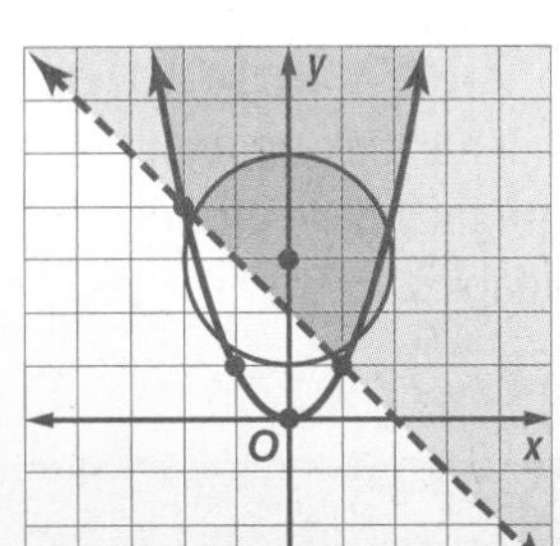

Formative Assessment

Key Vocabulary The page references after each word denote where that term was first introduced. If students have difficulty answering questions 1–10, remind them that they can use these page references to refresh their memories about the vocabulary.

Summative Assessment

CRM Vocabulary Test, p. 56

FL Math Online glencoe.com

Vocabulary PuzzleMaker improves students' mathematics vocabulary using four puzzle formats–crossword, scramble, word search using a word list, and word search using clues. Students can work online or from a printed worksheet.

Additional Answers

20.

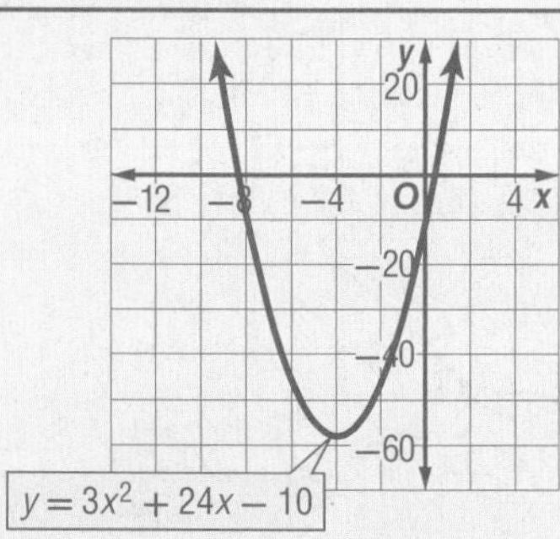

21.

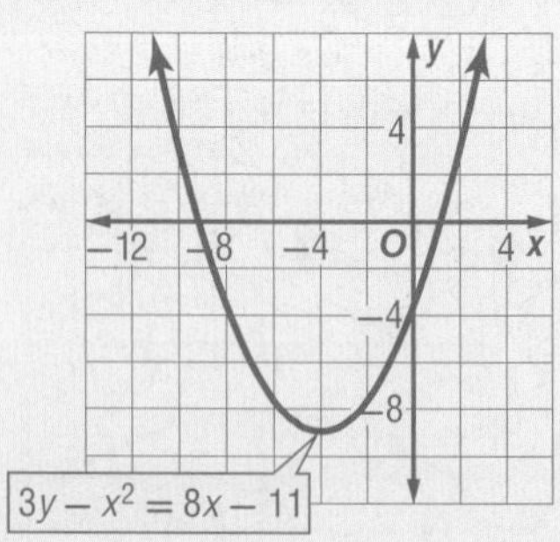

CHAPTER 10 Study Guide and Review

FL Math Online glencoe.com
- STUDY TO GO
- Vocabulary Review

Chapter Summary

Key Concepts

Midpoint and Distance Formulas (Lesson 10-1)

- $M = \left(\frac{x_1 + x_2}{2}, \frac{y_1 + y_2}{2}\right)$
- $d = \sqrt{(x_2 - x_1)^2 + (y_2 - y_1)^2}$

Circles (Lesson 10-2)

- The equation of a circle with center (h, k) and radius r can be written in the form $(x - h)^2 + (y - k)^2 = r^2$.

Parabolas (Lesson 10-3)

- Standard Form: $y = a(x - h)^2 + k$
  $x = a(y - k)^2 + h$

Ellipses (Lesson 10-4)

- Standard Form: horizontal $\frac{(x - h)^2}{a^2} + \frac{(y - k)^2}{b^2} = 1$
  vertical $\frac{(y - k)^2}{a^2} + \frac{(x - h)^2}{b^2} = 1$

Hyperbolas (Lesson 10-5)

- Standard Form: horizontal $\frac{(x - h)^2}{a^2} - \frac{(y - k)^2}{b^2} = 1$
  vertical $\frac{(y - k)^2}{a^2} - \frac{(x - h)^2}{b^2} = 1$

Solving Quadratic Systems (Lesson 10-7)

- Systems of quadratic equations can be solved using substitution and elimination.
- A system of quadratic equations can have zero, one, two, three, or four solutions.

FOLDABLES® Study Organizer

Be sure the Key Concepts are noted in your Foldable.

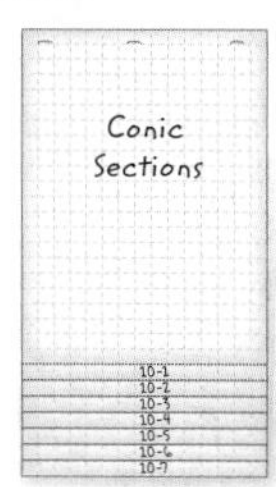

Key Vocabulary

- center (of a circle) (p. 631)
- center (of an ellipse) (p. 639)
- circle (p. 631)
- conjugate axis (p. 648)
- constant difference (p. 651)
- constant sum (p. 640)
- co-vertices (of a hyperbola) (p. 648)
- co-vertices (of an ellipse) (p. 639)
- directrix (p. 623)
- ellipse (p. 639)
- foci (of a hyperbola) (p. 648)
- foci (of an ellipse) (p. 639)
- focus (p. 623)
- hyperbola (p. 648)
- latus rectum (p. 623)
- major axis (p. 639)
- minor axis (p. 639)
- parabola (p. 623)
- radius (p. 631)
- transverse axis (p. 648)
- vertices (of a hyperbola) (p. 648)
- vertices (of an ellipse) (p. 639)

Vocabulary Check

6. false, conjugate axis

State whether each sentence is *true* or *false*. If *false*, replace the underlined term to make a true sentence.

1. The set of all points in a plane that are equidistant from a given point in the plane, called the focus, forms a circle. false, center
2. A(n) ellipse is the set of all points in a plane such that the sum of the distances from the two fixed points is constant. true
3. The endpoints of the major axis of an ellipse are the foci of the ellipse. false, vertices
4. The radius is the distance from the center of a circle to any point on the circle. true
5. The line segment with endpoints on a parabola, through the focus of the parabola, and perpendicular to the axis of symmetry is called the latus rectum. true
6. Every hyperbola has two axes of symmetry, the transverse axis and the major axis.
7. A directrix is the set of all points in a plane that are equidistant from a given point in the plane, called the center. false, circle
8. A hyperbola is the set of all points in a plane such that the absolute value of the sum of the distances from any point on the hyperbola to two given points is constant. false, difference
9. A parabola can be defined as the set of all points in a plane that are the same distance from the focus and a given line called the directrix. true
10. The major axis is the longer of the two axes of symmetry of an ellipse. true

FOLDABLES® Study Organizer

Dinah Zike's Foldables®
Have students look through the chapter to make sure they have included examples in their Foldables.

Suggest that students keep their Foldables handy while completing the Study Guide and Review pages. Point out that their Foldables can serve as a quick review tool when studying for the chapter test.

Lesson-by-Lesson Review

10-1 Midpoint and Distance Formulas (pp. 617–622)

912.G.1.1

Find the midpoint of the line segment with endpoints at the given coordinates.

11. $(-8, 6), (3, 4)$ $\left(-\frac{5}{2}, 5\right)$ **12.** $(-6, 0), (-1, 4)$ $\left(-\frac{7}{2}, 2\right)$

13. $\left(\frac{3}{4}, \frac{2}{3}\right), \left(-\frac{1}{3}, \frac{1}{4}\right)$ **14.** $(15, 20), (18, 21)$ $\left(\frac{33}{2}, \frac{41}{2}\right)$

Find the distance between each pair of points with the given coordinates.

15. $(10, -3), (1, -5)$ $\sqrt{85}$ **16.** $(0, 6), (-9, 7)$ $\sqrt{82}$

17. $\left(\frac{1}{4}, \frac{1}{2}\right), \left(\frac{3}{2}, \frac{5}{4}\right)$ $\frac{\sqrt{34}}{4}$ **18.** $(5, -3), (7, -1)$ $2\sqrt{2}$

19. **HIKING** Marc wants to hike from his camp to a waterfall. The waterfall is 5 miles south and 8 miles east of his campsite.

a. How far away is the waterfall?

b. Marc wants to stop for lunch halfway to the waterfall. Where should he stop? $\left(4, -\frac{5}{2}\right)$

19a. $\sqrt{89} \approx 9.4$ miles

EXAMPLE 1

Find the midpoint of a line segment whose endpoints are at (−4, 8) and (10, −1).

Let $(x_2, y_2) = (-4, 8)$ and $(x_2, y_2) = (10, -1)$.

$\left(\frac{x_1 + x_2}{2}, \frac{y_1 + y_2}{2}\right) = \left(\frac{-4 + 10}{2}, \frac{8 + (-1)}{2}\right)$

$= \left(\frac{6}{2}, \frac{7}{2}\right)$ or $\left(3, \frac{7}{2}\right)$

13. $\left(\frac{5}{24}, \frac{11}{24}\right)$

EXAMPLE 2

Find the distance between $P(5, -3)$ and $Q(-1, 5)$.
Let $(x_1, y_1) = (5, -3)$ and $(x_2, y_2) = (-1, 5)$.

$d = \sqrt{(x_2 - x_1)^2 + (y_2 - y_1)^2}$ Distance Formula

$= \sqrt{(-1 - 5)^2 + [5 - (-3)]^2}$ Substitute.

$= \sqrt{36 + 64}$ Subtract.

$= \sqrt{100}$ or 10 units Simplify.

10-2 Parabolas (pp. 623–629)

912.A.9.1, 912.A.9.2

Graph each equation. 20–23. See margin.

20. $y = 3x^2 + 24x - 10$ **21.** $3y - x^2 = 8x - 11$

22. $x = \frac{1}{2}y^2 - 4y + 3$ **23.** $x = y^2 - 14y + 25$

Write each equation in standard form. Identify the vertex, axis of symmetry, and direction of opening of the parabola. 24–27. See margin.

24. $y = -\frac{1}{2}x^2$ **25.** $y = 4x^2 - 16x + 9$

26. $x - 6y = y^2 + 4$ **27.** $x = y^2 + 14y + 20$

28. **SPORTS** When a football is kicked, the path it travels is shaped like a parabola. Suppose a football is kicked from ground level, reaches a maximum height of 50 feet, and lands 200 feet away. Assuming the football was kicked at the origin, write an equation of the parabola that models the flight of the football.

EXAMPLE 3

Write each equation in standard form. Identify the vertex, axis of symmetry, and direction of opening of $3y - x^2 = 4x + 7$.

Write the equation in the form $y = a(x - h)^2 + k$ by completing the square.

$3y = x^2 + 4x + 7$ Isolate the terms with x.

$3y = (x^2 + 4x + ■) + 7 - ■$ Complete the square.

$3y = (x^2 + 4x + 4) + 7 - 4$ $\left(\frac{4}{2}\right)^2 = 4$

$3y = (x + 2)^2 + 3$ $(x^2 + 4x + 4) = (x + 2)$

$y = \frac{1}{3}(x + 2)^2 + 1$ Divide each side by 3.

Vertex: $(-2, 1)$; axis of symmetry: $x = -2$; direction of opening: upward since $a > 0$.

28. $y = -\frac{1}{200}(x - 100)^2 + 50$

24. $y = -\frac{1}{2}x^2$; vertex: (0, 0); axis of symmetry: $x = 0$; opens: up

25. $y = 4(x - 2)^2 - 7$; vertex: (2, –7); axis of symmetry: $x = 2$; opens: up

26. $x = (y + 3)^2 - 5$; vertex: (–5, –3); axis of symmetry: $y = -3$; opens to the right

27. $x = (y + 7)^2 - 29$; vertex = (–29, –7); axis of symmetry $y = -7$; opens to the right

Lesson-by-Lesson Review

Intervention If the given examples are not sufficient to review the topics covered by the questions, remind students that the page references tell them where to review that topic in their textbook.

Two-Day Option Have students complete the Lesson-by-Lesson Review on pp. 669–672. Then you can use ExamView® Assessment Suite to customize another review worksheet that practices all the objectives of this chapter or only the objectives on which your students need more help.

Differentiated Instruction

Super DVD: Mindjogger Videoquizzes
Use this DVD as an alternative format of review for the test.

Additional Answers

22.

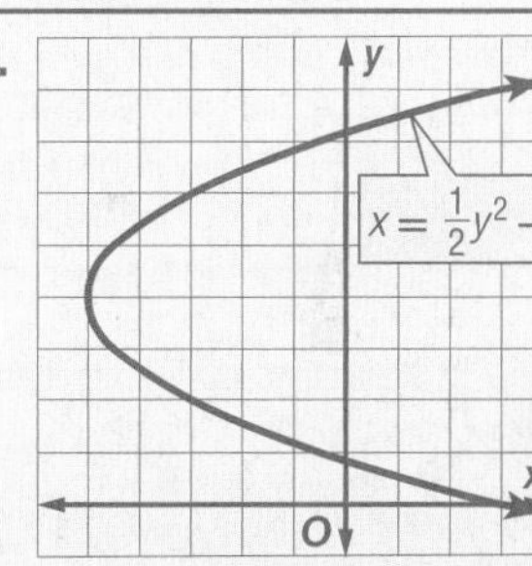

23.

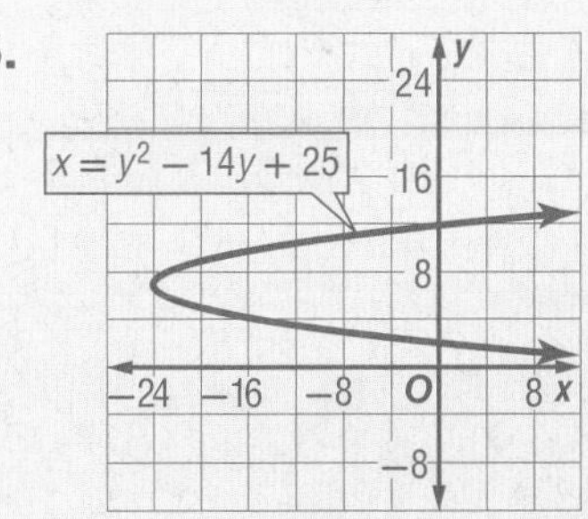

30. $(x-1)^2 + (y-2.5)^2 = \frac{29}{4}$ 31. $(x-1)^2 + (y+4)^2 = 13$

10-3 Circles (pp. 631–637)

912.G.6.6, 912.G.6.7

Write an equation for the circle that satisfies each set of conditions. 29. $(x+1)^2 + (y-6)^2 = 9$

29. center $(-1, 6)$, radius 3 units

30. endpoints of a diameter $(2, 5)$ and $(0, 0)$

31. endpoints of a diameter $(4, -2)$ and $(-2, -6)$

Find the center and radius of each circle. Then graph the circle. 32–35. See margin.

32. $(x+5)^2 + y^2 = 9$

33. $(x-3)^2 + (y+1)^2 = 25$

34. $(x+2)^2 + (y-8)^2 = 1$

35. $x^2 + 4x + y^2 - 2y - 11 = 0$

36. SOUND A loudspeaker in a school is located at the point (65, 40). The speaker can be heard in a circle with a radius of 100 feet. Write an equation to represent the possible boundary of the loudspeaker sound. $(x-65)^2 + (y-40)^2 = 100^2$

EXAMPLE 4

Find the center and radius of the circle with equation $x^2 - 2x + y^2 + 6y + 6 = 0$. Then graph the circle.

Complete the squares.

$$x^2 - 2x + y^2 + 6y + 6 = 0$$
$$(x^2 - 2x + \blacksquare) + (y^2 + 6y + \blacksquare) = -6 + \blacksquare + \blacksquare$$
$$(x^2 - 2x + 1) + (y^2 + 6y + 9) = -6 + 1 + 9$$
$$(x-1)^2 + (y+3)^2 = 4$$

The center of the circle is at $(1, -3)$ and the radius is 2.

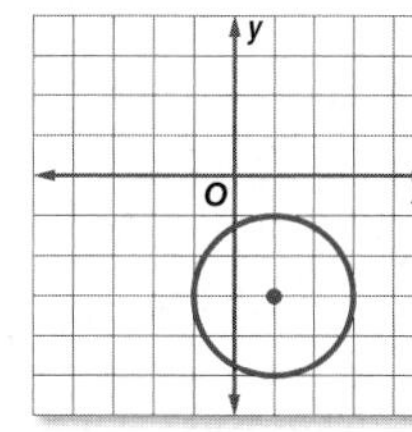

10-4 Ellipses (pp. 639–646) 37–44. See Chapter 10 Answer Appendix.

912.A.9.1

Find the coordinates of the center and foci and the lengths of the major and minor axes for the ellipse with the given equation. Then graph the ellipse.

37. $\frac{x^2}{9} + \frac{y^2}{36} = 1$

38. $\frac{y^2}{10} + \frac{x^2}{5} = 1$

39. $\frac{x^2}{36} + \frac{(y-4)^2}{4} = 1$

40. $27x^2 + 9y^2 = 81$

41. $\frac{(x+1)^2}{25} + \frac{(y-2)^2}{16} = 1$

42. $9x^2 + 4y^2 + 54x - 8y + 49 = 0$

43. $9x^2 + 25y^2 - 18x + 50y - 191 = 0$

44. $7x^2 + 3y^2 - 28x - 12y = -19$

45. LANDSCAPING The Martins have a garden in their front yard that is shaped like an ellipse. The major axis is 16 feet and the minor axis is 10 feet. Write an equation to model the garden. Assume the origin is at the center of the garden and the major axis is horizontal. $\frac{x^2}{64} + \frac{y^2}{25} = 1$

EXAMPLE 5

Find the coordinates of the center and foci and the lengths of the major and minor axes for the ellipse with equation $9x^2 + 16y^2 - 54x + 32y - 47 = 0$. Then graph the ellipse.

First, convert to standard form.

$$9x^2 + 16y^2 - 54x + 32y - 47 = 0$$
$$9(x^2 - 6x + \blacksquare) + 16(y^2 + 2y + \blacksquare) = 47 + 9(\blacksquare) + 16(\blacksquare)$$
$$9(x^2 - 6x + 9) + 16(y^2 + 2y + 1) = 47 + 9(9) + 16(1)$$
$$9(x-3)^2 + 16(y+1)^2 = 144$$
$$\frac{(x-3)^2}{16} + \frac{(y+1)^2}{9} = 1$$

The center of the ellipse is $(3, -1)$. The ellipse is horizontal. $a^2 = 16$, so $a = 4$. $b^2 = 9$, so $b = 3$. The length of the major axis is $2 \cdot 4$ or 8. The length of the minor axis is $2 \cdot 3$ or 6. To find the foci: $c^2 = 16 - 9$ or 7, so $c = \sqrt{7}$. The foci are $(3 + \sqrt{7}, -1)$ and $(3 - \sqrt{7}, -1)$.

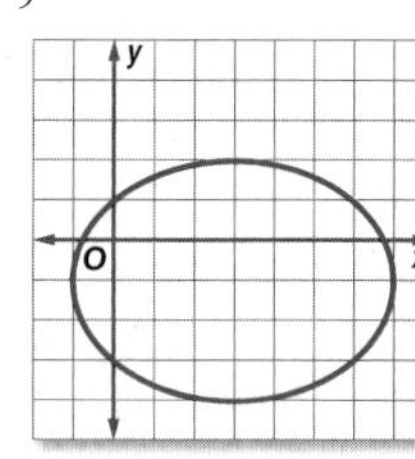

Additional Answers

32. $(-5, 0)$; $r = 3$

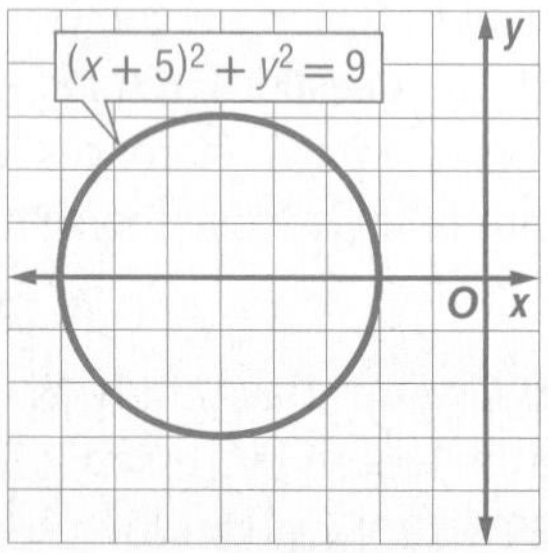

33. $(3, -1)$; $r = 5$

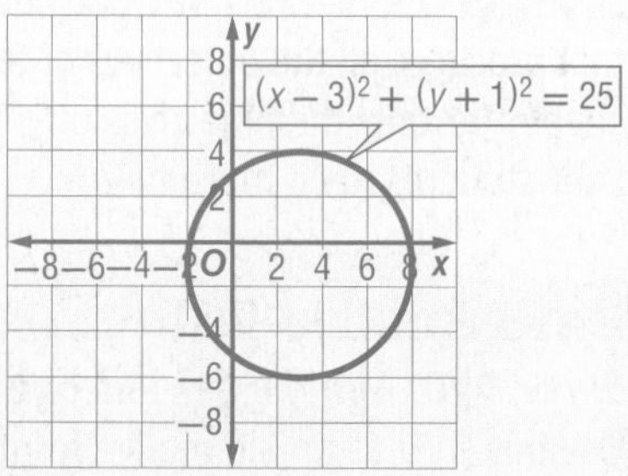

34. $(-2, 8)$; $r = 1$

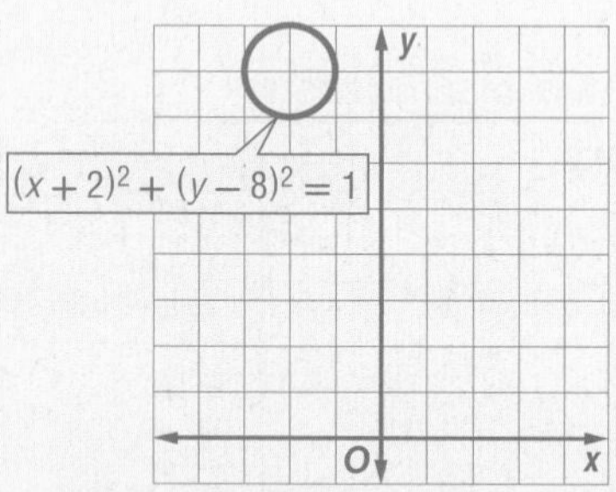

35. $(-2, 1)$; $r = 4$

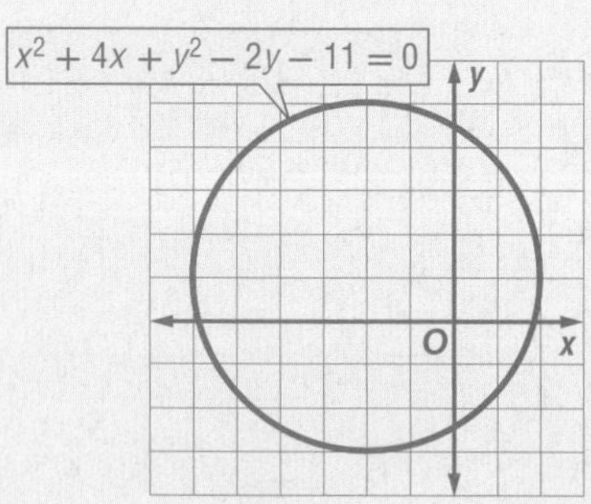

46. $(0, \pm 3)$; $(0, \pm\sqrt{13})$; $y = \pm\frac{3}{2}x$

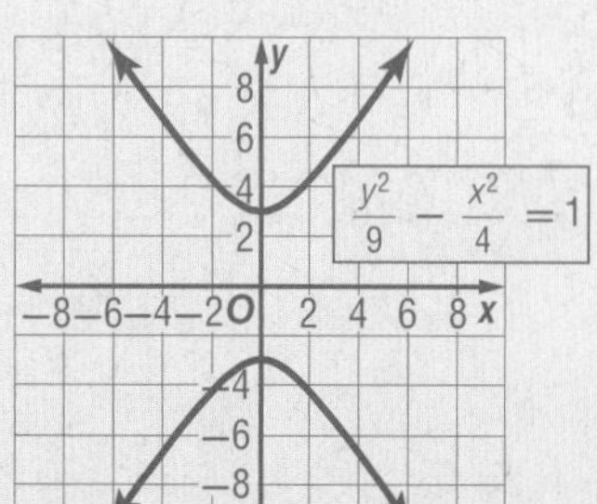

47. $(2, -2)$, $(4, -2)$; $(3 \pm \sqrt{5}, -2)$; $y + 2 = \pm 2(x - 3)$

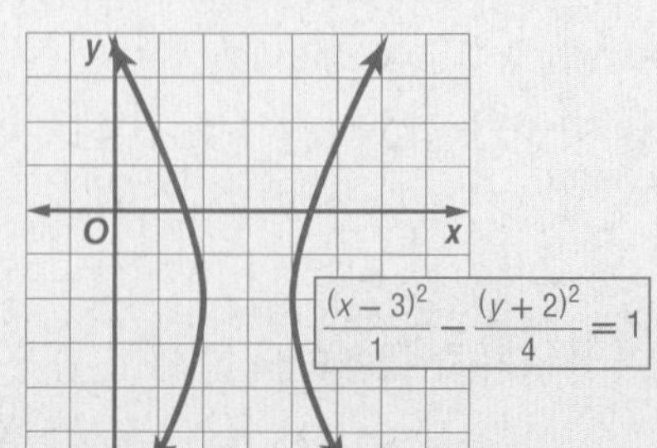

10-5 Hyperbolas (pp. 648–655)

912.A.9.1, 912.A.9.2

Graph each hyperbola. Identify the vertices, foci, and asymptotes. 46–50. See margin.

46. $\frac{y^2}{9} - \frac{x^2}{4} = 1$

47. $\frac{(x-3)^2}{1} - \frac{(y+2)^2}{4} = 1$

48. $\frac{(y+1)^2}{16} - \frac{(x-4)^2}{9} = 1$

49. $4x^2 - 9y^2 = 36$

50. $9y^2 - x^2 - 4x + 18y + 4 = 0$

51. MIRRORS A hyperbolic mirror is shaped like one branch of a hyperbola. It reflects light rays directed at one focus toward the other focus. Suppose a hyperbolic mirror is modeled by the upper branch of the hyperbola $\frac{y^2}{9} - \frac{x^2}{16} = 1$. A light source is located at $(-10, 0)$. Where should the light hit the mirror so that the light will be reflected to $(0, -5)$? See margin.

EXAMPLE 6

Graph $9x^2 - 4y^2 - 36x - 8y - 4 = 0$. Identify the vertices, foci, and asymptotes.

Complete the square.

$$9x^2 - 4y^2 - 36x - 8y - 4 = 0$$
$$9(x^2 - 4x + ■) - 4(y^2 + 2y + ■) = 4 + 9(■) - 4(■)$$
$$9(x^2 - 4x + 4) - 4(y^2 + 2y + 1) = 4 + 9(4) - 4(1)$$
$$9(x-2)^2 - 4(y+1)^2 = 36$$
$$\frac{(x-2)^2}{4} - \frac{(y+1)^2}{9} = 1$$

The center is at $(2, -1)$. The vertices are at $(0, -1)$ and $(4, -1)$. The foci are at $\left(2 + \sqrt{13}, -1\right)$ and $\left(2 - \sqrt{13}, -1\right)$. The equations of the asymptotes are $y + 1 = \pm\frac{3}{2}(x - 2)$.

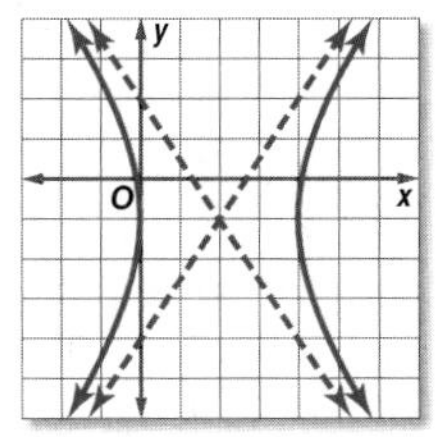

10-6 Identifying Conic Sections (pp. 656–660)

912.A.9.1, 912.A.9.2

Write each equation in standard form. State whether the graph of the equation is a *parabola*, *circle*, *ellipse*, or *hyperbola*. Then graph.

52. $3x^2 + 12x - y + 8 = 0$ 52–55. See Chapter 10 Answer Appendix.

53. $9x^2 + 16y^2 = 144$

54. $x^2 + y^2 - 8x - 2y + 8 = 0$

55. $-9x^2 + y^2 + 36x - 45 = 0$

Without writing the equation in standard form, state whether the graph of the equation is a *parabola*, *circle*, *ellipse*, or *hyperbola*.

56. $7x^2 + 9y^2 = 63$ ellipse

57. $5y^2 + 2y + 4x - 13x^2 = 81$ hyperbola

58. $x^2 - 8x + 16 = 6y$ parabola

59. $x^2 + 4x + y^2 - 285 = 0$ circle

60. LIGHT Suppose the edge of a shadow can be represented by the equation $16x^2 + 25y^2 - 32x - 100y - 284 = 0$.

a. What is the shape of the shadow? ellipse

b. Graph the equation. See margin.

EXAMPLE 7

Write $3x^2 + 3y^2 - 12x + 30y + 39 = 0$ in standard form. State whether the graph of the equation is a *parabola*, *circle*, *ellipse*, or *hyperbola*. Then graph the equation.

$$3x^2 + 3y^2 - 12x + 30y + 39 = 0$$
$$3(x^2 - 4x + ■) + 3(y^2 + 10y + ■) = -39 + 3(■) + 3(■)$$
$$3(x^2 - 4x + 4) + 3(y^2 + 10y + 25) = -39 + 3(4) + 3(25)$$
$$3(x-2)^2 + 3(y+5)^2 = 48$$
$$(x-2)^2 + (y+5)^2 = 16$$

In this equation $A = 3$ and $C = 3$. Since A and C are both positive and $A = C$, the graph is a circle. The center is at $(2, -5)$ and the radius is 4.

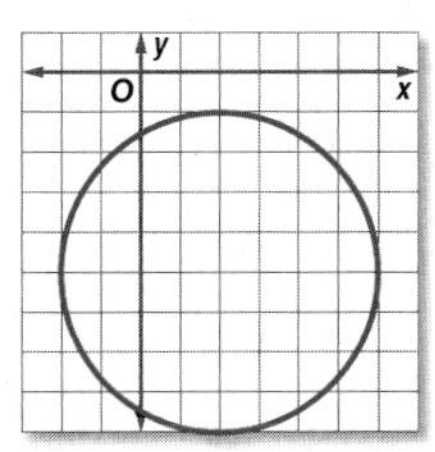

Additional Answers

48. $(4, -5), (4, 3), (4, -6), (4, 4)$; $y + 1 = \pm\frac{4}{3}(x - 4)$

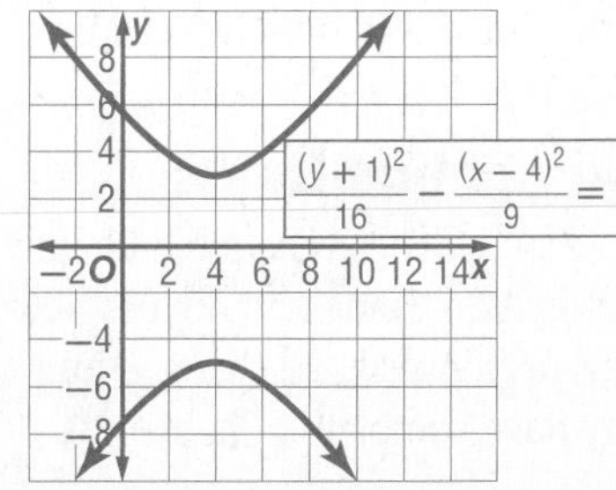

49. $(\pm3, 0)$; $(\pm\sqrt{13}, 0)$; $y = \pm\frac{2}{3}x$

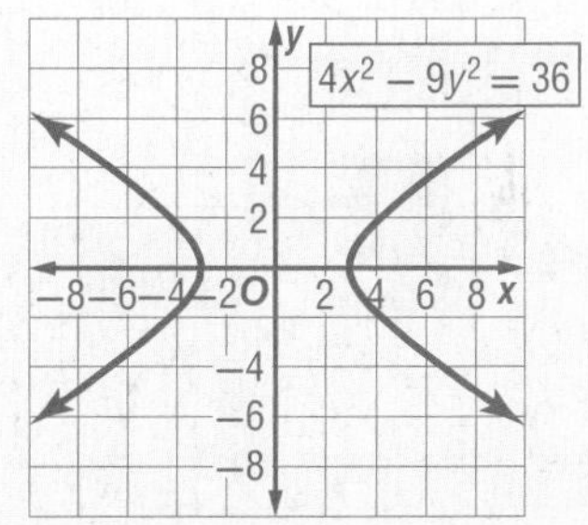

50. $\left(-2, -\frac{2}{3}\right), \left(-2, -\frac{4}{3}\right)$; $\left(-2, -1 \pm \frac{\sqrt{10}}{3}\right)$; $y + 1 = \pm\frac{1}{3}(x + 2)$

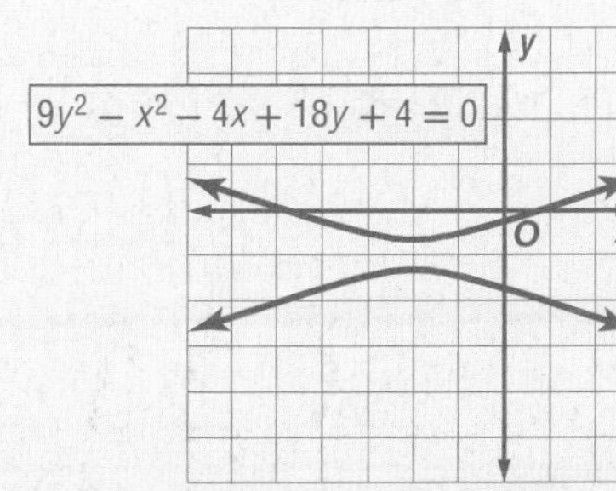

51. $\left(\frac{40 - 24\sqrt{5}}{5}, \frac{45 - 12\sqrt{5}}{5}\right)$

60b.

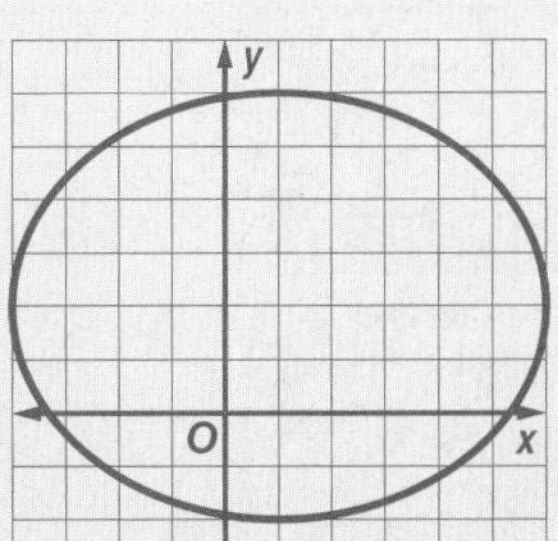

Problem Solving Review

For additional practice in problem solving for Chapter 10, see the Mixed Problem Solving Appendix, p. 980–993, in the Student Handbook section.

Anticipation Guide

Have students complete the Chapter 10 Anticipation Guide and discuss how their responses have changed now that they have completed Chapter 10.

Additional Answers

69.

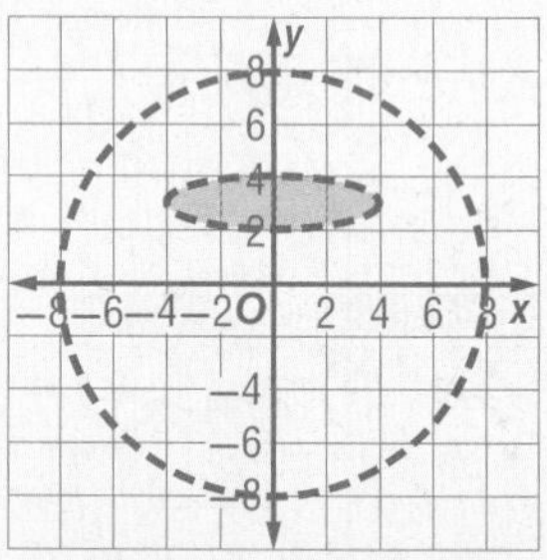

70.

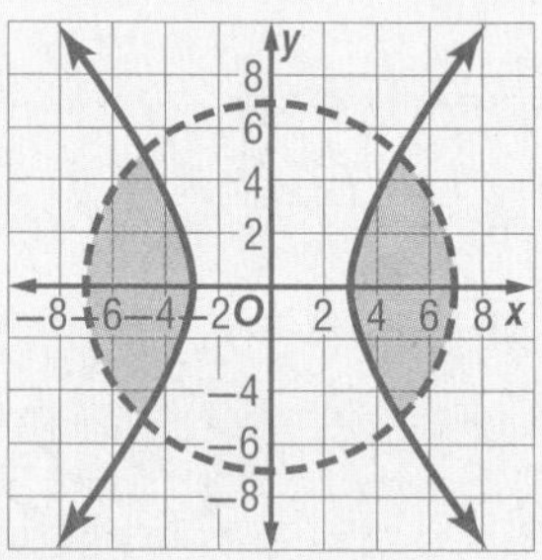

71.

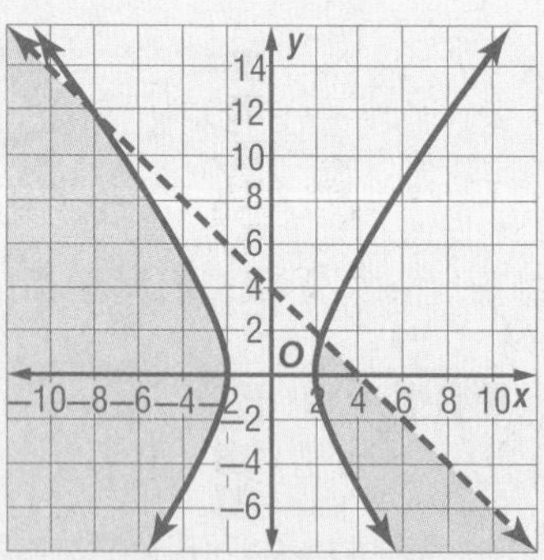

72.

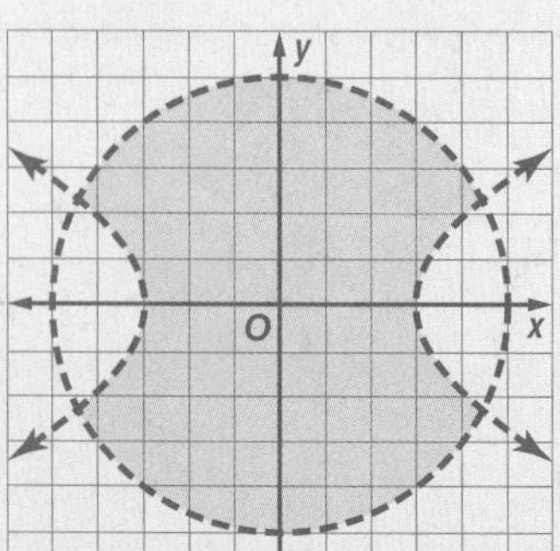

10-7 Solving Quadratics Systems (pp. 662–667)

64. (−2, −1), (−2, 1), (2, −1), (2, 1)

912.A.7.7

Solve each system of equations.

61. $x^2 + y^2 = 8$, $x + y = 0$ (2, −2), (−2, 2)

62. $x - 2y = 2$, $y^2 - x^2 = 2x + 4$ (−2, −2)

63. $y + x^2 = 4x$, $y + 4x = 16$ (4, 0)

64. $3x^2 - y^2 = 11$, $x^2 + 4y^2 = 8$

65. $5x^2 + y^2 = 30$, $9x^2 - y^2 = -16$ (1, ±5), (−1, ±5)

66. $\frac{x^2}{30} + \frac{y^2}{6} = 1$, $x = y$ $(\sqrt{5}, \sqrt{5})$, $(-\sqrt{5}, -\sqrt{5})$

67. **PHYSICAL SCIENCE** Two balls are launched into the air at the same time. The heights they are launched from are different. The height y in feet of one is represented by $y = -16t^2 + 80t + 25$ where t is the time in seconds. The height of the other ball is represented by $y = -16t^2 + 30t + 100$.

   a. After how many seconds are the balls at the same height? 1.5 seconds

   b. What is this height? 109 ft

68. **ARCHITECTURE** An architect is building the front entrance of a building in the shape of a parabola with the equation $y = -\frac{1}{10}(x - 10)^2 + 20$. While the entrance is being built, the construction team puts in two support beams with equations $y = -x + 10$ and $y = x - 10$. Where do the support beams meet the parabola? (0, 10) and (20, 10)

69–74. See margin.

Solve each system of inequalities by graphing.

69. $x^2 + y^2 < 64$, $x^2 + 16(y - 3)^2 < 16$

70. $x^2 + y^2 < 49$, $16x^2 - 9y^2 \geq 144$

71. $x + y < 4$, $9x^2 - 4y^2 \geq 36$

72. $x^2 + y^2 < 25$, $4x^2 - 9y^2 < 36$

73. $x^2 + y^2 < 36$, $4x^2 + 9y^2 > 36$

74. $y^2 < x$, $x^2 - 4y^2 < 16$

EXAMPLE 8

Solve the system of equations.

$x^2 + y^2 = 100$

$3x - y = 10$

Use substitution to solve the system.
First, rewrite $3x - y = 10$ as $y = 3x - 10$.

$$x^2 + y^2 = 100$$
$$x^2 + (3x - 10)^2 = 100$$
$$x^2 + 9x^2 - 60x + 100 = 100$$
$$10x^2 - 60x + 100 = 100$$
$$10x^2 - 60x = 0$$
$$10x(x - 6) = 0$$

$10x = 0$ or $x - 6 = 0$

$x = 0$ $\quad$ $x = 6$

Now solve for y.

$y = 3x - 10 = 3(0) - 10 = -10$

$y = 3x - 10 = 3(6) - 10 = 8$

The solutions of the system are (0, −10) and (6, 8).

EXAMPLE 9

Solve the system of inequalities by graphing.

$x^2 + y^2 \leq 9$

$2y \geq x^2 + 4$

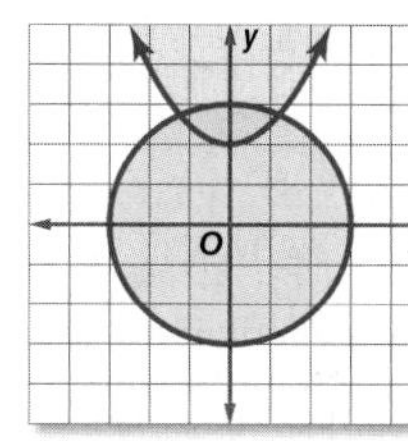

The solution is the green shaded region.

73.

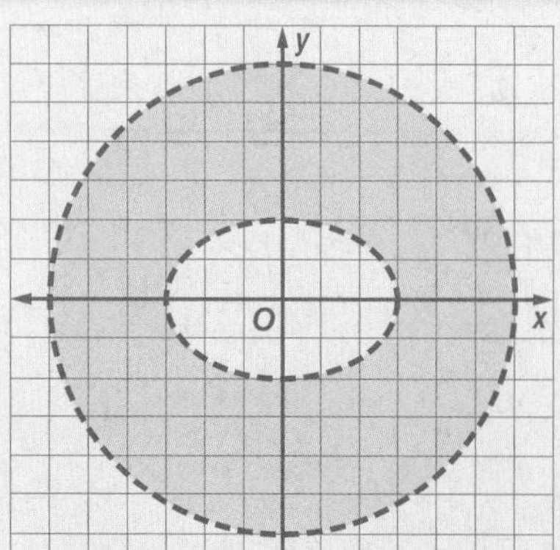

74.

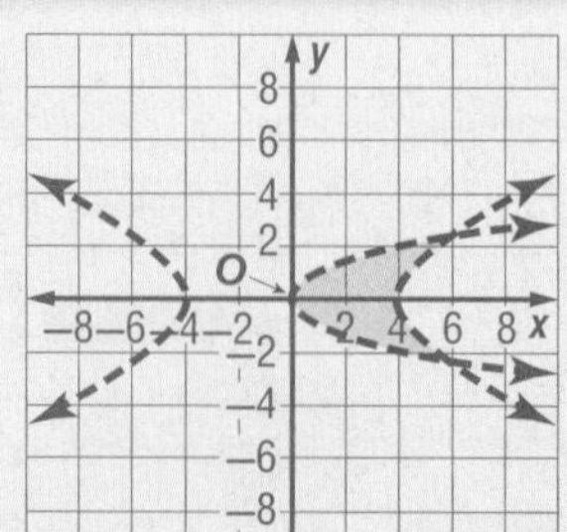

Practice Test

FL Math Online glencoe.com
Chapter Test

Find the midpoint of the line segment with endpoints at the given coordinates.

1. (8, 3), (−4, 9) (2, 6)
2. $\left(\frac{3}{4}, 0\right), \left(\frac{1}{2}, -1\right)$ $\left(\frac{5}{8}, -\frac{1}{2}\right)$
3. (−10, 0), (−2, 6) (−6, 3)

Find the distance between each pair of points with the given coordinates.

4. (−5, 8), (4, 3) $\sqrt{106}$
5. $\left(\frac{1}{3}, \frac{2}{3}\right), \left(-\frac{5}{6}, -\frac{11}{6}\right)$ $\frac{\sqrt{274}}{6}$
6. (4, −5), (4, 9) 14

State whether the graph of each equation is a *parabola*, *circle*, *ellipse*, or *hyperbola*. Then graph the equation. 7–16. See Chapter 10 Answer Appendix.

7. $y^2 = 64 - x^2$
8. $4x^2 + y^2 = 16$
9. $4x^2 - 9y^2 + 8x + 36y = 68$
10. $\frac{1}{2}x^2 - 3 = y$
11. $y = -2x^2 - 5$
12. $16x^2 + 25y^2 = 400$
13. $x^2 + 6x + y^2 = 16$
14. $\frac{y^2}{4} - \frac{x^2}{16} = 1$
15. $(x + 2)^2 = 3(y - 1)$
16. $4x^2 + 16y^2 + 32x + 63 = 0$

17. **NGSSS PRACTICE** Which equation represents a hyperbola that has vertices at (−3, −3) and (5, −3) and a conjugate axis of length 6 units? B

A. $\frac{(y-1)^2}{16} - \frac{(x+3)^2}{9} = 1$

B. $\frac{(x-1)^2}{16} - \frac{(y+3)^2}{9} = 1$

C. $\frac{(y+1)^2}{16} - \frac{(x-3)^2}{9} = 1$

D. $\frac{(x+1)^2}{16} - \frac{(y-3)^2}{9} = 1$

18. $10\sqrt{15}$ or about 38.73 inches

18. **CARPENTRY** Ellis built a window frame shaped like the top half of an ellipse. The window is 40 inches tall at its highest point and 160 inches wide at the bottom. What is the height of the window 20 inches from the center of the base?

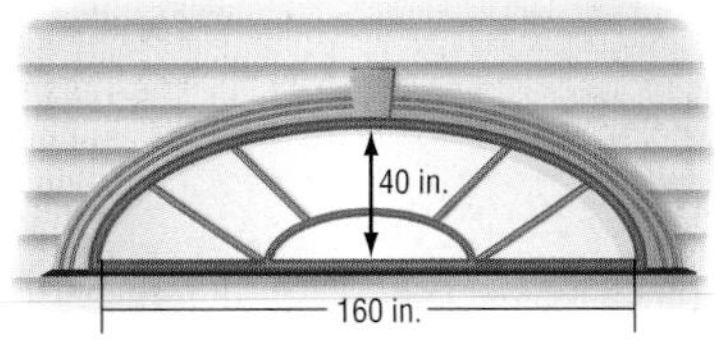

Solve each system of equations.

19. $x^2 + y^2 = 100$, $y = -x - 2$ (−8, 6), (6, −8)
20. $x^2 + 2y^2 = 11$, $x + y = 2$ $(3, -1), \left(-\frac{1}{3}, \frac{7}{3}\right)$
21. $x^2 + y^2 = 34$, $y^2 - x^2 = 9$ $\left(\pm\frac{5\sqrt{2}}{2}, \pm\frac{\sqrt{86}}{2}\right)$

Solve each system of inequalities. 22, 23. See margin.

22. $x^2 + y^2 \le 9$, $y > -x^2 + 2$

23. $\frac{(x-2)^2}{4} - \frac{(y-4)^2}{9} \ge 1$, $x - 4y < 8$

24. **NGSSS PRACTICE** Which is NOT the equation of a parabola? I

F. $y = 3x^2 + 5x - 3$

G. $2y + 3x^2 + x - 9 = 0$

H. $x = 3(y + 1)^2$

I. $x^2 + 2y^2 + 6x = 10$

25. **FORESTRY** A forest ranger at an outpost in the Sam Houston National Forest and another ranger at the primary station both heard an explosion. The outpost and the primary station are 6 kilometers apart. a, b. See margin.

a. If one ranger heard the explosion 6 seconds before the other, write an equation that describes all the possible locations of the explosion. Place the two ranger stations on the x-axis with the midpoint between the stations at the origin. The transverse axis is horizontal. (*Hint*: The speed of sound is about 0.35 kilometer per second.)

b. Draw a sketch of the possible locations of the explosion. Include the ranger stations in the drawing.

ExamView Assessment Suite Customize and create multiple versions of your chapter test and their answer keys. All of the questions from the leveled chapter tests in the *Chapter 10 Resource Masters* are also available on ExamView® Assessment Suite.

Additional Answers

22.

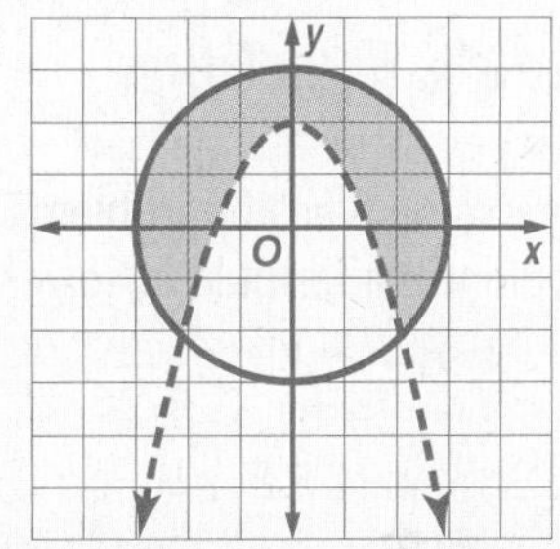

23.

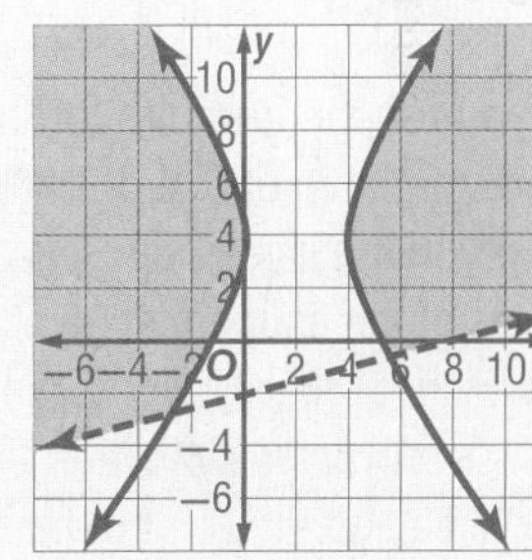

25a. $\frac{x^2}{1.1025} - \frac{y^2}{7.8975} = 1$

25b.

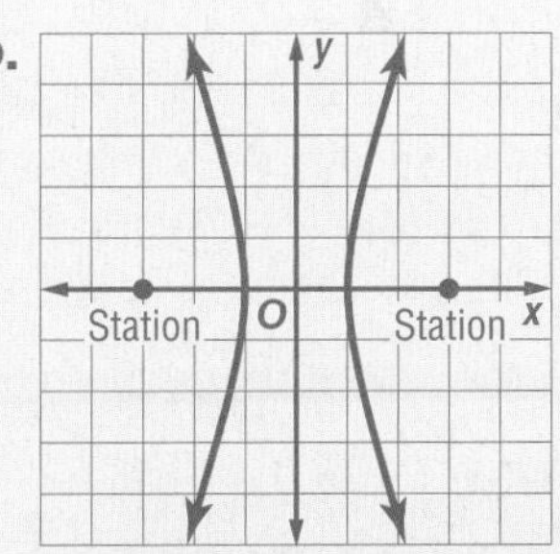

Intervention Planner

Tier 1 On Level	Tier 2 Strategic Intervention approaching grade level	Tier 3 Intensive Intervention 2 or more grades below level
If students miss about 25% of the exercises or less,	**If** students miss about 50% of the exercises,	**If** students miss about 75% of the exercises,
Then choose a resource: **SE** Lessons 10-1, 10-2, 10-3, 10-4, 10-5, 10-6, and 10-7 **CRM** Skills Practice, pp. 7, 13, 20, 27, 34, 41, and 47 **TE** Chapter Project, p. 614	**Then** choose a resource: **CRM** Study Guide and Intervention, Chapter 10, pp. 5, 11, 18, 25, 32, 39, and 45	**Then** use *Math Triumphs, Alg. 2*
FL Math Online Self-Check Quiz	FL Math Online Extra Examples, Personal Tutor, Homework Help	FL Math Online Extra Examples, Personal Tutor, Homework Help, Review Vocabulary

1 FOCUS

Objective Use the strategy of use a formula to solve standardized test problems.

2 TEACH

Scaffolding Questions

Ask:

- What are some types of problems you would use a formula to solve? Sample answers: finding a distance, finding the perimeter, area or volume of various geometric figures, solving a quadratic equation with the Quadratic Formula
- How do you use the formulas for the coordinates of the midpoint of a line segment if you are given both sets of coordinates of the endpoints? Sample answer: For the x-coordinate, add the endpoint's x-coordinates together and divide by 2. To find the y-coordinate, add the endpoint's y-coordinates then divide by 2.

CHAPTER 10 Preparing for Standardized Tests

Use a Formula

Sometimes it is necessary to use a formula to solve problems on standardized tests. In some cases you may even be given a sheet of formulas that you are permitted to reference while taking the test.

Strategies for Using a Formula

Step 1

Read the problem statement carefully.

Ask yourself:

- What am I being asked to solve?
- What information is given in the problem?
- Are there any formulas that I can use to help me solve the problem?

Step 2

Solve the problem and check your solution.

- Substitute the known quantities that are given in the problem statement into the formula.
- Simplify to solve for the unknown values in the formula.
- Check to make sure your answer makes sense. If time permits, check your answer.

NGSSS PRACTICE EXAMPLE

Read the problem. Identify what you need to know. Then use the information in the problem to solve. Show your work.

What is the distance between points A and B on the coordinate plane? Round your answer to the nearest tenth if necessary.

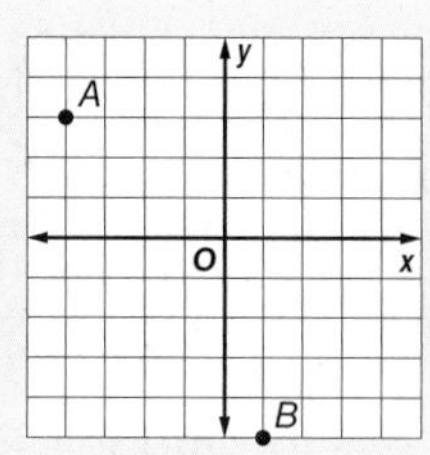

Scoring Rubric	
Criteria	**Score**
Full Credit: The answer is correct and a full explanation is provided that shows each step.	2
Partial Credit: • The answer is correct, but the explanation is incomplete. • The answer is incorrect, but the explanation is correct.	1
No Credit: Either an answer is not provided or the answer does not make sense.	0

Read the problem statement carefully. You are given the coordinates of two points on a coordinate plane and asked to find the distance between them. To solve this problem, you must use the **Distance Formula**.

Example of a 2-point response:

> Use the Distance Formula to find the distance between points $A(-4, 3)$ and $B(1, -5)$.
>
> $d = \sqrt{(x_2 - x_1)^2 + (y_2 - y_1)^2}$
>
> $= \sqrt{[1 - (-4)]^2 + [(-5) - 3]^2}$
>
> $= \sqrt{5^2 + (-8)^2}$
>
> $= \sqrt{25 + 64}$
>
> $= \sqrt{89}$ or about 9.4
>
> The distance between points A and B is about 9.4 units.

The steps, calculations, and reasoning are clearly stated. The student also arrives at the correct answer. So, this response is worth the full 2 points.

Exercises

Read each problem. Identify what you need to know. Then use the information in the problem to solve. Show your work.

1. What is the midpoint of segment CD with endpoints $C(5, -12)$ and $D(-9, 4)$? $M(-2, -4)$

2. Katrina is making a map of her hometown on a coordinate plane. She plots the school at $S(7, 3)$ and the park at $P(-4, 12)$. If the scale of the map is 1 unit = 250 yards, what is the actual distance between the school and the park? Round to the nearest yard. **about 3553 yd**

3. Mr. Washington is making a concrete table for his backyard. The tabletop will be circular with a diameter of 6 feet and a depth of 6 inches. How much concrete will Mr. Washington need to make the top of the table? Round to the nearest cubic foot. **14 ft³**

4. What is the equation, in standard form, of the hyperbola graphed below? $\frac{(y+1)^2}{9} - \frac{(x-2)^2}{16} = 1$

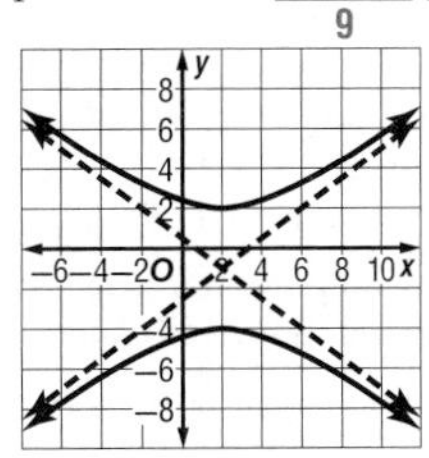

5. If the surface area of a cube is increased by a factor of 9, what is the change in the length of the sides of the cube? **B**

   A. The length is 2 times the original length.

   B. The length is 3 times the original length.

   C. The length is 6 times the original length.

   D. The length is 9 times the original length.

Additional Example

STANDARDIZED TEST PRACTICE
Find the exact solution for the following system of equations. D

$y = 5 - x^2$

$y = 2x^2 + 2$

A (2, 2), (−2, 2)
B (1, 2), (−1, 2)
C (4, −1), (4, 1)
D (−1, 4), (1, 4)

3 ASSESS

Use Exercises 1–5 to assess students' understanding.

Chapter 10 Preparing for Standardized Tests 675

Diagnose Student Errors

Survey student responses for each item. Class trends may indicate common errors and misconceptions.

1. A. this line is *not* incorrect
B. correct
C. this is the *second* incorrect step
D. since there is an incorrect step, this is not true

2. F. doesn't pass through (1, 9)
G. guess
H. correct
I. doesn't have (–3, –23) as focus

6. A. multiplied by x but not by 2
B. multiplied by 2 but not by x
C. correct
D. did not apply the Distributive Property consistently

7. F. found $-\frac{1}{3}$ slope
G. found $\frac{3}{4}$ slope
H. found $-\frac{7}{3}$ slope
I. correct

8. A. correct
B. guess
C. guess
D. guess

9. F. correct
G. guess
H. solved $\sqrt{x+5} = 4$
I. solved $\sqrt{x+5} - 1 = 4$

14. A. these are the co-vertices
B. guess
C. correct
D. guess

15. F. mistakenly divided 40 by 5
G. mistakenly added 14 and 5
H. correct
I. guess

Read each question. Then fill in the correct answer on the answer document provided by your teacher or on a sheet of paper.

1. Which is the first *incorrect* step in simplifying $\log_3 \frac{3}{48}$? B

Step 1: $\log_3 \frac{3}{48} = \log_3 3 - \log_3 48$
Step 2: $= 1 - 16$
Step 3: $= -15$

A. Step 1
B. Step 2
C. Step 3
D. Each step is correct.

2. Which is the equation for the parabola that has vertex (−3, −23) and passes through the point (1, 9)? H

F. $y = x^2 + 10x + 7$
G. $y = x^2 - 6x + 19$
H. $y = 2x^2 + 12x - 5$
I. $y = 2x^2 - 3x + 10$

3a. 82, 66

3. **EXTENDED RESPONSE** The Colonial High School Yearbook Staff is selling yearbooks and chrome picture frames engraved with the year. The number of yearbooks and frames sold to members of each grade is shown in the table.

Sales for Each Class

Grade	Yearbooks	Frames
9th	423	256
10th	464	278
11th	546	344
12th	575	497

a. Find the difference in the sales of yearbooks and frames made to the 10th and 11th grade classes.

b. Find the total number of yearbooks and frames sold. 2008, 1375

c. A yearbook costs \$48 and a frame costs \$18. Find the sales of yearbooks and frames for each class. yearbooks: \$20,304, \$22,272, \$26,208, \$27,600; frames: \$4608, \$5004, \$6192, \$8946

Test-TakingTip

Question 2 You can check your answer by substituting 1 for x and making sure that the y-value is 9.

4. **SHORT RESPONSE** A placekicker kicks a ball upward with a velocity of 32 feet per second. Ignoring the height of the kicking tee, how long after the football is kicked does it hit the ground? Use the formula $h(t) = v_0t - 16t^2$, where $h(t)$ is the height of an object in feet, v_0 is the object's initial velocity in feet per second, and t is the time in seconds. 2 seconds

5. **GRIDDED RESPONSE** What is the maximum number of solutions of a system of equations that consists of a circle and a hyperbola? 4

6. The area of the base of a rectangular suitcase measures $3x^2 + 5x - 4$ square units. The height of the suitcase measures $2x$ units. Which polynomial expression represents the volume of the suitcase? C

A. $3x^3 + 5x^2 - 4x$
B. $6x^2 + 10x - 8$
C. $6x^3 + 10x^2 - 8x$
D. $3x^3 + 10x^2 - 4$

7. Malina was given this geoboard to model the slope $-\frac{3}{4}$.

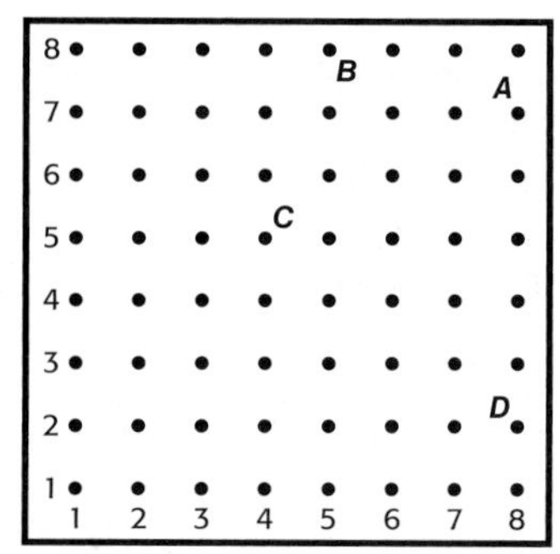

If the peg in the upper right-hand corner represents the origin on a coordinate plane, where could Malina place a rubber band to represent the given slope? I

F. from peg A to peg B
G. from peg A to peg C
H. from peg B to peg D
I. from peg C to peg D

8. Angela is making a map of her backyard on a coordinate grid. She plots point $G(-4, -6)$ to represent her mom's garden and point $S(3, 7)$ to represent the rope swing hanging on an oak tree. If the scale of the map is 1 unit = 5 feet, what is the approximate distance between the garden and the rope swing? **A**

A. 74 feet
B. 79 feet
C. 82 feet
D. 90 feet

9. If $\sqrt{x+5} + 1 = 4$, what is the value of x? **F**

F. 4
G. 10
H. 11
I. 20

10. **SHORT RESPONSE** Lupe is preparing boxes of assorted chocolates. Chocolate-covered peanuts cost \$7 per pound. Chocolate-covered caramels cost \$6.50 per pound. The boxes of assorted candies contain five more pounds of peanut candies than caramel candies. If the total amount sold was \$575, how many pounds of each candy were needed to make the boxes? **40 lb caramel, 45 lb peanut**

11. **GRIDDED RESPONSE** What is the y-coordinate of the midpoint of segment AB with endpoints $A(0.8, 5.32)$ and $B(0.44, 2.2)$? **3.76**

12. **SHORT RESPONSE** Marc went shopping and bought two shirts, three pairs of pants, one belt, and two pairs of shoes. The following matrix shows the prices for each item respectively.

$$[\ \$20.15 \quad \$32 \quad \$15 \quad \$25.99\ ]$$

Use matrix multiplication to find the total amount of money Marc spent while shopping. **\$203.28**

13. **EXTENDED RESPONSE** Clarence graphed the quadratic equation $h(t) = -16t^2 + 128t$ to model the flight of a firework. The parabola shows the height, in feet, of the firework t seconds after it was launched. **13b. the maximum height of the rocket**

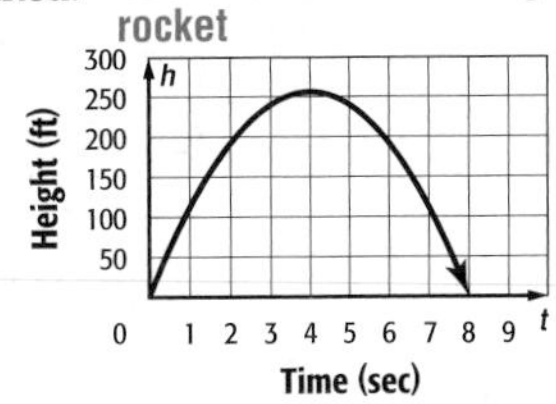

a. What is the vertex of the parabola? **(4, 256)**

b. What does the vertex of the parabola represent?

c. How long is the firework in the air before it lands? **8 seconds**

14. What are the vertices of the ellipse with equation $\frac{(x-3)^2}{36} + \frac{(y-2)^2}{144} = 1$? **C**

A. $(-3, 2)$ and $(9, 2)$
B. $(-2, 3)$ and $(10, 3)$
C. $(3, -10)$ and $(3, 14)$
D. $(2, -11)$ and $(4, 13)$

15. Hooke's Law states that the force needed to keep a spring stretched x units is directly proportional to x. If a force of 40 N is required to maintain a spring stretched to 5 centimeters, what force is needed to keep the spring stretched 14 centimeters? **H**

F. 8 N
G. 19 N
H. 112 N
I. 1600 N

Need Extra Help?

If you missed Question...	1	2	3	4	5	6	7	8	9	10	11	12	13	14	15
Go to Lesson or Page...	8-5	10-2	1-3	5-2	10-7	6-1	2-3	10-1	7-7	3-2	10-1	4-3	10-2	10-4	9-5
For help with NGSSS...	912.A.8.2	912.A.9.1	912.A.3.1	912.A.7.5	912.A.7.7	912.A.4.2	912.A.3.8	912.G.1.1	912.A.6.5	912.A.3.15	912.D.8.2	912.G.1.1	912.A.9.1	912.A.9.1	912.A.2.12

Formative Assessment

You can use these two pages to benchmark student progress.

Standardized Test Practice, pp. 70–72

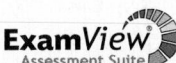

ExamView Assessment Suite Create practice worksheets or tests that align to your state's standards as well as TIMSS and NAEP tests.

Homework Option

Get Ready for Chapter 11 Assign students the exercises on p. 679 as homework to assess whether they possess the prerequisite skills needed for the next chapter.

Pages 624–625, Lesson 10-2 (Guided Practice)

2A.

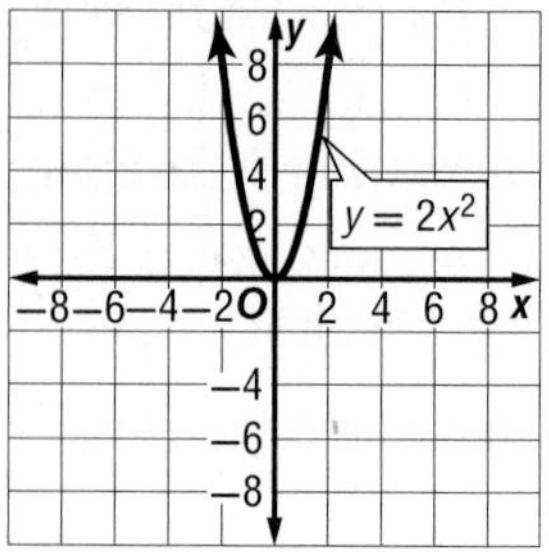

2B.

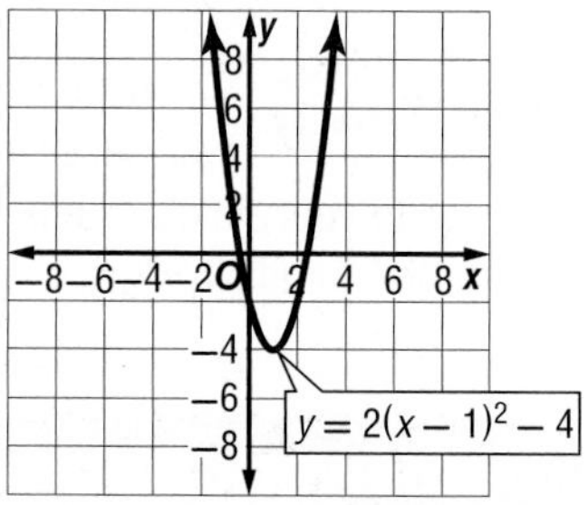

3A. $x = \frac{1}{3}(y + 2)^2 + 7$

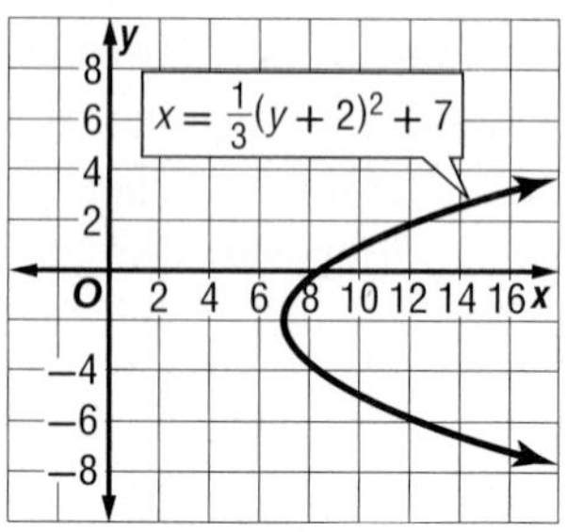

3B. $y = (x + 3)^2 - 13$

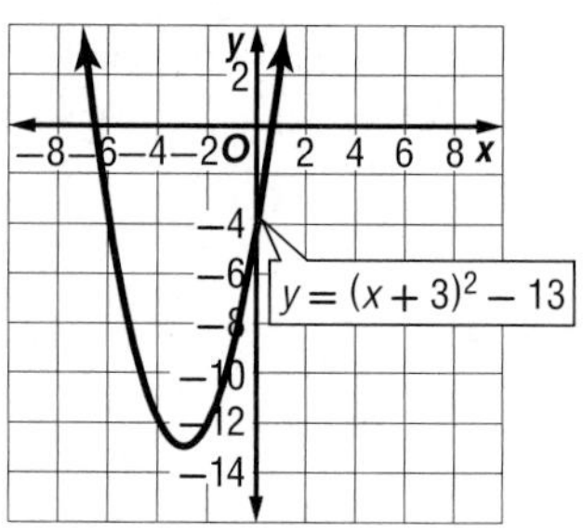

Page 627, Lesson 10-2

5.

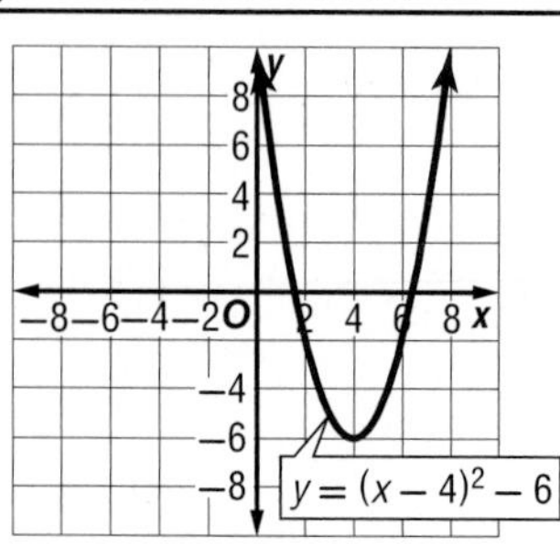

6.

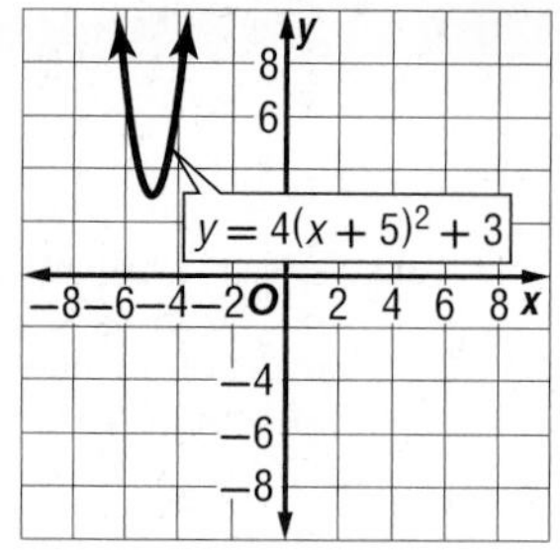

7.

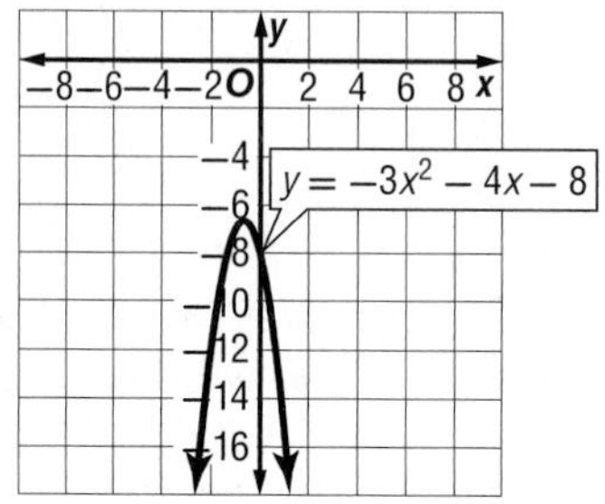

8.

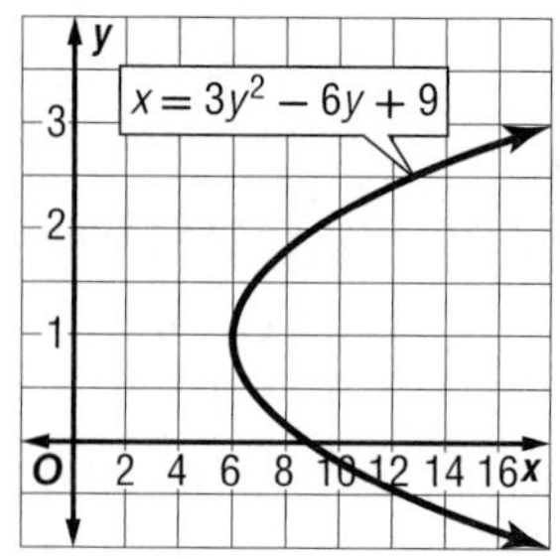

9. $y = \frac{1}{8}x^2 + 2$

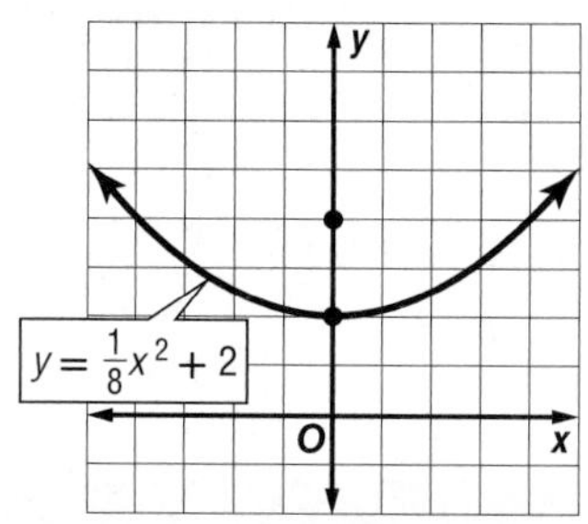

10. $x = -\frac{1}{4}(y - 4)^2 - 2$

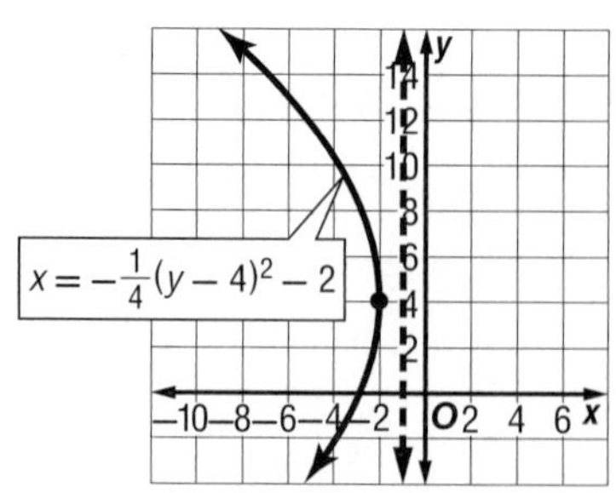

11. $y = -\frac{1}{12}(x - 3)^2 + 5$

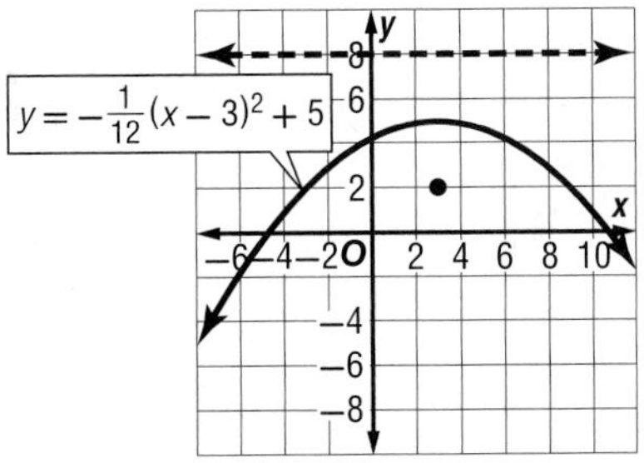

12. $x = -\frac{1}{16}(y + 5)^2 - 1$

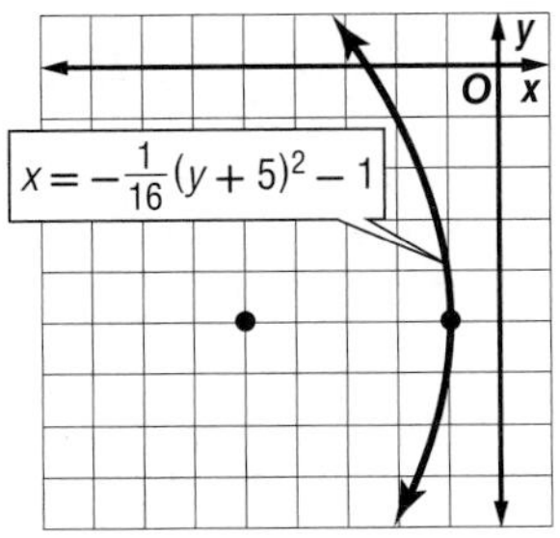

20.

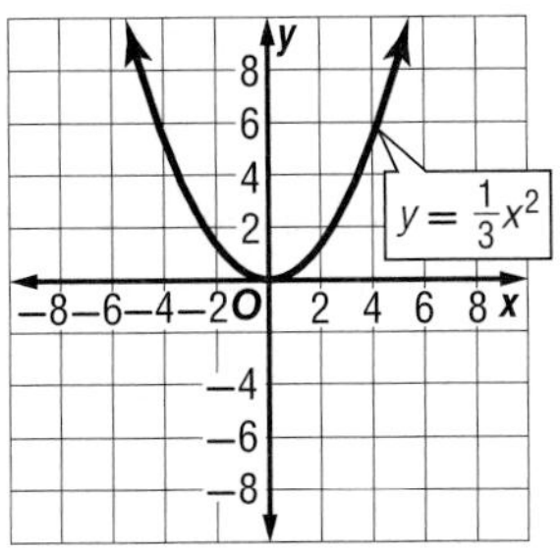

21.

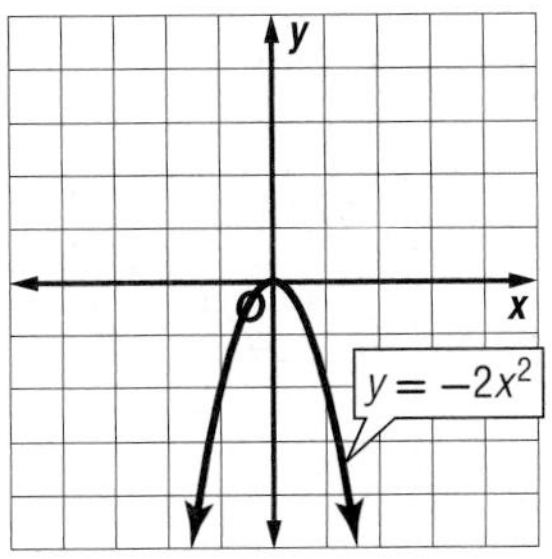

22.

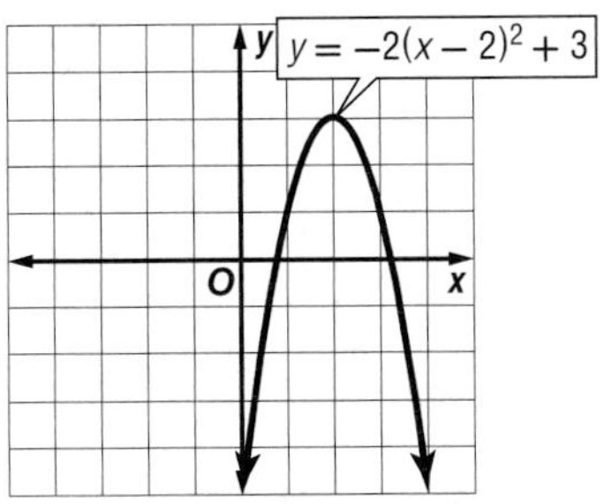

23.

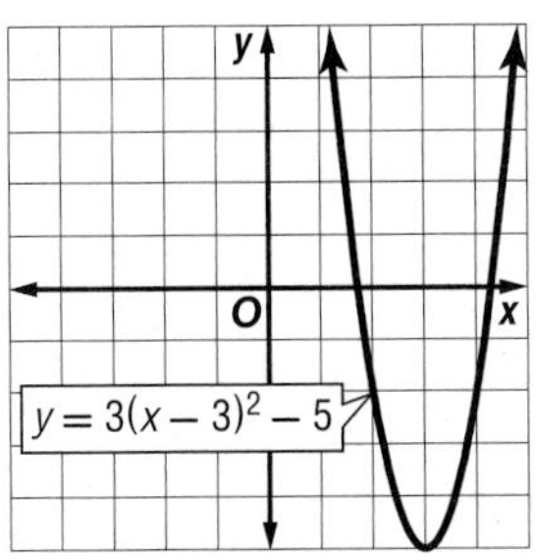

24.

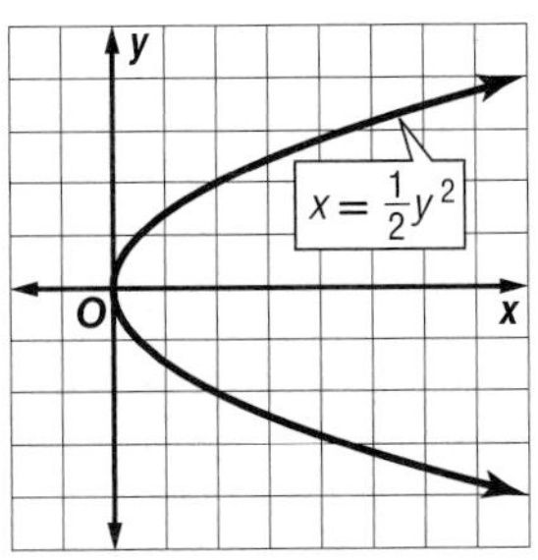

25.

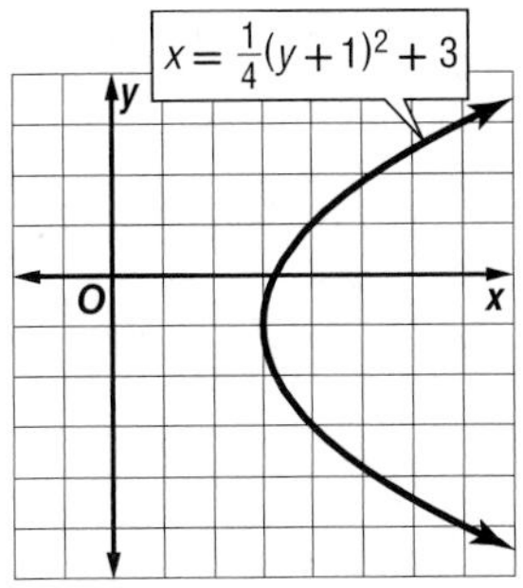

26. $y = \frac{1}{12}x^2 + 1$

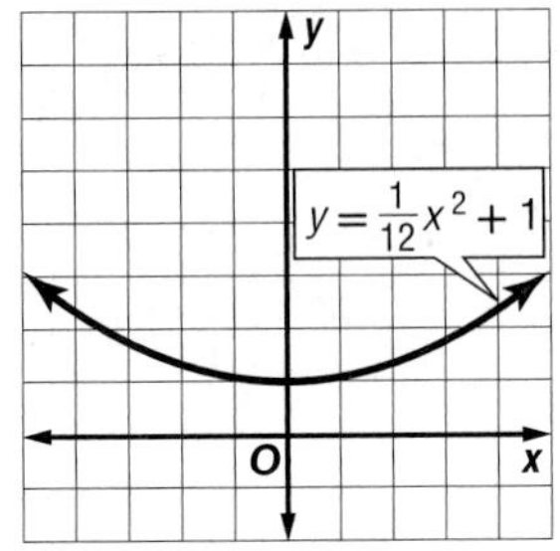

27. $y = \frac{1}{20}(x - 1)^2 + 8$

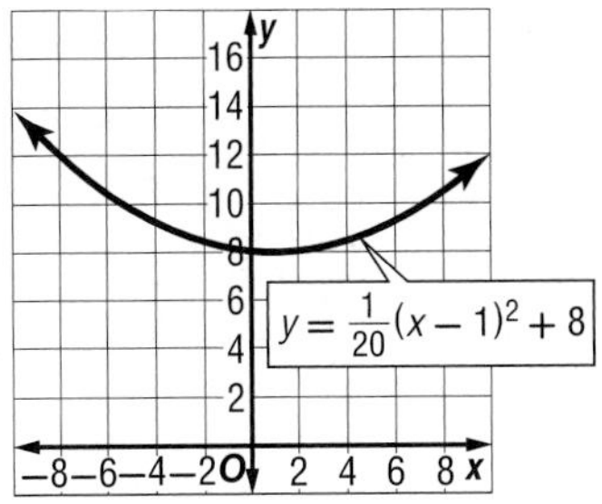

28. $x = \frac{1}{8}(y + 4)^2 - 4$

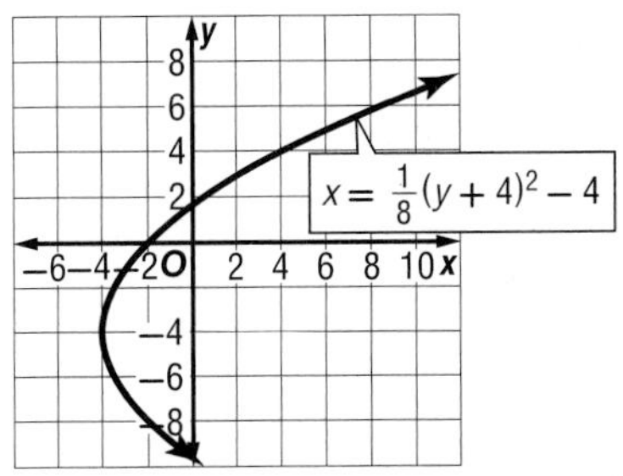

29. $x = -\frac{1}{16}(y - 4)^2 + 6$

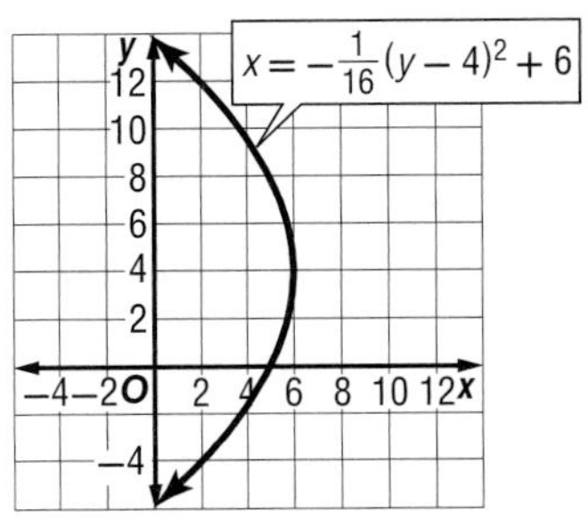

30. $x = -\frac{1}{32}y^2 - 6$

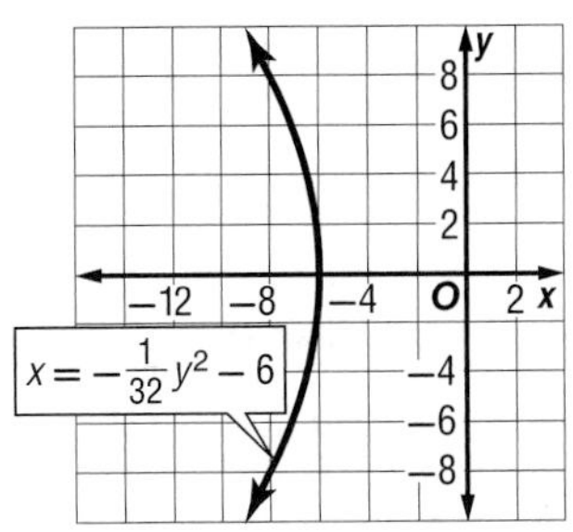

31. $y = -\frac{1}{4}(x - 9)^2 + 6$

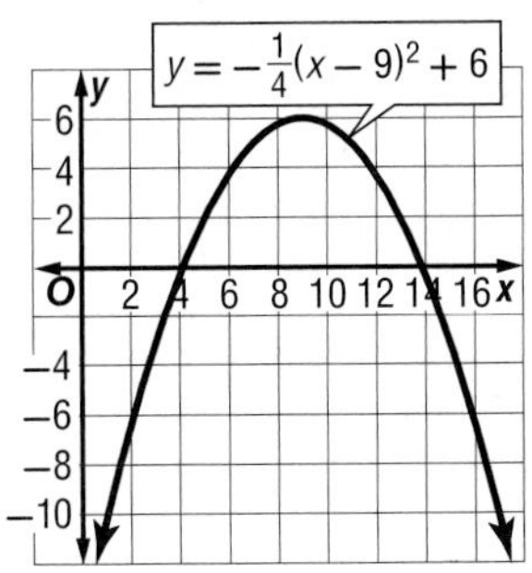

33a.

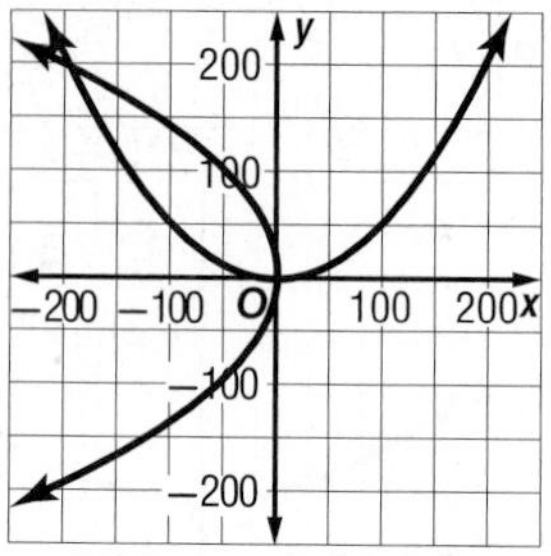

Pages 635–637, Lesson 10-3

31. center: (0,0); radius: $5\sqrt{3}$

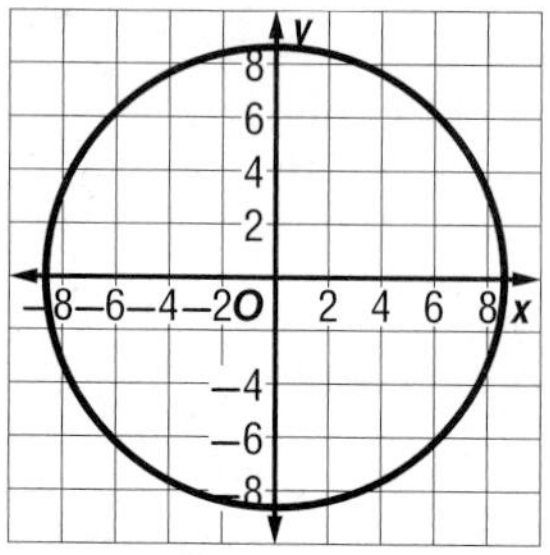

32. center: (3, 0); radius: 2

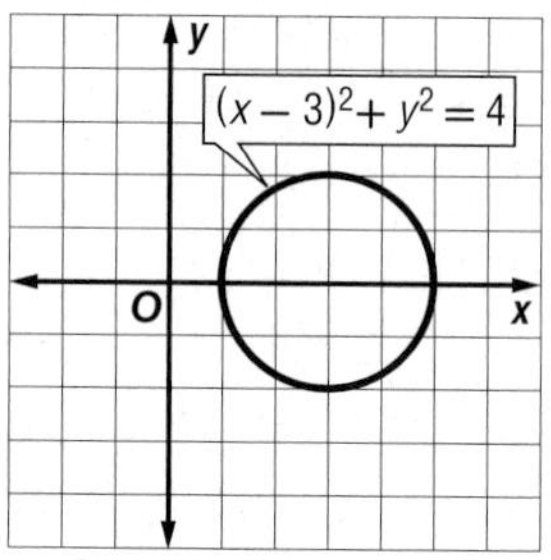

33. center: (1, 4); radius: $\sqrt{34}$

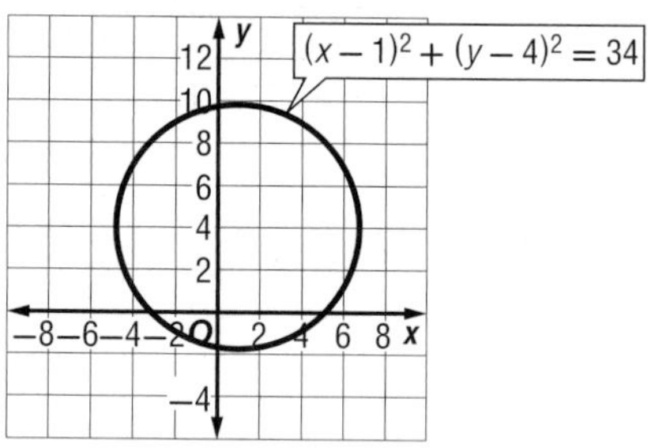

34. center: (0, 14); radius: 12

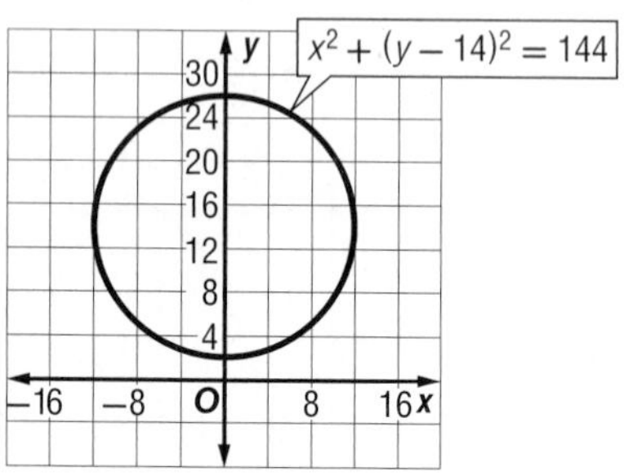

35. center: (5, –2); radius: 4

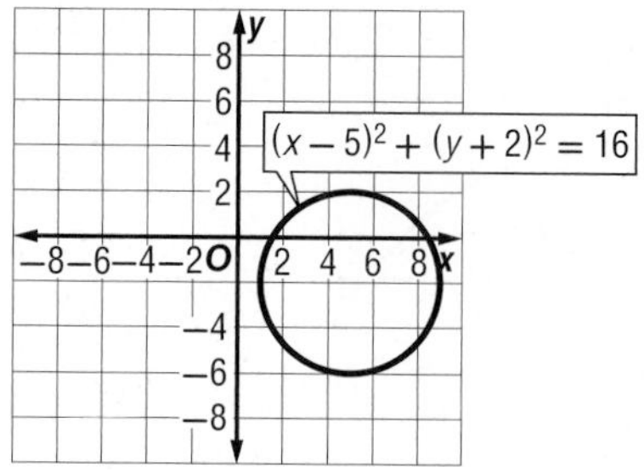

36. center: (0, 0); radius: 16

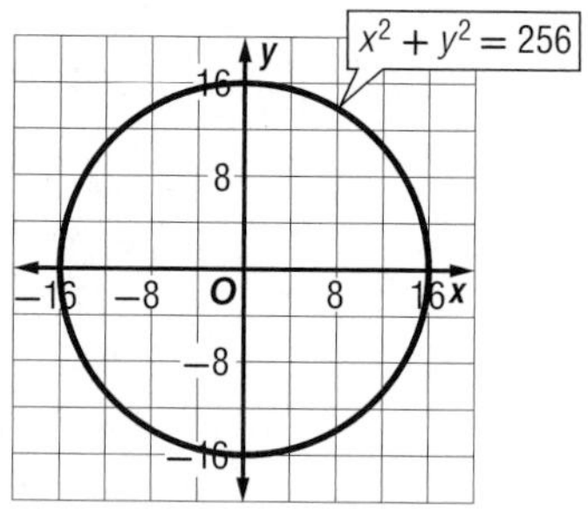

37. center: (4, 0); radius: $\frac{\sqrt{8}}{3}$

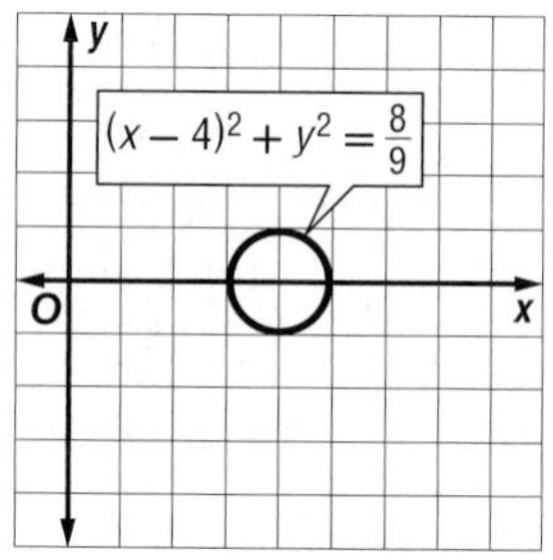

38. center: $\left(-\frac{2}{3}, \frac{1}{2}\right)$; radius: $\frac{4}{5}$

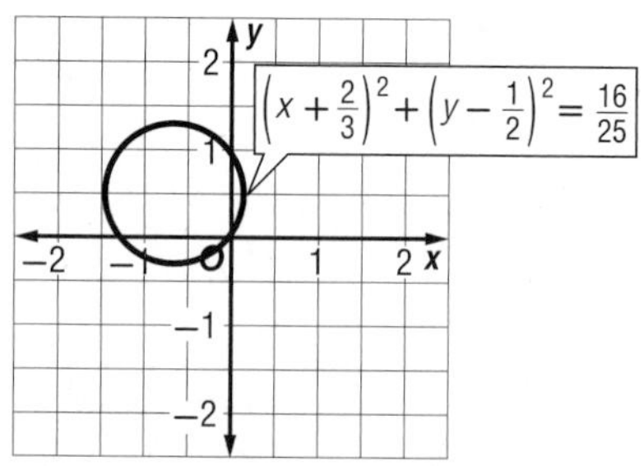

39. center: (–2, 0); radius: $\sqrt{13}$

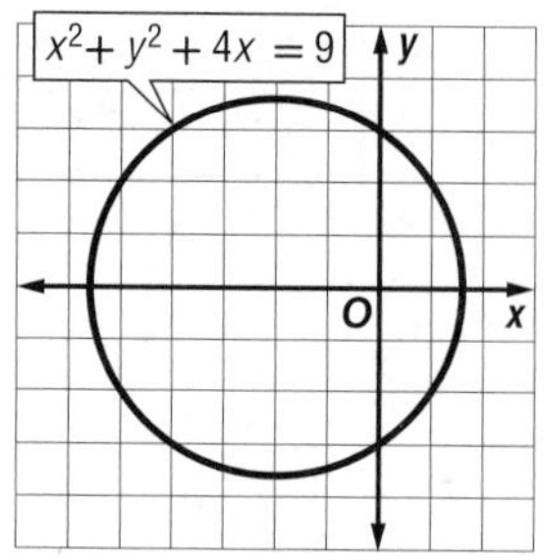

40. center: (–4, 3); radius: 5

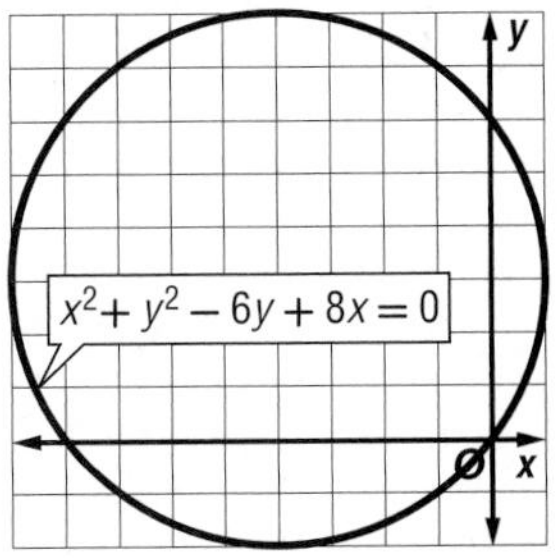

41. center: (–1, –2); radius: $\sqrt{14}$

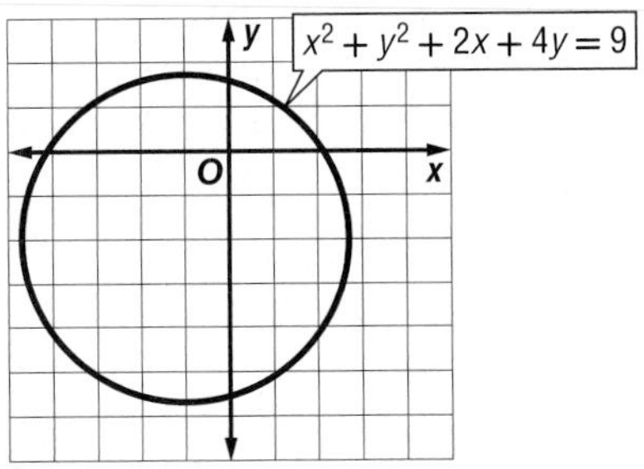

42. center: $\left(\frac{3}{2}, -4\right)$; radius: $\frac{3\sqrt{17}}{2}$

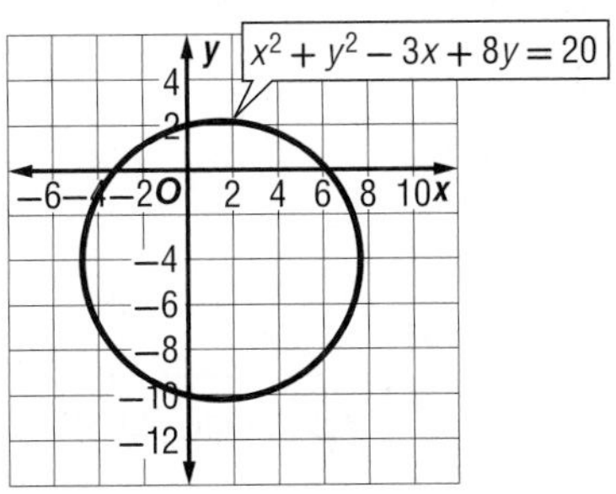

43. center: (–7, –3); radius: $2\sqrt{2}$ units

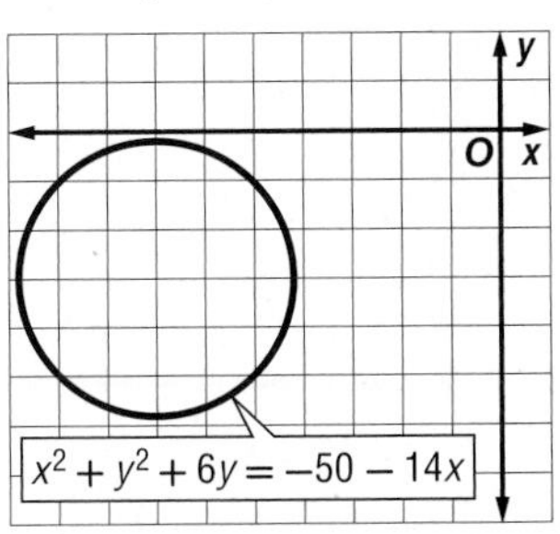

44. center: (9, 9); radius: $\sqrt{109}$ units

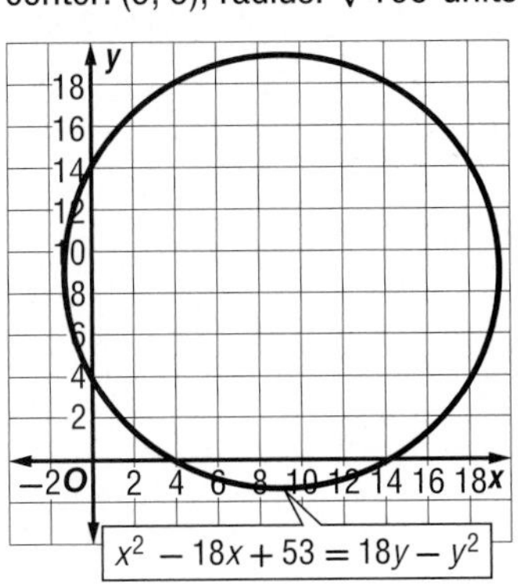

45. center: (1, –2); radius: $\sqrt{21}$

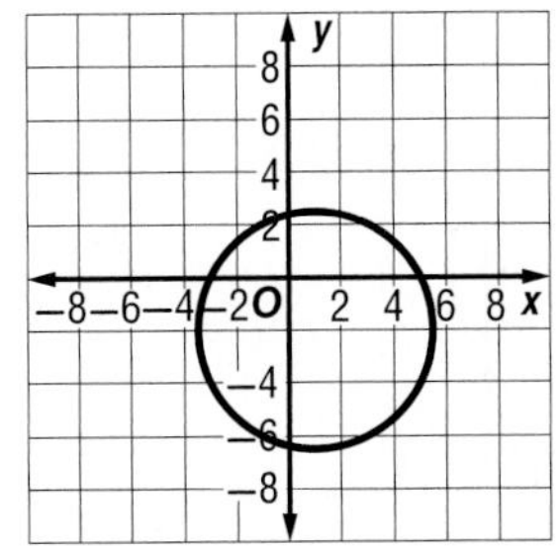

46. center: (–2, 1); radius: $\sqrt{13}$

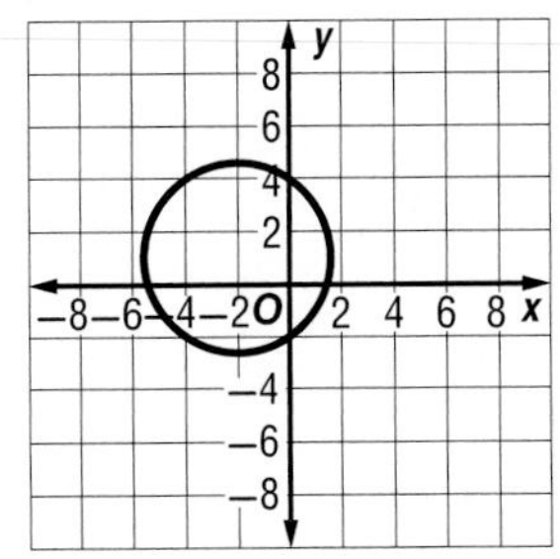

58. center: (6, 8), radius: 4

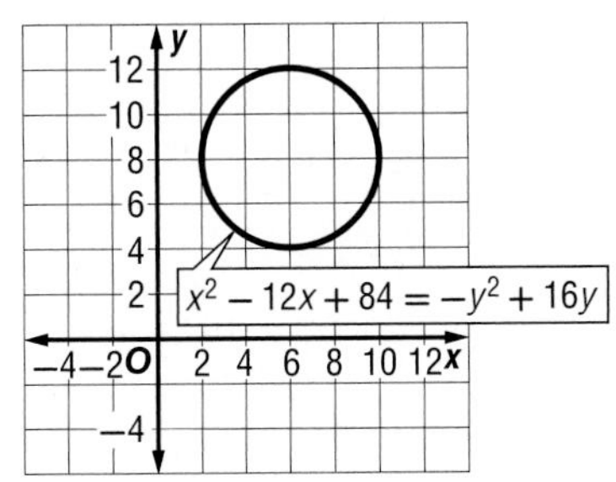

59. center: $\left(0, -\frac{9}{2}\right)$; radius: $2\sqrt{19}$

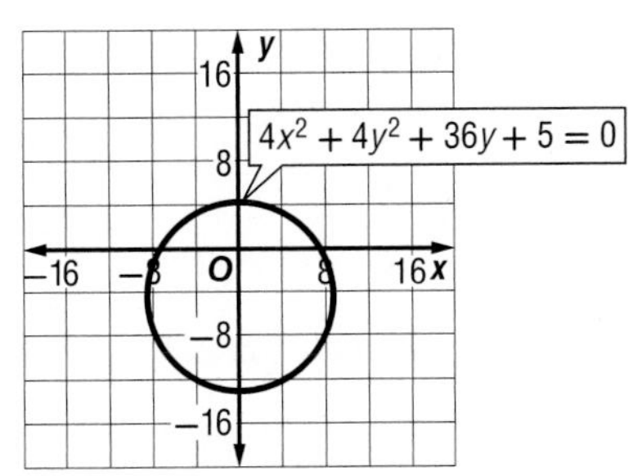

60. center: $(-\sqrt{5}, 4)$; radius: 5

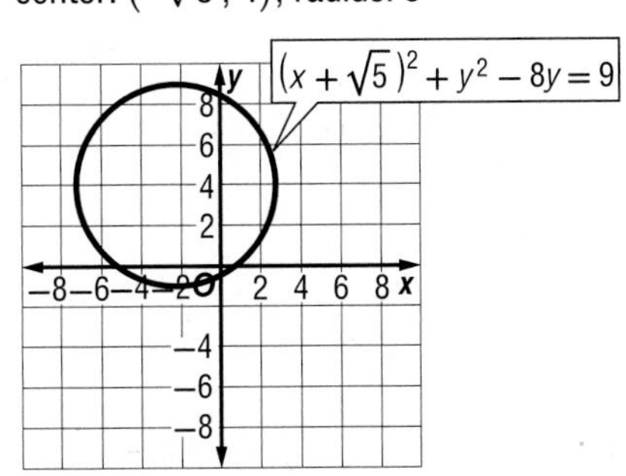

61. center: $(-\sqrt{7}, \sqrt{11})$; radius: $\sqrt{11}$

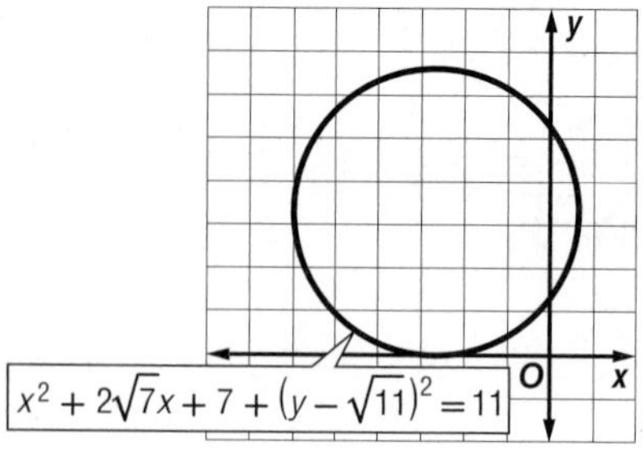

67. Quadrant I
$a > 0, b > 0, a = b, r > 0$

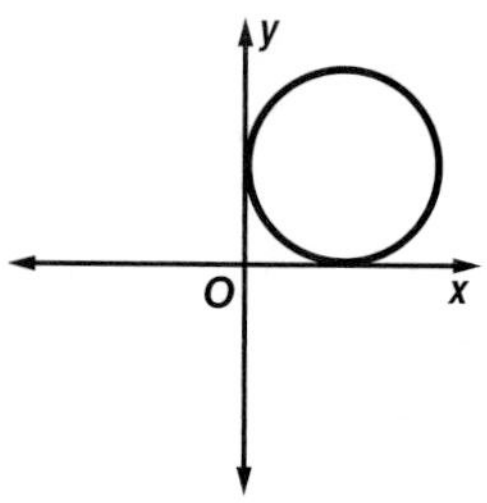

Quadrant II
$a < 0, b > 0, a = -b, r > 0$

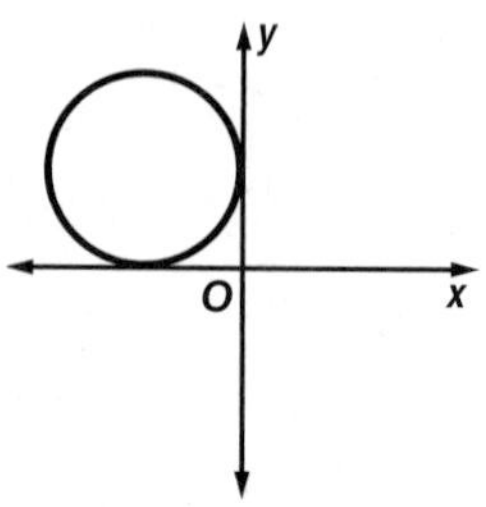

Quadrant III
$a < 0, b < 0, a = b, r > 0$

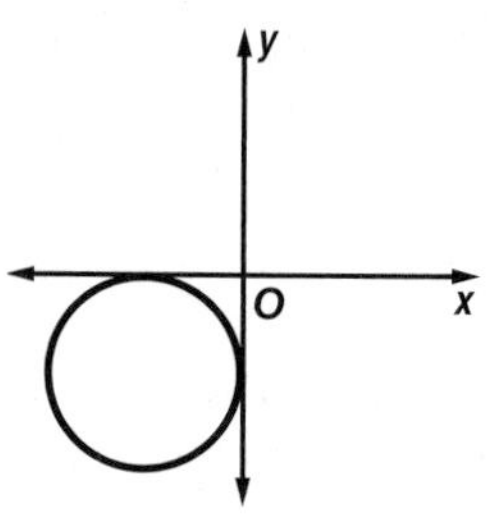

Quadrant IV
$a > 0, b < 0, a = -b, r > 0$

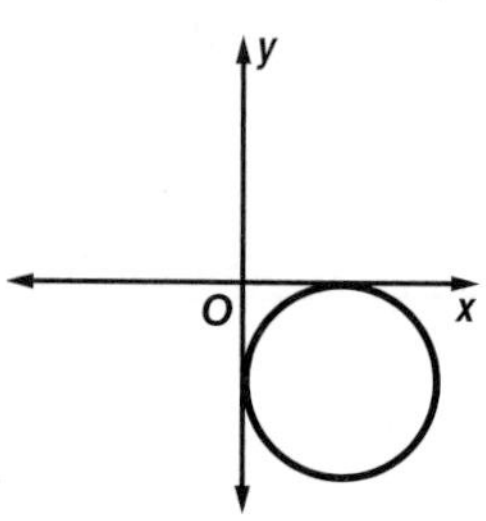

Sample answer: The circle is rotated 90° about the origin from one quadrant to the next.

72.

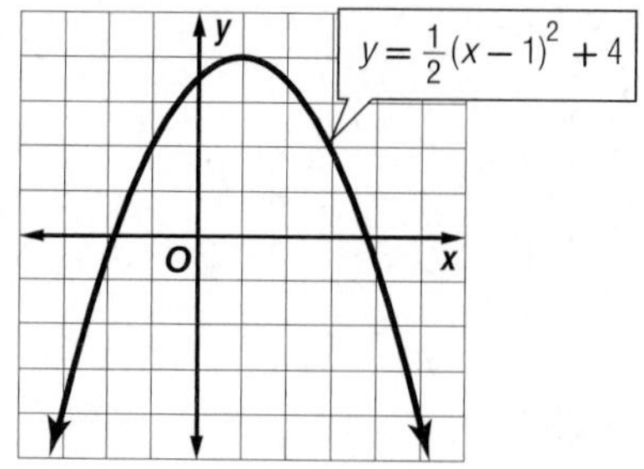

73.

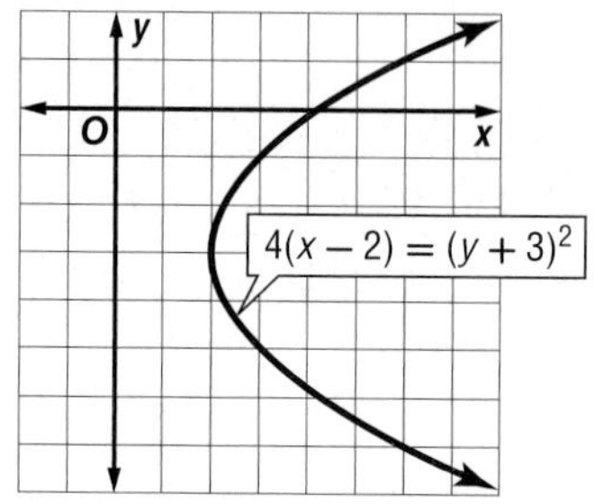

74.

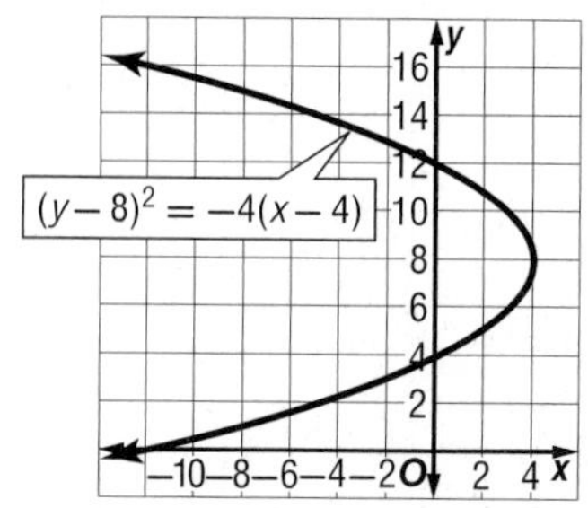

Pages 644–645, Lesson 10-4

24. center (3, 2); foci (3, 11.59) and (3, –7.59); major axis: ≈22.63; minor axis: 12

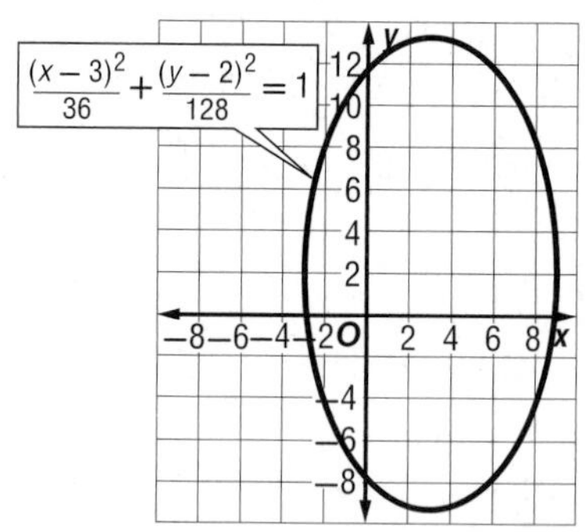

25. center (–6, 3); foci (–6, 7.69) and (–6, –1.69); major axis: ≈16.97; minor axis: ≈14.14

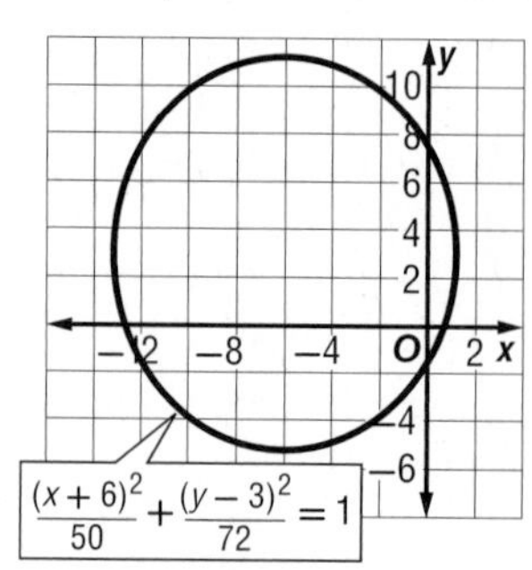

26. center (0, 5); foci (0, 11.08) and (1, –1.08); major axis: 16; minor axis: ≈10.39

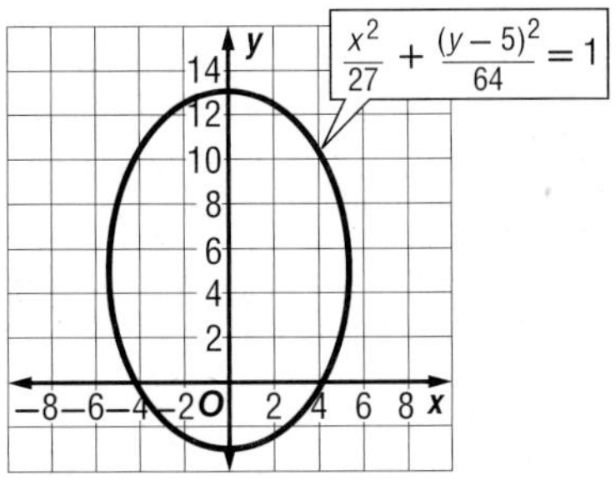

27. center (–4, 0); foci (–4, 7.68) and (–4, –7.68); major axis: ≈17.32; minor axis: 8

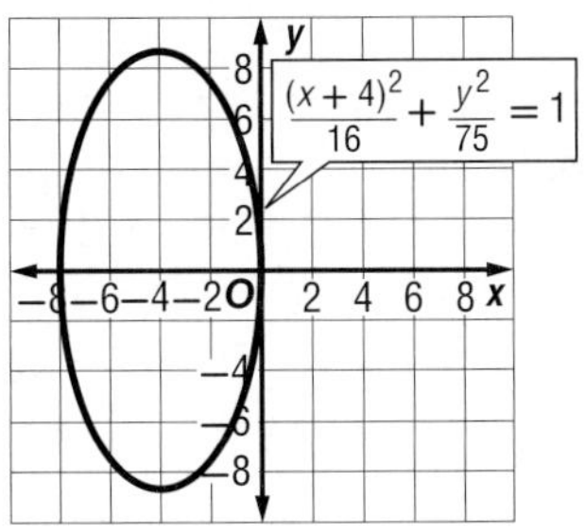

28. center (1, 4); foci (1, 8) and (1, 0); major axis: ≈9.80; minor axis: ≈5.66

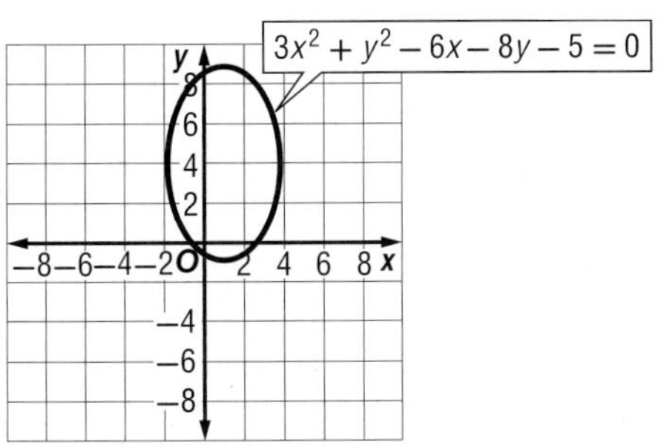

29. center (3, –3); foci (5.24, –3) and (0.76, –3); major axis: ≈8.94; minor axis: ≈7.75

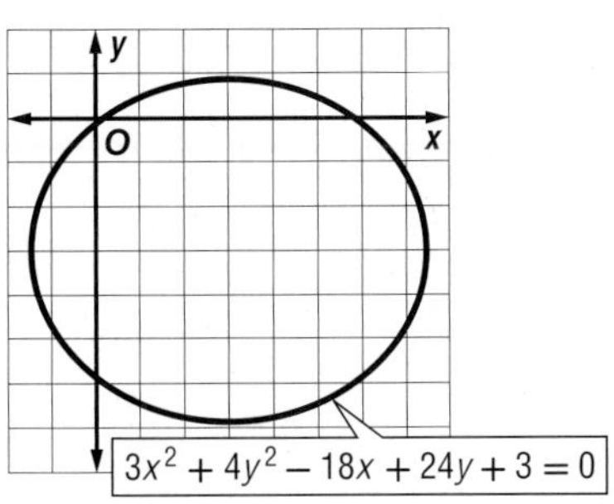

30. center (4, –3); foci (4, 1.90) and (4, –7.90); major axis: ≈10.58; minor axis: 4

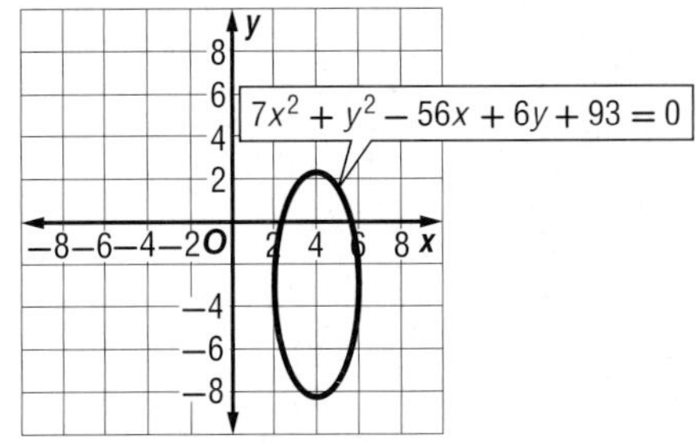

31. center (–2, 5); foci (–2, 7.83) and (–2, 2.17); major axis: ≈9.80; minor axis: 8

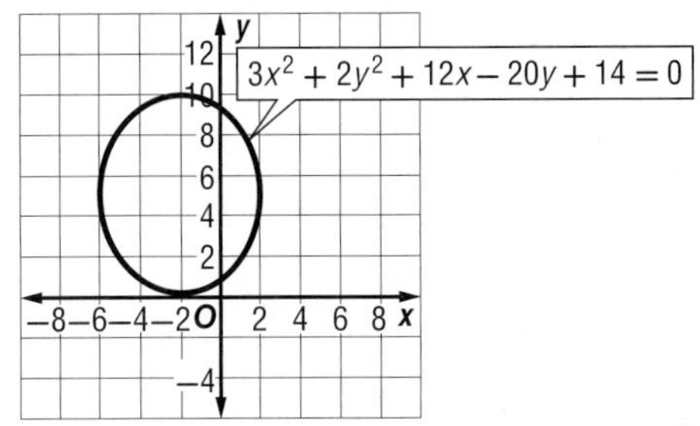

46. Sample answer: The domain is $\{x \mid -a \leq x \leq a\}$ because, if $|x| > a$, then $\frac{x^2}{a^2}$ would be greater than 1. This will force $\frac{y^2}{b^2}$ to be negative since $\frac{x^2}{a^2} + \frac{y^2}{b^2}$ must equal 1. In order for $\frac{y^2}{b^2}$ to be negative, either y^2 or b^2 must be negative, which cannot happen with real numbers. For any values of $\{x \mid -a \leq x \leq a\}$, $\frac{x^2}{a^2}$ will be between 0 and 1. The value of $\frac{y^2}{b^2}$ will also be between 0 and 1 for $\{y \mid -b \leq y \leq b\}$ and there are infinite combinations of $\frac{x^2}{a^2}$ and $\frac{y^2}{b^2}$ for which $\frac{x^2}{a^2} + \frac{y^2}{b^2} = 1$. Thus, the domain must be $\{x \mid -a \leq x \leq a\}$. The same method proves that the range must be $\{y \mid -b \leq y \leq b\}$.

Page 647, Mid-Chapter Quiz

11. (–3, –4); $\left(-3, -\frac{15}{4}\right)$; $x = -3$; $y = -\frac{17}{4}$; opens up; 1 unit

12. (3, 1); $\left(\frac{23}{8}, 1\right)$; $y = 1$; $x = \frac{25}{8}$; opens to the left; $\frac{1}{2}$ unit

13. (1, 0); 3 units

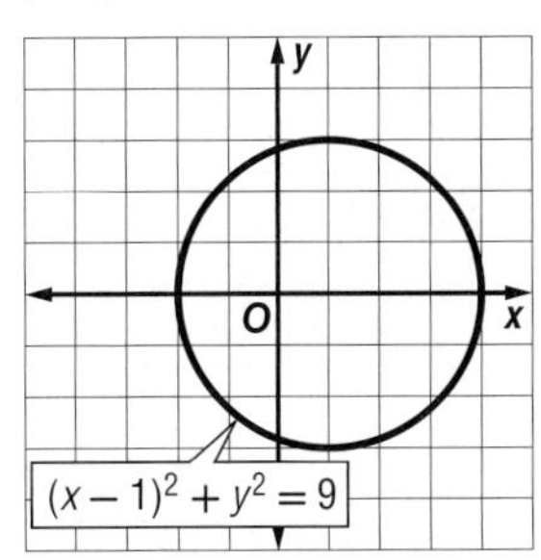

17. $(-4, 2)$; $(-4 \pm \sqrt{7}, 2)$; 8; 6

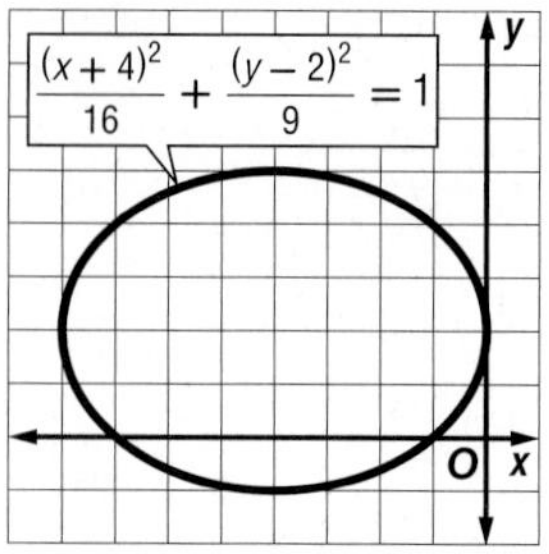

18. $(1, -2)$; $(5, -2)$, $(-3, -2)$; $4\sqrt{5}$; 4

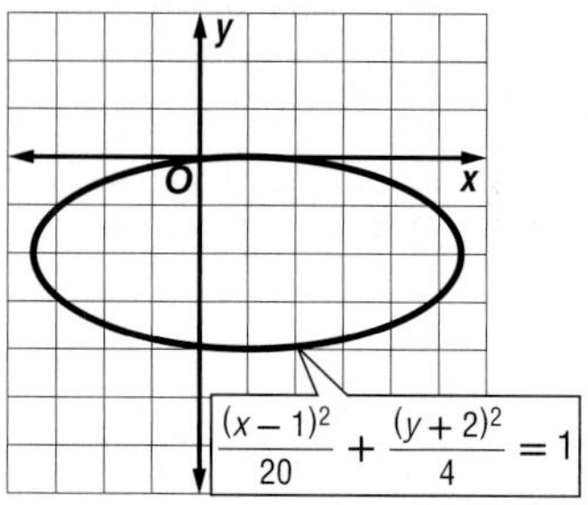

19. $(5, -2)$; $(5, -2 \pm \sqrt{5})$; 6; 4

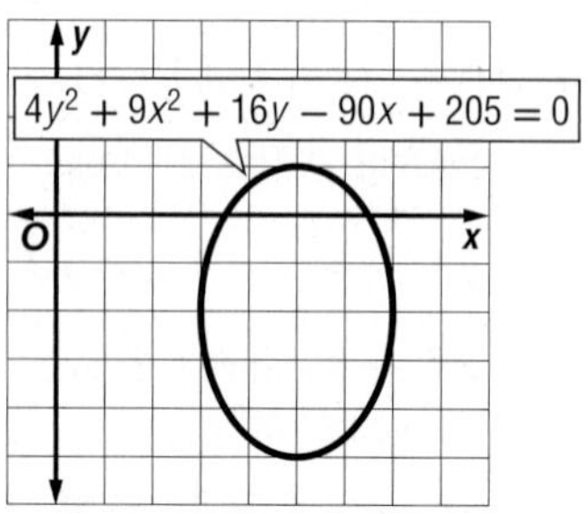

Page 653, Lesson 10-5

14.

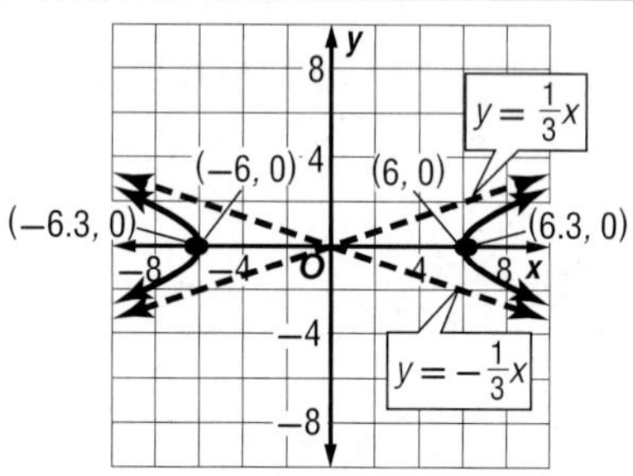

15.

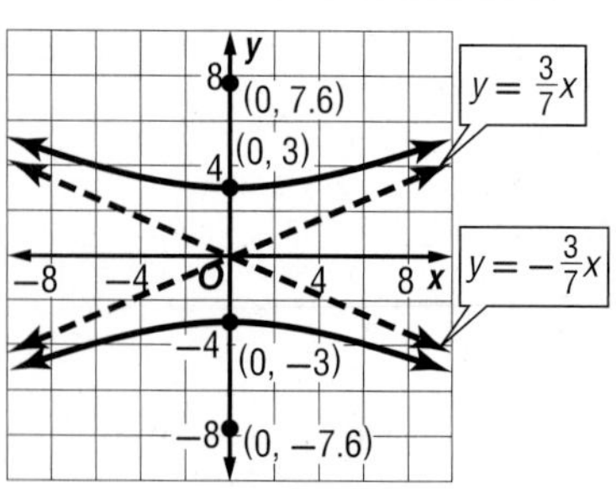

16.

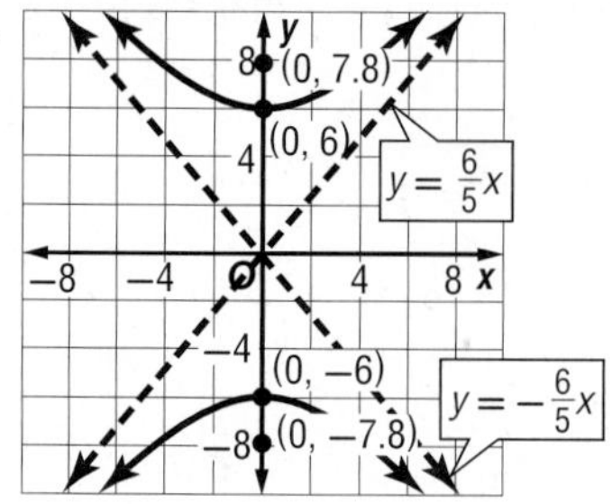

17.

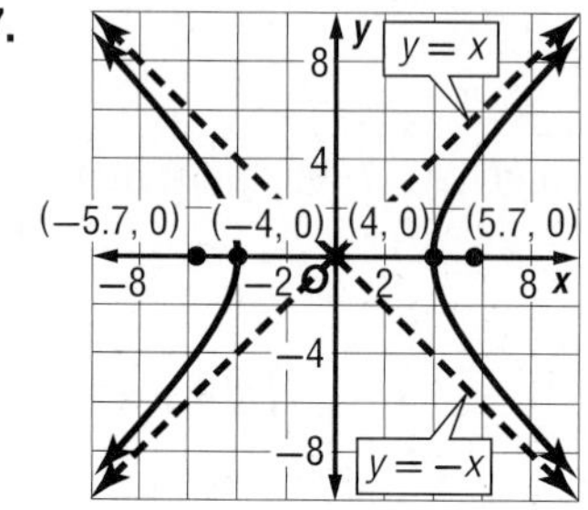

18.

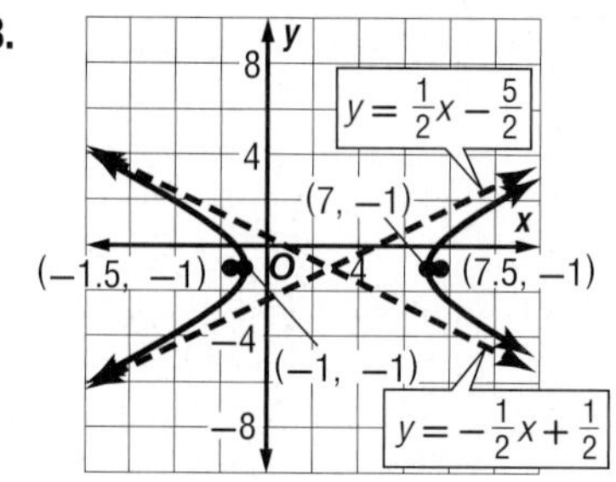

19.

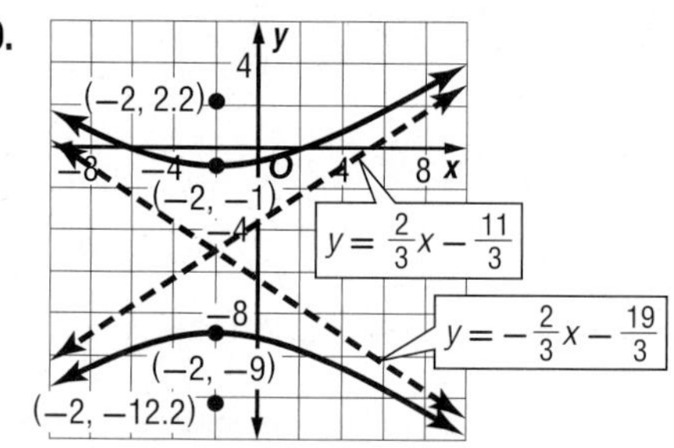

20.

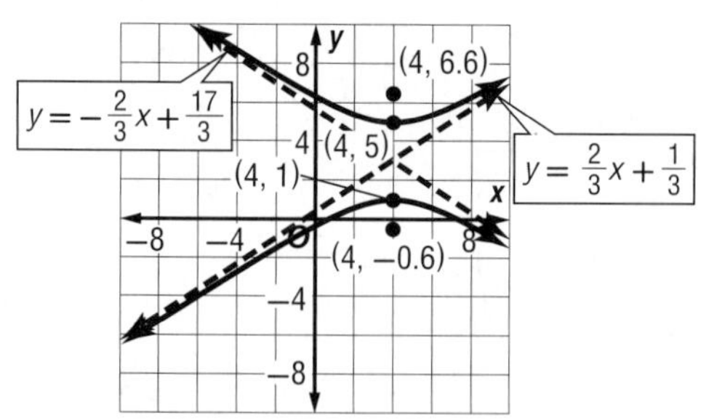

21.

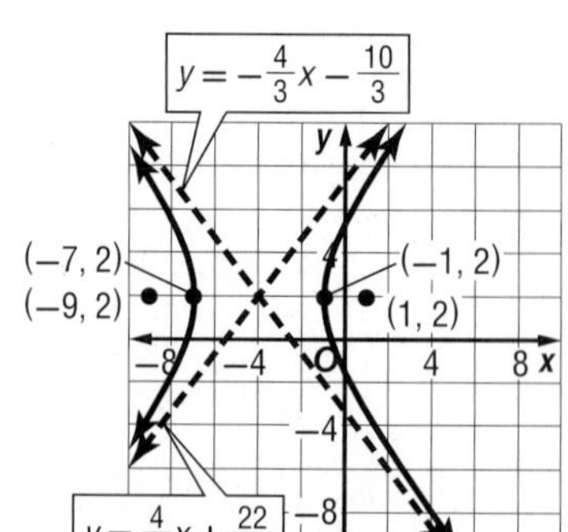

22.

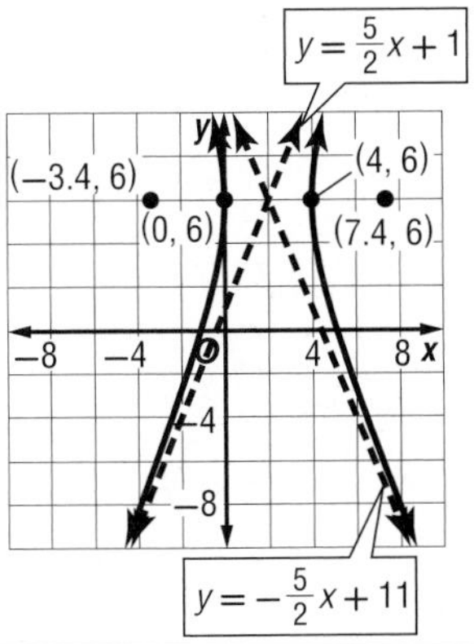

23.

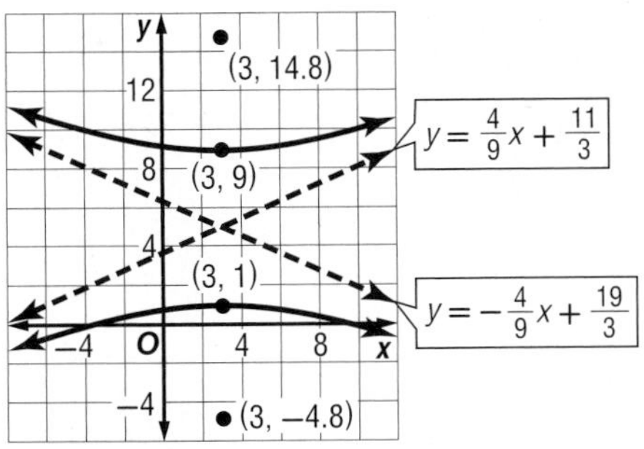

33a.

x	y
−12	−1.33
−10	−1.6
−8	−2
−6	−2.67
−4	−4
−2	−8
0	undef
2	8
4	4
6	2.67
8	2
10	1.6
12	1.33

33b.

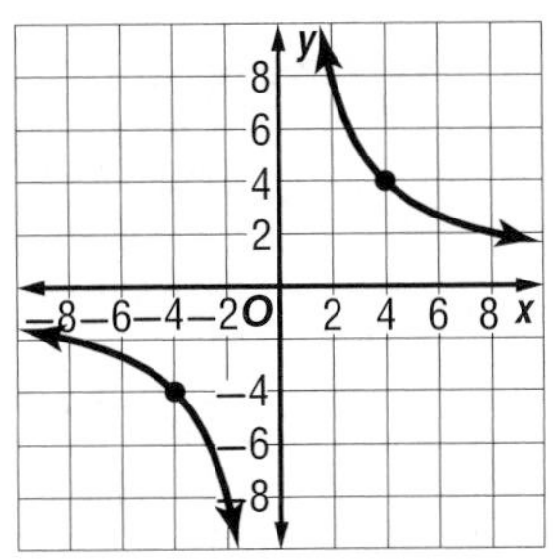

33c. The asymptotes are $y = 0$ and $x = 0$.

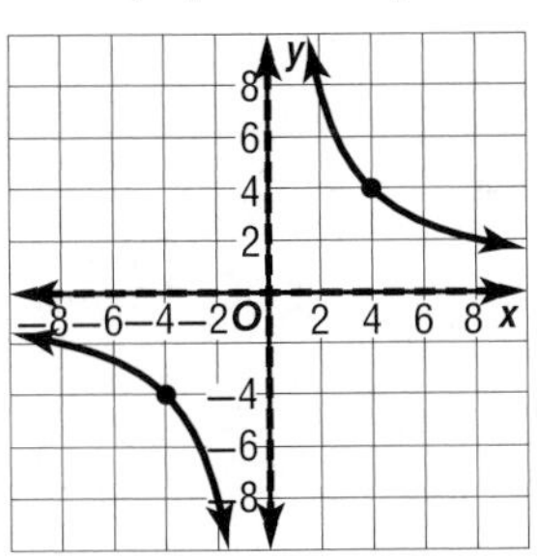

Page 656, Lesson 10-6 (Guided Practice)

1. $\frac{(x-2)^2}{9} + \frac{(y+4)^2}{36} = 1$; ellipse

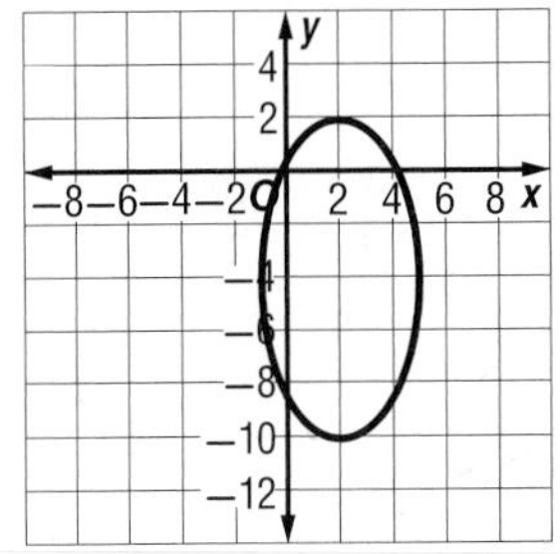

Pages 658–660, Lesson 10-6

1. $\frac{(x-3)^2}{36} + \frac{(y+2)^2}{9} = 1$; ellipse

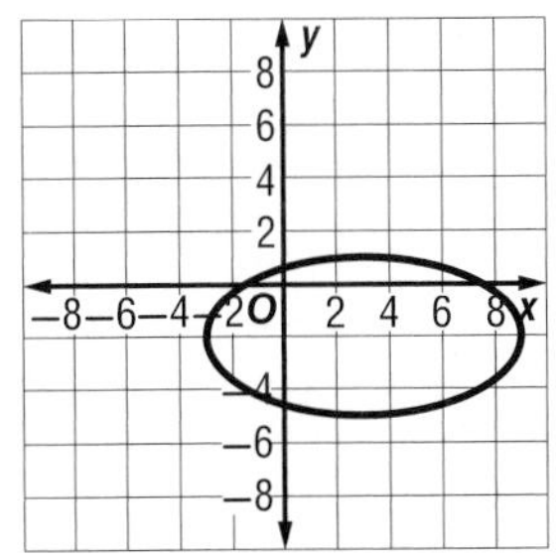

2. $(x+6)^2 + (y-4)^2 = 16$; circle

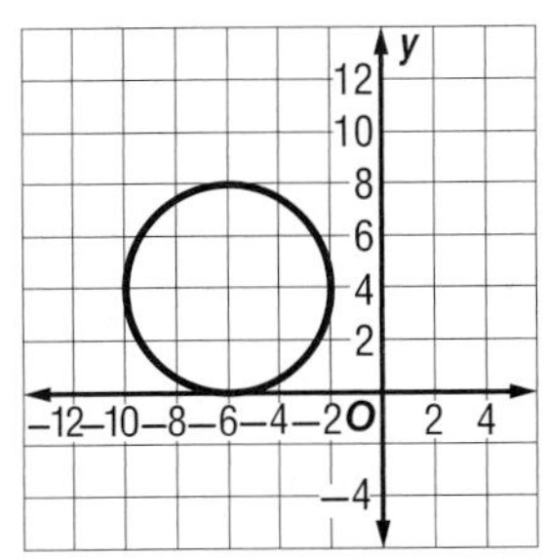

3. $\frac{(y-1)^2}{16} - \frac{(x+2)^2}{9}$; hyperbola

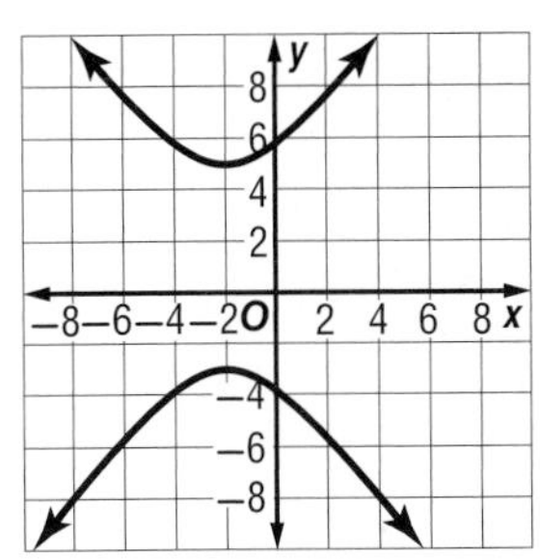

4. $x = 6(y - 2)^2 + 4$; parabola

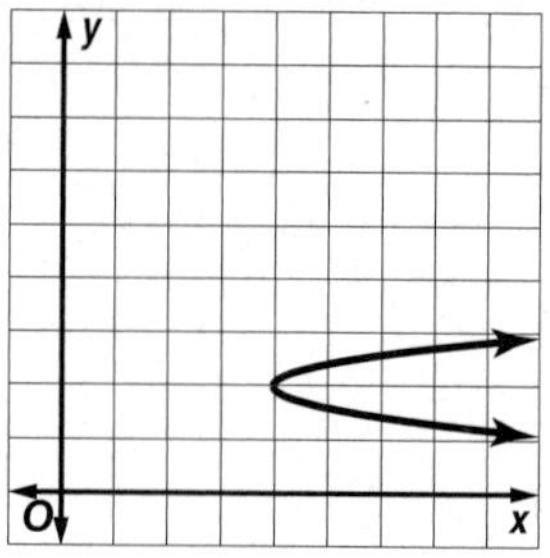

14. $\dfrac{(x + 3)^2}{18} - \dfrac{(y - 2)^2}{27} = 1$; hyperbola

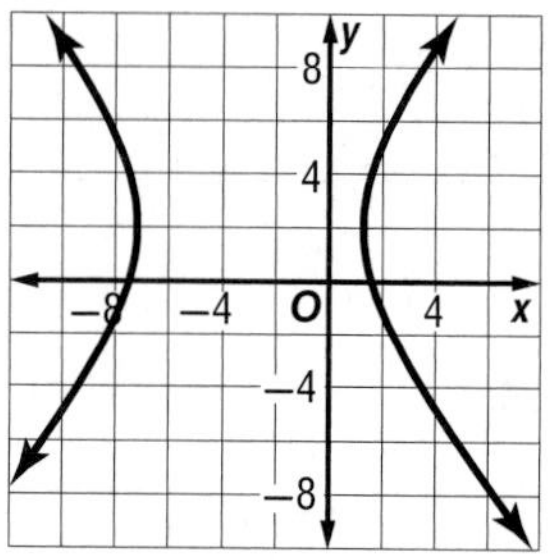

15. $\dfrac{(x + 4)^2}{32} + \dfrac{(y - 5)^2}{24} = 1$; ellipse

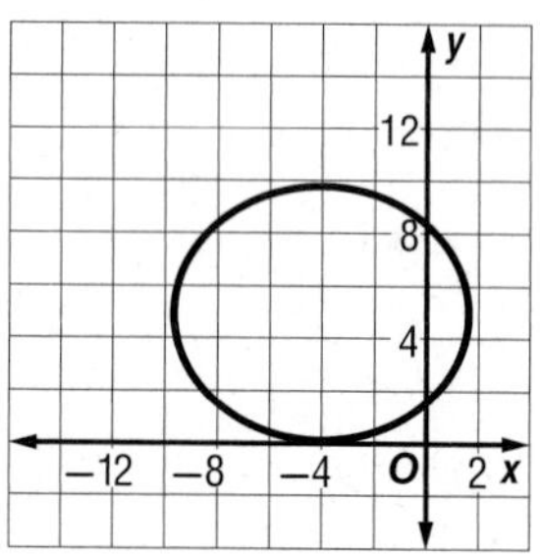

16. $x^2 + (y - 3)^2 = 25$; circle

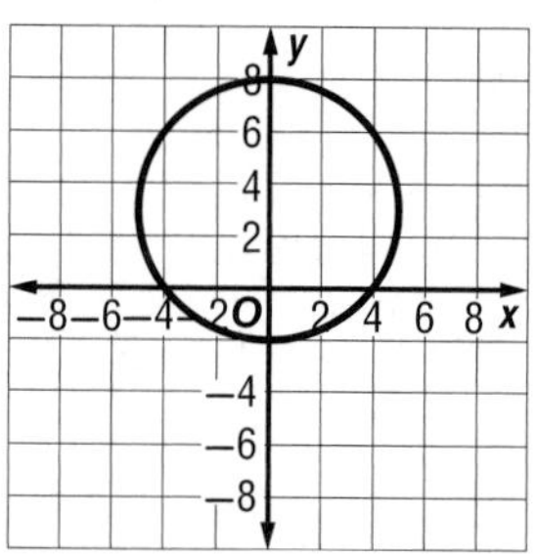

17. $y = 8(x + 2)^2 - 4$; parabola

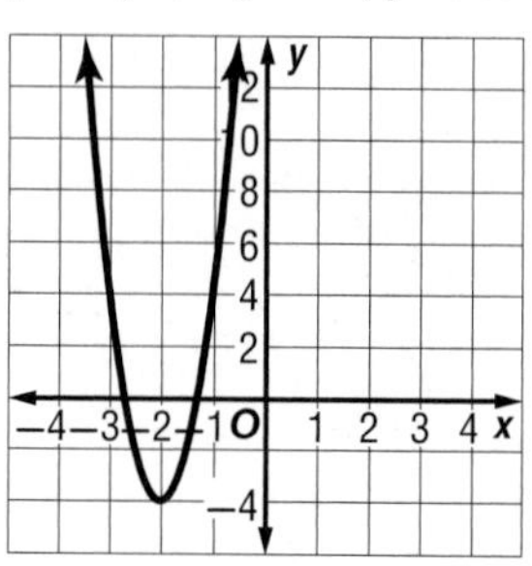

18. $\dfrac{(y - 2)^2}{42} + \dfrac{(x - 6)^2}{12} = 1$; ellipse

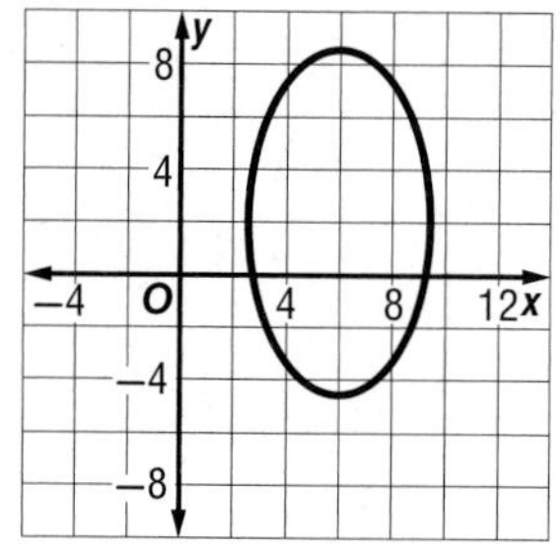

19. $(x - 3)^2 + (y + 4)^2 = 36$; circle

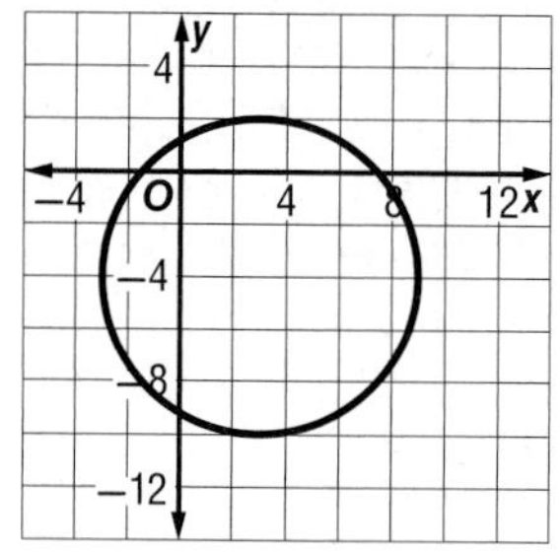

20. $x = -4(y - 3)^2 + 5$; parabola

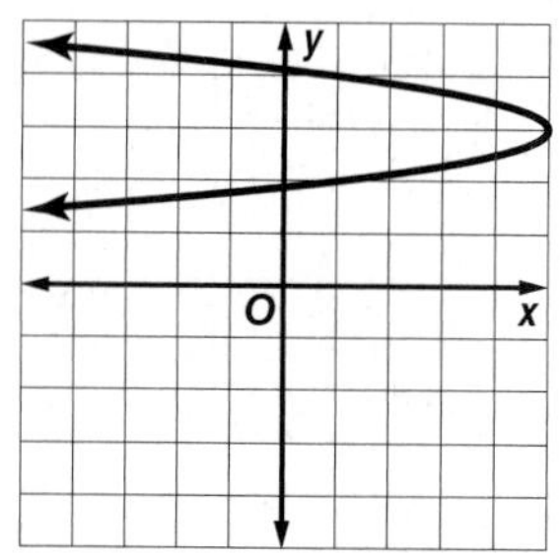

21. $\dfrac{(x + 4)^2}{21} - \dfrac{(y - 8)^2}{24} = 1$; hyperbola

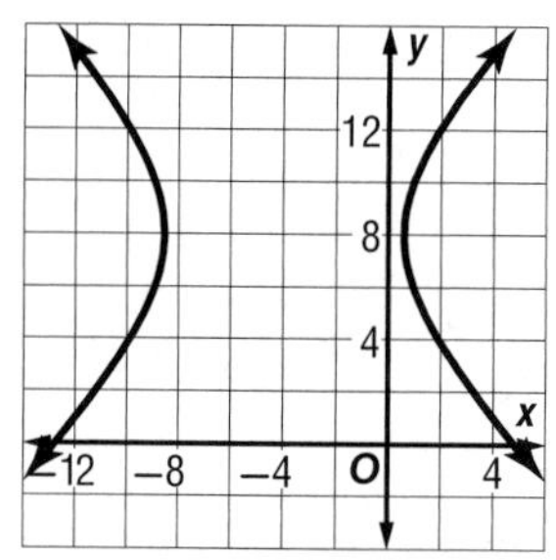

22. $\dfrac{(y + 2)^2}{28} + \dfrac{(x - 1)^2}{9} = 1$; ellipse

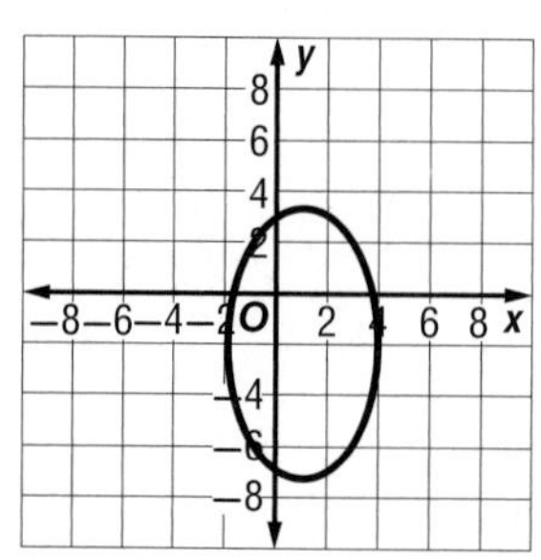

23. $\frac{(x+4)^2}{64} - \frac{(y-3)^2}{25} = 1$; hyperbola

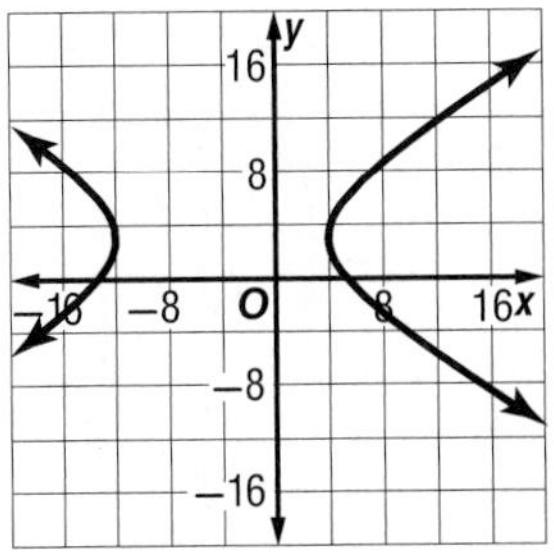

47. Sample answer: An ellipse is a flattened circle. Both circles and ellipses are enclosed regions while hyperbolas and parabolas are not. A parabola has one branch, which is a smooth curve that never ends, and a hyperbola has two such branches that are reflections of each other. In standard form and when there is no *xy*-term: an equation for a parabola consists of only one squared term, an equation for a circle has values for *A* and *C* that are equal, an equation for an ellipse has values for *A* and *C* that are the same sign but not equal, and an equation for a hyperbola has values of *A* and *C* that have opposite signs.

56.

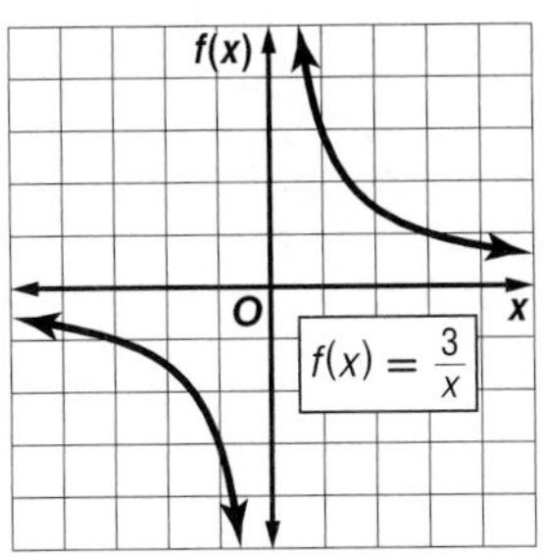

57.

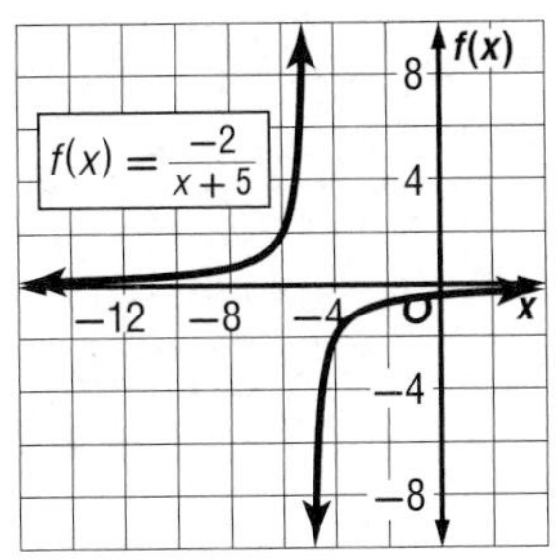

58.

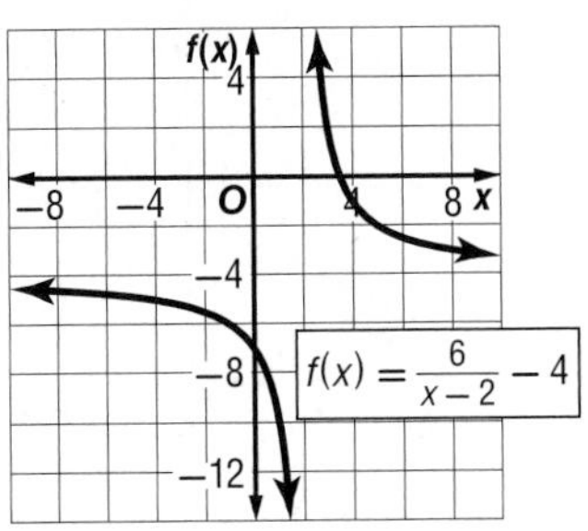

Page 661, Extend 10-6

1. $\frac{(x+4)^2}{32} - \frac{y^2}{32} = 1$; hyperbola

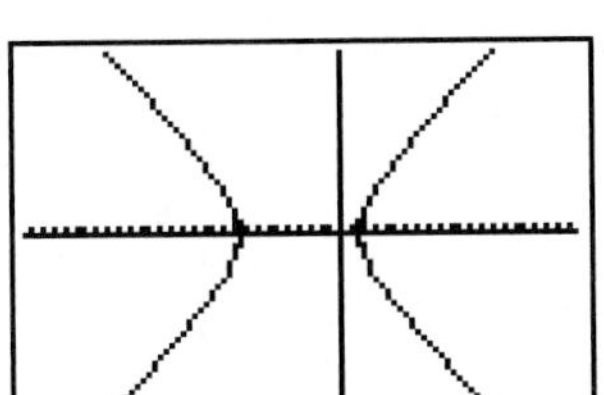

2. $\frac{y^2}{16} - \frac{x^2}{8} = 1$; hyperbola

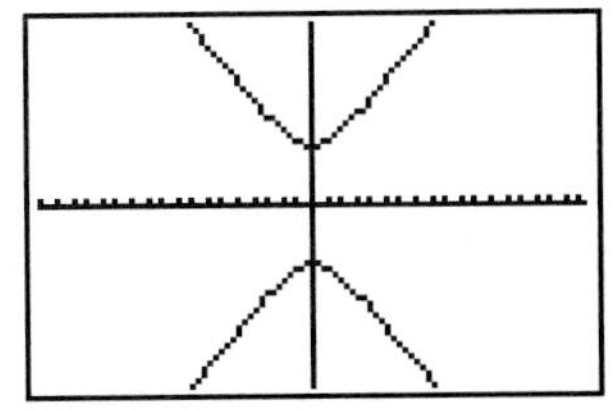

3. $\frac{(x-1)^2}{9} + \frac{y^2}{\frac{9}{2}} = 1$; ellipse

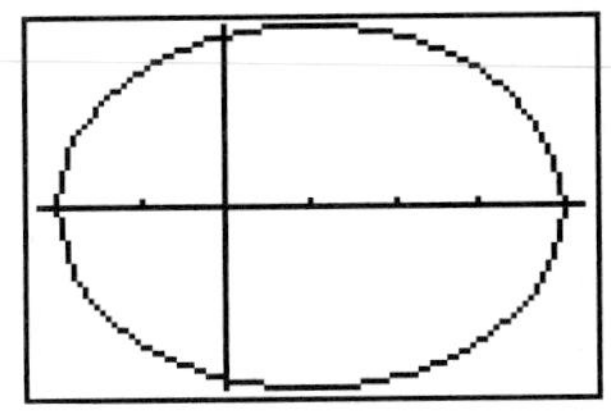

4. $x^2 + (y-4)^2 = 5$; circle

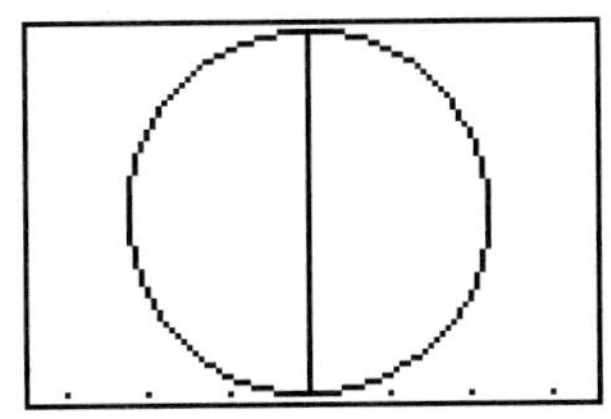

5. $\frac{(y+1)^2}{25} - \frac{x^2}{9} = 1$; hyperbola

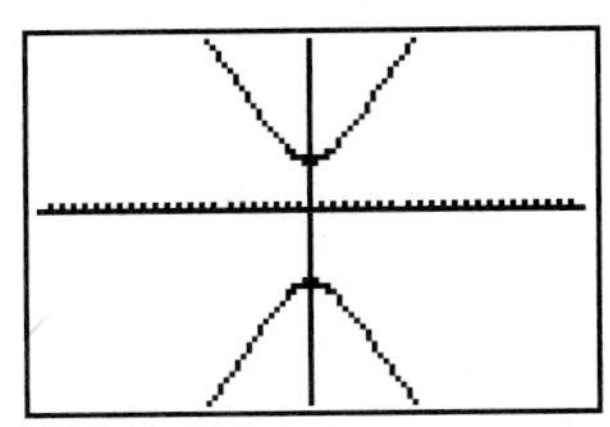

6. $\frac{(x+1)^2}{4} + \frac{(y-3)^2}{1} = 1$; ellipse

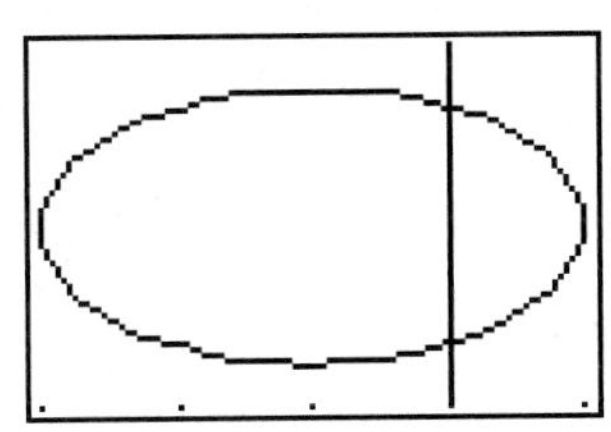

7. $\frac{x^2}{4} + \frac{(y+1)^2}{3} = 1$; ellipse

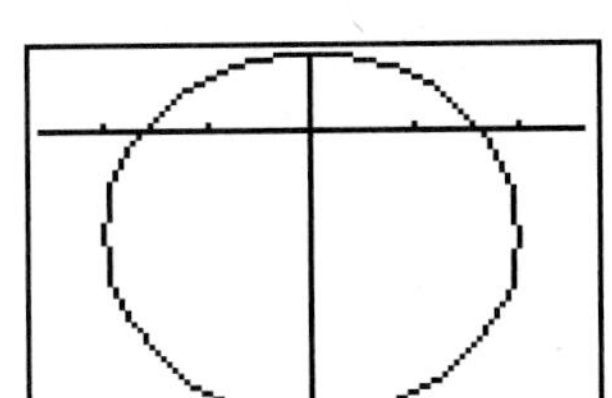

8. $\frac{(x+1)^2}{16} + \frac{(y-1)^2}{4} = 1$; ellipse

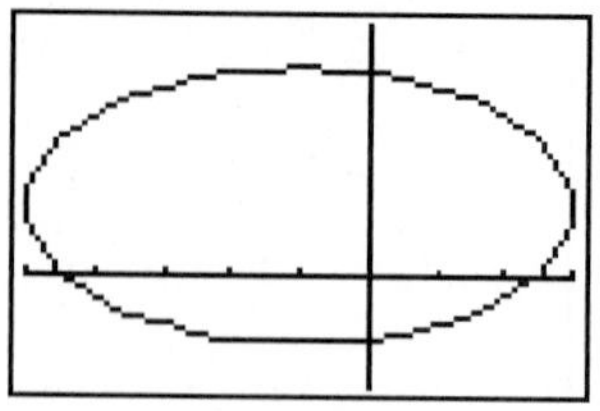

9. $\frac{(x-2)^2}{5} - \frac{(y+1)^2}{6} = 1$; hyperbola

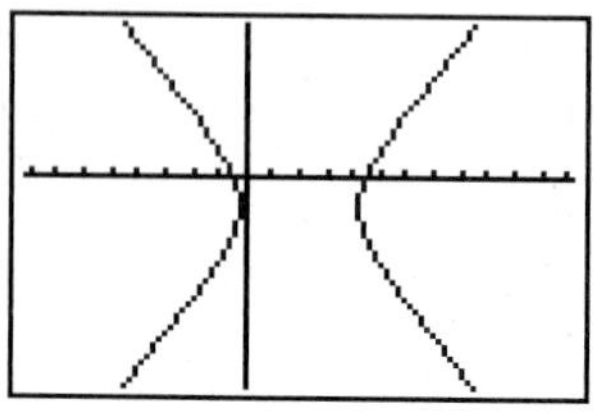

10. $\frac{(x-3)^2}{25} + \frac{(y-1)^2}{9} = 1$; ellipse

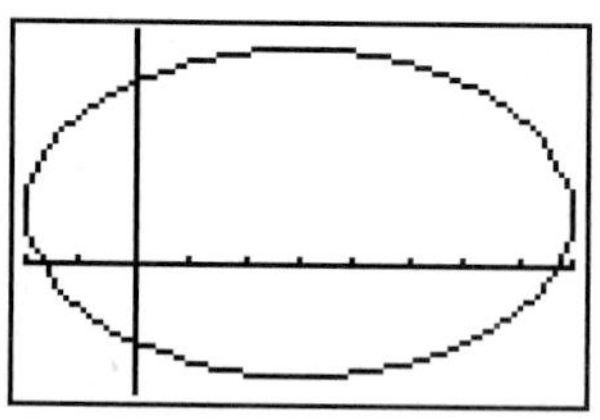

Pages 663–664, Lesson 10-7 (Guided Practice)

3A. 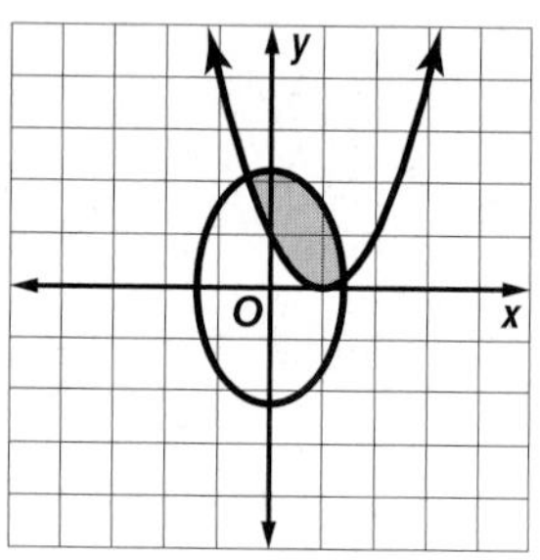

3B. 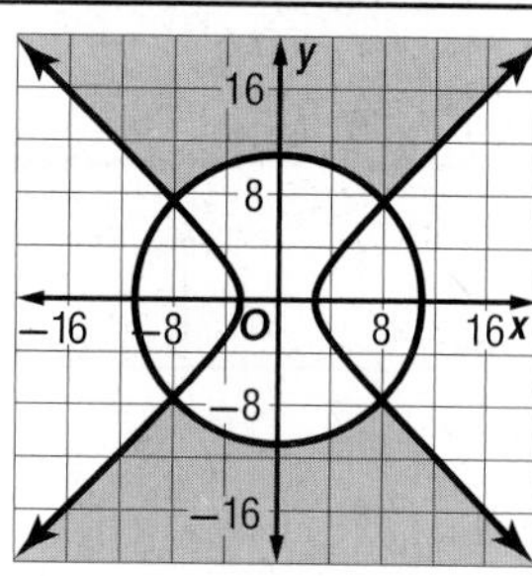

4A. 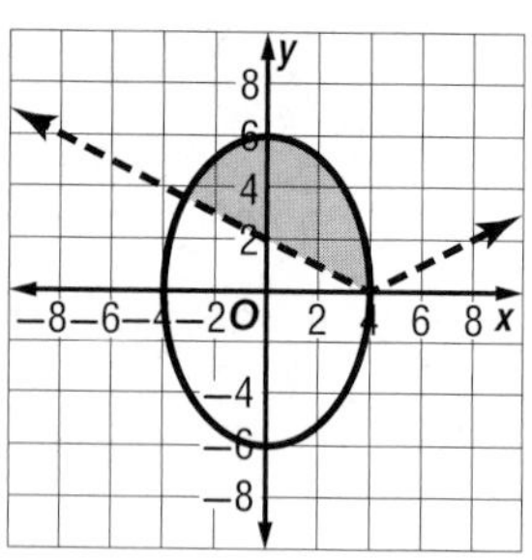

4B. 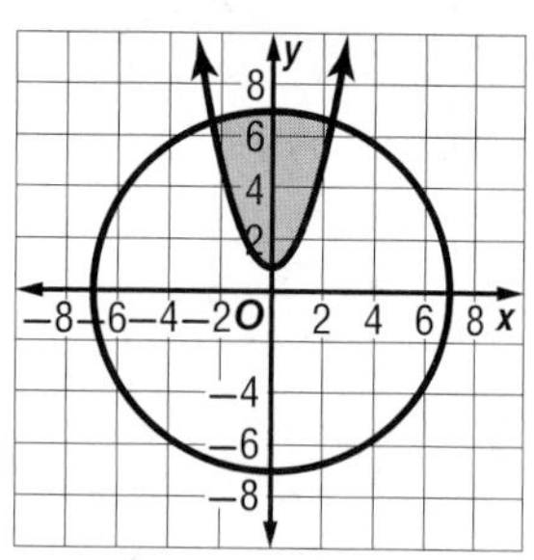

Pages 664–667, Lesson 10-7

10. 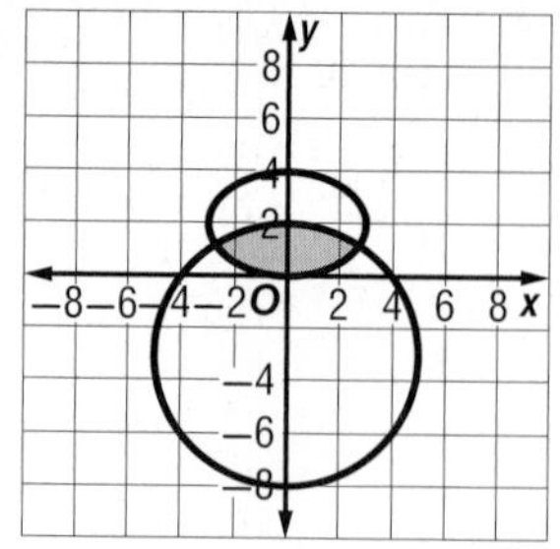

11. 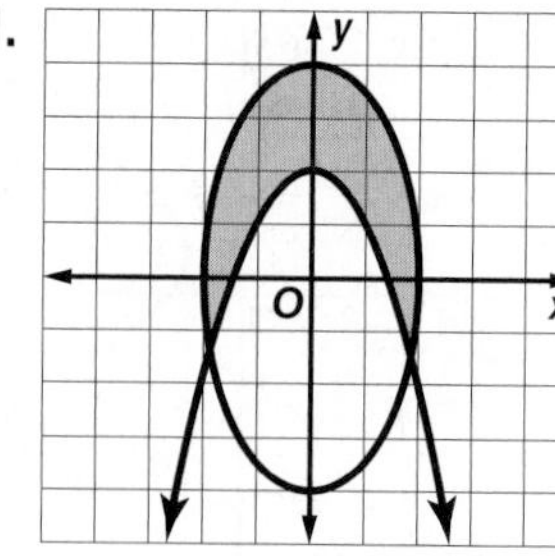

12. 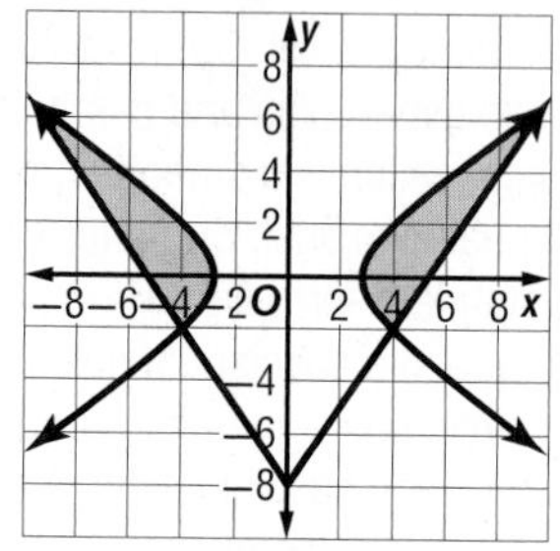

13. 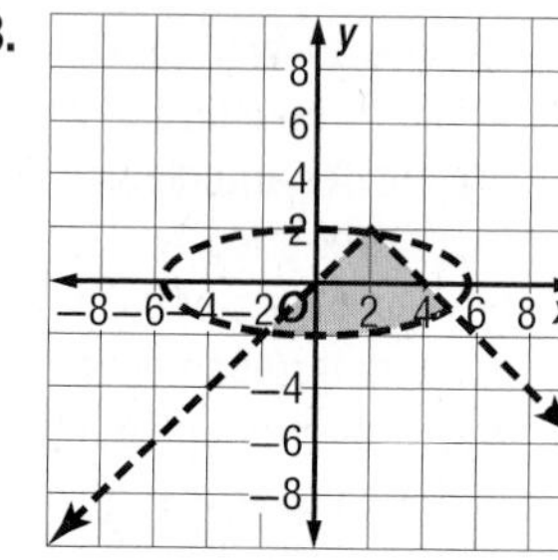

27. 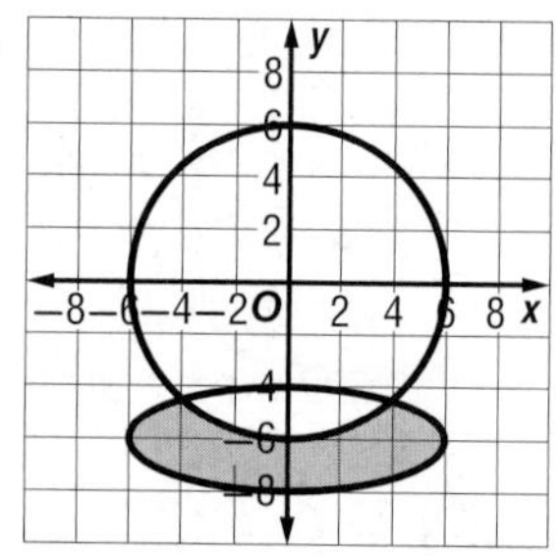

28. 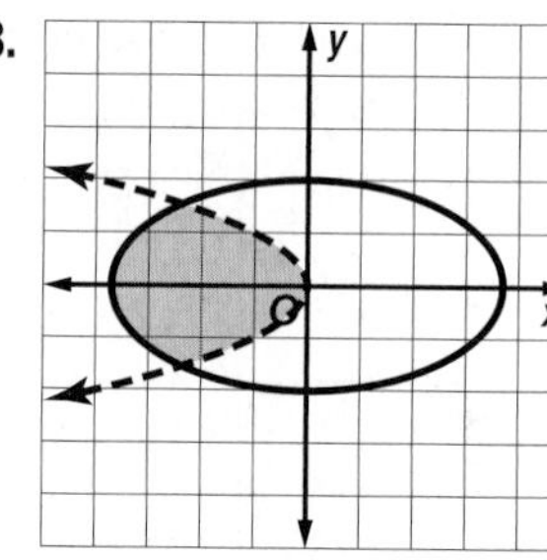

29. 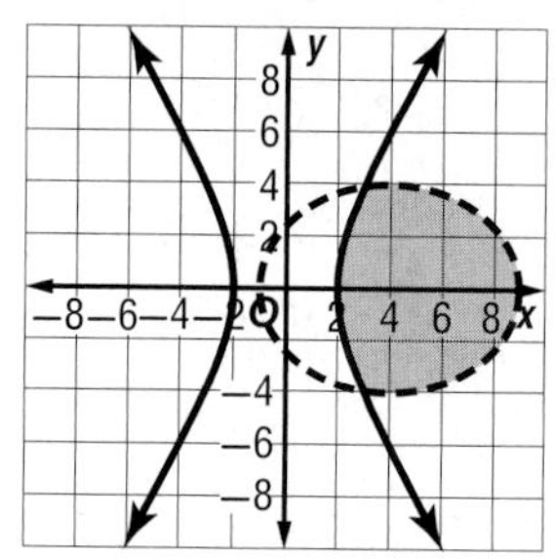

30. 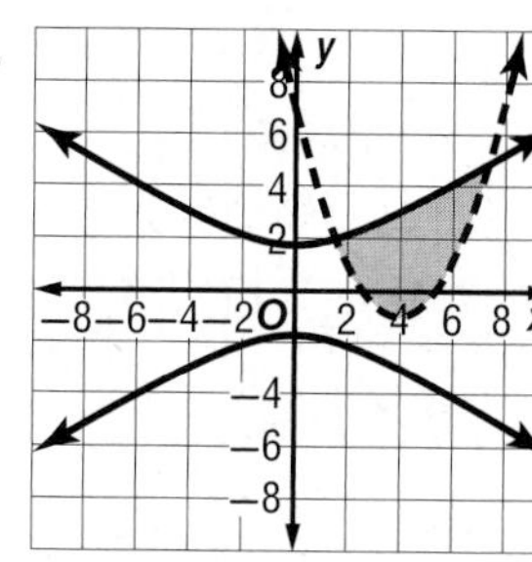

31. 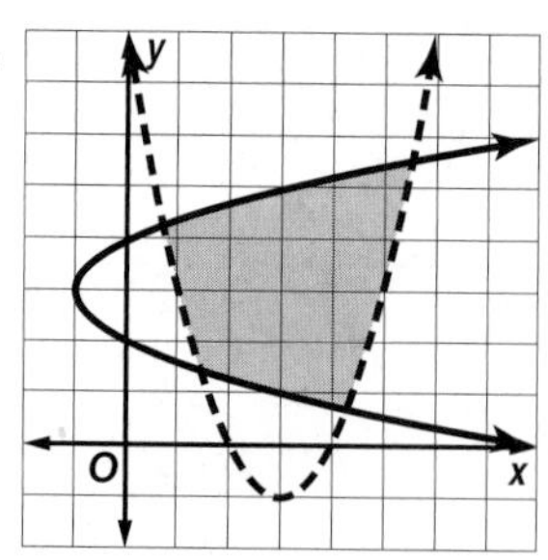

32. 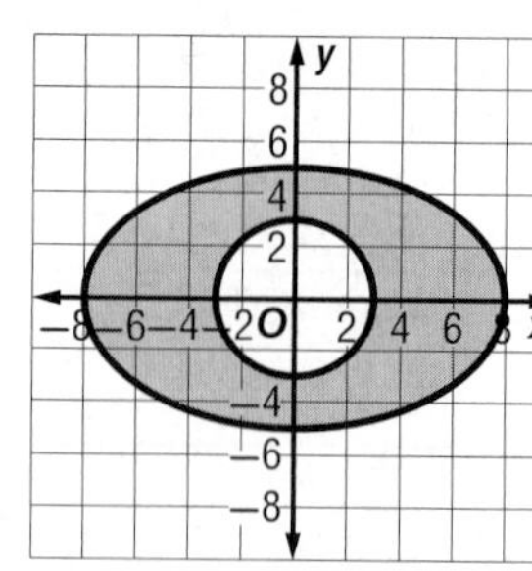

33. 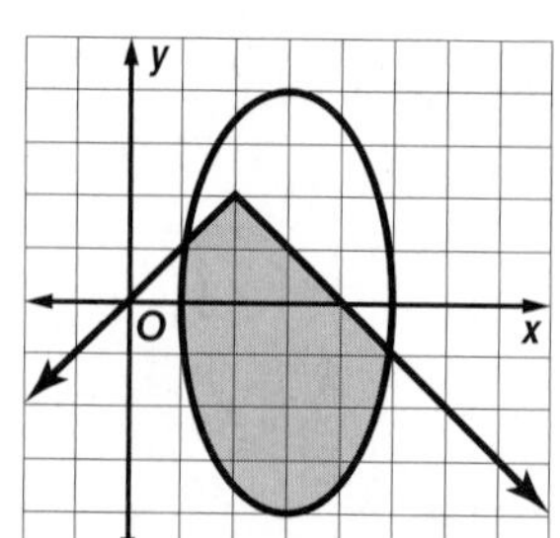

34. 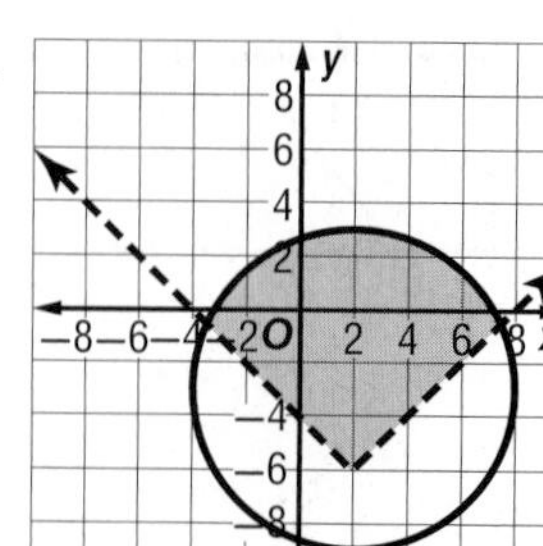

35. 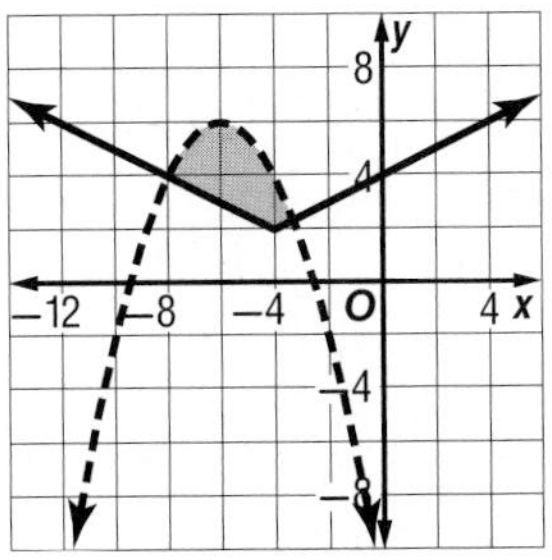

36. 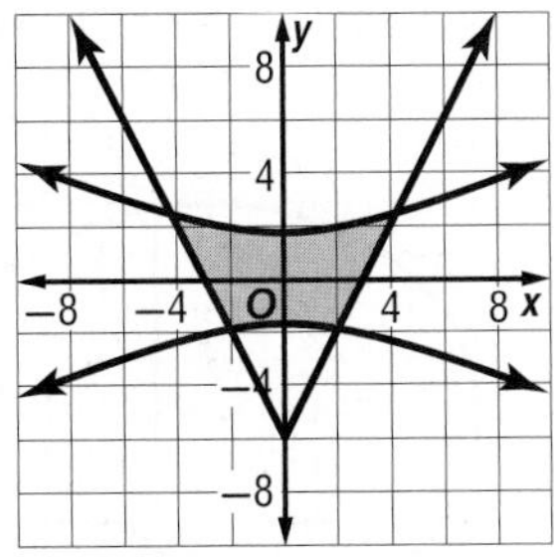

43. Sample answer: $\frac{x^2}{16} + \frac{y^2}{36} = 1$ and $(x + 10)^2 + y^2 = 36$

44. Sample answer: $y = x^2$ and $\frac{x^2}{16} + \frac{y^2}{36} = 1$

45. Sample answer: $x^2 + y^2 = 1$ and $\frac{x^2}{16} - \frac{y^2}{36} = 1$

46. Sample answer: $y = x^2$ and $\frac{x^2}{64} + \frac{(y-4)^2}{16} = 1$

47. Sample answer: $\frac{x^2}{64} + \frac{y^2}{100} = 1$ and $x^2 - y^2 = 1$

49. Sample answer: No; if one player is in one of the shaded areas and the other player is in the other shaded area, they will not be able to hear each other.

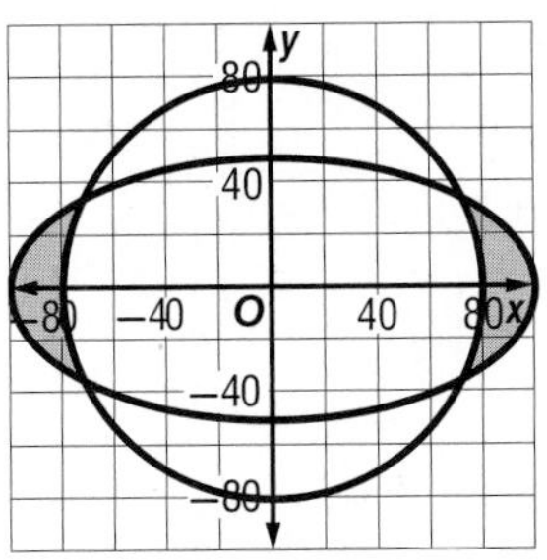

50a. 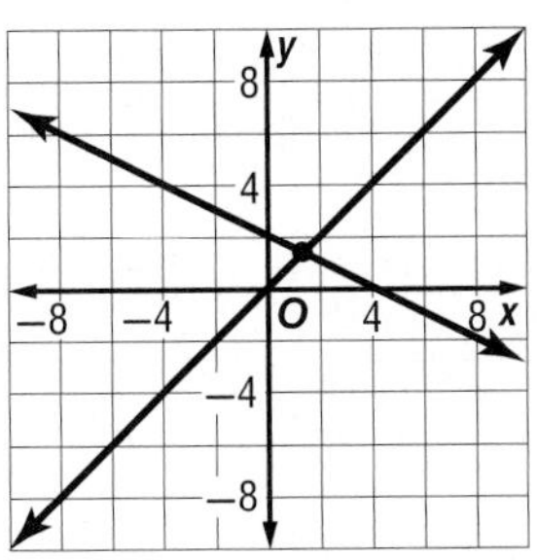 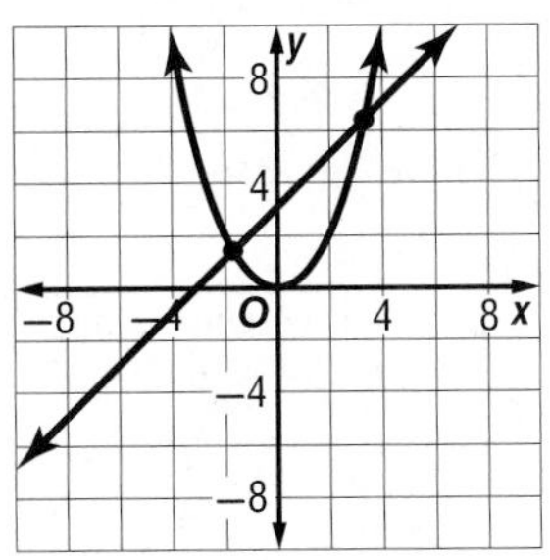

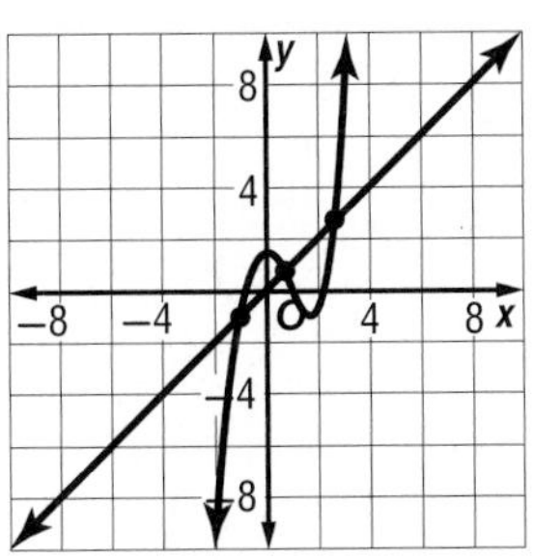 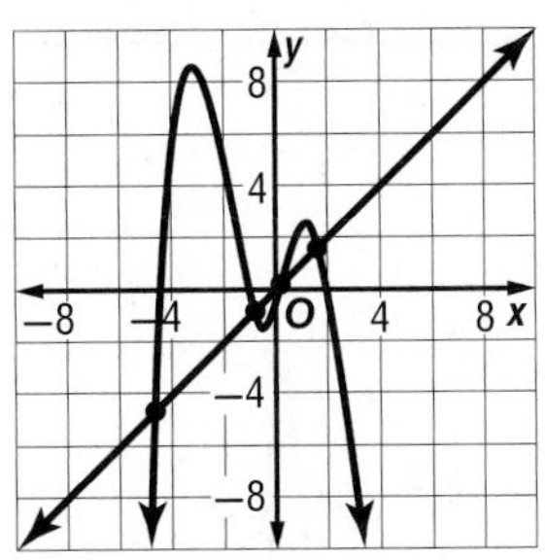

50c. 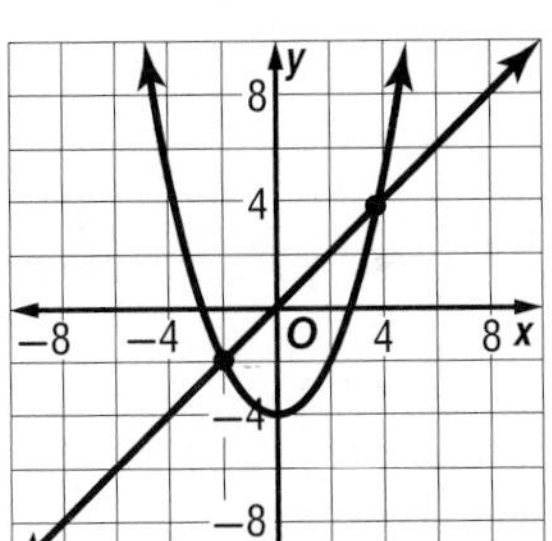 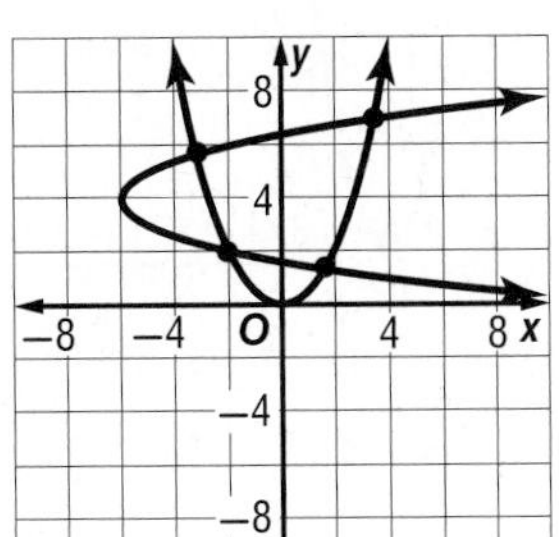

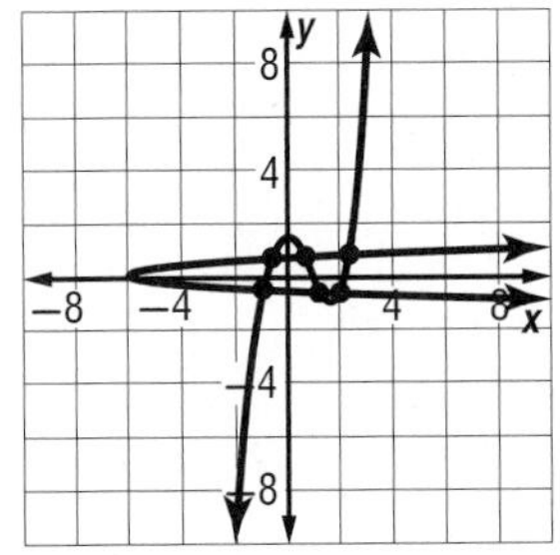 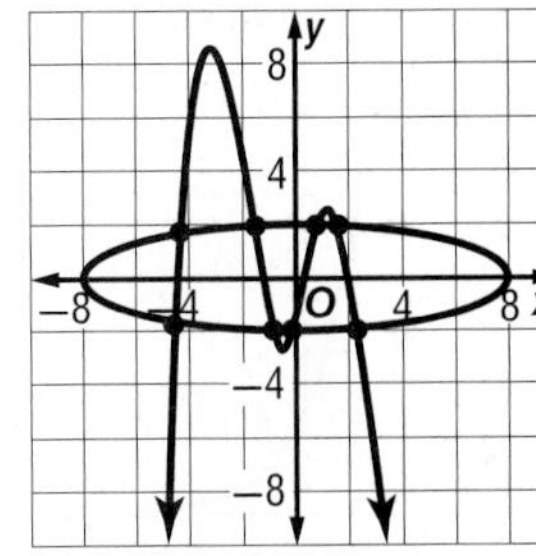

52. 1, 2 or 3; the parabola could be tangent to the ellipse and have one solution. The parabola could intersect the ellipse at three points like this.

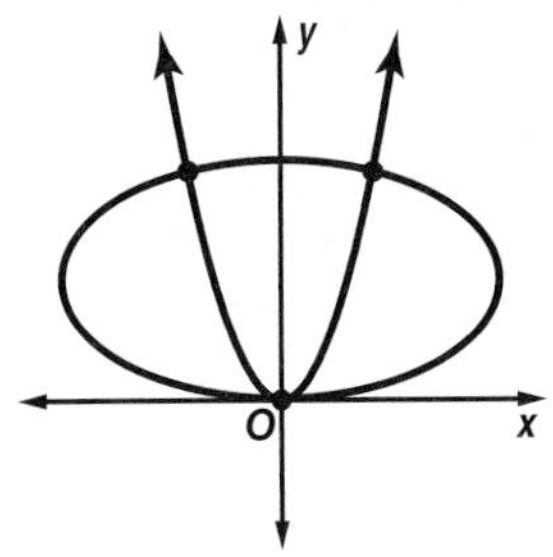

Or it could have two solutions like this.

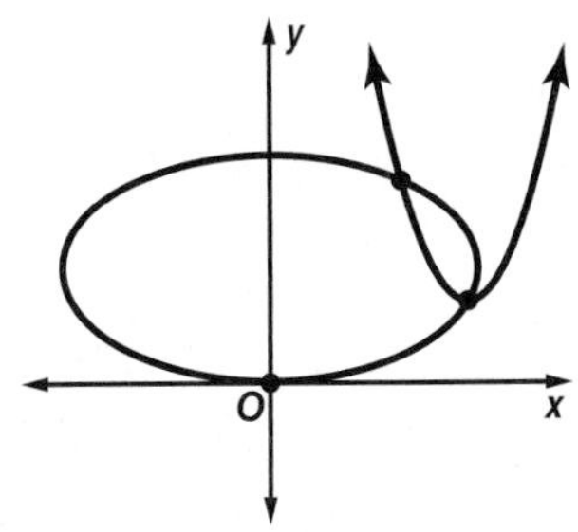

68. D = {all real numbers}, R = $\{f(x) \mid f(x) < 0\}$

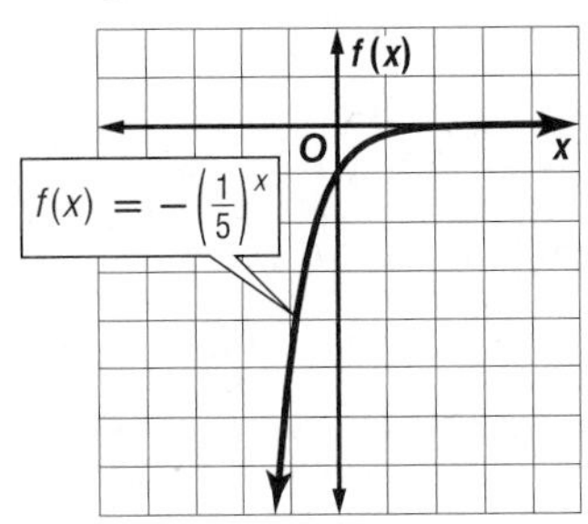

69. D = {all real numbers}, R = $\{y \mid y < 0\}$

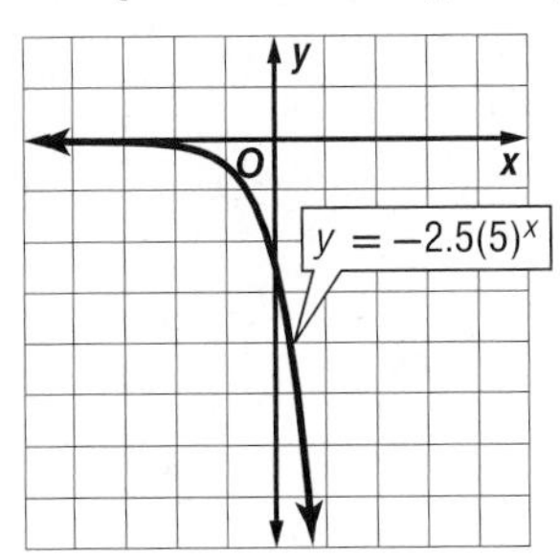

Chapter 10 Answer Appendix

70. D = {all real numbers}, R = $\{f(x) \mid f(x) > 0\}$

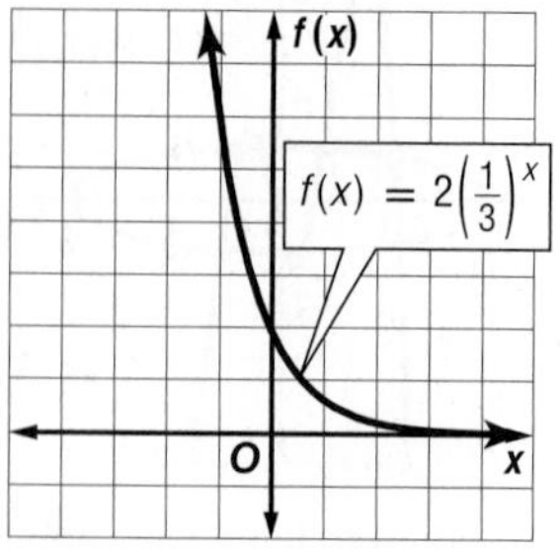

Pages 670–672, Study Guide and Review

37. (0, 0); $(0, \pm 3\sqrt{3})$; 12; 6

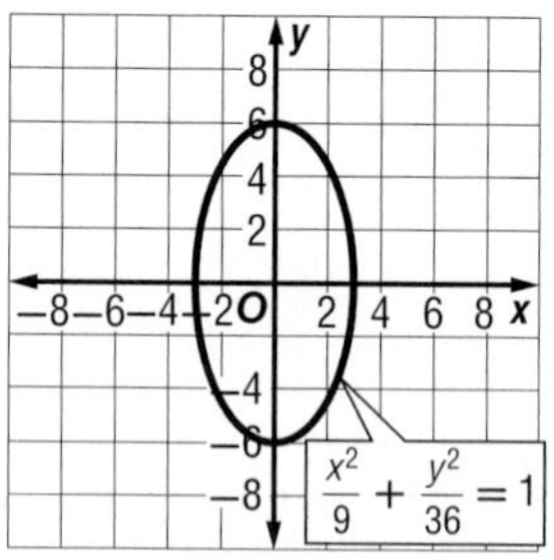

38. (0, 0); $(0, \pm\sqrt{5})$; $2\sqrt{10}$; $2\sqrt{5}$

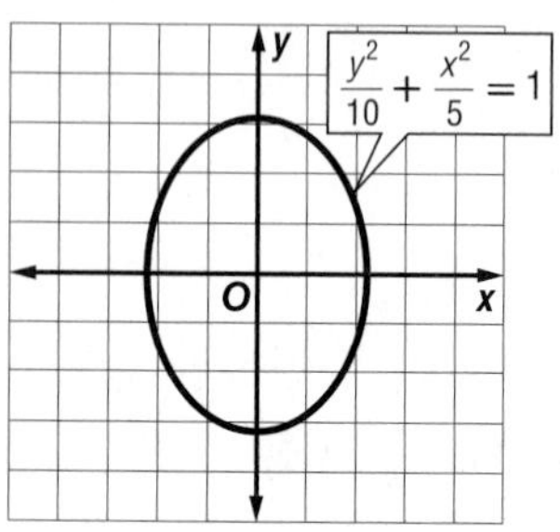

39. (0, 4); $(\pm 4\sqrt{2}, 4)$; 12; 4

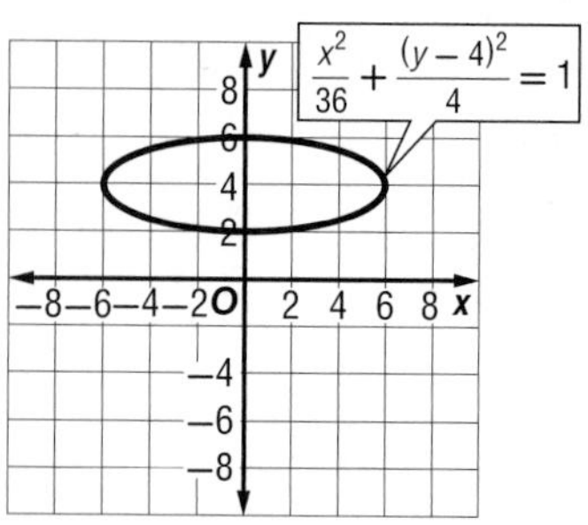

40. (0, 0); $(0, \pm\sqrt{6})$; 6; $2\sqrt{3}$

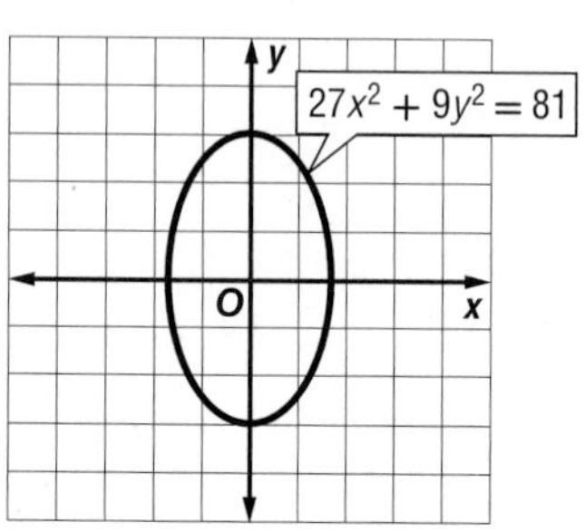

41. (–1, 2); (–4, 2), (2, 2); 10; 8

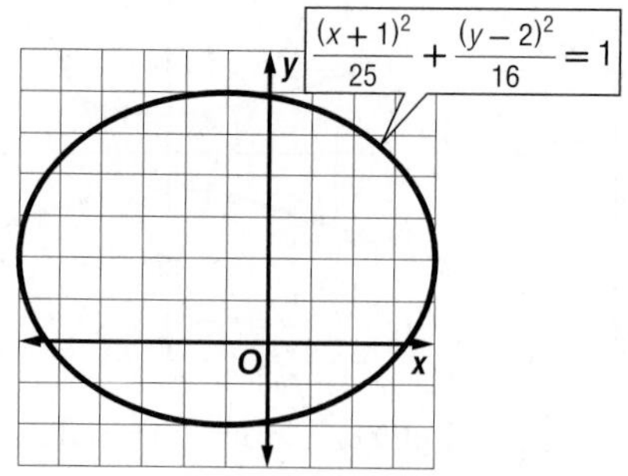

42. (–3, 1); $(-3, 1 \pm \sqrt{5})$; 6; 4

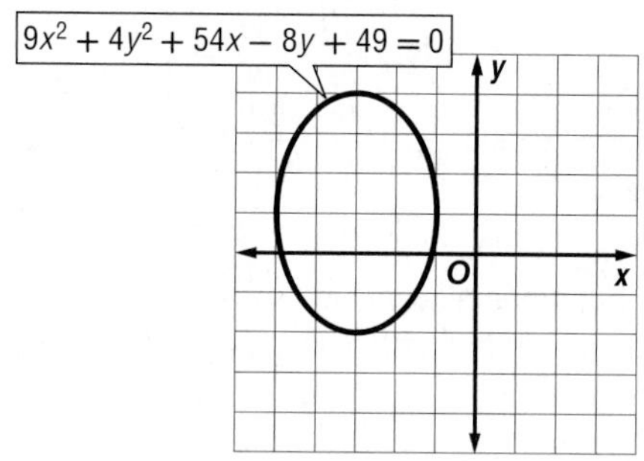

43. (1, –1); (–3, –1), (5, –1); 10; 6

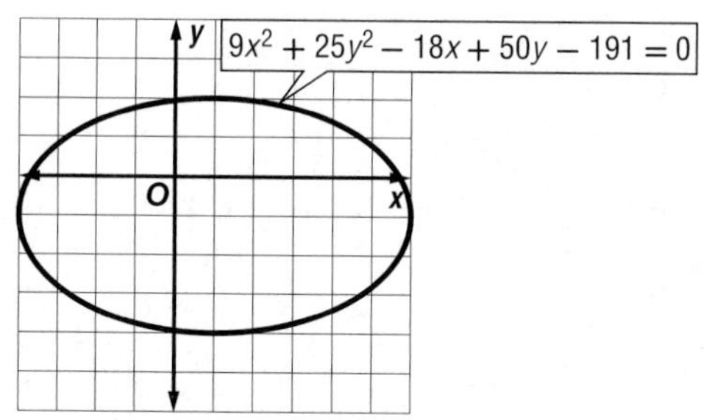

44. (2, 2); (2, 4), (2, 0); $2\sqrt{7}$; $2\sqrt{3}$

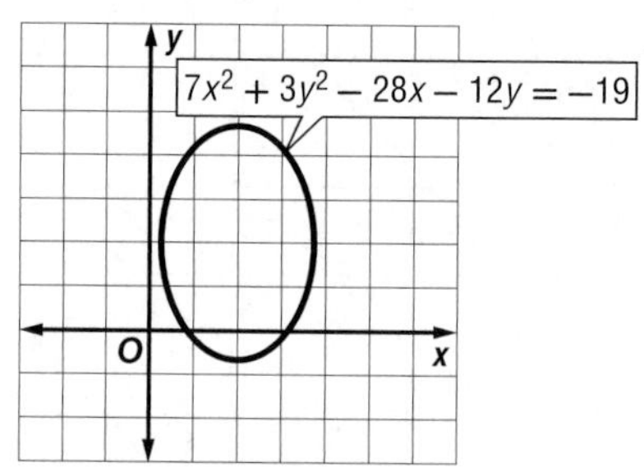

52. $y = 3(x + 2)^2 - 4$; parabola

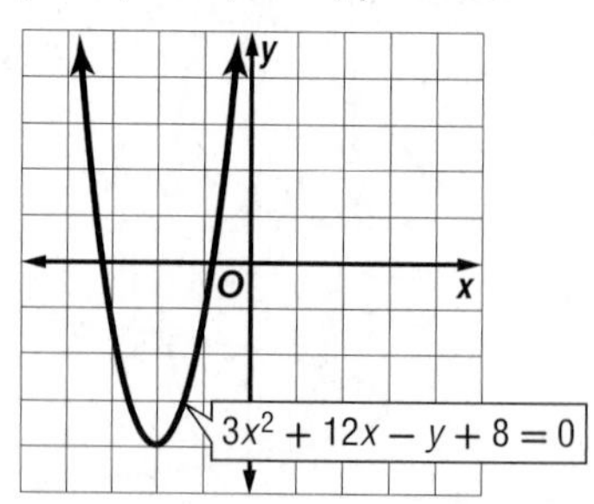

53. $\frac{x^2}{16} + \frac{y^2}{9} = 1$; ellipse

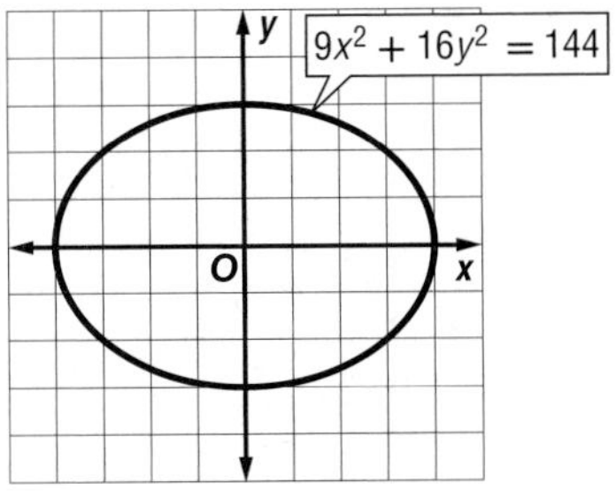

54. $(x - 4)^2 + (y - 1)^2 = 9$; circle

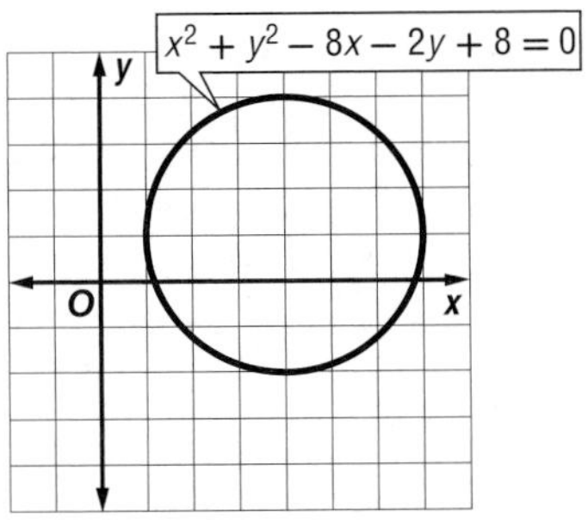

55. $\frac{y^2}{9} - \frac{(x - 2)^2}{1} = 1$; hyperbola

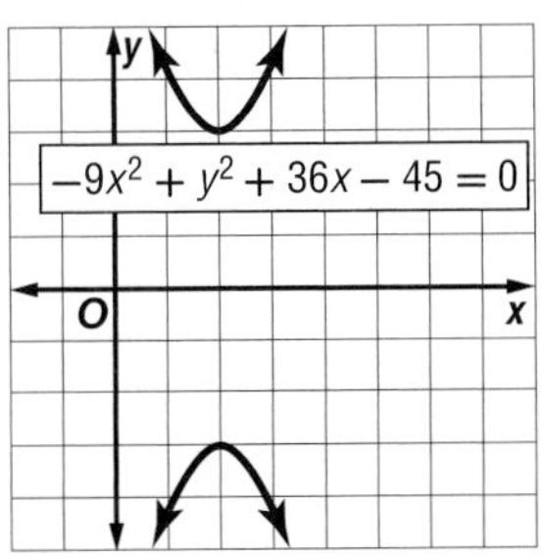

Page 673, Practice Test

7. circle

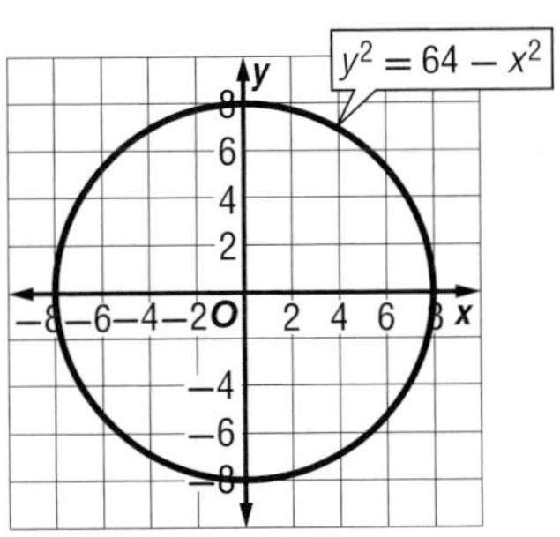

8. ellipse

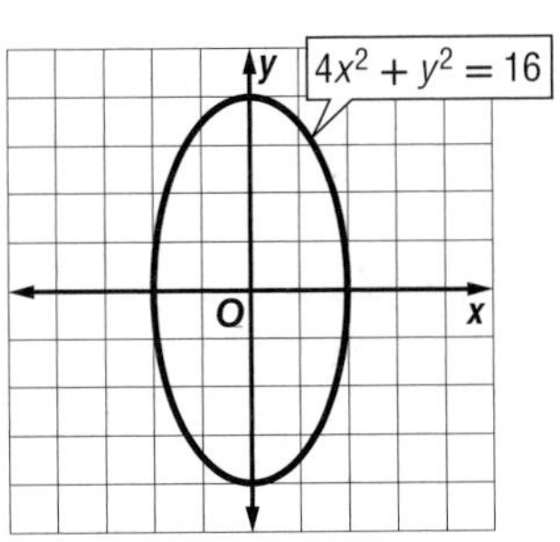

9. hyperbola

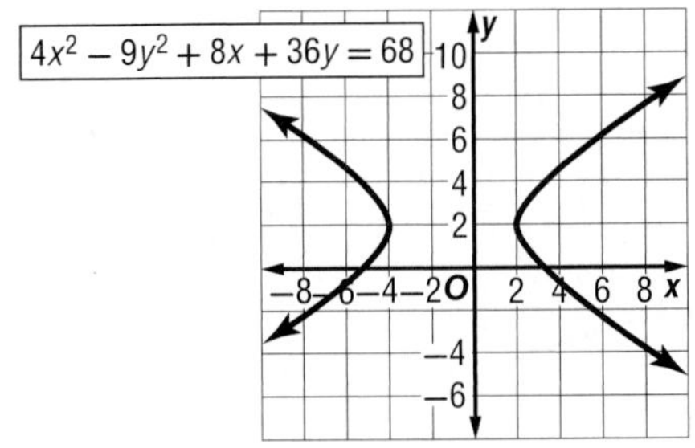

10. parabola

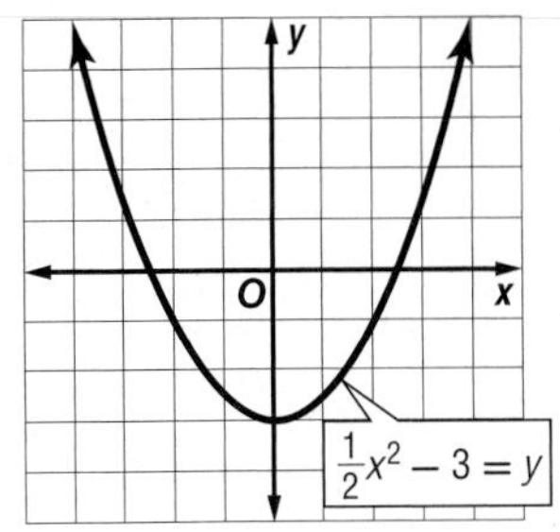

11. parabola

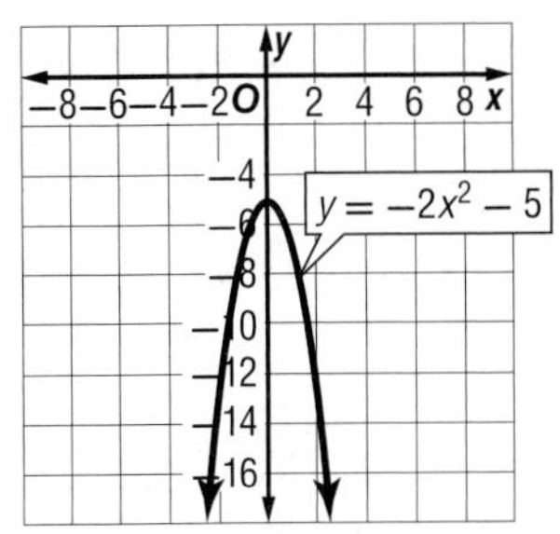

12. ellipse

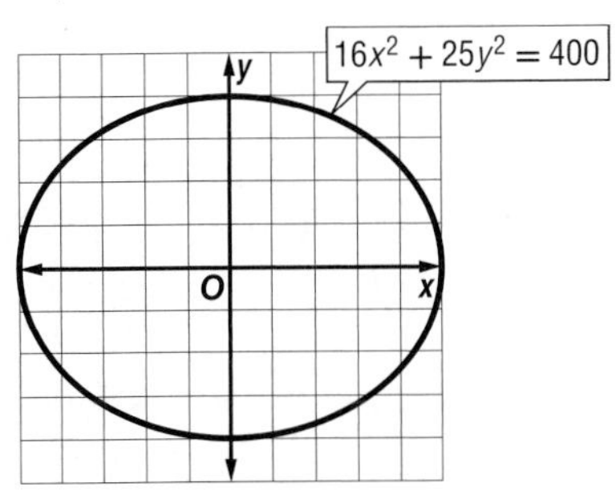

13. circle

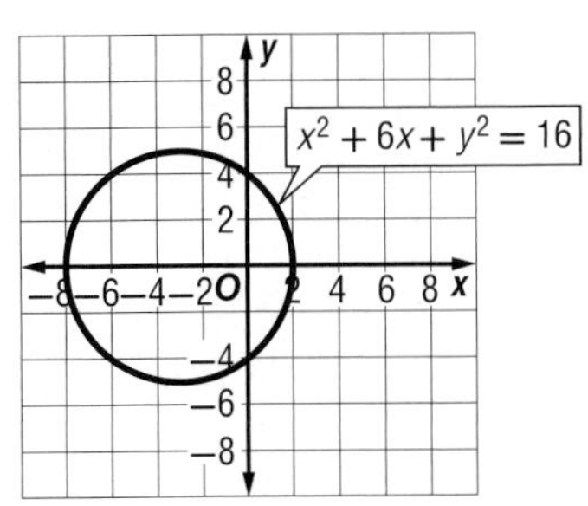

14. hyperbola

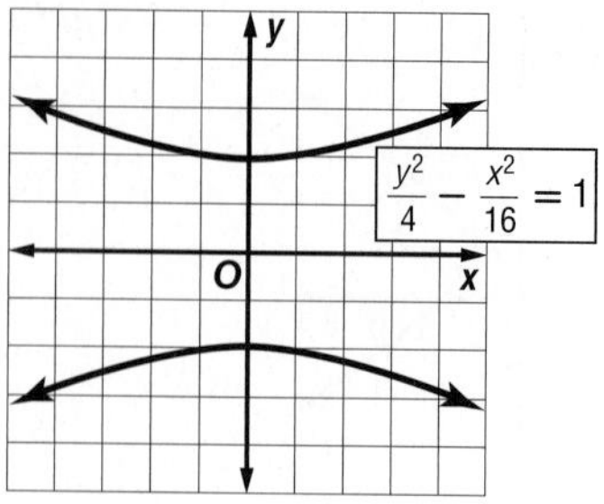

15. parabola

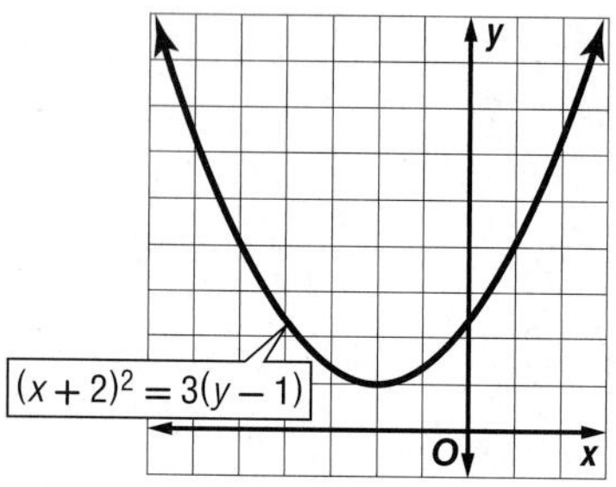

16. ellipse

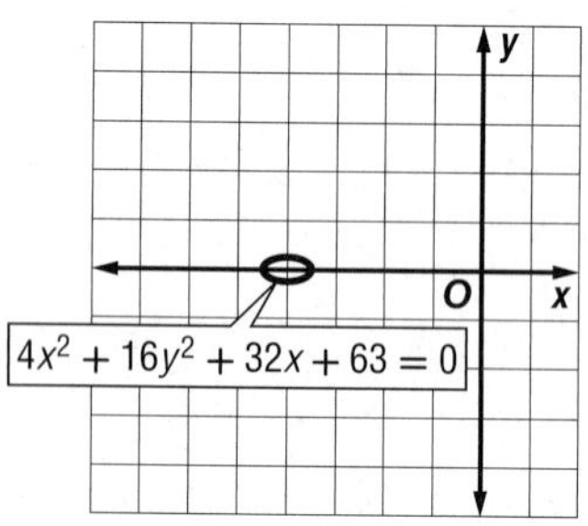

NOTES

CHAPTER 11

Chapter Planner

Diagnostic Assessment
Quick Check, p. 679

	Lesson 11-1 Pacing: 1 day	Lesson 11-2 Pacing: 1.5 days	Lesson 11-3 Pacing: 1.5 days
Title	**Sequences as Functions**	**Arithmetic Sequences and Series**	**Geometric Sequences and Series**
Objectives	• Relate arithmetic sequences to linear functions. • Relate geometric sequences to exponential functions.	• Use arithmetic sequences. • Find sums of arithmetic series.	• Use geometric sequences. • Find sums of geometric series.
Key Vocabulary	sequence term finite sequence infinite sequence arithmetic sequence common difference geometric sequence common ratio	arithmetic means series arithmetic series partial sum sigma notation	geometric means geometric series
NGSSS	MA.912.D.11.1, MA.912.D.11.3	MA.912.D.11.3, MA.912.D.11.4	MA.912.D.11.3, MA.912.D.11.4
Multiple Representations		p. 694	
Lesson Resources	**Chapter 11 Resource Masters** • Study Guide and Intervention, pp. 5–6 AL OL ELL • Skills Practice, p. 7 AL OL ELL • Practice, p. 8 AL OL BL ELL • Word Problem Practice, p. 9 AL OL BL ELL • Enrichment, p. 10 OL BL **Transparencies** • 5-Minute Check Transparency 11-1 AL OL BL ELL **Additional Print Resources** • Study Notebook AL OL BL ELL • Teaching Algebra with Manipulatives, p. 248 AL OL ELL	**Chapter 11 Resource Masters** • Study Guide and Intervention, pp. 11–12 AL OL ELL • Skills Practice, p. 13 AL OL ELL • Practice, p. 14 AL OL BL ELL • Word Problem Practice, p. 15 AL OL BL ELL • Enrichment, p. 16 OL BL • Spreadsheet Activity, p. 17 OL • TI-Nspire Activity, p. 18 OL • Quiz 1, p. 53 AL OL BL ELL **Transparencies** • 5-Minute Check Transparency 11-2 AL OL BL ELL **Additional Print Resources** • Study Notebook AL OL BL ELL	**Chapter 11 Resource Masters** • Study Guide and Intervention, pp. 19–20 AL OL ELL • Skills Practice, p. 21 AL OL ELL • Practice, p. 22 AL OL BL ELL • Word Problem Practice, p. 23 AL OL BL ELL • Enrichment, p. 24 OL BL • Graphing Calculator Activity, p. 25 OL **Transparencies** • 5-Minute Check Transparency 11-3 AL OL BL ELL **Additional Print Resources** • Study Notebook AL OL BL ELL
Technology for Every Lesson	FL Math Online glencoe.com • Extra Examples • Self-Check Quizzes • Personal Tutor • Homework Help	**CD/DVD Resources** IWB INTERACTIVE WHITEBOARD READY IWB StudentWorks Plus IWB Interactive Classroom IWB Diagnostic and Assessment Planner	• TeacherWorks Plus • eSolutions Manual Plus • ExamView Assessment Suite
Get Animated	Interactive Lab	Animation	
Differentiated Instruction	pp. 684, 687	pp. 690, 693	pp. 698, 702

KEY: AL Approaching Level OL On Level BL Beyond Level ELL English Learners

Sequences and Series

Suggested Pacing			
Time Periods	Instruction	Review & Assessment	Total
45-minute	11	2	13
90-minute	6	1	7

Explore 11-4 Pacing: 0.5 day	Lesson 11-4 Pacing: 1 day	Extend 11-4 Pacing: 0.5 day	Lesson 11-5 Pacing: 1.5 days
Algebra Lab: Area Under a Curve	**Infinite Geometric Series**	**Graphing Technology Lab: Limits**	**Recursion and Iteration**
• Approximate the area under a curve between a specified interval, using the sum of rectangular areas under the curve.	• Find sums of infinite geometric series. • Write repeating decimals as fractions.	• Use a graphing calculator to investigate limits of sequences.	• Recognize and use special sequences. • Iterate functions.
	convergent series divergent series infinity		Fibonacci sequence recursive sequence explicit formula recursive formula iteration
	MA.912.D.11.2, MA.912.D.11.4		MA.912.D.11.1
	p. 709		
Materials • grid paper **Additional Print Resources** • Teaching Algebra with Manipulatives, pp. 1, 249–250 AL OL ELL	**Chapter 11 Resource Masters** • Study Guide and Intervention, pp. 26–27 AL OL ELL • Skills Practice, p. 28 AL OL ELL • Practice, p. 29 AL OL BL ELL • Word Problem Practice, p. 30 AL OL BL ELL • Enrichment, p. 31 OL BL • Quiz 2, p. 53 AL OL BL ELL **Transparencies** • 5-Minute Check Transparency 11-4 AL OL BL ELL **Additional Print Resources** • Study Notebook AL OL BL ELL	**Materials** • TI-83/84 Plus or other graphing calculator	**Chapter 11 Resource Masters** • Study Guide and Intervention, pp. 32–33 AL OL ELL • Skills Practice, p. 34 AL OL ELL • Practice, p. 35 AL OL BL ELL • Word Problem Practice, p. 36 AL OL BL ELL • Enrichment, p. 37 OL BL • Graphing Calculator Activity, p. 38 OL **Transparencies** • 5-Minute Check Transparency 11-5 AL OL BL ELL **Additional Print Resources** • Study Notebook AL OL BL ELL • Teaching Algebra with Manipulatives, pp. 251–252 AL OL ELL

FL Math Online glencoe.com
- Extra Examples
- Self-Check Quizzes
- Personal Tutor
- Homework Help

CD/DVD Resources IWB INTERACTIVE WHITEBOARD READY
- IWB StudentWorks Plus
- IWB Interactive Classroom
- IWB Diagnostic and Assessment Planner
- TeacherWorks Plus
- eSolutions Manual Plus
- ExamView Assessment Suite

	pp. 707, 711		pp. 716, 719

Formative Assessment
Mid-Chapter Quiz, p. 713

CHAPTER 11 Chapter Planner

	Extend 11-5 Pacing: 0.5 day	Lesson 11-6 Pacing: 1.5 days	Extend 11-6 Pacing: 0.5 day	Lesson 11-7 Pacing: 1 day
Title	**Spreadsheet Lab: Amortizing Loans**	**The Binomial Theorem**	**Algebra Lab: Combinations and Pascal's Triangle**	**Proof by Mathematical Induction**
Objectives	• Use a spreadsheet to analyze the payments, interest, and balance on a loan.	• Use Pascal's triangle to expand powers of binomials. • Use the Binomial Theorem to expand powers of binomials.	• Use combinations and Pascal's triangle to determine the number of ways the prizes of a game can be chosen.	• Prove statements by using mathematical induction. • Disprove statements by finding a counterexample.
Key Vocabulary		Pascal's triangle		mathematical induction induction hypothesis
NGSSS		MA.912.A.4.12	MA.912.P.1.2	MA.912.D.1.3
Multiple Representations				
Lesson Resources	**Materials** • computer and spreadsheet program	**Chapter 11 Resource Masters** • Study Guide and Intervention, pp. 39–40 AL OL ELL • Skills Practice, p. 41 AL OL ELL • Practice, p. 42 AL OL BL ELL • Word Problem Practice, p. 43 AL OL BL • Enrichment, p. 44 OL BL • Quiz 3, p. 54 AL OL BL ELL **Transparencies** • 5-Minute Check Transparency 11-6 AL OL BL ELL **Additional Print Resources** • Study Notebook AL OL BL ELL	**Additional Print Resources** • Teaching Algebra with Manipulatives, p. 253 AL OL ELL	**Chapter 11 Resource Masters** • Study Guide and Intervention, pp. 45–46 AL OL ELL • Skills Practice, p. 47 AL OL ELL • Practice, p. 48 AL OL BL ELL • Word Problem Practice, p. 49 AL OL BL • Enrichment, p. 50 OL BL • Quiz 4, p. 54 AL OL BL ELL **Transparencies** • 5-Minute Check Transparency 11-7 AL OL BL ELL **Additional Print Resources** • Study Notebook AL OL BL ELL
Technology for Every Lesson	FL Math Online glencoe.com • Extra Examples • Personal Tutor • Self-Check Quizzes • Homework Help	**CD/DVD Resources** IWB INTERACTIVE WHITEBOARD READY IWB StudentWorks Plus IWB Interactive Classroom IWB Diagnostic and Assessment Planner		• TeacherWorks Plus • eSolutions Manual Plus • ExamView Assessment Suite
Get Animated				
Differentiated Instruction		pp. 722, 725		pp. 728, 731

Summative Assessment
- Study Guide and Review, pp. 732–736
- Practice Test, p. 737

KEY: AL Approaching Level OL On Level BL Beyond Level ELL English Learners

What the Research Says . . .

Stohl Drier (2001) states that interactive spreadsheets can promote open-ended exploration of mathematical concepts, allow learners to extend beyond or significantly enhance what could be done using paper-and-pencil, and give teachers and students an opportunity to discover mathematical concepts in a laboratory-like setting.

- In Extend 11-5, students use a computer spreadsheet to investigate sequences involved in loan amortization.
- Suggest that students use a spreadsheet to explore answers to some of the financially-oriented exercises in Lesson 11-5, such as Exercises 7, 28, and 36.

Teacher to Teacher

Holly K. Plunkett
University High School, Morgantown, WV

"I have students investigate geometric sequences by bouncing rubber balls and using a CBL."

NOTES:

CHAPTER 11

Assessment and Intervention

SE = Student Edition, **TE** = Teacher Edition, **CRM** = Chapter Resource Masters

	Diagnosis	Prescription
Diagnostic Assessment	**Beginning Chapter 11**	
	Get Ready for Chapter 11 **SE,** p. 679	Response to Intervention **TE,** p. 679
	Beginning Every Lesson	
	Then, Now, Why? **SE** 5-Minute Check Transparencies	Chapter 0 **SE,** pp. P1 through P19 Concepts and Skills Bank **SE,** pp. 994–1007
Formative Assessment	**During/After Every Lesson**	
	Guided Practice **SE,** every example Check Your Understanding **SE** H.O.T. Problems **SE** Spiral Review **SE** Additional Examples **TE** Watch Out! **TE** Step 4, Assess **TE** Chapter 11 Quizzes **CRM,** pp. 53–54 Self-Check Quizzes glencoe.com	**Tier 1 Intervention** Concepts and Skills Bank **SE,** pp. 994–1007 Skills Practice **CRM,** Ch. 1–11 glencoe.com **Tier 2 Intervention** Differentiated Instruction **TE** Study Guide and Intervention Masters **CRM,** Ch. 1–11 **Tier 3 Intervention** *Math Triumphs, Alg. 2*
	Mid-Chapter	
	Mid-Chapter Quiz **SE,** p. 713 Mid-Chapter Test **CRM,** p. 55 ExamView Assessment Suite	**Tier 1 Intervention** Concepts and Skills Bank **SE,** pp. 994–1007 Skills Practice **CRM,** Ch. 1–11 glencoe.com **Tier 2 Intervention** Study Guide and Intervention Masters **CRM,** Ch. 1–11 **Tier 3 Intervention** *Math Triumphs, Alg. 2*
	Before Chapter Test	
	Chapter Study Guide and Review **SE,** pp. 732–736 Practice Test **SE,** p. 737 Standardized Test Practice **SE,** pp. 738–741 Chapter Test glencoe.com Standardized Test Practice glencoe.com Vocabulary Review glencoe.com ExamView Assessment Suite	**Tier 1 Intervention** Concepts and Skills Bank **SE,** pp. 994–1007 Skills Practice **CRM,** Ch. 1–11 glencoe.com **Tier 2 Intervention** Study Guide and Intervention Masters **CRM,** Ch. 1–11 **Tier 3 Intervention** *Math Triumphs, Alg. 2*
Summative Assessment	**After Chapter 11**	
	Multiple-Choice Tests, Forms 1, 2A, 2B **CRM,** pp. 57–62 Free-Response Tests, Forms 2C, 2D, 3 **CRM,** pp. 63–68 Vocabulary Test **CRM,** p. 56 Extended Response Test **CRM,** p. 69 Standardized Test Practice **CRM,** pp. 70–72 ExamView Assessment Suite	Study Guide and Intervention Masters **CRM,** Ch. 1–11 glencoe.com

CHAPTER 11

Differentiated Instruction

Option 1 Reaching All Learners AL OL BL ELL

LOGICAL Have students make a chart that compares and contrasts arithmetic and geometric sequences and series, explaining what the variables represent in each formula.

INTERPERSONAL Create a friendly competition between two groups of students, the *Binomial Theorem Expanders* and the *Polynomial Multipliers.* Write an expression such as $(2x + y)^5$ on the board. Have each group expand the expression using the method for which their group is named. Compare the expanded expressions and the times the groups take to find them.

Option 2 Approaching Level AL

To explain conceptually how mathematical induction works, set up a series of 5 evenly spaced dominoes in a line, one behind the other. Knock the first domino over. Ask students to describe what they observe. Tell students that you think, based on what was just observed, that the 29th domino will get knocked over if you knock over the first domino. Set up 30 dominos to test and prove your assumption is true. Then ask the class what they think would happen to the 500th domino. Tell students that they just used inductive reasoning.

Explain that when they say that a mathematical statement is true for $n = 1$, it is the same as proving the first domino can be knocked down. Then proving it is true for $k + 1$ if it is true for k, means that you have proved that if any domino falls, the next one in line will fall. So, if #1 falls, #2 will fall, and if #2 falls, then #3 will fall, and so on.

Option 3 English Learners ELL

Have students create a list of the different mathematical notations (symbols) as they are presented in this chapter. As each notation is presented, ask students to record the notation, an example, its name, and why it is useful in their study of mathematics.

For example,

Notation	Name	Example	why it is useful
...	ellipsis	2, 4, 6, ...	indicates that a series is infinite
$\sum$	sigma	$\sum_{k=1}^{y} 3K$	represents the sum of a series

Option 4 Beyond Level BL

With manipulatives or sketches, students use various geometric elements to model problems involving arithmetic or geometric sequences. Then have students write a general rule for the nth term of their sequence.

For example, the figures below show an arithmetic sequence in the number of red dots. The rule for the sequence is $a_n = 3 + 2(n - 1)$.

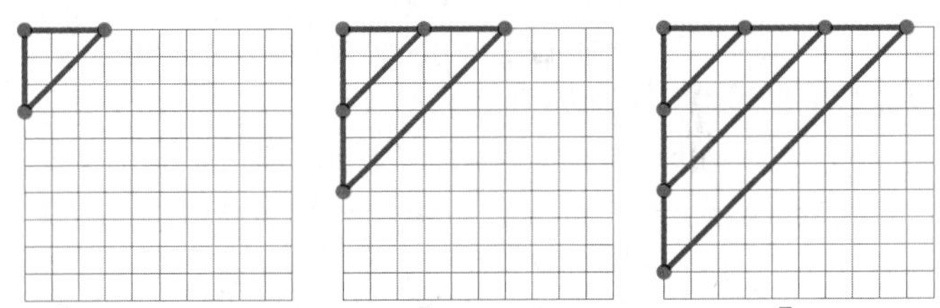

3 5 7

FL Math Online Access Point Activities

CHAPTER 11

Focus on Mathematical Content

Vertical Alignment

Before Chapter 11

Related Topics before Algebra 1

- find and evaluate an algebraic expression to determine any term on an arithmetic sequence

Related Topics from Algebra 1

- look for patterns and represent generalizations algebraically
- transform and solve equations
- simplify polynomial expressions

Related Topics from Geometry

- use inductive reasoning to formulate a conjecture

Chapter 11

Related Topics from Algebra 2

- relate arithmetic sequences to linear functions and relate geometric sequences to exponential functions
- find specific terms and sums of arithmetic and geometric series
- find the sum of an infinite geometric series and write repeating decimals as fractions
- recognize and use special sequences and iterate functions
- use Pascal's triangle and the Binomial Theorem to expand powers of binomials
- use mathematical induction to prove statements

After Chapter 11

Preparation for Precalculus

- represent patterns using arithmetic and geometric sequences and series
- use arithmetic, geometric, and other sequences and series to solve real-life problems
- describe limits of sequences and apply their properties to investigate convergent and divergent series
- apply sequences and series to solve problems including sums and binomial expansion

Lesson-by-Lesson Preview

11-1 Sequences as Functions

A set of numbers arranged in a particular order is called a sequence. Each number is a term of the sequence. A sequence is

- *finite* when there are a limited number of terms, or
- *infinite* when the terms continue without end.

A sequence is

- *arithmetic* when the terms are determined by adding a constant value (a common difference) to the previous term,
- *geometric* when each term is determined by multiplying a nonzero constant (the common ratio) by the previous term, or
- *neither* arithmetic nor geometric when there is no common difference or ratio.

Sequences are functions whose domains consist of natural numbers and whose ranges consist of real numbers. Arithmetic sequences are linear. Geometric sequences are exponential.

11-2 Arithmetic Sequences and Series

Any term a_n in an arithmetic sequence can be determined when you know the first term a_1 and the common difference d. The formula to use is $a_n = a_1 + (n - 1)d$, where n is any natural number.

An *arithmetic series* is formed when the terms of an arithmetic sequence are added. The formulas $S_n = \left(\frac{na_1 + a_n}{2}\right)$ or $S_n = \frac{n}{2}[2a_1 + (n - 1)d]$ can be used to find the sum of the first n terms of any arithmetic series. Sigma notation can be used to indicate the sum of a series. For example, $\sum_{n=1}^{3}(n^2 + 2)$ represents a sum of three terms in which n is successively replaced by each of the values 1, 2, and 3.

11-3 Geometric Sequences and Series

The formula $a_n = a_1 \cdot r^{n-1}$ can be used to find any term a_n in a geometric sequence when you know the first term a_1 and the common ratio r.

A *geometric series* is formed when the terms of a geometric sequence are added. The formulas $S_n = \frac{a_1 + a_1r^n}{1 - r}, r \neq 1$ or $S_n = \frac{a_1 + a_nr}{1 - r}, r \neq 1$ can be used to find the sum of the first n terms of a geometric sequence. Sigma notation can be used to represent the sum of a geometric series.

11-4 Infinite Geometric Series

If the sum of an infinite geometric series

- approaches a finite value, it is called a *convergent series* and $|r| < 1$. The formula $S = \frac{a_1}{1 - r}$ can be used to find its sum.
- does not approach a finite value, it is called a *divergent series* and $|r| \geq 1$.

The formula for the sum of an infinite series can be used to convert a repeating decimal to a fraction as shown below.

$0.353535... = 0.35 + 0.0035 + 0.000035 + ...$

Common ratio: $r = \frac{0.0035}{0.35} = 0.01$

$S = \frac{a_1}{1 - r} = \frac{0.35}{1 - 0.01} = \frac{0.35}{0.99} = \frac{35}{99}$

11-5 Recursion and Iteration

The formulas for terms of sequences that were investigated in previous lessons are called *explicit formulas.* They give a_n as a function of n. In *recursive formula, s* terms are determined by a formula using one or more of the previous terms. For example, a recursive formula for the sequence 3, 7, 11, 15, 19, . . . is

$$a_1 = 3, a_n = a_{n-1} + 4$$

Iteration is a process of repeatedly composing a function with itself. This process can be used to generate a sequence recursively. For example, how to find the first three iterates x_1, x_2, and x_3 of $f(x) = 2x + 1$ for an initial value $x_0 = 2$ is shown below.

$f(x) = 2x + 1$ when $x_0 = 2$

$x_1 = f(x_0)$	$x_2 = f(x_1)$	$x_3 = f(x_2)$
$= 2(2) + 1 = 5$	$= 2(5) + 1 = 11$	$= 2(11) + 1 = 23$

The first three iterates are 5, 11, and 23.

11-6 The Binomial Theorem

The pattern found in Pascal's triangle (shown below) can be used to determine the coefficients of an expanded binomial $(a + b)^n$.

$(a + b)^0$	1
$(a + b)^1$	1 1
$(a + b)^2$	1 2 1
$(a + b)^3$	1 3 3 1
$(a + b)^4$	1 4 6 4 1
$(a + b)^5$	1 5 10 10 5 1

To expand the binomial $(a + b)^n$ for nonnegative values of n requires finding the coefficient and the exponents for a and b in each term. Binomial expansions, such as in $(a + b)^4 = a^4 + 4a^3b + 6a^2b^2 + 4ab^3 + b^4$, contain many patterns.

- The sum of the exponents in each term is n.
- The exponent of a in the first term and b in the last term is n.
- The coefficients are the entries in Pascal's triangle.
- There are $n + 1$ terms.

The Binomial Theorem can be used to expand a binomial.

Written in sigma notation, $(a + b)^n = \sum_{k=0}^{n} \frac{n!}{k!\,(n-k)!} a^{n-k} b^k$.

11-7 Proof by Mathematical Induction

Mathematical induction is a powerful method of proving conjectures. It consists of two parts.

- First, a property is shown to be true for a particular number (often the number 1).
- The second, *inductive,* part involves demonstrating that if the property is true for *some* positive integer, it must be true for the *next* integer. As a result, the property is shown to be true for *all* integers, beginning with a certain value. Properties of series, divisibility, and proving a formula to be false by finding a counterexample are all examined in this lesson.

McGraw Hill Professional Development

Targeted professional development has been articulated throughout *Algebra 2.* More quality, customized professional development is available from McGraw-Hill Professional Development. Visit glencoe.com for details on each product.

- **Online Lessons** emphasize the strategies and techniques used to teach Algebra 2. Includes streaming video, interactive pages, and online tools.
- **Video Workshops** allow mentors, coaches, or leadership personnel to facilitate on-site workshops on educational strategies in mathematics and mathematical concepts.
- **MHPD Online** (www.mhpdonline.com) offers online professional development with video clips of instructional strategies, links, student activities, and news and issues in education.
- **Teaching Today** (teachingtoday.glencoe.com) gives secondary teachers practical strategies and materials that inspire excellence and innovation in teaching.

CHAPTER 11 Notes

Chapter Project

Animal Populations

Students use what they have learned about sequences to predict changes in wildlife populations.

- Have students, working in pairs, choose a national park and find information about the number of a particular kind of animal in the park. For example, there were about 370 wolves in Yellowstone National Park in 2007, according to the park Web site. If possible, have students also find the number of that animal in the previous year; otherwise assume a value.
- Assuming a constant numerical increase or decrease each year, ask students to write a recursive formula for a sequence that would give the animal population for any year.
- Ask them to calculate a percent of change. Then have them assume a constant percent of change and use that percent to write a recursive formula for the animal population in any year.
- Ask them to predict how long it would take for the animal population to increase or decrease by 25 percent using each of their sequences.

Key Vocabulary Introduce the key vocabulary in the chapter using the routine below.

Define: A term is each number in a sequence or series.

Example: The fourth term in the following series is 29. 2, 11, 20, 29, 39, . . .

Ask: What is the first term in the series above? 2

CHAPTER 11 Sequences and Series

Then

In Chapter 1, you simplified and evaluated algebraic expressions.

Now

In Chapter 11, you will:

- Use arithmetic and geometric sequences and series.
- Use special sequences and iterate functions.
- Expand powers by using the Binomial Theorem.
- Prove statements by using mathematical induction.

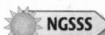

NGSSS

MA.912.D.11.3
MA.912.D.11.4

Why?

CONSERVATION AND NATURE

Mathematics occurs in aspects of nature in astonishing ways. The Fibonacci sequence manifests itself in seeds, flowers, pine cones, fruits, and vegetables. Sequences and series can further help us conserve our natural resources by making water filtration systems more efficient.

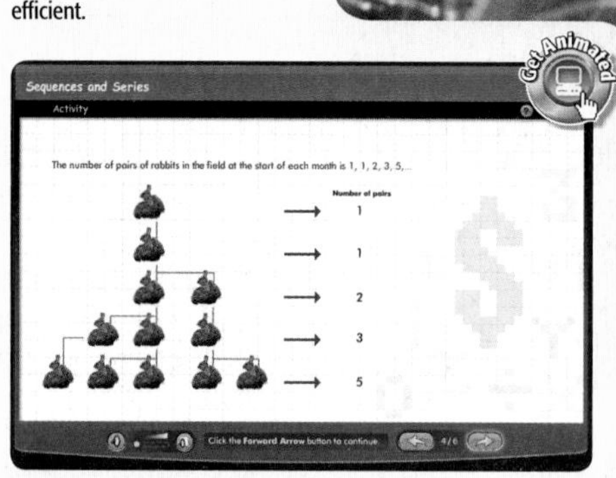

Additional Answers (Get Ready for Chapter 11)

6.

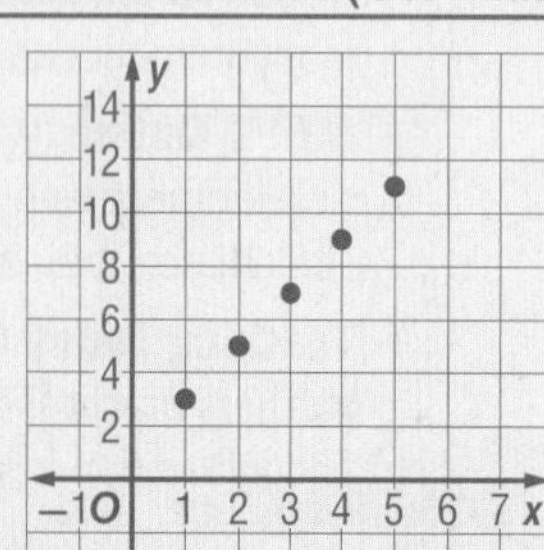

7.

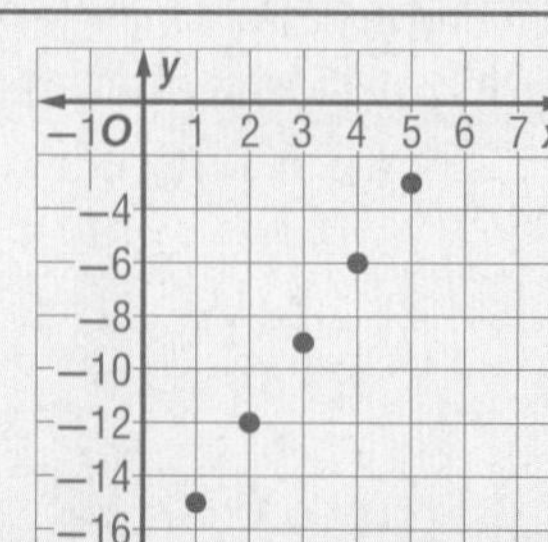

Get Ready for Chapter 11

Diagnose Readiness You have two options for checking Prerequisite Skills.

Text Option Take the Quick Check below. Refer to the Quick Review for help.

QuickCheck

(Used in Lessons 11-1 through 11-3)

Solve each equation. (Lesson 1-3)

1. $-6 = 7x + 78$ $x = -12$
2. $768 = 3x^4$ $x = \pm 4$
3. $23 - 5x = 8$ $x = 3$
4. $2x^3 + 4 = -50$ $x = -3$
5. **PLANTS** Lauri has 48 plants for her two gardens. She plants 12 in the small garden. In the other garden she wants 4 plants in each row. How many rows will she have? **9 rows**

QuickReview

EXAMPLE 1

Solve $25 = 3x^3 + 400$.

$-375 = 3x^3$	Subtract 400 from each side.
$-125 = x^3$	Divide each side by 3.
$\sqrt[3]{-125} = \sqrt[3]{x^3}$	Take the cube root of each side.
$-5 = x$	Simplify.

(Used in Lessons 11-1 through 11-5)

Graph each function. (Lesson 0-1) **6–9. See margin.**

6. $\{(1, 3), (2, 5), (3, 7), (4, 9), (5, 11)\}$
7. $\{(1, -15), (2, -12), (3, -9), (4, -6), (5, -3)\}$
8. $\left\{(1, 27), (2, 9), (3, 3), (4, 1), \left(5, \frac{1}{3}\right)\right\}$
9. $\left\{(1, 1), (2, 2), \left(3, \frac{5}{2}\right), \left(4, \frac{11}{4}\right), \left(5, \frac{23}{8}\right)\right\}$
10. **DAYCARE** A child care center has expenses of \$125 per day. They charge \$50 per child per day. The function $P(c) = 50c - 125$ gives the amount of money the center makes when there are c children there. How much will they make if there are 8 children? **\$275**

EXAMPLE 2

Graph the function $\{(1, 1), (2, 4), (3, 9), (4, 16), (5, 25)\}$. State the domain and range.

The domain of a function is the set of all possible x-values. So, the domain of the function is $\{1, 2, 3, 4, 5\}$. The range of a function is the set of all possible y-values. So, the range of this function is $\{1, 4, 9, 16, 25\}$.

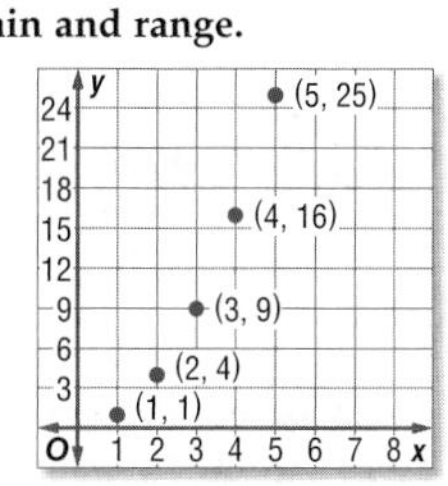

(Used in Lessons 11-1 through 11-5, and 11-8)

Evaluate each expression for the given value(s) of the variable(s). (Lesson 1-1)

11. $\frac{a}{3}(b + c)$ if $a = 9$, $b = -2$, and $c = -8$ -30
12. $r + (n - 2)t$ if $r = 15$, $n = 5$, and $t = -1$ 12
13. $x \cdot y^{z+1}$ if $x = -2$, $y = \frac{1}{3}$, and $z = 5$ $-\frac{2}{729}$
14. $\frac{a(1 - bc)^2}{1 - b}$ if $a = -3$, $b = -4$, and $c = 1$ -15

EXAMPLE 3

Evaluate $2 \cdot 3^{x+y}$ if $x = -2$ and $y = -3$.

$2 \cdot 3^{x+y} = 2 \cdot 3^{-2+-3}$	Substitute.
$= 2 \cdot 3^{-5}$	Simplify.
$= \frac{2}{3^5}$	Rewrite with positive exponent.
$= \frac{2}{243}$	Evaluate the power.

Online Option FL Math Online Take a self-check Chapter Readiness Quiz at glencoe.com.

Additional Answers

8.

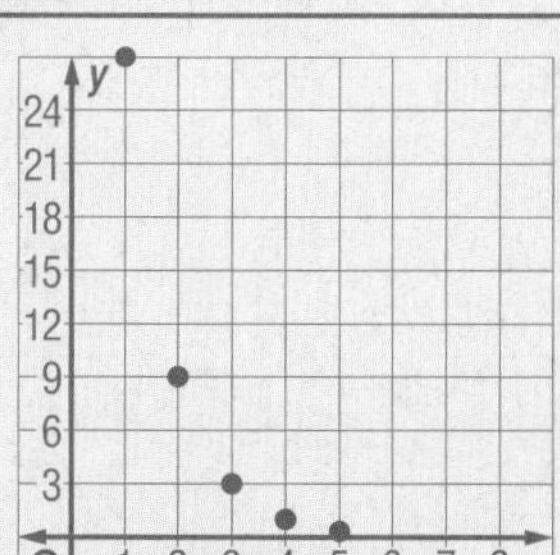

9.

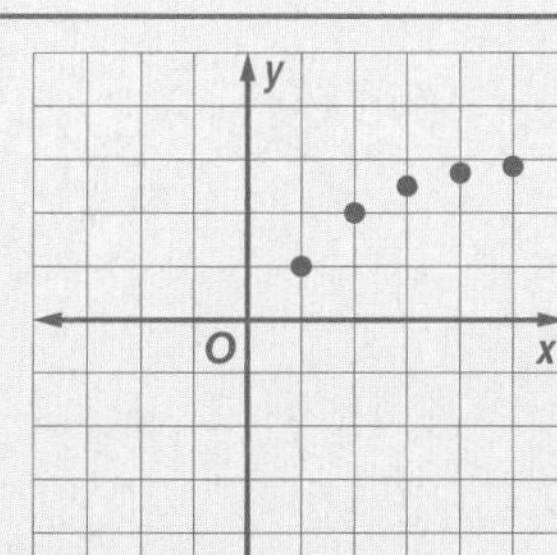

Get Ready for Chapter 11

Response to Intervention (RtI)

Use the *Quick Check* results and the Intervention Planner to help you determine your Response to Intervention. The If-Then statements in the chart below help you decide the appropriate tier of RtI and suggest intervention resources for each tier.

Intervention Planner

Tier 1 On Level

If students miss about 25% of the exercises or less,

Then choose a resource:

- **SE** Lessons 1-1, 1-3, and 0-1
- **CRM** Skills Practice, Chapter 1, pp. 7 and 19
- **TE** Chapter Project, p. 678
- FL Math Online Self-Check Quiz

Tier 2 Strategic Intervention approaching grade level

If students miss about 50% of the exercises,

Then choose a resource:

- **CRM** Study Guide and Intervention, Chapter 1, pp. 5 and 17
- FL Math Online Extra Examples, Personal Tutor, Homework Help

Tier 3 Intensive Intervention 2 or more years below grade level

If students miss about 75% of the exercises,

Then use *Math Triumphs, Alg. 2*

FL Math Online Extra Examples, Personal Tutor, Homework Help, Review Vocabulary

CHAPTER 11 Notes

FOLDABLES® Study Organizer

Dinah Zike's Foldables®

Focus Students record notes and examples about sequences and series on index cards and place them in the appropriate pocket of their Foldables.

Teach Have students make and label their Foldables as illustrated. Students should use their Foldables to write notes, define terms, record concepts, and give examples of sequences and series on index cards. The cards should then be placed in the appropriate pocket.

When to Use It Encourage students to add to their Foldables as they work through the chapter and to use them to review for the chapter test.

Differentiated Instruction

CRM Student-Built Glossary, pp. 1–2
Students should complete the chart by providing a definition of each term and an example as they progress through Chapter 11. This study tool can also be used to review for the chapter test.

Get Started on Chapter 11

You will learn several new concepts, skills, and vocabulary terms as you study Chapter 11. To get ready, identify important terms and organize your resources. You may wish to refer to **Chapter 0** to review prerequisite skills.

FOLDABLES® Study Organizer

Sequences and Series Make this Foldable to help you organize your Chapter 11 notes about sequences and series. Begin with one $8\frac{1}{2}$" by 11" sheet of paper.

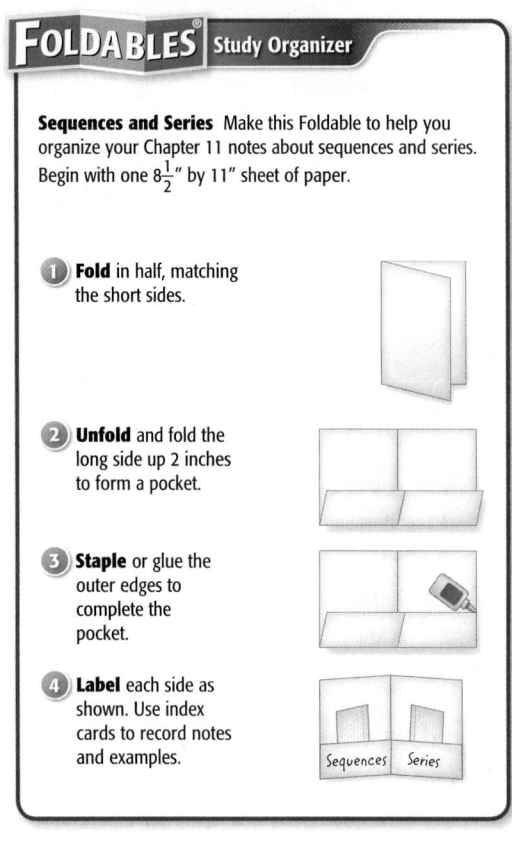

1. **Fold** in half, matching the short sides.

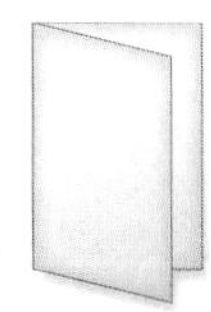

2. **Unfold** and fold the long side up 2 inches to form a pocket.

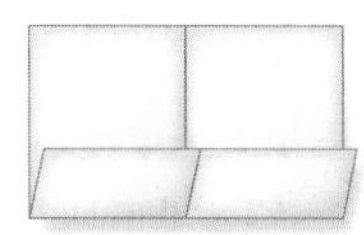

3. **Staple** or glue the outer edges to complete the pocket.

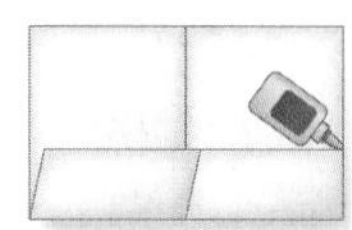

4. **Label** each side as shown. Use index cards to record notes and examples.

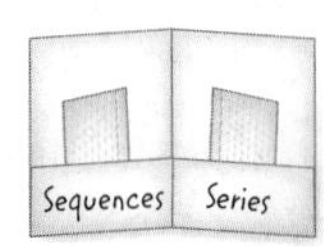

FL Math Online glencoe.com
- Study the chapter online
- Explore **Get Animated**
- Get extra help from your own **Personal Tutor**
- Use **Extra Examples** for additional help
- Take a **Self-Check Quiz**
- **Review Vocabulary** in fun ways

New Vocabulary

English		Español
sequence	• p. 681 •	sucesión
finite sequence	• p. 681 •	sucesión finita
infinite sequence	• p. 681 •	sucesión infinita
arithmetic sequence	• p. 681 •	sucesión arithmética
common difference	• p. 681 •	diferencia común
geometric sequence	• p. 683 •	sucesión geométrica
common ratio	• p. 683 •	razón común
arithmetic means	• p. 689 •	media arithmética
series	• p. 690 •	serie
arithmetic series	• p. 690 •	serie arithmética
partial sum	• p. 690 •	suma parcial
geometric means	• p. 697 •	media geométrica
geometric series	• p. 698 •	serie geométrica
convergent series	• p. 705 •	serie convergente
divergent series	• p. 705 •	serie divergente
recursive sequence	• p. 714 •	sucesión recursiva
iteration	• p. 716 •	iteración
mathematical induction	• p. 727 •	inducción mathemática
induction hypothesis	• p. 727 •	hipótesis inductiva

Review Vocabulary

coefficient • p. P7 • coeficiante the numerical factor of a monomial

coefficient
coeficiante

$15x^3$

formula • p. 6 • fórmula a mathematical sentence that expresses the relationship between certain quantities

function • p. P4 • función a relation in which each element of the domain is paired with exactly one element in the range

Multilingual eGlossary glencoe.com

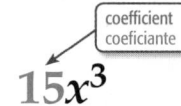

11-1 Sequences as Functions

Why?

During their routine, a high school marching band marches in rows. There is one performer in the first row, three performers in the next row, and five in the third row. This pattern continues for the rest of the rows.

Then
You analyzed linear and exponential functions. (Lessons 2-2 and 8-1)

Now
- Relate arithmetic sequences to linear functions.
- Relate geometric sequences to exponential functions.

NGSSS

MA.912.D.11.1 Define arithmetic and geometric sequences and series.
MA.912.D.11.3 Find specified terms of arithmetic and geometric sequences.

New Vocabulary
sequence
term
finite sequence
infinite sequence
arithmetic sequence
common difference
geometric sequence
common ratio

FL Math Online
glencoe.com

Arithmetic Sequences A **sequence** is a set of numbers in a particular order or pattern. Each number in a sequence is called a **term**. A sequence may be a **finite sequence** containing a limited number of terms, such as $\{-2, 0, 2, 4, 6\}$, or an **infinite sequence** that continues without end, such as $\{0, 1, 2, 3, \ldots\}$. The first term of a sequence is denoted a_1, the second term is denoted a_2, and so on.

Key Concept — Sequences as Functions

Get Animated

Words A sequence is a function in which the domain consists of natural numbers, and the range consists of real numbers.

Symbols Domain: $1 \quad 2 \quad 3 \quad \cdots \quad n$ — the position of a term

Range: $a_1 \quad a_2 \quad a_3 \quad \cdots \quad a_n$ — the terms of the sequence

Examples

Finite Sequence	Infinite Sequence
{3, 6, 9, 12, 15}	{3, 6, 9, 12, 15, ...}
Domain: {1, 2, 3, 4, 5} Range: {3, 6, 9, 12, 15}	Domain: {all natural numbers} Range: $\{y \mid y$ is a multiple of 3, $y \geq 3\}$

In an **arithmetic sequence**, each term is determined by adding a constant value to the previous term. This constant value is called the **common difference**.

Consider the sequence 3, 6, 9, 12, 15. This sequence is arithmetic because the terms share a common difference. Each term is 3 more than the previous term.

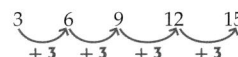

$$3 \quad 6 \quad 9 \quad 12 \quad 15$$
$$+3 \quad +3 \quad +3 \quad +3$$

EXAMPLE 1 Identify Arithmetic Sequences

Determine whether each sequence is arithmetic.

a. $5, -6, -17, -28, \ldots$

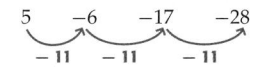

$$5 \quad -6 \quad -17 \quad -28$$
$$-11 \quad -11 \quad -11$$

The common difference is -11. The sequence is arithmetic.

b. $-4, 12, 28, 42, \ldots$

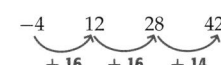

$$-4 \quad 12 \quad 28 \quad 42$$
$$+16 \quad +16 \quad +14$$

There is no common difference. This is not an arithmetic sequence.

Guided Practice

1A. 7, 12, 16, 20, ... no

1B. −6, 3, 12, 21, ... yes

Personal Tutor glencoe.com

11-1 Lesson Notes

1 FOCUS

Vertical Alignment

Before Lesson 11-1
Analyze linear and exponential functions.

Lesson 11-1
Relate arithmetic sequences to linear functions.
Relate geometric sequences to exponential functions.

After Lesson 11-1
Use arithmetic, geometric, and other sequences and series to solve real-life problems.

2 TEACH

Scaffolding Questions

Have students read the *Why?* section of the lesson.

Ask:

- What pattern do the rows of marching performers make? 1, 3, 5, 7, . . .
- How can you find the next four numbers in the pattern? Add 2 to each successive row to find the number of performers in that row.
- What are the next four numbers? 9, 11, 13, 15
- Would you expect this pattern to continue infinitely? No, there is a limit to the number of rows of performers.

Lesson 11-1 Resources

Resource	Approaching-Level	On-Level	Beyond-Level	English Learners
Teacher Edition	• Differentiated Instruction, p. 684	• Differentiated Instruction, p. 687	• Differentiated Instruction, p. 687	• Differentiated Instruction, p. 684
Chapter Resource Masters	• Study Guide and Intervention, pp. 5–6 • Skills Practice, p. 7 • Practice, p. 8 • Word Problem Practice, p. 9	• Study Guide and Intervention, pp. 5–6 • Skills Practice, p. 7 • Practice, p. 8 • Word Problem Practice, p. 9 • Enrichment, p. 10	• Practice, p. 8 • Word Problem Practice, p. 9 • Enrichment, p. 10	• Study Guide and Intervention, pp. 5–6 • Skills Practice, p. 7 • Practice, p. 8 • Word Problem Practice, p. 9
Transparencies	• 5-Minute Check Transparency 11-1	• 5-Minute Check Transparency 11-1	• 5-Minute Check Transparency 11-1	• 5-Minute Check Transparency 11-1
Other	• Study Notebook • Teaching Algebra with Manipulatives	• Study Notebook • Teaching Algebra with Manipulatives	• Study Notebook	• Study Notebook • Teaching Algebra with Manipulatives

Arithmetic Sequences

Example 1 shows how to determine if there is a common difference for a sequence and, if there is one, how to identify the sequence as arithmetic. **Example 2** shows how to use the common difference to find terms of an arithmetic sequence and how to graph the terms of the sequence. **Example 3** shows how to find a term of a given arithmetic sequence to solve a real-world problem.

Formative Assessment

Use the Guided Practice exercises after each example to determine students' understanding of concepts.

Additional Examples

1 Determine whether each sequence is arithmetic. Write *yes* or *no*.

a. −3, −8, −13, −23, . . . no

b. −8, −2, 4, 10, . . . yes

2 Consider the arithmetic sequence −8, −6, −4, . . .

a. Find the next four terms of the sequence. −2, 0, 2, 4

b. Graph the first seven terms of the sequence.

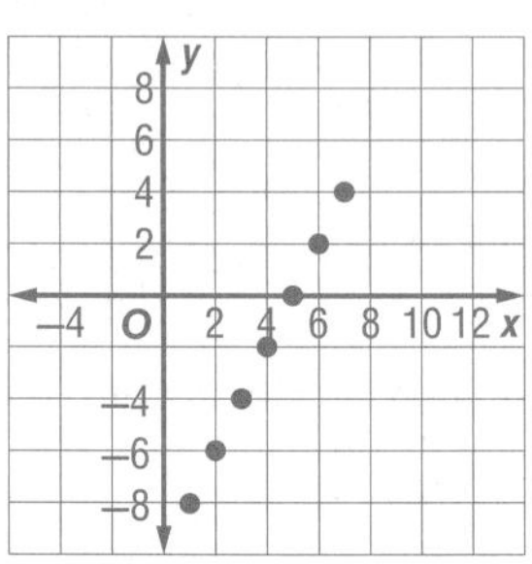

3 **MARCHING BAND** Use the information in Example 3 to determine how many performers will be in the 20th row during the routine. 39

Additional Examples also in Interactive Classroom PowerPoint® Presentations

IWB INTERACTIVE WHITEBOARD READY

You can use the common difference to find terms of an arithmetic sequence.

EXAMPLE 2 Graph an Arithmetic Sequence

Consider the arithmetic sequence 18, 14, 10, … .

a. Find the next four terms of the sequence.

Step 1 To determine the common difference, subtract any term from the term directly after it. The common difference is 10 − 14 or −4.

Step 2 To find the next term, add −4 to the last term. Continue to add −4 to find the following terms.

10 → 6 → 2 → −2 → −6 (each step + (−4))

The next four terms are 6, 2, −2, and −6.

b. Graph the first seven terms of the sequence.

The domain contains the terms {1, 2, 3, 4, 5, 6, 7} and the range contains the terms {18, 14, 10, 6, 2, −2, −6}. So, graph the corresponding ordered pairs.

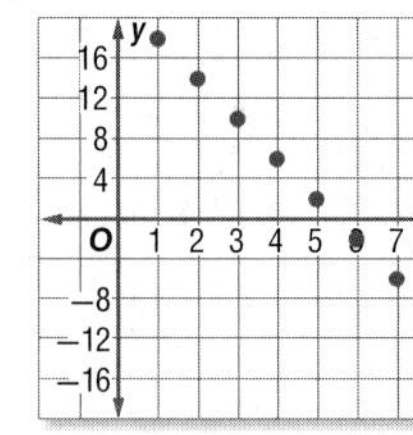

Guided Practice

2. Find the next four terms of the arithmetic sequence 18, 11, 4, … . Then graph the first seven terms. **See margin.**

Personal Tutor glencoe.com

Real-World Link

Each year, about 100 bands compete in the Bands of America Grand National Championships.

Source: Bands of America

Notice that the graph of the terms of the arithmetic sequence lie on a line. An arithmetic sequence is a linear function in which the term number n is the independent variable, the term a_n is the dependent variable, and the common difference is the slope.

Real-World EXAMPLE 3 Find a Term

MARCHING BANDS Refer to the beginning of the lesson. Suppose the director wants to determine how many performers will be in the 14th row during the routine.

Understand Because the difference between any two consecutive rows is 2, the common difference for the sequence is 2.

Plan Use point-slope form to write an equation for the sequence. Let $m = 2$ and $(x_1, y_1) = (3, 5)$. Then solve for $x = 14$.

Solve

$(y - y_1) = m(x - x_1)$	**Point-slope form**
$(y - 5) = 2(x - 3)$	**$m = 2$ and $(x_1, y_1) = (3, 5)$**
$y - 5 = 2x - 6$	**Multiply.**
$y = 2x - 1$	**Add 5 to each side.**
$y = 2(14) - 1$	**Replace x with 14.**
$y = 28 - 1$ or 27	**Simplify.**

There will be 27 performers in the 14th row.

Check You can find the terms of the sequence by adding 2, starting with row 1, until you reach row 14.

Guided Practice

3. MONEY Geraldo's employer offers him a pay rate of \$9 per hour with a \$0.15 raise every three months. How much will Geraldo earn per hour after 3 years? **\$10.80**

Personal Tutor glencoe.com

Watch Out!

Preventing Misconceptions Make sure all students understand that the subscript in a_n refers to a term, and that it is not an exponent.

Additional Answer (Guided Practice)

2. −3, −10, −17, −24

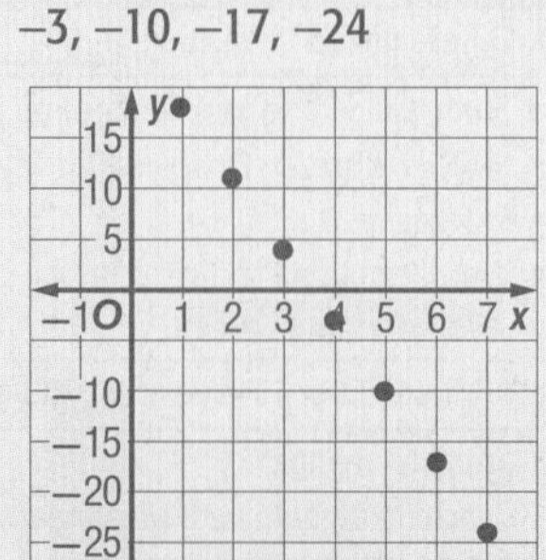

Geometric Sequences Another type of sequence is a geometric sequence. In a **geometric sequence**, each term is determined by multiplying a nonzero constant by the previous term. This constant value is called the **common ratio**.

Consider the sequence $\frac{1}{16}, \frac{1}{4}, 1, 4, 16$. This sequence is geometric because the terms share a common ratio. Each term is 4 times as much as the previous term.

$$\frac{1}{16} \xrightarrow{\times 4} \frac{1}{4} \xrightarrow{\times 4} 1 \xrightarrow{\times 4} 4 \xrightarrow{\times 4} 16$$

Watch Out!

Ratios If you find the ratio of a term to the previous term, set up the remaining ratios the same way.

EXAMPLE 4 Identify Geometric Sequences

Determine whether each sequence is geometric.

a. **−2, 6, −18, 54, ...**

Find the ratios of the consecutive terms.

$\frac{6}{-2} = -3 \quad \frac{-18}{6} = -3 \quad \frac{54}{-18} = -3$

The ratios are the same, so the sequence is geometric.

b. **8, 16, 24, 32, ...**

$\frac{16}{8} = 2 \quad \frac{24}{16} = 1.5 \quad \frac{32}{24} = 1.\overline{3}$

The ratios are not the same, so the sequence is not geometric.

Guided Practice

4A. −8, 2, −0.5, 0.125, ... yes **4B.** 1, 3, 7, 15, ... no

Personal Tutor glencoe.com

You can use the common ratio to determine more terms of a geometric sequence.

EXAMPLE 5 Graph a Geometric Sequence

Consider the geometric sequence 32, 8, 2, ...

a. **Find the next three terms of the sequence.**

Step 1 Find the value of the common ratio: $\frac{2}{8}$ or $\frac{1}{4}$.

Step 2 To find the next term, multiply the previous term by $\frac{1}{4}$.

Continue multiplying by $\frac{1}{4}$ to find the following terms.

$$2 \xrightarrow{\times \frac{1}{4}} \frac{1}{2} \xrightarrow{\times \frac{1}{4}} \frac{1}{8} \xrightarrow{\times \frac{1}{4}} \frac{1}{32}$$

The next three terms are $\frac{1}{2}, \frac{1}{8}$, and $\frac{1}{32}$.

b. **Graph the first six terms of the sequence.**

Domain: {1, 2, 3, 4, 5, 6}

Range: $\left\{32, 8, 2, \frac{1}{2}, \frac{1}{8}, \frac{1}{32}\right\}$

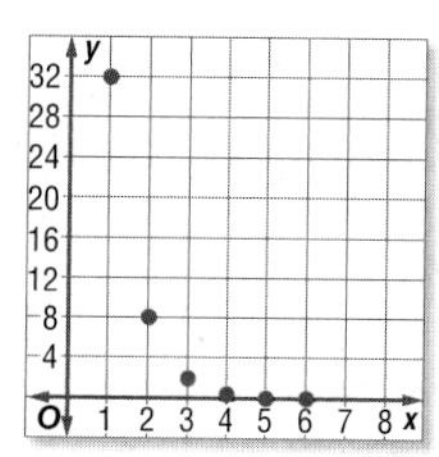

Guided Practice

5. Find the next two terms of 7, 21, 63, ... Then graph the first five terms. See margin.

Personal Tutor glencoe.com

Geometric Sequences

Example 4 shows how to determine if a sequence has a common ratio, and, if it does, how to identify the sequence as geometric. **Example 5** shows how to use the common ratio to determine more terms of a geometric sequence and how to graph the terms of the sequence. **Example 6** shows how to determine whether a sequence is arithmetic, geometric, or neither.

Additional Examples

4 Determine whether each sequence is geometric. Write *yes* or *no*.

a. 8, 20, 50, 125, ... yes

b. 19, 30, 41, 52, ... no

5 Consider the geometric sequence 10, 15, 22.5, ...

a. Find the next three terms of the sequence. 33.75, 50.625, 75.9375

b. Graph the first six terms of the sequence.

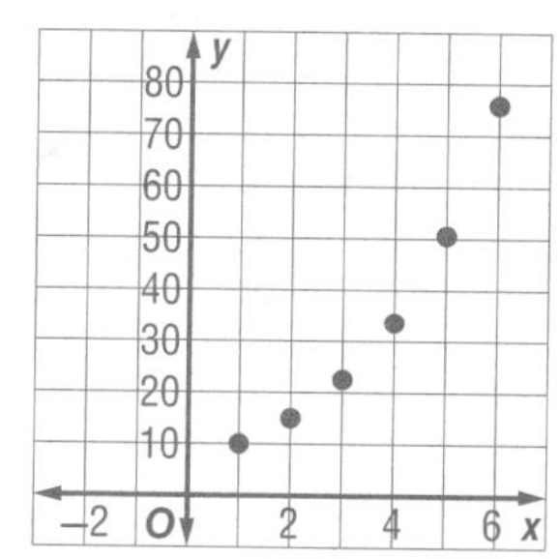

Additional Answer (Guided Practice)

5. 189, 567

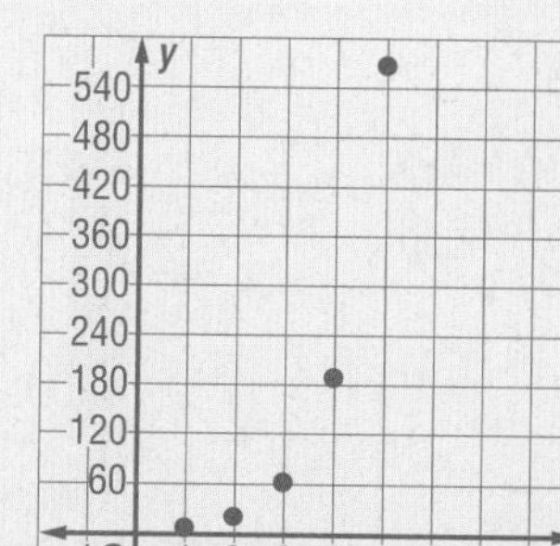

Additional Example

6 Determine whether each sequence is *arithmetic, geometric,* or *neither.* Explain your reasoning.

a. 13, 25, 37, 49, . . . Arithmetic; the common difference is 12.

b. 2, 5, 9, 14, . . . Neither; there is no common difference or common ratio.

c. 6, –12, 24, –48, . . . Geometric; the common ratio is 2.

Focus on Mathematical Content

Sequences Not all lists of numbers that follow a pattern are geometric or arithmetic. Knowing this will prepare students for Lesson 11-5 on special sequences called recursive sequences.

TEACH with TECH

INSTANT MESSAGING Have students work in pairs. Each student will write an equation to create a sequence, and send a message with only the sequence to the other student. Each student should then find and reply with the equation for the sequence he or she received.

Review Vocabulary

exponential function a function of the form $f(x) = b^x$, where $b > 0$ and $b \neq 1$ (Lesson 8-1)

Examine the graph in Example 5. While the graph of an arithmetic sequence is linear, the graph of a geometric sequence is exponential and can be represented by $f(x) = r^x$, where r is the common ratio, $r > 0$, and $r \neq 1$.

Arithmetic

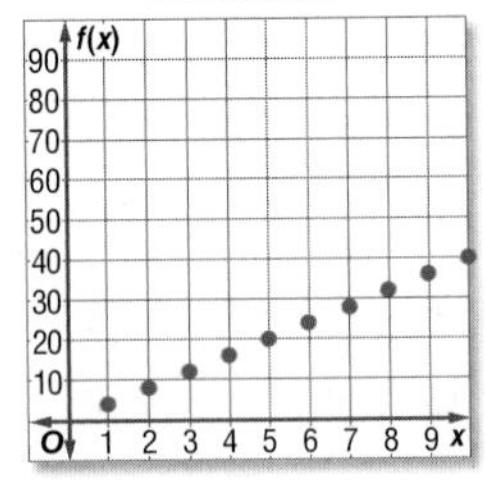

x	1	2	3	4	5	6	7	8	9	10
f(x)	4	8	12	16	20	24	28	32	36	40

Geometric

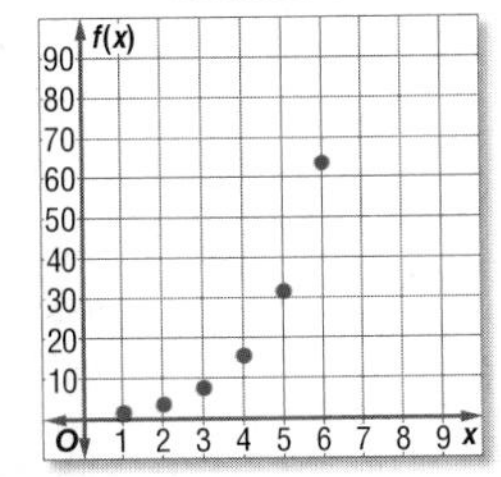

x	1	2	3	4	5	6
f(x)	2	4	8	16	32	64

The characteristics of arithmetic and geometric sequences can be used to classify sequences.

EXAMPLE 6 Classify Sequences

Determine whether each sequence is *arithmetic, geometric,* or *neither.* Explain your reasoning.

a. 16, 24, 36, 54, ...

Check for a common difference.

$54 - 36 = 18$ $\quad 36 - 24 = 12$ ✗

Check for a common ratio.

$\frac{54}{36} = \frac{3}{2}$ $\quad \frac{36}{24} = \frac{3}{2}$ $\quad \frac{24}{16} = \frac{3}{2}$ ✓

Because there is a common ratio, the sequence is geometric.

b. 1, 4, 9, 16, ...

Check for a common difference.

$16 - 9 = 7$ $\quad 9 - 4 = 5$ ✗

Check for a common ratio.

$\frac{16}{9} = 1.\overline{7}$ $\quad \frac{9}{4} = 2.25$ ✗

Because there is no common difference or ratio, the sequence is neither arithmetic nor geometric.

c. 23, 17, 11, 5, ...

Check for a common difference.

$5 - 11 = -6$ $\quad 11 - 17 = -6$ $\quad 17 - 23 = -6$ ✓

Because there is a common difference, the sequence is arithmetic.

Guided Practice

6A. $\frac{5}{3}, 2, \frac{7}{3}, \frac{8}{3}, \ldots$

6B. $2, -\frac{3}{2}, \frac{9}{8}, -\frac{27}{32}, \ldots$

6C. $-4, 4, 5, -5, \ldots$

6A. Arithmetic; the common difference is $\frac{1}{3}$.
6B. Geometric; the common ratio is $-\frac{3}{4}$.
6C. Neither; there is no common difference or ratio.

Personal Tutor glencoe.com

Differentiated Instruction AL ELL

Interpersonal Learners Have students in small groups discuss any confusions they may have about the key concepts for arithmetic and geometric sequences. Suggest they help each other organize and complete their notes on these topics.

684 Chapter 11 Sequences and Series

Check Your Understanding

Example 1 p. 681

Determine whether each sequence is arithmetic. Write *yes* or *no*.

1. 8, −2, −12, −22, … **yes**
2. −19, −12, −5, 2, 9 **yes**
3. 1, 2, 4, 8, 16 **no**
4. 0.6, 0.9, 1.2, 1.8, … **no**

Example 2 p. 682

Find the next four terms of each arithmetic sequence. Then graph the sequence.

5. 6, 18, 30, … **5–8. See margin.**
6. 15, 6, −3, …
7. −19, −11, −3, …
8. −26, −33, −40, …

Example 3 p. 682

9. **FINANCIAL LITERACY** Kelly is saving her money to buy a car. She has \$250, and she plans to save \$75 per week from her job as a waitress.
   a. How much will Kelly have saved after 8 weeks? **\$850**
   b. If the car costs \$2000, how long will it take her to save enough money at this rate? **24 wk**

Example 4 p. 683

Determine whether each sequence is geometric. Write *yes* or *no*.

10. −8, −5, −1, 4, … **no**
11. 4, 12, 36, 108, … **yes**
12. 27, 9, 3, 1, … **yes**
13. 7, 14, 21, 28, … **no**

Example 5 p. 683

14–17. See Chapter 11 Answer Appendix.

Find the next three terms of each geometric sequence. Then graph the sequence.

14. 8, 12, 18, 27, …
15. 8, 16, 32, 64, …
16. 250, 50, 10, 2, …
17. 9, −3, 1, $-\frac{1}{3}$, …

Example 6 p. 684

Determine whether each sequence is *arithmetic, geometric,* or *neither*. Explain your reasoning. **18. Neither; there is no common difference or ratio.**

18. 5, 1, 7, 3, 9, …
19. 200, −100, 50, −25, …
20. 12, 16, 20, 24, …

19. Geometric; the common ratio is $-\frac{1}{2}$. **20. Arithmetic; the common difference is 4.**

Practice and Problem Solving

● = **Step-by-Step Solutions** begin on page R20. **Extra Practice** begins on page 947.

Example 1 p. 681

Determine whether each sequence is arithmetic. Write *yes* or *no*.

21. $\frac{1}{2}, \frac{1}{3}, \frac{1}{4}, \frac{1}{5}, \ldots$ **no**
22. −9, −3, 0, 3, 9 **no**
23. 14, −5, −19, … **no**
24. $\frac{2}{9}, \frac{5}{9}, \frac{8}{9}, \frac{11}{9}, \ldots$ **yes**

Example 2 p. 682

25–30. See Chapter 11 Answer Appendix.

Find the next four terms of each arithmetic sequence. Then graph the sequence.

25. −4, −1, 2, 5, …
26. 10, 2, −6, −14, …
27. −5, −11, −17, −23, …
28. −19, −2, 15, …
29. $\frac{1}{5}, \frac{4}{5}, \frac{7}{5}, \ldots$
30. $\frac{2}{3}, -\frac{1}{3}, -\frac{4}{3}$

Example 3 p. 682

31. **THEATER** There are 28 seats in the front row of a theater. Each successive row contains two more seats than the previous row. If there are 24 rows, how many seats are in the last row of the theater? **74**

32. **EXERCISE** Mario began an exercise program to get back in shape. He plans to row 5 minutes on his rowing machine the first day and increase his rowing time by one minute and thirty seconds each day.
    a. How long will he row on the 18th day? **30 minutes and 30 seconds**
    b. On what day will Mario first row an hour or more? **on the 38th day**
    c. Is it reasonable for this pattern to continue indefinitely? Explain.

32c. Sample answer: It is unreasonable because there are only so many hours in the day that can be dedicated to rowing.

Differentiated Homework Options

Level	Assignment	Two-Day Option	
AL Basic	21–50, 54–55, 57–80	21–49 odd, 61–64	22–50 even, 54–55, 57–60, 65–80
OL Core	21–49 odd, 51–53, 54–55, 57–60, 61–80	21–50, 61–64	51–55, 57–60, 65–80
BL Advanced	51–74, (optional: 75–80)		

3 PRACTICE

Formative Assessment

Use Exercises 1–20 to check for understanding.

Use the chart at the bottom of this page to customize assignments for your students.

Exercise Alert

Grid Paper For Exercises 5–8, 14–17, 25–30, 39–44, and 68–73, students will need grid paper.

Additional Answers

5. 42, 54, 66, 78

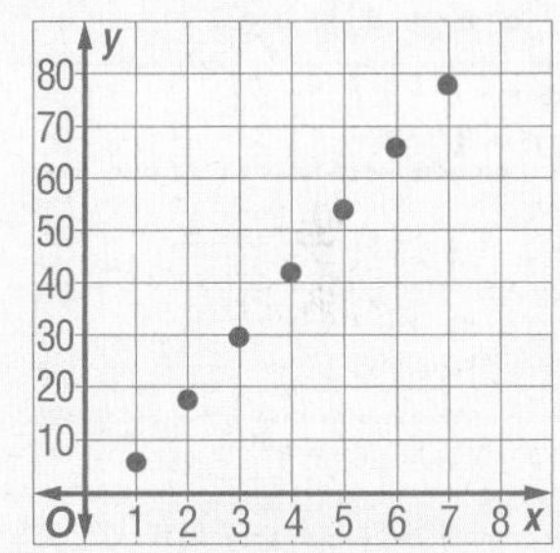

6. −12, −21, −30, −39

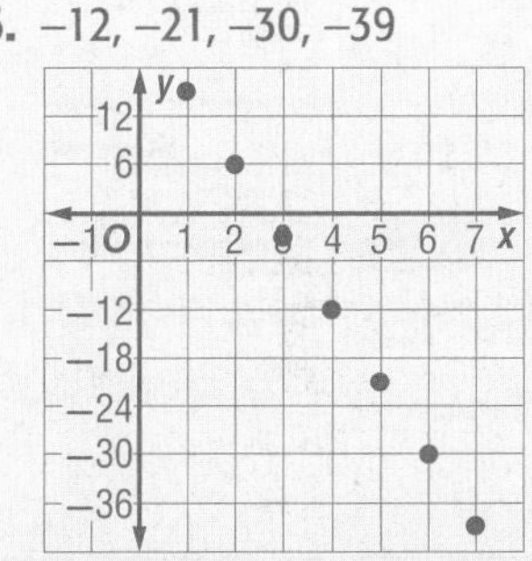

7. 5, 13, 21, 29

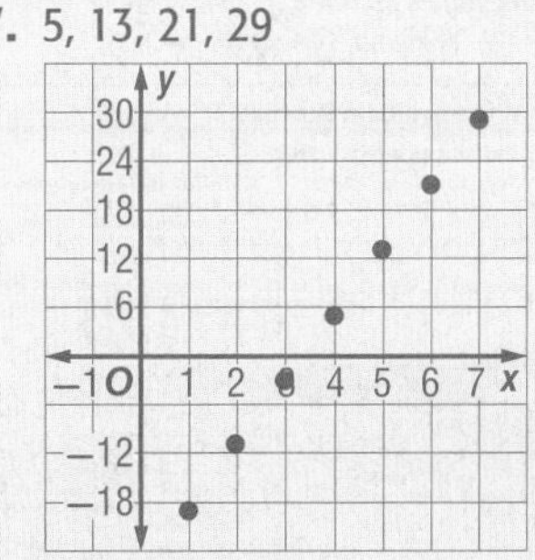

8. −47, −54, −61, −68

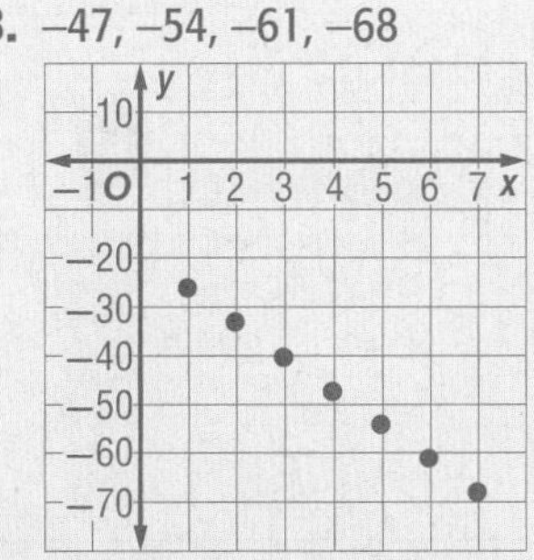

Study Guide and Intervention

CRM pp. 5–6 AL OL ELL

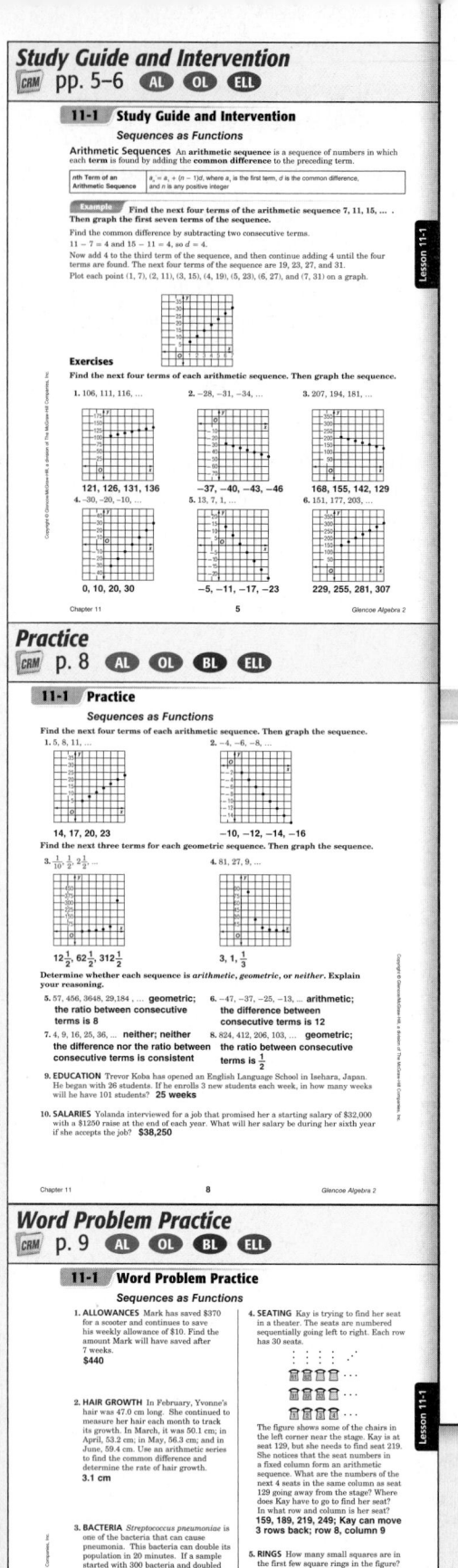

11-1 Study Guide and Intervention

Sequences as Functions

Arithmetic Sequences An **arithmetic sequence** is a sequence of numbers in which each **term** is found by adding the **common difference** to the preceding term.

nth Term of an Arithmetic Sequence	$a_n = a_1 + (n - 1)d$, where a_1 is the first term, d is the common difference, and n is any positive integer

Example **Find the next four terms of the arithmetic sequence 7, 11, 15, … . Then graph the first seven terms of the sequence.**

Find the common difference by subtracting two consecutive terms.

$11 - 7 = 4$ and $15 - 11 = 4$, so $d = 4$.

Now add 4 to the third term of the sequence, and then continue adding 4 until the four terms are found. The next four terms of the sequence are 19, 23, 27, and 31.

Plot each point (1, 7), (2, 11), (3, 15), (4, 19), (5, 23), (6, 27), and (7, 31) on a graph.

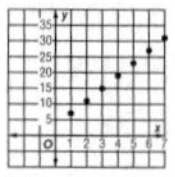

Lesson 11-1

Exercises

Find the next four terms of each arithmetic sequence. Then graph the sequence.

1. 106, 111, 116, …

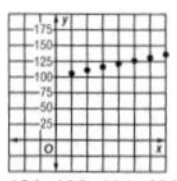

121, 126, 131, 136

2. −28, −31, −34, …

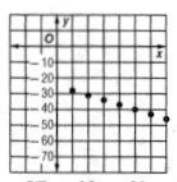

−37, −40, −43, −46

3. 207, 194, 181, …

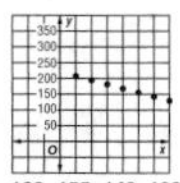

168, 155, 142, 129

4. −30, −20, −10, …

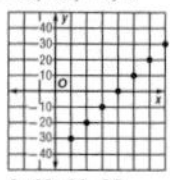

0, 10, 20, 30

5. 13, 7, 1, …

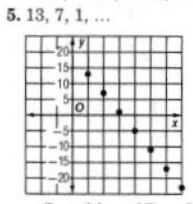

−5, −11, −17, −23

6. 151, 177, 203, …

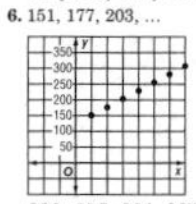

229, 255, 281, 307

Chapter 11 5 Glencoe Algebra 2

Practice

CRM p. 8 AL OL BL ELL

11-1 Practice

Sequences as Functions

Find the next four terms of each arithmetic sequence. Then graph the sequence.

1. 5, 8, 11, …

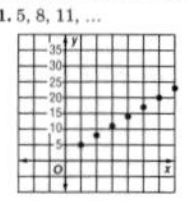

14, 17, 20, 23

2. −4, −6, −8, …

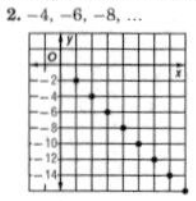

−10, −12, −14, −16

Find the next three terms for each geometric sequence. Then graph the sequence.

3. $\frac{1}{10}, \frac{1}{2}, 2\frac{1}{2}, \ldots$

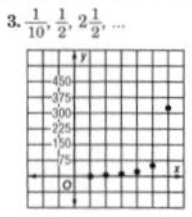

$12\frac{1}{2}, 62\frac{1}{2}, 312\frac{1}{2}$

4. 81, 27, 9, …

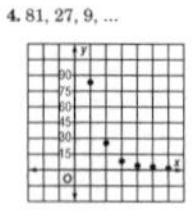

$3, 1, \frac{1}{3}$

Determine whether each sequence is *arithmetic*, *geometric*, or *neither*. Explain your reasoning.

5. 57, 456, 3648, 29,184 , … **geometric; the ratio between consecutive terms is 8**
6. −47, −37, −25, −13, … **arithmetic; the difference between consecutive terms is 12**
7. 4, 9, 16, 25, 36, … **neither; neither the difference nor the ratio between consecutive terms is consistent**
8. 824, 412, 206, 103, … **geometric; the ratio between consecutive terms is $\frac{1}{2}$**
9. **EDUCATION** Trevor Koba has opened an English Language School in Isehara, Japan. He began with 26 students. If he enrolls 3 new students each week, in how many weeks will he have 101 students? **25 weeks**
10. **SALARIES** Yolanda interviewed for a job that promised her a starting salary of $32,000 with a $1250 raise at the end of each year. What will her salary be during her sixth year if she accepts the job? **$38,250**

Chapter 11 8 Glencoe Algebra 2

Word Problem Practice

CRM p. 9 AL OL BL ELL

11-1 Word Problem Practice

Sequences as Functions

1. **ALLOWANCES** Mark has saved $370 for a scooter and continues to save his weekly allowance of $10. Find the amount Mark will have saved after 7 weeks.
$440

2. **HAIR GROWTH** In February, Yvonne's hair was 47.0 cm long. She continued to measure her hair each month to track its growth. In March, it was 50.1 cm; in April, 53.2 cm; in May, 56.3 cm; and in June, 59.4 cm. Use an arithmetic series to find the common difference and determine the rate of hair growth.
3.1 cm

3. **BACTERIA** *Streptococcus pneumoniae* is one of the bacteria that can cause pneumonia. This bacteria can double its population in 20 minutes. If a sample started with 300 bacteria and doubled every 20 minutes, use the geometric series formula to calculate the number of bacteria in the sample after 80 minutes.
4800 bacteria

4. **SEATING** Kay is trying to find her seat in a theater. The seats are numbered sequentially going left to right. Each row has 30 seats.

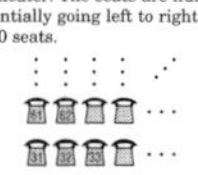

The figure shows some of the chairs in the left corner near the stage. Kay is at seat 129, but she needs to find seat 219. She notices that the seat numbers in a fixed column form an arithmetic sequence. What are the numbers of the next 4 seats in the same column as seat 129 going away from the stage? Where does Kay have to go to find her seat? In what row and column is her seat?
159, 189, 219, 249; Kay can move 3 rows back; row 8, column 9

5. **RINGS** How many small squares are in the first few square rings in the figure?

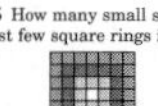

8, 16, 24

a. If the pattern is continued, write a formula for the number of squares in the nth ring.
8n

b. What is the side length of the nth ring?
2n + 1

Lesson 11-1

Chapter 11 9 Glencoe Algebra 2

Example 4 p. 683

Determine whether each sequence is geometric. Write *yes* or *no*.

33. 21, 14, 7, … **no**
34. 124, 186, 248, … **no**
35. −27, 18, −12, … **yes**
36. 162, 108, 72, … **yes**
37. $\frac{1}{2}, -\frac{1}{4}, 1, -\frac{1}{2}, \ldots$ **no**
38. −4, −2, 0, 2, … **no**

Example 5 p. 683

Find the next three terms of the sequence. Then graph the sequence. **39–44. See Chapter 11 Answer Appendix.**

39. 0.125, −0.5, 2, …
40. 18, 12, 8, …
41. 64, 48, 36, …
42. 81, 108, 144, …
43. $\frac{1}{3}, 1, 3, 9, \ldots$
44. 1, 0.1, 0.01, 0.001, …

Example 6 p. 684

Determine whether each sequence is *arithmetic*, *geometric*, or *neither*. Explain your reasoning.

45. 3, 12, 27, 48, …
46. 1, −2, −5, −8, …
47. 12, 36, 108, 324, …
48. $-\frac{2}{5}, -\frac{2}{25}, -\frac{2}{125}, -\frac{2}{625}, \ldots$
49. $\frac{5}{2}, 3, \frac{7}{2}, 4, \ldots$
50. 6, 9, 14, 21, …

45. Neither; there is no common difference or ratio.

46. Arithmetic; the common difference is −3.

47. Geometric; the common ratio is 3.

48. Geometric; the common ratio is $\frac{1}{5}$.

49. Arithmetic; the common difference is $\frac{1}{2}$.

50. Neither; there is no common difference or ratio.

51. **READING** Sareeta took an 800-page book on vacation. If she was already on page 112 and is going to be on vacation for 8 days, what is the minimum number of pages she needs to read per day to finish the book by the end of her vacation? **86 pg/day**

52. **DEPRECIATION** Tammy's car is expected to depreciate at a rate of 15% per year. If her car is currently valued at $24,000, to the nearest dollar, how much will it be worth in 6 years? **$9052**

Real-World Link

According to *Car and Driver*, a car loses 15% to 20% of its value each year.

53. **PAPER FOLDING** When a piece of paper is folded onto itself, it doubles in thickness. If a piece of paper that is 0.1 mm thick could be folded 37 times, how thick would it be? **about 13,744 km**

H.O.T. Problems

Use Higher-Order Thinking Skills

54. **REASONING** Explain why the sequence 8, 10, 13, 17, 22 is not arithmetic.

55. **OPEN ENDED** Describe a real-life situation that can be represented by an arithmetic sequence with a common difference of 8.

56. **CHALLENGE** The sum of three consecutive terms of an arithmetic sequence is 6. The product of the terms is −42. Find the terms. **−3, 2, 7**

57. **ERROR ANALYSIS** Brody and Gen are determining whether the sequence 8, 8, 8, … is *arithmetic*, *geometric*, *neither*, or *both*. Is either of them correct? Explain your reasoning.

Brody	Gen
The sequence has a common difference of 0. The sequence is arithmetic.	The sequence has a common ratio of 1. The sequence is geometric.

58. **OPEN ENDED** Find a geometric sequence, an arithmetic sequence, and a sequence that is neither geometric nor arithmetic that begins 3, 9, … .

59. **REASONING** If a geometric sequence has a ratio r such that $|r| < 1$, what happens to the terms as n increases? What would happen to the terms if $|r| \geq 1$? **See margin.**

60. **WRITING IN MATH** Describe what happens to the terms of a geometric sequence when the common ratio is doubled. What happens when it is halved? Explain your reasoning. **See Chapter 11 Answer Appendix.**

54. Sample answer: The consecutive terms do not share a common difference. For instance, 22 − 17 = 5, while 17 − 13 = 4.

55. Sample answer: A babysitter earns $20 for cleaning the house and $8 extra for every hour she watches the children.

57. Sample answer: Neither; the sequence is both arithmetic and geometric.

58. Sample answer: geometric: 3, 9, 27, 81, 243, … arithmetic: 3, 9, 15, 21, 27, … neither geometric nor arithmetic: 3, 9, 21, 45, 93, …

Enrichment

CRM p. 10 OL BL

11-1 Enrichment

Fibonacci Sequence

Leonardo Fibonacci first discovered the sequence of numbers named for him while studying rabbits. He wanted to know how many pairs of rabbits would be produced in n months, starting with a single pair of newborn rabbits. He made the following assumptions.

1. Newborn rabbits become adults in one month.
2. Each pair of rabbits produces one pair each month.
3. No rabbits die.

Let F_n represent the number of pairs of rabbits at the end of n months. If you begin with one pair of newborn rabbits, $F_0 = F_1 = 1$. This pair of rabbits would produce one pair at the end of the second month, so $F_2 = 1 + 1$, or 2. At the end of the third month, the first pair of rabbits would produce another pair. Thus, $F_3 = 2 + 1$, or 3.

The chart below shows the number of rabbits each month for several months.

Month	Adult Pairs	Newborn Pairs	Total
F_0	0	1	1
F_1	1	0	1
F_2	1	1	2
		1	3

Additional Answer

59. Sample answer: If a geometric sequence has a ratio r such that $|r| < 1$, as n increases, the absolute value of the terms will decrease and approach zero because they are continuously being multiplied by a fraction. When $|r| \geq 1$, the absolute value of the terms will increase and approach infinity because they are continuously being multiplied by a value greater than 1.

NGSSS PRACTICE 912.G.2.5, 912.D.11.1, 912.S.3.3, 912.D.11.3

61. THINK SOLVE EXPLAIN **SHORT RESPONSE** Mrs. Aguilar's rectangular bedroom measures 13 feet by 11 feet. She wants to purchase carpet for the bedroom that costs \$2.95 per square foot, including tax. How much will it cost to carpet her bedroom? **\$421.85**

62. The pattern of filled circles and white circles below can be described by a relationship between two variables.

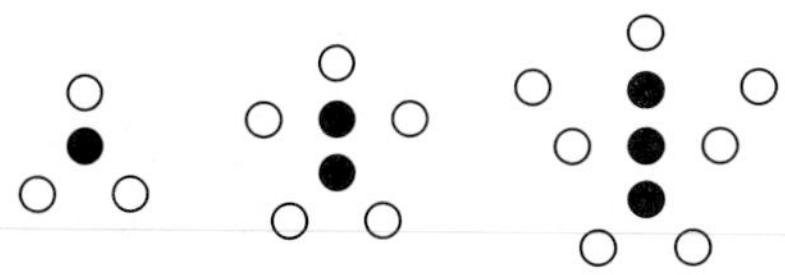

Which rule relates w, the number of white circles, to f, the number of dark circles? **C**

A. $w = 3f$

B. $f = \frac{1}{2}w - 1$

C. $w = 2f + 1$

D. $f = \frac{1}{3}w$

63. **ACT/SAT** Donna wanted to determine the average of her six test scores. She added the scores correctly to get T, but divided by 7 instead of 6. Her average was 12 less than the actual average. Which equation could be used to determine the value of T? **H**

F. $6T + 12 = 7T$

G. $\frac{T}{7} = \frac{T - 12}{6}$

H. $\frac{T}{7} + 12 = \frac{T}{6}$

I. $\frac{T}{6} = \frac{T - 12}{7}$

64. Find the next term in the geometric sequence $8, 6, \frac{9}{2}, \frac{27}{8}, \ldots$. **D**

A. $\frac{11}{8}$

B. $\frac{27}{16}$

C. $\frac{9}{4}$

D. $\frac{81}{32}$

Spiral Review

Solve each system of equations. (Lesson 10-7)

65. $y = 5$, $y^2 = x^2 + 9$ **(±4, 5)**

66. $y - x = 1$, $x^2 + y^2 = 25$ **(−4, −3), (3, 4)**

67. $3x = 8y^2$, $8y^2 - 2x^2 = 16$ **no solution**

Write each equation in standard form. State whether the graph of the equation is a *parabola, circle, ellipse,* or *hyperbola*. Then graph the equation. (Lesson 10-6) **68–70. See margin.**

68. $6x^2 + 6y^2 = 162$

69. $4y^2 - x^2 + 4 = 0$

70. $x^2 + y^2 + 6y + 13 = 40$

Graph each function. (Lesson 9-4) **71–73. See Chapter 11 Answer Appendix.**

71. $f(x) = \frac{6}{(x - 2)(x + 3)}$

72. $f(x) = \frac{-3}{(x - 2)^2}$

73. $f(x) = \frac{x^2 - 36}{x + 6}$

74. **HEALTH** A certain medication is eliminated from the bloodstream at a steady rate. It decays according to the equation $y = ae^{-0.1625t}$, where t is in hours. Find the half-life of this substance. (Lesson 8-8) **about 4.27 hours**

Skills Review

Write an equation of each line. (Lesson 2-4)

75. passes through (6, 4), $m = 0.5$ $y = 0.5x + 1$

76. passes through $\left(2, \frac{1}{2}\right)$, $m = -\frac{3}{4}$ $y = -\frac{3}{4}x + 2$

77. passes through (0, −6), $m = 3$ $y = 3x - 6$

78. passes through (0, 4), $m = \frac{1}{4}$ $y = \frac{1}{4}x + 4$

79. passes through (1, 3) and $\left(8, -\frac{1}{2}\right)$ $y = -\frac{1}{2}x + \frac{7}{2}$

80. passes through (−5, 1) and (5, 16) $y = \frac{3}{2}x + \frac{17}{2}$

Watch Out!

Error Analysis For Exercise 57, ask students to find a sequence, other than 8, 8, 8, . . . , that is both arithmetic and geometric. Discuss how that sequence is similar to 8, 8, 8, ...

4 ASSESS

Name the Math Have students explain how to find any term of an arithmetic sequence or geometric sequence when the first few terms are given.

Additional Answers

68. circle; $x^2 + y^2 = 27$

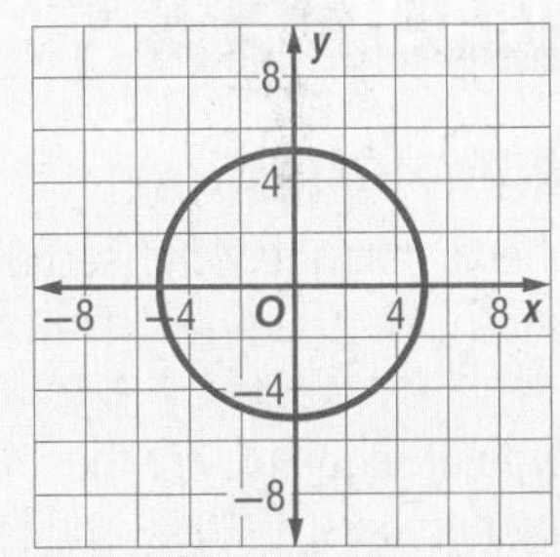

69. hyperbola; $\frac{x^2}{4} - \frac{y^2}{1} = 1$

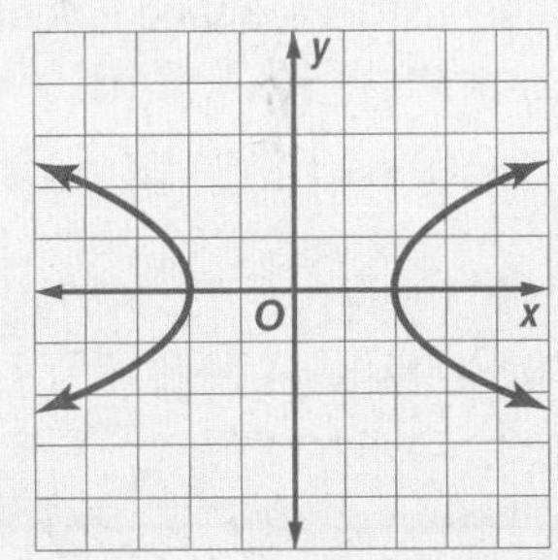

70. circle; $x^2 + (y + 3)^2 = 36$

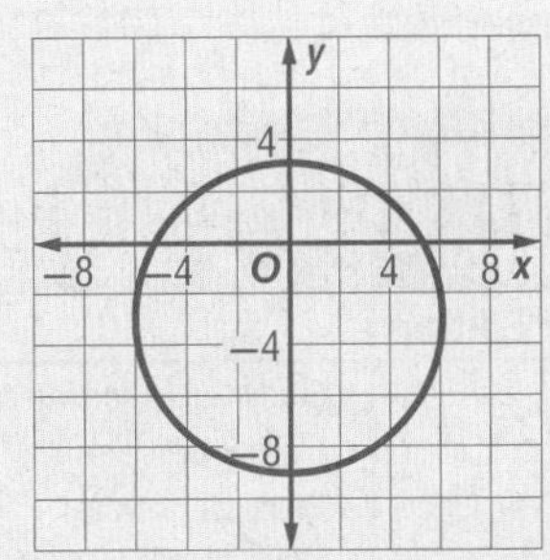

Differentiated Instruction

OL BL

Extension Ask students this question: "Is 1, 2, 4, 8, 16, . . . an arithmetic or geometric sequence? How do you know?" Geometric; the common ratio is 2. Then ask, "If each term in the sequence 1, 2, 4, 8, 16, . . . were replaced with its reciprocal, would the sequence still be a geometric sequence? How do you know?" Yes; the common ratio is $\frac{1}{2}$. Ask students to write their own geometric sequence and determine if its reciprocal counterpart is also a geometric sequence.

11-2 Lesson Notes

1 FOCUS

Vertical Alignment

Before Lesson 11-2
Determine whether a sequence is arithmetic.

Lesson 11-2
Use arithmetic sequences.
Find sums of arithmetic series.

After Lesson 11-2
Prove statements by using mathematical induction.

2 TEACH

Scaffolding Questions

Have students read the *Why?* section of the lesson.

Ask:

- What type of sequence are the counting numbers, 1–100? arithmetic
- What is the value of the first term? 1
- How could you quickly determine the sum of the first 10 counting numbers? Sample answer: $5 \times 11 = 55$

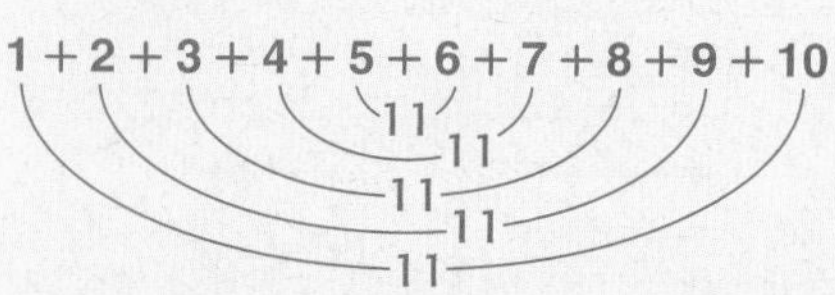

11-2 Arithmetic Sequences and Series

Then
You determined whether a sequence was arithmetic. (Lesson 11-1)

Now
- Use arithmetic sequences.
- Find sums of arithmetic series.

NGSSS
MA.912.D.11.3 Find specified terms of arithmetic and geometric sequences. MA.912.D.11.4 Find partial sums of arithmetic and geometric series, and find sums of infinite convergent geometric series. Use Sigma notation where applicable. *Also addresses MA.912.D.11.1 and MA.912.D.11.2.*

New Vocabulary
arithmetic means
series
arithmetic series
partial sum
sigma notation

FL Math Online
glencoe.com

Why?

In the 18th century, a teacher asked his class of elementary students to find the sum of the counting numbers 1 through 100. A pupil named Karl Gauss correctly answered within seconds, astonishing the teacher. Gauss went on to become a great mathematician.

He solved this problem by using an arithmetic series.

Arithmetic Sequences In Lesson 11-1, you used the point-slope form to find a specific term of an arithmetic sequence. It is possible to develop an equation for any term of an arithmetic sequence using the same process.

Consider the arithmetic sequence $a_1, a_2, a_3, \ldots, a_n$ in which the common difference is d.

$(y - y_1) = m(x - x_1)$	**Point-slope form**
$(a_n - a_1) = d(n - 1)$	**$(x, y) = (n, a_n)$, $(x_1, y_1) = (1, a_1)$, and $m = d$**
$a_n = a_1 + d(n - 1)$	**Add a_1 to each side.**

You can use this equation to find any term in an arithmetic sequence when you know the first term and the common difference.

Key Concept — ***n*th Term of an Arithmetic Sequence**

The *n*th term a_n of an arithmetic sequence in which the first term is a_1 and the common difference is d is given by the following formula, where n is any natural number.

$$a_n = a_1 + (n - 1)d$$

You will prove this formula in Exercise 80.

EXAMPLE 1 Find the *n*th Term

Find the 12th term of the arithmetic sequence 9, 16, 23, 30, … .

Step 1 Find the common difference.
$16 - 9 = 7 \qquad 23 - 16 = 7 \qquad 30 - 23 = 7$

So, $d = 7$.

Step 2 Find the 12th term.

$a_n = a_1 + (n - 1)d$	***n*th term of an arithmetic sequence**
$a_{12} = 9 + (12 - 1)(7)$	**$a_1 = 9$, $d = 7$, and $n = 12$**
$= 9 + 77$ or 86	**Simplify.**

Guided Practice

Find the indicated term of each arithmetic sequence.

1A. $a_1 = -4, d = 6, n = 9$ 44

1B. a_{20} for $a_1 = 15, d = -8$ −137

Personal Tutor glencoe.com

Lesson 11-2 Resources

Resource	Approaching-Level	On-Level	Beyond-Level	English Learners
Teacher Edition		• Differentiated Instruction, pp. 690, 693	• Differentiated Instruction, p. 693	• Differentiated Instruction, p. 690
Chapter Resource Masters	• Study Guide and Intervention, pp. 11–12 • Skills Practice, p. 13 • Practice, p. 14 • Word Problem Practice, p. 15	• Study Guide and Intervention, pp. 11–12 • Skills Practice, p. 13 • Practice, p. 14 • Word Problem Practice, p. 15 • Enrichment, p. 16 • Spreadsheet Activity, p. 17 • Graphing Calculator Activity, p. 18	• Practice, p. 14 • Word Problem Practice, p. 15 • Enrichment, p. 16	• Study Guide and Intervention, pp. 11–12 • Skills Practice, p. 13 • Practice, p. 14 • Word Problem Practice, p. 15
Transparencies	• 5-Minute Check Transparency 11-2	• 5-Minute Check Transparency 11-2	• 5-Minute Check Transparency 11-2	• 5-Minute Check Transparency 11-2
Other	• Study Notebook	• Study Notebook	• Study Notebook	• Study Notebook

If you are given some terms of an arithmetic sequence, you can write an equation for the nth term of the sequence.

EXAMPLE 2 Write Equations for the nth Term

Write an equation for the nth term of each arithmetic sequence.

a. $5, -13, -31, \ldots$

$d = -13 - 5$ or -18; 5 is the first term.

$a_n = a_1 + (n - 1)d$	**nth term of an arithmetic sequence**
$a_n = 5 + (n - 1)(-18)$	**$a_1 = 5$ and $d = -18$**
$a_n = 5 + (-18n + 18)$	**Distributive Property**
$a_n = -18n + 23$	**Simplify.**

b. $a_5 = 19, d = 6$

First, find a_1.

$a_n = a_1 + (n - 1)d$	**nth term of an arithmetic sequence**
$19 = a_1 + (5 - 1)(6)$	**$a_5 = 19$, $n = 5$, and $d = 6$**
$19 = a_1 + 24$	**Multiply.**
$-5 = a_1$	**Subtract 24 from each side.**

Then write the equation.

$a_n = a_1 + (n - 1)d$	**nth term of an arithmetic sequence**
$a_n = -5 + (n - 1)(6)$	**$a_1 = -5$ and $d = 6$**
$a_n = -5 + (6n - 6)$	**Distributive Property**
$a_n = 6n - 11$	**Simplify.**

Guided Practice

2A. $12, 3, -6, \ldots$ $a_n = -9n + 21$

2B. $a_6 = 12, d = 8$ $a_n = 8n - 36$

Personal Tutor glencoe.com

StudyTip

Checking Solutions Check your solution by using it to determine the first three terms of the sequence.

Sometimes you are given two terms of a sequence, but they are not consecutive terms of that sequence. The terms between any two nonconsecutive terms of an arithmetic sequence, called **arithmetic means**, can be used to find missing terms of a sequence.

ReadingMath

arithmetic mean the average of two or more numbers

arithmetic means the terms between any two nonconsecutive terms of an arithmetic sequence

EXAMPLE 3 Find Arithmetic Means

Find the arithmetic means in the sequence $-8, \underline{?}, \underline{?}, \underline{?}, \underline{?}, 22, \ldots$.

Step 1 Since there are four terms between the first and last terms given, there are $4 + 2$ or 6 total terms, so $n = 6$.

Step 2 Find d.

$a_n = a_1 + (n - 1)d$	**nth term of an arithmetic sequence**
$22 = -8 + (6 - 1)d$	**$a_1 = -8$, $a_6 = 22$, and $n = 6$**
$30 = 5d$	**Distributive Property**
$6 = d$	**Divide each side by 5.**

Step 3 Use d to find the four arithmetic means.

$-8 \xrightarrow{+6} -2 \xrightarrow{+6} 4 \xrightarrow{+6} 10 \xrightarrow{+6} 16 \xrightarrow{+6} 22$

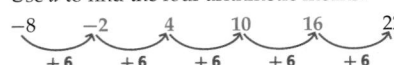

The arithmetic means are -2, 4, 10, and 16.

Guided Practice

3. Find the five arithmetic means between -18 and 36. $-9, 0, 9, 18, 27$

Personal Tutor glencoe.com

Arithmetic Sequences

Example 1 shows how to find the nth term of an arithmetic sequence when you know the first term and the common difference. **Example 2** shows how to write an equation for the nth term of an arithmetic sequence when given some terms of the sequence. **Example 3** shows how to find the arithmetic means between two nonconsecutive terms of an arithmetic sequence.

Formative Assessment

Use the Guided Practice exercises after each example to determine students' understanding of concepts.

Additional Examples

1 Find the 20th term of the arithmetic sequence 3, 10, 17, 24, ... 136

2 Write an equation for the nth term of each arithmetic sequence.

a. $-8, -6, -4, \ldots$

$a_n = 2n - 10$

b. $a_6 = 11, d = -11$

$a_n = -11n + 77$

3 Find the arithmetic means in the sequence 21, ___, ___, ___, 45, ... 27, 33, 39

Additional Examples also in Interactive Classroom PowerPoint® Presentations

IWB INTERACTIVE WHITEBOARD READY

Focus on Mathematical Content

Formula for an Arithmetic Sequence Any term of a sequence can be found from the value of the preceding term if the common difference is known, but a formula for the nth term requires knowledge of the first term in the sequence.

Arithmetic Series

Example 4 shows how to use a formula to find the sum of an arithmetic sequence. **Example 5** shows how to use a sum formula to find terms in an arithmetic sequence. **Example 6** shows how to find the sum of a series written in sigma notation.

Additional Examples

4 Find the sum $8 + 12 + 16 + \ldots + 80$. 836

5 Find the first three terms of the arithmetic series. $S_n = 129$, $a_1 = 14$, and $a_n = 29$ 14, 17, 20

TEACH with TECH

INTERACTIVE WHITEBOARD
Show an example on the board to help explain the formula for finding the sum of an arithmetic series. Write a sequence of numbers from 1 to 10, and drag the numbers to form the sums $1 + 10$, $2 + 9$, $3 + 8$, etc., and find the sum of the series. Then show how the formula simplifies this calculation.

Arithmetic Series A **series** is formed when the terms of a sequence are added. An **arithmetic series** is the sum of an arithmetic sequence. The sum of the first n terms is called the **partial sum** and is denoted S_n.

Key Concept — Partial Sum of an Arithmetic Series

Formula	Given	The sum S_n of the first n terms is:
General	a_1 and a_n	$S_n = n\left(\frac{a_1 + a_n}{2}\right)$
Alternate	a_1 and d	$S_n = \frac{n}{2}[2a_1 + (n - 1)d]$

Sometimes a_1, a_n, or n must be determined before the sum of an arithmetic series can be found. When this occurs, use the formula for the nth term.

EXAMPLE 4 Use the Sum Formulas

Find the sum of $12 + 19 + 26 + \cdots + 180$.

Step 1 $a_1 = 12$, $a_n = 180$, and $d = 19 - 12$ or 7.
We need to find n before we can use one of the formulas.

$a_n = a_1 + (n - 1)d$ — **nth term of an arithmetic sequence**
$180 = 12 + (n - 1)(7)$ — **$a_n = 180$, $a_1 = 12$, and $d = 7$**
$168 = 7n - 7$ — **Simplify.**
$25 = n$ — **Solve for n.**

Step 2 Use either formula to find S_n.

$S_n = \frac{n}{2}[2a_1 + (n - 1)d]$ — **Sum formula**
$S_{25} = \frac{25}{2}[2(12) + (25 - 1)(7)]$ — **$n = 25$, $a_1 = 12$, and $d = 7$**
$S_{25} = 12.5(192)$ or 2400 — **Simplify.**

Guided Practice

Find the sum of each arithmetic series.

4A. $2 + 4 + 6 \cdots + 100$ 2550

4B. $n = 16$, $a_n = 240$, and $d = 8$. 2880

Personal Tutor glencoe.com

You can use a sum formula to find terms of a series.

Watch Out!

Common Difference Don't confuse the sign of the common difference in an arithmetic sequence. Check that the rule actually produces the terms of a sequence.

EXAMPLE 5 Find the First Three Terms

Find the first three terms of the arithmetic series in which $a_1 = 7$, $a_n = 79$, and $S_n = 430$.

Step 1 Find n.

$S_n = n\left(\frac{a_1 + a_n}{2}\right)$ — **Sum formula**
$430 = n\left(\frac{7 + 79}{2}\right)$ — **$S_n = 430$, $a_1 = 7$, and $a_n = 79$**
$430 = n(43)$ — **Simplify.**
$10 = n$ — **Divide each side by 43.**

Differentiated Instruction (OL) (ELL)

Interpersonal Learners Discuss the difference between a sequence and a series, and ask students to suggest ways to remember which is which.

Step 2 Find d.

$a_n = a_1 + (n - 1)d$ — **nth term of an arithmetic sequence**

$79 = 7 + (10 - 1)d$ — **$a_n = 79$, $a_1 = 7$, and $n = 10$**

$72 = 9d$ — **Subtract 7 from each side.**

$8 = d$ — **Divide each side by 9.**

Step 3 Use d to determine a_2 and a_3.

$a_2 = 7 + 8$ or 15 $\quad$ $a_3 = 15 + 8$ or 23

The first three terms are 7, 15, and 23.

Guided Practice

Find the first three terms of each arithmetic series. 5B. −24 −16, −8

5A. $S_n = 120, n = 8, a_n = 36$ −6, 0, 6 $\quad$ **5B.** $a_1 = -24, a_n = 288, S_n = 5280$

Personal Tutor glencoe.com

ReadingMath

Sigma Notation The name comes from the Greek letter sigma, which is used in the notation.

The sum of a series can be written in shorthand by using **sigma notation**.

Key Concept — Sigma Notation

Get Animated

Symbols $\sum_{k=1}^{n} f(k)$ — n: last value of k; $k = 1$: first value of k; $f(k)$: formula for the terms of the series

Example $\sum_{k=1}^{12} (4k + 2) = [4(1) + 2] + [4(2) + 2] + [4(3) + 2] + \cdots + [4(12) + 2]$

$= 6 + 10 + 14 + \cdots + 50$

NGSSS PRACTICE EXAMPLE 6 — 912.D.11.4

Find $\sum_{k=4}^{18} (6k - 1)$.

A. 846 $\quad$ **B.** 910 $\quad$ **C.** 975 $\quad$ **D.** 1008

Test-TakingTip

Solve a Simpler Problem Sometimes it is necessary to break a problem into parts, solve each part, then combine the solutions of the parts.

Read the Test Item

You need to find the sum of the series. Find a_1, a_n, and n.

Solve the Test Item

There are $18 - 4 + 1$ or 15 terms, so $n = 15$.

$a_1 = 6(4) - 1$ or 23 $\quad$ $a_n = 6(18) - 1$ or 107

Find the sum.

$S_n = n\left(\frac{a_1 + a_n}{2}\right)$ — **Sum formula**

$S_{15} = 15\left(\frac{23 + 107}{2}\right)$ — **$n = 15$, $a_1 = 23$, and $a_n = 107$**

$S_{15} = 15(65)$ or 975 $\quad$ The correct answer is C.

Guided Practice

6. **Find $\sum_{m=9}^{21} (5m + 6)$.** G

F. 972 $\quad$ **G.** 1053 $\quad$ **H.** 1281 $\quad$ **I.** 1701

Personal Tutor glencoe.com

Focus on Mathematical Content

Finite Series Although most of the sequences studied in this lesson are infinite, the series in this lesson are not. The formula $S_n = \frac{n}{2}(a_1 + a_n)$ for the sum of an arithmetic series is valid only for a stated finite number n of terms.

Additional Example

6 **STANDARDIZED TEST PRACTICE**

Find $\sum_{k=3}^{10} (2k + 1)$. D

A 23

B 70

C 98

D 112

Watch Out!

Preventing Errors Help students become comfortable with sigma notation by having them read aloud several expressions written in this notation. Explain that sigma is the uppercase letter S in the Greek alphabet. Ask them for other examples of mathematical notation that use Greek letters. Sample answer: π

3 PRACTICE

Formative Assessment

Use Exercises 1–13 to check for understanding.

Use the chart at the bottom of this page to customize assignments for your students.

Additional Answer

32c. Sample answer: No; there are a maximum of 300 points in a bowling game, so it would be impossible for the average to continue to climb indefinitely.

Check Your Understanding

Example 1 p. 688 — Find the indicated term of each arithmetic sequence.

1. $a_1 = 14, d = 9, n = 11$ **104**
2. a_{18} for 12, 25, 38, … **233**

Example 2 p. 689 — Write an equation for the nth term of each arithmetic sequence.

3. 13, 19, 25, … $a_n = 6n + 7$
4. $a_5 = -12, d = -4$ $a_n = -4n + 8$

Example 3 p. 689 — Find the arithmetic means in each sequence.

5. 6, ?, ?, ?, 42 **15, 24, 33**
6. −4, ?, ?, ?, 8 **−1, 2, 5**

Example 4 p. 690 — Find the sum of each arithmetic series.

7. the first 50 natural numbers **1275**
8. $4 + 8 + 12 + \cdots + 200$ **5100**
9. $a_1 = 12, a_n = 188, d = 4$ **4500**
10. $a_n = 145, d = 5, n = 21$ **1995**

Example 5 pp. 690, 691 — Find the first three terms of each arithmetic series.

11. $a_1 = 8, a_n = 100, S_n = 1296$ **8, 12, 16**
12. $n = 18, a_n = 112, S_n = 1098$ **10, 16, 22**

Example 6 p. 691

13. NGSSS PRACTICE Find $\sum_{k=1}^{12}(3k + 9)$. **C**

A. 45
B. 78
C. 342
D. 410

Practice and Problem Solving

● = **Step-by-Step Solutions** begin on page R20. **Extra Practice** begins on page 947.

Example 1 p. 688 — Find the indicated term of each arithmetic sequence.

14. $a_1 = -18, d = 12, n = 16$ **162**
15. $a_1 = -12, n = 66, d = 4$ **248**
16. $a_1 = 9, n = 24, d = -6$ **−129**
17. a_{15} for −5, −12, −19, … **−103**
18. a_{10} for −1, 1, 3, … **17**
19. a_{24} for 8.25, 8.5, 8.75, … **14**

Example 2 p. 689 — Write an equation for the nth term of each arithmetic sequence.

20. 24, 35, 46, …
21. 31, 17, 3, …
22. $a_9 = 45, d = -3$
23. $a_7 = 21, d = 5$
24. $a_4 = 12, d = 0.25$
25. $a_5 = 1.5, d = 4.5$
26. 9, 2, −5, …
27. $a_6 = 22, d = 9$
28. $a_8 = -8, d = -2$
29. $a_{15} = 7, d = \frac{2}{3}$
30. −12, −17, −22, …
31. $a_3 = -\frac{4}{5}, d = \frac{1}{2}$

20. $a_n = 11n + 13$
21. $a_n = -14n + 45$
22. $a_n = -3n + 72$
23. $a_n = 5n - 14$
24. $a_n = 0.25n + 11$
25. $a_n = 4.5n - 21$
26. $a_n = -7n + 16$
27. $a_n = 9n - 32$
28. $a_n = -2n + 8$
29. $a_n = \frac{2}{3}n - 3$
30. $a_n = -5n - 7$
31. $a_n = \frac{1}{2}n - \frac{23}{10}$

32. **SPORTS** José averaged 123 total pins per game in his bowing league this season. He is taking bowling lessons and hopes to bring his average up by 8 pins each new season. **b. 9th season**
    a. Write an equation to represent the nth term of the sequence. $a_n = 115 + 8n$
    b. If the pattern continues, during what season will José average 187 per game?
    c. Is it reasonable for this pattern to continue indefinitely? Explain. **See margin.**

Example 3 p. 689 — Find the arithmetic means in each sequence.

33. 24, ?, ?, ?, ?, −1 **19, 14, 9, 4**
34. −6, ?, ?, ?, ?, 49 **5, 16, 27, 38**
35. −28, ?, ?, ?, ?, 7 **−21, −14, −7, 0**
36. 84, ?, ?, ?, ?, 39 **75, 66, 57, 48**
37. −12, ?, ?, ?, ?, ?, −66
38. 182, ?, ?, ?, ?, ?, 104

37. −21, −30, −39, −48, −57
38. 169, 156, 143, 130, 117

Differentiated Homework Options

Level	Assignment	Two-Day Option	
AL Basic	14–60, 74–75, 78–82, 83–100	15–59 odd, 83–86	14–60 even, 74–75, 78–82, 87–100
OL Core	15–59 odd, 61–71, 73–75, 78–100	14–60, 83–86	61–73, 74–75, 78–82, 87–100
BL Advanced	61–96, (optional: 97–100)		

Example 4 p. 690

Find the sum of each arithmetic series. **39. 10,100 40. 40,000 41. 10,000**

39. the first 100 even natural numbers

40. the first 200 odd natural numbers

41. the first 100 odd natural numbers

42. the first 300 even natural numbers **42. 90,300**

43. $-18 + (-15) + (-12) + \cdots + 66$ **696**

44. $-24 + (-18) + (-12) + \cdots + 72$ **408**

45. $a_1 = -16, d = 6, n = 24$ **1272**

46. $n = 19, a_n = 154, d = 8$ **1558**

47. CONTESTS The prizes in a weekly radio contest began at \$150 and increased by \$50 for each week that the contest lasted. If the contest lasted for eleven weeks, how much was awarded in total? **\$4400**

Example 5 pp. 690–691

Find the first three terms of each arithmetic series.

48. $n = 32, a_n = -86, S_n = 224$ **100, 94, 88**

49. $a_1 = 48, a_n = 180, S_n = 1368$ **48, 60, 72**

50. $a_1 = 3, a_n = 66, S_n = 759$ **3, 6, 9**

51. $n = 28, a_n = 228, S_n = 2982$ **−15, −6, 3**

52. $a_1 = -72, a_n = 453, S_n = 6858$

53. $n = 30, a_n = 362, S_n = 4770$

54. $a_1 = 19, n = 44, S_n = 9350$ **19, 28, 37**

55. $a_1 = -33, n = 36, S_n = 6372$

52. −72, −57, −42
53. −44, −30, −16
55. −33, −21, −9
56. \$400 and \$1300

56. PRIZES A radio station is offering a total of \$8500 in prizes over ten hours. Each hour, the prize will increase by \$100. Find the amounts of the first and last prize.

Example 6 p. 691

Find the sum of each arithmetic series. **60. −208**

57. $\sum_{k=1}^{16}(4k-2)$ **512**

58. $\sum_{k=4}^{13}(4k+1)$ **350**

59. $\sum_{k=5}^{16}(2k+6)$ **324**

60. $\sum_{k=0}^{12}(-3k+2)$

B

61. FINANCIAL LITERACY Daniela borrowed some money from her parents. She agreed to pay \$50 at the end of the first month and \$25 more each additional month for 12 months. How much does she pay in total after the 12 months? **\$2250**

62. GRAVITY When an object is in free fall and air resistance is ignored, it falls 16 feet in the first second, an additional 48 feet during the next second, and 80 feet during the third second. How many total feet will the object fall in 10 seconds? **1600 ft**

Real-World Link

Some sources recommend that teens who borrow from their parents should sign a contract, deduct advances from future allowances, and pay interest on the loan.

Source: North Dakota State University

Use the given information to write an equation that represents the nth term in each arithmetic sequence. **64.** $a_n = -9n + 177$

63. The 100th term of the sequence is 245. The common difference is 13. $a_n = 13n - 1055$

64. The eleventh term of the sequence is 78. The common difference is −9.

65. The sixth term of the sequence is −34. The 23rd term is 119. $a_n = 9n - 88$

66. The 25th term of the sequence is 121. The 80th term is 506. $a_n = 7n - 54$

67. SEATING The rectangular tables in a reception hall are often placed end-to-end to form one long table. The diagrams below show the number of people who can sit at each of the table arrangements.

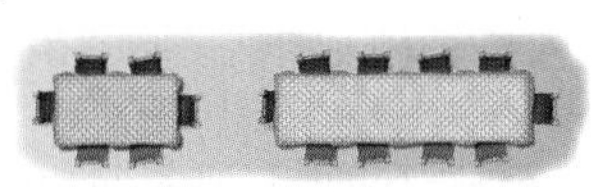

a. Make drawings to find the next three numbers as tables are added one at a time to the arrangement. **See margin.**

b. Write an equation representing the nth number in this pattern. $p_n = 4n + 2$

c. Is it possible to have seating for exactly 100 people with such an arrangement? Explain. **No; there is no whole number n for which $4n + 2 = 100$.**

Exercise Alert

Grid Paper For Exercises 71, 90–92, and 94–96, students will need grid paper.

Additional Answer

67a. 14, 18, 22

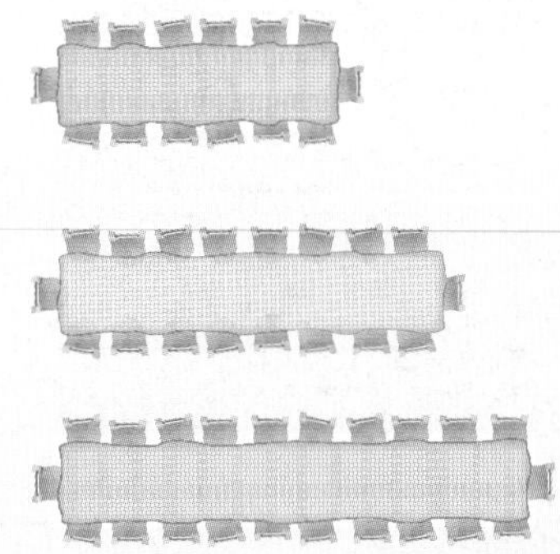

Differentiated Instruction

OL BL

Extension Write an arithmetic series such as 5 + 9 + 13 + 17 + 21 on the board and ask students to write the sum in terms of n using sigma notation with n starting at 1. $\sum_{n=1}^{5}(4n+1)$

Study Guide and Intervention
CRM pp. 11–12 AL OL ELL

11-2 Study Guide and Intervention

Arithmetic Sequences and Series

Arithmetic Sequences

Term	Definition	Example
Common Difference	$d = a_{n+1} - a_n$	The common difference in an arithmetic sequence with consecutive terms ... 5, 7, ... is $7 - 5 = 2$.
*n*th Term of an Arithmetic Sequence	$a_n = a_1 + (n - 1)d$ where a_1 is the common difference and n is any positive integer.	The fourth term of the arithmetic sequence with first term 3 and common difference 2 is $3 + (4 \times 2) = 11$.

Example 1 **Find the thirteenth term of the arithmetic sequence with $a_1 = 21$ and $d = -6$.**

Use the formula for the *n*th term of an arithmetic sequence with $a_1 = 21$, $n = 13$, and $d = -6$.

$a_n = a_1 + (n - 1)d$ Formula for the *n*th term
$a_{13} = 21 + (13 - 1)(-6)$ $n = 13, a_1 = 21, d = -6$
$a_{13} = -51$

Example 2 **Write an equation for the *n*th term of the arithmetic sequence −14, −5, 4, 13, ...**

In this sequence, $a_1 = -14$ and $d = 9$. Use the formula for a_n to write an equation.
$a_n = a_1 + (n - 1)d$ Formula for the *n*th term
$a_n = -14 + (n - 1)(9)$ $a_1 = -14, d = 9$
$a_n = -14 + 9n - 9$ Distributive Property
$a_n = 9n - 23$ Simplify.

Exercises

Find the indicated term of each arithmetic sequence.

1. Find the twentieth term of the arithmetic sequence with $a_1 = 15$ and $d = 4$. **91**
2. Find the seventh term of the arithmetic sequence with $a_1 = -81$ and $d = 12$. **−9**
3. Find the eleventh term of the arithmetic sequence with $a_1 = 42$ and $d = -5$. **−8**
4. Find a_{31} of the arithmetic sequence 18, 15, 12, 9, ... **−72**
5. Find a_{100} of the arithmetic sequence −63, −58, −53, −48, ... **432**

Write an equation for the *n*th term of each arithmetic sequence.

6. $a_1 = 15$ and $d = 38$ **$a_n = 38n - 23$**
7. $a_1 = 72$ and $d = -13$ **$a_n = -13n + 85$**
8. −56, −39, −22, −5, ... **$a_n = 17n - 73$**
9. −94, −52, −10, 32, ... **$a_n = 42n - 136$**
10. 63, 70, 77, 84, ... **$a_n = 7n + 56$**

Chapter 11 11 Glencoe Algebra 2

Lesson 11-2

Practice
CRM p. 14 AL OL BL ELL

11-2 Practice

Arithmetic Sequences and Series

Find the indicated term of each arithmetic sequence.

1. Find the sixtieth term of the arithmetic sequence if $a_1 = 418$ and $d = 12$. **1126**
2. Find a_{23} in the sequence, −18, −34, −50, −66, ... **−370**

Write an equation for the *n*th term of each arithmetic sequence.

3. 45, 30, 15, 0, ... **$a_n = -15n + 60$**
4. −87, −73, −59, −45, ... **$a_n = 14n - 101$**

Find the sum of each arithmetic series.

5. $5 + 7 + 9 + 11 + ... + 27$ **192**
6. $-4 + 1 + 6 + 11 + ... + 91$ **870**
7. $13 + 20 + 27 + ... + 272$ **5415**
8. $89 + 86 + 83 + 80 + ... + 20$ **1308**
9. $\sum_{n=1}^{4}(1 - 2n)$ **−16**
10. $\sum_{j=1}^{6}(5 + 3n)$ **93**
11. $\sum_{n=1}^{5}(9 - 4n)$ **−15**
12. $\sum_{k=4}^{10}(2k + 1)$ **105**
13. $\sum_{n=3}^{8}(5n - 10)$ **105**
14. $\sum_{n=1}^{101}(4 - 4n)$ **−20,200**

Find the first three terms of each arithmetic series described.

15. $a_1 = 14, a_n = -85, S_n = -1207$ **14, 11, 8**
16. $a_1 = 1, a_n = 19, S_n = 100$ **1, 3, 5**
17. $n = 16, a_n = 15, S_n = -120$ **−30, −27, −24**
18. $n = 15, a_n = 5\frac{4}{5}, S_n = 45$ **$\frac{1}{5}, \frac{3}{5}, 1$**
19. **STACKING** A health club rolls its towels and stacks them in layers on a shelf. Each layer of towels has one less towel than the layer below it. If there are 20 towels on the bottom layer and one towel on the top layer, how many towels are stacked on the shelf?
210 towels
20. **BUSINESS** A merchant places $1 in a jackpot on August 1, then draws the name of a regular customer. If the customer is present, he or she wins the $1 in the jackpot. If the customer is not present, the merchant adds $2 to the jackpot on August 2 and draws another name. Each day the merchant adds an amount equal to the day of the month. If the first person to win the jackpot wins $496, on what day of the month was her or his name drawn?
August 31

Chapter 11 14 Glencoe Algebra 2

Word Problem Practice
CRM p. 15 AL OL BL ELL

11-2 Word Problem Practice

Arithmetic Sequences and Series

1. **WINDOWS** A side of an apartment building is shaped like a steep staircase. The windows are arranged in columns. The first column has 2 windows, the next has 4, then 6, and so on. How many windows are on the side of the apartment building if it has 15 columns?

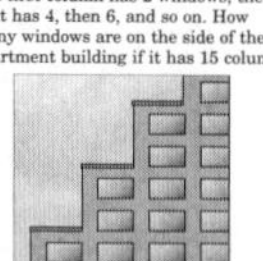

240

2. **WEIGHTS** Nathan has a collection of barbells for his home gym. He has 2 barbells for every 5 pounds starting at 5 pounds and going up to 80 pounds. What is the total weight of all his barbells?
1360 lb
3. **TRAINING** More than 380,000 people run in U.S. marathons each year. Matthew is training to run a marathon. He runs 20 miles his first week of training. Each week, he increases the number of miles he runs by 4 miles. How many total miles did he run in 8 weeks of training?
272 mi
4. **VOLUNTEERING** Maryland Public Schools requires all high school students to complete 75 hours of volunteer service as a condition for graduation. One school includes grades 1–12, with 50 students in each grade. The school decides that students in grade *g* will volunteer 0.25*g* hours per week of their time. How many hours will all the school's students collectively donate to charity each week?
975 hours
5. **TRIANGLES** A triangle is made of congruent equilateral triangles as shown in the figure.

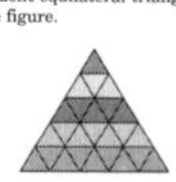

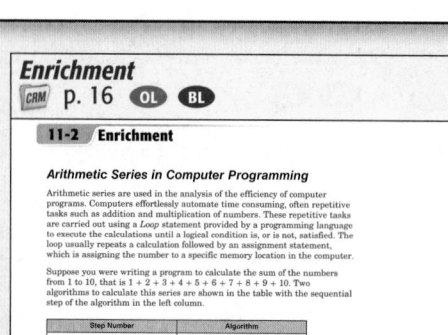

a. Starting from the top, each colored row of triangles has more and more triangles. Write a formula for the number of triangles in row *n*.
$a_n = 2n - 1$
b. If the large triangle consists of *N* rows of small triangles, how many small triangles are there in the large triangle? Write your answer using sigma notation.
$\sum_{n=1}^{N} 2n - 1$
c. Evaluate the sum you wrote for part b.
N^2

Chapter 11 15 Glencoe Algebra 2

Lesson 11-2

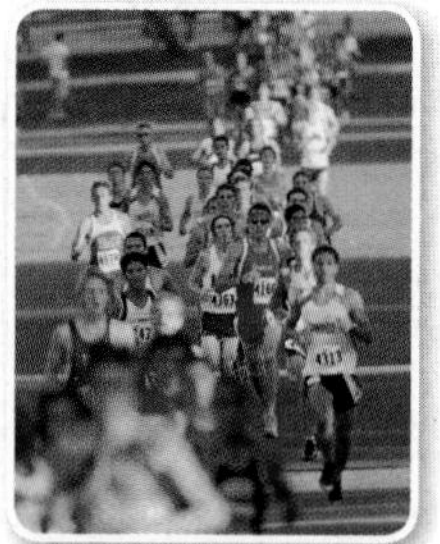

Real-World Link

An estimated 384,000 American high school students participate in cross country every year.

Source: National Federation of State High School Associations

70c. Sample answer: No; eventually the number of miles per day will become unrealistic.
71d. Sample answer: The graphs cover the same range. The domain of the series is the natural numbers, while the domain of the quadratic function is all real numbers, $0 \leq x \leq 10$.
71e. Sample answer: For every partial sum of an arithmetic series, there is a corresponding quadratic function that shares the same range.
74. Sample answer: Eric; Juana missed the step of multiplying *d* by $n - 1$.

68. **PERFORMANCE** A certain company pays its employees according to their performance. Belinda is paid a flat rate of $200 per week plus $24 for every unit she completes. If she earned $512 in one week, how many units did she complete? **13**

69. **SALARY** Terry currently earns $28,000 per year. If Terry expects a $4000 increase in salary every year, after how many years will he have a salary of $100,000 per year? **the 19th year**

70. **SPORTS** While training for cross country, Silvia plans to run 3 miles per day for the first week, and then increase the distance by a half mile each of the following weeks.
   a. Write an equation to represent the *n*th term of the sequence. **$a_n = 2.5 + 0.5n$**
   b. If the pattern continues, during which week will she be running 10 miles per day? **15th wk**
   c. Is it reasonable for this pattern to continue indefinitely? Explain.

C

71. **MULTIPLE REPRESENTATIONS** Consider $\sum_{k=1}^{x}(2k + 2)$. **a–c. See Chapter 11 Answer Appendix.**
   a. **TABULAR** Make a table of the partial sums of the series for $1 \leq k \leq 10$.
   b. **GRAPHICAL** Graph (*k*, partial sum).
   c. **GRAPHICAL** Graph $f(x) = x^2 + 3x$ on the same grid.
   d. **VERBAL** What do you notice about the two graphs?
   e. **ANALYTICAL** What conclusions can you make about the relationship between quadratic functions and the sum of arithmetic series?
   f. **ALGEBRAIC** Find the arithmetic series that relates to $g(x) = x^2 + 8x$. **$\sum_{k=1}^{x} 2k + 7$**

Find the value of *x*.

72. $\sum_{k=3}^{x}(6k - 5) = 928$ **18**

73. $\sum_{k=5}^{x}(8k + 2) = 1032$ **16**

H.O.T. Problems
Use Higher-Order Thinking Skills

74. **ERROR ANALYSIS** Eric and Juana are determining the formula for the *n*th term for the sequence −11, −2, 7, 16, ... Is either of them correct? Explain your reasoning.

Eric	Juana
$d = 16 - 7$ or 9, $a_1 = -11$ $a_n = -11 + (n - 1)9$ $= 9n - 20$	$d = 16 - 7$ or 9, $a_1 = -11$ $a_n = 9n - 11$

75. **REASONING** If *a* is the third term in an arithmetic sequence, *b* is the fifth term, and *c* is the eleventh term, express *c* in terms of *a* and *b*. **$4b - 3a$**

76. **CHALLENGE** There are three arithmetic means between *a* and *b* in an arithmetic sequence. The average of the arithmetic means is 16. What is the average of *a* and *b*? **16**

77. **CHALLENGE** Find S_n for $(x + y) + (x + 2y) + (x + 3y) + \dots$.

78. **OPEN ENDED** Write an arithmetic series with 8 terms and a sum of 324.

79. **WRITING IN MATH** Compare and contrast arithmetic sequences and series.

80. **PROOF** Prove the formula for the *n*th term of an arithmetic sequence.

81. **PROOF** Derive a sum formula that does not include a_1.

82. **PROOF** Derive the Alternate Sum Formula using the General Sum Formula.

77. $S_n = nx + y\left(\frac{n^2 + n}{2}\right)$
78. Sample answer: $9 + 18 + 27 + \dots + 72$
79. See margin.
80–81. See Chapter 11 Answer Appendix.
82. See margin.

Enrichment
CRM p. 16 OL BL

11-2 Enrichment

Arithmetic Series in Computer Programming

Arithmetic series are used in the analysis of the efficiency of computer programs. Computers effortlessly automate time consuming, often repetitive tasks such as addition and multiplication of numbers. These repetitive tasks are carried out using a *Loop* statement provided by a programming language to execute the calculations until a logical condition is, or is not, satisfied. The loop usually repeats a calculation followed by an assignment statement, which is assigning the number to a specific memory location in the computer.

Suppose you were writing a program to calculate the sum of the numbers from 1 to 10, that is $1 + 2 + 3 + 4 + 5 + 6 + 7 + 8 + 9 + 10$. Two algorithms to calculate this series are shown in the table with the sequential step of the algorithm in the left column.

Step Number	Algorithm
1	Assign in memory s = 1
2	Assign j = 2
3	If j < 11 then do steps 4 and 5
4	Assign s = s + j
5	Assign j = j + 1

Multiple Representations In Exercise 71, students use a table of values, a graph, and algebraic analysis to relate a quadratic function to the sum of an arithmetic series.

NGSSS PRACTICE 912.D.11.3, 912.A.4.4, 912.D.11.4, 912.A.2.12

83. ACT/SAT The measures of the angles of a triangle form an arithmetic sequence. If the measure of the smallest angle is 36°, what is the measure of the largest angle? B

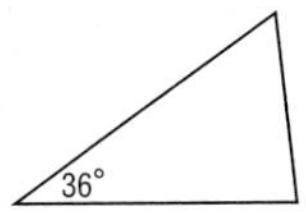

A. 75°
B. 84°
C. 90°
D. 97°

84. The area of a triangle is $\frac{1}{2}q^2 - 8$ and the height is $q + 4$. Which expression best describes the triangle's length? I

F. $(q + 1)$
G. $(q + 2)$
H. $(q - 3)$
I. $(q - 4)$

85. The expression $1 + \sqrt{2} + \sqrt[3]{3}$ is equivalent to A

A. $\sum_{k=1}^{3} k^{\frac{1}{k}}$
B. $\sum_{k=1}^{3} k^{k}$
C. $\sum_{k=1}^{3} k^{-k}$
D. $\sum_{k=1}^{3} \sqrt{k}$

86. SHORT RESPONSE Trevor can type a 200-word essay in 6 hours. Minya can type the same essay in $4\frac{1}{2}$ hours. If they work together, how many hours will it take them to type the essay? $2\frac{4}{7}$

Spiral Review

Determine whether each sequence is arithmetic. Write *yes* or *no*. (Lesson 11-1)

87. $-6, 4, 14, 24, \ldots$ yes

88. $2, \frac{7}{5}, \frac{4}{5}, \frac{1}{5}, \ldots$ yes

89. $10, 8, 5, 1, \ldots$ no

Solve each system of inequalities by graphing. (Lesson 10-7) 90–92. See Chapter 11 Answer Appendix.

90. $x + 2y > 1$
$x^2 + y^2 \leq 25$

91. $x + y \leq 2$
$4x^2 - y^2 \geq 4$

92. $x^2 + y^2 \geq 4$
$4y^2 + 9x^2 \leq 36$

93. PHYSICS The distance a spring stretches is related to the mass attached to the spring. This is represented by $d = km$, where d is the distance, m is the mass, and k is the spring constant. When two springs with spring constants k_1 and k_2 are attached in a series, the resulting spring constant k is found by the equation $\frac{1}{k} = \frac{1}{k_1} + \frac{1}{k_2}$. (Lesson 9-6)

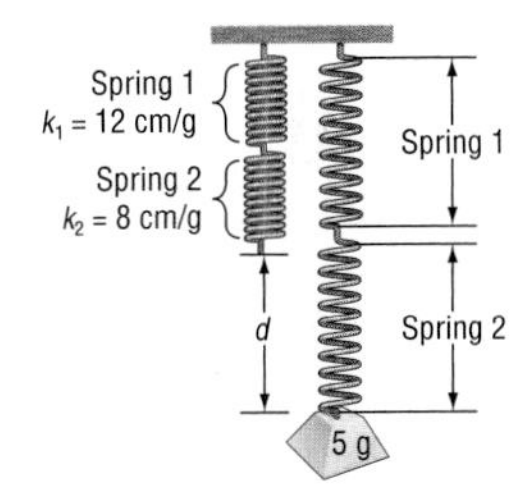

a. If one spring with constant of 12 centimeters per gram is attached in a series with another spring with constant of 8 centimeters per gram, find the resultant spring constant. 4.8 cm/g

b. If a 5-gram object is hung from the series of springs, how far will the springs stretch? Is this answer reasonable in this context? See margin.

Graph each function. State the domain and range. (Lesson 8-1) 94–96. See Chapter 11 Answer Appendix.

94. $f(x) = \frac{2}{3}(2^x)$

95. $f(x) = 4^x + 3$

96. $f(x) = 2\left(\frac{1}{3}\right)^x - 1$

Skills Review

Solve each equation. Round to the nearest ten-thousandth. (Lesson 8-6)

97. $5^x = 52$ 2.4550

98. $4^{3p} = 10$ 0.5537

99. $3^{n+2} = 14.5$ 0.4341

100. $16^{d-4} = 3^{3-d}$ 3.7162

Watch Out!

Error Analysis For Exercise 74, tell students that to avoid errors such as the one Juana made, it is helpful to write the formula, then in the next line, show the substitution of known values.

Preventing Errors Make sure that all students can demonstrate understanding of sigma notation by asking them to write out the terms of a series described in sigma notation.

4 ASSESS

Yesterday's News Ask students to describe how their work with sequences in the previous lesson helped them with this lesson.

Formative Assessment

Check for student understanding of Lessons 11-1 and 11-2.

CRM Quiz 1, p. 53

Additional Answer

93b. 24 cm; The answer is reasonable. The object would stretch the first spring 60 cm and would stretch the second spring 40 cm. The object would have to stretch the combined springs less than it would stretch either of the springs individually.

79. Sample answer: An arithmetic sequence is a list of terms such that any pair of successive terms has a common difference. An arithmetic series is the sum of the terms of an arithmetic sequence.

82.
$S_n = (a_1 + a_n) \cdot \left(\frac{n}{2}\right)$ General sum formula
$a_n = a_1 + (n - 1)d$ Formula for *n*th term
$S_n = [a_1 + a_1 + (n - 1)d] \cdot \left(\frac{n}{2}\right)$ Substitution
$S_n = [2a_1 + (n - 1)d] \cdot \left(\frac{n}{2}\right)$ Simplify.

Lesson 11-2 Arithmetic Sequences and Series 695

11-3 Lesson Notes

1 FOCUS

Vertical Alignment

Before Lesson 11-3
Determine whether a sequence is geometric.

Lesson 11-3
Use geometric sequences.
Find the sums of geometric series.

After Lesson 11-3
Find the sum of an infinite geometric series.

2 TEACH

Scaffolding Questions

Have students read the *Why?* section of the lesson.

Ask:

- What are the first 3 terms of the pattern? 5, 25, 125
- Why is this sequence not an arithmetic sequence? There is no common difference between the terms.
- What is the common ratio in the sequence? $r = 5$
- Compare a common difference with a common ratio. The first involves addition; the second involves multiplication.

11-3 Geometric Sequences and Series

Then
You determined whether a sequence was geometric. (Lesson 11-1)

Now
- Use geometric sequences.
- Find sums of geometric series.

NGSSS
MA.912.D.11.3 Find specified terms of arithmetic and geometric sequences. MA.912.D.11.4 Find partial sums of arithmetic and geometric series, and find sums of infinite convergent geometric series. Use Sigma notation where applicable.
Also addresses MA.912.D.11.1 and MA.912.D.11.2.

New Vocabulary
geometric means
geometric series

FL Math Online
glencoe.com

Why?

Julian hears a song by a new band. He e-mails a link for the band's Web site to five of his friends. They each forward the link to five of their friends. The link is forwarded again following the same pattern. How many people will receive the link on the eighth round of E-mails?

Geometric Sequences As with arithmetic sequences, there is a formula for the nth term of a geometric sequence. This formula can be used to determine any term of the sequence.

Key Concept — *n*th Term of a Geometric Sequence

The nth term a_n of a geometric sequence in which the first term is a_1 and the common ratio is r is given by the following formula, where n is any natural number.

$$a_n = a_1 r^{n-1}$$

You will prove this formula in Exercise 68.

Real-World EXAMPLE 1 Find the *n*th Term

MUSIC If the pattern continues, how many E-mails will be sent in the eighth round?

Understand We need to determine the number of forwarded E-mails on the eighth round. Five E-mails were sent on the first round. Each of the five recipients sent five E-mails on the second round, and so on.

Plan This is a geometric sequence, and the common ratio is 5. Use the formula for the nth term of a geometric sequence.

Solve

$a_n = a_1 r^{n-1}$ — ***n*th term of a geometric sequence**

$a_8 = 5(5)^{8-1}$ — $a_1 = 5$, $r = 5$, **and** $n = 8$

$a_8 = 5(78{,}125)$ or $390{,}625$ — $5^7 = 78{,}125$

Check Write out the first eight terms by multiplying by the common ratio.

5, 25, 125, 625, 3125, 15,625, 78,125, 390,625

There will be 390,625 E-mails sent on the 8th round.

Guided Practice

1. **E-MAILS** Shira receives a joke in an E-mail that asks her to forward it to four of her friends. She forwards it, then each of her friends forwards it to four of their friends, and so on. If the pattern continues, how many people will receive the E-mail on the ninth round of forwarding? 262,144

Personal Tutor glencoe.com

Lesson 11-3 Resources

Resource	Approaching-Level	On-Level	Beyond-Level	English Learners
Teacher Edition		• Differentiated Instruction, pp. 698, 702	• Differentiated Instruction, pp. 698, 702	• Differentiated Instruction, p. 698
Chapter Resource Masters	• Study Guide and Intervention, pp. 19–20 • Skills Practice, p. 21 • Practice, p. 22 • Word Problem Practice, p. 23	• Study Guide and Intervention, pp. 19–20 • Skills Practice, p. 21 • Practice, p. 22 • Word Problem Practice, p. 23 • Enrichment, p. 24 • Graphing Calculator Activity, p. 25	• Practice, p. 22 • Word Problem Practice, p. 23 • Enrichment, p. 24	• Study Guide and Intervention, pp. 19–20 • Skills Practice, p. 21 • Practice, p. 22 • Word Problem Practice, p. 23
Transparencies	• 5-Minute Check Transparency 11-3	• 5-Minute Check Transparency 11-3	• 5-Minute Check Transparency 11-3	• 5-Minute Check Transparency 11-3
Other	• Study Notebook	• Study Notebook	• Study Notebook	• Study Notebook

If you are given some of the terms of a geometric sequence, you can determine an equation for finding the nth term of the sequence.

EXAMPLE 2 Write an Equation for the nth Term

Write an equation for the nth term of each geometric sequence.

a. 0.5, 2, 8, 32, ...

$r = 8 \div 2$ or 4; 0.5 is the first term.

$a_n = a_1 r^{n-1}$ — **nth term of a geometric sequence**
$a_n = 0.5(4)^{n-1}$ — **$a_1 = 0.5$ and $r = 4$**

b. $a_4 = 5$ and $r = 6$

Step 1 Find a_1.

$a_n = a_1 r^{n-1}$ — **nth term of a geometric sequence**
$5 = a_1(6^{4-1})$ — **$a_n = 5$, $r = 6$, and $n = 4$**
$5 = a_1(216)$ — **Evaluate the power.**
$\frac{5}{216} = a_1$ — **Divide each side by 216.**

Step 2 Write the equation.

$a_n = a_1 r^{n-1}$ — **nth term of a geometric sequence**
$a_n = \frac{5}{216}(6)^{n-1}$ — **$a_1 = \frac{5}{216}$ and $r = 6$**

Guided Practice 2A. $a_n = -0.25(-8)^{n-1}$

Write an equation for the nth term of each geometric sequence.

2A. −0.25, 2, −16, 128, ...

2B. $a_3 = 16$, $r = 4$ $a_n = 1(4)^{n-1}$

Personal Tutor glencoe.com

Like arithmetic means, **geometric means** are the terms between two nonconsecutive terms of a geometric sequence. The common ratio r can be used to find the geometric means.

EXAMPLE 3 Find Geometric Means

Find three geometric means between 2 and 1250.

Step 1 Since there are three terms between the first and last term, there are 3 + 2 or 5 total terms, so $n = 5$.

Step 2 Find r.

$a_n = a_1 r^{n-1}$ — **nth term of a geometric sequence**
$1250 = 2r^{5-1}$ — **$a_n = 1250$, $a_1 = 2$, and $n = 5$**
$625 = r^4$ — **Divide each side by 2.**
$\pm 5 = r$ — **Take the 4th root of each side.**

Step 3 Use r to find the three geometric means.

2, 10, 50, 250, 1250 (× 5, × 5, × 5, × 5) or 2, −10, 50, −250, 1250 (× −5, × −5, × −5, × −5)

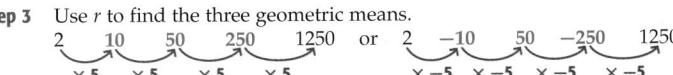

The geometric means are 10, 50, and 250 or −10, 50, and −250.

Guided Practice

3. Find four geometric means between 0.5 and 512. 2, 8, 32, 128

Personal Tutor glencoe.com

Math History Link

Archytas (428–347 B.C.) Geometric sequences, or geometric progressions, were first studied by the Greek mathematician Archytas. His studies of these sequences came from his interest in music and octaves.

ReadingMath

Geometric Means A geometric mean can also be represented geometrically. In the figure below, h is the geometric mean between x and y.

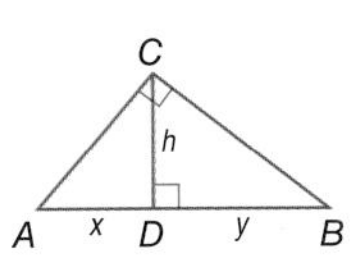

Geometric Sequences

Example 1 shows how to find a term in a geometric sequence when the first term and the common ratio are given. **Example 2** illustrates writing an equation for the nth term of a geometric sequence. **Example 3** shows how to find geometric means between two given numbers.

Formative Assessment

Use the Guided Practice exercises after each example to determine students' understanding of concepts.

Additional Examples

1 Find the sixth term of a geometric sequence for which $a_1 = -3$ and $r = -2$. $a_6 = 96$

2 Write an equation for the nth term of each geometric sequence.

a. 5, 10, 20, 40, . . .
$a_n = 5 \cdot 2^{n-1}$

b. $a_5 = 4$ and $r = 3$
$a_n = \frac{4}{81}(3^{n-1})$

3 Find three geometric means between 3.12 and 49.92. 6.24, 12.48, 24.96, or −6.24, 12.48, −24.96

Additional Examples also in Interactive Classroom PowerPoint® Presentations

IWB INTERACTIVE WHITEBOARD READY

Focus on Mathematical Content

Increasing or Decreasing Geometric Sequences Many of the sequences in this lesson are either increasing or decreasing, and the common ratio for these sequences is positive. But if the common ratio in a geometric sequence is negative, the sequence will be neither increasing nor decreasing.

Watch Out!

Preventing Errors Encourage students to begin a geometric sequence problem by writing the known values for each of the variables n, a, and r.

Tips for New Teachers

Sense-Making You may wish to have students calculate one or more sums with and without using the formula in order to verify the formula. This will also demonstrate the formula's efficiency.

Watch Out!

Preventing Errors Emphasize the importance of writing every step of calculations as an equation, so that each numeric value found during the process is clearly identified.

Geometric Series

Example 4 illustrates finding the sum of the first *n* terms of a geometric series. **Example 5** shows how to evaluate a sum written in sigma notation. **Example 6** shows how to find the first term in a geometric series for which the sum of a specified number of terms and the common ratio are known.

Additional Examples

4 MUSIC Use the information in Example 4. How many E-mails will be sent after the sixth round? 19,530

5 Find $\sum_{n=1}^{12} 3 \cdot 2^{n-1}$. 12,285

Geometric Series A **geometric series** is the sum of the terms of a geometric sequence. The sum of the first n terms of a series is denoted S_n. You can use either of the following formulas to find the partial sum S_n of the first n terms of a geometric series.

Key Concept — Partial Sum of a Geometric Series

Given	The sum S_n of the first n terms is:
a_1 and n	$S_n = \frac{a_1 - a_1r^n}{1 - r}, r \neq 1$
a_1 and a_n	$S_n = \frac{a_1 - a_nr}{1 - r}, r \neq 1$

Real-World EXAMPLE 4 Find the Sum of a Geometric Series

MUSIC Refer to the beginning of the lesson. If the pattern continues, what is the total number of E-mails sent in the eight rounds?

Five E-mails are sent in the first round and there are 8 rounds of E-mails. So, $a_1 = 5$, $r = 5$ and $n = 8$.

$S_n = \frac{a_1 - a_1r^n}{1 - r}$ — Sum formula

$S_8 = \frac{5 - 5 \cdot 5^8}{1 - 5}$ — $a_1 = 5$, $r = 5$, and $n = 8$

$S_8 = \frac{-1{,}953{,}120}{-4}$ — Simplify the numerator and denominator.

$S_8 = 488{,}280$ — Divide.

There will be 488,280 E-mails sent after 8 rounds.

Guided Practice Find the sum of each geometric series.

4A. $a_1 = 2, n = 10, r = 3$ 59,048

4B. $a_1 = 2000, a_n = 125, r = \frac{1}{2}$ 3875

Personal Tutor glencoe.com

As with arithmetic series, sigma notation can also be used to represent geometric series.

Watch Out!

Sigma Notation Notice in Example 5 that you are being asked to evaluate the sum from the 3rd term to the 10th term.

EXAMPLE 5 Sum in Sigma Notation

Find $\sum_{k=3}^{10} 4(2)^{k-1}$.

Find a_1, r, and k. In the first term, $k = 3$ and $a_1 = 4 \cdot 2^{3-1}$ or 16. The base of the exponential function is r, so $r = 2$. There are $10 - 3 + 1$ or 8 terms, so $k = 8$.

$S_n = \frac{a_1 - a_1r^k}{1 - r}$ — Sum formula

$= \frac{16 - 16(2)^8}{1 - 2}$ — $a_1 = 16$, $r = 2$, and $k = 8$

$= 4080$ — Use a calculator.

Guided Practice Find each sum.

5A. $\sum_{k=4}^{12} \frac{1}{4} \cdot 3^{k-1}$ 66,426.75

5B. $\sum_{k=2}^{9} \frac{2}{3} \cdot 4^{k-1}$ 58,253.333

Personal Tutor glencoe.com

Differentiated Instruction OL BL ELL

If you think students might be interested in learning how this lesson applies to real-world situations,

Then have students research how biologists and ecologists use geometric series in their work to count and predict the population changes for various organisms.

698 Chapter 11 Sequences and Series

You can use the formula for the sum of a geometric series to help find a particular term of the series.

EXAMPLE 6 **Find the First Term of a Series**

Find a_1 in a geometric series for which $S_n = 13{,}116$, $n = 7$, and $r = 3$.

$S_n = \frac{a_1 - a_1 r^n}{1 - r}$ — Sum formula

$13{,}116 = \frac{a_1 - a_1(3^7)}{1 - 3}$ — $S_n = 13{,}116$, $r = 3$, and $n = 7$

$13{,}116 = \frac{a_1(1 - 3^7)}{1 - 3}$ — Distributive Property

$13{,}116 = \frac{-2186a_1}{-2}$ — Subtract.

$13{,}116 = 1093a_1$ — Simplify.

$12 = a_1$ — Divide each side by 1093.

Guided Practice

6. Find a_1 in a geometric series for which $S_n = -26{,}240$, $n = 8$, and $r = -3$. 16

Personal Tutor glencoe.com

Check Your Understanding

Example 1 p. 696

1. GENEOLOGY Dean is making a family tree for his grandfather. He was able to trace many generations. If Dean could trace his family back 10 generations, starting with his parents, how many ancestors would there be? 2046

Example 2 p. 697

Write an equation for the *n*th term of each geometric sequence. 3. $a_n = 18 \cdot \left(\frac{1}{3}\right)^{n-1}$

2. 2, 4, 8, … $a_n = 2 \cdot 2^{n-1}$ **3.** 18, 6, 2, … **4.** −4, 16, −64, …

4. $a_n = (-4) \cdot (-4)^{n-1}$

5 $a_2 = 4$, $r = 3$ $a_n = \frac{4}{3}(3)^{n-1}$ **6.** $a_6 = \frac{1}{8}$, $r = \frac{3}{4}$ $a_n = \frac{128}{243}\left(\frac{3}{4}\right)^{n-1}$ **7.** $a_2 = -96$, $r = -8$ $a_n = 12(-8)^{n-1}$

Example 3 p. 697

Find the geometric means of each sequence.

8. 0.25, ?, ?, ?, 64 1, 4, 16 or −1, 4, −16 **9.** 0.20, ?, ?, ?, 125 1, 5, 25 or −1, 5, −25

Example 4 p. 698

10. GAMES Miranda arranges some rows of dominoes so that after she knocks over the first one, each domino knocks over two more dominoes when it falls. If there are ten rows, how many dominoes does Miranda use? 1023

Example 5 p. 698

Find the sum of each geometric series.

11. $\sum_{k=1}^{6} 3(4)^{k-1}$ 4095 **12.** $\sum_{k=1}^{8} 4\left(\frac{1}{2}\right)^{k-1}$ 7.96875

Example 6 p. 699

Find a_1 for each geometric series described.

13. $S_n = 85\frac{5}{16}$, $r = 4$, $n = 6$ $\frac{1}{16}$ **14.** $S_n = 91\frac{1}{12}$, $r = 3$, $n = 7$ $\frac{1}{12}$

15. $S_n = 1020$, $a_n = 4$, $r = \frac{1}{2}$ 512 **16.** $S_n = 121\frac{1}{3}$, $a_n = \frac{1}{3}$, $r = \frac{1}{3}$ 81

Additional Example

6 Find a_1 in a geometric series for which $S_8 = 765$, $n = 8$, and $r = 2$. 3

Focus on Mathematical Content

Two Formulas The formula for the sum of a geometric series $S_n = \frac{a_1 - a_n r}{1 - r}$ is used when the number of terms is not given. If n is known, the formula $S_n = \frac{a_1(1 - r^n)}{1 - r}$ can be used, since in this case it is not necessary to calculate a_n.

TEACH with TECH

DOCUMENT CAMERA Assign several exercises to the class, and give students time to work through them independently. Then choose students to share and explain their work to the class.

3 PRACTICE

Formative Assessment

Use Exercises 1–16 to check for understanding.

Use the chart at the bottom of the next page to customize assignments for your students.

Exercise Alert

Grid Paper For Exercises 81–83, students will need grid paper.

Additional Answers

64. $S_n = \frac{a_1 - a_1r^n}{1 - r}$

$= \frac{a_1 - a_1r^{n-1} \cdot r}{1 - r}$

$= \frac{a_1 - a_nr}{1 - r}$

65. $S_n = \frac{a_1 - a_nr}{1 - r}$

Alternate sum formula

$a_n = a_1 \cdot r^{n-1}$

Formula for *nth* term

$\frac{a_n}{r^{n-1}} = a_1$

Divide each side by r^{n-1}.

$S_n = \frac{\frac{a_n}{r^{n-1}} - a_nr}{1 - r}$

Substitution.

$= \frac{\frac{a_n}{r^{n-1}} - \frac{a_nr \cdot r^{n-1}}{r^{n-1}}}{1 - r}$

Multiply by $\frac{\frac{r^{n-1}}{r^{n-1}}}{1}$.

$= \frac{\frac{a_n(1 - r^n)}{r^{n-1}}}{1 - r}$

Simplify.

$= \frac{a_n(1 - r^n)}{r^{n-1}(1 - r)}$

Divide by $(1 - r)$.

$= \frac{a_n(1 - r^n)}{r^{n-1} - r^n}$

Simplify.

Practice and Problem Solving

= **Step-by-Step Solutions** begin on page R20.
Extra Practice begins on page 947.

23. $a_n = (-3)(-2)^{n-1}$
24. $a_n = 288\left(-\frac{1}{3}\right)^{n-1}$
25. $a_n = (-1)(-1)^{n-1}$
26. $a_n = \frac{1}{3}\left(\frac{2}{3}\right)^{n-1}$
27. $a_n = 8 \cdot \left(\frac{1}{4}\right)^{n-1}$
28. $a_n = 12 \cdot \left(-\frac{4}{3}\right)^{n-1}$
29. $a_n = 7(2)^{n-1}$
30. $a_n = -64(0.5)^{n-1}$
31. $a_n = \frac{1}{15{,}552}(6)^{n-1}$
32. $a_n = 32\left(\frac{1}{2}\right)^{n-1}$
33. $a_n = 648\left(\frac{1}{3}\right)^{n-1}$
35. 270, 90, 30 or −270, 90, −30
36. 160, 40, 10 or −160, 40, −10
37. $\frac{7}{3}, \frac{14}{9}, \frac{28}{27}$ or $-\frac{7}{3}, \frac{14}{9}, -\frac{28}{27}$
38. $\frac{243}{16}, \frac{81}{4}, 27$ or $-\frac{243}{16}, \frac{81}{4}, -27$

Example 1 p. 696

17. WEATHER Heavy rain in Brieanne's town caused the river to rise. The river rose three inches the first day, and each day after rose twice as much as the previous day. How much did the river rise in five days? **93 in.**

Find a_n for each geometric sequence.

18. $a_1 = 2400, r = \frac{1}{4}, n = 7$ **$\frac{75}{128}$ or 0.5859375**
19. $a_1 = 800, r = \frac{1}{2}, n = 6$ **25**

20. $a_1 = \frac{2}{9}, r = 3, n = 7$ **162**
21. $a_1 = -4, r = -2, n = 8$ **512**

22. BIOLOGY A certain bacteria grows at a rate of 3 cells every 2 minutes. If there were 260 cells initially, how many are there after 21 minutes? **864,567**

Example 2 p. 697

Write an equation for the *n*th term of each geometric sequence.

23. −3, 6, −12, …
24. 288, −96, 32, …
25. −1, 1, −1, …

26. $\frac{1}{3}, \frac{2}{9}, \frac{4}{27}, \ldots$
27. $8, 2, \frac{1}{2}, \ldots$
28. $12, -16, \frac{64}{3}, \ldots$

29. $a_3 = 28, r = 2$
30. $a_4 = -8, r = 0.5$
31. $a_6 = 0.5, r = 6$

32. $a_3 = 8, r = \frac{1}{2}$
33. $a_4 = 24, r = \frac{1}{3}$
34. $a_4 = 80, r = 4$ **$a_n = \frac{5}{4}(4)^{n-1}$**

Example 3 p. 697

Find the geometric means of each sequence.

35. 810, ?, ?, ?, 10
36. 640, ?, ?, ?, 2.5

37. $\frac{7}{2}$, ?, ?, ?, $\frac{56}{81}$
38. $\frac{729}{64}$, ?, ?, ?, $\frac{324}{9}$

39. Find two geometric means between 3 and 375. **15, 75**

40. Find two geometric means between 16 and −2. **−8, 4**

Example 4 p. 698

41. WATER TREATMENT A certain water filtration system can remove 70% of the contaminants each time a sample of water is passed through it. If the same water is passed through the system four times, what percent of the original contaminants will be removed from the water sample? **97.3%**

Find the sum of each geometric series.

42. $a_1 = 36, r = \frac{1}{3}, n = 8$ **53.9918**
43. $a_1 = 16, r = \frac{1}{2}, n = 9$ **31.9375**

44. $a_1 = 240, r = \frac{3}{4}, n = 7$ **831.855**
45. $a_1 = 360, r = \frac{4}{3}, n = 8$ **9707.82**

46. VACUUMS A vacuum claims to pick up 80% of the dirt every time it is run over the carpet. Assuming this is true, what percent of the original amount of dirt is picked up after the seventh time the vacuum is run over the carpet? **99.19%**

Example 5 p. 698

Find the sum of each geometric series. **47. 2188 48. 255 49. −87, 381**

47. $\sum_{k=1}^{7} 4(-3)^{k-1}$
48. $\sum_{k=1}^{8} (-3)(-2)^{k-1}$
49. $\sum_{k=1}^{9} (-1)(4)^{k-1}$
50. $\sum_{k=1}^{10} 5(-1)^{k-1}$ **0**

Example 6 p. 699

Find a_1 for each geometric series described.

51. $S_n = -2912, r = 3, n = 6$ **−8**
52. $S_n = -10{,}922, r = 4, n = 7$ **−2**

53. $S_n = 1330, a_n = 486, r = \frac{3}{2}$ **64**
54. $S_n = 4118, a_n = 128, r = \frac{2}{3}$ **1458**

55. $a_n = 1024, r = 8, n = 5$ **0.25**
56. $a_n = 1875, r = 5, n = 7$ **$\frac{3}{25}$**

Differentiated Homework Options

Level	Assignment	Two-Day Option	
AL Basic	17–57, 64–68, 71–89	17–57 odd, 73–76	18–56 even, 64–68, 71–72, 77–89
OL Core	17–57 odd, 58–68, 71–89	17–57, 73–76	58–68, 71–72, 77–89
BL Advanced	58–85, (optional: 86–89)		

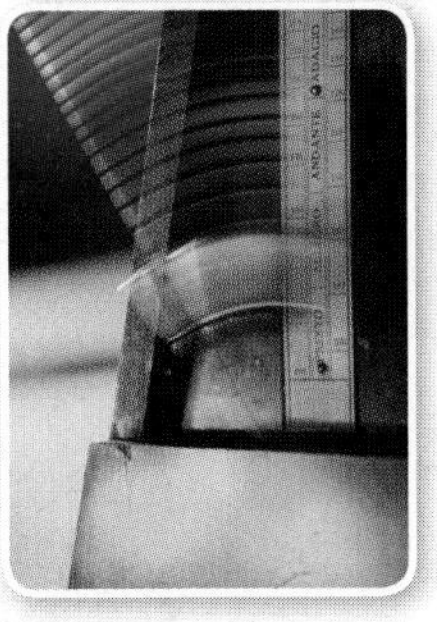

Real-World Link

A metronome is a pendulum device that produces a pulse, usually to establish a steady beat or tempo for the performance of musical compositions.

Source: *Glide Magazine*

57. **SCIENCE** One minute after it is released, a gas-filled balloon has risen 100 feet. In each succeeding minute, the balloon rises only 50% as far as it rose in the previous minute. How far will it rise in 5 minutes? **193.75 ft**

58. **CHEMISTRY** Radon has a half-life of about 4 days. This means that about every 4 days, half of the mass of radon decays into another element. How many grams of radon remain from an initial 60 grams after 4 weeks? **about 0.46875 g**

59. **COMPUTERS** A virus goes through a computer, infecting the files. If one file was infected initially and the total number of files infected doubles every minute, how many files will be infected in 20 minutes? **524,288**

60. **GEOMETRY** In the figure, the sides of each equilateral triangle are twice the size of the sides of its inscribed triangle. If the pattern continues, find the sum of the perimeters of the first eight triangles. **about 119.5 cm**

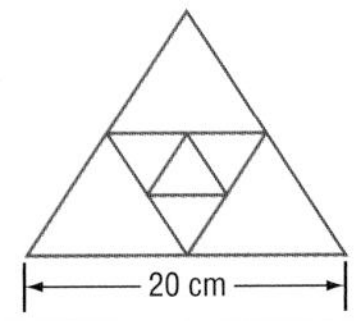

61. **PENDULUMS** The first swing of a pendulum travels 30 centimeters. If each subsequent swing travels 95% as far as the previous swing, find the total distance traveled by the pendulum after the 30th swing. **about 471 cm**

62. **PHONE CHAINS** A school established a phone chain in which every staff member calls two other staff members to notify them when the school closes due to weather. The first round of calls begins with the superintendent calling both principals. If there are 94 total staff members and employees at the school, how many rounds of calls are there? **7**

63. **TELEVISIONS** High Tech Electronics advertises a weekly installment plan for the purchase of a popular brand of high definition television. The buyer pays \$5 at the end of the first week, \$5.50 at the end of the second week, \$6.05 at the end of the third week, and so on for one year. (Assume 1 yr = 52 wk.)
    a. What will the payments be at the end of the 10th, 20th, and 40th weeks?
    b. Find the total cost of the TV. **\$7052.15**
    c. Why is the cost found in part **b** not entirely accurate?

63a. \$11.79, \$30.58, \$205.72
63c. Each payment made is rounded to the nearest penny, so the sum of the payments will actually be more than the sum found in part b.
64. See margin.
66. Sample answer: $256 + 192 + 144 + 108 + 81 + \frac{243}{4}$
68. See Chapter 11 Answer Appendix.

H.O.T. Problems Use Higher-Order Thinking Skills

64. **PROOF** Derive the General Sum Formula using the Alternate Sum Formula.

65. **PROOF** Derive a sum formula that does not include a_1. **See margin.**

66. **OPEN ENDED** Write a geometric series for which $r = \frac{3}{4}$ and $n = 6$.

67. **REASONING** Explain how $\sum_{k=1}^{10} 3(2)^{k-1}$ needs to be altered to refer to the same series if $k = 1$ changes to $k = 0$. Explain your reasoning. **See Chapter 11 Answer Appendix.**

68. **PROOF** Prove the formula for the *n*th term of a geometric sequence.

69. **CHALLENGE** The fifth term of a geometric sequence is $\frac{1}{27}$th of the eighth term. If the ninth term is 702, what is the eighth term? **234**

70. **CHALLENGE** Use the fact that h is the geometric mean between x and y in the figure at the right to find h^4 in terms of x and y. x^2y^2

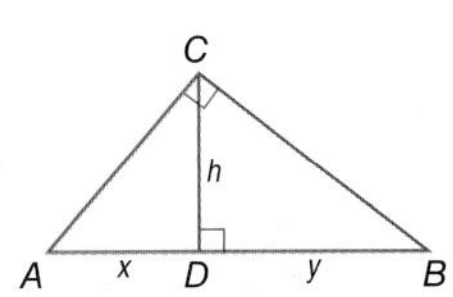

71. **OPEN ENDED** Write a geometric series with 6 terms and a sum of 252. **Sample answer: $4 + 8 + 16 + 32 + 64 + 128$**

72. **WRITING IN MATH** Explain how you determine whether a series is *arithmetic*, *geometric*, *neither*, or *both*. **See margin.**

Study Guide and Intervention
CRM pp. 19–20 AL OL ELL

11-3 Study Guide and Intervention
Geometric Sequences and Series

Geometric Sequences A **geometric sequence** is a sequence in which each term after the first is the product of the previous term and a constant called the **constant ratio**.

*n*th Term of a Geometric Sequence	$a_n = a_1 \cdot r^{n-1}$, where a_1 is the first term, r is the common ratio, and n is any positive integer

Example 1 **Find the next two terms of the geometric sequence 1200, 480, 192, ...**

Since $\frac{480}{1200} = 0.4$ and $\frac{190}{480} = 0.4$, the sequence has a common ratio of 0.4. The next two terms in the sequence are $192(0.4) = 76.8$ and $76.8(0.4) = 30.72$.

Example 2 **Write an equation for the *n*th term of the geometric sequence 3.6, 10.8, 32.4, ...**

In this sequence $a_1 = 3.6$ and $r = 3$. Use the *n*th term formula to write an equation.

$a_n = a_1 \cdot r^{n-1}$ Formula for *n*th term
$= 3.6 \cdot 3^{n-1}$ $a_1 = 3.6, r = 3$

An equation for the *n*th term is $a_n = 3.6 \cdot 3^{n-1}$.

Exercises

Find a_n for each geometric sequence.

1. $a_1 = -10, r = 4, n = 2$ **−40**
2. $a_1 = -6, r = -\frac{1}{2}, n = 8$ $\frac{3}{64}$
3. $a_3 = 9, r = -3, n = 7$ **729**
4. $a_4 = 16, r = 2, n = 10$ **1024**
5. $a_4 = -54, r = -3, n = 6$ **−486**
6. $a_1 = 8, r = \frac{2}{3}, n = 5$ $\frac{128}{81}$
7. $a_1 = 7, r = 3, n = 5$ **567**
8. $a_1 = 46{,}875, r = \frac{1}{5}, n = 7$ **3**
9. $a_1 = -34{,}816, r = \frac{1}{2}, n = 6$ **−1088**

Write an equation for the *n*th term of each geometric sequence.

10. 500, 350, 245, ... $a_n = 500(0.7^{n-1})$
11. 8, 32, 128, ... $a_n = 8(4^{n-1})$
12. 11, −24.2, 53.24, ... $a_n = 11(-2.2)^{n-1}$
13. 9, 54, 324, 1944, ... $a_n = 9(6^{n-1})$
14. 17; 187; 2057; 22,627; ... $a_n = 17(11^{n-1})$
15. −53; −424; −3392; −27,136; ... $a_n = -53(8^{n-1})$

Lesson 11-3

Chapter 11 19 Glencoe Algebra 2

Practice
CRM p. 22 AL OL BL ELL

11-3 Practice
Geometric Sequences and Series

Find a_n for each geometric sequence.

1. $a_1 = 5, r = 3, n = 6$ **1215**
2. $a_1 = 20, r = -3, n = 6$ **−4860**
3. $a_1 = -4, r = -2, n = 10$ **2048**
4. a_8 for $-\frac{1}{250}, -\frac{1}{50}, -\frac{1}{10}, \ldots$ $-\frac{625}{2}$
5. a_{12} for 96, 48, 24, ... $\frac{3}{64}$
6. $a_1 = 8, r = \frac{1}{2}, n = 9$ $\frac{1}{32}$
7. $a_1 = -3125, r = -\frac{1}{5}, n = 9$ $-\frac{1}{125}$
8. $a_1 = 3, r = \frac{1}{10}, n = 8$ $\frac{3}{10{,}000{,}000}$

Write an equation for the *n*th term of each geometric sequence.

9. 1, 4, 16, ... $a_n = (4)^{n-1}$
10. −1, −5, −25, ... $a_n = -1(5)^{n-1}$
11. $1, \frac{1}{2}, \frac{1}{4}, \ldots$ $a_n = \left(\frac{1}{2}\right)^{n-1}$
12. −3, −6, −12, ... $a_n = -3(2)^{n-1}$

Find the sum of each geometric series.

13. $\sum_{k=3}^{10}(-4)(-2)^{k-1}$ **1360**
14. $\sum_{k=1}^{8}(-3)(3)^{k-1}$ **−9840**
15. $\sum_{k=2}^{32}9(-1)^{k-1}$ **9**

Find a_1 for each geometric series described.

16. $S_n = 1550, n = 3, r = 5$ **50**
17. $S_n = 1512, n = 6, r = 2$ **24**
18. $S_n = 3478.2, r = 2, a_n = 3481.6$ **3.4**
19. $S_n = 4860, r = 3, a_n = 3280.5$ **121.5**

20. **BIOLOGY** A culture initially contains 200 bacteria. If the number of bacteria doubles every 2 hours, how many bacteria will be in the culture at the end of 12 hours? **12,800**

21. **LIGHT** If each foot of water in a lake screens out 60% of the light above, what percent of the light passes through 5 feet of water? **1.024%**

22. **INVESTING** Raul invests \$1000 in a savings account that earns 5% interest compounded annually. How much money will he have in the account at the end of 5 years? **\$1276.28**

Chapter 11 22 Glencoe Algebra 2

Word Problem Practice
CRM p. 23 AL OL BL ELL

11-3 Word Problem Practice
Geometric Sequences and Series

1. **BASE 10** When the common ratio of a geometric series is 10, the sum is sometimes easier to computer because we use a decimal number system. For example, what is the sum of $1 + 10 + 10^2 + 10^3 + 10^4 + 10^5$? **111, 111**

2. **INVITATIONS** Amanda wants to host a party. She invites 3 friends and tells them to invite 3 of their friends. The 3 friends do invite 3 others and ask each to invite 3 more people. This invitation process goes on for 5 generations of invitations. Including herself, how many people can Amanda expect at her party? **364**

3. **MOORE'S LAW** Gordon Moore, co-founder of Intel, suggested that the number of transistors on a square inch of integrated circuit in a computer chip would double every 18 months. Assuming Moore's law is true, how many times as many transistors would you expect on a square inch of integrated circuit every 18 months for the next 6 years? **2, 4, 8, 16**

4. **TEACHING** A teacher teaches 8 students how to fold an origami model. Each of these students goes on to teach 8 students of their own how to fold the same model. If this teaching process goes on for *n* generations, how many people will know how to fold the origami model? 8^{n-1}

5. **BIOLOGY** Mitosis is a process of cell division that results in two identical daughter cells from a single parent cell. The table illustrates the number of cells produced after each of the first 5 cell divisions.

Division Number	0	1	2	3	4	5
Number of Cells	1	2	4	8	16	32

a. Do the entries in the "Number of Cells" row form a geometric series? If so, find *r*. **Yes; $r = 2$**

b. Write an expression to find the *n*th term of the sequence. $a_n = 2^{n-1}$

c. Find the number of cells after 100 divisions. 6.34×10^{29}

Lesson 11-3

Chapter 11 23 Glencoe Algebra 2

Additional Answer

72. Sample answer: A series is arithmetic if every pair of consecutive terms shares a common difference. A series is geometric if every pair of consecutive terms shares a common ratio. If the series displays both qualities, then it is both arithmetic and geometric. If the series displays neither quality, then it is neither geometric nor arithmetic.

Enrichment
CRM p. 24 OL BL

11-3 Enrichment

Half the Distance

Suppose you are 200 feet from a fixed point, *P*. Suppose that you are able to move to the halfway point in one minute, to the next halfway point one minute after that, and so on.

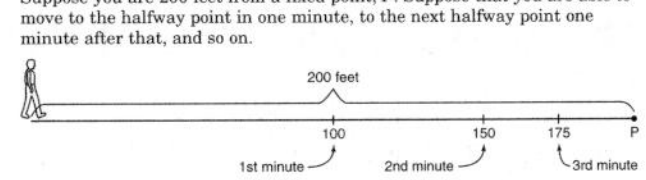

An interesting sequence results because according to the problem, you never actually reach the point *P*, although you do get arbitrarily close to it.

You can compute how long it will take to get within some specified small distance of the point. On a calculator, you enter the distance to be covered and then count the number of successive divisions by 2 necessary to get within the desired distance.

Example **How many minutes are needed to get within 0.1 foot of a point 200 feet away?**

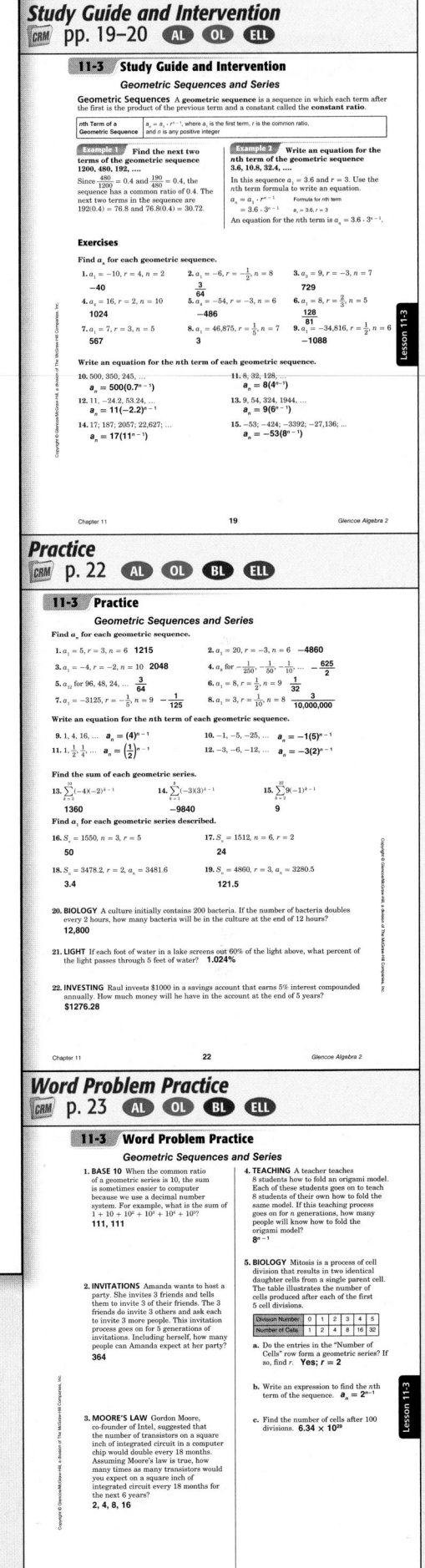

Lesson 11-3 Geometric Sequences and Series 701

4 ASSESS

Crystal Ball Ask students to describe how they think their knowledge of sums of geometric series might help them learn about sums of infinite geometric series in the next lesson.

Additional Answers

81. (3, 1), 5 units

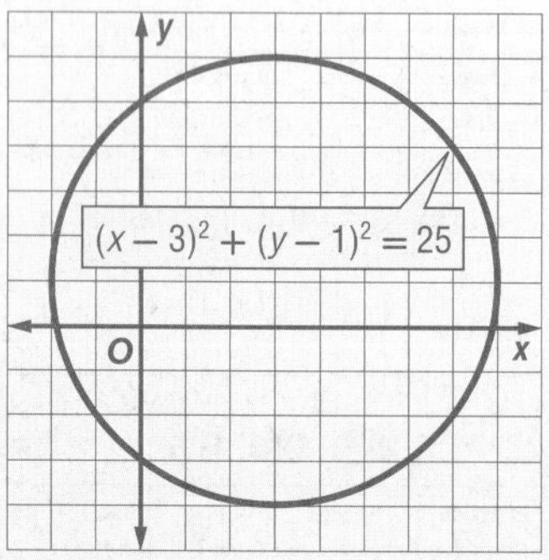

82. (−3, −7), 9 units

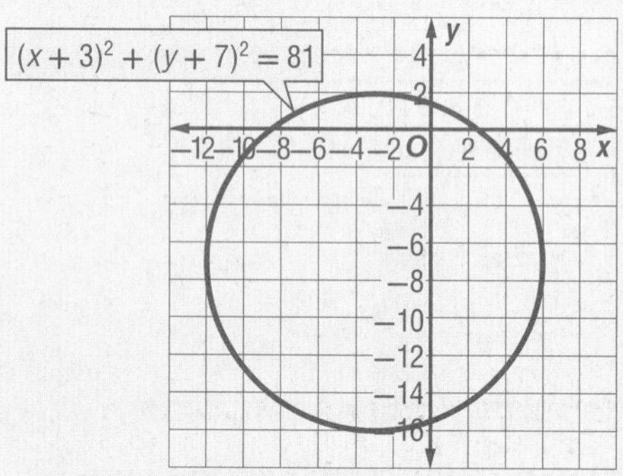

83. (3, −7), $5\sqrt{2}$ units

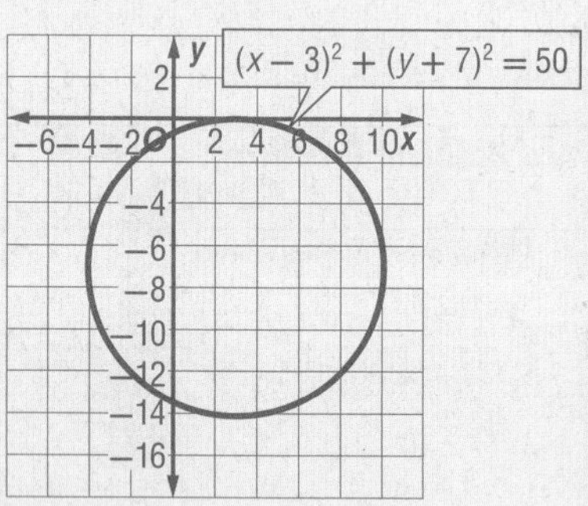

NGSSS PRACTICE 912.D.11.4, 912.A.8.5, 912.A.2.6

73. Which of the following is closest to $\sqrt[3]{7.32}$? **B**

A. 1.8
B. 1.9
C. 2.0
D. 2.1

74. The first term of a geometric series is 5, and the common ratio is −2. How many terms are in the series if its sum is $6828\frac{1}{3}$? **I**

F. 5
G. 9
H. 10
I. 12

75. THINK SOLVE EXPLAIN **SHORT RESPONSE** Danette has a savings account. She withdraws half of the contents every year. After 4 years, she has $2000 left. How much did she have in the savings account originally? **$32,000**

76. **ACT/SAT** The curve below could be part of the graph of which function? **C**

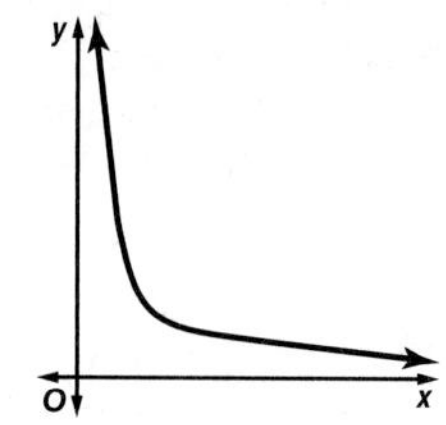

A. $y=\sqrt{x}$
B. $y=x^2-5x+4$
C. $xy=4$
D. $y=-x+20$

Spiral Review

77. **MONEY** Elena bought a high-definition LCD television at the electronics store. She paid $200 immediately and $75 each month for a year and a half. How much did Elena pay in total for the TV? (Lesson 11-2) **$1550**

Determine whether each sequence is *arithmetic*, *geometric*, or *neither*. Explain your reasoning. (Lesson 11-1) **78. Neither; there is no common difference or ratio.**

79. Arithmetic; the common difference is $\frac{1}{50}$.
80. Neither; there is no common difference or ratio.

78. $\frac{1}{10}, \frac{3}{5}, \frac{7}{20}, \frac{17}{20}, \ldots$

79. $-\frac{7}{25}, -\frac{13}{50}, -\frac{6}{25}, -\frac{11}{50}, \ldots$

80. $-\frac{22}{3}, -\frac{68}{9}, -\frac{208}{27}, -\frac{632}{81}, \ldots$

Find the center and radius of each circle. Then graph the circle. (Lesson 10-3) **81–83. See margin.**

81. $(x-3)^2+(y-1)^2=25$

82. $(x+3)^2+(y+7)^2=81$

83. $(x-3)^2+(y+7)^2=50$

84. Suppose y varies jointly as x and z. Find y when $x=9$ and $z=-5$, if $y=-90$ when $z=15$ and $x=-6$. (Lesson 9-5) **−45**

85. **SHOPPING** A certain store found that the number of customers who will attend a sale can be modeled by $N=125\sqrt[3]{100Pt}$, where N is the number of customers expected, P is the percent of the sale discount, and t is the number of hours the sale will last. Find the number of customers the store should expect for a sale that is 50% off and will last four hours. (Lesson 7-4) **731 customers**

Skills Review

Evaluate each expression if $a=-2$, $b=\frac{1}{3}$, and $c=-12$. (Lesson 1-1)

86. $\frac{3ab}{c}$ **$\frac{1}{6}$**

87. $\frac{a-c}{a+c}$ **$-\frac{5}{7}$**

88. $\frac{a^3-c}{b^2}$ **36**

89. $\frac{c+3}{ab}$ **$\frac{27}{2}$**

Differentiated Instruction OL BL

Extension Write the expression for the *n*th term of a geometric sequence, a_1r^{n-1}, on the board. Ask students to write an expression for the *next* term, with term number $(n+1)$, by replacing n with $(n+1)$ in the expression a_1r^{n-1}. Then have them show that $\frac{a_{n+1}}{a_n}$ is equal to the common ratio r. $\frac{a_1r^{(n+1)-1}}{a_1r^{n-1}}=\frac{r^n}{r^{n-1}}=r^{n-(n-1)}=r^1=r$

Area Under a Curve

The Morgans are renovating the outside of their house so that there is an archway above the front entrance. Mr. Morgan made a scale drawing of the archway in which each line on the grid paper represents one foot of the actual archway. Mrs. Morgan modeled the shape of the top with the quadratic equation $y = -0.25x^2 + 3x$.

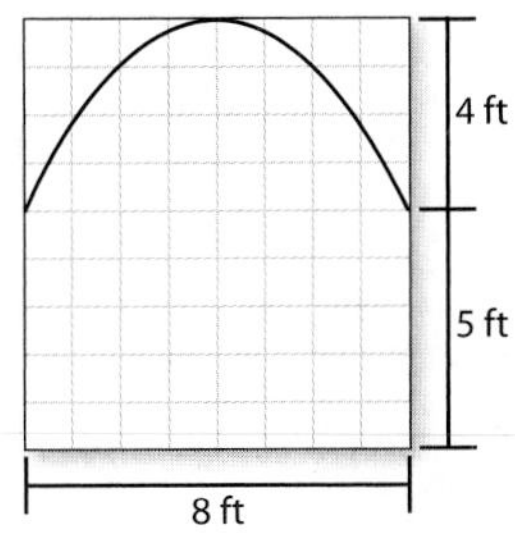

ACTIVITY

Find the area of the opening under the archway.

Method 1

Step 1 Make a table of values for $y = -0.25x^2 + 3x$. Then graph the equation.

x	0	1	2	3	4	5	6	7	8	9	10	11	12
y	0	2.75	5	6.75	8	8.75	9	8.75	8	6.75	5	2.75	0

Step 2 Divide the figure into regions.

To estimate the area inside the archway, you can divide the archway into rectangles as shown in blue.

Because the left and right sides of the archway are 5 feet high and $y = 5$ when $x = 2$ and when $x = 10$, the opening of the entrance extends from $x = 2$ to $x = 10$.

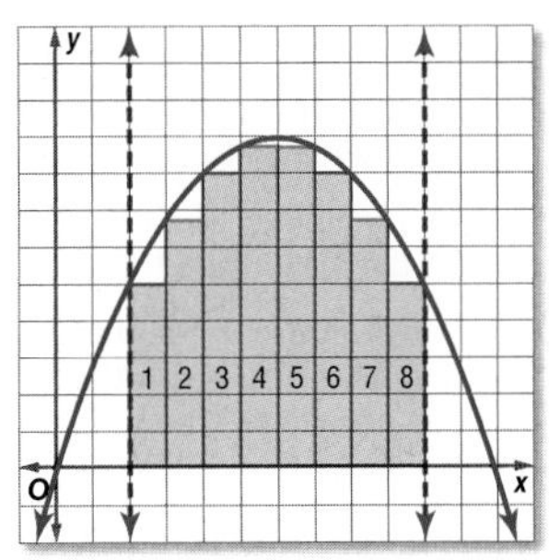

Step 3 Find the area of the regions.

Rectangle	1	2	3	4	5	6	7	8
Width (ft)	1	1	1	1	1	1	1	1
Height (ft)	5	6.75	8	8.75	8.75	8	6.75	5
Area (ft²)	5	6.75	8	8.75	8.75	8	6.75	5

The approximate area of the archway is the sum of the areas of the rectangles.

$5 + 6.75 + 8 + 8.75 + 8.75 + 8 + 6.75 + 5 = 57 \text{ ft}^2$

EXPLORE 11-4 Lesson Notes

1 FOCUS

Objective Approximate the area under a curve between a specified interval, using the sum of rectangular areas under the curve.

Materials for Each Group

- grid paper

Easy to Make Manipulatives

Teaching Algebra with Manipulatives
Template for:
- grid paper, p.1

Teaching Tip

Students should be familiar with finding the area of irregular figures. In a sense, this lesson is also about finding the area of an irregular figure. Each rectangle the students divide the area into should have the same width. You might suggest that students number the rectangles they draw under the curve 1–8.

2 TEACH

Working in Cooperative Groups

Pair students with different abilities. Have students work through the Steps for both Methods 1 and 2 of the Activity and then answer Exercises 1–4.

Ask:

- What does the width of each grid on your graph represent? 1 foot
- In Method 1, will your rectangles go beyond the graph of the quadratic equation? no
- How can you find the height of each rectangle? Use the values for *x* and *y* found in the table made in Step 1.

Practice Have students complete Exercises 5–7.

3 ASSESS

Formative Assessment

Use Exercise 5 to assess whether students can approximate the area under a curve for a specified interval.

From Concrete to Abstract

Ask students to repeat the Activity letting each grid represent 0.5 feet instead of 1 foot, thus using 16 rectangles instead of 8. Ask students if they think the results are closer to the actual area under the curve. Then ask how they might get even closer to the actual number of square feet found under the curve.

Additional Answer

4.

Rectangle	1	2	3	4
Width	2	2	2	2
Height	6.75	9	9	6.75
Area	13.5	18	18	13.5

Estimate of area: $2(13.5 + 18) = 63$ ft^2. The estimate will be greater than the actual area because there are 4 portions of the rectangles that lie outside the area under the curve and 2 portions of the area under the curve that are not in the rectangles. This estimate is probably more accurate than the other two estimates.

Method 2

Step 1 Draw a second graph of the equation and divide into regions. Divide the archway into rectangles as shown in blue.

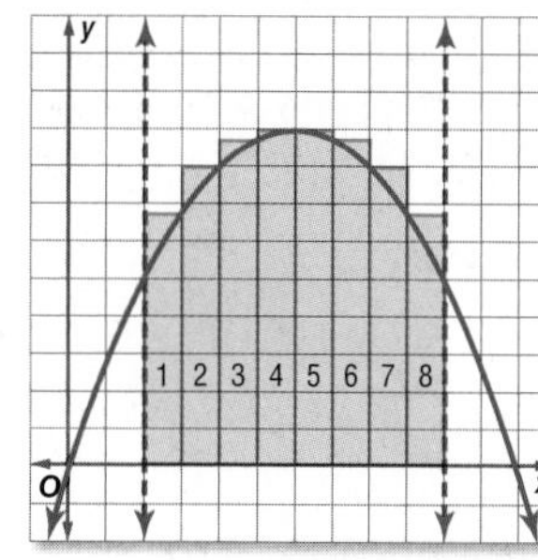

Step 2 Find the area of the regions.

Rectangle	1	2	3	4	5	6	7	8
Width (ft)	1	1	1	1	1	1	1	1
Height (ft)	6.75	8	8.75	9	9	8.75	8	6.75
Area (ft^2)	6.75	8	8.75	9	9	8.75	8	6.75

The approximate area of the archway is the sum of the areas of the rectangles.

$6.75 + 8 + 8.75 + 9 + 9 + 8.75 + 8 + 6.75 = 65$ ft^2

Both Method 1 and Method 2 illustrate how to approximate the area under a curve within a specified interval.

1. Less; sample answer: The rectangles are inside the curve leaving some area unaccounted for.
2. Greater; sample answer: The rectangles include area outside the curve.
3. Sample answer: Find the mean of the estimates: $(65 + 57) \div 2 = 61$.

Analyze the Results

1. Is the area of the regions calculated using Method 1 greater than or less than the actual area of the archway? Explain your reasoning.
2. Is the area of the regions calculated using Method 2 greater than or less than the actual area of the archway? Explain your reasoning.
3. Compare the area estimates for both methods. How could you find the best estimate for the area inside the archway? Explain your reasoning.
4. The diagram shows a third method for finding an estimate of the area of the archway. Is this estimate for the area greater than or less than the actual area? How does this estimate compare to the other two estimates of the area? See margin.

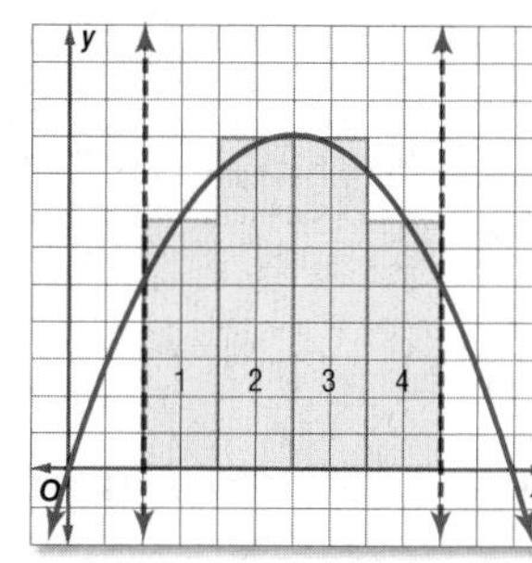

Exercises

Estimate the area described by any method. Make a table of values, draw graphs with rectangles, and make a table for the areas of the rectangles. Compare each estimate to the actual area. 5–7. See Chapter 11 Answer Appendix.

5. the area under the curve for $y = -x^2 + 4$, from $x = -2$ to $x = 2$, and above the x–axis
6. the area under the curve for $y = x^3$, from $x = 0$ to $x = 4$, and above the x–axis
7. the area under the curve for $y = x^2$, from $x = -3$ to $x = 3$, and above the x–axis

704 Chapter 11 Sequences and Series

11-4 Infinite Geometric Series

Why?

With their opponent on the 10-yard line, the defense is penalized half the distance to the goal, placing the ball on the 5-yard line. If they continue to be penalized in this way, where will the ball eventually be placed? Will they ever reach the goal line? How many total penalty yards will the defense have incurred? These questions can be answered by looking at infinite geometric series.

Then
You found sums of finite geometric series. (Lesson 11-4)

Now
- Find sums of infinite geometric series.
- Write repeating decimals as fractions.

NGSSS
MA.912.D.11.2 Use sigma notation to describe series. **MA.912.D.11.4** Find partial sums of arithmetic and geometric series, **and find sums of infinite convergent geometric series.** Use Sigma notation where applicable. *Also addresses MA.912.D.11.1.*

New Vocabulary
infinite geometric series
convergent series
divergent series
infinity

FL Math Online
glencoe.com

Infinite Geometric Series An **infinite geometric series** is a geometric series with an infinite number of terms. A series that has a sum is a **convergent series**, because its sum converges to a specific value. A series that does *not* have a sum is a **divergent series**.

When you evaluated the sum S_n of an infinite geometric series for the first n terms, you were finding the partial sum of the series. It is also possible to find the sum of an entire series. In the application above, it seems that the ball will eventually reach the goal line, and the defense will be penalized a total of 10 yards. This value is the actual sum of the infinite series $5 + 2.5 + 1.25 + \dots$. The graph of S_n for $1 \leq n \leq 10$ is shown on the left below. As n increases, S_n approaches 10.

Key Concept: Convergent and Divergent Series

	Convergent Series	Divergent Series
Words	The sum approaches a finite value.	The sum does not approach a finite value.
Ratio	$\lvert r \rvert < 1$	$\lvert r \rvert \geq 1$
Example	$5 + 2.5 + 1.25 + \dots$	$\frac{1}{16} + \frac{1}{8} + \frac{1}{4} + \dots$

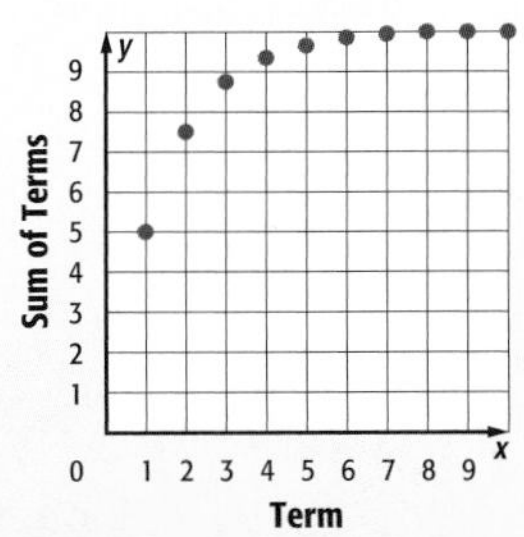

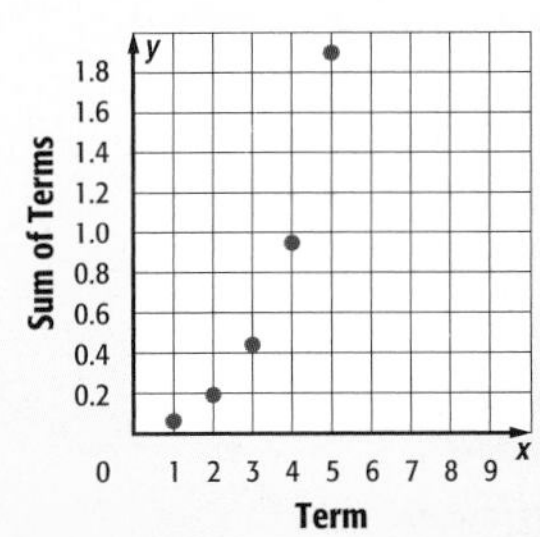

EXAMPLE 1 Convergent and Divergent Series

Determine whether each infinite geometric series is *convergent* or *divergent*.

a. $54 + 36 + 24 + \dots$

Find the value of r.

$r = \frac{36}{54}$ or $\frac{2}{3}$; since $-1 < \frac{2}{3} < 1$, the series is convergent.

11-4 Lesson Notes

1 FOCUS

Vertical Alignment

Before Lesson 11-4
Find sums of finite geometric series.

Lesson 11-4
Find sums of infinite geometric series.
Write repeating decimals as fractions.

After Lesson 11-4
Write recursive formulas for sequences.

2 TEACH

Scaffolding Questions

Have students read the *Why?* section of the lesson.

Ask:
- To write a geometric series to model this situation, what would the first term be? 5
- What would the second term be? 2.5
- Write the first four terms of the series. $5 + 2.5 + 1.25 + 0.625 + \dots$
- Why is this series called an infinite series? Sample answer: It goes on forever.

Lesson 11-4 Resources

Resource	Approaching-Level	On-Level	Beyond-Level	English Learners
Teacher Edition		• Differentiated Instruction, pp. 707, 711	• Differentiated Instruction, pp. 707, 711	
Chapter Resource Masters	• Study Guide and Intervention, pp. 26–27 • Skills Practice, p. 28 • Practice, p. 29 • Word Problem Practice, p. 30	• Study Guide and Intervention, pp. 26–27 • Skills Practice, p. 28 • Practice, p. 29 • Word Problem Practice, p. 30 • Enrichment, p. 31	• Practice, p. 29 • Word Problem Practice, p. 30 • Enrichment, p. 31	• Study Guide and Intervention, pp. 26–27 • Skills Practice, p. 28 • Practice, p. 29 • Word Problem Practice, p. 30
Transparencies	• 5-Minute Check Transparency 11-4	• 5-Minute Check Transparency 11-4	• 5-Minute Check Transparency 11-4	• 5-Minute Check Transparency 11-4
Other	• Study Notebook	• Study Notebook	• Study Notebook	• Study Notebook

Infinite Geometric Series

Example 1 shows how to determine whether an infinite geometric series is convergent or divergent. **Example 2** shows how to find the sum of an infinite geometric series, while **Example 3** does the same for a series given in sigma notation.

Formative Assessment

Use the Guided Practice exercises after each example to determine students' understanding of concepts.

Additional Examples

1 Determine whether each infinite geometric series is *convergent* or *divergent.*

a. $729 + 243 + 81 + \ldots$ convergent

b. $2 + 5 + 12.5 + \ldots$ divergent

2 Find the sum of each infinite geometric series, if it exists.

a. $-\frac{4}{3} + 4 - 12 + 36 - 108 + \ldots$ no sum

b. $3 - \frac{3}{2} + \frac{3}{4} - \frac{3}{8} + \ldots$ 2

Additional Examples also in Interactive Classroom PowerPoint® Presentations

IWB INTERACTIVE WHITEBOARD READY

Tips for New Teachers

Reasoning Make sure students can explain why $|r| < 1$ can also be written as $-1 < r < 1$. Graphing this inequality on a number line may help students understand what is meant by these two different mathematical notations.

StudyTip

Absolute Value Recall that $|r| < 1$ means $-1 < r < 1$.

b. $8 + 12 + 18 + \ldots$

$r = \frac{12}{8}$ or 1.5; since $1.5 > 1$, the series is divergent.

Guided Practice

1A. $2 + 3 + 4.5 + \ldots$ divergent

1B. $100 + 50 + 25 + \ldots$ convergent

Personal Tutor glencoe.com

When $|r| < 1$, the value of r^n will approach 0 as n increases. Therefore, the partial sums of the infinite geometric series will approach $\frac{a_1 - a_1(0)}{1 - r}$ or $\frac{a_1}{1 - r}$.

Key Concept **Sum of an Infinite Geometric Series**

The sum S of an infinite geometric series with $|r| < 1$ is given by

$$S = \frac{a_1}{1 - r}.$$

If $|r| \geq 1$, the series has no sum.

When an infinite geometric series is divergent, $|r| \geq 1$ and the series has no sum because the value of r^n will increase infinitely as n increases.

The table at the right shows the partial sums for the divergent series $4 + 16 + 64 + \ldots$. As n increases, S_n increases rapidly without limit.

n	S_n
5	1364
10	1,398,100
15	1,431,655,764

EXAMPLE 2 **Sum of an Infinite Series**

Find the sum of each infinite series, if it exists.

a. $\frac{2}{3} + \frac{6}{15} + \frac{18}{75} + \ldots$

Step 1 Find the value of r to determine if the sum exists.

$r = \frac{6}{15} \div \frac{2}{3}$ or $\frac{3}{5}$ — Divide consecutive terms.

Since $\left|\frac{3}{5}\right| < 1$, the sum exists.

Step 2 Use the formula to find the sum.

$S = \frac{a_1}{1 - r}$ — Sum formula

$= \frac{\frac{2}{3}}{1 - \frac{3}{5}}$ — $a_1 = \frac{2}{3}$ and $r = \frac{3}{5}$

$= \frac{2}{3} \div \frac{2}{5}$ or $\frac{5}{3}$ — Simplify.

b. $6 + 9 + 13.5 + 20.25 + \ldots$

$r = \frac{9}{6}$ or 1.5; since $|1.5| \geq 1$, the series diverges and the sum does not exist.

StudyTip

Convergence and Divergence A sequence converges when the absolute value of a term is smaller than the absolute value of the previous term. An infinite arithmetic series will always be divergent.

Guided Practice

2A. $4 - 2 + 1 - 0.5 + \ldots$ $\frac{8}{3}$

2B. $16 + 20 + 25 + \ldots$ No sum exists.

Personal Tutor glencoe.com

Focus on Mathematical Content

Sum of an Infinite Geometric Series Whether an infinite geometric series has a sum depends on the product of any term and the common ratio r. The absolute value of the product of any number and a fraction between −1 and 1 will always be less than the absolute value of the original number, so the series will have a sum if $-1 < r < 1$.

Sigma notation can be used to represent infinite series. If a sequence goes to **infinity**, it continues without end. The infinity symbol ∞ is placed above the $\sum$ to indicate that a series is infinite.

EXAMPLE 3 Infinite Series in Sigma Notation

Find $\sum_{k=1}^{\infty} 18\left(\frac{4}{5}\right)^{k-1}$.

$S = \frac{a_1}{1-r}$ **Sum formula**

$= \frac{18}{1-\frac{4}{5}}$ $a_1 = 18$ **and** $r = \frac{4}{5}$

$= \frac{18}{\frac{1}{5}}$ or 90 **Simplify.**

Guided Practice

3. Find $\sum_{k=1}^{\infty} 12\left(\frac{3}{4}\right)^{k-1}$. **48**

Personal Tutor glencoe.com

Repeating Decimals A repeating decimal is the sum of an infinite geometric series. For instance, $0.\overline{45} = 0.454545\ldots$ or $0.45 + 0.0045 + 0.000045 + \ldots$. The formula for the sum of an infinite series can be used to convert the decimal to a fraction.

Problem-Solving Tip

Choose the Best Method of Computation In many cases, it is possible to solve a problem in more than one way. Use the method with which you are most comfortable.

EXAMPLE 4 Write a Repeating Decimal as a Fraction

Write $0.\overline{63}$ as a fraction.

Method 1 Use the sum of an infinite series.

$0.\overline{63} = 0.63 + 0.0063 + \ldots$

$= \frac{63}{100} + \frac{63}{10{,}000} + \ldots$

$S = \frac{a_1}{1-r}$ **Sum formula**

$= \frac{\frac{63}{100}}{1-\frac{1}{100}}$ $a_1 = \frac{63}{100}$ **and** $r = \frac{1}{100}$

$= \frac{63}{99}$ or $\frac{7}{11}$ **Simplify.**

Method 2 Use algebraic properties.

$x = 0.\overline{63}$	**Let $x = 0.\overline{63}$.**
$x = 0.636363\ldots$	**Write as a repeating decimal.**
$100x = 63.636363\ldots$	**Multiply each side by 100.**
$99x = 63$	**Subtract x from $100x$ and $0.\overline{63}$ from $63.\overline{63}$.**
$x = \frac{63}{99}$ or $\frac{7}{11}$	**Divide each side by 99.**

Study Tip

Repeating Decimals Every repeating decimal is a rational number and can be written as a fraction.

Guided Practice

4. Write $0.\overline{21}$ as a fraction. $\frac{7}{33}$

Personal Tutor glencoe.com

Additional Example

3 Find $\sum_{k=1}^{\infty} 5\left(\frac{1}{2}\right)^{k-1}$. 10

Watch Out!

Preventing Errors Ask students to write a few terms of the series in Example 3 to make sure they know how to read the notation.

Repeating Decimals

Example 4 shows how to write a repeating decimal as a fraction.

Additional Example

4 Write $0.\overline{25}$ as a fraction. $\frac{25}{99}$

TEACH with TECH

INSTANT MESSAGING Have students work in pairs. The first student will send a message including a repeating decimal. The second student must then write the decimal as a fraction. Have students switch roles and repeat.

Differentiated Instruction OL BL

Logical Learners Have students research and read about the famous mathematical puzzle called Zeno's paradox. Have them discuss this story of the tortoise's race in terms of the content of this lesson.

3 PRACTICE

Formative Assessment

Use Exercises 1–15 to check for understanding.

Use the chart on the bottom of this page to customize assignments for your students.

Check Your Understanding

Example 1 p. 705

Determine whether each infinite geometric series is *convergent* or *divergent*.

1. $16 - 8 + 4 - \ldots$ convergent

2. $32 - 48 + 72 - \ldots$ divergent

3. $0.5 + 0.7 + 0.98 + \ldots$ divergent

4. $1 + 1 + 1 + \ldots$ divergent

Example 2 p. 706

Find the sum of each infinite series, if it exists.

5. $440 + 220 + 110 + \ldots$ 880

6. $520 + 130 + 32.5 + \ldots$ $693\frac{1}{3}$

7. $\frac{1}{4} + \frac{3}{8} + \frac{9}{16} + \ldots$ No sum exists.

8. $\frac{32}{9} + \frac{16}{3} + 8 + \ldots$ No sum exists.

9. MEDICINE A certain drug has a half-life of 8 hours after it is administered to a patient. What percent of the drug is still in the patient's system after 24 hours? 12.5%

Example 3 p. 707

Find the sum of each infinite series, if it exists.

10. $\sum_{k=1}^{\infty} 5 \cdot 4^{k-1}$ No sum exists.

11. $\sum_{k=1}^{\infty} (-2) \cdot (0.5)^{k-1}$ -4

12. $\sum_{k=1}^{\infty} 3 \cdot \left(\frac{4}{5}\right)^{k-1}$ 15

13. $\sum_{k=1}^{\infty} \frac{1}{2} \cdot \left(\frac{3}{4}\right)^{k-1}$ 2

Example 4 p. 707

Write each repeating decimal as a fraction.

14. $0.\overline{35}$ $\frac{35}{99}$

15. $0.\overline{642}$ $\frac{214}{333}$

Practice and Problem Solving

● = **Step-by-Step Solutions** begin on page R20.
Extra Practice begins on page 947.

Example 1 p. 705

Determine whether each infinite geometric series is *convergent* or *divergent*.

16. $21 + 63 + 189 + \ldots$ divergent

17. $480 + 360 + 270 + \ldots$ convergent

18. $\frac{3}{4} + \frac{9}{8} + \frac{27}{16} + \ldots$ divergent

19. $\frac{5}{6} + \frac{10}{9} + \frac{40}{27} + \ldots$ divergent

20. $0.1 + 0.01 + 0.001 + \ldots$ convergent

21. $0.008 + 0.08 + 0.8 + \ldots$ divergent

Example 2 p. 706

Find the sum of each infinite series, if it exists.

22. $18 + 21.6 + 25.92 + \ldots$ No sum exists.

23. $-3 - 4.2 - 5.88 - \ldots$ No sum exists.

24. $\frac{1}{2} + \frac{1}{6} + \frac{1}{18} + \ldots$ $\frac{3}{4}$

25 $\frac{12}{5} + \frac{6}{5} + \frac{3}{5} + \ldots$ $\frac{24}{5}$

26. $21 + 14 + \frac{28}{3} + \ldots$ 63

27. $32 + 40 + 50 + \ldots$ No sum exists.

28. SWINGS If Kerry does not push any harder after his initial swing, the distance traveled per swing will decrease by 10% with each swing. If his initial swing traveled 6 feet, find the total distance traveled when he comes to rest. 60 ft

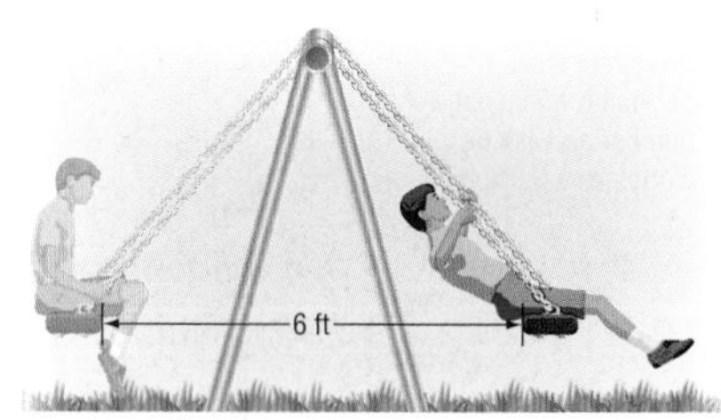

Differentiated Homework Options

Level	Assignment	Two-Day Option	
AL Basic	16–40, 60–61, 63–76	17–39 odd, 68–71	16–40 even, 60–61, 63–67, 72–76
OL Core	17–39 odd, 41–43, 45–49 odd, 50–61, 63–76	16–40, 68–71	41–61, 63–67, 72–76
BL Advanced	41–73, (optional: 74–76)		

Example 3 p. 707

Find the sum of each infinite series, if it exists. **29, 30, 32. No sum exists.**

29. $\sum_{k=1}^{\infty} \frac{4}{3} \cdot \left(\frac{5}{4}\right)^{k-1}$

30. $\sum_{k=1}^{\infty} \frac{1}{4} \cdot 3^{k-1}$

31. $\sum_{k=1}^{\infty} \frac{5}{3} \cdot \left(\frac{3}{7}\right)^{k-1}$ **$\frac{35}{12}$**

32. $\sum_{k=1}^{\infty} \frac{2}{3} \cdot \left(\frac{4}{3}\right)^{k-1}$

33. $\sum_{k=1}^{\infty} \frac{8}{3} \cdot \left(\frac{5}{6}\right)^{k-1}$ **16**

34. $\sum_{k=1}^{\infty} \frac{1}{8} \cdot \left(\frac{1}{12}\right)^{k-1}$ **$\frac{3}{22}$**

Example 4 p. 707

Write each repeating decimal as a fraction.

35. $0.\overline{321}$ **$\frac{53}{165}$**

36. $0.1\overline{45}$ **$\frac{8}{55}$**

37. $2.\overline{18}$ **$\frac{24}{11}$**

38. $4.\overline{96}$ **$\frac{164}{33}$**

39. $0.12\overline{14}$ **$\frac{601}{4950}$**

40. $0.43\overline{36}$ **$\frac{477}{1100}$**

B

41. **FANS** A fan is running at 10 revolutions per second. After it is turned off, its speed decreases at a rate of 75% per second. Determine the number of revolutions completed by the fan after it is turned off. **$\frac{40}{3}$**

42. **FINANCIAL LITERACY** Kamiko deposited $5000 into an account at the beginning of the year. The account earns 8% interest each year.

 a. How much money will be in the account after 20 years? (*Hint*: Let $5000(1 + 0.08)^1$ represent the end of the first year.) **$23,304.79**

 b. Is this series *convergent* or *divergent*? Explain. **It is a diverging series. The ratio is 1.08, which is greater than 1.**

43. **RECHARGEABLE BATTERIES** A certain rechargeable battery is advertised to recharge back to 99.9% of its previous capacity with every charge. If its initial capacity is 8 hours of life, how many total hours should the battery last? **8000 hrs**

Real-World Link

Batteries have been in use in the United States for over 100 years, and they are in demand like never before. As a result, about 3 billion single-use batteries are disposed of each year. One rechargeable battery can replace up to 100 single-use alkaline batteries.

Find the sum of each infinite series, if it exists. **47, 48. No sum exists.**

44. $\frac{7}{5} + \frac{21}{20} + \frac{63}{80} + \ldots$ **$\frac{28}{5}$**

45. $\frac{15}{4} + \frac{5}{2} + \frac{5}{3} + \ldots$ **$\frac{45}{4}$**

46. $-\frac{16}{9} + \frac{4}{3} - 1 + \ldots$ **$-\frac{64}{63}$**

47. $\frac{15}{8} + \frac{5}{2} + \frac{10}{3} + \ldots$

48. $\frac{21}{16} + \frac{7}{4} + \frac{7}{3} + \ldots$

49. $-\frac{18}{7} + \frac{12}{7} - \frac{8}{7} + \ldots$ **$-\frac{54}{35}$**

50. **MULTIPLE REPRESENTATIONS** In this problem, you will use a square of paper that is at least 8 inches on a side.

 a. **CONCRETE** Let the square be one unit. Cut away one half of the square. Call this piece Term 1. Next, cut away one half of the remaining sheet of paper. Call this piece Term 2. Continue cutting the remaining paper in half and labeling the pieces with a term number as long as possible. List the fractions represented by the pieces. **$\frac{1}{2}, \frac{1}{4}, \frac{1}{8}, \frac{1}{16}, \ldots$**

 b. **NUMERICAL** If you could cut the squares indefinitely, you would have an infinite series. Find the sum of the series. **1**

 c. **VERBAL** How does the sum of the series relate to the original square of paper?

50c. The original square has area 1 unit and the area of all the pieces cannot exceed 1.

51. **PHYSICS** In a physics experiment, a steel ball on a flat track is accelerated, and then allowed to roll freely. After the first minute, the ball has rolled 120 feet. Each minute the ball travels only 40% as far as it did during the preceding minute. How far does the ball travel? **200 ft**

C

52. **PENDULUMS** A pendulum travels 12 centimeters on its first swing and 95% of that distance on each swing thereafter. Find the total distance traveled by the pendulum when it comes to rest. **240 cm**

53. **TOYS** If a rubber ball can bounce back to 95% of its original height, what is the total vertical distance that it will travel if it is dropped from an elevation of 30 feet? **1170 ft**

54. **CARS** During a maintenance inspection, a tire is removed from a car and spun on a diagnostic machine. When the machine is turned off, the spinning tire completes 20 revolutions the first second and 98% of the revolutions each additional second. How many revolutions does the tire complete before it stops spinning? **1000 revolutions**

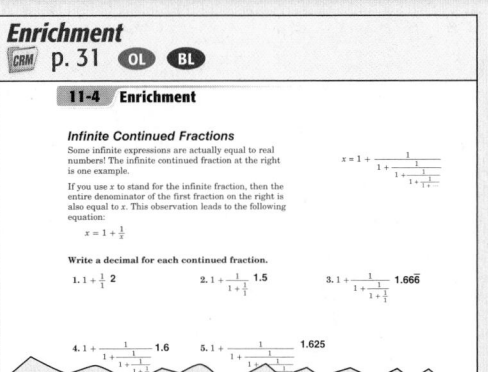

Study Guide and Intervention

CRM pp. 26–27 AL OL ELL

11-4 Study Guide and Intervention

Infinite Geometric Series

Infinite Geometric Series A geometric series that does not end is called an **infinite geometric** series. Some infinite geometric series have sums, but others do not because the **partial sums** increase without approaching a limiting value.

Sum of an Infinite Geometric Series	$S = \frac{a_1}{1-r}$ for $-1 < r < 1$. If $\lvert r \rvert \geq 1$, the infinite geometric series does not have a sum.

Example Find the sum of each infinite series, if it exists.

a. $75 + 15 + 3 + \ldots$

First, find the value of r to determine if the sum exists. $a_1 = 75$ and $a_2 = 15$, so $r = \frac{15}{75}$ or $\frac{1}{5}$. Since $\left|\frac{1}{5}\right| < 1$, the sum exists. Now use the formula for the sum of an infinite geometric series.

$S = \frac{a_1}{1-r}$ Sum formula

$= \frac{75}{1-\frac{1}{5}}$ $a_1 = 75, r = \frac{1}{5}$

$= \frac{75}{\frac{4}{5}}$ or 93.75 Simplify.

The sum of the series is 93.75.

b. $\sum_{n=1}^{\infty} 48\left(-\frac{1}{3}\right)^{n-1}$

In this infinite geometric series, $a_1 = 48$ and $r = -\frac{1}{3}$.

$S = \frac{a_1}{1-r}$ Sum formula

$= \frac{48}{1-\left(-\frac{1}{3}\right)}$ $a_1 = 48, r = -\frac{1}{3}$

$= \frac{48}{\frac{4}{3}}$ or 36 Simplify.

Thus $\sum_{n=1}^{\infty} 48\left(-\frac{1}{3}\right)^{n-1} = 36$.

Exercises

Find the sum of each infinite series, if it exists.

1. $a_1 = -7, r = \frac{5}{8}$ **$-18\frac{2}{3}$**
2. $1 + \frac{5}{4} + \frac{25}{16} + \ldots$ **No sum exists.**
3. $a_1 = 4, r = \frac{1}{2}$ **8**
4. $\frac{2}{9} + \frac{5}{27} + \frac{25}{162} + \ldots$ **$1\frac{1}{3}$**
5. $15 + 10 + 6\frac{2}{3} + \ldots$ **45**
6. $18 - 9 + 4\frac{1}{2} - 2\frac{1}{4} + \ldots$ **12**
7. $\frac{1}{10} + \frac{1}{20} + \frac{1}{40} + \ldots$ **$\frac{1}{5}$**
8. $1000 + 800 + 640 + \ldots$ **5000**
9. $6 - 12 + 24 - 48 + \ldots$ **No sum exists.**
10. $\sum_{n=1}^{\infty} 50\left(\frac{4}{5}\right)^{n-1}$ **250**
11. $\sum_{k=1}^{\infty} 22\left(-\frac{1}{2}\right)^{k-1}$ **$14\frac{2}{3}$**
12. $\sum_{s=1}^{\infty} 24\left(\frac{7}{12}\right)^{s-1}$ **$57\frac{3}{5}$**

Chapter 11 26 Glencoe Algebra 2

Practice

CRM p. 29 AL OL BL ELL

11-4 Practice

Infinite Geometric Series

Find the sum of each infinite series, if it exists.

1. $a_1 = 35, r = \frac{2}{7}$ **49**
2. $a_1 = 26, r = \frac{1}{2}$ **52**
3. $a_1 = 98, r = -\frac{3}{4}$ **56**
4. $a_1 = 42, r = \frac{6}{5}$ **No sum exists.**
5. $a_1 = 112, r = -\frac{3}{5}$ **70**
6. $a_1 = 500, r = \frac{1}{5}$ **625**
7. $a_1 = 135, r = -\frac{1}{2}$ **90**
8. $18 - 6 + 2 - \ldots$ **$\frac{27}{2}$**
9. $2 + 6 + 18 + \ldots$ **No sum exists.**
10. $6 + 4 + \frac{8}{3} + \ldots$ **18**
11. $\frac{4}{25} + \frac{2}{5} + 1 + \ldots$ **No sum exists.**
12. $10 + 1 + 0.1 + \ldots$ **$\frac{100}{9}$**
13. $100 + 20 + 4 + \ldots$ **125**
14. $-270 + 135 - 67.5 + \ldots$ **−180**
15. $0.5 + 0.25 + 0.125 + \ldots$ **1**
16. $\frac{7}{10} + \frac{7}{100} + \frac{7}{1000} + \ldots$ **$\frac{7}{9}$**
17. $0.8 + 0.08 + 0.008 + \ldots$ **$\frac{8}{9}$**
18. $\frac{1}{12} - \frac{1}{6} + \frac{1}{3} - \ldots$ **No sum exists.**
19. $3 + \frac{9}{7} + \frac{27}{49} + \ldots$ **$\frac{21}{4}$**
20. $0.3 - 0.003 + 0.00003 - \ldots$ **$\frac{30}{101}$**
21. $0.06 + 0.006 + 0.0006 + \ldots$ **$\frac{1}{15}$**
22. $\frac{2}{3} - 2 + 6 - \ldots$ **No sum exists.**
23. $\sum_{n=1}^{\infty} 3\left(\frac{1}{4}\right)^{n-1}$ **4**
24. $\sum_{n=1}^{\infty} \frac{2}{3}\left(-\frac{3}{4}\right)^{n-1}$ **$\frac{8}{21}$**
25. $\sum_{n=1}^{\infty} 18\left(\frac{2}{3}\right)^{n-1}$ **54**
26. $\sum_{n=1}^{\infty} 5(-0.1)^{n-1}$ **$\frac{50}{11}$**

Write each repeating decimal as a fraction.

27. $0.\overline{6}$ **$\frac{2}{3}$**
28. $0.\overline{09}$ **$\frac{1}{11}$**
29. $0.\overline{43}$ **$\frac{43}{99}$**
30. $0.\overline{27}$ **$\frac{3}{11}$**
31. $0.\overline{243}$ **$\frac{9}{37}$**
32. $0.8\overline{4}$ **$\frac{28}{33}$**
33. $0.\overline{990}$ **$\frac{110}{111}$**
34. $0.\overline{150}$ **$\frac{50}{333}$**

35. **PENDULUMS** On its first swing, a pendulum travels 8 feet. On each successive swing, the pendulum travels $\frac{4}{5}$ the distance of its previous swing. What is the total distance traveled by the pendulum when it stops swinging? **40 ft**

36. **ELASTICITY** A ball dropped from a height of 10 feet bounces back $\frac{9}{10}$ of that distance. With each successive bounce, the ball continues to reach $\frac{9}{10}$ of its previous height. What is the total vertical distance (both up and down) traveled by the ball when it stops bouncing? (*Hint*: Add the total distance the ball falls to the total distance it rises.) **190 ft**

Lesson 11-4

Chapter 11 29 Glencoe Algebra 2

Word Problem Practice

CRM p. 30 AL OL BL ELL

11-4 Word Problem Practice

Infinite Geometric Series

1. **PARADOX** If the formula for the sum of a geometric series is applied to the series whose first term is 1 and common ratio is 2, the result is the equation $-1 = 1 + 2 + 2^2 + 2^3 + \ldots$. Is this equality really true? Explain.
No, it is not true. An infinite geometric series must have $r < 1$ to have a sum.

2. **BONDS** British consols are government bonds that pay out interest annually forever. If an investor receives $2 interest on British consols this year and the rate remains the same, what is the total of all interest the investor will eventually receive if the bonds are held indefinitely?
infinite

3. **BASES** The infinite repeating decimal 0.999... is equal to 1. This can be shown by using the sum of a geometric series with common ratio $\frac{1}{10}$ and first term $\frac{9}{10}$. In a similar vein, compute the sum of the infinite geometric series $\frac{b-1}{b} + \frac{b-1}{b^2} + \frac{b-1}{b^3} + \cdots$, where b is a positive integer greater than 1. How is this sum related to the fact that $0.999\ldots = 1$?
1; It is similar to 0.999... in base b.

4. **CLIMBING** A robot is designed to climb a wall each time a button is pressed. The first time the button is pressed, it climbs 10 feet. Each time after, the robot climbs only 75% of what it climbed the last time. What is the smallest upper limit on how high the robot can climb?
40 ft

5. **INSTALLMENTS** Jade lends Jack a 100-pound chunk of pure gold for one year. After one year, she wants to start getting the gold back. One year later, Jack begins returning the gold, by giving Jade 1 pound of gold. The next day, Jack gives her 0.99 pounds of gold. The next day, Jack gives her $(0.99)^2$ or 0.9801 pounds of gold. Each successive day, Jack gives 0.99 times as much gold as the previous day.

 a. How much gold does Jade get back on the nth day that Jack begins returning the gold?
 $(0.99)^{n-1}$ lb

 b. How much gold has Jade received after 10 days? 100 days? Infinitely many days? Round your answers to the nearest hundredth of a pound.
 9.56 lb after 10 days; 63.40 lb after 100 days; about 100 lb after infinitely many days

 c. Will Jade have all her gold back at any specific date in the future? Explain.
 No. At the rate Jack is returning there will always be a small amount of the gold that will never be returned.

Chapter 11 30 Glencoe Algebra 2

Multiple Representations In Exercise 50, students use a model, numerical analysis, and verbal description to represent an infinite series and its sum.

Enrichment

CRM p. 31 OL BL

11-4 Enrichment

Infinite Continued Fractions

Some infinite expressions are actually equal to real numbers! The infinite continued fraction at the right is one example.

$$x = 1 + \cfrac{1}{1 + \cfrac{1}{1 + \cfrac{1}{1 + \cfrac{1}{1 + \cdots}}}}$$

If you use x to stand for the infinite fraction, then the entire denominator of the first fraction on the right is also equal to x. This observation leads to the following equation:

$x = 1 + \frac{1}{x}$

Write a decimal for each continued fraction.

1. $1 + \frac{1}{1}$ **2**
2. $1 + \cfrac{1}{1 + \frac{1}{1}}$ **1.5**
3. $1 + \cfrac{1}{1 + \cfrac{1}{1 + \frac{1}{1}}}$ **$1.6\overline{6}$**
4. $1 + \cfrac{1}{1 + \cfrac{1}{1 + \cfrac{1}{1 + \frac{1}{1}}}}$ **1.6**
5. $1 + \cfrac{1}{1 + \cfrac{1}{1 + \cdots}}$ **1.625**

Watch Out!

Error Analysis For Exercise 60, remind students that the value of r determines whether the infinite geometric series is convergent or divergent.

Exercise Alert

Formula For Exercise 71, students may need to be reminded that the formula for the volume of a sphere is $V = \frac{4}{3}\pi r^3$.

Additional Answers

60. Sample answer: Austin; the common ratio of the series $r = -1$, so the absolute value of $r = 1$ and the series diverges.

61. Sample answer: The sum of a geometric series is $S_n = \frac{a_1 - a_1 r^n}{1 - r}$. For an infinite series with $|r| < 1$, $r^n \to 0$ as $n \to \infty$. Thus, $S = \frac{a_1 - a_1(0)}{1 - r}$ or $\frac{a_1}{1 - r}$.

67. An arithmetic series has a common difference, so each term will eventually become more positive or more negative, but never approach 0. With the terms not approaching 0, the sum will never reach a limit and the series cannot converge.

Real-World Link

In 2001, the federal government enacted a tax cut that sent checks ranging from \$300 to \$600 to every taxpayer in the United States.

Source: *The Economist*

62. $-\frac{1}{3} < b < \frac{1}{3}$

63. Sample answer: An infinite geometric series has a sum when the common ratio is less than 1. When this occurs, the terms will approach 0 as n approaches infinity. With the future terms almost 0, the sum of the series will approach a limit. When the common ratio is 1 or greater, the terms will keep increasing and approach infinity as n approaches infinity and the sum of the series will have no limit.

64. Sample answer: Sometimes; the statement is true for all *infinite* geometric series.

65. Sample answer: $3 + 2 + \frac{4}{3} + \ldots$

66. $\sum_{k=1}^{\infty} 3(-2)^{k-1}$; $\sum_{k=0}^{\infty} 3(-2)^k$

55. ECONOMICS A state government decides to stimulate its economy by giving \$500 to every adult. The government assumes that everyone who receives the money will spend 80% on consumer goods and that the producers of these goods will in turn spend 80% on consumer goods. How much money is generated for the economy for every \$500 that the government provides? **\$2500**

56. SCIENCE MUSEUM An exhibit at a science museum offers visitors the opportunity to experiment with the motion of an object on a spring. One visitor pulls the object down and lets it go. The object travels 1.2 feet upward before heading back the other way. Each time the object changes direction, it decreases its distance by 20% when compared to the previous direction. Find the total distance traveled by the object. **6 ft**

Match each graph with its corresponding description.

57. b

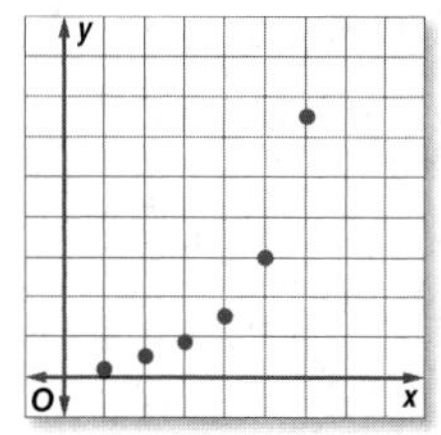

58. d

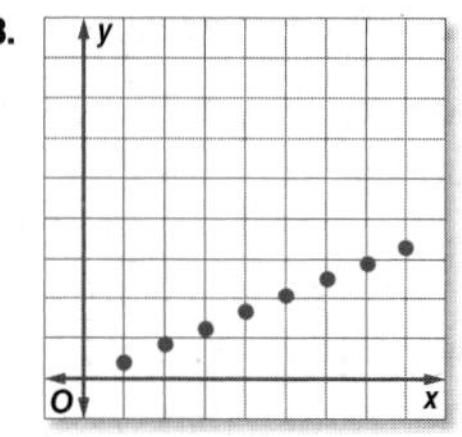

59. a

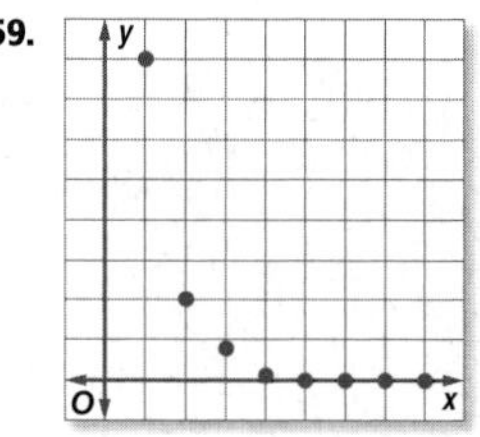

a. converging geometric series
b. diverging geometric series
c. converging arithmetic series
d. diverging arithmetic series

H.O.T. Problems

Use **H**igher-**O**rder **T**hinking Skills

60. ERROR ANALYSIS Emmitt and Austin are asked to find the sum of $1 - 1 + 1 - \ldots$. Is either of them correct? Explain your reasoning. **See margin.**

Emmitt	Austin
The sum is 0 because the sum of each pair of terms in the sequence is 0.	There is no sum because $\lvert r \rvert \geq 1$, and the series diverges.

61. PROOF Derive the formula for the sum of an infinite geometric series. **See margin.**

62. CHALLENGE For what values of b does $3 + 9b + 27b^2 + 81b^3 + \ldots$ have a sum?

63. REASONING When does an infinite geometric series have a sum, and when does it not have a sum? Explain your reasoning.

64. REASONING Determine whether the following statement is *sometimes*, *always*, or *never* true. Explain your reasoning.

If the absolute value of a term of any geometric series is greater than the absolute value of the previous term, then the series is divergent.

65. OPEN ENDED Write an infinite series with a sum that converges to 9.

66. OPEN ENDED Write $3 - 6 + 12 - \ldots$ using sigma notation in two different ways.

67. WRITING IN MATH Explain why an arithmetic series is always divergent. **See margin.**

710 Chapter 11 Sequences and Series

NGSSS PRACTICE 912.D.11.4, 912.A.4.1, 912.A.8.2, 912.A.2.12

68. ACT/SAT What is the sum of an infinite geometric series with a first term of 27 and a common ratio of $\frac{2}{3}$? **A**

A. 81 **C.** 34

B. 65 **D.** 18

69. Adelina, Michelle, Masao, and Brandon each simplified the same expression at the board. Each student's work is shown below. The teacher said that while two of them had a correct answer, only one of them had arrived at the correct conclusion using correct steps. **H**

Adelina's work

$$x^2x^{-5} = \frac{x^2}{x^{-5}} = x^7, x \neq 0$$

Masao's work

$$x^2x^{-5} = \frac{x^2}{x^5} = \frac{1}{x^3}, x \neq 0$$

Michelle's work

$$x^2x^{-5} = \frac{x^2}{x^{-5}} = x^{-3}, x \neq 0$$

Brandon's work

$$x^2x^{-5} = \frac{x^2}{x^5} = x^3, x \neq 0$$

Which is a completely accurate simplification?

F. Adelina's work **H.** Masao's work

G. Michelle's work **I.** Brandon's work

70. GRIDDED RESPONSE Evaluate $\log_8 60$ to the nearest hundredth. **1.97**

71. GEOMETRY The radius of a large sphere was multiplied by a factor of $\frac{1}{3}$ to produce a smaller sphere. **C**

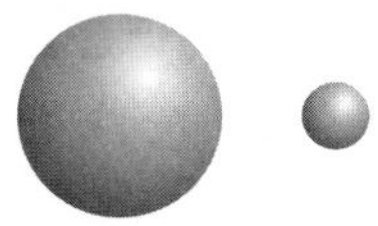

Radius = r Radius = $\frac{1}{3}r$

How does the volume of the smaller sphere compare to the volume of the larger sphere?

A. The volume of the smaller sphere is $\frac{1}{9}$ as large.

B. The volume of the smaller sphere is $\frac{1}{\pi^3}$ as large.

C. The volume of the smaller sphere is $\frac{1}{27}$ as large.

D. The volume of the smaller sphere is $\frac{1}{3}$ as large.

Spiral Review

72. GAMES An audition is held for a TV game show. At the end of each round, one half of the prospective contestants are eliminated from the competition. On a particular day, 524 contestants begin the audition. (Lesson 11-3)

a. Write an equation for finding the number of contestants who are left after n rounds. $a_n = 524\left(\frac{1}{2}\right)^n$

b. Using this method, will the number of contestants who are to be eliminated always be a whole number? Explain. **No; at the beginning of the third round there will be 131 contestants and one-half of that is 65.5.**

73. CLUBS A quilting club consists of 9 members. Every week, each member must bring one completed quilt square. (Lesson 11-2)

a. Find the first eight terms of the sequence that describes the total number of squares that have been made after each meeting. **9, 18, 27, 36, 45, 54, 63, 72**

b. One particular quilt measures 72 inches by 84 inches and is being designed with 4-inch squares. After how many meetings will the quilt be complete? **42 meetings**

Skills Review

Find each function value. (Lesson 2-1)

74. $f(x) = 5x - 9, f(6)$ **21**

75. $g(x) = x^2 - x, g(4)$ **12**

76. $h(x) = x^2 - 2x - 1, h(3)$ **2**

Differentiated Instruction OL BL

Extension Have students work in pairs taking turns writing a repeating decimal and challenging their partners to express them as fractions.

4 ASSESS

Ticket Out the Door Make several copies of each of five different infinite geometric series–some that have sums and some that do not. Give a copy of one series to each student. As students leave the room, ask them to tell whether the series are convergent or divergent.

Formative Assessment

Check for student understanding of Lessons 11-3 and 11-4.

CRM Quiz 2, p. 53

Lesson 11-4 Infinite Geometric Series 711

1 FOCUS

Objective Use a graphing calculator to investigate limits of sequences.

Materials

- TI-83/84 Plus or other graphing calculator

Teaching Tip

Stat plots for sequences are graphed in the same way as any other stat plot. It is essential that lists L1 and L2 contain the same number of elements.

2 TEACH

Working in Cooperative Groups

Have students work in pairs so they can help each other correct keystroke errors. Then have the students complete Steps 1–2 of the Activity, and Exercises 1–2.

- If students are having trouble generating the sequence list, make sure they place the cursor on the *name* of the list, rather than on the first element in the list.
- Students may need to be reminded about how to read scientific notation as displayed on a calculator (e.g., 4.572E-4 represents the number 4.572×10^{-4}).
- Make sure students realize that for a sequence to have a limit, values of succeeding terms must continue to get closer and closer to the limiting value.

Practice Have students complete Exercises 3–6.

Limits

FL Math Online glencoe.com
- Other Calculator Keystrokes
- Graphing Technology Personal Tutor

You may have noticed that in some geometric sequences, the later the term in the sequence, the closer the value is to 0. Another way to describe this is that as n increases, a_n approaches 0. The value that the terms of a sequence approach, in this case 0, is called the **limit** of the sequence. Other types of infinite sequences may also have limits. But if the terms of a sequence do not approach a unique value, we say that the limit of the sequence does not exist.

You can use a TI-83/84 Plus graphing calculator to help find the limits of infinite sequences.

ACTIVITY

Find the limit of the geometric sequence $1, \frac{1}{4}, \frac{1}{16}, \ldots$.

Step 1 Enter the sequence.

The formula for this sequence is $a_n = \left(\frac{1}{4}\right)^{n-1}$.

- Position the cursor on L1 in the STAT EDIT 1: Edit… screen and enter the formula seq(N,N,1,10,1). This generates the values 1, 2, …, 10 of the index N.

KEYSTROKES: [STAT] [ENTER] [▲] [2nd] [STAT] [▶] 5 [X,T,θ,n] [,] [X,T,θ,n] [,] 1 [,] 10 [,] 1 [)] [ENTER]

- Position the cursor on L2 and enter the formula seq((1/4)^(N-1),N,1,10,1). This generates the first ten terms of the sequence.

KEYSTROKES: [▶] [▲] [2nd] [STAT] [▶] 5 [(] 1 [÷] 4 [)] [^] [(] [X,T,θ,n] [−] 1 [)] [,] [X,T,θ,n] [,] 1 [,] 10 [,] 1 [)] [ENTER]

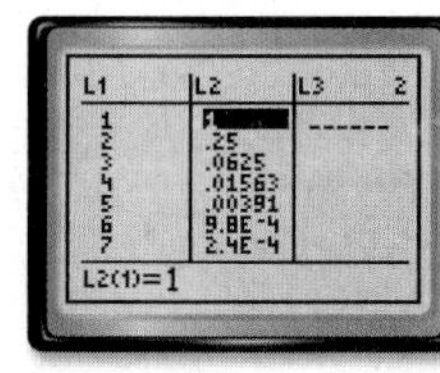

Notice that as n increases, the terms of the given sequence get closer and closer to 0. If you scroll down, you can see that for $n \geq 6$ the terms are so close to 0 that the calculator expresses them in scientific notation. This suggests that the limit of the sequence is 0.

Step 2 Graph the sequence.

Use STAT PLOT to graph the sequence. Use L1 as the Xlist and L2 as the Ylist.

The graph also shows that, as n increases, the terms approach 0. In fact, for $n \geq 3$, the marks appear to lie on the horizontal axis. This strongly suggests that the limit of the sequence is 0.

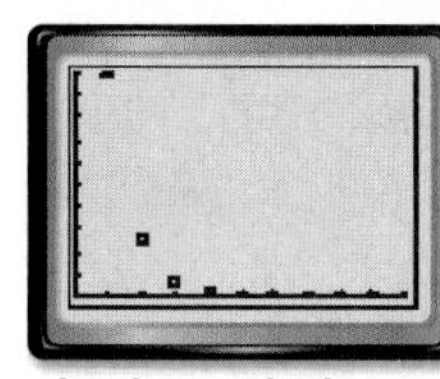

[0, 10] scl: 1 by [0, 1] scl: 0.1

Exercises

Find the limit of each sequence.

1. $a_n = \left(\frac{1}{3}\right)^n$ **0**

2. $a_n = \left(-\frac{1}{3}\right)^n$ **0**

3. $a_n = 5^n$ **does not exist**

4. $a_n = \frac{1}{n^2}$ **0**

5. $a_n = \frac{3^n}{3^n + 1}$ **1**

6. $a_n = \frac{n^2}{n + 2}$ **does not exist**

3 ASSESS

Formative Assessment

Use Exercise 6 to assess whether students comprehend how to recognize when a sequence has no limit.

From Concrete to Abstract

Have students examine the sequence $a_n = \frac{3^n}{3^n + 1}$ in Exercise 5. Have them divide the numerator and denominator by 3^n and ask them to use the result to explain why the limit of the sequence must be 1.

NGSSS 912.D.11.3, 912.D.11.4

Determine whether each sequence is *arithmetic*, *geometric*, or *neither*. Explain your reasoning. (Lesson 11-1)

1. 5, −3, −12, −22, −33… Neither; no common ratio or difference
2. $\frac{1}{5}, \frac{7}{10}, \frac{6}{5}, \frac{17}{10}, \frac{11}{5}, \ldots$ Arithmetic; common difference of $\frac{1}{2}$
3. **HOUSING** Laura is a real estate agent. She needs to sell 15 houses in 6 months. (Lesson 11-1)
   a. By the end of the first 2 months she has sold 4 houses. If she sells 2 houses each month for the rest of the 6 months, will she meet her goal? Explain. See margin.
   b. If she has sold 5 houses by the end of the first month, how many will she have to sell on average each month in order to meet her goal? 2 houses
4. **GEOMETRY** The figures below show a pattern of filled squares and white squares. (Lesson 11-1)

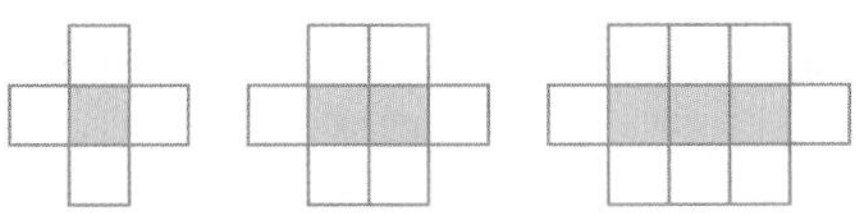

Figure 1 Figure 2 Figure 3

   a. Write an equation representing the nth number in this pattern where n is the number of white squares. $a_n = 2n + 2$
   b. Is it possible to have exactly 84 white squares in an arrangement? Explain. See margin.

Find the indicated term of each arithmetic sequence. (Lesson 11-2)

5. $a_1 = 10, d = -5, n = 9$ −30
6. $a_1 = -8, d = 4, n = 99$ 384

Find the sum of each arithmetic series. (Lesson 11-2)

7. $-15 + (-11) + (-7) + \cdots + 53$ 342
8. $a_1 = -12, d = 8, n = 22$ 1584
9. What is the sum of the arithmetic series $\sum_{k=11}^{50} (-3k + 1)$? (Lesson 11-2) −3620
10. **NGSSS PRACTICE** What is the sum of the first 50 odd numbers? (Lesson 11-2) B
    A. 625
    B. 2500
    C. 2499
    D. 2401

Find the indicated term for each geometric sequence. (Lesson 11-3)

11. $a_2 = 8, r = 2, a_8 = ?$ 512
12. $a_3 = 0.5, r = 8, a_{10} = ?$ 1,048,576
13. **NGSSS PRACTICE** What are the geometric means of the sequence below? I
    0.5, _____, _____, _____, 2048
    F. 512.375, 1024.25, 1536.125
    G. 683, 1365.5, 2048
    H. 2, 8, 32
    I. 4, 32, 256
14. **INCOME** Peter works for a house building company for 4 months per year. He starts out making \$3000 per month. At the end of each month, his salary increases by 5%. How much money will he make in those 4 months? (Lesson 11-3) \$12,930.38

Evaluate the sum of each geometric series. (Lesson 11-3)

15. $\sum_{k=1}^{8} 3 \cdot 2^{k-1}$ 765
16. $\sum_{k=1}^{9} 4 \cdot (-1)^{k-1}$ 4
17. $\sum_{k=1}^{20} -2\left(\frac{2}{3}\right)^{k-1}$ −5.998

Find the sum of each infinite series, if it exists. (Lesson 11-4)

18. $\sum_{n=1}^{\infty} 9 \cdot 2^{n-1}$ No sum exists.
19. $\sum_{n=1}^{\infty} (4) \cdot (0.5)^{n-1}$ 8
20. $\sum_{n=1}^{\infty} 12 \cdot \left(\frac{2}{3}\right)^{n-1}$ 36

CHAPTER 11 Mid-Chapter Quiz

Formative Assessment

Use the Mid-Chapter Quiz to assess students' progress in the first half of the chapter.

For problems answered incorrectly, have students review the lessons indicated in parentheses.

ExamView Assessment Suite Customize and create multiple versions of your Mid-Chapter Quiz and their answer keys.

FOLDABLES® Follow-Up

Before students complete the Mid-Chapter Quiz, encourage them to review the information for Lessons 11-1 through 11-4 in their Foldables.

Additional Answers

3a. No, she will have 11 houses left to sell in 4 months. If she sold 2 houses per month for the remaining 4 months, she would only sell 8 more houses.

4b. Yes, when $2n + 2 = 84$, $n = 41$. In the 41st figure there will be 84 white squares.

Intervention Planner

Tier 1 On Level	Tier 2 Strategic Intervention approaching grade level	Tier 3 Intensive Intervention 2 or more grades below level
If students miss about 25% of the exercises or less,	**If** students miss about 50% of the exercises,	**If** students miss about 75% of the exercises,
Then choose a resource: **SE** Lessons 11–1, 11–2, 11–3, and 11–4 **CRM** Skills Practice, pp. 7, 13, 21, and 28 **TE** Chapter Project, p. 678	**Then** choose a resource: **CRM** Study Guide and Intervention, Chapter 11, pp. 5, 11, 19, and 26	**Then** use *Math Triumphs, Alg. 2*
FL Math Online Self-Check Quiz	FL Math Online Extra Examples, Personal Tutor, Homework Help	FL Math Online Extra Examples, Personal Tutor, Homework Help, Review Vocabulary

11-5 Lesson Notes

1 FOCUS

Vertical Alignment

Before Lesson 11-5
Explore compositions of functions.

Lesson 11-5
Recognize and use special sequences.
Iterate functions.

After Lesson 11-5
Use mathematical induction to prove statements.

2 TEACH

Scaffolding Questions

Have students read the *Why?* section of the lesson.

Ask:

- What number follows 8 in this sequence? 13
- Is this sequence an arithmetic sequence? no
- Is it a geometric sequence? no Explain. There is neither a common difference nor a common ratio.

Special Sequences

Example 1 shows how to use a recursive formula to find terms of a sequence. **Example 2** shows how to write a recursive formula. **Example 3** shows how to use a recursive formula to model a real-world situation.

11-5 Recursion and Iteration

Then
You explored compositions of functions. (Lesson 7-1)

Now
- Recognize and use special sequences.
- Iterate functions.

NGSSS
MA.912.D.11.1 Define arithmetic and geometric sequences and series.

New Vocabulary
Fibonacci sequence
recursive sequence
explicit formula
recursive formula
iteration

FL Math Online
glencoe.com

Why?

The female honeybee is produced after the queen mates with a male, so the female has two parents, a male and a female. The male honeybee, however, is produced by the queen's unfertilized eggs and thus has only one parent, a female. The family tree for the honeybee follows a special sequence.

Generation	1	2	3	4	5	6
Ancestors	1	1	2	3	5	8

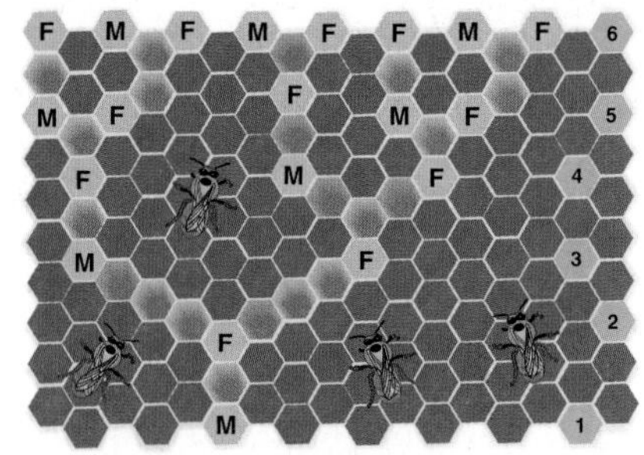

Special Sequences Notice that every term in the list of ancestors is the sum of the previous two terms. This special sequence is called the **Fibonacci sequence**, and it is found in many places in nature. The Fibonacci sequence is an example of a **recursive sequence**. In a recursive sequence, each term is determined by one or more of the previous terms.

The formulas you have used for sequences thus far have been explicit formulas. An **explicit formula** gives a_n as a function of n, such as $a_n = 3n + 1$. The formula that describes the Fibonacci sequence, $a_n = a_{n-2} + a_{n-1}$, is a **recursive formula**, which means that every term will be determined by one or more of the previous terms. An initial term must be given in a recursive formula.

Key Concept Recursive Formulas for Sequences

Arithmetic Sequence $a_n = a_{n-1} + d$, where d is the common difference

Geometric Sequence $a_n = r \cdot a_{n-1}$, where r is the common ratio

EXAMPLE 1 Use a Recursive Formula

Find the first five terms of the sequence in which $a_1 = -3$ and $a_{n+1} = 4a_n - 2$, if $n \geq 1$.

$a_{n+1} = 4a_n - 2$	Recursive formula
$a_{1+1} = 4a_1 - 2$	$n = 1$
$a_2 = 4(-3) - 2$ or -14	$a_1 = -3$
$a_3 = 4(-14) - 2$ or -58	$a_2 = -14$
$a_4 = 4(-58) - 2$ or -234	$a_3 = -58$
$a_5 = 4(-234) - 2$ or -938	$a_4 = -234$

The first five terms of the sequence are −3, −14, −58, −234, and −938.

Guided Practice

1. Find the first five terms of the sequence in which $a_1 = 8$ and $a_{n+1} = -3a_n + 6$, if $n \geq 1$. **8, −18, 60, −174, 528**

Personal Tutor glencoe.com

Lesson 11-5 Resources

Resource	Approaching-Level	On-Level	Beyond-Level	English Learners
Teacher Edition		• Differentiated Instruction, pp. 716, 719	• Differentiated Instruction, p. 719	
Chapter Resource Masters	• Study Guide and Intervention, pp. 32–33 • Skills Practice, p. 34 • Practice, p. 35 • Word Problem Practice, p. 36	• Study Guide and Intervention, pp. 32–33 • Skills Practice, p. 34 • Practice, p. 35 • Word Problem Practice, p. 36 • Enrichment, p. 37 • Graphing Calculator Activity, p. 38	• Practice, p. 35 • Word Problem Practice, p. 36 • Enrichment, p. 37	• Study Guide and Intervention, pp. 32–33 • Skills Practice, p. 34 • Practice, p. 35 • Word Problem Practice, p. 36
Transparencies	• 5-Minute Check Transparency 11-5	• 5-Minute Check Transparency 11-5	• 5-Minute Check Transparency 11-5	• 5-Minute Check Transparency 11-5
Other	• Study Notebook • Teaching Algebra with Manipulatives	• Study Notebook • Teaching Algebra with Manipulatives	• Study Notebook	• Study Notebook • Teaching Algebra with Manipulatives

In order to find a recursive formula, first determine the initial term. Then evaluate the pattern to generate the later terms.

StudyTip

Recursive Formula The recursive formula that generates a sequence does not include the value of the initial term.

EXAMPLE 2 Write Recursive Formulas

Write a recursive formula for each sequence.

a. **2, 10, 18, 26, 34, ...**

Step 1 Determine whether the sequence is arithmetic or geometric.
The sequence is arithmetic because each term after the first can be found by adding a common difference.

Step 2 Find the common difference.
$d = 10 - 2$ or 8

Step 3 Write the recursive formula.

$a_n = a_{n-1} + d$ **Recursive formula for arithmetic sequence**

$a_n = a_{n-1} + 8$ **$d = 8$**

A recursive formula for the sequence is $a_n = a_{n-1} + 8$, $a_1 = 2$.

b. **16, 56, 196, 686, 2401, ...**

Step 1 Determine whether the sequence is arithmetic or geometric.
The sequence is geometric because each term after the first can be found after multiplying by a common ratio.

Step 2 Find the common ratio.
$r = \frac{56}{16}$ or 3.5

Step 3 Write the recursive formula.

$a_n = r \cdot a_{n-1}$ **Recursive formula for geometric sequence**

$a_n = 3.5a_{n-1}$ **$r = 3.5$**

A recursive formula for the sequence is $a_n = 3.5a_{n-1}$, $a_1 = 16$.

c. **$a_4 = 108$ and $r = 3$**

Step 1 Determine whether the sequence is arithmetic or geometric.
Because r is given, the sequence is geometric.

Step 2 Write the recursive formula.

$a_n = r \cdot a_{n-1}$ **Recursive formula for geometric sequence**

$a_n = 3a_{n-1}$ **$r = 3$**

A recursive formula for the sequence is $a_n = 3a_{n-1}$, $a_1 = 4$.

Guided Practice

Write a recursive formula for each sequence.

2A. 8, 20, 50, 125, 312.5, ... **2B.** 8, 17, 26, 35, 44, ... **2C.** $a_3 = 16$ and $r = 4$

Personal Tutor glencoe.com

2A. $a_n = 2.5a_{n-1}$, $a_1 = 8$
2B. $a_n = a_{n-1} + 9$, $a_1 = 8$
2C. $a_n = 4a_{n-1}$, $a_1 = 1$

Formative Assessment

Use the Guided Practice exercises after each example to determine students' understanding of concepts.

Additional Examples

1 Find the first five terms of the sequence in which $a_1 = 5$ and $a_{n+1} = 2a_n + 7, n \geq 1$. 5, 17, 41, 89, 185

2 Write a recursive formula for each sequence.

a. 3, 10, 17, 24, 31, . . .
$a_1 = 3; a_n = a_{n-1} + 7$

b. 5, 20, 80, 320, 1280, . . .
$a_1 = 5; a_n = 4 \cdot a_{n-1}$

c. $a_3 = 6$ and $d = 5$
$a_1 = -4; a_n = a_{n-1} + 5$

Additional Examples also in Interactive Classroom PowerPoint® Presentations

IWB INTERACTIVE WHITEBOARD READY

Watch Out!

Preventing Misconceptions Make sure students understand that you use the value of one term to find the value of the next term when a sequence is given in recursive form. Point out that $a_n = a_1 + (n - 1)d$ and $a_n = a_1r^{n-1}$ are not recursive formulas. These *explicit* formulas determine each term by the number n of the term rather than by the value of the preceding term.

Additional Example

3 **BIOLOGY** Dr. Elliot is growing cells in lab dishes. She starts with 108 cells Monday morning and then removes 20 of these for her experiment. By Tuesday, the remaining cells have multiplied in number by 1.5. She again removes 20. This pattern repeats each day of the week. Write a recursive formula for the number of cells Dr. Elliot finds each day before she removes any. Then determine how many cells she will find on Friday morning. $c_{n+1} = 1.5(c_n - 20)$ or $c_{n+1} = 1.5c_n - 30$, $c_1 = 108$; 303

TEACH with TECH

INTERACTIVE WHITEBOARD Show students how to calculate successive terms using a recursive formula. Use different colors and the highlight tool in your calculations to help show how each term is linked to the pervious terms.

Iteration

Example 4 shows how to find the first few iterates, or iterated values, of a function.

Additional Example

4 Find the first three iterates x_1, x_2, and x_3 of $f(x) = 3x - 1$ for an initial value of $x_0 = 5$. 14, 41, 122

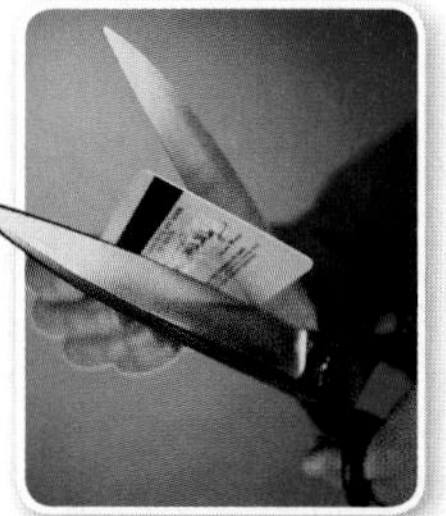

Real-World Link

In 2007, the average credit card debt for college students was about $2700.

Source: *Money Magazine*

Real-World EXAMPLE 3 Use a Recursive Formula

FINANCIAL LITERACY **Nate had $15,000 in credit card debt when he graduated from college. The balance increased by 2% each month due to interest, and Nate could only make payments of $400 per month. Write a recursive formula for the balance on his account each month. Then determine the balance after five months.**

Step 1 Write the recursive formula.

Let a_n represent the balance on the account in the nth month. The initial balance a_1 is $15,000. After one month, interest is added and a payment is made.

	initial balance	+	balance times 2%	−	monthly payment
$a_2 =$	a_1	+	$(a_1 \times 0.02)$	−	400

$a_2 = 1.02a_1 - 400$

The formula is $a_n = 1.02a_{n-1} - 400$.

Step 2 Find the next five terms.

$a_n = 1.02a_{n-1} - 400$
$a_2 = (15{,}000 \times 1.02) - 400$ or 14,900
$a_3 = (14{,}900 \times 1.02) - 400$ or 14,798
$a_4 = (14{,}798 \times 1.02) - 400$ or 14,693.96
$a_5 = (14{,}693.96 \times 1.02) - 400$ or 14,587.84
$a_6 = (14{,}587.84 \times 1.02) - 400$ or 14,479.60

Recursive formula
$a_1 = 15{,}000$
$a_2 = 14{,}900$
$a_3 = 14{,}798$
$a_4 = 14{,}693.96$
$a_5 = 14{,}587.84$

After the fifth month, the balance will be $14,479.60.

Guided Practice

3. $a_n = 1.025a_{n-1} - 600$; $a_1 = 10{,}000$; $10,000, $9650, $9291.25, $8923.53, $8546.62

3. Write a recursive formula for a $10,000 debt, at 2.5% interest per month, with a $600 monthly payment. Then find the first five balances.

Personal Tutor glencoe.com

Iteration

Iteration is the process of repeatedly composing a function with itself. Consider x_0. The first iterate is $f(x_0)$, the second iterate is $f(f(x_0))$, the third iterate is $f(f(f(x_0)))$, and so on.

Iteration can be used to recursively generate a sequence. Start with the initial value x_0. Let $x_1 = f(x_0)$, $x_2 = f(f(x_0))$, and so on.

Review Vocabulary

composition of functions A function is performed, and then a second function is performed on the result of the first function. (Lesson 7-1)

EXAMPLE 4 Iterate a Function

Find the first three iterates x_1, x_2, and x_3 of $f(x) = 5x + 4$ for an initial value of $x_0 = 2$.

$x_1 = f(x_0)$	Iterate the function.
$= 5(2) + 4$ or 14	$x_0 = 2$
$x_2 = f(x_1)$	Iterate the function.
$= 5(14) + 4$ or 74	$x_1 = 14$
$x_3 = f(x_2)$	Iterate the function.
$= 5(74) + 4$ or 374	$x_2 = 74$

The first three iterates are 14, 74, and 374.

Guided Practice

4. Find the first three iterates x_1, x_2, and x_3 of $f(x) = -3x + 8$ for an initial value of $x_0 = 6$. −10, 38, −106

Personal Tutor glencoe.com

Differentiated Instruction OL

Kinesthetic Learners Have students research and then play the game Tower of Hanoi. The object of the Tower of Hanoi game is to move a stack of 8 disks of graduated sizes from one of 3 pegs to a vacant peg in the fewest number of moves by following these rules:

- You may move only one disk at a time.
- A disk must be placed on top of another disk, not underneath.
- A smaller disk may be placed on top of a larger disk, but not vice versa.

Check Your Understanding

Example 1 p. 714

Find the first five terms of each sequence described. 4. −4, −14, −34, −74, −154

1. $a_1 = 16, a_{n+1} = a_n + 4$ 16, 20, 24, 28, 32 **2.** $a_1 = -3, a_{n+1} = a_n + 8$ −3, 5, 13, 21, 29

3. $a_1 = 5, a_{n+1} = 3a_n + 2$ 5, 17, 53, 161, 485 **4.** $a_1 = -4, a_{n+1} = 2a_n - 6$

Example 2 p. 715

Write a recursive formula for each sequence. 6. $a_{n+1} = 3a_n - 1$; $a_1 = 5$

5. 3, 8, 18, 38, 78, ... $a_{n+1} = 2a_n + 2$; $a_1 = 3$ **6.** 5, 14, 41, 122, 365, ...

Example 3 p. 716

7. FINANCING Ben financed a $1500 rowing machine to help him train for the college rowing team. He could only make a $100 payment each month, and his bill increased by 1% due to interest at the end of each month. a. $a_n = 1.01a_{n-1} - 100$, $a_1 = 1500$

a. Write a recursive formula for the balance owed at the end of each month.

b. Find the balance owed after the first four months.

c. How much interest has accumulated after the first six months? $77.08

7b. $1415, $1329.15, $1242.44, $1154.87

Example 4 p. 716

Find the first three iterates of each function for the given initial value.

8. $f(x) = 5x + 2, x_0 = 8$ 42, 212, 1062 **9.** $f(x) = -4x + 2, x_0 = 5$ −18, 74, −294

10. $f(x) = 6x + 3, x_0 = -4$ **11.** $f(x) = 8x - 4, x_0 = -6$

10. −21, −123, −735
11. −52, −420, −3364
12. 10, 41, 165, 661, 2645 13. −9, −10, −12, −16, −24

Practice and Problem Solving

● = **Step-by-Step Solutions** begin on page R20. **Extra Practice** begins on page 947.

Example 1 p. 714

Find the first five terms of each sequence described. 15. −4, −7, −12, −21, −38

12. $a_1 = 10, a_{n+1} = 4a_n + 1$ **13.** $a_1 = -9, a_{n+1} = 2a_n + 8$

14. $a_1 = 12, a_{n+1} = a_n + n$ 12, 13, 15, 18, 22 **15.** $a_1 = -4, a_{n+1} = 2a_n + n$

16. $a_1 = 6, a_{n+1} = 3a_n - n$ **17.** $a_1 = -2, a_{n+1} = 5a_n + 2n$

18. $a_1 = 7, a_2 = 10, a_{n+2} = 2a_n + a_{n+1}$ **19.** $a_1 = 4, a_2 = 5, a_{n+2} = 4a_n - 2a_{n+1}$

20. $a_1 = 4, a_2 = 3x, a_n = a_{n-1} + 4a_{n-2}$ **21.** $a_1 = 3, a_2 = 2x, a_n = 4a_{n-1} - 3a_{n-2}$

22. $a_1 = 2, a_2 = x + 3, a_n = a_{n-1} + 6a_{n-2}$ **23.** $a_1 = 1, a_2 = x, a_n = 3a_{n-1} + 6a_{n-2}$

16. 6, 17, 49, 144, 428
17. −2, −8, −36, −174, −862
18. 7, 10, 24, 44, 92
19. 4, 5, 6, 8, 8
20. 4, $3x$, $3x + 16$, $15x + 16$, $27x + 80$

Example 2 p. 715

Write a recursive formula for each sequence. 24–31. See margin.

24. 16, 10, 7, 5.5, 4.75, ... **25.** 32, 12, 7, 5.75, ...

26. 4, 15, 224, 50,175, ... **27.** 1, 2, 9, 730, ...

28. 9, 33, 129, 513, ... **29.** 480, 128, 40, 18, ...

30. 393, 132, 45, 16, ... **31.** 68, 104, 176, 320, ...

21. 3, $2x$, $8x - 9$, $26x - 36$, $80x - 117$
22. 2, $x + 3$, $x + 15$, $7x + 33$, $13x + 123$
23. 1, x, $3x + 6$, $15x + 18$, $63x + 90$

Example 3 p. 716

32. FINANCIAL LITERACY Mr. Edwards and his company deposit $20,000 into his retirement account at the end of each year. The account earns 8% interest before each deposit.

a. Write a recursive formula for the balance in the account at the end of each year.

b. Determine how much is in the account at the end of each of the first 8 years.

32a. $a_n = 1.08a_{n-1} + 20000$
32b. See margin.

Example 4 p. 716

Find the first three iterates of each function for the given initial value.

33. $f(x) = 12x + 8, x_0 = 4$ 56, 680, 8168 **34.** $f(x) = -9x + 1, x_0 = -6$ 55, −494, 4447

35. $f(x) = -6x + 3, x_0 = 8$ −45, 273, −1635 **36.** $f(x) = 8x + 3, x_0 = -4$

37. $f(x) = -3x^2 + 9, x_0 = 2$ −3, −18, −963 **38.** $f(x) = 4x^2 + 5, x_0 = -2$

39. $f(x) = 2x^2 - 5x + 1, x_0 = 6$ **40.** $f(x) = -0.25x^2 + x + 6, x_0 = 8$

41. $f(x) = x^2 + 2x + 3, x_0 = \frac{1}{2}$ **42.** $f(x) = 2x^2 + x + 1, x_0 = -\frac{1}{2}$ 1, 4, 37

36. −29, −229, −1829
38. 21, 1769, 12,517,449
39. 43, 3484, 24,259,093
40. −2, 3, 6.75
41. 4.25, 29.5625, 936.0664

3 PRACTICE

Formative Assessment

Use Exercises 1–11 to check for understanding.

Use the chart at the bottom of this page to customize assignments for your students.

Additional Answers

24. $a_{n+1} = 0.5a_n + 2; a_1 = 16$

25. $a_{n+1} = 0.25a_n + 4; a_1 = 32$

26. $a_{n+1} = (a_n)^2 - 1; a_1 = 4$

27. $a_{n+1} = (a_n)^3 + 1; a_1 = 1$

28. $a_{n+1} = 4n - 3; a_1 = 9$

29. $a_{n+1} = 0.25a_n + 8; a_1 = 480$

30. $a_{n+1} = \frac{a_n}{3} + 1 + 1; a_1 = 393$

31. $a_{n+1} = 2a_n - 32; a_1 = 84$

32b. $a_1 = \$20,000$, $a_2 = \$41,600$, $a_3 = \$64,928$, $a_4 = \$90,122.24$, $a_5 = \$117,332.02$, $a_6 = \$146,718.58$, $a_7 = \$178,456.07$, $a_8 = \$212,732.56$

Differentiated Homework Options

Level	Assignment	Two-Day Option	
AL Basic	12–42, 49, 51–69	13–41 odd, 54–57	12–42 even, 49, 51–53, 58–69
OL Core	13– 41 odd, 43–49, 51–69	12–42, 54–57	43–49, 51–53, 58–69
BL Advanced	43–63, (optional: 64–69)		

Study Guide and Intervention

CRM pp. 32–33 AL OL ELL

11-5 Study Guide and Intervention

Recursion and Iteration

Special Sequences In a **recursive formula,** each succeeding term is formulated from one or more previous terms. A recursive formula for a sequence has two parts:

1. the value(s) of the first term(s), and
2. an equation that shows how to find each term from the term(s) before it.

Example **Find the first five terms of the sequence in which $a_1 = 6$, $a_2 = 10$, and $a_n = 2a_{n-2}$ for $n \geq 3$.**

$a_1 = 6$
$a_2 = 10$
$a_3 = 2a_1 = 2(6) = 12$
$a_4 = 2a_2 = 2(10) = 20$
$a_5 = 2a_3 = 2(12) = 24$

The first five terms of the sequence are 6, 10, 12, 20, 24.

Exercises

Find the first five terms of each sequence described.

1. $a_1 = 1, a_2 = 1, a_n = 2(a_{n-1} + a_{n-2}), n \geq 3$ **1, 1, 4, 10, 28**
2. $a_1 = 1, a_n = \frac{1}{1 + a_{n-1}}, n \geq 2$ **$1, \frac{1}{2}, \frac{2}{3}, \frac{3}{5}, \frac{5}{8}$**
3. $a_1 = 3, a_n = a_{n-1} + 2(n-2), n \geq 2$ **3, 3, 5, 9, 15**
4. $a_1 = 5, a_n = a_{n-1} + 2, n \geq 2$ **5, 7, 9, 11, 13**
5. $a_1 = 0.5, a_n = a_{n-1} + 2n, n \geq 2$ **0.5, 4.5, 10.5, 18.5, 28.5**
6. $a_1 = 100, a_n = \frac{a_{n-1}}{n}, n \geq 2$ **$100, 50, \frac{50}{3}, \frac{25}{6}, \frac{5}{6}$**

Write a recursive formula for each sequence.

7. $1, \frac{1}{2}, \frac{1}{6}, \frac{1}{24}, \frac{1}{120}, \ldots$ **$a_n = \frac{1}{n}a_{n-1}$**
8. $1, -1, 2, -3, 5, -8, \ldots$ **$a_n = a_{n-2} - a_{n-1}$**

Practice

CRM p. 35 AL OL BL ELL

11-6 Practice

Recursion and Iteration

Find the first five terms of each sequence described.

1. $a_1 = 3, a_{n+1} = a_n + 5$ **3, 8, 13, 18, 23**
2. $a_1 = -7, a_{n+1} = a_n + 8$ **−7, 1, 9, 17, 25**
3. $a_1 = -3, a_{n+1} = 3a_n + 2$ **−3, −7, −19, −55, −163**
4. $a_1 = -8, a_{n+1} = 10 - a_n$ **−8, 18, −8, 18, −8**
5. $a_1 = 2, a_2 = -3, a_{n+1} = 5a_n - 8a_{n-1}$ **2, −3, −31, −131, −407**
6. $a_1 = -2, a_2 = 1, a_{n+1} = -2a_n + 6a_{n-1}$ **−2, 1, −14, 34, −152**

Write a recursive formula for each sequence.

7. 2, 5, 7, 13, 20, … **$a_n = a_{n-1} + a_{n-2}$**
8. 1, −2, −2, 4, −8, −32, 256, … **$a_n = (a_{n-1})(a_{n-2})$**
9. −3, 9, 81, 6561, … **$a_n = (a_{n-1})^2$**
10. 3, 7, 4, −3, −7, −4, 3, 7, … **$a_n = (a_{n-1}) - (a_{n-2})$**
11. −1, 2, 1, 3, 4, 7, 11, … **$a_n = a_{n-1} + a_{n-2}$**
12. $3, 1, \frac{1}{3}, \frac{1}{3}, 1, 3, 3, 1, \ldots$ **$a_n = (a_{n-1}) \div (a_{n-2})$**

Find the first three iterates of each function for the given initial value.

13. $f(x) = 3x + 4, x_0 = -1$ **1, 7, 25**
14. $f(x) = 10x + 2, x_0 = -1$ **−8, −78, −778**
15. $f(x) = 8 + 3x, x_0 = 1$ **11, 41, 131**
16. $f(x) = 8 - x, x_0 = -3$ **11, −3, 11**
17. $f(x) = 4x + 5, x_0 = -1$ **1, 9, 41**
18. $f(x) = 5(x + 3), x_0 = -2$ **5, 40, 215**
19. $f(x) = -8x + 9, x_0 = 1$ **1, 1, 1**
20. $f(x) = -4x^2, x_0 = -1$ **−4; −64; −16,384**
21. $f(x) = x^2 - 1, x_0 = 3$ **8, 63, 3968**
22. $f(x) = 2x^2; x_0 = 5$ **50; 5000; 50,000,000**
23. **INFLATION** Iterating the function $c(x) = 1.05x$ gives the future cost of an item at a constant 5% inflation rate. Find the cost of a $2000 ring in five years at 5% inflation. **$2552.56**
24. **FRACTALS** Replacing each side of the square shown with the combination of segments below it gives the figure to its right.

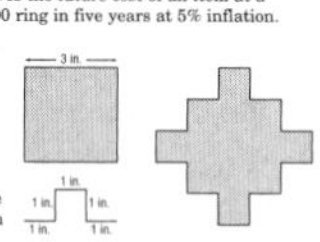

   a. What is the perimeter of the original square? **12 in.**
   b. What is the perimeter of the new shape? **20 in.**
   c. If you repeat the process by replacing each side of the new shape by a proportional combination of 5 segments, what will the perimeter of the third shape be? **$33\frac{1}{3}$ in.**
   d. What function $f(x)$ can you iterate to find the perimeter of each successive shape if you continue this process? **$f(x) = \frac{5}{3}x$**

Word Problem Practice

CRM p. 36 AL OL BL ELL

11-5 Word Problem Practice

Recursion and Iteration

1. **GEOMETRIC SEQUENCES** The geometric sequence with first term a and common ratio r goes like this: a, ar, ar^2, ar^3, etc. It happens that this sequence can also be seen from the point of view of iterative sequences. What function $f(x)$ can be used to define the geometric sequence above iteratively? **$f(x) = rx$**

2. **BACTERIA** The bacteria *Staphylococcus aureus* has a generation or doubling time of half an hour. Also, every hour, 1000 bacteria are removed from the culture. If the initial population consisted of 1100 bacteria, what are the population sizes every hour for the next four half hours? **Starting with 1100, the population increases to 1200, 1400, 1800, then 2600.**

3. **WORK** The company that Robert works for has a policy where the number of hours you have to work one week depends on the number of hours worked the previous week. If you worked h hours one week, then the next week you must work at least $80 - h$ hours. Robert worked 20 hours his first week with the company. From then on, he always worked the minimum number of hours required of him. Describe the number of hours Robert worked from week to week. **Robert alternated 20-hour weeks with 60-hour weeks.**

4. **GEOMETRY** A sequence of triangular shapes is made using squares as shown in the figure.

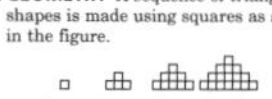

Let x_n be the number of squares to make the nth figure. Write a recursive formula for x_n. **$x_1 = 1; x_{n+1} = x_n + 2n + 1$ for $n > 0$**

5. **PATHS** Gregory makes walking paths out of two different rectangles. One is a 1-yard by 1-yard square and the other is a 1-yard by 2-yard rectangle. He makes paths by lining up the squares and rectangles as shown in the figure.

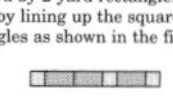

Gregory wants to know how many different paths he can make of a fixed length. Let a_n denote the number of paths he can make of length n yards.

   a. What are the first 5 values of a_n? **1, 2, 3, 5, 8**
   b. Write a recursive formula for a_n. Explain. **$a_1 = 1; a_2 = 2; a_{n+1} = a_n + a_{n-1}$ for $n > 1$. Every path of length $n - 1$ can be extended to a path of length $n + 1$ by adding a 1 by 2 rectangle and every path of length n can be extended to a path of length $n + 1$ by adding a 1 by 1 rectangle.**

Real-World Career

Conservation Scientist Conservation scientists work with private landowners and the government to manage, improve, and protect natural resources. A conservation scientist must have a bachelor's degree in forestry, biology, natural resource management, or the environmental sciences.

B **43. FRACTALS** Consider the figures at the right. The number of blue triangles increases according to a specific pattern.

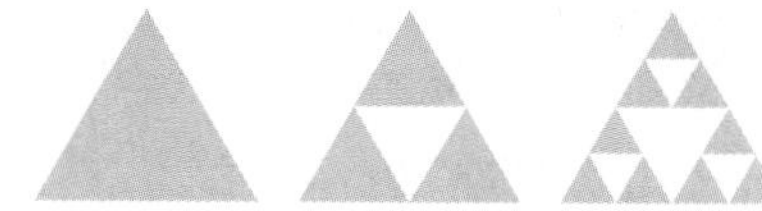

a. Write a recursive formula for the number of blue triangles in the sequence of figures. **$a_n = 3a_{n-1}, a_1 = 1$**

b. How many blue triangles will be in the sixth figure? **243**

44. FINANCIAL LITERACY Miguel's monthly car payment is $234.85. The recursive formula $b_n = 1.005b_{n-1} - 234.85$ describes the balance left on the loan after n payments. Find the balance of the $10,000 loan after each of the first eight payments.

45. CONSERVATION Suppose a lake is populated with 10,000 fish. A year later, 80% of the fish have died or been caught, and the lake is replenished with 10,000 new fish. If the pattern continues, will the lake eventually run out of fish? If not, will the population of the lake converge to any particular value? Explain.

46. GEOMETRY Consider the pattern at the right.

C a. Write a sequence of the total number of triangles in the first six figures. **1, 4, 10, 19, 31, 46**

b. Write a recursive formula for the number of triangles. **$a_n = a_{n-1} + 3(n-1)$**

c. How many triangles will be in the tenth figure? **136**

47. SPREADSHEETS Consider the sequence with $x_0 = 20{,}000$ and $f(x) = 0.3x + 5000$.

a. Enter x_0 in cell A1 of your spreadsheet. Enter "= (0.3)*(A1) + 5000" in cell A2. What answer does it provide? **11,000**

b. Copy cell A2, highlight cells A3 through A70, and paste. What do you notice about the sequence? **It converges to 7142.857.**

c. How do spreadsheets help analyze recursive sequences? **See margin.**

48. VIDEO GAMES The final monster in Helena's video game has 100 health points. During the final battle, the monster regains 10% of its health points after every 10 seconds. If Helena can inflict damage to the monster that takes away 10 health points every 10 seconds without getting hurt herself, will she ever kill the monster? If so, when? **yes; between 250 and 260 seconds**

H.O.T. Problems

Use **H**igher-**O**rder **T**hinking Skills

49. ERROR ANALYSIS Marcus and Armando are finding the first three iterates of $f(x) = 5x - 3$ for an initial value of $x_0 = 4$. Is either of them correct? Explain.

Marcus	Armando
f(4) = 5(4) − 3 or 17	f(4) = 5(4) − 3 or 17
f(17) = 5(17) − 3 or 82	f(17) = 5(17) − 3 or 82
The first three iterates are 4, 17, and 82.	f(82) = 5(82) − 3 or 407
	The first three iterates are 17, 82, and 407.

50. CHALLENGE Find a recursive formula for 5, 23, 98, 401, … . **$a_{n+1} = 4a_n + 3n, a_1 = 5$**

51. REASONING Is the statement "*If the first three terms of a sequence are identical, then the sequence is not recursive*" *sometimes*, *always*, or *never* true? Explain your reasoning.

52. OPEN ENDED Write a function for which the first three iterates are 9, 19, and 39.

53. WRITING IN MATH Explain the difference between a recursive sequence and a recursive formula. **See margin.**

44. $9815.15, $9629.38, $9442.67, $9255.04, $9066.46, $8876.94, $8686.48, $8495.06

45. No; the population of fish will reach 12,500. Each year, 20% of 12,500 or 2500 fish, plus 10,000 additional fish, yields 12,500 fish.

49. Armando; Marcus included x_0 with the iterates and only showed the first 2 iterates.

51. See margin.

52. Sample answer: $f(x) = 2x + 1$, $x_0 = 4$

Enrichment

CRM p. 37 OL BL

11-5 Enrichment

Continued Fractions

The fraction below is an example of a continued fraction. Note that each fraction in the continued fraction has a numerator of 1.

$$2 + \cfrac{1}{3 + \cfrac{1}{4 + \frac{1}{5}}}$$

Example 1 **Evaluate the continued fraction above. Start at the bottom and work your way up.**

Step 1 $4 + \frac{1}{5} = \frac{20}{5} + \frac{1}{5} = \frac{21}{5}$
Step 2 $\frac{1}{\frac{21}{5}} = \frac{5}{21}$
Step 3 $3 + \frac{5}{21} = \frac{63}{21} + \frac{5}{21} = \frac{68}{21}$
Step 4 $\frac{1}{\frac{68}{21}} = \frac{21}{68}$
Step 5 $2 + \frac{21}{68} = 2\frac{21}{68}$

Example 2 **Change $\frac{25}{11}$ into a continued fraction.**

Follow the steps.

Step 1 $\frac{25}{11} = \frac{22}{11} + \frac{3}{11} = 2 + \frac{3}{11}$
Step 2 $\frac{3}{11} = \frac{1}{\frac{11}{3}}$
Step 3 $\frac{11}{3} = \frac{9}{3} + \frac{2}{3} = 3 + \frac{2}{3}$
Step 4 $\frac{2}{3} = \frac{1}{\frac{3}{2}}$
Step 5 $\frac{3}{2} = \frac{2}{2} + \frac{1}{2} = 1 + \frac{1}{2}$

Stop, because the numerator is 1.

Additional Answers

47c. Sample answer: They make it easier to analyze recursive sequences because they can produce the first 100 terms instantaneously; it would take a long time to calculate the terms by hand.

51. Sample answer: Sometimes; the recursive formula could involve the first three terms. For example, 2, 2, 2, 8, 20, . . . is recursive with $a_n + 3 = a_n + a_{n+1} + 2a_{n+2}$.

NGSSS PRACTICE 912.G.2.2, 912.A.9.1, 912.A.7.5

54. GEOMETRY In the figure shown, $a + b + c = ?$ **C**

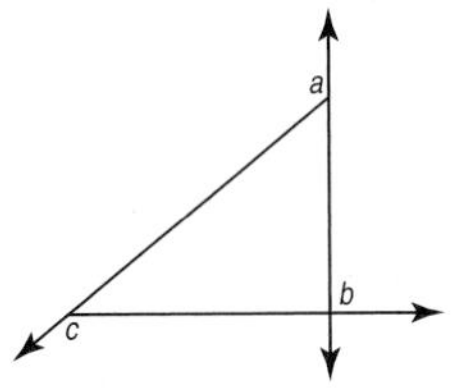

A. 180°
B. 270°
C. 360°
D. 450°

55. EXTENDED RESPONSE Bill launches a model rocket from ground level. The rocket's height h in meters is given by the equation $h = -4.9t^2 + 56t$, where t is the time in seconds after the launch.

a. What is the maximum height the rocket will reach?

b. How long after it is launched will the rocket reach its maximum height? Round to the nearest tenth of a second. **5.7 s**

c. How long after it is launched will the rocket land? Round to the nearest tenth of a second.

56. Which of the following is true about the graphs of $y = 3(x - 4)^2 + 5$ and $y = 3(x + 4)^2 + 5$? **G**

F. Their vertices are maximums.
G. The graphs have the same shape with different vertices.
H. The graphs have different shapes with different vertices.
I. One graph has a vertex that is a maximum, while the other graph has a vertex that is a minimum.

57. Which factors could represent the length times the width? **C**

$A = 16x^4 - 25y^2$

A. $(4x - 5y)(4x - 5y)$
B. $(4x + 5y)(4x - 5y)$
C. $(4x^2 - 5y)(4x^2 + 5y)$
D. $(4x^2 + 5y)(4x^2 + 5y)$

55a. 100 m 55c. 11.4 s

Spiral Review

Write each repeating decimal as a fraction. (Lesson 11-4)

58. $0.\overline{7}$ $\frac{7}{9}$ **59.** $5.\overline{126}$ $5\frac{14}{111}$ **60.** $6.\overline{259}$ $6\frac{7}{27}$

61. SPORTS Adrahan is training for a marathon, about 26 miles. He begins by running 2 miles. Then, when he runs every other day, he runs one and a half times the distance he ran the time before. (Lesson 11-3)

a. Write the first five terms of a sequence describing his training schedule. **2, 3, 4.5, 6.75, 10.125**

b. When will he exceed 26 miles in one run? **the eighth session**

c. When will he have run 100 total miles? **during the ninth session**

State whether the events are *independent* or *dependent*. (Lesson 0-4)

62. tossing a penny and rolling a number cube **independent**

63. choosing first and second place in an academic competition **dependent**

Skills Review

Find each product. (Lesson 0-2)

64. $(y + 4)(y + 3)$ $y^2 + 7y + 12$ **65.** $(x - 2)(x + 6)$ $x^2 + 4x - 12$ **66.** $(a - 8)(a + 5)$ $a^2 - 3a - 40$

67. $(4h + 5)(h + 7)$ $4h^2 + 33h + 35$ **68.** $(9p - 1)(3p - 2)$ $27p^2 - 21p + 2$ **69.** $(2g + 7)(5g - 8)$ $10g^2 + 19g - 56$

Watch Out!

Error Analysis For Exercise 49, remind students that $x_1 = f(x_0)$, where x_0 is the initial value and x_1 is the first iterate. Be sure students understand that the initial value does not count as an iterate. The first iterate is obtained by applying the function to the initial value.

Tips for New Teachers

Understanding Language Make sure that students understand the terminology used in this lesson, particularly *iteration* and *iterate*.

4 ASSESS

Name the Math Have students explain what it means to say that a formula or a function is *recursive*.

Additional Answer

53. Sample answer: In a recursive sequence, each term is determined by one or more of the previous terms. A recursive formula is used to produce the terms of the recursive sequence.

Differentiated Instruction OL BL

Extension Write a sequence like 2, 5, 7, 12, 19, 31, . . ., on the board and see if students can identify the pattern. Such a sequence, called a Lucas sequence, is similar to the Fibonacci sequence in that each term beginning with the third term is the sum of the two terms immediately preceding it. Have them write their own Lucas sequences with any two starting terms.

Lesson 11-5 Recursion and Iteration 719

1 FOCUS

Objective Use a spreadsheet to analyze the payments, interest, and balance on a loan.

Materials for Each Student

- computer spreadsheet (optional)

Teaching Tip

Suggest to students that they always type descriptive labels in cells adjacent to entered or computed values as well as at the tops of columns. This will make it easier to understand and interpret the results.

2 TEACH

Working in Cooperative Groups

You may want to have students work in pairs of mixed abilities so that they can help each other with keystrokes and commands. Then have groups follow the Example and complete Exercises 1–2.

- Before students begin this investigation, point out that a spreadsheet can express a relationship in which the calculation of the value of the next term involves using the value of the previous term.
- Ask students why the balance is multiplied by 1.0075 rather than 0.0075. You need to find the balance plus the interest.

Practice Have students complete Exercises 3–6.

3 ASSESS

Formative Assessment

Use Exercise 1 to assess whether students comprehend how to relate the spreadsheet formula to the algebraic formulas they have studied.

EXTEND 11-5 Spreadsheet Lab: Amortizing Loans

FL Math Online glencoe.com
Graphing Technology Personal Tutor

When a payment is made on a loan, part of the payment is used to cover the interest that has accumulated since the last payment. The rest is used to reduce the *principal*, or original amount of the loan. This process is called *amortization*. You can use a spreadsheet to analyze the payments, interest, and balance on a loan. A table that shows this kind of information is called an *amortization schedule*.

EXAMPLE

LOANS Gloria just bought a new computer for $695. The store is letting her make monthly payments of $60.78 at an interest rate of 9% for one year. How much will she still owe after six months?

Every month, the interest on the remaining balance will be $\frac{9\%}{12}$ or 0.75%. You can find the balance after a payment by multiplying the balance after the previous payment by 1 + 0.0075 or 1.0075 and then subtracting 60.78.

In a spreadsheet, the column of numbers represents the number of payments, and Column B shows the balance. Enter the interest rate and monthly payment in cells in Column A so that they can be easily updated if the information changes.

The spreadsheet at the right shows the formulas for the balances after each of the first six payments. After six months, Gloria still owes $355.28.

Computer Loan

	A	B	C
1	Interest Rate	=695*(1+A2)–A5	
2	0.0075	=B1*(1+A2)–A5	
3		=B2*(1+A2)–A5	
4	Monthly payment	=B3*(1+A2)–A5	
5	60.78	=B4*(1+A2)–A5	
6		=B5*(1+A2)–A5	
7			

Sheet 1 / Sheet 2 / Sheet 3

Model and Analyze

1. Let b_n be the balance left on Gloria's loan after n months. Write an equation relating b_n and b_{n+1}. $b_{n+1} = 1.0075b_n - 60.78$, $b_1 = 695$
2. Payments at the beginning of a loan go more toward interest than payments at the end. What percent of Gloria's loan remains to be paid after half a year? about 51%
3. Extend the spreadsheet to the whole year. What is the balance after 12 payments? Why is it not 0? About –$0.01; the balance is not exactly 0 due to rounding.
4. Suppose Gloria decides to pay $70 every month. How long would it take her to pay off the loan? 11 mo
5. Suppose that, based on how much she can afford, Gloria will pay a variable amount each month in addition to the $60.78. Explain how the flexibility of a spreadsheet can be used to adapt to this situation. The variable amount can just be subtracted after A5.
6. Ethan has a three-year, $12,000 motorcycle loan. The annual interest rate is 6%, and his monthly payment is $365.06. After fifteen months, he receives an inheritance which he wants to use to pay off the loan. How much does he owe at that point? $7260.42

From Concrete to Abstract

Use Exercise 5 to see how well students can incorporate a variable payment amount into their spreadsheet models.

Extending the Concept

Ask students to try to create columns in their spreadsheets that will show just the interest paid each month.

11-6 The Binomial Theorem

Why?

A manager plans to hire 8 new employees. Not wanting to appear biased, the manager wants to hire a combination of males and females that has at least a 10% chance of occurring randomly. If there are an equal number of male and female applicants, is the probability of randomly hiring 6 men and 2 women less than 10%?

Then
You worked with combinations.
(Concepts and Skills Bank, Lesson 0-5)

Now
- Use Pascal's triangle to expand powers of binomials.
- Use the Binomial Theorem to expand powers of binomials.

NGSSS
MA.912.A.4.12 Apply the Binomial Theorem.

New Vocabulary
Pascal's triangle

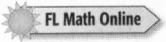

FL Math Online
glencoe.com

Pascal's Triangle In the 13th century, the Chinese discovered a pattern of numbers that would later be referred to as **Pascal's triangle**. This pattern can be used to determine the coefficients of an expanded binomial $(a + b)^n$.

$(a + b)^0$						1					
$(a + b)^1$					1		1				
$(a + b)^2$				1		2		1			
$(a + b)^3$			1		3		3		1		
$(a + b)^4$		1		4		6		4		1	
$(a + b)^5$	1		5		10		10		5		1

For example, the expanded form of
$(a + b)^5 = 1a^5 + 5a^4b + 10a^3b^2 + 10a^2b^3 + 5ab^4 + 1b^5$.

Real-World EXAMPLE 1 Use Pascal's Triangle

Find the probability of hiring 6 men and 2 women by expanding $(m + f)^8$.

Write three more rows of Pascal's triangle and use the pattern to write the expansion.

5				1		5		10		10		5		1			
6			1		6		15		20		15		6		1		
7		1		7		21		35		35		21		7		1	
8	1		8		28		56		70		56		28		8		1

$(m + f)^8 = m^8 + 8m^7f + 28m^6f^2 + 56m^5f^3 + 70m^4f^4 + 56m^3f^5 + 28m^2f^6 + 8mf^7 + f^8$

By adding the coefficients of the polynomial, we determine that there are 256 combinations of males and females that could be hired.

$28m^6f^2$ represents the number of combinations with 6 males and 2 females. Therefore, there is a $\frac{28}{256}$ or about an 11% chance of randomly hiring 6 males and 2 females.

Guided Practice

1. Expand $(c + d)^9$.

1. $c^9 + 9c^8d + 36c^7d^2 + 84c^6d^3 + 126c^5d^4 + 126c^4d^5 + 84c^3d^6 + 36c^2d^7 + 9cd^8 + d^9$

Personal Tutor glencoe.com

The Binomial Theorem Instead of writing out row after row of Pascal's triangle, you can use the **Binomial Theorem** to expand a binomial. Recall that ${}_nC_r = \frac{n!}{r!(n - r)!}$.

11-6 Lesson Notes

1 FOCUS

Vertical Alignment

Before Lesson 11-6
Work with combinations.

Lesson 11-6
Use Pascal's triangle to expand powers of binomials.
Use the Binomial Theorem to expand powers of binomials.

After Lesson 11-6
Find probabilities for binomial experiments.

2 TEACH

Scaffolding Questions

Have students read the *Why?* section of the lesson.

Ask:

- Suppose only 2 men and 2 women are hired. How many sequences of 2 men and 2 women would there be? List them. 6; MMWW, MWMW, MWWM, WMMW, WMWM, WWMM
- Expand $(a + b)^4$. Which term has the coefficient 6? $a^4 + 4a^3b^1 + 6a^2b^2 + 4a^1b^3 + b^4$; $6a^2b^2$
- How many sequences of 3 men and 1 woman would there be? Use your expanded form of $(a + b)^4$. Then list them. 4; MMMW, MWMM, WMMM, MMWM

Lesson 11-6 Resources

Resource	Approaching-Level	On-Level	Beyond-Level	English Learners
Teacher Edition		• Differentiated Instruction, pp. 722, 725	• Differentiated Instruction, p. 725	• Differentiated Instruction, p. 722
Chapter Resource Masters	• Study Guide and Intervention, pp. 39–40 • Skills Practice, p. 41 • Practice, p. 42 • Word Problem Practice, p. 43	• Study Guide and Intervention, pp. 39–40 • Skills Practice, p. 41 • Practice, p. 42 • Word Problem Practice, p. 43 • Enrichment, p. 44	• Practice, p. 42 • Word Problem Practice, p. 43 • Enrichment, p. 44	• Study Guide and Intervention, pp. 39–40 • Skills Practice, p. 41 • Practice, p. 42 • Word Problem Practice, p. 43
Transparencies	• 5-Minute Check Transparency 11-6	• 5-Minute Check Transparency 11-6	• 5-Minute Check Transparency 11-6	• 5-Minute Check Transparency 11-6
Other	• Study Notebook	• Study Notebook	• Study Notebook	• Study Notebook

Pascal's Triangle

Example 1 shows how to use Pascal's triangle to write the expansion of a power of a binomial.

Formative Assessment

Use the Guided Practice exercises after each example to determine students' understanding of concepts.

Additional Example

1 Expand $(p + t)^5$. $p^5 + 5p^4t + 10p^3t^2 + 10p^2t^3 + 5pt^4 + t^5$

Additional Examples also in Interactive Classroom PowerPoint® Presentations

IWB INTERACTIVE WHITEBOARD READY

The Binomial Theorem

Example 2 shows how to use the Binomial Theorem to expand a power of a binomial. **Example 3** uses the factorial form of the Binomial Theorem to expand a power of a binomial with coefficients other than 1. **Example 4** shows how to use the Binomial Theorem to find a particular term of a binomial expansion.

Additional Examples

2 Expand $(t - w)^8$. $t^8 - 8t^7w + 28t^6w^2 - 56t^5w^3 + 70t^4w^4 - 56t^3w^5 + 28t^2w^6 - 8tw^7 + w^8$

3 Expand $(3x - y)^4$. $81x^4 - 108x^3y + 54x^2y^2 - 12xy^3 + y^4$

Key Concept — Binomial Theorem

If n is a natural number, then $(a + b)^n =$

$${}_nC_0\, a^nb^0 + {}_nC_1\, a^{n-1}b^1 + {}_nC_2\, a^{n-2}b^2 + \cdots + {}_nC_n\, a^0b^n = \sum_{k=0}^{n} \frac{n!}{k!(n-k)!} a^{n-k}b^k.$$

StudyTip

Combinations Recall that both ${}_nC_0$ and ${}_nC_n$ equal 1.

To use the theorem, replace n with the value of the exponent. Notice how the terms will follow the pattern of Pascal's triangle, and the coefficients will be symmetric.

EXAMPLE 2 Use the Binomial Theorem

Expand $(a + b)^7$.

Method 1 Use combinations.

Replace n with 7 in the Binomial Theorem.

$$(a + b)^7 = a^7 + {}_7C_1\, a^6b + {}_7C_2\, a^5b^2 + {}_7C_3\, a^4b^3 + {}_7C_4\, a^3b^4 + {}_7C_5\, a^2b^5 + {}_7C_6\, ab^6 + b^7$$

$$= a^7 + \frac{7!}{6!} a^6b + \frac{7!}{2!5!} a^5b^2 + \frac{7!}{3!4!} a^4b^3 + \frac{7!}{4!3!} a^3b^4 + \frac{7!}{5!2!} a^2b^5 + \frac{7!}{6!} ab^6 + b^7$$

$$= a^7 + 7a^6b + 21a^5b^2 + 35a^4b^3 + 35a^3b^4 + 21a^2b^5 + 7ab^6 + b^7$$

Method 2 Use Pascal's triangle.

Use the Binomial Theorem to determine exponents, but instead of finding the coefficients by using combinations, look at the seventh row of Pascal's triangle.

6		1	6	15	20	15	6	1	
7		1	7	21	35	35	21	7	1
8	1	8	28	56	70	56	28	8	1

$$(a + b)^7 = a^7 + 7a^6b + 21a^5b^2 + 35a^4b^3 + 35a^3b^4 + 21a^2b^5 + 7ab^6 + b^7$$

Guided Practice

2. Expand $(x + y)^{10}$.

2. $x^{10} + 10x^9y + 45x^8y^2 + 120x^7y^3 + 210x^6y^4 + 252x^5y^5 + 210x^4y^6 + 120x^3y^7 + 45x^2y^8 + 10xy^9 + y^{10}$

Personal Tutor glencoe.com

When the binomial to be expanded has coefficients other than 1, the coefficients will no longer be symmetrical. In these cases, you may want to use the Binomial Theorem.

StudyTip

Graphing Calculator You can calculate ${}_nC_r$ by using a graphing calculator.

Press MATH and choose PRB 3.

EXAMPLE 3 Coefficients Other Than 1

Expand $(5a - 4b)^4$.

$(5a - 4b)^4$

$$= (5a)^4 + {}_4C_1\,(5a)^3(-4b) + {}_4C_2\,(5a)^2(-4b)^2 + {}_4C_3\,(5a)(-4b)^3 + {}_4C_4\,(-4b)^4$$

$$= 625a^4 + \frac{4!}{3!}(125a^3)(-4b) + \frac{4!}{2!2!}(25a^2)(16b^2) + \frac{4!}{3!}(5a)(-64b^3) + 256b^4$$

$$= 625a^4 - 2000a^3b + 2400a^2b^2 - 1280ab^3 + 256b^4$$

Guided Practice

3. Expand $(3x + 2y)^5$. $243x^5 + 810x^4y + 1080x^3y^2 + 720x^2y^3 + 240xy^4 + 32y^5$

Personal Tutor glencoe.com

Sometimes you may need to find only one term in a binomial expansion. To do this, you can use the summation formula for the Binomial Theorem, $\sum_{k=0}^{n} \frac{n!}{k!(n-k)!} a^{n-k}b^k$.

Differentiated Instruction

OL ELL

If you want to give students the opportunity to be creative,

Then have pairs of students work together to make up a jingle or a poem that describes the patterns in the Binomial Theorem. Ask students to incorporate at least three of the five items listed in the Concept Summary on page 723 of the Student Edition.

EXAMPLE 4 Determine a Single Term

Find the fifth term of $(y + z)^{11}$.

Step 1 Use the Binomial Theorem to write the expansion in sigma notation.

$$(y + z)^{11} = \sum_{k=0}^{11} \frac{11!}{k!(11-k)!} y^{11-k}z^k$$

Step 2 $\frac{11!}{k!(11-k)!} y^{11-k}z^k = \frac{11!}{4!(11-4)!} y^{11-4}z^4$ **For the fifth term, $k = 4$.**

$= 330y^7z^4$ **$C(11, 4) = 330$**

Guided Practice

4. Find the sixth term of $(c + d)^{10}$. $252c^5d^5$

Personal Tutor glencoe.com

Concept Summary Binomial Expansion

In a binomial expansion of $(a + b)^n$,

- there are $n + 1$ terms.
- n is the exponent of a in the first term and b in the last term.
- in successive terms, the exponent of a decreases by 1, and the exponent of b increases by 1.
- the sum of the exponents in each term is n.
- the coefficients are symmetric.

1. $c^5 + 5c^4d + 10c^3d^2 + 10c^2d^3 + 5cd^4 + d^5$ 2. $g^7 + 7g^6h + 21g^5h^2 + 35g^4h^3 + 35g^3h^4 + 21g^2h^5 + 7gh^6 + h^7$

Check Your Understanding

3. $x^6 - 24x^5 + 240x^4 - 1280x^3 + 3840x^2 - 6144x + 4096$
4. $32y^5 - 80y^4z + 80y^3z^2 - 40y^2z^3 + 10yz^4 - z^5$

Examples 1–3 pp. 721–722

5. $x^5 + 15x^4 + 90x^3 + 270x^2 + 405x + 243$
6. $y^4 - 16y^3z + 96y^2z^2 - 256yz^3 + 256z^4$

Expand each binomial.

1. $(c + d)^5$ **2.** $(g + h)^7$ **3.** $(x - 4)^6$

4. $(2y - z)^5$ **5.** $(x + 3)^5$ **6.** $(y - 4z)^4$

7. GENETICS If a woman is equally as likely to have a baby boy or a baby girl, use binomial expansion to determine the probability that 5 of her 6 children are girls. Do not consider identical twins. $\frac{3}{32}$ or 0.09375

Example 4 p. 723

8. $84b^6c^3$
9. $5670x^4y^4$
10. $240a^4b^2$
11. $-108{,}864c^3d^5$
12. y^5
13. $243a^5$

Find the indicated term of each expression.

8. fourth term of $(b + c)^9$ **9** fifth term of $(x + 3y)^8$ **10.** third term of $(a - 4b)^6$

11. sixth term of $(2c - 3d)^8$ **12.** last term of $(5x + y)^5$ **13.** first term of $(3a + 8b)^5$

14. FLOWERS The color of a particular flower is determined by the combination of two genes, also called *alleles*. If the flower has two red alleles r, the flower is red. If the flower has two white alleles w, the flower is white. If the flower has one allele of each color, the flower will be pink. In a lab, two pink flowers are mated and eventually produce 1000 offspring. How many of the 1000 offspring will be pink? 500

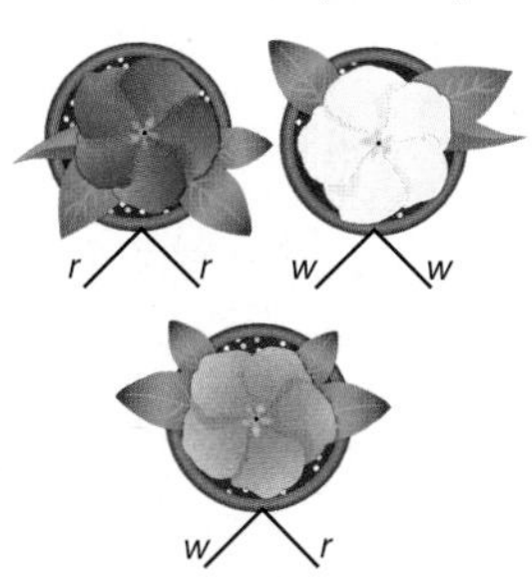

TEACH with TECH

VIDEO RECORDING Have students work in groups to create videos about expanding powers of binomials. Have students explain how to use either Pascal's triangle or the Binomial Theorem to expand the power. Share each group's video with the entire class.

Focus on Mathematical Content

Patterns and the Binomial Theorem For the expansion of $(a + b)^n$, the signs of the terms depend on the signs of a and b. The sign of each term is + if both a and b are positive; the sign of each even-numbered term is – if b alone is negative.

Additional Example

4 Find the fourth term of $(a + 3b)^4$. $108ab^3$

3 PRACTICE

Formative Assessment

Use Exercises 1–14 to check for understanding.

Use the chart at the bottom of this page to customize assignments for your students.

Differentiated Homework Options

Level	Assignment	Two-Day Option	
AL Basic	15–28, 35–52	15–27 odd, 39–42	16–28 even, 35–38, 43–52
OL Core	15–35 odd, 36–52	15–28, 39–42	29–33, 35–38, 43–52
BL Advanced	29–49, (optional: 50–52)		

Study Guide and Intervention
CRM pp. 39–40 AL OL BL

11-6 Study Guide and Intervention
The Binomial Theorem

Pascal's Triangle **Pascal's triangle** is the pattern of coefficients of powers of binomials displayed in triangular form. Each row begins and ends with 1 and each coefficient is the sum of the two coefficients above it in the previous row.

Pascal's Triangle		
	$(a+b)^0$	1
	$(a+b)^1$	1 1
	$(a+b)^2$	1 2 1
	$(a+b)^3$	1 3 3 1
	$(a+b)^4$	1 4 6 4 1
	$(a+b)^5$	1 5 10 10 5 1

Example Use Pascal's triangle to find the number of possible sequences consisting of 3 *a*s and 2 *b*s.

The coefficient 10 of the a^3b^2-term in the expansion of $(a+b)^5$ gives the number of sequences that result in three *a*s and two *b*s.

Exercises

Expand each binomial.

1. $(a+5)^4$ $a^4 + 20a^3 + 150a^2 + 500a + 625$
2. $(x-2y)^6$ $x^6 - 12x^5y + 60x^4y^2 - 160x^3y^3 + 240x^2y^4 - 192xy^5 + 64y^6$
3. $(j-3k)^5$ $j^5 - 15j^4k + 90j^3k^2 - 270j^2k^3 + 405jk^4 - 243k^5$
4. $(2r+t)^7$ $128r^7 + 448r^6t + 672r^5t^2 + 560r^4t^3 + 280r^3t^4 + 84r^2t^5 + 14rt^6 + t^7$
5. $(2p+3m)^6$ $64p^6 + 576p^5m + 2160p^4m^2 + 4320p^3m^3 + 4860p^2m^4 + 2916pm^5 + 729m^6$
6. $\left(a - \frac{b}{2}\right)^4$ $a^4 - 2a^3b + \frac{3}{2}a^2b^2 - \frac{1}{2}ab^3 + \frac{1}{16}b^4$
7. **COIN TOSS** Ray tosses a coin 15 times. How many different sequences of tosses could result in 4 heads and 11 tails? **1365**
8. **QUIZZES** There are 9 true/false questions on a quiz. If twice as many of the statements are true as false, how many different sequences of true/false answers are possible? **84**

Chapter 11 39 Glencoe Algebra 2

Lesson 11-6

Practice
CRM p. 42 AL OL BL ELL

11-6 Practice
The Binomial Theorem

Expand each binomial.

1. $(n+v)^5$ $n^5 + 5n^4v + 10n^3v^2 + 10n^2v^3 + 5nv^4 + v^5$
2. $(x-y)^4$ $x^4 - 4x^3y + 6x^2y^2 - 4xy^3 + y^4$
3. $(x+y)^6$ $x^6 + 6x^5y + 15x^4y^2 + 20x^3y^3 + 15x^2y^4 + 6xy^5 + y^6$
4. $(r+3)^5$ $r^5 + 15r^4 + 90r^3 + 270r^2 + 405r + 243$
5. $(m-5)^5$ $m^5 - 25m^4 + 250m^3 - 1250m^2 + 3125m - 3125$
6. $(x+4)^4$ $x^4 + 16x^3 + 96x^2 + 256x + 256$
7. $(3x+y)^4$ $81x^4 + 108x^3y + 54x^2y^2 + 12xy^3 + y^4$
8. $(2m-y)^4$ $16m^4 - 32m^3y + 24m^2y^2 - 8my^3 + y^4$
9. $(w-3z)^3$ $w^3 - 9w^2z + 27wz^2 - 27z^3$
10. $(2d+3)^6$ $64d^6 + 576d^5 + 2160d^4 + 4320d^3 + 4860d^2 + 2916d + 729$
11. $(x+2y)^5$ $x^5 + 10x^4y + 40x^3y^2 + 80x^2y^3 + 80xy^4 + 32y^5$
12. $(2x-y)^5$ $32x^5 - 80x^4y + 80x^3y^2 - 40x^2y^3 + 10xy^4 - y^5$
13. $(a-3b)^4$ $a^4 - 12a^3b + 54a^2b^2 - 108ab^3 + 81b^4$
14. $(3-2z)^4$ $16z^4 - 96z^3 + 216z^2 - 216z + 81$
15. $(3m-4p)^3$ $27p^3 - 108m^2p + 144mp^2 - 64p^3$
16. $(5x-2y)^4$ $625x^4 - 1000x^3y + 600x^2y^2 - 160xy^3 + 16y^4$

Find the indicated term of each expansion.

17. sixth term of $(x+4y)^6$ $6{,}144xy^5$
18. fourth term of $(5x+2y)^6$ $8{,}000x^2y^4$
19. eighth term of $(x-y)^{11}$ $204x^3y^8$
20. third term of $(x-2)^8$ $36x^6y^2$
21. seventh term of $(a+b)^{10}$ $210a^4b^6$
22. sixth term of $(m-p)^{10}$ $-252m^5p^5$
23. ninth term of $(r-t)^{14}$ $3003r^6t^8$
24. tenth term of $(2x+y)^{12}$ $1760x^3y^9$
25. fourth term of $(x-3y)^6$ $-540x^3y^3$
26. fifth term of $(2x-1)^9$ $4032x^5$
27. **GEOMETRY** How many line segments can be drawn between ten points, no three of which are collinear, if you use exactly two of the ten points to draw each segment? **45**
28. **PROBABILITY** If you toss a coin 4 times, how many different sequences of tosses will give exactly 3 heads and 1 tail or exactly 1 head and 3 tails? **8**

Chapter 11 42 Glencoe Algebra 2

Word Problem Practice
CRM p. 43 AL OL BL ELL

11-6 Word Problem Practice
The Binomial Theorem

1. **AREA** The square shown has a side length of $x + y$. The area must therefore be $(x+y)^2 = x^2 + xy + xy + y^2$. Each of these four terms corresponds to a different part of the area. Place each term in the corresponding region of the square.

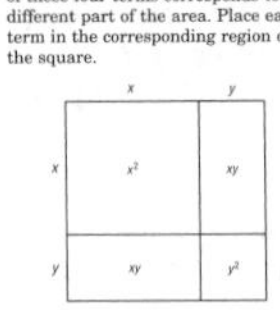

2. **POWERS** The binomial theorem states $(x+y)^n = \sum_{k=0}^{n} \frac{n!}{k!(n-k)} x^{n-k}y^k$. Explain what this implies about powers of 2 if you substitute $x = y = 1$ into the equation.
The sum of the entries in a row of Pascal's triangle is a power of 2.

3. **SUPREME COURT** There are nine judges on the Supreme Court, and for most rulings, a majority is needed. How many combinations of votes are possible for a majority to be reached? (*Hint:* The majority could be 5, 6, 7, 8, or 9 votes.)
${}_9C_5 + {}_9C_6 + {}_9C_7 + {}_9C_8 + {}_9C_9 = 256$

4. **SYMMETRY** Each row of Pascal's triangle is like a palindrome. That is, the numbers read the same left to right as they do right to left. Explain why this is the case.
Possible answer: If you switch x and y in the Binomial Theorem, the coefficients reverse their order, yet $(x+y)^n = (y+x)^n$ because $x + y = y + x$. Therefore, the coefficients must read the same forward and back.

5. **VOLUME** The length of each side of this cube is $x + y$ units.

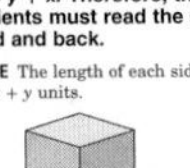

a. Expand $(x+y)^3$ using the Binomial Theorem.
$x^3 + 3x^2y + 3xy^2 + y^3$

b. Make a picture similar to the one used in Exercise 1 for the cube. For the three-dimensional cube, it helps to make a blow-up version of the drawing.

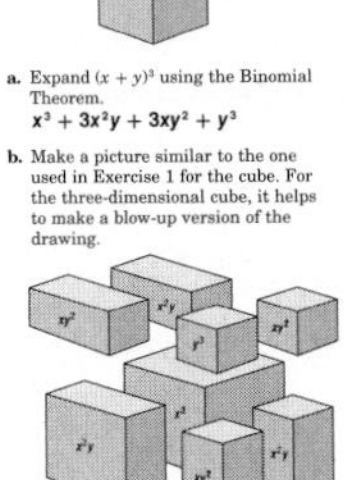

Chapter 11 43 Glencoe Algebra 2

Lesson 11-6

Practice and Problem Solving

● = **Step-by-Step Solutions** begin on page R20.
Extra Practice begins on page 947.

Examples 1–3 pp. 721–722

Expand each binomial. **15.** $a^6 - 6a^5b + 15a^4b^2 - 20a^3b^3 + 15a^2b^4 - 6ab^5 + b^6$

15. $(a-b)^6$ **16.** $(c-d)^7$ **17.** $(x+6)^6$

18. $(y-5)^7$ **19.** $(2a+4b)^4$ **20.** $(3a-4b)^5$

18. $y^7 - 35y^6 + 525y^5 - 4375y^4 + 21{,}875y^3 - 65{,}625y^2 + 109{,}375y - 78{,}125$

16. $c^7 - 7c^6d + 21c^5d^2 - 35c^4d^3 + 35c^3d^4 - 21c^2d^5 + 7cd^6 - d^7$

17. $x^6 + 36x^5 + 540x^4 + 4320x^3 + 19{,}440x^2 + 46{,}656x + 46{,}656$

19. $16a^4 + 128a^3b + 384a^2b^2 + 512ab^3 + 256b^4$

21. **COMMITTEES** If an equal number of men and women applied to be on a community planning committee and the committee needs a total of 10 people, find the probability that 7 of the members will be women. Assume that committee members will be chosen randomly. $\frac{120}{1024} = \frac{15}{128} \approx 0.117$

22. **BASEBALL** If a pitcher is just as likely to throw a ball as a strike, find the probability that 11 of his first 12 pitches are balls. $\frac{12}{4096} = \frac{3}{1024} \approx 0.00293$

Example 4 p. 723

20. $243a^5 - 1620a^4b + 4320a^3b^2 - 5760a^2b^3 + 3840ab^4 - 1024b^5$

Find the indicated term of each expression.

23. third term of $(x+2z)^7$ $84x^5z^2$

24. fourth term of $(y-3x)^6$ $-540y^3x^3$

25. seventh term of $(2a-2b)^8$ $7168a^2b^6$

26. sixth term of $(4x+5y)^6$ $75{,}000xy^5$

27. fifth term of $(x-4)^9$ $32{,}256x^5$

28. fourth term of $(c+6)^8$ $12{,}096c^5$

B **Expand each binomial.** **29–32. See margin.**

29. $\left(x + \frac{1}{2}\right)^5$ **30.** $\left(x - \frac{1}{3}\right)^4$

31. $\left(2b + \frac{1}{4}\right)^5$ **32.** $\left(3c + \frac{1}{3}\right)^5$

Real-World Link

As of 2007, Mike Vanderjagt of the Dallas Cowboys had the highest field goal percentage in the history of the NFL, at over 86%.

Source: NFL

33. **FOOTBALL** In $\frac{n!}{k!(n-k)!}p^kq^{n-k}$, let p represent the likelihood of a success and q represent the likelihood of a failure.

a. If a place-kicker makes 70% of his kicks within 40 yards, find the likelihood that he makes 9 of his next 10 attempts from within 40 yards. **0.121**

b. If a quarterback completes 60% of his passes, find the likelihood that he completes 8 of his next 10 attempts. **0.121**

c. If a team converts 30% of their two-point conversions, find the likelihood that they convert 2 of their next 5 conversions. **0.309**

H.O.T. Problems
Use Higher-Order Thinking Skills

C **34.** **CHALLENGE** Find the sixth term of the expansion of $(\sqrt{a} + \sqrt{b})^{12}$. Explain your reasoning. $792a^3b^2\sqrt{ab}$

35. **REASONING** Explain how the terms of $(x+y)^n$ and $(x-y)^n$ are the same and how they are different.

35. Sample answer: While they have the same terms, the signs for $(x+y)^n$ will all be positive, while the signs for $(x-y)^n$ will alternate.

36. **REASONING** Determine whether the following statement is *true* or *false*. Explain your reasoning. **See margin.**

The eighth and twelfth terms of $(x+y)^{20}$ have the same coefficients.

37. **OPEN ENDED** Write a power of a binomial for which the second term of the expansion is $6x^4y$. **Sample answer: $\left(x + \frac{6}{5}y\right)^5$**

38. **WRITING IN MATH** Explain how to write out the terms of Pascal's triangle. **See margin.**

Enrichment
CRM p. 44 OL BL

11-6 Enrichment

Patterns in Pascal's Triangle

You have learned that the coefficients in the expansion of $(x+y)^n$ yield a number pyramid called **Pascal's triangle.**

Row 1 →	1
Row 2 →	1 1
Row 3 →	1 2 1
Row 4 →	1 3 3 1
Row 5 →	1 4 6 4 1
Row 6 →	1 5 10 10 5 1
Row 7 →	1 6 15 20 15 6 1

As many rows can be added to the bottom of the pyramid as you please.

This activity explores some of the interesting properties of this famous number pyramid.

1. Pick a row of Pascal's triangle.

a. What is the sum of all the numbers in all the rows *above* the row you picked? **See students' work.**

b. What is the sum of all the numbers in the row you picked? **See students' work.**

Additional Answers

29. $x^5 + \frac{5}{2}x^4 + \frac{5}{2}x^3 + \frac{5}{4}x^2 + \frac{5}{16}x + \frac{1}{32}$

30. $x^4 - \frac{4}{3}x^3 + \frac{2}{3}x^2 - \frac{4}{27}x + \frac{1}{81}$

31. $32b^5 + 20b^4 + 5b^3 + \frac{5}{8}b^2 + \frac{5}{128}b + \frac{1}{1024}$

32. $243c^5 + 135c^4 + 30c^3 + \frac{10}{3}c^2 + \frac{5}{27}c + \frac{1}{243}$

NGSSS PRACTICE 912.P.3.1, 912.A.2.12, 912.G.7.5, 912.A.3.1

39. PROBABILITY A desk drawer contains 7 sharpened red pencils, 5 sharpened yellow pencils, 3 unsharpened red pencils, and 5 unsharpened yellow pencils. If a pencil is taken from the drawer at random, what is the probability that it is yellow, given that it is one of the sharpened pencils? **A**

A. $\frac{5}{12}$

B. $\frac{7}{20}$

C. $\frac{5}{8}$

D. $\frac{1}{5}$

40. GRIDDED RESPONSE Two people are 17.5 miles apart. They begin to walk toward each other along a straight line at the same time. One walks at the rate of 4 miles per hour, and the other walks at the rate of 3 miles per hour. In how many hours will they meet? **2.5**

41. GEOMETRY Christie has a cylindrical block that she needs to paint for an art project.

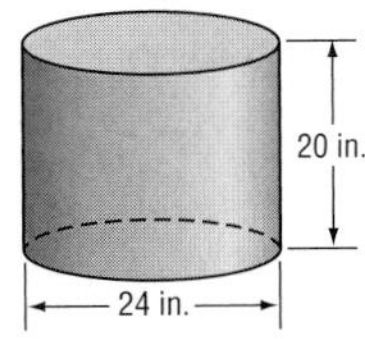

What is the surface area of the cylinder in square inches rounded to the nearest square inch? **G**

F. 1960

G. 2413

H. 5127

I. 6635

42. Which of the following is a linear function? **C**

A. $y = \frac{x+3}{x+2}$

B. $y = (3x + 2)^2$

C. $y = \frac{x+3}{2}$

D. $y = |3x| + 2$

Spiral Review

Find the first five terms of each sequence. (Lesson 11-5)

43. $a_1 = -2, a_{n+1} = a_n + 5$ **−2, 3, 8, 13, 18**

44. $a_1 = 3, a_{n+1} = 4a_n - 10$ **3, 2, −2, −18, −82**

45. $a_1 = 4, a_{n+1} = 3a_n - 6$ **4, 6, 12, 30, 84**

Find the sum of each infinite geometric series, if it exists. (Lesson 11-4)

46. $-6 + 3 - \frac{3}{2} + \ldots$ **−4**

47. $\frac{3}{4} + \frac{1}{4} + \frac{1}{12} + \ldots$ **$1\frac{1}{8}$**

48. $\sqrt{3} + 3 + \sqrt{27} + \ldots$ **No sum exists.**

49. TRAVEL A trip between two towns takes 4 hours under ideal conditions. The first 150 miles of the trip is on an interstate, and the last 130 miles is on a highway with a speed limit that is 10 miles per hour less than on the interstate. (Lesson 9-6)

a. If x represents the speed limit on the interstate, write expressions for the time spent at that speed and for the time spent on the other highway. **$\frac{150}{x}, \frac{130}{x-10}$**

b. Write and solve an equation to find the speed limits on the two highways. **$\frac{150}{x} + \frac{130}{x-10} = 4$; 75 mph, 65 mph**

Skills Review

50. true; $\frac{(1+1)(1+1)}{2} = 2$

State whether each statement is *true* or *false* when $n = 1$. Explain. (Lesson 1-1)

50. $\frac{(n+1)(n+1)}{2} = 2$

51. $3n + 5$ is even. **true; $3(1) + 5 = 8$, which is even**

52. $n^2 - 1$ is odd. **false; $1^2 - 1 = 0$, which is not odd**

Differentiated Instruction OL BL

Extension Write $(1.002)^5$ on the board and ask students how they could write this expression as the 5th power of a binomial. Then have them use the Binomial Theorem to find the decimal value of $(1.002)^5$ to five decimal places. 1.01004

Exercise Alert

Formula For Exercise 41, students will need to know the formula for the volume of a cylinder is $V = \pi r^2 h$.

4 ASSESS

Ticket Out the Door Give the students small pieces of paper. Have them write the first seven rows of Pascal's triangle on the papers and hand them to you as they leave the room.

Additional Answers

36. Sample answer: False; a binomial to the 20th power will have 21 terms. The eleventh term will be in the middle and the rest of the terms will be symmetric. The tenth term corresponds with the twelfth term.

38. Sample answer: The first row is a 1. The second row is two 1s. Each new row begins and ends with 1. Each coefficient is the sum of the two coefficients above it in the previous row.

Lesson 11-6 The Binomial Theorem 725

EXTEND **11-6** Lesson Notes

1 FOCUS

Objective Use combinations and Pascal's triangle to determine the number of ways the prizes of a game can be chosen.

Teaching Tip

The main difference between a permutation and a combination is whether order is considered. In a permutation, order matters. In a combination, order does not matter. To help students understand the difference, you may wish to show the number of combinations possible when choosing 2 snacks from a possible 6 different choices.

2 TEACH

Working in Cooperative Groups

Pair students with different abilities. Have students work through the Activity and then answer Exercises 1–2.

Ask:

- What do you notice about ${}_5C_2$ and ${}_5C_3$? They are the same: 10.
- Can you ever have ${}_5C_6$? no
- How can you extend Pascal's triangle to include more rows? Sample answer: Use the patterns found in the triangle: the first and the last numbers are always 1, each next number is then the sum of the two numbers closest to it in the line above the number. Each line has one more number in it than the line above it.

Practice Have students complete Exercise 3.

EXTEND **11-6** Algebra Lab

Combinations and Pascal's Triangle

NGSSS **MA.912.A.9.2** Use formulas for permutations and combinations to count outcomes and determine probabilities of events.

Recall that an arrangement or selection of objects in which order is not important is called a *combination*. For example, selecting 2 snacks from a choice of 6 is a combination of 6 objects taken 2 at a time and can be written ${}_6C_2$ or C(6, 2).

ACTIVITY

A contestant on a game show has the opportunity to win up to five prizes, one for each of five rounds of the game. If the contestant wins a round, he or she may choose one prize. Determine the number of ways that prizes can be chosen.

Step 1 If a contestant does not win any rounds, he or she receives 0 prizes. This represents 5 items taken 0 at a time.

$${}_nC_r = \frac{n!}{(n-r)!\,r!}$$ **Definition of combination**

$${}_5C_0 = \frac{5!}{(5-0)!\,0!}$$ **$n = 5$ and $r = 0$**

$$= \frac{120}{120(1)} \text{ or } 1$$ **$5! = 120$ and $0! = 1$**

There is 1 way to receive 0 prizes.

If a contestant wins one round, any one of the prizes can be selected. If a contestant wins two rounds, two prizes can be chosen. If three rounds are won, three prizes can be chosen, and so on. In how many ways can 1 prize be chosen? 2 prizes? 3, 4, and 5 prizes? We can determine these answers by examining Pascal's triangle.

Step 2 Examine Pascal's triangle.

List Rows 0 through 5 of Pascal's triangle.

Row 0						1					
Row 1					1		1				
Row 2				1		2		1			
Row 3			1		3		3		1		
Row 4		1		4		6		4		1	
Row 5	1		5		10		10		5		1

The number of ways one prize can be chosen from 5 can be determined by looking at Row 5. The first number in Row 5 represents the number of ways to choose 0 prizes, the second number represents the number of ways to choose 1 prize, and so on.

Analyze the Results

1. Sample answer: There are n objects, so use Row n to find the number of choices. The first number is 0 objects selected, the second number is 1 object selected, and so on.

1. Make a conjecture about how the numbers in one of the rows can be used to find the number of ways that 0, 1, 2, 3, 4, …, n objects can be selected from n objects.
2. Suppose the rules of the game are changed so that there are 6 rounds and 6 prizes from which to choose. Find the number of ways that 0, 1, 2, 3, 4, 5, or 6 prizes can be chosen. Which row of Pascal's triangle can be used to find the answers? **1, 6, 15, 20, 15, 6, 1; Row 6**
3. Use Pascal's triangle to find ${}_8C_0$, ${}_8C_1$, ${}_8C_2$, ${}_8C_3$, ${}_8C_4$, ${}_8C_5$, ${}_8C_6$, ${}_8C_7$, and ${}_8C_8$. State the row number that you used to find the answers. **1, 8, 28, 56, 70, 56, 28, 8, 1; Row 8**

3 ASSESS

Formative Assessment

Use Exercise 3 to assess whether students understand how to use combinations and Pascal's triangle to find the number of ways prizes can be chosen.

From Concrete to Abstract

Ask students to use Pascal's triangle to show that ${}_nC_k = {}_nC_{n-k}$. When Pascal's triangle is folded across a vertical center line, the numbers match. The corresponding numbers match k with $n - k$.

726 Chapter 11 Sequences and Series

Proof by Mathematical Induction

Then
You have proved the sum of an arithmetic series. (Lesson 11-2)

Now
- Prove statements by using mathematical induction.
- Disprove statements by finding a counterexample.

NGSSS
Preparation for MA.912.D.1.3 Use mathematical induction to prove various concepts in number theory (such as sums of infinite integer series, divisibility statements, and parity statements), recurrence relations, and other applications.

New Vocabulary
mathematical induction
induction hypothesis

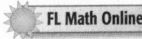

FL Math Online
glencoe.com

Why?

When dominoes are set up closely and the first domino is knocked down, the rest of the dominoes come tumbling down. All that is needed with this setup is for the first domino to fall, and the rest will follow. The same is true with mathematical induction.

Mathematical Induction **Mathematical induction** is a method of proving statements involving natural numbers.

Key Concept Mathematical Induction

To prove that a statement is true for all natural numbers n,

Step 1 Show that the statement is true for $n = 1$.

Step 2 Assume that the statement is true for some natural number k. This assumption is called the **induction hypothesis**.

Step 3 Show that the statement is true for the next natural number $k + 1$.

EXAMPLE 1 Prove Summation

Prove that $1^3 + 2^3 + 3^3 + \cdots + n^3 = \frac{n^2(n+1)^2}{4}$.

Step 1 When $n = 1$, the left side of the equation is 1^3 or 1.
The right side is $\frac{1^2(1+1)^2}{4}$ or 1. Thus, the statement is true for $n = 1$.

Step 2 Assume that $1^3 + 2^3 + 3^3 + \cdots + k^3 = \frac{k^2(k+1)^2}{4}$ for a natural number k.

Step 3 Show that the given statement is true for $n = k + 1$.

$$1^3 + 2^3 + 3^3 + \cdots + k^3 = \frac{k^2(k+1)^2}{4} \quad \text{Inductive hypothesis}$$

$$1^3 + 2^3 + \cdots + k^3 + (k+1)^3 = \frac{k^2(k+1)^2}{4} + (k+1)^3 \quad \text{Add } (k+1)^3 \text{ to each side.}$$

$$= \frac{k^2(k+1)^2 + 4(k+1)^3}{4} \quad \text{The LCD is 4.}$$

$$= \frac{(k+1)^2[k^2 + 4(k+1)]}{4} \quad \text{Factor.}$$

$$= \frac{(k+1)^2(k^2 + 4k + 4)}{4} \quad \text{Simplify.}$$

$$= \frac{(k+1)^2(k+2)^2}{4} \quad \text{Factor.}$$

The last expression is the statement to be proved, where n has been replaced by $k + 1$. This proves the conjecture.

Guided Practice

1. Prove that $1^2 + 2^2 + 3^2 + \cdots + n^2 = \frac{n(n+1)(2n+1)}{6}$. **See Chapter 11 Answer Appendix.**

Personal Tutor glencoe.com

1 FOCUS

Vertical Alignment

Before Lesson 11-7
Prove the sum of an arithmetic series.

Lesson 11-7
Prove statements by using mathematical induction.
Disprove statements by finding a counterexample.

After Lesson 11-7
Prove limits of sequences using mathematical induction.

2 TEACH

Scaffolding Questions

Have students read the *Why?* section of the lesson.

Ask:
- Imagine the positive integers are assigned to each of the dominoes. What will make domino number 2 fall down? Domino number 1 must fall.
- What will make domino number 3 fall down? Domino number 2 must fall.
- If the domino n falls down, what happens to domino $n + 1$? It falls.

Mathematical Induction

Examples 1 and 2 illustrate the three-step procedure for proof by mathematical induction.

Lesson 11-7 Resources

Resource	Approaching-Level	On-Level	Beyond-Level	English Learners
Teacher Edition	• Differentiated Instruction, p. 728	• Differentiated Instruction, pp. 728, 731	• Differentiated Instruction, p. 731	
Chapter Resource Masters	• Study Guide and Intervention, pp. 45–46 • Skills Practice, p. 47 • Practice, p. 48 • Word Problem Practice, p. 49	• Study Guide and Intervention, pp. 45–46 • Skills Practice, p. 47 • Practice, p. 48 • Word Problem Practice, p. 49 • Enrichment, p. 50	• Practice, p. 48 • Word Problem Practice, p. 49 • Enrichment, p. 50	• Study Guide and Intervention, pp. 45–46 • Skills Practice, p. 47 • Practice, p. 48 • Word Problem Practice, p. 49
Transparencies	• 5-Minute Check Transparency 11-7	• 5-Minute Check Transparency 11-7	• 5-Minute Check Transparency 11-7	• 5-Minute Check Transparency 11-7
Other	• Study Notebook	• Study Notebook	• Study Notebook	• Study Notebook

Formative Assessment

Use the Guided Practice exercises after each example to determine students' understanding of concepts.

TEACH with TECH

VIDEO RECORDING Record yourself as you teach the class about mathematical induction and work through several examples. Post the video to a video sharing Web site for students to use as a reference outside of class.

Additional Examples

1 Prove that $1 + 4 + 7 + \ldots + (3n - 2) = \frac{n(3n-1)}{2}$.

Step 1: When $n = 1$, the left side of the given equation is 1. The right side is $\frac{1[3(1)-1]}{2}$ or 1. Thus, the statement is true for $n = 1$.

Step 2: Assume $1 + 4 + 7 + \ldots + (3k - 2) = \frac{k(3k-1)}{2}$ for a natural number k.

Step 3: $1 + 4 + 7 + \ldots + (3k - 2) + [3(k + 1) - 2]$

$= \frac{k(3k-1)}{2} + [3(k+1) - 2]$

$= \frac{3k^2 - k + 6k + 2}{2}$

$= \frac{3k^2 + 5k + 2}{2}$

$= \frac{(k+1)(3k+2)}{2}$.

The last expression is the statement to be proved, where n has been replaced by $k + 1$.

2 Prove that $6^n - 1$ is divisible by 5 for all positive integers n. Proof uses steps similar to those in Example 2 in the Student Edition.

Additional Examples also in Interactive Classroom PowerPoint® Presentations

IWB INTERACTIVE WHITEBOARD READY

Along with summation, mathematical induction can be used to prove divisibility.

EXAMPLE 2 Prove Divisibility

Prove that $8^n - 1$ is divisible by 7 for all natural numbers n.

Step 1 When $n = 1$, $8^n - 1 = 8^1 - 1$ or 7. Since 7 is divisible by 7, the statement is true for $n = 1$.

Step 2 Assume that $8^k - 1$ is divisible by 7 for some natural number k. This means that there is a natural number r such that $8^k - 1 = 7r$.

Step 3 Show that the statement is true for $n = k + 1$.

$8^k - 1 = 7r$	**Inductive hypothesis**
$8^k = 7r + 1$	**Add 1 to each side.**
$8(8^k) = 8(7r + 1)$	**Multiply each side by 8.**
$8^{k+1} = 56r + 8$	**Simplify.**
$8^{k+1} - 1 = 56r + 7$	**Subtract 1 from each side.**
$8^{k+1} - 1 = 7(8r + 1)$	**Factor.**

Since r is a natural number, $8r + 1$ is a natural number and $7(8r + 1)$ is divisible by 7. Therefore, $8^{k+1} - 1$ is divisible by 7.

This proves that $8^{n} - 1$ is divisible by 7 for all natural numbers n.

StudyTip

Divisibility The r is a whole number used to show divisibility in proof. When a value equals $4r$, then it must be divisible by 4.

Guided Practice

2. Prove that $7^n - 1$ is divisible by 6 for all natural numbers n. **See Chapter 11 Answer Appendix.**

Personal Tutor glencoe.com

Counterexamples Statements can be proved false by using mathematical induction. An easier method is by finding a counterexample, which is a specific case in which the statement is false.

Review Vocabulary

counterexample One of the synonyms of *counter* is to *contradict*, so a counterexample is an example that contradicts a hypothesis.

EXAMPLE 3 Use a Counterexample to Disprove

Find a counterexample to disprove the statement that $2^n + 2n^2$ is divisible by 4 for any natural number n.

Test different values of n.

n	$2^n + 2n^2$	Divisible by 4?
1	$2^1 + 2(1)^2 = 2 + 2$ or 4	yes
2	$2^2 + 2(2)^2 = 4 + 8$ or 12	yes
3	$2^3 + 2(3)^2 = 8 + 18$ or 26	no

The value $n = 3$ is a counterexample for the statement.

Guided Practice

3. Find a counterexample to disprove $1^2 + 2^2 + 3^2 + \cdots + n^2 = \frac{n(3n-1)}{2}$. $n = 3$

Personal Tutor glencoe.com

Differentiated Instruction

AL OL

Kinesthetic Learners Have students demonstrate proof by induction by organizing themselves into a line. Instruct each person to tell any message he hears to the person behind him. Tell the first person a message. Explain that the first person telling the next person assures that $n = 1$ is true. And, your instructions to tell all messages heard to the next person assures that $k + 1$ is true.

Check Your Understanding

Example 1 p. 727

Prove that each statement is true for all natural numbers.

1. $1 + 3 + 5 + \cdots + (2n - 1) = n^2$ See margin.
2. $1 + 2 + 3 + \cdots + n = \frac{n(n+1)}{2}$ See Chapter 11 Answer Appendix.

3. **NUMBER THEORY** A number is *triangular* if it can be represented visually by a triangular array. c. See Chapter 11 Answer Appendix.

10

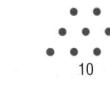

   a. The first triangular number is 1. Find the next 5 triangular numbers. 3, 6, 10, 15, 21
   b. Write a formula for the nth triangular number. $a_n = \frac{n(n+1)}{2}$
   c. Prove that the sum of the first n triangular numbers equals $\frac{n(n+1)(n+2)}{6}$.

Example 2 p. 728

Prove that each statement is true for all natural numbers. 4, 5. See Chapter 11 Answer Appendix.

4. $10^n - 1$ is divisible by 9.
5. $4^n - 1$ is divisible by 3.

Example 3 p. 728

Find a counterexample to disprove each statement.

6. $3^n + 1$ is divisible by 4. $n = 2$
7. $2^n + 3^n$ is divisible by 4. $n = 1$

Practice and Problem Solving

= **Step-by-Step Solutions** begins on page R20. **Extra Practice** begins on page 947.

Example 1 p. 727

Prove that each statement is true for all natural numbers. 8–15. See Chapter 11 Answer Appendix.

8. $\frac{1}{2} + \frac{1}{2^2} + \frac{1}{2^3} + \cdots + \frac{1}{2^n} = 1 - \frac{1}{2^n}$
9. $2 + 5 + 8 + \cdots + (3n - 1) = \frac{n(3n+1)}{2}$
10. $1 + 2 + 4 + \cdots + 2^{n-1} = 2^n - 1$
11. $1 + 5 + 9 + \cdots + (4n - 3) = n(2n - 1)$
12. $1 + 4 + 7 + \cdots + (3n - 2) = \frac{n(3n-1)}{2}$
13. $3 + 7 + 11 + \cdots + (4n - 1) = 2n^2 + n$
14. $\frac{1}{2} + \frac{1}{6} + \frac{1}{12} + \cdots + \frac{1}{n(n+1)} = \frac{n}{n+1}$
15. $1^2 + 3^2 + 5^2 + \cdots + (2n - 1)^2 = \frac{n(2n-1)(2n+1)}{3}$

16. **GEOMETRY** According to the Interior Angle Sum Formula, if a convex polygon has n sides, then the sum of the measures of the interior angles of a polygon equals $180(n - 2)$. Prove this formula for $n \geq 3$ using mathematical induction and geometry. See Chapter 11 Answer Appendix.

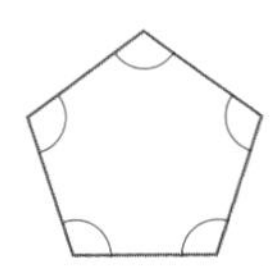

Example 2 p. 728

Prove that each statement is true for all natural numbers. 17–20. See Chapter 11 Answer Appendix.

17. $5^n + 3$ is divisible by 4.
18. $9^n - 1$ is divisible by 8.
19. $12^n + 10$ is divisible by 11.
20. $13^n + 11$ is divisible by 12.

Example 3 p. 728

Find a counterexample to disprove each statement.

21. $1 + 2 + 3 + \cdots + n = n^2$ $n = 2$
22. $1 + 8 + 27 + \cdots + n^3 = (2n + 2)^2$ $n = 3$
23. $n^2 - n + 15$ is prime. $n = 1$
24. $n^2 + n + 23$ is prime. $n = 1$

Counterexamples

Example 3 illustrates proving that a formula is not true by finding a counterexample.

Additional Example

3 Find a counterexample for the statement that $n^2 + n + 5$ is always a prime number for any positive integer n. Sample answer: $n = 4$

3 PRACTICE

Formative Assessment

Use Exercises 1–7 to check for understanding.

Use the chart at the bottom of this page to customize assignments for your students.

Additional Answer

1. Step 1: When $n = 1$, the left side of the given equation is 1. The right side is 1^2 or 1, so the equation is true for $n = 1$.
Step 2: Assume that $1 + 3 + 5 + \ldots + (2k - 1) = k^2$ for some natural number k.
Step 3: $1 + 3 + 5 + \ldots + (2k - 1) + (2(k + 1) - 1)$
$= k^2 + (2(k + 1) - 1)$
$= k^2 + (2k + 2 - 1)$
$= k^2 + 2k + 1$
$= (k + 1)^2$
The last expression is the right side of the equation to be proved, where $n = k + 1$. Thus, the equation is true for $n = k + 1$.
Therefore, $1 + 3 + 5 + \ldots + (2n - 1) = n^2$ for all natural numbers n.

Differentiated Homework Options

Level	Assignment	Two-Day Option	
AL Basic	8–24, 34–35, 37–62	9–23 odd, 41–45	8–24 even, 34–35, 38–40, 45–62
OL Core	9–31 odd, 32, 34–35, 37–62	8–24, 41–44	25–32, 34–35, 37–40
BL Advanced	25–50, (optional: 51–62)		

Study Guide and Intervention

CRM pp. 45–46 AL OL ELL

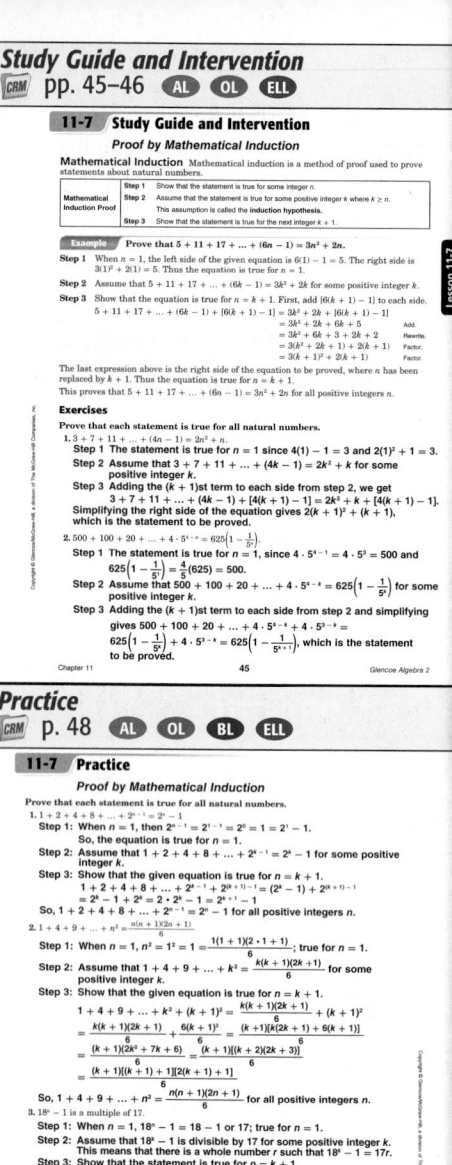

11-7 Study Guide and Intervention

Proof by Mathematical Induction

Mathematical Induction Mathematical induction is a method of proof used to prove statements about natural numbers.

Mathematical Induction Proof	Step 1	Show that the statement is true for some integer n.
	Step 2	Assume that the statement is true for some positive integer k where $k \geq n$. This assumption is called the **induction hypothesis.**
	Step 3	Show that the statement is true for the next integer $k + 1$.

Example Prove that $5 + 11 + 17 + ... + (6n - 1) = 3n^2 + 2n$.

Step 1 When $n = 1$, the left side of the given equation is $6(1) - 1 = 5$. The right side is $3(1)^2 + 2(1) = 5$. Thus the equation is true for $n = 1$.

Step 2 Assume that $5 + 11 + 17 + ... + (6k - 1) = 3k^2 + 2k$ for some positive integer k.

Step 3 Show that the equation is true for $n = k + 1$. First, add $[6(k + 1) - 1]$ to each side.

$$5 + 11 + 17 + ... + (6k - 1) + [6(k + 1) - 1] = 3k^2 + 2k + [6(k + 1) - 1]$$
$$= 3k^2 + 2k + 6k + 5 \quad \text{Add.}$$
$$= 3k^2 + 6k + 3 + 2k + 2 \quad \text{Rewrite.}$$
$$= 3(k^2 + 2k + 1) + 2(k + 1) \quad \text{Factor.}$$
$$= 3(k + 1)^2 + 2(k + 1) \quad \text{Factor.}$$

The last expression above is the right side of the equation to be proved, where n has been replaced by $k + 1$. Thus the equation is true for $n = k + 1$.

This proves that $5 + 11 + 17 + ... + (6n - 1) = 3n^2 + 2n$ for all positive integers n.

Exercises

Prove that each statement is true for all natural numbers.

1. $3 + 7 + 11 + ... + (4n - 1) = 2n^2 + n$.
   Step 1 The statement is true for $n = 1$ since $4(1) - 1 = 3$ and $2(1)^2 + 1 = 3$.
   Step 2 Assume that $3 + 7 + 11 + ... + (4k - 1) = 2k^2 + k$ for some positive integer k.
   Step 3 Adding the $(k + 1)$st term to each side from step 2, we get $3 + 7 + 11 + ... + (4k - 1) + [4(k + 1) - 1] = 2k^2 + k + [4(k + 1) - 1]$.
   Simplifying the right side of the equation gives $2(k + 1)^2 + (k + 1)$, which is the statement to be proved.

2. $500 + 100 + 20 + ... + 4 \cdot 5^{4-n} = 625\left(1 - \frac{1}{5^n}\right)$.
   Step 1 The statement is true for $n = 1$, since $4 \cdot 5^{4-1} = 4 \cdot 5^3 = 500$ and $625\left(1 - \frac{1}{5^1}\right) = \frac{4}{5}(625) = 500$.
   Step 2 Assume that $500 + 100 + 20 + ... + 4 \cdot 5^{4-k} = 625\left(1 - \frac{1}{5^k}\right)$ for some positive integer k.
   Step 3 Adding the $(k + 1)$st term to each side from step 2 and simplifying gives $500 + 100 + 20 + ... + 4 \cdot 5^{4-k} + 4 \cdot 5^{3-k} = 625\left(1 - \frac{1}{5^k}\right) + 4 \cdot 5^{3-k} = 625\left(1 - \frac{1}{5^{k+1}}\right)$, which is the statement to be proved.

Chapter 11 45 Glencoe Algebra 2

Lesson 11-7

Practice

CRM p. 48 AL OL BL ELL

11-7 Practice

Proof by Mathematical Induction

Prove that each statement is true for all natural numbers.

1. $1 + 2 + 4 + 8 + ... + 2^{n-1} = 2^n - 1$
   Step 1: When $n = 1$, then $2^{n-1} = 2^{1-1} = 2^0 = 1 = 2^1 - 1$. So, the equation is true for $n = 1$.
   Step 2: Assume that $1 + 2 + 4 + 8 + ... + 2^{k-1} = 2^k - 1$ for some positive integer k.
   Step 3: Show that the given equation is true for $n = k + 1$.
   $1 + 2 + 4 + 8 + ... + 2^{k-1} + 2^{(k+1)-1} = (2^k - 1) + 2^{(k+1)-1}$
   $= 2^k - 1 + 2^k = 2 \cdot 2^k - 1 = 2^{k+1} - 1$
   So, $1 + 2 + 4 + 8 + ... + 2^{n-1} = 2^n - 1$ for all positive integers n.

2. $1 + 4 + 9 + ... + n^2 = \frac{n(n + 1)(2n + 1)}{6}$
   Step 1: When $n = 1$, $n^2 = 1^2 = 1 = \frac{1(1 + 1)(2 \cdot 1 + 1)}{6}$; true for $n = 1$.
   Step 2: Assume that $1 + 4 + 9 + ... + k^2 = \frac{k(k + 1)(2k + 1)}{6}$ for some positive integer k.
   Step 3: Show that the given equation is true for $n = k + 1$.
   $1 + 4 + 9 + ... + k^2 + (k + 1)^2 = \frac{k(k + 1)(2k + 1)}{6} + (k + 1)^2$
   $= \frac{k(k + 1)(2k + 1)}{6} + \frac{6(k + 1)^2}{6} = \frac{(k + 1)[k(2k + 1) + 6(k + 1)]}{6}$
   $= \frac{(k + 1)(2k^2 + 7k + 6)}{6} = \frac{(k + 1)[(k + 2)(2k + 3)]}{6}$
   $= \frac{(k + 1)[(k + 1) + 1][2(k + 1) + 1]}{6}$
   So, $1 + 4 + 9 + ... + n^2 = \frac{n(n + 1)(2n + 1)}{6}$ for all positive integers n.

3. $18^n - 1$ is a multiple of 17.
   Step 1: When $n = 1$, $18^n - 1 = 18 - 1$ or 17; true for $n = 1$.
   Step 2: Assume that $18^k - 1$ is divisible by 17 for some positive integer k. This means that there is a whole number r such that $18^k - 1 = 17r$.
   Step 3: Show that the statement is true for $n = k + 1$.
   $18^k - 1 = 17r$, so $18^k = 17r + 1$, and $18(18^k) = 18(17r + 1)$. This is equivalent to $18^{k+1} = 306r + 18$, so $18^{k+1} - 1 = 306r + 17$, and $18^{k+1} - 1 = 17(18r + 1)$.
   Since r is a whole number, $18r + 1$ is a whole number, and $18^{k+1} - 1$ is divisible by 17. The statement is true for $n = k + 1$. So, $18^n - 1$ is divisible by 17 for all positive integers n.

Find a counterexample to disprove each statement.

4. $1 + 4 + 7 + ... + (3n - 2) = n^3 - n^2 + 1$ **Sample answer: $n = 3$**
5. $5^n - 2n - 3$ is divisible by 3. **Sample answer: $n = 3$**
6. $1 + 3 + 5 + ... + (2n - 1) = \frac{n^2 + 3n - 2}{2}$ **Sample answer: $n = 3$**
7. $1^3 + 2^3 + 3^3 + ... + n^3 = n^4 - n^3 + 1$ **Sample answer: $n = 3$**

Chapter 11 48 Glencoe Algebra 2

Word Problem Practice

CRM p. 49 AL OL BL ELL

11-7 Word Problem Practice

Proof by Mathematical Induction

1. **AREA** Cathy claims that there are only 4 pairs of consecutive odd prime numbers, namely, (3, 5), (5, 7), (11, 13), and (17, 19). Is this true or false? If it is true, prove it. If it is false, give a counterexample.
   Cathy's claim is false. (29, 31).

2. **PROOFS** Mrs. Smith has written the following "proof" on the board. Mrs. Smith asks her students to verify her work.
   For all natural numbers n, $2 + 4 + 6 + ... + (2n) = n^2 + n + 1$.
   Mrs. Smith's proof goes like this: "Assume that the identity is true for $n = k$, that is $2 + 4 + 6 + ... + (2k) = k^2 + k + 1$. Add $2k + 2$ to both sides.
   $2 + 4 + 6 + ... + (2k) + (2k + 2)$
   $= k^2 + k + 1 + (2k + 2)$
   $= k^2 + 2k + 1 + k + 1 + 1$
   $= (k + 1)^2 + (k + 1) + 1$.
   The last equality shows that the identity holds for $n = k + 1$ as well. Therefore, by induction, the identity is true for all n." What response should the students give?
   She forgot to show that the statement is true for a particular value of n, which is impossible because the identity is not true.

3. **INDUCTION** A mathematics institute is offering a million dollars to the first person who proves the solution to one of the "millennium prize" problems. Luke is trying to prove that is true for all natural numbers n. He succeeds in proving the statement for $n = 1$. However, instead of proving the $n = k$ implies $n = k + 1$, he proves that $n = k$ implies $n = 2k$ AND $n = k$ implies $n = k - 1$. Is the statement true for all natural numbers n?
   yes

4. **PARITY** Numbers can be either odd or even. If they are divisible by 2, they are even. Otherwise, they are odd. One fact about parity is that $n^2 - n$ is even for all natural numbers n. Note that $1^2 - 1 = 0$, so the statement is obvious for $n = 1$. Assume that the statement is true for $n = k$ and prove that it is then also true for $n = k + 1$.
   Sample answer: Assume $k^2 - k$ is even. $(k + 1)^2 - (k + 1) = k^2 + 2k + 1 - k - 1 = k^2 - k = k^2 - k + 2k$. This shows that $(k + 1)^2 - (k + 1)$ differs from the even number $k^2 - k$ by $2k$ which is also even, and so $(k + 1)^2 - (k + 1)$ must be even.

5. **VOLUME** Let F_n be the Fibonacci numbers. In other words, $F_1 = F_2 = 1$ and $F_{n+1} = F_n + F_{n-1}$ for $n > 1$. You will prove by induction that
   $F_1 + F_3 + F_5 + ... + F_{2n+1} = F_{2n+2}$,
   for all positive integers n.
   a. Show that the identity holds for $n = 1$.
   $F_1 + F_3 = 1 + 2 = 3$ and $F_4 = 3$.
   b. Assume the identity for $n = k$. Show that the identity holds for $n = k + 1$.
   Possible answer: We assume $F_1 + F_3 + F_5 + ... + F_{2n+1} = F_{2n+2}$. Add F_{2n+3} to both sides. The left side becomes the left side of the identity for $n = k + 1$. The right side is $F_{2n+2} + F_{2n+3} = F_{2n+4}$, by definition of sequence. Because this is the right side of the identity for $n = k + 1$, the induction hypothesis follows.

Chapter 11 49 Glencoe Algebra 2

Lesson 11-7

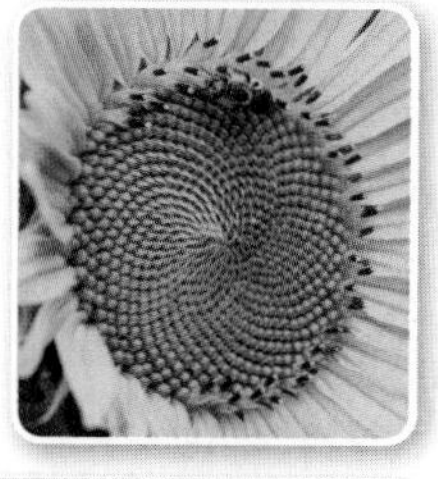

Real-World Link

Fibonacci spirals are found everywhere in nature, because they provide optimal spacing and packaging.

Source: Mathematica

25. **NATURE** The terms of the Fibonacci sequence are found in many places in nature. The number of spirals of seeds in sunflowers is a Fibonacci number, as is the number of spirals of scales on a pinecone. The Fibonacci sequence begins 1, 1, 2, 3, 5, 8, …. Each element after the first two is found by adding the previous two terms. If f_n stands for the nth Fibonacci number, prove that $f_1 + f_2 + \cdots + f_n = f_{n+2} - 1$. **See margin.**

26, 27. See Chapter 11 Answer Appendix.

Prove that each statement is true for all natural numbers or find a counterexample.

26. $7^n + 5$ is divisible by 6.

27. $18^n - 1$ is divisible by 17.

28. $n^2 + 21n + 7$ is a prime number. **$n = 6$**

29. $n^2 + 3n + 3$ is a prime number. **$n = 3$**

30. $500 + 100 + 20 + \cdots + 4 \cdot 5^{4-n} = 625\left(1 - \frac{1}{5^n}\right)$ **See Chapter 11 Answer Appendix.**

31. $\frac{1}{1 \cdot 2 \cdot 3} + \frac{1}{2 \cdot 3 \cdot 4} + \frac{1}{3 \cdot 4 \cdot 5} + \cdots + \frac{1}{n(n + 1)(n + 2)} = \frac{n(n + 3)}{4(n + 1)(n + 2)}$ **See Chapter 11 Answer Appendix.**

32. **CHECKERBOARDS** Refer to the figures below.

Figure 1 Figure 2 Figure 3

a. There is a total of 5 squares in the second figure. How many squares are there in the third figure? **14**

b. Write a sequence for the first five figures. **1, 5, 14, 30, 55**

c. How many squares are there in a standard 8 × 8 checkerboard? **204**

d. Write a formula to represent the number of squares in an $n \times n$ grid. **$\frac{n(n + 1)(2n + 1)}{6}$**

H.O.T. Problems Use Higher-Order Thinking Skills

33. **CHALLENGE** Suggest a formula to represent $2 + 4 + 6 + \cdots + 2n$, and prove your hypothesis using mathematical induction. **See Chapter 11 Answer Appendix.**

REASONING Determine whether the following statements are *true* or *false*. Explain.

34. If you cannot find a counterexample to a statement, then it is true.

35. If a statement is true for $n = k$ and $n = k + 1$, then it is also true for $n = 1$.

36. **CHALLENGE** Prove $\sum_{k=1}^{n} k^3 = \left(\frac{n(n + 1)}{2}\right)^2$. **See Chapter 11 Answer Appendix.**

37. **REASONING** Find a counterexample to $x^3 + 30 > x^2 + 20x$. **$x = 3$**

38. **OPEN ENDED** Write a sequence, the formula that produces it, and determine the formula for the sum of the terms of the sequence. Then prove the formula with mathematical induction. **See Chapter 11 Answer Appendix.**

39. **WRITING IN MATH** Explain how the concept of dominoes can help you understand the power of mathematical induction.

40. **WRITING IN MATH** Provide a real-world example other than dominoes that describes mathematical induction. **Sample answer: Climbing a ladder; each step leads to the next step.**

34. Sample answer: False; Even if a counterexample cannot immediately be found, it does not mean that one doesn't exist. A statement can easily be proven false, but it is more difficult to prove that it is true. Statements need to be proven true by mathematical induction, geometrically, or by another method.

35. Sample answer: False; assume $k = 2$, just because a statement is true for $n = 2$ and $n = 3$ does not mean that it is true for $n = 1$.

39. Sample answer: When dominoes are set up, after the first domino falls, the rest will fall as well. With induction, once it is proved that the statement is true for $n = 1$ (the first domino), $n = k$ (the second domino), and $n = k + 1$ (the next domino), it will be true for any integer value (any domino).

730 Chapter 11 Sequences and Series

Enrichment

CRM p. 50 OL BL

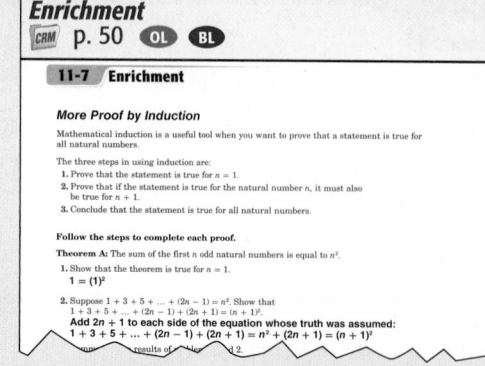

11-7 Enrichment

More Proof by Induction

Mathematical induction is a useful tool when you want to prove that a statement is true for all natural numbers.

The three steps in using induction are:

1. Prove that the statement is true for $n = 1$.
2. Prove that if the statement is true for the natural number n, it must also be true for $n + 1$.
3. Conclude that the statement is true for all natural numbers.

Follow the steps to complete each proof.

Theorem A: The sum of the first n odd natural numbers is equal to n^2.

1. Show that the theorem is true for $n = 1$.
   $1 = (1)^2$
2. Suppose $1 + 3 + 5 + ... + (2n - 1) = n^2$. Show that $1 + 3 + 5 + ... + (2n - 1) + (2n + 1) = (n + 1)^2$.
   Add $2n + 1$ to each side of the equation whose truth was assumed: $1 + 3 + 5 + ... + (2n - 1) + (2n + 1) = n^2 + (2n + 1) = (n + 1)^2$

results of d 2.

NGSSS PRACTICE 912.P.1.2, 912.A.4.4

41. Which of the following is a counterexample to the statement below? **B**

$n^2 + n - 11$ is prime.

A. $n = -6$ C. $n = 5$
B. $n = 4$ D. $n = 6$

42. PROBABILITY Latisha wants to create a 7-character password. She wants to use an arrangement of the first 3 letters of her first name (lat), followed by an arrangement of the 4 digits in 1986, the year she was born. How many possible passwords can she create in this way? **G**

F. 72 H. 288
G. 144 I. 576

43. GRIDDED RESPONSE A gear that is 8 inches in diameter turns a smaller gear that is 3 inches in diameter. If the larger gear makes 36 revolutions, how many revolutions does the smaller gear make in that time? **96**

44. $3x + 8\overline{)3x^4 + 32x^3 + 46x^2 - 66x - 44} =$ **B**

A. $2x^3 + 16x^2 - 12x - 12 - \frac{4}{3x+8}$

B. $x^3 + 8x^2 - 6x - 6 + \frac{4}{3x+8}$

C. $x^3 + 8x^2 - 6x - 6 - \frac{4}{3x+8}$

D. $x^3 - 8x^2 + 6x - 6 + \frac{4}{3x+8}$

Spiral Review

Find the indicated term of each expansion. (Lesson 11-6)

45. fourth term of $(x + 2y)^6$ **$160x^3y^3$**
46. fifth term of $(a + b)^6$ **$15a^2b^4$**
47. fourth term of $(x - y)^9$ **$-84x^6y^3$**

48. BIOLOGY In a particular forest, scientists are interested in how the population of wolves will change over the next two years. One model for animal population is the Verhulst population model, $p_{n+1} = p_n + rp_n(1 - p_n)$, where n represents the number of time periods that have passed, p_n represents the percent of the maximum sustainable population that exists at time n, and r is the growth factor. (Lesson 11-5) **b. 0.45 represents the maximum sustainable population of 45% and 1.5 is the growth factor.**

a. To find the population of the wolves after one year, evaluate $p_1 = 0.45 + 1.5(0.45)(1 - 0.45)$. **0.82125**

b. Explain what each number in the expression in part **a** represents.

c. The current population of wolves is 165. Find the new population by multiplying 165 by the value in part **a**. **about 136 wolves**

Find the exact solution(s) of each system of equations. (Lesson 10-7)

49. $x^2 + y^2 - 18x + 24y + 200 = 0$, $4x + 3y = 0$ **(6, −8), (12, −16)**

50. $4x^2 + y^2 = 16$, $x^2 + 2y^2 = 4$ **(± 2, 0)**

Skills Review

Evaluate each expression. (Lesson 0-5)

51. $P(8, 2)$ **56**
52. $P(9, 1)$ **9**
53. $P(12, 6)$ **665,280**
54. $C(5, 2)$ **10**
55. $C(8, 4)$ **70**
56. $C(20, 17)$ **1140**
57. $P(12, 2)$ **132**
58. $P(7, 2)$ **42**
59. $C(8, 6)$ **28**
60. $C(9, 4) \cdot C(5, 3)$ **1260**
61. $C(6, 1) \cdot C(4, 1)$ **24**
62. $C(10, 5) \cdot C(8, 4)$ **17,640**

Exercise Alert

Grid Paper For Exercise 32, students may benefit from drawing the first five figures on grid paper.

4 ASSESS

Name the Math Write an equation with one variable on the board that is not true for all values of the variable, and ask students to hand you pieces of paper on which they have written counterexamples to show that the equation is not always true.

Formative Assessment

Check for student understanding of concepts in Lesson 11-7.

CRM Quiz 4, p. 54

Additional Answer

25. Step 1: When $n = 1$, the left side of the given equation is f_1. The right side is $f\,3 - 1$. Since $f_1 = 1$ and $f_3 = 2$ the equation becomes $1 = 2 - 1$ and is true for $n = 1$.

Step 2: Assume that $f_1 + f_2 + \ldots + f_k = f_{k+2} - 1$ for some natural number k.

Step 3: $f_1 + f_2 + \ldots + f_k + f_{k+1}$
$= f_{k+2} - 1 + f_{k+1}$
$= f_{k+1} + f_{k+2} - 1$
$= f_{k+3} - 1$, since Fibonacci numbers are produced by adding the two previous Fibonacci numbers.

The last expression is the right side of the equation to be proved, where $n = k + 1$. Thus, the equation is true for $n = k + 1$. Therefore, $f_1 + f_2 + \ldots + f_n = f_{n+2} - 1$ for all natural numbers n.

Differentiated Instruction

OL BL

Extension Tell students that the number $n!$ is defined as the product of all the natural numbers less than or equal to n. Then ask students to prove $1 \cdot 2 \cdot 3 \cdot \ldots \cdot (n-1)(n) = n!$.
Step 1: When $n = 1$, the left side of the given equation is 1! or 1. The right side is 1. Thus, the statement is true for $n = 1$. **Step 2:** Assume $1 \cdot 2 \cdot 3 \cdot \ldots \cdot (k-1)(k) = k!$ for a natural number k.
Step 3: Show that the given statement is true for $n = k + 1$.

$1 \cdot 2 \cdot 3 \cdot \ldots \cdot (k-1)(k)(k+1) = k!(k+1)$
$= [k(k-1) \cdot \ldots \cdot 3 \cdot 2 \cdot 1](k+1)$
$= (k+1)k(k-1) \cdot \ldots \cdot 3 \cdot 2 \cdot 1$ or $(k+1)!$

Formative Assessment

Key Vocabulary The page references after each word denote where that term was first introduced. If students have difficulty answering questions 1–10, remind them that they can use these page references to refresh their memories about the vocabulary.

Summative Assessment

CRM Vocabulary Test, p. 56

FL Math Online glencoe.com

Vocabulary PuzzleMaker improves students' mathematics vocabulary using four puzzle formats– crossword, scramble, word search using a word list, and word search using clues. Students can work online or from a printed worksheet.

CHAPTER 11 Study Guide and Review

FL Math Online glencoe.com
- STUDY TO GO
- Vocabulary Review

Chapter Summary

Key Concepts

Arithmetic Sequences and Series (Lessons 11-1 and 11-2)

- The *n*th term a_n of an arithmetic sequence with first term a_1 and common difference d is given by $a_n = a_1 + (n - 1)d$, where n is any positive integer.
- The sum S_n of the first n terms of an arithmetic series is given by $S_n = \frac{n}{2}[2a_1 + (n - 1)d]$ or $S_n = \frac{n}{2}(a_1 + a_n)$.

Geometric Sequences and Series (Lessons 11-3 and 11-4)

- The *n*th term a_n of a geometric sequence with first term a_1 and common ratio r is given by $a_n = a_1 \cdot r^{n-1}$, where n is any positive integer.
- The sum S_n of the first n terms of a geometric series is given by $S_n = \frac{a_1(1 - r^n)}{1 - r}$ or $S_n = \frac{a_1 - a_1 r^n}{1 - r}$, where $r \neq 1$.
- The sum S of an infinite geometric series with $-1 < r < 1$ is given by $S_n = \frac{a_1}{1 - r}$.

Recursion and Iteration (Lesson 11-5)

- In a recursive formula, each term is formulated from one or more previous terms.

The Binomial Theorem (Lesson 11-6)

- The Binomial Theorem: $(a + b)^n = \sum_{k=0}^{n} \frac{n!}{(n - k)!k!} a^{n-k} b^k$

Mathematical Induction (Lesson 11-7)

- Mathematical induction is a method of proof used to prove statements about the positive integers.

FOLDABLES® Study Organizer

Be sure the Key Concepts are noted in your Foldable.

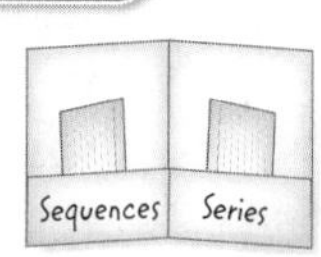

Key Vocabulary

arithmetic means (p. 689)
arithmetic sequence (p. 681)
arithmetic series (p. 690)
common difference (p. 681)
common ratio (p. 683)
convergent series (p. 705)
divergent series (p. 705)
explicit formula (p. 714)
Fibonacci sequence (p. 714)
finite sequence (p. 681)
geometric means (p. 697)
geometric sequence (p. 683)
geometric series (p. 698)
induction hypothesis (p. 727)
infinite geometric series (p. 705)
infinite sequence (p. 681)
infinity (p. 707)
iteration (p. 716)
mathematical induction (p. 727)
partial sum (p. 690)
Pascal's triangle (p. 721)
recursive formula (p. 714)
recursive sequence (p. 714)
series (p. 690)
sequence (p. 681)
sigma notation (p. 691)
term (p. 681)

Vocabulary Check

State whether each sentence is *true* or *false*. If *false*, replace the underlined term to make a true sentence.

1. An infinite geometric series that has a sum is called a convergent series. **true**
2. Mathematical induction is the process of repeatedly composing a function with itself. **false, iteration**
3. The arithmetic means of a sequence are the terms between any two non-successive terms of an arithmetic sequence. **true**
4. A term is a list of numbers in a particular order. **false, sequence**
5. The sum of the first n terms of a series is called the partial sum. **true**
6. The formula $a_n = a_{n-2} + a_{n-1}$ is a recursive formula. **true**
7. A geometric sequence is a sequence in which every term is determined by adding a constant value to the previous term. **false, arithmetic sequence**
8. An infinite geometric series that does not have a sum is called a partial sum. **false, divergent series**
9. Eleven and 17 are two geometric means between 5 and 23 in the sequence 5, 11, 17, 23. **false, arithmetic means**
10. Using the Binomial Theorem, $(x - 2)^4$ can be expanded to $x^4 - 8x^3 + 24x^2 - 32x + 16$. **true**

FOLDABLES® Study Organizer

Dinah Zike's Foldables®
Have students look through the chapter to make sure they have included examples in their Foldables.

Suggest that students keep their Foldables handy while completing the Study Guide and Review pages. Point out that their Foldables can serve as a quick review tool when studying for the chapter test.

Lesson-by-Lesson Review

11-1 Sequences as Functions (pp. 681–687)

912.D.11.1, 912.D.11.3

Find the indicated term of each arithmetic sequence.

11. $a_1 = 9, d = 3, n = 14$ **48**
12. $a_1 = -3, d = 6, n = 22$ **123**
13. $a_1 = 10, d = -4, n = 9$ **−22**
14. $a_1 = -1, d = -5, n = 18$ **−86**

EXAMPLE 1

Find the 11th term of an arithmetic sequence if $a_1 = -15$ and $d = 6$.

$a_n = a_1 + (n - 1)d$	Formula for the *n*th term
$a_{11} = -15 + (11 - 1)6$	$n = 11, a_1 = -15, d = 6$
$a_{11} = 45$	Simplify.

11-2 Arithmetic Sequences and Series (pp. 688–695)

912.D.11.3, 912.D.11.4

Find the arithmetic means in each sequence.

15. $-12, \_, \_, \_, 8$ **−7, −2, 3**
16. $15, \_, \_, 29$ $\frac{59}{3}, \frac{73}{3}$
17. $12, \_, \_, \_, \_, -8$ **8, 4, 0, −4**
18. $72, \_, \_, \_, 24$ **60, 48, 36**
19. **BANKING** Carson saves \$40 every 2 months. If he saves at this rate for two years, how much will he have at the end of two years? **\$480**

Find S_n for each arithmetic series.

20. $a_1 = 16, a_n = 48, n = 6$ **192**
21. $a_1 = 8, a_n = 96, n = 20$ **1040**
22. $9 + 14 + 19 + \cdots + 74$ **581**
23. $16 + 7 + -2 + \cdots + -65$ **−245**
24. **DRAMA** Laura has a drama performance in 12 days. She plans to practice her lines each night. On the first night she rehearses her lines 2 times. The next night she rehearses her lines 4 times. The third night she rehearses her lines 6 times. On the eleventh night, how many times has she rehearsed her lines? **132**

Find the sum of each arithmetic series.

25. $\sum_{k=5}^{21}(3k - 2)$ **629**
26. $\sum_{k=0}^{10}(6k - 1)$ **319**
27. $\sum_{k=4}^{12}(-2k + 5)$ **−99**

EXAMPLE 2

Find the two arithmetic means between 3 and 39.

$a_n = a_1 + (n - 1)d$	Formula for the *n*th term
$a_4 = 3 + (4 - 1)d$	$n = 4, a_1 = 3$
$39 = 3 + 3d$	$a_4 = 39$
$12 = d$	Simplify.

The arithmetic means are 3 + 12 or 15 and 15 + 12 or 27.

EXAMPLE 3

Find S_n for the arithmetic series with $a_1 = 18$, $a_n = 56$, and $n = 8$.

$S_n = \frac{n}{2}(a_1 + a_n)$	Sum formula
$S_8 = \frac{8}{2}(18 + 56)$	$n = 8, a_1 = 18, a_n = 56$
$= 296$	Simplify.

EXAMPLE 4

Evaluate $\sum_{k=3}^{15} 5k + 1$.

Use the formula $S_n = \frac{n}{2}(a_1 + a_n)$. There are 13 terms, $a_1 = 5(3) + 1$ or 16, and $a_{13} = 5(15) + 1$ or 76.

$S_{13} = \frac{13}{2}(16 + 76)$

$= 598$

Lesson-by-Lesson Review

Intervention If the given examples are not sufficient to review the topics covered by the questions, remind students that the page references tell them where to review that topic in their textbook.

Two-Day Option Have students complete the Lesson-by-Lesson Review on pp. 733–736. Then you can use ExamView® Assessment Suite to customize another review worksheet that practices all the objectives of this chapter or only the objectives on which your students need more help.

Differentiated Instruction

Super DVD: Mindjogger Videoquizzes Use this DVD as an alternative format of review for the test.

CHAPTER 11 Study Guide and Review

11-3 Geometric Sequences and Series (pp. 696–702)

912.D.11.3, 912.D.11.4

Find the indicated term for each geometric sequence.

28. $a_1 = 5, r = 2, n = 7$ **320**

29. $a_1 = 11, r = 3, n = 3$ **99**

30. $a_1 = 128, r = -\frac{1}{2}, n = 5$ **8**

31. a_8 for $\frac{1}{8}, \frac{3}{8}, \frac{9}{8} \ldots$ $\frac{2187}{8}$

Find the geometric means in each sequence.

32. 6, __, __, 162 **18, 54**

33. 8, __, __, __, 648 **±24, 72, ±216**

34. −4, __, __, 108 **12, −36**

35. **SAVINGS** Nolan has a savings account with a current balance of $1500. What would be Nolan's account balance after 4 years if he receives 5% interest annually? **$1823.26**

Find S_n for each geometric series.

36. $a_1 = 15, r = 2, n = 4$ **225**

37. $a_1 = 9, r = 4, n = 6$ **12,285**

38. $5 - 10 + 20 - \ldots$ to 7 terms **215**

39. $243 + 81 + 27 + \ldots$ to 5 terms **363**

Evaluate the sum of each geometric series.

40. $\sum_{k=1}^{7} 3 \cdot (-2)^{k-1}$ **129** **41.** $\sum_{k=1}^{8} -1\left(\frac{2}{3}\right)^{k-1}$ $-\frac{6305}{2187}$

42. **ADVERTISING** Natalie is handing out fliers to advertise the next student council meeting. She hands out fliers to 4 people. Then, each of those 4 people hand out 4 fliers to 4 other people. Those 4 then hand out 4 fliers to 4 new people. If Natalie is considered the first round, how many people will have been given fliers after 4 rounds? **85**

EXAMPLE 5

Find the sixth term of a geometric sequence for which $a_1 = 9$ and $r = 4$.

$a_n = a_1 \cdot r^{n-1}$ Formula for the *n*th term

$a_6 = 9 \cdot 4^{6-1}$ $n = 6, a_1 = 9, r = 4$

$a_6 = 9216$

The sixth term is 9216.

EXAMPLE 6

Find two geometric means between 1 and 27.

$a_n = a_1 \cdot r^{n-1}$ Formula for the *n*th term

$a_4 = 1 \cdot r^{4-1}$ $n = 4$ and $a_1 = 1$

$27 = r^3$ $a_4 = 27$

$3 = r$ Simplify.

The geometric means are 1(3) or 3 and 3(3) or 9.

EXAMPLE 7

Find the sum of a geometric series for which $a_1 = 3$, $r = 5$, and $n = 11$.

$S_n = \frac{a_1 - a_1 r^n}{1 - r}$ Sum formula

$S_{11} = \frac{3 - 3 \cdot 5^{11}}{1 - 5}$ $n = 11, a_1 = 3, r = 5$

$S_{11} = 36{,}621{,}093$ Use a calculator.

EXAMPLE 8

Evaluate $\sum_{k=1}^{6} 2 \cdot (4)^{k-1}$.

$S_6 = \frac{2 - 2 \cdot 4^6}{1 - 4}$ $n = 6, a_1 = 2, r = 4$

$= \frac{-8190}{-3}$ Simplify.

$= 2730$ Simplify.

734 Chapter 11 Sequences and Series

MIXED PROBLEM SOLVING
For mixed problem-solving practice, see page 989.

11-4 Infinite Geometric Series (pp. 705–711)

912.D.11.2, 912.D.11.4

Find the sum of each infinite series, if it exists.

43. $a_1 = 8, r = \frac{3}{4}$ **32**

44. $\frac{5}{6} - \frac{20}{18} + \frac{80}{54} - \frac{320}{162} + \ldots$ **does not exist**

45. $\sum_{k=1}^{\infty} 3\left(\frac{1}{2}\right)^{k-1}$ **6**

46. **PHYSICAL SCIENCE** Maddy drops a ball off of a building that is 60 feet high. Each time the ball bounces, it bounces back to $\frac{2}{3}$ its previous height. If the ball continues to follow this pattern, what will be the total distance that the ball travels? **300 ft**

EXAMPLE 9

Find the sum of the infinite geometric series for which $a_1 = 15$ and $r = \frac{1}{3}$.

$S = \frac{a_1}{1 - r}$ — Sum formula

$= \frac{15}{1 - \frac{1}{3}}$ — $a_1 = 15, r = \frac{1}{3}$

$= \frac{15}{\frac{2}{3}}$ or 22.5 — Simplify.

11-5 Recursion and Special Sequences (pp. 714–719)

912.D.11.1

Find the first five terms of each sequence.

47. $a_1 = -3, a_{n+1} = a_n + 4$ **−3, 1, 5, 9, 13**

48. $a_1 = 5, a_{n+1} = 2a_n - 5$ **5, 5, 5, 5, 5**

49. $a_1 = 1, a_{n+1} = a_n + 5$ **1, 6, 11, 16, 21**

50. **SAVINGS** Sari has a savings account with a $12,000 balance. She has a 5% interest rate that is compounded monthly. Every month Sari adds $500 to the account. The recursive formula $b_n = 1.05b_{n-1} + 500$ describes the balance in Sari's savings account after n months. Find the balance of Sari's account after 3 months. Round your answer to the nearest penny. **$15,467.75**

Find the first three iterates of each function for the given initial value.

51. $f(x) = 2x + 1, x_0 = 3$ **7, 15, 31**

52. $f(x) = 5x - 4, x_0 = 1$ **1, 1, 1**

53. $f(x) = 6x - 1, x_0 = 2$ **11, 65, 389**

54. $f(x) = 3x + 1, x_0 = 4$ **13, 40, 121**

EXAMPLE 10

Find the first five terms of the sequence in which $a_1 = 1, a_{n+1} = 3a_n + 2$.

$a_{n+1} = 3a_n + 2$	Recursive formula
$a_{1+1} = 3a_1 + 2$	$n = 1$
$a_2 = 3(1) + 2$ or 5	$a_1 = 1$
$a_{2+1} = 3a_2 + 2$	$n = 2$
$a_3 = 3(5) + 2$ or 17	$a_2 = 5$
$a_{3+1} = 3a_3 + 2$	$n = 3$
$a_4 = 3(17) + 2$ or 53	$a_3 = 17$
$a_{4+1} = 3a_4 + 2$	$n = 4$
$a_5 = 3(53) + 2$ or 161	$a_4 = 53$

The first five terms of the sequence are 1, 5, 17, 53, and 161.

EXAMPLE 11

Find the first three iterates of the function $f(x) = 3x - 2$ for the initial value of $x_0 = 2$.

$x_1 = f(x_0)$	$x_2 = f(x_1)$	$x_3 = f(x_2)$
$= f(2)$	$= f(4)$	$= f(10)$
$= 3(2) - 2$	$= 3(4) - 2$	$= 3(10) - 2$
$= 4$	$= 10$	$= 28$

The first three iterates are 4, 10, and 28.

Chapter 11 Study Guide and Review 735

Problem Solving Review

For additional practice in problem solving for Chapter 11, see the Mixed Problem Solving Appendix, p. 990, in the Student Handbook section.

Anticipation Guide

Have students complete the Chapter 11 Anticipation Guide and discuss how their responses have changed now that they have completed Chapter 11.

Additional Answers

56. $y^7 - 21y^6 + 189y^5 - 945y^4 + 2835y^3 - 5103y^2 + 5103y - 2187$

57. $-32z^5 + 240z^4 - 720z^3 + 1080z^2 - 810z + 243$

58. $256a^4 - 768a^3b + 864a^2b^2 - 432ab^3 + 81b^4$

59. $x^5 - \frac{5}{4}x^4 + \frac{5}{8}x^3 - \frac{5}{32}x^2 + \frac{5}{256}x - \frac{1}{1024}$

63. Step 1: When $n = 1$, the left side of the equation is equal to 2. The right side of the equation is also equal to 2. So the equation is true for $n = 1$.
Step 2: Assume that $2 + 6 + 12 + \ldots + k(k + 1) = \frac{k(k + 1)(k + 2)}{3}$ for some positive integer k.

Step 3: $1 \ldots 2 + 2 \ldots 3 + \ldots + k(k + 1) + (k + 1)(k + 2)$

$= \frac{k(k + 1)(k + 2)}{3} + (k + 1)(k + 2)$

$= \frac{k(k + 1)(k + 2)}{3} + \frac{3(k + 1)(k + 2)}{3}$

$= \frac{(k + 1)[k(k + 2) + 3(k + 2)]}{3}$

$= \frac{(k + 1)(k + 2)(k + 3)}{3}$

$= \frac{(k + 1)[(k + 1) + 1][(k + 1) + 2]}{3}$

The last expression is the right side of the equation to be proved, where $n = k + 1$. Thus, the equation is true for $n = k + 1$. Therefore, $2 + 6 + 12 + \ldots + k(k + 1) = \frac{k(k + 1)(k + 2)}{3}$ for all positive integers n.

11-6 The Binomial Theorem (pp. 721–725)

912.A.4.12

Expand each binomial. 56–59. See margin.

55. $(a + b)^3$ $a^3 + 3a^2b + 3ab^2 + b^3$

56. $(y - 3)^7$

57. $(3 - 2z)^5$

58. $(4a - 3b)^4$

59. $\left(x - \frac{1}{4}\right)^5$

Find the indicated term of each expression.

60. third term of $(a + 2b)^8$ $112a^6b^2$

61. sixth term of $(3x + 4y)^7$ $193{,}536x^2y^3$

62. second term of $(4x - 5)^{10}$ $-13{,}107{,}200x^9$

EXAMPLE 12

Expand $(x - 3y)^4$.

$(x - 3y)^4$
$= x^4 + {}_4C_1x^3(-3y) + {}_4C_2x^2(-3y)^2 + {}_4C_3(-3y)^4 + {}_4C_4(-3y)^4$
$= x^4 + \frac{4!}{3!}x^3(-3y) + \frac{4!}{2!2!}x^2(9y^2) + \frac{4!}{3!}x(-27y^3) + 81y^4$
$= x^4 + -12x^3y + 54x^2y^2 + -108xy^3 + 81y^4$

EXAMPLE 13

Find the fourth term of $(x + y)^8$.

Use the binomial Theorem to write the expansion in sigma notation.

$(x + y)^8 = \sum_{k=0}^{8} \frac{8!}{k!(8 - k)!}x^{8-k}y^k$

For the fourth term, $k = 3$.

$\frac{8!}{k!(8 - k)!}x^{8-k}y^k = \frac{8!}{3!(8 - 3)!}x^{8-3}y^3$
$= 56x^5y^3$

11-7 Proof and Mathematical Induction (pp. 727–731)

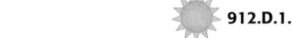

912.D.1.3

Prove that each statement is true for all positive integers. 63. See margin.

63. $2 + 6 + 12 + \cdots + n(n + 1) = \frac{n(n + 1)(n + 2)}{3}$

64. $7^n - 1$ is divisible by 6.

65. $5^n - 1$ is divisible by 4.

64, 65. See Chapter 11 Answer Appendix.

Find a counterexample for each statement.

66. $8^n + 3$ is divisible by 11. $n = 2$

67. $6^{n+1} - 2$ is divisible by 17. $n = 2$

68. $n^2 + 2n + 4$ is prime. $n = 2$

69. $n + 19$ is prime. $n = 1$

EXAMPLE 14

Prove that $9^n + 3$ is divisible by 4.

Step 1 When $n = 1$, $9^n + 3 = 9^1 + 3$ or 12. Since 12 divided by 4 is 3, the statement is true for $n = 1$.

Step 2 Assume that $9^k + 3$ is divisible by 4 for some positive integer k. This means that $9^k + 3 = 4r$ for some whole number r.

Step 3
$9^k + 3 = 4r$
$9^k = 4r - 3$
$9^{k+1} = 36r - 27$
$9^{k+1} + 3 = 36r - 27 + 3$
$9^{k+1} + 3 = 36r - 24$
$9^{k+1} + 3 = 4(9r - 6)$

Since r is a whole number, $9r - 6$ is a whole number. Thus, $9^{k+1} + 3$ is divisible by 4, so the statement is true for $n = k + 1$.

Therefore, $9^n + 3$ is divisible by 4 for all positive integers n.

FL Math Online > glencoe.com
Chapter Test

1. Find the next 4 terms of the arithmetic sequence 81, 72, 63, … . **54, 45, 36, 27**

2. Find the 25th term of an arithmetic sequence for which $a_1 = 9$ and $d = 5$. **129**

3. NGSSS PRACTICE What is the eighth term in the arithmetic sequence that begins 18, 20.2, 22.4, 24.6, …? **D**

A. 26.8

B. 29

C. 31.2

D. 33.4

4. Find the four arithmetic means between −9 and 11. **4. −5, −1, 3, 7**

5. Find the sum of the arithmetic series for which $a_1 = 11$, $n = 14$, and $a_n = 22$. **231**

6. NGSSS PRACTICE What is the next term in the geometric sequence below? **H**

$$10, \frac{5}{2}, \frac{5}{8}, \frac{5}{32} \dots$$

F. $\frac{13}{32}$

G. $\frac{5}{32}$

H. $\frac{5}{128}$

I. $\frac{5}{8}$

7. Find the three geometric means between 6 and 1536. **24, 96, 384**

8. Find the sum of the geometric series for which $a_1 = 15$, $r = \frac{2}{3}$, and $n = 5$. $\frac{1055}{27}$

Find the sum of each series, if it exists.

9. $\sum_{k=2}^{12}(3k - 1)$ **220**

10. $\sum_{k=1}^{\infty}\frac{1}{2}(3^k)$ **does not exist**

11. $45 + 37 + 29 + \cdots + -11$ **136**

12. $\frac{1}{8} + \frac{2}{24} + \frac{4}{72} + \dots$ $\frac{3}{8}$

13. Write $0.\overline{65}$ as a fraction. $\frac{65}{99}$

Find the first five terms of each sequence.

14. $a_1 = -1, a_{n+1} = 3a_n + 5$ **−1, 2, 11, 38, 119**

15. $a_1 = 4, a_{n+1} = a_n + n$ **4, 5, 7, 10, 14**

16. NGSSS PRACTICE What are the first 3 iterates of $f(x) = -5x + 4$ for an initial value of $x_0 = 3$? **B**

A. 3, −11, 59

B. −11, 59, −291

C. −1, −6, −11

D. 59, −291, 1459

17. Expand $(2a - 3b)^4$. $16a^4 - 96a^3b + 216a^2b^2 - 216ab^3 + 81b^4$

18. What is the coefficient of the fifth term of $(m + 3n)^6$? **1215**

19. Find the fourth term of the expansion of $(c + d)^9$. $84c^6d^3$

Prove that each statement is true for all positive integers. **20, 21. See Chapter 11 Answer Appendix.**

20. $1 + 6 + 36 + \cdots + 6^{n-1} = \frac{1}{5}(6^n - 1)$.

21. $11^n - 1$ is divisible by 10.

22. Find a counterexample for the following statement.

$2^n + 4^n$ is divisible by 4. $n = 1$

23. **SCHOOL** There are an equal number of girls and boys in Mr. Marshall's science class. He needs to choose 8 students to represent his class at the science fair. What is the probability that 5 are boys? **about 21.9%**

24. **PENDULUM** Laurie swings a pendulum. The distance traveled per swing decreases by 15% with each swing. If the pendulum initially traveled 10 inches, find the total distance traveled when the pendulum comes to a rest. **about 66.7 inches**

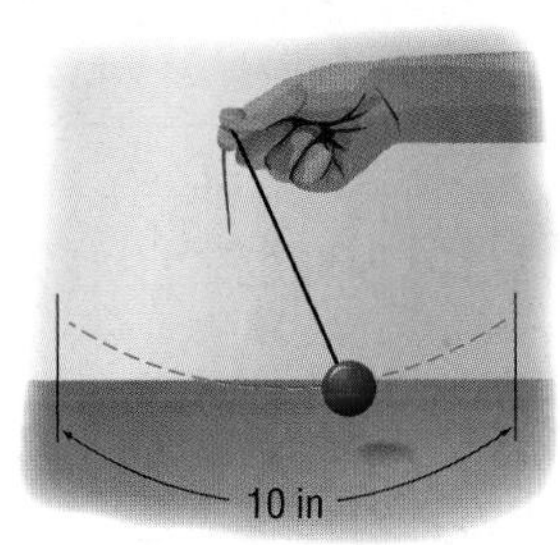

CHAPTER 11 Practice Test

ExamView Assessment Suite Customize and create multiple versions of your chapter test and their answer keys. All of the questions from the leveled chapter tests in the *Chapter 11 Resource Masters* are also available on ExamView® Assessment Suite.

Intervention Planner

Tier 1 On Level	Tier 2 Strategic Intervention approaching grade level	Tier 3 Intensive Intervention 2 or more grades below level
If students miss about 25% of the exercises,	**If** students miss about 50% of the exercises,	**If** students miss about 75% of the exercises,
Then choose a resource: **SE** Lessons 11-1, 11-2, 11-3, 11-4, 11-5, 11-6, and 11-7 **CRM** Skills Practice, pp. 7, 13, 21, 28, 34, 41, and 47 **TE** Chapter Project, p. 678 FL Math Online > Self-Check Quiz	**Then** choose a resource: **CRM** Study Guide and Intervention, Chapter 11, pp. 5, 11, 19, 26, 32, 39, and 45 FL Math Online > Extra Examples, Personal Tutor, Homework Help	**Then** use *Math Triumphs, Alg. 2* FL Math Online > Extra Examples, Personal Tutor, Homework Help, Review Vocabulary

1 FOCUS

Objective Use the strategy of look for a pattern to solve standardized test problems.

2 TEACH

Scaffolding Questions

Ask:

- What types of questions do you think the strategy of look for a pattern works best? Possible answer: Questions such as, "What is the next term in the sequence?" or "What is an expression that models this pattern?"
- How do you find a pattern? Possible answer: See how the terms of the pattern are related and find common operations that express the pattern.

CHAPTER 11 Preparing for Standardized Tests

Look For a Pattern

One of the most common problem-solving strategies is to look for a pattern. The ability to recognize patterns, model them algebraically, and extend them is a valuable problem-solving tool.

Strategies for Looking For a Pattern

Step 1

Identify the pattern.

- Compare the numbers, shapes, or graphs in the pattern.
- **Ask yourself:** How are the terms of the pattern related?
- **Ask yourself:** Are there any common operations that lead from one term to the next?

Step 2

Generalize the pattern.

- Write a rule using words to describe how the terms of the pattern are generated.
- Assign variables and write an algebraic expression to model the pattern if appropriate.

Step 3

Find missing terms, extend the pattern, and solve the problem.

- Use your pattern or your rule to finding missing terms and/or extend the pattern to solve the problem.
- Check your answer to make sure it makes sense.

NGSSS PRACTICE EXAMPLE

Read the problem. Identify what you need to know. Then use the information in the problem to solve.

Use the sequence of squares shown. How many squares will be needed to make the ninth figure of the sequence?

A. 55 **C.** 74

B. 65 **D.** 82

Figure 1 **Figure 2** **Figure 3**

Read the problem statement carefully. You are given three figures of a sequence and asked to find how many squares will be needed to make the ninth figure.

Look for a pattern in the figures of squares. Count the number of squares in each figure.

Write an expression to model this pattern.

Words	The number of squares is equal to the square of the figure number plus one.
Variable	Let n represent the figure number.
Equation	$a_n = n^2 + 1$

Use your expression to extend the pattern and find the number of squares in the ninth figure.

$a_9 = 9^2 + 1 = 82$

So, the ninth figure will have 82 squares. The correct answer is D.

Exercises

Read each problem. Use a pattern to solve the problem.

1. The numbers below form a famous mathematical sequence of numbers known as the Fibonacci sequence. What is the next Fibonacci number in the sequence? **B**

1, 1, 2, 3, 5, 8, 13, 21, …

A. 36

B. 34

C. 31

D. 29

2. What is the missing number in the table? **H**

n	a_n
1	0
2	2
3	6
4	12
5	??
6	30

F. 17

G. 18

H. 20

I. 21

Additional Example

STANDARDIZED TEST PRACTICE Jonas has $2100 in a savings account. At the end of each month, the balance is increased by 0.3%. How much money will Jonas have in his savings account at the end of one year? **B**

A $2170.35

B $2176.86

C $2106.89

D $2994.09

3 ASSESS

Use Exercises 1 and 2 to assess students' understanding.

Chapter 11 Preparing for Standardized Tests 739

NGSSS Practice

Cumulative, Chapters 1 through 11

Read each question. Then fill in the correct answer on the answer document provided by your teacher or on a sheet of paper.

1. THINK SOLVE EXPLAIN **SHORT RESPONSE** Use the Binomial Theorem to expand the expression $(c + d)^6$. $c^6 + 6c^5d + 15c^4d^2 + 20c^3d^3 + 15c^2d^4 + 6cd^5 + d^6$

2. Find the next term of the arithmetic sequence. B

   7, 13, 19, 25, 31, …

   A. 36 C. 38
   B. 37 D. 39

3. Which of the following geometric series does *not* converge to a sum? G

   F. $\sum_{k=1}^{\infty} 4 \cdot \left(\frac{9}{10}\right)^{k-1}$ H. $\sum_{k=1}^{\infty} \frac{7}{6} \cdot \left(\frac{1}{3}\right)^{k-1}$

   G. $\sum_{k=1}^{\infty} \frac{1}{5} \cdot \left(\frac{3}{2}\right)^{k-1}$ I. $\sum_{k=1}^{\infty} (-2) \cdot \left(\frac{5}{6}\right)^{k-1}$

4. An air filter claims to remove 90% of the contaminants in the air each time air is circulated through the filter. If the same volume of air is circulated through the filter three times, what percent of the original contaminants will be removed from the air? D

   A. 0.1% B. 0.01% C. 99.99% D. 99.9%

5. THINK SOLVE EXPLAIN **SHORT RESPONSE** What are the dimensions of the matrix that results from the multiplication shown? 4×1

$$\begin{bmatrix} a & b & c \\ d & e & f \\ g & h & i \\ j & k & l \end{bmatrix} \cdot \begin{bmatrix} 7 \\ 4 \\ 6 \end{bmatrix}$$

Test-Taking Tip

Question 3 Understand the terms used in Algebra and how to apply them. A geometric series converges to a sum if the common ratio r has an absolute value less than 1.

6. **GRIDDED RESPONSE** Consider the pattern below. Into how many pieces will the sixth figure of the pattern be divided? 1024

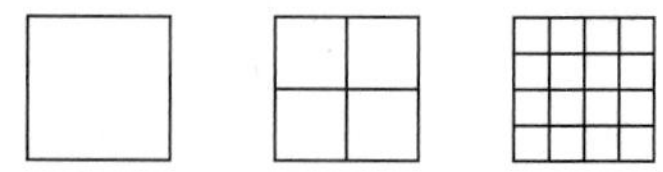

Figure 1	Figure 2	Figure 3
1 piece	4 pieces	16 pieces

7. **GRIDDED RESPONSE** Kara has a cylindrical container that she needs to fill with dirt so she can plant some flowers.

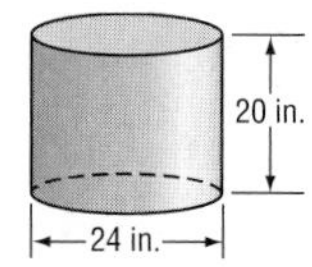

What is the volume of the cylinder in cubic inches rounded to the nearest cubic inch? 9048

8. The table shows a dimension of a square tent and the number of people that the tent can fit.

Length of Tent (yards)	Number of People
2	7
5	28
6	39
8	67
12	147

Let ℓ represent the length of the tent and n represent the number of people that can fit in the tent. Identify the equation that best represents the relationship between the length of the tent and the number of people that can fit in the tent. G

   F. $\ell = n^2 + 3$ H. $\ell = 3n + 1$
   G. $n = \ell^2 + 3$ I. $n = 3\ell + 1$

9. At the movies, the cost of 2 boxes of popcorn and 1 soft drink is \$11.50. The cost of 3 boxes of popcorn and 4 soft drinks is \$27.25. Which pair of equations can be used to determine p, the cost of a box of popcorn, and s, the cost of a soft drink? C

   A. $2p + s = 27.25$, $3p + 4s = 11.50$ C. $2p + s = 11.50$, $3p + 4s = 27.25$
   B. $2p - s = 11.50$, $3p - 4s = 27.25$ D. $p + s = 11.50$, $p + 4 = 27.25$

Diagnose Student Errors

Survey student responses for each item. Class trends may indicate common errors and misconceptions.

2. A. did not add the common difference and 31 correctly
B. correct
C. mistakenly found 7 as a common difference
D. mistakenly found a pattern that every third term ends with 9

3. F. the absolute value of the common ratio will be less than one
G. correct
H. the absolute value of the common ratio will be less than one
I. the absolute value of the common ratio will be less than one

4. A. found contaminants that remain after two times through the filter
B. found contaminants that remain after three times through the filter
C. found contaminants that were removed after four times through the filter
D. correct

8. F. confused the meanings of the variables
G. correct
H. did not recognize a geometric sequence
I. did not recognize a geometric sequence

9. A. transposed totals
B. subtracted soda costs instead of added
C. correct
D. guess

11. F. guess
G. only one dimension was taken into consideration
H. mistakenly multiplied 4 by 2 instead of squaring 4
I. correct

12. A. guess
B. correct
C. transposed constant and base
D. missed a_1

14. F. only evaluated $9k - 1$ for $k = 15$
G. found summation for $k = 1$ to 14
H. correct
I. found summation for $k = 1$ to 16

16. A. guess
B. guess
C. mistakenly thought a lessor coefficient of x^2 causes the graph to become narrower
D. correct

10a. (2, −4); The center is the midpoint of the diameter.

10. **EXTENDED RESPONSE** The endpoints of a diameter of a circle are at (−1, 0) and (5, −8).

a. What are the coordinates of the center of the circle? Explain your method.

b. Find the radius of the circle. Explain your method. See margin.

c. Write an equation of the circle. $(x - 2)^2 + (y + 4)^2 = 25$

11. Lynette gets an enlargement of a 4-inch by 6-inch picture so that the new print has dimensions that are 4 times the dimensions of her original. How does the area of the enlargement compare to the area of the original picture? I

F. The area is twice as large.

G. The area is four times as large.

H. The area is eight times as large.

I. The area is sixteen times as large.

12. Write the formula for the nth term of the geometric sequence shown in the table. B

n	a_n
1	5
2	10
3	20
4	40
5	80

A. $a_n = (5)^n$

B. $a_n = 5(2)^{n-1}$

C. $a_n = 2(5)^{n-1}$

D. $a_n = 5(2)^n$

13. **GRIDDED RESPONSE** What is the value of $f[g(6)]$ if $f(x) = 2x + 4$ and $g(x) = x^2 + 5$? 86

14. Evaluate $\sum_{k=1}^{15}(8k - 1)$. H

F. 119

G. 826

H. 945

I. 1072

15. **SHORT RESPONSE** Bacteria in a culture are growing exponentially with time, as shown in the table.

Hours	Bacteria
0	1000
1	2000
2	4000

Write an equation to express the number of bacteria, y, with respect to time, t. $y = (1000) \cdot (2)^t$

16. What is the effect on the graph of the equation $y = 3x^2$ when the equation is changed to $y = 2x^2$? D

A. The graph of $y = 2x^2$ is a reflection of the graph of $y = 3x^2$ across the y-axis.

B. The graph is rotated 90 degrees about the origin.

C. The graph is narrower.

D. The graph is wider.

17. **EXTENDED RESPONSE** Prove that the sum of any two odd integers is even. See margin.

18. **EXTENDED RESPONSE** A cyclist travels from Centerville to Springfield in 2.5 hours. If she increases her speed, she can make the trip in 2 hours.

a. Does this situation represent a *direct* or *inverse* variation? Explain your reasoning. See margin.

b. If the trip from Centerville to Springfield takes 2.5 hours when traveling at 12 miles per hour, what must the speed be to make the trip in 2 hours? 15 mph

Need Extra Help?

If you missed Question...	1	2	3	4	5	6	7	8	9	10	11	12	13	14	15	16	17	18
Go to Lesson or Page...	11-6	11-2	11-4	11-3	4-3	11-5	6-7	2-4	3-1	10-3	1-1	11-3	7-1	11-2	8-8	5-7	11-7	9-5
For help with NGSSS...	912.A.4.12	912.D.11.3	912.D.11.4	912.D.11.4	912.D.8.2	912.D.11.1	912.G.7.5	912.A.3.1	912.A.3.15	912.G.1.1	912.G.2.5	912.D.11.3	912.A.2.8	912.D.11.4	912.A.8.5	912.A.2.10	912.D.1.3	912.S.2.12

Formative Assessment

You can use these two pages to benchmark student progress.

CRM *Chapter 11 Resource Masters*

- Standardized Test Practice, pp. 70–72

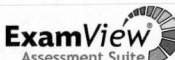

ExamView Assessment Suite Create practice worksheets or tests that align to your state's standards as well as TIMSS and NAEP tests.

Homework Option

Get Ready for Chapter 12 Assign students the exercises on p. 743 as homework to assess whether they possess the prerequisite skills needed for the next chapter.

Additional Answers

10b. 5; the radius is the distance between the center and any point on the circle. $(x - 2)^2 + (y + 4)^2 = 25$

17. Sample answer: Let $2n + 1$ and $2k + 1$ represent any two odd integers where n and k are both integers. Then their sum is $(2n + 1) + (2k + 1)$, or $2n + 2k + 2$. This can be written as $2(n + k + 1)$ which is the product of 2 and an integer, $n + k + 1$. So, the sum $2n + 2k + 2$ is even.

18a. Inverse; the slower speed takes more time to travel the same distance.

Pages 685–687, Lesson 11-1

14. 40.5, 60.75, 91.125

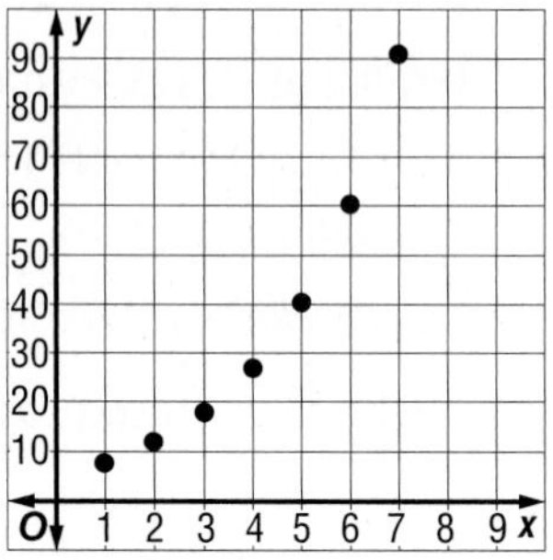

15. 128, 256, 512

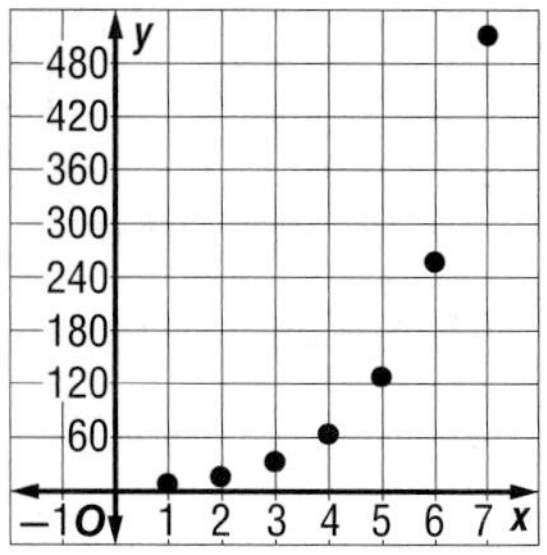

16. $\frac{2}{5}, \frac{2}{25}, \frac{2}{125}$

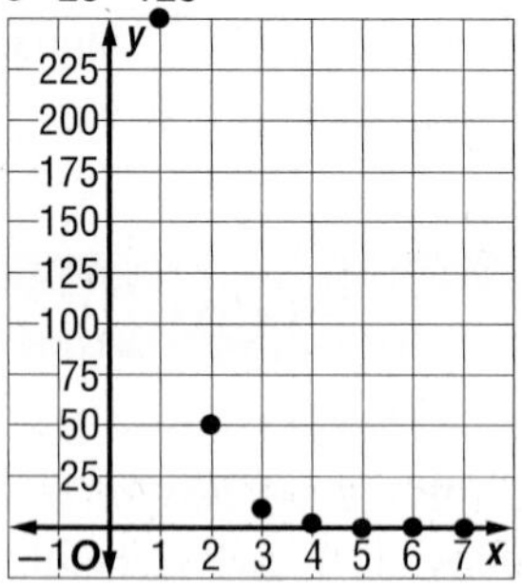

17. $\frac{1}{9}, \frac{-1}{27}, \frac{1}{81}$

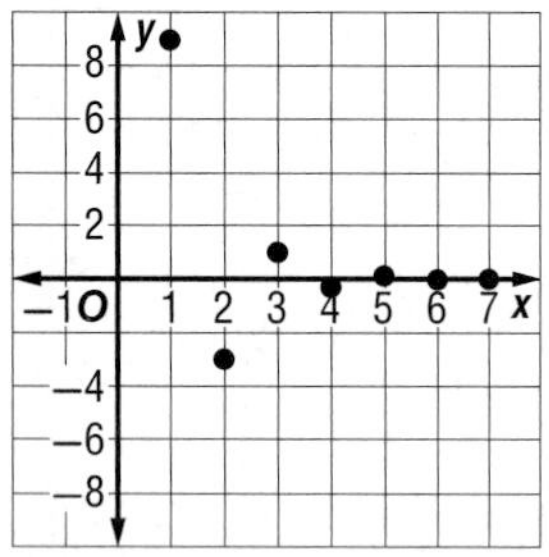

25. 8, 11, 14, 17

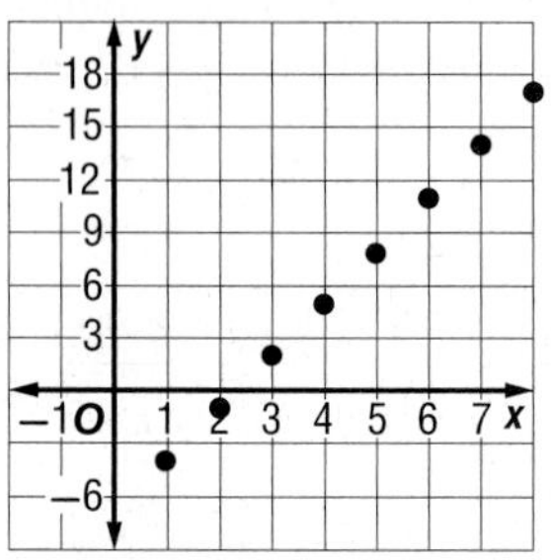

26. −22, −30, −38, −46

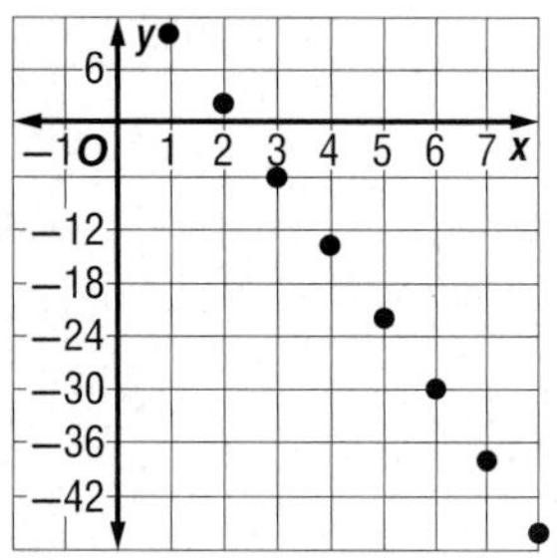

27. −29, −35, −41, −47

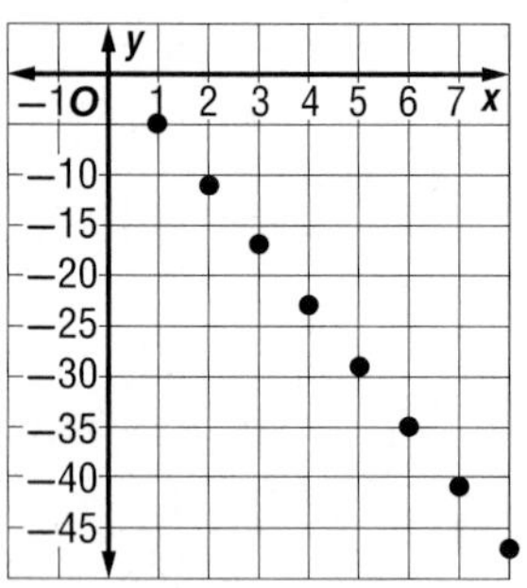

28. 32, 49, 66, 83

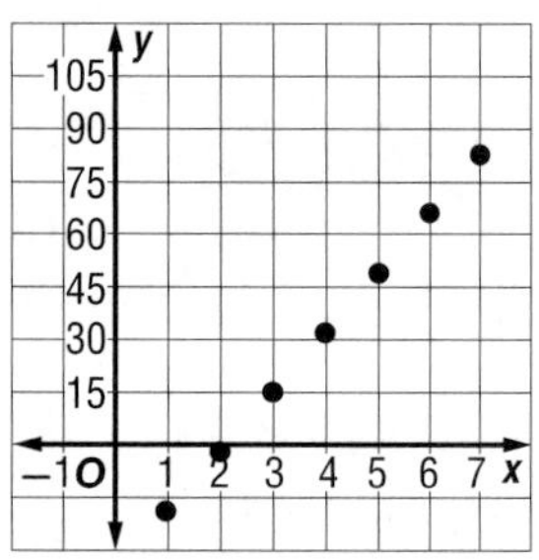

29. $2, \frac{13}{5}, \frac{16}{5}, \frac{19}{5}$

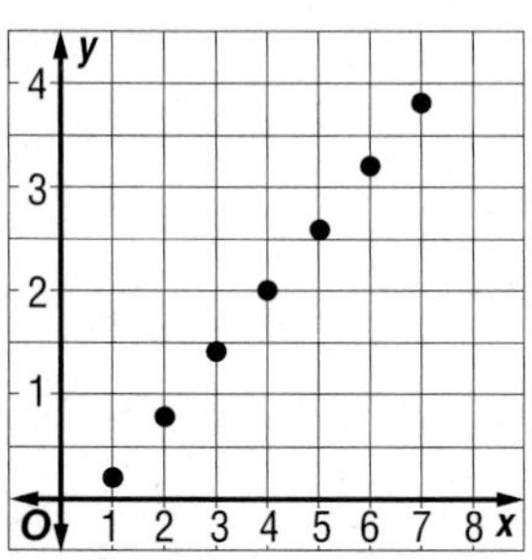

30. $-\frac{7}{3}, -\frac{10}{3}, -\frac{13}{3}, -\frac{16}{3}$

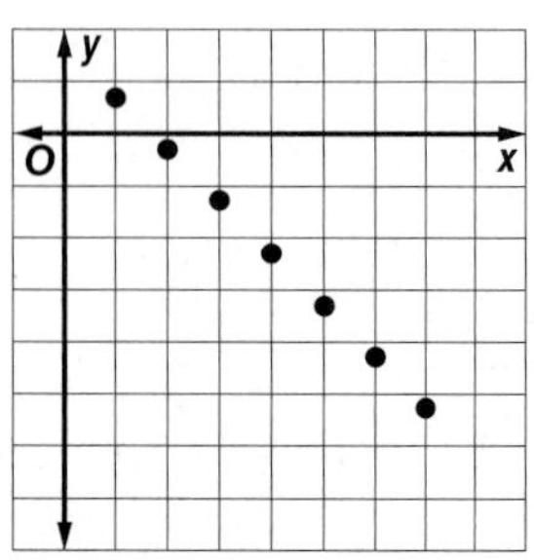

39. −8, 32, −128

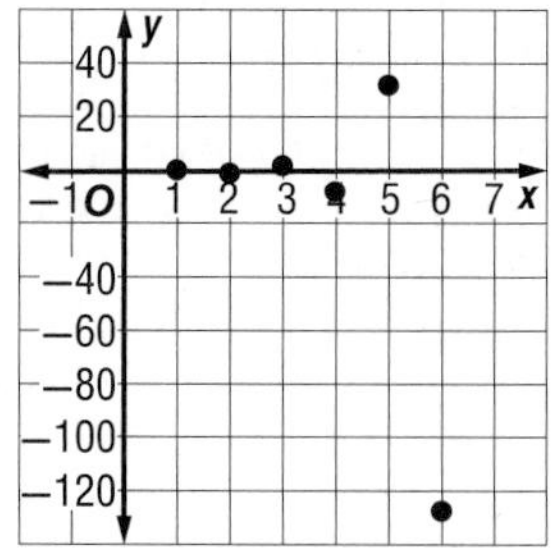

40. $\frac{16}{3}, \frac{32}{9}, \frac{64}{27}$

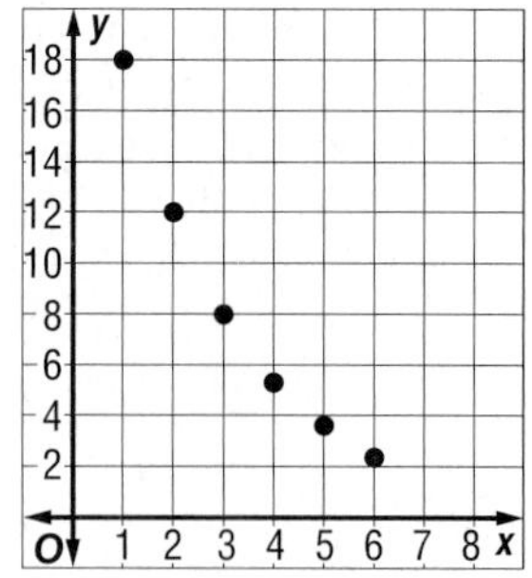

41. $27, \frac{81}{4}, \frac{243}{16}$

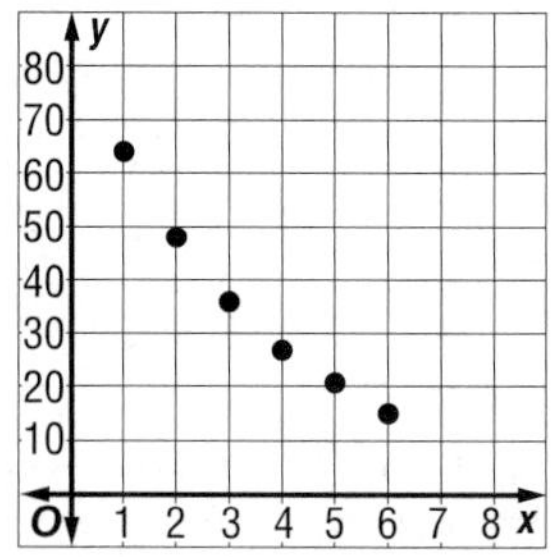

42. $192, 256, \frac{1024}{3}$

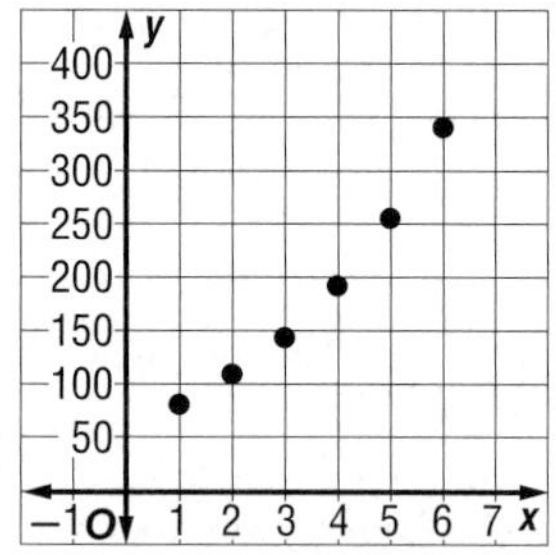

43. 27, 81, 243

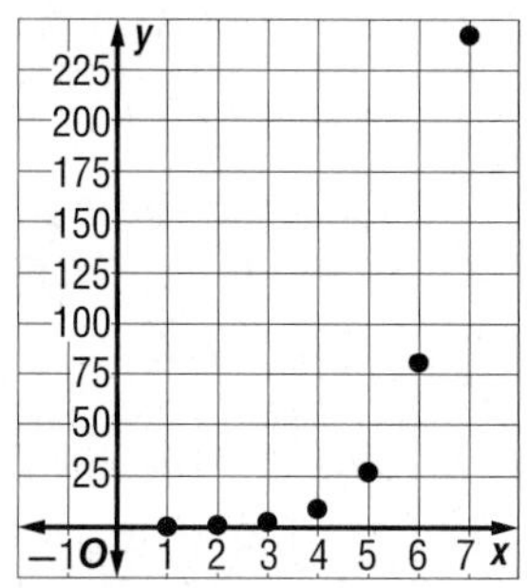

44. 0.0001, 0.00001, 0.000001

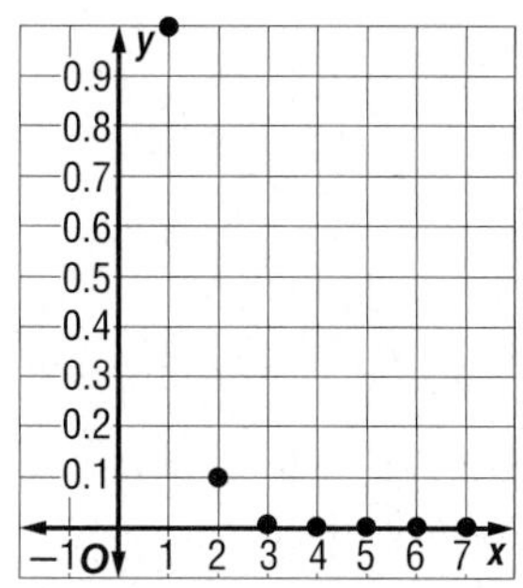

60. Sample answer: When the value of r is doubled, a_2 doubles, a_3 quadruples, a_4 is multiplied by 8, a_5 is multiplied by 2^4 or 16, and so on. So, the new terms are $a_n = a_n \cdot 2^{n-1}$. When the value of r is halved, the new terms are $a_n = a_n \cdot \left(\frac{1}{2}\right)^{n-1}$.

71.

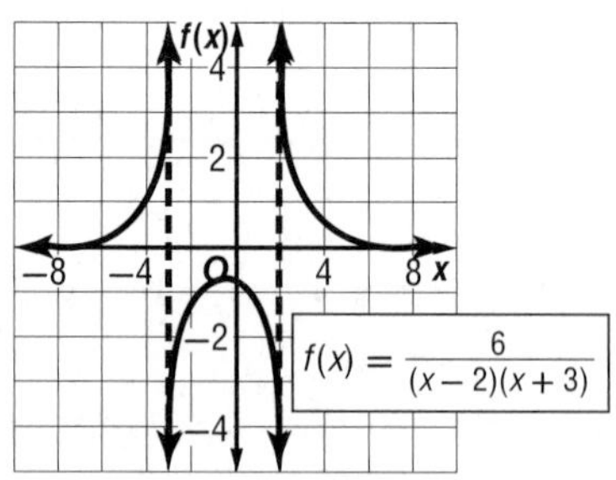

Chapter 11 Answer Appendix

72. 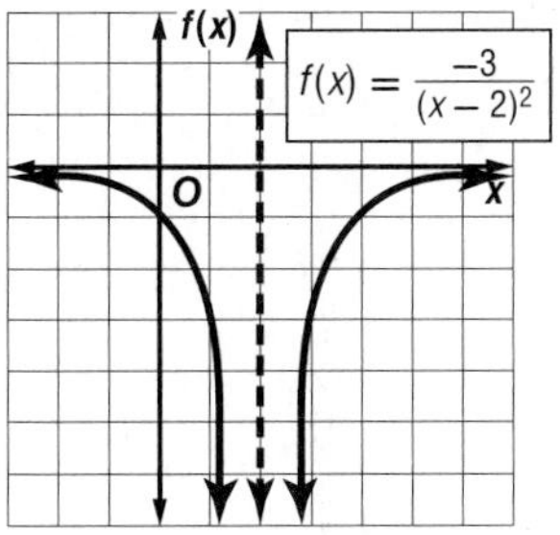

73. 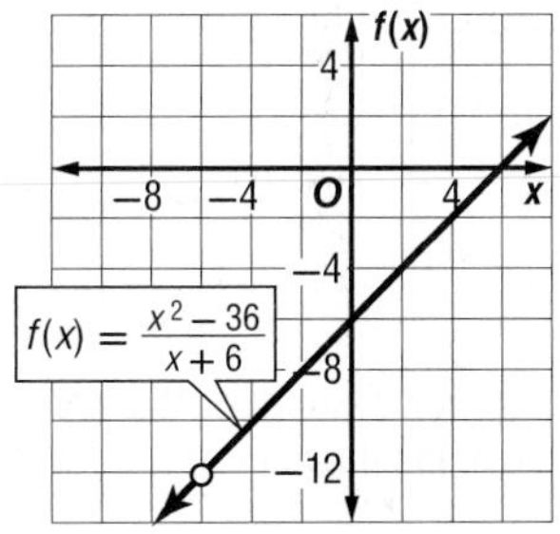

Pages 694–695, Lesson 11-2

71a.

n	S_n
1	4
2	10
3	18
4	28
5	40
6	54
7	70
8	88
9	108
10	130

71b. 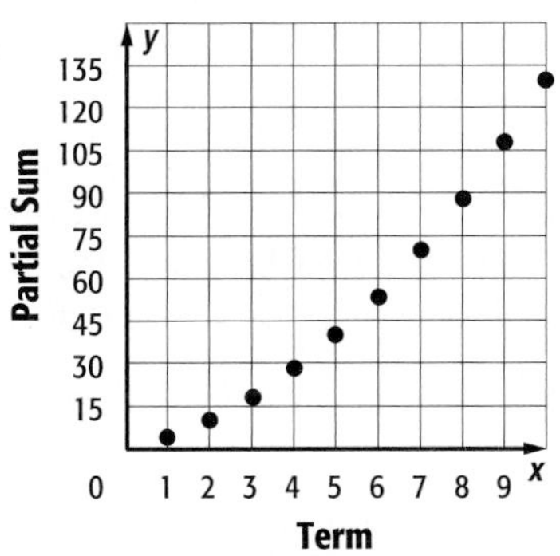

71c. 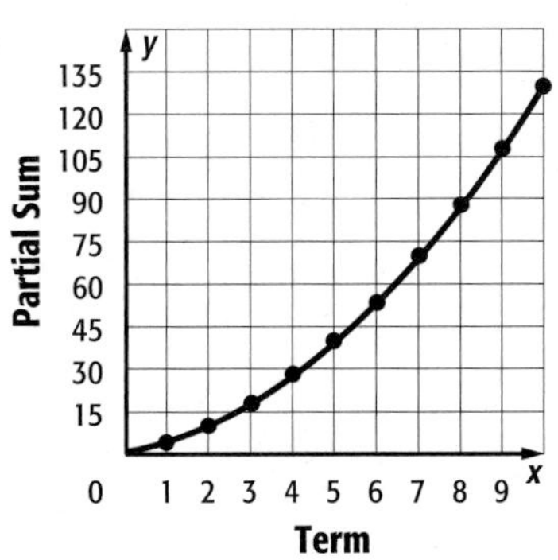

80. Sample answer:
Let a_n = the nth term of the sequence and d = the common difference

$a_2 = a_1 + d$	Definition of the second term of an arithmetic sequence
$a_3 = a_2 + d$	Definition of the third term of an arithmetic sequence
$a_3 = (a_1 + d) + d$	Substitution
$a_3 = a_1 + 2d$	Associative Property of Addition
$a_3 = a_1 + (3 - 1)d$	$3 - 1 = 2$
$a_n = a_1 + (n - 1)d$	$n = 3$

81.

$S_n = (a_1 + a_n) \cdot \left(\frac{n}{2}\right)$	General sum formula
$a_n = a_1 + (n - 1)d$	Formula for *nth* term
$a_n - (n - 1)d = a_1$	Subtract $(n - 1)d$ from both sides.
$S_n = [a_n - (n - 1)d + a_n] \cdot \left(\frac{n}{2}\right)$	Substitution
$S_n = [2a_n - (n - 1)d] \cdot \left(\frac{n}{2}\right)$	Simplify.

90. 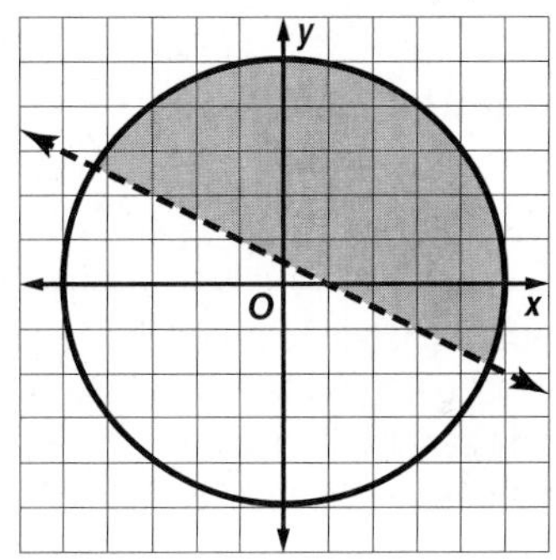

91. 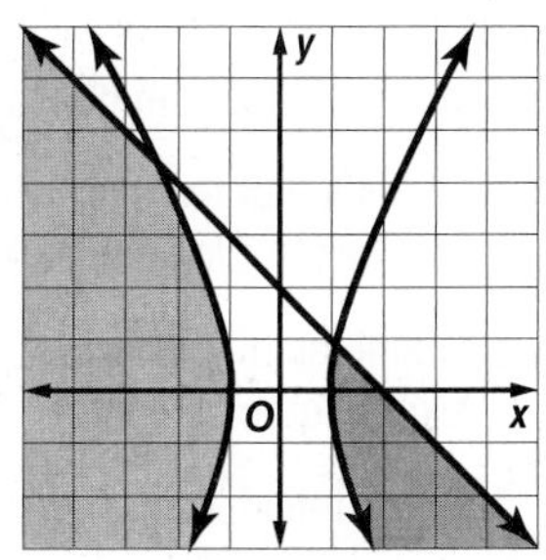

92. 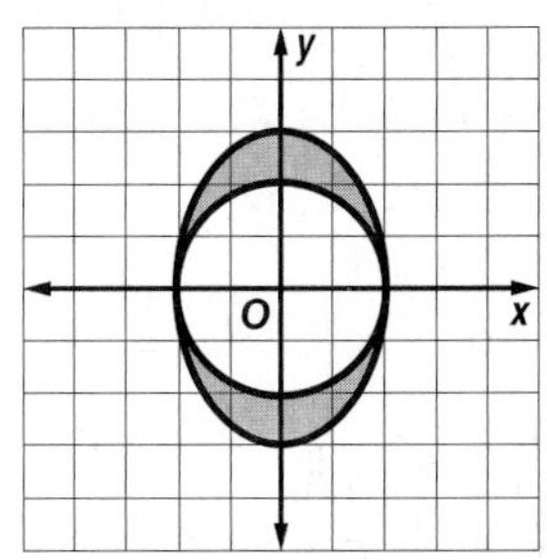

94. 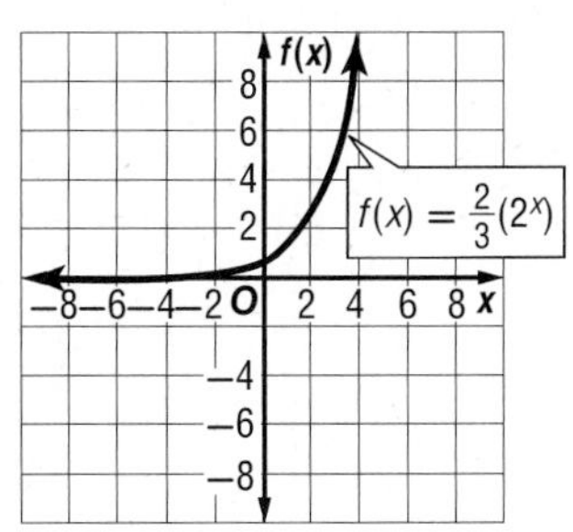

D = {all real numbers}, R = $\{f(x) \mid f(x) > 0\}$

95.

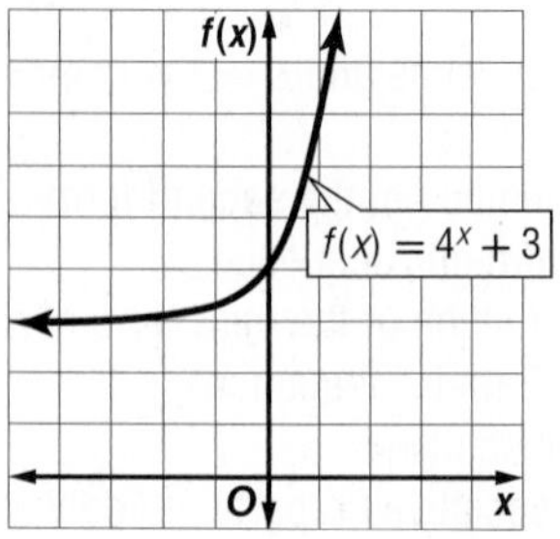

D = {all real numbers}, R = {$f(x)$ | $f(x) > 3$}

96.

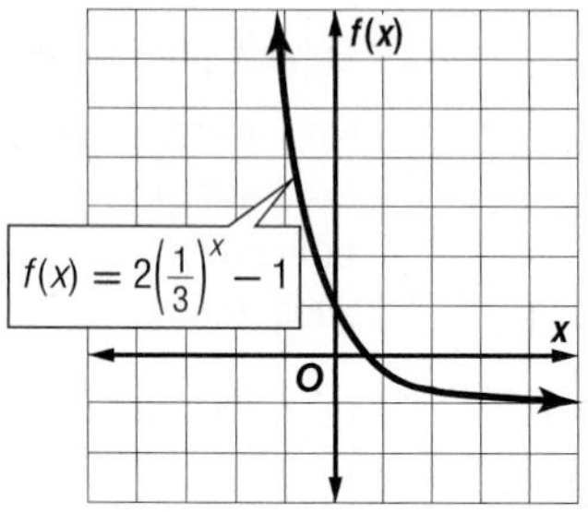

D = {all real numbers}, R = {$f(x)$ | $f(x) > -1$}

Page 701, Lesson 11-3

67. Sample answer: $n - 1$ needs to change to n, and the 10 needs to change to a 9. When this happens, the terms for both series will be identical (a_1 in the first series will equal a_0 in the second series, and so on), and the series will be equal to each other.

68. Sample answer:

Let a_n = the nth term of the sequence and r = the common ratio.

$a_2 = a_1 \cdot r$	Definition of the second term of a geometric sequence
$a_3 = a_2 \cdot r$	Definition of the third term of a geometric sequence
$a_3 = a_1 \cdot r \cdot r$	Substitution
$a_3 = a_1 \cdot r^2$	Associative Property of Multiplication
$a_3 = a_1 \cdot r^{3-1}$	$3 - 1 = 2$
$a_n = a_1 \cdot r^{n-1}$	$n = 3$

Page 704, Explore 11-4

5. Sample answer:

x	−2	−1	0	1	2
y	0	3	4	3	0

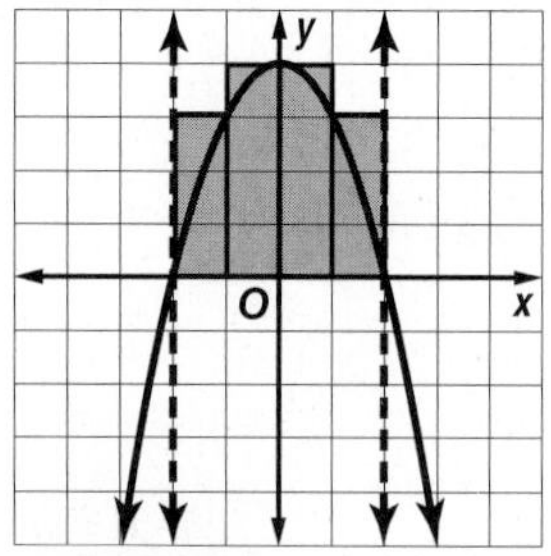

Rectangle	1	2	3	4
Width	1	1	1	1
Height	3	4	4	3
Area	3	4	4	3

14 units^2; The estimate will be greater than the actual area, because the rectangles extend outside the area under the curve.

6. Sample answer:

x	0	1	2	3	4
y	0	1	8	27	64

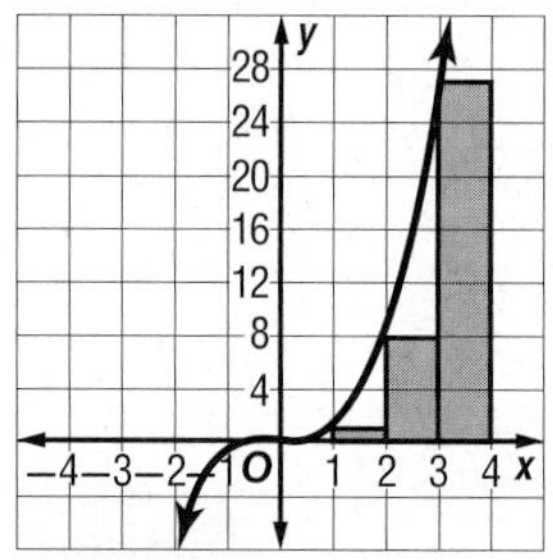

Rectangle	1	2	3
Width	1	1	1
Height	1	8	27
Area	1	8	27

36 units^2; The estimate will be less than the actual area, because rectangles are inside the curve leaving some area unaccounted for.

7. Sample answer:

x	−3	−2	−1	0	1	2	3
y	9	4	1	0	1	4	9

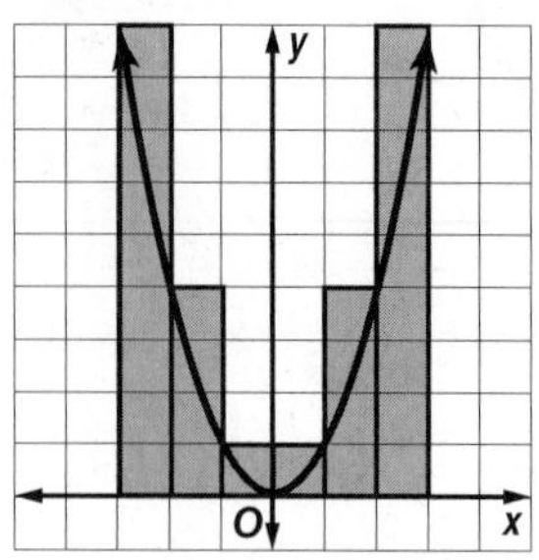

Rectangle	1	2	3	4	5	6
Width	1	1	1	1	1	1
Height	9	4	1	1	4	9
Area	9	4	1	1	4	9

28 units^2; The estimate will be greater than the actual area, because the rectangles extend outside the area under the curve.

Pages 727–728, Lesson 11-7 (Guided Practice)

1. Step 1: When $n = 1$, the left side of the given equation is 1^2 or 1. The right side is $\frac{1(1+1)(1+2)}{6}$ or 1, so the equation is true for $n = 1$.
Step 2: Assume that $1^2 + 2^2 + 3^2 + \ldots + k^2 = \frac{k(k+1)(2k+1)}{6}$ for some natural number k.
Step 3: $1^2 + 2^2 + 3^2 + \ldots + k^2 + (k+1)^2$

$$= \frac{k(k+1)(2k+1)}{6} + (k+1)^2$$
$$= \frac{k(k+1)(2k+1)}{6} + \frac{6(k+1)^2}{6}$$
$$= \frac{(k+1)[k(2k+1)+6(k+1)]}{6}$$
$$= \frac{(k+1)(2k^2+7k+6)}{6}$$
$$= \frac{(k+1)(k+2)(2k+3)}{6}$$
$$= \frac{(k+1)[(k+1)+1][2(k+1)+1]}{6}$$

The last expression is the right side of the equation to be proved, when $n = k + 1$. Thus, the equation is true for $n = k + 1$.

Therefore, $1^2 + 2^2 + 3^2 + \ldots + n^2 = \frac{n(n+1)(2n+1)}{6}$ for all natural numbers n.

2. Step 1: $7^1 - 1 = 6$, which is divisible by 6. The statement is true for $n = 1$.
Step 2: Assume that $7^k - 1$ is divisible by 6 for some natural number k. This means that $7^k - 1 = 6r$ for some natural number r.
Step 3: $7^k - 1 = 6r$

$$7^k = 6r + 1$$
$$7^{k+1} = 7(6r + 1)$$
$$7^{k+1} - 1 = 42r + 6$$
$$7^{k+1} - 1 = 6(7r + 1)$$

Since r is a natural number, $7r + 1$ is a natural number. Thus, $7^{k+1} - 1$ is divisible by 6, so the statement is true for $n = k + 1$. Therefore, $7^n - 1$ is divisible by 6 for all natural numbers n.

Pages 729–730, Lesson 11-7

2. Step 1: When $n = 1$, the left side of the given equation is 1. The right side is $\frac{1(1+1)}{2}$ or 1, so the equation is true for $n = 1$.
Step 2: Assume that $1 + 2 + 3 + \ldots + k = \frac{k(k+1)}{2}$ for some natural number k.
Step 3: $1 + 2 + 3 + \ldots + k + (k+1)$

$$= \frac{k(k+1)}{2} + (k+1)$$
$$= \frac{k(k+1) + 2(k+1)}{2}$$
$$= \frac{(k+1)(k+2)}{2}$$

The last expression is the right side of the equation to be proved, where $n = k + 1$. Thus, the equation is true for $n = k + 1$. Therefore, $1 + 2 + 3 + \text{L} + n = \frac{n(n+1)}{2}$ for all natural numbers n.

3c. Step 1: When $n = 1$, the left side of the given equation is $\frac{1(1+1)}{2}$ or 1. The right side is $\frac{1(1+1)(1+2)}{6}$ or 1, so the equation is true for $n = 1$.
Step 2: Assume that $1 + 3 + 6 + \ldots + \frac{k(k+1)}{2} = \frac{k(k+1)(k+2)}{6}$ for some natural number k.
Step 3: $1 + 3 + 6 + \ldots + \frac{k(k+1)}{2} + \frac{(k+1)(k+1+1)}{2}$

$$= \frac{k(k+1)(k+2)}{6} + \frac{(k+1)(k+1+1)}{2}$$
$$= \frac{k(k+1)(k+2)}{6} + \frac{3(k+1)(k+2)}{6}$$
$$= \frac{(k+1)(k+2)(k+3)}{6}$$
$$= \frac{(k+1)[(k+1)+1][(k+1)+2]}{6}$$

The last expression is the right side of the equation to be proved, where $n = k + 1$. Thus, the equation is true for $n = k + 1$. Therefore, $1 + 3 + 6 + \ldots + \frac{n(n+1)}{2} = \frac{n(n+1)(n+2)}{6}$ for all natural numbers n.

4. Step 1: $10^1 - 1 = 9$, which is divisible by 9. The statement is true for $n = 1$.
Step 2: Assume $10^k - 1$ is divisible by 9 for some natural number k. This means that $10^k - 1 = 9r$ for some whole number r.
Step 3: $10^k - 1 = 9r$

$$10^k = 9r + 1$$
$$10^{k+1} = 90r + 10$$
$$10^{k+1} - 1 = 90r + 9$$
$$10^{k+1} - 1 = 9(10r + 1)$$

Since r is a whole number, $10r + 1$ is a whole number. Thus, $10^{k+1} - 1$ is divisible by 9, so the statement is true for $n = k + 1$. Therefore, $10^n - 1$ is divisible by 9 for all natural numbers n.

5. Step 1: $4^1 - 1 = 3$, which is divisible by 3. The statement is true for $n = 1$.
Step 2: Assume that $4^k - 1$ is divisible by 3 for some natural number k. This means that $4^k - 1 = 3r$ for some whole number r.
Step 3: $4^k - 1 = 3r$

$$4^k = 3r + 1$$
$$4^{k+1} = 12r + 4$$
$$4^{k+1} - 1 = 12r + 3$$
$$4^{k+1} - 1 = 3(4r + 1)$$

Since r is a whole number, $4r + 1$ is a whole number. Thus, $4^{k+1} - 1$ is divisible by 3, so the statement is true for $n = k + 1$. Therefore, $4^n - 1$ is divisible by 3 for all natural numbers n.

8. Step 1: When $n = 1$, the left side of the given equation is $\frac{1}{2}$. The right side is $1 - \frac{1}{2}$ or $\frac{1}{2}$, so the equation is true for $n = 1$.
Step 2: Assume that $\frac{1}{2} + \frac{1}{2^2} + \frac{1}{2^3} + \ldots + \frac{1}{2^k} = 1 - \frac{1}{2^k}$ for some natural number k.
Step 3: $\frac{1}{2} + \frac{1}{2^2} + \frac{1}{2^3} + \ldots + \frac{1}{2^k} + \frac{1}{2^{k+1}}$
$= 1 - \frac{1}{2^k} + \frac{1}{2^{k+1}}$
$= 1 - \frac{2}{2^{k+1}} + \frac{1}{2^{k+1}}$
$= 1 - \frac{1}{2^{k+1}}$
The last expression is the right side of the equation to be proved, where $n = k + 1$. Thus, the equation is true for $n = k + 1$.
Therefore, $\frac{1}{2} + \frac{1}{2^2} + \frac{1}{2^3} + \ldots + \frac{1}{2^n} = 1 - \frac{1}{2^n}$ for all natural numbers n.

9. Step 1: When $n = 1$, the left side of the given equation is 2. The right side is $\frac{1[3(1) + 1]}{2}$ or 2, so the equation is true for $n = 1$.
Step 2: Assume that $2 + 5 + 8 + \ldots + (3k - 1) = \frac{k(3k + 1)}{2}$ for some natural number k.
Step 3: $2 + 5 + 8 + \ldots + (3k - 1) + [3(k + 1) - 1]$
$= \frac{k(3k + 1)}{2} + [3(k + 1) - 1]$
$= \frac{k(3k + 1) + 2[3(k + 1) - 1]}{2}$
$= \frac{3k^2 + k + 6k + 6 - 2}{2}$
$= \frac{3k^2 + 7k + 4}{2}$
$= \frac{(k + 1)(3k + 4)}{2}$
$= \frac{(k + 1)[3(k + 1) + 1]}{2}$
The last expression is the right side of the equation to be proved, where $n = k + 1$. Thus, the equation is true for $n = k + 1$.
Therefore, $2 + 5 + 8 + \ldots + (3n - 1) = \frac{n(3n + 1)}{2}$ for all natural numbers n.

10. Step 1: When $n = 1$, the left side of the given equation is 1. The right side is $2^1 - 1$ or 1, so the equation is true for $n = 1$.
Step 2: Assume that $1 + 2 + 4 + \ldots + 2^{k-1} = 2^k - 1$ for some natural number k.
Step 3: $1 + 2 + 4 + \ldots + 2^{k-1} + 2^{k-1+1}$
$= 2^k - 1 + 2^{k-1+1}$
$= 2^k + 2^k - 1$
$= 2(2^k) - 1$
$= 2^{k+1} - 1$
The last expression is the right side of the equation to be proved, where $n = k + 1$. Thus, the equation is true for $n = k + 1$.
Therefore, $1 + 2 + 4 + \ldots + 2^{n-1} = 2^n - 1$ for all natural numbers n.

11. Step 1: When $n = 1$, the left side of the given equation is 1. The right side is $1[2(1) - 1]$ or 1, so the equation is true for $n = 1$.
Step 2: Assume that $1 + 5 + 9 + \ldots + (4k - 3) = k(2k - 1)$ for some natural number k.
Step 3: $1 + 5 + 9 + \ldots + (4k - 3) + [4(k + 1) - 3]$
$= k(2k - 1) + [4(k + 1) - 3]$
$= 2k^2 - k + 4k + 4 - 3$
$= 2k^2 + 3k + 1$
$= (k + 1)(2k + 1)$
$= (k + 1)[2(k + 1) - 1]$
The last expression is the right side of the equation to be proved, where $n = k + 1$. Thus, the equation is true for $n = k + 1$. Therefore, $1 + 5 + 9 + \ldots + (4n - 3) = n(2n - 1)$ for all natural numbers n.

12. Step 1: When $n = 1$, the left side of the given equation is 1. The right side is $\frac{1[3(1) - 1]}{2}$ or 1, so the equation is true for $n = 1$.
Step 2: Assume that $1 + 4 + 7 + \ldots + (3k - 2) = \frac{k(3k - 1)}{2}$ for some natural number k.
Step 3: $1 + 4 + 7 + \ldots + (3k - 2) + [3(k + 1) - 2]$
$= \frac{k(3k - 1)}{2} + [3(k + 1) - 2]$
$= \frac{k(3k - 1)}{2} + 3k + 1$
$= \frac{k(3k - 1)}{2} + \frac{6k + 2}{2}$
$= \frac{3k^2 + 5k + 2}{2}$
$= \frac{(k + 1)(3k + 2)}{2}$
$= \frac{(k + 1)[3(k + 1) - 1]}{2}$
The last expression is the right side of the equation to be proved, where $n = k + 1$. Thus, the equation is true for $n = k + 1$.
Therefore, $1 + 4 + 7 + \ldots + (3n - 2) = \frac{n(3n - 1)}{2}$ for all natural numbers n.

13. Step 1: When $n = 1$, the left side of the given equation is $4(1) - 1$ or 3. The right side is $2(1)^2 + 1$ or 3, so the equation is true for $n = 1$.
Step 2: Assume that $3 + 7 + 11 + \ldots + (4k - 1) = 2k^2 + k$ for some natural number k.
Step 3: $3 + 7 + 11 + \ldots + (4k - 1) + [4(k + 1) - 1]$
$= 2k^2 + k + [4(k + 1) - 1]$
$= 2k^2 + k + 4k + 3$
$= 2k^2 + 5k + 3$
$= 2k^2 + 4k + 2 + k + 1$
$= [2(k + 1)^2] + (k + 1)$
The last expression is the right side of the equation to be proved, where $n = k + 1$. Thus, the equation is true for $n = k + 1$.
Therefore, $3 + 7 + 11 + \ldots + (4n - 1) = 2n^2 + n$ for all natural numbers n.

14. Step 1: When $n = 1$, the left side of the given equation is $\frac{1}{1(1 + 1)}$ or $\frac{1}{2}$. The right side is $\frac{1}{1 + 1}$ or $\frac{1}{2}$, so the equation is true for $n = 1$.
Step 2: Assume that $\frac{1}{2} + \frac{1}{6} + \frac{1}{12} + \ldots + \frac{1}{k(k + 1)} = \frac{k}{k + 1}$ for some natural number k.
Step 3: $\frac{1}{2} + \frac{1}{6} + \frac{1}{12} + \ldots + \frac{1}{k(k + 1)} + \frac{1}{(k + 1)(k + 1 + 1)}$
$= \frac{k}{k + 1} + \frac{1}{(k + 1)(k + 1 + 1)}$
$= \frac{k(k + 2)}{(k + 1)(k + 2)} + \frac{1}{(k + 1)(k + 2)}$
$= \frac{k^2 + 2k + 1}{(k + 1)(k + 2)}$

$= \frac{(k+1)(k+1)}{(k+1)(k+2)}$

$= \frac{k+1}{(k+1)+1}$

The last expression is the right side of the equation to be proved, where $n = k + 1$. Thus, the equation is true for $n = k + 1$. Therefore, $\frac{1}{2} + \frac{1}{6} + \frac{1}{12} + \ldots + \frac{1}{n(n+1)} = \frac{n}{n+1}$ for all natural numbers n.

15. Step 1: When $n = 1$, the left side of the given equation is 1^2 or 1. The right side is $\frac{1[2(1)-1][2(1)+1]}{3}$ or 1, so the equation is true for $n = 1$.
Step 2: Assume that $1^2 + 3^2 + 5^2 + \ldots + (2k-1)^2 = \frac{k(2k-1)(2k+1)}{3}$ for some natural number k.
Step 3: $1^2 + 3^2 + 5^2 + \ldots + (2k-1)^2 + [2(k+1)-1]^2$

$= \frac{k(2k-1)(2k+1)}{3} + [2(k+1)-1]^2$

$= \frac{k(2k-1)(2k+1) + 3(2k+1)^2}{3}$

$= \frac{(2k+1)[k(2k-1) + 3(2k+1)]}{3}$

$= \frac{(2k+1)(2k^2 - k + 6k + 3)}{3}$

$= \frac{(2k+1)(2k^2 + 5k + 3)}{3}$

$= \frac{(2k+1)(k+1)(2k+3)}{3}$

$= \frac{(k+1)[2(k+1)-1][2(k+1)+1]}{3}$

The last expression is the right side of the equation to be proved, where $n = k + 1$. Thus, the equation is true for $n = k + 1$.
Therefore, $1^2 + 3^2 + 5^2 + \ldots + (2n-1)^2 = \frac{n(2n-1)(2n+1)}{3}$ for all natural numbers n.

16. Step 1: When $n = 3$, $180(3 - 2) = 180$. When a polygon has 3 sides or 3 vertices, there are 180 degrees. The statement is true for $n = 3$.
Step 2: Assume that the statement is true for $n \geq 3$.
Step 3: Consider a convex polygon with $n + 1$ vertices. Since $n + 1 \geq 4$, if we take one vertex x there is another vertex y such that there is one vertex between x and y in one direction, and $n - 2$ in the other direction. Join x and y by a new edge, dividing our original polygon into two polygons. The new polygons' interior angles summed together make up the sum of the original polygon's interior angles. One of the new polygons is a triangle and the other a polygon of n vertices (all but the one isolated between x and y). The triangle has interior angle sum 180°, and by the inductive hypothesis the other polygon has interior angle sum $(n - 2) \cdot 180°$. Summing these we get $(n + 1 - 2) \cdot 180°$, and the theorem is proved.

17. Step 1: $5^1 + 3 = 8$, which is divisible by 4. The statement is true for $n = 1$.
Step 2: Assume $5^k + 3$ is divisible by 4 for some natural number k. This means that $5^k + 3 = 4r$ for some natural number r.
Step 3: $5^k + 3 = 4r$

$5^k = 4r - 3$

$5^{k+1} = 20r - 15$

$5^{k+1} + 3 = 20r - 12$

$5^{k+1} + 3 = 4(5r - 3)$

Since r is a natural number, $5r - 3$ is a natural number. Thus, $5^{k+1} + 3$ is divisible by 4, so the statement is true for $n = k + 1$. Therefore, $5^n + 3$ is divisible by 4 for all natural numbers n.

18. Step 1: $9^1 - 1 = 8$, which is divisible by 8. The statement is true for $n = 1$.
Step 2: Assume that $9^k - 1$ is divisible by 8 for some natural number k. This means that $9^k - 1 = 8r$ for some whole number r.
Step 3: $9^k - 1 = 8r$

$9^k = 8r + 1$

$9^{k+1} = 72r + 9$

$9^{k+1} - 1 = 72r + 8$

$9^{k+1} - 1 = 8(9r + 1)$

Since r is a whole number, $9r + 1$ is a whole number. Thus, $9^{k+1} - 1$ is divisible by 8, so the statement is true for $n = k + 1$. Therefore, $9^n - 1$ is divisible by 8 for all natural numbers n.

19. Step 1: $12^1 + 10 = 22$, which is divisible by 11. The statement is true for $n = 1$.
Step 2: Assume that $12^k + 10$ is divisible by 11 for some natural number k. This means that $12^k + 10 = 11r$ for some natural number r.
Step 3: $12^k + 10 = 11r$

$12^k = 11r - 10$

$12^{k+1} = 132r - 120$

$12^{k+1} + 10 = 132r - 110$

$12^{k+1} + 10 = 11(12r - 10)$

Since r is a natural number, $12r - 10$ is a natural number. Thus, $12^{k+1} + 10$ is divisible by 11, so the statement is true for $n = k + 1$. Therefore, $12^n + 10$ is divisible by 11 for all natural numbers n.

20. Step 1: $13^1 + 11 = 24$, which is divisible by 12. The statement is true for $n = 1$.
Step 2: Assume that $13^k + 11$ is divisible by 12 for some natural number k. This means that $13^k + 11 = 12r$ for some natural number r.
Step 3: $13^k + 11 = 12r$

$13^k = 12r - 11$

$13^{k+1} = 156r - 143$

$13^{k+1} + 11 = 156r - 132$

$13^{k+1} + 11 = 12(13r - 11)$

Since r is a natural number, $13r - 11$ is a natural number. Thus, $13^{k+1} + 11$ is divisible by 12, so the statement is true for $n = k + 1$. Therefore, $13^n + 11$ is divisible by 12 for all natural numbers n.

26. Step 1: $7^1 + 5 = 12$, which is divisible by 6. The statement is true for $n = 1$.
Step 2: Assume that $7^k + 5$ is divisible by 6 for some natural number k. This means that $7^k + 5 = 6r$ for some whole number r.
Step 3: $7^k + 5 = 6r$

$$\begin{aligned} 7^k &= 6r - 5 \\ 7^{k+1} &= 7(6r - 5) \\ 7^{k+1} &= 42r - 35 \\ 7^{k+1} + 5 &= 42r - 30 \\ 7^{k+1} + 5 &= 6(7r - 5) \end{aligned}$$

Since r is a natural number, $7r - 5$ is a natural number. Thus, $7^{k+1} + 5$ is divisible by 6, so the statement is true for $n = k + 1$. Therefore, $7^n + 5$ is divisible by 6 for all natural numbers n.

27. Step 1: $18^1 - 1 = 17$, which is divisible by 17. The statement is true for $n = 1$.
Step 2: Assume that $18^k - 1$ is divisible by 17 for some natural number k. This means that $18^k - 1 = 17r$ for some natural number r.
Step 3: $18^k - 1 = 17r$

$$\begin{aligned} 18^k &= 17r + 1 \\ 18^{k+1} &= 18(17r + 1) \\ 18^{k+1} &= 306r + 18 \\ 18^{k+1} - 1 &= 306r + 17 \\ 18^{k+1} - 1 &= 17(18r + 1) \end{aligned}$$

Since r is a natural number, $18r + 1$ is a natural number. Thus, $18^{k+1} - 1$ is divisible by 17, so the statement is true for $n = k + 1$. Therefore, $18^n - 1$ is divisible by 17 for all natural numbers n.

30. Step 1: When $n = 1$, the left side of the given equation is $4 \cdot 5^{4-1}$ or 500. The right side is $625\left(1 - \frac{1}{5^1}\right)$ or 500, so the equation is true for $n = 1$.
Step 2: Assume that $500 + 100 + 20 + \dots + 4 \cdot 5^{4-k} = 625\left(1 - \frac{1}{5^k}\right)$ for some natural number k.
Step 3: $500 + 100 + 20 + \dots + 4 \cdot 5^{4-k} + 4 \cdot 5^{4-(k+1)}$

$$\begin{aligned} &= 625\left(1 - \frac{1}{5^k}\right) + 4 \cdot 5^{4-(k+1)} \\ &= 625\left(\frac{5^k - 1}{5^k}\right) + 4 \cdot 5^{3-k} \\ &= 625\left(\frac{5^{k+1} - 5}{5^{k+1}}\right) + \frac{4 \cdot 5^4}{5^{k+1}} \\ &= \frac{5^4(5^{k+1} - 5) + 4 \cdot 5^4}{5^{k+1}} \\ &= \frac{5^4(5^{k+1} - 5 + 4)}{5^{k+1}} \\ &= 625\left(\frac{5^{k+1} - 1}{5^{k+1}}\right) \\ &= 625\left(1 - \frac{1}{5^{k+1}}\right) \end{aligned}$$

The last expression is the right side of the equation to be proved, where $n = k + 1$. Thus, the equation is true for $n = k + 1$. Therefore, $500 + 100 + 20 + \dots + 4 \cdot 5^{4-n} = 625\left(1 - \frac{1}{5^n}\right)$ for all natural numbers n.

31. Step 1: When $n = 1$, the left side of the given equation is $\frac{1}{1(1+1)(1+2)}$ or $\frac{1}{6}$. The right side is $\frac{1(1+3)}{4(1+1)(1+2)}$ or $\frac{1}{6}$, so the equation is true for $n = 1$.

Step 2: Assume that $\frac{1}{1 \dots 2 \dots 3} + \frac{1}{2 \dots 3 \dots 4} + \frac{1}{3 \dots 4 \dots 5} + \dots + \frac{1}{k(k+1)(k+2)} = \frac{k(k+3)}{4(k+1)(k+2)}$ for some natural number k.

Step 3:

$$\begin{aligned} &\frac{1}{1 \cdot 2 \cdot 3} + \frac{1}{2 \cdot 3 \cdot 4} + \dots + \frac{1}{k(k+1)(k+2)} + \frac{1}{(k+1)(k+2)(k+3)} \\ &= \frac{k(k+3)}{4(k+1)(k+2)} + \frac{1}{(k+1)(k+2)(k+3)} \\ &= \frac{k(k+3)(k+3)}{4(k+1)(k+2)(k+3)} + \frac{4}{4(k+1)(k+2)(k+3)} \\ &= \frac{k^3 + 6k^2 + 9k + 4}{4(k+1)(k+2)(k+3)} \\ &= \frac{(k+1)(k^2 + 5k + 4)}{4(k+1)(k+2)(k+3)} \\ &= \frac{(k+1)(k+4)}{4(k+2)(k+3)} \\ &= \frac{(k+1)[(k+1)+3]}{4[(k+1)+1][(k+1)+2]} \end{aligned}$$

The last expression is the right side of the equation to be proved, where $n = k + 1$. Thus, the equation is true for $n = k + 1$. Therefore, $\frac{1}{1 \dots 2 \dots 3} + \frac{1}{2 \dots 3 \dots 4} + \frac{1}{3 \dots 4 \dots 5} + \dots + \frac{1}{n(n+1)(n+2)} = \frac{n(n+3)}{4(n+1)(n+2)}$ for all natural numbers n.

33. $n(n + 1)$
Step 1: When $n = 1$, the left side of the given equation is 2(1) or 2. The right side is $1(1 + 1)$ or 2, so the equation is true for $n = 1$.

Step 2: Assume that $2 + 4 + 6 + \dots + 2k = k(k + 1)$ for some natural number k.

Step 3: $2 + 4 + 6 + \dots + 2k + 2(k + 1)$

$$\begin{aligned} &= k(k+1) + 2(k+1) \\ &= (k+1)(k+2) \\ &= (k+1)[(k+1)+1] \end{aligned}$$

The last expression is the right side of the equation to be proved, where $n = k + 1$. Thus, the equation is true for $n = k + 1$. Therefore, $2 + 4 + 6 + \dots + n^2 = n(n + 1)$ for all natural numbers n.

36. Step 1: When $n = 1$, the left side of the given equation is 1^3 or 1. The right side is $\left(\frac{1(1+1)}{2}\right)^2$ or 1, so the equation is true for $n = 1$.

Step 2: Assume that $1 + 8 + 27 + \dots + k^3 = \left(\frac{k(k+1)}{2}\right)^2$ for some natural number k.
Step 3:
$1 + 8 + \dots + k^3 + (k+1)^3 = \left(\frac{k(k+1)}{2}\right)^2 + (k+1)^3$

$$= \frac{k^2(k+1)^2}{4} + (k+1)^3$$
$$= \frac{k^2(k+1)^2}{4} + \frac{4(k+1)^3}{4}$$
$$= \frac{(k+1)^2\,[k^2 + 4(k+1)]}{4}$$
$$= \frac{(k+1)^2\,(k^2 + 4k + 4)}{4}$$
$$= \frac{(k+1)^2(k+2)^2}{2^2}$$
$$= \left(\frac{(k+1)[(k+1)+1]}{2}\right)^2$$

The last expression is the right side of the equation to be proved, where $n = k + 1$. Thus, the equation is true for $n = k + 1$. Therefore, $1 + 8 + \ldots + k^3 = \left(\frac{k(k+1)}{2}\right)^2$ for all natural numbers n.

38. Sample answer: $6 + 10 + 14 + \ldots$. The sequence is produced by $a_n = 4n + 2$. The sum of the sequence is represented by $2n(n + 2)$.
Step 1: When $n = 1$, the left side of the given equation is $4(1) + 2$ or 6. The right side is $2(1)(1 + 2)$ or 6, so the equation is true for $n = 1$.
Step 2: Assume that $6 + 10 + 14 + \ldots 4k + 2 = 2k(k + 2)$ for some natural number k.
Step 3: $6 + 10 + 14 + \ldots 4k + 2 + 4(k + 1) + 2$
$= 2k(k + 2) + 4(k + 1) + 2$
$= 2k^2 + 4k + 4k + 4 + 2$
$= 2k^2 + 8k + 6$
$= 2(k + 1)(k + 3)$
$= 2(k + 1)[(k + 1) + 2]$
The last expression is the right side of the equation to be proved, where $n = k + 1$. Thus, the equation is true for $n = k + 1$. Therefore, $6 + 10 + 14 + \ldots (4n + 2) = 2n(n + 2)$ for all natural numbers n.

Page 736, Study Guide and Review

64. Step 1: When $n = 1$, $7^1 - 1 = 7 - 1$ or 6. Since 6 divided by 6 is 1, the statement is true for $n = 1$.

Step 2: Assume that $7^k - 1$ is divisible by 6 for some positive integer k. This means that $7^k - 1 = 6r$ for some whole number r.

Step 3:
$7^k - 1 = 6r$
$7^k = 6r + 1$
$7^{k+1} = 42r + 7$
$7^{k+1} - 1 = 42r + 7 - 1$
$7^{k+1} - 1 = 42r + 6$
$7^{k+1} - 1 = 6(7r + 1)$
Since r is a whole number, $7r + 1$ is a whole number. Thus, $7^{k+1} - 1$ is divisible by 6, so the statement is true for $n = k + 1$. Therefore, $7^n - 1$ is divisible by 6 for all positive integers n.

65. Step 1: When $n = 1$, $5^1 - 1 = 5 - 1$ or 4. Since 4 divided by 4 is 1, the statement is true for $n = 1$.
Step 2: Assume that $5^k - 1$ is divisible by 4 for some positive integer k. This means that $5^k - 1 = 4r$ for some whole number r.
Step 3:
$5^k - 1 = 4r$
$5^k = 4r + 1$
$5^{k+1} = 20r + 5$
$5^{k+1} - 1 = 20r + 5 - 1$
$5^{k+1} - 1 = 20r + 4$
$5^{k+1} - 1 = 4(5r + 1)$
Since r is a whole number, $5r + 1$ is a whole number. Thus, $5^{k+1} - 1$ is divisible by 4, so the statement is true for $n = k + 1$. Therefore, $5^n - 1$ is divisible by 4 for all positive integers n.

Page 737, Practice Test

20. Step 1: When $n = 1$, the left side of the given equation is 1. The right side is 1 also, so the equation is true for $n = 1$.
Step 2: Assume $1 + 6 + 36 + \ldots + 6^{k-1} = \frac{1}{5}(6^k - 1)$ for some positive integer k.
Step 3: Show that the given equation is true for $n = k + 1$.
$$1 + 6 + 36 + \ldots + 6^{k-1} + 6^{k+1-1} = \frac{1}{5}(6^k - 1) + 6^{k+1-1}$$
$$= \frac{1}{5}(6^k - 1) + 6^k$$
$$= \frac{1}{5} \cdot 6^k - \frac{1}{5} + 6^k$$
$$= \frac{6}{5} \cdot 6^k - \frac{1}{5}$$
$$= \frac{1}{5} \cdot 6^{k+1} - \frac{1}{5}$$
$$= \frac{1}{5} \cdot (6^{k+1} - 1)$$
The last expression is the right side of the equation to be proved, where $n = k + 1$. Therefore, $1 + 6 + 36 + \ldots + 6^{n-1} = \frac{1}{5}(6^n - 1)$ for all positive integers n.

21. Step 1: $11^1 - 1 = 10$, which is divisible by 10. The statement is true for $n = 1$.
Step 2: Assume that $11^k - 1$ is divisible by 10 for some positive integer k. This means that $11^k - 1 = 10r$ for some whole number r.
Step 3:
$11^k - 1 = 10r$
$11^k = 10r + 1$
$11(11^k) = (10r + 1)\,11$
$11^{k+1} = 110r + 11$
$11^{k+1} - 1 = 110r + 11 - 1$
$11^{k+1} - 1 = 110r + 10$
$11^{k+1} - 1 = 10(11r + 1)$

Since r is a whole umber, $11r + 1$ is a whole number. Thus, $11^{k+1} - 1$ is divisible by 10, so the statement is true for $n = k + 1$. Therefore, $11^n - 1$ is divisible by 10 for all positive integers n.

CHAPTER 12

Chapter Planner

Diagnostic Assessment
Quick Check, p. 743

	Lesson 12-1 Pacing: 1 day	Extend 12-1 Pacing: 0.5 day	Lesson 12-2 Pacing: 1 day
Title	**Experiments, Surveys, and Observational Studies**	**Graphing Technology Lab: Evaluating Published Data**	**Statistical Analysis**
Objectives	• Evaluate surveys, studies, and experiments. • Distinguish between correlation and causation.	• Use the CelSheet application of a graphing calculator to evaluate data found in the media.	• Use measures of central tendency and variation to compare sets of data. • Explore measures of variation.
Key Vocabulary	survey population census sample biased unbiased observational study experiment treated group control group correlation causation		univariate data measure of central tendency parameter statistic margin of sampling error measure of variation variance standard deviation
NGSSS	MA.912.S.2.1, MA.912.S.2.3		MA.912.S.3.3, MA.912.S.3.4
Multiple Representations			
Lesson Resources	**Chapter 12 Resource Masters** • Study Guide and Intervention, pp. 5–6 AL OL ELL • Skills Practice, p. 7 AL OL ELL • Practice, p. 8 AL OL BL ELL • Word Problem Practice, p. 9 AL OL BL ELL • Enrichment, p. 10 OL BL **Transparencies** • 5-Minute Check Transparency 12-1 AL OL BL ELL **Additional Print Resources** • Study Notebook AL OL BL ELL	**Materials** • TI-83/84 Plus graphing calculator	**Chapter 12 Resource Masters** • Study Guide and Intervention, pp. 11–12 AL OL ELL • Skills Practice, p. 13 AL OL ELL • Practice, p. 14 AL OL BL ELL • Word Problem Practice, p. 15 AL OL BL ELL • Enrichment, p. 16 OL BL • Graphing Calculator Activity, p. 17 OL • Quiz 1, p. 51 AL OL BL ELL **Transparencies** • 5-Minute Check Transparency 12-2 AL OL BL ELL **Additional Print Resources** • Study Notebook AL OL BL ELL
Technology for Every Lesson	FL Math Online glencoe.com • Extra Examples • Self-Check Quizzes • Personal Tutor • Homework Help	**CD/DVD Resources** IWB INTERACTIVE WHITEBOARD READY IWB StudentWorks Plus IWB Interactive Classroom IWB Diagnostic and Assessment Planner	• TeacherWorks Plus • eSolutions Manual Plus • ExamView Assessment Suite
Get Animated	Interactive Lab		
Differentiated Instruction	pp. 747, 750		pp. 753, 758

KEY: AL Approaching Level OL On Level BL Beyond Level ELL English Learners

Probability and Statistics

Suggested Pacing			
Time Periods	Instruction	Review & Assessment	Total
45-minute	9	2	11
90-minute	7	1	8

Lesson 12-3 Pacing: 1 day	Lesson 12-4 Pacing: 1 day	Lesson 12-5 Pacing: 1 day	Extend 12-5 Pacing: 0.5 day
Conditional Probability	**Probability and Probability Distributions**	**The Normal Distribution**	**Algebra Lab: The Empirical Rule and Percentiles**
• Find probabilities of events given the occurrence of other events. • Use contingency tables to find conditional probabilities.	• Find probabilities by using combinations and permutations. • Create and use graphs of probability distributions.	• Determine whether a set of data appears to be normally distributed or skewed. • Use the Empirical Rule to find probabilities.	• Use the Empirical Rule to associate percentiles with a normal distribution.
conditional probability contingency table relative frequency	probability success failure sample space random variable probability distribution uniform distribution relative-frequency histogram discrete probability distribution theoretical probability expected value	continuous probability distribution normal distribution skewed distribution	
MA.912.P.2.3	MA.912.P.1.2, MA.912.P.3.1	MA.912.P.3.1, MA.912.P.3.2, MA.912.P.3.3	MA.912.S.3.6
	p. 771		
Chapter 12 Resource Masters • Study Guide and Intervention, pp. 18–19 AL OL ELL • Skills Practice, p. 20 AL OL ELL • Practice, p. 21 AL OL BL ELL • Word Problem Practice, p. 22 AL OL BL ELL • Enrichment, p. 23 OL BL **Transparencies** • 5-Minute Check Transparency 12-3 AL OL BL ELL **Additional Print Resources** • Study Notebook AL OL BL ELL	**Chapter 12 Resource Masters** • Study Guide and Intervention, pp. 24–25 AL OL ELL • Skills Practice, p. 26 AL OL ELL • Practice, p. 27 AL OL BL ELL • Word Problem Practice, p. 28 AL OL BL ELL • Enrichment, p. 29 OL BL • Quiz 2, p. 51 AL OL BL ELL **Transparencies** • 5-Minute Check Transparency 12-4 AL OL BL ELL **Additional Print Resources** • Study Notebook AL OL BL ELL • Teaching Algebra with Manipulatives, pp. 256–257 AL OL ELL	**Chapter 12 Resource Masters** • Study Guide and Intervention, pp. 30–31 AL OL ELL • Skills Practice, p. 32 AL OL ELL • Practice, p. 33 AL OL BL ELL • Word Problem Practice, p. 34 AL OL BL ELL • Enrichment, p. 35 OL BL **Transparencies** • 5-Minute Check Transparency 12-5 AL OL BL ELL **Additional Print Resources** • Study Notebook AL OL BL ELL	**Additional Print Resources** • Teaching Algebra with Manipulatives, p. 258 AL OL ELL

FL Math Online glencoe.com
- Extra Examples
- Self-Check Quizzes
- Personal Tutor
- Homework Help

CD/DVD Resources IWB INTERACTIVE WHITEBOARD READY
- IWB StudentWorks Plus
- IWB Interactive Classroom
- IWB Diagnostic and Assessment Planner
- TeacherWorks Plus
- eSolutions Manual Plus
- ExamView Assessment Suite

		Animation	
pp. 760, 763	pp. 765, 771	pp. 775, 778	

Formative Assessment
Mid-Chapter Quiz, p. 772

CHAPTER 12

Chapter Planner

	Lesson 12-6 Pacing: 1 day	Explore 12-7 Pacing: 0.5 day	Lesson 12-7 Pacing: 1.5 days
Title	**Hypothesis Testing**	**Algebra Lab: Simulations**	**Binomial Distributions**
Objectives	• Compare sample statistics and population statistics. • Design experiments to test hypotheses.	• Simulate a real-life situation, collect data, and do a statistical analysis.	• Find probabilities for binomial experiments. • Find probabilities by using binomial distributions and expansions.
Key Vocabulary	inferential statistics statistical inference confidence interval hypothesis null hypothesis alternative hypothesis		binomial distribution binomial experiment experimental probability
NGSSS	MA.912.S.5.2, MA.912.S.5.3	MA.912.S.4.2	MA.912.P.3.1, MA.912.P.3.2
Multiple Representations			
Lesson Resources	**Chapter 12 Resource Masters** • Study Guide and Intervention, pp. 36–37 AL OL ELL • Skills Practice, p. 38 AL OL ELL • Practice, p. 39 AL OL BL ELL • Word Problem Practice, p. 40 AL OL BL ELL • Enrichment, p. 41 OL BL • Graphing Calculator Activity, p. 42 OL • Quiz 3, p. 52 AL OL BL ELL **Transparencies** • 5-Minute Check Transparency 12-6 AL OL BL ELL **Additional Print Resources** • Study Notebook AL OL BL ELL	**Materials** • six-sided die **Additional Print Resources** • Teaching Algebra with Manipulatives, p. 259 AL OL ELL	**Chapter 12 Resource Masters** • Study Guide and Intervention, pp. 43–44 AL OL ELL • Skills Practice, p. 45 AL OL ELL • Practice, p. 46 AL OL BL ELL • Word Problem Practice, p. 47 AL OL BL ELL • Enrichment, p. 48 OL BL • Quiz 4, p. 52 AL OL BL ELL **Transparencies** • 5-Minute Check Transparency 12-7 AL OL BL ELL **Additional Print Resources** • Study Notebook AL OL BL ELL • Teaching Algebra with Manipulatives, p. 246 AL OL ELL
Technology for Every Lesson	FL Math Online glencoe.com • Extra Examples • Self-Check Quizzes • Personal Tutor • Homework Help	**CD/DVD Resources** IWB INTERACTIVE WHITEBOARD READY IWB StudentWorks Plus IWB Interactive Classroom IWB Diagnostic and Assessment Planner	• TeacherWorks Plus • eSolutions Manual Plus • ExamView Assessment Suite
Get Animated			
Differentiated Instruction	pp. 781, 784		pp. 787, 793

KEY: AL Approaching Level · OL On Level · BL Beyond Level · ELL English Learners

Summative Assessment
- Study Guide and Review, pp. 794–798
- Practice Test, p. 799

What the Research Says . . .

According to Wilkins (1999), the Cereal Box problem serves as a great introduction to situations of uncertainty and the ideas associated with expected value. Using Monte Carlo methods, students can make reasonable estimates about the number of cereal boxes one would have to buy.

- In Lesson 12-7B, students use a die to simulate prizes that come on a soft drink cap and draw conclusions about the average number of caps that are required to get all six prizes.
- In Exercise 7 of Lesson 12-7B, students design and carry out their own simulation of a related problem.

NOTES:

CHAPTER 12

Assessment and Intervention

SE = Student Edition, **TE** = Teacher Edition, **CRM** = Chapter Resource Masters

	Diagnosis	Prescription
Diagnostic Assessment	**Beginning Chapter 12**	
	Get Ready for Chapter 12 **SE,** p. 743	Response to Intervention **TE,** p. 743
	Beginning Every Lesson	
	Then, Now, Why? **SE** 5-Minute Check Transparencies	Chapter 0 **SE,** pp. P1–P19 Concepts and Skills Bank **SE,** pp. 994–1007
Formative Assessment	**During/After Every Lesson**	
	Guided Practice **SE,** every example Check Your Understanding **SE** H.O.T. Problems **SE** Spiral Review **SE** Additional Examples **TE** Watch Out! **TE** Step 4, Assess **TE** Chapter 12 Quizzes **CRM,** pp. 51–52 Self-Check Quizzes glencoe.com	**Tier 1 Intervention** Concepts and Skills Bank **SE,** pp. 994–1007 Skills Practice **CRM,** Ch. 1–12 glencoe.com **Tier 2 Intervention** Differentiated Instruction **TE** Study Guide and Intervention Masters **CRM,** Ch. 1–12 **Tier 3 Intervention** *Math Triumphs, Alg. 2,* Ch. 5
	Mid-Chapter	
	Mid-Chapter Quiz **SE,** p. 772 Mid-Chapter Test **CRM,** p. 53 ExamView Assessment Suite	**Tier 1 Intervention** Concepts and Skills Bank **SE,** pp. 994–1007 Skills Practice **CRM,** Ch. 1–12 glencoe.com **Tier 2 Intervention** Study Guide and Intervention Masters **CRM,** Ch. 1–12 **Tier 3 Intervention** *Math Triumphs, Alg. 2,* Ch. 5
	Before Chapter Test	
	Chapter Study Guide and Review **SE,** pp. 794–798 Practice Test **SE,** p. 799 Standardized Test Practice **SE,** pp. 800–803 Chapter Test glencoe.com Standardized Test Practice glencoe.com Vocabulary Review glencoe.com ExamView Assessment Suite	**Tier 1 Intervention** Concepts and Skills Bank **SE,** pp. 994–1007 Skills Practice **CRM,** Ch. 1–12 glencoe.com **Tier 2 Intervention** Study Guide and Intervention Masters **CRM,** Ch. 1–12 **Tier 3 Intervention** *Math Triumphs, Alg. 2,* Ch. 5
Summative Assessment	**After Chapter 12**	
	Multiple-Choice Tests, Forms 1, 2A, 2B **CRM,** pp. 55–60 Free-Response Tests, Forms 2C, 2D, 3 **CRM,** pp. 61–66 Vocabulary Test **CRM,** p. 54 Extended Response Test **CRM,** p. 67 Standardized Test Practice **CRM,** pp. 68–70 ExamView Assessment Suite	Study Guide and Intervention Masters **CRM,** Ch. 1–12 glencoe.com

Differentiated Instruction

Option 1 Reaching All Learners AL OL BL ELL

KINESTHETIC Ask each student to use a tape measure to measure the distance around the wrists of 15 classmates to the nearest tenth of a centimeter. Have students find the mean and standard deviation of their data. Then have them determine if their data appears to be normally distributed, positively skewed, or negatively skewed.

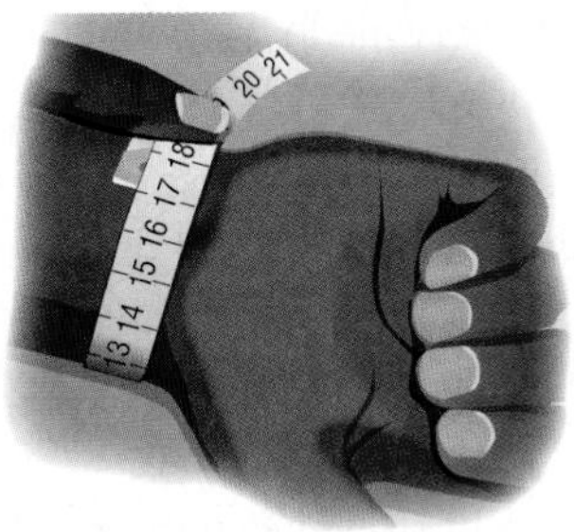

VISUAL/SPATIAL Have students work in pairs to make up a crossword puzzle using the terms studied in this chapter. Use either the definition or an example of the terms in the *across* and *down* hints. Make photocopies of the puzzle to distribute to the class. Ask students to keep the puzzles to use as a chapter review.

Option 2 Approaching Level AL

Have students work in groups of three or four. Ask each student to choose either the mean, median, or mode and to create a set of at least 15 data values that would be best represented using the chosen measure of central tendency. Each student, in turn, presents his/her set of data to the group, who then decides which measure to use. As a group, students actually find the measure of central tendency that best represents each set of data.

FL Math Online Access Point Activities

Option 3 English Learners ELL

Ask students to work with a partner. One partner writes an expression, such as ${}_{12}C_3$, and hands it to the other partner, who reads the notation aloud (for example, "the number of combinations of 12 items taken 3 at a time") and calculates the value. 220 The partners discuss and correct this value as necessary. Then they exchange roles.

Option 4 Beyond Level BL

Ask students to make a chart showing the relationship between the binomial coefficients and combinatorial notation. An example is shown below.

Binomial notation:

$$(x+y)^n = x^n + nx^{n-1}y + \frac{n(n-1)}{2!}x^{n-2}y^2 + \frac{n(n-1)(n-2)}{3!}x^{n-3}y^3 + \dots + \frac{n(n-1)(n-2)\dots(n-r+2)}{(r-1)!}x^{n-r+1}y^{r-1} + \dots + nxy^{n-1} + y^n$$

Combinatorial notation:

$$(x+y)^n = {}_nC_0x^n + {}_nC_1x^{n-1}y + {}_nC_2x^{n-2}y^2 + {}_nC_3x^{n-3}y^3 + \dots + {}_nC_{r-1}x^{n-r+1}y^{r-1} + \dots + {}_nC_{n-1}xy^{n-1} + {}_nC_ny^n$$

Focus on Mathematical Content

Vertical Alignment

Before Chapter 12

Related Topics from Algebra 1

- construct sample spaces for simple or composite experiments
- find the probabilities of dependent and independent events
- use theoretical probabilities and experimental results to make predictions and decisions
- select the appropriate measure of central tendency or range to describe a set of data
- select and use an appropriate representation for presenting and displaying relationships among collected data
- evaluate methods of sampling to determine validity of an inference made from a set of data

Previous Topics from Algebra 2

- simplify polynomial expressions

Chapter 12

Reinforcement of Topics Before Algebra 2

- use combinations and permutations to find probability and use them to solve problems
- find probabilities of two independent and two dependent events
- find the probability of mutually exclusive and inclusive events

Related Topics from Algebra 2

- use a measure of central tendency to represent a set of data and find measures of variation for a set of data
- determine whether a sample is biased and find margins of sampling error
- create and use graphs of probability distributions
- solve problems involving normally distributed data
- use binomial expressions to find probabilities
- identify and calculate conditional probabilities

After Chapter 12

This chapter reinforces skills needed in AP-Statistics

Lesson-by-Lesson Preview

12-1 Experiments, Surveys, and Observational Studies

In this lesson, students

- explore and discuss how the response from a *sample survey* relates to what the responses might be if the entire population were surveyed (a *census*). For a random or unbiased sample, everyone in the population has the same chance of being included.
- learn how to determine when to use a survey, an *observational study* (individuals are observed without any outside influences), or an *experiment* (something is done to a treated group and their response is observed against those in a control group) to collect the data needed.
- learn to distinguish between when there is a *correlation* between two events (the two events are related) or when there is a *causation* (one event is the direct cause of another event).

12-2 Statistical Analysis

In this lesson, students assess whether the mean, median, or mode is the most appropriate measure of *central tendency* to represent a given set of data. They also decide if the results of a survey are a characteristic of a *population* or of a *sample.*

When a single sample is drawn from a population, there is a risk of incurring a sampling error.

The *margin of sampling error* (sometimes referred to as *ME*) provides an interval that shows how much the responses from the sample could differ from the population.

Measures of variation describe the dispersions or spread of a set of data. The *range* is one type of measure of variation. Two other measures of variation are the *variance* and the *standard deviation.* These two measures describe how closely a set of data clusters about the mean.

- The formula for calculating the sample standard deviation is

$$s = \sqrt{\frac{\sum_{k=1}^{n}(x_n - \bar{x})^2}{n-1}}$$ ($\bar{x}$ is the sample mean).

- The formula for calculating the population standard deviation is

$$\sigma = \sqrt{\frac{\sum_{k=1}^{n}(x_n - \mu)^2}{n}}$$ (μ is the population mean).

12-3 Conditional Probability

The probability of an event given that another event has already occurred is called *conditional probability.* The conditional probability of an event *B,* given that the probability of an event *A* has already occurred, is defined as $P(B \mid A) = \frac{P(A \text{ and } B)}{P(A)}$, where $P(A) \neq 0$.

Contingency tables are used to record data in which different possible situations result in different possible outcomes. The data in these tables can be used to determine conditional probabilities.

12-4 Probability and Probability Distributions

The likelihood of an event happening can be described in terms of *probability.*

- The probability that an event can succeed $P(S)$ is the ratio of the number of ways an event can succeed to the number of ways the event can happen.
- A probability is always a number from 0 to 1.
- The sum of the probability that an event occurs and the probability that it does not occur is 1.

Students investigate *discrete probability distributions* by looking at theoretical tables of probability distributions and by graphing those distributions as *relative-frequency histograms.* Students use what they have learned about weighted averages to find the *expected value, $E(x)$* of the values in a probability distribution.

12-5 The Normal Distribution

The *normal distribution* is one of the most important *continuous probability distributions,* in which the value of an outcome can be any real number in an interval. A continuous distribution is represented by a curve. The graph of a normal distribution is a *symmetric, bell-shaped curve.* The *Empirical Rule* describes the characteristics of normal distributions.

Distributions with nonsymmetric curves are called *skewed distributions.* They can be skewed positively or negatively.

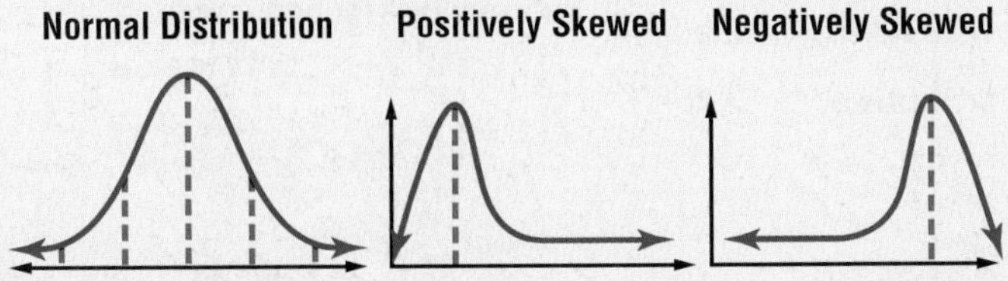

12-6 Hypothesis Testing

Inferential statistics can be used to draw conclusions about a population by using a sample. A 95% *confidence interval* can be found by using the formula $CI = \bar{x} \pm 2 \cdot \frac{s}{\sqrt{n}}$, where $\bar{x}$ is the mean of the sample, *s* is the standard of deviation of the sample, and *n* is the size of the sample.

A *hypothesis* is a statement to be tested. Testing a hypothesis involves these five steps:

- State the null hypothesis H_0 and the alternative hypothesis H_1.
- Design the experiment.
- Conduct the experiment and collect the data.
- Find the confidence interval.
- Make the correct statistical inference. Accept the null hypothesis if the population parameter falls into the confidence interval.

12-7 Binomial Distributions

A *binomial experiment* is a random experiment with an outcome that is one of two simple events. A *binomial distribution* shows the probabilities of the outcomes of a binomial experiment. Tree diagrams are often used to show these distributions.

The full probability distribution for a binomial experiment can be found by expanding the binomial $(s + f)^n$ where *n* is the number of independent trials, *s* is the probability of success, and *f* is the probability of failure. To graph a binomial distribution, the possible outcomes are shown on the *x*-axis and the probabilities of success are on the *y*-axis.

McGraw-Hill Professional Development

Targeted professional development has been articulated throughout *Algebra 2.* More quality, customized professional development is available from McGraw-Hill Professional Development. Visit glencoe.com for details on each product.

- **Online Lessons** emphasize the strategies and techniques used to teach Algebra 2. Includes streaming video, interactive pages, and online tools.
- **Video Workshops** allow mentors, coaches, or leadership personnel to facilitate on-site workshops on educational strategies in mathematics and mathematical concepts.
- **MHPD Online** (www.mhpdonline.com) offers online professional development with video clips of instructional strategies, links, student activities, and news and issues in education.
- **Teaching Today** (teachingtoday.glencoe.com) gives secondary teachers practical strategies and materials that inspire excellence and innovation in teaching.

CHAPTER 12 Notes

Chapter Project

Educational Statistics

Students use what they have learned about probability and statistics to design and analyze a survey about their high school.

- Have students work in groups of three or four. Each group should design a survey question to examine a characteristic of students in the school. (Possible topics: favorite/hardest course, favorite sport, preferred after-school activity, plans for after high school graduation, etc.) Make sure that the question is unbiased.
- Compile the questions into a single questionnaire which the students can give to a sample of the students in the school. Have students decide how to ensure that the selection of the sample is random.
- Have each group make a bar graph of the responses to their question.
- Finally, ask each group to pose a binomial probability question related to their graph and then answer it. (Sample question: "What is the probability that more than 3 out of 8 randomly selected students would say that math is their favorite course?")

CHAPTER 12 Probability and Statistics

Then
In Chapter 9, you calculated weighted averages.

Now
In Chapter 12, you will:
- Evaluate surveys, studies, and experiments.
- Create and use graphs of probability distributions.
- Use the Empirical Rule to find probabilities.
- Compare sample statistics and population statistics.

NGSSS
MA.912.P.2.3
MA.912.P.3.1

Why?
EDUCATION
Probability and statistics are used in all facets of education. Surveys and experiments are done to find out which teaching methods promote the most learning. Statistics are used to determine grades when classes are curved, or when college professors weight their grades.

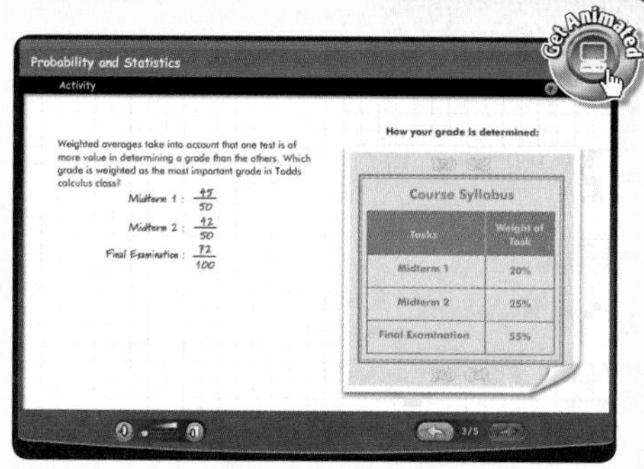

Key Vocabulary Introduce the key vocabulary in the chapter using the routine below.

Define: Normal distribution is a frequency distribution that often occurs when there is a large number of values in a set of data: about 68% of the values are within one standard deviation of the mean, 95% of the values are within two standard deviations of the mean, and 99% of the values are within three standard deviations.

Example:

This diagram shows a normal distribution.

Normal Distribution

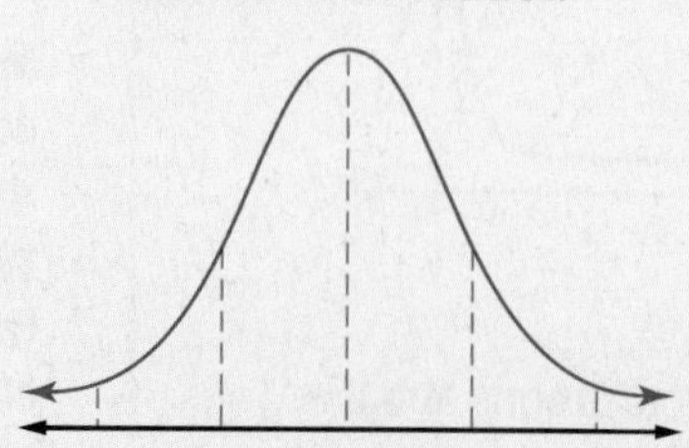

Ask: What do you notice about the normal distribution curve? It is shaped like a bell and is symmetrical.

Get Ready for Chapter 12

Diagnose Readiness You have two options for checking Prerequisite Skills.

Text Option Take the Quick Check below. Refer to the Quick Review for help.

QuickCheck

(Used in Lessons 12-3 and 12-4)

State whether the events are *independent* or *dependent*. (Concepts and Skills Bank 4)

1. selecting a fiction book and a nonfiction book at the library **independent**
2. choosing a president, vice-president, secretary, and treasurer for Key Club, assuming that a person can hold only one office **dependent**
3. choosing a junior, a senior and a faculty member to coordinate a food drive **independent**

(Used in Lesson 12-4) **4. permutation**

Determine whether each situation involves a *permutation* or a *combination*. (Lesson 0-5)

4. seven shoppers in line at a checkout counter
5. an arrangement of the letters in the word *intercept* **permutation**
6. choosing 2 different pizza toppings from a list of 6 **combination**

(Used in Lesson 12-7)

Expand each binomial. (Lesson 11-6)

7. $(a - 2)^4$
8. $(m - a)^5$
9. $(2b - x)^4$
10. $(2a + b)^6$
11. $(3x - 2y)^5$
12. $(3x + 2y)^4$
13. $\left(\frac{a}{2} + 2\right)^5$
14. $\left(3 + \frac{m}{3}\right)^5$

7–14. See margin.

QuickReview

EXAMPLE 1

Mary wants to take 7 different classes next year. Assuming that each class is offered each period, how many different schedules could she have?

When Mary schedules a class for a given period, she cannot schedule that class for any other period. Therefore, the choices of which class to schedule each period are dependent events.

There are $7 \cdot 6 \cdot 5 \cdot 4 \cdot 3 \cdot 2 \cdot 1$ or 5040 different schedules that Mary could have.

EXAMPLE 2

Determine whether the situation involves a *permutation* or a *combination*.

choosing 6 students from a class of 25

Because the order of the students that are chosen does not matter, this is a combination.

EXAMPLE 3

Expand $(a + b)^4$.

Replace n with 4 in the Binomial Theorem.

$$(a + b)^4$$
$$= a^4 + {}_4C_1\, a^3b + {}_4C_2\, a^2b^2 + {}_4C_3\, ab^3 + {}_4C_4\, b^4$$
$$= a^4 + \frac{4!}{(4-1)! \cdot 1!}a^3b + \frac{4!}{(4-2)! \cdot 2!}a^2b^2 + \frac{4!}{(4-3)! \cdot 3!}ab^3 + \frac{4!}{(4-4)! \cdot 4!}b^4$$
$$= a^4 + \frac{4!}{3! \cdot 1!}a^3b + \frac{4!}{2! \cdot 2!}a^2b^2 + \frac{4!}{1! \cdot 3!}ab^3 + \frac{4!}{0! \cdot 4!}b^4$$
$$= a^4 + \frac{24}{6 \cdot 1}a^3b + \frac{24}{2 \cdot 2}a^2b^2 + \frac{24}{1 \cdot 6}ab^3 + \frac{24}{1 \cdot 4}b^4$$
$$= a^4 + 4a^3b + 6a^2b^2 + 4ab^3 + b^4$$

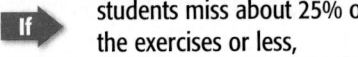

Online Option FL Math Online Take a self-check Chapter Readiness Quiz at glencoe.com.

Additional Answers

7. $a^4 - 8a^3 + 24a^2 - 32a + 16$
8. $m^5 - 5m^4a + 10m^3a^2 - 10m^2a^3 + 5ma^4 - a^5$
9. $16b^4 - 32b^3x + 24b^2x^2 - 8bx^3 + x^4$
10. $64a^6 + 192a^5b + 240a^4b^2 + 160a^3b^3 + 60a^2b^4 + 12ab^5 + b^6$
11. $243x^5 - 810x^4y + 1080x^3y^2 - 720x^2y^3 + 240xy^4 - 32y^5$
12. $81x^4 + 216x^3y + 216x^2y^2 + 96xy^3 + 16y^4$
13. $\frac{a^5}{32} + \frac{5a^4}{8} + 5a^3 + 20a^2 + 40a + 32$
14. $243 + 135m + 30m^2 + \frac{10m^3}{3} + \frac{5m^4}{27} + \frac{m^5}{243}$

Response to Intervention (RtI)

Use the *Quick Check* results and the Intervention Planner to help you determine your Response to Intervention. The If-Then statements in the chart below help you decide the appropriate tier of RtI and suggest intervention resources for each tier.

Intervention Planner

Tier 1 — On Level

If students miss about 25% of the exercises or less,

Then choose a resource:

- **SE** Concepts and Skills Bank, p. 999, Lessons 0-5 and 11-6
- **CRM** Skills Practice, Chapter 11, p. 41
- **TE** Chapter Project, P. 742

FL Math Online Self-Check Quiz

Tier 2 — Strategic Intervention approaching grade level

If students miss about 50% of the exercises,

Then choose a resource:

- **CRM** Study Guide and Intervention, Chapter 11, p. 39

FL Math Online Extra Examples, Personal Tutor, Homework Help

Tier 3 — Intensive Intervention 2 or more years below grade level

If students miss about 75% of the exercises,

Then use *Math Triumphs, Alg. 2*, Ch. 5

FL Math Online Extra Examples, Personal Tutor, Homework Help, Review Vocabulary

CHAPTER 12 Notes

FOLDABLES® Study Organizer

Dinah Zike's Foldables®

Focus Students write notes about probability and statistics.

Teach Have students make and label their Foldables as illustrated. At the end of each lesson, ask students to write about their experiences with the statistics and probability topics presented in the lessons. Encourage students to explain what they found interesting or challenging.

When to Use It Encourage students to add to their Foldables as they work through the chapter and to use them to review for the chapter test.

Differentiated Instruction

CRM Student-Built Glossary, pp. 1–2 Students should complete the chart by providing a definition of each term and an example as they progress through Chapter 12. This study tool can also be used to review for the chapter test.

Get Started on Chapter 12

You will learn several new concepts, skills, and vocabulary terms as you study Chapter 12. To get ready, identify important terms and organize your resources. You may wish to refer to **Chapter 0** to review prerequisite skills.

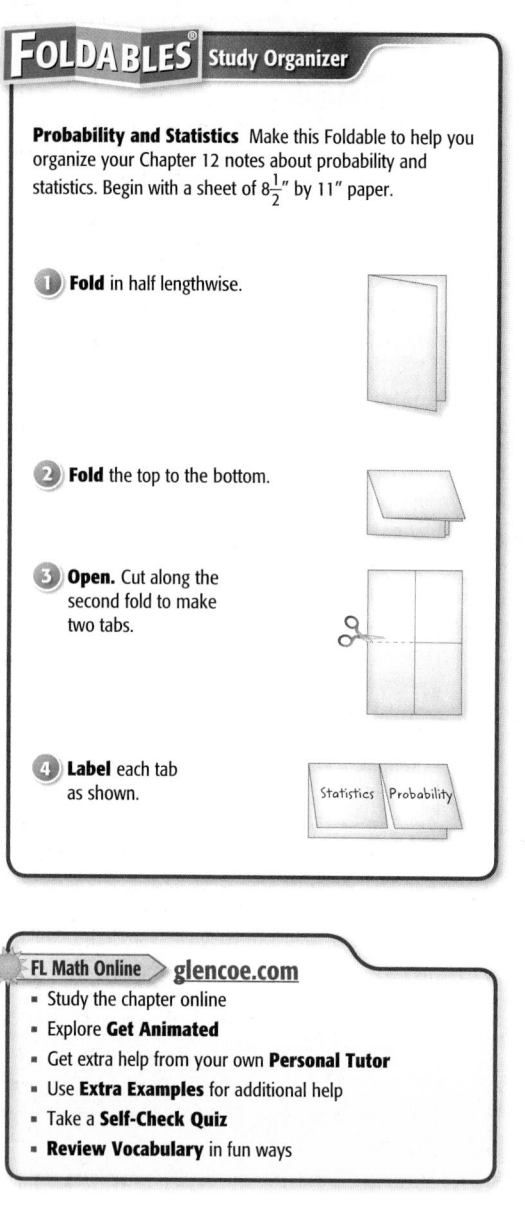

FOLDABLES® Study Organizer

Probability and Statistics Make this Foldable to help you organize your Chapter 12 notes about probability and statistics. Begin with a sheet of $8\frac{1}{2}$" by 11" paper.

1. **Fold** in half lengthwise.

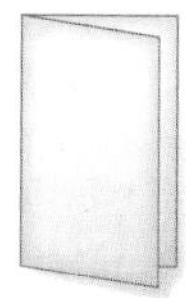

2. **Fold** the top to the bottom.

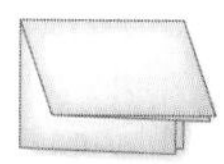

3. **Open.** Cut along the second fold to make two tabs.

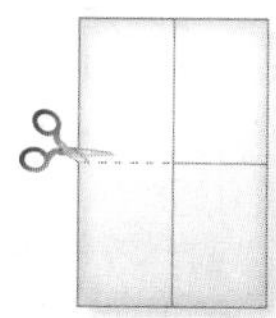

4. **Label** each tab as shown.

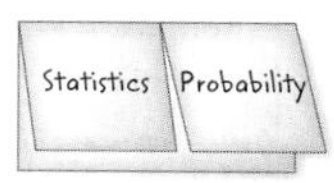

FL Math Online glencoe.com

- Study the chapter online
- Explore **Get Animated**
- Get extra help from your own **Personal Tutor**
- Use **Extra Examples** for additional help
- Take a **Self-Check Quiz**
- **Review Vocabulary** in fun ways

New Vocabulary

English		Español
survey	p. 745	exámenes
population	p. 745	población
sample	p. 745	muestra
biased	p. 745	en polarización negativa
unbiased	p. 745	imparcial
observational study	p. 746	estudio de observación
experiment	p. 746	experimento
treatment group	p. 746	grupo tratado
control group	p. 746	grupo de control
parameter	p. 752	parámetro
statistic	p. 752	estadística
conditional probability	p. 759	probabilidad condicional
relative frequency	p. 760	frecuencia relativa
probability	p. 764	probabilidad
random variable	p. 766	variable aleatoria
expected value	p. 767	valor previsto
normal distribution	p. 773	distribución normal
skewed distribution	p. 773	distribución asimétrica
inferential statistics	p. 780	estadística deductiva
confidence interval	p. 780	intervalo de la confianza
null hypothesis	p. 781	hipótesis nula
alternative hypothesis	p. 781	hipótesis alternativa
binomial distribution	p. 786	distribución binomial
binomial experiment	p. 786	experimento binomio

Review Vocabulary

combination • p. P12 • combinación an arrangement or selection of objects in which order is *not* important

permutation • p. P12 • permutación a group of objects or people arranged in a certain order

random • arbitrario Unpredictable, or not based on any predetermined characteristics of the population; when a die is tossed, a coin is flipped, or a spinner is spun, the outcome is a random event.

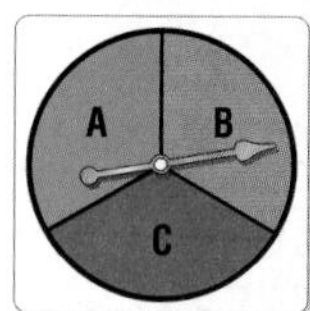

Multilingual eGlossary glencoe.com

Additional Answer (Lesson 12-1, Guided Practice)

1B. Yes; the people are randomly selected from the population. (at least, the population who have listed numbers)

Experiments, Surveys, and Observational Studies

Then
You studied inductive and deductive reasoning. (Geometry)

Now
- Evaluate surveys, studies, and experiments.
- Distinguish between correlation and causation.

NGSSS
MA.912.S.2.1 Compare the difference between surveys, experiments, and observational studies.
MA.912.S.2.3 Identify sources of bias, including sampling and nonsampling errors.

New Vocabulary
survey
population
census
sample
biased
unbiased
observational study
experiment
treatment group
control group
correlation
causation

FL Math Online
glencoe.com

Why?

Students at a new school wanted to form a basketball team. In order to get funding for the program, they carried out a survey of students and their parents to determine who was in favor of starting the team.

Surveys, Studies, and Experiments **Surveys** are used to collect information. If everyone involved with the school were surveyed, then the survey would involve the entire **population**. A survey in which every member of the population is polled is called a **census**. If only 100 people selected at random from the school were surveyed, then the survey would involve a **sample**.

A survey is **biased** if its design favors certain outcomes. If the students above only surveyed basketball players and their parents, then the survey would be biased toward accepting the team. A sample is **unbiased** if it is *random*, or not based on any predetermined characteristics of the population. If they sent surveys to 100 students selected at random, then the survey would be unbiased.

Real-World EXAMPLE 1 Biased and Unbiased Samples

SURVEYS **State whether each survey would produce a random sample. Write *yes* or *no*. Explain.**

a. asking every tenth person coming out of a theater how many times a week they go to the theater to determine how often city residents support the performing arts

No; the people surveyed probably go to the theater more often than the average person.

b. surveying people going into a pet store to find out if the city's residents support the building and maintaining of a dog park

No; the people surveyed would probably be more likely than others to support pet activities.

c. A box contains the name of every student in the school. A hundred names are randomly pulled out of the box. Those students are asked their opinions on the new cafeteria rules.

Yes; everyone in the population has an equal chance to be part of the sample.

Guided Practice 1A. No; they will likely be biased toward watching golf. 1B. See margin. 1C. No; they will likely prefer football.

1A. asking every player at a golf course what sport they prefer to watch on TV

1B. calling 100 randomly selected numbers and asking for their opinions on a local tax

1C. going to a football game and asking 100 random fans about their favorite sport

Personal Tutor glencoe.com

To avoid bias in a survey, two things are needed: a strong random sample and unbiased survey techniques. A strong random sample is an unbiased sample with a large number of participants.

1 FOCUS

Vertical Alignment

Before Lesson 12-1
Study inductive and deductive reasoning.

Lesson 12-1
Evaluate surveys, studies, and experiments.
Distinguish between correlation and causation.

After Lesson 12-1
Use results from a survey sample to draw conclusions about a population.

2 TEACH

Scaffolding Questions

Have students read the *Why?* section of the lesson.

Ask:
- Would the survey results be valid even if the survey did not include all students at the school? Sample answer: possibly, depending on which people were surveyed
- Would the survey results be valid if the survey were conducted by interviewing people who attended a school football game? Probably not, because people who attend football games may be more likely than the average person to also like basketball.

Lesson 12-1 Resources

Resource	Approaching-Level	On-Level	Beyond-Level	English Learners
Teacher Edition		• Differentiated Instruction, pp. 747, 750	• Differentiated Instruction, p. 750	• Differentiated Instruction, p. 747
Chapter Resource Masters	• Study Guide and Intervention, pp. 5–6 • Skills Practice, p. 7 • Practice, p. 8 • Word Problem Practice, p. 9	• Study Guide and Intervention, pp. 5–6 • Skills Practice, p. 7 • Practice, p. 8 • Word Problem Practice, p. 9 • Enrichment, p. 10	• Practice, p. 8 • Word Problem Practice, p. 9 • Enrichment, p. 10	• Study Guide and Intervention, pp. 5–6 • Skills Practice, p. 7 • Practice, p. 8 • Word Problem Practice, p. 9
Transparencies	• 5-Minute Check Transparency 12-1	• 5-Minute Check Transparency 12-1	• 5-Minute Check Transparency 12-1	• 5-Minute Check Transparency 12-1
Other	• Study Notebook	• Study Notebook	• Study Notebook	• Study Notebook

Surveys, Studies, and Experiments

Examples 1 and 2 contrast biased and random (unbiased) sampling and questioning. **Examples 3 and 4** contrast surveys, observational studies, and experiments.

Formative Assessment

Use the Guided Practice exercises after each example to determine students' understanding of concepts.

Additional Examples

1 **SURVEYS** State whether each survey would produce a random sample. Write *yes* or *no*. Explain.

a. surveying people watching a drama to find out the most popular kind of movie No; they will likely think dramas are the best.

b. calling every 10th person on a newspaper's list of subscribers to ask about the quality of service Yes; no obvious bias exists.

c. conducting an online survey to determine what percent of people use travel agents No; the people surveyed online are less likely to use a travel agent.

2 **SPORTS** Which question will determine the most popular spectator sport?

a. Isn't football an exciting sport to watch? This question is biased in favor of football.

b. What is your favorite sport to watch? This is an unbiased question that will produce the answer being sought.

c. Do you like to watch tennis matches? This question is biased in favor of tennis.

Additional Examples also in Interactive Classroom PowerPoint® Presentations

IWB INTERACTIVE WHITEBOARD READY

Real-World EXAMPLE 2 Survey Design

SCHOOL SURVEYS Christopher wants to determine the most desired location for the senior class trip. Which questions will get him the answer he is seeking?

a. Do you like Disneyland?
This question is biased in favor of Disneyland.

b. Which is better, King's Island or Cedar Point?
This question is biased because it only gives two options.

c. Where would you most like to go on the senior trip?
This is an unbiased question that will produce the answer he is seeking.

Guided Practice

Which question will determine the most popular horror movie at school?

2A. Did you enjoy the last horror movie you saw?

2B. Which is better, romance or comedy?

2C. What is your favorite horror movie?

2A. This is biased in favor of one movie and does not mention any other movies at all.

2B. This allows for selection between two other types of movies and does not mention horror movies at all.

2C. This is an unbiased question that will get the desired response.

Personal Tutor glencoe.com

In an **observational study**, individuals are observed and no attempt is made to influence the results. In an **experiment**, something is intentionally done to people, animals, or objects, and then the response is observed.

Observational Study	Experiment
• Find 100 people, 50 of whom have been taking a treatment.	• Find 100 people. Randomly select 50 people for treatment. Give the other 50 a placebo.
• Collect the data.	• Collect and analyze the data.
• Analyze and interpret the data.	

In an experiment, the people, animals, or objects given the treatment are called the **treatment group**. Those given the *placebo*, or false treatment, are the **control group**. The placebo is given so none of the participants will know which group he or she is in, and the experiment will be unbiased.

StudyTip

Experiments An experiment is biased when the participants know which group they are in.

Real-World EXAMPLE 3 Experiments and Observational Studies

EXPERIMENTS State whether each situation represents an *experiment* or an *observational study*. If it is an experiment, identify the *control* group and the *treatment* group. Then determine whether there is bias.

a. Find 200 students, half of whom participated in extracurricular activities, and compare their grade-point averages.
This is an observational study.

b. Find 200 people and randomly split them into two groups. One group jogs 2 miles per day and the other group does not jog at all.
This is an experiment because the people are put into groups at random. The treatment group is the joggers, and the control is the other group. This is a biased experiment because the participants all know which group they are in.

Guided Practice

3. Find 80 college students, half of whom took a statistics course in high school, and compare their grades in a college statistics course. observational study

Personal Tutor glencoe.com

Focus on Mathematical Content

Survey and Census Since a census measures an entire population, its results are known to be correct. But since a survey investigates only part of the population, its results always contain some uncertainty.

TEACH with TECH

WEB PAGE Ask students to create a survey and post it on a secure class Web page. Have them examine the group they have surveyed, and identify possible sources of bias in this sample.

How do you know when to use a survey, an observational study, or an experiment? A survey involves the random sampling of subjects from a population, while experiments involve the random assignment of treatments to subjects. In an experiment, you have control. In an observational study, you do not.

EXAMPLE 4 Experiments and Observational Studies

Determine whether each situation calls for a *survey*, an *observational study*, or an *experiment*. Explain the process.

a. You want to test a treatment for a disease.

This calls for an experiment. The test subjects are people with the disease. The treatment group receives the treatment while the control group gets a placebo.

b. You want to find opinions on a presidential election.

This calls for a survey. It is best to call random numbers throughout the country in order to get an unbiased sample.

c. You want to find out if 10 years of smoking affects lung capacity.

This calls for an observational study. The lung capacity of people who have smoked for 10 years is compared to the lung capacity of an equal number of nonsmokers.

Guided Practice 4. Survey; randomly select 200 students, ask the question, and have them rate their opinions from 1 to 5.

4. Two hundred randomly selected high school students rate their opinions regarding the new lunch rules from 1 (Totally Disagree) to 5 (Totally Agree).

Personal Tutor glencoe.com

Distinguish Between Correlation and Causation An observed association between the results of an experiment and the treatment does not necessarily imply that the treatment caused the results.

When there is a **correlation** between two events, the two events are related. When there is a **causation**, one event is shown to be the direct cause of another event. While a correlation between two events can be shown, causation is much more difficult to prove.

StudyTip

Causation If nothing else could have possibly caused the event, then you can assume causation.

EXAMPLE 5 Correlation Versus Causation

Determine whether the following statements show *correlation* or *causation*. Explain your reasoning.

a. Studies have shown that students are less energetic after they eat lunch.

Correlation; the statement ignores crucial factors that might have a causal influence on both.

b. If I lift weights, I can make the football team.

Correlation; there are more factors involved.

c. When the Sun is visible, we have daylight.

A good way to determine causation is to look for other alternatives that could cause daylight. Since there are none, it shows causation.

Guided Practice 5. Correlation; while studying can help you get an A, it does not guarantee it.

5. When I study, I will get an A.

Personal Tutor glencoe.com

Additional Examples

3 **EXPERIMENT** State whether each situation represents an *experiment* or an *observational study*. If it is an experiment, identify the *control* group and the *treatment* group. Then determine whether there is bias.

a. Find 100 students and randomly split them into two groups. One group walks to school and the other group does not. Experiment; treatment group: group that walks to school; control: other group; biased; students know which group they are in.

b. Find 100 students, half of whom work after school. Compare their grade point averages. Observational study

4 Determine whether each situation calls for a *survey*, an *observational study*, or an *experiment*. Explain the process.

a. You want to find out if jogging increases muscle mass. Observational; compare the muscle mass of people who jog to that of an equal number of nonjoggers.

b. You want to find out who are the most popular teachers in your school. Survey; it is best to interview randomly identified students to get an unbiased sample.

c. You want to test a vaccine for cats. Experiment; test subjects are cats, treatment group receives the vaccine, control group gets a placebo.

Differentiated Instruction

OL ELL

Verbal/Linguistic Learners Have students in small groups design a survey question and practice asking it in such a way that there is bias built into the tone of voice and facial expression of the questioner. Then have them try out the question on other groups to see if they get a high percentage of the answer that the bias is designed to elicit.

Distinguishing Between Correlation and Causation

Example 5 contrasts correlation and causation.

Additional Example

5 Determine whether the following statements show *correlation* or *causation.* Explain your reasoning.

a. Tides are higher during a full Moon. Causation; the phase of the Moon has a direct effect on the height of the tides.

b. Laboratory mice deprived of sleep have a lower average weight. Correlation; while lack of sleep may help lower the weight, it does not necessarily guarantee it.

c. People who live in cities drink more bottled water. Correlation; there are more factors involved.

3 PRACTICE

Formative Assessment

Use Exercises 1–9 to check for understanding.

Use the chart at the bottom of this page to customize assignments for your students.

Watch Out!

Error Analysis For Exercise 28, remind students that in an unbiased experiment, no one should know if they are in the treated group or in the control group.

Additional Answer

1. No; the people surveyed would probably be more likely than others to love ice cream.

Check Your Understanding

Example 1 p. 745

State whether each survey would produce a random sample. Write *yes* or *no*. Explain.

1. Survey every third person coming out of an ice cream shop to find people's favorite type of dessert. See margin.
2. A teacher sends every student whose last name ends with a chosen letter to the blackboard.

2. Yes; everyone in the population has an equal chance to be part of the sample.

Example 2 p. 746

Determine the survey question that will best obtain the desired answer.

3. Taylor wants to determine the most popular football team at the school. b
   - **a.** What is your favorite college football team?
   - **b.** What is your favorite football team?
   - **c.** Do you like the Dallas Cowboys or the Pittsburgh Steelers?

4. See Chapter 12 Answer Appendix.

Example 3 p. 746

State whether each situation represents an *experiment* or an *observational study*. If it is an experiment, identify the *control* group and the *treatment* group. Then determine whether there is bias.

4. A teacher has his first class complete review activities the day before the test. His second class does no review activities. He compares their test results.
5. Jaime finds 100 people, half of whom volunteer at a homeless shelter, and compares their average annual incomes. See Chapter 12 Answer Appendix.

7. Survey; it is best to call random numbers throughout the country in order to get an unbiased sample.

Example 4 p. 747

Determine whether the situation calls for a *survey*, an *observational study*, or an *experiment*. Explain the process.

6. You want to test a drug that reverses male pattern baldness. See Chapter 12 Answer Appendix.
7. You want to find voters' opinions on recent legislation.

Example 5 p. 747

Determine whether the following statements show *correlation* or *causation*. Explain.

8. When I exercise, I am in a better mood. See Chapter 12 Answer Appendix.
9. If we have a Level 2 snow emergency, we do not have school.

9. Causation; the Level 2 emergency is a direct cause of the school closing.

Practice and Problem Solving

● = **Step-by-Step Solutions** begin on page R20. **Extra Practice** begins on page 947.

Example 1 p. 745

State whether each survey would produce a random sample. Write *yes* or *no*. Explain.

10. A sporting goods store owner sends a survey to everyone whose address ends in a particular digit.
11. Students in an honors science class are asked what their favorite subject is.
12. Every other shopper coming out of a mall is surveyed to determine how much people spend during the holidays.
13. Every twentieth person coming out of your high school is asked for whom they will vote in the upcoming student council race. See Chapter 12 Answer Appendix.

10. Yes; everyone in the population has an equal chance to be part of the sample.
11. No; the people surveyed would probably be more likely than others to like science.

Example 2 p. 746

Determine the survey question that will best obtain the desired answer.

14. Sabrina wants to determine interest in starting a chess club at her school. c
    - **a.** What day do you have free to stay after school?
    - **b.** Do you like chess?
    - **c.** Would you be willing to join a chess club at school?
15. Lauren wants to determine the most popular presidential candidate. a
    - **a.** For whom would you vote in the upcoming election?
    - **b.** Do you prefer a particular political party?
    - **c.** If you could vote, would you?

12. No; because the people surveyed would probably be more likely than others to spend more during the holidays.

Differentiated Homework Options

Level	Assignment	Two-Day Option	
AL Basic	10–25, 28, 30–61	11–25 odd, 33–36	10–24 even, 28, 30–32, 37–61
OL Core	11–25 odd, 26–28, 30–61	10–25, 33–36	26–28, 30–32, 37–61
BL Advanced	26–59, (optional: 60–61)		

Example 3 p. 746

State whether each situation represents an *experiment* or an *observational study*. If it is an experiment, identify the *control* group and the *treatment* group. Then determine whether there is bias.

16. Find 300 people and randomly split them into two groups. One group listens to Mozart for an hour every night before bed, and the other group does not listen to anything. Then compare how well they slept. **See margin.**
17. Find 250 students, half of whom are in the marching band, and compare the amounts of time spent on homework. **observational study**
18. Find 100 students, half of whom are in the French Club, and compare their grades in French class. **See Chapter 12 Answer Appendix.**

Example 4 p. 747

Determine whether each situation calls for a *survey*, an *observational study*, or an *experiment*. Explain the process. **19–21. See Chapter 12 Answer Appendix.**

19. You want to find out if years of running affect knee movement.
20. You want to find out if drinking soda affects stomach linings.
21. You want to test a treatment that keeps deer out of your garden.

Example 5 p. 747

Determine whether the following statements show *correlation* or *causation*. Explain.

22. When it is very hot in the summer, there are ice cream vendors outside in New York.
23. Reading more will enable you to become more intelligent.
24. Researchers have concluded that Americans who speak more than one language are less likely to become ill.
25. Sleeping with your shoes on will cause you to have a headache.

22. Causation; the heat in the summer is direct cause for the vendors being in business outside.
23. Correlation; while the two may be related, reading does not directly increase intelligence.
24. Correlation; while a study may have found a relationship between the two, one does not cause the other.
25. Correlation; while there may be a relationship between the two, one does not cause the other.

26. **SELECTION BIAS** In a call-in poll, 81% of the more than 6000 respondents said that a certain businessman "symbolizes what makes the U.S.A. a great country." How is this an example of sampling bias? **See Chapter 12 Answer Appendix.**
27. **QUESTIONNAIRES** A company gives an exit questionnaire to employees who are leaving the company. One of the questions asks how the employee felt about his or her experience with the company. Is this survey biased? Explain why or why not. **See Chapter 12 Answer Appendix.**

H.O.T. Problems

Use Higher-Order Thinking Skills **28–32. See Chapter 12 Answer Appendix.**

28. **ERROR ANALYSIS** Jordan and Kyle were asked to design an unbiased experiment. Is either of them correct? Explain your reasoning.

Jordan
- Get a group of 20 random people.
- Randomly put half of them on an all-fruit diet for 3 weeks.
- Compare their weight gain/loss at the end of the 3 weeks.

Kyle
- Get a group of 20 football players.
- Make half of them do 500 push-ups per day.
- Compare the number of push-ups each group can do after 3 weeks.

29. **CHALLENGE** How could a telephone survey introduce sampling bias into the results?
30. **WRITING IN MATH** Compare and contrast the random sampling of units from a population and the random assignment of treatments to experimental units.
31. **OPEN ENDED** Design one of each of the following.
    a. survey
    b. observational study
    c. experiment
32. **REASONING** How can bias occur in an experiment, and how does it affect the results? Provide an example to explain your reasoning.

Real-World Link

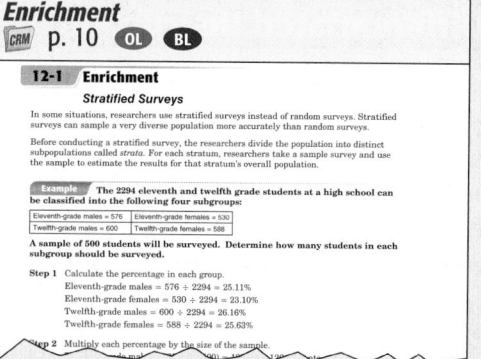

Phone surveys can cost up to five times as much as online surveys.

Source: Yahoo! Small Business

Study Guide and Intervention

CRM pp. 5–6 AL OL ELL

12-1 Study Guide and Intervention

Experiments, Surveys, and Observational Studies

Surveys, Studies, and Experiments

Term	Definition	Example
Survey	a means of obtaining information from a population or a sample of the population	taking a poll to learn who people will vote for in an upcoming election
Observational Study	an examination in which individuals are observed and no attempt is made to influence the results	observing a group of 100 people, 50 of whom have been taking a treatment; collecting, analyzing, and interpreting the data
Experiment	an operation in which something is intentionally done to people, animals, or objects, and then the response is observed	studying the differences between two groups of people, one of which receives a treatment and the other a placebo

Example 1 **State whether the following situation represents an *experiment* or an *observational study*. Identify the *control* group and the *treatment* group. If it is an experiment, determine whether there is bias.**

Find twenty adult ducks, half of which are domesticated, and compare their weights.

This is an observational study. Domesticated ducks are the *treated* group, and the wild ducks are the *control* group. This is unbiased.

Example 2 **Determine whether the following situation calls for a *survey*, an *observational study*, or an *experiment*. Explain the process.**

You want to know how students and parents feel about school uniforms.

This calls for a survey. It is best to ask a random sample of students and a random sample of parents to give their opinions.

Exercises

State whether each situation represents an *experiment* or an *observational study*. Identify the *control* group and the *treatment* group. If it is an experiment, determine whether there is bias.

1. Find 300 students and randomly split them into two groups. One group practices basketball three times per week and the other group does not practice basketball at all. After three months, you interview the students to find out how they feel about school. **Experiment; the treated group is the students that practice basketball, and the control is the other group. This is a biased experiment because all students know which group they are in.**
2. Find 100 students, half of whom participated on the school math team, and compare their grade point average. **Observational study; the students who participated on the math team are the treated group, and the other students are the control; unbiased.**

Chapter 12 5 Glencoe Algebra 2

Lesson 12-1

Practice

CRM p. 8 AL OL BL ELL

12-1 Practice

Experiments, Surveys, and Observational Studies

State whether each situation represents an *experiment* or an *observational study*. Identify the *control* group and the *treatment* group. If it is an experiment, determine whether there is bias.

1. Find 300 students, half of whom are on the chess team, and compare their grade point averages. **Observational study; the students who are on the chess team are the treated group and the other students are the control group; unbiased.**
2. Find 1000 people and randomly split them into two groups. Give a new vitamin to one group and a placebo to the other group. **Experiment; treated group includes the people who take the vitamin and the control group includes the people who take the placebo; unbiased.**

Determine whether each situation call for a *survey*, an *observational study*, or an *experiment*. Explain the process.

3. You want to compare the health of students who walk to school to the health of students who ride the bus. **Observational study; compare the medical records of students who walk to school to those of students who ride the bus.**
4. You want to find out if people who eat a candy bar immediately before a math test get higher scores than people who do not. **Experiment; randomly divide the students taking a math test into two groups. Give the treated group a candy bar to eat before the test but do not give the control group anything to eat.**

Determine whether the following statements show *correlation* or *causation*. Explain.

5. If I jog every day, I can complete a marathon in three hours. **Correlation; other factors affect whether you can complete a marathon in three hours.**
6. When there are no clouds in the sky, it does not rain. **Causation; rain comes from clouds.**
7. Studies show that taking a multivitamin leads to a longer life. **Correlation; other factors determine the length of your life.**
8. If I study for three hours, I will earn a grade of 100% on my history test. **Correlation; other factors determine how you perform on your history test.**

Chapter 12 8 Glencoe Algebra 2

Word Problem Practice

CRM p. 9 AL OL BL ELL

12-1 Word Problem Practice

Experiments, Surveys, and Observational Studies

1. **SURGERY** A new technique for knee surgery includes fitting knees with titanium and plastic caps instead of cutting through the muscles and tendons in the knee. A study observes the recovery time after 100 knee surgeries, half of which use the new knee surgery technique. Which group of surgeries is the control group? **The control group consists of knee surgeries done using the old knee surgery technique.**
2. **SPORTS DRINKS** A sports drink company gives out free samples of their new sports drink at the mall. They record the number of teens versus the number of adults that take the sample. Does this situation represent an experiment, an observational study, or a survey? **Observational study**
3. **ELECTION** At the Democratic National Convention, people are asked if they are going to vote for a Democratic or Republican candidate for president.

Who Do You Support for President?		
Democratic Candidate	Republican Candidate	Other Candidate
94%	3%	3%

Is this a biased or unbiased survey? **Biased; there are many more Democrats at the Democratic National Convention.**

4. **COUNTRY CLUB** A research study finds that 75% of the members of an exclusive country club are either doctors or lawyers. Does this demonstrate *correlation* or *causation*? **Correlation; membership in the club does not cause people to be doctors and lawyers. Similarly, being a doctor or lawyer does not cause people to become a member of the club.**
5. **VIDEO GAMES** A behavioral scientist studies the influence of violent video games on teens.
   a. Describe an observational study the scientist can perform to study the influence of violent video games on teens. **Sample answer: The scientist can observe the number of crimes committed by teens that play violent video games versus the number of crimes committed by teens that don't play violent video games.**
   b. Describe an experiment the scientist can set up to test the influence of violent video games on teens. **Sample answer: Have a treated group play 8 hours of violent video games and observe their behavior. Then observe the behavior of a control group that does not play violent video games.**
   c. How can the scientist show that violence is caused by video games, and is not just a correlation? **The scientist would have to prove that playing the video games directly leads to violence.**

Chapter 12 9 Glencoe Algebra 2

Lesson 12-1

Additional Answer

16. Experiment; the people are put into groups at random. The treatment group is the Mozart listeners, and the control is the other group. This is a biased experiment because the participants all know which group they are in.

Enrichment

CRM p. 10 OL BL

12-1 Enrichment

Stratified Surveys

In some situations, researchers use stratified surveys instead of random surveys. Stratified surveys can sample a very diverse population more accurately than random surveys.

Before conducting a stratified survey, the researchers divide the population into distinct subpopulations called *strata*. For each stratum, researchers take a sample survey and use the sample to estimate the results for that stratum's overall population.

Example **The 2294 eleventh and twelfth grade students at a high school can be classified into the following four subgroups:**

Eleventh-grade males = 576	Eleventh-grade females = 530
Twelfth-grade males = 600	Twelfth-grade females = 588

A sample of 500 students will be surveyed. Determine how many students in each subgroup should be surveyed.

Step 1 Calculate the percentage in each group.
Eleventh-grade males = 576 ÷ 2294 = 25.11%
Eleventh-grade females = 530 ÷ 2294 = 23.10%
Twelfth-grade males = 600 ÷ 2294 = 26.16%
Twelfth-grade females = 588 ÷ 2294 = 25.63%

Step 2 Multiply each percentage by the size of the sample.

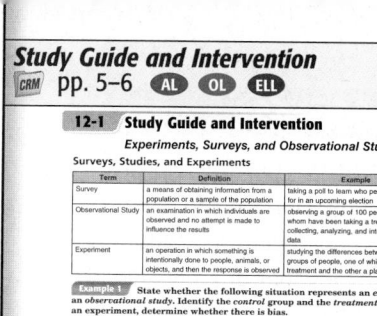

4 ASSESS

Ticket Out the Door Have each student write an outline for an experiment of their own choosing, identifying the treated group and the control group.

Additional Answers

37. Step 1: $9^1 - 1 = 8$, which is divisible by 8. The statement is true for $n = 1$.

Step 2: Assume that $9^k - 1$ is divisible by 8 for some positive integer k. This means that $9^k - 1 = 8r$ for some whole number r.

Step 3:
$$9^k - 1 = 8r$$
$$9^k = 8r + 1$$
$$9^{k+1} = 72r + 9$$
$$9^{k+1} - 1 = 72r + 8$$
$$9^{k+1} - 1 = 8(9r + 1)$$

Since r is a whole number, $9r + 1$ is a whole number. Thus, $9^{k+1} - 1$ is divisible by 8, so the statement is true for $n = k + 1$. Therefore, $9^n - 1$ is divisible by 8 for all positive integers n.

42. $(0, 3), \left(\pm\frac{\sqrt{23}}{2}, -\frac{11}{4}\right)$

NGSSS PRACTICE 912.A.8.5, 912.A.9.1

33. GEOMETRY In $\triangle ABC$, $BC > AB$. Which of the following must be true? **C**

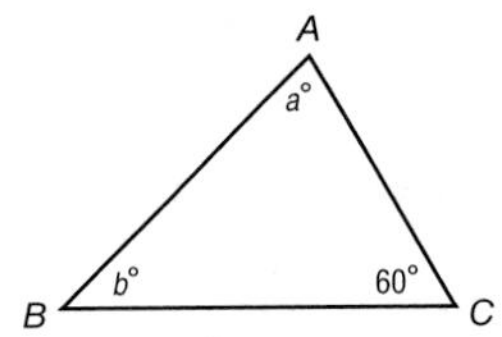

A. $AB = BC$

B. $AC > AB$

C. $a > 60$

D. $a = b$

34. THINK SOLVE EXPLAIN **SHORT RESPONSE** What is the solution set of $4^{4x^2 - 2x - 4} = 4^{-2}$? **{1, −0.5}**

35. SAT/ACT A pie is divided evenly between 3 boys and a girl. If one boy gives one half of his share to the girl and a second boy keeps two thirds of his share and gives the rest to the girl, what portion will the girl have in all? **G**

F. $\frac{5}{24}$ G. $\frac{11}{24}$ H. $\frac{1}{2}$ I. $\frac{13}{24}$

36. Which equation represents a hyperbola? **D**

A. $y^2 = 49 - x^2$

B. $y = 49 - x^2$

C. $y = 49x^2$

D. $y = \frac{49}{x}$

Spiral Review

37. Prove that the statement $9^n - 1$ *is divisible by 8* is true for all natural numbers. (Lesson 11-7) **See margin.**

38. INTRAMURALS Ofelia is taking ten shots in the intramural free-throw shooting competition. How many sequences of hits and misses are there that result in her making eight shots and missing two? (Lesson 11-6) **45**

Solve each system of equations. (Lesson 10-7) **40.** $(-1 + \sqrt{17}, 1 + \sqrt{17}), (-1 - \sqrt{17}, 1 - \sqrt{17})$

39. $y = x + 3$, $y = 2x^2$ $\left(\frac{3}{2}, \frac{9}{2}\right), (-1, 2)$

40. $x^2 + y^2 = 36$, $y = x + 2$

41. $y^2 + x^2 = 9$, $y = 7 - x$ **no solution**

42. $y + x^2 = 3$, $x^2 + 4y^2 = 36$ **See margin.**

43. $x^2 + y^2 = 64$, $x^2 + 64y^2 = 64$ $(\pm 8, 0)$

44. $y^2 = x^2 - 25$, $x^2 - y^2 = 7$ **no solution**

Find the distance between each pair of points with the given coordinates. (Lesson 10-1) **49.** $\sqrt{70.25}$ **units**

45. (9, −2), (12, −14) $3\sqrt{17}$ **units**

46. (−4, −10), (−3, −11) $\sqrt{2}$ **units**

47. (1, −14), (−6, 10) **25 units**

48. (−4, 9), (1, −3) **13 units**

49. (2.3, −1.2), (−4.5, 3.7)

50. (0.23, 0.4), (0.68, −0.2) **0.75 unit**

Simplify. Assume that no variable equals 0. (Lesson 6-1)

51. $(5cd^2)(-c^4d)$ $-5c^5d^3$

52. $(7x^3y^{-5})(4xy^3)$ $\frac{28x^4}{y^2}$

53. $\frac{a^2n^6}{an^5}$ an

54. $(n^4)^4$ n^{16}

55. $\frac{-y^5z^7}{y^2z^5}$ $-y^3z^2$

56. $(-2r^2t)^3(3rt^2)$ $-24r^7t^5$

Write a quadratic equation with the given root(s). Write the equation in the form $ax^2 + bx + c = 0$, where a, b, and c are integers. (Lesson 5-3)

57. −3, 9 $x^2 - 6x - 27 = 0$

58. $-\frac{1}{3}, -\frac{3}{4}$ $12x^2 + 13x + 3 = 0$

59. 4, −5 $x^2 + x - 20 = 0$

Skills Review

60. TESTS Ms. Bonilla's class of 30 students took a biology test. If 20 of her students had an average of 83 on the test and the other students had an average score of 74, what was the average score of the whole class? (Lesson 9-6) **80**

61. DRIVING During a 10-hour trip, Kwan drove 4 hours at 60 miles per hour and 6 hours at 65 miles per hour. What was her average rate, in miles per hour, for the entire trip? (Lesson 9-6) **63**

Differentiated Instruction OL BL

Extension Have students investigate methods for producing random samples. A random number table, found in the appendix of many statistics texts, can be used to select randomly from a numbered list. Assign a two-digit number to each student and use a column of the table to select a random sample of students. The random number generator of a calculator or spreadsheet could also be used.

750 Chapter 12 Probability and Statistics

Graphing Technology Lab
Evaluating Published Data

FL Math Online glencoe.com
- Other Calculator Keystrokes
- Graphing Technology Personal Tutor

You can use a TI-83/84 Plus graphing calculator with the CelSheet application to evaluate data found in the media.

A newspaper ran a series of articles about high school students who study abroad for at least one semester. To support the claim that international study was gaining in popularity, the reporter presented the graph at the right. It includes information from a state university about the number of students earning credit through the university while studying abroad in the International Academic Programs.

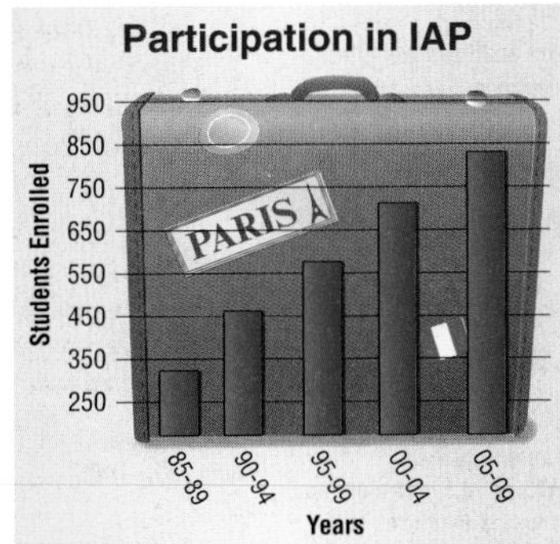

Years	1985–1989	1990–1994	1995–1999	2000–2004	2005–2009
Students in IAP	316	451	561	704	823

ACTIVITY

Evaluate the graph of the data.

Step 1 Enter data in the CelSheet application.

- Press [APPS] then press [▼] until CelSheet is highlighted.
  Press [ENTER]. Then press any key to exit the title and help pages.
- Press [ALPHA] ["] 85 [—] 89 [ENTER] to enter the first range of years into cell A1. Repeat for the remaining years.
- Use the arrow keys to highlight cell B1. Enter the data for each range of years.

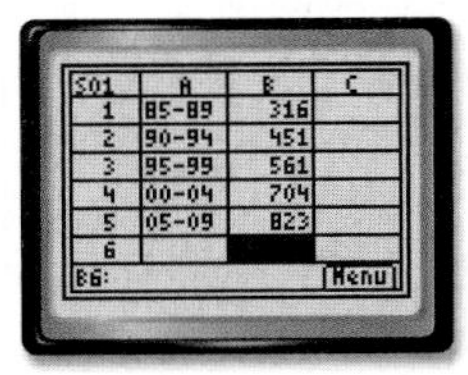

Step 2 Make a bar graph of the data.

- Press [Graph] to access Menu. Press 4: Charts. Then press 5: Bar.
- Enter the Category range: press [ALPHA] [A] 1 [ALPHA] [:] [ALPHA] [A] 5 [ENTER].
- Enter Series1: press [ALPHA] [B] 1 [ALPHA] [:] [ALPHA] [B] 5 [ENTER].
- For Ser1Name enter STDNTS. At this prompt, the alpha is assumed.
- Use the arrow keys to scroll past Series 2 and Series 3 information. At Title, enter IAP. Press [ENTER] three times to display graph.
- Press [TRACE] then [▶] and [◀] to see information about each bar.

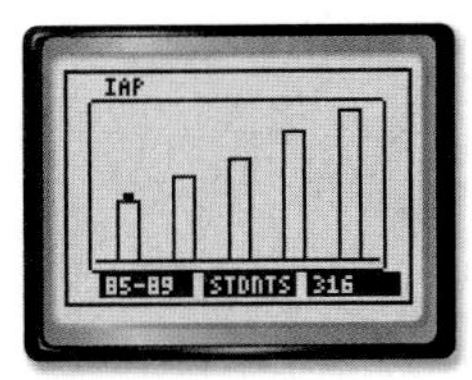

Analyze the Results

2. Sample answer: The newspaper's graph; the vertical scale does not start at 0.

Compare your graph to the newspaper's graph.

1. Do the graphs display the same information? yes
2. Which graph seems to show a more dramatic increase? Why?
3. Why would the reporter choose to display the graph in this way? Is it acceptable? Why or why not? Sample answer: The newspaper wanted the increase to appear to be dramatic. It is not acceptable. Data should be presented clearly.

EXTEND 12-1 Lesson Notes

1 FOCUS

Objective Use the CelSheet application of a graphing calculator to evaluate data found in the media.

Materials for Each Student

- TI-83/84 Plus graphing calculator

Teaching Tip

If an old CelSheet appears when starting the application, students must access the menu by pressing [Graph], then choose **1: File** and then **3: New** to start a new CelSheet.

2 TEACH

Working in Cooperative Groups

Have students work in pairs, mixing abilities, to complete the Activity.

- The upper left corner of the CelSheet will contain whatever title students enter.
- [ALPHA] ["] preceding an entry denotes the entry as text. This should not be used to enter numerical data.

Practice Have students complete Exercises 1–3.

3 ASSESS

Formative Assessment

Use Exercise 1 to assess whether students can create a bar graph of data using the CelSheet application.

From Concrete to Abstract

Ask:

- What is the percent of increase in the popularity of the International Academic Program from the first time interval to the last? about 160%
- How did the reporter's graph distort the information? The reporter's graph makes it look as if the increase were about 350%.

12-2 Lesson Notes

1 FOCUS

Vertical Alignment

Before Lesson 12-2
Analyze weighted averages.

Lesson 12-2
Use measures of central tendency and variation to compare sets of data.
Explore measures of variation.

After Lesson 12-2
Compare sample statistics and population statistics.

2 TEACH

Scaffolding Questions

Have students read the *Why?* section of the lesson.

Ask:

- Why is it helpful to put a list in order when studying data? Sample answer: If the data are in order, it is much easier to find the least value, median, mode, and greatest value.
- What observations can you make about Denny's times without doing any calculations, or by using only mental math? Sample answers may include: greatest and least values (7:29 and 6:48) and the range (41 seconds).

12-2 Statistical Analysis

Then
You analyzed weighted averages. (Lesson 9-6)

Now
- Use measures of central tendency and variation to compare sets of data.
- Explore measures of variation.

NGSSS
MA.912.S.3.3 Calculate and interpret measures of the center of a set of data, including mean, median, and weighted mean, and use these measures to make comparisons among sets of data.
MA.912.S.3.4 Calculate and interpret measures of variance and standard deviation. Use these measures to make comparisons among sets of data.

New Vocabulary
variable
univariate data
measure of central tendency
parameter
statistic
margin of sampling error
measure of variation
variance
standard deviation

FL Math Online
glencoe.com

Why?

Denny has raced in 18 mountain bike races in the past year. His times are listed in the table shown. Which measure of central tendency should Denny use to describe the finishing times?

6:51	7:03	6:49	7:29	6:59	7:20
6:57	6:49	7:01	6:50	6:52	6:48
7:02	7:09	6:56	6:54	7:07	6:53

Measures of Central Tendency Data in one **variable**, or data type, like the finishing times are called **univariate data**. These data can be described by a **measure of central tendency** because it represents the center or middle of the data. The most commonly used measures of central tendency are the *mean*, *median*, and *mode*.

When deciding which measure of central tendency to use to represent a set of data, look closely at the data values.

Key Concept — Measures of Central Tendency

Use	Which Is...	When...
mean	the sum of the data divided by the number of items in the data set	The data set has no outliers.
median	the middle number of the ordered data, or the mean of the middle two numbers	The data set has outliers, but there are no big gaps in the middle of the data.
mode	the number or numbers that occur most often	The data set has many repeated numbers.

Real-World EXAMPLE 1 — Measures of Central Tendency

a. RACING TIMES Refer to the information above. Which measure of central tendency best represents the data, and why?

Since the data are spread out and there do not appear to be any outliers, the mean best represents the data.

b. Which measure of central tendency best represents the data at the right, and why?

16	17	15	17
12	16	16	15
2	18	18	18
40	16	48	1

Since there are outliers and no big gaps in the middle, the median best represents the data.

Guided Practice 1. Mode; almost all of the values are the same.

1. RAFFLE A raffle is offering a grand prize worth $1000 and thirty other prizes worth $5 each. Which measure of central tendency best represents the data, and why?

Personal Tutor glencoe.com

Two types of measures can be applied to sets of data. A **parameter** is a measure that describes a characteristic of a *population*. One example of a parameter is the mean income of the United States. A **statistic** is a measure that describes a characteristic of a *sample*. An example of a statistic is the mean income of the people who live on your street.

Lesson 12-2 Resources

Resource	Approaching-Level	On-Level	Beyond-Level	English Learners
Teacher Edition	• Differentiated Instruction, p. 753	• Differentiated Instruction, pp. 753, 758	• Differentiated Instruction, pp. 753, 758	
Chapter Resource Masters	• Study Guide and Intervention, pp. 11–12 • Skills Practice, p. 13 • Practice, p. 14 • Word Problem Practice, p. 15	• Study Guide and Intervention, pp. 11–12 • Skills Practice, p. 13 • Practice, p. 14 • Word Problem Practice, p. 15 • Enrichment, p. 16 • Graphing Calculator Activity, p. 17	• Practice, p. 14 • Word Problem Practice, p. 15 • Enrichment, p. 16	• Study Guide and Intervention, pp. 11–12 • Skills Practice, p. 13 • Practice, p. 14 • Word Problem Practice, p. 15
Transparencies	• 5-Minute Check Transparency 12-2	• 5-Minute Check Transparency 12-2	• 5-Minute Check Transparency 12-2	• 5-Minute Check Transparency 12-2
Other	• Study Notebook	• Study Notebook	• Study Notebook	• Study Notebook

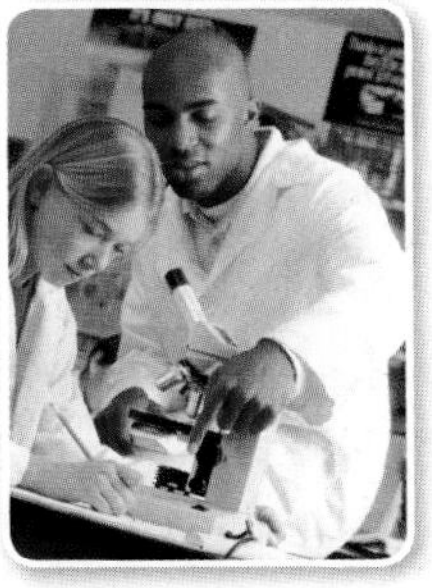

Real-World Career

Teacher
Teachers need a bachelor's degree and they need to be working toward their master's degree in education. High school teachers need to specialize in their chosen field. Many teachers also go through a rigorous testing process to be certified to teach in their states.

EXAMPLE 2 Samples Versus Populations

Determine whether each of the following represents a *population* or a *sample*.

a. The Nielsen Poll estimates the average number of hours of television watched per week for U.S. households.

This represents a sample because only a fraction of U.S. residents are polled.

b. A mathematics exam is given to every graduating senior in the country to analyze certain mathematics skills.

This represents a population because the exam tests *every* graduating senior.

Guided Practice

2A. A teacher compares the scores on a test in her class. population

2B. A teacher compares her class with the rest of the country on a national test. sample

Personal Tutor glencoe.com

When a single sample is drawn from a population, there is a risk of incurring a sampling error. As the size of the sample increases, the margin of error decreases. The **margin of sampling error** provides the interval that shows how much the responses from the sample would differ from the population.

Key Concept Margin of Sampling Error

When a random sample n is taken from a population, the margin of sampling error can be approximated by $\pm\frac{1}{\sqrt{n}}$.

EXAMPLE 3 Margin of Sampling Error

In a random survey of 2148 people, 58% said that football is their favorite sport.

a. What is the margin of sampling error?

$$\text{Margin of sampling error} = \pm\frac{1}{\sqrt{n}} \quad \text{Margin of Sampling Error Formula}$$
$$= \pm\frac{1}{\sqrt{2148}} \quad n = 2148$$
$$\approx \pm 0.0216 \quad \text{Simplify.}$$

The margin of sampling error is about ±2.16%.

b. What is the likely interval that contains the percentage of the population that claims football is their favorite sport?

$0.58 + 0.0216 = 0.6016$ $\qquad$ $0.58 - 0.0216 = 0.5584$

The likely interval that contains the percentage of the population that claims football is their favorite sport is between 55.84% and 60.16%.

Guided Practice

In a random survey of 3247 people, 41% said that they are satisfied with the government's performance.

3A. What is the margin of sampling error? ±1.75%

3B. What is the likely interval that contains the percentage of the population that is satisfied with the government? 39.25%–42.75%

Personal Tutor glencoe.com

StudyTip

Data Types *Categorical data* can be put into categories, such as race, gender, age group, and so on. *Measurement data* involve an actual measurement of something, like height, weight, and capacity. The data in Example 1a are measurement data.

Measures of Central Tendency

Example 1 shows how to decide which measure of central tendency best represents a set of data. **Example 2** contrasts samples and populations. **Example 3** shows how to find the margin of sampling error for a survey.

Formative Assessment

Use the Guided Practice exercises after each example to determine students' understanding of concepts.

Additional Examples

1 **SALARIES** A new Internet company has 3 employees who are each paid \$300,000, ten who are paid \$100,000, and sixty who are paid \$50,000.

a. Which measure of central tendency best represents the pay at this company, and why? Mode or median; there are no large gaps in the middle of the data, and there are many repeated numbers.

b. Which measure of central tendency best represents the following data, and why? 37, 33, 40, 31, 33, 38, 35 Mean; there are no outliers.

2 Determine whether each of the following represents a *population* or a *sample*.

a. A company has each of its employees complete a survey on commuting habits. population

b. Every 5th table in the cafeteria is interviewed to find out what students eat for lunch. sample

Additional Examples also in Interactive Classroom PowerPoint® Presentations

IWB INTERACTIVE WHITEBOARD READY

Differentiated Instruction

AL OL BL

Intrapersonal Learners Have students find an example of a poll in a magazine, newspaper, or on the Internet and compare the stated margin of sampling error to their own calculations based on the methods in this lesson.

Additional Example

3 In a random survey of 1710 teens, 76% said they had downloaded music from the Internet.

a. What is the margin of sampling error? $\approx \pm 0.0242$

b. What is the likely interval that contains the percentage of the population that have downloaded music from the Internet? between 73.58% and 78.42%

Measure of Variation

Example 4 shows how to calculate and compare standard deviation for two data sets.

Additional Example

4 **WEATHER** The daily high temperatures (in °F) in a city for the first 10 days of last year were 38, 48, 51, 53, 64, 69, 51, 53, 43, 36. For the first 10 days of this year, they were 32, 17, 30, 34, 35, 40, 43, 36, 38, 28.

a. Find the standard deviation for last year's temperatures. 10.4

b. Use a calculator to find the standard deviation of this year's temperatures. 7.3

c. Compare the standard deviations for the two years. There was a greater variation in temperature for the first 10 days of last year.

Measures of Variation **Measures of variation** describe the *dispersion* or spread of a set of data. Two common measures of variation are the **variance** and **standard deviation**. These measures describe how closely a set of data clusters about the mean.

The sample mean $\bar{x}$, read *x bar*, and the population mean μ, or mu, are calculated the same way. The formulas for calculating the sample standard deviation s and the population standard deviation σ, or sigma, are given below.

Real-World Link

College professors often weight their grades to put more emphasis on tests, essays, and research papers.

Source: The Ohio State University

Key Concept — Standard Deviation Formulas

Sample	Population
$s = \sqrt{\dfrac{\sum_{k=1}^{n}(x_k - \bar{x})^2}{n-1}}$	$\sigma = \sqrt{\dfrac{\sum_{k=1}^{n}(x_k - \mu)^2}{n}}$

Real-World EXAMPLE 4 — Standard Deviation

TEST SCORES **The Chapter 3 and Chapter 4 scores from Mr. Hoff's class both have a mean of 75. Find and compare their standard deviations.**

Mr. Hoff's 2nd Period Chapter 3 Scores
85, 80, 75, 75, 70, 75, 75, 65, 75, 75, 75, 80, 75, 75, 70, 80, 70, 75, 75, 75, 75, 75, 75

Mr. Hoff's 2nd Period Chapter 4 Scores
100, 100, 90, 10, 100, 95, 10, 95, 100, 100, 85, 15, 95, 20, 95, 90, 100, 100, 90, 10, 100, 100, 25

a. Find the standard deviation for the Chapter 3 scores.

Step 1 This is a population. Since the mean of each set was 75, $\mu = 75$.

Step 2 Find the standard deviation.

$$\sigma = \sqrt{\frac{\sum_{k=1}^{n}(x_k - \mu)^2}{n}} \quad \text{Standard Deviation Formula}$$

$$= \sqrt{\frac{(85-75)^2 + (80-75)^2 + \ldots + (75-75)^2 + (75-75)^2}{23}} \approx 3.9$$

The class mean of the Chapter 3 test is 75 with a standard deviation of about 3.9.

b. Use a calculator to find the standard deviation of the Chapter 4 scores.

Clear all lists. Then press STAT ENTER and enter each data value, pressing ENTER after each value. To view the statistics, press STAT ▶ 1 ENTER.

The class mean of the Chapter 4 test is 75 with a standard deviation of about 36.

c. Compare the standard deviations of the two tests.

The standard deviation of the Chapter 4 test is far greater than for Chapter 3. Therefore, the scores are more dispersed in the Chapter 4 test, and they are much closer to the mean in the Chapter 3 test. Mr. Hoff can conclude that 75 is a stronger mean for Chapter 3, meaning that the majority of his students scored very close to 75.

StudyTip

Population Mean When the population mean μ is known, then the symbol can be interchanged with $\bar{x}$.

Watch Out!

Common Misconceptions Explain to students that the standard deviation is a number representing the typical or representative variation for the data items in that set. It tells how far a data value will typically be from the mean of the entire data set.

Focus on Mathematical Content

Variability of a Normal Distribution For a normal distribution, 68.3% of the data are always within one standard deviation of the mean; 95.4% are always within two standard deviations, and 99.7% are always within three standard deviations, because of the way standard deviation is defined.

TEACH with TECH

INTERACTIVE WHITEBOARD Use a spreadsheet or other software program to calculate various statistics from data collected from a survey. Keep this information displayed on the board as you teach students what it means and how to interpret it.

754 Chapter 12 Probability and Statistics

4B. Sample answer: The mean should increase by a little while the standard deviation should increase by a large amount. $\mu = 32.2$, $\sigma = 8.19$

Guided Practice

4A. Calculate the mean and standard deviation of the population of data. $\mu = 30.6$, $\sigma = 2.74$

4B. Change 30 to 70. What should happen to the mean and standard deviation? Recalculate to confirm your results.

28	34	33	33	31
33	29	34	36	31
30	29	32	28	36
29	33	29	28	28
26	31	28	27	29

Personal Tutor glencoe.com

StudyTip

Standard Deviation The greater the standard deviation, the more the data deviate from the mean.

In a given set of data, the majority of the values fall within one standard deviation of the mean. Almost all of the data will fall within 2 standard deviations. Mr. Hoff's Chapter 3 scores had a mean of 75 and a standard deviation σ of 3.9. We can illustrate this graphically on a number line.

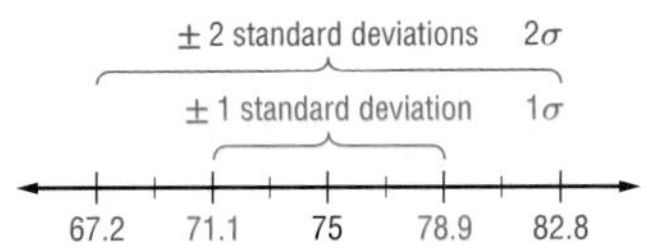

If Mr. Hoff were to compare his students' scores with other students throughout the country on a national test, the class would be considered a sample of all of the students who took the test. He would then need to calculate a sample mean $\bar{x}$ and a sample standard deviation σ.

Check Your Understanding

Example 1 p. 752

Which measure of central tendency best represents the data, and why? 1–4. See margin.

1. {833, 796, 781, 776, 758}
2. {27.2, 36.8, 50.4, 71.6, 194.7}
3. {65, 21, 17, 52, 25, 17, 11, 22, 60, 44}
4. {53, 61, 46, 59, 61, 55, 49}

Example 2 p. 753

Determine whether each of the following represents a *population* or a *sample*.

5. Jerry's math club wants to compare their SAT scores to the scores of all students who took the SAT. sample
6. The tennis team wants to compare their first-serve percentages with each other.
7. Jennifer conducts an online survey on political opinions. sample
8. Veronica compares the student-teacher ratios of all of the schools in her county.

6. population
8. population

Example 3 p. 753

9. **OLYMPICS** In a random survey of 5824 people, 29% said they will watch some of the Summer Olympics on television.
   a. What is the margin of sampling error? ± 0.0131
   b. What is the likely interval that contains the percentage of the population that will watch the Summer Olympics on television? between 27.7% and 30.3%

Example 4 p. 754

10. **DRIVING** The maximum speed limits in miles per hour for interstate highways are given.
   a. Is this a sample or a population? population
   b. Find the standard deviation of the speeds. ≈ 4.3

Maximum Speed Limits Per State

70	65	75	70	70	75	65	65	70	70
55	75	65	65	65	70	65	70	65	65
65	70	70	70	70	65	75	75	65	65
75	65	70	70	65	75	65	65	75	65
70	75	65	65	70	70	65	75	65	65

Source: National Motorists Association

3 PRACTICE

Formative Assessment

Use Exercises 1–10 to check for understanding.

Use the chart on the bottom of this page to customize assignments for your students.

Additional Answers

1. Mean; there are no extreme values.
2. Median; there is one value that is much greater than the rest of the data.
3. Median; there is one value that is much less than the rest of the data.
4. Mean; there are no extreme values.

Differentiated Homework Options

Level	Assignment	Two-Day Option	
AL Basic	11–24, 28, 30–45	11–23 odd, 34–37	12–24 even, 28, 30–33, 38–45
OL Core	11–23 odd, 25–28, 30–45	11–24, 34–37	25–28, 30–33, 38–45
BL Advanced	25–41, (optional: 42–45)		

Tips for New Teachers

Choice of Calculator Scientific calculators, as well as graphing calculators, have special keys and functions that can be used to find mean, median, and standard deviation. Since a scientific calculator costs only a fraction of what a graphing calculator costs, more students may have their own calculator of this type.

Additional Answers

28. Sample answer:

Bowling Scores			
189	211	201	178
232	228	199	206
181	186	203	212
175	182	171	197

There is no mode, the median is 198, and the mean is 196.9375. The variance is 308, and the standard deviation is about 18.

31. Sample answer: The median will also increase by 10. For example, in a data set with a middle or median value of 18, if all of the data are increased by 10, the 18 increases to 28 and remains in the middle. Thus, the new median is 18 + 10 or 28. The mean will also increase by 10 because all of the data have increased by 10. For example, the data set of 2, 2, 2, 2, 2 has a mean of 2. If they are all increased by 10, then the new data set will be 12, 12, 12, 12, 12 and the mean will be 2 + 10 or 12. The standard deviation will be unaffected because even though the data all increase by 10, they are still the same distance from the mean, which also increased by 10.

33. Sample answer: While the average heights of both teams are the same, the West team will have more players that are much taller than 6 feet as well as more players that are shorter than 6 feet. For the East team, most of the players will be between 5 ft 11 and 6 ft 1, while for the West team, most of the players will be between 5 ft 8 and 6 ft 4.

Practice and Problem Solving

● = **Step-by-Step Solutions** begin on page R20.
Extra Practice begins on page 947.

Example 1 p. 752

Which measure of central tendency best represents the data, and why?

11. Median; there is one value that is much greater than the rest of the data, 66.

12. Mean; the set of data has no extreme values or numbers that are identical.

11. NUTRITION The table shows the number of Calories per serving of each vegetable.

Vegetable	Calories	Vegetable	Calories	Vegetable	Calories	Vegetable	Calories
asparagus	14	broccoli	25	cauliflower	10	lettuce	9
beans	30	cabbage	17	celery	17	spinach	9
bell pepper	20	carrots	28	corn	66	zucchini	17

12. WEATHER The table below shows daytime high temperatures for a week.

Day	Sun.	Mon.	Tues.	Wed.	Thurs.	Fri.	Sat.
Temperature	64°F	73°F	69°F	70°F	71°F	75°F	74°F

Example 2 p. 753

Determine whether each of the following represents a *population* or a *sample*.

13. Carissa calculates the average number of pineapples in 25 cans of pineapple. **sample**

14. The IRS calculates the mean income per household. **population**

15. Middleburg Elementary School calculates the average height of all of its students.

15. population

16. Members of the football team want to compare their times in the 40 meter dash to those of the rest of the conference. **sample**

17. Jermaine asks 100 random people at the mall for their opinions on education. **sample**

18. The NFL compares the yards per game allowed by each team's defense. **population**

19. Tomás compares the populations of every state. **population**

20. Dona asks 400 random people what their favorite season is. **sample**

Example 3 p. 753

21. MOVIES A survey of 5669 random people found that 31% go to the movies at least once a month.

a. What is the margin of sampling error? **±0.0133**

b. What is the likely interval that contains the percentage of the population that goes to the movies at least once a month? **between 29.7% and 32.3%**

22. EXERCISE A survey of 4213 people found that 78% exercise at least one hour each week.

a. What is the margin of sampling error? **±0.0154**

b. What is the likely interval that contains the percentage of the population that do at least one hour of exercise each week? **between 76.5% and 79.5%**

Example 4 p. 754

23. DOGSLED The Iditarod is a 1150-mile dogsled race across Alaska. At the right are the winning times, in days, for recent years.

Iditarod Winning Times									
9	9	10	9	9	8	9	9	9	9
17	15	15	14	12	16	13	13	18	12
11	11	11	11	13	11	11	11		

a. Is this a sample or a population? **sample**

b. Find the standard deviation of the winning times. **2.7**

24. TRAINING While training, Aiden recorded his times in the 40-meter dash. Find the standard deviation of the data. **0.12**

40-Meter Dash Times									
4.8	4.9	4.8	4.7	5.0	4.9	4.8	4.9	4.8	5.0
5.0	5.1	4.8	4.9	4.6	4.8	4.7	4.9	4.8	4.8
5.0	4.9	4.9	5.0	4.9	5.0	4.8	4.8	4.7	4.6

25. EDUCATION Below are ACT scores for a recent year.

B

Mean ACT Scores by State									
20.2	21.3	21.5	20.4	21.6	20.3	22.5	21.5	17.8	20.5
20.0	21.7	21.3	20.2	21.6	22.0	21.6	20.3	19.8	22.6
20.8	22.4	21.4	22.2	18.8	21.5	21.7	21.7	21.2	22.5
21.2	20.1	22.3	20.3	21.2	21.4	20.6	22.5	21.8	21.9
19.3	21.5	20.5	20.3	21.5	22.7	20.9	22.5	22.2	21.4

Source: ACT, Inc.

a. Compare the mean and median of the data. **The mean is 21.18, and the median is 21.4. They are very close.**

b. Is this a sample or a population? **population**

c. Find the standard deviation of the data. Round to the nearest hundredth. **1.02**

d. Suppose the state with a mean score of 20.0 incorrectly reported the results. The score for the state is actually 22.5. How are the mean and median of the data affected by this change?

Real-World Link

In 2007, the ACT was taken by more than 1.3 million students nationally with an average of 21.2.

Source: ACT, Inc.

26. STUDENT-TEACHER RATIOS The table at the right shows the number of students in every math class at Principal Johnson's high school.

Students Per Math Class					
25	27	26	26	19	27
24	23	19	28	25	24
20	22	22	24	26	18
28	29	29	26	24	24
23	23	25	25	29	28

a. Which measure of central tendency best represents the data? Why?

b. Is this a sample or a population? **population**

c. Find the standard deviation of the data. Round to the nearest hundredth. **2.96**

27. VACATIONS The table shows the number of annual vacation days for nine countries. Which measure of central tendency best represents the data? Justify your selection, and then find the measure of central tendency. **Median; 13 is much lower than the rest of the data and is lowering the mean. The median is 28.**

Annual Vacation Days			
Country	**Days**	**Country**	**Days**
Brazil	34	Japan	25
Canada	26	Korea	25
France	37	U.K.	28
Germany	35	U.S.	13
Italy	42		

Source: *USA TODAY*

H.O.T. Problems Use Higher-Order Thinking Skills

28. OPEN ENDED Find and analyze a set of univariate real-world data of interest to you. Describe its measures of central tendency and variation. **See margin.**

C

29. CHALLENGE If 67% of the people surveyed responded positively and the likely interval that contains the percentage of the population is 64.8%–69.2%, how many people were surveyed? **2066**

30. REASONING A large outlier is eliminated from a set of data. How does this affect the mean and the standard deviation of the data? Explain.

31. REASONING With a linear transformation of data, all of the values are increased or decreased by the same value. If all of the values of the data are increased by 10, how does this affect the median, mean, and standard deviation? Explain. **See margin.**

32. WRITING IN MATH Compare and contrast the mean and median as measures of central tendency for a univariate data set.

33. REASONING The East basketball team has an average height of 6 feet with a standard deviation of 1.1 inches. The West basketball team has an average height of 6 feet with a standard deviation of 4.1 inches. Compare and contrast the heights of the players on the two teams. **See margin.**

25d. The new mean is 21.23, and the median is 21.45. The mean and median are each slightly greater.

26a. Mean; the set of data has no extreme values and no single mode.

30. Sample answer: When the large outlier is eliminated, the remaining data will be much closer together, so the spread and the standard deviation will decrease. The mean of the remaining data will also decrease because the large outlier was causing the average to be high.

32. Sample answer: While the median and mean both represent the center or middle of the data, the median only measures the value of the data in the middle of the data set. The mean considers the entire data set and finds the average of all of the data.

Study Guide and Intervention

CRM pp. 11–12 AL OL ELL

12-2 Study Guide and Intervention

Statistical Analysis

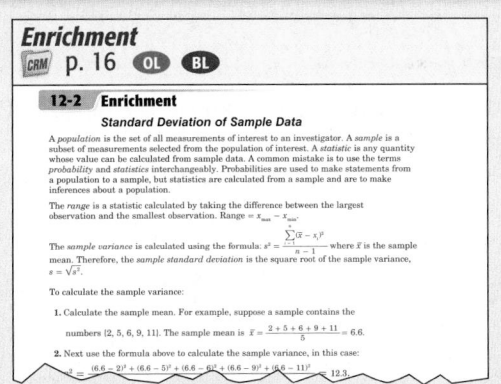

Measures of Central Tendency

Term	Definition	Best Used When
Mean	sum of the data divided by number of items in the data	the data set has no outliers
Median	the middle number or mean of two middle numbers of the ordered data	the data set has outliers but no big gaps in the middle of the data
Mode	the number or numbers that occur most often	the data has many repeated numbers
Margin of Sampling Error	$\pm\frac{1}{\sqrt{n}}$, for a random sample of n items	estimating how well a sample represents the whole population

Example 1 **Which measure of central tendency best represents the data and why?**

{2.1, 21.5, 22.3, 22.8, 23.1, 159.4}

There are outliers, but no large gaps in the middle, the median best represents this data.

Example 2 **What is the margin of sampling error and the likely interval that contains the percentage of the population?**

Of 400 people surveyed in a national poll, 51% say they will vote for candidate González.

Since 400 people are surveyed, the margin of sampling error is $\pm\frac{1}{\sqrt{400}}$ or ± 5%. The percentage of people who are likely to vote for candidate González is the percentage found in the survey plus or minus 5%, so the likely interval is from 46% to 56%.

Exercises

Which measure of central tendency best represents the data, and why?

1. {45, 16, 30, 45, 29, 45} **Mode; the data set has repeated numbers.**
2. {100, 92, 105, 496, 77, 121} **Median; there is an outlier—496.**
3. {2.5, 99.5, 110.5, 76} **Median; there is an outlier—2.5.**
4. {60, 50, 55, 62, 44, 65, 51} **Mean; there are no outliers or repeating numbers in the data.**
5. **BOOKS** A survey of 28 random people found that 40% read at least three books each month. What is the margin of sampling error? What is the likely interval that contains the percentage of the population that reads at least three books each month? **margin of sampling error = ±0.1890 or ±18.9%; likely interval between 21.1% and 58.9%**

Chapter 12 11 Glencoe Algebra 2

Lesson 12-2

Practice

CRM p. 14 AL OL BL ELL

12-2 Practice

Statistical Analysis

Which measure of central tendency best represents the data, and why?

1. {12.1, 14.9, 6.7, 10, 12.8, 14, 18} **Mean; there are no outliers or repeating numbers in the data.**
2. {77.9, 101, 78.9, 105, 4.2, 110, 87.9} **Median; there is an outlier—4.2.**
3. {10, 14.7, 14.7, 21, 7.4, 14.7, 8, 14.7} **Mode; the data set has repeated numbers.**
4. {29, 36, 14, 99, 16, 15, 12, 30} **Median; there is an outlier—99.**

Determine whether the following represents a *population* or a *sample*.

5. a list of the times every student in gym class took to run a mile **population**
6. the test scores of seven students in a chemistry class are compared **sample**
7. friends compare the batting averages of players who are listed in their collections of baseball cards **sample**
8. every student in a high school votes in a class president election **population**
9. **CARS** A survey of 56 random people in a small town found that 14% drive convertibles year-round. What is the margin of sampling error? What is the likely interval that contains the percentage of the population that drives convertibles year-round? **margin of sampling error = ±0.1336; likely interval between 0.64% and 27.36%**
10. **BEACHES** A survey of 812 random people in Hawaii found that 57% went to the beach at least four times last July. What is the margin of sampling error? What is the likely interval that contains the percentage of the population that went to the beach at least four times last July? **margin of sampling error = ±0.0351; likely interval between 53.49% and 60.51%**
11. Determine whether each is a sample or a population. Then find the standard deviation of the data. Round to the nearest hundredth.

a.

The Number of Wins for Each Player on a Tennis Team Last Season					
10	2	9	17	4	8
9	9	10	15	19	5

population; standard deviation = 4.88

b.

The Number of Medals Earned by 18 High School Debaters					
7	10	4	5	10	9
11	5	6	4	4	3
12	7	8	5	3	9

sample; standard deviation = 2.86

Chapter 12 14 Glencoe Algebra 2

Word Problem Practice

CRM p. 15 AL OL BL ELL

12-2 Word Problem Practice

Statistical Analysis

1. **BASEBALL** The following shows the number of wins for Major League Baseball's American League East teams at the end of the 2007 regular season.

Team	Number of Wins
Boston	96
New York	94
Toronto	83
Baltimore	69
Tampa Bay	66

The American League also has Central and Western divisions. If the data is used to study the number of wins for all American League baseball teams, is it a sample or a population? **sample**

2. **VOTING** A poll was taken of registered voters to see if they planned to vote in the next presidential election. What is the margin of sampling error if the likely interval of those who plan on voting is between 46.5% and 49.5%? **margin of sampling error = ±0.015**

3. **APPLES** The following data set depicts the number of apples in 20 different bushel baskets: {80, 75, 68, 82, 77, 74, 81, 85, 73, 79, 75, 73, 80, 71, 82, 81, 77, 80, 78, 84}. What is the median number of apples in a bushel basket? **median = 78.5 apples**

4. **CARS** A police officer clocked the following speed of cars (in miles per hour) on the highway: {65, 61, 72, 54, 78, 61, 74, 75, 61, 55, 64, 66, 70}. What is the mode of the data set? **mode = 61 miles per hour**

5. **SOLAR SYSTEM** For much of the 20th century, astronomers considered the solar system to have nine planets. The table below lists the masses of these planets.

Planet	Mercury	Venus	Earth	Mars	Jupiter
Mass (10^{21} tons)	0.364	5.37	6.58	0.708	2093

Planet	Saturn	Uranus	Neptune	Pluto
Mass (10^{21} tons)	627	95.7	113	0.0138

a. Which measure of central tendency best represents the data, and why? **Median; the data set has outliers, but there are no big gaps in the middle of the data.**

b. What is the correct number for the measurement that best represents the data? **median; $\frac{(5.37 + 6.58)}{2} = 5.975$**

c. What is the standard deviation of the data? **standard deviation = 626.025**

d. How many of the planets have masses within the range of the central measure of the data plus or minus one standard deviation? **8**

Chapter 12 15 Glencoe Algebra 2

Lesson 12-2

Enrichment

CRM p. 16 OL BL

12-2 Enrichment

Standard Deviation of Sample Data

A *population* is the set of all measurements of interest to an investigator. A *sample* is a subset of measurements selected from the population of interest. A *statistic* is any quantity whose value can be calculated from sample data. A common mistake is to use the terms *probability* and *statistics* interchangeably. Probabilities are used to make statements from a population to a sample, but statistics are calculated from a sample and are to make inferences about a population.

The *range* is a statistic calculated by taking the difference between the largest observation and the smallest observation. Range = $x_{max} - x_{min}$.

The *sample variance* is calculated using the formula: $s^2 = \frac{\sum_{i=1}^{n}(\bar{x} - x_i)^2}{n - 1}$ where $\bar{x}$ is the sample mean. Therefore, the *sample standard deviation* is the square root of the sample variance, $s = \sqrt{s^2}$.

To calculate the sample variance:

1. Calculate the sample mean. For example, suppose a sample contains the numbers {2, 5, 6, 9, 11}. The sample mean is $\bar{x} = \frac{2 + 5 + 6 + 9 + 11}{5} = 6.6$.
2. Next use the formula above to calculate the sample variance, in this case: $s^2 = \frac{(6.6 - 2)^2 + (6.6 - 5)^2 + (6.6 - 6)^2 + (6.6 - 9)^2 + (6.6 - 11)^2}{[illegible]} = 12.3$.

4 ASSESS

Yesterday's News Have students explain how their study of samples and populations in Lesson 12-1 helped them with today's lesson.

Formative Assessment

Check for student understanding of Lessons 12-1 and 12-2.

CRM Quiz 1, p. 51

Additional Answers

39. No; basketball players are more likely to be taller than the average high school student, so a sample of basketball players would not give representative heights for the whole school.

40. **Step 1:** After the first guest has arrived, no handshakes have taken place. $\frac{1(1-1)}{2} = 0$, so the formula is correct for $n = 1$.

Step 2: Assume that after k guests have arrived, a total of $\frac{k(k-1)}{2}$ handshakes have taken place, for some positive integer k.

Step 3: When the $(k+1)$st guest arrives, he or she shakes hands with the k guests already there, so the total number of handshakes that have then taken place is $\frac{k(k-1)}{2} + k$.

$$\frac{k(k-1)}{2} + k = \frac{k(k-1)+2k}{2} = \frac{k[(k-1)+2]}{2} = \frac{k(k+1)}{2} \text{ or } \frac{(k+1)k}{2}$$

The last expression is the formula to be proved, where $n = k + 1$. Thus, the formula is true for $n = k + 1$.

Therefore, the total number of handshakes is $\frac{n(n-1)}{2}$ for all positive integers n.

NGSSS PRACTICE 912.S.3.3, 912.A.1.6, 912.A.8.3

34. **STATISTICS** In a set of nine different numbers, which of the following cannot affect the value of the median? **D**

A. doubling each number
B. increasing each number by 10
C. increasing the smallest number only
D. increasing the largest number only

35. **SHORT RESPONSE** The average of the test scores of a class of c students is 80, and the average test scores of a class of d students is 85. When the scores of both classes are combined, the average score is 82. What is the value of $\frac{c}{d}$? $\frac{3}{2}$

36. **SAT/ACT** What is the multiplicative inverse of $2i$? **I**

F. $-2i$ G. $\frac{1}{2}$ H. -2 I. $\frac{-i}{2}$

37. Which equation best represents the graph? **C**

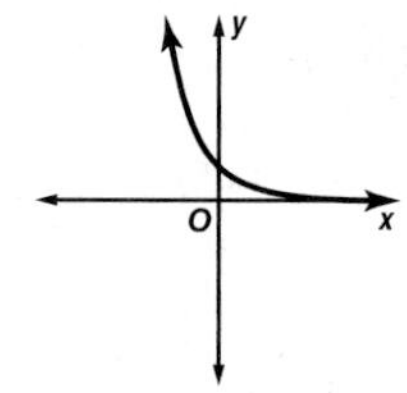

A. $y = 4x$ C. $y = 4^{-x}$
B. $y = x^2 + 4$ D. $y = -4^x$

Spiral Review

State whether each survey would produce a random sample. Explain. (Lesson 12-1)

38. the government sending a tax survey to everyone whose social security number ends in a particular digit **Yes; everyone in the population has an equal chance to be part of the sample.**

39. finding the heights of all the boys on the varsity basketball team to determine the average height of all the boys in your school **See margin.**

40. **PARTIES** Suppose each time a new guest arrives at a party, he or she shakes hands with each person already at the party. Prove that after n guests have arrived, a total of $\frac{n(n-1)}{2}$ handshakes have taken place. (Lesson 11-7) **See margin.**

41. **ASTRONOMY** The orbit of Pluto can be modeled by the equation $\frac{x^2}{39.5^2} + \frac{y^2}{38.3^2} = 1$, where the units are astronomical units. Suppose a comet is following a path modeled by the equation $x = y^2 + 20$. (Lesson 10-7)

a. Find the point(s) of intersection of the orbits of Pluto and the comet. **(39.2, ±4.4)**

b. Will the comet necessarily hit Pluto? Explain. **No; the comet and Pluto may not be at either point of intersection at the same time.**

c. Where do the graphs of $y = 2x + 1$ and $2x^2 + y^2 = 11$ intersect? **41c.** $\left(-\frac{5}{3}, -\frac{7}{3}\right)$, **(1, 3)**

d. What are the coordinates of the points that lie on the graphs of both $x^2 + y^2 = 25$ and $2x^2 + 3y^2 = 66$? **(3, ±4), (−3, ±4)**

Skills Review

Determine whether each situation involves a *permutation* or a *combination*. Then find the number of possibilities. (Lesson 0-5)

42. the winner of the first, second, and third prizes in a contest with 8 finalists **permutation; 336**

43. selecting two of eight employees to attend a business seminar **combination; 28**

44. an arrangement of the letters in the word *algebra* **permutation; 2520**

45. placing an algebra book, a geometry book, a chemistry book, an English book, and a health book on a shelf **permutation; 120**

Differentiated Instruction

OL BL

Extension Have students compute the range and the standard deviation for a few different data sets. Ask them to compare the values and see if they can make any generalizations about the relationship between range and standard deviation. For large data sets, the range is usually from 4 to 6 times as large as the standard deviation. This provides a rule of thumb that is sometimes used to find a quick estimate of standard deviation without going through the complete calculation.

758 Chapter 12 Probability and Statistics

12-3 Conditional Probability

Why?

Alexis is testing a drug that protects people from getting sick. There are two groups; one group gets the experimental drug, while the other group receives a placebo.

After getting the results, Alexis needs to find the probability that a subject's staying healthy was a result of using the experimental drug.

This is an example of a conditional probability.

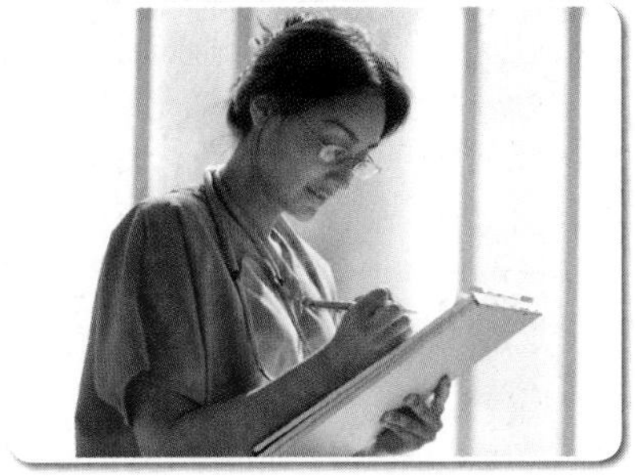

Then
You calculated probabilities.
(Lesson PS 4)

Now
- Find probabilities of events given the occurrence of other events.
- Use contingency tables to find conditional probabilities.

NGSSS
MA.912.P.2.3 Understand and use the concept of conditional probability, including: understanding how conditioning affects the probability of events; finding conditional probabilities from a two-way frequency table.

New Vocabulary
conditional probability
contingency table
relative frequency

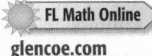

FL Math Online
glencoe.com

Conditional Probability The probability of an event given that another event has already occurred is called **conditional probability**. The conditional probability that event B occurs given that event A has already occurred can be represented by $P(B \mid A)$. This is read *the probability of B given A*.

Key Concept — Conditional Probability

Given that A and B are dependent events, the conditional probability of an event B, given that an event A has already occurred, is defined as

$$P(B \mid A) = \frac{P(A \text{ and } B)}{P(A)}, \text{ where } P(A) \neq 0.$$

EXAMPLE 1 Conditional Probability

Carolina rolls a six-sided die. What is the probability that she has rolled a 3 given that she has rolled an odd number?

There are 6 possible results of rolling a six-sided die.

Let event A be that she rolled an odd number.
Let event B be that she rolled a 3.

$P(A) = \frac{1}{2}$ — **Three of the six outcomes are an odd number.**

$P(A \text{ and } B) = \frac{1}{6}$ — **One of the six outcomes is 3 and odd.**

$P(B \mid A) = \frac{P(A \text{ and } B)}{P(A)}$ — **Probability of B given A**

$= \frac{1}{6} \div \frac{1}{2} \text{ or } \frac{1}{3}$ — **$P(A) = \frac{1}{2}$ and $P(A \text{ and } B) = \frac{1}{6}$**

The probability of rolling a 3 given that the roll is odd is $\frac{1}{3}$.

Guided Practice

1. Chen draws a card from a standard deck of 52 cards. Find the probability that he drew a king given that he drew a king, a queen, or a jack. $\frac{1}{3}$

Personal Tutor glencoe.com

12-3 Lesson Notes

1 FOCUS

Vertical Alignment

Before Lesson 12-3
Calculate probabilities.

Lesson 12-3
Find probabilities of events given the occurrence of other events.
Use contingency tables to find conditional probabilities.

After Lesson 12-3
Use the Empirical Rule to find probabilities.

2 TEACH

Scaffolding Questions

Have students read the *Why?* section of the lesson.

Ask:
- In this experiment, what is the group called that gets the experimental drug? treatment group
- What is the group called that gets the placebo? control group

Conditional Probability

Example 1 shows how to find a conditional probability.

Lesson 12-3 Resources

Resource	Approaching-Level	On-Level	Beyond-Level	English Learners
Teacher Edition	• Differentiated Instruction, p. 760	• Differentiated Instruction, p. 760	• Differentiated Instruction, p. 763	
Chapter Resource Masters	• Study Guide and Intervention, pp. 18–19 • Skills Practice, p. 20 • Practice, p. 21 • Word Problem Practice, p. 22	• Study Guide and Intervention, pp. 18–19 • Skills Practice, p. 20 • Practice, p. 21 • Word Problem Practice, p. 22 • Enrichment, p. 23	• Practice, p. 21 • Word Problem Practice, p. 22 • Enrichment, p. 23	• Study Guide and Intervention, pp. 18–19 • Skills Practice, p. 20 • Practice, p. 21 • Word Problem Practice, p. 22
Transparencies	• 5-Minute Check Transparency 12-3	• 5-Minute Check Transparency 12-3	• 5-Minute Check Transparency 12-3	• 5-Minute Check Transparency 12-3
Other	• Study Notebook	• Study Notebook	• Study Notebook	• Study Notebook

Formative Assessment

Use the Guided Practice exercises after each Example to determine students' understanding of concepts.

Additional Example

1 Kim draws a card from a standard 52-card deck. What is the probability that she draws a heart given that the card is from a red suit? $\frac{1}{2}$

Additional Examples also in Interactive Classroom PowerPoint® Presentations

IWB INTERACTIVE WHITEBOARD READY

Contingency Tables

Examples 2 and 3 show how to use a contingency table to find conditional probabilities.

Additional Examples

2 COLLEGE Find the probability that a student plans to attend college after high school if the student is a girl.

Going to College?	Number of Students	
	Boys	Girls
Yes	342	376
No	151	138

0.73 or 73%

3 STANDARDIZED TEST EXAMPLE Using the data in Example 3, find the probability that a student is non-varsity given that he or she is a senior. D

A 16.6% **C** 50.4%

B 19.8% **D** 83.4%

ReadingMath

Contingency Tables Contingency tables are also called *two-way frequency tables*.

Contingency Tables A **contingency table** records data in which different possible situations result in different possible outcomes. Each value represents the **relative frequency** of an outcome. These tables can be used to find conditional probabilities.

Real-World EXAMPLE 2 Contingency Tables

MEDICINE Find the probability that a test subject stayed healthy, given that he or she used an experimental drug.

Condition	Number of Subjects	
	Using Drug (D)	Using Placebo (P)
sick (S)	1600	1200
healthy (H)	800	400

There is a total of 1600 + 800 + 1200 + 400 or 4000 people in the study. We need to find the probability of H given that D occurs.

$P(H \mid D) = \frac{P(H \text{ and } D)}{P(D)}$ **Conditional Probability Formula**

$= \frac{800}{4000} \div \frac{2400}{4000}$ **$P(H$ and $D) = \frac{800}{4000}$ and $P(D) = \frac{1600 + 800}{4000}$**

$= \frac{800}{2400}$ or $\frac{1}{3}$ **Simplify.**

The probability that a subject stayed healthy given that he or she used the drug is $\frac{1}{3}$.

StudyTip

Independent Events If A and B are independent events, then $P(B \mid A) = P(B)$.

Guided Practice

2. Find the probability that a test subject remained healthy, given that he or she used the placebo. $\frac{1}{4}$

Personal Tutor glencoe.com

Contingency tables can be used to represent any number of possible situations.

NGSSS PRACTICE EXAMPLE 3 912.P.3.1

The table below shows the number of students who are varsity athletes. Find the probability that a student is a varsity athlete given he or she is a junior.

A. 19.8% **C.** 11.5%

B. 13.0% **D.** 16.6%

Class	Freshman	Sophomore	Junior	Senior
varsity	7	22	36	51
nonvarsity	269	262	276	257

Read the Test Item

We need to find the probability that a student is a varsity athlete given that he or she is a junior. There is a total of 1180 students.

Solve the Test Item

$P(V \mid J) = \frac{P(V \text{ and } J)}{P(J)}$ **Conditional Probability Formula**

$= \frac{36}{1180} \div \frac{312}{1180}$ **$P(V$ and $J) = \frac{36}{1180}$ and $P(J) = \frac{36 + 276}{1180}$**

$\approx 11.5\%$ The correct answer is C.

Guided Practice

3. Find the probability that a student plays varsity given that he or she is a freshman. G

F. 2.6% **G.** 2.5% **H.** 8.4% **I.** 7.7%

Personal Tutor glencoe.com

Differentiated Instruction AL OL

If you think students might benefit from using a graphic organizer,

Then a Venn diagram can help students understand how to compute conditional probabilities from contingency tables. To find $P(B \mid A)$, let overlapping circles represent the two events. Write the number of joint occurrences of A and B in the overlapping region, with numbers representing occurrence of only one of the events in the appropriate circle outside the overlap. The conditional probability $P(B \mid A)$ equals the number in the overlap divided by the total of the numbers within circle B.

Check Your Understanding

Example 1 p. 759

A bag contains 8 blue marbles, 6 red marbles, and 5 green marbles. The marbles are drawn one at a time. Find each probability.

1. The second marble is green, given that the first marble is blue and not replaced. $\frac{5}{18}$
2. The second marble is red, given that the first marble is green and is replaced. $\frac{6}{19}$
3. The third marble is red, given that the first two are red and blue and not replaced. $\frac{5}{17}$
4. The third marble is green, given that the first two are red and are replaced. $\frac{5}{19}$

Example 2 p. 760

5. **DRIVING TESTS** The table shows how students in Mr. Diaz's class fared on their first driving test. Some took a class to prepare, while others did not.

	Class	No Class
Passed	64	48
Failed	18	32

   a. Find the probability that Paige passed, given that she took the class. $\frac{32}{41}$
   b. Find the probability that Elizabeth failed, given that she did not take the class. $\frac{2}{5}$
   c. Find the probability that Terrence did not take the class, given that he passed. $\frac{3}{7}$

Example 3 p. 760

6. **NGSSS PRACTICE** The number of students who have attended a football game at North Coast High School is listed below. Find the probability that a student who has attended a game is a junior or a senior. B

Class	Freshman	Sophomore	Junior	Senior
attended	48	90	224	254
not attended	182	141	36	8

A. 48.6% B. 77.6% C. 86.2% D. 91.6%

Practice and Problem Solving

● = **Step-by-Step Solutions** begin on page R20.
Extra Practice begins on page 947.

Example 1 p. 759

Three dice are rolled. Find each probability.

7. One of the rolls is a 6, given that all of the rolls are even. $\frac{12}{27}$
8. One of the rolls is a 3, given that two of the rolls are odd. $\frac{4}{9}$
9. Two of the rolls are 4s, given that all three rolls are the same. 0
10. At least two of the rolls are even, given that all three rolls are the same. $\frac{1}{2}$

Example 2 p. 760

11. **SCHOOL CLUBS** King High School tallied the number of males and females that were members of at least one after school club. Find each probability.

	Clubs	No Clubs
Male	156	242
Female	312	108

   a. A student is a member of a club given that he is male.
   b. A student is not a member of a club given that she is female. $\frac{9}{35}$ or 25.7%
   c. A student is a male given that he is not a member of a club. $\frac{121}{175}$ or 69.1%

11a. $\frac{78}{199}$ or 39.2%

Example 3 p. 760

12. **NGSSS PRACTICE** Naoko, Keisha, and Joshua compared the music on their MP3 players. Find the probability that a selected song is country given that it is not on Naoko's player. I

Person	Rock	Country	R & B
Naoko	521	316	44
Keisha	119	145	302
Joshua	244	4	182

F. 17.2% G. 24.8% H. 35.9% I. 15.0%

TEACH with TECH

INTERACTIVE WHITEBOARD Draw a tree diagram on the board to show students how to find the conditional probabilities. Save your work and send the diagram to students for reference.

Focus on Mathematical Content

Conditional Probability If the probability of event B is altered by the occurrence of event A, a conditional probability must be used for event B. The occurrence of A can be thought of as reducing the sample space for event B.

3 PRACTICE

Formative Assessment

Use Exercises 1–6 to check for understanding.

Use the chart at the bottom of this page to customize assignments for your students.

Differentiated Homework Options

Level	Assignment	Two-Day Option	
AL Basic	7–12, 24–41	7–11 odd, 28–31	8–12 even, 24–27, 32–41
OL Core	7–11 odd, 13–22, 24–41	7–12, 28–31	13–22, 24–27, 32–41
BL Advanced	13–35, (optional: 36–41)		

Study Guide and Intervention
CRM pp. 18–19 AL OL ELL

12-3 Study Guide and Intervention

Conditional Probability

Conditional Probability The probability of an event, given that another event has already occurred, is called **conditional probability**. The conditional probability that event B occurs, given that event A has already occurred, can be represented by $P(B \mid A)$.

Example SPINNER **Naomi is playing a game with the spinner shown. What is the probability that the spinner lands on 7, given that Naomi has spun a number greater than 5?**

There are 8 possible results of spinning the spinner shown.
Let event A be that she spun a number greater than 5.
Let event B be that she spun a 7.

$P(A) = \frac{3}{8}$ — Three of the eight outcomes are greater than 5.

$P(A \text{ and } B) = \frac{1}{8}$ — One out of eight outcomes is both greater than 5 and equal to 7.

$P(B \mid A) = \frac{P(A \text{ and } B)}{P(B)}$ — Conditional Probability Formula

$P(B \mid A) = \frac{1}{8} \div \frac{3}{8}$ — Substitute values for $P(A)$ and $P(A$ and $B)$

$P(B \mid A) = \frac{1}{3}$

The probability of spinning a 7, given that the spin is greater than 5, is $\frac{1}{3}$.

Exercises

Cards are drawn from a standard deck of 52 cards. Find each probability.

1. The card is a heart, given that an ace is drawn. $\frac{1}{4}$
2. The card is the six of clubs, given that a club is drawn. $\frac{1}{13}$
3. The card is a spade, given that a black card is drawn. (Hint: The black cards are the suits of clubs and spades.) $\frac{1}{2}$

A six-sided die is rolled. Find each probability.

4. A 4 is rolled, given that the roll is even. $\frac{1}{3}$
5. A 2 is rolled, given that the roll is less than 6. $\frac{1}{5}$
6. An even number is rolled, given that the roll is 3 or 4. $\frac{1}{2}$

Practice
CRM p. 21 AL OL BL ELL

12-3 Practice

Conditional Probability

Four dice are thrown. Find each probability.

1. All of the rolls are 5, given that all of the rolls show the same number. $\frac{1}{6}$
2. One of the rolls is a 4, given that all of the rolls are greater than 3. $\frac{8}{81}$
3. None of the rolls are 2, given that all of the rolls are even. $\frac{16}{81}$
4. One of the rolls is a 6, given that one of the rolls is a 2. $\frac{25}{216}$
5. CHEMISTRY Cheryl and Jerome are testing the pH of 32 unknown substances as part of science class. Cheryl and Jerome split the work between them as shown in the table. Find each probability.

Results	Cheryl's Tests	Jerome's Tests
Acidic	12	8
Basic	9	3

   a. The substance is acidic, given that Cheryl is testing it. $\frac{4}{7}$
   b. Jerome is testing the substance, given that it is basic. $\frac{1}{4}$

6. ELECTIONS Rose Heck is running against Joe Coniglio in a district that includes the towns of Hasbrouck, Clinton, Eastwick, and Abletown. The table shows how many votes each candidate received in each town. Find each probability.

	Hasbrouck	Clinton	Eastwick	Abletown
Joe Coniglio	1743	1782	886	7790
Rose Heck	2616	2178	1329	5876

   a. A voter cast a ballot for Joe Coniglio, given that the voter cast a ballot in Clinton. $\frac{9}{20}$
   b. A voter cast a ballot for Rose Heck, given that the voter cast a ballot in Eastwick. $\frac{3}{5}$
   c. A voter cast a ballot in Hasbrouck, given that the voter cast a ballot for Joe Coniglio. $\frac{1}{7}$

7. BASEBALL Derek Jeter, a player for the New York Yankees, had 206 hits in the 2007 Major League Baseball season and has 2356 career hits. The table below shows the number of singles, doubles, triples, and home runs Derek Jeter had in the 2007 season and during his career. Find each probability.

	Singles	Doubles	Triples	Home Runs
2007 Season	151	39	4	12
Career	1721	386	54	195

   a. A hit was a home run, given that the hit happened in the 2007 season. $\frac{1}{17}$
   b. A hit was a double, given that the hit happened during Jeter's career. $\frac{193}{1178}$

Lesson 12-3

Word Problem Practice
CRM p. 22 AL OL BL ELL

12-3 Word Problem Practice

Conditional Probability

1. SPINNERS Majorie is playing a game that uses the spinner shown. What is the probability that Majorie spins the number 6, given that she spins a number greater than 2? $\frac{1}{4}$

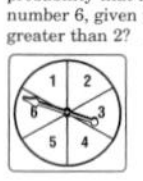

2. CARDS Monique is playing a card game. To win the game, she needs to draw a card that is a club. What is the probability that Monique wins the card game if the card she draws is black? $\frac{1}{2}$

3. PET GROOMING At the CleanPaws pet grooming salon, owners can bring their cats or dogs in to get bathed only, or bathed and groomed. The table shows how many animals the salon serviced this week.

Animal	Bathed Only	Bathed and Groomed
Dog	48	51
Cat	3	12

Find the probability that an animal was bathed and groomed, given that the animal was a cat. $\frac{4}{5}$

4. DICE Stan rolls a pair of dice. What is the probability that the total of the two dice is 11, given that one of the dice rolls is a 5? $\frac{1}{6}$

5. WOMEN IN POLITICS The table shows the gender of United States governors who served in 2007, 1997, and 1987.

Year	Male Governors	Female Governors
2007	42	8
1997	47	3
1987	47	3

Source: National Governors Association

   a. Find the probability that a governor is female, given that the governor served in 1987. $\frac{3}{50}$
   b. Find the probability that a governor is female, given that the governor served in 2007. $\frac{4}{25}$
   c. Find the probability that a governor listed in the table served in 1997, given that the governor is male. $\frac{47}{50}$

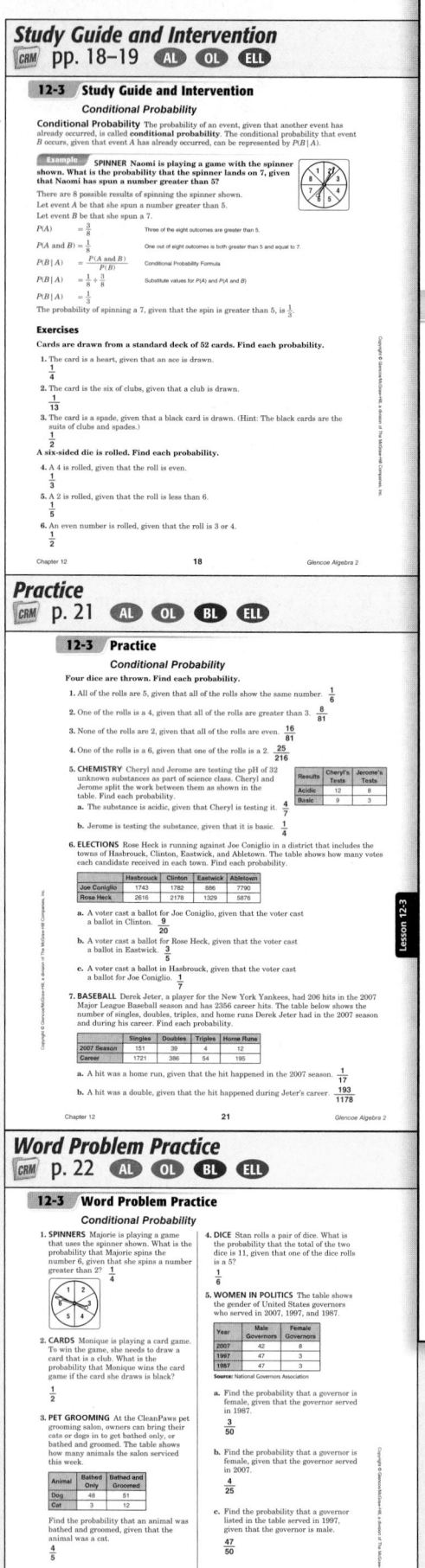

B **Four coins are flipped. Find each probability.**

13. Two are heads, given that at least one is tails. $\frac{2}{5}$
14. Three are tails, given that at least one is heads. $\frac{4}{15}$
15. None are heads, given that at least one is tails. $\frac{1}{15}$
16. None are tails, given that at least three are heads. $\frac{1}{5}$
17. **SOFTBALL** Paloma gets a hit 65% of the times she is at bat. What is the probability that she does not get a hit in five consecutive at-bats? **0.5%**
18. **WEATHER** According to the meteorologist, there will be a 20% chance of snow for each of the next five days. What is the probability that it snows for each of the next five days? **0.032%**

Real-World Link

Male teens spend about one fifth of their own money on video games.

Source: NOP World 2003

19. **COMPUTER GAMES** The table shows a distribution of computer games sold by a company.

Type	P
strategy	0.19
children's	0.12
family	0.08
action	0.25
role playing	0.17
sports	0.16
other	0.03

   a. Find the probability that a game is an action game, given that it is not a sports or role playing game. **37.3%**
   b. Find the probability that a game is a family game, given that it is not a strategy or action game. **14.3%**

20. **POP QUIZZES** His students have determined that Mr. Woodruff gives a pop quiz at the beginning of class 15% of the time. What is the probability that there will be no quizzes during a five-day week? **44.4%**
21. **C** **FUNDRAISING** Mercedes and Victoria are trying to raise funds for their charity by calling numbers in the local phone book and asking for donations. They only reach 40% of the people they call. Of the people they reach, 20% promise to donate funds. Of the people who promise to donate, only 25% actually send money. What is the probability that a person who is called will actually contribute? **2%**
22. **HONORS CLASS** The probability that a student is in honors, given that he or she is in Mrs. Rollins' class, is $\frac{28}{51}$. The probability that a student is not in Mrs. Rollins' class, given that he or she is not in honors, is $\frac{33}{56}$. If there are 165 students that are neither in Mrs. Rollins' class nor in honors, how many students *are* in Mrs. Rollins' class and in honors? **140**

H.O.T. Problems
Use Higher-Order Thinking Skills

23. **CHALLENGE** The probability that a student has a MyRoom page, given that he or she is a freshman, is $\frac{43}{55}$. The probability that a student does not have a MyRoom page, given that he or she is a sophomore, is $\frac{4}{27}$. If there are 82 students, determine the probability that a student is a freshman, given that he or she does have a MyRoom page. $\frac{43}{66}$
24. **WRITING IN MATH** Explain the difference between conditional probability for dependent events and conditional probability for independent events. Provide examples of each type.
25. **REASONING** Which branches of a tree diagram represent conditional probability? Provide a sample tree diagram and explain your reasoning. **See margin.**
26. **REASONING** If a fair coin is flipped 20 times in a row and comes up heads every single time, what is the probability that it comes up heads on the 21st flip? Explain your reasoning.
27. **OPEN ENDED** Create a contingency table and calculate a conditional probability using the students in your class. **See margin.**

24. Sample answer: When two events are independent, the probability of event A happening has no effect on event B happening. For example, rolling a die has no effect on drawing a card, so the probability of drawing a king given that a three was rolled is equal to the probability of drawing a king $P(A \mid B) = P(B)$. When two events are dependent, then the conditional probability holds. For example, drawing a king and not replacing it has an effect on drawing a spade. If the king of spades is drawn, then there is one fewer spade in the deck, and the probability of drawing a spade is affected.

26. Sample answer: 50%; the previous tosses have no effect on the 21st toss. They are independent events.

Enrichment
CRM p. 23 AL OL

12-3 Enrichment

Probability and Tic-Tac-Toe

What would be the chances of winning at tic–tac–toe if it were turned into a game of pure chance? To find out, the nine cells of the tic–tac–toe board are numbered from 1 to 9 and nine chips (also numbered from 1 to 9) are put into a bag. Player A draws a chip at random and enters an X in the corresponding cell. Player B does the same and enters an O.

To solve the problem, assume that both players draw all their chips without looking and all X and O entries are made at the same time. There are four possible outcomes: a draw, A wins, B wins, and either A or B can win.

There are 16 arrangements that result in a draw. Reflections and rotations must be counted as shown below.

```
o x o      x o x      o o x
x o x 4    o o x 4    x x o 8
x o x      x x o      o x x
```

There are 36 arrangements in which either player may win because both players have winning triples.

```
x x x      x x x      x o x      x x x      x x x      x x o
o o o 4    x o x 4    x x x 4    x x o 8    o o o 8    x x x 8
x o x      o o o      o o o      o o o      x x o      o o o
```

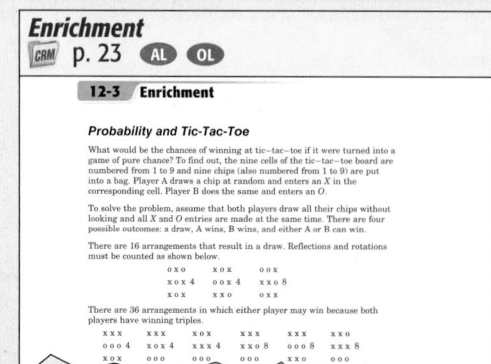

NGSSS PRACTICE 912.A.5.3, 912.A.6.2, 912.P.3.1, 912.A.2.12

28. GEOMETRY If the perimeter of an equilateral triangle is 45, then what is the length of the altitude of the triangle? **D**

A. 9 C. 7.5
B. $9\sqrt{3}$ D. $7.5\sqrt{3}$

29. Which expression is equivalent to $\dfrac{\frac{1}{4}+\frac{1}{4x}}{\frac{1}{x}+\frac{1}{4}}$? **F**

F. $\dfrac{x+1}{x+4}$ H. $\dfrac{4x+4}{x+4}$
G. 4 I. $\dfrac{1}{4}$

30. SAT/ACT Aisha is late to practice 30% of the time each Wednesday because of French Club. What is the probability that she will be late on at least 3 of the next 5 Wednesdays? **C**

A. 3% C. 16%
B. 13% D. 84%

31. THINK SOLVE EXPLAIN **SHORT RESPONSE** If $\frac{12}{7}+\frac{15}{x}=1$, what is the value of x? **−21**

32a. The mean is $26,489 and the median is $25,738. The median is about 3% less than the mean.

Spiral Review

32c. The mean increased to $26,655.67 and the median remained the same.

32. FINANCIAL LITERACY The list shows the median income per capita in a recent year for 12 states in a region of the country. (Lesson 12-2)

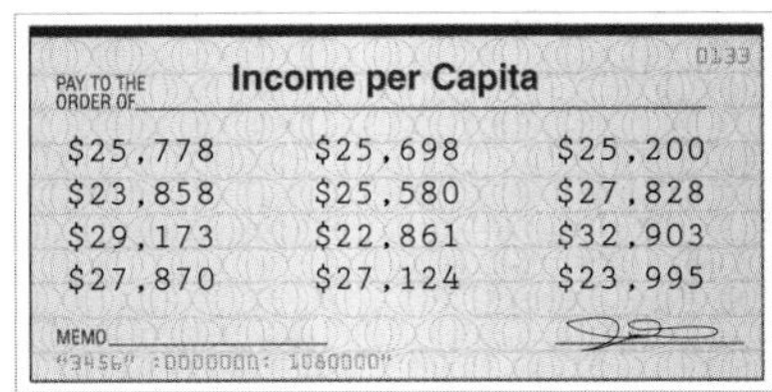

PAY TO THE ORDER OF
Income per Capita
0133
$25,778 $25,698 $25,200
$23,858 $25,580 $27,828
$29,173 $22,861 $32,903
$27,870 $27,124 $23,995
MEMO

a. Compare the mean and median for the region.

b. Find the standard deviation of the data. Round to the nearest hundredth. **$2736.46**

c. Suppose the state's reported per capita income of $22,861 is incorrect, and the actual value is $24,861. How are the mean and median for the region affected?

Determine whether each situation would produce a random sample. Write *yes* or *no* and explain your answer. (Lesson 12-1)

33. surveying band members to find the most popular type of music at your school **no**

34. surveying people coming into a post office to find out what color cars are most popular **yes**

35. ENTERTAINMENT A basketball team has a halftime promotion in which a fan gets to shoot a 3-pointer to try to win a jackpot. The jackpot starts at $5000 for the first game and increases $500 each time there is no winner. Ellis has tickets to the fifteenth game of the season. How much will the jackpot be for that game if no one wins by then? (Lesson 11-2) **$12,000**

Skills Review

Find *x*. Round to the nearest tenth if necessary. (Lesson 0-7)

36. **20**
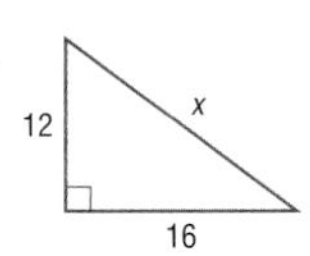

37. **8.9**
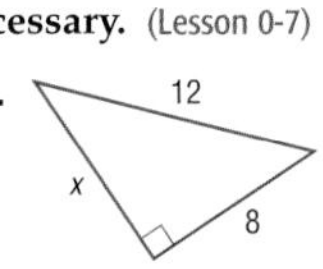

38. **5.8**
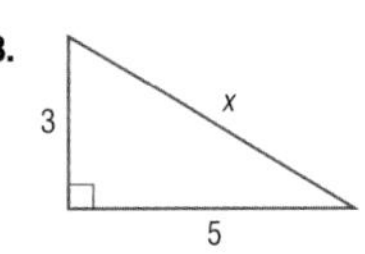

39. **10**
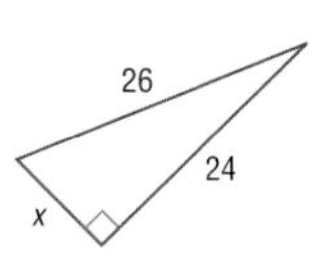

40. **10.8**
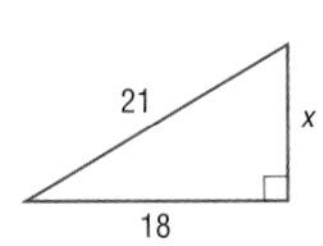

41. **15**
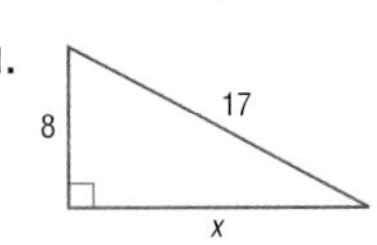

4 ASSESS

Ticket Out the Door Put a contingency table on the board that compares the numbers of girls and boys in the class with respect to some trait, like participation in school sports, playing in the band, working after school, and so on. Then ask students to write a conditional probability related to the data in the table.

Tips for New Teachers

Reasoning Remind students to use the Commutative and Associative Properties and look for pairs of numbers that will make calculations easier.

Additional Answers

25. Sample answer: The final branches represent conditional probability. For example, consider the probabilities of students being sophomores and licensed to drive. The 0.4 represents the probability that a student is licensed given he or she is a sophomore.

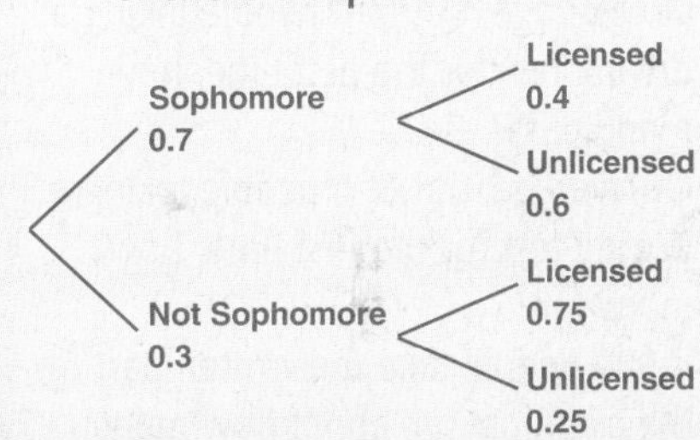

27. Sample answer:

Class	Male	Female
Freshman	6	9
Sophomore	8	5

the probability that a student is a female given she is a freshman: $\frac{3}{5}$

Differentiated Instruction BL

Extension The probability that two events A and B both occur is always found by multiplying their individual probabilities. But if A and B are dependent events, a conditional probability must be used for one of them: $P(A \text{ and } B) = P(A) \cdot P(B \mid A)$. Use this formula to find the probability that, when two cards are drawn from a standard 52-card deck, the first will be an ace and the second will be a king. $\frac{4}{52} \times \frac{4}{51} = \frac{4}{663}$ or about 0.006

12-4 Lesson Notes

1 FOCUS

Vertical Alignment

Before Lesson 12-4
Solve problems involving combinations and permutations.

Lesson 12-4
Find probabilities by using combinations and permutations.
Create and use graphs of probability distributions.

After Lesson 12-4
Create a graph of a binomial probability distribution.

2 TEACH

Scaffolding Questions

Have students read the *Why?* section of the lesson.

Ask:

- On average, out of 6 people taking a driving test for the first time, how many pass? 5
- On average, out of 6 people taking a driving test for the first time, how many fail? 1
- If 500 people take the written part of the examination, about how many will pass? about 450

12-4 Probability and Probability Distributions

Then
You solved problems involving combinations and permutations. (Lesson 0-5)

Now
- Find probabilities by using combinations and permutations.
- Create and use graphs of probability distributions.

NGSSS
MA.912.P.1.2 Use formulas for permutations and combinations to count outcomes and determine probabilities of events. **MA.912.P.3.1 Determine probabilities of events from distributions, including: discrete** uniform, binomial, normal, and exponential.

New Vocabulary
probability
success
failure
sample space
random variable
probability distribution
uniform distribution
relative-frequency graph
discrete probability distribution
theoretical probability
expected value

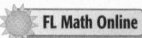

FL Math Online
glencoe.com

Why?

Suppose the chances of passing a driving test the first time you take it are 5 in 6. The chances of passing the written part of the examination the first time are 9 in 10. What is the probability that you will pass both tests on the first try?

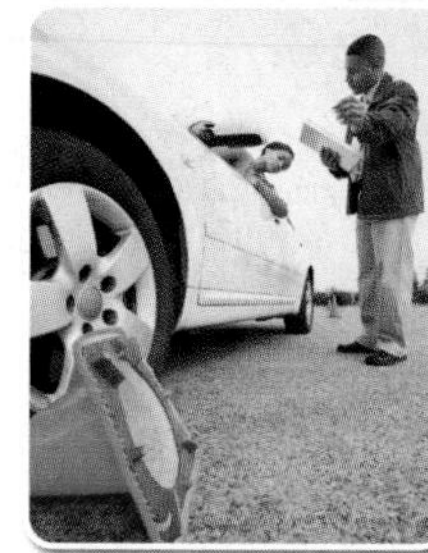

Probability The **probability** of an event is a ratio that measures the chances of the event occurring. A desired outcome is called a **success**. Any other outcome is called a **failure**. The set of all possible outcomes is called the **sample space**. The closer the probability of an event is to 1, the more likely the event is to occur.

> **Key Concept** — Probability of Success and Failure
>
> **Words** If an event can succeed in s ways and fail in f ways, then the probabilities of success $P(S)$ and of failure $P(F)$ are as follows.
>
> **Symbols** $P(S) = \frac{s}{s+f}$ $\quad P(F) = \frac{f}{s+f}$

EXAMPLE 1 Probability with Combinations

Twelve male and 16 female students have been selected as equal qualifiers for 6 college scholarships. If the qualifiers interviewed on the first day are to be chosen at random, what is the probability that 3 will be male and 3 will be female?

Step 1 Determine the number of successes.

$_{12}C_3$ **3 males chosen from 12 males**
$_{16}C_3$ **3 females chosen from 16 females**

Use combinations and the Fundamental Counting Principle to find s.

$$_{12}C_3 \cdot {}_{16}C_3 = \frac{12!}{9!3!} \cdot \frac{16!}{13!3!} \text{ or } 123{,}200 \text{ possible groups}$$

Step 2 Determine the number of possibilities, $s + f$.

$$_{28}C_6 = \frac{28!}{22!6!} \text{ or } 376{,}740 \text{ total possible groups}$$

Step 3 Find the probability.

$P(3 \text{ males and } 3 \text{ females}) = \frac{s}{s+f}$ **Probability of success**

$= \frac{123{,}200}{376{,}740}$ **$s = 123{,}200$ and $s + f = 376{,}740$**

≈ 0.327016 **Use a calculator.**

The probability of selecting 3 males and 3 females is about 0.327016 or 33%.

Guided Practice

1. Three juniors and eleven seniors have been nominated for 4 spots to represent the school at a city-wide charity event. If the winners are drawn at random, what is the probability that 2 juniors and 2 seniors are selected? 16.5%

Personal Tutor glencoe.com

Lesson 12-4 Resources

Resource	Approaching-Level	On-Level	Beyond-Level	English Learners
Teacher Edition	• Differentiated Instruction, p. 765	• Differentiated Instruction, p. 765	• Differentiated Instruction, pp. 765, 771	
Chapter Resource Masters	• Study Guide and Intervention, pp. 24–25 • Skills Practice, p. 26 • Practice, p. 27 • Word Problem Practice, p. 28	• Study Guide and Intervention, pp. 24–25 • Skills Practice, p. 26 • Practice, p. 27 • Word Problem Practice, p. 28 • Enrichment, p. 29	• Practice, p. 27 • Word Problem Practice, p. 28 • Enrichment, p. 29	• Study Guide and Intervention, pp. 24–25 • Skills Practice, p. 26 • Practice, p. 27 • Word Problem Practice, p. 28
Transparencies	• 5-Minute Check Transparency 12-4	• 5-Minute Check Transparency 12-4	• 5-Minute Check Transparency 12-4	• 5-Minute Check Transparency 12-4
Other	• Study Notebook • Teaching Algebra with Manipulatives	• Study Notebook • Teaching Algebra with Manipulatives	• Study Notebook	• Study Notebook • Teaching Algebra with Manipulatives

Review Vocabulary

permutations and combinations When a group of objects or people is arranged in a certain order, the arrangement is called a *permutation*. An arrangement or selection of objects in which order is *not* important is called a *combination*. (Lesson 0-5)

Real-World EXAMPLE 2 Probability with Permutations

MUSIC Courtney has a playlist of 6 songs on her MP3 player. What is the probability that the player will randomly play her favorite song first, then her second favorite song, and the three least favorite songs last?

Step 1 Determine the number of successes.

$_1P_1$ **Play two favorite songs first and in order.**

$_3P_3$ **Play the least favorite songs last, but in any order.**

Use permutations and the Fundamental Counting Principle to find s.

$_1P_1 \cdot {_3P_3} = 1! \cdot 3!$ or 6

Step 2 Determine the number of possibilities, $s + f$.

$_6P_6 = 6!$ or 720 possible orders of 6 songs

Step 3 Find the probability.

$P(\text{Courtney's desired order}) = \frac{s}{s+f}$ **Probability of success**

$= \frac{6}{720}$ **$s = 6$ and $s + f = 720$**

≈ 0.0083 **Use a calculator.**

The probability of the songs playing in Courtney's desired order is about 0.8%.

Guided Practice 2. $\frac{1}{56}$ or about 2%

2. RACING Taryn, Stephanie, and Julie are in the 400-meter race with 5 other athletes. What is the probability that they all finish in the top three?

Personal Tutor glencoe.com

Sometimes, permutations and combinations are *both* used in determining a probability.

EXAMPLE 3 Probability with Combinations and Permutations

Suppose Hernanda pulls 5 marbles without replacement from a bag of 28 marbles in which 7 are red, 7 are black, 7 are blue, and 7 are white. What is the probability that 2 are of one color and 3 are of another color?

Step 1 Determine the number of successes.

$_4P_2$ **2 colors chosen from 4 if order matters**

$_7C_2$ **2 marbles of one color chosen from a group of 7**

$_7C_3$ **3 marbles of another color chosen from a group of 7**

Use permutations and combinations, along with the Fundamental Counting Principle, to find s.

$_4P_2 \cdot {_7C_2} \cdot {_7C_3} = 12 \cdot 21 \cdot 35$ or 8820

Step 2 Determine the number of possibilities, $s + f$.

$_{28}C_5 = 98{,}280$ ways to pull 5 marbles from a bag of 28

Step 3 Find the probability.

$P(\text{3 of one color, 2 of another}) = \frac{s}{s+f}$ **Probability of success**

$= \frac{8820}{98{,}280}$ **Substitute.**

≈ 0.0897 **Use a calculator.**

The probability of pulling 2 of one color and 3 of another is about 9%.

StudyTip

Replacement *With replacement* means that the object is *replaced*, or put back into the bag after it is drawn.

Probability

Example 1 shows how to use combinations to find probabilities.
Example 2 shows how to use permutations to find probabilities.
Example 3 shows how to use both combinations and permutations to find probabilities.

Formative Assessment

Use the Guided Practice exercises after each example to determine students' understanding of concepts.

Additional Examples

1 Roman has a collection of 26 books—16 are fiction and 10 are nonfiction. If he randomly chooses 8 books to take with him on vacation, what is the probability that he happens to choose 4 fiction and 4 nonfiction? about 0.24464 or about 24.5%

2 For next semester, Alisa has signed up for English, precalculus, Spanish, geography, and chemistry classes. If class schedules are assigned randomly and each class is equally likely to be at any time of day, what is the probability that Alisa's first two classes in the morning will be precalculus and chemistry, in either order? $\frac{1}{10}$

3 Suppose Alice draws 4 cards without replacement from a standard 52-card deck. What is the probability that those 4 cards contain 2 of one suit and 2 of another? about 27.0%

Additional Examples also in Interactive Classroom PowerPoint® Presentations

IWB INTERACTIVE WHITEBOARD READY

Differentiated Instruction AL OL BL

Social Learners It is important to be aware that some students may have cultural or familial prohibitions against cards, dice, or gambling of any kind. Explain that, historically, the laws of probability were actually developed in the context of gambling but are now used in many other ways, including medicine and meteorology.

Probability Distributions

Example 4 shows how to use a graph or a table to visualize a probability distribution. **Example 5** shows how to find the expected value of a probability distribution.

Additional Example

4 A bag of 10 marbles contains 3 blue, 1 red, 2 yellow, and 4 green marbles.

a. Create a relative-frequency graph of the probability distribution.

D = Draw	Blue	Red	Yellow	Green
Probability	$\frac{3}{10}$	$\frac{1}{10}$	$\frac{1}{5}$	$\frac{2}{5}$

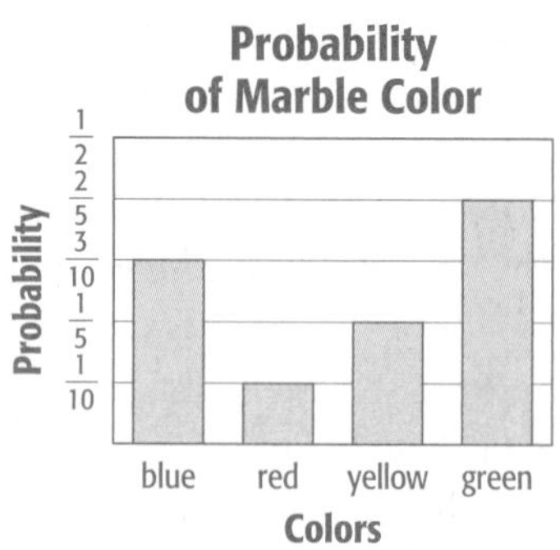

b. Use the graph to determine which outcome is most likely. What is its probability? green; $\frac{2}{5}$

c. What is the probability of drawing a red or blue marble? $\frac{2}{5}$

TEACH with TECH

DOCUMENT CAMERA Choose two students to work through an example in front of the class. Have one student explain how to calculate a frequency distribution, and have the other student explain how to create a histogram from that distribution.

Guided Practice

3. If 7 green marbles are added to the bag, what is the probability that Hernanda pulls out 4 of one color and 3 of another? **about 0.36%**

Personal Tutor glencoe.com

ReadingMath

Random Variables The notation $P(R = n)$ is used with random variables. $P(R = 4) = \frac{1}{6}$ is read *The probability that R equals 4 is one sixth.*

Probability Distributions The value of a **random variable** is the numerical outcome of a random event. A **probability distribution** for a particular random variable is a function that maps the sample space to its probabilities of the outcomes in the sample space.

A variable is said to be *random* if the sum of its probabilities is 1. The table below illustrates the probability distribution for rolling a die.

Sample space: $R = \{1, 2, 3, 4, 5, 6\}$

R = roll	1	2	3	4	5	6
Probability	$\frac{1}{6}$	$\frac{1}{6}$	$\frac{1}{6}$	$\frac{1}{6}$	$\frac{1}{6}$	$\frac{1}{6}$

$P(R = 4) = \frac{1}{6}$

A distribution in which all of the probabilities are equal is called a **uniform distribution**. For example, the distribution for rolling a die is uniform.

To help visualize a probability distribution, you can use a table or a bar graph or histogram of probabilities called a **relative-frequency graph**.

Real-World Link

There are currently 120 Crayola crayon colors. More than 400 have been introduced since 1903.

Source: Crayola

EXAMPLE 4 Probability Distribution

The spinner shows the probability distribution of the spinner landing on each color.

a. Create a relative-frequency bar graph.

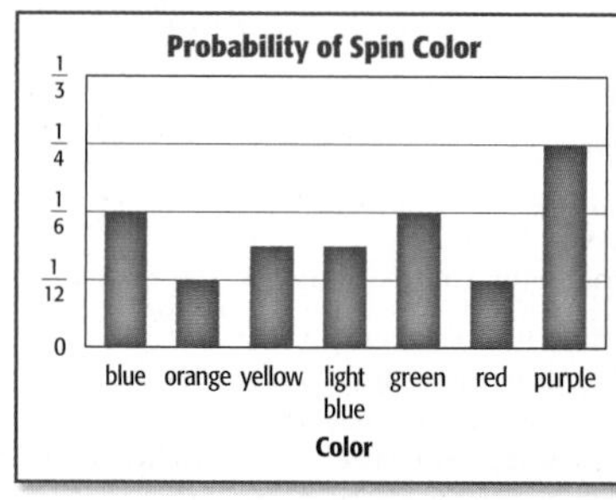

b. Use the graph to determine which outcome is most likely.

The most likely outcome is purple, and its probability is $\frac{1}{4}$.

c. Find P(blue or green).

The probability of spinning blue or green is $\frac{1}{6} + \frac{1}{6}$ or $\frac{1}{3}$.

Guided Practice 4A. See margin. 4B. 2 and 12; $\frac{1}{36}$

Two six-sided dice are rolled, and their sum is recorded.

4A. Create a frequency table and a relative-frequency graph of the data.

4B. Which outcomes are the least likely to occur? What is their probability?

4C. Find $P(5 \text{ or } 11)$. $\frac{1}{6}$

Personal Tutor glencoe.com

Additional Answer (Guided Practice)

4A.

Sum	2	3	4	5	6	7
	8	9	10	11	12	
Probability	$\frac{1}{36}$	$\frac{1}{18}$	$\frac{1}{12}$	$\frac{1}{9}$	$\frac{5}{36}$	$\frac{1}{6}$
	$\frac{5}{36}$	$\frac{1}{9}$	$\frac{1}{12}$	$\frac{1}{18}$	$\frac{1}{36}$	

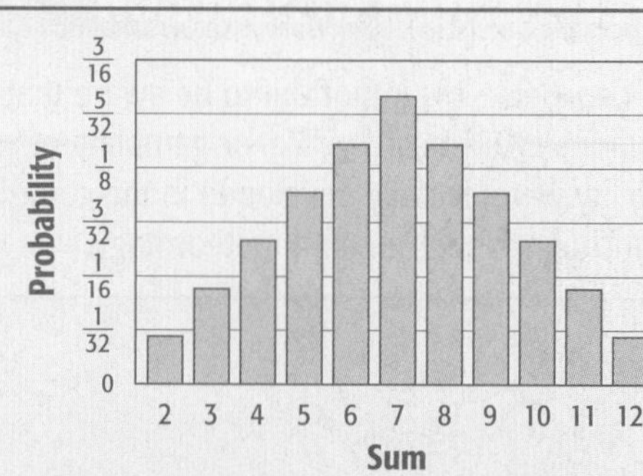

Probability distributions like the one in Example 4 are called **discrete probability distributions** because there are only a finite number of possible outcomes.

The probabilities discussed here are **theoretical probabilities** because they are based on assumptions of what is expected to happen. The **expected value** $E(x)$ is the weighted average of the values in a probability distribution if the weight applied to each value is its theoretical probability. It tells you what you could expect in the "long run"—that is, after many trials. This is not to be confused with *expected number*. When there are multiple trials, the expected number of times an event occurs is the probability of success in one trial multiplied by the total number of trials.

StudyTip

Law of Large Numbers The *Law of Large Numbers* states that as the number of trials increases, the experimental probability gets closer to the expected value.

EXAMPLE 5 Expected Value

a. A die is rolled. Find the expected value of one roll of the die.

$E(x) = \left(1 \cdot \frac{1}{6}\right) + \left(2 \cdot \frac{1}{6}\right) + \left(3 \cdot \frac{1}{6}\right) + \left(4 \cdot \frac{1}{6}\right) + \left(5 \cdot \frac{1}{6}\right) + \left(6 \cdot \frac{1}{6}\right)$ **Weighted Average Formula**

$= \frac{1}{6} + \frac{2}{6} + \frac{3}{6} + \frac{4}{6} + \frac{5}{6} + \frac{6}{6}$ **Multiply.**

$= \frac{21}{6}$ or 3.5 **Add.**

b. If the die is rolled 4 times, find the expected number of *even* rolls.

$E(n) = P(S) \cdot n$ **Expected number**

$= \frac{1}{6} \cdot 4$ or $\frac{2}{3}$ **Multiply.**

Guided Practice

5. Find the expected value of the sum of two dice. What is the expected number of 7s in 100 rolls? 7; 17

Personal Tutor glencoe.com

Check Your Understanding

1. about 13.9%

Example 1 p. 764

1. **ART** A museum curator at the Art Institute of Chicago is randomly selecting 4 paintings out of the 20 on display to showcase the work in a special exhibit. What is the probability that 3 of the 8 Paul Gauguin paintings are selected?

Example 2 p. 765

2. **TOURNAMENTS** Eight players entered a tournament. If the names are drawn randomly, what is the probability that the first four players selected are, in order, Alicia, Andrew, Marco, and Zack? $\frac{1}{1680}$ or about 0.06%

Example 3 p. 765

3. **CARDS** Suppose Justin draws 5 cards from a standard deck of 52 cards. What is the probability that those 5 cards contain 3 of one suit and two of another suit? about 10.3%

Examples 4 and 5 pp. 766–767

4. **FLOWERS** The relative-frequency histogram shows the distribution of the number of red flowers if 4 seeds are planted.

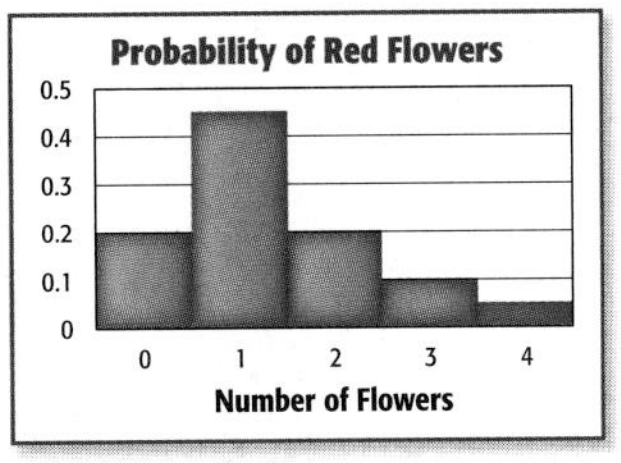

   a. Find $P(R = 0)$. $\frac{1}{5}$ or 20%

   b. What is the probability that at least 2 are red? 35%

   c. If ten pots are planted with 4 seeds each, how many would you expect to have 1 red flower? 5

Example 5 p. 767

5. **RAFFLES** The French Club sold 500 raffle tickets for \$1 each. The first prize ticket will win \$100, 2 second prize tickets will each win \$10, and 5 third prize tickets each win \$5. What is the expected value of a single ticket? \$0.29

Additional Example

5 A tetrahedral die has four sides numbered 1, 2, 3, and 4.

a. Find the expected value of one roll of this die. $\frac{5}{2}$ or 2.5

b. If the die is rolled 8 times, find the expected number of rolls that are 1 or 2. 4

3 PRACTICE

Formative Assessment

Use Exercises 1–5 to check for understanding.

Use the chart on the bottom of the next page to customize assignments for your students.

Additional Answer

14a.

Red / Red	11%
Red / Black	16%
Red / Green	18%
Red / White	12%
Black / Black	5%
Black / Green	12%
Black / White	8%
Green / White	9%
Green / Green	6%
White / White	3%

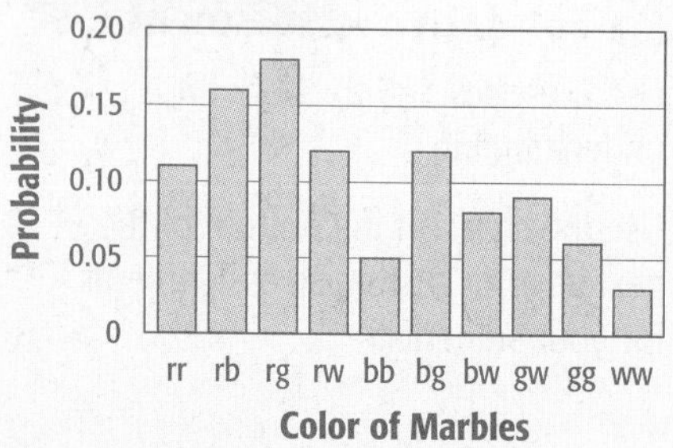

Practice and Problem Solving

= **Step-by-Step Solutions** begin on page R20.
Extra Practice begins on page 947.

Example 1 p. 764

6. **DRAWINGS** Twenty-four students entered a random drawing for 10 new calculators. What is the probability that 3 of the 5 students who entered from Mr. Kline's class won a calculator? **about 26%**

7. **RAFFLES** Fifty kids, including Lorena, Rebecca, and Melia, entered a raffle for 4 game consoles. What is the probability that two of these girls won? $\frac{69}{4900}$ **or about 1.4%**

8. **PERFORMANCES** During a magic show, the magician selects at random five members of the audience to assist in his performance. If there are 124 people in the audience, what is the probability that at least one of ten friends is selected? **about 34.8%**

Example 2 p. 765

9. **SEATING CHARTS** The new seating chart in Mr. Lian's class of 26 students was randomly generated. What is the probability that Jamila, Candace, and Haley are in the first, second, and third seats, respectively? $\frac{1}{15,600}$

10. **LOTTERIES** In a lottery, 3 numbers from 1 through 10 are drawn without replacement, and the person who selects the correct numbers in the order in which they are drawn wins the prize. If Eva buys 5 different tickets, what is the probability that she will win? $\frac{1}{144}$

Example 3 p. 765

11. $\frac{1,306,800}{73,629,072}$ or about 2%

11. **BALLOONS** A package of 48 balloons contains an equal number of red, white, blue, and purple balloons. If Shelby is given a handful of them to blow up, what is the probability that she gets 3 balloons of one color and 4 of another color?

12. **TRIVIA CONTESTS** Ten students from every grade level at West High were invited to a district-wide trivia contest. At the contest, 6 students are randomly selected to be alternates. What is the probability that 4 of these students are seniors and 2 are sophomores? $\frac{113,400}{3,838,380}$ **or about 3%**

Example 4 p. 766

13. **RAFFLES** The table and relative-frequency histogram show the distribution of winning a raffle if 100 tickets are sold. There is 1 prize for first, 10 prizes for second, and 25 prizes for third. Find $P(Z > 0)$. **0.36**

Z = Prize	no prize	1st	2nd	3rd
Probability	0.64	0.01	0.1	0.25

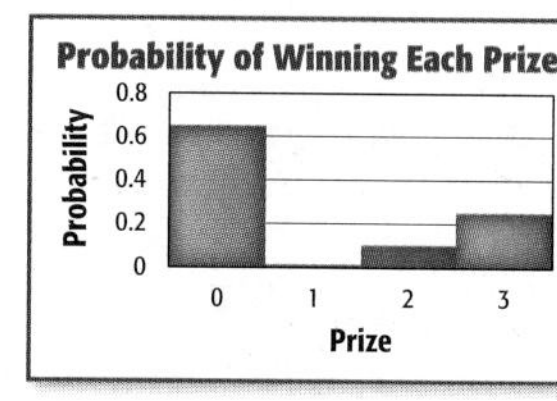

14. **MARBLES** Tai has a sack of 35 marbles. Eight are black, 12 are red, 9 are green, and the rest are white. Brianna pulls 2 marbles out of the bag. **a. See margin.**

   a. Create a frequency table and a relative-frequency graph of the data.

   b. Which outcome is the most likely to occur? **a red and a green marble**

   c. Find *P*(black and green). **12%**

Example 5 p. 767

15. **CARDS** In a standard deck of 52 cards, there are 4 different suits.

   a. If jacks = 11, queens = 12, kings = 13, and aces = 1, what is the expected value of a cord that is drawn from a standard deck? **7**

   b. If you are dealt 7 cards, what is the expected number of spades? **2**

Differentiated Homework Options

Level	Assignment	Two-Day Option	
AL Basic	6–16, 26–53	5–15 odd, 29–32	6–16 even, 26–28, 33–53
OL Core	5–15 odd, 17–53	6–16, 29–32	17–28, 33–53
BL Advanced	17–47, (optional: 48–53)		

16. BILLIARD BALLS In a rack of 16 billiard balls, there are 9 different colors, including the black eight ball and the white cue ball. Of the remaining 14 balls, 7 are striped and 7 are solid.

a. If 5 balls are randomly selected, what is the expected number of stripes? **2.1875**

b. If 4 balls are randomly selected, what is the expected number of white balls? **0.25**

c. If the value of the cue ball is 0 and the other balls are numbered 1–15, what is the expected value of a randomly-selected ball? **7.5**

17 B **SNOW DAYS** The following probability distribution lists the probable number of snow days per school year at North High School. Use this information to determine the expected number of snow days per year. **3.34**

Real-World Link

Before closing schools, superintendents use a system that could include field operatives traveling hazardous streets, Internet forecasts, and a school district's own Doppler radar.

Source: The Associated Press

Number of Snow Days Per Year

Days	0	1	2	3	4	5	6	7	8
Probability	0.1	0.1	0.15	0.15	0.25	0.1	0.08	0.05	0.02

18. BASKETBALL The distribution lists the probability of the number of upsets in the first round of a basketball tournament. Determine the expected number of upsets. **4.34**

Number of Upsets Per Year

Upsets	0	1	2	3	4	5	6	7	8
Probability	$\frac{1}{32}$	$\frac{1}{16}$	$\frac{3}{32}$	$\frac{1}{8}$	$\frac{1}{8}$	$\frac{5}{16}$	$\frac{1}{8}$	$\frac{3}{32}$	$\frac{1}{32}$

19. STUDENT GOVERNMENT Based on previous data, the probability distribution of the number of students running for class president per year is listed at the right. Determine the expected number of students who will run. **4.7**

Number of Students Running

Students	1	2	3	4	5	6
Probability	0.05	0.15	0.2	0.2	0.35	0.2

20. about 0.56%

20. MARBLES In a bag of 25 marbles with an equal amount of red, blue, green, black, and clear marbles, what is the probability of pulling out 4 of one color and 2 of another?

21. CONTESTS The bar graph at the right shows the probability of each student winning a prize.

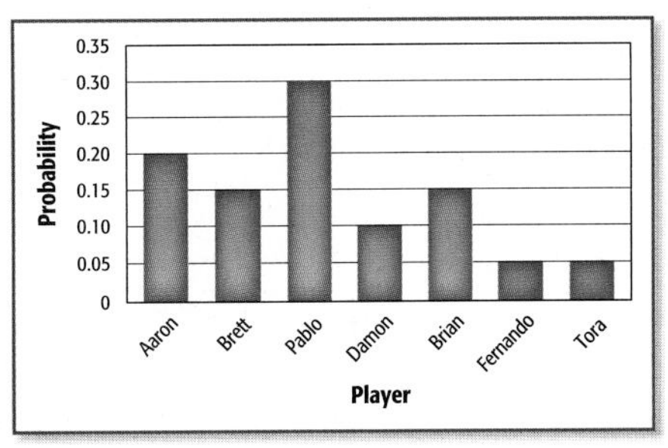

a. Who has the best chance to win, and what is the probability? **Pablo; 30%**

b. Which two players combined have the same chance of winning as Brian?

21b. Damon and Tora or Damon and Fernando

c. Who has a better chance of winning, Damon or Brett? **Brett**

d. Find P(Aaron or Pablo). **50%**

e. Find P(neither Damon nor Tora). **85%**

22. CARDS Three eights, 2 tens, 4 sixes, 3 fives, 2 twos, and a three are drawn from a deck of cards. If one card is drawn from these cards, what is its expected value? **6**

Lesson 12-4 Probability and Probability Distributions 769

Math History Link

Christian Huygens (1629–1695)
This Dutchman was the first to discuss games of chance. "Although in a pure game of chance the results are uncertain, the chance that one player has to win or to lose depends on a determined value." This became known as the *expected value*.

23. VOLUNTEERING Twenty girls and 25 boys sign up to volunteer at a shelter. If only eight students are allowed to go, what is the probability that 3 will be boys? **About 16.5%**

24. HORSE RACING In a race involving seven horses, Delsin randomly chose three horses to place first through third. What is the probability that he wins? $\frac{1}{210}$

25. MULTIPLE REPRESENTATIONS In this problem, you will investigate geometric probability.

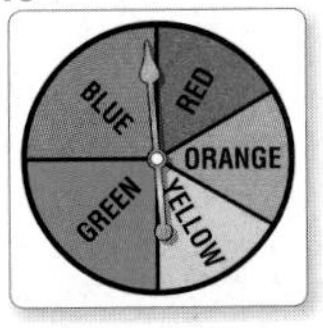

a. TABULAR The spinner shown has a radius of 2.5 inches. Copy and complete the table below.

Color	Probability	Sector Area	Total Area	Sector Area / Total Area
red	$\frac{1}{6}$	3.27 in^2	19.63 in^2	0.166
orange	$\frac{1}{6}$	3.27 in^2	19.63 in^2	0.166
yellow	$\frac{1}{6}$	3.27 in^2	19.63 in^2	0.166
green	$\frac{1}{4}$	4.91 in^2	19.63 in^2	0.25
blue	$\frac{1}{4}$	4.91 in^2	19.63 in^2	0.25

b. VERBAL Make a conjecture about the relationship between the ratio of the area of the sector to the total area and the probability of the spinner landing on each color.

25b. Sample answer: The probability is equal to the ratio of the sector area to the total area.

c. ANALYTICAL Consider the dartboard shown. Predict the probability of a dart landing in each area of the board. Assume that any dart thrown will land on the board and is equally likely to land at any point on the board.
red: $\frac{1}{9}$; yellow: $\frac{1}{3}$; blue: $\frac{5}{9}$

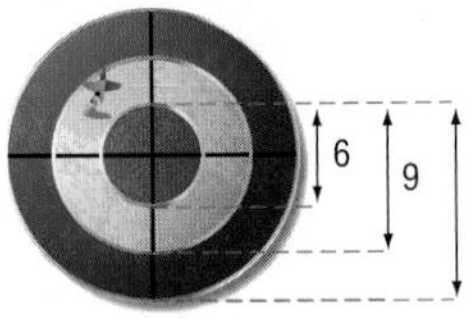

H.O.T. Problems Use Higher-Order Thinking Skills

26. ERROR ANALYSIS Liana and Shannon created probability distributions for the sum of two spins on the spinner at the right. Is either of them correct? Explain your reasoning.

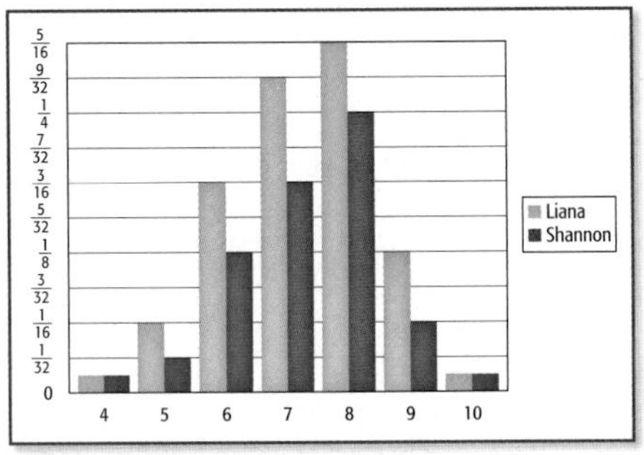

26. Sample answer: Liana; Shannon did not consider every scenario in determining the total probability. For example, in calculating the probability of a sum of 5, she considered spinning a 3 then a 2, but not a 2 then a 3.

27. REASONING Determine whether the following statement is *true* or *false*. Explain your reasoning.

Theoretical probabilities are based on results of experiments.

27. Sample answer: False; experimental probability is based on experiments, and theoretical probability is based on mathematical methods and assumptions.

28. OPEN ENDED Create a discrete probability distribution that shows five different outcomes and their associated probabilities. **See margin.**

Study Guide and Intervention
CRM pp. 24–25 AL OL ELL

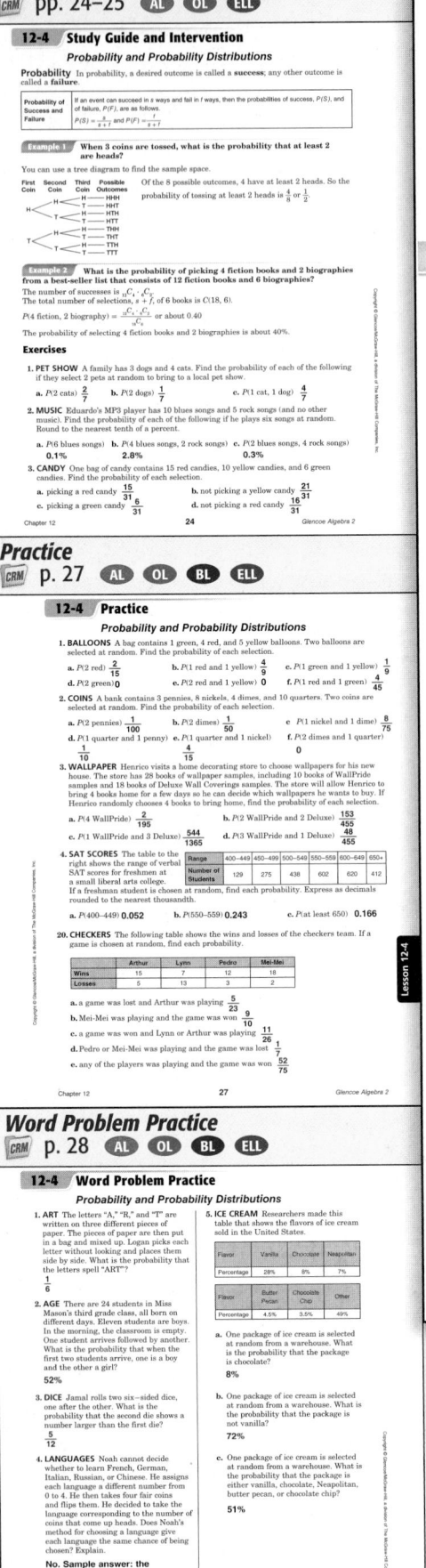

12-4 Study Guide and Intervention
Probability and Probability Distributions

Probability In probability, a desired outcome is called a **success**; any other outcome is called a **failure**.

Probability of Success and Failure	If an event can succeed in s ways and fail in f ways, then the probabilities of success, $P(S)$, and of failure, $P(F)$, are as follows. $P(S) = \frac{s}{s+f}$ and $P(F) = \frac{f}{s+f}$

Example 1 **When 3 coins are tossed, what is the probability that at least 2 are heads?**

You can use a tree diagram to find the sample space.

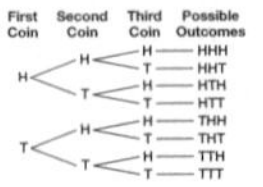

Of the 8 possible outcomes, 4 have at least 2 heads. So the probability of tossing at least 2 heads is $\frac{4}{8}$ or $\frac{1}{2}$.

Example 2 **What is the probability of picking 4 fiction books and 2 biographies from a best-seller list that consists of 12 fiction books and 6 biographies?**

The number of successes is ${}_{12}C_4 \cdot {}_6C_2$.
The total number of selections, $s + f$, of 6 books is $C(18, 6)$.

$P(\text{4 fiction, 2 biography}) = \frac{{}_{12}C_4 \cdot {}_6C_2}{{}_{18}C_6}$ or about 0.40

The probability of selecting 4 fiction books and 2 biographies is about 40%.

Exercises

1. **PET SHOW** A family has 3 dogs and 4 cats. Find the probability of each of the following if they select 2 pets at random to bring to a local pet show.
   a. P(2 cats) $\frac{2}{7}$ b. P(2 dogs) $\frac{1}{7}$ c. P(1 cat, 1 dog) $\frac{4}{7}$
2. **MUSIC** Eduardo's MP3 player has 10 blues songs and 5 rock songs (and no other music). Find the probability of each of the following if he plays six songs at random. Round to the nearest tenth of a percent.
   a. P(6 blues songs) **0.1%** b. P(4 blues songs, 2 rock songs) **2.8%** c. P(2 blues songs, 4 rock songs) **0.3%**
3. **CANDY** One bag of candy contains 15 red candies, 10 yellow candies, and 6 green candies. Find the probability of each selection.
   a. picking a red candy $\frac{15}{31}$ b. not picking a yellow candy $\frac{21}{31}$
   c. picking a green candy $\frac{6}{31}$ d. not picking a red candy $\frac{16}{31}$

Chapter 12 24 Glencoe Algebra 2

Practice
CRM p. 27 AL OL BL ELL

12-4 Practice
Probability and Probability Distributions

1. **BALLOONS** A bag contains 1 green, 4 red, and 5 yellow balloons. Two balloons are selected at random. Find the probability of each selection.
   a. P(2 red) $\frac{2}{15}$ b. P(1 red and 1 yellow) $\frac{4}{9}$ c. P(1 green and 1 yellow) $\frac{1}{9}$
   d. P(2 green) 0 e. P(2 red and 1 yellow) 0 f. P(1 red and 1 green) $\frac{4}{45}$
2. **COINS** A bank contains 3 pennies, 8 nickels, 4 dimes, and 10 quarters. Two coins are selected at random. Find the probability of each selection.
   a. P(2 pennies) $\frac{1}{100}$ b. P(2 dimes) $\frac{1}{50}$ c P(1 nickel and 1 dime) $\frac{8}{75}$
   d. P(1 quarter and 1 penny) $\frac{1}{10}$ e. P(1 quarter and 1 nickel) $\frac{4}{15}$ f. P(2 dimes and 1 quarter) 0
3. **WALLPAPER** Henrico visits a home decorating store to choose wallpapers for his new house. The store has 28 books of wallpaper samples, including 10 books of WallPride samples and 18 books of Deluxe Wall Coverings samples. The store will allow Henrico to bring 4 books home for a few days so he can decide which wallpapers he wants to buy. If Henrico randomly chooses 4 books to bring home, find the probability of each selection.
   a. P(4 WallPride) $\frac{2}{195}$ b. P(2 WallPride and 2 Deluxe) $\frac{153}{455}$
   c. P(1 WallPride and 3 Deluxe) $\frac{544}{1365}$ d. P(3 WallPride and 1 Deluxe) $\frac{48}{455}$
4. **SAT SCORES** The table to the right shows the range of verbal SAT scores for freshmen at a small liberal arts college.

Range	400–449	450–499	500–549	550–559	600–649	650+
Number of Students	129	275	438	602	620	412

   If a freshman student is chosen at random, find each probability. Express as decimals rounded to the nearest thousandth.
   a. P(400–449) 0.052 b. P(550–559) 0.243 c. P(at least 650) 0.166

20. **CHECKERS** The following table shows the wins and losses of the checkers team. If a game is chosen at random, find each probability.

	Arthur	Lynn	Pedro	Mei-Mei
Wins	15	7	12	18
Losses	5	13	3	2

   a. a game was lost and Arthur was playing $\frac{5}{23}$
   b. Mei-Mei was playing and the game was won $\frac{9}{10}$
   c. a game was won and Lynn or Arthur was playing $\frac{11}{26}$
   d. Pedro or Mei-Mei was playing and the game was lost $\frac{1}{7}$
   e. any of the players was playing and the game was won $\frac{52}{75}$

Chapter 12 27 Glencoe Algebra 2

Lesson 12-4

Word Problem Practice
CRM p. 28 AL OL BL ELL

12-4 Word Problem Practice
Probability and Probability Distributions

1. **ART** The letters "A," "R," and "T" are written on three different pieces of paper. The pieces of paper are then put in a bag and mixed up. Logan picks each letter without looking and places them side by side. What is the probability that the letters spell "ART"?
   $\frac{1}{6}$
2. **AGE** There are 24 students in Miss Mason's third grade class, all born on different days. Eleven students are boys. In the morning, the classroom is empty. One student arrives followed by another. What is the probability that when the first two students arrive, one is a boy and the other a girl?
   52%
3. **DICE** Jamal rolls two six–sided dice, one after the other. What is the probability that the second die shows a number larger than the first die?
   $\frac{5}{12}$
4. **LANGUAGES** Noah cannot decide whether to learn French, German, Italian, Russian, or Chinese. He assigns each language a different number from 0 to 4. He then takes four fair coins and flips them. He decided to take the language corresponding to the number of coins that come up heads. Does Noah's method for choosing a language give each language the same chance of being chosen? Explain.
   No. Sample answer: the probability of getting 0 is 1 in 16 but the probability of getting 1 is 1 in 4.
5. **ICE CREAM** Researchers made this table that shows the flavors of ice cream sold in the United States.

Flavor	Vanilla	Chocolate	Neapolitan
Percentage	28%	8%	7%

Flavor	Butter Pecan	Chocolate Chip	Other
Percentage	4.5%	3.5%	49%

   a. One package of ice cream is selected at random from a warehouse. What is the probability that the package is chocolate?
   8%
   b. One package of ice cream is selected at random from a warehouse. What is the probability that the package is not vanilla?
   72%
   c. One package of ice cream is selected at random from a warehouse. What is the probability that the package is either vanilla, chocolate, Neapolitan, butter pecan, or chocolate chip?
   51%

Chapter 12 28 Glencoe Algebra 2

Enrichment
CRM p. 29 OL BL

12-4 Enrichment

Geometric Probability

If a dart, thrown at random, hits the triangular board shown at the right, what is the chance that it will hit the shaded region? This chance, also called a probability, can be determined by comparing the area of the shaded region to the area of the board. This ratio indicates what fraction of the tosses should hit in the shaded region.

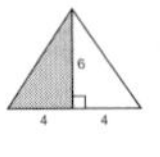

$$\frac{\text{area of shaded region}}{\text{area of triangular board}} = \frac{\frac{1}{2}(4)(6)}{\frac{1}{2}(8)(6)} = \frac{12}{24} \text{ or } \frac{1}{2}$$

In general, if S is a subregion of some region R, then the probability, $P(S)$, that a point, chosen at random, belongs to subregion S is given by the following.

$$P(S) = \frac{\text{area of subregion } S}{\text{area of region } R}$$

Find the probability that a point, chosen at random, belongs to the shaded subregions of the following regions.

Additional Answer

28. Sample answer: A spinner with 5 equal-sided areas shaded red, blue, yellow, green, and brown.

Color	red	blue	yellow	green	brown
Probability	0.2	0.2	0.2	0.2	0.2

770 Chapter 12 Probability and Statistics

NGSSS PRACTICE 912.A.8.5, 912.P.3.2, 912.G.6.5, 912.A.4.1

29. **GRIDDED RESPONSE** The height $f(x)$ of a bouncing ball after x bounces is represented by $f(x) = 140(0.8)^x$. How many times higher is the first bounce than the fifth bounce? 2.4

30. **PROBABILITY** Andres has a bag that contains 4 red, 6 yellow, 2 blue, and 4 green marbles. If he reaches into the bag and removes a marble without looking, what is the probability that it will not be yellow? D

A. $\frac{1}{8}$ C. $\frac{3}{8}$

B. $\frac{1}{4}$ D. $\frac{5}{8}$

31. **GEOMETRY** Find the area of the shaded portion of the figure to the nearest square inch. H

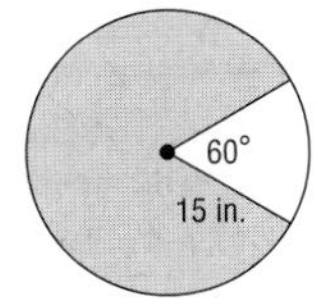

F. 79

G. 94

H. 589

I. 707

32. **SAT/ACT** If x and y are positive integers, which of the following expressions is equivalent to $\frac{(5^x)^y}{5^x}$? D

A. 1^y C. 5^{xy-1}

B. 5^y D. 5^{xy-x}

Spiral Review

38. 0.125, 0.1875, 0.28125, 0.421875, 0.632813
39. 0.5, 1.25, 3.125, 7.8125, 19.53125

33. **JOBS** A computer company is interviewing 8 men and 7 women for 5 computer programming positions. If the applicants are chosen at random, what is the probability that the company will hire 3 men and 2 women? (Lesson 12-3) 0.39

Determine whether each of the following represents a *population* or a *sample*. (Lesson 12-2)

34. Shenae calculates the average number of people on 50 bus rides. sample

35. The U.S. Census Bureau conducts a demographics survey every 10 years. population

36. East State College calculates the average cost of tuition of the entire student body. population

37. Jared conducts a survey in his department to determine what time employees usually arrive in the morning. sample

Find the first five terms of each geometric sequence described. (Lesson 11-3) 43. 80, 100, 125, $\frac{625}{4}$, $\frac{3125}{16}$

38. $a_1 = 0.125, r = 1.5$

39. $a_1 = 0.5, r = 2.5$

40. $a_1 = 4, r = 0.5$ 4, 2, 1, 0.5, 0.25

41. $a_1 = 12, r = \frac{1}{3}$ 12, 4, $\frac{4}{3}$, $\frac{4}{9}$, $\frac{4}{27}$

42. $a_1 = 21, r = \frac{2}{3}$ 21, 14, $\frac{28}{3}$, $\frac{56}{9}$, $\frac{112}{27}$

43. $a_1 = 80, r = \frac{5}{4}$

44. **COMMUNICATION** A microphone is placed at the focus of a parabolic reflector to collect sound for the television broadcast of a football game. Write an equation for the cross section, assuming that the focus is at the origin, the focus is 6 inches from the vertex, and the parabola opens to the right. (Lesson 10-2) $x = \frac{1}{24}y^2 - 6$

Solve each equation. Check your solutions. (Lesson 8-4)

45. $\log_9 x = \frac{3}{2}$ 27

46. $\log_{\frac{1}{10}} x = -3$ 1000

47. $\log_b 9 = 2$ 3

Skills Review

Find each percent. Round to the nearest tenth.

48. 65% of 27 17.6

49. 89% of 120 106.8

50. 11% of 30 3.3

51. 25% of 373 93.3

52. 77% of 200 154

53. 30% of 48 14.4

Multiple Representations In Exercise 25, students use a diagram, information organized in a table, symbolic formulas, and verbal analysis to determine geometric probabilities.

Watch Out!

Error Analysis For Exercise 26, ask students how many ways you can spin the spinner twice and get a sum of 4. Repeat for sums of 5, 6, 7, 8, 9, and 10.

4 ASSESS

Crystal Ball Ask students how they think today's study of probability distributions will help them with their study of normal distributions in the next lesson.

Formative Assessment

Check for student understanding of concepts in Lessons 12-3 and 12-4.

CRM Quiz 2, p. 51

Differentiated Instruction

BL

Extension Write the numbers 1, 1, 1, 2, 2, 3, 4, 4 on eight slips of paper and mix them up in a paper bag. Have students construct a probability distribution for the number that results when one slip is drawn at random from the bag. Then have them take turns drawing (with replacement) and compare the relative frequencies with the theoretical probability distribution. The theoretical probabilities are: $P(1) = \frac{3}{8}$, $P(2) = \frac{1}{4}$, $P(3) = \frac{1}{8}$, $P(4) = \frac{1}{4}$.

Lesson 12-4 Probability and Probability Distributions 771

CHAPTER 12 Mid-Chapter Quiz

Formative Assessment

Use the Mid-Chapter Quiz to assess students' progress in the first half of the chapter.

For problems answered incorrectly, have students review the lessons indicated in parentheses.

ExamView Assessment Suite Customize and create multiple versions of your Mid-Chapter Quiz and their answer keys.

FOLDABLES Follow-Up

Before students complete the Mid-Chapter Quiz, encourage them to review the information for Lessons 12-1 through 12-4 in their Foldables.

Additional Answers

1. No; because the people surveyed would probably be more likely than others to have children
2. Yes; everyone in the office is the population and each have an equal opportunity to become part of the sample.
3. Yes; every student in the school is the population and each have an equal opportunity to become part of the sample.
9. Mean; the data has no outliers.

CHAPTER 12 Mid-Chapter Quiz

Lessons 12-1 through 12-4

NGSSS 912.P.3.1, 912.P.3.2, 912.S.3.3

1–3. See margin.

State whether each survey would produce a random sample. Write *yes* or *no*. Explain. (Lesson 12-1)

1. Every other shopper coming out of a mall is surveyed to determine how many children they have.
2. Every tenth person in an office is surveyed to determine their feelings about their jobs.
3. Every other student in a high school is asked who their vote for Teacher of the Year is.
4. Henry surveys thirty random friends to determine who should be Homecoming Queen. No; his friends do not represent the entire population.
5. NGSSS PRACTICE Determine which of the following statements show a *causation*. (Lesson 12-1) D
   - A. If you practice every day, you can become a professional basketball player.
   - B. If you read your textbook, you will pass the test.
   - C. If you apply for ten different jobs, you will get an offer from at least one.
   - D. If you stand outside in the rain with no shelter, you will get wet.

6. observational study

State whether each situation represents an *experiment* or an *observational study*. If it is an experiment, identify the *control* group and the *treatment* group. Then determine whether there is bias. (Lesson 12-1)

6. Find 250 students, half of whom are on the honor roll, and compare their study habits.
7. Give a random half of the employees an extra hour lunch break every day and compare their attitudes toward work with their coworkers. See Chapter 12 Answer Appendix.
8. NGSSS PRACTICE Determine which of the following represents a *population*. (Lesson 12-2) G
   - F. Mr. Noble compares 100 random times in the 400 meter run in his gym classes.
   - G. Heather compares the ratings of every quarterback in the NFL.
   - H. Omar completes an online survey regarding the state of education in the United States.
   - I. A national newspaper sends out a survey with every paper asking for public opinion on the upcoming presidential election.

9. Which measure of central tendency best represents the data, and why? (Lesson 12-2) See margin.

Number of Years Playing an Instrument

2	2	3	2	4	1	2
2	3	1	3	4	2	1
3	2	3	2	3	1	4
2	3	4	1	1	1	0
1	2	1	2	2	2	3

10. **SCHOOL CLUBS** The table below shows the number of students who took algebra in eighth grade and the number who took calculus in high school. Use this information to determine the probability of each of the following. (Lesson 12-3)

	Did take calculus	Did not take calculus
Did take algebra	48	42
Did not take algebra	6	144

   a. Lori took calculus given that she took algebra in eighth grade. $\frac{8}{15}$

   b. Kenny did not take algebra in eighth grade given that he did not take calculus. $\frac{24}{31}$

Two dice are rolled. Determine each probability. (Lesson 12-3) 12. $\frac{1}{3}$ or 33% 13. $\frac{1}{2}$ or 50%

11. One of the rolls was odd, given that at least one was a 3. $\frac{1}{2}$ or 50%
12. One of the rolls was a 4, given one was even.
13. Both of the rolls were even, given at least one was a 2.
14. **FOOTBALL** The number of freshmen that make the varsity roster for Eddie's school each year is listed in the table below. Find the number of freshmen expected to make the next varsity roster. (Lesson 12-4) 2.875

Year	Freshmen	Year	Freshmen
2000	4	2004	4
2001	2	2005	2
2002	1	2006	3
2003	5	2007	2

15. **RAFFLES** Sixty students, including Michelle and her 8 friends, entered a raffle for 5 gift certificates. What is the probability that only Michelle or one of her friends wins a gift certificate? (Lesson 12-4) about 41%

Intervention Planner

Tier 1 On Level	Tier 2 Strategic Intervention approaching grade level	Tier 3 Intensive Intervention 2 or more grades below level
If students miss about 25% of the exercises or less,	**If** students miss about 50% of the exercises,	**If** students miss about 75% of the exercises,
Then choose a resource: SE Lessons 12-1, 12-2, 12-3, and 12-4 CRM Skills Practice, pp. 7, 13, 20, and 26 TE Chapter Project, p. 742	**Then** choose a resource: CRM Study Guide and Intervention, Chapter 12, pp. 5, 11, 18, and 24	**Then** use *Math Triumph, Alg. 2*, Ch. 5
FL Math Online Self-Check Quiz	FL Math Online Extra Examples, Personal Tutor, Homework Help	FL Math Online Extra Examples, Personal Tutor, Homework Help, Review Vocabulary

12-5 The Normal Distribution

Why?

The graph lists the Scholastic Assessment Test (SAT) math scores for Ms. Fuentes's students. The data are clustered in the center, and the graph is shaped like a bell. This discrete probability distribution is close to being *normally* distributed.

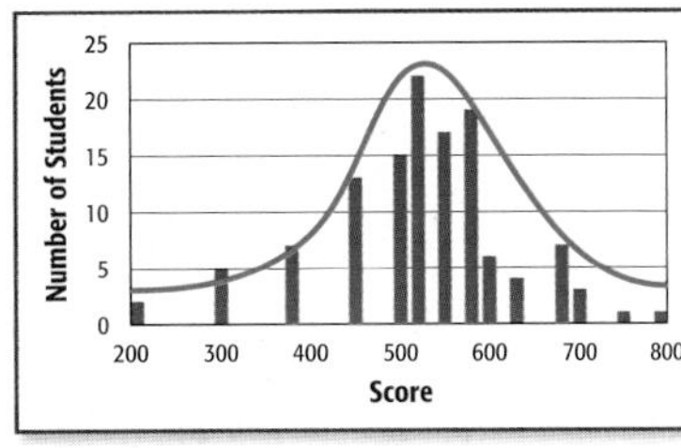

Then
You analyzed probability distributions. (Lesson 12-3)

Now
- Determine whether a set of data appears to be normally distributed or skewed.
- Use the Empirical Rule to find probabilities.

NGSSS
MA.912.P.3.1, MA.912.P.3.2 Determine probabilities of events from distributions, and determine the mean and variance of distributions, including: discrete uniform, binomial, **normal,** and exponential. **MA.912.P.3.3 Apply the properties of the normal distribution.**

New Vocabulary
continuous probability distribution
normal distribution
skewed distribution

FL Math Online
glencoe.com

Normal and Skewed Distributions In a **continuous probability distribution**, the outcome can be any value in an interval of real numbers. A continuous probability distribution is best represented by a curve. The **normal distribution** is the most common example of a continuous probability distribution.

> **Key Concept** Characteristics of the Normal Distribution
>
> - The maximum occurs at the mean. The mean, median, and mode are equal.
> - The distribution can extend from negative infinity to positive infinity, but never touches the x-axis.
> - The population mean μ and standard deviation σ are used to determine probabilities. Probabilities are cumulative and are expressed as inequalities.
> - Because the area under the normal curve represents probabilities, this area is 1.

While the normal distribution is continuous, discrete distributions like the one above can have a *normal* shape. Distributions with other shapes are called **skewed distributions**.

Normal Distribution

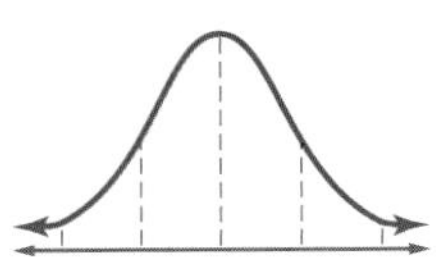

shaped like a bell and symmetric

Positively Skewed

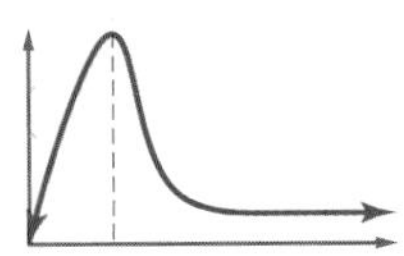

mass of distribution at the left and tail to the right

Negatively Skewed

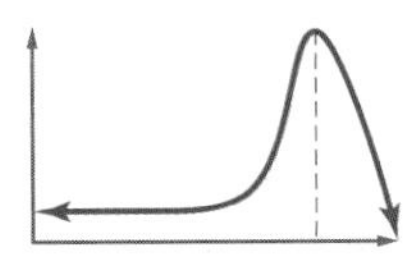

mass of distribution at the right and tail to the left

EXAMPLE 1 Classify a Data Distribution

Determine whether the following data appear to be *positively skewed, negatively skewed,* or *normally distributed.*

a.

10	12	13	15	13	15	15	14	14	16	15	18	16	18	19	16	14	13
16	16	15	14	18	17	11	19	17	18	13	15	14	21	14	15	15	17

Use the frequency table to make a graph. Since the graph is high in the middle and appears to be somewhat symmetric, the data are normally distributed.

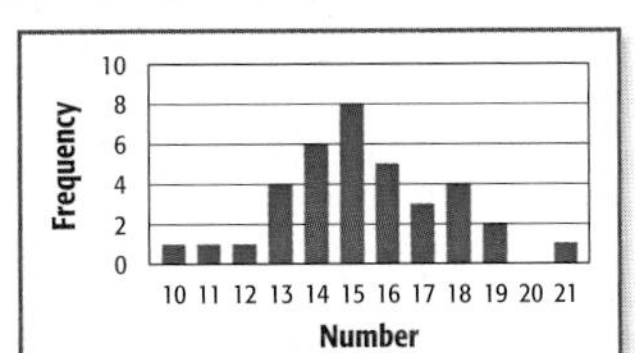

12-5 Lesson Notes

1 FOCUS

Vertical Alignment

Before Lesson 12-5
Analyze probability distributions.

Lesson 12-5
Determine whether a set of data appears to be normally distributed or skewed.
Use the Empirical Rule to find probabilities.

After Lesson 12-5
Find probabilities for binomial experiments.

2 TEACH

Scaffolding Questions

Have students read the *Why?* section of the lesson and answer the questions.

Ask:
- What SAT score is most common for Ms. Fuentes's students? about 520
- What is the range of the scores? about 600
- Why are SAT scores discrete? Only certain whole number values are allowed.

Normal and Skewed Distributions

Example 1 shows how to use a histogram to determine whether a data set is skewed or normally distributed.

Lesson 12-5 Resources

Resource	Approaching-Level	On-Level	Beyond-Level	English Learners
Teacher Edition	• Differentiated Instruction, p. 775	• Differentiated Instruction, p. 775	• Differentiated Instruction, p. 778	
Chapter Resource Masters	• Study Guide and Intervention, pp. 30–31 • Skills Practice, p. 32 • Practice, p. 33 • Word Problem Practice, p. 34	• Study Guide and Intervention, pp. 30–31 • Skills Practice, p. 32 • Practice, p. 33 • Word Problem Practice, p. 34 • Enrichment, p. 35	• Practice, p. 33 • Word Problem Practice, p. 34 • Enrichment, p. 35	• Study Guide and Intervention, pp. 30–31 • Skills Practice, p. 32 • Practice, p. 33 • Word Problem Practice, p. 34
Transparencies	• 5-Minute Check Transparency 12-5	• 5-Minute Check Transparency 12-5	• 5-Minute Check Transparency 12-5	• 5-Minute Check Transparency 12-5
Other	• Study Notebook	• Study Notebook	• Study Notebook	• Study Notebook

b.

24	24	35	33	25	27	26	26	28	30	31	24	28	27	25	26	28	26
25	32	31	35	24	26	27	29	32	34	29	28	27	25	25	26	27	25

Use the frequency table to make a graph. Since the graph is high on the left and low in the middle and right, the data are positively skewed.

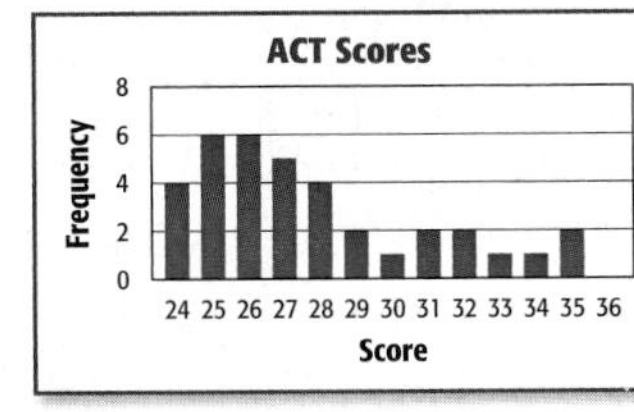

Guided Practice

1. Determine whether the data at the right appear to be *positively skewed*, *negatively skewed*, or *normally distributed*. **positively skewed**

Shoe Size	6	7	8	9	10	11	12
Frequency	4	8	9	7	4	2	3

Personal Tutor glencoe.com

The Empirical Rule The Empirical Rule describes other characteristics of normal distributions.

StudyTip

Discrete vs Continuous A discrete probability distribution can take a discrete number of values that are usually integers. A continuous probability distribution is defined for an infinite number of points over a continuous interval, the probability at a single point is always zero.

Key Concept The Empirical Rule

A normal distribution with mean μ and standard deviation σ has the following properties.

- About 68% of the values are within 1σ of the mean.
- About 95% of the values are within 2σ of the mean.
- About 99% of the values are within 3σ of the mean.

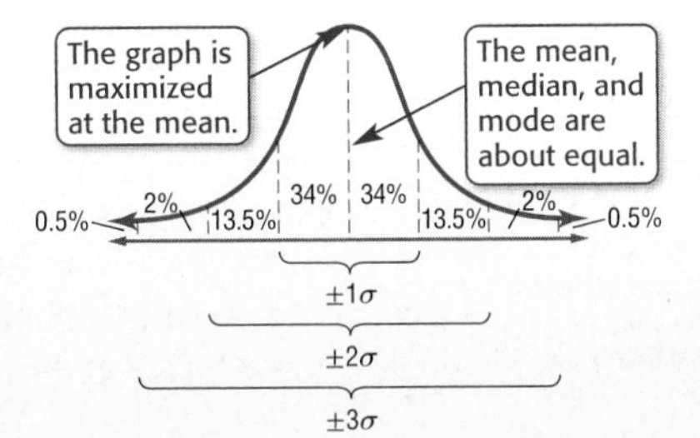

StudyTip

Normal Distributions In all of these cases, the number of data values must be large for the distribution to be approximately normal.

EXAMPLE 2 Normal Distribution

A normal distribution of data has a mean of 34 and standard deviation of 5. Find the probability that random value x is greater than 24, that is, $P(x > 24)$.

$\mu = 34$ and $\sigma = 5$

The probability that a randomly selected value in the distribution is greater than $\mu - 2\sigma$, that is, $34 - 2(5)$ or 24, is the shaded area under the normal curve.

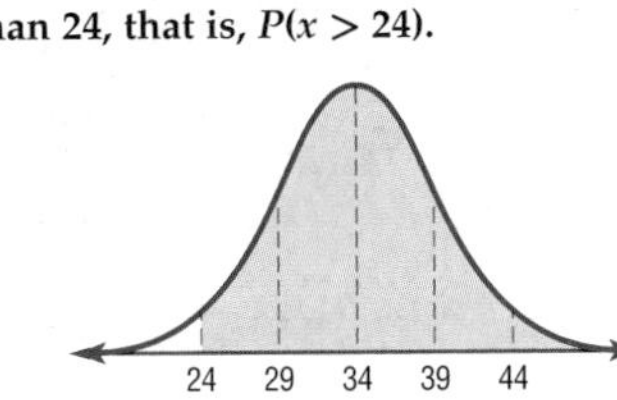

$P(x > 24) = 13.5 + 34 + 34 + 13.5 + 2 + 0.5$
$= 97.5\%$

Guided Practice

2. Find the probability that a randomly selected value in the distribution above is less than 49. **99.5%**

Personal Tutor glencoe.com

Formative Assessment

Use the Guided Practice exercises after each example to determine students' understanding of concepts.

Additional Example

1 Determine whether the following data appear to be *positively skewed, negatively skewed,* or *normally distributed.*

a. 31, 37, 35, 36, 34, 36, 32, 36, 33, 32, 34, 34, 35, 34 normally distributed

b. 14, 15, 11, 13, 13, 14, 15, 14, 12, 13, 14, 15 negatively skewed

Additional Examples also in Interactive Classroom PowerPoint® Presentations

IWB INTERACTIVE WHITEBOARD READY

The Empirical Rule

Examples 2 and 3 show how to use the Empirical Rule to find probabilities for a random value in a normal distribution.

Additional Example

2 A normal distribution of data has a mean of 66 and standard deviation of 11. Find the probability that random value x is less than 44, that is $P(x < 44)$. 2.5%

TEACH with TECH

INSTANT MESSAGING Have students work in pairs and send each other questions about a normal distribution (for example: "What percent of the values are within 2 standard deviations above the mean?"). Students should reply with the answers and check each others' work.

Focus on Mathematical Content

Normal Distributions The graphs of all normally distributed variables have essentially the same shape. With appropriate labeling of the mean and the points that are one standard deviation from the mean, the same normal curve can represent any normal distribution.

774 Chapter 12 Probability and Statistics

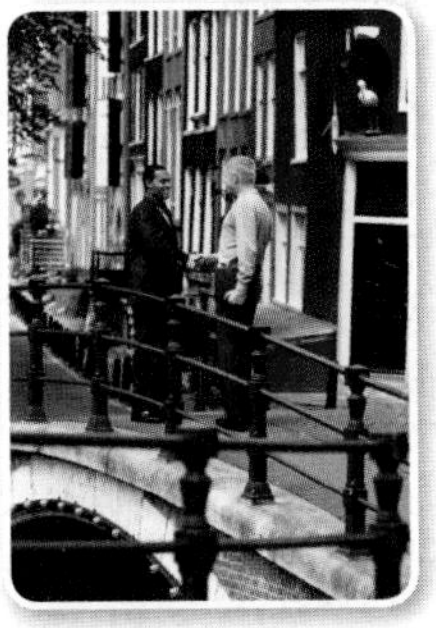

Real-World Link

While the average adult American male is 5 feet 10 inches, the average height of adult males in the Netherlands is the highest worldwide, at almost 6 feet 1 inch.

Source: *Eurostats Statistical Yearbook*

A sample that is normally distributed can be represented by the normal curve as if it were a population.

Real-World EXAMPLE 3 Normally Distributed Sample

HEIGHTS The heights of 1800 teenagers are normally distributed with a mean of 66 inches and a standard deviation of 2 inches.

a. About how many teens are between 62 and 70 inches?

Draw a normal curve.

62 and 70 are 2σ away from the mean. Therefore, about 95% of the data are between 62 and 70.

Since $1800 \times 95\% = 1710$, we know that about 1710 of the teenagers are between 62 and 70 inches tall.

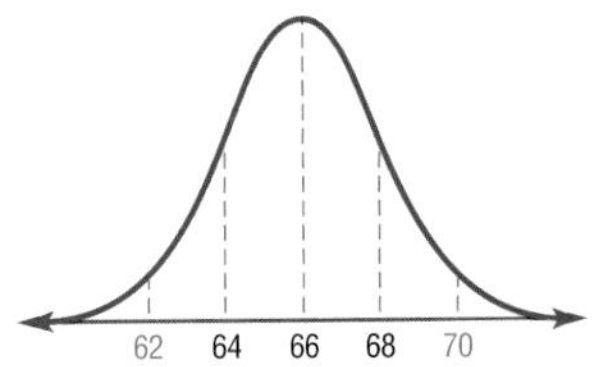

b. What is the probability that a teenager selected at random has a height greater than 68 inches?

From the curve, values greater than 68 are more than 1σ from the mean. 13.5% are between 1σ and 2σ, 2% are between 2σ and 3σ, and 0.5% are greater than 3σ.

So, the probability that a teenager selected at random has a height greater than 68 inches is $13.5 + 2 + 0.5$ or 16%.

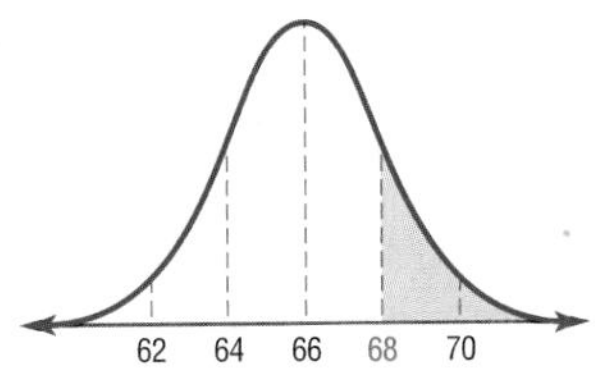

Guided Practice

GRADES The grade-point averages of 1200 students at East High School are normally distributed with a mean of 2.6 and a standard deviation of 0.6.

3A. About how many students have a grade-point average between 2.0 and 3.2? **816**

3B. What is the probability that a randomly selected student has an average less than 3.8? **97.5%**

Personal Tutor glencoe.com

Check Your Understanding

Example 1 pp. 773–774

1. ACT The table at the right shows recent composite ACT scores. Determine whether the data appear to be *positively skewed*, *negatively skewed*, or *normally distributed*. **positively skewed**

Score	% of Students
33–36	1
28–32	9
24–27	19
20–23	29
16–19	27
13–15	12

Source: ACT, Inc.

Example 2 p. 774

2. A normal distribution of data has a mean of 161 and standard deviation of 12. Find the probability that random value x is less than 149, that is $P(x < 149)$. **16%**

Example 3 p. 775

3. SCHOOL Mr. Bash gave a quiz in his social studies class. The scores were normally distributed with a mean of 21 and a standard deviation of 2.

a. What percent would you expect to score between 19 and 23? **68%**

b. What percent would you expect to score between 23 and 25? **13.5%**

c. What is the probability that a student scored between 17 and 25? **95%**

Additional Example

3 **PACKAGING** Students counted the number of candies in 100 small packages. They found that the number of candies per package was normally distributed, with a mean of 23 candies per package and a standard deviation of 1 piece of candy.

a. About how many packages have between 22 and 24 candies? about 68 packages

b. What is the probability that a package selected at random has more than 25 candies? about 2.5%

3 PRACTICE

Formative Assessment

Use Exercises 1–3 to check for understanding.

Use the chart at the bottom of the next page to customize assignments for your students.

Tips for New Teachers

Sense-Making Show students that the skewness of a distribution of data indicates the direction of the tail of the distribution. For example, a positively skewed distribution has a *tail* that extends to the right, therefore the distribution is skewed to the right.

Differentiated Instruction

AL OL

If students need an aid in drawing a normal curve,

Then it may be useful to know that the concave side of the curve switches from facing downward to facing upward at points that are one standard deviation from the mean. Drawing a normal curve for each problem can help students with their estimates.

Watch Out!

Error Analysis In Exercise 16, remind students that 68% of any normal distribution is within one standard deviation of the mean.

Additional Answers

14c. Sample answer: I would expect people with several traffic citations to lie to the far right of the distribution where insurance costs are highest, because I think insurance companies would charge them more.

14d. Sample answer: I think auto insurance companies would charge younger people more than older people because they have not been driving as long. I think they would charge more for expensive cars and sports cars and less for cars that have good safety ratings. I think they would charge a person less if they have a good driving record and more if they have had tickets and accidents.

18. Sample answer: When the data set includes the height of everyone in an elementary school, most of the data will be on the left side (the students), while a comparatively small amount will be on the right (the teachers and staff). This is a positively skewed distribution. When the batting averages of a baseball lineup are listed, most of the data will be at a certain level while the pitcher will typically be much lower. This is a negatively skewed distribution. When test scores are calculated for an entire state, most of the students will place in the middle, while some will place above or below. This is a normal distribution.

Practice and Problem Solving

● = **Step-by-Step Solutions** begin on page R20.
Extra Practice begins on page 947.

Example 1 pp. 773–774

Determine whether the data appear to be *positively skewed*, *negatively skewed*, or *normally distributed*.

4.

20 Most Visited National Parks	
Visitors (millions)	**Number of Parks**
3–4	10
4–5	2
5–6	2
6–7	1
7–8	1
8+	4

positively skewed

5.

Tallest Buildings in the World	
Stories	**Number of Buildings**
0–39	1
40–59	11
60–79	35
80–99	9
100+	6

normally distributed

Example 2 p. 774

A normal distribution of data has each mean and standard deviation. Find each probability.

6. $\mu = 74, \sigma = 6, P(x > 86)$ **2.5%**

7. $\mu = 13, \sigma = 0.4, P(x < 12.6)$ **16%**

8. $\mu = 63, \sigma = 4, P(59 < x < 71)$ **81.5%**

9. $\mu = 91, \sigma = 6, P(73 < x < 103)$ **97%**

Example 3 p. 775

10. CAR BATTERIES The useful life of a certain car battery is normally distributed with a mean of 100,000 miles and a standard deviation of 10,000 miles. The company makes 20,000 batteries a month.

a. About how many batteries will last between 90,000 and 110,000 miles? **13,600**

b. About how many batteries will last more than 120,000 miles? **500**

c. About how many batteries will last less than 90,000 miles? **3200**

d. What is the probability that if you buy a car battery at random, it will last between 80,000 and 110,000 miles? **81.5%**

Real-World Link

Car batteries typically last between 5 and 7 years.

Source: National Tire and Battery

B

11. HEALTH The cholesterol level for adult males of a specific racial group is normally distributed with a mean of 158.3 and a standard deviation of 6.6.

a. About what percent of the males have cholesterol below 151.7? **16%**

b. How many of the 900 men in a study have cholesterol between 145.1 and 171.5? **855**

12. FOOD The shelf life of a particular snack chip is normally distributed with a mean of 180 days and a standard deviation of 30 days.

a. About what percent of the product lasts between 150 and 210 days? **68%**

b. About what percent of the product lasts between 180 and 210 days? **34%**

c. About what percent of the product lasts less than 90 days? **0.5%**

d. About what percent of the product lasts more than 210 days? **16%**

13. VENDING A vending machine dispenses about 8 ounces of coffee. The amount varies and is normally distributed with a standard deviation of 0.3 ounce.

a. What percent of the time will you get more than 8 ounces of coffee? **50%**

b. What percent of the time will you get less than 8 ounces of coffee? **50%**

c. What percent of the time will you get between 7.4 and 8.6 ounces of coffee? **95%**

Differentiated Homework Options

Level	Assignment	Two-Day Option	
AL Basic	4–11, 16, 18–36	5–11 odd, 23–26	4–10 even, 16, 18–36
OL Core	5–11 odd, 12–16, 18–36	4–11, 23–26	12–16, 18–22, 27–36
BL Advanced	12–32, (optional: 33–36)		

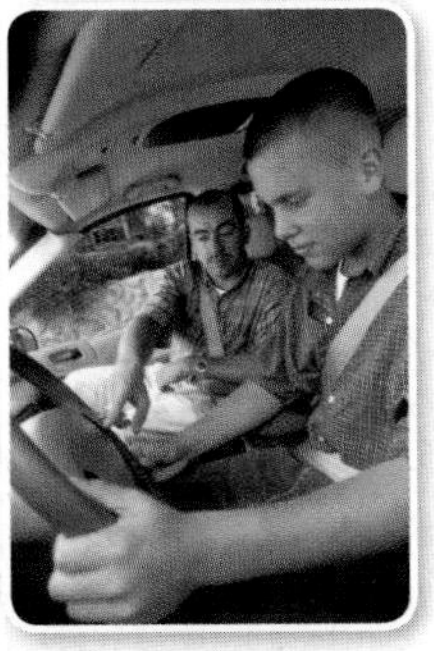

Real-World Link

Insurance rates for teenagers are affected by the type of car that is driven, the driving history, and the grades of the student.

Source: Esurance

14a. between $714 and $944

14. FINANCIAL LITERACY The insurance industry uses various factors including age, type of car driven, and driving record to determine an individual's insurance rate. Suppose insurance rates for a sample population are normally distributed. **c, d. See margin.**

a. If the mean annual cost per person is $829 and the standard deviation is $115, what is the range of rates you would expect 68% of the population to pay annually?

b. If 900 people were sampled, how many would you expect to pay more than $1059 annually? **22 or 23**

c. Where on the distribution would you expect a person with several traffic citations to lie? Explain your reasoning.

d. How do you think auto insurance companies use each factor to calculate risk?

15. RAINFALL Use the table at the right.

a. Find the mean. **12.17 in.**

b. Find the standard deviation. **4.81**

c. If the data are normally distributed, what percent of the time will annual precipitation in these cities be between 7.36 and 16.98 inches? **68%**

Average Annual Precipitation

City	Precipitation (in.)
Albuquerque	9
Boise	12
Phoenix	8
Reno	7
Salt Lake City	17
San Francisco	20

Problem-Solving Tip

Use a Graph You can use a graph to visualize data, analyze trends, and make predictions.

H.O.T. Problems

Use **H**igher-**O**rder **T**hinking Skills

16. ERROR ANALYSIS A set of normally distributed tree diameters have mean 11.5 cm, standard deviation 2.5, and range 3.6 to 19.8. Monica and Hiroko are to find the range that represents the middle 68% of the data. Is either of them correct? Explain.

Monica	Hiroko
The data span 16.2 cm. 68% of 16.2 is about 11 cm. Center this 11-cm range around the mean of 11.5 cm. This 68% group will range from about 6 cm to about 17 cm.	The middle 68% span from $\mu + \sigma$ to $\mu - \sigma$. So we move 2.5 cm below 11.5 and then 2.5 cm above 11.5. The 68% group will range from 9 cm to 14 cm.

17. CHALLENGE A case of digital audio players has an average battery life of 8.0 hours with a standard deviation of 0.7 hour. Eight of the players have a battery life greater than 10.1 hours. If the sample is normally distributed, how many players are in the case? **1600**

18. WRITING IN MATH Explain the difference between *positively skewed*, *negatively skewed*, and *normally distributed* sets of data and describe an example of each. **See margin.**

19. REASONING *True* or *false*: *According to the Empirical Rule, in a normal distribution, most of the data will fall within one standard deviation of the mean.* Explain.

20. OPEN ENDED Find a real-world data set that appears to represent a normal distribution. Describe the characteristics of the distribution, including its mean and standard deviation. Create a visual representation of the data.

21. OPEN ENDED Provide examples of a discrete probability distribution and a continuous probability distribution. Describe the differences between them.

22. REASONING The term *six sigma process* comes from the notion that if one has six standard deviations between the mean of a process and the nearest specification limit, there will be practically no items that fail to meet the specifications. Is this a true assumption? Explain. **See margin.**

16. Hiroko; Monica's solution would work with a uniform distribution.

19. Sample answer: True; according to the Empirical Rule, 68% of the data lie within 1 standard deviation of the mean.

20. See Chapter 12 Answer Appendix.

21. Sample answer: A discrete probability distribution can be the uniform distribution of the roll of a die. In this type of distribution, there are only a finite number of possibilities. A continuous probability distribution can be the distribution of the lives of 400 batteries. In this distribution, there are an infinite number of possibilities.

Additional Answer

22. Sample answer: True; according to the Empirical Rule, 99% of the data lie within 3 standard deviations of the mean. Therefore, only 1% will fall outside of three-sigma. An infinitesimally small amount will fall outside of six-sigma.

Enrichment

CRM p. 35 OL BL

12-5 Enrichment

Calculating Z-Scores

The normal distribution is the most important probability distribution. Many physical measurements have distributions approximately normal. Examples include height, weight, and measures of intelligence. More importantly, even if the individual variables are not normally distributed, sums and averages tend to still be normally distributed. Unfortunately, normal probability distribution functions are difficult to calculate. Fortunately, statisticians have compiled a table for a normal distribution with mean of zero and standard deviation of one. This is called the Standard Normal Distribution and is typically denoted by N(0, 1), where the N indicates a normal distribution which has mean, μ (mu) = 0, and standard deviation, σ (sigma) = 1.

Suppose the variable x is normally distributed with mean μ and standard deviation σ. In order to calculate probabilities of this normal distribution, we must standardize the variable x by an appropriate transformation. The letter Z denotes the transformed variable and is called the Z–score, which is a measure of relative standing. The following steps are needed to complete the transformation.

- If the mean and standard deviation are not given, then calculate the mean and standard deviation of the given (population) data.
- Define $Z = \frac{x - \mu}{\sigma}$.

Example 1 Find the standard normal variable Z given and $\mu = 15$ and $\sigma = 3$.
Apply the transform to the variable X using the definition above, that is: $Z = \frac{X - 15}{3}$.

Study Guide and Intervention

CRM pp. 30–31 AL OL ELL

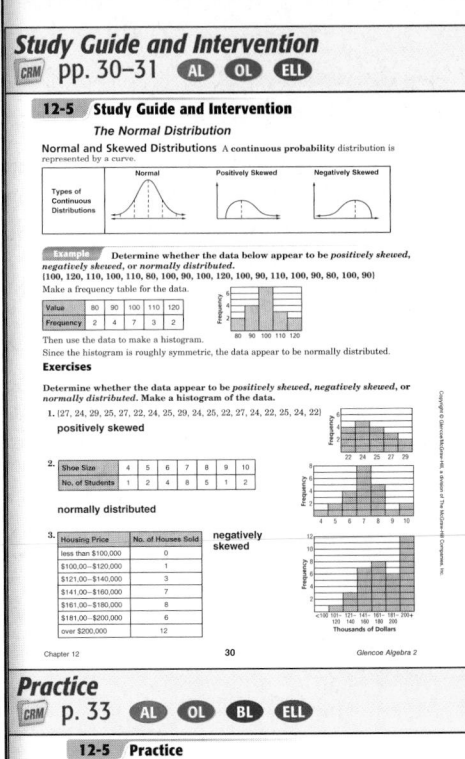

12-5 Study Guide and Intervention

The Normal Distribution

Normal and Skewed Distributions A **continuous probability** distribution is represented by a curve.

Types of Continuous Distributions

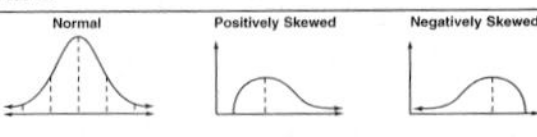

Example **Determine whether the data below appear to be *positively skewed, negatively skewed,* or *normally distributed.***
{100, 120, 110, 100, 110, 80, 100, 90, 100, 120, 100, 90, 110, 100, 90, 80, 100, 90}

Make a frequency table for the data.

Value	80	90	100	110	120
Frequency	2	4	7	3	2

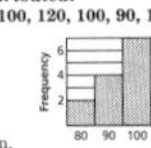

Then use the data to make a histogram.
Since the histogram is roughly symmetric, the data appear to be normally distributed.

Exercises

Determine whether the data appear to be *positively skewed, negatively skewed,* or *normally distributed.* Make a histogram of the data.

1. {27, 24, 29, 25, 27, 22, 24, 25, 29, 24, 25, 22, 27, 24, 22, 25, 24, 22}
positively skewed

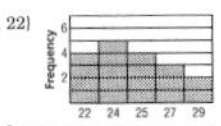

2.

Shoe Size	4	5	6	7	8	9	10
No. of Students	1	2	4	8	5	1	2

normally distributed

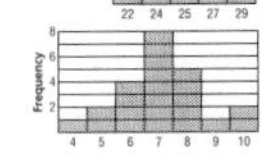

3.

Housing Price	No. of Houses Sold
less than $100,000	0
$100,00–$120,000	1
$121,00–$140,000	3
$141,00–$160,000	7
$161,00–$180,000	8
$181,00–$200,000	6
over $200,000	12

negatively skewed

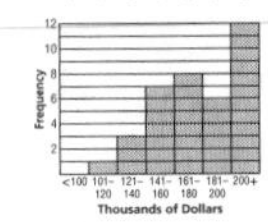

Chapter 12 30 Glencoe Algebra 2

Practice

CRM p. 33 AL OL BL ELL

12-5 Practice

The Normal Distribution

Determine whether the data appear to be *positively skewed, negatively skewed,* or *normally distributed.*

1. Time Spent at a Museum Exhibit

Minutes	Frequency
0–25	27
26–50	46
51–75	89
75–100	57
1001	24

normally distributed

2. Average Age of High School Principals

Age in Years	Number
31–35	3
36–40	8
41–45	15
46–50	32
51–55	40
56–60	38
60+	4

negatively skewed

3. **STUDENTS** The frequency table to the right shows the number of hours worked per week by 100 high school students.

Hours	Number of Students
0–8	30
9–17	45
18–25	20
26+	5

a. What percentage of the students worked between 9 and 17 days? **45%**

b. Do the data appear to be *positively skewed, negatively skewed,* or *normally distributed*? Explain.
Positively skewed; the histogram is high at the left and has a tail to the right.

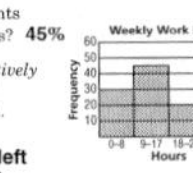

4. **TESTING** The scores on a test administered to prospective employees are normally distributed with a mean of 100 and a standard deviation of 15.

a. About what percent of the scores are between 70 and 130? **95%**

b. About what percent of the scores are between 85 and 130? **81.5%**

c. About what percent of the scores are over 115? **16%**

d. About what percent of the scores are lower than 85 or higher than 115? **32%**

e. If 80 people take the test, how many would you expect to score higher than 130? **2**

f. If 75 people take the test, how many would you expect to score lower than 85? **12**

5. **TEMPERATURE** The daily July surface temperature of a lake at a resort has a mean of 82° and a standard deviation of 4.2°. If you prefer to swim when the temperature is at least 77.8°, about what percent of the days does the temperature meet your preference? **84%**

Chapter 12 33 Glencoe Algebra 2

Lesson 12-5

Word Problem Practice

CRM p. 34 AL OL BL ELL

12-5 Word Problem Practice

The Normal Distribution

1. **PARKING** Over several years, Bertram conducted a study of how far into parking spaces people tend to park by measuring the distance from the end of a parking space to the front fender of a car parked in the space. He discovered that the distribution of the data closely approximated a normal distribution with mean 8.5 inches. He found that about 5% of cars parked more than 11.5 inches away from the end of the parking space. What percentage of cars would you expect parked less than 5.5 inches away from the end of the parking space?
5%

2. **HEIGHT** Chandra's graph of the number of tenth grade students of different heights is shown below.

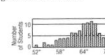

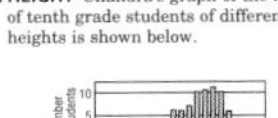

Is the data positively skewed, negatively skewed, or normally distributed?
Negatively skewed

3. **OVENS** An oven manufacturer tries to make the temperature setting on its ovens as accurate as possible. However, if one measures the actual temperatures in the ovens when the temperature setting is 350°F, they will differ slightly from 350°F. The set of actual temperatures for all the ovens is normally distributed around 350°F with a standard deviation of 0.5°F. About what percentage of ovens will be between 350°F and 351°F when their temperature setting is 350°F?
47.5%

4. **LIGHT BULBS** The time that a certain brand of light bulb will last before burning out is normally distributed. About 2.5% of the bulbs last longer than 6800 hours and about 16% of the bulbs last longer than 6500 hours. How long does the average bulb last?
6200 hours

5. **DOGS** The weights of adult male greyhound dogs are normally distributed. The mean weight is about 68 pounds and the standard deviation is about 10 pounds.

a. Approximately what percentage of adult male greyhound dogs would you expect weigh between 58 and 78 pounds?
68%

b. Approximately what percentage of adult male greyhound dogs would you expect weigh more than 98 pounds?
0.5%

c. Approximately what percentage of adult male greyhound dogs would you expect weigh less than 48 pounds?
2.5%

d. What would you expect an adult male greyhound dog to weigh if it weighed less than 0.5% of an average adult greyhound?
39 lbs or less.

Chapter 12 34 Glencoe Algebra 2

Lesson 12-5 The Normal Distribution 777

4 ASSESS

Ticket Out the Door Have students draw sketches of normal distributions, distributions that are skewed to the left, and distributions that are skewed to the right.

NGSSS PRACTICE 912.P.3.3, 912.D.11.3

23. The lifetimes of 10,000 light bulbs are normally distributed. The mean lifetime is 300 days, and the standard deviation is 40 days. How many light bulbs will last between 260 and 340 days? **D**

A. 2500 C. 5000
B. 3400 D. 6800

24. Which description best represents the graph? **J**

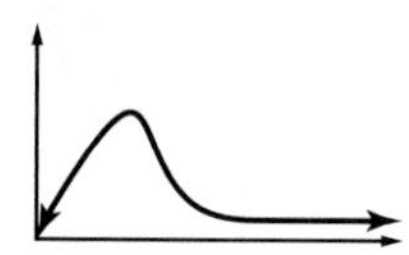

F. negatively skewed H. normal distribution
G. no correlation J. positively skewed

25. THINK SOLVE EXPLAIN **SHORT RESPONSE** In the figure below, $RT = TS$ and $QR = QT$. What is the value of x? **32.5**

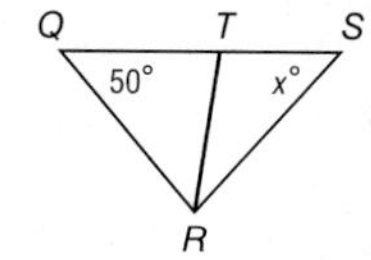

26. SAT/ACT The integer 99 can be expressed as a sum of n consecutive positive integers. The value of n could be which of the following? **D**

I. 2
II. 3
III. 6

A. I only C. I and II only
B. II only D. I, II, and III

Spiral Review

27. DOGS Three spaniels and eleven retrievers have been nominated for 4 spots to visit people at a hospital. If the winners are drawn at random, what is the probability that 2 spaniels and 2 retrievers are selected? (Lesson 12-4) **16.5%**

28. GAMES To begin a game, Kaylee, Abbey, and Brent agree to roll two dice and the player who rolls the greatest sum will go first. Kaylee rolled a sum of 5 and Abbey rolled a sum of 7. Assuming there is no tie, what is the probability that Brent will go first? (Lesson 12-3) $\frac{15}{36}$

29. BRIDGES The Bayonne Bridge connects Staten Island, New York, to New Jersey. It has an arch in the shape of a parabola that opens downward. Write an equation of a parabola to model the arch, assuming that the origin is at the surface of the water, beneath the vertex of the arch. (Lesson 10-2) **about $y = -0.00046x^2 + 325$**

Identify the type of function represented by each graph. (Lesson 2-7)

30. 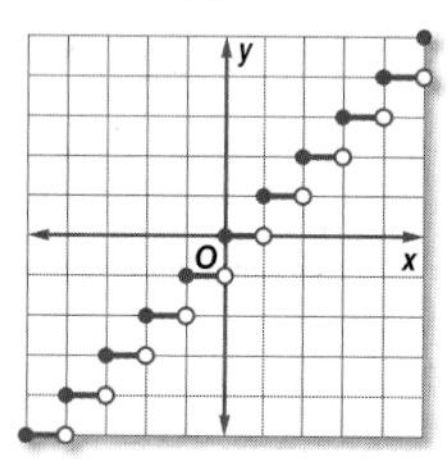

greatest integer

31. 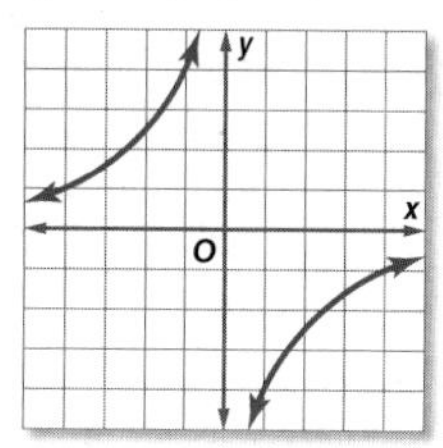

inverse variation or rational

32. 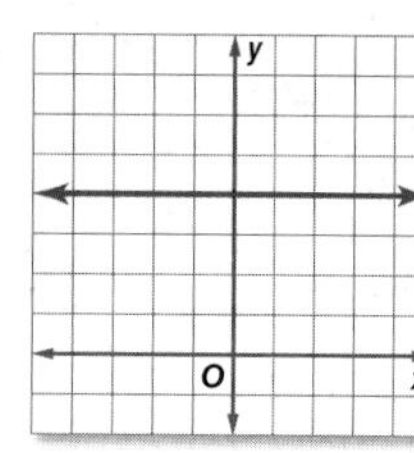

constant

Skills Review

Find the standard deviation for each sample set of data. (Lesson 12-2)

33. {3, 11, 27, 14, 18, 19, 2, 33, 16, 12} **9.6**

34. {45, 47, 49, 49, 51, 53, 46, 47, 50, 48} **2.4**

35. {320, 400, 350, 410, 380, 390, 330, 400, 370, 360} **30.7**

36. {505, 527, 512, 517, 509, 513, 522, 520, 516, 511} **6.6**

Differentiated Instruction

BL

Extension Write the formula $z = \frac{x - \mu}{\sigma}$ on the board, and explain that μ = population mean, σ = standard deviation, x = value of a normally distributed variable, and z = standard normal variable. Ask students to find a z-value for two reaction times of 0.32 seconds and 0.38 seconds in a situation where the reaction times are normally distributed, $\mu = 0.35$ s and $\sigma = 0.05$ s. −0.6, +0.6 Then use a graphing calculator and the z-values for 0.32 and 0.38 seconds to evaluate **normalcdf (−.6, .6)**, to get the percent of teens having reaction times in the interval (0.32 s, 0.38 s). about 45% In a similar way, probabilities for *any* two values of x can be determined, not just those that are an integral number of standard deviations from the mean.

EXTEND 12-5

Algebra Lab: The Empirical Rule and Percentiles

NGSSS MA.912.S.3.6 Use empirical rules to estimate spread of distributions and to make comparisons among sets of data.

If you know the mean and standard deviation of a normal distribution, you know that about 68%, 95%, and 99% of the data are within 1, 2, and 3 standard deviations of the mean, respectively. This is called the **Empirical Rule**. You can use the Empirical Rule to report percentiles. A **percentile** describes what percent of the data were at or below a given level.

Here is some additional information about percentiles.

- Percentiles measure rank from the bottom.
- There is no 0 percentile rank. The lowest score is at the 1st percentile.
- There is no 100th percentile rank. The highest score is at the 99th percentile.

ACTIVITY

A county-wide math contest was held for students in grades 9–12. Participants took at least three different tests during the competition. For the Problem-Solving Test, the scores were normally distributed with a mean of 30 and a standard deviation of 5.

Step 1 Draw a normal curve for the Problem-Solving Test scores, similar to the one shown at the right. Label the mean and the mean plus or minus multiples of the standard deviation. Label the percents as shown.

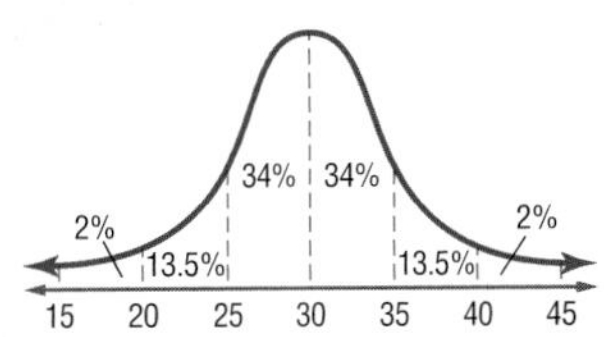

Step 2 The score of 30 is the mean. Looking at the diagram you can see that 50% of the scores are at or below the score of 30. You can say that a score of 30 is at the 50th percentile. What percent of the total scores was at or below a score of 25? **This means that a score of 25 is at the 15.5th percentile.**

Step 3 What percent of the total scores was at or below a score of 40? **This means that a score of 40 is at the 97th percentile.**

Step 4 What score is at the 99th percentile? **45**
What score is at the 0th percentile? **No score, because there is no 0th percentile.**

Exercises 1, 2. See margin.

Make a drawing similar to the drawing in Step 1. Then find the percentiles or scores.

1. For the geometry test, the scores were normally distributed with a mean of 15 and a standard deviation of 2. Find the percentiles for the following scores: 21, 15, 13, 9.
2. For the chemistry test, the scores were normally distributed with a mean of 40 and a standard deviation of 4. Find the scores for the following percentiles: 99th, 2nd, 50th, 84th.

EXTEND 12-5

Lesson Notes

1 FOCUS

Objective Use the Empirical Rule to associate percentiles with a normal distribution.

Teaching Tip

Remind students that in Lesson 12-5 they learned that 0.5% of a normal distribution is more than 3 standard deviations above or below the mean.

2 TEACH

Working in Cooperative Groups

Have students work in pairs, mixing abilities, to complete the Activity.

Ask:

- At what percentile is the median of a normally distributed variable? 50th
- What can you say about the percentile for a test score of 37? It is between the 84th and the 97th percentile.

Practice Have students complete Exercises 1 and 2.

Additional Answers

1.

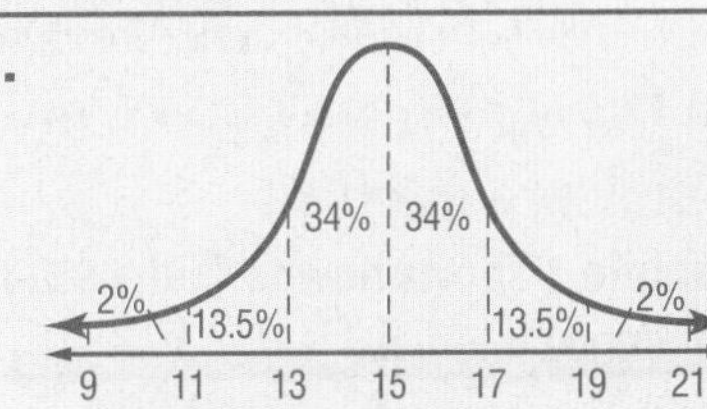

21 is at the 99th percentile; 15 is at the 50th percentile; 13 is at the 15.5 or about 16th percentile; 9 is at the 1st percentile.

2.

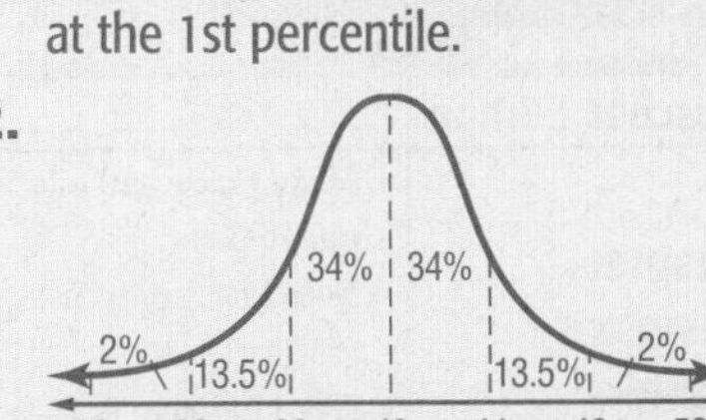

The 99th percentile is a score of 52; the 1st percentile is a score of 28; the 50th percentile is a score of 40; the 84th percentile is a score of about 44.

3 ASSESS

Formative Assessment

Use Exercise 1 to assess whether students can assign percentiles to values located at 0, 1, 2, or 3 standard deviations from the mean.

From Concrete to Abstract

Why is there no 100th percentile rank?
Sample answer: There is no theoretical upper limit for a normal distribution.

Extending the Concept

For other than normal distributions, would the 50th percentile be the same as the mean?

No, but the 50th percentile would be the median.

Extend 12-5 Algebra Lab: The Empirical Rule and Percentiles 779

12-6 Lesson Notes

1 FOCUS

Vertical Alignment

Before Lesson 12-6
Find standard deviations.

Lesson 12-6
Compare sample statistics and population statistics.
Design experiments to test hypotheses.

After Lesson 12-6
Draw conclusions about populations based on sample statistics.

2 TEACH

Scaffolding Questions

Have students read the *Why?* section of the lesson.

Ask:

- What part of the disclaimer mentions a probability? 95% confidence
- What does the word *confidence* mean? Sample answer: trust
- What is the answer to the question *To what are they referring?* They are referring to the accuracy of the survey. 92%–98% of all teens would respond in the same way as those surveyed.

Confidence Intervals

Example 1 shows how to find a 95% confidence interval.

12-6 Hypothesis Testing

Then
You found standard deviations. (Lesson 12-2)

Now
- Compare sample statistics and population statistics.
- Design experiments to test hypotheses.

NGSSS
MA.912.S.5.2 Apply the general principles of hypothesis testing.
MA.912.S.5.3 Explain and identify the following: null hypothesis, alternative hypotheses.

New Vocabulary
inferential statistics
statistical inference
confidence interval
hypothesis
null hypothesis
alternative hypothesis

FL Math Online
glencoe.com

Why?

In a recent Gallup Poll published by *USA TODAY*, 1014 teens were surveyed. The end of the poll had the following disclaimer: "For results based on the total sample of national teens, one can say with 95% confidence that the margin of sampling error is ±3 percentage points." To what are they referring?

Confidence Interval While a distribution can provide general data about populations, it cannot give you any specifics. You can use **inferential statistics** to draw conclusions about a population by using a sample. When you use information from a sample to draw conclusions about the entire population, you are making a **statistical inference**.

To account for differences between sample statistics and population parameters, you can use an estimate. A **confidence interval** is an estimate of a population parameter stated as a range with a specific degree of certainty. Typically, statisticians use 90%, 95%, and 99% confidence intervals, but any other percentage can be considered. The most often used interval is 95%.

Key Concept **95% Confidence Interval Formula**

A 95% confidence interval estimate can be found by using the formula $CI = \bar{x} \pm 1.96 \cdot \frac{s}{\sqrt{n}}$, where $\bar{x}$ is the mean of the sample, s is the standard deviation of the sample, and n is the size of the sample.

These intervals are an estimation of the mean of the population, μ.

Real-World EXAMPLE 1 Find Confidence Intervals

SCHOOL WORK A sample of 200 students was asked for the average amount of time they spend on their homework during a week night. The mean time was 52.5 minutes with a standard deviation of 5.1 minutes. Determine a 95% confidence interval.

$CI = \bar{x} \pm 1.96 \cdot \frac{s}{\sqrt{n}}$ — **Confidence Interval Formula**

$= 52.5 \pm 1.96 \cdot \frac{5.1}{\sqrt{200}}$ — **$\bar{x} = 52.5$, $s = 5.1$, and $n = 200$**

$\approx 52.5 \pm 0.71$ — **Use a calculator.**

The 95% confidence interval is $51.79 \le \mu \le 53.21$.

Guided Practice **1. $46.9 \le \bar{x} \le 49.7$**

1. Find a 95% confidence interval for $\bar{x} = 48.3$, $s = 6.4$, and $n = 80$.

Personal Tutor glencoe.com

Lesson 12-6 Resources

Resource	Approaching-Level	On-Level	Beyond-Level	English Learners
Teacher Edition		• Differentiated Instruction, p. 781	• Differentiated Instruction, p. 784	• Differentiated Instruction, p. 781
Chapter Resource Masters	• Study Guide and Intervention, pp. 36–37 • Skills Practice, p. 38 • Practice, p. 39 • Word Problem Practice, p. 40	• Study Guide and Intervention, pp. 36–37 • Skills Practice, p. 38 • Practice, p. 39 • Word Problem Practice, p. 40 • Enrichment, p. 41 • Graphing Calculator, p. 42	• Practice, p. 39 • Word Problem Practice, p. 40 • Enrichment, p. 41	• Study Guide and Intervention, pp. 36–37 • Skills Practice, p. 38 • Practice, p. 39 • Word Problem Practice, p. 40
Transparencies	• 5-Minute Check Transparency 12-6	• 5-Minute Check Transparency 12-6	• 5-Minute Check Transparency 12-6	• 5-Minute Check Transparency 12-6
Other	• Study Notebook	• Study Notebook	• Study Notebook	• Study Notebook

Hypothesis Testing A hypothesis is an assumption that can be verified by testing. A specific hypothesis to be tested is called the **null hypothesis** H_0 (read *H null*). It is expressed as an equality and is considered true until evidence indicates otherwise.

If you conclude that the null hypothesis is false, then the alternative hypothesis must be true. The **alternative hypothesis** H_1 is mutually exclusive to the null hypothesis. It is stated as an inequality using $<$, $\leq$, $\neq$, $\geq$, or $>$. The alternative hypothesis represents the conclusion reached by rejecting the null hypothesis. Use these steps to test a hypothesis.

Key Concept **Hypothesis Testing**

Step 1 State the null hypothesis H_0 and the alternative hypothesis H_1.

Step 2 Design the experiment.

Step 3 Conduct the experiment and collect the data.

Step 4 Find the confidence interval.

Step 5 Make the correct statistical inference. Accept the null hypothesis if the population parameter falls into the confidence interval.

StudyTip

Randomness and Inferential Statistics On any single observation, every outcome that is possible is equally likely to occur, but in the long run, predictable patterns of responses will emerge. This is the basis for inferential statistics.

Real-World EXAMPLE 2 Hypothesis Test

STUDENT COUNCIL Lindsey, the president of the junior class, has heard complaints that the cafeteria lunch line moves too slowly. The dining services coordinator assures her that the average wait time is 6 minutes. The students think it is much longer. Test the hypothesis that the average wait time is 6 minutes.

Step 1 State the hypotheses: H_0: $\mu = 6$ and H_1: $\mu > 6$.

Step 2 Design the experiment.
Lindsey will collect data and decide whether the data provide evidence for or against the null hypothesis. The results must differ enough from the null hypothesis to reject it, so Libby will use a 95% confidence level.

Step 3 Conduct the experiment and collect the data.
Lindsey selected a random sample of 40 students and measured their wait times. She found that $\bar{x} = 7.3$ and $s = 2.821$.

Step 4 Find the confidence interval.

$CI = \bar{x} \pm 1.96 \cdot \frac{s}{\sqrt{n}}$ **Confidence Interval Formula**

$= 7.3 \pm 1.96 \cdot \frac{2.821}{\sqrt{40}}$ **$n = 40$, $\bar{x} = 7.3$, and $s = 2.821$**

≈ 6.426 or 8.174 **Use a calculator.**

This means that 95% of the time, the experiment will produce a mean between 6.426 and 8.174.

Step 5 Make the correct statistical inference.
The 95% confidence interval does not include H_0, so Lindsey can reject the null hypothesis. She can assume that the average wait time is longer than 6 minutes.

StudyTip

95% Confidence 95% confidence implies that for samples of the same size, approximately 95% of those samples will generate a confidence interval that captures the true mean.

Guided Practice 2. $2.8 \leq \bar{x} \leq 3.6$; $H_0 = 2$ is rejected and $H_1 > 2$ is accepted.

2. FIRE DRILLS Ms. Guzman was told that it takes an average of 2 minutes to evacuate the building during a fire drill. She believes it takes longer. After collecting data for 20 fire drills, she arrives at a mean of 3.2 minutes and a standard deviation of 0.9 minute. Test the hypothesis that the average length of time is greater than 2 minutes.

Personal Tutor glencoe.com

Differentiated Instruction OL ELL

Linguistic Learners The formal conclusion of a hypothesis test is stated as "Reject the null hypothesis" or "Do not reject the null hypothesis." Students should always restate conclusions in their own words.

Formative Assessment

Use the Guided Practice exercises after each example to determine students' understanding of concepts.

Additional Example

1 COMMUTING In a sample of 400 commuters, the mean travel distance to work was 12.4 miles with a standard deviation of 3.5 miles. Determine a 95% confidence interval. $12.05 \leq \mu \leq 12.75$

Additional Examples also in Interactive Classroom PowerPoint® Presentations

IWB INTERACTIVE WHITEBOARD READY

Hypothesis Testing

Example 2 show how to perform a hypothesis test.

Additional Example

2 GRADES The average grade point average in Algebra 2 at one high school was 2.6, with 2.0 being a C. For a random sample of 34 students who work part-time, the mean grade was 2.4, with a standard deviation of 0.6. Test the hypothesis that the average grade for students who work part-time is the same as the overall average. The 95% confidence interval is $2.19 \leq \mu \leq 2.61$, so the null hypothesis is not rejected. Grades of working students are not significantly different from the average.

TEACH with TECH

BLOG Have students write a blog entry to describe hypothesis testing in their own words. Check students' entries to be sure they understand the concept and importance of hypothesis testing.

Focus on Mathematical Content

Tests and Confidence Intervals While a confidence interval is used to estimate the value of a quantity, a hypothesis test is performed in order to answer a *yes* or *no* question about whether a null hypothesis is true. A confidence interval can be used to help answer that question.

3 PRACTICE

Formative Assessment

Use Exercises 1–10 to check for understanding.

Use the chart at the bottom of this page to customize assignments for your students.

Check Your Understanding

Example 1 p. 780

Find a 95% confidence interval for each of the following.

1. $\bar{x} = 90, s = 5.6$, and $n = 50$
2. $\bar{x} = 72, s = 4.6$, and $n = 100$
3. $\bar{x} = 84, s = 3.5$, and $n = 120$
4. $\bar{x} = 62.5, s = 2.3$, and $n = 150$
5. **VIDEO GAMES** A sample of 100 students was asked for the average amount of time they spend playing video games each day. The mean time was 75 minutes with a standard deviation of 5.1 minutes. Determine a 95% confidence interval.

1. $88.45 \leq \bar{x} \leq 91.55$
2. $71.10 \leq \bar{x} \leq 72.90$
3. $83.37 \leq \bar{x} \leq 84.63$
4. $62.13 \leq \bar{x} \leq 62.87$
5. $74.00 \leq \bar{x} \leq 76.00$

Example 2 p. 781

Test each null hypothesis. Write *accept* or *reject*.

6. $H_0 = 10, H_1 < 10, n = 50, \bar{x} = 8.75$, and $s = 0.9$ **reject**
7. $H_0 = 48.8, H_1 > 48.8, n = 100, \bar{x} = 49$, and $s = 1.5$ **accept**
8. $H_0 = 75, H_1 > 75, n = 150, \bar{x} = 77$, and $s = 2$ **reject**
9. $H_0 = 90, H_1 > 90, n = 200, \bar{x} = 93$, and $s = 3.5$ **reject**
10. **SWIMMING** Yolanda's average time for the 400-meter butterfly was 8 minutes. She wants to test to see if that time is still accurate. After timing herself for 25 drills, she came to a mean of 8 minutes 10 seconds and a standard deviation of 30 seconds. Test the hypothesis that the average time is 8 minutes. **accept**

Practice and Problem Solving

= **Step-by-Step Solutions** begin on page R20. **Extra Practice** begins on page 947.

Example 1 p. 780

Find a 95% confidence interval for each of the following.

11. $\bar{x} = 26, s = 3.7$, and $n = 180$
12. $\bar{x} = 47, s = 5.9$, and $n = 200$
13. $\bar{x} = 58, s = 7.1$, and $n = 225$
14. $\bar{x} = 66, s = 6.3$, and $n = 250$
15. $\bar{x} = 92, s = 8.4$, and $n = 300$
16. $\bar{x} = 74, s = 6.8$, and $n = 350$
17. **FINANCIAL LITERACY** A sample of 500 students was asked for the average amount of money they spend a day. The mean amount was \$6.55 with a standard deviation of \$2.75.
    a. Determine a 95% confidence interval. **$\$6.31 \leq \bar{x} \leq \$6.79$**
    b. Suppose the sample is expanded to 750 students, but the mean and standard deviation remain the same. Determine a new 95% confidence interval.
    c. How does a larger sample affect the confidence interval?

11. $25.46 \leq \bar{x} \leq 26.54$
12. $46.18 \leq \bar{x} \leq 47.82$
13. $57.07 \leq \bar{x} \leq 58.93$
14. $65.22 \leq \bar{x} \leq 66.78$
15. $91.05 \leq \bar{x} \leq 92.95$
16. $73.29 \leq \bar{x} \leq 74.71$

17b. $\$6.35 \leq \bar{x} \leq \$6.75$

17c. Sample answer: A larger sample decreases the range of the confidence interval.

Example 2 p. 781

Test each null hypothesis. Write *accept* or *reject*.

18. $H_0 = 14, H_1 < 14, n = 80, \bar{x} = 12.75$, and $s = 0.8$ **reject**
19. $H_0 = 64.2, H_1 > 64.2, n = 200, \bar{x} = 64$, and $s = 2.5$ **accept**
20. $H_0 = 95, H_1 > 95, n = 150, \bar{x} = 97$, and $s = 1.5$ **reject**
21. $H_0 = 50, H_1 < 50, n = 400, \bar{x} = 49.5$, and $s = 0.9$ **reject**
22. $H_0 = 81, H_1 > 81, n = 300, \bar{x} = 81.5$, and $s = 3.4$ **reject**
23. $H_0 = 72, H_1 < 72, n = 350, \bar{x} = 71.7$, and $s = 4.1$ **accept**
24. **WALKING** Evan thought it took about 5 minutes to walk to school, while his sister Angela thought it took longer. They timed themselves for 40 days and calculated a mean of 5.8 minutes with a standard deviation of 0.6 minutes. Test the hypothesis. **reject**

Differentiated Homework Options

Level	Assignment	Two-Day Option	
AL Basic	11–24, 30–51	11–23 odd, 34–37	12–24 even, 30–33, 38–51
OL Core	11–23 odd, 25–28, 30–51	11–24, 34–37	25–28, 30–33, 38–51
BL Advanced	25–48, (optional: 49–51)		

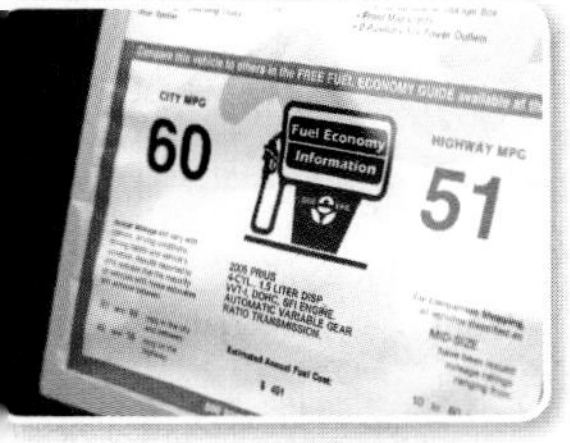

Real-World Link

Some hybrid vehicles can average over 50 miles per gallon in the city.

Source: EPA

25. **GAS MILEAGE** The manufacturer of Diana's car claimed that the car averages 28 miles per gallon in the city, but Diana believes it is less than that. The following data represent her calculations for the last 30 tanks of gas for her car. Conduct a hypothesis test to see if she is correct. **reject**

28.2	25.3	24.6	27.2	29.3	27.1	26.4	29.1	26.2	25.9
26.6	25.8	24.9	27.3	28.6	28.4	28.3	25.8	25.8	28.2
27.2	28.1	29.3	26.3	25.9	28.0	27.2	26.1	27.4	26.4

26. **QUALITY CONTROL** Grace is a quality tester for a manufacturing company. The company wants to claim that their new rechargeable battery lasts 8 hours. Grace tests 50 different batteries to see if they actually last fewer than 8 hours. Use the data below to conduct a hypothesis test. **accept**

8.1	7.9	7.8	8.0	8.2	7.8	7.7	8.1	7.8	7.7
8.2	8.4	8.2	7.8	7.7	7.7	7.9	8.3	8.1	8.0
8.0	7.9	7.9	8.4	8.1	8.2	8.0	7.6	7.7	7.9
7.8	7.9	8.0	8.0	8.1	8.1	8.2	7.6	7.8	7.8
8.0	8.1	8.1	7.9	7.9	7.9	8.1	7.8	7.8	8.0

StudyTip

Sample Size Larger samples will have a smaller error but will be more costly to obtain.

27. **COOKIES** A cookie manufacturer stated that there were 20 chocolate chips in every cookie. Lamar thought there were fewer than 20, so he tested 40 random cookies. Use the data below to conduct a hypothesis test. **reject**

21	19	20	20	19	19	18	21	19	17
19	18	18	20	20	19	18	20	18	19
21	21	19	17	17	18	19	19	19	21
22	21	21	20	20	19	17	17	17	20

28. **CANNED FOOD** The label on Leah's can of sliced peaches promises 12 slices in every can. Leah decides to test her hypothesis that there are more than 12 slices in every can by finding the number in 40 random cans. Test her hypothesis. **reject**

13	14	13	14	12	12	12	11	15	12
13	13	14	13	14	12	15	11	11	14
13	14	14	13	12	12	12	12	13	13
11	14	14	13	14	13	13	14	12	12

H.O.T. Problems

Use **H**igher-**O**rder **T**hinking Skills

29. **CHALLENGE** A 95% confidence interval for the mean weight of a 20-ounce box of cereal was $19.996 \le \bar{x} \le 20.004$ with a sample standard deviation of 0.128 ounces. Determine the sample size that led to this interval. **45**

30. **WRITING IN MATH** Describe how the size of the sample affects hypothesis testing. **See margin.**

31. **REASONING** Determine whether the following statement is *sometimes*, *always*, or *never* true. Explain your reasoning.

If a confidence interval contains H_0, then it is not rejected.

32. **OPEN ENDED** Conduct your own research study, and draw conclusions based on the results of a hypothesis test. Write a brief summary of your findings.

33. **CHALLENGE** If $H_0 = 85$, $H_1 > 85$, $\bar{x} = 85.5$, and $n = 300$, what is the minimum sample standard deviation for which the null hypothesis will be accepted? **4.38**

31. Sample answer: Always; if the null hypothesis falls within the confidence interval, then it is accepted, not rejected.

32. Sample answer: A pizza company claims to put 100 pepperonis on its large pizza. H_0: $\mu = 100$ and H_1: $\mu > 100$; data collected: 100, 102, 101, 101, 100, 99, 99, 103, 102, 103, 103, 101, 102, 99, 105, 103, 102, 100, 101, 104; $\bar{x} = 101.5$, $s = 1.70$; a 95% confidence interval is $100.74 < \bar{x} < 102.26$. H_0 does not fall within the confidence interval, so we reject the null hypothesis and accept the alternative hypothesis.

Additional Answer

30. Sample answer: A larger sample size will make the confidence interval smaller and the sample will more accurately reflect the true population mean, making a more accurate test.

Study Guide and Intervention

CRM pp. 36–37 AL OL ELL

12-6 Study Guide and Intervention

Hypothesis Testing

Confidence Interval

Term	Definition
Confidence Interval	the estimated range within which a number will fall with a stated degree of certainty
95% Confidence Interval Formula	$CI = \bar{x} \pm 2 \cdot \frac{s}{\sqrt{n}}$

Example **A survey asked 100 random people how many minutes they exercised each day. The mean of their answers was 25.3 minutes with a standard deviation of 9.4 minutes. Determine a 95% confidence interval. Round to the nearest tenth.**

$CI = \bar{x} \pm 2 \cdot \frac{s}{\sqrt{n}}$ Confidence Interval Formula

$= 25.3 \pm 2 \cdot \frac{9.4}{\sqrt{100}}$ $\bar{x} = 25.3, s = 9.4, n = 100$

$= 25.3 \pm 1.88$

The 95% confidence interval to the nearest tenth is $23.4 \le \mu \le 27.2$.

Exercises

Find a 95% confidence interval for each of the following.

1. $\bar{x} = 10$, $s = 6$, and $n = 100$ **$8.8 \le \bar{x} \le 11.2$**
2. $\bar{x} = 100$, $s = 5.4$, and $n = 5$ **$95.17 \le \bar{x} \le 104.83$**
3. $\bar{x} = 90$, $s = 1.8$, and $n = 170$ **$89.7 \le \bar{x} \le 90.3$**
4. $\bar{x} = 82$, $s = 4.5$, and $n = 8000$ **$81.90 \le \bar{x} \le 82.10$**
5. $\bar{x} = 1088$, $s = 7.8$, and $n = 200$ **$1086.90 \le \bar{x} \le 1089.10$**
6. $\bar{x} = 70$, $s = 10$, and $n = 50$ **$67.2 \le \bar{x} \le 72.8$**
7. $\bar{x} = 120$, $s = 8$, and $n = 1000$ **$149.90 \le \bar{x} \le 125.10$** **$118.3 \le \bar{x} \le 121.8$**
8. $\bar{x} = 147$, $s = 39$, and $n = 100$ **$139.20 \le \bar{x} \le 154.80$**
9. $\bar{x} = 70.5$, $s = 5.5$, and $n = 150$ **$69.6 \le \bar{x} \le 71.4$**
10. $\bar{x} = 788.2$, $s = 52$, and $n = 8$ **$751.43 \le \bar{x} \le 824.97$**

Practice

CRM p. 39 AL OL BL ELL

12-6 Practice

Hypothesis Testing

Lesson 12-6

Find a 95% confidence interval for each of the following.

1. $\bar{x} = 56$, $s = 2$, and $n = 50$ **$55.5 \le \bar{x} \le 56.6$**
2. $\bar{x} = 99$, $s = 22$, and $n = 121$ **$95 \le \bar{x} \le 103$**
3. $\bar{x} = 34$, $s = 4$, and $n = 200$ **$33.5 \le \bar{x} \le 34.6$**
4. $\bar{x} = 12$, $s = 4.5$, and $n = 100$ **$11.1 \le \bar{x} \le 12.9$**
5. $\bar{x} = 37$, $s = 2.5$, and $n = 50$ **$36.3 \le \bar{x} \le 37.7$**
6. $\bar{x} = 78$, $s = 2$, and $n = 225$ **$77.7 \le \bar{x} \le 78.3$**
7. $\bar{x} = 36$, $s = 6$, and $n = 36$ **$34 \le \bar{x} \le 38$**
8. $\bar{x} = 121$, $s = 2.5$, and $n = 100$ **$120.5 \le \bar{x} \le 121.5$**

Test each null hypothesis. Write *accept* or *reject*.

9. $H_0 = 200.1$, $H_1 < 200.1$, $n = 200$, $\bar{x} = 50$, and $\sigma = 2$ **reject**
10. $H_0 = 75.6$, $H_1 < 75.6$, $n = 100$, $\bar{x} = 77$, and $\sigma = 7$ **accept**
11. $H_0 = 89.3$, $H_1 < 89.3$, $n = 100$, $\bar{x} = 89$ and $\sigma = 1.5$ **accept**
12 $H_0 = 75$, $H_1 < 75$, $n = 150$, $\bar{x} = 74.2$, and $\sigma = 2.5$ **reject**
13. $H_0 = 121$, $H_1 < 121$, $n = 64$, $\bar{x} = 120$, and $\sigma = 2$ **reject**
14. $H_0 = 198.5$, $H_1 > 198.5$, $n = 100$, $\bar{x} = 200$, and $\sigma = 7.5$ **accept**
15. $H_0 = 38.5$, $H_1 > 38.5$, $n = 50$, $\bar{x} = 40$, and $\sigma = 4.5$ **reject**
16. $H_0 = 112.5$, $H_1 < 112.5$, $n = 100$, $\bar{x} = 110.5$, and $\sigma = 10$ **accept**

17. **RUNNING** Josh and his sister Megan run together each morning and do not use a stopwatch to keep track of their time. Josh thinks they usually run the mile under 7 minutes, while Megan thinks it takes them longer. They borrow a stopwatch and time themselves each day for 20 days. Their mean time to run one mile is 7.4 minutes with a standard deviation of 0.2 minutes. Test Megan's hypothesis.
accept

18. **QUALITY CONTROL** Kim is a quality tester for a tropical fruit company. The company claims that their canned pineapple stays fresh for at least 16 hours after opening. Kim tests 15 different cans to see if they actually stay fresh for at least 16 hours. Use the data below to conduct a hypothesis test.

Number of Hours Each Can Stays Fresh				
12	14	7	12	10
12	12	13	16	9
5	11	19	18	6

reject

Word Problem Practice

CRM p. 40 AL OL BL ELL

12-6 Word Problem Practice

Hypothesis Testing

1. **COLD REMEDY** A medical company claims that its new cold pill will shorten the length of a cold by at least 24 hours. The company wants to test its claim. What should the null hypothesis and alternate hypothesis be?
Null hypothesis: The cold pill will not shorten the length of a cold by at least 24 hours. Alternate hypothesis: The cold pill shortens the length of a cold by more than 24 hours.

2. **HYBRID CAR** A car company believes that its new experimental hybrid car will get at least 50 miles per gallon. If the confidence interval is 49 to 58 miles per hour, should the null hypothesis be accepted or rejected? Explain your answer.
The null hypothesis, that the car will get less than 50 miles per gallon, should be accepted. The null hypothesis overlaps within the confidence interval; thus the null hypothesis is accepted.

3. **POLITICS** A candidate running for governor hires a survey company to conduct a poll. The company reports that the candidate has a mean of 45% of voters supporting her with a standard deviation of 6%. What is the confidence interval for this poll?
$43.8 \le x \le 46.2$ votes

4. **VOCATIONS** Recent labor statistics show that 22,000 Americans work as statisticians. One statistician tests the null hypothesis that statisticians earn less than $65,000 per year. Five statisticians are polled and their mean income is $69,000 with a standard deviation of $1,000.

Statistician Salaries				
$69,500	$68,255	$68,895	$67,630	$69,720

Should the null hypothesis be rejected or accepted? Explain your answer.
The null hypothesis should be rejected. The alternate hypothesis is statisticians earn more than $65,000 per year. The confidence interval is $\$68,123 \le x \le \$69,877$ and does not overlap the null hypothesis.

5. **BOOKS** Ferdinand works at a bookstore. He believes that the bookstore sells more than 20 books on any randomly chosen day. Specifically, $H_0 \le 20$.
   a. What experiment can Ferdinand do to test the null hypothesis?
   Record the number of books sold each day for 30 days. Find a confidence interval and then reject or accept the null hypothesis depending on whether it overlaps the null hypothesis.
   b. If Ferdinand found a mean of 24 books with a standard deviation of 2 books, should he reject or accept the null hypothesis? Explain your answer.
   He should reject the null hypothesis. The confidence interval is $23.3 \le x \le 24.7$, which does not overlap his null hypothesis.

Enrichment

CRM p. 41 OL BL

12-6 Enrichment

Sample Mean and Standard Error

Lesson 12-6

The mean of a sample of size n is an estimate of the mean of the entire population under study. A different sample of size n probably will have a different mean, and a third sample yet another. For example, suppose the means for three different samples were 9, 5, and 11. What prediction would you make for the mean of a fourth sample? Clearly there is some uncertainty involved in the prediction. Therefore the sample mean must have a probability distribution associated with it. If the standard deviation of the population is known, σ (sigma), then the standard deviation of the sample mean, called the *standard error*, is given by: $SE = \frac{\sigma}{\sqrt{n}}$, where n is the sample size.

A 95% confidence interval for the population mean is given by:
$(\bar{x} - 2SE, \bar{x} + 2SE) = \left(\bar{x} - 2\frac{\sigma}{\sqrt{n}}, \bar{x} + 2\frac{\sigma}{\sqrt{n}}\right)$. That is, there is a 95% chance that the *true* population mean will be contained in this interval.

Suppose a high school football team has 50 players. The coach wants to know what the average amount a player can bench press. The only exact way to calculate this average would be to measure, in the weight room, each player on the team. Instead the coach randomly samples 10 players and computes the average of these 10 to estimate the mean bench press weight for the entire team. Suppose the coach knew that $\sigma = 41.6$. (This data is unknown to the coach but presented here for the purpose of the exercises.)

185	185	200	205	215

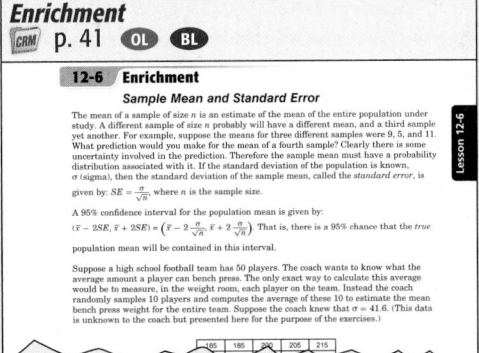

4 ASSESS

Yesterday's News Ask students to describe how their study of normal distributions relates to their study of confidence intervals and hypothesis testing.

Formative Assessment

Check for student understanding of Lessons 12-5 and 12-6.

CRM Quiz 3, p. 52

Additional Answers

43. ellipse

$$\frac{y^2}{4} + \frac{x^2}{2} = 1$$

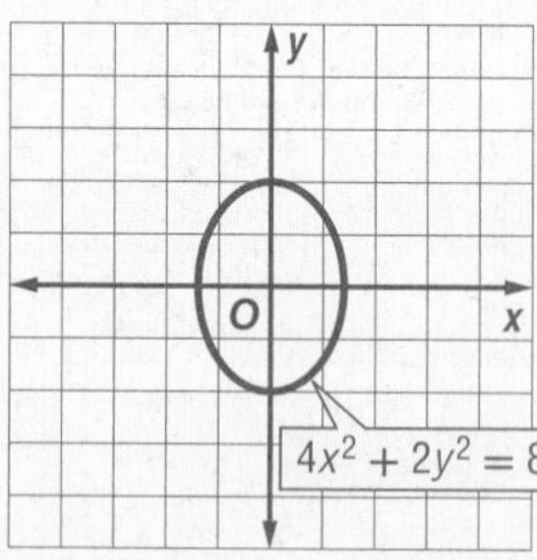

44. parabola

$$y = \frac{1}{8}x^2$$

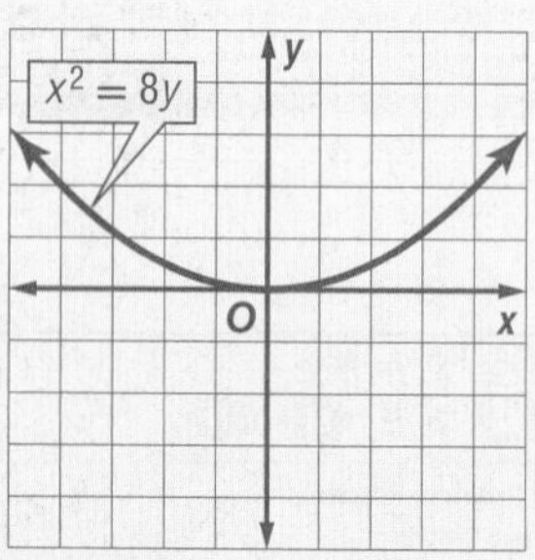

45. hyperbola

$$\frac{(x-1)^2}{36} - \frac{(y-4)^2}{4} = 1$$

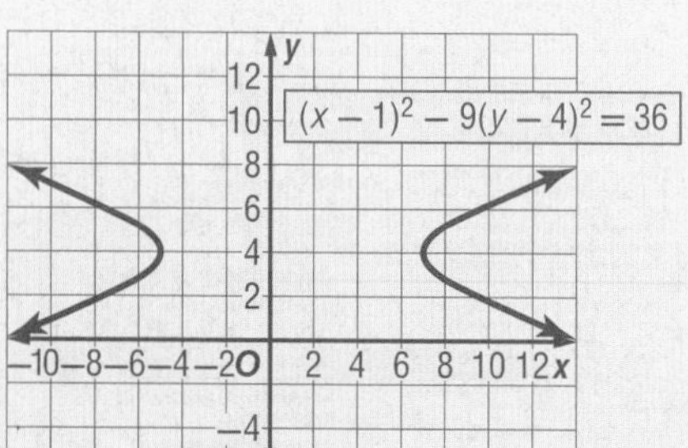

NGSSS PRACTICE 912.A.3.9, 912.A.7.5, 912.A.3.1, 912.A.8.5

34. GEOMETRY In the graph below, line ℓ passes through the origin. What is the value of $\frac{a}{b}$? **B**

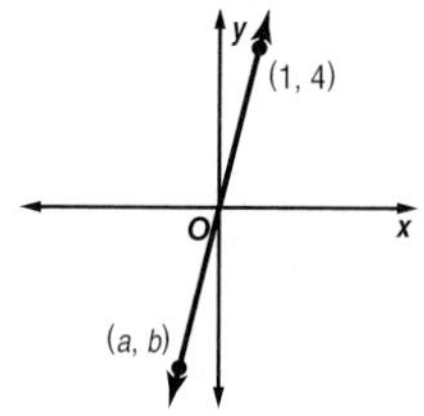

A. 4 B. $\frac{1}{4}$ C. −4 D. $-\frac{1}{4}$

35. SAT/ACT If $5 + i$ and $5 - i$ are the roots of $x^2 - 10x + c = 0$, what is the value of c? **I**

F. −25 G. −26 H. 25 I. 26

36. The Service Club at Corey's school was founded 8 years ago. The number of members of the club by year is shown in the table. Which linear equation best models the data? **B**

Year	Participation
0	11
2	13
4	15
6	19
8	22

A. $y = 1.4x$ C. $y = 1.6x$
B. $y = 1.4x + 10.4$ D. $y = 1.6x + 11.1$

37. GRIDDED RESPONSE Solve for x: $\log_2 (x - 6) = 3$. **14**

Spiral Review

38. HEALTH The heights of students at Madison High School are normally distributed with a mean of 66 inches and a standard deviation of 2 inches. Of the 1080 students in the school, how many would you expect to be less than 62 inches tall? (Lesson 12-5) **27 students**

39. RETAIL The posters for 8 newly released DVDs can be displayed a store window. If there are 6 new comedies, 9 new family movies, and 4 new dramas this week, what is the probability that 4 posters will be for comedies and 4 will be for family movies if the posters are chosen at random? (Lesson 12-4) **about 2.5%**

Find a_n for each geometric sequence. (Lesson 11-3)

40. $a_1 = \frac{1}{3}, r = 3, n = 8$ **729** **41.** $a_1 = \frac{1}{64}, r = 4, n = 9$ **1024** **42.** $a_4 = 16, r = 0.5, n = 8$ **1**

Write each equation in standard form. State whether the graph of the equation is a *parabola, circle, ellipse,* or *hyperbola.* Then graph the equation. (Lesson 10-6) **43–45. See margin.**

43. $4x^2 + 2y^2 = 8$ **44.** $x^2 = 8y$ **45.** $(x - 1)^2 - 9(y - 4)^2 = 36$

Write an equation in slope-intercept form for each graph. (Lesson 2-4) **47.** $y = -\frac{5}{3}x + \frac{29}{3}$

46. $y = 0.8x$

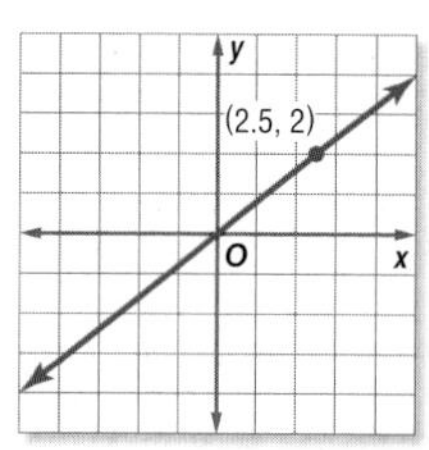

47.

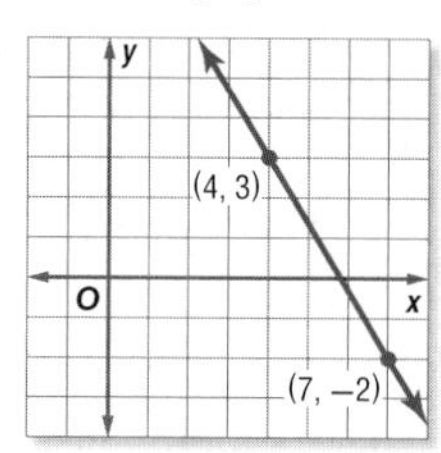

48. $y = -4$

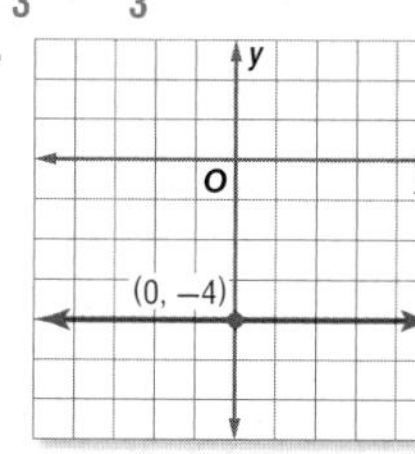

Skills Review

50. $m^4 + 4m^3n + 6m^2n^2 + 4mn^3 + n^4$
51. $r^8 + 8r^7n + 28r^6n^2 + 56r^5n^3 + 70r^4n^4 + 56r^3n^5 + 28r^2n^6 + 8rn^7 + n^8$

Expand each power. (Lesson 11-7)

49. $(a - b)^3$ $a^3 - 3a^2b + 3ab^2 - b^3$ **50.** $(m + n)^4$ **51.** $(r + n)^8$

Differentiated Instruction BL

Extension Point out to students that the reason that $2 \cdot \frac{s}{\sqrt{n}}$ is used to form a 95% confidence interval is that 95% of a normal distribution is within 2 standard deviations of the mean. Then ask students to rework Example 1 on page 780 to find a 99% confidence interval for mean time spent on homework. $52.5 \pm 3 \cdot \frac{5.1}{\sqrt{200}} \approx 52.5 \pm 1.08$

784 Chapter 12 Probability and Statistics

EXPLORE 12-7

Algebra Lab: Simulations

NGSSS MA.912.S.4.2 Use a simulation to approximate sampling distributions for the mean, using repeated sampling simulations from a given population.

A **simulation** uses a probability experiment to mimic a real-life situation. You can use a simulation to solve the following problem.

A fast food restaurant is offering one of six different food prize tickets on every soft drink cup. If the prizes are equally and randomly distributed, how many drinks, on average, would you have to buy in order to get at least one of each prize?

ACTIVITY

Work in pairs or small groups to complete Steps 1 through 4.

Step 1 Use the six numbers on a die to represent the six different food prizes.

Step 2 Roll the die and record which food prize was on the first soft drink cup. Use a tally sheet like the one shown at the right.

Step 3 Continue to roll the die and record the prize number until you have a complete set of food prizes. Stop as soon as you have a complete set. This is the end of one trial in your simulation. Record the number of drinks required for this trial.

Step 4 Repeat Steps 1, 2, and 3 until your group has carried out 25 trials. Use a new tally sheet for each trial.

Simulation Tally Sheet

Prize Number	Drinks Purchased
1	
2	
3	
4	
5	
6	
Total Needed	

Analyze the Data

2. Sample answer: mean = 13.56; median = 12; maximum = 41; minimum = 7; standard deviation ≈ 7.3

1. Create two different statistical graphs of the data collected for 25 trials. See Chapter 12 Answer Appendix.
2. Determine the mean, median, maximum, minimum, and standard deviation of the total number of drinks needed in the 25 trials.
3. Combine the small-group results and determine the mean, median, maximum, minimum, and standard deviation of the number of drinks required for all the trials conducted by the class. See students' work.

Make a Conjecture

5. The class results should be better since it is a much larger set of data.

4. If you carry out 25 additional trials, will your results be the same as in the first 25 trials? Explain. Probably not; the outcomes of the trials are random since you are rolling a die.
5. Should the small-group results or the class results give a better idea of the average number of drinks required to get a complete set of food prizes? Explain.
6. If there were 8 prizes instead of 6, would you need to buy more drinks or fewer drinks on average? more
7. **DESIGN A SIMULATION** What if one of the 6 prizes was more common than the other 5? For instance, suppose that one prize, a free ice cream sundae, appears on 25% of all the drinks and the other 5 prizes are equally and randomly distributed among the remaining 75% of the drinks. Design and carry out a new simulation to predict the average number of drinks you would need to buy to get a complete set. Include some measures of central tendency and dispersion with your data. See Chapter 12 Answer Appendix.

EXPLORE 12-7

Lesson Notes

1 FOCUS

Objective Simulate a real-life situation, collect data, and do a statistical analysis.

Materials

- one six-sided die for each group

Easy to Make Manipulatives

Teaching Algebra with Manipulatives
Template for:

- die patterns, p. 22

Teaching Tip

After students have read the problem, ask them why rolling a die can simulate this problem. because it has 6 possible equally likely random outcomes

2 TEACH

Working in Cooperative Groups

Put students in groups of two or three, mixing abilities. Students should take turns rolling the die during the activity, switching after each complete trial. One student can fill out the tally sheet while another rolls.

- Before students collect their data, ask them if they would expect every group in the class to have the same results. probably not, since you are finding experimental and not theoretical probabilities
- Point out that the first cup (first roll) will always contain a prize, but the second cup may not have a different prize (if the first two rolls are identical). Also note that, within a trial, the number of cups (rolls) is not fixed. The total number of cups required to collect all six prizes will vary from trial to trial.
- Have each group write the results of their 25 trials on the board so that everyone can see the results for the entire class.

Practice Have students complete Exercises 1–7.

3 ASSESS

Formative Assessment

Use Exercise 2 to assess whether students comprehend how to use numerical measure to summarize data.

From Concrete to Abstract

Exercise 7 asks students to use what they have learned to design their own simulations.

12-7 Lesson Notes

1 FOCUS

Vertical Alignment

Before Lesson 12-7
Use the Binomial Theorem.

Lesson 12-7
Find probabilities for binomial experiments.
Find probabilities by using binomial distributions and expansions.

After Lesson 12-7
Solve for probabilities of particular events in finite space.

2 TEACH

Scaffolding Questions

Have students read the *Why?* section of the lesson.

Ask:

- What is the probability that the player does not get a hit on a particular at-bat? 64%
- Are two successive at-bats independent events? yes
- If successive at-bats are independent, what is the probability that the player gets no hits in two successive at-bats? 0.4096
- What is the answer to the question *Is their assumption correct?* The probability for success is the same for every at-bat.

12-7 Binomial Distributions

Then
You used the Binomial Theorem. (Lesson 11-6)

Now
- Find probabilities for binomial experiments.
- Find probabilities by using binomial distributions and expansions.

NGSSS
MA.912.P.3.1, MA.912.P.3.2 Determine probabilities of events from distributions, and determine the mean and variance of distributions, including: discrete uniform, binomial, normal, and exponential.

New Vocabulary
binomial distribution
binomial experiment
experimental probability

FL Math Online
glencoe.com

Why?

During a baseball game, a player who gets a hit 36% of the time is at the plate. However, he has been in a hitting slump recently, failing to get a hit in his last 20 at-bats. The commentators notice this and declare that he is "due" to get a hit this time. Is their assumption correct?

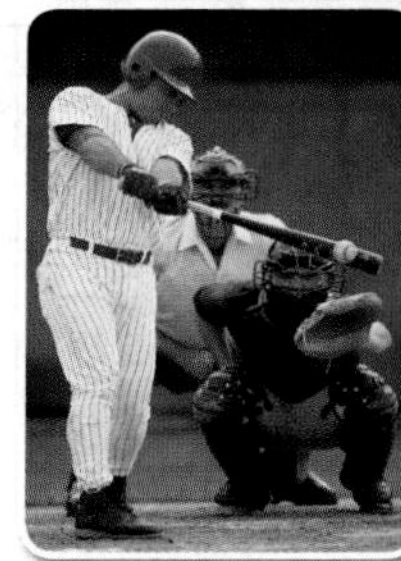

Binomial Experiments Another type of discrete probability distribution is the binomial distribution. A **binomial distribution** shows the probabilities of the outcomes of a binomial experiment. A **binomial experiment** is a random experiment with an outcome that is one of two simple events. In a binomial experiment, the following are true.

Key Concept Binomial Experiments

- There are only two possible outcomes, success or failure.
- There is a fixed number of trials, n.
- The probability of success is the same in every trial.
- The trials are independent.
- The random variable is the number of successes in n trials.

The **experimental probability** is what is estimated from observed simulations or experiments. When a simulation is conducted, the observed data are analyzed and the experimental probability is determined from these results.

EXAMPLE 1 Design a Binomial Experiment

In a certain dice game, a player tries to roll a total of 7 or 11 with two dice. Design and conduct a binomial experiment for 10 rolls of the dice.

Step 1 Describe the trial for the situation.
Each roll is a trial. There will be 10 trials.

Step 2 Describe a success. What is the probability of a success?
A success is rolling 7 or 11. The probability of success is $\frac{6}{36} + \frac{2}{36}$ or $\frac{2}{9}$.

Step 3 Design and conduct a simulation to determine the experimental probability of rolling a 7 or 11 at least two out of ten times. Let s represent success, and let f represent failure.

Roll	1	2	3	4	5	6	7	8	9	10	Total Successes
Simulation 1	f	f	f	f	f	s	f	f	s	f	2
Simulation 2	f	f	f	f	s	f	f	f	f	f	1
Simulation 3	s	s	f	f	f	f	f	f	f	f	2
Simulation 4	f	f	f	f	f	s	f	s	f	f	2

Three of the four simulations produced at least 2 successes, so the experimental probability of rolling a 7 or 11 twice in 10 rolls is 75%.

Lesson 12-7 Resources

Resource	Approaching-Level	On-Level	Beyond-Level	English Learners
Teacher Edition		• Differentiated Instruction, pp. 787, 793	• Differentiated Instruction, pp. 787, 793	
Chapter Resource Masters	• Study Guide and Intervention, pp. 43–44 • Skills Practice, p. 45 • Practice, p. 46 • Word Problem Practice, p. 47	• Study Guide and Intervention, pp. 43–44 • Skills Practice, p. 45 • Practice, p. 46 • Word Problem Practice, p. 47 • Enrichment, p. 48	• Practice, p. 46 • Word Problem Practice, p. 47 • Enrichment, p. 48	• Study Guide and Intervention, pp. 43–44 • Skills Practice, p. 45 • Practice, p. 46 • Word Problem Practice, p. 47
Transparencies	• 5-Minute Check Transparency 12-7	• 5-Minute Check Transparency 12-7	• 5-Minute Check Transparency 12-7	• 5-Minute Check Transparency 12-7
Other	• Study Notebook • Teaching Algebra with Manipulatives	• Study Notebook • Teaching Algebra with Manipulatives	• Study Notebook	• Study Notebook • Teaching Algebra with Manipulatives

786 Chapter 12 Probability and Statistics

Real-World Link

The Georgia State Fair, held in Macon since 1851, has raised over $4 million for education and charities.

Source: Georgia State Fair

StudyTip

Tree Diagrams Multiply all of the probabilities along the branch to calculate its probability.

Guided Practice

1. Design and conduct an experiment, and then find the experimental probability of a fair coin landing on heads 6 out of 10 tosses. See margin.

Personal Tutor glencoe.com

Binomial distributions are often represented graphically, usually with a tree diagram.

Real-World EXAMPLE 2 Find a Probability

STATE FAIR Antonia earned 3 prize tokens for shooting baskets at the state fair. According to the advertisement, 30% of the tokens win prizes. Find the probability that *exactly* 2 of Antonia's tokens win a prize.

Each token has a probability of success of 0.3.
The probability of failure is 1 − 0.3 or 0.7.
The tree diagram shows all of the possibilities and the probability of each.

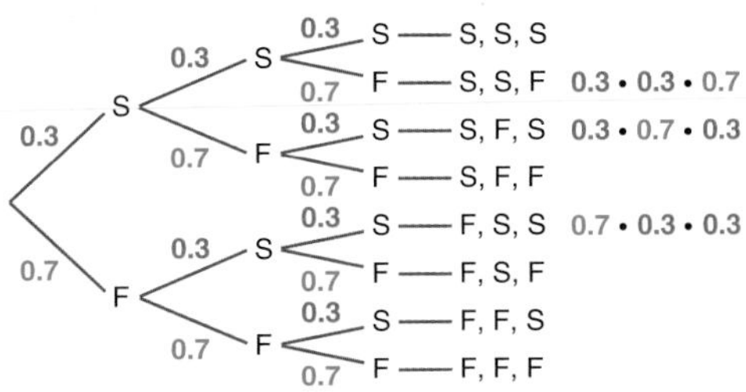

Three distinct branches of the tree indicate exactly two successes.
The sum of the probabilities of these branches will produce the overall probability.

$$0.3 \cdot 0.3 \cdot 0.7 + 0.3 \cdot 0.7 \cdot 0.3 + 0.7 \cdot 0.3 \cdot 0.3 = 0.189 \text{ or } 18.9\%$$

Guided Practice

2. Becky bought 5 game cards at the store. Each game card has a 10% chance of winning. Find the probability that at least 2 of her game cards are winners. 8.1%

Personal Tutor glencoe.com

Binomial Distribution The tree diagram in Example 2 is an example of a binomial distribution. This distribution can be simplified by the following formula.

Key Concept — Binomial Distribution Functions

The probability of x successes in n independent trials is

$$P(x) = C(n, x)\, s^x f^{n-x},$$

where s is the probability of success of an individual trial and f is the probability of failure on that same individual trial ($s + f = 1$).

The expected value of a binomial distribution can also be determined.

Key Concept — Expected Value of a Binomial Distribution

The expected value for a binomial distribution is $E(X) = ns$, where n is the total number of trials and s is the probability of success.

Binomial Experiments

Example 1 shows how to design and conduct a binomial experiment.
Example 2 shows how to find a binomial probability using a tree diagram.

Formative Assessment

Use the Guided Practice exercises after each example to determine students' understanding of concepts.

Additional Examples

1. Design and conduct an experiment to find the experimental probability of two fair coins both landing on heads for 10 tosses of the coins. Results should usually be between 10% and 40%.

2. **SALES** A report said that approximately 1 out of 6 cars sold in a certain year was green. Suppose a salesperson sells 4 cars per week. Find the probability that exactly 3 of the 4 cars in a particular week are green. about 0.0154 or 1.54%

Additional Examples also in Interactive Classroom PowerPoint® Presentations

IWB INTERACTIVE WHITEBOARD READY

Additional Answer (Guided Practice)

1. Sample answer:

	Flips	Total Successes
Simulation 1	sssffsffsf	5
Simulation 2	fsffssfsfs	5
Simulation 3	ssffsffsss	6
Simulation 4	fsfffsfssf	4

25%

Differentiated Instruction OL BL

Kinesthetic Learners Have students in small groups do a binomial experiment by tossing a ball into the wastebasket about 20 times to establish the probability of scoring a goal. Then have them find the probability that they will score exactly 4 goals in 8 tries.

Binomial Distribution

Example 3 shows how to find a probability by using the Binomial Distribution Formula and to find an expected value. **Example 4** shows how to determine a full probability distribution for a binomial experiment. **Example 5** shows how to graph a binomial distribution. **Example 6** shows how to use a normal distribution to approximate a binomial distribution.

Additional Examples

3 A candy company produces bags of strawberry and vanilla flavored candies, 65% of which are strawberry on average. The production line mixes the candies randomly and packages 10 per bag.

a. What is the probability that *at least* 4 candies in a bag are strawberry? 97.4%

b. What is the expected number of strawberry candies in a bag? 6.5

4 A family has 4 children. Determine the probabilities associated with the number of girl children in the family. 4 girls, 6.25%; 3 girls, 25%; 2 girls, 37.5%; 1 girl, 25%; 0 girl, 6.25%

Focus on Mathematical Content

Binomial Distributions A binomial distribution is called a *two-parameter* distribution, with the parameters being the number of trials (n) and the probability for one of the outcomes (p). Probabilities for a binomial distribution are completely determined once the parameters are specified.

StudyTip

Selecting Probabilities Sometimes it is easier to find the probability of failure and subtract from 1 to get the probability of success. These probabilities are complements of each other.

EXAMPLE 3 Binomial Probability

A chocolate company makes boxes of assorted chocolates, 40% of which are dark chocolate on average. The production line mixes the chocolates randomly and packages 10 per box.

a. What is the probability that *at least* 3 chocolates in a box are dark?

A success is a dark chocolate, so $s = 0.4$ and $f = 1 - 0.4$ or 0.6.

Calculate the probability of the box having exactly 0, 1, or 2 dark chocolates, and then subtract that sum from 1.

$P(\geq 3 \text{ dark chocolates})$

$= 1 - P(< 3 \text{ dark chocolates})$ — **$s + f = 1$**

$= 1 - [P(0) + P(1) + P(2)]$ — **Mutually exclusive events**

$= 1 - [C(10, 0)(0.4)^0(0.6)^{10} + C(10, 1)(0.4)^1(0.6)^9 + C(10, 2)(0.4)^2(0.6)^8]$

$= 1 - 0.1673$ or 0.8327 — **Simplify.**

The probability of at least 3 chocolates being dark is 0.8327 or 83.27%.

b. What is the expected number of dark chocolates in a box?

$E(X) = np$ — **Expected Value of a Binomial Distribution**

$= 10(0.4)$ or 4 — **$n = 10$ and $s = 0.4$**

The expected number of dark chocolates in a box is 4.

StudyTip

Expected Values and Probability A probability is not a guarantee that something will occur. For example, if the probability shows that a ball team is expected to win 3 of the next 5 games, it does not mean they will.

Guided Practice

3. If 20% of the chocolates are white chocolates, what is the probability that at least one chocolate in a given box of 10 is a white chocolate? **89.3%**

Personal Tutor glencoe.com

You can find the full probability distribution for a binomial experiment by expanding the binomial.

EXAMPLE 4 Full Probability Distribution

Autumn ran out of time when she took her multiple-choice test so she randomly circled answers for the last 5 questions. Each question had 5 possible choices. Determine the probabilities associated with the number of answers she got correct on the last 5 questions.

We are asked to find the probability for each possible number of correct answers on the 5 she guessed on.

Expand the binomial $(s + f)^n$ with $n =$ the 5 questions.

There are five equal possibilities for each question, so $s = \frac{1}{5}$ or 0.2 and $f = \frac{4}{5}$ or 0.8.

$(s + f)^n$

$= 1s^5 + 5s^4f + 10s^3f^2 + 10s^2f^3 + 5sf^4 + 1f^5$

$= (0.2)^5 + 5(0.2)^4(0.8) + 10(0.2)^3(0.8)^2 + 10(0.2)^2(0.8)^3 + 5(0.2)(0.8)^4 + (0.8)^5$

$= 0.032\%$ (**5 correct**) $+ 0.64\%$ (**4 correct**) $+ 5.12\%$ (**3 correct**) $+ 20.48\%$ (**2 correct**) $+ 40.96\%$ (**1 correct**) $+ 32.768\%$ (**0 correct**)

Guided Practice

4. Ricky guessed on the last 6 questions of his test. Each question had 4 options. Determine the probabilities associated with the number of answers he got correct on the last 6 questions.

4.

Number Correct	Probability
6	0.02%
5	0.4%
4	3.3%
3	13.2%
2	29.7%
1	35.6%
0	17.8%

Personal Tutor glencoe.com

TEACH with TECH

WEB SEARCH Have students search the Web for binomial distribution applets. Allow students to create and explore binomial probability histograms, and search for additional examples of binomial experiments.

The graph of a binomial probability distribution can be drawn with the possible outcomes on the x-axis and their probabilities of success on the y-axis.

EXAMPLE 5 Graphing a Binomial Distribution

Graph the binomial probability distribution in Example 4. Describe the shape of the distribution.

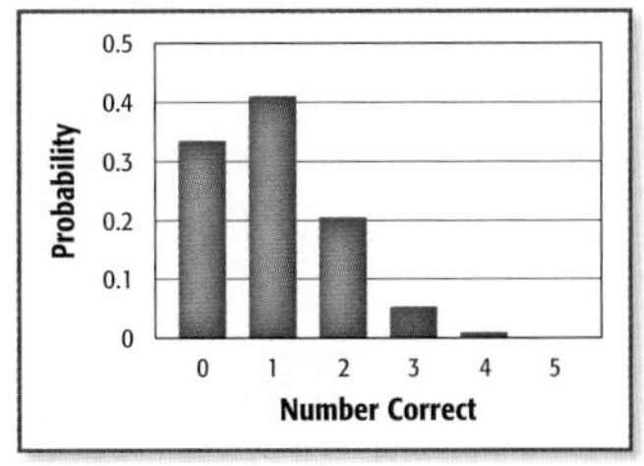

List the number of correct answers along the x-axis.

The maximum probability is 40.96%, so the y-axis should range from 0 to 0.5.

The graph is positively skewed.

Guided Practice

5. Graph the binomial probability distribution in Check Your Progress 4. Describe the shape of the distribution. **See margin.**

Personal Tutor glencoe.com

When the number of trials increases, a normal distribution can be used to approximate a binomial distribution.

Key Concept

Normal Approximation of a Binomial Distribution

In a binomial distribution with n trials, a probability of success s, and a probability of failure f, such that $ns \geq 5$ and $nf \geq 5$, the binomial distribution can be approximated by a normal distribution with $\bar{x} = ns$ and $\sigma = \sqrt{nsf}$.

EXAMPLE 6 Normal Approximation of a Binomial Distribution

According to an online poll, 64% of middle-aged college graduates feel that their college years were the most exciting. Bernardo conducts a survey of 300 random middle-aged adults with college degrees. What is the probability that at least 200 of the responses will agree?

The number of people surveyed who say that their college years were the most exciting has a binomial distribution with $n = 300$, $s = 0.64$, and $f = 0.36$. Use a normal distribution to approximate the probability.

$\bar{x} = ns$ — **Mean of a normal approximation**

$= 300(0.64)$ or 192 — **$n = 300$ and $s = 0.64$**

$\sigma = \sqrt{nsf}$ — **Standard deviation of a normal approximation**

$= \sqrt{300(0.64)(0.36)}$ — **$n = 300$, $s = 0.64$, and $f = 0.36$**

≈ 8.31 — **Use a calculator.**

200 is about 1 standard deviation greater than the mean, so the probability that at least 200 responses agree is 16%.

StudyTip

Normal Approximations The normal approximation is used because as n increases, using the binomial distribution function to find the probability becomes a tedious process.

Guided Practice

6. According to an online poll, 32% of adults feel that school should be in session year-round. Suki thinks the number should be lower, so she conducts a survey of 250 random adults. What is the probability that no more than 65 of the surveyed adults feel that school should be in session year-round? **2.5%**

Personal Tutor glencoe.com

Additional Examples

5 Graph the binomial probability distribution in Additional Example 4. Describe the shape of the distribution.

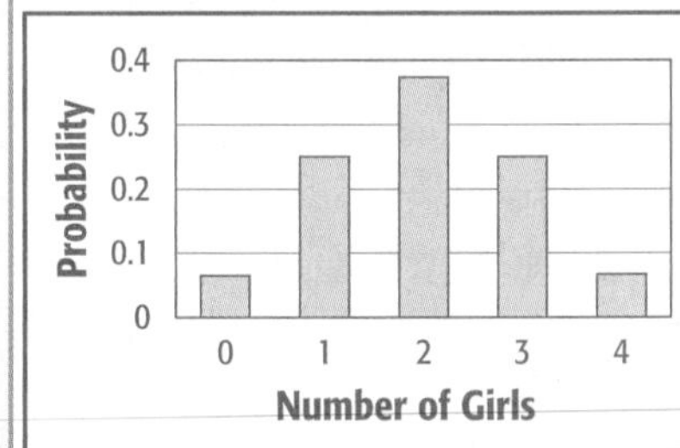

The graph is a normal distribution.

6 For the poll in Example 6, what is the probability that no more than 175 of the responses will agree? about 2.5%

Additional Answer (Guided Practice)

5.

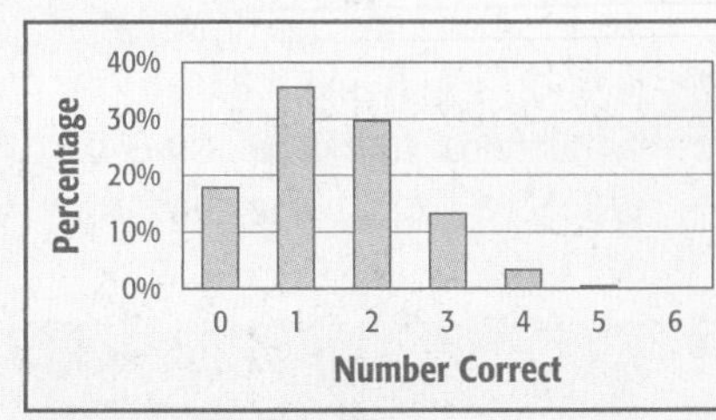

positively skewed

Lesson 12-7 Binomial Distributions 789

3 PRACTICE

Formative Assessment

Use Exercises 1–6 to check for understanding.

Use the chart at the bottom of this page to customize assignments for your students.

Additional Answers

1.

K	-	-	-	-	-	A	-	-	-
-	-	-	A	K	-	K	-	-	-
-	-	K	A	-	-	A	-	-	-
-	A	-	-	-	-	-	-	-	K
-	K	-	-	-	-	-	-	-	K
-	-	K	-	-	A	-	-	-	K
-	-	-	-	-	-	-	-	-	-
-	-	-	-	-	-	-	-	-	-
-	-	-	-	-	-	-	-	-	-
-	-	-	-	-	A	-	-	-	-

An ace or a king was drawn at least once in 8 out of the 10 simulations, so the experimental probability of drawing at least one ace or king is 0.8.

4.

Number Correct	Probability
0	0.098%
1	0.977%
2	4.395%
3	11.719%
4	20.508%
5	24.609%
6	20.508%
7	11.719%
8	4.395%
9	0.977%
10	0.098%

5a.

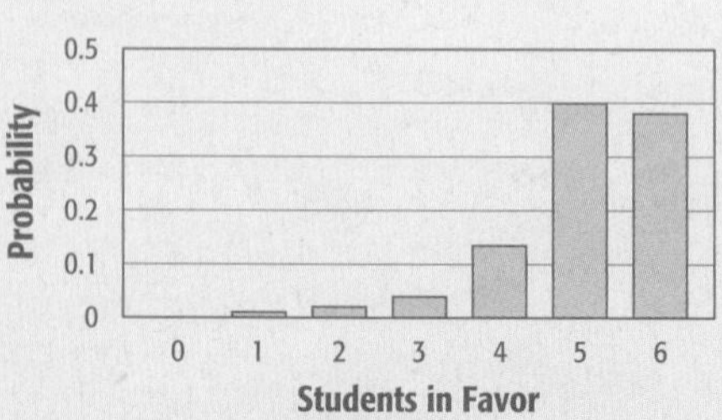

Check Your Understanding

Example 1 p. 786

1. **CARDS** Design and conduct an experiment, and use a table like the one at the right to find the experimental probability of drawing an ace or a king 1 out of 10 times when drawing from a deck of 52 cards with replacement. **See margin.**

Draw	Ace/King	Draw	Ace/King
1	Yes	6	No
2	No	7	Yes
3	No	8	No
4	No	9	No
5	No	10	No

Example 2 p. 787

2. **PETS** Chloe's cat is having kittens. The probability of a kitten being male is 0.5.
   a. If Chloe's cat has 4 kittens, what is the probability that at least 3 will be male? **31.25%**
   b. What is the expected number of males in a litter of 6? **3**

Example 3 p. 788

3. **BASEBALL** What is the probability that at least 5 of the 25 students trying out for the baseball team are left-handed if 11% of the population is left-handed? **13.3%**

Example 4 p. 788

4. **GUESSING** Loranzo had to guess on the last 10 questions of his test. Luckily, they were true and false questions. Determine the probabilities associated with the number of answers he guessed correctly and make a table listing the probability for 0 correct, 1 correct, 2 correct, etc. **See margin.**

Example 5 p. 789

5. **PARKING** A poll at Steve's high school showed that 85% of the students were in favor of expanding the junior-senior parking lot. Steve asked 6 random students who participated in the poll if they were in favor of expanding the parking lot.
   a. Graph the binomial probability distribution. **See margin.**
   b. What is the probability that all 6 of the students were in favor of expansion? **0.38**

Example 6 p. 789

6. **SUMMER JOBS** According to an online poll, 90% of high school upperclassmen have summer jobs. Tadeo thinks the number should be lower so he conducts a survey of 400 random upperclassmen. What is the probability that no more than 350 of the surveyed upperclassmen have summer jobs? **95%**

7–9. See margin.

Practice and Problem Solving

= **Step-by-Step Solutions** begin on page R20. **Extra Practice** begins on page 947.

Example 1 p. 786

7. **DICE** Design and conduct an experiment, and then find the experimental probability of rolling a 7 with 2 six-sided dice 2 out of 10 times.

8. **CARDS** Design and conduct an experiment, and then find the experimental probability of drawing a face card out of a standard deck of cards 4 out of 10 times with replacement.

9. **MARBLES** Design and conduct an experiment using a bag of 4 blue, 3 green, and 5 red marbles. Then find the experimental probability of pulling out a red marble 6 out of 10 times with replacement.

Examples 2 and 3 pp. 787–788

10. **MP3 PLAYERS** According to a recent survey, 85% of high school students own an MP3 player. What is the probability that at least 6 of 10 random high school students own an MP3 player? **0.99013 or 99%**

11. **CARS** According to a recent survey, 92% of high school seniors own their own car. What is the probability that fewer than 8 out of 10 random high school students own their own car? **0.0401 or 4.01%**

790 Chapter 12 Probability and Statistics

Differentiated Homework Options

Level	Assignment	Two-Day Option	
AL Basic	7–24, 43–72	7–23 odd, 48–51	8–24 even, 43–47, 52–72
OL Core	7–41 odd, 43–72	7–24, 48–51	25–41, 43–47, 52–72
BL Advanced	25–71, (optional: 72)		

12. **SENIOR PROM** According to a recent survey, 25% of high school upperclassmen think that the junior-senior prom is the most important event of the school year. What is the probability that no more than 3 out of 10 random high school upperclassmen think this way? **0.7759 or 78%**

13. **FOOTBALL** A certain football team has won 75.7% of their games. Find the probability that they win at least 7 of their next 10 games. **0.792 or 79.2%**

14. **GARDENING** Peter is planting 24 irises in his front yard. The flowers he bought were a combination of two varieties, blue and white. The flowers are not blooming yet, but Peter knows that the probability of having a blue flower is 75%. What is the probability that at least 20 of the flowers will be blue? **0.24665 or 24.7%**

15. **FOOTBALL** What is the probability that a field goal kicker makes at least 7 of his next 10 kicks from within 35 yards? **about 77.6%**

Range (yd)	Accuracy (%)
0–34	75
35–44	62
45+	20

16. **BABIES** Mr. and Mrs. Davis are planning to have 3 children and the probability of each child being a boy is 50%. What is the probability that they will have at least 2 boys? **0.5 or 50%**

Example 4 p. 788

17. **LAPTOPS** According to a recent survey, 95% of high school students own a laptop. Ten random students are chosen.
    a. Determine the probabilities associated with the number of students who own a laptop. **See Chapter 12 Answer Appendix.**
    b. What is the probability that at least 8 of the 10 students own a laptop? **98.9%**

18. **ATHLETICS** According to a recent survey, 80% of high school students have participated in at least one sport for their school. Six random students are chosen.
    a. Determine the probabilities associated with the number of students playing in at least one sport.
    b. What is the probability that no more than 2 of the students participated in a sport? **about 1.7%**

18a.

Number of Students	Probability
0	0.0064%
1	0.15%
2	1.5%
3	8.2%
4	24.6%
5	39.3%
6	26.2%

19. **CAR WASH** Some students are doing a car wash to raise money for the Spanish Club. They have determined that 65% of the time the customers donate more than the minimum amount for the car wash. What is the probability that at least 4 of the next 5 customers will donate more than the minimum? **42.8%**

20. **DRAWINGS** One in five students will win a prize in the class drawing. If there are 25 students in the drawing, including Jake, Leslie, Roberto, Ika, and Nicholas, what is the probability that at least one of them wins a prize? **67.2%**

Example 5 p. 789

21. **MUSIC** An online poll showed that 5% of adults still play vinyl records. Moe surveyed 8 random people from the population.
    a. Graph the binomial probability distribution. **See Chapter 12 Answer Appendix.**
    b. What is the probability that no more than 2 of the people surveyed still play vinyl records? **99.38%**

22. **PROMOTIONS** A beverage company has a promotion in which 30% of the bottles purchased during the promotion have bottle caps that win a free beverage. Melanie bought 10 bottles.
    a. Graph the binomial probability distribution. **See Chapter 12 Answer Appendix.**
    b. What is the probability that Melanie won at least 4 free beverages? **35%**

Example 6 p. 789

23. **REALITY SHOWS** According to an online poll, 70% of teens watch at least one reality show. Dillon surveyed 200 random teens. What is the probability that at least 146 of the teens surveyed watch at least one reality show? **16%**

Watch Out!

Preventing Errors Encourage students to think about the reasonableness of their solution. Emphasize the fact that a randomly selected item will most likely be clustered around the mean. The further that a value is from the mean, the lower the percentage should be.

Additional Answers

7.

5	11	5	3	8	6	7	11	6	8
8	3	6	5	6	5	2	8	7	8
6	7	7	9	11	8	8	4	7	6
7	8	9	5	8	7	8	5	5	8
10	6	9	6	7	6	5	8	4	9
7	4	4	8	10	7	9	7	4	8
5	3	11	12	7	11	7	7	3	7
7	12	6	2	6	8	9	9	6	9
8	6	10	6	8	7	11	6	8	9
6	9	7	6	3	6	6	11	7	6

A 7 was rolled at least 2 out of 10 times in 8 of 10 simulations, so the experimental probability is 0.8.

8.

-	-	-	-	-	-	F	F	-	-
-	F	-	F	-	-	F	-	-	F
-	-	-	-	F	F	-	-	F	F
-	-	F	F	F	-	-	F	-	F
-	-	-	F	-	-	-	F	-	-
F	-	-	F	-	F	F	F	F	F
-	-	-	-	-	-	-	F	F	-
-	-	-	-	-	-	F	-	-	-
-	-	-	-	F	-	-	-	-	-
-	-	F	-	-	F	F	F	-	F

A face card was drawn four times in 2 out of the 10 simulations, so the experimental probability of drawing a face card 4 out of 10 times is 0.2.

9.

-	R	R	R	-	-	-	-	R	-
-	-	-	-	-	-	-	R	R	-
-	R	R	-	R	-	-	R	-	-
R	-	-	R	R	R	-	R	-	-
-	R	-	-	-	-	-	-	-	R
-	R	-	R	R	-	-	R	R	R
R	-	R	-	R	R	-	R	-	-
-	R	-	-	R	-	R	-	R	-
R	-	-	R	-	-	R	R	-	R
-	-	-	R	-	-	-	-	-	-

A red marble was pulled six times in 1 out of the 10 simulations, so the experimental probability of pulling a red marble 6 out of 10 times is 0.1.

Study Guide and Intervention
CRM pp. 43–44 AL OL ELL

12-7 Study Guide and Intervention
Binomial Distributions

Binomial Experiments

Binomial Experiments	A binomial experiment is possible if and only if all of these conditions occur. • There are exactly two outcomes for each trial. • There is a fixed number of trials. • The trials are independent. • The probabilities for each trial are the same.

Example **Suppose a coin is weighted so that the probability of getting heads in any one toss is 90%. What is the probability of getting exactly 7 heads in 8 tosses?**

The probability of getting heads is $\frac{9}{10}$ and the probability of getting tails is $\frac{1}{10}$. There are $C(8, 7)$ ways to choose the 7 heads.

$$P(7 \text{ heads}) = C(8, 7)\left(\frac{9}{10}\right)^7\left(\frac{1}{10}\right)^1 = 8 \cdot \frac{9^7}{10^8} \approx 0.38$$

The probability of getting 7 heads in 8 tosses is about 38%.

Exercises

1. **BASKETBALL** For any one foul shot, Derek has a probability of 0.72 of getting the shot in the basket. As part of a practice drill, he shoots 8 shots from the foul line.
   a. What is the probability that he gets in exactly 6 foul shots? **about 31%**
   b. What is the probability that he gets in at least 6 foul shots? **about 60%**
2. **SCHOOL** A teacher is trying to decide whether to have 4 or 5 choices per question on her multiple choice test. She wants to prevent students who just guess from scoring well on the test.
   a. On a 5-question multiple-choice test with 4 choices per question, what is the probability that a student can score at least 60% by guessing? **10.4%**
   b. What is the probability that a student can score at least 60% by guessing on a test of the same length with 5 choices per question? **5.8%**
3. **DICE** Julie rolls two dice and adds the two numbers.
   a. What is the probability that the sum will be divisible by 3? $\frac{1}{3}$
   b. If she rolls the dice 5 times what is the chance that she will get exactly 3 sums that are divisible by 3? **about 16%**
4. **SKATING** During practice a skater falls 15% of the time when practicing a triple axel. During one practice session he attempts 20 triple axels.
   a. What is the probability that he will fall only once? **about 14%**
   b. What is the probability that he will fall 4 times? **about 18%**

Chapter 12 43 *Glencoe Algebra 2*

Lesson 12-7

Practice
CRM p. 46 AL OL BL ELL

12-7 Practice
Binomial Distributions

1. **COINS** Find each probability if a coin is tossed 6 times.
   a. P(exactly 3 tails) $\frac{5}{16}$
   b. P(exactly 5 tails) $\frac{3}{32}$
   c. P(0 tails) $\frac{1}{64}$
   d. P(at least 4 heads) $\frac{11}{32}$
   e. P(at least 4 tails) $\frac{11}{32}$
   f. P(at most 2 tails) $\frac{11}{32}$
2. **FREE THROWS** The probability of Chris making a free throw is $\frac{2}{3}$. If she shoots 5 times, find each probability.
   a. P(all missed) $\frac{1}{243}$
   b. P(all made) $\frac{32}{243}$
   c. P(exactly 2 made) $\frac{40}{243}$
   d. P(exactly 1 missed) $\frac{80}{243}$
   e. P(at least 3 made) $\frac{64}{81}$
   f. P(at most 2 made) $\frac{17}{81}$
3. **BOARD GAME** When Tarin and Sam play a certain board game, the probability that Tarin will win a game is $\frac{3}{4}$. If they play 5 games, find each probability.
   a. P(Sam wins only once) $\frac{405}{1024}$
   b. P(Tarin wins exactly twice) $\frac{45}{512}$
   c. P(Sam wins exactly 3 games) $\frac{45}{512}$
   d. P(Sam wins at least 1 game) $\frac{781}{1024}$
   e. P(Tarin wins at least 3 games) $\frac{459}{512}$
   f. P(Tarin wins at most 2 games) $\frac{53}{512}$
4. **SAFETY** In August 2001, the American Automobile Association reported that 73% of Americans use seat belts. In a random selection of 10 Americans in 2001, what is the probability that exactly half of them use seat belts? **about 7.5%**
5. **HEALTH** In 2001, the American Heart Association reported that 50 percent of the Americans who receive heart transplants are ages 50–64 and 20 percent are ages 35–49.
   a. In a randomly selected group of 10 heart transplant recipients, what is the probability that at least 8 of them are ages 50–64? $\frac{7}{128}$
   b. In a randomly selected group of 5 heart transplant recipients, what is the probability that 2 of them are ages 35–49? $\frac{128}{625}$

Chapter 12 46 *Glencoe Algebra 2*

Word Problem Practice
CRM p. 47 AL OL BL ELL

12-7 Word Problem Practice
Binomial Distributions

1. **GENETICS** Dagmar is conducting a genetic experiment. Before she performs the experiment, she would like to compute theoretically probabilities for some of the outcomes. One of these computations involves expanding $(p + q)^4$. What is this expansion?
   $p^4 + 4p^3q + 6p^2q^2 + 4pq^3 + q^4$
2. **GAMES** The probability that Kendra will win a card game is $\frac{2}{3}$. If Kendra plays 7 games what is the probability she wins exactly 4 games? Round your answer to the nearest thousandth.
   about 0.256
3. **DEFECTS** An electronics parts manufacturer produces capacitors for electronic circuits. The probability that a capacitor comes out defective is 1 in 1,000. In a batch of 10,000 capacitors, write an expression for the probability that 10 of the capacitors are defective.
   $C(10{,}000, 10)\left(\frac{1}{1000}\right)^{10}\left(\frac{999}{1000}\right)^{9990}$
4. **SUBWAYS** Fiona uses the subway to commute to work. During the morning commute, the trains run frequently and there is a 1 in 8 chance that she will find a train waiting for her as soon as she gets to the platform. Over the course of a five-day work week, what is the probability that she found a train waiting for her at least twice? Round your answer to the nearest thousandth.
   0.121
5. **SOCCER** The boys varsity soccer team at Lincoln High School has a 75% probability of winning each of their 17 games this season. What is the probability that the team will win at least 13 games this season? Round your answer to the nearest thousandth.
   0.574
5. **CHESS** Gary and Howard play chess. Their chess ratings are shown in the table below.

Chess Ratings	
Gary	Howard
2050	1948

This means that whenever they play, Gary has a 64% chance of defeating Howard. One day, Gary and Howard play three games against each other. Round your answers to the nearest thousandth.
   a. What is the probability that Gary will win all three of the matches? **0.262**
   b. What is the probability that Gary will win at least two of the three matches? **0.705**
   c. What is the probability that Gary will win only one of the matches? **0.249**

Chapter 12 47 *Glencoe Algebra 2*

Lesson 12-7

24. **COLLEGE** A poll of students at Jacqui's school determined that 88% of the students wanted to go to college. Jacqui surveyed 150 random students from the school. What is the probability that at least 10 of the polled students did not want to go to college? **98.9%**

B **A binomial distribution has a 60% rate of success. There are 18 trials.**

25. What is the probability that there will be at least 12 successes? **0.37 or 37%**
26. What is the probability that there will be 12 failures? **0.0145 or 1.45%**
27. What is the expected number of successes? **10.8**
28. **TENNIS** A player has won 85% of his matches over his career. Find each probability.
    a. He wins 3 of the next 5 matches. **13.8%**
    b. He wins at least 2 of his next 5 matches. **99.8%**
    c. He loses at least 1 of his next 5 matches. **55.6%**

Real-World Link

Sweepstakes hobbyists who enter by mail are often called "sweepstakers" or "sweepers." Many sweepstakers meet locally in clubs and nationally at a yearly convention, which 800 people attended in 2006.

Source: National Sweepstakes Convention

Each binomial distribution has n trials and p probability of success. Determine the most likely number of successes.

29. $n = 8, p = 0.6$ **5**
30. $n = 10, p = 0.4$ **4**
31. $n = 6, p = 0.8$ **5**
32. $n = 12, p = 0.55$ **7**
33. $n = 9, p = 0.75$ **7**
34. $n = 11, p = 0.35$ **4**
35. **SWEEPSTAKES** A beverage company is having a sweepstakes. The probability of winning selected prizes are shown at the right. If Ernesto purchases 8 beverages, what is the probability that he wins at least one prize? **60.3%**

Probability of Winning	
beverage	1 in 10
CD	1 in 200
hat	1 in 250
MP3 player	1 in 20,000
car	1 in 25,000,000

Each binomial distribution has n trials and p probability of success. Determine the probability of s successes. **36. 0.744 or 74.4% 37. 0.322 or 32.2% 38. 0.767 or 76.7%**

36. $n = 8, p = 0.3, s \geq 2$
37. $n = 10, p = 0.2, s > 2$
38. $n = 6, p = 0.6, s \leq 4$
39. $n = 9, p = 0.25, s \leq 5$ **0.99 or 99%**
40. $n = 10, p = 0.75, s \geq 8$ **0.526 or 52.6%**
41. $n = 12, p = 0.1, s < 3$ **0.1109 or 11.09%**

H.O.T. Problems
Use Higher-Order Thinking Skills

44–46. See margin.

42. **CHALLENGE** In a normal approximation of a binomial distribution, there is a 34% probability of there being between 60 and 66 successes. If $\bar{x} = 60$ and the probability of success is 36%, how many trials are there? **156**

C

43. **WRITING IN MATH** You poll a sample of your classmates to find out if they support using school funds for the science wing project. How could you use a binomial distribution to predict the number of people in the school who support the project?

43. Sample answer: The poll will give you a percent of people supporting the addition. The percent of supporters represents the probability of success. You can use the formula for the expected number of successes in a binomial distribution with the total number of students in the school to predict the number that will support the science wing addition.

44. **REASONING** Determine whether the following statement is *sometimes*, *always*, or *never* true. Explain your reasoning.

    It is more beneficial to find the probability of failure and subtract it from 1 in order to determine the probability of success.

45. **OPEN ENDED** Describe a real-world setting within your school or community activities that seems to fit a binomial distribution. Identify the key components of your setting that connect to binomial distributions.
46. **WRITING IN MATH** Describe how binomial distributions are connected to Pascal's triangle.
47. **WRITING IN MATH** Explain the relationship between a binomial experiment and a binomial distribution. **Sample answer: A binomial distribution shows the probabilities of the outcomes of a binomial experiment.**

Enrichment
CRM p. 48 OL BL

12-7 Enrichment
Multinomial Distributions

A multinomial is a generalization of a binomial. For example, $(a + b + c)^2$ is a multinomial. One way to determine the coefficients is by direct multiplication using the distributive property. Take each term in the first factor and multiply by each term (a, b, and c) in the second factor, then combine like terms. (Notice that the sum of the exponents is always equal to two.)

$$\begin{aligned}(a + b + c)^2 = (a + b + c)(a + b + c) &= a(a + b + c) + b(a + b + c) + c(a + b + c)\\ &= a^2 + ab + ac + ab + b^2 + bc + ac + bc + c^2\\ &= a^2 + b^2 + c^2 + 2ab + 2ac + 2bc\end{aligned}$$

Underlying this expansion is the notion of a *partition* into categories. The example partitions two 'items' among three categories. In this case the categories are the variables a, b, and c and the items are exponents. For example the partition, {1, 0, 1} represents the term ac in the expansion, which could also be written as $a^1b^0c^1$, whereas the partition {0, 2, 0} represents the b^2 term. The coefficients of each term can be computed by the formula:

$\frac{n!}{n_1! \cdot n_2! \cdot n_3! \ldots n_k!}$, where n is the exponent and $n_1 + n_2 + n_3 + \cdots + n_k = n$. Recall, $0! = 1$.

Term	Partition	Coefficient
a^2	{2,0,0}	$\frac{2!}{2! \cdot 0! \cdot 0!} = 1$
b^2	{0,2,0}	$\frac{2!}{0! \cdot 2! \cdot 0!} = 1$

Additional Answer

44. Sometimes; there may be times when you need to add the probabilities of many events, (for example D = 3, 4, 5, 6, and 7), when it would be easier to add the probabilities of failures (D = 0, 1 and 2) and then subtract the total from 1. Other times, it would be easier to add the successes.

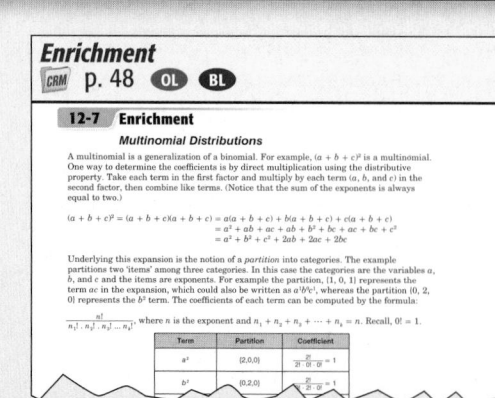

NGSSS PRACTICE 912.P.3.1, 912.A.9.1, 912.A.2.12

48. **EXTENDED RESPONSE** Carly is taking a 10-question multiple-choice test in which each question has four choices. If she guesses on each question, what is the probability that she will get

a. 7 questions correct? 0.003

b. 9 questions correct? 0.00003

c. 0 questions correct? 0.056

d. 3 questions correct? 0.25

49. What is the maximum point of the graph of the equation $y = -2x^2 + 16x + 5$? C

A. (−4, −59) C. (4, 37)

B. (−4, −91) D. (4, 101)

50. **GEOMETRY** On a number line, point X has coordinate −8 and point Y has coordinate 4. Point P is $\frac{2}{3}$ of the way from X to Y. What is the coordinate of P? H

F. −4 H. 0

G. −2 I. 2

51. **SAT/ACT** The cost of 4 CDs is d dollars. At this rate, what is the cost, in dollars, of 36 CDs? D

A. $\frac{9d}{4}$ C. $\frac{36}{d}$

B. $\frac{d}{36}$ D. $9d$

Spiral Review

Test each null hypothesis. Write *accept* or *reject*. (Lesson 12-6)

52. $H_0 = 33, H_1 > 33, n = 100, \bar{x} = 32.1$, and $s = 1.2$ reject

53. $H_0 = 5, H_1 < 5, n = 50, \bar{x} = 5.2$, and $s = 0.8$ accept

54. $H_0 = 0.04, H_1 > 0.04, n = 100, \bar{x} = 0.042$, and $s = 0.1$ accept

55. $H_0 = 300, H_1 < 300, n = 25, \bar{x} = 301$, and $s = 1.5$ reject

56. **SPEED** A system collected and recorded the speed of drivers on a road near a school. The speeds were normally distributed with a mean of 37 miles per hour and a standard deviation of 4 miles per hour. Of the 425 cars sampled, how many would you expect were driving less than 33 miles per hour? (Lesson 12-5) 68

Find the missing value for each arithmetic sequence. (Lesson 11-1)

57. $a_5 = 12, a_{16} = 133, d = ?$ 11

58. $a_9 = -34, a_{22} = 44, d = ?$ 6

59. $a_4 = 18, a_n = 95, d = 7, n = ?$ 15

60. $a_8 = ?, a_{19} = 31, d = 8$ −57

61. $a_6 = ?, a_{20} = 64, d = 7$ −32

62. $a_7 = -28, a_n = 76, d = 8, n = ?$ 20

63. **ASTRONOMY** The table at the right shows the closest and farthest distances of Venus and Jupiter from the center of the Sun in millions of miles. (Lesson 10-4)

Planet	Closest	Farthest
Venus	66.8	67.7
Jupiter	460.1	507.4

a. Write an equation for the orbit of each planet. Assume that the center of the orbit is the origin and the center of the Sun is a focus that lies on the x-axis.

b. Which planet has an orbit that is closer to a circle? Venus

63a. Venus: $\frac{x^2}{4522.5625} + \frac{y^2}{4522.36} = 1$; Jupiter: $\frac{x^2}{234{,}014.06} + \frac{y^2}{233{,}454.74} = 1$

Write an equivalent exponential or logarithmic function. (Lesson 8-7)

64. $e^{-x} = 5$ $-x = \ln 5$

65. $e^2 = 6x$ $2 = \ln 6x$

66. $\ln e = 1$ $e^1 = e$

67. $\ln 5.2 = x$ $e^x = 5.2$

68. $e^{x+1} = 9$ $x + 1 = \ln 9$

69. $e^{-1} = x^2$ $-1 = \ln x^2$

70. $\ln \frac{7}{3} = 2x$ $e^{2x} = \frac{7}{3}$

71. $\ln e^x = 3$ $e^3 = e^x$

Skills Review

72. **MUSIC** Tina owns 11 pop, 6 country, 16 rock, and 7 rap CDs. Find each probability if she randomly selects 4 CDs. (Lesson 12-3)

a. P(2 rock) 0.15

b. P(1 rap) 0.18

c. P(1 rock and 2 country) 0.02

4 ASSESS

Name the Math Have each student use his or her own family or the family of a friend (for example, 2 boys and a girl), and find the probabilities for that particular group of siblings. Then have students explain the steps they used.

Formative Assessment

Check for student understanding of Lesson 12-7.

CRM Quiz 4, p. 52

Additional Answers

45. Sample answer: During May and June, lunches are held outside, weather permitting. Also during this time, there has historically been a 15% chance of rain. So, to determine the probability of not having rain for at least 24 of these 28 days, the binomial distribution would use $s = 0.85$, $f = 0.15$, and $n = 28$.

46. Sample answer: A full binomial distribution can be determined by expanding the binomial, which itself utilizes Pascal's triangle.

Differentiated Instruction OL BL

Extension Have students look at a histogram of a binomial distribution created on a graphing calculator for $n = 20$ and $p = 0.5$. Point out that they can use the histogram to answer a question like "What is the probability that x is at least 12?" by adding the heights of all the bars beginning with $x = 12$. Then have them find the probability that x is at least 12. 0.2517

Formative Assessment

Key Vocabulary The page references after each word denote where that term was first introduced. If students have difficulty answering questions 1–5, remind them that they can use these page references to refresh their memories about the vocabulary.

Summative Assessment

CRM Vocabulary Test, p. 54

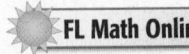

FL Math Online glencoe.com

Vocabulary PuzzleMaker improves students' mathematics vocabulary using four puzzle formats–crossword, scramble, word search using a word list, and word search using clues. Students can work online or from a printed worksheet.

CHAPTER 12 Study Guide and Review

FL Math Online glencoe.com
- STUDY TO GO
- Vocabulary Review

Chapter Summary

Key Concepts

Samples and Populations (Lessons 12-1 and 12-2)

- A sample is biased if its design favors certain outcomes.
- A sample is unbiased if it is random or unpredictable.

Standard Deviation	
Sample	Population
$\sqrt{\dfrac{\sum_{k=1}^{n}(x_k - \bar{x})^2}{n-1}}$	$\sqrt{\dfrac{\sum_{k=1}^{n}(x_k - \mu)^2}{n}}$

Conditional Probability (Lesson 12-3)

- The probability of an event given that another event has already occurred is the conditional probability.
- A contingency table records data in which different possible situations result in different possible outcomes.

Probability Distributions (Lessons 12-4, 12-5, and 12-7)

Sample	Population
uniform	All probabilities are equal.
discrete	finite number of possible outcomes
continuous	infinite number of possible outcomes
normal	symmetric curves
skewed	non-symmetric curves
binomial	Outcomes are one of two simple events.

Hypothesis Testing (Lesson 12-6)

- Inferential statistics draw conclusions about a population by using a sample.
- A hypothesis is an assumption that can be verified by testing.

FOLDABLES® Study Organizer

Be sure the Key Concepts are noted in your Foldable.

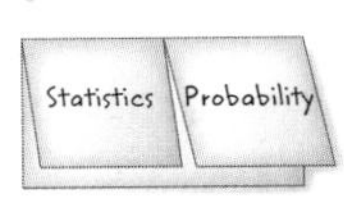

Key Vocabulary

alternative hypothesis (p. 781)
biased (p. 745)
binomial distribution (p. 786)
binomial experiment (p. 786)
causation (p. 747)
conditional probability (p. 759)
confidence interval (p. 780)
continuous probability distribution (p. 773)
control group (p. 746)
correlation (p. 747)
discrete probability distribution (p. 767)
expected value (p. 767)
experiment (p. 746)
inferential statistics (p. 780)
margin of sampling error (p. 753)
measure of central tendency (p. 752)
measure of variation (p. 754)
normal distribution (p. 773)
null hypothesis (p. 781)
observational study (p. 746)
parameter (p. 752)
population (p. 745)
probability (p. 764)
probability distribution (p. 766)
random variable (p. 766)
relative frequency (p. 760)
sample (p. 745)
skewed distribution (p. 773)
standard deviation (p. 754)
statistic (p. 752)
survey (p. 745)
theoretical probability (p. 767)
treatment group (p. 746)
unbiased (p. 745)
variable (p. 752)

Vocabulary Check

Choose a word or term from the list above that best completes each statement. 1. probability distribution

1. A(n) ________ for a particular random variable is a function that maps the sample space to the probabilities of the outcomes of the sample space.
2. When two events are related, there is a(n) ________. correlation
3. A survey is ________ if its design favors certain outcomes. biased
4. The group given the placebo is the ________. control group
5. The ________ provides the interval that shows how much responses from the sample would differ from the population. margin of sampling error
6. A probability distribution with only a finite number of possible outcomes is a(n) ________. discrete probability distribution

FOLDABLES® Study Organizer

Dinah Zike's Foldables

Have students look through the chapter to make sure they have included examples in their Foldables.

Suggest that students keep their Foldables handy while completing the Study Guide and Review pages. Point out that their Foldables can serve as a quick review tool when studying for the chapter test.

Lesson-by-Lesson Review

12-1 Experiments, Surveys, and Observational Studies (pp. 745–750)

912.S.2.1, 912.S.2.3

State whether each survey would produce a random sample. Write *yes* or *no*. Explain.

7. Every tenth shopper coming out of a hardware store is surveyed to determine his or her satisfaction with the store. See margin.
8. Every tenth person coming out of a high school is asked what their favorite class is. See margin.
9. A fast food restaurant asks their customers to complete a survey asking what their favorite fast food restaurant is. See margin.

Determine whether each situation calls for a *survey*, an *observational study*, or an *experiment*. Explain the process. 10. observational study

10. Find 100 students, half of which have part-time jobs, and compare their grade-point averages.
11. Find 100 people and randomly split them into two equal groups. One group eats a specific diet while the other group does not. Compare the results. experiment

EXAMPLE 1

A car dealership selects 100 random customers who recently took their vehicles in for work and asks them how the service was. Would this produce a random sample? Explain.

Yes. Everyone in the population of customers has an equal chance to be part of the sample.

EXAMPLE 2

A teacher has his first class take their test while listening to headphones. His second class does not. He compares their test results. Is this a *survey*, an *observational study*, or an *experiment*? Explain the process.

Experiment. The treatment group is the first class and the control is the second class. This is a biased experiment because the treated group knows who they are.

12-2 Statistical Analysis (pp. 752–758)

912.S.3.3, 912.S.3.4

Determine whether each of the following represents a *population* or a *sample*. 12. sample

12. Jarred conducts an online survey on cancer.
13. The French club wants to compare their AP test scores with the national average. population
14. The field hockey team wants to compare their scoring average with everyone else in the league.
15. **SEASONS** In a random survey of 3446 people, 34% said that spring is their favorite season. What is the margin of sampling error? ±1.7%
16. **SWIMMING** While practicing, Kelly kept track of her times in the 400-meter individual medley. Find the standard deviation of her practice times.

Times in Seconds					
301	311	320	308	312	307
313	315	309	308	304	302
311	313	313	316	314	306
329	326	319	310	306	309
320	318	315	318	314	309

EXAMPLE 3

A national poll estimates that the average number of hours spent per week sitting in traffic is four. Is this a *population* or a *sample*?

This represents a sample because only a fraction of the residents of the United States are polled.

EXAMPLE 4

In a random survey of 2645 people, 12% said that hockey is their favorite sport. What is the margin of sampling error?

$$\text{Margin of sampling error} = \pm\frac{1}{\sqrt{n}}$$
$$= \pm\frac{1}{\sqrt{2645}}$$
$$\approx \pm 0.0194$$

The margin of sampling error ≈ ±1.9%.

14. population
16. 6.37 seconds

Lesson-by-Lesson Review

Intervention If the given examples are not sufficient to review the topics covered by the questions, remind students that the page references tell them where to review that topic in their textbook.

Two-Day Option Have students complete the Lesson-by-Lesson Review on pp. 795–798. Then you can use ExamView® Assessment Suite to customize another review worksheet that practices all the objectives of this chapter or only the objectives on which your students need more help.

Differentiated Instruction

Super DVD: MindJogger Videoquizzes
Use this DVD as an alternative format of review for the test.

Additional Answers

7. Yes; everyone in the population of customers has an equal chance to be part of the sample.
8. Yes; everyone in the population of students has an equal chance to be part of the sample.
9. No; the sample is biased towards the restaurant.

Additional Answer

23a.

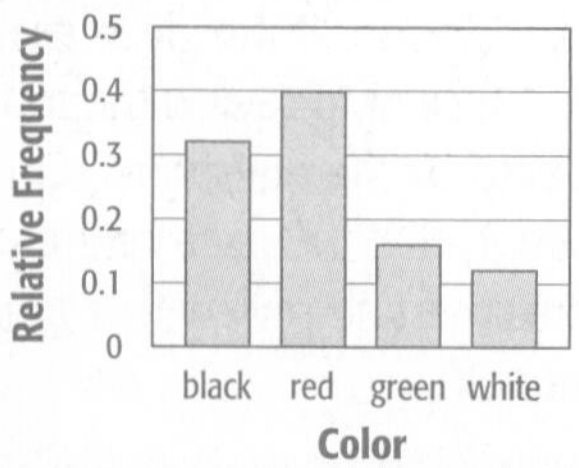

Color	Black	Red	Green	White
Frequency	8	10	4	3

CHAPTER 12 Study Guide and Review

12-3 Conditional Probability (pp. 759–763)

912.P.2.3

17. SOFTBALL Jillian gets a hit 65% of the times she is at bat. What is the probability that she does not get a hit in five consecutive at-bats? **0.005**

18. BASEBALL The results of who made the varsity baseball team are listed in the table below. Find the probability of each.

	Yes	No
Left-Handed	6	5
Right-Handed	15	22

a. Peter made the team given that he is left-handed. $\frac{6}{11}$

b. Paul is right-handed given he did not make the team. $\frac{22}{27}$

EXAMPLE 5

MEDICINE Find the probability that Lori has a Health class, given that she is a freshman.

	Health Class	No Health Class
Freshmen	126	84
Sophomores	98	72

$P(H \mid F)$

$= \frac{P(H \text{ and } F)}{P(F)}$ — **Conditional Probability**

$= \frac{126}{380} \div \frac{210}{380}$ — $P(H \text{ and } F) = \frac{126}{380}$, $P(D) = \frac{210}{380}$

$= \frac{126}{210}$ or $\frac{3}{5}$ — **Simplify.**

12-4 Probability and Probability Distributions (pp. 764–771)

912.P.1.2, 912.P.3.1

SPORTS CARDS Bob is moving and all of his sports cards are mixed up in a box. Twelve cards are baseball, eight are football, and five are basketball. If he reaches in the box and selects them at random, find each probability.

19. P(3 football) $\frac{14}{575}$

20. P(3 baseball) $\frac{11}{115}$

21. P(1 basketball, 2 football) $\frac{7}{115}$

22. P(2 basketball, 1 baseball) $\frac{6}{115}$

23. MARBLES Sammy has a sack of 25 marbles. Eight are black, 10 are red, 4 are green, and the rest are white. He pulls two marbles out of the bag.

a. Create a frequency table and a relative-frequency graph of the data. **See margin.**

b. Which outcome is the most likely to occur? **red**

c. Find P(black and green). $\frac{12}{25}$

24. CARDS Three nines, 4 tens, 5 sixes, 4 fives, 2 twos, and a three are pulled from a deck of cards. If one card is drawn from the cards that were pulled out, what is its expected value? **6.5**

EXAMPLE 6

Ramon has five books on the floor, one for each of his classes: Algebra 2, chemistry, English, Spanish, and history. Ramon is going to put the books on a shelf. If he picks the books up at random and places them in a row on the same shelf, what is the probability that his English, Spanish, and Algebra 2 books will be the leftmost books on the shelf, but not necessarily in that order?

Step 1 Determine how many book arrangements meet the conditions.
$P(3, 3)$ **Place the 3 leftmost books.**
$P(2, 2)$ **Place the other 2 books.**

Step 2 Use the Fundamental Counting Principle to find the number of successes.
$P(3, 3) \cdot P(2, 2) = 3! \cdot 2!$ or 12

Step 3 Find the total number, $s + f$, of possible 5-book arrangements.
$P(5, 5) = 5!$ or 120 $\quad s + f = 120$

Step 4 Determine the probability.
$P = \frac{s}{s+f} = \frac{12}{120}$ or 0.1

The probability of placing English, Spanish, and Algebra 2 before the other two books is 0.1 or 10%.

MIXED PROBLEM SOLVING
For mixed problem-solving practice, see page 990.

12-5 The Normal Distribution (pp. 773–778)

912.P.3.1, 912.P.3.2, 912.P.3.3

A normal distribution of data has each mean and standard deviation. Find each probability.

25. $\mu = 121, \sigma = 9, P(x > 103)$ 97.5%

26. $\mu = 84, \sigma = 8, P(x > 108)$ 0.5%

27. $\mu = 181, \sigma = 12, P(x > 169)$ 84%

28. RUNNING TIMES The times in the 40-meter dash for a select group of professional football players is normally distributed with a mean of 4.7 and a standard deviation of 0.15.

a. About what percent of the players have times below 4.4? 2.5%

b. About how many of the 800 players have times between 4.55 and 4.85? 544

EXAMPLE 7

A normal distribution of data has a mean of 78 and standard deviation of 5. Find the probability that random value x is greater than 83.

$\mu = 78$ and $\sigma = 5$

The probability that a randomly selected value in the distribution is greater than $\mu + \sigma$, that is, $78 + 5$ or 83, is $13.5\% + 2\% + 0.5\% = 16\%$

In the normal curve, this includes the area that is greater than $\mu + \sigma$.

12-6 Hypothesis Testing (pp. 780–784)

912.S.5.2, 912.S.5.3

Find a 95% confidence interval for each of the following.

29. $\bar{x} = 23.3, s = 2.4$, and $n = 80$ $22.8 \leq \bar{x} \leq 23.8$

30. $\bar{x} = 72.2, s = 5.8$, and $n = 120$ $71.1 \leq \bar{x} \leq 73.3$

31. $\bar{x} = 81.4, s = 6.1$, and $n = 200$ $80.5 \leq \bar{x} \leq 82.3$

32. INTERNET A sample of 300 students was asked for the average amount of time they spend online during a week night. The mean time was 64.3 minutes with a standard deviation of 7.3 minutes. Determine a 95% confidence interval. $63.5 \leq \bar{x} \leq 65.1$

33. accept 34. reject 35. reject

Test each null hypothesis. Write *accept* or *reject*.

33. $H_0 = 60, H_1 < 60, n = 100, \bar{x} = 59.4$, and $s = 3.1$

34. $H_0 = 5.5, H_1 > 5.5, n = 80, \bar{x} = 5.8$, and $s = 0.7$

35. $H_0 = 32, H_1 < 32, n = 60, \bar{x} = 31.5$, and $s = 1.8$

36. INTERSECTIONS A light at an intersection is timed to let 10 cars turn left each rotation. Danny believes it is less than 10 and tests the light. After collecting data for 50 rotations, he arrives at a mean of 9.1 cars and a standard deviation of 0.8 cars. Test the hypothesis that the average number of cars is less than 10. Reject the null hypothesis.

EXAMPLE 8

Find a 95% confidence interval for $\bar{x} = 65$, $s = 1.6$, and $n = 100$.

$CI = \bar{x} \pm 1.96 \cdot \frac{s}{\sqrt{n}}$ **Confidence Interval Formula**

$= 65 \pm 1.96 \cdot \frac{1.6}{\sqrt{100}}$ **$\bar{x} = 65, s = 1.6, n = 100$**

$\approx 65 \pm 0.31$ **Simplify.**

The 95% confidence interval is $64.69 \leq \mu \leq 65.31$.

EXAMPLE 9

Test the null hypothesis. Write *accept* or *reject*. $H_0 = 8$, $H_1 < 8$, $n = 90$, $\bar{x} = 8.1$, and $s = 0.7$

$CI = \bar{x} \pm 1.96 \cdot \frac{s}{\sqrt{n}}$ **Confidence Interval Formula**

$= 8.1 \pm 1.96 \cdot \frac{0.7}{\sqrt{90}}$ **$\bar{x} = 8.1, s = 0.7, n = 90$**

$\approx 8.1 \pm 0.15$ **Simplify.**

The 95% confidence interval is $7.95 \leq \mu \leq 8.25$. The confidence interval includes H_0, so we accept the null hypothesis.

Chapter 12 Study Guide and Review 797

Problem Solving Review

For additional practice in problem solving for Chapter 11, see the Mixed Problem Solving Appendix, p. 990, in the Student Handbook section.

Anticipation Guide

Have students complete the Chapter 12 Anticipation Guide and discuss how their responses have changed now that they have completed Chapter 12.

CHAPTER 12 Study Guide and Review

12-7 Binomial Distributions (pp. 786–793)

912.P.3.1, 912.P.3.2

A binomial distribution has a 40% rate of success. There are 10 trials. Calculate the probability of each.

37. exactly 3 successes 21.5%
38. less than 8 successes 98.8%
39. no more than 3 successes 38.2%
40. at least 4 successes 61.8%
41. In a certain dice game, a player tries to roll a total of 3 or 10 with two dice. Kevin designed and conducted a binomial experiment for 7 rolls of the dice. 60%

Simulation	1	2	3	4	5	6	7	Total Successes
1	f	f	f	f	f	f	f	0
2	f	s	f	f	s	f	f	2
3	s	f	f	f	f	f	f	1
4	f	f	f	s	f	s	f	2
5	f	s	f	f	f	f	s	2

From Kevin's experiment, what is the experimental probability of rolling a 3 or 10 twice in seven rolls?

42. **SENIOR TRIP** A poll of students at Ryan's school determined that 76% of the students wanted to go to a theme park for their senior trip. Ryan surveyed 180 random students from the school. What is the probability that at least 60 of the polled students did not want to go to a theme park? 0.5%
43. **WORK** According to an online poll, 28% of adults feel that the standard 40-hour work-week should be increased. Sheila thinks the number should be lower, so she conducts a survey of 250 random adults. What is the probability that more than 55 of the surveyed adults feel that the standard 40-hour work-week should be increased? 97.5%
44. **WATCHES** According to an online poll, 74% of adults wear watches. Timmy surveyed 200 random adults. What is the probability that at least 160 of the adults surveyed wear a watch? 2.5%

EXAMPLE 10

A binomial distribution has a 55% rate of success. There are 8 trials. What is the probability that there will be at least 2 successes?

Calculate the probability of 0 and 1 successes.

$P(1) = C(8, 1)(0.55)^1(0.45)^7$
$= 0.01644$

$P(0) = C(8, 0)(0.55)^0(0.45)^8$
$= 0.00168$

$P(\geq 2 \text{ successes}) = 1 - P(< 2 \text{ successes})$
$= 1 - P(1) - P(0)$
$= 1 - 0.01644 - 0.00168$
$= 0.98188$

There is about a 98% probability that there will be at least 2 successes.

EXAMPLE 11

VACATIONS According to an online poll, 70% of high school students take a vacation during the summer. Louie thinks the number should be lower so he conducts a survey of 650 random students. What is the probability that no more than 420 of the surveyed students go on a vacation in the summer?

The number of people surveyed has a binomial distribution with $n = 650$, $s = 0.70$, and $f = 0.30$.

Use a normal distribution to approximate the probability.

Mean of a normal approximation:

$\bar{x} = ns$
$= 650(0.70)$ or 455 — **$n = 650, s = 0.7$**

Standard deviation of a normal approximation:

$\sigma = \sqrt{nsf}$
$= \sqrt{650(0.7)(0.3)}$ — **$n = 300, s = 0.7, f = 0.3$**
≈ 11.68 — **Use a calculator.**

420 is about 3 standard deviations less than the mean, so the probability that no more than 420 responses agree is 0.5%.

FL Math Online glencoe.com
Chapter Test

Determine whether the following statements show *correlation* or *causation*. Explain. **1, 2. See margin.**

1. When a baseball player hits the ball over the outfielder's head and into the bleachers, he has hit a home run.
2. When Jimmy is running in the hallways, he is late for class.

State whether each survey would produce a random sample. Write *yes* or *no*. Explain. **3, 4. See margin.**

3. An online store surveys its customers asking how much money they spend online per month.
4. A teacher selects the names of 5 students from a hat to determine who gives their speeches in class that day.

Which measure of central tendency best represents the data, and why?

5. **Mean; the data set has no outliers.**

AP Test Scores				
4	4	3	3	3
4	5	5	4	4
3	3	3	3	4
3	3	3	4	4
4	5	3	4	3

6. **Median; the data set has outliers, but there are no big gaps in the middle of the data.**

Height in Inches				
61	64	62	61	64
63	65	61	66	73
74	63	62	65	61
61	62	66	63	61

Determine whether each of the following represents a *population* or a *sample*. **9. population**

7. Olivia records the addresses of every student at her high school. **population**
8. Bridgette compares her class's test results to the national average. **sample**
9. Joey separates the candy in his bag by color.
10. Paul asks 100 random people what their favorite movie is. **sample**
11. NGSSS PRACTICE A survey of 6225 random people found that 48% eat fast food at least once per week. What is the likely interval that contains the percentage of the population that eats fast food at least once per week? **C**

    A. 0.78% B. 1.27% C. ±1.27% D. ±0.78%

A normal distribution of data has each mean and standard deviation. Find each probability.

12. $\mu = 54, \sigma = 5, P(x > 44)$ **97.5%**
13. $\mu = 35, \sigma = 2.4, P(x < 37.4)$ **84%**
14. **TESTS** Mr. Holt's class was given the opportunity to retake a test. He also held an optional review session at school the Sunday before. Some students improved and some did not. **b. $\frac{6}{9} \approx 67\%$**

	Improved	Did not Improve
Attended	12	3
Did not Attend	4	6

a. Find the probability that Michael improved, given he attended the session. **$\frac{12}{15}$ or 80%**

b. Find the probability that Melissa did not attend the session, given she did not improve.

A bag contains 10 blue marbles, 8 red marbles, and 12 green marbles. The marbles are drawn one at a time. Find each probability.

15. The second marble is red, given that the first marble is blue and not replaced. **$\frac{8}{29}$**
16. The second marble is blue, given that the first marble is green and is replaced. **$\frac{10}{30}$ or $\frac{1}{3}$**
17. NGSSS PRACTICE In a box of paper clips, 45 are red, 25 are yellow, and 30 are green. If 12 paperclips are drawn, what is the expected number of green paperclips? **I**

    F. 2.5 G. 4.8 H. 3.0 I. 3.6

18. **DRAWINGS** Ten male and 12 female students have been selected for a drawing for 5 free mp3 players. If the five names will be drawn at random, what is the probability that 3 winners will be male and 2 will be female? **about 30%**

19. reject 20. accept

Test each null hypothesis. Write *accept* or *reject*.

19. $H_0 = 77, H_1 > 77, n = 150, \bar{x} = 78.1$, and $s = 1.3$
20. $H_0 = 65, H_1 < 65, n = 120, \bar{x} = 64.8$, and $s = 2.1$
21. A binomial distribution has a 65% rate of success. There are 15 trials. What is the probability that there will be at least 10 successes? **about 56.4%**
22. **WEATHER** The weatherman says that there is a 40% chance of snow for each of the next seven days. Find the probability that it snows at least 2 of those days. **about 84.1%**

CHAPTER 12 Practice Test

ExamView Assessment Suite — Customize and create multiple versions of your chapter test and their answer keys. All of the questions from the leveled chapter tests in the *Chapter 12 Resource Masters* are also available on ExamView® Assessment Suite.

Additional Answers

1. Causation; the ball going over the outfielder's head and into the bleachers is a direct cause of the homerun.
2. Correlation; while the two may be related, Jimmy could be running in the hallways for another reason.
3. No; because the people surveyed would probably be more likely than others to spend more online.
4. Yes; everyone in the population has an equal chance to be part of the sample.

Intervention Planner

Tier 1 On Level

If students miss about 25% of the exercises or less,

Then choose a resource:

- SE Lessons 12-1, 12-2, 12-3, 12-4, 12-5, 12-6, and 12-7
- CRM Skills Practice, pp. 7, 13, 20, 26, 32, 38, and 45
- TE Chapter Project, p. 742

FL Math Online Self-Check Quiz

Tier 2 Strategic Intervention approaching grade level

If students miss about 50% of the exercises,

Then choose a resource:

- CRM Study Guide and Intervention, Chapter 12, pp. 5, 11, 18, 24, 30, 36, and 43

FL Math Online Extra Examples, Personal Tutor, Homework Help

Tier 3 Intensive Intervention 2 or more grades below level

If students miss about 75% of the exercises,

Then use *Math Triumphs, Alg. 2*, Ch. 5

FL Math Online Extra Examples, Personal Tutor, Homework Help, Review Vocabulary

1 FOCUS

Objective Use the strategy for solving multi-step problems to solve standardized test problems.

2 TEACH

Scaffolding Questions

Ask:

- What is another question to ask yourself when you think that the problem might require multiple steps to solve it? Sample answer: What information am I missing?
- How do you know if you have completed all the steps needed to solve the problem? Sample answer: Go back and check the steps you originally listed. Reread the original problem and see if your solution fits.

Solve Multi-Step Problems

Some problems that you will encounter on standardized tests require you to solve multiple parts in order to come up with the final solution. Use this lesson to practice these types of problems.

Strategies for Solving Multi-Step Problems

Step 1

Read the problem statement carefully.

Ask yourself:

- What am I being asked to solve? What information is given?
- Are there any intermediate steps that need to be completed before I can solve the problem?

Step 2

Organize your approach.

- List the steps you will need to complete in order to solve the problem.
- Remember that there may be more than one possible way to solve the problem.

Step 3

Solve and check.

- Work as efficiently as possible to complete each step and solve.
- If time permits, check your answer.

NGSSS PRACTICE EXAMPLE

Read the problem. Identify what you need to know. Then use the information in the problem to solve.

There are 15 boys and 12 girls in Mrs. Lawrence's homeroom. Suppose a committee is to be made up of 6 randomly selected students. What is the probability that the committee will contain 3 boys and 3 girls? Round your answer to the nearest tenth of a percent.

A. 27.2% **C.** 31.5%

B. 29.6% **D.** 33.8%

Read the problem statement carefully. You are asked to find the probability that a committee will be made up of 3 boys and 3 girls. Finding this probability involves successfully completing several steps.

Step 1 Find the number of possible successes.

There are $C(15, 3)$ ways to choose 3 boys from 15, and there are $C(12, 3)$ to choose 3 girls from 12. Use the Fundamental Counting Principle to find s, the number of possible successes.

$s = C(15, 3) \times C(12, 3) = \frac{15!}{12!3!} \times \frac{12!}{9!3!}$ or 100,100

Step 2 Find the total number of possible outcomes.

Compute the number of ways 6 people can be chosen from a group of 27 students.

$C(27, 6) = 296{,}010$

Step 3 Compute the probability.

Find the probability by comparing the number of successes to the number of possible outcomes.

$P(\text{3 boys, 3 girls}) = \frac{100{,}100}{296{,}010} \approx 0.33816$

So, there is about a 33.8% chance of selecting 3 boys and 3 girls for the committee. The answer is D.

Exercises

Read the problem. Identify what you need to know. Then use the information in the problem to solve.

1. There are 52 cards in a standard deck. Of these, 4 of the cards are Aces. What is the probability of a randomly dealt 5-card hand containing a pair of Aces? Round your answer to the nearest whole percent. A

   A. 4%

   B. 5%

   C. 6%

   D. 7%

2. According to the table, what is the probability that a randomly selected camper went on the horse ride, given that the camper is an 8th grader? H

Grade	Camp Activities		
	Canoe Trip	Horse Ride	Nature Hike
6th	8	6	3
7th	5	4	7
8th	11	9	6

   F. 0.731

   G. 0.441

   H. 0.346

   I. 0.153

Additional Example

STANDARDIZED TEST PRACTICE
A bakery has 8 fudge cakes and 10 yellow cakes, each in a separate, identical box, Anna needs to ice 4 cakes. What is the probability that she will randomly choose 2 fudge cakes and 2 yellow cakes to ice? B

A about 9.7%

B about 12.1%

C about 25.7%

D about 50%

3 ASSESS

Use Exercises 1 and 2 to assess students' understanding.

Diagnose Student Errors

Survey student responses for each item. Class trends may indicate common errors and misconceptions.

1. A. found the probability that the score is more than 2 or more standard deviations above the mean
B. found the probability that the score is more than 2 standard deviations above the mean
C. correct
D. found the probability that the score is above the mean, but no more than 1 standard deviation above the mean

4. F. missed multiplying $-\frac{1}{4}$
G. ignored $-\frac{1}{4}$
H. multiplied $12b$ by $\frac{1}{4}$ instead of $-\frac{1}{4}$
I. correct

5. A. found σx instead of Sx
B. correct
C. guess
D. eliminated duplicate grades

7. F. thinks coefficient determines decay
G. correct
H. thinks base greater than 1 determines decay
I. thinks fractional base determines decay

9. A. found equation that works for only (1, 6)
B. found equation that works for only (1, 6)
C. found incorrect initial term
D. correct

11. F. correct
G. subtracted incorrectly
H. used exterior angle measure instead of its supplement
I. used exterior angle measure instead of its supplement

12. A. correct
B. transposed x and y
C. found inverse of slope
D. found equation that works for only (9, 10.80)

13. F. thinks a greater coefficient gives a wider graph
G. thinks a lessor coefficient gives a wider graph
H. correct
I. thinks a coefficient with a greater absolute value gives a wider graph

15. A. took cube root of 27 and divided 6 by 3 instead of dividing 3 by 6
B. took cube root of 27 and misapplied laws of exponents
C. failed to include x in square root
D. correct

16. F. found one fourth of diameter
G. correct
H. guess
I. found diameter

CHAPTER 12 NGSSS Practice

Cumulative, Chapters 1 through 12

Read each question. Then fill in the correct answer on the answer document provided by your teacher or on a sheet of paper.

1. Suppose the test scores on a final exam are normally distributed with a mean of 74 and a standard deviation of 3. What is the probability that a randomly selected test has a score higher than 77? **C**

 A. 2.5% C. 16%
 B. 13.5% D. 34%

2. **SHORT RESPONSE** Determine whether each of the following situations calls for a *survey*, an *observational study*, or an *experiment*. Explain the process. **a. experiment**

 a. Caroline wants to find out if a particular plant food helps plants to grow faster than just water.
 b. Allison wants to find opinions on favorite candidates in the upcoming student counsel elections. **survey**
 c. Manuel wants to find out if people who get regular exercise sleep better at night. **observational study**

3. **EXTENDED RESPONSE** Christine had one dress and three sweaters cleaned at the dry cleaner and the charge was $19.50. The next week, she had two dresses and two sweaters cleaned for a total charge of $23.00.

 a. Let d represent the price of cleaning a dress and s represent the price of cleaning a sweater. Write a system of linear equations to represent the prices of cleaning each item. **$d + 3s = 19.5$; $2d + 2s = 23$**
 b. Solve the system of equations using substitution or elimination. Explain your choice of method.
 c. What will the charge be if Christine takes two dresses and four sweaters to be cleaned? **$31.00**
 3b. $d = \$7.50$; $s = \$4.00$; substitution, because the variable d in the first equation has a coefficient of 1.

Test-TakingTip

Question 5 You can use a scientific calculator to find the standard deviation. Enter the data values as a list and calculate the 1-Var statistics.

4. Which expression is equivalent to $(6a - 2b) - \frac{1}{4}(4a + 12b)$? **I**

 F. $5a + 10b$ H. $5a + b$
 G. $10a + 10b$ I. $5a - 5b$

5. The table at the right shows the grades earned by students on a science test. Calculate the standard deviation of the test scores. **B**

76	84	91	75	83
82	65	94	90	71
92	84	83	88	80
78	84	89	95	93

 A. 7.82 B. 8.03 C. 8.23 D. 8.75

6. **EXTENDED RESPONSE** Martin is taking a multiple choice test that has 8 questions. Each question has four possible answers: A, B, C, or D. Martin forgot to study for the test, so he must guess at each answer.

 a. What is the probability of guessing a correct answer on the test? **0.25**
 b. What is the expected number of correct answers if Martin guesses at each question? **2**
 c. What is the probability that Martin will get at least half of the questions correct? Round your answer to the nearest tenth of a percent. **about 11.4%**

7. Which of the following functions represents exponential decay? **G**

 F. $y = 0.2(7)^x$ H. $y = 4(9)^x$
 G. $y = (0.5)^x$ I. $y = 5\left(\frac{4}{3}\right)^x$

8. **GRIDDED RESPONSE** Perry drove to the gym at an average rate of 30 miles per hour. It took him 45 minutes. Going home, he took the same route, but drove at a rate of 45 miles per hour. How many miles is it to his house from the gym? **22.5**

802 Chapter 12 Probability and Statistics

9. Using the table below, which expression can be used to determine the nth term of the sequence? D

n	1	2	3	4
y	6	10	14	18

A. $y = 6n$ **C.** $y = 2n + 1$
B. $y = n + 5$ **D.** $y = 2(2n + 1)$

10. THINK SOLVE EXPLAIN **SHORT RESPONSE** Alex wants to find the area of a triangle. He draws the triangle on a coordinate plane and finds that it has vertices at (2, 1), (3, 4), and (1, 4). Find the area of the triangle using determinants. 3 units^2

11. In the figure below, lines a and b are parallel. What are the measures of the angles in the triangle? F

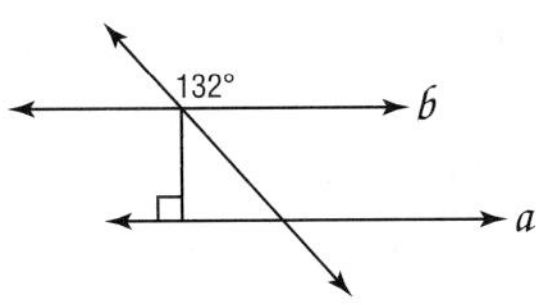

F. 42, 48, 90 **H.** 48, 52, 90
G. 42, 90, 132 **I.** 48, 90, 132

12. An equation can be used to find the total cost of a pizza with a certain diameter. Using the table below, find the equation that best represents y, the total cost, as a function of x, the diameter in inches. A

Diameter, x (in.)	Total Cost, y
9	$10.80
12	$14.40
20	$24.00

A. $y = 1.2x$ **C.** $y = 0.83x$
B. $x = 1.2y$ **D.** $y = x + 1.80$

13. Which shows the functions correctly listed in order from widest to narrowest graph? H

F. $y = 8x^2, y = 2x^2, y = \frac{1}{2}x^2, y = -\frac{4}{5}x^2$

G. $y = -\frac{4}{5}x^2, y = \frac{1}{2}x^2, y = 2x^2, y = 8x^2$

H. $y = \frac{1}{2}x^2, y = -\frac{4}{5}x^2, y = 2x^2, y = 8x^2$

I. $y = 8x^2, y = 2x^2, y = -\frac{4}{5}x^2, y = \frac{1}{2}x^2$

14. **GRIDDED RESPONSE** Carla received a map of some walking paths through her college campus. Paths A, B, and C are parallel. What is the length x to the nearest tenth of a foot? 17.1

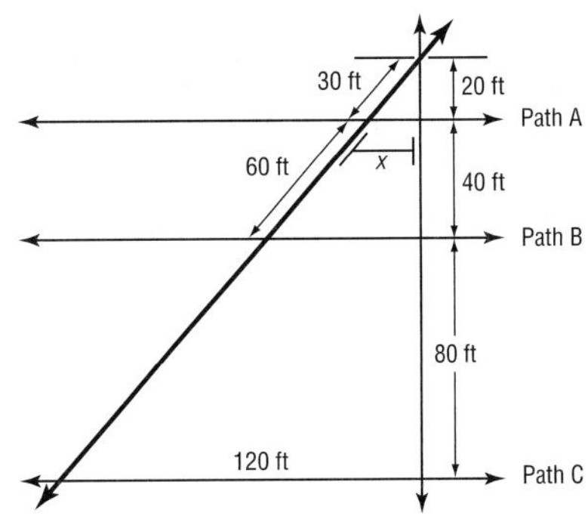

15. Simplify $\sqrt[6]{27x^3}$. D

A. $3x^2$ **B.** $3x$ **C.** $\sqrt{3}x$ **D.** $\sqrt{3x}$

16. A diameter of a circle has endpoints $A(4, 6)$ and $B(-3, -1)$. Find the approximate length of the radius. G

F. 2.5 units **H.** 5.1 units
G. 4.9 units **I.** 9.9 units

Need Extra Help?

If you missed Question...	1	2	3	4	5	6	7	8	9	10	11	12	13	14	15	16
Go to Lesson or Page...	12-5	12-1	3-2	6-1	12-2	12-7	8-1	9-5	11-2	4-5	3-1	2-4	5-7	1-4	7-6	10-1
For help with NGSSS...	912.P.3.1	912.S.2.1	912.A.3.15	912.A.4.2	912.S.3.4	912.S.3.2	912.A.8.3	912.A.2.12	912.D.11.3	912.D.8.2	912.A.3.15	912.A.3.1	912.A.2.10	912.A.3.15	912.A.6.3	912.G.1.1

Formative Assessment

You can use these two pages to benchmark student progress.

CRM *Chapter 12 Resource Masters*

- Standardized Test Practice, pp. 68–70

ExamView Assessment Suite Create practice worksheets or tests that align to your state's standards as well as TIMSS and NAEP tests.

Homework Option

Get Ready for Chapter 13 Assign students the exercises on p. 805 as homework to assess whether they possess the prerequisite skills needed for the next chapter.

Pages 748–749, Lesson 12-1

4. Experiment; students are put into groups at random. The treatment group is the review activities class, and the control is the other class. This is a biased experiment because the participants all know which group they are in.

5. Observational study

6. Experiment; the test subjects are people who are bald or balding. The treatment group gets the treatment, while the control gets a placebo.

8. Correlation; while exercising and being in a better mood can be related, one does not specifically cause the other.

13. Yes; everyone in the population has an equal chance to be part of the sample.

18. Observational study

19. Observational study; the people who run are the treatment group, and people who do not run are the control.

20. Observational study; people who drink soda are the treatment group, people who do not are the control group.

21. Experiment; the test subjects are gardens with deer. The treatment group of gardens gets the treatment, while the control gets a placebo.

26. Sample answer: In call-in surveys, people who call in often have strong opinions and may call more than once.

27. Sample answer: Yes; the majority of employees who leave are not happy about some facet of their employment. The majority of employees who are happy will not leave, and will thus not complete the questionnaire. Biased or not, the goal of these questionnaires is to determine why the employee left.

28. Sample answer: Neither; both experiments are biased because the people in the treatment group *know* they are in the treatment group.

29. Sample answer: A telephone survey can introduce bias because unlisted phone numbers are not called and people without phones are not called.

30. Sample answer: Random sampling of units from a population is done to get a sample that reflects the population as a whole and to avoid bias. Random assignment of treatments to experimental units is done to ensure that the subjects all have an equal chance of getting the treatment and do not know if they are getting the treatment. This is also done to avoid bias.

31a. Sample answer: Survey 50 students at school on their opinions about changing to block scheduling.
Sample: List all of the students at the school and randomly draw 50 names.
Subject of survey: "Rate your opinion about block scheduling at school from 1 to 5, 1 being strongly against and 5 being strongly in favor."

31b. Sample answer: Observe 20 students, half of whom have study halls, and compare their grades at the end of the semester. Control: no study hall; treatment: study hall.

31c. Sample answer: Select a sample of 20 random students with the common cold. Give half of them a pill and the other half a placebo, and compare the results after 3 weeks. Control: placebo; treatment: pill.

32. Sample answer: Bias can occur in an experiment when the treatment group is aware. For example, if a group of people knows they are testing a pill to increase their energy level, they may be preordained to hoping the pill works or doesn't work. Also, if the control group knows they are taking a placebo, they will have no motivation to complete the experiment.

Page 772, Mid-Chapter Quiz

7. Experiment; The treatment group is the half that gets the extra hour. This is biased because everyone knows what group they are in.

Page 777, Lesson 12-5

20. Sample answer: the heights of the players on the Pittsburgh Steelers roster

Heights of the Players on the 2007 Pittsburgh Steelers Roster (inches)							
74	69	75	73	70	75	76	77
74	73	77	70	76	73	72	75
74	71	77	75	75	71	73	69
75	72	72	77	70	73	70	71
70	77	68	71	75	75	77	71
77	79	75	75	80	73	73	70
72	75	73	70	74			

The mean of the data is 73.47 in or 6 ft 1.47 in. The standard deviation is 2.73 in.

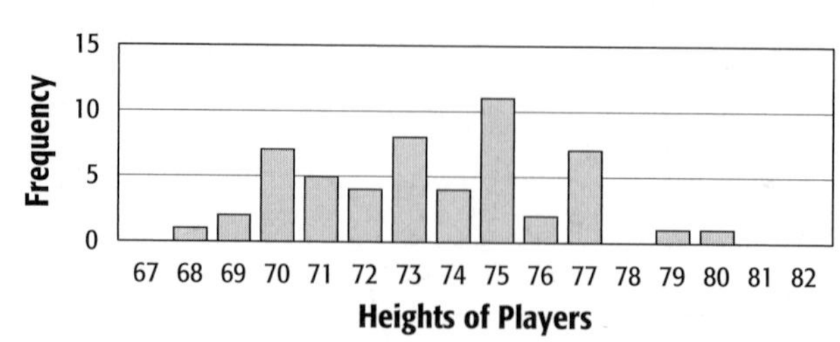

Page 785, Explore 12-7

1. Sample graphs:

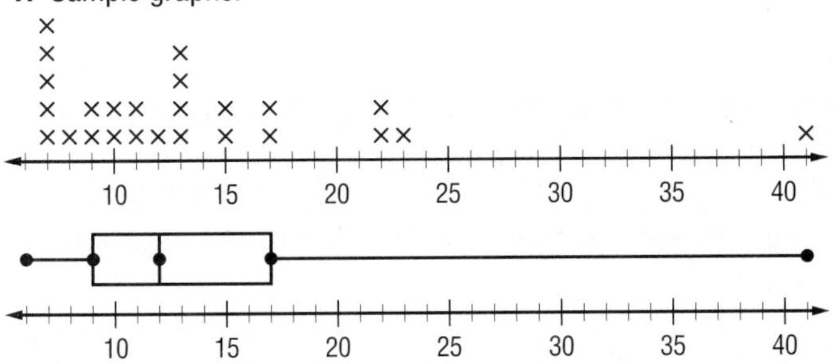

7. Sample answer:

Trial	Complete Set	Trial	Complete Set
1	67	6	49
2	53	7	61
3	20	8	69
4	75	9	43
5	18	10	58

The mean of the data is 51.3 drinks with a standard deviation of 19.5.

Page 791, Lesson 12-7

17a.

Number of Students	Probability
0	0.00000000001%
1	0.000000002%
2	0.000002%
3	0.000008%
4	0.0003%
5	0.006%
6	0.1%
7	1.0%
8	7.5%
9	31.5%
10	59.9%

21a.

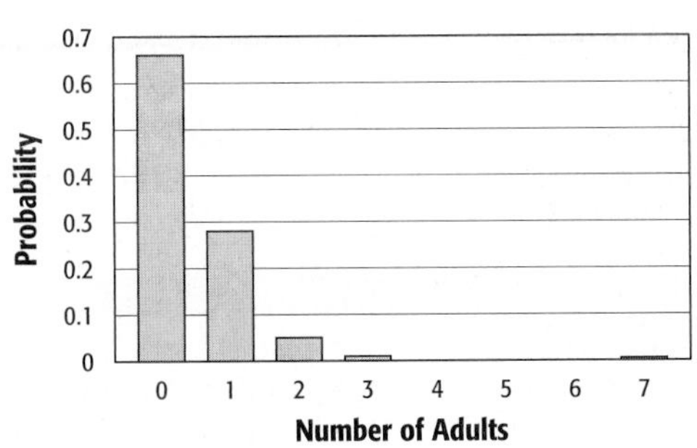

22a.

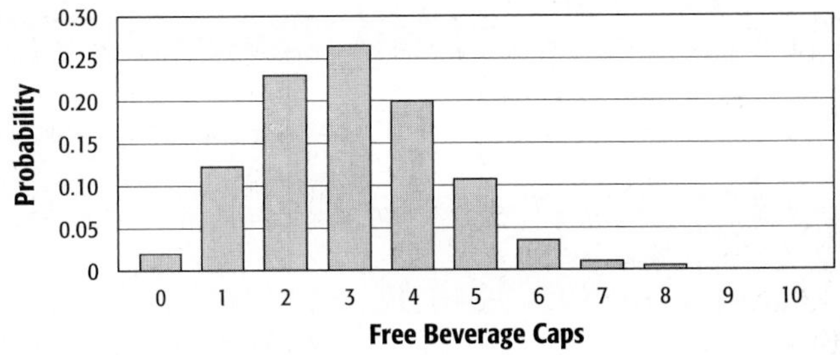

Chapter 12 Answer Appendix

CHAPTER 13

Chapter Planner

Diagnostic Assessment
Quick Check, p. 805

	Explore 13-1 Pacing: 0.5 day	Lesson 13-1 Pacing: 1.5 days	Lesson 13-2 Pacing: 1 day
Title	**Spreadsheet Lab: Investigating Special Right Triangles**	**Trigonometric Functions in Right Triangles**	**Angles and Angle Measures**
Objectives	• Use a spreadsheet to investigate ratios of side lengths is special right triangles.	• Find values of trigonometric functions. • Use trigonometric functions to find side lengths and angle measures of right triangles.	• Draw and find angles in standard position. • Convert between degree measures and radian measures.
Key Vocabulary		trigonometry trigonometric ratio trigonometric function sine cosine tangent cosecant secant cotangent reciprocal functions angle of elevation angle of depression	standard position initial side terminal side coterminal angles radian central angle
NGSSS		MA.912.T.2.1, MA.912.T.2.2	LA.910.1.6.1, MA.912.T.1.1
Multiple Representations			p. 822
Lesson Resources	**Materials** • spreadsheet program and computer	**Chapter 13 Resource Masters** • Study Guide and Intervention, pp. 5–6 AL OL ELL • Skills Practice, p. 7 AL OL ELL • Practice, p. 8 AL OL BL ELL • Word Problem Practice, p. 9 AL OL BL ELL • Enrichment, p. 10 OL BL **Transparencies** • 5-Minute Check Transparency 13-1 AL OL BL ELL **Additional Print Resources** • Study Notebook AL OL BL ELL • Teaching Algebra with Manipulatives, pp. 263–264 AL OL ELL	**Chapter 13 Resource Masters** • Study Guide and Intervention, pp. 11–12 AL OL ELL • Skills Practice, p. 13 AL OL ELL • Practice, p. 14 AL OL BL ELL • Word Problem Practice, p. 15 AL OL BL ELL • Enrichment, p. 16 OL BL **Transparencies** • 5-Minute Check Transparency 13-2 AL OL BL ELL **Additional Print Resources** • Study Notebook AL OL BL ELL
Technology for Every Lesson	FL Math Online glencoe.com • Extra Examples • Self-Check Quizzes • Personal Tutor • Homework Help	**CD/DVD Resources** IWB INTERACTIVE WHITEBOARD READY IWB StudentWorks Plus IWB Interactive Classroom IWB Diagnostic and Assessment Planner	• TeacherWorks Plus • eSolutions Manual Plus • ExamView Assessment Suite
Get Animated			Animation
Differentiated Instruction		pp. 811, 816	pp. 819, 823

KEY: AL Approaching Level OL On Level BL Beyond Level ELL English Learners

Trigonometric Functions

Suggested Pacing			
Time Periods	Instruction	Review & Assessment	Total
45-minute	13	2	15
90-minute	7	1	8

Extend 13-2 Pacing: 0.5 day	Lesson 13-3 Pacing: 1.5 days	Lesson 13-4 Pacing: 1.5 days	Extend 13-4 Pacing: 0.5 day
Geometry Lab: Area of Parallelograms	**Trigonometric Functions of General Angles**	**Law of Sines**	**Geometry Lab: Regular Polygons**
• Use the sine ratio to find the area of a parallelogram.	• Find values of trigonometric functions for general angles. • Find values of trigonometric functions by using reference angles.	• Find the area of a triangle using two sides and an included angle. • Use the Law of Sines to solve triangles.	• Investigate measures in regular polygons using trigonometry.
	quadrantal angle reference angle	Law of Sines solving a triangle	
MA.912.T.1.4	MA.912.T.1.2, MA.912.T.1.3	MA.912.T.2.3, MA.912.T.2.4	MA.912.T.2.3
Additional Print Resources • Teaching Algebra with Manipulatives, p. 265 AL OL ELL	**Chapter 13 Resource Masters** • Study Guide and Intervention, pp. 17–18 AL OL ELL • Skills Practice, p. 19 AL OL ELL • Practice, p. 20 AL OL BL ELL • Word Problem Practice, p. 21 AL OL BL ELL • Enrichment, p. 22 OL BL • Quiz 1, p. 61 AL OL BL ELL **Transparencies** • 5-Minute Check Transparency 13-3 AL OL BL ELL **Additional Print Resources** • Study Notebook AL OL BL ELL	**Chapter 13 Resource Masters** • Study Guide and Intervention, pp. 23–24 AL OL ELL • Skills Practice, p. 25 AL OL ELL • Practice, p. 26 AL OL BL ELL • Word Problem Practice, p. 27 AL OL BL ELL • Enrichment, p. 28 OL BL **Transparencies** • 5-Minute Check Transparency 13-4 AL OL BL ELL **Additional Print Resources** • Study Notebook AL OL BL ELL	**Materials** • compass • straightedge • protractor **Additional Print Resources** • Teaching Algebra with Manipulatives, p. 266 AL OL ELL

FL Math Online glencoe.com
- Extra Examples
- Self-Check Quizzes
- Personal Tutor
- Homework Help

CD/DVD Resources IWB INTERACTIVE WHITEBOARD READY
- IWB StudentWorks Plus
- IWB Interactive Classroom
- IWB Diagnostic and Assessment Planner
- TeacherWorks Plus
- eSolutions Manual Plus
- ExamView Assessment Suite

	Animation		
	pp. 828, 831	pp. 835, 839	

CHAPTER 13

Chapter Planner

	Lesson 13-5 Pacing: 1 day	Lesson 13-6 Pacing: 1 day	Lesson 13-7 Pacing: 1 day
Title	**Law of Cosines**	**Circular Functions**	**Graphing Trigonometric Functions**
Objectives	• Use the Law of Cosines to solve triangles. • Choose methods to solve triangles.	• Find values of trigonometric functions based on the unit circle. • Use the properties of periodic functions to evaluate trigonometric functions.	• Describe and graph the sine, cosine, and tangent functions. • Describe and graph other trigonometric functions.
Key Vocabulary	Law of Cosines	unit circle circular function periodic function cycle period	amplitude frequency
NGSSS	MA.912.T.1.8, MA.912.T.2.3	MA.912.T.1.5, MA.912.T.1.8	MA.912.T.1.5, MA.912.T.1.6
Multiple Representations		p. 853	
Lesson Resources	**Chapter 13 Resource Masters** • Study Guide and Intervention, pp. 29–30 AL OL ELL • Skills Practice, p. 31 AL OL ELL • Practice, p. 32 AL OL BL ELL • Word Problem Practice, p. 33 AL OL BL ELL • Enrichment, p. 34 OL BL • Quiz 2, p. 61 AL OL BL ELL **Transparencies** • 5-Minute Check Transparency 13-5 AL OL BL ELL **Additional Print Resources** • Study Notebook AL OL BL ELL	**Chapter 13 Resource Masters** • Study Guide and Intervention, pp. 35–36 AL OL ELL • Skills Practice, p. 37 AL OL ELL • Practice, p. 38 AL OL BL ELL • Word Problem Practice, p. 39 AL OL BL ELL • Enrichment, p. 40 OL BL **Transparencies** • 5-Minute Check Transparency 13-6 AL OL BL ELL **Additional Print Resources** • Study Notebook AL OL BL ELL	**Chapter 13 Resource Masters** • Study Guide and Intervention, pp. 41–42 AL OL ELL • Skills Practice, p. 43 AL OL ELL • Practice, p. 44 AL OL BL ELL • Word Problem Practice, p. 45 AL OL BL ELL • Enrichment, p. 46 OL BL • Quiz 3, p. 62 AL OL BL ELL **Transparencies** • 5-Minute Check Transparency 13-7 AL OL BL ELL **Additional Print Resources** • Study Notebook AL OL BL ELL
Technology for Every Lesson	FL Math Online glencoe.com • Extra Examples • Self-Check Quizzes • Personal Tutor • Homework Help	**CD/DVD Resources** IWB INTERACTIVE WHITEBOARD READY IWB StudentWorks Plus IWB Interactive Classroom IWB Diagnostic and Assessment Planner	• TeacherWorks Plus • eSolutions Manual Plus • ExamView Assessment Suite
Get Animated			Animation
Differentiated Instruction	pp. 843, 846	pp. 850, 854	pp. 856, 861

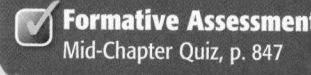

Formative Assessment
Mid-Chapter Quiz, p. 847

KEY: AL Approaching Level OL On Level BL Beyond Level ELL English Learners

Explore 13-8 Pacing: 0.5 day	Lesson 13-8 Pacing: 1.5 days	Lesson 13-9 Pacing: 1 day
Graphing Technology Lab: Trigonometric Graphs	**Translations of Trigonometric Graphs**	**Inverse Trigonometric Functions**
• Use a graphing calculator to explore transformations of the graphs of trigonometric functions.	• Graph horizontal translations of trigonometric graphs and find phase shifts. • Graph vertical translations of trigonometric graphs.	• Find values of inverse trigonometric functions. • Solve equations by using inverse trigonometric functions.
	phase shift vertical shift midline	principal values Arcsine function Arccosine function Arctangent function
MA.912.T.1.6	MA.912.T.1.6, MA.912.T.1.8	MA.912.T.1.7, MA.912.T.1.8
		p. 875
Materials • TI-83/84 Plus or other graphing calculator	**Chapter 13 Resource Masters** • Study Guide and Intervention, pp. 47–48 AL OL ELL • Skills Practice, p. 49 AL OL ELL • Practice, p. 50 AL OL BL ELL • Word Problem Practice, p. 51 AL OL BL ELL • Enrichment, p. 52 OL BL **Transparencies** • 5-Minute Check Transparency 13-8 AL OL BL ELL **Additional Print Resources** • Study Notebook AL OL BL ELL	**Chapter 13 Resource Masters** • Study Guide and Intervention, pp. 53–54 AL OL ELL • Skills Practice, p. 55 AL OL ELL • Practice, p. 56 AL OL BL ELL • Word Problem Practice, p. 57 AL OL BL ELL • Enrichment, p. 58 OL BL • Quiz 4, p. 62 AL OL BL ELL **Transparencies** • 5-Minute Check Transparency 13-9 AL OL BL ELL **Additional Print Resources** • Study Notebook AL OL BL ELL

FL Math Online glencoe.com
- Extra Examples
- Self-Check Quizzes
- Personal Tutor
- Homework Help

CD/DVD Resources IWB INTERACTIVE WHITEBOARD READY
- IWB StudentWorks Plus
- IWB Interactive Classroom
- IWB Diagnostic and Assessment Planner
- TeacherWorks Plus
- eSolutions Manual Plus
- ExamView Assessment Suite

	Animation	Animation
	pp. 864, 870	pp. 873, 876

Summative Assessment
- Study Guide and Review, pp. 877–882
- Practice Test, p. 883

CHAPTER 13 Assessment and Intervention

SE = Student Edition, **TE** = Teacher Edition, **CRM** = Chapter Resource Masters

	Diagnosis	Prescription
Diagnostic Assessment	**Beginning Chapter 13**	
	Get Ready for Chapter 13 **SE,** p. 805	Response to Intervention **TE,** p. 805
	Beginning Every Lesson	
	Then, Now, Why? **SE** 5-Minute Check Transparencies	Chapter 0 **SE,** pp. P1–P19 Concepts and Skills Bank **SE** pp. 993–1006
Formative Assessment	**During/After Every Lesson**	
	Guided Practice **SE,** every example Check Your Understanding **SE** H.O.T. Problems **SE** Spiral Review **SE** Additional Examples **TE** Watch Out! **TE** Step 4, Assess **TE** Chapter 13 Quizzes **CRM,** pp. 61–62 Self-Check Quizzes glencoe.com	Tier 1 Intervention Concepts and Skills Bank **SE,** pp. 993–1006 Skills Practice **CRM,** Ch. 1–13 glencoe.com Tier 2 Intervention Differentiated Instruction **TE** Study Guide and Intervention Masters **CRM,** Ch. 1–13 Tier 3 Intervention *Math Triumphs, Alg. 2,* Ch. 6
	Mid-Chapter	
	Mid-Chapter Quiz **SE,** p. 847 Mid-Chapter Test **CRM,** p. 63 ExamView Assessment Suite	Tier 1 Intervention Concepts and Skills Bank **SE,** pp. 993–1006 Skills Practice **CRM,** Ch. 1–13 glencoe.com Tier 2 Intervention Study Guide and Intervention Masters **CRM,** Ch. 1–13 Tier 3 Intervention *Math Triumphs, Alg. 2,* Ch. 6
	Before Chapter Test	
	Chapter Study Guide and Review **SE,** pp. 877–882 Practice Test **SE,** p. 883 Standardized Test Practice **SE,** pp. 884–887 Chapter Test glencoe.com Standardized Test Practice glencoe.com Vocabulary Review glencoe.com ExamView Assessment Suite	Tier 1 Intervention Concepts and Skills Bank **SE,** pp. 993–1006 Skills Practice **CRM,** Ch. 1–13 glencoe.com Tier 2 Intervention Study Guide and Intervention Masters **CRM,** Ch. 1–13 Tier 3 Intervention *Math Triumphs, Alg. 2,* Ch. 6
Summative Assessment	**After Chapter 13**	
	Multiple-Choice Tests, Forms 1, 2A, 2B **CRM,** pp. 65–70 Free-Response Tests, Forms 2C, 2D, 3 **CRM,** pp. 71–76 Vocabulary Test **CRM,** p. 64 Extended Response Test **CRM,** p. 77 Standardized Test Practice **CRM,** pp. 78–80 ExamView Assessment Suite	Study Guide and Intervention Masters **CRM,** Ch. 1–13 glencoe.com

CHAPTER 13

Differentiated Instruction

Option 1 Reaching All Learners AL OL BL ELL

INTRAPERSONAL Have students choose an angle measure that is greater than 90°, draw an angle with that measure in standard position, find the reference angle, and give the values of all 6 of the trigonometric functions in both degrees and radians.

KINESTHETIC Have students work in groups of three or four. Provide each group with drinking straws, scissors, and glue. Ask students to make a poster of the Key Concepts in Lesson 13-4 and Lesson 13-5, using straws to form the triangles.

Option 2 Approaching Level AL

Working in groups of three or four, students draw a variety of right triangles, each having one angle that measures 30°. Have students measure the lengths of the hypotenuse and the leg opposite the 30° angle to the nearest millimeter. Then ask students to find the sine of 30° in each triangle to determine that sin 30° is the same for each triangle, 0.5. Discuss results with students. Then draw a right triangle with a 30° angle on the board. Label the hypotenuse 8 cm. Ask students how they could find the length of the leg opposite the 30° angle.

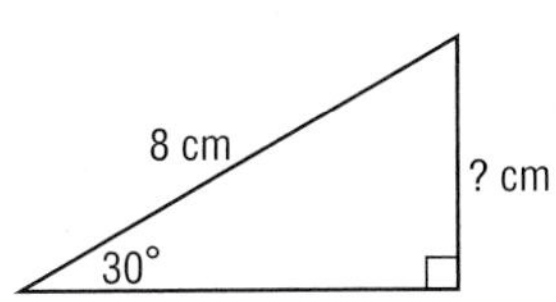

$$\sin 30° = \frac{1}{2} = \frac{?\text{ cm}}{8\text{ cm}}$$

Option 3 English Learners ELL

Have students work in small groups to decide on an informal explanation of what a radian is and what coterminal angles are. Then have a reporter from each group share that explanation with the whole class.

Option 4 Beyond Level BL

Tell students that you want them to draw a triangle and determine its area using each of the following three different ways:

- using the basic formula for the area of a triangle $A = \frac{1}{2}bh$ The lengths of the base and height are needed.
- using Heron's formula The lengths of all three sides are needed.
- using the formula $A = \frac{1}{2}bc \sin A$ The lengths of two sides and the sine of their included angle are needed.

Students may use a protractor and a ruler as needed. Then have students tell what information about the triangle they needed to know when using each method.

FL Math Online Access Point Activities

CHAPTER 13

Focus on Mathematical Content

Vertical Alignment

Before Chapter 13

Related Topics before Algebra 1

- use the Pythagorean Theorem
- apply formulas to solve problems

Previous Topics from Algebra 2

- introduce new notations for inverse functions when logarithmic functions are explored
- restrict domains when inverses for functions, such as $y = x^2$, are found

Chapter 13

Related Topics from Algebra 2

- explore trigonometric functions, first in acute angles in standard form, and also for points on the unit circle
- derive and use the Law of Sines and the Law of Cosines as applications of trigonometric functions
- develop inverses for the sine, cosine, and tangent functions
- use the trigonometric functions to explore amplitude and period
- investigate phase shifts and vertical shifts in the graphs of trigonometric functions

After Chapter 13

Preparation for Precalculus

- continue the study of amplitude, period, and frequency for trigonometric and other periodic functions
- explore trigonometric functions and periodic functions
- explore amplitude and frequency for periodic functions
- look at translations of graphs
- use trigonometric functions for sum and difference of angles
- solve equations involving trigonometric functions

Lesson-by-Lesson Preview

13-1 Trigonometric Functions in Right Triangles

A rule given by a ratio that compares the lengths of the sides of a right triangle is called a *trigonometric function.* The hypotenuse, the leg opposite θ, and leg adjacent to θ are used to define the six trigonometric functions.

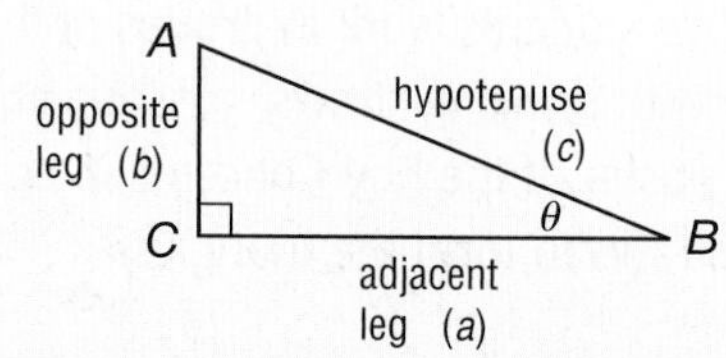

13-2 Angles and Angle Measures

An angle on a coordinate plane is in *standard position* if one ray of the angle (*initial side*) is placed on the positive x-axis and the other ray (*terminal side*) rotates about the origin. The terminal side rotates counterclockwise to show an angle with a positive measure and rotates clockwise to show an angle with a negative measure. It is important to note that the measure a $-210°$ angle is not less than the measure of a $210°$ angle.

Coterminal angles are angles in standard position that have the same terminal side. To find angles that are coterminal to another angle, add or subtract a multiple of 360°.

Angles can be measured in degrees or in *radians*–units that are based on arc length. The fact that π radians $= 180°$ can be used to convert between the two units.

13-3 Trigonometric Functions of General Angles

When a point $P(x, y)$ on the terminal side of the angle θ is known, the value of the six trigonometric functions can be found. Draw a segment from the point perpendicular to the x-axis, forming a right triangle with a leg measuring x units, a leg measuring y units, and a hypotenuse measuring r units, where $r = \sqrt{x^2 + y^2}$. Thus, $\sin \theta = \frac{y}{r}$ and $\cos \theta = \frac{x}{r}$.

To determine the values of trigonometric functions for any nonquadrantal angle θ, find the value of the function for the *reference angle* θ that is formed by the terminal side and the x-axis. The sign of the function is determined by the quadrant in which the terminal side of θ lies.

13-4 Law of Sines and 13-5 Law of Cosines

The *Law of Sines* can be used to solve a triangle if you know

- the measures of two angles and any side (AAS or ASA) or
- the measures of two sides and the angle opposite one of the sides (SSA). When solving a triangle in the SSA case, zero, one, or two solutions are possible.

The *Law of Cosines* can be used to solve a triangle if you know

- the measures of two sides and the included angle, (SAS) or
- the measures of the three sides (SSS).

13-6 Circular Functions

A unit circle–a circle centered at the origin with a radius of 1 unit–can be used to generalize the sine and cosine functions. If the terminal side of an angle θ in standard position intersects the unit circle at a point P with coordinates (x, y), then $\cos \theta = x$ and $\sin \theta = y$.

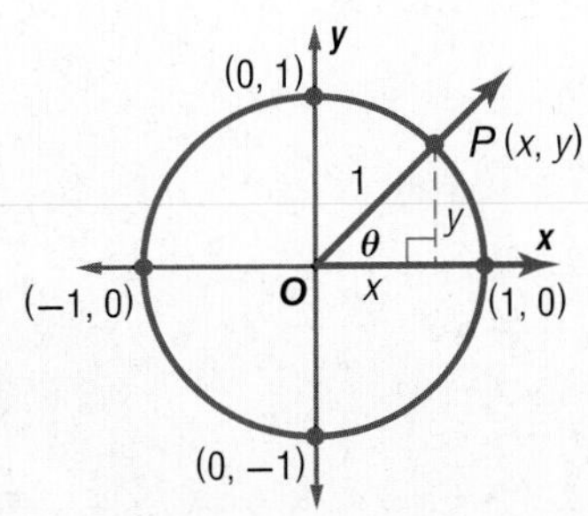

The exact values of $\cos \theta$ and $\sin \theta$ for special angles are shown on the unit circle below.

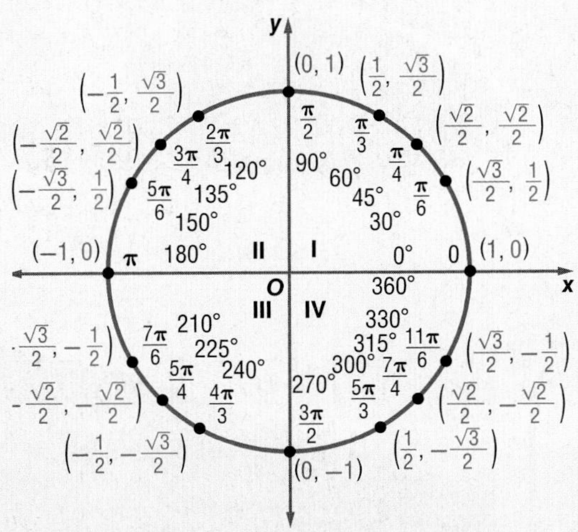

Cycles of the sine and cosine functions repeat every 360°, so they are *periodic functions.*

13-7 Graphing Trigonometric Functions

The graphs of sine, cosine, and tangent functions have repeating patterns (cycles). The horizontal length of each cycle is its *period.* For the sine and cosine functions, the period is 2π radians or 360°. For the tangent function, the period is π radians or 180°. For sine and cosine functions half the difference between the maximum or minimum value is called the *amplitude* of the graph.

Algebraically, for the sine function $y = a \sin b\theta$ and the cosine function $y = a \cos b\theta$, the period is $360° \div |b|$ and the amplitude is $|a|$. For the tangent function $y = a \tan b\theta$, the period is $180° \div |b|$. The graphs of the cosecant, secant, and cotangent functions are related to the graphs of the sine, cosine, and tangent, respectively.

13-8 Translations of Trigonometric Graphs

The graphs of the functions $y = a \sin b(\theta - h) + k$, $y = a \cos b(\theta - h) + k$, and $y = a \tan b(\theta - h) + k$ are affected by changing the values a, b, h, and k.

- A *horizontal translation* is a *phase shift.* If h is positive, the entire graph is shifted to the right; if h is negative, the entire graph is shifted to the left.
- A *vertical translation* is a *vertical shift* of the *horizontal midline.* If k is positive, the entire graph shifts upward; if k is negative, the entire graph shifts downward.
- The *amplitude* is determined by the value of $|a|$, so the maximum values of the function are $|a|$ above k and the minimum values of the function are $|a|$ below k.
- The *period* of a function can also change. As the value of $|b|$ increases, the period of the function decreases.

13-9 Inverse Trigonometric Functions

The section of the sine and tangent graphs between $-90° \left(-\frac{\pi}{2}\right)$ and $90° \left(\frac{\pi}{2}\right)$ and of the cosine graph between 0° (0) and 180° (π) pass the horizontal line test, so inverse functions can be identified for those domains. The functions $y = \sin x$, $y = \cos x$, and $y = \tan x$ are the restricted-domain functions. Their inverses are $y = \sin^{-1} x$ or $y = \arcsin x$, $y = \cos^{-1} x$ or $y = \arccos x$, and $y = \tan^{-1} x$ or $y = \arctan x$.

Professional Development

Targeted professional development has been articulated throughout *Algebra 2.* More quality, customized professional development is available from McGraw-Hill Professional Development. Visit glencoe.com for details on each product.

- **Online Lessons** emphasize the strategies and techniques used to teach Algebra 2. Includes streaming video, interactive pages, and online tools.
- **Video Workshops** allow mentors, coaches, or leadership personnel to facilitate on-site workshops on educational strategies in mathematics and mathematical concepts.
- **MHPD Online** (www.mhpdonline.com) offers online professional development with video clips of instructional strategies, links, student activities, and news and issues in education.
- **Teaching Today** (teachingtoday.glencoe.com) gives secondary teachers practical strategies and materials that inspire excellence and innovation in teaching.

Chapter 13 Notes

Chapter Project

On the Water

Students use what they have learned about trigonometry to describe characteristics of water sports.

- Divide students into small groups. Ask each group to use the Internet, sailing magazines, or books to research information about the sizes of sails for sailboats that are in the shapes of triangles. For example, a small sailboat might have a sail in the shape of an isosceles triangle with the two equal sides having length 13 feet 4 inches, and the third side 14 feet 7 inches.
- Once students have found adequate information, have them find both the area of the sail and the angles made by the edges of the sail at the corners.
- Have them assume that the sail is hung so that one of the sides is horizontal, forming a lower base for the triangle. Then have them find the shortest distance from the lower edge to the top corner of the sail when the sail is hanging flat (as it would be if there were no wind).
- Have each group make a scale model of their sail letting 1 inch = 1 foot. Display the models on a bulletin board.

Chapter 13 Trigonometric Functions

Then
Throughout this text, you have graphed and analyzed functions.

Now
In Chapter 13, you will:

- Find values of trigonometric functions.
- Solve problems by using right triangle trigonometry.
- Solve triangles by using the Law of Sines and Law of Cosines.
- Graph trigonometric functions.

NGSSS
MA.912.T.1.5
MA.912.T.1.6

Why?

WATER SPORTS Knowing trigonometric functions has practical applications in water sports. For instance, you can use right triangle trigonometry to find the distance a kayak has traveled down river. If you are familiar with angles and angle measures, then you have a better understanding of how impressive it is to be able to do a 540° rotation on a wakeboard.

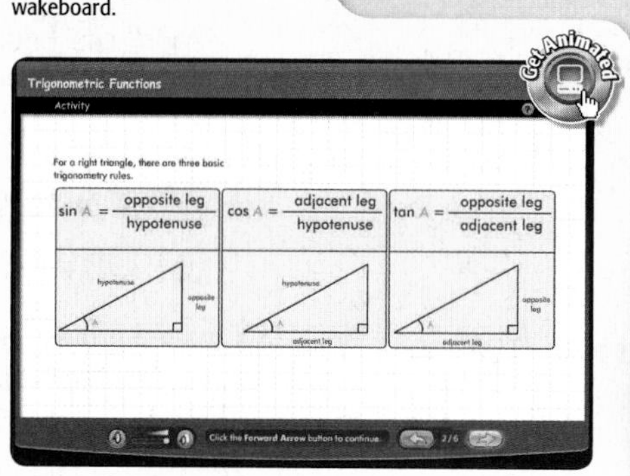

Key Vocabulary Introduce the key vocabulary in the chapter using the routine below.

Define: One radian is the measure of an angle θ in standard position whose rays intercept an arc of length 1 unit on the unit circle.

Example:

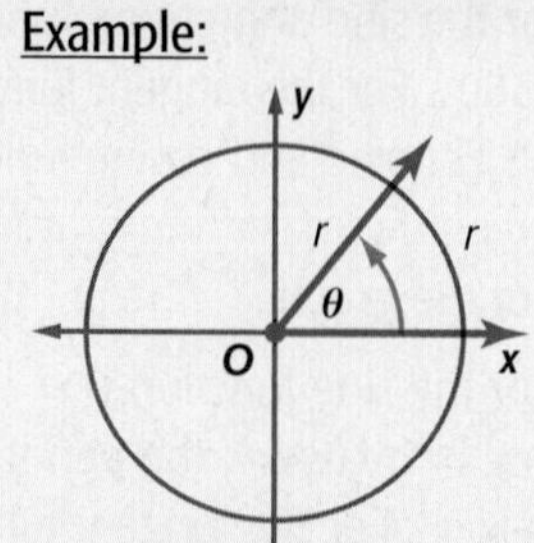

$\theta = 1$ radian

Ask: What does a radian measure? an angle

Get Ready for Chapter 13

Diagnose Readiness You have two options for checking Prerequisite Skills.

Text Option Take the Quick Check below. Refer to the Quick Review for help.

*Quick*Check

(Used in Lessons 13-1 and 13-3)
Find the value of x to the nearest tenth. (Lesson 0-7)

1. 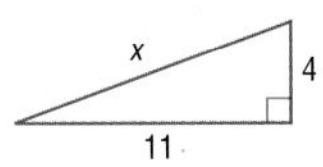

11.7

2. 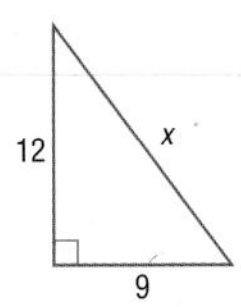

15

3. 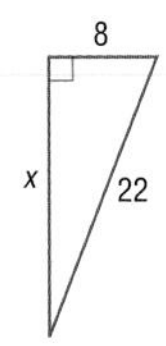

20.5

4. Laura has a rectangular garden in her backyard that measures 12 feet by 15 feet. She wants to put a rock walkway on the diagonal. How long will the walkway be? Round to the nearest tenth of a foot. 19.2 feet

(Used in Lesson 13-1)
Find each missing measure. Write all radicals in simplest form. (Geometry)

5. 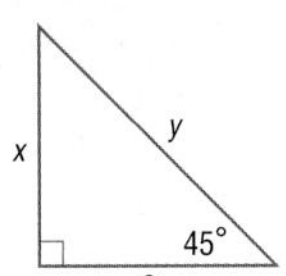

$x = 9,\ y = 9\sqrt{2}$

6. 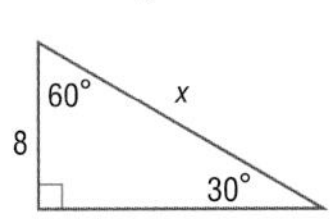

$x = 16,\ y = 8\sqrt{3}$

7. 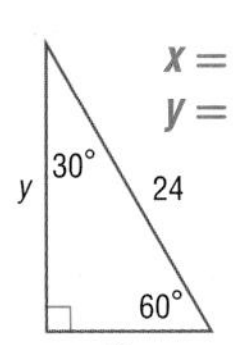

$x = 12,$
$y = 12\sqrt{3}$

8. A ladder leans against a wall at a 45° angle. If the ladder is 12 feet long, how far up the wall does the ladder reach?

*Quick*Review

EXAMPLE 1

Find the missing measure of the right triangle.

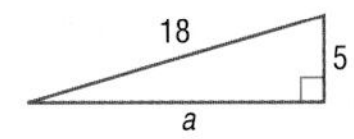

$c^2 = a^2 + b^2$	Pythagorean Theorem
$18^2 = a^2 + 5^2$	Replace c with 18 and b with 5.
$324 = a^2 + 25$	Simplify.
$299 = a^2$	Subtract 25 from each side.
$17.3 \approx a$	Take the positive square root of each side.

EXAMPLE 2

Find the missing measures. Write all radicals in simplest form.

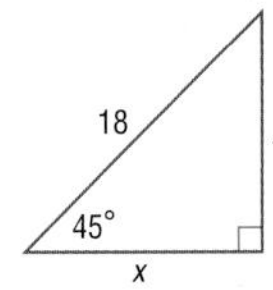

$x^2 + x^2 = 18^2$	Pythagorean Theorem
$2x^2 = 18^2$	Combine like terms.
$2x^2 = 324$	Simplify.
$x^2 = 162$	Divide each side by 2.
$x = \sqrt{162}$	Take the positive square root of each side.
$x = 9\sqrt{2}$	Simplify.

8. $6\sqrt{2}$ ft or about 8.5 ft

Online Option FL Math Online Take a self-check Chapter Readiness Quiz at glencoe.com.

Get Ready for Chapter 13

Response to Intervention (RtI)

Use the *Quick Check* results and the Intervention Planner to help you determine your Response to Intervention. The If-Then statements in the chart below help you decide the appropriate tier of RtI and suggest intervention resources for each tier.

Intervention Planner

Tier 1 — On Level

If students miss about 25% of the exercises or less,

Then choose a resource:

- **SE** Concepts and Skills Bank, p. 995; Lesson 0-7
- **TE** Chapter Project, p. 804
- FL Math Online Self-Check Quiz

Tier 2 — Strategic Intervention approaching grade level

If students miss about 50% of the exercises,

Then choose a resource:

FL Math Online Extra Examples, Personal Tutor, Homework Help

Tier 3 — Intensive Intervention 2 or more years below grade level

If students miss about 75% of the exercises,

Then use *Math Triumphs, Alg. 2,* Ch. 6

FL Math Online Extra Examples, Personal Tutor, Homework Help, Review Vocabulary

CHAPTER 13 Notes

FOLDABLES® Study Organizer

Dinah Zike's Foldables®

Focus Students write notes as they explore trigonometric functions in the lessons of this chapter.

Teach Have students make and label their Foldables as illustrated. Have students use the appropriate tab as they cover each lesson in this chapter. Lessons 13-8 and 13-9 should go on the last tab. Encourage students to apply what they have learned by writing their own examples as well.

When to Use It Encourage students to add to their Foldables as they work through the chapter and to use them to review for the chapter test.

Differentiated Instruction

CRM Student-Built Glossary, pp. 1–2 Students should complete the chart by providing a definition of each term and an example as they progress through Chapter 13. This study tool can also be used to review for the chapter test.

Get Started on Chapter 13

You will learn several new concepts, skills, and vocabulary terms as you study Chapter 13. To get ready, identify important terms and organize your resources. You may wish to refer to **Chapter 0** to review prerequisite skills.

Trigonometric Functions Make this Foldable to help you organize your Chapter 13 notes about trigonometric functions. Begin with four pieces of grid paper.

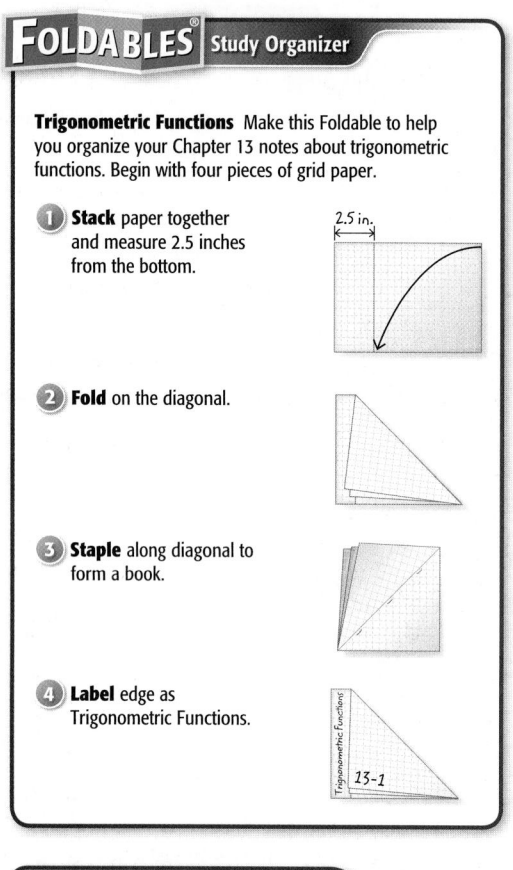

1. **Stack** paper together and measure 2.5 inches from the bottom.

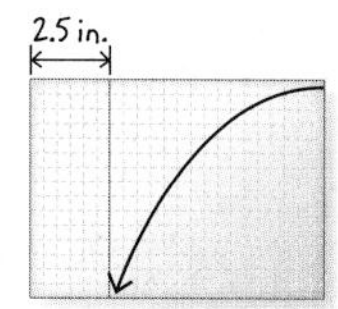

2. **Fold** on the diagonal.

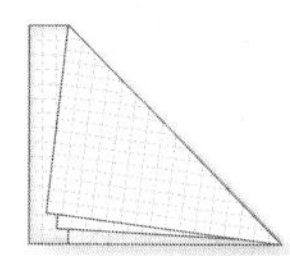

3. **Staple** along diagonal to form a book.

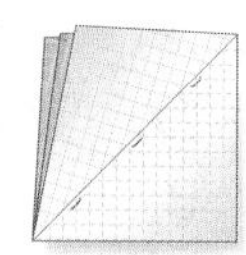

4. **Label** edge as Trigonometric Functions.

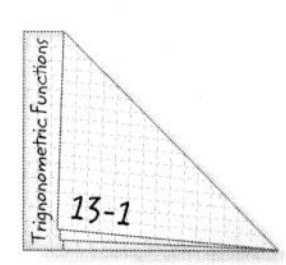

FL Math Online glencoe.com

- Study the chapter online
- Explore **Get Animated**
- Get extra help from your own **Personal Tutor**
- Use **Extra Examples** for additional help
- Take a **Self-Check Quiz**
- **Review Vocabulary** in fun ways

New Vocabulary

English		Español
trigonometry	• p. 808 •	trigonometría
sine	• p. 808 •	seno
cosine	• p. 808 •	coseno
tangent	• p. 808 •	tangente
cosecant	• p. 808 •	cosecante
secant	• p. 808 •	secante
cotangent	• p. 808 •	cotangente
angle of elevation	• p. 812 •	ángulo de depresión
angle of depression	• p. 812 •	ángulo de elevación
standard position	• p. 817 •	posición estándar
radian	• p. 819 •	radián
Law of Sines	• p. 833 •	Ley de los senos
Law of Cosines	• p. 841 •	Ley de los cosenos
unit circle	• p. 848 •	círculo unitario
circular function	• p. 848 •	funciones circulares
periodic function	• p. 849 •	función periódica
cycle	• p. 849 •	ciclo
period	• p. 849 •	período
amplitude	• p. 855 •	amplitud
frequency	• p. 856 •	frecuencia

Review Vocabulary

acute angle • prior course • ángulo agudo an angle with a measure between 0° and 90°

function • p. P4 • función a relation in which each element of the domain is paired with exactly one element in the range

inverse function • p. 417 • función inversa two functions f and g are inverse functions if and only if both of their compositions are the identity function

Pythagorean Theorem • p. P17 • Teorema de Pitágoras

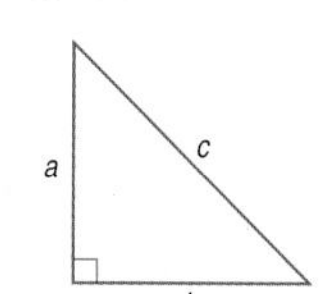

$a^2 + b^2 = c^2$

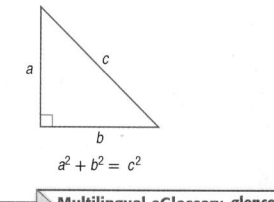

Multilingual eGlossary glencoe.com

Additional Answer (Explore 13-1)

1.

	A	B	C	D	E	F
1	a	b	c	b/a	b/c	a/c
2	1	1.732050808	2	1.732050808	0.866025404	0.5
3	2	3.464101615	4	1.732050808	0.866025404	0.5
4	3	5.196152423	6	1.732050808	0.866025404	0.5
5	4	6.92820323	8	1.732050808	0.866025404	0.5
6	5	8.660254038	10	1.732050808	0.866025404	0.5
7	6	10.39230485	12	1.732050808	0.866025404	0.5

EXPLORE

13-1 Spreadsheet Lab: Investigating Special Right Triangles

FL Math Online glencoe.com
Graphing Technology Personal Tutor

You can use a spreadsheet to investigate side measures of special right triangles.

ACTIVITY 45°-45°-90° Triangle

The legs of a 45°-45°-90° triangle, *a* and *b*, are equal in measure. What patterns do you observe in the ratios of the side measures of these triangles?

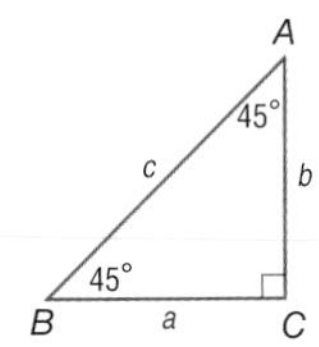

Step 1 Enter the indicated formulas in the spreadsheet. The formula uses the Pythagorean Theorem in the form $c = \sqrt{a^2 + b^2}$.

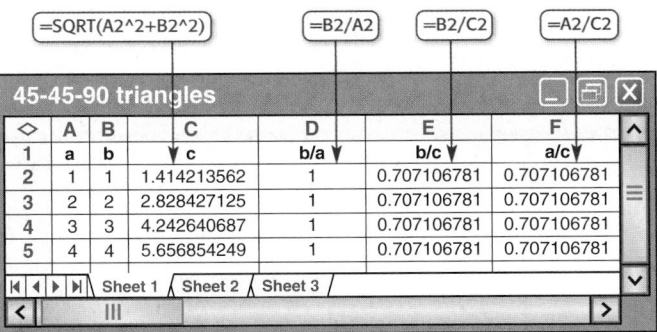

=SQRT(A2^2+B2^2) (column C), =B2/A2 (column D), =B2/C2 (column E), =A2/C2 (column F)

45-45-90 triangles

◇	A	B	C	D	E	F
1	a	b	c	b/a	b/c	a/c
2	1	1	1.414213562	1	0.707106781	0.707106781
3	2	2	2.828427125	1	0.707106781	0.707106781
4	3	3	4.242640687	1	0.707106781	0.707106781
5	4	4	5.656854249	1	0.707106781	0.707106781

Sheet 1 | Sheet 2 | Sheet 3

Step 2 Examine the results. Because 45°-45°-90° triangles share the same angle measures, these triangles are all similar. The ratios of the sides of these triangles are all the same. The ratios of side *b* to side *a* are 1. The ratios of side *b* to side *c* and of side *a* to side *c* are approximately 0.71.

Model and Analyze

Use the spreadsheet below for 30°-60°-90° triangles.

30-60-90 triangles

◇	A	B	C	D	E	F
1	a	b	c	b/a	b/c	a/c
2	1		2			
3	2		4			
4	3		6			
5	4		8			

Sheet 1 | Sheet 2 | Sheet 3

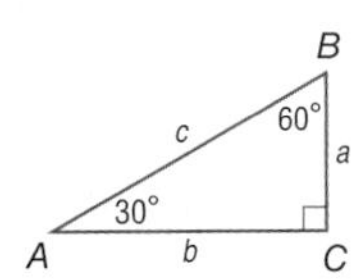

3. All of the ratios of side *b* to side *a* are approximately 1.73. All of the ratios of side *b* to side *c* are approximately 0.87. All of the ratios of side *a* to side *c* are 0.5.

1. Copy and complete the spreadsheet above. **See margin.**
2. Describe the relationship among the 30°-60°-90° triangles with the dimensions given. **The triangles are all similar.**
3. What patterns do you observe in the ratios of the side measures of these triangles?

Extending the Concept

Ask:

- Ask students what formula could have been used in column B for the 45°-45°-90° triangle instead of entering the data? in column C for the 30°-60°-90° triangle? $b = a$; $c = 2a$
- Ask students to compare the 30°-60°-90° triangles. What is the same? What is different? The angle measures are all the same, but the side measures are different. The triangles are similar but not congruent.

EXPLORE

13-1 Lesson Notes

1 FOCUS

Objective Use a spreadsheet to investigate ratios of side lengths in special right triangles.

Materials for Each Student

- spreadsheet program and computer

Teaching Tip Have students practice their skills in using a spreadsheet by entering the data in the example. Have students format the cells before they start to enter the data by using the Format Cells command. Format columns C, E, and F for numbers with 9 decimal places. Format columns A, B, and D for integers.

2 TEACH

Working in Cooperative Groups

Have students work with partners, mixing abilities so that a student with more knowledge of spreadsheets is paired with one who has less experience.

Practice Have students complete the Activity and Exercises 1–3.

3 ASSESS

Formative Assessment

Use Exercise 1 to assess whether students comprehend how to enter data into a spreadsheet.

From Concrete to Abstract

Ask students to describe the rule, pattern, or formula for various cells of the spreadsheet.

Explore 13-1 Spreadsheet Lab: Investigating Special Right Triangles 807

13-1 Lesson Notes

1 FOCUS

Vertical Alignment

Before Lesson 13-1
Use the Pythagorean Theorem to find side lengths of right triangles.

Lesson 13-1
Find values of trigonometric functions.
Use trigonometric functions to find side lengths and angle measures of right triangles.

After Lesson 13-1
Investigate graphs of the sine and cosine functions.

2 TEACH

Scaffolding Questions

Have students read the *Why?* section of the lesson.

Ask:

- What kind of angle is formed by the tow rope and the horizontal? acute
- Which side of the triangle is opposite the right angle? Which side is opposite the $x°$ angle? the hypotenuse ℓ; altitude
- If length ℓ is constant and x increases, how does the altitude change? It increases.

13-1 Trigonometric Functions in Right Triangles

Then
You used the Pythagorean Theorem to find side lengths of right triangles.

Now
- Find values of trigonometric functions for acute angles.
- Use trigonometric functions to find side lengths and angle measures of right triangles.

NGSSS
MA.912.T.2.1 Define and use the trigonometric ratios (sine, cosine, tangent, cotangent, secant, cosecant) in terms of angles of right triangles.
MA.912.T.2.2 Solve real-world problems involving right triangles using technology when appropriate.

New Vocabulary
trigonometry
trigonometric ratio
trigonometric function
sine
cosine
tangent
cosecant
secant
cotangent
reciprocal functions
angle of elevation
angle of depression

FL Math Online
glencoe.com

Why?

The altitude of a person parasailing depends on the length of the tow rope ℓ and the angle the rope makes with the horizontal $x°$. If you know these two values, you can use a ratio to find the altitude of the person parasailing.

Trigonometric Functions for Acute Angles **Trigonometry** is the study of relationships among the angles and sides of a right triangle. A **trigonometric ratio** compares the side lengths of a right triangle. A **trigonometric function** has a rule given by a trigonometric ratio.

The Greek letter *theta* θ is often used to represent the measure of an acute angle in a right triangle. The *hypotenuse*, the *leg opposite* θ, and the *leg adjacent to* θ are used to define the six trigonometric functions.

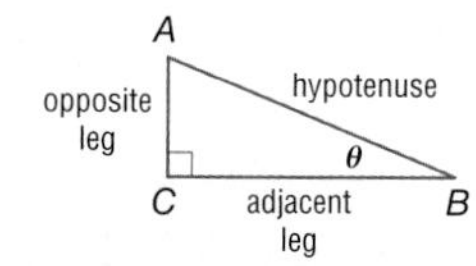

Key Concept — Trigonometric Functions in Right Triangles

Words If θ is the measure of an acute angle of a right triangle, then the following trigonometric functions involving the opposite side *opp*, the adjacent side *adj*, and the hypotenuse *hyp* are true.

Symbols

$\sin$ (**sine**) $\theta = \frac{\text{opp}}{\text{hyp}}$ $\qquad$ $\csc$ (**cosecant**) $\theta = \frac{\text{hyp}}{\text{opp}}$

$\cos$ (**cosine**) $\theta = \frac{\text{adj}}{\text{hyp}}$ $\qquad$ $\sec$ (**secant**) $\theta = \frac{\text{hyp}}{\text{adj}}$

$\tan$ (**tangent**) $\theta = \frac{\text{opp}}{\text{adj}}$ $\qquad$ $\cot$ (**cotangent**) $\theta = \frac{\text{adj}}{\text{opp}}$

Examples

$\sin\theta = \frac{4}{5}$ $\qquad$ $\cos\theta = \frac{3}{5}$ $\qquad$ $\tan\theta = \frac{4}{3}$

$\csc\theta = \frac{5}{4}$ $\qquad$ $\sec\theta = \frac{5}{3}$ $\qquad$ $\cot\theta = \frac{3}{4}$

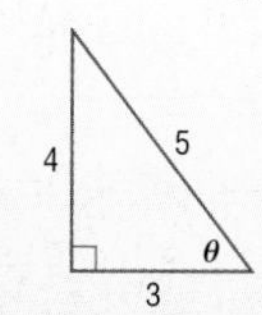

EXAMPLE 1 Evaluate Trigonometric Functions

Find the values of the six trigonometric functions for angle θ.

leg opposite θ: $BC = 8$ $\qquad$ leg adjacent θ: $AC = 15$ $\qquad$ hypotenuse: $AB = 17$

$\sin\theta = \frac{\text{opp}}{\text{hyp}} = \frac{8}{17}$ $\qquad$ $\cos\theta = \frac{\text{adj}}{\text{hyp}} = \frac{15}{17}$ $\qquad$ $\tan\theta = \frac{\text{opp}}{\text{adj}} = \frac{8}{15}$

$\csc\theta = \frac{\text{hyp}}{\text{opp}} = \frac{17}{8}$ $\qquad$ $\sec\theta = \frac{\text{hyp}}{\text{adj}} = \frac{17}{15}$ $\qquad$ $\cot\theta = \frac{\text{adj}}{\text{opp}} = \frac{15}{8}$

Guided Practice

1. Find the values of the six trigonometric functions for angle B. See margin.

Personal Tutor glencoe.com

Lesson 13-1 Resources

Resource	Approaching-Level	On-Level	Beyond-Level	English Learners
Teacher Edition	• Differentiated Instruction, p. 811	• Differentiated Instruction, pp. 811, 816	• Differentiated Instruction, p. 816	
Chapter Resource Masters	• Study Guide and Intervention, pp. 5–6 • Skills Practice, p. 7 • Practice, p. 8 • Word Problem Practice, p. 9	• Study Guide and Intervention, pp. 5–6 • Skills Practice, p. 7 • Practice, p. 8 • Word Problem Practice, p. 9 • Enrichment, p. 10	• Practice, p. 8 • Word Problem Practice, p. 9 • Enrichment, p. 10	• Study Guide and Intervention, pp. 5–6 • Skills Practice, p. 7 • Practice, p. 8 • Word Problem Practice, p. 9
Transparencies	• 5-Minute Check Transparency 13-1	• 5-Minute Check Transparency 13-1	• 5-Minute Check Transparency 13-1	• 5-Minute Check Transparency 13-1
Other	• Study Notebook • Teaching Algebra with Manipulatives	• Study Notebook • Teaching Algebra with Manipulatives	• Study Notebook	• Study Notebook • Teaching Algebra with Manipulatives

StudyTip

Memorize Trigonometric Ratios SOH-CAH-TOA is a mnemonic device for remembering the first letter of each word in the ratios for sine, cosine, and tangent.

$\sin\theta = \frac{\text{opp}}{\text{hyp}}$

$\cos\theta = \frac{\text{adj}}{\text{hyp}}$

$\tan\theta = \frac{\text{opp}}{\text{adj}}$

Notice that the cosecant, secant, and cotangent ratios are reciprocals of the sine, cosine, and tangent ratios, respectively. These are called the **reciprocal functions**. So, the following are also true.

$$\csc\theta = \frac{1}{\sin\theta} \qquad \sec\theta = \frac{1}{\cos\theta} \qquad \cot\theta = \frac{1}{\tan\theta}$$

The domain of any trigonometric function is the set of all acute angles θ of a right triangle. So, trigonometric functions depend only on the measures of the acute angles, not on the side lengths of a right triangle.

EXAMPLE 2 Find Trigonometric Ratios

In a right triangle, $\angle B$ is acute and $\sin B = \frac{5}{8}$. Find the value of $\tan B$.

Step 1 Draw a right triangle and label one acute angle B. Since $\sin B = \frac{5}{8} = \frac{\text{opp}}{\text{hyp}}$, label the opposite side 5 and the hypotenuse 8.

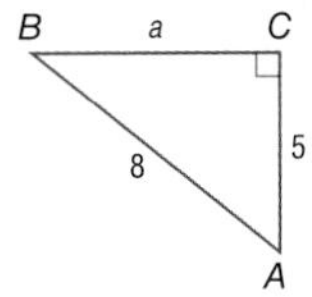

Step 2 Use the Pythagorean Theorem to find a.

$a^2 + b^2 = c^2$	**Pythagorean Theorem**
$a^2 + 5^2 = 8^2$	**$b = 5$ and $c = 8$**
$a^2 + 25 = 64$	**Simplify.**
$a^2 = 39$	**Subtract 25 from each side.**
$a = \pm\sqrt{39}$	**Take the square root of each side.**
$a = \sqrt{39}$	**Length cannot be negative.**

Step 3 Find $\tan B$.

$\tan B = \frac{\text{opp}}{\text{adj}}$	**Tangent function**
$= \frac{5}{\sqrt{39}}$	**Replace *opp* with 5 and *adj* with $\sqrt{39}$.**
$= \frac{5\sqrt{39}}{39}$	**Rationalize the denominator.**

Guided Practice

2. If $\tan B = \frac{3}{7}$, find the value of $\sin B$. $\frac{3\sqrt{58}}{58}$

Personal Tutor glencoe.com

ReadingMath

Labeling Triangles Throughout this chapter, a capital letter is used to represent both a vertex of a triangle and the measure of the angle at that vertex. The same letter in lowercase is used to represent both the side opposite that angle and the length of the side.

Angles that measure 30°, 45°, and 60° occur frequently in trigonometry. The table below gives the values of three trigonometric functions for these angles.

Key Concept Trigonometric Values for Special Angles

30°-60°-90°

$\sin 30° = \frac{1}{2}$ $\quad\cos 30° = \frac{\sqrt{3}}{2}$ $\quad\tan 30° = \frac{\sqrt{3}}{3}$

$\sin 60° = \frac{\sqrt{3}}{2}$ $\quad\cos 60° = \frac{1}{2}$ $\quad\tan 60° = \sqrt{3}$

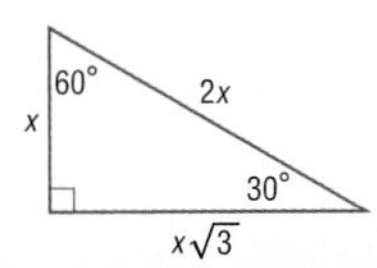

45°-45°-90°

$\sin 45° = \frac{\sqrt{2}}{2}$ $\quad\cos 45° = \frac{\sqrt{2}}{2}$ $\quad\tan 45° = 1$

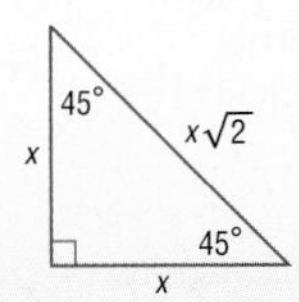

Trigonometric Functions for Acute Angles

Example 1 shows how to find the values of the six trigonometric functions for an angle. **Example 2** shows how to use one trigonometric ratio for an angle to find another.

Formative Assessment

Use the Guided Practice exercises after each example to determine students' understanding of concepts.

Additional Examples

1 Find the values of the six trigonometric functions for angle G.

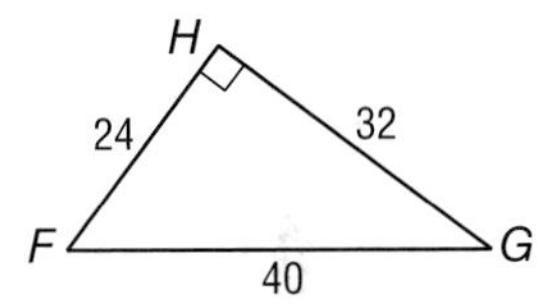

$\sin G = \frac{3}{5}$, $\cos G = \frac{4}{5}$,

$\tan G = \frac{3}{4}$, $\cot G = \frac{4}{3}$,

$\sec G = \frac{5}{4}$, $\csc G = \frac{5}{3}$

2 In a right triangle, $\angle A$ is acute and $\tan A = \frac{5}{3}$. Find the value of $\csc A$. $\frac{\sqrt{34}}{5}$

Additional Examples also in Interactive Classroom PowerPoint® Presentations

IWB INTERACTIVE WHITEBOARD READY

Additional Answer (Guided Practice)

1. $\sin B = \frac{15}{17}$, $\cos B = \frac{8}{17}$, $\tan B = \frac{15}{8}$, $\csc B = \frac{17}{15}$, $\sec B = \frac{17}{8}$, $\cot B = \frac{8}{15}$

TEACH with TECH

INTERACTIVE WHITEBOARD Draw a right triangle on the board and label each of the side lengths. To write the trigonometric ratios, drag the measurement from the side of the triangle to the ratio.

Tips for New Teachers

Reasoning The relative lengths of the sides of the two special triangles in the Key Concept box on this page are critical. Have students learn how to recreate these triangles themselves from memory. From the triangles, they can generate the values shown in the Key Concept box.

Use Trigonometric Functions

Examples 3 and 4 show how to use a trigonometric ratio to find a missing side length of a right triangle. **Example 5** shows how to find missing angle measures of a right triangle. **Example 6** shows how to use angles of elevation and depression to solve real-world problems.

Additional Examples

3 Use a trigonometric function to find the value of x. Round to the nearest tenth if necessary. 10.4

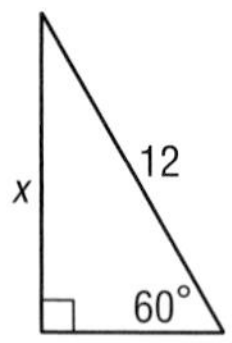

4 **BUILDINGS** In Example 4, what is the distance from the top of the building to Joel's eye? about 827 ft

---

Use Trigonometric Functions You can use trigonometric functions to find missing side lengths and missing angle measures of right triangles.

EXAMPLE 3 Find a Missing Side Length

Use a trigonometric function to find the value of x. Round to the nearest tenth if necessary.

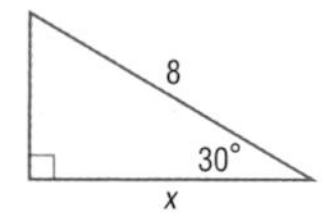

The length of the hypotenuse is 8. The missing measure is for the side adjacent to the 30° angle. Use the cosine function to find x.

$\cos\theta = \frac{\text{adj}}{\text{hyp}}$	**Cosine function**
$\cos 30° = \frac{x}{8}$	**Replace θ with 30°, *adj* with x, and *hyp* with 8.**
$\frac{\sqrt{3}}{2} = \frac{x}{8}$	**$\cos 30° = \frac{\sqrt{3}}{2}$**
$\frac{8\sqrt{3}}{2} = x$	**Multiply each side by 8.**
$6.9 \approx x$	**Use a calculator.**

StudyTip

Choose a Function If the length of the hypotenuse is unknown, then either the sine or cosine function must be used to find the missing measure.

Guided Practice

3A. 7

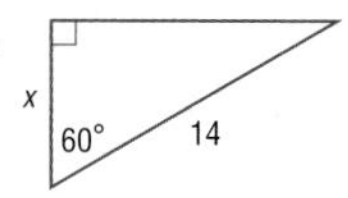

3B. 14.1

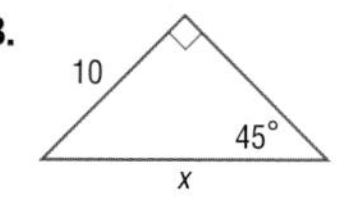

Personal Tutor glencoe.com

You can use a calculator to find the missing side lengths of triangles that do not have 30°, 45°, or 60° angles.

Real-World Link

Inclinometers measure the angle of Earth's magnetic field as well as the pitch and roll of vehicles, sailboats, and airplanes. They are also used for monitoring volcanoes and well drilling.

Source: *Science Magazine*

EXAMPLE 4 Find a Missing Side Length

BUILDINGS To calculate the height of a building, Joel walked 200 feet from the base of the building and used an inclinometer to measure the angle from his eye to the top of the building. If his eye level is at 6 feet, how tall is the building?

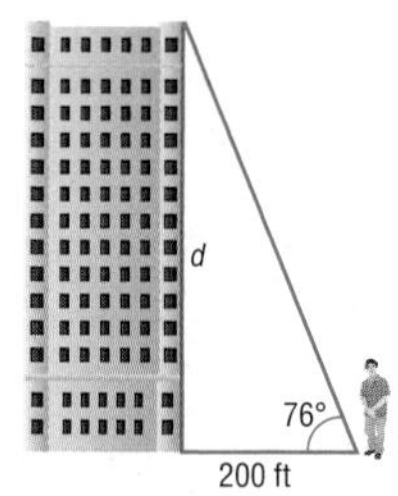

The measured angle is 76°. The side adjacent to the angle is 200 feet. The missing measure is the side opposite the angle. Use the tangent function to find d.

$\tan\theta = \frac{\text{opp}}{\text{adj}}$	**Tangent function**
$\tan 76° = \frac{d}{200}$	**Replace θ with 76°, *opp* with d, and *adj* with 200.**
$200 \tan 76° = d$	**Multiply each side by 200.**
$802 \approx d$	**Use a calculator to simplify: 200 [TAN] 76 [ENTER].**

Because the inclinometer was 6 feet above the ground, the height of the building is approximately 808 feet.

Guided Practice

4. Use a trigonometric function to find the value of x. Round to the nearest tenth if necessary. 27.0

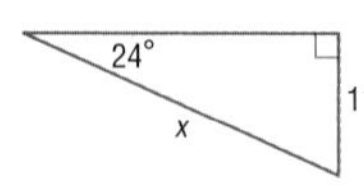

Personal Tutor glencoe.com

Focus on Mathematical Content

Trigonometric Functions Students may be familiar with finding values of trigonometric functions of any angle. However, at this point, the functions have been defined in terms of ratios of the sides of a right triangle. This means that the definitions are only valid for acute angles. The more general case will be considered later when reference angles are introduced.

When solving equations like $3x = -27$, you use the inverse of multiplication to find x. You also can find angle measures by using the inverse of sine, cosine, or tangent.

Key Concept — Inverse Trigonometric Ratios

Words If $\angle A$ is an acute angle and the sine of A is x, then the **inverse sine** of x is the measure of $\angle A$.

Symbols If $\sin A = x$, then $\sin^{-1} x = m\angle A$.

Example $\sin A = \frac{1}{2} \rightarrow \sin^{-1} \frac{1}{2} = m\angle A \rightarrow m\angle A = 30°$

Words If $\angle A$ is an acute angle and the cosine of A is x, then the **inverse cosine** of x is the measure of $\angle A$.

Symbols If $\cos A = x$, then $\cos^{-1} x = m\angle A$.

Example $\cos A = \frac{\sqrt{2}}{2} \rightarrow \cos^{-1} \frac{\sqrt{2}}{2} = m\angle A \rightarrow m\angle A = 45°$

Words If $\angle A$ is an acute angle and the tangent of A is x, then the **inverse tangent** of x is the measure of $\angle A$.

Symbols If $\tan A = x$, then $\tan^{-1} x = m\angle A$.

Example $\tan A = \sqrt{3} \rightarrow \tan^{-1} \sqrt{3} = m\angle A \rightarrow m\angle A = 60°$

ReadingMath

Inverse Trigonometric Ratios The expression $\sin^{-1} x$ is read *the inverse sine of x* and is interpreted as the angle whose sine is x. Be careful not to confuse this notation with the notation for negative exponents; $\sin^{-1} x \neq \frac{1}{\sin x}$. Instead, this notation is similar to the notation for an inverse function, $f^{-1}(x)$.

If you know the sine, cosine, or tangent of an acute angle, you can use a calculator to find the measure of the angle, which is the inverse of the trigonometric ratio.

EXAMPLE 5 Find a Missing Angle Measure

Find the measure of each angle. Round to the nearest tenth if necessary.

a. $\angle N$

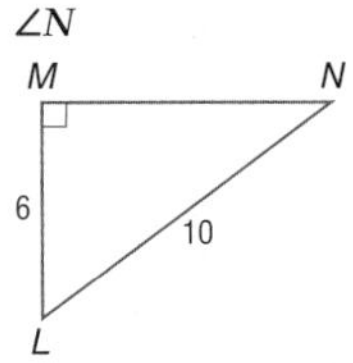

You know the measure of the side opposite $\angle N$ and the measure of the hypotenuse. Use the sine function.

$\sin N = \frac{6}{10}$ $\sin \theta = \frac{\text{opp}}{\text{hyp}}$

$\sin^{-1} \frac{6}{10} = m\angle N$ **Inverse sine**

$36.9° \approx m\angle N$ **Use a calculator.**

b. $\angle B$

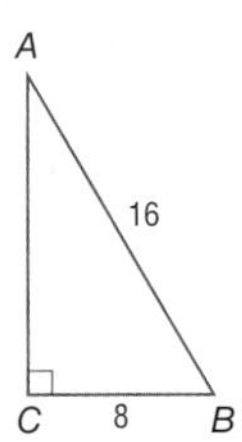

Use the cosine function.

$\cos B = \frac{8}{16}$ $\cos \theta = \frac{\text{adj}}{\text{hyp}}$

$\cos^{-1} \frac{8}{16} = m\angle B$ **Inverse cosine**

$60° = m\angle B$ **Use a calculator.**

Guided Practice

Find x. Round to the nearest tenth if necessary.

5A. 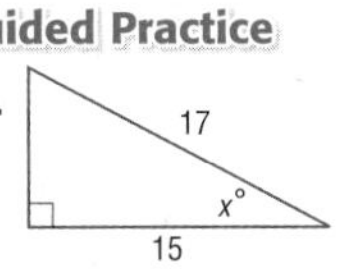

28.1

5B. 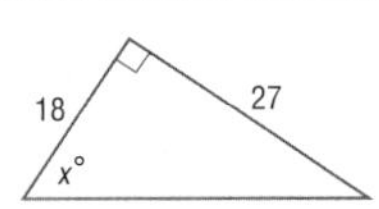

56.3

Personal Tutor glencoe.com

Additional Example

5 Find the measure of each angle. Round to the nearest tenth if necessary.

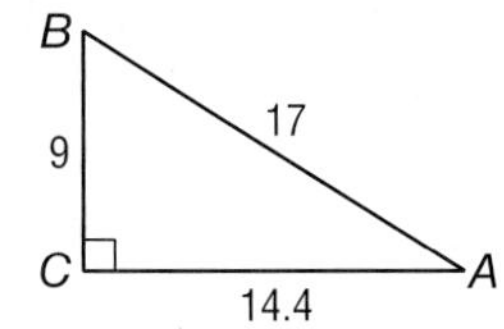

a. $\angle A$ 32°

b. $\angle B$ 58°

Differentiated Instruction

AL OL

Visual/Spatial Learners Have students use a stack of books and a notebook to model a ramp and investigate how steep the ramp needs to be for a toy car to roll down it without being pushed. Have them report their results in terms of the trigonometric functions of a right triangle.

Lesson 13-1 Right Triangle Trigonometry 811

Additional Example

6 **a. GOLF** From a camera in a blimp, the apparent distance between the golfer and the hole in Example 6a is the horizontal distance. Find the horizontal distance. 169.4 yd

b. ROLLER COASTER From a blimp, the apparent distance traveled by the roller coaster in Example 6b is the horizontal distance from the top of the hill to the bottom. Find the horizontal distance. 112.6 ft

StudyTip

Angles of Elevation and Depression The angle of elevation and the angle of depression are congruent since they are alternate interior angles of parallel lines.

In the figure at the right, the angle formed by the line of sight from the swimmer and a line parallel to the horizon is called the **angle of elevation**. The angle formed by the line of sight from the lifeguard and a line parallel to the horizon is called the **angle of depression**.

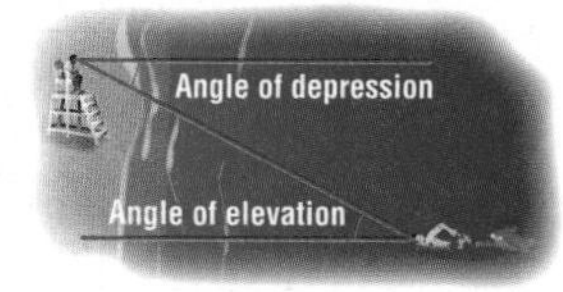

EXAMPLE 6 Use Angles of Elevation and Depression

a. GOLF A golfer is standing at the tee, looking up to the green on a hill. If the tee is 36 yards lower than the green and the angle of elevation from the tee to the hole is 12°, find the distance from the tee to the hole.

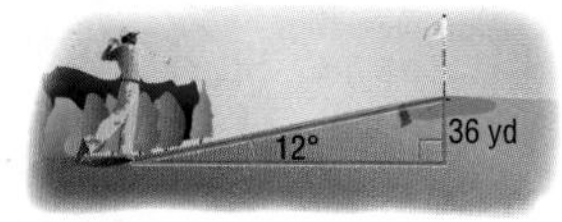

Write an equation using a trigonometric function that involves the ratio of the vertical rise (side opposite the 12° angle) and the distance from the tee to the hole (hypotenuse).

$\sin 12° = \frac{36}{x}$ **$\sin \theta = \frac{\text{opp}}{\text{hyp}}$**

$x \sin 12° = 36$ **Multiply each side by x.**

$x = \frac{36}{\sin 12°}$ **Divide each side by sin 12°.**

$x \approx 173.2$ **Use a calculator.**

So, the distance from the tee to the hole is about 173.2 yards.

Real-World Link

The steepest roller coasters in the world have angles of descent that are close to 90°.

Source: Ultimate Roller Coaster

b. ROLLER COASTER The hill of the roller coaster has an *angle of descent*, or an angle of depression, of 60°. Its vertical drop is 195 feet. Estimate the length of the hill.

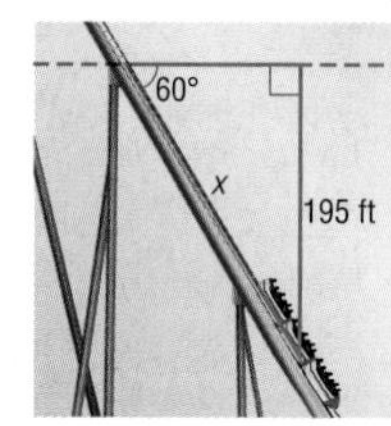

Write an equation using a trigonometric function that involves the ratio of the vertical drop (side opposite the 60° angle) and the length of the hill (hypotenuse).

$\sin 60° = \frac{195}{x}$ **$\sin \theta = \frac{\text{opp}}{\text{hyp}}$**

$x \sin 60° = 195$ **Multiply each side by x.**

$x = \frac{195}{\sin 60°}$ **Divide each side by sin 60°.**

$x \approx 225.2$ **Use a calculator.**

So, the length of the hill is about 225.2 feet.

Guided Practice

6A. MOVING A ramp for unloading a moving truck has an angle of elevation of 32°. If the top of the ramp is 4 feet above the ground, estimate the length of the ramp. about 7.5 ft

6B. LADDERS A 14-ft long ladder is placed against a house at an angle of elevation of 72°. How high above the ground is the top of the ladder? about 13.3 ft

Personal Tutor glencoe.com

Check Your Understanding

Example 1 p. 808

Find the values of the six trigonometric functions for angle θ. 1, 2. See margin.

1.

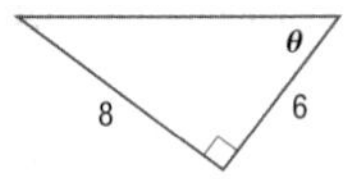

2.

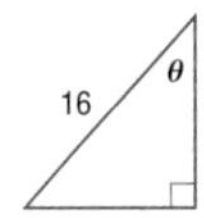

Example 2 p. 809

In a right triangle, $\angle A$ is acute.

3. If $\cos A = \frac{4}{7}$, what is $\sin A$? $\frac{\sqrt{33}}{7}$

4. If $\tan A = \frac{20}{21}$, what is $\cos A$? $\frac{21}{29}$

Examples 3 and 4 p. 810

Use a trigonometric function to find the value of x. Round to the nearest tenth.

5. 25.4

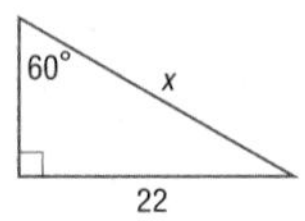

6. 7.7

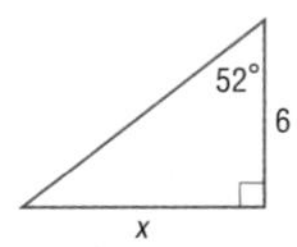

7. 8.3

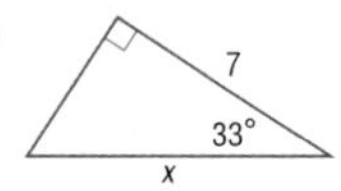

Example 5 p. 811

Find the value of x. Round to the nearest tenth.

8. 61.9

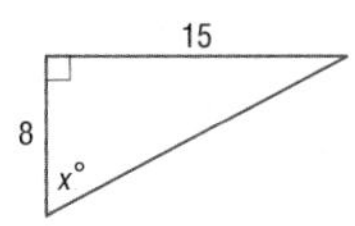

9. 25.4

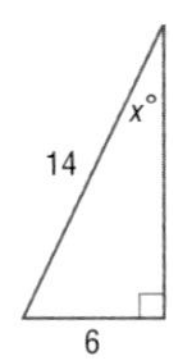

10. 68.0

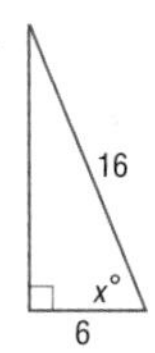

Example 6 p. 812

11. GEOGRAPHY Christian found two trees directly across from each other in a canyon. When he moved 100 feet from the tree on his side (parallel to the edge of the canyon), the angle formed by the tree on his side, Christian, and the tree on the other side was 70°. Find the distance across the canyon. about 274.7 ft

12. LADDERS The recommended angle of elevation for a ladder used in fire fighting is 75°. At what height on a building does a 21-foot ladder reach if the recommended angle of elevation is used? Round to the nearest tenth. 20.3 ft

Practice and Problem Solving

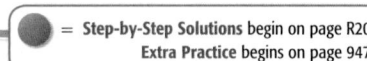

= **Step-by-Step Solutions** begin on page R20.
Extra Practice begins on page 947.

Example 1 p. 808

Find the values of the six trigonometric functions for angle θ. 13–16. See margin.

13.

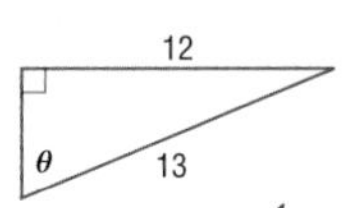

14.

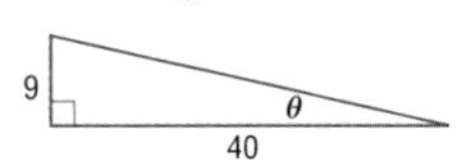

15.

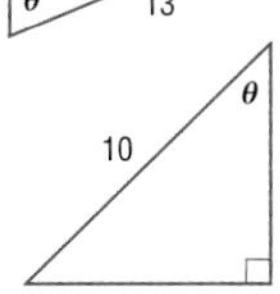

16.

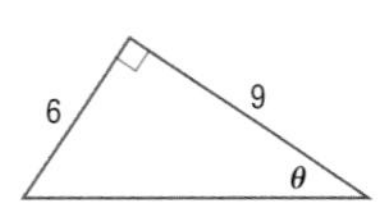

Example 2 p. 809

In a right triangle, $\angle A$ and $\angle B$ are acute.

17. If $\tan A = \frac{8}{15}$, what is $\cos A$? $\frac{15}{17}$

18. If $\cos A = \frac{3}{10}$, what is $\tan A$? $\frac{\sqrt{91}}{3}$

19. If $\tan B = 3$, what is $\sin B$? $\frac{3\sqrt{10}}{10}$

20. If $\sin B = \frac{4}{9}$, what is $\tan B$? $\frac{4\sqrt{65}}{65}$

3 PRACTICE

Formative Assessment

Use Exercises 1–12 to check for understanding.

Use the chart on the bottom of this page to customize assignments for your students.

Additional Answers

1. $\sin B = \frac{4}{5}$; $\cos B = \frac{3}{5}$; $\tan B = \frac{4}{3}$; $\csc B = \frac{5}{4}$; $\sec B = \frac{5}{3}$; $\cot B = \frac{3}{4}$

2. $\sin\theta = \frac{\sqrt{7}}{4}$; $\cos\theta = \frac{3}{4}$; $\tan\theta = \frac{\sqrt{7}}{3}$; $\csc\theta = \frac{4\sqrt{7}}{7}$; $\sec\theta = \frac{4}{3}$; $\cot\theta = \frac{3\sqrt{7}}{7}$

13. $\sin\theta = \frac{12}{13}$; $\cos\theta = \frac{5}{13}$; $\tan\theta = \frac{12}{5}$; $\csc\theta = \frac{13}{12}$; $\sec\theta = \frac{13}{5}$; $\cot\theta = \frac{5}{12}$

14. $\sin\theta = \frac{9}{41}$; $\cos\theta = \frac{40}{41}$; $\tan\theta = \frac{9}{40}$; $\csc\theta = \frac{41}{9}$; $\sec\theta = \frac{41}{40}$; $\cot\theta = \frac{40}{9}$

15. $\sin\theta = \frac{\sqrt{51}}{10}$; $\cos\theta = \frac{7}{10}$; $\tan\theta = \frac{\sqrt{51}}{7}$; $\csc\theta = \frac{10\sqrt{51}}{51}$; $\sec\theta = \frac{10}{7}$; $\cot\theta = \frac{7\sqrt{51}}{51}$

16. $\sin\theta = \frac{2\sqrt{13}}{13}$; $\cos\theta = \frac{3\sqrt{13}}{13}$; $\tan\theta = \frac{2}{3}$; $\csc\theta = \frac{\sqrt{13}}{2}$; $\sec\theta = \frac{\sqrt{13}}{3}$; $\cot\theta = \frac{3}{2}$

Differentiated Homework Options

Level	Assignment	Two-Day Option	
AL Basic	13–36, 55–74	13–35 odd, 58–61	14–36 even, 55–57, 62–74
OL Core	13–35 odd, 37–45 odd, 46–53, 55–74	13–36, 58–61	37–53, 55–57, 62–74
BL Advanced	37–68, (optional: 69–74)		

Tips for New Teachers

Calculators On a scientific calculator (in contrast to a graphing calculator), the sequence for finding the sine, cosine, or tangent of an angle may be to enter the angle measure, such as 20, first, and then press the SIN, COS, or TAN key.

Additional Answers

46a. Sample answer:

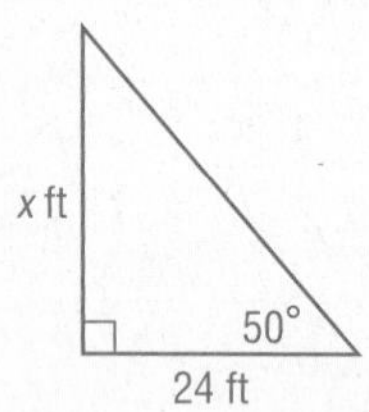

55. True; $\sin \theta = \frac{\text{opp}}{\text{hyp}}$ and the values of the opposite side and the hypotenuse of an acute triangle are positive, so the value of the sine function is positive.

57. Sample answer: The slope describes the ratio of the vertical rise to the horizontal run of the roof. The vertical rise is opposite the angle that the roof makes with the horizontal. The horizontal run is the adjacent side. So, the tangent of the angle of elevation equals the ratio of the rise to the run, or the slope of the roof; $\theta = 33.7°$.

Examples 3 and 4 p. 810

Use a trigonometric function to find each value of x. Round to the nearest tenth.

21. 12.7

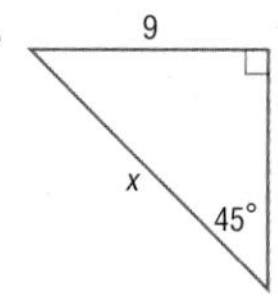

22. 3.6

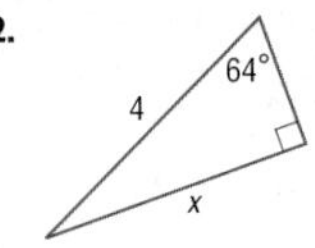

23. 10.4

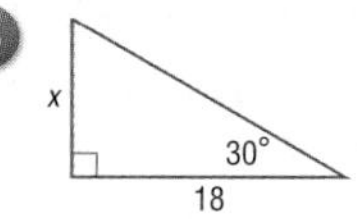

24. 32.9

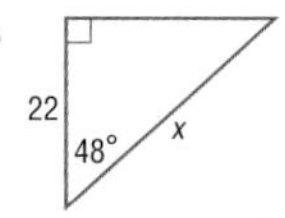

25. 8.7

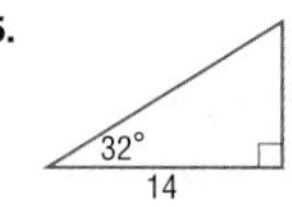

26. 5.1

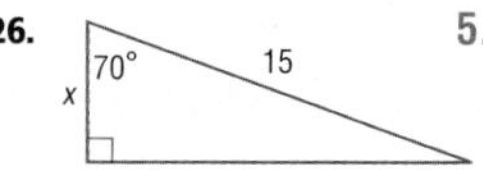

27. PARASAILING Refer to the beginning of the lesson and the figure at the right. Find a, the altitude of a person parasailing, if the tow rope is 250 feet long and the angle formed is 32°. Round to the nearest tenth. **132.5 ft**

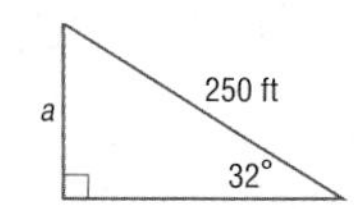

28. BRIDGES Devon wants to build a rope bridge between his treehouse and Cheng's treehouse. Suppose Devon's treehouse is directly behind Cheng's treehouse. At a distance of 20 meters to the left of Devon's treehouse, an angle of 52° is measured between the two treehouses. Find the length of the rope. **25.6 m**

Example 5 p. 811

Find the value of x. Round to the nearest tenth.

29. 30

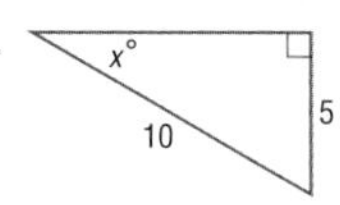

30. 67.2

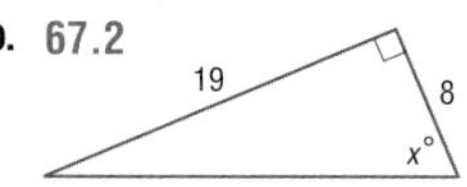

31. 36.9

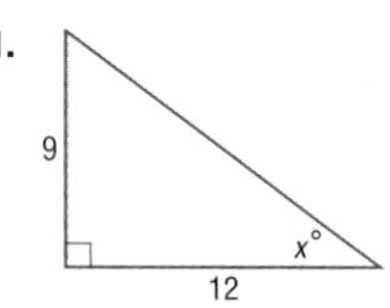

32. 55.2

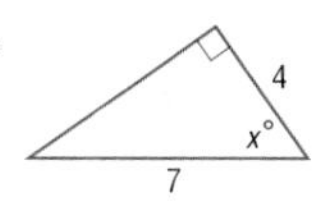

33. 32.5

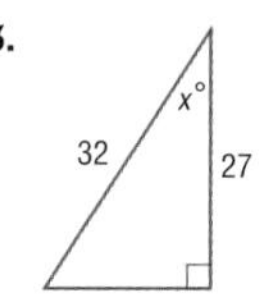

34. 23.6

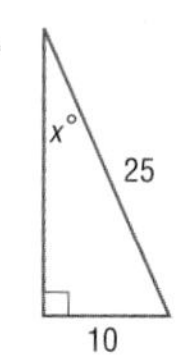

Example 6 p. 812

35. SQUIRRELS Adult flying squirrels can make glides of up to 160 feet. If a flying squirrel glides a horizontal distance of 160 feet and the angle of descent is 9°, find its change in height. **25.3 ft**

36. HANG GLIDING A hang glider climbs at a 20° angle of elevation. Find the change in altitude of the hang glider when it has flown a horizontal distance of 60 feet. **21.8 ft**

B **Use trigonometric functions to find the values of x and y. Round to the nearest tenth.**

37. $x = 21.9$, $y = 20.8$
38. $x = 93.7$, $y = 60.2$
39. $x = 19.3$, $y = 70.7$

37.

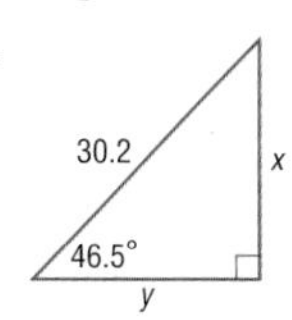

38.

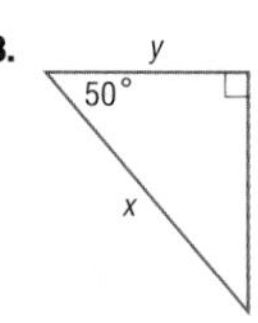

39.

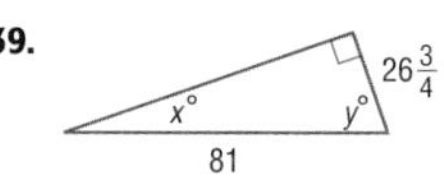

Solve each equation.

40. $\cos A = \frac{3}{19}$ **80.9**

41. $\sin N = \frac{9}{11}$ **54.9**

42. $\tan X = 15$ **86.2**

43. $\sin T = 0.35$ **20.5**

44. $\tan G = 0.125$ **7.1**

45. $\cos Z = 0.98$ **11.5**

46. **MONUMENTS** A monument casts a shadow 24 feet long. The angle of elevation from the end of the shadow to the top of the monument is 50°.

a. Draw and label a right triangle to represent this situation. **See margin.**

b. Write a trigonometric function that can be used to find the height of the monument. $\tan 50° = \frac{x}{24}$

c. Find the value of the function to determine the height of the monument to the nearest tenth. **28.6 ft**

C 47. **NESTS** Tabitha's eyes are 5 feet above the ground as she looks up to a bird's nest in a tree. If the angle of elevation is 74.5° and she is standing 12 feet from the tree's base, what is the height of the bird's nest? Round to the nearest foot. **48 ft**

48. **RAMPS** Two bicycle ramps each cover a horizontal distance of 8 feet. One ramp has a 20° angle of elevation, and the other ramp has a 35° angle of elevation, as shown at the right.

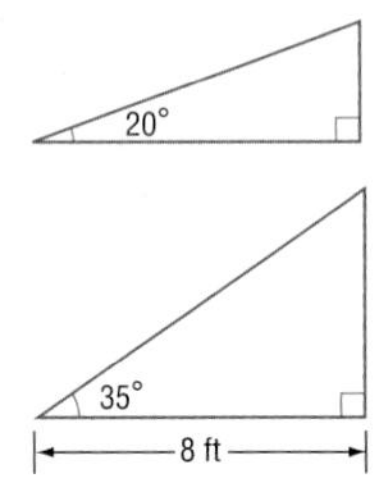

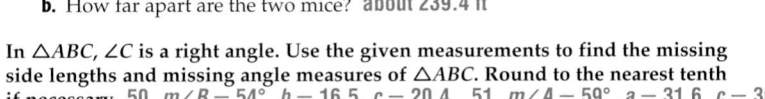

a. How much taller is the second ramp than the first? Round to the nearest tenth. **2.7 ft**

b. How much longer is the second ramp than the first? Round to the nearest tenth. **1.3 ft**

Real-World Link

A falcon can see an object 10 centimeters long from a distance of 1.5 kilometers away. A falcon can also sharp images when diving at 100 miles per hour.

Source: Neuroscience for Kids

49. **FALCONS** A falcon at a height of 200 feet sees two mice A and B, as shown in the diagram.

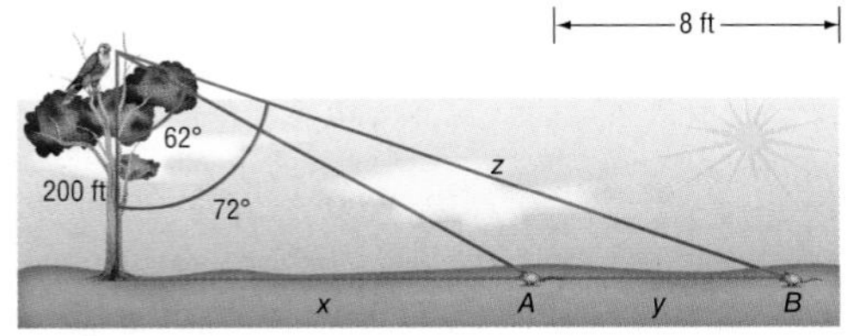

a. What is the approximate distance z between the falcon and mouse B? **about 647.2 ft**

b. How far apart are the two mice? **about 239.4 ft**

In $\triangle ABC$, $\angle C$ is a right angle. Use the given measurements to find the missing side lengths and missing angle measures of $\triangle ABC$. Round to the nearest tenth if necessary. **50. $m\angle B = 54°$, $b = 16.5$, $c = 20.4$ 51. $m\angle A = 59°$, $a = 31.6$, $c = 36.9$**

50. $m\angle A = 36°, a = 12$

51. $m\angle B = 31°, b = 19$

52. $a = 8, c = 17$ **$m\angle A = 28.1°$, $m\angle B = 61.9°$, $b = 15$**

53. $\tan A = \frac{4}{5}, a = 6$ **$m\angle A = 38.7°$, $m\angle B = 51.3°$, $b = 7.5$, $c = 9.6$**

H.O.T. Problems

Use **H**igher-**O**rder **T**hinking Skills

54. **CHALLENGE** A line segment has endpoints $A(2, 0)$ and $B(6, 5)$, as shown in the figure at the right. What is the measure of the acute angle θ formed by the line segment and the x-axis? Explain how you found the measure.

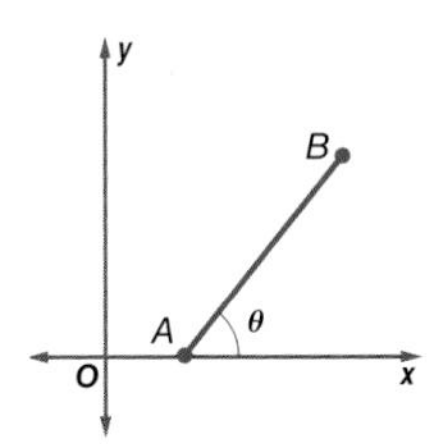

55. **REASONING** Determine whether the following statement is *true* or *false*. Explain your reasoning. **See margin.**

For any acute angle, the sine function will never have a negative value.

56. **OPEN ENDED** In right triangle ABC, $\sin A = \sin C$. What can you conclude about $\triangle ABC$? Justify your reasoning.

57. **WRITING IN MATH** A roof has a slope of $\frac{2}{3}$. Describe the connection between the slope and the angle of elevation θ that the roof makes with the horizontal. Then use an inverse trigonometric function to find θ. **See margin.**

54. About 51.3°; if a right triangle is drawn with $\overline{AB}$ as the hypotenuse, then the side opposite angle θ is 5 and the side adjacent angle θ is 4. Tan $A = \frac{5}{4}$, so $A \approx 51.3°$.

56. Sin A = sin C, so $\frac{\text{side opp } A}{\text{hyp}} = \frac{\text{side opp } C}{\text{hyp}}$. Since the hypotenuse is the same, the length of the side opposite angle A must equal the length of the side opposite angle C. Since the two sides have the same measure, the triangle is isosceles.

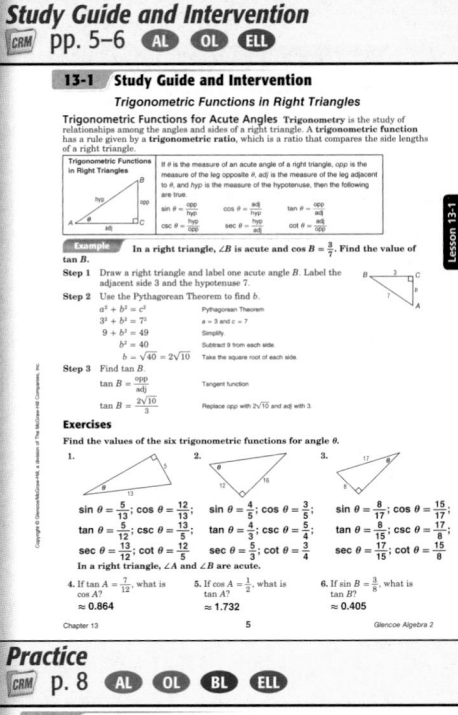

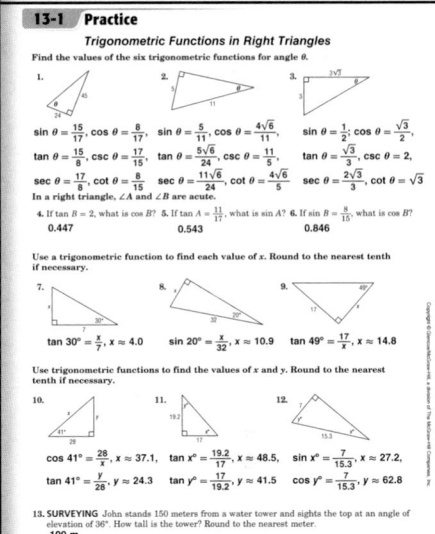

Study Guide and Intervention

CRM pp. 5–6 AL OL ELL

13-1 Study Guide and Intervention

Trigonometric Functions in Right Triangles

Trigonometric Functions for Acute Angles **Trigonometry** is the study of relationships among the angles and sides of a right triangle. A **trigonometric function** has a rule given by a **trigonometric ratio**, which is a ratio that compares the side lengths of a right triangle.

Trigonometric Functions in Right Triangles	If θ is the measure of an acute angle of a right triangle, *opp* is the measure of the leg opposite θ, *adj* is the measure of the leg adjacent to θ, and *hyp* is the measure of the hypotenuse, then the following are true. $\sin \theta = \frac{opp}{hyp}$ $\cos \theta = \frac{adj}{hyp}$ $\tan \theta = \frac{opp}{adj}$ $\csc \theta = \frac{hyp}{opp}$ $\sec \theta = \frac{hyp}{adj}$ $\cot \theta = \frac{adj}{opp}$

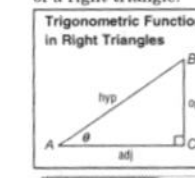

Example **In a right triangle, $\angle B$ is acute and $\cos B = \frac{3}{7}$. Find the value of $\tan B$.**

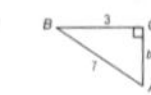

Step 1 Draw a right triangle and label one acute angle B. Label the adjacent side 3 and the hypotenuse 7.

Step 2 Use the Pythagorean Theorem to find b.

$a^2 + b^2 = c^2$ Pythagorean Theorem
$3^2 + b^2 = 7^2$ $a = 3$ and $c = 7$
$9 + b^2 = 49$ Simplify.
$b^2 = 40$ Subtract 9 from each side.
$b = \sqrt{40} = 2\sqrt{10}$ Take the square root of each side.

Step 3 Find $\tan B$.

$\tan B = \frac{opp}{adj}$ Tangent function
$\tan B = \frac{2\sqrt{10}}{3}$ Replace *opp* with $2\sqrt{10}$ and *adj* with 3.

Exercises

Find the values of the six trigonometric functions for angle θ.

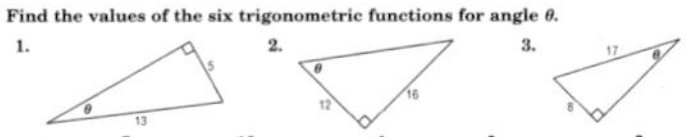

1. $\sin \theta = \frac{5}{13}$; $\cos \theta = \frac{12}{13}$; $\tan \theta = \frac{5}{12}$; $\csc \theta = \frac{13}{5}$; $\sec \theta = \frac{13}{12}$; $\cot \theta = \frac{12}{5}$

2. $\sin \theta = \frac{4}{5}$; $\cos \theta = \frac{3}{5}$; $\tan \theta = \frac{4}{3}$; $\csc \theta = \frac{5}{4}$; $\sec \theta = \frac{5}{3}$; $\cot \theta = \frac{3}{4}$

3. $\sin \theta = \frac{8}{17}$; $\cos \theta = \frac{15}{17}$; $\tan \theta = \frac{8}{15}$; $\csc \theta = \frac{17}{8}$; $\sec \theta = \frac{17}{15}$; $\cot \theta = \frac{15}{8}$

In a right triangle, $\angle A$ and $\angle B$ are acute.

4. If $\tan A = \frac{7}{12}$, what is $\cos A$? ≈ 0.864

5. If $\cos A = \frac{1}{2}$, what is $\tan A$? ≈ 1.732

6. If $\sin B = \frac{3}{8}$, what is $\tan B$? ≈ 0.405

Chapter 13 5 *Glencoe Algebra 2*

Lesson 13-1

Practice

CRM p. 8 AL OL BL ELL

13-1 Practice

Trigonometric Functions in Right Triangles

Find the values of the six trigonometric functions for angle θ.

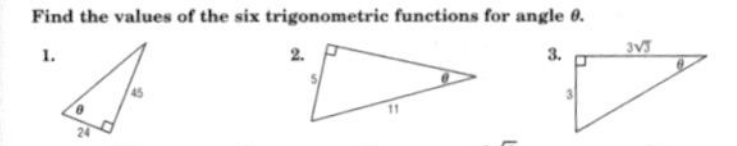

1. $\sin \theta = \frac{15}{17}$, $\cos \theta = \frac{8}{17}$, $\tan \theta = \frac{15}{8}$, $\csc \theta = \frac{17}{15}$, $\sec \theta = \frac{17}{8}$, $\cot \theta = \frac{8}{15}$

2. $\sin \theta = \frac{5}{11}$, $\cos \theta = \frac{4\sqrt{6}}{11}$, $\tan \theta = \frac{5\sqrt{6}}{24}$, $\csc \theta = \frac{11}{5}$, $\sec \theta = \frac{11\sqrt{6}}{24}$, $\cot \theta = \frac{4\sqrt{6}}{5}$

3. $\sin \theta = \frac{1}{2}$; $\cos \theta = \frac{\sqrt{3}}{2}$, $\tan \theta = \frac{\sqrt{3}}{3}$, $\csc \theta = 2$, $\sec \theta = \frac{2\sqrt{3}}{3}$, $\cot \theta = \sqrt{3}$

In a right triangle, $\angle A$ and $\angle B$ are acute.

4. If $\tan B = 2$, what is $\cos B$? 0.447

5. If $\tan A = \frac{11}{17}$, what is $\sin A$? 0.543

6. If $\sin B = \frac{8}{15}$, what is $\cos B$? 0.846

Use a trigonometric function to find each value of x. Round to the nearest tenth if necessary.

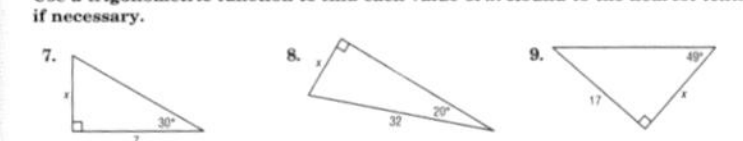

7. $\tan 30° = \frac{x}{7}$, $x \approx 4.0$

8. $\sin 20° = \frac{x}{32}$, $x \approx 10.9$

9. $\tan 49° = \frac{17}{x}$, $x \approx 14.8$

Use trigonometric functions to find the values of x and y. Round to the nearest tenth if necessary.

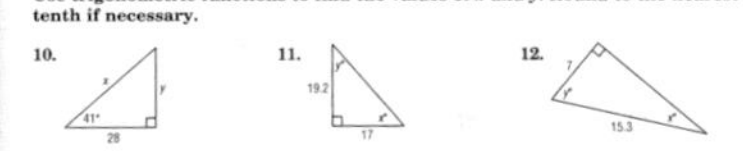

10. $\cos 41° = \frac{28}{x}$, $x \approx 37.1$, $\tan 41° = \frac{y}{28}$, $y \approx 24.3$

11. $\tan x° = \frac{19.2}{17}$, $x \approx 48.5$, $\tan y° = \frac{17}{19.2}$, $y \approx 41.5$

12. $\sin x° = \frac{7}{15.3}$, $x \approx 27.2$, $\cos y° = \frac{7}{15.3}$, $y \approx 62.8$

13. **SURVEYING** John stands 150 meters from a water tower and sights the top at an angle of elevation of 36°. How tall is the tower? Round to the nearest meter. 109 m

Chapter 13 8 *Glencoe Algebra 2*

Word Problem Practice

CRM p. 9 AL OL BL ELL

13-1 Word Problem Practice

Trigonometric Functions in Right Triangles

1. **ROOFS** The roof on a house is built with a pitch of 10/12, meaning that the roof rises 10 feet for every 12 feet of horizontal run. The side view of the roof is shown in the figure below.

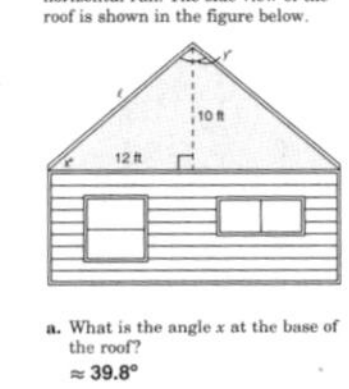

a. What is the angle x at the base of the roof? $\approx 39.8°$

b. What is the angle y at the peak of the roof? $\approx 100.4°$

c. What is the length ℓ of the roof? ≈ 15.6 ft

d. If the width of the house is 26 feet, what is the total area of the roof? ≈ 812.3 ft^2

2. **BUILDINGS** Jessica stands 150 feet from the base of a tall building. She measures the angle from her eye to the top of the building to be 84°. If her eye level is 5 feet above the ground, how tall is the building? ≈ 1427 ft

3. **SCALE DRAWING** The collection pool for a fountain is in the shape of a right triangle. A scale drawing shows that the angles of the triangle are 40°, 50°, and 90°. If the hypotenuse of the actual fountain will be 30 feet, what are the lengths of the other two sides of the fountain? about 19.3 ft and 23.0 ft

4. **GEOMETRY** A regular hexagon is inscribed in a circle with a diameter of 8 inches.

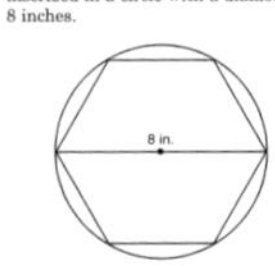

a. What is the perimeter of the hexagon? 24 in.

b. What is the area of the hexagon? $24\sqrt{3}$ or about 41.6 in^2

Chapter 13 9 *Glencoe Algebra 2*

Lesson 13-1

Enrichment

CRM p. 10 OL BL

13-1 Enrichment

The Angle of Repose

Suppose you place a block of wood on an inclined plane, as shown at the right. If the angle, θ, at which the plane is inclined from the horizontal is very small, the block will not move. If you increase the angle, the block will eventually overcome the force of friction and start to slide down the plane.

At the instant the block begins to slide, the angle formed by the plane is called the angle of friction, or the angle of repose.

For situations in which the block and plane are smooth but unlubricated, the angle of repose depends *only* on the types of materials in the block and the plane. The angle is independent of the area of contact between the two surfaces and of the weight of the block.

The drawing at the right shows how to use vectors to find a coefficient of friction. This coefficient varies with different materials and is denoted by the Greek letter mu, μ.

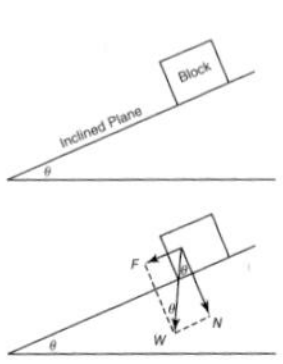

$F = W \sin \theta$ $N = W \cos \theta$

$F = \mu N$

$\mu = \frac{\sin \theta}{\cos \theta} = \tan \theta$

4 ASSESS

Ticket Out the Door Have students write the minimum information one must have about a right triangle in order to solve it for a missing side or angle value. two of the following: measure of an acute angle, length of a leg, length of the hypotenuse

NGSSS PRACTICE 912.A.3.15, 912.D.8.2, 912.G.2.5

58. **EXTENDED RESPONSE** Your school needs 5 cases of yearbooks. Neighborhood Yearbooks lists a case of yearbooks at \$153.85 with a 10% discount on an order of 5 cases. Yearbooks R Us lists a case of yearbooks at \$157.36 with a 15% discount on 5 cases. **a. Yearbooks R Us**

a. Which company would you choose?

b. What is the least amount that you would have to spend for the yearbooks? **\$668.78**

59. **SHORT RESPONSE** As a fundraiser, the marching band sold T-shirts and hats. They sold a total of 105 items and raised \$1170. If the cost of a hat was \$10 and the cost of a T-shirt was \$15, how many T-shirts were sold? **24**

60. A hot dog stand charges price x for a hot dog and price y for a drink. Two hot dogs and one drink cost \$4.50. Three hot dogs and two drinks cost \$7.25. Which matrix could be multiplied by $\begin{bmatrix} 4.50 \\ 7.25 \end{bmatrix}$ to find x and y? **B**

A. $\begin{bmatrix} -1 & 1 \\ 2 & -1 \end{bmatrix}$ **C.** $\begin{bmatrix} 1 & 2 \\ -1 & 3 \end{bmatrix}$

B. $\begin{bmatrix} 2 & -1 \\ -3 & 2 \end{bmatrix}$ **D.** $\begin{bmatrix} 1 & -1 \\ -1 & 2 \end{bmatrix}$

61. **SAT/ACT** The length and width of a rectangle are in the ratio of 5:12. If the rectangle has an area of 240 square centimeters, what is the length, in centimeters, of its diagonal? **F**

F. 26 H. 30
G. 28 I. 32

Spiral Review

62. **POLLS** A polling company wants to estimate how many people are in favor of a new environmental law. The polling company polls 20 people. The probability that a person is in favor of the law is 0.5. (Lesson 12-7)

a. What is the probability that exactly 12 people are in favor of the new law? **0.12**

b. What is the expected number of people in favor of the law? **10**

Text each null hypothesis. Write *accept* or *reject*. (Lesson 12-6)

63. $H_0 = 92, H_1 > 92, n = 80, \bar{x} = 92.75$, and $s = 2.8$ **reject**

64. $H_0 = 48, H_1 > 48, n = 240, \bar{x} = 48.2$, and $s = 2.2$ **accept**

65. $H_0 = 71, H_1 > 71, n = 180, \bar{x} = 72.4$, and $s = 3.5$ **reject**

66. $H_0 = 55, H_1 < 55, n = 300, \bar{x} = 54.5$, and $s = 1.9$ **reject**

Find each probability. (Lesson 12-3)

67. A city council consists of six Democrats, two of whom are women, and six Republicans, four of whom are men. A member is chosen at random. If the member chosen is a man, what is the probability that he is a Democrat? $\frac{1}{2}$

68. Two boys and two girls are lined up at random. What is the probability that the girls are separated if a girl is on an end? $\frac{3}{5}$

Skills Review

Find each product. Include the appropriate units with your answer. (Lesson 6-1B)

69. $4.3 \text{ miles}\left(\frac{5280 \text{ feet}}{1 \text{ mile}}\right)$ **22,704 ft**

70. $8 \text{ gallons}\left(\frac{8 \text{ pints}}{1 \text{ gallon}}\right)$ **64 pt**

71. $\left(\frac{5 \text{ dollars}}{3 \text{ meters}}\right)21 \text{ meters}$ **35 dollars**

72. $\left(\frac{18 \text{ cubic inches}}{5 \text{ seconds}}\right)24 \text{ seconds}$ **86.4 in^3**

73. $65 \text{ degrees}\left(\frac{10 \text{ centimeters}}{3 \text{ degrees}}\right)$ **$216\frac{2}{3}$ cm**

74. $\left(\frac{7 \text{ liters}}{30 \text{ minutes}}\right)10 \text{ minutes}$ **$2\frac{1}{3}$ L**

Differentiated Instruction OL BL

Extension Have students compute the value of $\sin^2 x + \cos^2 x$ for some values of x. Have them make a conjecture about the value of the expression and use the definitions of the trigonometric functions to prove their conjecture. The value is always 1.

$$\sin^2 x + \cos^2 x \stackrel{?}{=} 1$$
$$\left(\frac{\text{opp}}{\text{hyp}}\right)^2 + \left(\frac{\text{adj}}{\text{hyp}}\right)^2 \stackrel{?}{=} 1$$

$\text{opp}^2 + \text{adj}^2 = \text{hyp}^2$, which is true by the Pythagorean Theorem

13-2

Angles and Angle Measure

Why?

A sundial is an instrument that indicates the time of day by the shadow that it casts on a surface marked to show hours or fractions of hours. The shadow moves around the dial 15° every hour.

Then
You used angles with degree measures. (Lesson 13-1)

Now
- Draw and find angles in standard position.
- Convert between degree measures and radian measures.

NGSSS
LA.910.1.6.1 The student will use new vocabulary that is introduced and taught directly.
MA.912.T.1.1 Convert between degree and radian measures.

New Vocabulary
standard position
initial side
terminal side
coterminal angles
radian
central angle
arc length

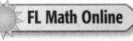

FL Math Online
glencoe.com

Angles in Standard Position An angle on the coordinate plane is in **standard position** if the vertex is at the origin and one ray is on the positive x-axis.

- The ray on the x-axis is called the **initial side** of the angle.
- The ray that rotates about the center is called the **terminal side**.

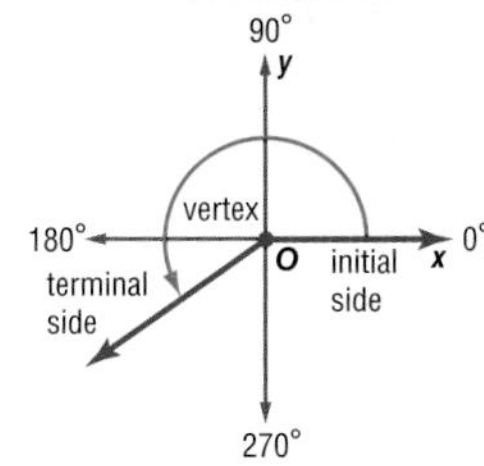

Key Concept — Angle Measures

If the measure of an angle is positive, the terminal side is rotated counterclockwise.

If the measure of an angle is negative, the terminal side is rotated clockwise.

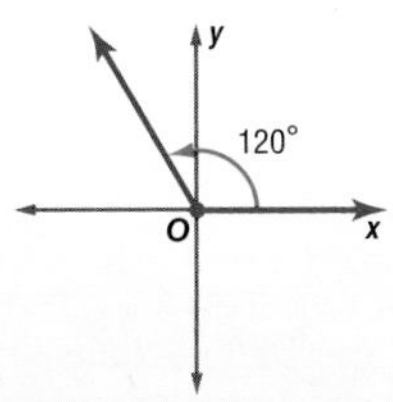

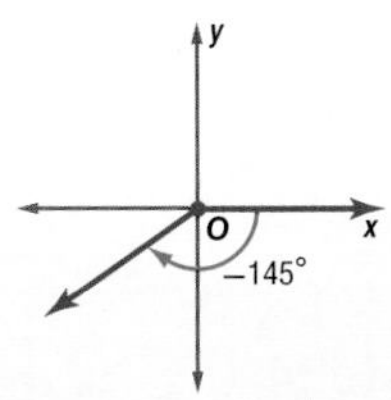

EXAMPLE 1 Draw an Angle in Standard Position

Draw an angle with the given measure in standard position.

a. 215° $215° = 180° + 35°$

Draw the terminal side of the angle 35° counterclockwise past the negative x-axis.

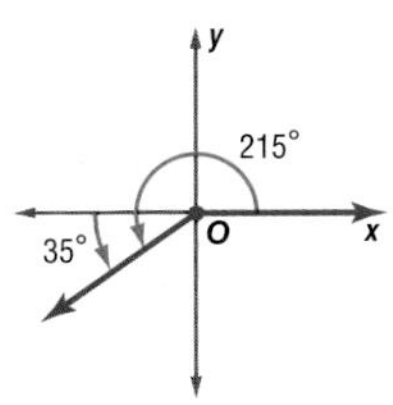

b. −40°

The angle is negative. Draw the terminal side of the angle 40° clockwise from the positive x-axis.

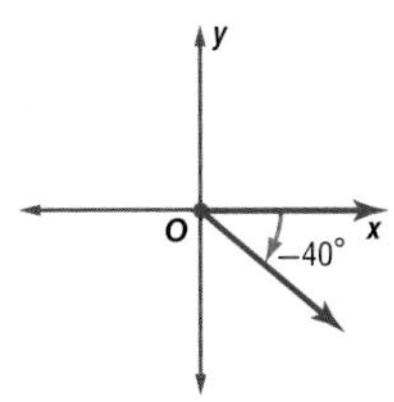

Guided Practice 1A, 1B. See Chapter 13 Answer Appendix.

1A. 80° **1B.** −105°

Personal Tutor glencoe.com

13-2 Lesson Notes

1 FOCUS

Vertical Alignment

Before Lesson 13-2
Use angles with degree measures.

Lesson 13-2
Draw and find angles in standard position.
Convert between degree measures and radian measures.

After Lesson 13-2
Investigate graphs of the sine and cosine functions.

2 TEACH

Scaffolding Questions

Have students read the *Why?* section of the lesson.

Ask:
- In what direction does the shadow point in the morning? west
- At what time do you get the shortest shadow? noon
- Explain why the shadow moves 15° every hour. The shadow "returns" to any particular position every 24 hours, and the entire circle, divided by 24, is 360° ÷ 24, or 15°.

Lesson 13-2 Resources

Resource	Approaching-Level	On-Level	Beyond-Level	English Learners
Teacher Edition	• Differentiated Instruction, p. 819	• Differentiated Instruction, p. 823	• Differentiated Instruction, p. 823	
Chapter Resource Masters	• Study Guide and Intervention, pp. 11–12 • Skills Practice, p. 13 • Practice, p. 14 • Word Problem Practice, p. 15	• Study Guide and Intervention, pp. 11–12 • Skills Practice, p. 13 • Practice, p. 14 • Word Problem Practice, p. 15 • Enrichment, p. 16	• Practice, p. 14 • Word Problem Practice, p. 15 • Enrichment, p. 16	• Study Guide and Intervention, pp. 11–12 • Skills Practice, p. 13 • Practice, p. 14 • Word Problem Practice, p. 15
Transparencies	• 5-Minute Check Transparency 13-2	• 5-Minute Check Transparency 13-2	• 5-Minute Check Transparency 13-2	• 5-Minute Check Transparency 13-2
Other	• Study Notebook	• Study Notebook	• Study Notebook	• Study Notebook

Angles in Standard Position

Example 1 shows how to draw an angle in standard position with a given measure. **Example 2** shows how to represent an angle greater than 360°. **Example 3** shows how to represent coterminal angles with a positive or a negative measure.

Formative Assessment

Use the Guided Practice exercises after each example to determine students' understanding of concepts.

Additional Examples

1 Draw an angle with the given measure in standard position.

a. 210°

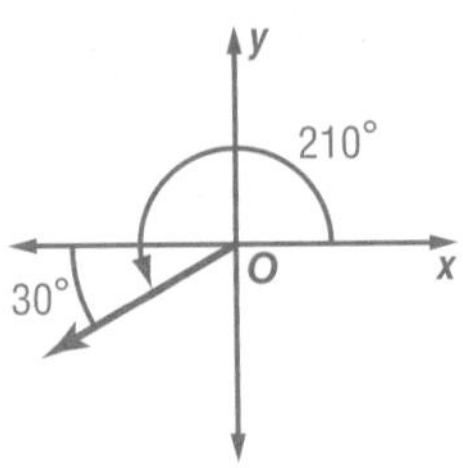

b. –45°

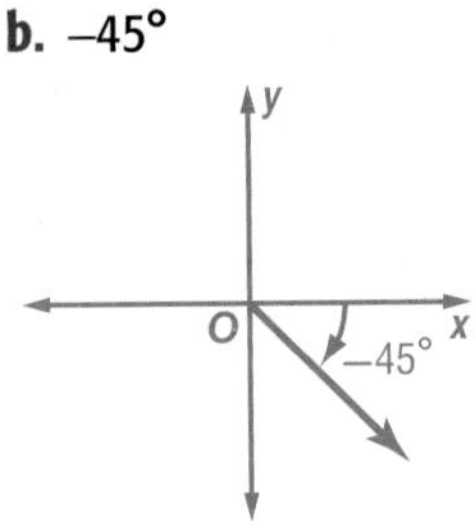

2 **DIVING** In a springboard diving competition, a diver made a 900-degree rotation before slicing into the water. Draw an angle in standard position that measures 900°.

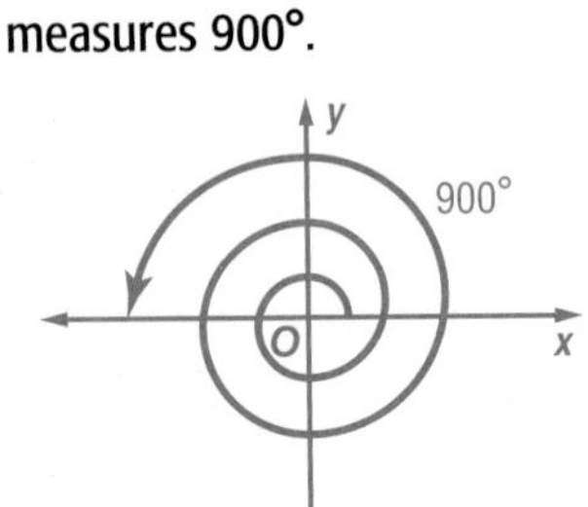

Real-World Link

Wakeboarding is one of the fastest-growing water sports in the United States. Participation increased more than 100% in recent years.

Source: King of Wake

The terminal side of an angle can make more than one complete rotation. For example, a complete rotation of 360° plus a rotation of 120° forms an angle that measures 360° + 120° or 480°.

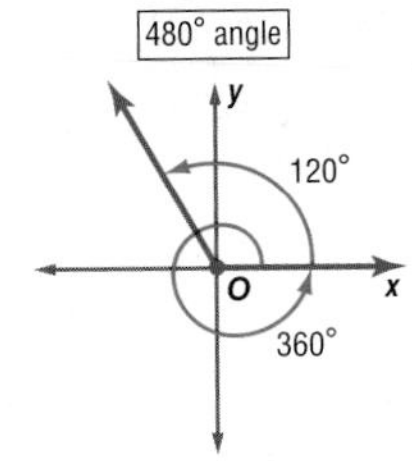

Real-World EXAMPLE 2 Draw an Angle in Standard Position

WAKEBOARDING ***Wakeboarding* is a combination of surfing, skateboarding, snowboarding, and water skiing. One maneuver involves a 540-degree rotation in the air. Draw an angle in standard position that measures 540°.**

540° = 360° + 180°

Draw the terminal side of the angle 180° past the positive x-axis.

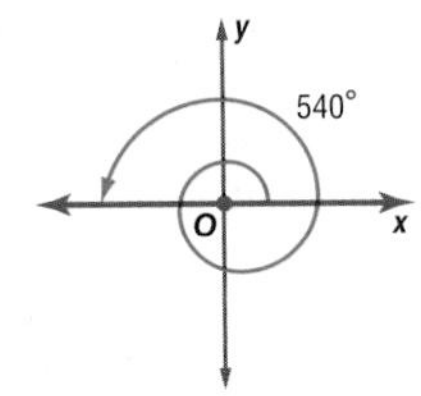

Guided Practice

2. Draw an angle in standard position that measures 600°. **See margin.**

Personal Tutor glencoe.com

Two or more angles in standard position with the same terminal side are called **coterminal angles**. For example, angles that measure 60°, 420°, and –300° are coterminal, as shown in the figure at the right.

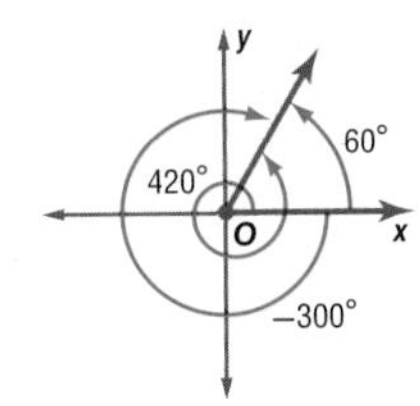

An angle that is coterminal with another angle can be found by adding or subtracting a multiple of 360°.

- 60° + 360° = 420°
- 60° – 360° = –300°

EXAMPLE 3 Find Coterminal Angles

Find an angle with a positive measure and an angle with a negative measure that are coterminal with each angle.

a. 130°

positive angle: 130° + 360° = 490° **Add 360°.**
negative angle: 130° – 360° = –230° **Subtract 360°.**

b. –200°

positive angle: –200° + 360° = 160° **Add 360°.**
negative angle: –200° – 360° = –560° **Subtract 360°.**

ReadingMath

Angle of Rotation In trigonometry, an angle is sometimes referred to as an *angle of rotation.*

Guided Practice

3A. 15° **375°, –345°**

3B. –45° **315°, –405°**

Personal Tutor glencoe.com

Tips for New Teachers

Drawing Angles Discuss with students the importance of marking the drawings of angles with the arrows as shown, and labeling the degrees.

Additional Answer (Guided Practice)

2.

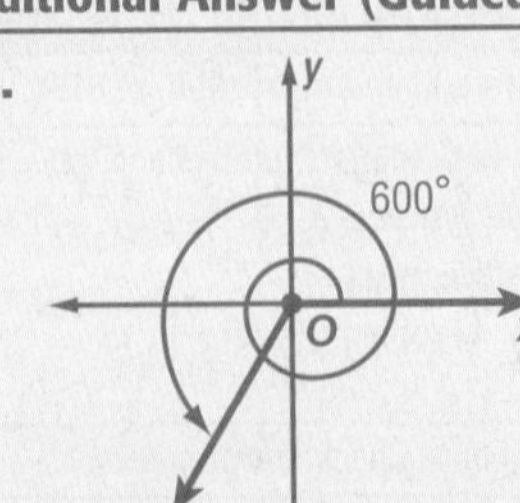

StudyTip

Radians As with degrees, radians measure the amount of rotation from the initial side to the terminal side.

- The measure of an angle in radians is positive if its rotation is counterclockwise.
- The measure is negative if the rotation is clockwise.

Convert Between Degrees and Radians Angles can also be measured in units that are based on arc length. One **radian** is the measure of an angle θ in standard position with a terminal side that intercepts an arc with the same length as the radius of the circle.

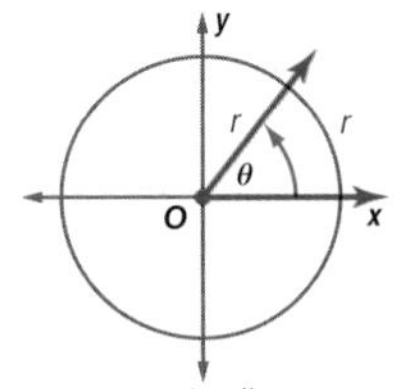

$\theta = 1$ radian

The circumference of a circle is $2\pi r$. So, one complete revolution around a circle equals 2π radians. Since 2π radians $= 360°$, degree measure and radian measure are related by the following equations.

$$2\pi \text{ radians} = 360° \qquad \pi \text{ radians} = 180°$$

Key Concept: Convert Between Degrees and Radians

Degrees to Radians	Radians to Degrees
To convert from degrees to radians, multiply the number of degrees by $\frac{\pi \text{ radians}}{180°}$.	To convert from radians to degrees, multiply the number of radians by $\frac{180°}{\pi \text{ radians}}$.

ReadingMath

Radian Measures The word *radian* is usually omitted when angles are expressed in radian measure. Thus, when no units are given for an angle measure, radian measure is implied.

EXAMPLE 4 Convert Between Degrees and Radians

Rewrite the degree measure in radians and the radian measure in degrees.

a. $-30°$

$$-30° = -30° \cdot \frac{\pi \text{ radians}}{180°}$$
$$= \frac{-30\pi}{180} \text{ or } -\frac{\pi}{6} \text{ radians}$$

b. $\frac{5\pi}{2}$

$$\frac{5\pi}{2} = \frac{5\pi}{2} \text{ radians} \cdot \frac{180°}{\pi \text{ radians}}$$
$$= \frac{900°}{2} \text{ or } 450°$$

Guided Practice

4A. $120°$ $\frac{2\pi}{3}$

4B. $-\frac{3\pi}{8}$ $-67.5°$

Personal Tutor glencoe.com

Concept Summary: Degrees and Radians

The diagram shows equivalent degree and radian measures for special angles.

You may find it helpful to memorize the following equivalent degree and radian measures. The other special angles are multiples of these angles.

$30° = \frac{\pi}{6}$ $\qquad 45° = \frac{\pi}{4}$

$60° = \frac{\pi}{3}$ $\qquad 90° = \frac{\pi}{2}$

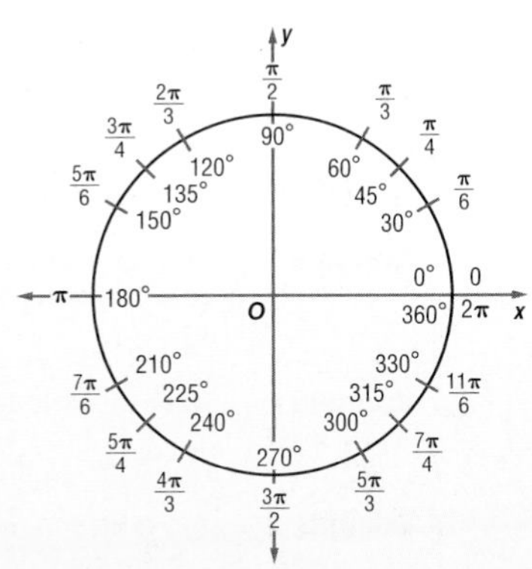

Additional Example

3 Find an angle with a positive measure and an angle with a negative measure that are coterminal with each angle.

a. 210° Sample answers: 570°, –150°

b. –120° Sample answers: 240°, –480°

Additional Examples also in Interactive Classroom PowerPoint® Presentations

IWB INTERACTIVE WHITEBOARD READY

TEACH with TECH

INSTANT MESSAGING Have students work in pairs. One student should send a message with the measure of an angle. The other student should reply with the measures of two angles coterminal with the given angle. Students should then switch roles and repeat.

Convert Between Degrees and Radians

Example 4 shows how to convert between degrees and radians. **Example 5** shows how to convert and use angle measures in a real-world situation.

Additional Example

4 Rewrite the degree measure in radians and the radian measure in degrees.

a. 30° $\frac{\pi}{6}$

b. $-\frac{5\pi}{3}$ –300°

Differentiated Instruction

AL

If students need further practice with coterminal angles,

Then have them work with a partner so that one person models an angle with two pencils or yardsticks. The other partner then names a positive and negative angle, less than or more than a full circle, that is coterminal with the modeled angle.

Additional Example

5 **TRUCKS** The steering wheel on a monster truck has a radius of 11 inches. How far does a point on the steering wheel travel if the wheel makes four fifths of a rotation? about 55.3 in.

Additional Answers

1.

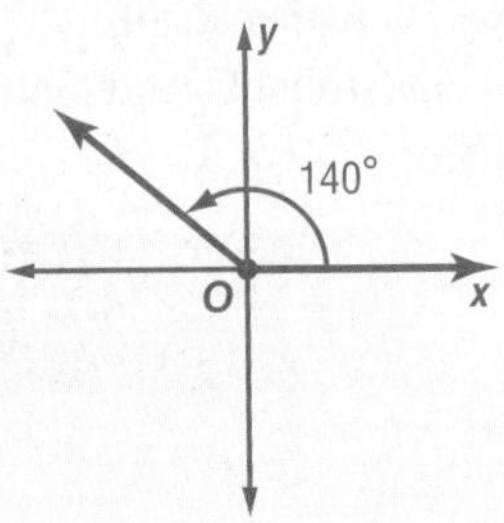

2.

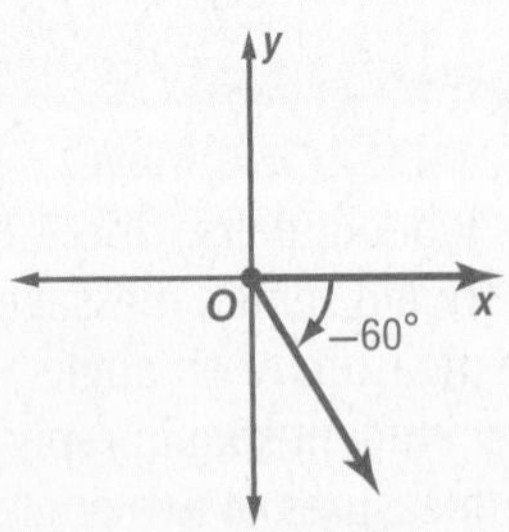

3.

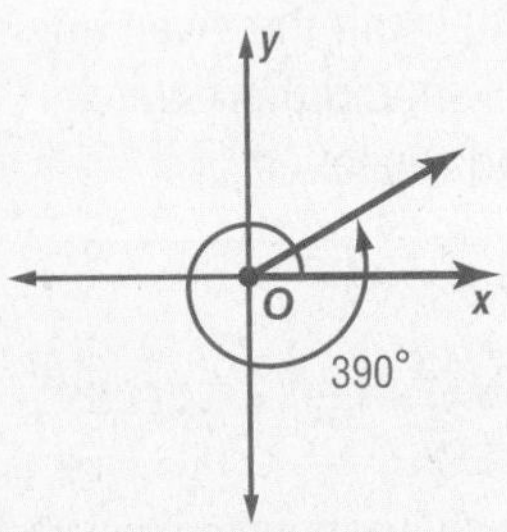

11.

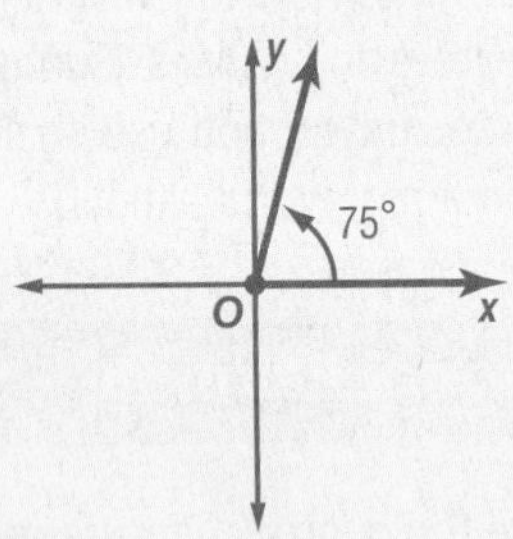

12.

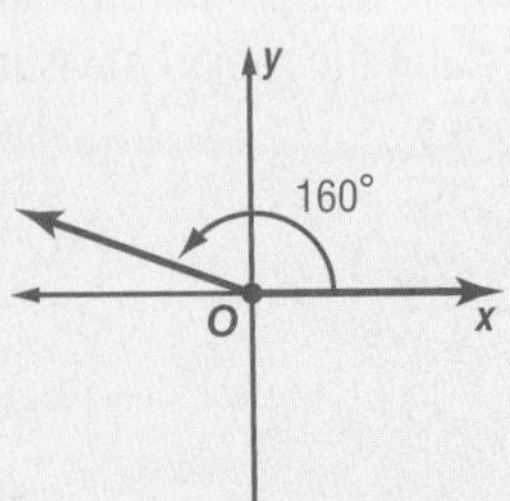

A **central angle** of a circle is an angle with a vertex at the center of the circle. If you know the measure of a central angle and the radius of the circle, you can find the length of the arc that is intercepted by the angle.

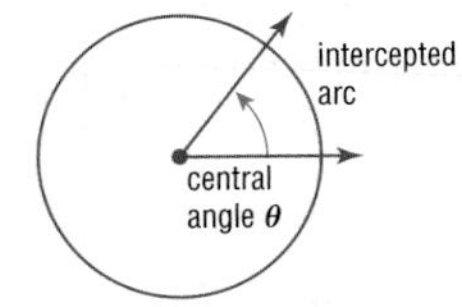

Key Concept Arc Length

Words For a circle with radius r and central angle θ (in radians), the **arc length** s equals the product of r and θ.

Symbols $s = r\theta$

Model

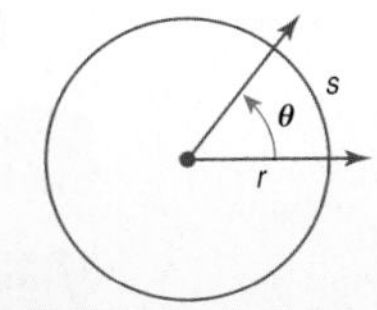

You will justify this formula in Exercise 52.

Real-World EXAMPLE 5 Find Arc Length

TRUCKS Monster truck tires have a radius of 33 inches. How far does a monster truck travel in feet after just three fourths of a tire rotation?

Step 1 Find the central angle in radians.

$\theta = \frac{3}{4} \cdot 2\pi$ or $\frac{3\pi}{2}$ The angle is $\frac{3}{4}$ of a complete rotation.

Step 2 Use the radius and central angle to find the arc length.

$s = r\theta$ Write the formula for arc length.

$= 33 \cdot \frac{3\pi}{2}$ Replace r with 33 and θ with $\frac{3\pi}{2}$.

≈ 155.5 in. Use a calculator to simplify.

≈ 13.0 ft Divide by 12 to convert to feet.

So, the truck travels about 13 feet after three fourths of a tire rotation.

Watch Out!

Arc Length Remember to write the angle measure in radians, not degrees, when finding arc length. Also, recall that the number of radians in a complete rotation is 2π.

Guided Practice

5. A circle has a diameter of 9 centimeters. Find the arc length if the central angle is 60°. Round to the nearest tenth. 4.7 cm

Personal Tutor glencoe.com

Check Your Understanding

5. Sample answer: 535°, −185°
6. Sample answer: 260°, −460°

Examples 1 and 2 pp. 817–818 **Draw an angle with the given measure in standard position.** 1–3. See margin.

1. 140° **2.** −60° **3.** 390°

Example 3 p. 818 **Find an angle with a positive measure and an angle with a negative measure that are coterminal with each angle.** 4. Sample answer: 385°, −335°

4. 25° **5.** 175° **6.** −100°

Example 4 p. 819 **Rewrite each degree measure in radians and each radian measure in degrees.**

7. $\frac{\pi}{4}$ 45° **8.** 225° $\frac{5\pi}{4}$ **9.** −40° $-\frac{2\pi}{9}$

Example 5 p. 820 **10. TENNIS** A tennis player's swing moves along the path of an arc. If the radius of the arc's circle is 4 feet and the angle of rotation is 100°, what is the length of the arc? Round to the nearest tenth. 7.0 ft

13.

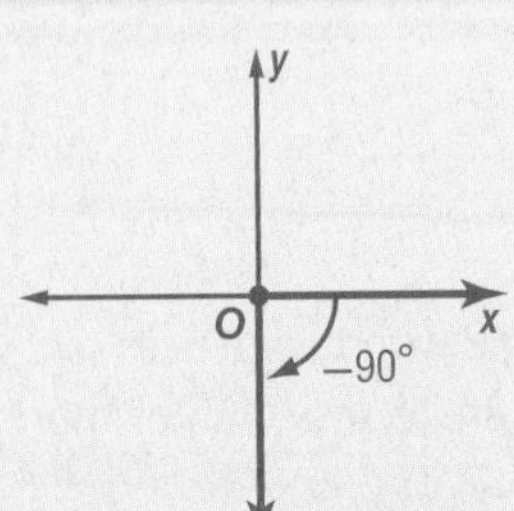

Practice and Problem Solving

● = **Step-by-Step Solutions** begin on page R20.
Extra Practice begins on page 947.

Examples 1 and 2 pp. 817–818

Draw an angle with the given measure in standard position. 11–16. See margin.

11. 75°	**12.** 160°	**13.** −90°
14. −120°	**15.** 295°	**16.** 510°

17. GYMNASTICS A gymnast on the uneven bars swings to make a 240° angle of rotation.

18. FOOD The lid on a jar of pasta sauce is turned 420° before it comes off.
17, 18. See margin.

Example 3 p. 818

Find an angle with a positive measure and an angle with a negative measure that are coterminal with each angle.

19. 50°	**20.** 95°	**21.** 205°
22. 350°	**23.** −80°	**24.** −195°

Example 4 p. 819

Rewrite each degree measure in radians and each radian measure in degrees.

25. 330° $\frac{11\pi}{6}$	**26.** $\frac{5\pi}{6}$ 150°	**27.** $-\frac{\pi}{3}$ −60°
28. −50° $-\frac{5\pi}{18}$	**29.** 190° $\frac{19\pi}{18}$	**30.** $-\frac{7\pi}{3}$ −420°

Example 5 p. 820

31. SKATEBOARDING The skateboard ramp at the right is called a *quarter pipe*. The curved surface is determined by the radius of a circle. Find the length of the curved part of the ramp. about 12.6 ft

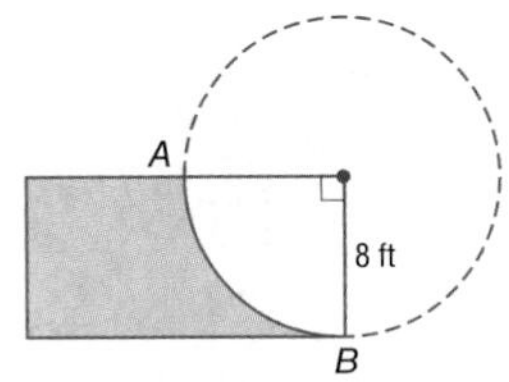

32. RIVERBOATS The paddlewheel of a riverboat has a diameter of 24 feet. Find the arc length of the circle made when the paddlewheel rotates 300°. about 62.8 ft

Find the length of each arc. Round to the nearest tenth.

33. 6.7 cm

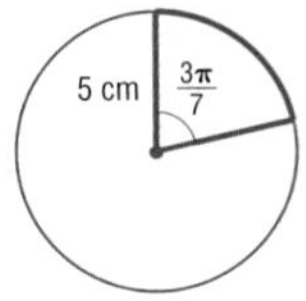

34. 94.2 m

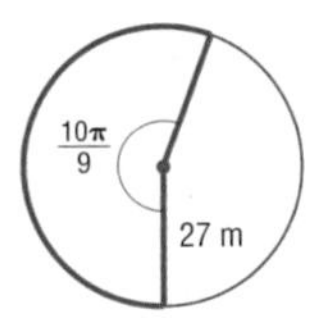

35. CLOCKS How long does it take for the minute hand on a clock to pass through 2.5π radians? 1 h 15 min

36. SUNDIALS Refer to the beginning of the lesson. A shadow moves around a sundial 15° every hour.

a. After how many hours is the angle of rotation of the shadow $\frac{8\pi}{5}$ radians? 19.2 h

b. What is the angle of rotation in radians after 5 hours? $\frac{5\pi}{12}$

c. A sundial has a radius of 8 inches. What is the arc formed by a shadow after 14 hours? Round to the nearest tenth. 29.3 in.

Find an angle with a positive measure and an angle with a negative measure that are coterminal with each angle.

37. 620°	**38.** −400°	**39.** $-\frac{3\pi}{4}$	**40.** $\frac{19\pi}{6}$

19. Sample answer: 410°, −310°
20. Sample answer: 455°, −265°
21. Sample answer: 565°, −155°
22. Sample answer: 710°, −10°
23. Sample answer: 280°, −440°
24. Sample answer: 165°, −555°
37. Sample answer: 260°, −100°
38. Sample answer: 320°, −40°
39. Sample answer: $\frac{5\pi}{4}$, $-\frac{11\pi}{4}$
40. Sample answer: $\frac{7\pi}{6}$, $-\frac{5\pi}{6}$

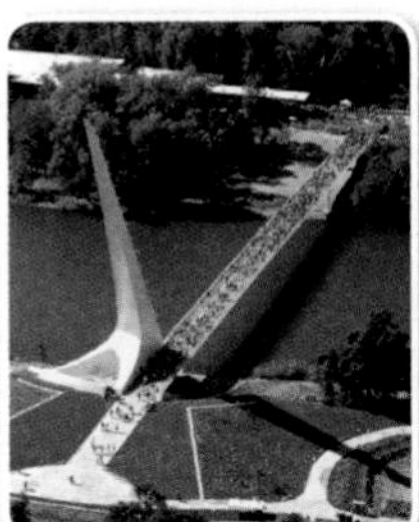

Real-World Link

The Sundial Bridge at Turtle Bay in Redding, California, is the world's largest sundial. It is 700 feet long, 23 feet wide, and 217 feet high.

Source: Turtle Bay Exploration Park

3 PRACTICE

Formative Assessment

Use Exercises 1–10 to check for understanding.

Use the chart at the bottom of this page to customize assignments for your students.

Additional Answers

14.

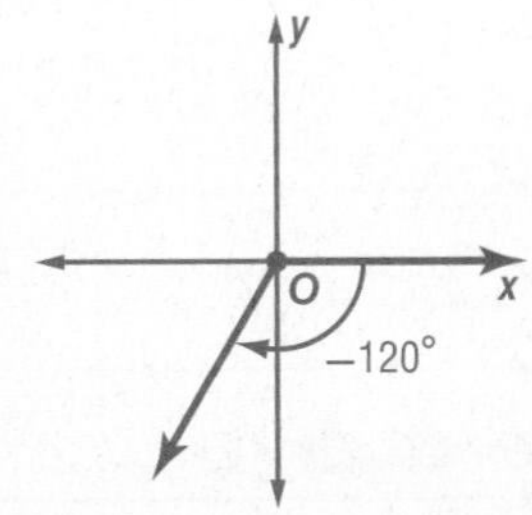

15.

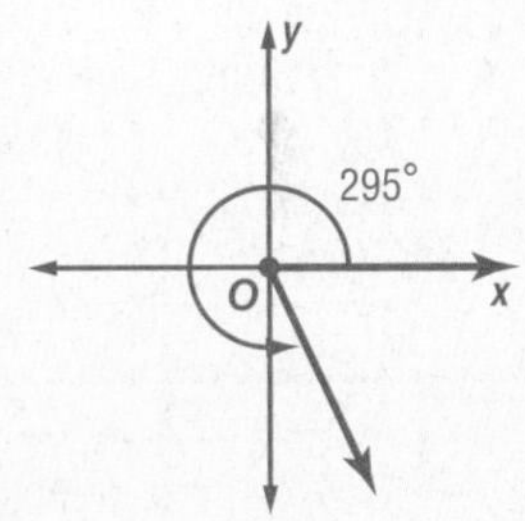

16.

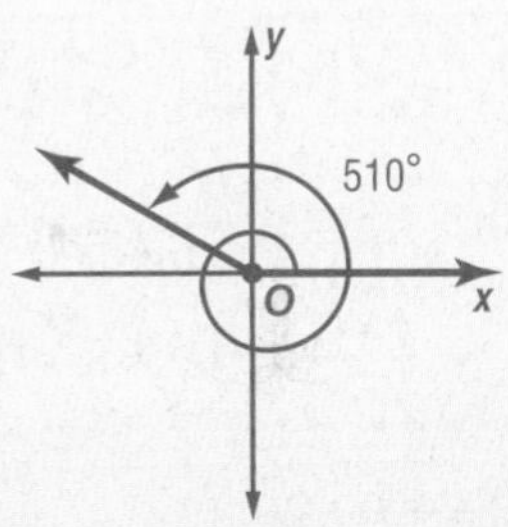

17.

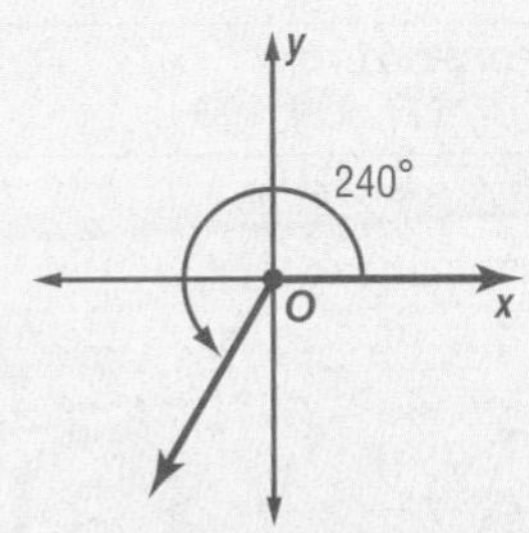

18.

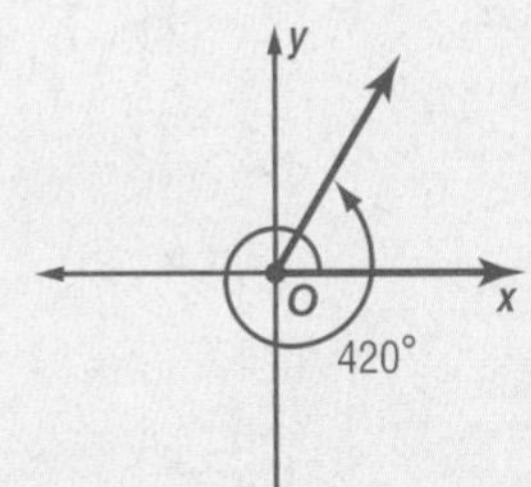

Differentiated Homework Options

Level	Assignment	Two-Day Option	
AL Basic	11–34, 48, 50–67	11–33 odd, 54–57	12–34 even, 48, 50–53, 58–67
OL Core	11–39 odd, 41–48, 50–67	11–34, 54–57	35–48, 50–53, 58–67
BL Advanced	35–64, (optional: 65–67)		

Study Guide and Intervention
CRM pp. 11–12 AL OL ELL

13-2 Study Guide and Intervention
Angles and Angle Measure

Angles in Standard Position An angle is determined by two rays. The degree measure of an angle in standard position is described by the amount and direction of rotation from the **initial side**, which lies along the positive x-axis, to the **terminal side**. A counterclockwise rotation is associated with positive angle measure and a clockwise rotation is associated with negative angle measure. Two or more angles in standard position with the same terminal side are called **coterminal angles**.

Example 1 Draw an angle with measure 290° in standard position.

The negative y-axis represents a positive rotation of 270°. To generate an angle of 290°, rotate the terminal side 20° more in the counterclockwise direction

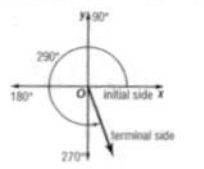

Example 2 Find an angle with a positive measure and an angle with a negative measure that are coterminal with each angle.

a. 250°
A positive angle is 250° + 360° or 610°. Add 360°.
A negative angle is 250° − 360° or −110°. Subtract 360°.

b. −140°
A positive angle is −140° + 360° or 220°. Add 360°.
A negative angle is −140° − 360° or −500°. Subtract 360°.

Exercises

Draw an angle with the given measure in standard position.

1. 160° 2. 280° 3. 400°

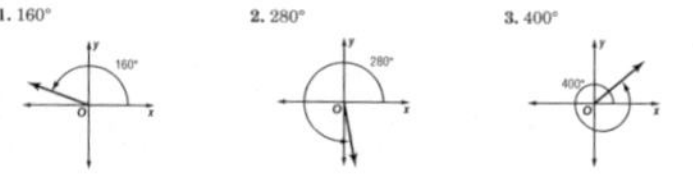

Find an angle with a positive measure and an angle with a negative measure that are coterminal with each angle.

4. 65° **425°, −295°** 5. −75° **285°, −435°** 6. 230° **590°, −130°** 7. 420° **60°, −300°**

Chapter 13 11 *Glencoe Algebra 2*

Lesson 13-2

Practice
CRM p. 14 AL OL BL ELL

13-2 Practice
Angles and Angle Measure

Draw an angle with the given measure in standard position.

1. 210° 2. 305° 3. 580°
4. 135° 5. −450° 6. −560°

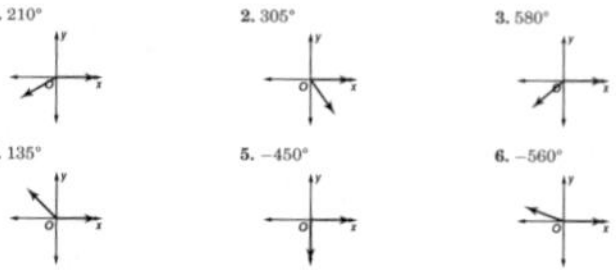

Find an angle with a positive measure and an angle with a negative measure that are coterminal with each angle.

7. 65° **425°, −295°** 8. 80° **440°, −280°** 9. 110° **470°, −250°**

10. $\frac{2\pi}{5}$ **$\frac{12\pi}{5}, -\frac{8\pi}{5}$** 11. $\frac{5\pi}{6}$ **$\frac{17\pi}{6}, -\frac{7\pi}{6}$** 12. $-\frac{3\pi}{2}$ **$\frac{\pi}{2}, -\frac{7\pi}{2}$**

Rewrite each degree measure in radians and each radian measure in degrees.

13. 18° **$\frac{\pi}{10}$** 14. 6° **$\frac{\pi}{30}$** 15. −72° **$-\frac{2\pi}{5}$** 16. −820° **$-\frac{41\pi}{9}$**

17. 4π **720°** 18. $\frac{5\pi}{2}$ **450°** 19. $-\frac{9\pi}{2}$ **−810°** 20. $-\frac{7\pi}{12}$ **−105°**

Find the length of each arc. Round to the nearest tenth.

21. 22. 23.

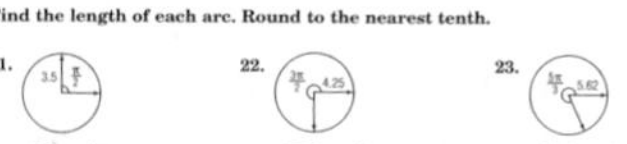

5.5 units **20.0 units** **29.4 units**

24. **TIME** Find both the degree and radian measures of the angle through which the hour hand on a clock rotates from 5 A.M. to 10 P.M. **−510°; $-\frac{17\pi}{6}$**

25. **ROTATION** A truck with 16-inch radius wheels is driven at 77 feet per second (52.5 miles per hour). Find the measure of the angle through which a point on the outside of the wheel travels each second. Round to the nearest degree and nearest radian. **3309°/s; 58 radians/s**

Chapter 13 14 *Glencoe Algebra 2*

Word Problem Practice
CRM p. 15 AL OL BL ELL

13-2 Word Problem Practice
Angles and Angle Measure

1. **AMUSEMENT PARKS** The carousel at an amusement park has 20 horses spaced evenly around its circumference. The horses are numbered consecutively from 1 to 20. The carousel completes one rotation about its axis every 40 seconds.

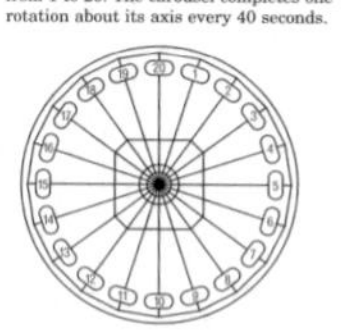

a. What is the central angle, in degrees, formed by horse #1 and horse #8? **126°**

b. What is the speed of the carousel in rotations per minute? **1.5 rotations per minute**

c. What is the speed of the carousel in radians per minute? **3π radians per minute**

d. A child rides the carousel for 6 minutes. Through how many radians will the child pass in the course of the carousel ride? **18π radians**

2. **TIME** Through what angle, in degrees and radians, does the hour hand on a clock rotate between 4 P.M. and 7 P.M.? Assuming the length of the hour hand is 6 inches, find the arc length of the circle made by the hour hand during that time. **90°, $\frac{\pi}{2}$ radians**

3. **TIME** Through what angle, in degrees and radians, does the minute hand rotate between 4 P.M. and 7 P.M.? **1080°, 6π radians**

4. **PLANETS** Earth makes one full rotation on its axis every 24 hours. How long does it take Earth to rotate through 150°? Neptune makes one full rotation on its axis every 16 hours. How long does it take Neptune to rotate through 150°? **10 hours, $6\frac{2}{3}$ hours**

Chapter 13 15 *Glencoe Algebra 2*

Lesson 13-2

41d. The arc length would double. Since $s = r\theta$, if r is doubled and θ remains unchanged, then the value of s is also doubled.

42b. $\tan \angle BEA = -\frac{3}{2}$, $\tan \angle DEC = \frac{4}{3}$

42c. slope of $\overline{BE} = -\frac{3}{2}$, slope of $ED = \frac{4}{3}$

42d. Sample answer: In the coordinate plane, the tangent of the angle in standard position equals the slope of the terminal side of the angle.

41. **SWINGS** A swing has a 165° angle of rotation.
 a. Draw the angle in standard position. **See margin.**
 b. Write the angle measure in radians. **$\frac{11\pi}{12}$**
 c. If the chains of the swing are $6\frac{1}{2}$ feet long, what is the length of the arc that the swing makes? Round to the nearest tenth. **18.7 ft**
 d. Describe how the arc length would change if the lengths of the chains of the swing were doubled.

42. **MULTIPLE REPRESENTATIONS** Consider $A(-4, 0)$, $B(-4, 6)$, $C(6, 0)$, and $D(6, 8)$.
 a. **GEOMETRIC** Draw $\triangle EAB$ and $\triangle ECD$ with E at the origin. **See margin.**
 b. **ALGEBRAIC** Find the values of the tangent of $\angle BEA$ and the tangent of $\angle DEC$.
 c. **ALGEBRAIC** Find the slope of $\overline{BE}$ and $\overline{ED}$.
 d. **VERBAL** What conclusions can you make about the relationship between slope and tangent?

Rewrite each degree measure in radians and each radian measure in degrees.

43. $\frac{21\pi}{8}$ **472.5°** 44. 124° **$\frac{31\pi}{45}$** 45. −200° **$-\frac{10\pi}{9}$** 46. 5 **$\frac{900}{\pi} \approx 286.5°$**

C

47. **CAROUSELS** A carousel makes 5 revolutions per minute. The circle formed by riders sitting in the outside row has a radius of 17.2 feet. The circle formed by riders sitting in the inside row has a radius of 13.1 feet.

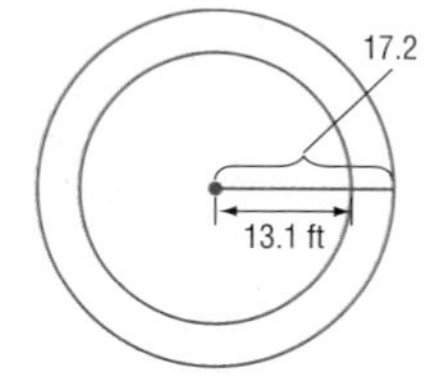

 a. Find the angle θ in radians through which the carousel rotates in one second. **$\frac{\pi}{6}$**
 b. In one second, what is the difference in arc lengths between the riders sitting in the outside row and the riders sitting in the inside row? **2.1 ft**

Real-World Link

In the United States, carousels rotate counterclockwise, while carousels in Europe rotate clockwise.

Source: The Discovery Channel

H.O.T. Problems
Use Higher-Order Thinking Skills

48. **ERROR ANALYSIS** Tarshia and Alan are writing an expression for the measure of an angle coterminal with the angle shown at the right. Is either of them correct? Explain your reasoning.

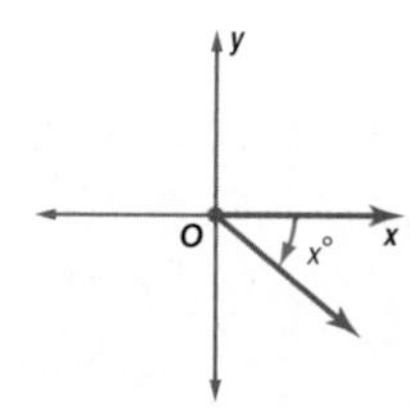

Tarshia	Alan
The measure of a coterminal angle is $(x - 360)°$.	The measure of a coterminal angle is $(360 - x)°$.

48. Tarshia; a coterminal can be found by adding a multiple of 360° or by subtracting a multiple of 360°. Alan incorrectly subtracted the original angle measure from 360°.

49. **CHALLENGE** A line makes an angle of $\frac{\pi}{2}$ radians with the positive x-axis at the point (2, 0). Find an equation for this line. **$x = 2$**

50. **REASONING** Express $\frac{1}{8}$ of a revolution in degrees and in radians. Explain your reasoning.

50. 45°, $\frac{\pi}{4}$; $\frac{1}{8}$ of 360° is 45° and $\frac{1}{8}$ of 2π is $\frac{\pi}{4}$.

51. **OPEN ENDED** Draw and label an acute angle in standard position. Find two angles, one positive and one negative, that are coterminal with the angle. **See margin.**

52. **REASONING** Justify the formula for the length of an arc. **See Chapter 13 Answer Appendix.**

53. **WRITING IN MATH** Use a circle with radius r to describe what one degree and one radian represent. Then explain how to convert between the measures. **See Chapter 13 Answer Appendix.**

Enrichment
CRM p. 16 OL BL

13-2 Enrichment

Making and Using a Hypsometer

A **hypsometer** is a device that can be used to measure the height of an object. To construct your own hypsometer, you will need a rectangular piece of heavy cardboard that is at least 7 cm by 10 cm, a straw, transparent tape, a string about 20 cm long, and a small weight that can be attached to the string.

Mark off 1-cm increments along one short side and one long side of the cardboard. Tape the straw to the other short side. Then attach the weight to one end of the string, and attach the other end of the string to one corner of the cardboard, as shown in the figure below. The diagram below shows how your hypsometer should look.

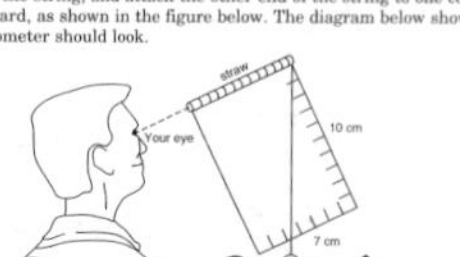

Multiple Representations In Exercise 42, students use coordinate geometry, trigonometry, algebra, and analysis to relate the slope of a line to the tangent of the angle it makes with the x-axis.

NGSSS PRACTICE 912.A.7.5, 912.A.2.12, 912.G.2.5, 912.D.11.3

54. THINK SOLVE EXPLAIN **SHORT RESPONSE** If $(x + 6)(x + 8) - (x - 7)(x - 5) = 0$, find x. $-\frac{1}{2}$

55. Which of the following represents an inverse variation? A

A.

x	2	5	10	20	25	50
y	50	20	10	5	4	2

B.

x	2	4	6	8	10	12
y	−4	−8	−12	−16	−20	−24

C.

x	1	2	3	4	5	6
y	5	10	15	20	25	30

D.

x	10	9	8	7	6	5
y	5	6	7	8	9	10

56. GEOMETRY If the area of the figure is 60 square units, what is the length of side $\overline{XZ}$? G

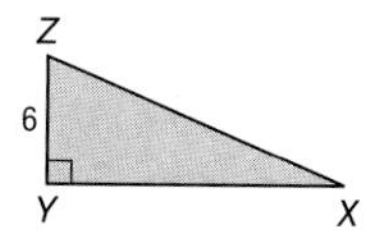

F. $2\sqrt{34}$ H. $4\sqrt{109}$
G. $2\sqrt{109}$ I. $4\sqrt{34}$

57. SAT/ACT The first term of a sequence is −6, and every term after the first is 8 more than the term immediately preceding it. What is the value of the 101st term? B

A. 788 C. 802
B. 794 D. 808

Spiral Review

Find the values of the six trigonometric functions for angle θ. (Lesson 13-1) 58–60. See Chapter 13 Answer Appendix.

58.

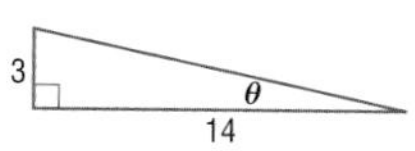

59.

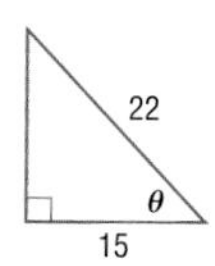

60.

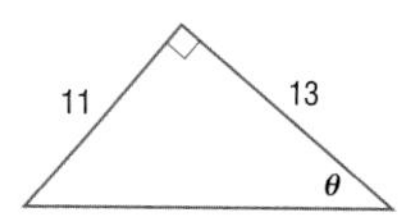

A binomial distribution has a 40% rate of success. There are 12 trials. (Lesson 12-7)

61. What is the probability that there will be at least 8 successes? exactly 5 failures? 5.7%; 10.1%

62. What is the expected number of successes? 4.8

63. MANUFACTURING The sizes of CDs made by a company are normally distributed with a standard deviation of 1 millimeter. The CDs are supposed to be 120 millimeters in diameter, and they are made for drives that are 122 millimeters wide. (Lesson 12-5)

a. What percent of the CDs would you expect to be greater than 120 millimeters? 50%

b. If the company manufactures 1000 CDs per hour, how many of the CDs made in one hour would you expect to be between 119 and 122 millimeters? 815

c. About how many CDs per hour will be too large to fit in the drives? 25

64. FINANCIAL LITERACY If the rate of inflation is 2%, the cost of an item in future years can be found by iterating the function $c(x) = 1.02x$. Find the cost of a $70 digital audio player in four years if the rate of inflation remains constant. (Lesson 11-5) $75.77

Skills Review

Use the Pythagorean Theorem to find the length of the hypotenuse for each right triangle with the given side lengths. (Lesson 0-7)

65. $a = 12, b = 15$ $3\sqrt{41}$ **66.** $a = 8, b = 17$ $\sqrt{353}$ **67.** $a = 14, b = 11$ $\sqrt{317}$

Watch Out!

Error Analysis For Exercise 48, if students think that Alan is correct, point out that if the angle shown is measured clockwise, then the angle measure x is a negative quantity and $(360 - x)°$ will be greater, not less, than 360°.

4 ASSESS

Yesterday's News Ask students to describe how yesterday's topic of angles in right triangles helped them understand and illustrate today's topic of angles in standard position.

Additional Answers

41a.

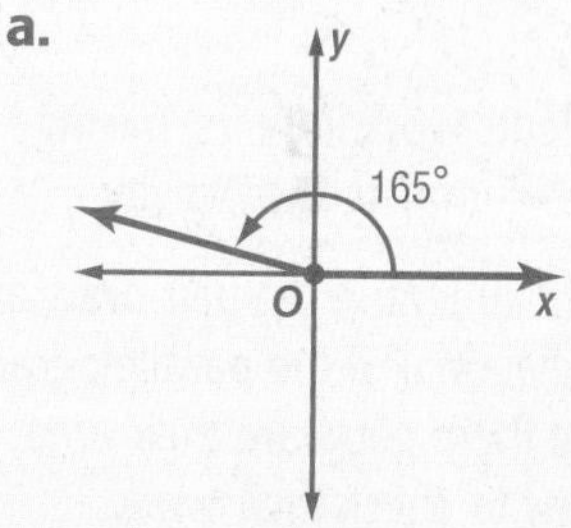

42a.

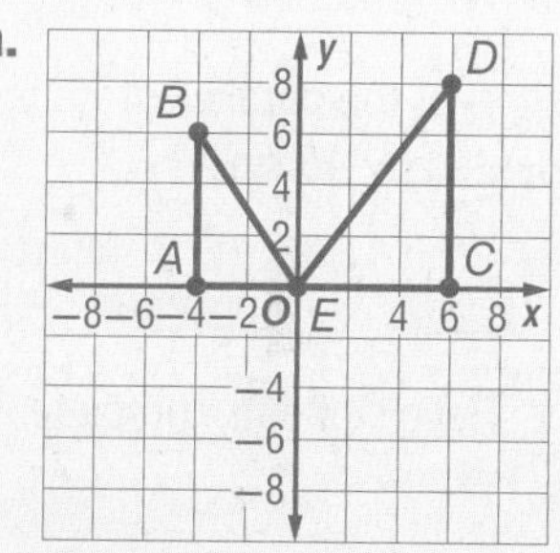

51. Sample answer: 440° and −280°

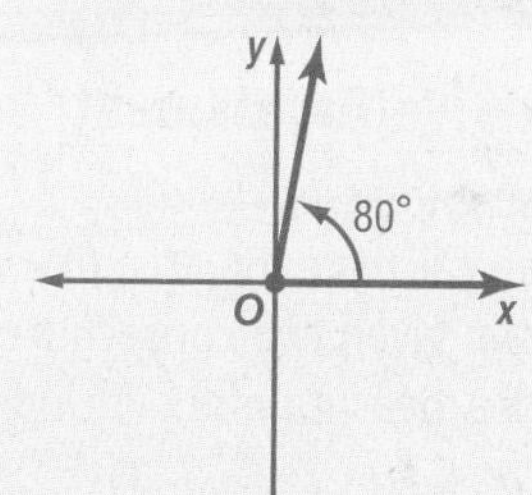

Differentiated Instruction

OL BL

Extension There are infinitely many angles coterminal with a given angle. Have students write an expression that gives the angle measure of all angles coterminal with an angle of 50°. $50° + k \cdot 360°$, where k is any integer.

1 FOCUS

Objective Use the sine ratio to find the area of a parallelogram.

Teaching Tip

If students use calculators to approximate areas, remind them to make sure that their calculators are in degree mode.

2 TEACH

Working in Cooperative Groups

Have students work in pairs, mixing abilities, to complete the Activity.

Have each student in the pair draw a different diagonal of the parallelogram. Then have them compare their area calculations to check their work.

Ask:

- What part of the parallelogram is represented by *AB* sin *A*?

  $\sin A = \frac{h}{AB}$, so *AB* sin *A* is the height *h* of the parallelogram.

Practice Have students complete Exercise 1–3.

3 ASSESS

Formative Assessment

Use Exercise 2 to assess whether students can calculate the area of a parallelogram given two consecutive sides and the measure of the included angle.

Areas of Parallelograms

NGSSS **MA.912.T.1.4** Find approximate values of trigonometric and inverse trigonometric functions using appropriate technology.

The area of any triangle can be found using the sine ratios in the triangle. A similar process can be used to find the area of a parallelogram.

ACTIVITY

Find the area of parallelogram *ABCD*.

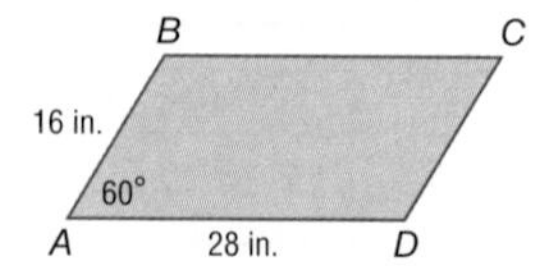

Step 1 Draw diagonal $\overline{BD}$.
$\overline{BD}$ divides the parallelogram into two congruent triangles, $\triangle ABD$ and $\triangle CDB$.

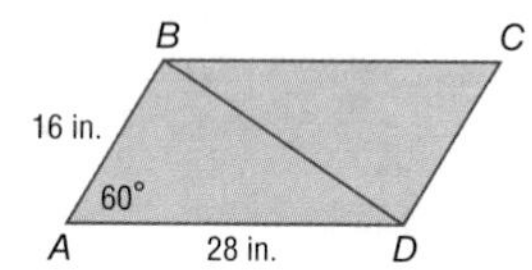

Step 2 Find the area of $\triangle ABD$.

$\text{Area} = \frac{1}{2}(AB)(AD)\sin A$	**Area of a triangle**
$= \frac{1}{2}(16)(28)\sin 60°$	**$AB = 16$, $AD = 28$, and $A = 60°$**
$= 224\left(\frac{\sqrt{3}}{2}\right)$	**Multiply and evaluate sin 60°.**
$= 112\sqrt{3}$	**Simplify.**

Step 3 Find the area of ▱*ABCD*.

The area of ▱*ABCD* is equal to the sum of the areas of $\triangle ABD$ and $\triangle CDB$. Because $\triangle ABD \cong \triangle CDB$, the areas of $\triangle ABD$ and $\triangle CDB$ are equal. So, the area of ▱*ABCD* equals twice the area of $\triangle ABD$.

$2 \cdot 112\sqrt{3} = 224\sqrt{3}$ or about 387.98 square inches.

Exercises

1a. 106.07 m^2 1b. 57.40 m^2 1c. 150 m^2 2a. 22.5 in^2 2b. 11.65 in^2 2c. 38.97 in^2 3a. 19,318.52 ft^2 3b. 12,175.23 ft^2 3c. 10,000 ft^2

For each of the following,

a. **find the area of each parallelogram.**

b. **find the area of each parallelogram when the included angle is half the given measure.**

c. **find the area of each parallelogram when the included angle is twice the given measure.**

1.

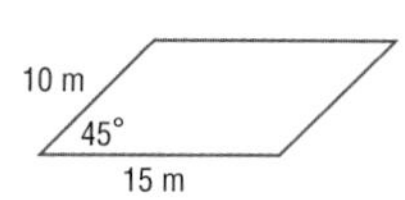

2.

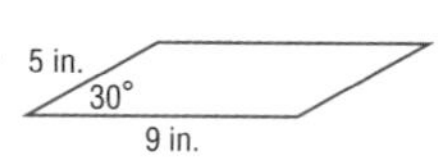

3.

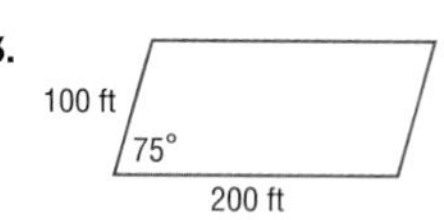

From Concrete to Abstract

Ask students to develop a formula for the area of a parallelogram if the measures of two consecutive sides are *a* and *b*, and one of the angles of the parallelogram is θ. $A = ab\sin\theta$

Additional Answer (Lesson 13-3, Guided Practice)

1. $\sin\theta = \frac{\sqrt{10}}{10}$, $\cos\theta = -\frac{3\sqrt{10}}{10}$, $\tan\theta = -\frac{1}{3}$, $\csc\theta = \sqrt{10}$, $\sec\theta = -\frac{\sqrt{10}}{3}$, $\cot\theta = -3$

824 Chapter 13 Trigonometric Functions

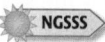

Trigonometric Functions of General Angles

Then

You found values of trigonometric functions for acute angles. (Lesson 13-1)

Now

- Find values of trigonometric functions for general angles.
- Find values of trigonometric functions by using reference angles.

NGSSS

MA.912.T.1.2 Define and determine sine and cosine using the unit circle.
MA.912.T.1.3 State and use exact values of trigonometric functions for special angles, i.e. multiples of $\frac{P}{6}$ and $\frac{P}{4}$ (degree and radian measures).

New Vocabulary

quadrantal angle
reference angle

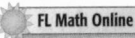

FL Math Online

glencoe.com

Why?

In the ride at the right, the cars rotate back and forth about a central point. The current positions of two of the arms can be described as 220° clockwise and 50° counterclockwise from the standard position.

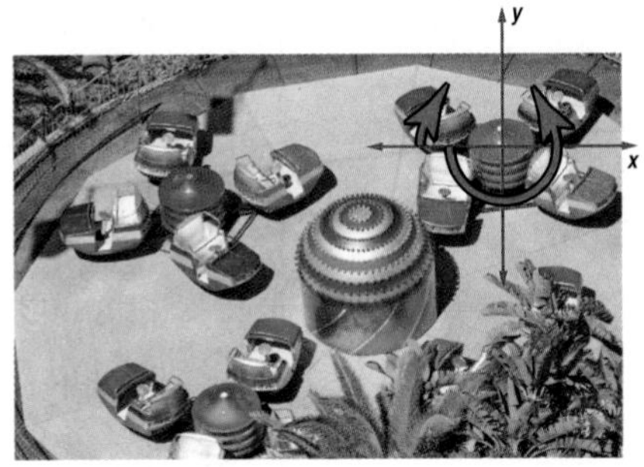

Trigonometric Functions for General Angles You can find values of trigonometric functions for angles greater than 90° or less than 0°.

Key Concept

Trigonometric Functions of General Angles

Let θ be an angle in standard position and let $P(x, y)$ be a point on its terminal side. Using the Pythagorean Theorem, $r = \sqrt{x^2 + y^2}$. The six trigonometric functions of θ are defined below.

$\sin\theta = \frac{y}{r}$ $\cos\theta = \frac{x}{r}$ $\tan\theta = \frac{y}{x}, x \neq 0$

$\csc\theta = \frac{r}{y}, y \neq 0$ $\sec\theta = \frac{r}{x}, x \neq 0$ $\cot\theta = \frac{x}{y}, y \neq 0$

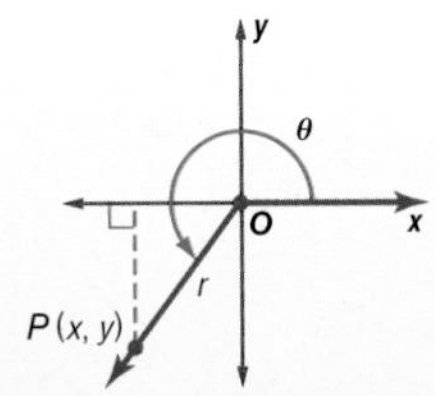

EXAMPLE 1 Evaluate Trigonometric Functions Given a Point

The terminal side of θ in standard position contains the point at (–3, –4). Find the exact values of the six trigonometric functions of θ.

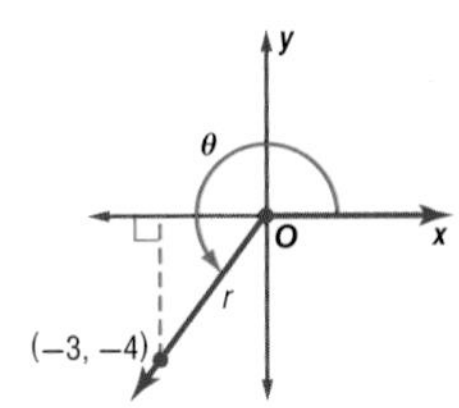

Step 1 Draw the angle, and find the value of r.

$$r = \sqrt{x^2 + y^2}$$
$$= \sqrt{(-3)^2 + (-4)^2}$$
$$= \sqrt{25} \text{ or } 5$$

Step 2 Use $x = -3$, $y = -4$, and $r = 5$ to write the six trigonometric ratios.

$\sin\theta = \frac{y}{r} = \frac{-4}{5}$ or $-\frac{4}{5}$ $\cos\theta = \frac{x}{r} = \frac{-3}{5}$ or $-\frac{3}{5}$ $\tan\theta = \frac{y}{x} = \frac{-4}{-3}$ or $\frac{4}{3}$

$\csc\theta = \frac{r}{y} = \frac{5}{-4}$ or $-\frac{5}{4}$ $\sec\theta = \frac{r}{x} = \frac{5}{-3}$ or $-\frac{5}{3}$ $\cot\theta = \frac{x}{y} = \frac{-3}{-4}$ or $\frac{3}{4}$

Guided Practice

1. The terminal side of θ in standard position contains the point at (–6, 2). Find the exact values of the six trigonometric functions of θ. **See margin.**

Personal Tutor glencoe.com

1 FOCUS

Vertical Alignment

Before Lesson 13-3
Find values of trigonometric functions for acute angles.

Lesson 13-3
Find values of trigonometric functions for general angles.
Find values of trigonometric functions by using reference angles.

After Lesson 13-3
Investigate graphs of the tangent, cotangent, secant, and cosecant functions.

2 TEACH

Scaffolding Questions

Have students read the *Why?* section of the lesson.

Ask:

- Which quadrant is indicated by "20° clockwise"? Quadrant IV
- Which is indicated by "200° counterclockwise"? Quadrant III
- How can you describe the position "20° clockwise" in terms of a counterclockwise rotation? 340° counterclockwise

Lesson 13-3 Resources

Resource	Approaching-Level	On-Level	Beyond-Level	English Learners
Teacher Edition	• Differentiated Instruction, p. 828	• Differentiated Instruction, pp. 828, 831	• Differentiated Instruction, p. 831	
Chapter Resource Masters	• Study Guide and Intervention, pp. 17–18 • Skills Practice, p. 19 • Practice, p. 20 • Word Problem Practice, p. 21	• Study Guide and Intervention, pp. 17–18 • Skills Practice, p. 19 • Practice, p. 20 • Word Problem Practice, p. 21 • Enrichment, p. 22	• Practice, p. 20 • Word Problem Practice, p. 21 • Enrichment, p. 22	• Study Guide and Intervention, pp. 17–18 • Skills Practice, p. 19 • Practice, p. 20 • Word Problem Practice, p. 21
Transparencies	• 5-Minute Check Transparency 13-3	• 5-Minute Check Transparency 13-3	• 5-Minute Check Transparency 13-3	• 5-Minute Check Transparency 13-3
Other	• Study Notebook	• Study Notebook	• Study Notebook	• Study Notebook

Trigonometric Functions for General Angles

Example 1 shows how to evaluate trigonometric functions for a given point. **Example 2** shows how to find the values of the six trigonometric functions for a quadrantal angle.

Formative Assessment

Use the Guided Practice exercises after each example to determine students' understanding of concepts.

Additional Examples

1 The terminal side of θ in standard position contains the point (8, –15). Find the exact values of the six trigonometric functions of θ. $\sin\theta = -\frac{15}{17}$; $\cos\theta = \frac{8}{17}$; $\tan\theta = -\frac{15}{8}$; $\sec\theta = \frac{17}{8}$; $\csc\theta = -\frac{17}{15}$; $\cot\theta = -\frac{8}{15}$

2 The terminal side of θ in standard position contains the point at (0, –2). Find the values of the six trigonometric functions of θ. $\sin\theta = -1$; $\cos\theta = 0$; $\tan\theta$ is undefined; $\csc\theta = -1$; $\sec\theta$ is undefined; $\cot\theta = 0$

Additional Examples also in Interactive Classroom PowerPoint® Presentations

IWB INTERACTIVE WHITEBOARD READY

If the terminal side of angle θ in standard position lies on the x- or y-axis, the angle is called a **quadrantal angle**.

StudyTip

Quadrantal Angles The measure of a quadrantal angle is a multiple of 90° or $\frac{\pi}{2}$.

Key Concept: Quadrantal Angles

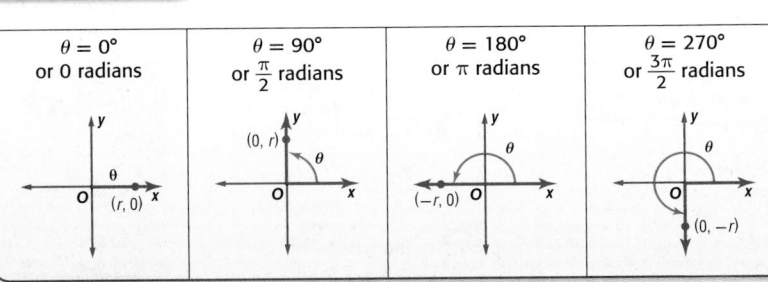

$\theta = 0°$ or 0 radians	$\theta = 90°$ or $\frac{\pi}{2}$ radians	$\theta = 180°$ or π radians	$\theta = 270°$ or $\frac{3\pi}{2}$ radians
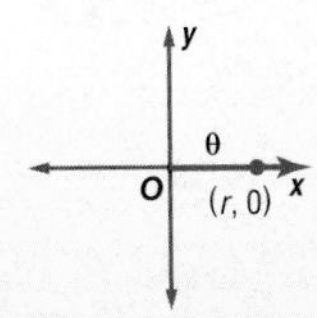	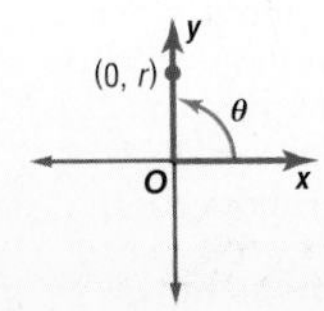	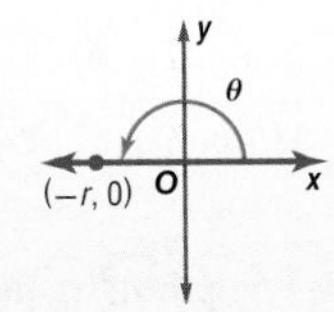	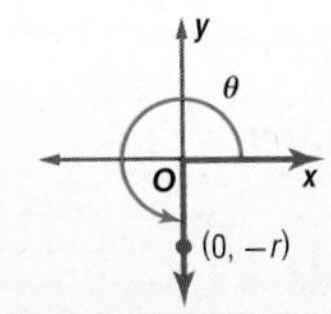

EXAMPLE 2 Quadrantal Angles

The terminal side of θ in standard position contains the point at (0, 6). Find the values of the six trigonometric functions of θ.

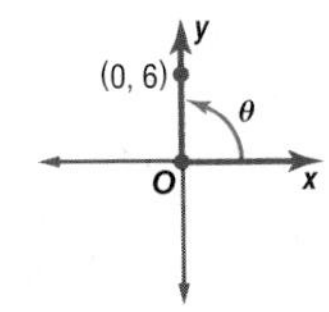

The point at (0, 6) lies on the positive y-axis, so the quadrantal angle θ is 90°. Use $x = 0$, $y = 6$, and $r = 6$ to write the trigonometric functions.

$\sin\theta = \frac{y}{r} = \frac{6}{6}$ or 1 $\quad \cos\theta = \frac{x}{r} = \frac{0}{6}$ or 0 $\quad \tan\theta = \frac{y}{x} = \frac{6}{0}$ undefined

$\csc\theta = \frac{r}{y} = \frac{6}{6}$ or 1 $\quad \sec\theta = \frac{r}{x} = \frac{6}{0}$ undefined $\quad \cot\theta = \frac{x}{y} = \frac{0}{6}$ or 0

Guided Practice

2. The terminal side of θ in standard position contains the point at (–2, 0). Find the values of the six trigonometric functions of θ.

2. $\sin\theta = 0$ $\cos\theta = -1$, $\tan\theta = 0$, $\csc\theta =$ undefined, $\sec\theta = -1$, $\cot\theta =$ undefined

Personal Tutor glencoe.com

Trigonometric Functions with Reference Angles If θ is a nonquadrantal angle in standard position, its **reference angle** θ' is the acute angle formed by the terminal side of θ and the x-axis. The rules for finding the measures of reference angles for $0° < \theta < 360°$ or $0° < \theta < 2\pi$ are shown below.

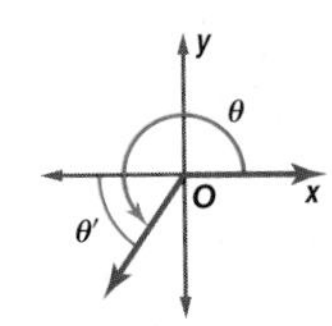

ReadingMath

Theta Prime θ' is read *theta prime*.

Key Concept: Reference Angles

Quadrant I	Quadrant II	Quadrant III	Quadrant IV
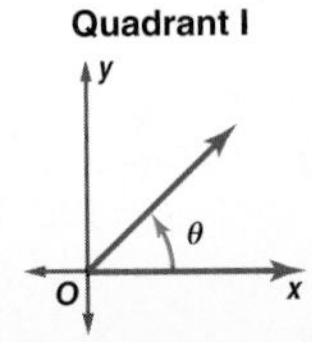	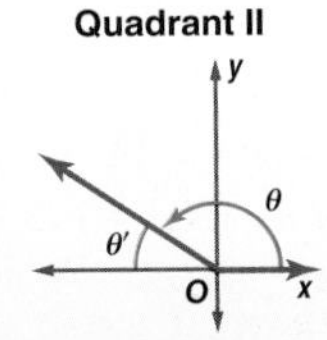	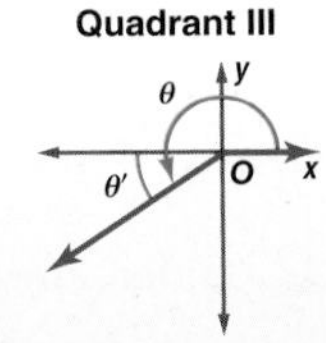	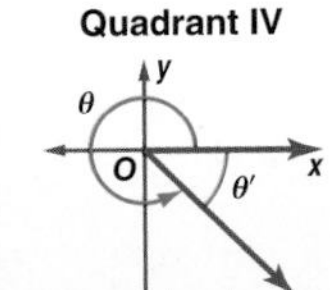
$\theta' = \theta$	$\theta' = 180° - \theta$ $\theta' = \pi - \theta$	$\theta' = \theta - 180°$ $\theta' = \theta - \pi$	$\theta' = 360° - \theta$ $\theta' = 2\pi - \theta$

Watch Out!

Unlocking Misconceptions In Example 1, watch for students who think that r must be a negative number any time either x or y has a negative value.

TEACH with TECH

STUDENT RESPONSE SYSTEM Present students with a number of examples (such as cos 120°, csc (–35°), and tan (–165°)). Ask students if the value of each trigonometric function is positive or negative. Have students respond with A for positive and B for negative.

If the measure of θ is greater than 360° or less than 0°, then use a coterminal angle with a positive measure between 0° and 360° to find the reference angle.

EXAMPLE 3 **Find Reference Angles**

Sketch each angle. Then find its reference angle.

a. 210°

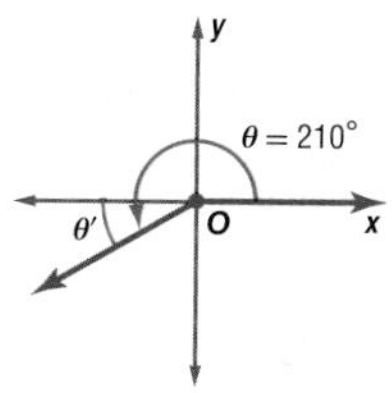

The terminal side of 210° lies in Quadrant III.

$\theta' = \theta - 180°$

$= 210° - 180°$ or $30°$

b. $-\frac{5\pi}{4}$

coterminal angle: $-\frac{5\pi}{4} + 2\pi = \frac{3\pi}{4}$

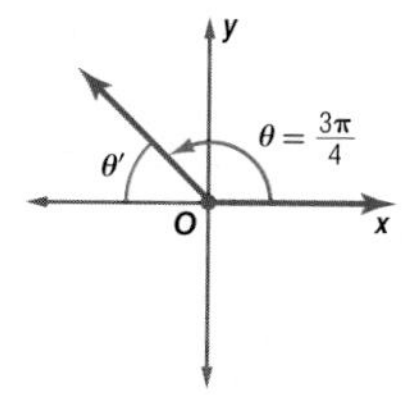

The terminal side of $\frac{3\pi}{4}$ lies in Quadrant III.

$\theta' = \pi - \theta$

$= \pi - \frac{3\pi}{4}$ or $\frac{\pi}{4}$

Guided Practice **3A, 3B. See margin.**

3A. −110°

3B. $\frac{2\pi}{3}$

Personal Tutor glencoe.com

StudyTip

Graphing Angles You can refer to the diagram in the Lesson 13-2 Concept Summary to help you sketch angles.

You can use reference angles to evaluate trigonometric functions for any angle θ. The sign of a function is determined by the quadrant in which the terminal side of θ lies. Use these steps to evaluate a trigonometric function for any angle θ.

Key Concept **Evaluate Trigonometric Functions**

Step 1 Find the measure of the reference angle θ'.

Step 2 Evaluate the trigonometric function for θ'.

Step 3 Determine the sign of the trigonometric function value. Use the quadrant in which the terminal side of θ lies.

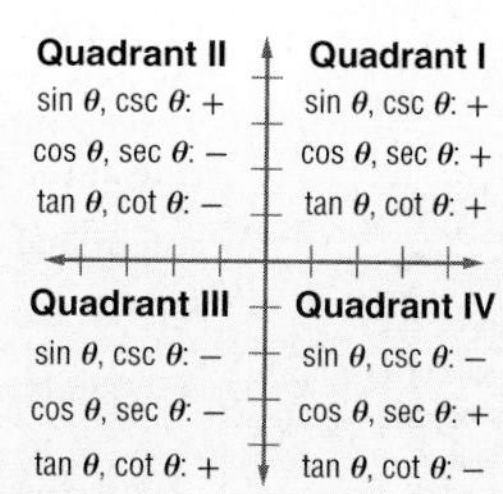

You can use the trigonometric values of angles measuring 30°, 45°, and 60° that you learned in Lesson 13-1.

Trigonometric Values for Special Angles

Sine	Cosine	Tangent	Cosecant	Secant	Cotangent
$\sin 30° = \frac{1}{2}$	$\cos 30° = \frac{\sqrt{3}}{2}$	$\tan 30° = \frac{\sqrt{3}}{3}$	$\csc 30° = 2$	$\sec 30° = \frac{2\sqrt{3}}{3}$	$\cot 30° = \sqrt{3}$
$\sin 45° = \frac{\sqrt{2}}{2}$	$\cos 45° = \frac{\sqrt{2}}{2}$	$\tan 45° = 1$	$\csc 45° = \sqrt{2}$	$\sec 45° = \sqrt{2}$	$\cot 45° = 1$
$\sin 60° = \frac{\sqrt{3}}{2}$	$\cos 60° = \frac{1}{2}$	$\tan 60° = \sqrt{3}$	$\csc 60° = \frac{2\sqrt{3}}{3}$	$\sec 60° = 2$	$\cot 60° = \frac{\sqrt{3}}{3}$

Trigonometric Functions with Reference Angles

Example 3 shows how to find the reference angle for a given angle. **Example 4** shows how to use a reference angle to find a trigonometric value. **Example 5** shows how to solve a real-world problem involving reference angles.

Additional Example

3 Sketch each angle. Then find its reference angle.

a. 330° 30°

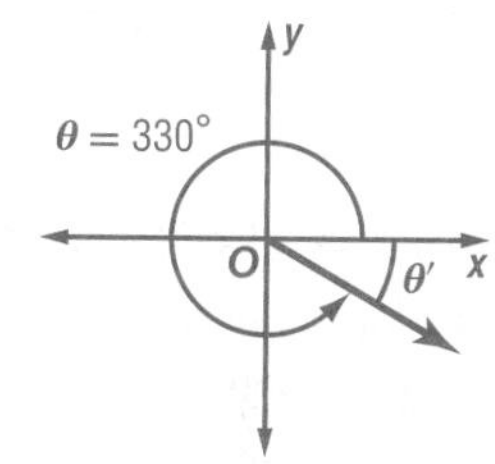

b. $-\frac{5\pi}{6}$ $\frac{\pi}{6}$

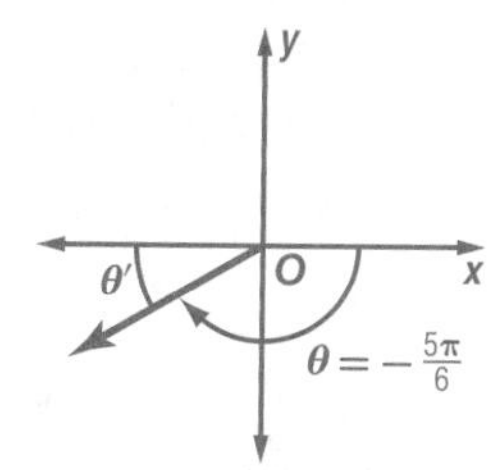

Additional Answers (Guided Practice)

3A. 70°

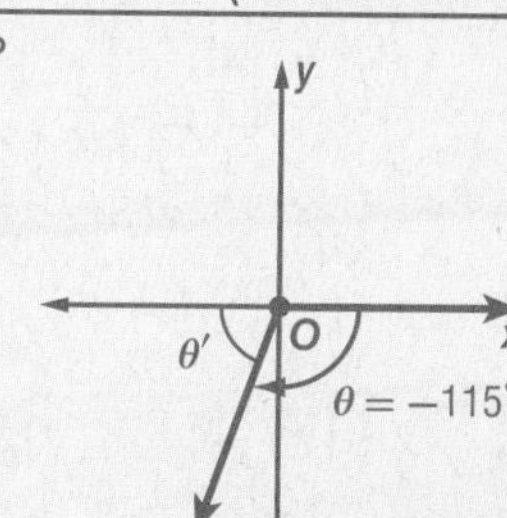

3B. $\frac{\pi}{3}$

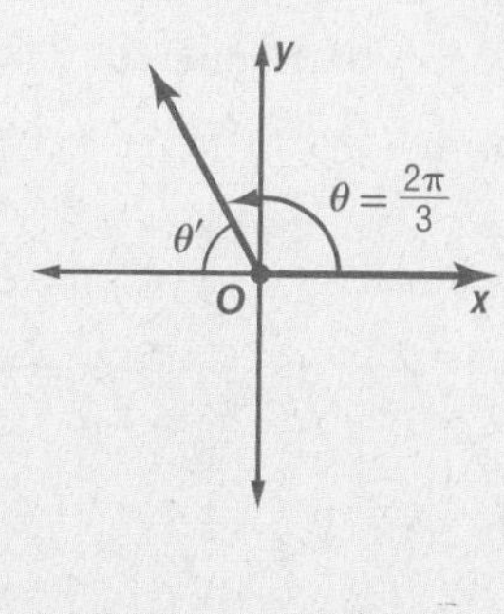

Watch Out!

Preventing Errors When finding trigonometric values for an angle, students may find it helpful to sketch an angle in standard position and drop a perpendicular to the x-axis to form a right triangle. Then they can see that, as the angle increases from 90° to 180°, the y value approaches 0, and the values of the other two sides approach each other.

Lesson 13-3 Trigonometric Functions of General Angles **827**

Additional Examples

4 Find the exact value of each trigonometric function.

a. sin 135° $\frac{\sqrt{2}}{2}$

b. cot $\frac{7\pi}{3}$ $\frac{\sqrt{3}}{3}$

5 **RIDES** Suppose a ride similar to the one in Example 5 has a swing arm 89 feet long. The height of the axis is 99 feet, and the angles are the same. What is the total height of the new ride at the peak of the arc?
$y = 89 \sin 20° = 30.4$ ft; $30.4 + 99 = 129.4$ ft

Focus on Mathematical Content

Reference Angles In Lesson 13-1 the trigonometric functions were defined only for acute angles. The introduction of reference angles allows one to find the values of the trigonometric functions for any angle. Every reference angle is an acute angle.

Additional Answers

1. $\sin\theta = \frac{2\sqrt{5}}{5}$, $\cos\theta = \frac{\sqrt{5}}{5}$, $\tan\theta = 2$, $\csc\theta = \frac{\sqrt{5}}{2}$, $\sec\theta = \sqrt{5}$, $\cot\theta = \frac{1}{2}$

2. $\sin\theta = -\frac{15}{17}$, $\cos\theta = -\frac{8}{17}$, $\tan\theta = \frac{15}{8}$, $\csc\theta = -\frac{17}{15}$, $\sec\theta = -\frac{17}{8}$, $\cot\theta = \frac{8}{15}$

3. $\sin\theta = -1$, $\cos\theta = 0$, $\tan\theta =$ undefined, $\csc\theta = -1$, $\sec\theta =$ undefined, $\cot\theta = 0$

4. 60°

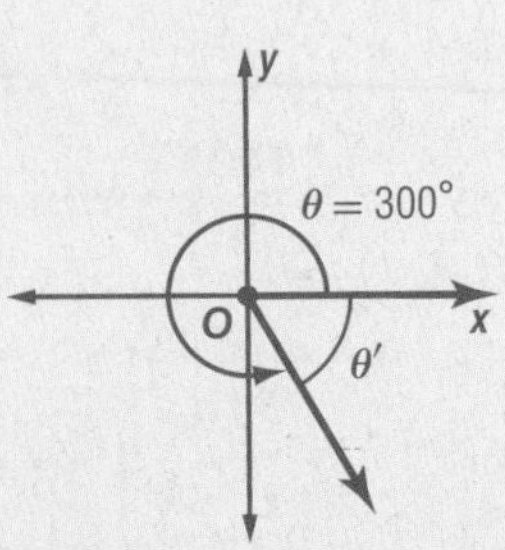

EXAMPLE 4 Use a Reference Angle to Find a Trigonometric Value

Find the exact value of each trigonometric function.

a. cos 240°

The terminal side of 240° lies in Quadrant III.

$\theta' = \theta - 180°$ — **Find the measure of the reference angle.**

$= 240° - 180°$ or $60°$ — **$\theta = 240°$**

$\cos 240° = -\cos 60°$ or $-\frac{1}{2}$ — **The cosine function is negative in Quadrant III.**

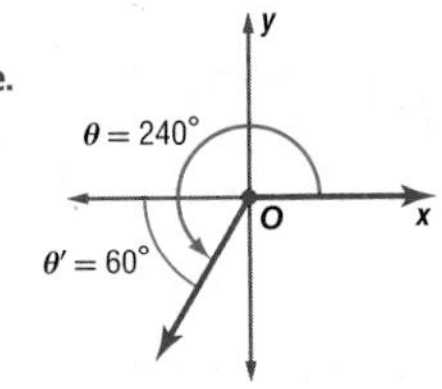

b. csc $\frac{5\pi}{6}$

The terminal side of $\frac{5\pi}{6}$ lies in Quadrant II.

$\theta' = \pi - \theta$ — **Find the measure of the reference angle.**

$= \pi - \frac{5\pi}{6}$ or $\frac{\pi}{6}$ — **$\theta = \frac{5\pi}{6}$**

$\csc\frac{5\pi}{6} = \csc\frac{\pi}{6}$ — **The cosecant function is positive in Quadrant II.**

$= \csc 30°$ — **$\frac{\pi}{6}$ radians = 30°**

$= 2$ — **$\csc 30° = \frac{1}{\sin 30}$**

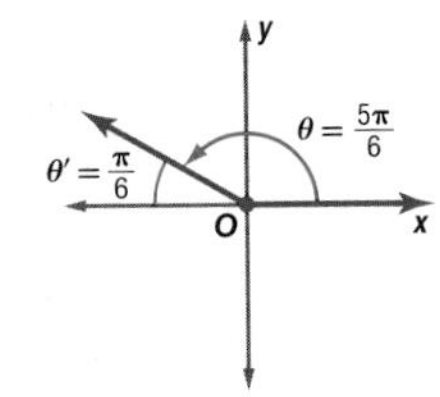

Guided Practice

4A. cos 135° $-\frac{\sqrt{2}}{2}$

4B. tan $\frac{5\pi}{6}$ $\frac{-\sqrt{3}}{3}$

Personal Tutor glencoe.com

Real-World Link

On a swing ride, riders experience weightlessness just like the drop side of a roller coaster. The ride lasts one minute and reaches speeds of 60 miles per hour in both directions.

Source: Cedar Point

Real-World EXAMPLE 5 Use Trigonometric Functions

RIDES The swing arms of the ride at the right are 84 feet long and the height of the axis from which the arms swing is 97 feet. What is the total height of the ride at the peak of the arc?

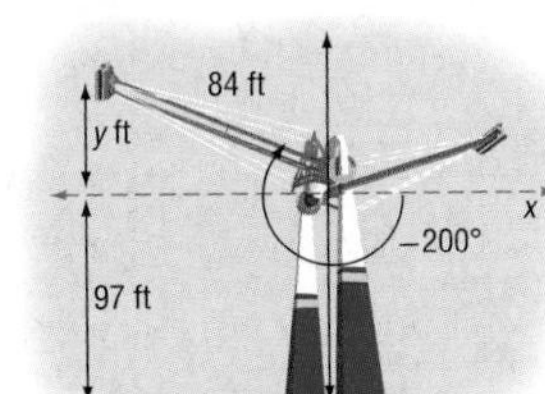

coterminal angle: $-200° + 360° = 160°$

reference angle: $180° - 160° = 20°$

$\sin\theta = \frac{y}{r}$ — **Sine function**

$\sin 20° = \frac{y}{84}$ — **$\theta = 20°$ and $r = 84$**

$84 \sin 20° = y$ — **Multiply each side by 84.**

$28.7 \approx y$ — **Use a calculator to solve for y.**

Since y is approximately 28.7 feet, the total height of the ride at its peak is 28.7 + 97 or about 125.7 feet.

Guided Practice

5. RIDES A similar ride that is smaller has swing arms that are 72 feet long. The height of the axis from which the arms swing is 88 feet, and the angle of rotation from the standard position is −195°. What is the total height of the ride at the peak of the arc? **about 106.6 ft**

Personal Tutor glencoe.com

Differentiated Instruction AL OL

Auditory/Musical Learners Have students work in small groups to create a jingle, song, rap, or short poem to help them remember the trigonometric values for special angles.

Check Your Understanding

Examples 1 and 2 pp. 825–826

The terminal side of θ in standard position contains each point. Find the exact values of the six trigonometric functions of θ. 1–3. See margin.

1. (1, 2) **2.** (−8, −15) **3.** (0, −4)

Example 3 p. 827

Sketch each angle. Then find its reference angle. 4–6. See margin.

4. 300° **5.** 115° **6.** $-\frac{3\pi}{4}$

Example 4 p. 828

Find the exact value of each trigonometric function.

7. $\sin\frac{3\pi}{4}$ $\frac{\sqrt{2}}{2}$ **8.** $\tan\frac{5\pi}{3}$ $-\sqrt{3}$ **9.** sec 120° −2 **10.** sin 300° $-\frac{\sqrt{3}}{2}$

Example 5 p. 828

11. ENTERTAINMENT Alejandra opens her portable DVD player so that it forms a 125° angle. The screen is $5\frac{1}{2}$ inches long.

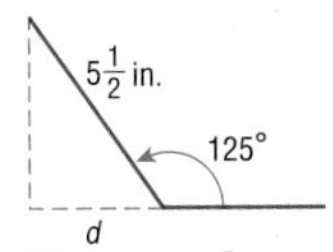

a. Redraw the diagram so that the angle is in standard position on the coordinate plane. See Chapter 13 Answer Appendix.

b. Find the reference angle. Then write a trigonometric function that can be used to find the distance to the wall d that she can place the DVD player. 55°; $\cos 55° = \frac{d}{5\frac{1}{2}}$

c. Use the function to find the distance. Round to the nearest tenth. 3.2 in.

Practice and Problem Solving

● = Step-by-Step Solutions begin on page R20. Extra Practice begins on page 947.

Examples 1 and 2 pp. 825–826

The terminal side of θ in standard position contains each point. Find the exact values of the six trigonometric functions of θ. 12–17. See margin.

12. (5, 12) **13.** (−6, 8) **14.** (3, 0)

15. (0, −7) **16.** (4, −2) **17.** (−9, −3)

Example 3 p. 827

Sketch each angle. Then find its reference angle. 18–23. See Chapter 13 Answer Appendix.

18. 195° **19.** 285° **20.** −250°

21. $\frac{7\pi}{4}$ **22.** $-\frac{\pi}{4}$ **23.** 400°

Example 4 p. 828

Find the exact value of each trigonometric function.

24. sin 210° $-\frac{1}{2}$ **25.** tan 315° −1 **26.** cos 150° $-\frac{\sqrt{3}}{2}$ **27.** csc 225° $-\sqrt{2}$

28. $\sin\frac{4\pi}{3}$ $-\frac{\sqrt{3}}{2}$ **29.** $\cos\frac{5\pi}{3}$ $\frac{1}{2}$ **30.** $\cot\frac{5\pi}{4}$ 1 **31.** $\sec\frac{11\pi}{6}$ $\frac{2\sqrt{3}}{3}$

Example 5 p. 828

32. SOCCER A soccer player x feet from the goalie kicks the ball toward the goal, as shown in the figure. The goalie jumps up and catches the ball 7 feet in the air.

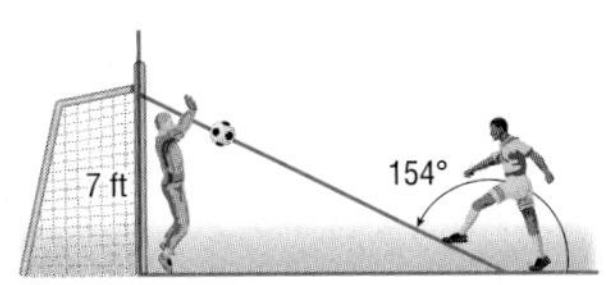

a. Find the reference angle. Then write a trigonometric function that can be used to find how far from the goalie the soccer player was when he kicked the ball. 26°; $\tan 26° = \frac{7}{x}$

b. About how far away from the goalie was the soccer player? about 14.4 ft

Differentiated Homework Options

Level	Assignment	Two-Day Option	
AL Basic	12–32, 48–78	13–31 odd, 52–55	12–32 even, 48–51, 56–78
OL Core	13–31 odd, 33–36, 37–45 odd, 48–78	12–32, 52–55	33–46, 48–51, 56–78
BL Advanced	33–75, (optional: 76–78)		

3 PRACTICE

Formative Assessment

Use Exercises 1–11 to check for understanding.

Use the chart at the bottom of this page to customize assignments for your students.

Additional Answers

5. 65°

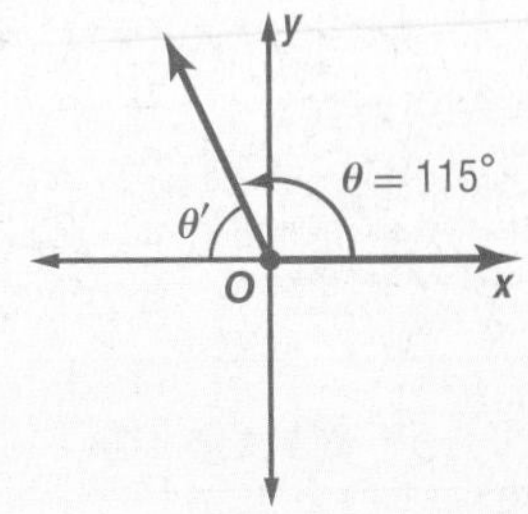

6. $\frac{\pi}{4}$

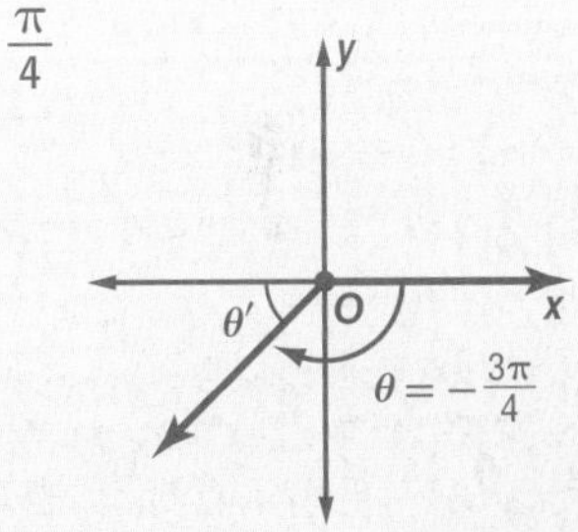

12. $\sin\theta = \frac{12}{13}$, $\cos\theta = \frac{5}{13}$, $\tan\theta = \frac{12}{5}$, $\csc\theta = \frac{13}{12}$, $\sec\theta = \frac{13}{5}$, $\cot\theta = \frac{5}{12}$

13. $\sin\theta = \frac{4}{5}$, $\cos\theta = -\frac{3}{5}$, $\tan\theta = -\frac{4}{3}$, $\csc\theta = \frac{5}{4}$, $\sec\theta = -\frac{5}{3}$, $\cot\theta = -\frac{3}{4}$

14. $\sin\theta = 0$, $\cos\theta = 1$, $\tan\theta = 0$, $\csc\theta =$ undefined, $\sec\theta = 1$, $\cot\theta =$ undefined

15. $\sin\theta = -1$, $\cos\theta = 0$, $\tan\theta =$ undefined, $\csc\theta = -1$, $\sec\theta =$ undefined, $\cot\theta = 0$

16. $\sin\theta = -\frac{\sqrt{5}}{5}$, $\cos\theta = \frac{2\sqrt{5}}{5}$, $\tan\theta = -\frac{1}{2}$, $\csc\theta = -\sqrt{5}$, $\sec\theta = \frac{\sqrt{5}}{2}$, $\cot\theta = -2$

17. $\sin\theta = -\frac{\sqrt{10}}{10}$, $\cos\theta = -\frac{3\sqrt{10}}{10}$, $\tan\theta = \frac{1}{3}$, $\csc\theta = -\sqrt{10}$, $\sec\theta = -\frac{\sqrt{10}}{3}$, $\cot\theta = 3$

Study Guide and Intervention
CRM pp. 17–18 AL OL ELL

13-3 Study Guide and Intervention

Trigonometric Functions of General Angles

Trigonometric Functions for General Angles

Trigonometric Functions, θ in Standard Position	Let θ be an angle in standard position and let $P(x, y)$ be a point on the terminal side of θ. By the Pythagorean Theorem, the distance r from the origin is given by $r = \sqrt{x^2 + y^2}$. The trigonometric functions of an angle in standard position may be defined as follows. $\sin\theta = \frac{y}{r}$, $\cos\theta = \frac{x}{r}$, $\tan\theta = \frac{y}{x}, x \neq 0$; $\csc\theta = \frac{r}{y}, y \neq 0$, $\sec\theta = \frac{r}{x}, x \neq 0$, $\cot\theta = \frac{x}{y}, y \neq 0$

Example Find the exact values of the six trigonometric functions of θ if the terminal side of θ in standard position contains the point $(-5, 5\sqrt{2})$.

You know that $x = -5$ and $y = 5$. You need to find r.

$r = \sqrt{x^2 + y^2}$ Pythagorean Theorem

$= \sqrt{(-5)^2 + (5\sqrt{2})^2}$ Replace x with -5 and y with $5\sqrt{2}$.

$= \sqrt{75}$ or $5\sqrt{3}$

Now use $x = -5$, $y = 5\sqrt{2}$, and $r = 5\sqrt{3}$ to write the six trigonometric ratios.

$\sin\theta = \frac{y}{r} = \frac{5\sqrt{2}}{5\sqrt{3}} = \frac{\sqrt{6}}{3}$ $\cos\theta = \frac{x}{r} = \frac{-5}{5\sqrt{3}} = -\frac{\sqrt{3}}{3}$ $\tan\theta = \frac{y}{x} = \frac{5\sqrt{2}}{-5} = -\sqrt{2}$

$\csc\theta = \frac{r}{y} = \frac{5\sqrt{3}}{5\sqrt{2}} = \frac{\sqrt{6}}{2}$ $\sec\theta = \frac{r}{x} = \frac{5\sqrt{3}}{-5} = -\sqrt{3}$ $\cot\theta = \frac{x}{y} = \frac{-5}{5\sqrt{2}} = -\frac{\sqrt{2}}{2}$

Exercises

The terminal side of θ in standard position contains each point. Find the exact values of the six trigonometric functions of θ.

1. (8, 4) $\sin\theta = \frac{\sqrt{5}}{5}$, $\cos\theta = \frac{2\sqrt{5}}{5}$, $\tan\theta = \frac{1}{2}$, $\csc\theta = \sqrt{5}$, $\sec\theta = \frac{\sqrt{5}}{2}$, $\cot\theta = 2$
2. (4, 4) $\sin\theta = \frac{\sqrt{2}}{2}$, $\cos\theta = \frac{\sqrt{2}}{2}$, $\tan\theta = 1$, $\csc\theta = \sqrt{2}$, $\sec\theta = \sqrt{2}$, $\cot\theta = 1$
3. (0, 4) $\sin\theta = 1$, $\cos\theta = 0$, $\tan\theta$ = undefined, $\csc\theta = 1$, $\sec\theta$ = undefined, $\cot\theta = 0$
4. (6, 2) $\sin\theta = \frac{\sqrt{10}}{10}$, $\cos\theta = \frac{3\sqrt{10}}{10}$, $\tan\theta = \frac{1}{3}$, $\csc\theta = \sqrt{10}$, $\sec\theta = \frac{\sqrt{10}}{3}$, $\cot\theta = 3$

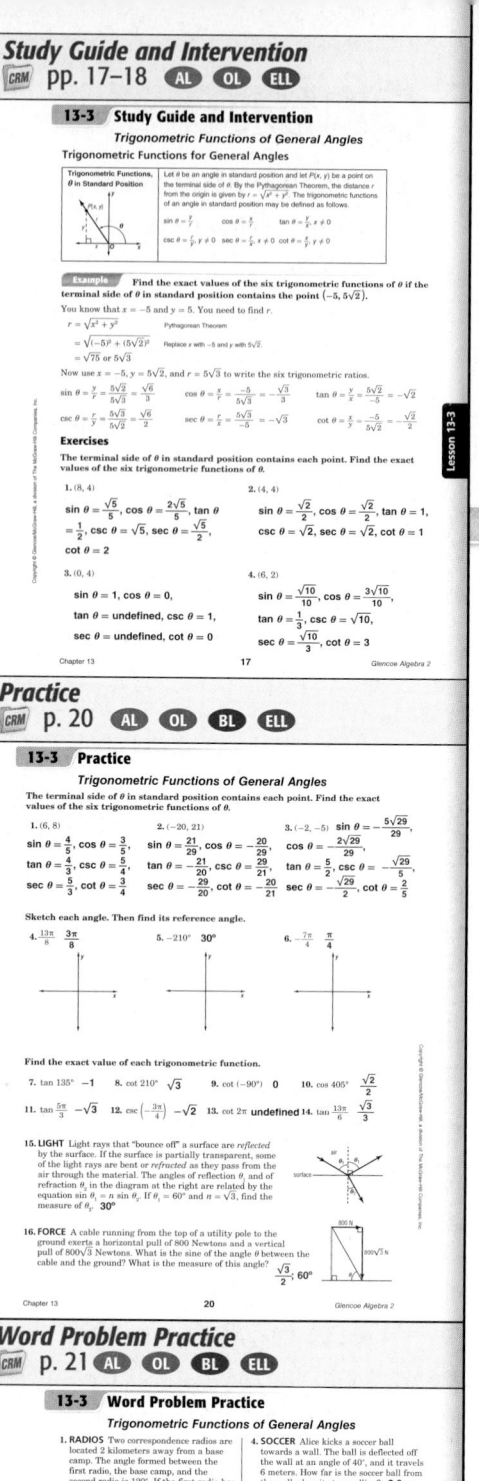

Chapter 13 17 Glencoe Algebra 2

Practice
CRM p. 20 AL OL BL ELL

13-3 Practice

Trigonometric Functions of General Angles

The terminal side of θ in standard position contains each point. Find the exact values of the six trigonometric functions of θ.

1. (6, 8) $\sin\theta = \frac{4}{5}$, $\cos\theta = \frac{3}{5}$, $\tan\theta = \frac{4}{3}$, $\csc\theta = \frac{5}{4}$, $\sec\theta = \frac{5}{3}$, $\cot\theta = \frac{3}{4}$
2. (−20, 21) $\sin\theta = \frac{21}{29}$, $\cos\theta = -\frac{20}{29}$, $\tan\theta = -\frac{21}{20}$, $\csc\theta = \frac{29}{21}$, $\sec\theta = -\frac{29}{20}$, $\cot\theta = -\frac{20}{21}$
3. (−2, −5) $\sin\theta = -\frac{5\sqrt{29}}{29}$, $\cos\theta = -\frac{2\sqrt{29}}{29}$, $\tan\theta = \frac{5}{2}$, $\csc\theta = -\frac{\sqrt{29}}{5}$, $\sec\theta = -\frac{\sqrt{29}}{2}$, $\cot\theta = \frac{2}{5}$

Sketch each angle. Then find its reference angle.

4. $\frac{13\pi}{8}$ $\frac{3\pi}{8}$
5. −210° 30°
6. $-\frac{7\pi}{4}$ $\frac{\pi}{4}$

Find the exact value of each trigonometric function.

7. tan 135° −1
8. cot 210° $\sqrt{3}$
9. cot (−90°) 0
10. cos 405° $\frac{\sqrt{2}}{2}$
11. $\tan\frac{5\pi}{3}$ $-\sqrt{3}$
12. $\csc\left(-\frac{3\pi}{4}\right)$ $-\sqrt{2}$
13. $\cot 2\pi$ undefined
14. $\tan\frac{13\pi}{6}$ $\frac{\sqrt{3}}{3}$

15. LIGHT Light rays that "bounce off" a surface are *reflected* by the surface. If the surface is partially transparent, some of the light rays are bent or *refracted* as they pass from the air through the material. The angles of reflection θ_1 and of refraction θ_2 in the diagram at the right are related by the equation $\sin\theta_1 = n \sin\theta_2$. If $\theta_1 = 60°$ and $n = \sqrt{3}$, find the measure of θ_2. 30°

16. FORCE A cable running from the top of a utility pole to the ground exerts a horizontal pull of 800 Newtons and a vertical pull of $800\sqrt{3}$ Newtons. What is the sine of the angle θ between the cable and the ground? What is the measure of this angle? $\frac{\sqrt{3}}{2}$; 60°

Chapter 13 20 Glencoe Algebra 2

Word Problem Practice
CRM p. 21 AL OL BL ELL

13-3 Word Problem Practice

Trigonometric Functions of General Angles

1. RADIOS Two correspondence radios are located 2 kilometers away from a base camp. The angle formed between the first radio, the base camp, and the second radio is 120°. If the first radio has coordinates (2, 0) relative to the base camp, what is the position of the second radio relative to the base camp? $-1, \sqrt{2}$

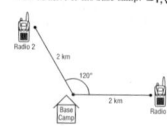

2. CLOCKS The pendulum of a grandfather clock swings back and forth through an arc. The angle θ of the pendulum is given by $\theta = 0.3\cos\left(\frac{\pi}{2} + 5t\right)$ where t is the time in seconds after leaving the bottom of the swing. Determine the measure of the angles in radians for t = 0, 0.5, 1, 1.5, 2, 2.5, and 3 seconds. 0, −0.18, 0.28, −0.28, 0.16, 0.02, −0.20

3. FERRIS WHEELS Janice rides a Ferris wheel in Japan called the Sky Dream Fukuoka, which has a radius of about 60 m and is 5 m off the ground. After she enters the bottom car, the wheel rotates 210.5° counterclockwise before stopping. How high above the ground is Janice when the car has stopped? about 56.7m

4. SOCCER Alice kicks a soccer ball towards a wall. The ball is deflected off the wall at an angle of 40°, and it travels 6 meters. How far is the soccer ball from the wall when it stops rolling? 3.9 m

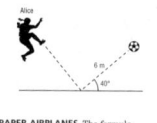

5. PAPER AIRPLANES The formula $R = \frac{V_0^2 \sin 2\theta}{32} + 15\cos\theta$ gives the distance traveled by a paper airplane that is thrown with an initial velocity of V_0 feet per second at an angle of θ with the ground.

a. If the airplane is thrown with an initial velocity of 15 feet per second at an angle of 25°, how far will the airplane travel? 19 ft

b. Two airplanes are thrown with an initial velocity of 10 feet per second. One airplane is thrown at an angle of 15° to the ground, and the other airplane is thrown at an angle of 45° to the ground. Which will travel further? The airplane thrown at 15° will travel further.

Chapter 13 21 Glencoe Algebra 2

B **33.** **SPRINKLER** A sprinkler rotating back and forth shoots water out a distance of 10 feet. From the horizontal position, it rotates 145° before reversing its direction. At a 145° angle, about how far to the left of the sprinkler does the water reach? **about 8.2 ft**

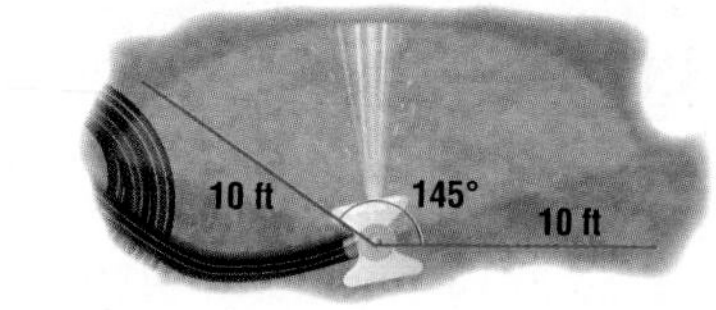

Real-World Link

The Wonder Wheel, which holds 144 people, is different from most Ferris wheels. It has eight stationary cars and sixteen cars that roll along tracks within the wheel's structure.

Source: Amusement Park History

34. **BASKETBALL** The formula $R = \frac{V_0^2 \sin 2\theta}{32}$ gives the distance of a basketball shot with an initial velocity of V_0 feet per second at an angle θ with the ground.

a. If the basketball was shot with an initial velocity of 24 feet per second at an angle of 75°, how far will the basketball travel? **9 ft**

b. If the basketball was shot at an angle of 65° and traveled 10 feet, what was its initial velocity? **about 20.4 feet per second**

c. If the basketball was shot with an initial velocity of 30 feet per second and traveled 12 feet, at what angle was it shot? **about 12.6°**

35. **PHYSICS** A rock is shot off the edge of a ravine with a slingshot at an angle of 65° and with an initial velocity of 6 meters per second. The equation that represents the horizontal distance of the rock x is $x = v_0 (\cos\theta)t$, where v_0 is the initial velocity, θ is the angle at which it is shot, and t is the time in seconds. About how far does the rock travel after 4 seconds? **about 10.1 m**

36. **FERRIS WHEELS** The Wonder Wheel Ferris wheel at Coney Island has a radius of about 68 feet and is 15 feet off the ground. After a person gets on the bottom car, the Ferris wheel rotates 202.5° counterclockwise before stopping. How high above the ground is this car when it has stopped? **145.8 ft**

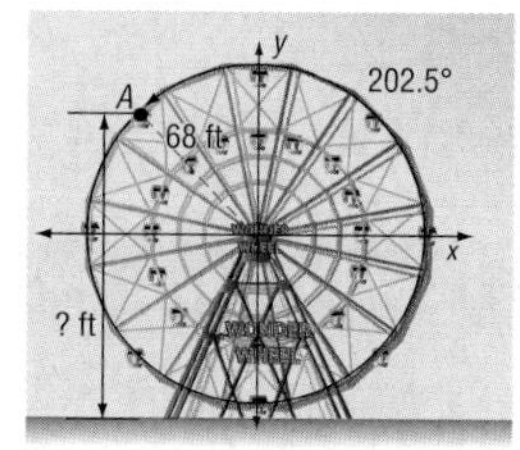

C Suppose θ is an angle in standard position whose terminal side is in the given quadrant. For each function, find the exact values of the remaining five trigonometric functions of θ. **37–40. See margin.**

37. $\sin\theta = \frac{4}{5}$, Quadrant II

38. $\tan\theta = -\frac{2}{3}$, Quadrant IV

39. $\cos\theta = -\frac{8}{17}$, Quadrant III

40. $\cot\theta = -\frac{12}{5}$, Quadrant IV

Find the exact value of each trigonometric function.

41. cot 270° **0**

42. csc 180° **undefined**

43. sin 570° $-\frac{1}{2}$

44. $\tan\left(-\frac{7\pi}{6}\right)$ $-\frac{\sqrt{3}}{3}$

45. $\cos\left(-\frac{11\pi}{6}\right)$ $\frac{\sqrt{3}}{2}$

46. $\cot\frac{9\pi}{4}$ **1**

H.O.T. Problems

Use Higher-Order Thinking Skills

47. **CHALLENGE** For an angle θ in standard position, $\sin\theta = \frac{\sqrt{2}}{2}$ and $\tan\theta = -1$. Can the value of θ be 225°? Justify your reasoning.

48. **REASONING** Determine whether 3 sin 60° = sin 180° is *true* or *false*. Explain your reasoning.

49. **REASONING** Use the sine and cosine functions to explain why cot 180° is undefined.

50. **OPEN ENDED** Give an example of a negative angle θ for which $\sin\theta > 0$ and $\cos\theta < 0$.

51. **WRITING IN MATH** Describe the steps for evaluating a trigonometric function for an angle θ that is greater than 90°. Include a description of a reference angle. **See margin.**

47. No; for $\sin\theta = \frac{\sqrt{2}}{2}$ and $\tan\theta = -1$, the reference angle is 45°. However, for $\sin\theta$ to be positive and $\tan\theta$ to be negative, the reference angle must be in the second quadrant. So, the value of θ must be 135° or an angle coterminal with 135°.

48. False; $3 \sin 60° = 3 \cdot \frac{\sqrt{3}}{2}$ or $\frac{3\sqrt{3}}{2}$ and $\sin 180° = 0.0$

49. See margin.

50. Sample answer: $\theta = -200°$

Enrichment
CRM p. 22 OL BL

13-3 Enrichment

Areas of Polygons and Circles

A regular polygon has sides of equal length and angles of equal measure. A regular polygon can be inscribed in or circumscribed about a circle. For n-sided regular polygons, the following area formulas can be used.

Area of circle $A_C = \pi r^2$

Area of inscribed polygon $A_I = \frac{nr^2}{2} \times \sin\frac{360°}{n}$

Area of circumscribed polygon $A_C = nr^2 \times \tan\frac{180°}{n}$

Use a calculator to complete the chart below for a unit circle (a circle of radius 1).

Number of Sides	Area of Inscribed Polygon	Area of Circle minus Area of Polygon	Area of Circumscribed Polygon	Area of Polygon minus Area of Circle
3	1.2990381	1.84[illegible]	5.19[illegible]	2.054597

Additional Answers

37. $\cos\theta = -\frac{3}{5}$, $\tan\theta = -\frac{4}{3}$, $\csc\theta = \frac{5}{4}$, $\sec\theta = -\frac{5}{3}$, $\cot\theta = -\frac{3}{4}$

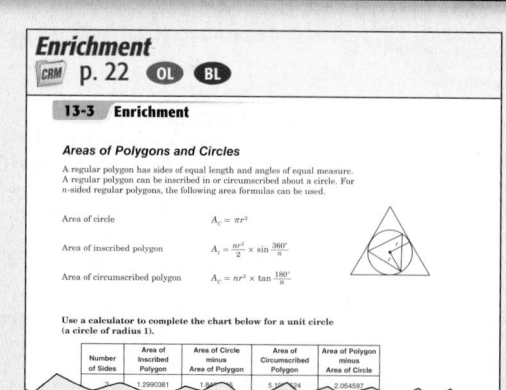

38. $\sin\theta = -\frac{2\sqrt{13}}{13}$, $\cos\theta = \frac{3\sqrt{13}}{13}$, $\csc\theta = -\frac{\sqrt{13}}{2}$, $\sec\theta = \frac{\sqrt{13}}{3}$, $\cot\theta = -\frac{3}{2}$

NGSSS PRACTICE 912.A.3.15, 912.G.1.1, 912.A.1.6

52. **GRIDDED RESPONSE** If the sum of two numbers is 21 and their difference is 3, what is their product? **108**

53. **GEOMETRY** D is the midpoint of $\overline{BC}$, and A and E are the midpoints of $\overline{BD}$ and $\overline{DC}$, respectively. If the length of $\overline{AE}$ is 12, what is the length of $\overline{BC}$? **C**

A. 6 C. 24
B. 12 D. 48

54. The expression $(-6 + i)^2$ is equivalent to which of the following expressions? **I**

F. $-12i$ H. $36 - 12i$
G. $36 - i$ I. $35 - 12i$

55. **SAT/ACT** Of the following, which is least? **C**

A. $1 + \frac{1}{4}$ C. $\frac{1}{4} - 1$
B. $1 - \frac{1}{4}$ D. $1 \times \frac{1}{4}$

Spiral Review

Rewrite each radian measure in degrees. (Lesson 13-2)

56. $\frac{4}{3}\pi$ **240°**
57. $\frac{11}{6}\pi$ **330°**
58. $-\frac{17}{4}\pi$ **−765°**

Solve each equation. (Lesson 13-1)

59. $\cos a = \frac{13}{17}$ **40.1°**
60. $\sin 30 = \frac{b}{6}$ **3**
61. $\tan c = \frac{9}{4}$ **66.0°**

62. **ARCHITECTURE** A memorial being constructed in a city park will be a brick wall, with a top row of six gold-plated bricks engraved with the names of six local war veterans. Each row has two more bricks than the row above it. Prove that the number of bricks in the top n rows is $n^2 + 5n$. (Lesson 11-7) **See Chapter 13 Answer Appendix.**

63. **LEGENDS** There is a legend of a king who wanted to reward a boy for a good deed. The king gave the boy a choice. He could have \$1,000,000 at once, or he could be rewarded daily for a 30-day month, with one penny on the first day, two pennies on the second day, and so on, receiving twice as many pennies each day as the previous day. How much would the second option be worth? (Lesson 11-3) **\$10,737,418.23**

Write an equation for each circle given the endpoints of a diameter. (Lesson 10-3)

64. (2, −4), (10, 2) $(x - 6)^2 + (y + 1)^2 = 25$
65. (−1, −10), (−7, 6) $(x + 4)^2 + (y + 2)^2 = 73$
66. (9, 0), (4, −7) $(x - 6.5)^2 + (y + 3.5)^2 = 18.5$

Simplify each expression. (Lesson 9-2) **67–69. See margin.**

67. $\frac{5}{x^2 + 6x + 8} + \frac{x}{x^2 - 3x - 28}$
68. $\frac{3x}{x^2 + 8x - 20} - \frac{6}{x^2 + 7x - 18}$
69. $\frac{4}{3x^2 + 12x} + \frac{2x}{x^2 - 2x - 24}$

Solve each equation or inequality. Round to the nearest ten-thousandth. (Lesson 8-6)

70. $8^x = 30$ **1.6356**
71. $5^x = 64$ **2.5841**
72. $3^{x+2} = 41$ **1.3802**

Evaluate each expression. (Lesson 7-6)

73. $16^{-\frac{1}{4}}$ $\frac{1}{2}$
74. $27^{\frac{4}{3}}$ **81**
75. $25^{-\frac{5}{2}}$ $\frac{1}{3125}$

Skills Review

Solve for x. (Concepts and Skills Bank 1)

76. $\frac{x + 2}{18} = \frac{x - 2}{9}$ **6**
77. $\frac{x + 5}{x - 1} = \frac{7}{4}$ **9**
78. $\frac{5}{x + 8} = \frac{15}{2x + 20}$ **−4**

4 ASSESS

Crystal Ball Have students look ahead to Lesson 13-4. Have them write how they think what they learned today will connect with the theme in Lesson 13-4.

Formative Assessment

Check for student understanding of concepts in Lessons 13-1, 13-2, and 13-3.

CRM Quiz 1, p. 61

Additional Answers

39. $\sin \theta = -\frac{15}{17}$, $\tan \theta = \frac{15}{8}$, $\csc \theta = -\frac{17}{15}$, $\sec \theta = -\frac{17}{8}$, $\cot \theta = \frac{8}{15}$

40. $\sin \theta = -\frac{5}{13}$, $\cos \theta = \frac{12}{13}$, $\csc \theta = -\frac{13}{5}$, $\sec \theta = \frac{13}{12}$, $\tan \theta = -\frac{5}{12}$

49. Sample answer: We know that $\cot \theta = \frac{x}{y}$, $\sin \theta = \frac{y}{r}$, and $\cos \theta = \frac{x}{r}$. Since $\sin 180° = 0$, it must be true that $y = 0$. Thus $\cot 180° = \frac{x}{0}$, which is undefined.

51. Sample answer: First, sketch the angle and determine in which quadrant it is located. Then use the appropriate rule for finding its reference angle θ'. A reference angle is the acute angle formed by the terminal side of θ and the x-axis. Next, find the value of the trigonometric function for θ'. Finally, use the quadrant location to determine the sign of the trigonometric function value of θ.

67. $\frac{x^2 + 7x - 35}{(x + 2)(x + 4)(x - 7)}$

68. $\frac{3(x^2 + 7x - 20)}{(x + 10)(x + 9)(x - 2)}$

69. $\frac{2(3x^2 + 2x - 12)}{3x(x + 4)(x - 6)}$

Differentiated Instruction

OL BL

Extension For an angle with a measure between 0° and 90°, the angle is its own reference angle. Have students write expressions for the measure of the reference angle of θ,

if $90° < \theta < 180°$. $180° - \theta$

if $180° < \theta < 270°$. $\theta - 180°$

if $270° < \theta < 360°$. $360° - \theta$

13-4 Lesson Notes

1 FOCUS

Vertical Alignment

Before Lesson 13-4
Find side lengths and angle measures of right triangles.

Lesson 13-4
Find the area of a triangle using two sides and an included angle. Use the Law of Sines to solve triangles.

After Lesson 13-4
Use the Law of Cosines to solve problems.

2 TEACH

Scaffolding Questions

Have students read the *Why?* section of the lesson.

Ask:

- What is the size of the angle opposite the side connecting Wahoo and Naukan? Wahoo and Wabash? 102°; 23°
- What is the measure of the angle opposite the side connecting Wabash and Naukan? 55°
- What is the distance between Wahoo and Wabash? 1.2 km
- Which crater is at the vertex of the largest angle? Wabash

13-4 Law of Sines

Then
You found side lengths and angle measures of right triangles. (Lesson 13-1)

Now
- Find the area of a triangle using two sides and an included angle.
- Use the Law of Sines to solve triangles.

NGSSS
MA.912.T.2.3 **Apply the laws of sines** and cosines to solve real-world problems using technology.
MA.912.T.2.4 Use the area of triangles given two sides and an angle or three sides to solve real-world problems.

New Vocabulary
Law of Sines
solving a triangle

FL Math Online
glencoe.com

Why?

Mars has hundreds of thousands of craters. These craters are named after famous scientists, science fiction authors, and towns on Earth. The craters named Wahoo, Wabash, and Naukan are shown in the figure. You can use trigonometry to find the distance between Wahoo and Naukan.

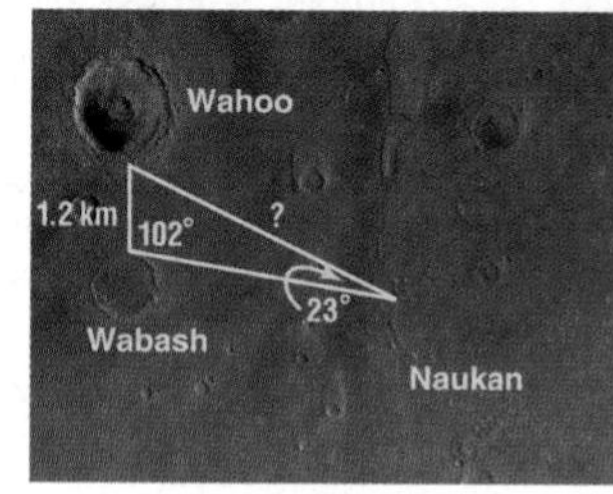

Find the Area of a Triangle In the triangle at the right, $\sin A = \frac{h}{c}$, or $h = c \sin A$.

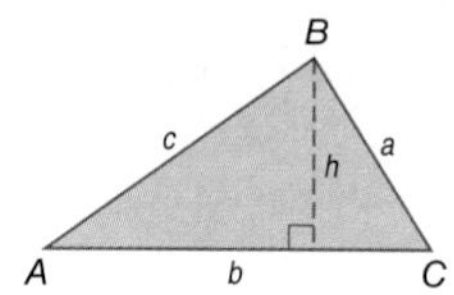

$\text{Area} = \frac{1}{2}bh$	**Formula for area of a triangle**
$\text{Area} = \frac{1}{2}b(c \sin A)$	**Replace h with $c \sin A$.**
$\text{Area} = \frac{1}{2}bc \sin A$	**Simplify.**

You can use this formula or two other formulas to find the area of a triangle if you know the lengths of two sides and the measure of the included angle.

Key Concept — Area of a Triangle

Words The area of a triangle is one half the product of the lengths of two sides and the sine of their included angle.

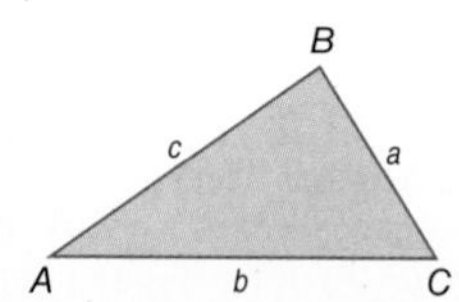

Symbols $\text{Area} = \frac{1}{2}bc \sin A$ $\text{Area} = \frac{1}{2}ac \sin B$ $\text{Area} = \frac{1}{2}ab \sin C$

EXAMPLE 1 Find the Area of a Triangle

Find the area of $\triangle ABC$ to the nearest tenth.

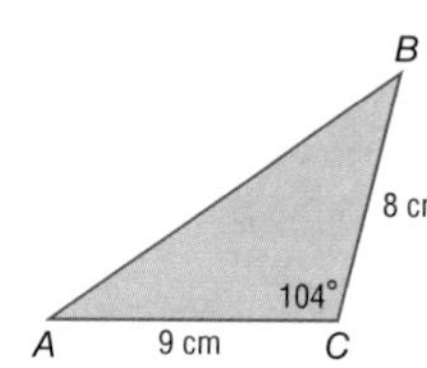

In $\triangle ABC$, $a = 8$, $b = 9$, and $C = 104°$.

$\text{Area} = \frac{1}{2}ab \sin C$	**Based on the known measures, use the third area formula.**
$= \frac{1}{2}(8)(9) \sin 104°$	**Substitution**
≈ 34.9	**Simplify.**

So, the area is about 34.9 square centimeters.

Guided Practice

1. Find the area of $\triangle ABC$ to the nearest tenth if $A = 31°$, $b = 18$ meters, and $c = 22$ meters. 102.0 m^2

Personal Tutor glencoe.com

Lesson 13-4 Resources

Resource	Approaching-Level	On-Level	Beyond-Level	English Learners
Teacher Edition	• Differentiated Instruction, p. 835	• Differentiated Instruction, pp. 835, 839	• Differentiated Instruction, pp. 835, 839	• Differentiated Instruction, p. 835
Chapter Resource Masters	• Study Guide and Intervention, pp. 23–24 • Skills Practice, p. 25 • Practice, p. 26 • Word Problem Practice, p. 27	• Study Guide and Intervention, pp. 23–24 • Skills Practice, p. 25 • Practice, p. 26 • Word Problem Practice, p. 27 • Enrichment, p. 28	• Practice, p. 26 • Word Problem Practice, p. 27 • Enrichment, p. 28	• Study Guide and Intervention, pp. 23–24 • Skills Practice, p. 25 • Practice, p. 26 • Word Problem Practice, p. 27
Transparencies	• 5-Minute Check Transparency 13-4	• 5-Minute Check Transparency 13-4	• 5-Minute Check Transparency 13-4	• 5-Minute Check Transparency 13-4
Other	• Study Notebook	• Study Notebook	• Study Notebook	• Study Notebook

Use the Law of Sines to Solve Triangles You can use the area formulas to derive the **Law of Sines**, which shows the relationships between side lengths of a triangle and the sines of the angles opposite them.

$\frac{1}{2}bc \sin A = \frac{1}{2}ac \sin B = \frac{1}{2}ab \sin C$	**Set the area formulas equal to each other.**
$bc \sin A = ac \sin B = ab \sin C$	**Multiply each expression by 2.**
$\frac{bc \sin A}{abc} = \frac{ac \sin B}{abc} = \frac{ab \sin C}{abc}$	**Divide each expression by *abc*.**
$\frac{\sin A}{a} = \frac{\sin B}{b} = \frac{\sin C}{c}$	**Simplify.**

Key Concept Law of Sines

In $\triangle ABC$, if sides with lengths a, b, and c are opposite angles with measures A, B, and C, respectively, then the following is true.

$$\frac{\sin A}{a} = \frac{\sin B}{b} = \frac{\sin C}{c}$$

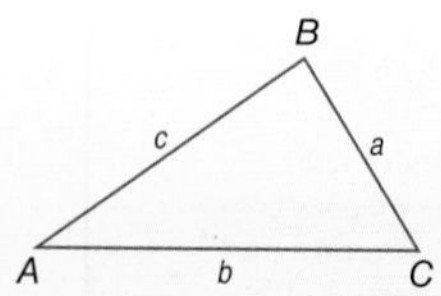

You can use the Law of Sines to solve a triangle if you know either one of the following.

- the measures of two angles and any side (angle-angle-side AAS or angle-side-angle ASA cases)

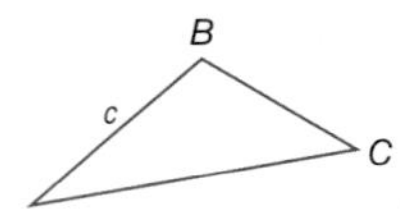

- the measures of two sides and the angle opposite one of the sides (side-side-angle SSA case)

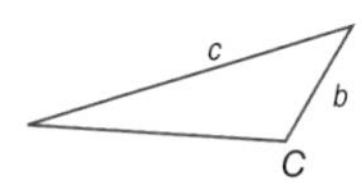

Using given measures to find all unknown side lengths and angle measures of a triangle is called **solving a triangle**.

EXAMPLE 2 Solve a Triangle Given Two Angles and a Side

Solve $\triangle ABC$. Round to the nearest tenth if necessary.

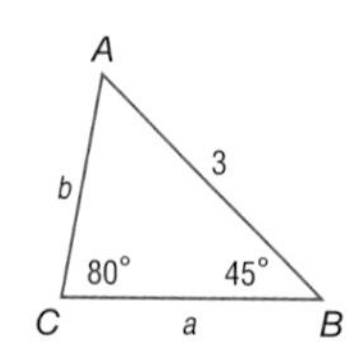

Step 1 Find the measure of the third angle.
$m\angle A = 180 - (80 + 45)$ or $55°$

Step 2 Use the Law of Sines to find side lengths a and b. Write an equation to find each variable.

$\frac{\sin A}{a} = \frac{\sin C}{c}$	**Law of Sines**	$\frac{\sin B}{b} = \frac{\sin C}{c}$
$\frac{\sin 55°}{a} = \frac{\sin 80°}{3}$	**Substitution**	$\frac{\sin 45°}{b} = \frac{\sin 80°}{3}$
$a = \frac{3 \sin 55°}{\sin 80°}$	**Solve for each variable.**	$b = \frac{3 \sin 45°}{\sin 80°}$
$a \approx 2.5$	**Use a calculator.**	$b \approx 2.2$

So, $A = 55°$, $a \approx 2.5$, and $b \approx 2.2$.

Guided Practice

2. Solve $\triangle NPQ$ if $P = 42°$, $Q = 65°$, and $n = 5$. **$N = 73°$, $p \approx 3.5$, $q \approx 4.7$**

Personal Tutor glencoe.com

StudyTip

Alternative Representations The Law of Sines may also be written as $\frac{a}{\sin A} = \frac{b}{\sin B} = \frac{c}{\sin C}$. So, the expressions below could also be used to solve the triangle in Example 2.

- $\frac{a}{\sin 55°} = \frac{3}{\sin 80°}$
- $\frac{b}{\sin 45°} = \frac{3}{\sin 80°}$

Find the Area of a Triangle

Example 1 shows how to use the sine of an angle to find the area of a triangle.

Formative Assessment

Use the Guided Practice exercises after each example to determine students' understanding of concepts.

Additional Example

1 Find the area of $\triangle ABC$ to the nearest tenth. 3.8 cm^2

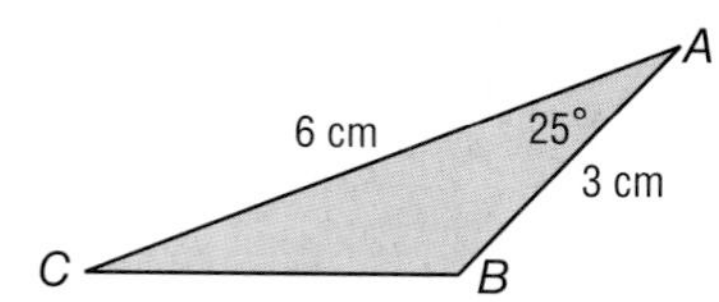

Additional Examples also in Interactive Classroom PowerPoint® Presentations

IWB INTERACTIVE WHITEBOARD READY

Use the Law of Sines to Solve Triangles

Example 2 shows how to use the Law of Sines to solve a triangle when two angles and a side are given. **Example 3** shows how to use the Law of Sines to solve a triangle that has zero, one, or two solutions. **Example 4** shows how to use the Law of Sines to solve a real-world problem.

Additional Example

2 Solve $\triangle ABC$. Round to the nearest tenth if necessary.

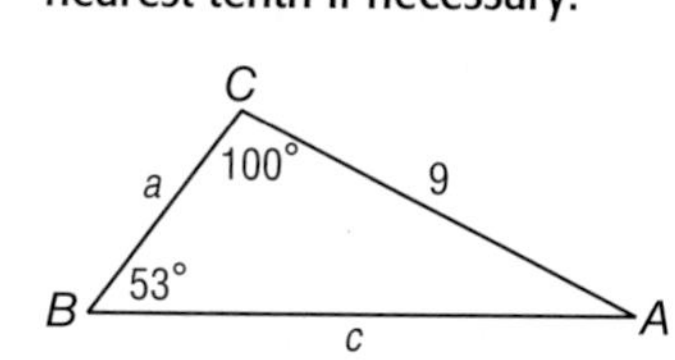

$A = 27°$, $a \approx 5.1$, $c \approx 11.1$

Watch Out!

Unlocking Misconceptions Students may think the Law of Sines only works for right trangles. Clarify that this formula works for any triangle, as does the Law of Cosines explored in Lesson 13-5.

Additional Example

3 Determine whether each triangle has *no* solution, *one* solution, or *two* solutions. Then solve the triangle. Round side lengths to the nearest tenth and angle measures to the nearest degree.

a. In $\triangle NPQ$, $Q = 110°$, $q = 11$, and $n = 8$. $P = 27°$, $N = 43°$, $p = 5.3$

b. In $\triangle DEF$, $E = 52°$, $e = 5$, and $f = 9$. no solution

c. In $\triangle XYZ$, $X = 28°$, $z = 15$, and $x = 9$. One solution is $Z = 51°$, $Y = 101°$, and $y = 18.8$; another solution is $Z = 129°$, $Y = 23°$, and $y = 7.5$.

TEACH with TECH

INTERACTIVE WHITEBOARD Use the board to demonstrate the ambiguous case with the Law of Sines. Use a drawing program to accurately draw the two given sides of the triangle and the given angle. Draw one of the possible third sides of the triangle. Then drag the segment to show how to construct the other possible triangle.

StudyTip

Two Solutions A situation in which two solutions for a triangle exist is called the *ambiguous case.*

StudyTip

A is Acute In the figures at the right, the altitude h is compared to a because h is the minimum distance from C to $\overline{AB}$ when A is acute.

$\sin A = \frac{\text{opp}}{\text{hyp}}$

$\sin A = \frac{h}{b}$

If you are given the measures of two angles and a side, exactly one triangle is possible. However, if you are given the measures of two sides and the angle opposite one of them, zero, one, or two triangles may be possible. So, when solving a triangle using the SSA case, zero, one, or two solutions are possible.

Key Concept — Possible Triangles in SSA Case

Consider a triangle in which a, b, and $m\angle A$ are given.

$\angle A$ is Acute.

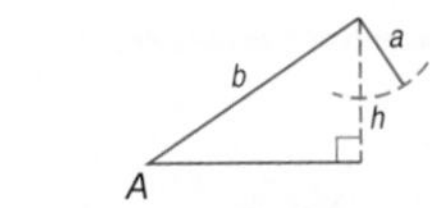

$a < h$
no solution

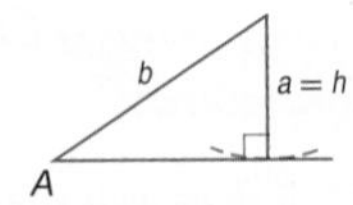

$a = h$
one solution

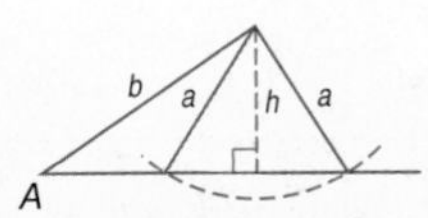

$h < a < b$
two solutions

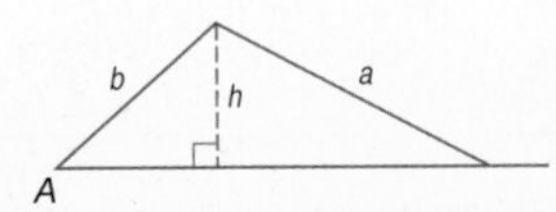

$a \geq b$
one solution

$\angle A$ is Right or Obtuse.

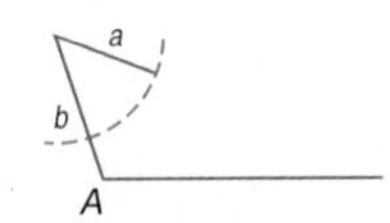

$a \leq b$
no solution

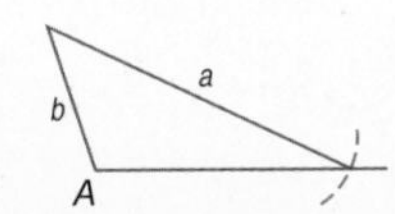

$a > b$
one solution

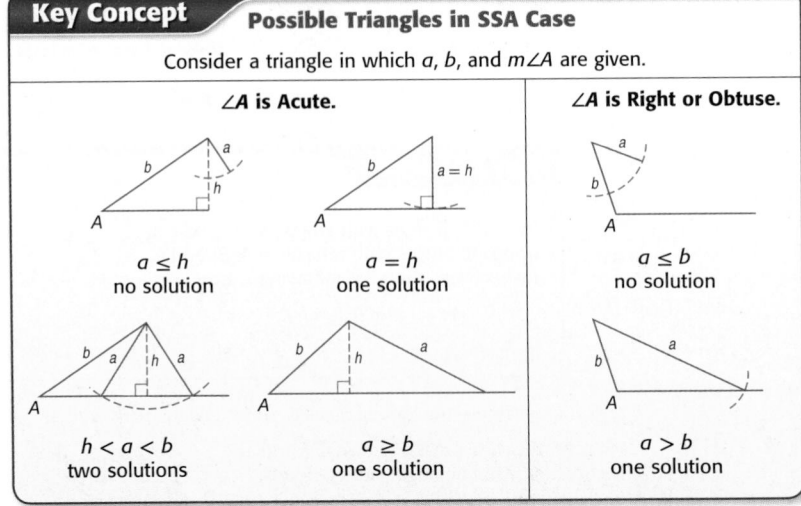

Since $\sin A = \frac{h}{b}$, you can use $h = b \sin A$ to find h in the acute triangles.

EXAMPLE 3 Solve a Triangle Given Two Sides and an Angle

Determine whether each triangle has *no* solution, *one* solution, or *two* solutions. Then solve the triangle. Round side lengths to the nearest tenth and angle measures to the nearest degree.

a. In $\triangle RST$, $R = 105°$, $r = 9$, and $s = 6$.

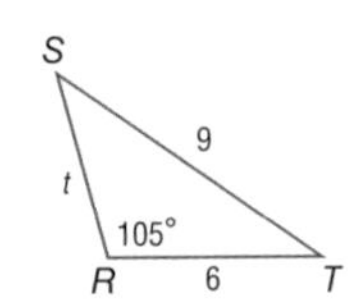

Because $\angle R$ is obtuse and $9 > 6$, you know that one solution exists.

Step 1 Use the Law of Sines to find $m\angle S$.

$\frac{\sin S}{6} = \frac{\sin 105°}{9}$ **Law of Sines**

$\sin S = \frac{6 \sin 105°}{9}$ **Multiply each side by 6.**

$\sin S \approx 0.6440$ **Use a calculator.**

$S \approx 40°$ **Use the $\sin^{-1}$ function.**

Step 2 Find $m\angle T$.

$m\angle T \approx 180 - (105 + 40)$ or $35°$

Step 3 Use the Law of Sines to find t.

$\frac{\sin 35°}{t} \approx \frac{\sin 105°}{9}$ **Law of Sines**

$t \approx \frac{9 \sin 35°}{\sin 105°}$ **Solve for t.**

$t \approx 5.3$ **Use a calculator.**

So, $S \approx 40°$, $T \approx 35°$, and $t \approx 5.3$.

b. **In $\triangle ABC$, $A = 54°$, $a = 6$, and $b = 8$.**

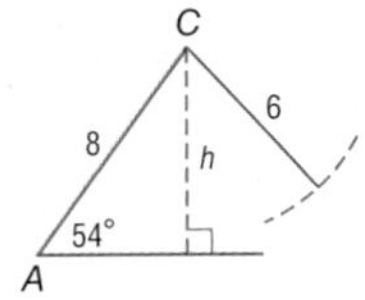

Since $\angle A$ is acute and $6 < 8$, find h and compare it to a.

$b \sin A = 8 \sin 54°$	**$b = 8$ and $A = 54°$**
≈ 6.5	**Use a calculator.**

Since $6 \le 6.5$ or $a \le h$, there is no solution.

c. **In $\triangle ABC$, $A = 35°$, $a = 17$, and $b = 20$.**

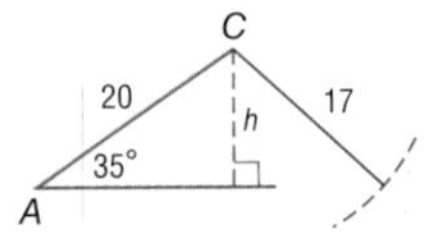

Since $\angle A$ is acute and $17 < 20$, find h and compare it to a.

$b \sin A = 20 \sin 35°$	**$b = 20$ and $A = 35°$**
≈ 11.5	**Use a calculator.**

Since $11.5 < 17 < 20$ or $h < a < b$, there are two solutions. So, there are two triangles to be solved.

Case 1 $\angle B$ is acute.

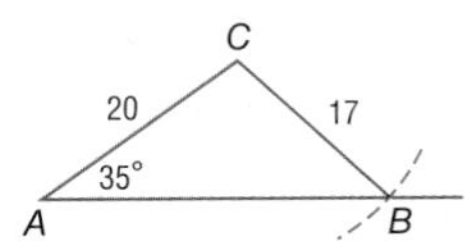

Step 1 Find $m\angle B$.

$\frac{\sin B}{20} = \frac{\sin 35°}{17}$	**Law of Sines**
$\sin B = \frac{20 \sin 35°}{17}$	**Solve for sin *B*.**
$\sin B \approx 0.6748$	**Use a calculator.**
$B \approx 42°$	**Find $\sin^{-1}$ 0.6748.**

Step 2 Find $m\angle C$.

$m\angle C \approx 180 - (35 + 42)$ or $103°$

Step 3 Find c.

$\frac{\sin 103°}{c} = \frac{\sin 35°}{17}$	**Law of Sines**
$c = \frac{17 \sin 103°}{\sin 35°}$	**Solve for *c*.**
$c \approx 28.9$	**Simplify.**

Case 2 $\angle B$ is obtuse.

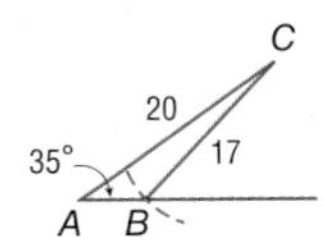

Step 1 Find $m\angle B$.

The sine function also has a positive value in Quadrant II. So, find an obtuse angle B for which $\sin B \approx 0.6748$.

$m\angle B \approx 180° - 42°$ or $138°$

Step 2 Find $m\angle C$.

$m\angle C \approx 180 - (35 + 138)$ or $7°$

Step 3 Find c.

$\frac{\sin 7°}{c} \approx \frac{\sin 35°}{17}$	**Law of Sines**
$c \approx \frac{17 \sin 7°}{\sin 35°}$	**Solve for *c*.**
$c \approx 3.6$	**Simplify.**

So, one solution is $B \approx 42°$, $C \approx 103°$, and $c \approx 28.9$, and another solution is $B \approx 138°$, $C \approx 7°$, and $c \approx 3.6$.

Guided Practice

Determine whether each triangle has *no* solution, *one* solution, or *two* solutions. Then solve the triangle. Round side lengths to the nearest tenth and angle measures to the nearest degree.

3A. In $\triangle RST$, $R = 95°$, $r = 10$, and $s = 12$. **no solution**

3B. In $\triangle MNP$, $N = 32°$, $n = 7$, and $p = 4$. **one; $P \approx 18°$, $M \approx 130°$, $m \approx 10.1$**

3C. In $\triangle ABC$, $A = 47°$, $a = 15$, and $b = 18$.

Personal Tutor glencoe.com

StudyTip

Reference Angle In the triangle in Case 2, you are using the reference angle 42° to find the other value of *B*.

3C. two; $B \approx 61°$, $C \approx 72°$, $c \approx 19.5$; $B \approx 119°$, $C \approx 14°$, $c \approx 5.0$

Focus on Mathematical Content

Law of Sines In one case for which the Law of Sines may be used, more than one solution of the triangle is possible. For this ambiguous case, the process of solving the triangle must be performed twice. However, there may still be only one solution for the triangle.

Differentiated Instruction

AL OL BL ELL

Intrapersonal Learners Have students write a journal entry about which example they found the most challenging and why. Ask them to include any questions they still have about the lesson.

Additional Example

4 **BASEBALL** In Example 4, suppose the angles at second base and third base are 58° and 41°, respectively. How far away from second base was the ball caught? about 59.8 ft

3 PRACTICE

Formative Assessment

Use Exercises 1–12 to check for understanding.

Use the chart at the bottom of the next page to customize assignments for your students.

Real-World Link

High school and college baseball fields share the same infield dimensions as professional baseball fields. The outfield dimensions vary greatly.

Source: *Baseball Digest Magazine*

Real-World EXAMPLE 4 Use the Law of Sines to Solve a Problem

BASEBALL A baseball is hit between second and third bases and is caught at point *B*, as shown in the figure. How far away from second base was the ball caught?

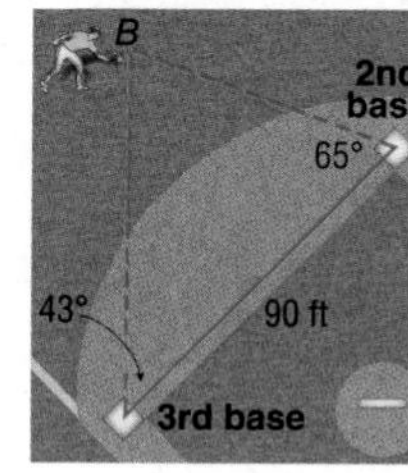

$\frac{\sin 72°}{90} = \frac{\sin 43°}{x}$ **Law of Sines**

$x \sin 72° = 90 \sin 43°$ **Cross products**

$x = \frac{90 \sin 43°}{\sin 72°}$ **Solve for *x*.**

$x \approx 64.5$ **Use a calculator.**

So, the distance is about 64.5 feet.

Guided Practice

4. How far away from third base was the ball caught? 85.8 ft

Personal Tutor glencoe.com

Check Your Understanding

Example 1 p. 832

Find the area of $\triangle ABC$ to the nearest tenth, if necessary.

1. 27.9 mm^2

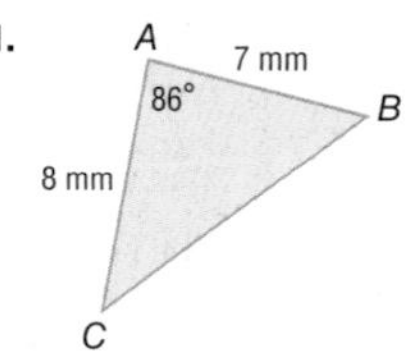

2. 3 yd^2

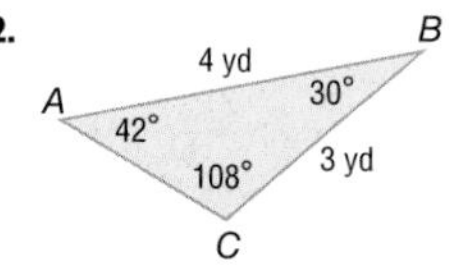

3. $A = 40°, b = 11$ cm, $c = 6$ cm 21.2 cm^2

4. $B = 103°, a = 20$ in., $c = 18$ in. 175.4 in^2

Example 2 p. 833

Solve each triangle. Round side lengths to the nearest tenth and angle measures to the nearest degree.

5. $E = 107°$, $d \approx 7.9$, $f \approx 7.0$
6. $C = 33°$, $a \approx 6.9$, $c \approx 4.9$

5.

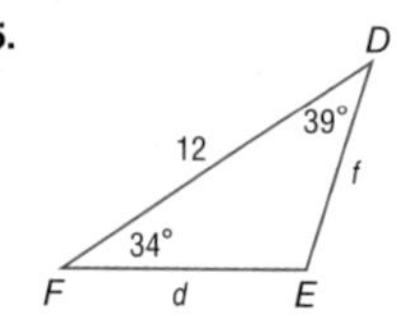

6.

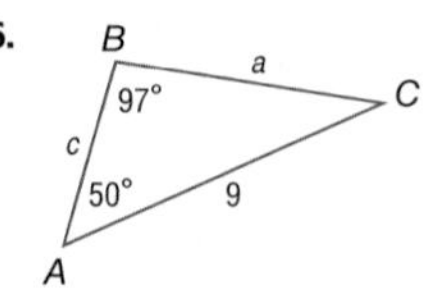

7. Solve $\triangle FGH$ if $G = 80°, H = 40°$, and $g = 14$. $F = 60°$, $f \approx 12.3$, $h \approx 9.1$

Example 3 pp. 834–835

Determine whether each $\triangle ABC$ has *no* solution, *one* solution, or *two* solutions. Then solve the triangle. Round side lengths to the nearest tenth and angle measures to the nearest degree. 8. one; $B \approx 39°$, $C \approx 46°$, $c \approx 13.7$

10. two; $B \approx 65°$, $C \approx 81°$, $c \approx 14.1$; $B \approx 115°$, $C \approx 31°$, $c \approx 7.4$
11. one; $B = 90°$, $C = 60°$, $c \approx 5.2$

8. $A = 95°, a = 19, b = 12$

9. $A = 60°, a = 15, b = 24$ no solution

10. $A = 34°, a = 8, b = 13$

11. $A = 30°, a = 3, b = 6$

Example 4 p. 836

12. SPACE Refer to the beginning of the lesson. Find the distance between the Wahoo Crater and the Naukan Crater on Mars. 3 kilometers

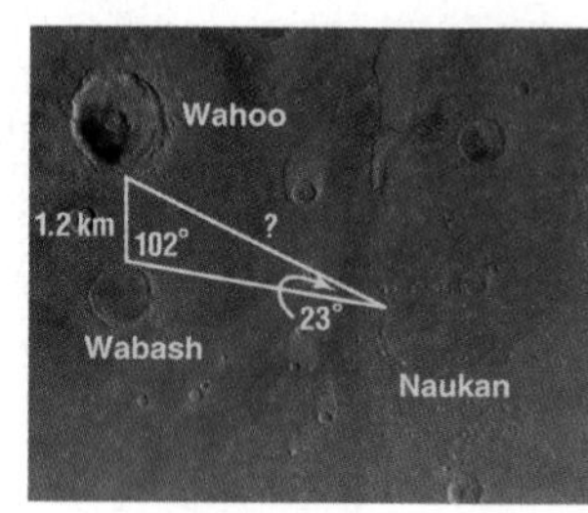

836 Chapter 13 Trigonometric Functions

Practice and Problem Solving

● = **Step-by-Step Solutions** begin on page R20.
Extra Practice begins on page 947.

Example 1 p. 832

Find the area of $\triangle ABC$ to the nearest tenth.

13. 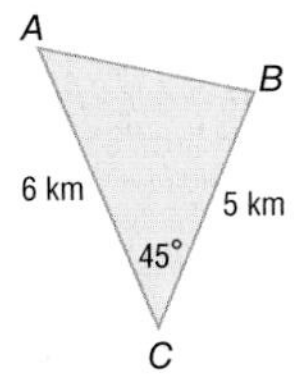

10.6 km²

14. 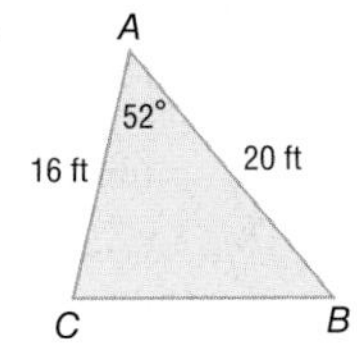

126.1 ft²

15. 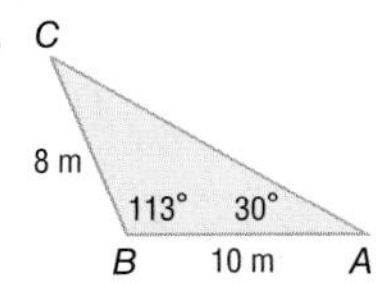

36.8 m²

16. 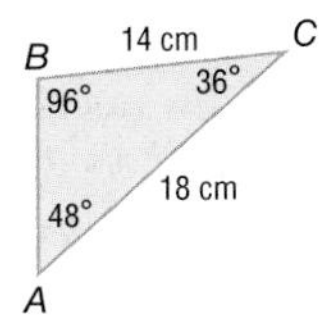

74.1 cm²

17. $C = 25°, a = 4$ ft, $b = 7$ ft 5.9 ft²

18. $A = 138°, b = 10$ in., $c = 20$ in. 66.9 in²

19. $B = 92°, a = 14.5$ m, $c = 9$ m 65.2 m²

20. $C = 116°, a = 2.7$ cm, $b = 4.6$ cm 5.6 cm²

Example 2 p. 833

Solve each triangle. Round side lengths to the nearest tenth and angle measures to the nearest degree.

21. $C = 30°$, $b \approx 11.1$, $c \approx 5.8$
22. $R = 80°$, $r \approx 17.5$, $t \approx 14.2$
23. $L = 74°$, $m \approx 4.9$, $n \approx 3.1$
24. $B = 38°$, $a \approx 19.5$, $c \approx 36.1$

21. 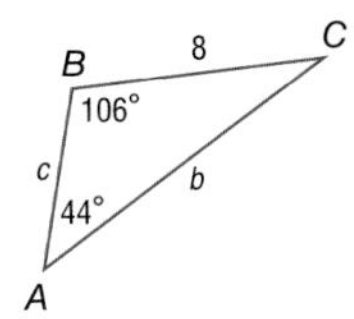

22. 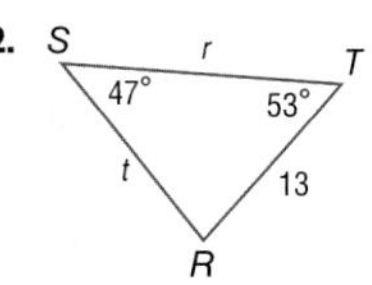

23. 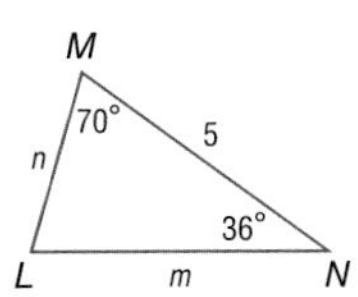

24. 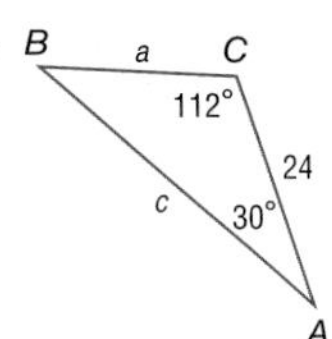

29. one; $B \approx 25°$, $C \approx 55°$, $c \approx 5.8$
30. one; $B \approx 49°$, $C \approx 56°$, $c \approx 12.0$
31. one; $B \approx 32°$, $C \approx 110°$, $c \approx 32.1$
33. two; $B \approx 53°$, $C \approx 85°$, $c \approx 7.4$; $B \approx 127°$, $C \approx 11°$, $c \approx 1.4$

25 Solve $\triangle HJK$ if $H = 53°$, $J = 20°$, and $h = 31$. $K = 107°$, $j \approx 13.3$, $k \approx 37.1$

26. Solve $\triangle NPQ$ if $P = 109°$, $Q = 57°$, and $n = 22$. $N = 14°$, $p \approx 86.0$, $q \approx 76.3$

27. Solve $\triangle ABC$ if $A = 50°$, $a = 2.5$, and $C = 67°$. $B \approx 63°$, $b \approx 2.9$, $c \approx 3.0$

28. Solve $\triangle ABC$ if $B = 18°$, $C = 142°$, and $b = 20$. $A = 20°$, $a \approx 22.1$, $c \approx 39.8$

Example 3 pp. 834–835

Determine whether each $\triangle ABC$ has *no* solution, *one* solution, or *two* solutions. Then solve the triangle. Round side lengths to the nearest tenth and angle measures to the nearest degree.

34. two; $B \approx 71°$, $C \approx 65°$, $c \approx 18.3$; $B \approx 109°$, $C \approx 27°$, $c \approx 9.1$
36. one; $B = 90°$, $C = 60°$, $c \approx 29.4$

29. $A = 100°, a = 7, b = 3$

30. $A = 75°, a = 14, b = 11$

31. $A = 38°, a = 21, b = 18$

32. $A = 52°, a = 9, b = 20$ no solution

33. $A = 42°, a = 5, b = 6$

34. $A = 44°, a = 14, b = 19$

35. $A = 131°, a = 15, b = 32$ no solution

36. $A = 30°, a = 17, b = 34$

Differentiated Homework Options

Level	Assignment	Two-Day Option	
AL Basic	13–38, 43, 46–69	13–37 odd, 49–52	14–38 even, 43, 46–48, 53–69
OL Core	13–37 odd, 39–43, 46–69	13–38, 49–52	39–43, 46–48, 53–69
BL Advanced	39–66, (optional: 67–69)		

Lesson 13-4 Law of Sines 837

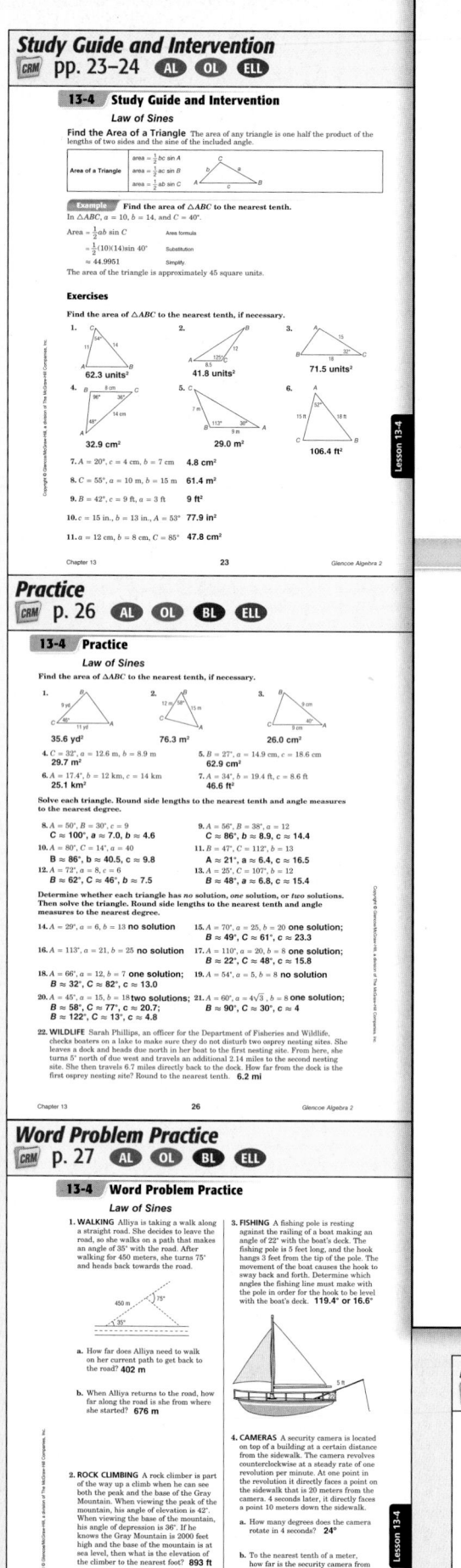

Study Guide and Intervention
CRM pp. 23–24 AL OL ELL

13-4 Study Guide and Intervention

Law of Sines

Find the Area of a Triangle The area of any triangle is one half the product of the lengths of two sides and the sine of the included angle.

Area of a Triangle	area $= \frac{1}{2}bc \sin A$; area $= \frac{1}{2}ac \sin B$; area $= \frac{1}{2}ab \sin C$

Example Find the area of $\triangle ABC$ to the nearest tenth.

In $\triangle ABC$, $a = 10$, $b = 14$, and $C = 40°$.

Area $= \frac{1}{2}ab \sin C$ — Area formula

$= \frac{1}{2}(10)(14)\sin 40°$ — Substitution

≈ 44.9951 — Simplify.

The area of the triangle is approximately 45 square units.

Exercises

Find the area of $\triangle ABC$ to the nearest tenth, if necessary.

1. 62.3 units² 2. 41.8 units² 3. 71.5 units²
4. 32.9 cm² 5. 29.0 m² 6. 106.4 ft²
7. $A = 20°$, $c = 4$ cm, $b = 7$ cm **4.8 cm²**
8. $C = 55°$, $a = 10$ m, $b = 15$ m **61.4 m²**
9. $B = 42°$, $c = 9$ ft, $a = 3$ ft **9 ft²**
10. $c = 15$ in., $b = 13$ in., $A = 53°$ **77.9 in²**
11. $a = 12$ cm, $b = 8$ cm, $C = 85°$ **47.8 cm²**

Chapter 13 23 Glencoe Algebra 2

Practice
CRM p. 26 AL OL BL ELL

13-4 Practice

Law of Sines

Find the area of $\triangle ABC$ to the nearest tenth, if necessary.

1. 35.6 yd² 2. 76.3 m² 3. 26.0 cm²
4. $C = 32°$, $a = 12.6$ m, $b = 8.9$ m **29.7 m²**
5. $B = 27°$, $a = 14.9$ cm, $c = 18.6$ cm **62.9 cm²**
6. $A = 17.4°$, $b = 12$ km, $c = 14$ km **25.1 km²**
7. $A = 34°$, $b = 19.4$ ft, $c = 8.6$ ft **46.6 ft²**

Solve each triangle. Round side lengths to the nearest tenth and angle measures to the nearest degree.

8. $A = 50°$, $B = 30°$, $c = 9$ **C ≈ 100°, a ≈ 7.0, b ≈ 4.6**
9. $A = 56°$, $B = 38°$, $a = 12$ **C ≈ 86°, b ≈ 8.9, c ≈ 14.4**
10. $A = 80°$, $C = 14°$, $a = 40$ **B ≈ 86°, b ≈ 40.5, c ≈ 9.8**
11. $B = 47°$, $C = 112°$, $b = 13$ **A ≈ 21°, a ≈ 6.4, c ≈ 16.5**
12. $A = 72°$, $a = 8$, $c = 6$ **B ≈ 62°, C ≈ 46°, b ≈ 7.5**
13. $A = 25°$, $C = 107°$, $b = 12$ **B ≈ 48°, a ≈ 6.8, c ≈ 15.4**

Determine whether each triangle has *no* solution, *one* solution, or *two* solutions. Then solve the triangle. Round side lengths to the nearest tenth and angle measures to the nearest degree.

14. $A = 29°$, $a = 6$, $b = 13$ **no solution**
15. $A = 70°$, $a = 25$, $b = 20$ **one solution; B ≈ 49°, C ≈ 61°, c ≈ 23.3**
16. $A = 113°$, $a = 21$, $b = 25$ **no solution**
17. $A = 110°$, $a = 20$, $b = 8$ **one solution; B ≈ 22°, C ≈ 48°, c ≈ 15.8**
18. $A = 66°$, $a = 12$, $b = 7$ **one solution; B ≈ 32°, C ≈ 82°, c ≈ 13.0**
19. $A = 54°$, $a = 5$, $b = 8$ **no solution**
20. $A = 45°$, $a = 15$, $b = 18$ **two solutions; B ≈ 58°, C ≈ 77°, c ≈ 20.7; B ≈ 122°, C ≈ 13°, c ≈ 4.8**
21. $A = 60°$, $a = 4\sqrt{3}$, $b = 8$ **one solution; B ≈ 90°, C ≈ 30°, c ≈ 4**

22. **WILDLIFE** Sarah Phillips, an officer for the Department of Fisheries and Wildlife, checks boaters on a lake to make sure they do not disturb two osprey nesting sites. She leaves a dock and heads due north in her boat to the first nesting site. From here, she turns 5° north of due west and travels an additional 2.14 miles to the second nesting site. She then travels 6.7 miles directly back to the dock. How far from the dock is the first osprey nesting site? Round to the nearest tenth. **6.2 mi**

Chapter 13 26 Glencoe Algebra 2

Word Problem Practice
CRM p. 27 AL OL BL ELL

13-4 Word Problem Practice

Law of Sines

1. **WALKING** Alliya is taking a walk along a straight road. She decides to leave the road, so she walks on a path that makes an angle of 35° with the road. After walking for 450 meters, she turns 75° and heads back towards the road.
   a. How far does Alliya need to walk on her current path to get back to the road? **402 m**
   b. When Alliya returns to the road, how far along the road is she from where she started? **676 m**

2. **ROCK CLIMBING** A rock climber is part of the way up a climb when he can see both the peak and the base of the Gray Mountain. When viewing the peak of the mountain, his angle of elevation is 42°. When viewing the base of the mountain, his angle of depression is 36°. If he knows the Gray Mountain is 2000 feet high and the base of the mountain is at sea level, then what is the elevation of the climber to the nearest foot? **893 ft**

3. **FISHING** A fishing pole is resting against the railing of a boat making an angle of 22° with the boat's deck. The fishing pole is 5 feet long, and the hook hangs 3 feet from the tip of the pole. The movement of the boat causes the hook to sway back and forth. Determine which angles the fishing line must make with the pole in order for the hook to be level with the boat's deck. **119.4° or 16.6°**

4. **CAMERAS** A security camera is located on top of a building at a certain distance from the sidewalk. The camera revolves counterclockwise at a steady rate of one revolution per minute. At one point in the revolution it directly faces a point on the sidewalk that is 20 meters from the camera. 4 seconds later, it directly faces a point 10 meters down the sidewalk.
   a. How many degrees does the camera rotate in 4 seconds? **24°**
   b. To the nearest tenth of a meter, how far is the security camera from the sidewalk? **19.6 m**

Chapter 13 27 Glencoe Algebra 2

Lesson 13-4

Example 4 p. 836

GEOGRAPHY In Hawaii, the distance from Hilo to Kailua is 57 miles, and the distance from Hilo to Captain Cook is 55 miles.

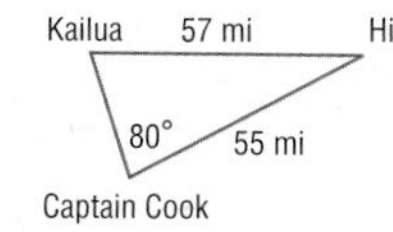

37. What is the measure of the angle formed at Hilo? **about 28°**

38. What is the distance between Kailua and Captain Cook? **about 27.2 mi**

B ▶ 39. **TORNADOES** Tornado sirens A, B, and C form a triangular region in one area of a city. Sirens A and B are 8 miles apart. The angle formed at siren A is 112°, and the angle formed at siren B is 40°. How far apart are sirens B and C? **about 15.8 mi**

40. **MYSTERIES** The Bermuda Triangle is a region of the Atlantic Ocean between Bermuda, Miami, Florida, and San Juan, Puerto Rico. It is an area where ships and airplanes have been rumored to mysteriously disappear.

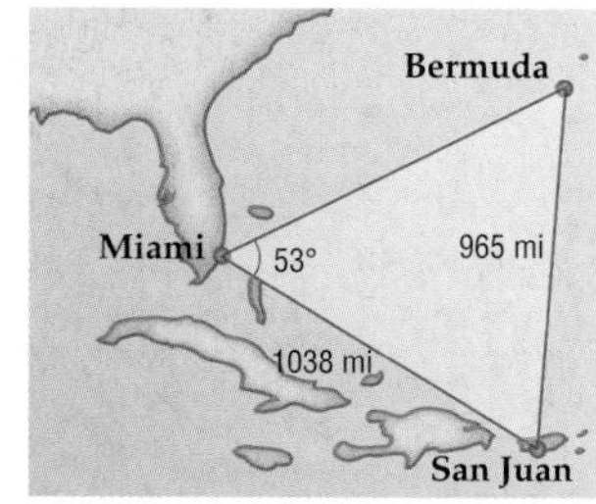

a. What is the distance between Miami and Bermuda? **about 1120.3 mi**

b. What is the approximate area of the Bermuda Triangle? **about 464,366.1 mi²**

Real-World Link

At 65 feet high, one of the tallest indoor rock climbing walls in the world is located in Bloomington, Illinois.

Source: Hi am
a n

41. **BICYCLING** One side of a triangular cycling path is 4 miles long. The angle opposite this side is 64°. Another angle formed by the triangular path measures 66°.

a. Sketch a drawing of the situation. Label the missing sides a and b. **See margin.**

b. Write equations that could be used to find the lengths of the missing sides.

c. What is the perimeter of the path? **about 11.5 mi**

42. **ROCK CLIMBING** Savannah S and Leon L are standing 8 feet apart in front of a rock climbing wall, as shown at the right. What is the height of the wall? Round to the nearest tenth. **19.0 ft**

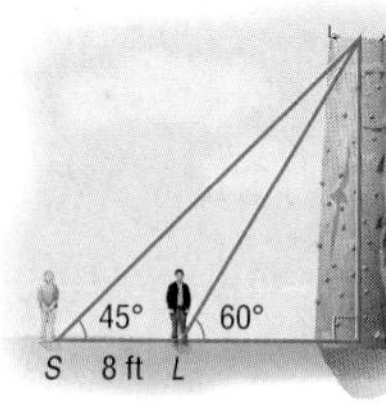

41b. Sample answer: $\frac{\sin 66°}{a} = \frac{\sin 64°}{4}$; $\frac{\sin 50°}{b} = \frac{\sin 64°}{4}$

46. Sample answer: $a = 12$, $b \approx 14.2$, $c \approx 5.0$; $a = 6$, $b \approx 7.1$, $c \approx 2.5$

47. Sample answer: In the triangle, $B = 115°$. Using the Law of Sines, $\frac{\sin 50°}{a} = \frac{\sin 115°}{b}$. This equation cannot be solved because there are two unknown sides. To solve a triangle using the Law of Sines, two sides and an angle must be given or two angles and a side opposite one of the angles must be given.

H.O.T. Problems
Use **H**igher-**O**rder **T**hinking Skills

C ▶ 43. **ERROR ANALYSIS** In $\triangle RST$, $R = 56°$, $r = 24$, and $t = 12$. Cameron and Gabriela are using the Law of Sines to find T. Is either of them correct? Explain your reasoning. **Cameron; R is acute and $r > t$, so there is one solution.**

Cameron	Gabriela
$\frac{\sin T}{12} = \frac{\sin 56°}{24}$ $\sin T \approx 0.4145$ $T \approx 24.5°$	Since $r > t$, there is no solution.

44. **CHALLENGE** In $\triangle ABC$, $B = 30°$, and $a = 6$. How many triangles can be formed if $b = 5$? Explain your reasoning. **See margin.**

45. **CHALLENGE** Using the figure at the right, derive the formula Area $= \frac{1}{2}bc \sin A$. **See Chapter 13 Answer Appendix.**

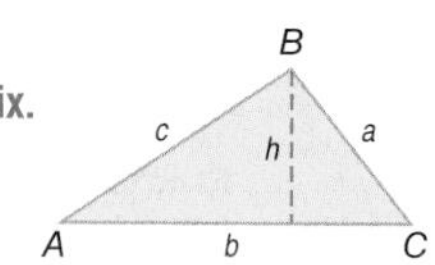

46. **REASONING** Find the side lengths of two different triangles ABC that can be formed if $A = 55°$ and $C = 20°$.

47. **WRITING IN MATH** Use the Law of Sines to explain why a and b do not have unique values in the figure shown.

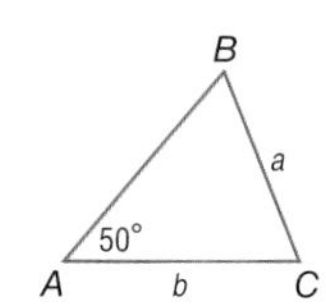

48. **OPEN ENDED** Given that $E = 62°$ and $d = 38$, find a value for e such that no triangle DEF can exist. Explain your reasoning. **See margin.**

Enrichment
CRM p. 28 OL BL

13-4 Enrichment

Navigation

The bearing of a boat is an angle showing the direction the boat is heading. Often, the angle is measured from north, but it can be measured from any of the four compass directions. At the right, the bearing of the boat is 155°. Or, it can be described as 25° east of south (S25°E).

Example A boat A sights the lighthouse B in the direction N65°E and the spire of a church C in the direction S75°E. According to the map, B is 7 miles from C in the direction N30°W. In order for A to avoid running aground, find the bearing it should keep to pass B at 4 miles distance.

In $\triangle ABC$, $\angle \alpha = 180° - 65° - 75°$ or 40°

$\angle C = 180° - 30° - (180° - 75°)$

$= 45°$

$a = 7$ miles

With the Law of Sines,

$AB = \frac{a \sin C}{\sin \alpha} = \frac{7(\sin 45°)}{\sin 40°} = 7.7$ mi.

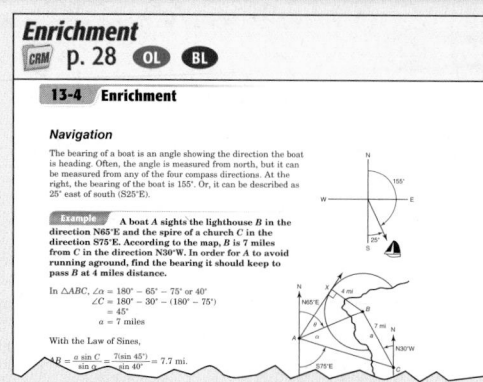

NGSSS PRACTICE 912.A.2.7, 912.S.3.3, 912.A.7.5

49. **SHORT RESPONSE** Given the graphs of $f(x)$ and $g(x)$, what is the value of $f(g(4))$? **2**

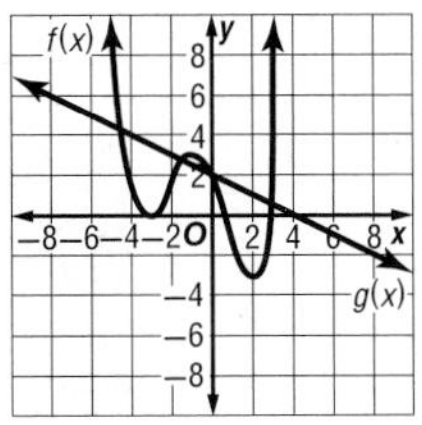

50. **STATISTICS** If the average of seven consecutive odd integers is n, what is the median of these seven integers? **C**

A. 0
B. 7
C. n
D. $n - 2$

51. One zero of $f(x) = x^3 - 7x^2 - 6x + 72$ is 4. What is the factored form of the expression $x^3 - 7x^2 - 6x + 72$? **G**

F. $(x - 6)(x + 3)(x + 4)$
G. $(x - 6)(x + 3)(x - 4)$
H. $(x + 6)(x + 3)(x - 4)$
I. $(x + 12)(x - 1)(x - 4)$

52. **SAT/ACT** Three people are splitting \$48,000 using the ratio 5 : 4 : 3. What is the amount of the greatest share? **C**

A. \$12,000
B. \$16,000
C. \$20,000
D. \$24,000

Spiral Review

Find the exact value of each trigonometric function. (Lesson 13-3)

53. $\sin 210°$ $-\frac{1}{2}$

54. $\cos \frac{3}{4}\pi$ $-\frac{\sqrt{2}}{2}$

55. $\cot 60°$ $\frac{\sqrt{3}}{3}$

Find an angle with a positive measure and an angle with a negative measure that are coterminal with each angle. (Lesson 13-2)

56. $125°$ $485°, -235°$

57. $-32°$ $328°, -392°$

58. $\frac{2}{3}\pi$ $\frac{8}{3}\pi, -\frac{4}{3}\pi$

59. **CLOCKS** Jun's grandfather clock is broken. When she sets the pendulum in motion by holding it against the side of the clock and letting it go, it swings 24 centimeters to the other side, then 18 centimeters back, then 13.5 centimeters, and so on. What is the total distance that the pendulum swings before it stops? (Lesson 11-5) **96 cm**

Find the sum of each infinite series, if it exists. (Lesson 11-4)

60. $64 + 48 + 36 + \ldots$ **256**

61. $27 + 36 + 48 + \ldots$ **No sum exists.**

62. $\sum_{n=1}^{\infty} 0.5(1.1)^n$ **No sum exists.**

63. **ASTRONOMY** At its closest point, Earth is 91.8 million miles from the center of the Sun. At its farthest point, Earth is 94.9 million miles from the center of the Sun. Write an equation for the orbit of Earth, assuming that the center of the orbit is the origin and the Sun lies on the x-axis. (Lesson 10-4) $\frac{x^2}{8.714 \times 10^{15}} + \frac{y^2}{8.710 \times 10^{15}} = 1$

Simplify. (Lesson 7-4)

64. $\sqrt{(x-4)^2}$ $|x - 4|$

65. $\sqrt{(y+2)^4}$ $(y + 2)^2$

66. $\sqrt[3]{(a-b)^6}$ $(a - b)^2$

Skills Review

Evaluate each expression if $w = 6$, $x = -4$, $y = 1.5$, and $z = \frac{3}{4}$. (Lesson 1-1)

67. $w^2 + y^2 - 6xz$ **56.25**

68. $x^2 + z^2 + 5wy$ $61\frac{9}{16}$

69. $wy + xz + w^2 - x^2$ **26**

Watch Out!

Error Analysis For Exercise 43, students should see that neither answer is correct. Cameron has probably made a calculator error, because $\sin T = \frac{12 \cdot \sin 56°}{24} = \frac{(12)(0.8290)}{24} \approx 0.4145$ and so $T \approx 24.5°$. Gabriela is incorrect because this is not a "no solution" situation. Explain to students that the "no solution" situation is when the side opposite the given angle θ is less than $\sin \theta$ times the length of the side adjacent to θ.

4 ASSESS

Name the Math Ask students to state the steps that are necessary for solving a triangle when one side and two angle measures are given.

Additional Answers

41a. Sample answer:

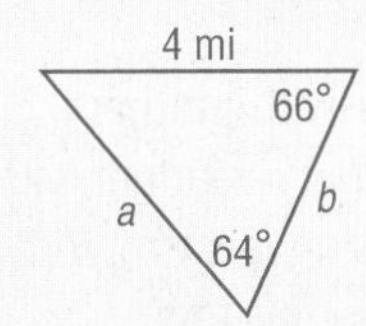

44. Sample answer: 2 triangles; the altitude $h = 3$ so $h < 5 < 6$.

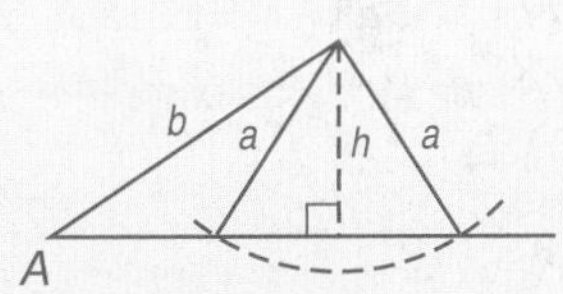

48. Sample answer: $e = 30$; for no triangle to exist, the length of the side opposite angle E must be less than 33.6 to satisfy the Law of Sines.

Differentiated Instruction OL BL

Extension Have students compute the area of a 3-4-5 right triangle using the area formula presented in this lesson. Have them use the formula for all three angles of the triangle. 6; 6; 6

EXTEND 13-4 Lesson Notes

1 FOCUS

Objective Investigate measures in regular polygons using trigonometry.

Materials for Each Student

- compass
- straightedge
- protractor

Teaching Tip

Have students draw a diameter for each circle. This will make it easier to use the protractor to draw the angles in each circle.

2 TEACH

Working in Cooperative Groups

Have students work with partners, mixing abilities so that a student with more experience using drawing tools is paired with one who has less experience. Have students complete the Activity.

Practice Have students complete Exercises 1–7.

3 ASSESS

Formative Assessment

Use Exercise 1 to assess whether students understand how to inscribe regular polygons in a circle.

From Concrete to Abstract

Exercises 5–7 require students to determine formulas that express relationships between the number of sides of a regular polygon and the length of the apothem. Students should use the results of Exercise 1 to determine the formulas.

EXTEND 13-4 Geometry Lab

Regular Polygons

NGSSS **MA.912.T.2.3** Apply the laws of sines and cosines to solve real-world problems using technology.

You can use central angles of circles to investigate characteristics of regular polygons inscribed in a circle. Recall that a regular polygon is inscribed in a circle if each of its vertices lies on the circle.

ACTIVITY Collect the Data

Step 1 Use a compass to draw a circle with a radius of one inch.

Step 2 Inscribe an equilateral triangle inside the circle. To do this, use a protractor to measure three angles of 120° at the center of the circle, since $\frac{360°}{3} = 120°$. Then connect the points where the sides of the angles intersect the circle using a straightedge.

Step 3 The **apothem** of a regular polygon is a segment that is drawn from the center of the polygon perpendicular to a side of the polygon. Use the cosine of angle θ to find the length of an apothem, labeled a in the diagram.

Model and Analyze

1. Make a table like the one shown below and record the length of the apothem of the equilateral triangle. Inscribe each regular polygon named in the table in a circle with radius one inch. Copy and complete the table.

Number of Sides, n	θ	a	Number of Sides, n	θ	a
3	60	0.50	7	25.7	0.90
4	45	0.71	8	22.5	0.92
5	36	0.81	9	20	0.94
6	30	0.87	10	18	0.95

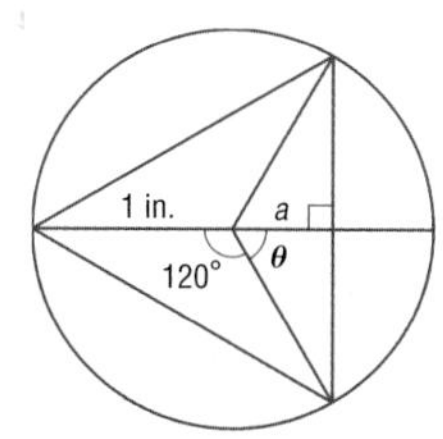

2. What do you notice about the measure of θ as the number of sides of the inscribed polygon increases? **The measure of θ decreases.**
3. What do you notice about the value of a? **The length of the apothem increases as the number of sides increases, approaching 1.**
4. **MAKE A CONJECTURE** Suppose you inscribe a 30-sided regular polygon inside a circle. Find the measure of angle θ. **6°**
5. Write a formula that gives the measure of angle θ for a polygon with n sides. **$\theta = 360 \div 2n$ or $\theta = 180 \div n$**
6. Write a formula that gives the length of the apothem of a regular polygon inscribed in a circle with radius one inch. **$a = \cos\theta$**
7. How would the formula you wrote in Exercise 5 change if the apothem of the circle was not one inch? **See margin.**

Extending the Concept

Ask:

- What happens to the area of the inscribed regular polygons as n increases? The area increases.
- What value does that area approach? the area of the circle

Additional Answer

7. To find the length of the apothem, you need to write the equation $\cos\theta = \frac{a}{\text{length of radius}}$. If the radius is 1, then $\cos\theta = a$. If the radius is not 1, then $a = \text{length of radius} \cdot \cos\theta$.

13-5 Law of Cosines

Why?

Submersibles, which are lowered into the ocean from ships, are used to take humans to depths they cannot reach by any other means. A submersible 520 meters from its ship shines a light on a shipwreck 338 meters away, as shown in the diagram. You can use trigonometry to find the distance from the ship to the shipwreck.

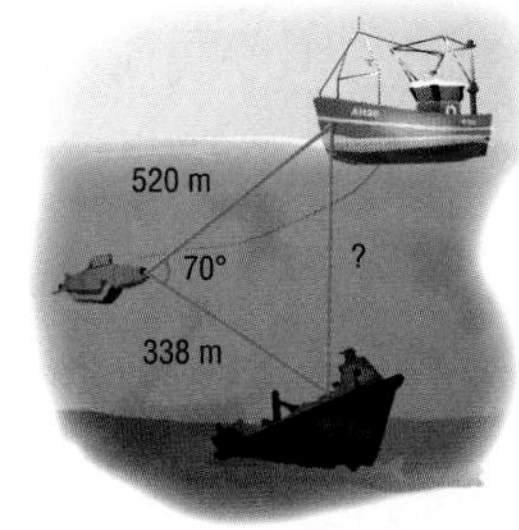

Then
You solved triangles by using the Law of Sines. (Lesson 13-4)

Now
- Use the Law of Cosines to solve triangles.
- Choose methods to solve triangles.

NGSSS
MA.912.T.1.8 Solve real-world problems involving applications of trigonometric functions using graphing technology when appropriate.
MA.912.T.2.3 Apply the laws of sines and **cosines** to solve real-world problems using technology.

New Vocabulary
Law of Cosines

FL Math Online
glencoe.com

Use Law of Cosines to Solve Triangles You cannot use the Law of Sines to solve a triangle like the one shown above. You can use the **Law of Cosines** to solve a triangle if you know either one of the following.

- the measures of two sides and the included angle (side-angle-side SAS case)
- the measures of three sides (side-side-side SSS case)

Key Concept Law of Cosines

In $\triangle ABC$, if sides with lengths a, b, and c are opposite angles with measures A, B, and C, respectively, then the following are true.

$$a^2 = b^2 + c^2 - 2bc \cos A$$
$$b^2 = a^2 + c^2 - 2ac \cos B$$
$$c^2 = a^2 + b^2 - 2ab \cos C$$

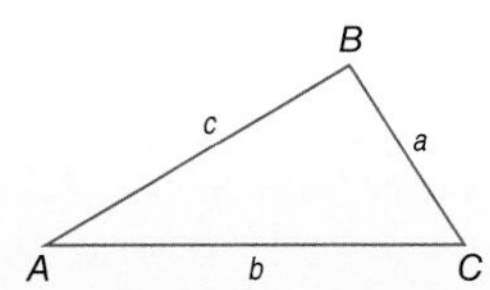

EXAMPLE 1 Solve a Triangle Given Two Sides and the Included Angle

Solve $\triangle ABC$.

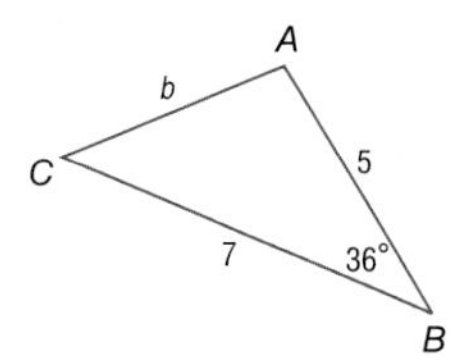

Step 1 Use the Law of Cosines to find the missing side length.

$b^2 = a^2 + c^2 - 2ac \cos B$ — **Law of Cosines**
$b^2 = 7^2 + 5^2 - 2(7)(5) \cos 36°$ — **$a = 7, c = 5, B = 36°$**
$b^2 \approx 17.4$ — **Use a calculator to simplify.**
$b \approx 4.2$ — **Take the square root of each side.**

Step 2 Use the Law of Sines to find a missing angle measure.

$\frac{\sin A}{7} \approx \frac{\sin 36°}{4.2}$ — $\frac{\sin A}{a} = \frac{\sin B}{b}$
$\sin A \approx \frac{7 \sin 36°}{4.2}$ — **Multiply each side by 7.**
$A \approx 78°$ — **Use the $\sin^{-1}$ function.**

Step 3 Find the measure of the other angle.
$m\angle C \approx 180° - (36° + 78°)$ or $66°$

So, $b \approx 4.2$, $A \approx 78°$, and $C \approx 66°$.

Guided Practice

1. Solve $\triangle FGH$ if $G = 82°$, $f = 6$, and $h = 4$. $H \approx 36°$, $F = 62°$, $g = 6.7$

Personal Tutor glencoe.com

13-5 Lesson Notes

1 FOCUS

Vertical Alignment

Before Lesson 13-5
Solve triangles by using the Law of Sines.

Lesson 13-5
Use the Law of Cosines to solve triangles.
Choose methods to solve triangles.

After Lesson 13-5
Use the Law of Sines and the Law of Cosines to solve problems.

2 TEACH

Scaffolding Questions

Have students read the *Why?* section of the lesson.

Ask:

- Is the triangle in the diagram acute, right, or obtuse? acute
- Explain why the angle with vertex at the ship has greater measure than the angle with vertex at the shipwreck. The side opposite the angle with vertex at the ship is longer.
- Explain why the distance between the ship and the shipwreck must be less than 858 m. Triangle Inequality tells us that the third side of the triangle must be less than 520 + 338 = 858 m.

Lesson 13-5 Resources

Resource	Approaching-Level	On-Level	Beyond-Level	English Learners
Teacher Edition	• Differentiated Instruction, p. 843	• Differentiated Instruction, pp. 843, 846	• Differentiated Instruction, p. 846	• Differentiated Instruction, p. 843
Chapter Resource Masters	• Study Guide and Intervention, pp. 29–30 • Skills Practice, p. 31 • Practice, p. 32 • Word Problem Practice, p. 33	• Study Guide and Intervention, pp. 29–30 • Skills Practice, p. 31 • Practice, p. 32 • Word Problem Practice, p. 33 • Enrichment, p. 34	• Practice, p. 32 • Word Problem Practice, p. 33 • Enrichment, p. 34	• Study Guide and Intervention, pp. 29–30 • Skills Practice, p. 31 • Practice, p. 32 • Word Problem Practice, p. 33
Transparencies	• 5-Minute Check Transparency 13-5	• 5-Minute Check Transparency 13-5	• 5-Minute Check Transparency 13-5	• 5-Minute Check Transparency 13-5
Other	• Study Notebook	• Study Notebook	• Study Notebook	• Study Notebook

Use Law of Cosines to Solve Triangles

Example 1 shows how to solve a triangle given two sides and the included angle. **Example 2** shows how to solve a triangle given three sides.

Formative Assessment

Use the Guided Practice exercises after each example to determine students' understanding of concepts.

Additional Examples

1 Solve $\triangle ABC$.

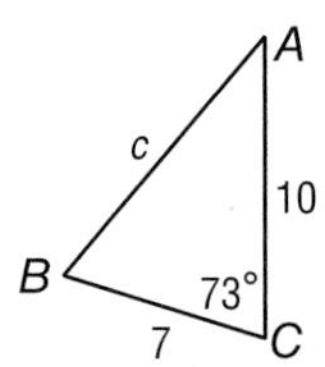

$A \approx 40°$; $B \approx 67°$; $c \approx 10.4$

2 Solve $\triangle ABC$.

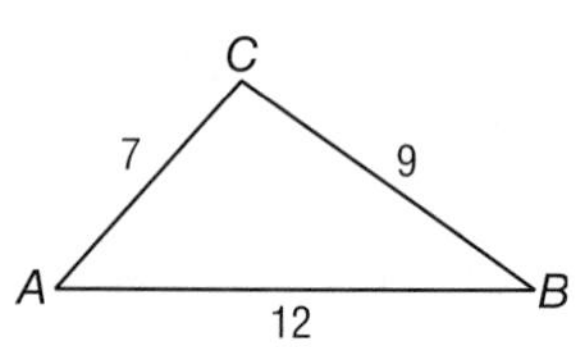

$A \approx 48°$; $B \approx 35°$; $C \approx 97°$

Additional Examples also in Interactive Classroom PowerPoint® Presentations

IWB INTERACTIVE WHITEBOARD READY

When you are only given the three side lengths of a triangle, you can solve it by using the Law of Cosines. The first step is to find the measure of the largest angle. This is done to ensure the other two angles are acute when using the Law of Sines.

EXAMPLE 2 Solve a Triangle Given Three Sides

Solve $\triangle ABC$.

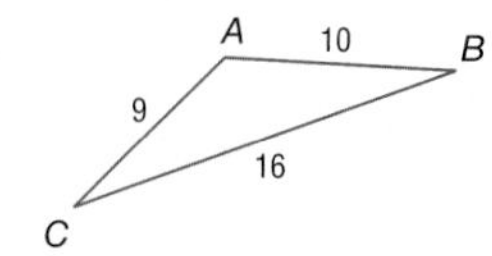

Step 1 Use the Law of Cosines to find the measure of the largest angle, $\angle A$.

$a^2 = b^2 + c^2 - 2bc \cos A$	**Law of Cosines**
$16^2 = 9^2 + 10^2 - 2(9)(10) \cos A$	**$a = 16$, $b = 9$, and $c = 10$**
$16^2 - 9^2 - 10^2 = -2(9)(10) \cos A$	**Subtract 9^2 and 10^2 from each side.**
$\frac{16^2 - 9^2 - 10^2}{-2(9)(10)} = \cos A$	**Divide each side by $-2(9)(10)$.**
$-0.4167 \approx \cos A$	**Use a calculator to simplify.**
$115° \approx A$	**Use the $\cos^{-1}$ function.**

Step 2 Use the Law of Sines to find the measure of $\angle B$.

$\frac{\sin B}{9} \approx \frac{\sin 115°}{16}$	$\frac{\sin B}{b} = \frac{\sin A}{a}$
$\sin B \approx \frac{9 \sin 115°}{16}$	**Multiply each side by 9.**
$\sin B \approx 0.5098$	**Use a calculator.**
$B \approx 31°$	**Use the $\sin^{-1}$ function.**

Step 3 Find the measure of $\angle C$.

$m\angle C \approx 180° - (115° + 31°)$ or about $34°$

So, $A \approx 115°$, $B \approx 31°$, and $C \approx 34°$.

StudyTip

Alternative Method After finding *b* in Step 1, the Law of Cosines could be used again to find the measure of a second angle.

Guided Practice

1. Solve $\triangle ABC$ if $a = 5$, $b = 11$, and $c = 8$. **$A = 24.6°$, $B = 113.6°$, $C = 41.8°$**

Personal Tutor glencoe.com

Review Vocabulary

oblique a triangle that has no right angle

Choose a Method to Solve Triangles You can use the Law of Sines and the Law of Cosines to solve problems involving oblique triangles. You need to know the measure of at least one side and any two other parts. If the triangle has a solution, you must decide whether to use the Law of Sines or the Law of Cosines to begin solving it.

Concept Summary Solving Oblique Triangles

Given	Begin by Using
two angles and any sides	Law of Sines
two sides and an angle opposite one of them	Law of Sines
two sides and their included angle	Law of Cosines
three sides	Law of Cosines

Focus on Mathematical Content

Law of Cosines The Law of Cosines can be used to solve a triangle if all three sides of the triangle are given or if two sides and the included angle are given. Unlike the Law of Sines cases, if a solution does exist for cases in which the Law of Cosines can be used, the solution is unique.

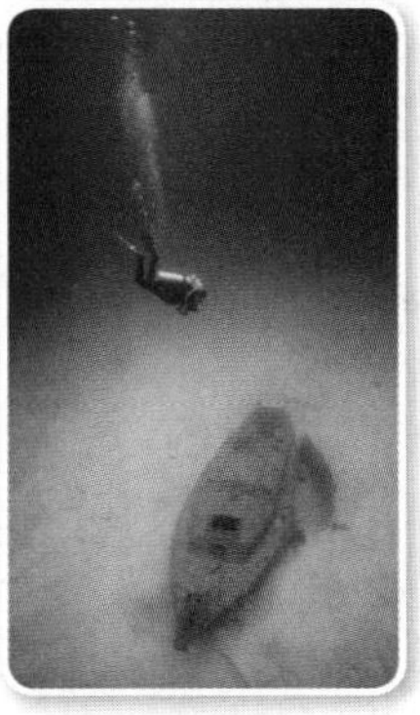

Real-World Link

The record for the deepest seawater scuba dive was 1044 feet, made by a scuba diver in the Red Sea.

Source: *Guinness Book of World Records*

Real-World EXAMPLE 3 Use the Law of Cosines

SCUBA DIVING A scuba diver looks up 20° and sees a turtle 9 feet away. She looks down 40° and sees a blue parrotfish 12 feet away. How far apart are the turtle and the blue parrotfish?

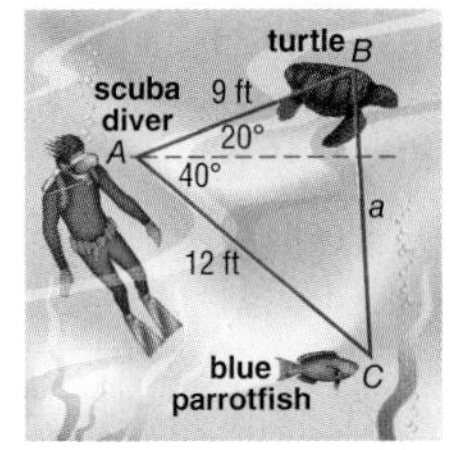

Understand You know the angles formed when the scuba diver looks up and when she looks down. You also know how far away the turtle and the blue parrotfish are from the scuba diver.

Plan Use the information to draw and label a diagram. Since two sides and the included angle of a triangle are given, you can use the Law of Cosines to solve the problem.

Solve

$a^2 = b^2 + c^2 - 2bc \cos A$	Law of Cosines
$a^2 = 12^2 + 9^2 - 2(12)(9) \cos 60$	$b = 12$, $c = 9$, and $A = 60$
$a^2 = 117$	Use a calculator.
$a \approx 10.8$	Find the positive value of a.

So, the turtle and the blue parrotfish are about 10.8 feet apart.

Check Using the Law of Sines, you can find that $B \approx 74°$ and $C \approx 46°$. Since $C < A < B$ and $c < a < b$, the solution is reasonable.

Guided Practice

3. **MARATHONS** Amelia ran 6 miles in one direction. She then turned 79° and ran 7 miles. At the end of the run, how far was Amelia from her starting point? about 8.3 mi

Personal Tutor glencoe.com

Check Your Understanding

Examples 1 and 2 pp. 841–842

Solve each triangle. Round side lengths to the nearest tenth and angle measures to the nearest degree.

1. 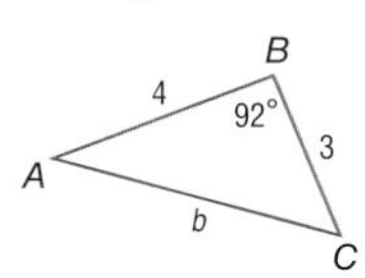

2. 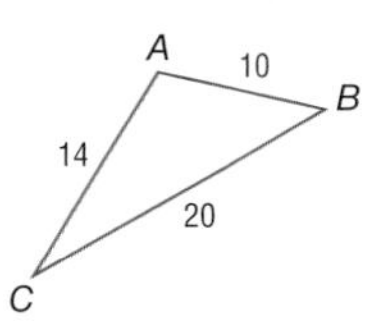

3. $a = 5, b = 8, c = 12$

4. $B = 110°, a = 6, c = 3$

1. $A \approx 36°$, $C \approx 52°$, $b \approx 5.1$
2. $A \approx 112°$, $B \approx 40°$, $C \approx 28°$
3. $A \approx 18°$, $B \approx 29°$, $C \approx 133°$
4. $A \approx 48°$, $C \approx 22°$, $b \approx 7.6$

Example 3 p. 843

Determine whether each triangle should be solved by beginning with the Law of *Sines* or the Law of *Cosines*. Then solve the triangle.

5. 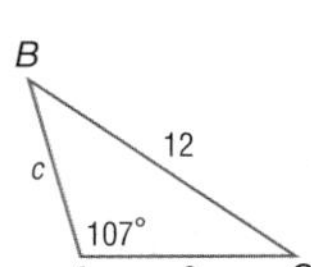

Sines; $B \approx 40°$, $C \approx 33°$, $c \approx 6.8$

6. 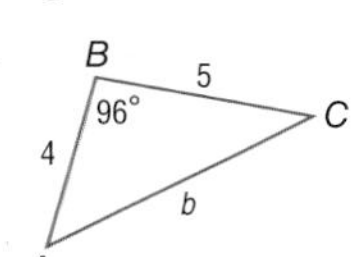

Cosines; $A \approx 48°$, $C \approx 36°$, $b \approx 6.7$

7. In $\triangle RST$, $R = 35°$, $s = 16$, and $t = 9$. Cosines; $S \approx 31°$, $T \approx 114°$, $r \approx 10.1$

8. **FOOTBALL** In a football game, the quarterback is 20 yards from Receiver A. He turns 40° to see Receiver B, who is 16 yards away. How far apart are the two receivers? about 12.9 yd

Choose a Method to Solve Triangles

Example 3 shows how to apply the Law of Cosines to solve a real-world problem.

Additional Example

3 **AIRPORT** Two pilots in a stationary airplane look 38° to the left of their runway and see a bus 75 feet away. They look 28° to the right of their runway and see a truck 110 feet away. How far apart are the bus and the truck? about 105 ft

TEACH with TECH

DOCUMENT CAMERA Assign several problems to the class, and give students time to work through them. Then choose several students to share and explain their work to the class. Be sure the students sketch a diagram and explain how they decided whether to use the Law of Sines or the Law of Cosines to solve the problem.

Watch Out!

Preventing Errors When students must decide which method to use to solve, watch for students who think the angle is included. Review the definition of included angles with them.

Differentiated Instruction

AL OL ELL

If students struggle with any of the methods shown to solve a triangle,

Then have students discuss in small groups how to choose which method to use when solving a triangle. Have them compare their approaches and develop a brief explanation to help others decide. Then have each group share their conclusions with the class.

3 PRACTICE

Formative Assessment

Use Exercises 1–8 to check for understanding.

Use the chart at the bottom of this page to customize assignments for your students.

4 ASSESS

Yesterday's News Ask students to describe how yesterday's topic, using the Law of Sines, was similar to and was different from today's topic, using the Law of Cosines.

Formative Assessment

Check for student understanding of concepts in Lessons 13-4 and 13-5.

CRM Quiz 2, p. 61

Additional Answers

29a. Sample answer:

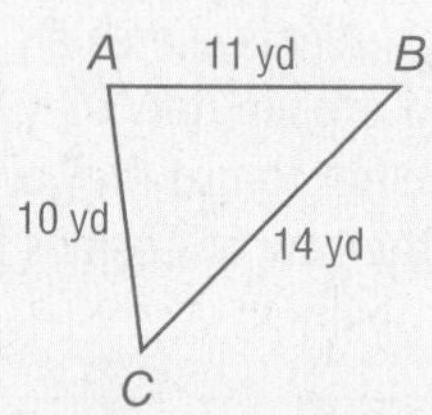

34. $a^2 = (b - x)^2 + h^2$ Use the Pythagorean Theorem for $\triangle DBC$.
$= b^2 - 2bx + x^2 + h^2$
Expand $(b - x)^2$.
$= b^2 - 2bx + c^2$
In $\triangle ADB$, $c^2 = x^2 + h^2$.
$= b^2 - 2b(c \cos A) + c^2$
$\cos A = \frac{x}{c}$, so $x = c \cos A$.
$= b^2 + c^2 - 2bc \cos A$
Commutative Property

37. When two angles and a side are given or when two sides and an angle opposite one of the sides are given, you can use the Law of Sines to solve a triangle. When two sides and an included angle are given or when three sides are given, you can use the Law of Cosines to solve a triangle.

Practice and Problem Solving

● = **Step-by-Step Solutions** begin on page R20. **Extra Practice** begins on page 947.

Examples 1 and 2 pp. 841–842

Solve each triangle. Round side lengths to the nearest tenth and angle measures to the nearest degree.

9. $A \approx 70°$, $B \approx 40°$, $c \approx 3.0$
10. $A \approx 48°$, $C \approx 40°$, $b \approx 18.8$
11. $A \approx 31°$, $B \approx 108°$, $C \approx 41°$
12. $A \approx 102°$, $B \approx 44°$, $C \approx 34°$
13. $a \approx 6.9$, $B \approx 41°$, $C \approx 23°$
14. $c \approx 8.9$, $A \approx 87°$, $B \approx 13°$
15. $F \approx 65°$, $G \approx 94°$, $H \approx 21°$

9.

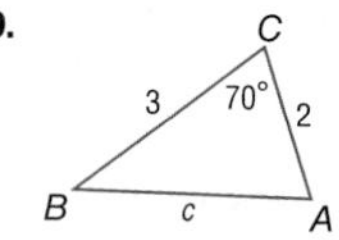

10.

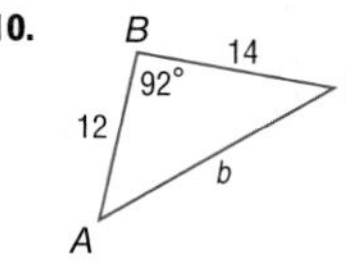

11.

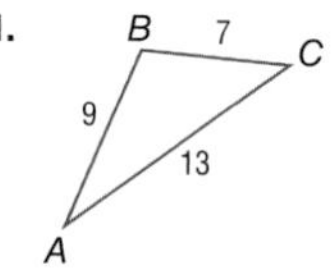

12.

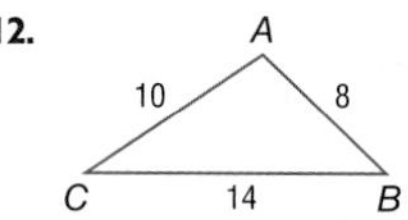

13. $A = 116°, b = 5, c = 3$

14. $C = 80°, a = 9, b = 2$

15. $f = 10, g = 11, h = 4$

16. $w = 20, x = 13, y = 12$

Example 3 p. 843

16. $W \approx 106°$, $X \approx 39°$, $Y \approx 35°$
17. Sines; $C \approx 45°$, $A \approx 85°$, $a \approx 18.2$
18. Cosines; $s \approx 28.9$, $R \approx 42°$, $T \approx 32°$
19. Cosines; $A \approx 27°$, $B \approx 115°$, $C \approx 38°$
20. Sines; $N \approx 53°$, $p \approx 38.2$, $m \approx 28.4$

Determine whether each triangle should be solved by beginning with the Law of *Sines* or the Law of *Cosines*. Then solve the triangle.

17.

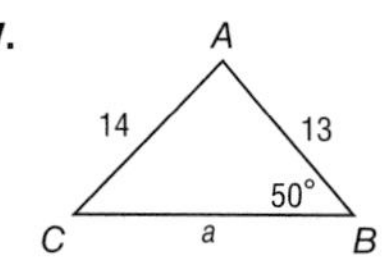

18.

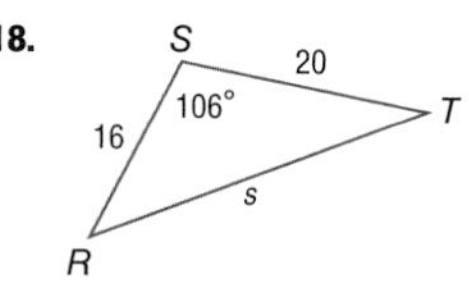

19.

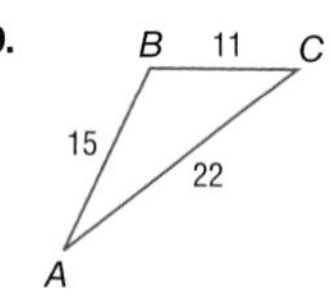

20.

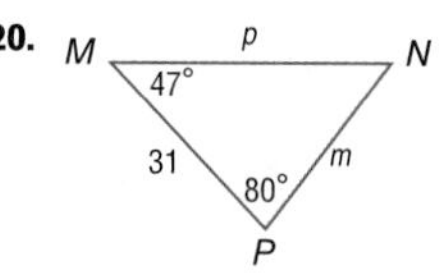

21. Sines; $A \approx 17°$, $B \approx 79°$, $b \approx 6.9$
22. Cosines; $H \approx 48°$, $J = 25°$, $K = 107°$

21. In $\triangle ABC$, $C = 84°$, $c = 7$, and $a = 2$.

22. In $\triangle HJK$, $h = 18$, $j = 10$, and $k = 23$.

23 **EXPLORATION** Refer to the beginning of the lesson. Find the distance between the ship and the shipwreck. Round to the nearest tenth. **514.215 m**

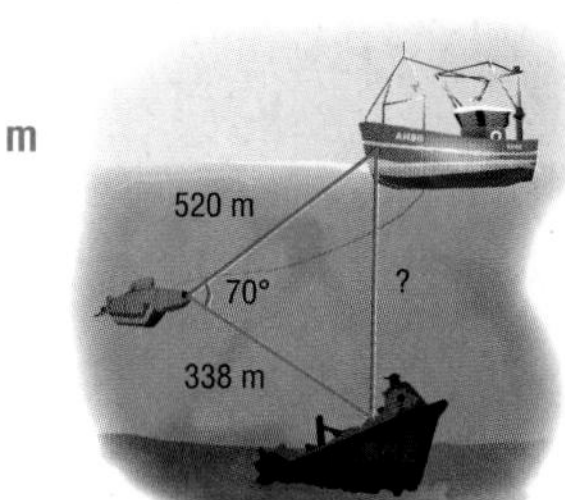

24. GEOMETRY A parallelogram has side lengths 8 centimeters and 12 centimeters. One angle between them measures 42°. To the nearest tenth, what is the length of the shorter diagonal? **8.1 cm**

25. RACING A triangular cross-country course has side lengths 1.8 kilometers, 2 kilometers, and 1.2 kilometers. What are the angles formed between each pair of sides? **81°, 36°, 63°**

B

26. SURVEYING A triangular plot of farm land measures 0.9 by 0.5 by 1.25 miles.

a. If the plot of land is fenced on the border, what will be the angles at which the fences of the three sides meet? Round to the nearest degree. **19°, 37°, 124°**

b. What is the area of the plot of land? **about 0.19 mi²**

27. LAND Some land is in the shape of a triangle. The distances betwen each vertex of the triangle are 140 yd, 210 yd and 300 yd, respectively. Use the Law of Cosines to find the area of the land to the nearest square yard. **about 13,148 yd²**

Problem-Solving Tip

Work Backward When the information needed to solve a problem is not given in an organized manner, begin with what you need to find and arrange the information from end to beginning.

Differentiated Homework Options

Level	Assignment	Two-Day Option	
AL Basic	9–24, 35–55	9–23 odd, 38–41	10–24 even, 35–37, 42–55
OL Core	9–23 odd, 25–31, 33, 35–55	9–24, 38–41	25–33, 35–37, 42–55
BL Advanced	25–52, (optional: 53–55)		

StudyTip

Rounding Sometimes rounding can lead to ambiguous answers, such as a triangle appearing to be 181 degrees.

28. RIDES Two bumper cars at an amusement park ride collide as shown below.

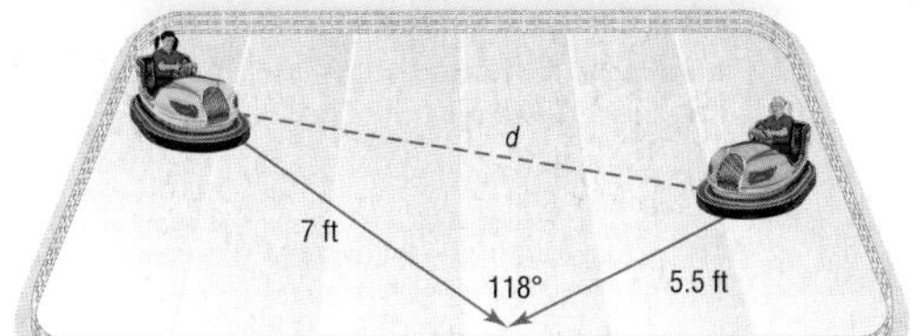

a. How far apart d were the two cars before they collided? **about 10.7 ft**

b. Before the collision, a third car was 10 feet from car 1 and 13 feet from car 2. Describe the angles formed by cars 1, 2, and 3 before the collision. **78°, 49°, 53°**

29. PICNICS A triangular picnic area is 11 yards by 14 yards by 10 yards.

a. Sketch and label a drawing to represent the picnic area. **See margin.**

b. Describe how you could find the area of the picnic area.

c. What is the area? Round to the nearest tenth. **54.6 yd²**

29b. Sample answer: Use the Law of Cosines to find the measure of ∠A. Then use the formula Area $= \frac{1}{2}bc \sin A$.

30. WATERSPORTS A person on a personal watercraft makes a trip from point A to point B to point C traveling 28 miles per hour. She then returns from point C back to her starting point traveling 35 miles per hour. How many minutes did the entire trip take? Round to the nearest tenth. **1.6 min**

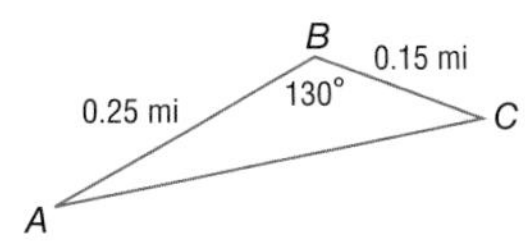

Real-World Link

Personal watercraft were first developed in the 1960s and became popular in the mid 1970s. Today, personal watercraft account for about $\frac{1}{3}$ of all powerboat sales.

Source: Personal Watercraft Industry Association

Solve each triangle. Round side lengths to the nearest tenth and angle measures to the nearest degree.

31.

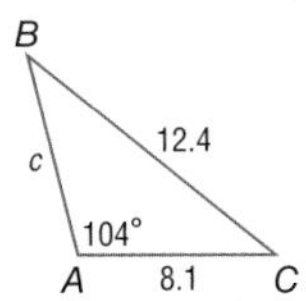

32.

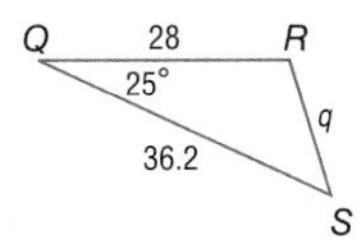

33.

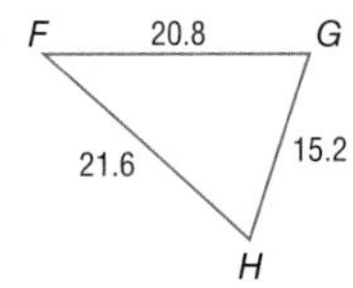

31. $B \approx 39°$, $C \approx 37°$, $c \approx 7.7$
32. $R \approx 107°$, $S \approx 48°$, $q \approx 16.0$
33. $F \approx 42°$, $G \approx 72°$, $H \approx 66°$

H.O.T. Problems

Use Higher-Order Thinking Skills

34. CHALLENGE Use the figure and the Pythagorean Theorem to derive the Law of Cosines. Use the hints below. **See margin.**

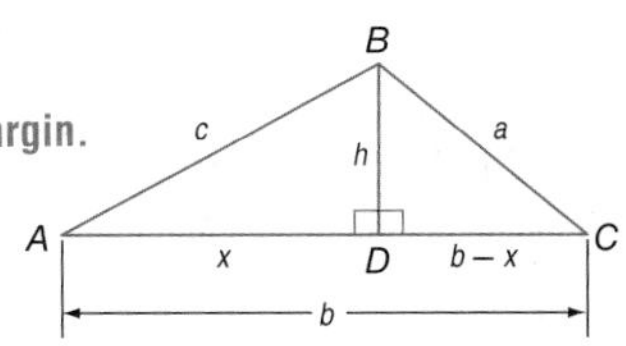

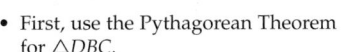

- First, use the Pythagorean Theorem for $\triangle DBC$.
- In $\triangle ADB$, $c^2 = x^2 + h^2$.
- $\cos A = \frac{x}{c}$

35. REASONING Three sides of a triangle measure 10.6 centimeters, 8 centimeters, and 14.5 centimeters. Explain how to find the measure of the largest angle. Then find the measure of the angle to the nearest degree.

36. OPEN ENDED Find three measures of a triangle so that the Law of Cosines can be used to solve the triangle. Then solve the triangle.

37. WRITING IN MATH Compare the circumstances in which you can use the Law of Sines and the Law of Cosines to solve a triangle. **See margin.**

35. The longest side is 14.5 centimeters. Use the Law of Cosines to find the measure of the angle opposite the longest side; 102°.

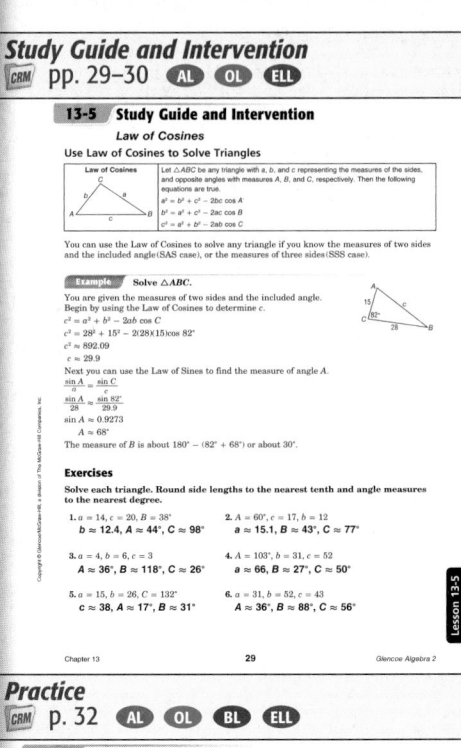

36. Sample answer: In $\triangle ABC$, $A = 40°$, $b = 3$ and $c = 6$. Then $a \approx 4.2$, $B \approx 27°$, and $C \approx 113°$.

Study Guide and Intervention

CRM pp. 29–30 AL OL ELL

13-5 Study Guide and Intervention

Law of Cosines

Use Law of Cosines to Solve Triangles

Law of Cosines	Let $\triangle ABC$ be any triangle with a, b, and c representing the measures of the sides, and opposite angles with measures A, B, and C, respectively. Then the following equations are true. $a^2 = b^2 + c^2 - 2bc \cos A$; $b^2 = a^2 + c^2 - 2ac \cos B$; $c^2 = a^2 + b^2 - 2ab \cos C$

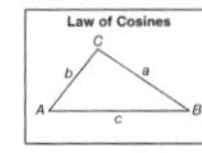

You can use the Law of Cosines to solve any triangle if you know the measures of two sides and the included angle (SAS case), or the measures of three sides (SSS case).

Example Solve $\triangle ABC$.

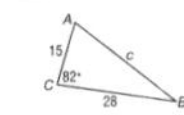

You are given the measures of two sides and the included angle. Begin by using the Law of Cosines to determine c.

$c^2 = a^2 + b^2 - 2ab \cos C$
$c^2 = 28^2 + 15^2 - 2(28)(15)\cos 82°$
$c^2 \approx 892.09$
$c \approx 29.9$

Next you can use the Law of Sines to find the measure of angle A.

$\frac{\sin A}{a} = \frac{\sin C}{c}$
$\frac{\sin A}{28} \approx \frac{\sin 82°}{29.9}$
$\sin A \approx 0.9273$
$A \approx 68°$

The measure of B is about $180° - (82° + 68°)$ or about 30°.

Exercises

Solve each triangle. Round side lengths to the nearest tenth and angle measures to the nearest degree.

1. $a = 14$, $c = 20$, $B = 38°$ **$b \approx 12.4$, $A \approx 44°$, $C \approx 98°$**
2. $A = 60°$, $c = 17$, $b = 12$ **$a \approx 15.1$, $B \approx 43°$, $C \approx 77°$**
3. $a = 4$, $b = 6$, $c = 3$ **$A \approx 36°$, $B \approx 118°$, $C \approx 26°$**
4. $A = 103°$, $b = 31$, $c = 52$ **$a \approx 66$, $B \approx 27°$, $C \approx 50°$**
5. $a = 15$, $b = 26$, $C = 132°$ **$c \approx 38$, $A \approx 17°$, $B \approx 31°$**
6. $a = 31$, $b = 52$, $c = 43$ **$A \approx 36°$, $B \approx 88°$, $C \approx 56°$**

Lesson 13-5

Practice

CRM p. 32 AL OL BL ELL

13-5 Practice

Law of Cosines

Determine whether each triangle should be solved by beginning with the Law of *Sines* or Law of *Cosines*. Then solve the triangle.

1.

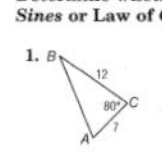

cosines; $c \approx 12.8$, $A \approx 67°$, $B \approx 33°$

2.

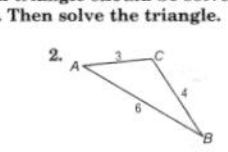

cosines; $A \approx 36°$, $B \approx 26°$, $C \approx 117°$

3.

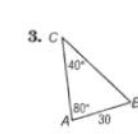

sines; $B = 60°$, $a \approx 46.0$, $b \approx 40.4$

4. $a = 16$, $b = 20$, $C = 54°$ **cosines; $A \approx 51°$, $B \approx 75°$, $c \approx 16.7$**
5. $B = 71°$, $c = 6$, $a = 11$ **cosines; $A \approx 77°$, $C \approx 32°$, $b \approx 10.7$**
6. $A = 37°$, $a = 20$, $b = 18$ **sines; $B \approx 33°$, $C \approx 110°$, $c \approx 31.2$**
7. $C = 35°$, $a = 18$, $b = 24$ **cosines; $A \approx 48°$, $B \approx 97°$, $c \approx 13.9$**
8. $a = 8$, $b = 6$, $c = 9$ **cosines; $A \approx 61°$, $B \approx 41°$, $C \approx 79°$**
9. $A = 23°$, $b = 10$, $c = 12$ **cosines; $B \approx 54°$, $C \approx 103°$, $a \approx 4.8$**
10. $a = 4$, $b = 5$, $c = 8$ **cosines; $A \approx 24°$, $B \approx 31°$, $C \approx 125°$**
11. $B = 46.6°$, $C = 112°$, $b = 13$ **sines; $A = 21°$, $a \approx 6.5$, $c \approx 16.6$**
12. $A = 46.3°$, $a = 35$, $b = 30$ **sines; $B \approx 38°$, $C \approx 95°$, $c \approx 48.2$**
13. $a = 16.4$, $b = 21.1$, $c = 18.5$ **cosines; $A \approx 48°$, $B \approx 74°$, $C \approx 57°$**
14. $C = 43.5°$, $b = 8$, $c = 6$ **sines; $A \approx 70°$, $B \approx 67°$, $a \approx 8.2$**
15. $A = 78.3°$, $b = 7$, $c = 11$ **cosines; $B \approx 36°$, $C \approx 66°$, $a \approx 11.8$**

16. **SATELLITES** Two radar stations 2.4 miles apart are tracking an airplane. The straight-line distance between Station A and the plane is 7.4 miles. The straight-line distance between Station B and the plane is 6.9 miles. What is the angle of elevation from Station A to the plane? Round to the nearest degree. **69°**

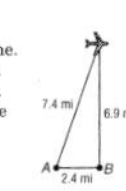

17. **DRAFTING** Marion is using a computer-aided drafting program to produce a drawing for a client. She begins a triangle by drawing a segment 4.2 inches long from point A to point B. From B, she moves 42° degrees counterclockwise from the segment connecting A and B and draws a second segment that is 6.4 inches long, ending at point C. To the nearest tenth, how long is the segment from C to A? **9.9 in.**

Word Problem Practice

CRM p. 33 AL OL BL ELL

13-5 Word Problem Practice

Law of Cosines

1. **POOLS** The Perth County pool has a lifeguard station in both the deep water and shallow water sections of the pool. The distance between each station and the bottom of the slide is known, but the manager would like to calculate more information about the pool setup.

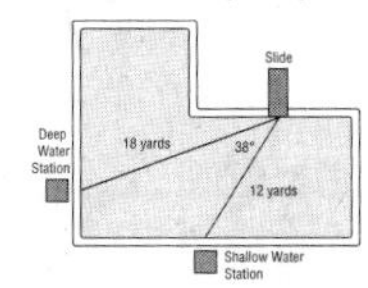

a. When the lifeguards switch positions, the lifeguard at the deep water station swims to the shallow water station. How far does the lifeguard swim? **13.8 yards**

b. If the lifeguard at the deepwater station is directly facing the bottom of the slide, what angle does she need to turn in order to face the lifeguard at the shallow water station? **41.8°**

2. **CAMPING** At Shady Pines Campground, Campsites A and B are situated 80 meters apart. The camp office is 95 meters from Campsite A and 115 meters from Campsite B. When the ranger is standing at the office, what is the angle of separation between Campsites A and B? **43.5°**

3. **SKATING** During a figure skating routine, Jackie and Peter skate apart with an angle of 15° between them. Jackie skates for 5 meters and Peter skates for 7 meters. How far apart are the skaters? **2.5 m**

4. **TECHNOLOGY** Gina's handheld PDA can send and receive e-mails if it is within 40 miles of a transmission tower. On a trip, Gina drives past the transmission tower on Highway 7 for 32 miles, and then she turns onto Oakville Road and drives for another 19 miles.

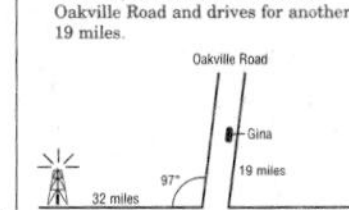

a. Is Gina close enough to the transmission tower to be able to send and receive e-mails? Explain your reasoning. **Yes. She is 39.2 miles from the tower.**

b. If Gina is within range of the tower, how much further can she drive on Oakville Road before she is out of range? If she is out of range and drives back towards Highway 7, how far will she travel before she is back in range? **She is within range and can drive 1.4 miles further.**

Lesson 13-5

Enrichment

CRM p. 34 OL BL

13-5 Enrichment

The Law of Cosines and the Pythagorean Theorem

The Law of Cosines bears strong similarities to the Pythagorean theorem. According to the Law of Cosines, if two sides of a triangle have lengths a and b and if the angle between them has a measure of $x°$, then the length, y, of the third side of the triangle can be found by using the equation

$y^2 = a^2 + b^2 - 2ab \cos x°$.

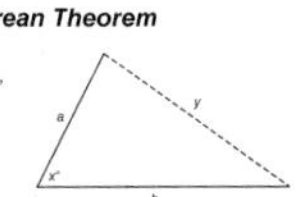

Answer the following questions to clarify the relationship between the Law of Cosines and the Pythagorean theorem.

1. If the value of $x°$ becomes less and less, what number does $\cos x°$ approach? **1**
2. If the value of $x°$ is very close to zero but then increases, what happens to $\cos x°$ as $x°$ approaches 90°? **decreases, approaches 0**
3. If $x°$ equals 90°, what is the value of $\cos x°$? What does the equation of $y^2 = a^2 + b^2 - 2ab \cos x°$ simplify to if $x°$ equals 90°? **0, $y^2 = a^2 + b^2$**

Additional Answers

45. $\sin \theta = \frac{5\sqrt{89}}{89}$, $\cos \theta = \frac{8\sqrt{89}}{89}$,
$\tan \theta = \frac{5}{8}$, $\csc \theta = \frac{\sqrt{89}}{5}$,
$\sec \theta = \frac{\sqrt{89}}{8}$, $\cot \theta = \frac{8}{5}$

46. $\sin \theta = \frac{-\sqrt{5}}{5}$, $\cos \theta = \frac{-2\sqrt{5}}{5}$,
$\tan \theta = 0.5$, $\csc \theta = -\sqrt{5}$,
$\sec \theta = \frac{-\sqrt{5}}{2}$, $\cot \theta = 2$

47. $\sin \theta = -\frac{3\sqrt{13}}{13}$, $\cos \theta = \frac{2\sqrt{13}}{13}$,
$\tan \theta = -1.5$, $\csc \theta = \frac{-\sqrt{13}}{3}$,
$\sec \theta = \frac{\sqrt{13}}{2}$, $\cot \theta = -\frac{2}{3}$

53.

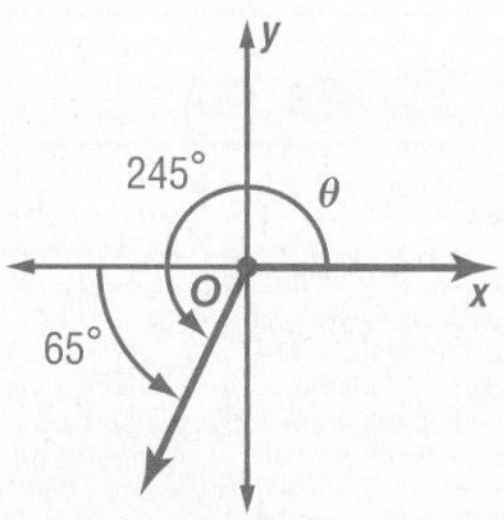

54.

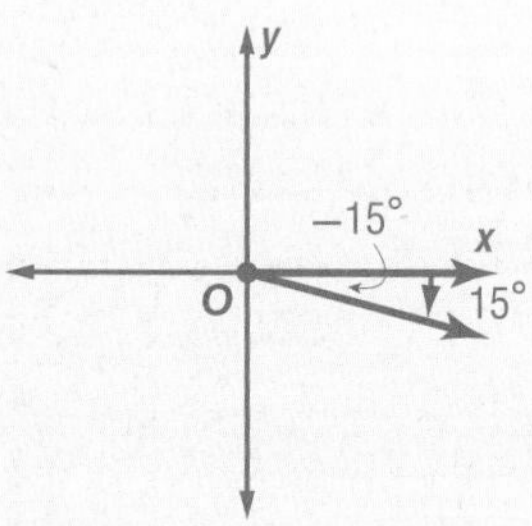

55.

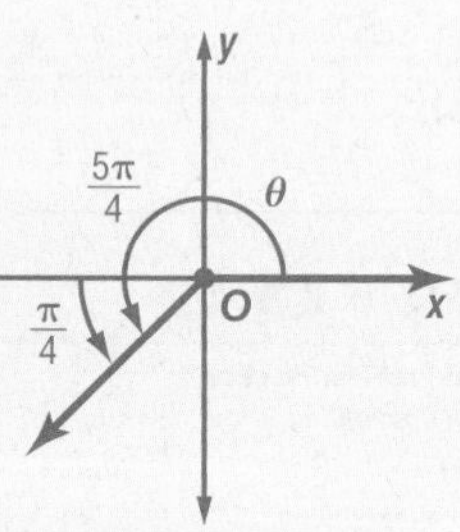

NGSSS PRACTICE 912.A.8.5, 912.G.5.3, 912.A.6.5

38. SAT/ACT If c and d are different positive integers and $4c + d = 26$, what is the sum of all possible values of c? **D**

A. 6 C. 15
B. 10 D. 21

39. If $6^y = 21$, what is y? **G**

F. $\log 12 - \log 6$
H. $\frac{\log 6}{\log 21}$
G. $\frac{\log 21}{\log 6}$
I. $\log\left(\frac{6}{21}\right)$

40. GEOMETRY Find the perimeter of the figure. **C**

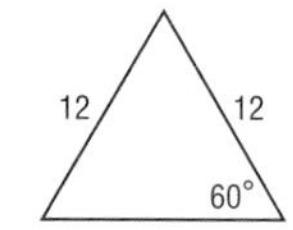

A. 24 B. 30 C. 36 D. 48

41. THINK SOLVE EXPLAIN **SHORT RESPONSE** Solve the equation below for x. **4, $\frac{23}{15}$**

$$\frac{1}{x-1} + \frac{5}{8} = \frac{23}{6x}$$

Spiral Review

Find the area of $\triangle ABC$ to the nearest tenth. (Lesson 13-4)

42. **65.2 cm²**

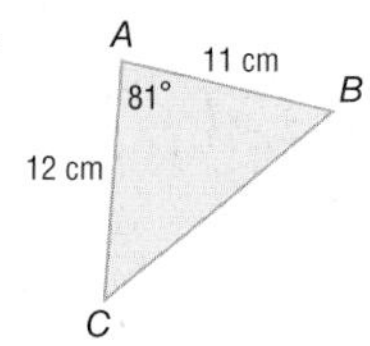

43. **7.5 yd²**

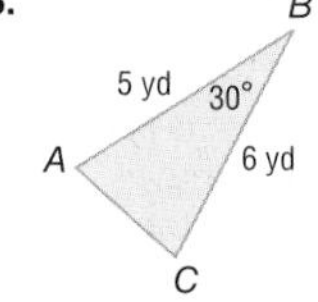

44. **35.1 ft²**

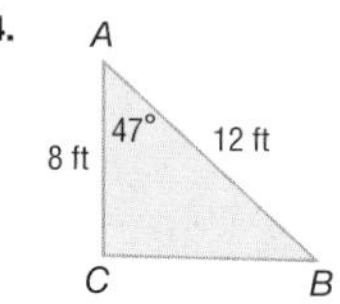

The terminal side of θ in standard position contains each point. Find the exact values of the six trigonometric functions of θ. (Lesson 13-3) **45–47. See margin.**

45. (8, 5) **46.** (−4, −2) **47.** (6, −9)

48. EDUCATION The Millersburg school board is negotiating a pay raise with the teachers' union. Three of the administrators have salaries of \$90,000 each. However, a majority of the teachers have salaries of about \$45,000 per year. (Lesson 12-2)

a. You are a member of the school board and would like to show that the current salaries are reasonable. Would you quote the mean, median, or mode as the "average" salary to justify your claim? Explain. **Mean; it is highest.**

b. You are the head of the teachers' union and maintain that a pay raise is in order. Which of the mean, median, or mode would you quote to justify your claim? Explain your reasoning. **Mode; it is lower and is what most of the employees earn. It reflects the most representative worker.**

49. CELL PHONES A person using a cell phone can be located with respect to three cellular towers. In a coordinate system where a unit represents one mile, a caller is determined to be 50 miles from the tower at the origin. He is also 40 miles from a tower at (0, 30) and 13 miles from a tower at (35, 18). Where is the caller? (Lesson 10-7) **(40, 30)**

Without writing the equation in standard form, state whether the graph of each equation is a *parabola, circle, ellipse,* or *hyperbola.* (Lesson 10-6)

50. $x^2 + y^2 - 8x - 6y + 5 = 0$ **circle**
51. $3x^2 - 2y^2 + 32y - 134 = 0$ **hyperbola**
52. $y^2 + 18y - 2x = -84$ **parabola**

Skills Review

Sketch each angle. Then find its reference angle. (Lesson 13-3) **53–55. See margin.**

53. 245° **54.** −15° **55.** $\frac{5}{4}\pi$

Differentiated Instruction OL BL

Extension Have students use the Law of Cosines to attempt to solve a "triangle" with sides 5, 12, and 18 (such a triangle does not exist). Have them explain what they discover and what it means. Students will get an error when attempting to find the inverse cosine because the value is not between −1 and 1. This means that no such triangle exists.

NGSSS 912.T.1.1, 912.T.2.1, 912.T.2.2

Solve $\triangle XYZ$ by using the given measurements. Round measures of sides to the nearest tenth and measures of angles to the nearest degree. (Lesson 13-1)

1. $X = 25°$, $y = 34.3$, $z = 37.9$
2. $Y = 65°$, $y = 17.2$, $z = 18.9$

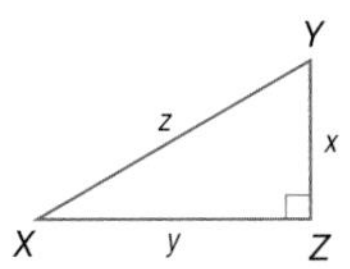

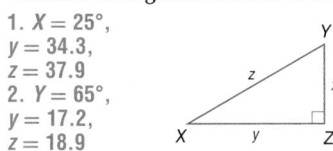

1. $Y = 65°, x = 16$ **2.** $X = 25°, x = 8$

3. Find the values of the six trigonometric functions for angle θ. (Lesson 13-1) See margin.

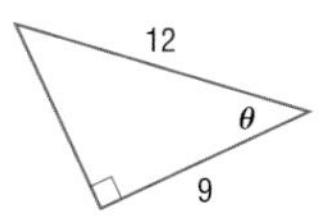

4. Draw an angle measuring $-80°$ in standard position. (Lesson 13-2) See margin.

Rewrite each degree measure in radians and each radian measure in degrees. (Lesson 13-2)

5. $215°$ $\frac{43\pi}{36}$ **6.** $-350°$ $-\frac{35\pi}{18}$

7. $\frac{8\pi}{5}$ $288°$ **8.** $\frac{9\pi}{2}$ $810°$

9. NGSSS PRACTICE What is the length of the arc below rounded to the nearest tenth? (Lesson 13-2) C

A. 4.2 cm

B. 17.1 cm

C. 53.9 cm

D. 2638.9 cm

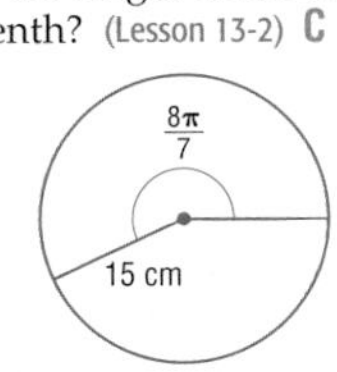

Find the exact value of each trigonometric function. (Lesson 13-3)

10. $\tan \pi$ 0 **11.** $\cos \frac{3\pi}{4}$ $-\frac{\sqrt{2}}{2}$

12, 13. See Chapter 13 Answer Appendix.

The terminal side of θ in standard position contains each point. Find the exact values of the six trigonometric functions of θ. (Lesson 13-3)

12. $(0, -5)$ **13.** $(6, 8)$

14. GARDEN Lana has a garden in the shape of a triangle as pictured below. She wants to fill the garden with top soil. What is the area of the triangle? (Lesson 13-4) about 38.8 m^2

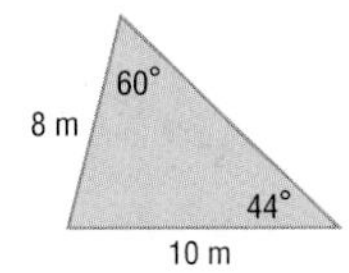

Determine whether each triangle has *no* solution, *one* solution, or *two* solutions. Then solve the triangle. Round side lengths to the nearest tenth and angle measures the nearest degree. (Lesson 13-4)

15. $A = 38°, a = 18, c = 25$ See Chapter 13 Answer Appendix.

16. $A = 65°, a = 5, b = 7$ no solution

17. $A = 115°, a = 12, b = 8$ one solution: $B = 37°$, $C = 28°$, $c = 6.2$

Solve each triangle. Round side lengths to the nearest tenth and angle measures to the nearest degree. (Lesson 13-5) 19. $A = 40°$, $C = 35°$, $c = 10.7$

18.

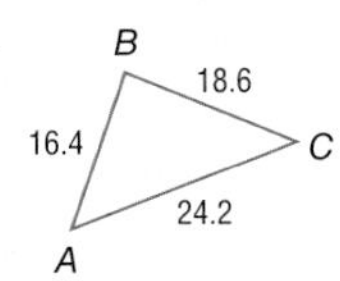

$A = 50°$, $B = 87°$, $C = 43°$

19.

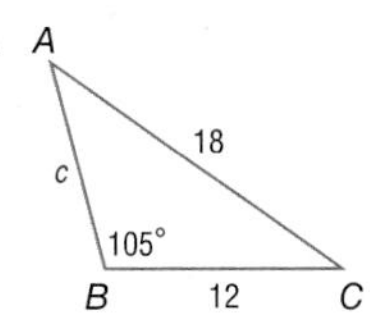

20. Eric and Zach are camping. Erik leaves Zach at the campsite and walks 4.5 miles. He then turns at a 120°angle and walks another 2.5 miles. If Eric were to walk directly back to Zach, how far would he walk? (Lesson 13-5) about 6.1 mi

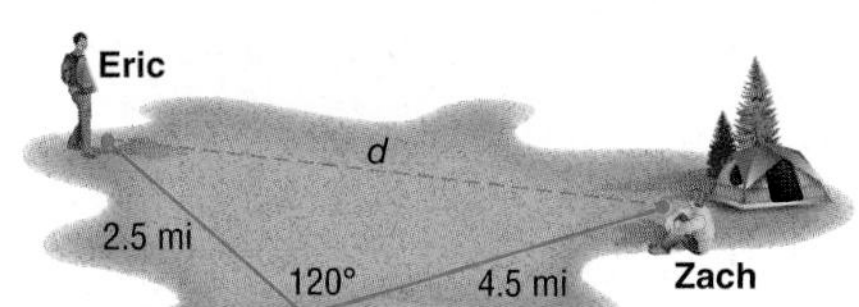

21. NGSSS PRACTICE Suppose θ is an angle in standard position with $\cos \theta > 0$. In which quadrant(s) does the terminal side of θ lie? (Lesson 13-2) I

F. I

G. II

H. III

I. I and IV

CHAPTER 13 Mid-Chapter Quiz

Formative Assessment

Use the Mid-Chapter Quiz to assess students' progress in the first half of the chapter.

For problems answered incorrectly, have students review the lessons indicated in parentheses.

ExamView Assessment Suite Customize and create multiple versions of your Mid-Chapter Test and their answer keys.

FOLDABLES Follow-Up

Before students complete the Mid-Chapter Test, encourage them to review the information for Lessons 13-1 through 13-5 in their Foldables.

Additional Answers

3. $\sin \theta = \frac{\sqrt{7}}{4}$, $\cos \theta = \frac{3}{4}$, $\tan \theta = \frac{\sqrt{7}}{3}$, $\csc \theta = \frac{4\sqrt{7}}{7}$, $\sec \theta = \frac{4}{3}$, $\cot \theta = \frac{3\sqrt{7}}{7}$

4.

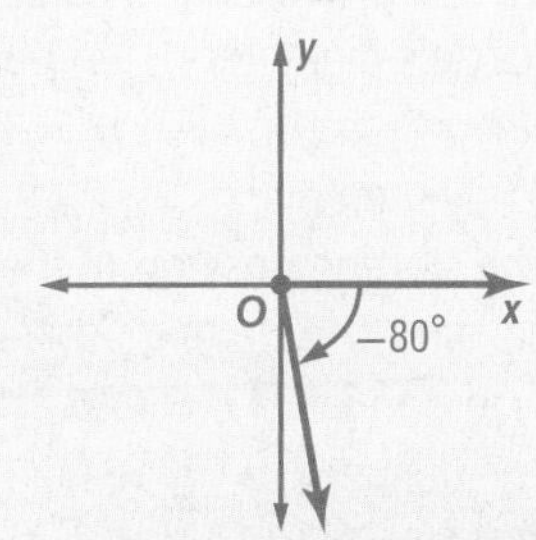

Intervention Planner

Tier 1 On Level	Tier 2 Strategic Intervention approaching grade level	Tier 3 Intensive Intervention 2 or more grades below level
If students miss about 25% of the exercises,	**If** students miss about 50% of the exercises,	**If** students miss about 75% of the exercises,
Then choose a resource:	**Then** choose a resource:	**Then** use *Math Triumphs, Alg. 2*, Ch. 6
SE Lessons 13-1, 13-2, 13-3, 13-4, and 13-5 **CRM** Skills Practice, pp. 7, 13, 19, 25, and 31 **TE** Chapter Project, p. 804	**CRM** Study Guide and Intervention, Chapter 13, pp. 5, 11, 17, 23, and 29	
FL Math Online Self-Check Quiz	FL Math Online Extra Examples, Personal Tutor, Homework Help	FL Math Online Extra Examples, Personal Tutor, Homework Help, Review Vocabulary

13-6 Lesson Notes

1 FOCUS

Vertical Alignment

Before Lesson 13-6
Evaluate trigonometric functions using reference angles.

Lesson 13-6
Find values of trigonometric functions based on the unit circle. Use the properties of periodic functions to evaluate trigonometric functions.

After Lesson 13-6
Sketch and interpret graphs of the sine and cosine functions.

2 TEACH

Scaffolding Questions

Have students read the *Why?* section of the lesson.

Ask:

- Use the maximum and minimum heights of the pedal to find the diameter of the circle. diameter = maximum − minimum = 18 − 4 = 14 in.
- Use the height of the circle's center to find the circle's diameter. The radius is 18 − 11 = 7 in., or 11 − 4 = 7 in., so the diameter is 2 • 7 = 14 in.
- What is the starting position of the pedal? Explain. The starting position would correspond with $t = 0$ seconds; at that time the pedal is at the top of the diagram.

13-6 Circular Functions

Then
You evaluated trigonometric functions using reference angles. (Lesson 13-3)

Now
- Find values of trigonometric functions based on the unit circle.
- Use the properties of periodic functions to evaluate trigonometric functions.

NGSSS
MA.912.T.1.5 Make connections between right triangle ratios, trigonometric functions, and circular functions.
MA.912.T.1.8 Solve real-world problems involving applications of trigonometric functions using graphing technology when appropriate.

New Vocabulary
unit circle
circular function
periodic function
cycle
period

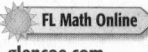

FL Math Online
glencoe.com

Why?

The pedals on a bicycle rotate as the bike is being ridden. The height of a pedal is a function of time, as shown in the figure at the right.

Notice that the pedal makes one complete rotation every two seconds.

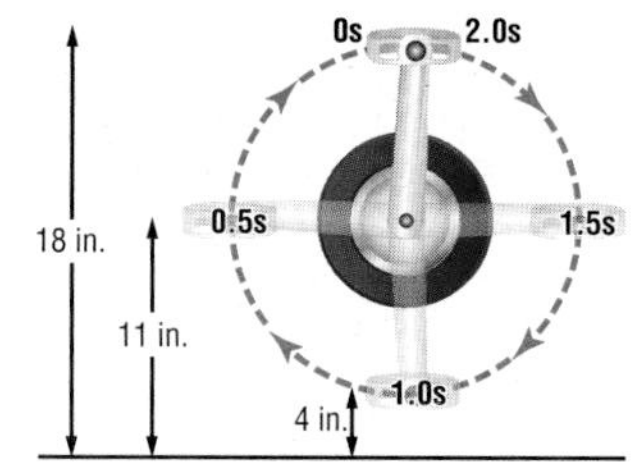

Circular Functions A **unit circle** is a circle with a radius of 1 unit centered at the origin on the coordinate plane. You can use a point P on the unit circle to generalize sine and cosine functions.

$$\sin \theta = \frac{y}{r} = \frac{y}{1} \text{ or } y \qquad \cos \theta = \frac{x}{r} = \frac{x}{1} \text{ or } x$$

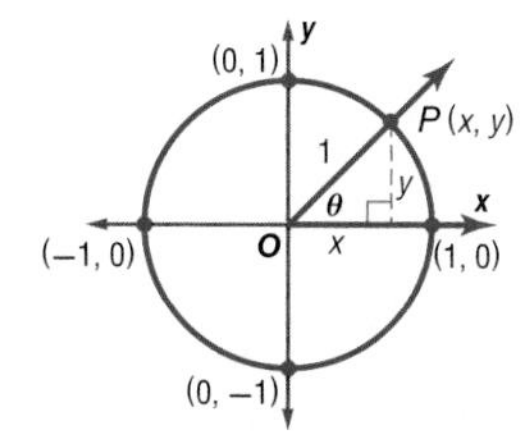

So, the values of $\sin \theta$ and $\cos \theta$ are the y-coordinate and x-coordinate, respectively, of the point where the terminal side of θ intersects the unit circle.

Key Concept — Functions on a Unit Circle

Words If the terminal side of an angle θ in standard position intersects the unit circle at $P(x, y)$, then $\cos \theta = x$ and $\sin \theta = y$.

Symbols $P(x, y) = P(\cos \theta, \sin \theta)$

Example If $\theta = 120°$, $P(x, y) = P(\cos 120°, \sin 120°)$.

Model

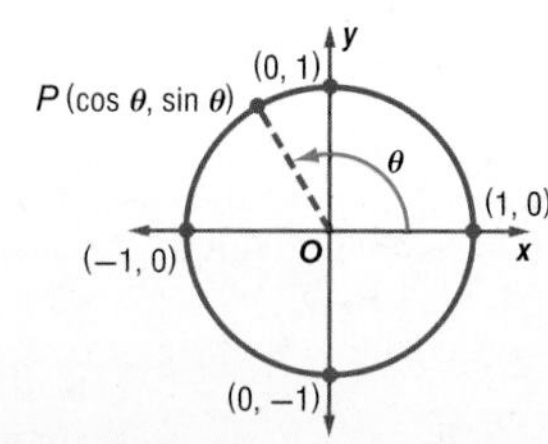

Both $\cos \theta = x$ and $\sin \theta = y$ are functions of θ. Because they are defined using a unit circle, they are called **circular functions**.

EXAMPLE 1 Find Sine and Cosine Given a Point on the Unit Circle

The terminal side of angle θ in standard position intersects the unit circle at $P\left(\frac{1}{2}, \frac{\sqrt{3}}{2}\right)$. Find $\cos \theta$ and $\sin \theta$.

$$P\left(\frac{1}{2}, \frac{\sqrt{3}}{2}\right) = P(\cos \theta, \sin \theta)$$

$$\cos \theta = \frac{1}{2} \qquad \sin \theta = \frac{\sqrt{3}}{2}$$

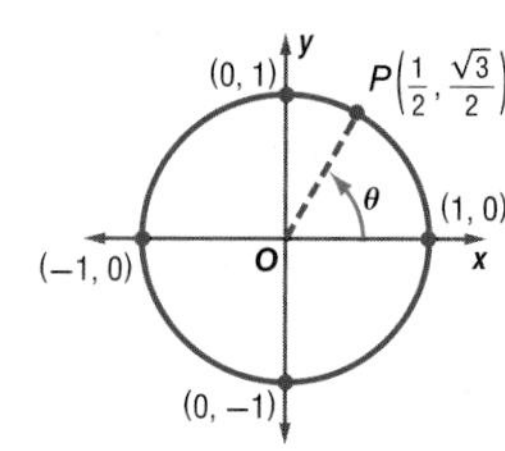

Guided Practice

1. The terminal side of angle θ in standard position intersects the unit circle at $P\left(\frac{3}{5}, -\frac{4}{5}\right)$. Find $\cos \theta$ and $\sin \theta$. $\cos \theta = \frac{3}{5}$, $\sin \theta = -\frac{4}{5}$

Personal Tutor glencoe.com

Lesson 13-6 Resources

Resource	Approaching-Level	On-Level	Beyond-Level	English Learners
Teacher Edition	• Differentiated Instruction, p. 850	• Differentiated Instruction, pp. 850, 854	• Differentiated Instruction, p. 854	
Chapter Resource Masters	• Study Guide and Intervention, pp. 35–36 • Skills Practice, p. 37 • Practice, p. 38 • Word Problem Practice, p. 39	• Study Guide and Intervention, pp. 35–36 • Skills Practice, p. 37 • Practice, p. 38 • Word Problem Practice, p. 39 • Enrichment, p. 40	• Practice, p. 38 • Word Problem Practice, p. 39 • Enrichment, p. 40	• Study Guide and Intervention, pp. 35–36 • Skills Practice, p. 37 • Practice, p. 38 • Word Problem Practice, p. 39
Transparencies	• 5-Minute Check Transparency 13-6	• 5-Minute Check Transparency 13-6	• 5-Minute Check Transparency 13-6	• 5-Minute Check Transparency 13-6
Other	• Study Notebook	• Study Notebook	• Study Notebook	• Study Notebook

Periodic Functions A **periodic function** has y-values that repeat at regular intervals. One complete pattern is a **cycle**, and the horizontal length of one cycle is a **period**.

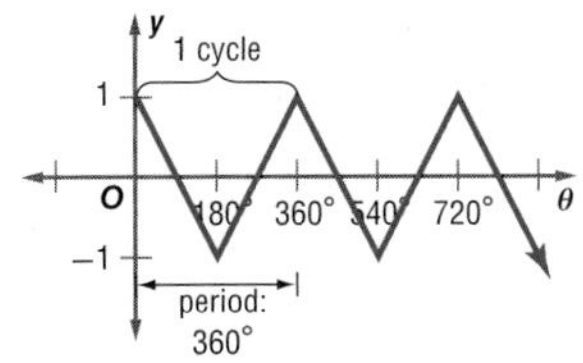

θ	y
0°	1
180°	−1
360°	1
540°	−1
720°	1

The cycle repeats every 360°.

StudyTip

Cycles A cycle can begin at any point on the graph of a periodic function. In Example 2, if the beginning of the cycle is at $\frac{\pi}{2}$, then the pattern repeats at $\frac{3\pi}{2}$. The period is $\frac{3\pi}{2} - \frac{\pi}{2}$ or π.

EXAMPLE 2 Identify the Period

Determine the period of the function.

The pattern repeats at π, 2π, and so on. So, the period is π.

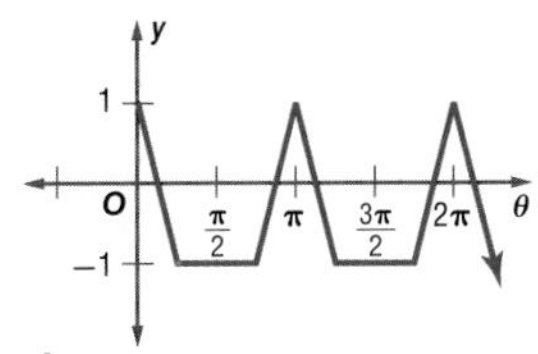

Guided Practice

2. Graph a function with a period of 4. See margin.

Personal Tutor glencoe.com

The rotations of wheels, pedals, carousels, and objects in space are all periodic.

Real-World Link

Most competitive cyclists pedal at rates of more than 200 rotations per minute. Most other people pedal at between 90 and 120 rotations per minute.

Source: SpringerLink

Real-World EXAMPLE 3 Use Trigonometric Functions

CYCLING Refer to the beginning of the lesson. The height of a bicycle pedal varies periodically as a function of time, as shown in the figure.

a. Make a table showing the height of a bicycle pedal at 0, 0.5, 1.0, 1.5, 2.0, 2.5, and 3.0 seconds.

At 0 seconds, the pedal is 18 inches high. At 0.5 second, the pedal is 11 inches high. At 1.0 second, the pedal is 4 inches high, and so on.

Time (s)	Height (in.)
0	18
0.5	11
1.0	4
1.5	11
2.0	18
2.5	11
3.0	4

b. Identify the period of the function.

The period is the time it takes to complete one rotation. So, the period is 2 seconds.

c. Graph the function. Let the horizontal axis represent the time t and the vertical axis represent the height h in inches that the pedal is from the ground.

The maximum height of the pedal is 18 inches, and the minimum height is 4 inches. Because the period of the function is 2 seconds, the pattern of the graph repeats in intervals of 2 seconds.

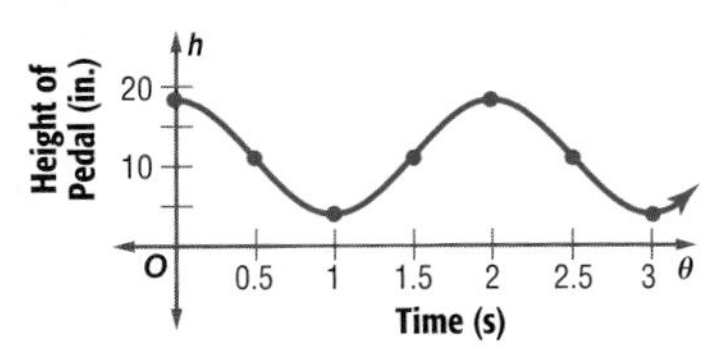

Guided Practice

3. CYCLING Another cyclist pedals the same bike at a rate of 1 revolution per second.

A. Make a table showing the height of a bicycle pedal at times 0, 0.5, 1.0, 1.5, 2.0, 2.5, and 3.0 seconds.

B. Identify the period and graph the function. 1; See margin for graph.

Personal Tutor glencoe.com

3A.

Time (s)	Height of Pedal (in.)
0	18
0.5	4
1.0	18
1.5	4
2.0	18
2.5	4
3.0	18

Additional Answers (Guided Practice)

2.

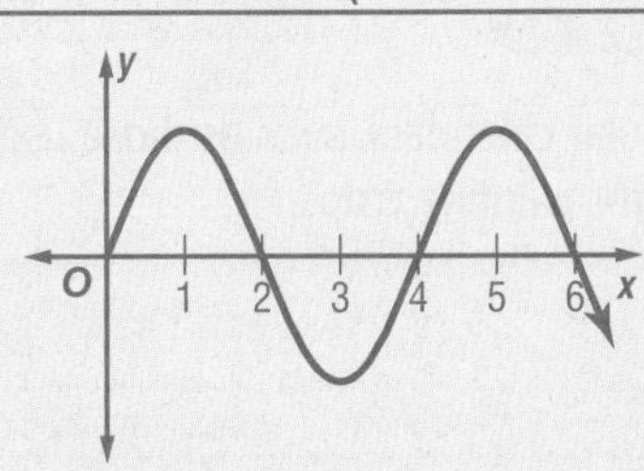

3B.

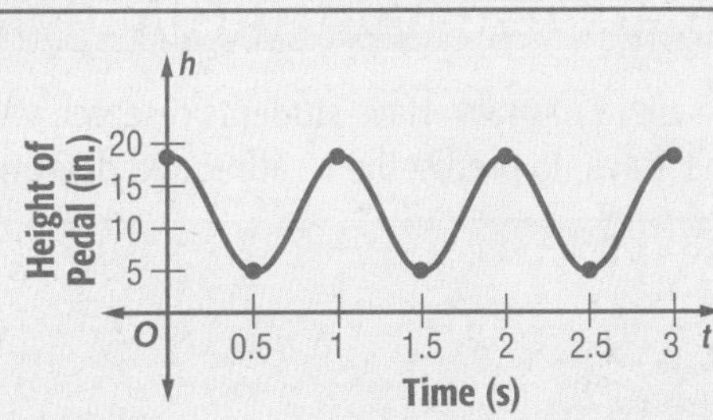

Circular Functions

Example 1 Shows how to find the sine and cosine of a point on the unit circle.

Formative Assessment

Use the Guided Practice exercises after each example to determine students' understanding of concepts.

Additional Example

1 The terminal side of angle θ in standard position intersects the unit circle at $P\left(\frac{\sqrt{7}}{4}, \frac{3}{4}\right)$. Find $\cos\theta$ and $\sin\theta$. $\sin\theta = \frac{3}{4}$, $\cos\theta = \frac{\sqrt{7}}{4}$.

Additional Examples also in Interactive Classroom PowerPoint® Presentations

IWB INTERACTIVE WHITEBOARD READY

Periodic Functions

Example 2 shows how to use a graph to identify the period of the function.
Example 3 shows how to solve a real-world problem using the periodic nature of trigonometric functions.
Example 4 shows how to find the value of a trigonometric function using the period of the function.

Additional Example

2 Determine the period of the function. $\frac{\pi}{3}$

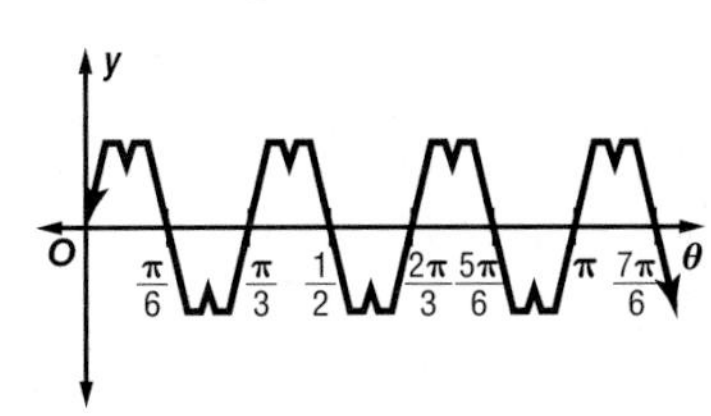

Additional Examples

3 **CYCLING** Refer to the application at the beginning of the lesson. The height of a bicycle pedal varies periodically as a function of the time, as shown in the figure.

a. Make a table showing the height of a bicycle pedal at 3.0, 3.5, 4.0, 4.5, and 5.0 seconds.

Time (s)	Height (in.)
3.0	4
3.5	11
4.0	18
4.5	11
5.0	4

b. Identify the period of the function. 2 seconds

c. Graph the function. Let the horizontal axis represent the time t and the vertical axis represent the height h in inches that the pedal is from the ground.

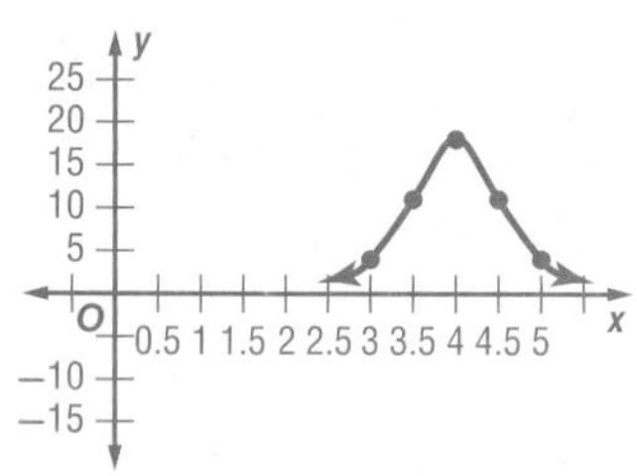

4 Find the exact value of each function.

a. $\cos 690°$ $\frac{\sqrt{3}}{2}$

b. $\sin\left(-\frac{3\pi}{4}\right)$ $-\frac{\sqrt{2}}{2}$

TEACH with TECH

AUDIO RECORDING Have students create audio recordings explaining how to find the exact value of a trigonometric function for an angle greater than 360° (or less than −360°). Give students specific examples to explain.

StudyTip

Sine and Cosine To help you remember that for (x, y) on a unit circle, $x = \cos\theta$ and $y = \sin\theta$, notice that alphabetically x comes before y and *cosine* comes before *sine*.

The exact values of $\cos\theta$ and $\sin\theta$ for special angles are shown on the unit circle at the right. The cosine values are the x-coordinates of the points on the unit circle, and the sine values are the y-coordinates.

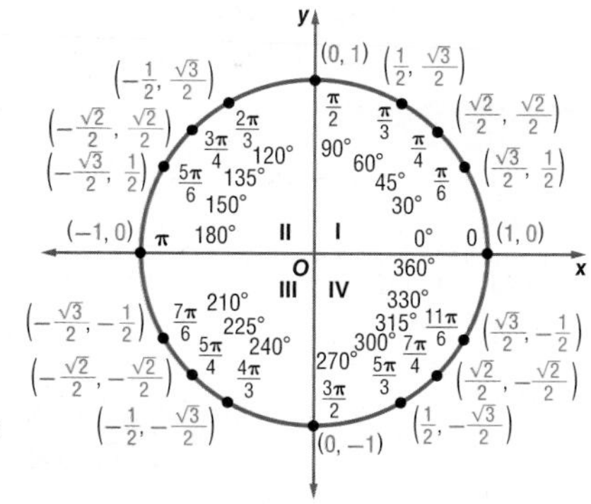

You can use this information to graph the sine and cosine functions. Let the horizontal axis represent the values of θ and the vertical axis represent the values of $\sin\theta$ or $\cos\theta$.

The cycles of the sine and cosine functions repeat every 360°. So, they are periodic functions. The period of each function is 360° or 2π.

Consider the points on the unit circle for $\theta = 45°$, $\theta = 150°$, and $\theta = 270°$.

$(\cos 45°, \sin 45°) = \left(\frac{\sqrt{2}}{2}, \frac{\sqrt{2}}{2}\right)$

$(\cos 150°, \sin 150°) = \left(-\frac{\sqrt{3}}{2}, \frac{1}{2}\right)$

$(\cos 270°, \sin 270°) = (0, -1)$

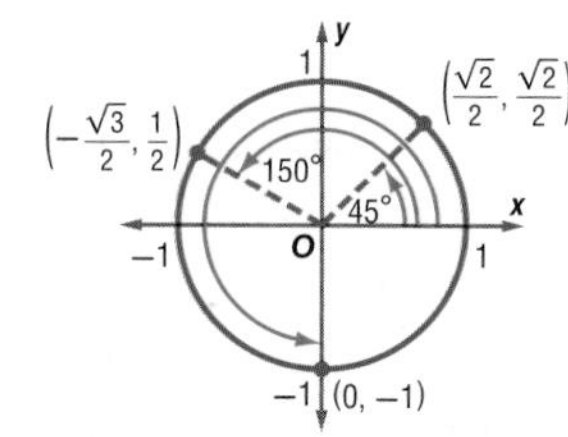

StudyTip

Radians The sine and cosine functions can also be graphed using radians as the units on the θ-axis.

These points can also be shown on the graphs of the sine and cosine functions.

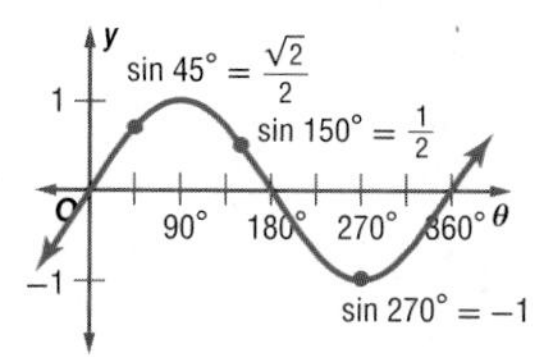

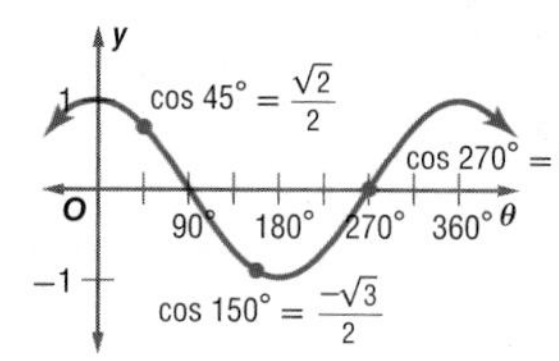

Since the period of the sine and cosine functions is 360°, the values repeat every 360°. So, $\sin(x + 360°) = \sin x$, and $\cos(x + 360°) = \cos x$.

EXAMPLE 4 Evaluate Trigonometric Functions

Find the exact value of each function.

a. $\cos 480°$

$$\cos 480° = \cos(120° + 360°)$$
$$= \cos 120°$$
$$= -\frac{1}{2}$$

b. $\sin\frac{11\pi}{4}$

$$\sin\frac{11\pi}{4} = \sin\left(\frac{3\pi}{4} + \frac{8\pi}{4}\right)$$
$$= \sin\frac{3\pi}{4}$$
$$= \frac{\sqrt{2}}{2}$$

Guided Practice

4A. $\cos\left(-\frac{3\pi}{4}\right)$ $-\frac{\sqrt{2}}{2}$

4B. $\sin 420°$ $\frac{\sqrt{3}}{2}$

Personal Tutor glencoe.com

Differentiated Instruction

AL OL

Naturalist Learners Have students research various kinds of circular calendars, such as those used by the Maya, to predict the weather and determine the best time for planting crops.

850 Chapter 13 Trigonometric Functions

Check Your Understanding

Example 1 p. 848

The terminal side of angle θ in standard position intersects the unit circle at each point P. Find $\cos\theta$ and $\sin\theta$.

1. $P\left(\frac{15}{17}, \frac{8}{17}\right)$ $\cos\theta = \frac{15}{17}, \sin\theta = \frac{8}{17}$

2. $P\left(-\frac{\sqrt{2}}{2}, \frac{\sqrt{2}}{2}\right)$ $\cos\theta = -\frac{\sqrt{2}}{2}, \sin\theta = \frac{\sqrt{2}}{2}$

Example 2 p. 849

Determine the period of each function.

3. 2

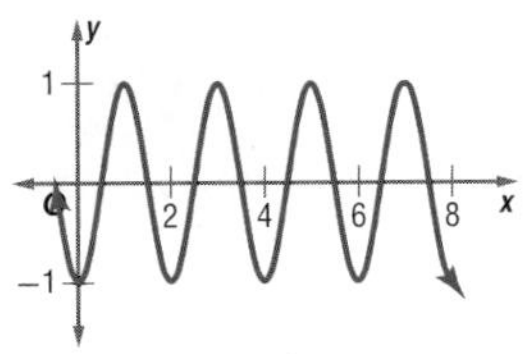

4. 4π

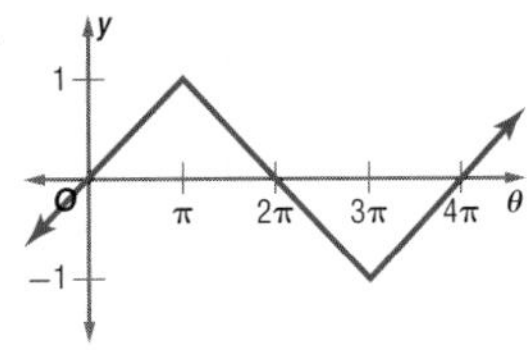

Example 3 p. 849

5. SWINGS The height of a swing varies periodically as the function of time. The swing goes forward and reaches its high point of 6 feet. It then goes backward and reaches 6 feet again. Its lowest point is 2 feet. The time it takes to swing from its high point to its low point is 1 second.

a. How long does it take for the swing to go forward and back one time? **4 seconds**

b. Graph the height of the swing h as a function of time t. **See margin.**

Example 4 p. 850

Find the exact value of each function.

6. $\sin\frac{13\pi}{6}$ $\frac{1}{2}$

7. $\sin(-60°)$ $-\frac{\sqrt{3}}{2}$

8. $\cos 540°$ -1

Practice and Problem Solving

● = **Step-by-Step Solutions** begin on page R20.
Extra Practice begins on page 947.

Example 1 p. 848

The terminal side of angle θ in standard position intersects the unit circle at each point P. Find $\cos\theta$ and $\sin\theta$.

9. $P\left(\frac{6}{10}, -\frac{8}{10}\right)$ $\cos\theta = \frac{3}{5}, \sin\theta = -\frac{4}{5}$

10. $P\left(-\frac{10}{26}, -\frac{24}{26}\right)$ $\cos\theta = -\frac{5}{13}, \sin\theta = -\frac{12}{13}$

11. $P\left(\frac{\sqrt{3}}{2}, \frac{1}{2}\right)$ $\cos\theta = \frac{\sqrt{3}}{2}, \sin\theta = \frac{1}{2}$

12. $P\left(\frac{\sqrt{6}}{5}, \frac{\sqrt{19}}{5}\right)$ $\cos\theta = \frac{\sqrt{6}}{5}, \sin\theta = \frac{\sqrt{19}}{5}$

Example 2 p. 849

Determine the period of each function.

13. 3

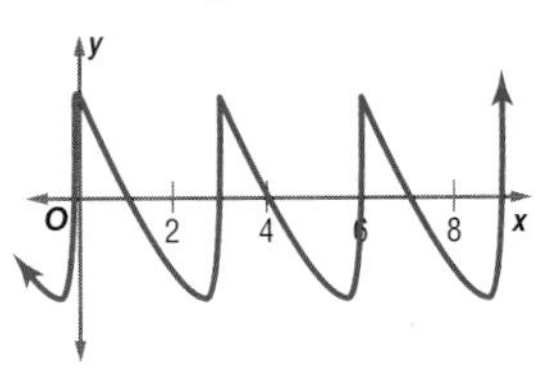

14. 8

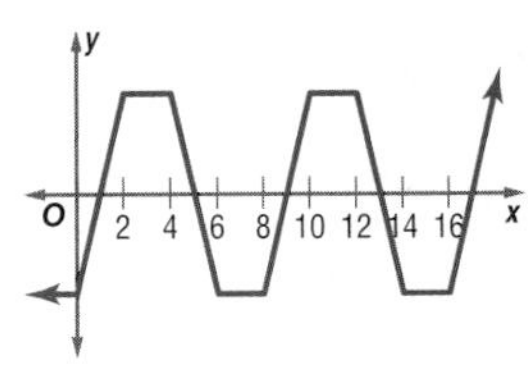

15. 12

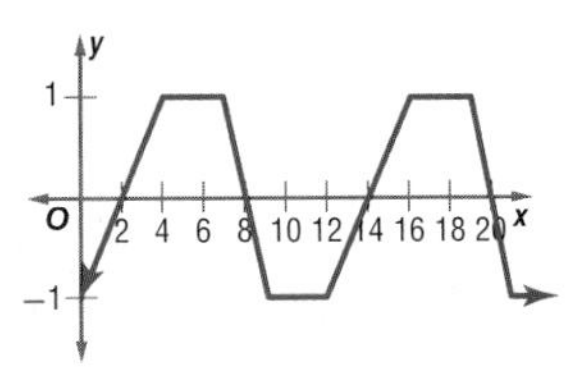

16. 6

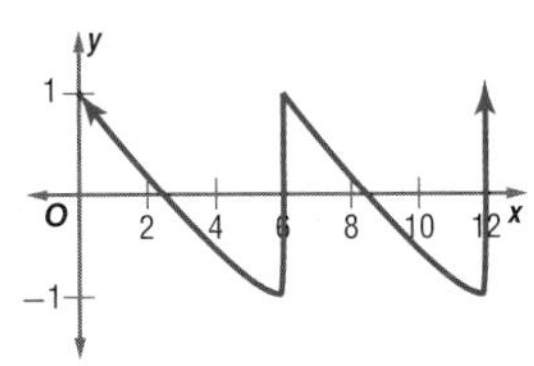

3 PRACTICE

Formative Assessment

Use Exercises 1–8 to check for understanding.

Then use the chart at the bottom of this page to customize assignments for your students.

Additional Answer

5b. Sample answer:

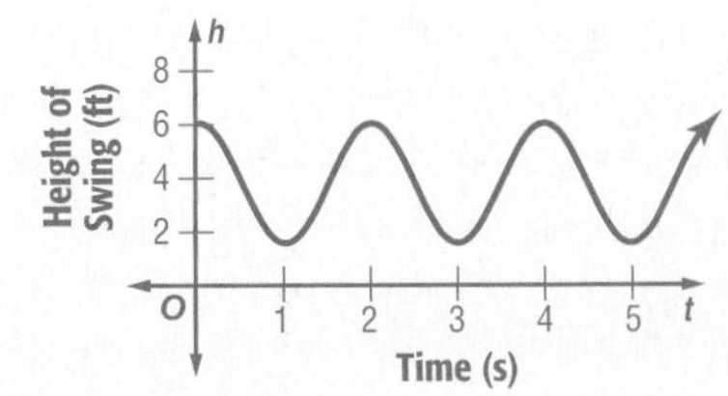

Differentiated Homework Options

Level	Assignment	Two-Day Option	
AL Basic	9–25, 37, 39–62	9–25 odd, 42–46	10–24 even, 37, 39–41, 47–62
OL Core	9–25 odd, 26–30, 31–35 odd, 37, 39–62	9–25, 42–46	26–37, 39–41, 47–62
BL Advanced	26–59, (optional: 60–62)		

Multiple Representations In Exercise 29, students draw a diagram and use a table of values and analysis to investigate the relationship between the terminal side of an angle and the slope of the line representing it.

Additional Answers

19a. Average High Temperatures

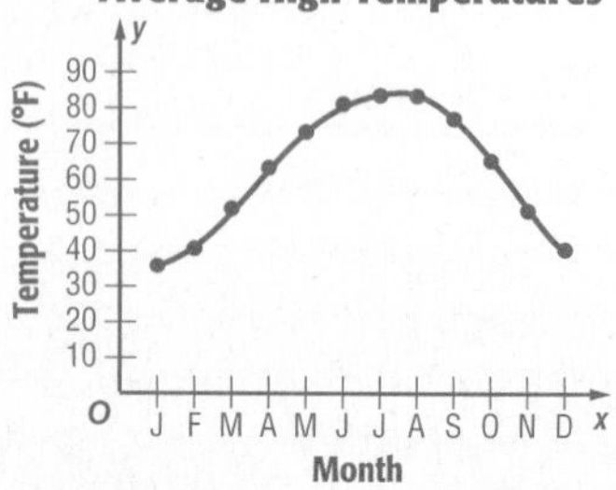

26b. Sample answer:

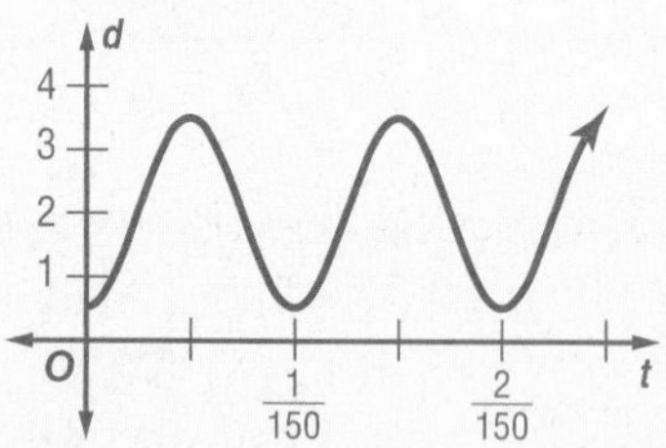

27b. Sample answer:

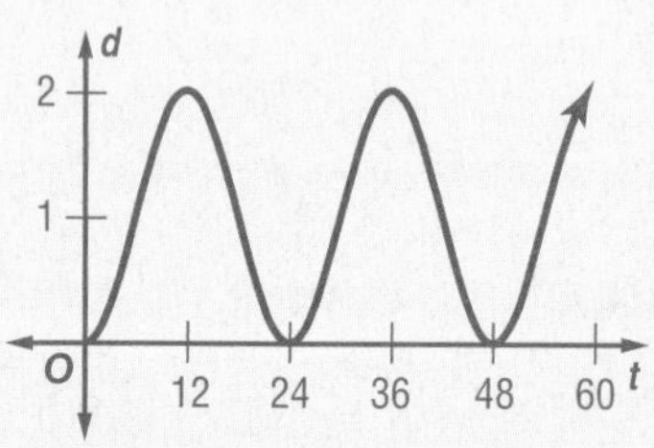

28. Sample answer:

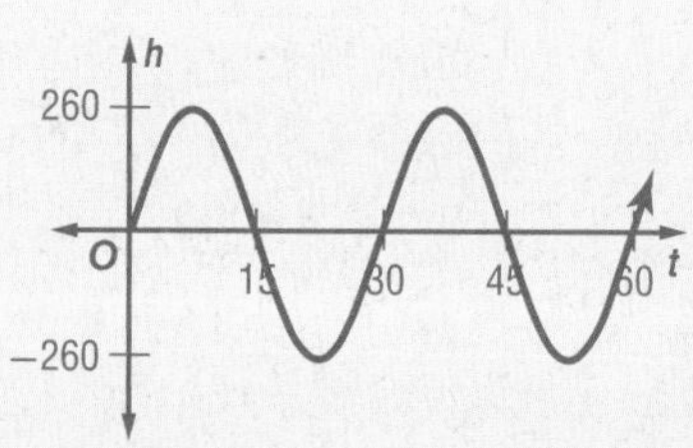

Determine the period of each function.

17. 180°

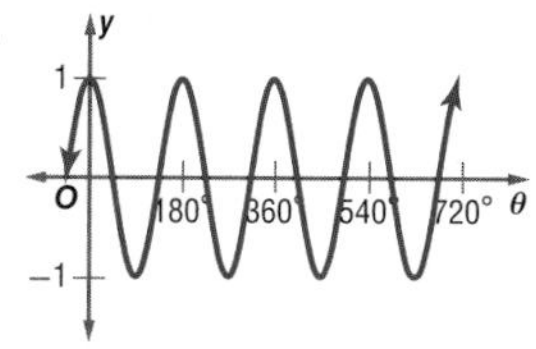

18. 2π

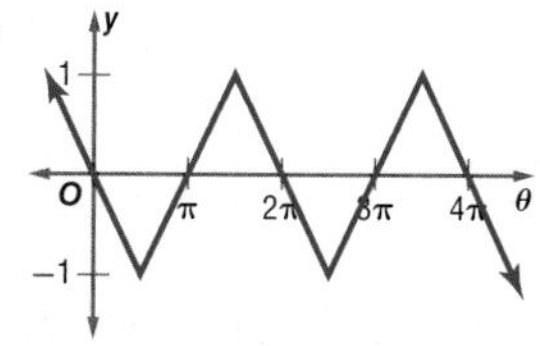

Example 3 p. 849

19. WEATHER In a city, the average high temperature for each month is shown in the table.

a. Sketch a graph of the function representing this situation. **See margin.**

b. Describe the period of the function. **12 mo or 1 yr**

Average High Temperatures			
Month	Temperature (°F)	Month	Temperature (°F)
Jan	36	July	85
Feb.	41	Aug.	84
Mar.	52	Sept.	78
Apr.	64	Oct.	66
May	74	Nov.	52
Jun.	82	Dec.	41

Source: The Weather Channel

Example 4 p. 850

Find the exact value of each function.

20. $\sin \frac{7\pi}{3}$ $\frac{\sqrt{3}}{2}$

21. $\cos(-60°)$ $\frac{1}{2}$

22. $\cos 450°$ **0**

23. $\sin \frac{11\pi}{4}$ $\frac{\sqrt{2}}{2}$

24. $\sin(-45°)$ $-\frac{\sqrt{2}}{2}$

25. $\cos 570°$ $-\frac{\sqrt{3}}{2}$

B

26. ENGINES In the engine at the right, the distance d from the piston to the center of the circle, called the *crankshaft*, is a function of the speed of the piston rod. Point R on the piston rod rotates 150 times per second.

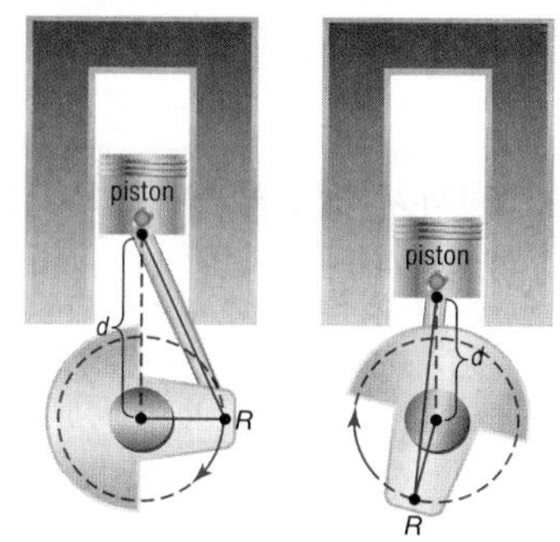

a. Identify the period of the function as a fraction of a second. $\frac{1}{150}$

b. The shortest distance d is 0.5 inch, and the longest distance is 3.5 inches. Sketch a graph of the function. Let the horizontal axis represent the time t. Let the vertical axis represent the distance d. **See margin.**

Real-World Link

Tornadoes can have whirling winds that reach 300 miles per hour. The forward speed of a tornado can reach up to 70 miles per hour.

Source: FEMA

27. TORNADOES A tornado siren makes 2.5 rotations per minute and the beam of sound has a radius of 1 mile. Ms. Miller's house is 1 mile from the siren. The distance of the sound beam from her house varies periodically as a function of time.

a. Identify the period of the function in seconds. **24 seconds**

b. Sketch a graph of the function. Let the horizontal axis represent the time t from 0 seconds to 60 seconds. Let the vertical axis represent the distance d the sound beam is from Ms. Miller's house at time t. **See margin.**

28. FERRIS WHEEL A Ferris wheel in China has a diameter of approximately 520 feet. The height of a compartment h is a function of time t. It takes about 30 seconds to make one complete revolution. Let the height at the center of the wheel represent the height at time 0. Sketch a graph of the function. **See margin.**

30b.

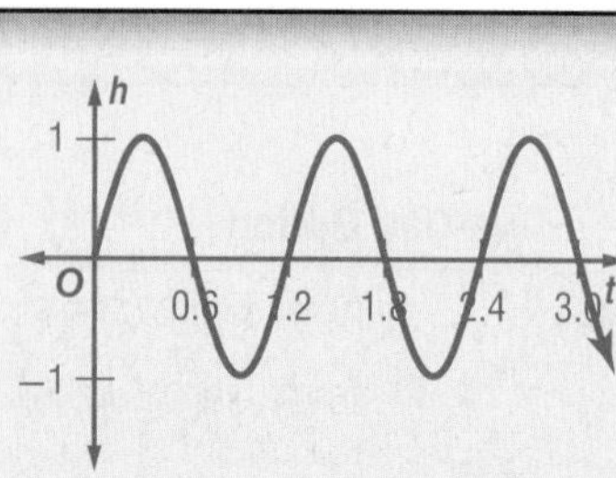

40. Sample answer:

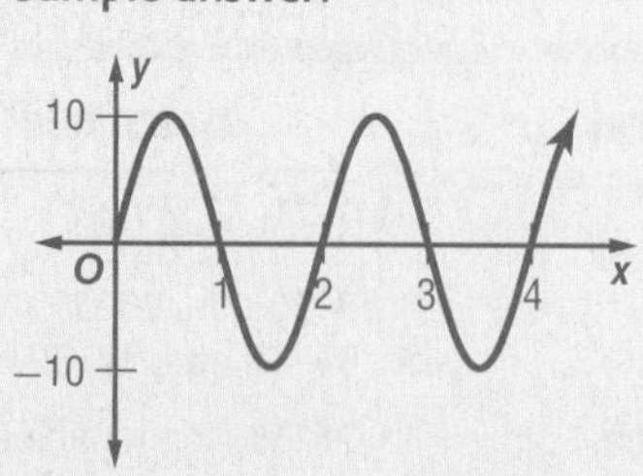

period: 2

Math History Link

Pauline Sperry (1885–1967) Pauline Sperry was born in Peabody, Massachusetts. During the 1920s, she wrote two textbooks, *Short Course in Spherical Trigonometry* and *Plane Trigonometry*. In 1923, she became the first woman to be promoted to assistant professor in the mathematics department at Berkeley.

29a–c. See Chapter 13 Answer Appendix.
30a. Sample answer: independent variable: time t in seconds; dependent variable: height h in feet; period: 1.2 seconds
37. Benita; Francis incorrectly wrote $\cos\frac{-\pi}{3} = -\cos\frac{\pi}{3}$.
39. Sometimes; the period of a sine curve could be $\frac{\pi}{2}$, which is not a multiple of π.
41. The period of a periodic function is the horizontal distance of the part of the graph that is nonrepeating. Each nonrepeating part of the graph is one cycle.

29. **MULTIPLE REPRESENTATIONS** The terminal side of an angle in standard position intersects the unit circle at P, as shown in the figure.

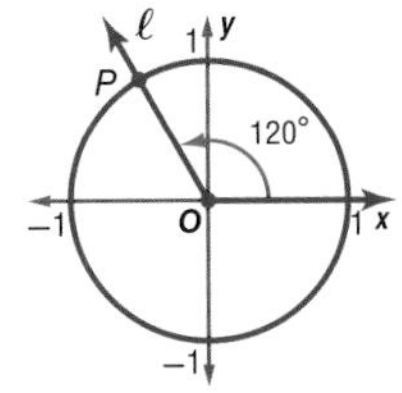

a. **GEOMETRIC** Copy the figure. Draw lines representing 30°, 60°, 150°, 210°, and 315°.

b. **TABULAR** Use a table of values to show the slope of each line to the nearest tenth.

c. **ANALYTICAL** What conclusions can you make about the relationship between the terminal side of the angle and the slope? Explain your reasoning.

30. **POGO STICK** A person is jumping up and down on a pogo stick at a constant rate. The difference between his highest and lowest points is 2 feet. He jumps 50 times per minute.

a. Describe the independent variable and dependent variable of the periodic function that represents this situation. Then state the period of the function in seconds.

b. Sketch a graph of the jumper's change in height in relation to his starting point. Assume that his starting point is halfway between his highest and lowest points. Let the horizontal axis represent the time t in seconds. Let the vertical axis represent the height h. **See margin.**

C **Find the exact value of each function.**

31. $\cos 45° - \cos 30°$ $\;\frac{\sqrt{2}-\sqrt{3}}{2}$

32. $6(\sin 30°)(\sin 60°)$ $\;\frac{3\sqrt{3}}{2}$

33. $2\sin\frac{4\pi}{3} - 3\cos\frac{11\pi}{6}$ $\;-\frac{5\sqrt{3}}{2}$

34. $\cos\left(-\frac{2\pi}{3}\right) + \frac{1}{3}\sin 3\pi$ $\;-\frac{1}{2}$

35. $(\sin 45°)^2 + (\cos 45°)^2$ $\;1$

36. $\frac{(\cos 30°)(\cos 150°)}{\sin 315°}$ $\;\frac{3\sqrt{2}}{4}$

H.O.T. Problems
Use **H**igher-**O**rder **T**hinking Skills

37. **ERROR ANALYSIS** Francis and Benita are finding the exact value of $\cos\frac{-\pi}{3}$. Is either of them correct? Explain your reasoning.

Francis	Benita
$\cos\frac{-\pi}{3} = -\cos\frac{\pi}{3}$ $= -0.5$	$\cos\frac{-\pi}{3} = \cos\left(-\frac{\pi}{3} + 2\pi\right)$ $= \cos\frac{5\pi}{3}$ $= 0.5$

38. **CHALLENGE** A ray has its endpoint at the origin of the coordinate plane, and point $P\left(\frac{1}{2}, -\frac{\sqrt{3}}{2}\right)$ lies on the ray. Find the angle θ formed by the positive x-axis and the ray. **−60°**

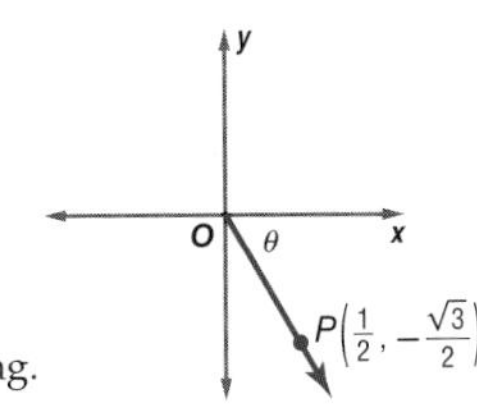

39. **REASONING** Is the period of a sine curve *sometimes*, *always*, or *never* a multiple of π? Justify your reasoning.

40. **OPEN ENDED** Draw the graph of a periodic function that has a maximum value of 10 and a minimum value of −10. Describe the period of the function. **See margin.**

41. **WRITING IN MATH** Explain how to determine the period of a periodic function from its graph. Include a description of a cycle.

Watch Out!

Error Analysis For Exercise 37, students should see that Benita is correct because the cosine function repeats every 2π radians. Francis is incorrect because $\cos(-\theta) = \cos\theta$. Explain to students that if they consider θ in Quadrant I and $-\theta$ in Quadrant IV, the x coordinates are the same and so $\cos(-\theta) = \cos\theta$. (Students can see the same result for θ in Quadrant II and $-\theta$ in Quadrant III.)

Enrichment
CRM p. 40 OL BL

13-6 Enrichment

Polar Coordinates

Consider an angle in standard position with its vertex at a point O called the *pole*. Its initial side is on a coordinated axis called the *polar axis*. A point P on the terminal side of the angle is named by the *polar coordinates* (r, θ) where r is the directed distance of the point from O and θ is the measure of the angle.

Graphs in this system may be drawn on polar coordinate paper such as the kind shown at the right.

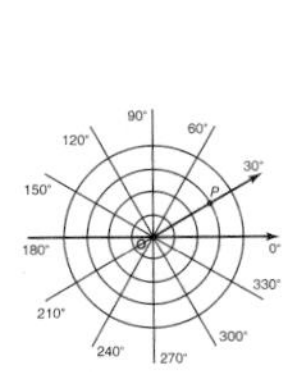

The polar coordinates of a point are not unique. For example, (3, 30°) names point P as well as (3, 390°). Another name for P is (−3, 210°). Can you see why? The coordinates of the pole are $(0, \theta)$ where θ may be any angle.

Example **Draw the graph of the function $r = \cos\theta$. Make a table of convenient values for θ and r. Then plot the points.**

θ	0°	30°	60°	90°	120°	150°	180°

Study Guide and Intervention
CRM pp. 35–36 AL OL ELL

13-6 Study Guide and Intervention

Circular Functions

Circular Functions

Definition of Sine and Cosine	If the terminal side of an angle θ in standard position intersects the unit circle at $P(x, y)$, then $\cos\theta = x$ and $\sin\theta = y$. Therefore, the coordinates of P can be written as $P(\cos\theta, \sin\theta)$.

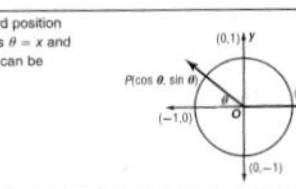

Example **The terminal side of angle θ in standard position intersects the unit circle at $P\left(-\frac{5}{6}, \frac{\sqrt{11}}{6}\right)$. Find $\cos\theta$ and $\sin\theta$.**

$P\left(-\frac{5}{6}, \frac{\sqrt{11}}{6}\right) = P(\cos\theta, \sin\theta)$, so $\cos\theta = -\frac{5}{6}$ and $\sin\theta = \frac{\sqrt{11}}{6}$.

Exercises

The terminal side of angle θ in standard position intersects the unit circle at each point P. Find $\cos\theta$ and $\sin\theta$.

1. $P\left(-\frac{\sqrt{3}}{2}, \frac{1}{2}\right)$ $\;\sin\theta = \frac{1}{2}$, $\cos\theta = -\frac{\sqrt{3}}{2}$
2. $P(0, -1)$ $\;\sin\theta = -1$, $\cos\theta = 0$
3. $P\left(-\frac{2}{3}, \frac{\sqrt{5}}{3}\right)$ $\;\sin\theta = \frac{\sqrt{5}}{3}$, $\cos\theta = -\frac{2}{3}$
4. $P\left(-\frac{4}{5}, -\frac{\sqrt{3}}{5}\right)$ $\;\sin\theta = -\frac{3}{5}$, $\cos\theta = -\frac{4}{5}$
5. $P\left(\frac{1}{6}, -\frac{\sqrt{35}}{6}\right)$ $\;\sin\theta = -\frac{\sqrt{35}}{6}$, $\cos\theta = \frac{1}{6}$
6. $P\left(\frac{\sqrt{7}}{4}, \frac{3}{4}\right)$ $\;\sin\theta = \frac{3}{4}$, $\cos\theta = \frac{\sqrt{7}}{4}$
7. P is on the terminal side of $\theta = 45°$. $\;\sin\theta = \frac{\sqrt{2}}{2}$, $\cos\theta = \frac{\sqrt{2}}{2}$
8. P is on the terminal side of $\theta = 120°$. $\;\sin\theta = \frac{\sqrt{3}}{2}$, $\cos\theta = -\frac{1}{2}$
9. P is on the terminal side of $\theta = 240°$. $\;\sin\theta = \frac{\sqrt{3}}{2}$, $\cos\theta = -\frac{1}{2}$
10. P is on the terminal side of $\theta = 330°$. $\;\sin\theta = -\frac{1}{2}$, $\cos\theta = \frac{\sqrt{3}}{2}$

Lesson 13-5

Practice
CRM p. 38 AL OL BL ELL

13-6 Practice

Circular Functions

The terminal side of angle θ in standard position intersects the unit circle at each point P. Find $\cos\theta$ and $\sin\theta$.

1. $P\left(-\frac{1}{2}, \frac{\sqrt{3}}{2}\right)$ $\;\sin\theta = \frac{\sqrt{3}}{2}$, $\cos\theta = -\frac{1}{2}$
2. $P\left(\frac{20}{29}, -\frac{21}{29}\right)$ $\;\sin\theta = -\frac{21}{29}$, $\cos\theta = \frac{20}{29}$
3. $P(0.8, 0.6)$ $\;\sin\theta = 0.6$, $\cos\theta = 0.8$
4. $P(0, -1)$ $\;\sin\theta = -1$, $\cos\theta = 0$
5. $P\left(-\frac{\sqrt{2}}{2}, -\frac{\sqrt{2}}{2}\right)$ $\;\sin\theta = -\frac{\sqrt{2}}{2}$, $\cos\theta = -\frac{\sqrt{2}}{2}$
6. $P\left(\frac{\sqrt{3}}{2}, \frac{1}{2}\right)$ $\;\sin\theta = \frac{1}{2}$, $\cos\theta = \frac{\sqrt{3}}{2}$

Determine the period of each function.

7.

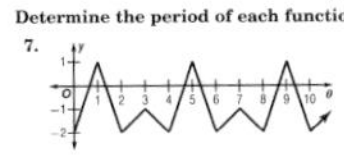

4

8.

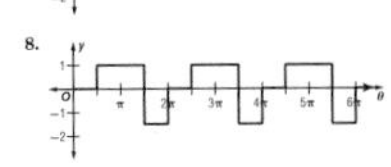

2π

Find the exact value of each function.

9. $\cos\frac{7\pi}{4}$ $\;\frac{\sqrt{2}}{2}$
10. $\sin(-30°)$ $\;-\frac{1}{2}$
11. $\sin\left(-\frac{2\pi}{3}\right)$ $\;-\frac{\sqrt{3}}{2}$
12. $\cos(-330°)$ $\;\frac{\sqrt{3}}{2}$
13. $\cos 600°$ $\;-\frac{1}{2}$
14. $\sin\frac{9\pi}{2}$ $\;1$
15. $\cos 7\pi$ $\;-1$
16. $\cos\left(-\frac{11\pi}{4}\right)$ $\;-\frac{\sqrt{2}}{2}$
17. $\sin(-225°)$ $\;\frac{\sqrt{2}}{2}$
18. $\sin 585°$ $\;-\frac{\sqrt{2}}{2}$
19. $\cos\left(-\frac{10\pi}{3}\right)$ $\;-\frac{1}{2}$
20. $\sin 840°$ $\;\frac{\sqrt{3}}{2}$

21. **FERRIS WHEELS** A Ferris wheel with a diameter of 100 feet completes 2.5 revolutions per minute. What is the period of the function that describes the height of a seat on the outside edge of the Ferris wheel as a function of time? **24 s**

Word Problem Practice
CRM p. 39 AL OL BL ELL

13-6 Word Problem Practice

Circular Functions

1. **TIRES** A point on the edge of a car tire is marked with paint. As the car moves slowly, the marked point on the tire varies in distance from the surface of the road. The height in inches of the point is given by the expression $h = -8\cos t + 8$, where t is the time in seconds.

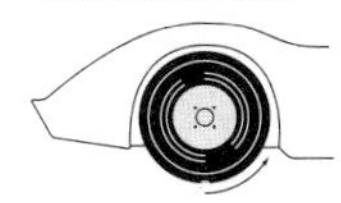

a. What is the maximum height above ground that the point on the tire reaches? **16 inches**

b. What is the minimum height above ground that the point on the tire reaches? **0 inches**

c. How many rotations does the tire make per second? **1**

d. How far does the marked point travel in 30 seconds? How far does the marked point travel in one hour? **1508 ft; 2.9 mi**

2. **GEOMETRY** The temperature T in degrees Fahrenheit of a city t months into the year is approximated by the formula $T = 42 + 30\sin\left(\frac{\pi}{6}t\right)$.

a. What is the highest monthly temperature for the city? **72°F**

b. In what month does the highest temperature occur? **March**

c. What is the lowest monthly temperature for the city? **12°F**

d. In what month does the lowest temperature occur? **September**

3. **THE MOON** The moon's period of revolution is the number of days it takes for the moon to revolve around the Earth. The period can be determined by graphing the percentage of sunlight reflected by the moon each day, as seen by an observer on the Earth. Use the graph to determine the moon's period of revolution. **approximately 28 days**

Lesson 13-6

Lesson 13-6 Circular Functions **853**

4 ASSESS

Name the Math Ask students to describe how they can find points on the unit circle in each of the quadrants and on each of the axes.

Additional Answer

42. Sample answer: Move the graph of $f(x)$ 4 units to the left and 3 units down to obtain the graph of $g(x)$.

NGSSS PRACTICE 912.A.2.10, 912.A.8.7, 912.A.3.15

42. THINK SOLVE EXPLAIN **SHORT RESPONSE** Describe the translation of the graph of $f(x) = x^2$ to the graph of $g(x) = (x + 4)^2 - 3$. **See margin.**

43. The rate of population decline of Hampton Cove is modeled by $P(t) = 24{,}000e^{-0.0064t}$, where t is time in years from this year and 24,000 is the current population. In how many years will the population be 10,000? **C**

A. 14 B. 104 C. 137 D. 375

44. SAT/ACT If $d^2 + 8 = 21$, then $d^2 - 8 =$ **F**

F. 5 G. 13 H. 31 I. 161

45. STATISTICS If the average of three different positive integers is 65, what is the greatest possible value of one of the integers? **A**

A. 192 B. 193 C. 194 D. 195

46. **GRIDDED RESPONSE** If $8xy + 3 = 3$, what is the value of xy? **0**

Spiral Review

Solve each triangle. Round side lengths to the nearest tenth and angle measures to the nearest degree. (Lesson 13-5)

47.

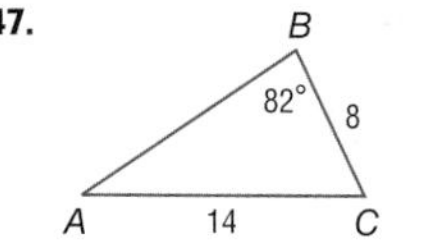

$A \approx 34°$, $C \approx 64°$, $c \approx 12.7$

48.

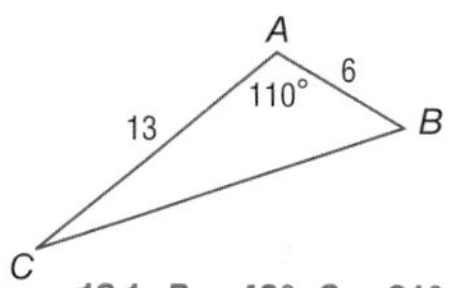

$a \approx 16.1$, $B \approx 49°$, $C \approx 21°$

49.

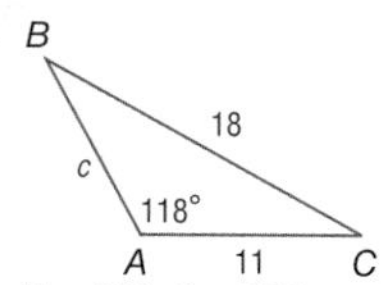

$B \approx 33°$, $C \approx 29°$, $c \approx 9.9$

Determine whether each triangle has *no* solution, *one* solution, or *two* solutions. Then solve the triangle. Round side lengths to the nearest tenth and angle measures to the nearest degree. (Lesson 13-4) **51. one solution; $B \approx 35°$, $C \approx 99°$, $c \approx 13.7$ 52. one solution; $B \approx 31°$, $C \approx 39°$, $c \approx 6.0$**

50. $A = 72°, a = 6, b = 11$ **no solution** **51.** $A = 46°, a = 10, b = 8$ **52.** $A = 110°, a = 9, b = 5$

A binomial distribution has a 70% rate of success. There are 10 trials. (Lesson 12-7)

53. What is the probability that there will be 3 failures? **0.267**

54. What is the probability that there will be at least 7 successes? **0.6496**

55. What is the expected number of successes? **7**

56. GAMES The diagram shows the board for a game in which spheres are dropped down a chute. A pattern of nails and dividers causes the spheres to take various paths to the sections at the bottom. For each section, how many paths through the board lead to that section? (Lesson 11-6) **1, 4, 6, 4, 1**

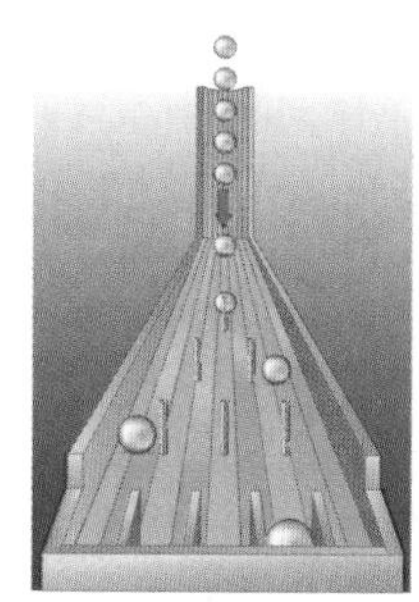

57. SALARIES Phillip's current salary is \$40,000 per year. His annual pay raise is always a percent of his salary at the time. What would his salary be if he got four consecutive 4% increases? (Lesson 11-2) **\$46,794.34**

Find the exact solution(s) of each system of equations. (Lesson 10-7)

58. $y = x + 2$ **(2, 4), (−1, 1)**
$y = x^2$

59. $4x + y^2 = 20$ **(5, 0), (−4, ±6)**
$4x^2 + y^2 = 100$

Skills Review

Simplify each expression. (Lesson 1-4)

60. $\dfrac{240}{\left|1 - \frac{5}{4}\right|}$ **960** **61.** $\dfrac{180}{\left|2 - \frac{1}{3}\right|}$ **108** **62.** $\dfrac{90}{\left|2 - \frac{11}{4}\right|}$ **120**

Differentiated Instruction OL BL

Extension Show students the graphs of $y = \cos x$, $y = \cos 2x$, and $y = \cos 3x$. Ask them to state the period of each function. 360°, 180°, 120° Ask them to determine the period of the function $y = \cos kx$. $\dfrac{360°}{k}$

13-7 Graphing Trigonometric Functions

Why?

Visible light waves have different wavelengths or periods. Red has the longest wavelength and violet has the shortest wavelength.

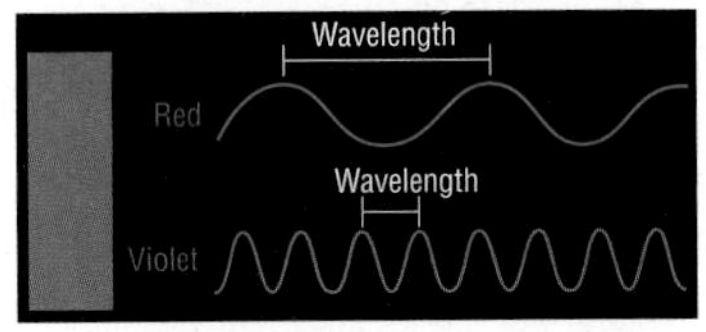

Then
You examined periodic functions. (Lesson 13-6)

Now
- Describe and graph the sine, cosine, and tangent functions.
- Describe and graph other trigonometric functions.

NGSSS
MA.912.T.1.5 Make connections between right triangle ratios, trigonometric functions, and circular functions.
MA.912.T.1.6 Define and graph trigonometric functions using domain, range, intercepts, period, amplitude, phase shift, vertical shift, and asymptotes with and without the use of graphing technology.

New Vocabulary
amplitude
frequency

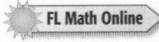

FL Math Online
glencoe.com

Sine, Cosine, and Tangent Functions Trigonometric functions can also be graphed on the coordinate plane. Recall that graphs of periodic functions have repeating patterns, or *cycles*. The horizontal length of each cycle is the *period*. The **amplitude** of the graph of a sine or cosine function equals half the difference between the maximum and minimum values of the function.

Key Concept — Sine and Cosine Functions

Parent Function	$y = \sin \theta$	$y = \cos \theta$
Graph	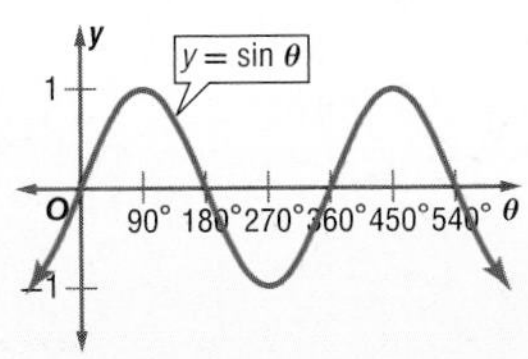	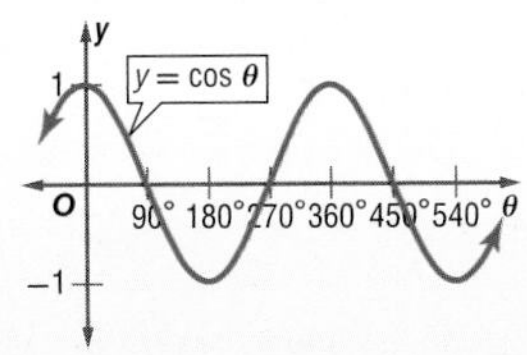
Domain	{all real numbers}	{all real numbers}
Range	$\{y \mid -1 \le y \le 1\}$	$\{y \mid -1 \le y \le 1\}$
Amplitude	1	1
Period	360°	360°

As with other functions, trigonometric functions can be transformed. For the graphs of $y = a \sin b\theta$ and $y = a \cos b\theta$, the amplitude $= |a|$ and the period $= \frac{360°}{|b|}$.

EXAMPLE 1 Find Amplitude and Period

Find the amplitude and period of $y = 4 \cos 3\theta$.

amplitude: $|a| = |4|$ or 4

period: $\frac{360°}{|b|} = \frac{360°}{|3|}$ or 120°

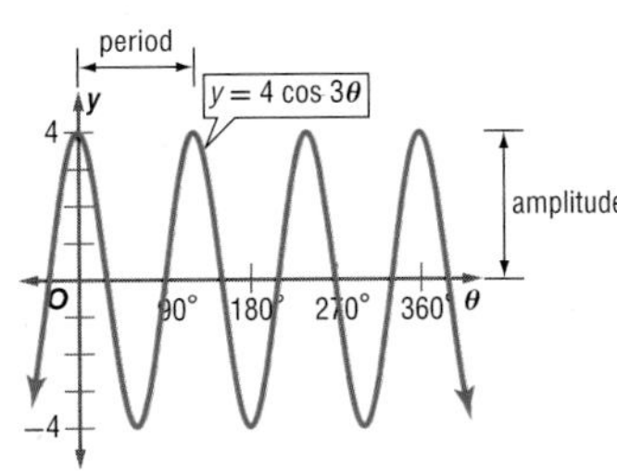

Guided Practice

Find the amplitude and period of each function.

1A. $y = \cos \frac{1}{2}\theta$ amplitude: 1; period: 720° **1B.** $y = 3 \sin 5\theta$ amplitude: 3; period: 72°

Personal Tutor glencoe.com

13-7 Lesson Notes

1 FOCUS

Vertical Alignment

Before Lesson 13-7
Examine periodic functions.

Lesson 13-7
Describe and graph the sine, cosine, and tangent functions. Describe and graph other trigonometric functions

After Lesson 13-7
Graph functions and interpret them in terms of their amplitude, frequency, period, and phase shift.

2 TEACH

Scaffolding Questions

Have students read the *Why?* section of the lesson.

Ask:

- How are wavelengths measured in the diagram? In the diagram, wavelengths are measured between the highest points of two sequential waves.
- What is another way to measure a wavelength? The wavelengths could be measured as the distance between any two corresponding points of sequential waves.
- In the diagram, how many violet wavelengths are equivalent to one red wavelength? 3

Lesson 13-7 Resources

Resource	Approaching-Level	On-Level	Beyond-Level	English Learners
Teacher Edition	• Differentiated Instruction, p. 856	• Differentiated Instruction, pp. 856, 861	• Differentiated Instruction, p. 861	
Chapter Resource Masters	• Study Guide and Intervention, pp. 41–42 • Skills Practice, p. 43 • Practice, p. 44 • Word Problem Practice, p. 45	• Study Guide and Intervention, pp. 41–42 • Skills Practice, p. 43 • Practice, p. 44 • Word Problem Practice, p. 45 • Enrichment, p. 46	• Practice, p. 44 • Word Problem Practice, p. 45 • Enrichment, p. 46	• Study Guide and Intervention, pp. 41–42 • Skills Practice, p. 43 • Practice, p. 44 • Word Problem Practice, p. 45
Transparencies	• 5-Minute Check Transparency 13-7	• 5-Minute Check Transparency 13-7	• 5-Minute Check Transparency 13-7	• 5-Minute Check Transparency 13-7
Other	• Study Notebook	• Study Notebook	• Study Notebook	• Study Notebook

Sine, Cosine, and Tangent Functions

Example 1 shows how to find the amplitude and period of a trigonometric function. **Example 2** shows how to use the amplitude and period to graph a trigonometric function. **Example 3** shows how to write a trigonometric function to model a real-world situation. **Example 4** shows how to use the period and asymptotes of a tangent function to graph the function.

Formative Assessment

Use the Guided Practice exercises after each example to determine students' understanding of concepts.

Additional Examples

1 Find the amplitude and period of $y = \sin \frac{1}{3}\theta$. amplitude: 1; period: 1080°

2 Graph each function.

a. $y = \sin 3\theta$

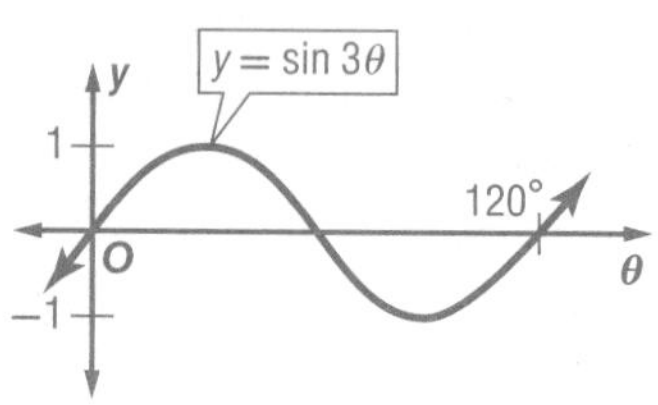

b. $y = \frac{1}{2} \cos \theta$

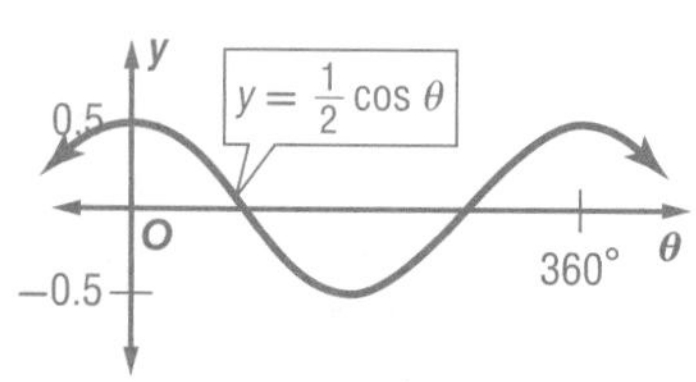

Additional Examples also in Interactive Classroom PowerPoint® Presentations

IWB INTERACTIVE WHITEBOARD READY

StudyTip

Periods In $y = a \sin b\theta$ and $y = a \cos b\theta$, b represents the number of cycles in 360°. In Example 1, the 3 in $y = 4 \cos 3\theta$ indicates that there are three cycles in 360°. So, there is one cycle in 120°.

Use the graphs of the parent functions to graph $y = a \sin b\theta$ and $y = a \cos b\theta$. Then use the amplitude and period to draw the appropriate sine and cosine curves. You can also use θ-intercepts to help you graph the functions.

The θ-intercepts of $y = a \sin b\theta$ and $y = a \cos b\theta$ in one cycle are as follows.

$y = a \sin b\theta$	$y = a \cos b\theta$
$(0, 0), \left(\frac{1}{2} \cdot \frac{360°}{b}, 0\right) \left(\frac{360°}{b}, 0\right)$	$\left(\frac{1}{4} \cdot \frac{360°}{b}, 0\right), \left(\frac{3}{4} \cdot \frac{360°}{b}, 0\right)$

EXAMPLE 2 Graph Sine and Cosine Functions

Graph each function.

a. $y = 2 \sin \theta$

Find the amplitude, the period, and the x-intercepts: $a = 2$ and $b = 1$.

amplitude: $|a| = |2|$ or 2 → The graph is stretched vertically so that the maximum value is 2 and the minimum value is −2.

period: $\frac{360°}{|b|} = \frac{360°}{|1|}$ or 360° → One cycle has a length of 360°.

x-intercepts: (0, 0)

$\left(\frac{1}{2} \cdot \frac{360°}{b}, 0\right) = (180°, 0)$

$\left(\frac{360°}{b}, 0\right) = (360°, 0)$

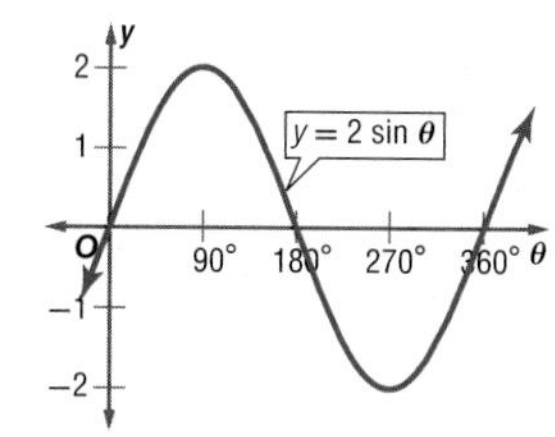

StudyTip

Amplitude The graphs of $y = a \sin b\theta$ and $y = a \cos b\theta$ with amplitude of $|a|$ have maxima at $y = a$ and minima at $y = -a$.

b. $y = \cos 4\theta$

amplitude: $|a| = |1|$ or 1

period: $\frac{360°}{|b|} = \frac{360°}{|4|}$ or 90°

x-intercepts: $\left(\frac{1}{4} \cdot \frac{360°}{b}, 0\right) = (22.5°, 0)$

$\left(\frac{3}{4} \cdot \frac{360°}{b}, 0\right) = (67.5°, 0)$

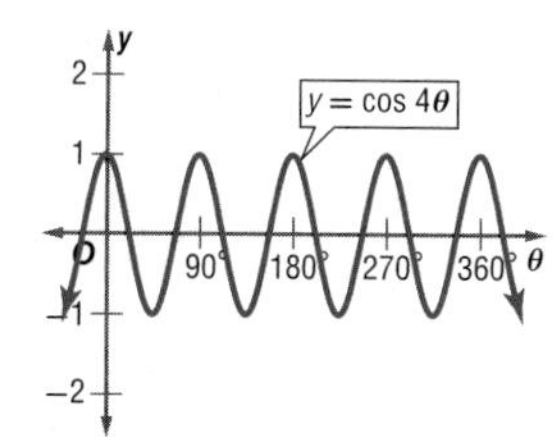

Guided Practice 2A, 2B. See margin.

2A. $y = 3 \cos \theta$ **2B.** $y = \frac{1}{2} \sin 2\theta$

Personal Tutor glencoe.com

Trigonometric functions are useful for modeling real-world periodic motion such as electromagnetic waves or sound waves. Often these waves are described using *frequency*. **Frequency** is the number of cycles in a given unit of time.

The frequency of the graph of a function is the reciprocal of the period of the function. So, if the period of a function is $\frac{1}{100}$ second, then the frequency is 100 cycles per second.

Differentiated Instruction AL OL

Visual/Spatial Learners Have groups of students make posters showing sketches of the graphs of the six trigonometric functions. Encourage students to color-code the key features of all the graphs, such as period, amplitude, asymptotes, and so on.

Real-World EXAMPLE 3 Model Periodic Situations

Real-World Link

Elephants are able to hear sound coming from up to 5 miles away. Humans can hear sounds with frequencies between 20 Hz and 20,000 Hz.

Source: School for Champions

SOUND Sound that has a frequency below the human range is known as *infrasound*. Elephants can hear sounds in the infrasound range, with frequencies as low as 5 hertz (Hz), or 5 cycles per second.

a. Find the period of the function that models the sound waves.

There are 5 cycles per second, and the period is the time it takes for one cycle. So, the period is $\frac{1}{5}$ or 0.2 second.

b. Let the amplitude equal 1 unit. Write a sine equation to represent the sound wave y as a function of time t. Then graph the equation.

$\text{period} = \frac{2\pi}{\lvert b \rvert}$	Write the relationship between the period and b.
$0.2 = \frac{2\pi}{\lvert b \rvert}$	Substitution
$0.2\lvert b \rvert = 2\pi$	Multiply each side by $\lvert b \rvert$.
$b = 10\pi$	Multiply each side by 5; b is positive.
$y = a \sin b\theta$	Write the general equation for the sine function.
$y = 1 \sin 10\pi t$	$a = 1$, $b = 10\pi$, and $\theta = t$
$y = \sin 10\pi t$	Simplify.

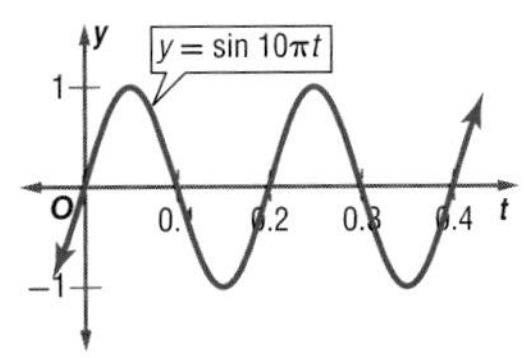

StudyTip

Amplitude and Period Note that the amplitude affects the graph along the vertical axis, and the period affects it along the horizontal axis.

Guided Practice

3. SOUND Humans can hear sounds with frequencies as low as 20 hertz.

A. Find the period of the function. $\frac{1}{20}$ or 0.05 second

B. Let the amplitude equal 1 unit. Write a cosine equation to model the sound waves. Then graph the equation. $y = \cos 40\pi t$; See Chapter 13 Answer Appendix for graph.

Personal Tutor glencoe.com

Tangent is one of the trigonometric functions whose graphs have asymptotes.

Key Concept Tangent Function

Parent Function	$y = \tan \theta$	Graph
Domain	$\{\theta \mid \theta \neq 90 + 180n$, n is an integer$\}$	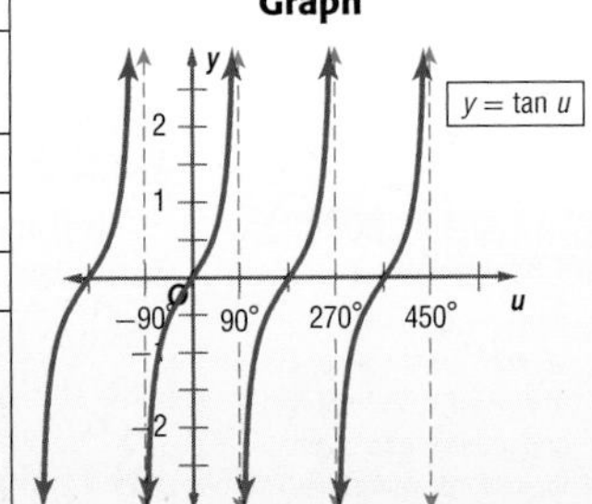
Range	{all real numbers}	
Amplitude	undefined	
Period	180°	
θ intercepts in one cycle	$(0, 0)$, $\left(\frac{1}{2} \cdot \frac{360°}{b}, 0\right)$, $\left(\frac{360°}{b}, 0\right)$	

For the graph of $y = a \tan b\theta$, the period $= \frac{180°}{\lvert b \rvert}$, there is no amplitude, and the asymptotes are odd multiples of $\frac{180°}{2\lvert b \rvert}$.

Additional Example

3 SOUND Humans can hear sounds with a frequency of 40 Hz.

a. Find the period of the function that models the sound waves. $\frac{1}{40}$ or 0.025 second

b. Let the amplitude equal 1 unit. Write a sine equation to represent the sound wave y as a function of time t. Then graph the equation. $y = \sin 80\pi t$

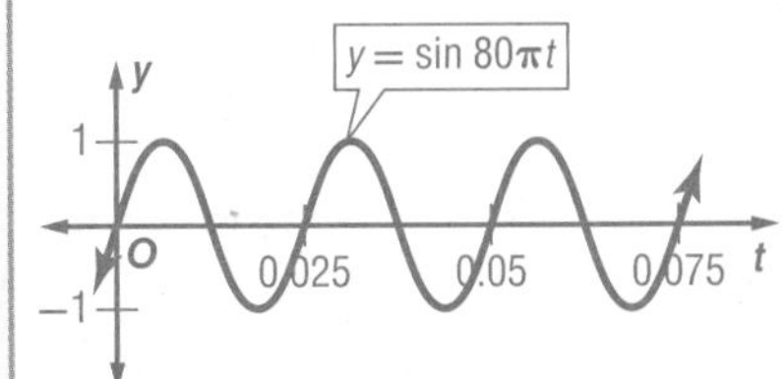

Focus on Mathematical Content

Amplitude and Period The graphs of the sine and cosine functions have an amplitude. The graphs of the other trigonometric functions do not have an amplitude because there is no maximum or minimum value. The period is the distance along the horizontal axis required for the graph to complete one cycle. The period is easy to determine from the graph.

Tips for New Teachers

Graphing You might wish to have students draw their own graphs of the sine, cosine, and tangent functions. Their graphs can be compared to those shown on pp. 856 and 858. This immediate feedback can be beneficial in helping students acquire the skills for graphing trigonometric functions, which are more complicated than most of the graphing students have done to this point.

Additional Answers (Guided Practice)

2A.

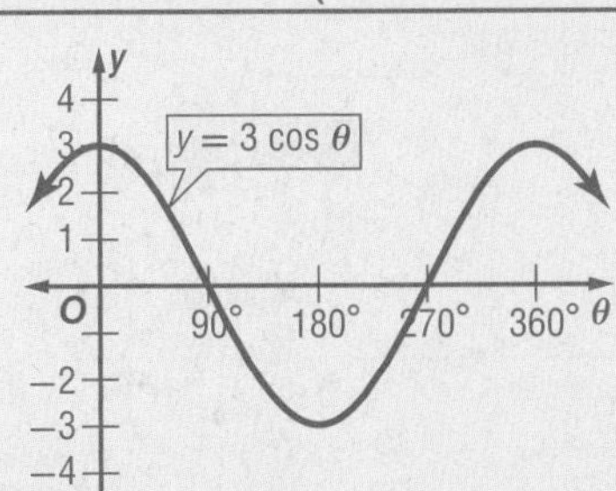

2B.

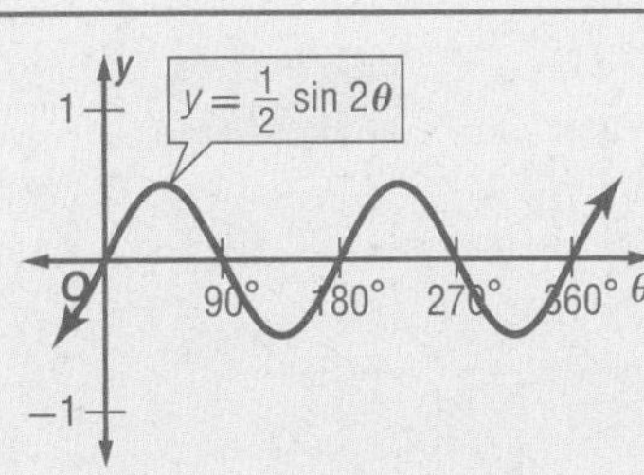

Additional Example

4 Find the period of $y = \tan \frac{1}{2}\theta$. Then graph the function.
period: 360°

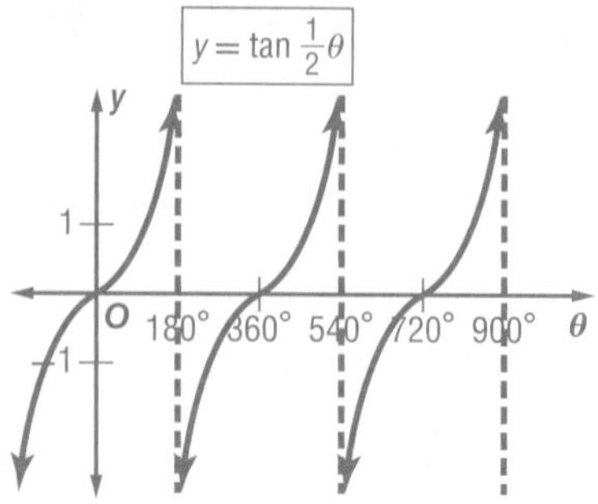

Graphs of Other Trigonometric Functions

Example 5 shows how to use the period of one of the three basic functions to graph another trigonometric function.

Additional Example

5 Find the period of $y = 3 \csc \theta$. Then graph the function.
period: 360°

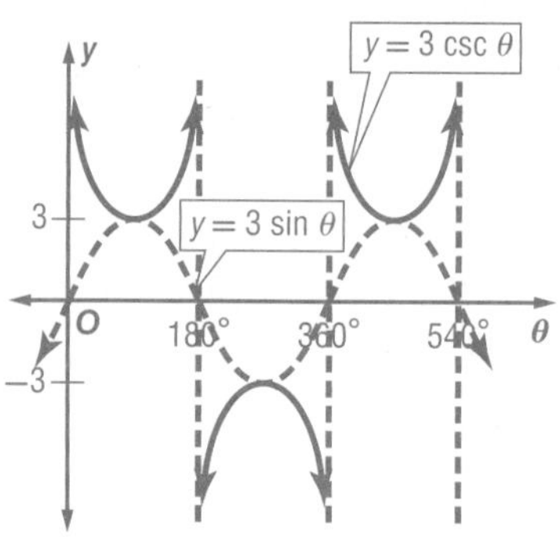

TEACH with TECH

DOCUMENT CAMERA Choose students to show and explain to the class how to sketch the graph of a trigonometric function. Be sure each student explains how to create a table of values, choose a scale for the graph, and plot the points to draw the graph.

StudyTip

Tangent The tangent function does not have an amplitude because it has no maximum or minimum values.

EXAMPLE 4 Graph Tangent Functions

Find the period of $y = \tan 2\theta$. Then graph the function.

period: $\frac{180°}{|b|} = \frac{180°}{|2|}$ or 90°

asymptotes: $\frac{180°}{2|b|} = \frac{180°}{2|2|}$ or 45°

Sketch asymptotes at $-1 \cdot 45°$ or $-45°$, $1 \cdot 45°$ or 45°, $3 \cdot 45°$ or 135°, and so on.

Use $y = \tan \theta$, but draw one cycle every 90°.

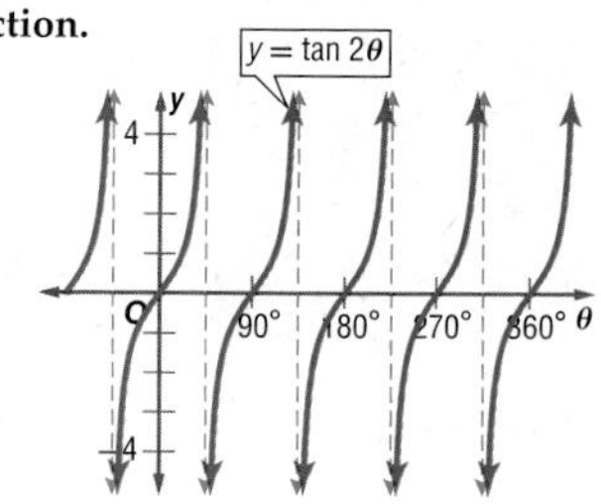

Guided Practice

4. Find the period of $y = \frac{1}{2} \tan \theta$. Then graph the function. See margin.

Personal Tutor glencoe.com

Graphs of Other Trigonometric Functions The graphs of the cosecant, secant, and cotangent functions are related to the graphs of the sine, cosine, and tangent functions.

Key Concept Cosecant, Secant, and Cotangent Functions

Parent Function	$y = \csc \theta$	$y = \sec \theta$	$y = \cot \theta$
Graph	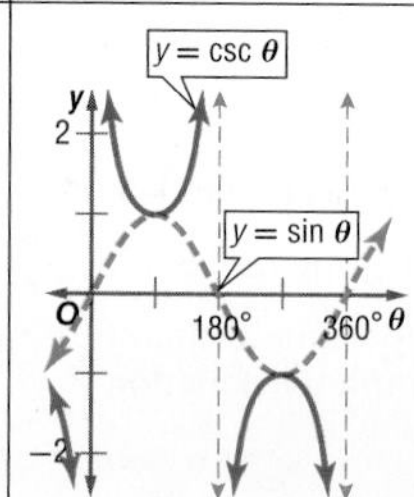	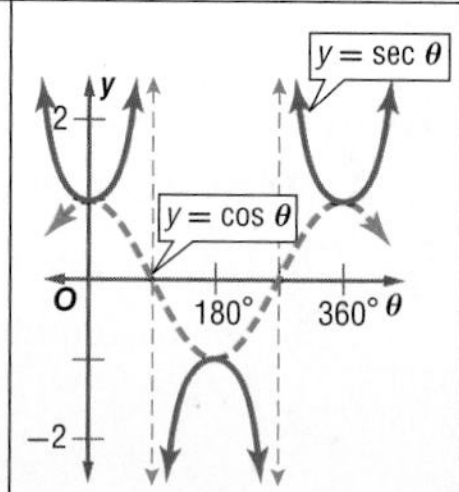	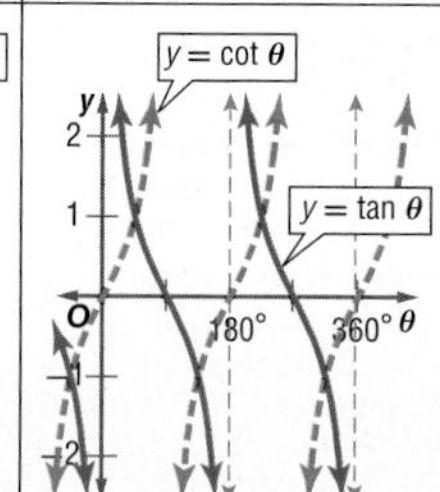
Domain	{θ | θ ≠ 180n, n is an integer}	{θ | θ ≠ 90 + 180n, n is an integer}	{θ | θ ≠ 180n, n is an integer}
Range	{y | −1 > y or y > 1}	{y | −1 > y or y > 1}	{all real numbers}
Amplitude	undefined	undefined	undefined
Period	360°	360°	180°

EXAMPLE 5 Graph Other Trigonometric Functions

Find the period of $y = 2 \sec \theta$. Then graph the function.

Since $2 \sec \theta$ is a reciprocal of $2 \cos \theta$, the graphs have the same period, 360°. The vertical asymptotes occur at the points where $2 \cos \theta = 0$. So, the asymptotes are at $\theta = 90°$ and $\theta = 270°$.

Sketch $y = 2 \cos \theta$ and use it to graph $y = 2 \sec \theta$.

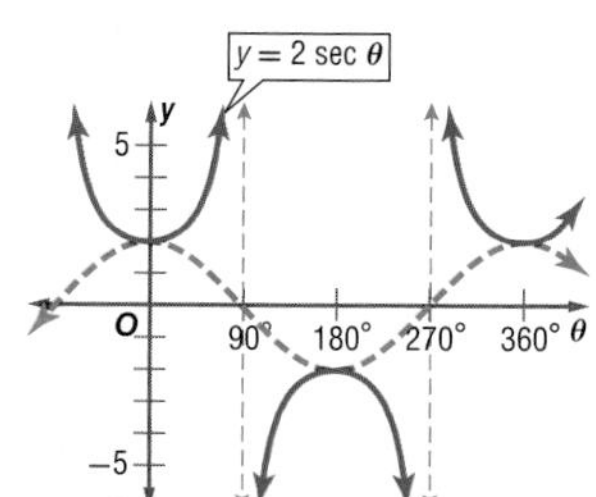

Guided Practice

5. Find the period of $y = \csc 2\theta$. Then graph the function. See margin.

Personal Tutor glencoe.com

StudyTip

Reciprocal Functions You can use the graphs of $y = \sin \theta$, $y = \cos \theta$, and $y = \tan \theta$ to graph the reciprocal functions, but these graphs are not part of the graphs of the cosecant, secant, and cotangent functions.

Additional Answers (Guided Practice)

4. period: 180°

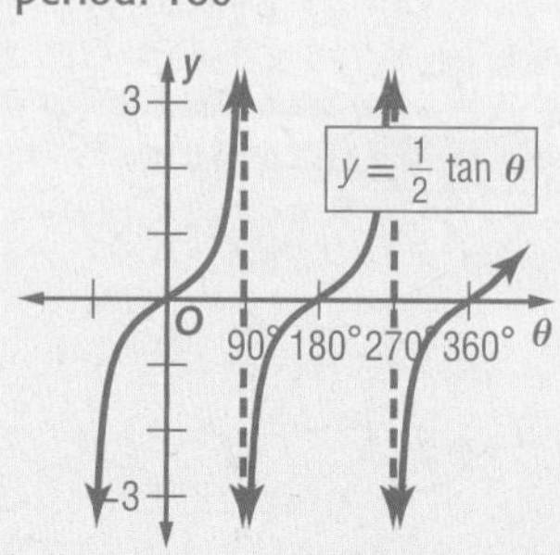

5. period: 180°

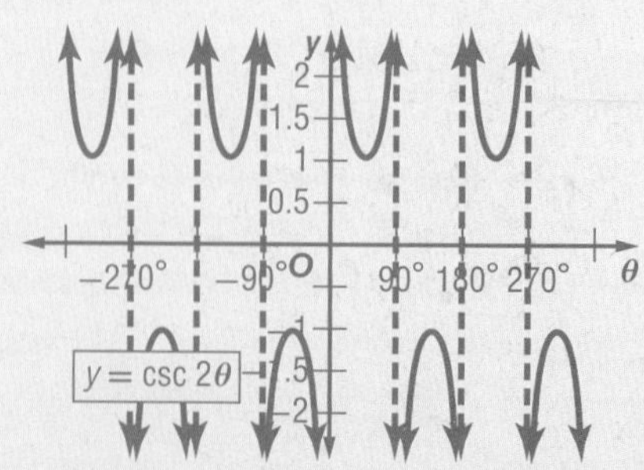

858 Chapter 13 Trigonometric Functions

Check Your Understanding

1–4. See margin.

Examples 1 and 2 pp. 855–856

Find the amplitude and period of each function. Then graph the function.

1. $y = 4 \sin \theta$
2. $y = \sin 3\theta$
3. $y = \cos 2\theta$
4. $y = \frac{1}{2} \cos 3\theta$

Example 3 p. 857

5. **SPIDERS** When an insect gets caught in a spider web, the web vibrates with a frequency of 14 hertz.
   a. Find the period of the function. $\frac{1}{14}$ or about 0.07 second
   b. Let the amplitude equal 1 unit. Write a sine equation to represent the vibration of the web y as a function of time t. Then graph the equation. See margin.

Examples 4 and 5 p. 858

Find the period of each function. Then graph the function. 6–8. See Chapter 13 Answer Appendix.

6. $y = 3 \tan \theta$
7. $y = 2 \csc \theta$
8. $y = \cot 2\theta$

Practice and Problem Solving

● = **Step-by-Step Solutions** begin on page R20. **Extra Practice** begins on page 947.

Examples 1 and 2 pp. 855–856

9–20. See Chapter 13 Answer Appendix.

Find the amplitude and period of each function. Then graph the function.

9. $y = 2 \cos \theta$
10. $y = 3 \sin \theta$
11. $y = \sin 2\theta$
12. $y = \cos 3\theta$
13. $y = \cos \frac{1}{2}\theta$
14. $y = \sin 4\theta$
15. $y = \frac{3}{4} \cos \theta$
16. $y = \frac{3}{2} \sin \theta$
17. $y = \frac{1}{2} \sin 2\theta$
18. $y = 4 \cos 2\theta$
19. $y = 3 \cos 2\theta$
20. $y = 5 \sin \frac{2}{3}\theta$

Example 3 p. 857

21. **WAVES** A boat on a lake bobs up and down with the waves. The difference between the lowest and highest points of the boat is 8 inches. The boat is at *equilibrium* when it is halfway between the lowest and highest points. Each cycle of the periodic motion lasts 3 seconds.
    a. Write an equation for the motion of the boat. Let h represent the height in inches and let t represent the time in seconds. Assume that the boat is at equilibrium at $t = 0$ seconds. $h = 4 \sin \frac{2}{3}\pi t$
    b. Draw a graph showing the height of the boat as a function of time. See Chapter 13 Answer Appendix.
22. **ELECTRICITY** The voltage supplied by an electrical outlet is a periodic function that *oscillates*, or goes up and down, between −165 volts and 165 volts with a frequency of 50 cycles per second.
    a. Write an equation for the voltage V as a function of time t. Assume that at $t = 0$ seconds, the current is 165 volts. $V = 165 \cos 100\pi t$
    b. Graph the function. See Chapter 13 Answer Appendix.

Examples 4 and 5 p. 858

Find the period of each function. Then graph the function. 23–28. See Chapter 13 Answer Appendix.

23. $y = \tan \frac{1}{2}\theta$
24. $y = 3 \sec \theta$
25. $y = 2 \cot \theta$
26. $y = \csc \frac{1}{2}\theta$
27. $y = 2 \tan \theta$
28. $y = \sec \frac{1}{3}\theta$

3 PRACTICE

Formative Assessment

Use Exercises 1–8 to check for understanding.

Use the chart at the bottom of this page to customize assignments for your students.

Additional Answers

1. amplitude: 4; period: 360°

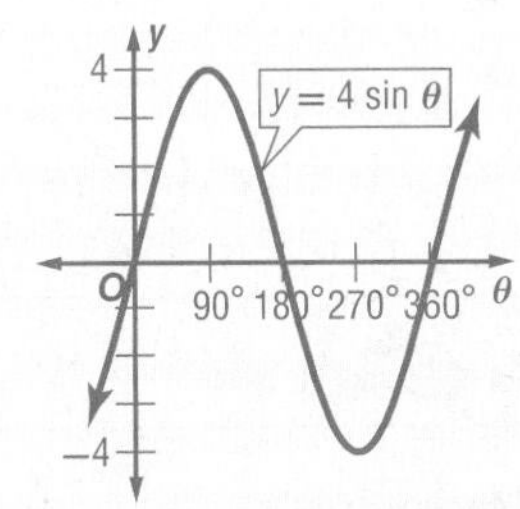

2. amplitude: 1; period: 120°

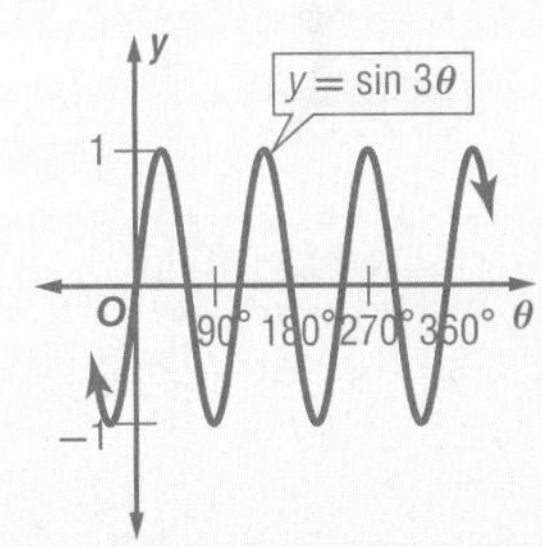

3. amplitude: 1; period: 180°

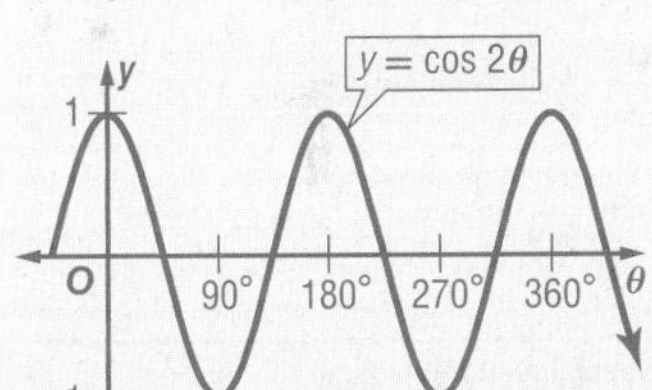

4. amplitude: $\frac{1}{2}$; period: 120°

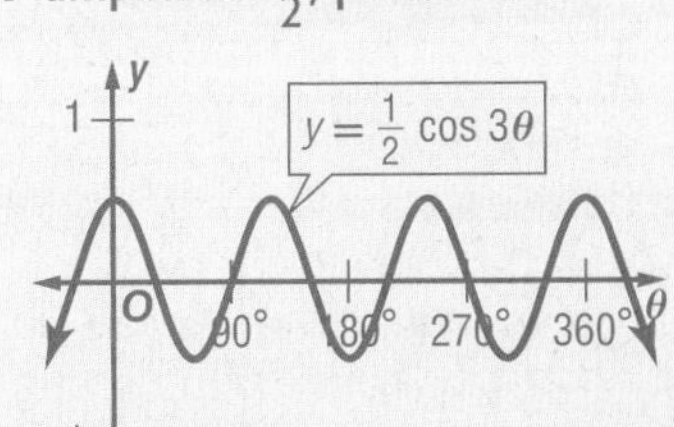

5b. $y = \sin 28\pi t$

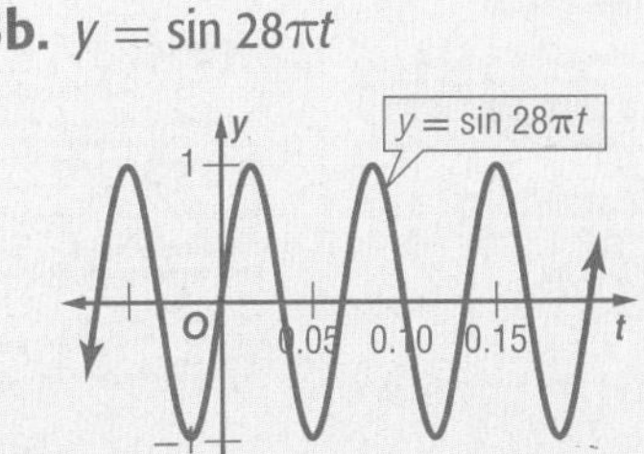

Differentiated Homework Options

Level	Assignment	Two-Day Option	
AL Basic	9–28, 42–63	9–27 odd, 45–48	10–28 even, 42–44, 49–63
OL Core	9–27 odd, 29–31, 33–39 odd, 42–63	9–28, 45–48	29–40, 42–44, 49–63
BL Advanced	29–60, (optional: 61–63)		

Study Guide and Intervention
CRM pp. 41–42 AL OL ELL

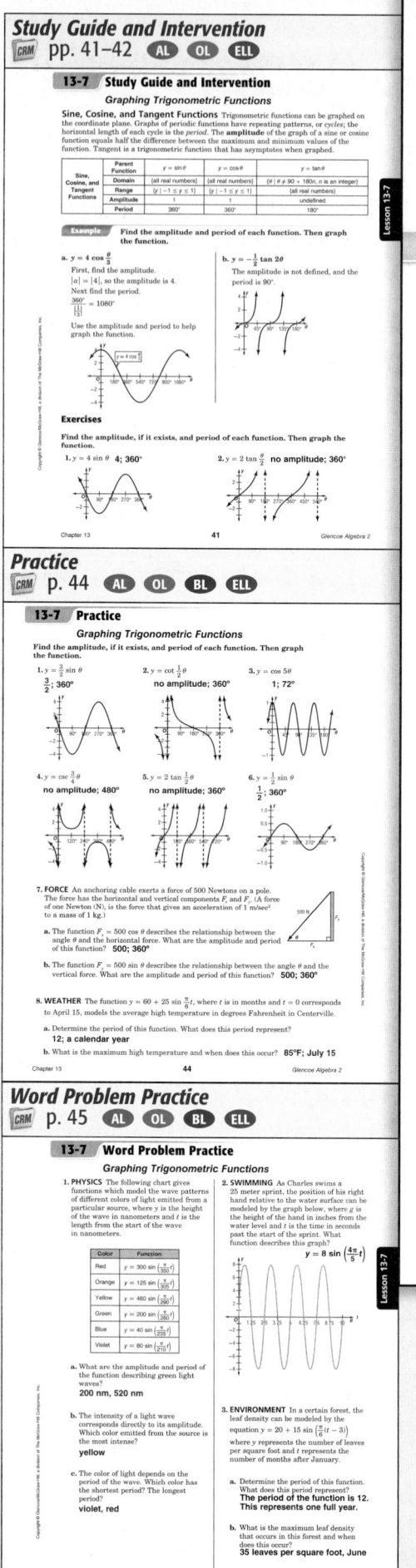

13-7 Study Guide and Intervention
Graphing Trigonometric Functions

Sine, Cosine, and Tangent Functions Trigonometric functions can be graphed on the coordinate plane. Graphs of periodic functions have repeating patterns, or *cycles*; the horizontal length of each cycle is the *period*. The **amplitude** of the graph of a sine or cosine function equals half the difference between the maximum and minimum values of the function. Tangent is a trigonometric function that has asymptotes when graphed.

Sine, Cosine, and Tangent Functions	Parent Function	$y = \sin\theta$	$y = \cos\theta$	$y = \tan\theta$
	Domain	{all real numbers}	{all real numbers}	$\{\theta \mid \theta \neq 90 + 180n$, n is an integer$\}$
	Range	$\{y \mid -1 \le y \le 1\}$	$\{y \mid -1 \le y \le 1\}$	{all real numbers}
	Amplitude	1	1	undefined
	Period	360°	360°	180°

Example **Find the amplitude and period of each function. Then graph the function.**

a. $y = 4 \cos \frac{\theta}{3}$

First, find the amplitude.
$|a| = |4|$, so the amplitude is 4.
Next find the period.
$\frac{360°}{\left|\frac{1}{3}\right|} = 1080°$

Use the amplitude and period to help graph the function.

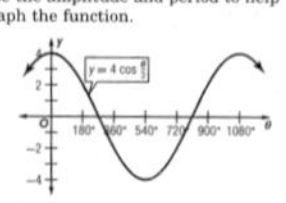

b. $y = -\frac{1}{2} \tan 2\theta$

The amplitude is not defined, and the period is 90°.

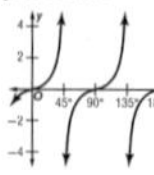

Exercises

Find the amplitude, if it exists, and period of each function. Then graph the function.

1. $y = 4 \sin \theta$ **4; 360°**

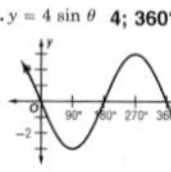

2. $y = 2 \tan \frac{\theta}{2}$ **no amplitude; 360°**

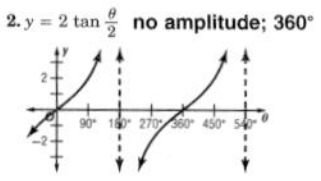

Practice
CRM p. 44 AL OL BL ELL

13-7 Practice
Graphing Trigonometric Functions

Find the amplitude, if it exists, and period of each function. Then graph the function.

1. $y = \frac{3}{2} \sin \theta$
$\frac{3}{2}$; 360°

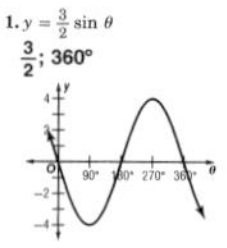

2. $y = \cot \frac{1}{2}\theta$
no amplitude; 360°

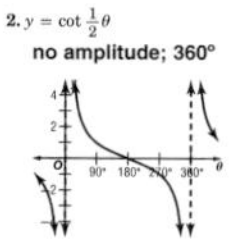

3. $y = \cos 5\theta$
1; 72°

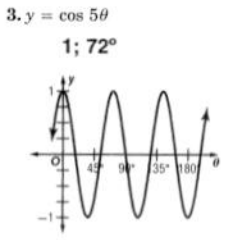

4. $y = \csc \frac{3}{4}\theta$
no amplitude; 480°

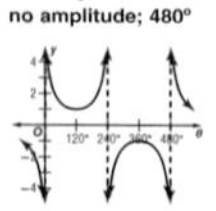

5. $y = 2 \tan \frac{1}{2}\theta$
no amplitude; 360°

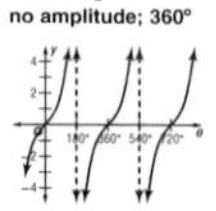

6. $y = \frac{1}{2} \sin \theta$
$\frac{1}{2}$; 360°

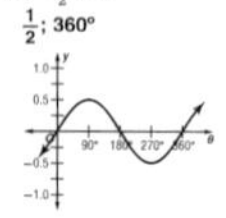

7. **FORCE** An anchoring cable exerts a force of 500 Newtons on a pole. The force has the horizontal and vertical components F_x and F_y. (A force of one Newton (N), is the force that gives an acceleration of 1 m/sec² to a mass of 1 kg.)

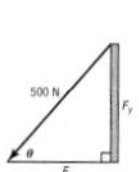

a. The function $F_x = 500 \cos \theta$ describes the relationship between the angle θ and the horizontal force. What are the amplitude and period of this function? **500; 360°**

b. The function $F_y = 500 \sin \theta$ describes the relationship between the angle θ and the vertical force. What are the amplitude and period of this function? **500; 360°**

8. **WEATHER** The function $y = 60 + 25 \sin \frac{\pi}{6}t$, where t is in months and $t = 0$ corresponds to April 15, models the average high temperature in degrees Fahrenheit in Centerville.

a. Determine the period of this function. What does this period represent?
12; a calendar year

b. What is the maximum high temperature and when does this occur? **85°F; July 15**

Word Problem Practice
CRM p. 45 AL OL BL ELL

13-7 Word Problem Practice
Graphing Trigonometric Functions

1. **PHYSICS** The following chart gives functions which model the wave patterns of different colors of light emitted from a particular source, where y is the height of the wave in nanometers and t is the length from the start of the wave in nanometers.

Color	Function
Red	$y = 300 \sin\left(\frac{\pi}{350}t\right)$
Orange	$y = 125 \sin\left(\frac{\pi}{305}t\right)$
Yellow	$y = 460 \sin\left(\frac{\pi}{290}t\right)$
Green	$y = 200 \sin\left(\frac{\pi}{260}t\right)$
Blue	$y = 40 \sin\left(\frac{\pi}{235}t\right)$
Violet	$y = 80 \sin\left(\frac{\pi}{210}t\right)$

a. What are the amplitude and period of the function describing green light waves?
200 nm, 520 nm

b. The intensity of a light wave corresponds directly to its amplitude. Which color emitted from the source is the most intense?
yellow

c. The color of light depends on the period of the wave. Which color has the shortest period? The longest period?
violet, red

2. **SWIMMING** As Charles swims a 25 meter sprint, the position of his right hand relative to the water surface can be modeled by the graph below, where g is the height of the hand in inches from the water level and t is the time in seconds past the start of the sprint. What function describes this graph?
$y = 8 \sin\left(\frac{4\pi}{5}t\right)$

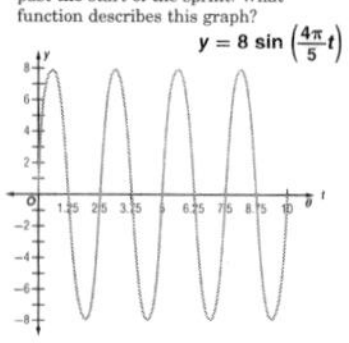

3. **ENVIRONMENT** In a certain forest, the leaf density can be modeled by the equation $y = 20 + 15 \sin\left(\frac{\pi}{6}(t - 3)\right)$ where y represents the number of leaves per square foot and t represents the number of months after January.

a. Determine the period of this function. What does this period represent?
The period of the function is 12. This represents one full year.

b. What is the maximum leaf density that occurs in this forest and when does this occur?
35 leaves per square foot, June

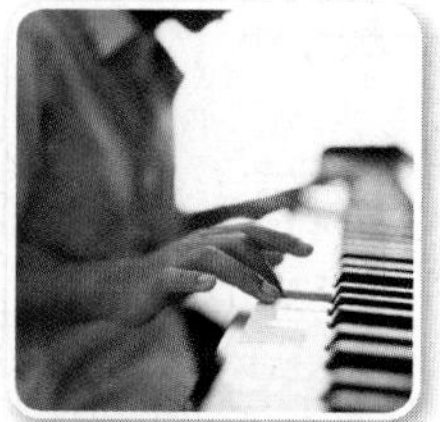

Real-World Link

Of all of the music lessons that teens take, piano lessons are the most popular.

Source: *Piano Magazine*

29. **EARTHQUAKES** A seismic station detects an earthquake wave that has a frequency of 0.5 hertz and an amplitude of 1 meter. **b. See margin.**

a. Write an equation involving sine to represent the height of the wave h as a function of time t. Assume that the equilibrium point of the wave, $h = 0$, is halfway between the lowest and highest points. **$h = \sin \pi t$**

b. Graph the function. Then determine the height of the wave after 20.5 seconds.

30. **PHYSICS** An object is attached to a spring as shown at the right. It oscillates according to the equation $y = 20 \cos \pi t$, where y is the distance in centimeters from its equilibrium position at time t.

a. Describe the motion of the object by finding the following: the amplitude in centimeters, the frequency in vibrations per second, and the period in seconds.

b. Find the distance of the object from its equilibrium position at $t = \frac{1}{4}$ second. **about 14.1 cm**

c. The equation $v = (-20 \text{ cm})(\pi \text{ rad/s}) \cdot \sin(\pi \text{ rad/s} \cdot t)$ represents the velocity v of the object at time t. Find the velocity at $t = \frac{1}{4}$ second. **about −44.4 cm/s**

30a. amplitude: 20 cm; frequency: 0.5 vibrations per second; period: 2 seconds

31a. $y = \cos 260\pi t$; See Chapter 13 Answer Appendix for graph.

31b. The amplitude remains the same. The period decreases because it is the reciprocal of the frequency.

31. **PIANOS** A piano string vibrates at a frequency of 130 hertz.

a. Write and graph an equation using cosine to model the vibration of the string y as a function of time t. Let the amplitude equal 1 unit.

b. Suppose the frequency of the vibration doubles. Do the amplitude and period increase, decrease, or remain the same? Explain.

Find the amplitude, if it exists, and period of each function. Then graph the function.

32. $y = 3 \sin \frac{2}{3}\theta$
33. $y = \frac{1}{2} \cos \frac{3}{4}\theta$
34. $y = 2 \tan \frac{1}{2}\theta$
35. $y = 2 \sec \frac{4}{5}\theta$
36. $y = 5 \csc 3\theta$
37. $y = 2 \cot 6\theta$

32–37. See Chapter 13 Answer Appendix.

Identify the period of the graph and write an equation for each function.

38.

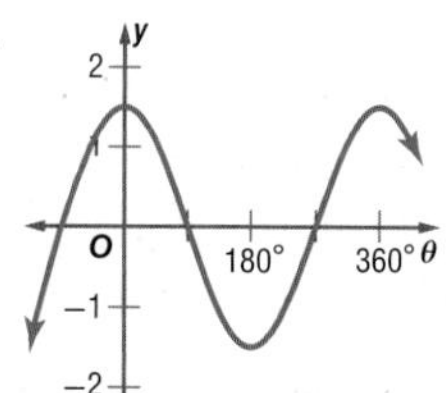

360°; $y = \frac{3}{2} \cos \theta$

39.

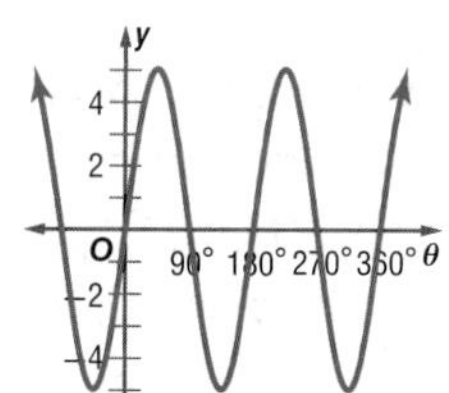

180°; $y = 5 \sin 2\theta$

40.

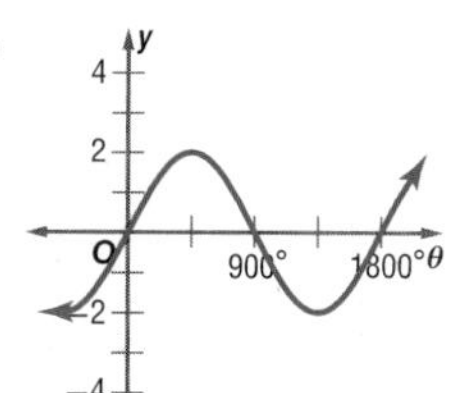

1800°; $y = 2 \sin \frac{1}{5}\theta$

H.O.T. Problems
Use **H**igher-**O**rder **T**hinking Skills

41. **CHALLENGE** Describe the domain and range of $y = a \cos \theta$ and $y = a \sec \theta$, where a is any positive real number.

42. **REASONING** Compare and contrast the graphs of $y = \frac{1}{2} \sin \theta$ and $y = \sin \frac{1}{2}\theta$.

43. **OPEN ENDED** Write a trigonometric function that has an amplitude of 3 and a period of 180°. Then graph the function. **See margin.**

44. **WRITING IN MATH** Explain how to find the amplitude of $y = -2 \sin \theta$, and describe how the negative coefficient affects the graph. **Find the absolute value of −2, which is 2. The negative coefficient causes the graph to be reflected over the x-axis.**

41. The domain of $y = a \cos \theta$ is the set of all real numbers. The domain of $y = a \sec \theta$ is the set of all real numbers except the values for which $\cos \theta = 0$. The range of $y = a \cos \theta$ is $-a \le y \le a$. The range of $y = a \sec \theta$ is $y \le -a$ and $y \ge a$.

42. The graph of $y = \frac{1}{2} \sin \theta$ has an amplitude of $\frac{1}{2}$ and a period of 360°. The graph of $y = \sin \frac{1}{2}\theta$ has an amplitude of 1 and a period of 720°.

Enrichment
CRM p. 46 OL BL

13-7 Enrichment

Blueprints

Interpreting blueprints requires the ability to select and use trigonometric functions and geometric properties. The figure below represents a plan for an improvement to a roof. The metal fitting shown makes a 30° angle with the horizontal. The vertices of the geometric shapes are *not* labeled in these plans. Relevant information must be selected and the appropriate function used to find the unknown measures.

Example **Find the unknown measures in the figure at the right.**

The measures x and y are the legs of a right triangle.

The measure of the hypotenuse is $\frac{15}{16}$ in. + $\frac{5}{16}$ in. or $\frac{20}{16}$ in.

$\frac{y}{\frac{20}{16}} = \cos 30°$ $\frac{x}{\frac{20}{16}} = \sin 30°$

$y = 1.08$ in. $x = 0.63$ in.

Roofing Improvement

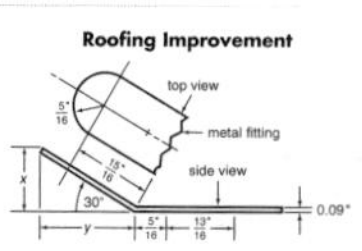

Additional Answer

29b.

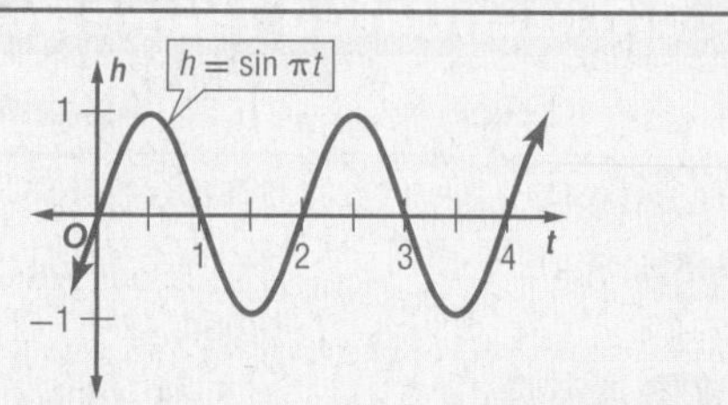

NGSSS PRACTICE 912.D.11.3, 912.S.3.3, 912.A.8.7

45. **SHORT RESPONSE** Find the 100,001st term of the sequence. **700,013**

13, 20, 27, 34, 41, …

46. **STATISTICS** You bowled five games and had the following scores: 143, 171, 167, 133, and 156. What was your average? **C**

A. 147 B. 153 C. 154 D. 156

47. Your city had a population of 312,430 ten years ago. If its current population is 418,270, by what percentage has it grown over the past 10 years? **G**

F. 25% G. 34% H. 66% I. 75%

48. **SAT/ACT** If $h + 4 = b - 3$, then $(h - 2)^2 =$ **B**

A. $h^2 + 4$
B. $b^2 - 18b + 81$
C. $b^2 - 14b + 49$
D. $b^2 - 10b + 25$

Spiral Review

Find the exact value of each expression. (Lesson 13-6)

49. $\cos 120° - \sin 30°$ **-1**

50. $3(\sin 45°)(\sin 60°)$ **$\frac{3\sqrt{6}}{4}$**

51. $4 \sin \frac{4\pi}{3} - 2 \cos \frac{\pi}{6}$ **$-3\sqrt{3}$**

Solve each triangle. Round side lengths to the nearest tenth and angle measures to the nearest degree. (Lesson 13-5) **52. $B \approx 17°$, $C \approx 139°$, $c \approx 7.2$ 53. $R \approx 103°$, $S \approx 45°$, $q \approx 11.2$ 54. $F \approx 49°$, $G \approx 62°$, $H \approx 69°$**

52. 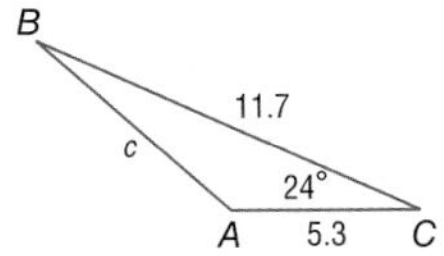

53. 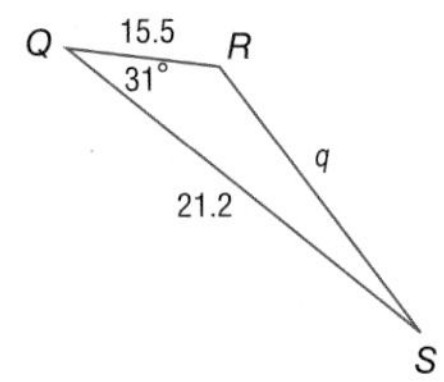

54. 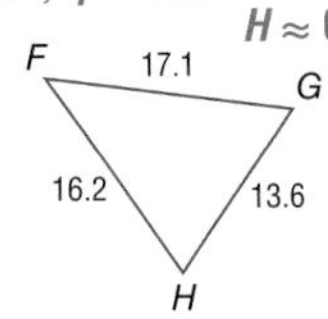

A bag contains 12 blue marbles, 9 red marbles, and 8 green marbles. The marbles are drawn one at a time. Find each probability. (Lesson 12-3)

55. The second marble is blue, given that the first marble is green and is replaced. **$\frac{12}{29}$**

56. The third marble is green, given that the first two are red and blue and not replaced. **$\frac{8}{27}$**

57. The third marble is red, given that the first two are red and not replaced. **$\frac{7}{27}$**

58. **BANKING** Rita has deposited $1000 in a bank account. At the end of each year, the bank posts interest to her account in the amount of 3% of the balance, but then takes out a $10 annual fee. (Lesson 11-6)

a. Let b_0 be the amount Rita deposited. Write a recursive equation for the balance b_n in her account at the end of n years. **$b_n = 1.03b_{n-1} - 10$**

b. Find the balance in the account after four years. **$1083.67**

Write an equation for an ellipse that satisfies each set of conditions. (Lesson 10-4)

59. center at (6, 3), focus at (2, 3), co-vertex at (6, 1) **$\frac{(x-2)^2}{20} + \frac{(y-3)^2}{4} = 1$**

60. foci at (2, 1) and (2, 13), co-vertex at (5, 7) **$\frac{(x-2)^2}{9} + \frac{(y-7)^2}{45} = 1$**

Skills Review

Graph each function. (Lesson 5-7) **61–63. See margin.**

61. $y = 2(x - 3)^2 - 4$

62. $y = \frac{1}{3}(x + 5)^2 + 2$

63. $y = -3(x + 6)^2 + 7$

Differentiated Instruction OL BL

Extension Ask students to graph $y = \sin(\theta - \pi)$, $y = \sin\left(\theta - \frac{\pi}{2}\right)$, and $y = \sin\left(\theta - \frac{\pi}{4}\right)$. Ask them to describe the effect of the term being subtracted from θ. The value being subtracted from θ determines how far to the right the graph of $y = \sin \theta$ is translated.

4 ASSESS

Ticket Out the Door Have students write a function of the form $y = a \sin b\theta$ or $y = a \cos b\theta$. Then have them state the amplitude and period of the graph.

Formative Assessment

Check student understanding of concepts in Lessons 13-6 and 13-7.

CRM Quiz 3, p. 62

Additional Answers

43. Sample answer: $y = 3 \sin 2\theta$

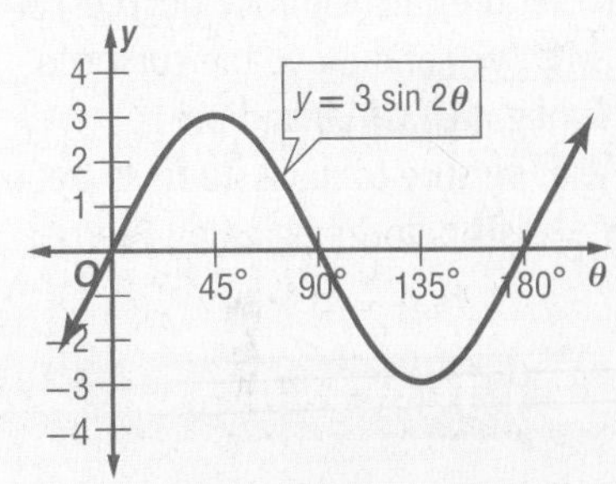

61. 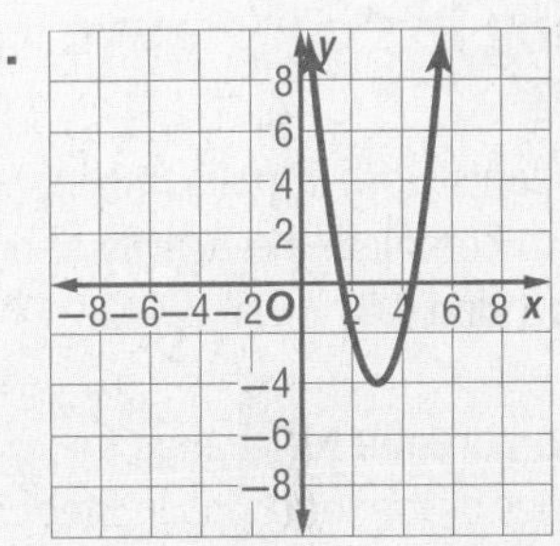

62. 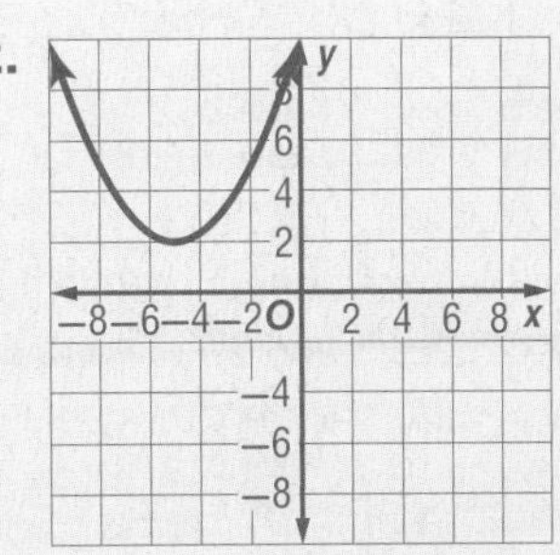

63. 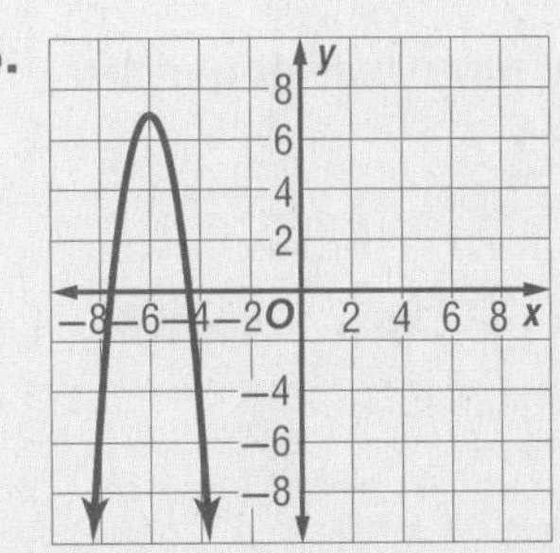

1 FOCUS

Objective Use a graphing calculator to explore transformations of the graphs of trigonometric functions.

Materials for Each Student

- TI-83/84 Plus or other graphing calculator

Teaching Tip

To set the calculator for degrees, press MODE and move the cursor to highlight **DEGREE** and press .
Also, be sure to have students clear the **Y** = lists before beginning Exercise 1.

2 TEACH

Working in Cooperative Groups

Have students work in pairs, mixing abilities, to complete the Activity and Exercises 1 and 2.

Ask:

- How do parentheses change the meanings of the functions in Steps 1 and 2? In Step 1, a number is added to the value of sin θ, while in Step 2, a number is added to θ before finding the sine.
- How do the parentheses change the graphs in Steps 1 and 2? The graphs in Step 1 "move" up or down, while the graphs in Step 2 "move" right or left.

Practice Have students complete Exercises 3–7.

Graphing Technology Lab
Trigonometric Graphs

FL Math Online glencoe.com
- Other Calculator Keystrokes
- Graphing Technology Personal Tutor

Objective
Use a graphing calculator to transform graphs of trigonometric functions.

NGSSS
MA.912.T.1.6 Define and graph trigonometric functions using domain, range, intercepts, period, amplitude, phase shift, vertical shift, and asymptotes with and without the use of graphing technology.

You can use a TI-83/84 Plus graphing calculator to explore transformations of the graphs of trigonometric functions.

ACTIVITY

Step 1 Graph $y = \sin\theta$, $y = \sin\theta + 2$, and $y = \sin\theta - 3$ on the same coordinate plane. Use the window shown at right. Let $Y1 = \sin\theta$, $Y2 = \sin\theta + 2$, and $Y3 = \sin\theta - 3$.

KEYSTROKES: [Y=] [SIN] [X,T,θ,n] [)] [ENTER]
[SIN] [X,T,θ,n] [)] [+] 2 [ENTER]
[SIN] [X,T,θ,n] [)] [−] 3 [GRAPH]

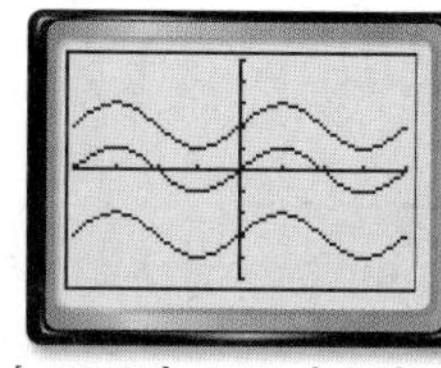

[−360, 360] scl: 90 by [−5, 5] scl: 1

Describe the relationship among the graphs.

Step 2 Graph $y = \sin\theta$, $y = \sin(\theta + 45°)$, and $y = \sin(\theta - 90°)$ on the same coordinate plane. Let $Y1 = \sin\theta$, $Y2 = \sin(\theta + 45)$, and $Y3 = \sin(\theta - 90)$. **Be sure to clear the entries from Step 1.**

KEYSTROKES: [Y=] [SIN] [X,T,θ,n] [)] [ENTER]
[SIN] [X,T,θ,n] [+] 45 [)] [ENTER]
[SIN] [X,T,θ,n] [−] 90 [)] [GRAPH]

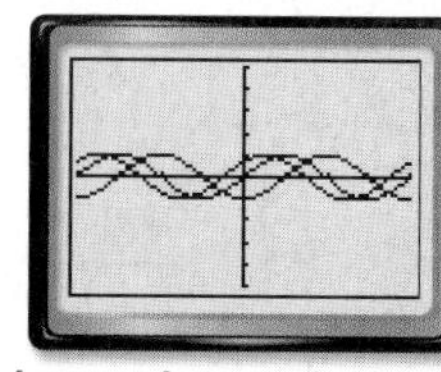

[−360, 360] scl: 90 by [−5, 5] scl: 1

Describe the relationship among the graphs.

Model and Analyze 1. Sample answer: Adding a constant to a trigonometric function translates the graph of the function vertically.

Repeat the activity for the cosine and tangent functions.

1. What is the effect of adding a constant to a trigonometric function?
2. What is the effect of adding a constant to θ in a trigonometric function? Sample answer: Adding a constant to θ translates the graph of the function horizontally.

Repeat the activity for each of the following. Describe the relationship between each pair of graphs. 3–6. See Chapter 13 Answer Appendix.

3. $y = \sin\theta + 4$
   $y = \sin(2\theta) + 4$
4. $y = \cos\left(\frac{1}{2}\theta\right)$
   $y = \cos\frac{1}{2}(\theta + 45°)$
5. $y = 2\sin\theta$
   $y = 2\sin\theta - 1$
6. $y = \cos\theta - 3$
   $y = \cos(\theta - 90°) - 3$
7. Write a general equation for the sine, cosine, and tangent functions after changes in amplitude a, period b, horizontal position h, and vertical position k.
   $y = a\sin(b\theta - h) + k$

3 ASSESS

Formative Assessment

Use Exercises 1 and 2 to assess whether students can describe the effect of adding a constant to a trigonometric function or to the value of θ in a trigonometric function.

From Concrete to Abstract

Ask students to describe how the value of n affects the graphs of $y = \sin\theta + n$ and $y = \sin(\theta + n)$. The graph of $y = \sin\theta + n$ is n units above $y = \sin\theta$; the graph of $y = \sin(\theta + n)$ is n units left of $y = \sin\theta$.

Translations of Trigonometric Graphs

Then
You translated exponential functions. (Lesson 8-1)

Now
- Graph horizontal translations of trigonometric graphs and find phase shifts.
- Graph vertical translations of trigonometric graphs.

NGSSS

MA.912.T.1.6 Define and graph trigonometric functions using domain, range, intercepts, period, amplitude, phase shift, vertical shift, and asymptotes with and without the use of graphing technology.
MA.912.T.1.8 Solve real-world problems involving applications of trigonometric functions using graphing technology when appropriate.

New Vocabulary
phase shift
vertical shift
midline

FL Math Online
glencoe.com

Why?

The graphs at the right represent the waves in a bay during high and low tides. Notice that the shape of the waves does not change.

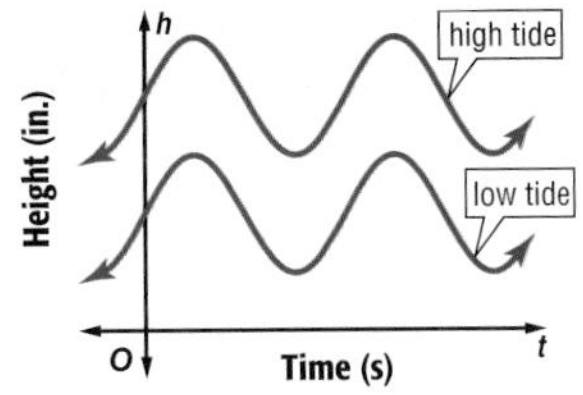

Horizontal Translations Recall that a *translation* occurs when a figure is moved from one location to another on the coordinate plane without changing its orientation. A horizontal translation of a periodic function is called a **phase shift**.

Key Concept — Phase Shift

Words The phase shift of the functions $y = a \sin b(\theta - h)$, $y = a \cos b(\theta - h)$, and $y = a \tan b(\theta - h)$ is h, where $b > 0$.

Models

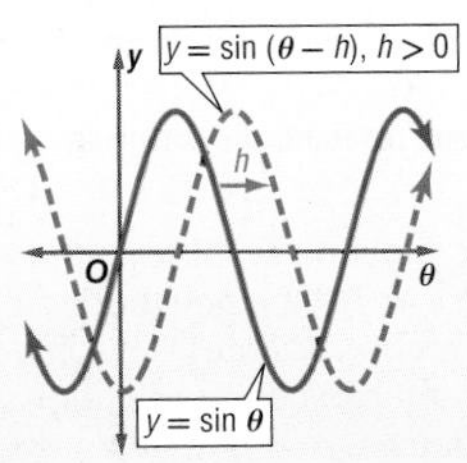

If $h > 0$, the shift is h units to the right.

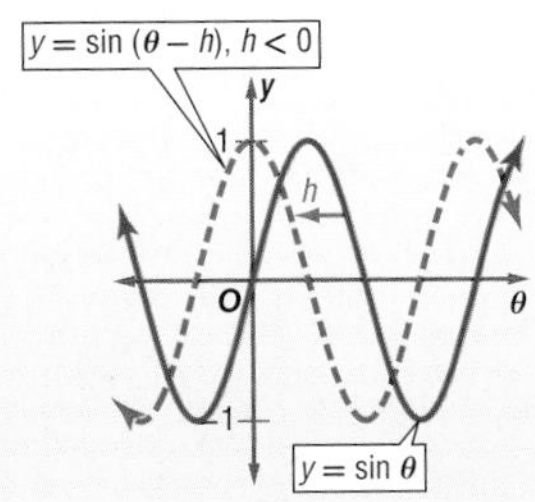

If $h < 0$, the shift is h units to the left.

Examples $y = \cos(\theta - 90°)$ The phase shift is 90° to the right.
$y = \tan(\theta + 30°)$ The phase shift is 30° to the left.

The secant, cosecant, and cotangent can be graphed using the same rules.

EXAMPLE 1 Graph Horizontal Translations

State the amplitude, period, and phase shift for $y = \sin(\theta - 90°)$. Then graph the function.

amplitude: $a = 1$

period: $\frac{360°}{|b|} = \frac{360°}{1}$ or 360°

phase shift: $h = 90°$

Graph $y = \sin\theta$ shifted 90° to the right.

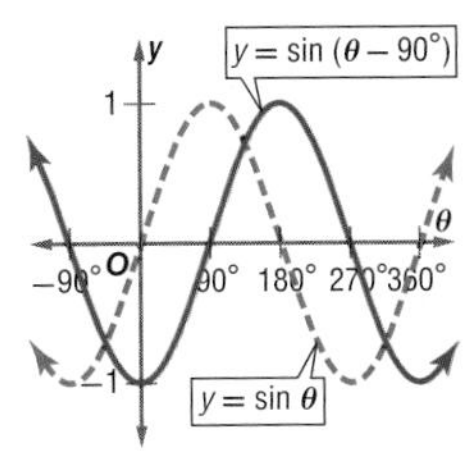

Guided Practice

1. State the amplitude, period, and phase shift for $y = 2\cos(\theta + 45°)$. Then graph the function. **2; 360°; $h = -45°$; See Chapter 13 Answer Appendix for graph.**

Personal Tutor glencoe.com

1 FOCUS

Vertical Alignment

Before Lesson 13-8
Translate exponential functions.

Lesson 13-8
Graph horizontal translations of trigonometric graphs and find phase shifts.
Graph vertical translations of trigonometric graphs.

After Lesson 13-8
Use trigonometry in a variety of applications and word problems.

2 TEACH

Scaffolding Questions

Have students read the *Why?* section of the lesson.

Ask:
- Compare the waves for high and low tides on their periods and amplitudes. The two waves have the same period and amplitude.
- What is represented by the horizontal axis? The horizontal axis represents time measured in seconds.
- What is represented by the vertical axis? The vertical axis shows the height above the bottom of the bay, measured in inches.
- According to the diagram, is the greatest level at low tide greater than the lowest level at high tide? no

Lesson 13-8 Resources

Resource	Approaching-Level	On-Level	Beyond-Level	English Learners
Teacher Edition	• Differentiated Instruction, p. 864	• Differentiated Instruction, p. 870	• Differentiated Instruction, p. 870	
Chapter Resource Masters	• Study Guide and Intervention, pp. 47–48 • Skills Practice, p. 49 • Practice, p. 50 • Word Problem Practice, p. 51	• Study Guide and Intervention, pp. 47–48 • Skills Practice, p. 49 • Practice, p. 50 • Word Problem Practice, p. 51 • Enrichment, p. 52	• Practice, p. 50 • Word Problem Practice, p. 51 • Enrichment, p. 52	• Study Guide and Intervention, pp. 47–48 • Skills Practice, p. 49 • Practice, p. 50 • Word Problem Practice, p. 51
Transparencies	• 5-Minute Check Transparency 13-8	• 5-Minute Check Transparency 13-8	• 5-Minute Check Transparency 13-8	• 5-Minute Check Transparency 13-8
Other	• Study Notebook	• Study Notebook	• Study Notebook	• Study Notebook

Horizontal Translations

Example 1 shows how to graph horizontal translations of trigonometric functions.

Formative Assessment

Use the Guided Practice exercises after each example to determine students' understanding of concepts.

Additional Example

1 State the amplitude, period, and phase shift for $y = 2 \sin(\theta + 20°)$. Then graph the function.
amplitude: 2; period: 360°; phase shift: 20° left

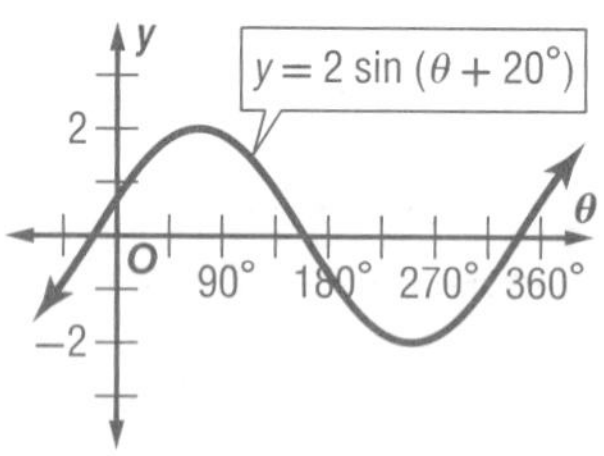

Additional Examples also in Interactive Classroom PowerPoint® Presentations

IWB INTERACTIVE WHITEBOARD READY

Vertical Translations

Example 2 shows how to graph vertical translations of trigonometric functions. **Example 3** shows how to graph a function that combines a horizontal and a vertical translation of a trigonometric function. **Example 4** shows how to solve a real-world problem using translations.

Additional Answer (Guided Practice)

2. no amplitude; 180°; $k = 3$; $y = 3$

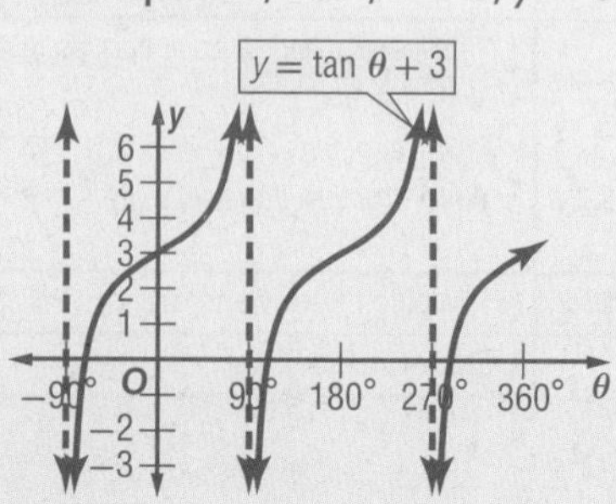

Vertical Translations Recall that the graph of $y = x^2 + 5$ is the graph of the parent function $y = x^2$ shifted up 5 units. Similarly, graphs of trigonometric functions can be translated vertically through a **vertical shift**.

StudyTip

Notation Note that $\sin(\theta + x) \neq \sin \theta + x$. The first expression indicates a phase shift. The second expression indicates a vertical shift.

Key Concept — Vertical Shift

Words The vertical shift of the functions $y = a \sin b\theta + k$, $y = a \cos b\theta + k$, and $y = a \tan b\theta + k$ is k.

Models

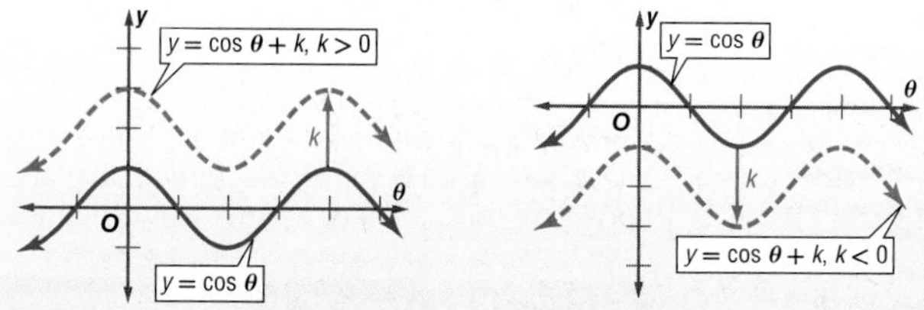

If $k > 0$, the shift is k units up. If $k < 0$, the shift is k units down.

Examples $y = \sin \theta + 4$ The vertical shift is 4 units up.
$y = \tan \theta - 3$ The vertical shift is 3 units down.

The secant, cosecant, and cotangent can be graphed using the same rules.

When a trigonometric function is shifted up or down k units, the line $y = k$ is the new horizontal axis about which the graph oscillates. This line is called the **midline**, and it can be used to help draw vertical translations.

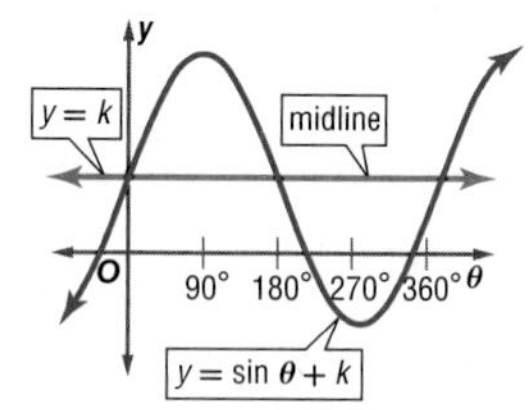

StudyTip

Using Color It may be helpful to first graph the parent function in one color. Next, apply the vertical shift and graph the function in another color. Then apply the change in amplitude and graph the function in the final color.

EXAMPLE 2 Graph Vertical Translations

State the amplitude, period, vertical shift, and equation of the midline for $y = \frac{1}{2} \cos \theta - 2$. Then graph the function.

amplitude: $|a| = \frac{1}{2}$

period: $\frac{2\pi}{|b|} = \frac{2\pi}{|1|}$ or 2π

vertical shift: $k = -2$

midline: $y = -2$

To graph $y = \frac{1}{2} \cos \theta - 2$, first draw the midline. Then use it to graph $y = \frac{1}{2} \cos \theta$ shifted 2 units down.

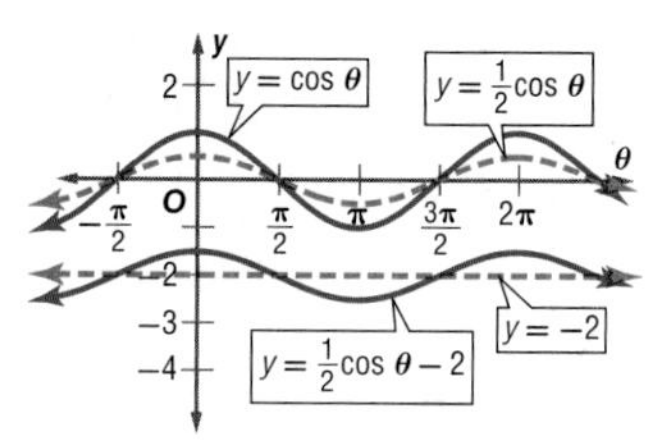

Guided Practice

2. State the amplitude, period, vertical shift, and equation of the midline for $y = \tan \theta + 3$. Then graph the function. **See margin.**

Personal Tutor glencoe.com

Differentiated Instruction AL

If students struggle with translations of trigonometric graphs,

Then make coordinate axes with masking tape on the classroom floor. Give students at least 15 feet of rope and have them stand along the x-axis, positioning the rope to model the graph of $y = \sin x$. As you call out equations of functions with graphs being horizontal phase shifts of the graph of $y = \sin x$, students can step left or right to model the translated graph. Similarly, call out functions with graphs being vertical shifts of the graph $y = \sin x$.

You can use the following steps to graph trigonometric functions involving phase shifts and vertical shifts.

Concept Summary **Graph Trigonometric Functions**

$$y = a \sin b(\theta - h) + k$$

amplitude: a; period: b; phase shift: h; vertical shift: k

Step 1 Determine the vertical shift, and graph the midline.

Step 2 Determine the amplitude, if it exists. Use dashed lines to indicate the maximum and minimum values of the function.

Step 3 Determine the period of the function, and graph the appropriate function.

Step 4 Determine the phase shift, and translate the graph accordingly.

EXAMPLE 3 **Graph Transformations**

State the amplitude, period, phase shift, and vertical shift for $y = 3 \sin \frac{2}{3}(\theta - \pi) + 4$. Then graph the function.

amplitude: $|a| = 3$

period: $\frac{2\pi}{|b|} = \frac{2\pi}{\left|\frac{2}{3}\right|}$ or 3π — **The period indicates that the graph will be stretched.**

phase shift: $h = \pi$ — **The graph will shift π to the right.**

vertical shift: $k = 4$ — **The graph will shift 4 units up.**

midline: $y = 4$ — **The graph will oscillate around the line $y = 4$.**

Step 1 Graph the midline.

Step 2 Since the amplitude is 3, draw dashed lines 3 units above and 3 units below the midline.

Step 3 Graph $y = 3 \sin \frac{2}{3}\theta + 4$ using the midline as a reference.

Step 4 Shift the graph π to the right.

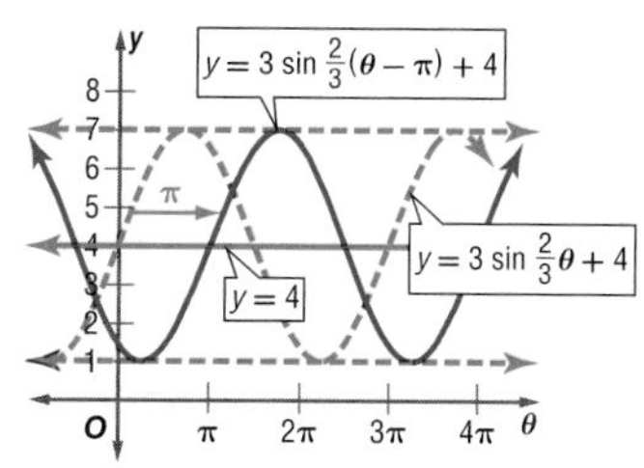

CHECK You can check the accuracy of your transformation by evaluating the function for various values of θ and confirming their location on the graph.

StudyTip

Verifying a Graph After drawing the graph of a trigonometric function, select values of θ and evaluate them in the equation to verify your graph.

Guided Practice

3. State the amplitude, period, phase shift, and vertical shift for $y = 2 \cos \frac{1}{2}\left(\theta + \frac{\pi}{2}\right) - 2$. Then graph the function. **See margin.**

Personal Tutor glencoe.com

Additional Examples

2 State the amplitude, period, vertical shift, and equation of the midline for $y = \frac{1}{2}\cos \theta + 3$. Then graph the function.

amplitude: $\frac{1}{2}$; period: 360° or 2π; vertical shift: 3 units up; midline: $y = 3$

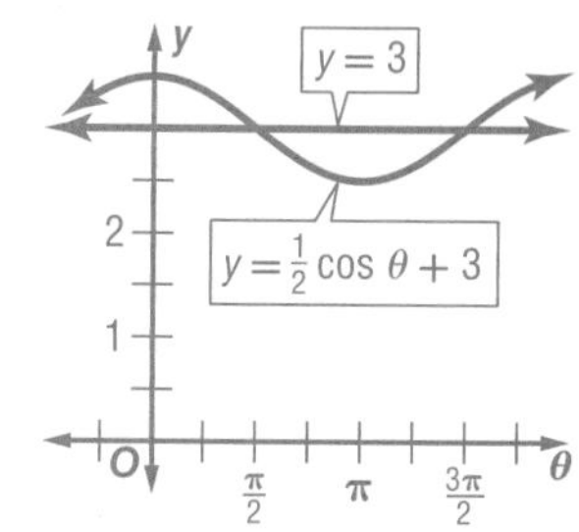

3 State the amplitude, period, phase shift, and vertical shift for $y = 3 \sin \left[2\left(\theta - \frac{\pi}{2}\right)\right] + 4$. Then graph the function.

amplitude: 3; period: π; phase shift: $\frac{\pi}{2}$ to the right; vertical shift: 4 units up

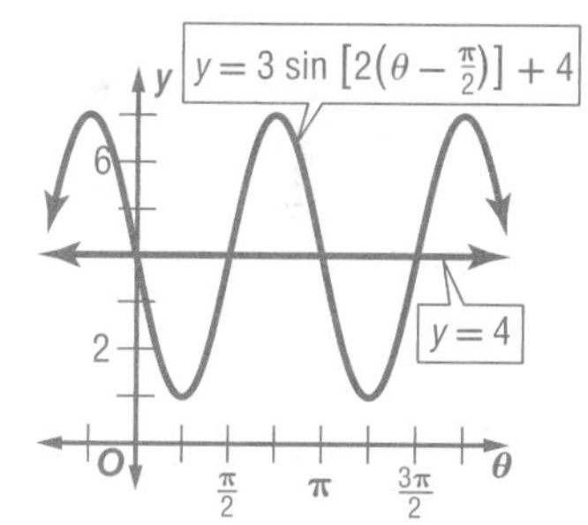

Additional Answer (Guided Practice)

3. 2; 4π; $h = -\frac{\pi}{2}$; $k = -2$

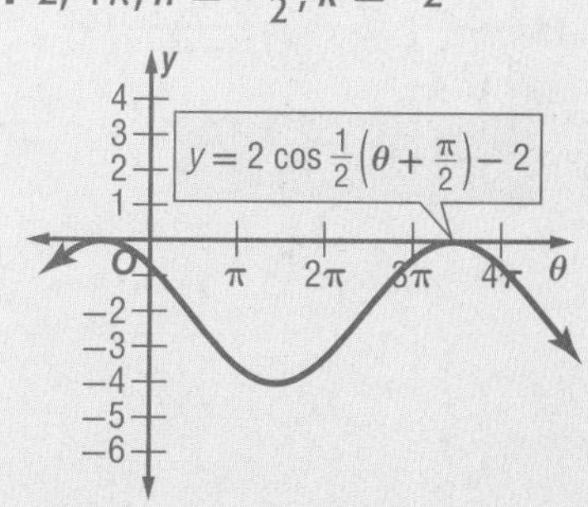

Tips for New Teachers

Reading Math Make sure students are clear about the difference between the terms *vertical* and *horizontal.* Students can use the words *vertigo* (a sense of dizziness some people experience when looking down from a great height) and *horizon* to help link vertical and horizontal to their relative direction.

TEACH with TECH

INTERACTIVE WHITEBOARD Show a coordinate grid on the board. Draw a sine or cosine graph on the grid and have students find the equation of the graph. Drag the graph up or down along the y-axis and left or right along the x-axis. After each time you move the graph, have students find its equation. Discuss how the equations are similar and different.

Lesson 13-8 Translations of Trigonometric Graphs **865**

Additional Example

4 **WAVE POOL** In Example 4, suppose the height of water oscillates between a maximum of 10 feet and a minimum of 6 feet, and the wave generator pumps 3 waves per minute. Write a sine function that represents the height of the water at time *t* seconds. Then graph the function. $h = 2 \sin \frac{\pi}{10}t + 8$

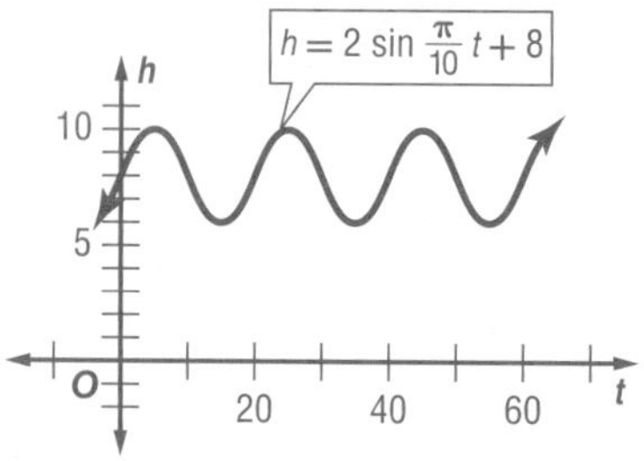

Focus on Mathematical Content

Horizontal and Vertical Translations Students often confuse which parameter in $y = a \sin b(\theta - h) + k$ affects which transformation: h determines the horizontal translation, a determines the amplitude, b changes the period, and k determines the vertical translation.

Additional Answer (Guided Practice)

4. $h = 4 \cos \frac{\pi}{6}t + 10$

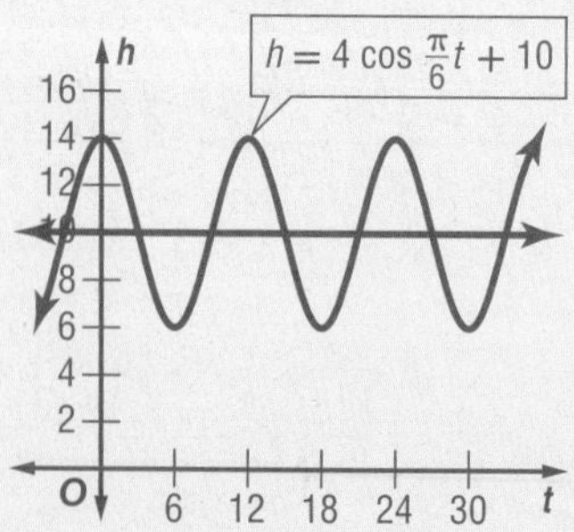

Real-World Link

In some wave pools, surfers can ride waves up to 70 meters.

Source: Orlando Wave Pool

The sine wave occurs often in physics, signal processing, music, electrical engineering, and many other fields.

Real-World EXAMPLE 4 Represent Periodic Functions

WAVE POOL The height of water in a wave pool oscillates between a maximum of 13 feet and a minimum of 5 feet. The wave generator pumps 6 waves per minute. Write a sine function that represents the height of the water at time *t* seconds. Then graph the function.

Step 1 Write the equation for the midline, and determine the vertical shift.

$y = \frac{13 + 5}{2}$ or 9 — **The midline lies halfway between the maximum and minimum values.**

Since the midline is $y = 9$, the vertical shift is $k = 9$.

Step 2 Find the amplitude.

$|a| = |13 - 9|$ or 4 — **Find the difference between the midline value and the maximum value.**

So, $a = 4$.

Step 3 Find the period.

Since there are 6 waves per minute, there is 1 wave every 10 seconds. So, the period is 10 seconds.

$10 = \frac{2\pi}{|b|}$ — **period** $= \frac{2\pi}{|b|}$

$|b| = \frac{2\pi}{10}$ — **Solve for** $|b|$.

$b = \pm\frac{\pi}{5}$ — **Simplify.**

Step 4 Write an equation for the function.

$h = a \sin b(t - h) + k$ — **Write the equation for sine relating height *h* and time *t*.**

$= 4 \sin \frac{\pi}{5}(t - 0) + 9$ — **Substitution:** $a = 4, b = \frac{\pi}{5}, h = 0, k = 9$

$= 4 \sin \frac{\pi}{5}t + 9$ — **Simplify.**

Then graph the function.

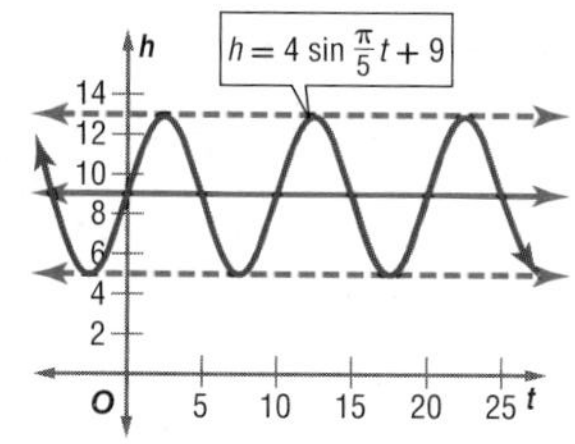

Guided Practice

4. WAVE POOL The height of water in a wave pool oscillates between a maximum of 14 feet and a minimum of 6 feet. The wave generator pumps 5 waves per minute. Write a cosine function that represents the height of water at time *t* seconds. Then graph the function. **See margin.**

Personal Tutor glencoe.com

Additional Answers

1. 1; 360°; $h = 180°$

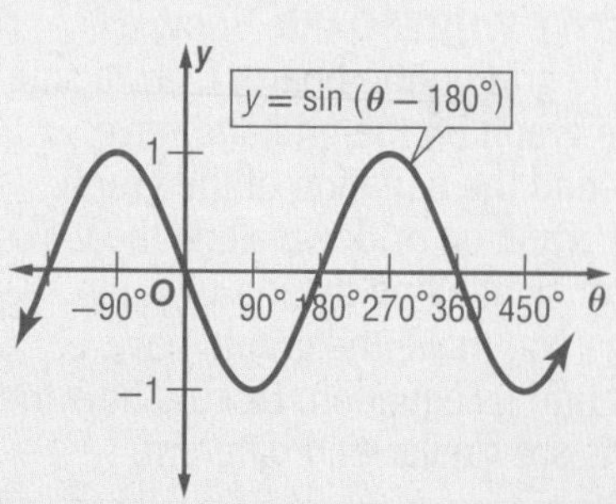

2. no amplitude; 180°; $h = \frac{\pi}{4}$

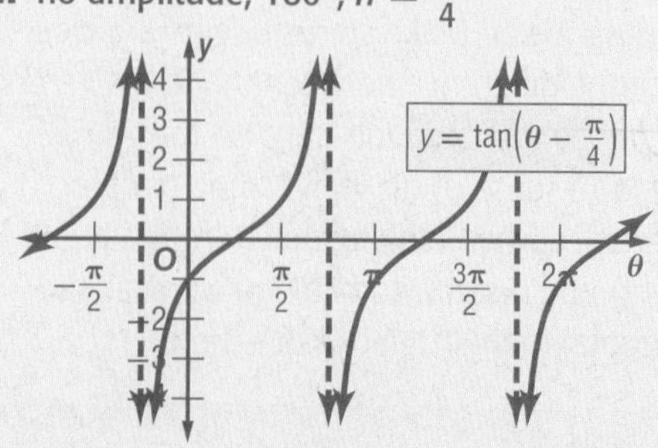

866 Chapter 13 Trigonometric Functions

Check Your Understanding

Example 1 p. 863

State the amplitude, period, and phase shift for each function. Then graph the function. 1–4. See margin.

1. $y = \sin(\theta - 180°)$
2. $y = \tan\left(\theta - \frac{\pi}{4}\right)$
3. $y = \sin\left(\theta - \frac{\pi}{2}\right)$
4. $y = \frac{1}{2}\cos(\theta + 90°)$

Example 2 p. 864

State the amplitude, period, vertical shift, and equation of the midline for each function. Then graph the function. 5–8. See margin.

5. $y = \cos\theta + 4$
6. $y = \sin\theta - 2$
7. $y = \frac{1}{2}\tan\theta + 1$
8. $y = \sec\theta - 5$

Example 3 p. 865

State the amplitude, period, phase shift, and vertical shift for each function. Then graph the function. 9–12. See Chapter 13 Answer Appendix.

9. $y = 2\sin(\theta + 45°) + 1$
10. $y = \cos 3(\theta - \pi) - 4$
11. $y = \frac{1}{4}\tan 2(\theta + 30°) + 3$
12. $y = 4\sin\frac{1}{2}\left(\theta - \frac{\pi}{2}\right) + 5$

Example 4 p. 866

13. **EXERCISE** While doing some moderate physical activity, a person's blood pressure oscillates between a maximum of 130 and a minimum of 90. The person's heart rate is 90 beats per minute. Write a sine function that represents the person's blood pressure P at time t seconds. Then graph the function. See Chapter 13 Answer Appendix.

Practice and Problem Solving

= **Step-by-Step Solutions** begin on page R20.
Extra Practice begins on page 947.

Example 1 p. 863

State the amplitude, period, and phase shift for each function. Then graph the function. 14–19. See Chapter 13 Answer Appendix.

14. $y = \cos(\theta + 180°)$
15. $y = \tan(\theta - 90°)$
16. $y = \sin(\theta + \pi)$
17. $y = 2\sin\left(\theta + \frac{\pi}{2}\right)$
18. $y = \tan\frac{1}{2}(\theta + 30°)$
19. $y = 3\cos\left(\theta - \frac{\pi}{3}\right)$

Example 2 p. 864

State the amplitude, period, vertical shift, and equation of the midline for each function. Then graph the function. 20–25. See Chapter 13 Answer Appendix.

20. $y = \cos\theta + 3$
21. $y = \tan\theta - 1$
22. $y = \tan\theta + \frac{1}{2}$
23. $y = 2\cos\theta - 5$
24. $y = 2\sin\theta - 4$
25. $y = \frac{1}{3}\sin\theta + 7$

Example 3 p. 865

State the amplitude, period, phase shift, and vertical shift for each function. Then graph the function. 26–33. See Chapter 13 Answer Appendix.

26. $y = 4\sin(\theta - 60°) - 1$
27. $y = \cos\frac{1}{2}(\theta - 90°) + 2$
28. $y = \tan(\theta + 30°) - 2$
29. $y = 2\tan 2\left(\theta + \frac{\pi}{4}\right) - 5$
30. $y = \frac{1}{2}\sin\left(\theta - \frac{\pi}{2}\right) + 4$
31. $y = \cos 3(\theta - 45°) + \frac{1}{2}$
32. $y = 3 + 5\sin 2(\theta - \pi)$
33. $y = -2 + 3\sin\frac{1}{3}\left(\theta - \frac{\pi}{2}\right)$

Example 4 p. 866

34. **TIDES** The height of the water in a harbor rose to a maximum height of 15 feet at 6:00 P.M. and then dropped to a minimum level of 3 feet by 3:00 A.M. The water level can be modeled by the sine function. Write an equation that represents the height h of the water t hours after noon on the first day. $h = 9 + 6\sin\left[\frac{\pi}{9}(t - 1.5)\right]$

3 PRACTICE

Formative Assessment

Use Exercises 1–13 to check for understanding.

Use the chart at the bottom of the next page to customize assignments for your students.

Additional Answers

3. $1; 2\pi; \frac{\pi}{2}$

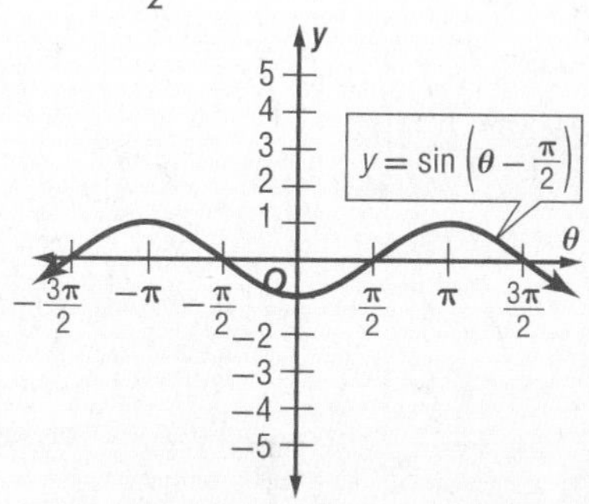

4. $\frac{1}{2}; 360°; h = -90°$

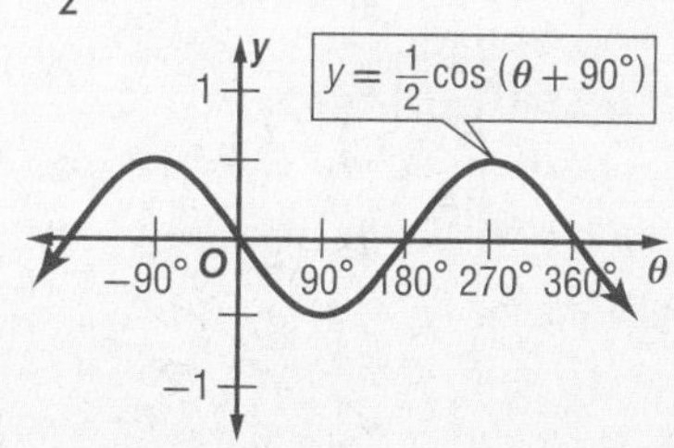

5. $1; 360°; k = 4; y = 4$

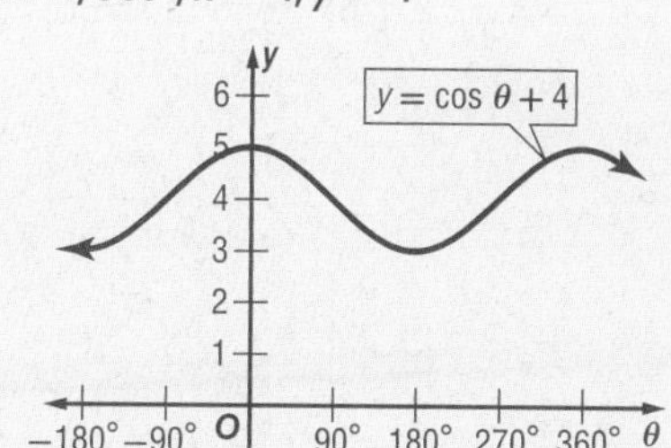

6. $1; 360°; k = -2; y = -2$

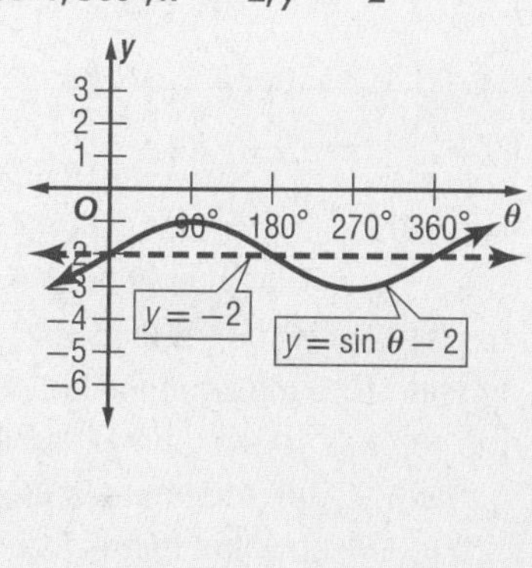

7. no amplitude; $180°; k = 1; y = 1$

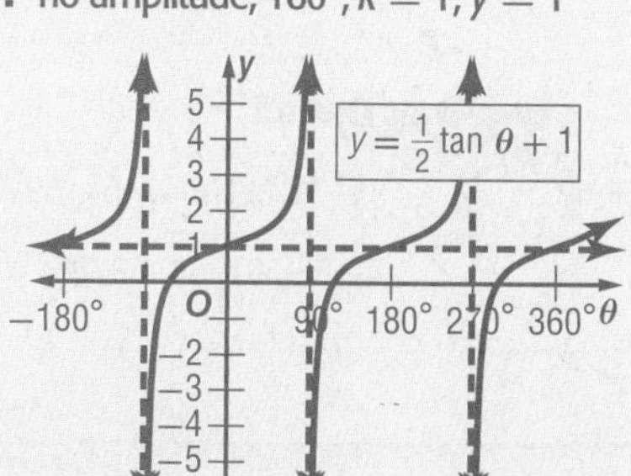

8. $k = -5; y = -5$; no amplitude; $360°$

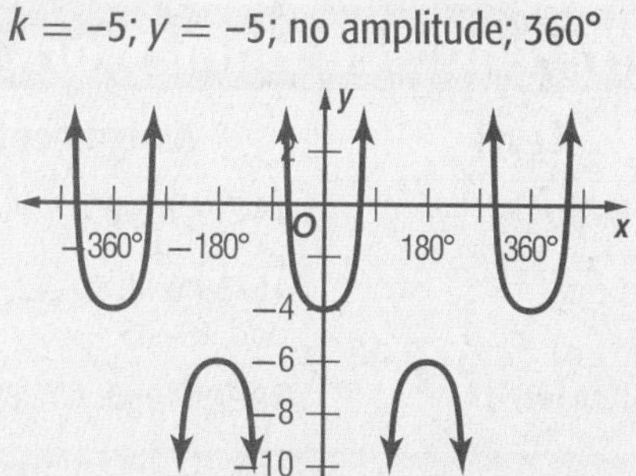

Additional Answers

35.

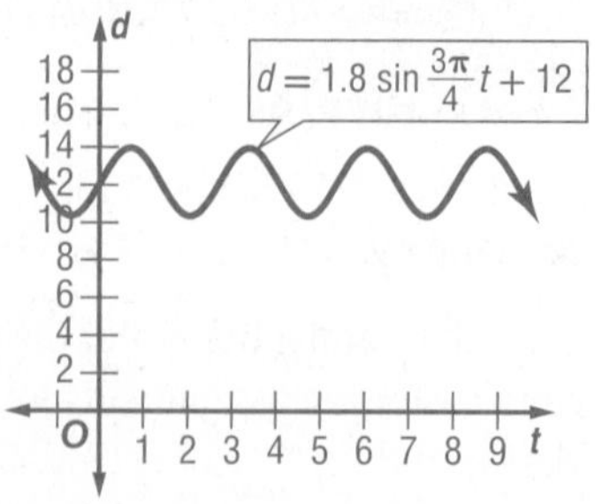

min: 10.2 ft; max: 13.8 ft

36. $h = 260 \cos \frac{\pi}{15}t + 265$

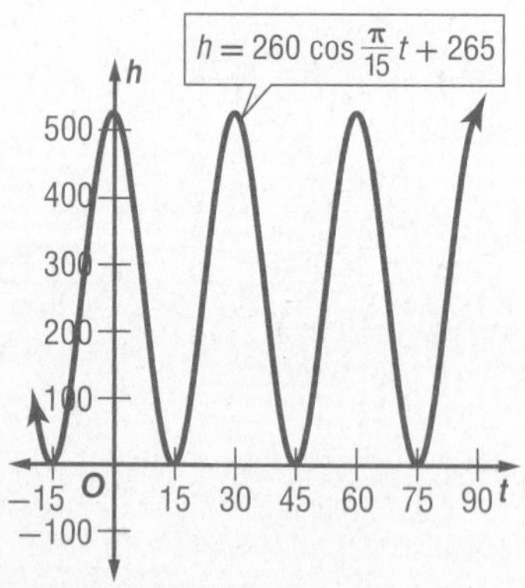

41b.

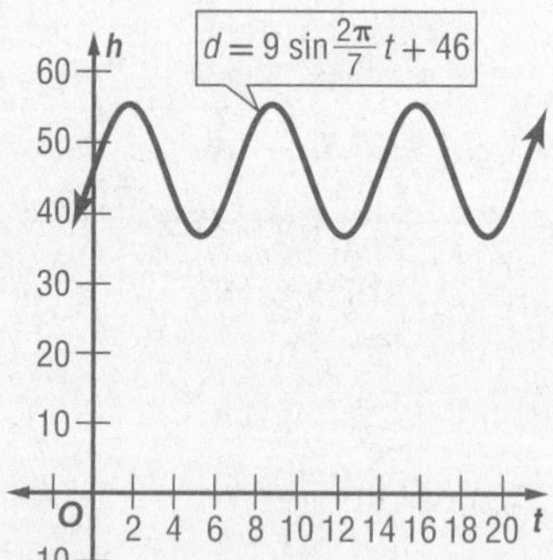

42c.

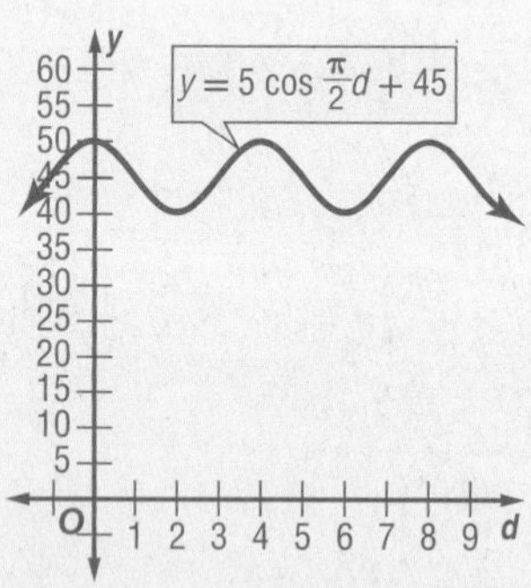

60. Sometimes; if the function is shifted vertically, then you also need to know the value of the midline. The maximum value is the value of the midline plus the amplitude. The minimum value is the midline value minus the amplitude.

35. LAKES A buoy marking the swimming area in a lake oscillates each time a speed boat goes by. Its distance d in feet from the bottom of the lake is given by $d = 1.8 \sin \frac{3\pi}{4}t + 12$, where t is the time in seconds. Graph the function. Describe the minimum and maximum distances of the buoy from the bottom of the lake when a boat passes by. **See margin.**

36. FERRIS WHEEL Suppose a Ferris wheel has a diameter of approximately 520 feet and makes one complete revolution in 30 minutes. Suppose the lowest car on the Ferris wheel is 5 feet from the ground. Let the height at the top of the wheel represent the height at time 0. Write an equation for the height of a car h as a function of time t minutes. Then graph the function. **See margin.**

Write an equation for each translation.

37. $y = \sin x$, 4 units to the right and 3 units up $y = \sin (x - 4) + 3$

38. $y = \cos x$, 5 units to the left and 2 units down $y = \cos (x + 5) - 2$

39. $y = \tan x$, π units to the right and 2.5 units up $y = \tan (x - \pi) + 2.5$

40a. At 1.25 seconds, the height of the rope is 68 inches; at 2.75 seconds, the height of the rope is 2 inches.

B

40. JUMP ROPE The graph at the right approximates the height of a jump rope h in inches as a function of time t in seconds. A maximum point on the graph is (1.25, 68), and a minimum point is (2.75, 2).

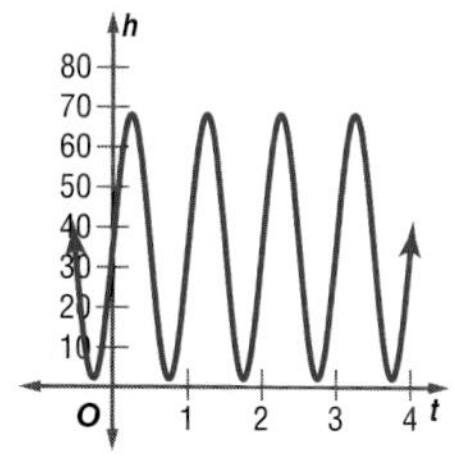

a. Describe what the maximum and minimum points mean in the context of the situation.

b. What is the equation for the midline, the amplitude, and the period of the function? $y = 35$; 33, 1

c. Write an equation for the function. $h = 33 \sin 2\pi t + 35$

Real-World Link

The record for jump rope is 151,036 jumps of rope in 24 hours. That is an average of 104 skips every minute for the entire day.

Source: *Guinness Book of World Records*

41 CAROUSEL A horse on a carousel goes up and down 3 times as the carousel makes one complete rotation. The maximum height of the horse is 55 inches, and the minimum height is 37 inches. The carousel rotates once every 21 seconds. Assume that the horse starts and stops at its median height. a. $h = 9 \sin \frac{2\pi}{7}t + 46$

a. Write an equation to represent the height of the horse h as a function of time t seconds.

b. Graph the function. **See margin.**

c. Use your graph to estimate the height of the horse after 8 seconds. Then use a calculator to find the height to the nearest tenth. **Sample answer: 8 s; 53.0 in.**

42. TEMPERATURES During one month, the outside temperature fluctuates between 40°F and 50°F. A cosine curve approximates the change in temperature, with a high of 50°F being reached every four days.

a. Describe the amplitude, period, and midline of the function that approximates the temperature y on day d. 5; 4; $y = 45$

b. Write a cosine function to estimate the temperature y on day d. $y = 5 \cos \frac{\pi}{2}d + 45$

c. Sketch a graph of the function. **See margin.**

d. Estimate the temperature on the 7th day of the month. **about 45°F**

Find a coordinate that represents a maximum for each graph.

43. $y = -2 \cos \left(x - \frac{\pi}{2}\right)$ $\left(\frac{3\pi}{2}, 2\right)$

44. $y = 4 \sin \left(x + \frac{\pi}{3}\right)$ $\left(\frac{\pi}{6}, 4\right)$

45. $y = 3 \tan \left(x + \frac{\pi}{2}\right) + 2$ no maximum values

46. $y = -3 \sin \left(x - \frac{\pi}{4}\right) - 4$ $\left(\frac{7\pi}{4}, -1\right)$

Differentiated Homework Options

Level	Assignment	Two-Day Option	
AL Basic	14–39, 61–85	15–39 odd, 65–68	16–38 even, 61–64, 69–85
OL Core	15–39 odd, 40–42, 43–59 odd, 61–85	15–39, 65–68	40–59, 61–64, 69–85
BL Advanced	40–79, (optional: 80–85)		

868 Chapter 13 Trigonometric Functions

47. The graphs are reflections of each other over the x-axis.

Compare each pair of graphs.

47. $y = -\cos 3\theta$ and $y = \sin 3(\theta - 90°)$

48. $y = 2 + 0.5 \tan \theta$ and $y = 2 + 0.5 \tan (\theta + \pi)$ **The graphs are identical.**

49. $y = 2 \sin \left(\theta - \frac{\pi}{6}\right)$ and $y = -2 \sin \left(\theta + \frac{5\pi}{6}\right)$ **The graphs are identical.**

C Identify the period of each function. Then write an equation for the graph using the given trigonometric function.

50. sine

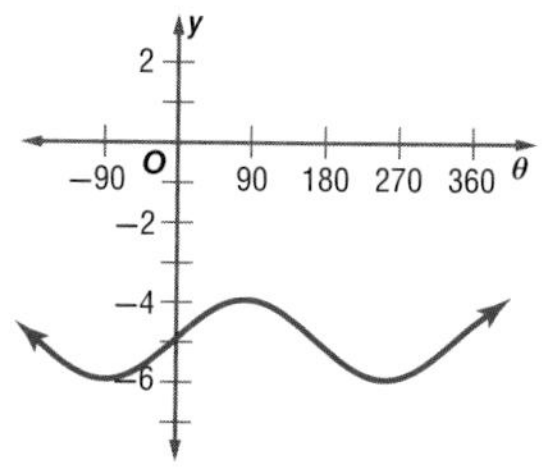

51. cosine

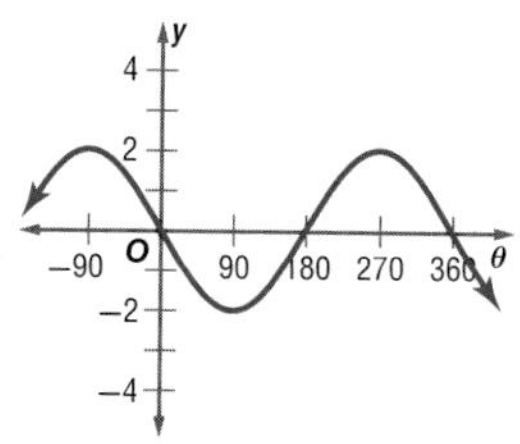

52. cosine

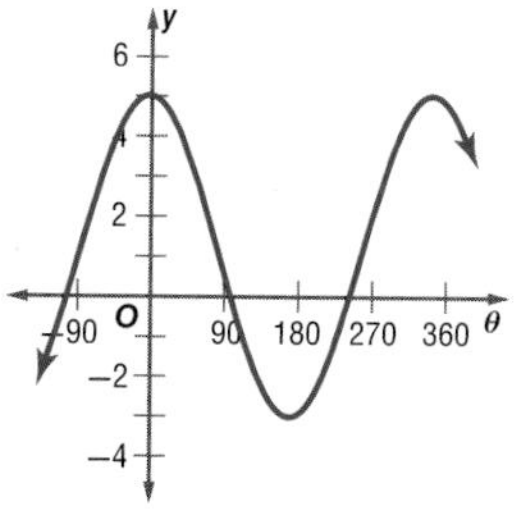

53 sine

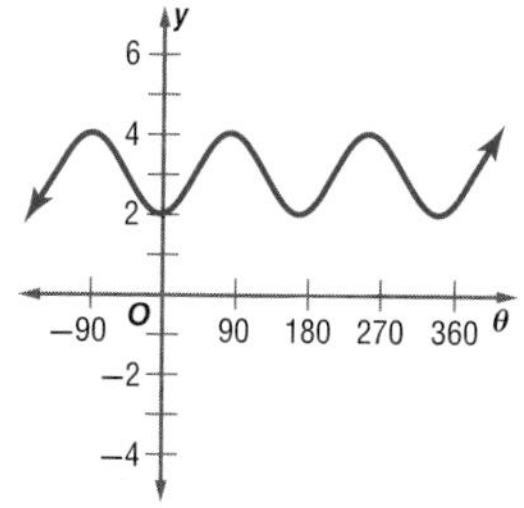

Watch Out!

Parent Functions Often the graph of a trigonometric function can be represented by more than one equation. For example, the graphs of $y = \cos \theta$ and $y = \sin (\theta + 90°)$ are the same.

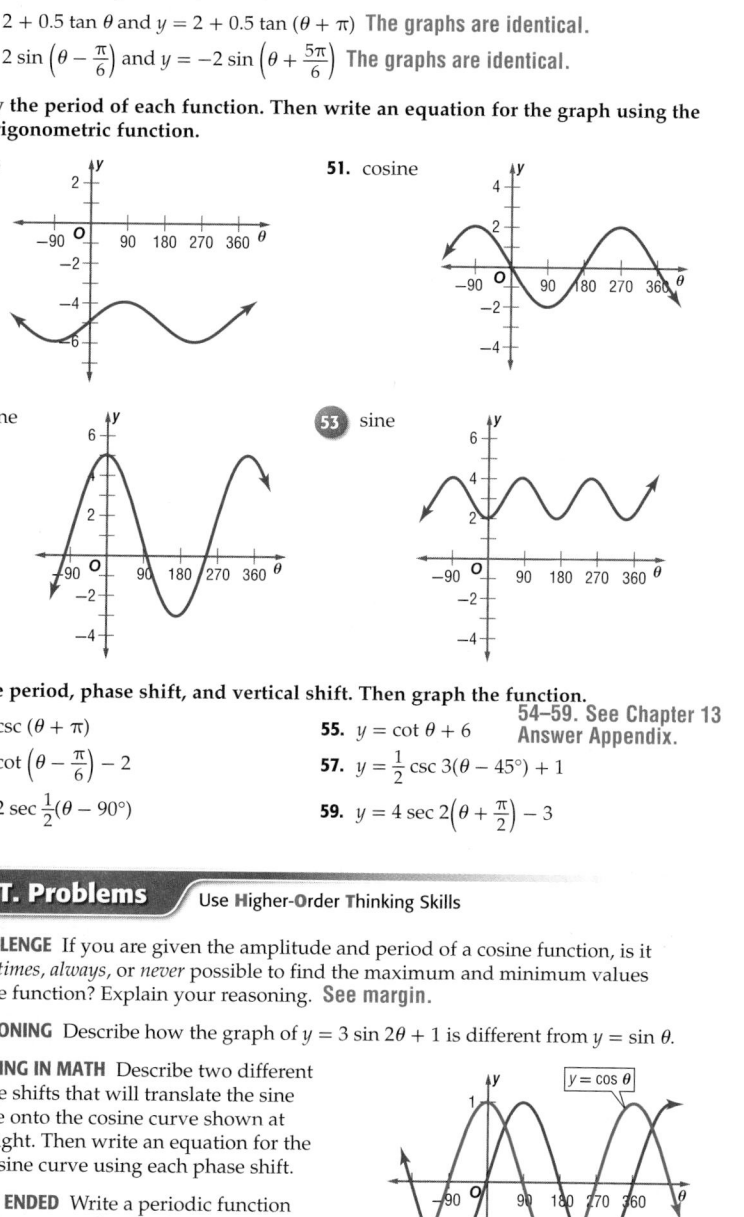

50. 360°; Sample answer: $y = \sin \theta - 5$
51. 360°; Sample answer: $y = 2 \cos (\theta + 90°)$
52. 360°; Sample answer: $y = 4 \cos \theta + 1$
53. 180°; Sample answer: $y = \sin 2(\theta - 45°) + 3$

State the period, phase shift, and vertical shift. Then graph the function. **54–59. See Chapter 13 Answer Appendix.**

54. $y = \csc (\theta + \pi)$

55. $y = \cot \theta + 6$

56. $y = \cot \left(\theta - \frac{\pi}{6}\right) - 2$

57. $y = \frac{1}{2} \csc 3(\theta - 45°) + 1$

58. $y = 2 \sec \frac{1}{2}(\theta - 90°)$

59. $y = 4 \sec 2\left(\theta + \frac{\pi}{2}\right) - 3$

H.O.T. Problems
Use Higher-Order Thinking Skills

60. CHALLENGE If you are given the amplitude and period of a cosine function, is it *sometimes*, *always*, or *never* possible to find the maximum and minimum values of the function? Explain your reasoning. **See margin.**

61. REASONING Describe how the graph of $y = 3 \sin 2\theta + 1$ is different from $y = \sin \theta$.

62. WRITING IN MATH Describe two different phase shifts that will translate the sine curve onto the cosine curve shown at the right. Then write an equation for the new sine curve using each phase shift.

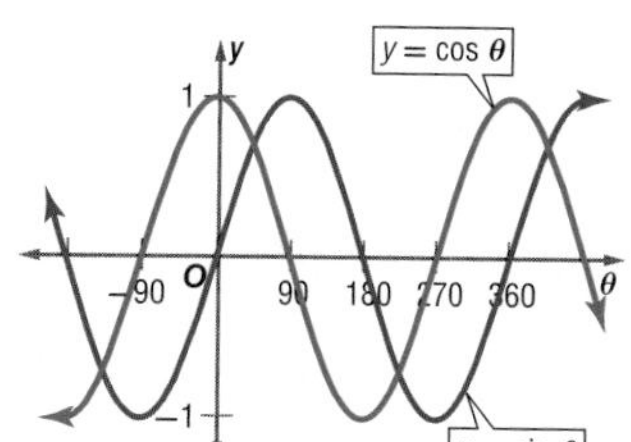

63. OPEN ENDED Write a periodic function that has an amplitude of 2 and midline at $y = -3$. Then graph the function.

64. REASONING How many different sine graphs pass through the origin $(n\pi, 0)$? Explain your reasoning.

61. The graph of $y = 3 \sin 2\theta + 1$ has an amplitude of 3 rather than an amplitude of 1. It is shifted up 1 unit from the parent graph and is compressed so that it has a period of 180°.
62. Sample answer: a phase shift 90° left, $y = \sin (\theta + 90°)$; a phase shift 270° right, $y = \sin (\theta - 270°)$
63. See margin.
64. Sample answer: Infinitely many; any change in amplitude will create a different graph that has the same θ-intercepts.

Additional Answer

63. Sample answer: $y = 2 \sin \theta - 3$

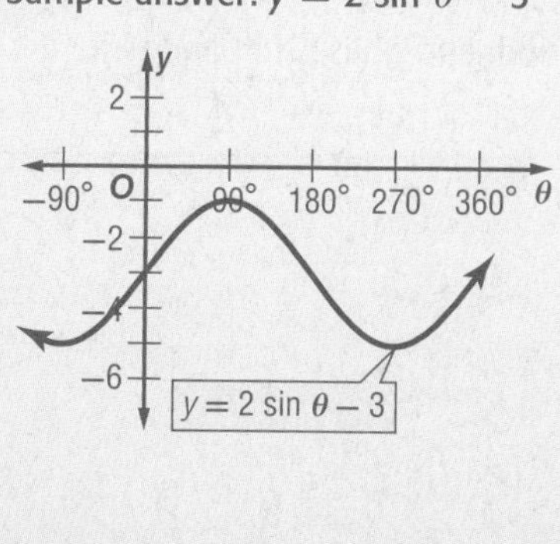

Study Guide and Intervention
CRM pp. 47–48 AL OL ELL

13-8 Study Guide and Intervention

Translations of Trigonometric Graphs

Horizontal Translations When a constant is subtracted from the angle measure in a trigonometric function, a **phase shift** of the graph results.

Phase Shift	The phase shift of the graphs of the functions $y = a \sin b(\theta - h)$, $y = a \cos b(\theta - h)$, and $y = a \tan b(\theta - h)$ is h, where $b > 0$. If $h > 0$, the shift is h units to the right. If $h < 0$, the shift is h units to the left.

Example State the amplitude, period, and phase shift for $y = \frac{1}{2} \cos 3\left(\theta - \frac{\pi}{2}\right)$. Then graph the function.

Amplitude: $|a| = \left|\frac{1}{2}\right|$ or $\frac{1}{2}$
Period: $\frac{2\pi}{|b|} = \frac{2\pi}{|3|}$ or $\frac{2\pi}{3}$
Phase Shift: $h = \frac{\pi}{2}$
The phase shift is to the right since $\frac{\pi}{2} > 0$.

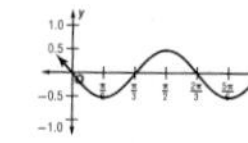

Exercises

State the amplitude, period, and phase shift for each function. Then graph the function.

1. $y = 2 \sin (\theta + 60°)$
2; 360°; 60° to the left

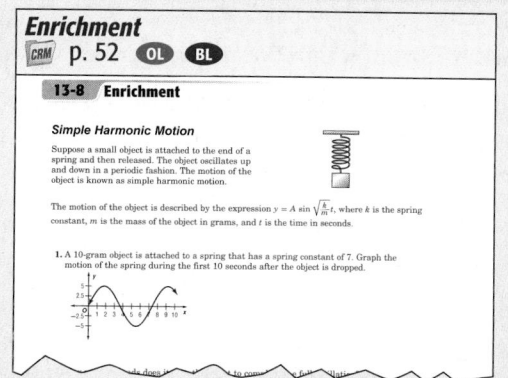

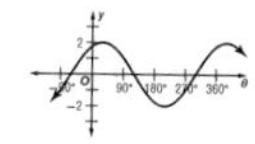

2. $y = \tan \left(\theta - \frac{\pi}{2}\right)$
no amplitude; π; $\frac{\pi}{2}$ to the right

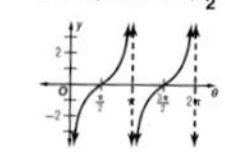

3. $y = 3 \cos (\theta - 45°)$
3; 360°; 45° to the right

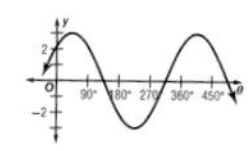

4. $y = \frac{1}{2} \sin 3\left(\theta - \frac{\pi}{3}\right)$
$\frac{1}{2}$; $\frac{2\pi}{3}$; $\frac{\pi}{3}$ to the right

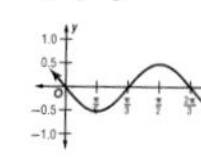

Chapter 13 47 Glencoe Algebra 2

Lesson 13-8

Practice
CRM p. 50 AL OL BL ELL

13-8 Practice

Translations of Trigonometric Graphs

State the amplitude, period, phase shift, and vertical shift for each function. Then graph the function.

1. $y = \frac{1}{2} \tan \left(\theta - \frac{\pi}{2}\right)$
no vertical shift; no amplitude; π; $\frac{\pi}{2}$

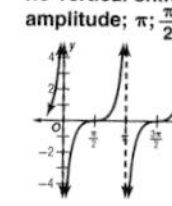

2. $y = 2 \cos (\theta + 30°) + 3$
3; 2; 360; –30°

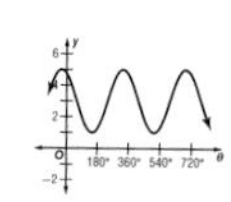

3. $y = 3 \sin (2\theta + 60°) - 2.5$
–2.5; no amplitude; 180°; –60°

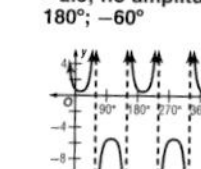

4. $y = -3 + 2 \sin 2\left(\theta + \frac{\pi}{4}\right)$
amplitude: 2, period: π, phase shift: $-\frac{\pi}{4}$, vertical shift: –3;

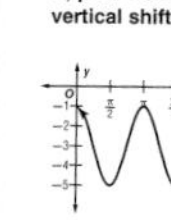

5. $y = 3 \cos 2 (\theta + 45°) + 1$
amplitude: 3, period: 180°, phase shift: –45°, vertical shift: 1;

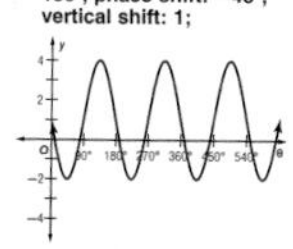

6. $y = -1 + 4 \tan (\theta + \pi)$
amplitude: 4, period: 2π, phase shift: $-\pi$, vertical shift: –1;

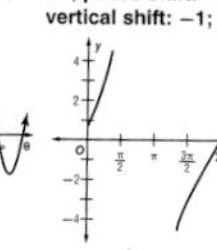

7. **ECOLOGY** The population of an insect species in a stand of trees follows the growth cycle of a particular tree species. The insect population can be modeled by the function $y = 40 + 30 \sin 6t$, where t is the number of years since the stand was first cut in November, 1920.

a. How often does the insect population reach its maximum level?
every 60 yr

b. When did the population last reach its maximum?
1995

c. What condition in the stand do you think corresponds with a minimum insect population?
Sample answer: The species on which the insect feeds has been cut.

Chapter 13 50 Glencoe Algebra 2

Word Problem Practice
CRM p. 51 AL OL BL ELL

13-8 Word Problem Practice

Translations of Trigonometric Graphs

1. **CLOCKS** A town hall has a tower with a clock on its face. The center of the clock is 40 feet above street level. The minute hand of the clock has a length of four feet.

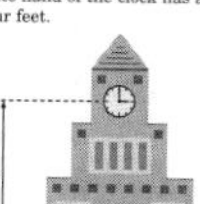

a. What is the maximum height of the tip of the minute hand above street level?
44 feet

b. What is the minimum height of the tip of the minute hand above street level?
36 feet

c. Write a sine function that represents the height above street level of the tip of the minute hand for t minutes after midnight.
$y = \sin \left(\frac{\pi}{30}t + \frac{\pi}{2}\right) + 40$?

d. Graph the function from your answer to Exercise 3.

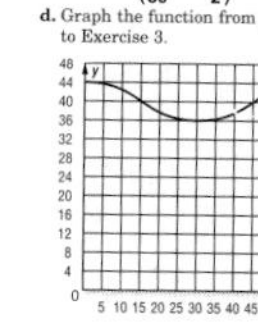

2. **ANIMAL POPULATION** The population of predators and prey in a closed ecological system tends to vary periodically over time. In a certain system, the population of snakes S can be represented by $S = 100 + 20 \sin \left(\frac{\pi}{5}t\right)$, where t is the number of years since January 1, 2000. In that same system, the population of rats can be represented by $R = 200 + 75 \sin. \left(\frac{\pi}{5}t + \frac{\pi}{10}\right)$

a. What is the maximum snake population?
120

b. When is this population first reached?
2.5 yr

c. What is the minimum rat population?
125

d. When is this population first reached?
7 yr

Chapter 13 51 Glencoe Algebra 2

Lesson 13-8

Enrichment
CRM p. 52 OL BL

13-8 Enrichment

Simple Harmonic Motion

Suppose a small object is attached to the end of a spring and then released. The object oscillates up and down in a periodic fashion. The motion of the object is known as simple harmonic motion.

The motion of the object is described by the expression $y = A \sin \sqrt{\frac{k}{m}}t$, where k is the spring constant, m is the mass of the object in grams, and t is the time in seconds.

1. A 10-gram object is attached to a spring that has a spring constant of 7. Graph the motion of the spring during the first 10 seconds after the object is dropped.

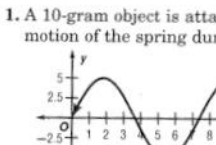

4 ASSESS

Name the Math Have students write a function for which the graph involves both a horizontal and a vertical translation of a trigonometric function. Then have them describe the translations.

Additional Answers

69. amplitude: 2; period: 360°

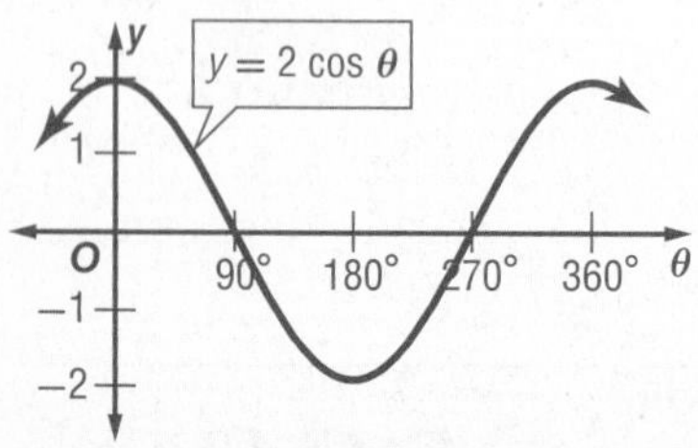

70. amplitude: 3; period: 360°

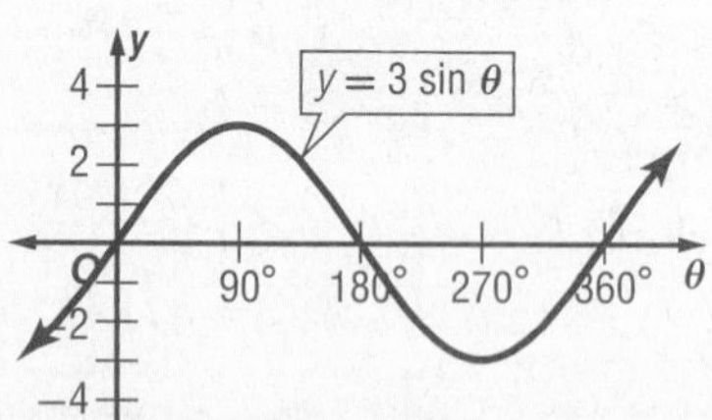

71. amplitude: 1; period: 180°

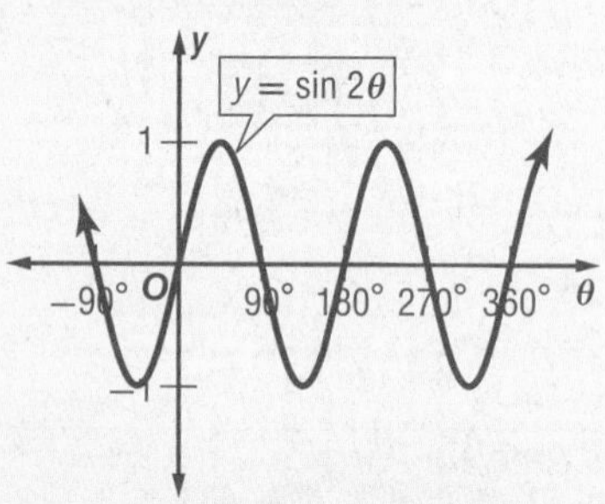

75. Experiment; the people are put into groups at random. The treatment group is the exercisers, and the control is the other group. This is a biased experiment because the participants all know which group they are in.

77. Observational study; the students who have part-time jobs are the treatment group, and the other students are the control; unbiased.

NGSSS PRACTICE 912.A.6.3, 912.A.4.12, 912.A.6.5, 912.A.3.15

65. **GRIDDED RESPONSE** The expression $\frac{3x-1}{4} + \frac{x+6}{4}$ is how much greater than x? **1.25**

66. Expand $(a - b)^4$. **D**

A. $a^4 - b^4$

B. $a^4 - 4ab + b^4$

C. $a^4 + 4a^3b + 6a^2b^2 + 4ab^3 + b^4$

D. $a^4 - 4a^3b + 6a^2b^2 - 4ab^3 + b^4$

67. Solve $\sqrt{x-3} + \sqrt{x+2} = 5$. **F**

F. 7

G. 0, 7

H. 7, 13

I. no solution

68. **GEOMETRY** Using the figures below, what is the average of a, b, c, d, and f? **D**

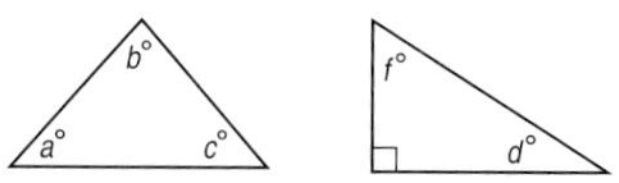

A. 21 B. 45 C. 50 D. 54

Spiral Review

Find the amplitude and period of each function. Then graph the function. (Lesson 13-7) **69–71. See margin.**

69. $y = 2 \cos \theta$

70. $y = 3 \sin \theta$

71. $y = \sin 2\theta$

Find the exact value of each expression. (Lesson 13-6)

72. $\sin \frac{4\pi}{3}$ $-\frac{\sqrt{3}}{2}$

73. $\sin (-30°)$ $-\frac{1}{2}$

74. $\cos 405°$ $\frac{\sqrt{2}}{2}$

State whether each situation represents an *experiment* or an *observational study*. If it is an experiment, identify the *control* group and the *treatment* group. Then determine whether there is bias. (Lesson 12-1) **75, 77. See margin.**

75. Find 220 people and randomly split them into two groups. One group exercises for an hour a day and the other group does not. Then compare their body mass indexes.

76. Find 200 students, half of whom play soccer, and compare the amounts of time spent sleeping. **observational study**

77. Find 100 students, half of whom have part-time jobs, and compare their grades.

78. **GEOMETRY** Equilateral triangle ABC has a perimeter of 39 centimeters. If the midpoints of the sides are connected, a smaller equilateral triangle results. Suppose the process of connecting midpoints of sides and drawing new triangles is continued indefinitely. (Lesson 11-4)

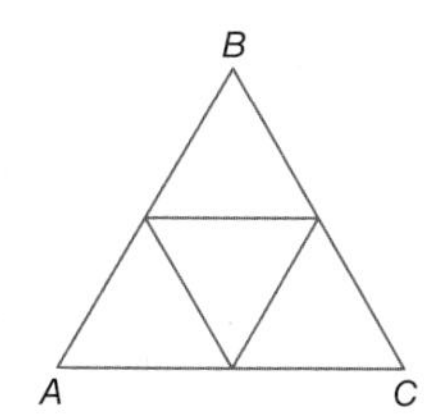

a. Write an infinite geometric series to represent the sum of the perimeters of all of the triangles. **39 + 19.5 + 9.75 + ...**

b. Find the sum of the perimeters of all of the triangles. **78 cm**

79. **CONSTRUCTION** A construction company will be fined for each day it is late completing a bridge. The daily fine will be $4000 for the first day and will increase by $1000 each day. Based on its budget, the company can only afford $60,000 in total fines. What is the maximum number of days it can be late? (Lesson 11-3) **8 days**

Skills Review

Find each value of θ. Round to the nearest degree. (Lesson 13-1)

80. $\sin \theta = \frac{7}{8}$ **61°**

81. $\tan \theta = \frac{9}{10}$ **42°**

82. $\cos \theta = \frac{1}{4}$ **76°**

83. $\cos \theta = \frac{4}{5}$ **37°**

84. $\sin \theta = \frac{5}{6}$ **56°**

85. $\tan \theta = \frac{2}{7}$ **16°**

Differentiated Instruction OL BL

Extension Have students choose a vertical shift, amplitude, period, and phase shift and write a function with these characteristics.

13-9 Inverse Trigonometric Functions

Why?

The leaning bookshelf at the right is 15 inches from the wall and reaches a height of 75 inches. In Lesson 13-1, you learned how to use the inverse of a trigonometric function to find the measure of acute angle θ.

$\tan \theta = \frac{15}{75}$ or 0.2 **Use the tangent function.**

Find an angle that has a tangent of 0.2.

[2nd] [TAN^{-1}] .2 [ENTER] 11.30993247

So, the measure of θ is about 11°.

Then
You graphed trigonometric functions. (Lesson 13-7)

Now
- Find values of inverse trigonometric functions.
- Solve equations by using inverse trigonometric functions.

NGSSS
MA.912.T.1.7 Define and graph inverse trigonometric relations and functions.
MA.912.T.1.8 Solve real-world problems involving applications of trigonometric functions using graphing technology when appropriate.

New Vocabulary
principal values
Arcsine function
Arccosine function
Arctangent function

FL Math Online
glencoe.com

Inverse Trigonometric Functions If you know the value of a trigonometric function for an angle, you can use the *inverse* to find the angle. Recall that an inverse function is the relation in which all values of x and y are reversed. The inverse of $y = \sin x$, $x = \sin y$, is graphed at the right.

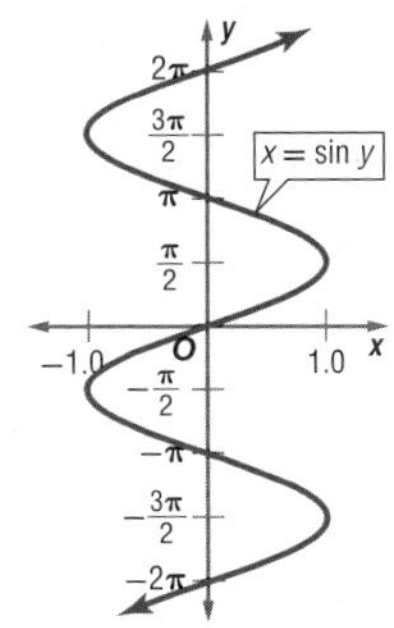

Notice that the inverse is not a function because there are many values of y for each value of x. If you restrict the domain of the sine function so that $-\frac{\pi}{2} \leq x \leq \frac{\pi}{2}$, then the inverse is a function.

The values in this restricted domain are called **principal values**. Trigonometric functions with restricted domains are indicated with capital letters.

- $y = \text{Sin } x$ if and only if $y = \sin x$ and $-\frac{\pi}{2} \leq x \leq \frac{\pi}{2}$.
- $y = \text{Cos } x$ if and only if $y = \cos x$ and $0 \leq x \leq \pi$.
- $y = \text{Tan } x$ if and only if $y = \tan x$ and $-\frac{\pi}{2} \leq x \leq \frac{\pi}{2}$.

You can use functions with restricted domains to define inverse trigonometric functions. The inverses of the sine, cosine, and tangent functions are the **Arcsine**, **Arccosine**, and **Arctangent** functions, respectively.

Key Concept — Inverse Trigonometric Functions

Inverse Function	Symbols	Domain	Range	Model
Arcsine	$y = \text{Arcsin } x$ $y = \text{Sin}^{-1} x$	$-1 \leq x \leq 1$	$-\frac{\pi}{2} \leq y \leq \frac{\pi}{2}$ $-90° \leq y \leq 90°$	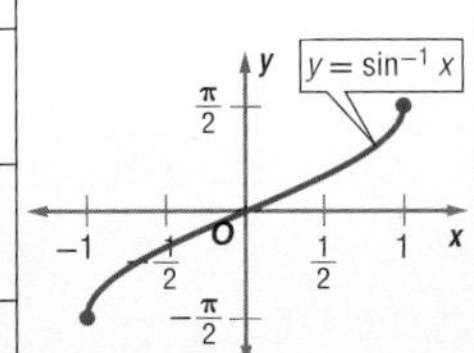
Arccosine	$y = \text{Arccos } x$ $y = \text{Cos}^{-1} x$	$-1 \leq x \leq 1$	$0 \leq y \leq \pi$ $0° \leq y \leq 180°$	
Arctangent	$y = \text{Arctan } x$ $y = \text{Tan}^{-1} x$	all real numbers	$-\frac{\pi}{2} \leq y \leq \frac{\pi}{2}$ $-90° \leq y \leq 90°$	

13-9 Lesson Notes

1 FOCUS

Vertical Alignment

Before Lesson 13-9
Graph trigonometric functions.

Lesson 13-9
Find values of inverse trigonometric functions.
Solve equations by using inverse trigonometric functions.

After Lesson 13-9
Define and graph the inverse trigonometric functions.

2 TEACH

Scaffolding Questions

Have students read the *Why?* section of the lesson.

Ask:
- How can you find the length of the leaning bookshelf? Find that length. Use the Pythagorean Theorem; $s^2 = 15^2 + 75^2 = 5850$; $s \approx 76.485$ in.
- What ratio represents $\sin \theta$? $\frac{15}{76.485}$
- What ratio represents $\cos \theta$? $\frac{75}{76.485}$
- Use your values for $\sin \theta$ and $\cos \theta$ to find θ. Do you get the same value? The same value for θ, 11.3088°, is obtained using $\sin \theta$ and $\cos \theta$.

Lesson 13-9 Resources

Resource	Approaching-Level	On-Level	Beyond-Level	English Learners
Teacher Edition		• Differentiated Instruction, pp. 873, 876	• Differentiated Instruction, pp. 873, 876	
Chapter Resource Masters	• Study Guide and Intervention, pp. 53–54 • Skills Practice, p. 55 • Practice, p. 56 • Word Problem Practice, p. 57	• Study Guide and Intervention, pp. 53–54 • Skills Practice, p. 55 • Practice, p. 56 • Word Problem Practice, p. 57 • Enrichment, p. 58	• Practice, p. 56 • Word Problem Practice, p. 57 • Enrichment, p. 58	• Study Guide and Intervention, pp. 53–54 • Skills Practice, p. 55 • Practice, p. 56 • Word Problem Practice, p. 57
Transparencies	• 5-Minute Check Transparency 13-9	• 5-Minute Check Transparency 13-9	• 5-Minute Check Transparency 13-9	• 5-Minute Check Transparency 13-9
Other	• Study Notebook	• Study Notebook	• Study Notebook	• Study Notebook

Inverse Trigonometric Functions

Example 1 shows how to evaluate inverse trigonometric functions for angles measured in degrees or radians. **Example 2** shows how to use a calculator to find values of expressions involving inverse trigonometric functions.

Formative Assessment

Use the Guided Practice exercises after each example to determine students' understanding of concepts.

Additional Examples

1 Find each value. Write angle measures in degrees and radians.

a. $\text{Sin}^{-1}\left(\frac{\sqrt{2}}{2}\right)$ $45°; \frac{\pi}{4}$

b. Arcsin (–1) $-90°; -\frac{\pi}{2}$

2 Find $\tan\left(\text{Cos}^{-1}\frac{4}{7}\right)$. Round to the nearest hundredth. 1.44

Additional Examples also in Interactive Classroom PowerPoint® Presentations

IWB INTERACTIVE WHITEBOARD READY

Tips for New Teachers

Sense-Making It may help students to understand the nature of inverse functions if they read arcsin x and $\sin^{-1} x$ as "the angle with sine of x."

TEACH with TECH

VIDEO RECORDING Create a video explaining how to find the values of inverse trigonometric functions. Post the video to a class Web site so students can use it as an additional reference outside of class.

Review Vocabulary

inverse functions If f and f^{-1} are inverse functions, then $f(a) = b$ if and only if $f^{-1}(b) = a$. (Lesson 7-2)

In the relation $y = \cos^{-1} x$, if $x = \frac{1}{2}$, $y = 60°, 300°$, and all angles that are coterminal with those angles. In the function $y = \text{Cos}^{-1} x$, if $x = \frac{1}{2}$, $y = 60°$ only.

EXAMPLE 1 Evaluate Inverse Trigonometric Functions

Find each value. Write angle measures in degrees and radians.

a. $\text{Cos}^{-1}\left(-\frac{1}{2}\right)$

Find the angle θ for $0° \le \theta \le 180°$ that has a cosine value of $-\frac{1}{2}$.

Method 1 Use a unit circle.

Find a point on the unit circle that has an x-coordinate of $-\frac{1}{2}$.

When $\theta = 120°$, $\cos\theta = -\frac{1}{2}$.

So, $\text{Cos}^{-1}\left(-\frac{1}{2}\right) = 120°$ or $\frac{2\pi}{3}$.

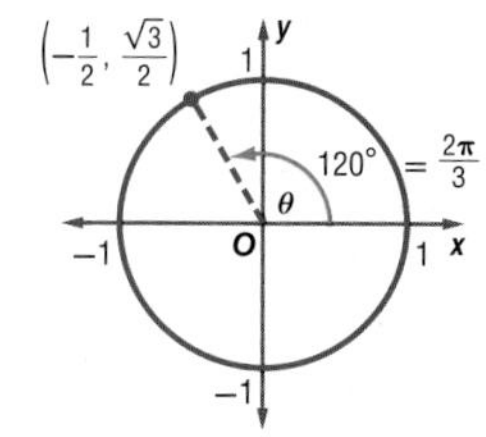

Method 2 Use a calculator.

KEYSTROKES: [2nd] [COS⁻¹] [(–)] 1 [÷] 2 [)] [ENTER] 120

Therefore, $\text{Cos}^{-1}\left(-\frac{1}{2}\right) = 120°$ or $\frac{2\pi}{3}$.

StudyTip

Angle Measure Remember that when evaluating an inverse trigonometric function, the result is an angle measure.

b. Arctan 1

Find the angle θ for $-90° \le \theta \le 90°$ that has a tangent value of 1.

KEYSTROKES: [2nd] [TAN⁻¹] 1 [ENTER] 45

Therefore, Arctan $1 = 45°$ or $\frac{\pi}{4}$.

Guided Practice

1A. $\text{Cos}^{-1} 0$ $90; \frac{\pi}{2}$

1B. $\text{Arcsin}\left(-\frac{\sqrt{2}}{2}\right)$ $-45°; -\frac{\pi}{4}$

Personal Tutor glencoe.com

When finding a value when there are multiple trigonometric functions involved, use the order of operations to solve.

EXAMPLE 2 Find a Trigonometric Value

Find $\tan\left(\text{Cos}^{-1}\frac{1}{2}\right)$. Round to the nearest hundredth.

Use a calculator.

KEYSTROKES: [TAN] [2nd] [COS⁻¹] 1 [÷] 2 [)] [ENTER] 1.732050808

So, $\tan\left(\text{Cos}^{-1}\frac{1}{2}\right) \approx 1.73$.

CHECK $\text{Cos}^{-1}\frac{1}{2} = 60°$ and $\tan 60° \approx 1.73$. So, the answer is correct.

Guided Practice

Find each value. Round to the nearest hundredth.

2A. $\sin\left(\text{Tan}^{-1}\frac{3}{8}\right)$ 0.35

2B. $\cos\left(\text{Arccos} -\frac{\sqrt{2}}{2}\right)$ –0.71

Personal Tutor glencoe.com

872 Chapter 13 Trigonometric Functions

Focus on Mathematical Content

Inverse Trigonometric Functions Because the trigonometric functions are periodic, many angles correspond to the same function value. Therefore, the inverse of any of the trigonometric functions is not a function (since the value inverse would not be unique). However, if the domain is restricted to an appropriate interval, the inverse is a function. While there are infinitely many intervals that would work, standard intervals (centered at 0 or with 0 as an endpoint) have been chosen.

Solve Equations by Using Inverses You can rewrite trigonometric equations to solve for the measure of an angle.

Test-TakingTip

Eliminate Possibilities The function Sin restricts the possible angle measures to Quadrants I or IV. Because −0.35 is negative, look for an angle measure in Quadrant IV.

NGSSS PRACTICE EXAMPLE 3 912.T.2.1

If Sin $\theta = -0.35$, find θ.

A. $-20.5°$ B. $-0.6°$ C. $0.6°$ D. $20.5°$

Read the Test Item

The sine of angle θ is −0.35. This can be written as Arcsin $(-0.35) = \theta$.

Solve the Test Item

Use a calculator.

KEYSTROKES: [2nd] [SIN⁻¹] [(−)] .35 [ENTER] −20.48731511

So, $\theta \approx -20.5°$. The answer is A.

Guided Practice

3. If Tan $\theta = 1.8$, find θ. H

F. 0.03° G. 29.1° H. 60.9° I. no solution

Personal Tutor glencoe.com

Inverse trigonometric functions can be used to determine angles of inclination, depression, and elevation.

Real-World EXAMPLE 4 **Use Inverse Trigonometric Functions**

WATER SKIING A water ski ramp is 6 feet tall and 9 feet long, as shown at the right. Write an inverse trigonometric function that can be used to find θ, the angle the ramp makes with the water. Then find the measure of the angle. Round to the nearest tenth.

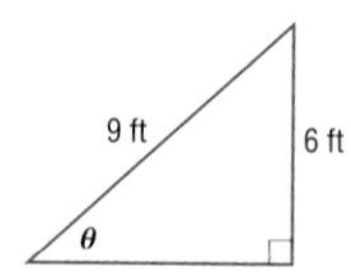

Because the measures of the opposite side and the hypotenuse are known, you can use the sine function.

$\sin \theta = \frac{6}{9}$ **Sine function**

$\theta = \text{Sin}^{-1} \frac{6}{9}$ **Inverse sine function**

$\theta \approx 41.8°$ **Use a calculator.**

So, the angle of the ramp is about 41.8°.

CHECK Using your calculator, $\sin 41.8 \approx 0.66653 \approx \frac{6}{9}$. So, the answer is correct.

Guided Practice

4. **SKIING** A ski trail is shown at the right. Write an inverse trigonometric function that can be used to find θ, the angle the trail makes with the ground in the valley. Then find the angle. Round to the nearest tenth. $\theta = \text{Tan}^{-1} \frac{5}{12}$; 22.6°

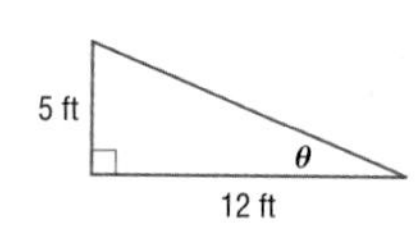

Personal Tutor glencoe.com

Solve Equations by Using Inverses

Example 3 shows how to solve an equation by using an inverse trigonometric function. **Example 4** shows how to apply an inverse trigonometric function to solve a real-world problem.

Additional Examples

3 **STANDARDIZED TEST EXAMPLE** If Cos $\theta = -0.86$, find θ. D

A −149.3° C 59.3°

B −59.3° D 149.3°

4 **WATER SKIING** In Example 4, suppose the ramp is 5.5 feet tall and 12 feet long. Write an inverse trigonometric function that can be used to find θ. Then find the measure of θ. Round to the nearest tenth. $\sin \theta = \frac{5.5}{12}$; $\theta = \text{Sin}^{-1} \frac{5.5}{12} \approx 27.3°$

Differentiated Instruction

OL BL

Visual/Spatial Learners Ask students to find arcsin 2. If they use a calculator, suggest that they study the graph of $y = \sin x$ to explain why an error message was the result. The graph of $y = \sin x$ has no y values greater than 1 or less than −1.

3 PRACTICE

Formative Assessment

Use Exercises 1–11 to check for understanding.

Use the chart at the bottom of this page to customize assignments for your students.

Tips for New Teachers

Calculator Mode Remind students to put their calculator into the correct mode (degree or radian), depending on how the answer is to be stated.

Multiple Representations In Exercise 40, students use a graph, symbolic notation, and numeric evaluation to investigate the inverse cosine function.

Additional Answers

40a.

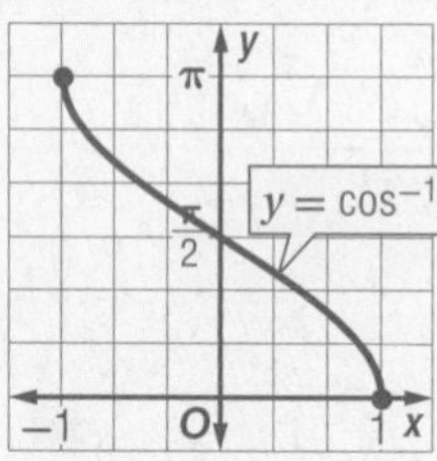

domain: $-1 \le x \le 1$; range: $0 \le y \le \pi$

40d. Sample answer: The graph of $y = \cos x$ has a domain of all real numbers and a range from −1 to 1. The graph of $y = \cos^{-1} x$ has a domain from −1 to 1 and a range of 0 to 180°.

45. Sample answer: $y = \tan^{-1} x$ is a relation that has a domain of all real numbers and a range of all real numbers except odd multiples of $\frac{\pi}{2}$. The relation is not a function. $y = \text{Tan}^{-1} x$ is a function that has a domain of all real numbers and a range of $-\frac{\pi}{2} \le y \le \frac{\pi}{2}$.

Check Your Understanding

Example 1 p. 872

Find each value. Write angle measures in degrees and radians.

1. $\text{Sin}^{-1} \frac{1}{2}$ **30°; $\frac{\pi}{6}$**
2. $\text{Arctan}\,(-\sqrt{3})$ **−60°; $-\frac{\pi}{3}$**
3. $\text{Arccos}\,(-1)$ **180°; π**

Example 2 p. 872

Find each value. Round to the nearest hundredth if necessary.

4. $\cos\left(\text{Arcsin}\,\frac{4}{5}\right)$ **0.6**
5. $\tan\,(\text{Cos}^{-1} 1)$ **0**
6. $\sin\left(\text{Sin}^{-1} \frac{\sqrt{3}}{2}\right)$ **0.87**

Example 3 p. 873

7. NGSSS PRACTICE If $\text{Sin}\,\theta = 0.422$, find θ. **A**

A. 25° B. 42° C. 48° D. 65°

Solve each equation. Round to the nearest tenth if necessary.

8. $\text{Cos}\,\theta = 0.9$ **25.8°**
9. $\text{Sin}\,\theta = -0.46$ **−27.4°**
10. $\text{Tan}\,\theta = 2.1$ **64.5°**

Example 4 p. 873

11. **SNOWBOARDING** A cross section of a superpipe for snowboarders is shown at the right. Write an inverse trigonometric function that can be used to find θ, the angle that describes the steepness of the superpipe. Then find the angle to the nearest degree. **Arctan $\frac{6.2}{18}$; 19°**

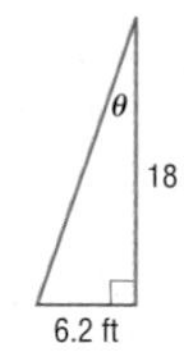

Practice and Problem Solving

= **Step-by-Step Solutions** begin on page R20. **Extra Practice** begins on page 947.

Example 1 p. 872

Find each value. Write angle measures in degrees and radians.

12. $\text{Arcsin}\left(\frac{\sqrt{3}}{2}\right)$ **60°; $\frac{\pi}{3}$**
13. $\text{Arccos}\left(\frac{\sqrt{3}}{2}\right)$ **30°; $\frac{\pi}{6}$**
14. $\text{Sin}^{-1}(-1)$ **−90°; $-\frac{\pi}{2}$**
15. $\text{Tan}^{-1}\sqrt{3}$ **60°; $\frac{\pi}{3}$**
16. $\text{Cos}^{-1}\left(-\frac{\sqrt{3}}{2}\right)$ **150°; $\frac{5\pi}{6}$**
17. $\text{Arctan}\left(-\frac{\sqrt{3}}{3}\right)$ **−30°; $-\frac{\pi}{6}$**

Example 2 p. 872

Find each value. Round to the nearest hundredth if necessary.

18. $\tan\,(\text{Cos}^{-1} 1)$ **0**
19. $\tan\left[\text{Arcsin}\left(-\frac{1}{2}\right)\right]$ **−0.58**
20. $\cos\left(\text{Tan}^{-1} \frac{3}{5}\right)$ **0.86**
21. $\sin\,(\text{Arctan}\,\sqrt{3})$ **0.87**
22. $\cos\left(\text{Sin}^{-1} \frac{4}{9}\right)$ **0.90**
23. $\sin\left[\text{Cos}^{-1}\left(-\frac{\sqrt{2}}{2}\right)\right]$ **0.71**

Example 3 p. 873

Solve each equation. Round to the nearest tenth if necessary.

24. $\text{Tan}\,\theta = 3.8$ **75.3°**
25. $\text{Sin}\,\theta = 0.9$ **64.2°**
26. $\text{Sin}\,\theta = -2.5$ **no solution**
27. $\text{Cos}\,\theta = -0.25$ **104.5°**
28. $\text{Cos}\,\theta = 0.56$ **55.9°**
29. $\text{Tan}\,\theta = -0.2$ **−11.3°**

Example 4 p. 873

30. **BOATS** A boat is traveling west to cross a river that is 190 meters wide. Because of the current, the boat lands at point Q, which is 59 meters from its original destination point P. Write an inverse trigonometric function that can be used to find θ, the angle at which the boat veered south of the horizontal line. Then find the measure of the angle to the nearest tenth.

Arctan $\frac{59}{190} = \theta$; 17.3°

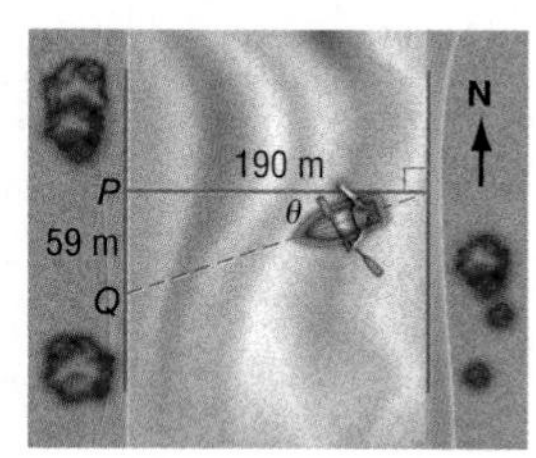

Differentiated Homework Options

Level	Assignment	Two-Day Option	
AL Basic	12–31, 42–60	13–31 odd, 47–50	12–30 even, 42–46, 51–60
OL Core	13–39 odd, 40, 42–60	12–31, 47–50	32–40, 42–46, 51–60
BL Advanced	32–56, (optional: 57–60)		

31. **TREES** A 24-foot tree is leaning 2.5 feet left of vertical, as shown in the figure. Write an inverse trigonometric function that can be used to find θ, the angle at which the tree is leaning. Then find the measure of the angle to the nearest degree. **Arcsin $\frac{2.5}{24}$; 6°**

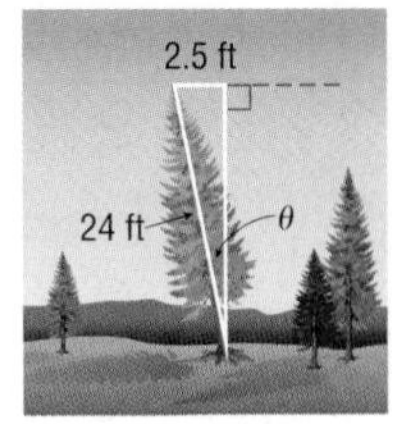

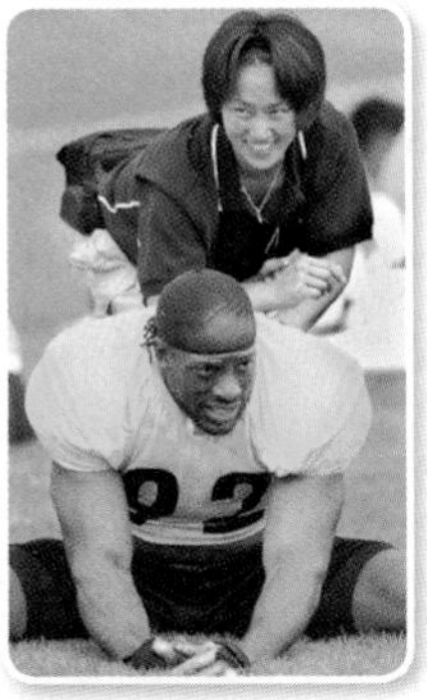

Real-World Career

Sport Science Administrator
A sport science administrator provides sport science information to players, coaches, and parents. He or she implements testing, training, and treatment programs for athletes. A master's degree in sport science or a related area is recommended.

32. **DRIVING** An expressway off-ramp curve has a radius of 52 meters and is designed for vehicles to safely travel at speeds up to 45 kilometers per hour (or 12.5 meters per second). The equation below represents the angle θ of the curve. What is the measure of the angle to the nearest degree? **17°**

$$\tan \theta = \frac{(12.5 \text{ m/s})^2}{(52 \text{ m})(9.8 \text{ m/s}^2)}$$

33. **TRACK AND FIELD** A shot-putter throws the shot with an initial speed of 15 meters per second. The expression $\frac{15 \text{ m/s} (\sin x)}{9.8 \text{ m/s}^2}$ represents the time in seconds at which the shot reached its maximum height. In the expression, x is the angle at which the shot was thrown. If the maximum height of the shot was reached in 1.0 second, at what angle was it thrown? Round to the nearest tenth. **40.8°**

Solve each equation for $0 \leq \theta \leq 2\pi$.

34. $\csc \theta = 1$ **$\frac{\pi}{2}$**
35. $\sec \theta = -1$ **π**
36. $\sec \theta = 1$ **0, 2π**
37. $\csc \theta = \frac{1}{2}$ **no solution**
38. $\cot \theta = 1$ **$\frac{\pi}{4}$, $\frac{5\pi}{4}$**
39. $\sec \theta = 2$ **$\frac{\pi}{3}$, $\frac{5\pi}{3}$**

40. **MULTIPLE REPRESENTATIONS** Consider $y = \text{Cos}^{-1}\, x$. **a. See margin.**

a. **GRAPHICAL** Sketch a graph of the function. Describe the domain and the range.

b. **SYMBOLIC** Write the function using different notation. **$y =$ Arccos x**

c. **NUMERICAL** Choose a value for x between −1 and 0. Then evaluate the inverse cosine function. Round to the nearest tenth. **Sample answer: $x = -0.2$; $y = 101.5$**

d. **ANALYTICAL** Compare the graphs of $y = \cos x$ and $y = \text{Cos}^{-1}\, x$. **See margin.**

H.O.T. Problems
Use Higher-Order Thinking Skills

41. **CHALLENGE** Determine whether *cos (Arccos x) = x for all values of x* is *true* or *false*. If false, give a counterexample. **false; $x = 2\pi$**

42. **ERROR ANALYSIS** Desiree and Oscar are solving $\cos \theta = 0.3$ where $90 < \theta < 180$. Is either of them correct? Explain your reasoning.

Desiree	Oscar
$\cos \theta = 0.3$	$\cos \theta = 0.3$
$\cos^{-1} 0.3 = 162.5°$	$\cos^{-1} 0.3 = 72.5°$

43. **REASONING** Explain how the domain of $y = \text{Sin}^{-1}\, x$ is related to the range of $y = \text{Sin}\, x$.

44. **OPEN ENDED** Write an equation with an Arcsine function and an equation with a Sine function that both involve the same angle measure.

45. **WRITING IN MATH** Compare and contrast the relations $y = \tan^{-1} x$ and $y = \text{Tan}^{-1}\, x$. Include information about the domains and ranges. **See margin.**

46. **REASONING** Explain how $\text{Sin}^{-1}\, 8$ and $\text{Cos}^{-1}\, 8$ are undefined while $\text{Tan}^{-1}\, 8$ is defined.

42. Sample answer: Neither; cosine is not positive in the second quadrant.
43. The domain of $y = \text{Sin}^{-1}\, x$ is $-1 \leq x \leq 1$. This is the same as the range of $y = \text{Sin}\, x$.
44. Sample answer: Arcsin $\frac{1}{2} = 30°$; $\frac{1}{2} = \text{Sin}\, 30°$
46. Sample answer: The range of $y = \text{Sin}\, x$ and $y = \text{Cos}\, x$ is $-1 \leq x \leq 1$. The range of $y = \text{Tan}^{-1}\, x$ is all real numbers.

Watch Out!

Error Analysis For Exercise 42, students should see that neither student is correct because this is a "trick question." Explain to students that when $90° < \theta < 180°$, then $\cos \theta$ must have a negative value.

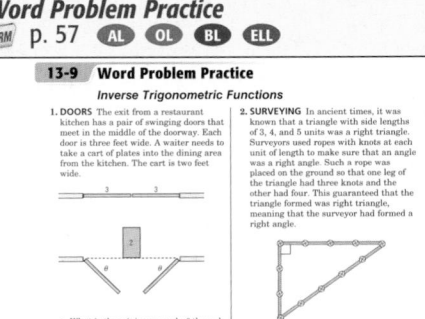

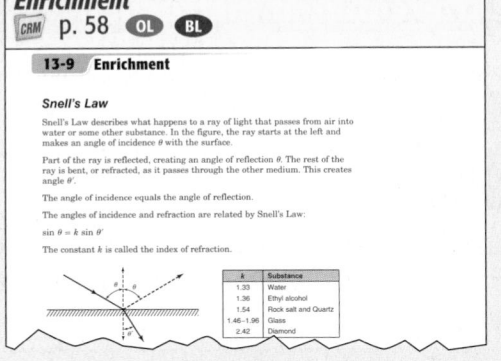

Enrichment
CRM p. 58 OL BL

13-9 Enrichment

Snell's Law

Snell's Law describes what happens to a ray of light that passes from air into water or some other substance. In the figure, the ray starts at the left and makes an angle of incidence θ with the surface.

Part of the ray is reflected, creating an angle of reflection θ. The rest of the ray is bent, or refracted, as it passes through the other medium. This creates angle θ'.

The angle of incidence equals the angle of reflection.

The angles of incidence and refraction are related by Snell's Law:

$\sin \theta = k \sin \theta'$

The constant k is called the index of refraction.

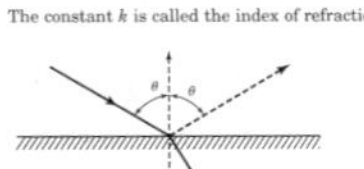

k	Substance
1.33	Water
1.36	Ethyl alcohol
1.54	Rock salt and Quartz
1.46–1.96	Glass
2.42	Diamond

Study Guide and Intervention
CRM pp. 53–54 AL OL ELL

13-9 Study Guide and Intervention

Inverse Trigonometric Functions

Inverse Trigonometric Functions If you know the value of a trigonometric function for an angle, you can use the *inverse* to find the angle. If you restrict the function's domain, then the inverse is a function. The values in this restricted domain are called **principal values**.

Principal Values of Sine, Cosine, and Tangent	$y = \text{Sin}\, x$ if and only if $y = \sin x$ and $-\frac{\pi}{2} \leq x \leq \frac{\pi}{2}$. $y = \text{Cos}\, x$ if and only if $y = \cos x$ and $0 \leq x \leq \pi$. $y = \text{Tan}\, x$ if and only if $y = \tan x$ and $-\frac{\pi}{2} \leq x \leq \frac{\pi}{2}$.
Inverse Sine, Cosine, and Tangent	Given $y = \text{Sin}\, x$, the inverse sine function is defined by $y = \text{Sin}^{-1}\, x$ or $y = \text{Arcsin}\, x$. Given $y = \text{Cos}\, x$, the inverse cosine function is defined by $y = \text{Cos}^{-1}\, x$ or $y = \text{Arccos}\, x$. Given $y = \text{Tan}\, x$, the inverse tangent function is given by $y = \text{Tan}^{-1}\, x$ or $y = \text{Arctan}\, x$.

Example 1 **Find the value of $\text{Sin}^{-1}\left(\frac{\sqrt{3}}{2}\right)$. Write angle measures in degrees and radians.**

Find the angle θ for $-\frac{\pi}{2} \leq \theta \leq \frac{\pi}{2}$ that has a sine value of $\frac{\sqrt{3}}{2}$.
Using a unit circle, the point on the circle that has y-coordinate of $\frac{\sqrt{3}}{2}$ is $\frac{\pi}{3}$ or 60°.
So, $\text{Sin}^{-1}\left(\frac{\sqrt{3}}{2}\right) = \frac{\pi}{3}$ or 60°.

Example 2 **Find $\tan\left(\text{Sin}^{-1}\frac{1}{2}\right)$. Round to the nearest hundredth.**

Let $\theta = \text{Sin}^{-1}\frac{1}{2}$. Then $\text{Sin}\,\theta = \frac{1}{2}$ with $-\frac{\pi}{2} < \theta < \frac{\pi}{2}$. The value $\theta = \frac{\pi}{6}$ satisfies both conditions. $\tan\frac{\pi}{6} = \frac{\sqrt{3}}{3}$ so $\tan\left(\text{Sin}^{-1}\frac{1}{2}\right) = \frac{\sqrt{3}}{3}$.

Exercises

Find each value. Write angle measures in degrees and radians.

1. $\text{Cos}^{-1}\left(\frac{\sqrt{3}}{2}\right)$ **30°, $\frac{\pi}{6}$**
2. $\text{Sin}^{-1}\left(-\frac{\sqrt{3}}{2}\right)$ **−60°, $-\frac{\pi}{3}$**
3. $\text{Arccos}\left(-\frac{1}{2}\right)$ **120°, $\frac{2\pi}{3}$**
4. $\text{Arctan}\,\sqrt{3}$ **60°, $\frac{\pi}{3}$**
5. $\text{Arccos}\left(-\frac{\sqrt{2}}{2}\right)$ **135°, $\frac{3\pi}{4}$**
6. $\text{Tan}^{-1}(-1)$ **−45°, $-\frac{\pi}{4}$**

Find each value. Round to the nearest hundredth if necessary.

7. $\cos\left[\text{Sin}^{-1}\left(-\frac{\sqrt{2}}{2}\right)\right]$ **0.71**
8. $\tan\left[\text{Arcsin}\left(-\frac{5}{7}\right)\right]$ **−1.02**
9. $\sin\left(\text{Tan}^{-1}\frac{5}{12}\right)$ **0.38**
10. $\text{Cos}\,[\text{Arcsin}\,(-0.7)]$ **0.71**
11. $\cos\,(\text{Arctan}\, 5)$ **0.20**
12. $\sin\,(\text{Cos}^{-1}\, 0.3)$ **0.95**

Lesson 13-9

Chapter 13 53 Glencoe Algebra 2

Practice
CRM p. 56 AL OL BL ELL

13-9 Practice

Inverse Trigonometric Functions

Find each value. Write angle measures in degrees and radians.

1. Arcsin 1 **90°, $\frac{\pi}{2}$**
2. $\text{Cos}^{-1}\left(\frac{-\sqrt{2}}{2}\right)$ **135°, $\frac{3\pi}{4}$**
3. $\text{Tan}^{-1}\left(\frac{-\sqrt{3}}{3}\right)$ **−30°, $-\frac{\pi}{6}$**
4. $\text{Arccos}\,\frac{\sqrt{2}}{2}$ **45°, $\frac{\pi}{4}$**
5. $\text{Arctan}\,(-\sqrt{3})$ **−60°, $-\frac{\pi}{3}$**
6. $\text{Sin}^{-1}\left(-\frac{1}{2}\right)$ **−30°, $-\frac{\pi}{6}$**

Find each value. Round to the nearest hundredth if necessary.

7. $\tan\left(\text{Cos}^{-1}\frac{1}{2}\right)$ **1.73**
8. $\cos\left[\text{Sin}^{-1}\left(-\frac{3}{5}\right)\right]$ **0.8**
9. $\cos\,[\text{Arctan}\,(-1)]$ **0.71**
10. $\tan\left(\text{Sin}^{-1}\frac{12}{13}\right)$ **2.4**
11. $\sin\left(\text{Arctan}\,\frac{\sqrt{3}}{3}\right)$ **0.5**
12. $\cos\left(\text{Arctan}\,\frac{3}{4}\right)$ **0.8**

Solve each equation. Round to the nearest tenth if necessary.

13. $\text{Tan}\,\theta = 10$ **84.3°**
14. $\text{Sin}\,\theta = 0.7$ **44.4°**
15. $\text{Sin}\,\theta = -0.5$ **−30.0°**
16. $\text{Cos}\,\theta = 0.05$ **87.1°**
17. $\text{Tan}\,\theta = 0.22$ **12.4°**
18. $\text{Sin}\,\theta = -0.03$ **−1.7°**

19. **PULLEYS** The equation $\cos \theta = 0.95$ describes the angle through which pulley A moves, and $\cos \theta = 0.17$ describes the angle through which pulley B moves. Which pulley moves through a greater angle?
pulley A

20. **FLYWHEELS** The equation $\text{Tan}\,\theta = 1$ describes the counterclockwise angle through which a flywheel rotates in 1 millisecond. Through how many degrees has the flywheel rotated after 25 milliseconds?
1125°

Chapter 13 56 Glencoe Algebra 2

Word Problem Practice
CRM p. 57 AL OL BL ELL

13-9 Word Problem Practice

Inverse Trigonometric Functions

1. **DOORS** The exit from a restaurant kitchen has a pair of swinging doors that meet in the middle of the doorway. Each door is three feet wide. A waiter needs to take a cart of plates into the dining area from the kitchen. The cart is two feet wide.

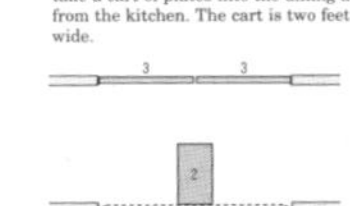

a. What is the minimum angle θ through which the doors must each be opened to prevent the cart from hitting either door? **48.2°**

b. If only one of the two doors could be opened, what is the minimum angle θ through which the door must be opened to prevent the cart from hitting the door? **70.5°**

c. If the pair of swinging doors were replaced by a single door the full width of the opening, what is the minimum angle θ through which the door must be opened to prevent the cart from hitting the door? **48.2°**

2. **SURVEYING** In ancient times, it was known that a triangle with side lengths of 3, 4, and 5 units was a right triangle. Surveyors used ropes with knots at each unit of length to make sure that an angle was a right angle. Such a rope was placed on the ground so that one leg of the triangle had three knots and the other had four. This guaranteed that the triangle formed was right triangle, meaning that the surveyor had formed a right angle.

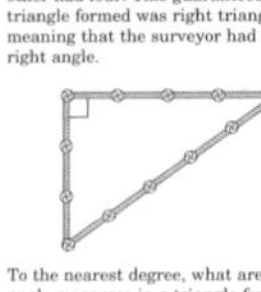

To the nearest degree, what are the angle measures in a triangle formed in this way? **37°, 53°, 90°**

3. **TRAVEL** Beth is riding her bike to her friend Marco's house. She can only ride on the streets, which run north-south or east-west.

a. Beth rides two miles east and four miles south to get to Marco's. If Beth could have traveled directly from her house to Marco's, in what direction would she have traveled?
63.4° south of east

b. Beth then rides three miles west and one mile north to get to the grocery store. If Beth could have traveled directly from Marco's house to the store, in what direction would she have traveled? **18.4° north of west**

Lesson 13-9

Chapter 13 57 Glencoe Algebra 2

4 ASSESS

Ticket Out the Door Have students write the domain and range for the arcsin, arccos, and arctan functions.

Formative Assessment

Check for student understanding of concepts in Lessons 13-8 and 13-9.

CRM Quiz 4, p. 62

NGSSS PRACTICE 912.A.6.3, 912.A.9.1, 912.A.2.8

47. Simplify $\dfrac{\frac{2}{x}+2}{\frac{2}{x}-2}$. A

A. $\dfrac{1+x}{1-x}$ C. $\dfrac{1-x}{1+x}$

B. $\dfrac{2}{x}$ D. $-x$

48. **SHORT RESPONSE** What is the equation of the graph below? $(x-3)^2+(y+4)^2=25$

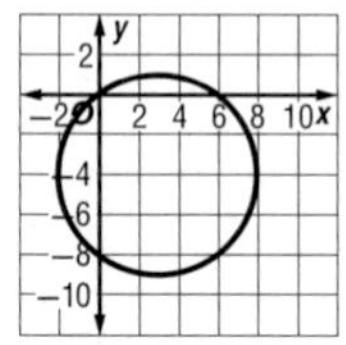

49. If $f(x)=2x^2-3x$ and $g(x)=4-2x$, what is $g[f(x)]$? G

F. $g[f(x)]=4+6x-8x^2$

G. $g[f(x)]=4+6x-4x^2$

H. $g[f(x)]=20-26x+8x^2$

I. $g[f(x)]=44-38x+8x^2$

50. If g is a positive number, which of the following is equal to $12g$? D

A. $\sqrt{144g}$

B. $\sqrt{12g^2}$

C. $\sqrt{24g^2}$

D. $6\sqrt{4g^2}$

Spiral Review

51. **RIDES** The Cosmoclock 21 is a huge Ferris wheel in Japan. The diameter is 328 feet. Suppose a rider enters the ride at 0 feet, and then rotates in 90° increments counterclockwise. The table shows the angle measures of rotation and the height above the ground of the rider. (Lesson 13-8)

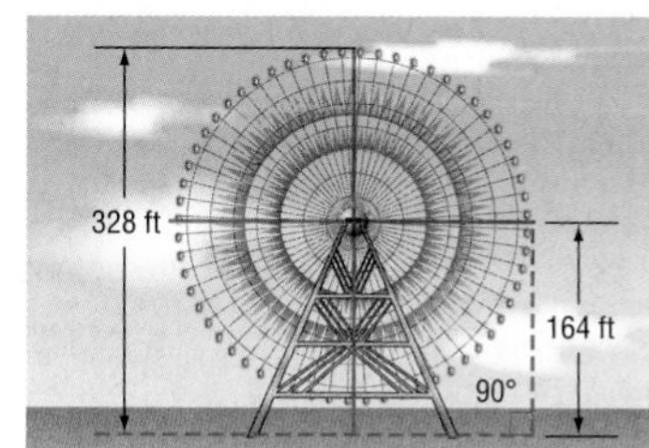

Angle	Height	Angle	Height
0°	0	450°	164
90°	164	540°	328
180°	328	630°	164
270°	164	720°	0
360°	0		

a. A function that models the data is $y=164\cdot[\sin(x-90°)]+164$. Identify the vertical shift, amplitude, period, and phase shift of the graph. 164; 164; 360°, 90°

b. Write an equation using the sine that models the position of a rider on the Vienna Giant Ferris Wheel in Austria, with a diameter of 200 feet. Check your equation by plotting the points and the equation with a graphing calculator. $y=100\,[\sin(x-90°)]+100$

52. **TIDES** The world's record for the highest tide is held by the Minas Basin in Nova Scotia, Canada, with a tidal range of 54.6 feet. A tide is at equilibrium when it is at its normal level halfway between its highest and lowest points. Write an equation to represent the height h of the tide. Assume that the tide is at equilibrium at $t=0$, that the high tide is beginning, and that the tide completes one cycle in 12 hours. (Lesson 13-7) $y=27.3\sin\frac{\pi}{6}t$

Solve each equation. (Lesson 8-4)

53. $\log_3 5+\log_3 x=\log_3 10$ 2

54. $\log_4 a+\log_4 9=\log_4 27$ 3

55. $\log_{10} 16-\log_{10} 2t=\log_{10} 2$ 4

56. $\log_7 24-\log_7 (y+5)=\log_3 8$ −2

Skills Review

Find the exact value of each trigonometric function. (Lesson 13-3)

57. $\cos 3\pi$ -1

58. $\tan 120°$ $-\sqrt{3}$

59. $\sin 300°$ $-\frac{\sqrt{3}}{2}$

60. $\sec\frac{7\pi}{6}$ $-\frac{2\sqrt{3}}{3}$

Differentiated Instruction OL BL

Extension Have students consider the function $y=\sin^{-1}x+\cos^{-1}x$ and complete the table.

x	0	$\frac{1}{2}$	$\frac{\sqrt{2}}{2}$	$\frac{\sqrt{3}}{2}$	1	$-\frac{1}{2}$	$-\frac{\sqrt{2}}{2}$	$-\frac{\sqrt{3}}{2}$	−1
y	$\frac{\pi}{2}$	$\frac{\pi}{2}$	$\frac{\pi}{2}$	$\frac{\pi}{2}$	$\frac{\pi}{2}$	$\frac{\pi}{2}$	$\frac{\pi}{2}$	$\frac{\pi}{2}$	$\frac{\pi}{2}$

Have them make a conjecture about the function $y=\sin^{-1}x+\cos^{-1}x$. $\sin^{-1}x+\cos^{-1}x=\frac{\pi}{2}$ for all values of x. Have them make a conjecture about the functions $y=\tan^{-1}x+\cot^{-1}x$ and $y=\sec^{-1}x+\csc^{-1}x$. Both functions are equal to 1 for all values of x.

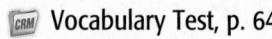

FL Math Online glencoe.com
- STUDY TO GO
- Vocabulary Review

Chapter Summary

Key Concepts

Right Triangle Trigonometry (Lesson 13-1)

- $\sin\theta = \frac{\text{opp}}{\text{hyp}}$, $\cos\theta = \frac{\text{adj}}{\text{hyp}}$, $\tan\theta = \frac{\text{opp}}{\text{adj}}$,
  $\csc\theta = \frac{\text{hyp}}{\text{opp}}$, $\sec\theta = \frac{\text{hyp}}{\text{adj}}$, $\cot\theta = \frac{\text{adj}}{\text{opp}}$

Angle Measures and Trigonometric Functions of General Angles (Lessons 13-2 and 13-3)

- The measure of an angle is determined by the amount of rotation from the initial side to the terminal side.
- You can find the exact values of the six trigonometric functions of θ, given the coordinates of a point $P(x, y)$ on the terminal side of the angle.

Law of Sines and Law of Cosines (Lessons 13-4 and 13-5)

- $\frac{\sin A}{a} = \frac{\sin B}{b} = \frac{\sin C}{c}$
- $a^2 = b^2 + c^2 - 2bc\cos A$
  $b^2 = a^2 + c^2 - 2ac\cos B$
  $c^2 = a^2 + b^2 - 2ab\cos C$

Circular and Inverse Trigonometric Functions (Lessons 13-6 and 13-9)

- If the terminal side of an angle θ in standard position intersects the unit circle at $P(x, y)$, then $\cos\theta = x$ and $\sin\theta = y$.
- $y = \text{Sin } x$ if $y = \sin x$ and $-\frac{\pi}{2} \leq x \leq \frac{\pi}{2}$

Graphing Trigonometric Functions (Lesson 13-7)

- For trigonometric functions of the form $y = a\sin b\theta$ and $y = a\cos b\theta$, the amplitude is $|a|$, and the period is $\frac{360°}{|b|}$ or $\frac{2\pi}{|b|}$.
- The period of $y = a\tan b\theta$ is $\frac{180°}{|b|}$ or $\frac{\pi}{|b|}$.

FOLDABLES® Study Organizer

Be sure the Key Concepts are noted in your Foldable.

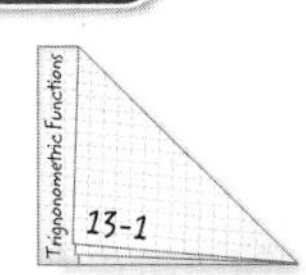

Key Vocabulary

- **amplitude** (p. 855)
- **angle of depression** (p. 812)
- **angle of elevation** (p. 812)
- **Arccosine function** (p. 871)
- **Arcsine function** (p. 871)
- **Arctangent function** (p. 871)
- **central angle** (p. 820)
- **circular function** (p. 848)
- **cosecant** (p. 808)
- **cosine** (p. 808)
- **cotangent** (p. 808)
- **coterminal angles** (p. 818)
- **cycle** (p. 849)
- **frequency** (p. 856)
- **initial side** (p. 817)
- **Law of Cosines** (p. 841)
- **Law of Sines** (p. 833)
- **midline** (p. 864)
- **period** (p. 849)
- **periodic function** (p. 849)
- **phase shift** (p. 863)
- **principle values** (p. 871)
- **quadrantal angle** (p. 826)
- **radian** (p. 819)
- **reference angle** (p. 826)
- **secant** (p. 808)
- **sine** (p. 808)
- **solving a triangle** (p. 833)
- **standard position** (p. 817)
- **tangent** (p. 808)
- **terminal side** (p. 817)
- **trigonometric function** (p. 808)
- **trigonometric ratio** (p. 808)
- **trigonometry** (p. 808)
- **unit circle** (p. 848)
- **vertical shift** (p. 864)

Vocabulary Check

State whether each sentence is *true* or *false*. If *false*, replace the underlined term to make a true sentence.

1. The Law of Cosines is used to solve a triangle when two angles and any sides are known. **1. false, Law of Sines**
2. An angle on the coordinate plane is in standard position if the vertex is at the origin and one ray is on the positive x-axis. **true**
3. Coterminal angles are angles in standard position that have the same terminal side. **true**
4. A horizontal translation of a periodic function is called a phase shift. **true**
5. The inverse of the sine function is the cosecant function. **false, arcsine function**
6. The cycle of the graph of a sine or cosine function equals half the difference between the maximum and minimum values of the function. **false, amplitude**

CHAPTER 13 Study Guide and Review

Formative Assessment

Key Vocabulary The page references after each word denote where that term was first introduced. If students have difficulty answering questions 1–6, remind them that they can use these page references to refresh their memories about the vocabulary.

Summative Assessment

CRM Vocabulary Test, p. 64

FL Math Online glencoe.com

Vocabulary PuzzleMaker improves students' mathematics vocabulary using four puzzle formats–crossword, scramble, word search using a word list, and word search using clues. Students can work online or from a printed worksheet.

FOLDABLES® Study Organizer

Dinah Zike's Foldables®

Have students look through the chapter to make sure they have included examples in their Foldables.

Suggest that students keep their Foldables handy while completing the Study Guide and Review pages. Point out that their Foldables can serve as a quick review tool when studying for the chapter test.

CHAPTER 13 Study Guide and Review

Lesson-by-Lesson Review

Intervention If the given examples are not sufficient to review the topics covered by the questions, remind students that the page references tell them where to review that topic in their textbook.

Two-Day Option Have students complete the Lesson-by-Lesson Review on pp. 878–882. Then you can use ExamView® Assessment Suite to customize another review worksheet that practices all the objectives of this chapter or only the objectives on which your students need more help.

Differentiated Instruction

Super DVD: MindJogger Videoquizzes Use this DVD as an alternative format of review for the test.

CHAPTER 13 Study Guide and Review

Lesson-by-Lesson Review

13-1 Right Triangle Trigonometry (pp. 808–816)

912.T.2.1, 912.T.2.2

Solve $\triangle ABC$ by using the given measurements. Round measures of sides to the nearest tenth and measures of angles to the nearest degree.

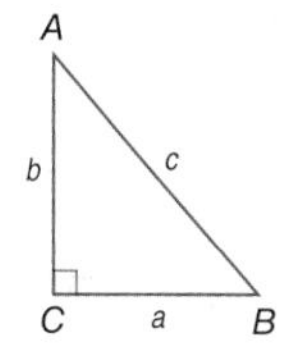

7. $c = 12, b = 5$ $a = 10.9$; $A = 65°$; $B = 25°$

8. $a = 10, B = 55°$ $A = 35°$; $c = 17.4$; $b = 14.3$

9. $B = 75°, b = 15$ $A = 15°$; $a = 4.0$; $c = 15.5$

10. $B = 45°, c = 16$ $a = 11.3$; $b = 11.3$; $A = 45°$

11. $A = 35°, c = 22$ $B = 55°$; $a = 12.6$; $b = 18.0$

12. $\sin A = \frac{2}{3}, a = 6$ $A = 42°$; $B = 48°$; $b = 6.7$; $c = 9.0$

13. TRUCK The back of a moving truck is 3 feet off of the ground. What length does a ramp off the back of the truck need to be in order for the angle of elevation of the ramp to be 20°? about 8.8 ft

EXAMPLE 1

Solve $\triangle ABC$ by using the given measurements. Round measures of sides to the nearest tenth and measures of angles to the nearest degree.

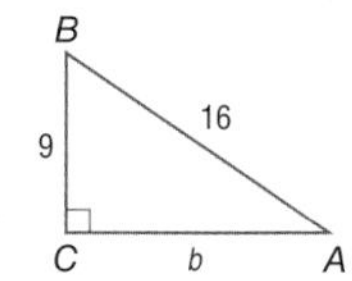

Find b.
$a^2 + b^2 = c^2$
$9^2 + b^2 = 16^2$
$b = \sqrt{16^2 - 9^2}$
$b \approx 13.2$

Find A. $\sin A = \frac{9}{16}$
Use a calculator.
To the nearest degree, $A = 34°$.

Find B. $34° + B \approx 90°$
$B \approx 56°$

Therefore, $b \approx 13.2$, $A \approx 34°$, and $B \approx 56°$.

13-2 Angles and Angle Measures (pp. 817–823)

912.T.1.1

Rewrite each degree measure in radians and each radian measure in degrees.

14. 215° $\frac{43\pi}{36}$

15. $\frac{5\pi}{2}$ 450°

16. -3π $-540°$

17. $-315°$ $-\frac{7\pi}{4}$

Find one angle with positive measure and one angle with negative measure coterminal with each angle.

18. 265° 625°, −95°

19. −65° 295°, −425°

20. $\frac{7\pi}{2}$ $\frac{11\pi}{2}$, $-\frac{\pi}{2}$

21. BICYCLE A bicycle tire makes 8 revolutions in one minute. The tire has a radius of 15 inches. Find the angle θ in radians through which the tire rotates in one second. $\frac{4\pi}{15}$

EXAMPLE 2

Rewrite 160° in radians.

$160° = 160°\left(\frac{\pi \text{ radians}}{180°}\right)$

$= \frac{160\pi}{180}$ radians or $\frac{8\pi}{9}$

EXAMPLE 3

Find one angle with positive measure and one angle with negative measure coterminal with 150°.

positive angle:

$150° + 360° = 510°$ **Add 360°.**

negative angle:

$150° - 360° = -210°$ **Subtract 360°.**

13-3 Trigonometric Functions of General Angles (pp. 825–831)

912.T.1.2, 912.T.1.3

Find the exact value of each trigonometric function.

22. $\cos 135°$ $-\frac{\sqrt{2}}{2}$

23. $\tan 150°$ $-\frac{\sqrt{3}}{3}$

24. $\sin 2\pi$ 0

25. $\cos \frac{3\pi}{2}$ 0

The terminal side of θ in standard position contains each point. Find the exact values of the six trigonometric functions of θ. 26–28. See margin.

26. $P(-4, 3)$

27. $P(5, 12)$

28. $P(16, -12)$

29. BALL A ball is thrown off the edge of a building at an angle of 70° and with an initial velocity of 5 meters per second. The equation that represents the horizontal distance of the ball x is $x = v_0(\cos \theta)t$, where v_0 is the initial velocity, θ is the angle at which it is thrown, and t is the time in seconds. About how far will the ball travel in 10 seconds? about 17.1 meters

EXAMPLE 4

Find the exact value of sin 120°.

Because the terminal side of 120° lies in Quadrant II, the reference angle θ' is 180° − 120° or 60°. The sine function is positive in Quadrant II, so $\sin 120° = \sin 60°$ or $\frac{\sqrt{3}}{2}$.

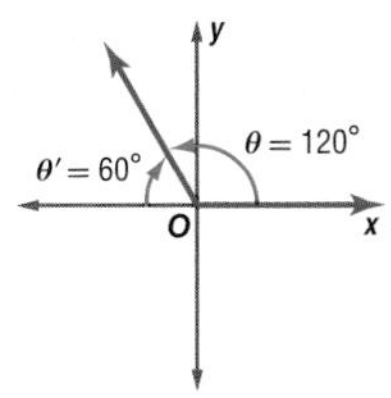

EXAMPLE 5

The terminal side of θ in standard position contains the point (6, 5). Find the exact values of the six trigonometric functions of θ.

$\sin \theta = \frac{y}{r}$ or $\frac{5\sqrt{61}}{61}$	$\cos \theta = \frac{x}{r}$ or $\frac{6\sqrt{61}}{61}$	$\tan \theta = \frac{y}{x}$ or $\frac{5}{6}$
$\csc \theta = \frac{r}{y}$ or $\frac{\sqrt{61}}{5}$	$\sec \theta = \frac{r}{x}$ or $\frac{\sqrt{61}}{6}$	$\cot \theta = \frac{x}{y}$ or $\frac{6}{5}$

13-4 Law of Sines (pp. 832–839)

912.T.2.3, 912.T.2.4

Determine whether each triangle has *no* solution, *one* solution, or *two* solutions. Then solve each triangle. Round measures of sides to the nearest tenth and measures of angles to the nearest degree.

30. $C = 118°, c = 10, a = 4$ See margin.

31. $A = 25°, a = 15, c = 18$ See margin.

32. $A = 70°, a = 5, c = 16$ no solution

33. BOAT Kira and Mallory are standing on opposite sides of a river. How far is Kira from the boat? Round to the nearest tenth if necessary. 105.5 ft

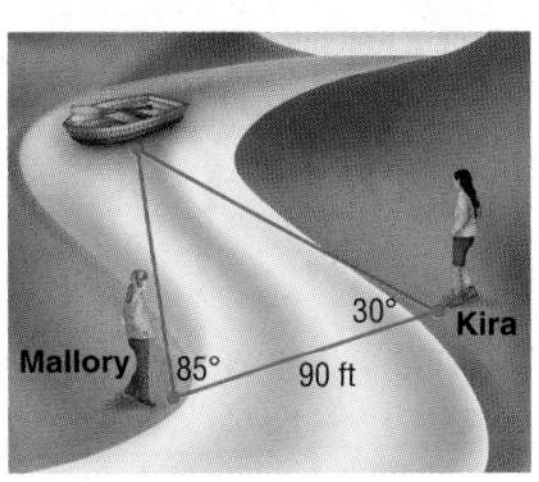

EXAMPLE 6

Solve $\triangle ABC$.

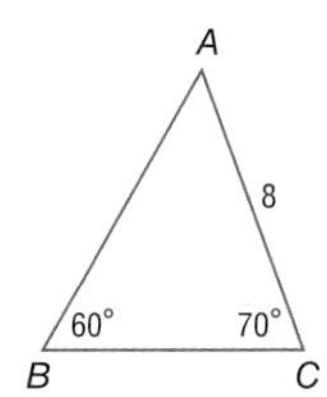

First, find the measure of the third angle.

$$60° + 70° + a = 180°$$
$$A = 50°$$

Now use the Law of Sines to find a and c. Write two equations, each with one variable.

$$\frac{\sin B}{b} = \frac{\sin C}{c} \qquad \frac{\sin B}{b} = \frac{\sin A}{a}$$
$$\frac{\sin 60°}{8} = \frac{\sin 70°}{c} \qquad \frac{\sin 60°}{8} = \frac{\sin 50°}{a}$$
$$c = \frac{8 \sin 70°}{\sin 60°} \qquad a = \frac{8 \sin 50°}{\sin 60°}$$
$$c \approx 8.7 \qquad a \approx 7.1$$

Therefore, $A = 50°$, $c \approx 8.7$, and $a \approx 7.1$.

Additional Answers

26. $\sin \theta = \frac{3}{5}$, $\cos \theta = -\frac{4}{5}$, $\tan \theta = -\frac{3}{4}$, $\csc \theta = \frac{5}{3}$, $\sec \theta = -\frac{5}{4}$, $\cot \theta = -\frac{4}{3}$

27. $\sin \theta = \frac{12}{13}$, $\cos \theta = \frac{5}{13}$, $\tan \theta = \frac{12}{5}$, $\csc \theta = \frac{13}{12}$, $\sec \theta = \frac{13}{5}$, $\cot \theta = \frac{5}{12}$

28. $\sin \theta = -\frac{3}{5}$, $\cos \theta = \frac{4}{5}$, $\tan \theta = -\frac{3}{4}$, $\csc \theta = -\frac{5}{3}$, $\sec \theta = \frac{5}{4}$, $\cot \theta = -\frac{4}{3}$

30. one solution; $A \approx 21°$, $B \approx 41°$, $b \approx 7.4$

31. two solutions; first solution: $C = 30°$, $B = 125°$, $b = 29.1$; second solution: $C = 150°$, $B = 5°$, $b = 3.1$

Chapter 13 Study Guide and Review 879

CHAPTER 13 Study Guide and Review

13-5 Law of Cosines (pp. 841–846)

912.T.1.8, 912.T.2.3

Determine whether each triangle should be solved by beginning with the Law of *Sines* or Law of *Cosines*. Then solve each triangle. Round measures of sides to the nearest tenth and measures of angles to the nearest degree.

34.

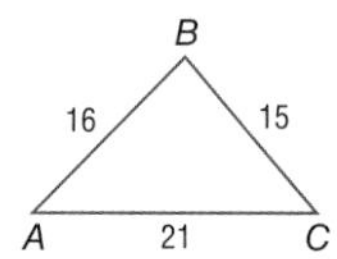

35.

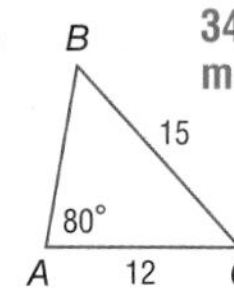

34–38. See margin.

36. $C = 75°, a = 5, b = 7$

37. $A = 42°, a = 9, b = 13$

38. $b = 8.2, c = 15.4, A = 35°$

39. FARMING A farmer wants to fence a piece of his land. Two sides of the triangular field have lengths of 120 feet and 325 feet. The measure of the angle between those sides is 70°. How much fencing will the farmer need? **about 750.5 ft**

EXAMPLE 7

Solve $\triangle ABC$ for $C = 55°$, $b = 11$, and $a = 18$.

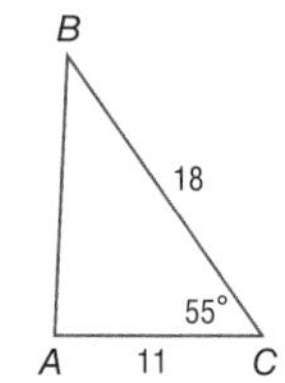

You are given the measure of two sides and the included angle. Begin by drawing a diagram and using the Law of Cosines to determine c.

$c^2 = a^2 + b^2 - 2ab \cos C$

$c^2 = 18^2 + 11^2 - 2(18)(11) \cos 55°$

$c^2 \approx 217.9$

$c \approx 14.8$

Next, you can use the Law of Sines to find the measure of angle A.

$\frac{\sin A}{18} \approx \frac{\sin 55°}{14.8}$

$\sin A \approx \frac{18 \sin 55°}{14.2}$ or A is about 85.0°

The measure of the angle B is approximately $180 - (85.0 + 55)$ or 40.0°.

Therefore, $c \approx 14.8$, $A \approx 85.0°$, and $B \approx 40.0°$.

13-6 Circular Functions (pp. 848–854)

912.T.1.5, 912.T.1.8

Find the exact value of each function.

40. $\cos(-210°)$ $-\frac{\sqrt{3}}{2}$

41. $(\cos 45°)(\cos 210°)$ $-\frac{\sqrt{6}}{4}$

42. $\sin -\frac{7\pi}{4}$ $\frac{\sqrt{2}}{2}$

43. $\left(\cos \frac{\pi}{2}\right)\left(\sin \frac{\pi}{2}\right)$ **0**

44. Determine the period of the function. **6**

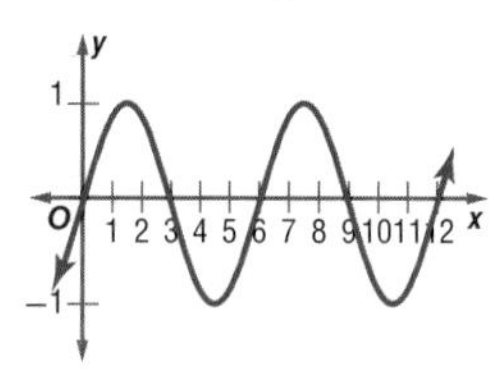

45. A wheel with a diameter of 18 inches completes 4 revolutions in 1 minute. What is the period of the function that describes the height of one spot on the outside edge of the wheel as a function of time? **15 seconds**

EXAMPLE 8

Find the exact value of sin 510°.

$\sin 510° = \sin(360° + 150°)$

$= \sin 150°$

$= \frac{1}{2}$

EXAMPLE 9

Determine the period of the function below.

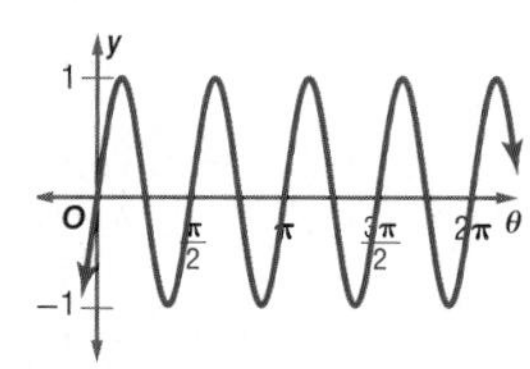

The pattern repeats itself at $\frac{\pi}{2}$, π, and so on. So, the period is $\frac{\pi}{2}$.

Additional Answers

34. Cosines; $A \approx 46°$, $B \approx 85°$, $C \approx 49°$

35. Sines; $B \approx 52°$, $C \approx 48°$, $c \approx 11.3$

36. Cosines; $A \approx 40°$, $B \approx 65°$, $c \approx 7.5$

37. Sines; $B \approx 75°$, $C \approx 63°$, $c \approx 12.0$ or $B \approx 105°$, $C \approx 33°$, $c \approx 7.3$

38. Cosines; $a \approx 9.9$, $B \approx 28°$, $C \approx 117°$

46. amplitude: 4, period: 180°

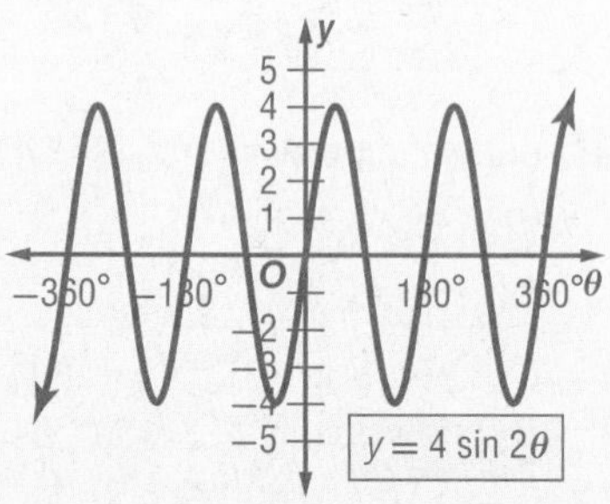

47. amplitude: 1, period: 720°

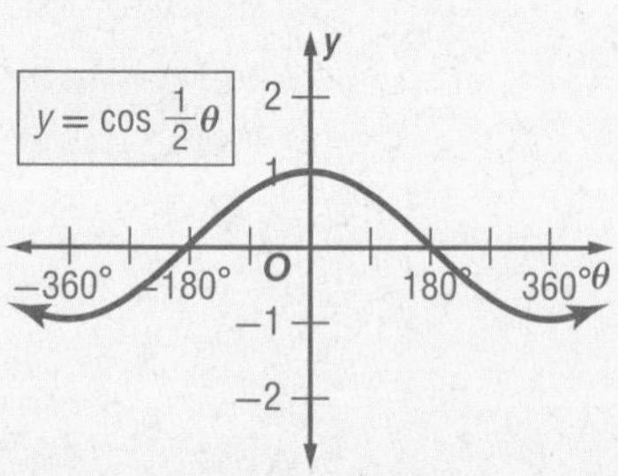

48. amplitude: not defined, period: 360°

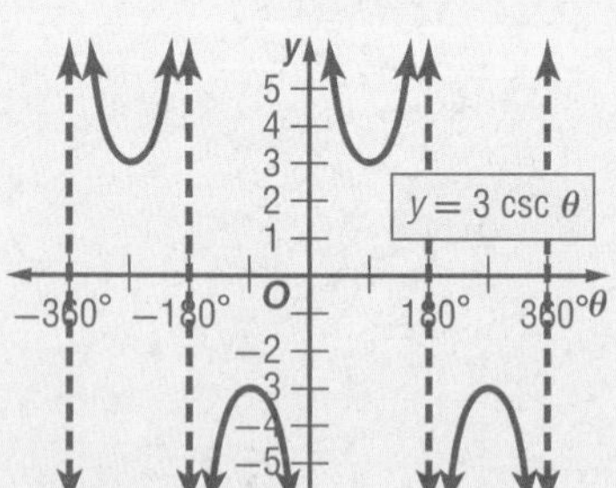

49. amplitude: not defined, period: 360°

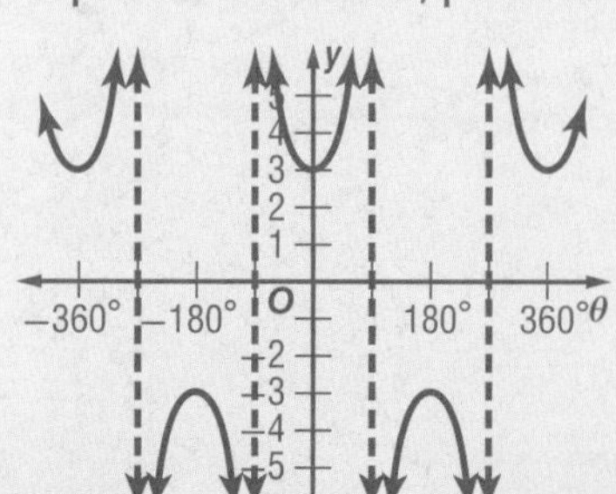

50. amplitude: not defined, period: 90°

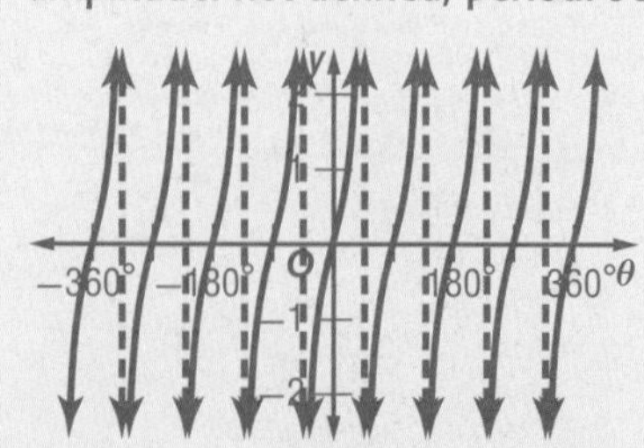

MIXED PROBLEM SOLVING
For mixed problem-solving practice, see page 991.

13-7 Graphing Trigonometric Functions (pp. 855–861)

912.T.1.5, 912.T.1.6

Find the amplitude, if it exists, and period of each function. Then graph the function. 46–51. See margin.

46. $y = 4 \sin 2\theta$

47. $y = \cos \frac{1}{2}\theta$

48. $y = 3 \csc \theta$

49. $y = 3 \sec \theta$

50. $y = \tan 2\theta$

51. $y = 2 \csc \frac{1}{2}\theta$

52. When Lauren jumps on a trampoline it vibrates with a frequency of 10 hertz. Let the amplitude equal 5 feet. Write a sine equation to represent the vibration of the trampoline y as a function of time t. $y = 5 \sin 20\pi t$

EXAMPLE 10

Find the amplitude and period of $y = 2 \cos 4\theta$. Then graph the function.

amplitude: $|a| = |2|$ or 2. The graph is stretched vertically so that the maximum value is 2 and the minimum value is −2.

period: $\frac{360°}{|b|} = \frac{360°}{|4|}$ or 90°

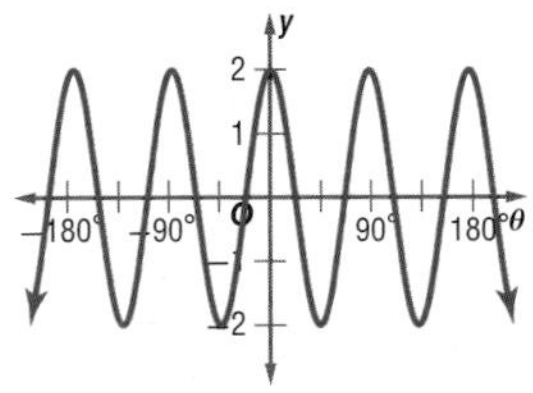

13-8 Translations of Trigonometric Graphs (pp. 863–870)

912.T.1.6, 912.T.1.8

State the vertical shift, amplitude, period, and phase shift of each function. Then graph the function. 53–57. See margin.

53. $y = 3 \sin [2(\theta - 90°)] + 1$

54. $y = \frac{1}{2} \tan [2(\theta - 30°)] - 3$

55. $y = 2 \sec \left[3\left(\theta - \frac{\pi}{2}\right)\right] + 2$

56. $y = \frac{1}{2} \cos \left[\frac{1}{4}\left(\theta + \frac{\pi}{4}\right)\right] - 1$

57. $y = \frac{1}{3} \sin \left[\frac{1}{3}(\theta - 90°)\right] + 2$

58. The graph below approximates the height y of a rope that two people are twirling as a function of time t in seconds. Write an equation for the function. $y = 4 \sin 360t + 4$

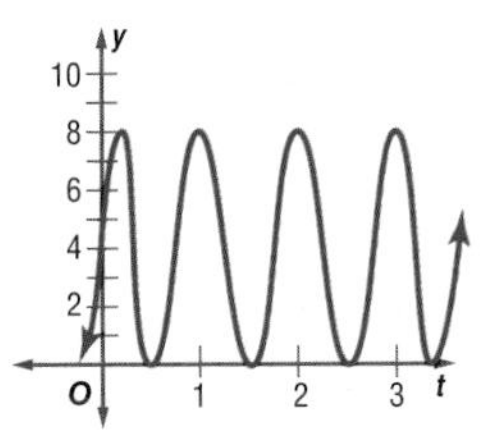

EXAMPLE 11

State the vertical shift, amplitude, period, and phase shift of $y = 2 \sin \left[3\left(\theta + \frac{\pi}{2}\right)\right] + 4$. Then graph the function.

Identify the values of k, a, b, and h.

$k = 4$, so the vertical shift is 4.

$a = 2$, so the amplitude is 2.

$b = 3$, so the period is $\frac{2\pi}{|3|}$ or $\frac{2\pi}{3}$.

$h = -\frac{\pi}{2}$, so the phase shift is $\frac{\pi}{2}$ to the left.

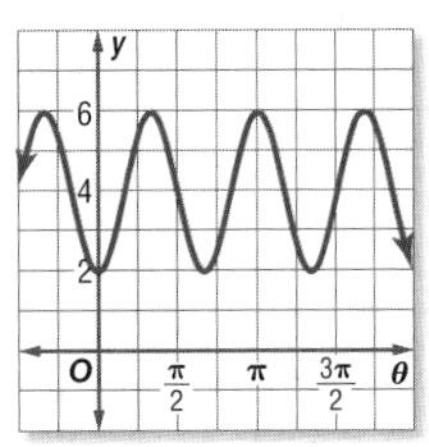

Additional Answers

51. amplitude: not defined, period: 720°

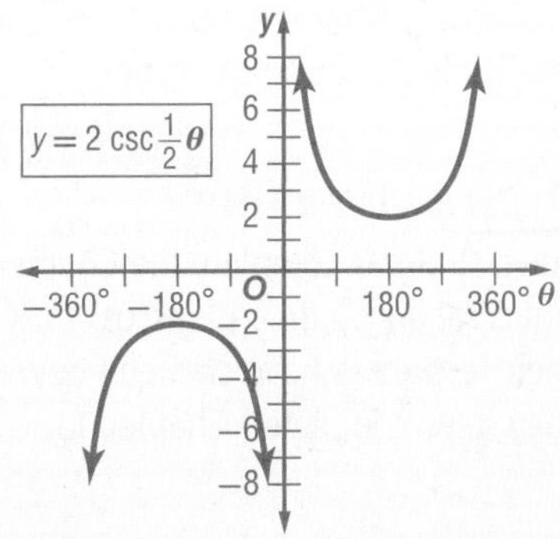

53. vertical shift: up 1, amplitude: 3, period: 180°, phase shift: 90° right

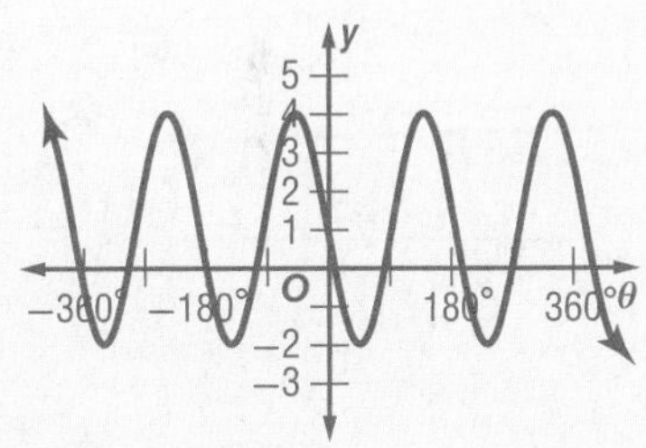

54. vertical shift: down 3, amplitude: undefined, period: 90°, phase shift: 30° right

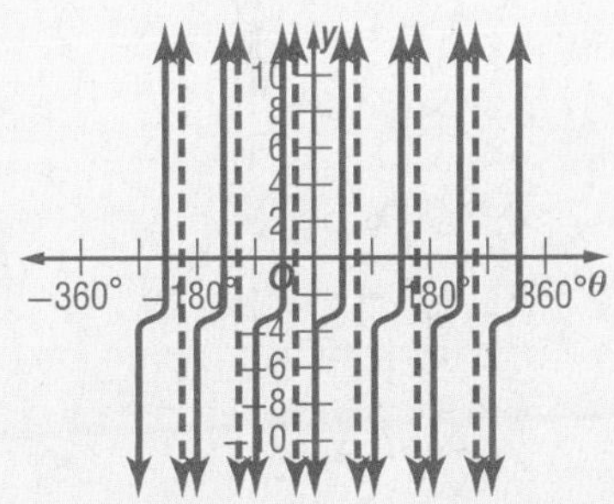

55. vertical shift: up 2, amplitude: not defined, period: $\frac{2\pi}{3}$ phase shift: $\frac{\pi}{2}$ right

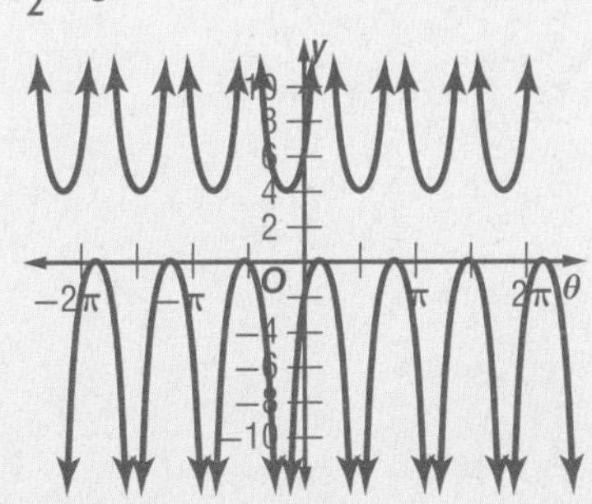

Additional Answers

56. vertical shift: down 1, amplitude: $\frac{1}{2}$, period: 4π, phase shift: $\frac{\pi}{4}$ left

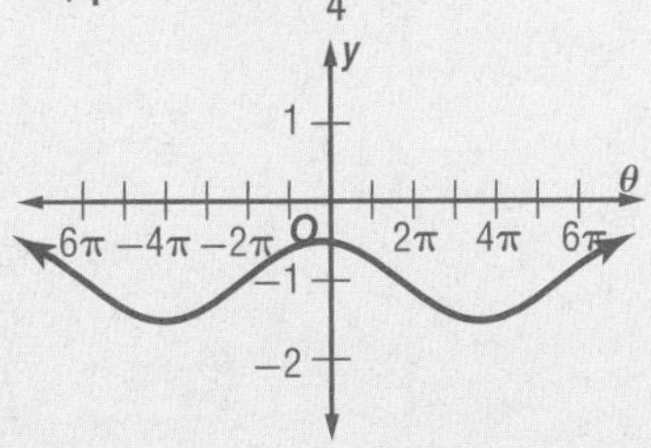

57. vertical shift: up 2, amplitude: $\frac{1}{3}$, period: 1080°, phase shift: 90° right

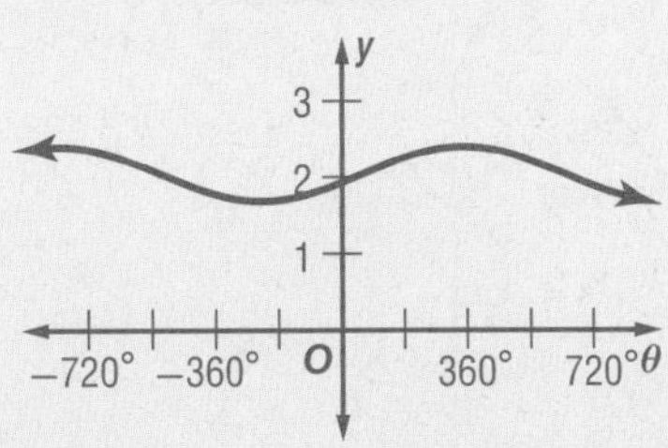

Problem Solving Review

For additional practice in problem solving for Chapter 13, see the Mixed Problem Solving Appendix, p. 992, in the Student Handbook section.

Anticipation Guide

Have students complete the Chapter 13 Anticipation Guide and discuss how their responses have changed now that they have completed Chapter 13.

Additional Answers (Practice Test)

19.

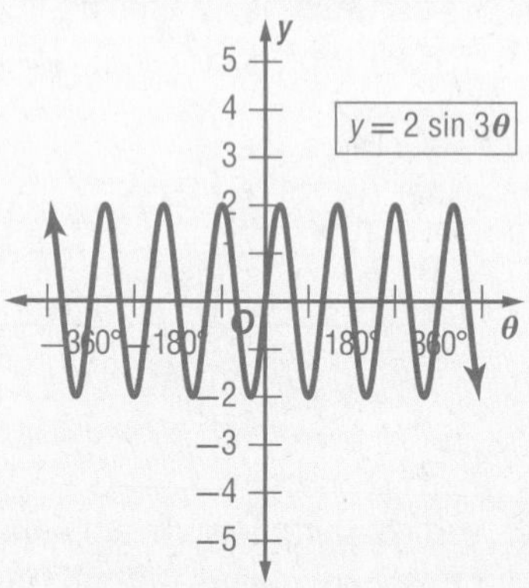

20.

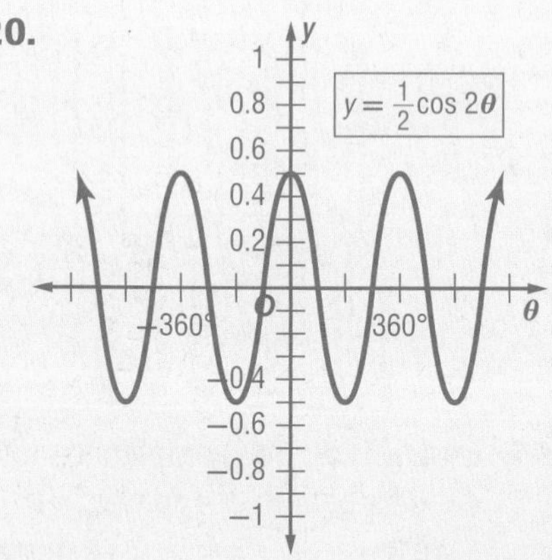

13-9 Inverse Trigonometric Functions (pp. 871–876)

912.T.1.7, 912.T.1.8

Evaluate each inverse trigonometric function. Write angle measures in degrees and radians.

59. $\text{Sin}^{-1}(1)$ **90°, $\frac{\pi}{2}$**
60. Arctan (0) **0°, 0**
61. Arcsin $\frac{\sqrt{3}}{2}$ **60°, $\frac{\pi}{3}$**
62. $\text{Cos}^{-1} \frac{\sqrt{2}}{2}$ **45°, $\frac{\pi}{4}$**
63. $\text{Tan}^{-1} 1$ **45°, $\frac{\pi}{4}$**
64. Arccos 0 **90°, $\frac{\pi}{2}$**
65. **RAMPS** A bicycle ramp is 5 feet tall and 10 feet long, as shown below. Write an inverse trigonometric function that can be used to find θ, the angle the ramp makes with the ground. Then find the angle. **$\sin^{-1} \frac{5}{10} = \theta$; 30°**

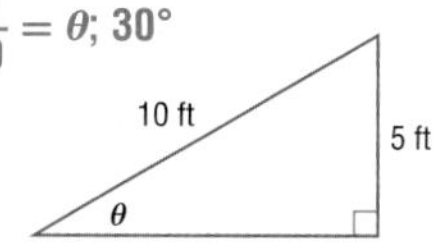

Evaluate each inverse trigonometric function. Round to the nearest hundredth if necessary.

66. $\tan\left(\text{Cos}^{-1} \frac{1}{3}\right)$ **2.83**
67. $\text{Sin}\left(\text{Arcsin} -\frac{\sqrt{2}}{2}\right)$ **−0.71**
68. $\sin(\text{Tan}^{-1} 0)$ **0**

Solve each equation. Round to the nearest tenth if necessary.

69. $\text{Tan}\ \theta = -1.43$ **−55.0°**
70. $\text{Sin}\ \theta = 0.8$ **53.1°**
71. $\text{Cos}\ \theta = 0.41$ **65.8°**

EXAMPLE 12

Evaluate $\text{Cos}^{-1} \frac{1}{2}$. Write angle measures in degrees and radians.

Find the angle θ for $0° \leq \theta \leq 180°$ that has a cosine value of $\frac{1}{2}$.

Use a unit circle.

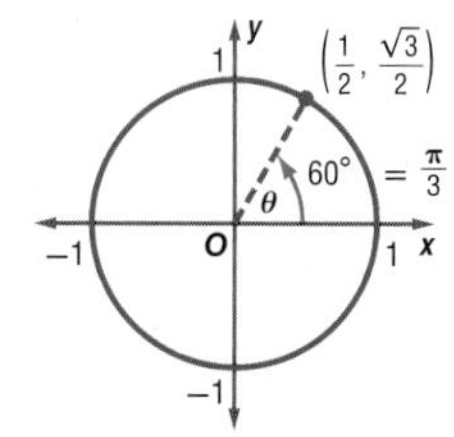

Find a point on the unit circle that has an x-coordinate of $\frac{1}{2}$. When $\theta = 60°$, $\text{Cos}\ \theta = \frac{1}{2}$.

So, $\text{Cos}^{-1} = 60°$ or $\frac{\pi}{3}$.

EXAMPLE 13

Evaluate $\sin\left(\text{Tan}^{-1} \frac{1}{2}\right)$. Round to the nearest hundredth.

Use a calculator.

KEYSTROKES: SIN 2nd [TAN^{-1}] 1 ÷ 2) ENTER

0.4472135955

So, $\sin\left(\text{Tan}^{-1} \frac{1}{2}\right) \approx 0.45$.

EXAMPLE 14

If $\text{Cos}\ \theta = 0.72$, find θ.

Use a calculator.

KEYSTROKES: 2nd [COS^{-1}] .72 ENTER 43.9455195623

So, $\theta \approx 43.9°$.

23.

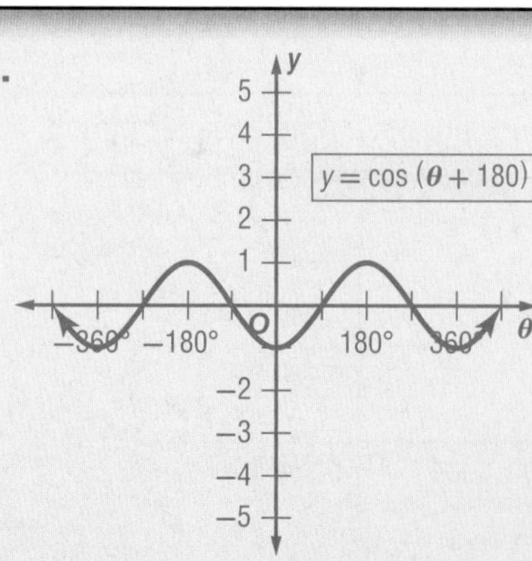

CHAPTER 13 Practice Test

FL Math Online glencoe.com
Chapter Test

Solve $\triangle ABC$ by using the given measurements. Round measures of sides to the nearest tenth and measures of angles to the nearest degree.

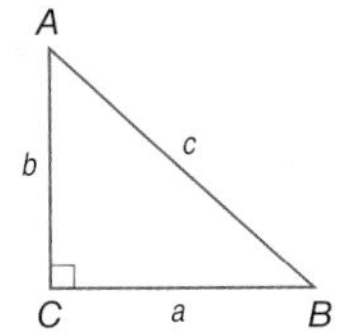

1. $A = 36°, c = 9$ **$B = 54°, a = 5.3, b = 7.3$**
2. $a = 12, A = 58°$ **$B = 32°, c = 14.2, b = 7.5$**
3. $B = 85°, b = 8$ **$A = 5°, c = 8.0, a = 0.7$**
4. $a = 9, c = 12$ **$b = 7.9, B = 41°, A = 49°$**

Rewrite each degree measure in radians and each radian measure in degrees.

5. $325°$ **$\frac{65\pi}{36}$**
6. $-175°$ **$-\frac{35\pi}{36}$**
7. $\frac{9\pi}{4}$ **$405°$**
8. $-\frac{5\pi}{6}$ **$-150°$**

9. Determine whether $\triangle ABC$, with $A = 110°, a = 16$, and $b = 21$, has *no* solution, *one* solution, or *two* solutions. Then solve the triangle, if possible. Round measures of sides to the nearest tenth and measures of angles to the nearest degree. **no solution**

Find the exact value of each function. Write angle measures in degrees.

10. $\cos(-90°)$ **0**
11. $\sin 585°$ **$-\frac{\sqrt{2}}{2}$**
12. $\cot \frac{4\pi}{3}$ **$\frac{\sqrt{3}}{3}$**
13. $\sec\left(-\frac{9\pi}{4}\right)$ **$\sqrt{2}$**
14. $\tan\left(\text{Cos}^{-1}\frac{4}{5}\right)$ **$\frac{3}{4}$**
15. $\text{Arccos}\,\frac{1}{2}$ **$60°$**

16. The terminal side of angle θ in standard position intersects the unit circle at point $P\left(\frac{1}{2}, \frac{\sqrt{3}}{2}\right)$. Find $\cos\theta$ and $\sin\theta$. **$\cos\theta = \frac{1}{2}, \sin\theta = \frac{\sqrt{3}}{2}$**

17. **NGSSS PRACTICE** What angle has a tangent and sine that are both negative? **B**

A. 65°

B. 310°

C. 120°

D. 265°

18. **NAVIGATION** Airplanes and ships measure distance in nautical miles. The formula 1 nautical mile = $6077 - 31\cos 2\theta$ feet, where θ is the latitude in degrees, can be used to find the approximate length of a nautical mile at a certain latitude. Find the length of a nautical mile when the latitude is 120°. **6092.5 ft**

Find the amplitude and period of each function. Then graph the function. **19, 20. See margin for graphs.**

19. $y = 2\sin 3\theta$ **2, 120°**
20. $y = \frac{1}{2}\cos 2\theta$ **$\frac{1}{2}$, 180°**

21. **NGSSS PRACTICE** What is the period of the function $y = 3\cot\theta$? **G**

F. 120°

G. 180°

H. 360°

I. 1080°

22. Determine whether $\triangle XYZ$, with $y = 15, z = 9$, and $X = 105°$, should be solved by beginning with the Law of Sines or Law of Cosines. Then solve the triangle. Round measures of sides to the nearest tenth and measures of angles to the nearest degree. **Law of Cosines; $Y \approx 48°$, $x \approx 19.4$, $Z \approx 27°$**

23, 24. See margin for graphs.

State the amplitude, period, and phase shift for each function. Then graph the function.

23. $y = \cos(\theta + 180)$ **1, 360°, −180°**
24. $y = \frac{1}{2}\tan\left(\theta - \frac{\pi}{2}\right)$ **does not exist, π, $\frac{\pi}{2}$**

25. **WHEELS** A water wheel has a diameter of 20 feet. It makes one complete revolution in 45 seconds. Let the height at the top of the wheel represent the height at time 0. Write an equation for the height of point h in the diagram below as a function of time t. Then graph the function. **$h = 10\cos 8t$; See margin for graph.**

CHAPTER 13 Practice Test

ExamView Assessment Suite — Customize and create multiple versions of your chapter test and their answer keys. All of the questions from the leveled chapter tests in the *Chapter 13 Resource Masters* are also available on ExamView® Assessment Suite.

Additional Answers

24.

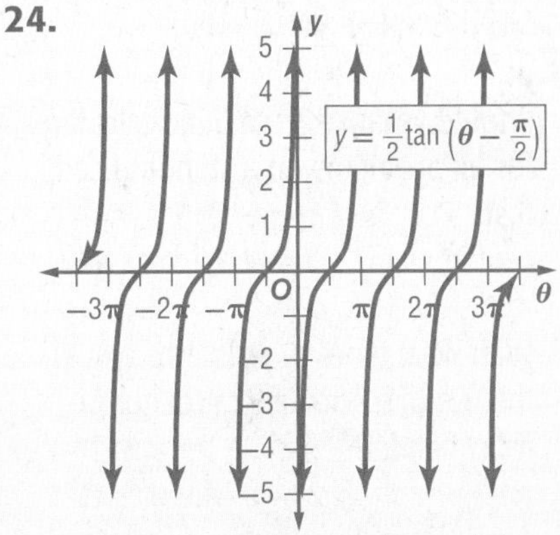

25.

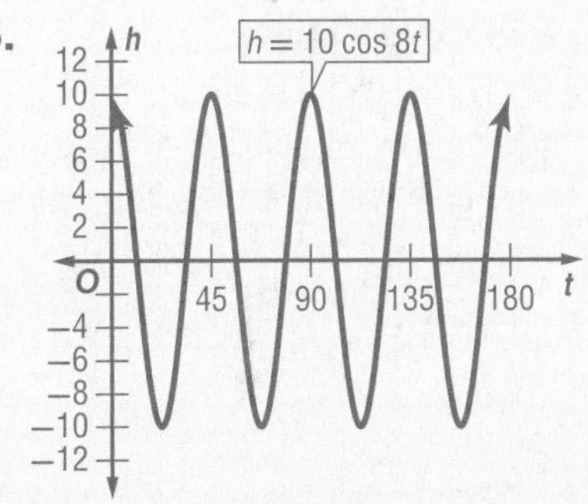

Intervention Planner

Tier 1 **On Level**	Tier 2 **Strategic Intervention** approaching grade level	Tier 3 **Intensive Intervention** 2 or more grades below level
If students miss about 25% of the exercises,	**If** students miss about 50% of the exercises,	**If** students miss about 75% of the exercises,
Then choose a resource: **SE** Lessons 13-1, 13-2, 13-3, 13-4, 13-5, 13-6, 13-7, 13-8, and 13-9 **CRM** Skills Practice, pp. 7, 13, 19, 25, 31, 37, 43, 49, and 55 **TE** Chapter Project, p. 804	**Then** choose a resource: **CRM** Study Guide and Intervention, Chapter 13, pp. 5, 11, 17, 23, 29, 35, 41, 47, and 53	**Then** use *Math Triumphs, Alg. 2*, Ch. 6
FL Math Online Self-Check Quiz	FL Math Online Extra Examples, Personal Tutor, Homework Help	FL Math Online Extra Examples, Personal Tutor, Homework Help, Review Vocabulary

1 FOCUS

Objective Use the strategy of using a scientific calculator to solve standardized test problems.

2 TEACH

Scaffolding Questions

Ask:

- Should you use a scientific calculator for all problems on a standardized test? Possible answer: No, some problems are more efficiently solved mentally or by hand.
- With what types of problems would the use of a scientific calculator be most helpful? Possible answer: Those problems that involve complicated calculations, logarithmic functions, exponential functions, trigonometric functions, square roots are among those problems with which the use of a scientific calculator would be most helpful.

CHAPTER 13 Preparing for Standardized Tests

Using a Scientific Calculator

Scientific calculators and graphing calculators are powerful problem-solving tools. As you have likely seen, some test problems that you encounter have steps or computations that require the use of a scientific calculator.

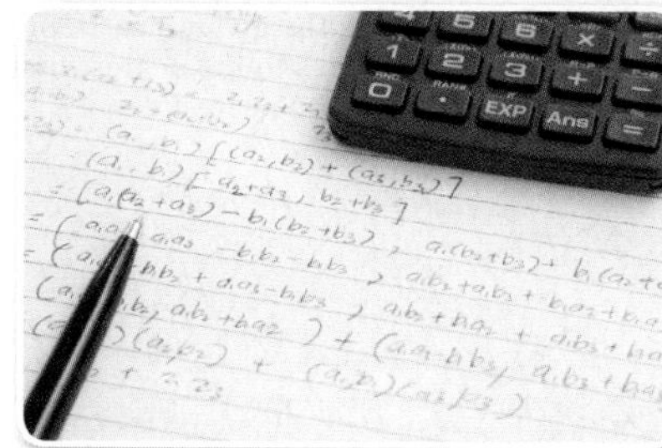

Strategies for Using a Scientific Calculator

Step 1

Familiarize yourself with the various functions of a scientific calculator as well as when they should be used.

- **Scientific notation**—for calculating large numbers
- **Logarithmic and exponential functions**—growth and decay problems, compound interest
- **Trigonometric functions**—problems involving angles, triangle problems, indirect measurement problems
- **Square roots and *n*th roots**—distance on a coordinate plane, Pythagorean Theorem

Step 2

Use your scientific or graphing calculator to solve the problem.

- Remember to work as efficiently as possible. Some steps may be done mentally or by hand, while others must be done using your calculator.
- If time permits, check your answer.

NGSSS PRACTICE EXAMPLE

Read the problem. Identify what you need to know. Then use the information in the problem to solve.

When Molly stands at a distance of 18 feet from the base of a tree, she forms an angle of 57° with the top of the tree. What is the height of the tree to the nearest tenth?

A. 27.7 ft

B. 28.5 ft

C. 29.2 ft

D. 30.1 ft

884 Chapter 13 Trigonometric Functions

Read the problem carefully. You are given some measurements and asked to find the height of a tree. It may be helpful to first sketch a model of the problem.

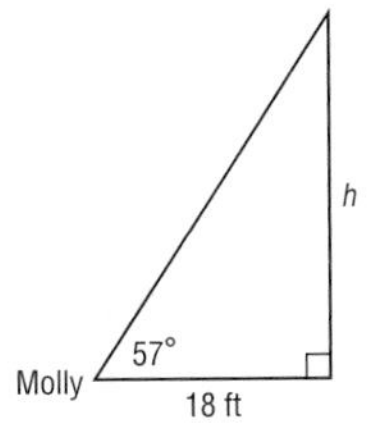

Use a trigonometric function to relate the lengths and the angle measure in the right triangle.

$\text{tangent } \theta = \frac{\text{opposite}}{\text{adjacent}}$ **Definition of tangent ratio**

$\tan 57° = \frac{h}{18}$ **Substitute.**

You need to evaluate tan 57° to solve for the height of a tree h. Use a scientific calculator.

$1.53986 \approx \frac{h}{18}$ **Use a calculator.**

$27.71748 \approx h$ **Multiply each side by 18.**

The height of the tree is about 27.7 feet. The correct answer is A.

Exercises

Read each problem. Identify what you need to know. Then use the information in the problem to solve.

1. An airplane takes off and climbs at a constant rate. After traveling 800 yards horizontally, the plane has climbed 285 yards vertically. What is the plane's angle of elevation during the takeoff and initial climb? **C**

A. 15.6°

B. 18.4°

C. 19.6°

D. 22.3°

2. What is the angle of the bike ramp below? **I**

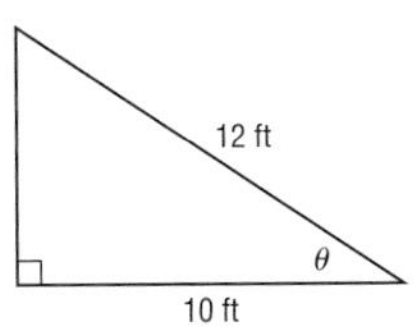

F. 26.3°

G. 28.5°

H. 30.4°

I. 33.6°

Additional Example

STANDARDIZED TEST PRACTICE The sum of three numbers is 35. The sum of the first two numbers is five greater than the third number. Twice the second number is equal to three times the first number. What are the three numbers? C

A 6, 9, 20

B 6, 10, 21

C 8, 12, 15

D 8, 10, 17

3 ASSESS

Use Exercises 1 and 2 to assess students' understanding.

Chapter 13 Preparing for Standardized Tests 885

Diagnose Student Errors

Survey student responses for each item. Class trends may indicate common errors and misconceptions.

1. A. correct
B. guess
C. guess
D. used diameter instead of radius in circumference formula

3. F. unfamiliar with point-slope form
G. unfamiliar with point-slope form
H. unfamiliar with point-slope form
I. correct

5. A. correct
B. guess
C. used wrong angle measures with side measures
D. used cosine instead of sine

7. F. guess
G. guess
H. correct
I. guess

9. A. found cos 240°
B. guess
C. correct
D. found sin 120°

10. F. did not calculate x and y correctly
G. correct
H. guess
I. guess

12. A. the coefficient of the x term prevents the graph from being symmetrical about the y-axis
B. the coefficient of the x term prevents the graph from being symmetrical about the y-axis
C. correct
D. the coefficient of the x term prevents the graph from being symmetrical about the y-axis

14. F. error in final subtraction of the division algorithm
G. correct
H. error in final subtraction of the division algorithm
I. error in final subtraction of the division algorithm

15. A. used cosine instead of tangent
B. guess
C. rounded answer incorrectly
D. correct

17. F. this is a valid conclusion but the problem asked for a conclusion that is not valid
G. this is a valid conclusion but the problem asked for a conclusion that is not valid
H. this is a valid conclusion but the problem asked for a conclusion that is not valid
I. correct

NGSSS Practice

Cumulative, Chapters 1 through 13

Read each question. Then fill in the correct answer on the answer document provided by your teacher or on a sheet of paper.

1. Suppose a Ferris wheel has a diameter of 68 feet. The wheel rotates 12° each time a new passenger is picked up. How far would you travel when the wheel rotates 12°? Round to the nearest tenth if necessary. **A**

A. 7.1 ft
B. 7.5 ft
C. 7.8 ft
D. 14.2 ft

2. **EXTENDED RESPONSE** Amanda's hours at her summer job for one week are listed in the table below. She earns $6 per hour.

Amanda's Work Hours	
Sunday	0
Monday	6
Tuesday	4
Wednesday	0
Thursday	2
Friday	6
Saturday	8

a. Write an expression for Amanda's total weekly earnings. **$6(0 + 6 + 4 + 0 + 2 + 6 + 8)**

b. Evaluate the expression from part **a** by using the Distributive Property. **$156**

c. Michael works with Amanda and also earns $6 per hour. If Michael's earnings were $192 this week, write and solve an equation to find how many more hours Michael worked than Amanda. **$6h + 156 = 192$; 6 hours**

3. What is the slope of a line parallel to $y - 2 = 4(x + 1)$? **I**

F. -4
G. $-\frac{1}{4}$
H. $\frac{1}{4}$
I. 4

Test-Taking Tip

Question 5 Use the Law of Sines to solve the triangle.

4. **GRIDDED RESPONSE** What is the radius of the circle with equation $x^2 + y^2 + 8x + 8y + 28 = 0$? **2**

5. Find m in triangle MNO if $n = 12.4$ centimeters, $M = 35°$, and $N = 74°$. Round to the nearest tenth. **A**

A. 7.4 cm
B. 8.5 cm
C. 14.6 cm
D. 35.9 cm

6. **SHORT RESPONSE** Anna is training to run a 10-kilometer race. The table below lists the times she received in different races. The times are listed in minutes. What was her mean time in minutes for a 10-kilometer race? **7.385**

7.25	8.10
7.40	6.75
7.20	7.35
7.10	7.25
8.00	7.45

7. Marvin rides his bike at a speed of 21 miles per hour and can ride his training loop 10 times in the time that it takes his younger brother to complete the training loop 8 times. Which is a reasonable estimate for Marvin's younger brother's speed? **H**

F. between 14 mph and 15 mph
G. between 15 mph and 16 mph
H. between 16 mph and 17 mph
I. between 17 mph and 18 mph

8. **SHORT RESPONSE** The speed a tsunami, or tidal wave, can travel is modeled by the equation $s = 356\sqrt{d}$, where s is the speed in kilometers per hour and d is the average depth of the water in kilometers. A tsunami is found to be traveling at 145 kilometers per hour. What is the average depth of the water? Round to the nearest hundredth. **0.17 km**

9. What is the exact value of sin 240°? **C**

A. $-\frac{1}{2}$
B. $\frac{\sqrt{2}}{3}$
C. $-\frac{\sqrt{3}}{2}$
D. $\frac{\sqrt{3}}{2}$

10. What is the solution of the system of equations shown below? **G**

$$\begin{cases} x - y + z = 0 \\ -5x + 3y - 2z = -1 \\ 2x - y + 4z = 11 \end{cases}$$

F. (0, 3, 3)
G. (2, 5, 3)
H. no solution
I. infinitely many solutions

11. **SHORT RESPONSE** In order to remain healthy, a horse requires 10 pounds of hay per day.

a. Write an equation to represent the amount of hay needed to sustain x horses for d days. $h = 10xd$

b. Is your equation a direct, joint, or inverse variation? Explain. **See margin.**

c. How much hay do three horses need for the month of July? **930 lb**

12. The graph of which of the following equations is symmetrical about the y-axis? **C**

A. $y = x^2 + 3x - 1$
B. $y = -x^2 + x$
C. $y = 6x^2 + 9$
D. $y = 3x^2 - 3x + 1$

13. **GRIDDED RESPONSE** Suppose you deposit \$500 in an account paying 4.5% interest compounded semiannually. Find the dollar value of the account rounded to the nearest penny after 10 years. **780.25**

14. What is the remainder when $x^3 - 7x + 5$ is divided by $x + 3$? **G**

F. −11
G. −1
H. 1
I. 11

15. What is the value of x? Round to the nearest tenth if necessary. **D**

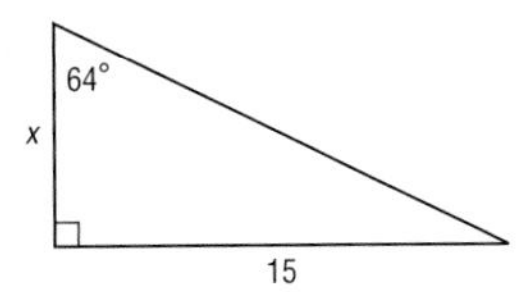

A. 6.5
B. 6.9
C. 7.1
D. 7.3

16. **GRIDDED RESPONSE** The pattern of squares below continues infinitely, with more squares being added at each step. How many squares are in the tenth step? **22**

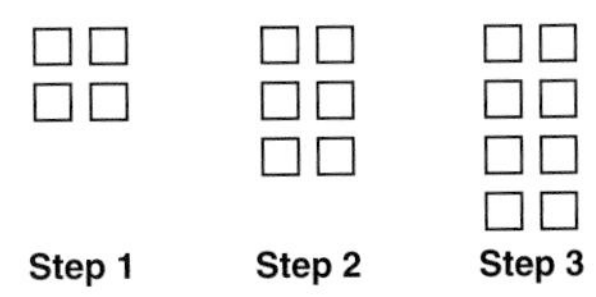

17. The results of a recent poll are organized in the matrix.

	For	Against
Proposition 1	1553	771
Proposition 2	689	1633
Proposition 3	2088	229

Based on these results, which conclusion is **not** valid? **I**

F. There were 771 votes cast against Proposition 1.
G. More people voted against Proposition 1 than voted for Proposition 2.
H. Proposition 2 has little chance of passing.
I. More people voted for Proposition 1 than for Proposition 3.

Need Extra Help?

If you missed Question...	1	2	3	4	5	6	7	8	9	10	11	12	13	14	15	16	17
Go to Lesson or Page...	13-2	1-3	2-4	10-3	13-4	12-2	1-3	7-3	13-3	3-5	9-5	5-1	8-2	6-2	13-1	11-2	4-1
For help with NGSSS...	912.T.2.2	912.A.3.1	912.A.3.10	912.G.6.7	912.T.2.3	912.S.3.3	912.A.3.1	912.A.6.5	912.T.1.3	912.A.3.14	912.A.2.12	612.A.2.6	912.A.8.7	612.A.4.4	912.T.2.1	912.D.11.3	912.D.8.2

Formative Assessment

You can use these two pages to benchmark student progress.

CRM Standardized Test Practice, pp. 78–80

ExamView Assessment Suite Create practice worksheets or tests that align to your state's standards as well as TIMSS and NAEP tests.

Homework Option

Get Ready for Chapter 14 Assign students the exercises on p. 889 as homework to assess whether they possess the prerequisite skills needed for the next chapter.

Additional Answer

11b. joint; Sample answer: The amount of hay needed is dependent upon both the number of days and the number of horses.

Page 817, Lesson 13-2, (Guided Practice)

1A.

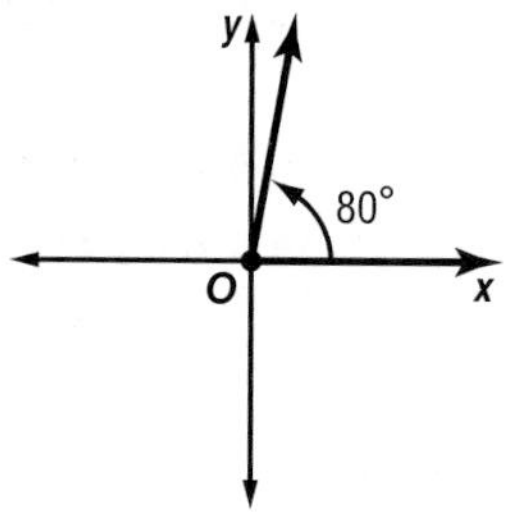

1B.

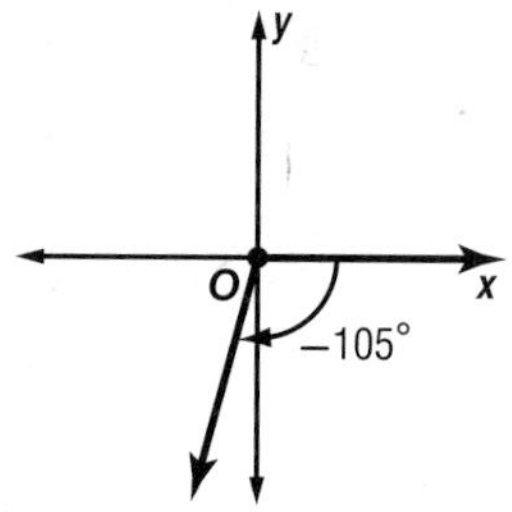

Pages 822–823, Lesson 13-2

52. Use a proportion.

$$\frac{\text{measure of the central angle}}{\text{measure of an entire circle}} = \frac{\text{the length of the arc}}{\text{the circumference}}$$

$\frac{\theta}{2\pi} = \frac{s}{2\pi r}$ Substitute.

$2\pi r\theta = 2\pi s$ Find the cross products.

$r\theta = s$ Divide each side by 2π.

53. One degree represents an angle measure that equals $\frac{1}{360}$ rotation around a circle. One radian represents the measure of an angle in standard position that intercepts an arc of length *r*. To change from degrees to radians, multiply the number of degrees by $\frac{\pi \text{ radians}}{180°}$. To change from radians to degrees, multiply the number of radians by $\frac{180°}{\pi \text{ radians}}$.

58. $\sin\theta = \frac{3}{\sqrt{205}}$ or $\frac{3\sqrt{205}}{205}$, $\cos\theta = \frac{14}{\sqrt{205}}$ or $\frac{14\sqrt{205}}{205}$, $\tan\theta = \frac{3}{14}$, $\csc\theta = \frac{\sqrt{205}}{3}$, $\sec\theta = \frac{\sqrt{205}}{14}$, $\cot\theta = \frac{14}{3}$

59. $\sin\theta = \frac{\sqrt{259}}{22}$, $\cos\theta = \frac{15}{22}$, $\tan\theta = \frac{\sqrt{259}}{15}$, $\csc\theta = \frac{22}{\sqrt{259}}$ or $\frac{22\sqrt{259}}{259}$, $\sec\theta = \frac{22}{15}$, $\cot\theta = \frac{15}{\sqrt{259}}$ or $\frac{15\sqrt{259}}{259}$

60. $\sin\theta = \frac{11}{\sqrt{290}}$ or $\frac{11\sqrt{290}}{290}$, $\cos\theta = \frac{13}{\sqrt{290}}$ or $\frac{13\sqrt{290}}{290}$, $\tan\theta = \frac{11}{13}$, $\csc\theta = \frac{\sqrt{290}}{11}$, $\sec\theta = \frac{\sqrt{290}}{13}$, $\cot\theta = \frac{13}{11}$

Pages 829–831, Lesson 13-3

11a.

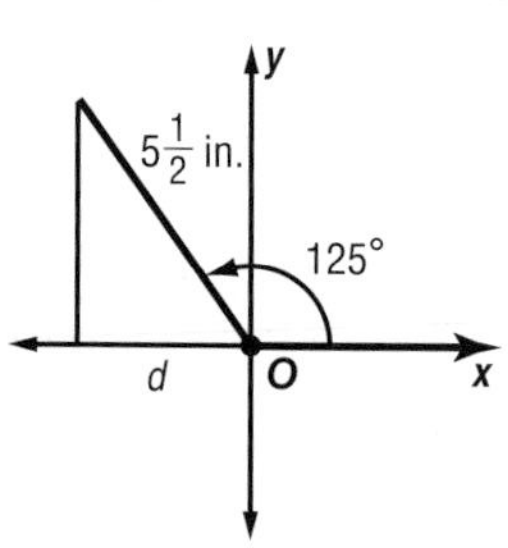

18. 15°

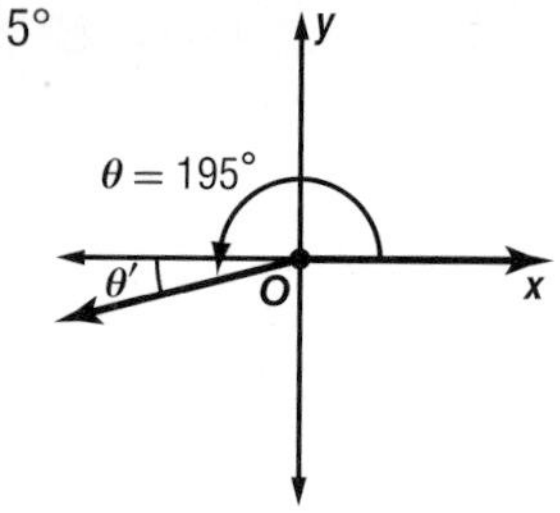

19. 75°

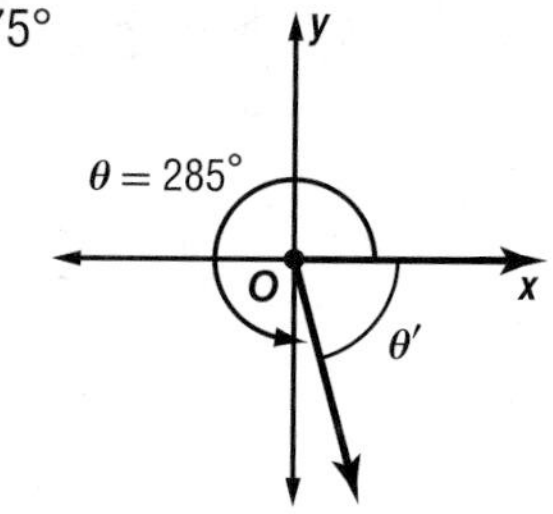

20. 70°

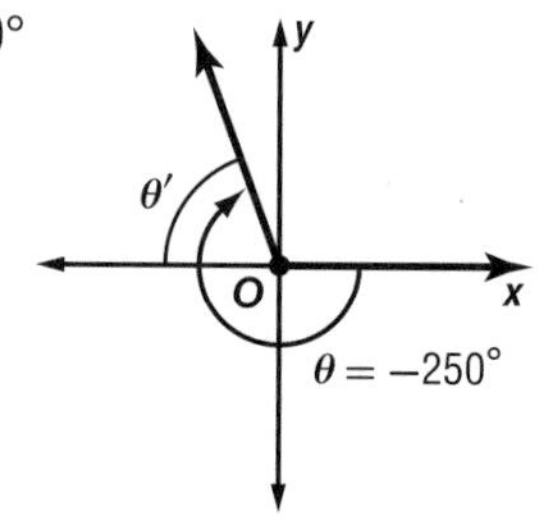

21. $\frac{\pi}{4}$

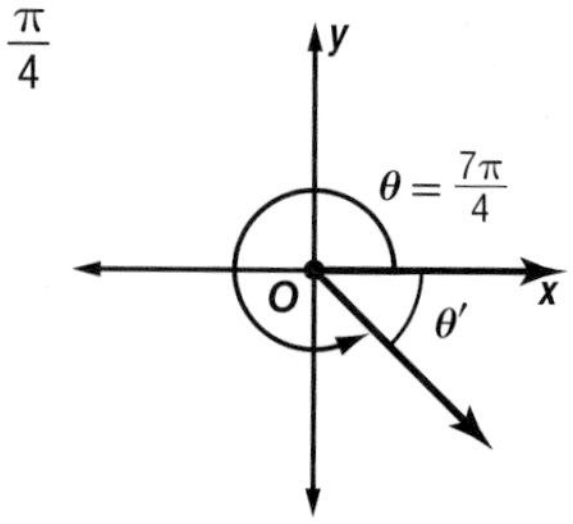

22. $\frac{\pi}{4}$

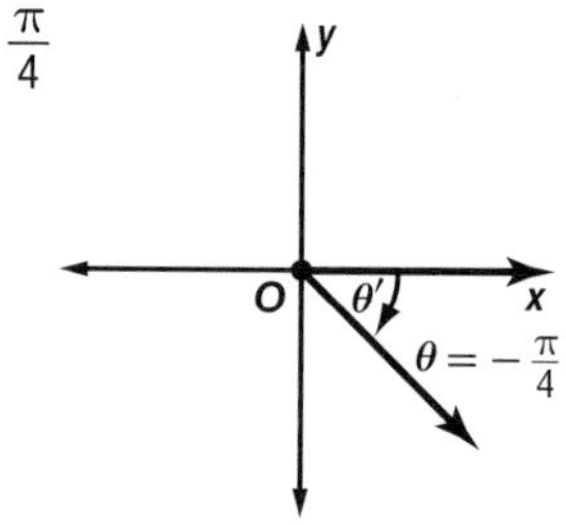

23. 40°

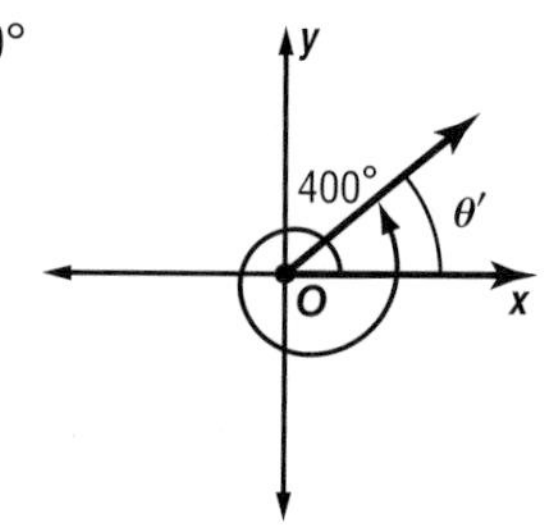

62. Sample answer:

Step 1: There are 6 bricks in the top row, and $1^2 + 5(1) = 6$, so the formula is true for $n = 1$.

Step 2: Assume that there are $k^2 + 5k$ bricks in the top *k* rows for some positive integer *k*.

Step 3: Since each row has 2 more bricks than the one above, the numbers of bricks in the rows form an arithmetic sequence. The number of bricks in the $(k + 1)$st row is $6 + [(k + 1) - 1](2)$ or $2k + 6$. Then the number of bricks in the top $k + 1$ rows is $k^2 + 5k + (2k + 6)$ or $k^2 + 7k + 6$. $k^2 + 7k + 6 = (k + 1)^2 + 5(k + 1)$, which is the formula to be proved, where $n = k + 1$. Thus, the formula is true for $n = k + 1$. Therefore, the number of bricks in the top *n* rows in $n^2 + 5n$ for all positive integers *n*.

Page 838, Lesson 13-4

45. Sample answer:

$\sin A = \frac{\text{opposite}}{\text{hypotenuse}}$	Definition of sine
$\sin A = \frac{h}{c}$	h = opposite side, c = hypotenuse
$c\sin A = h$	Multiply both sides by c.
$\text{Area} = \frac{1}{2} \cdot \text{base} \cdot \text{height}$	Area of a triangle
$\text{Area} = \frac{1}{2}bh$	b = base, h = height
$\text{Area} = \frac{1}{2}bc\sin A$	Substitution

Page 847, Mid-Chapter Quiz

12. $\sin\theta = -1$, $\cos\theta = 0$, $\tan\theta =$ undefined, $\csc\theta = -1$, $\sec\theta =$ undefined, $\cot\theta = 0$

13. $\sin\theta = \frac{4}{5}$, $\cos\theta = \frac{3}{5}$, $\tan\theta = \frac{4}{3}$, $\csc\theta = \frac{5}{4}$, $\sec\theta = \frac{5}{3}$, $\cot\theta = \frac{3}{4}$

15. two solutions: $C = 59°$, $B = 83°$, $b = 29.0$ or $C = 121°$, $B = 21°$, $b = 10.5$

Page 853, Lesson 13-6

29a.

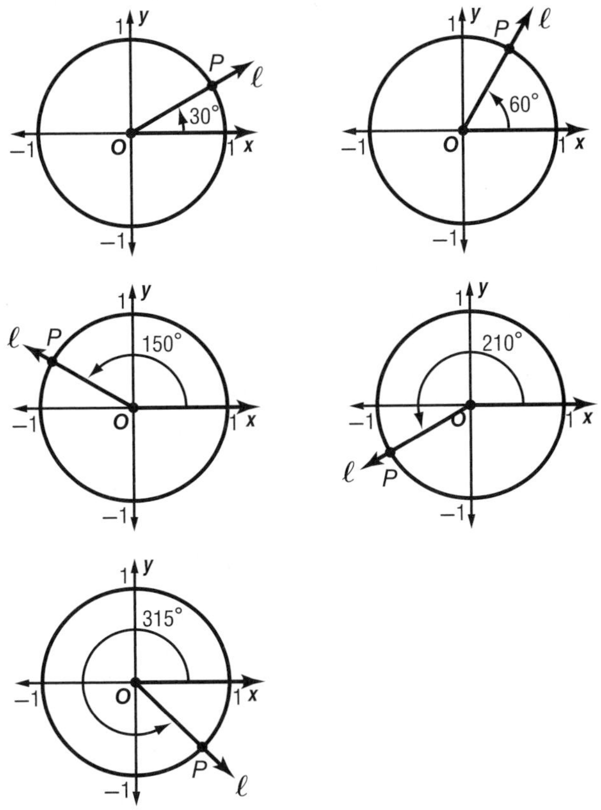

29b.

Angle	Slope
30	0.6
60	1.7
120	–1.7
150	–0.6
210	0.6
315	–1

29c. Sample answer: The slope corresponds to the tangent of the angle. For $\theta = 120°$, the x-coordinate of P is $-\frac{1}{2}$ and the y-coordinate is $= \frac{\sqrt{3}}{2}$; slope $= \frac{\text{change in } y}{\text{change in } x}$. Since change in $x = -\frac{1}{2}$ and change in $y = \frac{\sqrt{3}}{2}$, slope $= \frac{\sqrt{3}}{2} \div \left(-\frac{1}{2}\right)$ $= -\sqrt{3}$ or about -1.7.

Page 857, Lesson 13-7, (Guided Practice)

3B.

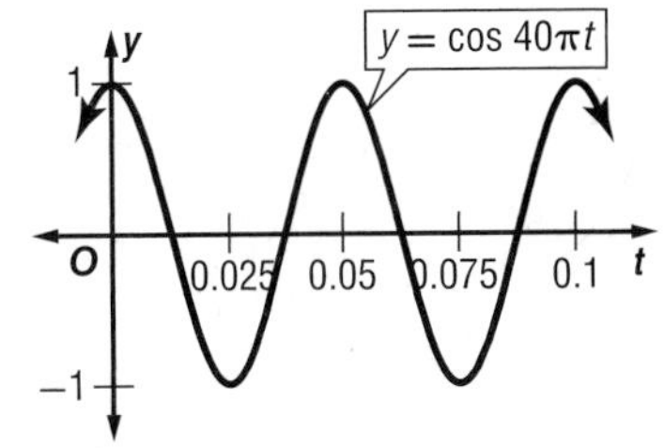

Pages 859–860, Lesson 13-7

6. period: 180°

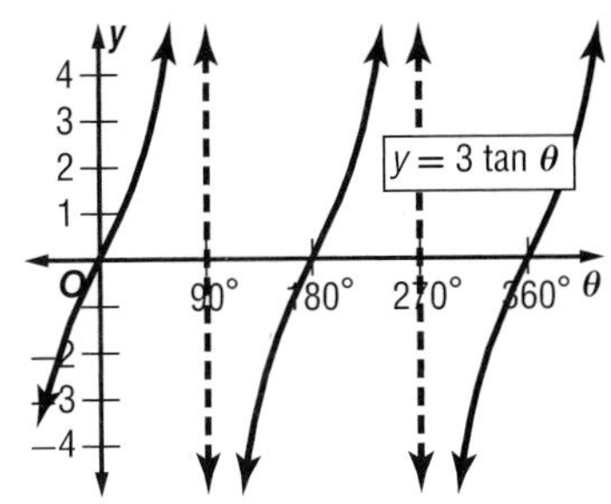

7. period: 360°

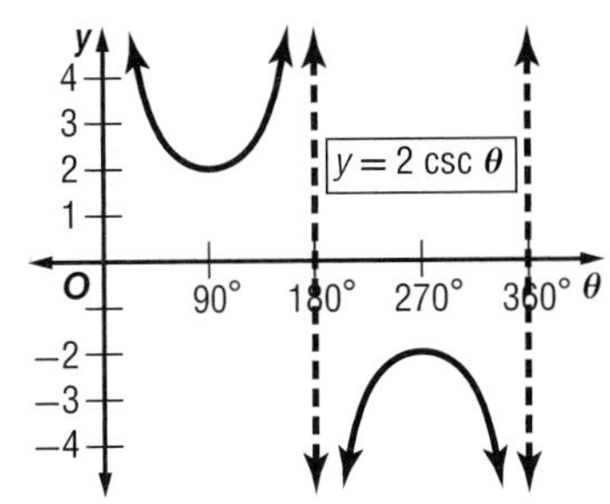

8. period: 90°

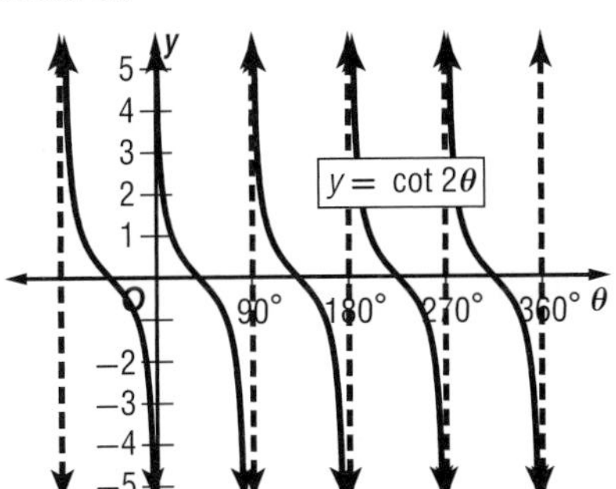

9. amplitude: 2; period: 360°

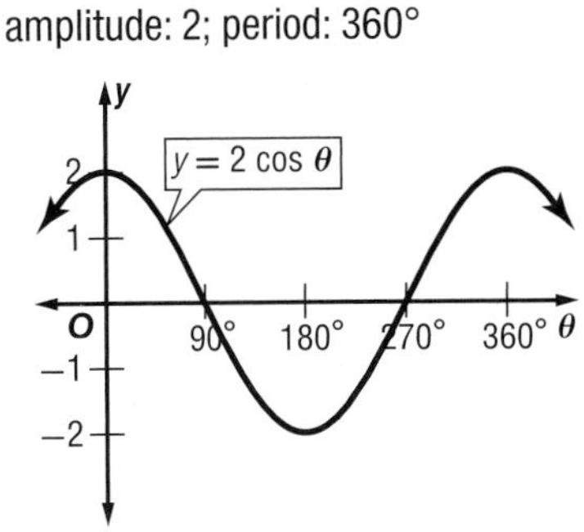

10. amplitude: 3; period: 360°

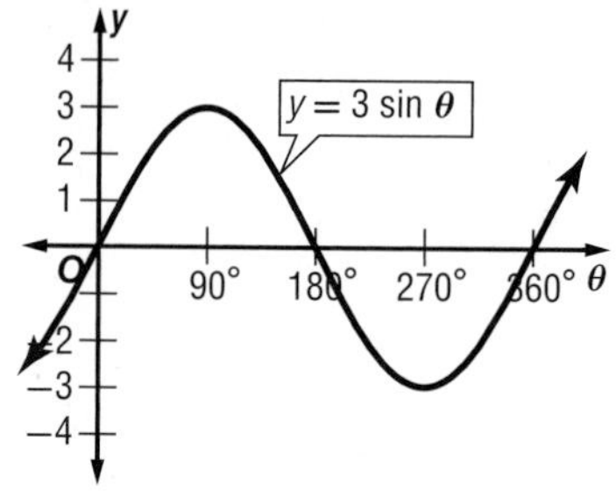

11. amplitude: 1; period: 180°

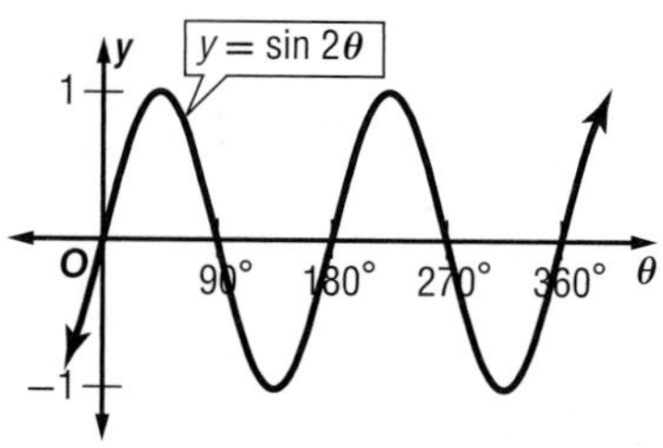

12. amplitude: 1; period: 120°

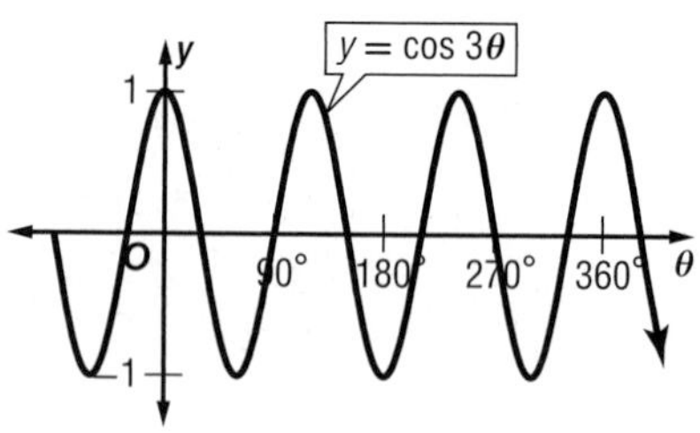

13. amplitude: 1; period: 720°

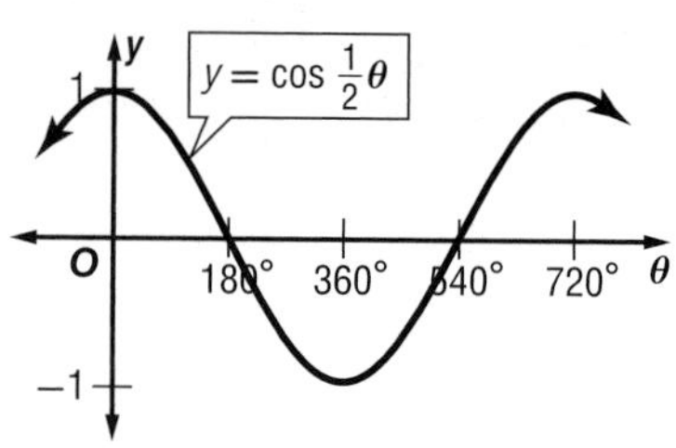

14. amplitude: 1; period: 90°

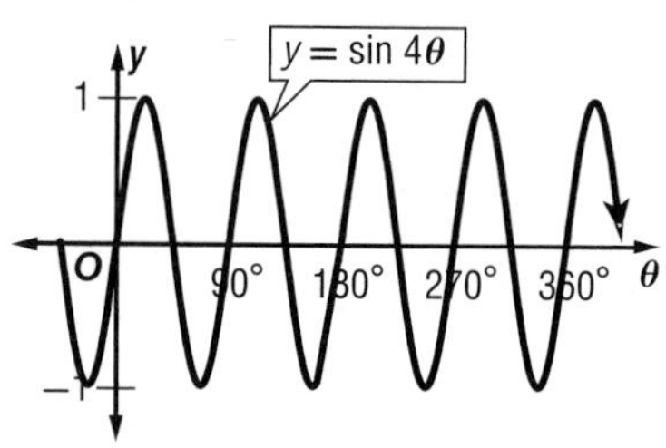

15. amplitude: $\frac{3}{4}$; period: 360°

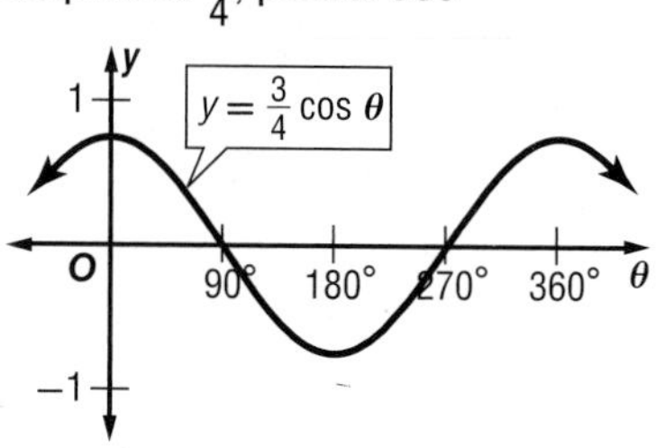

16. amplitude: $\frac{3}{2}$; period: 360°

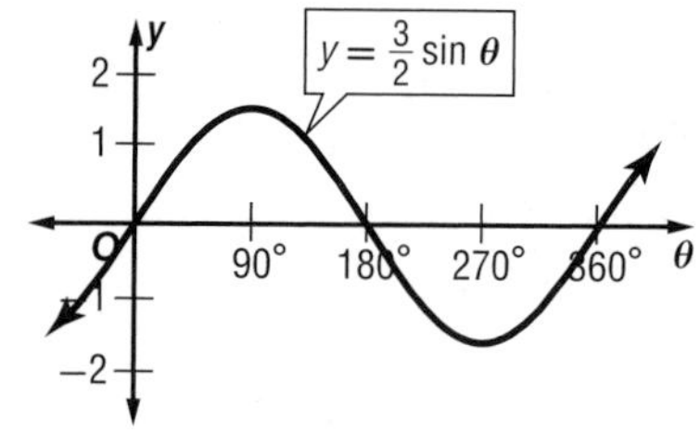

17. amplitude: $\frac{1}{2}$; period: 180°

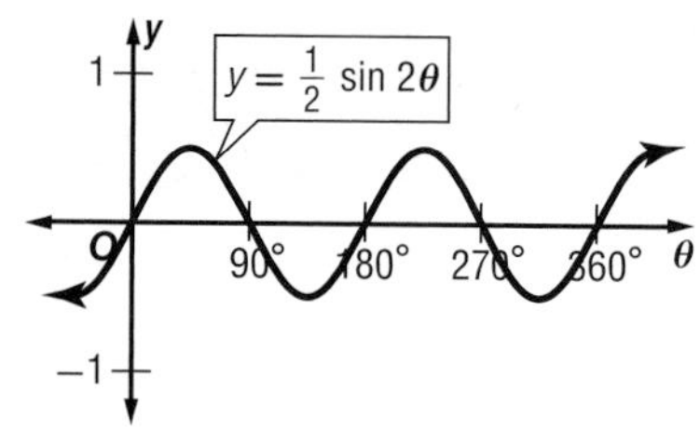

18. amplitude: 4; period: 180°

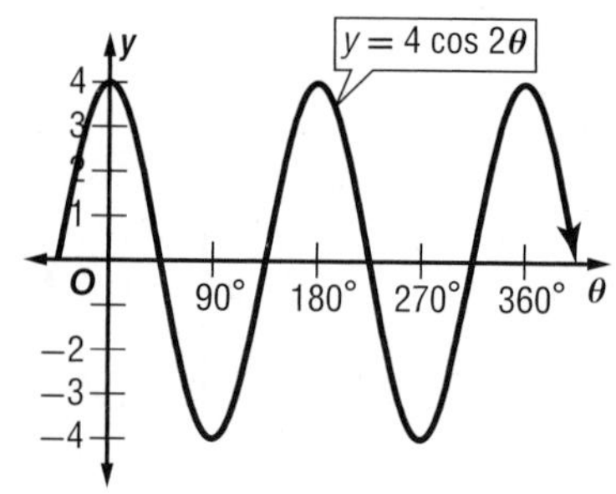

19. amplitude: 3; period: 180°

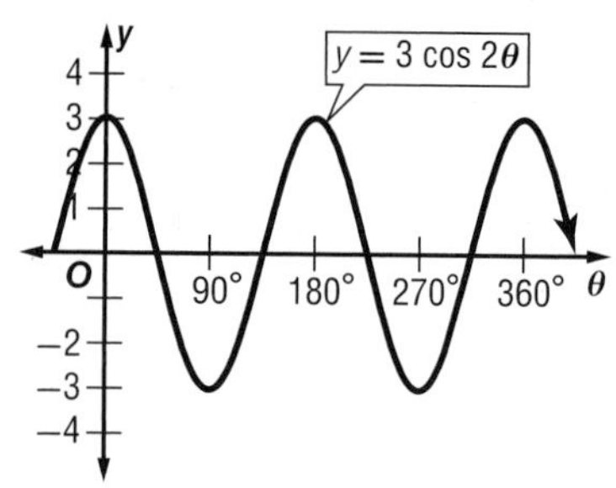

20. amplitude: 5; period: 540°

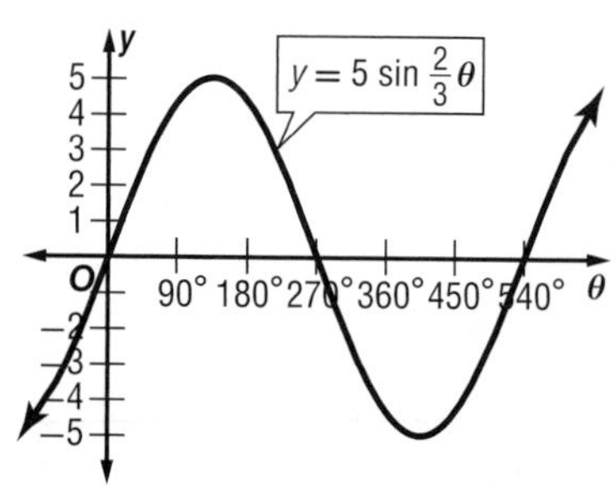

21b.

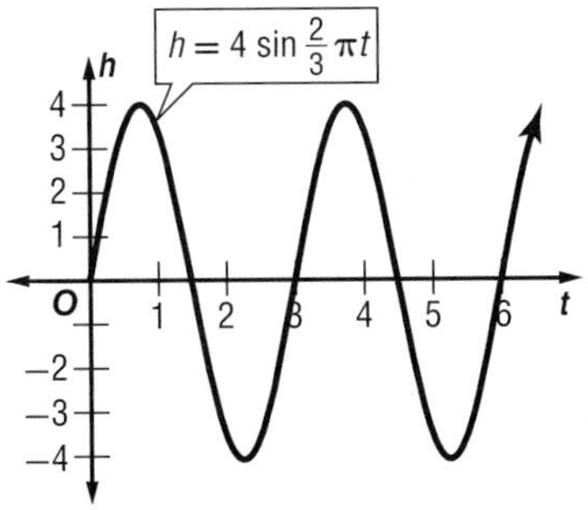

22b.

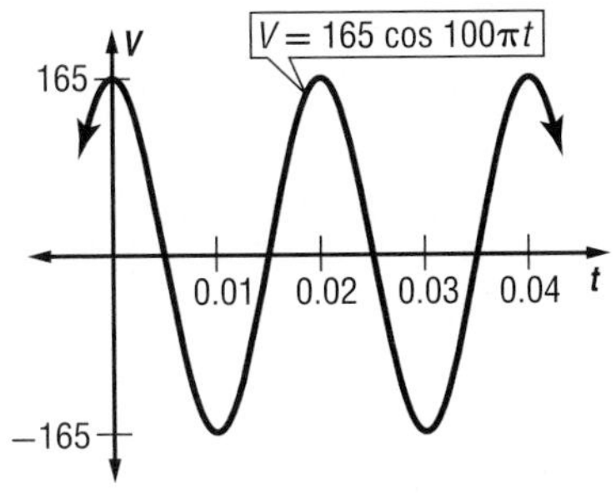

23. period: 360°

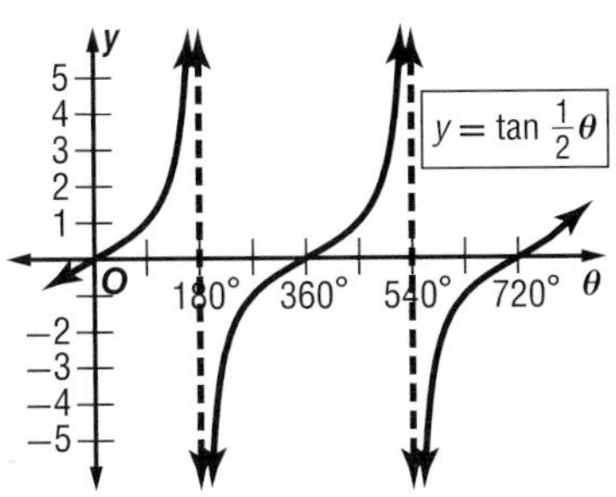

24. period: 360°

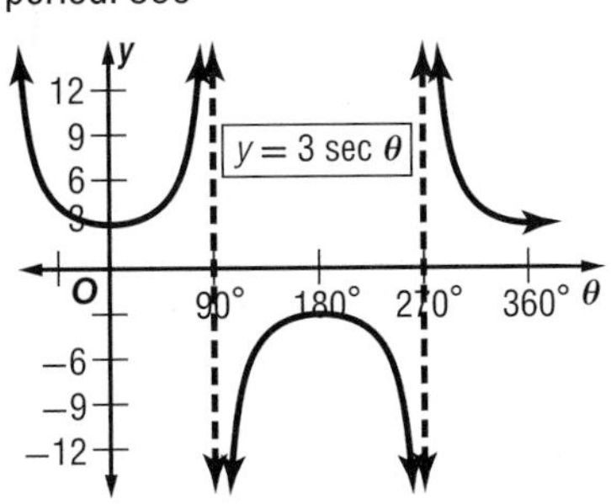

25. period: 180°

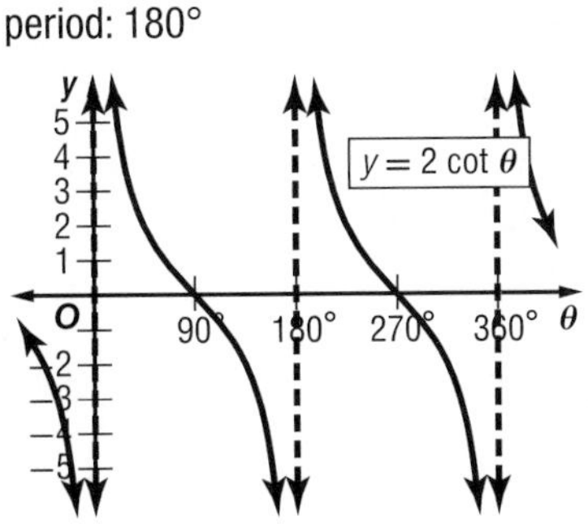

26. period: 720°

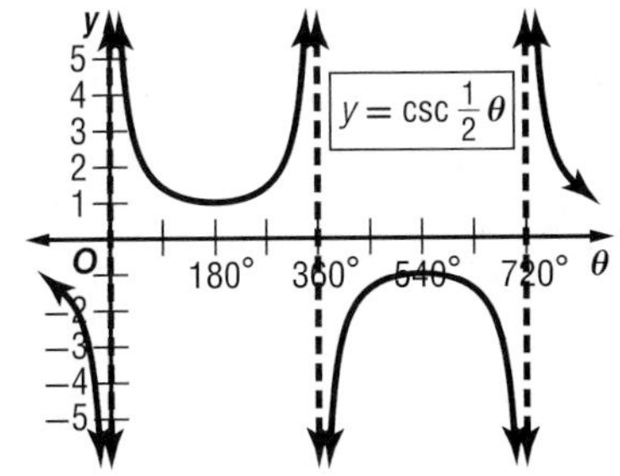

27. period: 180°

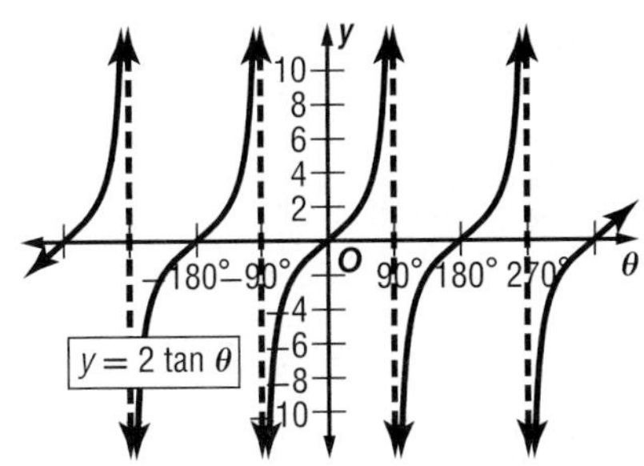

28. period: 1080°

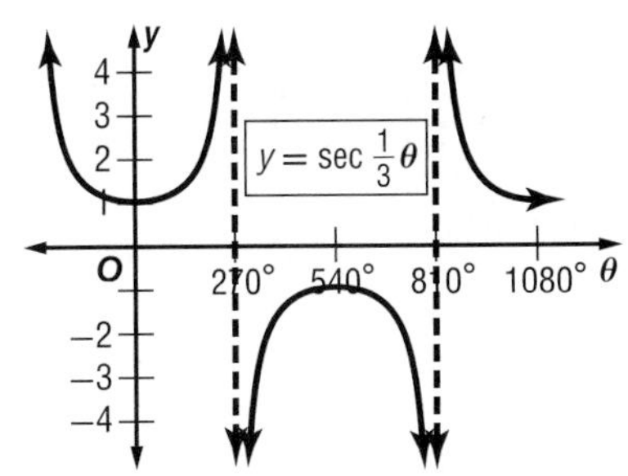

31a.

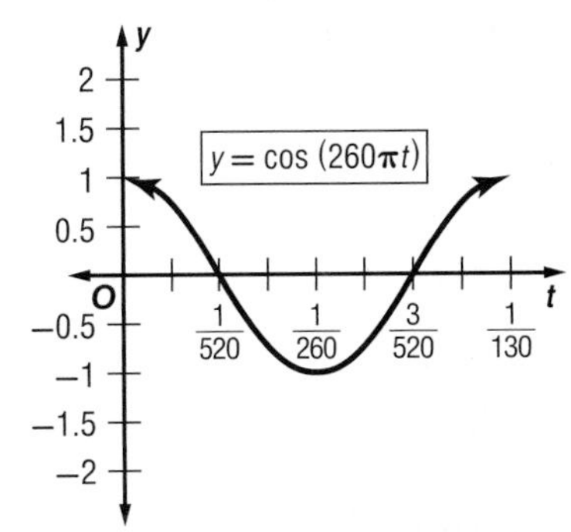

32. amplitude: 3; period: 540°

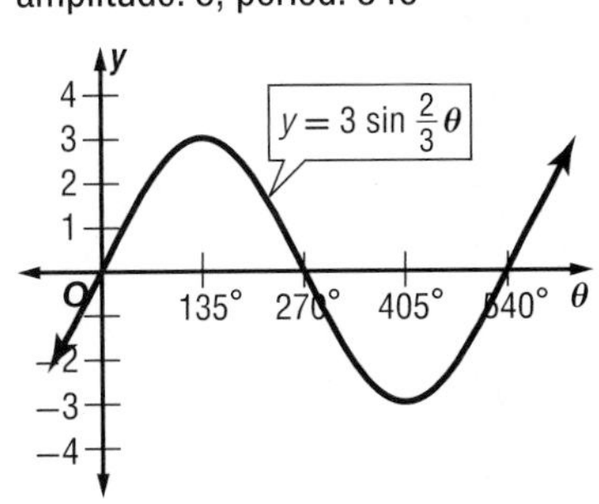

33. amplitude: $\frac{1}{2}$; period: 480°

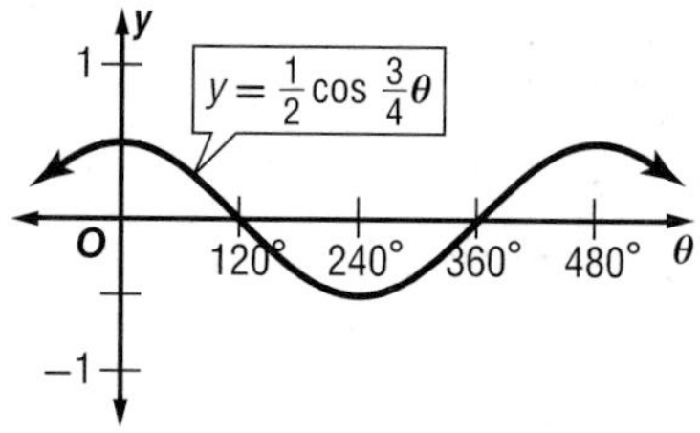

34. amplitude: does not exist; period: 360°

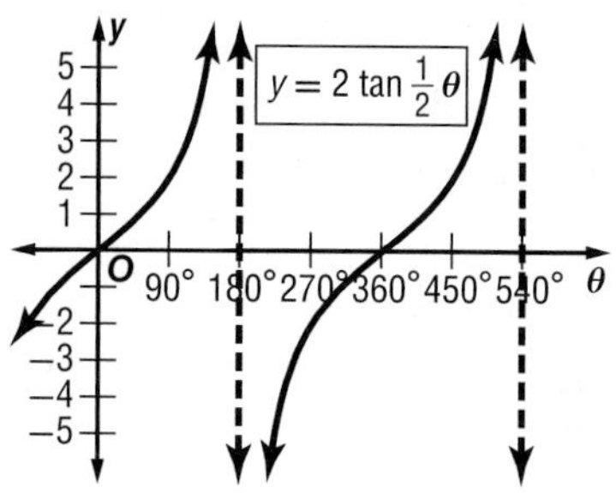

35. amplitude: does not exist; period: 450°

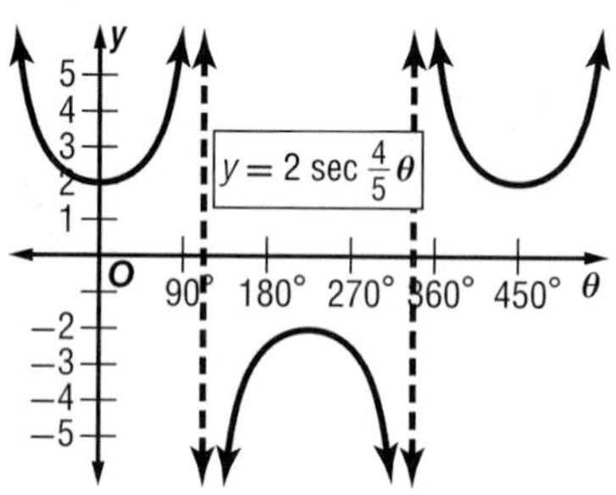

36. amplitude: does not exist; period: 120°

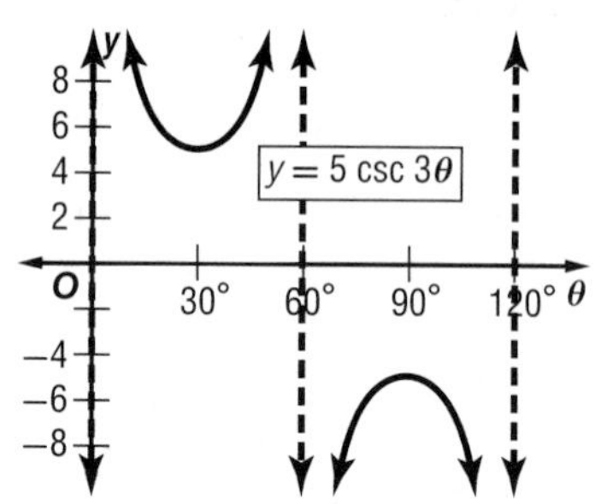

37. amplitude: does not exist; period: 30°

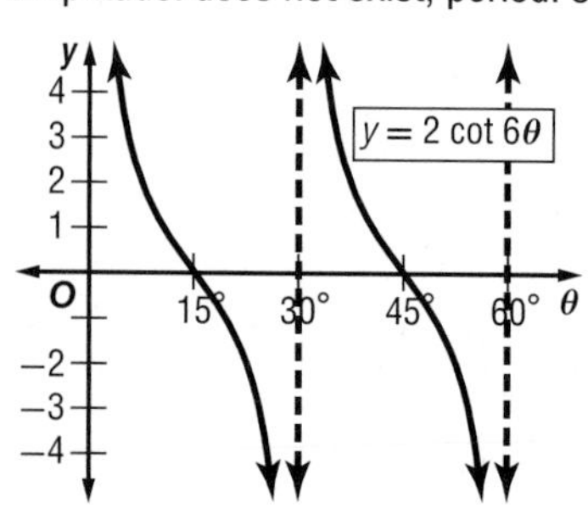

Page 862, Explore 13-8

3. Sample answer: The graph of $y = \sin(2\theta) + 4$ goes through two cycles in 360°, and the graph of $y = \sin\theta + 4$ goes through one cycle in 360°.

4. Sample answer: The graph of $y = \cos\frac{1}{2}(\theta + 45°)$ has been translated 45° left from the graph of $y = \cos\left(\frac{1}{2}\theta\right)$.

5. Sample answer: The graph of $y = 2\sin\theta - 1$ has been translated down 1 unit from the graph of $y = 2\sin\theta$.

6. Sample answer: The graph of $y = \cos(\theta - 90°) - 3$ has been translated 90° right from the graph of $y = \cos\theta - 3$.

Page 863, Lesson 13-8, (Guided Practice)

1.

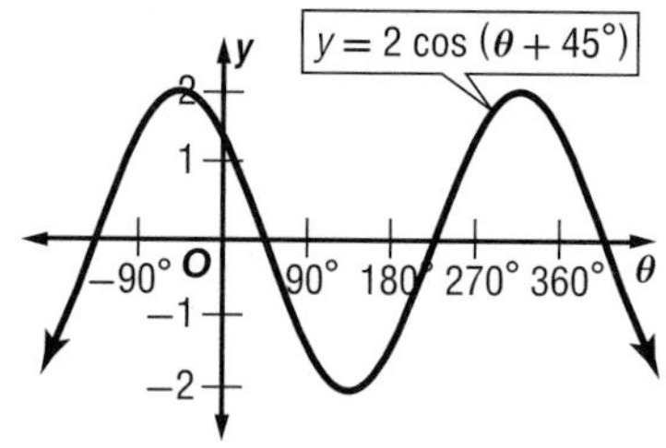

Pages 867–869, Lesson 13-8

9. 2; 360°; $h = -45°$; $k = 1$

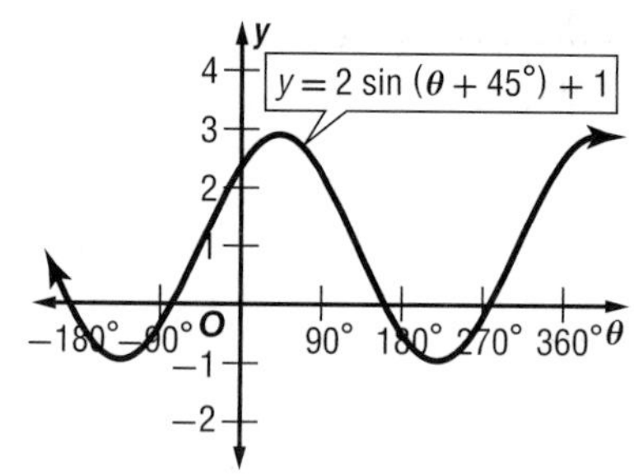

10. 1; 120°; $h = \pi$; $k = -4$

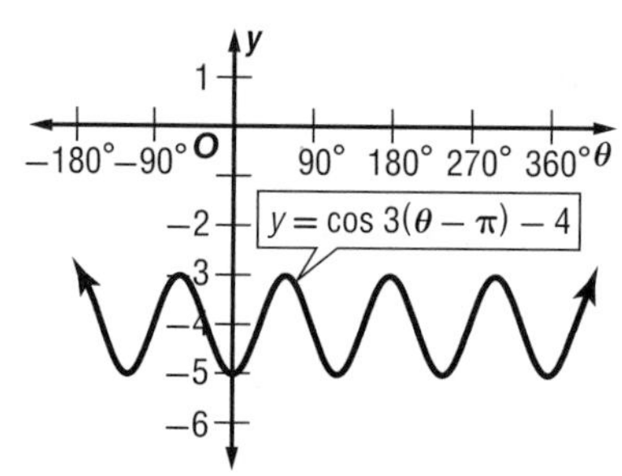

11. no amplitude; 90°; $h = -30°$; $k = 3$

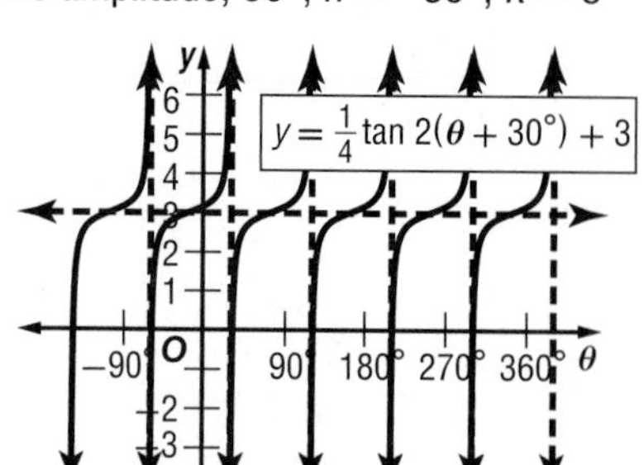

12. 4; 4π; $h = \frac{\pi}{2}$; $k = 5$

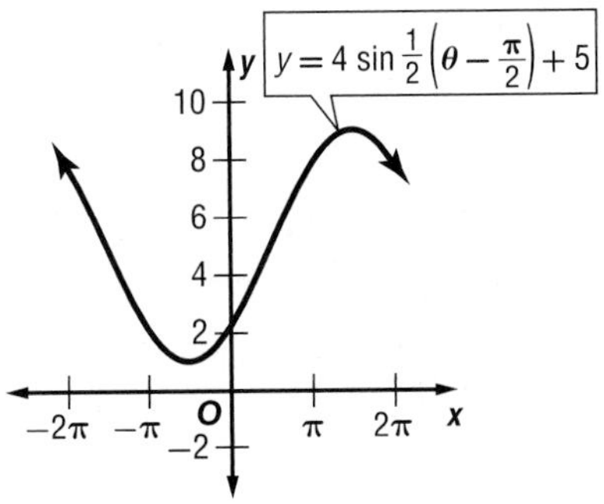

13. $P = 20 \sin 3\pi t + 110$

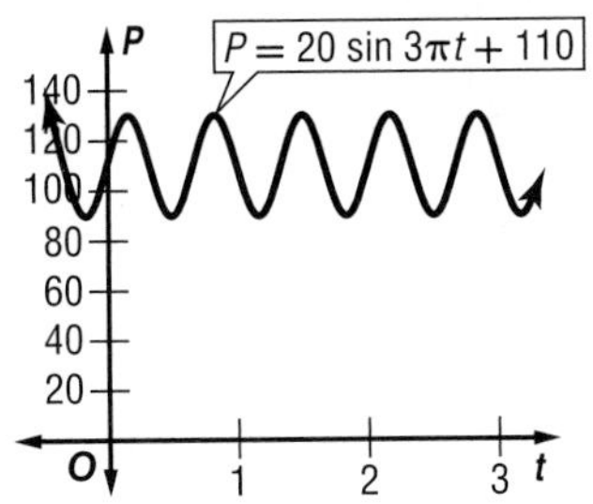

14. 1; 360°; $h = -180°$

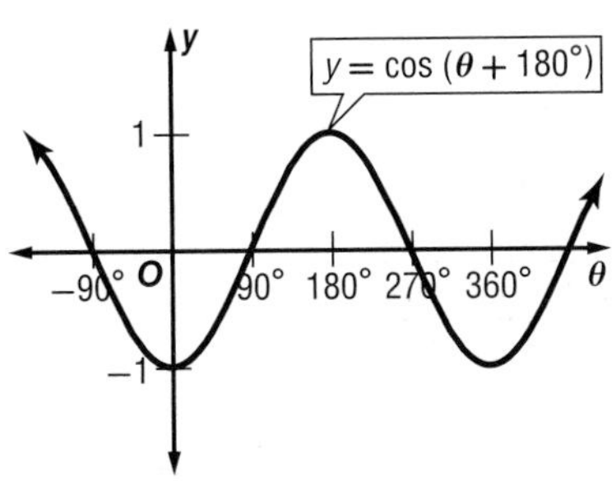

15. no amplitude; 180°; $h = 90°$

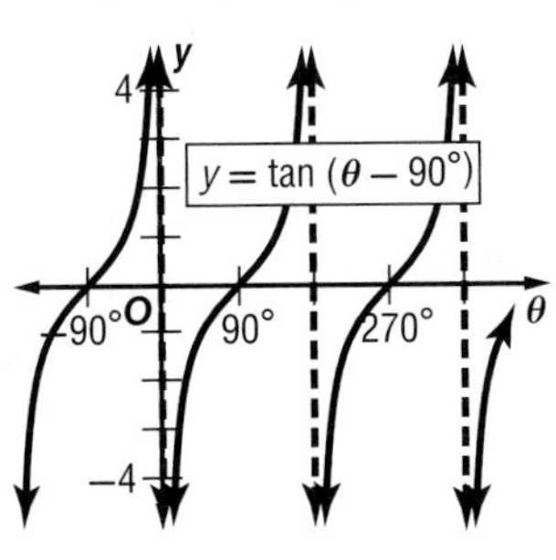

16. 1; 2π; $h = -\pi$

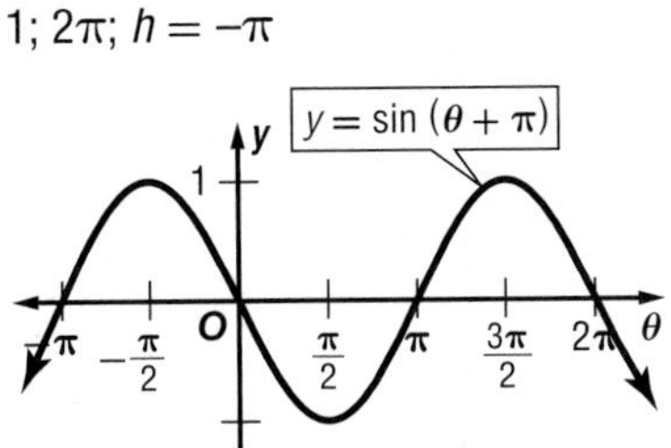

17. 2; 2π; $h = -\frac{\pi}{2}$

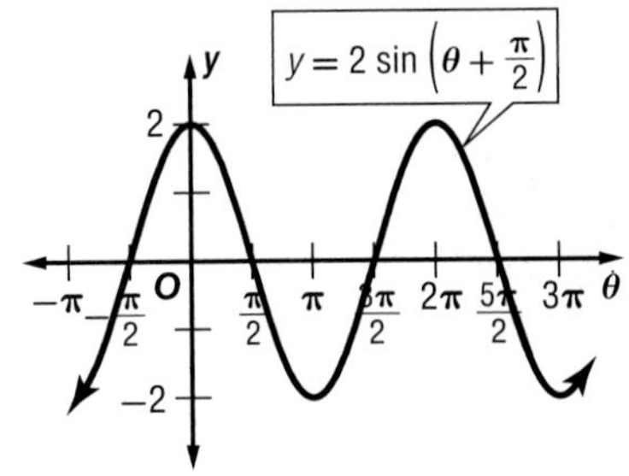

18. no amplitude; 360°; $h = -30°$

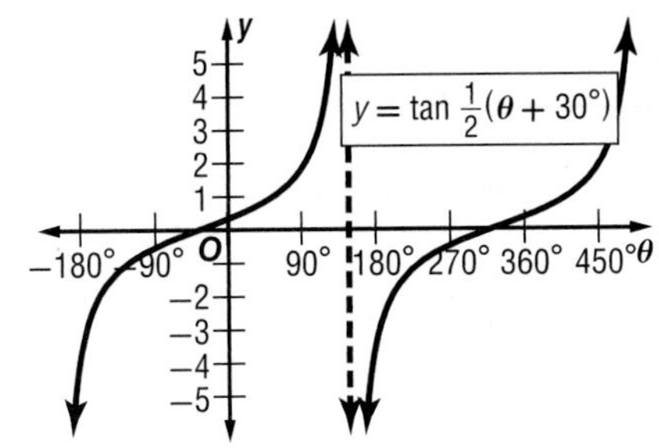

19. 3; 2π; $h = \frac{\pi}{3}$

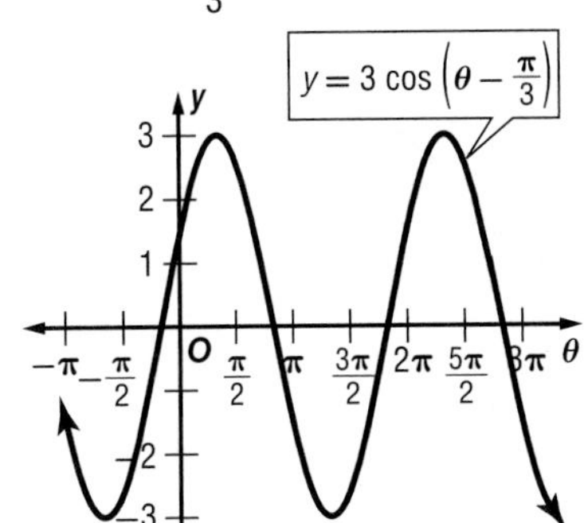

20. 1; 360°; $k = 3$; $y = 3$

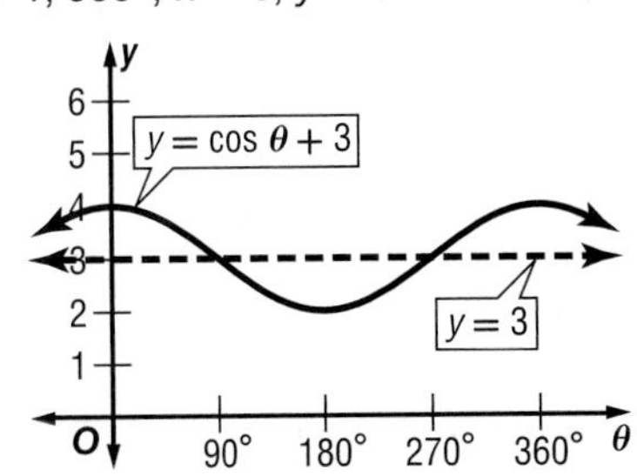

21. no amplitude; 180°; $k = -1$; $y = -1$

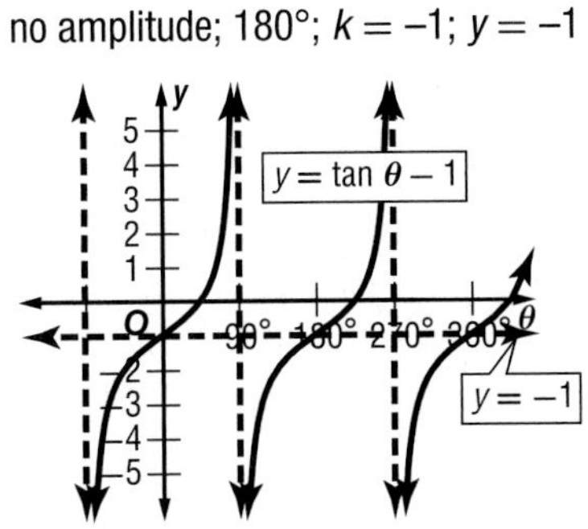

Chapter 13 Answer Appendix

22. no amplitude; 180°; $k = \frac{1}{2}$; $y = \frac{1}{2}$

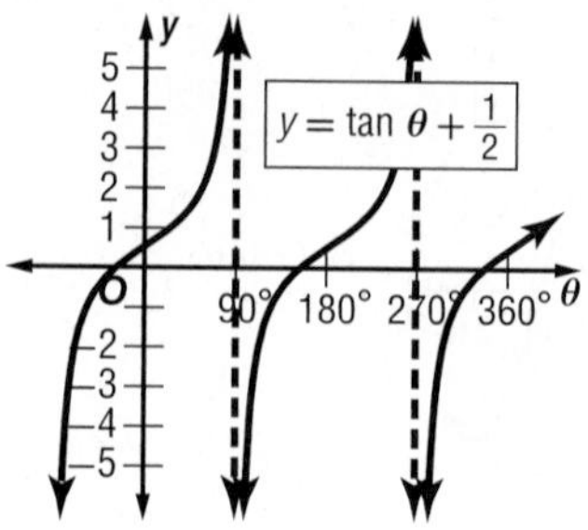

23. 2; 360°; $k = -5$; $y = -5$

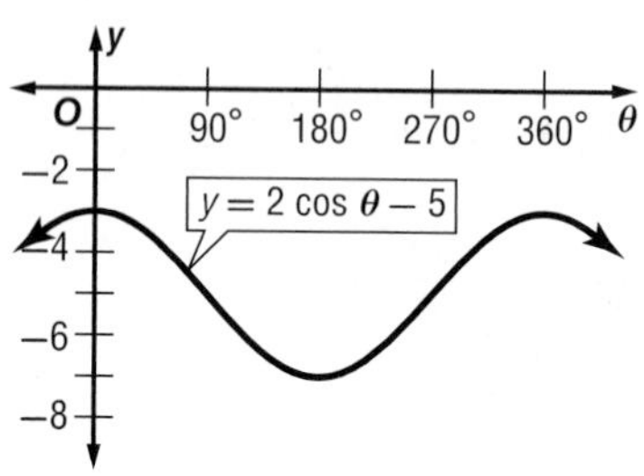

24. 2; 360°; $k = -4$; $y = -4$

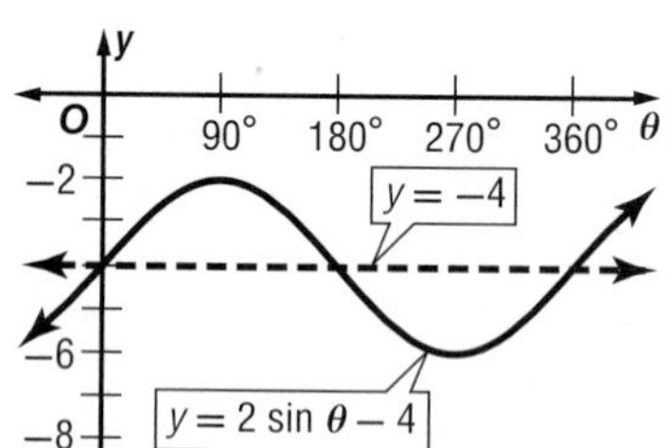

25. $\frac{1}{3}$; 360°; $k = 7$; $y = 7$

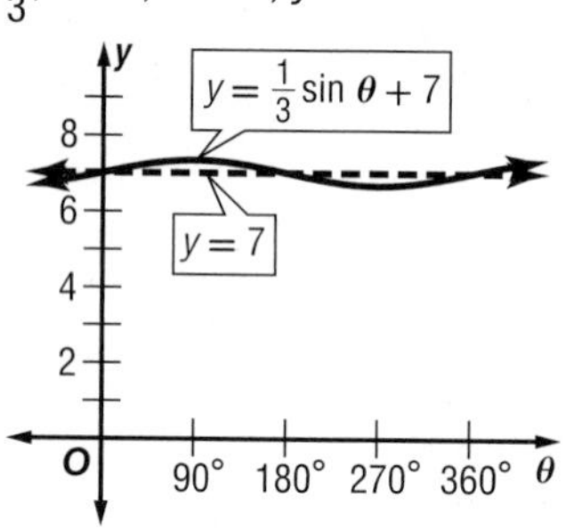

26. 4; 360°; $h = 60°$; $k = -1$

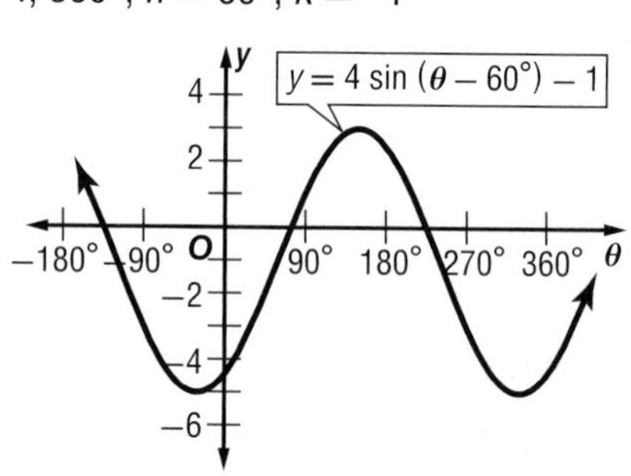

27. 1; 720°; $h = 90°$; $k = 2$

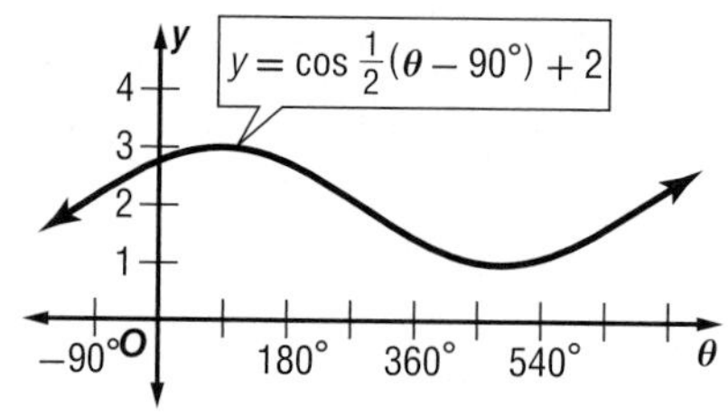

28. no amplitude; 180°; $h = -30°$; $k = -2$

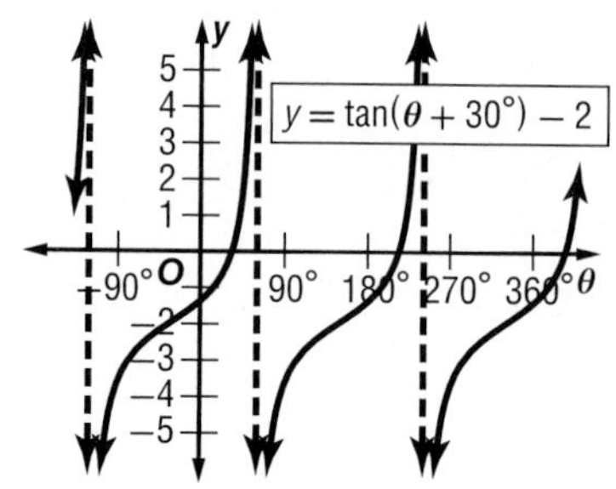

29. no amplitude; $\frac{\pi}{2}$; $h = -\frac{\pi}{4}$; $k = -5$

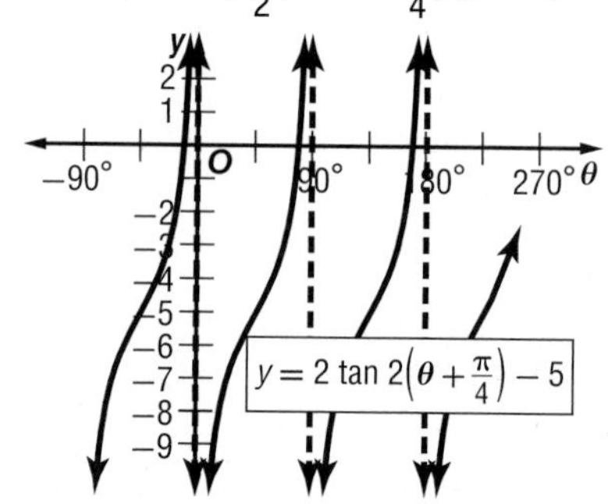

30. $\frac{1}{2}$; 2π; $h = \frac{\pi}{2}$; $k = 4$

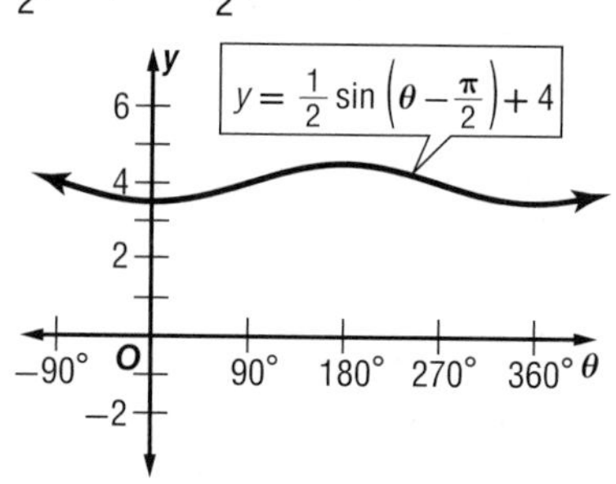

31. 1; 120°; $h = 45°$; $k = \frac{1}{2}$

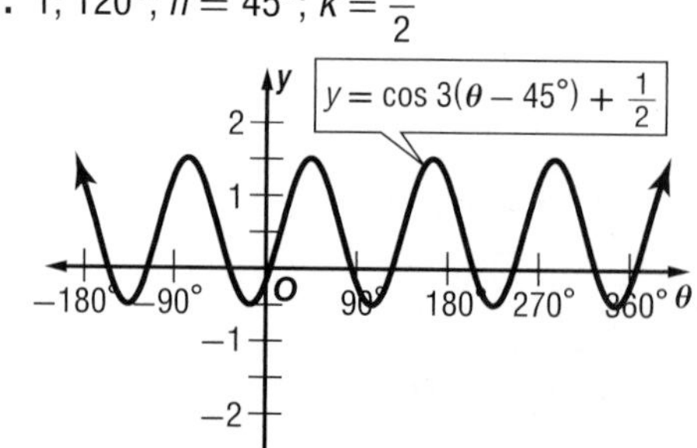

32. 5; π; $h = \pi$; $k = 3$

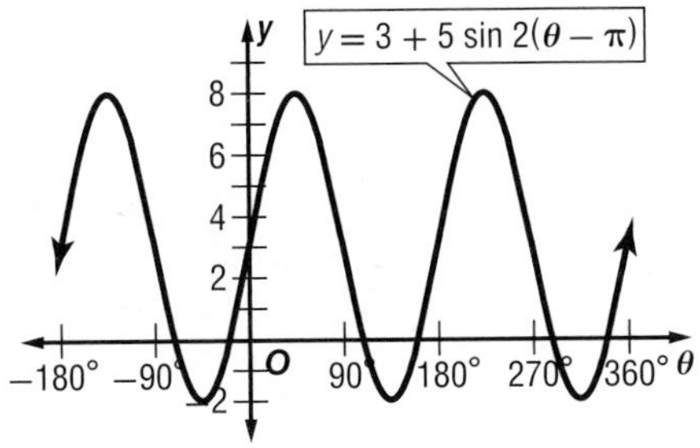

33. 3; 6π; $h = \frac{\pi}{2}$; $k = -2$

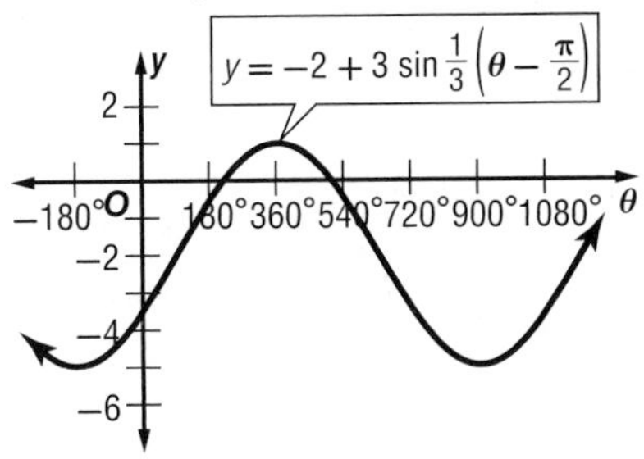

54. 360°; $h = -\pi$; no vertical shift

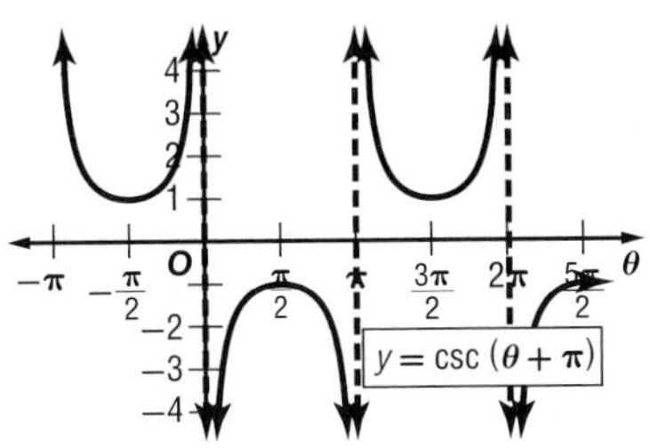

55. 180°; no phase shift; $k = 6$

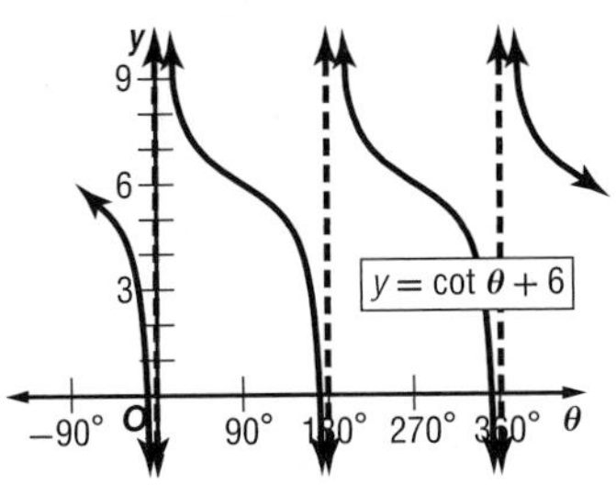

56. π; $h = \frac{\pi}{6}$; $k = -2$

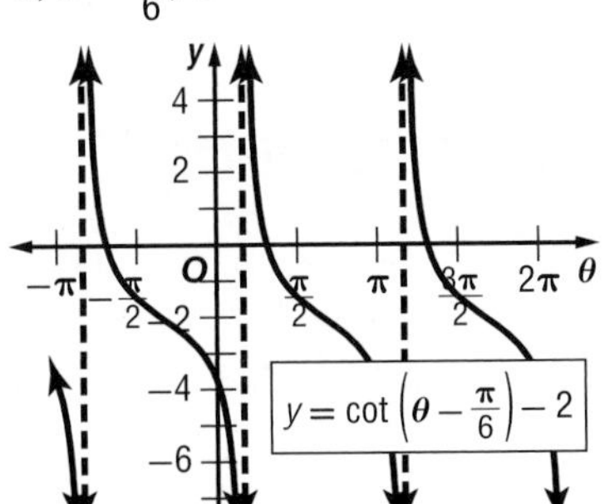

57. 120°; $h = 45°$; $k = 1$

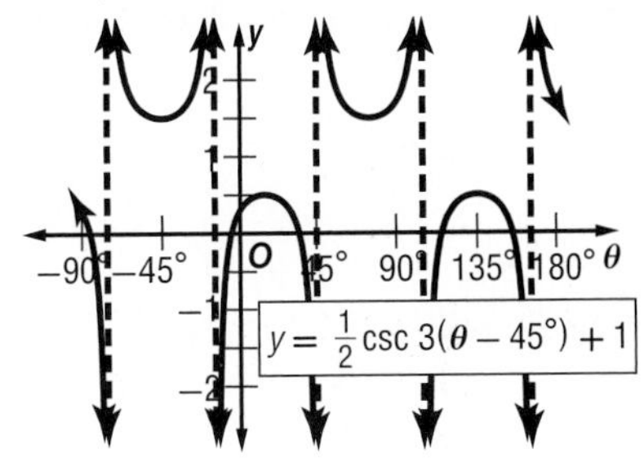

58. 720°; $h = 90°$; no vertical shift

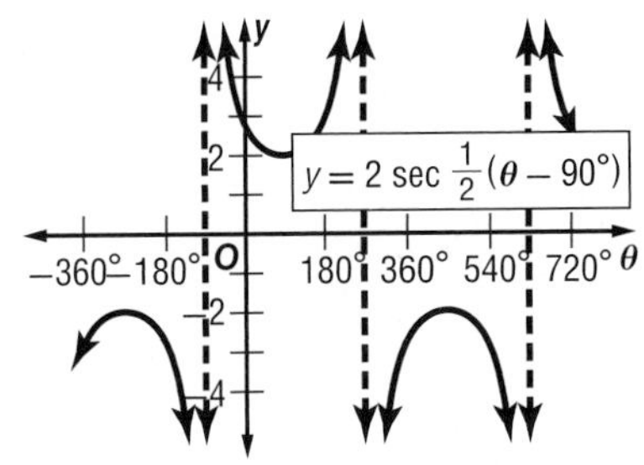

59. π; $h = -\frac{\pi}{2}$; $k = -3$

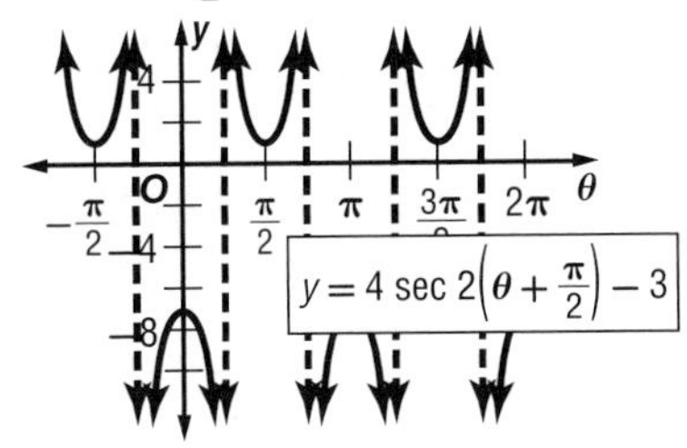

CHAPTER 14

Chapter Planner

Diagnostic Assessment
Quick Check, p. 889

	Lesson 14-1 Pacing: 1 day	Lesson 14-2 Pacing: 1 day	Lesson 14-3 Pacing: 1 day
Title	**Trigonometric Identities**	**Verifying Trigonometric Identities**	**Sum and Difference of Angles Identities**
Objectives	• Use trigonometric identities to find trigonometric values. • Use trigonometric identities to simplify expressions.	• Verify trigonometric identities by transforming one side of an equation into the form of the other side. • Verify trigonometric identities by transforming each side of the equation into the same form.	• Find values of sine and cosine by using sum and difference identities. • Verify trigonometric identities by using sum and difference identities.
Key Vocabulary	trigonometric identity		
NGSSS	MA.912.T.3.1	MA.912.T.3.2	MA.912.T.3.2, MA.912.T.3.3
Multiple Representations	p. 895		p. 908
Lesson Resources	**Chapter 14 Resource Masters** • Study Guide and Intervention, pp. 5–6 AL OL ELL • Skills Practice, p. 7 AL OL ELL • Practice, p. 8 AL OL BL ELL • Word Problem Practice, p. 9 AL OL BL ELL • Enrichment, p. 10 OL BL **Transparencies** • 5-Minute Check Transparency 14–1 AL OL BL ELL **Additional Print Resources** • Study Notebook AL OL BL ELL	**Chapter 14 Resource Masters** • Study Guide and Intervention, pp. 11–12 AL OL ELL • Skills Practice, p. 13 AL OL ELL • Practice, p. 14 AL OL BL ELL • Word Problem Practice, p. 15 AL OL BL ELL • Enrichment, p. 16 OL BL • Quiz 1, p. 37 AL OL BL ELL **Transparencies** • 5-Minute Check Transparency 14–2 AL OL BL ELL **Additional Print Resources** • Study Notebook AL OL BL ELL	**Chapter 14 Resource Masters** • Study Guide and Intervention, pp. 17–18 AL OL ELL • Skills Practice, p. 19 AL OL ELL • Practice, p. 20 AL OL BL ELL • Word Problem Practice, p. 21 AL OL BL ELL • Enrichment, p. 22 OL BL • Quiz 2, p. 37 AL OL BL ELL **Transparencies** • 5-Minute Check Transparency 14–3 AL OL BL ELL **Additional Print Resources** • Study Notebook AL OL BL ELL
Technology for Every Lesson	FL Math Online glencoe.com • Extra Examples • Self-Check Quizzes • Personal Tutor • Homework Help	**CD/DVD Resources** IWB INTERACTIVE WHITEBOARD READY IWB StudentWorks Plus IWB Interactive Classroom IWB Diagnostic and Assessment Planner	• TeacherWorks Plus • eSolutions Manual Plus • ExamView Assessment Suite
Get Animated			
Differentiated Instruction	pp. 892, 893, 897	pp. 899, 903	pp. 905, 909

Formative Assessment
Mid-Chapter Quiz, p. 910

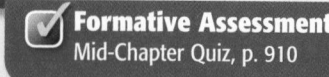

KEY: AL Approaching Level OL On Level BL Beyond Level ELL English Learners

Trigonometric Identities and Equations

Suggested Pacing			
Time Periods	Instruction	Review & Assessment	Total
45-minute	6	2	8
90-minute	3	1	4

Lesson 14-4 — Pacing: 1 day	Explore 14-5 — Pacing: 0.5 day	Lesson 14-5 — Pacing: 1.5 day
Double-Angle and Half-Angle Identities	**Graphing Technology Lab: Solving Trigonometric Equations**	**Solving Trigonometric Equations**
• Find values of sine and cosine by using double-angle identities. • Find values of sine and cosine by using half-angle identities.	• Use a graphing calculator to solve trigonometric equations.	• Solve trigonometric equations. • Find extraneous solutions from trigonometric equations.
		trigonometric equations
MA.912.T.3.2, MA.912.T.3.3	MA.912.T.3.4	MA.912.T.3.4
Chapter 14 Resource Masters • Study Guide and Intervention, pp. 23–24 AL OL ELL • Skills Practice, p. 25 AL OL ELL • Practice, p. 26 AL OL BL ELL • Word Problem Practice, p. 27 AL OL BL ELL • Enrichment, p. 28 OL BL • Quiz 3, p. 38 AL OL BL ELL **Transparencies** • 5-Minute Check Transparency 14–4 AL OL BL ELL **Additional Print Resources** • Study Notebook AL OL BL ELL	**Materials** • TI–83/84 Plus or other graphing calculator	**Chapter 14 Resource Masters** • Study Guide and Intervention, pp. 29–30 AL OL ELL • Skills Practice, p. 31 AL OL ELL • Practice, p. 32 AL OL BL ELL • Word Problem Practice, p. 33 AL OL BL ELL • Enrichment, p. 34 OL BL • Quiz 4, p. 38 AL OL BL ELL **Transparencies** • 5-Minute Check Transparency 14–5 AL OL BL ELL **Additional Print Resources** • Study Notebook AL OL BL ELL • Teaching Algebra with Manipulatives, p. 268 AL OL ELL

FL Math Online glencoe.com
- Extra Examples
- Self-Check Quizzes
- Personal Tutor
- Homework Help

CD/DVD Resources IWB INTERACTIVE WHITEBOARD READY
- IWB StudentWorks Plus
- IWB Interactive Classroom
- IWB Diagnostic and Assessment Planner
- TeacherWorks Plus
- eSolutions Manual Plus
- ExamView Assessment Suite

pp. 914, 917		pp. 921, 925

Summative Assessment
- Study Guide and Review, pp. 926–928
- Practice Test, p. 929

CHAPTER 14

Assessment and Intervention

SE = Student Edition, **TE** = Teacher Edition, **CRM** = Chapter Resource Masters

	Diagnosis	Prescription
Diagnostic Assessment	**Beginning Chapter 14**	
	Get Ready for Chapter 14 **SE,** p. 889	Response to Intervention **TE,** p. 889
	Beginning Every Lesson	
	Then, Now, Why? **SE** 5-Minute Check Transparencies	Chapter 0 **SE,** pp. P1 through P19 Concepts and Skills Bank **SE** pp. 994–1007
Formative Assessment	**During/After Every Lesson**	
	Guided Practice **SE,** every example Check Your Understanding **SE** H.O.T. Problems **SE** Spiral Review **SE** Additional Examples **TE** Watch Out! **TE** Step 4, Assess **TE** Chapter 14 Quizzes **CRM,** pp. 37–38 Self-Check Quizzes glencoe.com	**Tier 1 Intervention** Concepts and Skills Bank **SE,** pp. 994–1007 Skills Practice **CRM,** Ch. 1–14 glencoe.com **Tier 2 Intervention** Differentiated Instruction **TE** Study Guide and Intervention Masters **CRM,** Ch. 1–14 **Tier 3 Intervention** *Math Triumphs, Alg. 2*
	Mid-Chapter	
	Mid-Chapter Quiz **SE,** p. 910 Mid-Chapter Test **CRM,** p. 39 ExamView Assessment Suite	**Tier 1 Intervention** Concepts and Skills Bank **SE,** pp. 994–1007 Skills Practice **CRM,** Ch. 1–14 glencoe.com **Tier 2 Intervention** Study Guide and Intervention Masters **CRM,** Ch. 1–14 **Tier 3 Intervention** *Math Triumphs, Alg. 2*
	Before Chapter Test	
	Chapter Study Guide and Review **SE,** pp. 926–928 Practice Test **SE,** p. 929 Standardized Test Practice **SE,** pp. 930–933 Chapter Test glencoe.com Standardized Test Practice glencoe.com Vocabulary Review glencoe.com ExamView Assessment Suite	**Tier 1 Intervention** Concepts and Skills Bank **SE,** pp. 994–1007 Skills Practice **CRM,** Ch. 1–14 glencoe.com **Tier 2 Intervention** Study Guide and Intervention Masters **CRM,** Ch. 1–14 **Tier 3 Intervention** *Math Triumphs, Alg. 2*
Summative Assessment	**After Chapter 14**	
	Multiple-Choice Tests, Forms 1, 2A, 2B **CRM,** pp. 41–46 Free-Response Tests, Forms 2C, 2D, 3 **CRM,** pp. 47–52 Vocabulary Test **CRM,** p. 40 Extended Response Test **CRM,** p. 53 Standardized Test Practice **CRM,** pp. 54–56 ExamView Assessment Suite	Study Guide and Intervention Masters **CRM,** Ch. 1–14 glencoe.com

Differentiated Instruction

Option 1 Reaching All Learners AL OL BL ELL

KINESTHETIC Put students into pairs. Have each pair of students make up a set of Basic Trigonometric Identities cards. Pairs should make up two cards for every type of identity within each category (quotient, reciprocal, Pythagorean, cofunction, and negative angle). For example, for the quotient identities, four cards will be made: $\tan \theta$, $\frac{\sin \theta}{\cos \theta}$, $\cot \theta$, and $\frac{\cos \theta}{\sin \theta}$. A total of 28 should be made. Then, pairs will play a game of "Memory." The first partner will turn over two cards. The two cards are removed if they represent equal basic trigonometric values. If not, both are turned back over. The other partner then takes a turn.

$\cot \theta$	$\frac{\cos \theta}{\sin \theta}$					

LOGICAL Have students work in pairs to create their own Trigonometric Identity equations. Ask students to start with a true statement, such as, $\cos \theta = \cos \theta$. Then, transform each side by substituting equivalent expressions. For example, $\cos \theta = \cos \theta$ can be transformed using the quotient identities to give the following result, $\frac{\sin \theta}{\tan \theta} + \frac{\cos \theta}{\sin \theta} = \frac{1}{\sec \theta} + \cot \theta$. Then have pairs trade and try to verify that each other's equation is an identity.

FL Math Online Access Point Activities

Option 2 Approaching Level AL

Work with students to create and complete a table like the one below that they can use as a reference for knowing the sign of each function of θ in each quadrant.

Quadrant	I	II	III	IV
Sine	+	+	−	−
Cosine	+	−	−	+
Tangent	+	−	+	−

Option 3 English Learners ELL

Have students make up a half-angle identity. Then ask them to verify that it actually is an identity by explaining in words or in writing each step needed to do so.

Option 4 Beyond Level BL

Have students make up a crossword puzzle using any of the terms related to trigonometry used in this chapter. Use either the definition or an example of the terms in the *across* and *down* hints. Have each student make photocopies of his/her puzzles to distribute to other class members. Ask students to complete the puzzles.

Focus on Mathematical Content

Vertical Alignment

Before Chapter 14

Previous Topics from Algebra 2

- investigate the six trigonometric functions
- work with angles measured in degrees or radians
- investigate angles as rays in standard position and as points on the unit circle
- explore periodicity and inverse trigonometric functions

Chapter 14

Related Topics from Algebra 2

- learn how to verify and use trigonometric identities
- prove trigonometric identities
- solve trigonometric equations using the ideas of factoring, the zero product property, trigonometric inverses, and periodic behavior

After Chapter 14

Preparation for Precalculus

- use trigonometric formulas and identities while analyzing vertical and horizontal translations of graphs and how these translations are related to changes in the algebraic description of the graphs

Lesson-by-Lesson Preview

14-1 Trigonometric Identities

An equation that involves trigonometric functions that is true for all values for which every expression in the equation is defined is called a *trigonometric identity*. There are five categories of identities: Quotient, Reciprocal, Pythagorean, Cofunction, and Negative Angle Identities. These are shown in the table below:

Basic Trigonometric Identities		
Quotient Identities (no denominator equals 0)		
$\tan \theta = \frac{\sin \theta}{\cos \theta}$	$\cot \theta = \frac{\cos \theta}{\sin \theta}$	
Reciprocal Identities (no denominator equals 0)		
$\csc \theta = \frac{1}{\sin \theta}$	$\sec \theta = \frac{1}{\cos \theta}$	$\cot \theta = \frac{1}{\tan \theta}$
Pythagorean Identities		
$\cos^2 \theta + \sin^2 \theta = 1$	$\tan^2 \theta + 1 = \sec^2 \theta$	$\cot^2 \theta + 1 = \csc^2 \theta$
Cofunction Identities		
$\sin\left(\frac{\pi}{2} - \theta\right) = \cos \theta$	$\cos\left(\frac{\pi}{2} - \theta\right) = \sin \theta$	$\tan\left(\frac{\pi}{2} - \theta\right) = \cot \theta$
Negative Angle Identities		
$\sin(-\theta) = -\sin \theta$	$\cos(-\theta) = \cos \theta$	$\tan(-\theta) = -\tan \theta$

These identities are helpful when simplifying trigonometric expressions and solving real-world problems.

14-2 Verifying Trigonometric Identities

Basic trigonometric identities and definitions can be used to verify identities. To verify an identity, the goal is to either transform one side of the equation, replacing expressions with equivalent expressions, until the two sides are identical or transform both sides of an equation separately into a common form. There are several approaches for writing equivalent expressions.

- Make substitutions using the Pythagorean Identities.
- Use the Distributive Property to factor an expression or to collect like terms.
- Transform a term by multiplying the term by an expression equivalent to 1.
- Rewrite all the trigonometric functions in terms of $\sin \theta$ or $\cos \theta$ by using the Quotient and Reciprocal Identities.

Warning: Do not perform operations to each side of the unverified identity because the properties of equality do not apply to identities as they do to equations.

14-3 Sum and Difference of Angles Identities

The identities for the sum and difference of two angles, $\sin(a \pm b)$, $\cos(a \pm b)$, and $\tan(a \pm b)$, can be used to find values of sine and cosine. They can also be used to help verify identities such as $\sin(180^\circ + \theta) = -\sin \theta$.

The sum and difference of angles identities are as follows.

- $\sin (a + b) = \sin a \cos b + \cos a \sin b$
- $\sin (a - b) = \sin a \cos b - \cos a \sin b$
- $\cos (a + b) = \cos a \cos b - \sin a \sin b$
- $\cos (a - b) = \cos a \cos b + \sin a \sin b$
- $\tan (a + b) = \dfrac{\tan a + \tan b}{1 - \tan a \tan b}$
- $\tan (a - b) = \dfrac{\tan a - \tan b}{1 + \tan a \tan b}$

14-4 Double-Angle and Half-Angle Identities

Using the identities for $\sin(a + b)$, $\cos(a + b)$, and $\tan(a + b)$, and replacing both a and b with θ, results in identities called the Double-Angle Identities. These identities are:

- $\sin 2\theta = 2 \sin \theta \cos \theta$
- $\cos 2\theta = 2 \cos^2 \theta - 1$ or

  $\cos 2\theta = \cos^2 \theta - \sin^2 \theta$ or

  $\cos 2\theta = 1 - 2 \sin^2 \theta$
- $\tan 2\theta = \dfrac{2 \tan \theta}{1 - \tan^2 \theta}$

Three identities called Half-Angle Identities can be derived from the Double-Angle Identities. These identities are:

- $\sin \frac{a}{2} = \pm\sqrt{\frac{1 - \cos a}{2}}$
- $\cos \frac{a}{2} = \pm\sqrt{\frac{1 + \cos a}{2}}$
- $\sin \frac{a}{2} = \pm\sqrt{\frac{1 - \cos a}{1 + \cos a}}$, $\cos \theta \neq 1$

The Half-Angle and Double-Angle Identities, along with other identities, can be used to find exact values for particular trigonometric expressions. They can also be used to verify trigonometric identities.

14-5 Solving Trigonometric Equations

Trigonometric equations are true for only certain values of the variable. Solving a trigonometric equation is similar to solving an algebraic equation.

- The first step in solving a trigonometric equation is to use factoring, the Zero Product Property, and/or identities to rewrite a complicated equation as a string of simpler trigonometric equations.
- The second step is to use trigonometric inverses to isolate the variable; that is, to solve an equation such as $\cos \theta = -1$, for θ.
- The third step is to use ideas of periodicity to include all the occurrences of that value.

Some equations have infinitely many solutions and some equations have no solution. Hence, it is necessary to check your solutions in the original equation.

Mc Graw Hill Professional Development

Targeted professional development has been articulated throughout *Algebra 2.* More quality, customized professional development is available from McGraw-Hill Professional Development. Visit glencoe.com for details on each product.

- **Online Lessons** emphasize the strategies and techniques used to teach Algebra 2. Includes streaming video, interactive pages, and online tools.
- **Video Workshops** allow mentors, coaches, or leadership personnel to facilitate on-site workshops on educational strategies in mathematics and mathematical concepts.
- **MHPD Online** (www.mhpdonline.com) offers online professional development with video clips of instructional strategies, links, student activities, and news and issues in education.
- **Teaching Today** (teachingtoday.glencoe.com) gives secondary teachers practical strategies and materials that inspire excellence and innovation in teaching.

CHAPTER 14 Notes

Chapter Project

Electronics Professions

Students use what they have learned about trigonometric identities and equations to interview people who use trigonometry in their jobs.

- Have students work in groups of three or four. Ask them to research professions that deal with alternating current, for example, electrical engineers and computer technicians.
- Either by phone or in person, have students interview one or two people in their identified professions, asking how they use trigonometry in their jobs. If possible, have them take a digital photo of the people interviewed.
- Once the interview is complete, have students write a short paper explaining how the person they interviewed uses trigonometry.
- Use papers and photos to create a "Careers in Electronics" bulletin board.

CHAPTER 14 Trigonometric Identities and Equations

Then
In Chapter 13, you graphed trigonometric functions and determined the period, amplitude, phase shifts, and vertical shifts.

Now
In Chapter 14, you will:

- Use and verify trigonometric identities.
- Use the sum and difference of angles identities.
- Use the double- and half-angle identities.
- Solve trigonometric equations.

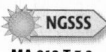

NGSSS
MA.912.T.3.2
MA.912.T.3.4

Why?
ELECTRONICS Many aspects of electronics can be modeled by trigonometric functions. Radio, television, cellular telephones, and wireless Internet all communicate through radio waves that are modeled by trigonometric functions. The amount of power in an electronic gadget can be found by using a trigonometric equation.

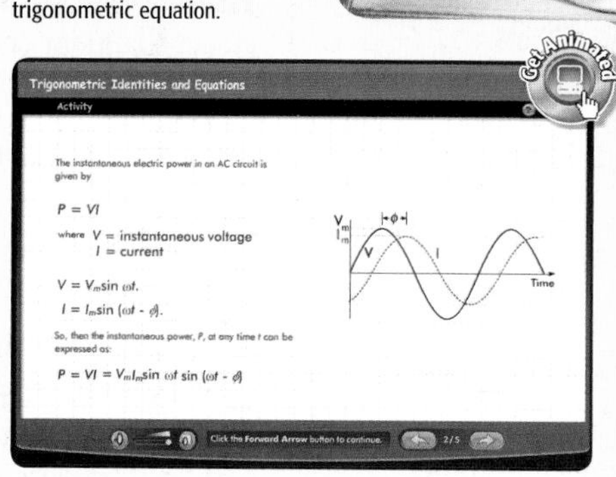

Key Vocabulary Introduce the key vocabulary in the chapter using the routine below.

Define: A trigonometric identity is an equation involving a trigonometric function that is true for all values of the variable.

Example: The identity $\sin(-\theta) = -\sin\theta$ is a Negative Angle Identity.

Ask: What other identities have you learned about this year? Answers may vary; students may mention identity matrices or the identity function.

Get Ready for Chapter 14

Diagnose Readiness You have two options for checking Prerequisite Skills.

Text Option

Take the Quick Check below. Refer to the Quick Review for help.

QuickCheck

(Used in Lesson 14-2)

Factor completely. If the polynomial is not factorable, write *prime*. (Lesson 6-5)

1. $-16a^2 + 4a$
2. $5x^2 - 20$
3. $x^3 + 9$ prime
4. $2y^2 - y - 15$
5. **GEOMETRY** The area of a rectangular piece of cardboard is $x^2 + 6x + 8$ square inches. If the cardboard has a length of $(x + 4)$ inches, what is the width? $(x + 2)$ in.

(Used in Lesson 14-7)

Solve each equation by factoring. (Lesson 5-3)

6. $x^2 + 6x = 0$ $\{-6, 0\}$
7. $x^2 + 2x - 35 = 0$
8. $x^2 - 9 = 0$ $\{-3, 3\}$
9. $x^2 - 7x + 12 = 0$ $\{3, 4\}$
10. **GARDENING** Peyton is building a flower bed in her back yard. The area of the flower bed will be 42 square feet. Find the possible values for x. 6

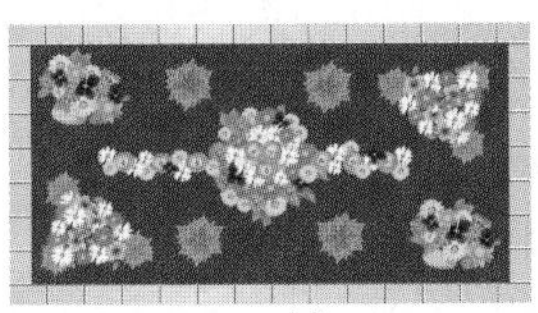

x ft

x + 1 ft

(Used in Lesson 14-3)

Find the exact value of each trigonometric function. (Lesson 13-3)

11. $\sin 45°$ $\frac{\sqrt{2}}{2}$
12. $\cos 225°$ $-\frac{\sqrt{2}}{2}$
13. $\tan 150°$ $-\frac{\sqrt{3}}{3}$
14. $\sin 120°$ $\frac{\sqrt{3}}{2}$
15. **RIDES** The distance from the highest point of a Ferris wheel to the ground can be found by multiplying 90 feet by sin 90°. What is the height of the Ferris wheel when it is halfway between the tallest point and the ground? 45 ft

QuickReview

EXAMPLE 1 1. $-4a(4a - 1)$

Factor $x^3 + 2x^2 - 24x$ completely.

$x^3 + 2x^2 - 24x = x(x^2 + 2x - 24)$

The product of the coefficients of the x terms must be -24, and their sum must be 2. The product of 6 and -4 is -24 and their sum is 2.

$x(x^2 + 2x - 24) = x(x + 6)(x - 4)$

2. $5(x + 2)(x - 2)$ 4. $(2y + 5)(y - 3)$

EXAMPLE 2

Solve $x^2 + 6x + 5 = 0$ by factoring.

$x^2 + 6x + 5 = 0$ **Original equation**

$(x + 5)(x + 1) = 0$ **Factor.**

$x + 5 = 0$ or $x + 1 = 0$

$x = -5$ $\quad x = -1$

The solution set is $\{-5, -1\}$.

7. $\{-7, 5\}$

EXAMPLE 3

Find the exact value of cos 135°.

The reference angle is $180° - 135°$ or $45°$.

$\cos 45°$ is $\frac{\sqrt{2}}{2}$. Since 135° is in the second quadrant, $\cos 135° = -\frac{\sqrt{2}}{2}$.

Online Option

FL Math Online Take a self-check Chapter Readiness Quiz at glencoe.com.

Get Ready for Chapter 14

Response to Intervention (RtI)

Use the *Quick Check* results and the Intervention Planner to help you determine your Response to Intervention. The If-Then statements in the chart below help you decide the appropriate tier of RtI and suggest intervention resources for each tier.

Intervention Planner

Tier 1 — On Level

If students miss about 25% of the exercises or less,

Then choose a resource:

- **SE** Lessons 6-5, 5-3, and 13-3
- **CRM** Skills Practice, Chapter 6, p. 37; Chapter 5, p. 19 and Chapter 13, p. 19
- **TE** Chapter Project, p. 888
- FL Math Online Self-Check Quiz

Tier 2 — Strategic Intervention approaching grade level

If students miss about 50% of the exercises,

Then choose a resource:

- **CRM** Study Guide and Intervention, Chapter 6, pp. 35–36, Chapter 5, pp. 17–18, Chapter 13, pp. 17–18
- FL Math Online Extra Examples, Personal Tutor, Homework Help

Tier 3 — Intensive Intervention 2 or more years below grade level

If students miss about 75% of the exercises,

Then use *Math Triumphs, Alg. 2*

FL Math Online Extra Examples, Personal Tutor, Homework Help, Review Vocabulary

FOLDABLES® Study Organizer

Dinah Zike's Foldables®

Focus Students write notes as they explore trigonometric identities and equations in the lessons of this chapter.

Teach Have students make and label their Foldables as illustrated. Have students use the appropriate tab as they cover each lesson in this chapter. Encourage students to apply what they have learned about trigonometric identities by writing their own examples as well.

When to Use It Suggest that students add to their Foldables as they work through the chapter and to use them to review concepts for the chapter test.

Differentiated Instruction

CRM Student-Built Glossary, pp. 1–2
Students should complete the chart by providing a definition of each term and an example as they progress through Chapter 14. This study tool can also be used to review for the chapter test.

Get Started on Chapter 14

You will learn several new concepts, skills, and vocabulary terms as you study Chapter 14. To get ready, identify important terms and organize your resources. You may wish to refer to **Chapter 0** to review prerequisite skills.

FOLDABLES® Study Organizer

Trigonometric Identities and Equations Make this Foldable to help you organize your Chapter 14 notes about trigonometric identities and equations. Begin with one sheet of 11″ × 17″ paper and four sheets of grid paper.

1. **Fold** the short sides of the 11″ × 17″ paper to meet in the middle.

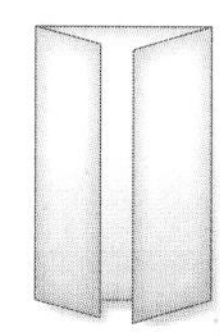

2. **Cut** each tab in half as shown.

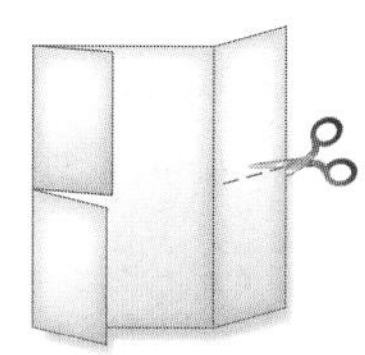

3. **Cut** four sheets of grid paper in half and fold the half-sheets in half.

4. **Insert** two folded half-sheets under each of the four tabs and staple along the fold. Label each tab as shown.

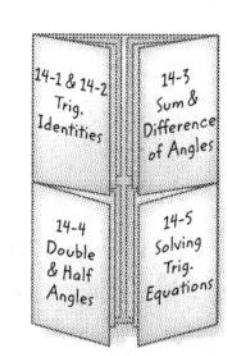

FL Math Online glencoe.com
- Study the chapter online
- Explore **Get Animated**
- Get extra help from your own **Personal Tutor**
- Use **Extra Examples** for additional help
- Take a **Self-Check Quiz**
- **Review Vocabulary** in fun ways

New Vocabulary

English		Español
trigonometric identity	• p. 891 •	identidad trigométrica
quotient identity	• p. 891 •	identidad de cociente
reciprocal identity	• p. 891 •	identidad recíproca
Pythagorean identity	• p. 891 •	identidad Pitagórica
cofunction identity	• p. 891 •	identidad de función conjunta
negative angle identity	• p. 891 •	identidad negativa de ángulo
trigonometric equation	• p. 919 •	ecuación trigométrica

Review Vocabulary

formula • p. 6 • fórmula a mathematical sentence that expresses the relationship between certain quantities

identity • p. 229 • identidad an equality that remains true regardless of the values of any variables that are in it

trigonometric functions • p. 808 • funciones trigonométricas For any angle, with measure θ, a point $P(x, y)$ on its terminal side, $r = \sqrt{x^2 + y^2}$, the trigonometric functions of θ are as follows.

$\sin \theta = \frac{y}{r}$ $\cos \theta = \frac{x}{r}$ $\tan \theta = \frac{y}{x}$

$\csc \theta = \frac{r}{y}$ $\sec \theta = \frac{r}{x}$ $\cot \theta = \frac{x}{y}$

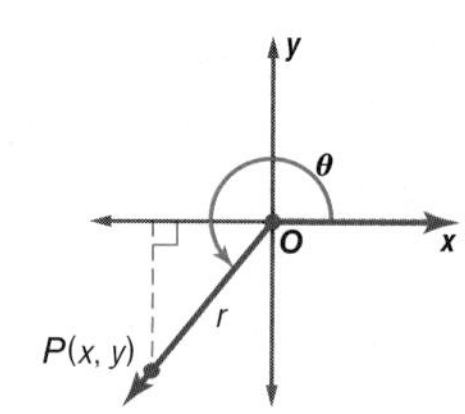

Multilingual eGlossary glencoe.com

14-1 Trigonometric Identities

Then
You evaluated trigonometric functions. (Lesson 13-7)

Now
- Use trigonometric identities to find trigonometric values.
- Use trigonometric identities to simplify expressions.

NGSSS

MA.912.T.3.1 Verify the basic Pythagorean identities, e.g., $\sin^2 x + \cos^2 x = 1$, and show they are equivalent to the Pythagorean Theorem.

New Vocabulary
trigonometric identity

FL Math Online
glencoe.com

Why?

The amount of light that a source provides to a surface is called the *illuminance*. The illuminance E in foot candles on a surface is related to the distance R in feet from the light source.

The formula $\sec \theta = \frac{I}{ER^2}$, where I is the intensity of the light source measured in candles and θ is the angle between the light beam and a line perpendicular to the surface, can be used in situations in which lighting is important, as in photography.

Find Trigonometric Values The equation above can also be written as $E = \frac{I \cos \theta}{R^2}$. This is an example of a trigonometric identity. A **trigonometric identity** is an equation involving trigonometric functions that is true for all values for which every expression in the equation is defined.

If you can show that a specific value of the variable in an equation makes the equation false, then you have produced a *counterexample*. It only takes one counterexample to prove that an equation is not an identity.

Key Concept — Basic Trigonometric Identities

Quotient Identities

$\tan \theta = \frac{\sin \theta}{\cos \theta}$, $\cos \theta \neq 0$

$\cot \theta = \frac{\cos \theta}{\sin \theta}$, $\sin \theta \neq 0$

Reciprocal Identities

$\sin \theta = \frac{1}{\csc \theta}$, $\csc \theta \neq 0$ $\qquad$ $\csc \theta = \frac{1}{\sin \theta}$, $\sin \theta \neq 0$

$\cos \theta = \frac{1}{\sec \theta}$, $\sec \theta \neq 0$ $\qquad$ $\sec \theta = \frac{1}{\cos \theta}$, $\cos \theta \neq 0$

$\tan \theta = \frac{1}{\cot \theta}$, $\cot \theta \neq 0$ $\qquad$ $\cot \theta = \frac{1}{\tan \theta}$, $\tan \theta \neq 0$

Pythagorean Identities

$\cos^2 \theta + \sin^2 \theta = 1$ $\qquad$ $\tan^2 \theta + 1 = \sec^2 \theta$ $\qquad$ $\cot^2 \theta + 1 = \csc^2 \theta$

Cofunction Identities

$\sin\left(\frac{\pi}{2} - \theta\right) = \cos \theta$ $\qquad$ $\cos\left(\frac{\pi}{2} - \theta\right) = \sin \theta$ $\qquad$ $\tan\left(\frac{\pi}{2} - \theta\right) = \cot \theta$

Negative Angle Identities

$\sin(-\theta) = -\sin \theta$ $\qquad$ $\cos(-\theta) = \cos \theta$ $\qquad$ $\tan(-\theta) = -\tan \theta$

The identity $\tan \theta = \frac{\sin \theta}{\cos \theta}$ is true except for angle measures such as $90°, 270°, \ldots, 90° + k180°$, where k is an integer. The cosine of each of these angle measures is 0, so $\tan \theta$ is not defined when $\cos \theta = 0$. These identities are sometimes called *quotient identities*. An identity similar to this is $\cot \theta = \frac{\cos \theta}{\sin \theta}$.

14-1 Lesson Notes

1 FOCUS

Vertical Alignment

Before Lesson 14-1
Evaluate trigonometric functions.

Lesson 14-1
Use trigonometric identities to find trigonometric values.
Use trigonometric identities to simplify expressions.

After 14-1
Use trigonometry to solve real-world problems.

2 TEACH

Scaffolding Questions

Have students read the *Why?* section of the lesson.

Ask:

- On the right-hand side of the illuminance formula, which variables appear in the numerator? In the denominator? intensity; illuminance and distance
- In a right triangle, what is the ratio for $\sec \theta$? $\sec \theta = \frac{\text{hypotenuse}}{\text{adjacent side}}$
- What is the reciprocal identity of $\sec \theta$? $\frac{1}{\cos \theta}$, $\cos \theta \neq 0$

Lesson 14-1 Resources

Resource	Approaching-Level	On-Level	Beyond-Level	English Learners
Teacher Edition	• Differentiated Instruction, p. 892	• Differentiated Instruction, pp. 892, 897	• Differentiated Instruction, pp. 893, 897	
Chapter Resource Masters	• Study Guide and Intervention, pp. 5–6 • Skills Practice, p. 7 • Practice, p. 8 • Word Problem Practice, p. 9	• Study Guide and Intervention, pp. 5–6 • Skills Practice, p. 7 • Practice, p. 8 • Word Problem Practice, p. 9 • Enrichment, p. 10	• Practice, p. 8 • Word Problem Practice, p. 9 • Enrichment, p. 10	• Study Guide and Intervention, pp. 5–6 • Skills Practice, p. 7 • Practice, p. 8 • Word Problem Practice, p. 9
Transparencies	• 5-Minute Check Transparency 14-1	• 5-Minute Check Transparency 14-1	• 5-Minute Check Transparency 14-1	• 5-Minute Check Transparency 14-1
Other	• Study Notebook	• Study Notebook	• Study Notebook	• Study Notebook

Find Trigonometric Values

Example 1 shows how to find values of a trigonometric function for an angle in a specified quadrant.

Formative Assessment

Use the Guided Practice exercises after each example to determine students' understanding of concepts.

Additional Example

1 **a.** Find the exact value of tan θ if sec $\theta = -2$ and $180° < \theta < 270°$. $\tan \theta = \sqrt{3}$

b. Find the exact value of sin θ if $\cos \theta = -\frac{1}{2}$ and $90° < \theta < 180°$. $\sin \theta = \frac{\sqrt{3}}{2}$

Additional Examples also in Interactive Classroom PowerPoint® Presentations

IWB INTERACTIVE WHITEBOARD READY

You can use trigonometric identities to find exact values of trigonometric functions. You can find approximate values by using a graphing calculator.

EXAMPLE 1 Use Trigonometric Identities

a. Find the exact value of cos θ if $\sin \theta = \frac{1}{4}$ and $90° < \theta < 180°$.

$\cos^2 \theta + \sin^2 \theta = 1$	Pythagorean identity
$\cos^2 \theta = 1 - \sin^2 \theta$	Subtract $\sin^2 \theta$ from each side.
$\cos^2 \theta = 1 - \left(\frac{1}{4}\right)^2$	Substitute $\frac{1}{4}$ for sin θ.
$\cos^2 \theta = 1 - \frac{1}{16}$	Square $\frac{1}{4}$.
$\cos^2 \theta = \frac{15}{16}$	Subtract: $\frac{16}{16} - \frac{1}{16} = \frac{15}{16}$.
$\cos \theta = \pm\frac{\sqrt{15}}{4}$	Take the square root of each side.

Since θ is in the second quadrant, cos θ is negative. Thus, $\cos \theta = -\frac{\sqrt{15}}{4}$.

CHECK Use a calculator to find an approximate answer.

Step 1 Find Arcsin $\frac{1}{4}$.

$\sin^{-1} \frac{1}{4} \approx 14.48°$ **Use a calculator.**

Because $90° < \theta < 180°$, $\theta \approx 180° - 14.48°$ or about 165.52°.

Step 2 Find cos θ.
Replace θ with 165.52°.
$\cos 165.52° \approx -0.97$

Step 3 Compare with the exact value.

$-\frac{\sqrt{15}}{4} \stackrel{?}{\approx} 0.97$

$-0.968 \approx 0.97$ ✓

b. Find the exact value of csc θ if $\cot \theta = -\frac{3}{5}$ and $270° < \theta < 360°$.

$\cot^2 \theta + 1 = \csc^2 \theta$	Pythagorean identity
$\left(-\frac{3}{5}\right)^2 + 1 = \csc^2 \theta$	Substitute $-\frac{3}{5}$ for cot θ.
$\frac{9}{25} + 1 = \csc^2 \theta$	Square $-\frac{3}{5}$.
$\frac{34}{25} = \csc^2 \theta$	Add: $\frac{9}{25} + \frac{25}{25} = \frac{34}{25}$.
$\pm\frac{\sqrt{34}}{5} = \csc \theta$	Take the square root of each side.

Since θ is in the fourth quadrant, csc θ is negative. Thus, $\csc \theta = -\frac{\sqrt{34}}{5}$.

Guided Practice

1A. Find sin θ if $\cos \theta = \frac{1}{3}$ and $270° < \theta < 360°$. $-\frac{2\sqrt{2}}{3}$

1B. Find sec θ if $\sin \theta = -\frac{2}{7}$ and $180° < \theta < 270°$. $-\frac{7\sqrt{5}}{15}$

Personal Tutor glencoe.com

StudyTip

Quadrants Here is a table to help you remember which ratios are positive and which are negative in each quadrant.

Function	+	−
sin θ	1, 2	3, 4
cos θ	1, 4	2, 3
tan θ	1, 3	2, 4
csc θ	1, 2	3, 4
sec θ	1, 4	2, 3
cot θ	1, 3	2, 4

Simplify Expressions Simplifying an expression that contains trigonometric functions means that the expression is written as a numerical value or in terms of a single trigonometric function, if possible.

Differentiated Instruction AL OL

If students have difficulty with trigonometric identities,

Then have students work in groups of three. Ask each group to choose one of the identities in the Key Concept box on p. 891 and work together to demonstrate that it is true. Students should verify their results using the definitions of sine, cosine, and tangent in terms of the sides of a right triangle.

StudyTip

Simplifying It is often easiest to write all expressions in terms of sine and/or cosine.

EXAMPLE 2 Simplify an Expression

Simplify $\frac{\sin\theta\csc\theta}{\cot\theta}$.

$\frac{\sin\theta\csc\theta}{\cot\theta} = \frac{\sin\theta\cdot\frac{1}{\sin\theta}}{\frac{1}{\tan\theta}}$	$\csc\theta = \frac{1}{\sin\theta}$ and $\cot\theta = \frac{1}{\tan\theta}$
$= \frac{1}{\frac{1}{\tan\theta}}$	$\frac{\sin\theta}{\sin\theta} = 1$
$= \frac{1}{1}\cdot\frac{\tan\theta}{1}$ or $\tan\theta$	$\frac{a}{b}\div\frac{c}{d} = \frac{a}{b}\cdot\frac{d}{c}$

Guided Practice

Simplify each expression.

2A. $\frac{\tan^2\theta\csc^2\theta - 1}{\sec^2\theta}$ $\sin^2\theta$

2B. $\frac{\sec\theta}{\sin\theta}(1-\cos^2\theta)$ $\tan\theta$

Personal Tutor glencoe.com

Simplifying trigonometric expressions can be helpful when solving real-world problems.

Math History Link

Aryabhatta (476–550 A.D.) Among Indian mathematicians, Aryabhatta is probably the most famous. His name is closely associated with trigonometry. He was the first to introduce inverse trig functions and spherical trigonometry. Aryabhatta also calculated approximations for pi and trig functions.

Real-World EXAMPLE 3 Simplify and Use an Expression

LIGHTING Refer to the beginning of the lesson.

a. Solve the formula in terms of E.

$\sec\theta = \frac{I}{ER^2}$	Original equation
$ER^2\sec\theta = I$	Multiply each side by ER^2.
$ER^2\frac{1}{\cos\theta} = I$	$\frac{1}{\cos\theta} = \sec\theta$
$\frac{E}{\cos\theta} = \frac{I}{R^2}$	Divide each side by R^2.
$E = \frac{I\cos\theta}{R^2}$	Multiply each side by $\cos\theta$.

b. Is the equation in part a equivalent to $R^2 = \frac{I\tan\theta\cos\theta}{E}$? Explain.

$R^2 = \frac{I\tan\theta\cos\theta}{E}$	Original equation
$ER^2 = I\tan\theta\cos\theta$	Multiply each side by E.
$E = \frac{I\tan\theta\cos\theta}{R^2}$	Divide each side by R^2.
$E = \frac{I\frac{\sin\theta}{\cos\theta}\cos\theta}{R^2}$	$\tan\theta = \frac{\sin\theta}{\cos\theta}$
$E = \frac{I\sin\theta}{R^2}$	Simplify.

No; the equations are not equivalent. $R^2 = \frac{I\tan\theta\cos\theta}{E}$ simplifies to $E = \frac{I\sin\theta}{R^2}$.

Guided Practice

3. Rewrite $\cot^2\theta - \tan^2\theta$ in terms of $\sin\theta$. $\frac{1-2\sin^2\theta}{\sin^2\theta - \sin^4\theta}$

Personal Tutor glencoe.com

Simplify Expressions

Example 2 shows how to simplify an expression by writing it in terms of one trigonometric function. **Example 3** illustrates simplifying a real-world expression involving trigonometric functions.

Additional Examples

2 Simplify $\sin\theta(\csc\theta - \sin\theta)$. $\cos^2\theta$

3 **LIGHTING** Refer to the beginning of the lesson.

a. Solve the illuminance formula in terms of R. $R = \sqrt{\frac{I\cos\theta}{E}}$

b. Is the equation in part **a** equivalent to $\frac{1}{R^2} = \frac{E}{I\sec\theta}$? no

Focus on Mathematical Content

Identities Students must have good recall of the quotient, reciprocal, and Pythagorean identities. While it is helpful to remember other identities, the other identities can be derived from the basic identities.

TEACH with TECH

WEB PAGE Create a class Web page that includes all of the trigonometric identities and formulas from this chapter. Have students subscribe to an RSS feed so that they can easily tell when you update the page.

Differentiated Instructions

BL

Extension Beyond-level students are often interested in learning how certain mathematical ideas came into existence. Provide an extension to the math history link about the Indian mathematician, Aryabhatta. Students can investigate the prior mathematical discoveries of Aryabhatta that led to the need for inverse trigonometric functions in the context of his work.

Lesson 14-1 Trigonometric Identities 893

3 PRACTICE

Formative Assessment

Use Exercises 1–8 to check for understanding.

Use the chart at the bottom of this page to customize assignments for your students.

Tips for New Teachers

Trigonometric Ratios You can use the familiar definitions of sine, cosine, and tangent as the ratios of the opposite side, adjacent side, and hypotenuse of a right triangle to show why $\frac{\sin\theta}{\cos\theta} = \tan\theta$.

Check Your Understanding

Example 1 p. 892

Find the exact value of each expression if $0° < \theta < 90°$.

1. If $\cot\theta = 2$, find $\tan\theta$. $\frac{1}{2}$
2. If $\sin\theta = \frac{4}{5}$, find $\cos\theta$. $\frac{3}{5}$
3. If $\cos\theta = \frac{2}{3}$, find $\sin\theta$. $\frac{\sqrt{5}}{3}$
4. If $\cos\theta = \frac{2}{3}$, find $\csc\theta$. $\frac{3\sqrt{5}}{5}$

Example 2 p. 893

Simplify each expression.

5. $\tan\theta\cos^2\theta$ $\sin\theta\cos\theta$
6. $\csc^2\theta - \cot^2\theta$ 1
7. $\frac{\cos\theta\csc\theta}{\tan\theta}$ $\cot^2\theta$

Example 3 p. 893

8. **OPTICS** When unpolarized light passes through polarized sunglass lenses, the intensity of the light is cut in half. If the light then passes through another polarized lens with its axis at an angle of θ to the first, the intensity of the light is again diminished. The intensity of the emerging light can be found by using the formula $I = I_0 - \frac{I_0}{\csc^2\theta}$, where I_0 is the intensity of the light incoming to the second polarized lens, I is the intensity of the emerging light, and θ is the angle between the axes of polarization.

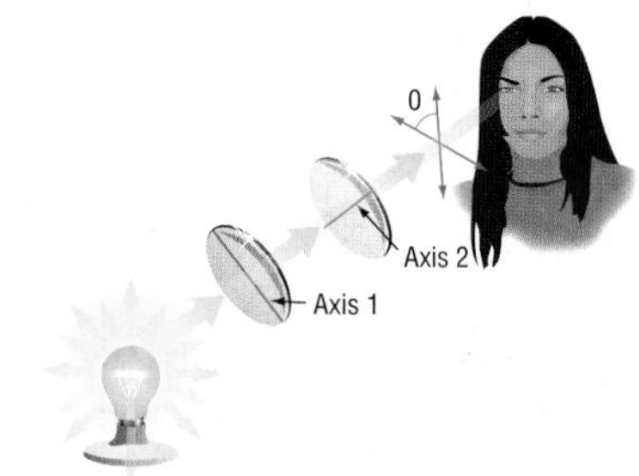

a. Simplify the formula in terms of $\cos\theta$. $I = I_0\cos^2\theta$

b. Use the simplified formula to determine the intensity of light that passes through a second polarizing lens with axis at 30° to the original. $I = \frac{3}{4}I_0$; The light has three fourths the intensity it had before passing through the second polarizing lens.

Practice and Problem Solving

● = **Step-by-Step Solutions** begin on page R20. **Extra Practice** begins on page 947.

Example 1 p. 892

Find the exact value of each expression if $0° < \theta < 90°$.

9. If $\cos\theta = \frac{3}{5}$, find $\csc\theta$. $\frac{5}{4}$
10. If $\sin\theta = \frac{1}{2}$, find $\tan\theta$. $\frac{\sqrt{3}}{3}$
11. If $\sin\theta = \frac{3}{5}$, find $\cos\theta$. $\frac{4}{5}$
12. If $\tan\theta = 2$, find $\sec\theta$. $\sqrt{5}$

Find the exact value of each expression if $180° < \theta < 270°$.

13. If $\cos\theta = -\frac{3}{5}$, find $\csc\theta$. $-\frac{5}{4}$
14. If $\sec\theta = -3$, find $\tan\theta$. $2\sqrt{2}$
15. If $\cot\theta = \frac{1}{4}$, find $\csc\theta$. $\frac{-\sqrt{17}}{4}$
16. If $\sin\theta = -\frac{1}{2}$, find $\cos\theta$. $-\frac{\sqrt{3}}{2}$

Find the exact value of each expression if $270° < \theta < 360°$.

17. If $\cos\theta = \frac{5}{13}$, find $\sin\theta$. $-\frac{12}{13}$
18. If $\tan\theta = -1$, find $\sec\theta$. $\sqrt{2}$
19. If $\sec\theta = \frac{5}{3}$, find $\cos\theta$. $\frac{3}{5}$
20. If $\csc\theta = -\frac{5}{3}$, find $\cos\theta$. $\frac{4}{5}$

Example 2 p. 893

Simplify each expression.

21. $\sec\theta\tan^2\theta + \sec\theta$ $\sec^3\theta$
22. $\cos\left(\frac{\pi}{2} - \theta\right)\cot\theta$ $\cos\theta$
23. $\cot\theta\sec\theta$ $\csc\theta$
24. $\sin\theta(1 + \cot^2\theta)$ $\csc\theta$
25. $\sin\left(\frac{\pi}{2} - \theta\right)\sec\theta$ 1
26. $\frac{\cos(-\theta)}{\sin(-\theta)}$ $-\cot\theta$

Differentiated Homework Options

Level	Assignment	Two-Day Option	
AL Basic	9–27, 42, 44–48, 50–67	9–27 odd, 51–54	10–26 even, 42, 44–48, 50, 55–67
OL Core	9–33 odd, 34–42, 44–48, 50–67	9–27, 51–54	28–42, 44–48, 50, 55–67
BL Advanced	28–64, (optional: 65–67)		

Example 3 p. 893

27 **ELECTRONICS** When there is a current in a wire in a magnetic field, such as in a hairdryer, a force acts on the wire. The strength of the magnetic field can be determined using the formula $B = \frac{F \csc \theta}{I\ell}$, where F is the force on the wire, I is the current in the wire, ℓ is the length of the wire, and θ is the angle the wire makes with the magnetic field. Rewrite the equation in terms of $\sin \theta$. (*Hint:* Solve for F.) $F = I\ell B \sin \theta$

B **Simplify each expression.**

28. $\frac{1 - \sin^2 \theta}{\sin^2 \theta}$ $\cot^2 \theta$

29. $\tan \theta \csc \theta$ $\sec \theta$

30. $\frac{1}{\sin^2 \theta} - \frac{\cos^2 \theta}{\sin^2 \theta}$ 1

31. $2(\csc^2 \theta - \cot^2 \theta)$ 2

32. $(1 + \sin \theta)(1 - \sin \theta)$ $\cos^2 \theta$

33. $2 - 2\sin^2 \theta$ $2\cos^2 \theta$

34. **SUN** The ability of an object to absorb energy is related to a factor called the emissivity e of the object. The emissivity can be calculated by using the formula $e = \frac{W \sec \theta}{AS}$, where W is the rate at which a person's skin absorbs energy from the Sun, S is the energy from the Sun in watts per square meter, A is the surface area exposed to the Sun, and θ is the angle between the Sun's rays and a line perpendicular to the body. a. $W = eAS \cos \theta$

a. Solve the equation for W. Write your answer using only $\sin \theta$ or $\cos \theta$.

b. Find W if $e = 0.80$, $\theta = 40°$, $A = 0.75$ m^2, and $S = 1000$ W/m^2. Round to the nearest hundredth. 459.63 W

Real-World Link

Research has shown that skin cancer is related to Sun exposure. If current trends continue, 1 in 5 Americans will develop skin cancer during their lifetimes.

Source: Skin Cancer Net

35. **MAPS** The map shows some of the buildings in Maria's neighborhood that she visits on a regular basis. The sine of the angle θ formed by the roads connecting the dance studio, the school, and Maria's house is $\frac{4}{9}$. c. $\frac{4}{9}$, $\frac{\sqrt{65}}{9}$, $\frac{4\sqrt{65}}{65}$

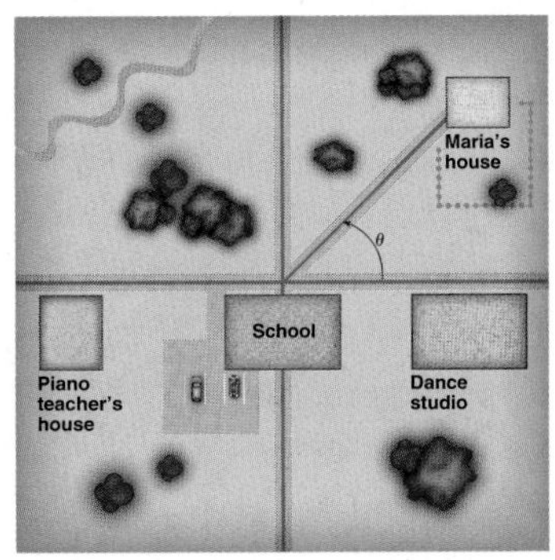

a. What is the cosine of the angle? $\frac{\sqrt{65}}{9}$

b. What is the tangent of the angle? $\frac{4\sqrt{65}}{65}$

c. What are the sine, cosine, and tangent of the angle formed by the roads connecting the piano teacher's house, the school, and Maria's house?

36. **MULTIPLE REPRESENTATIONS** In this problem, you will use a graphing calculator to determine whether an equation may be a trigonometric identity. Consider the trigonometric identity $\tan^2 \theta - \sin^2 \theta = \tan^2 \theta \sin^2 \theta$.

a. TABULAR Complete the table below.

θ	0°	30°	45°	60°
$\tan^2 \theta - \sin^2$	0	$\frac{1}{12}$	$\frac{1}{2}$	$\frac{9}{4}$
$\tan^2 \theta \sin^2 \theta$	0	$\frac{1}{12}$	$\frac{1}{2}$	$\frac{9}{4}$

b. GRAPHICAL Use a graphing calculator to graph $\tan^2 \theta - \sin^2 \theta = \tan^2 \theta \sin^2 \theta$ as two separate functions. Sketch the graph. See margin.

c. ANALYTICAL If the graphs of the two functions do not match, then the equation is not an identity. Do the graphs coincide? yes

d. ANALYTICAL Use a graphing calculator to determine whether the equation $\sec^2 x - 1 = \sin^2 x \sec^2 x$ may be an identity. (Be sure your calculator is in degree mode.) yes

Multiple Representations In Exercise 36, students use a table of values and a graphing calculator to determine whether an equation is a trigonometric identity.

Additional Answer

36b.

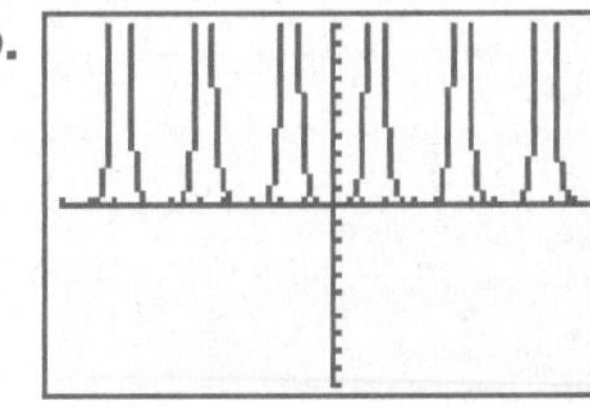

[–540, 540] scl: 90 by [–10, 10] scl: 1

Lesson 14-1 Trigonometric Identities 895

Study Guide and Intervention
CRM pp. 5–6 AL OL ELL

14-1 Study Guide and Intervention
Trigonometric Identities

Find Trigonometric Values A **trigonometric identity** is an equation involving trigonometric functions that is true for all values for which every expression in the equation is defined.

Basic Trigonometric Identities	Quotient Identities	$\tan\theta = \frac{\sin\theta}{\cos\theta}$	$\cot\theta = \frac{\cos\theta}{\sin\theta}$	
	Reciprocal Identities	$\csc\theta = \frac{1}{\sin\theta}$	$\sec\theta = \frac{1}{\cos\theta}$	$\cot\theta = \frac{1}{\tan\theta}$
	Pythagorean Identities	$\cos^2\theta + \sin^2\theta = 1$	$\tan^2\theta + 1 = \sec^2\theta$	$\cot^2\theta + 1 = \csc^2\theta$

Example Find the exact value of $\cot\theta$ if $\csc\theta = -\frac{11}{5}$ and $180° < \theta < 270°$.

$\cot^2\theta + 1 = \csc^2\theta$ Trigonometric identity
$\cot^2\theta + 1 = \left(-\frac{11}{5}\right)^2$ Substitute $-\frac{11}{5}$ for $\csc\theta$.
$\cot^2\theta + 1 = \frac{121}{25}$ Square $-\frac{11}{5}$.
$\cot^2\theta = \frac{96}{25}$ Subtract 1 from each side.
$\cot\theta = \pm\frac{4\sqrt{6}}{5}$ Take the square root of each side.

Since θ is in the third quadrant, $\cot\theta$ is positive. Thus, $\cot\theta = \frac{4\sqrt{6}}{5}$.

Exercises

Find the exact value of each expression if $0° < \theta < 90°$.

1. If $\cot\theta = 4$, find $\tan\theta$. $\frac{1}{4}$
2. If $\cos\theta = \frac{\sqrt{3}}{2}$, find $\csc\theta$. **2**
3. If $\sin\theta = \frac{3}{5}$, find $\cos\theta$. $\frac{4}{5}$
4. If $\sin\theta = \frac{1}{3}$, find $\sec\theta$. $\frac{3\sqrt{2}}{4}$
5. If $\tan\theta = \frac{4}{3}$, find $\cos\theta$. $\frac{3}{5}$
6. If $\sin\theta = \frac{3}{7}$, find $\tan\theta$. $\frac{3\sqrt{10}}{20}$

Find the exact value of each expression if $90° < \theta < 180°$.

7. If $\cos\theta = -\frac{7}{8}$, find $\sec\theta$. $-\frac{8}{7}$
8. If $\csc\theta = \frac{12}{5}$, find $\cot\theta$. $-\frac{\sqrt{119}}{5}$

Find the exact value of each expression if $270° < \theta < 360°$.

9. If $\cos\theta = \frac{6}{7}$, find $\sin\theta$. $-\frac{\sqrt{13}}{7}$
10. If $\csc\theta = -\frac{9}{4}$, find $\sin\theta$. $-\frac{4}{9}$

Chapter 14 5 Glencoe Algebra 2

Lesson 14-1

Practice
CRM p. 8 AL OL BL ELL

14-1 Practice
Trigonometric Identities

Find the exact value of each expression if $0° < \theta < 90°$.

1. If $\cos\theta = \frac{5}{13}$, find $\sin\theta$. $\frac{12}{13}$
2. If $\cot\theta = \frac{1}{2}$, find $\sin\theta$. $\frac{2\sqrt{5}}{5}$
3. If $\tan\theta = 4$, find $\sec\theta$. $\sqrt{17}$
4. If $\tan\theta = \frac{2}{5}$, find $\cot\theta$. $\frac{5}{2}$

Find the exact value of each expression if $180° < \theta < 270°$.

5. If $\sin\theta = -\frac{15}{17}$, find $\sec\theta$. $-\frac{17}{8}$
6. If $\csc\theta = -\frac{3}{2}$, find $\cot\theta$. $\frac{\sqrt{5}}{2}$

Find the exact value of each expression if $270° < \theta < 360°$.

7. If $\cos\theta = \frac{3}{10}$, find $\cot\theta$. $-\frac{3\sqrt{91}}{91}$
8. If $\csc\theta = -8$, find $\sec\theta$. $\frac{8\sqrt{7}}{21}$
9. If $\tan\theta = -\frac{1}{2}$, find $\sin\theta$. $-\frac{\sqrt{5}}{5}$
10. If $\cos\theta = \frac{1}{3}$, find $\cot\theta$. $-\frac{\sqrt{2}}{4}$

Simplify each expression.

11. $\csc\theta\tan\theta$ **$\sec\theta$**
12. $\frac{\sin^2\theta}{\tan^2\theta}$ **$\cos^2\theta$**
13. $\sin^2\theta\cot^2\theta$ **$\cos^2\theta$**
14. $\cot^2\theta + 1$ **$\csc^2\theta$**
15. $\frac{\csc^2\theta - \cot^2\theta}{1 - \cos^2\theta}$ **$\csc^2\theta$**
16. $\frac{\csc\theta - \sin\theta}{\cos\theta}$ **$\cot\theta$**
17. $\sin\theta + \cos\theta\cot\theta$ **$\csc\theta$**
18. $\frac{\cos\theta}{1 - \sin\theta} - \frac{\cos\theta}{1 + \sin\theta}$ **$2\tan\theta$**
19. $\sec^2\theta\cos^2\theta - \tan^2\theta$ **$\sec^2\theta$**

20. **AERIAL PHOTOGRAPHY** The illustration shows a plane taking an aerial photograph of point A. Because the point is directly below the plane, there is no distortion in the image. For any point B not directly below the plane, however, the increase in distance creates distortion in the photograph. This is because as the distance from the camera to the point being photographed increases, the exposure of the film reduces by $(\sin\theta)(\csc\theta - \sin\theta)$. Express $(\sin\theta)(\csc\theta - \sin\theta)$ in terms of $\cos\theta$ only. **$\cos^2\theta$**

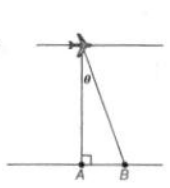

21. **WAVES** The equation $y = a\sin\theta t$ represents the height of the waves passing a buoy at a time t in seconds. Express a in terms of $\csc\theta t$. **$a = y\csc\theta t$**

Chapter 14 8 Glencoe Algebra 2

Word Problem Practice
CRM p. 9 AL OL BL ELL

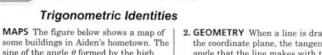

14-1 Word Problem Practice
Trigonometric Identities

1. **MAPS** The figure below shows a map of some buildings in Aiden's hometown. The sine of the angle θ formed by the high school, the middle school, and Aiden's house is $\frac{3}{7}$.

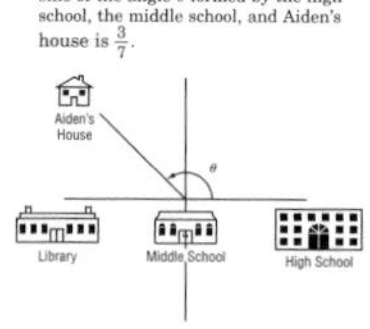

a. What is the cosine of the angle? $2\frac{\sqrt{10}}{7}$

b. What is the tangent of the angle? $\frac{3\sqrt{10}}{20}$

c. What are the sine, cosine, and tangent of the angle formed by the library, the middle school, and Aiden's house? $\frac{3}{7}, \frac{2\sqrt{10}}{7}, \frac{3\sqrt{10}}{20}$

2. **GEOMETRY** When a line is drawn in the coordinate plane, the tangent of the angle that the line makes with the horizontal axis is equal to the slope of the line (for non-vertical lines).

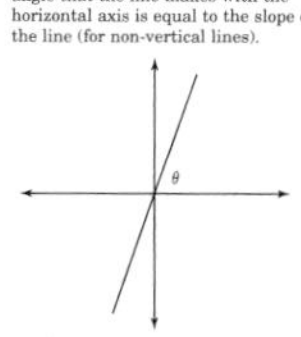

The cosine of the angle θ the line in the figure makes with the horizontal is $\frac{1}{3}$.

a. Explain two ways to determine the slope of the line. Draw a representative triangle with the length of the side adjacent to angle θ equal to 1 and the hypotenuse equal to 3. **Use the Pythagorean Theorem to find the length of the other leg. Compute the tangent from the definition. Or use the given value of cosine of θ and the Pythagorean Identity to compute sine of θ. Finally, use the identity $\tan\theta = \frac{\sin\theta}{\cos\theta}$.**

b. Compute the sine and tangent of the angle. $\frac{2\sqrt{2}}{3}$, $2\sqrt{2}$

c. What is the slope of the line? $2\sqrt{2}$

Chapter 14 9 Glencoe Algebra 2

Lesson 14-1

C

37. **SKIING** A skier of mass m descends a θ-degree hill at a constant speed. When Newton's laws are applied to the situation, the following system of equations is produced: $F_n - mg\cos\theta = 0$ and $mg\sin\theta - \mu_k F_n = 0$, where g is the acceleration due to gravity, F_n is the normal force exerted on the skier, and μ_k is the coefficient of friction. Use the system to define μ_k as a function of θ. **$\mu_k = \tan\theta$**

Simplify each expression.

38. $\frac{\tan\left(\frac{\pi}{2} - \theta\right)\sec\theta}{1 - \csc^2\theta}$ **$-\tan\theta\sec\theta$**

39. $\frac{\cos\left(\frac{\pi}{2} - \theta\right) - 1}{1 + \sin(-\theta)}$ **-1**

40. $\frac{\sec\theta\sin\theta + \cos\left(\frac{\pi}{2} - \theta\right)}{1 + \sec\theta}$ **$\sin\theta$**

41. $\frac{\cot\theta\cos\theta}{\tan(-\theta)\sin\left(\frac{\pi}{2} - \theta\right)}$ **$-\cot^2\theta$**

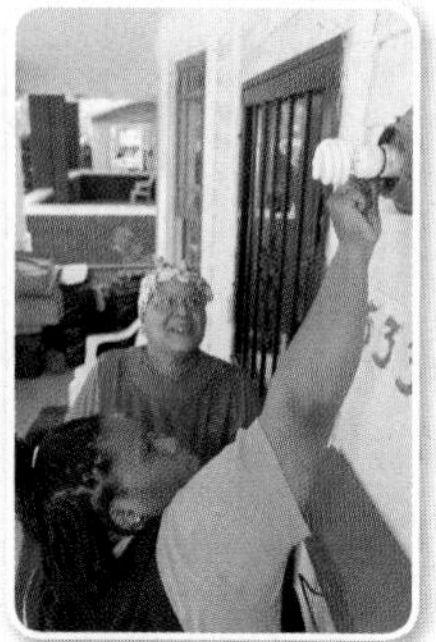

Real-World Link

Compact fluorescent lights, or CFLs, typically have a lifespan of between 6000 and 15,000 hours, whereas incandescent lights are usually manufactured to have a life span of 750 to 1000 hours.

Source: Osram

H.O.T. Problems
Use Higher-Order Thinking Skills

42. **ERROR ANALYSIS** Clyde and Rosalina are debating whether an equation from their homework assignment is an identity. Clyde says that since he has tried ten specific values for the variable and all of them worked, it must be an identity. Rosalina argues that specific values could only be used as counterexamples to prove that an equation is not an identity. Is either of them correct? Explain your reasoning. **Rosalina; there may be other values for which the equation is not true.**

43. **CHALLENGE** Find a counterexample to show that $1 - \sin x = \cos x$ is *not* an identity. **Sample answer: $x = 45°$**

44. **REASONING** Demonstrate how the formula about illuminance from the beginning of the lesson can be rewritten to show that $\cos\theta = \frac{ER^2}{I}$. **See margin.**

45. **WRITING IN MATH** Pythagoras is most famous for the Pythagorean Theorem. The identity $\cos^2\theta + \sin^2\theta = 1$ is an example of a Pythagorean identity. Why do you think that this identity is classified in this way?

46. **PROOF** Prove that $\tan(-a) = -\tan a$ by using the quotient and negative angle identities. **See margin.**

47. **OPEN ENDED** Write two expressions that are equivalent to $\tan\theta\sin\theta$.

48. **REASONING** Explain how you can use division to rewrite $\sin^2\theta + \cos^2\theta = 1$ as $1 + \cot^2\theta = \csc^2\theta$. **Divide all of the terms by $\sin^2\theta$.**

49. **CHALLENGE** Find $\cot\theta$ if $\sin\theta = \frac{3}{5}$ and $90° \le \theta < 180°$. **$-\frac{4}{3}$**

50. **FIND THE ERROR** Jordan and Ebony are simplifying $\frac{\sin^2\theta}{\cos^2\theta + \sin^2\theta}$. Is either of them correct? Explain your reasoning.

Jordan

$$\frac{\sin^2\theta}{\cos^2\theta + \sin^2\theta} = \frac{\sin^2\theta}{\cos^2\theta} + \frac{\sin^2\theta}{\sin^2\theta}$$
$$= \tan^2\theta + 1$$
$$= \sec^2\theta$$

Ebony

$$\frac{\sin^2\theta}{\cos^2\theta + \sin^2\theta} = \frac{\sin^2\theta}{1}$$
$$= \sin^2\theta$$

45. Sample answer: The functions $\cos\theta$ and $\sin\theta$ can be thought of as the lengths of the legs of a right triangle, and the number 1 can be thought of as the measure of the corresponding hypotenuse.

47. Sample answer: $\frac{\sin\theta}{\cos\theta} \cdot \sin\theta$ and $\frac{\sin^2\theta}{\cos\theta}$

50. Ebony; Jordan did not use the identity $\sin^2\theta + \cos^2\theta = 1$ and made an error adding rational expressions.

Enrichment
CRM p. 10 OL BL

14-1 Enrichment

Planetary Orbits

The orbit of a planet around the sun is an ellipse with the Sun at one focus. Let the pole of a polar coordinate system be that focus and the polar axis be toward the other focus. The polar equation of an ellipse is

$r = \frac{2ep}{1 - e\cos\theta}$. Since $2p = \frac{b^2}{c}$ and $b^2 = a^2 - c^2$,

$2p = \frac{a^2 - c^2}{c} = \frac{a^2}{c}\left(1 - \frac{c^2}{a^2}\right)$. Because $e = \frac{c}{a}$,

$2p = a\left(\frac{a}{c}\right)\left(1 - \left(\frac{c}{a}\right)^2\right) = a\left(\frac{1}{e}\right)(1 - e^2)$.

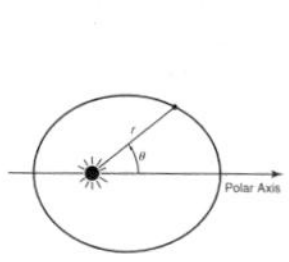

Therefore, $2ep = a(1 - e^2)$. Substituting into the polar equation of an ellipse yields an equation that is useful for finding distances from the planet to the Sun.

$r = \frac{a(1 - e^2)}{1 - e\cos\theta}$

Note that e is the eccentricity of the orbit and a is the length of the semi-major axis of the ellipse. Also, a is the mean distance of the planet from the Sun.

Additional Answer

44. $\sec\theta = \frac{I}{ER^2}$

$\frac{1}{\cos\theta} = \frac{I}{ER^2}$ $\quad$ $\sec\theta = \frac{1}{\cos\theta}$

$ER^2 = I\cos\theta$ $\quad$ Cross multiply.

$\cos\theta = \frac{ER^2}{I}$ $\quad$ Divide each side by I.

NGSSS PRACTICE 912.T.2.1, 912.P.3.1, 912.A.3.1, 912.A.8.7

51. Refer to the figure below. If $\cos D = 0.8$, what is the length of $\overline{DF}$? **A**

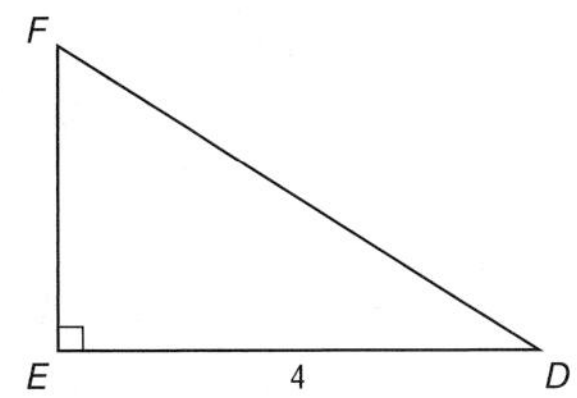

A. 5 C. 3.2
B. 4 D. $\frac{4}{5}$

52. PROBABILITY There are 16 green marbles, 2 red marbles, and 6 yellow marbles in a jar. How many yellow marbles need to be added to the jar in order to double the probability of selecting a yellow marble? **I**

F. 4 H. 8
G. 6 I. 12

53. ACT/SAT Ella is 6 years younger than Amanda. Zoe is twice as old as Amanda. The total of their ages is 54. Which equation can be used to find Amanda's age? **D**

A. $x + (x - 6) + 2(x - 6) = 54$
B. $x - 6x + (x + 2) = 54$
C. $x - 6 + 2x = 54$
D. $x + (x - 6) + 2x = 54$

54. Which of the following functions represents exponential growth? **G**

F. $y = (0.3)^x$
G. $y = (1.3)^x$
H. $y = x^3$
I. $y = x^{\frac{1}{3}}$

Spiral Review

Find each value. Write angle measures in radians. Round to the nearest hundredth. (Lesson 13-9)

55. $\text{Cos}^{-1}\left(-\frac{1}{2}\right)$ **2.09**

56. $\text{Sin}^{-1}\frac{\pi}{2}$ **does not exist**

57. $\text{Arctan}\,\frac{\sqrt{3}}{3}$ **0.52**

58. $\tan\left(\text{Cos}^{-1}\frac{6}{7}\right)$ **0.60**

59. $\sin\left(\text{Arctan}\,\frac{\sqrt{3}}{3}\right)$ **0.5**

60. $\cos\left(\text{Arcsin}\,\frac{3}{5}\right)$ **0.8**

61. PHYSICS A weight is attached to a spring and suspended from the ceiling. At equilibrium, the weight is located 4 feet above the floor. The weight is pulled down 1 foot and released. Write the equation for the height h of the weight above the floor as a function of time t seconds if the weight returns to its lowest position every 4 seconds. (Lesson 13-8) **$h = 4 - \cos\frac{\pi}{2}t$ or $h = 4 - \cos 90°t$**

Evaluate the sum of each geometric series. (Lesson 11-3)

62. $\sum_{k=1}^{5} \frac{1}{4} \cdot 2^{k-1}$ **$\frac{31}{4}$**

63. $\sum_{k=1}^{7} 81\left(\frac{1}{3}\right)^{k-1}$ **$\frac{1093}{9}$**

64. $\sum_{k=1}^{8} \frac{1}{3} \cdot 5^{k-1}$ **32,552**

Skills Review

Solve each equation. (Lesson 9-6)

65. $a + 1 = \frac{6}{a}$ **−3, 2**

66. $\frac{9}{t-3} = \frac{t-4}{t-3} + \frac{1}{4}$ **11**

67. $\frac{5}{x+1} - \frac{1}{3} = \frac{x+2}{x+1}$ **2**

Watch Out!

Error Analysis For Exercise 42, students should see that Rosalina is correct. Explain to students that inductive reasoning (generalizing from several examples) can never prove that an identity is true, but that any specific counterexample is enough to show that an equation is not an identity.

For Exercise 50, students should see that Ebony is correct (because $\cos^2\theta + \sin^2\theta = 1$) and that Jordan is not correct $\left(\text{because } \frac{a}{b+c} \neq \frac{a}{b} + \frac{a}{c}\right)$. Explain to students that when they simplify a trigonometric expression, they use the same properties as when they simplify any rational expression.

4 ASSESS

Crystal Ball Tell students to look ahead to Lesson 14-2. Ask them to write how they think what they learned today will help them with Lesson 14-2.

Additional Answer

46.
$$\tan(-A) = \frac{\sin(-A)}{\cos(-A)} = \frac{-\sin A}{\cos A} = -\frac{\sin A}{\cos A} = -\tan A$$

Differentiated Instruction

OL BL

Extension Ask students if it is always possible to simplify a trigonometric expression by writing it in terms of one trigonometric function. Ask them to provide an example if it is not possible or explain why it is possible.

Lesson 14-1 Trigonometric Identities 897

14-2 Lesson Notes

1 FOCUS

Vertical Alignment

Before Lesson 14-2
Use identities to find trigonometric values and simplify expressions.

Lesson 14-2
Verify trigonometric identities by transforming one side of an equation into the form of the other side.
Verify trigonometric identities by transforming each side of the equation into the same form.

After Lesson 14-2
Use sum and difference identities to prove or simplify other trigonometric identities.

2 TEACH

Scaffolding Questions

Have students read the *Why?* section of the lesson.

Ask:

- On the right-hand side of the *angle of incline* equation, which variables appear in the numerator? In the denominator? *v; g and R*
- How can you express $\tan\theta$ in terms of $\sin\theta$ and $\cos\theta$? $\tan\theta = \frac{\sin\theta}{\cos\theta}$
- Does $\frac{\sin\theta}{\cos\theta}$ equal $\frac{v^2}{gR}$ or $\frac{gR}{v^2}$? $\frac{v^2}{gR}$

14-2 Verifying Trigonometric Identities

Then
You used identities to find trigonometric values and simplify expressions. (Lesson 14-1)

Now
- Verify trigonometric identities by transforming one side of an equation into the form of the other side.
- Verify trigonometric identities by transforming each side of the equation into the same form.

NGSSS
MA.912.T.3.2 Use basic trigonometric identities to verify other identities and simplify expressions.

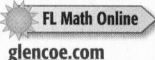

FL Math Online
glencoe.com

Why?

While running on a circular track, Lamont notices that his body is not perpendicular to the ground. Instead, it leans away from a vertical position. The nonnegative acute angle θ that Lamont's body makes with the vertical is called the *angle of incline* and is described by the equation $\tan\theta = \frac{v^2}{gR}$.

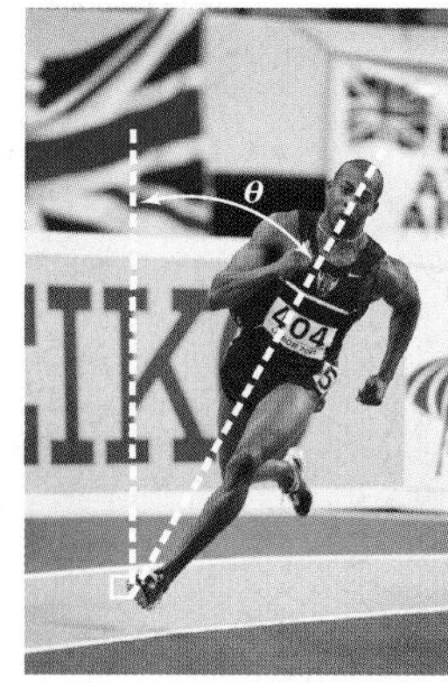

This is not the only equation that describes the angle of incline in terms of trigonometric functions. Another such equation is $\sin\theta = \cos\frac{v^2}{gR}\theta$, where $0 \le \theta \le 90°$. Are these two equations completely independent of one another or are they merely different versions of the same relationship?

Transform One Side of an Equation You can use the basic trigonometric identities along with the definitions of the trigonometric functions to verify identities. If you wish to show an identity, you need to show that it is true for all values of θ.

Key Concept

Verifying Identities by Transforming One Side

Step 1 Simplify one side of an equation until the two sides of the equation are the same. It is often easier to work with the more complicated side of the equation.

Step 2 Transform that expression into the form of the simpler side.

EXAMPLE 1 Transform One Side of an Equation

Verify that $\frac{\sin^2\theta}{1-\cos\theta} = 1 + \cos\theta$ is an identity.

$\frac{\sin^2\theta}{1-\cos\theta} \stackrel{?}{=} 1 + \cos\theta$ — **Original equation**

$\frac{1+\cos\theta}{1+\cos\theta} \cdot \frac{\sin^2\theta}{1-\cos\theta} \stackrel{?}{=} 1 + \cos\theta$ — **Multiply the numerator and denominator by $1 + \cos\theta$.**

$\frac{\sin^2\theta(1+\cos\theta)}{1-\cos^2\theta} \stackrel{?}{=} 1 + \cos\theta$ — **$(1+\cos\theta)(1-\cos\theta) = 1-\cos^2\theta$**

$\frac{\sin^2\theta(1+\cos\theta)}{\sin^2\theta} \stackrel{?}{=} 1 + \cos\theta$ — **$\sin^2\theta = 1-\cos^2\theta$**

$1 + \cos\theta = 1 + \cos\theta$ ✓ — **Divide the numerator and denominator by $\sin^2\theta$.**

Guided Practice

1. Verify that $\cot^2\theta - \cos^2\theta = \cot^2\theta\cos^2\theta$ is an identity. **See margin.**

Personal Tutor glencoe.com

Lesson 14-2 Resources

Resource	Approaching-Level	On-Level	Beyond-Level	English Learners
Teacher Edition	• Differentiated Instruction, p. 899	• Differentiated Instruction, p. 899	• Differentiated Instruction, pp. 899, 903	• Differentiated Instruction, p. 899
Chapter Resource Masters	• Study Guide and Intervention, pp. 11–12 • Skills Practice, p. 13 • Practice, p. 14 • Word Problem Practice, p. 15	• Study Guide and Intervention, pp. 11–12 • Skills Practice, p. 13 • Practice, p. 14 • Word Problem Practice, p. 15 • Enrichment, p. 16	• Practice, p. 14 • Word Problem Practice, p. 15 • Enrichment, p. 16	• Study Guide and Intervention, pp. 11–12 • Skills Practice, p. 13 • Practice, p. 14 • Word Problem Practice, p. 15
Transparencies	• 5-Minute Check Transparency 14-2	• 5-Minute Check Transparency 14-2	• 5-Minute Check Transparency 14-2	• 5-Minute Check Transparency 14-2
Other	• Study Notebook	• Study Notebook	• Study Notebook	• Study Notebook

When you verify a trigonometric identity, you are really working backward. In Example 1, consider the last step $1 + \cos\theta = 1 + \cos\theta$. Since that step is clearly true, you can conclude that the next-to-last step is also true, and so on, all the way back to the original equation.

Watch Out!

Simplify Separately Verifying an identity is like checking the solution of an equation. You must simplify one or both sides separately until they are the same.

NGSSS PRACTICE EXAMPLE 2 — 912.T.3.2

$\dfrac{\cos\theta \csc\theta}{\tan\theta} =$

A. $\cot\theta$ **B.** $\csc\theta$ **C.** $\cot^2\theta$ **D.** $\csc^2\theta$

Read the Test Item

Find an expression that is always equal to the given expression. Notice that all of the answer choices involve either $\cot\theta$ or $\csc\theta$. So work toward eliminating the other trigonometric functions.

Solve the Test Item

Transform the given expression to match one of the choices.

$$\frac{\cos\theta\csc\theta}{\tan\theta} = \frac{\cos\theta\frac{1}{\sin\theta}}{\frac{\sin\theta}{\cos\theta}} \qquad \csc\theta = \frac{1}{\sin\theta} \text{ and } \tan\theta = \frac{\sin\theta}{\cos\theta}$$

$$= \frac{\frac{\cos\theta}{\sin\theta}}{\frac{\sin\theta}{\cos\theta}} \qquad \text{Multiply.}$$

$$= \frac{\cos\theta}{\sin\theta}\cdot\frac{\cos\theta}{\sin\theta} \qquad \text{Invert the denominator and multiply.}$$

$$= \cot\theta\cdot\cot\theta \qquad \cot\theta = \frac{\cos\theta}{\sin\theta}$$

$$= \cot^2\theta \qquad \text{Multiply.}$$

The answer is C.

Test-TakingTip

Checking Answers Verify your answer by choosing values for θ. Then evaluate the original expression and compare to your answer choice.

Guided Practice

2. $\tan^2\theta(\cot^2\theta - \cos^2\theta) =$ H

F. $\cot^2\theta$ **G.** $\tan^2\theta$ **H.** $\cos^2\theta$ **I.** $\sin^2\theta$

Personal Tutor glencoe.com

Transform Each Side of an Equation Sometimes it is easier to transform each side of an equation separately into a common form. The following suggestions may be helpful as you verify trigonometric identities.

Key Concept — **Suggestions for Verifying Identities**

- Substitute one or more basic trigonometric identities to simplify the expression.
- Factor or multiply as necessary. You may have to multiply both the numerator and denominator by the same trigonometric expression.
- Write each side of the identity in terms of sine and cosine only. Then simplify each side as much as possible.
- The properties of equality do not apply to identities as with equations. Do not perform operations to the quantities from each side of an unverified identity.

Transform One Side of an Equation

Example 1 shows how to verify a trigonometric identity by transforming one side of an equation. **Example 2** shows how to find an expression equivalent to a given trigonometric expression.

Formative Assessment

Use the Guided Practice exercises after each example to determine students' understanding of concepts.

Additional Examples

1 Verify that $\csc\theta\cos\theta\tan\theta = 1$ is an identity.

$$\csc\theta\cos\theta\tan\theta \stackrel{?}{=} 1$$
$$\frac{1}{\sin\theta}\cdot\cos\theta\cdot\frac{\sin\theta}{\cos\theta} \stackrel{?}{=} 1$$
$$1 = 1 \ \checkmark$$

2 **STANDARDIZED TEST PRACTICE**

$\dfrac{\csc\theta}{\cos\theta} - \tan\theta =$ A

A $\cot\theta$ **C** 0

B $\dfrac{1-\sin\theta}{\cos^2\theta}$ **D** $\cos^2\theta$

Additional Examples also in Interactive Classroom PowerPoint® Presentations

IWB INTERACTIVE WHITEBOARD READY

Additional Answer (Guided Practice)

1. $\cot^2\theta - \cos^2\theta \stackrel{?}{=} \cot^2\theta\cos^2\theta$

$$\frac{\cos^2\theta}{\sin^2\theta} - \cos^2\theta \stackrel{?}{=} \cot^2\theta\cos^2\theta$$
$$\cos^2\theta\left(\frac{1}{\sin^2\theta} - 1\right) \stackrel{?}{=} \cot^2\theta\cos^2\theta$$
$$\cos^2\theta(\csc^2\theta - 1) \stackrel{?}{=} \cot^2\theta\cos^2\theta$$
$$\cot^2\theta\cos^2\theta = \cot^2\theta\cos^2\theta \ \checkmark$$

Differentiated Instruction

AL OL BL ELL

Interpersonal Learners Have groups or pairs of students work together to verify some of the identities in Exercises 8–17. Have students record the techniques they found helpful. Ask students to compare their list of techniques to the list of suggestions given at the bottom of p. 899. Also have them discuss failed strategies. What did and did not work, and why?

Lesson 14-2 Verifying Trigonometric Identities 899

EXAMPLE 3 Verify by Transforming Each Side

Verify that $1 - \tan^4 \theta = 2\sec^2 \theta - \sec^4 \theta$ is an identity.

$1 - \tan^4 \theta \stackrel{?}{=} 2\sec^2 \theta - \sec^4 \theta$	Original equation
$(1 - \tan^2 \theta)(1 + \tan^2 \theta) \stackrel{?}{=} \sec^2 \theta\,(2 - \sec^2 \theta)$	Factor each side.
$[1 - (\sec^2 \theta - 1)]\sec^2 \theta \stackrel{?}{=} (2 - \sec^2 \theta)\sec^2 \theta$	$1 + \tan^2 \theta = \sec^2 \theta$
$(2 - \sec^2 \theta)\sec^2 \theta = (2 - \sec^2 \theta)\sec^2 \theta$ ✓	Simplify.

Guided Practice

3. Verify that $\csc^2 \theta - \cot^2 \theta = \cot \theta \tan \theta$ is an identity. See margin.

Personal Tutor glencoe.com

Check Your Understanding

Examples 1 and 3 pp. 898–900

Verify that each equation is an identity. 1–6. See Chapter 14 Answer Appendix.

1. $\cot \theta + \tan \theta = \dfrac{\sec^2 \theta}{\tan \theta}$

2. $\cos^2 \theta = (1 + \sin \theta)(1 - \sin \theta)$

3. $\sin \theta = \dfrac{\sec \theta}{\tan \theta + \cot \theta}$

4. $\tan^2 \theta = \dfrac{1 - \cos^2 \theta}{\cos^2 \theta}$

5. $\tan^2 \theta \csc^2 \theta = 1 + \tan^2 \theta$

6. $\tan^2 \theta = (\sec \theta + 1)(\sec \theta - 1)$

Example 2 p. 899

7 NGSSS **PRACTICE** Which expression can be used to form an identity with $\dfrac{\tan^2 \theta + 1}{\tan^2 \theta}$? D

A. $\sin^2 \theta$ **B.** $\cos^2 \theta$ **C.** $\tan^2 \theta$ **D.** $\csc^2 \theta$

Practice and Problem Solving

● = Step-by-Step Solutions begin on page R20. Extra Practice begins on page 947.

Example 1 p. 898

Verify that each equation is an identity. 8–17. See Chapter 14 Answer Appendix.

8. $\cos^2 \theta + \tan^2 \theta \cos^2 \theta = 1$

9. $\cot \theta(\cot \theta + \tan \theta) = \csc^2 \theta$

10. $1 + \sec^2 \theta \sin^2 \theta = \sec^2 \theta$

11. $\sin \theta \sec \theta \cot \theta = 1$

12. $\dfrac{1 - \cos \theta}{1 + \cos \theta} = (\csc \theta - \cot \theta)^2$

13. $\dfrac{1 - 2\cos^2 \theta}{\sin \theta \cos \theta} = \tan \theta - \cot \theta$

14. $\tan \theta = \dfrac{\sec \theta}{\csc \theta}$

15. $\cos \theta = \sin \theta \cot \theta$

16. $(\sin \theta - 1)(\tan \theta + \sec \theta) = -\cos \theta$

17. $\cos \theta \cos(-\theta) - \sin \theta \sin(-\theta) = 1$

Example 2 p. 899

18. LADDER Some students derived an expression for the length of a ladder that, when carried flat, could fit around a corner from a 5-foot-wide hallway into a 7-foot-wide hallway, as shown. They determined that the maximum length ℓ of a ladder that would fit was given by $\ell(\theta) = \dfrac{7\sin \theta + 5\cos \theta}{\sin \theta \cos \theta}$. When their teacher worked the problem, she concluded that $\ell(\theta) = 7\sec \theta + 5\csc \theta$. Are the two expressions equivalent? yes

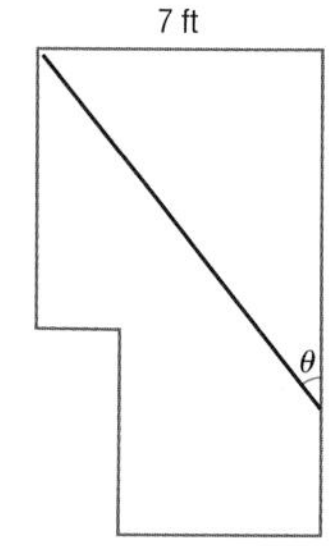

TEACH with TECH

INTERACTIVE WHITEBOARD Work through the examples on the whiteboard and save your work as notes pages. At the end of class, post your notes to a class Web page. This may help students to focus on the lesson rather than copying notes for each step of the proofs.

Transform Each Side of an Equation

Example 3 shows how to verify a trigonometric identity by transforming both sides of an equation.

Additional Example

3 Verify that $\csc \theta + \sec \theta = \dfrac{1 + \cot \theta}{\cos \theta}$ is an identity.

$$\csc \theta + \sec \theta \stackrel{?}{=} \frac{1 + \cot \theta}{\cos \theta}$$

$$\frac{1}{\sin \theta} + \frac{1}{\cos \theta} \stackrel{?}{=} \frac{1 + \frac{\cos \theta}{\sin \theta}}{\cos \theta}$$

$$\frac{\cos \theta + \sin \theta}{\sin \theta \cos \theta} \stackrel{?}{=} \frac{\sin \theta\left(1 + \frac{\cos \theta}{\sin \theta}\right)}{\sin \theta \cos \theta}$$

$$\frac{\cos \theta + \sin \theta}{\sin \theta \cos \theta} = \frac{\sin \theta + \cos \theta}{\sin \theta \cos \theta} \checkmark$$

3 PRACTICE

Formative Assessment

Use Exercises 1–7 to check for understanding.

Use the chart at the bottom of this page to customize assignments for your students.

Additional Answers (Guided Practice)

3. $\csc^2 \theta - \cot^2 \theta \stackrel{?}{=} \cot \theta \tan \theta$

$$\frac{1}{\sin^2 \theta} - \frac{\cos^2 \theta}{\sin^2 \theta} \stackrel{?}{=} \frac{\cos \theta}{\sin \theta} \cdot \frac{\sin \theta}{\cos \theta}$$

$$\frac{1 - \cos^2 \theta}{\sin^2 \theta} \stackrel{?}{=} 1$$

$$\frac{\sin^2 \theta}{\sin^2 \theta} \stackrel{?}{=} 1$$

$$1 = 1 \checkmark$$

Differentiated Homework Options

Level	Assignment	Two-Day Option	
AL Basic	8–32, 52, 54–57, 59–76	9–31 odd, 60–63	8–32 even, 52, 54–57, 59, 64–76
OL Core	9–31 odd, 33–34, 35–49 odd, 50–52, 54–57, 59–76	8–32, 60–63	33–52, 54–57, 59, 64–76
BL Advanced	33–72, (optional: 73–76)		

Example 3 p. 900

19–32. See Chapter 14 Answer Appendix.

Verify that each equation is an identity.

19. $\sec\theta - \tan\theta = \frac{1-\sin\theta}{\cos\theta}$

20. $\frac{1+\tan\theta}{\sin\theta+\cos\theta} = \sec\theta$

21. $\sec\theta\csc\theta = \tan\theta + \cot\theta$

22. $\sin\theta + \cos\theta = \frac{2\sin^2\theta - 1}{\sin\theta - \cos\theta}$

23. $(\sin\theta + \cos\theta)^2 = \frac{2+\sec\theta\csc\theta}{\sec\theta\csc\theta}$

24. $\frac{\cos\theta}{1-\sin\theta} = \frac{1+\sin\theta}{\cos\theta}$

25. $\csc\theta - 1 = \frac{\cot^2\theta}{\csc\theta+1}$

26. $\cos\theta\cot\theta = \csc\theta - \sin\theta$

27. $\sin\theta\cos\theta\tan\theta + \cos^2\theta = 1$

28. $(\csc\theta - \cot\theta)^2 = \frac{1-\cos\theta}{1+\cos\theta}$

29. $\csc^2\theta = \cot^2\theta + \sin\theta\csc\theta$

30. $\frac{\sec\theta - \csc\theta}{\csc\theta\sec\theta} = \sin\theta - \cos\theta$

31. $\sin^2\theta + \cos^2\theta = \sec^2\theta - \tan^2\theta$

32. $\sec\theta - \cos\theta = \tan\theta\sin\theta$

B

33. TETHERBALL The diagram at the right represents a game of tetherball. As the ball rotates around the pole, a conical surface is swept out by line segment $\overline{SP}$. A formula for the relationship between the length L of the string and the angle θ that the string makes with the pole is given by the equation $L = \frac{g\sec\theta}{\omega^2}$. Is $L = \frac{g\tan\theta}{\omega^2\sin\theta}$ also an equation for the relationship between L and θ? **yes**

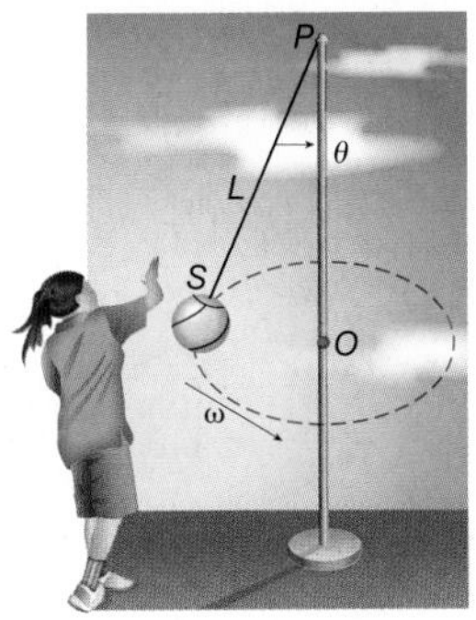

34. RUNNING A portion of a racetrack has the shape of a circular arc with a radius of 16.7 meters. As a runner races along the arc, the sine of her angle of incline θ is found to be $\frac{1}{4}$. Find the speed of the runner. Use the Angle of Incline Formula given at the beginning of the lesson, $\tan\theta = \frac{v^2}{gR}$, where $g = 9.8$ and R is the radius. (*Hint*: Find $\cos\theta$ first.) **6.5 m/s**

Real-World Link

Running games were organized in ancient Egypt as early as 3800 B.C. The first marathon race, which was 24 miles long, was held during the 1896 Olympic Games in Athens, Greece.

When simplified, would the expression be equal to 1 or −1?

35. $\cot(-\theta)\tan(-\theta)$ **1**

36. $\sin\theta\csc(-\theta)$ **−1**

37. $\sin^2(-\theta) + \cos^2(-\theta)$ **1**

38. $\sec(-\theta)\cos(-\theta)$ **1**

39. $\sec^2(-\theta) - \tan^2(-\theta)$ **1**

40. $\cot(-\theta)\cot\left(\frac{\pi}{2} - \theta\right)$ **−1**

Simplify the expression to either a constant or a basic trigonometric function.

41. $\frac{\tan\left(\frac{\pi}{2}-\theta\right)\csc\theta}{\csc^2\theta}$ **$\cos\theta$**

42. $\frac{1+\tan\theta}{1+\cot\theta}$ **$\tan\theta$**

43. $(\sec^2\theta + \csc^2\theta) - (\tan^2\theta + \cot^2\theta)$ **2**

44. $\frac{\sec^2\theta - \tan^2\theta}{\cos^2 x + \sin^2 x}$ **1**

45. $\tan\theta\cos\theta$ **$\sin\theta$**

46. $\cot\theta\tan\theta$ **1**

47. $\sec\theta\sin\left(\frac{\pi}{2}-\theta\right)$ **1**

48. $\frac{1+\tan^2\theta}{\csc^2\theta}$ **$\tan^2\theta$**

49. $y = -\frac{gx^2}{2v_0^2}(1 + \tan^2\theta) + x\tan\theta$

49. PHYSICS When a firework is fired from the ground, its height y and horizontal displacement x are related by the equation $y = \frac{-gx^2}{2v_0^2\cos^2\theta} + \frac{x\sin\theta}{\cos\theta}$, where v_0 is the initial velocity of the projectile, θ is the angle at which it was fired, and g is the acceleration due to gravity. Rewrite this equation so that $\tan\theta$ is the only trigonometric function that appears in the equation.

Focus on Mathematical Content

Transform One or Two Sides An identity can be verified by transforming one or both sides of an equation at the same time. Some students may prefer to work on only one side at a time to avoid confusion.

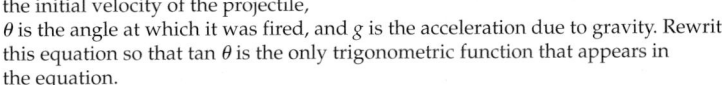

Lesson 14-2 Verifying Trigonometric Identities 901

Study Guide and Intervention
CRM p. 11–12 AL OL ELL

14-2 Study Guide and Intervention
Verifying Trigonometric Identities

Transform One Side of an Equation Use the basic trigonometric identities along with the definitions of the trigonometric functions to verify trigonometric identities. Often it is easier to begin with the more complicated side of the equation and transform that expression into the form of the simpler side.

Example Verify that each equation is an identity.

a. $\frac{\sin\theta}{\cot\theta} - \sec\theta = -\cos\theta$

Transform the left side.

$\frac{\sin\theta}{\cot\theta} - \sec\theta \stackrel{?}{=} -\cos\theta$

$\frac{\sin\theta}{\frac{\cos\theta}{\sin\theta}} - \frac{1}{\cos\theta} \stackrel{?}{=} -\cos\theta$

$\frac{\sin^2\theta}{\cos\theta} - \frac{1}{\cos\theta} \stackrel{?}{=} -\cos\theta$

$\frac{\sin^2 - 1}{\cos\theta} \stackrel{?}{=} -\cos\theta$

$\frac{-\cos^2\theta}{\cos\theta} \stackrel{?}{=} -\cos\theta$

$-\cos\theta = -\cos\theta$

b. $\frac{\tan\theta}{\csc\theta} + \cos\theta = \sec\theta$

Transform the left side.

$\frac{\tan\theta}{\csc\theta} + \cos\theta \stackrel{?}{=} \sec\theta$

$\frac{\frac{\sin\theta}{\cos\theta}}{\frac{1}{\sin\theta}} + \cos\theta \stackrel{?}{=} \sec\theta$

$\frac{\sin^2\theta}{\cos\theta} + \cos\theta \stackrel{?}{=} \sec\theta$

$\frac{\sin^2\theta + \cos^2\theta}{\cos\theta} \stackrel{?}{=} \sec\theta$

$\frac{1}{\cos\theta} \stackrel{?}{=} \sec\theta$

$\sec\theta = \sec\theta$

Exercises

Verify that each equation is an identity.

1. $1 + \csc^2\theta \cdot \cos^2\theta = \csc^2\theta$

$1 + \frac{1}{\sin^2\theta} \cdot \cos^2\theta \stackrel{?}{=} \csc^2\theta$

$\frac{\sin^2\theta + \cos^2\theta}{\sin^2\theta} \stackrel{?}{=} \csc^2\theta$

$\frac{1}{\sin^2\theta} \stackrel{?}{=} \csc^2\theta$

$\csc^2\theta = \csc^2\theta$

2. $\frac{\sin\theta}{1 - \cos\theta} - \frac{\cot\theta}{1 + \cos\theta} = \frac{1 - \cos^3\theta}{\sin^3\theta}$

$\frac{\sin\theta(1 + \cos\theta) - \frac{\cos\theta}{\sin\theta}(1 - \cos\theta)}{(1 - \cos\theta)(1 + \cos\theta)} \stackrel{?}{=} \frac{1 - \cos^3\theta}{\sin^3\theta}$

$\frac{\sin\theta + \sin\theta \cdot \cos\theta - \frac{\cos\theta}{\sin\theta} + \frac{\cos^2\theta}{\sin\theta}}{1 - \cos^2\theta} \stackrel{?}{=} \frac{1 - \cos^3\theta}{\sin^3\theta}$

$\frac{\frac{\sin^2\theta + \sin^2\theta\cos\theta - \cos\theta + \cos^2\theta}{\sin\theta}}{\sin^2\theta} \stackrel{?}{=} \frac{1 - \cos^3\theta}{\sin^3\theta}$

$\frac{\sin^2\theta + \cos^2\theta + \cos\theta(\sin^2\theta - 1)}{\sin^3\theta} \stackrel{?}{=} \frac{1 - \cos^3\theta}{\sin^3\theta}$

$\frac{1 + \cos\theta(-\cos^2\theta)}{\sin^3\theta} \stackrel{?}{=} \frac{1 - \cos^3\theta}{\sin^3\theta}$

$\frac{1 - \cos^3\theta}{\sin^3\theta} = \frac{1 - \cos^3\theta}{\sin^3\theta}$

Lesson 14-2

Practice
CRM p. 14 AL OL BL ELL

14-2 Practice
Verifying Trigonometric Identities

Verify that each equation is an identity.

1. $\frac{\sin^2\theta + \cos^2\theta}{\cos^2\theta} = \sec^2\theta$

$\frac{\sin^2\theta + \cos^2\theta}{\cos^2\theta} \stackrel{?}{=} \sec^2\theta$

$\frac{1}{\cos^2\theta} \stackrel{?}{=} \sec^2\theta$

$\sec^2\theta = \sec^2\theta$

2. $\frac{\cos^2\theta}{1 - \sin^2\theta} = 1$

$\frac{\cos^2\theta}{1 - \sin^2\theta} \stackrel{?}{=} 1$

$\frac{\cos^2\theta}{\cos^2\theta} \stackrel{?}{=} 1$

$1 = 1$

3. $(1 + \sin\theta)(1 - \sin\theta) = \cos^2\theta$

$(1 + \sin\theta)(1 - \sin\theta) \stackrel{?}{=} \cos^2\theta$

$1 - \sin^2\theta \stackrel{?}{=} \cos^2\theta$

$\cos^2\theta = \cos^2\theta$

4. $\tan^4\theta + 2\tan^2\theta + 1 = \sec^4\theta$

$\tan^4\theta + 2\tan^2\theta + 1 \stackrel{?}{=} \sec^4\theta$

$(\tan^2\theta + 1)^2 \stackrel{?}{=} \sec^4\theta$

$(\sec^2\theta)^2 \stackrel{?}{=} \sec^4\theta$

$\sec^4\theta = \sec^4\theta$

5. $\cos^2\theta\cot^2\theta = \cot^2\theta - \cos^2\theta$

$\cos^2\theta\cot^2\theta \stackrel{?}{=} \cot^2\theta - \cos^2\theta$

$\cos^2\theta\cot^2\theta \stackrel{?}{=} \frac{\cos^2\theta}{\sin^2\theta} - \cos^2\theta$

$\cos^2\theta\cot^2\theta \stackrel{?}{=} \frac{\cos^2\theta - \cos^2\theta\sin^2\theta}{\sin^2\theta}$

$\cos^2\theta\cot^2\theta \stackrel{?}{=} \frac{(\cos^2\theta)(1 - \sin^2\theta)}{\sin^2\theta}$

$\cos^2\theta\cot^2\theta \stackrel{?}{=} \frac{\cos^2\theta}{1} \cdot \frac{\cos^2\theta}{\sin^2\theta}$

$\cos^2\theta\cot^2\theta = \cos^2\theta\cot^2\theta$

6. $(\sin^2\theta)(\csc^2\theta + \sec^2\theta) = \sec^2\theta$

$(\sin^2\theta)(\csc^2\theta + \sec^2\theta) \stackrel{?}{=} \sec^2\theta$

$(\sin^2\theta)\left(\frac{1}{\sin^2\theta} + \frac{1}{\cos^2\theta}\right) \stackrel{?}{=} \sec^2\theta$

$\frac{1 + \sin^2\theta}{\cos^2\theta} \stackrel{?}{=} \sec^2\theta$

$1 + \tan^2\theta \stackrel{?}{=} \sec^2\theta$

$\sec^2\theta = \sec^2\theta$

7. **PROJECTILES** The square of the initial velocity of an object launched from the ground is $v^2 = \frac{2gh}{\sin^2\theta}$, where θ is the angle between the ground and the initial path, h is the maximum height reached, and g is the acceleration due to gravity. Verify the identity $\frac{2gh}{\sin^2\theta} = \frac{2gh\sec^2\theta}{\sec^2\theta - 1}$.

$\frac{2gh}{\sin^2\theta} = \frac{2gh}{1 - \cos^2\theta} = \frac{2gh}{1 - \frac{1}{\sec^2\theta}} = \frac{2gh}{\frac{\sec^2\theta - 1}{\sec^2\theta}} = \frac{2gh\sec^2\theta}{\sec^2\theta - 1}$

8. **LIGHT** The intensity of a light source measured in candles is given by $I = ER^2\sec\theta$, where E is the illuminance in foot candles on a surface, R is the distance in feet from the light source, and θ is the angle between the light beam and a line perpendicular to the surface. Verify the identity $ER^2(1 + \tan^2\theta)\cos\theta = ER^2\sec\theta$.

$ER^2(1 + \tan^2\theta)\cos\theta = ER^2\sec^2\theta\cos\theta = ER^2\sec^2\theta \cdot \frac{1}{\sec\theta} = ER^2\sec\theta$

Word Problem Practice
CRM p. 15 AL OL BL ELL

14-2 Word Problem Practice
Verifying Trigonometric Identities

1. **EXPERIMENTS** Kyle is performing an experiment for his physics class. He uses a motion detector connected to a computer to collect data. The first time he performs the experiment, the computer produces the graph below. The graph is of the function $y = \frac{\cos^2 x}{1 - \sin x}$.

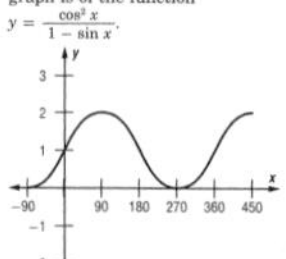

The second time he performs the experiment, the computer produces the graph below. The graph is of the $y = \sin x$.

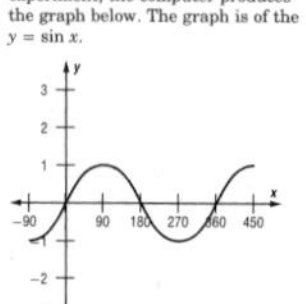

Use the graphs to write an identity involving $\frac{\cos^2 x}{1 - \sin x}$ and $\sin x$.

$\frac{\cos^2 x}{1 - \sin x} = 1 + \sin x$

or $\frac{\cos^2 x}{1 - \sin x} - 1 = \sin x$

2. **GRAPHING FUNCTIONS** Brandi is doing her trigonometry homework and needs to graph the function $y = \frac{\sin^2 x - \tan^2 x}{\sec^2 x}$. She thinks that it would be easier to graph the function if she could rewrite it in a simpler way, either without a denominator or as an expression containing only one trigonometric function. After some work, Brandi decides that she can graph $y = -\sin^4 x$ instead of the given function.

a. Is it possible for Brandi to simplify the function in the way she claims?

yes

b. If Brandi graphs the given function and her simpler function on the same set of axes, what will she find?

She will see only one graph.

c. What does this mean about $\frac{\sin^2 x - \tan^2 x}{\sec^2 x}$ and $-\sin^4 x$?

The expressions are equal, meaning that $\frac{\sin^2 x - \tan^2 x}{\sec^2 x} = -\sin^4 x$ is an identity.

Lesson 14-2

Real-World Career

Electrician
An electrician specializes in the wiring of electrical components. Electricians serve an apprenticeship lasting 3–5 years. Schooling in electrical theory and building codes is required. Certification requires work experience and a passing score on a written test.

50. **ELECTRONICS** When an alternating current of frequency f and peak current I_0 passes through a resistance R, then the power delivered to the resistance at time t seconds is $P = I_0^2 R\sin^2 2\pi ft$.

a. Write an expression for the power in terms of $\cos^2 2\pi$ ft. $P = I_0^2 R(1 - \cos^2 2\pi ft)$

b. Write an expression for the power in terms of $\csc^2 2\pi$ ft. $P = \frac{I_0^2 R}{\csc^2 2\pi ft}$

51. **THROWING A BALL** In this problem, you will investigate the path of a ball represented by the equation $h = \frac{v_0^2\sin^2\theta}{2g}$, where θ is the measure of the angle between the ground and the path of the ball, v_0 is its initial velocity in meters per second, and g is the acceleration due to gravity. The value of g is 9.8 m/s².

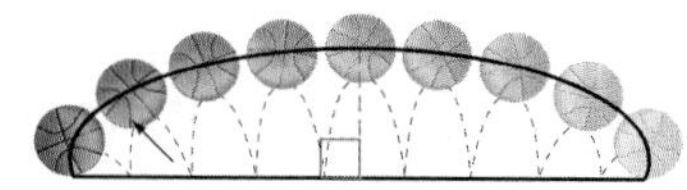

a. If the initial velocity of the ball is 47 meters per second, find the height of the ball at 30°, 45°, 60°, and 90°. Round to the nearest tenth. **See Chapter 14 Answer Appendix.**

b. Graph the equation on a graphing calculator. **See Chapter 14 Answer Appendix.**

c. Show that the formula $h = \frac{v_0^2\tan^2\theta}{2g\sec^2\theta}$ is equivalent to the one given above. **See Chapter 14 Answer Appendix.**

H.O.T. Problems Use Higher-Order Thinking Skills

52. **WHICH ONE DOESN'T BELONG?** Identify the equation that does not belong with the other three. Explain your reasoning.

$\sin^2\theta + \cos^2\theta = 1$	$1 + \cot^2\theta = \csc^2\theta$
$\sin^2\theta - \cos^2\theta = 2\sin^2\theta$	$\tan^2\theta + 1 = \sec^2\theta$

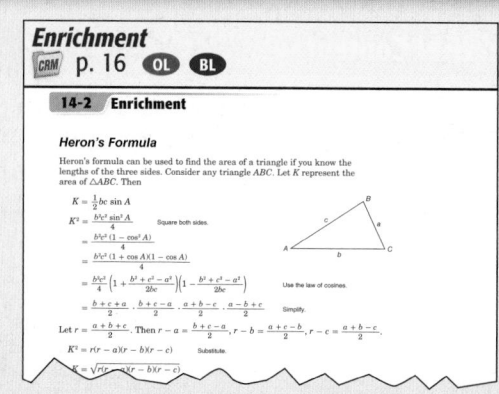

52. $\sin^2\theta - \cos^2\theta = 2\sin^2\theta$**; the other three are Pythagorean identities, but this is not.**

53. **CHALLENGE** Transform the right side of $\tan^2\theta = \frac{\sin^2\theta}{\cos^2\theta}$ to show that $\tan^2\theta = \sec^2\theta - 1$.

53. $\tan^2\theta = \frac{\sin^2\theta}{\cos^2\theta}$

$\tan^2\theta = \tan^2\theta$

$\tan^2\theta = \sec^2\theta - 1$

54. **WRITING IN MATH** Explain why you cannot square each side of an equation when verifying a trigonometric identity.

54. The properties of equality do not apply to identities as they do with equations. Do not perform operations to the quantities from each side of an unverified identity.

55. **REASONING** Explain why $\sin^2\theta + \cos^2\theta = 1$ is an identity, but $\sin\theta = \sqrt{1 - \cos\theta}$ is not. **Sample answer: counterexample 45°, 30°**

56. **WRITE A QUESTION** A classmate is having trouble trying to verify a trigonometric identity involving multiple trigonometric functions to multiple degrees. Write a question to help her work through the problem. **Sample answer: Have you tried using the most common identity, $\sin^2\sigma + \cos^2\sigma = 1$, to simplify?**

57. **WRITING IN MATH** Write about why you think terms of a trigonometric identity are often rewritten in terms of sine and cosine. **Sample answer: They are the trigonometric functions with which most people are familiar.**

58. **CHALLENGE** Let $x = \frac{1}{2}\tan\theta$, where $-\frac{\pi}{2} < \theta < \frac{\pi}{2}$. Write $f(x) = \frac{x}{\sqrt{1 + 4x^2}}$ in terms of a single trigonometric function of θ. $f(\theta) = \frac{1}{2}\sin\theta$

59. **REASONING** Justify the three basic Pythagorean identities. **See Chapter 14 Answer Appendix.**

Enrichment
CRM p. 16 OL BL

14-2 Enrichment

Heron's Formula

Heron's formula can be used to find the area of a triangle if you know the lengths of the three sides. Consider any triangle ABC. Let K represent the area of $\triangle ABC$. Then

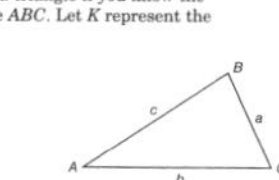

$K = \frac{1}{2}bc\sin A$

$K^2 = \frac{b^2c^2\sin^2 A}{4}$ Square both sides.

$= \frac{b^2c^2(1 - \cos^2 A)}{4}$

$= \frac{b^2c^2(1 + \cos A)(1 - \cos A)}{4}$

$= \frac{b^2c^2}{4}\left(1 + \frac{b^2 + c^2 - a^2}{2bc}\right)\left(1 - \frac{b^2 + c^2 - a^2}{2bc}\right)$ Use the law of cosines.

$= \frac{b + c + a}{2} \cdot \frac{b + c - a}{2} \cdot \frac{a + b - c}{2} \cdot \frac{a - b + c}{2}$ Simplify.

Let $r = \frac{a + b + c}{2}$. Then $r - a = \frac{b + c - a}{2}$, $r - b = \frac{a + c - b}{2}$, $r - c = \frac{a + b - c}{2}$.

$K^2 = r(r - a)(r - b)(r - c)$ Substitute.

$K = \sqrt{r(r - a)(r - b)(r - c)}$

NGSSS PRACTICE 912.S.3.3, 912.A.9.1, 912.A.3.14, 912.A.6.3

60. ACT/SAT A small business owner must hire seasonal workers as the need arises. The following list shows the number of employees hired monthly for a 5-month period.

5, 14, 6, 8, 12

If the mean of these data is 9, what is the population standard deviation for these data? (Round your answer to the nearest tenth.) **A**

A. 3.5
B. 5.7
C. 8.6
D. 12.3

61. Find the center and radius of the circle with equation $(x-4)^2 + y^2 - 16 = 0$. **H**

F. $C(-4, 0)$; $r = 4$ units
G. $C(-4, 0)$; $r = 16$ units
H. $C(4, 0)$; $r = 4$ units
I. $C(4, 0)$; $r = 16$ units

62. GEOMETRY The perimeter of a right triangle is 36 inches. Twice the length of the longer leg minus twice the length of the shorter leg is 6 inches. What are the lengths of all three sides? **C**

A. 3 in., 4 in., 5 in.
B. 6 in., 8 in., 10 in.
C. 9 in., 12 in., 15 in.
D. 12 in., 16 in., 20 in.

63. Simplify $128^{\frac{1}{4}}$. **G**

F. $2\sqrt[4]{2}$
G. $2\sqrt[4]{8}$
H. 4
I. $4\sqrt[4]{2}$

Spiral Review

Find the exact value of each expression. (Lesson 14-1)

64. $\tan\theta$, if $\cot\theta = 2$; $0° \le \theta < 90°$ $\frac{1}{2}$

65. $\sin\theta$, if $\cos\theta = \frac{2}{3}$; $0° \le \theta < 90°$ $\frac{\sqrt{5}}{3}$

66. $\csc\theta$, if $\cos\theta = -\frac{3}{5}$; $90° < \theta < 180°$ $\frac{5}{4}$

67. $\cos\theta$, if $\sec\theta = \frac{5}{3}$; $270° < \theta < 360°$ $\frac{3}{5}$

68. ARCHITECTURE The support for a roof is shaped like two right triangles, as shown at the right. Find θ. (Lesson 13-9) **30°**

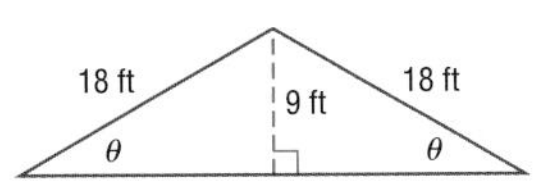

69. PROBABILITY An administrative assistant has 4 blue file folders, 3 red folders, and 3 yellow folders on her desk. Each folder contains different information, so two folders of the same color should be viewed as being different. She puts the file folders randomly in a box to take to a meeting. Find each probability. (Lesson 12-3)

a. P(4 blue, 3 red, 3 yellow, in that order) $\frac{1}{4200}$

b. P(first 2 blue, last 2 blue) $\frac{1}{210}$

Find the coordinates of the vertices and foci and the equations of the asymptotes for the hyperbolas with the given equations. Then graph the hyperbola. (Lesson 10-5) **70–72. See margin.**

70. $\frac{y^2}{18} - \frac{x^2}{20} = 1$

71. $\frac{(y+6)^2}{20} - \frac{(x-1)^2}{25} = 1$

72. $x^2 - 36y^2 = 36$

Skills Review

Simplify. (Lesson 7-5)

73. $\frac{2+\sqrt{2}}{5-\sqrt{2}}$ $\frac{12+7\sqrt{2}}{23}$

74. $\frac{x+1}{\sqrt{x^2-1}}$ $\frac{\sqrt{x^2-1}}{x-1}$

75. $\frac{x-1}{\sqrt{x}-1}$ $\sqrt{x}+1$

76. $\frac{-2-\sqrt{3}}{1+\sqrt{3}}$ $\frac{-1-\sqrt{3}}{2}$

Differentiated Instruction

BL

Extension $\sin x + \cos x = 1$ is not an identity, meaning that it is not true for all real values of x. Find the values of x for which the equation is true. $0° + k \cdot 360°$ or $90° + k \cdot 360°$, where k is any integer

4 ASSESS

Yesterday's News Have students write how learning basic trigonometric identities in Lesson 14-1 has helped them with verifying the more complex identities in today's lesson.

Formative Assessment

Check for student understanding of concepts in Lessons 14-1 and 14-2.

CRM Quiz 1, p. 37

Additional Answers

70. $(0, \pm3\sqrt{2})$; $(0, \pm\sqrt{38})$; $y = \pm\frac{3\sqrt{10}}{10}x$

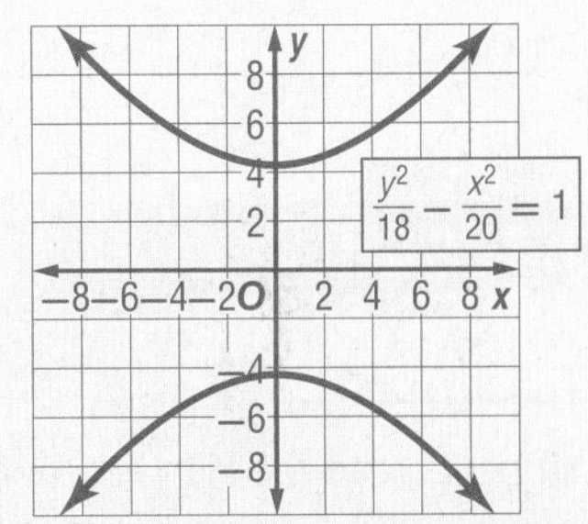

71. $(1, -6 \pm 2\sqrt{5})$; $(1, -6 \pm 3\sqrt{5})$; $y + 6 = \pm\frac{2\sqrt{5}}{5}(x-1)$

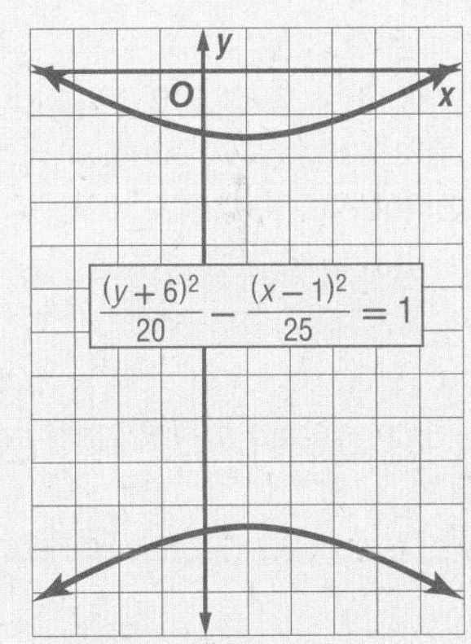

72. $(\pm6, 0)$; $(\pm\sqrt{37}, 0)$; $y = \pm\frac{1}{6}x$

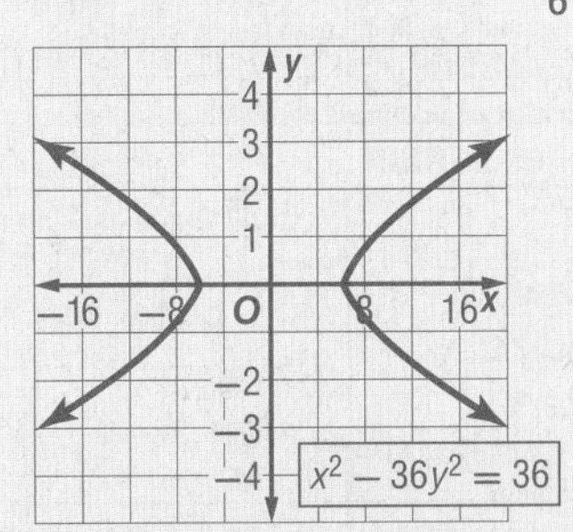

14-3 Lesson Notes

1 FOCUS

Vertical Alignment

Before Lesson 14-3
Find values of trigonometric functions for general angles.

Lesson 14-3
Find values of sine and cosine by using sum and difference identities.
Verify trigonometric identities by using sum and difference identities.

After Lesson 14-3
Use double-angle and half-angle identities.

2 TEACH

Scaffolding Questions

Have students read the *Why?* section of the lesson.

Ask:

- Where else have you heard the term *interference?* Sample answer: television and radio
- At its peak, how does the amplitude of the combined wave compare to the amplitude of the initial two waves? The amplitude of the combined wave is the sum of the amplitudes of the two initial waves.

(continued on the next page)

14-3 Sum and Difference of Angles Identities

Then
You found values of trigonometric functions for general angles. (Lesson 13-3)

Now
- Find values of sine and cosine by using sum and difference identities.
- Verify trigonometric identities by using sum and difference identities.

NGSSS
MA.912.T.3.2 Use basic trigonometric identities to verify other identities and simplify expressions.
MA.912.T.3.3 Use the sum and difference, half-angle and double-angle formulas for sine, cosine, and tangent, when formulas are provided.

FL Math Online
glencoe.com

Why?

Have you ever been using a wireless Internet provider and temporarily lost the signal? Waves that pass through the same place at the same time cause interference. Interference occurs when two waves combine to have a greater, or smaller, amplitude than either of the component waves.

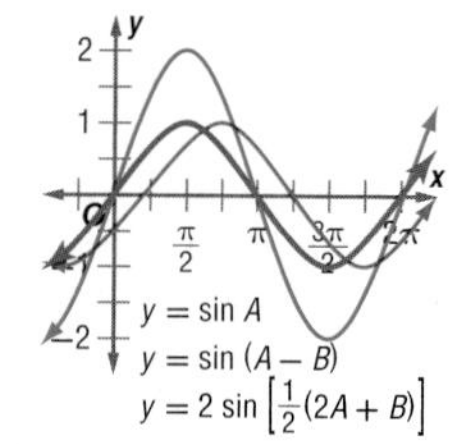

Sum and Difference Identities Notice that the third equation shown above involves the sum of A and B. It is often helpful to use formulas for the trigonometric values of the difference or sum of two angles. For example, you could find the exact value of sin 15° by evaluating sin (60° − 45°). Formulas exist that can be used to evaluate expressions like sin ($A - B$) or cos ($A + B$).

Key Concept

Sum Identities
- $\sin (A + B) = \sin A \cos B + \cos A \sin B$
- $\cos (A + B) = \cos A \cos B - \sin A \sin B$
- $\tan (A + B) = \dfrac{\tan A + \tan B}{1 - \tan A \tan B}$

Difference Identities
- $\sin (A - B) = \sin A \cos B - \cos A \sin B$
- $\cos (A - B) = \cos A \cos B + \sin A \sin B$
- $\tan (A - B) = \dfrac{\tan A - \tan B}{1 + \tan A \tan B}$

EXAMPLE 1 Find Trigonometric Values

Find the exact value of each expression.

a. sin 105°

Use the identity $\sin (A + B) = \sin A \cos B + \cos A \sin B$.

$\sin 105° = \sin (60° + 45°)$ — **$A = 60°$ and $B = 45°$**

$= \sin 60° \cos 45° + \cos 60° \sin 45°$ — **Sum identity**

$= \left(\frac{\sqrt{3}}{2} \cdot \frac{\sqrt{2}}{2}\right) + \left(\frac{1}{2} \cdot \frac{\sqrt{2}}{2}\right)$ — **Evaluate each expression.**

$= \frac{\sqrt{6}}{4} + \frac{\sqrt{2}}{4}$ or $\frac{\sqrt{6} + \sqrt{2}}{4}$ — **Multiply.**

b. cos (−120°)

Use the identity $\cos (A - B) = \cos A \cos B + \sin A \sin B$.

$\cos (-120) = \cos (60° - 180°)$ — **$A = 60°$ and $B = 180°$**

$= \cos 60° \cos 180° + \sin 60° \sin 180°$ — **Difference identity**

$= \frac{1}{2} \cdot (-1) + \frac{\sqrt{3}}{2} \cdot 0$ — **Evaluate each expression.**

$= -\frac{1}{2}$ — **Multiply.**

Guided Practice

1A. sin 15° $\frac{\sqrt{6} - \sqrt{2}}{4}$

1B. cos (−15°) $\frac{\sqrt{6} + \sqrt{2}}{4}$

Personal Tutor glencoe.com

Lesson 14-3 Resources

Resource	Approaching-Level	On-Level	Beyond-Level	English Learners
Teacher Edition		• Differentiated Instruction, pp. 905, 909	• Differentiated Instruction, pp. 905, 909	• Differentiated Instruction, p. 905
Chapter Resource Masters	• Study Guide and Intervention, pp. 17–18 • Skills Practice, p. 19 • Practice, p. 20 • Word Problem Practice, p. 21	• Study Guide and Intervention, pp. 17–18 • Skills Practice, p. 19 • Practice, p. 20 • Word Problem Practice, p. 21 • Enrichment, p. 22	• Practice, p. 20 • Word Problem Practice, p. 21 • Enrichment, p. 22	• Study Guide and Intervention, pp. 17–18 • Skills Practice, p. 19 • Practice, p. 20 • Word Problem Practice, p. 21
Transparencies	• 5-Minute Check Transparency 14-3	• 5-Minute Check Transparency 14-3	• 5-Minute Check Transparency 14-3	• 5-Minute Check Transparency 14-3
Other	• Study Notebook	• Study Notebook	• Study Notebook	• Study Notebook

You can use the sum and difference of angles identities to solve real-world applications.

Real-World EXAMPLE 2 Sum and Difference of Angles Identities

A geologist measures the angle between one side of a rectangular lot and the line from her position to the opposite corner of the lot as 30°. She then measures the angle between that line and the line to the point on the property where a river crosses as 45°. She stands 100 yards from the opposite corner of the property. How far is she from the point at which the river crosses the property line?

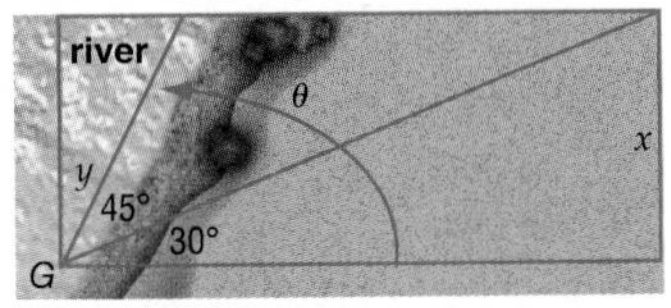

Understand The question asks for the distance between the geologist and the point where the river crosses the property line, or y.

Plan Draw a picture that labels all the things that you know from the information given.

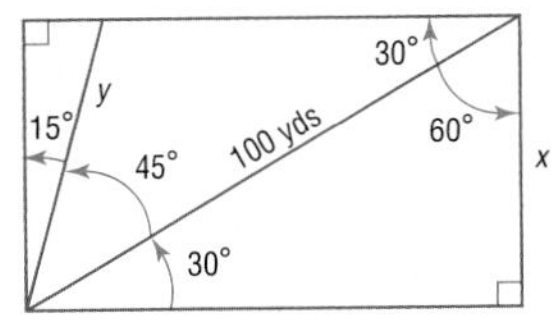

Solve Solve for x.

$\sin 30° = \frac{x}{100}$ **Definition of sine**

$x = 100 \sin 30°$

$x = 50$ **Since the lot is rectangular, opposite sides are equal.**

Now look at the triangle on the far left and solve for y.

$\cos 15° = \frac{50}{y}$ **Definition of cosine**

$\cos (45° - 30°) = \frac{50}{y}$ **15 = 45 − 30**

$\cos 45° \cos 30° + \sin 45° \sin 30° = \frac{50}{y}$ **Difference identity**

$\frac{\sqrt{2}}{2} \cdot \frac{\sqrt{3}}{2} + \frac{\sqrt{2}}{2} \cdot \frac{1}{2} = \frac{50}{y}$ **Evaluate.**

$\frac{\sqrt{6} + \sqrt{2}}{4} = \frac{50}{y}$ **Simplify.**

$(\sqrt{6} + \sqrt{2})y = 200$ **Cross products**

$$y = \frac{200}{(\sqrt{6} + \sqrt{2})} \cdot \frac{(\sqrt{6} - \sqrt{2})}{(\sqrt{6} - \sqrt{2})}$$

$$y = 50(\sqrt{6} - \sqrt{2})$$

$$y = 50\sqrt{6} - 50\sqrt{2} \text{ or about } 51.8$$

The geologist is about 51.8 yards from the point where the river crosses the property line.

Check Use a calculator to find the Arccos of $\frac{50}{51.8} \approx 15°$. ✓

Guided Practice

2. The harmonic motion of an object can be described by $x = 4 \cos \left(2\pi t - \frac{\pi}{4}\right)$, where x is distance from the equilibrium point in inches and t is time in minutes. Find the exact distance from the equilibrium point at 45 seconds. **$2\sqrt{2}$ inches below**

Personal Tutor glencoe.com

Problem-SolvingTip

Make a Model Make a model to visualize a problem situation. A model can be a drawing or a figure made of different objects, such as algebra tiles or folded paper.

ReadingMath

Greek Letters The Greek letter phi, ϕ, is used in Check Your Progress 2 to represent latitude.

- Why does the combined wave cross the x-axis at a point where neither of the two initial waves are crossing the axis? The combined wave is the sum of the other two waves. It crosses the x-axis at points where one of the initial waves is above the x-axis and the other wave is an equal distance below the x-axis.

Sum and Difference Identities

Example 1 shows how to use the sum and difference identities to find exact values of trigonometric expressions. **Example 2** shows how to use a difference identity to solve a real-world problem.

Formative Assessment

Use the Guided Practice exercises after each example to determine students' understanding of concepts.

Additional Examples

1 Find the exact value of each expression.

a. $\sin 75°$ $\frac{\sqrt{2} + \sqrt{6}}{4}$

b. $\cos (-75°)$ $\frac{\sqrt{6} - \sqrt{2}}{4}$

2 **DISTANCE** Refer to Example 2. If z represents the distance between the upper left corner of the property and the point where the river crosses the top boundary, then $\tan 15° = \frac{z}{50}$ or $\tan (45° - 30°) = \frac{z}{50}$. Use the identity for $\tan (A - B)$ to find an exact value for z.

$$z = \frac{50\left(1 - \frac{1}{\sqrt{3}}\right)}{1 + \frac{1}{\sqrt{3}}},$$

which can be simplified to $z = 100 - 50\sqrt{3}$.

Additional Examples also in Interactive Classroom PowerPoint® Presentations

IWB INTERACTIVE WHITEBOARD READY

Differentiated Instruction

OL BL ELL

Verbal/Linguistic Learners Ask students to identify patterns, similarities, and differences in the sum and difference identities. Then ask the students to write short sentences describing what they have identified.

Lesson 14-3 Sum and Difference of Angles Identities **905**

TEACH with TECH

DOCUMENT CAMERA Choose several students to work through examples and explain how to apply the sum and difference of angles formulas.

Verify Trigonometric Identities

Example 3 shows how to use the sum and difference identities to verify trigonometric identities.

Additional Example

3 Verify that each equation is an identity.

a. $\cos(360° - \theta) = \cos\theta$

$\cos(360° - \theta) \stackrel{?}{=} \cos\theta$

$\cos 360° \cos\theta + \sin 360° \sin\theta \stackrel{?}{=} \cos\theta$

$1 \cdot \cos\theta + 0 \cdot \sin\theta \stackrel{?}{=} \cos\theta$

$\cos\theta = \cos\theta$ ✓

b. $\cos(\pi - \theta) = -\cos\theta$

$\cos(\pi - \theta) \stackrel{?}{=} -\cos\theta$

$\cos\pi\cos\theta + \sin\pi\sin\theta \stackrel{?}{=} -\cos\theta$

$-1 \cdot \cos\theta + 0 \cdot \sin\theta \stackrel{?}{=} -\cos\theta$

$-\cos\theta = -\cos\theta$ ✓

3 PRACTICE

Formative Assessment

Use Exercises 1–11 to check for understanding.

Use the chart at the bottom of the next page to customize assignments for your students.

StudyTip

Make a List Make a list of the trigonometric values for the angles between 0° and 360° for which the sum and difference identities can be easily used. Use your list as a reference.

Verify Trigonometric Identities You can also use the sum and difference identities to verify identities.

EXAMPLE 3 Verify Trigonometric Identities

Verify that each equation is an identity.

a. $\cos(90° - \theta) = \sin\theta$

$\cos(90° - \theta) \stackrel{?}{=} \sin\theta$	Original equation
$\cos 90° \cos\theta + \sin 90° \sin\theta \stackrel{?}{=} \sin\theta$	Sum identity
$0 \cdot \cos\theta + 1 \cdot \sin\theta \stackrel{?}{=} \sin\theta$	Evaluate each expression.
$\sin\theta = \sin\theta$ ✓	Simplify.

b. $\sin\left(\theta + \frac{\pi}{2}\right) = \cos\theta$

$\sin\left(\theta + \frac{\pi}{2}\right) \stackrel{?}{=} \cos\theta$	Original equation
$\sin\theta\cos\frac{\pi}{2} + \cos\theta\sin\frac{\pi}{2} \stackrel{?}{=} \cos\theta$	Sum identity
$\sin\theta \cdot 0 + \cos\theta \cdot 1 \stackrel{?}{=} \cos\theta$	Evaluate each expression.
$\cos\theta = \cos\theta$ ✓	Simplify.

Guided Practice

Verify that each equation is an identity.

3A. $\sin(90° - \theta) = \cos\theta$ **3B.** $\cos(90° + \theta) = -\sin\theta$

3A. $\sin(90° - \theta) \stackrel{?}{=} \cos\theta$; $\sin 90° \cos\theta - \cos 90° \sin\theta \stackrel{?}{=} \cos\theta$; $1\cos\theta - 0\sin\theta \stackrel{?}{=} \cos\theta$; $\cos\theta = \cos\theta$

3B. $\cos(90° + \theta) \stackrel{?}{=} -\sin\theta$; $\cos 90° \cos\theta - \sin 90° \sin\theta \stackrel{?}{=} -\sin\theta$; $0\cos\theta - 1\sin\theta \stackrel{?}{=} -\sin\theta$; $-\sin\theta = -\sin\theta$

Personal Tutor glencoe.com

Check Your Understanding

Example 1 p. 904 Find the exact value of each expression.

1. $\cos 165°$ $-\frac{\sqrt{2}+\sqrt{6}}{4}$
2. $\cos 105°$ $\frac{\sqrt{2}-\sqrt{6}}{4}$
3. $\cos 75°$ $\frac{\sqrt{6}-\sqrt{2}}{4}$
4. $\sin(-30°)$ $-\frac{1}{2}$
5. $\sin 135°$ $\frac{\sqrt{2}}{2}$
6. $\sin(-210°)$ $\frac{1}{2}$

Example 2 p. 905

7. **ELECTRONICS** Refer to the beginning of the lesson. *Constructive interference* occurs when two waves combine to have a greater amplitude than either of the component waves. *Destructive interference* occurs when the component waves combine to have a smaller amplitude. The first signal can be modeled by the equation $y = 20\sin(3\theta + 45°)$. The second signal can be modeled by the equation $y = 20\sin(3\theta + 225°)$.
   a. Find the sum of the two functions. **0**
   b. What type of interference results when signals modeled by the two equations are combined? **The interference is destructive. The signals cancel each other completely.**

Example 3 p. 906 Verify that each equation is an identity. **8–11. See margin.**

8. $\sin(90° + \theta) = \cos\theta$
9. $\cos\left(\frac{3\pi}{2} - \theta\right) = -\sin\theta$
10. $\tan\left(\theta + \frac{\pi}{2}\right) = -\cot\theta$
11. $\sin(\theta + \pi) = -\sin\theta$

Additional Answers

8.

$\sin(90° + \theta) \stackrel{?}{=} \cos\theta$

$\sin 90° \cos\theta + \cos 90° \sin\theta \stackrel{?}{=} \cos\theta$

$1 \cdot \cos\theta + 0 \cdot \sin\theta \stackrel{?}{=} \cos\theta$

$\cos\theta = \cos\theta$ ✓

9.

$\cos\left(\frac{3\pi}{2} - \theta\right) \stackrel{?}{=} -\sin\theta$

$\cos\frac{3\pi}{2}\cos\theta + \sin\frac{3\pi}{2}\sin\theta \stackrel{?}{=} -\sin\theta$

$0 \cdot \cos\theta - 1 \cdot \sin\theta \stackrel{?}{=} -\sin\theta$

$-\sin\theta = -\sin\theta$ ✓

Practice and Problem Solving

● = **Step-by-Step Solutions** begin on page R20. **Extra Practice** begins on page 947.

Example 1 p. 904

Find the exact value of each expression.

12. $\sin 165°$ $\frac{\sqrt{6}-\sqrt{2}}{4}$ **13.** $\cos 135°$ $-\frac{\sqrt{2}}{2}$ **14.** $\cos \frac{7\pi}{12}$ $\frac{\sqrt{2}-\sqrt{6}}{4}$

15. $\sin \frac{\pi}{12}$ $\frac{\sqrt{6}-\sqrt{2}}{4}$ **16.** $\tan 195°$ $2-\sqrt{3}$ **17.** $\cos\left(-\frac{\pi}{12}\right)$ $\frac{\sqrt{2}+\sqrt{6}}{4}$

Example 2 p. 905

18. ELECTRONICS In a certain circuit carrying alternating current, the formula $c = 2 \sin (120t)$ can be used to find the current c in amperes after t seconds.

a. Rewrite the formula using the sum of two angles. **Sample answer: $c = 2 \sin (90t + 30t)$**

b. Use the sum of angles formula to find the exact current at $t = 1$ second. **$\sqrt{3}$ amperes**

Example 3 p. 906

Verify that each equation is an identity. **19–22. See margin.**

19. $\cos\left(\frac{\pi}{2}+\theta\right) = -\sin \theta$ **20.** $\cos (60° + \theta) = \sin (30° - \theta)$

21. $\cos (180° + \theta) = -\cos \theta$ **22.** $\tan (\theta + 45°) = \frac{1+\tan\theta}{1-\tan\theta}$

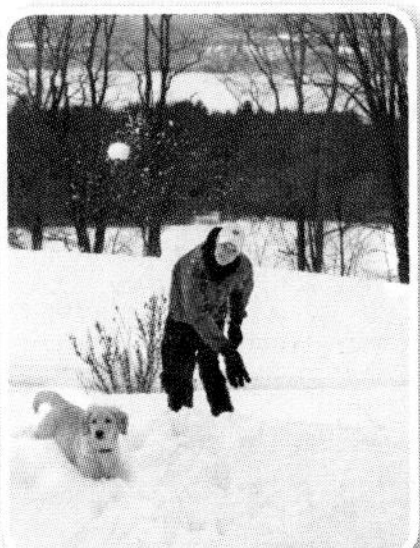

Real-World Link

The most snow that Minneapolis, Minnesota, received in one year was 101.5 inches in 1983. On average, Minneapolis receives 40 inches of snow per year.

Source: Minnesota Climatology

23b. The new function represents the average of the high and low temperatures for each month.

23. WEATHER The monthly high temperatures for Minneapolis, Minnesota, can be modeled by the equation $y = 31.65 \sin\left(\frac{\pi}{6}x - 2.09\right) + 52.35$, where the months x are represented by January = 1, February = 2, and so on. The monthly low temperatures for Minneapolis can be modeled by the equation $y = 30.15 \sin\left(\frac{\pi}{6}x - 2.09\right) + 32.95$.

a. Write a new function by adding the expressions on the right side of each equation and dividing the result by 2. **$y = 30.9 \sin\left(\frac{\pi}{6}x - 2.09\right) + 42.65$**

b. What is the meaning of the function you wrote in part **a**?

Find the exact value of each expression.

24. $\tan 165°$ $-2+\sqrt{3}$ **25.** $\sec 1275°$ $\sqrt{2}-\sqrt{6}$ **26.** $\sin 735°$ $\frac{\sqrt{6}-\sqrt{2}}{4}$

27. $\tan \frac{23\pi}{12}$ $-2+\sqrt{3}$ **28.** $\csc \frac{5\pi}{12}$ $\sqrt{6}-\sqrt{2}$ **29.** $\cot \frac{113\pi}{12}$ $2-\sqrt{3}$

30. FORCE In the figure at the right, the effort F necessary to hold a safe in position on a ramp is given by $F = \frac{W(\sin A + \mu \cos A)}{\cos A - \mu \sin A}$, where W is the weight of the safe and $\mu = \tan \theta$. Show that $F = W \tan (A + \theta)$. **See Chapter 14 Answer Appendix.**

31. QUILTING As part of a quilt that is being made, the quilter places two right triangular swatches together to make a new triangular piece. One swatch has sides 6 inches, 8 inches, and 10 inches long. The other swatch has sides 8 inches, $8\sqrt{3}$ inches, and 16 inches long. The pieces are placed with the sides of eight inches against each other, as shown in the figure, to form triangle ABC.

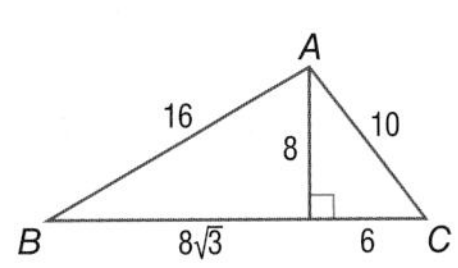

a. What is the exact value of the sine of angle BAC? $\frac{3+4\sqrt{3}}{10}$

b. What is the exact value of the cosine of angle BAC? $\frac{4-3\sqrt{3}}{10}$

c. What is the measure of angle BAC? **96.9°**

d. Is the new triangle formed from the two triangles also a right triangle? **no**

Additional Answers

10.
$$\tan\left(\theta+\frac{\pi}{2}\right) \stackrel{?}{=} -\cot\theta$$
$$\frac{\sin\left(\theta+\frac{\pi}{2}\right)}{\cos\left(\theta+\frac{\pi}{2}\right)} \stackrel{?}{=} -\cot\theta$$
$$\frac{\sin\theta\cos\frac{\pi}{2}+\cos\theta\sin\frac{\pi}{2}}{\cos\theta\cos\frac{\pi}{2}-\sin\theta\sin\frac{\pi}{2}} \stackrel{?}{=} -\cot\theta$$
$$\frac{(\sin\theta)\cdot 0+(\cos\theta)\cdot 1}{(\cos\theta)\cdot 0-(\sin\theta)\cdot 1} \stackrel{?}{=} -\cot\theta$$
$$-\frac{\cos\theta}{\sin\theta} \stackrel{?}{=} -\cot\theta$$
$$-\cot\theta = -\cot\theta\ \checkmark$$

11.
$$\sin(\theta+\pi) \stackrel{?}{=} -\sin\theta$$
$$\sin\theta\cos\pi+\cos\theta\sin\pi \stackrel{?}{=} -\sin\theta$$
$$(\sin\theta)(-1)+(\cos\theta)(0) \stackrel{?}{=} -\sin\theta$$
$$-\sin\theta = -\sin\theta\ \checkmark$$

19.
$$\cos\left(\frac{\pi}{2}+\theta\right) \stackrel{?}{=} -\sin\theta$$
$$\cos\frac{\pi}{2}\cos\theta-\sin\frac{\pi}{2}\sin\theta \stackrel{?}{=} -\sin\theta$$
$$(0)(\cos\theta)-(1)(\sin\theta) \stackrel{?}{=} -\sin\theta$$
$$-\sin\theta = -\sin\theta\ \checkmark$$

20.
$$\cos(60°+\theta) \stackrel{?}{=} \sin(30°-\theta)$$
$$\cos 60°\cos\theta-\sin 60°\sin\theta \stackrel{?}{=} \sin 30°\cos\theta-\cos 30°\sin\theta$$
$$\frac{1}{2}\cos\theta-\frac{\sqrt{3}}{2}\sin\theta = \frac{1}{2}\cos\theta-\frac{\sqrt{3}}{2}\sin\theta\ \checkmark$$

21.
$$\cos(180°+\theta) \stackrel{?}{=} -\cos\theta$$
$$\cos 180°\cos\theta-\sin 180°\sin\theta \stackrel{?}{=} -\cos\theta$$
$$-1\cdot\cos\theta-0\cdot\sin\theta \stackrel{?}{=} -\cos\theta$$
$$-\cos\theta = -\cos\theta\ \checkmark$$

22.
$$\tan(\theta+45°) \stackrel{?}{=} \frac{1+\tan\theta}{1-\tan\theta}$$
$$\frac{\tan\theta+\tan 45°}{1-\tan\theta\tan 45°} \stackrel{?}{=} \frac{1+\tan\theta}{1-\tan\theta}$$
$$\frac{\tan\theta+1}{1-(\tan\theta)(1)} \stackrel{?}{=} \frac{1+\tan\theta}{1-\tan\theta}$$
$$\frac{1+\tan\theta}{1-\tan\theta} = \frac{1+\tan\theta}{1-\tan\theta}\ \checkmark$$

Differentiated Homework Options

Level	Assignment	Two-Day Option	
AL Basic	12–22, 38–39, 41–57	13–21 odd, 43–46	12–22 even 38–39, 41–42, 47–57
OL Core	13–29 odd, 30–33, 35, 37–39, 41–57	12–22, 43–46	23–39, 41–42, 47–57
BL Advanced	23–54, (optional: 55–57)		

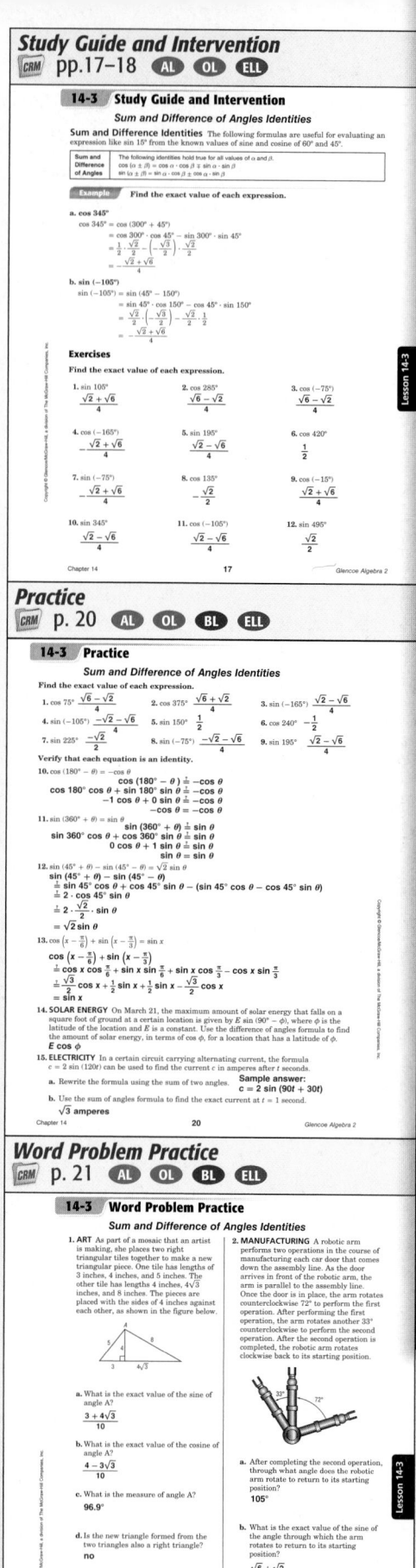

Study Guide and Intervention
CRM pp.17–18 AL OL ELL

14-3 Study Guide and Intervention

Sum and Difference of Angles Identities

Sum and Difference Identities The following formulas are useful for evaluating an expression like sin 15° from the known values of sine and cosine of 60° and 45°.

Sum and Difference of Angles	The following identities hold true for all values of α and β. $\cos(\alpha \pm \beta) = \cos\alpha \cdot \cos\beta \mp \sin\alpha \cdot \sin\beta$; $\sin(\alpha \pm \beta) = \sin\alpha \cdot \cos\beta \pm \cos\alpha \cdot \sin\beta$

Example Find the exact value of each expression.

a. cos 345°

$\cos 345° = \cos(300° + 45°)$
$= \cos 300° \cdot \cos 45° - \sin 300° \cdot \sin 45°$
$= \frac{1}{2} \cdot \frac{\sqrt{2}}{2} - \left(-\frac{\sqrt{3}}{2}\right) \cdot \frac{\sqrt{2}}{2}$
$= \frac{\sqrt{2} + \sqrt{6}}{4}$

b. sin (−105°)

$\sin(-105°) = \sin(45° - 150°)$
$= \sin 45° \cdot \cos 150° - \cos 45° \cdot \sin 150°$
$= \frac{\sqrt{2}}{2} \cdot \left(-\frac{\sqrt{3}}{2}\right) - \frac{\sqrt{2}}{2} \cdot \frac{1}{2}$
$= -\frac{\sqrt{2} + \sqrt{6}}{4}$

Exercises

Find the exact value of each expression.

1. sin 105° $\frac{\sqrt{2} + \sqrt{6}}{4}$
2. cos 285° $\frac{\sqrt{6} - \sqrt{2}}{4}$
3. cos (−75°) $\frac{\sqrt{6} - \sqrt{2}}{4}$
4. cos (−165°) $-\frac{\sqrt{2} + \sqrt{6}}{4}$
5. sin 195° $\frac{\sqrt{2} - \sqrt{6}}{4}$
6. cos 420° $\frac{1}{2}$
7. sin (−75°) $-\frac{\sqrt{2} + \sqrt{6}}{4}$
8. cos 135° $-\frac{\sqrt{2}}{2}$
9. cos (−15°) $\frac{\sqrt{2} + \sqrt{6}}{4}$
10. sin 345° $\frac{\sqrt{2} - \sqrt{6}}{4}$
11. cos (−105°) $\frac{\sqrt{2} - \sqrt{6}}{4}$
12. sin 495° $\frac{\sqrt{2}}{2}$

Chapter 14 17 Glencoe Algebra 2

Practice
CRM p. 20 AL OL BL ELL

14-3 Practice

Sum and Difference of Angles Identities

Find the exact value of each expression.

1. cos 75° $\frac{\sqrt{6} - \sqrt{2}}{4}$
2. cos 375° $\frac{\sqrt{6} + \sqrt{2}}{4}$
3. sin (−165°) $\frac{\sqrt{2} - \sqrt{6}}{4}$
4. sin (−105°) $\frac{-\sqrt{2} - \sqrt{6}}{4}$
5. sin 150° $\frac{1}{2}$
6. cos 240° $-\frac{1}{2}$
7. sin 225° $\frac{-\sqrt{2}}{2}$
8. sin (−75°) $\frac{-\sqrt{2} - \sqrt{6}}{4}$
9. sin 195° $\frac{\sqrt{2} - \sqrt{6}}{4}$

Verify that each equation is an identity.

10. $\cos(180° - \theta) = -\cos\theta$

$\cos(180° - \theta) \stackrel{?}{=} -\cos\theta$
$\cos 180° \cos\theta + \sin 180° \sin\theta \stackrel{?}{=} -\cos\theta$
$-1\cos\theta + 0\sin\theta \stackrel{?}{=} -\cos\theta$
$-\cos\theta = -\cos\theta$

11. $\sin(360° + \theta) = \sin\theta$

$\sin(360° + \theta) \stackrel{?}{=} \sin\theta$
$\sin 360° \cos\theta + \cos 360° \sin\theta \stackrel{?}{=} \sin\theta$
$0\cos\theta + 1\sin\theta \stackrel{?}{=} \sin\theta$
$\sin\theta = \sin\theta$

12. $\sin(45° + \theta) - \sin(45° - \theta) = \sqrt{2}\sin\theta$

$\sin(45° + \theta) - \sin(45° - \theta)$
$\stackrel{?}{=} \sin 45° \cos\theta + \cos 45° \sin\theta - (\sin 45° \cos\theta - \cos 45° \sin\theta)$
$\stackrel{?}{=} 2 \cdot \cos 45° \sin\theta$
$\stackrel{?}{=} 2 \cdot \frac{\sqrt{2}}{2} \cdot \sin\theta$
$= \sqrt{2}\sin\theta$

13. $\cos\left(x - \frac{\pi}{6}\right) + \sin\left(x - \frac{\pi}{3}\right) = \sin x$

$\cos\left(x - \frac{\pi}{6}\right) + \sin\left(x - \frac{\pi}{3}\right)$
$\stackrel{?}{=} \cos x \cos\frac{\pi}{6} + \sin x \sin\frac{\pi}{6} + \sin x \cos\frac{\pi}{3} - \cos x \sin\frac{\pi}{3}$
$\stackrel{?}{=} \frac{\sqrt{3}}{2}\cos x + \frac{1}{2}\sin x + \frac{1}{2}\sin x - \frac{\sqrt{3}}{2}\cos x$
$= \sin x$

14. **SOLAR ENERGY** On March 21, the maximum amount of solar energy that falls on a square foot of ground at a certain location is given by $E \sin(90° - \phi)$, where ϕ is the latitude of the location and E is a constant. Use the difference of angles formula to find the amount of solar energy, in terms of cos ϕ, for a location that has a latitude of ϕ. **$E\cos\phi$**

15. **ELECTRICITY** In a certain circuit carrying alternating current, the formula $c = 2\sin(120t)$ can be used to find the current c in amperes after t seconds.

a. Rewrite the formula using the sum of two angles. **Sample answer: $c = 2\sin(90t + 30t)$**

b. Use the sum of angles formula to find the exact current at $t = 1$ second. **$\sqrt{3}$ amperes**

Chapter 14 20 Glencoe Algebra 2

Word Problem Practice
CRM p. 21 AL OL BL ELL

14-3 Word Problem Practice

Sum and Difference of Angles Identities

1. **ART** As part of a mosaic that an artist is making, she places two right triangular tiles together to make a new triangular piece. One tile has lengths of 3 inches, 4 inches, and 5 inches. The other tile has lengths 4 inches, $4\sqrt{3}$ inches, and 8 inches. The pieces are placed with the sides of 4 inches against each other, as shown in the figure below.

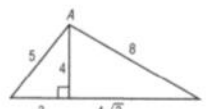

a. What is the exact value of the sine of angle A? $\frac{3 + 4\sqrt{3}}{10}$

b. What is the exact value of the cosine of angle A? $\frac{4 - 3\sqrt{3}}{10}$

c. What is the measure of angle A? **96.9°**

d. Is the new triangle formed from the two triangles also a right triangle? **no**

2. **MANUFACTURING** A robotic arm performs two operations in the course of manufacturing each car door that comes down the assembly line. As the door arrives in front of the robotic arm, the arm is parallel to the assembly line. Once the door is in place, the arm rotates counterclockwise 72° to perform the first operation. After performing the first operation, the arm rotates another 33° counterclockwise to perform the second operation. After the second operation is completed, the robotic arm rotates clockwise back to its starting position.

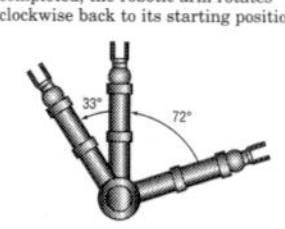

a. After completing the second operation, through what angle does the robotic arm rotate to return to its starting position? **105°**

b. What is the exact value of the sine of the angle through which the arm rotates to return to its starting position? $\frac{\sqrt{6} + \sqrt{2}}{4}$

c. What is the exact value of the cosine of the angle through which the arm rotates to return to its starting position? $\frac{\sqrt{2} - \sqrt{6}}{4}$

Chapter 14 21 Glencoe Algebra 2

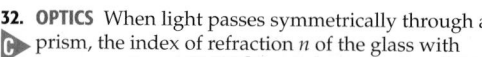

Real-World Link

Dispersive prisms break light into its constituent spectral colors. White light entering a prism is a mixture of different frequencies, each of which gets bent differently. Blue light is slowed down more than red light and will therefore be bent more than red light.

39. Sample answer: To determine wireless Internet interference, you need to determine the sine or cosine of the sum or difference of two angles. Interference occurs when waves pass through the same space at the same time. When the combined waves have a greater amplitude, constructive interference results. When the combined waves have a smaller amplitude, destructive interference results.

40. See Chapter 14 Answer Appendix.

41. See Chapter 14 Answer Appendix.

42. Sample answer: $A = 35°$, $B = 60°$, $C = 85°$; $0.7002 + 1.7321 + 11.4301 \stackrel{?}{=} (0.7002) \cdot (1.7321)(11.4301)$; $13.86 = 13.86$ ✓

32. **OPTICS** When light passes symmetrically through a prism, the index of refraction n of the glass with respect to air is $n = \frac{\sin\left[\frac{1}{2}(a + b)\right]}{\sin\frac{b}{2}}$, where a is the measure of the deviation angle and b is the measure of the prism apex angle.

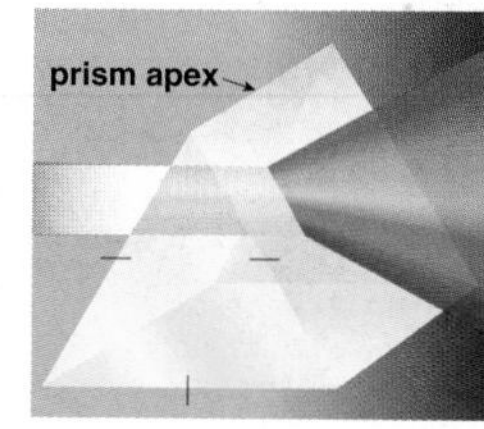

a. Show that for the prism shown, $n = \sqrt{3}\sin\frac{a}{2} + \cos\frac{a}{2}$. **See margin.**

b. Find n for the prism shown. **$\sqrt{3}$**

33. **MULTIPLE REPRESENTATIONS** In this problem, you will disprove the hypothesis that $\sin(A + B) = \sin A + \sin B$. **b, c. See Chapter 14 Answer Appendix.**

a. **TABULAR** Complete the table.

A	B	sin A	sin B	sin (A + B)	sin A + sin B
30°	90°	$\frac{1}{2}$	1	$\frac{\sqrt{3}}{2}$	$\frac{3}{2}$
45°	60°	$\frac{\sqrt{2}}{2}$	$\frac{\sqrt{3}}{2}$	$\frac{\sqrt{2} + \sqrt{6}}{4}$	$\frac{\sqrt{2} + \sqrt{3}}{2}$
60°	45°	$\frac{\sqrt{3}}{2}$	$\frac{\sqrt{2}}{2}$	$\frac{\sqrt{2} + \sqrt{6}}{4}$	$\frac{\sqrt{2} + \sqrt{3}}{2}$
90°	30°	1	$\frac{1}{2}$	$\frac{\sqrt{3}}{2}$	$\frac{3}{2}$

b. **GRAPHICAL** Assume that B is always 15° less than A. Use a graphing calculator to graph $y = \sin(x + x - 15)$ and $y = \sin x + \sin(x - 15)$ on the same screen.

c. **ANALYTICAL** Determine whether $\cos(A + B) = \cos A + \cos B$ is an identity. Explain your reasoning.

Verify that each equation is an identity. **34–37. See Chapter 14 Answer Appendix.**

34. $\sin(A + B) = \frac{\tan A + \tan B}{\sec A \sec B}$

35. $\cos(A + B) = \frac{1 - \tan A \tan B}{\sec A \sec B}$

36. $\sec(A - B) = \frac{\sec A \sec B}{1 + \tan A \tan B}$

37. $\sin(A + B)\sin(A - B) = \sin^2 A - \sin^2 B$

H.O.T. Problems
Use Higher-Order Thinking Skills

38. **REASONING** Simplify the following expression without expanding any of the sums or differences. **$\sin(-2\theta)$**

$$\sin\left(\frac{\pi}{3} - \theta\right)\cos\left(\frac{\pi}{3} + \theta\right) - \cos\left(\frac{\pi}{3} - \theta\right)\sin\left(\frac{\pi}{3} + \theta\right)$$

39. **WRITING IN MATH** Use the information at the beginning of the lesson and in Exercise 7 to explain how the sum and difference identities are used to describe wireless Internet interference. Include an explanation of the difference between constructive and destructive interference.

40. **CHALLENGE** Derive an identity for cot $(A + B)$ in terms of cot A and cot B.

41. **PROOF** The figure at the right shows two angles A and B in standard position on the unit circle. Use the Distance Formula to find d, where $(x_1, y_1) = (\cos B, \sin B)$ and $(x_2, y_2) = (\cos A, \sin A)$.

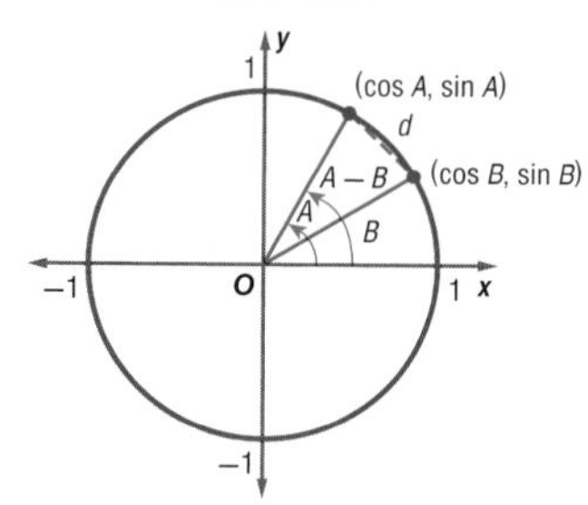

42. **OPEN ENDED** Consider the following theorem. *If A, B, and C are the angles of an oblique triangle, then tan A + tan B + tan C = tan A tan B tan C.* Choose values for A, B, and C. Verify that the conclusion is true for your specific values.

Enrichment
CRM p. 22 OL BL

14-3 Enrichment

Identities for the Products of Sines and Cosines

By adding the identities for the sines of the sum and difference of the measures of two angles, a new identity is obtained.

$\sin(\alpha + \beta) = \sin\alpha\cos\beta + \cos\alpha\sin\beta$
$\sin(\alpha - \beta) = \sin\alpha\cos\beta - \cos\alpha\sin\beta$
(i) $\sin(\alpha + \beta) + \sin(\alpha - \beta) = 2\sin\alpha\cos\beta$

This new identity is useful for expressing certain products as sums.

Example Write sin 3θ cos θ as a sum.

In the identity let $\alpha = 3\theta$ and $\beta = \theta$ so that $2\sin 3\theta\cos\theta = \sin(3\theta + \theta) + \sin(3\theta - \theta)$. Thus, $\sin 3\theta\cos\theta = \frac{1}{2}\sin 4\theta + \frac{1}{2}\sin 2\theta$.

By subtracting the identities for $\sin(\alpha + \beta)$ and $\sin(\alpha - \beta)$, a similar identity for expressing a product as a difference is obtained.

(ii) $\sin(\alpha + \beta) - \sin(\alpha - \beta) = 2\cos\alpha\sin\beta$

Multiple Representations In Exercise 33, students use information organized in a table and a graphing calculator to disprove a hypothesis about trigonometric operations.

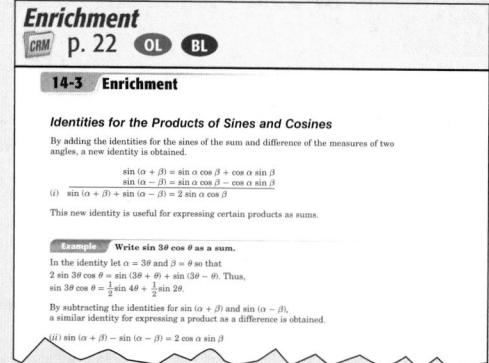

NGSSS PRACTICE 912.S.3.3, 912.D.11.3, 912.A.4.11, 912.S.3.1

43. **GRIDDED RESPONSE** The mean of seven numbers is 0. The sum of three of the numbers is −9. What is the sum of the remaining four numbers? **9**

44. The variables a, b, c, d, and f are integers in a sequence, where $a = 2$ and $b = 12$. To find the next term, double the last term and add that result to one less than the next-to-last term. For example, $c = 25$, because $2(12) = 24$, $2 - 1 = 1$, and $24 + 1 = 25$. What is the value of f? **C**

A. 74
B. 144
C. 146
D. 256

45. **ACT/SAT** Solve $x^2 - 5x < 14$. **H**

F. $\{x \mid -7 < x < 2\}$
G. $\{x \mid -7 < x > 2\}$
H. $\{x \mid -2 < x < 7\}$
I. $\{x \mid -2 < x > 7\}$

46. **PROBABILITY** A math teacher is randomly distributing 15 yellow pencils and 10 green pencils. What is the probability that the first pencil she hands out will be yellow and the second pencil will be green? **B**

A. $\frac{1}{24}$ C. $\frac{2}{5}$
B. $\frac{1}{4}$ D. $\frac{23}{25}$

Spiral Review

Verify that each equation is an identity. (Lesson 14-2) **47, 48. See margin.**

47. $\frac{\sin\theta}{\tan\theta} + \frac{\cos\theta}{\cot\theta} = \cos\theta + \sin\theta$

48. $\sec\theta(\sec\theta - \cos\theta) = \tan^2\theta$

Simplify each expression. (Lesson 14-1)

49. $\sin\theta\csc\theta - \cos^2\theta$ **$\sin^2\theta$**

50. $\cos^2\theta\sec\theta\csc\theta$ **$\cot\theta$**

51. $\cos\theta + \sin\theta\tan\theta$ **$\sec\theta$**

52. **GUITAR** When a guitar string is plucked, it is displaced from a fixed point in the middle of the string and vibrates back and forth, producing a musical tone. The exact tone depends on the frequency, or number of cycles per second, that the string vibrates. To produce an A, the frequency is 440 cycles per second, or 440 hertz (Hz). (Lesson 13-6)

a. Find the period of this function. **$\frac{1}{440}$ second**

b. Graph the height of the fixed point on the string from its resting position as a function of time. Let the maximum distance above the resting position have a value of 1 unit, and let the minimum distance below this position have a value of 1 unit. **See Chapter 14 Answer Appendix.**

Prove that each statement is true for all positive integers. (Lesson 11-7) **53, 54. See Chapter 14 Answer Appendix.**

53. $4^n - 1$ is divisible by 3.

54. $5^n + 3$ is divisible by 4.

Skills Review

Solve each equation. (Lesson 7-7)

55. $7 + \sqrt{4x + 8} = 9$ **−1**

56. $\sqrt{y + 21} - 1 = \sqrt{y + 12}$ **4**

57. $\sqrt{4z + 1} = 3 + \sqrt{4z - 2}$ **no solution**

Differentiated Instruction OL BL

Extension Tell students that sin 20° is approximately 0.3420. Tell them to use this information to find sin 65° and cos 65°. 0.9063, 0.4226

4 ASSESS

Ticket Out the Door Have students make a list of angles between 0° and 360° for which the sum and difference formulas can easily be used. Then have them tell what the angles have in common.

Formative Assessment

Check for student understanding of concepts in Lesson 14-3.

CRM Quiz 2, p. 37

Additional Answers

32a.
$$\frac{\sin\left[\frac{1}{2}(a+b)\right]}{\sin\frac{b}{2}} = \frac{\sin\left[\frac{1}{2}(a+60^\circ)\right]}{\sin\frac{60^\circ}{2}}$$
$$= \frac{\sin\left(\frac{a}{2}+30^\circ\right)}{\sin 30^\circ}$$
$$= \frac{\sin\frac{a}{2}\cos 30^\circ + \cos\frac{a}{2}\sin 30^\circ}{\sin 30^\circ}$$
$$= \frac{\left(\sin\frac{a}{2}\right)\left(\frac{\sqrt{3}}{2}\right) + \left(\cos\frac{a}{2}\right)\left(\frac{1}{2}\right)}{\frac{1}{2}}$$
$$= \sqrt{3}\sin\frac{a}{2} + \cos\frac{a}{2}$$

47.
$$\frac{\sin\theta}{\tan\theta} + \frac{\cos\theta}{\cot\theta} \stackrel{?}{=} \cos\theta + \sin\theta$$
$$\frac{\sin\theta}{\frac{\sin\theta}{\cos\theta}} + \frac{\cos\theta}{\frac{\cos\theta}{\sin\theta}} \stackrel{?}{=} \cos\theta + \sin\theta$$
$$\sin\theta \cdot \frac{\cos\theta}{\sin\theta} + \cos\theta \cdot \frac{\sin\theta}{\cos\theta} \stackrel{?}{=} \cos\theta + \sin\theta$$
$$\cos\theta + \sin\theta = \cos\theta + \sin\theta \checkmark$$

48.
$$\sec\theta(\sec\theta - \cos\theta) \stackrel{?}{=} \tan^2\theta$$
$$\frac{1}{\cos\theta}\left(\frac{1}{\cos\theta} - \cos\theta\right) \stackrel{?}{=} \tan^2\theta$$
$$\frac{1}{\cos\theta} - 1 \stackrel{?}{=} \tan^2\theta$$
$$\sec^2\theta - 1 \stackrel{?}{=} \tan^2\theta$$
$$\tan^2\theta = \tan^2\theta \checkmark$$

CHAPTER 14 Mid-Chapter Quiz

Formative Assessment

Use the Mid-Chapter Quiz to assess students' progress in the first half of the chapter.

For problems answered incorrectly, have students review the lessons indicated in parentheses.

ExamView Assessment Suite — Customize and create multiple versions of your Mid-Chapter Quiz and their answer keys.

FOLDABLES Follow-Up

Before students complete the Mid-Chapter Quiz, encourage them to review the information for Lessons 14-1 through 14-3 in their Foldables.

Additional Answer

5. $(31.5)^2 + 51^2 = c^2$; $992.25 + 2601 = c^2$; $3593.25 = c^2$; $c = \sqrt{3593.25}$; $\sin\theta = \dfrac{31.5}{\sqrt{3593.25}} = \dfrac{31.5\sqrt{3593.25}}{3593.25}$

CHAPTER 14 Mid-Chapter Quiz

Lessons 14-1 through 14-3

NGSSS 912.T.3.2, 912.T.3.3

Simplify each expression. (Lesson 14-1)

1. $\cot\theta\sec\theta$ **$\csc\theta$**
2. $\dfrac{1-\cos^2\theta}{\sin^2\theta}$ **1**
3. $\dfrac{1}{\cos\theta} - \dfrac{\sin^2\theta}{\cos\theta}$ **$\cos\theta$**
4. $\cos\left(\frac{\pi}{2} - \theta\right)\csc\theta$ **1**

5. **HISTORY** In 1861, the United States 34-star flag was adopted. For this flag, $\tan\theta = \frac{31.5}{51}$. Find $\sin\theta$. **See margin.**

Find the value of each expression. (Lesson 14-1)

6. $\sin\theta$, if $\cos\theta = \frac{3}{5}$; $0° < \theta < 90°$ **$\frac{4}{5}$**
7. $\csc\theta$, if $\cot\theta = \frac{1}{2}$; $270° < \theta < 360°$ **$-\frac{\sqrt{5}}{2}$**
8. $\tan\theta$, if $\sec\theta = \frac{4}{3}$; $0° < \theta < 90°$ **$\frac{\sqrt{7}}{3}$**

9. **NGSSS PRACTICE** Which of the following is equivalent to $\dfrac{\cos\theta}{1-\sin^2\theta}$? (Lesson 14-1) **D**

   A. $\cos\theta$
   B. $\csc\theta$
   C. $\tan\theta$
   D. $\sec\theta$

10. **AMUSEMENT PARKS** Suppose a child on a merry-go-round is seated on an outside horse. The diameter of the merry-go-round is 16 meters. The angle of inclination is represented by the equation $\tan\theta = \frac{v^2}{gR}$, where R is the radius of the circular path, v is the speed in meters per second, and g is 9.8 meters per second squared. (Lesson 14-1)

    a. If the sine of the angle of inclination of the child is $\frac{1}{5}$, what is the angle of inclination made by the child? **about 11.5°**

    b. What is the velocity of the merry-go-round? **about 4 m/s**

    c. If the speed of the merry-go-round is 3.6 meters per second, what is the value of the angle of inclination of a rider? **about 9.4°**

Verify that each of the following is an identity. (Lesson 14-2) **11–14. See Chapter 14 Answer Appendix.**

11. $\cot^2\theta + 1 = \dfrac{\cot\theta}{\cos\theta \cdot \sin\theta}$
12. $\dfrac{\cos\theta\csc\theta}{\cot\theta} = 1$
13. $\dfrac{\sin\theta\tan\theta}{1-\cos\theta} = (1+\cos\theta)\sec\theta$
14. $\tan\theta(1-\sin\theta) = \dfrac{\cos\theta\sin\theta}{1+\sin\theta}$

15. **COMPUTER** The front of a computer monitor is usually measured along the diagonal of the screen as shown below. (Lesson 14-2)

    a. Find h. **9**

    b. Using the diagram shown, show that $\cot\theta = \frac{\cos\theta}{\sin\theta}$. **See Chapter 14 Answer Appendix.**

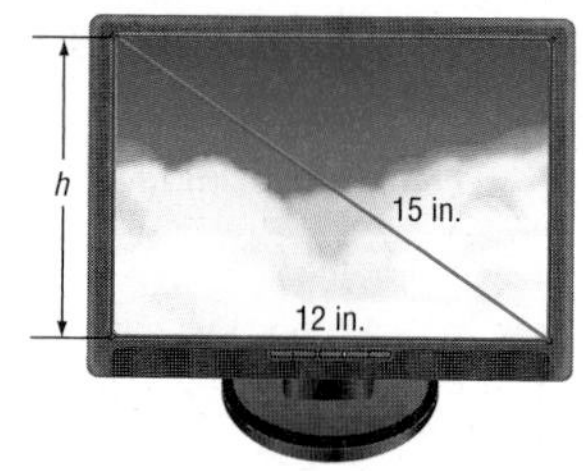

Verify that each of the following is an identity. (Lesson 14-2) **16–19. See Chapter 14 Answer Appendix.**

16. $\tan^2\theta + 1 = \dfrac{\tan\theta}{\cos\theta \cdot \sin\theta}$
17. $\dfrac{\sin\theta \cdot \sec\theta}{\sec\theta - 1} = (\sec\theta + 1)\cot\theta$
18. $\sin^2\theta \cdot \tan^2\theta = \tan^2\theta - \sin^2\theta$
19. $\cot\theta(1-\cos\theta) = \dfrac{\cos\theta \cdot \sin\theta}{1+\cos\theta}$

Find the exact value of each expression. (Lesson 14-3)

20. $\cos 105°$ **$\frac{\sqrt{2}-\sqrt{6}}{4}$**
21. $\sin(-135°)$ **$-\frac{\sqrt{2}}{2}$**
22. $\tan 15°$ **$2-\sqrt{3}$**
23. $\cot 75°$ **$2-\sqrt{3}$**

24. **NGSSS PRACTICE** What is the exact value of $\cos\frac{5\pi}{12}$? (Lesson 14-3) **H**

    F. $\sqrt{2}$
    G. $\dfrac{\sqrt{6}+\sqrt{2}}{2}$
    H. $\dfrac{\sqrt{6}-\sqrt{2}}{4}$
    I. $\dfrac{\sqrt{6}+\sqrt{2}}{4}$

25. Verify that $\cos 30°\cos\theta + \sin 30°\sin\theta = \sin 60°\cos\theta + \cos 60°\sin\theta$ is an identity. (Lesson 14-3) **See Chapter 14 Answer Appendix.**

Intervention Planner

Tier 1 On Level	Tier 2 Strategic Intervention approaching grade level	Tier 3 Intensive Intervention 2 or more grades below level
If students miss about 25% of the exercises or less,	**If** students miss about 50% of the exercises,	**If** students miss about 75% of the exercises,
Then choose a resource: **SE** Lessons 14-1, 14-2, and 14-3 **CRM** Skills Practice, pp. 7, 13, and 19 **TE** Chapter Project, p. 888 **FL Math Online** Self-Check Quiz	**Then** choose a resource: **CRM** Study Guide and Intervention, Chapter 14, pp. 5, 11, and 17 **FL Math Online** Extra Examples, Personal Tutor, Homework Help	**Then** use *Math Triumphs, Alg. 2* **FL Math Online** Extra Examples, Personal Tutor, Homework Help, Review Vocabulary

14-4 Double-Angle and Half-Angle Identities

Then

You found values of sine and cosine by using sum and difference identities. (Lesson 14-3)

Now

- Find values of sine and cosine by using double-angle identities.
- Find values of sine and cosine by using half-angle identities.

NGSSS

MA.912.T.3.2 Use basic trigonometric identities to verify other identities and simplify expressions.
MA.912.T.3.3 **Use the sum and difference,** half-angle and double-angle formulas for sine, cosine, and tangent, **when formulas are provided.**

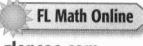

FL Math Online
glencoe.com

Why?

Chicago's Buckingham Fountain contains jets placed at specific angles that shoot water into the air to create arcs. When a stream of water shoots into the air with velocity v at an angle of θ with the horizontal, the model predicts that the water will travel a horizontal distance of $D = \frac{v^2}{g} \sin 2\theta$ and reach a maximum height of $H = \frac{v^2}{2g} \sin^2 \theta$. The ratio of H to D helps determine the total height and width of the fountain. Express $\frac{H}{D}$ as a function of θ.

Double-Angle Identities It is sometimes useful to have identities to find the value of a function of twice an angle or half an angle.

Key Concept — Double-Angle Identities

The following identities hold true for all values of θ.

$\sin 2\theta = 2 \sin \theta \cos \theta$

$\cos 2\theta = \cos^2 \theta - \sin^2 \theta$
$\cos 2\theta = 2 \cos^2 \theta - 1$
$\cos 2\theta = 1 - 2 \sin^2 \theta$

$\tan 2\theta = \frac{2 \tan \theta}{1 - \tan^2 \theta}$

EXAMPLE 1 Double-Angle Identities

Find the exact value of $\sin 2\theta$ if $\sin \theta = \frac{2}{3}$ and θ is between 0° and 90°.

Step 1 Use the identity $\sin 2\theta = 2 \sin \theta \cos \theta$ to find the value of $\cos \theta$.

$\cos^2 \theta = 1 - \sin^2 \theta$ — $\cos^2 \theta + \sin^2 \theta = 1$

$\cos^2 \theta = 1 - \left(\frac{2}{3}\right)^2$ — $\sin \theta = \frac{2}{3}$

$\cos^2 \theta = \frac{5}{9}$ — Subtract.

$\cos \theta = \pm\frac{\sqrt{5}}{3}$ — Take the square root of each side.

Since θ is in the first quadrant, cosine is positive. Thus, $\cos \theta = \frac{\sqrt{5}}{3}$.

Step 2 Find $\sin 2\theta$.

$\sin 2\theta = 2 \sin \theta \cos \theta$ — Double-angle identity

$= 2\left(\frac{2}{3}\right)\left(\frac{\sqrt{5}}{3}\right)$ — $\sin \theta = \frac{2}{3}$ and $\cos \theta = \frac{\sqrt{5}}{3}$

$= \frac{4\sqrt{5}}{9}$ — Multiply.

Guided Practice

1. Find the exact value of $\sin 2\theta$ if $\cos \theta = -\frac{1}{3}$ and $90° < \theta < 180°$. $-\frac{4\sqrt{2}}{9}$

Personal Tutor glencoe.com

14-4 Lesson Notes

1 FOCUS

Vertical Alignment

Before Lesson 14-4
Find values of sine and cosine by using sum and difference identities.

Lesson 14-4
Find values of sine and cosine by using double-angle identities.
Find values of sine and cosine using half-angle identities.

After Lesson 14-4
Solve trigonometric equations.

2 TEACH

Scaffolding Questions

Have students read the *Why?* section of the lesson.

Ask:

- What is the difference between $\sin 2\theta$ and $\sin^2\theta$? Explain. $\sin 2\theta$ represents the sine of the angle that is two times θ; $\sin^2\theta$ represents the square of the value of $\sin \theta$.
- Will expressing $\frac{H}{D}$ as a function of θ include the variable v? No, when simplifying, $\frac{v^2}{v^2} = 1$.
- Will it include g? Explain. No, $\frac{1}{2g} \div \frac{1}{g}$ is $\frac{1}{2}$, so it will not include the variable g.

Lesson 14-4 Resources

Resource	Approaching-Level	On-Level	Beyond-Level	English Learners
Teacher Edition	• Differentiated Instruction, p. 914	• Differentiated Instruction, p. 914	• Differentiated Instruction, p. 917	
Chapter Resource Masters	• Study Guide and Intervention, pp. 23–24 • Skills Practice, p. 25 • Practice, p. 26 • Word Problem Practice, p. 27	• Study Guide and Intervention, pp. 23–24 • Skills Practice, p. 25 • Practice, p. 26 • Word Problem Practice, p. 27 • Enrichment, p. 28	• Practice, p. 26 • Word Problem Practice, p. 27 • Enrichment, p. 28	• Study Guide and Intervention, pp. 23–24 • Skills Practice, p. 25 • Practice, p. 26 • Word Problem Practice, p. 27
Transparencies	• 5-Minute Check Transparency 14-4	• 5-Minute Check Transparency 14-4	• 5-Minute Check Transparency 14-4	• 5-Minute Check Transparency 14-4
Other	• Study Notebook	• Study Notebook	• Study Notebook	• Study Notebook

Double-Angle Identities

Examples 1 and 2 show how to find the exact value of an expression using the double-angle identities.

Formative Assessment

Use the Guided Practice exercises after each example to determine students' understanding of concepts.

Additional Examples

1 Find the exact value of $\cos 2\theta$ if $\sin \theta = \frac{3}{4}$ and θ is between 0° and 90°. -0.125

2 Find the exact value of each expression if $\cos \theta = \frac{4}{5}$ and θ is between 0° and 90°.

a. $\tan 2\theta$ $\frac{24}{7}$

b. $\sin 2\theta$ $\frac{24}{25}$

Additional Examples also in Interactive Classroom PowerPoint® Presentations

IWB INTERACTIVE WHITEBOARD READY

Tips for New Teachers

Sense-Making Remind students of the identity $\sin^2\theta + \cos^2\theta = 1$, and its two variations that occur by subtracting either $\sin^2\theta$ or $\cos^2\theta$ from both sides. Explain that there are three versions of the formula for $\cos 2\theta$ because of the three variations of the identity $\sin^2\theta + \cos^2\theta = 1$.

StudyTip

Deriving Formulas You can use the identity for $\sin (A + B)$ to find the sine of twice an angle θ, $\sin 2\theta$, and the identity for $\cos (A + B)$ to find the cosine of twice an angle θ, $\cos 2\theta$.

EXAMPLE 2 Double-Angle Identities

Find the exact value of each expression if $\sin \theta = \frac{2}{3}$ and θ is between 0° and 90°.

a. $\cos 2\theta$

Since we know the values of $\cos \theta$ and $\sin \theta$, we can use any of the double-angle identities for cosine. We will use the identity $\cos 2\theta = 1 - 2\sin^2\theta$.

$\cos 2\theta = 1 - 2\sin^2\theta$ — **Double-angle identity**

$= 1 - 2\left(\frac{2}{3}\right)^2$ or $\frac{1}{9}$ — $\sin \theta = \frac{2}{3}$

b. $\tan 2\theta$

Step 1 Find $\tan \theta$ to use the double-angle identity for $\tan 2\theta$.

$\tan \theta = \frac{\sin \theta}{\cos \theta}$ — **Definition of tangent**

$= \frac{\frac{2}{3}}{\frac{\sqrt{5}}{3}}$ — $\sin \theta = \frac{2}{3}$ and $\cos \theta = \frac{\sqrt{5}}{3}$

$= \frac{2}{\sqrt{5}}$ or $\frac{2\sqrt{5}}{5}$ — **Rationalize the denominator.**

Step 2 Find $\tan 2\theta$.

$\tan 2\theta = \frac{2\tan \theta}{1 - \tan^2\theta}$ — **Double-angle identity**

$= \frac{2\left(\frac{2\sqrt{5}}{5}\right)}{1 - \left(\frac{2\sqrt{5}}{5}\right)^2}$ — $\tan \theta = \frac{2\sqrt{5}}{5}$

$= \frac{2\left(\frac{2\sqrt{5}}{5}\right)}{\frac{25}{25} - \frac{20}{25}}$ — **Square the denominator.**

$= \frac{\frac{4\sqrt{5}}{5}}{\frac{1}{5}}$ — **Simplify.**

$= \frac{4\sqrt{5}}{5} \cdot \frac{5}{1}$ or $4\sqrt{5}$ — $\frac{a}{b} \div \frac{c}{d} = \frac{a}{b} \cdot \frac{d}{c}$

Guided Practice

Find the exact value of each expression if $\cos \theta = -\frac{1}{3}$ and $90° < \theta < 180°$.

2A. $\cos 2\theta$ $-\frac{7}{9}$

2B. $\tan 2\theta$ $\frac{4\sqrt{2}}{7}$

Personal Tutor glencoe.com

Half-Angle Identities It is sometimes useful to have identities to find the value of a function of half an angle.

Key Concept Half-Angle Identities

The following identities hold true for all values of θ.

$\sin \frac{\theta}{2} = \pm\sqrt{\frac{1 - \cos \theta}{2}}$ $\cos \frac{\theta}{2} = \pm\sqrt{\frac{1 + \cos \theta}{2}}$ $\tan \frac{\theta}{2} = \pm\sqrt{\frac{1 - \cos \theta}{1 + \cos \theta}}$, $\cos \theta \neq -1$

912 Chapter 14 Trigonometric Identities and Equations

StudyTip

Choosing the Sign In the first step of the solution, you may want to determine the quadrant in which the terminal side of $\frac{\theta}{2}$ will lie. Then you can use the correct sign from that point on.

ReadingMath

Plus or Minus The first sign of the half-angle identity is read *plus or minus*. Unlike with the double-angle identities, you must determine the sign.

EXAMPLE 3 Half-Angle Identities

a. Find the exact value of $\cos \frac{\theta}{2}$ if $\sin \theta = -\frac{4}{5}$ and θ is in the third quadrant.

$\cos^2 \theta = 1 - \sin^2 \theta$ — Use a Pythagorean identity to find $\cos \theta$.

$\cos^2 \theta = 1 - \left(-\frac{4}{5}\right)^2$ — $\sin \theta = -\frac{4}{5}$

$\cos^2 \theta = 1 - \frac{16}{25}$ — Evaluate exponent.

$\cos^2 \theta = \frac{9}{25}$ — Subtract.

$\cos \theta = \pm\frac{3}{5}$ — Take the square root of each side.

Since θ is in the third quadrant, $\cos \theta = -\frac{3}{5}$.

$\cos \frac{\theta}{2} = \pm\sqrt{\frac{1 + \cos \theta}{2}}$ — Half-angle identity

$= \pm\sqrt{\frac{1 - \frac{3}{5}}{2}}$ — $\cos \theta = -\frac{3}{5}$

$= \pm\sqrt{\frac{1}{5}}$ — Simplify.

$= \pm\frac{1}{\sqrt{5}} \cdot \frac{\sqrt{5}}{\sqrt{5}}$ or $\pm\frac{\sqrt{5}}{5}$ — Rationalize the denominator.

If θ is between 180° and 270°, $\frac{\theta}{2}$ is between 90° and 135°. So, $\cos \frac{\theta}{2}$ is $-\frac{\sqrt{5}}{5}$.

b. Find the exact value of cos 67.5°.

$\cos 67.5° = \cos \frac{135°}{2}$ — $67.5° = \frac{135°}{2}$

$= \sqrt{\frac{1 + \cos 135°}{2}}$ — $\cos \frac{\theta}{2} = \pm\sqrt{\frac{1 + \cos \theta}{2}}$

$= \sqrt{\frac{1 - \frac{\sqrt{2}}{2}}{2}}$ — 67.5° is in Quadrant I; the value is positive.

$= \sqrt{\frac{\frac{2}{2} - \frac{\sqrt{2}}{2}}{2}}$ — $1 = \frac{2}{2}$

$= \sqrt{\frac{\frac{2 - \sqrt{2}}{2}}{2}}$ — Subtract fractions.

$= \sqrt{\frac{2 - \sqrt{2}}{2} \cdot \frac{1}{2}}$ — $\frac{a}{b} \div \frac{c}{d} = \frac{a}{b} \cdot \frac{d}{c}$

$= \sqrt{\frac{2 - \sqrt{2}}{4}}$ — Multiply.

$= \frac{\sqrt{2 - \sqrt{2}}}{\sqrt{4}}$ — $\sqrt{\frac{a}{b}} = \frac{\sqrt{a}}{\sqrt{b}}$

$= \frac{\sqrt{2 - \sqrt{2}}}{2}$ — Simplify.

Guided Practice

3. Find the exact value of $\sin \frac{\theta}{2}$ if $\sin \theta = \frac{2}{3}$ and θ is in the second quadrant. $\frac{\sqrt{18 + 6\sqrt{5}}}{6}$

Personal Tutor glencoe.com

Half-Angle Identities

Example 3 shows how to use the half-angle identities to find the exact value of a trigonometric function for an angle in a given quadrant. **Example 4** shows how to simplify an equation that contains trigonometric expressions. **Example 5** shows how to verify trigonometric identities using double-angle identities.

Additional Example

3 **a.** Find the exact value of $\cos \frac{\theta}{2}$ if $\sin \theta = \frac{3}{5}$ and θ is in the second quadrant. $\sqrt{\frac{1}{10}}$ or $\frac{\sqrt{10}}{10}$

b. Find the exact value of sin 165°. $\frac{\sqrt{2 - \sqrt{3}}}{2}$

Watch Out!

Preventing Errors Stress the Study Tip provided in the margin next to Example 3. Determining the proper sign for the answer at the beginning of the computation will help some students avoid forgetting this step at the end of their computations.

TEACH with TECH

VIDEO RECORDING Split the class into groups, and assign each group a double-angle or half-angle problem. Have the group create a video recording showing how to apply the appropriate formula to solve the problem. Try to assign as many different types of problems as possible to the class.

Focus on Mathematical Content

Deriving Formulas The Double-Angle Formulas are special cases of the Sum of Angles Formulas studied in the previous lesson. The Double-Angle Formulas are obtained by setting *A* and *B* equal to each other in the Sum of Angles Formulas.

Additional Examples

4 **FOUNTAIN** Refer to the beginning of the lesson. Find $\frac{D}{H}$.

$4 \cot \theta$ or $\frac{4}{\tan \theta}$

5 Verify that $\sin \theta(\cos^2 \theta - \cos 2\theta) = \sin^3 \theta$ is an identity.

$\sin \theta (\cos^2 \theta - \cos 2\theta) \stackrel{?}{=} \sin^3 \theta$

$\sin \theta [\cos^2 \theta - (\cos^2 \theta - \sin^2 \theta)] \stackrel{?}{=} \sin^3 \theta$

$\sin \theta (\cos^2 \theta - \cos^2 \theta + \sin^2 \theta) \stackrel{?}{=} \sin^3 \theta$

$\sin \theta (\sin^2 \theta) \stackrel{?}{=} \sin^3 \theta$

$\sin^3 \theta = \sin^3 \theta$ ✓

Additional Answer (Guided Practice)

5. $4 \cos^2 x - \sin^2 2x \stackrel{?}{=} 4 \cos^4 x$

$4 \cos^2 x - 4 \sin^2 x \cos^2 x \stackrel{?}{=} 4 \cos^4 x$

$4 \cos^2 x(1 - \sin^2 x) \stackrel{?}{=} 4 \cos^4 x$

$4 \cos^2 x \cos^2 x \stackrel{?}{=} 4 \cos^4 x$

$4 \cos^4 x = 4 \cos^4 x$ ✓

Real-World Link

The City Hall Park Fountain in New York City is located in the heart of Manhattan in front of City Hall.

Source: *Fodor's*

Real-World EXAMPLE 4 Simplify Using Double-Angle Identities

FOUNTAIN Refer to the beginning of the lesson. Find $\frac{H}{D}$.

$\frac{H}{D} = \dfrac{\frac{v^2}{2g}\sin^2 \theta}{\frac{v^2}{g}\sin 2\theta}$	Original equation
$= \dfrac{\frac{v^2 \sin^2 \theta}{2g}}{\frac{v^2 \sin 2\theta}{g}}$	Simplify the numerator and denominator.
$= \frac{v^2 \sin^2 \theta}{2g} \cdot \frac{g}{v^2 \sin 2\theta}$	$\frac{a}{b} \div \frac{c}{d} = \frac{a}{b} \cdot \frac{d}{c}$
$= \frac{\sin^2 \theta}{2 \sin 2\theta}$	Simplify.
$= \frac{\sin^2 \theta}{4 \sin \theta \cos \theta}$	$\sin 2\theta = 2 \sin \theta \cos \theta$
$= \frac{1}{4} \cdot \frac{\sin \theta}{\cos \theta}$	Simplify.
$= \frac{1}{4} \tan \theta$	$\frac{\sin \theta}{\cos \theta} = \tan \theta$

Guided Practice

Find each value.

4A. $\sin 135°$ $\frac{\sqrt{2}}{2}$

4B. $\cos \frac{7\pi}{8}$ $-\frac{\sqrt{2 + \sqrt{2}}}{2}$

Personal Tutor glencoe.com

Recall that you can use the sum and difference identities to verify identities. Double- and half-angle identities can also be used to verify identities.

EXAMPLE 5 Verify Identities

Verify that $\frac{\cos 2\theta}{1 + \sin 2\theta} = \frac{\cot \theta - 1}{\cot \theta + 1}$ is an identity.

$\frac{\cos 2\theta}{1 + \sin 2\theta} \stackrel{?}{=} \frac{\cot \theta - 1}{\cot \theta + 1}$	Original equation
$\frac{\cos 2\theta}{1 + \sin 2\theta} \stackrel{?}{=} \dfrac{\frac{\cos \theta}{\sin \theta} - 1}{\frac{\cos \theta}{\sin \theta} + 1}$	$\cot \theta = \frac{\cos \theta}{\sin \theta}$
$\frac{\cos 2\theta}{1 + \sin 2\theta} \stackrel{?}{=} \frac{\cos \theta - \sin \theta}{\cos \theta + \sin \theta}$	Multiply numerator and denominator by $\sin \theta$.
$\frac{\cos 2\theta}{1 + \sin 2\theta} \stackrel{?}{=} \frac{\cos \theta - \sin \theta}{\cos \theta + \sin \theta} \cdot \frac{\cos \theta + \sin \theta}{\cos \theta + \sin \theta}$	Multiply the right side by 1.
$\frac{\cos 2\theta}{1 + \sin 2\theta} \stackrel{?}{=} \frac{\cos^2 \theta - \sin^2 \theta}{\cos^2 \theta + 2 \cos \theta \sin \theta + \sin^2 \theta}$	Multiply.
$\frac{\cos 2\theta}{1 + \sin 2\theta} \stackrel{?}{=} \frac{\cos^2 \theta - \sin^2 \theta}{1 + 2 \cos \theta \sin \theta}$	Simplify.
$\frac{\cos 2\theta}{1 + \sin 2\theta} = \frac{\cos 2\theta}{1 + \sin 2\theta}$ ✓	$\cos^2 \theta - \sin^2 \theta = \cos 2\theta$; $2 \cos \theta \sin \theta = \sin 2\theta$

Guided Practice

5. Verify that $4 \cos^2 x - \sin^2 2x = 4 \cos^4 x$. See margin.

Personal Tutor glencoe.com

Differentiated Instruction

Auditory/Musical Learners If possible, ask a music teacher at your school to talk to students about harmonics. Students playing stringed instruments may also be willing to share what they have learned about harmonics and waves. If a music teacher is not available, a physics teacher may also be able to demonstrate harmonics or bring a device that creates standing waves in class.

914 **Chapter 14** Trigonometric Identities and Equations

Check Your Understanding

Examples 1–3 pp. 911–913

Find the exact values of $\sin 2\theta$, $\cos 2\theta$, $\sin \frac{\theta}{2}$, and $\cos \frac{\theta}{2}$.

1. $\sin \theta = \frac{1}{4}$; $0° < \theta < 90°$ — $\frac{\sqrt{15}}{8}, \frac{7}{8}, \frac{\sqrt{8 - 2\sqrt{15}}}{4}, \frac{\sqrt{8 + 2\sqrt{15}}}{4}$
2. $\sin \theta = \frac{4}{5}$; $90° < \theta < 180°$ — $-\frac{24}{25}, -\frac{7}{25}, \frac{2\sqrt{5}}{5}, \frac{\sqrt{5}}{5}$
3. $\cos \theta = -\frac{5}{13}$; $\frac{\pi}{2} < \theta < \pi$ — $-\frac{120}{169}, -\frac{119}{169}, \frac{3\sqrt{13}}{13}, \frac{2\sqrt{13}}{13}$
4. $\cos \theta = \frac{3}{5}$; $270° < \theta < 360°$ — $-\frac{24}{25}, -\frac{7}{25}, \frac{\sqrt{5}}{5}, -\frac{2\sqrt{5}}{5}$
5. $\tan \theta = -\frac{8}{15}$; $90° < \theta < 180°$ — $-\frac{240}{289}, \frac{161}{289}, \frac{4\sqrt{17}}{17}, \frac{\sqrt{17}}{17}$
6. $\tan \theta = \frac{5}{12}$; $\pi < \theta < \frac{3\pi}{2}$ — $\frac{120}{169}, \frac{119}{169}, \frac{5\sqrt{26}}{26}, -\frac{\sqrt{26}}{26}$

Find the exact value of each expression.

7. $\sin \frac{\pi}{8}$ $\frac{\sqrt{2 - \sqrt{2}}}{2}$
8. $\cos 15°$ $\frac{\sqrt{2 + \sqrt{3}}}{2}$

Example 4 p. 914

9. **SOCCER** A soccer player kicks a ball at an angle of 37° with the ground with an initial velocity of 52 feet per second. The distance d that the ball will go in the air if it is not blocked is given by $d = \frac{2v^2 \sin \theta \cos \theta}{g}$. In this formula, g is the acceleration due to gravity and is equal to 32 feet per second squared, and v is the initial velocity.

   a. Simplify this formula by using a double-angle identity. $d = \frac{v^2 \sin 2\theta}{g}$
   b. Using the simplified formula, how far will this ball go? ≈ 81 ft

Example 5 p. 914

Verify that each equation is an identity. **10, 11. See margin.**

10. $\tan \theta = \frac{1 - \cos 2\theta}{\sin 2\theta}$
11. $(\sin \theta + \cos \theta)^2 = 1 + 2 \sin \theta \cos \theta$

Practice and Problem Solving

● = **Step-by-Step Solutions** begin on page R20. **Extra Practice** begins on page 947.

Examples 1–3 pp. 911–913

Find the exact values of $\sin 2\theta$, $\cos 2\theta$, $\sin \frac{\theta}{2}$, and $\cos \frac{\theta}{2}$.

12. $\sin \theta = \frac{2}{3}$; $90° < \theta < 180°$ — $-\frac{4\sqrt{5}}{9}, \frac{1}{9}, \frac{\sqrt{6} \cdot \sqrt{3 + \sqrt{5}}}{6}, \frac{\sqrt{6} \cdot \sqrt{3 - \sqrt{5}}}{6}$
13. $\sin \theta = -\frac{15}{17}$; $\pi < \theta < \frac{3\pi}{2}$ — $\frac{240}{289}, -\frac{161}{189}, \frac{5\sqrt{34}}{34}, -\frac{3\sqrt{34}}{34}$
14. $\cos \theta = \frac{3}{5}$; $\frac{3\pi}{2} < \theta < 2\pi$ — $-\frac{24}{25}, -\frac{7}{25}, \frac{\sqrt{5}}{5}, \frac{2\sqrt{5}}{5}$
15. $\cos \theta = \frac{1}{5}$; $270° < \theta < 360°$ — $-\frac{4\sqrt{6}}{25}, -\frac{23}{25}, \frac{\sqrt{10}}{5}, -\frac{\sqrt{15}}{5}$
16. $\tan \theta = \frac{4}{3}$; $180° < \theta < 270°$ — $\frac{24}{25}, -\frac{7}{25}, \frac{2\sqrt{5}}{5}, -\frac{\sqrt{5}}{5}$
17. $\tan \theta = -2$; $\frac{\pi}{2} < \theta < \pi$ — $-\frac{4}{5}, -\frac{3}{5}, \sqrt{\frac{\sqrt{5} + 1}{2\sqrt{5}}}, \sqrt{\frac{\sqrt{5} - 1}{2\sqrt{5}}}$

Find the exact value of each expression.

18. $\sin 75°$ $\frac{\sqrt{2 + \sqrt{3}}}{2}$
19. $\sin \frac{3\pi}{8}$ $\frac{\sqrt{2 + \sqrt{2}}}{2}$
20. $\cos \frac{7\pi}{12}$ $-\frac{\sqrt{2 - \sqrt{3}}}{2}$
21. $\tan 165°$ $\sqrt{3} - 2$
22. $\tan \frac{5\pi}{12}$ $2 + \sqrt{3}$
23. $\tan 22.5°$ $\sqrt{2} - 1$
24. **GEOGRAPHY** The Mercator projection of the globe is a projection on which the distance between the lines of latitude increases with their distance from the equator. The calculation of the location of a point on this projection involves the expression $\tan\left(45° + \frac{L}{2}\right)$, where L is the latitude of the point.

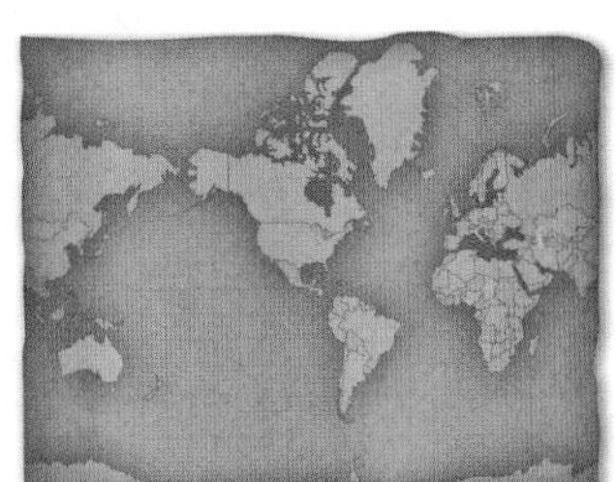

   a. Write this expression in terms of a trigonometric function of L. **See margin.**
   b. The latitude of Tallahassee, Florida, is 30° north. Find the value of the expression if $L = 30°$. $\sqrt{3}$

3 PRACTICE

Formative Assessment

Use Exercises 1–11 to check for understanding.

Then use the chart at the bottom of this page to customize assignments for your students.

Additional Answers

10. $\tan \theta \stackrel{?}{=} \frac{1 - \cos 2\theta}{\sin 2\theta}$

$\stackrel{?}{=} \frac{1 - (1 - 2\sin^2 \theta)}{2 \sin \theta \cos \theta}$

$\stackrel{?}{=} \frac{2\sin^2 \theta}{2 \sin \theta \cos \theta}$

$\stackrel{?}{=} \frac{\sin \theta}{\cos \theta}$

$= \tan \theta$ ✓

11. $(\sin \theta + \cos \theta)^2 \stackrel{?}{=} 1 + 2 \sin \theta \cos \theta$

$(\sin \theta + \cos \theta)(\sin \theta + \cos \theta) \stackrel{?}{=} 1 + 2 \sin \theta \cos \theta$

$\sin^2 \theta + 2 \sin \theta \cos \theta + \cos^2 \theta \stackrel{?}{=} 1 + 2 \sin \theta \cos \theta$

$1 + 2 \sin \theta \cos \theta = 1 + 2 \sin \theta \cos \theta$ ✓

24a. $\frac{1 \pm \sqrt{\frac{1 - \cos L}{1 + \cos L}}}{1 \mp \sqrt{\frac{1 - \cos L}{1 + \cos L}}}$

Differentiated Homework Options

Level	Assignment	Two-Day Option	
AL Basic	12–29, 37, 39–60	13–29 odd, 43–46	12–28 even, 37, 39–42, 47–60
OL Core	13–29 odd, 30, 31–37 odd, 39–60	12–29, 43–46	30–37, 39–42, 47–60
BL Advanced	30–57, (optional: 58–60)		

Study Guide and Intervention
CRM pp. 23-24 AL OL ELL

14-4 Study Guide and Intervention
Double-Angle and Half-Angle Identities

Double-Angle Identities

Double-Angle Identities	The following identities hold true for all values of θ. $\sin 2\theta = 2\sin 2\theta \cdot \cos\theta$; $\cos 2\theta = \cos^2\theta - \sin^2\theta$; $\cos 2\theta = 1 - 2\sin^2\theta$; $\cos 2\theta = 2\cos^2\theta - 1$

Example Find the exact values of $\sin 2\theta$, and $\cos 2\theta$ if $\sin\theta = -\frac{9}{10}$ and θ is between 180° and 270°.

First, find value of $\cos\theta$.

$\cos^2\theta = 1 - \sin^2\theta$ $\cos^2\theta + \sin^2\theta = 1$

$\cos^2\theta = 1 - \left(-\frac{9}{10}\right)^2$ $\sin\theta = -\frac{9}{10}$

$\cos^2\theta = \frac{19}{100}$

$\cos\theta = \pm\frac{\sqrt{19}}{10}$

Since θ is in the third quadrant, $\cos\theta$ is negative. Thus $\cos\theta = -\frac{\sqrt{19}}{10}$.

To find $\sin 2\theta$, use the identity $\sin 2\theta = 2\sin\theta \cdot \cos\theta$.

$\sin 2\theta = 2\sin\theta \cdot \cos\theta$

$= 2\left(-\frac{9}{10}\right)\left(-\frac{\sqrt{19}}{10}\right)$

$= \frac{9\sqrt{19}}{50}$

The value of $\sin 2\theta$ is $\frac{9\sqrt{19}}{50}$.

To find $\cos 2\theta$, use the identity $\cos 2\theta = 1 - 2\sin^2\theta$.

$\cos 2\theta = 1 - 2\sin^2\theta$

$= 1 - 2\left(-\frac{9}{10}\right)^2$

$= -\frac{31}{50}$.

The value of $\cos 2\theta$ is $= -\frac{31}{50}$.

Exercises

Find the exact values of $\sin 2\theta$ and $\cos 2\theta$.

1. $\sin\theta = \frac{1}{4}$, $0° < \theta < 90°$ $\frac{\sqrt{15}}{8}, \frac{7}{8}$
2. $\sin\theta = -\frac{1}{8}$, $270° < \theta < 360°$ $-\frac{3\sqrt{7}}{32}, \frac{31}{32}$
3. $\cos\theta = -\frac{3}{5}$, $180° < \theta < 270°$ $\frac{24}{25}, -\frac{7}{25}$
4. $\cos\theta = -\frac{4}{5}$, $90° < \theta < 180°$ $-\frac{24}{25}, \frac{7}{25}$
5. $\sin\theta = -\frac{3}{5}$, $270° < \theta < 360°$ $-\frac{24}{25}, \frac{7}{25}$
6. $\cos\theta = -\frac{2}{3}$, $90° < \theta < 180°$ $-\frac{4\sqrt{5}}{9}, -\frac{1}{9}$

Lesson 14-4

Practice
CRM p. 26 AL OL BL ELL

14-4 Practice
Double-Angle and Half-Angle Identities

Find the exact values of $\sin 2\theta$, $\cos 2\theta$, $\sin\frac{\theta}{2}$, and $\cos\frac{\theta}{2}$ for each of the following.

1. $\cos\theta = \frac{5}{13}$, $0° < \theta < 90°$ $\frac{120}{169}, -\frac{119}{169}, \frac{2\sqrt{13}}{13}, \frac{3\sqrt{13}}{13}$
2. $\sin\theta = \frac{8}{17}$, $90° < \theta < 180°$ $-\frac{240}{289}, \frac{161}{289}, \frac{4\sqrt{17}}{17}, \frac{\sqrt{17}}{17}$
3. $\cos\theta = \frac{1}{4}$, $270° < \theta < 360°$ $-\frac{\sqrt{15}}{8}, -\frac{7}{8}, \frac{\sqrt{6}}{4}, \frac{\sqrt{10}}{4}$
4. $\sin\theta = -\frac{2}{3}$, $180° < \theta < 270°$ $\frac{4\sqrt{5}}{9}, \frac{1}{9}, \frac{\sqrt{18+6\sqrt{5}}}{6}, \frac{\sqrt{18-6\sqrt{5}}}{6}$

Find the exact value of each expression.

5. $\tan 105°$ $-2-\sqrt{3}$
6. $\tan 15°$ $2-\sqrt{3}$
7. $\cos 67.5°$ $\frac{\sqrt{2-\sqrt{2}}}{2}$
8. $\sin\left(-\frac{\pi}{8}\right)$ $-\frac{\sqrt{2-\sqrt{2}}}{2}$

Verify that each equation is an identity.

9. $\sin\frac{\theta}{2} = \frac{\tan\theta - \sin\theta}{2\tan\theta}$

$$\frac{1-\cos\theta}{2} \stackrel{?}{=} \frac{\tan\theta - \sin\theta}{2\tan\theta};\quad \frac{1-\cos\theta}{2} \stackrel{?}{=} \frac{\frac{\tan\theta}{\tan\theta} - \frac{\sin\theta}{\tan\theta}}{2\frac{\tan\theta}{\tan\theta}};\quad \frac{1-\cos\theta}{2} = \frac{1-\cos\theta}{2}$$

10. $\sin 4\theta = 4\cos 2\theta \sin\theta\cos\theta$

$$\sin 4\theta \stackrel{?}{=} 4\cos 2\theta \sin\theta\cos\theta$$
$$\sin 2(2\theta) \stackrel{?}{=} 4\cos 2\theta \sin\theta\cos\theta$$
$$2\sin 2\theta\cos 2\theta \stackrel{?}{=} 4\cos 2\theta \sin\theta\cos\theta$$
$$2(2\sin\theta\cos\theta)(\cos 2\theta) \stackrel{?}{=} 4\cos 2\theta \sin\theta\cos\theta$$
$$4\cos 2\theta\sin\theta\cos\theta = 4\cos 2\theta \sin\theta\cos\theta$$

11. **AERIAL PHOTOGRAPHY** In aerial photography, there is a reduction in film exposure for any point X not directly below the camera. The reduction E_θ is given by $E_\theta = E_0\cos^4\theta$, where θ is the angle between the perpendicular line from the camera to the ground and the line from the camera to point X, and E_0 is the exposure for the point directly below the camera. Using the identity $2\sin^2\theta = 1 - \cos 2\theta$, verify that $E_0\cos^4\theta = E_0\left(\frac{1}{2} + \frac{\cos 2\theta}{2}\right)^2$.

$$E_0\cos^4\theta = E_0(\cos^2\theta)^2 = E_0(1-\sin^2\theta)^2 = E_0\left(1 - \frac{2\sin^2\theta}{2}\right)^2 = E_0\left(1 - \frac{1-\cos 2\theta}{2}\right)^2 = E_0\left(\frac{1}{2} + \frac{\cos 2\theta}{2}\right)^2$$

12. **IMAGING** A scanner takes thermal images from altitudes of 300 to 12,000 meters. The width W of the swath covered by the image is given by $W = 2H'\tan\theta$, where H' is the height and θ is half the scanner's field of view. Verify that $\frac{2H'\sin 2\theta}{1+\cos 2\theta} = 2H'\tan\theta$.

$$\frac{2H'\sin 2\theta}{1+\cos 2\theta} = \frac{4H'\sin\theta\cos\theta}{1+(2\cos^2\theta - 1)} = \frac{4H'\sin\theta\cos\theta}{2\cos^2\theta} = \frac{2H'\sin\theta}{\cos\theta} = 2H'\tan\theta$$

Word Problem Practice
CRM p. 27 AL OL BL ELL

14-4 Word Problem Practice
Double-Angle and Half-Angle Identities

1. **GEOMETRY** The large triangle shown in the figure below is an isosceles right triangle. The small triangle inside the large triangle was formed by bisecting each of the isosceles angles of the right triangle.

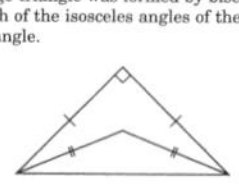

a. What is the exact value of the sine of either of the congruent angles of the small triangle? $\frac{\sqrt{2-\sqrt{2}}}{2}$

b. What is the exact value of the cosine of either of the congruent angles of the small triangle? $\frac{\sqrt{2+\sqrt{2}}}{2}$

c. What is the exact value of the sine of the obtuse angle of the small triangle? $\frac{\sqrt{2}}{2}$

d. What is the exact value of the cosine of the obtuse angle of the small triangle? $-\frac{\sqrt{2}}{2}$

2. **RAMPS** A ramp for loading goods onto a truck was mistakenly built with the dimensions shown in the figure below. The degree measure of the angle the ramp makes with the ground should have been twice the degree measure of the angle shown in the figure.

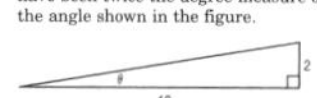

a. Find the exact values of the sine and cosine of the angle the ramp should have made with the ground. $\frac{9}{41}, \frac{40}{41}$

b. If the ramp had been built properly, what would the degree measures of the two acute angles have been? 12.7°, 77.3°

Lesson 14-4

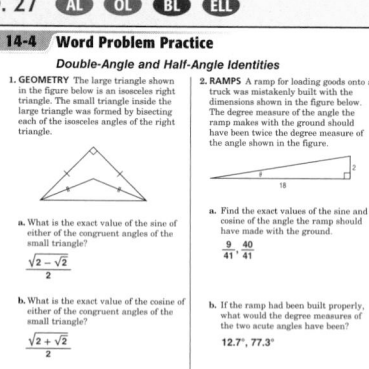

Example 4 p. 914

25. **ELECTRONICS** Consider an AC circuit consisting of a power supply and a resistor. If the current I_0 in the circuit at time t is $I_0 \sin t\theta$, then the power delivered to the resistor is $P = {I_0}^2 R \sin^2 t\theta$, where R is the resistance. Express the power in terms of $\cos 2t\theta$. $P = \frac{1}{2}{I_0}^2 R - \frac{1}{2}{I_0}^2 R \cos 2t\theta$

Example 5 p. 914

Verify that each equation is an identity. 26. See margin.

27–29. See Chapter 14 Answer Appendix.

26. $\tan 2\theta = \frac{2}{\cot\theta - \tan\theta}$
27. $1 + \frac{1}{2}\sin 2\theta = \frac{\sec\theta + \sin\theta}{\sec\theta}$
28. $\sin\frac{\theta}{2}\cos\frac{\theta}{2} = \frac{\sin\theta}{2}$
29. $\tan\frac{\theta}{2} = \frac{\sin\theta}{1+\cos\theta}$

Real-World Link

On average, a place kick travels about 15 yards farther than a punt, assuming the kicker is at least 13 years old.

30. **FOOTBALL** Suppose a place kicker consistently kicks a football with an initial velocity of 95 feet per second. Prove that the horizontal distance the ball travels in the air will be the same for $\theta = 45° + A$ as for $\theta = 45° - A$. Use the formula given in Exercise 9. See Chapter 14 Answer Appendix.

Find the exact values of $\sin 2\theta$, $\cos 2\theta$, and $\tan 2\theta$.

31. $\cos\theta = \frac{4}{5}$; $0° < \theta < 90°$ $\frac{24}{25}, \frac{7}{25}, \frac{24}{7}$
32. $\sin\theta = \frac{1}{3}$; $0 < \theta < \frac{\pi}{2}$ $\frac{4\sqrt{2}}{9}, \frac{7}{9}, \frac{4\sqrt{2}}{7}$
33. $\tan\theta = -3$; $90° < \theta < 180°$ $-\frac{3}{5}, -\frac{4}{5}, \frac{3}{4}$
34. $\sec\theta = -\frac{4}{3}$; $90° < \theta < 180°$
35. $\csc\theta = -\frac{5}{2}$; $\frac{3\pi}{2} < \theta < 2\pi$ $-\frac{4\sqrt{21}}{25}, \frac{17}{25}, -\frac{4\sqrt{21}}{17}$
36. $\cot\theta = \frac{3}{2}$; $180° < \theta < 270°$ $\frac{12}{13}, \frac{5}{13}, \frac{12}{5}$

34. $-\frac{3\sqrt{7}}{8}, \frac{1}{8}, -3\sqrt{7}$

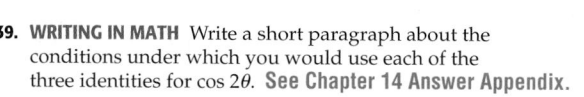

H.O.T. Problems
Use Higher-Order Thinking Skills

37. **ERROR ANALYSIS** Teresa and Nathan are calculating the exact value of sin 15°. Is either of them correct? Explain your reasoning. See Chapter 14 Answer Appendix.

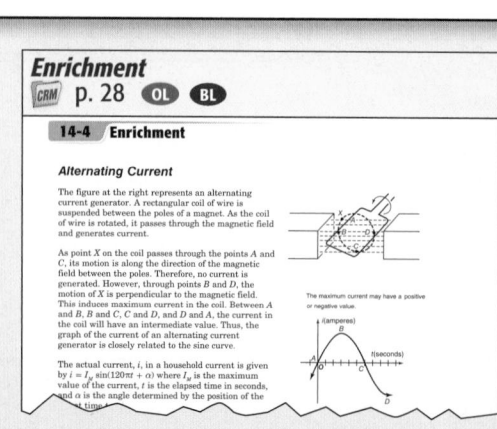

Teresa	Nathan
$\sin(A - B) = \sin A\cos B - \cos A\sin B$ $\sin(45 - 30) = \sin 45\cos 30 - \cos 45\sin 30$ $= \frac{\sqrt{2}}{2}\cdot\frac{\sqrt{3}}{2} - \frac{\sqrt{2}}{2}\cdot\frac{1}{2}$ $= \frac{\sqrt{4}}{4}$	$\sin\frac{A}{2} = \pm\sqrt{\frac{1-\cos A}{2}}$ $\sin\frac{30}{2} = \pm\sqrt{\frac{1-\frac{1}{2}}{2}}$ $= 0.5$

38. **CHALLENGE** Circle O is a unit circle. Use the figure to prove that $\tan\frac{1}{2}\theta = \frac{\sin\theta}{1+\cos\theta}$.

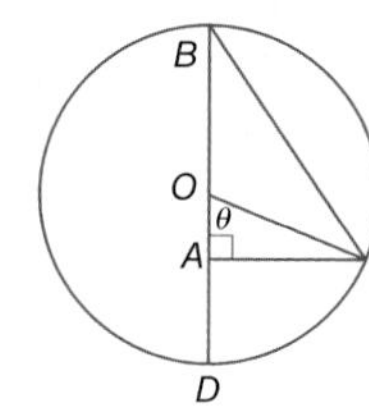

38. $\angle PBD$ is an inscribed angle that subtends the same arc as the central angle $\angle POD$, so $m\angle PBD = \frac{1}{2}\theta$. By right triangle trigonometry, $\tan\frac{1}{2}\theta = \frac{PA}{BA} = \frac{PA}{1+OA} = \frac{\sin\theta}{1+\cos\theta}$.

39. **WRITING IN MATH** Write a short paragraph about the conditions under which you would use each of the three identities for $\cos 2\theta$. See Chapter 14 Answer Appendix.

40. **PROOF** Use the formula for $\sin(A + B)$ to derive the formula for $\sin 2\theta$, and use the formula for $\cos(A + B)$ to derive the formula for $\cos 2\theta$. See Chapter 14 Answer Appendix.

41. **REASONING** Derive the half-angle identities from the double-angle identities. See Chapter 14 Answer Appendix.

42. **OPEN ENDED** Suppose a golfer consistently hits the ball so that it leaves the tee with an initial velocity of 115 feet per second and $d = \frac{2v^2\sin\theta\cos\theta}{g}$. Explain why the maximum distance is attained when $\theta = 45°$.

42. Sample answer: Since $d = \frac{v^2\sin 2\theta}{g}$, d is at a maximum when $\sin 2\theta = 1$, that is, when $2\theta = 90°$ or $\theta = 45°$.

Enrichment
CRM p. 28 OL BL

14-4 Enrichment

Alternating Current

The figure at the right represents an alternating current generator. A rectangular coil of wire is suspended between the poles of a magnet. As the coil of wire is rotated, it passes through the magnetic field and generates current.

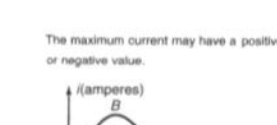

As point X on the coil passes through the points A and C, its motion is along the direction of the magnetic field between the poles. Therefore, no current is generated. However, through points B and D, the motion of X is perpendicular to the magnetic field. This induces maximum current in the coil. Between A and B, B and C, C and D, and D and A, the current in the coil will have an intermediate value. Thus, the graph of the current of an alternating current generator is closely related to the sine curve.

The maximum current may have a positive or negative value.

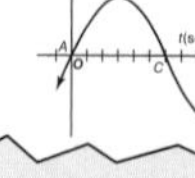

The actual current, i, in a household current is given by $i = I_M \sin(120\pi t + \alpha)$ where I_M is the maximum value of the current, t is the elapsed time in seconds, and α is the angle determined by the position of the ... at time ...

Additional Answer

26. $\tan 2\theta \stackrel{?}{=} \frac{2}{\cot\theta - \tan\theta}$

$\tan 2\theta \stackrel{?}{=} \frac{2}{\cot\theta - \tan\theta}\cdot\frac{\tan\theta}{\tan\theta}$

$\tan 2\theta \stackrel{?}{=} \frac{2\tan\theta}{\cot\theta\tan\theta - \tan^2\theta}$

$\tan 2\theta \stackrel{?}{=} \frac{2\tan\theta}{1 - \tan^2\theta}$

$\tan 2\theta = \tan 2\theta$ ✓

NGSSS PRACTICE 912.A.2.12, 912.S.3.3, 912.A.2.4, 912.G.6.2

43. THINK SOLVE EXPLAIN **SHORT RESPONSE** Angles *C* and *D* are supplementary. The measure of angle *C* is seven times the measure of angle *D*. Find the measure of angle *D* in degrees. 22.5

44. ACT/SAT Ms. Romero has a list of the yearly salaries of the staff members in her department. Which measure of data describes the middle income value of the salaries? B

- **A.** mean
- **B.** median
- **C.** mode
- **D.** range

45. Identify the domain and range of the function $f(x) = |4x + 1| - 8$. G

- **F.** $D = \{x \mid -3 \le x \le 1\}$, $R = \{y \mid y \ge -8\}$
- **G.** D = {all real numbers}, $R = \{y \mid y \ge -8\}$
- **H.** $D = \{x \mid -3 \le x \le 1\}$, R = {all real numbers}
- **I.** D = {all real numbers}, R = {all real numbers}

46. GEOMETRY Angel is putting a stone walkway around a circular pond. He has enough stones to make a walkway 144 feet long. If he uses all of the stones to surround the pond, what is the radius of the pond? B

- **A.** $\frac{144}{\pi}$ ft
- **B.** $\frac{72}{\pi}$ ft
- **C.** 144π ft
- **D.** 72π ft

Spiral Review

Find the exact value of each expression. (Lesson 14-3) 48. $\frac{\sqrt{2} - \sqrt{6}}{4}$

47. $\sin 135°$ $\frac{\sqrt{2}}{2}$

48. $\cos 105°$

49. $\sin 285°$ $\frac{-\sqrt{6} - \sqrt{2}}{4}$

50. $\cos(-30°)$ $\frac{\sqrt{3}}{2}$

51. $\sin(-240°)$ $\frac{\sqrt{3}}{2}$

52. $\cos(-120°)$ $-\frac{1}{2}$

Verify that each equation is an identity. (Lesson 14-2) 53, 54. See margin.

53. $\cot\theta + \sec\theta = \frac{\cos^2\theta + \sin\theta}{\sin\theta\cos\theta}$

54. $\sin^2\theta + \tan^2\theta = (1 - \cos^2\theta) + \frac{\sec^2\theta}{\csc^2\theta}$

Determine whether each triangle should be solved by beginning with the Law of *Sines* or Law of *Cosines*. Then solve each triangle. Round measures of sides to the nearest tenth and measures of angles to the nearest degree. (Lesson 13-5)

55.

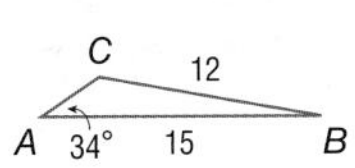

sines; $B \approx 102°$, $C \approx 44°$, $b \approx 21.1$ or $B \approx 10°$, $C \approx 136°$, $b \approx 3.7$

56.

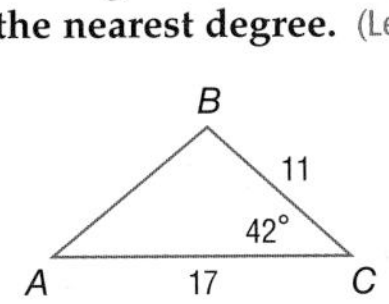

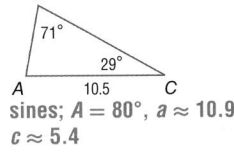

cosines; $A \approx 40°$, $B \approx 98°$, $c \approx 11.5$

57.

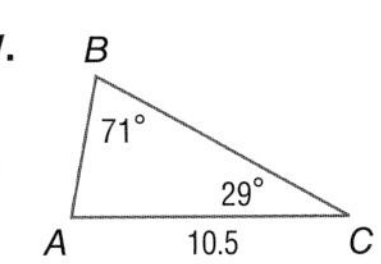

sines; $A = 80°$, $a \approx 10.9$, $c \approx 5.4$

Skills Review

Solve each equation by factoring. (Lesson 5-3)

58. $x^2 + 5x - 24 = 0$ {−8, 3}

59. $x^2 - 3x - 28 = 0$ {−4, 7}

60. $x^2 - 4x = 21$ {−3, 7}

Differentiated Instruction BL

Extension Ask students to write an expression for $\sin 4\theta$ in terms of $\sin\theta$ and $\cos\theta$.
Sample answer: $\sin 4\theta = 4\sin\theta\cos\theta - 8\sin^3\theta\cos\theta$

Watch Out!

Error Analysis For Exercise 37, students should see that Teresa incorrectly replaced $\frac{\sqrt{6}}{4} - \frac{\sqrt{2}}{4}$ with $\frac{\sqrt{4}}{4}$, while Nathan incorrectly replaced $\cos 30°$ with $\frac{1}{2}$ rather than with $\frac{\sqrt{3}}{2}$. Explain to students that both first steps, $\sin 15° = \sin(45° - 30°)$ and $\sin 15° = \sin\frac{30°}{2}$, are valid first steps. However, Teresa's fourth step should be $\frac{\sqrt{6} - \sqrt{2}}{4}$ and Nathan's steps, after the first line, should be $\sin\frac{30°}{2} = \sqrt{\frac{1 - \frac{\sqrt{3}}{2}}{2}} = \sqrt{\frac{2 - \sqrt{3}}{4}} = \frac{\sqrt{2 - \sqrt{3}}}{2}$

4 ASSESS

Name the Math Have students tell how they determine whether a problem involves a double-angle or half-angle identity and how they use each type of equation.

Formative Assessment

Check for students' understanding of concepts in Lesson 14-4.

CRM Quiz 3, p. 38

Additional Answers

53.
$$\cot\theta + \sec\theta \stackrel{?}{=} \frac{\cos^2\theta + \sin\theta}{\sin\theta\cos\theta}$$
$$\cot\theta + \sec\theta \stackrel{?}{=} \frac{\cos^2\theta}{\sin\theta\cos\theta} + \frac{\sin\theta}{\sin\theta\cos\theta}$$
$$\cot\theta + \sec\theta \stackrel{?}{=} \frac{\cos\theta}{\sin\theta} + \frac{1}{\cos\theta}$$
$$\cot\theta + \sec\theta = \cot\theta + \sec\theta \checkmark$$

54.
$$\sin^2\theta + \tan^2\theta \stackrel{?}{=} (1 - \cos^2\theta) + \frac{\sec^2\theta}{\csc^2\theta}$$
$$\sin^2\theta + \tan^2\theta \stackrel{?}{=} \sin^2\theta + \frac{\sec^2\theta}{\csc^2\theta}$$
$$\sin^2\theta + \tan^2\theta \stackrel{?}{=} \sin^2\theta + \frac{1}{\cos^2\theta} \div \frac{1}{\sin^2\theta}$$
$$\sin^2\theta + \tan^2\theta \stackrel{?}{=} \sin^2\theta + \frac{\sin^2\theta}{\cos^2\theta}$$
$$\sin^2\theta + \tan^2\theta = \sin^2\theta + \tan^2\theta \checkmark$$

EXPLORE 14-5 Lesson Notes

1 FOCUS

Objective Use a graphing calculator to solve trigonometric equations.

Materials for Each Student

TI-83/84 Plus or other graphing calculator

Teaching Tip

In Example 1, approximate solutions can also be found by using the Trace feature. In most situations, however, the Intersect feature will give more accurate solutions.

Remind students to use appropriate windows for their graphs.

2 TEACH

Working in Cooperative Groups

Have students work in pairs so they can help each other correct keystroke errors. Have them complete Examples 1 and 2 and Exercise 1.

Ask:

- How are the solutions of the equations related to the points where the graphs intersect? The solutions are the x values of the points of intersection.
- How can you tell if an equation has no solution? The graphs of Y1 and Y2 do not intersect.

Practice Have students complete Exercises 2–6.

3 ASSESS

Formative Assessment

Use Exercise 6 to assess whether students understand how the specified interval affects the solutions.

EXPLORE 14-5

Graphing Technology Lab

Solving Trigonometric Equations

FL Math Online glencoe.com
- Other Calculator Keystrokes
- Graphing Technology Personal Tutor

NGSSS **MA.912.T.3.4** **Solve trigonometric equations** and real-world problems involving applications of trigonometric equations using technology when appropriate.

The graph of a trigonometric function is made up of points that represent all values that satisfy the function. To solve a trigonometric equation, you need to find all values of the variable that satisfy the equation. You can use a TI-83/84 Plus graphing calculator to solve trigonometric equations by graphing each side of the equation as a function and then locating the points of intersection.

ACTIVITY 1 Real Solutions

Use a graphing calculator to solve $\sin x = 0.4$ if $0° \le x < 360°$.

Step 1 Enter and graph related equations. Rewrite the equation as two equations, Y1 = $\sin x$ and Y2 = 0.4. Then graph the two equations. Because the interval is in degrees, set your calculator to degree mode.

KEYSTROKES: [MODE] [▼] [▼] [▶] [ENTER]
[Y=] [SIN] [X,T,θ,n] [)]
[ENTER] 0.4 [ENTER] [GRAPH]

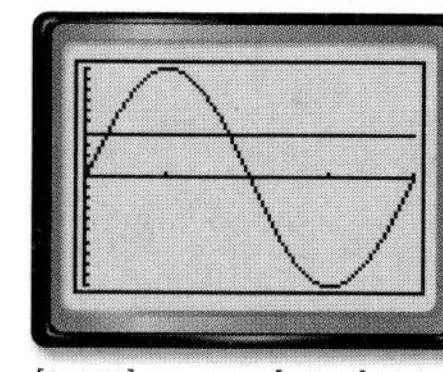

[0, 360] scl: 90 by [−1, 1] scl: 0.1

Step 2 Approximate the solutions. Based on the graph, you can see that there are two points of intersection in the interval $0° \le x < 360°$. Use the CALC feature to determine the x-values at which the two graphs intersect.

The solutions are $x \approx 23.57°$ and $x \approx 156.4°$.

ACTIVITY 2 No Real Solutions

Use a graphing calculator to solve $\tan^2 x \cos x + 3 \cos x = 0$ if $0° \le x < 360°$.

Step 1 Enter and graph related equations. The related equations to be graphed are $y_1 = \tan^2 x \cos x + 3 \cos x$ and $y_2 = 0$.

KEYSTROKES: [Y=] [TAN] [X,T,θ,n] [)] [x^2] [COS]
[X,T,θ,n] [)] [+] 3 [COS] [X,T,θ,n]
[)] [ENTER] 0 [ENTER]

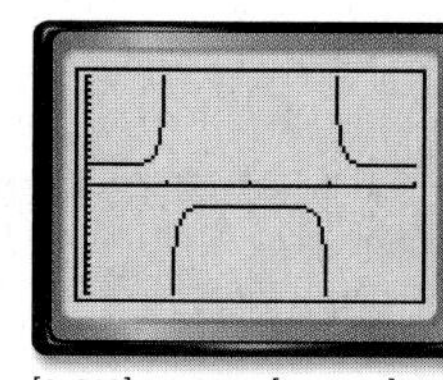

[0, 360] scl: 90 by [−15, 15] scl: 1

Step 2 These two functions do not intersect.

Therefore, the equation $\tan^2 x \cos x + 3 \cos x = 0$ has no real solutions.

Exercises

Use a graphing calculator to solve each equation for the values of x indicated.

1. $\sin x = 0.7$; $0° \le x < 360°$ **44.4°, 135.6°**
2. $\tan x = \cos x$; $0° \le x < 360°$ **38.17°, 141.8°**
3. $3 \cos x + 4 = 0.5$; $0° \le x < 360°$ **no real solution**
4. $0.25 \cos x = 3.4$; $-720° \le x < 720°$ **no real solution**
5. $\sin 2x = \sin x$; $0° \le x < 360°$ **0°, 60°, 180°, 300°**
6. $\sin 2x - 3 \sin x = 0$ if $-360° \le x < 360°$ **−360°, −180°, 0°, 180°**

From Concrete to Abstract

Have students consider Exercises 1–6 with a different interval or no interval and explain how this affects the solutions.

14-5 Solving Trigonometric Equations

Why?

When you ride a Ferris wheel that has a diameter of 40 meters and turns at a rate of 1.5 revolutions per minute, the height above the ground, in meters, of your seat after t minutes can be modeled by the equation

$$h = 21 - 20 \cos 3\pi t.$$

After the ride begins, how long is it before your seat is 31 meters above the ground for the first time?

Then
You verified trigonometric identities. (Lessons 14-2 through 14-4)

Now
- Solve trigonometric equations.
- Find extraneous solutions from trigonometric equations.

NGSSS
MA.912.T.3.4 Solve trigonometric equations and real-world problems involving applications of trigonometric equations **using technology when appropriate.**

New Vocabulary
trigonometric equations

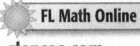

FL Math Online
glencoe.com

Solve Trigonometric Equations So far in this chapter, we have studied a special type of trigonometric equation called an identity. Trigonometric identities are equations that are true for all values of the variable for which both sides are defined. In this lesson, we will examine **trigonometric equations** that are true for only certain values of the variable. Solving these equations resembles solving algebraic equations.

EXAMPLE 1 Solve Equations for a Given Interval

Solve $\sin \theta \cos \theta - \frac{1}{2}\cos \theta = 0$ if $0 \le \theta \le 180°$.

$\sin \theta \cos \theta - \frac{1}{2}\cos \theta = 0$ — **Original equation**

$\cos \theta \left(\sin \theta - \frac{1}{2}\right) = 0$ — **Factor.**

$\cos \theta = 0$ or $\sin \theta - \frac{1}{2} = 0$ — **Zero Product Property**

$\theta = 90°$ or $270°$ $\qquad \sin \theta = \frac{1}{2}$

$\theta = 30°$ or $150°$

The solutions are 30°, 90°, and 150°.

CHECK You can check the answer by graphing $y = \sin \theta \cos \theta$ and $y = \frac{1}{2}\cos \theta$ in the same coordinate plane on a graphing calculator. Then find the points where the graphs intersect. You can see that there are infinitely many such points, but we are only interested in the points between 0° and 180°.

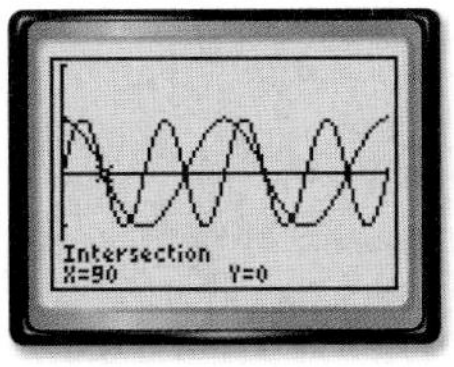

Guided Practice

1. Find all solutions of $\sin 2\theta = \cos \theta$ if $0 \le \theta \le 2\pi$. $\frac{\pi}{6}, \frac{\pi}{2}, \frac{5\pi}{6}, \frac{3\pi}{2}$

Personal Tutor glencoe.com

Trigonometric equations are usually solved for values of the variable between 0° and 360° or between 0 radians and 2π radians. There are solutions outside that interval. These other solutions differ by integral multiples of the period of the function.

14-5 Lesson Notes

1 FOCUS

Vertical Alignment

Before Lesson 14-5
Verify trigonometric identities.

Lesson 14-5
Solve trigonometric equations. Find extraneous solutions from trigonometric equations.

After Lesson 14-5
Use trigonometry to solve real-world problems.

2 TEACH

Scaffolding Questions

Have students read the *Why?* section of the lesson.

Ask:
- Take any point on the Ferris wheel. How far does that point travel in 1 revolution? 40π or about 125.66 meters
- How far does a position on the Ferris wheel travel in 1 minute? 60π or about 188.5 meters
- When $t = 0$, what is the value of $20 \cos 3\pi t$? 20

Lesson 14-5 Resources

Resource	Approaching-Level	On-Level	Beyond-Level	English Learners
Teacher Edition	• Differentiated Instruction, p. 921	• Differentiated Instruction, p. 921	• Differentiated Instruction, p. 925	
Chapter Resource Masters	• Study Guide and Intervention, pp. 29–30 • Skills Practice, p. 31 • Practice, p. 32 • Word Problem Practice, p. 33	• Study Guide and Intervention, pp. 29–30 • Skills Practice, p. 31 • Practice, p. 32 • Word Problem Practice, p. 33 • Enrichment, p. 34	• Practice, p. 32 • Word Problem Practice, p. 33 • Enrichment, p. 34	• Study Guide and Intervention, pp. 29–30 • Skills Practice, p. 31 • Practice, p. 32 • Word Problem Practice, p. 33
Transparencies	• 5-Minute Check Transparency 14-5	• 5-Minute Check Transparency 14-5	• 5-Minute Check Transparency 14-5	• 5-Minute Check Transparency 14-5
Other	• Study Notebook • Teaching Algebra with Manipulatives	• Study Notebook • Teaching Algebra with Manipulatives	• Study Notebook	• Study Notebook • Teaching Algebra with Manipulatives

Solve Trigonometric Equations

Example 1 shows how to solve trigonometric equations for a given interval. **Example 2** shows how to solve trigonometric equations for angles measured in radians. **Example 3** shows how to solve real-world problems involving trigonometric equations.

Formative Assessment

Use the Guided Practice exercises after each example to determine students' understanding of concepts.

Additional Examples

1 Solve $2\cos^2\theta - 1 = \sin\theta$ if $0° \leq \theta \leq 180°$. $30°, 150°$

2 **a.** Solve $\cos\theta + \frac{1}{4} = \sin^2\theta$ for all values of θ if θ is measured in degrees. $60° + k \cdot 360°, 300° + k \cdot 360°$, where k is any interger

b. Solve $2\cos\theta = -1$ for all values of θ if θ is measured in radians. $\frac{2\pi}{3} + 2k\pi$ and $\frac{4\pi}{3} + 2k\pi$, where k is any integer

3 **AMUSEMENT PARKS** Refer to the beginning of the lesson. How long after the Ferris wheel starts will your seat first be $(10\sqrt{2} + 21)$ meters above the ground?

$$10\sqrt{2} + 21 = 21 - 20\cos 3\pi t;$$
$$10\sqrt{2} = -20\cos 3\pi t;$$
$$-\frac{\sqrt{2}}{2} = \cos 3\pi t;$$
$$\cos^{-1}\left(-\frac{\sqrt{2}}{2}\right) = 3\pi t;$$
$$\frac{3}{4}\pi = 3\pi t$$
$$\frac{1}{4} = t$$

$\frac{1}{4}$ min or 15 sec

Tips for New Teachers

Reasoning In Example 2, show students how to look for patterns in the solutions. Students should look for pairs of solutions that differ by exactly π or 2π.

EXAMPLE 2 Infinitely Many Solutions

Solve $\cos\theta + 1 = 0$ for all values of θ if θ is measured in radians.

$\cos\theta + 1 = 0$
$\cos\theta = -1$

Look at the graph of $y = \cos\theta$ to find solutions of $\cos\theta = -1$.

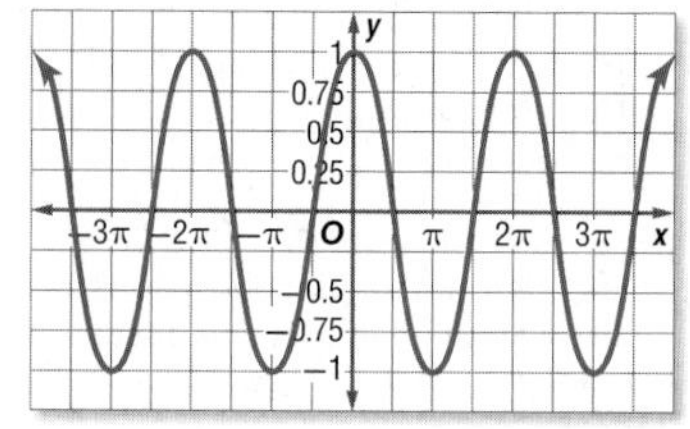

The solutions are π, 3π, 5π, and so on, and $-\pi$, -3π, -5π, and so on. The only solution in the interval 0 radians to 2π radians is π. The period of the cosine function is 2π radians. So the solutions can be written as $\pi + 2k\pi$, where k is any integer.

StudyTip

Expressing Solutions as Multiples The expression $\pi + 2k\pi$ includes 3π and its multiples, so it is not necessary to list them separately.

Guided Practice

2A. Solve $\cos 2\theta + \cos\theta + 1 = 0$ for all values of θ if θ is measured in degrees.

2B. Solve $2\sin\theta = -1$ for all values of θ if θ is measured in radians.

2A. $90° + k \cdot 180°$, $120° + k \cdot 360°$, and $240° + k \cdot 360°$
2B. $\frac{7\pi}{6} + 2k\pi$ and $\frac{11\pi}{6} + 2k\pi$

Personal Tutor glencoe.com

Trigonometric equations are often used to solve real-world problems.

Real-World EXAMPLE 3 Solve Trigonometric Equations

AMUSEMENT PARKS **Refer to the beginning of the lesson. How long after the Ferris wheel starts will your seat first be 31 meters above the ground?**

$h = 21 - 20\cos 3\pi t$	Original equation
$31 = 21 - 20\cos 3\pi t$	Replace h with 31.
$10 = -20\cos 3\pi t$	Subtract 21 from each side.
$-\frac{1}{2} = \cos 3\pi t$	Divide each side by −20.
$\cos^{-1} -\frac{1}{2} = 3\pi t$	Take the Arccosine.
$\frac{2\pi}{3} = 3\pi t$ or $\frac{4\pi}{3} = 3\pi t$	The Arccosine of $-\frac{1}{2}$ is $\frac{2\pi}{3}$ or $\frac{4\pi}{3}$.
$\frac{2\pi}{3} + 2\pi k = 3\pi t$ or $\frac{4\pi}{3} + 2\pi k = 3\pi t$	k is any integer.
$\frac{2}{9} + \frac{2}{3}k = t$ $\quad$ $\frac{4}{9} + \frac{2}{3}k = t$	Divide each term by 3π.

The least positive value for t is obtained by letting $k = 0$ in the first expression. Therefore, $t = \frac{2}{9}$ of a minute or about 13 seconds.

Guided Practice

3. How long after the Ferris wheel starts will your seat first be 41 meters above the ground? about 20 seconds

Personal Tutor glencoe.com

Problem-Solving Tip

Look for a Pattern Look for patterns in your solutions. Look for pairs of solutions that differ by exactly π or 2π and write your solutions with the simplest possible pattern.

Extraneous Solutions Some trigonometric equations have no solution. For example, the equation $\cos \theta = 4$ has no solution because all values of $\cos \theta$ are between −1 and 1, inclusive. Thus, the solution set for $\cos \theta = 4$ is empty.

EXAMPLE 4 Determine Whether a Solution Exists

Solve each equation.

a. $2 \sin^2 \theta - 3 \sin \theta - 2 = 0$ **if** $0 \le \theta \le 2\pi$

$2 \sin^2 \theta - 3 \sin \theta - 2 = 0$ **Original equation**

$(\sin \theta - 2)(2 \sin \theta + 1) = 0$ **Factor.**

$\sin \theta - 2 = 0$ or $2 \sin \theta + 1 = 0$ **Zero Product Property**

$\sin \theta = 2$ $\quad$ $2 \sin \theta = -1$

This is not a solution since all values of $\sin \theta$ are between −1 and 1, inclusive. $\quad$ $\sin \theta = -\frac{1}{2}$

$\theta = \frac{7\pi}{6}$ or $\frac{11\pi}{6}$

The solutions are $\frac{7\pi}{6}$ or $\frac{11\pi}{6}$.

CHECK

$2 \sin \theta - 3 \sin \theta - 2 = 0$ $\qquad$ $2 \sin^2 \theta - 3 \sin \theta - 2 = 0$

$2 \sin^2 \left(\frac{7\pi}{6}\right) - 3 \sin \left(\frac{7\pi}{6}\right) - 2 \stackrel{?}{=} 0$ $\qquad$ $2 \sin^2 \left(\frac{11\pi}{6}\right) - 3 \sin \left(\frac{11\pi}{6}\right) - 2 \stackrel{?}{=} 0$

$2\left(\frac{1}{4}\right) - 3\left(-\frac{1}{2}\right) - 2 \stackrel{?}{=} 0$ $\qquad$ $2\left(\frac{1}{4}\right) - 3\left(-\frac{1}{2}\right) - 2 \stackrel{?}{=} 0$

$\frac{1}{2} + \frac{3}{2} - 2 \stackrel{?}{=} 0$ $\qquad$ $\frac{1}{2} + \frac{3}{2} - 2 \stackrel{?}{=} 0$

$0 = 0$ ✓ $\qquad$ $0 = 0$ ✓

b. $\sin \theta = 1 + \cos \theta$ **if** $0° \le \theta < 360°$

$\sin \theta = 1 + \cos \theta$ **Original equation**

$\sin^2 \theta = (1 + \cos \theta)^2$ **Square each side.**

$1 - \cos^2 \theta = 1 + 2 \cos \theta + \cos^2 \theta$ **$\sin^2 \theta = 1 - \cos^2 \theta$**

$0 = 2 \cos \theta + 2 \cos^2 \theta$ **Set the left side equal to 0.**

$0 = 2 \cos \theta (1 + \cos \theta)$ **Factor.**

$1 + \cos \theta = 0$ or $2 \cos \theta = 0$ **Zero Product Property**

$\cos \theta = -1$ $\quad$ $\cos \theta = 0$

$\theta = 180$ $\quad$ $\theta = 90°$ or $270°$

CHECK

$\sin \theta = 1 + \cos \theta$ $\qquad$ $\sin \theta = 1 + \cos \theta$

$\sin 90° \stackrel{?}{=} 1 + \cos 90°$ $\qquad$ $\sin 180° \stackrel{?}{=} 1 + \cos 180°$

$1 \stackrel{?}{=} 1 + 0$ $\qquad$ $0 \stackrel{?}{=} 1 + (-1)$

$1 = 1$ ✓ $\qquad$ $0 = 0$ ✓

$\sin \theta = 1 + \cos \theta$

$\sin 270° \stackrel{?}{=} 1 + \cos 270°$

$-1 \stackrel{?}{=} 1 + 0$

$-1 \ne 1$ ✗

The solutions are 90° and 180°.

Guided Practice 4B. identity; therefore, infinitely many solutions

Solve each equation.

4A. $\sin^2 \theta + 2 \cos^2 \theta = 4$ no solution $\qquad$ **4B.** $\cos^2 \theta + 3 = 4 - \sin^2 \theta$

Personal Tutor glencoe.com

If an equation cannot be solved easily by factoring, try rewriting the expression using trigonometric identities. However, using identities and some algebraic operations, such as squaring, may result in extraneous solutions. So, it is necessary to check your solutions using the original equation.

Extraneous Solutions

Example 4 shows how to solve a trigonometric equation and test for extraneous solutions. **Example 5** shows how to use identities to solve a trigonometric equation.

Additional Example

4 Solve each equation.

a. $\sin \theta \cos \theta = \cos^2 \theta$ if $0 \le \theta \le 2\pi$ $\quad \frac{\pi}{4}, \frac{\pi}{2}, \frac{5\pi}{4}, \frac{3\pi}{2}$

b. $\cos \theta = 1 - \sin \theta$ if $0° \le \theta \le 360°$ $\quad$ 0°, 90°, 360°

Focus on Mathematical Content

Infinitely Many Solutions Many trigonometric equations have an infinite number of solutions. If no interval is specified to restrict the number of solutions, the infinite number of solutions must be specified by using an expression rather than by simply using a number. There is a solution that occurs for each full rotation about the origin, a solution has the form $a° + k \cdot 360°$, where k is any integer.

TEACH with TECH

BLOG Have students write blog entries about how to solve trigonometric equations. Have them describe how the process is similar to and different from solving other types of equations.

Differentiated Instruction AL OL

Interpersonal Learners As students work through this lesson, have them create a class list on the board that identifies common errors they made. Encourage students to add suggestions for how to avoid their errors. For example, one common error is having one's calculator set to degrees when it needs to be set to radians for a problem, and vice versa.

Additional Example

5 Solve $\tan^4\theta - 4\sec^2\theta = -7$ for all values of θ if θ is measured in degrees. $\theta = 60° + 180°k$, $120° + 180°k$, or $45° + 90° \cdot k$, where k is any integer.

3 PRACTICE

Formative Assessment

Use Exercises 1–29 to check for understanding.

Then use the chart at the bottom of this page to customize assignments for your students.

Additional Answer

21b. Every day from February 19 to October 20; sample explanation: Since the longest day of the year occurs around June 22, the days between February 19 and October 20 must increase in length until June 22 and then decrease in length until October 20.

StudyTip

Solving Trigonometric Equations Remember that *solving a trigonometric equation* means solving for all values of the variable.

EXAMPLE 5 Solve Trigonometric Equations by Using Identities

Solve $2\sec^2\theta - \tan^4\theta = -1$ for all values of θ if θ is measured in degrees.

$2\sec^2\theta - \tan^4\theta = -1$	**Original equation**
$2(1 + \tan^2\theta) - \tan^4\theta = -1$	**$\sec^2\theta = 1 + \tan^2\theta$**
$2 + 2\tan^2\theta - \tan^4\theta = -1$	**Distributive Property**
$\tan^4\theta - 2\tan^2\theta - 3 = 0$	**Set one side of the equation equal to 0.**
$(\tan^2\theta - 3)(\tan^2\theta + 1) = 0$	**Factor.**

$\tan^2\theta - 3 = 0$ or $\tan^2\theta + 1 = 0$ **Zero Product Property**

$\tan^2\theta = 3$ $\quad$ $\tan^2\theta = -1$

$\tan\theta = \pm\sqrt{3}$ $\quad$ This part gives no solutions since $\tan^2\theta$ is never negative.

$\theta = 60° + 180°k$ and $\theta = -60° + 180°k$, where k is any integer. The solutions are $60° + 180°k$ and $-60° + 180°k$.

Guided Practice 5A. $90° + k \cdot 180°$

Solve each equation. 5B. $\frac{7\pi}{6} + 2k \cdot \pi$, and $\frac{11\pi}{6} + 2k \cdot \pi$

5A. $\sin\theta\cot\theta - \cos^2\theta = 0$

5B. $\frac{\cos\theta}{\cot\theta} + 2\sin^2\theta = 0$

Personal Tutor glencoe.com

Check Your Understanding

Example 1 p. 919

Solve each equation if $0° \le \theta \le 360°$.

1. $2\sin\theta + 1 = 0$ 210°, 330°

2. $\cos^2\theta + 2\cos\theta + 1 = 0$ 180°

3. $\cos 2\theta + \cos\theta = 0$ 60°, 180°, or 300°

4. $2\cos\theta = 1$ 60°, 300°

5. $\cos\theta = -\frac{\sqrt{3}}{2}$ 150°, 210°

6. $\sin 2\theta = -\frac{\sqrt{3}}{2}$ 120°, 150°, 300°, 330°

7. $\cos 2\theta = 8 - 15\sin\theta$ 30°, 150°

8. $\sin\theta + \cos\theta = 1$ 0°, 90°

Example 2 p. 920

Solve each equation for all values of θ if θ is measured in radians.

9. $4\sin^2\theta - 1 = 0$

10. $2\cos^2\theta = 1$ $\frac{\pi}{4} + \frac{k}{2}\pi$

11. $\cos 2\theta\sin\theta = 1$ $\frac{3\pi}{2} + 2k\pi$

12. $\sin\frac{\theta}{2} + \cos\frac{\theta}{2} = \sqrt{2}$ $\frac{\pi}{2} + 4\pi k$

13. $\cos 2\theta + 4\cos\theta = -3$ $\pi + 2k\pi$

14. $\sin\frac{\theta}{2} + \cos\theta = 1$

Solve each equation for all values of θ if θ is measured in degrees.

15. $\cos 2\theta - \sin^2\theta + 2 = 0$

16. $\sin^2\theta - \sin\theta = 0$

17. $2\sin^2\theta - 1 = 0$ $45° + k \cdot 90°$

18. $\cos\theta - 2\cos\theta\sin\theta = 0$

19. $\cos 2\theta\sin\theta = 1$ $270° + k \cdot 360°$

20. $\sin\theta\tan\theta - \tan\theta = 0$ $0° + k \cdot 180°$, $90° + k \cdot 360°$

Example 3 p. 920

21. LIGHT The number of hours of daylight d in Hartford, Connecticut, may be approximated by the equation $d = 3\sin\frac{2\pi}{365}t + 12$, where t is the number of days after March 21.

a. On what days will Hartford have exactly $10\frac{1}{2}$ hours of daylight?

b. Using the results in part **a**, tell what days of the year have at least $10\frac{1}{2}$ hours of daylight. Explain how you know. See margin.

9. $\pm\frac{\pi}{6} + 2k\pi$ or $\pm\frac{5\pi}{6} + 2k\pi$

14. $0 + 2k\pi$; $\frac{\pi}{3} + 4k\pi$; $\frac{5\pi}{3} + 4k\pi$

15. $90° + k \cdot 180°$

16. $0° + k \cdot 180°$, $90° + k \cdot 360°$

18. $30° + k \cdot 360°$, $150° + k \cdot 360°$, $90° + k \cdot 180°$

21a. There will be $10\frac{1}{2}$ hours of daylight 213 and 335 days after March 21; that is, on October 20 and February 19.

Differentiated Homework Options

Level	Assignment	Two-Day Option	
AL Basic	30–48, 58, 60–62, 64–83	31–47 odd, 64–67	30–48 even, 58, 60–62, 68–83
OL Core	31–55 odd, 56–58, 60–62, 64–83	30–48, 64–67	49–58, 60–62, 68–83
BL Advanced	49–80, (optional: 81–83)		

922 Chapter 14 Trigonometric Identities and Equations

Examples 4 and 5
pp. 921–922

Solve each equation. **25.** $\frac{\pi}{2} + \pi k, \frac{\pi}{6} + 2\pi k, \frac{5\pi}{6} + 2\pi k$

22. $\sin^2 2\theta + \cos^2 \theta = 0$ $\frac{\pi}{2} + \pi k$

23. $\tan^2 \theta + 2 \tan \theta + 1 = 0$ $\frac{3\pi}{4} + \pi k$

24. $\cos^2 \theta + 3 \cos \theta = -2$ $\pi + 2\pi k$

25. $\sin 2\theta - \cos \theta = 0$

26. $\tan \theta = 1$ $45° + k \cdot 180°$ or $\frac{\pi}{4} + k \cdot \pi$

27. $\cos 8\theta = 1$ $0° + k \cdot 45°$ or $0 + k \cdot \frac{\pi}{4}$

28. $\sin \theta + 1 = \cos 2\theta$ $0° + k \cdot 180°, 210° + k \cdot 360°, 330° + k \cdot 360°$

29. $2 \cos^2 \theta = \cos \theta$ $\frac{\pi}{3} + 2k\pi, \frac{\pi}{2} + k\pi, \frac{5\pi}{3} + 2k\pi$

Practice and Problem Solving

= **Step-by-Step Solutions** begin on page R20.
Extra Practice begins on page 947.

Example 1
p. 919

Solve each equation for the given interval.

30. $\cos^2 \theta = \frac{1}{4}; 0° \leq \theta \leq 360°$

31. $2 \sin^2 \theta = 1; 90° < \theta < 270°$ $135°, 225°$

32. $\sin 2\theta - \cos \theta = 0; 0 \leq \theta \leq 2\pi$

33. $3 \sin^2 \theta = \cos^2 \theta; 0 \leq \theta \leq \frac{\pi}{2}$ $\frac{\pi}{6}$

34. $2 \sin \theta + \sqrt{3} = 0; 180° < \theta < 360°$ $240°, 300°$

35. $4 \sin^2 \theta - 1 = 0; 180° < \theta < 360°$ $210°, 330°$

30. $60°, 120°, 240°, 300°$

32. $\frac{\pi}{6}, \frac{\pi}{2}, \frac{5\pi}{6}, \frac{3\pi}{2}$

Example 2
p. 920

Solve each equation for all values of θ if θ is measured in radians.

36. $\cos 2\theta + 3 \cos \theta = 1$

37 $2 \sin^2 \theta = \cos \theta + 1$

38. $\cos^2 \theta - \frac{3}{2} = \frac{5}{2} \cos \theta$

39. $3 \cos \theta - \cos \theta = 2$ $0 + 2k\pi$

36. $\frac{\pi}{3} + 2k\pi, \frac{5\pi}{3} + 2k\pi$

37. $\pi + 2k\pi, \frac{\pi}{3} + 2k\pi, \frac{5\pi}{3} + 2k\pi$

38. $\frac{2\pi}{3} + 2k\pi, \frac{4\pi}{3} + 2k\pi$

Solve each equation for all values of θ if θ is measured in degrees.

40. $\sin \theta - \cos \theta = 0$ $45° + k \cdot 180°$

41. $\tan \theta - \sin \theta = 0$ $0° + k \cdot 180°$

42. $\sin^2 \theta = 2 \sin \theta + 3$ $270° + k \cdot 360°$

43. $4 \sin^2 \theta = 4 \sin \theta - 1$ $30° + k \cdot 360°, 150° + k \cdot 360°$

Example 3
p. 920

44. **ELECTRONICS** One of the tallest structures in the world is a television transmitting tower located near Fargo, North Dakota, with a height of 2064 feet. What is the measure of θ if the length of the shadow is 1 mile? **about 21°**

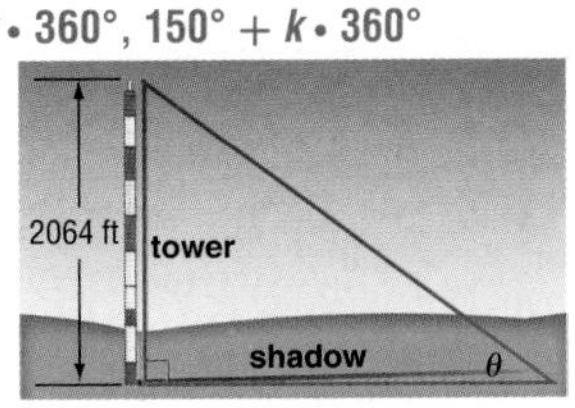

46. $\frac{\pi}{6} + 2k\pi, \frac{5\pi}{6} + 2k\pi, \frac{\pi}{2} + 2k\pi$ or $30° + k \cdot 360°, 150° + k \cdot 360°, 90° + k \cdot 360°$

Examples 4 and 5
pp. 921–922

Solve each equation. **45.** $\frac{7\pi}{6} + 2k\pi, \frac{11\pi}{6} + 2k\pi$ or $210° + k \cdot 360°, 330° + k \cdot 360°$

45. $2 \sin^2 \theta = 3 \sin \theta + 2$

46. $2 \cos^2 \theta + 3 \sin \theta = 3$

47. $\sin^2 \theta + \cos 2\theta = \cos \theta$ $0 + 2k\pi, \frac{\pi}{2} + k\pi$ or $0° + k \cdot 360°, 90° + k \cdot 180°$

48. $2 \cos^2 \theta = -\cos \theta$

48. $\frac{\pi}{2} + k\pi, \frac{2\pi}{3} + 2k\pi, \frac{4\pi}{3} + 2k\pi$ or $90° + k \cdot 180°, 120° + k \cdot 360°, 240° + k \cdot 360°$

49. **RIVERS** Due to ocean tides, the depth y in meters of the River Thames in London varies as a sine function of x, the hour of the day. On a certain day that function was $y = 3 \sin \left[\frac{\pi}{6}(x - 4)\right] + 8$, where $x = 0, 1, 2, \ldots, 24$ corresponds to 12:00 midnight, 1:00 A.M., 2:00 A.M., …, 12:00 midnight the next night.

a. What is the maximum depth of the River Thames on that day? **11 m**

b. At what times does the maximum depth occur? **7:00 A.M. and 7:00 P.M.**

Solve each equation if θ is measured in radians.

50. $(\cos \theta)(\sin 2\theta) - 2 \sin \theta + 2 = 0$ $\frac{\pi}{2} + 2\pi k$

51. $2 \sin^2 \theta + (\sqrt{2} - 1) \sin \theta = \frac{\sqrt{2}}{2}$ $\frac{\pi}{6} + 2\pi k, \frac{5\pi}{6} + 2\pi k, \frac{5\pi}{4} + 2\pi k, \frac{7\pi}{4} + 2\pi k$

Solve each equation if θ is measured in degrees.

52. $\sin 2\theta + \frac{\sqrt{3}}{2} = \sqrt{3} \sin \theta + \cos \theta$

53. $1 - \sin^2 \theta - \cos \theta = \frac{3}{4}$

52. $30° + 360°k, 150° + 360°k, 330° + 360°k$

53. $120° + 360°k, 240° + 360°k$

Study Guide and Intervention
CRM pp. 29–30 AL OL ELL

14-5 Study Guide and Intervention

Solving Trigonometric Equations

Solve Trigonometric Equations You can use trigonometric identities to solve trigonometric equations, which are true for only certain values of the variable.

Example 1 Solve $4 \sin^2 \theta - 1 = 0$ if $0° < \theta < 360°$.

$4 \sin^2 \theta - 1 = 0$
$4 \sin^2 \theta = 1$
$\sin^2 \theta = \frac{1}{4}$
$\sin \theta = \pm\frac{1}{2}$
$\theta = 30°, 150°, 210°, 330°$

Example 2 Solve $\sin 2\theta + \cos \theta = 0$ for all values of θ. Give your answer in both radians and degrees.

$\sin 2\theta + \cos \theta = 0$
$2 \sin \theta \cos \theta + \cos \theta = 0$
$\cos \theta (2 \sin \theta + 1) = 0$
$\cos \theta = 0$ or $2 \sin \theta + 1 = 0$
$\sin \theta = -\frac{1}{2}$
$\theta = 90° + k \cdot 180°$; $\theta = 210° + k \cdot 360°, 330° + k \cdot 360°$;
$\theta = \frac{\pi}{2} + k \cdot \pi$; $\theta = \frac{7\pi}{6} + k \cdot 2\pi, \frac{11\pi}{6} + k \cdot 2\pi$

Exercises

Solve each equation for the given interval.

1. $2 \cos^2 \theta + \cos \theta = 1, 0 \leq \theta < 2\pi$ $\frac{\pi}{3}, \pi, \frac{5\pi}{3}$
2. $\sin^2 \theta \cos^2 \theta = 0, 0 \leq \theta < 2\pi$ $0, \frac{\pi}{2}, \pi, \frac{3\pi}{2}$
3. $\cos 2\theta = \frac{\sqrt{3}}{2}, 0° \leq \theta < 360°$ $15°, 165°, 195°, 345°$
4. $2 \sin \theta - \sqrt{3} = 0, 0 \leq \theta < 2\pi$ $\frac{\pi}{3}, \frac{2\pi}{3}$

Solve each equation for all values of θ if θ is measured in radians.

5. $4 \sin^2 \theta - 3 = 0$ $\frac{\pi}{3} + k \cdot \pi, \frac{2\pi}{3} + k \cdot \pi$
6. $2 \cos \theta \sin \theta + \cos \theta = 0$ $\frac{\pi}{2} + k \cdot 2\pi, \frac{3\pi}{2} + k \cdot 2\pi, \frac{7\pi}{6} + k \cdot 2\pi, \frac{11\pi}{6} + k \cdot 2\pi$

Solve each equation for all values of θ if θ is measured in degrees.

7. $\cos 2\theta + \sin^2 \theta = \frac{1}{2}$ $45° + k \cdot 90°$
8. $\tan 2\theta = -1$ $67.5° + k \cdot 360°, 157.5° + k \cdot 360°$

Lesson 14-5

Chapter 14 29 Glencoe Algebra 2

Practice
CRM p. 32 AL OL BL ELL

14-5 Practice

Solving Trigonometric Equations

Solve each equation for the given interval.

1. $\sin 2\theta = \cos \theta, 90° \leq \theta < 180°$ $90°, 150°$
2. $\sqrt{2} \cos \theta = \sin 2\theta, 0° \leq \theta, 360°$ $45°, 90°, 135°, 270°$
3. $\cos 4\theta = \cos 2\theta, 180° \leq \theta < 360°$ $180°, 240°, 300°$
4. $\cos \theta + \cos (90 - \theta) = 0, 0 \leq \theta < 2\pi$ $\frac{3\pi}{4}, \frac{7\pi}{4}$
5. $2 + \cos \theta = 2 \sin^2 \theta, \pi \leq \theta \leq \frac{3\pi}{2}$ $\frac{4\pi}{3}, \frac{3\pi}{2}$
6. $\tan^2 \theta + \sec \theta = 1, \frac{\pi}{2} \leq \theta < \pi$ $\frac{2\pi}{3}$

Solve each equation for all values of θ if θ is measured in radians.

7. $\cos^2 \theta = \sin^2 \theta$ $\frac{\pi}{4} + k\frac{\pi}{2}$
8. $\cot \theta = \cot^3 \theta$ $\frac{\pi}{2} + k\pi$ and $\frac{\pi}{4} + k\frac{\pi}{2}$
9. $\sqrt{2} \sin^3 \theta = \sin^2 \theta$ $k\pi, \frac{\pi}{4} + 2k\pi$, and $\frac{3\pi}{4} + 2k\pi$
10. $\cos^2 \theta \sin \theta = \sin \theta$ $k\pi$
11. $2 \cos 2\theta = 1 - 2 \sin^2 \theta$ $\frac{\pi}{4} + k\frac{\pi}{2}$
12. $\sec^2 \theta = 2$ $\frac{\pi}{4} + k\frac{\pi}{2}$

Solve each equation for all values of θ if θ is measured in degrees.

13. $\sin^2 \theta \cos \theta = \cos \theta$ $90° + k \cdot 180°$
14. $\csc^2 \theta - 3 \csc \theta + 2 = 0$ $30° + k \cdot 360°, 90° + k \cdot 360°$, and $150° + k \cdot 360°$
15. $\frac{3}{1 + \cos \theta} = 4(1 - \cos \theta)$ $60° + k \cdot 180°$ and $120° + k \cdot 180°$
16. $\sqrt{2} \cos^2 \theta = \cos^2 \theta$ $90° + k \cdot 180°$ and $450° + k \cdot 360°$

Solve each equation.

17. $4 \sin^2 \theta = 3$ $\frac{\pi}{3} + k\pi$ and $\frac{2\pi}{3} + k\pi$, or $60° + k \cdot 180°$ and $120° + k \cdot 180°$
18. $4 \sin^2 \theta - 1 = 0$ $\frac{\pi}{6} + k\pi$ and $\frac{5\pi}{6} + k\pi$, or $30° + k \cdot 180°$ and $150° + k \cdot 180°$
19. $2 \sin^2 \theta - 3 \sin \theta = -1$ $\frac{\pi}{6} + \frac{\pi k}{3}$, or $30° + k \cdot 60°$
20. $\cos 2\theta + \sin \theta - 1 = 0$ $k\pi$ and $\frac{\pi}{6} + 2k\pi$, or $k \cdot 180°$ and $30° + k \cdot 360°$
21. **WAVES** Waves are causing a buoy to float in a regular pattern in the water. The vertical position of the buoy can be described by the equation $h = 2 \sin x$. Write an expression that describes the position of the buoy when its height is at its midline. $k\pi$ or $k \cdot 180°$
22. **ELECTRICITY** The electric current in a certain circuit with an alternating current can be described by the formula $i = 3 \sin 240t$, where i is the current in amperes and t is the time in seconds. Write an expression that describes the times at which there is no current. $0.75\ kt$

Chapter 14 32 Glencoe Algebra 2

Word Problem Practice
CRM p. 33 AL OL BL ELL

14-5 Word Problem Practice

Solving Trigonometric Equations

1. **SANDCASTLES** The water level on Sunset Beach can be modeled by the function $y = 7 + 7 \sin\left(\frac{\pi}{6}t\right)$, where y is the distance in feet of the shoreline above the low tide mark and t is the number of hours past 6 A.M. At 2 P.M., Victoria built her sandcastle 10 feet above the low tide mark. At what time will the shoreline reach Victoria's sandcastle? **7 P.M.**

2. **BATTERY** The amount of light emitted from a battery indicator bulb pulses while the battery is charging. This can be modeled by the equation $y = 60 + 60 \sin\left(\frac{\pi}{4}t\right)$, where y is the lumens emitted from the bulb and t is the number of seconds since the beginning of a pulse. At what time will the amount of light emitted be equal to 110 lumens? **1.3 seconds after the beginning of the pulse**

3. **BUILDINGS** In downtown Centerville, the length of the shadows of the hotel and the bank depends on the angle of inclination of the sun θ.

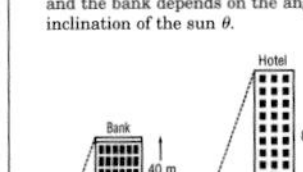

a. Express the length of the shadow of each building as a function of the angle of inclination. bank: $s_1 = \frac{40}{\tan \theta_1}$, hotel: $s_2 = \frac{82}{\tan \theta_2}$

b. What is the greatest angle of inclination of the sun such that the bank is entirely contained in the shadow of the hotel? **58.6°**

c. At what angle of inclination of the sun will the bank's shadow be equal to the height of the hotel? **26°**

Lesson 14-5

Chapter 14 33 Glencoe Algebra 2

Enrichment
CRM p. 34 OL BL

14-5 Enrichment

Families of Curves

Use these graphs for the problems below.

The Family $y = x^n$

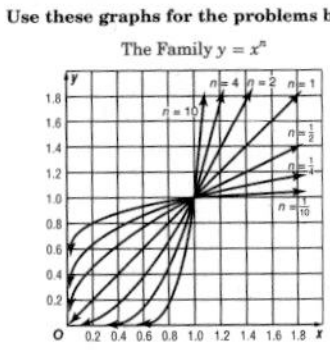

The Family $y = e^{mx}$

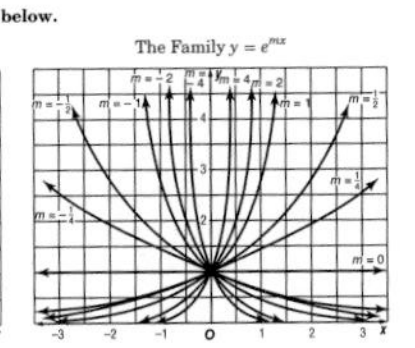

1. Use the graph on the left to describe the relationship among the curves $y = x^{\frac{1}{2}}, y = x^1$, and $y = x^2$.

…d n = 2, … are refle…s of … anoth… in the

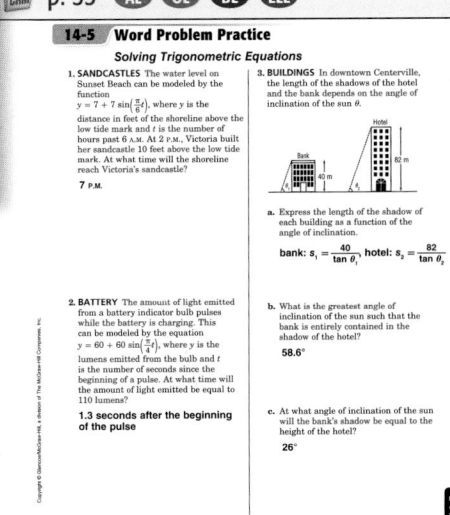

Watch Out!

Error Analysis For Exercise 58, students should see that Jennifer divided both sides of the equation by sin θ, and that Tat incorrectly rewrote 2sin θ cos θ − sin θ as 2cos θ. Explain to students that if cos $\theta = \frac{1}{2}$, then θ must be in Quadrant I or Quadrant IV, so θ = 60° or 300°. Also explain to students that the expression 2sin θ cos θ − sin θ has the form 2 • *B* • *C* − *B*, and that expression is *not* equal to 2 • *C*.

Additional Answers

60. Each type of equation may require adding, subtracting, multiplying, or dividing each side by the same number. Quadratic and trigonometric equations can often be solved by factoring. Linear and quadratic equations do not require identities. All linear and quadratic equations can be solved algebraically, whereas some trigonometric equations may be graphed more easily by using a graphing calculator. A linear equation has at most one solution. A quadratic equation has at most two solutions. A trigonometric equation usually has infinitely many solutions, unless the values of the variable are restricted.

72. $\sin(270° - \theta) \stackrel{?}{=} -\cos\theta$

$\sin 270° \cos\theta - \cos 270° \sin\theta \stackrel{?}{=} -\cos\theta$

$-1\cos\theta - 0 \stackrel{?}{=} -\cos\theta$

$-\cos\theta = -\cos\theta$ ✓

73. $\cos(90° + \theta) \stackrel{?}{=} -\sin\theta$

$\cos 90° \cos\theta - \sin 90° \sin\theta \stackrel{?}{=} -\sin\theta$

$0 - 1\sin\theta \stackrel{?}{=} -\sin\theta$

$-\sin\theta = -\sin\theta$ ✓

74. $\cos(90° - \theta) \stackrel{?}{=} \sin\theta$

$\cos 90° \cos\theta + \sin 90° \sin\theta \stackrel{?}{=} \sin\theta$

$0 \cdot \cos\theta + 1 \cdot \sin\theta \stackrel{?}{=} \sin\theta$

$\sin\theta = \sin\theta$ ✓

Solve each equation.

54. $2\sin\theta = \sin 2\theta$ **πk**

55. $\cos\theta\tan\theta - 2\cos^2\theta = -1$ **$\frac{\pi}{6} + 2\pi k, \frac{5\pi}{6} + 2\pi k$**

Real-World Link

The sparkle of a diamond is created by refracted light. Light travels at different speeds in various media. When light rays pass from one medium to another in which they travel at a different velocity, the light is bent or refracted.

56. DIAMONDS According to Snell's Law, $n_1 \sin i = n_2 \sin r$, where n_1 is the index of refraction of the medium the light is exiting, n_2 is the index of refraction of the medium the light is entering, i is the degree measure of the angle of incidence, and r is the degree measure of the angle of refraction.

a. The index of refraction of a diamond is 2.42, and the index of refraction of air is 1.00. If a beam of light strikes a diamond at an angle of 35°, what is the angle of refraction? **13.71°**

b. Explain how a gemologist might use Snell's Law to determine whether a diamond is genuine.

57. MUSIC A wave traveling in a guitar string can be modeled by the equation $D = 0.5\sin(6.5x)\sin(2500t)$, where D is the displacement in millimeters at the position x millimeters from the left end of the string at time t seconds. Find the first positive time when the point 0.5 meter from the left end has a displacement of 0.01 millimeter. **0.0026 second**

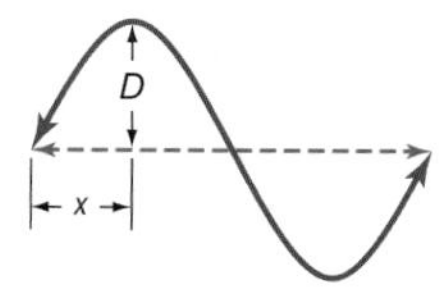

56b. Measure the angles of incidence and refraction to determine the index of refraction. If the index is 2.42, the diamond is genuine.

58. No; Jennifer divided both sides of the equation by sin θ, which is incorrect, and Tat subtracted sin θ incorrectly.

H.O.T. Problems
Use Higher-Order Thinking Skills

58. ERROR ANALYSIS Jennifer and Tat are solving $2\sin\theta\cos\theta = \sin\theta$ for $0° \leq \theta \leq 360°$. Is either of them correct? Explain your reasoning.

Jennifer	Tat
$2\sin\theta\cos\theta = \sin\theta$	$2\sin\theta\cos\theta = \sin\theta$
$\frac{2\sin\theta\cos\theta}{\sin\theta} = \frac{\sin\theta}{\sin\theta}$	$-\sin\theta = -\sin\theta$
$2\cos\theta = 1$	$2\cos\theta = 0$
$\cos\theta = \frac{1}{2}$	$\cos\theta = 0$
$\theta = 60°, 300°$	$\theta = 90°, 270°$

59. $\frac{\pi}{3} < x < \pi$ **or** $\frac{5\pi}{3} < x < 2\pi$

61. All trigonometric functions are periodic. Adding the least common multiple of the periods of the functions that appear to any solution of the equation will always produce another solution.

59. CHALLENGE Solve $\sin 2x < \sin x$ for $0 \leq x \leq 2\pi$ without a calculator.

60. WRITING IN MATH Compare and contrast solving trigonometric equations with solving linear and quadratic equations. What techniques are the same? What techniques are different? How many solutions do you expect? **See margin.**

61. REASONING Explain why many trigonometric equations have infinitely many solutions.

62. OPEN ENDED Write an example of a trigonometric equation that has exactly two solutions if $0° \leq \theta \leq 360°$. **Sample answer: $2\cos\theta = 0$, 90° and 270°**

63. CHALLENGE How many solutions in the interval $0° \leq \theta \leq 360°$ should you expect for $a\sin(b\theta + c) + d = d\left(\frac{a}{2}\right)$, if $a \neq 0$ and b is a positive integer? **$2b$**

75. $\sin(90° - \theta) \stackrel{?}{=} \cos\theta$

$\sin 90° \cos\theta - \cos 90° \sin\theta \stackrel{?}{=} \cos\theta$

$1 \cdot \cos\theta - 0 \cdot \sin\theta \stackrel{?}{=} \cos\theta$

$\cos\theta - 0 \stackrel{?}{=} \cos\theta$

$\cos\theta = \cos\theta$ ✓

76b.

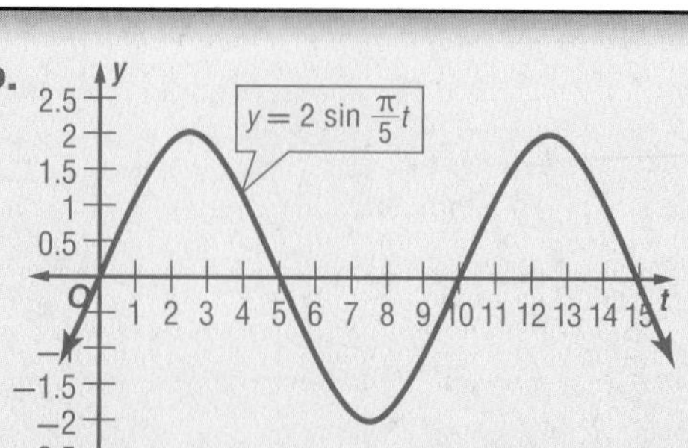

NGSSS PRACTICE 912.A.8.7, 912.S.3.3, 912.A.4.4, 912.D.11.3

64. **EXTENDED RESPONSE** Charles received \$2500 for a graduation gift. He put it into a savings account in which the interest rate was 5.5% per year.

a. How much did he have in his savings account after 5 years if he made no deposits or withdrawals? **\$3267.40**

b. After how many years will the amount in his savings account have doubled? **about 13 yr**

65. **PROBABILITY** Find the probability of rolling three 3s if a number cube is rolled three times. **A**

A. $\frac{1}{216}$ C. $\frac{1}{6}$

B. $\frac{1}{36}$ D. $\frac{1}{4}$

66. Use synthetic substitution to find $f(-2)$ for the function below. **F**

$$f(x) = x^4 + 10x^2 + x + 8$$

F. 62 H. 30

G. 38 I. 8

67. **ACT/SAT** The pattern of dots below continues infinitely, with more dots being added at each step.

Which expression can be used to determine the number of dots in the nth step? **D**

A. $2n$ C. $n(n + 1)$

B. $n(n + 2)$ D. $2(n + 1)$

Spiral Review

Find the exact value of each expression. (Lesson 14-4)

68. $\cos 165°$ $-\frac{\sqrt{2 + \sqrt{3}}}{2}$

69. $\sin 22\frac{1}{2}°$ $\frac{\sqrt{2 - \sqrt{2}}}{2}$

70. $\sin \frac{7\pi}{8}$ $\frac{\sqrt{2 - \sqrt{2}}}{2}$

71. $\cos \frac{7\pi}{12}$ $-\frac{\sqrt{2 - \sqrt{3}}}{2}$

Verify that each equation is an identity. (Lesson 14-3) **72–75. See margin.**

72. $\sin (270° - \theta) = -\cos \theta$

73. $\cos (90° + \theta) = -\sin \theta$

74. $\cos (90° - \theta) = \sin \theta$

75. $\sin (90° - \theta) = \cos \theta$

76. **WATER SAFETY** A harbor buoy bobs up and down with the waves. The distance between the highest and lowest points is 4 feet. The buoy moves from its highest point to its lowest point and back to its highest point every 10 seconds. (Lesson 13-7)

a. Write an equation for the motion of the buoy. Assume that it is at equilibrium at $t = 0$ and that it is on the way up from the normal water level. $y = 2 \sin \frac{\pi}{5}t$

b. Draw a graph showing the height of the buoy as a function of time. **See margin.**

c. What is the height of the buoy after 12 seconds? **about 1.9 ft**

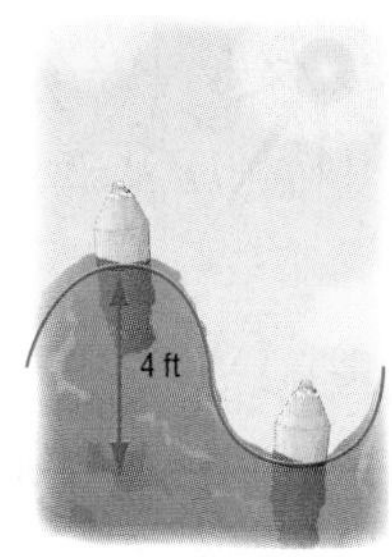

Find the first three terms of each arithmetic series described. (Lesson 11-2)

77. $a_1 = 17, a_n = 197, S_n = 2247$ **17, 26, 35**

78. $a_1 = -13, a_n = 427, S_n = 18{,}423$ **−13, −8, −3**

79. $n = 31, a_n = 78, S_n = 1023$ **−12, −9, −6**

80. $n = 19, a_n = 103, S_n = 1102$ **13, 18, 23**

Graph each rational function. (Lesson 9-4) **81–83. See margin.**

81. $f(x) = \frac{1}{(x + 3)^2}$

82. $f(x) = \frac{x + 4}{x - 1}$

83. $f(x) = \frac{x + 2}{x^2 - x - 6}$

4 ASSESS

Ticket Out the Door Have students write an equation involving $\sin^2\theta$ that has exactly one solution for the interval $90° < \theta < 270°$.

Formative Assessment

Check for students' understanding of concepts in Lessons 14-5.

CRM Quiz 4, p. 38

Additional Answers

81.

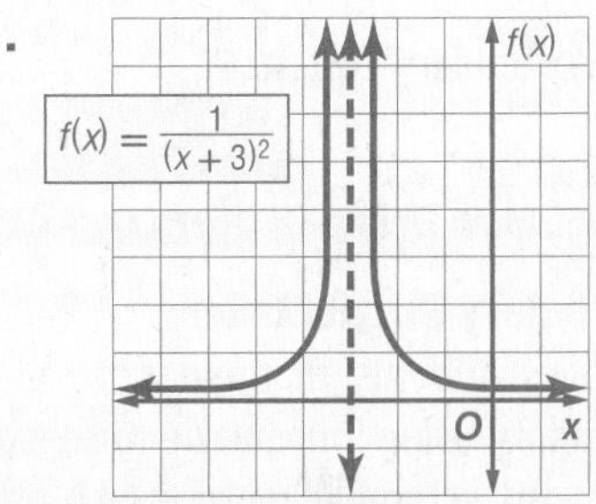

82.

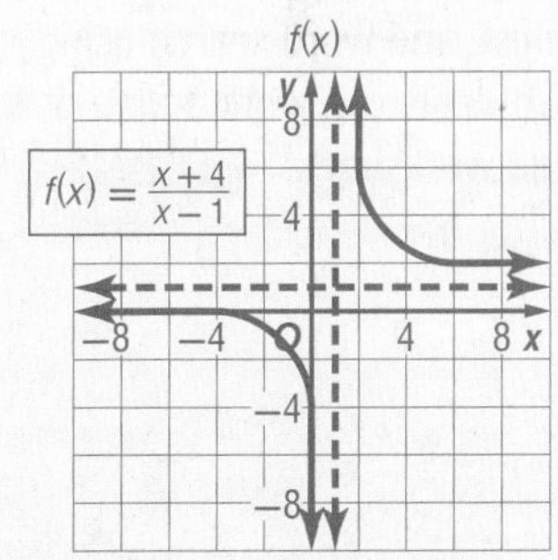

83.

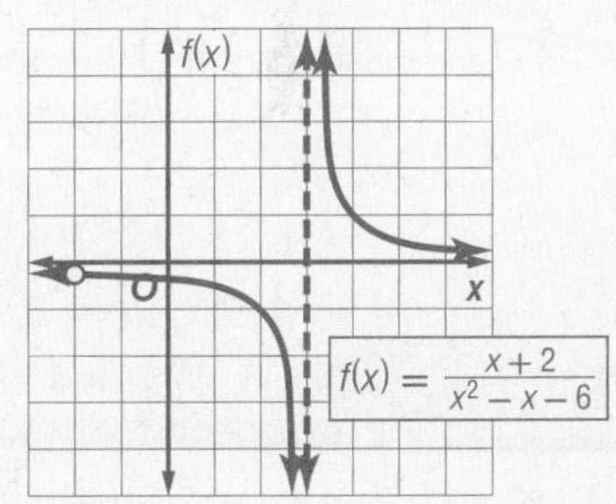

Differentiated Instruction

BL

Extension Ask students to explore the solutions of the equation $\sin x = \frac{x}{k}$, where k is a positive integer. Ask them to determine how the number of solutions to the equation changes as k changes. What value of x is a solution of the equation for every value of k? 0

Formative Assessment

Key Vocabulary The page references after each word denote where that term was first introduced. If students have difficulty answering questions 1–9, remind them that they can use these page references to refresh their memories about the vocabulary.

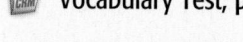

Summative Assessment

CRM Vocabulary Test, p. 40

FL Math Online glencoe.com

Vocabulary PuzzleMaker improves students' mathematics vocabulary using four puzzle formats–crossword, scramble, word search using a word list, and word search using clues. Students can work online or from a printed worksheet.

CHAPTER 14 Study Guide and Review

FL Math Online glencoe.com
- STUDY TO GO
- Vocabulary Review

Chapter Summary

Key Concepts

Trigonometric Identities (Lessons 14-1, 14-2, and 14-5)

- Trigonometric identities describe the relationships between trigonometric functions.
- Trigonometric identities can be used to simplify, verify, and solve trigonometric equations and expressions.

Sum and Difference of Angles Identities
(Lesson 14-3)

- For all values of A and B:
  $\cos(A \pm B) = \cos A \cos B \pm \sin A \sin B$
  $\sin(A \pm B) = \sin A \sin B \pm \cos A \sin B$

Double-Angle and Half-Angle Identities
(Lesson 14-4)

- Double-angle identities:
  $\sin 2\theta = 2 \sin \theta \cos \theta$
  $\cos 2\theta = \cos^2 \theta - \sin^2 \theta$
  $\cos 2\theta = 1 - 2 \sin^2 \theta$
  $\cos 2\theta = 2 \sin^2 \theta - 1$
- Half-angle identities:
  $\sin \frac{\theta}{2} = \pm\sqrt{\frac{1 - \cos \theta}{2}}$
  $\cos \frac{\theta}{2} = \pm\sqrt{\frac{1 + \cos \theta}{2}}$
  $\tan \frac{\theta}{2} = \sqrt{\frac{1 - \cos \theta}{1 + \cos \theta}}, \cos \theta \neq -1$

FOLDABLES® Study Organizer

Be sure the Key Concepts are noted in your Foldable.

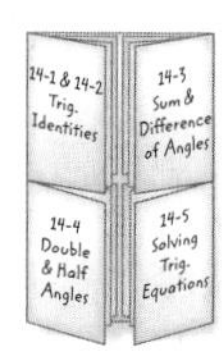

Key Vocabulary

cofunction identity (p. 891)
negative angle identity (p. 891)
Pythagorean identity (p. 891)
quotient identity (p. 891)
reciprocal identity (p. 891)
trigonometric equation (p. 919)
trigonometric identity (p. 891)

Vocabulary Check

Choose the correct term to complete each sentence.

1. The ________ can be used to find the sine or cosine of 75° if the sine and cosine of 90° and 15° are known. **difference of angles identity**
2. The identities $\tan \theta = \frac{\sin \theta}{\cos \theta}$ and $\cot \theta = \frac{\cos \theta}{\sin \theta}$ are examples of ________. **quotient identities**
3. A ________ is an equation involving trigonometric functions that is true for all values for which every expression in the equation is defined. **trigonometric identity**
4. The ________ can be used to find sin 60° using 30° as a reference. **double-angle identity**
5. A ________ is true for only certain values of the variable. **trigonometric equation**
6. The ________ formula can be used to find $\cos 22\frac{1}{2}°$. **half-angle**
7. The identities $\csc \theta = \frac{1}{\sin \theta}$ and $\sec \theta = \frac{1}{\cos \theta}$ are examples of ________. **reciprocal identities**
8. The ________ can be used to find the sine or cosine of 120° if the sine and cosine of 90° and 30° are known. **sum of angles identity**
9. $\cos^2 \theta + \sin^2 \theta = 1$ is an example of a ________. **Pythagorean identity**

FOLDABLES® Study Organizer

Dinah Zike's Foldables®

Have students look through the chapter to make sure they have included examples in their Foldables.

Suggest that students keep their Foldables handy while completing the Study Guide and Review pages. Point out that their Foldables can serve as a quick review tool when studying for the chapter test.

MIXED PROBLEM SOLVING
For mixed problem-solving practice, see page 992.

Lesson-by-Lesson Review

14-1 Trigonometric Identities (pp. 891–897)

912.T.3.1

Find the value of each expression.

10. $\sin\theta$, if $\cos\theta = \frac{\sqrt{2}}{2}$ and $270° < \theta < 360°$ $-\frac{\sqrt{2}}{2}$
11. $\sec\theta$, if $\cot\theta = \frac{\sqrt{2}}{2}$ and $90° < \theta < 180°$ $-\sqrt{3}$
12. $\tan\theta$, if $\cot\theta = 2$ and $0° < \theta < 90°$ $\frac{1}{2}$
13. $\cos\theta$, if $\sin\theta = -\frac{3}{5}$ and $180° < \theta < 270°$ $-\frac{4}{5}$
14. $\csc\theta$, if $\cot\theta = -\frac{4}{5}$ and $270° < \theta < 360°$ $-\frac{\sqrt{41}}{5}$
15. **SOCCER** For international matches, the maximum dimensions of a soccer field are 110 meters by 75 meters. Find $\sin\theta$. See margin.

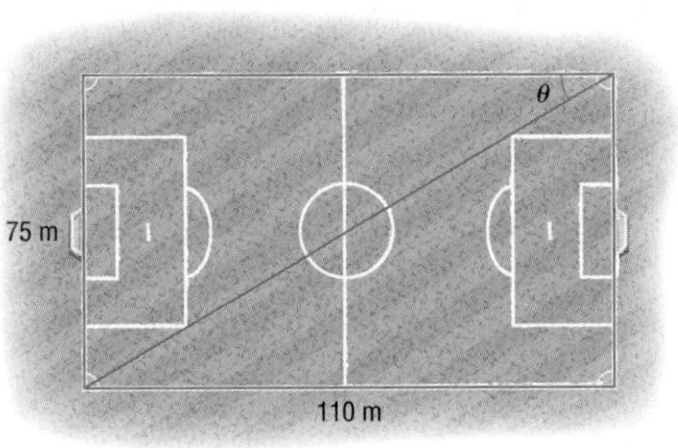

Simplify each expression.

16. $1 - \tan\theta\sin\theta\cos\theta$
17. $\tan\theta\csc\theta$ $\sec\theta$
18. $\sin\theta + \cos\theta\cot\theta$
19. $\cos\theta(1 + \tan^2\theta)$ $\sec\theta$

16. $\cos^2\theta$
18. $\csc\theta$

EXAMPLE 1

Find $\sin\theta$ if $\cos\theta = \frac{3}{4}$ and $0° < \theta < 90°$.

$\cos^2\theta + \sin^2\theta = 1$	Trigonometric identity
$\sin^2\theta = 1 - \cos^2\theta$	Subtract $\cos^2\theta$ from each side.
$\sin^2\theta = 1 - \left(\frac{3}{4}\right)^2$	Substitute $\frac{3}{4}$ for $\cos\theta$.
$\sin^2\theta = 1 - \frac{9}{16}$	Square $\frac{3}{4}$.
$\sin^2\theta = \frac{7}{16}$	Subtract.
$\sin\theta = \pm\frac{\sqrt{7}}{4}$	Take the square root of each side.

Because θ is in the first quadrant, $\sin\theta$ is positive. Thus, $\sin\theta = \frac{\sqrt{7}}{4}$.

EXAMPLE 2

Simplify $\cos\theta\sec\theta\cot\theta$.

$$\cos\theta\sec\theta\cot\theta = \cos\theta\left(\frac{1}{\cos\theta}\right)\left(\frac{\cos\theta}{\sin\theta}\right)$$
$$= \cot\theta$$

14-2 Verifying Trigonometric Identities (pp. 898–903)

912.T.3.2

Verify that each of the following is an identity.

20. $\tan\theta\cos\theta + \cot\theta\sin\theta = \sin\theta + \cos\theta$
21. $\frac{\cos\theta}{\cot\theta} + \frac{\sin\theta}{\tan\theta} = \sin\theta + \cos\theta$
22. $\sec^2\theta - 1 = \frac{\sin^2\theta}{1 - \sin^2\theta}$ 20–23. See margin.
23. **GEOMETRY** The right triangle shown at the right is used in a special quilt. Use the measures of the sides of the triangle to show that $\tan^2\theta + 1 = \sec^2\theta$.

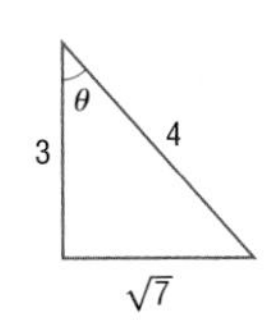

EXAMPLE 3

Verify that $\frac{\cos\theta + 1}{\sin\theta} = \cot\theta + \csc\theta$ is an identity.

$\frac{\cos\theta + 1}{\sin\theta} \stackrel{?}{=} \cot\theta + \csc\theta$	Original equation
$\frac{\cos\theta}{\sin\theta} + \frac{1}{\sin\theta} \stackrel{?}{=} \cot\theta + \csc\theta$	Simplify.
$\cot\theta + \csc\theta = \cot\theta + \csc\theta$ ✓	Simplify.

Lesson-by-Lesson Review

Intervention If the given examples are not sufficient to review the topics covered by the questions, remind students that the page references tell them where to review that topic in their textbook.

Two-Day Option Have students complete the Lesson-by-Lesson Review on pp. 927–928. Then you can use ExamView® Assessment Suite to customize another review worksheet that practices all the objectives of this chapter or only the objectives on which your students need more help.

Differentiated Instruction

Super DVD: MindJogger Videoquizzes Use this DVD as an alternative format of review for the test.

Additional Answers

15. First find the length of the diagonal: $75^2 + 110^2 = c^2$; $5625 + 12{,}100 = c^2$; $17{,}725 = c^2$; $c = 5\sqrt{709}$; $\sin\theta = \frac{75}{5\sqrt{709}} = \frac{15\sqrt{709}}{709}$

20. $\tan\theta\cos\theta + \cot\theta\sin\theta \stackrel{?}{=} \sin\theta + \cos\theta$
$\frac{\sin\theta}{\cos\theta}\cdot\cos\theta + \frac{\cos\theta}{\sin\theta}\cdot\sin\theta \stackrel{?}{=} \sin\theta + \cos\theta$
$\sin\theta + \cos\theta = \sin\theta + \cos\theta$ ✓

21. $\frac{\cos\theta}{\cot\theta} + \frac{\sin\theta}{\tan\theta} \stackrel{?}{=} \sin\theta + \cos\theta$
$\cos\theta \div \frac{\cos\theta}{\sin\theta} + \sin\theta \div \frac{\sin\theta}{\cos\theta} \stackrel{?}{=} \sin\theta + \cos\theta$
$\cos\theta\cdot\frac{\sin\theta}{\cos\theta} + \sin\theta\cdot\frac{\cos\theta}{\sin\theta} \stackrel{?}{=} \sin\theta + \cos\theta$
$\sin\theta + \cos\theta = \sin\theta + \cos\theta$ ✓

22. $\sec^2\theta - 1 \stackrel{?}{=} \frac{\sin^2\theta}{1 - \sin^2\theta}$
$\sec^2\theta - 1 \stackrel{?}{=} \frac{\sin^2\theta}{\cos^2\theta}$
$\sec^2\theta - 1 \stackrel{?}{=} \tan^2\theta$
$\sec^2\theta - 1 = \sec^2\theta - 1$ ✓

23. $\tan^2\theta + 1 = \left(\frac{\sqrt{7}}{3}\right)^2 + 1 = \frac{7}{9} + 1$
$= \frac{7}{9} + \frac{9}{9} = \frac{16}{9}$;
$\sec^2\theta = \left(\frac{4}{3}\right)^2 = \frac{16}{9}$

Problem Solving Review

For additional practice in problem solving for Chapter 14, see the Mixed Problem Solving Appendix, p. 980-993, in the Student Handbook section.

Additional Answers (Practice Test)

2. $\cos(30° - \theta) \stackrel{?}{=} \sin(60° + \theta)$

$\cos 30° \cos\theta + \sin 30° \sin\theta \stackrel{?}{=} \sin 60° \cos\theta + \cos 60° \sin\theta$

$\frac{\sqrt{3}}{2}\cos\theta + \frac{1}{2}\sin\theta = \frac{\sqrt{3}}{2}\cos\theta + \frac{1}{2}\sin\theta$ ✓

3. $\cos(\theta - \pi) \stackrel{?}{=} -\cos\theta$

$\cos\theta\cos\pi + \sin\theta\sin\pi \stackrel{?}{=} -\cos\theta$

$(\cos\theta)(-1) + (\sin\theta)(0) \stackrel{?}{=} -\cos\theta$

$-\cos\theta = -\cos\theta$ ✓

10. $\sin\theta(\cot\theta + \tan\theta) \stackrel{?}{=} \sec\theta$

$\sin\theta\left(\frac{\cos\theta}{\sin\theta} + \frac{\sin\theta}{\cos\theta}\right) \stackrel{?}{=} \sec\theta$

$\cos\theta + \frac{\sin^2\theta}{\cos\theta} \stackrel{?}{=} \sec\theta$

$\frac{\cos^2\theta + \sin^2\theta}{\cos\theta} \stackrel{?}{=} \sec\theta$

$\frac{1}{\cos\theta} \stackrel{?}{=} \sec\theta$

$\sec\theta = \sec\theta$ ✓

11. $\frac{\cos^2\theta}{1 - \sin\theta} \stackrel{?}{=} \frac{\cos\theta}{\sec\theta - \tan\theta}$

$\frac{\cos^2\theta}{1 - \sin\theta} \stackrel{?}{=} \frac{\cos\theta}{\frac{1}{\cos\theta} - \frac{\sin\theta}{\cos\theta}}$

$\frac{\cos^2\theta}{1 - \sin\theta} \stackrel{?}{=} \frac{\cos\theta}{\frac{1 - \sin\theta}{\cos\theta}}$

$\frac{\cos^2\theta}{1 - \sin\theta} \stackrel{?}{=} \cos\theta \cdot \frac{\cos\theta}{1 - \sin\theta}$

$\frac{\cos^2\theta}{1 - \sin\theta} = \frac{\cos^2\theta}{1 - \sin\theta}$ ✓

12. $(\tan\theta + \cot\theta)^2 \stackrel{?}{=} \csc^2\theta\sec^2\theta$

$\left(\frac{\sin\theta}{\cos\theta} + \frac{\cos\theta}{\sin\theta}\right)^2 \stackrel{?}{=} \csc^2\theta\sec^2\theta$

$\left(\frac{\sin^2\theta + \cos^2\theta}{\cos\theta\sin\theta}\right)^2 \stackrel{?}{=} \csc^2\theta\sec^2\theta$

$\left(\frac{1}{\cos\theta\sin\theta}\right)^2 \stackrel{?}{=} \csc^2\theta\sec^2\theta$

$\frac{1}{\cos^2\theta} \cdot \frac{1}{\sin^2\theta} \stackrel{?}{=} \csc^2\theta\sec^2\theta$

$\sec^2\theta\csc^2\theta = \csc^2\theta\sec^2\theta$ ✓

13. $\frac{1 + \sec\theta}{\sec\theta} \stackrel{?}{=} \frac{\sin^2\theta}{1 - \cos\theta}$

$\frac{1}{\sec\theta} + \frac{\sec\theta}{\sec\theta} \stackrel{?}{=} \frac{\sin^2\theta}{1 - \cos\theta} \cdot \frac{1 + \cos\theta}{1 + \cos\theta}$

$\cos\theta + 1 \stackrel{?}{=} \frac{\sin^2\theta(1 + \cos\theta)}{1 - \cos^2\theta}$

$\cos\theta + 1 \stackrel{?}{=} \frac{\sin^2\theta(1 + \cos\theta)}{\sin^2\theta}$

$\cos\theta + 1 = 1 + \cos\theta$ ✓

14-3 Sum and Difference of Angles Identities (pp. 904–909)

912.T.3.2

Find the exact value of each expression.

24. $\cos(-135°)$ $-\frac{\sqrt{2}}{2}$

25. $\cos 15°$ $\frac{\sqrt{6} + \sqrt{2}}{4}$

26. $\sin 210°$ $-\frac{1}{2}$

27. $\sin 105°$ $\frac{\sqrt{6} + \sqrt{2}}{4}$

28. $\tan 75°$ $\sqrt{3} + 2$

29. $\cos 105°$ $\frac{-\sqrt{6} + \sqrt{2}}{4}$

Verify that each of the following is an identity. 30–32. See Chapter 14 Answer Appendix.

30. $\sin(\theta + 90) = \cos\theta$

31. $\sin\left(\frac{3\pi}{2} - \theta\right) = -\cos\theta$

32. $\tan(\theta - \pi) = \tan\theta$

EXAMPLE 4

Find the exact value of sin 75°.

Use $\sin(A + B) = \sin A\cos B + \cos A\sin B$.

$\sin 75° = \sin(30° + 45°)$

$= \sin 30°\cos 45° + \cos 30°\sin 45°$

$= \left(\frac{1}{2}\right)\left(\frac{\sqrt{2}}{2}\right) + \left(\frac{\sqrt{3}}{2}\right)\left(\frac{\sqrt{2}}{2}\right)$

$= \frac{\sqrt{2}}{4} + \frac{\sqrt{6}}{4}$ or $\frac{\sqrt{2} + \sqrt{6}}{4}$

14-4 Double-Angle and Half-Angle Identities (pp. 911–917)

912.T.3.2, 912.T.3.3

Find the exact values of $\sin 2\theta$, $\cos 2\theta$, $\sin\frac{\theta}{2}$, and $\cos\frac{\theta}{2}$ for each of the following. 33–36. See Chapter 14 Answer Appendix.

33. $\cos\theta = \frac{4}{5}$; $0° < \theta < 90°$

34. $\sin\theta = -\frac{1}{4}$; $180° < \theta < 270°$

35. $\cos\theta = -\frac{2}{3}$; $\frac{\pi}{2} < \theta < \pi$

36. BASEBALL The infield of a baseball diamond is a square with side length 90 feet.

a. Find the length of the diagonal.

b. Write the ratio for sin 45° using the lengths of the baseball diamond.

c. Use the formula $\sin\frac{\theta}{2} = \pm\sqrt{\frac{1 - \cos\theta}{2}}$ to verify the ratio you wrote in part **b**.

EXAMPLE 5

Find the exact value of $\sin\frac{\theta}{2}$ if $\cos\theta = -\frac{3}{5}$ and θ is in the second quadrant.

$\sin\frac{\theta}{2} = \pm\sqrt{\frac{1 - \cos\theta}{2}}$ **Half-angle identity**

$= \pm\sqrt{\frac{1 - \left(-\frac{3}{5}\right)}{2}}$ **$\cos\theta = -\frac{3}{5}$**

$= \pm\sqrt{\frac{\frac{8}{5}}{2}}$ **Subtract.**

$= \pm\sqrt{\frac{4}{5}}$ **Divide.**

$= \pm\frac{2\sqrt{5}}{5}$ **Simplify.**

Since θ is in the second quadrant, $\sin\frac{\theta}{2} = \frac{2\sqrt{5}}{5}$.

14-5 Solving Trigonometric Equations (pp. 919–925)

912.T.3.4

Find all solutions of each equation for the given interval.

37. $2\cos\theta - 1 = 0$; $0° \le \theta < 360°$ **60°, 300°**

38. $4\cos^2\theta - 1 = 0$; $0 \le \theta < 2\pi$ $\frac{\pi}{3}, \frac{2\pi}{3}, \frac{4\pi}{3}, \frac{5\pi}{3}$

39. $\sin 2\theta + \cos\theta = 0$; $0° \le \theta < 360°$

40. $\sin^2\theta = 2\sin\theta + 3$; $0° \le \theta < 360°$ **270°**

41. $4\cos^2\theta - 4\cos\theta + 1 = 0$; $0 \le \theta < 2\pi$ $\frac{\pi}{3}, \frac{5\pi}{3}$

39. 90°, 210°, 270°, 330°

EXAMPLE 6

Find all solutions of $\sin 2\theta - \cos\theta = 0$ if $0 \le \theta < 2\pi$.

$\sin 2\theta - \cos\theta = 0$ **Original equation**

$2\sin\theta\cos\theta - \cos\theta = 0$ **Double-angle identity**

$\cos\theta(2\sin\theta - 1) = 0$ **Factor.**

$\cos\theta = 0$ or $2\sin\theta - 1 = 0$

$\theta = \frac{\pi}{2}, \frac{3\pi}{2}$ $\sin\theta = \frac{1}{2}$; $\theta = \frac{\pi}{6}, \frac{5\pi}{6}$

FL Math Online glencoe.com Chapter Test

1. NGSSS PRACTICE Which expression is equivalent to $\sin\theta + \cos\theta\cot\theta$? D

A. $\cot\theta$ C. $\sec\theta$

B. $\tan\theta$ D. $\csc\theta$

2. Verify that $\cos(30° - \theta) = \sin(60° + \theta)$ is an identity. See margin.

3. Verify that $\cos(\theta - \pi) = -\cos\theta$. See margin.

4. NGSSS PRACTICE What is the exact value of $\sin\theta$, if $\cos\theta = -\frac{3}{5}$ and $90° < \theta < 180°$? I

F. $\frac{5}{3}$

G. $\frac{\sqrt{34}}{8}$

H. $-\frac{4}{5}$

I. $\frac{4}{5}$

Find the value of each expression.

5. $\cot\theta$, if $\sec\theta = \frac{4}{3}$; $270° < \theta < 360°$ $-\frac{3\sqrt{7}}{7}$

6. $\tan\theta$, if $\cos\theta = -\frac{1}{2}$; $90° < \theta < 180°$ $-\sqrt{3}$

7. $\sec\theta$, if $\csc\theta = -2$; $180° < \theta < 270°$ $-\frac{2\sqrt{3}}{3}$

8. $\cot\theta$, if $\csc\theta = -\frac{5}{3}$; $270° < \theta < 360°$ $-\frac{4}{3}$

9. $\sec\theta$, if $\sin\theta = \frac{1}{2}$; $0° \le \theta < 90°$ $\frac{2\sqrt{3}}{3}$

Verify that each of the following is an identity.

10. $\sin\theta(\cot\theta + \tan\theta) = \sec\theta$ 10–14. See margin.

11. $\frac{\cos^2\theta}{1 - \sin\theta} = \frac{\cos\theta}{\sec\theta - \tan\theta}$

12. $(\tan\theta + \cot\theta)^2 = \csc^2\theta\sec^2\theta$

13. $\frac{1 + \sec\theta}{\sec\theta} = \frac{\sin^2\theta}{1 - \cos\theta}$

14. $\frac{\sin\theta}{1 - \cos\theta} = \csc\theta + \cot\theta$

15. NGSSS PRACTICE What is the exact value of $\tan\frac{\pi}{8}$? B

A. $\frac{\sqrt{2 - \sqrt{3}}}{2}$

B. $\sqrt{2} - 1$

C. $1 - \sqrt{2}$

D. $-\frac{\sqrt{2 - \sqrt{3}}}{2}$

16. **HISTORY** Some researchers believe that the builders of ancient pyramids, such as the Great Pyramid of Khufu, may have tried to build the faces as equilateral triangles. Later they had to change to other types of triangles. Suppose a pyramid is built such that a face is an equilateral triangle of side length 18 feet. a, b. See margin.

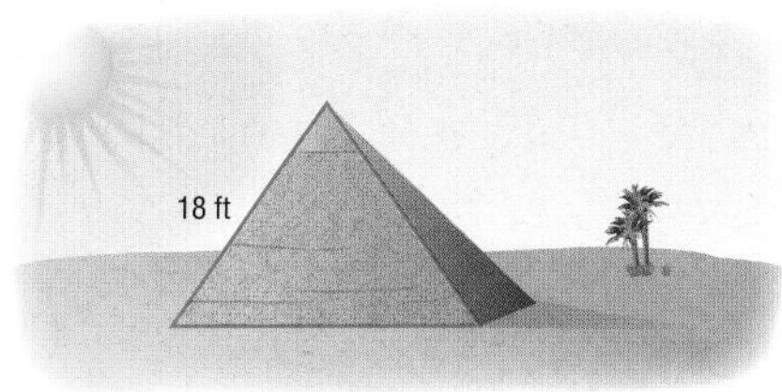

a. Find the height of the equilateral triangle.

b. Use the formula $\sin 2\theta = 2\sin\theta\cos\theta$ and the measures of the equilateral triangle and its height to show that $\sin 2(30°) = \sin 60°$. Find the exact values.

Find the exact value of each expression.

17. $\cos(-225°)$ $-\frac{\sqrt{2}}{2}$

18. $\sin 480°$ $\frac{\sqrt{3}}{2}$

19. $\cos 75°$ $\frac{\sqrt{6} - \sqrt{2}}{4}$

20. $\sin 165°$ $\frac{\sqrt{6} - \sqrt{2}}{4}$

21. **ROCKETS** A model rocket is launched with an initial velocity of 20 meters per second. The range of a projectile is given by the formula $R = \frac{v^2}{g}\sin 2\theta$, where R is the range, v is the initial velocity, g is acceleration due to gravity or 9.8 meters per second squared, and θ is the launch angle. What angle is needed in order for the rocket to reach a range of 25 meters? See margin.

Solve each equation for all values of θ if θ is measured in radians.

22. $2\cos^2\theta - 3\cos\theta - 2 = 0$ See margin.

23. $2\sin 3\theta - 1 = 0$ $\frac{\pi}{18} + \frac{2k\pi}{3}, \frac{5\pi}{18} + \frac{2k\pi}{3}$

Solve each equation for $0° \le \theta \le 360°$ if θ is measured in degrees.

24. $\cos 2\theta + \cos\theta = 2$ 0°, 360°

25. $\sin\theta\cos\theta - \frac{1}{2}\sin\theta = 0$ 0°, 60°, 180°, 300°, 360°

CHAPTER 14 Practice Test

ExamView Assessment Suite Customize and create multiple versions of your chapter test and their answer keys. All of the questions from the leveled chapter tests in the *Chapter 14 Resource Masters* are also available on ExamView® Assessment Suite.

Additional Answers

14. $\frac{\sin\theta}{1 - \cos\theta} \stackrel{?}{=} \cos\theta + \cot\theta$

$\frac{\sin\theta}{1 - \cos\theta} \stackrel{?}{=} \frac{1}{\sin\theta} + \frac{\cos\theta}{\sin\theta}$

$\frac{\sin\theta}{1 - \cos\theta} \stackrel{?}{=} \frac{1 + \cos\theta}{\sin\theta}$

$\frac{\sin\theta}{1 - \cos\theta} \stackrel{?}{=} \frac{1 + \cos\theta}{\sin\theta} \cdot \frac{1 - \cos\theta}{1 - \cos\theta}$

$\frac{\sin\theta}{1 - \cos\theta} \stackrel{?}{=} \frac{1 - \cos^2\theta}{\sin\theta(1 - \cos\theta)}$

$\frac{\sin\theta}{1 - \cos\theta} \stackrel{?}{=} \frac{\sin^2\theta}{\sin\theta(1 - \cos\theta)}$

$\frac{\sin\theta}{1 - \cos\theta} = \frac{\sin\theta}{1 - \cos\theta}$ ✓

16a. $18^2 = 9^2 + a^2$; $324 = 81 + a^2$; $243 = a^2$; $a = 9\sqrt{3}$

16b. $\sin 2\theta = 2\sin\theta\cos\theta$; $\sin 2(30) = 2\sin 30\cos 30$; $\sin 60 = 2\left(\frac{9}{18}\right)\left(\frac{9\sqrt{3}}{18}\right) = \frac{162\sqrt{3}}{324} = \frac{\sqrt{3}}{2}$; $\sin 60 = \frac{9\sqrt{3}}{18} = \frac{\sqrt{3}}{2}$

21. $R = \frac{v^2}{g}\sin 2\theta$; $25 = \frac{20^2}{9.8}\sin 2\theta$; $0.6125 = \sin 2\theta$; $\theta \approx 18.9°$

22. $\frac{2\pi}{3} + 2\pi k, \frac{4\pi}{3} + 2\pi k$

Intervention Planner

Tier 1 On Level	Tier 2 Strategic Intervention approaching grade level	Tier 3 Intensive Intervention 2 or more grades below level
If students miss about 25% of the exercises or less,	**If** students miss about 50% of the exercises,	**If** students miss about 75% of the exercises,
Then choose a resource: **SE** Lessons 14-1, 14-2, 14-3, 14-4, and 14-5 **CRM** Skills Practice, pp. 7, 13, 19, 25, and 31 **TE** Chapter Project, p. 888 FL Math Online Self-Check Quiz	**Then** choose a resource: **CRM** Study Guide and Intervention, Chapter 14, pp. 5, 11, 17, 23, and 29 FL Math Online Extra Examples, Personal Tutor, Homework Help	**Then** use *Math Triumphs, Alg. 2* FL Math Online Extra Examples, Personal Tutor, Homework Help, Review Vocabulary

1 FOCUS

Objective Use the strategy of simplifying expressions to solve standardized test problems.

2 TEACH

Scaffolding Questions

Ask:

- What kinds of problems might you have to simplify in order to solve? Possible answer: equations or inequalities where one or both sides need to be simplified before the equation or inequality is solved, trigonometric functions that need to be simplified.
- Why check if a problem could be simplified before using a calculator? Possible answer: if you start to use a calculator before simplifying you have more of a chance to enter information incorrectly. Also, you may find that simplifying the problem first gives you an answer without having to use the calculator.

CHAPTER 14 Preparing for Standardized Tests

Simplify Expressions

Some standardized test questions will require you to use the properties of algebra to simplify expressions. Follow the steps below to help prepare to solve these kinds of problems.

Strategies for Simplifying Expressions

Step 1

Study the expression that you are being asked to simplify.

Ask yourself:

- Are there any mathematical operations I can apply to help simplify the expression?
- Are there any laws or identities I can apply to help simplify the expression?

Step 2

Solve the problem and check your solution.

- Use the order of operations.
- Combine terms and factor as appropriate.
- Apply laws and identities.

Step 3

Check your solution if time permits.

- Retrace the steps in your work to make sure you answered the question thoroughly and accurately.
- If needed, sometimes you can use your scientific calculator to help you check your solution. Evaluate the original expression and your answer for some value and make sure they are the same.

NGSSS PRACTICE EXAMPLE

Solve the problem below. Responses will be graded using the short-response scoring rubric shown.

Simplify the trigonometric expression shown below by writing it in terms of sin θ. Show your work to receive full credit.

$$\frac{\cos \theta}{\sec \theta + \tan \theta}$$

Scoring Rubric

Criteria	Score
Full Credit: The answer is correct and a full explanation is provided that shows each step.	2
Partial Credit: • The answer is correct, but the explanation is incomplete. • The answer is incorrect, but the explanation is correct.	1
No Credit: Either an answer is not provided or the answer does not make sense.	0

Read the problem statement carefully. You are given a trigonometric expression and asked to simplify it by writing it in terms of sin θ. So, your final answer must contain only numbers and terms involving the sin θ. Show your work to receive full credit.

Example of a 2-point response:

Use trigonometric identities to simplify the expression.

$$\frac{\cos\theta}{\sec\theta + \tan\theta} = \frac{\cos\theta}{\frac{1}{\cos\theta} + \frac{\sin\theta}{\cos\theta}}$$ **Definition of sec θ and tan θ**

$$= \frac{\cos\theta}{\frac{1 + \sin\theta}{\cos\theta}}$$ **Simplify the denominator.**

$$= \frac{\cos^2\theta}{1 + \sin\theta}$$ **Simplify the complex fraction.**

$$= \frac{1 - \sin^2\theta}{1 + \sin\theta}$$ **Pythagorean identity**

$$= \frac{(1 + \sin\theta)(1 - \sin\theta)}{1 + \sin\theta}$$ **Factor.**

$$= 1 - \sin\theta$$ **Simplify.**

The simplified expression is $1 - \sin\theta$.

The steps, calculations, and reasoning are clearly stated. The student also arrives at the correct answer. So, this response is worth the full 2 points.

Exercises

Solve each problem. Show your work. Responses will be graded using the short-response scoring rubric given at the beginning of the lesson.

1. Simplify $\frac{\sec\theta}{\cot\theta + \tan\theta}$ by writing it in terms of sin θ. **sin θ**

2. What is $\frac{10a^{-3}}{29b^4} \div \frac{5a^{-5}}{16b^{-7}}$? $\frac{32a^2}{29b^{11}}$

3. Write $\frac{y+1}{y-1} + \frac{y+2}{y-2} + \frac{y}{y^2 - 3y + 2}$ in simplest form. $\frac{2y^2 + y - 4}{(y-1)(y-2)}$

4. Simplify $\frac{\cot^2\theta - \csc^2\theta}{\tan^2\theta - \sec^2\theta}$ by writing it as a constant. **1**

5. Multiply $(-5 + 2i)(6 - i)(4 + 3i)$. $-163 - 16i$

6. Simplify $(\cot\theta + 1)^2 - 2\cot\theta$ by writing it in terms of csc θ. $\csc^2\theta$

7. Express $\frac{4 - \sqrt{7}}{3 + \sqrt{7}}$ in simplest form. $\frac{19 - 7\sqrt{7}}{2}$

Additional Example

STANDARDIZED TEST PRACTICE
Simplify the expression
sec θ cot θ cos θ. B

A csc θ
B cot θ
C cos θ
D sin θ

3 ASSESS

Use Exercises 1–7 to assess students' understanding.

Diagnose Student Errors

Survey student responses for each item. Class trends may indicate common errors and misconceptions.

1. A. chose an amount not between \$650 and \$925
   B. chose an amount not between \$650 and \$925
   C. correct
   D. chose an amount not between \$650 and \$925
3. F. mistakenly identified the slope as the y-intercept
   G. mistakenly identified the slope as the x-intercept
   H. does not understand that the slopes of two lines must be additive inverses in order for the lines to be perpendicular
   I. correct
5. A. correct
   B. used $\cos^2 \theta = 1 + \sin^2 \theta$ instead of $\cos^2 \theta = 1 - \sin^2 \theta$
   C. incorrectly simplified fraction
   D. incorrectly multiplied denominator
7. F. mistakenly reversed the cosine and sine values and subtracted in the formula
   G. incorrect denominator, 2, found when multiplying values
   H. correct
   I. mistakenly subtracted when using the addition of angles formula
9. A. product should be a 1×2 matrix not 2×1 matrix
   B. correct
   C. product should be a 1×2 matrix not 3×2
   D. the first matrix is 1×3 and the second is 3×2 so the product of a 1×2 matrix is defined
10. F. added instead of multiplied to find x^2 coefficient
    G. added instead of multiplied to find x^2 coefficient
    H. placed incorrect signs on x-term and constant
    I. correct
12. A. did not understand that n represents the number of sides
    B. did not evalute expression with data in the table
    C. correct
    D. only used data from the first line of the table to determine the expression
13. F. does not recognize the difference of squares but pays attention to exponents of terms
    G. correct
    H. does not recognize the difference of squares
    I. does recognize the difference of squares but does not pay attention to exponents of terms
15. A. did not include $\frac{3}{5}$ in domain
    B. guess
    C. correct
    D. incorrectly solved $0 \leq 5x - 3$

Read each question. Then fill in the correct answer on the answer document provided by your teacher or on a sheet of paper.

1. The profit p that Selena's Shirt Store makes in a day can be represented by the inequality $10t + 200 < p < 15t + 250$, where t represents the number of shirts sold. If the store sold 45 shirts on Friday, which of the following is a reasonable amount that the store made? **C**

   A. \$200 B. \$625 C. \$850 D. \$950

2. **EXTENDED RESPONSE** Kyla's annual salary is \$50,000. Each year she gets a 6% raise.

   a. To the nearest dollar, what will her salary be in four years? **\$63,124**

   b. To the nearest dollar, what will her salary be in 10 years? **\$89,542**

3. Which of the following best describes the graphs of $y = 3x - 5$ and $4y = 12x + 16$? **I**

   F. The lines have the same y-intercept.
   G. The lines have the same x-intercept.
   H. The lines are perpendicular.
   I. The lines are parallel.

4. **GRIDDED RESPONSE** A coordinate grid is placed over a map. Emilee's house is located at $(-3, -2)$, and Oliver's house is located at $(2, 5)$. A side of each square represents one block. What is the approximate distance between Emilee's house and Oliver's house? **8.6**

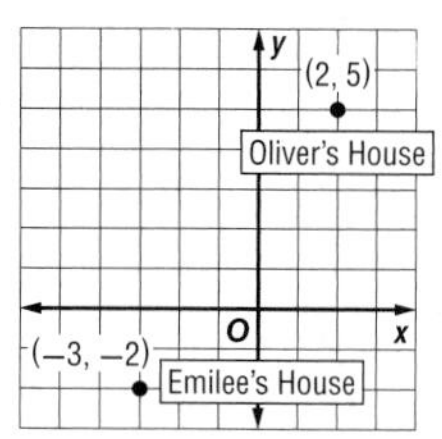

5. How can you express $\cos \theta \csc \theta \cot \theta$ in terms of $\sin \theta$? **A**

   A. $\frac{1 - \sin^2 \theta}{\sin^2 \theta}$ C. $\frac{\sin^2 \theta}{2}$

   B. $\frac{1 + \sin^2 \theta}{\sin^2 \theta}$ D. $\frac{1 - \sin^2 \theta}{\sin \theta}$

6. **SHORT RESPONSE** Kelly is designing a 12-inch by 12-inch scrapbook page. She cuts one picture that is 4 inches by 6 inches. She decides that she wants the next picture to be 75% as large as the first picture and the third picture to be 150% as large as the second picture. What are the approximate dimensions of the third picture? **4.5 in. by 6.75 in.**

7. Use a sum or difference of angles identity to find the exact value of cos 75°. **H**

   F. $\frac{\sqrt{2} - \sqrt{6}}{4}$ H. $\frac{\sqrt{6} - \sqrt{2}}{4}$

   G. $\frac{\sqrt{2} + \sqrt{6}}{2}$ I. $\frac{\sqrt{6} + \sqrt{2}}{4}$

8. **SHORT RESPONSE** Identify the amplitude and period of the function graphed below. Then write an equation for the function.

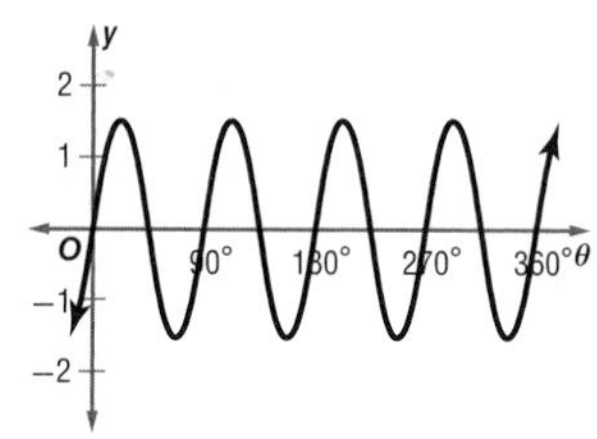

amplitude: 1.5, period: 90°, equation: $y = 1.5 \sin 4\theta$

9. What is the product of $\begin{bmatrix} 5 & -2 & 3 \end{bmatrix}$ and $\begin{bmatrix} 1 & -2 \\ 0 & 3 \\ 2 & 5 \end{bmatrix}$? **B**

   A. $\begin{bmatrix} 11 \\ -1 \end{bmatrix}$ C. $\begin{bmatrix} 5 & -10 \\ 0 & -6 \\ 6 & -15 \end{bmatrix}$

   B. $\begin{bmatrix} 11 & -1 \end{bmatrix}$ D. undefined

Test-Taking Tip

Question 7 You can check your answer using a scientific calculator. Find cos 75° and compare it to the value of your answer.

14. Sample answer: $\sin 2N = 2 \sin N \cos N = 2\frac{n}{m} \cdot \frac{\ell}{m} = \frac{2n\ell}{m^2}$

10. Which quadratic equation has roots $\frac{1}{2}$ and $\frac{1}{3}$? I

F. $5x^2 - 5x - 2 = 0$

G. $5x^2 - 5x + 1 = 0$

H. $6x^2 + 5x - 1 = 0$

I. $6x^2 - 5x + 1 = 0$

11. **GRIDDED RESPONSE** Solve the trigonometric equation below in the interval from 0 to 2π. Round your answer to the nearest hundredth if necessary. 2.52

$$3 \cos \frac{t}{3} = 2$$

12. Use the table to determine the expression that best represents the sum of the degree measures of the interior angles of a polygon with n sides. C

Polygon	Number of Sides	Sum of Measures
triangle	3	180
quadrilateral	4	360
pentagon	5	540
hexagon	6	720
heptagon	7	900
octagon	8	1080

A. $180 + n$

B. $180n$

C. $180(n - 2)$

D. $60n$

13. The area of a rectangle is $25a^4 - 16b^2$. Which factors could represent the length times width? G

F. $(5a^2 + 4b)(5a^2 + 4b)$

G. $(5a^2 + 4b)(5a^2 - 4b)$

H. $(5a - 4b)(5a - 4b)$

I. $(5a + 4b)(5a - 4b)$

14. **SHORT RESPONSE** Use right triangle LMN at the right to show that $\sin 2N = \frac{2n\ell}{m^2}$.

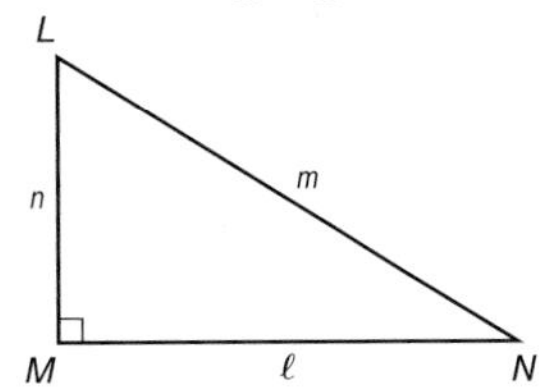

15. What is the domain of $f(x) = \sqrt{5x - 3}$? C

A. $\left\{x \mid x > \frac{3}{5}\right\}$

B. $\left\{x \mid x > -\frac{3}{5}\right\}$

C. $\left\{x \mid x \geq \frac{3}{5}\right\}$

D. $\left\{x \mid x \geq -\frac{3}{5}\right\}$

16. If the equation $y = 3^x$ is graphed, which of the following values of x would produce a point closest to the x-axis? I

F. $\frac{3}{4}$

G. $\frac{1}{4}$

H. 0

I. $-\frac{3}{4}$

17. **EXTENDED RESPONSE** When working at Taco King, Naomi wears a uniform that consists of a shirt, a pair of pants, and a tie. She has 6 uniform shirts, 3 uniform pants, and 4 uniform ties.

a. How many different combinations of shirt, pants, and tie can she make? 72

b. How many different combinations of shirts and pants can she make? 18

c. Two of her shirts are red, 3 are blue, and 1 is white. If she wears a different shirt for six days in a row and chooses the shirts at random, what is the probability that she wears a red shirt the first two days? $\frac{1}{15}$

Need Extra Help?

If you missed Question...	1	2	3	4	5	6	7	8	9	10	11	12	13	14	15	16	17
Go to Lesson or Page...	1-5	11-2	3-1	10-1	14-1	9-5	14-3	13-8	4-3	5-3	14-5	2-4	6-2	14-4	7-3	8-1	12-4
For help with NGSSS...	912.A.3.4	912.D.11.3	912.A.3.14	912.G.1.1	912.T.3.2	912.A.2.12	912.T.3.3	912.T.1.6	912.D.8.2	912.A.4.3	912.T.3.5	912.A.3.10	912.A.4.4	912.T.3.2	912.A.2.4	912.A.8.3	912.P.1.2

16. F. doesn't understand that exponential functions are everywhere increasing
G. doesn't understand that exponential functions are everywhere increasing
H. doesn't understand that exponential functions are everywhere increasing
I. correct

Formative Assessment

You can use these two pages to benchmark student progress.

Chapter 14 Resource Masters

- Standardized Test Practice, pp. 54–56

ExamView Assessment Suite — Create practice worksheets or tests that align to your state's standards as well as TIMSS and NAEP tests.

Pages 900–902, Lesson 14-2

1. $\cot\theta + \tan\theta \stackrel{?}{=} \dfrac{\sec^2\theta}{\tan\theta}$

$\cot\theta + \tan\theta \stackrel{?}{=} \dfrac{\tan^2\theta + 1}{\tan\theta}$

$\cot\theta + \tan\theta \stackrel{?}{=} \dfrac{\tan^2\theta}{\tan\theta} + \dfrac{1}{\tan\theta}$

$\cot\theta + \tan\theta = \tan\theta + \cot\theta$ ✓

2. $\cos^2\theta \stackrel{?}{=} (1 + \sin\theta)(1 - \sin\theta)$

$\cos^2\theta \stackrel{?}{=} 1 - \sin^2\theta$

$\cos^2\theta = \cos^2\theta$ ✓

3. $\sin\theta \stackrel{?}{=} \dfrac{\sec\theta}{\tan\theta + \cot\theta}$

$\sin\theta \stackrel{?}{=} \dfrac{\frac{1}{\cos\theta}}{\frac{\sin\theta}{\cos\theta} + \frac{\cos\theta}{\sin\theta}}$

$\sin\theta \stackrel{?}{=} \dfrac{\frac{1}{\cos\theta}}{\frac{\sin^2\theta + \cos^2\theta}{\cos\theta\sin\theta}}$

$\sin\theta \stackrel{?}{=} \dfrac{\frac{1}{\cos\theta}}{\frac{1}{\cos\theta\sin\theta}}$

$\sin\theta \stackrel{?}{=} \dfrac{1}{\cos\theta} \cdot \dfrac{\cos\theta\sin\theta}{1}$

$\sin\theta = \sin\theta$ ✓

4. $\tan^2\theta \stackrel{?}{=} \dfrac{1 - \cos^2\theta}{\cos^2\theta}$

$\tan^2\theta \stackrel{?}{=} \dfrac{\sin^2\theta}{\cos^2\theta}$

$\tan^2\theta = \tan^2\theta$ ✓

5. $\tan^2\theta\csc^2\theta \stackrel{?}{=} 1 + \tan^2\theta$

$\dfrac{\sin^2\theta}{\cos^2\theta} \cdot \dfrac{1}{\sin^2\theta} \stackrel{?}{=} \sec^2\theta$

$\dfrac{1}{\cos^2\theta} \stackrel{?}{=} \sec^2\theta$

$\sec^2\theta = \sec^2\theta$ ✓

6. $\tan^2\theta \stackrel{?}{=} (\sec\theta + 1)(\sec\theta - 1)$

$\tan^2\theta \stackrel{?}{=} \sin^2\theta - 1$

$\tan^2\theta = \tan^2\theta$ ✓

8. $\cos^2\theta + \tan^2\theta\cos^2\theta \stackrel{?}{=} 1$

$\cos^2\theta + \dfrac{\sin^2\theta}{\cos^2\theta} \cdot \cos^2\theta \stackrel{?}{=} 1$

$\cos^2\theta + \sin^2\theta \stackrel{?}{=} 1$

$1 = 1$ ✓

9. $\cot\theta(\cot\theta + \tan\theta) \stackrel{?}{=} \csc^2\theta$

$\cot^2\theta + \cot\theta\tan\theta \stackrel{?}{=} \csc^2\theta$

$\cot^2\theta + \dfrac{\sin\theta}{\cos\theta} \cdot \dfrac{\cos\theta}{\sin\theta} \stackrel{?}{=} \csc^2\theta$

$\cot^2\theta + 1 \stackrel{?}{=} \csc^2\theta$

$\csc^2\theta = \csc^2\theta$ ✓

10. $1 + \sec^2\theta\sin^2\theta \stackrel{?}{=} \sec^2\theta$

$1 + \dfrac{1}{\cos^2\theta} \cdot \sin^2\theta \stackrel{?}{=} \sec^2\theta$

$1 + \tan^2\theta \stackrel{?}{=} \sec^2\theta$

$\sec^2\theta = \sec^2\theta$ ✓

11. $\sin\theta\sec\theta\cot\theta \stackrel{?}{=} 1$

$\sin\theta \cdot \dfrac{1}{\cos\theta} \cdot \dfrac{\cos\theta}{\sin\theta} \stackrel{?}{=} 1$

$1 = 1$ ✓

12. $\dfrac{1 - \cos\theta}{1 + \cos\theta} \stackrel{?}{=} (\csc\theta - \cot\theta)^2$

$\dfrac{1 - \cos\theta}{1 + \cos\theta} \stackrel{?}{=} \csc^2\theta - 2\cot\theta\csc\theta + \cot^2\theta$

$\dfrac{1 - \cos\theta}{1 + \cos\theta} \stackrel{?}{=} \dfrac{1}{\sin^2\theta} - 2 \cdot \dfrac{\cos\theta}{\sin\theta} \cdot \dfrac{1}{\sin\theta} + \dfrac{\cos^2\theta}{\sin^2\theta}$

$\dfrac{1 - \cos\theta}{1 + \cos\theta} \stackrel{?}{=} \dfrac{1}{\sin^2\theta} - \dfrac{2\cos\theta}{\sin^2\theta} + \dfrac{\cos^2\theta}{\sin^2\theta}$

$\dfrac{1 - \cos\theta}{1 + \cos\theta} \stackrel{?}{=} \dfrac{1 - 2\cos\theta + \cos^2\theta}{\sin^2\theta}$

$\dfrac{1 - \cos\theta}{1 + \cos\theta} \stackrel{?}{=} \dfrac{(1 - \cos\theta)(1 - \cos\theta)}{1 - \cos^2\theta}$

$\dfrac{1 - \cos\theta}{1 + \cos\theta} \stackrel{?}{=} \dfrac{(1 - \cos\theta)(1 - \cos\theta)}{(1 - \cos\theta)(1 + \cos\theta)}$

$\dfrac{1 - \cos\theta}{1 + \cos\theta} = \dfrac{1 - \cos\theta}{1 + \cos\theta}$ ✓

13. $\dfrac{1 - 2\cos^2\theta}{\sin\theta\cos\theta} \stackrel{?}{=} \tan\theta - \cot\theta$

$\dfrac{(1 - \cos^2\theta) - \cos^2\theta}{\sin\theta\cos\theta} \stackrel{?}{=} \tan\theta - \cot\theta$

$\dfrac{\sin^2\theta - \cos^2\theta}{\sin\theta\cos\theta} \stackrel{?}{=} \tan\theta - \cot\theta$

$\dfrac{\sin^2\theta}{\sin\theta\cos\theta} - \dfrac{\cos^2\theta}{\sin\theta\cos\theta} \stackrel{?}{=} \tan\theta - \cot\theta$

$\dfrac{\sin\theta}{\cos\theta} - \dfrac{\cos\theta}{\sin\theta} \stackrel{?}{=} \tan\theta - \cot\theta$

$\tan\theta - \cot\theta = \tan\theta - \cot\theta$ ✓

14. $\tan\theta \stackrel{?}{=} \dfrac{\sec\theta}{\csc\theta}$

$\tan\theta \stackrel{?}{=} \dfrac{\frac{1}{\cos\theta}}{\frac{1}{\sin\theta}}$

$\tan\theta \stackrel{?}{=} \dfrac{\sin\theta}{\cos\theta}$

$\tan\theta = \tan\theta$ ✓

15. $\cos\theta \stackrel{?}{=} \sin\theta\cot\theta$

$\cos\theta \stackrel{?}{=} \sin\theta\left(\dfrac{\cos\theta}{\sin\theta}\right)$

$\cos\theta = \cos\theta$ ✓

16.
$$(\sin\theta - 1)(\tan\theta + \sec\theta) \stackrel{?}{=} -\cos\theta$$
$$\sin\theta\tan\theta + \sin\theta\sec\theta - \tan\theta - \sec\theta \stackrel{?}{=} -\cos\theta$$
$$\frac{\sin^2\theta}{\cos\theta} + \frac{\sin\theta}{\cos\theta} - \frac{\sin\theta}{\cos\theta} - \frac{1}{\cos\theta} \stackrel{?}{=} -\cos\theta$$
$$\frac{\sin^2\theta}{\cos\theta} - \frac{1}{\cos\theta} \stackrel{?}{=} -\cos\theta$$
$$\frac{\sin^2\theta - 1}{\cos\theta} \stackrel{?}{=} -\cos\theta$$
$$\frac{-\cos^2\theta}{\cos\theta} \stackrel{?}{=} -\cos\theta$$
$$-\cos\theta = -\cos\theta \checkmark$$

17.
$$\cos\theta\cos(-\theta) - \sin\theta\sin(-\theta) \stackrel{?}{=} 1$$
$$\cos\theta\cos\theta - \sin\theta(-\sin\theta) \stackrel{?}{=} 1$$
$$\cos^2\theta + \sin^2\theta \stackrel{?}{=} 1$$
$$1 = 1 \checkmark$$

19.
$$\sec\theta - \tan\theta \stackrel{?}{=} \frac{1 - \sin\theta}{\cos\theta}$$
$$\frac{1}{\cos\theta} - \frac{\sin\theta}{\cos\theta} \stackrel{?}{=} \frac{1 - \sin\theta}{\cos\theta}$$
$$\frac{1 - \sin\theta}{\cos\theta} = \frac{1 - \sin\theta}{\cos\theta} \checkmark$$

20.
$$\frac{1 + \tan\theta}{\sin\theta + \cos\theta} \stackrel{?}{=} \sec\theta$$
$$\frac{1 + \frac{\sin\theta}{\cos\theta}}{\sin\theta + \cos\theta} \stackrel{?}{=} \sec\theta$$
$$\frac{\frac{\cos\theta + \sin\theta}{\cos\theta}}{\sin\theta + \cos\theta} \stackrel{?}{=} \sec\theta$$
$$\frac{\cos\theta + \sin\theta}{\cos\theta} \cdot \frac{1}{\sin\theta + \cos\theta} \stackrel{?}{=} \sec\theta$$
$$\frac{1}{\cos\theta} \stackrel{?}{=} \sec\theta$$
$$\sec\theta = \sec\theta \checkmark$$

21.
$$\sec\theta\csc\theta \stackrel{?}{=} \tan\theta + \cot\theta$$
$$\frac{1}{\cos\theta} \cdot \frac{1}{\sin\theta} \stackrel{?}{=} \frac{\sin\theta}{\cos\theta} + \frac{\cos\theta}{\sin\theta}$$
$$\frac{1}{\cos\theta\sin\theta} \stackrel{?}{=} \frac{\sin^2\theta}{\sin\theta\cos\theta} + \frac{\cos^2\theta}{\sin\theta\cos\theta}$$
$$\frac{1}{\cos\theta\sin\theta} \stackrel{?}{=} \frac{\sin^2\theta + \cos^2\theta}{\sin\theta\cos\theta}$$
$$\frac{1}{\cos\theta\sin\theta} = \frac{1}{\cos\theta\sin\theta} \checkmark$$

22.
$$\sin\theta + \cos\theta \stackrel{?}{=} \frac{2\sin^2\theta - 1}{\sin\theta - \cos\theta}$$
$$\sin\theta + \cos\theta \stackrel{?}{=} \frac{2\sin^2\theta - (\sin^2\theta + \cos^2\theta)}{\sin\theta - \cos\theta}$$
$$\sin\theta + \cos\theta \stackrel{?}{=} \frac{\sin^2\theta - \cos^2\theta}{\sin\theta - \cos\theta}$$
$$\sin\theta + \cos\theta \stackrel{?}{=} \frac{(\sin\theta - \cos\theta)(\sin\theta - \cos\theta)}{\sin\theta - \cos\theta}$$
$$\sin\theta + \cos\theta = \sin\theta + \cos\theta \checkmark$$

23.
$$(\sin\theta + \cos\theta)^2 \stackrel{?}{=} \frac{2 + \sec\theta\csc\theta}{\sec\theta\csc\theta}$$
$$(\sin\theta + \cos\theta)^2 \stackrel{?}{=} \frac{2 + \frac{1}{\cos\theta} \cdot \frac{1}{\sin\theta}}{\frac{1}{\cos\theta} \cdot \frac{1}{\sin\theta}}$$
$$(\sin\theta + \cos\theta)^2 \stackrel{?}{=} \left(2 + \frac{1}{\cos\theta\sin\theta}\right) \cdot \frac{\cos\theta\sin\theta}{1}$$
$$(\sin\theta + \cos\theta)^2 \stackrel{?}{=} 2\cos\theta\sin\theta + 1$$
$$(\sin\theta + \cos\theta)^2 \stackrel{?}{=} 2\cos\theta\sin\theta + \cos^2\theta + \sin^2\theta$$
$$(\sin\theta + \cos\theta)^2 = (\sin\theta + \cos\theta)^2 \checkmark$$

24.
$$\frac{\cos\theta}{1 - \sin\theta} \stackrel{?}{=} \frac{1 + \sin\theta}{\cos\theta}$$
$$\frac{\cos\theta}{1 - \sin\theta} \stackrel{?}{=} \frac{1 + \sin\theta}{\cos\theta} \cdot \frac{1 - \sin\theta}{1 - \sin\theta}$$
$$\frac{\cos\theta}{1 - \sin\theta} \stackrel{?}{=} \frac{1 - \sin^2\theta}{\cos\theta(1 - \sin\theta)}$$
$$\frac{\cos\theta}{1 - \sin\theta} \stackrel{?}{=} \frac{\cos^2\theta}{\cos\theta(1 - \sin\theta)}$$
$$\frac{\cos\theta}{1 - \sin\theta} = \frac{\cos\theta}{1 - \sin\theta} \checkmark$$

25.
$$\csc\theta - 1 \stackrel{?}{=} \frac{\cot^2\theta}{\csc\theta + 1}$$
$$\csc\theta - 1 \stackrel{?}{=} \frac{\csc^2\theta - 1}{\csc\theta + 1}$$
$$\csc\theta - 1 \stackrel{?}{=} \frac{(\csc\theta - 1)(\csc\theta + 1)}{\csc\theta + 1}$$
$$\csc\theta - 1 = \csc\theta - 1 \checkmark$$

26.
$$\cos\theta\cot\theta \stackrel{?}{=} \csc\theta - \sin\theta$$
$$(\cos\theta)\frac{\cos\theta}{\sin\theta} \stackrel{?}{=} \frac{1}{\sin\theta} - \sin\theta$$
$$\frac{\cos^2\theta}{\sin\theta} \stackrel{?}{=} \frac{1}{\sin\theta} - \frac{\sin\theta}{1} \cdot \frac{\sin\theta}{\sin\theta}$$
$$\frac{\cos^2\theta}{\sin\theta} \stackrel{?}{=} \frac{1}{\sin\theta} - \frac{\sin^2\theta}{\sin\theta}$$
$$\frac{\cos^2\theta}{\sin\theta} \stackrel{?}{=} \frac{1 - \sin^2\theta}{\sin\theta}$$
$$\frac{\cos^2\theta}{\sin\theta} = \frac{\cos^2\theta}{\sin\theta} \checkmark$$

27.
$$\sin\theta\cos\theta\tan\theta + \cos^2\theta \stackrel{?}{=} 1$$
$$\sin\theta\cos\theta \cdot \frac{\sin\theta}{\cos\theta} + \cos^2\theta \stackrel{?}{=} 1$$
$$\sin^2\theta + \cos^2\theta \stackrel{?}{=} 1$$
$$1 = 1 \checkmark$$

28.
$$(\csc\theta - \cot\theta)^2 \stackrel{?}{=} \frac{1-\cos\theta}{1+\cos\theta}$$
$$\left(\frac{1}{\sin\theta} - \frac{\cos\theta}{\sin\theta}\right)^2 \stackrel{?}{=} \frac{1-\cos\theta}{1+\cos\theta}$$
$$\left(\frac{1-\cos\theta}{\sin\theta}\right)^2 \stackrel{?}{=} \frac{1-\cos\theta}{1+\cos\theta}$$
$$\frac{1-2\cos\theta+\cos^2\theta}{\sin^2\theta} \stackrel{?}{=} \frac{1-\cos\theta}{1+\cos\theta}$$
$$\frac{(1-\cos\theta)(1-\cos\theta)}{\sin^2\theta} \stackrel{?}{=} \frac{1-\cos\theta}{1+\cos\theta}$$
$$\frac{(1-\cos\theta)(1-\cos\theta)}{1-\cos^2\theta} \stackrel{?}{=} \frac{1-\cos\theta}{1+\cos\theta}$$
$$\frac{(1-\cos\theta)(1-\cos\theta)}{(1-\cos\theta)(1+\cos\theta)} \stackrel{?}{=} \frac{1-\cos\theta}{1+\cos\theta}$$
$$\frac{1-\cos\theta}{1+\cos\theta} = \frac{1-\cos\theta}{1+\cos\theta}\ \checkmark$$

29. $\csc^2\theta \stackrel{?}{=} \cot^2\theta + \sin\theta\csc\theta$
$$\csc^2\theta \stackrel{?}{=} \cot^2\theta + \sin\theta \cdot \frac{1}{\sin\theta}$$
$$\csc^2\theta \stackrel{?}{=} \cot^2\theta + 1$$
$$\csc^2\theta = \csc^2\theta\ \checkmark$$

30.
$$\frac{\sec\theta - \csc\theta}{\csc\theta\sec\theta} \stackrel{?}{=} \sin\theta - \cos\theta$$
$$\frac{\sec\theta}{\csc\theta\sec\theta} - \frac{\csc\theta}{\csc\theta\sec\theta} \stackrel{?}{=} \sin\theta - \cos\theta$$
$$\frac{1}{\csc\theta} - \frac{1}{\sec\theta} \stackrel{?}{=} \sin\theta - \cos\theta$$
$$\sin\theta - \cos\theta = \sin\theta - \cos\theta\ \checkmark$$

31. $\sin^2\theta + \cos^2\theta \stackrel{?}{=} \sec^2\theta - \tan^2\theta$
$$1 \stackrel{?}{=} \tan^2\theta + 1 - \tan^2\theta$$
$$1 = 1\ \checkmark$$

32.
$$\sec\theta - \cos\theta \stackrel{?}{=} \tan\theta\sin\theta$$
$$\frac{1}{\cos\theta} - \cos\theta \stackrel{?}{=} \tan\theta\sin\theta$$
$$\frac{1}{\cos\theta} - \frac{\cos^2\theta}{\cos\theta} \stackrel{?}{=} \tan\theta\sin\theta$$
$$\frac{1-\cos^2\theta}{\cos\theta} \stackrel{?}{=} \tan\theta\sin\theta$$
$$\frac{\sin^2\theta}{\cos\theta} \stackrel{?}{=} \tan\theta\sin\theta$$
$$\left(\frac{\sin\theta}{\cos\theta}\right)\sin\theta \stackrel{?}{=} \tan\theta\sin\theta$$
$$\tan\theta\sin\theta = \tan\theta\sin\theta\ \checkmark$$

51a.

Angle measure	Height
30°	28.2 m
45°	56.4 m
60°	84.5 m
90°	112.7 m

51b.

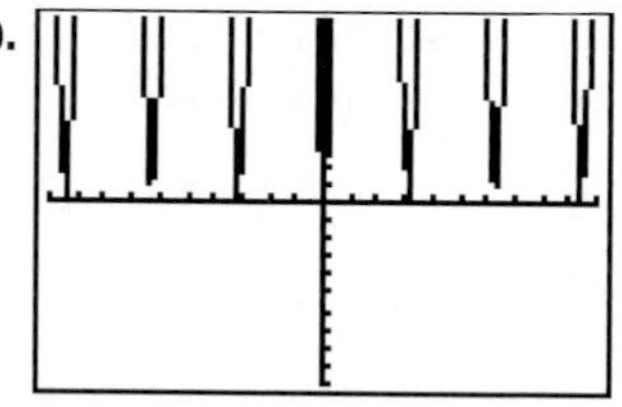

51c.
$$\frac{v_0^2\tan^2\theta}{2g\sec^2\theta} \stackrel{?}{=} \frac{v_0^2\sin^2\theta}{2g}$$
$$\frac{v_0^2\left(\frac{\sin^2\theta}{\cos^2\theta}\right)}{2g\left(\frac{1}{\cos^2\theta}\right)} \stackrel{?}{=} \frac{v_0^2\sin^2\theta}{2g}$$
$$\frac{v_0^2\sin^2\theta}{2g} = \frac{v_0^2\sin^2\theta}{2g}\ \checkmark$$

59. Using the unit circle and the Pythagorean Theorem, we can justify $\cos^2\theta + \sin^2\theta = 1$.

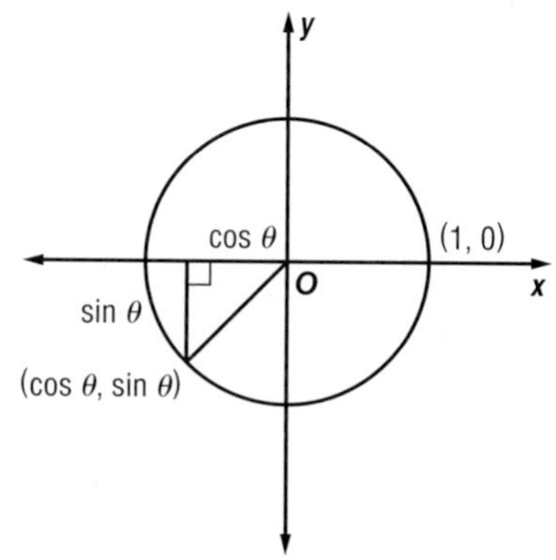

If we divide each term of the identity $\cos^2\theta + \sin^2\theta = 1$ by $\cos^2\theta$, we can justify $1 + \tan^2\theta = \sec^2\theta$.
$$\frac{\cos^2\theta}{\cos^2\theta} + \frac{\sin^2\theta}{\cos^2\theta} = \frac{1}{\cos^2\theta}$$
$$1 + \tan^2\theta = \sec^2\theta$$

If we divide each term of the identity $\cos^2\theta + \sin^2\theta = 1$ by $\sin^2\theta$, we can justify $\cot^2\theta + 1 = \csc^2\theta$.
$$\frac{\cos^2\theta}{\sin^2\theta} + \frac{\sin^2\theta}{\sin^2\theta} = \frac{1}{\sin^2\theta}$$
$$\cot^2\theta + 1 = \csc^2\theta$$

Pages 907–908, Lesson 14-3

30.
$$F = \frac{W(\sin A + \mu\cos A)}{\cos A - \mu\sin A}$$
$$= \frac{W(\sin A + \tan\theta\cos A)}{\cos A - \tan\theta\sin A}$$
$$= \frac{W\left(\frac{\sin A}{\cos A} + \frac{\tan\theta\cos A}{\cos A}\right)}{\frac{\cos A}{\cos A} - \frac{\tan\theta\sin A}{\cos A}}$$
$$= \frac{W(\tan A + \tan\theta)}{1 - \tan A\tan\theta}$$
$$= W\tan(A + \theta)$$

33b.

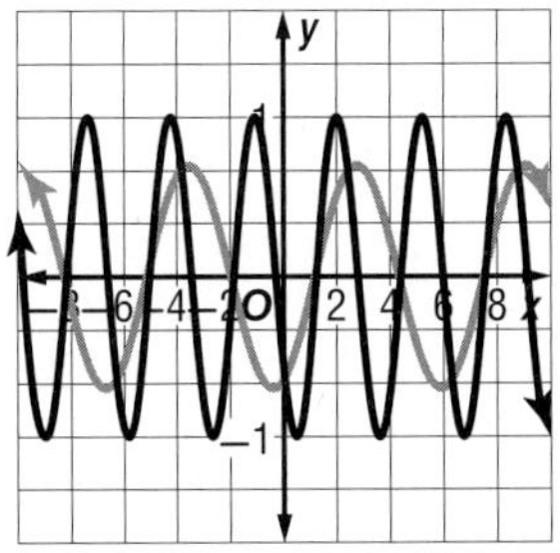

33c. No; a counterexample is: cos (30° + 45°) = cos 30° + cos 45°, which equals $\frac{\sqrt{3}}{2} + \frac{\sqrt{2}}{2}$ or about 1.5731. Since a cosine value cannot be greater than 1, this statement must be false.

34. $\sin(A+B) \stackrel{?}{=} \frac{\tan A + \tan B}{\sec A \sec B}$

$\sin(A+B) \stackrel{?}{=} \frac{\frac{\sin A}{\cos A} + \frac{\sin B}{\cos B}}{\frac{1}{\cos A} \cdot \frac{1}{\cos B}}$

$\sin(A+B) \stackrel{?}{=} \frac{\frac{\sin A}{\cos A} + \frac{\sin B}{\cos B}}{\frac{1}{\cos A} \cdot \frac{1}{\cos B}} \cdot \frac{\cos A \cos B}{\cos A \cos B}$

$\sin(A+B) \stackrel{?}{=} \frac{\sin A \cos B + \cos A \sin B}{1}$

$\sin(A+B) = \sin(A+B)$ ✓

35. $\cos(A+B) \stackrel{?}{=} \frac{1 - \tan A \tan B}{\sec A \sec B}$

$\cos(A+B) \stackrel{?}{=} \frac{1 - \frac{\sin A}{\cos A} \cdot \frac{\sin B}{\cos B}}{\frac{1}{\cos A} \cdot \frac{1}{\cos B}}$

$\cos(A+B) \stackrel{?}{=} \frac{1 - \frac{\sin A}{\cos A} \cdot \frac{\sin B}{\cos B}}{\frac{1}{\cos A} \cdot \frac{1}{\cos B}} \cdot \frac{\cos A \cos B}{\cos A \cos B}$

$\cos(A+B) \stackrel{?}{=} \frac{\cos A \cos B - \sin A \sin B}{1}$

$\cos(A+B) = \cos(A+B)$ ✓

36. $\sec(A-B) \stackrel{?}{=} \frac{\sec A \sec B}{1 + \tan A \tan B}$

$\sec(A-B) \stackrel{?}{=} \frac{\frac{1}{\cos A} \cdot \frac{1}{\cos B}}{1 + \frac{\sin A}{\cos A} \cdot \frac{\sin B}{\cos B}}$

$\sec(A-B) \stackrel{?}{=} \frac{\frac{1}{\cos A} \cdot \frac{1}{\cos B}}{1 + \frac{\sin A}{\cos A} \cdot \frac{\sin B}{\cos B}} \cdot \frac{\cos A \cos B}{\cos A \cos B}$

$\sec(A-B) \stackrel{?}{=} \frac{1}{\cos A \cos B + \sin A \sin B}$

$\sec(A-B) \stackrel{?}{=} \frac{1}{\cos(A-B)}$

$\sec(A-B) = \sec(A-B)$ ✓

37. $\sin(A+B)\sin(A-B) \stackrel{?}{=} \sin^2 A - \sin^2 B$

$(\sin A \cos B + \cos A \sin B)$
$(\sin A \cos B - \cos A \sin B) \stackrel{?}{=} \sin^2 A - \sin^2 B$

$(\sin A \cos B)^2 - (\cos A \sin B)^2 \stackrel{?}{=} \sin^2 A - \sin^2 B$

$\sin^2 B \cos^2 B - \cos^2 A \sin^2 B \stackrel{?}{=} \sin^2 A - \sin^2 B$

$\sin^2 A \cos^2 B + \sin^2 A \sin^2 B -$
$\sin^2 A \sin^2 B - \cos^2 A \sin^2 B \stackrel{?}{=} \sin^2 A - \sin^2 B$

$\sin^2 A(\cos^2 B + \sin^2 B) - \sin^2 B(\sin^2 A + \cos^2 A) \stackrel{?}{=} \sin^2 A - \sin^2 B$

$(\sin^2 A)(1) - (\sin^2 B)(1) \stackrel{?}{=} \sin^2 A - \sin^2 B$

$\sin^2 A - \sin^2 B = \sin^2 A - \sin^2 B$ ✓

40. $\cot(A+B) = \frac{1}{\tan(A+B)}$

$= \frac{1}{\frac{\tan A + \tan B}{1 - \tan A \tan B}}$

$= \frac{1 - \tan A \tan B}{\tan A + \tan B}$

$= \frac{1 - \frac{1}{\cot A} \cdot \frac{1}{\cot B}}{\frac{1}{\cot A} + \frac{1}{\cot B}} \cdot \frac{\cot A \cot B}{\cot A \cot B}$

$= \frac{\cot A \cot B - 1}{\cot A + \cot B}$

41. $d = \sqrt{(\cos\alpha - \cos\beta)^2 + (\sin\alpha - \sin\beta)^2}$

$d^2 = (\cos\alpha - \cos\beta)^2 + (\sin\alpha - \sin\beta)^2$

$d^2 = (\cos^2\alpha - 2\cos\alpha\cos\beta + \cos^2\beta) + (\sin^2\alpha - 2\sin\alpha$
$\sin\beta + \sin^2\beta)$

$d^2 = \cos^2\alpha + \sin^2\alpha + \cos^2\beta + \sin^2\beta - 2\cos\alpha\cos\beta -$
$2\sin\alpha\sin\beta$

$d^2 = 1 + 1 - 2\cos\alpha\cos\beta - 2\sin\alpha\sin\beta$

$d^2 = 2 - 2\cos\alpha\cos\beta - 2\sin\alpha\sin\beta$

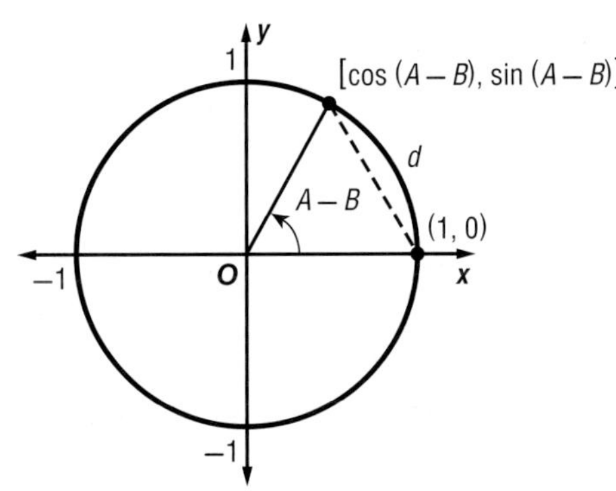

Now find the value of d^2 when the angle having measure $\alpha - \beta$ is in standard position on the unit circle, as shown in the figure above.

$$d = \sqrt{[\cos(\alpha - \beta) - 1]^2 + [\sin(\alpha - \beta) - 0]^2}$$
$$d^2 = [\cos(\alpha - \beta) - 1]^2 + [\sin(\alpha - \beta) - 0]^2$$
$$= [\cos^2(\alpha - \beta) - 2\cos(\alpha - \beta) + 1] + \sin^2(\alpha - \beta)$$
$$= \cos^2(\alpha - \beta) + \sin^2(\alpha - \beta) - 2\cos(\alpha - \beta) + 1$$
$$= 1 - 2\cos(\alpha - \beta) + 1$$
$$= 2 - 2\cos(\alpha - \beta)$$

52b.

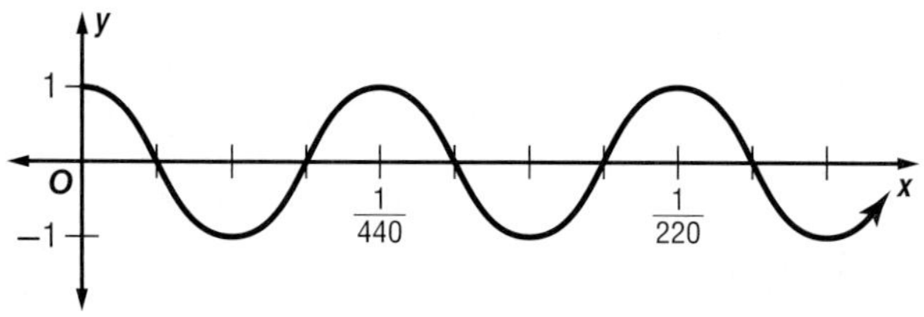

53. **Step 1:** $4^1 - 1 = 3$, which is divisible by 3. The statement is true for $n = 1$.
Step 2: Assume that $4^k - 1$ is divisible by 3 for some positive integer k. This means that $4^k - 1 = 3r$ for some whole number r.
Step 3: $4^k - 1 = 3r$

$$4^k = 3r + 1$$
$$4^{k+1} = 12r + 4$$
$$4^{k+1} - 1 = 12r + 3$$
$$4^{k+1} - 1 = 3(4r + 1)$$

Since r is a whole number, $4r + 1$ is a whole number. Thus, $4^{k+1} - 1$ is divisible by 3, so the statement is true for $n = k + 1$. Therefore, $4^n - 1$ is divisible by 3 for all positive integers n.

54. **Step 1:** $5^1 + 3 = 8$, which is divisible by 4. The statement is true for $n = 1$.
Step 2: Assume that $5^k + 3$ is divisible by 4 for some positive integer k. This means that $5^k + 3 = 4r$ for some positive integer r.
Step 3: $5^k + 3 = 4r$

$$5^k = 4r - 3$$
$$5^{k+1} = 20r - 15$$
$$5^{k+1} + 3 = 20r - 12$$
$$5^{k+1} + 3 = 4(5r - 3)$$

Since r is a positive integer, $5r - 3$ is a positive integer. Thus, $5^{k+1} + 3$ is divisible by 4, so the statement is true for $n = k + 1$. Therefore, $5^n + 3$ is divisible by 4 for all positive integers n.

Page 910, Mid-Chapter Quiz

11. $\sec^2\theta - 1 \stackrel{?}{=} \dfrac{\cot\theta}{\cos\theta \cdot \sin\theta}$

$$\csc^2\theta \stackrel{?}{=} \frac{\cos\theta}{\cos\theta \cdot \sin\theta \cdot \sin\theta}$$
$$\csc^2\theta \stackrel{?}{=} \frac{1}{\sin^2\theta}$$
$$\csc^2\theta = \csc^2\theta \ \checkmark$$

12. $\dfrac{\cos\theta\csc\theta}{\cot\theta} \stackrel{?}{=} 1$

$$\frac{\cos\theta}{\sin\theta} \cdot \tan\theta \stackrel{?}{=} 1$$
$$\frac{\cos\theta}{\sin\theta} \cdot \frac{\sin\theta}{\cos\theta} \stackrel{?}{=} 1$$
$$1 = 1 \ \checkmark$$

13. $\dfrac{\sin\theta\tan\theta}{1 - \cos\theta} \stackrel{?}{=} (1 + \cos\theta)\sec\theta$

$$\frac{\sin\theta\left(\frac{\sin\theta}{\cos\theta}\right)}{1 - \cos\theta} \stackrel{?}{=} (1 + \cos\theta)\frac{1}{\cos\theta}$$
$$\frac{\frac{\sin^2\theta}{\cos\theta}}{1 - \cos\theta} \stackrel{?}{=} \frac{1}{\cos\theta} + 1$$
$$\frac{\sin^2\theta}{\cos\theta} \cdot \frac{1}{1 - \cos\theta} \stackrel{?}{=} \frac{1}{\cos\theta} + 1$$
$$\frac{\sin^2\theta}{\cos\theta(1 - \cos\theta)} \stackrel{?}{=} \frac{1}{\cos\theta} + 1$$
$$\frac{1 - \cos^2\theta}{\cos\theta(1 - \cos\theta)} \stackrel{?}{=} \frac{1}{\cos\theta} + 1$$
$$\frac{(1 - \cos\theta)(1 + \cos\theta)}{\cos\theta(1 - \cos\theta)} \stackrel{?}{=} \frac{1}{\cos\theta} + 1$$
$$\frac{1 + \cos\theta}{\cos\theta} \stackrel{?}{=} \frac{1}{\cos\theta} + 1$$
$$\frac{1}{\cos\theta} + 1 = \frac{1}{\cos\theta} + 1 \ \checkmark$$

14. $\tan\theta(1 - \sin\theta) \stackrel{?}{=} \dfrac{\cos\theta\sin\theta}{1 + \sin\theta}$

$$\tan\theta(1 - \sin\theta) \stackrel{?}{=} \frac{\cos\theta\sin\theta}{1 + \sin\theta} \cdot \frac{1 - \sin\theta}{1 - \sin\theta}$$
$$\tan\theta(1 - \sin\theta) \stackrel{?}{=} \frac{\cos\theta\sin\theta(1 - \sin\theta)}{1 - \sin^2\theta}$$
$$\tan\theta(1 - \sin\theta) \stackrel{?}{=} \frac{\cos\theta\sin\theta(1 - \sin\theta)}{\cos^2\theta}$$
$$\tan\theta(1 - \sin\theta) \stackrel{?}{=} \frac{\sin\theta(1 - \sin\theta)}{\cos\theta}$$
$$\tan\theta(1 - \sin\theta) \stackrel{?}{=} \frac{\sin\theta}{\cos\theta} \cdot (1 - \sin\theta)$$
$$\tan\theta(1 - \sin\theta) = \tan\theta(1 - \sin\theta) \ \checkmark$$

15b. $\cot\theta = \dfrac{12}{9}$; $\dfrac{\cos\theta}{\sin\theta} = \dfrac{\frac{12}{15}}{\frac{9}{15}} = \dfrac{12}{9}$, so $\dfrac{12}{9} = \dfrac{12}{9}$

16. $\tan^2\theta + 1 \stackrel{?}{=} \dfrac{\tan\theta}{\cos\theta \cdot \sin\theta}$

$$\sec^2\theta \stackrel{?}{=} \frac{\tan\theta}{\cos\theta \cdot \sin\theta}$$
$$\sec^2\theta \stackrel{?}{=} \frac{\frac{\sin\theta}{\cos\theta}}{\cos\theta \cdot \sin\theta}$$
$$\sec^2\theta \stackrel{?}{=} \frac{\sin\theta}{\cos^2\theta \cdot \sin\theta}$$
$$\sec^2\theta \stackrel{?}{=} \frac{1}{\cos^2\theta}$$
$$\sec^2\theta = \sec^2\theta \ \checkmark$$

17. $\dfrac{\sin\theta \cdot \sec\theta}{\sec\theta - 1} \stackrel{?}{=} (\sec\theta + 1)\cot\theta$

$\dfrac{\sec\theta + 1}{\sec\theta + 1} \cdot \dfrac{\sin\theta \cdot \sec\theta}{\sec\theta - 1} \stackrel{?}{=} (\sec\theta + 1)\cot\theta$

$\dfrac{\sin\theta \cdot \sec\theta(\sec\theta + 1)}{\sec^2\theta - 1} \stackrel{?}{=} (\sec\theta + 1)\cot\theta$

$\dfrac{\sin\theta \cdot \frac{1}{\cos\theta}(\sec\theta + 1)}{\tan^2\theta} \stackrel{?}{=} (\sec\theta + 1)\cot\theta$

$\dfrac{\frac{\sin\theta}{\cos\theta}(\sec\theta + 1)}{\tan^2\theta} \stackrel{?}{=} (\sec\theta + 1)\cot\theta$

$\dfrac{\tan\theta(\sec\theta + 1)}{\tan^2\theta} \stackrel{?}{=} (\sec\theta + 1)\cot\theta$

$\dfrac{\sec\theta + 1}{\tan\theta} \stackrel{?}{=} (\sec\theta + 1)\cot\theta$

$\dfrac{\sec\theta + 1}{1} \cdot \dfrac{1}{\tan\theta} \stackrel{?}{=} (\sec\theta + 1)\cot\theta$

$(\sec\theta + 1)\cot\theta = (\sec\theta + 1)\cot\theta$ ✓

18. $\sin^2\theta \cdot \tan^2\theta \stackrel{?}{=} \tan^2\theta - \sin^2\theta$

$\sin^2\theta \cdot \tan^2\theta \stackrel{?}{=} \dfrac{\sin^2\theta}{\cos^2\theta} - \sin^2\theta$

$\sin^2\theta \cdot \tan^2\theta \stackrel{?}{=} \dfrac{\sin^2\theta - \sin^2\theta\cos^2\theta}{\cos^2\theta}$

$\sin^2\theta \cdot \tan^2\theta \stackrel{?}{=} \dfrac{\sin^2\theta(1 - \cos^2\theta)}{\cos^2\theta}$

$\sin^2\theta \cdot \tan^2\theta \stackrel{?}{=} \dfrac{\sin^2\theta(\sin^2\theta)}{\cos^2\theta}$

$\sin^2\theta \cdot \tan^2\theta \stackrel{?}{=} \sin^2\theta \cdot \dfrac{\sin^2\theta}{\cos^2\theta}$

$\sin^2\theta \cdot \tan^2\theta = \sin^2\theta \cdot \tan^2\theta$ ✓

19. $\cot\theta(1 - \cos\theta) \stackrel{?}{=} \dfrac{\cos\theta \cdot \sin\theta}{1 + \cos\theta}$

$\cot\theta(1 - \cos\theta) \stackrel{?}{=} \dfrac{\cos\theta \cdot \sin\theta}{1 + \cos\theta} \cdot \dfrac{1 - \cos\theta}{1 - \cos\theta}$

$\cot\theta(1 - \cos\theta) \stackrel{?}{=} \dfrac{\cos\theta \cdot \sin\theta(1 - \cos\theta)}{1 - \cos^2\theta}$

$\cot\theta(1 - \cos\theta) \stackrel{?}{=} \dfrac{\cos\theta \cdot \sin\theta(1 - \cos\theta)}{\sin^2\theta}$

$\cot\theta(1 - \cos\theta) \stackrel{?}{=} \dfrac{\cos\theta(1 - \cos\theta)}{\sin\theta}$

$\cot\theta(1 - \cos\theta) \stackrel{?}{=} \dfrac{\cos\theta}{\sin\theta}(1 - \cos\theta)$

$\cot\theta(1 - \cos\theta) = \cot\theta(1 - \cos\theta)$ ✓

25. $\cos 30^\circ\cos\theta + \sin 30^\circ\sin\theta \stackrel{?}{=} \sin 60^\circ\cos\theta + \cos 60^\circ\sin\theta$

$\dfrac{\sqrt{3}}{2}\cos\theta + \dfrac{1}{2}\sin\theta = \dfrac{\sqrt{3}}{2}\cos\theta + \dfrac{1}{2}\sin\theta$ ✓

Page 916, Lesson 14-4

27. $1 + \dfrac{1}{2}\sin^2\theta \stackrel{?}{=} \dfrac{\sec\theta + \sin\theta}{\sec\theta}$

$\stackrel{?}{=} \dfrac{\frac{1}{\cos\theta} + \sin\theta}{\frac{1}{\cos\theta}}$

$\stackrel{?}{=} \dfrac{\frac{1}{\cos\theta} + \sin\theta}{\frac{1}{\cos\theta}} \cdot \dfrac{\cos\theta}{\cos\theta}$

$\stackrel{?}{=} 1 + \dfrac{1}{2} \cdot 2\sin\theta\cos\theta$

$= 1 + \dfrac{1}{2}\sin 2\theta$ ✓

28. $\sin\dfrac{\theta}{2}\cos\dfrac{\theta}{2} \stackrel{?}{=} \dfrac{\sin\theta}{2}$

$\dfrac{2\sin\frac{\theta}{2}\cos\frac{\theta}{2}}{2} \stackrel{?}{=} \dfrac{\sin\theta}{2}$

$\dfrac{\sin 2\left(\frac{\theta}{2}\right)}{2} \stackrel{?}{=} \dfrac{\sin\theta}{2}$

$\dfrac{\sin\theta}{2} = \dfrac{\sin\theta}{2}$ ✓

29. $\tan\dfrac{\theta}{2} \stackrel{?}{=} \dfrac{\sin\theta}{1 + \cos\theta}$

$\tan\dfrac{\theta}{2} \stackrel{?}{=} \dfrac{\sin 2\left(\frac{\theta}{2}\right)}{1 + \cos 2\left(\frac{\theta}{2}\right)}$

$\tan\dfrac{\theta}{2} \stackrel{?}{=} \dfrac{2\sin\frac{\theta}{2}\cos\frac{\theta}{2}}{1 + 2\cos^2\frac{\theta}{2} - 1}$

$\tan\dfrac{\theta}{2} \stackrel{?}{=} \dfrac{2\sin\frac{\theta}{2}\cos\frac{\theta}{2}}{2\cos^2\frac{\theta}{2}}$

$\tan\dfrac{\theta}{2} \stackrel{?}{=} \dfrac{\sin\frac{\theta}{2}}{\cos\frac{\theta}{2}}$

$\tan\dfrac{\theta}{2} = \tan\dfrac{\theta}{2}$ ✓

30. For $\theta = 45° + \alpha$,

$$d = \frac{v^2 \sin 2\,(45° + \alpha)}{g}$$
$$= \frac{v^2 \sin (90° + 2\alpha)}{g}$$
$$= \frac{v^2(\sin 90° \cos 2\alpha + \cos 90° \sin 2\alpha)}{g}$$
$$= \frac{v^2(1 \cdot \cos 2\alpha + 0 \cdot \sin 2\alpha)}{g}$$
$$= \frac{v^2 \cos 2\alpha}{g}$$

For $\theta = 45° - \alpha$,

$$d = \frac{v^2 \sin 2\,(45° - \alpha)}{g}$$
$$= \frac{v^2 \sin (90° - 2\alpha)}{g}$$
$$= \frac{v^2(\sin 90° \cos 2\alpha - \cos 90° \sin 2\alpha)}{g}$$
$$= \frac{v^2(1 \cdot \cos 2\alpha - 0 \cdot \sin 2\alpha)}{g}$$
$$= \frac{v^2 \cos 2\alpha}{g}$$

37. No; Teresa incorrectly added the square roots, and Nathan used the half-angle identity incorrectly. He used sin 30° in the formula instead of first finding the cosine.

39. If you are only given the value of $\cos \theta$, then $\cos 2\theta = 2\cos^2 \theta - 1$ is the best identity to use. If you are only given the value of $\sin \theta$, then $\cos 2\theta = 1 - 2\sin^2 \theta$ is the best identity to use. If you are given the values of both $\cos \theta$ and $\sin \theta$, then $\cos 2\theta = \cos^2 \theta - \sin^2 \theta$ works just as well as the other two.

40. $\sin 2\theta = \sin(\theta + \theta)$
$= \sin \theta \cos \theta + \cos \theta \sin \theta$
$= 2 \sin \theta \cos \theta$

$\cos 2\theta = \cos(\theta + \theta)$
$= \cos \theta \cos \theta - \sin \theta \sin \theta$
$= \cos^2 \theta - \sin^2 \theta$

You can find alternate forms for $\cos 2\theta$ by making substitutions into the expression $\cos^2 \theta - \sin^2 \theta$.

$\cos^2 \theta - \sin^2 \theta = (1 - \sin^2 \theta) - \sin^2 \theta$
$= 1 - 2\sin^2 \theta$

Substitute $1 - \sin^2 \theta$ for $\cos^2 \theta$.
Simplify.

$\cos^2 \theta - \sin^2 \theta = \cos^2 \theta - (1 - \cos^2 \theta)$
$= 2\cos^2 \theta - 1$

Substitute $1 - \cos^2 \theta$ for $\sin^2 \theta$.
Simplify.

41. $1 - 2\sin^2 \theta = \cos 2\theta$ — Double-angle identity

$1 - 2\sin^2 \frac{A}{2} = \cos A$ — Substitute $\frac{A}{2}$ for θ and A for 2θ.

$\sin^2 \frac{A}{2} = \frac{1 - \cos A}{2}$ — Solve for $\sin^2 \frac{A}{2}$.

$\sin \frac{A}{2} = \pm\sqrt{\frac{1 - \cos A}{2}}$ — Take the square root of each side.

Find $\cos \frac{A}{2}$.

$2\cos^2 \theta - 1 = \cos 2\theta$ — Double-angle identity

$2\cos^2 \frac{A}{2} - 1 = \cos A$ — Substitute $\frac{A}{2}$ for θ and A for 2θ.

$\cos^2 \frac{A}{2} = \frac{1 + \cos A}{2}$ — Solve for $\cos^2 \frac{A}{2}$.

$\cos \frac{A}{2} = \pm\sqrt{\frac{1 + \cos A}{2}}$ — Take the square root of each side.

Page 928, Study Guide and Review

30. $\sin(\theta + 90) \stackrel{?}{=} \cos \theta$

$\sin \theta \cos 90° + \cos \theta \sin 90° \stackrel{?}{=} \cos \theta$

$(\sin \theta)(0) + (\cos \theta)(1) \stackrel{?}{=} \cos \theta$

$\cos \theta = \cos \theta$ ✓

31. $\sin\left(\frac{3\pi}{2} - \theta\right) \stackrel{?}{=} -\cos \theta$

$\sin \frac{3\pi}{2} \cos \theta - \cos \frac{3\pi}{2} \sin \theta \stackrel{?}{=} -\cos \theta$

$(-1)\cos \theta - (0)\sin \theta \stackrel{?}{=} -\cos \theta$

$-\cos \theta = -\cos \theta$ ✓

32. $\tan(\theta - \pi) \stackrel{?}{=} \tan \theta$

$\frac{\tan \theta - \tan \pi}{1 + \tan \theta \tan \pi} \stackrel{?}{=} \tan \theta$

$\frac{\tan \theta - 0}{1 + (\tan \theta)(0)} \stackrel{?}{=} \tan \theta$

$\frac{\tan \theta}{1} \stackrel{?}{=} \tan \theta$

$\tan \theta = \tan \theta$ ✓

33. $\sin 2\theta = \frac{24}{25}$, $\cos 2\theta = \frac{7}{25}$, $\sin \frac{\theta}{2} = \frac{\sqrt{10}}{10}$, and $\cos \frac{\theta}{2} = \frac{3\sqrt{10}}{10}$

34. $\sin 2\theta = \frac{\sqrt{15}}{8}$, $\cos 2\theta = \frac{7}{8}$, $\sin \frac{\theta}{2} = \frac{\sqrt{2}\sqrt{4 + \sqrt{15}}}{4}$, and $\cos \frac{\theta}{2} = -\frac{\sqrt{2}\sqrt{4 - \sqrt{15}}}{4}$

35. $\sin 2\theta = -\frac{4\sqrt{5}}{9}$, $\cos 2\theta = -\frac{1}{9}$, $\sin \frac{\theta}{2} = \frac{\sqrt{30}}{6}$, and $\cos \frac{\theta}{2} = \frac{\sqrt{6}}{6}$

36a. $c^2 = 90^2 + 90^2$; $c^2 = 8100 + 8100$; $c^2 = 16{,}200$; $c = 90\sqrt{2}$

36b. $\sin 45° = \frac{90}{90\sqrt{2}} = \frac{1}{\sqrt{2}} = \frac{\sqrt{2}}{2}$

36c. $\sin \frac{\alpha}{2} = \pm\sqrt{\frac{1 - \cos \alpha}{2}}$; $\sin \frac{90}{2} = \pm\sqrt{\frac{1 - \cos 90}{2}}$;

$\sin \frac{90}{2} = \pm \sqrt{\frac{1 - 0}{2}} = \frac{1}{\sqrt{2}} = \frac{\sqrt{2}}{2}$

Student Handbook

Built-In Workbooks

Reference

How to Use the Student Handbook

The Student Handbook is the additional skill and reference material found at the end of the text. This Handbook can help you answer these questions.

What If I Need Problem Solving Practice?
You have probably used several different problem solving strategies in previous math courses. The **Problem-Solving Handbook** section provides examples and problems for refreshing your skills at using various strategies.

What If I Need More Practice?
You, or your teacher, may decide that working through some additional problems would be helpful. The **Extra Practice** section provides these problems for each lesson so you have ample opportunity to practice new skills.

What If I Have Trouble with Word Problems?
The **Mixed Problem Solving** portion of the book provides additional word problems that use the skills presented in each lesson. These problems give you real-world situations where math can be applied.

What if I Forget What I Learned Last Year?
Use the **Concepts and Skills Bank** section to refresh your memory about things you have learned in other math classes. Here's a list of the topics covered in your book.

1. Proportional Reasoning
2. Square Roots
3. Scientific Notation
4. Adding and Multiplying Probabilities
5. Bar and Line Graphs
6. Frequency Tables and Histograms
7. Stem-and-Leaf Plots
8. Box-and-Whisker Plots

What If I Need to Check a Homework Answer?
The answers to odd-numbered problems are included in **Selected Answers and Solutions**. Check your answers to make sure you understand how to solve all of the assigned problems.

What If I Forget a Vocabulary Word?
The **English-Spanish Glossary** provides a list of important or difficult words used throughout the textbook. It provides a definition in English and Spanish as well as the page number(s) where the word can be found.

What If I Need to Find Something Quickly?
The **Index** alphabetically lists the subjects covered throughout the entire textbook and the pages on which each subject can be found.

What if I Forget a Formula?
Inside the back cover of your math book is a list of **Formulas and Symbols** that are used in the book.

Problem-Solving Handbook

Problem-Solving Strategy: Look for a Pattern

There are many problem-solving strategies in mathematics. One of the most common is to **look for a pattern**. To use this strategy, analyze the first few numbers in a pattern and identify a rule that is used to go from the first number in the pattern to the second, and then to the third, and so on. Then use the rule to extend the pattern and find a solution.

Real-World EXAMPLE

A function passes through the points shown. List the coordinates of each point. Describe the pattern in the coordinates and predict the next point in the pattern in the positive direction.

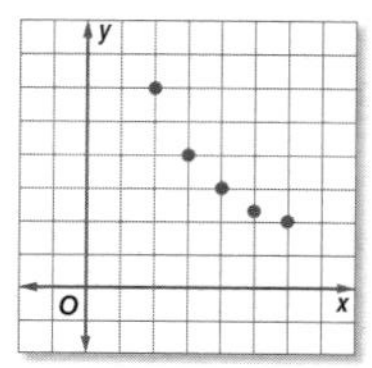

Step 1 List the coordinates of the points shown on the graph.

$(2, 6), (3, 4), (4, 3), \left(5, \frac{12}{5}\right)$, and $(6, 2)$

Step 2 Identify the pattern in the x-coordinates and the y-coordinates.

In each ordered pair, the product of the x- and y-coordinates is 12.

The next point is $\left(6 + 1, \frac{12}{6+1}\right)$ or $\left(7, \frac{12}{7}\right)$.

Practice

Solve each problem by looking for a pattern.

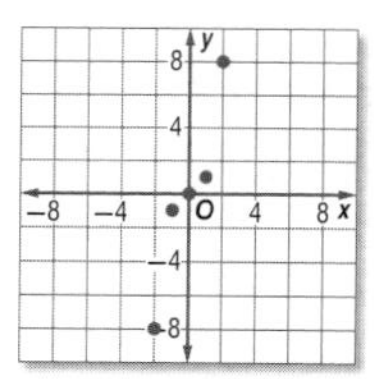

1. A function passes through the points shown.
   a. Describe the pattern in the coordinates, and predict the next point in the pattern in the positive direction.
   b. Predict the next point in the pattern in the negative direction. **(−3, −27)**

1a. The x-coordinates increase by 1; the y-coordinate is the cube of the x-coordinate. (3, 27)

2. Two workers can make two chairs in two days. How many chairs can 8 workers working at the same rate make in 20 days? **80**
3. The sum of the measures of the angles of a triangle is 180°.
   a. Use the sum of the angles of the triangles to determine the sum of the measures of the angles of each polygon by drawing all the diagonals from one vertex for a quadrilateral, a pentagon and a hexagon. **360°, 540°, 720°**
   b. Write a rule to find the sum of the measures of the angles of an n-gon. **$(n - 2)(180)$**

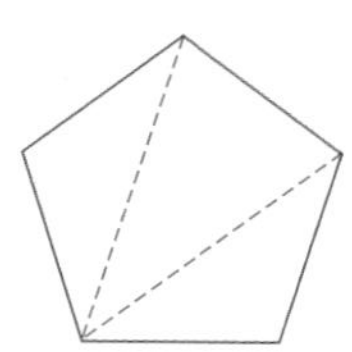

4. Courtney travels south on her bicycle riding 8 miles per hour. One hour later, her friend Horacio starts riding his bicycle from the same location. If he travels south at 10 miles per hour, how long will it take him to catch Courtney? **4 h**
5. A ball bounces back 0.6 of its height on every bounce. If a ball is dropped from 200 feet, how high does it bounce on the fifth bounce? Round to the nearest tenth. **15.6 ft**

Problem-Solving Strategy: Create a Table

One strategy for solving problems is to **create a table**. A table allows you to organize information in an understandable way.

Real-World EXAMPLE

A fruit machine accepts dollars, and each piece of fruit costs 65 cents. If the machine gives only nickels, dimes, and quarters, what combinations of those coins are possible as change for a dollar?

The machine will give back $1.00 − $0.65 or 35 cents in change in a combination of nickels, dimes, and quarters.

Make a table showing different combinations of nickels, dimes, and quarters that total 35 cents. Organize the table by starting with the combinations that include the most quarters.

The total for each combination of the coins is 35 cents. There are 6 combinations possible.

Quarters	Dimes	Nickels
1	1	0
1	0	2
0	3	1
0	2	3
0	1	5
0	0	7

Practice

Solve each problem by creating a table. **1–7. See Student Handbook Answer Appendix.**

1. How many ways can you make change for a half-dollar using only nickels, dimes, and quarters?
2. A penny, a nickel, a dime, and a quarter are in a purse. How many amounts of money are possible if you grab two coins at random?
3. Laura, Josie, and Marcus ate lunch together at the cafeteria. Each had a different item: a peanut butter sandwich, a hamburger, and a peanut butter and jelly sandwich. Josie ate the sandwich that had a bun. Laura does not like jelly. Marcus sat between the student eating the peanut butter sandwich and the student allergic to peanuts. Which student had which sandwich?
4. Johanna had a bag of four marbles. One marble is blue. Two marbles are green. One marble is orange. How many different ways are there to draw the marbles out of the bag one at a time?
5. At Midas High School, students are selling popcorn at a football game. Each small bag of popcorn is $1.25. Each large bag of popcorn is $2.25. Create a table to show the purchase prices of five bags of popcorn with every possible combination of large and/or small bags.
6. Aria asked her friends whether they used wrapping paper, gift bags, recycled paper, or no wrapping for birthday presents. Create a table to show how many students preferred each method of the 24 students she asked. Then predict how many would choose each method if 120 students were asked.

7. The equation for a semicircle is $y = \sqrt{16 - x^2}$. Create a table to show five ordered pairs with x-coordinates belonging to the set $\{-4, -2, 0, 2, 4\}$.

Problem-Solving Strategy: Make a Chart

Data presented in a problem can be organized by **making a chart**. This problem-solving strategy allows you to see patterns and relationships among data.

Real-World EXAMPLE

It takes an average driver 1.5 seconds to begin braking after they see an obstruction. The driver can safely decelerate a car or light truck with good tires on a dry street surface at the rate of about 15 feet per second (fps). The distance a vehicle will travel while braking can be found by multiplying the initial velocity by the deceleration time and dividing by 2. Find the stopping distance for a car traveling at 45, 55, 65, and 75 miles per hour.

Step 1 Make a chart that includes the given information and the information to be found. Before setting up your chart, think about how speed, distance, and time are related.

Since the distance is listed in feet, find the rate of speed it takes to stop in feet per second. To convert from miles per hour to feet per second, multiply by a conversion factor of $\frac{5280 \text{ ft}}{3600 \text{ s}}$. Then find the deceleration time by dividing the initial velocity by 15 fps.

Initial Velocity (mph)	Initial Velocity (fps)	Deceleration Time (s)	Distance Traveled before Braking (ft)	Distance Traveled while Braking (ft)	Total Stopping Distance (ft)
45	66	4.4			
55	80.7	5.38			
65	95.3	6.35			
75	110	7.33			

Step 2 To find the distance traveled before braking, multiply the initial velocity by the reaction time, 1.5 seconds. Then find the distance traveled while braking. Add to find the total stopping distance.

Initial Velocity (mph)	Initial Velocity (fps)	Deceleration Time (s)	Distance Traveled before Braking (ft)	Distance Traveled while Braking (ft)	Total Stopping Distance (ft)
45	66	4.4	99	145.2	244.2
55	80.7	5.38	121.05	217.08	338.13
65	95.3	6.35	142.95	302.58	445.53
75	110	7.33	165	403.15	568.15

Practice

Solve each problem by making a chart. 1–5. See Student Handbook Answer Appendix.

1. As the length of a square doubles, the area increases by a scale factor. Using the squares in the diagram, make a chart of each length and each area. Then find the scale factor.

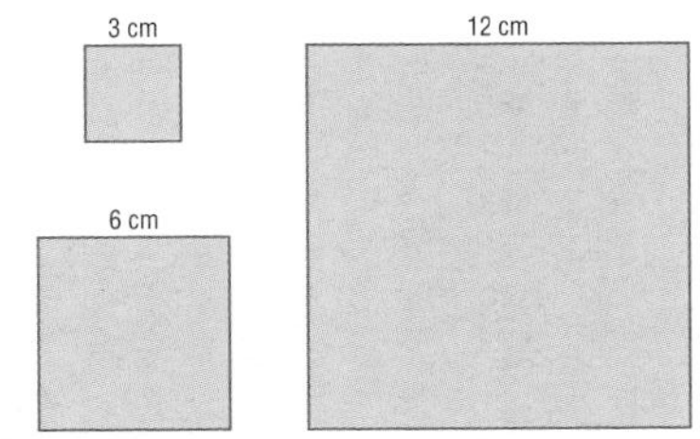

2. Given $f(x) = 2x + 3$ and $g(x) = -x - 3$, use a table to find $f(x) - g(x)$ for all positive integers less than or equal to 6.

3. **CONSTRUCTION** Nicole's new house has a small deck that measures 6 feet by 12 feet. She would like to build a larger deck. She can increase the dimensions in one-foot increments. Make a chart to show the possible dimensions if the area of the deck is doubled.

4. The diameters of the planets are given in the table. Make a box-and-whisker plot of the data. In which quartile are the data most closely clustered?

Planet	Mercury	Venus	Earth	Mars	Jupiter	Saturn	Uranus	Neptune
Diameter (mi)	3032	7521	7926	4194	88,736	74,978	32,193	30,775

5. The following table shows the official state reptile in each state. Make a tally chart that shows how many states have turtles (tortoise, terrapin), snakes, alligators, lizards, toads, or none. Find the ratio of states with alligators as their official state reptile compared to the states with no official state reptile.

AL	red-bellied turtle	LA	American alligator	OH	black racer
AK	none	ME	none	OK	collared lizard
AZ	ridge-nosed rattlesnake	MD	diamondback terrapin	OR	none
AR	none	MA	garter snake	PA	none
CA	desert tortoise	MI	painted turtle	RI	none
CO	none	MN	Blanding's turtle	SC	loggerhead turtle
CT	none	MS	American alligator	SD	none
DE	none	MO	three-toed box turtle	TN	eastern box turtle
FL	American alligator	MT	none	TX	horned lizard
GA	gopher tortoise	NE	none	UT	none
HI	none	NV	desert tortoise	VT	none
ID	none	NH	none	VA	none
IL	painted turtle	NJ	none	WA	none
IN	none	NM	whiptail lizard	WV	none
IA	none	NY	snapping turtle	WI	none
KS	ornate box turtle	NC	eastern box turtle	WY	horned toad
KY	none	ND	none		

Problem-Solving Strategy: Guess and Check

To solve some problems, you can make a reasonable guess and then check it in the problem. You can then use the results to improve your guess until you find the solution. This strategy is called **guess and check**.

Real-World EXAMPLE

Max needs to factor $2x^2 - x - 21$. He wants to use his graphing calculator to help him guess and check the answer. What steps would he use? What is the correct factorization?

Step 1 Use the calculator to graph $Y = 2x^2 - x - 21$.

Step 2 Find the root, or x-intercept, that has a whole number value. It is $x = -3$. Therefore, one factor is $(x + 3)$.

Step 3 By examining the first and last terms of the expression, guess the second factor. $(x + 3)(2x - 7)$

Step 4 Multiply the two factors to check for the desired product. $(x + 3)(2x - 7) = 2x^2 - 7x + 6x - 21 = 2x^2 - x - 21$.

Practice

Solve each problem by using the guess-and-check strategy.

1. Lacie bought four items at a school book fair. The prices of the books are shown in the table. Which four items did Lacie buy if she spent $25.20? **1. one calendar, one graphic novel, and two comic books**

Book	Price ($)
comic book	2.10
graphic novel	5.00
fiction book	5.90
atlas	22.40
calendar	16.00

2. This year, Mr. Jefferson's age is a multiple of 11. Next year, his age will be a multiple of 9. How old is Mr. Jefferson this year? **44**

3. Rafael is burning a CD for Selma. The CD will hold 35 minutes of music. Which songs should he select from the list to record the maximum time on the CD without going over? **Songs A, D, E, F, G, H, and J run for a total of 34 minutes 46 seconds.**

Song	A	B	C	D	E	F	G	H	I	J
Time	5 min 4 s	9 min 10 s	4 min 12 s	3 min 9 s	3 min 44 s	4 min 30 s	5 min 0 s	7 min 21 s	4 min 33 s	5 min 58 s

4. Larry wrote down 4 different numbers whose sum was 12. Give two possible combinations for the numbers. **1, 2, 4, 5 and 1, 2, 3, 6**

5. The Science Club sold candy bars and soft pretzels to raise money for an animal shelter. They raised a total of $62.75. They made $0.25 profit on each candy bar and $0.30 profit on each pretzel sold. How many of each did they sell? **5. Sample answer: 125 candy bars and 105 pretzels**

6. The product of two consecutive even integers is 4224. Find the integers. **64 and 66 or −64 and −66**

7. Jerrica has 8 coins, all dimes, quarters, and pennies. If she has $0.89, how many of each coin does she have? **4 pennies, 1 dime, 3 quarters**

8. One angle of a triangle is shown. Find the measures of the other two angles if their product is 1216. **32° and 38°**

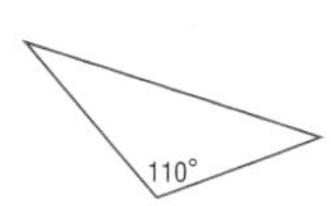

9. Anita sold tickets to the school musical. She had 12 bills worth $175 for the tickets she sold. If all the money was in $5 bills, $10 bills, and $20 bills, how many of each bill did she have? **Sample answer: 3-$5 bills, 2-$10 bills, and 7-$20 bills**

Problem-Solving Strategy: Work Backward

On most problems, a set of conditions or facts is given and an end result must be found. However, some problems start with the result and ask for something that happened earlier. The strategy of **working backward** can be used to solve problems like this. To use this strategy, start with the end result and *undo* each step.

Real-World EXAMPLE

Kendrick spent half of the money he had this morning on lunch. After lunch, he loaned his friend a dollar. Now he has $1.50. How much money did Kendrick have this morning?

Start with the end result, $1.50, and work backward to find the amount Kendrick had this morning.

Kendrick now has $1.50. → $1.50
Undo the $1.00 he loaned to his friend. → + 1.00 (Add $1.00 to undo giving his friend $1.00.)
$2.50
Undo the half he spent for lunch. → × 2 (Multiply by 2 to undo spending half the original amount.)
$5.00

Kendrick had $5.00 this morning.

CHECK Kendrick started with $5.00. If he spent half of that, or $2.50, on lunch, and loaned his friend $1.00, he would have $1.50 left. This matches the amount stated in the problem, so the solution is correct.

Practice

Solve each problem by working backward.

1. Tia used half of her allowance to buy a ticket to the class play. Then she spent $0.75 for an ice cream cone. Now she has $2.25 left. How much is her allowance? **$6**

2. Lawanda put $15 of her paycheck in savings. Then she spent one-half of what was left on clothes. She paid $24 for a concert ticket and later spent one-half of what was then left on a book. When she got home, she had $14 left. What was the amount of Lawanda's paycheck? **$119**

3. Mr. and Mrs. Delgado each own an equal number of shares of a stock. Mr. Delgado sells one-third of his shares for $2700. What was the total value of Mr. and Mrs. Delgado's stock before the sale? **$16,200**

4. A certain point was reflected across the x-axis, and then moved up three units and two units to the left. The final coordinates of the point are (3, 5). What were the original coordinates? **(5, −2)**

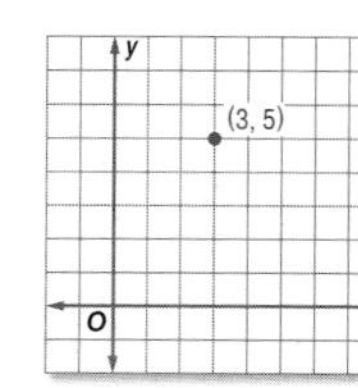

5. A certain bacteria doubles its population every 12 hours. After 3 full days, there are 1600 bacteria in a culture. How many bacteria were there at the beginning of the first day? **25 bacteria**

6. To catch a 7:30 A.M. bus, Don needs 30 minutes to get dressed, 30 minutes for breakfast, and 5 minutes to walk to the bus stop. What time should he wake up? **6:25 A.M.**

7. Troy walks $1\frac{1}{8}$ miles to his school. If he has walked along his route $\frac{1}{4}$ mile to meet a friend and then they walked another $\frac{1}{2}$ mile along the route to meet another friend, how far do they still need to walk to get to school? **$\frac{3}{8}$ mi**

Problem-Solving Strategy: Solve a Simpler Problem

One of the strategies you can use to solve a problem is to **solve a simpler problem**. To use this strategy, first solve a simpler or more familiar case of the problem. Then use the same concept and relationships to solve the original problem.

Real-World EXAMPLE

Find the sum of the numbers 1 through 500.

Consider a simpler problem. Find the sum of the numbers 1 through 10. Notice that you can group the addends into partial sums as shown below.

$1 + 2 + 3 + 4 + 5 + 6 + 7 + 8 + 9 + 10 = 55$

11
11
11
11
11

The number of sums is 5, or half the number of addends.

Each partial sum is 11, the sum of the first and last numbers.

The sum is 5×11 or 55.

Use the same concepts to find the sum of the numbers 1 through 500.

$1 + 2 + 3 + \cdots + 499 + 500 = 250 \times 501$

$= 125{,}250$

Multiply half the number of addends, 250, by the sum of the first and last numbers, 501.

Practice

Solve each problem by solving a simpler problem.

1. Find the number of squares of any size in the game board shown at the right. **204 squares**
2. Find the sum of the whole numbers through 1000. **500,500**
3. How many links are needed to join 30 pieces of chain into one long chain? **29 links**
4. Three people can pick six baskets of apples in one hour. How many baskets of apples can 2 people pick in one-half hour? **2 baskets**
5. Find the number of triangles of any size in the figure at the right. **27 triangles**
6. A shirt shop has 112 orders for T-shirt designs. Three designers can make 2 shirts in 2 hours. How many designers are needed to complete the orders in 8 hours? **42 designers**

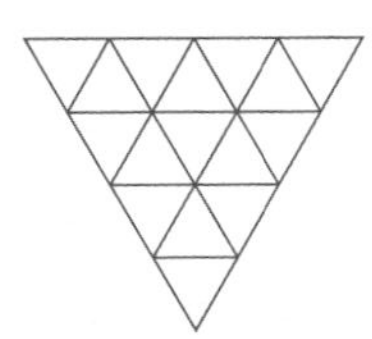

7. Find the area of the composite figure at the right with the given measures. **24 sq cm**
8. Stamps for postcards cost $0.24, and stamps for first-class letters cost $0.41. Diego wants to send postcards and letters to 10 friends. If he has $3.50 for stamps, how many postcards and how many letters can he send? **Sample answer: 5 postcards, 5 letters**

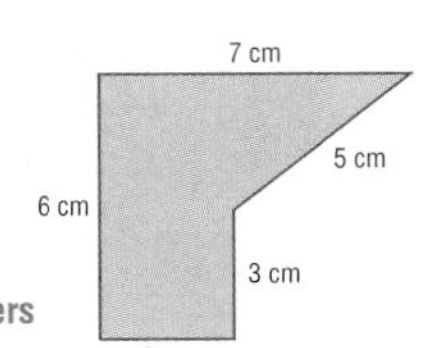

Problem-Solving Strategy: Draw a Diagram

Another strategy for solving problems is to **draw a diagram**. There will be times when a sketch or diagram will give you a better picture of how to tackle a mathematics problem. Adding details like units, labels, and numbers to the drawing or sketch can help you make decisions on how to solve the problem.

Real-World EXAMPLE

Cheng is designing a kite using similar triangles. One portion of the frame of the kite will look like the figure. If Cheng wants to place an upright strut 12 inches from the right angle, how long does it need to be?

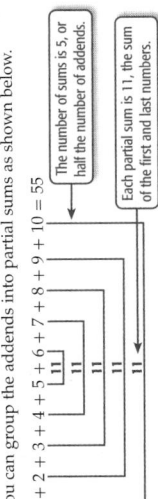

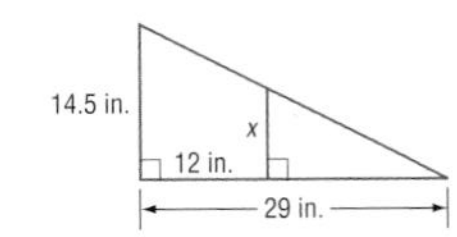

This problem can be solved using the concept of similar triangles. However, the two triangles overlap, making it difficult to compare the corresponding sides. It may be helpful to draw a diagram that shows the two triangles separately. Notice that the base of the triangle is $29 - 12$ or 17 inches.

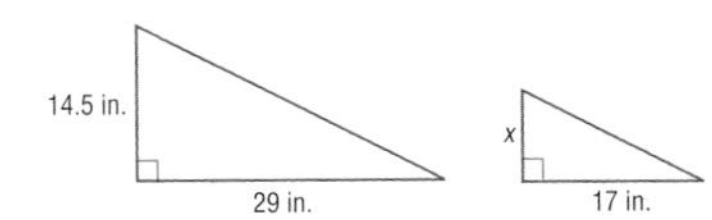

We can now set up the proportion $\frac{x}{14.5} = \frac{17}{29}$. Solving the proportion, we find that the strut should be 8.5 inches long.

Practice

Solve each problem by drawing a diagram.

1. Find the length of the horizontal side of the large triangle. **about 51.4 cm**
2. A 500-gallon water tank is being filled with water. Eighty gallons of water are in the tank after 4 minutes. How long will it take to fill the tank? **25 min**

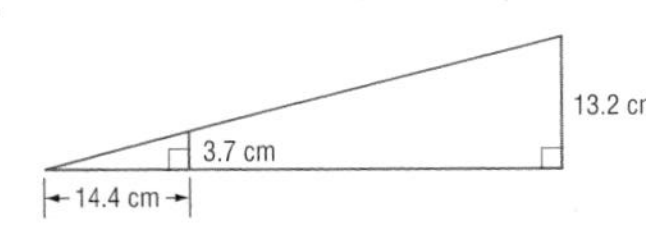

3. It takes 42 minutes to cut a 2-inch by 4-inch piece of wood into 7 equally sized pieces. How long will it take to cut a similar 2-inch by 4-inch piece into 4 equally sized pieces? **21 min**
4. Find the number of line segments that can be drawn between any two vertices of an octagon. **28**
5. There are 7 people in a meeting. If each person shakes hands with all the other people, how many handshakes take place? **21**

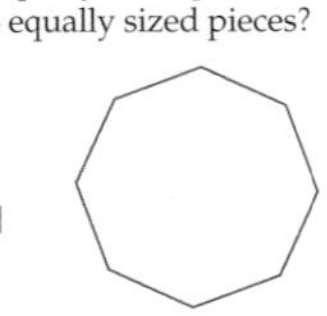

6. How many different teams of 3 players can be chosen from 8 players? **56**
7. Nitarren is trying to decide how many 9-inch diameter pies will fit on her dessert table that measures 4 feet by 2 feet. How many pies could Nitarren fit on the table? **10 pies**
8. Two distinct lines can share no points or one point. How many points can two distinct circles share? **0, 1, or 2**
9. Which of these shapes can be made by slicing a cone with a plane—a circle, an oval, a rectangle, a square, a triangle? **circle, oval, triangle**

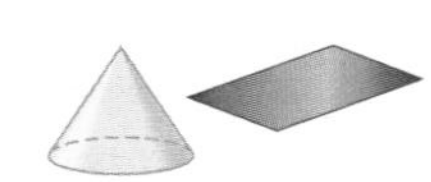

Problem Solving Handbook

Problem-Solving Strategy: Use Estimation

When you need to make a decision on the basis of inexact information, a common strategy is to **use estimation**. Often estimation is used when an exact answer is not required or when mental math is used rather than a calculator or paper and pencil. You should use estimation to determine if your answer is reasonable.

Real-World EXAMPLE

Recently, 51 million international visitors came to the United States. Given the information in the table, estimate what percentage of the visitors were from Japan.

Source: Travel Industry Association

Step 1 Determine about how many international visitors came to the United States.

51 million or 51,000,000 would be an easier number to work with if it was rounded to only one digit in the ten millions place, so round 51,000,000 to 50,000,000.

Step 2 Determine from the chart the number of visitors who were from Japan.

According to the chart, 5,000,000 visitors to the United States were from Japan.

Step 3 To determine the percentage, divide.

$$\frac{\text{number of visitors from Japan}}{\text{total number of visitors}} = \frac{5{,}000{,}000}{50{,}000{,}000}$$
$$= 0.1 \text{ or } 10\%$$

About 10% of the visitors to the United States in 2000 were from Japan.

Practice

Solve each problem by using estimation.

1. If Café Mocha charges $1.98 for each cup of coffee, about how much money did Café Mocha earn in March? **about $1200**

Coffee of the Month Sales	
Month	Number of Cups Sold
January	850
February	765
March	587
April	500
May	387

2. The length of Fun Center's go-kart track is 843 feet. If Nadia circled the track 9 times, about how many feet did she travel? **about 7650 ft**

3. In 2007, 82% of all Americans had at least one e-mail account. Of the 301,139,947 Americans, about how many checked their e-mail daily? **about 192,000,000**

Source: UCLA Center for Communication Policy

4. Sarah solves the following problem. Her answer is 8 doses. Use estimation to determine whether or not Sarah's answer is correct. Explain your reasoning.

How many $\frac{4}{5}$-ounce doses of medicine are in a 10-ounce jar?

4. Sarah is incorrect. Since there is a little less than an ounce in each dose, there should be a little more than 10 doses.

Problem-Solving Strategy: Eliminate Unnecessary Information

A useful problem-solving strategy is to learn how to **eliminate unnecessary information**. If there is a diagram, it is important to determine if all or some of the information is necessary to find a solution.

Real-World EXAMPLE

Twila is making a quilt that shows a repeating design of a house on each block of the quilt. Which information is unnecessary to find the area of the white door of the house?

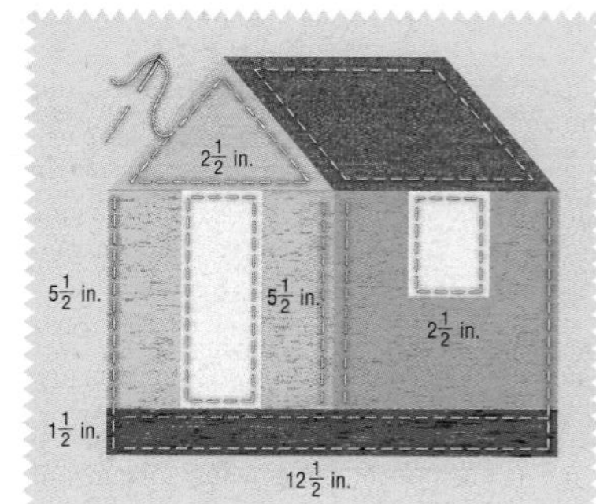

The dimensions needed to find the area of the door are the length and width of the door. So, the dimensions of $2\frac{1}{2}$ inches by $5\frac{1}{2}$ inches are needed. The other dimensions, such as the width of the window or the size of the square, are unnecessary.

Practice

Solve each problem by eliminating unnecessary information.

1. Many school districts are banning electronic devices for students. The chart shows what percentage of schools have banned specific devices. If there are 723 districts in Ohio, what information is not necessary to determine about how many school districts have banned handheld games? **the percentage of digital audio players banned, the percentage of cell phones banned, and the percentage of laptops banned**

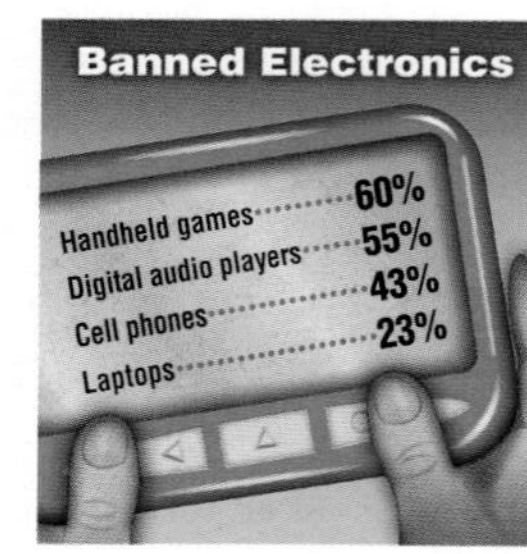

2. Miranda is making a mosaic with the tiles at the right. Which information is not needed to determine the area that each tile will cover? **the diagonal of the square, the hypotenuse of the triangle, the 10 cm side of the parallelogram**

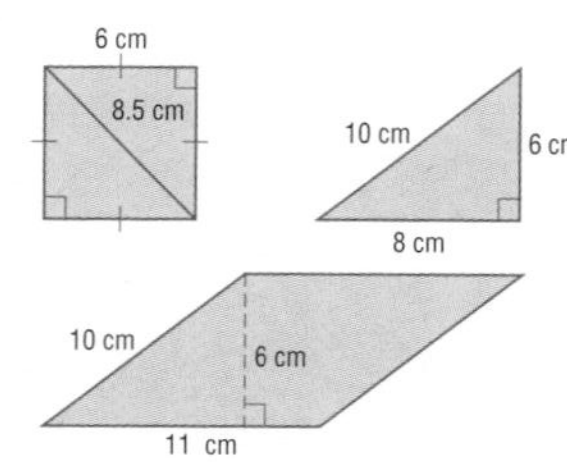

3. The Gemini North telescope was placed in Mauna Kea, Hawaii, in the year 2000. The Gemini South telescope was placed in Cerro Pachon, Chili, in the year 2001. Each of the twin cylindrical telescopes are 8.1 meters in diameter. What information is not necessary to find the circumference of the base of the telescopes? **the years and locations of the telescopes**

Problem-Solving Strategy: Write an Equation

A natural outcome of recognizing mathematical patterns and organizing data is to **write an equation**. Look at a set of data or read a word problem to determine which values are constants and which values vary. Figure out the dependent and independent variables in order to write an equation to reflect the given situation.

Real-World EXAMPLE

TelExcite Cell is offering the following cell phone plan. The first 60 minutes of phone use per month costs $20. Additional minutes, up to and including 400 minutes, the charge is $20 plus 10 cents a minute. For any number of minutes used past 400, the charge is a flat fee of $80.

a. Write a piecewise function to represent the plan.

Separate the domain as described. Pay careful attention to the category in which each boundary belongs. Write an expression for each condition.

$$f(x) = \begin{cases} 20 & \text{if } 0 \le x \le 60 \\ 20 + 0.10(x - 60) & \text{if } 60 < x \le 400 \\ 80 & \text{if } x > 400 \end{cases}$$

b. Find the charge for 325 minutes of phone use.

325 minutes fits the $60 < x \le 400$ portion of the domain. Therefore, the charge is $20 + 0.10(325 - 60)$ or $46.50.

c. When Anna uses more than 400 minutes of phone time in a month, she feels as if she does not get her money's worth if $80 is more than $20 plus 10 cents a minute she has used. For what amount of phone use does Anna feel the $80 charge is fair?

Solve $20 + 0.10(x - 60) = 80$ to find $x = 660$. Anna feels the $80 charge is fair for any number of minutes she uses over 660 minutes.

Practice

Solve each problem by writing an equation.

1. Isaac has been playing a massively multiplayer online game (MMOG) for the last two months. In the game, players are awarded levels of experience based on their actions in the game. For the first 10 hours of play, Isaac leveled 3 times each hour. For the next 5 hours of play, he only leveled once an hour. For the final nine hours of play, Isaac leveled once every three hours. **a. See Student Handbook Answer Appendix.**
   a. Write a piecewise function L to show level as a function of time t.
   b. What level had Isaac reached after 18 hours of play? **level 36**

2. The area of a rectangular parking lot is to be 20,000 square feet. The table shows some possible dimensions for the lot. Write an equation that can be used to find the width of the parking lot for any given length. $w = \frac{20{,}000}{\ell}$

Length (ft)	Width (ft)
20	1000
50	400
100	200
200	100
400	50

3. Iceland spent approximately 8.8% of its Gross Domestic Product on public health expenditures in 2006, the highest percentage of all countries. If Iceland had a GDP of $11,380,000,000 in 2006, write an equation to show how much money was spent on public health expenditures. $\frac{8.8}{100} = \frac{x}{11{,}380{,}000{,}000}$

Extra Practice

Lesson 1-1 Expressions and Formulas (pp. 5-10)

Evaluate each expression if $q = \frac{1}{2}$, $r = 1.2$, $v = -6$, and $t = 5$.

1. $qr - vt$ **30.6**
2. $qr \div v \cdot t$ **−0.5**
3. $qrvt$ **−18**
4. $qr + vt$ **−29.4**
5. $\frac{3q}{4v}$ **−2.25**
6. $\frac{5qr}{t}$ **0.6**
7. $\frac{2r(4v - 1)}{t}$ **−12**
8. $\frac{4q^3v + 1}{t - 1}$ **−0.5**

Evaluate each expression if $a = -0.5$, $b = 4$, $c = 5$, and $d = -3$.

9. $3b + 4d$ **0**
10. $ab^2 + c$ **−3**
11. $bc + d \div a$ **26**
12. $7ab - 3d$ **−5**
13. $ad + b^2 - c$ **12.5**
14. $\frac{4a + 3c}{3b}$ **$\frac{13}{12}$**
15. $\frac{3ab^2 - d^3}{a}$ **−6**
16. $\frac{5a + ad}{bc}$ **−0.05**

Lesson 1-2 Properties of Real Numbers (pp. 11-17)

Name the sets of numbers to which each number belongs. (Use N, W, Z, Q, I, and R.)

1. 8.2 **Q, R**
2. −9 **Z, Q, R**
3. $\sqrt{36}$ **N, W, Z, Q, R**
4. $-\frac{1}{3}$ **Q, R**
5. $\sqrt{2}$ **I, R**
6. $-0.\overline{24}$ **Q, R**

Name the property illustrated by each equation. **7. Comm. (×) 9. Distributive**

7. $(4 + 9a)2b = 2b(4 + 9a)$
8. $3\left(\frac{1}{3}\right) = 1$ **Mult. Inv.**
9. $a(3 - 2) = a \cdot 3 - a \cdot 2$
10. $(-3b) + 3b = 0$ **Add. Inv.**
11. $jk + 0 = jk$ **Add. Iden.**
12. $(2a)b = 2(ab)$ **Assoc. (×)**

Simplify each expression. **15. $-4x - 28y$**

13. $7r + 9t + 2r - 7t$ **$9r + 2t$**
14. $6(2a + 3b) + 5(3a - 4b)$ **$27a - 2b$**
15. $4(3x - 5y) - 8(2x + y)$
16. $0.2(5m - 8) + 0.3(6 - 2m)$ **$0.4m + 0.2$**
17. $\frac{1}{2}(7p + 3t) + \frac{3}{4}(6p - 4t)$ **$8p - \frac{3}{2}t$**
18. $\frac{4}{5}(3v - 2w) - \frac{1}{5}(7v - 2w)$ **$v - \frac{6}{5}w$**

Lesson 1-3 Solving Equations (pp. 18-25)

Write an algebraic expression to represent each verbal expression. **2. $2[n + (-9)]$**

1. twelve decreased by the square of a number **$12 - n^2$**
2. twice the sum of a number and negative nine
3. the product of the square of a number and 6 **$6n^2$**
4. the square of the sum of a number and 11 **$(n + 11)^2$**

Name the property illustrated by each statement.

5. If $a + 1 = 6$, then $3(a + 1) = 3(6)$. **Multiplication (=)**
6. If $x + (4 + 5) = 21$, then $x + 9 = 21$. **Substitution (=)**
7. If $7x = 42$, then $7x - 5 = 42 - 5$. **Subtraction (=)**
8. If $3 + 5 = 8$ and $8 = 2 \cdot 4$, then $3 + 5 = 2 \cdot 4$. **Transitive (=)**

Solve each equation. Check your solution.

9. $5t + 8 = 88$ **16**
10. $27 - x = -4$ **31**
11. $\frac{3}{4}y = \frac{2}{3}y + 5$ **60**
12. $8w - 3 = 5(2w + 1)$ **−4**
13. $3(k - 2) = k + 4$ **5**
14. $0.5z + 10 = z + 4$ **12**
15. $8q - \frac{q}{3} = 46$ **6**
16. $-\frac{2}{7}r + \frac{3}{7} = 5$ **−16**
17. $d - 1 = \frac{1}{2}(d - 2)$ **0**

Solve each equation or formula for the specified variable.

18. $C = \pi r$, for r **$r = \frac{C}{\pi}$**
19. $I = Prt$, for t **$t = \frac{I}{Pr}$**
20. $m = \frac{n - 2}{n}$, for n **$n = \frac{-2}{m - 1}$**

Extra Practice

Lesson 1-4 Solving Absolute Value Equations (pp. 27–32)

Evaluate each expression if $x = -5$, $y = 3$, and $z = -2.5$.

1. $|2x|$ 10
2. $|-3y|$ 9
3. $|2x + y|$ 7
4. $|y + 5z|$ 9.5
5. $-|x + z|$ −7.5
6. $8 - |5y - 3|$ −4
7. $2|x| - 4|2 + y|$ −10
8. $|x + y| - 6|z|$ −13

Solve each equation. Check your solutions.

9. $|d + 1| = 7$ {6, −8}
10. $|a - 6| = 10$ {−4, 16}
11. $2|x - 5| = 22$ {−6, 16}
12. $|t + 9| - 8 = 5$ {−22, 4}
13. $|p + 1| + 10 = 5$ ∅
14. $6|g - 3| = 42$ {−4, 10}
15. $2|y + 4| = 14$ {−11, 3}
16. $|3b - 10| = 2b$ {2, 10}
17. $|3x + 7| + 4 = 0$ ∅
18. $|2c + 3| - 15 = 0$ {−9, 6}
19. $7 - |m - 1| = 3$ {−3, 5}
20. $3 + |z + 5| = 10$ {−12, 2}
21. $2|2d - 7| + 1 = 35$ {−5, 12}
22. $|3t + 6| + 9 = 30$ {−9, 5}
23. $|d - 3| = 2d + 9$ {−2}
24. $|4y - 5| + 4 = 7y + 8$ $\left\{\frac{1}{11}\right\}$
25. $|2b + 4| - 3 = 6b + 1$ {0}
26. $|5t| + 2 = 3t + 18$ {−2, 8}

Lesson 1-5 Solving Inequalities (pp. 33–39)

Solve each inequality. Then graph the solution set on a number line. 12. $\{d \mid d \le -4\}$ 17. $\left\{x \,\middle|\, x \ge \frac{7}{2}\right\}$

1. $2z + 5 \le 7$ $\{z \mid z \le 1\}$
2. $3r - 8 > 7$ $\{r \mid r > 5\}$
3. $0.75b < 3$ $\{b \mid b < 4\}$
4. $-3x > 6$ $\{x \mid x < -2\}$
5. $2(3f + 5) \ge 28$ $\{f \mid f \ge 3\}$
6. $-33 > 5g + 7$ $\{g \mid g < -8\}$
7. $-3(y - 2) \ge -9$ $\{y \mid y \le 5\}$
8. $7a + 5 > 4a - 7$ $\{a \mid a > -4\}$
9. $5(b - 3) \le b - 7$ $\{b \mid b \le 2\}$
10. $3(2x - 5) < 5(x - 4)$ $\{x \mid x < -5\}$
11. $8(2c - 1) > 11c + 22$ $\{c \mid c > 6\}$
12. $2(d + 4) - 5 \ge 5(d + 3)$
13. $8 - 3t < 4(3 - t)$ $\{t \mid t < 4\}$
14. $-x \ge \frac{x + 4}{7}$ $\{x \mid x \le -0.5\}$
15. $\frac{a + 8}{4} \le \frac{7 + a}{3}$ $\{a \mid a \ge -4\}$
16. $-y < \frac{y + 5}{2}$ $\left\{y \,\middle|\, y > -\frac{5}{3}\right\}$
17. $5(x - 1) - 4x \ge 3(3 - x)$
18. $6k - (4k + 7) > 5 - k$ $\{k \mid k > 4\}$

Define a variable and write an inequality for each problem. Then solve. 19–22. Let n = the number.

19. The product of 7 and a number is greater than 42. $7n > 42$; $n > 6$
20. The difference of twice a number and 3 is at most 11. $2n - 3 \le 11$; $n \le 7$
21. The product of −10 and a number is greater than or equal to 20. $-10n \ge 20$; $n \le -2$
22. Thirty increased by a number is less than twice the number plus three. $30 + n < 2n + 3$; $n > 27$

Lesson 1-6 Solving Compound and Absolute Value Inequalities (pp. 41–48)

Write an absolute value inequality for each of the following. Then graph the solution set on a number line. 1–3. See Student Handbook Answer Appendix for graphs.

1. all numbers less than −9 or greater than 9 $|n| > 9$
2. all numbers between −5.5 and 5.5 $|n| < 5.5$
3. all numbers greater than or equal to −2 and less than or equal to 2 $|n| \le 2$

Solve each inequality. Graph the solution set on a number line. 4–24. See Student Handbook Answer Appendix.

4. $3m - 2 < 7$ or $2m + 1 > 13$
5. $2 < n + 4 < 7$
6. $-3 \le y - 2 \le 5$
7. $5t + 3 \le -7$ or $5t - 2 \ge 8$
8. $7 \le 4x + 3 \le 19$
9. $4x + 7 < 5$ or $2x - 4 > 12$
10. $|7x| \ge 21$
11. $|8p| \le 16$
12. $|7d| \ge -42$
13. $|a + 3| < 1$
14. $|t - 4| > 1$
15. $|2y - 5| < 3$
16. $|3d + 6| \ge 3$
17. $|4x - 1| < 5$
18. $|6v + 12| > 18$
19. $|2r + 4| < 6$
20. $|5w - 3| \ge 9$
21. $|z + 2| \ge 0$
22. $12 + |2q| < 0$
23. $|3h| + 15 < 0$
24. $|5n - 16| \ge 4$

Lesson 2-1 Relations and Functions (pp. 61–67)

State the domain and range of each relation. Then determine whether each relation is a *function*. If it is a function, determine if it is *one-to-one, onto, both*, or *neither*.

1.

Year	Population
1970	11,605
1980	13,468
1990	15,630
2000	18,140

D = {1970, 1980, 1990, 2000}; R = {11,605, 13,468, 15,630, 18,140}; yes; one-to-one

2.

x	y
1	5
2	5
3	5
4	5

D = {1, 2, 3, 4}; R = {5}; yes; neither

3. 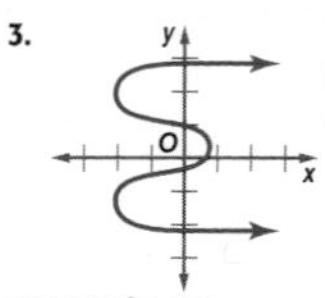

D = {x ≥ 2}; R = {all reals}; no

Graph each equation and determine the domain and range. Determine whether the equation is a *function*, is *one-to-one, onto, both*, or *neither*. Then state whether it is *discrete* or *continuous*. 4–9. See Student Handbook Answer Appendix.

4. {(1, 2), (2, 3), (3, 4), (4, 5)}
5. {(0, 3), (0, 2), (0, 1), (0, 0)}
6. $y = -x$
7. $y = 2x - 1$
8. $y = 2x^2$
9. $y = -x^2$

Find each value if $f(x) = x + 7$ and $g(x) = (x + 1)^2$.

10. $f(2)$ 9
11. $g(-2)$ 1
12. $f(a + 2)$ $a + 9$
13. $g(b - 1)$ b^2

Lesson 2-2 Linear Relations and Functions (pp. 69–74)

State whether each equation or function is a linear function. Write *yes* or *no*. If no, explain your reasoning.

1. $\frac{x}{2} - y = 7$ yes
2. $\sqrt{x} = y + 5$ no
3. $g(x) = \frac{2}{x - 3}$ no
4. $f(x) = 7$ yes

2, 3. See Student Handbook Answer Appendix for explanations.

Write each equation in standard form. Identify *A*, *B*, and *C*. 5–8. See Student Handbook Answer Appendix.

5. $x + 7 = y$
6. $x = -3y$
7. $5x = 7y + 3$
8. $-0.4x = 10$

Find the *x*-intercept and the *y*-intercept of the graph of each equation. Then graph the equation using intercepts. 9–12. See Student Handbook Answer Appendix for graphs.

9. $2x + y = 6$ 3; 6
10. $3x - 2y = -12$ −4; 6
11. $y = -x$ 0; 0
12. $y = -3$ none; −3

Lesson 2-3 Rate of Change and Slope (pp. 76–82)

Find the slope of the line that passes through each pair of points.

1. (0, 3), (5, 0) $-\frac{3}{5}$
2. (2, 8), (2, −8) undefined
3. (1.5, −1), (3, 1.5) $\frac{5}{3}$
4. (−3, *c*), (4, *c*) 0

Determine the rate of change of each graph.

7. 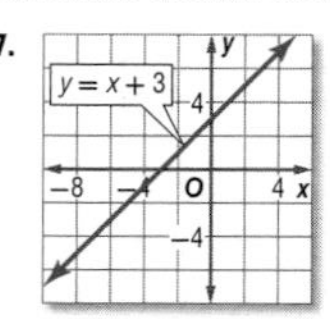

1

8. 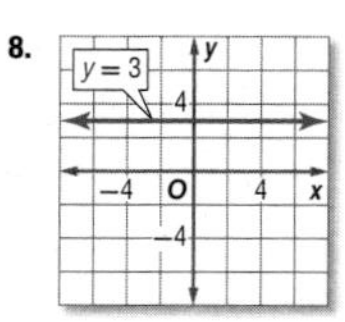

0

Find the rate of change for each set of data.

9.

Time (sec)	5	10	15	20
Distance (m)	15	30	45	60

3 m/sec

10.

Weight (lb)	2	4	6	8
Cost ($)	10	20	30	40

$5 per lb

Lesson 2-4 Writing Linear Equations (pp. 83–89)

Write an equation of each line.

1. 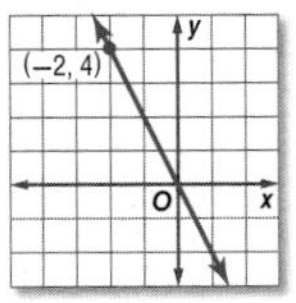

$y = -2x$

2. 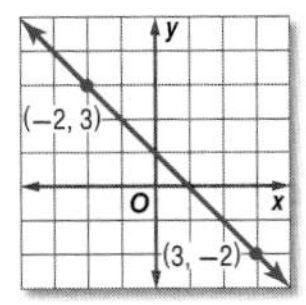

$y = -x + 1$

Write an equation in slope-intercept form for the line that satisfies each set of conditions.

3. slope −1, passes through (7, 2)
4. slope $\frac{3}{4}$, passes through the origin
5. passes through (1, −3) and (−1, 2)
6. x-intercept −5, y-intercept 2
7. passes through (1, 1), parallel to the graph of $2x + 3y = 5$
8. passes through (0, 0), perpendicular to the graph of $2y + 3x = 4$

3–8. See Student Handbook Answer Appendix.

Lesson 2-5 Scatter Plots and Lines of Regression (pp. 92–98)

Complete parts a–c for each set of data in Exercises 1–3. 1–3. See Student Handbook Answer Appendix.

a. Make a scatter plot and a line of fit, and describe the correlation.
b. Use two ordered pairs to write a prediction equation.
c. Use your prediction equation to predict the missing value.

1. Telephone Costs

Minutes	Cost ($)
1	0.20
3	0.52
4	0.68
6	1.00
9	1.48
15	?

2. Washington

Year	Population
1960	2,853,214
1970	3,413,244
1980	4,132,353
1990	4,866,669
2000	5,894,121
2010	?

Source: *The World Almanac*

3. Federal Minimum Wage

Year	Wage
1981	$3.35
1990	$3.80
1991	$4.25
1996	$4.75
1997	$5.15
2015	?

Source: *The World Almanac*

Lesson 2-6 Special Functions (pp. 101–107)

Write the piecewise function shown in each graph.

1. 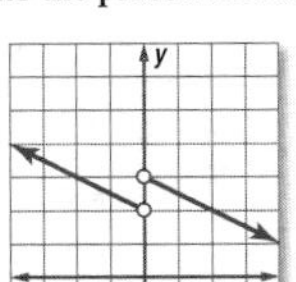

$y = \begin{cases} -\frac{1}{2}x + 2 \text{ if } x < 0 \\ -\frac{1}{2}x + 3 \text{ if } x > 0 \end{cases}$

2. 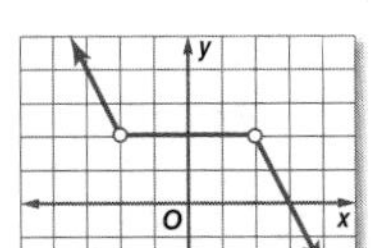

$y = \begin{cases} -2x - 2 \text{ if } x < 2 \\ 2 \text{ if } -2 < x < 2 \\ -2x + 6 \text{ if } x > 2 \end{cases}$

Graph each function. Identify the domain and range. 3–10. See Student Handbook Answer Appendix.

3. $f(x) = [\![x + 5]\!]$
4. $g(x) = [\![x]\!] - 2$
5. $f(x) = -2[\![x]\!]$
6. $h(x) = |x| - 3$
7. $h(x) = |x - 1|$
8. $g(x) = |2x| + 2$
9. $h(x) = \begin{cases} x \text{ if } x < -2 \\ 4 \text{ if } x \geq -2 \end{cases}$
10. $f(x) = \begin{cases} -3 \text{ if } x \leq 1 \\ -x \text{ if } x > 1 \end{cases}$

Lesson 2-7 Parent Functions and Transformations (pp. 109–116)

Identify the type of function represented by each graph.

1. 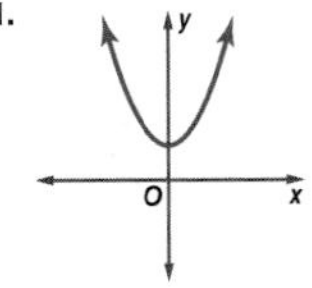

quadratic

2. 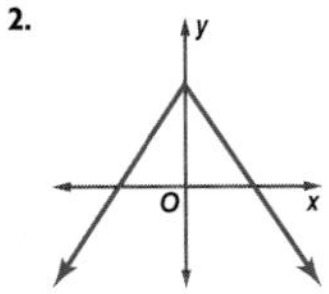

absolute value

3. 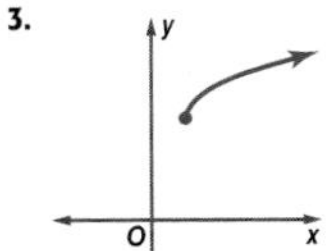

square root

Describe the translation of each function. Then graph the function. 4–9. See Student Handbook Answer Appendix for graphs.

4. $y = |x| + 3$ Translate the graph of $y = |x|$ up 3.
5. $y = x^2 - 2$ Translate the graph of $y = x^2$ down 2.

Describe the reflection in each function. Then graph the function.

6. $y = -x^2$ Reflect the graph of $y = x^2$ over the x-axis.
7. $y = -x$ Reflect the graph of $y = x$ over the x-axis.

Describe the dilation in each function. Then graph the function.

8. $y = \frac{3}{4}x$ Dilate the graph of $y = x$ by a scale factor of $\frac{3}{4}$.
9. $y = \frac{2}{x}$ Dilate the graph of $y = \frac{1}{x}$ by a scale factor of 2.

Lesson 2-8 Graphing Linear and Absolute Value Inequalities (pp. 117–121)

Graph each inequality. 1–21. See Student Handbook Answer Appendix.

1. $y \geq x - 2$
2. $y < -3x - 1$
3. $4y \leq -3x + 8$
4. $3x > y$
5. $x + 2 \geq y - 7$
6. $2x < 5 - y$
7. $y > \frac{1}{5}x - 8$
8. $2y - 5x \leq 8$
9. $-2x + 5 \leq \frac{2}{3}y$
10. $3x + 2y \geq 0$
11. $x \leq 2$
12. $\frac{y}{2} \leq x - 1$
13. $y - 3 < 5$
14. $y \geq -|x|$
15. $|x| \leq y + 3$
16. $y > |5x - 3|$
17. $y \leq |8 - x|$
18. $y < |x + 3| - 1$
19. $y + |2x| \geq 4$
20. $y \geq |2x - 1| + 5$
21. $y < \left|\frac{2x}{3}\right| - 1$

Lesson 3-1 Solving Systems of Equations by Graphing (pp. 135–141)

Solve each system of equations by graphing or by using a table.

1. $x + 3y = 18$, $-x + 2y = 7$ (3, 5)
2. $x - y = 2$, $2x - 2y = 10$ no solution
3. $2x + 6y = 6$, $\frac{1}{3}x + y = 1$ infinite solutions
4. $x + 3y = 0$, $2x + 6y = 5$ no solution
5. $2x - y = 7$, $\frac{2}{5}x - \frac{4}{3}y = -2$ (5, 3)
6. $y = \frac{1}{3}x + 1$, $y = 4x + 1$ (0, 1)

Graph each system of equations and describe it as *consistent and independent*, *consistent and dependent*, or *inconsistent*. 7–12. See Student Handbook Answer Appendix for graphs.

7. $2x + 3y = 5$, $-6x - 9y = -15$ consistent, dependent
8. $x - 2y = 4$, $y = x - 2$ consistent, independent
9. $y = 0.5x$, $2y = x + 4$ inconsistent
10. $9x - 5 = 7y$, $4.5x - 3.5y = 2.5$ consistent, dependent
11. $\frac{3}{4}x - y = 0$, $\frac{1}{3}y + \frac{1}{2}x = 6$ consistent, independent
12. $\frac{2}{3}x = \frac{5}{3}y$, $2x - 5y = 0$ consistent, dependent

Lesson 3-2 Solving Systems of Equations Algebraically (pp. 143–150)

Solve each system of equations by using substitution.

1. $2x + 3y = 10$, $x + 6y = 32$ (−4, 6)
2. $x = 4y - 10$, $5x + 3y = -4$ (−2, 2)
3. $3x - 4y = -27$, $2x + y = -7$ (−5, 3)

Solve each system of equations by using elimination.

4. $7x + y = 9$, $5x - y = 15$ (2, −5)
5. $r + 5t = -17$, $2r - 6t = -2$ (−7, −2)
6. $6n + 8q = 20$, $5n - 4q = -26$ (−2, 4)

Solve each system of equations by using either substitution or elimination.

7. $2x - 3y = 7$, $3x + 6y = 42$ (8, 3)
8. $2a + 5b = -13$, $3a - 4b = 38$ (6, −5)
9. $3c + 4d = -1$, $6c - 2d = 3$ $\left(\frac{1}{3}, -\frac{1}{2}\right)$
10. $7x - y = 35$, $y = 5x - 19$ (8, 21)
11. $3m + 4n = 28$, $5m - 3n = -21$ (0, 7)
12. $x = 2y - 1$, $4x - 3y = 21$ (9, 5)
13. $2.5x + 1.5y = -2$, $3.5x - 0.5y = 18$ (4, −8)
14. $\frac{5}{2}x + \frac{1}{3}y = 13$, $\frac{1}{2}x - y = -7$ (4, 9)
15. $\frac{2}{7}c - \frac{4}{3}d = 16$, $\frac{4}{7}c + \frac{8}{3}d = -16$ (14, −9)

Lesson 3-3 Solving Systems of Inequalities by Graphing (pp. 151–157)

Solve each system of inequalities by graphing. 1–12. See Student Handbook Answer Appendix.

1. $x \le 5$, $y \ge -3$
2. $y < 3$, $y - x \ge -1$
3. $x + y < 5$, $x < 2$
4. $y + x < 2$, $y \ge x$
5. $x + y \le 2$, $y - x \le 4$
6. $y \le x + 4$, $y - x \ge 1$
7. $y < \frac{1}{3}x + 5$, $y > 2x + 1$
8. $y + x \ge 1$, $y - x \ge -1$
9. $|x| > 2$, $|y| \le 5$
10. $|x - 3| \le 3$, $4y - 2x \le 6$
11. $4x + 3y \ge 12$, $2y - x \ge -1$
12. $y \le -1$, $3x - 2y \ge 6$

Find the coordinates of the vertices of the triangle formed by each system of inequalities. 13–15. See Student Handbook Answer Appendix for graphs.

13. $y \le 3$, $x \le 2$, $y \ge -\frac{3}{2}x + 3$ (0, 3), (2, 3), (2, 0)
14. $y \ge -1$, $y \le x$, $y \le -x + 4$ (2, 2), (−1, −1), (5, −1)
15. $y \le \frac{1}{3}x + \frac{7}{3}$, $4x - y \le 5$, $y \ge -\frac{3}{2}x + \frac{1}{2}$ (2, 3), (1, −1), (−1, 2)

Lesson 3-4 Optimization with Linear Programming (pp. 160–166)

Graph each system of inequalities. Name the coordinates of the vertices of the feasible region. Find the maximum and minimum values of the given function for this region. 1–6. See Student Handbook Answer Appendix for graphs.

1. $4x - 5y \le -10$, $y \le 6$, $2x + y \ge 2$; $f(x, y) = x + y$ (0, 2), (5, 6), (−2, 6); 11; 2
2. $x \le 5$, $y \ge 2$, $2x - 5y \ge -10$; $f(x, y) = 3x + y$ (0, 2), (5, 2), (5, 4); 19; 2
3. $x - 2y \ge -7$, $x + y \le 8$, $y \ge 5x + 8$; $f(x, y) = 3x - 4y$ (−1, 3); no maximum; 15
4. $y \le 4x + 6$, $x + 4y \ge 7$, $2x + y \le 7$; $f(x, y) = 2x - y$ (−1, 2), (3, 1) $\left(\frac{1}{6}, 6\frac{2}{3}\right)$; 5; $-6\frac{1}{3}$
5. $y \ge 0$, $y \le 5$, $y \le -x + 7$, $5x + 3y \ge 20$; $f(x, y) = x + 2y$ (4, 0), (7, 0), (2, 5), (1, 5); 12; 4
6. $y \ge 0$, $3x - 2y \ge 0$, $x + 3y \le 11$, $2x + 3y \le 16$; $f(x, y) = 4x + y$ (0, 0), (2, 3), (5, 2), (8, 0); 32; 0

Lesson 3-5 Systems of Equations in Three Variables (pp. 167–173)

Solve each system of equations.

1. $4x + 2y - 6z = -38$, $5x - 4y + z = -18$, $x + 3y + 7z = 38$ (−3, 2, 5)
2. $u + 3v + w = 14$, $2u - v + 3w = -9$, $4u - 5v - 2w = -17$ (1, 5, −2)
3. $x + y = -6$, $x + z = -2$, $y + z = 2$ (−5, −1, 3)
4. $5a = 5$, $6b - 3c = 15$, $2a + 7c = -5$ (1, 2, −1)
5. $w + 2t = 5$, $7r - 3w + t = 20$, $2t = 8$ (1, −3, 4)
6. $2u - 3v = 13$, $3v + w = -3$, $4u - w = 2$ (2, −3, 6)
7. $4a + 2b - c = 5$, $2a + b - 5c = -11$, $a - 2b + 3c = 6$ (1, 2, 3)
8. $x + 2y - z = 1$, $x + 3y + 2z = 7$, $2x + 6y + z = 8$ (3, 0, 2)
9. $2x + y - z = 7$, $3x - y + 2z = 15$, $x - 4y + z = 2$ (4, 1, 2)

Lesson 4-1 Introduction to Matrices (pp. 185–191)

State the dimensions of each matrix.

1. $\begin{bmatrix} 0 & 3 & -3 & 1 \\ -1 & 4 & 5 & 0 \end{bmatrix}$ 2 × 4
2. $\begin{bmatrix} 0 \\ -1 \\ 3 \\ -5 \end{bmatrix}$ 4 × 1
3. $\begin{bmatrix} -3 & 2 \\ 1 & 7 \\ 19 & 11 \end{bmatrix}$ 3 × 2

Identify each element of matrix $A = \begin{bmatrix} 0 & -6 & 2 & 11 \\ 2 & 3 & 0 & 9 \\ 7 & 4 & 3 & 12 \end{bmatrix}$.

4. a_{32} 4
5. a_{11} 0
6. a_{33} 3
7. a_{24} 9

Lesson 4-2 Operations with Matrices (pp. 193–199)

Perform the indicated matrix operations. If the matrix does not exist, write *impossible*. 1–6. See Student Handbook Answer Appendix.

1. $\begin{bmatrix} 3 & 5 \\ -7 & 2 \end{bmatrix} + \begin{bmatrix} -2 & 6 \\ 8 & -1 \end{bmatrix}$
2. $\begin{bmatrix} 0 & -1 & 3 \end{bmatrix} + \begin{bmatrix} 5 \\ -2 \\ -3 \end{bmatrix}$
3. $\begin{bmatrix} 45 & 36 & 18 \\ 63 & 29 & 5 \end{bmatrix} - \begin{bmatrix} 45 & -2 & 36 \\ 18 & 9 & -10 \end{bmatrix}$
4. $4\begin{bmatrix} -8 & 2 & 9 \end{bmatrix} - 3\begin{bmatrix} 2 & -7 & 6 \end{bmatrix}$
5. $5\begin{bmatrix} 6 & -2 \\ 5 & 4 \end{bmatrix} - 2\begin{bmatrix} 6 & -2 \\ 5 & 4 \end{bmatrix} + 4\begin{bmatrix} 7 & -6 \\ -4 & 2 \end{bmatrix}$
6. $1.3\begin{bmatrix} 3.7 \\ -5.4 \end{bmatrix} + 4.1\begin{bmatrix} 6.4 \\ -3.7 \end{bmatrix} - 6.2\begin{bmatrix} -0.8 \\ 7.4 \end{bmatrix}$

Use matrices A, B, C, D, and E to find the following. 7–14. See Student Handbook Answer Appendix.

$A = \begin{bmatrix} 1 & 0 \\ 0 & 1 \end{bmatrix}$, $B = \begin{bmatrix} -1 & 0 \\ 0 & -1 \end{bmatrix}$, $C = \begin{bmatrix} 2 & -2 \\ -3 & 3 \end{bmatrix}$, $D = \begin{bmatrix} -2 & 2 \\ 3 & -3 \end{bmatrix}$, $E = \begin{bmatrix} 5 & -3 \\ -2 & 4 \end{bmatrix}$

7. $A + B$
8. $C + D$
9. $A - B$
10. $4B$
11. $D - C$
12. $E + 2A$
13. $D - 2B$
14. $2A + 3E - D$

Lesson 4-3 Multiplying Matrices (pp. 200–207)

Find each product, if possible.

1. $\begin{bmatrix} -3 & 4 \end{bmatrix} \cdot \begin{bmatrix} -1 \\ 2 \end{bmatrix}$ $[11]$

2. $\begin{bmatrix} 2 & -4 \\ 0 & 5 \end{bmatrix} \cdot \begin{bmatrix} 1 & 3 \\ -2 & -1 \end{bmatrix}$ $\begin{bmatrix} 10 & 10 \\ -10 & -5 \end{bmatrix}$

3. $\begin{bmatrix} 1 & 3 \\ -2 & -1 \end{bmatrix} \cdot \begin{bmatrix} 2 & -4 \\ 0 & 5 \end{bmatrix}$ $\begin{bmatrix} 2 & 11 \\ -4 & 3 \end{bmatrix}$

4. $\begin{bmatrix} 3 & 2 \\ 5 & 2 \end{bmatrix} \cdot \begin{bmatrix} -8 \\ 15 \end{bmatrix}$ $\begin{bmatrix} 6 \\ -10 \end{bmatrix}$

5. $\begin{bmatrix} -1 \\ 2 \\ 1 \end{bmatrix} \cdot \begin{bmatrix} 7 & 6 & 1 \\ 2 & -4 & 0 \end{bmatrix}$ not possible

6. $\begin{bmatrix} 0 & 1 & -2 \\ 5 & 3 & -4 \\ -1 & 0 & 0 \end{bmatrix} \cdot \begin{bmatrix} 1 & -3 & 0 \\ 2 & 0 & -1 \\ 0 & 1 & -2 \end{bmatrix}$ $\begin{bmatrix} 2 & -2 & 3 \\ 11 & -19 & 5 \\ -1 & 3 & 0 \end{bmatrix}$

7. $\begin{bmatrix} 3 & -2 \\ 4 & 5 \end{bmatrix} \cdot \begin{bmatrix} 1 & 0 \\ 0 & 1 \end{bmatrix}$ $\begin{bmatrix} 3 & -2 \\ 4 & 5 \end{bmatrix}$

8. $\begin{bmatrix} -1 & 0 & 2 \\ -6 & 5 & -3 \end{bmatrix} \cdot \begin{bmatrix} -2 \\ 1 \\ 7 \end{bmatrix}$ $\begin{bmatrix} 16 \\ -4 \end{bmatrix}$

Lesson 4-4 Transformations with Matrices (pp. 209–217)

1, 2. See Student Handbook Answer Appendix.

1. The vertices of quadrilateral $ABCD$ are $A(1, 1)$, $B(-2, 3)$, $C(-4, -1)$, and $D(2, -3)$. The quadrilateral is dilated so that its perimeter is 2 times the original perimeter.
   a. Write the coordinates for $ABCD$ in a vertex matrix.
   b. Find the coordinates of the image $A'B'C'D'$.
   c. Graph $ABCD$ and $A'B'C'D'$.
2. The vertices of $\triangle MQN$ are $M(2, 4)$, $Q(3, -5)$, and $N(1, -1)$.
   a. Write the coordinates of $\triangle MQN$ in a vertex matrix.
   b. Write the reflection matrix for reflecting over the line $y = x$.
   c. Find the coordinates of $\triangle M'Q'N'$ after the reflection.
   d. Graph $\triangle MQN$ and $\triangle M'Q'N'$.
   e. Write a rotation matrix for rotating $\triangle MQN$ 90° counterclockwise about the origin.
   f. Find the coordinates of $\triangle M'Q'N'$ after the rotation.
   g. Graph $\triangle MQN$ and $\triangle M'Q'N'$.

Lesson 4-5 Determinants and Cramer's Rule (pp. 220–228)

Evaluate each determinant using diagonals.

1. $\begin{vmatrix} 2 & -3 & 5 \\ 1 & -2 & -7 \\ -1 & 4 & -3 \end{vmatrix}$ 48

2. $\begin{vmatrix} 0 & -1 & 2 \\ -2 & 1 & 0 \\ 2 & 0 & -1 \end{vmatrix}$ −2

3. $\begin{vmatrix} 4 & 3 & -2 \\ 2 & 5 & -8 \\ 6 & 4 & -1 \end{vmatrix}$ 14

4. $\begin{vmatrix} -3 & 0 & 2 \\ 1 & -2 & -1 \\ 0 & 5 & 0 \end{vmatrix}$ −5

5. $\begin{vmatrix} 3 & 2 & -1 \\ 2 & 3 & 0 \\ -1 & 0 & 3 \end{vmatrix}$ 12

6. $\begin{vmatrix} 1 & 0 & 0 \\ 0 & 1 & 0 \\ 0 & 0 & 1 \end{vmatrix}$ 1

7. $\begin{vmatrix} 6 & 4 & -1 \\ 2 & 5 & -8 \\ 4 & 3 & -2 \end{vmatrix}$ −14

8. $\begin{vmatrix} 6 & 12 & 15 \\ 9 & 3 & 14 \\ 5 & 6 & 3 \end{vmatrix}$ 651

Use Cramer's Rule to solve each system of equations.

9. $5x - y = 7$, $8x + 2y = 4$ $(1, -2)$
10. $3m + t = 4$, $2m + 2t = 3$ $\left(\frac{5}{4}, \frac{1}{4}\right)$
11. $6c + 5d = 7$, $3c - 10d = -4$ $\left(\frac{2}{3}, \frac{3}{5}\right)$
12. $3a - 5b = 1$, $a + 3b = 5$ $(2, 1)$
13. $2r - 7t = 24$, $-r + 8t = -21$ $(5, -2)$
14. $x + y = -3$, $3x - 10y = 43$ $(1, -4)$
15. $2m - 3t = 3$, $-4m + 9t = -8$ $\left(\frac{1}{2}, -\frac{2}{3}\right)$
16. $x + y = 1$, $2x - 2y = -12$ $(-2.5, 3.5)$

Lesson 4-6 Inverse Matrices and Systems of Equations (pp. 229–235)

Determine whether each pair of matrices are inverses of each other.

1. $A = \begin{bmatrix} -7 & -6 \\ 8 & 7 \end{bmatrix}$, $B = \begin{bmatrix} -7 & -6 \\ 8 & 7 \end{bmatrix}$ yes

2. $C = \begin{bmatrix} -3 & 4 \\ 2 & -2 \end{bmatrix}$, $D = \begin{bmatrix} -2 & -2 \\ -4 & -3 \end{bmatrix}$ no

Find the inverse of each matrix, if it exists. 3–6. See Student Handbook Answer Appendix.

3. $\begin{bmatrix} 2 & 4 \\ 2 & 3 \end{bmatrix}$
4. $\begin{bmatrix} 8 & -5 \\ -6 & 4 \end{bmatrix}$
5. $\begin{bmatrix} 10 & 3 \\ 5 & -2 \end{bmatrix}$
6. $\begin{bmatrix} -3 & 4 \\ -4 & 8 \end{bmatrix}$

Use a matrix equation to solve each system of equations.

7. $4c - 3d = -1$, $5c - 2d = 39$ (17, 23)
8. $x + 2y - z = 6$, $-2x + 3y + z = 1$, $x + y + 3z = 8$ (3, 2, 1)
9. $2a - 3b - c = 4$, $4a + b + c = 15$, $a - b - c = -2$ (2.6, −1.7, 6.3)

Lesson 5-1 Graphing Quadratic Functions (pp. 249–257)

Complete parts a–c for each quadratic function. 1–9. See Student Handbook Answer Appendix.

a. Find the y-intercept, the equation of the axis of symmetry, and the x-coordinate of the vertex.
b. Make a table of values that includes the vertex.
c. Use this information to graph the function.

1. $f(x) = 6x^2$
2. $f(x) = -x^2$
3. $f(x) = x^2 + 5$
4. $f(x) = -x^2 - 2$
5. $f(x) = 2x^2 + 1$
6. $f(x) = -3x^2 + 6x$
7. $f(x) = x^2 + 6x - 3$
8. $f(x) = x^2 - 2x - 8$
9. $f(x) = -3x^2 - 6x + 12$

Determine whether each function has a *maximum* or a *minimum* value and find that value. Then state the domain and range of the function. 10–15. See Student Handbook Answer Appendix for domains and ranges.

10. $f(x) = 9x^2$ min.; 0
11. $f(x) = 9 - x^2$ max.; 9
12. $f(x) = x^2 - 5x + 6$ min.; −0.25
13. $f(x) = 2 + 7x - 6x^2$ max.; $4\frac{1}{24}$
14. $f(x) = 4x^2 - 9$ min.; −9
15. $f(x) = x^2 + 2x + 1$ min.; 0

Lesson 5-2 Solving Quadratic Equations by Graphing (pp. 259–266)

Use the related graph of each equation to determine its solutions.

1. $x^2 + x - 6 = 0$ −3, 2

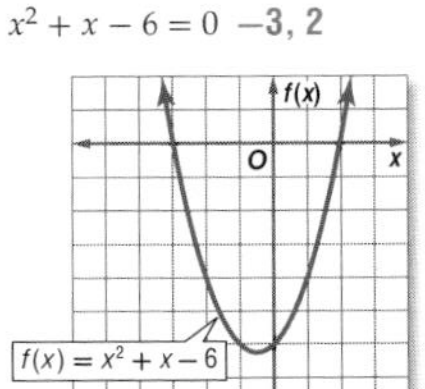

2. $-2x^2 = 0$ 0

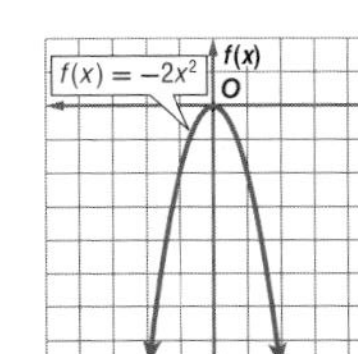

3. $x^2 - 4x - 5 = 0$ −1, 5

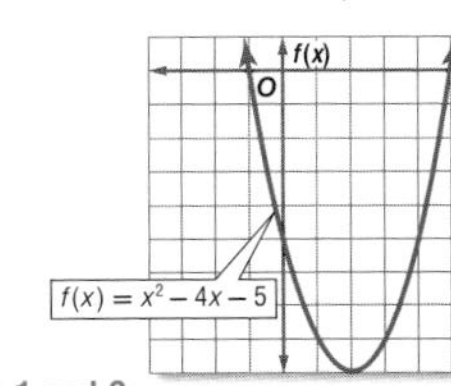

9. between −8 and −7; between 0 and 1 11. between −1 and 0; between 1 and 2

Solve each equation. If exact roots cannot be found, state the consecutive integers between which the roots are located. 6. between 0 and 1; between 4 and 5

4. $x^2 - 2x = 0$ 0, 2
5. $x^2 + 8x - 20 = 0$ −10, 2
6. $-2x^2 + 10x - 5 = 0$
7. $-5x + 2x^2 - 3 = 0$ $-\frac{1}{2}$, 3
8. $3x^2 - x + 8 = 0$ no real solutions
9. $-x^2 + 2 = 7x$
10. $4x^2 - 4x + 1 = 0$ 0.5
11. $4x + 1 = 3x^2$
12. $x^2 = -9x$ 0, −9

Lesson 5-3 Solving Quadratic Equations by Factoring (pp. 268–275)

Solve each equation by factoring. 11. −1.5, 0.25

1. $x^2 + 7x + 10 = 0$ −2, −5
2. $3x^2 = 75x$ 0, 25
3. $2x^2 + 7x = 9$ −4.5, 1
4. $8x^2 = 48 - 40x$ −6, 1
5. $5x^2 = 20x$ 0, 4
6. $16x^2 - 64 = 0$ ±2
7. $24x^2 - 15 = 2x$ $-\frac{3}{4}, \frac{5}{6}$
8. $x^2 = 72 - x$ −9, 8
9. $4x^2 + 9 = 12x$ $\frac{3}{2}$
10. $2x^2 - 8x = 0$ 0, 4
11. $8x^2 + 10x = 3$
12. $12x^2 - 5x = 3$ $\frac{3}{4}, -\frac{1}{3}$
13. $x^2 + 9x + 14 = 0$ −7, −2
14. $9x^2 + 1 = 6x$ $\frac{1}{3}$
15. $6x^2 + 7x = 3$ $\frac{1}{3}, -\frac{3}{2}$
16. $x^2 - 4x = 21$ −3, 7

Write a quadratic equation in standard form with the given roots.

17. 2, 1 $x^2 - 3x + 2 = 0$
18. −3, 4 $x^2 - x - 12 = 0$
19. −1, −7 $x^2 + 8x + 7 = 0$
20. $-1, \frac{1}{2}$ $2x^2 + x - 1 = 0$
21. $-5, \frac{1}{4}$ $4x^2 + 19x - 5 = 0$
22. $-\frac{1}{3}, -\frac{1}{2}$ $6x^2 + 5x + 1 = 0$

Lesson 5-4 Complex Numbers (pp. 276–282)

Simplify.

1. $\sqrt{-289}$ $17i$
2. $\sqrt{-\frac{25}{121}}$ $\frac{5}{11}i$
3. $\sqrt{-625b^8}$ $25b^4i$
4. $\sqrt{-\frac{28t^6}{27w^5}}$ $\frac{2|t^3|i\sqrt{21w}}{9w^3}$
5. $(7i)^2$ −49
6. $(6i)(-2i)(11i)$ $132i$
7. $(\sqrt{-8})(\sqrt{-12})$ $-4\sqrt{6}$
8. $-i^{22}$ 1
9. $i^{17} \cdot i^{12} \cdot i^{26}$ $-i$
10. $(14 - 5i) + (-8 + 19i)$ $6 + 14i$
11. $(7i) - (2 + 3i)$ $-2 + 4i$
12. $(2 + 2i) - (5 + i)$ $-3 + i$
13. $(7 + 3i)(7 - 3i)$ 58
14. $(8 - 2i)(5 + i)$ $42 - 2i$
15. $(6 + 8i)^2$ $-28 + 96i$
16. $\frac{3}{6 - 2i}$ $\frac{9 + 3i}{20}$
17. $\frac{5i}{3 + 4i}$ $\frac{4 + 3i}{5}$
18. $\frac{3 - 7i}{5 + 4i}$ $\frac{-13 - 47i}{41}$

Solve each equation.

19. $x^2 + 8 = 3$ $\pm i\sqrt{5}$
20. $\frac{4x^2}{49} + 6 = 3$ $\pm\frac{7i\sqrt{3}}{2}$
21. $8x^2 + 5 = 1$ $\pm\frac{i\sqrt{2}}{2}$
22. $12 - 9x^2 = 38$ $\pm\frac{i\sqrt{26}}{3}$
23. $9x^2 + 7 = 4$ $\pm\frac{i\sqrt{3}}{3}$
24. $\frac{1}{2}x^2 + 1 = 0$ $\pm i\sqrt{2}$

Lesson 5-5 Completing the Square (pp. 284–290)

Find the value of c that makes each trinomial a perfect square. Then write the trinomial as a perfect square. 1–8. See Student Handbook Answer Appendix for perfect squares.

1. $x^2 - 4x + c$ 4
2. $x^2 + 20x + c$ 100
3. $x^2 - 11x + c$ $\frac{121}{4}$
4. $x^2 - \frac{2}{3}x + c$ $\frac{1}{9}$
5. $x^2 + 30x + c$ 225
6. $x^2 + \frac{3}{8}x + c$ $\frac{9}{256}$
7. $x^2 - \frac{2}{5}x + c$ $\frac{1}{25}$
8. $x^2 - 3x + c$ $\frac{9}{4}$

Solve each equation by completing the square. 9–29. See Student Handbook Answer Appendix.

9. $x^2 + 3x - 4 = 0$
10. $x^2 + 5x = 0$
11. $x^2 + 2x - 63 = 0$
12. $3x^2 - 16x - 35 = 0$
13. $x^2 + 7x + 13 = 0$
14. $5x^2 - 8x + 2 = 0$
15. $x^2 - 6x + 11 = 0$
16. $x^2 - 12x + 36 = 0$
17. $8x^2 + 13x - 4 = 0$
18. $3x^2 + 5x + 6 = 0$
19. $x^2 + 14x - 1 = 0$
20. $4x^2 - 32x + 15 = 0$
21. $3x^2 - 11x - 4 = 0$
22. $x^2 + 8x - 84 = 0$
23. $x^2 - 7x + 5 = 0$
24. $x^2 + 3x - 8 = 0$
25. $x^2 - 5x - 10 = 0$
26. $3x^2 - 12x + 4 = 0$
27. $x^2 + 20x + 75 = 0$
28. $x^2 - 5x - 24 = 0$
29. $2x^2 + x - 21 = 0$

Lesson 5-6 The Quadratic Formula and the Discriminant (pp. 292–300)

Complete parts a–c for each quadratic equation. 1–15. See Student Handbook Answer Appendix.

a. Find the value of the discriminant.

b. Describe the number and type of roots.

c. Find the exact solutions by using the Quadratic Formula.

1. $x^2 + 7x + 13 = 0$
2. $6x^2 + 6x - 21 = 0$
3. $5x^2 - 5x + 4 = 0$
4. $9x^2 + 42x + 49 = 0$
5. $4x^2 - 16x + 3 = 0$
6. $2x^2 = 5x + 3$
7. $x^2 + 81 = 18x$
8. $3x^2 - 30x + 75 = 0$
9. $24x^2 + 10x = 43$
10. $9x^2 + 4 = 2x$
11. $7x = 8x^2$
12. $18x^2 = 9x + 45$
13. $x^2 - 4x + 4 = 0$
14. $4x^2 + 16x + 15 = 0$
15. $x^2 - 6x + 13 = 0$

Solve each equation by using the Quadratic Formula. 16–24. See Student Handbook Answer Appendix.

16. $x^2 + 4x + 29 = 0$
17. $4x^2 + 3x - 2 = 0$
18. $2x^2 + 5x = 9$
19. $x^2 = 8x - 16$
20. $7x^2 = 4x$
21. $2x^2 + 6x + 5 = 0$
22. $9x^2 - 30x + 25 = 0$
23. $3x^2 - 4x + 2 = 0$
24. $3x^2 = 108x$

Lesson 5-7 Transformations with Quadratic Functions (pp. 305–310)

Write each quadratic function in vertex form. Then identify the vertex, axis of symmetry, and direction of opening. 1–6. See Student Handbook Answer Appendix.

1. $y = (x + 6)^2 - 1$
2. $y = 2(x - 8)^2 - 5$
3. $y = -(x + 1)^2 + 7$
4. $y = -9(x - 7)^2 + 3$
5. $y = -x^2 + 10x - 3$
6. $y = -2x^2 + 16x + 7$

Graph each function. 7–15. See Student Handbook Answer Appendix.

7. $y = x^2 - 2x + 4$
8. $y = -3x^2 + 18x$
9. $y = -2x^2 - 4x + 1$
10. $y = 2x^2 - 8x + 9$
11. $y = \frac{1}{3}x^2 + 2x + 7$
12. $y = x^2 + 6x + 9$
13. $y = x^2 + 3x + 6$
14. $y = -0.5x^2 + 4x - 3$
15. $y = -2x^2 - 8x - 1$

Lesson 5-8 Quadratic Inequalities (pp. 312–318)

Graph each inequality. 1–8. See Student Handbook Answer Appendix.

1. $y \le 5x^2 + 3x - 2$
2. $y > -3x^2 + 2$
3. $y \ge x^2 - 8x$
4. $y \ge -x^2 - x + 3$
5. $y \le 3x^2 + 4x - 8$
6. $y \le -5x^2 + 2x - 3$
7. $y > 4x^2 + x$
8. $y \ge -x^2 - 3$

Solve each inequality by graphing.

9. $x^2 - 4 \le 0$ $-2 \le x \le 2$
10. $-x^2 + 6x - 9 \ge 0$ 3
11. $x^2 + 4x - 5 < 0$ $-5 < x < 1$

Solve each inequality algebraically. 12–19. See Student Handbook Answer Appendix.

12. $x^2 - 1 < 0$
13. $10x^2 - x - 2 \ge 0$
14. $-x^2 - 5x - 6 > 0$
15. $-3x^2 \ge 5$
16. $x^2 - 2x - 8 \le 0$
17. $2x^2 \ge 5x + 12$
18. $x^2 + 3x - 4 > 0$
19. $2x - x^2 \le -15$

Lesson 6-1 Operations with Polynomials (pp. 333–339)

Simplify. Assume that no variable equals 0. 10. $5.00315451 \times 10^{16}$

1. $x^7 \cdot x^3 \cdot x$ x^{11}
2. $m^8 \cdot m \cdot m^{10}$ m^{19}
3. $7^5 \cdot 7^2$ 823,543
4. $(-3)^4(-3)$ -243
5. $\frac{t^{12}}{t}$ t^{11}
6. $-\frac{16x^8}{8x^2}$ $-2x^6$
7. $\frac{6^5}{6^3}$ 36
8. $\frac{p^5t^7}{p^2t^5}$ p^3t^2
9. $-(m^3)^8$ $-m^{24}$
10. $(3^5)^7$
11. -3^4 -81
12. $(abc)^3$ $a^3b^3c^3$
13. $(5x^4)^{-2}$ $\frac{1}{25x^8}$
14. $(-3)^{-2}$ $\frac{1}{9}$
15. -3^{-2} $-\frac{1}{9}$
16. $\frac{x}{x^7}$ $\frac{1}{x^6}$
17. $-\left(\frac{x}{5}\right)^2$ $-\frac{x^2}{25}$
18. $\left(\frac{5a^7}{2b^5c}\right)^3$ $\frac{125a^{21}}{8b^{15}c^3}$
19. $\frac{1}{x^{-3}}$ x^3
20. $\frac{5^6a^{x+y}}{5^4a^{x-y}}$ $25a^{2y}$

Simplify. For answers not here, see Student Handbook Answer Appendix.

21. $(4x^3 + 5x - 7x^2) + (-2x^3 + 5x^2 - 7y^2)$
22. $(2x^2 - 3x + 11) + (7x^2 + 2x - 8)$
23. $(-3x^2 + 7x + 23) + (-8x^2 - 5x + 13)$
24. $(-3x^2 + 7x + 23) - (-8x^2 - 5x + 13)$
25. $\frac{7}{uw}\left(4u^2w^3 - 5uw + \frac{w}{7u}\right)$
26. $-4x^5(-3x^4 - x^3 + x + 7)$
27. $(2x - 3)(4x + 7)$
28. $(3x - 5)(-2x - 1)$
29. $(3x - 5)(2x - 1)$
30. $(2x + 5)(2x - 5)$ $4x^2 - 25$
31. $(-5x + 10)(-5x - 10)$
32. $(4x - 3)^2$ $16x^2 - 24x + 9$
33. $(5x + 6)^2$ $25x^2 + 60x + 36$
34. $(-x + 1)^2$ $x^2 - 2x + 1$
35. $\frac{3}{4}x(x^2 + 4x + 14)$ $\frac{3}{4}x^3 + 3x^2 + \frac{21}{2}x$
36. $-\frac{1}{2}a^2(a^3 - 6a^2 + 5a)$

Lesson 6-2 Dividing Polynomials (pp. 341–347)

Simplify. For answers not here, see Student Handbook Answer Appendix.

1. $\frac{18r^3t^2 + 36r^2t^3}{9r^2t^2}$ $2r + 4t$
2. $\frac{15v^3w^2 - 5v^4w^3}{-5v^4w^3}$ $\frac{-3}{vw} + 1$
3. $\frac{x^2 - x + 1}{x}$ $x - 1 + \frac{1}{x}$
4. $(5bh + 5ch) \div (b + c)$ $5h$
5. $(25c^4d + 10c^3d^2 - cd) \div (5cd)$
6. $(16f^{18} + 20f^9 - 8f^6) \div (4f^3)$ $4f^{15} + 5f^6 - 2f^3$
7. $(33m^5 + 55mp^5 - 11m^3)(11m)^{-1}$ $3m^4 + 5p^5 - m^2$
8. $(8g^3 + 19g^2 - 12g + 9) \div (g + 3)$ $8g^2 - 5g + 3$
9. $(p^{21} + 3p^{14} + p^7 - 2)(p^7 + 2)^{-1}$
10. $(q^4 + 8q^3 + 3q + 17) \div (q + 8)$
11. $(15v^3 + 8v^2 - 21v + 6) \div (5v - 4)$
12. $(-2x^3 + 15x^2 - 10x + 3) \div (x + 3)$
13. $(5k^3 + k^2 - 7) \div (k + 1)$
14. $(t^4 - 2t^3 + t^2 - 3t + 2) \div (t - 2)$
15. $(z^4 - 3z^3 - z^2 - 11z - 4) \div (z - 4)$
16. $(3r^4 - 6r^3 - 2r^2 + r - 6) \div (r + 1)$
17. $(2b^3 - 11b^2 + 12b + 9) \div (b - 3)$

Lesson 6-3 Polynomial Functions (pp. 348–355)

Find $p(5)$ and $p(-1)$ for each function.

1. $p(x) = 7x - 3$ 32; -10
2. $p(x) = -3x^2 + 5x - 4$ -54; -12
3. $p(x) = 5x^4 + 2x^2 - 2x$ 3165; 9
4. $p(x) = -13x^3 + 5x^2$ -1500; 18
5. $p(x) = x^6 - 2$ 15,623; -1
6. $p(x) = \frac{2}{3}x^2 + 5x$ $41\frac{2}{3}$; $-4\frac{1}{3}$
7. $p(x) = x^3 + x^2 - x + 1$ 146; 2
8. $p(x) = x^4 - x^2 - 1$ 599; -1
9. $p(x) = 1 - x^3$ -124; 2

If $p(x) = -2x^2 + 5x + 1$ and $m(x) = x^3 - 1$, find each value. 10–21. See Student Handbook Answer Appendix.

10. $m(n)$
11. $p(2b)$
12. $m(z^3)$
13. $p(3m^2)$
14. $m(x + 1)$
15. $p(3 - x)$
16. $m(a^2 - 2)$
17. $3m(h - 3)$
18. $5[p(c - 4)]$
19. $m(n - 2) + m(n^2)$
20. $-3p(4a) - p(a)$
21. $2[m(d^2 + 1)] + 3m(d)$

Lesson 6-4 Analyzing Graphs of Polynomial Functions (pp. 357–364)

Complete each of the following. 1–16. See Student Handbook Answer Appendix.

a. Graph each function by making a table of values.
b. Determine the consecutive integer values of x between which each real zero is located.
c. Estimate the x-coordinates at which the relative maxima and relative minima occur.

1. $f(x) = x^3 + x^2 - 3x$
2. $f(x) = -x^4 + x^3 + 5$
3. $f(x) = x^3 - 3x^2 + 8x - 7$
4. $f(x) = 2x^5 + 3x^4 - 8x^2 + x + 4$
5. $f(x) = x^4 - 5x^3 + 6x^2 - x - 2$
6. $f(x) = 2x^6 + 5x^4 - 3x^2 - 5$
7. $f(x) = -x^3 - 8x^2 + 3x - 7$
8. $f(x) = -x^4 - 3x^3 + 5x$
9. $f(x) = x^5 - 7x^4 - 3x^3 + 2x^2 - 4x + 9$
10. $f(x) = x^4 - 5x^3 + x^2 - x - 3$
11. $f(x) = x^4 - 128x^2 + 960$
12. $f(x) = -x^5 + x^4 - 208x^2 + 145x + 9$
13. $f(x) = x^5 - x^3 - x + 1$
14. $f(x) = x^3 - 2x^2 - x + 5$
15. $f(x) = 2x^4 - x^3 + x^2 - x + 1$
16. $f(x) = -x^3 - x^2 - x - 1$

Lesson 6-5 Solving Polynomial Equations (pp. 368–375)

Factor completely. If the polynomial is not factorable, write *prime*. 1–26. See Student Handbook Answer Appendix.

1. $14a^3b^3c - 21a^2b^4c + 7a^2b^3c$
2. $10ax - 2xy - 15ab + 3by$
3. $x^2 + x - 42$
4. $2x^2 + 5x + 3$
5. $6x^2 + 71x - 12$
6. $6x^4 - 12x^3 + 3x^2$
7. $x^2 - 6x + 2$
8. $x^2 - 2x - 15$
9. $6x^2 + 23x + 20$
10. $24x^2 - 76x + 40$
11. $6p^2 - 13pt - 28t^2$
12. $2x^2 - 6x + 3$
13. $x^2 + 49 - 14x$
14. $9x^2 - 64$
15. $36 - t^{10}$
16. $x^2 + 16$
17. $a^4 - 81b^4$
18. $3a^3 + 12a^2 - 63a$
19. $x^3 - 8x^2 + 15x$
20. $x^2 + 6x + 9$
21. $18x^3 - 8x$
22. $3x^2 - 42x + 40$
23. $2x^2 + 4x - 1$
24. $2x^3 + 6x^2 + x + 3$
25. $35ac - 3bf - 7af + 15bc$
26. $5h^2 - 10hj + h - 2j$

Lesson 6-6 The Remainder and Factor Theorems (pp. 377–382)

Use synthetic substitution to find $f(3)$ and $f(-4)$ for each function.

1. $f(x) = x^2 - 6x + 2$ -7, 42
2. $f(x) = x^3 + 5x - 6$ 36, -90
3. $f(x) = x^3 - x^2 - 3x + 1$ 10, -67
4. $f(x) = -3x^3 + 5x^2 + 7x - 3$ -18, 241
5. $f(x) = 3x^5 - 5x^3 + 2x - 8$ 592, -2768
6. $f(x) = 10x^3 + 2$ 272, -638

Given a polynomial and one of its factors, find the remaining factors of the polynomial. 7–18. See Student Handbook Answer Appendix.

7. $(x^3 - x^2 + x + 14)$; $(x + 2)$
8. $(5x^3 - 17x^2 + 6x)$; $(x - 3)$
9. $(2x^3 + x^2 - 41x + 20)$; $(x - 4)$
10. $(x^3 - 8)$; $(x - 2)$
11. $(x^2 + 6x + 5)$; $(x + 1)$
12. $(x^4 + x^3 + x^2 + x)$; $(x + 1)$
13. $(x^3 - 8x^2 + x + 42)$; $(x - 7)$
14. $(x^4 + 5x^3 - 27x - 135)$; $(x - 3)$
15. $(2x^3 - 15x^2 - 2x + 120)$; $(2x + 5)$
16. $(6x^3 - 17x^2 + 6x + 8)$; $(3x - 4)$
17. $(10x^3 + x^2 - 46x + 35)$; $(5x - 7)$
18. $(x^3 + 9x^2 + 23x + 15)$; $(x + 1)$

Lesson 6-7 Roots and Zeros (pp. 383–390)

Solve each equation. State the number and type of roots.

1. $-5x - 7 = 0$ $-\frac{7}{5}$; 1 real
2. $3x^2 + 10 = 0$ $\frac{\pm i\sqrt{30}}{3}$; 2 imaginary
3. $x^4 - 2x^3 = 23x^2 - 60x$ −5, 0, 3, 4; 4 real

State the number of positive real zeros, negative real zeros, and imaginary zeros of each function. 4–9. See Student Handbook Answer Appendix.

4. $f(x) = 5x^8 - x^6 + 7x^4 - 8x^2 - 3$
5. $f(x) = 6x^5 - 7x^2 + 5$
6. $f(x) = -2x^6 - 5x^5 + 8x^2 - 3x + 1$
7. $f(x) = 4x^3 + x^2 - 38x + 56$
8. $f(x) = 3x^4 - 5x^3 + 2x^2 - 7x + 5$
9. $f(x) = x^5 - x^4 + 7x^3 - 25x^2 + 8x - 13$

Find all zeros of each function. 10–15. See Student Handbook Answer Appendix.

10. $f(x) = x^3 - 7x^2 + 16x - 10$
11. $f(x) = 10x^3 + 7x^2 - 82x + 56$
12. $f(x) = x^3 - 16x^2 + 79x - 114$
13. $f(x) = -3x^3 + 6x^2 + 5x - 8$
14. $f(x) = 24x^3 + 64x^2 + 6x - 10$
15. $f(x) = 2x^3 + 2x^2 - 34x + 30$

Lesson 6-8 Rational Zero Theorem (pp. 391–396)

List all of the possible rational zeros of each function. 1–3. See Student Handbook Answer Appendix.

1. $f(x) = 3x^5 - 7x^3 - 8x + 6$
2. $f(x) = 4x^3 + 2x^2 - 5x + 8$
3. $f(x) = 6x^9 - 7$

Find all of the rational zeros of each function. 4–9. See Student Handbook Answer Appendix.

4. $f(x) = x^4 + 3x^3 - 7x^2 - 27x - 18$
5. $f(x) = 6x^4 - 31x^3 - 119x^2 + 214x + 560$
6. $f(x) = 20x^4 - 16x^3 + 11x^2 - 12x - 3$
7. $f(x) = 2x^4 - 30x^3 + 117x^2 - 75x + 280$
8. $f(x) = 3x^4 + 8x^3 + 9x^2 + 32x - 12$
9. $f(x) = x^5 - x^4 + x^3 + 3x^2 - x$

Find all of the zeros of each function. 10–12. See Student Handbook Answer Appendix.

10. $f(x) = x^4 + 8x^2 - 9$
11. $f(x) = 3x^4 - 9x^2 - 12$
12. $f(x) = 4x^4 + 19x^2 - 63$

Lesson 7-1 Operations on Functions (pp. 409–416)

Find $(f + g)(x)$, $(f - g)(x)$, $(f \cdot g)(x)$, and $\left(\frac{f}{g}\right)(x)$ for each $f(x)$ and $g(x)$. 1–4. See Student Handbook Answer Appendix.

1. $f(x) = 3x + 5$, $g(x) = x - 3$
2. $f(x) = \sqrt{x}$, $g(x) = x^2$
3. $f(x) = x^2 - 5$, $g(x) = x^2 + 5$
4. $f(x) = x^2 + 1$, $g(x) = x + 1$

For each pair of functions, find $f \circ g$ and $g \circ f$, if they exist. 5–8. See Student Handbook Answer Appendix.

5. $f = \{(-1, 1), (2, -1), (-3, 5)\}$, $g = \{(1, -1), (-1, 2), (5, -3)\}$
6. $f = \{(0, 6), (5, -8), (-9, 2)\}$, $g = \{(-8, 3), (6, 4), (2, 1)\}$
7. $f = \{(8, 2), (6, 5), (-3, 4), (1, 0)\}$, $g = \{(2, 8), (5, 6), (4, -3), (0, 1)\}$
8. $f = \{(10, 4), (-1, 2), (5, 6), (-1, 0)\}$, $g = \{(-4, 10), (2, -9), (-7, 5), (-2, -1)\}$

Find $[g \circ h](x)$ and $[h \circ g](x)$, if they exist.

9. $g(x) = 8 - 2x$, $h(x) = 3x$ $[g \circ h](x) = 8 - 6x$; $[h \circ g](x) = 24 - 6x$
10. $g(x) = x^2 - 7$, $h(x) = 3x + 2$ $[g \circ h](x) = 9x^2 + 12x - 3$; $[h \circ g](x) = 3x^2 - 19$
11. $g(x) = 2x + 7$, $h(x) = \frac{x - 7}{2}$ $[g \circ h](x) = x$; $[h \circ g](x) = x$
12. $g(x) = 3x + 2$, $h(x) = 5 - 3x$ $[g \circ h](x) = -9x + 17$; $[h \circ g](x) = -9x - 1$

Lesson 7-2 Inverse Functions and Relations (pp. 417–422)

Find the inverse of each relation. 1, 2. See Student Handbook Answer Appendix.

1. $\{(-2, 7), (3, 0), (5, -8)\}$
2. $\{(-3, 9), (-2, 4), (3, 9), (-1, 1)\}$

Find the inverse of each function. Then graph the function and its inverse. 3–14. See Student Handbook Answer Appendix.

3. $f(x) = x - 7$
4. $y = 2x + 8$
5. $g(x) = 3x - 8$
6. $y = -5x - 6$
7. $y = -2$
8. $g(x) = 5 - 2x$
9. $h(x) = \frac{x}{5} + 1$
10. $h(x) = -\frac{2}{3}x$
11. $y = \frac{x - 5}{3}$
12. $y = \frac{1}{2}x - 1$
13. $f(x) = \frac{3x + 8}{4}$
14. $g(x) = \frac{2x - 1}{3}$

Determine whether each pair of functions are inverse functions. Write *yes* or *no*.

15. $f(x) = \frac{2x - 3}{5}$, $g(x) = \frac{3x - 5}{3}$ no
16. $f(x) = 5x - 6$, $g(x) = \frac{x + 6}{5}$ yes
17. $f(x) = 6 - 3x$, $g(x) = 2 - \frac{1}{3}x$ yes
18. $f(x) = 3x - 7$, $g(x) = \frac{1}{3}x + 7$ no

Lesson 7-3 Square Root Functions and Inequalities (pp. 424–430)

Graph each function. State the domain and range. 1–18. See Student Handbook Answer Appendix.

1. $y = \sqrt{x - 4}$
2. $y = \sqrt{x + 3} - 1$
3. $y = \frac{1}{3}\sqrt{x + 2}$
4. $y = \sqrt{2x + 5}$
5. $y = -\sqrt{4x}$
6. $y = 2\sqrt{x}$
7. $y = -3\sqrt{x}$
8. $y = \sqrt{x} + 5$
9. $y = \sqrt{2x} - 1$
10. $y = 5\sqrt{x} + 1$
11. $y = \sqrt{x + 1} - 2$
12. $y = 6 - \sqrt{x + 3}$

Graph each inequality.

13. $y > \sqrt{2x}$
14. $y \le \sqrt{-5x}$
15. $y \ge \sqrt{x + 6} + 6$
16. $y < \sqrt{3x + 1} + 2$
17. $y \ge \sqrt{8x - 3} + 1$
18. $y < \sqrt{5x - 1} + 3$

Lesson 7-4 *n*th Roots (pp. 431–436)

Use a calculator to approximate each value to three decimal places.

1. $\sqrt{289}$ 17
2. $\sqrt{7832}$ 88.499
3. $\sqrt[4]{0.0625}$ 0.5
4. $\sqrt[3]{-343}$ −7
5. $\sqrt[10]{32^4}$ 4
6. $\sqrt[3]{49}$ 3.659
7. $\sqrt[5]{5}$ 1.380
8. $-\sqrt[4]{25}$ −2.236

Simplify. 14. not a real number

9. $\sqrt{9h^{22}}$ $3|h^{11}|$
10. $\sqrt[5]{0}$ 0
11. $\sqrt{\frac{16}{9}}$ $\frac{4}{3}$
12. $\sqrt{\left(-\frac{2}{3}\right)^4}$ $\frac{4}{9}$
13. $\sqrt[5]{-32}$ −2
14. $-\sqrt{-144}$
15. $\sqrt[4]{a^{16}b^8}$ a^4b^2
16. $\pm\sqrt[4]{81x^4}$ $\pm 3x$
17. $\sqrt[5]{\frac{1}{100{,}000}}$ $\frac{1}{10}$
18. $\sqrt[3]{-d^6}$ $-d^2$
19. $\sqrt[5]{n^{25}q^{15}r^5t^{20}}$ $n^5q^3rt^4$
20. $\sqrt[4]{(2x^2 - y^8)^8}$ $(2x^2 - y^8)^2$
21. $\pm\sqrt{16m^6p^2}$ $\pm 4m^3|p|$
22. $-\sqrt[3]{(2x - y)^3}$ $-(2x - y)$
23. $\sqrt[4]{(r + t)^4}$ $|r + t|$
24. $\sqrt{9a^2 + 6a + 1}$ $|3a + 1|$
25. $\sqrt{4y^2 + 12y + 9}$ $|2y + 3|$
26. $-\sqrt{x^2 - 2x + 1}$ $-|x - 1|$
27. $\pm\sqrt{x^2 + 2x + 1}$ $\pm|x + 1|$
28. $\sqrt[3]{a^3 + 6a^2 + 12a + 8}$ $a + 2$

Lesson 7-5 Operations with Radical Expressions (pp. 439–445)

Simplify. **1–24. See Student Handbook Answer Appendix.**

1. $\sqrt{75}$
2. $7\sqrt{12}$
3. $\sqrt[3]{81}$
4. $\sqrt{5r^5}$
5. $\sqrt[4]{7^8x^5y^6}$
6. $3\sqrt{5}+6\sqrt{5}$
7. $\sqrt{18}-\sqrt{50}$
8. $4\sqrt[3]{32}+\sqrt[3]{500}$
9. $(\sqrt{12})(\sqrt{27})$
10. $3\sqrt{12}+2\sqrt{300}$
11. $\sqrt[3]{54}-\sqrt[3]{24}$
12. $\sqrt{10}(2-\sqrt{5})$
13. $-\sqrt{3}(2\sqrt{6}-\sqrt{63})$
14. $(5+\sqrt{2})(3+\sqrt{3})$
15. $(2+\sqrt{5})(2-\sqrt{5})$
16. $(8+\sqrt{11})^2$
17. $(\sqrt{3}+\sqrt{6})(\sqrt{3}-\sqrt{6})$
18. $(\sqrt{8}+\sqrt{13})^2$
19. $(1-\sqrt{7})(4+\sqrt{7})$
20. $(5-2\sqrt{7})^2$
21. $\sqrt{\frac{3m^3}{24f^5}}$
22. $\frac{\sqrt{18}}{\sqrt{32}}$
23. $2\sqrt[3]{\frac{r^5}{2n^2t}}$
24. $\sqrt[3]{\frac{4}{7}}$

Lesson 7-6 Rational Exponents (pp. 446–452)

Write each expression in radical form or write each radical in exponential form.

1. $10^{\frac{1}{3}}$ **$\sqrt[3]{10}$**
2. $8^{\frac{1}{4}}$ **$\sqrt[4]{8}$**
3. $a^{\frac{2}{3}}$ **$\sqrt[3]{a^2}$**
4. $(b^2)^{\frac{3}{4}}$ **$|b|\sqrt{b}$**
5. $\sqrt{35}$ **$35^{\frac{1}{2}}$**
6. $\sqrt[4]{32}$ **$32^{\frac{1}{4}}$**
7. $\sqrt[3]{27a^2x}$ **$3a^{\frac{2}{3}}x^{\frac{1}{3}}$**
8. $\sqrt[5]{25ab^3c^4}$ **$5^{\frac{2}{5}}a^{\frac{1}{5}}b^{\frac{3}{5}}c^{\frac{4}{5}}$**

Evaluate each expression.

9. $2401^{\frac{1}{4}}$ **7**
10. $27^{\frac{4}{3}}$ **81**
11. $(-32)^{\frac{2}{5}}$ **4**
12. $-81^{\frac{3}{4}}$ **−27**
13. $(-125)^{-\frac{2}{3}}$ **$\frac{1}{25}$**
14. $16^{\frac{5}{2}}\cdot 16^{\frac{1}{2}}$ **4096**
15. $8^{-\frac{2}{3}}\cdot 64^{\frac{1}{6}}$ **0.5**
16. $\left(\frac{48}{1875}\right)^{-\frac{5}{4}}$ **$\frac{3125}{32}$**

Simplify each expression.

17. $7^{\frac{5}{9}}\cdot 7^{\frac{4}{9}}$ **7**
18. $32^{\frac{2}{3}}\cdot 32^{\frac{3}{5}}$ **$32^{\frac{19}{15}}$**
19. $\left(k^{\frac{8}{5}}\right)^5$ **k^8**
20. $x^{\frac{2}{5}}\cdot x^{\frac{8}{5}}$ **x^2**
21. $m^{\frac{2}{5}}\cdot m^{\frac{4}{5}}$ **$m^{\frac{6}{5}}$**
22. $\left(p^{\frac{5}{4}}\cdot r^{\frac{7}{2}}\right)^{\frac{8}{3}}$ **$p^{\frac{10}{3}}r^{\frac{28}{3}}$**
23. $\left(4^{\frac{9}{2}}c^{\frac{3}{2}}\right)^2$ **262, 144c^3**
24. $\frac{7^{\frac{3}{4}}}{7^{\frac{5}{3}}}$ **$\frac{7^{\frac{1}{12}}}{7}$**
25. $\frac{1}{t^{\frac{9}{5}}}$ **$\frac{t^{\frac{1}{5}}}{t^2}$**
26. $a^{-\frac{8}{7}}$ **$\frac{a^{\frac{6}{7}}}{a^2}$**
27. $\frac{r}{r^{\frac{7}{5}}}$ **$\frac{r^{\frac{3}{5}}}{r}$**
28. $\sqrt[4]{36}$ **$\sqrt{6}$**

Lesson 7-7 Solving Radical Equations and Inequalities (pp. 453–459)

Solve each equation.

1. $\sqrt{x}=16$ **256**
2. $\sqrt{z+3}=7$ **46**
3. $\sqrt[3]{a+5}=1$ **−4**
4. $g\sqrt{5}+4=g+4$ **0**
5. $\sqrt{x-8}=\sqrt{13+x}$ **no solution**
6. $\sqrt{3z-5}-3=1$ **7**
7. $(5n-1)^{\frac{1}{2}}=0$ **$\frac{1}{5}$**
8. $(7x-6)^{\frac{1}{3}}+1=3$ **2**
9. $(6a-8)^{\frac{1}{4}}+9=10$ **1.5**

Solve each inequality. **12, 16–18. See Student Handbook Answer Appendix.**

10. $\sqrt{3x+9}>2$ **$x>-\frac{5}{3}$**
11. $\sqrt{3n-1}\le 5$ **$\frac{1}{3}\le n\le\frac{26}{3}$**
12. $2-4\sqrt{21-6c}<-6$
13. $\sqrt{5y+4}>8$ **$y>12$**
14. $\sqrt{2w+3}+5\ge 7$ **$w\ge 0.5$**
15. $\sqrt{2c+3}-7>0$ **$c>23$**
16. $\sqrt{5y+1}+6<10$
17. $\sqrt{3n+1}-2\le 6$
18. $\sqrt{y-5}-\sqrt{y}\ge 1$

Lesson 8-1 Graphing Exponential Functions (pp. 475–482)

Sketch the graph of each function. State the domain and range. **1–8. See Student Handbook Answer Appendix.**

1. $y=3(5)^x$
2. $y=0.5(2)^x$
3. $y=3\left(\frac{1}{4}\right)^x$
4. $y=2(1.5)^x$
5. $y=3(4)^x$
6. $y=(0.5)^x$
7. $y=0.3(5)^x$
8. $y=\left(\frac{1}{5}\right)^x$

Lesson 8-2 Solving Exponential Equations and Inequalities (pp. 485–491)

Write an exponential function for the graph that passes through the given points.

1. (0, 6) and (2, 54) **$y=6(3)^x$**
2. (0, −4) and (−4, −64) **$y=-4(0.5)^x$**
3. (0, 1.5) and (3, 40.5) **$y=1.5(3)^x$**

Solve each equation or inequality. Check your solution.

4. $27^{2x-1}=3$ **$\frac{2}{3}$**
5. $8^{2+x}\ge 2$ **$x\ge-\frac{5}{3}$**
6. $4^{2x+5}<8^{x+1}$ **$x<-7$**
7. $6^{x+1}=36^{x-1}$ **3**
8. $10^{x-1}>100^{4-x}$ **$x>3$**
9. $\left(\frac{1}{5}\right)^{x-3}=125$ **0**
10. $2^{x^2+1}=32$ **±2**
11. $36^x=6^{x^2-3}$ **−1, 3**

Lesson 8-3 Logarithms and Logarithmic Functions (pp. 492–499)

Write each equation in logarithmic form.

1. $3^5=243$ **$\log_3 243=5$**
2. $10^3=1000$ **$\log_{10}1000=3$**
3. $4^{-3}=\frac{1}{64}$ **$\log_4\frac{1}{64}=-3$**

Write each equation in exponential form.

4. $\log_2\frac{1}{8}=-3$ **$2^{-3}=\frac{1}{8}$**
5. $\log_{25}5=\frac{1}{2}$ **$25^{\frac{1}{2}}=5$**
6. $\log_7\frac{1}{7}=-1$ **$7^{-1}=\frac{1}{7}$**

Evaluate each expression.

7. $\log_4 16$ **2**
8. $\log_{10}10{,}000$ **4**
9. $\log_3\frac{1}{9}$ **−2**
10. $\log_2 1024$ **10**
11. $\log_6 6^5$ **5**
12. $\log_{\frac{1}{2}}8$ **−3**
13. $\log_{11}121$ **2**
14. $5^{\log_5 10}$ **10**

Graph each function. **15–18. See Student Handbook Answer Appendix.**

15. $f(x)=\log_4 x$
16. $f(x)=\log_{\frac{1}{5}}x$
17. $f(x)=3\log_3(x-2)$
18. $f(x)=2\log_{\frac{1}{2}}x-5$

Lesson 8-4 Solving Logarithmic Equations and Inequalities (pp. 502–507)

Solve each equation or inequality. Check your solutions.

1. $\log_8 b=2$ **64**
2. $\log_4 x<3$ **$\{x \mid 0<x<64\}$**
3. $\log_{\frac{1}{9}}n=-\frac{1}{2}$ **3**
4. $\log_x 7=1$ **7**
5. $\log_{\frac{2}{3}}a<3$ **$\left\{a \,\middle|\, 0<a<\frac{8}{27}\right\}$**
6. $\log_2(x^2-9)=4$ **±5**
7. $\log_9 x=2$ **81**
8. $\log_{25}n=\frac{3}{2}$ **125**
9. $\log_{\frac{1}{7}}x=-1$ **7**
10. $\log_4 x<2$ **$\{x \mid 0<x<16\}$**
11. $\log_3(2x-1)\le 2$ **$\left\{x \,\middle|\, \frac{1}{2}<x\le 5\right\}$**
12. $\log_{16}x\ge\frac{1}{4}$ **$\{x \mid x\ge 2\}$**
13. $\log_5(3x-1)=\log_5(2x^2)$ **$\left\{\frac{1}{2}, 1\right\}$**
14. $\log_{10}(x^2-10x)=\log_{10}(-21)$ **no solution**
15. $\log_2(3x-5)>\log_2(x+7)$ **$\{x \mid x>6\}$**
16. $\log_2 c>8$ **$\{c \mid c>256\}$**
17. $\log_{64}y\le\frac{1}{2}$ **$\{y \mid 0<y\le 8\}$**
18. $\log_5(5x-7)\le\log_5(2x+5)$ **$\left\{x \,\middle|\, \frac{7}{5}<x\le 4\right\}$**
19. $\log_{\frac{1}{3}}p<0$ **$\{p \mid p>1\}$**
20. $\log_2(3x-8)\ge 6$ **$\{x \mid x\ge 24\}$**
21. $\log_6(2x-3)=\log_6(x+2)$ **5**
22. $\log_7(x^2+36)=\log_7 100$ **±8**
23. $\log_2(4y-10)\ge\log_2(y-1)$ **$\{y \mid y\ge 3\}$**
24. $\log_{10}(a^2-6)>\log_{10}a$ **$\{a \mid a>3\}$**

Lesson 8-5 Properties of Logarithms (pp. 509–515)

Use $\log_3 5 \approx 1.4651$ and $\log_3 7 \approx 1.7712$ to approximate the value of each expression.

1. $\log_3 \frac{7}{5}$ 0.3061
2. $\log_3 245$ 5.0075
3. $\log_3 35$ 3.2363

Solve each equation. Check your solutions.

4. $\log_2 x + \log_2 (x - 2) = \log_2 3$ 3
5. $\log_3 x = 2\log_3 3 + \log_3 5$ 45
6. $\log_5 (x^2 + 7) = \frac{2}{3}\log_5 64$ ±3
7. $\log_2 (x^2 - 9) = 4$ ±5
8. $\log_3 (x + 2) + \log_3 6 = 3$ 2.5
9. $\log_6 x + \log_6 (x - 5) = 2$ 9
10. $\log_5 (x + 3) = \log_5 8 - \log_5 2$ 1
11. $2\log_3 x - \log_3 (x - 2) = 2$ 3, 6
12. $\log_6 x = \frac{3}{2}\log_6 9 + \log_6 2$ 54
13. $\log_8 (x + 6) + \log_8 (x - 6) = 2$ 10
14. $\log_3 14 + \log_3 x = \log_3 42$ 3
15. $\log_{10} x = \frac{1}{2}\log_{10} 81$ 9

Lesson 8-6 Common Logarithms (pp. 516–522)

Use a calculator to evaluate each expression to four decimal places.

1. log 55 1.7404
2. log 6.7 0.8261
3. log 3.3 0.5185
4. log 0.08 −1.0969
5. log 9.9 0.9956
6. log 0.6 −0.2218

Solve each equation or inequality. Round to four decimal places.

7. $2^x = 15$ 3.9069
8. $4^{2a} > 45$ $a > 1.3730$
9. $7^{2x} = 35$ 0.9135
10. $11^{x+4} > 57$ $x > -2.3139$
11. $1.5^{a-7} = 9.6$ 12.5782
12. $3^{b^2} = 64$ ±1.9457
13. $7^{3c} < 35^{2c-1}$ $c < 2.7930$
14. $5^{m^2+1} = 30$ ±1.0551
15. $7^{3y-1} < 2^{2y+4}$ $y < 1.0600$
16. $9^{n-3} = 2^{n+3}$ 5.7651
17. $11^{t+1} \le 22^{t+3}$ $t \le -9.9189$
18. $2^{3a-1} = 3^{a+2}$ 2.9469

Express each logarithm in terms of common logarithms. Then approximate its value to four decimal places.

19. $\log_3 21$ $\frac{\log 21}{\log 3} \approx 2.7712$
20. $\log_4 62$ $\frac{\log 62}{\log 4} \approx 2.9771$
21. $\log_5 28$ $\frac{\log 28}{\log 5} \approx 2.0704$
22. $\log_2 25$ $\frac{\log 25}{\log 2} \approx 4.6439$

Lesson 8-7 Base *e* and Natural Logarithms (pp. 525–531)

Use a calculator to evaluate each expression to four decimal places.

1. e^3 20.0855
2. $e^{0.75}$ 2.1170
3. e^{-4} 0.0183
4. $e^{-2.5}$ 0.0821
5. ln 5 1.6094
6. ln 8 2.0794
7. ln 8.4 2.1282
8. ln 0.6 −0.5108

Write an equivalent exponential or logarithmic equation.

9. $e^x = 10$ $\ln 10 = x$
10. $\ln x \approx 2.3026$ $x \approx e^{2.3026}$
11. $e^3 = 9x$ $\ln 9x = 3$
12. $\ln 0.2 = x$ $e^x = 0.2$

Solve each equation or inequality. Round to the nearest ten-thousandth.

13. $25e^x = 1000$ 3.6889
14. $e^{0.075x} > 25$ $x > 42.9183$
15. $e^x < 3.8$ $x < 1.3350$
16. $-2e^x + 5 = 1$ 0.6931
17. $5 + 4e^{2x} = 17$ 0.5493
18. $e^{-3x} \le 15$ $x \ge -0.9027$
19. $\ln 7x = 10$ 3146.6380
20. $\ln 4x = 8$ 745.2395
21. $3\ln 2x \ge 9$ $x \ge 10.0428$
22. $\ln (x + 2) = 4$ 52.5982
23. $\ln (2x + 3) > 0$ $x > -1$
24. $\ln (3x - 1) = 5$ 49.8044

Lesson 8-8 Using Exponential and Logarithmic Functions (pp. 533–539)

1. **FARMING** Mr. Rogers purchased a combine for $175,000 for his farming operation. It is expected to depreciate at a rate of 18% per year. What will be the value of the combine in 3 years? $96,489.40

2. **REAL ESTATE** The Jacksons bought a house for $65,000 in 1992. Houses in the neighborhood have appreciated at the rate of 4.5% a year. How much is the house worth in 2003? $105,485.45

3. **POPULATION** In 1960, the population of a city was 50,000. Since then, the population has increased by 2.25% per year. If it continues to grow at this rate, what will the population be in 2015? about 170,000

4. **BEARS** In a particular state, the population of black bears has been decreasing at the rate of 0.75% per year. In 1995, it was estimated that there were 400 black bears in the state. If the population continues to decline at the same rate, what will the population be in 2015? 344 bears

Lesson 9-1 Multiplying and Dividing Rational Expressions (pp. 553–561)

Simplify each expression.

1. $\frac{25xy^2}{15y}$ $\frac{5xy}{3}$
2. $\frac{-4a^2b^3}{28ab^4}$ $-\frac{a}{7b}$
3. $\frac{(-2cd^3)^2}{8c^2d^5}$ $\frac{d}{2}$
4. $\frac{3x^3}{-2} \cdot \frac{-4}{9x}$ $\frac{2x^2}{3}$
5. $\frac{21x^2}{-5} \cdot \frac{10}{7x^3}$ $-\frac{6}{x}$
6. $\frac{2u^2}{3} \div \frac{6u^3}{5}$ $\frac{5}{9u}$
7. $\frac{15x^3}{14} \div \frac{18x}{7}$ $\frac{5x^2}{12}$
8. $\frac{xy^2}{2} \cdot \frac{x^2}{2y} \cdot \frac{2}{x^2y}$ $\frac{x}{2}$
9. $axy \div \frac{ax}{y}$ y^2
10. $\frac{9u^2}{28v} \div \frac{27u^2}{8v^2}$ $\frac{2v}{21}$
11. $\frac{x^2-4}{4x^2-1} \cdot \frac{2x-1}{x+2}$ $\frac{x-2}{2x+1}$
12. $\frac{x^2-1}{2x^2-x-1} \div \frac{x^2-4}{2x^2-3x-2}$ $\frac{x+1}{x+2}$
13. $\frac{2x^2+x-1}{2x^2+3x-2} \div \frac{x^2-2x+1}{x^2+x-2}$ $\frac{x+1}{x-1}$
14. $\frac{\frac{(ab)^2}{c}}{\frac{xa^3b}{cx^2}}$ $\frac{bx}{a}$
15. $\frac{x^4-y^4}{x^3+y^3} \div \frac{x^3-y^3}{x+y}$ $\frac{(x^2+y^2)(x+y)}{(x^2-xy+y^2)(x^2+xy+y^2)}$

Lesson 9-2 Adding and Subtracting Rational Expressions (pp. 562–568)

Find the LCM of each set of polynomials.

1. $2a^2b, 4ab^2, 20a$ $20a^2b^2$
2. $x^2 - 4x - 12, x^2 + 7x + 10$ $(x-6)(x+2)(x+5)$

Simplify each expression.

3. $\frac{12}{7d} - \frac{3}{14d}$ $\frac{3}{2d}$
4. $\frac{x+1}{x} - \frac{x-1}{x^2}$ $\frac{x^2+1}{x^2}$
5. $\frac{2x+1}{4x^2} - \frac{x+3}{6x}$ $\frac{3-2x^2}{12x^2}$
6. $\frac{7x}{13y^2} + \frac{4y}{6x^2}$ $\frac{21x^3+26y^3}{39x^2y^2}$
7. $\frac{x}{x-1} + \frac{1}{1-x}$ 1
8. $\frac{1}{3v^2} + \frac{1}{uv} + \frac{3}{4u^2}$ $\frac{4u^2+12uv+9v^2}{12u^2v^2}$
9. $\frac{1}{x^2-x} + \frac{1}{x^2+x}$ $\frac{2}{(x-1)(x+1)}$
10. $\frac{1}{x^2-1} - \frac{1}{(x-1)^2}$ $\frac{-2}{(x+1)(x-1)^2}$
11. $\frac{5}{x} - \frac{3}{x+5}$ $\frac{2x+25}{x(x+5)}$
12. $y - 1 + \frac{1}{y-1}$ $\frac{y^2-2y+2}{y-1}$
13. $3m + 1 - \frac{2m}{3m+1}$ $\frac{9m^2+4m+1}{3m+1}$
14. $\frac{3x}{x-y} + \frac{4x}{y-x}$ $\frac{-x}{x-y}$
15. $\frac{4}{a^2-4} - \frac{3}{a^2+4a+4}$ $\frac{a+14}{(a-2)(a+2)^2}$
16. $\frac{4}{3-3z^2} - \frac{2}{z^2+5z+4}$ $\frac{-10}{3(z-1)(z+4)}$
17. $\frac{2c}{c^2-9} - \frac{1}{c^2+6c+9}$ $\frac{(c+1)(2c+3)}{(c-3)(c+3)^2}$
18. $\frac{\frac{1}{x+y}}{\frac{1}{x}+\frac{1}{y}}$ $\frac{xy}{(x+y)^2}$
19. $\frac{1-\frac{1}{x+1}}{1+\frac{1}{x-1}}$ $\frac{x-1}{x+1}$
20. $\frac{4+\frac{1}{x-2}}{3-\frac{1}{x-2}}$ $\frac{4x-7}{3x-7}$

Lesson 9-3 Graphing Reciprocal Functions (pp. 569–575)

Graph each function. State the domain and range. 1–8. See Student Handbook Answer Appendix.

1. $f(x) = \frac{1}{x}$
2. $f(x) = \frac{3}{x}$
3. $f(x) = \frac{1}{x+2}$
4. $f(x) = \frac{-5}{x+1}$
5. $f(x) = \frac{-1}{x-4}$
6. $f(x) = \frac{3}{x+2}$
7. $f(x) = \frac{7}{x+10}$
8. $f(x) = \frac{4}{7-x}$

Lesson 9-4 Graphing Rational Functions (pp. 577–584)

Determine the equations of any vertical asymptotes and the values of x for any holes in the graph of each rational function. 3. asymptotes: $x = -1$, $x = 8$

1. $f(x) = \frac{1}{x+4}$ asymptote; $x = -4$
2. $f(x) = \frac{x-2}{x+3}$ asymptote; $x = -3$
3. $f(x) = \frac{5}{(x+1)(x-8)}$
4. $f(x) = \frac{x}{x+2}$ asymptote; $x = -2$
5. $f(x) = \frac{x^2-4}{x+2}$ hole; $x = -2$
6. $f(x) = \frac{x^2+x-6}{x^2+8x+15}$ asymptote; $x = -5$; hole: $x = -3$

Graph each rational function. 7–14. See Student Handbook Answer Appendix.

7. $f(x) = \frac{1}{x-5}$
8. $f(x) = \frac{3x}{x+1}$
9. $f(x) = \frac{x^2-16}{x-4}$
10. $f(x) = \frac{x}{x-6}$
11. $f(x) = \frac{1}{(x-3)^2}$
12. $f(x) = \frac{2}{(x+3)(x-4)}$
13. $f(x) = \frac{x+4}{x^2-1}$
14. $f(x) = \frac{x^2+5x-14}{x^2+9x+14}$

Lesson 9-5 Variation Functions (pp. 586–593)

State whether each equation represents a *direct*, *joint*, or *inverse* variation. Then name the constant of variation.

1. $xy = 10$ inverse; 10
2. $\frac{x}{7} = y$ direct; $\frac{1}{7}$
3. $\frac{x}{y} = -6$ direct; $-\frac{1}{6}$
4. $10x = y$ direct; 10
5. $x = \frac{2}{y}$ inverse; 2
6. $A = \ell w$ joint; 1
7. $\frac{1}{4}b = -\frac{3}{5}c$ direct; $-\frac{12}{5}$
8. $D = rt$ joint, 1
9. If y varies directly as x and $y = 16$ when $x = 4$, find y when $x = 12$. 48
10. If x varies inversely as y and $x = 12$ when $y = -3$, find x when $y = -18$. 2
11. If m varies directly as w and $m = -15$ when $w = 2.5$, find m when $w = 12.5$. −75
12. If y varies jointly as x and z and $y = 10$ when $z = 4$ and $x = 5$, find y when $x = 4$ and $z = 2$. 4

Lesson 9-6 Solving Rational Equations and Inequalities (pp. 594–602)

Solve each equation or inequality. Check your solutions. 6. $-4 < n < -2$ or $n > 0$

1. $\frac{x}{x-3} = \frac{1}{4}$ −1
2. $\frac{5}{x} + \frac{3}{5} = \frac{2}{x}$ −5
3. $\frac{5}{b-2} < 5$ $b < 2$ or $b > 3$
4. $\frac{4}{a+3} > 2$ $-3 < a < -1$
5. $\frac{x-2}{x} = \frac{x-4}{x-6}$ 3
6. $-6 - \frac{8}{n} < n$
7. $\frac{2}{d} + \frac{1}{d-2} = 1$ 1, 4
8. $\frac{1}{2+3x} + \frac{2}{2-3x} = 0$ −2
9. $\frac{1}{n+1} + \frac{1}{n-1} = \frac{2}{n^2-1}$ ∅
10. $\frac{p}{p+1} + \frac{3}{p-3} + 1 = 0$ 0, 1
11. $\frac{5z+2}{z^2-4} = \frac{-5z}{2-z} + \frac{2}{z+2}$ $\frac{3}{5}$
12. $\frac{1}{x-3} + \frac{2}{x^2-9} = \frac{5}{x+3}$ 5
13. $\frac{1}{m^2-1} = \frac{2}{m^2+m-2}$ 0
14. $\frac{12}{x^2-16} - \frac{24}{x-4} = 3$ −6, −2
15. $n + \frac{1}{n+3} = \frac{n^2}{n-1}$ −1

Lesson 10-1 Midpoint and Distance Formulas (pp. 617–622)

Find the midpoint of the line segment with endpoints at the given coordinates.

1. (7, −3), (−11, 13) (−2, 5)
2. (16, 29), (−7, 2) (4.5, 15.5)
3. (43, −18), (−78, −32) (−17.5, −25)
4. (−7.54, 3.42), (4.89, −9.28) (−1.325, −2.93)
5. $\left(\frac{1}{2}, \frac{1}{4}\right), \left(\frac{2}{3}, \frac{3}{5}\right)$ $\left(\frac{7}{12}, \frac{17}{40}\right)$
6. $\left(-\frac{1}{4}, \frac{2}{3}\right), \left(-\frac{1}{2}, -\frac{1}{2}\right)$ $\left(-\frac{3}{8}, \frac{1}{12}\right)$

Find the distance between each pair of points with the given coordinates.

7. (5, 7), (3, 19) $2\sqrt{37}$ units
8. (−2, −1), (5, 3) $\sqrt{65}$ units
9. (−3, 15), (7, −8) $\sqrt{629}$ units
10. (6, −3), (−4, −9) $2\sqrt{34}$ units
11. (3.89, −0.38), (4.04, −0.18) 0.25 unit
12. $(5\sqrt{3}, 2\sqrt{2}), (-11\sqrt{3}, -4\sqrt{2})$ $2\sqrt{210}$ units
13. $\left(\frac{1}{4}, 0\right), \left(-\frac{2}{3}, \frac{1}{2}\right)$ $\frac{\sqrt{157}}{12}$ units
14. $\left(4, -\frac{5}{6}\right), \left(-2, \frac{1}{6}\right)$ $\sqrt{37}$ units
15. A circle has a radius with endpoints at (−3, 1) and (2, −5). Find the circumference and area of the circle. Write the answer in terms of π. $2\pi\sqrt{61}$ units; 61π units^2
16. Triangle ABC has vertices $A(0, 0)$, $B(-3, 4)$, and $C(2, 6)$. Find the perimeter of the triangle. $5 + 2\sqrt{10} + \sqrt{29}$ units

Lesson 10-2 Parabolas (pp. 623–629)

1–15. See Student Handbook Answer Appendix.

Write each equation in standard form. Identify the vertex, the axis of symmetry, and the direction of opening of the parabola. Then graph the equation.

1. $y + 4 = x^2$
2. $y = 5(x + 2)^2$
3. $4(y + 2) = 3(x - 1)^2$
4. $5x + 3y^2 = 15$
5. $y = 2x^2 - 8x + 7$
6. $x = 2y^2 - 8y + 7$
7. $3(x - 8)^2 = 5(y + 3)$
8. $x = 3(y + 4)^2 + 1$
9. $8y + 5x^2 + 30x + 101 = 0$
10. $x = -\frac{1}{5}y^2 + \frac{8}{5}y - 7$
11. $6x = y^2 - 6y + 39$
12. $-8y = x^2$
13. $y = 4x^2 + 24x + 38$
14. $y = x^2 - 6x + 3$
15. $y = x^2 + 4x + 1$

16, 17. See Student Handbook Answer Appendix for graphs.

Write an equation for each parabola described below. Then graph the equation.

16. focus (1, 1), directrix $y = -1$ $y = \frac{1}{4}(x - 1)^2 + 0$
17. vertex (−1, 2), directrix $y = -4$ $y = \frac{1}{24}(x + 1)^2 + 2$

Lesson 10-3 Circles (pp. 631–637)

1–9. See Student Handbook Answer Appendix.

Write an equation for the circle that satisfies each set of conditions.

1. center (3, 2), $r = 5$ units
2. center (−5, 8), $r = 3$ units
3. center (1, −6), $r = \frac{2}{3}$ units
4. center (0, 7), tangent to x-axis
5. center (−2, −4), tangent to y-axis
6. endpoints of a diameter at (−9, 0) and (2, −5)
7. endpoints of a diameter at (4, 1) and (−3, 2)
8. center (6, −10), passes through origin
9. center (0.8, 0.5), passes through (2, 2)

10–18. See Student Handbook Answer Appendix.

Find the center and radius of each circle. Then graph the circle.

10. $x^2 + y^2 = 36$
11. $(x - 5)^2 + (y + 4)^2 = 1$
12. $x^2 + 3x + y^2 - 5y = 0.5$
13. $x^2 + y^2 = 14x - 24$
14. $x^2 + y^2 = 2(y - x)$
15. $x^2 + 10x + (y - \sqrt{3})^2 = 11$
16. $x^2 + y^2 = 4x + 9$
17. $x^2 + y^2 - 6x + 4y = 156$
18. $x^2 + y^2 - 2x + 7y = 1$

Lesson 10-4 Ellipses (pp. 639–646)

Write an equation for the ellipse that satisfies each set of conditions.

1. endpoints of major axis at $(-2, 7)$ and $(4, 7)$, endpoints of minor axis at $(1, 5)$ and $(1, 9)$ $\frac{(x-1)^2}{9} + \frac{(y-7)^2}{4} = 1$
2. endpoints of minor axis at $(1, -4)$ and $(1, 5)$, endpoints of major axis at $(-4, 0.5)$ and $(6, 0.5)$ $\frac{(x-1)^2}{25} + \frac{(y-0.5)^2}{20.25} = 1$
3. major axis 24 units long and parallel to the y-axis, minor axis 4 units long, center at $(0, 3)$ $\frac{(x-0)^2}{4} + \frac{(y-3)^2}{144} = 1$

Find the coordinates of the center and foci and the lengths of the major and minor axes for the ellipse with the given equation. Then graph the ellipse. 4–13. See Student Handbook Answer Appendix.

4. $\frac{x^2}{36} + \frac{y^2}{81} = 1$
5. $\frac{x^2}{121} + \frac{(y-5)^2}{16} = 1$
6. $\frac{(x+2)^2}{12} + \frac{(y+1)^2}{16} = 1$
7. $8x^2 + 2y^2 = 32$
8. $7x^2 + 3y^2 = 84$
9. $9x^2 + 16y^2 = 144$
10. $169x^2 - 338x + 169 + 25y^2 = 4225$
11. $x^2 + 4y^2 + 8x - 64y = -128$
12. $4x^2 + 5y^2 = 6(6x + 5y) + 658$
13. $9x^2 + 16y^2 - 54x + 64y + 1 = 0$

Lesson 10-5 Hyperbolas (pp. 648–655)

Graph each hyperbola. Identify the vertices, foci, and asymptotes. 1–11. See Student Handbook Answer Appendix.

1. $\frac{y^2}{25} - \frac{x^2}{9} = 1$
2. $\frac{x^2}{4} - \frac{y^2}{9} = 1$
3. $\frac{x^2}{81} - \frac{y^2}{36} = 1$
4. $\frac{(x-4)^2}{64} - \frac{(y+1)^2}{16} = 1$
5. $\frac{(y-7)^2}{2.25} - \frac{(x-3)^2}{4} = 1$
6. $(x+5)^2 - \frac{(y+3)^2}{48} = 1$
7. $x^2 - 9y^2 = 36$
8. $4x^2 - 9y^2 = 72$
9. $49x^2 - 16y^2 = 784$
10. $576y^2 = 49x^2 + 490x + 29{,}449$
11. $25(y+5)^2 - 20(x-1)^2 = 500$

Write an equation for the hyperbola that satisfies each set of conditions.

12. vertices $(-3, 0)$ and $(3, 0)$; conjugate axis of length 8 units $\frac{x^2}{9} - \frac{y^2}{16} = 1$
13. vertices $(0, -7)$ and $(0, 7)$; conjugate axis of length 25 units $\frac{y^2}{49} - \frac{x^2}{156.25} = 1$
14. center $(0, 0)$; horizontal transverse axis of length 12 units and a conjugate axis of length 10 units $\frac{x^2}{36} - \frac{y^2}{25} = 1$

Lesson 10-6 Identifying Conic Sections (pp. 656–660)

Write each equation in standard form. State whether the graph of the equation is a *parabola, circle, ellipse,* or *hyperbola.* Then graph the equation. 1–12. See Student Handbook Answer Appendix.

1. $9x^2 - 36x + 36 = 4y^2 + 24y + 72$
2. $x^2 + 4x + 2y^2 + 16y + 32 = 0$
3. $x^2 + 6x + y^2 - 6y + 9 = 0$
4. $9y^2 = 25x^2 + 400x + 1825$
5. $2y^2 + 12y - x + 6 = 0$
6. $x^2 + y^2 = 10x + 2y + 23$
7. $3x^2 + y = 12x - 17$
8. $9x^2 - 18x + 16y^2 + 160y = -265$
9. $x^2 + 10x + 5 = 4y^2 + 16$
10. $\frac{(y-5)^2}{4} - (x+1)^2 = 4$
11. $9x^2 + 49y^2 = 441$
12. $4x^2 - y^2 = 4$

Without writing in standard form, state whether the graph of each equation is a *parabola, circle, ellipse,* or *hyperbola.*

13. $(x+3)^2 = 8(y+2)$ parabola
14. $x^2 + 4x + y^2 - 8y = 2$ circle
15. $2x^2 - 13y^2 + 5 = 0$ hyperbola
16. $16(x-3)^2 + 81(y+4)^2 = 1296$ ellipse

Lesson 10-7 Solving Linear-Nonlinear Systems (pp. 662–667)

Solve each system of inequalities by graphing. 1–4. See Student Handbook Answer Appendix.

1. $x^2 - 16y^2 \geq 16$, $x^2 + y^2 \leq 49$
2. $16x^2 + 25y^2 \leq 400$, $y \leq x - 2$
3. $y \geq x + 3$, $x^2 + y^2 < 25$
4. $4x^2 + (y-3)^2 \leq 16$, $x + 2y \geq 4$

Solve each system of equations. 5–13. See Student Handbook Answer Appendix.

5. $x^2 + y^2 = 16$, $x - y = -3$
6. $x - y^2 = 0$, $(x+3)^2 + y^2 = 53$
7. $4x^2 - 3(y+2)^2 = 12$, $x^2 - y^2 = 11$
8. $2(x-1)^2 + 5y^2 = 10$, $x - y = -1$
9. $x^2 + y^2 = 13$, $x^2 - y^2 = -5$
10. $x^2 - 5y^2 = 25$, $x - y = 4$
11. $x^2 + y = 0$, $x + y = -2$
12. $x^2 - 9y^2 = 36$, $x - y = 0$
13. $4x^2 + 6y^2 = 360$, $x - y = 0$

Lesson 11-1 Sequences as Functions (pp. 681–687)

Find the next four terms of each arithmetic sequence.

1. 9, 7, 5, … 3, 1, −1, −3
2. 3, 4.5, 6, … 7.5, 9, 10.5, 12
3. 40, 35, 30, … 25, 20, 15, 10
4. 2, 5, 8, … 11, 14, 17, 20

Find the next two terms of each geometric sequence.

5. 5, 15, 45, … 135, 405
6. 2, 10, 50, … 250, 1250
7. 64, 16, 4, … 1, 0.25
8. −9, 27, −81, … 243, −729
9. 0.5, 0.75, 1.125, … 1.6875, 2.53125
10. $\frac{1}{2}, -\frac{3}{8}, \frac{9}{32}, \ldots$ $-\frac{27}{128}, \frac{81}{512}$

Lesson 11-2 Arithmetic Sequences and Series (pp. 688–695)

Find the sum of each arithmetic series.

1. $a_1 = 3, a_n = 20, n = 6$ 69
2. $a_1 = 90, a_n = -4, n = 10$ 430
3. $a_1 = 16, a_n = 14, n = 12$ 180
4. $a_1 = -1, d = 10, n = 30$ 4320
5. $a_1 = 4, d = -5, n = 11$ −231
6. $a_1 = 5, d = -\frac{1}{2}, n = 17$ 17

Find the sum of each arithmetic series.

7. $\sum_{k=1}^{6}(k+2)$ 33
8. $\sum_{k=5}^{10}(2k-5)$ 60
9. $\sum_{k=1}^{5}(40-2k)$ 170
10. $\sum_{k=8}^{12}(6-3k)$ −120

Find the first three terms of each arithmetic series.

11. $a_1 = 11, a_n = 38, S_n = 245$ 11, 14, 17
12. $n = 12, a_n = 13, S_n = -42$ −20, −17, −14
13. $n = 11, a_n = 5, S_n = 0$ −5, −4, −3

Find the first five terms of each arithmetic sequence.

14. $a_1 = 1, d = 7$ 1, 8, 15, 22, 29
15. $a_1 = -5, d = 2$ −5, −3, −1, 1, 3
16. $a_1 = 1.2, d = 3.7$ 1.2, 4.9, 8.6, 12.3, 16
17. $a_1 = -\frac{5}{4}, d = -\frac{1}{2}$ $-\frac{5}{4}, -\frac{7}{4}, -\frac{9}{4}, -\frac{11}{4}, -\frac{13}{4}$

Find the indicated term of each arithmetic sequence.

18. $a_1 = 4, d = 5, n = 10$ 49
19. $a_1 = -30, d = -6, n = 5$ −54
20. $a_1 = -3, d = 32, n = 8$ 221

Write an equation for the nth term of each arithmetic sequence.

21. 3, 5, 7, 9, … $a_n = 2n + 1$
22. 2, −1, −4, −7, … $a_n = -3n + 5$
23. 20, 28, 36, 44, … $a_n = 8n + 12$

Find the arithmetic means in each sequence.

24. 2, ?, ?, ?, 34 10, 18, 26
25. 0, ?, ?, ?, −28 −7, −14, −21
26. −10, ?, ?, ?, 14 −4, 2, 8

Lesson 11-3 Geometric Sequences and Series (pp. 696–702)

Find the first five terms of each geometric sequence. **1–4. See Student Handbook Answer Appendix.**

1. $a_1 = -2, r = 6$ **2.** $a_1 = 4, r = -5$ **3.** $a_1 = 0.8, r = 2.5$ **4.** $a_1 = -\frac{1}{3}, r = -\frac{3}{5}$

Find a_n for each geometric sequence.

5. $a_1 = 5, r = 7, n = 6$ **84,035** **6.** $a_1 = 200, r = -\frac{1}{2}, n = 10$ $-\frac{25}{64}$ **7.** $a_1 = 60, r = -2, n = 4$ **−480**

Write an equation for the nth term of each geometric sequence.

8. 20, 40, 80, … $a_n = 20(2)^{n-1}$ **9.** $-\frac{1}{2}, -\frac{1}{8}, -\frac{1}{32}, \ldots$ $a_n = -\frac{1}{2}\left(\frac{1}{4}\right)^{n-1}$

Find the geometric means in each sequence.

10. 1, ?, ?, ?, 81 **3, 9, 27 or −3, 9, −27** **11.** 5, ?, ?, ?, 6480 **30, 180, 1080 or −30, 180, −1080**

Find S_n for each geometric series described.

12. $a_1 = \frac{1}{81}, r = 3, n = 6$ $\frac{364}{81}$ **13.** $a_1 = 1, r = -2, n = 7$ **43** **14.** $a_1 = 5, r = 4, n = 5$ **1705**

15. $a_1 = -27, r = -\frac{1}{3}, n = 6$ $-\frac{182}{9}$ **16.** $a_1 = 1000, r = \frac{1}{2}, n = 7$ **1984.375** **17.** $a_1 = 125, r = -\frac{2}{5}, n = 5$ $\frac{451}{5}$

18. $a_1 = 10, r = 3, n = 6$ **3640** **19.** $a_1 = 1250, r = -\frac{1}{5}, n = 5$ **1042** **20.** $a_1 = 1215, r = \frac{1}{3}, n = 5$ **1815**

21. $a_1 = 16, r = \frac{3}{2}, n = 5$ **211** **22.** $a_1 = 7, r = 2, n = 7$ **889** **23.** $a_1 = -\frac{3}{2}, r = -\frac{1}{2}, n = 6$ $-\frac{63}{64}$

Find the sum of each geometric series.

24. $\sum_{k=1}^{5} 2^k$ **62** **25.** $\sum_{k=0}^{3} 3^{-k}$ $\frac{40}{27}$ **26.** $\sum_{k=0}^{3} 2(5^k)$ **312** **27.** $\sum_{k=2}^{5} -(-3)^{k-1}$ **−60**

Find the indicated term for each geometric series described.

28. $S_n = 300, a_n = 160, r = 2; a_1$ **20** **29.** $S_n = -171, n = 9, r = -2; a_5$ **−16** **30.** $S_n = -4372, a_n = -2916, r = 3; a_4$ **−108**

Lesson 11-4 Infinite Geometric Series (pp. 705–711)

Find the sum of each infinite geometric series, if it exists.

1. $a_1 = 54, r = \frac{1}{3}$ **81** **2.** $a_1 = 2, r = -1$ **does not exist** **3.** $a_1 = 1000, r = -0.2$ $833\frac{1}{3}$

4. $a_1 = 7, r = \frac{3}{7}$ $\frac{49}{4}$ **5.** $49 + 14 + 4 + \ldots$ $\frac{343}{5}$ **6.** $\frac{3}{4} + \frac{1}{2} + \frac{1}{3} + \ldots$ $\frac{9}{4}$

7. $12 - 4 + \frac{4}{3} - \ldots$ **9** **8.** $3 - 9 + 27 - \ldots$ **does not exist** **9.** $3 - 2 + \frac{4}{3} - \ldots$ $\frac{9}{5}$

10. $\sum_{k=1}^{\infty} 3\left(\frac{1}{4}\right)^{k-1}$ **4** **11.** $\sum_{k=1}^{\infty} 5\left(-\frac{1}{10}\right)^{k-1}$ $\frac{50}{11}$ **12.** $\sum_{k=1}^{\infty} -\frac{2}{3}\left(-\frac{3}{4}\right)^{k-1}$ $-\frac{8}{21}$

Write each repeating decimal as a fraction.

13. $0.\overline{4}$ $\frac{4}{9}$ **14.** $0.\overline{27}$ $\frac{3}{11}$ **15.** $0.\overline{123}$ $\frac{41}{333}$

16. $0.\overline{645}$ $\frac{215}{333}$ **17.** $0.\overline{67}$ $\frac{67}{99}$ **18.** $0.8\overline{53}$ $\frac{169}{198}$

Lesson 11-5 Recursion and Iteration (pp. 714–719)

Find the first five terms of each sequence described.

1. $a_1 = 4, a_{n+1} = 2a_n + 1$ **4, 9, 19, 39, 79** **2.** $a_1 = 6, a_{n+1} = a_n + 7$ **6, 13, 20, 27, 34**

3. $a_1 = 16, a_{n+1} = a_n + (n + 4)$ **16, 21, 27, 34, 42** **4.** $a_1 = 1, a_{n+1} = \frac{n}{n+2} \cdot a_n$ $1, \frac{1}{3}, \frac{1}{6}, \frac{1}{10}, \frac{1}{15}$

5. $a_1 = -\frac{1}{2}, a_{n+1} = 2a_n + \frac{1}{4}$ $-\frac{1}{2}, -\frac{3}{4}, -\frac{5}{4}, -\frac{9}{4}, -\frac{17}{4}$ **6.** $a_1 = \frac{1}{3}, a_2 = \frac{1}{4}, a_{n+1} = a_n + a_{n-1}$ $\frac{1}{3}, \frac{1}{4}, \frac{7}{12}, \frac{5}{6}, \frac{17}{12}$

Find the first three iterates of each function for the given initial value.

7. $f(x) = 3x - 1, x_0 = 3$ **8, 23, 68** **8.** $f(x) = 2x^2 - 8, x_0 = -1$ **−6, 64, 8184**

9. $f(x) = 4x + 5, x_0 = 0$ **5, 25, 105** **10.** $f(x) = 3x^2 + 1, x_0 = 1$ **4, 49, 7204**

11. $f(x) = x^2 + 4x + 4, x_0 = 1$ **9, 121, 15,129** **12.** $f(x) = x^2 + 9, x_0 = 2$ **13, 178, 31,693**

13. $f(x) = 2x^2 + x + 1, x_0 = -\frac{1}{2}$ **1, 4, 37** **14.** $f(x) = 3x^2 + 2x - 1, x_0 = \frac{2}{3}$ $\frac{5}{3}, \frac{32}{3}, \frac{1085}{3}$

Lesson 11-6 The Binomial Theorem (pp. 721–725)

Expand each binomial. **1–12. See Student Handbook Answer Appendix.**

1. $(z - 3)^5$ **2.** $(m + 1)^4$ **3.** $(x + 6)^4$ **4.** $(z - y)^2$

5. $(m + p)^5$ **6.** $(a - b)^4$ **7.** $(2n + 1)^4$ **8.** $(3n - 4)^3$

9. $(2n - m)^0$ **10.** $(4x - a)^4$ **11.** $(3r - 4t)^5$ **12.** $\left(\frac{b}{2} - 1\right)^4$

Find the indicated term of each expression.

13. sixth term of $(x + 3)^8$ $13{,}608x^3$ **14.** fourth term of $(x - 2)^7$ $-280x^4$ **15.** fifth term of $(a + b)^6$ $15a^2b^4$

16. fourth term of $(x - y)^9$ $-84x^6y^3$ **17.** sixth term of $(x + 4y)^7$ $21{,}504x^2y^5$ **18.** fifth term of $(3x + 5y)^{10}$ $95{,}681{,}250x^6y^4$

Lesson 11-7 Proof by Mathematical Induction (pp. 727–731)

Prove that each statement is true for all natural numbers. **1–5. See Student Handbook Answer Appendix.**

1. $2 + 4 + 6 + \ldots + 2n = n^2 + n$

2. $1^3 + 3^3 + 5^3 + \ldots + (2n - 1)^3 = n^2(2n^2 - 1)$

3. $\frac{1}{1 \cdot 3} + \frac{1}{2 \cdot 4} + \frac{1}{3 \cdot 5} + \ldots + \frac{1}{n(n+2)} = \frac{n(3n+5)}{4(n+1)(n+2)}$

4. $1 \cdot 3 + 2 \cdot 4 + 3 \cdot 5 + \ldots + n(n + 2) = \frac{n(n+1)(2n+7)}{6}$

5. $\frac{5}{1 \cdot 2} \cdot \frac{1}{3} + \frac{7}{2 \cdot 3} \cdot \frac{1}{3^2} + \frac{9}{3 \cdot 4} \cdot \frac{1}{3^3} + \ldots + \frac{2n+3}{n(n+1)} \cdot \frac{1}{3^n} = 1 - \frac{1}{3^n(n+1)}$

Find a counterexample to disprove each statement.

6. $n^2 + 2n - 1$ is divisible by 2. $n = 2$ **7.** $2^n + 3^n$ is prime. $n = 3$

8. $2^{n-1} + n = 2^n + 2 - n$ for all integers $n \geq 2$ $n = 4$ **9.** $3^n - 2n = 3^n - 2^n$ for all integers $n \geq 1$ $n = 3$

Lesson 12-1 Experiments, Surveys, and Observational Studies (pp. 745–750)

Determine whether each situation would produce a random sample. Write *yes* or *no* and explain your answer. 1. No; you would need to ask doctors at different locations, not just one hospital.

1. finding the most often prescribed pain reliever by asking all of the doctors at a hospital
2. taking a poll of the most popular baby girl names this year by studying birth announcements in newspapers from different cities across the country Yes; you are taking into account the different locations throughout the country.
3. polling people who are leaving a pizza parlor about their favorite restaurant in the city See Student Handbook Answer Appendix.

State whether each situation represents an *experiment* or an *observational study*. If it is an experiment, identify the control group and the treatment group. Then determine if there is bias.

4. A researcher stood at a busy intersection to see if the color of the automobile that a person drives is related to running a red light. observational study
5. Subjects were randomly assigned to two groups, and one group was given an herb and the other group a placebo. After six months the number of respiratory tract infections each group had were compared. 5. Experiment; the group given the herb is the treatment group. The group given the placebo is the control group. This is unbiased.

Determine if the following statements show a *correlation* or *causation*.

6. The more hours I work, the more spending money I have. correlation
7. When it snows heavily in the winter, there are snow plows outside. causation

Lesson 12-2 Statistical Analysis (pp. 752–758)

Which measure of central tendency best represents the data? Explain. 1–4. See Student Handbook Answer Appendix.

1. {86, 71, 74, 65, 45, 42, 76}
2. {20, 16, 15, 14, 24, 23, 25, 10, 19, 89}
3. {1, 2, 2, 2, 2, 4, 5}
4. {27, 33, 29, 37, 31, 28, 30, 34, 35}
5. **TEMPERATURES** The high temperatures at the right were recorded during a 38-day cold period in Cleveland, Ohio. Find the standard deviation. about 9.2

29°	26°	17°	12°	5°	4°	25°	17°
23°	18°	13°	6°	25°	20°	27°	22°
26°	30°	31°	2°	12°	27°	16°	27°
16°	30°	6°	16°	5°	0°	5°	29°
18°	16°	22°	29°	8°	23°		

Lesson 12-3 Conditional Probability (pp. 759–763)

Use the table to answer Exercises 1 and 2.

	Teacher Ratings			
	Explains well; Easy tests	Explains well; Hard tests	Explains poorly; Easy tests	Explains poorly; Hard tests
Junior	59	63	52	31
Senior	61	47	79	26

1. One of these students is randomly selected. If it is known that the student is a junior, find the probability that the student rated the teacher as "Explains well; Easy tests". $\frac{59}{205}$
2. One of these students is randomly selected. If it is known that the student rated the teacher as "Explains poorly; Hard tests", find the probability that the student is a senior. $\frac{26}{57}$
3. In a pizza restaurant, 95% of the customers order pizza. If 65% of the customers order pizza and a salad, find the probability that a customer will order a salad, given that he or she orders a pizza. $\frac{13}{19} \approx 68.4\%$

Lesson 12-4 Probability and Probability Distributions (pp. 764–771)

1. A small airline company employs 11 male flight attendants and 13 female flight attendants. As an economic move, the management decides to lay off two workers. Find the probability that both laid off workers will be male flight attendants. $\frac{55}{276} \approx 19.9\%$
2. Seven scientists are available to be the chairperson and assistant chairperson for a research project. If the names are drawn randomly, what is the probability that the two selected will be George and Sarah in that order? $\frac{1}{120} \approx 0.83\%$
3. The table shows the distribution of the number of heads tossed when tossing a coin three times.

X = Number of Heads	0	1	2	3
Probability	$\frac{1}{8}$	$\frac{3}{8}$	$\frac{3}{8}$	$\frac{1}{8}$

Find each of the following.

a. $P(X = 1)$ $\frac{3}{8}$ b. $P(X = 2)$ $\frac{3}{8}$ c. $P(X \neq 3)$ $\frac{7}{8}$

Lesson 12-5 The Normal Distribution (pp. 773–778)

1. Determine whether the data in the table appear to be *positively skewed*, *negatively skewed*, or *normally distributed*. The average size of a farm in each U.S. state was determined. positively skewed

Acres	85–559	560–1034	1035–1509	1510–1984	1985–2459	2460–2934	2935–3409	3410–3884
States	37	4	3	1	2	1	0	2

Source: *The World Almanac*

2. The diameters of metal fittings made by a machine are normally distributed. The diameters have a mean of 7.5 centimeters and a standard deviation of 0.5 centimeters.
   a. What percent of the fittings have diameters between 7.0 and 8.0 centimeters? 68%
   b. What percent of the fittings have diameters between 7.5 and 8.0 centimeters? 34%
   c. What percent of the fittings have diameters greater than 6.5 centimeters? 97.5%
   d. Of 100 fittings, how many will have a diameter between 6.0 and 8.5 centimeters? 97 fittings
3. A college extrance exam was administered at a state university. The scores were normally distributed with a mean of 510, and a standard deviation of 80.
   a. What percent would you expect to score above 510? 50%
   b. What percent would you expect to score between 430 and 590? 68%
   c. What is the probability that a student chosen at random scored between 350 and 670? 95%

Lesson 12-6 Hypothesis Testing (pp. 780–784)

Find a 95% confidence interval for each of the following.

1. $\overline{X} = 93$, $s = 2.7$, and $n = 125$ $92.52 \leq \overline{X} \leq 93.48$
2. $\overline{X} = 56$, $s = 1.9$, and $n = 75$ $55.56 \leq \overline{X} \leq 56.44$
3. A sample of 200 students was asked for the average amount of time they spent studying or working on homework assignments per day. The mean time was 50 minutes with a standard deviation of 6.7 minutes. Determine a 95% confidence interval. $49.05 \leq \overline{X} \leq 50.95$

Test each of the following hypotheses.

4. $H_0 = 45$, $H_1 < 45$, $n = 75$, $\overline{X} = 39.5$, and $s = 1.2$ The 95% confidence interval does not include H_0, so we reject the null hypothesis.
5. $H_0 = 18.0$, $H_1 > 18.0$, $n = 125$, $\overline{X} = 18.2$, and $s = 1.6$ The 95% confidence interval does include H_0, so we accept the null hypothesis.

Lesson 12-7 Binomial Distributions (pp. 786–793)

1. A fair coin is tossed 8 times. What is the probability of having at least 5 tails? 36.3%
2. A test is made of 20 true or false questions. If a student guesses at random, what is the probability that the student will answer at least 12 questions correctly? 25.2%
3. The Medicare program pays for 43% of all prescriptions filled at Bill's Pharmacy. If Bill's Pharmacy expects to fill 375 prescriptions this week, about how many can be expected to be paid by Medicare? 161.25
4. A research organization decides to mail 10 questionnaires to people selected at random. If the probability of any one person answering the questionnaire is $\frac{1}{7}$, find the probability that exactly 3 people will answer the questionnaire. 11.9%

Lesson 13-1 Right Triangle Trigonometry (pp. 808–816)

Find the values of the six trigonometric functions for angle θ. 1–3. See Student Handbook Answer Appendix.

1. 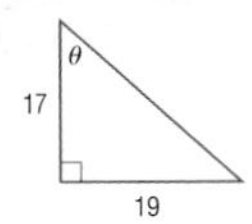

2. 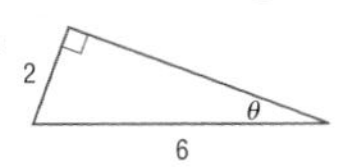

3. 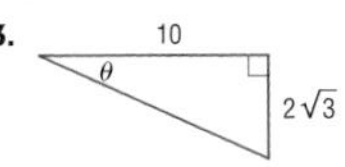

Solve $\triangle ABC$ using the diagram at the right and the given measurements. Round measures of sides to the nearest tenth and measures of angles to the nearest degree.

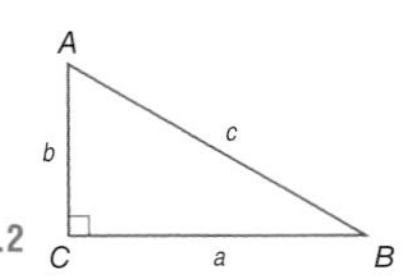

4. $B = 42°, c = 30$
5. $A = 84°, a = 4$ **$B = 6°, b = 0.4, c = 4.0$**
6. $B = 19°, b = 34$
7. $A = 75°, c = 55$ **$B = 15°, a = 53.1, b = 14.2$**
8. $b = 24, c = 36$
9. $a = 51, c = 115$ **$A = 26°, B = 64°, b = 103.1$**
10. $\cos B = \frac{2}{5}, a = 12$
11. $\tan A = \frac{3}{2}, b = 22$ **$A = 56°, B = 34°, a = 33, c = 39.7$**

4. $A = 48°, a = 22.3, b = 20.1$ 6. $A = 71°, a = 98.7, c = 104.4$
8. $A = 48°, B = 42°, a = 26.8$ 10. $A = 24°, B = 66°, b = 27.5, c = 30$

Lesson 13-2 Angles and Angle Measure (pp. 817–823)

Draw an angle with the given measure in standard position. 1–4. See Student Handbook Answer Appendix.

1. 60° 2. 250° 3. 315° 4. 150°

Rewrite each degree measure in radians and each radian measure in degrees.

5. −135° $-\frac{3\pi}{4}$
6. −315° $-\frac{7\pi}{4}$
7. 45° $\frac{\pi}{4}$
8. 80° $\frac{4\pi}{9}$
9. 24° $\frac{2\pi}{15}$
10. −54° $-\frac{3\pi}{10}$
11. $-\pi$ −180°
12. $\frac{9\pi}{4}$ 405°
13. $\frac{3\pi}{2}$ 270°
14. $-\frac{7\pi}{2}$ −630°
15. $\frac{9\pi}{10}$ 162°
16. $\frac{17\pi}{30}$ 102°
17. $\frac{7\pi}{12}$ 105°
18. 1 about 57.3°
19. $-2\frac{1}{3}$ about −133.7°

Find an angle with a positive measure and an angle with a negative measure that are coterminal with each angle.

20. 50° 410°, −310°
21. −75° 285°, −435°
22. 125° 485°, −235°
23. −400° 320°, −40°
24. 550° 190°, −170°
25. 3π $\pi, -\pi$
26. -2π $2\pi, -4\pi$
27. $\frac{2\pi}{3}$ $\frac{8\pi}{3}, -\frac{4\pi}{3}$
28. $\frac{12\pi}{5}$ $\frac{22\pi}{5}, -\frac{8\pi}{5}$
29. 0 $2\pi, -2\pi$

Lesson 13-3 Trigonometric Functions of General Angles (pp. 825–831)

The terminal side of θ in standard position contains each point. Find the exact values of the six trigonometric functions of θ. 1–5. See Student Handbook Answer Appendix.

1. $P(3, -4)$
2. $P(1, \sqrt{3})$
3. $P(0, 24)$
4. $P(-5, -5)$
5. $P(\sqrt{2}, -\sqrt{2})$

Find the exact value of each trigonometric function.

6. $\cos 225°$ $-\frac{\sqrt{2}}{2}$
7. $\sin\left(-\frac{5\pi}{3}\right)$ $\frac{\sqrt{3}}{2}$
8. $\tan \frac{7\pi}{6}$ $\frac{\sqrt{3}}{3}$
9. $\tan(-300°)$ $\sqrt{3}$
10. $\cos \frac{7\pi}{4}$ $\frac{\sqrt{2}}{2}$

Suppose θ is an angle in standard position whose terminal side is in the given quadrant. For each function, find the exact values of the remaining five trigonometric functions of θ.

11. $\cos \theta = -\frac{1}{3}$; Quadrant III
12. $\sec \theta = 2$; Quadrant IV
13. $\sin \theta = \frac{2}{3}$; Quadrant II
14. $\tan \theta = -4$; Quadrant IV
15. $\csc \theta = -5$; Quadrant III
16. $\cot \theta = -2$; Quadrant II
17. $\tan \theta = \frac{1}{3}$; Quadrant III
18. $\cos \theta = \frac{1}{4}$; Quadrant I
19. $\csc \theta = -\frac{5}{2}$; Quadrant IV

11–19. See Student Handbook Answer Appendix.

Lesson 13-4 Law of Sines (pp. 832–839)

Find the area of $\triangle ABC$ to the nearest tenth. 3. 55.2 cm²

1. $a = 11$ m, $b = 13$ m, $C = 31°$ 36.8 m²
2. $a = 15$ ft, $b = 22$ ft, $C = 90°$ 165 ft²
3. $a = 12$ cm, $b = 12$ cm, $C = 50°$

Solve each triangle. Round to the nearest tenth, if necessary. 4–9. See Student Handbook Answer Appendix.

4. $A = 18°, B = 37°, a = 15$
5. $A = 60°, C = 25°, c = 3$
6. $B = 40°, C = 32°, b = 10$
7. $B = 10°, C = 23°, c = 8$
8. $A = 12°, B = 60°, b = 5$
9. $A = 35°, C = 45°, a = 30$

Determine whether each triangle has *no* solution, *one* solution, or *two* solutions. Then solve the triangle. Round side lengths to the nearest tenth and angle measures to the nearest degree. 10–21. See Student Handbook Answer Appendix.

10. $A = 40°, B = 60°, c = 20$
11. $B = 70°, C = 58°, a = 84$
12. $A = 40°, a = 5, b = 12$
13. $A = 58°, a = 26, b = 29$
14. $A = 38°, B = 63°, c = 15$
15. $A = 150°, a = 6, b = 8$
16. $A = 57°, a = 12, b = 19$
17. $A = 25°, a = 125, b = 150$
18. $C = 98°, a = 64, c = 90$
19. $A = 46°, B = 63°, c = 12$
20. $A = 132°, a = 33, b = 50$
21. $A = 45°, a = 83, b = 79$

Lesson 13-5 Law of Cosines (pp. 841–846)

Determine whether each triangle should be solved by beginning with the Law of Sines or Law of Cosines. Then solve the triangle. Round side lengths to the nearest tenth and angle measures to the nearest degree. 1–18. See Student Handbook Answer Appendix.

1. 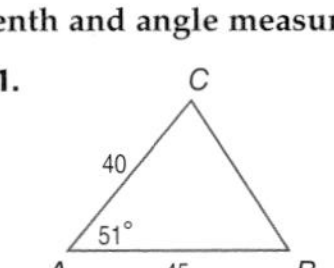

2. 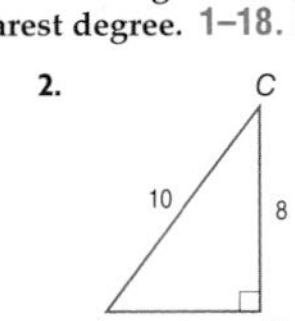

3. 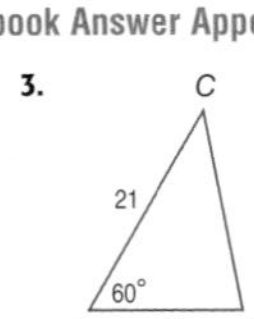

4. $a = 14, b = 15, c = 16$
5. $B = 41°, C = 52°, c = 27$
6. $a = 19, b = 24.3, c = 21.8$
7. $A = 112°, a = 32, c = 20$
8. $b = 8, c = 7, A = 28°$
9. $a = 5, b = 6, c = 7$
10. $C = 25°, a = 12, b = 9$
11. $a = 8, A = 49°, B = 58°$
12. $A = 42°, b = 120, c = 160$
13. $c = 10, A = 35°, C = 65°$
14. $a = 10, b = 16, c = 19$
15. $B = 45°, a = 40, c = 48$
16. $B = 100°, a = 10, c = 8$
17. $A = 40°, B = 45°, c = 4$
18. $A = 20°, b = 100, c = 84$

Lesson 13-6 Circular Functions (pp. 848–854)

The terminal side of angle θ in standard position intersects the unit circle at each point P. Find $\sin\theta$ and $\cos\theta$. **1–5. See Student Handbook Answer Appendix.**

1. $P\left(\frac{4}{5}, \frac{3}{5}\right)$ 2. $P\left(\frac{12}{13}, -\frac{5}{13}\right)$ 3. $P\left(-\frac{8}{17}, -\frac{15}{17}\right)$ 4. $P\left(\frac{3}{7}, \frac{2\sqrt{10}}{7}\right)$ 5. $P\left(-\frac{2}{3}, \frac{\sqrt{5}}{3}\right)$

Find the exact value of each function. **7.** $-\frac{\sqrt{3}}{2}$ **14.** $\frac{\sqrt{3}+1}{2}$ **17.** $-\frac{1}{5}$

6. $\sin 210°$ $-\frac{1}{2}$
7. $\cos 150°$
8. $\cos(2295°)$ $-\frac{\sqrt{2}}{2}$
9. $\cos\frac{3\pi}{4}$ $-\frac{\sqrt{2}}{2}$
10. $\sin 570°$ $-\frac{1}{2}$
11. $\sin 390°$ $\frac{1}{2}$
12. $\sin\frac{4\pi}{3}$ $-\frac{\sqrt{3}}{2}$
13. $\cos -\frac{7\pi}{3}$ $\frac{1}{2}$
14. $\cos 30° + \cos 60°$
15. $5(\sin 45°)(\cos 45°)$ $\frac{5}{2}$
16. $\frac{\sin 210° + \cos 240°}{3}$ $-\frac{1}{3}$
17. $\frac{6\cos 120° + 4\sin 150°}{5}$

Determine the period of each function.

18. **270°**

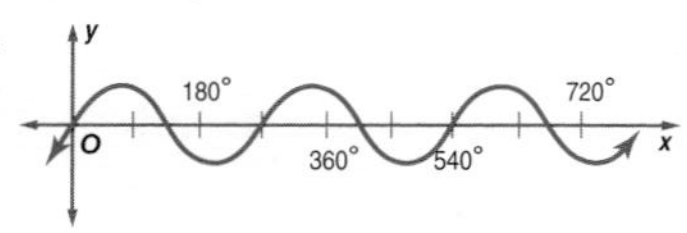

19. **3π**

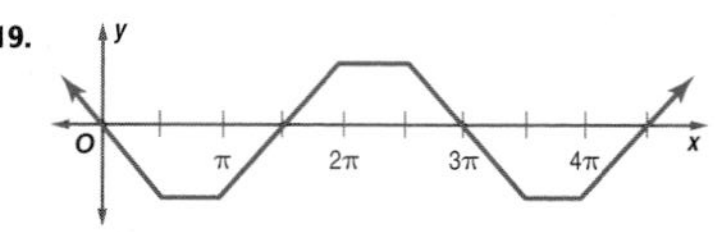

Lesson 13-7 Graphing Trigonometric Functions (pp. 855–861)

Find the amplitude and period of each function. Then graph the function.

1. $y = 2\cos\theta$ **2; 360° or 2π**
2. $y = \frac{1}{3}\sin\theta$ **$\frac{1}{3}$; 360° or 2π**
3. $y = \sin 3\theta$ **1; 120° or $\frac{2\pi}{3}$**
4. $y = 3\sec\theta$ **none; 360° or 2π**
5. $y = \sec\frac{1}{3}\theta$ **none; 1080° or 6π**
6. $y = 2\csc\theta$ **none; 360° or 2π**
7. $y = 3\tan\theta$ **none; 180° or π**
8. $y = 3\sin\frac{2}{3}\theta$ **3; 540° or 3π**
9. $y = 2\sin\frac{1}{5}\theta$ **2; 1800° or 10π**
10. $y = 3\sin 2\theta$ **3; 180° or π**
11. $y = \frac{1}{2}\cos\frac{3}{4}\theta$ **$\frac{1}{2}$; 480° or $\frac{8\pi}{3}$**
12. $y = 5\csc 3\theta$ **none; 120° or $\frac{2\pi}{3}$**
13. $y = 2\cot 6\theta$ **none; 30° or $\frac{\pi}{6}$**
14. $y = 2\csc 6\theta$ **none; 60° or $\frac{\pi}{3}$**
15. $y = 3\tan\frac{1}{3}\theta$ **none; 540° or 3π**

1–15. See Student Handbook Answer Appendix for graphs.

Lesson 13-8 Translations of Trigonometric Graphs (pp. 863–870)

State the amplitude, period, and phase shift for each function. Then graph the function.

1. $y = \sin(\theta + 60°)$ **1; 360°; −60°**
2. $y = \cos(\theta - 90°)$ **1; 360°; 90°**
3. $y = \tan\left(\theta + \frac{\pi}{2}\right)$ **none; π; $-\frac{\pi}{2}$**
4. $y = \sin\theta + \frac{\pi}{6}$ **1; 2π; $-\frac{\pi}{6}$**

1–4. See Student Handbook Answer Appendix for graphs.

State the amplitude, period, vertical shift, and the equation of the midline for each function. Then graph the function. **5–10. See Student Handbook Answer Appendix.**

5. $y = \cos\theta + 3$
6. $y = \sin\theta - 2$
7. $y = \sec\theta + 5$
8. $y = \csc\theta - 6$
9. $y = 2\sin\theta - 4$
10. $y = \frac{1}{3}\sin\theta + 7$

State the amplitude, period, vertical shift, and phase shift for each function. Then graph the function. **11–16. See Student Handbook Answer Appendix.**

11. $y = 3\cos[2(\theta + 30°)] + 4$
12. $y = 2\tan[3(\theta - 60°)] - 2$
13. $y = \frac{1}{2}\sin[4(\theta - 45°)] + 1$
14. $y = \frac{2}{5}\cos[6(\theta + 45°)] - 5$
15. $y = 6 + 2\sin\left[3\left(\theta + \frac{\pi}{2}\right)\right]$
16. $y = 3 + 3\cos\left[2\left(\theta - \frac{\pi}{3}\right)\right]$

Lesson 13-9 Inverse Trigonometric Functions (pp. 871–876)

Solve each equation.

1. $y = \text{Sin}^{-1}\, -\frac{\sqrt{2}}{2}$ **−45°**
2. $\text{Tan}^{-1}(1) = x$ **45°**
3. $a = \text{Arccos}\left(\frac{\sqrt{3}}{2}\right)$ **30°**
4. $\text{Arcsin}(0) = x$ **0**
5. $y = \text{Cos}^{-1}\frac{1}{2}$ **60°**
6. $y = \text{Sin}^{-1}(1)$ **90°**

Find each value. Round to the nearest hundredth if necessary.

7. $\text{Arccos}\left(-\frac{\sqrt{2}}{2}\right)$ **135°**
8. $\text{Sin}^{-1}(-1)$ **−90°**
9. $\cos\left[\text{Arcsin}\left(\frac{\sqrt{2}}{2}\right)\right]$ **0.71**
10. $\tan\left[\text{Sin}^{-1}\left(\frac{5}{13}\right)\right]$ **0.42**
11. $\sin\left[\text{Arccos}\frac{1}{2}\right]$ **0.87**
12. $\sin\left[\text{Arccos}\left(\frac{5}{17}\right)\right]$ **0.96**
13. $\sin\left[\text{Tan}^{-1}\left(\frac{5}{12}\right)\right]$ **0.38**
14. $\tan\left[\text{Arccos}-\left(\frac{\sqrt{3}}{2}\right)\right]$ **−0.58**
15. $\sin^{-1}[\text{Cos}^{-1}(1) - 1]$ **−90°**
16. $\text{Cos}^{-1}\left[\tan\frac{\pi}{4}\right]$ **0**
17. $\cos\left[\text{Sin}^{-1}\frac{1}{2}\right]$ **0.87**
18. $\sin[\text{Cos}^{-1}(0)]$ **1**

Lesson 14-1 Trigonometric Identities (pp. 891–897)

Find the value of each expression.

1. $\sin\theta$, if $\cos\theta = \frac{4}{5}$; $0° \le \theta \le 90°$ **$\frac{3}{5}$**
2. $\tan\theta$, if $\sin\theta = \frac{1}{2}$; $0° \le \theta \le 90°$ **$\frac{\sqrt{3}}{3}$**
3. $\csc\theta$, if $\sin\theta = \frac{3}{4}$; $90° \le \theta \le 180°$ **$\frac{4}{3}$**
4. $\cos\theta$, if $\tan\theta = -4$; $90° \le \theta \le 180°$ **$-\frac{\sqrt{17}}{17}$**
5. $\sec\theta$, if $\tan\theta = 24$; $90° \le \theta \le 180°$ **$-\sqrt{17}$**
6. $\sin\theta$, if $\cot\theta = -\frac{1}{4}$; $270° \le \theta \le 360°$ **$-\frac{\sqrt{17}}{17}$**
7. $\tan\theta$, if $\sec\theta = -3$; $90° \le \theta \le 180°$ **$-2\sqrt{2}$**
8. $\sin\theta$, if $\cos\theta = \frac{3}{5}$; $270° \le \theta \le 360°$ **$-\frac{4}{5}$**
9. $\cos\theta$, if $\sin\theta = -\frac{1}{2}$; $270° \le \theta \le 360°$ **$\frac{\sqrt{3}}{2}$**
10. $\csc\theta$, if $\cot\theta = -\frac{1}{4}$; $90° \le \theta \le 180°$ **$\frac{\sqrt{17}}{4}$**

Simplify each expression.

11. $\csc^2\theta - \cot^2\theta$ **1**
12. $\sin\theta\tan\theta\csc\theta$ **$\tan\theta$**
13. $\tan\theta\csc\theta$ **$\sec\theta$**
14. $\sec\theta\cot\theta\cos\theta$ **$\cot\theta$**
15. $\cos\theta(1 - \cos^2\theta)$ **$\cos\theta \cdot \sin^2\theta$**
16. $\frac{1 - \sin^2\theta}{\cos^2\theta}$ **1**
17. $\frac{\sin^2\theta + \cos^2\theta}{\cos^2\theta}$ **$\sec^2\theta$**
18. $\frac{1 + \tan^2\theta}{1 + \cot^2\theta}$ **$\tan^2\theta$**
19. $\frac{1}{1 + \sin\theta} + \frac{1}{1 - \sin\theta}$ **$2\sec^2\theta$**

Lesson 14-2 Verifying Trigonometric Identities (pp. 898–903)

Verify that each equation is an identity. **1–18. See Student Handbook Answer Appendix.**

1. $\sin^2\theta + \cos^2\theta + \tan^2\theta = \sec^2\theta$
2. $\frac{\tan\theta}{\sin\theta} = \sec\theta$
3. $\frac{\tan\theta}{\cot\theta} = \tan^2\theta$
4. $\csc^2\theta(1 - \cos^2\theta) = 1$
5. $1 - \cot^4\theta = 2\csc^2\theta - \csc^4\theta$
6. $\sin^4\theta - \cos^4\theta = \sin^2\theta - \cos^2\theta$
7. $\sin^2\theta + \cot^2\theta\sin^2\theta = 1$
8. $\frac{\cos\theta}{\csc\theta} - \frac{\csc\theta}{\sec\theta} = -\frac{\cos^3\theta}{\sin\theta}$
9. $\frac{\cos\theta}{\sec\theta - 1} - \frac{1 + \cos\theta}{\sec\theta + 1} = 2\cot^2\theta$
10. $\frac{1 + \cos\theta}{\sin\theta} = \frac{\sin\theta}{1 - \cos\theta}$
11. $\sec\theta + \tan\theta = \frac{\cos\theta}{1 - \sin\theta}$
12. $\tan\theta + \cot\theta = \csc\theta\sec\theta$
13. $\frac{\cot^2\theta}{1 + \cot^2\theta} = 1 - \sin^2\theta$
14. $\frac{\tan\theta - \sin\theta}{\sec\theta} = \frac{\sin^3\theta}{1 + \cos\theta}$
15. $\sin^2\theta(1 - \cos^2\theta) = \sin^4\theta$
16. $\sin^2\theta + \sin^2\theta\tan^2\theta = \tan^2\theta$
17. $\frac{\sec\theta - 1}{\sec\theta + 1} + \frac{\cos\theta - 1}{\cos\theta + 1} = 0$
18. $\tan^2\theta(1 - \sin^2\theta) = \sin^2\theta$

Lesson 14-3 Sum and Difference of Angles Identities (pp. 904–909)

Find the exact value of each expression. 1–12. See Student Handbook Answer Appendix.

1. sin 195° **2.** cos 285° **3.** sin 255°
4. sin 105° **5.** cos 15° **6.** sin 15°
7. cos 375° **8.** sin 165° **9.** sin (−225°)
10. cos (−210°) **11.** cos (−225°) **12.** sin (−30°)

Verify that each equation is an identity. 13–17. See Student Handbook Answer Appendix.

13. $\sin(90° + \theta) = \cos\theta$ **14.** $\cos(180° - \theta) = -\cos\theta$ **15.** $\sin(\pi + \theta) = -\sin\theta$

16. $\sin(\theta + 30°) + \sin(\theta + 60°) = \sqrt{3} + \frac{1}{2}(\sin\theta + \cos\theta)$ **17.** $\cos(30° - \theta) + \cos(30° + \theta) = \sqrt{3}\cos\theta$

Lesson 14-4 Double-Angle and Half-Angle Identities (pp. 911–917)

Find the exact value of $\sin 2\theta$, $\cos 2\theta$, $\sin\frac{\theta}{2}$, and $\cos\frac{\theta}{2}$ for each of the following. 2, 4. See Student Handbook Answer Appendix.

1. $\cos\theta = \frac{7}{25}$; $0 < \theta < 90°$ $\frac{336}{625}, -\frac{527}{625}, \frac{3}{5}, \frac{4}{5}$ **2.** $\sin\theta = \frac{2}{7}$; $0 < \theta < 90°$

3. $\cos\theta = -\frac{1}{8}$; $180° < \theta < 270°$ $\frac{3\sqrt{7}}{32}, -\frac{31}{32}, \frac{3}{4}, -\frac{\sqrt{7}}{4}$ **4.** $\sin\theta = -\frac{5}{13}$; $270° < \theta < 360°$

Find the exact value of each expression by using the half-angle formulas.

5. sin 75° **6.** cos 75° **7.** $\sin\frac{\pi}{8}$

8. $\cos\frac{13\pi}{12}$ $-\frac{\sqrt{2+\sqrt{3}}}{2}$ **9.** cos 22.5° $\frac{\sqrt{2+\sqrt{2}}}{2}$ **10.** $\cos\frac{\pi}{4}$ $\frac{\sqrt{2}}{2}$

5. $\frac{\sqrt{2+\sqrt{3}}}{2}$
6. $\frac{\sqrt{2-\sqrt{3}}}{2}$
7. $\frac{\sqrt{2-\sqrt{2}}}{2}$

Verify that each equation is an identity.

11. $\frac{\sin 2\theta}{2\sin^2\theta} = \cot\theta$ **12.** $1 + \cos 2\theta = \frac{2}{1 + \tan^2\theta}$ **13.** $\csc\theta\sec\theta = 2\csc 2\theta$

14. $\sin 2\theta(\cot\theta + \tan\theta) = 2$ **15.** $\frac{1 - \tan^2\theta}{1 + \tan^2\theta} = \cos 2\theta$ **16.** $\frac{\cos\theta + \sin\theta}{\cos\theta - \sin\theta} = \frac{1 + \sin 2\theta}{\cos 2\theta}$

11–16. See Student Handbook Answer Appendix.

Lesson 14-5 Solving Trigonometric Equations (pp. 919–925)

Find all the solutions for each equation for $0° \le \theta < 360°$.

1. $\cos\theta = -\frac{\sqrt{3}}{2}$ 150°, 210° **2.** $\sin 2\theta = -\frac{\sqrt{3}}{2}$ 120°, 150°, 300°, 330° **3.** $\cos 2\theta = 8 - 15\sin\theta$ 30°, 150°

Solve each equation for all values of θ if θ is measured in radians.

4. $\cos 2\theta\sin\theta = 1$ $\frac{3\pi}{2} + 2k\pi$ **5.** $\sin\frac{\theta}{2} + \cos\frac{\theta}{2} = \sqrt{2}$ $\frac{\pi}{2} + 4k\pi$ **6.** $\cos 2\theta + 4\cos\theta = -3$ $\pi + 2k\pi$

Solve each equation for all values of θ if θ is measured in degrees.

7. $2\sin^2\theta - 1 = 0$ $45° + k \cdot 90°$ **8.** $\cos\theta - 2\cos\theta\sin\theta = 0$ $30° + k \cdot 120°$; $90° + k \cdot 180°$ **9.** $\cos 2\theta\sin\theta = 1$ $270° + k \cdot 360°$

Solve each equation. 12–13. See Student Handbook Answer Appendix.

10. $\tan\theta = 1$ $45° + k \cdot 180°$ or $\frac{\pi}{4} + k \cdot \pi$ **11.** $\cos 8\theta = 1$ $0° + k \cdot 45°$ or $0 + k \cdot \frac{\pi}{4}$

12. $\sin\theta + 1 = \cos 2\theta$ **13.** $8\sin\theta\cos\theta = 2\sqrt{3}$

14. $\cos\theta = 1 + \sin\theta$ $0° + k \cdot 360°$ and $270° + k \cdot 360°$ or $0 + 2k\pi$ and $\frac{3\pi}{2} + 2k\pi$ **15.** $2\cos^2\theta = \cos\theta$ $90° + k \cdot 180°$, $60° + k \cdot 360°$, and $300° + k \cdot 360°$

Mixed Problem Solving

Chapter 1 Equations and Inequalities (pp. 2–57)

1. PACKAGING A can is 5 inches tall and has a diameter of 4 inches. Its volume can be determined by the equation $V = \pi r^2 h$. What is the volume of the can? (Lesson 1-1) 62.8 in³

2. SIGN A yield sign is 30 inches on a side and 26 inches tall. The formula for the area of a triangle is $A = \frac{1}{2}bh$. Find the area of a yield sign. (Lesson 1-1) 390 in²

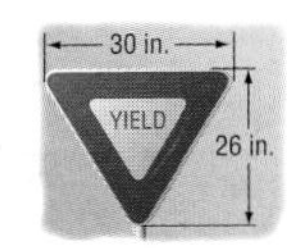

3. BILLBOARDS A standard roadside billboard is 14 feet by 48 feet. The area of a rectangle is $A = \ell w$. Find the area of a standard billboard. (Lesson 1-1) 672 ft²

4. AREA The area of a trapezoid is given by the formula $A = \frac{1}{2}(a + b)h$. Find A when $a = 2$ cm, $b = 5$ cm, and $h = 4$ cm. (Lesson 1-1) 14 cm²

5. CLOTHING A T-shirt shop has shirts on sale for \$9.99 each. Nina buys 2 of these shirts, Latisha buys 3, and Addie buys 1. (Lesson 1-2)

a. Illustrate the Distributive Property by writing two expressions to represent the cost of these shirts.

b. Use the Distributive Property to find how much money the store received from selling these shirts. \$59.94

5a. \$9.99(2 + 3 + 1); \$9.99 • 2 + \$9.99 • 3 + \$9.99 • 1

6. TEMPERATURE The formula for changing temperature in degrees Fahrenheit F to degrees Celsius C is given by the formula $C = \frac{5}{9}(F - 32)$. Find C if $F = 68°$. (Lesson 1-3) 20°

7. ALGEBRA Write an algebraic equation to represent the sentence *The quotient of two numbers is equal to the sum of those numbers.* (Lesson 1-3) $\frac{x}{y} = x + y$

8. ICE HOCKEY An ice hockey stick is 175 centimeters long, give or take 25 centimeters. Write and solve an absolute value equation to determine the least and greatest possible lengths of an ice hockey stick. (Lesson 1-4) $|x - 175| = 25$; $150 \le x \le 200$

9. SOCCER A regulation soccer ball is an air-filled sphere with a circumference of 68 to 70 centimeters. Write an absolute value equation to show the range of sizes allowable for a regulation soccer ball. (Lesson 1-4) $|x - 69| = 1$

10. COFFEE Coffee beans are typically roasted at 455°F, plus or minus 85°F. Write and solve an absolute value equation to determine the least and greatest temperatures at which coffee beans are typically roasted. (Lesson 1-4) $|x - 455| = 85$; $370 \le x \le 540$

11. PHONES Frieda's cell phone plan costs \$40 per month plus \$0.50 for each minute she goes beyond her free minutes. How many minutes can she go beyond her free minutes and still pay less than \$65? (Lesson 1-5) a. $40 + 0.5c \le 65$

a. Write an inequality to solve this problem.

b. Solve the problem. $c \le 50$

12. DATA Melissa's wireless handheld device service plan costs \$48 per month plus \$0.01 per kilobyte over her free usage. (Lesson 1-5)

a. Write an inequality to show how much she can go over her free usage and still pay less than \$58. $48 + 0.01d < 58$

b. Solve the inequality. $d < 1000$

13. MONEY Amy needs a new computer. They are on sale for \$350 but could vary in price by as much as \$125 from the sale price. (Lesson 1-6)

a. Write an absolute value inequality to describe this situation. $|350 - c| \le 125$

b. Solve the inequality to find the range of the prices of computers. $\{c \mid 225 \le c \le 475\}$

Chapter 2 Linear Relations and Functions (pp. 58–131)

1. **POLITICS** The table below shows the population of several states and the number of U.S. representatives from those states. (Lesson 2-1)

State	Population (millions)	Number of Representatives
Alabama	4.45	7
Delaware	0.78	1
Indiana	6.08	9
Michigan	9.94	15
New York	18.98	29
Ohio	11.35	18

a, b. See Student Handbook Answer Appendix.

a. Make a graph of the data with population on the horizontal axis and representatives on the vertical axis.

b. Identify the domain and range.

c. Is the relation *discrete* or *continuous*? discrete

d. Does the graph represent a function? Explain your reasoning. Yes; each domain value is paired with only one range value, so the relation is a function.

2. **TUTORING** Katrina is starting a business tutoring students in math. She rents an office for $450 per month and charges $40 per hour per student. She has 12 students. (Lesson 2-2)

a. Write an equation representing the situation if each student is tutored x hours per month.

b. How much profit will Katrina make if each student is tutored 4 hours per month? $1470

2a. $y = 40(12)x - 450$

3. **DRIVING** When driving up a certain hill, you rise 15 feet for every 1000 feet you drive forward. What is the slope of the road? (Lesson 2-3) $\frac{3}{200}$

4. **CELL PHONE** Mario bought a cell phone for $125. Monthly expenses for the cell phone total $85 per month. Write an equation that represents the total cost of buying and owning the cell phone for x months. (Lesson 2-4) $y = 85x + 125$

5a. $d = \frac{g}{250} + 3$

5. **GAMES** In Scott's favorite online game, virtual cash is earned from playing games. Playing a game earns 3 virtual dollars. Each 250 points scored in the game earns 1 additional virtual dollar. (Lesson 2-4)

a. Write an equation that models the virtual dollars earned d for a game score of g points.

b. How many virtual dollars did Scott earn when he had a game score of 12,500? 53

6. **BASEBALL** The table below shows the attendance for the Los Angeles Angels' home games. (Lesson 2-5)

Game	Attendance	Game	Attendance
1	43,906	4	34,970
2	42,463	5	31,397
3	35,701	6	30,876

a. Make a scatter plot of the data.

b. Find a regression equation for the data. $y = -2830.8x + 46{,}460.1$

6a. See Student Handbook Answer Appendix.

7. **RECREATION** The charge for renting inline skates from a rental shop for different amounts of time is shown. (Lesson 2-6) 7b, c. See Student Handbook Answer Appendix.

Inline Skate Rentals	
Time	Price ($)
1 hour	5
$\frac{1}{2}$ day	10
full day	17
full week	60

a. Identify the type of function that models this situation. step function

b. Write a function for the situation.

c. Graph the function.

8b. See Student Handbook Answer Appendix.

8. **HEALTH** Shooting baskets can burn up to 5.1 Calories per minute. The equation to represent how many Calories a person burns after m minutes of shooting baskets is $C(m) = 5.1m$. (Lesson 2-7)

a. Identify the transformation in the function.

b. Graph the function.

8a. The graph of the function is a dilation of the graph of $y = x$.

9. **CAR MAINTENANCE** Jerome needs to buy gas and oil for his car. Gas costs $4.03 a gallon and oil costs $2.99 a quart. He has $65 to spend. (Lesson 2-8) 9a, b. See Student Handbook Answer Appendix.

a. Write an inequality to represent the situation, where g is the number of gallons of gas he buys and q is the number of quarts of oil.

b. Graph the inequality.

c. Can Jerome buy 12 gallons of gasoline and 8 quarts of oil? No; (12, 8) is not in the shaded region.

Chapter 3 Systems of Equations and Inequalities (pp. 132–181)

1. **RECREATION** The admission fees for a fair are as shown in the table. On a certain day, 3400 people enter the fair and $12,250 is collected. (Lesson 3-1)

Admission Fee	
Age	Cost
adult	$5.00
child	$2.50

a. Write a system of equations to represent this situation. $a + c = 3400;\ 5a + 2.5c = 12{,}250$

b. How many adults and children attended? $a = 1500,\ c = 1900$

2. **LANDSCAPING** The school district placed two orders with a nursery. The first order was for 13 bushes and 4 trees and totaled $487. The second order was for 6 bushes and 2 trees and totaled $232. The bills do not list the per-item prices. (Lesson 3-1)

a. Write a system of equations to represent this situation. $13b + 4t = 487;\ 6b + 2t = 232$

b. What are the prices of one bush and of one tree? $b = \$23,\ t = \$47$

3. **DRAMA** Tickets to the next drama performance are as shown in the table. For the two-day run of the performance, 718 tickets are sold. The Drama Club collected $4269. (Lesson 3-2)

Tickets	
Age	Cost
adult	$8
child	$3

a. Write a system of equations to represent this situation. $a + c = 718;\ 8a + 3c = 4269$

b. Find how many adults and children attended. $a = 423,\ c = 295$

4. **NUMBERS** The sum of two numbers is 95. One number is 16 less than twice the other. (Lesson 3-2)

a. Write a system of equations to represent this situation. $x + y = 95;\ x = 2y - 16$

b. Find the numbers. $x = 58,\ y = 37$

5a. See Student Handbook Answer Appendix.

5. **CANDY** The most Jay can spend on chocolates is $35. White chocolates sell for $9.00 per pound, and dark chocolates sell for $7.50 per pound. He needs to buy at least 2.5 pounds of chocolate. (Lesson 3-3)

a. Graph the region that shows how many pounds of each type of chocolate he can purchase.

b. Give an example of three different purchases he can make. Sample answer: 2 lbs of dark, 2 lbs of white; 3 lbs of white, 1 lb of dark; 3 lbs of dark, 1 lb of white

6. **SALONS** Sierra King is a nail technician. When scheduling appointments, she allots 20 minutes for a manicure and 45 minutes for a pedicure in her 7-hour work day. The pedicure station must be sanitized after each use, so no more than 5 pedicures can be scheduled each day. The prices are $16 for a manicure and $38 for a pedicure. (Lesson 3-4)

a. Find a combination of manicures and pedicures that will maximize Ms. King's daily income. What is her maximum daily income? 21 manicures and 0 pedicures; $336

b. On avarage, clients tip $2 on a manicure and $7 on a pedicure. With tips, what combination of manicures and pedicures will maximize Ms. King's daily income? What is her maximum daily income with tips? 9 manicures and 5 pedicures; $387

7. **BUSINESS** Maura and Jeffrey use a shipping center for the pet accessories they sell. They want to track the sizes of t he packages shipped.

Joshua's Shipping Center	
Weight of Package	Cost
≤ 5 lb	$2.90
5 < weight < 10 lb	$5.20
≥ 10 lb	$8.00

The number of smallest packages shipped is 50% more than the number of largest packages shipped. One-day shipping charges for 300 packages is $1508. (Lesson 3-5)

a. Write a system of equations to represent this situation.

b. Find the number of packages shipped in each weight category.

7a, b. See Student Handbook Answer Appendix.

8. **PARKING** A parking lot has an area of 600 square meters. A car requires 6 square meters of space and a bus requires 30 square meters of space. The attendant can handle no more than 60 vehicles. If a car is charged $3 to park and a bus is charged $8, how many of each should the attendant accept to maximize income? (Lesson 3-5) 50 cars and 10 buses

9. **EDUCATION** In 2000, Harvard, Yale, and Stanford had combined endowments of $38.1 billion. Harvard had $0.1 billion more than Yale and Stanford together. Stanford's endowments trailed Harvard's by $10.2 billion. What were the endowments of each university? (Lesson 3-5) Harvard, $19.1 billion; Yale, $10.1 billion; Stanford, $8.9 billion

Chapter 4 Matrices (pp. 182–245)

1. **CELL PHONE USE** Four students' weekly cell phone use is summarized in the table. (Lesson 4-1)

Name	Cell Phone Minutes	Text Messages	Picture Messages
Lila	131	212	85
José	95	189	25
Tony	147	208	78
Abril	185	247	93

a, c. See Student Handbook Answer Appendix.

   a. Organize the cell phone usage in a matrix.

   b. Which student uses their cell phone the most?

   c. Add the elements of each row and interpret the results.

1b. Abril

2. **BUSINESS** An electronics store lists the prices for their most popular product in three categories at three stores. The manager has decided to put these products on sale for 25% off. (Lesson 4-2)

Store	Television	DVD Player	CD Player
1	582	132	85
2	621	129	89
3	594	131	95

   a. Write a matrix C to represent the current prices.

   b. What scalar can be used to determine a matrix N to represent the new prices? **0.75**

   c. Find N.

   d. What is $N - C$? What does this represent in this situation?

2a, c, d. See Student Handbook Answer Appendix.

3. **FUNDRAISING** Logan's band is selling boxes of fruit to raise money to go to Washington, D.C. The navel oranges are \$17 a box; red grapefruit are \$16 a box; and tangelos are \$27 a box. (Lesson 4-3)

Name	Oranges	Grapefruit	Tangelos
Logan	22	15	8
Lizzie	20	18	12
Jordan	10	3	7
Katherine	19	17	10

3a, b. See Student Handbook Answer Appendix.

   a. Write a matrix for the number of each type of fruit Logan and her friends sold.

   b. Use matrix multiplication to find the money raised by each person for each type of fruit.

   c. Find the total amount of money the friends raised for their trip. **\$3054**

4. **SPORTS** The Westfall Youth Baseball and Softball League charges the following registration fees: ages 7–8, \$45; ages 9–10, \$55; and ages 11–14, \$65. (Lesson 4-3)

Team Members		
Age	Baseball	Softball
7–8	350	280
9–10	320	165
11–14	180	120

   a. Write a matrix for the registration fees and a matrix for the number of players.

   b. Find the total amount of money the league received from baseball and softball registrations. **\$74,525**

4a. See Student Handbook Answer Appendix.

5. **SIGNS** For the election for student council, Michael wants to enlarge his campaign logo. He graphs it with vertices at $A(6, 0)$, $B(5, 7)$, and $C(0, 0)$. He enlarges it so that the perimeter is three times the original perimeter. State the coordinates of the vertices of the dilated image. (Lesson 4-4) **$A'(18, 0)$, $B'(15, 21)$, $C'(0, 0)$**

6. **ADVERTISING** Julie and Tonya are advertising a friend's new club. They are hanging flyers on poles at (3, 1), (4, 15), and (7, 12) according to their map. Each unit represents 1 kilometer. If they hang flyers everywhere, what is the area of town in which they are advertising? (Lesson 4-5) **22.5 km²**

7. **GEOGRAPHY** Dominic is calculating the amount of forest that is part of a metro park. He lays a coordinate grid in which 1 unit = 10 miles over a map of the forest with the origin at the entrance to the park. The coordinates of the two other exits are (7, 5) and (2.5, 10). Estimate the area of the forest. (Lesson 4-5) **2875 mi²**

8. **PILOT TRAINING** Flight instruction costs \$115 per hour, and the simulator costs \$65 per hour. Chia spent 4 more hours in airplane training than in the simulator. If Chia spent \$4780, how much time did she spend training in an airplane and in a simulator? (Lesson 4-6) **28 hours of flight instruction and 24 hours in the simulator**

9. **NUMBERS** The sum of the digits in a two-digit number is 14. The number itself is 2 greater than 11 times the tens digit. Find the number. (*Hint:* The number can be written as $10a + b$, where a is the tens digit and b is the ones digit.) (Lesson 4-6) **68**

Chapter 5 Quadratic Functions and Relations (pp. 246–326)

1. **ECONOMICS** A souvenir shop sells about 300 coffee mugs per month for \$7.50 each. The shop owner estimates that for each \$0.75 increase in the price, he will sell about 15 fewer coffee mugs per month. (Lesson 5-1)

   a. How much should the owner charge for each mug in order to maximize the monthly income from their sales? **\$11.25**

   b. What is the maximum monthly income the owner can expect to make from the mugs? **\$2531.25**

2a, b. See Student Handbook Answer Appendix.

2. **PHYSICS** An object is fired straight up from the top of a 150-foot tower at a velocity of 75 feet per second. The height $h(t)$ of the object t seconds after firing is given by $h(t) = -16t^2 + 75t + 150$. (Lesson 5-2) **c. 237.89 ft, 2.34 seconds**

   a. What are the domain and range of the function?

   b. What domain and range values are reasonable in the given situation?

   c. Find the maximum height reached by the object and the time that the height is reached.

   d. Interpret the meaning of the y-intercept in the context of this problem. **The y-intercept is the initial height of the object.**

3. **ARCHERY** An arrow is shot straight upward with a velocity of 85 feet per second. Use the formula $h(t) = v_0t - 16t^2 + h_0$, where $h(t)$ is the height of an object in feet, v_0 is the object's initial velocity in feet per second, h_0 is the intial height, and t is the time in seconds. (Lesson 5-2)

   a. Assuming the archer shoots the arrow from a height of 6 feet, how long after the arrow is released does it hit the ground? **5.4 s**

   b. How high does the arrow reach? **118.9 ft**

4. **NUMBERS** The sum of an integer and its square is 42. Find the integer. (Lesson 5-3) **6, −7**

5a. $(10 - x)(12 - x) = 63$, so $x^2 - 22x + 57 = 0$

5. **REMODELING** Sandy's closet was supposed to be 10 feet by 12 feet. The architect decided that this would not work and reduced the dimensions by the same amount x on each side. The area of the new closet is 63 square feet. (Lesson 5-3)

   a. Write a quadratic equation that represents the area of Sandy's closet now.

   b. Find the new dimensions of Sandy's closet. **7 ft by 9 ft**

9. See Student Handbook Answer Appendix.

6. **ELECTRICITY** In an AC circuit, voltage V, current C, and impedance I are related by the formula $V = CI$. (Lesson 5-4) **a. $22 + 14j$**

   a. Find the voltage in a circuit with current $3 + 5j$ amps and impedance $4 - 2j$ ohms.

   b. The voltage in a circuit is $76 - 10j$ volts, and the impedance is $8 - 7j$ ohms. What is the current? **$6 + 4j$**

7. **ARCHITECTURE** An architect's blueprints call for a room to be 12 feet by 12 feet. The customer would like the room to be square with an area of 275 square feet. How much will this add to each dimension? (Lesson 5-5) **4.58 ft**

8. **INSECTS** For a certain insect, the survival rate depends on temperature. A model of the number of larvae $N(t)$ that survive is given by $N(t) = -0.6t^2 + 32.1t - 350$, where t is the temperature in degrees Celsius. Find the range of temperatures where the insects can survive. (Lesson 5-6) **15.25 to 38.25**

9. **ARCHITECTURE** An architect designed a pool that is fenced on three sides. If she uses 60 yards of fencing to enclose an area of 352 square yards, then the dimensions ℓ and w can be modeled by $w = \ell^2 - 30\ell + 176$. Graph this function. (Lesson 5-7)

10. **ROCKETS** The height $h(t)$ of a model rocket in feet t seconds after its launch can be represented by the function $h(t) = -16t^2 + 96t + 0.75$. During what interval is the rocket at least 100 feet above the ground? (Lesson 5-8) **1.33 to 4.67 s**

11. **FUNDRAISING** The girls softball team is sponsoring a fundraising trip to see a baseball game. In order to earn a profit, they will charge \$15 per person if all seats on the bus are sold, but for each empty seat, they will increase the price by \$1.50 per person. (Lesson 5-8) **a. $P(n) = n[15 + 1.5(60 - n)] - 525 = -1.5n^2 + 105n - 525$**

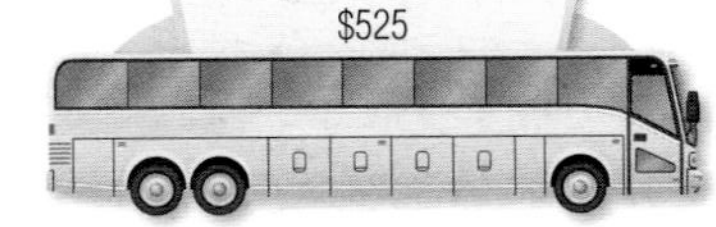

   a. Write a quadratic function giving the softball team's profit $P(n)$ from this fundraiser as a function of the number of passengers n.

   b. What is the minimum number of passengers needed for the team not to lose money? **6**

   c. What is the maximum profit the team can earn, and how many passengers will it take to achieve this maximum? **\$1312.50; 35 passengers**

Mixed Problem Solving

Chapter 6 Polynomials and Polynomial Functions (pp. 330–405)

1a. $-0.001x^2 + 5x - 500$ 1b. $5327.50

1. **E-SALES** A small online retailer estimates that the cost, in dollars, associated with selling x units of a particular product is given by the expression $0.001x^2 + 5x + 500$. The revenue from selling x units is given by $10x$. (Lesson 6-1)
   a. Write a polynomial to represent the profit generated by the product.
   b. Find the profit from sales of 1850 units.
2. **INVESTMENT** Charlene made $1235 working a summer job. She wants to invest it during the school year in a savings account that has an annual interest rate of 1.9% and a money market account that pays 3.9% per year. Write a polynomial to represent the amount of interest she will earn in one year if she invests x dollars in the savings account. (Lesson 6-1) $48.17 - 0.02x$
3. **CARS** The number of cars produced in a plant each day can be estimated by $6x^2 - 3x - 1$, where x is the number of worker teams. Divide by x to find the average number of cars produced per team. (Lesson 6-2) $6x - 3 - \frac{1}{x}$
4. **WOODWORKING** Arthur is building a rectangular table with an area of $3x^2 - 17x - 28$ square feet. If the length of the table is $3x + 4$ feet, what should the width of the table be? (Lesson 6-2) $x - 7$ ft
5. Consider the following graph. (Lesson 6-3)

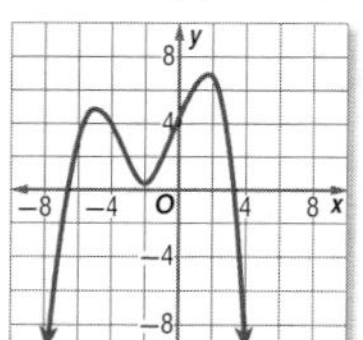

5a–c. See Student Handbook Answer Appendix.
   a. Describe the end behavior.
   b. Determine whether it represents an odd-degree or an even-degree function.
   c. State the number of real zeros.
6. **HEALTH** The weight w, in pounds, of a patient during a three-week illness is modeled by the cubic equation $w(n) = 0.3n^3 - 0.4n^2 + 95$, where n is the number of weeks since the patient became ill. (Lesson 6-4)
   a. Graph the function.
   b. Describe the turning points of the graph and its end behavior.
   c. What trends in the patient's weight does the graph suggest? Will the function model the patient's weight long term? Explain.

   6a–c. See Student Handbook Answer Appendix.
7. **SAILING** The area of a right triangular sail is $x^2 + 7x + 10$. The length of one leg of the sail is $2x + 10$. Find the length of the other leg. (Lesson 6-5) $x + 2$
8. **LANDSCAPING** A brick border that is x feet wide is built around a rectangular patio. The patio is 6 feet wide and 8 feet long. The combined area of the patio and the brick border is 120 square feet. What is the width of the brick border? (Lesson 6-5) 2 ft
9. **NUMBER SENSE** If the expression $ax^4 + bx^3 - x^2 + 2x + 3$ is divided by $x^2 + x - 2$, there is a remainder of $4x + 3$. Find the values of a and b. (Lesson 6-6) $a = 1$, $b = 2$
10. **CELL PHONES** DeQuan found that the equation $f(x) = 4x^3 + 4x^2 - 8x$ could be used to find the production volume of a certain type of cell phone, where x is time in minutes. Find the roots and type of roots for this equation. (Lesson 6-7) 0, 1, −2; real
11. **NUMBER SENSE** Write a polynomial function of least degree with real coefficients having zeros −1 and $6 - 3i$. (Lesson 6-7) $f(x) = x^3 - 11x^2 + 33x + 45$
12. **GEOMETRY** The volume of a rectangular solid is 160 cubic inches. The width is 3 inches more than the height, and the length is 1 inch less than the height. Find the dimensions of the solid. (Lesson 6-8) 4 in., 5 in., 8 in.

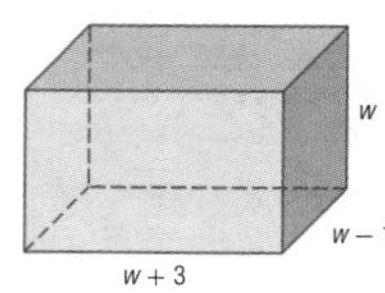

13a. $V = \pi r^3 + 6\pi r^2$
13. **FOOD** A restaurant orders spaghetti sauce in cylindrical metal cans. The volume of each can is about 160π cubic inches, and the height of the can is 6 inches more than the radius. (Lesson 6-8)
   a. Write a polynomial equation that represents the volume of a can. Use the formula for the volume of a cylinder, $V = \pi r^2 h$.
   b. What are the possible values of r? Which values are reasonable here? $4, -5 \pm i\sqrt{15}$; 4
   c. Find the dimensions of the can. $r = 4$ in., $h = 10$ in.

Chapter 7 Inverses and Radical Functions and Relations (pp. 406–471)

1. **TAXES** Claire has $150 deducted from every paycheck for retirement. She can have this deduction taken before state taxes are applied, which reduces her taxable income. Her state income tax is 7%. If Claire earns $1450 every pay period, find the difference in her net income if she has the retirement deduction taken before or after state taxes. (Lesson 7-1) See Student Handbook Answer Appendix.
2. **SHOPPING** The Sound Loft is offering both an in-store $25 rebate and a 25% discount on a stereo system that normally sells for $450. Which provides the better price: taking the discount before or after the rebate? (Lesson 7-1) See Student Handbook Answer Appendix.
3. **COMMISSION** Adelina works forty hours a week at a furniture store. She receives a $220 weekly salary, plus a 3% commission on sales over $5000. Assume that she sells enough this week to get the commission. (Lesson 7-1)
   a. Given the functions $f(x) = 0.03x$ and $g(x) = x - 5000$, which of $(f \circ g)(x)$ and $(g \circ f)(x)$ represents her commission? $(f \circ g)(x)$
   b. What is Adelina's commission on weekly sales of $11,675? $200.25
   c. How much is Adelina paid for working a week in which her sales total $17,381? $591.43
4. **GEOMETRY** The formula for the circumference of a circle is $C = 2\pi r$. (Lesson 7-2)
   a. Find the inverse of the function. $r = \frac{C}{2\pi}$
   b. Use the inverse to find the radius of a circle with a circumference of 150 inches. approx. 24 in.
5. **PHYSICS** The function $F = ma$ relates the acceleration a in meters per second squared to the force F in newtons for an object with mass m in kilograms. (Lesson 7-2)
   a. Find the inverse of the function. $a = \frac{F}{m}$
   b. Colby and his sled weigh 55 kilograms. They hit the bottom of a hill with a force of 275 newtons. How fast were they accelerating? 5 m/s²
6. **PENDULUM** The length of time it takes for a pendulum on a clock to make a complete motion is found by $f(\ell) = 2\pi\sqrt{\left(\frac{\ell}{g}\right)}$, where ℓ is the length of the pendulum and g is the acceleration due to gravity which is 9.8 meters per second squared. (Lesson 7-3)
   a. Graph the function. See Student Handbook Answer Appendix.
   b. How long is the pendulum for a period of 1.9 seconds? 0.9 m
7. **PACKAGING** Leroy needs a box to hold 3375 cubic centimeters. He is shipping cell phone parts and the packing material. If he makes the box a cube, how long is each side? (Lesson 7-4) a. $s = \sqrt[3]{V}$
   a. Write an equation to represent the situation.
   b. Find the length of each side. 15 cm
8. **GEOMETRY** Use the rectangle shown. (Lesson 7-5)

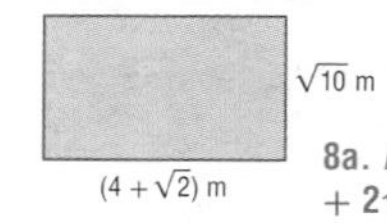

8a. $P = 8 + 2\sqrt{2} + 2\sqrt{10}$
   a. Find the perimeter of the rectangle.
   b. Find the area of the rectangle. $A = 4\sqrt{10} + 2\sqrt{5}$ in²
9. **PRICES** The formula $C = c(1 + r)^n$ can be used to estimate the future cost of an item due to inflation. C represents the future cost, c represents the current cost, r is the rate of inflation, and n is the number of years for the projection. (Lesson 7-6)
   a. Suppose a gallon of gas costs $3.98 now. How much would the price of gas be in 6 months with an inflation rate of 2.7%? $4.03
   b. Suppose a car costs $14,500 now. How much would the price of the car be in 6 months with an inflation rate of 2.9%? $14,709
10. **BODIES** The formula $p = \frac{1000\sqrt[3]{m}}{h}$ measures the ponderal index p, which is a measure of a person's body based on height h in centimeters and mass m in kilograms. A person who is 1.8 meters tall has a ponderal index of about 22.9. How much does the person weigh in kilograms? (Lesson 7-7) 70 kg
11. **GRAVITY** Hugo drops his keys from the top of a Ferris wheel. The formula $t = \frac{1}{4}\sqrt{65 - h}$ describes the time t in seconds when the keys are h feet above the boardwalk. If Hugo was 65 meters high when he dropped the keys, how many meters above the boardwalk will the keys be after 2 seconds? (Lesson 7-7) 1 m

Chapter 8 Exponential and Logarithmic Functions and Relations (pp. 472–542)

1. **CAFFEINE** A cup of coffee contains 95 milligrams of caffeine. The average teen can eliminate approximately 12.5% of the caffeine from their system per hour. (Lesson 8-1)
   a. Write an equation to represent the amount of caffeine remaining after drinking a cup of coffee. $y = 95(0.875)^x$
   b. Draw a graph for the equation. See Student Handbook Answer Appendix.
2. **BIOLOGY** A bacteria culture used in biology class grows continuously at a rate of 4.6% per day. The teacher starts with 250 bacteria. (Lesson 8-1)
   a. Write an equation to represent the amount of bacteria as time passes. $y = 250(0.954)^x$
   b. Draw a graph for the equation. See Student Handbook Answer Appendix.
3. **POPULATION** Every ten years, the Bureau of the Census counts the number of people living in the U.S. In 1790, the population of the U.S. was 3.93 million. By 1800, this number had grown to 5.31 million. (Lesson 8-2)
   a. Write an exponential function that could be used to model the U.S. population y in millions for 1790 to 1800. Write the equation in terms of x, the number of decades since 1790. $y = 3.93(1.35)^x$
   b. Assume that the U.S. population continued to grow at least that rapidly. Estimate the population for the years 1820, 1840, and 1860. Then compare your estimates with the actual population for those years, which were 9.64, 17.06, and 31.44 million, respectively.
   3b. See Student Handbook Answer Appendix.
4. **CHEMISTRY** The equation to determine the pH of a substance is $pH = -\log_{10}[H^+]$. (Lesson 8-3)
   a. What is the concentration of the hydrogen ion $[H^+]$ if the pH of an aqueous solution is 3.30? 5.0×10^{-4}
   b. What is the concentration of the hydrogen ion in an aqueous solution with pH = 13.22? 6.0×10^{-14}
   c. What is the concentration of the hydrogen ion in room temperature water with a pH of 7? 1.0×10^{-7}
   d. The runoff from a highway is measured at a pH of 3.6. What is the concentration of the hydrogen ions in this solution? 2.5×10^{-4}
   e. What is the pH of an aqueous solution in which $[H^+] = 2.7 \times 10^{-3}$ Moles? 2.57
   f. If the pH of an aqueous solution is 6.52, what is the concentration of hydrogen ions? 3.0×10^{-7}
5. **EARTHQUAKES** The Richter scale is based on logarithms. The equation is $R = \log_{10} M$, where M is the amount of ground movement and R is the strength of the earthquake on the Richter scale. (Lesson 8-4)
   a. How much ground movement is there in an earthquake that registers 5? 100,000 units
   b. How many times as much ground movement is there in a level 5 as in a level 3? $10^2 = 100$ times as much movement
6. **STAR LIGHT** The brightness, or apparent magnitude m of a star or planet is given by $m = 6 - 2.5 \log_{10} \frac{L}{L_0}$, where L is the amount of light coming to Earth from the star or planet and L_0 is the amount of light from a sixth magnitude star. Find the difference in the magnitudes of Sirius and the crescent moon. (Lesson 8-5) 5

The cresent moon is about 100 times as bright as the brightest star, Sirius.

7. **FLIGHT** An airplane takes off from an airport at sea level and its altitude h, in feet, at time t, in minutes, is given by $h = 2000 \ln (t + 1)$. Find the altitude at time $t = 2$ minutes. (Lesson 8-6) 2197 ft
8. **MONEY** The amount A in an account after t years when interest is compounded continuously is found using the formula $A = Pe^{rt}$, where P is the amount of principal and r is the annual interest rate. When Saul was born, his parents deposited $4000 into an account paying 5% interest compounded continuously. (Lesson 8-7)
   a. If the account is not touched, what is the balance after 10 years? $6594.89
   b. If they want to have $15,000 after 18 years, how much would they need to invest? $6098.54
9. **OLYMPICS** In 1928, the winning women's high jump was 62.5 inches, while the winning men's jump was 76.5 inches. Since then, the winning jump for women has increased by about 0.38% per year, while the winning jump for men has increased at a slower rate, 0.3%. If these rates continue, when will the women's winning high jump be higher than the men's? (Lesson 8-8) after the year 2182

Chapter 9 Rational Functions and Relations (pp. 550–613)

1. **BASKETBALL** At the end of the 2009–2010 season, a professional basketball player had made 5422 field goals out of 12,138 attempts during his NBA career. (Lesson 9-1)
   a. Write a ratio to represent the number of career field goals made to career field goals attempted by the professional basketball player at the end of the 2009–2010 season. $\frac{5422}{12,138}$
   b. Suppose the professional basketball player attempted a field goals and made m field goals during the 2010–2011 season. Write a rational expression to represent the ratio of the number of career field goals made to the number of career field goals attempted at the end of the 2010–2011 season. $\frac{5422 + m}{12,138 + a}$
2. **GEOMETRY** In the figure, the area of the rectangle is 111 square centimeters and the triangle is equilateral. Find the perimeter of the figure in terms of x. (Lesson 9-2)
   See Student Handbook Answer Appendix.

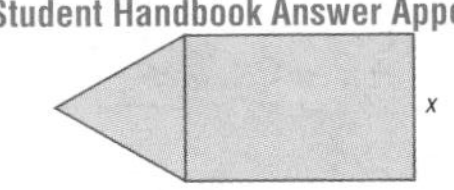

3. **GEOMETRY** Find the perimeter of the rectangle. (Lesson 9-2) $\frac{4}{(y - 4)}$

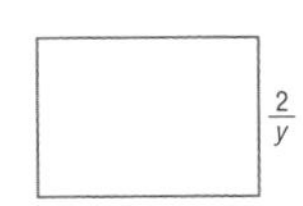

4. **AREA** A rectangle has an area equal to 100 cm^2 and a width x. (Lesson 9-3)
   a. Write an expression for the perimeter P in terms of x. $P(x) = 2\left(x + \frac{100}{x}\right)$
   b. Graph the perimeter as a function of x.
   c. What domain and range values are meaningful in the context of the problem?
   4b, c. See Student Handbook Answer Appendix.
5. **TRAVEL** A boat traveled upstream at r_1 miles per hour. During the return trip to its original starting point, the boat traveled at r_2 miles per hour. The average speed for the entire trip R is given by the formula $R = \frac{(2r_1r_2)}{(r_1 + r_2)}$. (Lesson 9-4)
   a. Draw the graph if $r_2 = 15$ miles per hour.
   b. What is the R-intercept of the graph?
   c. What domain and range values are meaningful in the context of the problem?
   5a–c. See Student Handbook Answer Appendix.
6. **NUTRITION** There are about 200 Calories in 50 grams of Swiss cheese. Susan ate 70 grams of this cheese. About how many Calories were in the cheese that she ate if the number of Calories varies directly as the weight of the cheese? (Lesson 9-5) 280
7. **PHYSICS** According to Hooke's law, the force needed to stretch a spring is proportional to the amount the spring is stretched. If 50 pounds stretches a spring five inches, how much will the spring be stretched by a force of 120 pounds? (Lesson 9-5) 12 in.
8. **PLANETS** Kepler's Third Law of Planetary Motion states that the square of the time required for a planet to make one revolution about the Sun varies directly as the cube of the average distance of the planet from the Sun. If you assume that Mars is 1.5 times as far from the Sun as is Earth, find the approximate length of a Martian year. (Lesson 9-5) The Martian year is approximately 1.837 Earth years.
9. **BIKING** Two cyclists start at the same time from opposite ends of a course that is 45 miles long. One cyclist is riding at 14 mph and the second cyclist is riding at 16 mph. How long after they begin will they meet? (Lesson 9-6) 1.5 hours
10. **MONEY** An investment advisor deposited $50,000 into two simple interest accounts. On the tax-free account the annual interest rate is 7%, and on the money market fund the annual simple interest rate is 13%. (Lesson 9-6) a. $0.07x = 0.13(50,000 - x)$
    a. Let x equal the amount put into the tax-free account. Write an expression for when both accounts earn the same amount of interest.
    b. How much should be invested in the tax-free account so that both accounts earn the same interest? $32,500
    c. How much should be invested in the market fund so that both accounts earn the same interest? $17,500
11. **CYCLING** On a particular day, the wind added 3 kilometers per hour to Alfonso's rate when he was cycling with the wind and subtracted 3 kilometers per hour from his rate on his return trip. Alfonso found that in the same amount of time he could cycle 36 kilometers with the wind, he could go only 24 kilometers against the wind. What is his normal bicycling speed with no wind? Determine whether your answer is reasonable. (Lesson 9-6) See Student Handbook Answer Appendix.

Chapter 10 Conic Sections (pp. 614–677)

1. **NEIGHBORHOOD** Katie and Angela agree to meet halfway between their houses. On a map, Katie lives at (1, −7). Angela lives at (−5, −3). (Lesson 10-1) **a. $2\sqrt{13}$ units**
   a. How far apart do Katie and Angela live?
   b. Where is the halfway point? **(−2, −5)**

2. **KEEP AWAY** Stephanie, standing at (2, 3), threw a ball to Heather, standing at (4, 1). (Lesson 10-1)
   a. How far did Stephanie throw the ball? **2.8 units**
   b. If Stephanie and Heather are keeping Alex from catching the ball and he is standing exactly between them, where is Alex standing? **(3, 2)**

3. **FLASHLIGHT** The parabolic reflector in a flashlight reflects the light from the bulb and makes it more intense. If the vertex of the parabola is at the origin, the focus is at (0, 2). (Lesson 10-2)
   a. Write an equation for the parabola formed by this flashlight reflector. **$y = \frac{1}{8}x^2$**
   b. Graph the equation. **See Student Handbook Answer Appendix.**

4. **INTERNET** A bagel shop offers free WiFi. Their transmitter has a 60-meter range in any direction. (Lesson 10-3)
   a. Write an equation to represent the area in which people can access the free WiFi. Place the bagel shop at the origin. **$x^2 + y^2 = 3600$**
   b. Graph the equation. **See Student Handbook Answer Appendix.** **5a. $\frac{x^2}{(884.5)^2} + \frac{y^2}{(883.3)^2} = 1$**

5. **SPACE** Saturn's distance from the Sun at the aphelion is about 930 million miles. Saturn's distance at the perihelion is 839 million miles. (Lesson 10-4)
   a. Determine an equation relating Saturn's orbit around the Sun in millions of miles with the center of the horizontal ellipse at the origin.
   b. Graph the equation. **See Student Handbook Answer Appendix.**

6. **VENUS** At its closest point, Venus is 0.719 astronomical units from the Sun. At its farthest point, Venus is 0.728 astronomical units from the Sun. Write an equation for the orbit of Venus. Assume that the center of the orbit is the origin, the Sun lies on the x-axis, and the radius of the Sun is 0.004 astronomical unit. (Lesson 10-4)
   $\frac{x^2}{0.5293} + \frac{y^2}{0.5292} = 1$

7. **BATS** Two bats that are 300 feet apart send out signals looking for prey. The concentric sound waves meet in a hyperbolic shape. The bats determine that a swarm of gnats is 80 feet farther from the first bat than from the second bat. Determine the equation of the hyperbola centered at the origin on which the swarm is located. (Lesson 10-5)

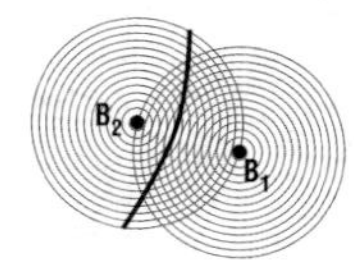

   a. Identify the vertices, foci, and asymptotes of the hyperbola.
   b. Write the equation. **$\frac{x^2}{1600} - \frac{y^2}{20{,}900} = 1$**
   7a. See Student Handbook Answer Appendix.

8. **DISCS** The movement of a flying disc can be described by the equation: $y + \left(\frac{1}{80}\right)x^2 - x = 0$, where x represents the time in seconds. (Lesson 10-6)
   a. Write the equation in standard form.
   b. State whether the graph of the equation is a *parabola*, *circle*, *ellipse*, or *hyperbola*. **parabola**
   c. Graph the equation.
   8a, c. See Student Handbook Answer Appendix.

9. **EARTHQUAKE** Seismographs are used to measure the intensity of earthquakes. Three seismographs can be used to find the center of the earthquake. Determine the location of the center of the earthquake on the grid. (Lesson 10-7) **(3, −4)**

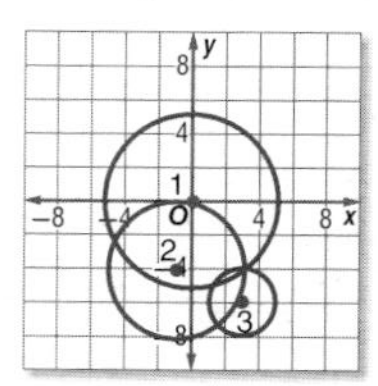

10. **ROCKETS** Two rockets are launched at the same time, but from different heights. The height y in feet of one rocket after t seconds is given by $y = -16t^2 + 150t + 5$. The height of the other rocket is given by $y = -16t^2 + 160t$. After how many seconds are the rockets at the same height? (Lesson 10-7) **0.5 s**

Chapter 11 Sequences and Series (pp. 678–741)

1. **FIELD HOUSE** The field house has a section where the seating can be arranged so that the first row has 11 seats, the second row has 15 seats, the third row has 19 seats, and so on. There is sufficient space for 30 rows in the section. (Lesson 11-1)
   a. How many seats are in the last row? **127**
   b. How many seats are in the whole section? **2070**

2. **SALARY** Mr. Patton starts his job at \$40,000 per year. He receives a \$1000 raise every year until he retires after 35 years. (Lesson 11-2)
   a. How much is Mr. Patton making the last year he works? **\$74,000**
   b. How much does Mr. Patton make over the course of his career? **\$1,995,500**

3. **ART** Alberta is making a beadwork design consisting of rows of colored beads. The first row consists of 10 beads, and each consecutive row will have 15 more beads than the previous row. (Lesson 11-2)
   a. Write an equation for the number of beads in the nth row. **$a_n = 15n - 5$**
   b. Find the number of beads in the design if it contains 25 rows. **4750 beads**

4. **PHYSICAL SCIENCE** A ball bounced in place recovers a certain percentage of its original height. Suppose a ball that recovers 70% of its height is dropped from 200 feet. After its first bounce, it reaches a height of 140 feet. After the second bounce, it reaches a height of 98 feet. (Lesson 11-3)
   a. How high will the ball bounce on its sixth bounce, which is the seventh height? **23.5 ft**
   b. What is the sum of the heights the ball has bounced through on its sixth bounce? **611.8 ft**

5. **RUBBER BALL** A rubber ball is dropped from a height of 10 meters. Supposed it rebounds one half the distance after each fall. Find the total distance the ball travels. (Lesson 11-4) **30 m**

6. **BUILDING** A 25-story building has a basement that is 4 feet below street level. Each floor is 13 feet high. (Lesson 11-5)
   a. Write a recursive formula for the height of each floor. **$a_{n+1} = a_n + 13$, $a_0 = -4$**
   b. Find the height of the first 5 floors.

Floor Number	Basement (0)	1	2	3	4	5
Height (ft)	−4	9	22	35	48	61

7. **FISH** In a city fishing pond, the city starts with 4000 trout. 20% of the fish are caught each year, so the city adds 1000 fish every spring. (Lesson 11-5)
   a. Write a recursive formula for the number of fish in the pond. **$a_n = 0.8a_{(n-1)} + 1000$**
   b. Determine the number of fish in the pond after 5 years. **4590**
   c. How many fish are needed to maintain a constant population? **5000**

8. **COMPETITION** Seventy-five teams take part in a competition organized so that teams meet one-on-one with the defeated team getting dropped out of the competition. How many games are needed before one team is declared a winner? (Lesson 11-6) **See Student Handbook Answer Appendix.**

9. **SCHOOL** Mr. Hopkins is giving a five-question quiz. How many ways could a student answer the questions with three trues and two falses? (Lesson 11-6) **10**

10. **GEOMETRY** Write an expanded expression for the volume of the cube. (Lesson 11-6)
   $27x^3 + 54x^2 + 36x + 8$ cm^3

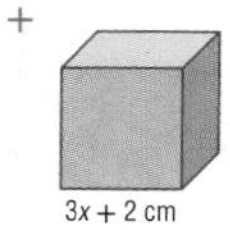

11. **PASCAL'S TRIANGLE** Study the first eight rows of Pascal's triangle. Write the sum of the terms in each row as a list. Make a conjecture about the sums of the rows of Pascal's triangle. (Lesson 11-7) **1, 2, 4, 8, 16, 32, 64, 128; The sum of the nth row is 2^n.**

12. **NUMBER THEORY** Two statements that can be proved using mathematical induction are $\frac{1}{3} + \frac{1}{3^2} + \frac{1}{3^3} + \cdots + \frac{1}{3^n} = \frac{1}{2}\left(1 - \frac{1}{3^n}\right)$ and $\frac{1}{4} + \frac{1}{4^2} + \frac{1}{4^3} + \cdots + \frac{1}{4^n} = \frac{1}{3}\left(1 - \frac{1}{4^n}\right)$. Write and prove a conjecture involving $\frac{1}{5}$ that is similar to the statements. (Lesson 11-7) **See Student Handbook Answer Appendix.**

Chapter 12 Probability and Statistics (pp. 742–803)

Determine if the statements show a *correlation* or a *causation*. (Lesson 12-1)

1. People who own red cars are twice as likely to have an accident as people who own blue cars. **correlation**
2. An apple that is red has color. **causation**
3. Tom is in a room that is not empty. **causation**
4. Men who have beards are happier than men who do not. **correlation**

5. **FOOTBALL** The tables show the Ohio State University football scores in the 2006 and 2007 seasons. (Lesson 12-2)

2006 Season

35	24	37	28
38	35	38	44
44	17	54	42

2007 Season

38	20	33	58
30	23	48	24
37	38	28	14

a. Find the mean for the 2006 season. **36.3**

b. Find the mean for the 2007 season. **32.6**

c. Find the standard deviation of scores from 2006. **about 9.4**

d. Find the standard deviation of scores from 2007. **about 11.8**

e. How do the standard deviations compare?

f. What conclusion can you make about the two seasons?

5e, f. See Student Handbook Answer Appendix.

6. **DRIVING** The table shows the number of students who have a driver's license and the number who own a personal vehicle. (Lesson 12-3)

Own?	License	No License
Y	148	2
N	124	86

a. Find the probability that Harry owns a vehicle, given that he has a license.

b. Find the probability that Anton does not have a license, given that he does not own a vehicle.

c. Find the probability that Morgan does not own a vehicle, given that she does not have a license.

6a–c. See Student Handbook Answer Appendix.

7. **MARBLES** A jar contains 3 white and 6 red marbles, all of equal size. Three marbles are drawn at random without replacement. What is the probability that at least 2 marbles drawn are red? (Lesson 12-4) $\frac{65}{84}$

8. **DRAWINGS** Twenty-four students entered the drawing below. What is the probability that 2 of 3 friends who entered won a ticket? (Lesson 12-4) **about 9.4%**

FREE
Concert Tickets!
Five tickets to tonight's show are being given away!
Enter to win!

9. **PINEAPPLES** The graph of the normal distribution of the number of pineapple rings in each can is shown. (Lesson 12-5)

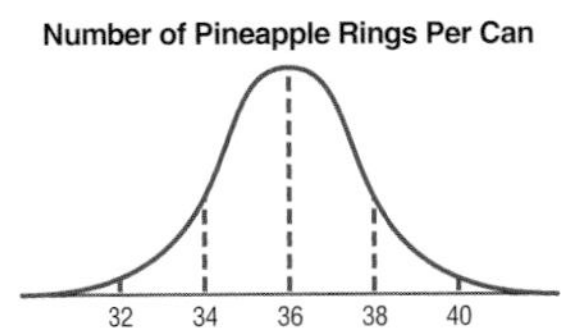

a. Find the mean and standard deviation. **36; 2**

b. What percent of the cans can be expected to contain at least 34 pineapple rings? **84%**

c. In a random sample of 840 cans, how many can be expected to contain less than 40 pineapple rings? **819**

10. **PHONES** A sample of 144 students was asked for the average amount of time they spent talking on the phone every day. The mean time was 85 minutes with a standard deviation of 3.5 minutes. Determine a 95% confidence interval. (Lesson 12-6) $84.42 \leq x \leq 85.58$

11. **COINS** A fair coin is tossed 10 times. What is the probability that exactly 6 heads will occur? (Lesson 12-7) **0.21**

12. **TELEPHONES** In the early days of telephone service, there was a probability of 0.8 of success in any attempt to make a telephone call. Calculate the probability of having 7 successes in 10 attempts. (Lesson 12-7) **0.201**

Chapter 13 Trigonometric Functions (pp. 804–887) **8c, 9a, 10b. See Student Handbook Answer Appendix.**

1. **TREES** From a point on the ground 25 feet from the foot of a tree, the angle of elevation of the top of the tree is 32°. Find the height of the tree to the nearest foot. (Lesson 13-1) **16 ft**

2. **LADDER** A ladder 6 feet long leans against a wall and makes an angle of 71° with the ground. Find to the nearest tenth of a foot how high up the wall the ladder will reach. (Lesson 13-1) **5.7 ft**

3. **BICYCLES** A bicycle tire has a diameter of 28 inches. How far does a bicycle travel in feet after $1\frac{1}{4}$ tire rotations? (Lesson 13-2) **9.16 ft**

4. **MUSIC** A metronome is a metal bar that is 5 inches long that swings back and forth to keep track of beats for music.

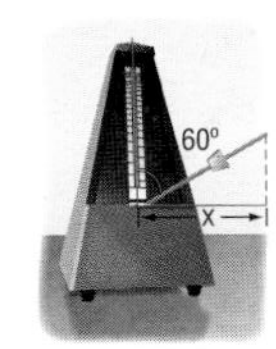

From the vertical position, it rotates 60° in each direction. How far outside the box, x, does the metronome arm reach? (Lesson 13-3) **4.33 in.**

5. **BOATS** Samuel sat on the deck of a river steamboat. As the paddle wheel turned, he noticed that a piece of seaweed was caught on one of the paddles. He started to keep track of the time and position above the water of the seaweed. When his stopwatch read 4 seconds, the seaweed was at its highest point, 16 feet above the surface of the water. The wheel's diameter was 18 ft and it completed its revolution every 10 seconds. (Lesson 13-3)

a. Make a table showing the height of the seaweed at 4, 6.5, 9, 11.5, 14, and 16.5 seconds.

b. Make a graph of the function. Let the horizontal axis represent the time t and the vertical axis represent the height h in inches that the paddle is from the water.

5a, b. See Student Handbook Answer Appendix.

6. **TOWER** Miguel needs to measure the height of the Leaning Tower of Pisa. He walks exactly 200 feet from the base of the tower and looks up. The angle from the ground to the top of the tower is 44.3°. The Leaning Tower of Pisa leans about 4° towards Miguel. How tall is the Leaning Tower of Pisa? (Lesson 13-4) **approx. 183 ft**

7. **SURVEYING** To approximate the length of a quarry, a surveyor starts at one end of the lake and walks 245 yards. He then turns 110° and walks 270 yards until he arrives at the other end of the lake. Approximately how long is the lake? (Lesson 13-5) **296 yd**

8. **FISH** Goldfish can hear sound with a lower frequency than humans can hear. Goldfish can hear as low as 20 hertz, or 20 cycles per second. (Lesson 13-6)

a. Find the period of the function that models the sound waves. **0.05 second**

b. Let the amplitude equal 1 unit. Write a sine function to represent the sound wave y as a function of time t. $y = \sin 40\pi t$

c. Graph the function.

9. **BIOLOGY** In a certain wildlife refuge, the population of field mice can be modeled by $y = 3000 + 1250 \sin \frac{\pi}{6}t$, where y represents the number of mice and t represents the number of months past March 1 of a given year. (Lesson 13-7)

a. Determine the period of the function. What does this period represent?

b. What is the maximum number of mice, and when does this occur? **4250; June 1**

10. **ECONOMY** An economist indicates that the demand for temporary employment (measured in thousands of job applications per week) in Sid's county can be modeled by the function $d = 4.3 \sin (0.82t + 0.3) + 7.3$, where t is the time in years since January 1995. (Lesson 13-8)

a. State the amplitude, period, and vertical shift of the function. **4.3, 7.7, 7.3**

b. Interpret the meaning of the function in the context of the situation.

11. **SQUIRRELS** A squirrel in a 10-foot tree was watching a cat that was sitting 9 feet from the base of the tree. At what angle to the horizontal was the squirrel looking? (Lesson 13-9) **48°**

Chapter 14 Trigonometric Identities and Equations (pp. 888–933)

1. **GEOMETRY** The area of a triangle can be determined by the formula $A = \frac{1}{2}ab \sin C$. (Lesson 14-1) $\frac{ab}{2 \csc C}$

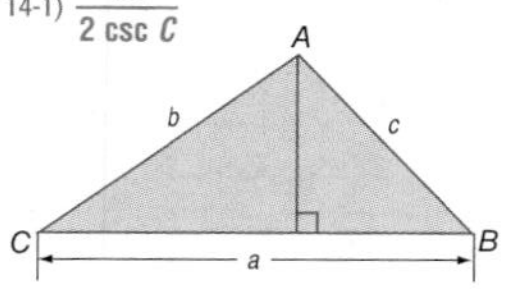

Rewrite the formula in terms of csc *C*.

2. **SCIENCE** Snell's Law describes the relationship between the angles of incidence and refraction passing through a boundary between two different media, such as air and glass. $\frac{\csc \theta_2}{\csc \theta_1} = \frac{v_1}{v_2}$ $\quad \frac{\sin \theta_1}{\sin \theta_2} = \frac{v_1}{v_2}$

Rewrite Snell's Law in terms of csc θ. (Lesson 14-1)

3. **ROCKETS** In the formula $h = \frac{v^2 \sin^2 \theta}{2g}$, h is the maximum height reached by a rocket, θ is the angle between the ground and the initial path of the object, v is the rocket's initial velocity, and g is the acceleration due to gravity. Verify the identity $\frac{v^2 \sin^2 \theta}{2g} = \frac{v^2 \cos^2 \theta}{2g \cot^2 \theta}$. (Lesson 14-2) **See Student Handbook Answer Appendix.**

4. **NEIGHBORHOOD** The following grid is a map of Newtown. Francine lives at *O*. Norman lives at *N*. Mark lives at *M*. School is at *J*. ∠*a* is 38° and ∠*b* is 42°. Francine lives 1 mile from school. Round to the nearest hundredth, if necessary. (Lesson 14-3)

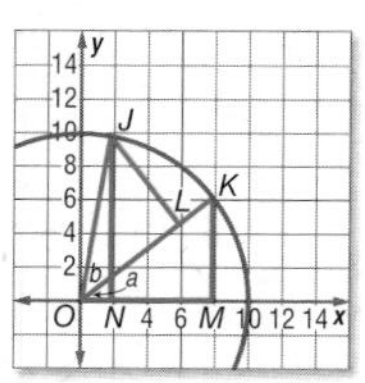

a. How far does Mark live from Francine? **0.79 mi**

b. How much closer does Norman live to school than Francine? **0.02 mi**

5. **COMMUNICATION** A radio transmitter sends out two signals, one for voice communication and another for data. Suppose the equation of the voice wave is $v = 10 \sin (2t - 30°)$, and the equation of the data wave is $d = 10 \cos (2t + 60°)$. Draw a graph of the waves when they are combined. (Lesson 14-3) **See Student Handbook Answer Appendix.**

6. **PHYSICAL SCIENCE** Scott was solving a series of equations concerning maximizing the distance for throwing a rock off a bridge when he came across this equation.

$$x = \frac{1}{g(v^2 \sin \theta \cos \theta)}$$

Use the double-angle identity to simplify this equation. (Lesson 14-4) $x = \frac{2}{g(v^2 \sin 2\theta)}$

7. **AVIATION** When a jet travels at speeds greater than the speed of sound, a sonic boom is created by the sound waves forming a cone behind the jet. If θ is the measure of the angle at the vertex of the cone, then the Mach number M can be determined using the formula $\sin \frac{\theta}{2} = \frac{1}{M}$. Find the Mach number of a jet if a sonic boom is created by a cone with a vertex angle of 75°. (Lesson 14-4) **1.64**

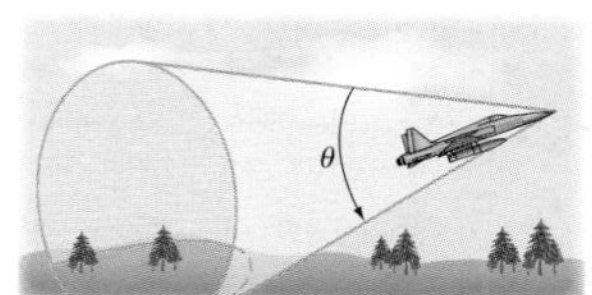

8. **LADDER** A ladder is leaning against the wall. What is the measure of the angle *A* that the ladder makes with the ground? (Lesson 14-5) **60°**

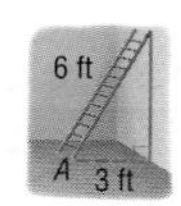

9. **LAKES** Determine the length ℓ of the pond. (Lesson 14-5) **19.5 ft**

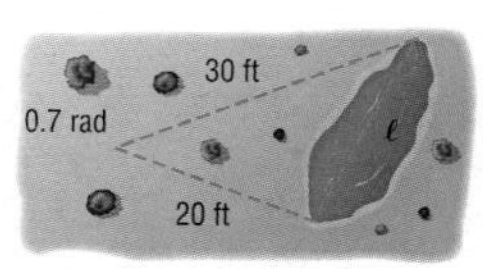

10. **MOUNTAIN** Determine the distance *d* to the top of the mountain. (Lesson 14-5) **1250.7 m**

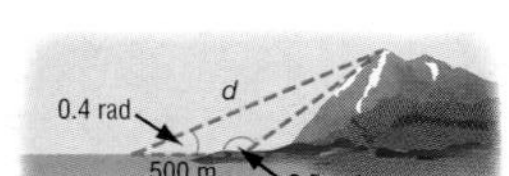

Concepts and Skills Bank

1 Proportional Reasoning

Two quantities are **proportional** if they have a constant ratio or rate. Relationships in which the ratios or rates are not constant are said to be **nonproportional**.

proportional

Distance (m)	3	9	12	21
Time (sec)	1	3	4	7

$\frac{3}{1} = \frac{9}{3} = \frac{12}{4} = \frac{21}{7}$

nonproportional

Distance (m)	1	4	7	9
Time (sec)	2	5	8	10

$\frac{1}{2} \neq \frac{4}{5} \neq \frac{7}{8} \neq \frac{9}{10}$

When two ratios are equal, they form a **proportion**. Consider the following proportion.

$\frac{a}{b} = \frac{c}{d}$ **Assume $b \neq 0$ and $d \neq 0$.**

$\frac{a}{\cancel{b}} \cdot \cancel{b}d = \frac{c}{\cancel{d}} \cdot b\cancel{d}$ **Multiply each side by bd.**

$ad = cb$ **Simplify.**

The products ad and cb are called the **cross products** of this proportion. You can use cross products to determine whether two ratios form a proportion.

EXAMPLE 1

Use cross products to determine whether each pair of ratios forms a proportion.

a. $\frac{4.8}{6.4}, \frac{2.1}{2.8}$

$\frac{4.8}{6.4} \stackrel{?}{=} \frac{2.1}{2.8}$ **Write a proportion.**

$4.8 \cdot 2.8 \stackrel{?}{=} 2.1 \cdot 6.4$ **Find the cross products.**

$13.44 = 13.44$ ✓ **Simplify.**

The cross products are equal, so the ratios form a proportion.

b. $\frac{6.25}{7.5}, \frac{9.75}{12}$

$\frac{6.25}{7.5} \stackrel{?}{=} \frac{9.75}{12}$ **Write a proportion.**

$6.25 \cdot 12 \stackrel{?}{=} 9.75 \cdot 7.5$ **Find the cross products.**

$75 \neq 73.125$ ✗ **Simplify.**

The cross products are not equal, so the ratios do not form a proportion.

You can use cross products to solve a proportion in which one of the quantities is not known.

1 Lesson CSB Notes

1 FOCUS

Vertical Alignment

Lesson CSB-1
Identify and solve proportions.

After Lesson CSB-1
Solve problems involving direct variation.

2 TEACH

Example 1 shows how to determine whether a pair of ratios forms a proportion. **Example 2** shows how to solve a proportion.

Additional Examples

1 Use cross products to determine whether each pair of ratios forms a proportion.

a. $\frac{6.5}{10.5}, \frac{8.75}{15}$ no

b. $\frac{3.2}{5.6}, \frac{4.4}{7.7}$ yes

2 Solve each proportion.

a. $\frac{y}{24} = \frac{27}{36}$ 18

b. $\frac{8}{t} = \frac{24}{4.8}$ 1.6

Tips for New Teachers

Alternative Method As an alternative to using cross products, students can solve proportions using the multiplication property of equality.

3 ASSESS

Formative Assessment

Use Exercises 1–24 to assess whether students understand how to identify and solve proportions.

Ticket Out the Door Ask students to write down two ratios that form a proportion.

EXAMPLE 2

Solve each proportion.

a. $\frac{9}{15} = \frac{n}{25}$

$\frac{9}{15} = \frac{n}{25}$	Original proportion
$9 \cdot 25 = n \cdot 15$	Cross products
$225 = 15n$	Multiply.
$\frac{225}{15} = n$	Divide each side by 15.
$15 = n$	Simplify.

b. $\frac{10}{8.4} = \frac{5}{x}$

$\frac{10}{8.4} = \frac{5}{x}$	Original proportion
$10 \cdot x = 5 \cdot 8.4$	Cross products
$10x = 42$	Multiply.
$x = \frac{42}{10}$	Divide each side by 10.
$x = 4.2$	Simplify.

Exercises

Concepts and Skills Bank

Determine whether each pair of ratios forms a proportion. Write *yes* or *no*.

1. $\frac{3}{2}, \frac{21}{14}$ yes
2. $\frac{8}{9}, \frac{12}{18}$ no
3. $\frac{2.3}{3.4}, \frac{3.0}{3.6}$ no
4. $\frac{5}{2}, \frac{4}{1.6}$ yes
5. $\frac{21.1}{14.4}, \frac{1.1}{1.2}$ no
6. $\frac{4.2}{5.6}, \frac{1.68}{2.24}$ yes
7. $\frac{4}{11}, \frac{12}{33}$ yes
8. $\frac{16}{17}, \frac{8}{9}$ no

Solve each proportion.

9. $\frac{p}{6} = \frac{24}{36}$ 4
10. $\frac{w}{11} = \frac{14}{22}$ 7
11. $\frac{4}{10} = \frac{8}{a}$ 20
12. $\frac{18}{12} = \frac{24}{q}$ 16
13. $\frac{5}{h} = \frac{10}{30}$ 15
14. $\frac{51}{z} = \frac{17}{7}$ 21
15. $\frac{7}{45} = \frac{x}{9}$ 1.4
16. $\frac{2}{15} = \frac{c}{72}$ 9.6
17. $\frac{7}{5} = \frac{10.5}{b}$ 7.5
18. $\frac{16}{7} = \frac{4.8}{h}$ 2.1
19. $\frac{2}{9.4} = \frac{0.2}{v}$ 0.94
20. $\frac{9}{7.2} = \frac{3.5}{k}$ 2.8

21. **DRIVING** Marci drove 238 miles in 3.5 hours. At that rate, how long will it take her to drive an additional 87 miles? about 1.28 hours

22. **TUTORING** Amanda earns $28.50 tutoring for 3 hours. Write an equation relating her earnings m to the number of hours h she tutors. How much would Amanda earn tutoring for 2 hours? for 4.5 hours? $m = 9.5h$; $19; $42.75

23. **PHOTOGRAPHY** A 3 inch-by-5 inch photo is enlarged so that the length of the new photo is 7 inches. Find the width of the new photo. $4\frac{1}{5}$ in.

24. **TRAVEL** The Lehmans' minivan requires 5 gallons of gasoline to travel 120 miles. How much gasoline will they need for a 350-mile trip? about 14.6 gal

2 Square Roots

You can estimate square roots by using perfect squares.

EXAMPLE 1

Estimate $\sqrt{45}$ to the nearest whole number.

- The first perfect square less than 45 is 36. $\sqrt{36} = 6$
- The first perfect square greater than 45 is 49. $\sqrt{49} = 7$
- Plot each square root on a number line.

The square root of 45 is between the whole numbers 6 and 7. Because 45 is closer to 49 than 36, you can expect that $\sqrt{45}$ is closer to 7 than 6.

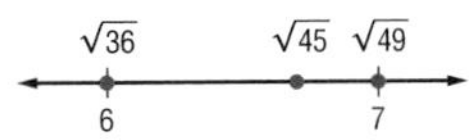

A radical expression is an expression that contains a square root. The expression is in simplest form when the following conditions have been met.

- No radicands have perfect square factors other than 1.
- No radicands contain fractions.
- No radicals appear in the denominator of a fraction.

The **Product Property of Square Roots** states that for two real numbers a and b, where $a \geq 0$ and $b \geq 0$, $\sqrt{ab} = \sqrt{a} \cdot \sqrt{b}$.

EXAMPLE 2

Simplify.

a. $\sqrt{96}$

$\sqrt{96}$	
$= \sqrt{2 \cdot 2 \cdot 2 \cdot 2 \cdot 6}$	Prime factorization of 96
$= \sqrt{2^2} \cdot \sqrt{2^2} \cdot \sqrt{6}$	Product Property of Square Roots
$= 2 \cdot 2 \cdot \sqrt{6}$	$\sqrt{2^2} = 2$
$= 4\sqrt{6}$	Simplify.

b. $\sqrt{32} \cdot \sqrt{75}$

$\sqrt{32} \cdot \sqrt{75}$	
$= \sqrt{32 \cdot 75}$	Product Property
$= \sqrt{2 \cdot 2 \cdot 2 \cdot 2 \cdot 2 \cdot 3 \cdot 5 \cdot 5}$	Prime factorization
$= \sqrt{2^2} \cdot \sqrt{2^2} \cdot \sqrt{2} \cdot \sqrt{3} \cdot \sqrt{5^2}$	Product Property
$= 2 \cdot 2 \cdot 5 \cdot \sqrt{2} \cdot \sqrt{3}$	$\sqrt{2^2} = 2$ and $\sqrt{5^2} = 5$
$= 20 \cdot \sqrt{2} \cdot \sqrt{3}$	Simplify.
$= 20\sqrt{2 \cdot 3}$ or $20\sqrt{6}$	Product Property

The **Quotient Property of Square Roots** states that for any real numbers a and b, where $a \geq 0$ and $b > 0$, $\sqrt{\frac{a}{b}} = \frac{\sqrt{a}}{\sqrt{b}}$.

EXAMPLE 3

Simplify $\sqrt{\frac{9}{64}}$.

$\sqrt{\frac{9}{64}} = \frac{\sqrt{9}}{\sqrt{64}}$	Quotient Property of Square Roots
$= \frac{3}{8}$	Simplify.

2 Lesson CSB Notes

1 FOCUS

Vertical Alignment

Lesson CSB-2
Estimate the value of a square root.
Simplify square roots.
Rationalize denominators involving square roots.

After Lesson CSB-2
Simplify algebraic expressions involving radicals.

2 TEACH

Example 1 shows how to estimate a square root to the nearest whole number. **Example 2** shows how to use the Product Property of Square Roots to simplify a square root. **Example 3** shows how to use the Quotient Property of Square Roots to simplify the square root of a fraction. **Example 4** shows how to rationalize a denominator. **Example 5** shows how to rationalize a binomial denominator.

Additional Examples

1. Estimate $\sqrt{68}$ to the nearest whole number. 8
2. Simplify.
   a. $\sqrt{50}$ $5\sqrt{2}$
   b. $\sqrt{15} \cdot \sqrt{27}$ $9\sqrt{5}$
3. Simplify $\sqrt{\frac{49}{16}}$. $\frac{7}{4}$

Additional Examples

4 Simplify $\frac{6}{\sqrt{7}}$. $\frac{6\sqrt{7}}{7}$

5 Simplify $\frac{2}{\sqrt{5}+3}$. $\frac{3-\sqrt{5}}{2}$

Tips for New Teachers

Common Error Remind students that expressions of the type $\sqrt{a+b}$ cannot be simplified, even if a and b are perfect squares.

3 ASSESS

Formative Assessment

Use Exercises 1–40 to assess whether students understand how to estimate and simplify square roots.

Name the Math Ask students to state the Product Property of Square Roots.

Rationalizing the denominator of a radical expression is a method used to eliminate radicals from the denominator of a fraction. To rationalize the denominator, multiply the expression by a fraction equivalent to 1 such that the resulting denominator is a perfect square.

EXAMPLE 4

Simplify $\frac{4}{\sqrt{5}}$.

$\frac{4}{\sqrt{5}} = \frac{4}{\sqrt{5}} \cdot \frac{\sqrt{5}}{\sqrt{5}}$ — **Multiply by $\frac{\sqrt{5}}{\sqrt{5}}$.**

$= \frac{4\sqrt{5}}{5}$ — **Simplify.**

Conjugates can be used to simplify radical expressions. Conjugates are binomials of the form $p\sqrt{a} + r\sqrt{b}$ and $p\sqrt{a} - r\sqrt{b}$.

EXAMPLE 5

Simplify $\frac{3}{1-\sqrt{2}}$.

$\frac{3}{1-\sqrt{2}} = \frac{3}{1-\sqrt{2}} \cdot \frac{1+\sqrt{2}}{1+\sqrt{2}}$ — **$\frac{1+\sqrt{2}}{1+\sqrt{2}} = 1$**

$= \frac{3(1+\sqrt{2})}{1^2 - (\sqrt{2})^2}$ — **$(a-b)(a+b) = a^2 - b^2$**

$= \frac{3+3\sqrt{2}}{1-2}$ — **$(\sqrt{2})^2 = 2$**

$= \frac{3+3\sqrt{2}}{-1}$ or $-\frac{3+3\sqrt{2}}{1}$ — **Simplify.**

Exercises

Estimate each square root to the nearest whole number.

1. $\sqrt{66}$ **8** **2.** $\sqrt{103}$ **10** **3.** $\sqrt{79}$ **9** **4.** $\sqrt{95}$ **10**

5. $\sqrt{54}$ **7** **6.** $\sqrt{125}$ **11** **7.** $\sqrt{200}$ **14** **8.** $\sqrt{396}$ **20**

Simplify.

9. $\sqrt{20}$ $2\sqrt{5}$ **10.** $\sqrt{52}$ $2\sqrt{13}$ **11.** $\sqrt{18}$ $3\sqrt{2}$ **12.** $\sqrt{24}$ $2\sqrt{6}$

13. $\sqrt{80}$ $4\sqrt{5}$ **14.** $\sqrt{75}$ $5\sqrt{3}$ **15.** $2\sqrt{32}$ $8\sqrt{2}$ **16.** $10\sqrt{90}$ $30\sqrt{10}$

17. $\sqrt{2} \cdot \sqrt{8}$ 4 **18.** $\sqrt{3} \cdot \sqrt{18}$ $3\sqrt{6}$ **19.** $\sqrt{5} \cdot \sqrt{6}$ $\sqrt{30}$ **20.** $\sqrt{3} \cdot \sqrt{8}$ $2\sqrt{6}$

21. $3\sqrt{10} \cdot 4\sqrt{10}$ 120 **22.** $7\sqrt{30} \cdot 2\sqrt{6}$ $84\sqrt{5}$ **23.** $2\sqrt{3} \cdot 5\sqrt{27}$ 90 **24.** $12\sqrt{5} \cdot 3\sqrt{45}$ 540

25. $\sqrt{\frac{81}{49}}$ $\frac{9}{7}$ **26.** $\sqrt{\frac{25}{64}}$ $\frac{5}{8}$ **27.** $\sqrt{\frac{42}{121}}$ $\frac{\sqrt{42}}{11}$ **28.** $\sqrt{\frac{3}{10}}$ $\frac{\sqrt{30}}{10}$

29. $\frac{4}{\sqrt{6}}$ $\frac{2\sqrt{6}}{3}$ **30.** $\frac{\sqrt{14}}{\sqrt{5}}$ $\frac{\sqrt{70}}{5}$ **31.** $\sqrt{\frac{2}{7}} \cdot \sqrt{\frac{7}{3}}$ $\frac{\sqrt{6}}{3}$ **32.** $\sqrt{\frac{3}{5}} \cdot \sqrt{\frac{6}{4}}$ $\frac{3\sqrt{10}}{10}$

33. $\frac{3}{2+\sqrt{2}}$ $\frac{6-3\sqrt{2}}{2}$ **34.** $\frac{7}{3-\sqrt{7}}$ $\frac{21+7\sqrt{7}}{2}$ **35.** $\frac{18}{6-\sqrt{2}}$ $\frac{54+9\sqrt{2}}{17}$ **36.** $\frac{3\sqrt{3}}{\sqrt{6}-2}$ $\frac{6\sqrt{3}+9\sqrt{2}}{2}$

37. $\frac{10}{\sqrt{7}+\sqrt{2}}$ $2\sqrt{7}-2\sqrt{2}$ **38.** $\frac{2}{\sqrt{3}+\sqrt{6}}$ $\frac{2\sqrt{3}-2\sqrt{6}}{-3}$ **39.** $\frac{4}{4-3\sqrt{3}}$ $\frac{16+12\sqrt{3}}{-11}$ **40.** $\frac{3\sqrt{7}}{5\sqrt{3}+3\sqrt{5}}$ $\frac{5\sqrt{21}-3\sqrt{35}}{10}$

Concepts and Skills Bank

3 Scientific Notation

A number is expressed in **scientific notation** when it is written as the product of a factor and a power of 10. The factor must be greater than or equal to 1 and less than 10.

$a \times 10^n$, where $1 \le a < 10$ and n is an integer

EXAMPLE 1

Express each number in scientific notation.

a. 32,500,000

$32{,}500{,}000 = 3.25 \times 10{,}000{,}000$ — The decimal point moves 7 places.

$= 3.25 \times 10^7$ — $10{,}000{,}000 = 10^7$

b. 0.00625

$0.00625 = 6.25 \times 0.001$ — The decimal point moves 3 places.

$= 6.25 \times 10^{-3}$ — $0.001 = 10^{-3}$

You can use a calculator to evaluate expressions involving scientific notation.

EXAMPLE 2

Evaluate.

a. $(6.58 \times 10^6)(3.97 \times 10^4)$

Enter the expression in a calculator. Use the [2nd] [EE] function to enter the base factor and the power of 10.

KEYSTROKES: 6.58 [2nd] [EE] 6 [×] 3.97 [2nd] [EE] 4 [ENTER] 2.61226E11

So, $(6.58 \times 10^6)(3.97 \times 10^4) = 2.61226 \times 10^{11}$.

b. $\dfrac{4.77 \times 10^{-8}}{1.02 \times 10^{-4}}$

KEYSTROKES: 4.77 [2nd] [EE] [(-)] 8 [÷] 1.02 [2nd] [EE] [(-)] 4 [ENTER] 4.676470588E−4

So, $\dfrac{4.77 \times 10^{-8}}{1.02 \times 10^{-4}} = 4.676470588 \times 10^{-4}$.

Exercises

Express each number in scientific notation.

1. 2,000,000 2×10^6
2. 499,000 4.99×10^5
3. 0.006 6×10^{-3}
4. 0.0125 1.25×10^{-2}
5. 50,000,000 5×10^7
6. 39,560 3.956×10^4
7. 0.000078 7.8×10^{-5}
8. 0.000425 4.25×10^{-4}

Evaluate.

9. $(4.24 \times 10^2)(5.72 \times 10^4)$ 2.42528×10^7
10. $(3.347 \times 10^{-1})(5.689 \times 10^{-3})$ 1.9041083×10^{-3}
11. $(1.399 \times 10^5)(1.5 \times 10^{-4})$ 2.0985×10^1
12. $\dfrac{9.01 \times 10^{-2}}{2.505 \times 10^3}$ $3.596806387 \times 10^{-5}$
13. $\dfrac{6.1 \times 10^4}{7.32 \times 10^7}$ $8.333333333 \times 10^{-4}$
14. $\dfrac{6.02 \times 10^{-12}}{9.931 \times 10^5}$ $6.0618266 \times 10^{-18}$

3 Lesson CSB Notes

1 FOCUS

Vertical Alignment

Lesson CSB-3
Express numbers in scientific notation.
Perform arithmetic operations with numbers expressed in scientific notation.

After Lesson CSB-3
Solve real-world problems involving scientific notation.

2 TEACH

Example 1 shows how to express a number in scientific notation. **Example 2** shows how to multiply and divide numbers expressed in scientific notation.

Additional Examples

1 Express each number in scientific notation.

a. 124,000 1.24×10^5

b. 0.0000047 4.7×10^{-6}

2 Evaluate.

a. $(5.9 \times 10^7)(2.46 \times 10^{-2})$ 1.4514×10^6

b. $\dfrac{6.12 \times 10^3}{3.6 \times 10^{-6}}$ 1.7×10^9

Tips for New Teachers

Using Scientific Notation Explain to students that scientific notation can be used to indicate the accuracy of a number. For example, if 600,000 is written as 6.00×10^5, it is clear that the number is accurate to the nearest thousand.

3 ASSESS

Formative Assessment

Use Exercises 1–14 to assess whether students understand how to use scientific notation.

Ticket Out the Door Give students a very large number and a very small number, and ask them to write each in scientific notation.

4 Lesson CSB Notes

1 FOCUS

Vertical Alignment

Lesson CSB-4
Evaluate compound probabilities.

After Lesson CSB-4
Construct discrete probability distributions.

2 TEACH

Example 1 shows how to find probabilities for independent events. **Example 2** shows how to find probabilities for dependent events. **Example 3** shows how to find probabilities for mutually exclusive events. **Example 4** shows how to find probabilities for inclusive events. **Example 5** shows how to find theoretical and experimental probabilities.

Additional Examples

1. A fair coin is flipped three times. What is the probability that the coin comes up heads the first time, tails the second, and heads the third? $\frac{1}{8}$
2. A bag contains 6 blue chips, 10 white chips, and 4 red chips. Three chips are randomly drawn from the bag one at a time and not replaced. Find the probability that a white chip, a blue chip, and a white chip are selected in order. $\frac{3}{38}$

Concepts and Skills Bank

4 Adding and Multiplying Probabilities

A single event, like rolling a 5 on a die, is called a **simple event**. Rolling a 5 on a die and drawing a 2 from a standard deck of cards is an example of a **compound event**, which is made up of two or more simple events. The roll of a die does not affect the selection of a card. These two events are called **independent events**. To find the probability of independent events, multiply the individual probabilities.

EXAMPLE 1

In a board game, three dice are rolled to determine the number of moves for the players. What is the probability that the first die shows a 6, the second die shows a 6, and the third die does not?

Let A be the event that the first die shows a 6. → $P(A) = \frac{1}{6}$

Let B be the event that the second die shows a 6. → $P(B) = \frac{1}{6}$

Let C be the event that the third die does *not* show a 6. → $P(C) = \frac{5}{6}$

$P(A, B, \text{and } C) = P(A) \cdot P(B) \cdot P(C)$ **Probability of independent events**

$= \frac{1}{6} \cdot \frac{1}{6} \cdot \frac{5}{6}$ **Substitute.**

$= \frac{5}{216}$ **Multiply.**

The probability that the first and second dice show a 6 and the third die does not is $\frac{5}{216}$.

When the outcome of one event affects the outcome of another event, such as drawing two cards from a standard deck without replacement, the events are **dependent events**.

EXAMPLE 2

A bag contains 12 red marbles, 9 blue marbles, 11 yellow marbles, and 8 green marbles. Three marbles are randomly drawn from the bag one at a time and not replaced. Find the probability that red, blue, and green marbles are selected in order.

The selection of the first marble affects the selection of the next marble because there is one less marble from which to choose. So, the events are dependent.

First marble: $P(\text{red}) = \frac{12}{40}$ or $\frac{3}{10}$ ← number of red marbles / ← total number of marbles

Second marble: $P(\text{blue}) = \frac{9}{39}$ or $\frac{3}{13}$ ← number of blue marbles / ← number of marbles remaining

Third marble: $P(\text{green}) = \frac{8}{38}$ or $\frac{4}{19}$ ← number of green marbles / ← number of marbles remaining

$P(\text{red, blue, green}) = P(\text{red}) \cdot P(\text{blue}) \cdot P(\text{green})$ **Probability of dependent events**

$= \frac{3}{10} \cdot \frac{3}{13} \cdot \frac{4}{19}$ **Substitute.**

$= \frac{36}{2470}$ or $\frac{18}{1235}$ **Multiply and simplify.**

The probability of selecting red, blue, and green marbles in order is $\frac{18}{1235}$.

Concepts and Skills Bank

Events that cannot occur at the same time are called **mutually exclusive**. Suppose you want to find the probability of rolling a 2 *or* a 4 on a die. Because a die cannot show both a 2 and a 4 at the same time, the events are mutually exclusive. To determine the probability of mutually exclusive events, add the individual probabilities.

EXAMPLE 3

Keisha has a stack of 8 baseball cards, 5 basketball cards, and 6 hockey cards. If she selects a card at random from the stack, what is the probability that it is a baseball or a hockey card?

These are mutually exclusive events, because the card cannot be both a baseball card *and* a hockey card.

$P(\text{baseball or hockey}) = P(\text{baseball}) + P(\text{hockey})$ **Mutually exclusive events**

$= \frac{8}{19} + \frac{6}{19} \text{ or } \frac{14}{19}$ **Substitute and add.**

The probability that Keisha selects a baseball or a hockey card is $\frac{14}{19}$.

What is the probability of drawing a king or a spade from a standard deck of cards? Since it is possible to draw a card that is both a king and a spade, these events are not mutually exclusive. These are called **inclusive events**. To determine the probability of inclusive events, add the individual probabilities and subtract the probability of both conditions.

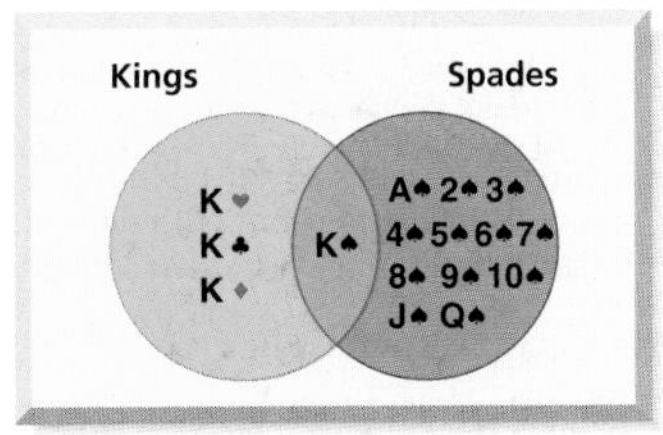

P(king)	+	*P*(spade)	−	*P*(king and spade)	=	*P*(king or spade)
$\frac{4}{52}$	+	$\frac{13}{52}$	−	$\frac{1}{52}$	=	$\frac{16}{52}$ or $\frac{4}{13}$

EXAMPLE 4

EDUCATION Suppose that of 1400 students, 550 take Spanish, 700 take biology, and 400 take both Spanish and biology. What is the probability that a student selected at random takes Spanish or biology?

$P(\text{Spanish}) = \frac{550}{1400}$ $\quad P(\text{biology}) = \frac{700}{1400}$ $\quad P(\text{Spanish and biology}) = \frac{400}{1400}$

$P(\text{Spanish or biology}) = P(\text{Spanish}) + P(\text{biology}) - P(\text{Spanish and biology})$

$= \frac{550}{1400} + \frac{700}{1400} - \frac{400}{1400}$ **Substitute.**

$= \frac{850}{1400}$ **Add and subtract.**

$= \frac{17}{28}$ **Simplify.**

The probability that a student selected at random takes Spanish or biology is $\frac{17}{28}$.

Probabilities based on known characteristics or facts are called **theoretical probabilities**. Probabilities that are based on the outcomes obtained by conducting an experiment are called **experimental probabilities**. Theoretical probabilities tell you what *should happen*, while experimental probabilities tell you what *actually happened*.

Concepts and Skills Bank

Additional Examples

3 Juan has 4 pennies, 3 nickels, and 2 dimes in his pocket. If he takes one coin at random out of his pocket, what is the probability that it is a penny or a nickel? $\frac{7}{9}$

4 **BREAKFAST** Of 200 students, 110 eat cereal for breakfast, 140 drink juice, and 85 have both cereal and juice. What is the probability that a randomly selected student has cereal or juice for breakfast? $\frac{33}{40}$

Tips for New Teachers

Mutually Exclusive Events Remind students that only one of a set of mutually exclusive events can occur in one trial of an experiment.

Concepts and Skills Bank

Additional Example

5 Find each probability.

a. A bag contains 12 blue marbles, 5 yellow marbles, and 3 red marbles. What is the theoretical probability of drawing a blue marble, replacing it, and then drawing another blue marble? $\frac{9}{25}$

b. The graph shows the results of drawing 50 marbles from a bag with replacement. Based on the experiment, what is the probability of drawing a yellow marble or a red marble? $\frac{3}{10}$

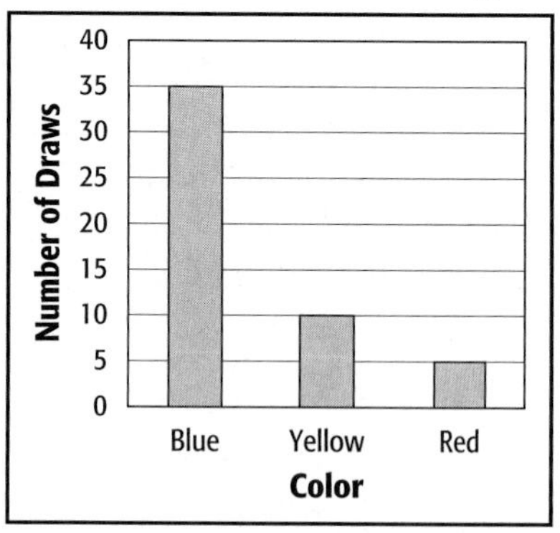

3 ASSESS

Formative Assessment

Use Exercises 1–22 to assess whether students understand how to find probabilities for compound events.

Name the Math Ask students to explain the difference between independent and dependent events.

EXAMPLE 5

Find each probability.

a. What is the theoretical probability of rolling a double 6 using two dice?

$P(6 \text{ and } 6) = \frac{1}{6} \cdot \frac{1}{6}$ or $\frac{1}{36}$

b. The graph shows the results of an experiment in which two number cubes were rolled. Based on the experiment, what is the probability that a sum of 6 or 12 occurs?

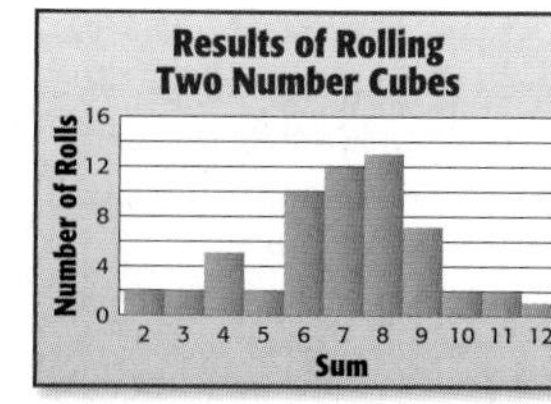

These are mutually exclusive events, because the sum cannot be both 6 and 12.

$P(\text{sum is 6 or 12}) = P(\text{sum is 6}) + P(\text{sum is 12})$ **Mutually exclusive events**

$= \frac{10}{58} + \frac{1}{58}$ or $\frac{11}{58}$ **Substitute and add.**

Exercises

Determine whether the events are *independent* or *dependent*. Then find the probability.

1. A black die and a white die are rolled. What is the probability that a 3 shows on the black die and a 5 shows on the white die? **independent; $\frac{1}{36}$**

2. Yana has 4 black socks, 6 blue socks, and 8 white socks in his drawer. If he selects three socks at random with no replacement, what is the probability that he will first select a blue sock, then a black sock, and then another blue sock? **dependent; $\frac{5}{204}$ or about 0.025**

A die is rolled twice. Find each probability.

3. $P(2, \text{then } 3)$ $\frac{1}{36}$

4. $P(\text{no 6s})$ $\frac{25}{36}$

5. $P(\text{two of the same number})$ $\frac{1}{6}$

6. $P(\text{two 4s})$ $\frac{1}{36}$

7. $P(1, \text{then any number})$ $\frac{1}{6}$

8. $P(\text{two different numbers})$ $\frac{5}{6}$

There are 8 action, 3 comedy, and 5 children's DVDs on a shelf. Suppose two DVDs are selected at random from the shelf. Find each probability.

9. $P(2 \text{ action DVDs})$, if replacement occurs $\frac{1}{4}$

10. $P(2 \text{ action DVDs})$, if no replacement occurs $\frac{7}{30}$

11. $P(\text{a comedy DVD, then a children's DVD})$, if no replacement occurs $\frac{1}{16}$

Six girls and eight boys walk into a video store at the same time. There are six salespeople available to help them. Find the probability that the salespeople will first help the given numbers of girls and boys.

12. $P(4 \text{ girls, 2 boys or 4 boys, 2 girls})$ $\frac{70}{143}$

13. $P(5 \text{ girls, 1 boy or 5 boys, 1 girl})$ $\frac{128}{1001}$

14. $P(\text{all girls or all boys})$ $\frac{29}{3003}$

15. $P(\text{at least 4 boys})$ $\frac{202}{429}$

Two cards are drawn from a standard deck of cards. Find each probability.

16. $P(\text{both queens or both red})$ $\frac{55}{221}$

17. $P(\text{both jacks or both face cards})$ $\frac{11}{221}$

18. $P(\text{both face cards or both black})$ $\frac{188}{663}$

19. $P(\text{both either black or ace})$ $\frac{63}{221}$

Determine whether each probability is *theoretical* or *experimental*. Then find the probability.

20. Two dice are rolled. What is the probability that the sum will be 10? **theoretical; $\frac{1}{12}$**

21. A baseball player has 126 hits in 410 at-bats this season. What is the probability that he gets a hit in his next at-bat? **experimental; about 0.307**

22. A hand of 2 cards is dealt from a standard deck of cards. What is the probability that both cards are clubs? **theoretical; $\frac{1}{17}$**

Concepts and Skills Bank

5 Bar and Line Graphs

A **bar graph** compares different categories of data by showing each as a bar whose length is related to the frequency. A **double bar graph** compares two sets of data. Another way to represent data is by using a **line graph**. A line graph usually shows how data changes over a period of time.

EXAMPLE 1

The table shows the average age at which Americans marry for the first time. Make a double bar graph to display the data.

Average Age to Marry		
Year	1990	2007
men	26	27
women	22	25

Step 1 Draw a horizontal and a vertical axis and label them as shown.

Step 2 Draw side-by-side bars to represent each category.

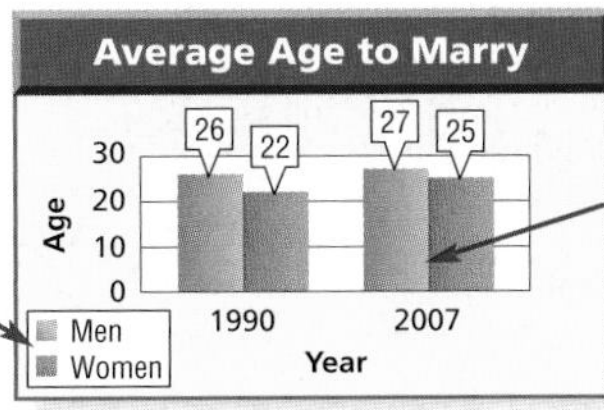

The legend indicates that the blue bars refer to men and the red bars refer to women.

The side-by-side bars compare the ages of men and women for each year.

EXAMPLE 2

The table shows Mark's height at 2-year intervals. Make a line graph to display the data.

Age	2	4	6	8	10	12	14	16
Height (feet)	2.8	3.5	4.0	4.6	4.9	5.2	5.8	6

Step 1 Draw a horizontal and a vertical axis. Label them as shown.

Step 2 Plot the points.

Step 3 Draw a line connecting each pair of consecutive points.

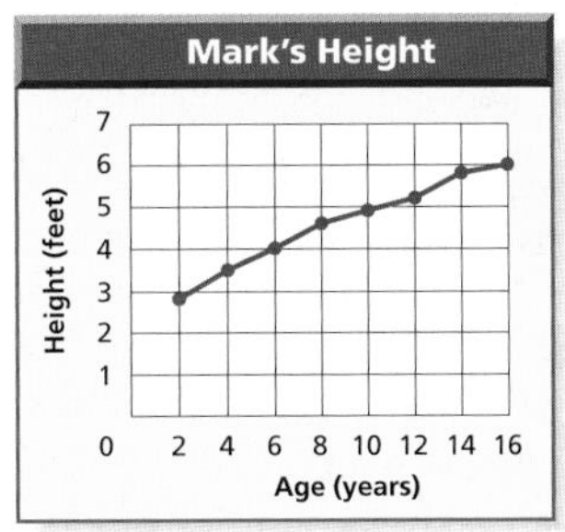

Exercises

1, 2. See Student Handbook Answer Appendix.

1. The table below shows the life expectancy for Americans born in each year listed. Make a double bar graph to display the data.

Life Expectancy		
Year of Birth	Male	Female
1980	70.0	77.5
1985	71.2	78.2
1990	71.8	78.8
1995	72.5	78.9
2004	75.2	80.4

Source: *World Almanac*

2. The amount of money in Becky's savings account from August through March is shown in the table below. Make a line graph to display the data.

Month	Amount	Month	Amount
August	\$300	December	\$780
September	\$400	January	\$800
October	\$700	February	\$950
November	\$780	March	\$900

5 Lesson CSB Notes

1 FOCUS

Vertical Alignment

Lesson CSB-5
Construct double bar and line graphs.

After Lesson CSB-5
Construct histograms.

2 TEACH

Example 1 shows how to construct a double bar graph. **Example 2** shows how to construct a line graph.

Additional Examples

1. The table shows the numbers of boys and girls participating in sports at a particular school. Make a double bar graph to display the data.

	Participation in Sports			
	Freshmen	Sophomores	Juniors	Seniors
Boys	65	78	62	54
Girls	72	80	56	48

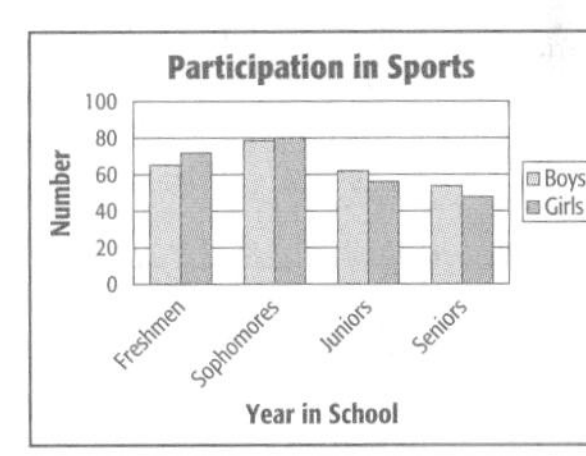

2. The table shows the daily high temperatures during the first week of April. Make a line graph to display the data.

Date	1	2	3	4	5	6	7
Temperature (°F)	48	50	54	60	56	58	62

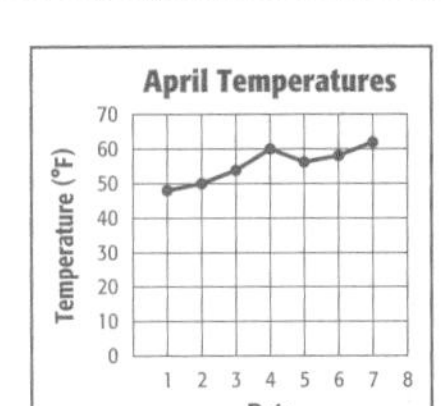

Tips for New Teachers

Appropriate Graphs Remind students that bar graphs are good for displaying categorical data, while line graphs are often used to show trends over time.

3 ASSESS

Formative Assessment

Use Exercise 1 to assess whether students understand how to construct double bar graphs. Use Exercise 2 to assess whether students understand how to construct line graphs.

Crystal Ball Ask students how they think their study of bar graphs will help them construct histograms in the next lesson.

6 Lesson CSB Notes

1 FOCUS

Vertical Alignment

Lesson CSB-6
Construct and interpret frequency tables. Construct and interpret histograms.

After Lesson CSB-6
Collect and analyze frequency data.

2 TEACH

Example 1 shows how to read and interpret a frequency table. **Example 2** shows how to construct and interpret a histogram.

Additional Example

1 **CARS** Use the frequency table.

Cars in School Parking Lot		
Color	Tally	Frequency
White	𝍸 𝍸	10
Silver	𝍸 𝍸 𝍸 ||	17
Green	𝍸	5
Blue	𝍸 ||	7
Red	𝍸 ||||	9
Black	𝍸 𝍸 ||	12
Brown	𝍸 |||	8

a. How many more silver cars are there than black? 5

b. What color appears twice as much as green? white

6 Frequency Tables and Histograms

A **frequency table** shows how often an item appears in a set of data. A tally mark is used to record each response. The total number of marks for a given response is the *frequency* of that response.

EXAMPLE 1

TELEVISION Use the frequency table.

a. How many more chose sports programs than news?

b. Which two programs together have the same frequency as adventures?

Favorite Television Shows		
Program	Tally	Frequency
Sports	𝍸 ||	7
Mysteries	𝍸	5
Soap operas	||||	4
News	𝍸	5
Quiz shows	𝍸 |	6
Music videos	||	2
Adventure	𝍸 ||||	9
Comedies	𝍸 ||	7

a. Seven people chose sports. Five people chose news. $7 - 5 = 2$, so 2 more people chose sports than news.

b. As many people chose adventures as the following pairs of programs.

sports and music videos — mysteries and soap operas
soap operas and news — comedies and music videos

Frequencies can be shown in a bar graph called a histogram. A **histogram** differs from other bar graphs in that no space is between the bars and the bars usually represent numbers grouped by intervals.

EXAMPLE 2

FITNESS A PE teacher tested the number of sit-ups students in two classes could do in 1 minute. The results are shown.

a. Make a histogram of the data. Title the histogram.

b. How many students were able to do 25–29 sit-ups in 1 minute?

c. How many students were unable to do 10 sit-ups in 1 minute?

d. Between which two consecutive intervals does the greatest increase in frequency occur? What is the increase?

Number of Sit-Ups	Frequency
0–4	8
5–9	12
10–14	15
15–19	6
20–24	18
25–29	10

a. Use the same intervals as those in the frequency table on the horizontal axis. Label the vertical axis with a scale that includes the frequency numbers from the table.

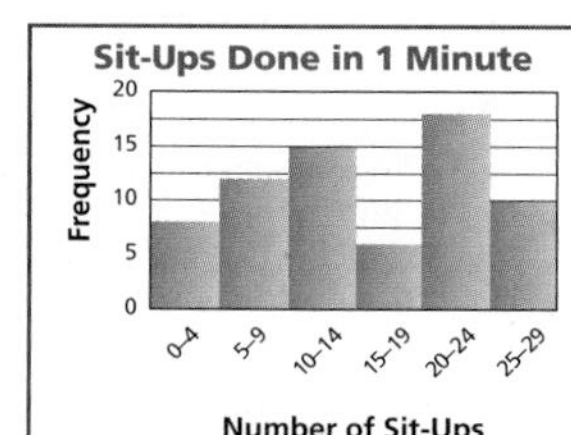

b. Ten students were able to do 25–29 sit-ups in 1 minute.

c. Add the students who did 0–4 sit-ups and 5–9 sit-ups. So $8 + 12$ or 20 students were unable to do 10 sit-ups in 1 min.

d. The greatest increase is between intervals 15–19 and 20–24. These frequencies are 6 and 18. So the increase is $18 - 6 = 12$.

1002 Concepts and Skills Bank

Exercises

Display each set of data in a histogram. 1, 2. See Student Handbook Answer Appendix.

1.

Weekly Study Time		
Time (hr)	**Tally**	**Frequency**
0–2	||	2
3–5	|||	3
6–8	卌 |||	8
9–11	卌 卌 ||	12
12–14	卌 卌	10

2.

Weekly Allowance		
Amount	**Tally**	**Frequency**
\$0–\$5	卌 卌 |	11
\$6–\$11	卌 ||||	9
\$12–\$17	卌 |||	8
\$18–\$23	|||	3
\$24–\$29	卌	5

3. **ART** The prices, in dollars, of paintings sold at an art auction are shown.

1800	750	600	600	1800	1350	300	1200	750	600	750	2700
600	750	300	750	600	450	2700	1200	600	450	450	300

a. Make a frequency table of the data. See Student Handbook Answer Appendix.

b. What price was paid most often for the artwork? \$600

c. What is the average price paid for artwork at this auction? \$931.25

d. How many paintings sold for at least \$600 and no more than \$1200? 13

4. **PETS** Refer to the table.

Number of Pets Per Family							
1	2	3	1	0	2	1	0
1	0	1	4	1	2	0	0
0	1	1	2	2	5	1	0

a. Use a frequency table to make a histogram of the data. See Student Handbook Answer Appendix.

b. How many families own two to three pets? 6

c. How many families own more than three pets? 2

d. To the nearest percent, what percent of families own no pets? 29%

e. Name the median, mode, and range of the data. median = 1; mode = 1; range = 5

5b–d. See Student Handbook Answer Appendix.

5. **TREES** Use the histogram shown.

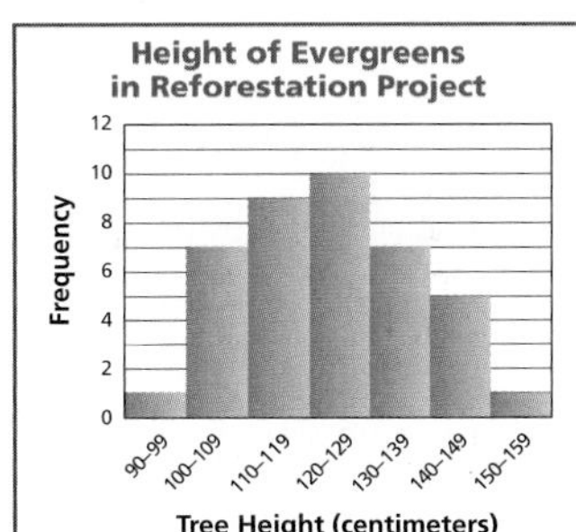

a. Which interval contains the most evergreen seedlings? 120–129

b. Which intervals contain an equal number of trees?

c. Which intervals contain 95% of the data?

d. Between which two consecutive intervals does the greatest increase in frequency occur? What is the increase?

6. **MARKET RESEARCH** Johanna is a civil engineer studying traffic patterns. She counts the number of cars that make it through one green light cycle during rush hour. Organize her data into a frequency table, and then make a histogram. See Student Handbook Answer Appendix.

15	16	10	8	8	14	9	7	6	9
10	11	14	10	7	8	9	11	14	10

Concepts and Skills Bank

Additional Example

2 **EARTHQUAKES** The table shows data on earthquakes worldwide with magnitudes 7.0 or greater.

Earthquakes Magnitude 7.0 or Greater	
Years	**Number**
1992–1995	79
1996–1999	81
2000–2003	59
2004–2007	56

a. Make a histogram of the data. Title the histogram.

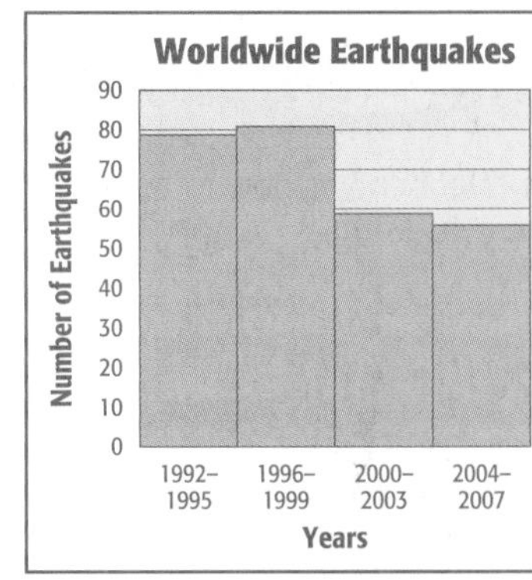

b. How many earthquakes of magnitude 7.0 or greater were there in the years 2000–2003? 59

c. Which period had the greatest number of earthquakes? 1996–1999

d. Can you tell from the histogram how many earthquakes with magnitude 7.0 or greater occurred during 2006? no

3 ASSESS

Formative Assessment

Use Exercises 1–6 to assess whether students understand how to construct and interpret frequency tables and histograms.

Yesterday's News Ask students to describe how the previous lesson's work with bar graphs helped them construct histograms.

Tips for New Teachers

Drawing Histograms Remind students that the bars in a histogram should touch each other.

Concepts and Skills Bank

7 Lesson CSB Notes

1 FOCUS

Vertical Alignment

Lesson CSB-7
Construct and interpret stem-and-leaf plots.

After Lesson CSB-7
Collect data and organize it in a stem-and-leaf plot.

2 TEACH

Example 1 shows how to construct a stem-and-leaf plot.

Additional Example

1 Students' scores on a test were 88, 72, 91, 65, 69, 97, 71, 77, 53, 68, 80, 79, 94, 85, and 70. Make a stem-and-leaf plot of the scores.

Stem	Leaf
5	3
6	5 8 9
7	0 1 2 7 9
8	0 5 8
9	1 4 7

$5|3 = 53$

Tips for New Teachers

Stem-and-Leaf Plots Point out to students that a stem-and-leaf plot is a graphical display that preserves all the original data.

3 ASSESS

Formative Assessment

Use Exercises 1–3 to assess whether students understand how to construct and interpret stem-and-leaf plots.

Ticket Out the Door Ask students to describe the difference between a stem and a leaf in a stem-and-leaf plot.

Concepts and Skills Bank

7 Stem-and-Leaf Plots

In a **stem-and-leaf plot**, data are organized in two columns. The greatest place value of the data is used for the stems. The next greatest place value forms the leaves. Stem-and-leaf plots are useful for organizing long lists of numbers.

EXAMPLE 1

Isabella has collected data on the GPAs (grade point average) of the 16 students in the art club. Display the data in a stem-and-leaf plot.
{4.0, 3.9, 3.1, 3.9, 3.8, 3.7, 1.8, 2.6, 4.0, 3.9, 3.5, 3.3, 2.9, 2.5, 1.1, 3.5}

Step 1 Find the least and greatest numbers. Then identify the greatest place-value digit in each number, in this case, ones.

least data: 1.1 — The least number has 1 in the ones place.

greatest data: 4.0 — The greatest number has 4 in the ones place.

Step 2 Draw a vertical line and write the stems from 1 to 4 to the left of the line.

Step 3 Write the leaves to the right of the line with the corresponding stem. For example, write 0 to the right of 4 for 4.0. Arrange the leaves so they are ordered from least to greatest.

Step 4 Include a key or an explanation.

Stem	Leaf
1	1 8
2	5 6 9
3	1 3 5 5 7 8 9 9 9
4	0 0

$3|1 = 3.1$

Exercises

2, 3. See Student Handbook Answer Appendix.

1. The stem-and-leaf plot at the right shows Charmaine's scores for her favorite computer game.
   a. What are Charmaine's highest and lowest scores? **90; 130**
   b. Which score(s) occurred most frequently? **90 and 98**
   c. How many scores were above 115? **6**

Stem	Leaf
9	0 0 0 1 3 4 5 5 7 8 8 8 9 9
10	0 3 4 4 5 6 9
11	0 3 9 9
12	1 2 6
13	0

$12|6 = 126$

2. The class scores on a 50-item test are shown in the table at the right. Make a stem-and-leaf plot of the data.

Test Scores					
45	15	30	40	28	35
39	29	38	18	43	49
46	44	48	35	36	30

3. **GEOGRAPHY** The table shows the land area of each county in Wyoming. Round each area to the nearest hundred square miles and organize the data in a stem-and-leaf plot.

County	Area (mi²)	County	Area (mi²)	County	Area (mi²)
Albany	4273	Hot Springs	2004	Sheridan	2523
Big Horn	3137	Johnson	4166	Sublette	4883
Campbell	4797	Laramie	2686	Sweetwater	10,425
Carbon	7896	Lincoln	4069	Teton	4008
Converse	4255	Natrona	5340	Unita	2082
Crook	2859	Niobrara	2626	Washakie	2240
Fremont	9182	Park	6942	Weston	2398
Goshen	2225	Platte	2085		

Source: *The World Almanac*

8 Box-and-Whisker Plots

In a set of data written in numerical order, **quartiles** are values that divide the data into four equal parts.

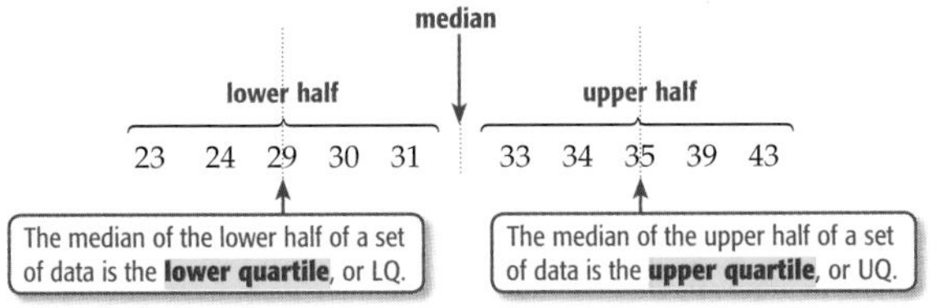

To make a **box-and-whisker plot**, draw a box around the quartile values, and draw lines or *whiskers* to represent the values in the lower fourth of the data and the upper fourth of the data.

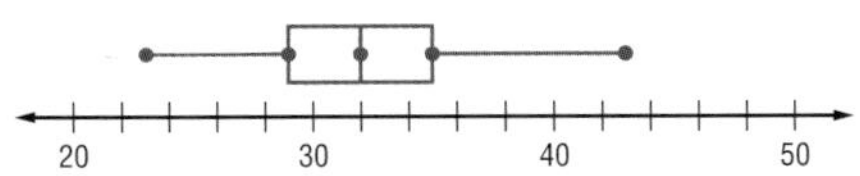

EXAMPLE 1

The amount spent in the cafeteria by 20 students is shown. Display the data in a box-and-whisker plot.

Amount Spent			
$2.00	$2.00	$1.00	$4.00
$1.00	$2.50	$2.50	$2.00
$2.50	$1.00	$4.00	$2.50
$3.50	$2.00	$3.00	$2.50
$4.00	$4.00	$5.50	$1.50

Step 1 Find the least and greatest number. Then draw a number line that covers the range of the data.

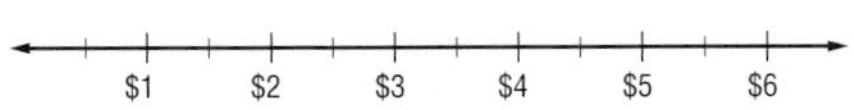

Step 2 Find the median, the extreme values, and the upper and lower quartiles. Mark these points above the number line.

1, 1, 1, 1.5, 2, 2, 2, 2, 2.5, 2.5, 2.5, 2.5, 2.5, 3, 3.5, 4, 4, 4, 4, 5.5

$LQ = \frac{2+2}{2}$ or 2 $\quad M = \frac{2.5+2.5}{2}$ or 2.5 $\quad UQ = \frac{3.5+4}{2}$ or 3.75

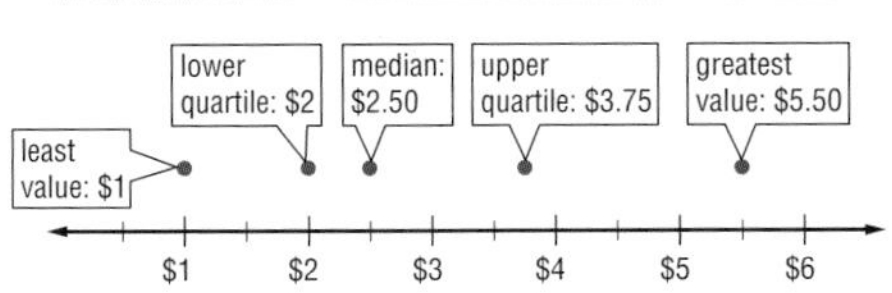

Step 3 Draw a box and the whiskers.

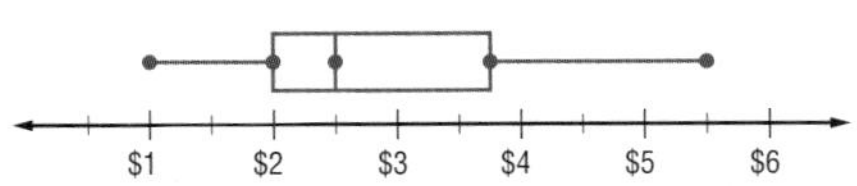

8 Lesson CSB Notes

1 FOCUS

Vertical Alignment

Lesson CSB-8
Construct and interpret box-and-whisker plots.

After Lesson CSB-8
Collect data and organize it in a box-and-whisker plot.

2 TEACH

Example 1 shows how to construct a box-and-whisker plot. **Example 2** shows how to interpret a box-and-whisker plot.

Additional Example

1 The commuting distances for 15 employees of a small company are shown. Display the data in a box-and-whisker plot.

Commuting Distance (miles)		
16	24	12
8	14	5
34	20	11
9	18	13
3	10	22

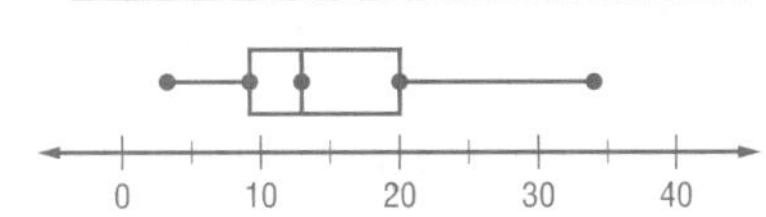

Additional Example

2 As a project, a group of students measure the wait times before getting served in two fast-food restaurants.

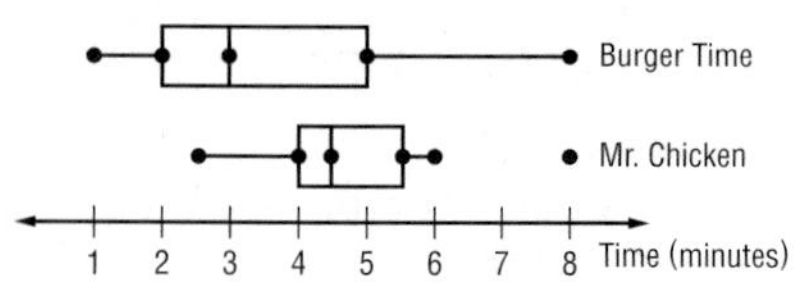

a. How do the wait times compare at the two restaurants? Sample answer: The times are usually shorter at Burger Time, but they are also more variable.

b. What was the shortest wait time at Mr. Chicken? $2\frac{1}{2}$ minutes

c. What is the interquartile range for the Burger Time plot? 3 min.

d. Identify any outliers in the data. one outlier of 8 minutes for Mr. Chicken

Tips for New Teachers

Point out to students that a box-and-whisker plot is useful for showing the variability of a data set.

3 ASSESS

Formative Assessment

Use Exercises 1–5 to assess whether students understand how to construct and interpret box-and-whisker plots.

Name the Math Ask students to list the five numbers that are needed in order to make a box-and-whisker plot.

The **interquartile range (IQR)** is the range of the middle half of the data and contains 50% of the data in the set.

$$\text{interquartile range} = UQ - LQ$$

An **outlier** is any element of a set that is at least 1.5 interquartile ranges less than the lower quartile or greater than the upper quartile. The whisker representing the data is drawn from the box to the least or greatest value that is not an outlier. *Parallel box-and-whisker plots* can be used to compare two sets of data.

EXAMPLE 2

Two students are analyzing the number of hours they spent studying each day for the last month.

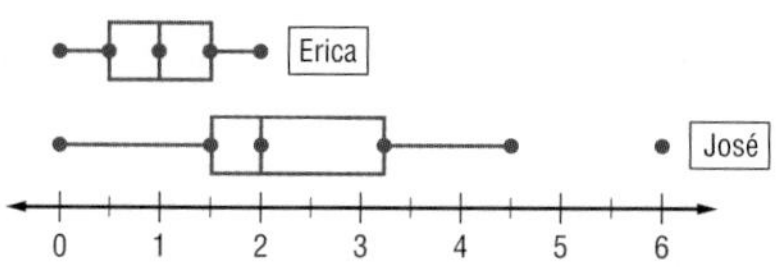

a. How does the time Erica spent studying compare to the time José spent studying?

The middle half of Erica's daily study time was between a half hour and an hour and a half. The middle half of José's daily study time was between an hour and a half and 3 hours 15 minutes. Thus, José's daily study time varies more than Erica's daily study time.

b. What was the greatest amount of time José studied in a day?

The greatest value in the plot is 6, so the greatest amount of time José studied in a day was 6 hours.

c. What is the interquartile range of José's study times?

The interquartile range is UQ – LQ. For this plot, the interquartile range is 3.25 – 1.5 or 1.75 hours.

d. Identify any outliers in José's study times.

An outlier is at least 1.5(1.75) less than the lower quartile or more than the upper quartile. Since $3.25 + (1.5)(1.75) = 5.9$ and $6 > 5.9$, the value 6 is an outlier and was not included in the whisker.

Exercises

3–5. See Student Handbook Answer Appendix.

Tyler surveys 20 randomly chosen students at his school about how many miles they drive in an average day. The results are shown in the box-and-whisker plot.

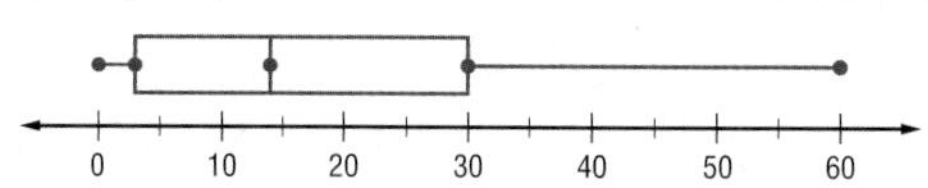

1. What percent of the students drive more than 30 miles in a day? about 25%
2. What is the interquartile range of the box-and-whisker plot? about 27 mi
3. Does a student at Tyler's school have a better chance to meet someone who drives the same mileage they do if they drive 50 miles in a day or 15 miles in a day? Why?
4. Carlos surveyed his friends to find the number of cans of soft drink they drink in an average week. Make a box-and-whisker plot of the data.
{0, 0, 0, 1, 1, 1, 2, 2, 3, 4, 4, 5, 5, 7, 10, 10, 10, 11, 11}
5. The average life span of some animals commonly found in a zoo are given below. Make a box-and-whisker plot of the data.
{1, 7, 7, 10, 12, 12, 15, 15, 18, 20, 20, 20, 25, 40, 100}

1006 Concepts and Skills Bank

Page 937, Problem-Solving Strategy: Create A Table

1. 10; Sample table:

quarters	dimes	nickels
2	0	0
1	2	1
1	1	3
1	0	5
0	5	0
0	4	2
0	3	4
0	2	6
0	1	8
0	0	10

2. 6; Sample table:

quarters	dimes	nickels	pennies	total (cents)
1	1	0	0	35
1	0	1	0	30
1	0	0	1	26
0	1	1	0	15
0	1	0	1	11
0	0	1	1	6

3. Josie: hamburger; Laura: peanut butter; Marcus: peanut butter and jelly; Sample table:

	Laura	Josie	Marcus
Peanut butter	√	X	X
Hamburger	X	√	X
Peanut butter and Jelly	X	X	√

4. 12 ways; Sample table:

B	G	G	0
B	0	G	G
B	G	0	G
G	B	G	0
G	G	B	0
G	B	0	G
G	G	0	B
G	0	B	G
G	0	G	B
0	B	G	G
0	G	B	G
0	G	G	B

5. Sample table:

Number of Small	Number of Large	Small Popcorn ($)	Large Popcorn ($)	Total ($)
0	5	0	11.25	11.25
1	4	1.25	9.00	10.25
2	3	2.50	6.75	9.25
3	2	3.75	4.50	8.25
4	1	5.00	2.25	7.75
5	0	6.25	0	6.25

6. Sample table:

Method of Wrapping	24 students surveyed	120 students surveyed
Recycled paper	3	15
Gift bags	6	30
Wrapping paper	12	60
No wrapping	3	15

7. Sample table:

x	$y = \sqrt{16 - x^2}$	y	(x, y)
-4	$\sqrt{16 - (-4)^2}$	0	$(-4, 0)$
-2	$\sqrt{16 - (-2)^2}$	$2\sqrt{3}$	$(-2, 2\sqrt{3})$
0	$\sqrt{16 - (0)^2}$	4	$(0, 4)$
2	$\sqrt{16 - (2)^2}$	$2\sqrt{3}$	$(2, 2\sqrt{3})$
4	$\sqrt{16 - (4)^2}$	0	$(4, 0)$

Page 939, Problem-Solving Strategy: Make a Chart

1. As the length is doubled, the area increases by a factor of 4. Sample chart:

Length of Square (cm)	Area of Square (cm^2)
3	9
6	36
12	144

2. 9, 12, 15, 18, 21, 24; sample chart:

Integer Value	$f(x) = 2x + 3$	$g(x) = -x - 3$	$f(x) - g(x)$
1	5	-4	9
2	7	-5	12
3	9	-6	15
4	11	-7	18
5	13	-8	21
6	15	-9	24

3. Sample chart:

Length	Width	Area
8	18	144
9	16	144
12	12	144

4. 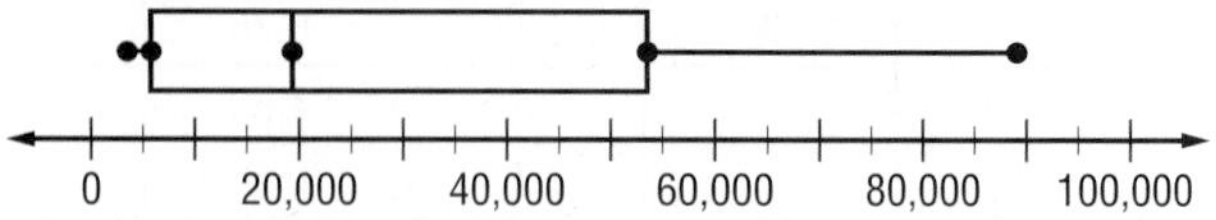

The data are most closely clustered in the first quartile.

5. $\frac{3}{26}$; sample chart:

Type of Reptile	Tally of States	Number of States
turtle, tortoise, terapin	𝍸 𝍸 ||||	14
snake	|||	3
alligator	|||	3
lizard	|||	3
toad	|	1
none	𝍸 𝍸 𝍸 𝍸 𝍸 |	26

Page 946, Problem-Solving Strategy: Write an Equation

1a. $$L(t) = \begin{cases} 3t & \text{if } 0 < t \leq 10 \\ 30 + (t - 10) & \text{if } 10 < t \leq 15 \\ 35 + \frac{1}{3}(t - 15) & \text{if } 15 < t \leq 24 \end{cases}$$

Page 948, Extra Practice (Lesson 1-6)

1. 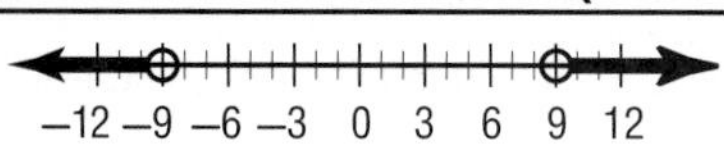

2. 

3. 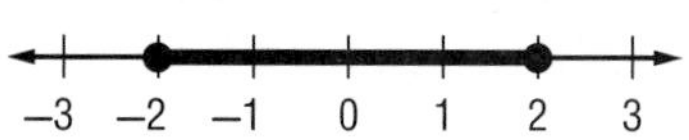

4. $\{m \mid m < 3 \text{ or } m > 6\}$ 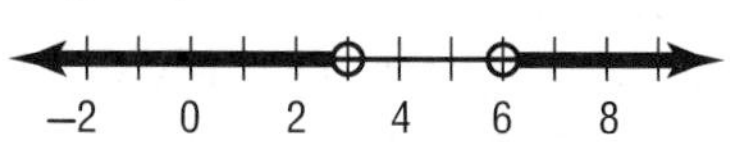

5. $\{n \mid -2 < n < 3\}$ 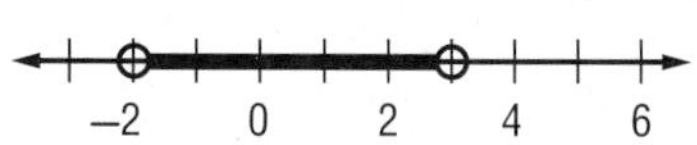

6. $\{y \mid -1 \leq y \leq 7\}$ 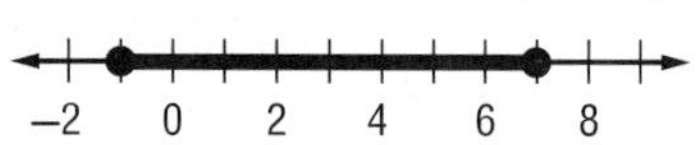

7. $\{t \mid t \leq -2 \text{ or } t \geq 2\}$ 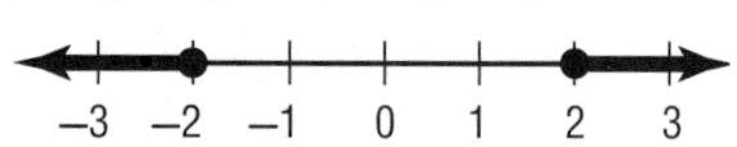

8. $\{x \mid 1 \leq x \leq 4\}$ 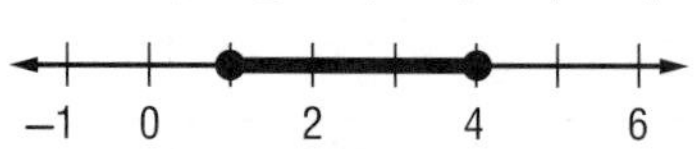

9. $\{x \mid x < -0.5 \text{ or } x > 8\}$ 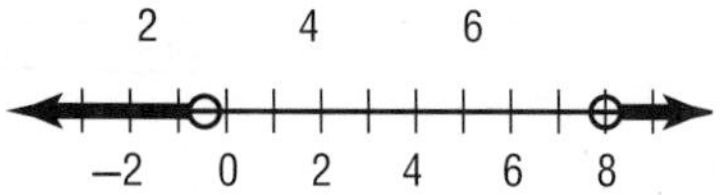

10. $\{x \mid x \leq -3 \text{ or } x \geq 3\}$ 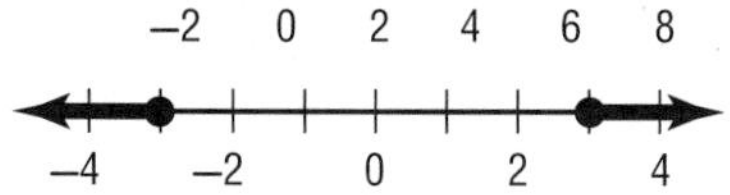

11. $\{p \mid -2 \leq p \leq 2\}$ 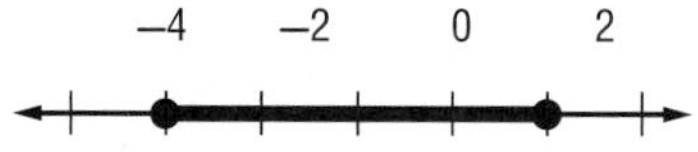

12. all real numbers 

13. $\{a \mid -4 < a < -2\}$ 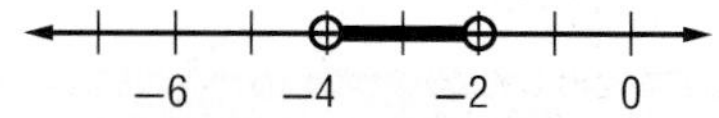

14. $\{t \mid t < 3 \text{ or } t > 5\}$ 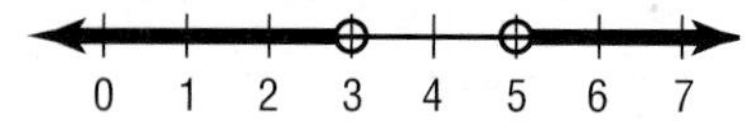

15. $\{y \mid 1 < y < 4\}$ 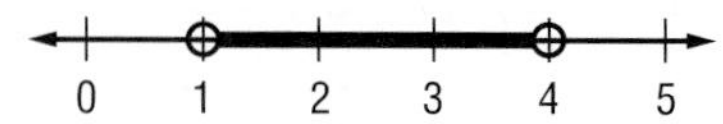

16. $\{d \mid d \leq -3 \text{ or } d \geq -1\}$

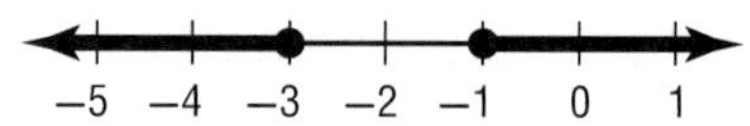

17. $\{x \mid -1 < x < 1.5\}$ 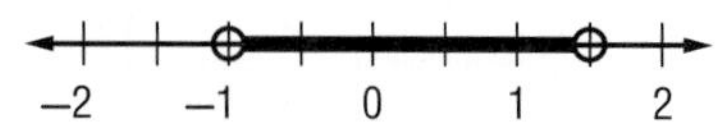

18. $\{v \mid v < -5 \text{ or } v > 1\}$ 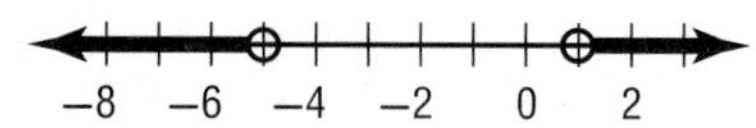

19. $\{r \mid -5 < r < 1\}$ 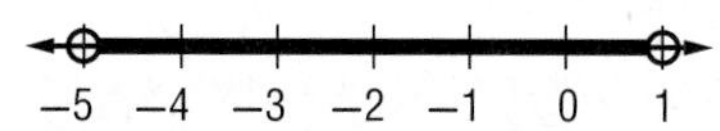

20. $\{w \mid w \leq -1.2 \text{ or } w \geq 2.4\}$

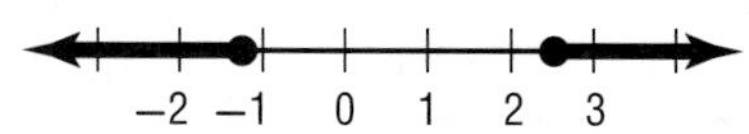

21. all real numbers 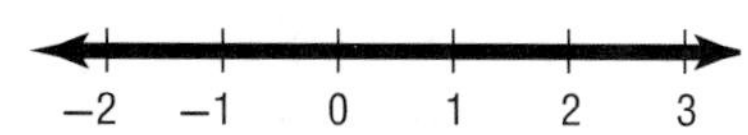

22. $\varnothing$ 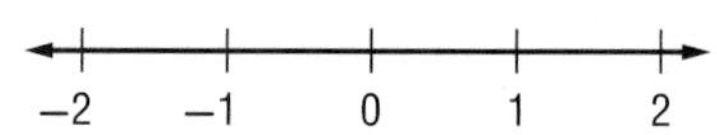

23. $\varnothing$ 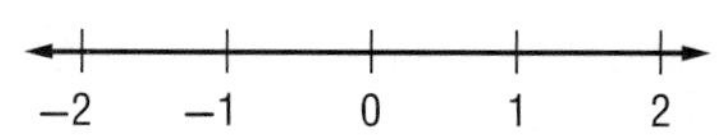

24. $\{n \mid n \leq 2.4 \text{ or } n \geq 4\}$ 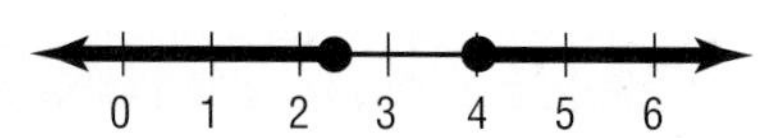

Page 949, Extra Practice (Lesson 2-1)

4. D = {1, 2, 3, 4}; R = {2, 3, 4, 5}: a function; both one-to-one and onto; discrete

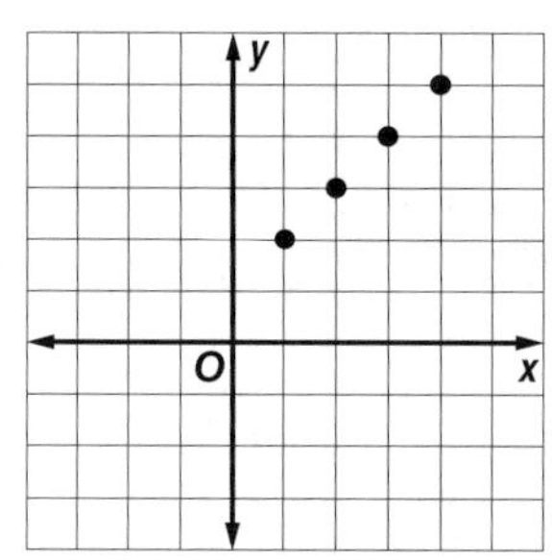

5. D = {0}; R = {0,1, 2, 3}: not a function; discrete

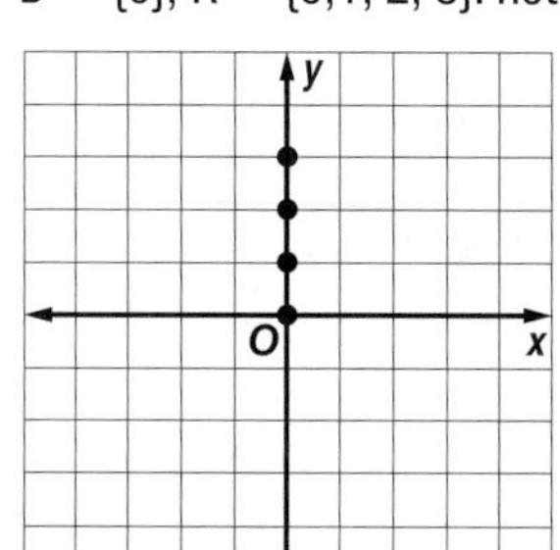

6. D = {all real numbers}; R = {all real numbers}; a function; both one-to one and onto; continuous

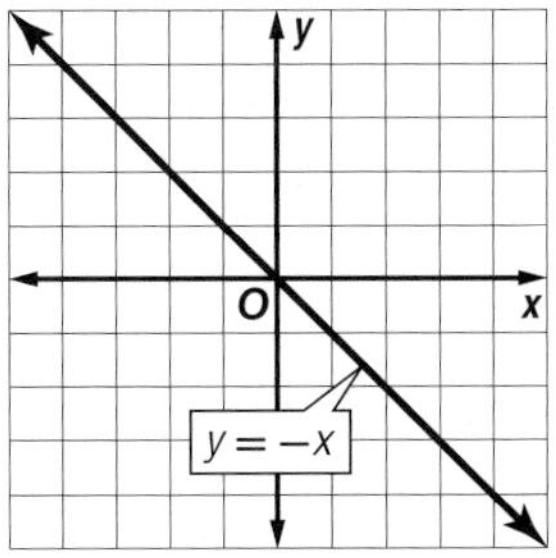

7. D = {all real numbers}; R = {all real numbers}; a function; both one-to-one and onto; continuous

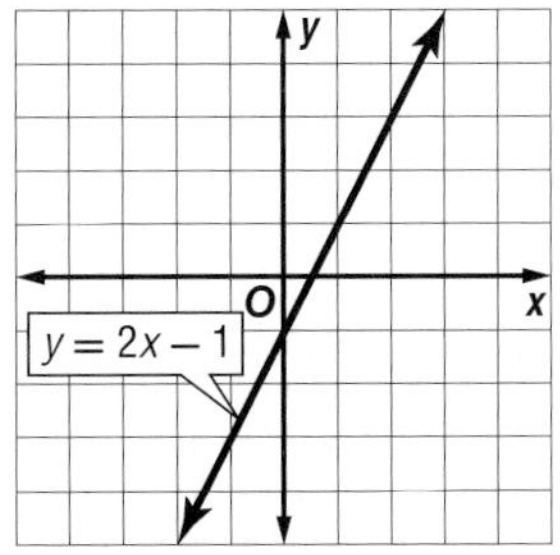

8. D = {all real numbers}; R = $\{y \mid y \geq 0\}$; a function; neither; continuous

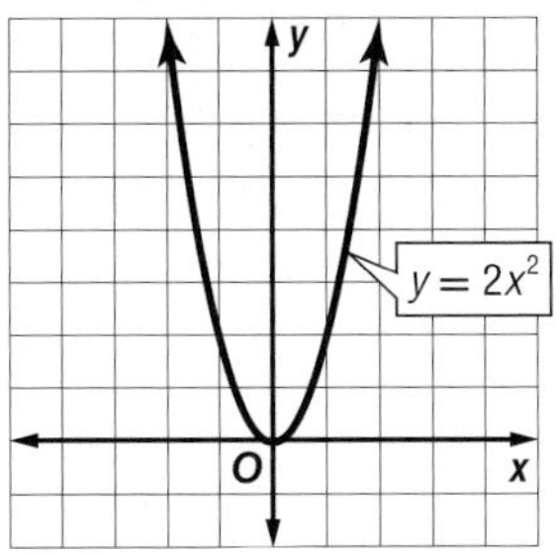

9. D = {all real numbers}; R = $\{y \mid y \leq 0\}$; a function; neither; continuous

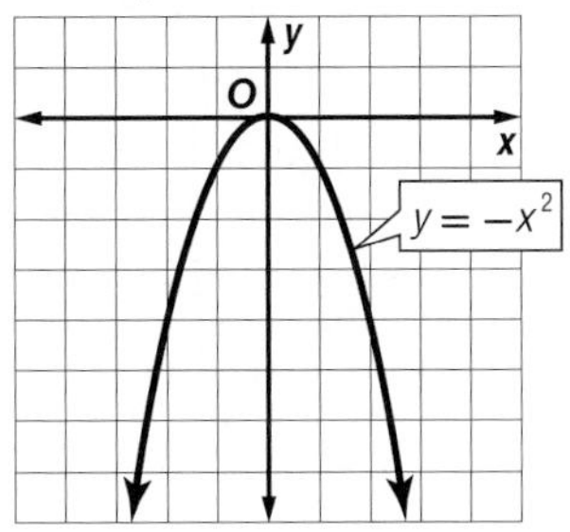

Page 949, Extra Practice (Lesson 2-2)

2. x is inside a radical.

3. x appears in a denominator.

5. $x - y = -7$; 1, –1, –7

6. $x + 3y = 0$; 1, 3, 0

7. $5x - 7y = 3$; 5, –7, 3

8. $x = -25$; 1, 0, –25

9.

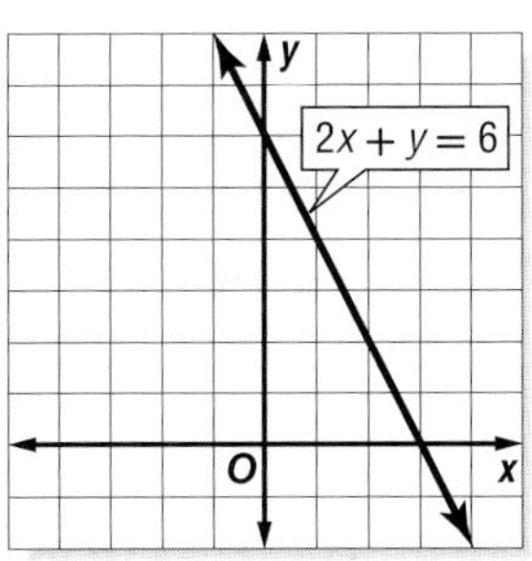

10.

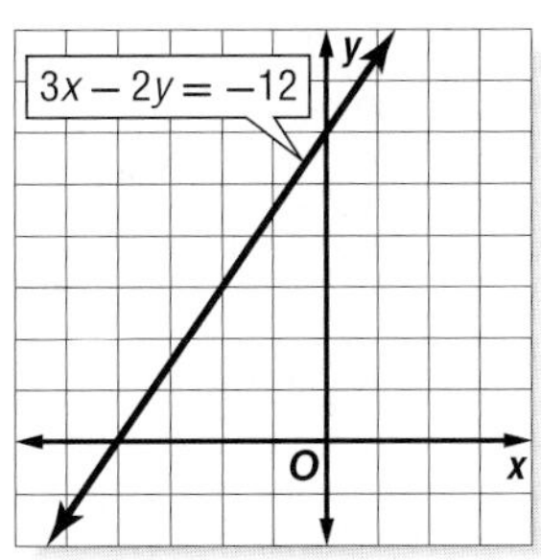

11.

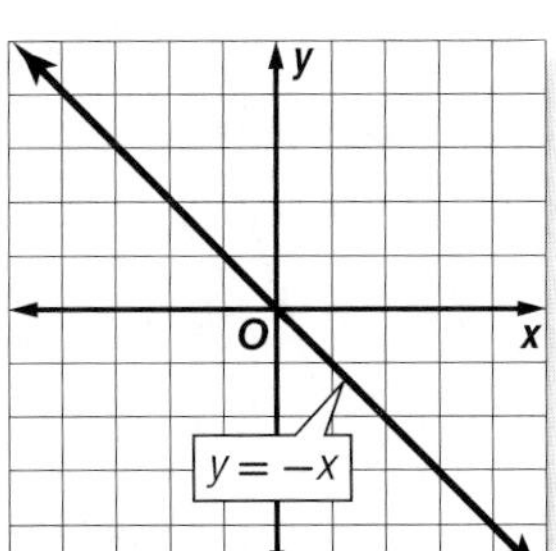

12.

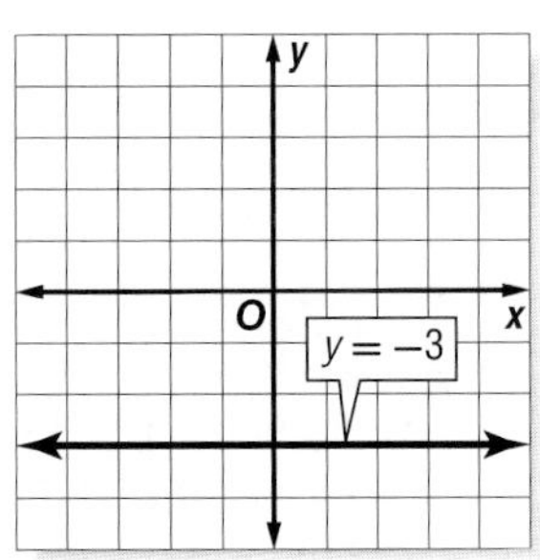

Page 950, Extra Practice (Lesson 2-4)

3. $y = -x + 9$

4. $y = \frac{3}{4}x$

5. $y = -\frac{5}{2}x - \frac{1}{2}$

6. $y = \frac{2}{5}x + 2$

7. $y = -\frac{2}{3}x + \frac{5}{3}$

8. $y = \frac{2}{3}x$

Page 950, Extra Practice (Lesson 2-5)

1a. positive correlation

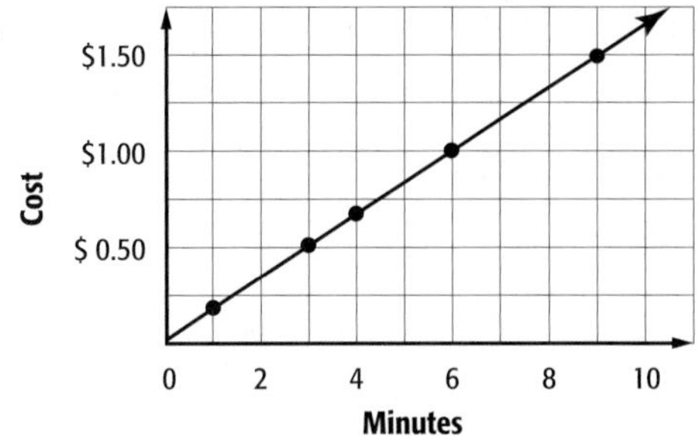

1b. $y = 0.16x + 0.04$

1c. $2.44

2a. positive correlation

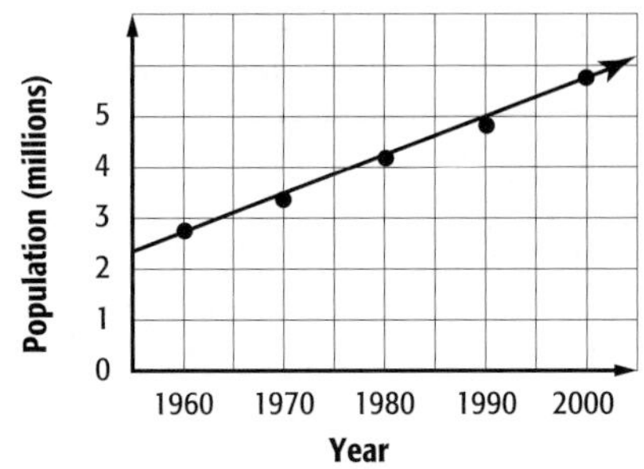

2b. Sample answer using (1960, 2,853,214) and (2000, 5,894,121): $y = 76{,}022.675x - 146{,}151{,}229$

2c. Sample answer: 6,654,348

3a. positive correlation

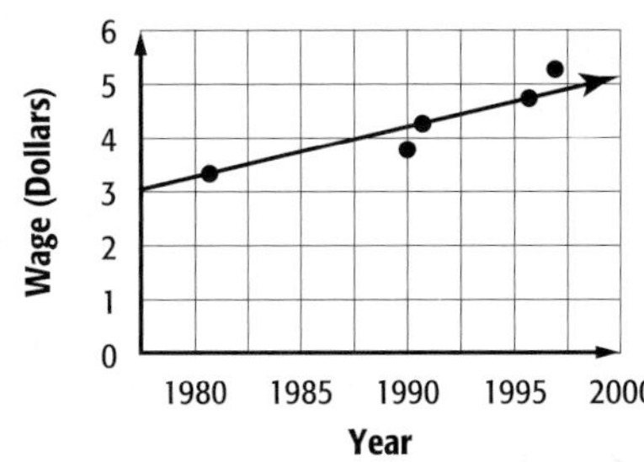

3b. Sample answer using (1991, 4.25) and (1996, 4.75): $y = 0.1x - 194.85$

3c. Sample answer: $6.65

Page 950, Extra Practice (Lesson 2-6)

3. D = {all real numbers}; R = {all integers}

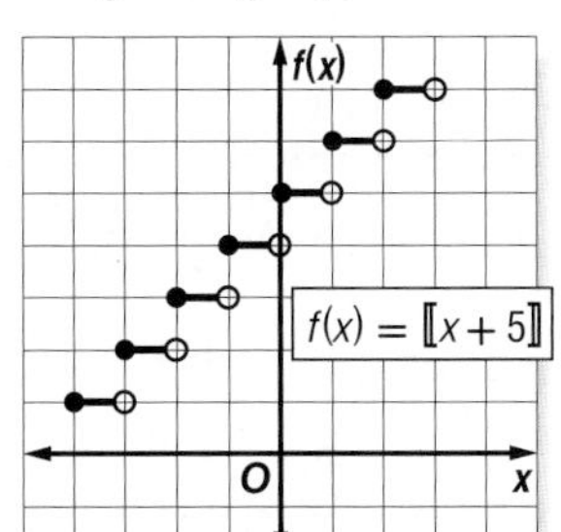

4. D = {all real numbers}; R = {all integers}

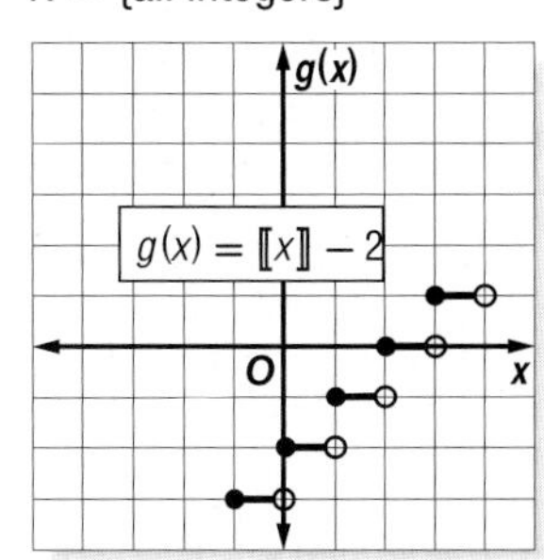

5. D = {all real numbers}; R = {even integers}

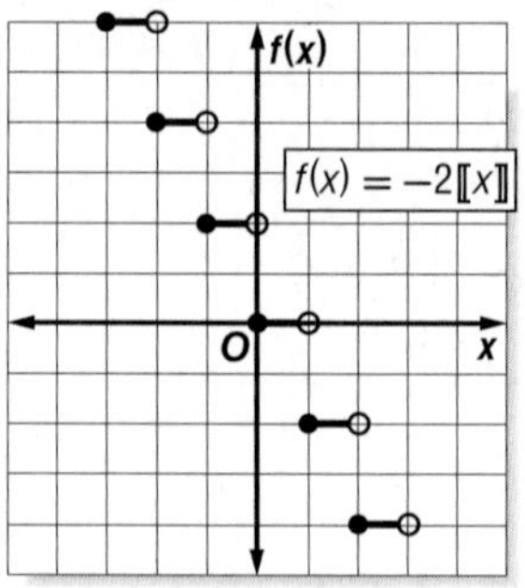

6. D = {all real numbers}; R = $\{h(x) \mid h(x) \geq -3\}$

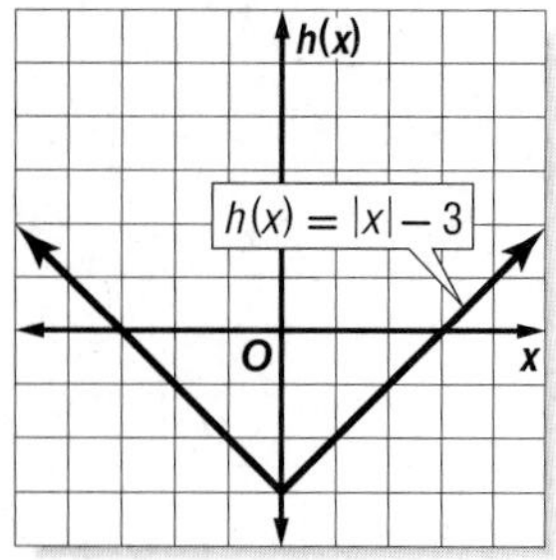

7. D = {all real numbers}; R = $\{h(x) \mid h(x) \geq 0\}$

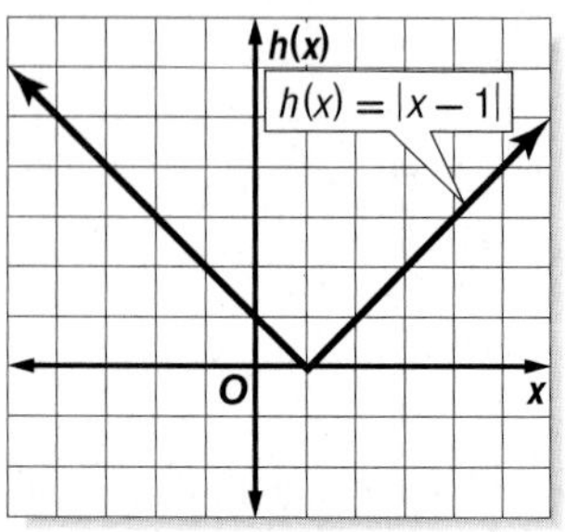

8. D = {all real numbers}; R = $\{g(x) \mid g(x) \geq 2\}$

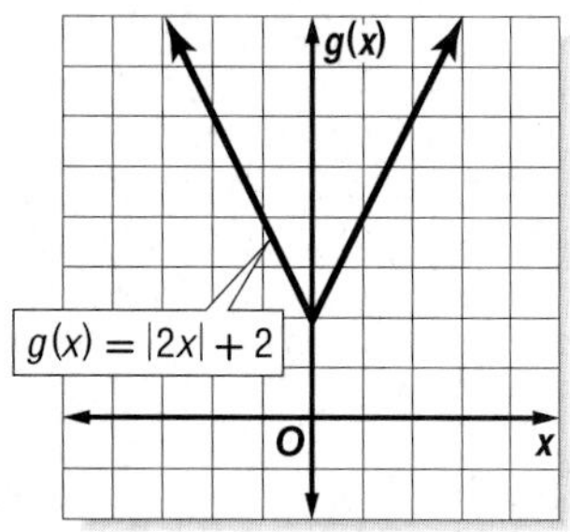

9. D = {all real numbers}; R = $\{h(x) \mid h(x) < -2 \text{ or } y = 4\}$

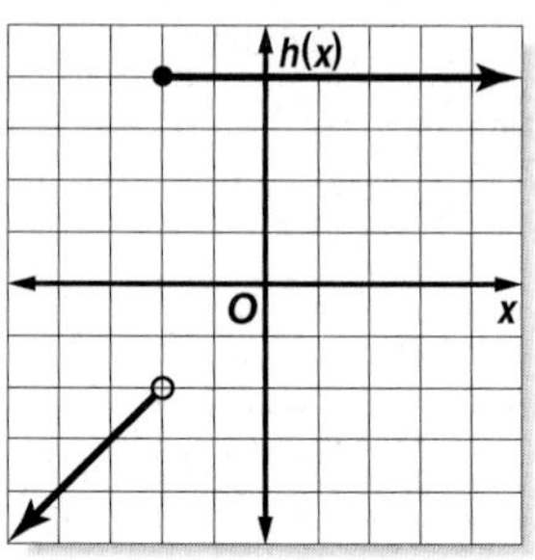

10. D = {all real numbers}; R = $\{f(x) \mid f(x) < -1\}$

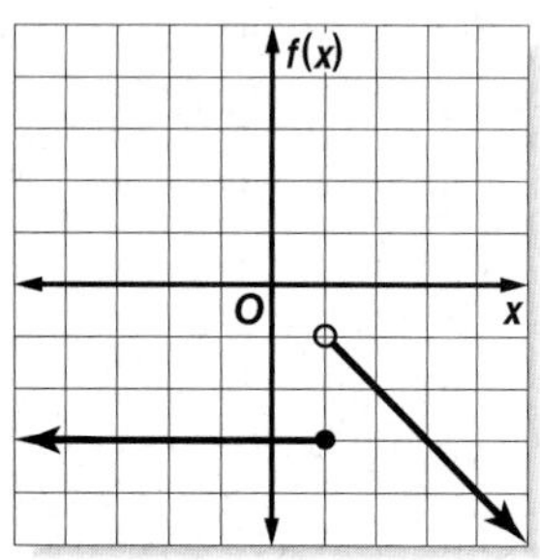

Page 951, Extra Practice (Lesson 2-7)

4.

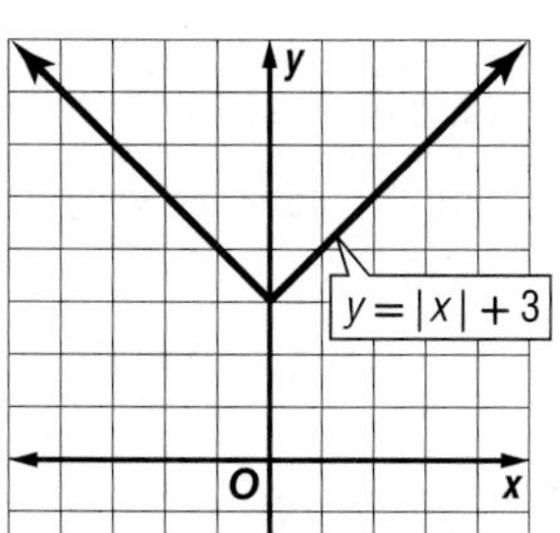

5.

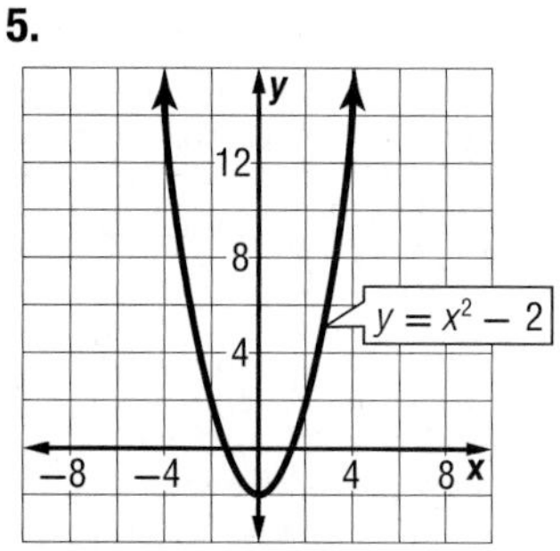

6.

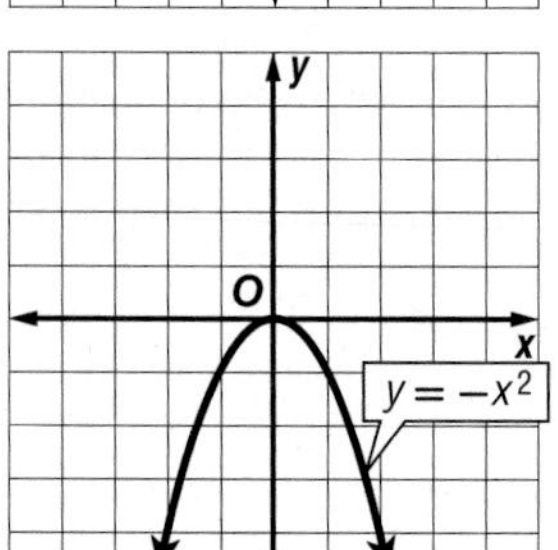

7.

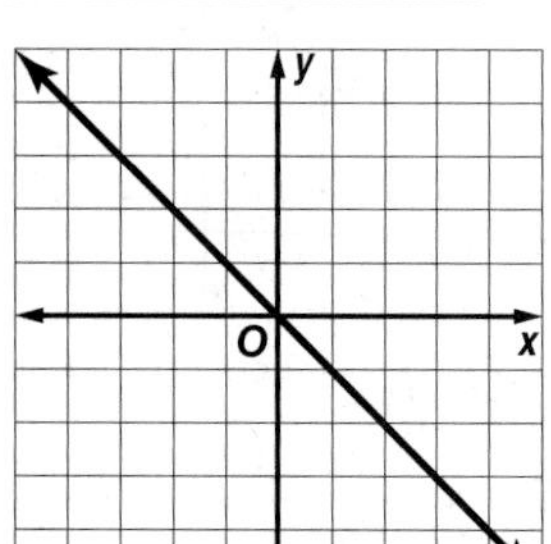

8.

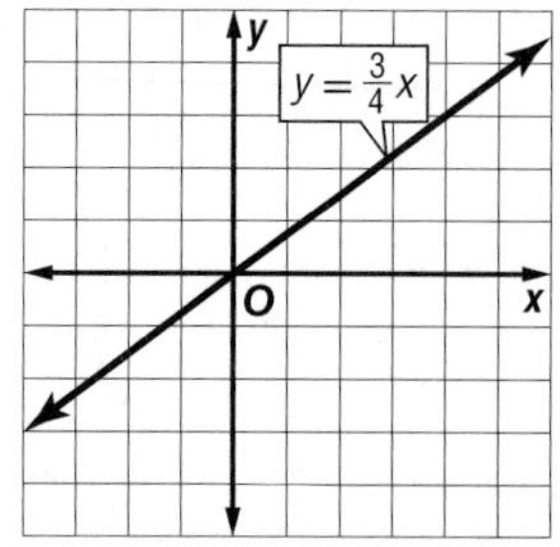

9.

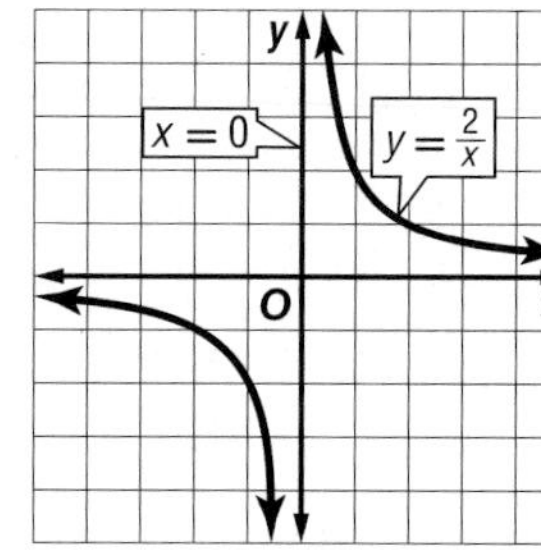

Page 951, Extra Practice (Lesson 2-8)

1.

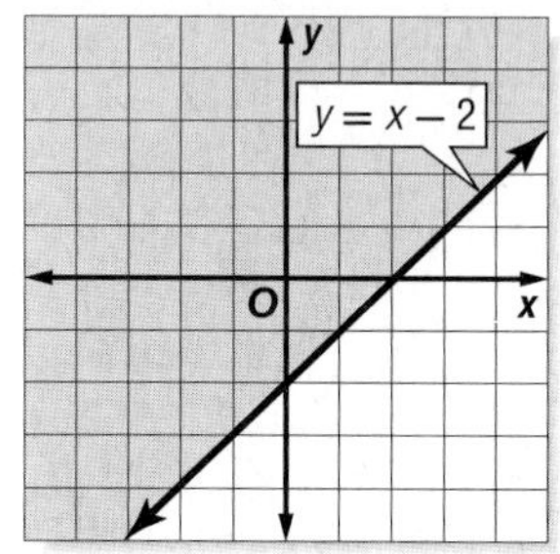

2.

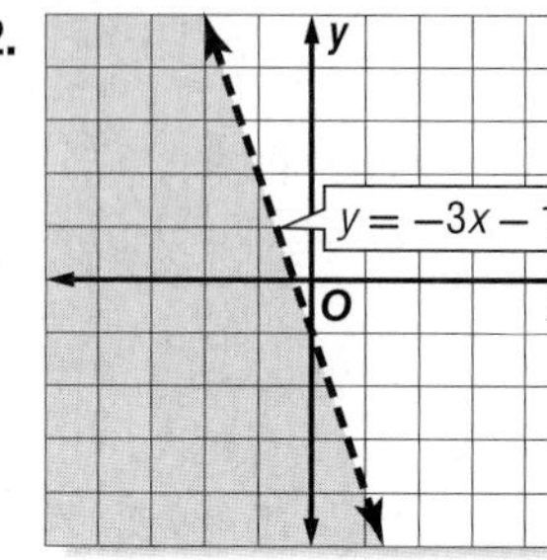

3.

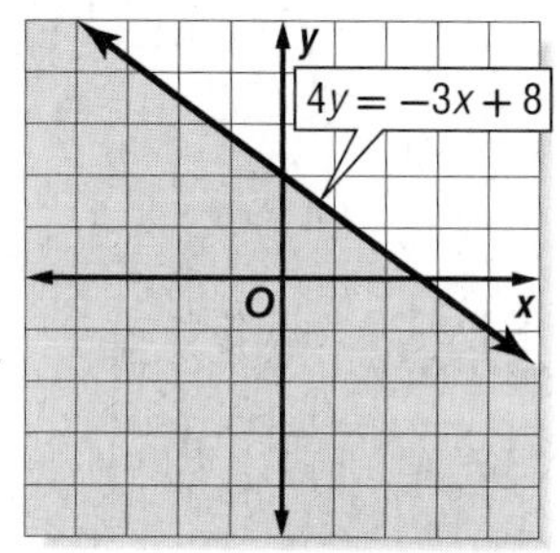

4.

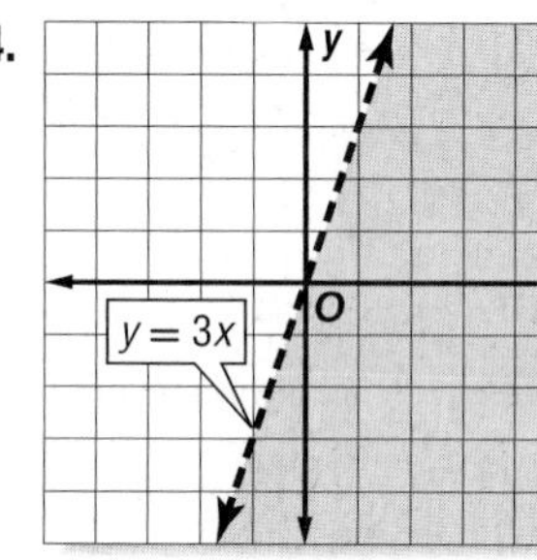

5.

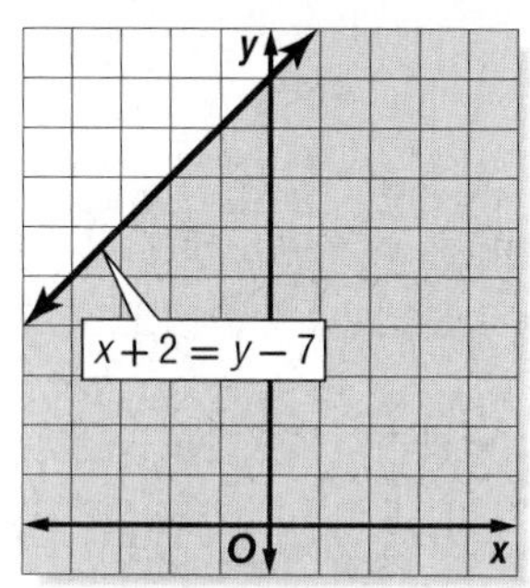

6.

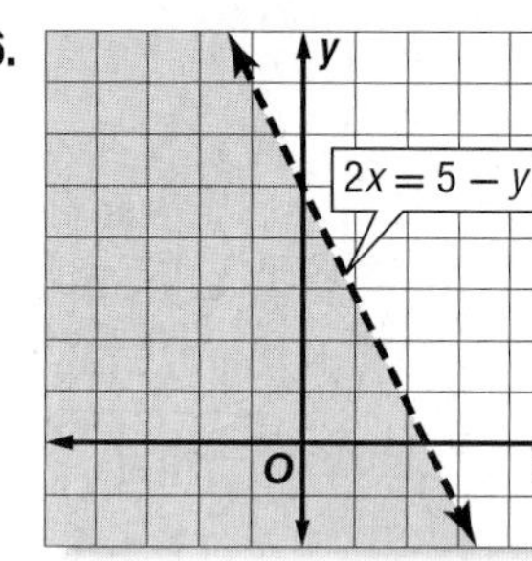

7.

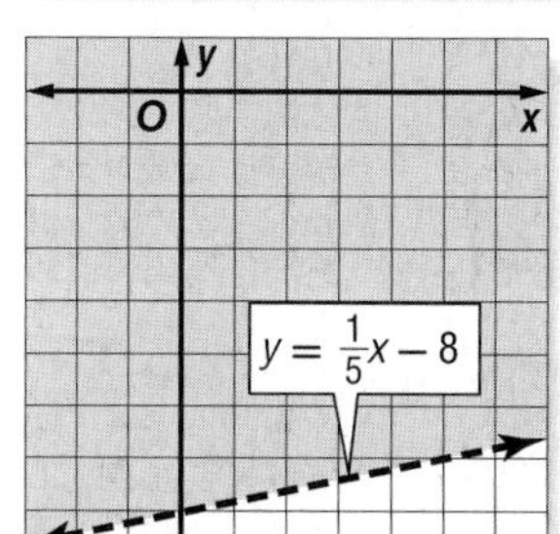

8.

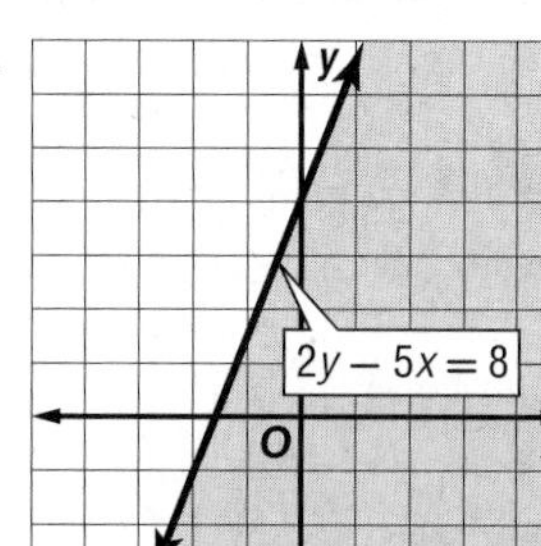

9.

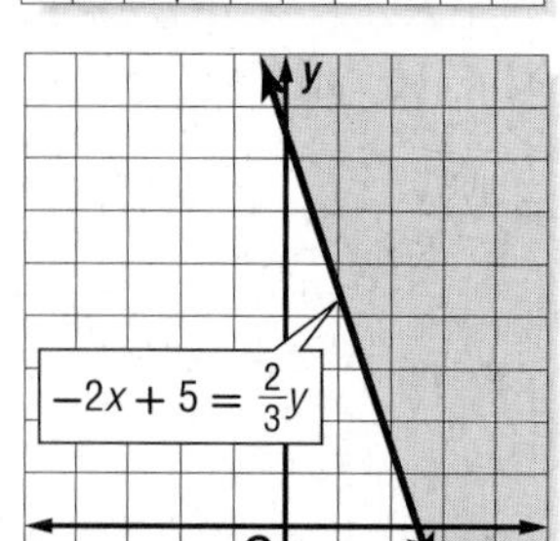

10.

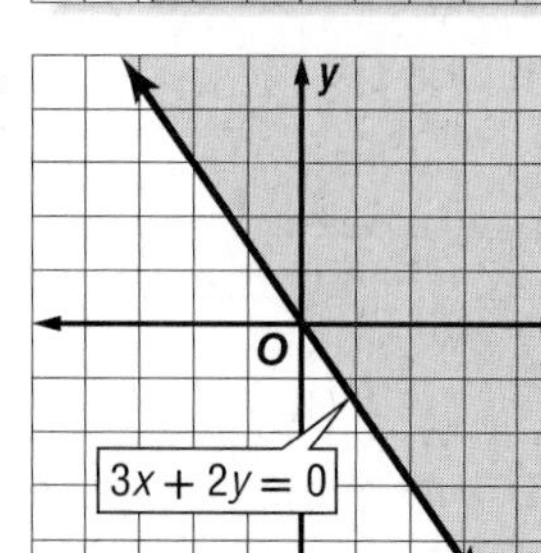

11.
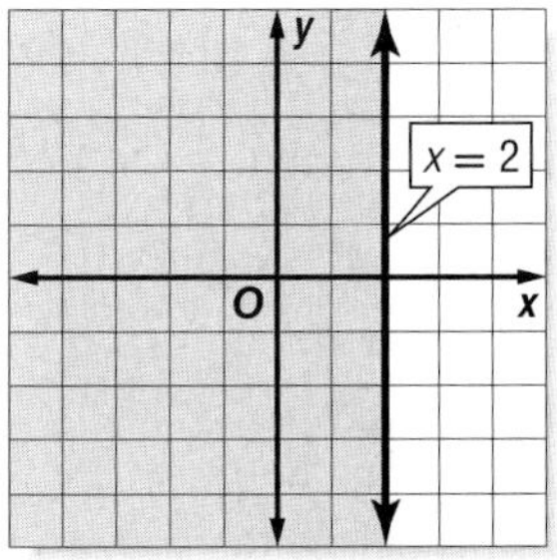

12.
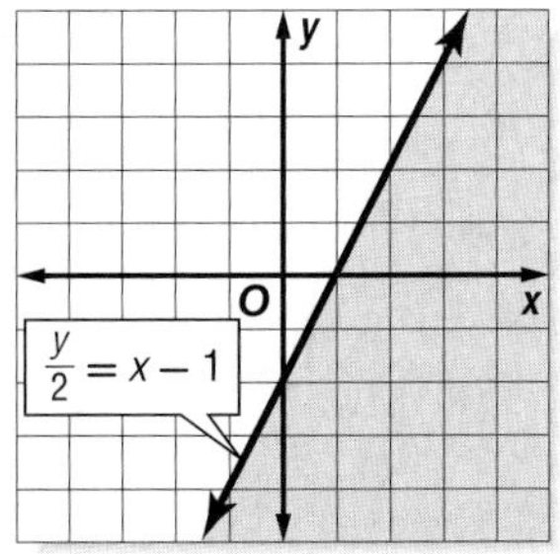

13.
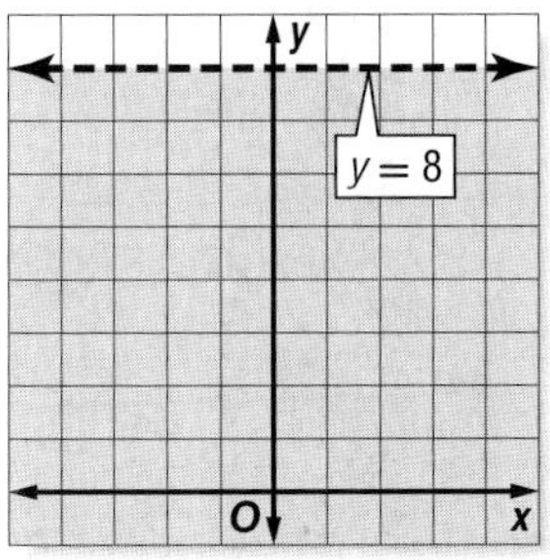

14.
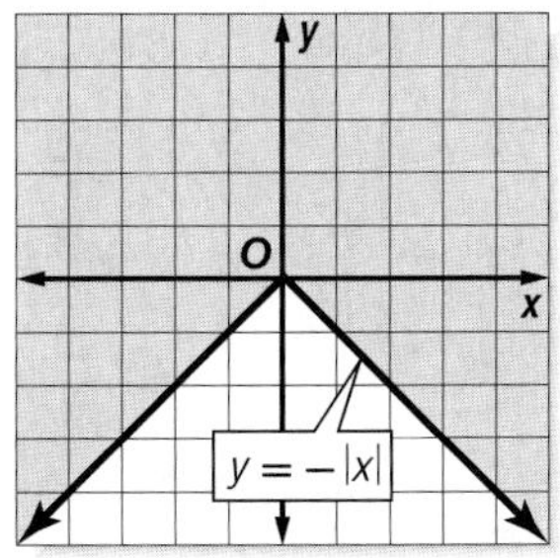

15.
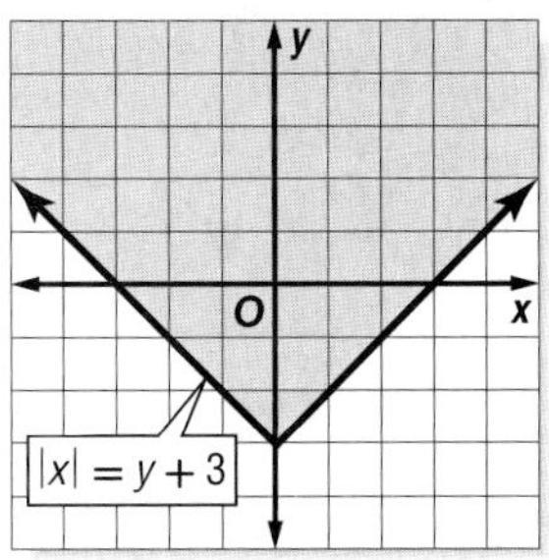

16.
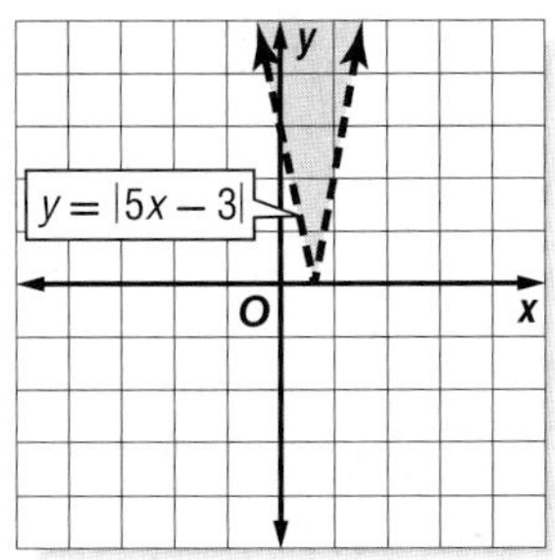

17.
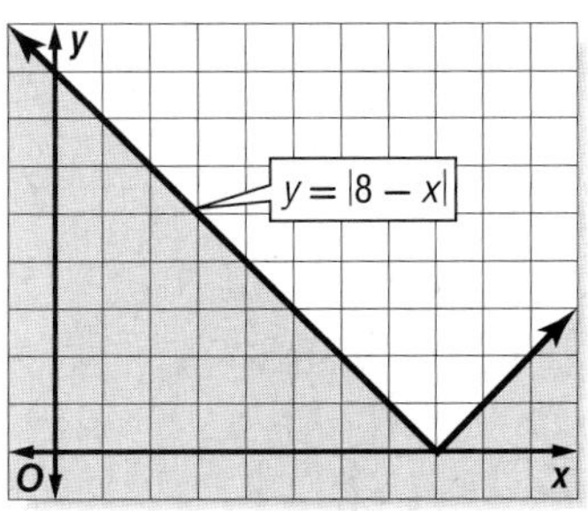

18.
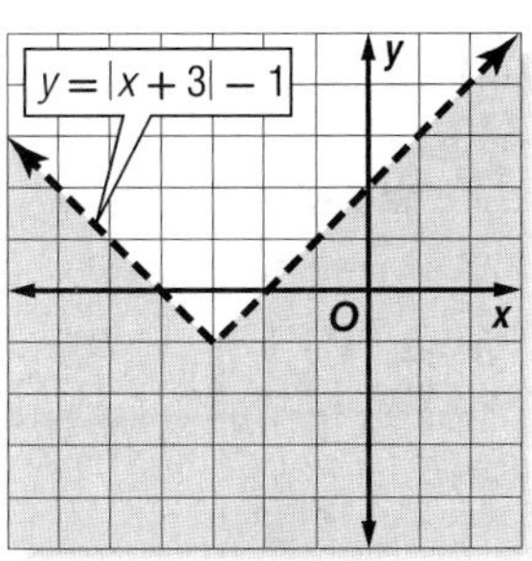

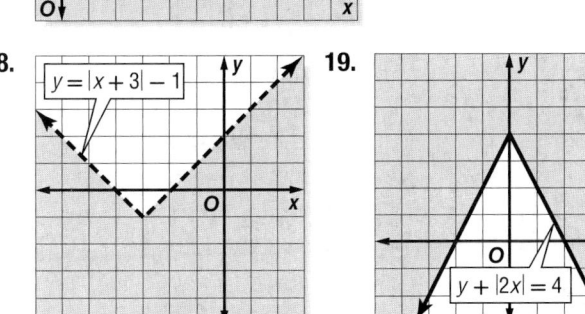

19.
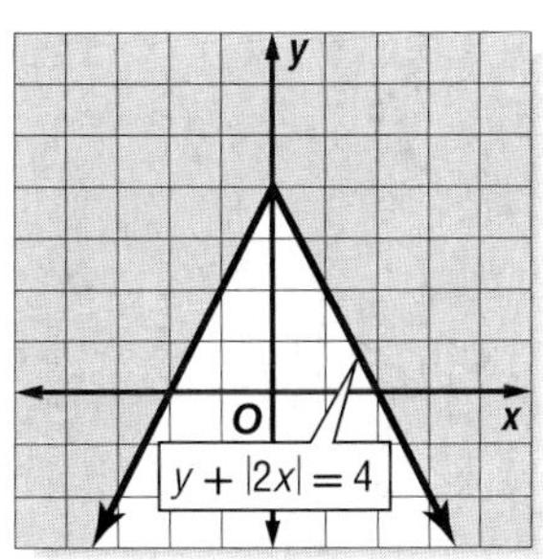

20.
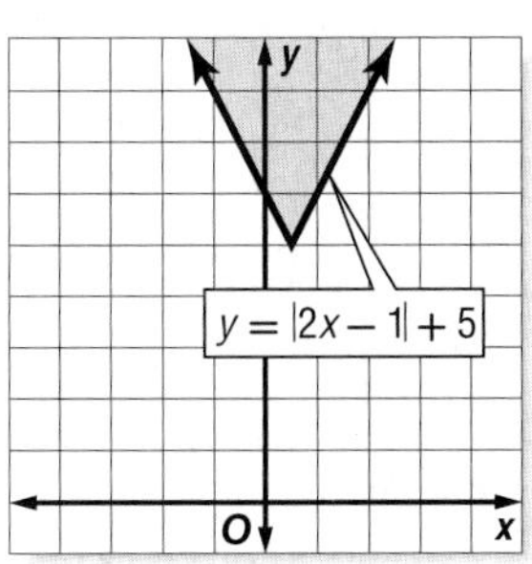

21.
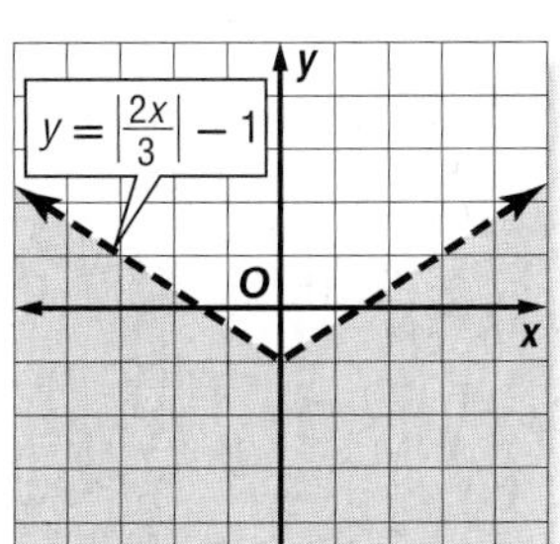

Page 951, Extra Practice (Lesson 3-1)

7.
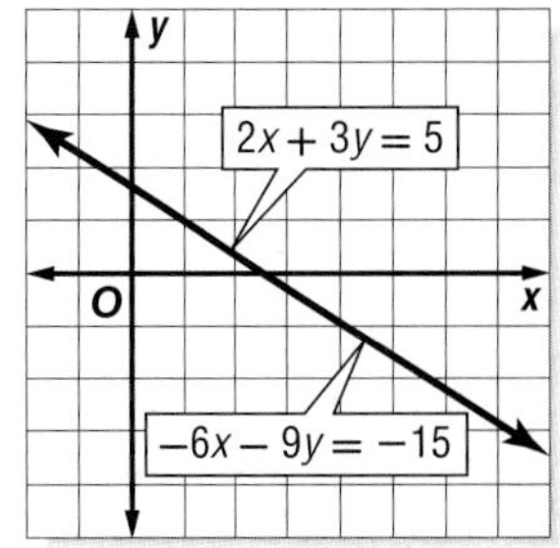

8.
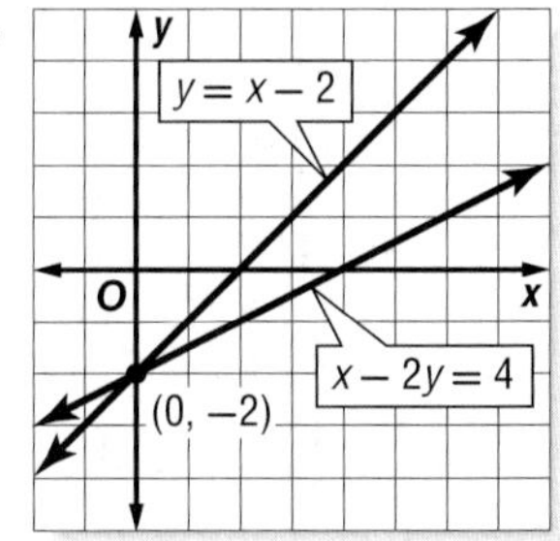

9.
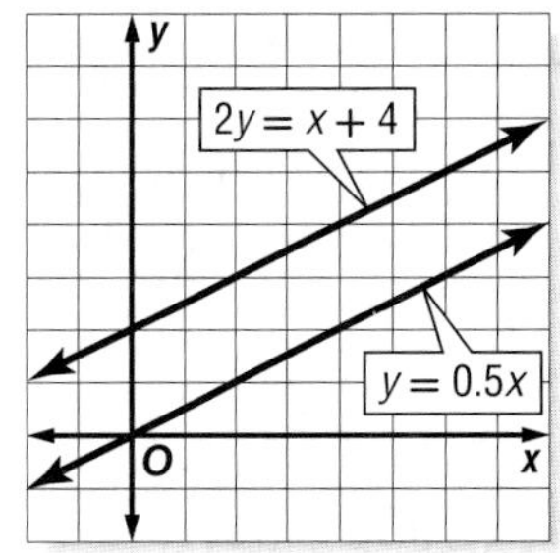

10.
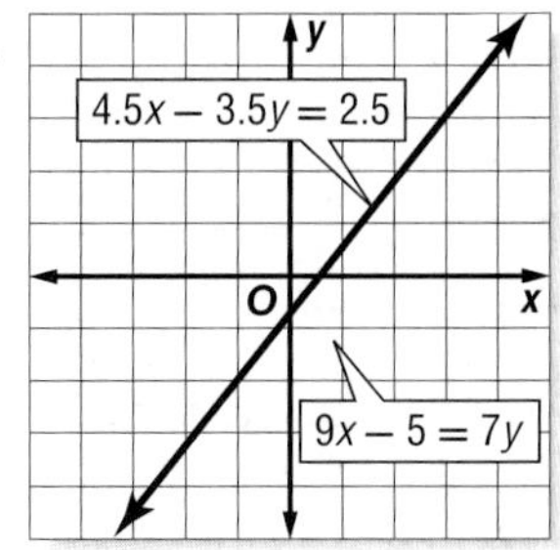

11.
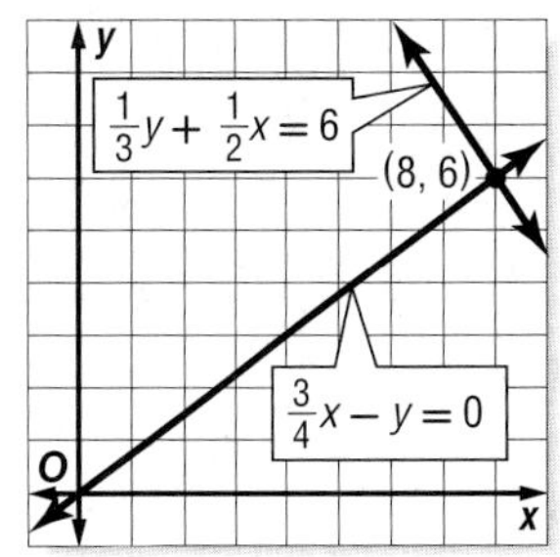

12.
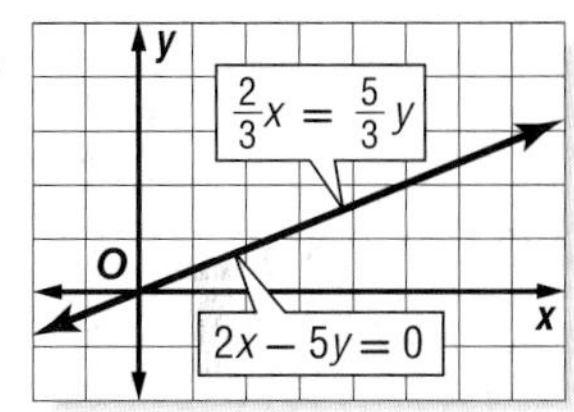

Page 952, Extra Practice (Lesson 3-3)

1.
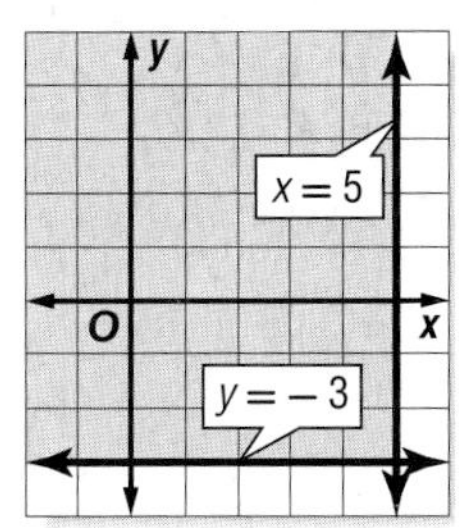

2.
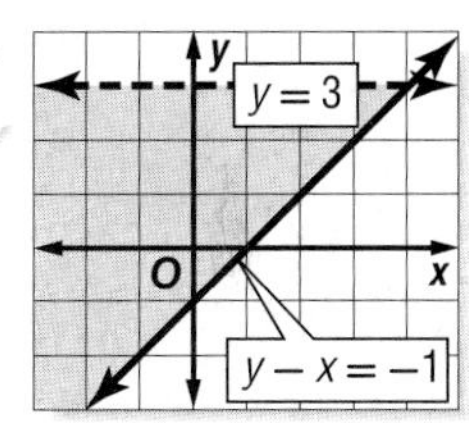

3.
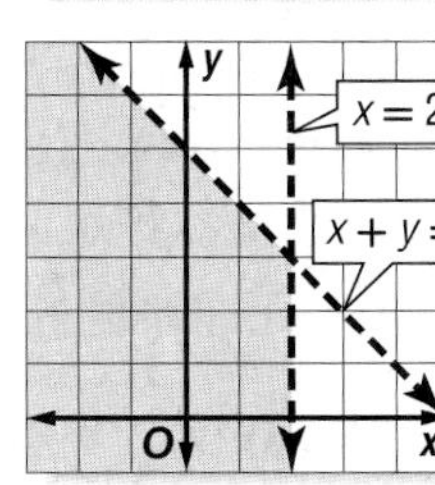

4.
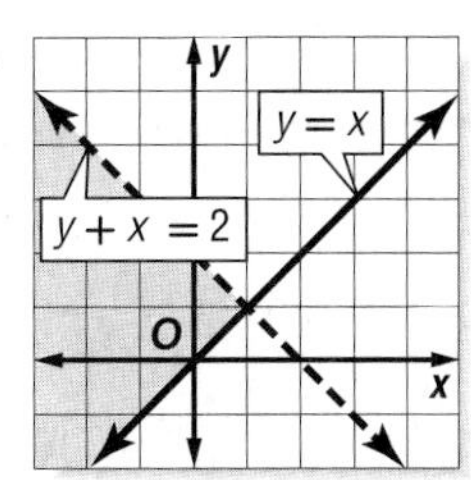

5.
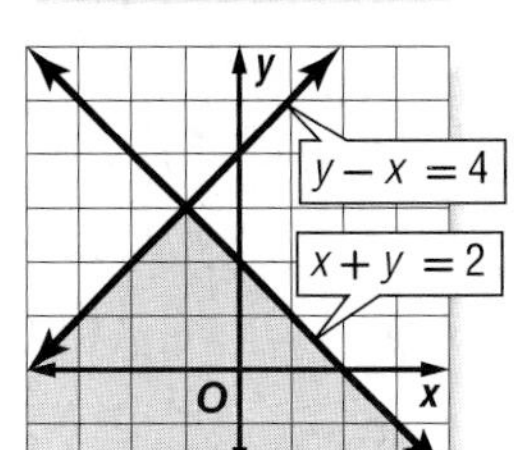

6.
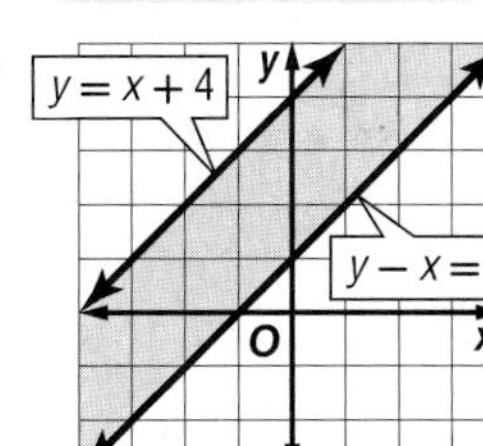

7.
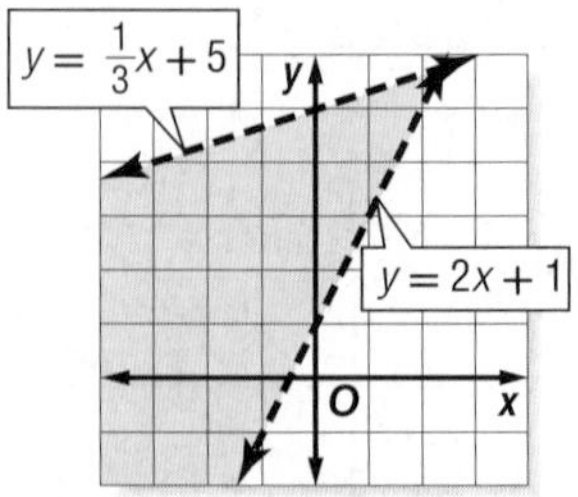

8.
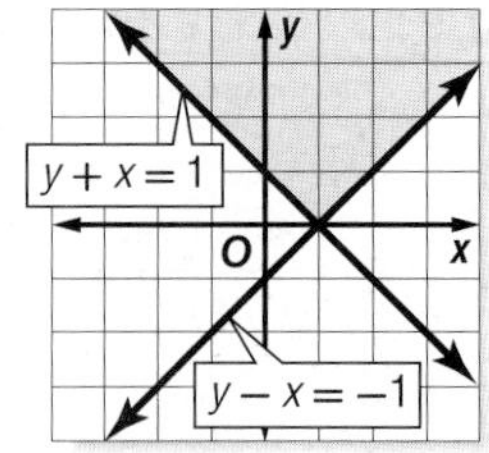

9.
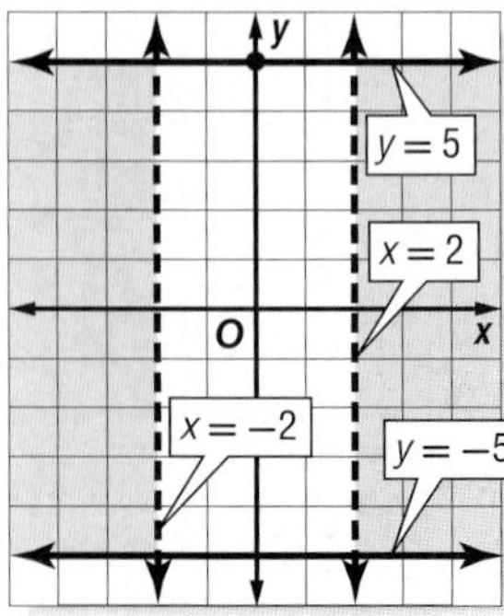

10.
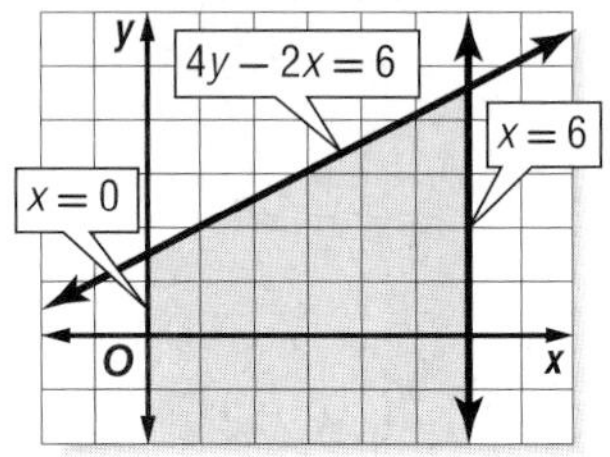

11.
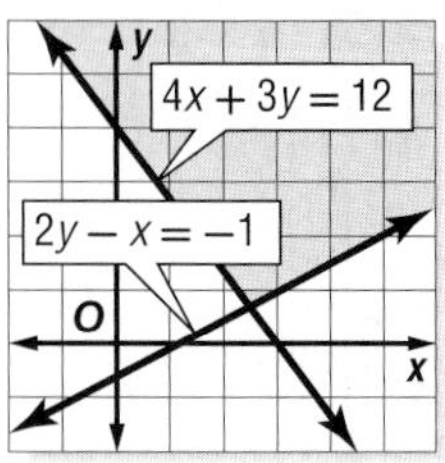

12.
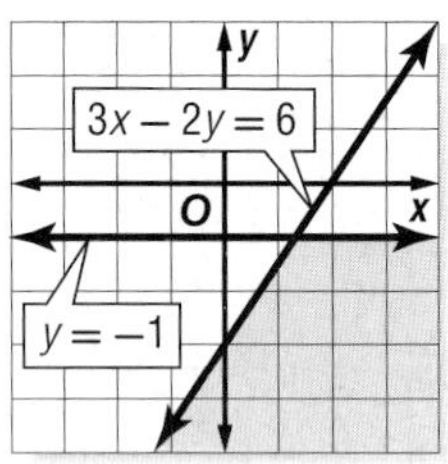

13.
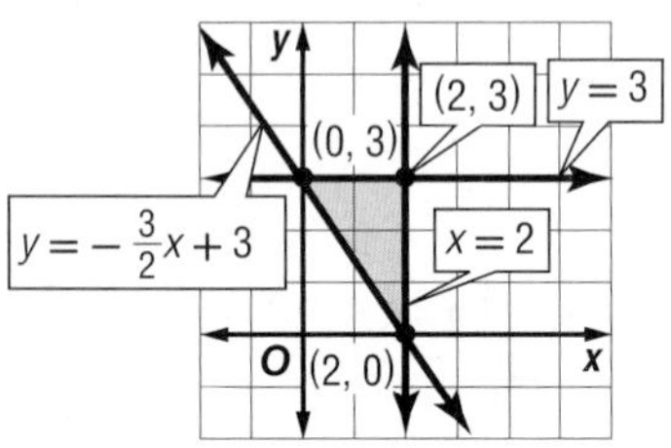

14.
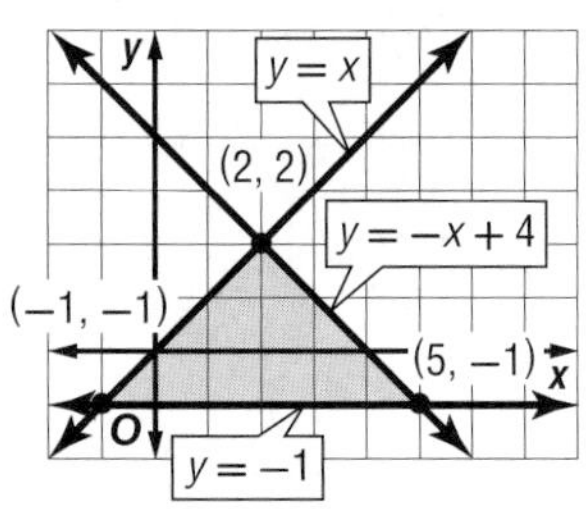

15.
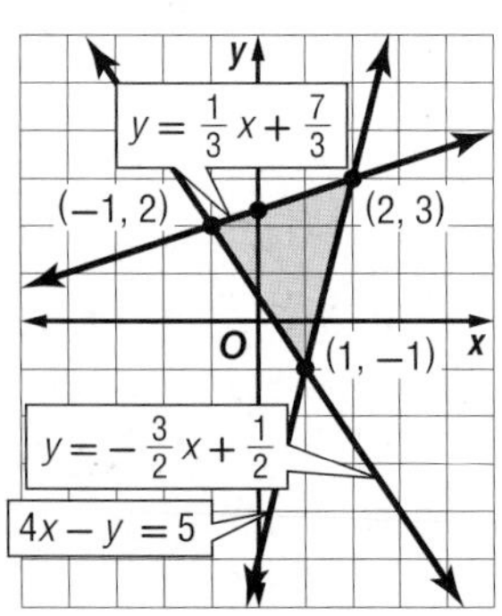

Page 952, Extra Practice (Lesson 3-4)

1.
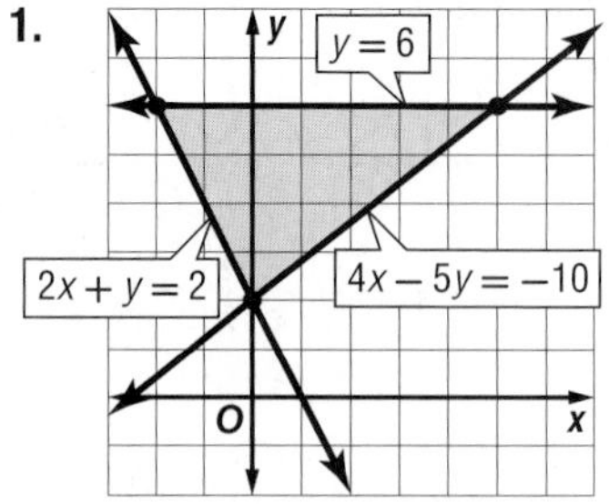

2A.
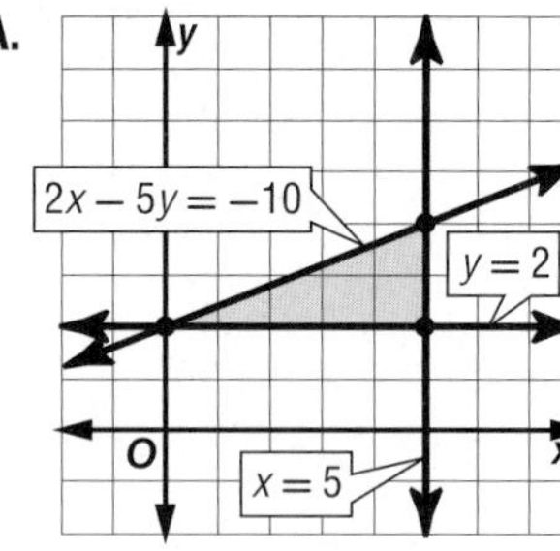

3.
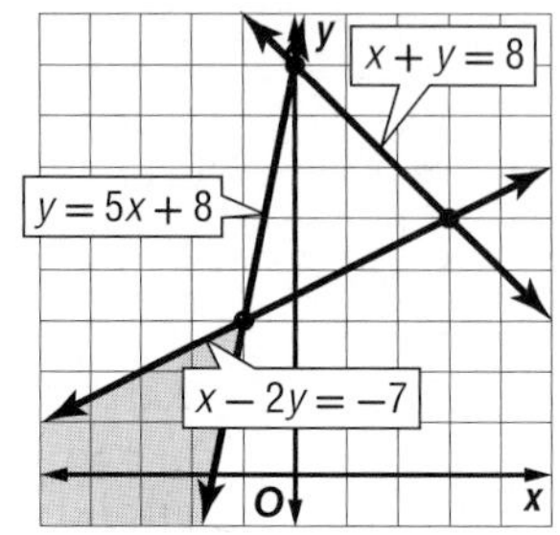

4.
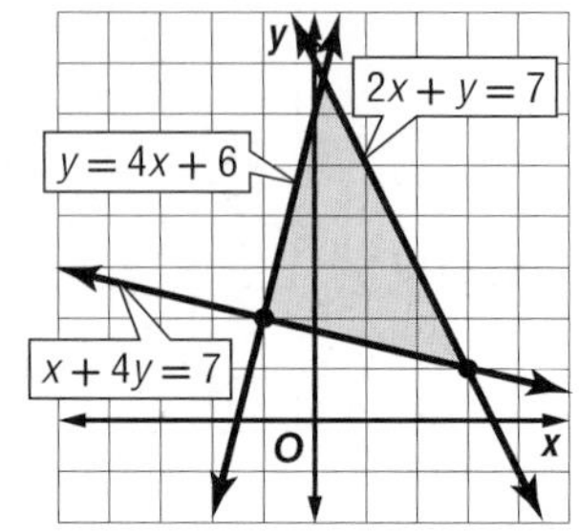

5.
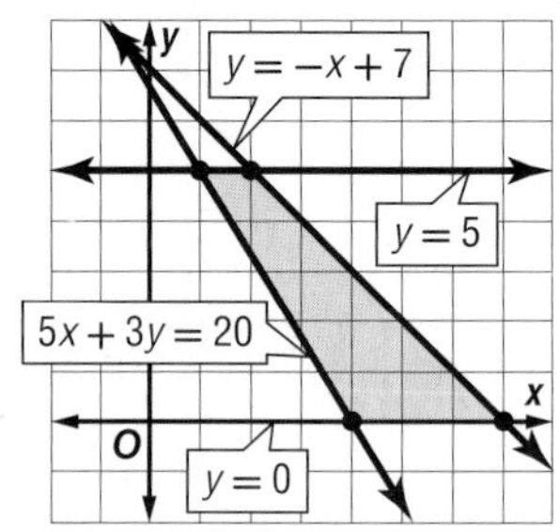

6.
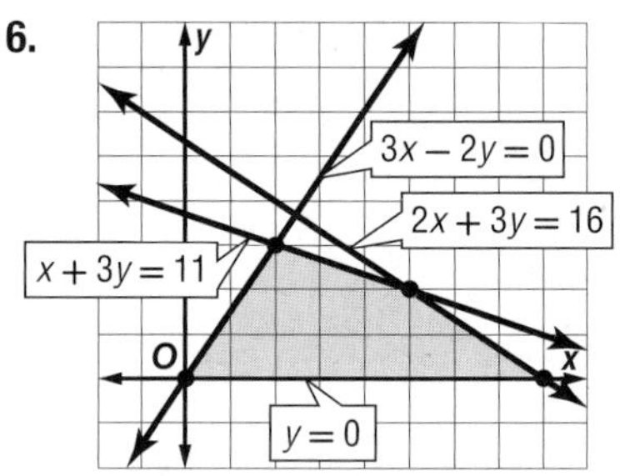

Page 953, Extra Practice (Lesson 4-2)

1. $\begin{bmatrix} 1 & 11 \\ 1 & 1 \end{bmatrix}$

2. impossible

3. $\begin{bmatrix} 0 & 38 & -18 \\ 45 & 20 & 15 \end{bmatrix}$

4. $\begin{bmatrix} -38 & 29 & 18 \end{bmatrix}$

5. $\begin{bmatrix} 46 & -30 \\ -1 & 20 \end{bmatrix}$

6. $\begin{bmatrix} 36.01 \\ -68.07 \end{bmatrix}$

7. $\begin{bmatrix} 0 & 0 \\ 0 & 0 \end{bmatrix}$

8. $\begin{bmatrix} 0 & 0 \\ 0 & 0 \end{bmatrix}$

9. $\begin{bmatrix} 2 & 0 \\ 0 & 2 \end{bmatrix}$

10. $\begin{bmatrix} -4 & 0 \\ 0 & -4 \end{bmatrix}$

11. $\begin{bmatrix} -4 & 4 \\ 6 & -6 \end{bmatrix}$

12. $\begin{bmatrix} 7 & -3 \\ -2 & 6 \end{bmatrix}$

13. $\begin{bmatrix} 0 & 2 \\ 3 & -1 \end{bmatrix}$

14. $\begin{bmatrix} 19 & -11 \\ -9 & 17 \end{bmatrix}$

Page 954, Extra Practice (Lesson 4-4)

1a. $\begin{bmatrix} 1 & -2 & -4 & 2 \\ 1 & 3 & -1 & -3 \end{bmatrix}$

1b. $A'(2, 2)$, $B'(-4, 6)$, $C'(-8, -2)$, $D'(4, -6)$

1c.

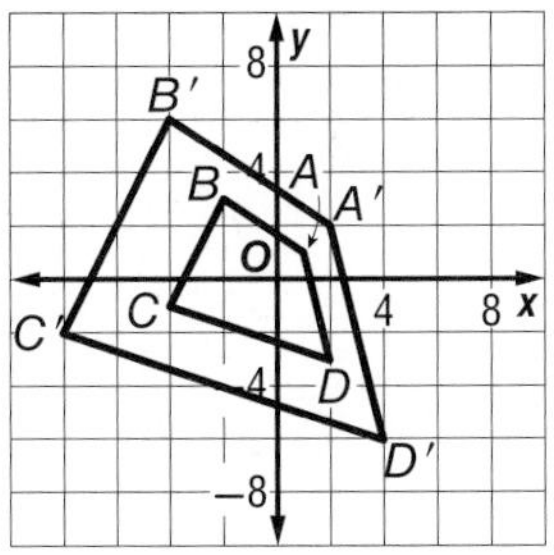

2a. $\begin{bmatrix} 2 & 3 & 1 \\ 4 & -5 & -1 \end{bmatrix}$

2b. $\begin{bmatrix} 0 & 1 \\ 1 & 0 \end{bmatrix}$

2c. $M'(4, 2)$, $Q'(-5, 3)$, $N'(-1, 1)$

2d.

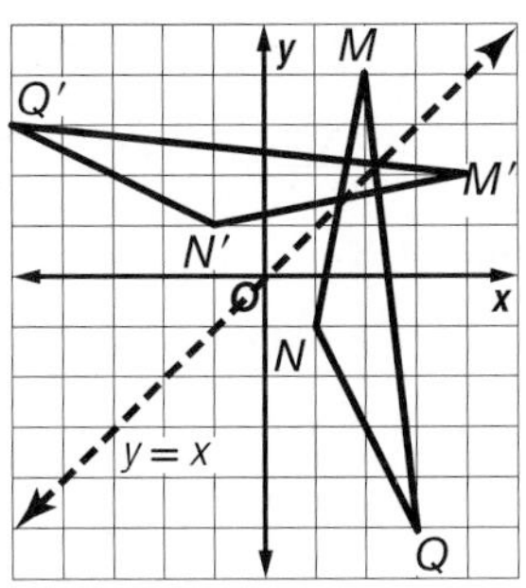

2e. $\begin{bmatrix} 0 & -1 \\ 1 & 0 \end{bmatrix}$

2f. $M'(-4, 2)$, $Q'(5, 3)$, $N'(1, 1)$

2g.

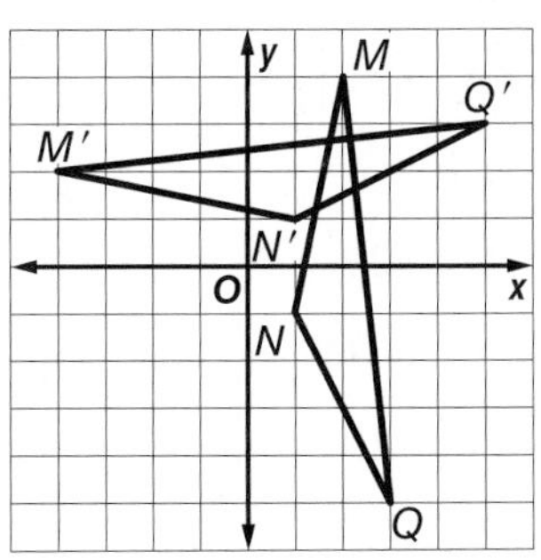

Page 955, Extra Practice (Lesson 4-6)

3. $-\frac{1}{2}\begin{bmatrix} 3 & -4 \\ -2 & 2 \end{bmatrix}$

4. $\frac{1}{2}\begin{bmatrix} 4 & 5 \\ 6 & 8 \end{bmatrix}$

5. $-\frac{1}{35}\begin{bmatrix} -2 & -3 \\ -5 & 10 \end{bmatrix}$

6. $-\frac{1}{8}\begin{bmatrix} 8 & -4 \\ 4 & -3 \end{bmatrix}$

Page 955, Extra Practice (Lesson 5-1)

1a. y-intercept: 0; axis of symmetry: $x = 0$; x-coordinate of vertex: 0

1b.

x	$f(x)$
−2	24
−1	6
0	0
1	6
2	24

1c.

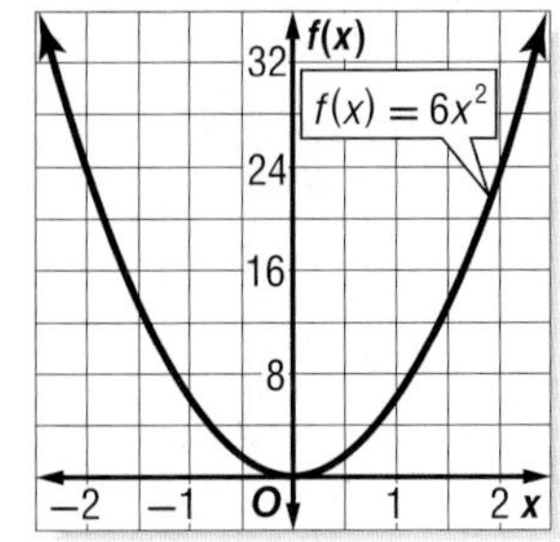

2a. y-intercept: 0; axis of symmetry: $x = 0$; x-coordinate of vertex: 0

2b.

x	$f(x)$
−2	−4
−1	−1
0	0
1	−1
2	−4

2c.

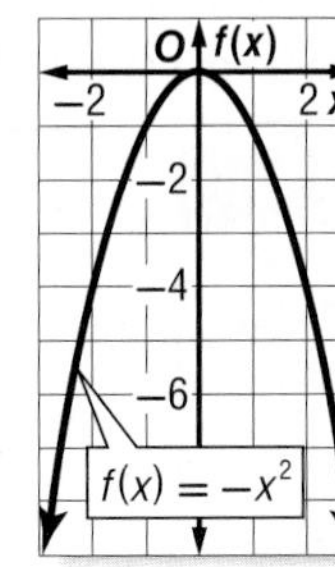

3a. y-intercept: 5; axis of symmetry: $x = 0$; x-coordinate of vertex: 0

3b.

x	$f(x)$
−2	9
−1	6
0	5
1	6
2	9

3c.

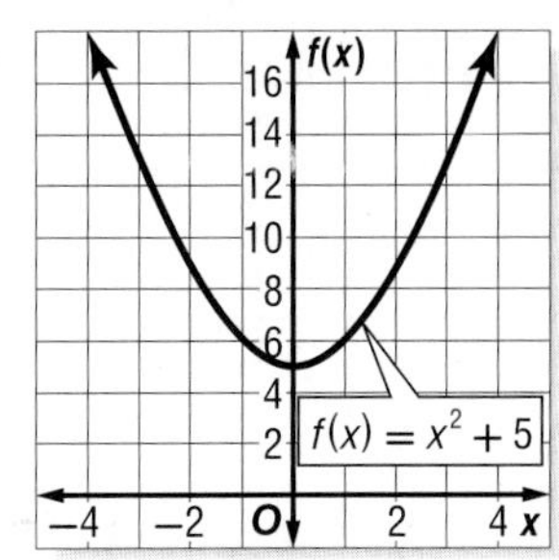

4a. y-intercept: −2; axis of symmetry: $x = 0$; x-coordinate of vertex: 0

4b.

x	$f(x)$
−2	−6
−1	−3
0	−2
1	−3
2	−6

4c.

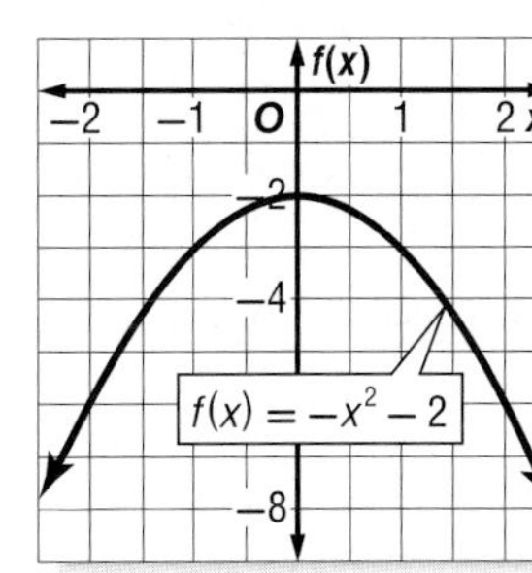

5a. y-intercept: 1; axis of symmetry: $x = 0$; x-coordinate of vertex: 0

5b.

x	$f(x)$
−2	9
−1	3
0	1
1	3
2	9

5c.

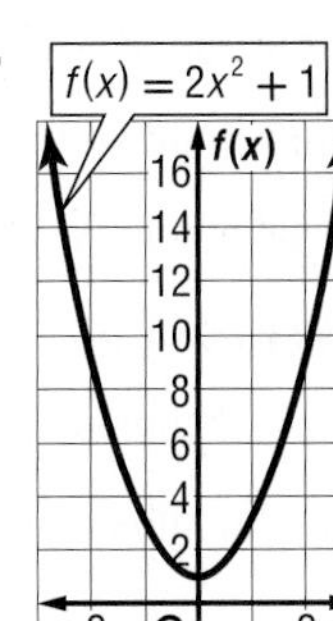

6a. y-intercept: 0; axis of symmetry: $x = 1$; x-coordinate of vertex: 1

6b.

x	$f(x)$
−1	−9
0	0
1	3
2	0
3	−9

6c.

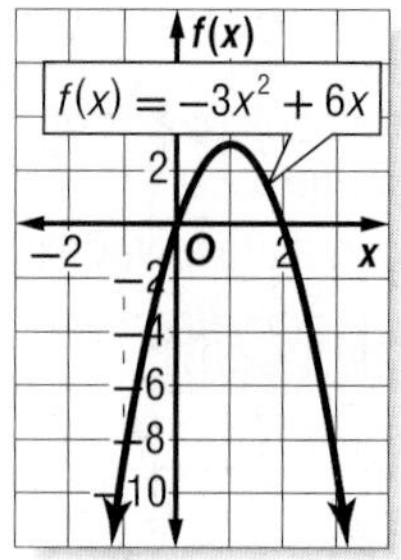

7a. y-intercept: −3; axis of symmetry: $x = -3$; x-coordinate of vertex: −3

7b.

x	$f(x)$
−7	4
−5	−8
−3	−12
−1	−8
1	4

7c.

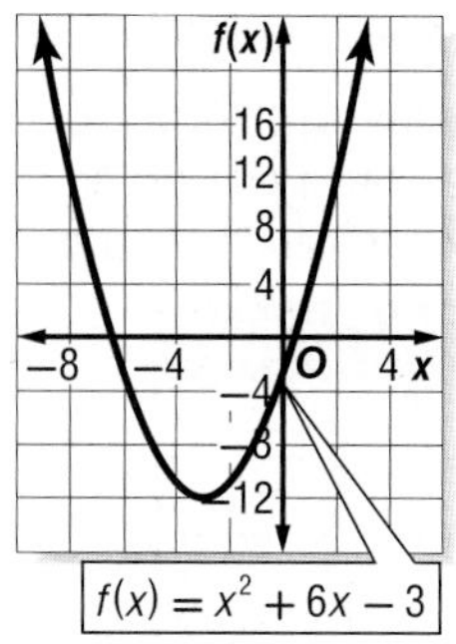

8a. y-intercept: −8; axis of symmetry: $x = 1$; x-coordinate of vertex: 1

8b.

x	$f(x)$
−2	0
0	−8
1	−9
2	−8
4	0

8c.

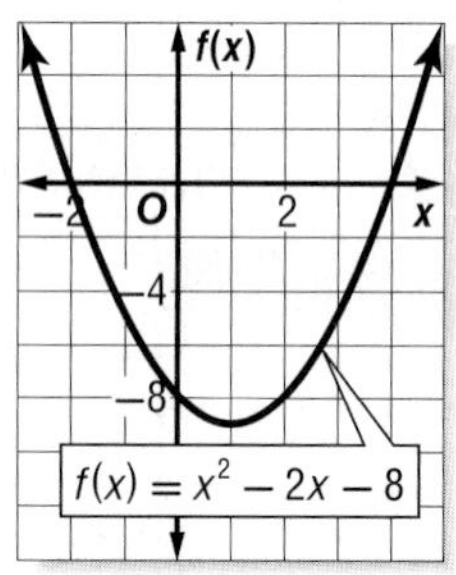

9a. y-intercept: 12; axis of symmetry: $x = -1$; x-coordinate of vertex: −1

9b.

x	$f(x)$
−3	3
−2	12
−1	15
0	12
1	3

9c.

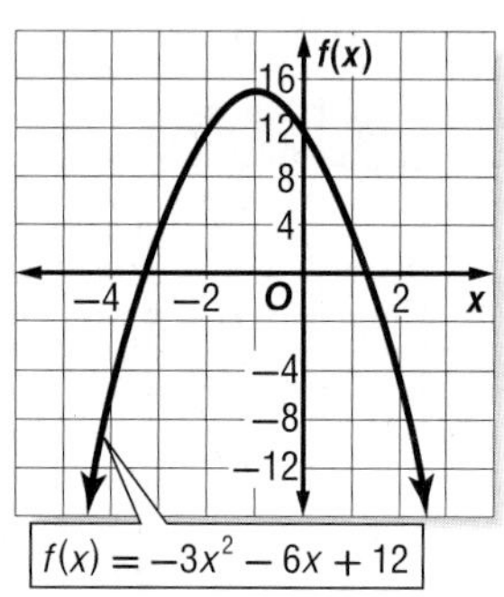

10. D = {all real numbers}, R = $\{f(x) \mid f(x) \geq 0\}$

11. D = {all real numbers}, R = $\{f(x) \mid f(x) \leq 9\}$

12. D = {all real numbers}, R = $\{f(x) \mid f(x) \geq -0.25\}$

13. D = {all real numbers}, R = $\left\{f(x) \mid f(x) \leq 4\frac{1}{4}\right\}$

14. D = {all real numbers}, R = $\{f(x) \mid f(x) \geq -9\}$

15. D = {all real numbers}, R = $\{f(x) \mid f(x) \geq 0\}$

Page 956, Extra Practice (Lesson 5-5)

1. $(x-2)^2$
2. $(x+10)^2$
3. $\left(x-\frac{11}{2}\right)^2$
4. $\left(x-\frac{1}{3}\right)^2$
5. $(x+15)^2$
6. $\left(x+\frac{3}{16}\right)^2$
7. $\left(x-\frac{1}{5}\right)^2$
8. $\left(x-\frac{3}{2}\right)^2$
9. −4, 1
10. −5, 0
11. −9, 7
12. $-\frac{5}{3}, 7$
13. $\frac{-7 \pm i\sqrt{3}}{2}$
14. $\frac{4 \pm \sqrt{6}}{5}$
15. $3 \pm i\sqrt{2}$
16. 6
17. $\frac{-13 \pm 3\sqrt{33}}{16}$
18. $\frac{-5 \pm i\sqrt{47}}{6}$
19. $-7 \pm 5\sqrt{2}$
20. 0.5, 7.5
21. $-\frac{1}{3}, 4$
22. −14, 6
23. $\frac{7 \pm \sqrt{29}}{2}$
24. $\frac{-3 \pm \sqrt{41}}{2}$
25. $\frac{5 \pm \sqrt{65}}{2}$
26. $\frac{6 \pm 2\sqrt{6}}{3}$
27. −15, −5
28. −3, 8
29. −3.5, 3

Page 957, Extra Practice (Lesson 5-6)

1a. −3
1b. 2 imaginary
1c. $\frac{-7 \pm i\sqrt{3}}{2}$
2a. 540
2b. 2 irrational
2c. $\frac{-1 \pm \sqrt{15}}{2}$
3a. −55
3b. 2 imaginary
3c. $\frac{5 \pm i\sqrt{55}}{10}$
4a. 0
4b. 1 rational
4c. $-2\frac{1}{3}$
5a. 208
5b. 2 irrational
5c. $\frac{4 \pm \sqrt{13}}{2}$
6a. 49
6b. 2 rational
6c. −0.5, 3
7a. 0
7b. 1 rational
7c. 9
8a. 0
8b. 1 rational
8c. 5
9a. 4228
9b. 2 irrational
9c. $\frac{-5 \pm \sqrt{1057}}{24}$
10a. −140
10b. 2 imaginary
10c. $\frac{1 \pm i\sqrt{35}}{9}$
11a. 49
11b. 2 rational
11c. $0, \frac{7}{8}$
12a. 3321
12b. 2 irrational
12c. $\frac{1 \pm \sqrt{41}}{4}$
13a. 0
13b. 1 rational
13c. 2
14a. 16

14b. 2 rational

14c. –1.5, –2.5

15a. –16

15b. 2 imaginary

15c. $3 \pm 2i$

16. $-2 \pm 5i$

17. $\frac{-3 \pm \sqrt{41}}{8}$

18. $\frac{-5 \pm \sqrt{97}}{4}$

19. 4

20. $0, \frac{4}{7}$

21. $\frac{-3 \pm i}{2}$

22. $\frac{5}{3}$

23. $\frac{2 \pm i\sqrt{2}}{3}$

24. 0, 36

Page 957, Extra Practice (Lesson 5-7)

1. $(-6, -1)$; $x = -6$; up

2. $(8, -5)$; $x = 8$; up

3. $(-1, 7)$; $x = -1$; down

4. $(7, 3)$; $x = 7$; down

5. $y = -(x - 5)^2 + 22$; $(5, 22)$; $x = 5$; down

6. $y = -2(x - 4)^2 + 39$; $(4, 39)$; $x = 4$; down

7.

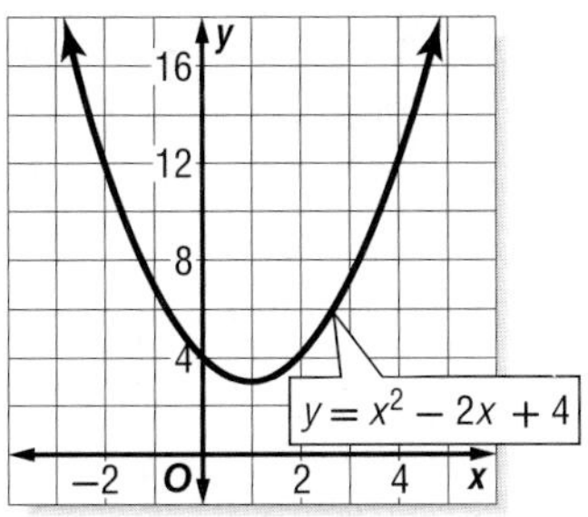

8.

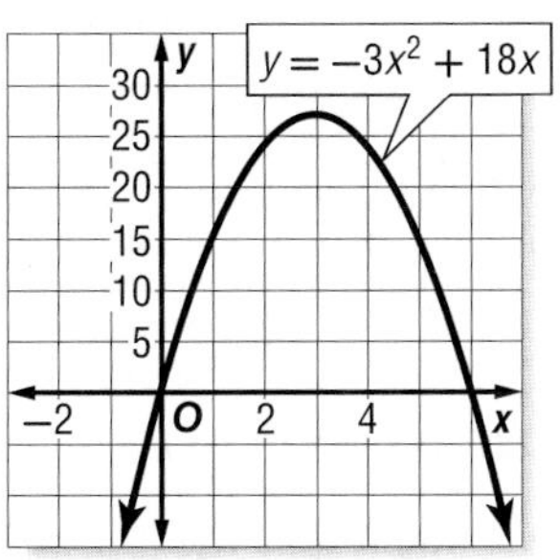

9.

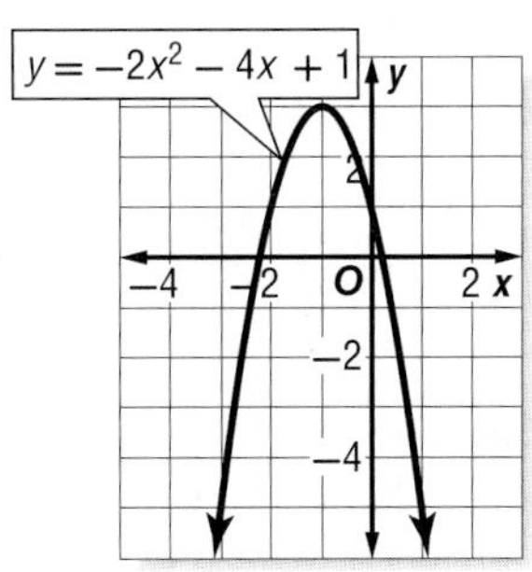

10.

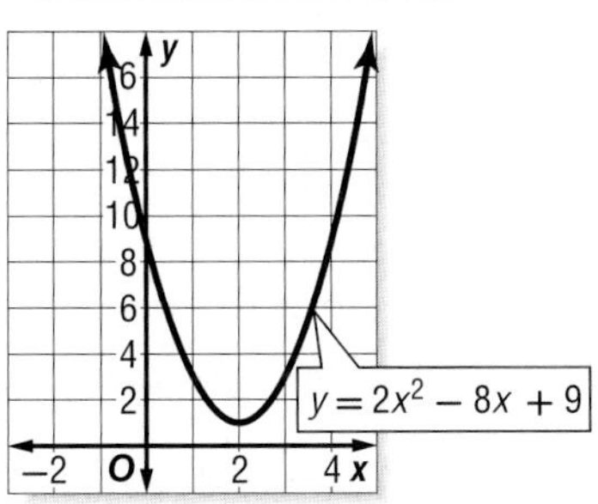

11.

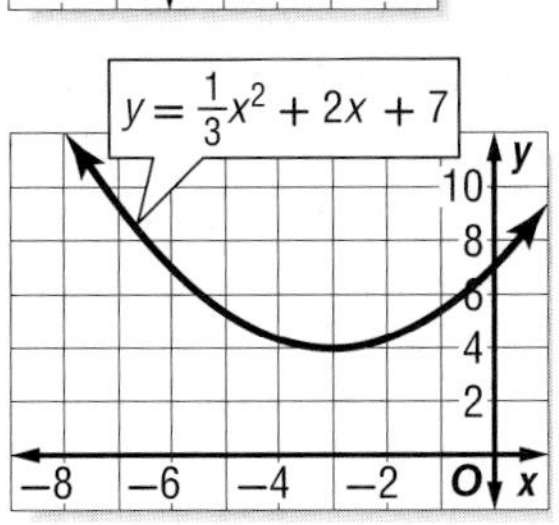

12.

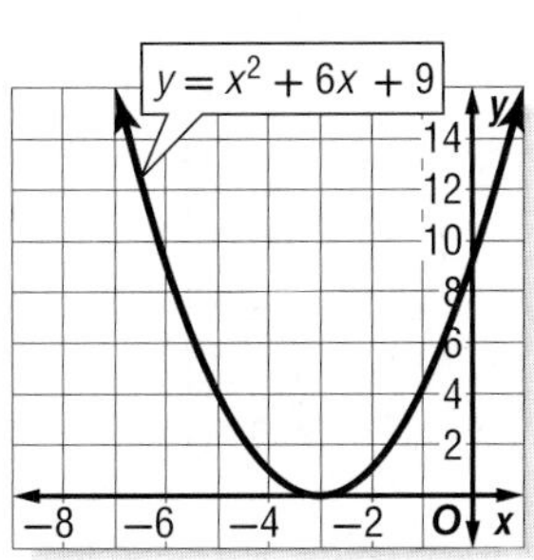

13.

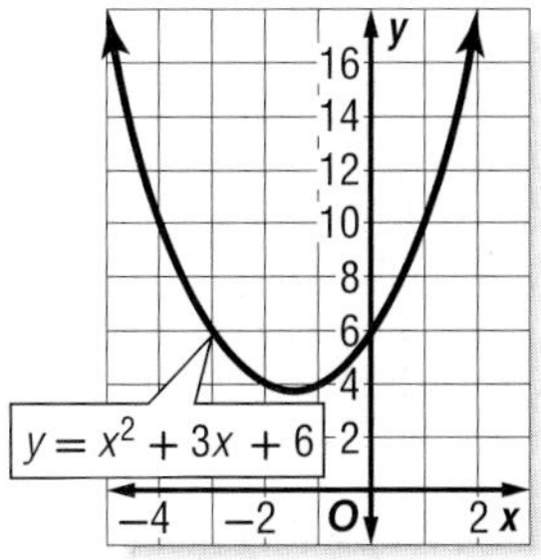

14.

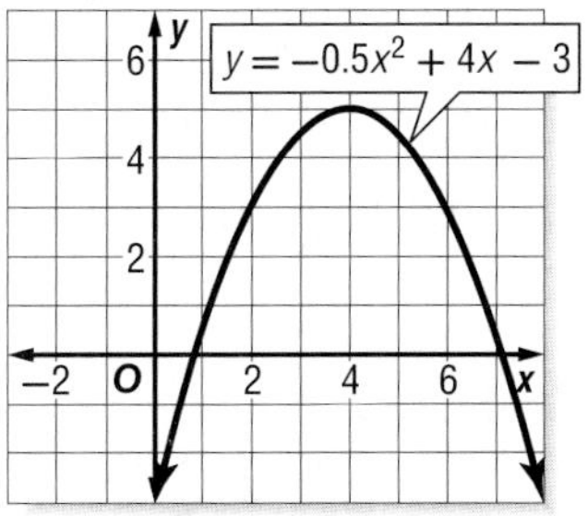

15.

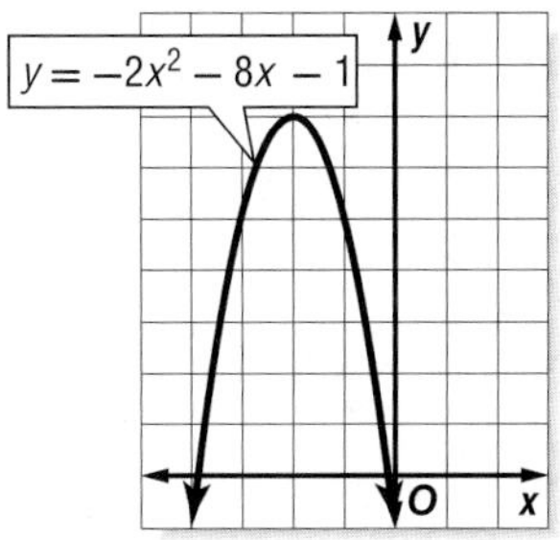

Page 957, Extra Practice (Lesson 5-8)

1.

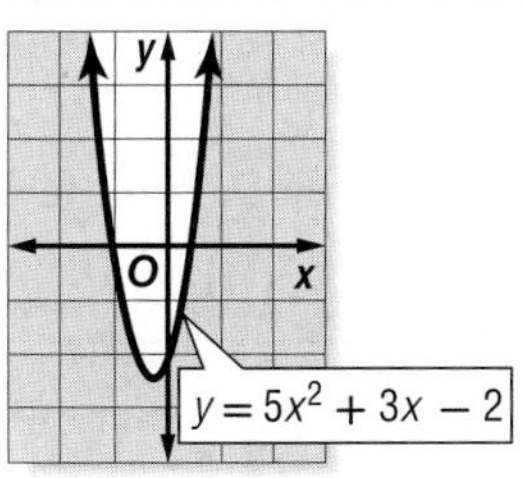

2.

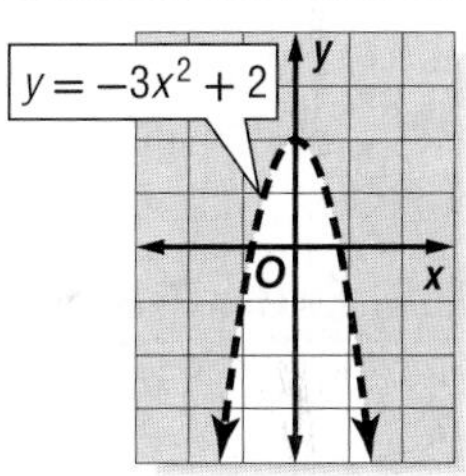

3.

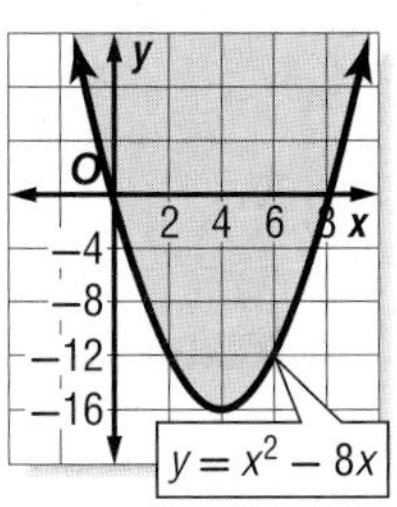

4.

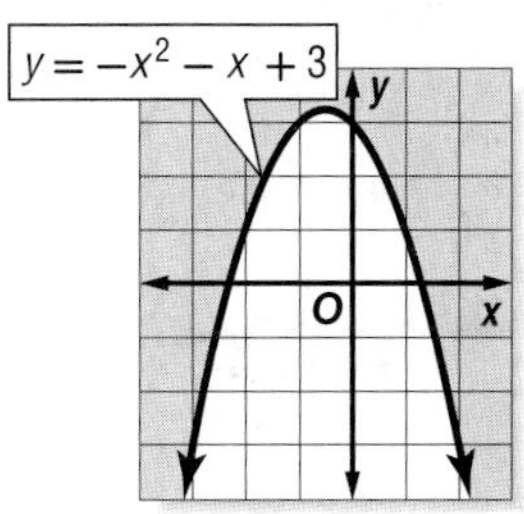

5.

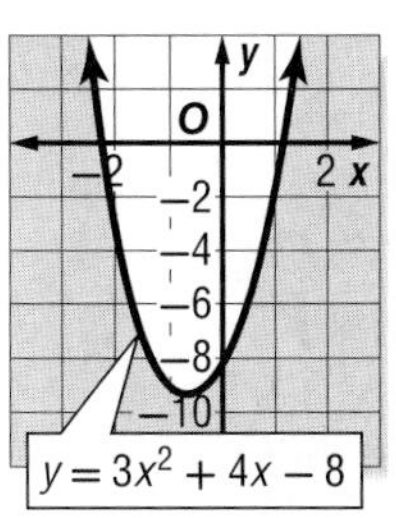

6.

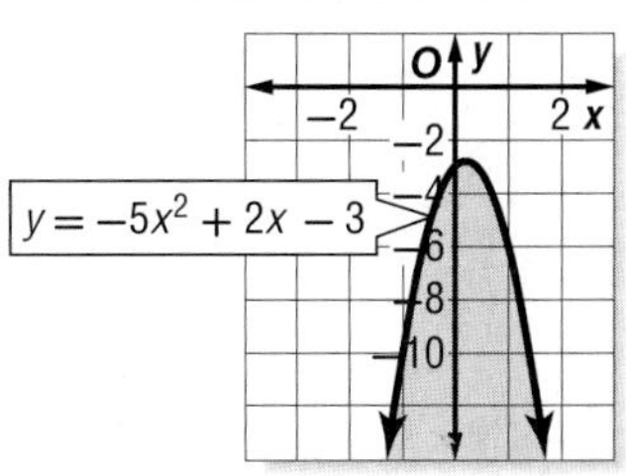

7. 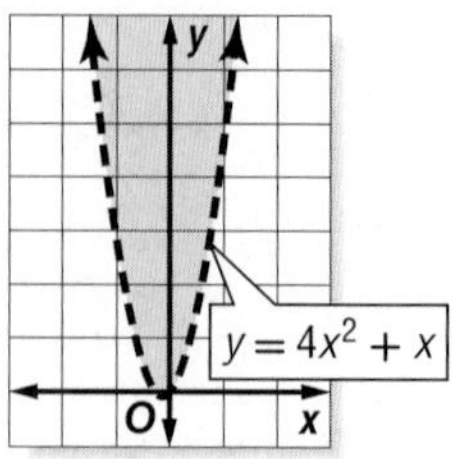

8. 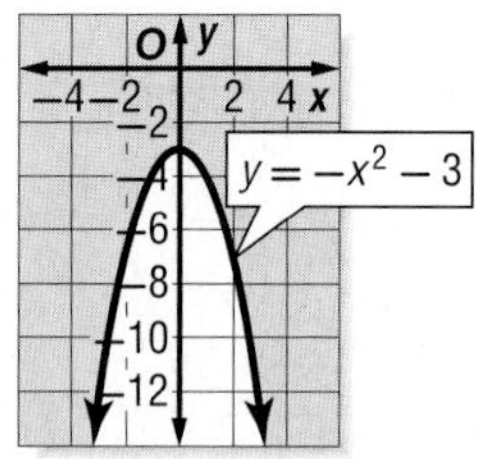

12. $\{x \mid -1 < x < 1\}$

13. $\{x \mid x \leq -0.4 \text{ or } x \geq 0.5\}$

14. $\{x \mid -3 < x < -2\}$

15. $\varnothing$

16. $\{x \mid -2 \leq x \leq 4\}$

17. $\{x \mid x \leq -1.5 \text{ or } x \geq 4\}$

18. $\{x \mid x < -4 \text{ or } x > 1\}$

19. $\{x \mid x \leq -3 \text{ or } x \geq 5\}$

Page 958, Extra Practice (Lesson 6-1)

21. $2x^3 - 2x^2 + 5x - 7y^2$

22. $9x^2 - x + 3$

23. $-11x^2 + 2x + 36$

24. $5x^2 + 12x + 10$

25. $28uw^2 - 35 + \frac{1}{u^2}$

26. $12x^9 + 4x^8 - 4x^6 - 28x^5$

27. $8x^2 + 2x - 21$

28. $-6x^2 + 7x + 5$

29. $6x^2 - 13x + 5$

31. $25x^2 - 100$

36. $-\frac{1}{2}a^5 + 3a^4 - \frac{5}{2}a^3$

Page 958, Extra Practice (Lesson 6-2)

5. $5c^3 + 2c^2d - \frac{1}{5}$

9. $p^{14} + p^7 - 1$

10. $q^3 + 3 - \frac{7}{q + 8}$

11. $3v^2 + 4v - 1 + \frac{2}{5v - 4}$

12. $-2x^2 + 21x - 73 + \frac{222}{x + 3}$

13. $5k^2 - 4k + 4 - \frac{11}{k + 1}$

14. $t^3 + t - 1$

15. $z^3 + z^2 + 3z + 1$

16. $3r^3 - 9r^2 + 7r - 6$

17. $2b^2 - 5b - 3$

Page 958, Extra Practice (Lesson 6-3)

10. $n^3 - 1$

11. $-8b^2 + 10b + 1$

12. $z^9 - 1$

13. $-18m^4 + 15m^2 + 1$

14. $x^3 + 3x^2 + 3x$

15. $-2x^2 + 7x - 2$

16. $a^6 - 6a^4 + 12a^2 - 9$

17. $3h^3 - 27h^2 + 81h - 84$

18. $-10c^3 + 105c - 255$

19. $n^6 + n^3 - 6n^2 + 12n - 10$

20. $98a^2 - 65a - 4$

21. $2d^6 + 6d^4 + 3d^3 + 6d^2 - 3$

Page 959, Extra Practice (Lesson 6-4)

1a. 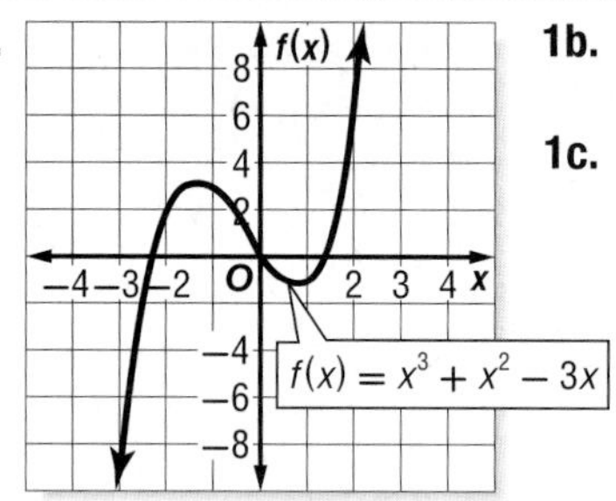

1b. between –3 and –2, at 0, between 1 and 2

1c. Sample answer: relative maximum at $x = -1.4$, relative minimum at $x = 0.7$

2a. 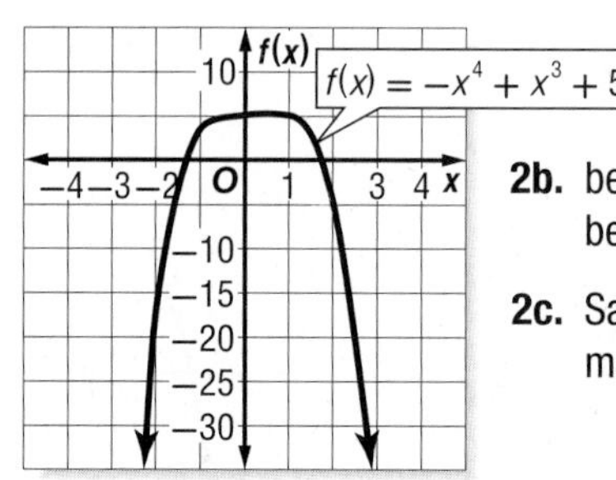

2b. between –2 and –1; between 1 and 2

2c. Sample answer: relative maximum at $x = 0.75$

3a. 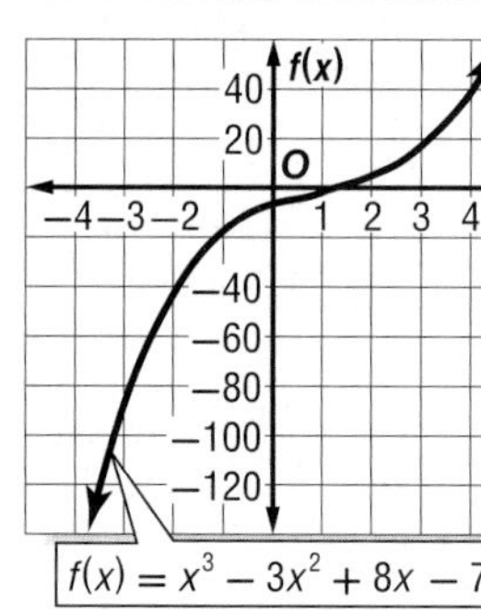

3b. between 1 and 2

3c. Sample answer: no relative maximum or minimum

4a. 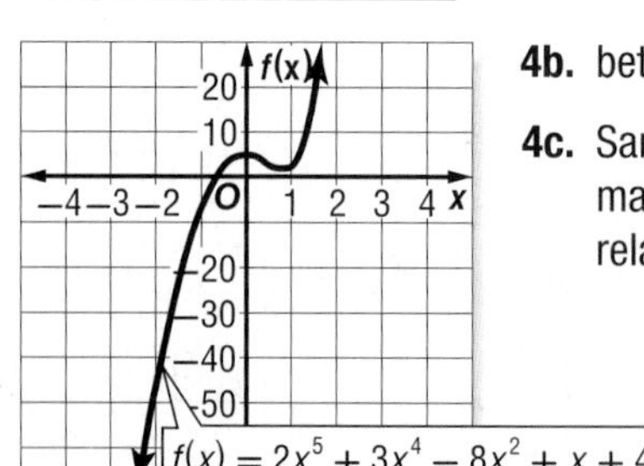

4b. between –1 and 0

4c. Sample answer: relative maximum at $x = 0.1$, relative minimum at $x = 0.9$

5a.

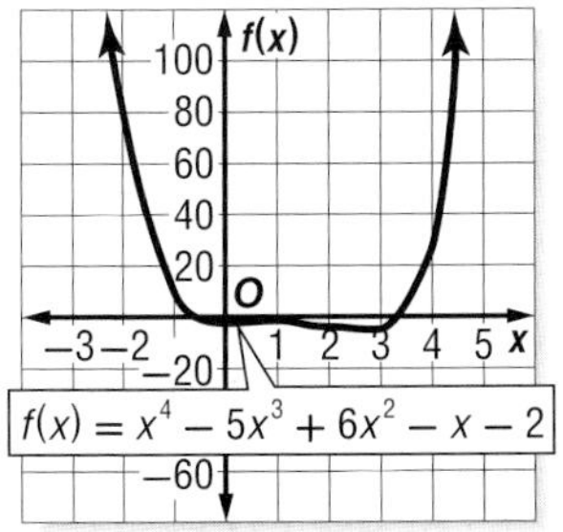

5b. between –1 and 0; between 3 and 4

5c. Sample answer: relative maximum at $x = 1.0$, relative minima at $x = 0.1$ and $x = 2.7$

6a.

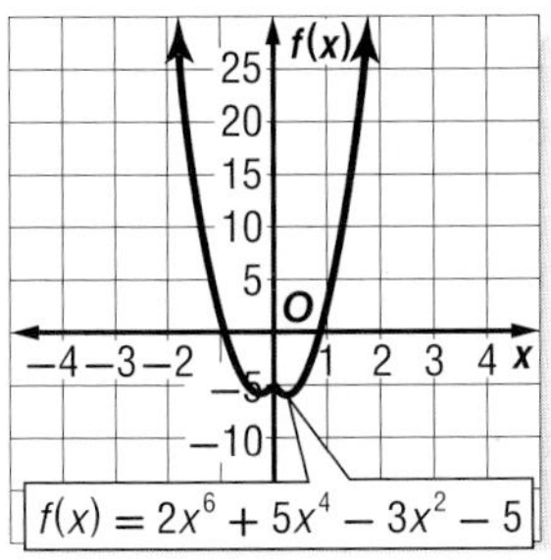

6b. between –2 and –1; between 1 and 2

6c. Sample answer: relative maximum at $x = 0$, relative minima at $x = -0.5$ and $x = 0.5$

7a.

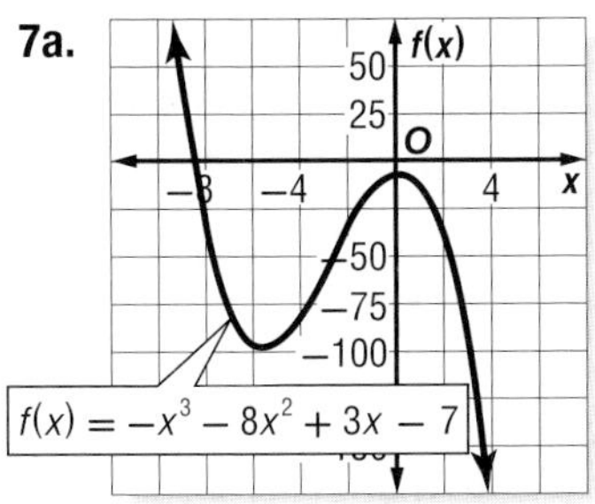

7b. between –9 and –8

7c. Sample answer: relative maximum at $x = 0.2$, relative minimum at $x = -5.5$

8a.

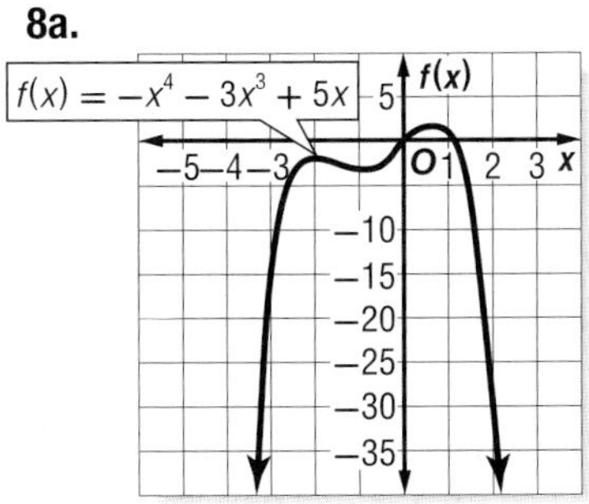

8b. at $x = 0$; between 1 and 2

8c. Sample answer: relative maxima at $x = -1.9$ and $x = 0.7$, relative minimum at $x = -1$

9a.

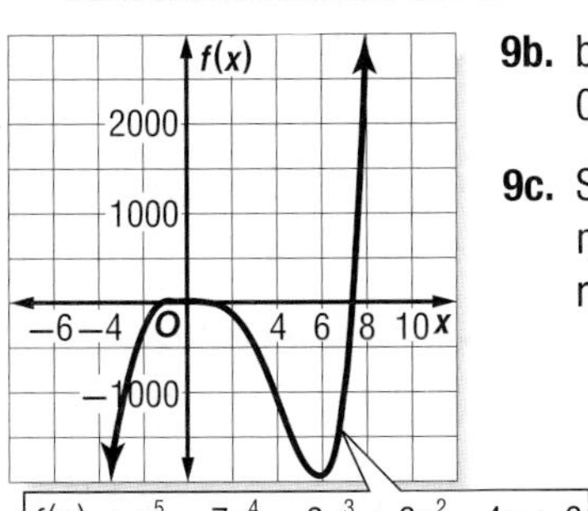

9b. between –2 and –1; 0 and 1; 7 and 8

9c. Sample answer: relative maximum at $x = -0.7$, relative minimum at $x = 5.9$

10a.

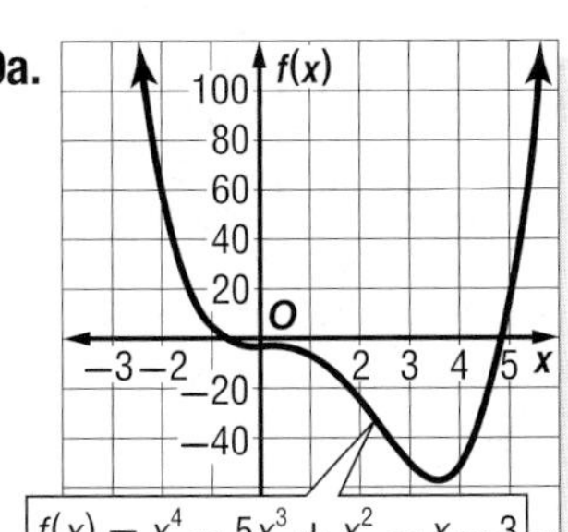

10b. between –1 and 0; between 4 and 5

10c. Sample answer: relative minimum at $x = 3.6$

11a.

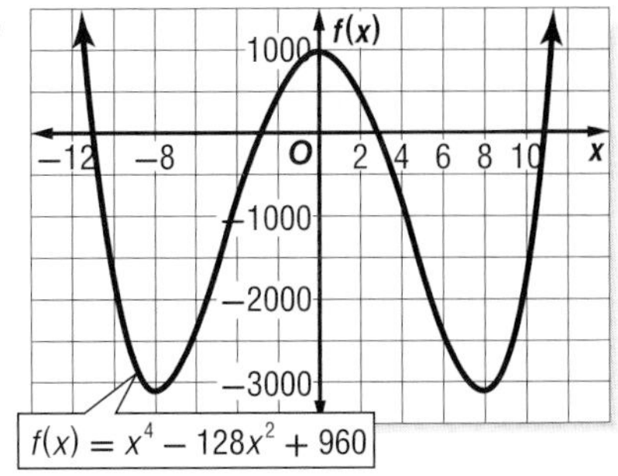

11b. between –11 and –10; between –3 and –2; between 2 and 3; between 10 and 11

11c. Sample answer: relative maximum at $x = 0$, relative minima at $x = -8$ and $x = 8$

12a.

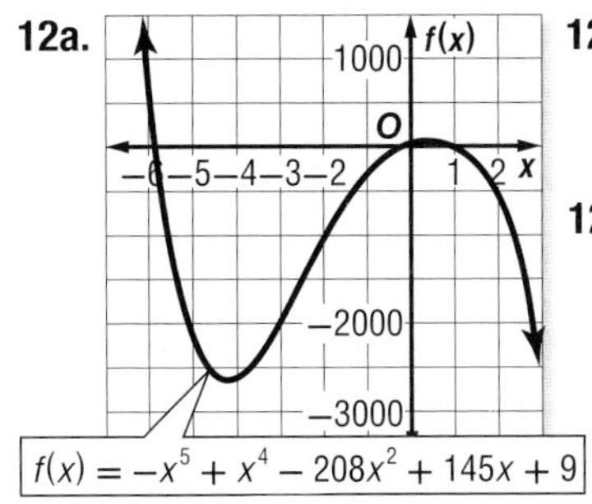

12b. between –6 and –5; between –1 and 0; between 0 and 1

12c. Sample answer: relative maximum at $x = 0.3$, relative minimum at $x = -4.2$

13a.

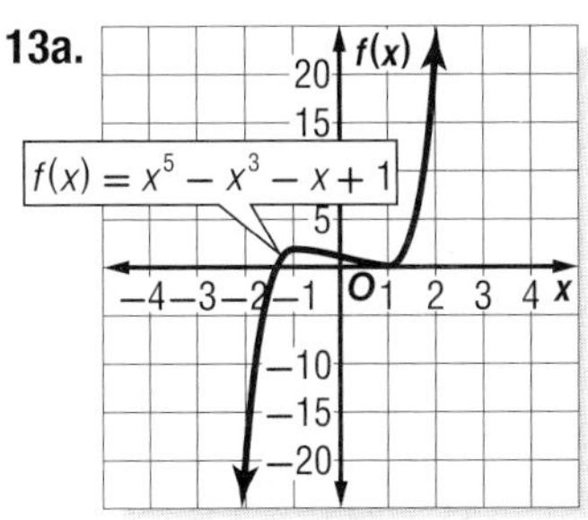

13b. between 0 and 1; at $x = 1$; between –2 and –1

13c. Sample answer: relative maximum at $x = -0.9$, relative minimum at $x = 0.9$

14a.

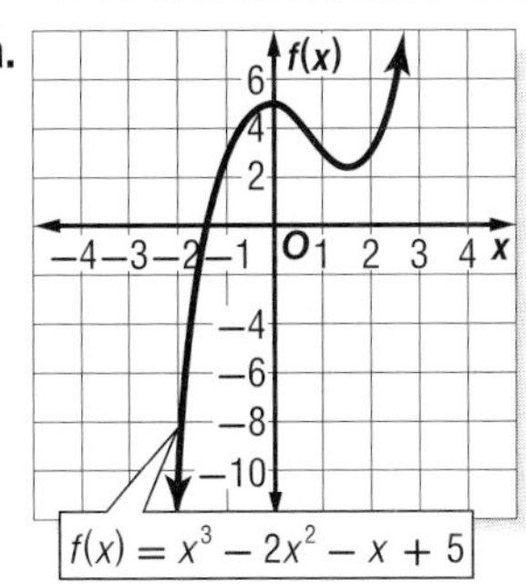

14b. between –2 and –1

14c. Sample answer: relative maximum at $x = -0.2$, relative minimum at $x = 1.5$

15a.

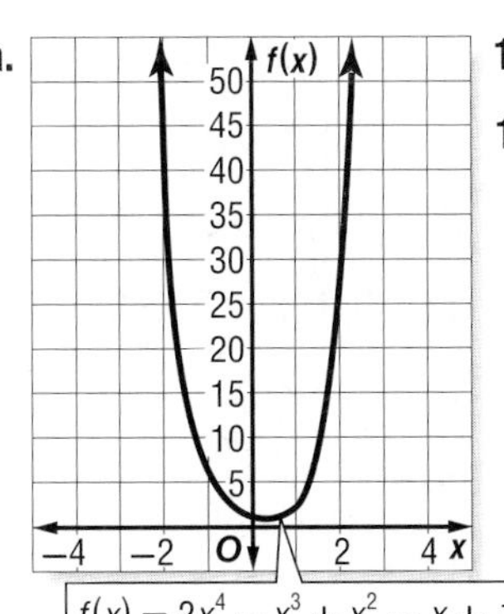

15b. no real roots

15c. Sample answer: relative minimum at $x = 0.4$

16a. 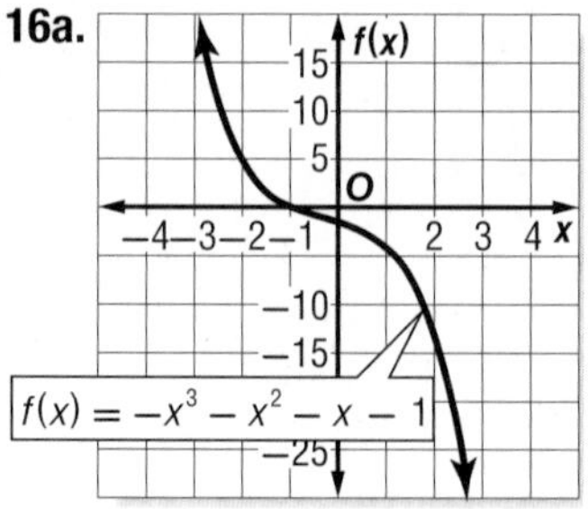

16b. $x = -1$

16c. no maxima or minima

Page 959, Extra Practice (Lesson 6-5)

1. $7a^2b^3c(2a - 3b + 1)$ **2.** $(2x - 3b)(5a - y)$
3. $(x + 7)(x - 6)$ **4.** $(2x + 3)(x + 1)$
5. $(6x - 1)(x + 12)$ **6.** $3x^2(2x^2 - 4x + 1)$
7. prime **8.** $(x - 5)(x + 3)$
9. $(2x + 5)(3x + 4)$ **10.** $4(2x - 5)(3x - 2)$
11. $(2p - 7t)(3p + 4t)$ **12.** prime
13. $(x - 7)^2$ **14.** $(3x - 8)(3x + 8)$
15. $(6 - t^5)(6 + t^5)$ **16.** prime
17. $(a + 3b)(a - 3b)(a^2 + 9b^2)$ **18.** $3a(a + 7)(a - 3)$
19. $x(x - 5)(x - 3)$ **20.** $(x + 3)^2$
21. $2x(3x - 2)(3x + 2)$ **22.** prime
23. prime **24.** $(2x^2 + 1)(x + 3)$
25. $(7a + 3b)(5c - f)$ **26.** $(5h + 1)(h - 2j)$

Page 959, Extra Practice (Lesson 6-6)

7. $x^2 - 3x + 7$ **8.** $x(5x - 2)$
9. $(x + 5)(2x - 1)$ **10.** $x^2 + 2x + 4$
11. $x + 5$ **12.** $x(x^2 + 1)$
13. $(x - 3)(x + 2)$ **14.** $(x + 5)(x^2 + 3x + 9)$
15. $(x - 6)(x - 4)$ **16.** $(2x + 1)(x - 2)$
17. $(2x + 5)(x - 1)$ **18.** $(x + 3)(x + 5)$

Page 960, Extra Practice (Lesson 6-7)

4. 3 or 1; 3 or 1; 2, 4, or 6 **5.** 2 or 0; 1; 2 or 4
6. 3 or 1; 1; 2 or 4 **7.** 2 or 0; 1; 0 or 2
8. 4, 2, or 0; 0; 4, 2, or 0 **9.** 5, 3, 1; 0; 4, 2, or 0
10. $1, 3 \pm i$ **11.** $-\frac{7}{2}, \frac{4}{5}, 2$
12. $6, 5 \pm \sqrt{6}$ **13.** $1, \frac{3 \pm \sqrt{105}}{6}$
14. $-\frac{5}{2}, -\frac{1}{2}, \frac{1}{3}$ **15.** −5, 1, 3

Page 960, Extra Practice (Lesson 6-8)

1. $\pm1, \pm\frac{1}{3}, \pm\frac{2}{3}, \pm2, \pm3, \pm6$
2. $\pm1, \pm2, \pm4, \pm8, \pm\frac{1}{2}, \pm\frac{1}{4}$
3. $\pm1, \pm7, \pm\frac{1}{6}, \pm\frac{7}{6}, \pm\frac{1}{2}, \pm\frac{7}{2}, \pm\frac{1}{3}, \pm\frac{7}{3}$
4. $\pm3, -1, -2$
5. $-\frac{5}{2}, -2, \frac{8}{3}, 7$ **6.** $1, -\frac{1}{5}$
7. 7, 8 **8.** $-3, \frac{1}{3}$
9. 0 **10.** $\pm1, \pm3i$
11. $\pm2, \pm i$ **12.** $\pm\frac{3}{2}, \pm i\sqrt{7}$

Page 960, Extra Practice (Lesson 7-1)

1. $(f + g)(x) = 4x + 2$; $(f - g)(x)\ 2x + 8$; $(f \cdot g)(x)\ 3x^2 - 4x - 15$; $\left(\frac{f}{g}\right)(x)\ \frac{3x + 5}{x - 3}, x \neq 3$

2. $(f + g)(x) = x^2 + \sqrt{x}$; $(f - g)(x)\ \sqrt{x} - x^2$; $(f \cdot g)(x)\ x^2\sqrt{x}$; $\left(\frac{f}{g}\right)(x)\ \frac{\sqrt{x}}{x^2}, x \neq 0$

3. $(f + g)(x) = 2x^2$; $(f - g)(x)\ -10$; $(f \cdot g)(x)\ x^4 - 25$; $\left(\frac{f}{g}\right)(x)\ \frac{x^2 - 5}{x^2 + 5}, x \neq \pm5i$

4. $(f + g)(x) = x^2 + x + 2$; $(f - g)(x)\ x^2 - x$; $(f \cdot g)(x)\ x^3 + x^2 + x + 1$; $\left(\frac{f}{g}\right)(x)\ \frac{x^2 + 1}{x + 1}, x \neq -1$

5. {(1, 1), (−1, −1), (5, 5)}; {(−1, −1), (2, 2), (−3, −3)}
6. does not exist; {(0, 4), (5, 3), (−9, 1)}
7. {(2, 2), (5, 5), (4, 4), (0, 0)}; {(8, 8), (6, 6), (−3, −3), (1, 1)}
8. {(−4, 4), (−7, 6), (−2, 0)}; {(−1, −9)}

Page 961, Extra Practice (Lesson 7-2)

1. {(7, −2), (0, 3), (−8, 5)}
2. {(9, −3), (4, −2), (9, 3), (1, −1)}
3. $f^{-1}(x) = x + 7$ **4.** $y = \frac{x - 8}{2}$

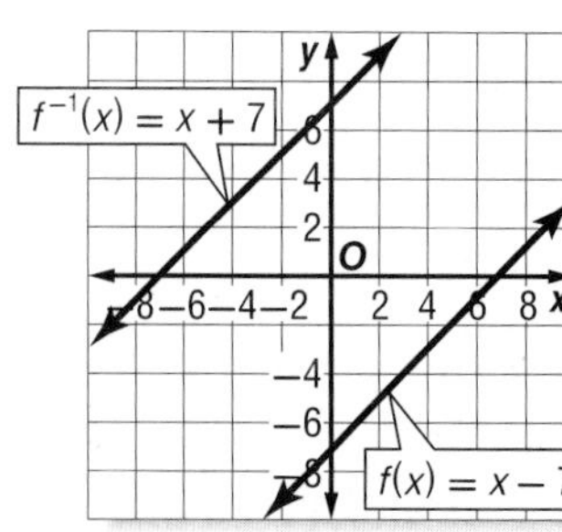

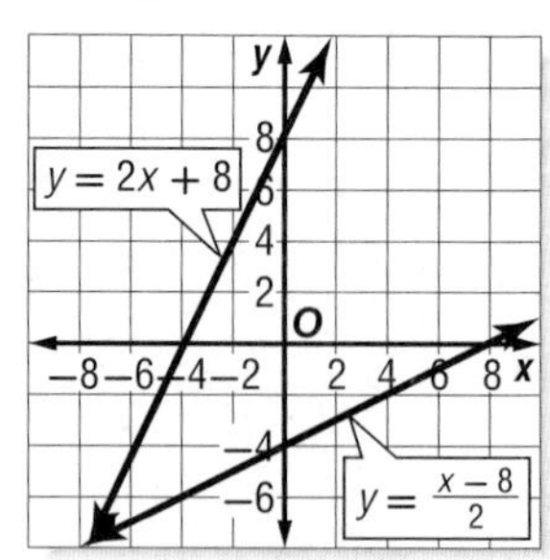

5. $g^{-1}(x) = \frac{x + 8}{3}$

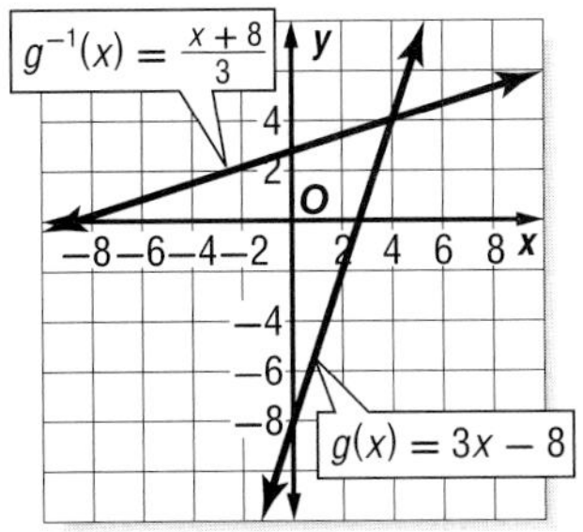

6. $y = \frac{x + 6}{-5}$

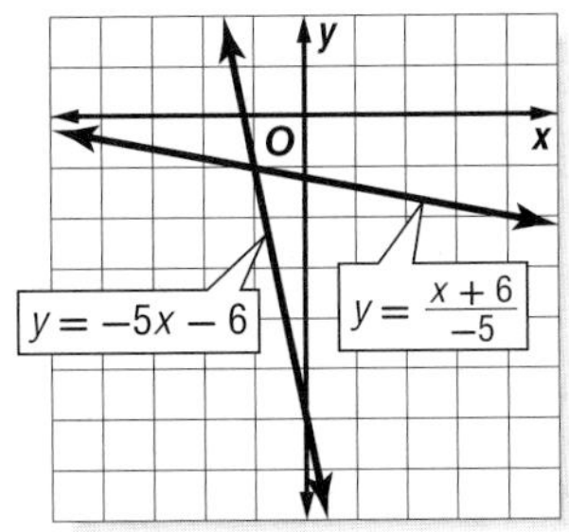

7. $x = -2$

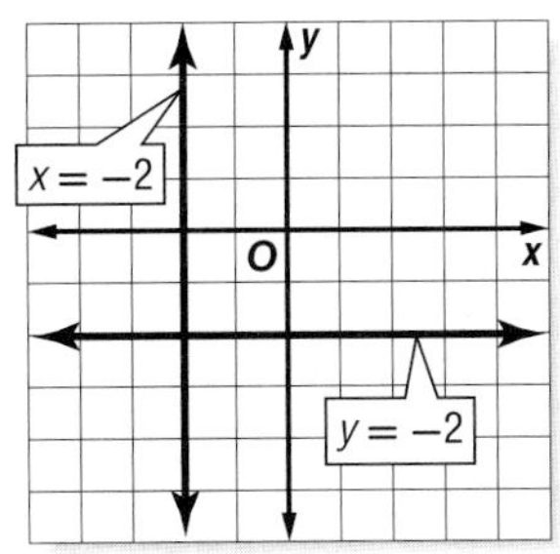

8. $g^{-1}(x) = \frac{x - 5}{-2}$

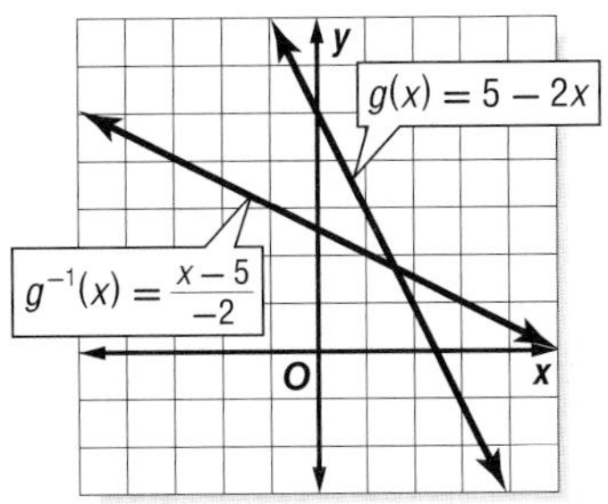

9. $h^{-1}(x) = 5x - 5$

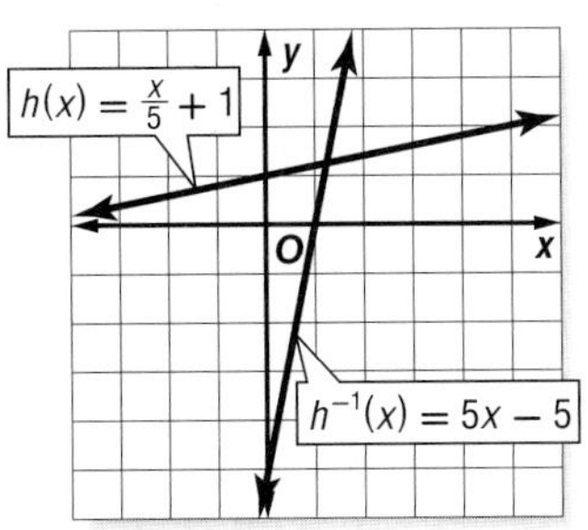

10. $h^{-1}(x) = -\frac{3}{2}x$

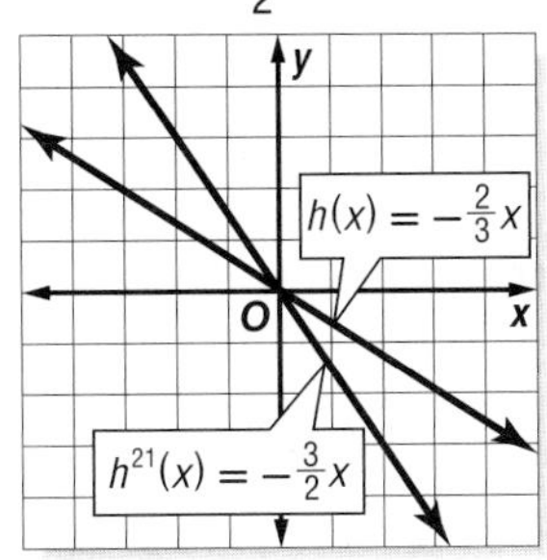

11. $y = 3x + 5$

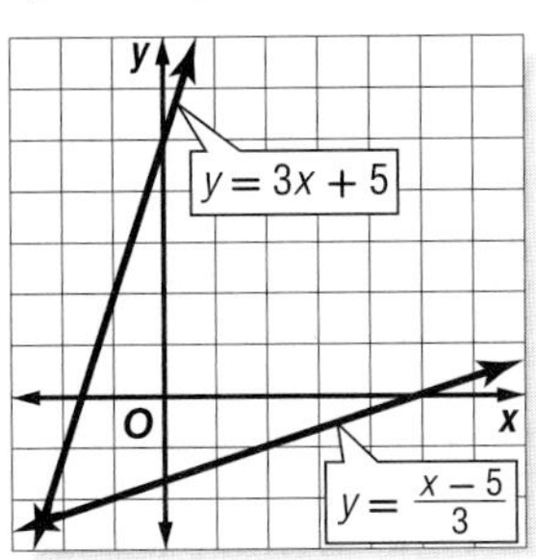

12. $y = 2x + 2$

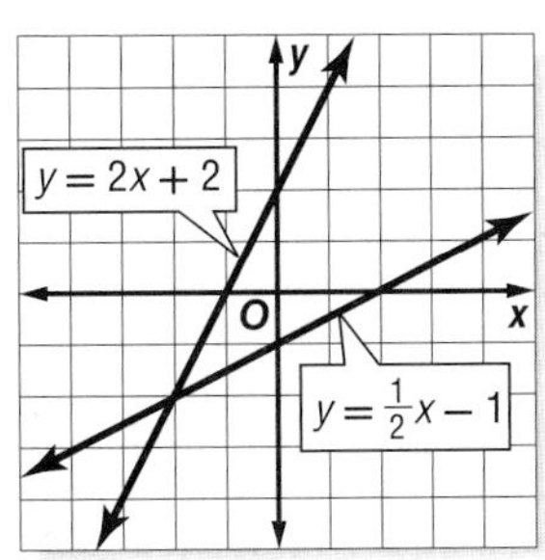

13. $f^{-1}(x) = \frac{4x - 8}{3}$

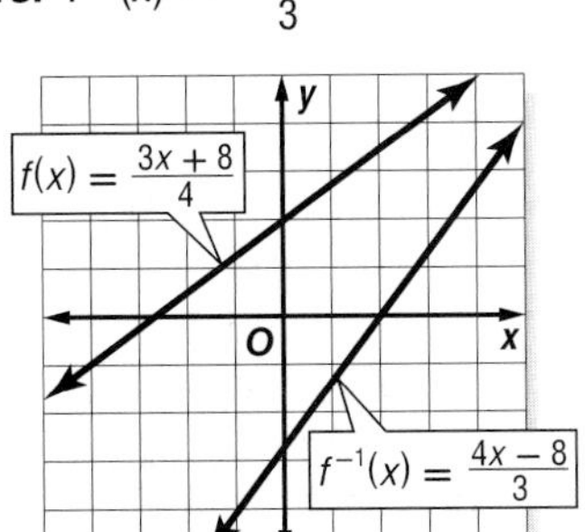

14. $g^{-1}(x) = \frac{3x + 1}{2}$

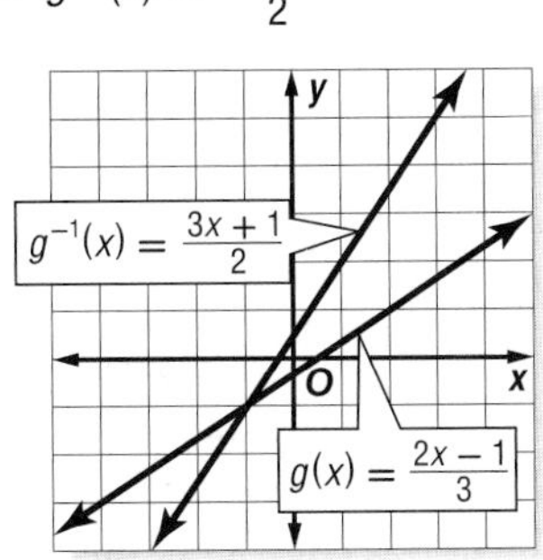

Page 961, Extra Practice (Lesson 7-3)

1. $D = \{x | x \geq 4\}, R = \{y | y \geq 0\}$

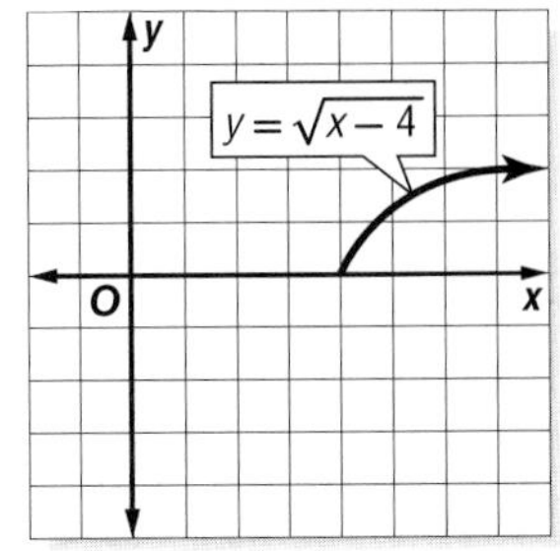

2. $D = \{x | x \geq -3\}, R = \{y | y \geq -1\}$

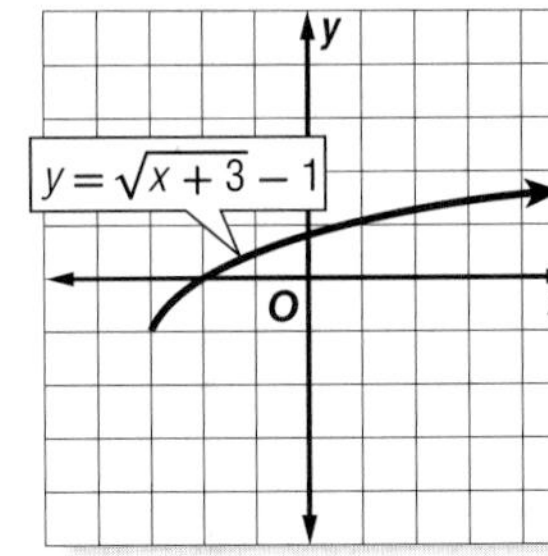

3. $D = \{x | x \geq -2\}, R = \{y | y \geq 0\}$

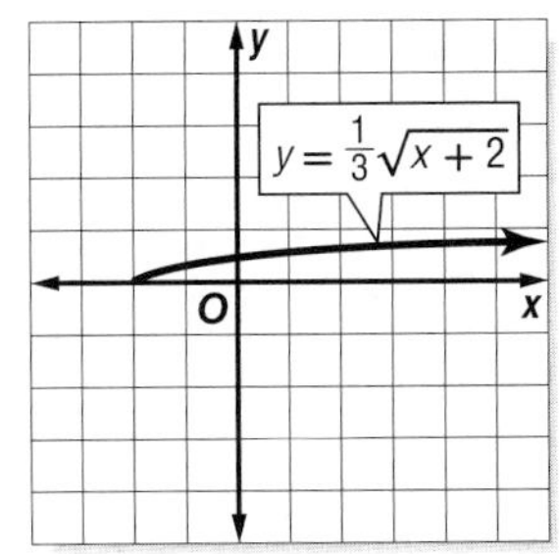

4. $D = \{x | x \geq -2.5, R = \{y | y \geq 0\}$

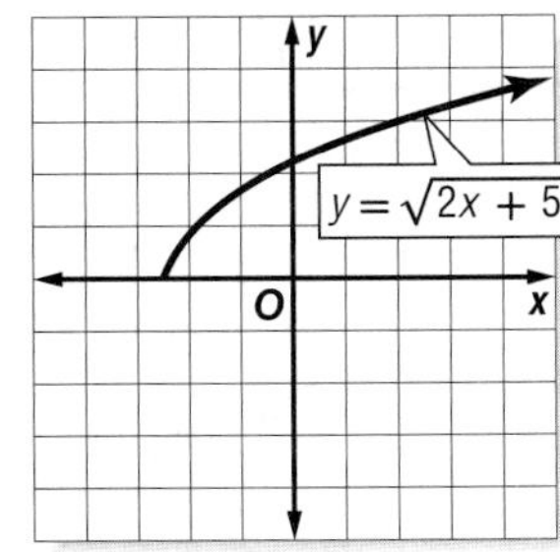

5. $D = \{x | x \geq 0\}, R = \{y | y \leq 0\}$

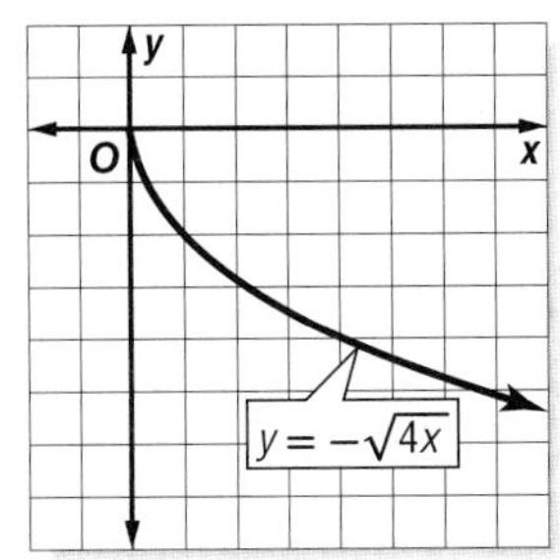

6. $D = \{x | x \geq 0\}, R = \{y | y \geq 0\}$

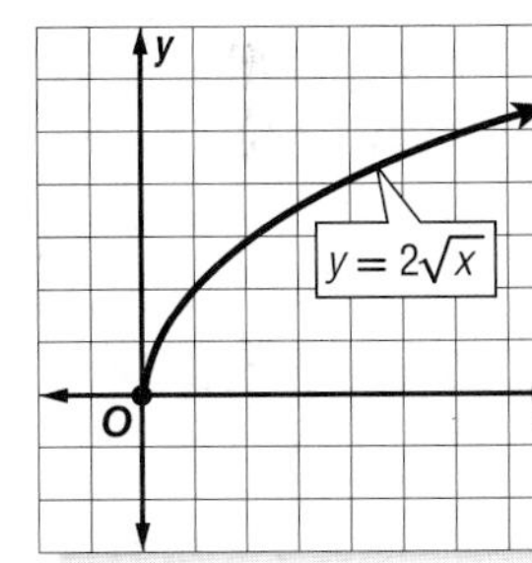

7. $D = \{x | x \geq 0\}, R = \{y | y \leq 0\}$

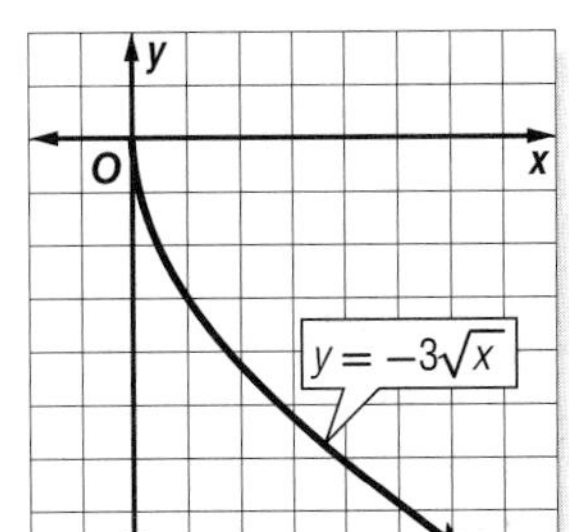

8. $D = \{x | x \geq 0\}, R = \{y | y \geq 5\}$

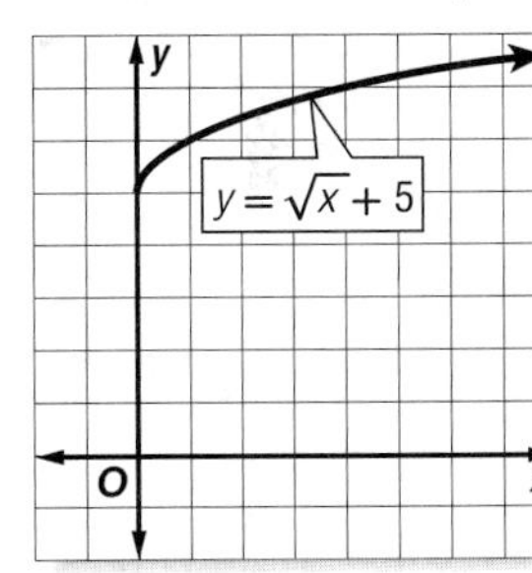

9. $D = \{x | x \geq 0\}, R = \{y | y \geq -1\}$

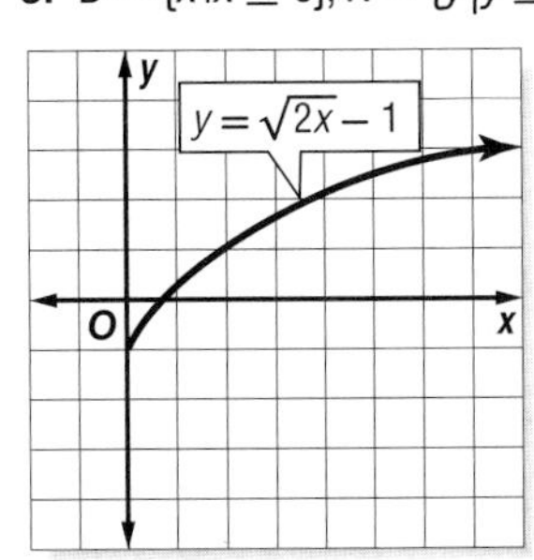

10. $D = \{x | x \geq 0\}, R = \{y | y \geq 1\}$

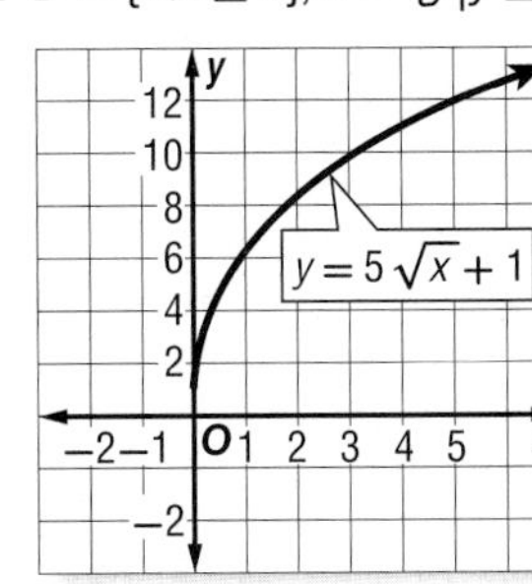

11. D = {x|x ≥ –1}, R = {y|y ≥ –2}

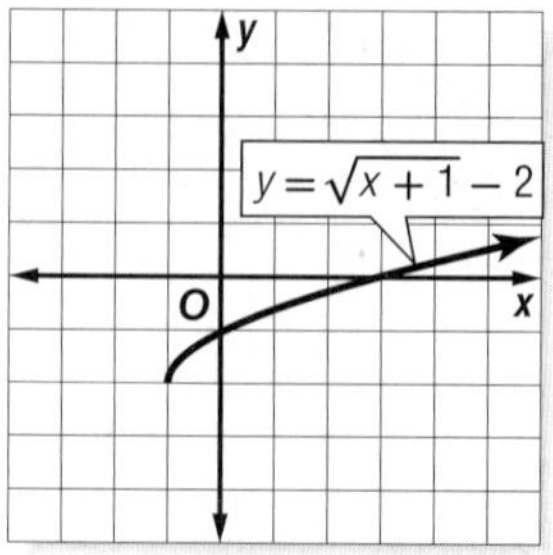

12. D = {x|x ≥ –3}, R = {y|y ≤ 6}

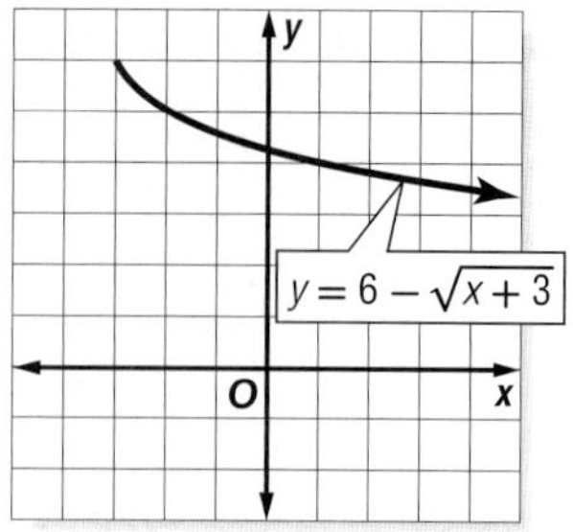

13.

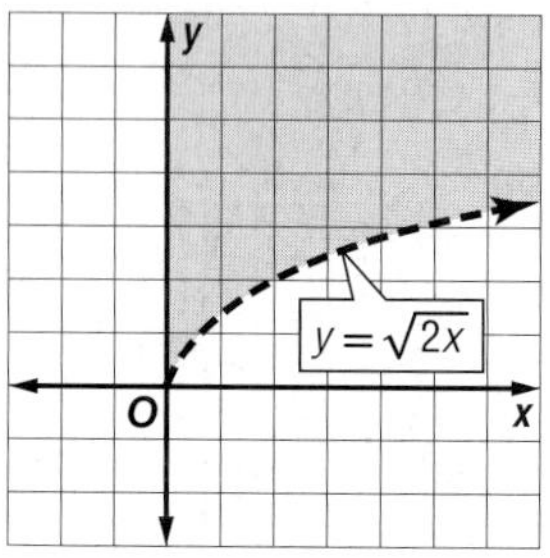

14.

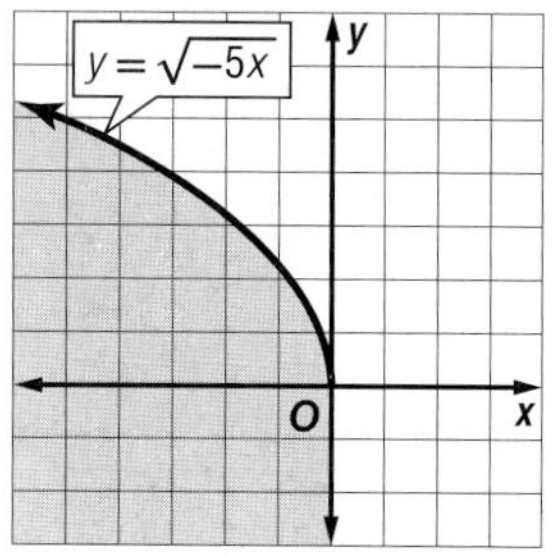

15.

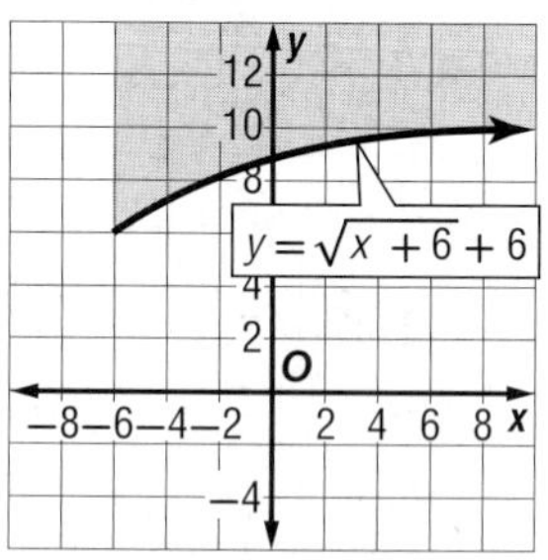

16.

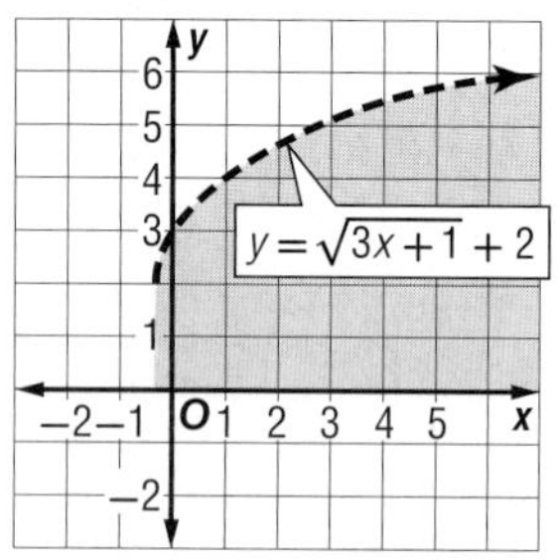

17.

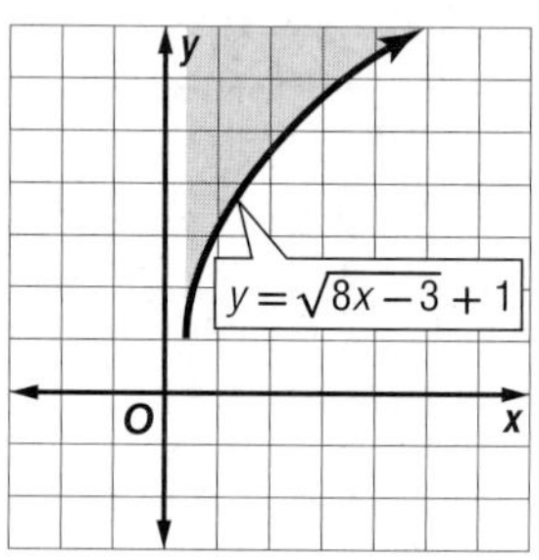

18.

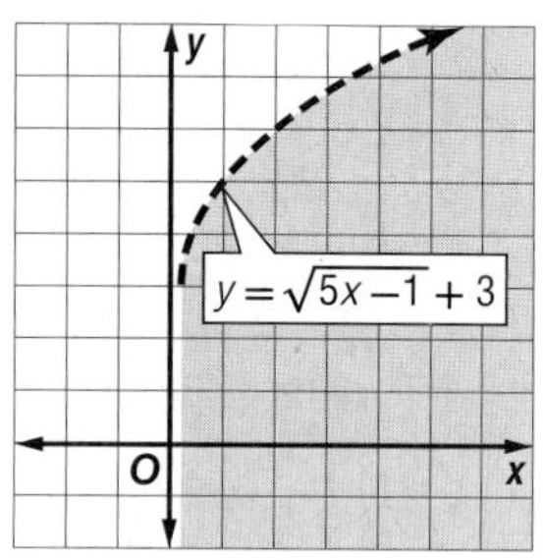

Page 962, Extra Practice (Lesson 7-5)

1. $5\sqrt{3}$
2. $14\sqrt{3}$
3. $3\sqrt[3]{3}$
4. $r^2\sqrt{5r}$
5. $49|xy|\sqrt[4]{xy^2}$
6. $9\sqrt{5}$
7. $-2\sqrt{2}$
8. $13\sqrt[3]{4}$
9. 18
10. $26\sqrt{3}$
11. $3\sqrt[3]{2} - 2\sqrt[3]{3}$
12. $2\sqrt{10} - 5\sqrt{2}$
13. $-6\sqrt{2} + 3\sqrt{21}$
14. $15 + 3\sqrt{2} + 5\sqrt{3} + \sqrt{6}$
15. –1
16. $75 + 16\sqrt{11}$
17. –3
18. $21 + 4\sqrt{26}$
19. $-3 - 3\sqrt{7}$
20. $53 - 20\sqrt{7}$
21. $\frac{m\sqrt{2mf}}{4f^3}$
22. $\frac{3}{4}$
23. $\frac{r\sqrt[3]{4r^2nt^2}}{nt}$
24. $\frac{\sqrt[3]{196}}{7}$

Page 962, Extra Practice (Lesson 7-7)

12. $c < \frac{17}{6}$
16. $-\frac{1}{5} \le y < 3$
17. $-\frac{1}{3} \le n \le 21$
18. no solution

Page 963, Extra Practice (Lesson 8-1)

1. D = {all real numbers}; R = {y|y > 0}

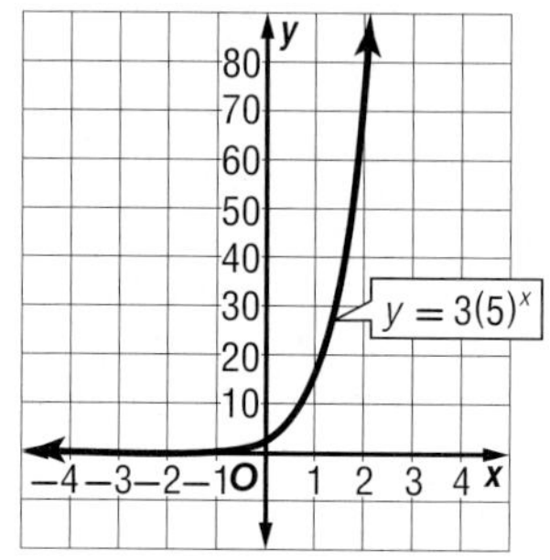

2. D = {all real numbers}; R = {y|y > 0}

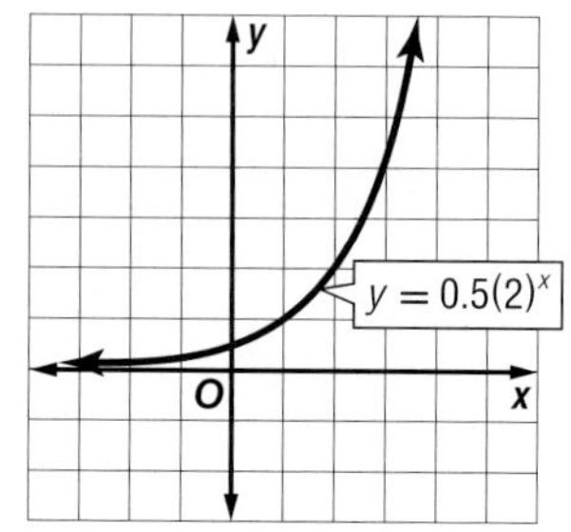

3. D = {all real numbers}; R = {y|y > 0}

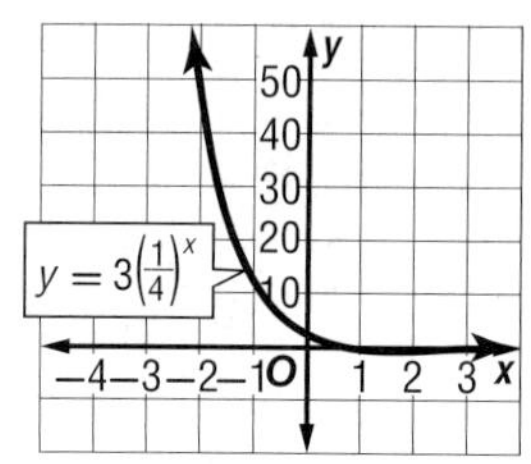

4. D = {all real numbers}; R = {y|y > 0}

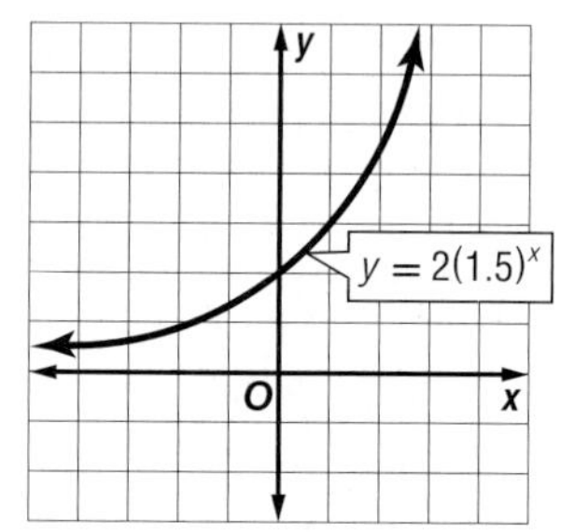

5. D = {all real numbers}; R = {y|y > 0}

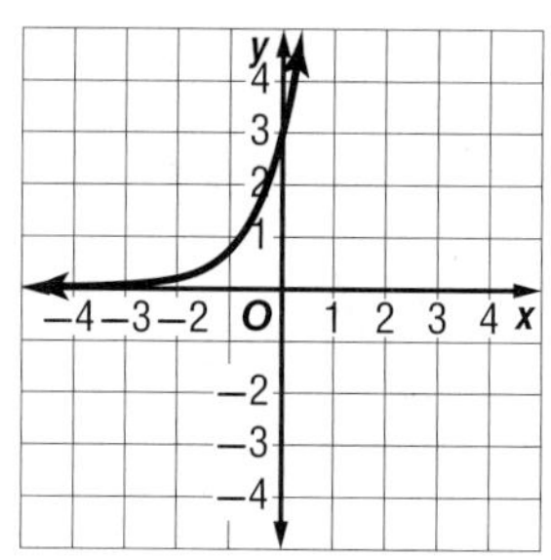

6. D = {all real numbers}; R = {y|y > 0}

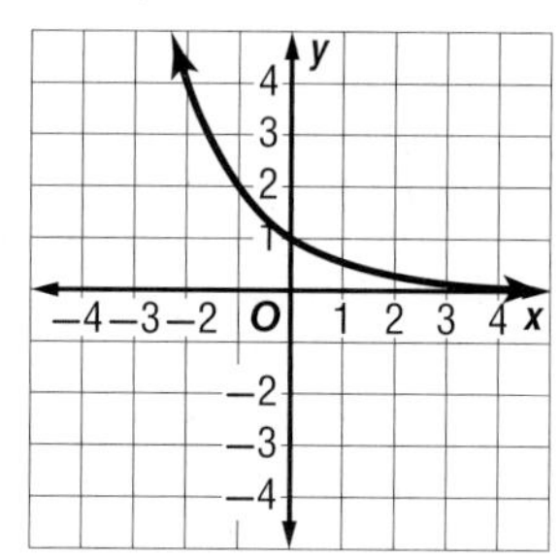

7. D = {all real numbers}; R = {y|y > 0}

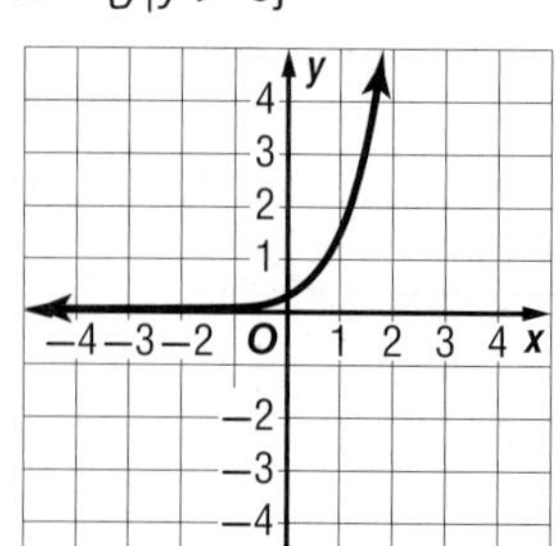

8. D = {all real numbers}; R = {y|y > 0}

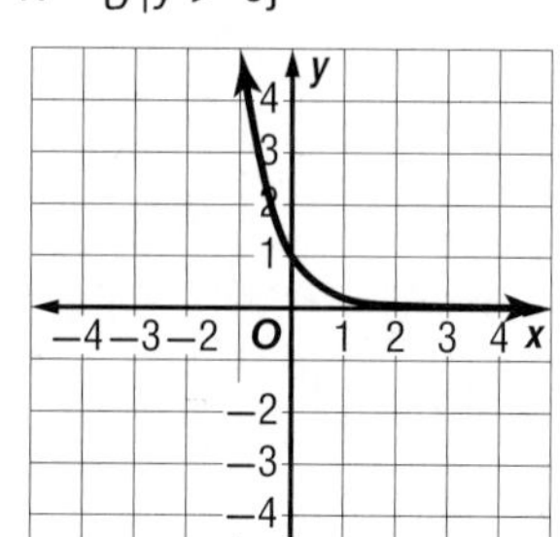

Page 963, Extra Practice (Lesson 8-3)

15.

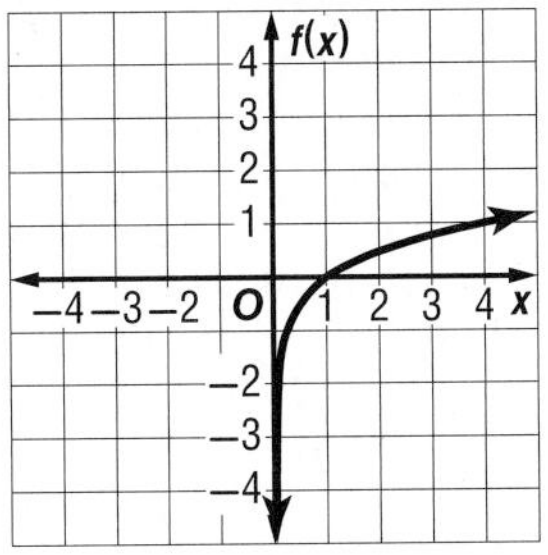

16.

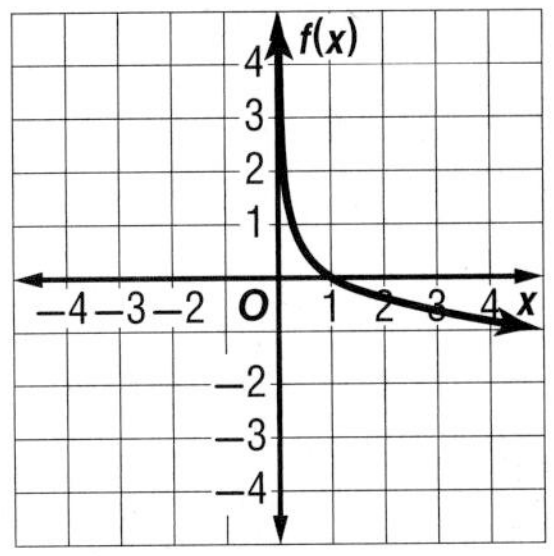

17.

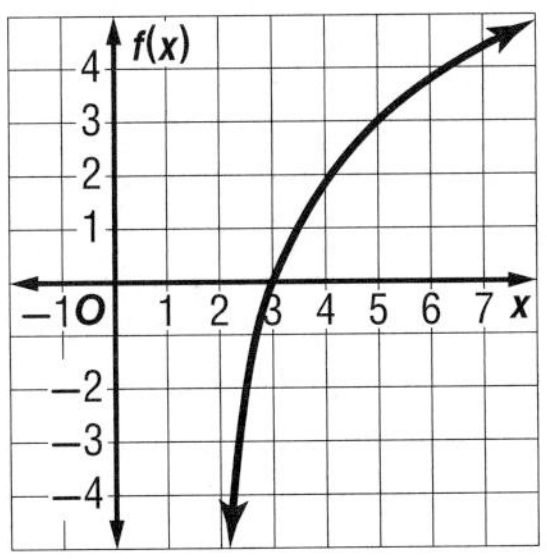

18.

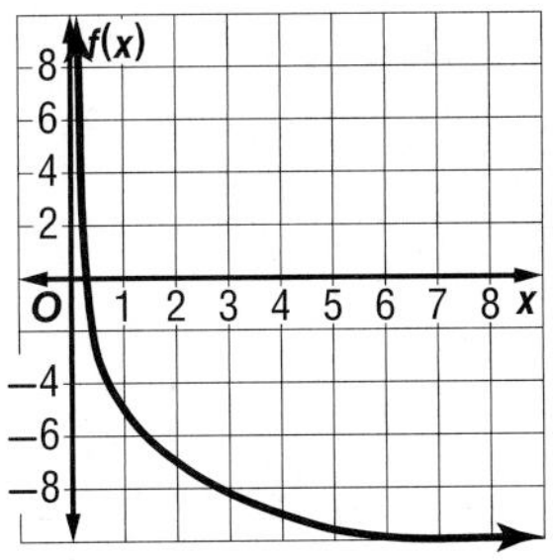

Page 966, Extra Practice (Lesson 9-3)

1. D = $\{x \mid x \neq 0\}$, R = $\{f(x) \mid f(x) \neq 0\}$

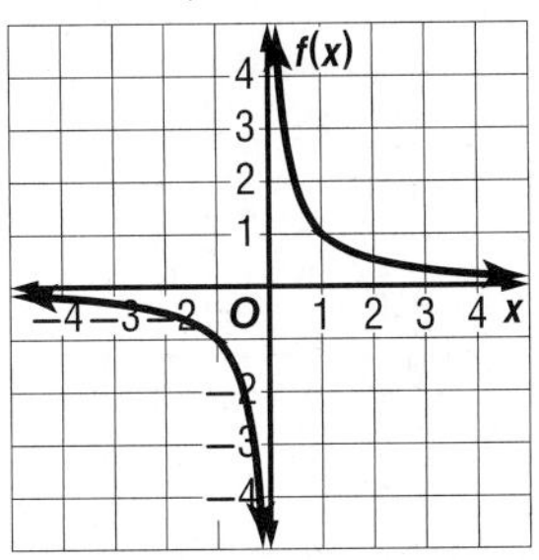

2. D = $\{x \mid x \neq 0\}$, R = $\{f(x) \mid f(x) \neq 0\}$

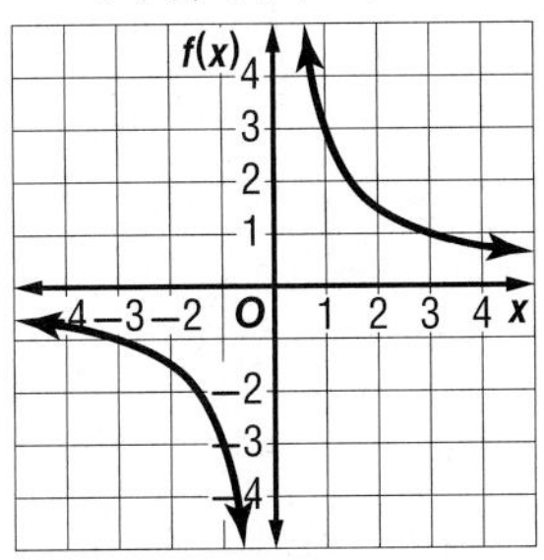

3. D = $\{x \mid x \neq -2\}$, R = $\{f(x) \mid f(x) \neq 0\}$

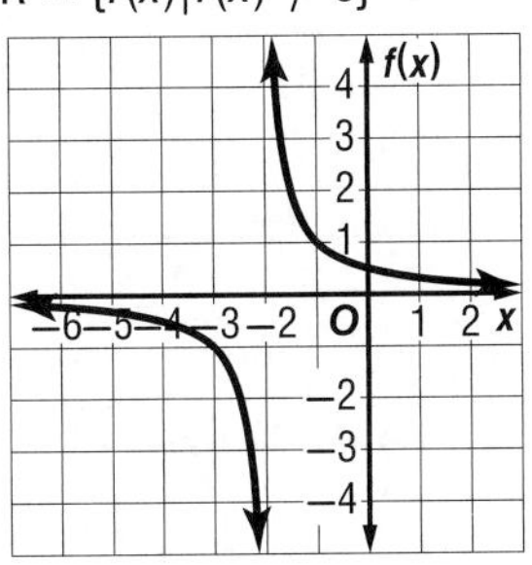

4. D = $\{x \mid x \neq -1\}$, R = $\{f(x) \mid f(x) \neq 0\}$

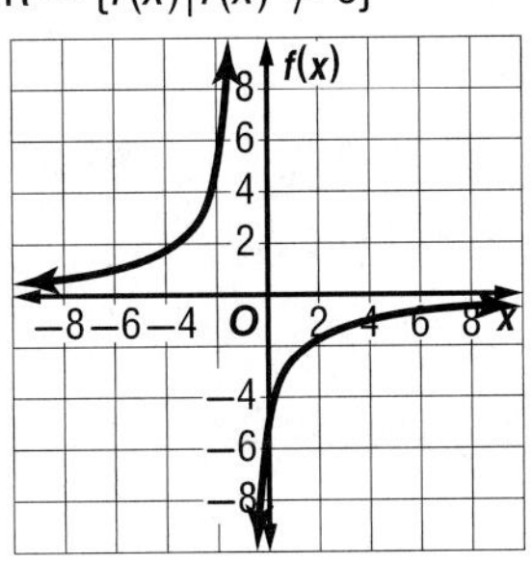

5. D = $\{x \mid x \neq 4\}$, R = $\{f(x) \mid f(x) \neq 0\}$

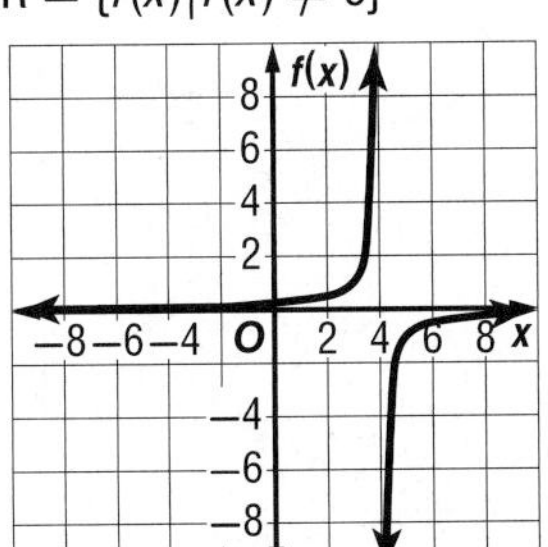

6. D = $\{x \mid x \neq -2\}$, R = $\{f(x) \mid f(x) \neq 0\}$

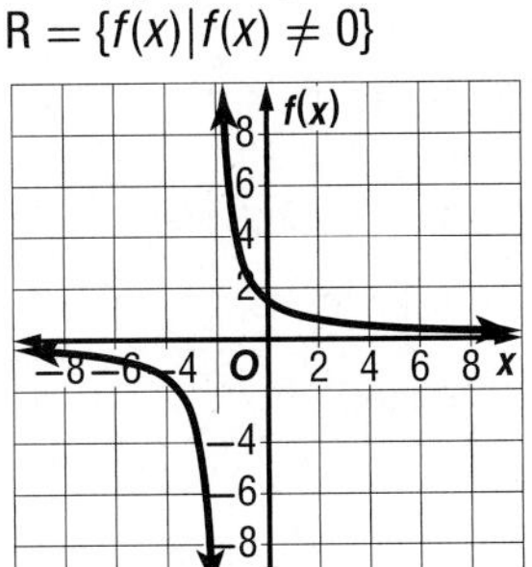

7. D = $\{x \mid x \neq -10\}$, R = $\{f(x) \mid f(x) \neq 0\}$

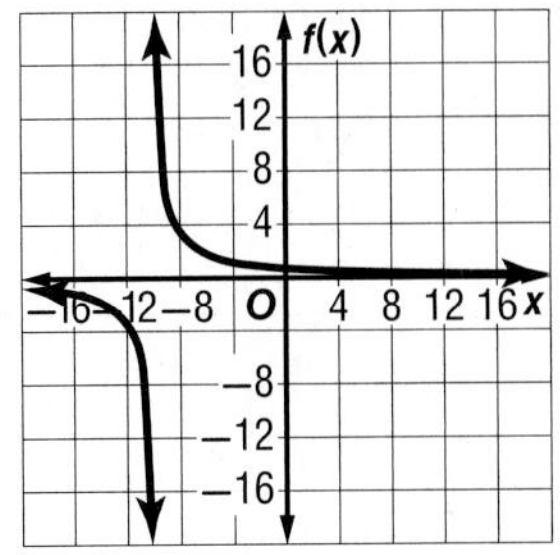

8. D = $\{x \mid x \neq 7\}$, R = $\{f(x) \mid f(x) \neq 0\}$

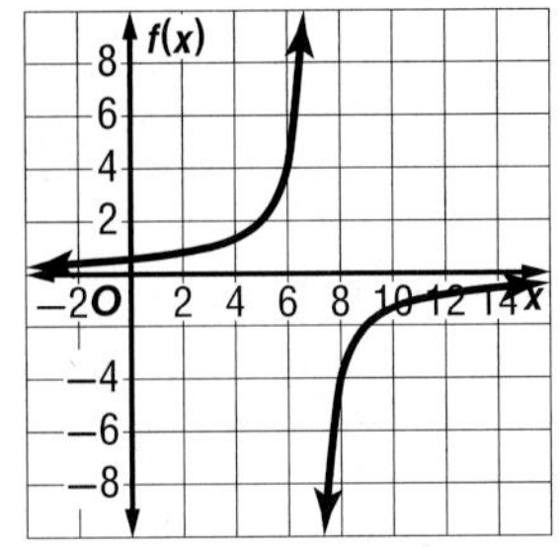

Page 966, Extra Practice (Lesson 9-4)

7.

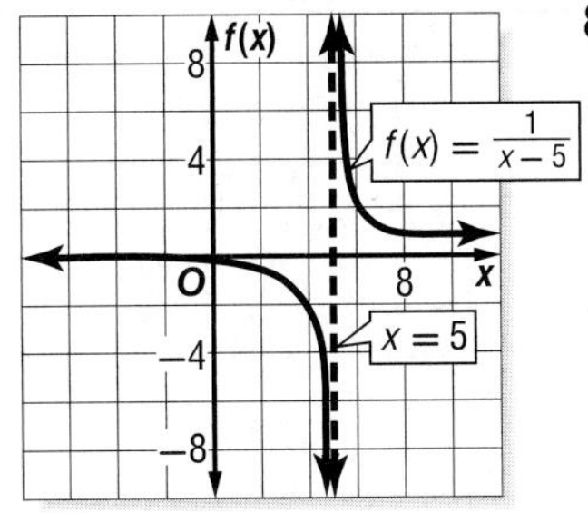

8.

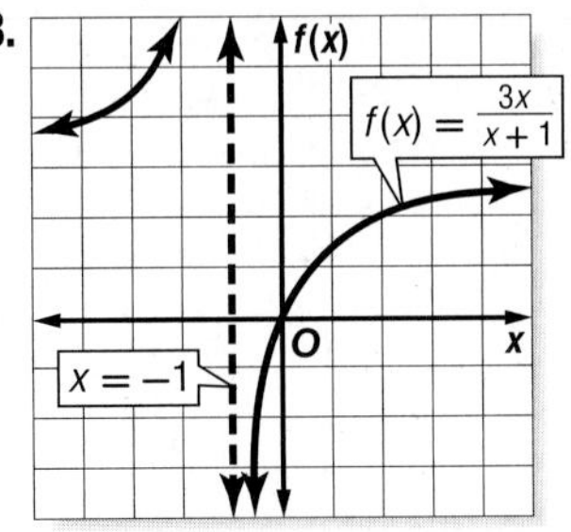

9.

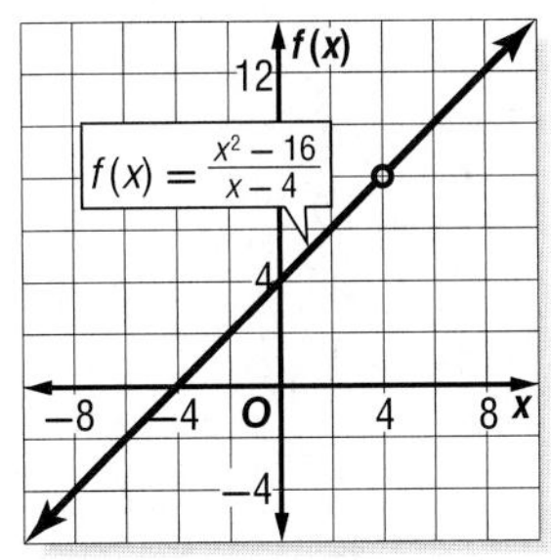

10.

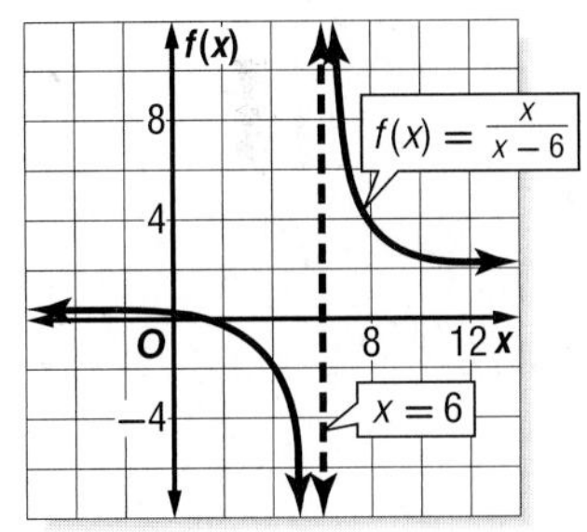

11.

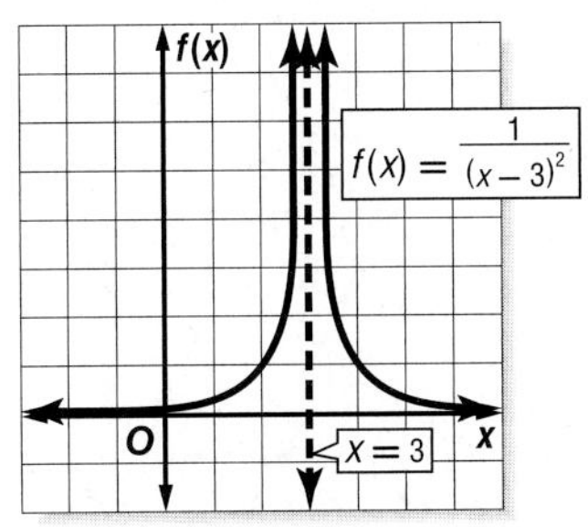

12.

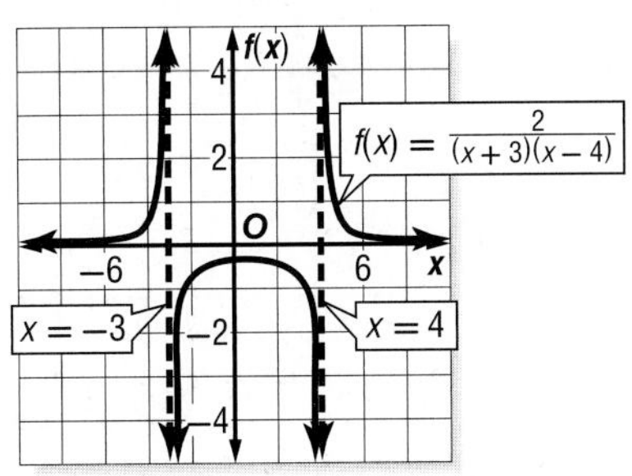

13.

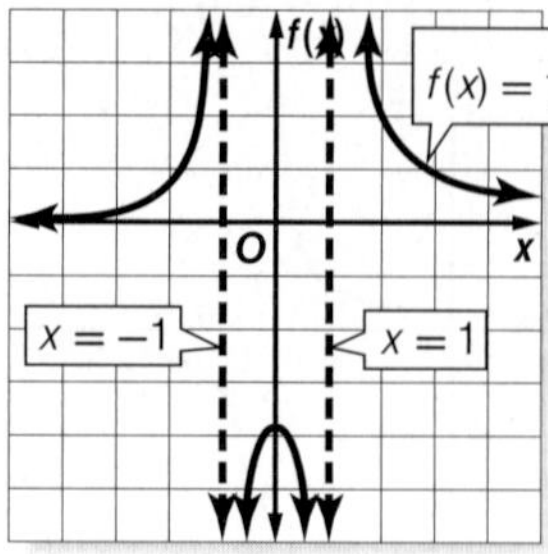

14.

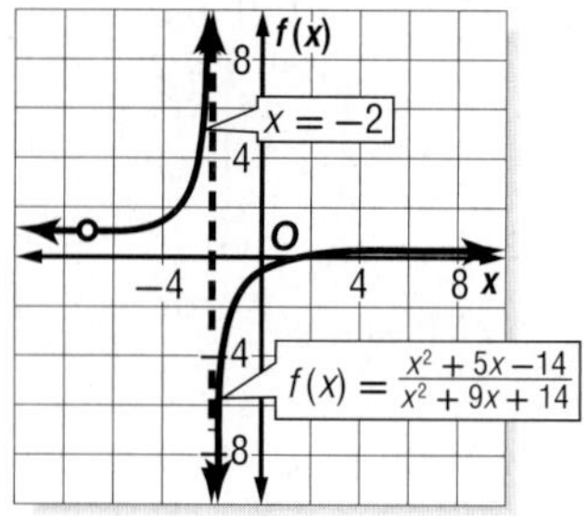

Page 967, Extra Practice (Lesson 10-2)

1. equation: $y = x^2 - 4$;
vertex: (0, –4);
axis: $x = 0$;
opens up

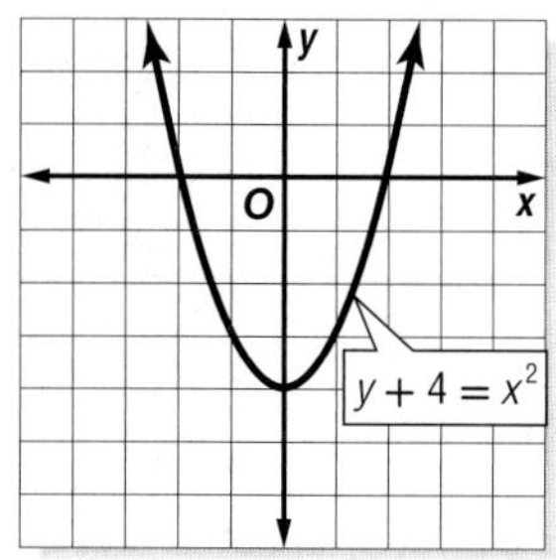

2. equation: $y = 5(x + 2)^2$;

vertex: (–2, 0);

axis: $x = -2$;

opens up

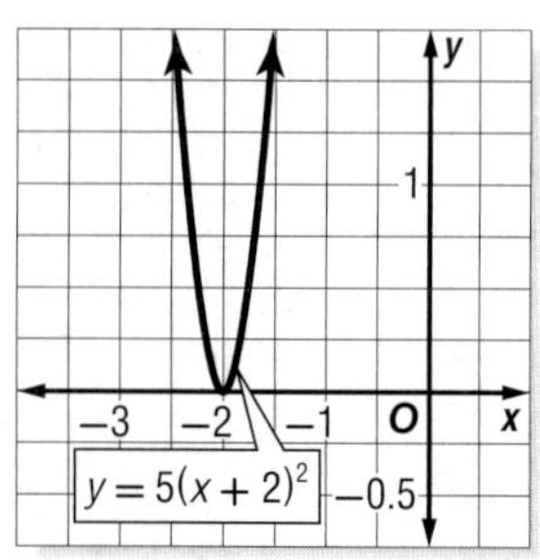

3. equation: $y = \frac{3}{4}(x - 1)^2 - 2$;

vertex: (1, –2);

axis: $x = 1$;

opens up

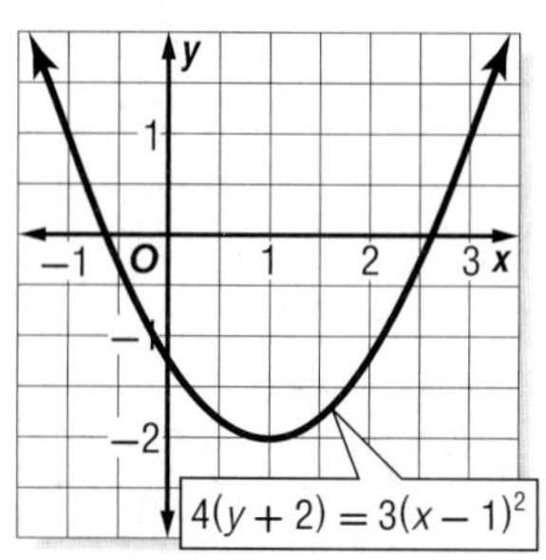

4. equation: $x = -\frac{3}{5}y^2 + 3$;

vertex: (3, 0);

axis: $y = 0$;
opens left

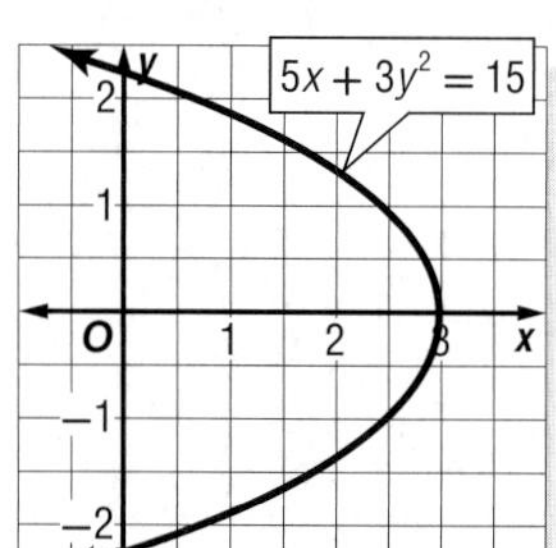

5. equation: $y = 2(x - 2)^2 - 1$;

vertex: (2, –1);

axis: $x = 2$;

opens up

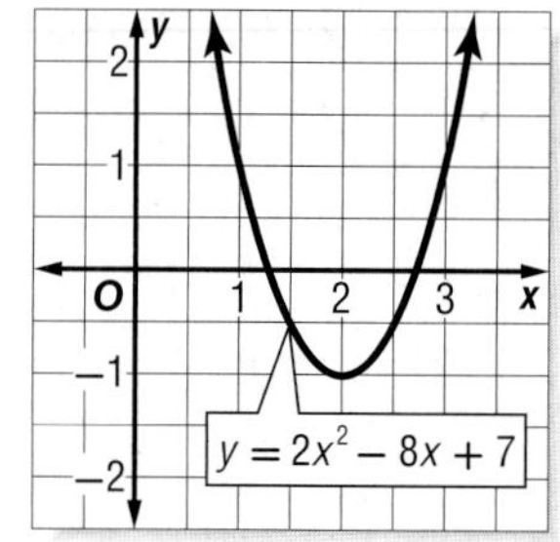

6. equation: $x = 2(y - 2)^2 - 1$;

vertex: (–1, 2);

axis: $y = 2$;

opens right

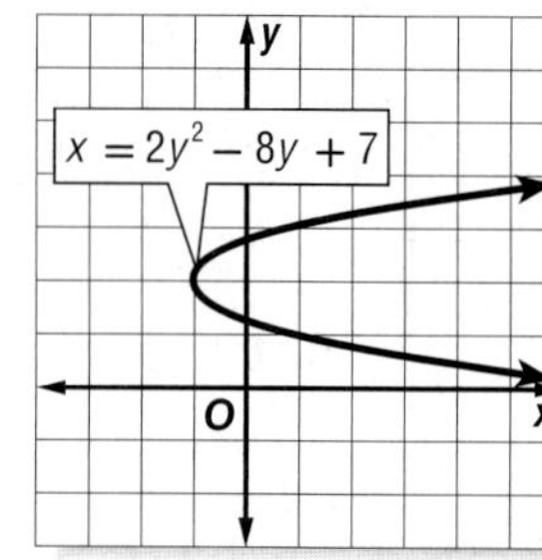

7. equation: $y = \frac{3}{5}(x - 8)^2 - 3$;

vertex: (8, –3);

axis: $x = 8$;
opens up

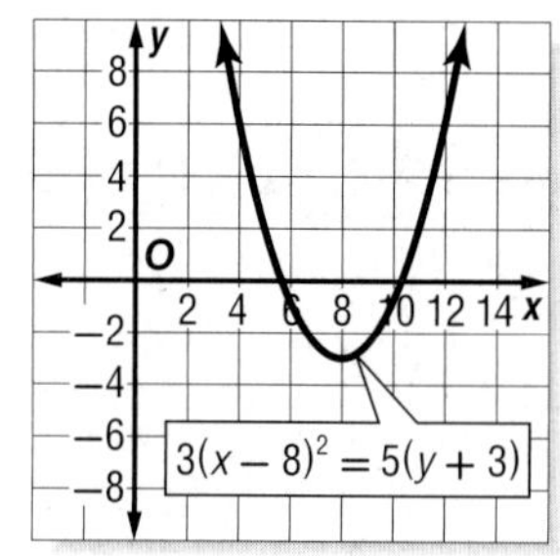

8. equation: $x = 3(y + 4)^2 + 1$;

vertex: (1, –4);

axis: $y = -4$;

opens right

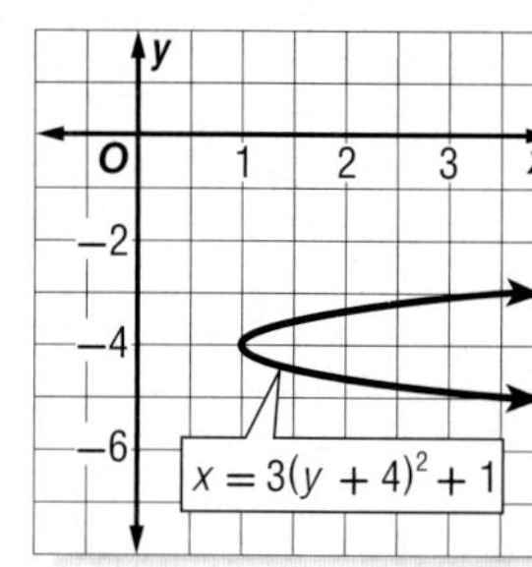

9. equation: $y = -\frac{5}{8}(x + 3)^2 - 7$;

vertex: (–3, –7);

axis: $x = -3$;

opens down

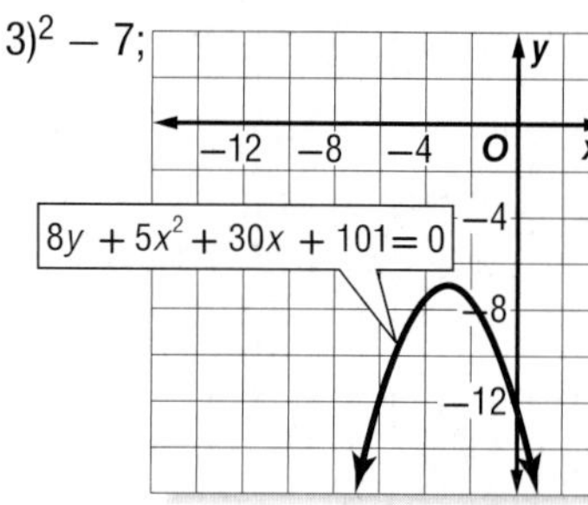

10. equation: $x = -\frac{1}{5}(y - 4)^2 - \frac{19}{5}$;

vertex: $\left(-3\frac{4}{5}, 4\right)$;

axis: $y = 4$;

opens left

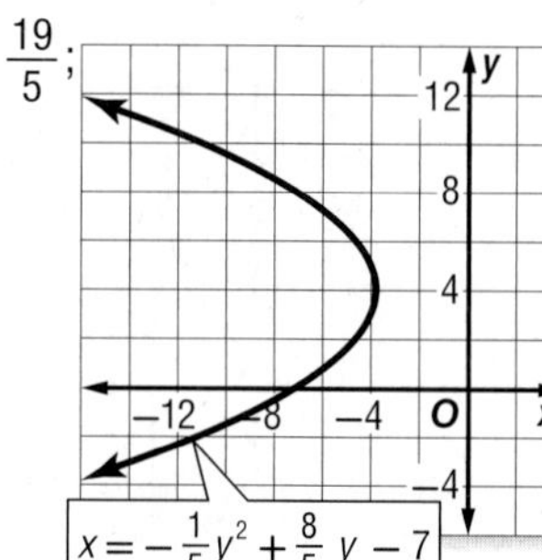

11. equation: $x = \frac{1}{6}(y - 3)^2 + 5$; vertex: (5, 3); axis: $y = 3$; opens right

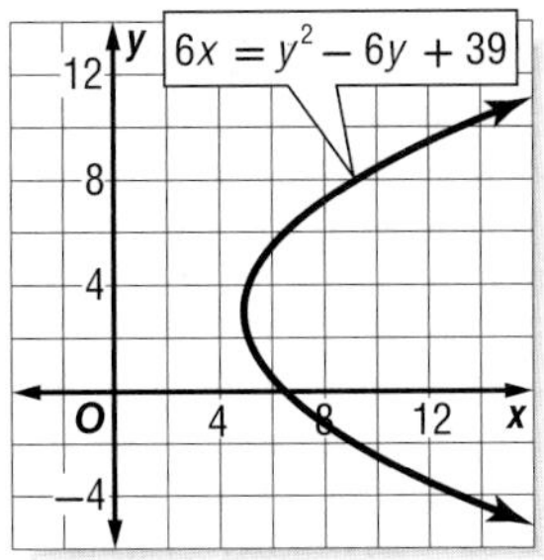

12. equation: $y = -\frac{1}{8}x^2$; vertex: (0, 0); axis: $x = 0$; opens down

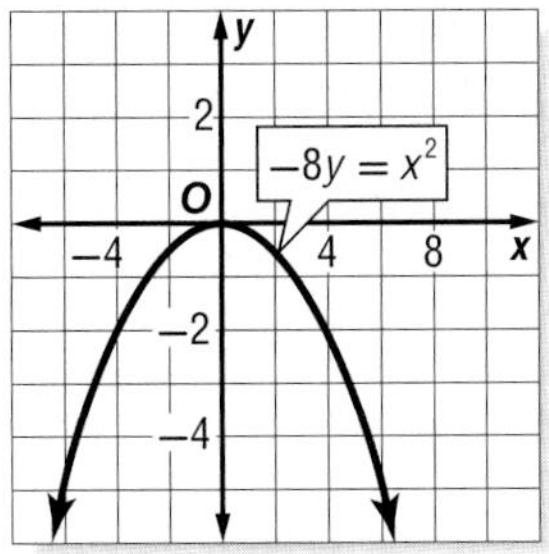

13. equation: $y = 4(x + 3)^2 + 2$; vertex: (–3, 2); axis: $x = -3$; opens up

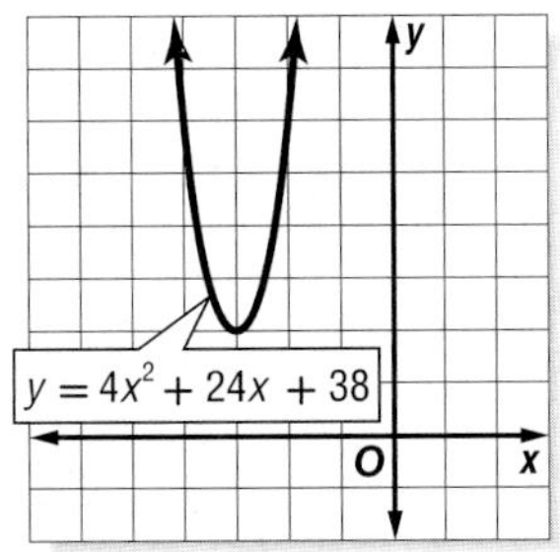

14. equation: $y = (x - 3)^2 - 6$; vertex: (3, –6); axis: $x = 3$; opens up

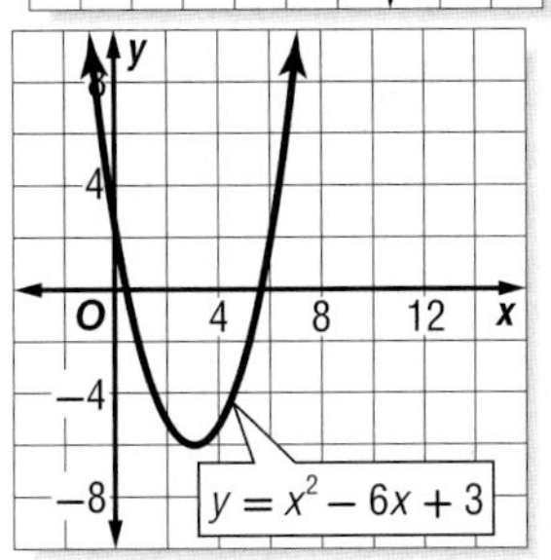

15. equation: $y = (x + 2)^2 - 3$; vertex: (–2, –3); axis: $x = -2$; opens up

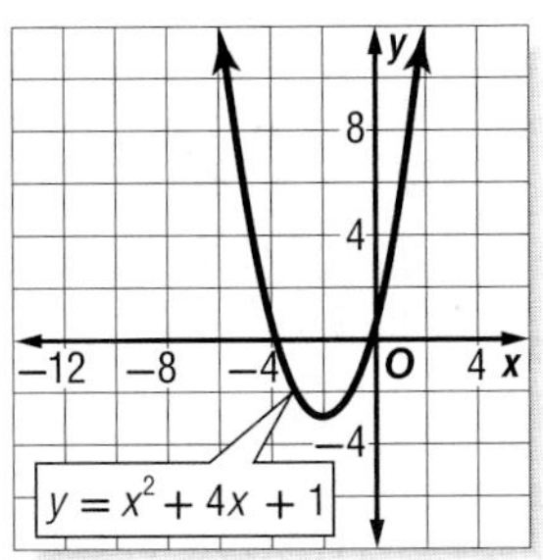

16.

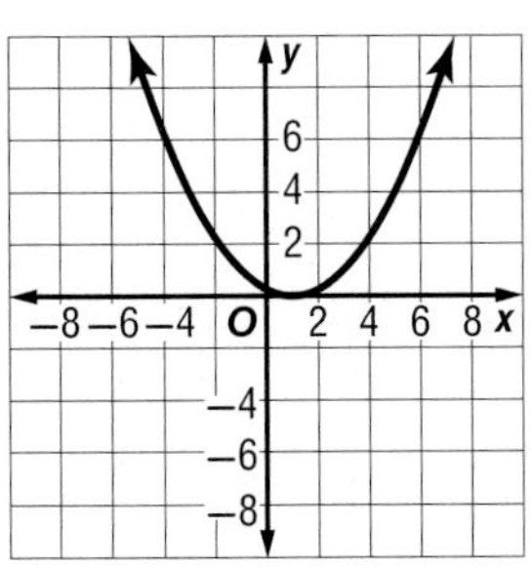

17.

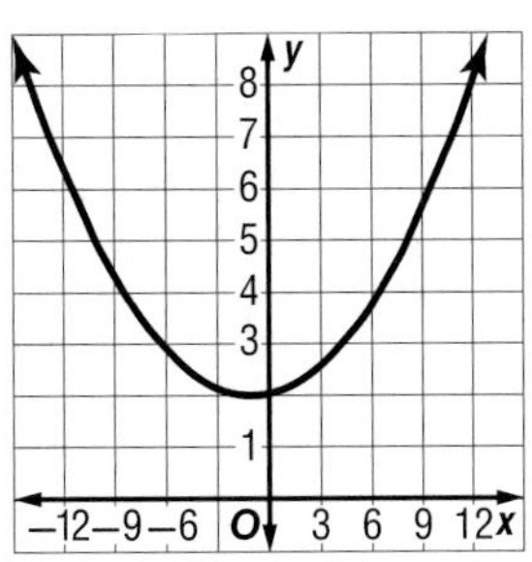

Page 967, Extra Practice (Lesson 10-3)

1. $(x - 3)^2 + (y - 2)^2 = 25$
2. $(x + 5)^2 + (y - 8)^2 = 9$
3. $(x - 1)^2 + (y + 6)^2 = \frac{4}{9}$
4. $(x - 0)^2 + (y - 7)^2 = 49$
5. $(x + 2)^2 + (y + 4)^2 = 4$
6. $(x + 3.5)^2 + (y + 2.5)^2 = 36.5$
7. $(x - 0.5)^2 + (y - 1.5)^2 = 12.5$
8. $(x - 6)^2 + (y + 10)^2 = 136$
9. $(x - 0.8)^2 + (y - 0.5)^2 = 3.69$
10. (0, 0); 6

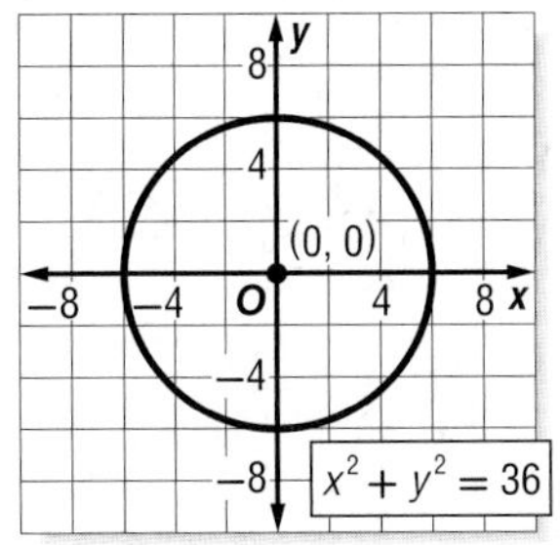

11. (5, –4); 1

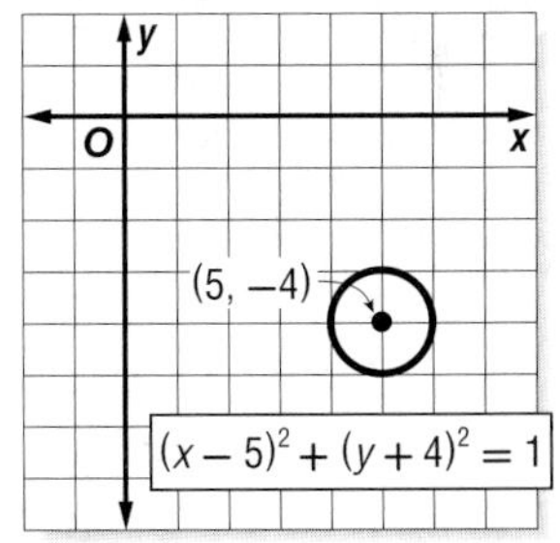

12. (–1.5, 2.5); 3

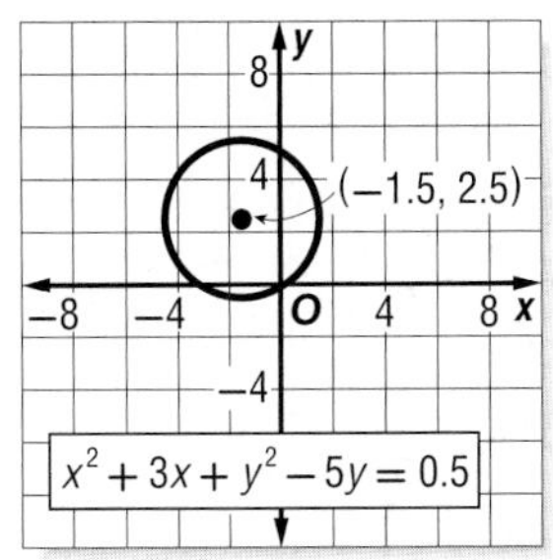

13. (7, 0); 5

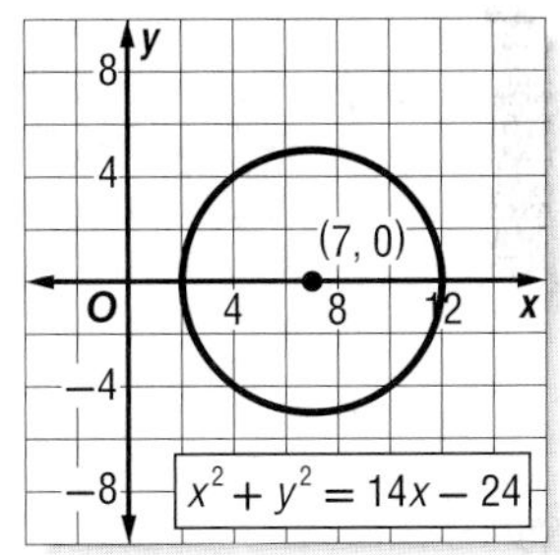

14. (–1, 1); $\sqrt{2}$

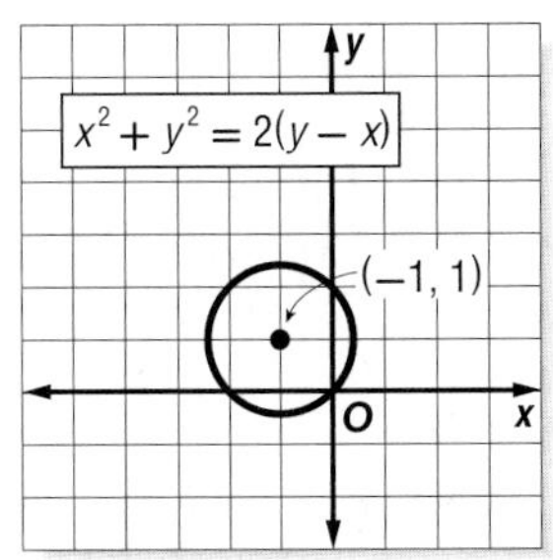

15. (–5, $\sqrt{3}$); 6

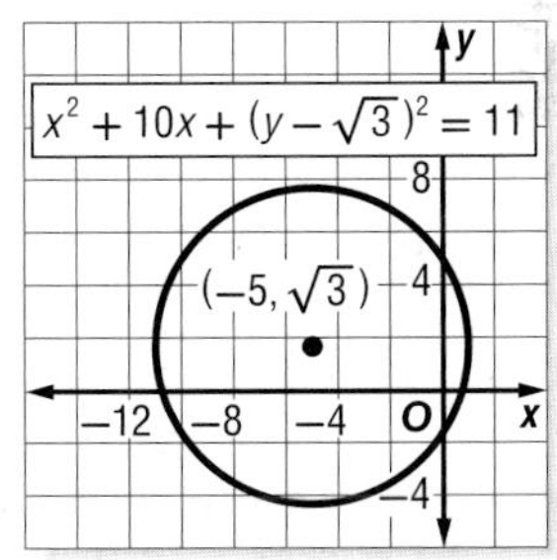

16. (2, 0); $\sqrt{13}$

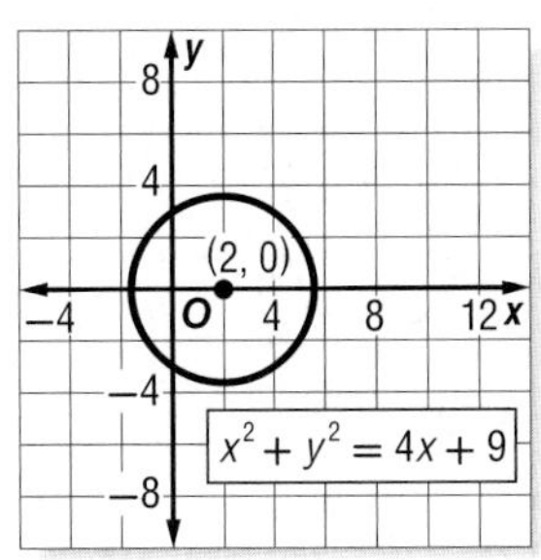

17. (3, –2); 13

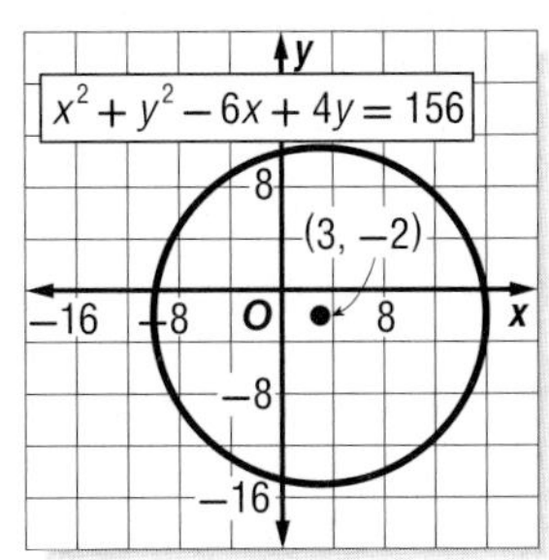

18. $(1, -3.5)$; $\sqrt{14.25}$

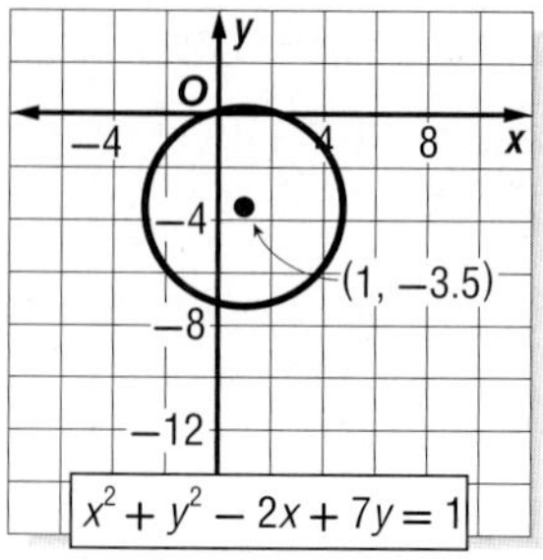

Page 968, Extra Practice (Lesson 10-4)

4. center: $(0, 0)$;
foci: $(0, \pm 3\sqrt{5})$;
major axis: 18;
minor axis: 12

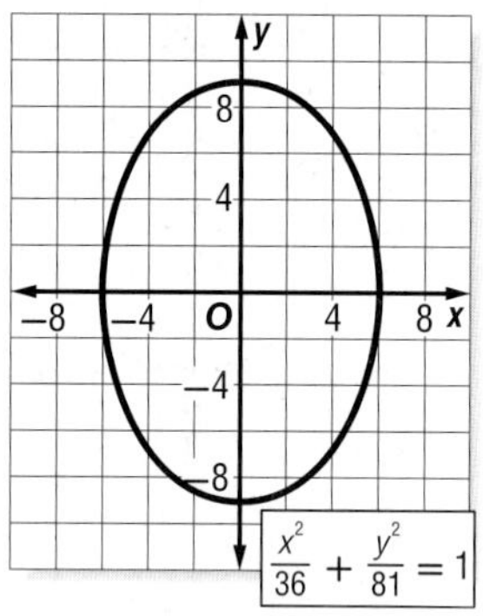

5. center: $(0, 5)$;
foci: $(\pm\sqrt{105}, 5)$;
major axis: 22;
minor axis: 8

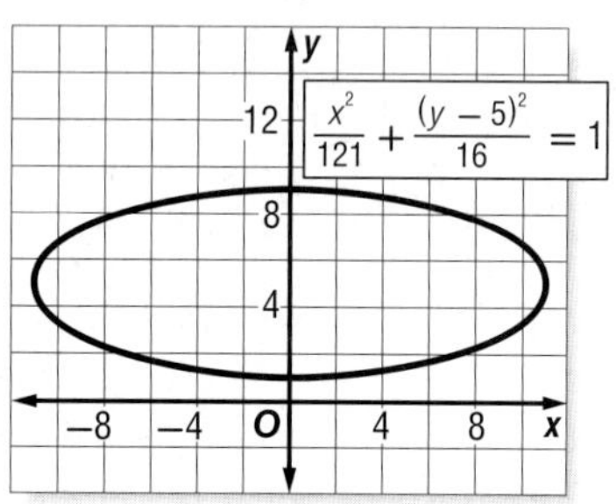

6. center: $(-2, -1)$;
foci: $(-2, -3)$, $(-2, -1)$;
major axis: 8;
minor axis: $4\sqrt{3}$

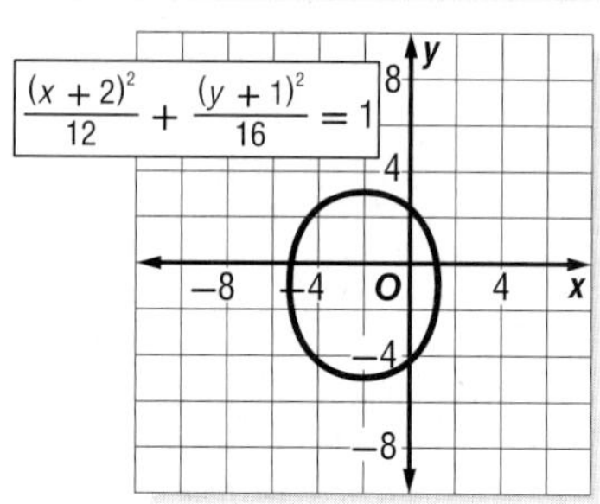

7. center: $(0, 0)$;
foci: $(0, \pm 2\sqrt{3})$;
major axis: 8;
minor axis: 4

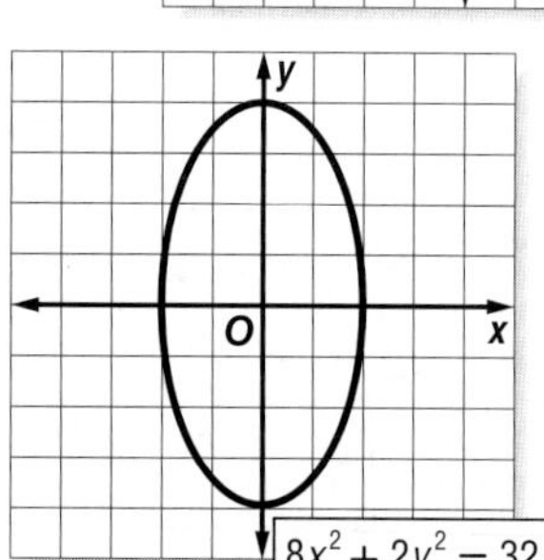

8. center: $(0, 0)$;
foci: $(0, \pm 4)$;
major axis: $4\sqrt{7}$;
minor axis: $4\sqrt{3}$

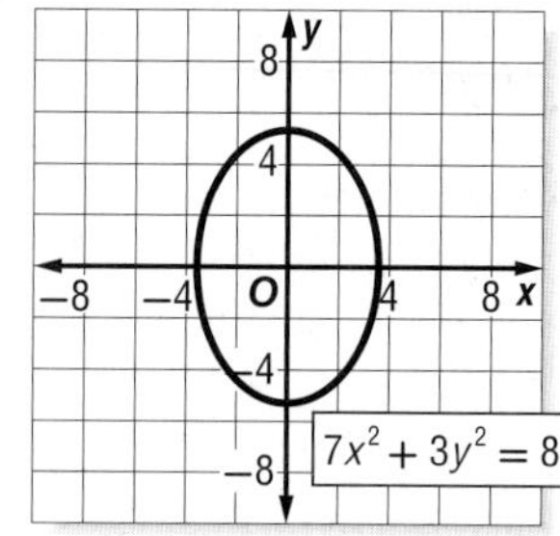

9. center: $(0, 0)$;
foci: $(\pm\sqrt{7}, 0)$;
major axis: 8;
minor axis: 6

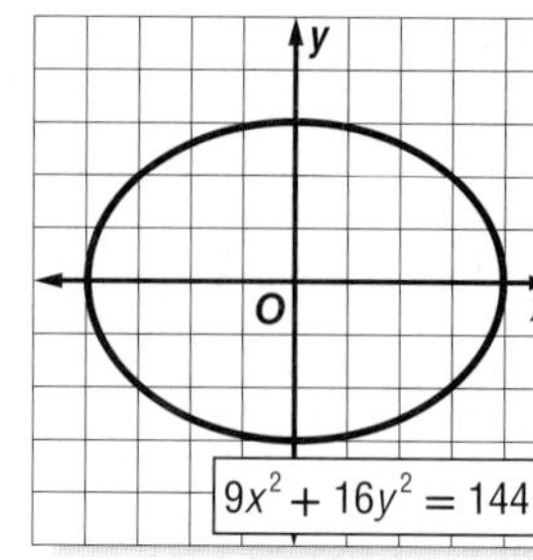

10. center: $(1, 0)$;
foci: $(1, \pm 12)$;
major axis: 26;
minor axis: 10

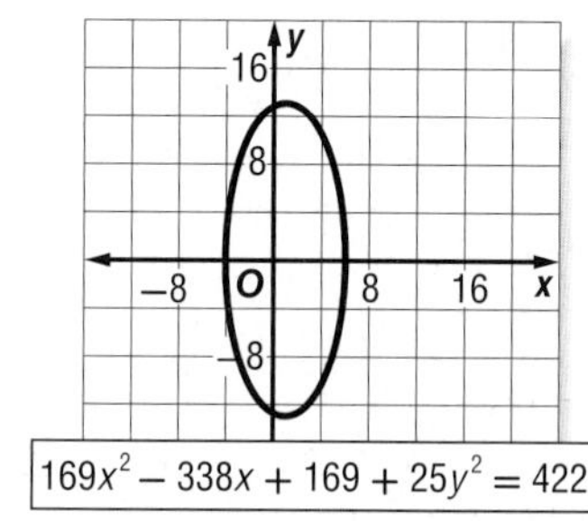

11. center: $(-4, 8)$;
foci: $(-4 \pm 6\sqrt{3}, 8)$;
major axis: 24;
minor axis: 12

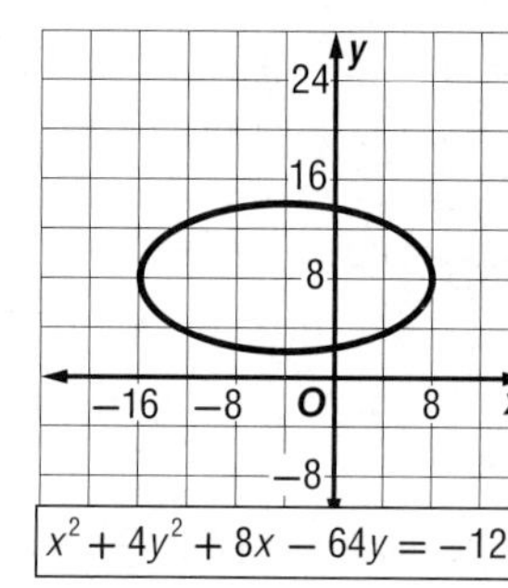

12. center: $(4.5, 3)$;
foci: $(4.5 \pm \sqrt{39.2}, 3)$;
major axis: 28;
minor axis: $2\sqrt{156.8}$

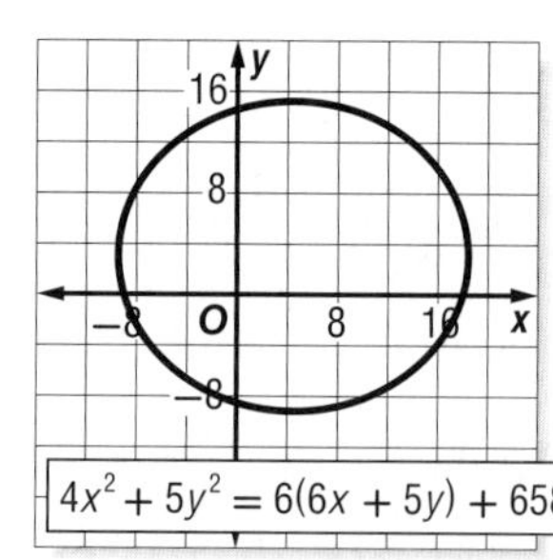

13. center: $(3, -2)$;
foci: $(3 \pm \sqrt{7}, -2)$;
major axis: 8;
minor axis: 6

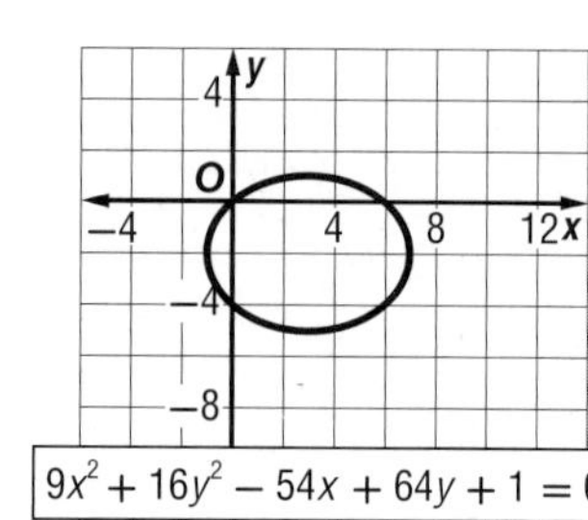

Page 968, Extra Practice (Lesson 10-5)

1. vertices: $(0, \pm 5)$;
foci: $(0, \pm\sqrt{34})$;
asymptotes:
$y = \pm\frac{5}{3}x$

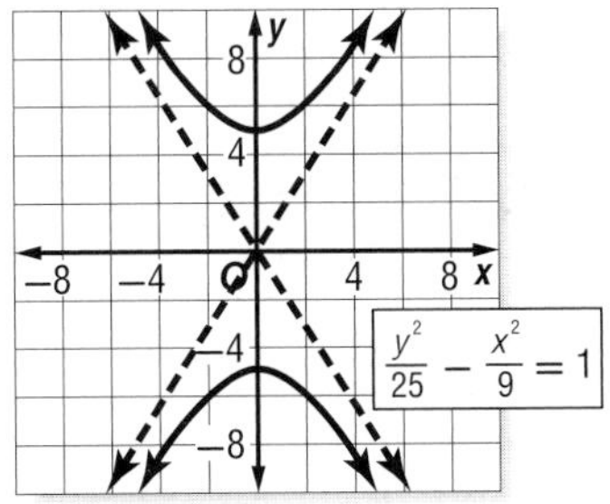

2. vertices: $(\pm 2, 0)$;
foci: $(\pm\sqrt{13}, 0)$;
asymptotes:
$y = \pm\frac{3}{2}x$

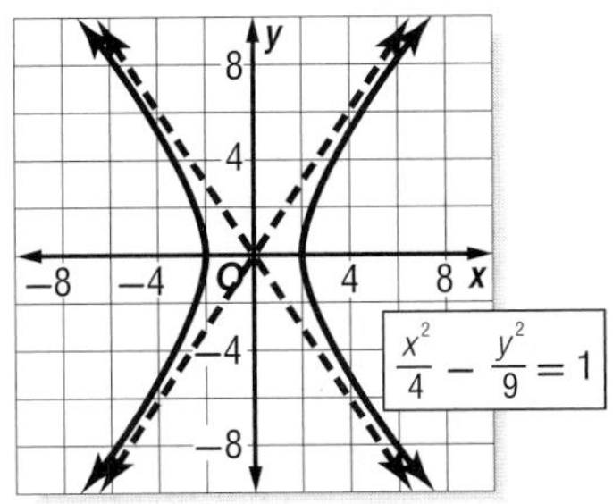

3. vertices: $(\pm 9, 0)$;
foci: $(\pm 3\sqrt{13}, 0)$;
asymptotes:
$y = \pm\frac{2}{3}x$

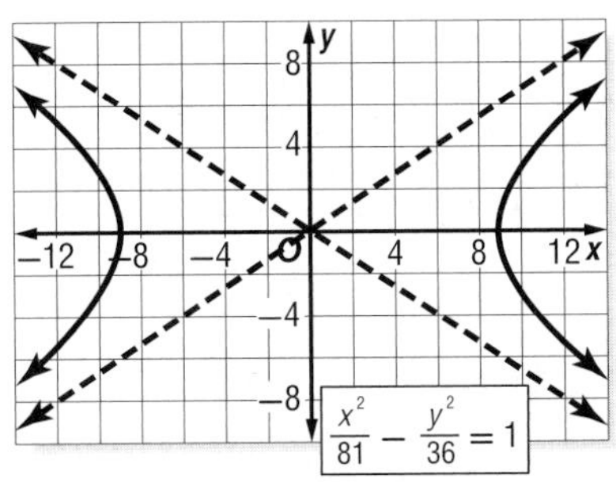

4. vertices: $(-4, -1)$, $(12, -1)$;
foci: $(4 + 4\sqrt{5}, -1)$, $(4 - 4\sqrt{5}, -1)$; asymptotes:
$y + 1 = \pm\frac{1}{2}(x - 4)$

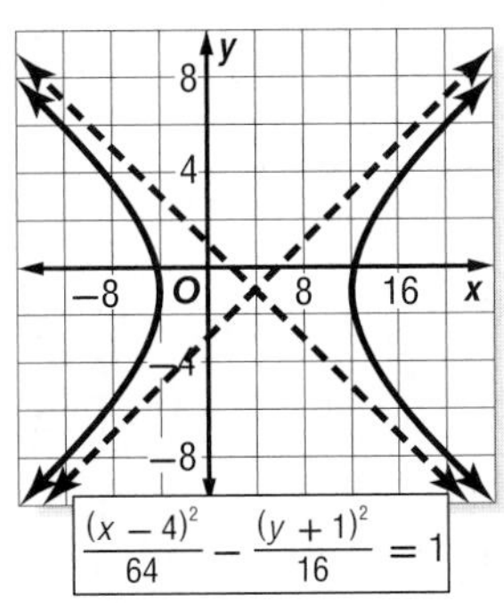

5. vertices: $(3, 5.5)$, $(3, 8.5)$;
foci: $(3, 4.5)$, $(3, 9.5)$;
asymptotes: $y - 7 = \frac{3}{4}(x - 3)$

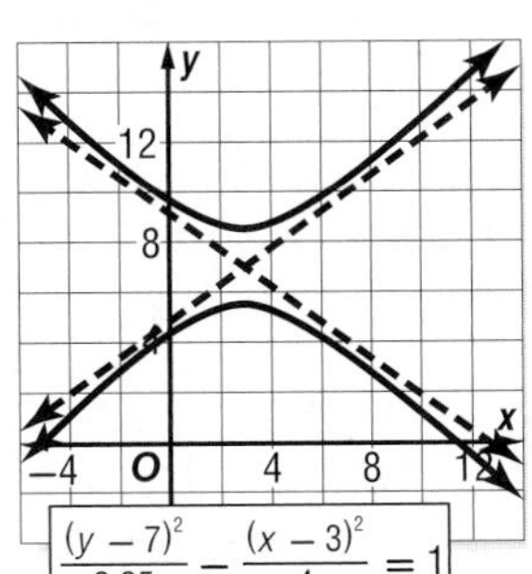

6. vertices: $(-4, -3)$, $(-6, -3)$; foci: $(2, -3)$, $(-12, -3)$;
asymptotes:
$y + 3 = \pm 4\sqrt{3}(x + 5)$

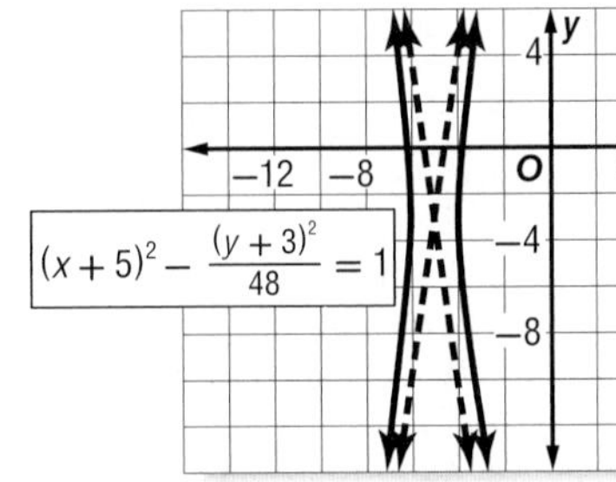

7. vertices: $(\pm 6, 0)$;
foci: $(\pm 2\sqrt{10}, 0)$;
asymptotes:
$y = \pm\frac{1}{3}x$

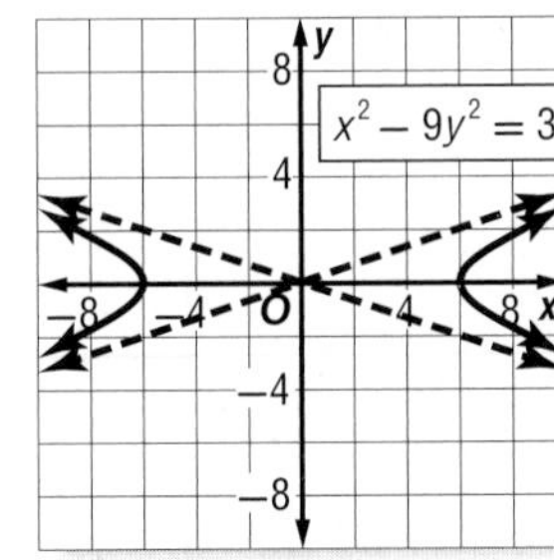

8. vertices: $(\pm 3\sqrt{2}, 0)$;
foci: $(\pm\sqrt{26}, 0)$;
asymptotes: $y = \pm\frac{2}{3}x$

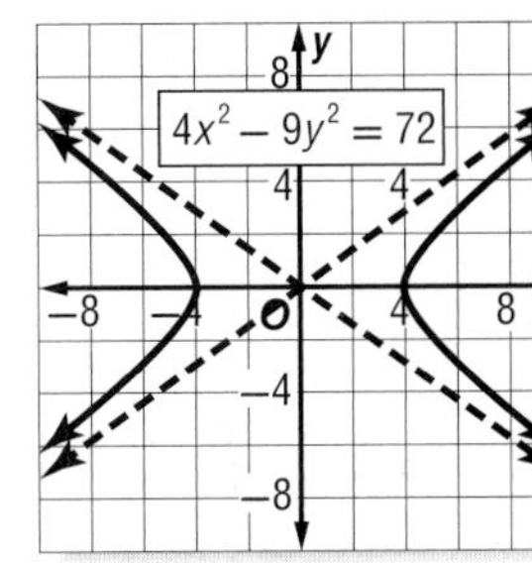

9. vertices: $(\pm 4, 0)$;
foci: $(\pm\sqrt{65}, 0)$;
asymptotes: $y = \pm\frac{7}{4}x$

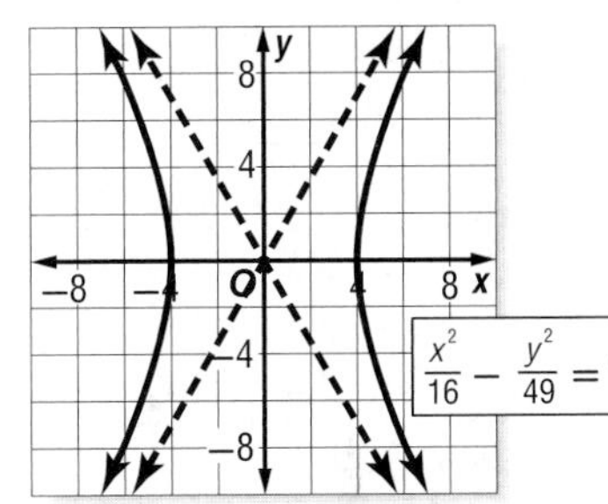

10. vertices: $(-5, \pm 7)$;
foci: $(-5, \pm 25)$;
asymptotes:
$y = \pm\frac{7}{24}(x + 5)$

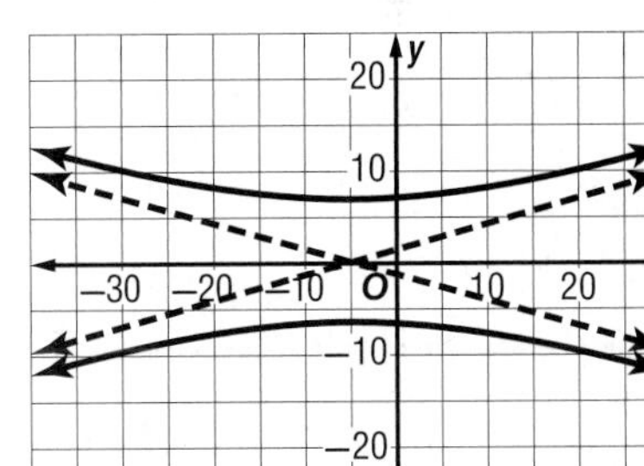

11. vertices: $(1, -5 \pm 2\sqrt{5})$;
foci: $(1, -5 \pm 3\sqrt{5})$;
asymptotes: $y + 5 = \pm\frac{2\sqrt{5}}{5}(x - 1)$

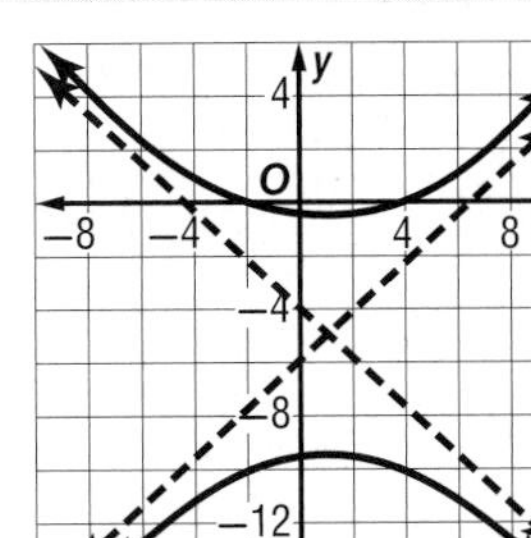

Page 968, Extra Practice (Lesson 10-6)

1. 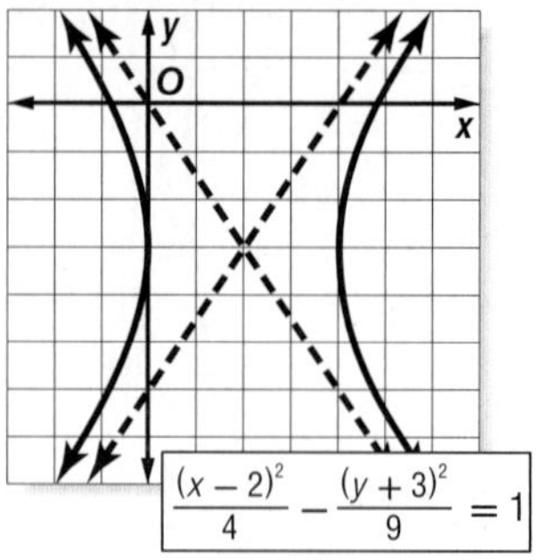

$\frac{(x-2)^2}{4} - \frac{(y+3)^2}{9} = 1$;
hyperbola

2. 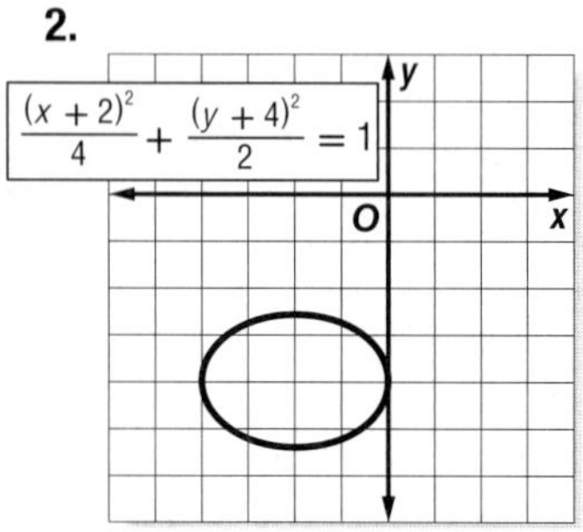

$\frac{(x+2)^2}{4} + \frac{(y+4)^2}{2} = 1$;
ellipse

3. 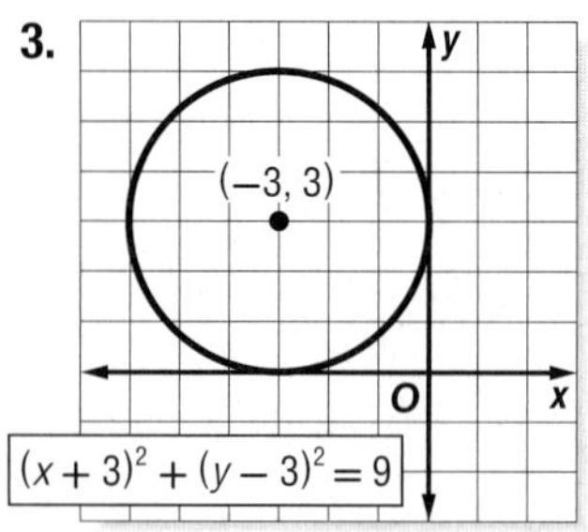

$(x+3)^2 + (y-3)^2 = 9$;
circle

4. 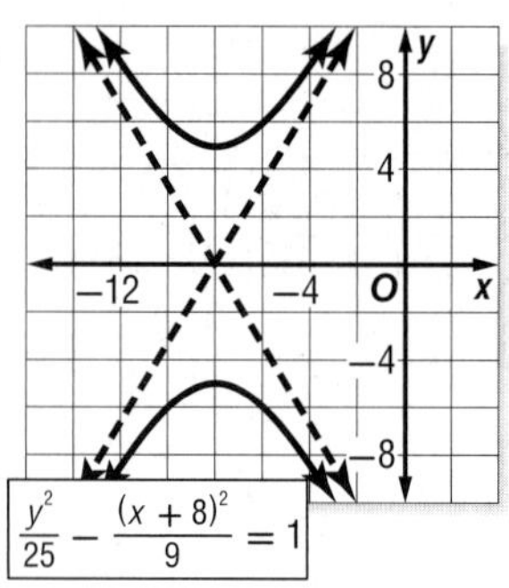

$\frac{(y-0)^2}{25} - \frac{(x+8)^2}{9} = 1$;
hyperbola

5. 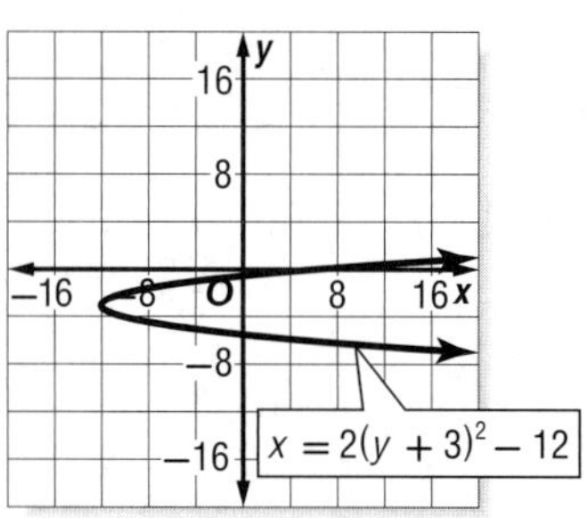

$x = 2(y+3)^2 - 12$;
parabola

6. 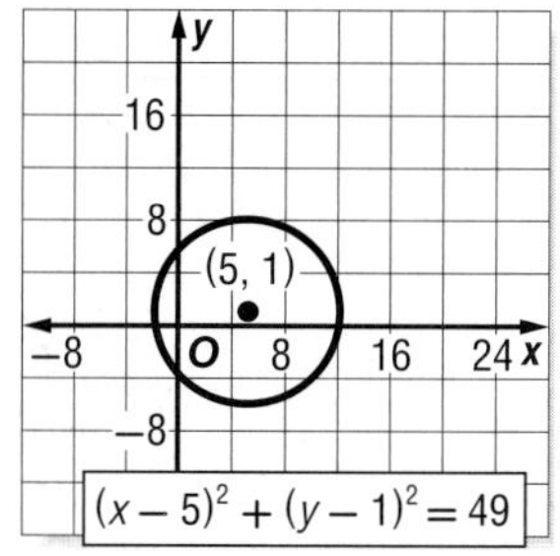

$(x-5)^2 + (y-3)^2 = 49$;
circle

7. 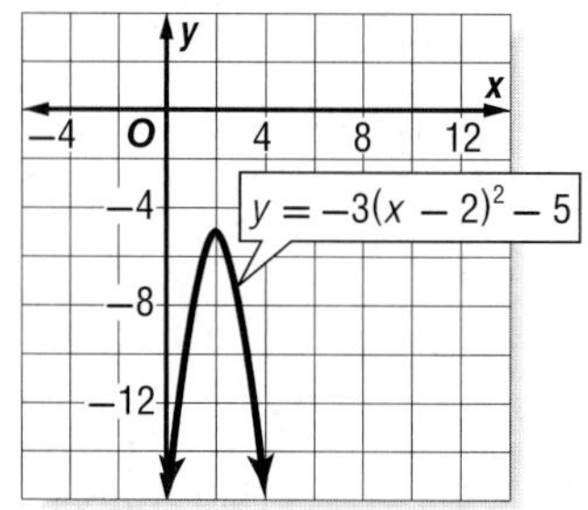

$y = -3(x-2)^2 - 5$;
parabola

8. 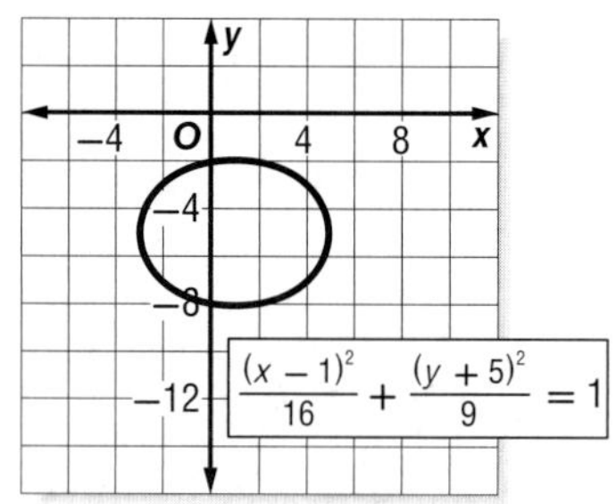

$\frac{(x-1)^2}{16} + \frac{(y+5)^2}{9} = 1$;
ellipse

9. 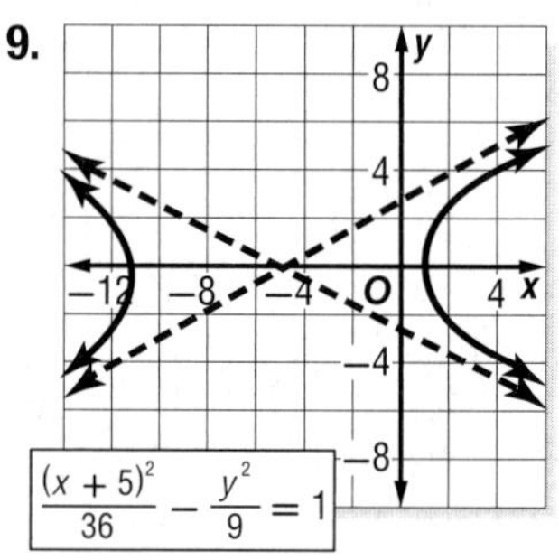

$\frac{(x+5)^2}{36} - \frac{(y-0)^2}{9} = 1$;
hyperbola

10. 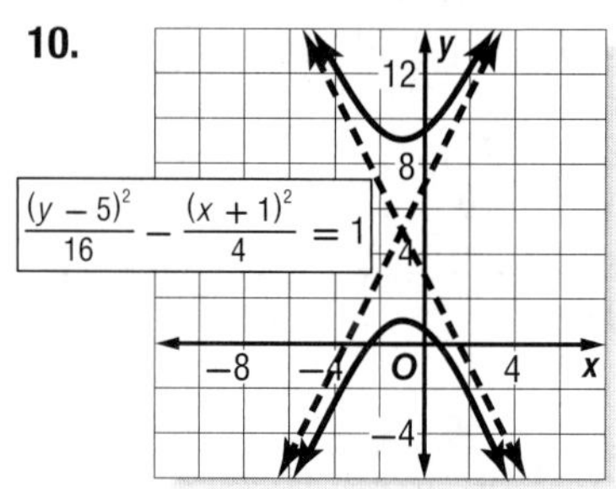

$\frac{(y-5)^2}{16} - \frac{(x+1)^2}{4} = 1$;
hyperbola

11. 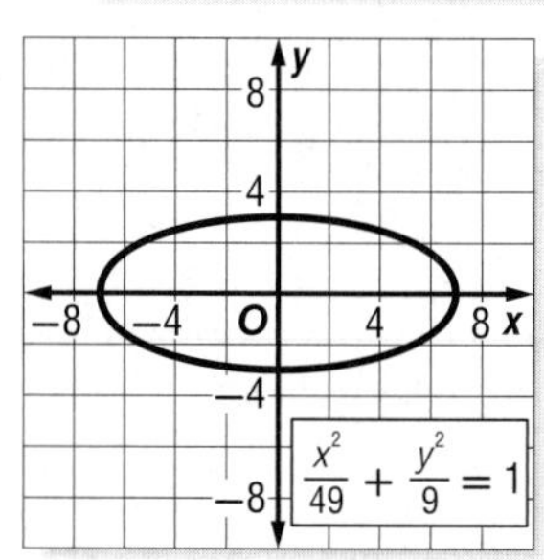

$\frac{x^2}{49} - \frac{y^2}{9} = 1$; ellipse

12. 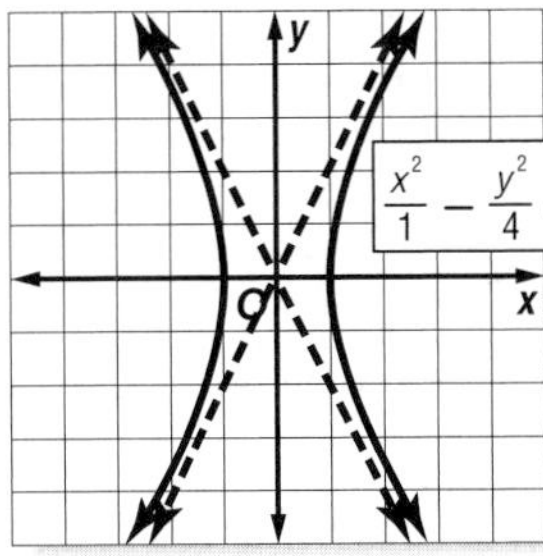

$\frac{x^2}{1} - \frac{y^2}{4} = 1$; hyperbola

Page 969, Extra Practice (Lesson 10-7)

1. 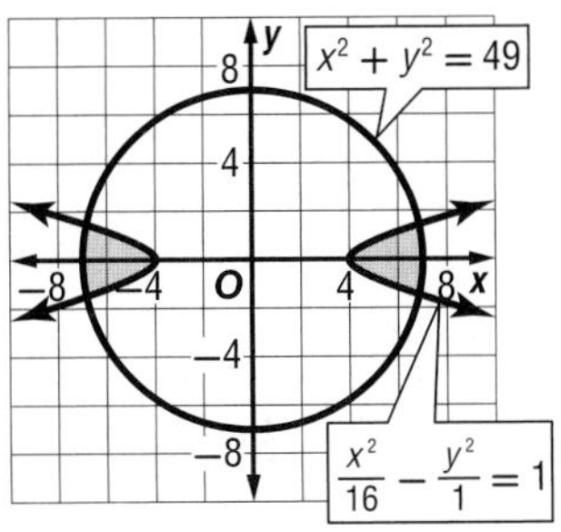

2. 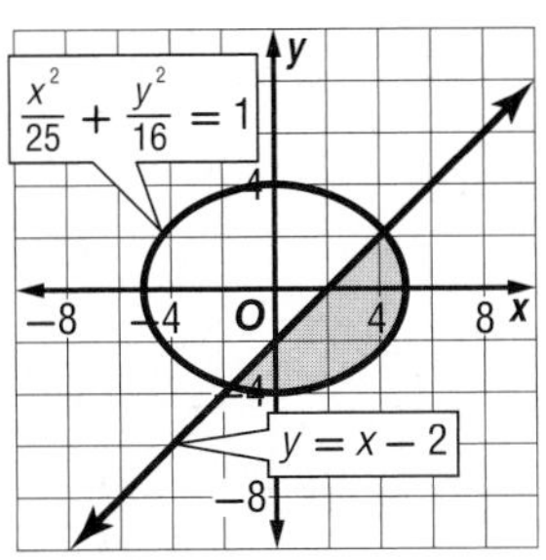

3. 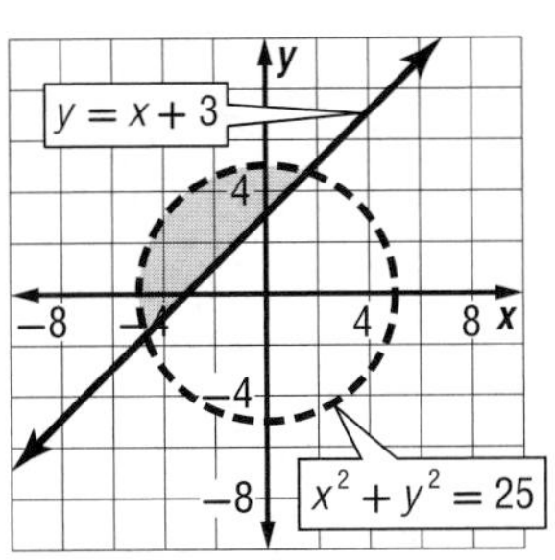

4. 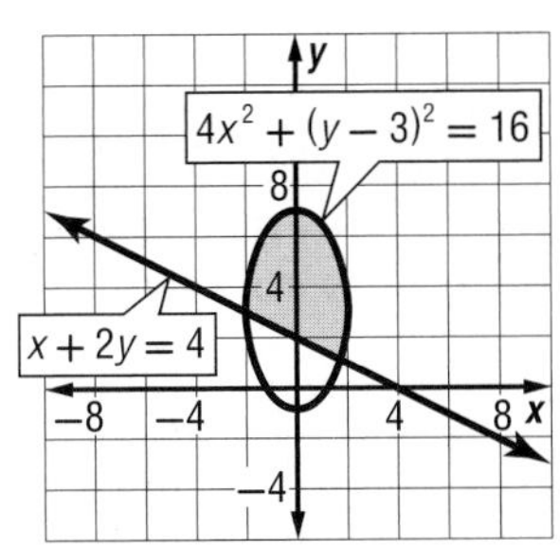

5. $\left(\frac{-3 + \sqrt{23}}{2}, \frac{3 + \sqrt{23}}{2}\right), \left(\frac{-3 - \sqrt{23}}{2}, \frac{3 - \sqrt{23}}{2}\right)$

6. (4, –2), (4, 2)

7. $(\sqrt{111}, 10), (-\sqrt{111}, 10), (\sqrt{15}, 2), (-\sqrt{15}, 2)$

8. $\left(\frac{-3 + \sqrt{30}}{7}, \frac{4 + \sqrt{30}}{7}\right), \left(\frac{-3 - \sqrt{30}}{7}, \frac{4 - \sqrt{30}}{7}\right)$

9. (2, 3), (2, –3), (–2, 3), (–2, –3)

10. no solutions

11. (2, –4), (–1, –1)

12. no solutions

13. (6, 6), (–6, –6)

Page 970, Extra Practice (Lesson 11-3)

1. –2, –12, –72, –432, –2592
2. 4, –20, 100, –500, 2500
3. 0.8, 2, 5, 12.5, 31.25
4. $-\frac{1}{3}, \frac{1}{5}, -\frac{3}{25}, \frac{9}{125}, -\frac{27}{625}$

Page 971, Extra Practice (Lesson 11-6)

1. $z^5 - 15z^4 + 90z^3 - 270z^2 + 405z - 243$
2. $m^4 + 4m^3 + 6m^2 + 4m + 1$
3. $x^4 + 24x^3 + 216x^2 + 864x + 1296$
4. $z^2 - 2zy + y^2$
5. $m^5 + 5m^4p + 10m^3p^2 + 10m^2p^3 + 5mp^4 + p^5$
6. $a^4 - 4a^3b + 6a^2b^2 - 4ab^3 + b^4$
7. $16n^4 + 32n^3 + 24n^2 + 8n + 1$
8. $27n^3 - 108n^2 + 144n - 64$
9. 1
10. $256x^4 - 256x^3a + 96x^2a^2 - 16xa^3 + a^4$
11. $243r^5 - 1620r^4t + 4320r^3t^2 - 5760r^2t^3 + 3840rt^4 - 1024t^5$
12. $\frac{b^4}{16} - \frac{b^3}{2} + \frac{3b^2}{2} - 2b + 1$

Page 971, Extra Practice (Lesson 11-7)

1. **Step 1:** When $n = 1$, the left side of the given equation is 2. The right side is $1^2 + 1$ or 2. Thus, the equation is true for $n = 1$.
Step 2: Assume that $2 + 4 + 6 + \ldots + 2k = k^2 + k$ for some positive integer k.
Step 3: Show that the given equation is true for $n = k + 1$.
$2 + 4 + 6 + \ldots + 2k + 2(k + 1)$
$= k^2 + k + 2(k + 1)$
$= k^2 + k + 2k + 2$
$= k^2 + 2k + 1 + k + 1$
$= (k + 1)^2 + (k + 1)$
The last expression above is the right side of the equation to be proved, where n has been replaced by $k + 1$. Thus, the equation is true for $n = k + 1$. Therefore, $2 + 4 + 6 + \ldots + 2n = n^2 + n$ for all positive integers n.

2. **Step 1:** When $n = 1$, the left side of the given equation is 1^3 or 1. The right side is $1^2[2(1)^2 - 1]$ or 1. Thus, the equation is true for $n = 1$.

Step 2: Assume that $1^3 + 3^3 + 5^3 + \ldots + (2k - 1)^3 = k^2(2k^2 - 1)$ for some positive integer k.

Step 3: Show that the given equation is true for $n = k + 1$.

$1^3 + 3^3 + 5^3 + \ldots + (2k - 1)^3 + [2(k + 1) - 1]^3$
$= k^2(2k^2 - 1) + [2(k + 1) - 1]^3$
$= 2k^4 - k^2 + (2k + 2 - 1)^3$
$= 2k^4 - k^2 + (2k + 1)^3$
$= 2k^4 - k^2 + (8k^3 + 12k^2 + 6k + 1)$
$= 2k^4 + 8k^3 + 11k^2 + 6k + 1$
$= (k^2 + 2k + 1)(2k^2 + 4k + 1)$
$= (k + 1)^2[2(k^2 + 2k + 1) - 1]$
$= (k + 1)^2[2(k + 1)^2 - 1]$

The last expression above is the right side of the equation to be proved, where n has been replaced by $k + 1$. Thus, the equation is true for $n = k + 1$. Therefore, $1^3 + 3^3 + 5^3 + \ldots + (2n - 1)^3 = n^2(2n^2 - 1)$ for all positive integers n.

3. **Step 1:** When $n = 1$, the left side of the given equation is $\frac{1}{1 \cdot 3}$ or $\frac{1}{3}$. The right side is $\frac{1[3(1) + 5]}{4(1 + 1)(1 + 2)}$ or $\frac{1}{3}$. Thus, the equation is true for $n = 1$.

Step 2: Assume that $\frac{1}{1 \cdot 3} + \frac{1}{2 \cdot 4} + \frac{1}{3 \cdot 5} + \ldots + \frac{1}{k(k + 2)} = \frac{k(3k + 5)}{4(k + 1)(k + 2)}$ for some positive integer k.

Step 3: Show that the given equation is true for $n = k + 1$.

$\frac{1}{1 \cdot 3} + \frac{1}{2 \cdot 4} + \frac{1}{3 \cdot 5} + \ldots + \frac{1}{k(k + 2)} + \frac{1}{(k + 1)[(k + 1) + 2]}$
$= \frac{k(3k + 5)}{4(k + 1)(k + 2)} + \frac{1}{(k + 1)[(k + 1) + 2]}$
$= \frac{3k^2 + 5k}{4(k + 1)(k + 2)} + \frac{1}{(k + 1)(k + 3)}$
$= \frac{(3k^2 + 5k)(k + 3) + 4(k + 2)}{4(k + 1)(k + 2)(k + 3)}$
$= \frac{3k^3 + 14k^2 + 15k + 4k + 8}{4(k + 1)(k + 2)(k + 3)}$
$= \frac{3k^3 + 14k^2 + 19k + 8}{4(k + 1)(k + 2)(k + 3)}$
$= \frac{3k^2 + 11k + 8}{4(k + 2)(k + 3)}$
$= \frac{(3k + 8)(k + 1)}{4(k + 2)(k + 3)}$
$= \frac{(k + 1)[3(k + 1) + 5]}{4[(k + 1) + 1][(k + 1) + 2]}$

The last expression above is the right side of the equation to be proved, where n has been replaced by $k + 1$. Thus, the equation is true for $n = k + 1$. Therefore, $\frac{1}{1 \cdot 3} + \frac{1}{2 \cdot 4} + \frac{1}{3 \cdot 5} + \ldots + \frac{1}{n(n + 2)} = \frac{n(3n + 5)}{4(n + 1)(n + 2)}$ for all positive integers n.

4. **Step 1:** When $n = 1$, the left side of the given equation is $1 \cdot 3$ or 3. The right side is $\frac{1(1 + 1)(2 + 7)}{6}$ or 3. Thus, the equation is true for $n = 1$.

Step 2: Assume that $1 \cdot 3 + 2 \cdot 4 + 3 \cdot 5 + \ldots + k(k + 2) = \frac{k(k + 1)(2k + 7)}{6}$ for some positive integer k.

Step 3: Show that the given equation is true for $n = k + 1$.

$1 \cdot 3 + 2 \cdot 4 + 3 \cdot 5 + \ldots + k(k + 2) + (k + 1)[(k + 1) + 2]$
$= \frac{k(k + 1)(2k + 7)}{6} + (k + 1)[(k + 1) + 2]$
$= \frac{2k^3 + 9k^2 + 7k}{6} + k^2 + 4k + 3$
$= \frac{2k^3 + 9k^2 + 7k}{6} + \frac{6(k^2 + 4k + 3)}{6}$
$= \frac{2k^3 + 9k^2 + 7k + 6k^2 + 24k + 18}{6}$
$= \frac{2k^3 + 15k^2 + 31k + 18}{6}$
$= \frac{(k + 1)(2k^2 + 13k + 18)}{6}$
$= \frac{(k + 1)[(k + 2)(2k + 9)]}{6}$
$= \frac{(k + 1)[(k + 1) + 1][2(k + 1) + 7]}{6}$

The last expression above is the right side of the equation to be proved, where n has been replaced by $k + 1$. Thus, the equation is true for $n = k + 1$. Therefore,

$1 \cdot 3 + 2 \cdot 4 + 3 \cdot 5 + \ldots + n(n + 2) = \frac{n(n + 1)(2n + 7)}{6}$ for all positive integers n.

5. **Step 1:** When $n = 1$, the left side of the given equation is $\frac{5}{2} \cdot \frac{1}{3}$ or $\frac{5}{6}$. The right side is $1 - \frac{1}{3(2)}$ or $\frac{5}{6}$. Thus, the equation is true for $n = 1$.

Step 2: Assume that $\frac{5}{1 \cdot 2} \cdot \frac{1}{3} + \frac{7}{2 \cdot 3} \cdot \frac{1}{3^2} + \frac{9}{3 \cdot 4} \cdot \frac{1}{3^3} + \ldots + \frac{2k + 3}{k(k + 1)} \cdot \frac{1}{3^k} = 1 - \frac{1}{3^k(k + 1)}$ for some positive integer k.

Step 3: Show that the given equation is true for $n = k + 1$.

$\frac{5}{1 \cdot 2} \cdot \frac{1}{3} + \frac{7}{2 \cdot 3} \cdot \frac{1}{3^2} + \frac{9}{3 \cdot 4} \cdot \frac{1}{3^3} + \ldots + \frac{2k + 3}{k(k + 1)} \cdot \frac{1}{3^k} + \frac{2(k + 1) + 3}{(k + 1)[(k + 1) + 1]} \cdot \frac{1}{3^{k+1}}$
$= 1 + \frac{-1}{3^k(k + 1)} + \frac{2(k + 1) + 3}{(k + 1)(k + 2)} \cdot \frac{1}{3^{k+1}}$
$= 1 + \frac{(-3)(k + 2) + 2k + 5}{3^{k+1}(k + 1)(k + 2)}$
$= 1 + \frac{(-k - 1)}{3^{k+1}(k + 1)(k + 2)}$
$= 1 - \frac{k + 1}{3^{k+1}(k + 1)(k + 2)}$
$= 1 - \frac{1}{3^{k+1}[(k + 1) + 1]}$

The last expression above is the right side of the equation to be proved, where n has been replaced by $k + 1$. Thus, the equation is true for $n = k + 1$.

Therefore, $\frac{5}{1 \cdot 2} \cdot \frac{1}{3} + \frac{7}{2 \cdot 3} \cdot \frac{1}{3^2} + \frac{9}{3 \cdot 4} \cdot \frac{1}{3^3} + \ldots + \frac{2n + 3}{n(n + 1)} \cdot \frac{1}{3^n} = 1 - \frac{1}{3^n(n + 1)}$ for all positive integers n.

Page 972, Extra Practice (Lesson 12-1)

3. No; people leaving a pizza parlor would probably favor pizza.

Page 972, Extra Practice (Lesson 12-2)

1. Mean; no extreme values
2. Median; there is one value much greater than the rest of the data. Also there is no large gap in the middle of the data
3. Mode; almost all the values are the same
4. Mean; no extreme values

Page 974, Extra Practice (Lesson 13-1)

1. $\sin\theta = \frac{19\sqrt{26}}{130}$; $\cos\theta = \frac{17\sqrt{26}}{130}$; $\tan\theta = \frac{19}{17}$; $\csc\theta = \frac{5\sqrt{26}}{19}$; $\sec\theta = \frac{5\sqrt{26}}{17}$; $\cot\theta = \frac{17}{19}$
2. $\sin\theta = \frac{1}{3}$; $\cos\theta = \frac{2\sqrt{2}}{3}$; $\tan\theta = \frac{\sqrt{2}}{4}$; $\csc\theta = 3$; $\sec\theta = \frac{3\sqrt{2}}{4}$; $\cot\theta = 2\sqrt{2}$
3. $\sin\theta = \frac{\sqrt{21}}{14}$; $\cos\theta = \frac{5\sqrt{7}}{14}$; $\tan\theta = \frac{\sqrt{3}}{5}$; $\csc\theta = \frac{2\sqrt{21}}{3}$; $\sec\theta = \frac{2\sqrt{7}}{5}$; $\cot\theta = \frac{5\sqrt{3}}{3}$

Page 974, Extra Practice (Lesson 13-2)

1.

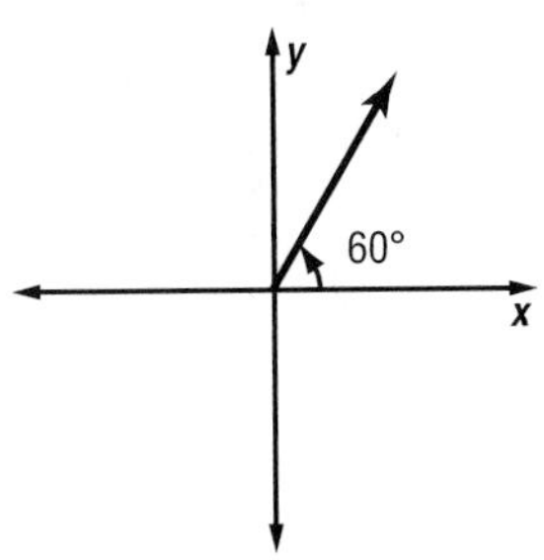

2.

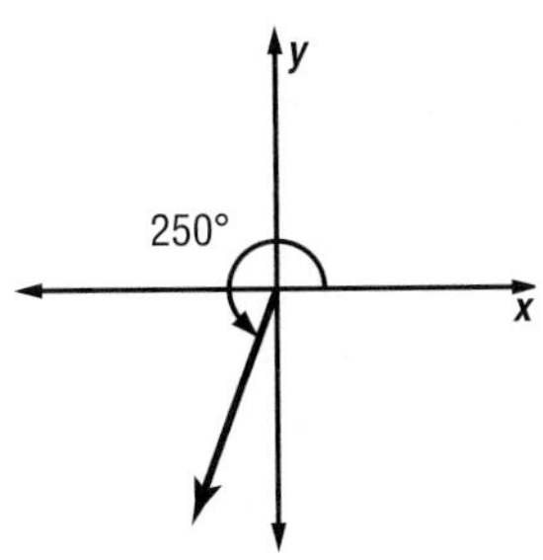

3.

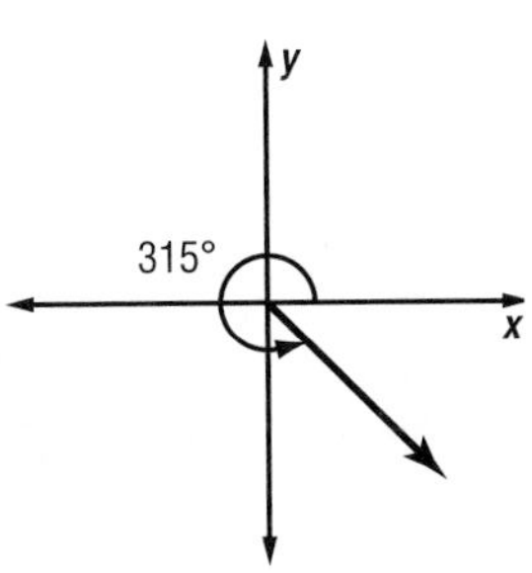

4.

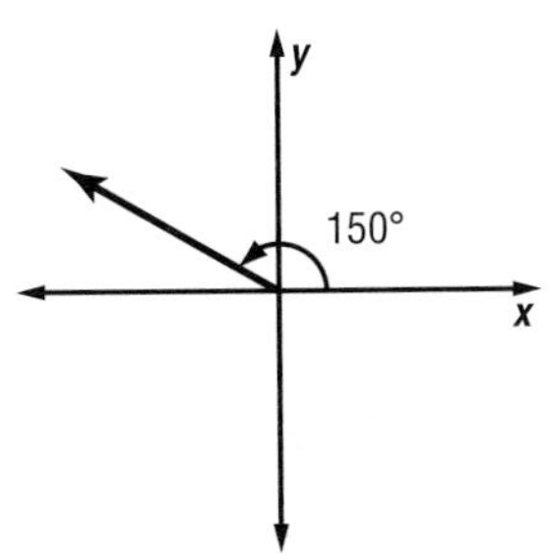

Page 975, Extra Practice (Lesson 13-3)

1. $\sin\theta = -\frac{4}{5}$, $\cos\theta = \frac{3}{5}$, $\tan\theta = -\frac{4}{3}$, $\csc\theta = -\frac{5}{4}$, $\sec\theta = \frac{5}{3}$, $\cot\theta = -\frac{3}{4}$
2. $\sin\theta = \frac{\sqrt{3}}{2}$, $\cos\theta = \frac{1}{2}$, $\tan\theta = \sqrt{3}$, $\csc\theta = \frac{2\sqrt{3}}{3}$, $\sec\theta = 2$, $\cot\theta = \frac{\sqrt{3}}{3}$
3. $\sin\theta = 1$, $\cos\theta = 0$, $\tan\theta$ undefined, $\csc\theta = 1$, $\sec\theta$ undefined, $\cot\theta = 0$
4. $\sin\theta = -\frac{\sqrt{2}}{2}$, $\cos\theta = \frac{\sqrt{2}}{2}$, $\tan\theta = -1$, $\csc\theta = -\sqrt{2}$, $\sec\theta = \sqrt{2}$, $\cot\theta = -1$
5. $\sin\theta = -\frac{\sqrt{2}}{2}$, $\cos\theta = -\frac{\sqrt{2}}{2}$, $\tan\theta = 1$, $\csc\theta = -\sqrt{2}$, $\sec\theta = -\sqrt{2}$, $\cot\theta = 1$

11. $\sin\theta = -\frac{2\sqrt{2}}{3}$, $\tan\theta = 2\sqrt{2}$, $\csc\theta = -\frac{3\sqrt{2}}{4}$, $\sec\theta = -3$, $\cot\theta = \frac{\sqrt{2}}{4}$
12. $\sin\theta = -\frac{\sqrt{3}}{2}$, $\cos\theta = \frac{1}{2}$, $\tan\theta = -\sqrt{3}$, $\csc\theta = -\frac{2\sqrt{3}}{3}$, $\cot\theta = -\frac{\sqrt{3}}{3}$
13. $\cos\theta = -\frac{\sqrt{5}}{3}$, $\tan\theta = -\frac{2\sqrt{5}}{5}$, $\csc\theta = \frac{3}{2}$, $\sec\theta = -\frac{3\sqrt{5}}{5}$, $\cot\theta = -\frac{\sqrt{5}}{2}$
14. $\sin\theta = -\frac{4\sqrt{17}}{17}$, $\cos\theta = \frac{\sqrt{17}}{17}$, $\csc\theta = -\frac{\sqrt{17}}{4}$, $\sec\theta = \sqrt{17}$, $\cot\theta = -\frac{1}{4}$
15. $\sin\theta = -\frac{1}{5}$, $\cos\theta = -\frac{2\sqrt{6}}{5}$, $\tan\theta = \frac{\sqrt{6}}{12}$, $\sec\theta = -\frac{5\sqrt{6}}{12}$, $\cot\theta = 2\sqrt{6}$
16. $\sin\theta = \frac{\sqrt{5}}{5}$, $\cos\theta = -\frac{2\sqrt{5}}{5}$, $\tan\theta = -\frac{1}{2}$, $\csc\theta = \sqrt{5}$, $\sec\theta = -\frac{\sqrt{5}}{2}$
17. $\sin\theta = -\frac{\sqrt{10}}{10}$, $\cos\theta = -\frac{3\sqrt{10}}{10}$, $\csc\theta = -\sqrt{10}$, $\sec\theta = -\frac{\sqrt{10}}{3}$, $\cot\theta = 3$
18. $\sin\theta = \frac{\sqrt{15}}{4}$, $\tan\theta = \sqrt{15}$, $\csc\theta = \frac{4\sqrt{15}}{15}$, $\sec\theta = 4$, $\cot\theta = \frac{\sqrt{15}}{15}$
19. $\sin\theta = -\frac{2}{5}$, $\cos\theta = \frac{\sqrt{21}}{5}$, $\tan\theta = -\frac{2\sqrt{21}}{21}$, $\sec\theta = \frac{5\sqrt{21}}{21}$, $\cot\theta = -\frac{\sqrt{21}}{2}$

Page 975, Extra Practice (Lesson 13-4)

4. $C = 125°$, $b \approx 29.2$, $c \approx 39.8$
5. $B = 95°$, $a \approx 6.1$, $b \approx 7.1$
6. $A = 108°$, $a \approx 14.8$, $c \approx 8.2$
7. $A = 147°$, $a \approx 11.2$, $b \approx 3.6$

8. $C = 108°$, $a \approx 1.2$, $c \approx 5.5$

9. $B = 100°$, $b \approx 51.5$, $c \approx 37.0$

10. one solution; $C = 80°$, $a \approx 13.1$, $b \approx 17.6$

11. one solution; $A = 52°$, $b = 100.2$, $c = 90.4$

12. no solution

13. two solutions; $B \approx 71°$, $C \approx 51°$, $c = 23.8$; $B \approx 109°$, $C \approx 13°$, $c \approx 6.9$

14. one solution; $C = 79°$, $a \approx 9.4$, $b \approx 13.6$

15. no solution

16. no solution

17. two solutions; $B \approx 30°$, $C \approx 125°$, $c \approx 243.8$; $B \approx 150°$, $C \approx 5°$, $c \approx 28.3$

18. one solution; $A \approx 44.8°$, $B \approx 37.2°$, $b \approx 54.9$

19. one solution; $C = 71°$, $a \approx 9.1$, $b \approx 11.3$

20. no solution

21. one solution; $B \approx 42°$, $C \approx 93°$, $c \approx 117.2$

Page 975, Extra Practice (Lesson 13-5)

1. cosines; $a \approx 36.9$, $B \approx 57°$, $C \approx 72°$
2. cosines; $A \approx 53°$, $B = 90°$, $C \approx 37°$
3. cosines; $a \approx 18.5$, $B \approx 79°$, $C \approx 41°$
4. cosines; $A \approx 54°$, $B \approx 60°$, $C \approx 67°$
5. sines; $A = 87°$, $a \approx 34.2$, $b \approx 22.5$
6. cosines; $A \approx 48°$, $B \approx 73°$, $C \approx 59°$
7. sines; $b \approx 18.6$, $B \approx 33°$, $C \approx 35°$
8. cosines; $a \approx 3.8$, $B \approx 91°$, $C \approx 61°$
9. cosines; $A \approx 44°$, $B \approx 57°$, $C \approx 79°$
10. cosines; $A \approx 110°$, $B \approx 45°$, $c \approx 5.4$
11. sines; $C = 73°$, $b \approx 9.0$, $c \approx 10.1$
12. cosines; $a \approx 107.1$, $B \approx 49°$, $C \approx 89°$
13. sines; $B = 80°$, $a \approx 6.3$, $b \approx 10.9$
14. cosines; $A \approx 32°$, $B \approx 57°$, $C \approx 91°$
15. cosines; $A \approx 55°$, $C \approx 80°$, $b \approx 34.5$
16. cosines; $A \approx 46°$, $C \approx 35°$, $b \approx 13.8$
17. sines; $C = 95°$, $a \approx 2.6$, $b \approx 2.8$
18. cosines; $B \approx 106°$, $C \approx 54°$, $a \approx 35.6$

Page 976, Extra Practice (Lesson 13-6)

1. $\sin\theta = \frac{3}{5}$, $\cos\theta = \frac{4}{5}$

2. $\sin\theta = -\frac{5}{13}$, $\cos\theta = \frac{12}{13}$

3. $\sin\theta = -\frac{15}{17}$, $\cos\theta = -\frac{8}{17}$

4. $\sin\theta = \frac{2\sqrt{10}}{7}$, $\cos\theta = \frac{3}{7}$

5. $\sin\theta = \frac{\sqrt{5}}{3}$, $\cos\theta = -\frac{2}{3}$

Page 976, Extra Practice (Lesson 13-7)

1.
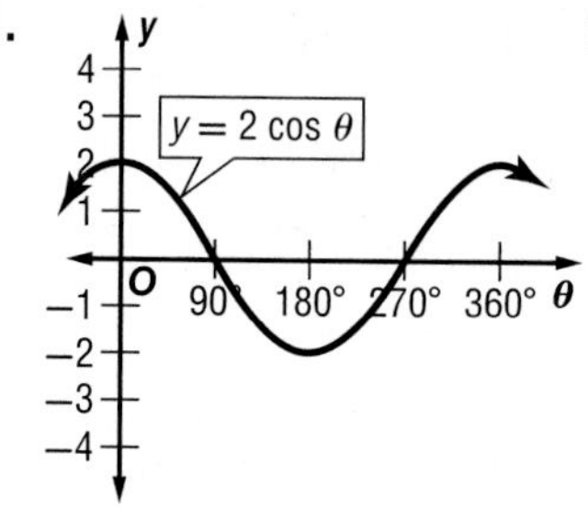

2.
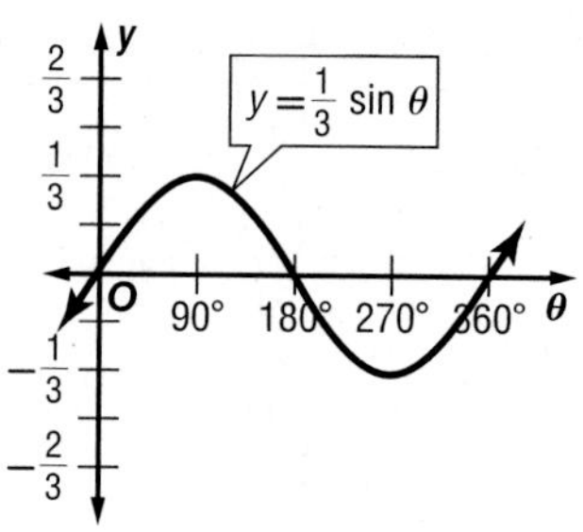

3.
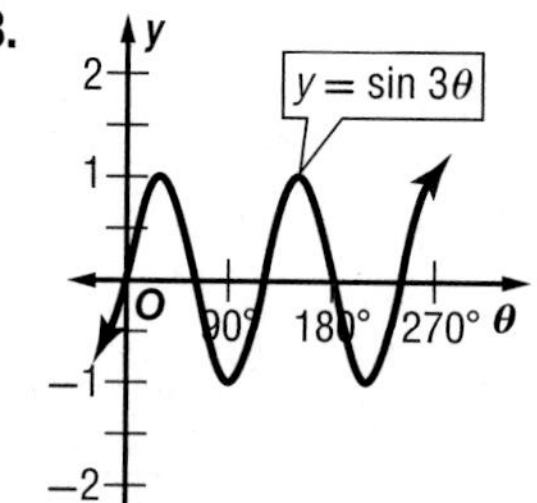

4.
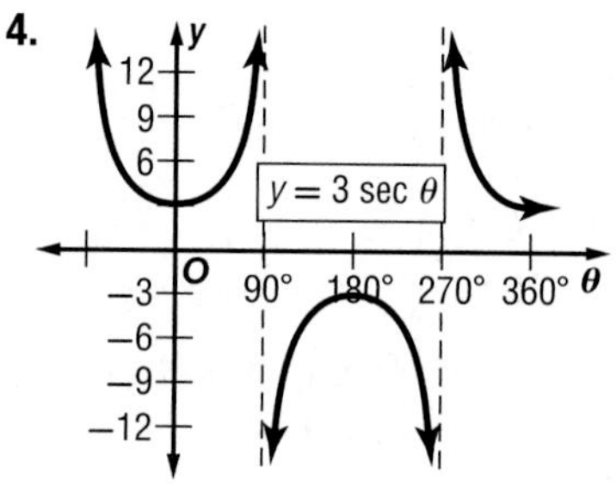

5.
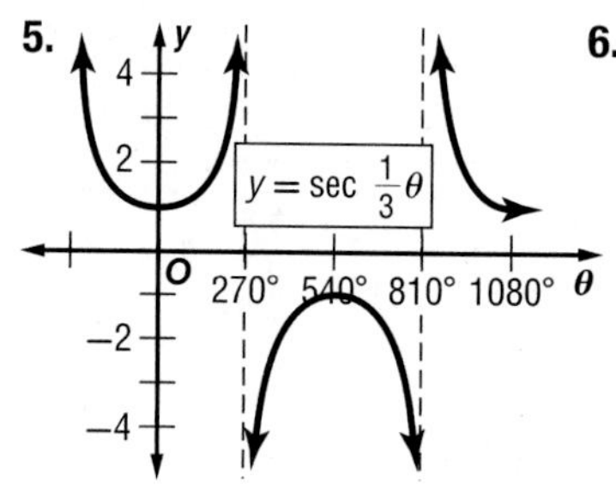

6.
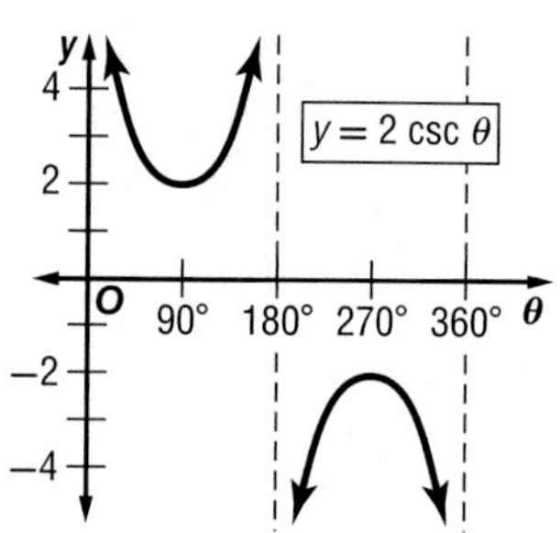

7.
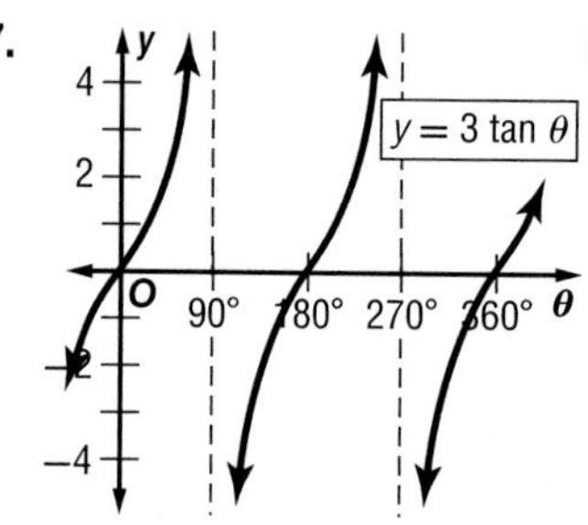

8.
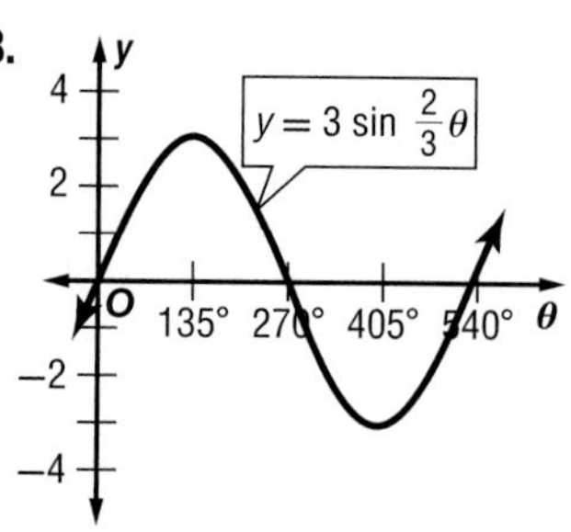

9.
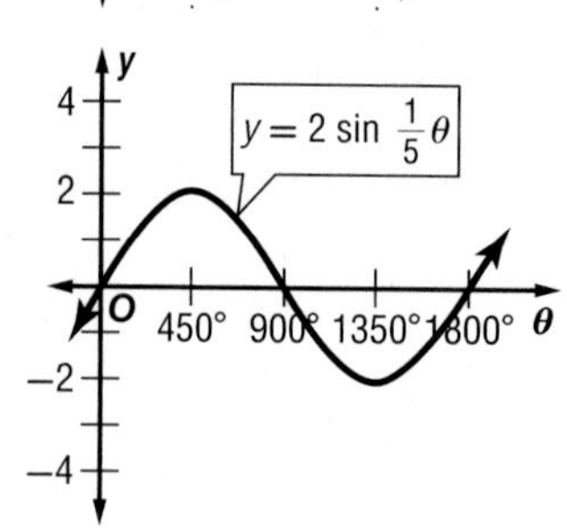

10.
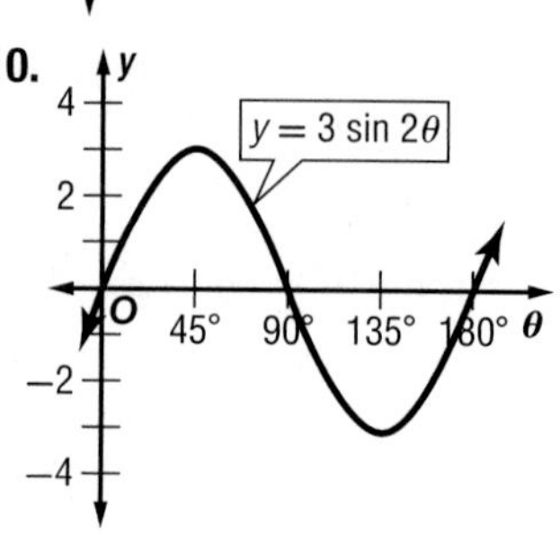

11.
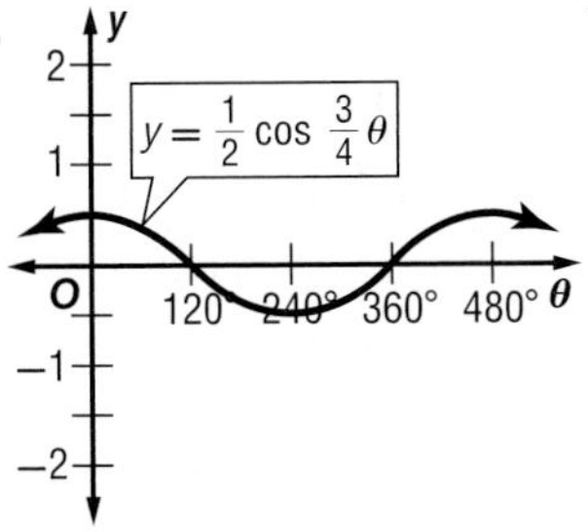

12.
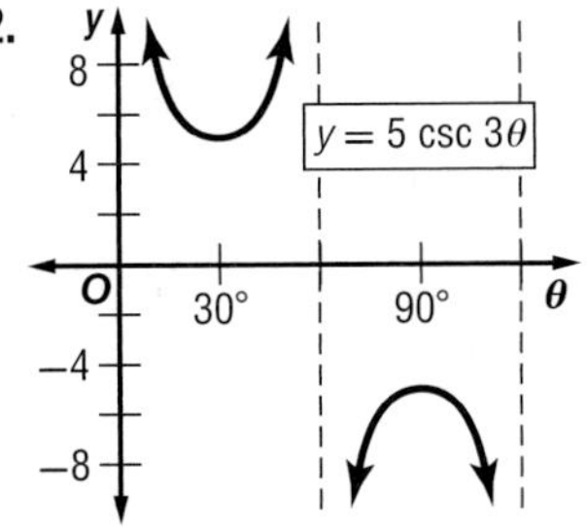

13.
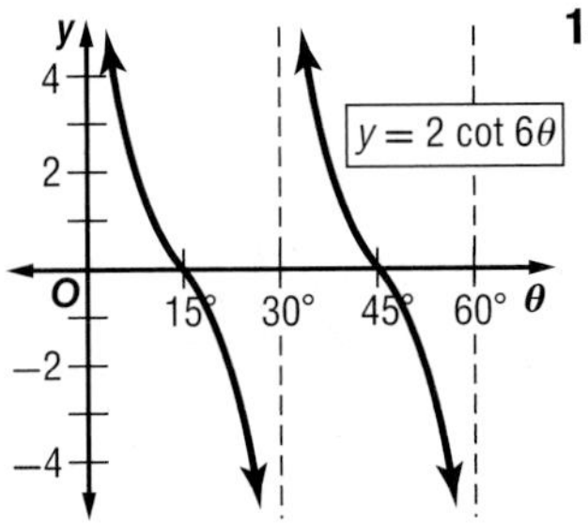

14.
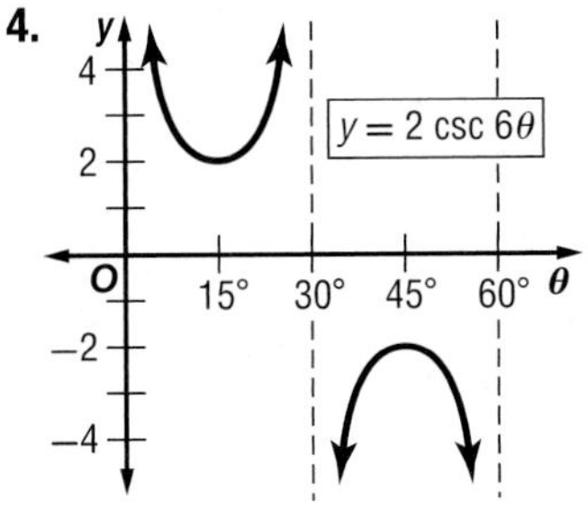

15.
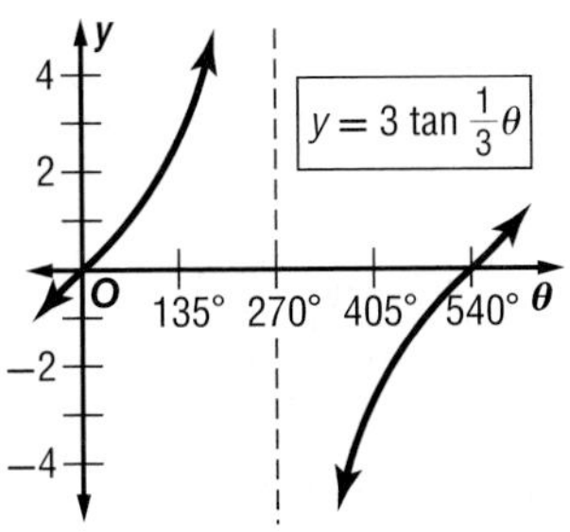

Page 976, Extra Practice (Lesson 13-8)

1.
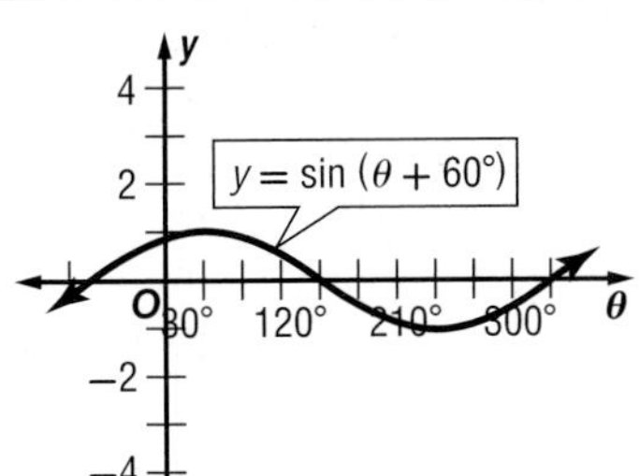

2.
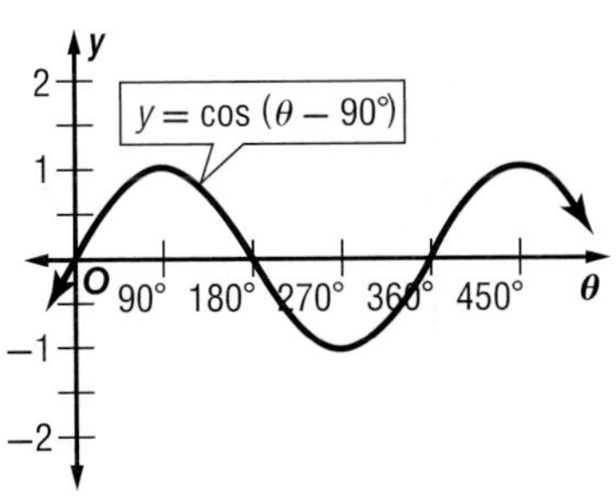

3.
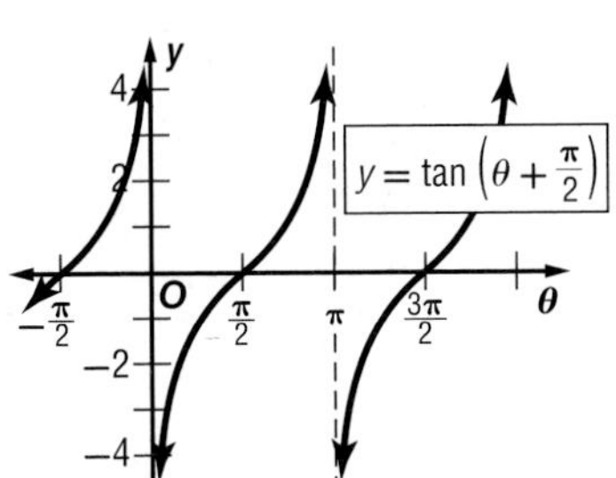

4.
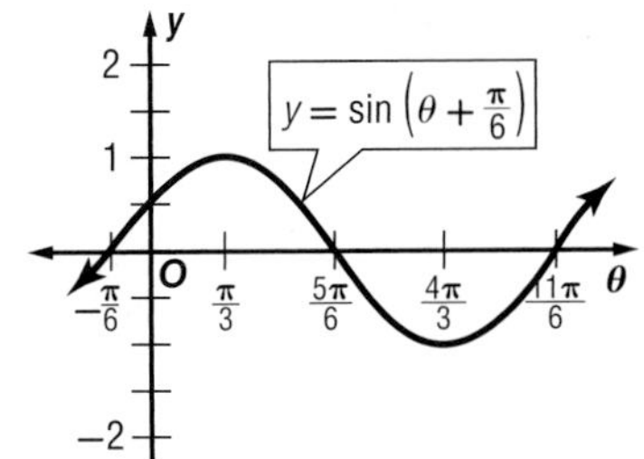

5. 1; 360°; 3; $y = 3$

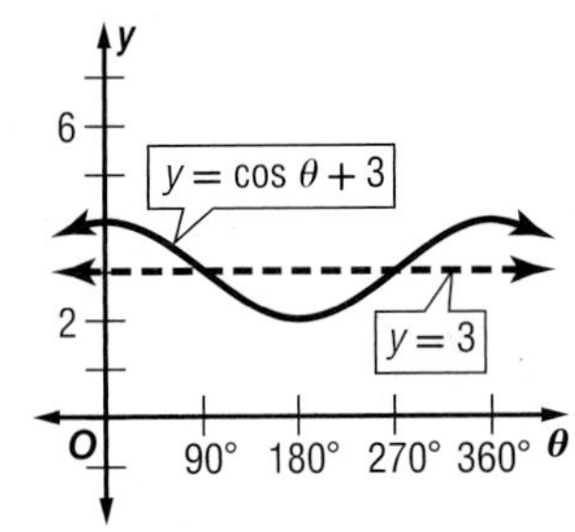

6. 1; 360°; –2; $y = -2$

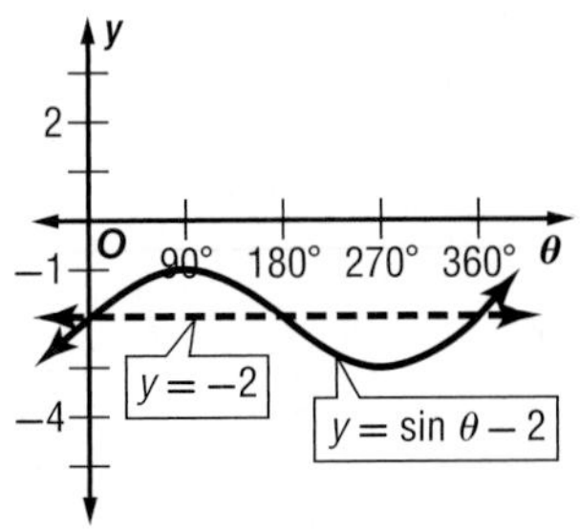

7. none; 360°; 5; $y = 5$

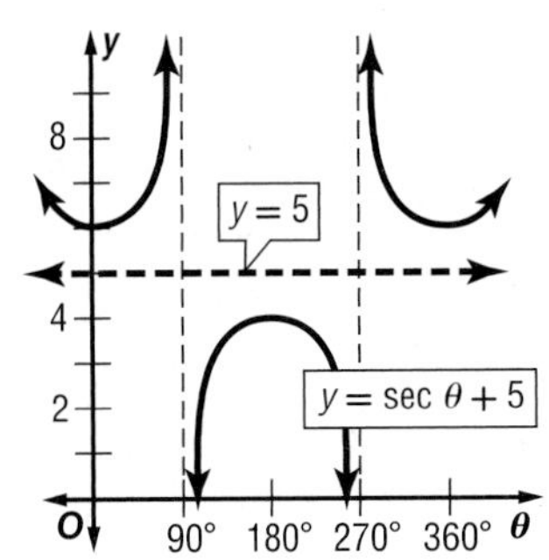

8. none; 360°; –6; $y = -6$

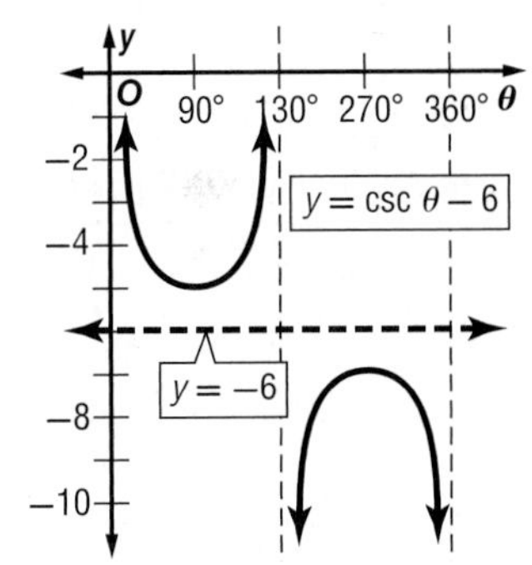

9. 2; 360°; –4; $y = -4$

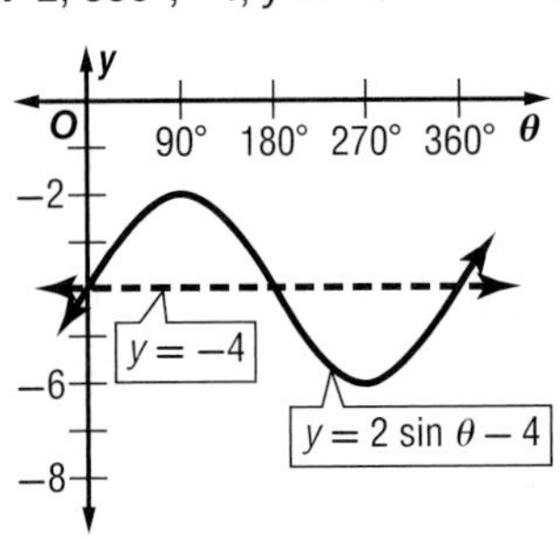

10. $\frac{1}{3}$; 360°; 7; $y = 7$

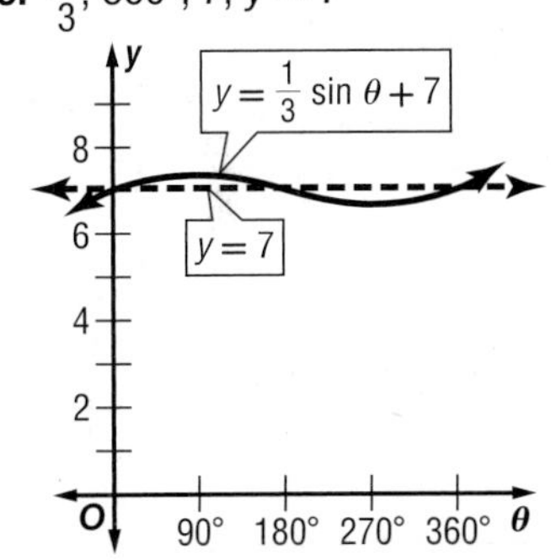

11. 3; 180°; 4; –30°

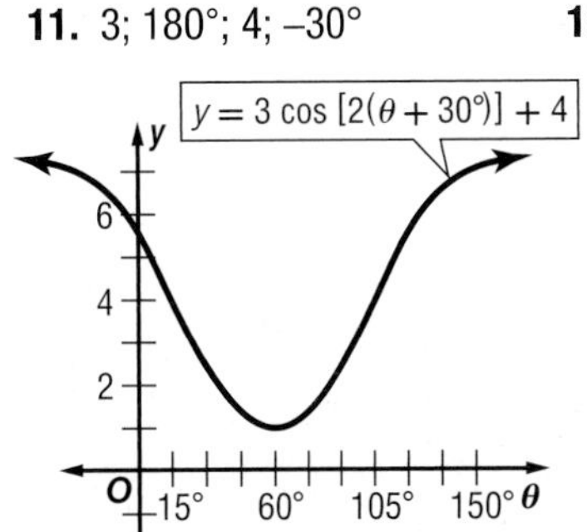

12. none; 60°; –2; 60°

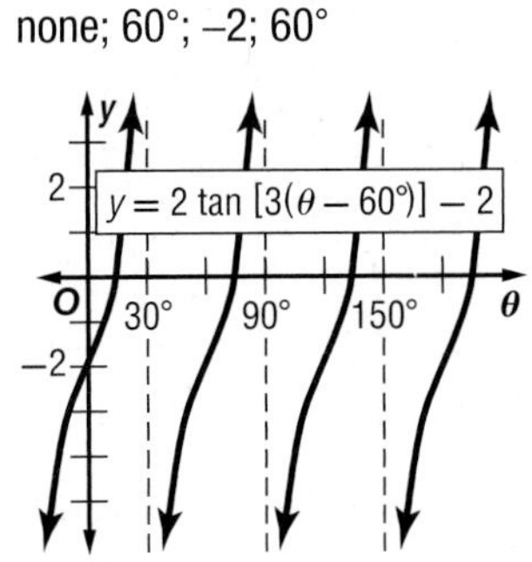

13. $\frac{1}{2}$; 90°; 1; 45°

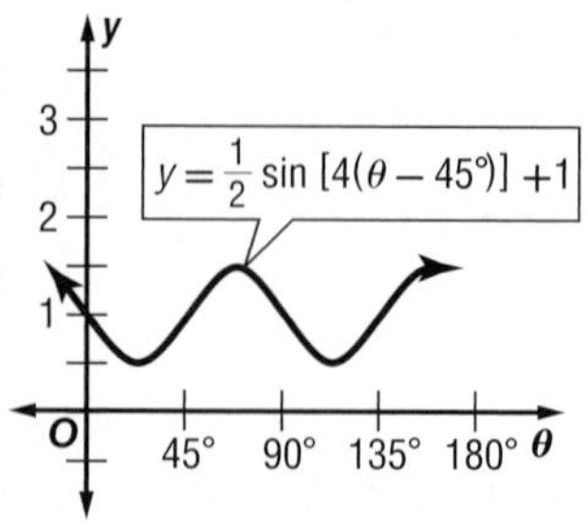

14. $\frac{2}{5}$; 60°; –5; –45°

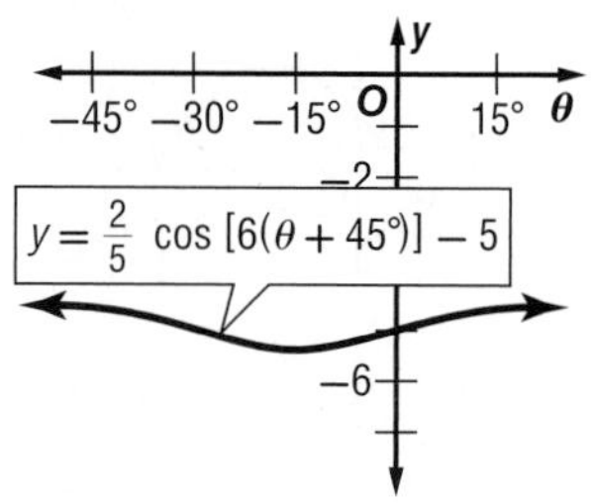

15. 2; $\frac{2\pi}{3}$; 6; $-\frac{\pi}{2}$

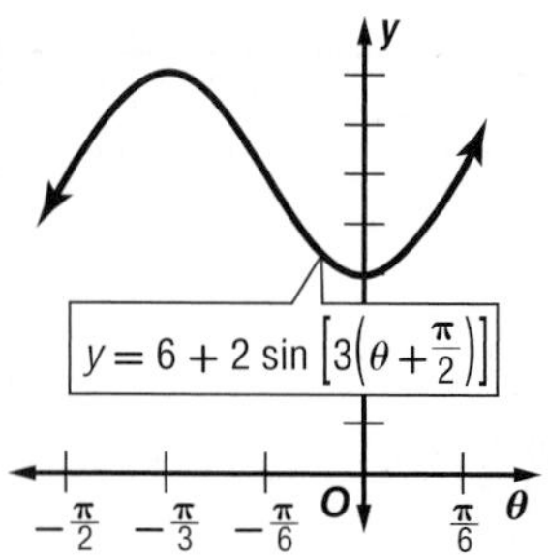

16. 3; π; 3; $\frac{\pi}{3}$

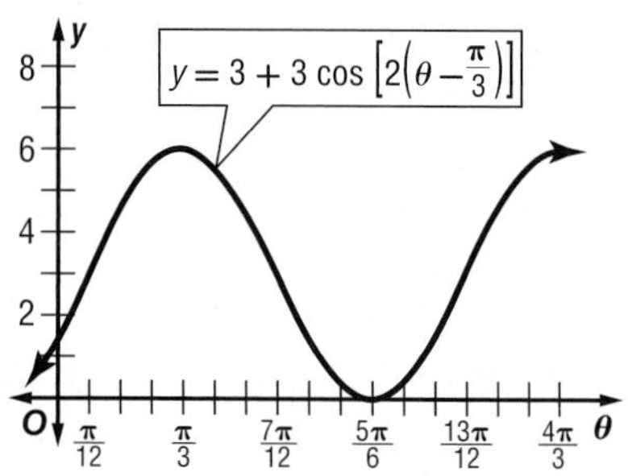

Page 977, Extra Practice (Lesson 14-2)

1. $\sin^2\theta + \cos^2\theta + \tan^2\theta \stackrel{?}{=} \sec^2\theta$

$1 + \tan^2\theta \stackrel{?}{=} \sec^2\theta$

$\sec^2\theta = \sec^2\theta$ ✓

2. $\frac{\tan\theta}{\sin\theta} \stackrel{?}{=} \sec\theta$

$\frac{\sin\theta}{\cos\theta} \cdot \frac{1}{\sin\theta} \stackrel{?}{=} \sec\theta$

$\frac{1}{\cos\theta} \stackrel{?}{=} \sec\theta$

$\sec\theta = \sec\theta$ ✓

3. $\frac{\tan\theta}{\cot\theta} \stackrel{?}{=} \tan^2\theta$

$\tan\theta \div \cot\theta \stackrel{?}{=} \tan^2\theta$

$\tan\theta \div \frac{1}{\tan\theta} \stackrel{?}{=} \tan^2\theta$

$\tan\theta \cdot \tan\theta = \tan^2\theta$ ✓

4. $\csc^2\theta\,(1 - \cos^2\theta) \stackrel{?}{=} 1$

$\csc^2\theta\,(\sin^2\theta) \stackrel{?}{=} 1$

$\frac{1}{\sin^2\theta}(\sin^2\theta) \stackrel{?}{=} 1$

$1 = 1$ ✓

5. $1 - \cot^4\theta \stackrel{?}{=} 2\csc^2\theta - \csc^4\theta$

$(1 - \cot^2\theta)(1 + \cot^2\theta) \stackrel{?}{=} 2\csc^2\theta - \csc^4\theta$

$(1 - \cot^2\theta)(\csc^2\theta) \stackrel{?}{=} 2\csc^2\theta - \csc^4\theta$

$[1 - (\csc^2\theta - 1)](\csc^2\theta) \stackrel{?}{=} 2\csc^2\theta - \csc^4\theta$

$(2 - \csc^2\theta)(\csc^2\theta) \stackrel{?}{=} 2\csc^2\theta - \csc^4\theta$

$2\csc^2\theta - \csc^4\theta = 2\csc^2\theta - \csc^4\theta$ ✓

6. $\sin^4\theta - \cos^4\theta \stackrel{?}{=} \sin^2\theta - \cos^2\theta$

$(\sin^2\theta - \cos^2\theta)(\sin^2\theta + \cos^2\theta) \stackrel{?}{=} \sin^2\theta - \cos^2\theta$

$(\sin^2\theta - \cos^2\theta)(1) \stackrel{?}{=} \sin^2\theta - \cos^2\theta$

$\sin^2\theta - \cos^2\theta = \sin^2\theta - \cos^2\theta$ ✓

7. $\sin^2\theta + \cot^2\theta\sin^2\theta \stackrel{?}{=} 1$

$\sin^2\theta\,(1 + \cot^2\theta) \stackrel{?}{=} 1$

$\sin^2\theta\,(\csc^2\theta) \stackrel{?}{=} 1$

$\sin^2\theta\left(\frac{1}{\sin^2\theta}\right) \stackrel{?}{=} 1$

$1 = 1$ ✓

8. $\frac{\cos\theta}{\csc\theta} - \frac{\csc\theta}{\sec\theta} \stackrel{?}{=} -\frac{\cos^3\theta}{\sin\theta}$

$\left(\cos\theta \div \frac{1}{\sin\theta}\right) - \left(\frac{1}{\sin\theta} \div \frac{1}{\cos\theta}\right) \stackrel{?}{=} -\frac{\cos^3\theta}{\sin\theta}$

$(\cos\theta \cdot \sin\theta) - \left(\frac{1}{\sin\theta} \cdot \cos\theta\right) \stackrel{?}{=} -\frac{\cos^3\theta}{\sin\theta}$

$\cos\theta\sin\theta - \frac{\cos\theta}{\sin\theta} \stackrel{?}{=} -\frac{\cos^3\theta}{\sin\theta}$

$\frac{\cos\theta\sin^2\theta - \cos\theta}{\sin\theta} \stackrel{?}{=} -\frac{\cos^3\theta}{\sin\theta}$

$\frac{-\cos\theta\,(1 - \sin^2\theta)}{\sin\theta} \stackrel{?}{=} -\frac{\cos^3\theta}{\sin\theta}$

$\frac{-\cos\theta(\cos^2\theta)}{\sin\theta} \stackrel{?}{=} -\frac{\cos^3\theta}{\sin\theta}$

$-\frac{\cos^3\theta}{\sin\theta} = -\frac{\cos^3\theta}{\sin\theta}$ ✓

9. $\frac{\cos\theta}{\sec\theta - 1} + \frac{\cos\theta}{\sec\theta + 1} \stackrel{?}{=} 2\cot^2\theta$

$\frac{\cos\theta(\sec\theta + 1) + \cos\theta(\sec\theta - 1)}{\sec^2\theta - 1} \stackrel{?}{=} 2\cot^2\theta$

$\frac{\cos\theta\sec\theta + \cos\theta + \cos\theta\sec\theta - \cos\theta}{\tan^2\theta} \stackrel{?}{=} 2\cot^2\theta$

$\frac{2}{\tan^2\theta} \stackrel{?}{=} 2\cot^2\theta$

$2\cot^2\theta = 2\cot^2\theta$ ✓

10. $\frac{1 + \cos\theta}{\sin\theta} \stackrel{?}{=} \frac{\sin\theta}{1 - \cos\theta}$

$\left(\frac{1 - \cos\theta}{1 - \cos\theta}\right)\left(\frac{1 + \cos\theta}{\sin\theta}\right) \stackrel{?}{=} \frac{\sin\theta}{1 - \cos\theta}$

$\frac{1 - \cos^2\theta}{\sin\theta\,(1 - \cos\theta)} \stackrel{?}{=} \frac{\sin\theta}{1 - \cos\theta}$

$\frac{\sin^2\theta}{\sin\theta\,(1 - \cos\theta)} \stackrel{?}{=} \frac{\sin\theta}{1 - \cos\theta}$

$\frac{\sin\theta}{1 - \cos\theta} = \frac{\sin\theta}{1 - \cos\theta}$ ✓

11. $$\sec\theta + \tan\theta \stackrel{?}{=} \frac{\cos\theta}{1-\sin\theta}$$
$$\frac{1}{\cos\theta} + \frac{\sin\theta}{\cos\theta} \stackrel{?}{=} \frac{\cos\theta}{1-\sin\theta}$$
$$\frac{1+\sin\theta}{\cos\theta} \stackrel{?}{=} \frac{\cos\theta}{1-\sin\theta}$$
$$\left(\frac{1-\sin\theta}{1-\sin\theta}\right)\left(\frac{1+\sin\theta}{\cos\theta}\right) \stackrel{?}{=} \frac{\cos\theta}{1-\sin\theta}$$
$$\frac{1-\sin^2\theta}{\cos\theta(1-\sin\theta)} \stackrel{?}{=} \frac{\cos\theta}{1-\sin\theta}$$
$$\frac{\cos^2\theta}{\cos\theta(1-\sin\theta)} \stackrel{?}{=} \frac{\cos\theta}{1-\sin\theta}$$
$$\frac{\cos\theta}{1-\sin\theta} = \frac{\cos\theta}{1-\sin\theta} \checkmark$$

12. $\tan\theta + \cot\theta \stackrel{?}{=} \csc\theta\sec\theta$
$$\frac{\sin\theta}{\cos\theta} + \frac{\cos\theta}{\sin\theta} \stackrel{?}{=} \csc\theta\sec\theta$$
$$\frac{\sin^2\theta+\cos^2\theta}{\cos\theta\sin\theta} \stackrel{?}{=} \csc\theta\sec\theta$$
$$\frac{1}{\cos\theta\sin\theta} \stackrel{?}{=} \csc\theta\sec\theta$$
$$\frac{1}{\cos\theta}\cdot\frac{1}{\sin\theta} \stackrel{?}{=} \csc\theta\sec\theta$$
$$\sec\theta\csc\theta \stackrel{?}{=} \csc\theta\sec\theta$$
$$\csc\theta\sec\theta = \csc\theta\sec\theta \checkmark$$

13. $$\frac{\cot^2\theta}{1+\cot^2\theta} \stackrel{?}{=} 1-\sin^2\theta$$
$$\frac{\cot^2\theta}{\csc^2\theta} \stackrel{?}{=} 1-\sin^2\theta$$
$$\frac{\cos^2\theta}{\sin^2\theta} \div \frac{1}{\sin^2\theta} \stackrel{?}{=} 1-\sin^2\theta$$
$$\frac{\cos^2\theta}{\sin^2\theta}\cdot\sin^2\theta \stackrel{?}{=} 1-\sin^2\theta$$
$$1-\sin^2\theta = 1-\sin^2\theta \checkmark$$

14. $$\frac{\tan\theta-\sin\theta}{\sec\theta} \stackrel{?}{=} \frac{\sin^3\theta}{1-\cos\theta}$$
$$\left(\frac{\sin\theta}{\cos\theta}-\sin\theta\right) \div \frac{1}{\cos\theta} \stackrel{?}{=} \frac{\sin^3\theta}{1-\cos\theta}$$
$$\left(\frac{\sin\theta-\sin\theta\cos\theta}{\cos\theta}\right)\cdot\cos\theta \stackrel{?}{=} \frac{\sin^3\theta}{1-\cos\theta}$$
$$\sin\theta-\sin\theta\cos\theta \stackrel{?}{=} \frac{\sin^3\theta}{1-\cos\theta}$$
$$\left(\frac{1+\cos\theta}{1+\cos\theta}\right)(\sin\theta-\sin\theta\cos\theta) \stackrel{?}{=} \frac{\sin^3\theta}{1-\cos\theta}$$
$$\frac{(1+\cos\theta)(1-\cos\theta)(\sin\theta)}{1+\cos\theta} \stackrel{?}{=} \frac{\sin^3\theta}{1-\cos\theta}$$
$$\frac{(1-\cos^2\theta)(\sin\theta)}{1+\cos\theta} \stackrel{?}{=} \frac{\sin^3\theta}{1-\cos\theta}$$
$$\frac{\sin^2\theta(\sin\theta)}{1+\cos\theta} \stackrel{?}{=} \frac{\sin^3\theta}{1-\cos\theta}$$
$$\frac{\sin^3\theta}{1-\cos\theta} = \frac{\sin^3\theta}{1-\cos\theta} \checkmark$$

15. $\sin^2\theta(1-\cos^2\theta) \stackrel{?}{=} \sin^4\theta$
$$\sin^2\theta(\sin^2\theta) \stackrel{?}{=} \sin^4\theta$$
$$\sin^4\theta = \sin^4\theta \checkmark$$

16. $\sin^2\theta + \sin^2\theta\tan^2\theta \stackrel{?}{=} \tan^2\theta$
$$\sin^2\theta(1+\tan^2\theta) \stackrel{?}{=} \tan^2\theta$$
$$\sin^2\theta(\sec^2\theta) \stackrel{?}{=} \tan^2\theta$$
$$\sin^2\theta\left(\frac{1}{\cos^2\theta}\right) \stackrel{?}{=} \tan^2\theta$$
$$\frac{\sin^2\theta}{\cos^2\theta} \stackrel{?}{=} \tan^2\theta$$
$$\tan^2\theta = \tan^2\theta \checkmark$$

17. $$\frac{\sec\theta-1}{\sec\theta+1} + \frac{\cos\theta-1}{\cos\theta+1} \stackrel{?}{=} 0$$
$$\frac{(\sec\theta-1)(\cos\theta+1)+(\cos\theta-1)(\sec\theta+1)}{(\sec\theta+1)(\cos\theta+1)} \stackrel{?}{=} 0$$
$$\frac{1+\sec\theta-\cos\theta-1+1-\sec\theta+\cos\theta-1}{(\sec\theta+1)(\cos\theta+1)} \stackrel{?}{=} 0$$
$$0 = 0 \checkmark$$

18. $\tan^2\theta(1-\sin^2\theta) \stackrel{?}{=} \sin^2\theta$
$$\tan^2\theta(\cos^2\theta) \stackrel{?}{=} \sin^2\theta$$
$$\frac{\sin^2\theta}{\cos^2\theta}(\cos^2\theta) \stackrel{?}{=} \sin^2\theta$$
$$\sin^2\theta = \sin^2\theta \checkmark$$

Page 978, Extra Practice (Lesson 14-3)

1. $\frac{\sqrt{2}-\sqrt{6}}{4}$
2. $\frac{\sqrt{6}-\sqrt{2}}{4}$
3. $\frac{-\sqrt{2}-\sqrt{6}}{4}$
4. $\frac{\sqrt{6}+\sqrt{2}}{4}$
5. $\frac{\sqrt{6}+\sqrt{2}}{4}$
6. $\frac{\sqrt{6}-\sqrt{2}}{4}$
7. $\frac{\sqrt{6}+\sqrt{2}}{4}$
8. $\frac{\sqrt{6}-\sqrt{2}}{4}$
9. $\frac{\sqrt{2}}{2}$
10. $-\frac{\sqrt{3}}{2}$
11. $-\frac{\sqrt{2}}{2}$
12. $-\frac{1}{2}$

13. $$\sin(90° + \theta) \stackrel{?}{=} \cos\theta$$
$$\sin 90°\cos\theta + \cos 90°\sin\theta \stackrel{?}{=} \cos\theta$$
$$(1)\cos\theta + (0)\sin\theta \stackrel{?}{=} \cos\theta$$
$$\cos\theta = \cos\theta \checkmark$$

14. $$\cos(180° - \theta) \stackrel{?}{=} -\cos\theta$$
$$\cos 180°\cos\theta + \sin 180°\sin\theta \stackrel{?}{=} -\cos\theta$$
$$(-1)\cos\theta + (0)\sin\theta \stackrel{?}{=} -\cos\theta$$
$$-\cos\theta = -\cos\theta \checkmark$$

15. $$\sin(\pi + \theta) \stackrel{?}{=} -\sin\theta$$
$$\sin\pi\cos\theta + \cos\pi\sin\theta \stackrel{?}{=} -\sin\theta$$
$$(0)\cos\theta + (-1)\sin\theta \stackrel{?}{=} -\sin\theta$$
$$-\sin\theta = -\sin\theta \checkmark$$

16. $\sin(\theta + 30°) + \sin(\theta + 60°) \stackrel{?}{=} \frac{\sqrt{3}+1}{2}(\sin\theta + \cos\theta)$

$$(\sin\theta\cos 30° + \cos\theta\sin 30°) + (\sin\theta\cos 60° + \cos\theta\sin 60°) \stackrel{?}{=} \frac{\sqrt{3}+1}{2}(\sin\theta + \cos\theta)$$

$$\left(\frac{\sqrt{3}}{2}\sin\theta + \frac{1}{2}\sin\theta\right) + \left(\frac{1}{2}\cos\theta + \frac{\sqrt{3}}{2}\cos\theta\right) \stackrel{?}{=} \frac{\sqrt{3}+1}{2}(\sin\theta + \cos\theta)$$

$$\frac{\sqrt{3}+1}{2}\sin\theta + \frac{\sqrt{3}+1}{2}\cos\theta \stackrel{?}{=} \frac{\sqrt{3}+1}{2}(\sin\theta + \cos\theta)$$

$$\frac{\sqrt{3}+1}{2}(\sin\theta + \cos\theta) = \frac{\sqrt{3}+1}{2}(\sin\theta + \cos\theta) \checkmark$$

17. $\cos(30° - \theta) + \cos(30° + \theta) \stackrel{?}{=} \sqrt{3}\cos\theta$

$$(\cos 30°\cos\theta + \sin 30°\sin\theta) + (\cos 30°\cos\theta - \sin 30°\sin\theta) \stackrel{?}{=} \sqrt{3}\cos\theta$$

$$\left(\frac{\sqrt{3}}{2}\cos\theta + \frac{1}{2}\sin\theta\right) + \left(\frac{\sqrt{3}}{2}\cos\theta - \frac{1}{2}\sin\theta\right) \stackrel{?}{=} \sqrt{3}\cos\theta$$

$$\left(\frac{\sqrt{3}}{2} + \frac{\sqrt{3}}{2}\right)\cos\theta \stackrel{?}{=} \sqrt{3}\cos\theta$$

$$\sqrt{3}\cos\theta = \sqrt{3}\cos\theta \checkmark$$

Page 978, Extra Practice (Lesson 14-4)

2. $\frac{12\sqrt{5}}{49}; \frac{41}{49}; \frac{\sqrt{98 - 42\sqrt{5}}}{14}; \frac{\sqrt{98 + 42\sqrt{5}}}{14}$

4. $-\frac{120}{169}; \frac{119}{169}; \frac{\sqrt{26}}{26}; -\frac{5\sqrt{26}}{26}$

11. $\frac{\sin 2\theta}{2\sin^2\theta} \stackrel{?}{=} \cot\theta$

$$\frac{2\sin\theta\cos\theta}{2\sin^2\theta} \stackrel{?}{=} \cot\theta$$

$$\frac{\cos\theta}{\sin\theta} \stackrel{?}{=} \cot\theta$$

$$\cot\theta = \cot\theta \checkmark$$

12. $1 + \cos 2\theta \stackrel{?}{=} \frac{2}{1 + \tan^2\theta}$

$$1 + (\cos^2\theta - \sin^2\theta) \stackrel{?}{=} \frac{2}{1 + \frac{\sin^2\theta}{\cos^2\theta}}$$

$$\cos^2\theta + \cos^2\theta \stackrel{?}{=} \frac{2}{\frac{\cos^2\theta + \sin^2\theta}{\cos^2\theta}}$$

$$2\cos^2\theta \stackrel{?}{=} \frac{2}{\frac{1}{\cos^2\theta}}$$

$$2\cos^2\theta = 2\cos^2\theta \checkmark$$

13. $\csc\theta\sec\theta \stackrel{?}{=} 2\csc 2\theta$

$$\frac{1}{\sin\theta}\cdot\frac{1}{\cos\theta} \stackrel{?}{=} \frac{2}{\sin 2\theta}$$

$$\frac{1}{\sin\theta\cos\theta} \stackrel{?}{=} \frac{2}{2\sin\theta\cos\theta}$$

$$\frac{1}{\sin\theta\cos\theta} = \frac{1}{\sin\theta\cos\theta} \checkmark$$

14. $\sin 2\theta(\cot\theta + \tan\theta) \stackrel{?}{=} 2$

$$2\sin\theta\cos\theta\left(\frac{\cos\theta}{\sin\theta} + \frac{\sin\theta}{\cos\theta}\right) \stackrel{?}{=} 2$$

$$\frac{2\sin\theta\cos\theta(\cos\theta)}{\sin\theta} + \frac{2\sin\theta\cos\theta(\sin\theta)}{\cos\theta} \stackrel{?}{=} 2$$

$$2\cos^2\theta + 2\sin^2\theta \stackrel{?}{=} 2$$

$$2(\cos^2\theta + \sin^2\theta) \stackrel{?}{=} 2$$

$$2 = 2 \checkmark$$

15. $\frac{1 - \tan^2\theta}{1 + \tan^2\theta} \stackrel{?}{=} \cos 2\theta$

$$\frac{1 - \frac{\sin^2\theta}{\cos^2\theta}}{1 + \frac{\sin^2\theta}{\cos^2\theta}} \stackrel{?}{=} \cos 2\theta$$

$$\frac{\cos^2\theta - \sin^2\theta}{\cos^2\theta}\cdot\frac{\cos^2\theta}{\cos^2\theta + \sin^2\theta} \stackrel{?}{=} \cos 2\theta$$

$$\frac{\cos^2\theta - \sin^2\theta}{\cos^2 + \sin^2\theta} \stackrel{?}{=} \cos 2\theta$$

$$\cos^2\theta - \sin^2 \stackrel{?}{=} \cos 2\theta$$

$$\cos 2\theta = \cos 2\theta \checkmark$$

16. $\frac{\cos\theta + \sin\theta}{\cos\theta - \sin\theta} \stackrel{?}{=} \frac{1 + \sin 2\theta}{\cos 2\theta}$

$$\left(\frac{\cos\theta + \sin\theta}{\cos\theta + \sin\theta}\right)\left(\frac{\cos\theta + \sin\theta}{\cos\theta - \sin\theta}\right) \stackrel{?}{=} \frac{1 + \sin 2\theta}{\cos 2\theta}$$

$$\frac{\cos^2\theta + 2\cos\theta\sin\theta + \sin^2\theta}{\cos^2\theta - \sin^2\theta} \stackrel{?}{=} \frac{1 + \sin 2\theta}{\cos 2\theta}$$

$$\frac{1 + 2\cos\theta\sin\theta}{\cos 2\theta} \stackrel{?}{=} \frac{1 + \sin 2\theta}{\cos 2\theta}$$

$$\frac{1 + \sin 2\theta}{\cos 2\theta} = \frac{1 + \sin 2\theta}{\cos 2\theta} \checkmark$$

Page 978, Extra Practice (Lesson 14-5)

12. $0° + k \cdot 180°$, $210° + k \cdot 360°$, and $330° + k \cdot 360°$ or $0 + k\pi$, $\frac{7\pi}{6} + 2k\pi$, and $\frac{11\pi}{6} + 2k\pi$

13. $30° + k \cdot 180°$ and $60° + k \cdot 180°$ or $\frac{\pi}{6} + k\pi$ and $\frac{\pi}{3} + k\pi$

Page 980, Mixed Problem Solving (Chapter 2)

1a.

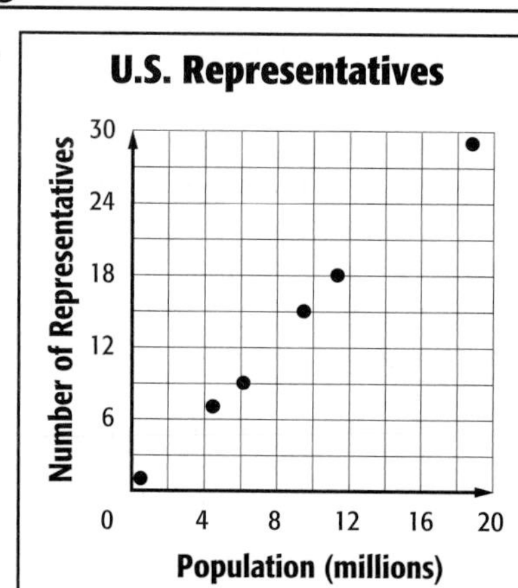

1b. D = {4.45, 0.78, 6.08, 9.94, 18.98, 11.35}, R = {7, 1, 9, 15, 29, 18}

6a.

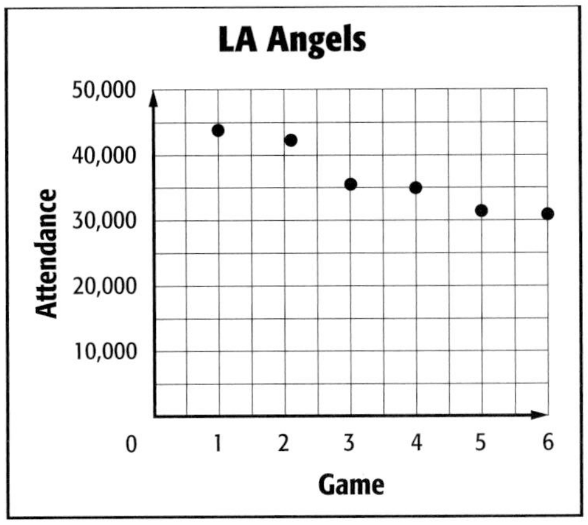

7b.

$$c(t) = \begin{cases} 5 \text{ if } t \leq 1 \\ 10 \text{ if } 1 < t \leq 12 \\ 17 \text{ if } 12 < t \leq 24 \\ 60 \text{ if } 24 < t \leq 168 \end{cases}$$

7c.

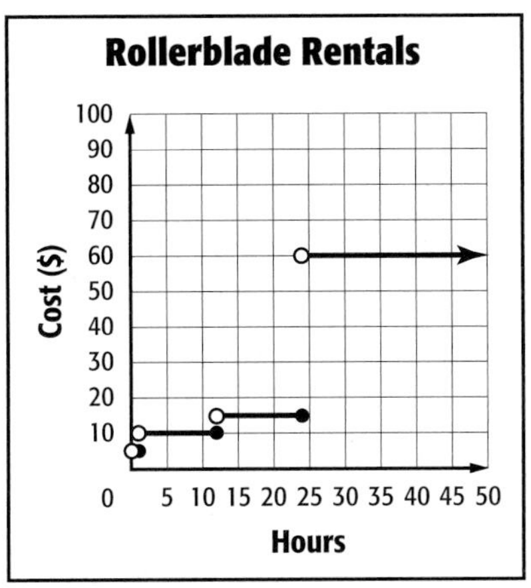

8b.

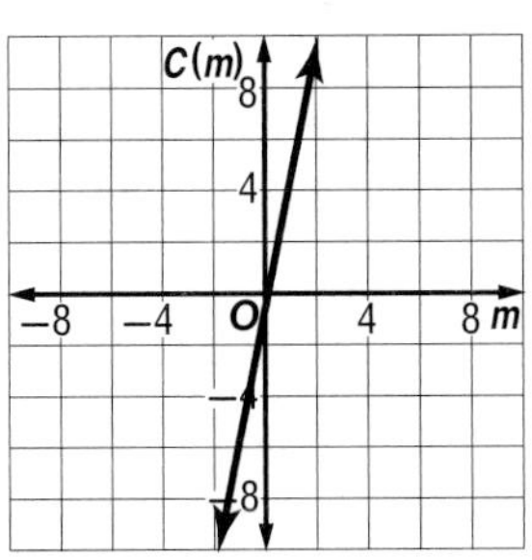

9a. $4.03g + 2.99q \leq 65$

9b.

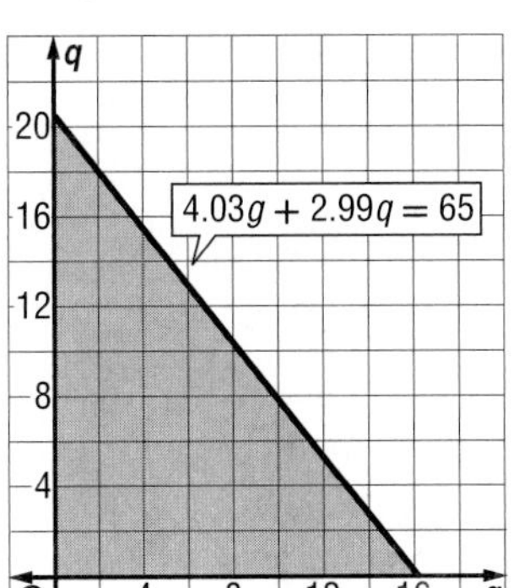

Page 981, Mixed Problem Solving (Chapter 3)

5a.

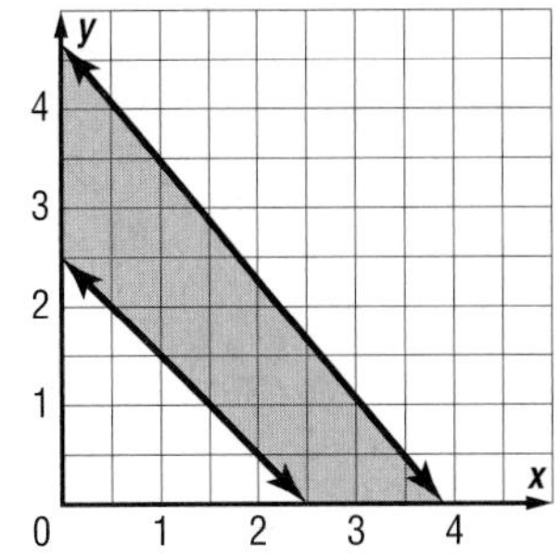

7a. $x + y + z = 300$; $2.9x + 5.2y + 8z = 1{,}508$; $x = 1.5z$

7b. ≤ 5 lbs : 120; 5 lbs < weight < 10 lbs : 100; ≥ 10 lb : 80

Page 982, Mixed Problem Solving (Chapter 4)

1a. $\begin{bmatrix} 131 & 212 & 85 \\ 95 & 189 & 25 \\ 147 & 208 & 78 \\ 185 & 247 & 93 \end{bmatrix}$

1c. Lila: 428; Jose: 309; Tony: 433; Abril: 525; The sum combines minutes and messages so it is irrelevant.

2a. $C = \begin{bmatrix} 582 & 132 & 85 \\ 621 & 129 & 89 \\ 594 & 131 & 95 \end{bmatrix}$

2c. $N = \begin{bmatrix} 436.50 & 99.00 & 63.75 \\ 465.75 & 96.75 & 66.75 \\ 445.50 & 98.25 & 71.25 \end{bmatrix}$

2d. $N - C = \begin{bmatrix} 145.50 & 33.00 & 21.25 \\ 155.25 & 32.25 & 22.25 \\ 148.50 & 32.75 & 23.75 \end{bmatrix}$

$N - C$ represents the amount the customer saved.

3a. $\begin{bmatrix} 22 & 15 & 8 \\ 20 & 18 & 12 \\ 10 & 3 & 7 \\ 19 & 17 & 10 \end{bmatrix}$

3b. $\begin{bmatrix} 374 & 240 & 216 \\ 340 & 288 & 324 \\ 170 & 48 & 189 \\ 323 & 272 & 270 \end{bmatrix}$

4a. $\begin{bmatrix} 45 & 55 & 65 \end{bmatrix} \begin{bmatrix} 350 & 280 \\ 320 & 165 \\ 180 & 120 \end{bmatrix}$

Page 983, Mixed Problem Solving (Chapter 5)

2a. D = {all real numbers}; R = $\{h(t) | h(t) \leq 237.89\}$

2b. The values of the domain that are reasonable are 0 to approximately 6.20, the time after the object is fired until it lands. The values of the range that are reasonable are 0 to 237.89, the minimum and maximum heights reached.

9.

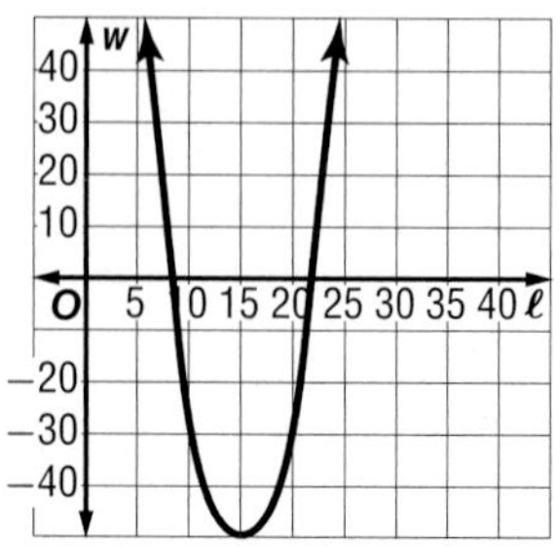

Page 984, Mixed Problem Solving (Chapter 6)

5a. $f(x) \to -\infty$ as $x \to -\infty$. $f(x) \to -\infty$ as $x \to +\infty$.

5b. Since the end behavior is in the same direction, it is an even-degree function.

5c. The graph intersects the x-axis at two points, so there are two real zeros.

6a.

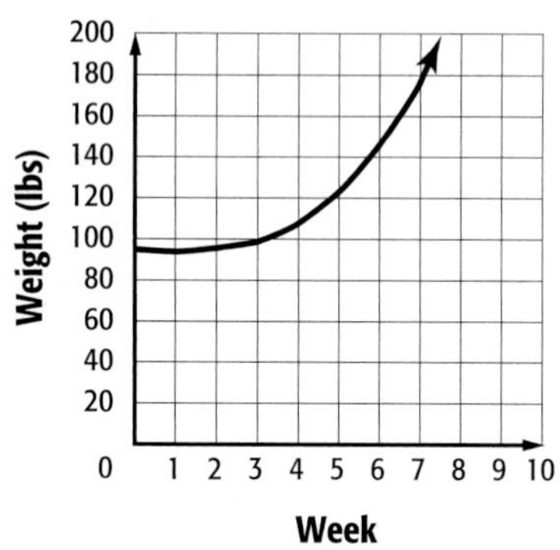

6b. There is a relative minimum at week 1. For the end behavior, $w(n)$ increases as n increases.

6c. The patient lost weight for the first week after becoming ill. After the first week, the patient gained weight and continue to gain weight. The function will not model weight long term because weight cannot continue to increase infinintely.

Page 985, Mixed Problem Solving (Chapter 7)

1. Claire saves $10.50 by taking the deduction before taxes.

2. It is better, by a difference of $6.25, to take the rebate after the discount.

6a.

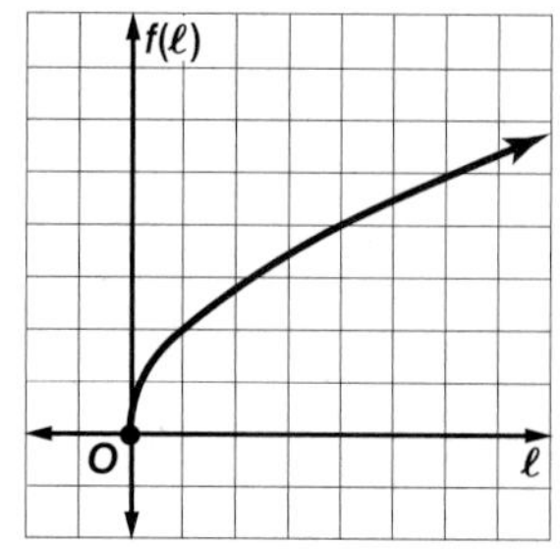

Page 986, Mixed Problem Solving (Chapter 8)

1b.

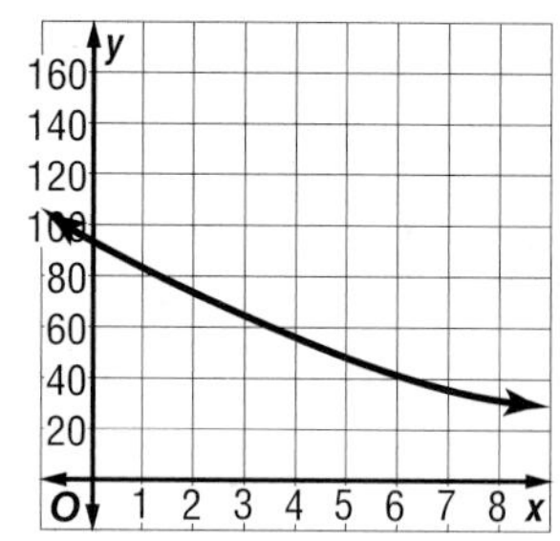

2b.

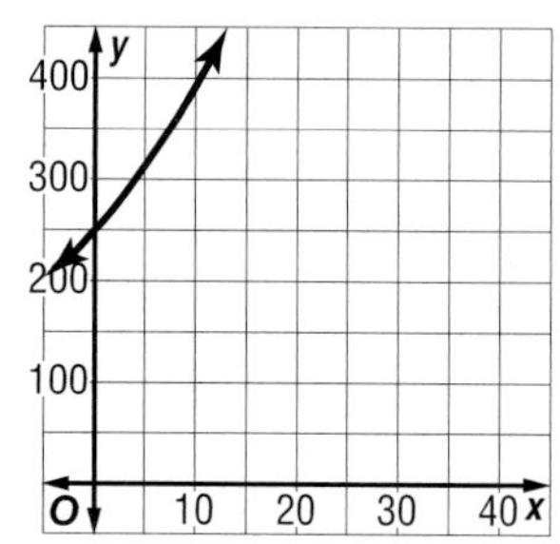

3b. at least 9.67 million; at least 17.62 million; at least 32.12 million; These answers are in close agreement with the actual populations in those years.

Page 987, Mixed Problem Solving (Chapter 9)

2. $A = x + x + x + \frac{111}{x} + \frac{111}{x} = 3x + \frac{222}{x}$

4b.

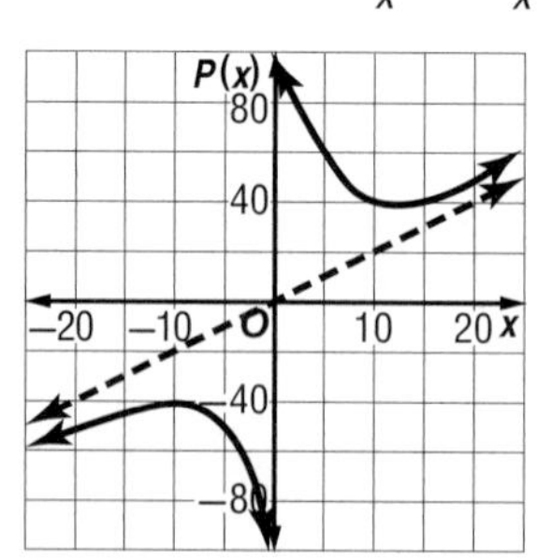

4c. The only meaningful measurements are nonnegative values.

5a.

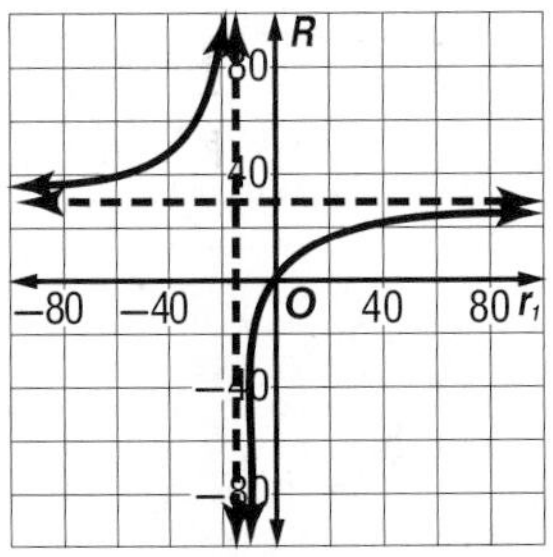

5b. The R-intercept is 0.

5c. $r_1 \geq 0$ and $0 \leq R \leq 30$ are meaningful.

11. 15 km/h; With the wind, Alfonso's speed would be 18 km/h, and his 36-km trip would take 2 hours. Against the wind, his speed would be 12 km/h, and his 24-km trip would take 2 hours. The answer makes sense.

Page 988, Mixed Problem Solving (Chapter 10)

3b.

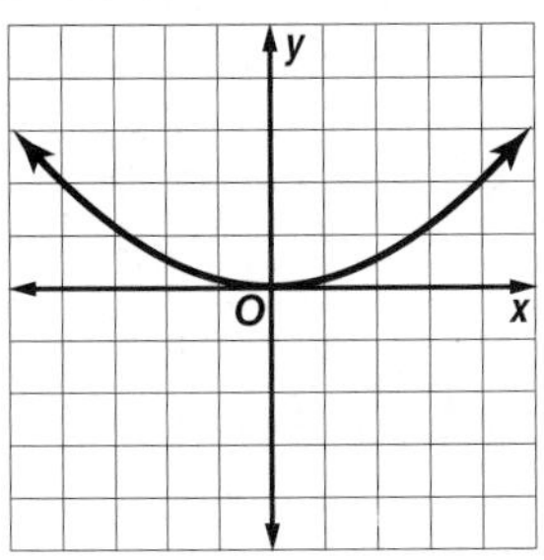

4b.

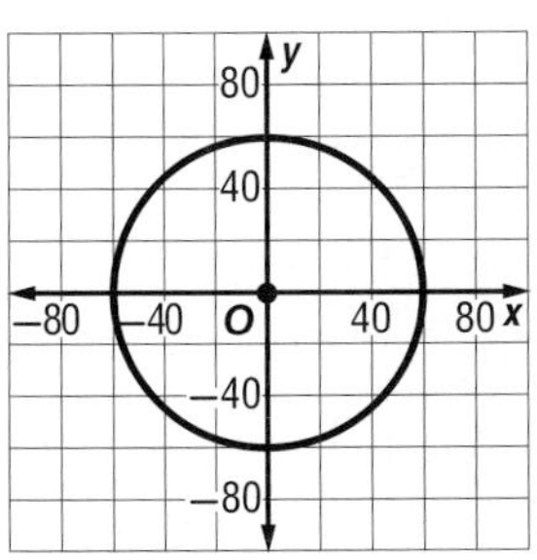

5b.

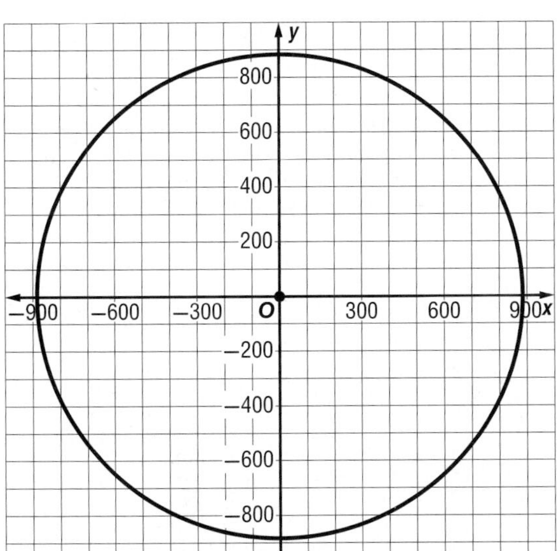

7a. vertices: (–40, 0), (40, 0); foci: (–150, 0), (150, 0); asymptotes: $y = \pm 3.615x$

8a. $y = -\frac{1}{80}(x - 40)^2 + 20$

8c.

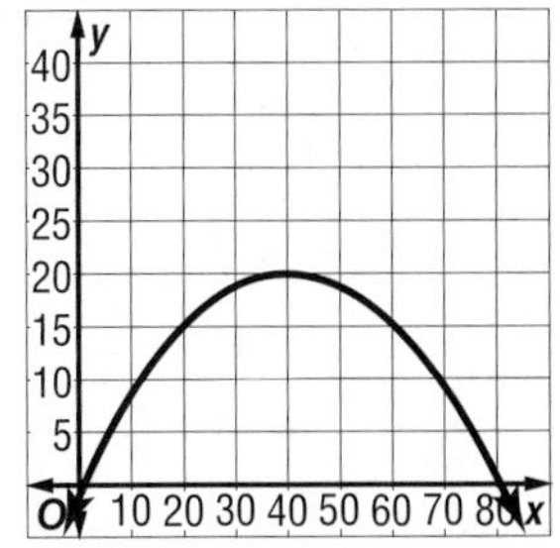

Page 989, Mixed Problem Solving (Chapter 11)

8. With each game, the number of teams in the competition is decreased by one. It takes 74 games to seed 1 team out of 75.

12. $\frac{1}{5} + \frac{1}{5^2} + \frac{1}{5^3} + \ldots + \frac{1}{5^n} = \frac{1}{4}\left(1 - \frac{1}{5^n}\right)$

Step 1: When $n = 1$, the left side of the given equation is $\frac{1}{5}$. The right side is $\frac{1}{4}\left(1 - \frac{1}{5}\right)$ or $\frac{1}{5}$. Thus, the equation is true for $n = 1$.

Step 2: Assume that $\frac{1}{5} + \frac{1}{5^2} + \frac{1}{5^3} + \ldots + \frac{1}{5^k} = \frac{1}{4}\left(1 - \frac{1}{5^k}\right)$ for some positive integer k.

Step 3: Show that the given equation is true for $n = k + 1$.

$$\frac{1}{5} = \frac{1}{5^2} + \frac{1}{5^3} + \ldots + \frac{1}{5^k} + \frac{1}{5^{k+1}}$$
$$= \frac{1}{4}\left(1 - \frac{1}{5^k}\right) + \frac{1}{5^{k+1}}$$
$$= \frac{1}{4} - \frac{1}{4(5^k)} + \frac{1}{5^{k+1}}$$
$$= \frac{5^{k+1} - 5 + 4}{4(5^{k+1})}$$
$$= \frac{5^{k+1}}{4(5^{k+1})} - \frac{1}{4(5^{k+1})}$$
$$= \frac{1}{4}\left(1 - \frac{1}{5^{k+1}}\right)$$

The last expression above is the right side of the equation to be proved, where n has been replaced by $k + 1$. Thus, the equation is true for $n = k + 1$.

Therefore, $\frac{1}{5} + \frac{1}{5^2} + \frac{1}{5^3} + \ldots + \frac{1}{5^n} = \frac{1}{4}\left(1 - \frac{1}{5^n}\right)$ for all positive integers n.

Page 990, Mixed Problem Solving (Chapter 12)

5e. The standard deviation for the 2007 season is larger than for the 2006 season.

5f. There was more variation in scores in 2007 than in 2006.

6a. $\frac{37}{68}$ or about 54%

6b. $\frac{43}{105}$ or about 41%

6c. $\frac{43}{44}$ or about 98%

Page 991, Mixed Problem Solving (Chapter 13)

5a.

Time (s)	Height of Green Object (ft)
4	16
6.5	7
9	–2
11.5	7
14	16
16.5	7

5b.

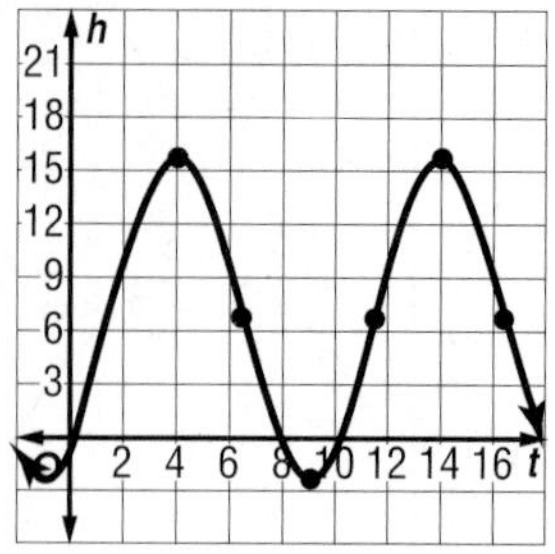

8c.

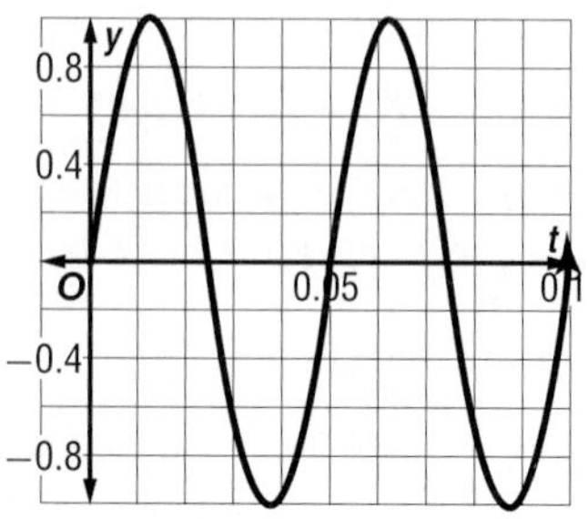

9a. 12 months; the pattern in the population will repeat every 12 months.

10b. The demand for temporary employment fluctuates in cycles of 7.7 years with a baseline of about 7300 job applications per week. Every cycle, the demand peaks at 11,600 applications per week and dips to a low of 3000.

Page 992, Mixed Problem Solving (Chapter 14)

3.

$$\frac{v^2 \sin^2 \theta}{2g} \stackrel{?}{=} \frac{v^2 \cos^2 \theta}{2g \cot^2 \theta}$$

$$\frac{v^2 \sin^2 \theta}{2g} \stackrel{?}{=} \frac{v^2 \cos^2 \theta}{2g\left(\frac{\cos^2 \theta}{\sin^2 \theta}\right)}$$

$$\frac{v^2 \sin^2 \theta}{2g} \stackrel{?}{=} \frac{v^2 \cos^2 \theta}{2g} \cdot \frac{\sin^2 \theta}{\cos^2 \theta}$$

$$\frac{v^2 \sin^2 \theta}{2g} = \frac{v^2 \sin^2 \theta}{2g} \quad \checkmark$$

5.

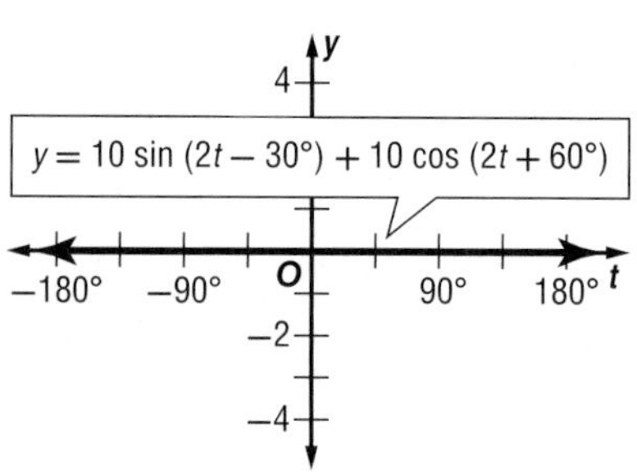

Page 1001, CSB 5 Bar and Line Graphs

1.

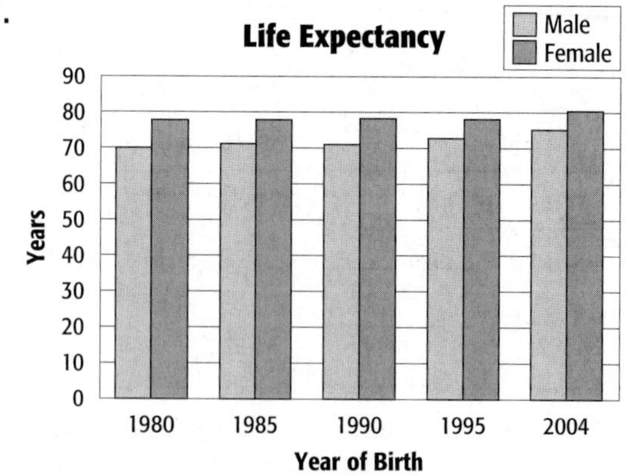

2.

Page 1003, CSB 6 Frequency Tables and Histograms

1.

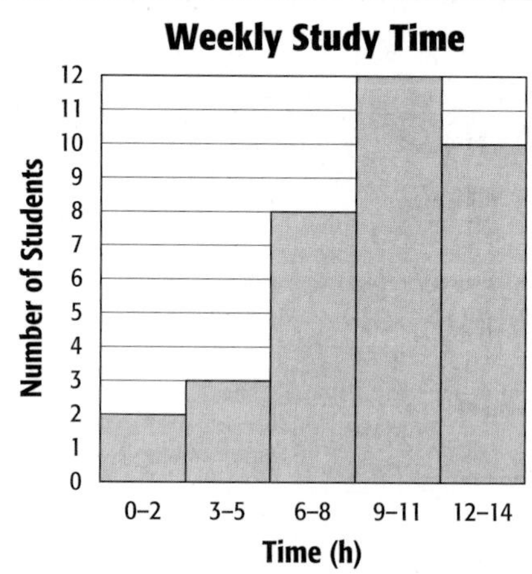

2.

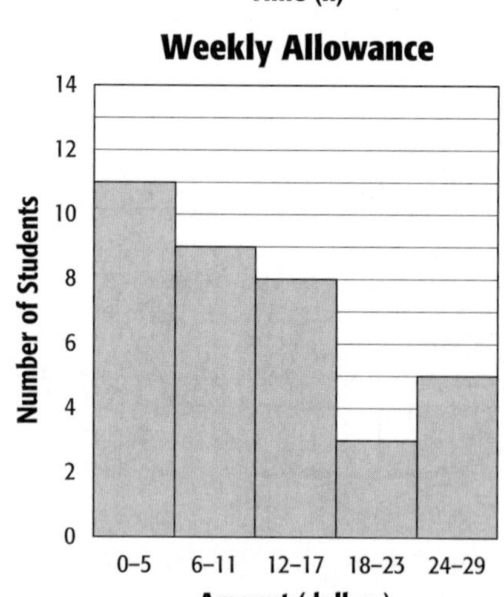

3a.

Price	Tally	Frequency
300	III	3
450	III	3
600	~~IIII~~ I	6
750	~~IIII~~	5
1200	II	2
1350	I	1
1800	II	2
2700	II	2

4a.

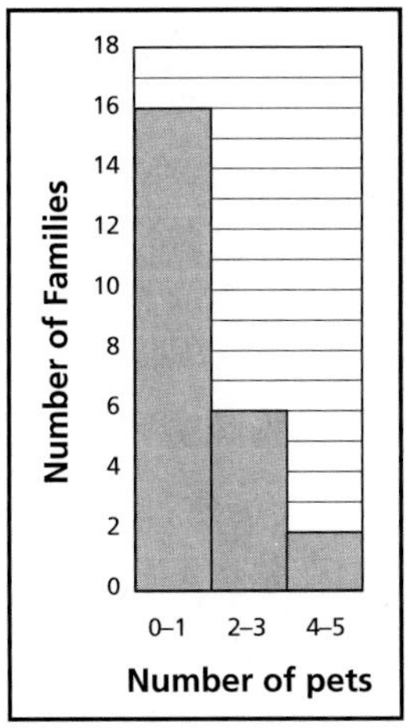

5b. 90–99 and 150–159; 100–109 and 130–139

5c. 100–109, 110–119, 120–129, 130–139, 140–149

5d. The greatest increase is between intervals 90–99 and 100–109. These frequencies are 1 and 7. So the increase is $7 - 1 = 6$.

6.

Number of Cars	Tally	Frequency
5–9	~~IIII~~ IIII	9
10–14	~~IIII~~ IIII	9
15–19	II	2

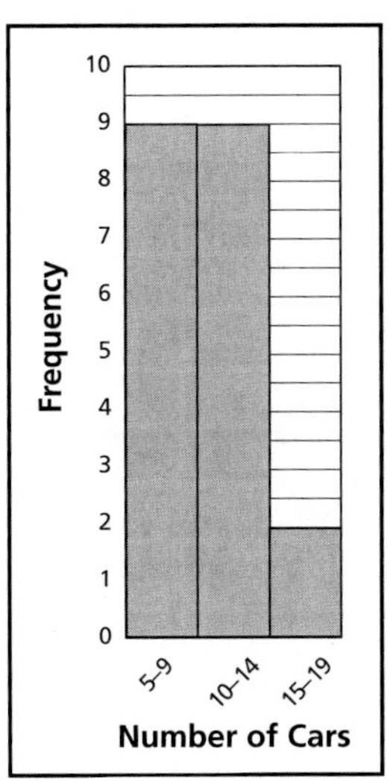

Page 1004, CSB 7 Stem-and-Leaf Plots

2.

Stem	Leaf
1	5 8
2	8 9
3	0 0 5 5 6 8 9
4	0 3 4 5 6 8 9 *2|8 = 28*

3.

Stem	Leaf
2	0 1 1 2 2 4 5 6 7 9
3	1
4	0 1 2 3 3 8 9
5	3
6	9
7	9
8	
9	2
10	4 *2|1 = 2100*

Page 1006, CSB 8 Box-and-Whisker Plots

3. You have a better chance to find someone who drives the same mileage if you drive 15 miles per day because more of the data is located closer to 15 miles than to 50 miles.

4.

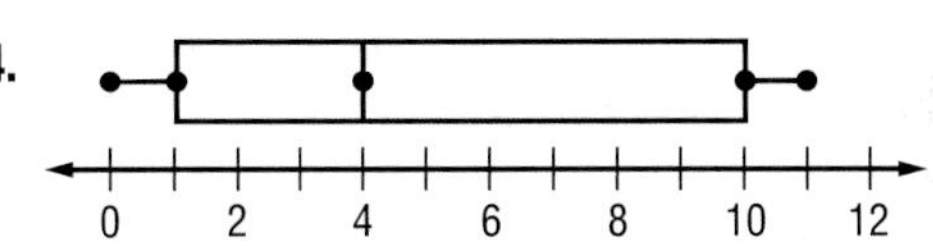

5.

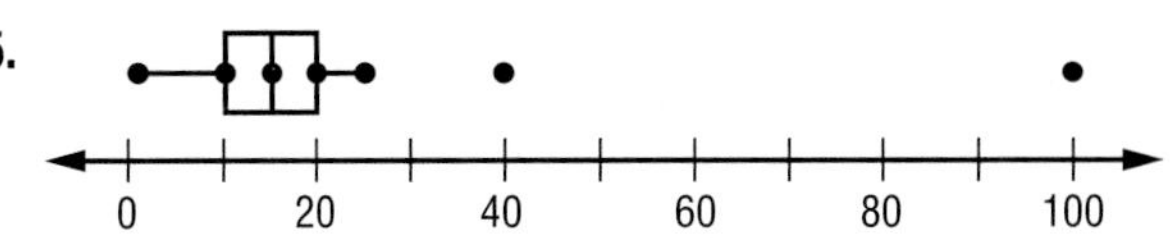

Student Handbook Answer Appendix

NOTES

Key Concepts

Preparing for Advanced Algebra — Chapter 0

Independent Events (p. P9) If the outcome of an event does not affect the outcome of another event, the two events are independent.

Dependent Events (p. P9) If the outcome of an event does affect the outcome of another event, the two events are dependent.

Fundamental Counting Principle (p. P9) If event M can occur in m ways and is followed by event N that can occur in n ways, then the event M followed by event N can occur in $m \cdot n$ ways.

Permutations (p. P12) The number of permutations of n distinct objects taken r at a time is given by

$$P(n, r) = \frac{n!}{(n - r)!}.$$

Permutations with Repetition (p. P13) The number of permutations of n of which p are alike and q are alike is

$$\frac{n!}{p!\,q!}.$$

Combinations (p. P13) The number of combinations of n distinct objects taken r at a time is given by

$$C(n, r) = \frac{n!}{(n - r)!r!}.$$

Equations and Inequalities — Chapter 1

Order of Operations (p. 5)
- **Step 1** Evaluate expressions inside grouping symbols.
- **Step 2** Evaluate all powers.
- **Step 3** Multiply and/or divide from left to right.
- **Step 4** Add and/or subtract from left to right.

Properties of Equality (p. 19)
- **Reflexive** For any real number a, $a = a$.
- **Symmetric** For all real numbers a and b, if $a = b$, then $b = a$.
- **Transitive** For all real numbers a, b, and c, if $a = b$ and $b = c$, then $a = c$.
- **Substitution** If $a = b$, then a may be replaced by b and b may be replaced by a.

Absolute Value (p. 27) For any real number a, $|a| = a$ if $a \geq 0$, and $|a| = -a$ if $a < 0$.

Addition Property of Inequality (p. 33)
For any real numbers, a, b, and c:
If $a > b$, then $a + c > b + c$.
If $a < b$, then $a + c < b + c$.

Subtraction Property of Inequality (p. 33)
For any real numbers, a, b, and c:
If $a > b$, then $a - c > b - c$.
If $a < b$, then $a - c < b - c$.

Key Concepts

'And' Compound Inequalities (p. 41) A compound inequality containing the word *and* is true if and only if *both* inequalities are true.

'Or' Compound Inequalities (p. 42) A compound inequality containing the word *or* is true if one or more of the inequalities is true.

Chapter 2 Linear Relations and Functions

One-to-one function (p. 61) Each element of the domain pairs to exactly one unique element of the range.

Onto function (p. 61) Each element of the range corresponds to an element of the domain.

Vertical Line Test (p. 62) If no vertical line intersects a graph in more than one point, the graph represents a function.

Standard Form of a Linear Equation (p. 70) The standard form of a linear equation is $Ax + By = C$, where A, B, and C are integers whose greatest common factor is 1, $A \geq 0$, and A and B are not both zero.

Slope of a Line (p. 78) The slope m of a line passing through (x_1, y_1) and (x_2, y_2) is given by $m = \frac{y_2 - y_1}{x_2 - x_1}$, where $x_1 \neq x_2$.

Slope-Intercept Form (p. 83) $y = mx + b$

slope → m; b ← y-intercept

Point-Slope Form (p. 84)

$$y - y_1 = m(x - x_1)$$

slope: m; coordinates of point on line: (x_1, y_1)

Parallel Lines (p. 85) Two nonvertical lines are parallel if and only if they have the same slope. All vertical lines are parallel.

Perpendicular Lines (p. 85) Two nonvertical lines are perpendicular if and only if the product of the slopes is −1. Vertical lines and horizontal lines are perpendicular.

Direct Variation (p. 90) y varies directly as x if there is some nonzero constant k such that $y = kx$. k is called the *constant of variation.*

Parent Function of Absolute Value (p. 103) $f(x) = |x|$, defined as

$$f(x) = \begin{cases} x \text{ if } x > 0 \\ 0 \text{ if } x = 0 \\ -x \text{ if } x < 0 \end{cases}$$

Parent Functions (p. 109)
Constant Function The general equation of a constant function is $f(x) = a$, where a is any number.
Identity Function The identity function $f(x) = x$ passes through all points with coordinates (a, a).
Absolute Value Function The parent function of absolute value functions is $f(x) = |x|$.
Quadratic Function The parent function of quadratic functions is $f(x) = x^2$.

Transformation of Functions (p. 112)

Translation	$f(x + h)$	Translates graph h units left.
	$f(x - h)$	Translates graph h units right.
	$f(x) + k$	Translates graph k units up.
	$f(x) - k$	Translates graph k units down.
Reflection	$-f(x)$	Reflects graph across the x-axis.
	$f(-x)$	Reflects graph across the y-axis.
Dilation	$a \cdot f(x)$, $a > 1$	Expands graph vertically.
	$a \cdot f(x)$, $0 < a < 1$	Compresses graph vertically
	$f(ax)$, $a > 1$	Compresses graph horizontally.
	$f(ax)$, $0 < a < 1$	Expands graph horizontally.

Chapter 3 Systems of Equations and Inequalities

Characteristics of Linear Systems (p. 138)
Consistent and independent intersecting lines; one solution
Consistent and dependent same line; infinitely many solutions
Inconsistent parallel lines; no solution

Substitution Method (p. 143)
Step 1 Solve one equation for one of the variables.
Step 2 Substitute the resulting expression into the other equation to replace the variable. Then solve the equation.
Step 3 Substitute to solve for the other variable.

Elimination Method (p. 144)
Step 1 Multiply one or both equations by a number to result in two equations that contain opposite terms.
Step 2 Add the equations, eliminating one variable. Then solve the equation.
Step 3 Substitute to solve for the other variable.

Solving Systems of Inequalities (p. 151)
Step 1 Graph each inequality, shading the correct area.
Step 2 Identify the region that is shaded for all of the inequalities. This is the solution of the system.

Feasible Regions (p. 160)
Bounded The feasible region is enclosed by the constraints. The maximum or minimum value of the related function *always* occurs at a vertex of the feasible region.
Unbounded The feasible region is open and can go on forever. Unbounded regions have either a maximum or a minimum.

Optimization with Linear Programming (p. 162)
Step 1 Define the variables.
Step 2 Write a system of inequalities.
Step 3 Graph the system of inequalities.
Step 4 Find the coordinates of the vertices of the feasible region.
Step 5 Write a linear function to be maximized or minimized.
Step 6 Substitute the coordinates of the vertices into the function.
Step 7 Select the greatest or least result. Answer the problem.

Matrices — Chapter 4

Adding and Subtracting Matrices (p. 193)

$$\underset{A}{\begin{bmatrix} a & b \\ c & d \end{bmatrix}} + \underset{B}{\begin{bmatrix} e & f \\ g & h \end{bmatrix}} = \underset{A+B}{\begin{bmatrix} a+e & b+f \\ c+g & d+h \end{bmatrix}} \qquad \underset{A}{\begin{bmatrix} a & b \\ c & d \end{bmatrix}} - \underset{B}{\begin{bmatrix} e & f \\ g & h \end{bmatrix}} = \underset{A-B}{\begin{bmatrix} a-e & b-f \\ c-g & d-h \end{bmatrix}}$$

Multiplying by a Scalar (p. 194)

$$k \cdot A = kA$$

$$k\begin{bmatrix} a & b \\ c & d \end{bmatrix} = \begin{bmatrix} ka & kb \\ kc & kd \end{bmatrix}$$

Properties of Matrix Operations (p. 194) For any matrices A, B, and C for which the matrix sum is defined and any scalar k, the following properties are true.

Commutative Property of Addition	$A + B = B + A$
Associative Property of Addition	$(A + B) + C = A + (B + C)$
Left Scalar Distributive Property	$k(A + B) = kA + kB$
Right Scalar Distributive Property	$(A + B)k = kA + kB$

Multiplying Matrices (p. 201)

$$\underset{A}{\begin{bmatrix} a & b \\ c & d \end{bmatrix}} \cdot \underset{B}{\begin{bmatrix} e & f \\ g & h \end{bmatrix}} = \underset{AB}{\begin{bmatrix} ae+bg & af+bh \\ ce+dg & cf+dh \end{bmatrix}}$$

Properties of Matrix Multiplication (p. 204)

Associative Property of Matrix Multiplication	$(AB)C = A(BC)$
Associative Property of Scalar Multiplication	$k(AB) = (kA)B = A(kB)$
Left Distributive Property	$C(A + B) = CA + CB$
Right Distributive Property	$(A + B)C = AC + BC$

Reflection Matrices (p. 212)

For a reflection across the:	x-axis	y-axis	line $y = x$
Multiply the vertex matrix on the left by:	$\begin{bmatrix} 1 & 0 \\ 0 & -1 \end{bmatrix}$	$\begin{bmatrix} -1 & 0 \\ 0 & 1 \end{bmatrix}$	$\begin{bmatrix} 0 & 1 \\ 1 & 0 \end{bmatrix}$

Rotation Matrices (p. 212)

For a counterclockwise rotation about the origin of:	90°	180°	270°
Multiply the vertex matrix on the left by:	$\begin{bmatrix} 0 & -1 \\ 1 & 0 \end{bmatrix}$	$\begin{bmatrix} -1 & 0 \\ 0 & -1 \end{bmatrix}$	$\begin{bmatrix} 0 & 1 \\ -1 & 0 \end{bmatrix}$

Second-Order Determinant (p. 220)

$$\det\begin{bmatrix} a & b \\ c & d \end{bmatrix} = \begin{vmatrix} a & b \\ c & d \end{vmatrix} = ad - bc$$

Diagonal Rule (p. 221)

Step 1 Rewrite the first two columns to the right of the determinant.
Step 2 Draw diagonals, beginning with the upper left-hand element. Multiply the elements in each diagonal.
Step 3 Find the sum of the products of the elements in the diagonals.
Step 4 Repeat the process, beginning with the upper right-hand element.
Step 5 Subtract the second sum from the first sum.

Area of a Triangle (p. 222) The area of a triangle with vertices (a, b), (c, d), and (e, f) is $|A|$,

where $A = \frac{1}{2}\begin{vmatrix} a & b & 1 \\ c & d & 1 \\ e & f & 1 \end{vmatrix}$.

Cramer's Rule (p. 223)

Let C be the coefficient matrix of the system. $\begin{matrix} ax + by = m \\ fx + gy = n \end{matrix} \rightarrow \begin{vmatrix} a & b \\ f & g \end{vmatrix}$

The solution of this system is $x = \dfrac{\begin{vmatrix} m & b \\ n & g \end{vmatrix}}{|C|}$, $y = \dfrac{\begin{vmatrix} a & m \\ f & n \end{vmatrix}}{|C|}$, if $C \neq 0$.

Cramer's Rule for a System of Three Equations (p. 224)

Let C be the coefficient matrix of the system. $\begin{matrix} ax + by + cz = m \\ fx + gy + hz = n \\ jx + ky + \ell z = p \end{matrix} \rightarrow \begin{vmatrix} a & b & c \\ f & g & h \\ j & k & \ell \end{vmatrix}$

The solution of this system is $x = \dfrac{\begin{vmatrix} m & b & c \\ n & g & h \\ p & k & \ell \end{vmatrix}}{|C|}$, $y = \dfrac{\begin{vmatrix} a & m & c \\ f & n & h \\ j & p & \ell \end{vmatrix}}{|C|}$, and

$z = y = \dfrac{\begin{vmatrix} a & b & m \\ f & g & n \\ j & k & p \end{vmatrix}}{|C|}$, if $C \neq 0$.

Identity Matrix for Multiplication (p. 229)

If $A = \begin{bmatrix} a & b \\ c & d \end{bmatrix}$, then $I = \begin{bmatrix} 1 & 0 \\ 0 & 1 \end{bmatrix}$ such that

$$\begin{bmatrix} a & b \\ c & d \end{bmatrix} \cdot \begin{bmatrix} 1 & 0 \\ 0 & 1 \end{bmatrix} = \begin{bmatrix} 1 & 0 \\ 0 & 1 \end{bmatrix} \cdot \begin{bmatrix} a & b \\ c & d \end{bmatrix} = \begin{bmatrix} a & b \\ c & d \end{bmatrix}.$$

Inverse of a 2 × 2 Matrix (p. 230)

The inverse of matrix $A = \begin{bmatrix} a & b \\ c & d \end{bmatrix}$ is $A^{-1} = \frac{1}{ad - bc}\begin{bmatrix} d & -b \\ -c & a \end{bmatrix}$, where $ad - bc \neq 0$.

Quadratic Functions and Relations — Chapter 5

Graph of a Quadratic Function (p. 250) Consider the graph of $y = ax^2 + bx + c$, where $a \neq 0$.

- The y-intercept is $a(0)^2 + b(0) + c$ or c.
- The equation of the axis of symmetry is $x = -\frac{b}{2a}$.
- The x-coordinate of the vertex is $-\frac{b}{2a}$.

Maximum and Minimum Value (p. 252) The graph of $f(x) = ax^2 + bx + c$, where $a \neq 0$,

- opens up and has a minimum value when $a > 0$, and
- opens down and has a maximum value when $a < 0$.

Solutions of a Quadratic Equation (p. 260) A quadratic equation can have one real solution, two real solutions, or no real solutions.

FOIL Method for Multiplying Binomials (p. 268) To multiply two binomials, find the sum of the products of F the *First* terms, O the *Outer* terms, I the *Inner* terms, and L the *Last* terms.

Zero Product Property (p. 271) For any real numbers a and b, if $ab = 0$, then either $a = 0$, $b = 0$, or both a and b equal zero.

Complex Numbers (p. 277) A complex number is any number that can be written in the form $a + bi$, where a and b are real numbers and i is the imaginary unit. A is called the real part, and b is called the imaginary part.

Completing the Square (p. 286) To complete the square for any quadratic expression of the form $x^2 + bx$, follow the steps below.

Step 1 Find one half of b, the coefficient of x.
Step 2 Square the result in Step 1.
Step 3 Add the result of Step 2 to $x^2 + bx$.

Quadratic Formula (p. 293) The solutions of a quadratic equation of the form $ax^2 + bx + c = 0$, where $a \neq 0$, are given by the following formula.

$$x = \frac{-b \pm \sqrt{b^2 - 4ac}}{2a}$$

Discriminant (p. 296) Consider $ax^2 + bx + c = 0$, where a, b, and c are rational numbers.

Value of Discriminant	$b^2 - 4ac > 0$; $b^2 - 4ac$ is a perfect square.	$b^2 - 4ac > 0$; $b^2 - 4ac$ is *not* a perfect square.	$b^2 - 4ac = 0$	$b^2 - 4ac < 0$
Type and Number of Roots	2 real, rational roots	2 real, irrational roots	1 real, rational root	2 complex roots

Sum and Product of Roots (p. 301) If the roots of $ax^2 + bx + c = 0$, with $a \neq 0$, are r_1 and r_2, then $r_1 + r_2 = -\frac{b}{a}$ and $r_1 \cdot r_2 = \frac{c}{a}$.

Transformations of Quadratic Functions (p. 307) $f(x) = a(x - h)^2 + k$

***h*, Horizontal Translation**	$\lvert h \rvert$ units to the right if h is positive $\lvert h \rvert$ units to the left if h is negative
***k*, Vertical Translation**	$\lvert k \rvert$ units up if k is positive $\lvert k \rvert$ units down if k is negative
***a*, Reflection**	If $a > 0$, the graph opens up. If $a < 0$, the graph opens down.
***a*, Dilation**	If $\lvert a \rvert > 1$, the graph is stretched vertically. If $0 < \lvert a \rvert < 1$, the graph is compressed vertically.

Chapter 6 Polynomials and Polynomial Functions

Properties of Exponents (p. 333)

Product of Powers	$x^a \cdot x^b = x^{a+b}$
Quotient of Powers	If $x \neq 0$, $\frac{x^a}{x^b} = x^{a-b}$.
Negative Exponent	$x^{-a} = \frac{1}{x^a}$ and $\frac{1}{x^{-a}} = x^a$, $x \neq 0$
Power of a Power	$(x^a)^b = x^{ab}$
Power of a Product	$(xy)^a = x^a y^a$
Power of a Quotient	$\left(\frac{x}{y}\right)^a = \frac{x^a}{y^a}$, $y \neq 0$, and $\left(\frac{x}{y}\right)^{-a} = \left(\frac{y}{x}\right)^a$ or $\frac{y^a}{x^a}$, $x \neq 0$, $y \neq 0$
Zero Power	$x^0 = 1$, $x \neq 0$

Simplifying Monomials (p. 334) A monomial expression is in simplified form when:

- there are no powers of powers,
- each base appears exactly once,
- all fractions are in simplest form, and
- there are no negative exponents.

Synthetic Division (p. 343)

Step 1 Write the coefficients of the dividend so that the degrees of the terms are in descending order. Write the constant r of the divisor $x - r$ in the box. Bring the first coefficient down.
Step 2 Multiply the first coefficient by r, and write the product under the second coefficient.
Step 3 Add the product and the second coefficient.
Step 4 Repeat Steps 2 and 3 until you reach a sum in the last column. The numbers along the bottom row are the coefficients of the quotient. The power of the first term is one less than the degree of the dividend. The final number is the remainder.

End Behavior of a Polynomial Function (p. 350)

Degree: even **Leading Coefficient:** positive **End Behavior:** $f(x) \to +\infty$ as $x \to -\infty$; $f(x) \to +\infty$ as $x \to +\infty$	**Degree:** odd **Leading Coefficient:** positive **End Behavior:** $f(x) \to -\infty$ as $x \to -\infty$; $f(x) \to +\infty$ as $x \to +\infty$
Degree: even **Leading Coefficient:** negative **End Behavior:** $f(x) \to -\infty$ as $x \to -\infty$; $f(x) \to -\infty$ as $x \to +\infty$	**Degree:** odd **Leading Coefficient:** negative **End Behavior:** $f(x) \to +\infty$ as $x \to -\infty$; $f(x) \to -\infty$ as $x \to +\infty$

Zeros of Even- and Odd-Degree Functions (p. 351) Odd-degree functions will always have an odd number of real zeros. Even-degree functions will always have an even number of real zeros or no real zeros at all.

Location Principle (p. 358) Suppose $y = f(x)$ represents a polynomial function and a and b are two real numbers such that $f(a) < 0$ and $f(b) > 0$. Then the function has at least one real zero between a and b.

Sum and Difference of Cubes (p. 368)

Sum of Two Cubes	$a^3 + b^3 = (a + b)(a^2 - ab + b^2)$
Difference of Two Cubes	$a^3 - b^3 = (a - b)(a^2 + ab + b^2)$

Factoring Techniques (p. 369)

Difference of Two Squares	$a^2 - b^2 = (a + b)(a - b)$
Sum of Two Cubes	$a^3 + b^3 = (a + b)(a^2 - ab + b^2)$
Difference of Two Cubes	$a^3 - b^3 = (a - b)(a^2 + ab + b^2)$
Perfect Square Trinomials	$a^2 + 2ab + b^2 = (a + b)^2$ $a^2 - 2ab + b^2 = (a - b)^2$
General Trinomials	$acx^2 + (ad + bc)x + bd$ $= (ax + b)(cx + d)$
Grouping	$ax + bx + ay + by$ $= x(a + b) + y(a + b)$ $= (a + b)(x + y)$

Quadratic Form (p. 371) An expression that is in quadratic form can be written as $au^2 + bu + c$ for any numbers a, b, and c, $a \neq 0$, where u is some expression in x. The expression $au^2 + bu + c$ is called the quadratic form of the original expression.

Remainder Theorem (p. 377) If a polynomial $P(x)$ is divided by $x - r$, the remainder is a constant $P(r)$, and

dividend equals quotient times divisor plus remainder

$$P(x) \quad = \quad Q(x) \quad \cdot \quad (x - r) \quad + \quad P(r),$$

where $Q(x)$ is a polynomial with degree one less than $P(x)$.

Factor Theorem (p. 379) The binomial $x - r$ is a factor of the polynomial $P(x)$ if and only if $P(r) = 0$.

Zeros, Factors, Roots, and Intercepts (p. 383) Let $P(x) = a_n x^n + \cdots + a_1 x + a_0$ be a polynomial function. Then the following statements are equivalent.
- c is a zero of $P(x)$.
- c is a root or solution of $P(x) = 0$.
- $x - c$ is a factor of $a_n x^n + \cdots + a_1 x + a_0$.
- If c is a real number, then $(c, 0)$ is an x-intercept of the graph of $P(x)$.

Fundamental Theorem of Algebra (p. 383) Every polynomial equation with degree greater than zero has at least one root in the set of complex numbers.

Corollary to the Fundamental Theorem of Algebra (p. 384) A polynomial equation of degree n has exactly n roots in the set of complex numbers, including repeated roots.

Descartes' Rule of Signs (p. 385) Let $P(x) = a_n x^n + \cdots + a_1 x + a_0$ be a polynomial function with real coefficients. Then:
- the number of *positive* real zeros of $P(x)$ is the same as the number of changes in sign of the coefficients of the terms, or is less than this by an even number; and
- the number of *negative* real zeros of $P(x)$ is the same as the number of changes in sign of the coefficients of the terms of $P(-x)$, or is less than this by an even number.

Complex Conjugates Theorem (p. 387) Let a and b be real numbers, and $b \neq 0$. If $a + bi$ is a zero of a polynomial function with real coefficients, then $a - bi$ is also a zero of the function.

Rational Zero Theorem (p. 391) If $P(x)$ is a polynomial function with integral coefficients, then every rational zero of $P(x) = 0$ is of the form $\frac{p}{q}$, a rational number in simplest form, where p is a factor of the constant term and q is a factor of the leading coefficient.

Corollary to the Rational Zero Theorem (p. 391) If $P(x)$ is a polynomial function with integral coefficients, a leading coefficient of 1, and a nonzero constant term, then any rational zeros of $P(x)$ must be factors of the constant term.

Chapter 7
Inverses and Radical Functions and Relations

Operations on Functions (p. 409)

Addition	$(f + g)(x) = f(x) + g(x)$
Subtraction	$(f - g)(x) = f(x) - g(x)$
Multiplication	$(f \cdot g)(x) = f(x) \cdot g(x)$
Division	$\left(\frac{f}{g}\right)(x) = \frac{f(x)}{g(x)}, g(x) \neq 0$

Composition of Functions (p. 411) Suppose f and g are functions such that the range of g is a subset of the domain of f. Then the composition function $f \circ g$ can be described by

$$[f \circ g](x) = f[g(x)].$$

Inverse Relations (p. 417) Two relations are inverse relations if and only if whenever one relation contains the element (a, b), the other relation contains the element (b, a).

Property of Inverses (p. 418) If f and f^{-1} are inverses, then $f(a) = b$ if and only if $f^{-1}(b) = a$.

Inverse Functions (p. 419) Two functions f and g are inverse functions if and only if both of their compositions are the identity function.

Parent Function of Square Root Functions (p. 424)

Parent function:	$f(x) = \sqrt{x}$
Domain:	$\{x \mid x \geq 0\}$
Range:	$\{f(x) \mid f(x) \geq 0\}$
Intercepts:	$x = 0, f(x) = 0$
Not defined:	$x < 0$
End behavior:	$x \to 0, f(x) \to 0$ $x \to +\infty, f(x) \to +\infty$

Transformations of Square Root Functions (p. 425) $f(x) = a\sqrt{x - h} + k$

***h*, Horizontal Translation**	$\lvert h \rvert$ units to the right if h is positive $\lvert h \rvert$ units to the left if h is negative
***k*, Vertical Translation**	$\lvert k \rvert$ units up if k is positive $\lvert k \rvert$ units down if k is negative
***a*, Orientation and Shape**	If $a < 0$, the graph is reflected across the x-axis. If $\lvert a \rvert > 1$, the graph is stretched vertically. If $0 < \lvert a \rvert < 1$, the graph is compressed vertically.

Definition of *n*th Root (p. 431) For any real numbers a and b, and any positive integer n, if $a^n = b$, then a is an nth root of b.

Real *n*th Roots (p. 432)

a	n is even	n is odd
$a > 0$	1 positive and 1 negative real root: $\pm\sqrt[n]{a}$	1 positive and 0 negative real root: $\sqrt[n]{a}$
$a < 0$	0 real roots	0 positive and 1 negative real root: $\sqrt[n]{a}$
$a = 0$	1 real root: $\sqrt[n]{0} = 0$	1 real root: $\sqrt[n]{0} = 0$

Product Property of Radicals (p. 439) For any real numbers a and b and any integer $n > 1$,
1. if n is even and a and b are both nonnegative, then $\sqrt[n]{ab} = \sqrt[n]{a} \cdot \sqrt[n]{b}$, and
2. if n is odd, then $\sqrt[n]{ab} = \sqrt[n]{a} \cdot \sqrt[n]{b}$.

Quotient Property of Radicals (p. 440) For any real numbers a and $b \neq 0$ and any integer $n > 1$, $\sqrt[n]{\frac{a}{b}} = \frac{\sqrt[n]{a}}{\sqrt[n]{b}}$, if all roots are defined.

Simplifying Radical Expressions (p. 441) A radical expression is in simplified form when the following conditions are met.
- The index n is as small as possible.
- The radicand contains no factors (other than 1) that are nth powers of an integer or polynomial.
- The radicand contains no fractions.
- No radicals appear in a denominator.

$b^{\frac{1}{n}}$ (p. 446) For any real number b and any positive integer n, $b^{\frac{1}{n}} = \sqrt[n]{b}$, except when $b < 0$ and n is even. When $b < 0$ and n is even, a complex root may exist.

Rational Exponents (p. 447) For any real nonzero number b, and any integers x and y, with $y > 1$, $b^{\frac{x}{y}} = \sqrt[y]{b^x} = \left(\sqrt[y]{b}\right)^x$, except when $b < 0$ and y is even. When $b < 0$ and y is even, a complex root may exist.

Expressions with Rational Exponents (p. 449) An expression with rational exponents is simplified when all of the following conditions are met.
- It has no negative exponents.
- It has no exponents that are not positive integers in the denominator.
- It is not a complex fraction.
- The index of any remaining radical is the least number possible.

Solving Radical Equations (p. 453)
Step 1 Isolate the radical on one side of the equation.
Step 2 Raise each side of the equation to a power equal to the index of the radical to eliminate the radical.
Step 3 Solve the resulting polynomial equation.

Solving Radical Inequalities (p. 455)
Step 1 If the index of the root is even, identify the values of the variable for which the radicand is nonnegative.
Step 2 Solve the inequality algebraically.
Step 3 Test values to check your solution.

Chapter 8
Exponential and Logarithmic Functions and Relations

Parent Function of Exponential Growth Functions (p. 475)

Parent function: $f(x) = b^x, b > 1$
Domain: all real numbers
Range: all nonzero real numbers
Asymptote: x-axis

Transformations of Exponential Functions (p. 476) $f(x) = ab^{x-h} + k$

h, Horizontal Translation	$\lvert h \rvert$ units to the right if h is positive $\lvert h \rvert$ units to the left if h is negative
k, Vertical Translation	$\lvert k \rvert$ units up if k is positive $\lvert k \rvert$ units down if k is negative
a, Orientation and Shape	If $a < 0$, the graph is reflected across the x-axis. If $\lvert a \rvert > 1$, the graph is stretched vertically. If $0 < \lvert a \rvert < 1$, the graph is compressed vertically.

Parent Function of Exponential Decay Functions (p. 477)

Parent function: $f(x) = b^x, 0 < b < 1$
Domain: all real numbers
Range: positive real numbers
Asymptote: x-axis

Property of Equality for Exponential Functions (p. 485) Let $b > 0$ and $b \neq 1$. Then $b^x = b^y$ if and only if $x = y$.

Property of Inequality for Exponential Functions (p. 487) Let $b > 1$. Then $b^x > b^y$ if and only if $x > y$, and $b^x < b^y$ if and only if $x < y$.

Logarithm with Base b (p. 492)

Suppose $b > 0, b \neq 1$, and $x > 0$, $\log_b x = y$ if and only if $b^y = x$.

Parent Function of Logarithmic Functions (p. 493)

Parent function: $f(x) = \log_b x$
Range: all real numbers
Asymptote: $f(x)$-axis

Transformations of Logarithmic Functions (p. 494) $f(x) = a \log_b (x - h) + k$

h, Horizontal Translation	$\lvert h \rvert$ units to the right if h is positive $\lvert h \rvert$ units to the left if h is negative
k, Vertical Translation	$\lvert k \rvert$ units up if k is positive $\lvert k \rvert$ units down if k is negative
a, Orientation and Shape	If $a < 0$, the graph is reflected across the x-axis. If $\lvert a \rvert > 1$, the graph is stretched vertically. If $0 < \lvert a \rvert < 1$, the graph is compressed vertically.

Property of Equality for Logarithmic Functions (p. 502) If b is a positive number other than 1, then $\log_b x = \log_b y$ if and only if $x = y$.

Property of Inequality for Logarithmic Functions (p. 503)
If $b > 1, x > 0$, and $\log_b x > y$, then $x > b^y$.
If $b > 1, x > 0$, and $\log_b x < y$, then $0 < x < b^y$.

Property of Inequality for Logarithmic Functions (p. 504) If $b > 1$, then $\log_b x > \log_b y$ if and only if $x > y$, and $\log_b x < \log_b y$ if and only if $x < y$.

Product Property of Logarithms (p. 509) For all positive numbers a, b, and x, where $x \neq 1$, $\log_x ab = \log_x a + \log_x b$.

Quotient Property of Logarithms (p. 510) For all positive numbers a, b, and x, where $x \neq 1$, $\log_x \frac{a}{b} = \log_x a - \log_x b$.

Power Property of Logarithms (p. 511) For any real number p, and positive numbers m and b, where $b \neq 1$, $\log_b m^p = p \log_b m$.

Change of Base Formula (p. 518) For all positive numbers a, b, and n, where $a \neq 1$ and $b \neq 1$, $\log_a n = \frac{\log_b n}{\log_b a}$.

Natural Base Functions (p. 525) The function $f(x) = e^x$ is used to model continuous exponential growth. The function $f(x) = e^{-x}$ is used to model continuous exponential decay. The inverse of a natural base exponential function is called the natural logarithm. This logarithm can be written as $\log_e x$, but is more often abbreviated as $\ln x$.

Exponential Growth (p. 533) Exponential growth can be modeled by the function $f(x) = ae^{kt}$

Exponential Decay (p. 533) Exponential decay can be modeled by the function $f(x) = ae^{-kt}$

Logistic Growth Function (p. 536) Let a, b, and c be positive constants where $b < 1$. The logistic growth function is represented by $f(t) = \frac{c}{1 + ae^{-bt}}$, where t represents time.

Chapter 9
Rational Functions and Relations

Multiplying Rational Expressions (p. 555) For all rational expressions $\frac{a}{b}$ and $\frac{c}{d}$ with $b \neq 0$ and $d \neq 0$, $\frac{a}{b} \cdot \frac{c}{d} = \frac{ac}{bd}$.

Dividing Rational Expressions (p. 555) For all rational expressions $\frac{a}{b}$ and $\frac{c}{d}$ with $b \neq 0, c \neq 0$, and $d \neq 0$, $\frac{a}{b} \div \frac{c}{d} = \frac{a}{b} \cdot \frac{d}{c} = \frac{ad}{bc}$.

Adding Rational Expressions (p. 563) For all rational expressions $\frac{a}{b}$ and $\frac{c}{d}$ with $b \neq 0$, and $d \neq 0$, $\frac{a}{b} + \frac{c}{d} = \frac{ad}{bd} + \frac{bc}{bd} = \frac{ad + bc}{bd}$.

Subtracting Rational Expressions (p. 563) For all rational expressions $\frac{a}{b}$ and $\frac{c}{d}$ with $b \neq 0$, and $d \neq 0$, $\frac{a}{b} - \frac{c}{d} = \frac{ad}{bd} - \frac{bc}{bd} = \frac{ad - bc}{bd}$.

Parent Function of Reciprocal Functions (p. 569)

Parent function: $f(x) = \frac{1}{x}$
Domain and range: all nonzero real numbers
Axes of symmetry: $x = 0$ and $f(x) = 0$
Not defined: $x = 0$ and $f(x) = 0$

Transformations of Reciprocal Functions (p. 571) $f(x) = \frac{a}{x - h} + k$

h, Horizontal Translation	$\lvert h \rvert$ units to the right if h is positive $\lvert h \rvert$ units to the left if h is negative The *vertical* asymptote is at $x = h$.
k, Vertical Translation	$\lvert k \rvert$ units up if k is positive $\lvert k \rvert$ units down if k is negative The *horizontal* asymptote is at $f(x) = k$.
a, Orientation and Shape	If $a < 0$, the graph is reflected across the x-axis. If $\lvert a \rvert > 1$, the graph is stretched vertically. If $0 < \lvert a \rvert < 1$, the graph is compressed vertically.

Vertical and Horizontal Asymptotes (p. 577) If $f(x) = \frac{a(x)}{b(x)}$, $a(x)$ and $b(x)$ are polynomial functions with no common factors other than 1, and $b(x) \neq 0$, then:

Vertical asymptote $f(x)$ has a vertical asymptote whenever $b(x) = 0$.
Horizontal asymptote $f(x)$ has at most one horizontal asymptote

- if the degree of $a(x)$ is greater than the degree of $b(x)$, there is no horizontal asymptote.
- if the degree of $a(x)$ is less than the degree of $b(x)$, the horizontal asymptote is the line $y = 0$.
- if the degree of $a(x)$ equals the degree of $b(x)$, the horizontal asymptote is the line $y = \frac{\text{leading coefficient of } a(x)}{\text{leading coefficient of } b(x)}$.

Oblique Asymptotes (p. 579) If $f(x) = \frac{a(x)}{b(x)}$, $a(x)$ and $b(x)$ are polynomial functions with no common factors other than 1 and $b(x) \neq 0$, then $f(x)$ has an oblique asymptote if the degree of $a(x)$ minus the degree of $b(x)$ equals 1. The equation of the asymptote is $\frac{a(x)}{b(x)}$ with no remainder.

Point Discontinuity (p. 581) If $f(x) = \frac{a(x)}{b(x)}$, $b(x) \neq 0$, and $x - c$ is a factor of both $a(x)$ and $b(x)$, then there is a point discontinuity at $x = c$.

Direct Variation (p. 586) y varies directly as x if there is some nonzero constant k such that $y = kx$. k is called the constant of variation.

Joint Variation (p. 587) y varies jointly as x and z if there is some nonzero constant k such that $y = kxz$.

Inverse Variation (p. 588) y varies inversely as x if there is some nonzero constant k such that $xy = k$ or $y = \frac{k}{x}$, where $x \neq 0$ and $y \neq 0$.

Solving Rational Inequalities (p. 599)

Step 1 State the excluded values. These are the values for which the denominator is 0.
Step 2 Solve the related equation.
Step 3 Use the values determined from the previous steps to divide a number line into intervals.
Step 4 Test a value in each interval to determine which intervals contain values that satisfy the inequality.

Conic Sections — Chapter 10

Midpoint Formula (p. 617) If a line segment has endpoints $P(x_1, y_1)$ and $Q(x_2, y_2)$, then the midpoint of the segment has coordinates $M\left(\frac{x_1 + x_2}{2}, \frac{y_1 + y_2}{2}\right)$.

Distance Formula (p. 618) The distance between two points with coordinates (x_1, y_1) and (x_2, y_2) is given by $\sqrt{(x_2 - x_1)^2 + (y_2 - y_1)^2}$.

Equations of Parabolas (p. 623)

Form of Equation	$y = a(x - h)^2 + k$	$x = a(y - k)^2 + h$
Direction of Opening	upward if $a > 0$, downward if $a < 0$	right if $a > 0$, left if $a < 0$
Vertex	(h, k)	(h, k)
Axis of Symmetry	$x = h$	$y = k$
Focus	$\left(h, k + \frac{1}{4a}\right)$	$\left(h + \frac{1}{4a}, k\right)$
Directrix	$y = k - \frac{1}{4a}$	$x = h - \frac{1}{4a}$
Length of Latus Rectum	$\left\lvert \frac{1}{a} \right\rvert$ units	$\left\lvert \frac{1}{a} \right\rvert$ units

Equations of Circles (p. 631)

Standard Form of Equation	$x^2 + y^2 = r^2$	$(x - h)^2 + (y - k)^2 = r^2$
Center	$(0, 0)$	(h, k)
Radius	r	r

Equations of Ellipses Centered at the Origin (p. 639)

Standard Form	$\frac{x^2}{a^2} + \frac{y^2}{b^2} = 1$	$\frac{y^2}{a^2} + \frac{x^2}{b^2} = 1$
Orientation	horizontal	vertical
Foci	$(c, 0), (-c, 0)$	$(0, c), (0, -c)$
Length of Major Axis	$2a$ units	$2a$ units
Length of Minor Axis	$2b$ units	$2b$ units

Equations of Ellipses Centered at (h, k) (p. 640)

Standard Form	$\frac{(x - h)^2}{a^2} + \frac{(y - k)^2}{b^2} = 1$	$\frac{(y - k)^2}{a^2} + \frac{(x - h)^2}{b^2} = 1$
Orientation	horizontal	vertical
Foci	$(h \pm c, k)$	$(h, k \pm c)$
Vertices	$(h \pm a, k)$	$(h, k \pm a)$
Co-vertices	$(h, k \pm b)$	$(h \pm b, k)$

Equations of Hyperbolas Centered at the Origin (p. 648)

Standard Form	$\frac{x^2}{a^2} - \frac{y^2}{b^2} = 1$	$\frac{y^2}{a^2} - \frac{x^2}{b^2} = 1$
Orientation	horizontal	vertical
Foci	$(\pm c, 0)$	$(0, \pm c)$
Length of Transverse Axis	$2a$ units	$2a$ units
Length of Conjugate Axis	$2b$ units	$2b$ units
Equations of Asymptotes	$y = \pm\frac{b}{a}x$	$y = \pm\frac{a}{b}x$

Equations of Hyperbolas Centered at (h, k) (p. 650)

Standard Form	$\frac{(x-h)^2}{a^2} - \frac{(y-k)^2}{b^2} = 1$	$\frac{(y-k)^2}{a^2} - \frac{(x-h)^2}{b^2} = 1$
Orientation	horizontal	vertical
Foci	$(h \pm c, k)$	$(k, h \pm c)$
Vertices	$(h \pm a, k)$	$(k, h \pm a)$
Co-vertices	$(h, k \pm b)$	$(k \pm b, h)$
Equations of Asymptotes	$y - k = \pm\frac{b}{a}(x - h)$	$y - k = \pm\frac{a}{b}(x - h)$

Standard Forms of Conic Sections (p. 656)

Circle	$(x-h)^2 + (y-k)^2 = r^2$	
	Horizontal Axis	Vertical Axis
Parabola	$y = a(x-h)^2 + k$	$x = a(y-k) + h$
Ellipse	$\frac{(x-h)^2}{a^2} + \frac{(y-k)^2}{b^2} = 1$	$\frac{(y-k)^2}{a^2} + \frac{(x-h)^2}{b^2} = 1$
Hyperbola	$\frac{(x-h)^2}{a^2} - \frac{(y-k)^2}{b^2} = 1$	$\frac{(y-k)^2}{a^2} - \frac{(x-h)^2}{b^2} = 1$

Classify Conics with the Discriminant (p. 657)

Circle	$B^2 - 4AC < 0$; $B = 0$ and $A = C$
Ellipse	$B^2 - 4AC < 0$; either $B \neq 0$ or $A \neq C$
Parabola	$B^2 - 4AC = 0$
Hyperbola	$B^2 - 4AC > 0$

Sequences and Series — Chapter 11

Sequences as Functions (p. 681) A sequence is a function in which the domain consists of natural numbers and the range consists of real numbers.

Domain: 1 2 3 … n
↓ ↓ ↓ ↓
Range: a_1 a_2 a_3 … a_n

*n*th Term of an Arithmetic Sequence (p. 688) The nth term a_n of an arithmetic sequence in which the first term is a_1 and the common difference is d is given by the following formula, where n is any natural number.

$$a_n = a_1 + (n - 1)d$$

Partial Sum of an Arithmetic Series (p. 690)

Given a_1 and a_n $S_n = n\left(\frac{a_1 + a_n}{2}\right)$

Given a_1 and d $S_n = \frac{n}{2}[2a_1 + (n - 1)d]$

Sigma Notation (p. 691)

$$\sum_{k=1}^{n} f(k)$$

last value of k → n; first value of k → $k = 1$; $f(k)$ ← formula for the terms of the series

*n*th Term of a Geometric Sequence (p. 696) The nth term a_n of a geometric sequence in which the first term is a_1 and the common ratio is r is given by the following formula, where n is any natural number.

$$a_n = a_1 r^{n-1}$$

Partial Sum of a Geometric Series (p. 698)

Given a_1 and n $S_n = \frac{a_1 - a_1 r^n}{1 - r}, r \neq 1$

Given a_1 and a_n $S_n = \frac{a_1 - a_n r}{1 - r}, r \neq 1$

Convergent Series (p. 705) The sum approaches a finite value. $|r| < 1$

Divergent Series (p. 705) The sum does not approach a finite value. $|r| \geq 1$

Sum of an Infinite Geometric Series (p. 706) The sum S of an infinite geometric series with $|r| < 1$ is given by

$$S = \frac{a_1}{1 - r}.$$

If $|r| \geq 1$, the series has no sum.

Recursive Formulas for Sequences (p. 714)
Arithmetic Sequence $a_n = a_{n-1} + d$, where d is the common difference
Geometric Sequence $a_n = r \cdot a_{n-1}$, where r is the common ratio

Binomial Theorem (p. 722) If n is a natural number, then $(a + b)^n =$

$${}_nC_0\, a^n b^0 + {}_nC_1\, a^{n-1} b^1 + {}_nC_2\, a^{n-2} b^2 + \cdots + {}_nC_n\, a^0 b^n = \sum_{k=0}^{n} \frac{n!}{k!(n-k)!} a^{n-k} b^k.$$

Binomial Expansion (p. 723) In a binomial expansion of $(a + b)^n$,
- There are $n + 1$ terms.
- n is the exponent of a in the first term and b in the last term.
- In successive terms, the exponent of a decreases by 1, and the exponent of b increases by 1.
- The sum of the exponents in each term is n.
- The coefficients are symmetric.

Mathematical Induction (p. 727)
Step 1 Show that the statement is true for $n = 1$.
Step 2 Assume that the statement is true for some natural number k. This assumption is called the inductive hypothesis.
Step 3 Show that the statement is true for the next natural number $k + 1$.

Probability and Statistics — Chapter 12

Measures of Central Tendency (p. 752)
mean the sum of the data divided by the number of items in the data set
median the middle number of the ordered data, or the mean of the middle two numbers
mode the number or numbers that occur most often

Margin of Sampling Error (p. 753) When a random sample n is taken from a population, the margin of sampling error can be approximated by $\pm \frac{1}{\sqrt{n}}$.

Standard Deviation Formula (p. 754)

Sample $s = \sqrt{\dfrac{\sum_{k=1}^{n}(x_k - \bar{x})^2}{n-1}}$ **Population** $\sigma = \sqrt{\dfrac{\sum_{k=1}^{n}(x_k - \mu)^2}{n}}$

Conditional Probability (p. 759) Given that A and B are dependent events, the conditional probability of an event B, given that an event A has already occurred, is defined as

$$P(B \mid A) = \frac{P(A \text{ and } B)}{P(A)}, \text{ where } P(A) \neq 0.$$

Probability of Success and Failure (p. 764) If an event can succeed in s ways and fail in f ways, then the probabilities of success $P(S)$ and of failure $P(F)$ are as follows.

$$P(S) = \frac{s}{s+f} \qquad P(F) = \frac{f}{s+f}$$

Characteristics of the Normal Distribution (p. 773)
- The maximum occurs at the mean. The mean, median, and mode are equal.
- The distribution extends from negative infinity to positive infinity, but never touches the x-axis.
- The population mean μ and standard deviation σ are used to determine probabilities. Probabilities are cumulative and are expressed as inequalities.
- Because the area under the normal curve represents probabilities, this area is 1.

The Empirical Rule (p. 774) A normal distribution with mean μ and standard deviation σ has the following properties.
- About 68% of the values are within 1σ of the mean.
- About 95% of the values are within 2σ of the mean.
- About 99% of the values are within 3σ of the mean.

95% Confidence Interval Formula (p. 780) A 95% confidence interval estimate can be found by using the formula $CI = \bar{x} \pm 2 \cdot \frac{s}{\sqrt{n}}$, where $\bar{x}$ is the mean of the sample, s is the standard deviation of the sample, and n is the size of the sample.

Hypothesis Testing (p. 781)
Step 1 State the null hypothesis H_0 and the alternative hypothesis H_1.
Step 2 Design the experiment.
Step 3 Conduct the experiment and collect the data.
Step 4 Find the confidence interval.
Step 5 Make the correct statistical inference. Accept the null hypothesis if the population parameter falls into the confidence interval.

Binomial Experiments (p. 786)
- There are only two possible outcomes, success or failure.
- There is a fixed number of trials, n.
- The probability of success is the same in every trial.
- The trials are independent.
- The random variable is the number of successes in n trials.

Binomial Distribution Functions (p. 787) The probability of x successes in n independent trials is

$$P(x) = C(n, x)\, s^x f^{n-x},$$

where s is the probability of success of an individual trial and f is the probability of failure on that same individual trial $(s + f = 1)$.

Expected Value of a Binomial Distribution (p. 787) The expected value for a binomial distribution is $E(X) = ns$, where n is the total number of trials and s is the probability of success.

Normal Approximation of a Binomial Distribution (p. 789) A binomial distribution with n trials and probability of success s and probability of failure f such that $ns \geq 5$ and $nf \geq 5$, then the binomial distribution can be approximated by a normal distribution with $\bar{x} = ns$ and $\sigma = \sqrt{nsf}$.

Trigonometric Functions — Chapter 13

Trigonometric Functions in Right Triangles (p. 808)

sine $\sin\theta = \frac{\text{opp}}{\text{hyp}}$	**cosine** $\cos\theta = \frac{\text{adj}}{\text{hyp}}$
tangent $\tan = \frac{\text{opp}}{\text{adj}}$	**cosecant** $\csc\theta = \frac{\text{hyp}}{\text{opp}}$
secant $\sec\theta = \frac{\text{hyp}}{\text{adj}}$	**cotangent** $\cot = \frac{\text{adj}}{\text{opp}}$

Inverse Trigonometric Ratios (p. 811)
inverse sine If $\sin A = x$, then $\sin^{-1} x = m\angle A$.
inverse cosine If $\cos A = x$, then $\cos^{-1} x = m\angle A$.
inverse tangent If $\tan A = x$, then $\tan^{-1} x = m\angle A$.

Angle Measures (p. 817) If the measure of an angle is positive, the terminal side is rotated counterclockwise. If the measure of an angle is negative, the terminal side is rotated clockwise.

Convert Degrees to Radians (p. 819) To convert from degrees to radians, multiply the number of degrees by $\frac{\pi \text{ radians}}{180°}$.

Convert Radians to Degrees (p. 819) To convert from radians to degrees, multiply the number of radians by $\frac{180°}{\pi \text{ radians}}$.

Arc Length (p. 820) For a circle with radius r and central angle θ (in radians), the arc length s equals the product of r and θ.

Trigonometric Functions of General Angles (p. 825) Let θ be an angle in standard position and let $P(x, y)$ be a point on its terminal side. Using the Pythagorean Theorem, $r = \sqrt{x^2 + y^2}$. The six trigonometric functions of θ are defined below.

$\sin\theta = \frac{y}{r}$	$\cos\theta = \frac{x}{r}$	$\tan\theta = \frac{y}{x}, x \neq 0$
$\csc\theta = \frac{r}{y}, y \neq 0$	$\sec\theta = \frac{r}{x}, x \neq 0$	$\cot\theta = \frac{x}{y}, y \neq 0$

Evaluate Trigonometric Functions (p. 827)
Step 1 Find the measure of the reference angle θ'.
Step 2 Evaluate the trigonometric function for θ'.
Step 3 Determine the sign of the trigonometric function value. Use the quadrant in which the terminal side of θ lies.

Area of a Triangle (p. 832)

Area $= \frac{1}{2}bc \sin A$

Area $= \frac{1}{2}ac \sin B$

Area $= \frac{1}{2}ab \sin C$

Law of Sines (p. 833) In $\triangle ABC$, if sides with lengths a, b, and c are opposite angles with measures A, B, and C, respectively, then the following is true.

$$\frac{\sin A}{a} = \frac{\sin B}{b} = \frac{\sin C}{c}$$

Law of Cosines (p. 841) In $\triangle ABC$, if sides with lengths a, b, and c are opposite angles with measures A, B, and C, respectively, then the following are true.

$$a^2 = b^2 + c^2 - 2bc \cos A$$
$$b^2 = a^2 + c^2 - 2ac \cos B$$
$$c^2 = a^2 + b^2 - 2ab \cos C$$

Sine and Cosine Functions on a Unit Circle (p. 848) If the terminal side of an angle θ in standard position intersects the unit circle at $P(x, y)$, then $\cos \theta = x$ and $\sin \theta = y$. $P(x, y) = P(\cos \theta, \sin \theta)$

θ-Intercepts of the Sine and Cosine Functions (p. 856)

$y = a \sin b\theta$: $(0, 0), \left(\frac{1}{2} \cdot \frac{360°}{b}, 0\right), \left(\frac{360°}{b}, 0\right)$

$y = a \cos b\theta$: $\left(\frac{1}{4} \cdot \frac{360°}{b}, 0\right), \left(\frac{3}{4} \cdot \frac{360°}{b}, 0\right)$

Phase Shift (p. 863) The phase shift of the functions $y = a \sin b(\theta - h)$, $y = a \cos b(\theta - h)$, and $y = a \tan b(\theta - h)$ is h, where $b > 0$.
- If $h > 0$, the shift is h units to the right.
- If $h < 0$, the shift is h units to the left.

Vertical Shift (p. 864) The vertical shift of the functions $y = a \sin b\theta + k$, $y = a \cos b\theta + k$, and $y = a \tan b\theta + k$ is k.
- If $k > 0$, the shift is k units up.
- If $k < 0$, the shift is k units down.

Graph Trigonometric Functions (p. 865)

Step 1 Determine the vertical shift and graph the midline.
Step 2 Determine the amplitude, if it exists. Use dashed lines to indicate the maximum and minimum values of the function.
Step 3 Determine the period of the function and graph the appropriate function.
Step 4 Determine the phase shift and translate the graph accordingly.

Inverse Trigonometric Functions (p. 871)

Arcsine $y = \text{Arcsin } x$, $y = \text{Sin}^{-1} x$
Arccosine $y = \text{Arccos } x$, $y = \text{Cos}^{-1} x$
Arctangent $y = \text{Arctan } x$, $y = \text{Tan}^{-1} x$

Trigonometric Identities and Equations — Chapter 14

Basic Trigonometric Identities (p. 891)

Quotient Identities	$\tan \theta = \frac{\sin \theta}{\cos \theta}, \cos \theta \neq 0$	$\cot \theta = \frac{\cos \theta}{\sin \theta}, \sin \theta \neq 0$	
Reciprocal Identities	$\csc \theta = \frac{1}{\sin \theta}, \sin \theta \neq 0$	$\sec \theta = \frac{1}{\cos \theta}, \cos \theta \neq 0$	$\cot \theta = \frac{1}{\tan \theta}, \tan \theta \neq 0$
Pythagorean Identities	$\cos^2 \theta + \sin^2 \theta = 1$	$\tan^2 \theta + 1 = \sec^2 \theta$	$\cot^2 \theta + 1 = \csc^2 \theta$
Cofunction Identities	$\sin\left(\frac{\pi}{2} - \theta\right) = \cos \theta$	$\cos\left(\frac{\pi}{2} - \theta\right) = \sin \theta$	$\tan\left(\frac{\pi}{2} - \theta\right) = \cot \theta$
Negative Angle Identities	$\sin(-\theta) = -\sin \theta$	$\cos(-\theta) = \cos \theta$	$\tan(-\theta) = -\tan \theta$

Verifying Identities by Transforming One Side (p. 898)

Step 1 Simplify one side of an equation until the two sides of the equation are the same. It is often easier to work with the more complicated side of the equation.
Step 2 Transform that expression into the form of the simpler side.

Suggestions for Verifying Identities (p. 899)
- Substitute one or more basic trigonometric identities to simplify the expression.
- Factor or multiply as necessary. You may have to multiply both the numerator and denominator by the same trigonometric expression.
- Write each side of the identity in terms of sine and cosine only. Then simplify each side as much as possible.
- The properties of equality do not apply to identities as they do with equations. Do not perform operations to the quantities from each side of an unverified identity.

Sum and Difference of Angles Identities (p. 904)

Sum Identities
- $\sin(A + B) = \sin A \cos B + \cos A \sin B$
- $\cos(A + B) = \cos A \cos B - \sin A \sin B$
- $\tan(A + B) = \frac{\tan A + \tan B}{1 - \tan A \tan B}$

Difference Identities
- $\sin(A - B) = \sin A \cos B - \cos A \sin B$
- $\cos(A - B) = \cos A \cos B + \sin A \sin B$
- $\tan(A - B) = \frac{\tan A - \tan B}{1 + \tan A \tan B}$

Double-Angle Identities (p. 911)

$\sin 2\theta = 2 \sin \theta \cos \theta$

$\cos 2\theta = \cos^2 \theta - \sin^2 \theta$
$\cos 2\theta = 2 \cos^2 \theta - 1$
$\cos 2\theta = 1 - 2 \sin^2 \theta$

$\tan 2\theta = \frac{2 \tan \theta}{1 - \tan^2 \theta}$

Half-Angle Identities (p. 912)

$\sin \frac{\theta}{2} = \pm\sqrt{\frac{1 - \cos \theta}{2}}$

$\cos \frac{\theta}{2} = \pm\sqrt{\frac{1 + \cos \theta}{2}}$

$\tan \frac{\theta}{2} = \pm\sqrt{\frac{1 - \cos \theta}{1 + \cos \theta}}$, $\cos \theta \neq -1$

Selected Answers and Solutions

For Homework Help, go to Hotmath.com
Complete, step-by-step solutions of most odd-numbered exercises are provided free of charge.

Chapter 0 Preparing for Advanced Algebra

Page P5 Lesson 0-1

1. D = {1, 2, 3}, R = {6, 7, 10}; yes **3.** D = {1, 2}, R = {5, 7, 9}; no **5.** D = {−2, −1, 0, 3}, R = {−3, −2, 2}; yes **7.** D = {−1, 0, 1, 2, 3}, R = {−3, −2, −1, 2, 3, 4}; no **9.** I **11.** none

Page P6 Lesson 0-2

1. $a^2 + 6a + 8$ **3.** $h^2 - 16$ **5.** $b^2 + b - 12$ **7.** $r^2 - 5r - 24$ **9.** $p^2 + 16p + 64$ **11.** $2c^2 - 9c - 5$ **13.** $6m^2 - 7m - 20$ **15.** $2q^2 - 13q - 34$ **17a.** $n - 7$, $n + 2$ **17b.** $n^2 - 5n - 14$

Page P8 Lesson 0-3

1. $4x(3x + 1)$ **3.** $4ab(2b - 3)$ **5.** $(y + 3)(y + 9)$ **7.** $(3y + 1)(y + 4)$ **9.** $(3x + 4)(x + 8)$ **11.** $(y - 4)(y - 1)$ **13.** $2(3a - b)(a - 8b)$ **15.** $(2x - 3y)(9x - 2y)$ **17.** $(3x - 4)^2$ **19.** $(x + 12)(x - 12)$ **21.** $(4y + 1)(4y - 1)$ **23.** $4(3y + 2)(3y - 2)$

Pages P10 and P11 Lesson 0-4

1. independent **3.** independent **5.** 6 **7.** 12 **9.** 48 **11.** 60,480 **13.** 358,800 **15.** 60

Page P14 Lesson 0-5

1. 60 **3.** 2520 **5.** 6 **7.** 15,120 **9.** permutation; 5040 **11.** combination; 715 **13.** combination; 15 **15.** permutation; 3360 **17.** 840 ways **19.** 220 ways

Page P16 Lesson 0-6

1. similar **3.** neither **5.** similar **7.** 8; 21 **9.** 10.2; 13.6 **11.** $4\frac{1}{2}$ in.

Page P18 Lesson 0-7

1. 39 ft **3.** 8.3 cm **5.** 5 **7.** 9.2 **9.** 8.5 **11.** yes **13.** no **15.** yes **17.** about 2.66 m

Chapter 1 Equations and Inequalities

Page 3 Chapter 1 Get Ready

1. 12.25 **3.** −66.15 **5.** $1\frac{13}{15}$ **7.** $-1\frac{1}{3}$ **9.** $10\frac{1}{2}$ yd **11.** −64 **13.** 15.625 **15.** $\frac{2401}{81}$ **17.** $-\frac{3375}{8}$ **19.** true **21.** false **23.** yes

Pages 7–10 Lesson 1-1

1. 4.6 **3.** 18.4 **5.** 11.6 **7.** 0.96875 **9.** 0.6 **11.** $6\frac{4}{15}$ **13.** 28 **15.** −13.4 **17a.** 1524.6 mi **17b.** 720 mi **19.** 20

21 $\frac{b^2c^2}{ad} = \frac{(-0.8)^2(5)^2}{(-4)\left(\frac{1}{5}\right)}$ $a = -4, b = -0.8, c = 5, d = \frac{1}{5}$
$= \frac{(0.64)(25)}{(-0.8)}$ Evaluate the numerator and denominator separately.
$= \frac{16}{-0.8}$ Simplify the numerator.
$= -20$ Simplify the fraction.

23. 3.71 **25.** $\frac{1}{2}(x + 7)(2x)$ **27a.** 584,336,233.6 mi **27b.** 8761 h **27c.** yes; $\frac{8761}{24} = 365$ days or 1 year **29.** 544 **31.** 13.8 **33.** 131.25 **35.** $6\pi x^3$

37 $t = 50 + \frac{n - 40}{4}$ Write the formula.
$= 50 + \frac{120 - 40}{4}$ $n = 120$
$= 50 + \frac{80}{4}$ Evaluate the numerator of the fraction.
$= 50 + 20$ Simplify the fraction.
$= 70$ Simplify.
If the number of chirps is 120, then the temperature is 70°F.

39a. \$3.91; \$5.36; \$7.31 **39b.** \$4.42; \$6.62; \$11.62; Sample answer: the average prices found in part b become increasingly higher with time.

41 $y = \sqrt{b^2\left(1 - \frac{x^2}{a^2}\right)}$ Write the equation.
$= \sqrt{8^2\left(1 - \frac{3^2}{6^2}\right)}$ $a = 6, b = 8, x = 3$
$= \sqrt{64\left(1 - \frac{9}{36}\right)}$ Evaluate the powers.
$= \sqrt{64\left(\frac{27}{36}\right)}$ Simplify inside the parentheses.
$= \sqrt{48}$ Simplify.
≈ 6.9 Use a calculator.

43. Lauren; −12 − 20 = −32. **45.** Subtract 8 from each side. Divide each side by 4. Add 12 to each side. Multiply each side by 3. Subtract 6 from each side. $k = -12$ **47.** Sample answer: $y\left(\frac{-4z}{x^2} - x\right) + z$

49. A table of on-base percentages is limited to those situations listed, while a formula can be used to find any on-base percentage. **51.** 9 mo **53.** B **55.** 10 cm **57.** $6x(x + 2)$ **59.** 3 and 11 **61.** 5 **63.** 11 **65.** −4 **67.** $\frac{5}{8}$

Pages 14–17 Lesson 1-2

1. N, W, Z, Q, R **3.** I, R **5.** Associative Property (×) **7.** Commutative Property (+) **9.** 7; $-\frac{1}{7}$ **11.** −3.8; $\frac{1}{3.8}$

13a. 22(2 + 4 + 3 + 1 + 5 + 6 + 7) or 22(2) + 22(4) + 22(3) + 22(1) + 22(5) + 22(6) + 22(7)
13b. \$616 **13c.** If she continues to mow the same number of lawns, at the end of next week she will have the money. This may not be reasonable because not all the lawns she mowed this week may need to be mowed again next week.

15. $24a + 9b$ **17.** $-16x + 22y$ **19.** Q, R **21.** Q, R

23 $-\sqrt{144} = -12$ belongs to the set of integers (Z), the set of rationals (Q), and the set of reals (R).

25. I, R **27.** Distributive Property **29.** Inverse Property (×) **31.** −12.1; $\frac{1}{12.1}$ **33.** $-\frac{6}{13}$; $\frac{13}{6}$ **35.** $-\sqrt{15}$; $\frac{1}{\sqrt{15}}$ **37.** $12b + 6c$ **39.** $40x - 20y$ **41.** $28g - 48k$ **43.** 53(60 + 60); 53(60) + 53(60); 6360 yd²

45 **a.** (2 + 1)4.50 = (3)4.50 Distributive Property
= \$13.50 Simplify.
b. The amount left over is \$20 − \$13.50 or \$6.50. \$6.50 ÷ 2 = 3.25
Because Billie cannot buy part of a sandwich, she can buy 3 cold sandwiches.
c. In two weeks, or ten school days, Billie buys a hot lunch 3 times and buys a cold sandwich 3 times. She has to pack lunch 10 − (3 + 3) = 10 − 6 or 4 times.

47. $\frac{27}{5}c - \frac{199}{20}d$ **49.** $-42x - 72y - 30z$

51 **a.** $-\sqrt{6}$ is an irrational number because the square root of 6 is not a perfect square.
3, or $\frac{3}{1}$, is a rational number, integer, whole number, and natural number.
$\frac{-15}{3}$, or −5, is a rational number and integer.
4.1, or $\frac{41}{10}$, is a rational number.
π is an irrational number.
0, or $\frac{0}{1}, \frac{0}{2}, \ldots$, is a rational number, integer, and whole number.
$\frac{3}{8}$ is a rational number.
$\sqrt{36}$, or 6, is a rational number, integer, whole number, and natural number.

irrational	rational	integer	whole	natural
$-\sqrt{6}$, π	3, $\frac{-15}{3}$, 4.1, 0, $\frac{3}{8}$, $\sqrt{36}$	3, $\frac{-15}{3}$, 0, $\sqrt{36}$	3, 0, $\sqrt{36}$	3, $\sqrt{36}$

b. Use a calculator to find the decimal form of $-\sqrt{6}$ and π; $-\sqrt{6} \approx -2.449$, 3 = 3.0, $\frac{-15}{3} = -5$, 4.1 = 4.1, π ≈ 3.14, 0 = 0, $\frac{3}{8} = 0.375$, $\sqrt{36} = 6$. Since −5 < −2.449 < 0 < 0.375 < 3.14 < 4.1 < 6, the numbers from least to greatest are $\frac{-15}{3}$, $-\sqrt{6}$, 0, $\frac{3}{8}$, π, 4.1, $\sqrt{36}$.
c. Draw a number line with tick marks at integers from −6 to 6. Then use the decimal forms in part d to graph each number.

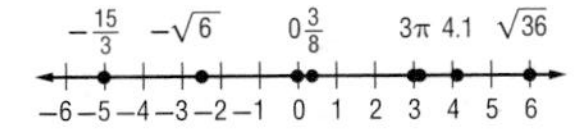

d. Sample answer: By converting the real numbers into decimal form, the decimal points can be easily lined up and the numbers compared.

53. $\sqrt{81}$; It is a rational number, while the other three are irrational numbers. **55.** No; Luna did not distribute the negative sign to the second term and Sophia switched the *a* and *b* terms because usually *a* comes first. The correct answer is $32a - 46b$.
57. Sample answer: $\sqrt{5} \cdot \sqrt{5} = \sqrt{25}$ or 5, which is not irrational **59.** Sample answer: (a) 3.2 and (b) $\sqrt{10}$
61. Sample answer: The Commutative Property does not hold for subtraction or division because order matters with these two operations. In addition or multiplication, the order does not matter. For example, 2 + 4 = 4 + 2 and 2 • 4 = 4 • 2. However, with subtraction, 2 − 4 ≠ 4 − 2, and with division, 2 ÷ 4 ≠ 4 ÷ 2. **63.** B **65.** B **67.** 24 **69.** about 2.66 m **71.** $3(3x^2 - x + 6)$ **73.** $10x(x - 2)$ **75.** $6(2x^2 - 3x - 4)$ **77.** $y^2 + y - 2$ **79.** $b^2 - 10b + 21$ **81.** $p^2 - 8p - 9$ **83.** $\frac{10}{9}$ **85.** 8 **87.** −1.176 **89.** −1.7

Pages 22–25 Lesson 1-3

1. $12[x + (-3)]$ **3.** The sum of five times a number and 7 equals 18. **5.** The difference between five times a number and the cube of that number is 12. **7.** Reflexive Property **9.** 53 **11.** −8 **13.** −6 **15.** 3 **17.** 4 **19.** $q = \frac{8r - 3}{5}$ **21.** B **23.** $8x^2$ **25.** $\frac{x}{4} + 5$
27. The quotient of the sum of 3 and a number and 4 is 5.

29 Let *n* = the number of home runs that Jacobs hit. Then *n* + 6 = the number of home runs that Cabrera hit.
$n + (n + 6) = 46$ Cabrera and Jacobs hit a combined total of 46 home runs.
$2n + 6 = 46$ Simplify.
$2n = 40$ Subtract 6 from each side.
$n = 20$ Divide each side by 2.
So, Jacobs hit 20 home runs and Cabrera hit *n* + 6 = 20 + 6 or 26 home runs.

31. Substitution **33.** Multiplication (=) **35.** 5 **37.** −3

39 $5(-2x - 4) - 3(4x + 5) = 97$ Original equation
$-10x - 20 - 12x - 15 = 97$ Apply the Distributive Property.
$-22x - 35 = 97$ Simplify the left side.
$-22x = 132$ Add 35 to each side.
$x = -6$ Divide each side by −22.

41. −3 **43.** *s* = length of a side; 5*s* = 100; 20 in. **45.** $m = \frac{E}{c^2}$ **47.** $h = \frac{z}{\pi q^3}$ **49.** $a = \frac{y - bx - c}{x^2}$ **51a.** $V = \pi \cdot r \cdot r \cdot h$ **51b.** $h = \frac{V}{\pi r^2}$ **53.** −2 **55.** −4 **57.** $-\frac{117}{11}$ **59.** *x* = the cost of rent each month; 622 + 428 + 240 + 144 + 12*x* = 10,734; \$775 per month

61 **a.** The integers from −5 to 5 are −5, −4, −3, −2, −1, 0, 1, 2, 3, 4, and 5. Draw a number line and plot a point at each integer.

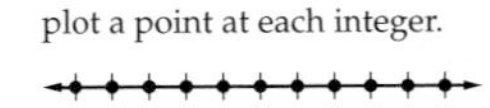

b. −5 and 5 are 5 units from zero, −4 and 4 are 4 units from zero, and so on.

For Homework Help, go to Hotmath.com

Integer	Distance from Zero
−5	5
−4	4
−3	3
−2	2
−1	1
0	0
1	1
2	2
3	3
4	4
5	5

c. The points (x, y) = (integer, distance from zero) are $(-5, 5)$, $(-4, 4)$, $(-3, 3)$, $(-2, 2)$, $(-1, 1)$, $(0, 0)$, $(1, 1)$, $(2, 2)$, $(3, 3)$, $(4, 4)$, and $(5, 5)$.

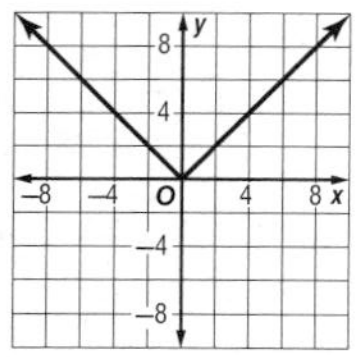

d. For positive integers, the distance from zero is the same as the integer. For negative integers, the distance is the integer with the opposite sign because distance is always positive.

63. $y_1 = y_2 - \sqrt{d^2 - (x_2 - x_1)^2}$ **65.** Sample answer: $3(x - 4) = 3x + 5$; $2(3x - 1) = 6x - 2$ **67.** D **69.** A **71.** $-3x + 6y + 6z$ **73.** 605 ft **75.** $4\frac{1}{5}$ **77.** $2x$ **79.** $-3\frac{2}{3}$ **81.** $-5x$

Pages 30–32 Lesson 1-4

1. 12 **3.** −108 **5a.** $|x - 78| = 2$ **5b.** least: 76°F; greatest: 80°F **5c.** 77°F; This would ensure a minimum temperature of 76°F. **7.** {15, −7} **9.** ∅ **11.** $\left\{\frac{6}{5}, -\frac{4}{5}\right\}$

13. 2 **15.** 25 **17.** 9.2 **19.** 49.2 **21.** −63 **23.** {34, −8} **25.** {4, −14} **27.** {−2, −10} **29.** 2

31 $2|3x - 4| + 8 = 6$ Original equation
$2|3x - 4| + 8 - 8 = 6 - 8$ Subtract 8 from each side.
$2|3x - 4| = -2$ Simplify.
$|3x - 4| = -1$ Divide each side by 2.

Because the absolute value of a number is always positive or zero, this sentence is never true. So, there is no solution.

33. ∅ **35.** $|x - 5.67| = 0.02$; heaviest: 5.69 g; lightest: 5.65 g **37.** 28 **39.** $\left\{1, \frac{1}{5}\right\}$ **41.** $-\frac{8}{3}$

43 The average altitude c is 100 ft. Since the altitude can be plus or minus 245 feet, the range r is 245.

$|x - c| = r$ Absolute value equation
$|x - 100| = 245$ $c = 100$ and $r = 245$
$|x - 100| = 245$ means $x - 100 = 245$ or $x - 100 = -245$.

Case 1	Case 2
$x - 100 = 245$	$x - 100 = -245$
$x - 100 + 100 = 245 + 100$	$x - 100 + 100 = -245 + 100$
$x = 345$	$x = -145$

The solutions are 345 and −145. This means the maximum is 345 ft above sea level; the minimum is −145 ft or 145 ft below sea level. The maximum is reasonable, but the minimum is not. Florida's lowest point should be at sea level where Florida meets the Atlantic Ocean and the Gulf of Mexico.

45. Ling; Ana included an extraneous solution. She would have caught this error if she had checked to see if her answers were correct by substituting the values into the original equation. **47.** Sometimes; this is only true for certain values of a. For example, it is true for $a = 8$; if $8 > 7$, then $11 > 10$. However, it is not true for $a = -8$; if $8 > 7$, then $5 \not> 10$. **49.** Always; starting with numbers between 1 and 5 and subtracting 3 will produce numbers between −2 and 2. These all have an absolute value less than or equal to 2. **51.** Sample answer: First, isolate the absolute value symbol by subtracting each side by c, and then dividing each side by a. You then have $|x - b|$ equals a mathematical expression. Take away the absolute value symbol, and form two new equations by setting $x - b$ equal to both the positive and negative values of the expression. Solve each equation for x. Then substitute each solution into the original equation, and confirm whether they are correct. **53.** $\frac{5}{8}$ **55.** C **57.** −2 **59a.** \$6800 **59b.** \$535.83 **59c.** 1 mo **61.** Distributive **63.** $10x + 2y$ **65.** $11m + 10a$ **67.** $32c - 46d$ **69.** 2 **71.** −8 **73.** $-\frac{4}{7}$

Pages 36–39 Lesson 1-5

1. $b < 8$

3. $x \le -6$

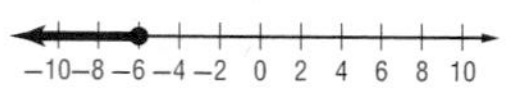

5. $w < 2$

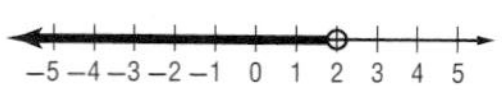

7 $s \ge \frac{s + 6}{5}$ Original inequality
$5s \ge s + 6$ Multiply each side by 5.
$4s \ge 6$ Subtract s from each side.
$s \ge 1.5$ Divide each side by 4.
The solution set is $\{s \mid s \ge 1.5\}$.

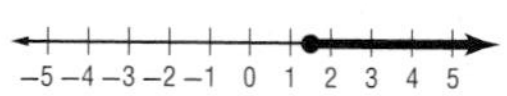

9. 40 bags

11. $n \le -3$

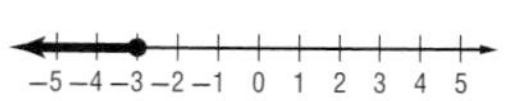

13. $t \le \frac{1}{2}$

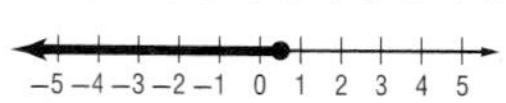

15. $k < 27$

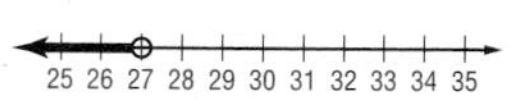

17. $z < 3$

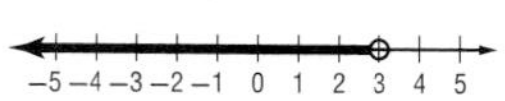

19 $12 < -4(3c - 6)$ Original inequality
$-3 > 3c - 6$ Divide each side by −4, reversing the inequality symbol.
$3 > 3c$ Add 6 to each side.
$1 > c$ Divide each side by 3.
The solution set is $\{c \mid c < 1\}$.

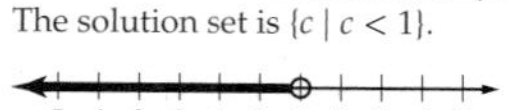

21. $z < 3$

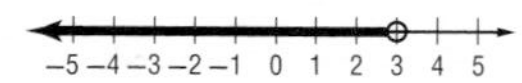

23. $3x - 12 < 21$; $x < 11$ **25.** $5x - 6 > x$; $x > 1.5$ **27.** 8 hours

29. $x > -\frac{3}{4}$

31. $y > 18.75$

33. $v > -4.5$

35. $r > -\frac{3}{4}$

37a. $250 + 0.03(500a) \ge 700$ **37b.** $a \ge 30$; He must sell at least 30 advertisements. **39.** $\frac{x}{3} + 4 \le 2x + 12$; $x \ge -4.8$

41 **a.** Let d = the number of miles by which Jamie should increase her average daily run. Then $5 + d$ = her average daily distance after the increase.

3 times	average daily distance	is at least	length of a marathon
3 •	$(5 + d)$	≥	26.2

So, the inequality is $3(5 + d) \ge 26.2$.

b. $3(5 + d) \ge 26.2$ Original inequality
$5 + d \ge 8.73$ Divide each side by 3. Round to the nearest hundredth.
$d \ge 3.73$ Subtract 5 from each side.

In order to have enough endurance to run a marathon, Jamie should increase the distance of her average daily run by at least 3.73 miles.

43a. Sample answer:

Point	Resulting Statement	True or False
(0, 0)	$0 \ge 3$	False
(1, 1)	$1 \ge \frac{5}{2}$	False
(2, 2)	$2 \ge 2$	True
(3, 3)	$3 \ge \frac{3}{2}$	True
(4, 4)	$4 \ge 1$	True

43b. Sample answer:

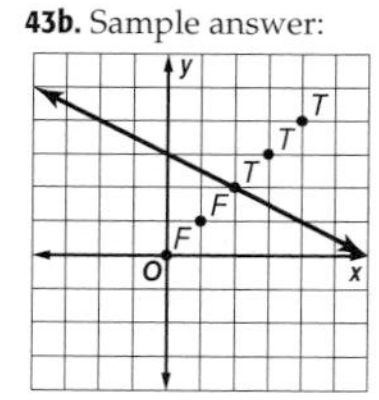

43c. Sample answer: The points on or above the line result in true statements, and the points below the line result in false statements. This is true for all points on the coordinate plane. **45.** No; Sample answer: Madlynn reversed the inequality sign when she added 1 to each side. Emilie did not reverse the inequality sign at all. **47.** Using the Triangle Inequality Theorem, we know that the sum of the lengths of any 2 sides of a triangle must be greater than the length of the remaining side. This generates 3 inequalities to examine.

$3x + 4 + 2x + 5 > 4x$ $3x + 4 + 4x > 2x + 5$
$x > -9$ $x > 0.2$
$2x + 5 + 4x > 3x + 4$
$x > -\frac{1}{3}$

In order for all 3 conditions to be true, x must be greater than 0.2. **49.** Sample answer: When one number is greater than another number, it is either more positive or less negative than that number. When these numbers are multiplied by a negative value, their roles are reversed. That is, the number that was more positive is now more negative than the other number. Thus, it is now *less than* that number and the inequality symbol needs to be reversed.

51. A **53.** D **55.** $\left\{-\frac{1}{3}, 3\right\}$ **57.** $|t - 3647.5| = 891.5$ **59a.** $SA = 2\pi r(r + h)$ **59b.** 78π cm² **59c.** Sample answer: The formula in part b is quicker. **61.** {−9, 9} **63.** $\left\{\frac{1}{2}, 7\right\}$ **65.** {−6, 2}

Pages 45–48 Lesson 1-6

1. $\{g \mid -12 < g < -2\}$

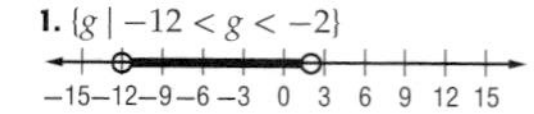

3. $\{z \mid z > -3$ or $z < -6\}$

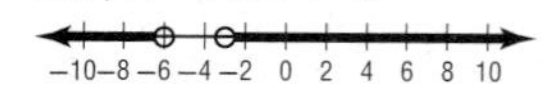

5. $\{c \mid c \ge 8$ or $c \le -8\}$

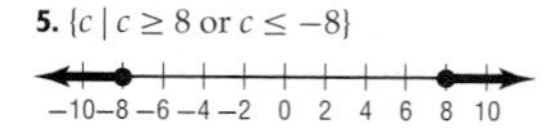

7. $\{z \mid -6 < z < 6\}$

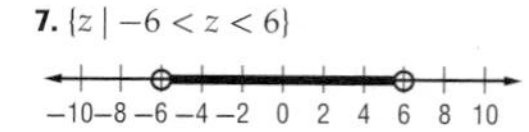

9. $\left\{v \,\middle|\, v > 3 \text{ or } v < -\frac{19}{3}\right\}$

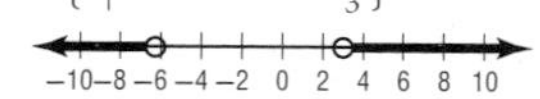

11. $43.96 \le c \le 77.94$; between \$43.96 and \$77.94

13. $\{d \mid -1 \le d \le 0.5\}$

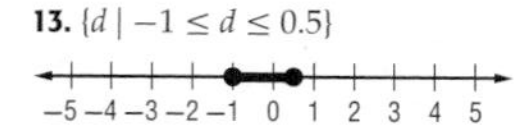

15. $\{y \mid y < -4$ or $y > 7\}$

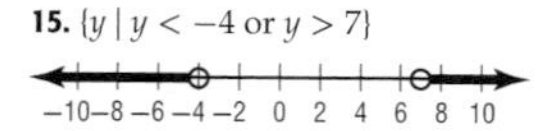

17. $\{k \mid -4 > k$ or $k > 4\}$

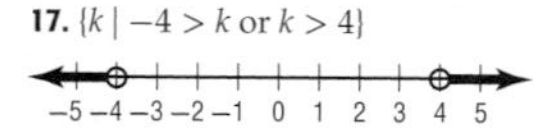

19 $|8t + 3| \le 4$ is equivalent to $-4 \le 8t + 3 \le 4$.

$$-4 \le 8t + 3 \le 4$$
$$-4 - 3 \le 8t + 3 - 3 \le 4 - 3$$
$$-7 \le 8t \le 1$$
$$-\frac{7}{8} \le \frac{8t}{8} \le \frac{1}{8}$$
$$-\frac{7}{8} \le t \le \frac{1}{8}$$

The solution set is $\left\{t \,\middle|\, -\frac{7}{8} \le t \le \frac{1}{8}\right\}$.

For Homework Help, go to Hotmath.com

21. $\left\{j \middle| j \geq \frac{8}{5} \text{ or } j \leq -\frac{16}{5}\right\}$

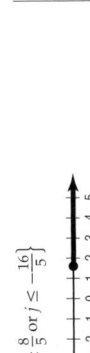

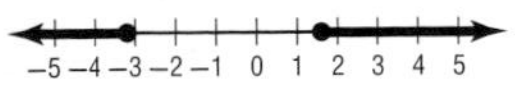

23. $|x - 1| \leq 5$ 25. $|x + 9| \leq 3$ 27. $|x - 2| \geq 10$
29. $|x + 3| > 1$

31 A healthy weight w for a fully grown female Labrador retriever is 55 pounds to 70 pounds. This can be represented by $55 \leq w \leq 70$.

33. $\{k \mid 2 < k < 4\}$

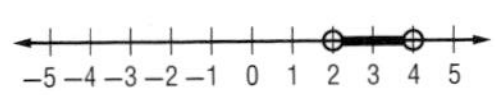

35. $\{h \mid h < -15 \text{ or } h > 15\}$

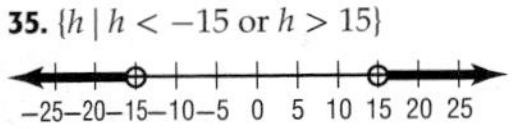

37. $\{z \mid z < -1 \text{ or } z > 5\}$

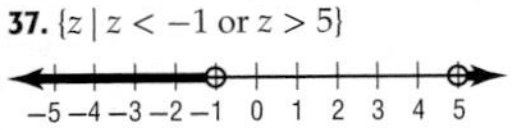

39. $\left\{f \middle| f > \frac{26}{5} \text{ or } f < -\frac{22}{5}\right\}$

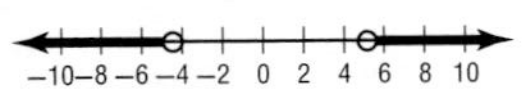

41. $|x + 5| \geq 4$ 43. $6 \leq |x - 2| \leq 10$

45. $\{n \mid -7 < n < 1\}$

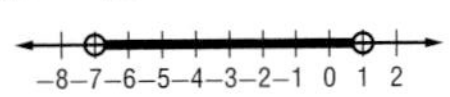

47. $\varnothing$

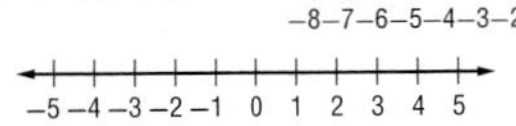

49. $\left\{g \middle| g \geq -\frac{2}{3}\right\}$

51. $|s - 88| > 38$; $\{s \mid s > 126 \text{ or } s < 50\}$ 53. Sample answer: David; when Sarah converted the absolute value into two inequalities, she mistakenly switched the inequality symbols. 55. False; sample answer: the graph of $x > 2$ and $x > 5$ is a ray bounded only on one end. 57. true 59. Sample answer: The graph on the left indicates a solution set from –3 to 5 for the inequality $|x - 1| \leq 4$. The graph on the right indicates a solution set of all numbers less than or equal to –3 or greater than or equal to 5 for the inequality $|x - 1| \geq 4$. 61. Each of these has a non-empty solution set except for $x > 5$ and $x < 1$. There are no values of x that are simultaneously greater than 5 and less than 1. 63. C 65. 60
67a. $750 \leq x \leq 990$ 67b. 110 g 69. $\{0, 10\}$ 71. $\varnothing$
73. Transitive (=)

Pages 49–52 Chapter 1 Study Guide and Review

1. false; nonnegative 3. true 5. true 7. false; or
9. true 11. 3 13. 10 15. 21 17. 169.65 in^3
19. N, W, Z, Q, R 21. $11x + 2y$ 23. $5m + 41n$
25. –7 27. $\frac{3}{2}$ 29. $8 31. $m = \frac{r + 5}{pn}$ 33. 8 in.
35. $\{2,10\}$ 37. $\{14\}$

39. $a \geq -6$

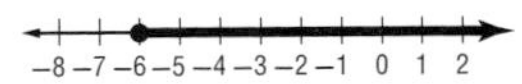

41. $x \leq -\frac{2}{9}$

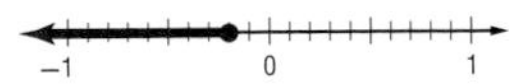

43. 3 or fewer slices each
45. $\{x \mid -2 < x < 4\}$

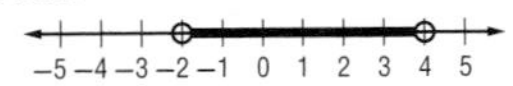

47. $\left\{m \middle| \frac{13}{5} \leq m < \frac{24}{5}\right\}$

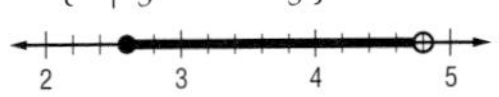

49. $\{p \mid -5 \leq p \leq 33\}$

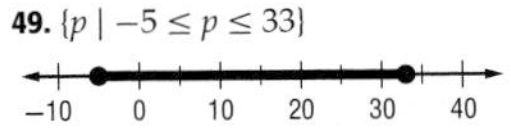

51. $\varnothing$ 53. $20 \leq 2.50(3) + 1.25b \leq 30$; $10 \leq b \leq 18$

Chapter 2 Linear Relations and Functions

Page 59 Chapter 2 Get Ready

1. (4, 1); I 3. (0, 0); origin 5. (–4, –4); III
7. –15 9. 10 11. $40 13. $b = \frac{a}{3} - 3$ 15. $x = \frac{8}{3} + \frac{4}{3}y$

Pages 64–67 Lesson 2-1

1. D = {5, 6, –2}, R = {3, –8, 1}; function; both

3 The domain is the set of x-values: {–2, 1, 4, 8}; the range is the set of y-values: {–4, –2, 6}. Since each element of the domain is paired with exactly one element of the range, the relation is a function. Since each element of the range corresponds to an element of the domain, the relation is an onto function.

5.

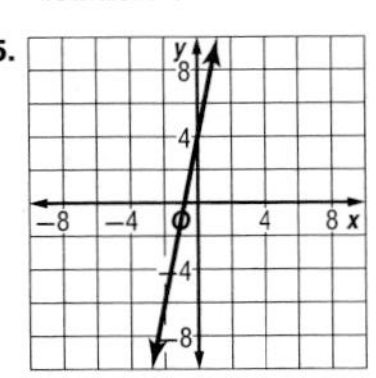

D = {all real numbers}, R = {all real numbers}; function; both; continuous

7.

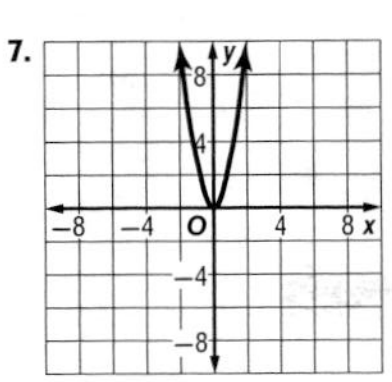

D = {all real numbers}, R = $\{y \mid y \geq 0\}$; function; neither; continuous
9. 4 11. D = {–0.3, 0.4, 1.2}, R = {–6, –3, –1, 4}; not a function 13. D = {–3, –1, 3, 5}, R = {–4, 0, 3}; function; one-to-one

15.

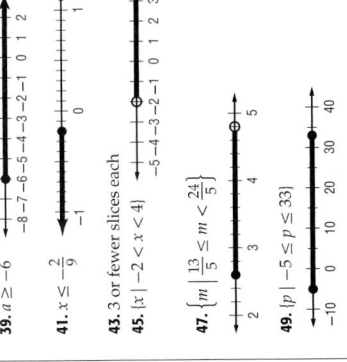

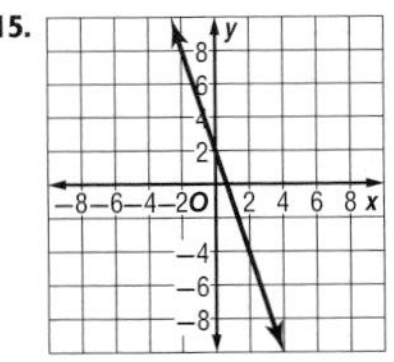

D = {all real numbers}, R = {all real numbers}; function; both; continuous

17.

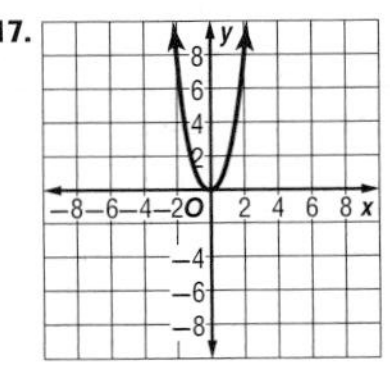

D = {all real numbers}, R = $\{y \mid y \geq 0\}$; function; neither; continuous

19.

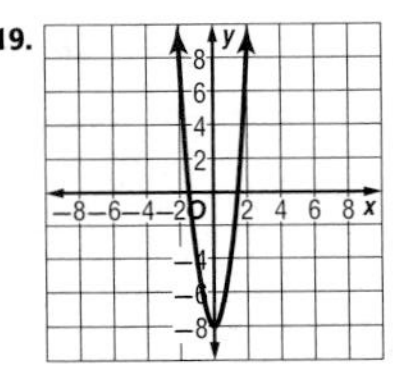

D = {all real numbers}, R = $\{y \mid y \geq -8\}$; function; neither; continuous

21

$f(x) = 5x^3 + 1$		Original function
$f(-8) = 5(-8)^3 + 1$		Substitute –8 for each x.
	$= 5(-512) + 1$	Evaluate $(-8)^3$.
	$= -2560 + 1$	Multiply.
	$= -2559$	Simplify.

23a. {(0, 1), (20, 1.6), (40, 2.2), (60, 2.8), (80, 3.4), (100, 4)}

23b.

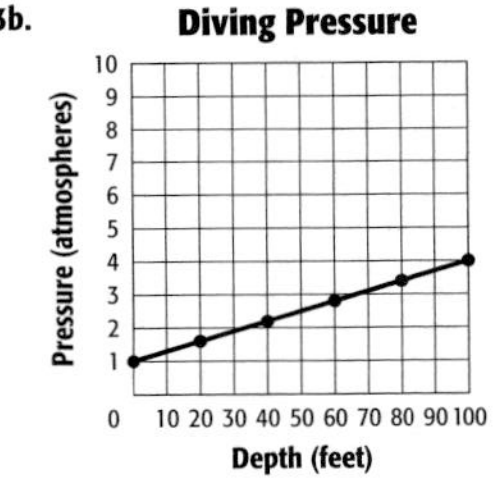

23c. D = $\{x \mid x \geq 0\}$, R = $\{y \mid y \geq 1\}$; continuous
23d. Yes; each domain value is paired with only one range value so the relation is a function. 25. 29
27. –72 29. –267 31. –4.5

33

$P(t) = 15 + 3t$		Original function
$P(8) = 15 + 3(8)$		Substitute 8 for each t.
	$= 15 + 24$	Multiply.
	$= 39$	Simplify.

After 8 months, Chaz will have 39 podcasts.

35. Sample answer: Omar; Madison did not square the 3 before multiplying by –4. 37. Never; if the graph crosses the y-axis twice, then there will be two separate y-values that correspond to $x = 0$, which violates the vertical line test. 39. Sample answer: False; a function is onto and not one-to-one if all of the elements of the domain correspond to an element of the range, but more than one element of the domain corresponds to the same element of the range. 41. A 43. I 45. $6 > y > 2$
47. $x > \frac{7}{4}$ or $x < -\frac{11}{4}$ 49. $15x \leq 120$; She can buy up to 8 shirts. 51. $\frac{3}{4}$ or $\frac{7}{4}$ 53. 33a 55. $10c + 36d$
57. 4 59. –4 61. –4 63. –6

Pages 71–74 Lesson 2-2

1. Yes; it can be written as $f(x) = \frac{x}{5} + \frac{12}{5}$. 3. No; x has an exponent that is not 1.

5 a.

$m(x) = 0.75x$		Original function
$m(4) = 0.75(4)$		Substitute 4 for x.
	$= 3$	Simplify.

If you have 4 CDs, you have 3 hours of music.

b.

$m(x) = 0.75x$	Original function
$6 = 0.75x$	Substitute 6 for $m(x)$.
$8 = x$	Divide each side by 0.75.

If the trip is 6 hours long, you should bring 8 CDs.
7. $6x - y = -5$; $A = 6, B = -1, C = -5$ 9. $8x + 9y = 6$; $A = 8, B = 9, C = 6$ 11. $2x - 3y = 12$; $A = 2, B = -3, C = 12$
13. $\frac{5}{2}$; –10 15. 7; $-\frac{21}{4}$

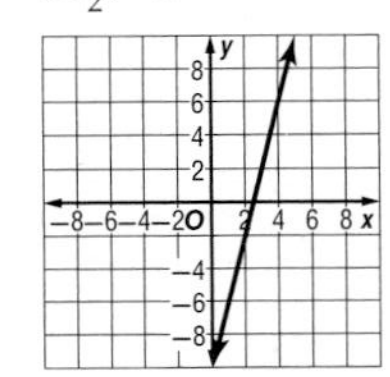

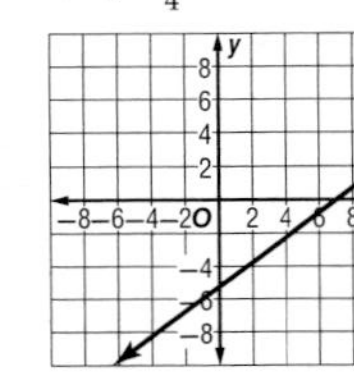

17. No; x has an exponent other than 1. 19. No; x has an exponent other than 1. 21. No; it cannot be written in $f(x) = mx + b$ form. 23. No; it cannot be written in $f(x) = mx + b$ form; There is an xy term. 25a. 260 m 25b. Kingda Ka; Sample answer: The Kingda Ka travels 847.5 meters in 25 seconds, so it travels a greater distance in the same amount of time. 27. $8x + 3y = -6$; $A = 8$, $B = 3$, $C = -6$ 29. $2x + y = -11$; $A = 2$, $B = 1$, $C = -11$

31

$2.4y = -14.4x$	Original equation
$14.4x + 2.4y = 0$	Add 14.4x to each side.
$144x + 24y = 0$	Multiply each side by 10.
$6x + y = 0$	Divide each side by 24.

$A = 6, B = 1, C = 0.$

For Homework Help, go to Hotmath.com

33. $5x + 32y = 160$; $A = 5$, $B = 32$, $C = 160$

35. -0.5; -4

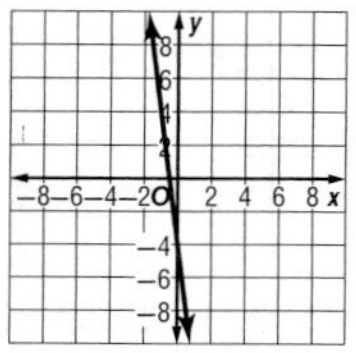

37. -7; 10.5

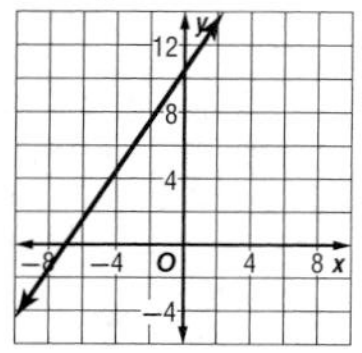

39. 12; -18

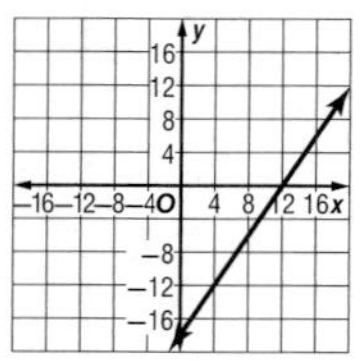

41a. $1.75m + 1.5n = 525$

41b.

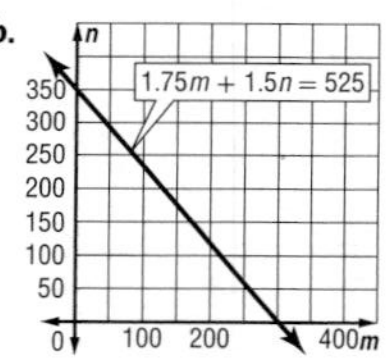

Yes; the graph passes the vertical line test.

41c. No; the amount that Latonya will sell is $1.75 \cdot 100 + 1.5 \cdot 200$, which is \$475.

43a. $y = 3x + 13$ **43b.** \$31 **45.** $4x - 40y = -59$; $A = 4$, $B = -40$, $C = -59$

47 The x-intercept is the value of x when $y = 0$.

$$\frac{6x+15}{4} = 3y - 12 \quad \text{Original equation}$$
$$\frac{6x+15}{4} = 3(0) - 12 \quad \text{Substitute 0 for } y.$$
$$\frac{6x+15}{4} = -12 \quad \text{Simplify.}$$
$$6x + 15 = -48 \quad \text{Multiply each side by 4.}$$
$$6x = -63 \quad \text{Subtract 15 from each side.}$$
$$x = -\frac{63}{6} \quad \text{Divide each side by 6.}$$
$$x = -10.5 \quad \text{Simplify.}$$

The x-intercept is -10.5.

The y-intercept is the value of y when $x = 0$.

$$\frac{6x+15}{4} = 3y - 12 \quad \text{Original equation}$$
$$\frac{6(0)+15}{4} = 3y - 12 \quad \text{Substitute 0 for } x.$$
$$\frac{15}{4} = 3y - 12 \quad \text{Simplify.}$$
$$\frac{63}{4} = 3y \quad \text{Add 12 to each side.}$$
$$5.25 = y \quad \text{Divide each side by 3.}$$

The y-intercept is 5.25.

49. $-1\frac{1}{75}$; $6\frac{1}{3}$ **51a.**

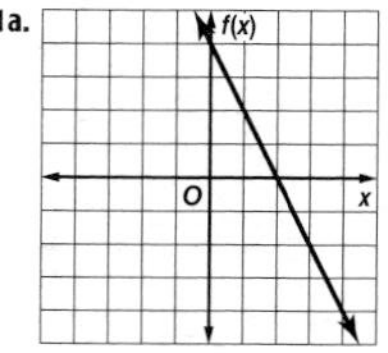

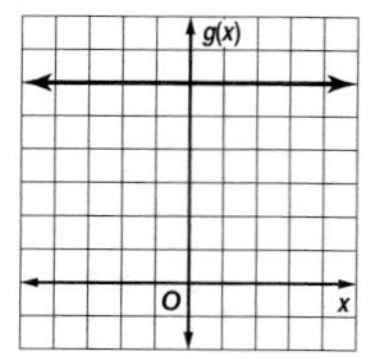

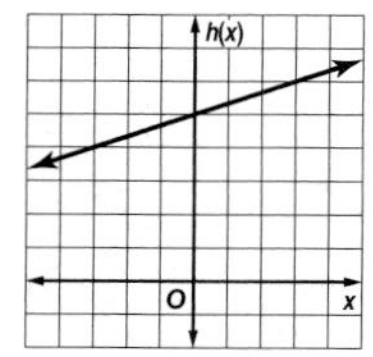

51b.

Function	One-to-One	Onto
$f(x) = -2x + 4$	yes	yes
$g(x) = 6$	no	no
$h(x) = \frac{1}{3}x + 5$	yes	yes

51c. No; horizontal lines are neither one-to-one nor onto because only one y-value is used and it is repeated for every x-value. Every other linear function is one-to-one and onto because every x-value has one unique y-value that is not used by any other x-element and every possible y-value is used. **53.** Sample answer: $f(x) = 2(x - 3)$ **55.** $y = 2xy$; Sample answer: $y = 2xy$ is not a linear function. **57.** C **59.** I **61.** D = {8, −4, −1}, R = {6, 3, 9}; not a function **63.** D = {−3, −4, 7}, R = {−1, −2, 9}; function; both **65.** 0.78 **67.** about −0.583 **69.** $\frac{2}{3}$ **71.** $-\frac{5}{4}$ **73.** $-\frac{1}{3}$ **75.** 9

Pages 79–82 Lesson 2-3

1. 6 feet/min **3a.** about 11,000 per year **3b.** about −5000 per year **3c.** The positive rate in part **a** represents an increase in the sales of digital cameras. The negative rate in part **b** represents a decrease in sales of film cameras. **5.** −3 **7.** $\frac{3}{5}$

9 Use the ordered pairs (3, 20) and (6, 40).

$$\text{rate of change} = \frac{\text{change in } y}{\text{change in } x}$$
$$= \frac{\text{change in height}}{\text{change in time}} \quad \begin{matrix}\leftarrow \text{mm} \\ \leftarrow \text{days}\end{matrix}$$
$$= \frac{40-20}{6-3}$$
$$= \frac{20}{3}$$

The rate of change is $\frac{20}{3}$ mm/day.

11a. 0.15°/h **11b.** −0.125°/h; Yes; the number should be negative because her temperature is dropping.

11c. Tuesday 8:00 A.M.–Tuesday 8:00 P.M. **13.** $\frac{14}{15}$ **15.** −2 **17.** $\frac{5}{3}$ **19.** 5

21 The line passes through (0, 20) and (5, 16).

$$m = \frac{y_2 - y_1}{x_2 - x_1} \quad \text{Slope Formula}$$
$$= \frac{16-20}{5-0} \quad (x_1, y_1) = (0, 20), (x_2, y_2) = (5, 16)$$
$$= \frac{-4}{5} \text{ or } -0.8 \quad \text{Simplify.}$$

23. $\frac{4}{3}$ **25.** 3 **27.** $\frac{6}{5}$

29 $$\text{slope} = \frac{\text{change in } y}{\text{change in } x}$$
$$= \frac{\text{change in vertical distance}}{\text{change in horizontal distance}}$$
$$= \frac{8.9}{2.8}$$
$$\approx 3.2$$

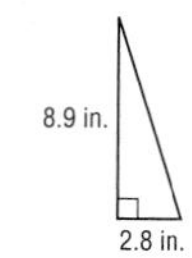

31. 9 **33.** 5 **35a.**

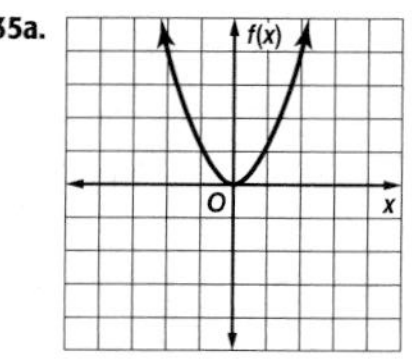

35b.

x	−4	−3	−2	−1	0	1	2	3	4
$f(x)$	16	9	4	1	0	1	4	9	16
slope		−7	−5	−3	−1	1	3	5	7

35c. Sample answer: The rate of change is not constant. The rate of change decreases as x approaches zero and then increases as x approaches infinity. **37.** Sample answer: Because the slope from (2, 3) to (5, 8) is the same as the slope from (5, 8) to (11, y), find the slope between each pair of points and set them equal to each other. Then solve for y.

$$\frac{8-3}{5-2} = \frac{y-8}{11-5}$$
$$\frac{5}{3} = \frac{y-8}{6}$$
$$30 = 3(y-8)$$
$$10 = y - 8$$
$$18 = y$$

39. Sometimes; the slope of a vertical line is undefined. **41.** $\frac{3}{2}$ **43.** G **45.** Yes; it can be written in $f(x) = mx + b$ form. **47.** No; it cannot be written in $f(x) = mx + b$ form. **49.** −46 **51.** 336 **53.** II **55.** 3.5 **57.** $\frac{7}{3}$

Pages 86–89 Lesson 2-4

1. $y = 1.5x + 5$ **3.** $y = -2x + 11$ **5.** A

7 The slope of the given line is $\frac{7}{8}$. Lines that are parallel have the same slope, so the slope of the line parallel to the given line is $\frac{7}{8}$.

$$y - y_1 = m(x - x_1) \quad \text{Point-slope form}$$
$$y - (-10) = \frac{7}{8}(x - 4) \quad (x_1, y_1) = (4, -10) \text{ and } m = \frac{7}{8}$$
$$y + 10 = \frac{7}{8}x - \frac{7}{2} \quad \text{Distributive Property}$$
$$y = \frac{7}{8}x - \frac{27}{2} \quad \text{Subtract 10 from each side.}$$

9. $y = -\frac{1}{2}x + 5$ **11.** $y = 4.5x - 6.5$ **13.** $y = 4x - 15$ **15.** $y = -\frac{1}{4}x - 1$ **17.** $y = 2x - 2$ **19.** $y = -8x - 20$ **21.** $y = -0.5x + 3.35$ **23.** $y = \frac{1}{2}x$ **25.** $y = -\frac{1}{2}x + 6$ **27.** $y = 180x + 5900$ **29.** $y = -25x + 250$

31 First, find the slope. The line passes through (−6, 2) and (0, 6).

$$m = \frac{y_2 - y_1}{x_2 - x_1} \quad \text{Slope Formula}$$
$$= \frac{6-2}{0-(-6)} \quad (x_1, y_1) = (-6, 2), (x_2, y_2) = (0, 6)$$
$$= \frac{4}{6} \text{ or } \frac{2}{3} \quad \text{Simplify.}$$

The graph intersects the y-axis at 6. So, $b = 6$. Substitute the values into the slope-intercept equation.

$$y = mx + b \quad \text{Slope-intercept form}$$
$$y = \frac{2}{3}x + 6 \quad m = \frac{2}{3}, b = 6$$

33. 10 mi

35 a. Let x be the number of people Ms. Cooper recruits and let y be the amount of money she earns. Use the points (10, 100) and (14, 120) to represent this situation.

$$m = \frac{y_2 - y_1}{x_2 - x_1} \quad \text{Slope Formula}$$
$$= \frac{120-100}{14-10} \quad (x_1, y_1) = (10, 100), (x_2, y_2) = (14, 120)$$
$$= 20 \div 4 \text{ or } 5 \quad \text{Simplify.}$$

Use the slope and either of the given points with the point-slope form to write the equation.

$$y - y_1 = m(x - x_1) \quad \text{Point-slope form}$$
$$y - 100 = 5(x - 10) \quad (x_1, y_1) = (10, 100), m = 5$$
$$y - 100 = 5x - 50 \quad \text{Distributive Property}$$
$$y = 5x + 50 \quad \text{Add 100 to each side.}$$

b. The y-intercept of the graph of $y = 5x + 50$ is 50. This represents the money Ms. Cooper would make if she had no recruits. So, \$50 is her daily salary.

c. Find the value of y when $x = 20$.

$$y = 5x + 50 \quad \text{Use the equation you found in part a.}$$
$$y = 5(20) + 50 \quad \text{Replace } x \text{ with 20.}$$
$$y = 150 \quad \text{Simplify.}$$

So, Ms. Cooper would earn \$150 in a day if she recruits 20 people.

37. Sample answer: Sometimes; while the two sets of parallel and perpendicular lines will always form a quadrilateral with four 90° angles, that figure will always be a rectangle, but not necessarily a square. **39.** Sample answer: $y - 0 = a\left(x + \frac{b}{a}\right)$ **41.** Sample answer: $y - d = -\frac{d}{c}(x - 0)$ **43.** A **45.** G **47.** $-\frac{5}{3}$ **49.** $\frac{1}{5}$ **51.** $x \geq -4$ **53.** $x \geq -\frac{21}{13}$ **55.** yes **57.** $8c^2 + 8c - 30$ **59.** $-6a^2 + 7a + 20$ **61.** $\frac{3}{2}$ **63.** $\frac{1}{5}$ **65.** $-\frac{1}{9}$

For Homework Help, go to Hotmath.com

Pages 95–98 Lesson 2-5

1 a. Graph the data as ordered pairs with the depth on the horizontal axis and the temperature on the vertical axis. Draw a line through two points that appear to represent the data well, such as (0, 22) and (2000, 6).

Ocean Temperature

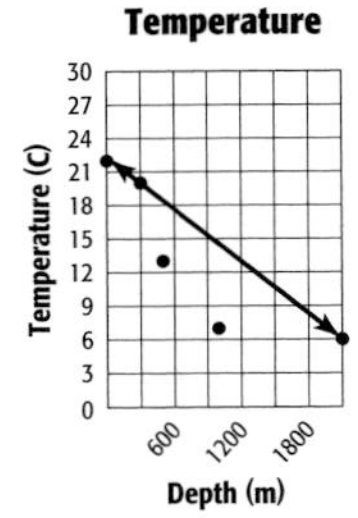

The data show a weak negative correlation.

b. Sample answer: Use (0, 22) and (2000, 6) to find an equation. First, find the slope of the line through (0, 22) and (2000, 6).

$m = \frac{y_2 - y_1}{x_2 - x_1}$ Slope Formula

$= \frac{6 - 22}{2000 - 0}$ $(x_1, y_1) = (0, 22), (x_2, y_2) = (2000, 6)$

≈ -0.008 Simplify.

Then write the equation.

$y - y_1 = m(x - x_1)$ Point-slope form

$y - 22 = -0.008(x - 0)$ $(x_1, y_1) = (0, 22), m = -0.008$

$y - 22 = -0.008x$ Simplify.

$y = -0.008x + 22$ Add 22 to each side.

c. Sample answer: Find y when $x = 2500$.

$y = -0.008x + 22$ Prediction equation

$= -0.008(2500) + 22$ $x = 2500$

$= -20 + 22$ or 2 Simplify.

So, at a depth of 2500 m, the temperature in the ocean is about 2°C.

3a. **Compact Disc Sales**

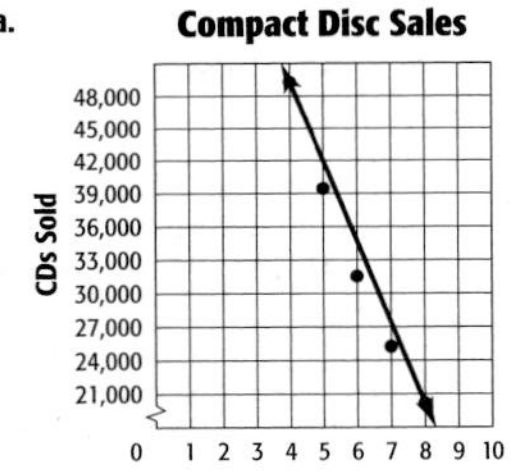

strong negative correlation

3b. Sample answer, using (4, 49,300) and (8, 20,193): $y = -7276.75x + 78,407$ **3c.** Sample answer: 12,916 CDs

5 a. Graph the data as ordered pairs with the month on the horizontal axis and the number of gallons sold on the vertical axis. Let 1 represent January, 2 represent February, and so on. Draw a line through two points that appear to represent the data well, such as (1, 37) and (8, 131).

Sunee's Homemade Ice Cream Sales

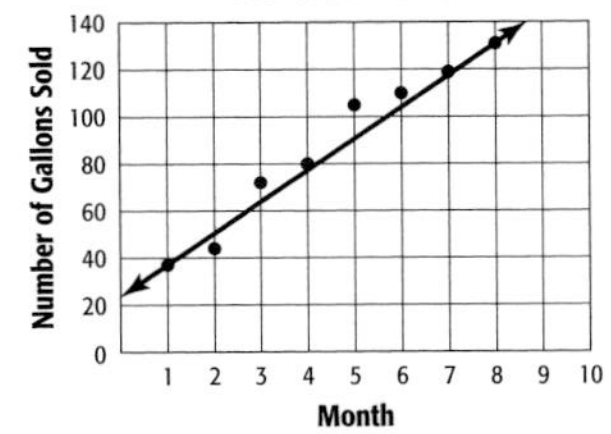

The data show a strong positive correlation.

b. Sample answer: Use (1, 37) and (8, 131) to find an equation. First, find the slope of the line through (1, 37) and (8, 131).

$m = \frac{y_2 - y_1}{x_2 - x_1}$ Slope Formula

$= \frac{131 - 37}{8 - 1}$ $(x_1, y_1) = (1, 37), (x_2, y_2) = (8, 131)$

$= \frac{94}{7}$ Simplify.

Then write the equation.

$y - y_1 = m(x - x_1)$ Point-slope form

$y - 37 = \frac{94}{7}(x - 1)$ $(x_1, y_1) = (1, 37), m = \frac{94}{7}$

$y - 37 = \frac{94}{7}x - \frac{94}{7}$ Distributive Property

$y = \frac{94}{7}x + \frac{165}{7}$ Add 37 to each side.

c. Sample answer: Find y when $x = 9$.

$y = \frac{94}{7}x + \frac{165}{7}$ Prediction equation

$= \frac{94}{7}(9) + \frac{165}{7}$ $x = 9$

$= \frac{1011}{7}$ Simplify.

≈ 144.4 Use a calculator.

So, about 144 gallons of ice cream are sold in September.

7.

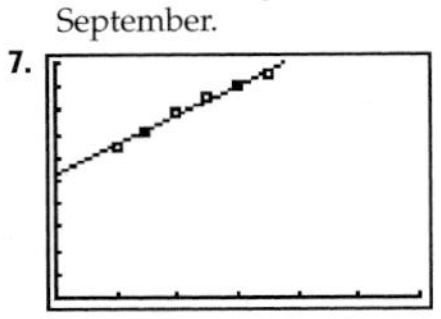

$y = 61.9x + 530.2$ (x is the number of years after 2002); \$1.149 million in sales

[0, 12] scl: 1 by [0, 1000] scl: 100

9 a. Graph the data as ordered pairs with the year on the horizontal axis and the attendance on the vertical axis.

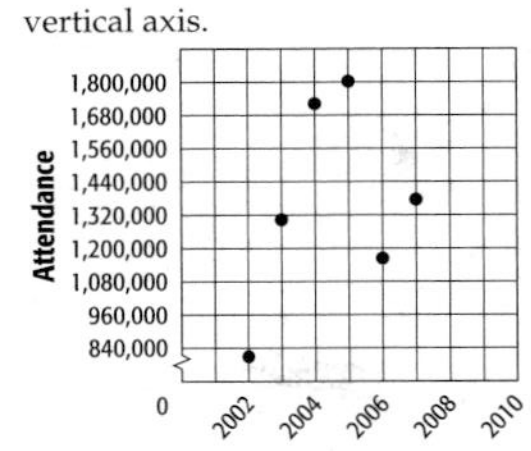

b. Use a graphing calculator to find a regression equation for the data. Enter the years in L1 and the attendance in L2. Then select LinReg(ax + b) on the STAT CALC menu. The regression equation is approximately $y = 71,406.4x - 141,763,070.9$.

c. On a graphing calculator, copy the regression equation to the Y= list. Then use VALUE on the CALC menu to find y when $x = 2020$. Be sure to reset the window size to accommodate the x-value of 2020. When $x = 2020$, $y \approx 2,477,915$. So, in the year 2020, the attendance will be about 2,477,915.

d. Sample answer: The prediction is unreasonable. The attendance will not increase without bound because attendance is largely dependent on the team's winning status.

11a. $y = 3.1x - 6177$; $r = 0.63$ **11b.** about \$64.2 million **11c.** $y = 2.6x - 5170$; $r = 0.986$ **11d.** about \$62.4 million **11e.** Sample answer: The new equation has a correlation coefficient, 0.986, that is extremely close to 1, so this equation should accurately represent the data. **13.** Sample answer: If a and b have a positive correlation, then they are both increasing. If b and c have a negative correlation and b is increasing, then c must be decreasing. If c and d have a positive correlation and c is decreasing, then d must be decreasing. If a is increasing and d is decreasing, then they must have a negative correlation.

15.

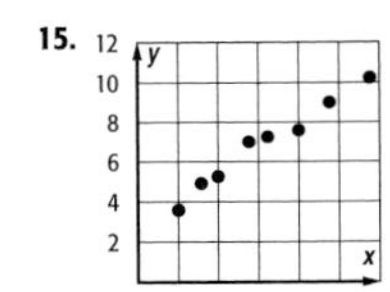

a; Sample answer: The data show a strong positive correlation which means that the correlation coefficient r should be close to 1.

17. 2 **19.** I **21.** $y = 2.5x - 6$ **23.** $y = -3x - 6$ **25.** 17.5 mi/hr **27.** 1.5 J/N **29.** 120 **31.** $\frac{17}{3}, -\frac{25}{3}$

Pages 104–107 Lesson 2-6

1.

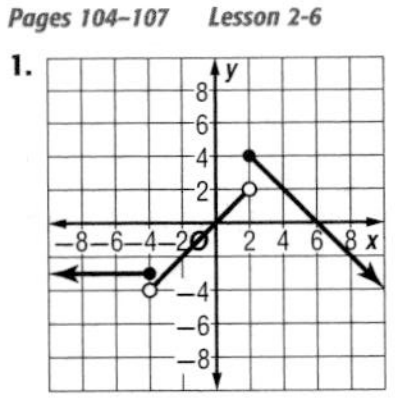

D = {all real numbers}; R = $\{y \mid y \leq 4\}$

3. $g(x) = \begin{cases} x + 4 \text{ if } x < -2 \\ -3 \text{ if } -2 \leq x \leq 3 \\ -2x + 12 \text{ if } x > 3 \end{cases}$

5 If the number of tickets sold is greater than 0 but less than or equal to 250, then the drama club must do 1 performance. If the number of tickets sold is greater than 250 but less than or equal to 500, then the drama club must do 2 performances, and so on. You can use the pattern to make a table, where x is the number of tickets sold and $P(x)$ is the number of performances. Then graph.

x	$P(x)$
$0 < x \leq 250$	1
$250 < x \leq 500$	2
$500 < x \leq 750$	3
$750 < x \leq 1000$	4
$1000 < x \leq 1250$	5

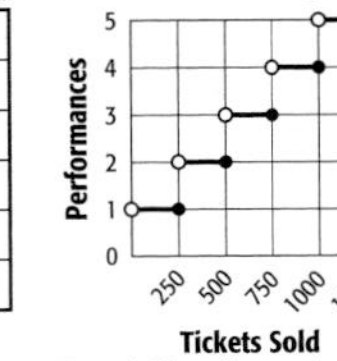

D = {all real numbers}; R = {all integers}

7.

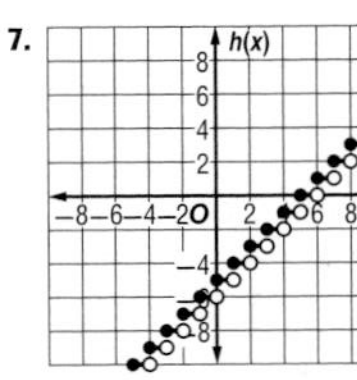

9.

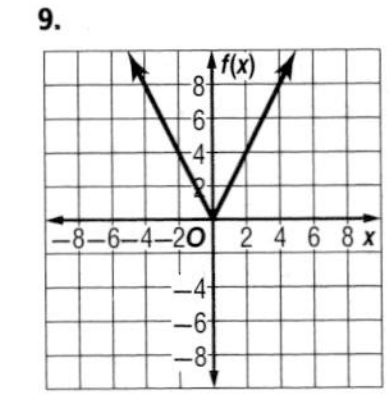

D = {all real numbers}; R = $\{f(x) \mid f(x) \geq 0\}$

11.

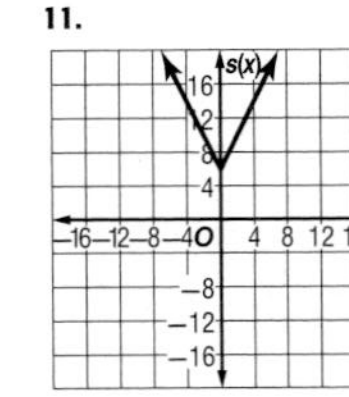

D = {all real numbers}; R = $\{s(x) \mid s(x) \geq 6\}$

13.

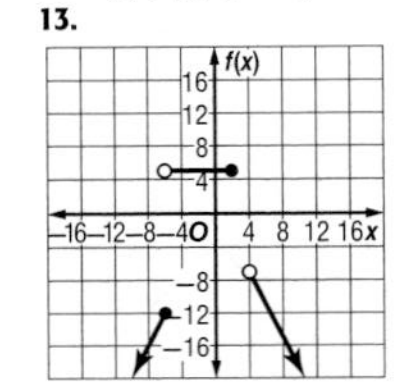

D = $\{x \mid x \leq 2 \text{ or } x > 4\}$; R = $\{f(x) \mid f(x) < -7$, or $f(x) = 5\}$

15.

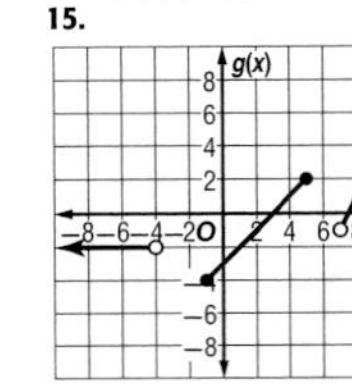

D = $\{x \mid x < -4$, $-1 \leq x \leq 5$, or $x > 7\}$; R = $\{g(x) \mid g(x) \geq -4\}$

17 The left portion of the graph is the graph of $g(x) = -x - 4$. There is a circle at $(-3, -1)$, so the linear function is defined for $\{x \mid x < -3\}$. The middle portion of the graph is the graph of $g(x) = x + 1$. There are dots at $(-3, -2)$ and $(1, 2)$, so the linear function is defined for $\{x \mid -3 \leq x \leq 1\}$. The right portion of the graph is the graph of $g(x) = -6$. There is a circle at $(4, -6)$, so the linear function is defined for $\{x \mid x > 4\}$. Write the piecewise-defined function.

$g(x) = \begin{cases} -x - 4 \text{ if } x < -3 \\ x + 1 \text{ if } -3 \leq x \leq 1 \\ -6 \text{ if } x > 4 \end{cases}$

For Homework Help, go to Hotmath.com

19. $g(x) = \begin{cases} 8 \text{ if } x \leq -1 \\ 2x \text{ if } 4 \leq x \leq 6 \\ 2x - 15 \text{ if } x > 7 \end{cases}$

21.

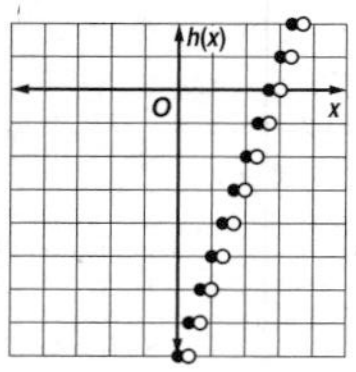

D = {all real numbers}; R = {all integers}

23.

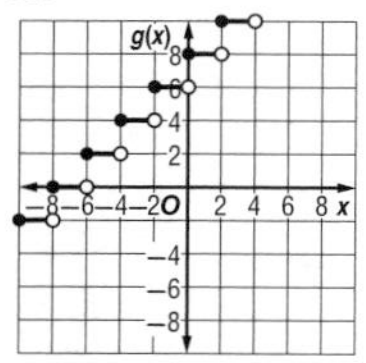

D = {all real numbers}; R = {all even integers}

25.

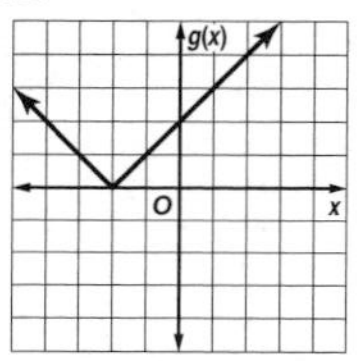

D = {all real numbers}; R = $\{g(x) \mid g(x) \geq 0\}$

27.

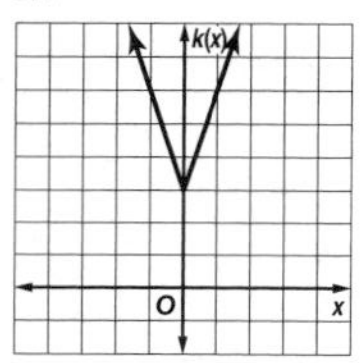

D = {all real numbers}; R = $\{k(x) \mid k(x) \geq 3\}$

29.

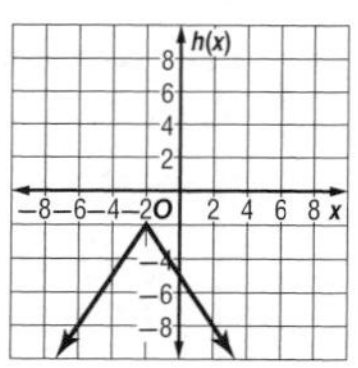

D = {all real numbers}; R = $\{h(x) \mid h(x) \leq -2\}$

31a. $f(a) = |a - 60|$
31b. $\{a \mid a \geq 0\}$

31c.

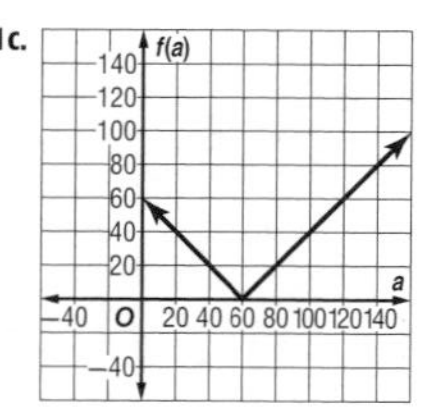

33 $f(x) = 0.5x$ if $x > 0$, $f(x) = 0$ if $x = 0$, and $f(x) = -0.5x$ if $x < 0$. So, according to the definition of absolute value, $f(x) = |0.5x|$.

35.

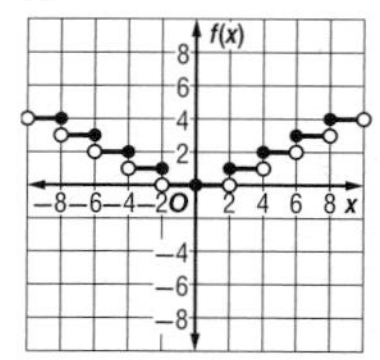

D = {all real numbers}; R = {all whole numbers}

37.

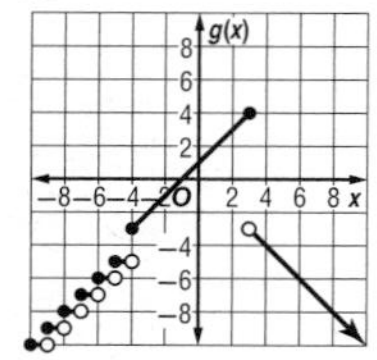

D = {all real numbers}; R = $\{g(x) \mid g(x) \leq 4\}$

39a.

x	−4	−3	−2	−1	0	1	2	3	4
f(x)	0	−1	−2	−3	−4	−3	−2	−1	0

x	−4	−3	−2	−1	0	1	2	3	4
g(x)	12	9	6	3	0	3	6	9	12

39b.

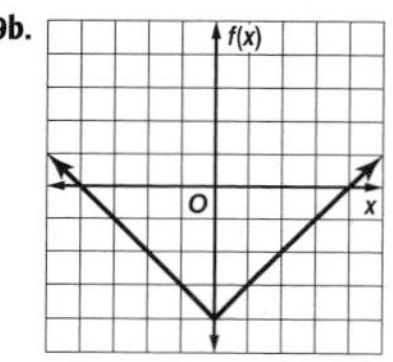

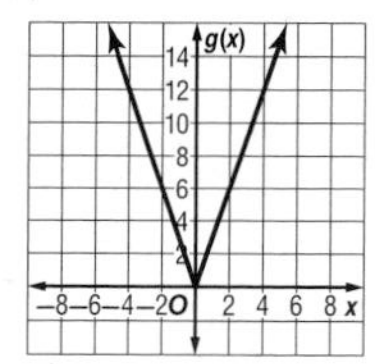

39c.

x	−4	−3	−2	−1	0	1	2	3	4
f(x)	0	−1	−2	−3	−4	−3	−2	−1	0
slope		−1	−1	−1	−1	1	1	1	1

x	−4	−3	−2	−1	0	1	2	3	4
g(x)	12	9	6	3	0	3	6	9	12
slope		−3	−3	−3	−3	3	3	3	3

39d. The two sections of an absolute value graph have opposite slopes. The slope is constant for each section of the graph.

41.

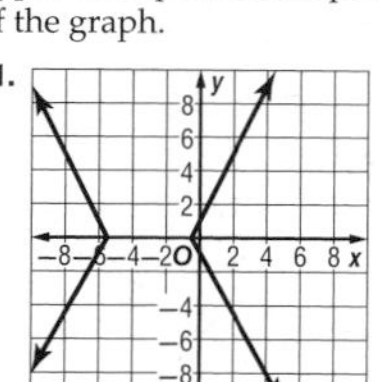

43. Sample answer: $f(x) = -|x - 2|$ **45.** $3n + 1$
47. I **49a.** $y = 0.10x + 30.34$ **49b.** $r = 0.987$
49c. about 110 **51.** $y = -\frac{3}{2}x + 6$ **53.** $-8c + 6$
55. −99

57.

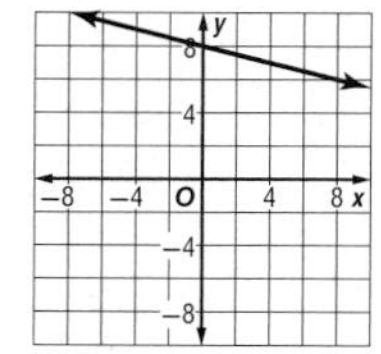

59.

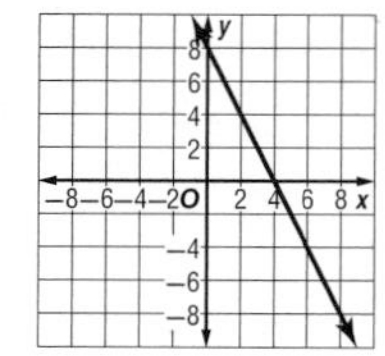

Pages 113–116 Lesson 2-7

1. linear
3. translation of the graph of $y = x^2$ down 4 units

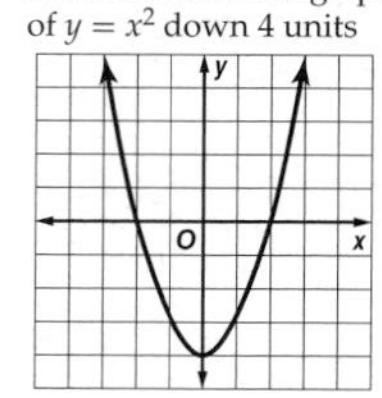

5. reflection of the graph of $y = |x|$ in the x-axis

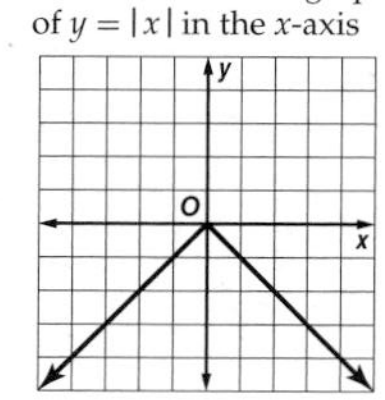

7. A vertical compression of the graph of $y = x$; the slope is not as steep as that of $y = x$.

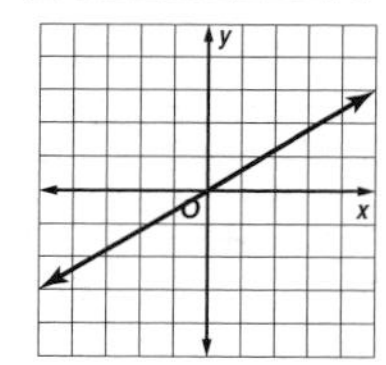

9. The function is a dilation and translation. The graph of $f(x) = \frac{1}{2}|x - 12|$ compresses the graph $f(x) = |x|$ vertically and translates it 12 units to the right.

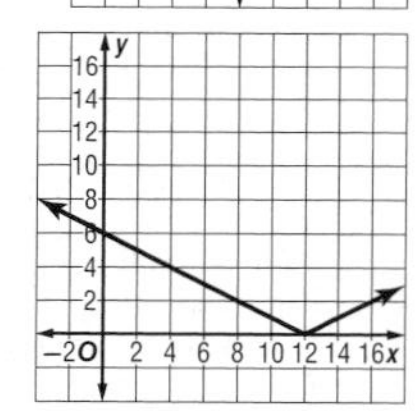

11 The graph is a curve that appears symmetrical. The graph represents a quadratic function.
13. linear
15. translation of the graph of $y = |x|$ down 3 units

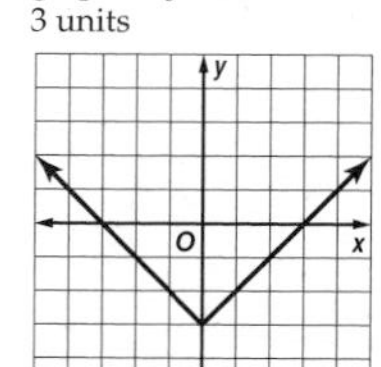

17. translation of the graph of $y = x$ up 2 units or left 2 units

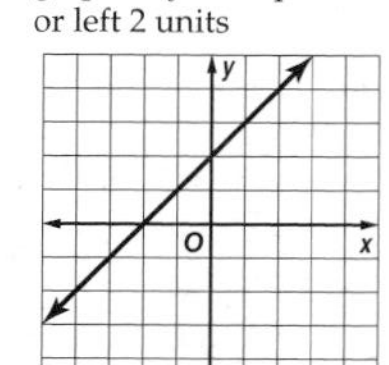

19. translation of the graph of $y = |x|$ left 6 units

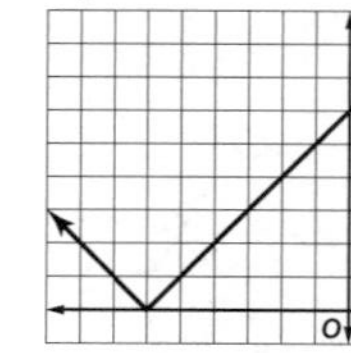

21. reflection of the graph of $y = x^2$ in the x-axis

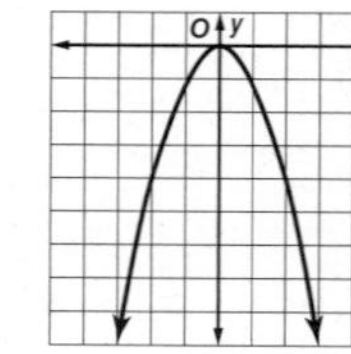

23. reflection of the graph of $y = |x|$ in the y-axis

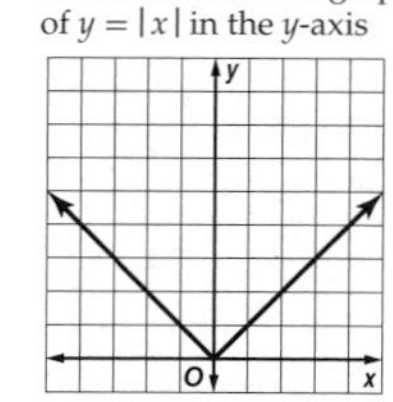

25. reflection of the graph of $y = x$ in the y-axis

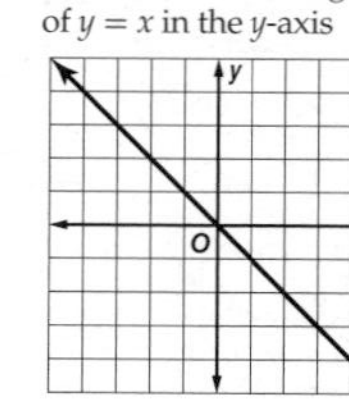

27. vertical stretch of the graph of $y = x$; The slope is steeper than that of $y = x$.

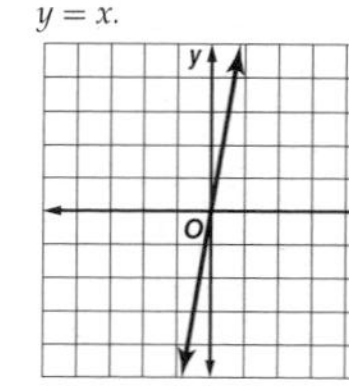

29. The dilation compressed the graph of $y = |x|$ horizontally.

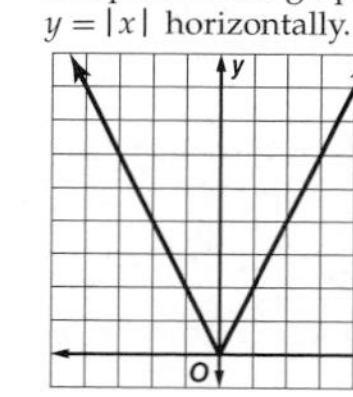

31. vertical compression of the graph of $y = x^2$

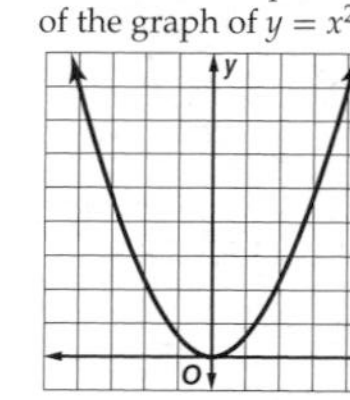

33. $y = x^2 + 1$ **35.** $y = x - 5$ **37.** $y = (x - 2)^2$

39 The blue line has a y-intercept of 4 and a slope of 1. So, an equation for the blue line is $y = x + 4$. The red line has a y-intercept of 2 and a slope of 1. So, an equation for the red line is $y = x + 2$. The red line is a translation of the blue line 2 units down.
41. $y = (x + 4)^2 - 6$ **43.** Sample answer: Since a vertical translation concerns only y-values and a horizontal translation concerns only x-values, order is irrelevant.

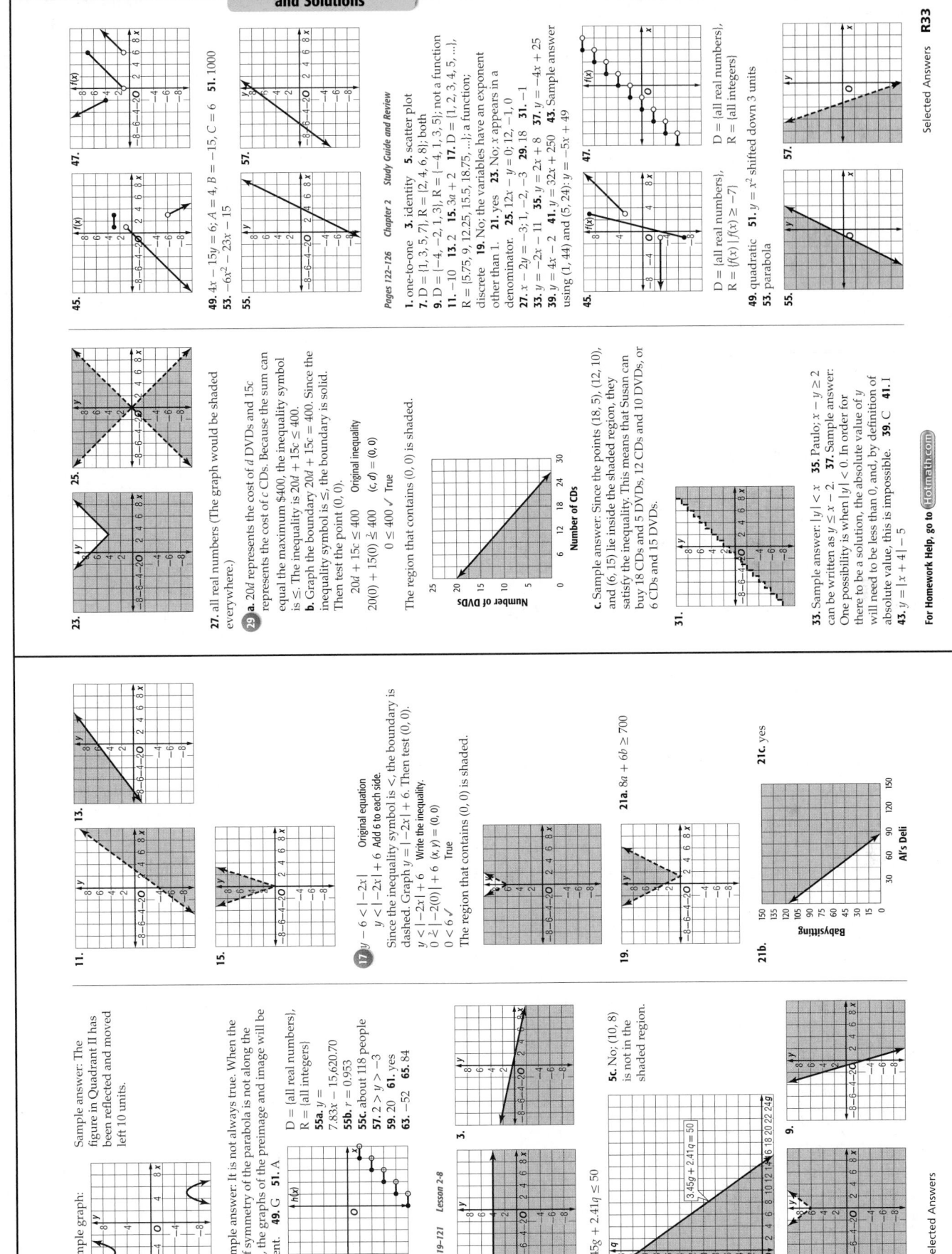

45. Sample graph:

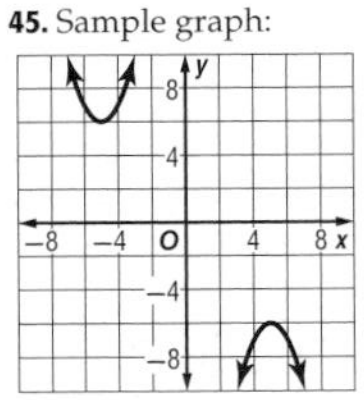

Sample answer: The figure in Quadrant II has been reflected and moved left 10 units.

47. Sample answer: It is not always true. When the axis of symmetry of the parabola is not along the y-axis, the graphs of the preimage and image will be different. **49.** G **51.** A

53.

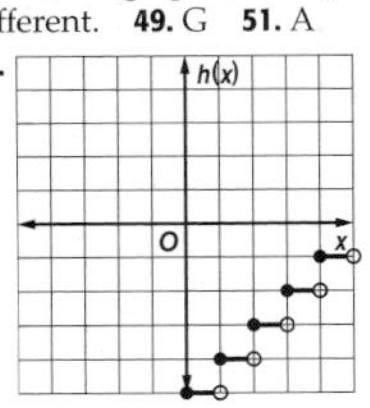

D = {all real numbers}, R = {all integers}
55a. $y = 7.83x - 15{,}620.70$
55b. $r = 0.953$
55c. about 118 people
57. $2 > y > -3$
59. 20 **61.** yes
63. −52 **65.** 84

Pages 119–121 Lesson 2-8

1.

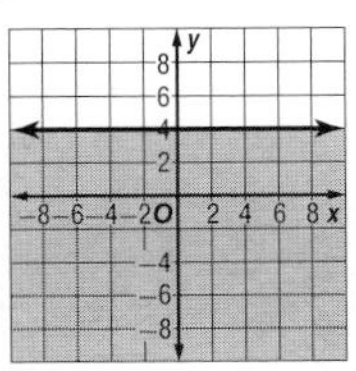

3.

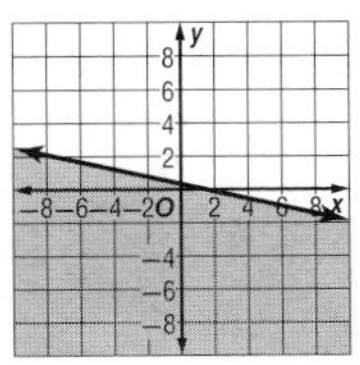

5a. $3.45g + 2.41q \le 50$

5b.

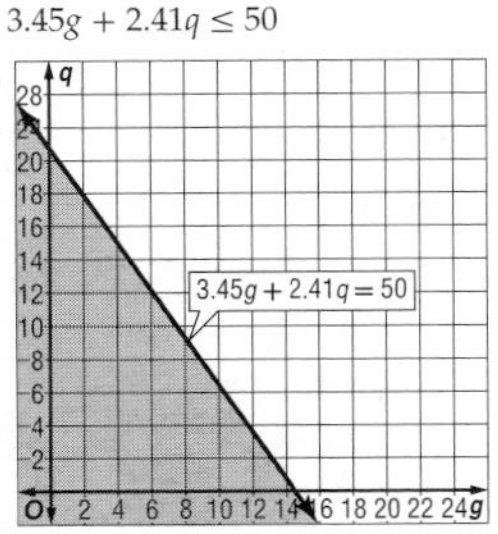

5c. No; (10, 8) is not in the shaded region.

7.

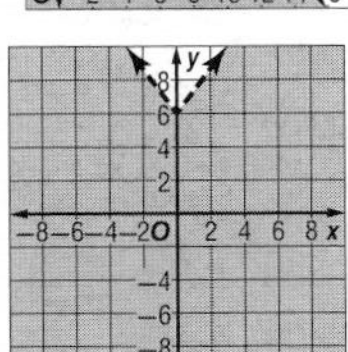

9.

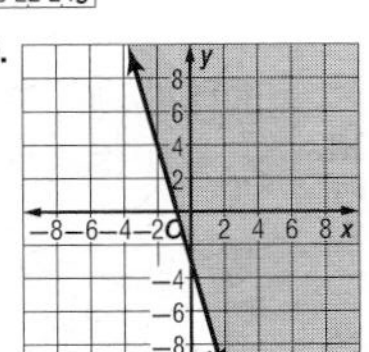

11.

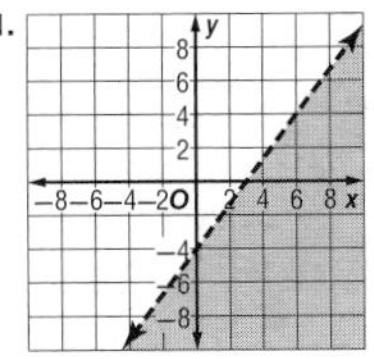

13.

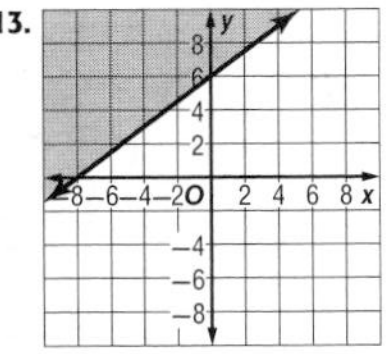

15.

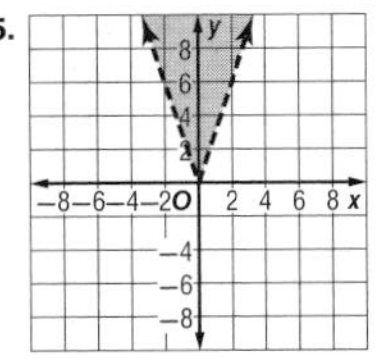

17 $y - 6 < |-2x|$ Original equation
$y < |-2x| + 6$ Add 6 to each side.
Since the inequality symbol is <, the boundary is dashed. Graph $y = |-2x| + 6$. Then test (0, 0).
$y < |-2x| + 6$ Write the inequality.
$0 \overset{?}{<} |-2(0)| + 6$ $(x, y) = (0, 0)$
$0 < 6$ ✓ True
The region that contains (0, 0) is shaded.

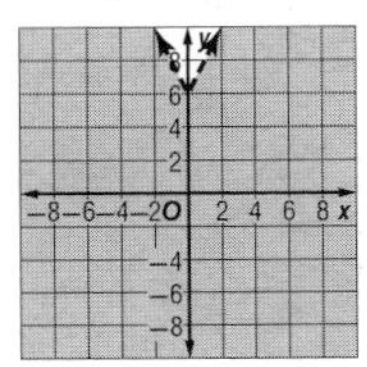

19.

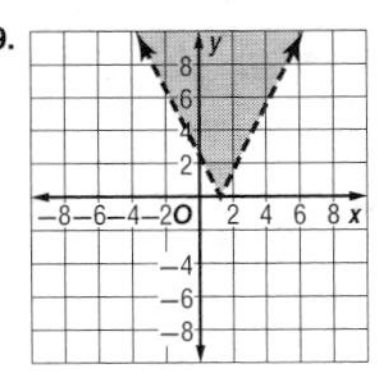

21a. $8a + 6b \ge 700$

21b.

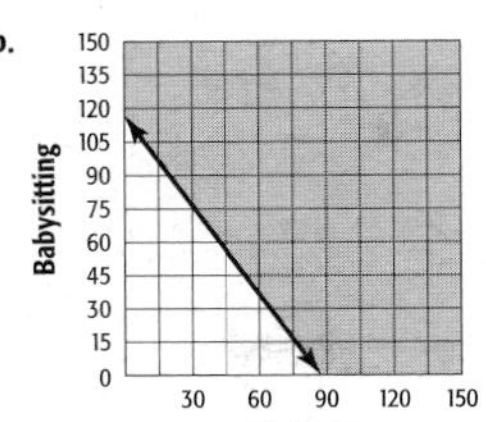

21c. yes

23.

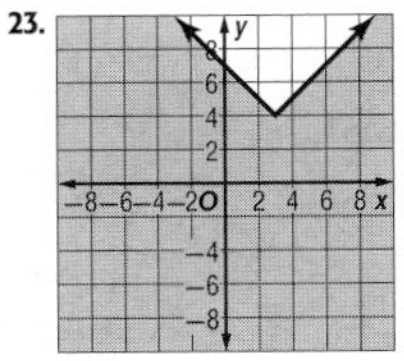

25.

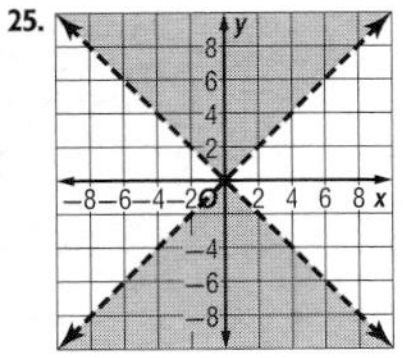

27. all real numbers (The graph would be shaded everywhere.)

29 **a.** $20d$ represents the cost of d DVDs and $15c$ represents the cost of c CDs. Because the sum can equal the maximum \$400, the inequality symbol is ≤. The inequality is $20d + 15c \le 400$.
b. Graph the boundary $20d + 15c = 400$. Since the inequality symbol is ≤, the boundary is solid. Then test the point (0, 0).
$20d + 15c \le 400$ Original inequality
$20(0) + 15(0) \overset{?}{\le} 400$ $(c, d) = (0, 0)$
$0 \le 400$ ✓ True
The region that contains (0, 0) is shaded.

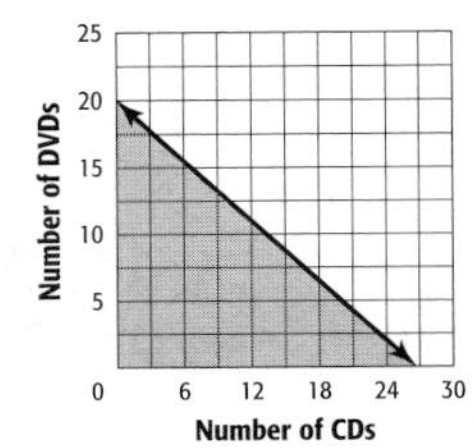

c. Sample answer: Since the points (18, 5), (12, 10), and (6, 15) lie inside the shaded region, they satisfy the inequality. This means that Susan can buy 18 CDs and 5 DVDs, 12 CDs and 10 DVDs, or 6 CDs and 15 DVDs.

31.

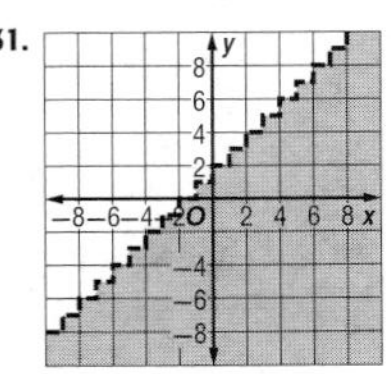

33. Sample answer: $|y| < x$ **35.** Paulo; $x - y \ge 2$ can be written as $y \le x - 2$. **37.** Sample answer: One possibility is when $|y| < 0$. In order for there to be a solution, the absolute value of y will need to be less than 0, and, by definition of absolute value, this is impossible. **39.** C **41.** I **43.** $y = |x + 4| - 5$

45.

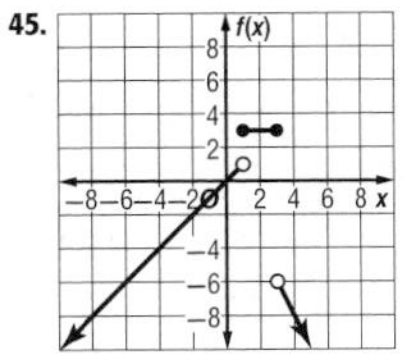

47.

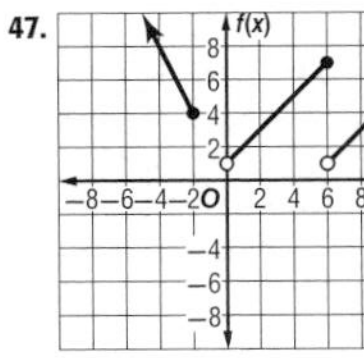

49. $4x - 15y = 6$; $A = 4$, $B = -15$, $C = 6$ **51.** 1000 **53.** $-6x^2 - 23x - 15$

55.

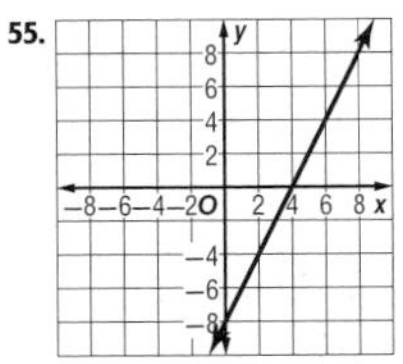

57.

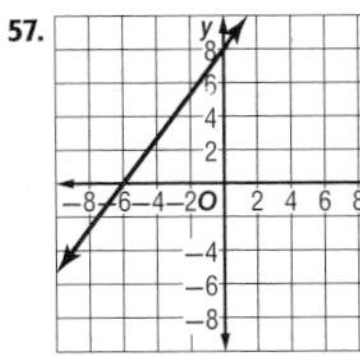

Pages 122–126 Chapter 2 Study Guide and Review

1. one-to-one **3.** identity **5.** scatter plot **7.** D = {1, 3, 5, 7}, R = {2, 4, 6, 8}; both **9.** D = {−4, −2, 1, 3}, R = {−4, 1, 3, 5}; not a function **11.** −10 **13.** 2 **15.** $3a + 2$ **17.** D = {1, 2, 3, 4, 5, ...}, R = {5.75, 9, 12.25, 15.5, 18.75, ...}; a function; discrete **19.** No; the variables have an exponent other than 1. **21.** yes **23.** No; x appears in a denominator. **25.** $12x - y = 0$; 12, −1, 0 **27.** $x - 2y = -3$; 1, −2, −3 **29.** 18 **31.** −1 **33.** $y = -2x - 11$ **35.** $y = 2x + 8$ **37.** $y = -4x + 25$ **39.** $y = 4x - 2$ **41.** $y = 32x + 250$ **43.** Sample answer using (1, 44) and (5, 24): $y = -5x + 49$

45.

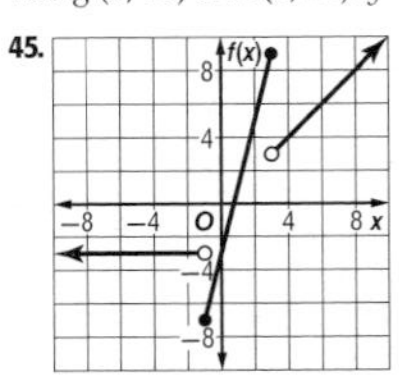

D = {all real numbers}, R = {$f(x)$ | $f(x) \ge -7$}

47.

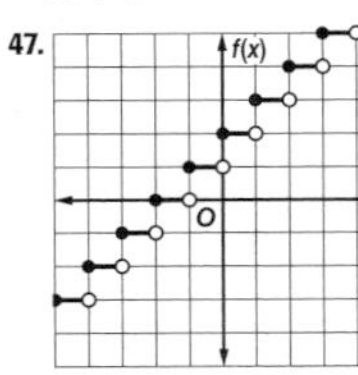

D = {all real numbers}, R = {all integers}

49. quadratic **51.** $y = x^2$ shifted down 3 units **53.** parabola

55.

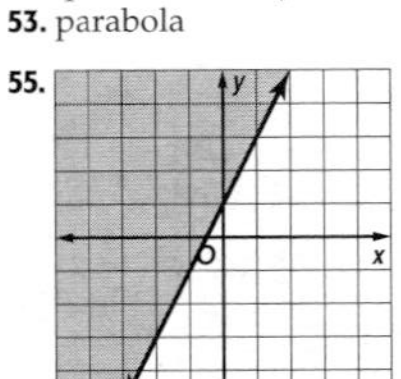

57.

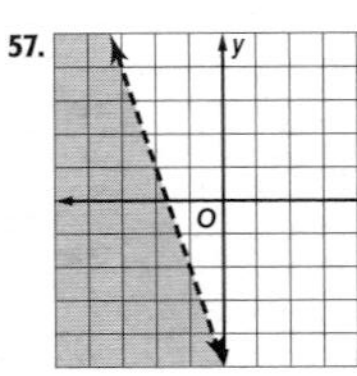

For Homework Help, go to Hotmath.com

59.

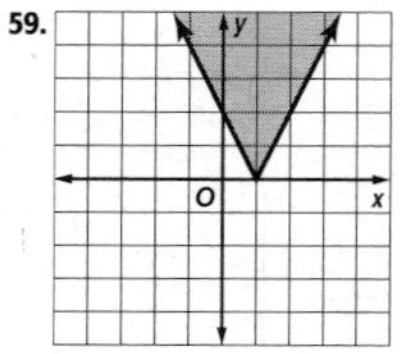

61.

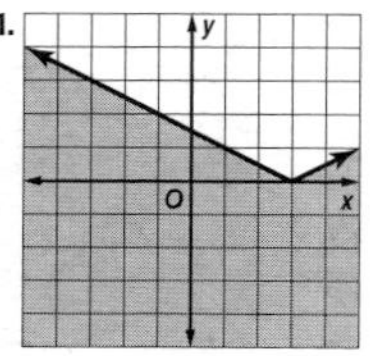

Chapter 3 Systems of Equations and Inequalities

Page 133 Chapter 3 Get Ready

1.

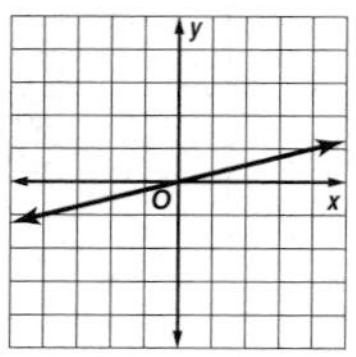

3.

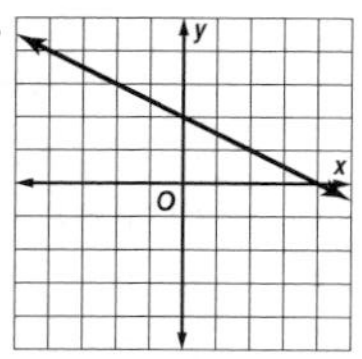

5.

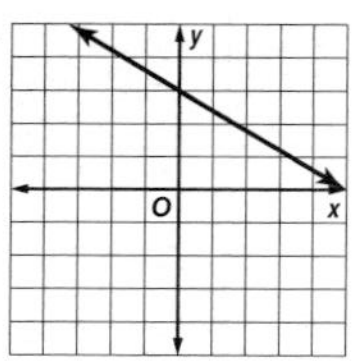

7a. $8.50a + 5.25c = 650$

7b.

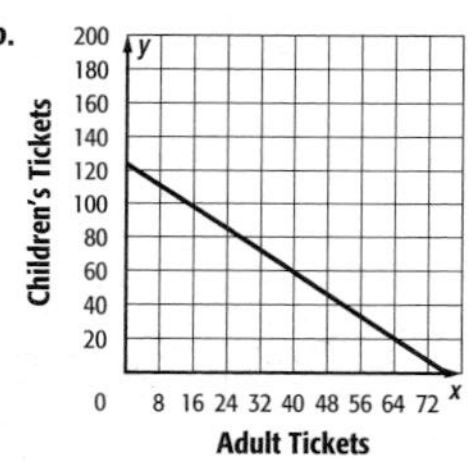

9.

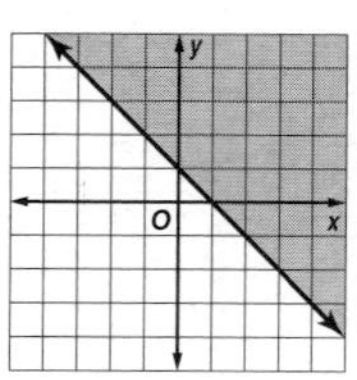

11.

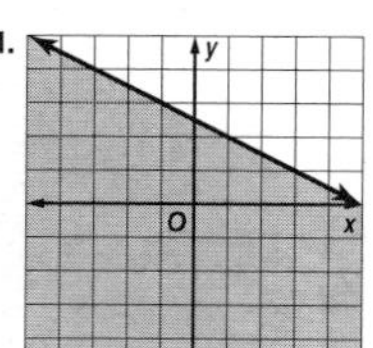

13.

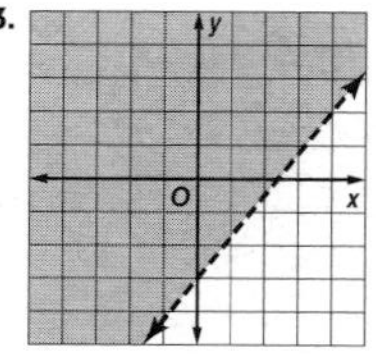

Pages 138–141 Lesson 3-1

1. (3, 5) **3.** (3, −3) **5.** (6, 7)

7 Write each equation in slope-intercept form. Then graph.

$4x + 5y = -41 \rightarrow y = -\frac{4}{5}x - \frac{41}{5}$

$3y - 5x = 5 \rightarrow y = \frac{5}{3}x + \frac{5}{3}$

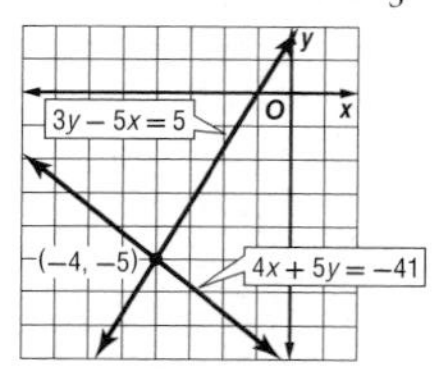

The graphs appear to intersect at (−4, −5). So, the solution is (−4, −5).

9a. $y = 0.15x + 2.70$, $y = 0.25x$
9b. $6.75 for 27 photos
9c. You should use EZ Online photos if you are printing more than 27 digital photos, and the local pharmacy if you are printing fewer than 27 photos.

11. consistent and dependent

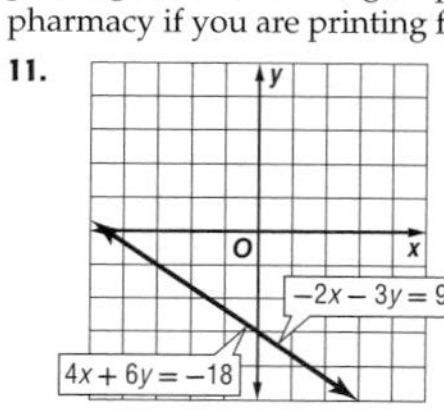

13. (−3, −12) **15.** (4, 3) **17.** (−3, −4) **19.** infinite solutions **21.** (−1.5, −2) **23.** $10 coupon for a purchase less than $66.67 and 15% discount coupon for a purchase over $66.67 **25.** (1, 3), (2, −1), (−2, −3)

27. consistent and independent

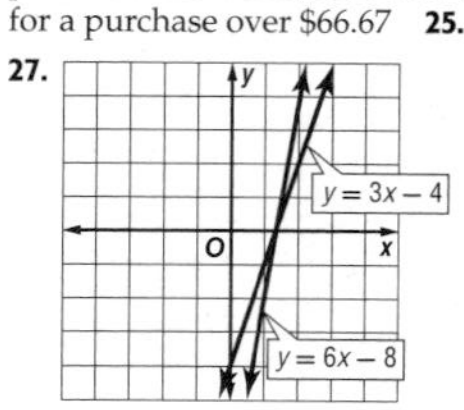

29. inconsistent

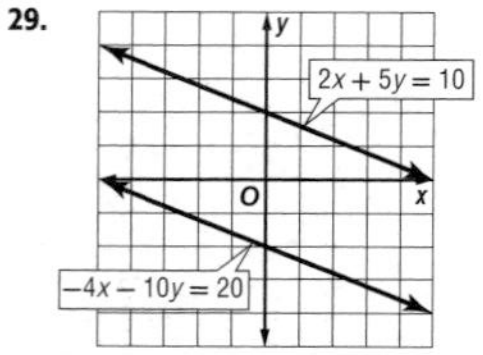

31 Write each equation in slope-intercept form. Then graph.

$-5x - 6y = 13 \rightarrow y = -\frac{5}{6}x - \frac{13}{6}$

$12y + 10x = -26 \rightarrow y = -\frac{5}{6}x - \frac{13}{6}$

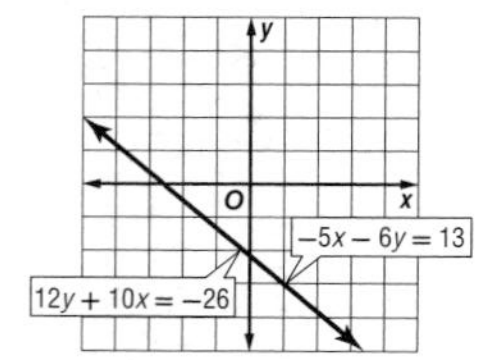

Because the equations are equivalent, their graphs are the same line. The system is consistent and dependent.

33. consistent and dependent

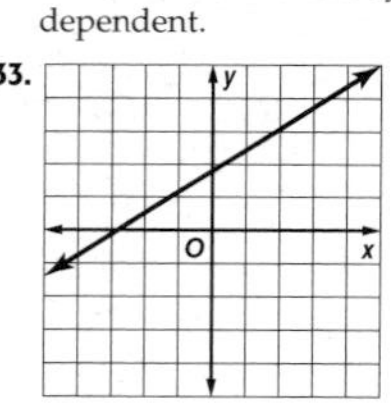

35. (4, 0.5) **37.** (−6, 3) **39.** (15.03, 10.98)

41 **a.** Sample answer: For men, you can use (0, 10) and (40, 9.85) to write an equation.

$m = \frac{y_2 - y_1}{x_2 - x_1}$ Slope Formula

$= \frac{9.85 - 10}{40 - 0}$ $(x_1, y_1) = (0, 10), (x_2, y_2) = (40, 9.85)$

$= -0.00375$ Simplify.

At $x = 0$, $y = 10.0$. So, the y-intercept is 10.

$y = mx + b$ Slope-intercept form

$y_m = -0.00375x + 10$ $m = -0.00375, b = 10$

For women, you can use (0, 11.4) and (40, 10.93) to write an equation.

$m = \frac{y_2 - y_1}{x_2 - x_1}$ Slope Formula

$= \frac{10.93 - 11.4}{40 - 0}$ $(x_1, y_1) = (0, 11.4), (x_2, y_2) = (40, 10.93)$

$= -0.01175$ Simplify.

At $x = 0$, $y = 11.4$. So, the y-intercept is 11.4.

$y = mx + b$ Slope-intercept form

$y_w = -0.01175x + 11.4$ $m = -0.01175, b = 11.4$

For Homework Help, go to Hotmath.com

b.

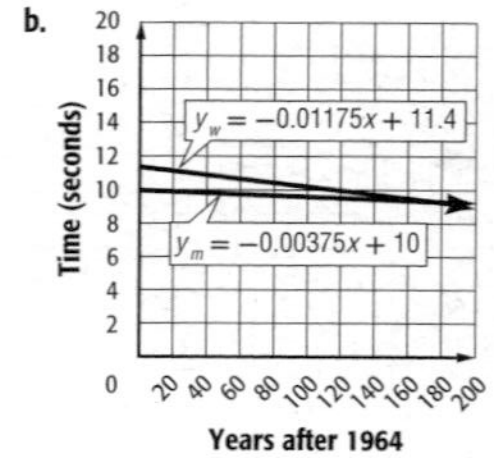

The graphs appear to intersect at (175, 9.3). This means that 175 years after 1964, the winning time for both men and women will be about 9.3 seconds. So, based on these data, the women's performance will catch up to the men's performance 175 years after 1964, or in the year 2139. The next Olympic year would be 2140.

c. Sample answer: No; it is unlikely that women's times will ever catch up to men's times because the times cannot continue to increase and decrease infinitely.

43. Alvin; Sample answer: Alvin used the **Intersect** command, while Victor used **Trace**. **45a.** Sample answer: $y = 2x$; $y = 2x + 1$ **45b.** Sample answer: $y = x$; $y = x$ **45c.** Sample answer: $y = x$; $y = 3x - 1$ **47.** $12xy + 18y^2 - 15y$ **49.** I **51a.** $10s + 15\ell \geq 350$

51b.

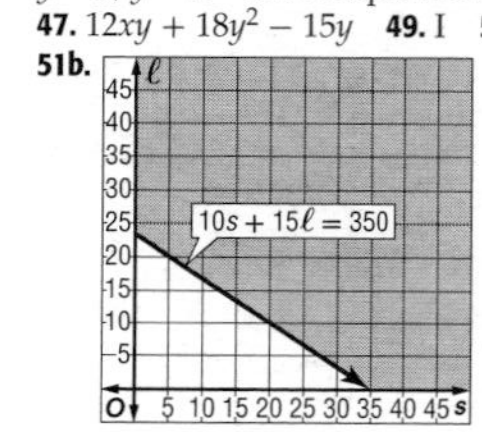

51c. no **53.** $-|x - 3|$ **55.** 7 **57.** 3.2 **59.** −8 **61.** $-x + 2$ **63.** $-2x + 3y$ **65.** $12x + 8y + 32$

Pages 146–150 Lesson 3-2

1. 250 T-shirts **3.** (−2, 1)

5
$2a + 8b = -8$ Multiply by 5. → $10a + 40b = -40$
$3a - 5b = 22$ Multiply by 8. → $24a - 40b = 176$

$10a + 40b = -40$ Equation 1 × 5
$(+)\ 24a - 40b = 176$ Equation 2 × 8
$34a = 136$ Add the equations.
$a = 4$ Divide each side by 34.

Substitute 4 for a into either original equation.

$2a + 8b = -8$ Equation 1
$2(4) + 8b = -8$ $a = 4$
$8 + 8b = -8$ Multiply.
$8b = -16$ Subtract 8 from each side.
$b = -2$ Divide each side by 8.

The solution is (4, −2).

7. (5, 1) **9.** (−2, 7) **11.** (−4, −3) **13.** no solution **15.** (5, 2) **17.** (6, −2) **19.** (−4, 3) **21.** infinite solutions **23.** (8, 4) **25.** (−3, −1) **27a.** $x + y = 13$ and $4x + 2y = 38$ **27b.** 6 doubles games and 7 singles games **29.** (0, 4) **31.** no solution **33.** (8, −6) **35.** (5, 4) **37.** (−4, 5) **39.** (6, −6) **41.** (−10, 4)

43 a. Let x represent the time in hours that Julian rides and let y represent the distance traveled.
Distance Julian travels after x hours: $y = 12x$
Distance Peter travels after x hours: $y = 16(x - 2)$

$y = 12x$ Equation representing Julian's distance
$16(x - 2) = 12x$ Substitute $16(x - 2)$ for y.
$16x - 32 = 12x$ Distributive Property
$4x - 32 = 0$ Subtract $12x$ from each side.
$4x = 32$ Add 32 to each side.
$x = 8$ Divide each side by 4.

So, after Julian rides 8 hours, or at 4:00 P.M., Peter catches up to him.

b. If Peter wants to catch up to Julian 1 hour sooner, or in 7 hours, then the total distance traveled y would be 12(7) or 84 miles.
Suppose Peter's speed remains the same but his starting time changes. Let t represent the number of hours after Julian that Peter starts.

$84 = 16(7 - t)$ Peter starts t hours after Julian.
$5.25 = 7 - t$ Divide each side by 16.
$-1.75 = -t$ Subtract 5.25 from each side.
$1.75 = t$ Divide each side by -1.

So, if Peter starts 1.75 hours after Julian and rides at a speed of 16 mph, then he will catch up to Julian in 7 hours. This answer is reasonable.
Suppose Peter's speed changes but his starting time remains the same. Let s represent Peter's new speed.

$84 = s(7 - 2)$ Peter cycles at s mph 2 hours after Julian.
$84 = s(5)$ Simplify.
$16.8 = s$ Divide each side by 5.

So, if Peter starts 2 hours after Julian and rides at a speed of 16.8 mph, then he will catch up to Julian in 7 hours. This answer is reasonable.

45. $(-5, 4)$ **47.** infinite solutions **49.** $(16, -8)$
51a. 7 16-ounce servings; If you drink 7 coffees, the price for each option is the same. **51b.** Sample answer: If you drink fewer than 7 coffees during that week, the disposable cup price is better. If you drink more than 7 coffees, the refillable mug price is better.
51c. Over a year's time, the refillable mug would be more economical because you would eventually have more than 7 coffees over the year. **53.** $m\angle A = 99°$, $m\angle B = 81°$

55 Let x represent the cost of an adult and y represent the cost of a student.
Van A: $2x + 5y = 77$
Van B: $2x + 7y = 95$

$2x + 5y = 77$ Multiply by -1. $\rightarrow$ $-2x - 5y = -77$
$-2x - 5y = -77$ Equation 1 × (−1)
$(+)\ 2x + 7y = 95$ Equation 2
$2y = 18$ Add the equations.
$y = 9$ Divide each side by 2.

$2x + 7y = 95$ Equation 2
$2x + 7(9) = 95$ $y = 9$
$2x + 63 = 95$ Multiply.
$2x = 32$ Subtract 63 from each side.
$x = 16$ Divide each side by 2.

The solution is (16, 9). So, the cost of an adult is \$16 and the cost of a student is \$9.
57. $(-4.3, -6.8)$ **59.** $(3.3, -6.5)$

61 Find an equation for the diagonal that goes through (6, 3) and (2, 9).

Slope:
$$m = \frac{y_2 - y_1}{x_2 - x_1} = \frac{9-3}{2-6} = \frac{6}{-4} \text{ or } -\frac{3}{2}$$
Equation:
$$y - y_1 = m(x - x_1)$$
$$y - 3 = -\frac{3}{2}(x - 6)$$
$$y - 3 = -\frac{3}{2}x + 9$$
$$y = -\frac{3}{2}x + 12$$

Find an equation for the diagonal that goes through (3, 4) and (11, 18).

Slope:
$$m = \frac{y_2 - y_1}{x_2 - x_1} = \frac{18-4}{11-3} = \frac{14}{8} \text{ or } \frac{7}{4}$$
Equation:
$$y - y_1 = m(x - x_1)$$
$$y - 4 = \frac{7}{4}(x - 3)$$
$$y - 4 = \frac{7}{4}x - \frac{21}{4}$$
$$y = \frac{7}{4}x - \frac{5}{4}$$

Find the point of intersection of the diagonals.

$y = -\frac{3}{2}x + 12$ Equation 1
$\frac{7}{4}x - \frac{5}{4} = -\frac{3}{2}x + 12$ Substitute $\frac{7}{4}x - \frac{5}{4}$ for y.
$\frac{13}{4}x - \frac{5}{4} = 12$ Add $\frac{3}{2}x$ to each side.
$\frac{13}{4}x = \frac{53}{4}$ Add $\frac{5}{4}$ to each side.
$x = \frac{53}{13}$ Multiply each side by $\frac{4}{13}$.

$y = -\frac{3}{2}x + 12$ Equation 1
$y = -\frac{3}{2}\left(\frac{53}{13}\right) + 12$ $x = \frac{53}{13}$
$y = -\frac{159}{26} + 12$ Multiply.
$y = \frac{153}{26}$ Simplify.

The diagonals intersect at $\left(\frac{53}{13}, \frac{153}{26}\right)$.

63a.

Equation 1	
x	y
0	$\frac{16}{3}$
1	5
2	$\frac{14}{3}$
3	$\frac{13}{3}$
4	4

Equation 2	
x	y
0	−4
1	−2
2	0
3	2
4	4

Equation 3	
x	y
0	10
1	5
2	0
3	−5
4	−10

63b. Equations 1 and 2 intersect at (4, 4), equations 2 and 3 intersect at (2, 0), and equations 1 and 3 intersect at (1, 5); there is no solution that satisfies all three equations.

63c.
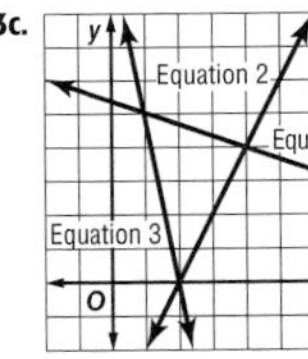

63d. If all three lines intersect at the same point, then the system has a solution. The system has no solution if the lines intersect at 3 different points, or if two or three lines are parallel.

65. $a \neq 0$, $b = 3$
67. Sample answer:
$4x + 5y = 21 \rightarrow 3(4x + 5y = 21)$
$3x - 2y = 10 \rightarrow 4(3x - 2y = 10)$

$12x + 15y = 63$
$(-)\ 12x - 8y = 40$
$23y = 23$
$y = 1$

$4x + 5(1) = 21$
$4x + 5 = 21$
$4x = 16$
$x = 4$

The solution is (4, 1).
69. 9 **71.** I **73a.** $y = 400$; $y = 150 + 5x$
73b.
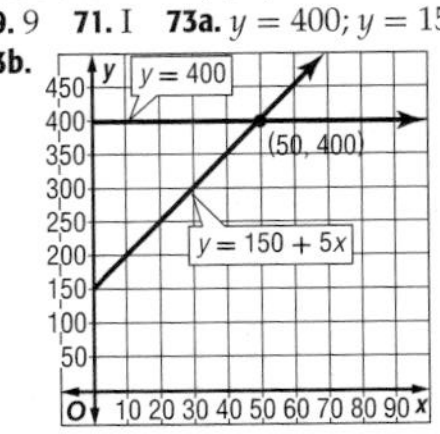

73c. It means that the options cost the same if you visit 50 times in a year.
73d. \$400 per year

75.
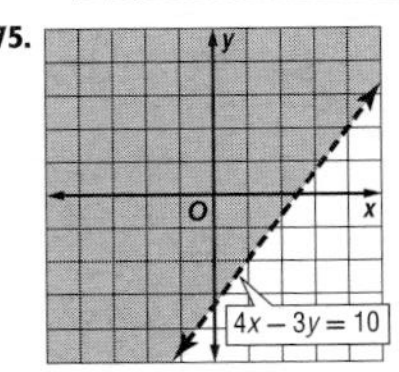

77. $y = -2x + 11$
79. $y = -4x - 25$
81. yes
83. no

Pages 154–157 Lesson 3-3

1.
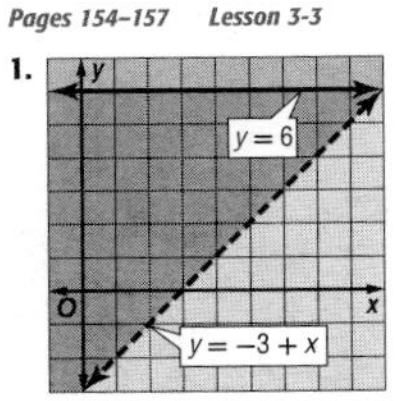

3.
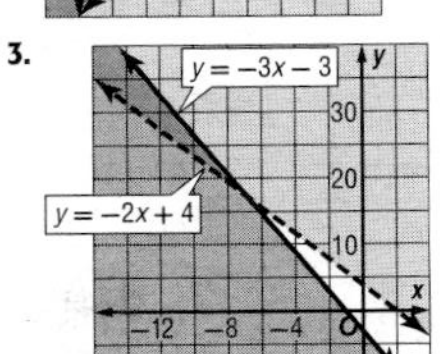

5.
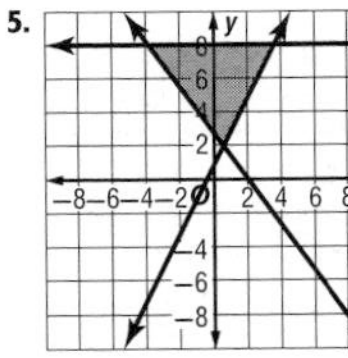

(3.5, 8), (−4, 8), (0.5, 2)

7.
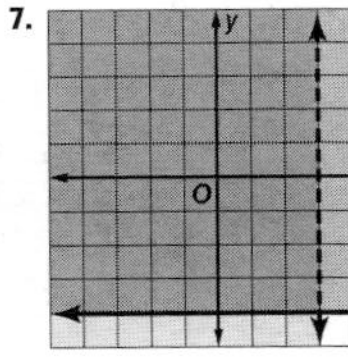

9 The solution of $y < -3x + 4$ is the region to the left of the boundary. The solution of $3y + x > -6$ is the region above the boundary. The intersection of the two regions is the solution of the system.

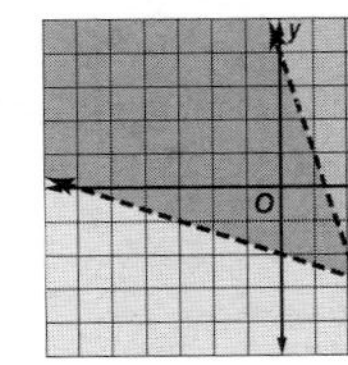

11.
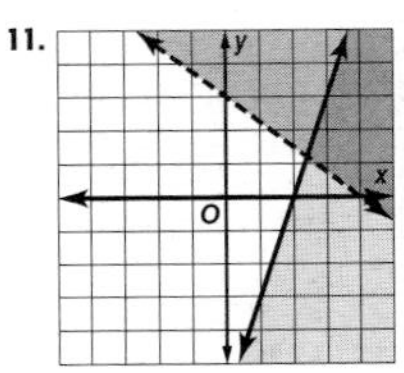

13.
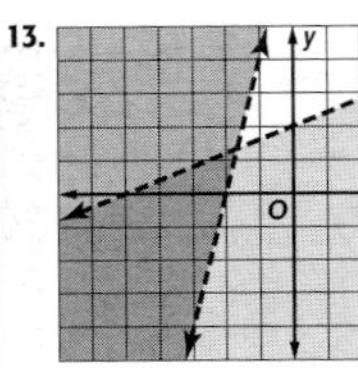

15.
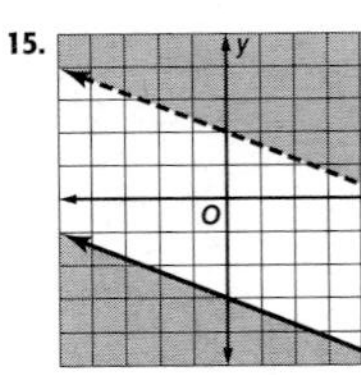

17.
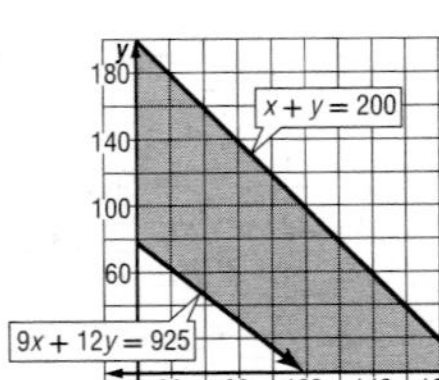

19. 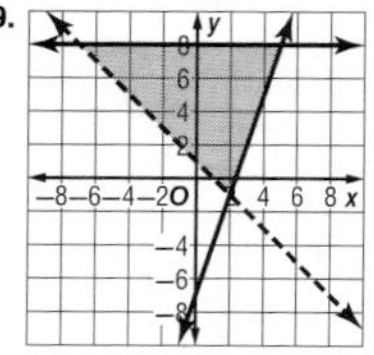
(2, −1), (5, 8), (−7, 8)

21. 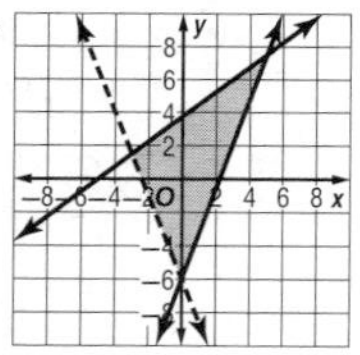
(−3, 1.5), (5, 7.5), (0, −6)

23. 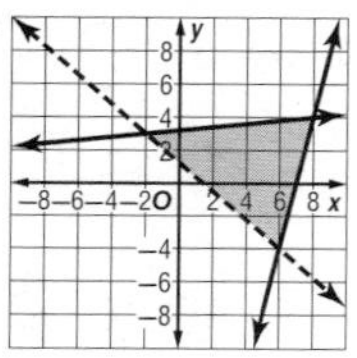
(8, 4), (6, −4), (−2, 3)

25. Let d represent the number of daytime minutes and n represent the number of nighttime minutes. Write a system of inequalities and then graph.

$d + n \leq 800$ Maximum number of minutes is 800.
$d \geq 2n$ At least twice as many daytime minutes as nighttime minutes
$n \geq 200$ At least 200 nighttime minutes

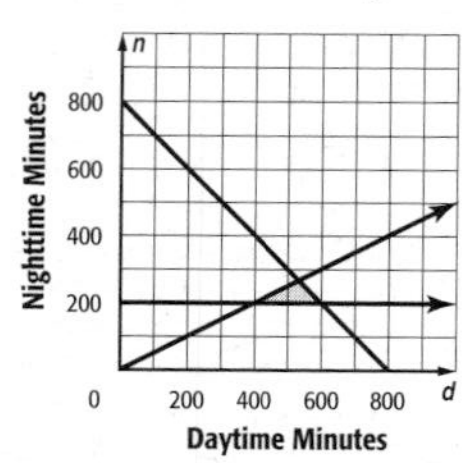

The intersection points are at (400, 200), (533.3, 266.7), and (600, 200).

$0.15d + 0.1n = 0.15(400) + 0.1(200)$ 400 daytime min., 200 nighttime min.
$= 60 + 20$ or \$80 Simplify.
$0.15d + 0.1n = 0.15(533.3) + 0.1(266.7)$ 533.3 daytime min., 266.7 nighttime min.
$\approx 80.0 + 26.7$ or \$106.70 Simplify.
$0.15d + 0.1n = 0.15(600) + 0.1(200)$ 600 daytime min., 200 nighttime min.
$= 90 + 20$ or \$110 Simplify.

So, his maximum bill is \$110 and his minimum bill is \$80.

27a. 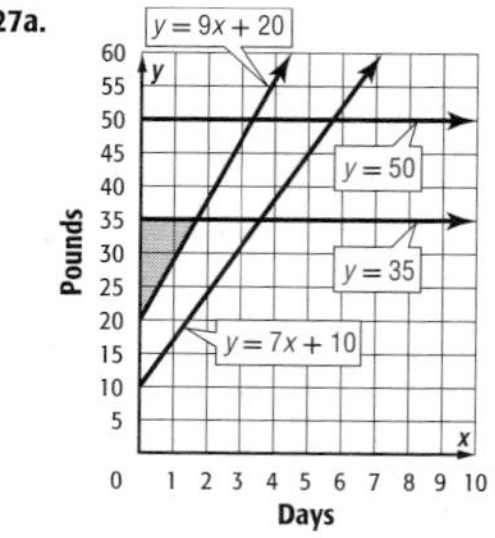

27b. $3\frac{1}{3}$ days **27c.** Marc; Jessica could last about a quarter of a day longer than Marc.

29. 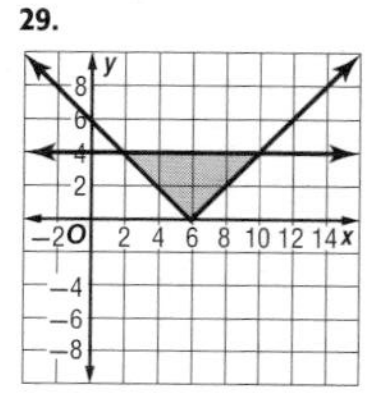

31. 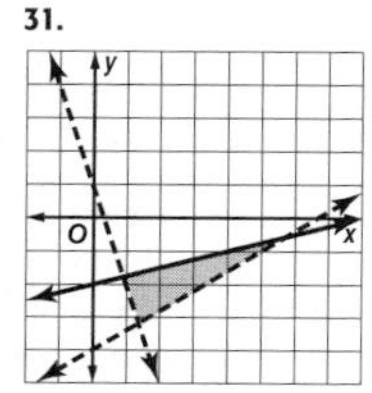

33. 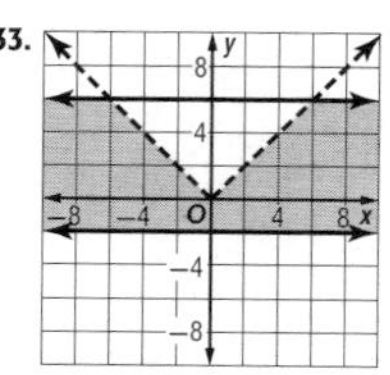

35. 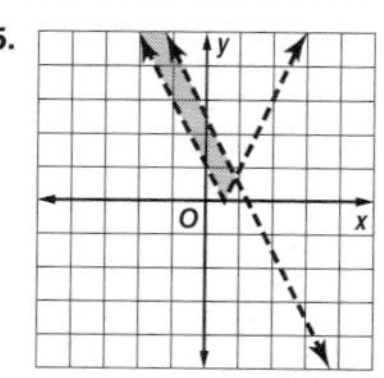

37. 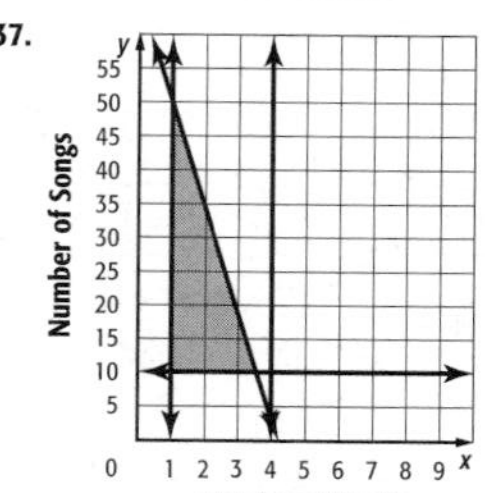

39. Let w = the number of hours writing, and let e = the number of hours exercising.
$w + e \leq 35$
$7 \leq e \leq 15$
$20 \leq w \leq 25$

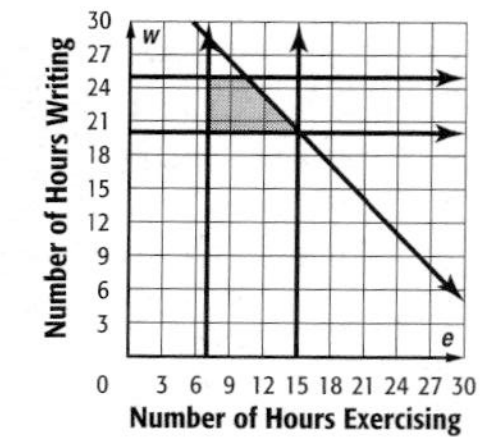

41. $(-6, -2)$, $\left(-3\frac{13}{17}, 6\frac{16}{17}\right)$, $\left(9\frac{1}{7}, 3\frac{5}{7}\right)$, $(0.8, -8.8)$

43. Let x represent the amount in the fund that pays 6% interest and y represent the amount in the fund that pays 10% interest. Write a system of inequalities and then graph.
$x + y \leq 10{,}000$ Total amount invested is up to \$10,000.
$0.06x + 0.10y \geq 740$ Total amount earned is at least \$740.

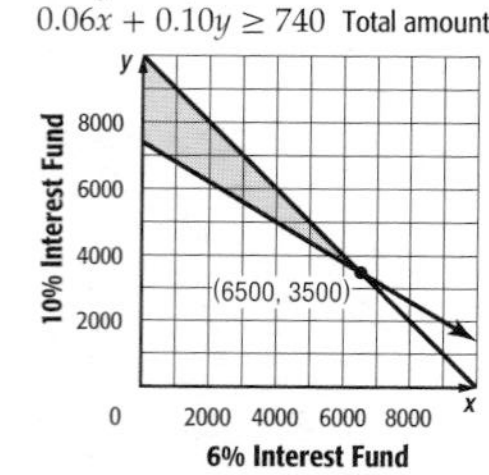

The least amount Mr. Hoffman can invest in the risky fund, or the 10% interest fund, is \$3500.

45. 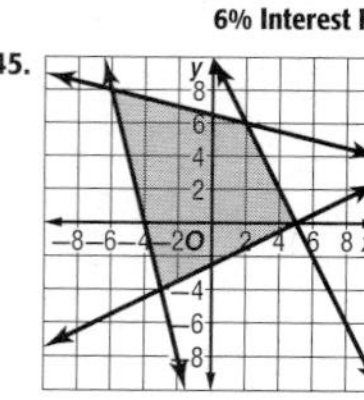
(−3, −4), (−6, 8), (2, 6), (5, 0); 75 units^2

47. Sample answer:
$y \geq 2x - 6$;
$y \leq -0.5x + 4$;
$y \geq -3x - 6$

49. Sample answer: Shade each inequality in their standard way, by shading above the line if $y >$ and shading below the line if $y <$ (or you can use test points). Once you determine where to shade for each inequality, the area where *every* inequality needs to be shaded is the actual solution. This is only the shaded area. **51.** A **53.** $\frac{4}{5}z$ **55.** (1.5, 3), (3.5, 7), (8, 3), (10, 7) **57.** no solution

59. 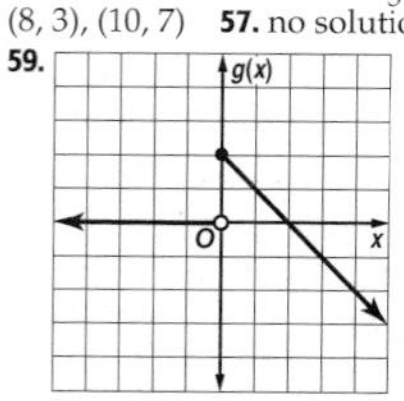
D = {all real numbers}, R = {g(x) | g(x) ≤ 2}

61. 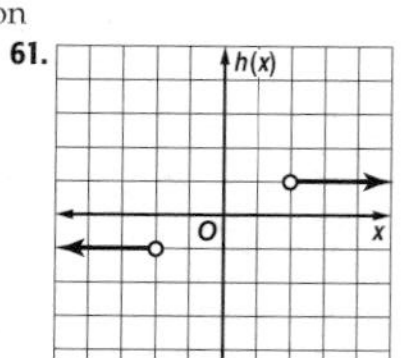
D = {x | x < −2 or x > 2}, R = {−1, 1}

63. −1 **65.** 3 **67.** 4.5

For Homework Help, go to Hotmath.com

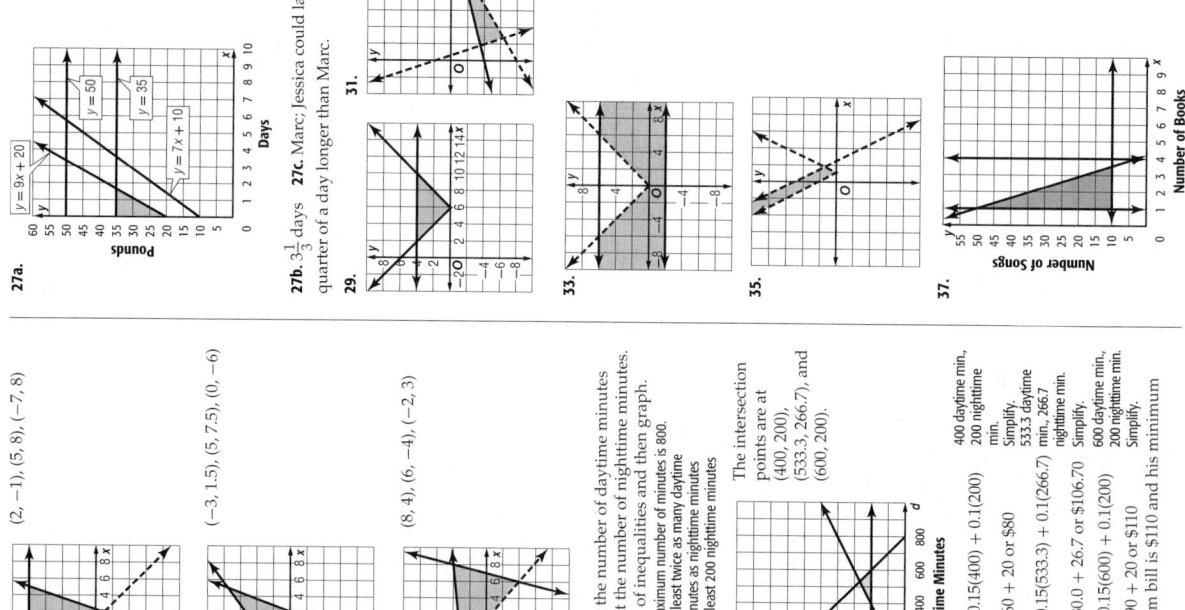

Pages 163–166 Lesson 3-4

1. 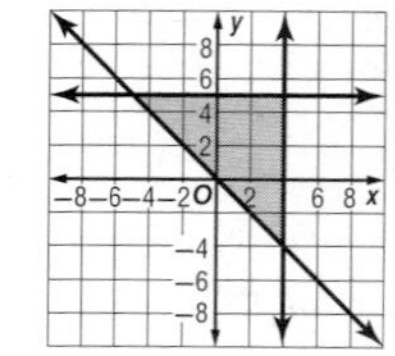
(4, 5), (4, −4), (−5, 5); max = 28, min = −35

3. 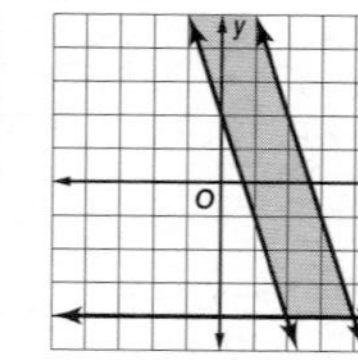
(2, −4), (4, −4); max does not exist, min = −52

5. 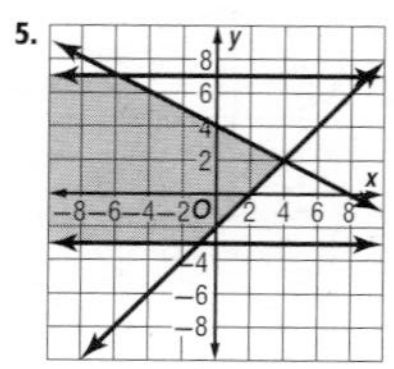
(4, 2), (−1, −3), (−6, 7); max does not exist; min = −30

7a. $g \geq 0$, $c \geq 0$, $1.5g + c \leq 85$, $2g + 0.5c \leq 40$

7b. 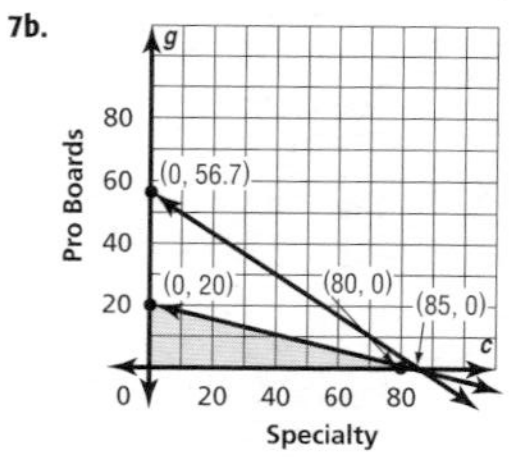

7c. (0, 0), (0, 20), (80, 0) **7d.** $f(c, g) = 65c + 50g$
7e. 80 specialty boards, 0 pro boards; \$5200

9. Graph the inequalities and locate the vertices.

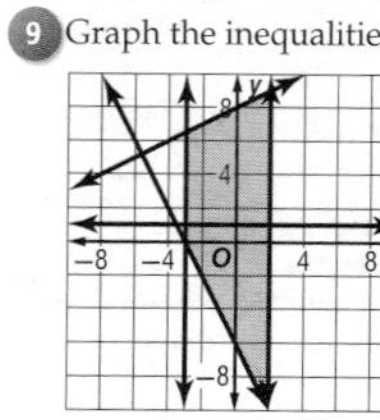

The vertices are at (2, −10), (−3, 0), (−3, 6.5), and (2, 9). Evaluate the function at each vertex.

(x, y)	−4x − 9y	f(x, y)
(2, −10)	−4(2) − 9(−10)	82
(−3, 0)	−4(−3) − 9(−0)	12
(−3, 6.5)	−4(−3) − 9(6.5)	70.5
(2, 9)	−4(2) − 9(9)	−89

The maximum value is 82 at (2, −10). The minimum value is −89 at (2, 9).

11.

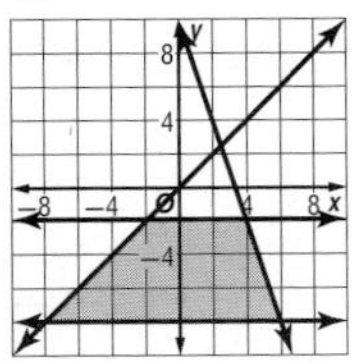

$(6, -8), (4, -2), (-2, -2), (-8, -8)$; max $= -8$, min $= -152$

13.

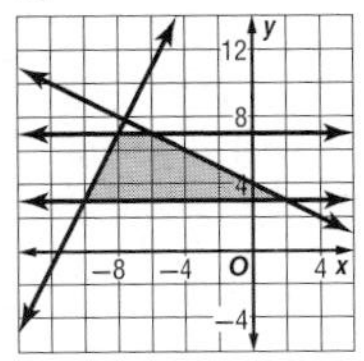

$(-10, 3), (2, 3), (-6, 7), (-8, 7)$; max $= 59$, min $= 9$

15 Graph the inequalities and locate the vertices.

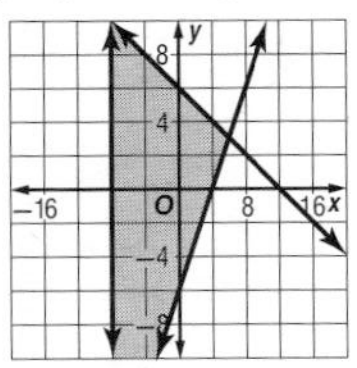

The vertices are at (6, 3), (−8, 10), and (−8, −18). Evaluate the function at each vertex.

(x, y)	10x − 6y	f(x, y)
(6, 3)	10(6) − 6(3)	42
(−8, 10)	10(−8) − 6(10)	−140
(−8, −18)	10(−8) − 6(−18)	28

The maximum value is 42 at (6, 3). The minimum value is −140 at (−8, 10).

17.

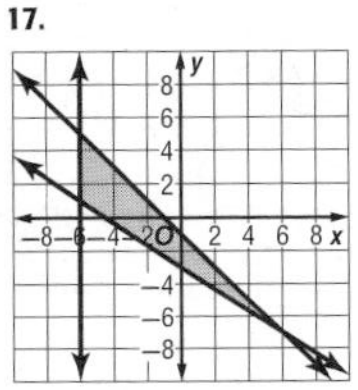

$(-6, 1), (6, -7), (-6, 5)$; max $= 48$, min $= 0$

19.

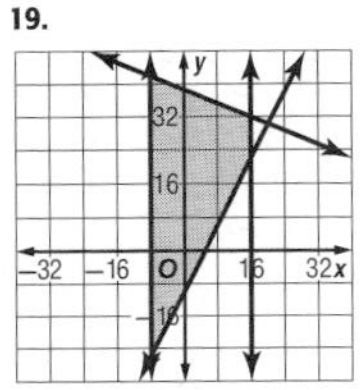

$(-8, 44), (16, 32), (-8, -26), (16, 22)$; max $= 672$, min $= -486$

21.

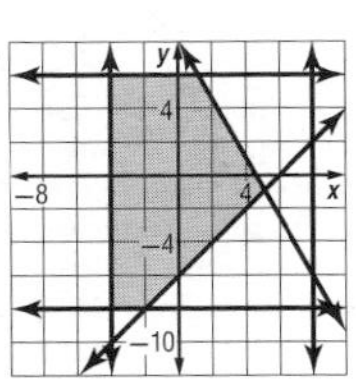

$(5, -1), (1, 6), (-2, -8), (-4, -8), (-4, 6)$, max $= 60$, min $= -112$

23. 225 yellow cakes, 0 strawberry cakes
25a. $a \geq 0, b \geq 0, a + b \leq 45, 4a + 5b \leq 200$

25b.

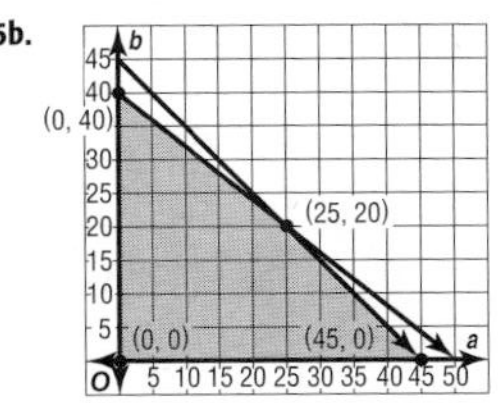

(0, 0), (0, 40), (25, 20), (45, 0)

25c. 25 sheds, 20 play houses
25d. $1250

27 **a.** Let x represent the number of small packages and y represent the number of large packages. Write a system of inequalities. Then graph the inequalities and locate the vertices.

$x \geq 0$ number of small packages ≥ 0
$y \geq 0$ number of large packages ≥ 0
$25x + 50y \leq 4200$ weight of packages ≤ 4200 lb
$3x + 5y \leq 480$ capacity of packages ≤ 480 cu ft

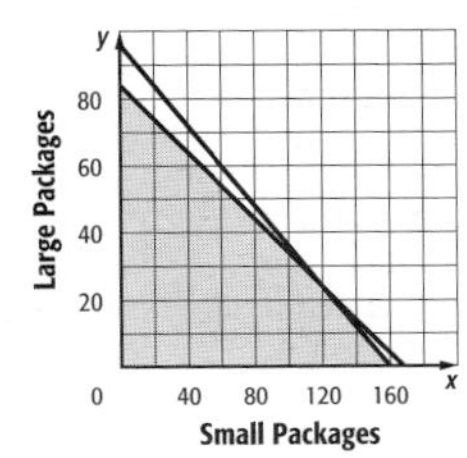

The vertices are at (0, 84), (120, 24), and (160, 0). Evaluate the function $f(x, y) = 5x + 8y$ at each vertex.

(x, y)	5x + 8y	f(x, y)
(0, 84)	5(0) + 8(84)	672
(120, 124)	5(120) + 8(24)	792
(160, 0)	5(160) + 8(0)	800

To maximize revenue, 160 small packages and 0 large packages should be placed on a train car.
b. The maximum revenue per train car is $800.
c. No; if revenue is maximized, the company will not deliver any large packages, and customers with large packages to ship will probably choose another carrier.
29. Sample answer: $-2 \geq y \geq -6, 4 \leq x \leq 9$
31. b; The feasible region of Graph b is unbounded while the other three are bounded.
33. Sample answer: Even though the region is bounded, multiple maximums occur at A and B and all of the points on the boundary of the feasible region containing both A and B. This happened because that boundary of the region has the same slope as the function. **35.** $70.20 **37.** D

39.

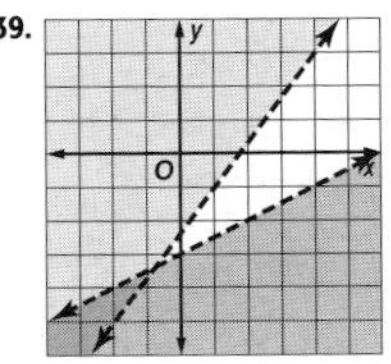

41. $7x + 15y = 330$, $8x + 16y = 360$; hats: 15, shirts: 15
43. $y = -\frac{1}{2}x + \frac{7}{2}$

45. 6; −2

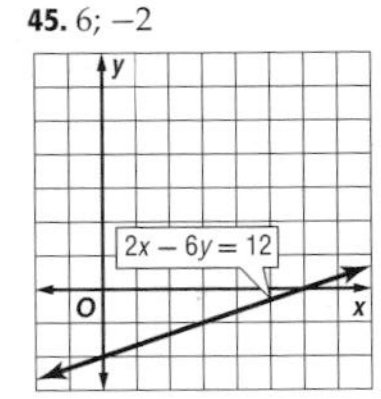

47. 5; 2

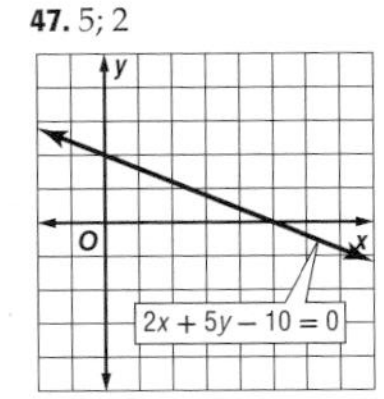

49. $\frac{1}{2}$; −2

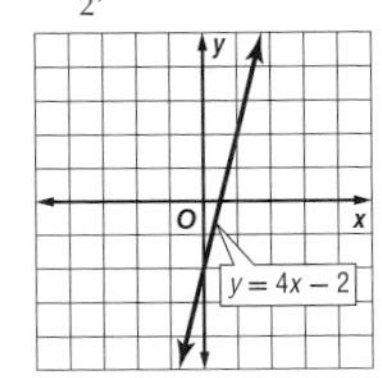

51. 9 **53.** −5 **55.** 15

Pages 171–173 Lesson 3-5

1. (−2, −3, 5) **3.** (−4, 3, 6) **5.** infinite solutions
7a. $s + d + t = 7, d = 2s, 0.3s + 0.6d + 0.6t = 3.6$
7b. 2 sitcoms, 4 dramas, 1 talk show

9 $-a + 4b + 2c = -13$ Multiply by 4. $\rightarrow$ $-4a + 16b + 8c = -52$

$-4a + 16b + 8c = -52$ Equation 3 (× 4)
$(+)\ 4a + 5b - 6c = 2$ Equation 1
$21b + 2c = -50$

$-a + 4b + 2c = -13$ Multiply by −3. $\rightarrow$ $3a - 12b - 6c = 39$

$3a - 12b - 6c = 39$ Equation 3 × (−3)
$(+)\ -3a - 2b + 7c = -15$ Equation 2
$-14b + c = 24$

The resulting system of two equations and two variables is shown below.
$21b + 2c = -50$ New Equation 1
$-14b + c = 24$ New Equation 2

$-14b + c = 24$ Multiply by −2. $\rightarrow$ $28b - 2c = -48$

$21b + 2c = -50$ New Equation 1
$(+)\ 28b - 2c = -48$ New Equation 2 × (−2)
$49b = -98$ Add the equations.
$b = -2$ Divide each side by 49.

$-14b + c = 24$ New Equation 2
$-14(-2) + c = 24$ Replace b with −2.
$28 + c = 24$ Multiply.
$c = -4$ Subtract 28 from each side.

$-a + 4b + 2c = -13$ Original Equation 3
$-a + 4(-2) + 2(-4) = -13$ $b = -2$ and $c = -4$
$-a - 8 - 8 = -13$ Multiply.
$-a = 3$ Add 16 to each side.
$a = -3$ Multiply each side by −1.

The solution is (−3, −2, −4).
11. (−2, −1, 4) **13.** infinite solutions **15.** (−4, −1, 6)
17. no solution **19.** infinite solutions **21.** roller coasters: 5; bumper cars: 1; water slides: 4

23 a = the amount invested in account A
b = the amount invested in account B
c = the amount invested in account C
$a + b + c = 100{,}000$ She invested a total of $100,000.
$a = c + 30{,}000$ She invested $30,000 more in account A than account C.
$0.04a + 0.08b + 0.1c = 6300$ The expected interest earned is $6300.

Substitute $a = c + 30{,}000$ in Equations 1 and 3.
$a + b + c = 100{,}000$ Equation 1
$c + 30{,}000 + b + c = 100{,}000$ $a = c + 30{,}000$
$30{,}000 + b + 2c = 100{,}000$ Add.
$b + 2c = 70{,}000$ Simplify.

$0.04a + 0.08b + 0.1c = 6300$ Equation 3
$0.04(c + 30{,}000) + 0.08b + 0.1c = 6300$ $a = c + 30{,}000$
$0.04c + 1200 + 0.08b + 0.1c = 6300$ Distribute.
$1200 + 0.08b + 0.14c = 6300$ Add.
$0.08b + 0.14c = 5100$ Simplify.

Solve the system of two equations in two variables.
$b + 2c = 70{,}000$ Multiply by −0.08. $\rightarrow$ $0.08b + 0.14c = 5100$

$-0.08b - 0.16c = -5600$
$(+)\ 0.08b + 0.14c = 5100$
$-0.02c = -500$
$c = 25{,}000$

Substitute to find b.
$b + 2c = 70{,}000$ Remaining equation in two variables
$b + 2(25{,}000) = 70{,}000$ $c = 25{,}000$
$b + 50{,}000 = 70{,}000$ Distribute.
$b = 20{,}000$ Simplify.

Substitute to find a.
$a + b + c = 100{,}000$ Equation 1
$a + 20{,}000 + 25{,}000 = 100{,}000$ $b = 20{,}000, c = 25{,}000$
$a + 45{,}000 = 100{,}000$ Add.
$a = 55{,}000$ Simplify.

The solution is (55,000, 20,000, 25,000). She invested $55,000 in account A, $20,000 in account B, and $25,000 in account C.
25. $y = -3x^2 + 4x - 6$; $a = -3, b = 4, c = -6$
27. Sample answer:
$3x + 4y + z = -17$
$3(-5) + 4(-2) + 6 = -17$
$-15 + (-8) + 6 = -17$
$-23 + 6 = -17$

$2x - 5y - 3z = -18$
$2(-5) - 5(-2) - 3(6) = -18$
$-10 + 10 - 18 = -18$
$-18 = -18$

$-x + 3y + 8z = 47$
$-(-5) + 3(-2) + 8(6) = 47$
$5 - 6 + 48 = 47$
$-1 + 48 = 47$

29. Sample answer: First, combine two of the original equations using elimination to form a new equation with three variables. Next, combine a different pair of the original equations using elimination to eliminate the same variable and form a second equation with three variables. Do the same thing with a third pair of the original equations. You now have a system of three equations with three variables. Follow the same procedure you learned in this section. Once you find the three variables, you need to use them to find the eliminated variable. **31.** I **33.** A **35.** 16; −8 **37.** 9; −8 **39.** (6, 1) **41.** (8, −5)

Pages 174–176 Chapter 3 Study Guide and Review

1. linear programming **3.** consistent **5.** unbounded **7.** dependent **9.** inconsistent **11.** (0, 2) **13.** (−3, 4) **15.** 4 h **17.** (−2, −7) **19.** (3, 5)

21.

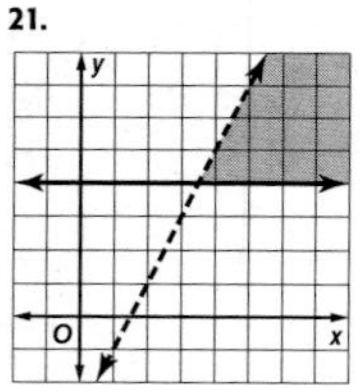

23.

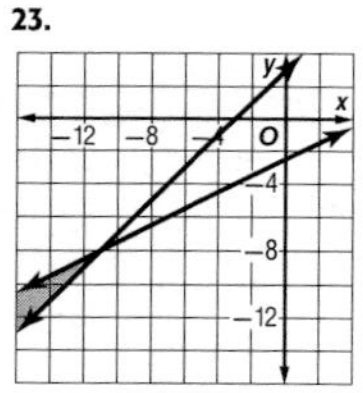

25.

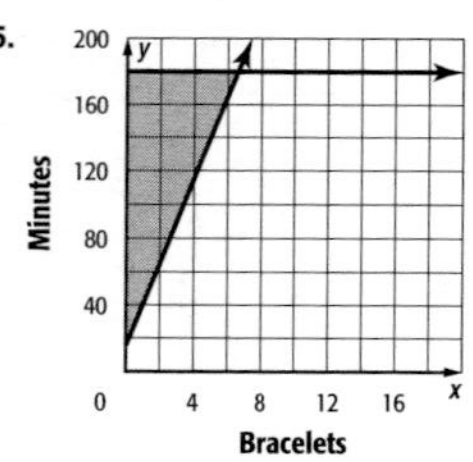

27. $480; 12 outdoor, 16 indoor **29.** (5, −5, −4)

Chapter 4 Matrices

Page 183 Chapter 4 Get Ready

1. $-4, \frac{1}{4}$ **3.** −0.2, 5 **5.** $\frac{3}{4}, -\frac{4}{3}$ **7.** $6x + 12y$ **9.** $-19x + 6$ **11.** $17x - 3y - 9$ **13.** (1, 4) **15.** (−2, 6)

Pages 188–191 Lesson 4-1

1. 2 × 4 **3.** 3 × 2 **5.** 1 **7.** 9 **9.** 1 × 2 **11.** 2 × 4 **13.** 3 × 1 **15.** −9

17 Since b_{13} is the element in row 1, column 3 of matrix B, the value of b_{13} is $2x$.

19.

John	221	201	185	607
Hideo	168	233	159	560
Paulo	187	189	211	587

21a. $\begin{bmatrix} 3 & 2 & 2 & 1 \\ 4 & 3 & 2 & 3 \\ 5 & 5 & 4 & 4 \\ 1 & 5 & 5 & 2 \end{bmatrix}$

21b. Sample answer: Brand C; it was given the highest rating possible for cost and comfort, and a high rating for looks, and it will last a fairly long time.
21c. Sample answer: Yes; finding the sum of the rows and then calculating the average will provide an easy way to compare the data. **23.** $4x$ **25.** x

27 **a.** Write a matrix with three rows and two columns. Let the rows represent the seating areas and let the columns represent the days.

	Weekday	Weekend
Coach	249	259
Business	279	289
First Class	319	339

b. Write a matrix with two rows and three columns. Let the rows represent the days and let the columns represent the seating areas.

	Coach	Business	First Class
Weekday	249	279	319
Weekend	259	289	339

29. $x^2 + 4$ **31.** $-y$

33 **a.** Write a matrix with one row for each planet and one column for each of the two types of distances.

	Sun	Earth
Mercury	36.00	57
Venus	67.24	26
Mars	141.71	35
Jupiter	483.88	370
Saturn	887.14	744
Uranus	1783.98	1607
Neptune	2796.46	2680

b. There are seven rows and two columns. So, the dimensions are 7 × 2.
c. The element a_{42} is in the fourth row and second column. So, the value is 370.
35. Sample answer: False; a square matrix with 4 columns has only 4 rows and cannot contain an element in a fifth row. **37.** No; element b_{32} is the second element in the third row, which is 2.

39. Sample answer:

	Hits	Walks	HR
Joe	95	12	8
John	102	16	5
Jim	109	13	12

41. D **43.** 780,000 ft² **45.** 45 first, 298 second, 147 third **47.** $-\frac{3}{2}$ **49.** $\frac{5}{3}$ **51.** $y^2 - 2y - 48$ **53.** −31 **55.** 52

Pages 196–199 Lesson 4-2

1. $\begin{bmatrix} 3 & -5 & 7 \end{bmatrix}$ **3.** $\begin{bmatrix} -2 & -18 \\ 11 & 13 \end{bmatrix}$

5. $\begin{bmatrix} 18 & 12 & 0 \\ -6 & 42 & -24 \\ -12 & -18 & 21 \end{bmatrix}$ **7.** $\begin{bmatrix} 20 & 4 \\ -14 & 38 \end{bmatrix}$

9. impossible **11a.** Test 1: $\begin{bmatrix} 85 \\ 75 \\ 96 \end{bmatrix}$ Test 2: $\begin{bmatrix} 72 \\ 74 \\ 83 \end{bmatrix}$

11b. $\begin{bmatrix} 157 \\ 149 \\ 179 \end{bmatrix}$ **11c.** $\begin{bmatrix} 13 \\ 1 \\ 13 \end{bmatrix}$

13 To find the sum of two matrices, they must have the same dimensions. Since the dimensions of the matrices are 2 × 2 and 3 × 2, it is impossible to find the sum.

15. $\begin{bmatrix} -24 \\ 10 \\ -3 \\ -7 \end{bmatrix}$ **17.** impossible **19.** $\begin{bmatrix} -7 \\ -32 \end{bmatrix}$

21a. Library A: $\begin{bmatrix} 10{,}000 \\ 5000 \\ 5000 \end{bmatrix}$; Library B: $\begin{bmatrix} 15{,}000 \\ 10{,}000 \\ 2500 \end{bmatrix}$;

Library C: $\begin{bmatrix} 4000 \\ 700 \\ 800 \end{bmatrix}$ **21b.** $\begin{bmatrix} 29{,}000 \\ 15{,}700 \\ 8300 \end{bmatrix}$ **21c.** $\begin{bmatrix} 6000 \\ 4300 \\ 4200 \end{bmatrix}$

21d. $\begin{bmatrix} 25{,}000 \\ 15{,}000 \\ 7500 \end{bmatrix}$; Sample answer: The sum represents the combined size of the two libraries.

23. $\begin{bmatrix} -8a & 32b & 8c - 8b \\ -104 & 80 & -40c \end{bmatrix}$

25 $-5\left(\begin{bmatrix} 4 & -8 \\ 8 & -9 \end{bmatrix} + \begin{bmatrix} 4 & -2 \\ -3 & -6 \end{bmatrix}\right)$

$= -5\begin{bmatrix} 4+4 & -8+(-2) \\ 8+(-3) & -9+(-6) \end{bmatrix}$ Add corresponding elements.

$= -5\begin{bmatrix} 8 & -10 \\ 5 & -15 \end{bmatrix}$ Simplify.

$= \begin{bmatrix} -5(8) & -5(-10) \\ -5(5) & -5(-15) \end{bmatrix}$ Distribute the scalar.

$= \begin{bmatrix} -40 & 50 \\ -25 & 75 \end{bmatrix}$ Multiply.

27. impossible **29.** $\begin{bmatrix} 68.6 & 19 \\ -19.99 & 18.3 \\ 11.83 & 38.7 \end{bmatrix}$

31. $\begin{bmatrix} 5 & 24 \\ -\frac{167}{12} & -10 \end{bmatrix}$

33 **a.** Write a matrix to show the American records and a matrix to show the world records. Then subtract.

$\begin{bmatrix} 24.63 \text{ s} \\ 53.99 \text{ s} \\ 1{:}57.41 \text{ min} \\ 8{:}16.22 \text{ min} \end{bmatrix} - \begin{bmatrix} 24.13 \text{ s} \\ 53.52 \text{ s} \\ 1{:}56.54 \text{ min} \\ 8{:}16.22 \text{ min} \end{bmatrix}$

$= \begin{bmatrix} 24.63 \text{ s} - 24.13 \text{ s} \\ 53.99 \text{ s} - 53.52 \text{ s} \\ 1{:}57.41 \text{ min} - 1{:}56.54 \text{ min} \\ 8{:}16.22 \text{ min} - 8{:}16.22 \text{ min} \end{bmatrix}$ Subtract corresponding elements.

$= \begin{bmatrix} 0.5 \text{ s} \\ 0.47 \text{ s} \\ 0.87 \text{ s} \\ 0 \text{ s} \end{bmatrix}$ Simplify.

b. In the 50-meter, the fastest American time is 0.5 second behind the world record. In the 100 m, the fastest American time is 0.47 second behind the world record. In the 200 m, the fastest American time is 0.87 second behind the world record. In the 800 m, the American and world records are the same. So, it was an American who set the world record.
c. In the 50-meter and 100-meter events, the fastest times were set at the Olympics. These times became world records.

35. To show that the Commutative Property of Matrix Addition is true for 2 × 2 matrices,
let $A = \begin{bmatrix} a & b \\ c & d \end{bmatrix}$ and $B = \begin{bmatrix} e & f \\ g & h \end{bmatrix}$. Show that $A + B = B + A$.

$A + B = \begin{bmatrix} a & b \\ c & d \end{bmatrix} + \begin{bmatrix} e & f \\ g & h \end{bmatrix}$ Substitution

$= \begin{bmatrix} a+e & b+f \\ c+g & d+h \end{bmatrix}$ Definition of matrix addition

$= \begin{bmatrix} e+a & f+b \\ g+c & h+d \end{bmatrix}$ Commutative Property of Addition for Real Numbers

$= \begin{bmatrix} e & f \\ g & h \end{bmatrix} + \begin{bmatrix} a & b \\ c & d \end{bmatrix}$ Definition of matrix addition

$= B + A$ Substitution

37. $\begin{bmatrix} 7 & 5 \\ -1 & -5 \end{bmatrix}$ **39.** Sample answer: $A = \begin{bmatrix} 6 & 1 \\ 6 & 3 \end{bmatrix}$ and $B = \begin{bmatrix} 3 & 2 \\ 4 & 2 \end{bmatrix}$ **41.** C **43.** F **45.** $4y$

47. does not exist **49.** (−2, 1, 6)

51.

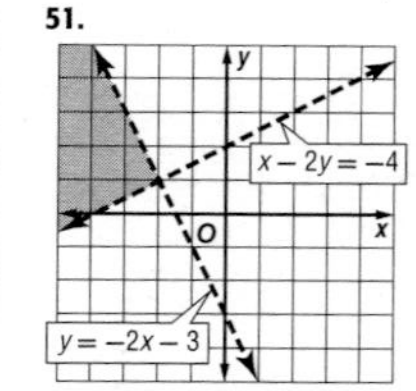

53.

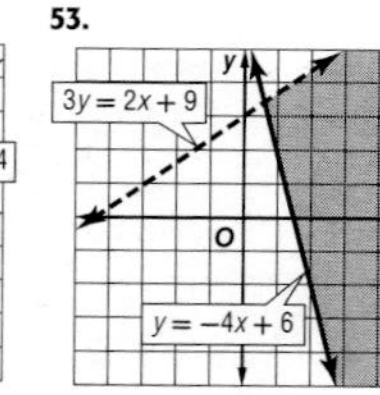

55. 350,349 − x = 15,991; 334,358 **57.** $-10a - b$

Pages 204–207 Lesson 4-3

1. 2 × 3 **3.** 8 × 10 **5.** $\begin{bmatrix} 0 & 44 \\ 8 & -34 \end{bmatrix}$

7 The product of a 2 × 1 matrix and a 1 × 3 matrix is a 2 × 3 matrix.

$\begin{bmatrix} -9 \\ 6 \end{bmatrix} \cdot \begin{bmatrix} 1 & -10 & 1 \end{bmatrix}$

$= \begin{bmatrix} -9(-1) & -9(-10) & -9(1) \\ 6(-1) & 6(-10) & 6(1) \end{bmatrix}$ Multiply the column by the row.

$= \begin{bmatrix} 9 & 90 & -9 \\ -6 & -60 & 6 \end{bmatrix}$ Simplify.

9. $\begin{bmatrix} -44 \\ 25 \end{bmatrix}$ **11.** $\begin{bmatrix} -16 & -1 \\ -6 & 10 \end{bmatrix}$

13. No; $\begin{bmatrix} 53 & -87 \\ -2 & -60 \end{bmatrix} \neq \begin{bmatrix} 62 & -33 \\ 28 & -69 \end{bmatrix}$.

15. 2×4 **17.** undefined **19.** undefined **21.** $[\ 26\ ]$

23 $\begin{bmatrix} -3 & -7 \\ -2 & -1 \end{bmatrix} \cdot \begin{bmatrix} 4 & 4 \\ 9 & -3 \end{bmatrix}$

$= \begin{bmatrix} -3(4) + (-7)(9) & -3(4) + (-7)(-3) \end{bmatrix}$ Multiply the 1st row in the 1st matrix by each column in the 2nd matrix.

$\begin{bmatrix} -3 & -7 \\ -2 & -1 \end{bmatrix} \cdot \begin{bmatrix} 4 & 4 \\ 9 & -3 \end{bmatrix}$

$= \begin{bmatrix} -3(4) + (-7)(9) & -3(4) + (-7)(-3) \\ -2(4) + (-1)(9) & -2(4) + (-1)(-3) \end{bmatrix}$ Multiply the 2nd row in the 1st matrix by each column in the 2nd matrix.

$= \begin{bmatrix} -12 + (-63) & -12 + 21 \\ -8 + (-9) & -8 + 3 \end{bmatrix}$ Multiply.

$= \begin{bmatrix} -75 & 9 \\ -17 & -5 \end{bmatrix}$ Add.

25. undefined **27.** $\begin{bmatrix} -40 & 64 \\ 22 & 1 \end{bmatrix}$

29a. $I = \begin{bmatrix} 3 & 2 & 2 \\ 2 & 3 & 1 \\ 4 & 3 & 0 \end{bmatrix}, C = \begin{bmatrix} 220 \\ 250 \\ 360 \end{bmatrix}$ **29b.** $\begin{bmatrix} \$1880 \\ \$1550 \\ \$1630 \end{bmatrix}$

29c. \$5060 **31.** $PQR = \begin{bmatrix} -22 & 240 \\ 44 & -12 \end{bmatrix}$ and

$RQP = \begin{bmatrix} 34 & -40 \\ -220 & -44 \end{bmatrix}$

33. No; $R(P + Q) = \begin{bmatrix} 34 & -6 \\ -64 & -30 \end{bmatrix}$ and

$PR + QR = \begin{bmatrix} 22 & 72 \\ 14 & -18 \end{bmatrix}$.

35 a. The bonuses can be found by multiplying the number of cars sold by the amount of bonus given for each new and used car sold.

Cars: $C = \begin{bmatrix} 27 & 49 \\ 35 & 36 \\ 9 & 56 \\ 15 & 62 \end{bmatrix}$ Bonus: $B = \begin{bmatrix} 1000 \\ 500 \end{bmatrix}$

$CB = \begin{bmatrix} 27 & 49 \\ 35 & 36 \\ 9 & 56 \\ 15 & 62 \end{bmatrix} \cdot \begin{bmatrix} 1000 \\ 500 \end{bmatrix}$ Write an equation.

$= \begin{bmatrix} 27(1000) + 49(500) \\ 35(1000) + 36(500) \\ 9(1000) + 56(500) \\ 15(1000) + 62(500) \end{bmatrix}$ Multiply columns by rows.

$= \begin{bmatrix} 51{,}500 \\ 53{,}000 \\ 37{,}000 \\ 46{,}000 \end{bmatrix}$ Simplify.

Westin earned the most, \$53,000.

b. total amount on bonuses = 51,500 + 53,000 + 37,000 + 46,000 or \$187,500

37. $\begin{bmatrix} -10 - 4.5y & 36.75 \\ 2x + 4 + 3y^2 & -6x - 4.5y - 12 \\ 3.6y + 26 & -83.4 \end{bmatrix}$

39. $\begin{bmatrix} -1.5x - 1.5y + 15 \\ y^2 + xy + 3x - 6 \\ 1.2x + 1.2y - 39 \end{bmatrix}$

41. undefined

43. $\begin{bmatrix} 15x + 69y - 12 \\ -18y^2 + 42.75y - 18xy + 20.25x \end{bmatrix}$

45a. A: \$421; B: \$274; C: \$150; D: \$68

45b. A: \$357.85; B: \$232.90; C: \$127.50; D: \$57.80

47a. $c(A + B)$

$= c\left(\begin{bmatrix} a & b \\ d & e \end{bmatrix} + \begin{bmatrix} w & x \\ y & z \end{bmatrix}\right)$ Substitution

$= c\begin{bmatrix} a + w & b + x \\ d + y & e + z \end{bmatrix}$ Definition of matrix addition

$= \begin{bmatrix} ca + cw & cb + cx \\ cd + cy & ce + cz \end{bmatrix}$ Definition of scalar multiplication

$= \begin{bmatrix} ca & cb \\ cd & ce \end{bmatrix} + \begin{bmatrix} cw & cx \\ cy & cz \end{bmatrix}$ Definition of matrix addition

$= cA + cB$ Substitution

47b. $C(A + B) = \begin{bmatrix} a & b \\ c & d \end{bmatrix}\left(\begin{bmatrix} e & f \\ g & h \end{bmatrix} + \begin{bmatrix} j & k \\ m & n \end{bmatrix}\right)$ Substitution

$= \begin{bmatrix} a & b \\ c & d \end{bmatrix}\begin{bmatrix} e + j & f + k \\ g + m & h + n \end{bmatrix}$ Definition of matrix addition

$= \begin{bmatrix} a(e + j) + b(g + m) & a(f + k) + b(h + n) \\ c(e + j) + d(g + m) & c(f + k) + d(h + n) \end{bmatrix}$ Definition of matrix multiplication

$= \begin{bmatrix} ea + ja + gb + mb & fa + ka + hb + nb \\ ec + jc + gd + md & fc + kc + hd + nd \end{bmatrix}$ Distributive Property

$= \begin{bmatrix} ea + gb + ja + mb & fa + hb + ka + nb \\ ec + gd + jc + md & fc + hd + kc + nd \end{bmatrix}$ Commutative Property of Addition

$= \begin{bmatrix} ea + gb & fa + hb \\ ec + gd & fc + hd \end{bmatrix} + \begin{bmatrix} ja + mb & ka + nb \\ jc + md & kc + nd \end{bmatrix}$ Definition of matrix addition

$= CA + CB$ Definition of matrix multiplication

$(A + B)C = \left(\begin{bmatrix} a_{11} & a_{12} \\ a_{21} & a_{22} \end{bmatrix} + \begin{bmatrix} b_{11} & b_{12} \\ b_{21} & b_{22} \end{bmatrix}\right)\begin{bmatrix} c_{11} & c_{12} \\ c_{21} & c_{22} \end{bmatrix}$ Substitution

$= \begin{bmatrix} a_{11} + b_{11} & a_{12} + b_{12} \\ a_{21} + b_{21} & a_{22} + b_{22} \end{bmatrix}\begin{bmatrix} c_{11} & c_{12} \\ c_{21} & c_{22} \end{bmatrix}$ Definition of matrix addition

$= \begin{bmatrix} (a_{11} + b_{11})c_{11} + (a_{12} + b_{12})c_{21} & (a_{11} + b_{11})c_{12} + (a_{12} + b_{12})c_{22} \\ (a_{11} + b_{11})c_{11} + (a_{12} + b_{12})c_{21} & (a_{21} + b_{21})c_{12} + (a_{22} + b_{22})c_{22} \end{bmatrix}$ Definition of matrix multiplication

$= \begin{bmatrix} a_{11}c_{11} + b_{11}c_{11} + a_{12}c_{21} + b_{12}c_{21} & a_{11}c_{12} + b_{11}c_{12} + a_{12}c_{22} + b_{12}c_{22} \\ a_{21}c_{11} + b_{21}c_{11} + a_{22}c_{21} + b_{22}c_{21} & a_{21}c_{12} + b_{21}c_{12} + a_{22}c_{22} + b_{22}c_{22} \end{bmatrix}$ Distributive Property

$= \begin{bmatrix} a_{11}c_{11} + a_{12}c_{21} + b_{11}c_{11} + b_{12}c_{21} & a_{11}c_{12} + a_{12}c_{22} + b_{11}c_{12} + b_{12}c_{22} \\ a_{21}c_{11} + a_{22}c_{21} + b_{21}c_{11} + b_{22}c_{21} & a_{21}c_{12} + a_{22}c_{22} + b_{21}c_{12} + b_{22}c_{22} \end{bmatrix}$ Commutative Property of Addition

$= \begin{bmatrix} a_{11}c_{11} + a_{12}c_{21} & a_{11}c_{12} + a_{12}c_{22} \\ a_{21}c_{11} + a_{22}c_{21} & a_{21}c_{12} + a_{22}c_{22} \end{bmatrix} + \begin{bmatrix} b_{11}c_{11} + b_{12}c_{21} & b_{11}c_{12} + b_{12}c_{22} \\ b_{21}c_{11} + b_{22}c_{21} & b_{21}c_{12} + b_{22}c_{22} \end{bmatrix}$ Definition of matrix addition

$= AC + BC$ Definition of matrix multiplication

47c. $(AB)C = \left(\begin{bmatrix} a_{11} & a_{12} \\ a_{21} & a_{22} \end{bmatrix}\begin{bmatrix} b_{11} & b_{12} \\ b_{21} & b_{22} \end{bmatrix}\right)\begin{bmatrix} c_{11} & c_{12} \\ c_{21} & c_{22} \end{bmatrix}$ Substitution

$= \begin{bmatrix} a_{11}b_{11} + a_{12}b_{21} & a_{11}b_{12} + a_{12}b_{22} \\ a_{21}b_{11} + a_{22}b_{21} & a_{21}b_{12} + a_{22}b_{22} \end{bmatrix}\begin{bmatrix} c_{11} & c_{12} \\ c_{21} & c_{22} \end{bmatrix}$ Definition of matrix multiplication

$= \begin{bmatrix} (a_{11}b_{11} + a_{12}b_{21})c_{11} + (a_{11}b_{12} + a_{12}b_{22})c_{21} & (a_{11}b_{11} + a_{12}b_{21})c_{12} + (a_{11}b_{12} + a_{12}b_{22})c_{22} \\ (a_{21}b_{11} + a_{22}b_{21})c_{11} + (a_{21}b_{12} + a_{22}b_{22})c_{21} & (a_{21}b_{11} + a_{22}b_{21})c_{12} + (a_{21}b_{12} + a_{22}b_{22})c_{22} \end{bmatrix}$ Definition of matrix multiplication

$= \begin{bmatrix} a_{11}b_{11}c_{11} + a_{12}b_{21}c_{11} + a_{11}b_{12}c_{21} + a_{12}b_{22}c_{21} & a_{11}b_{11}c_{12} + a_{12}b_{21}c_{12} + a_{11}b_{12}c_{22} + a_{12}b_{22}c_{22} \\ a_{21}b_{11}c_{11} + a_{22}b_{21}c_{11} + a_{21}b_{12}c_{21} + a_{22}b_{22}c_{21} & a_{21}b_{11}c_{12} + a_{22}b_{21}c_{12} + a_{21}b_{12}c_{22} + a_{22}b_{22}c_{22} \end{bmatrix}$ Distributive Property

$= \begin{bmatrix} a_{11}b_{11}c_{11} + a_{11}b_{12}c_{21} + a_{12}b_{21}c_{11} + a_{12}b_{22}c_{21} & a_{11}b_{11}c_{12} + a_{11}b_{12}c_{22} + a_{12}b_{21}c_{12} + a_{12}b_{22}c_{22} \\ a_{21}b_{11}c_{11} + a_{21}b_{12}c_{21} + a_{22}b_{21}c_{11} + a_{22}b_{22}c_{21} & a_{21}b_{11}c_{12} + a_{21}b_{12}c_{22} + a_{22}b_{21}c_{12} + a_{22}b_{22}c_{22} \end{bmatrix}$ Commutative Property of Addition

$= \begin{bmatrix} a_{11}(b_{11}c_{11} + b_{12}c_{21}) + a_{12}(b_{21}c_{11} + b_{22}c_{21}) & a_{11}(b_{11}c_{12} + b_{12}c_{22}) + a_{12}(b_{21}c_{12} + b_{22}c_{22}) \\ a_{11}(b_{11}c_{11} + b_{12}c_{21}) + a_{22}(b_{21}c_{11} + b_{22}c_{21}) & a_{21}(b_{11}c_{12} + b_{12}c_{22}) + a_{22}(b_{21}c_{12} + b_{22}c_{22}) \end{bmatrix}$ Definition of Distributive Property

$= \begin{bmatrix} a_{11} & a_{12} \\ a_{21} & a_{22} \end{bmatrix}\begin{bmatrix} b_{11}c_{11} + b_{12}c_{21} & b_{11}c_{12} + b_{12}c_{22} \\ b_{21}c_{11} + b_{22}c_{21} & b_{21}c_{12} + b_{22}c_{22} \end{bmatrix}$ Definition of matrix multiplication

$= \begin{bmatrix} a_{11} & a_{12} \\ a_{21} & a_{22} \end{bmatrix}\left(\begin{bmatrix} b_{11} & b_{12} \\ b_{21} & b_{22} \end{bmatrix}\begin{bmatrix} c_{11} & c_{12} \\ c_{21} & c_{22} \end{bmatrix}\right)$ Definition of matrix multiplication

$= A(BC)$ Substitution

47d. $c(AB) = c\left(\begin{bmatrix} a_{11} & a_{12} \\ a_{21} & a_{22} \end{bmatrix}\begin{bmatrix} b_{11} & b_{12} \\ b_{21} & b_{22} \end{bmatrix}\right)$ Substitution

$= c\begin{bmatrix} a_{11}b_{11} + a_{12}b_{21} & a_{11}b_{12} + a_{12}b_{22} \\ a_{21}b_{11} + a_{22}b_{21} & a_{21}b_{12} + a_{22}b_{22} \end{bmatrix}$ Definition of matrix addition

$= \begin{bmatrix} c(a_{11}b_{11} + a_{12}b_{21}) & c(a_{11}b_{12} + a_{12}b_{22}) \\ c(a_{21}b_{11} + a_{22}b_{21}) & c(a_{21}b_{12} + a_{22}b_{22}) \end{bmatrix}$ Definition of scalar multiplication

$= \begin{bmatrix} ca_{11}b_{11} + ca_{12}b_{21} & ca_{11}b_{12} + ca_{12}b_{22} \\ ca_{21}b_{11} + ca_{22}b_{21} & ca_{21}b_{12} + ca_{22}b_{22} \end{bmatrix}$ Distributive Property

$= \begin{bmatrix} ca_{11} & ca_{12} \\ ca_{21} & ca_{22} \end{bmatrix}\begin{bmatrix} b_{11} & b_{12} \\ b_{21} & b_{22} \end{bmatrix}$ Definition of matrix multiplication

$= c\begin{bmatrix} a_{11} & a_{12} \\ a_{21} & a_{22} \end{bmatrix}\begin{bmatrix} b_{11} & b_{12} \\ b_{21} & b_{22} \end{bmatrix}$ Definition of scalar multiplication

$= (cA)B$ Substitution

$c(AB) = c\left(\begin{bmatrix} a_{11} & a_{12} \\ a_{21} & a_{22} \end{bmatrix}\begin{bmatrix} b_{11} & b_{12} \\ b_{21} & b_{22} \end{bmatrix}\right)$ Substitution

$= c\begin{bmatrix} a_{11}b_{11} + a_{12}b_{21} & a_{11}b_{12} + a_{12}b_{22} \\ a_{21}b_{11} + a_{22}b_{21} & a_{21}b_{12} + a_{22}b_{22} \end{bmatrix}$ Definition of matrix multiplication

$= \begin{bmatrix} c(a_{11}b_{11} + a_{12}b_{21}) & c(a_{11}b_{12} + a_{12}b_{22}) \\ c(a_{21}b_{11} + a_{22}b_{21}) & c(a_{21}b_{12} + a_{22}b_{22}) \end{bmatrix}$ Definition of scalar multiplication

For Homework Help, go to Hotmath.com

$= \begin{bmatrix} ca_{11}b_{11} + ca_{12}b_{21} & ca_{11}b_{12} + ca_{12}b_{22} \\ ca_{21}b_{11} + ca_{22}b_{21} & ca_{21}b_{12} + ca_{22}b_{22} \end{bmatrix}$ Distributive Property

$= \begin{bmatrix} a_{11}cb_{11} + a_{12}cb_{21} & a_{11}cb_{12} + a_{12}cb_{22} \\ a_{21}cb_{11} + a_{22}cb_{21} & a_{21}cb_{12} + a_{22}cb_{22} \end{bmatrix}$ Commutative Property

$= \begin{bmatrix} a_{11} & a_{12} \\ a_{21} & a_{22} \end{bmatrix}\begin{bmatrix} cb_{11} & cb_{12} \\ cb_{21} & cb_{22} \end{bmatrix}$ Definition of matrix multiplication

$= A(cB)$ Substitution

49. $a = 2, b = 1, c = 3, d = 4$ **51.** 12 **53.** H

55. $\begin{bmatrix} 42 & -24 \\ -42 & -31 \end{bmatrix}$ **57.** $\begin{bmatrix} -80 & -44 \\ 68 & 4 \end{bmatrix}$ **59.** 2 × 2

61a. Sample answer: $y = 116.25x + 231{,}176.97$

61b. Sample answer: $2950.53 **61c.** The value predicted by the equation is significantly lower than the one given in the graph.

63. translation 4 units right and 3 units up

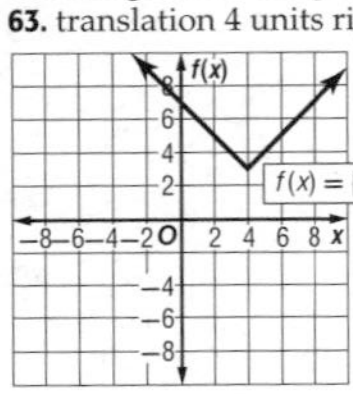

65. translation 2 units left and 6 units down

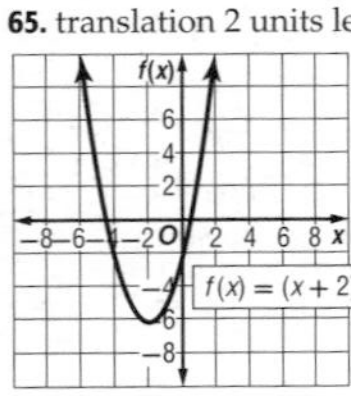

Pages 213–217 Lesson 4-4

1. $A'(2, -6), B'(1, -1), C'(6, -3)$

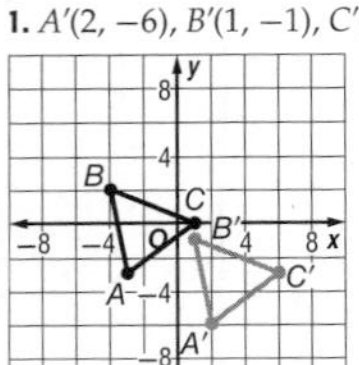

3 Find the translation matrix that moves $T(-3, -1)$ to $T'(-4, 1)$.

$\overset{T}{\begin{bmatrix} -3 \\ -1 \end{bmatrix}} + \begin{bmatrix} x \\ y \end{bmatrix} = \overset{T'}{\begin{bmatrix} -4 \\ 1 \end{bmatrix}}$ Write an equation.

$\begin{bmatrix} -3 + x \\ -1 + y \end{bmatrix} = \begin{bmatrix} -4 \\ 1 \end{bmatrix}$ Add.

The matrices are equal, so corresponding elements are equal.

$-3 + x = -4$ Solve for x. $\quad -1 + y = 1$ Solve for y.

$x = -1 \quad y = 2$

The translation matrix is $\begin{bmatrix} x \\ y \end{bmatrix} = \begin{bmatrix} -1 \\ 2 \end{bmatrix}$. So, rectangle $RSTU$ is translated by adding −1 to the x-coordinate and adding 2 to the y-coordinate.

Vertex Matrix of $RSTU$ + Translation Matrix:

$\begin{bmatrix} -3 & 1 & -3 & 1 \\ 2 & 2 & -1 & -1 \end{bmatrix} + \begin{bmatrix} -1 & -1 & -1 & -1 \\ 2 & 2 & 2 & 2 \end{bmatrix} =$

Vertex Matrix of $R'S'T'U'$

$\begin{bmatrix} -4 & 0 & -4 & 0 \\ 4 & 4 & 1 & 1 \end{bmatrix}$

The vertices of $R'S'T'U'$ are $R'(-4, 4)$, $S'(0, 4)$, $T'(-4, 1)$, and $U'(0, 1)$. So, the correct answer is A.

5. $S'\left(\frac{1}{2}, 0\right), T'\left(2, -1\frac{1}{2}\right), U'\left(\frac{1}{2}, -3\right), V'\left(-1, -1\frac{1}{2}\right)$

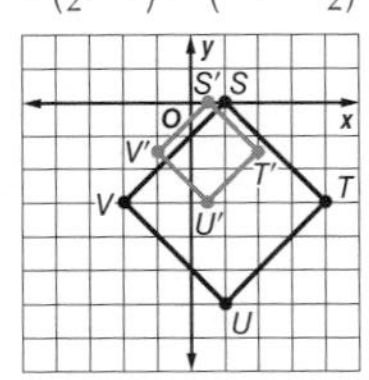

7. $P'(2, -1), Q'(-4, 4), R'(-4, -1)$

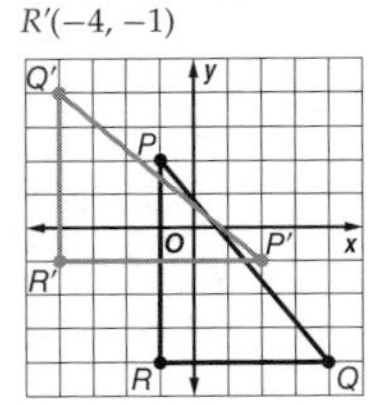

9. $A'(-1, -4), B'(-4, -3), C'(-4, 0), D'(-1, 1)$

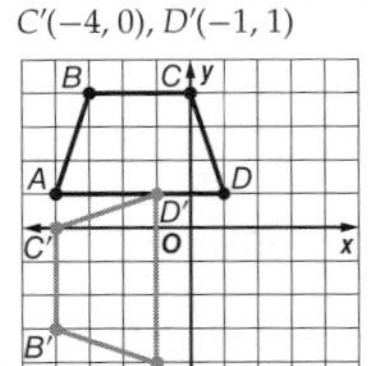

11. $E'(-8, 4), F'(-2, -1), G'(-6, -3), H'(-7, -2)$

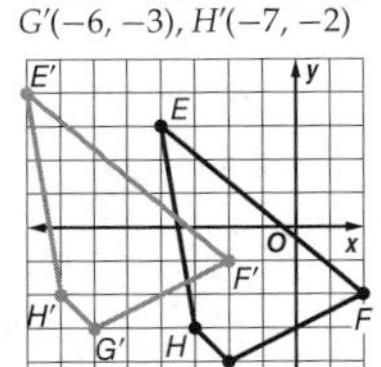

13. $J'(4, 0), K'(5, -3), L'(2, -6)$

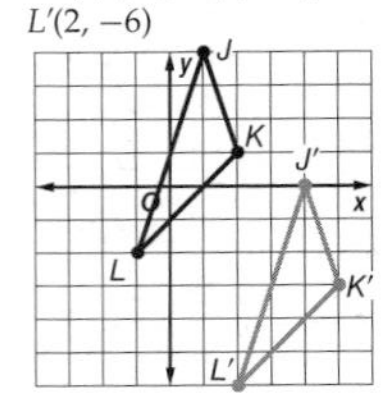

15. $W'(1, 5), X'(1, 9), Y'(5, 9), Z'(5, 5)$

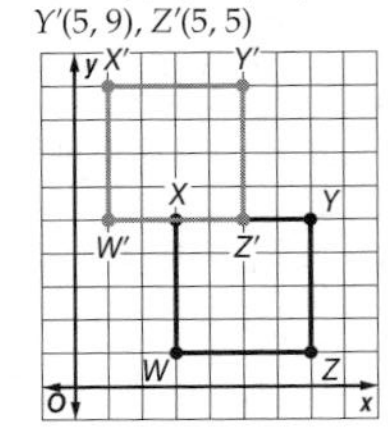

17 a. Three blocks east is 3 units to the right. Four blocks north is 4 units up. To translate 3 units to the right, add 3 to each x-coordinate. To translate 4 units up, add 4 to each y-coordinate. This can be represented by the translation matrix $\begin{bmatrix} 3 \\ 4 \end{bmatrix}$.

b. $\begin{bmatrix} 5.5 \\ 7 \end{bmatrix} + \begin{bmatrix} 3 \\ 4 \end{bmatrix} = \begin{bmatrix} 8.5 \\ 11 \end{bmatrix}$

The coordinates of the mall are (8.5, 11).

19. $D'(0, 16), E'(8, 8), F'(0, 0), G'(-8, 8)$

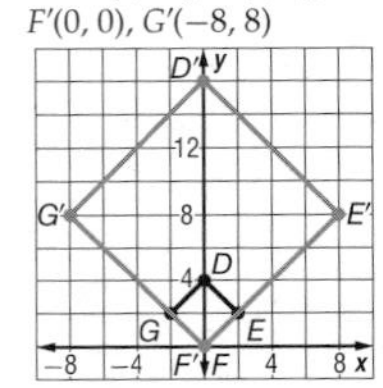

21. $Q'\left(1\frac{1}{2}, 1\right), R'(2, 0), S'\left(0, \frac{1}{4}\right)$

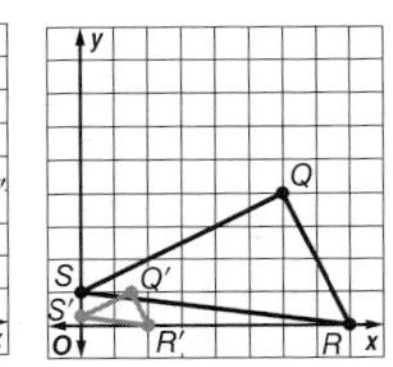

23 Reflection Matrix · Vertex Matrix of DEF = Vertex Matrix of $D'E'F'$

$\begin{bmatrix} 1 & 0 \\ 0 & -1 \end{bmatrix} \cdot \begin{bmatrix} 7 & 4 & -3 \\ 4 & 0 & 2 \end{bmatrix} = \begin{bmatrix} 7 & 4 & -3 \\ -4 & 0 & -2 \end{bmatrix}$

The coordinates of the vertices of $\triangle D'E'F'$ are $D'(7, -4)$, $E'(4, 0)$, and $F'(-3, -2)$.

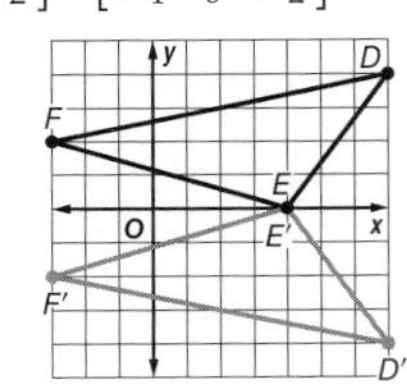

25. $L'(-1, -2), M'(5, -1), N'(4, 5), P'(-2, 4)$

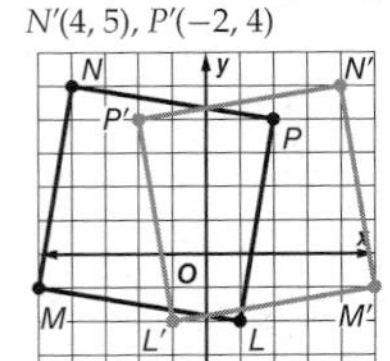

27. $T'(5, -4), U'(3, 1), V'(0, -2)$

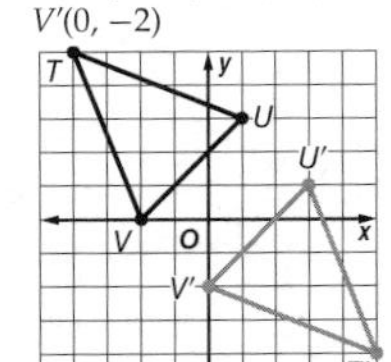

29. $X'(-1, -2), Y'(-1, -4), Z'(-5, -2)$

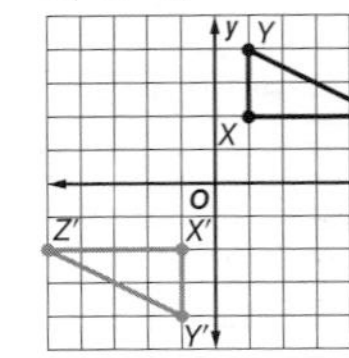

31. $E'(2, -3), F'(-4, -3), G'(-4, -2), H'(2, -2)$

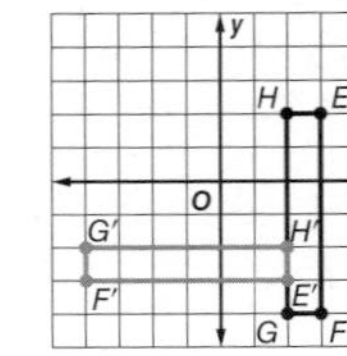

33. $N'(1, -2), P'(5, -3), Q'(5, -6), R'(1, -6)$

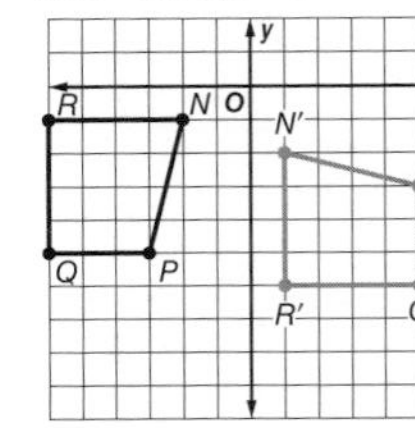

35. (−165, 0)

37. $X''(-8, -5), Y''(-6, -3), Z''(-5, -7)$

39. $A''(4, -4), B''(-4, -4), C''(-4, 4), D''(4, 4)$

41 a. vertex matrix for $\triangle ABC$: $\begin{bmatrix} -2 & 4 & 2 \\ 3 & 0 & -5 \end{bmatrix}$

matrix for $\triangle A'B'C'$: $\begin{bmatrix} 1 & 0 \\ 0 & -1 \end{bmatrix} \cdot \begin{bmatrix} -2 & 4 & 2 \\ 3 & 0 & -5 \end{bmatrix} = \begin{bmatrix} -2 & 4 & 2 \\ -3 & 0 & 5 \end{bmatrix}$

b.

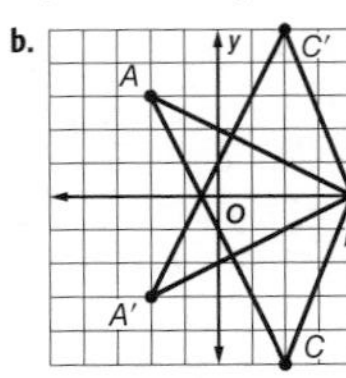

c. Conjecture: The reflection of $\triangle A'B'C'$ in the x-axis is $\triangle ABC$.

$\begin{bmatrix} 1 & 0 \\ 0 & -1 \end{bmatrix} \cdot \begin{bmatrix} -2 & 4 & 2 \\ -3 & 0 & 5 \end{bmatrix} = \begin{bmatrix} -2 & 4 & 2 \\ 3 & 0 & -5 \end{bmatrix}$

d. Reflection Matrix · Reflection Matrix

$\begin{bmatrix} 1 & 0 \\ 0 & -1 \end{bmatrix} \cdot \begin{bmatrix} 1 & 0 \\ 0 & -1 \end{bmatrix} = \begin{bmatrix} 1 & 0 \\ 0 & 1 \end{bmatrix}$

The matrix is the identity matrix because reflecting a triangle in the same line twice produces the original figure.

43. Sometimes; the image and preimage are only congruent if the scale factor is 1 or −1. **45.** Sample answer: A reflection in the x-axis produces an image of $\begin{bmatrix} 3 \\ 2 \end{bmatrix}$. This is the same as applying the translation $\begin{bmatrix} 0 \\ 4 \end{bmatrix}$.

For Homework Help, go to Hotmath.com

47. 180° counterclockwise rotation:

$$\begin{bmatrix} -1 & 0 \\ 0 & -1 \end{bmatrix} \cdot \begin{bmatrix} x_1 & x_2 & x_3 \\ y_1 & y_2 & y_3 \end{bmatrix}$$

$$= \begin{bmatrix} -1(x_1) + 0(y_1) & -1(x_2) + 0(y_2) & -1(x_3) + 0(y_3) \\ 0(x_1) - 1(y_1) & 0(x_2) - 1(y_2) & 0(x_3) - 1(y_3) \end{bmatrix}$$

$$= \begin{bmatrix} -x_1 & -x_2 & -x_3 \\ -y_1 & -y_2 & -y_3 \end{bmatrix}$$

Reflection in the x-axis:

$$\begin{bmatrix} 1 & 0 \\ 0 & -1 \end{bmatrix} \cdot \begin{bmatrix} x_1 & x_2 & x_3 \\ y_1 & y_2 & y_3 \end{bmatrix}$$

$$= \begin{bmatrix} 1(x_1) + 0(y_1) & 1(x_2) + 0(y_2) & 1(x_3) + 0(y_3) \\ 0(x_1) - 1(y_1) & 0(x_2) - 1(y_2) & 0(x_3) - 1(y_3) \end{bmatrix}$$

$$= \begin{bmatrix} x_1 & x_2 & x_3 \\ -y_1 & -y_2 & -y_3 \end{bmatrix}$$

followed by a reflection in the y-axis:

$$\begin{bmatrix} -1 & 0 \\ 0 & 1 \end{bmatrix} \cdot \begin{bmatrix} x_1 & x_2 & x_3 \\ -y_1 & -y_2 & -y_3 \end{bmatrix}$$

$$= \begin{bmatrix} -1(x_1) + 0(y_1) & -1(x_2) + 0(y_2) & -1(x_3) + 0(y_3) \\ 0(x_1) + 1(-y_1) & 0(x_2) + 1(-y_2) & 0(x_3) + 1(-y_3) \end{bmatrix}$$

$$= \begin{bmatrix} -x_1 & -x_2 & -x_3 \\ -y_1 & -y_2 & -y_3 \end{bmatrix}$$

49. B **51.** $\begin{bmatrix} \$29.99 & \$149.99 \\ \$39.99 & \$179.99 \\ \$49.99 & \$209.99 \\ \$69.99 & \$349.99 \end{bmatrix}, \begin{bmatrix} \$34.49 & \$172.49 \\ \$45.99 & \$206.99 \\ \$57.49 & \$241.49 \\ \$80.49 & \$402.49 \end{bmatrix}$

53. $\begin{bmatrix} 34 & 10 \\ -21 & -5 \end{bmatrix}$ **55.** impossible

57.

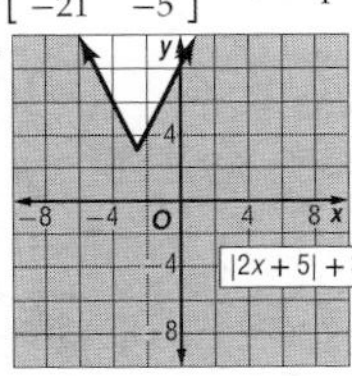

59.

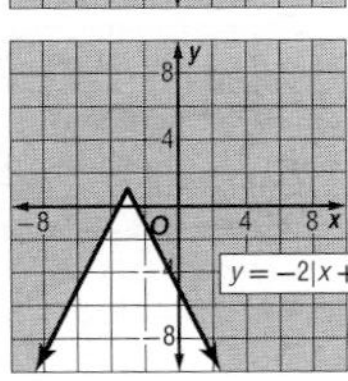

61. independent **63.** (5, –1)

Pages 225–228 Lesson 4-5

1. 26 **3.** –128

5 Rewrite the first two columns to the right of the determinant. Then find the products of the elements of the diagonals.

$$\begin{vmatrix} 3 & -2 & 2 \\ -4 & 2 & -5 \\ -3 & 1 & 4 \end{vmatrix} \begin{matrix} 3 & -2 \\ -4 & 2 \\ -3 & 1 \end{matrix} \quad \begin{matrix} 3(2)(4) = 24 \\ -2(-5)(-3) = -30 \\ 2(-4)(1) = -8 \end{matrix}$$

$$\begin{vmatrix} 3 & -2 & 2 \\ -4 & 2 & -5 \\ -3 & 1 & 4 \end{vmatrix} \begin{matrix} 3 & -2 \\ -4 & 2 \\ -3 & 1 \end{matrix} \quad \begin{matrix} -3(2)(2) = -12 \\ 1(-5)(3) = -15 \\ 4(-4)(-2) = 32 \end{matrix}$$

The sum of the first group is 24 + (–30) + (–8) or –14. The sum of the second group is –12 + (–15) + 32 or 5. The first sum minus the second sum is –14 – 5 or –19.

7. –284 **9.** 72 **11.** 182 **13.** (6, –3) **15.** (4, –1) **17a.** 15.75 units^2 **17b.** 482,343.75 mi^2

19. $\left(\frac{66}{7}, -\frac{116}{7}, -\frac{41}{7}\right)$ **21.** (–4, –2, 8)

23. (–1, –3, 7) **25.** (4, 0, 8) **27.** 3 **29.** –135 **31.** –459 **33.** 0 **35.** 728 **37.** –952 **39.** (8, –5)

41 $x = \dfrac{\begin{vmatrix} m & b \\ n & g \end{vmatrix}}{|C|} = \dfrac{\begin{vmatrix} -39 & -5 \\ 54 & 8 \end{vmatrix}}{\begin{vmatrix} -4 & -5 \\ 5 & 8 \end{vmatrix}}$

$x = \dfrac{-39(8) - 54(-5)}{-4(8) - 5(-5)}$

$= \dfrac{-312 + 270}{-32 + 25}$

$= \dfrac{-42}{-7}$ or 6

$y = \dfrac{\begin{vmatrix} a & m \\ f & n \end{vmatrix}}{|C|} = \dfrac{\begin{vmatrix} -4 & -39 \\ 5 & 54 \end{vmatrix}}{\begin{vmatrix} -4 & -5 \\ 5 & 8 \end{vmatrix}}$

$y = \dfrac{-4(54) - 5(-39)}{-4(8) - 5(-5)}$

$= \dfrac{-216 + 195}{-32 + 25}$

$= \dfrac{-21}{-7}$ or 3

The solution of the system is (6, 3).

43. (–3, –7) **45.** (4, –2, 5) **47.** 6 **49.** 2 m^2

51. (4, 8, –5) **53.** $\left(-\frac{6187}{701}, -\frac{2904}{701}, -\frac{4212}{701}\right)$

55 **a.** Let x = the number of medium drinks. Then $2x$ = the number of small drinks. Let y = the number of large drinks.

number of drinks: $x + 2x + y = 1385 \rightarrow 3x + y = 1385$

total sales: $1.75x + 1.15(2x) + 2.25y = 2238.75$

$\rightarrow 4.05x + 2.25y = 2238.75$

$x = \dfrac{\begin{vmatrix} m & b \\ n & g \end{vmatrix}}{|C|} = \dfrac{\begin{vmatrix} 1385 & 1 \\ 2238.75 & 2.25 \end{vmatrix}}{\begin{vmatrix} 3 & 1 \\ 4.05 & 2.25 \end{vmatrix}}$

$x = \dfrac{1385(2.25) - 2238.75(1)}{3(2.25) - 4.05(1)}$

$= \dfrac{3116.25 - 2238.75}{6.75 - 4.05}$

$= \dfrac{877.5}{2.7}$ or 325

$y = \dfrac{\begin{vmatrix} a & m \\ f & n \end{vmatrix}}{|C|} = \dfrac{\begin{vmatrix} 3 & 1385 \\ 4.05 & 2238.75 \end{vmatrix}}{\begin{vmatrix} 3 & 1 \\ 4.05 & 2.25 \end{vmatrix}}$

$y = \dfrac{3(2238.75) - 4.05(1385)}{3(2.25) - 4.05(1)}$

$= \dfrac{6716.25 - 5609.25}{6.75 - 4.05}$

$= \dfrac{1107}{2.7}$ or 410

He sold 325 medium drinks, 2(325) or 650 small drinks, and 410 large drinks.

b. total sales = sales of small + sales of medium + sales of large

= 1.25(650 – 140) + 1.75(325 + 125) + 2.25(410 + 35)

= 637.50 + 787.50 + 1001.25

= \$2426.25

c. It seems like it was a good move for the vendor. Although he sold 140 fewer small drinks, he sold 125 more medium drinks and 35 more large drinks. On the whole, he made \$2,426.25 – \$2,238.75 or \$187.50 more this week than in the previous week.

57. Sample answer: There is no unique solution of the system. There are either infinite or no solutions.

59. 0 **61.** Sample answer: Given a 2 × 2 system of linear equations, if the determinant of the matrix of coefficients is 0, then the system does not have a unique solution. The system may have no solution and the graphical representation shows two parallel lines. The system may have infinitely many solutions in which the graphical representation will be the same line. **63.** H **65.** B

67. $E'(5, -2), (-3, 5), G'(-6, -1)$ **69.** no

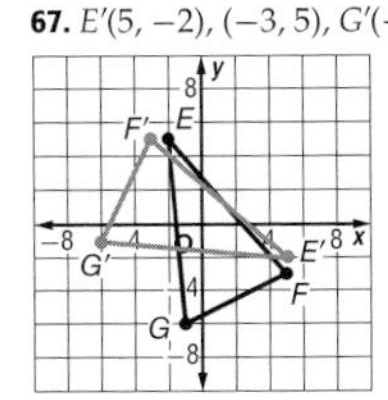

71.

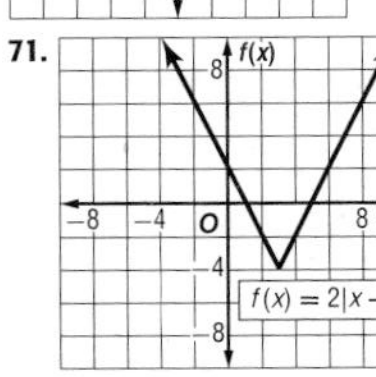

73.

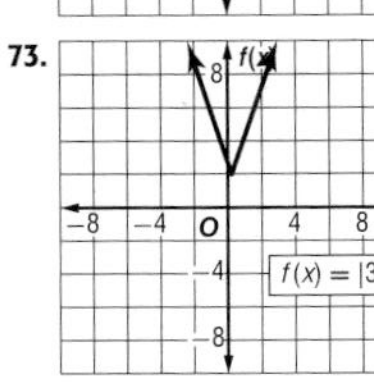

75. $\left(\frac{79}{25}, -\frac{56}{25}\right)$

Pages 233–235 Lesson 4-6

1. no **3.** yes **5.** $\begin{bmatrix} 0 & -1 \\ -\frac{1}{3} & -2 \end{bmatrix}$ **7.** $\begin{bmatrix} -\frac{1}{3} & 0 \\ \frac{5}{6} & \frac{1}{2} \end{bmatrix}$

9. (–2, 5) **11.** (1, –2) **13.** no **15.** no **17.** $\begin{bmatrix} \frac{1}{3} & 0 \\ 0 & \frac{1}{2} \end{bmatrix}$

19. $\begin{bmatrix} \frac{1}{3} & 0 \\ -\frac{5}{3} & 1 \end{bmatrix}$

21 $\begin{vmatrix} -5 & -4 \\ 4 & 2 \end{vmatrix} = -5(2) - 4(-4)$ or 6 Find the determinant.

Since the determinant ≠ 0, the inverse exists.

$A^{-1} = \dfrac{1}{ad - bc}\begin{bmatrix} d & -b \\ -c & a \end{bmatrix}$ Definition of inverse

$= \dfrac{1}{-5(2) - (-4)(4)}\begin{bmatrix} 2 & 4 \\ -4 & -5 \end{bmatrix}$ $a = -5, b = -4, c = 4, d = 2$

$= \dfrac{1}{6}\begin{bmatrix} 2 & 4 \\ -4 & -5 \end{bmatrix}$ or $\begin{bmatrix} \frac{1}{3} & \frac{2}{3} \\ -\frac{2}{3} & -\frac{5}{6} \end{bmatrix}$ Simplify.

23. $\begin{bmatrix} \frac{9}{74} & \frac{5}{74} \\ -\frac{2}{37} & \frac{3}{37} \end{bmatrix}$ **25.** $\begin{bmatrix} \frac{7}{22} & \frac{4}{11} \\ \frac{4}{11} & \frac{3}{11} \end{bmatrix}$ **27.** no solution

29. (–1, 5) **31.** no solution **33.** (–5, 0)

35. $\left(\frac{3}{4}, 3\right)$

37 **a.** Let x = the number of people who own CD players and let y = the number of people who own digital audio players. The following expressions represent the change in player ownership.

Keeping or switching to CD players: $0.35x + 0.12y$

Keeping or switching to digital audio players: $0.65x + 0.88y$

		From	
		CD	DAP
To	CD	0.35	0.12
	DAP	0.65	0.88

b. Let x = the number of people who will own CD players next year and let y = the number of people who will own digital audio players next year. Write a matrix equation.

$$\begin{bmatrix} 0.35 & 0.12 \\ 0.65 & 0.88 \end{bmatrix} \cdot \begin{bmatrix} 7748 \\ 17{,}252 \end{bmatrix} = \begin{bmatrix} x \\ y \end{bmatrix}$$

$$\begin{bmatrix} 4782 \\ 20{,}218 \end{bmatrix} = \begin{bmatrix} x \\ y \end{bmatrix}$$

So, about 20,218 people will own digital audio players next year.

c. Let x = the number of people who owned CD players last year and let y = the number of people who owned digital audio players last year. Write a matrix equation.

$$\begin{bmatrix} 0.35 & 0.12 \\ 0.65 & 0.88 \end{bmatrix} \cdot \begin{bmatrix} x \\ y \end{bmatrix} = \begin{bmatrix} 7748 \\ 17{,}252 \end{bmatrix}$$

Find the inverse of the coefficient matrix.

A^{-1}

$= \dfrac{1}{0.35(0.88) - 0.12(0.65)}\begin{bmatrix} 0.88 & -0.12 \\ -0.65 & 0.35 \end{bmatrix}$ $a = 0.35, b = 0.12, c = 0.65, d = 0.88$

$= \dfrac{1}{0.23}\begin{bmatrix} 0.88 & -0.12 \\ -0.65 & 0.35 \end{bmatrix}$ Simplify.

Multiply each side of the matrix equation by the inverse matrix.

$\frac{1}{0.23}\begin{bmatrix} 0.88 & -0.12 \\ -0.65 & 0.35 \end{bmatrix} \cdot \begin{bmatrix} 0.35 & 0.12 \\ 0.65 & 0.88 \end{bmatrix} \cdot \begin{bmatrix} x \\ y \end{bmatrix} =$

$\frac{1}{0.23}\begin{bmatrix} 0.88 & -0.12 \\ -0.65 & 0.35 \end{bmatrix} \cdot \begin{bmatrix} 7748 \\ 17{,}252 \end{bmatrix}$

$\begin{bmatrix} 1 & 0 \\ 0 & 1 \end{bmatrix} \cdot \begin{bmatrix} x \\ y \end{bmatrix} = \frac{1}{0.23}\begin{bmatrix} 4748 \\ 1002 \end{bmatrix}$

$\begin{bmatrix} x \\ y \end{bmatrix} = \begin{bmatrix} 20{,}643 \\ 4357 \end{bmatrix}$

So, about 4357 people owned digital audio players last year.

39. The system would have to consist of two equations that are the same or one equation that is a multiple of the other.

41. Sample answer: $\begin{bmatrix} 2 & 3 \\ 4 & 6 \end{bmatrix} \cdot \begin{bmatrix} x \\ y \end{bmatrix} = \begin{bmatrix} 9 \\ 10 \end{bmatrix}$; any matrix that has a determinant equal to 0, such as $\begin{bmatrix} 1 & 0 \\ 0 & 1 \end{bmatrix}$ **43.** C **45.** $\left(\frac{1}{2}, \frac{1}{4}\right)$ **47.** −54 **49.** 551

51. 179 gal of skim and 21 gal of whole milk

53. absolute value

Pages 237–240 Chapter 4 Study Guide and Review

1. matrix **3.** constant matrix **5.** dimensions **7.** identity **9.** determinant **11a.** $\begin{bmatrix} 64 & 108 & 31 \\ 42 & 9 & 68 \end{bmatrix}$

11b. 2 × 3 **11c.** 68 **11d.** 64 **11e.** The sum of column 1 is 106. This is the total number of customers for store A. The sum of column 2 is 117. This is the total number of customers for store B. **11f.** No, the stores are competing. **13.** $\begin{bmatrix} -3 & 27 \\ 9 & 12 \end{bmatrix}$ **15.** [42] **17.** undefined

19. $A'(3, 7)$, $B'(1, 1)$, $C'(-3, 4)$ **21.** $A'(5, -4)$, $B'(3, 2)$, $C'(-1, -1)$ **23.** $A'(2, 12)$, $B'(16, 12)$, $C'(16, 4)$, $D'(2, 4)$

25. −44 **27.** (2, −3, 6)

29. $\frac{1}{2}\begin{bmatrix} 2 & -4 \\ -3 & 7 \end{bmatrix}$ **31.** does not exist **33.** (2, 1)

Chapter 5 Quadratic Functions and Relations

Page 247 Chapter 5 Get Ready

1. 6 **3.** 4 **5.** 3 **7a.** $f(x) = 9x$ **7b.** 157,680 mi

9. $(x + 8)(x + 5)$ **11.** $(2x - 1)(x + 4)$ **13.** prime

15. $(x + 8)$ feet

Pages 254–257 Lesson 5-1

1a. y-int = 0; axis of symmetry: $x = 0$; x-coordinate = 0

1b.

x	f(x)
−2	12
−1	3
0	0
1	3
2	12

1c.

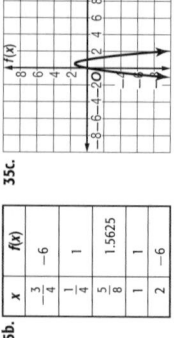

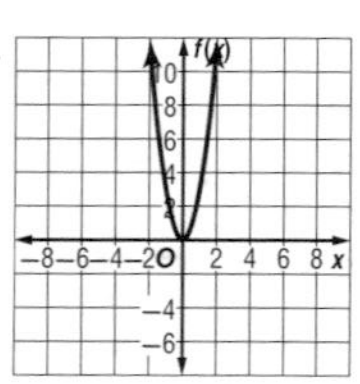

3a. y-int = 0; axis of symmetry: $x = 2$; x-coordinate = 2

3b.

x	f(x)
0	0
1	−3
2	−4
3	−3
4	0

3c.

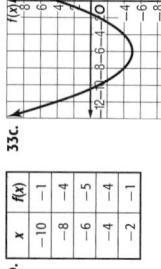

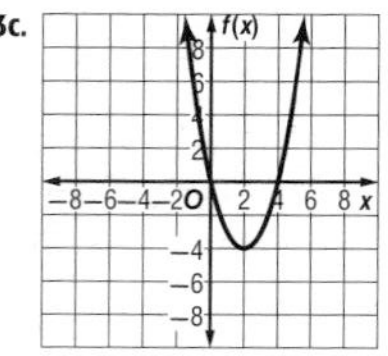

5a. y-int = −3; axis of symmetry: $x = 0.75$; x-coordinate = 0.75

5b.

x	f(x)
−1	7
0	−3
0.75	−5.25
1.5	−3
2.5	7

5c.

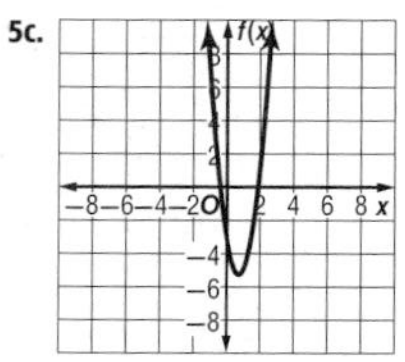

7. max = 8; D = {all real numbers}, R = $\{f(x) \mid f(x) \leq 8\}$

9. min = $-\frac{1}{3}$; D = {all real numbers}, R = $\left\{f(x) \mid f(x) \geq -\frac{1}{3}\right\}$ **11.** \$2.88 **13a.** y-int = 0; axis of symmetry: $x = 0$; x-coordinate = 0

13b.

x	f(x)
−2	−8
−1	−2
0	0
1	−2
2	−8

13c.

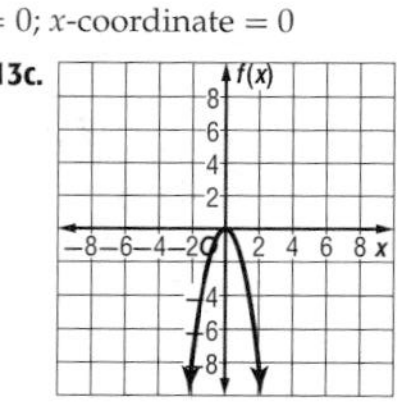

15a. y-int = 3; axis of symmetry: $x = 0$; x-coordinate = 0

15b.

x	f(x)
−2	7
−1	4
0	3
1	4
2	7

15c.

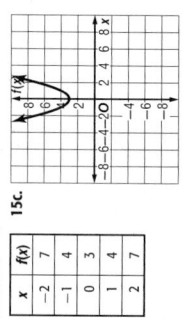

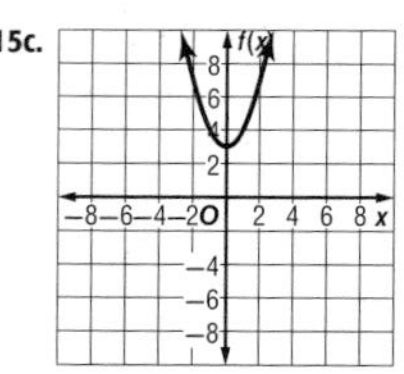

17a. y-int = 5; axis of symmetry: $x = 0$; x-coordinate = 0

17b.

x	f(x)
−2	−7
−1	2
0	5
1	2
2	−7

17c.

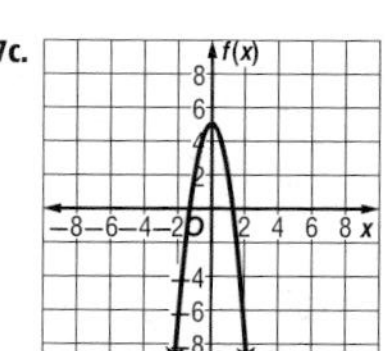

19 a. $f(x) = ax^2 + bx + c$

$f(x) = 1x^2 - 3x - 10$ $a = 1, b = -3, c = -10$

The y-intercept is $c = -10$.

$x = -\frac{b}{2a}$ Equation of the axis of symmetry

$= -\frac{(-3)}{2(1)}$ $a = 1$ and $b = -3$

$= \frac{3}{2}$ or 1.5 Simplify.

The equation of the axis of symmetry is $x = 1.5$. So, the x-coordinate of the vertex is 1.5.

b. Select five points, with the vertex in the middle and two points on either side of the vertex, including the y-intercept and its reflection.

x	f(x)	
0	−10	←reflection of y-intercept
1	−12	
1.5	−12.25	←vertex
2	−12	
3	−10	←y-intercept

c. Graph the five points from the table, connecting them with a smooth curve.

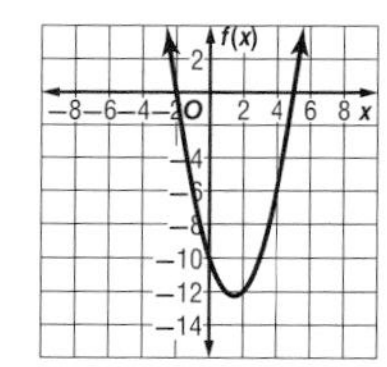

21a. y-int = 9; axis of symmetry: $x = 0.75$; x-coordinate = 0.75

21b.

x	f(x)
−1	4
0	9
0.75	10.125
1.5	9
2.5	4

21c.

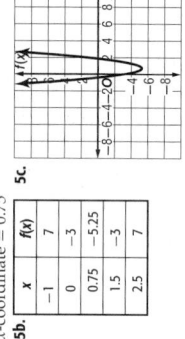

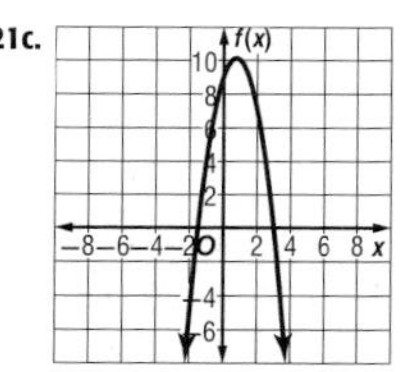

23. max = −12; D = {all real numbers}, R = $\{f(x) \mid f(x) \leq -12\}$ **25.** max = 13.25; D = {all real numbers}, R = $\{f(x) \mid f(x) \leq 13.25\}$ **27.** max = 7; D = {all real numbers}, R = $\{f(x) \mid f(x) \leq 7\}$

29. min = −9; D = {all real numbers}, R = $\{f(x) \mid f(x) \geq -9\}$ **31.** min = −74; D = {all real numbers}, R = $\{f(x) \mid f(x) \geq -74\}$ **33a.** y-int = −9; axis of symmetry: $x = 1.5$; x-coordinate of vertex = 1.5

33b.

x	f(x)
0	−9
1	−13
1.5	−13.5
2	−13
3	−9

33c.

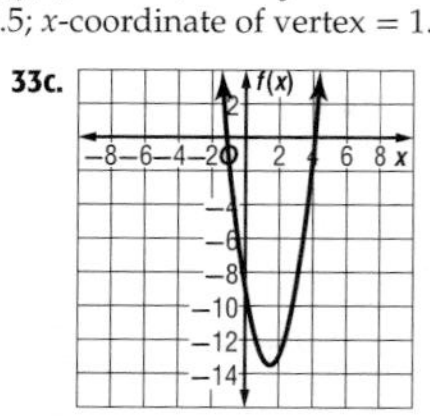

35a. y-int = 0; axis of symmetry: $x = \frac{5}{8}$; x-coordinate of vertex = $\frac{5}{8}$

35b.

x	f(x)
$-\frac{3}{4}$	−6
$\frac{1}{4}$	1
$\frac{5}{8}$	1.5625
1	1
2	−6

35c.

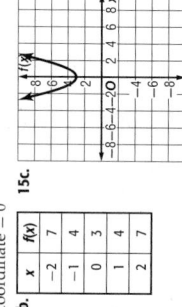

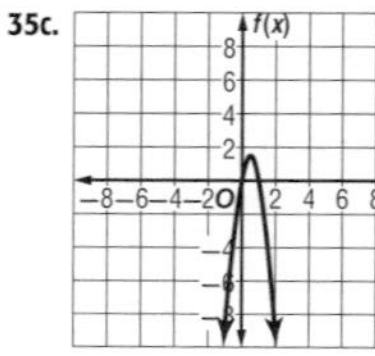

37a. y-int = 4; axis of symmetry: $x = -6$; x-coordinate of vertex = −6

37b.

x	f(x)
−10	−1
−8	−4
−6	−5
−4	−4
−2	−1

33c.

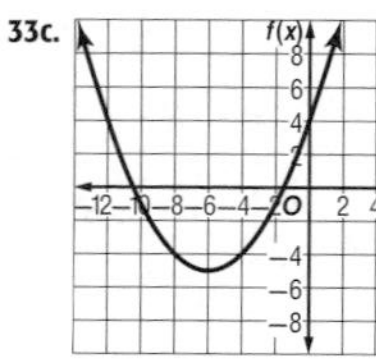

39a. y-int = −2.5; axis of symmetry: $x = -\frac{4}{3}$; x-coordinate of vertex = $-\frac{4}{3}$

39b.

x	f(x)
$-\frac{11}{3}$	3
$-\frac{8}{3}$	−2.5
$-\frac{4}{3}$	$-5\frac{1}{6}$
0	−2.5
1	3

39c.

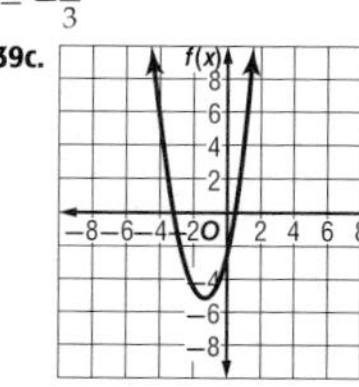

41a. $I(x) = -x^2 + 6x + 475$ **41b.** D = $\{x \mid 0 \leq x \leq 25\}$, R = $\{y \mid 0 \leq y \leq 484\}$ **41c.** \$11; Because the function has a maximum at $x = 3$, it is in the domain. Therefore, three \$0.50 increases is reasonable. **41d.** \$484

43. max = 23 **45.** max = −0.10 **47.** max = −4.11

49 $a = -5$, so the graph opens down and has a maximum value. The maximum value is the y-coordinate of the vertex.

$x = -\frac{b}{2a}$ Equation of the axis of symmetry

$= -\frac{4}{2(-5)}$ or 0.4 $a = -5$ and $b = 4$

The x-coordinate of the vertex is 0.4. Find the y-coordinate of the vertex by evaluating the function for $x = 0.4$.

$f(x) = -5x^2 + 4x - 8$ Original function

$= -5(0.4)^2 + 4(0.4) - 8$ $x = 0.4$

$= -7.2$ The maximum value of the function is −7.2.

The domain is all real numbers. The range is all real numbers less than or equal to the maximum value, or $\{f(x) \mid f(x) \leq -7.2\}$.

51. min = −9.375; D = {all real numbers}, R = $\{f(x) \mid f(x) \geq -9.375\}$ **53.** min = −23.5; D = {all real numbers}, R = $\{f(x) \mid f(x) \geq -23.5\}$

For Homework Help, go to Hotmath.com

55. $f(x) = x^2 - 4x - 5$ **57.** $f(x) = x^2 - 6x + 8$

59 a. Let x = the number of 5-cent increases. Then $65 + 5x$ = price per can in cents and $600 - 100x$ = number of cans. Let $f(x)$ = income as a function of x.

Income = number of cans times the price per can

$f(x) = (600 - 100x) \cdot (65 + 5x)$

Solve for x in the equation.

$f(x) = (600 - 100x) \cdot (65 + 5x)$
$= 600(65) + 600(5x) + (-100x)(65) + (-100x)(5x)$ Distribute.
$= 39{,}000 + 3000x - 6500x - 500x^2$ Multiply.
$= 39{,}000 - 3500x - 500x^2$ Simplify.

So, the equation is $f(x) = 39{,}000 - 3500x - 500x^2$ or $f(x) = -500x^2 - 3500x + 39{,}000$.

$x = -\frac{b}{2a}$ Equation of the axis of symmetry

$x = -\frac{(-3500)}{2(-500)}$ or -3.5 $a = -500$ and $b = -3500$

$f(x) = -500x^2 - 3500x + 39{,}000$ Original function
$= -500(-3.5)^2 - 3500(-3.5) + 39{,}000$ $x = -3.5$
$= 45{,}125$ Simplify.

The coordinates of the vertex are $(-3.5, 45{,}125)$. The y-intercept is 39,000.

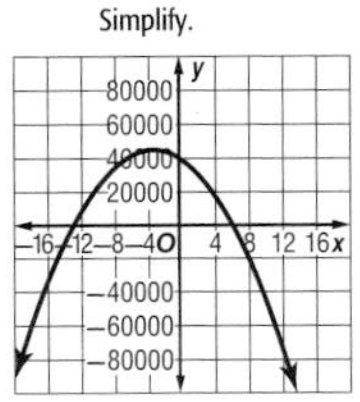

b. Let x = the number of 5-cent decreases. Then $65 - 5x$ = price per can and $600 + 100x$ = number of cans. Let $f(x)$ = income as a function of x.

Income = number of cans times the price per can

$f(x) = (600 + 100x) \cdot (65 - 5x)$

Solve for x in the equation.

$f(x) = (600 + 100x) \cdot (65 - 5x)$
$= 600(65) + 600(-5x) + (100x)(65) + (100x)(-5x)$ Distribute.
$= 39{,}000 - 3000x + 6500x - 500x^2$ Multiply.
$= 39{,}000 + 3500x - 500x^2$ Simplify.

So, the equation is $f(x) = 39{,}000 + 3500x - 500x^2$ or $f(x) = -500x^2 + 3500x + 39{,}000$.

$x = -\frac{b}{2a}$ Equation of the axis of symmetry

$x = -\frac{(3500)}{2(-500)}$ or 3.5 $a = -500$ and $b = 3500$

$f(x) = -500x^2 + 3500x + 39{,}000$ Original function
$= -500(-3.5)^2 + 3500(3.5) + 39{,}000$ $x = -3.5$
$= 45{,}125$ Simplify.

The coordinates of the vertex are (3.5, 45,125). So, Omar should have 3 price decreases and charge $65 - 3(5)$ or 50 cents. Or, he should have 4 price decreases and charge $65 - 4(5)$ or 45 cents.

c. $f(x) = -500x^2 + 3500x + 39{,}000$ Income function
$= -500(3)^2 + 3500(3) + 39{,}000$ Replace x with 3.
$= 45{,}000$ Simplify.

So, his income would be 45,000 cents or $450 per week.

61. Sample answer: Madison is correct; when Trent found the x-coordinate of the vertex, he multiplied two negatives and mistakenly kept a negative. **63a.** $a = 22$; $b = 26$; $c = -6$; $d = 2$ **63b.** 0 **63c.** maximum **65.** Sample answer: A function is quadratic if it has no other terms than a quadratic term, linear term, and constant term. The function has a maximum if the coefficient of the quadratic term is negative and has a minimum if the coefficient of the quadratic term is positive. **67.** I **69.** C

71. $\begin{bmatrix} -\frac{1}{4} & -\frac{1}{24} \\ 0 & \frac{1}{6} \end{bmatrix}$ **73.** 45 **75.** 0 **77.** No; it cannot be written as $y = mx + b$. **79.** Yes; it is written in $y = mx + b$ form, $m = 0$. **81.** -13

Pages 263–266 Lesson 5-2

1. no real solution
3. -4

5 Graph the related function $f(x) = x^2 - 3x - 18$. The equation of the axis of symmetry is $x = -\frac{(-3)}{2(1)}$ or 1.5. Make a table using x-values around 1.5. Then graph each point.

x	-3	0	1.5	3	6
$f(x)$	0	-18	-20.25	-18	0

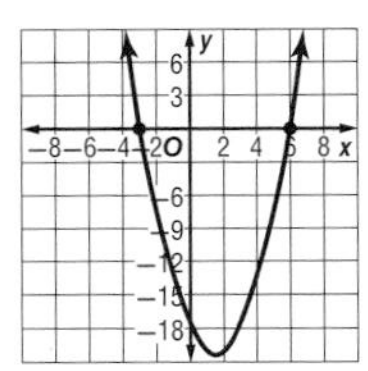

The zeros of the function are -3 and 6. So, the solutions of the equation are -3 and 6.

7.

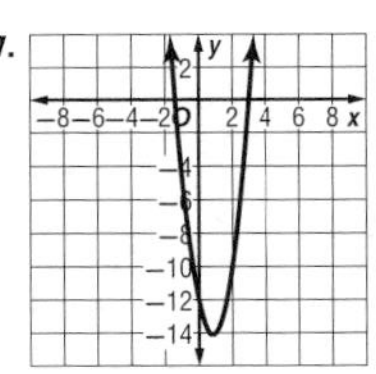

$3, -\frac{4}{3}$

9.

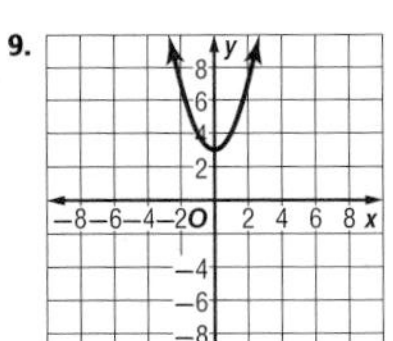

no real solution

11.

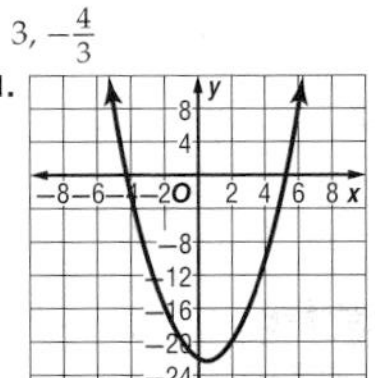

between -5 and -4, between 5 and 6

13. 5 seconds **15.** no real solution **17.** -2 **19.** $-3, 4$

21.

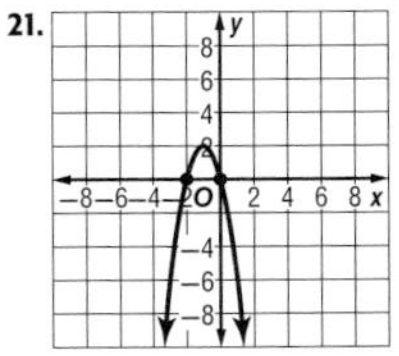

$-2, 0$

23.

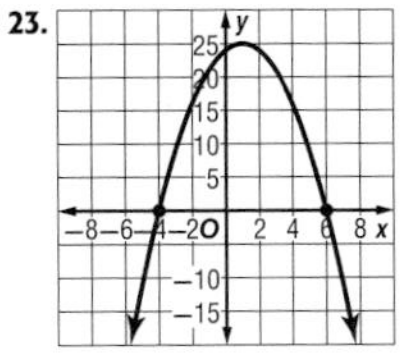

$-4, 6$

25.

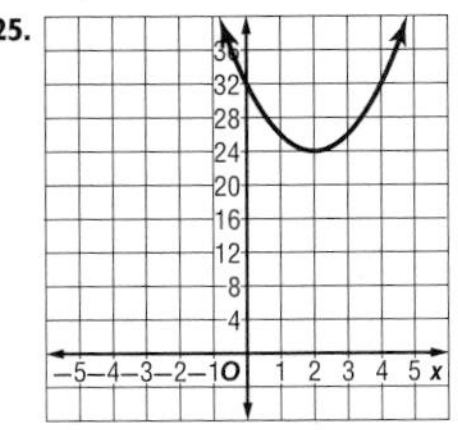

no real solution

27.

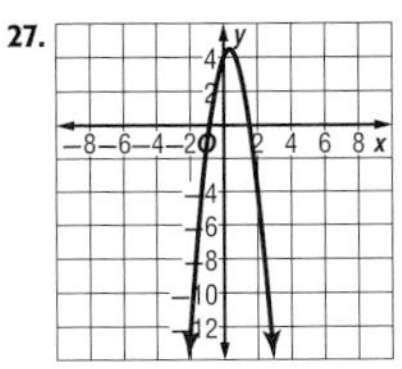

between -1 and 0, between 1 and 2

29.

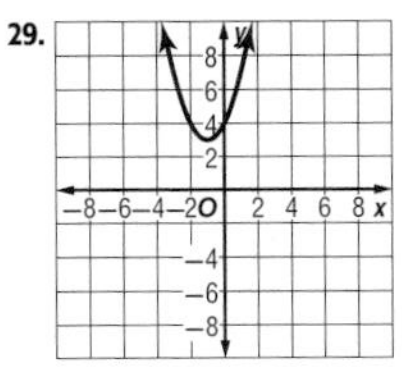

no real solution

31. between 0 and 1; between 2 and 3

33 Let x = one of the numbers. Then $-15 - x$ = the other number.

$x(-x - 15) = -54$ The product is -54.
$-x^2 - 15x = -54$ Distributive Property
$-x^2 - 15x + 54 = 0$ Add 54 to each side.

Graph the related function $f(x) = -x^2 - 15x + 54$. The equation of the axis of symmetry is $x = -\frac{(-15)}{2(-1)}$ or -7.5. Make a table using x-values around -7.5. Then graph each point.

x	-20	-15	-10	-7.5	-5	0	5
$f(x)$	-46	54	104	110.25	104	54	-46

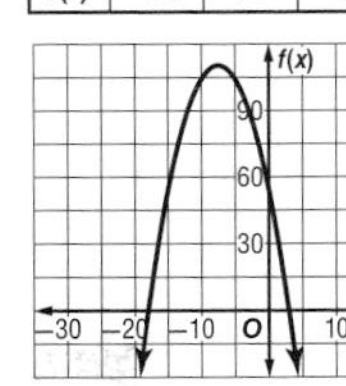

The zeros of the function are -18 and 3. So, the numbers are -18 and 3.

35. about -5.0 and 17.0 **37.** 11 and -19
39. about 3.4375 seconds

41.

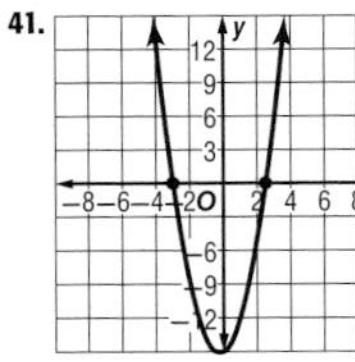

-3, between 2 and 3

43.

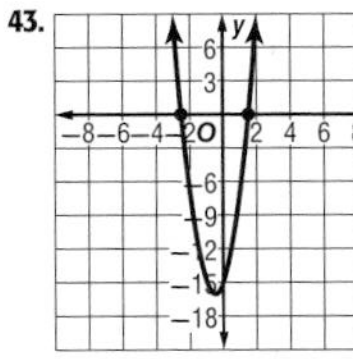

between -3 and -2, between 1 and 2

45.

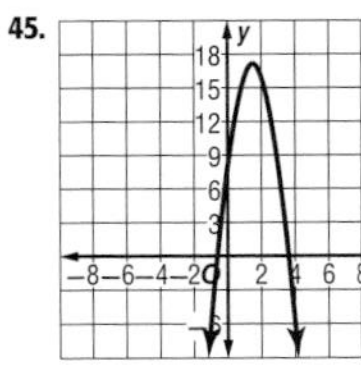

between -1 and 0, between 4 and 5

47.

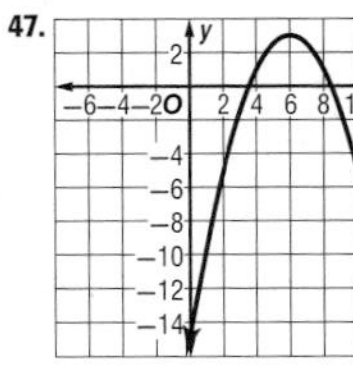

between 3 and 4, between 8 and 9

49 Find t when $h_0 = 60$ and $h(t) = 0$.

$h(t) = -16t^2 + h_0$ Original equation
$0 = -16t^2 + 60$ $h(t) = 0$ and $h_0 = 60$

Graph the related function $f(t) = -16t^2 + 60$ on a graphing calculator.

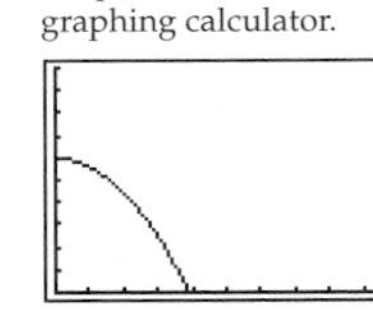

Use the **Zero** feature in the **CALC** menu to find the positive zero of the function, since time cannot be negative. $x \approx 1.94$, so it would take the balloon about 1.94 seconds to hit the ground. Tony's brother should be 4.4 ft/s • 1.94 s or about 8.5 feet from the target when Tony lets go of the balloon.

51. 25 seconds **53.** $k = 8$ **55.** $f(x) = -5x^2 + 30x + 80$ **57.** $\frac{1}{20}$ **59.** H **61.** maximum, -12; D = {all real numbers}, R = $\{f(x) \mid f(x) \le -12\}$

63. maximum, 15; D = {all real numbers}, R = $\{f(x) \mid f(x) \le 15\}$ **65.** no **67a.** The object is reflected over the x-axis, and then translated 6 units to the right. **67b.** Multiply the coordinates by $\begin{bmatrix} 1 & 0 \\ 0 & -1 \end{bmatrix}$, and then add the result to $\begin{bmatrix} 6 \\ 0 \end{bmatrix}$.

67c. Sample answer: No; since the translation does not change the y-coordinate, it does not matter whether or not you do the translation or reflection first. However, if the translation did change the y-coordinate, the order would be important.

67d. (17, −2), (23, 2) **69.** (−3, 4) **71.** $x \le -\frac{8}{3}$
73. $x \le \frac{19}{9}$ **75.** 1

Pages 272–275 Lesson 5-3

1. $x^2 + 3x - 40 = 0$ **3.** $6x^2 - 11x - 10 = 0$
5. $(6x - 1)(3x + 4)$ **7.** $(x - 7)(x + 3)$ **9.** $(4x - 3)(4x - 1)$
11. $6xy(2x - 3)$ **13.** 0, 9 **15.** 6 **17.** $x^2 - 14x + 49 = 0$
19. $5x^2 - 31x + 6 = 0$ **21.** $17c(3c^2 - 2)$
23. $3(x + 2)(x - 2)$

25 $48cg + 36cf - 4dg - 3df$ — Original expression
$= (48cg + 36cf) + (-4dg - 3df)$ — Group terms with common factors.
$= 12c(4g + 3f) + (-d)(4g + 3f)$ — Factor the GCF from each group.
$= (12c - d)(4g + 3f)$ — Distributive Property

27. $(x - 11)(x + 2)$ **29.** $(5x - 1)(3x + 2)$
31. $3(2x - 1)(3x + 4)$ **33.** $(3x + 5)(3x - 5)$
35. $3(5x + 2)(x - 6)$ **37.** $12x(y + 3)(y - 3)$ **39.** 8, −3
41. 2, −2 **43.** $5, \frac{3}{4}$ **45.** 24 and 26 or −24 and −26
47. $x = 20$; 24 in. by 18 in. **49.** $-\frac{1}{2}, \frac{5}{6}$ **51.** $-\frac{3}{2}$
53. 6, −6

55 To find the number of movie screens that produces a profit, first find the number of movie screens in which the profit is zero. Solve $-x^2 + 48x - 512 = 0$.
$ac = -1(-512)$ or 512
$m = 16$; $p = 32$ $mp = 512$ and $ac = 512$; $m + p = 48$ and $b = 48$
$-x^2 + 16x + 32x - 512 = 0$ — Write the pattern.
$(-x^2 + 16x) + (32x - 512) = 0$ — Group terms with common factors.
$-x(x - 16) + 32(x - 16) = 0$ — Group terms with common factors.
$(-x + 32)(x - 16) = 0$ — Distributive Property
$-x + 32 = 0$ or $x - 16 = 0$ — Zero Product Property
$x = 32$ $x = 16$ — Solve each equation.
The solutions are 16 and 32. When there are 16 or 32 movie screens, the profit is zero. Since a is positive, the graph of the function opens down and has a maximum value. So, $P(x)$ is nonnegative for $16 \le x \le 32$. When there are 16 to 32 movie screens, the company will not lose money.

57. $25x^2 - 100x + 51 = 0$ **59.** $-3, \frac{1}{2}$ **61.** $1, -\frac{5}{4}$
63. $-\frac{3}{2}, \frac{5}{6}$ **65.** $x^2 - 6^2$; $(x + 6)(x - 6)$ **67.** 20 in. by 15 in. **69.** 13 cm **71.** $2(3 - 4y)(3a + 8b)$

73 $6a^2b^2 - 12ab^2 - 18b^3$ — Original expression
$= 6b^2(a^2 - 2a - 3b)$ — Factor the GCF, $6b^2$.

75. $2(2x - 3y)(8a + 3b)$ **77.** $(x + y)(x - y)(5a + 2b)$
79. Sample answer: Neither is correct; Gwen didn't have like terms in the parentheses in the third line; Morgan made a sign error in the fourth line.
81. $5x^2(2x - 3y)(4x^2 + 6xy + 9y^2)$
83. Sample answer:
$(x - p)(x - q) = 0$ — Original equation
$x^2 - px - qx + pq = 0$ — Multiply.
$x^2 - (p + q)x + pq = 0$ — Simplify.

$x = -\frac{b}{2a}$ — Formula for axis of symmetry
$x = -\frac{-(p + q)}{2(1)}$ — $a = 1$ and $b = -(p + q)$
$x = \frac{p + q}{2}$ — Simplify.
x is midway between p and q. — Definition of midpoint

85. Sample answer: Always; in order to factor using perfect square trinomials, the coefficient of the linear term, bx, must be a multiple of 2, or even. **87.** 192 square units **89.** H **91.** −2, 4 **93.** −2

95.
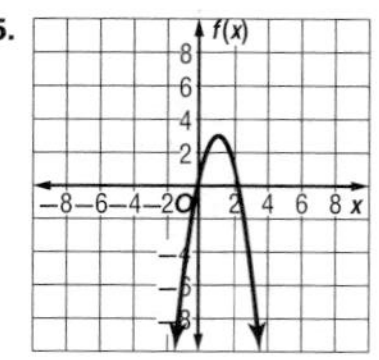

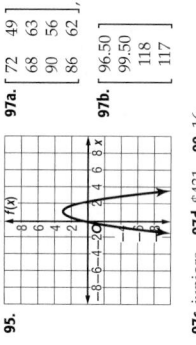

97a. $\begin{bmatrix} 72 & 49 \\ 68 & 63 \\ 90 & 56 \\ 86 & 62 \end{bmatrix}, \begin{bmatrix} 1.00 \\ 0.50 \end{bmatrix}$

97b. $\begin{bmatrix} 96.50 \\ 99.50 \\ 118 \\ 117 \end{bmatrix}$

97c. juniors **97d.** $431 **99.** 16

Pages 280–282 Lesson 5-4

1. $9i$ **3.** 12 **5.** 1 **7.** $\pm 2i\sqrt{2}$ **9.** 3, −2 **11.** $-3 + 2i$
13. $70 - 60i$ **15.** $\frac{1}{2} - \frac{1}{2}i$ **17.** $12 + 6j$ amps **19.** $13i$
21. $9i$ **23.** $-144i$ **25.** i **27.** −7 **29.** 9 **31.** $30 + 16i$
33. $1 + i$ **35.** $\frac{1}{3} - \frac{5}{3}i$

37 $3x^2 + 48 = 0$ — Original equation
$3x^2 = -48$ — Subtract 48 from each side.
$x^2 = -16$ — Divide each side by 3.
$x = \pm\sqrt{-16}$ — Square Root Property
$x = \pm 4i$ — $\sqrt{-16} = \sqrt{16} \cdot \sqrt{-1}$ or $4i$

39. $\pm i\sqrt{5}$ **41.** $\pm 4i$ **43.** 2, −3 **45.** $\frac{4}{3}, 4$ **47.** 25, −2
49. $4i$ **51.** 8 **53.** $-21 + 15i$ **55.** $\frac{15}{13} + \frac{16}{13}i$
57. $11 + 23i$ **59.** $\frac{1}{7} - \frac{4\sqrt{3}}{7}i$

61 $V = C \cdot I$ — Electricity formula
$= (3 + 6j) \cdot (5 - j)$ — $C = 3 + 6j$ and $I = 5 - j$
$= 3(5) + 3(-j) + 6j(5) + 6j(-j)$ — FOIL Method
$= 15 - 3j + 30j - 6j^2$ — Multiply.
$= 15 - 3j + 30j - 6(-1)$ — $j^2 = -1$
$= 21 + 27j$ — Simplify.
The voltage is $21 + 27j$ volts.

63. $(3 + i)x^2 + (-2 + i)x - 8i + 7$

65a.
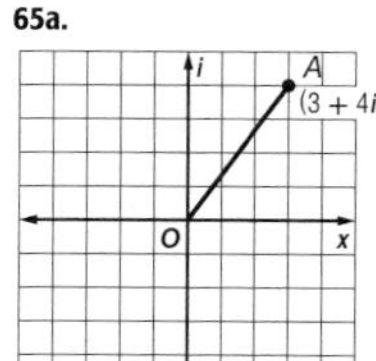

65b.
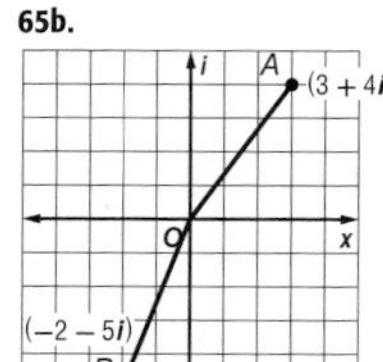

65c.
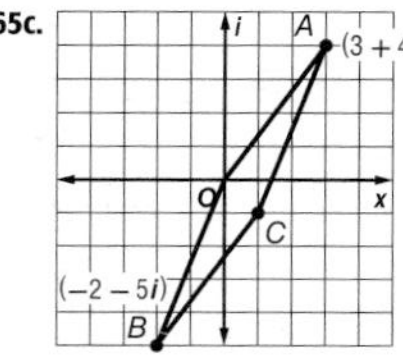

65d. $1 - i$; $A + B = C$
67. $-11 - 2i$
69. Sample answer: $(4 + 2i)(4 - 2i)$
71a. $\triangle CBE \cong \triangle ADE$

71b. $\angle AED \cong \angle CEB$ (Vertical angles)
$\overline{DE} \cong \overline{BE}$ (Both have length x.)
$\angle ADE \cong \angle CBE$ (Given)
Consecutive angles and the included side are all congruent, so the triangles are congruent by the ASA Property. **71c.** $\overline{EC} \cong \overline{EA}$ by CPCTC (corresponding parts of congruent triangles are congruent.) $EA = 7$, so $EC = 7$. **73.** H **75.** $-5, \frac{3}{2}$
77. $-\frac{1}{2}, \frac{4}{3}$ **79.** 3, 16 **81.** −9, −12

83.
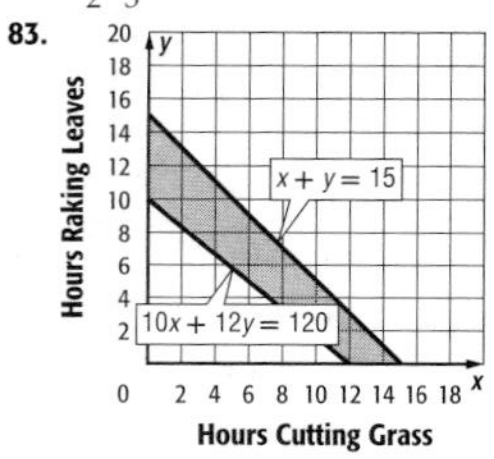

85. yes
87. no
89. yes

Pages 288–290 Lesson 5-5

1. {−8.45, −3.55} **3.** {−12.87, −5.13} **5.** 25 ft
7. 6.25; $(x - 2.5)^2$ **9.** $\{2 - i\sqrt{5}, 2 + i\sqrt{5}\}$
11. {−4.37, 1.37} **13.** {−6.45, −1.55} **15.** {−1.47, 7.47}
17. {−7.65, −2.35} **19.** {−1, 3} **21.** {4.67, 10.33}
23. {−0.95, 3.95} **25.** {4, 5} **27.** 64; $(x + 8)^2$
29. 20.25; $(x + 4.5)^2$ **31.** {−4.61, 2.61} **33.** {1, 3}
35. $\left\{\frac{3 - i\sqrt{31}}{4}, \frac{3 + i\sqrt{31}}{4}\right\}$

37 $3x^2 - 6x - 9 = 0$ — Original equation
$x^2 - 2x - 3 = 0$ — Divide by the coefficient of the quadratic term, 3.
$x^2 - 2x = 3$ — Add 3 to each side.
$x^2 - 2x + 1 = 3 + 1$ — Since $\left(\frac{-2}{2}\right)^2 = 1$, add 1 to each side.
$(x - 1)^2 = 4$ — Write the left side as a perfect square.
$x - 1 = \pm 2$ — Square Root Property
$x = \pm 2 + 1$ — Add 1 to each side.
$x = 2 + 1$ or $x = -2 + 1$ — Write as two equations.
$= 3$ $= -1$ — Simplify.
The solution set is {−1, 3}.

39. $\{-2 - i\sqrt{7}, -2 + i\sqrt{7}\}$ **41.** $\{5 - 2i, 5 + 2i\}$
43. $\left\{\frac{7 - i\sqrt{47}}{4}, \frac{7 + i\sqrt{47}}{4}\right\}$ **45.** $\{2.65 - i\sqrt{1.5775}, 2.65 + i\sqrt{1.5775}\}$ **47.** {−0.89, 5.39} **49.** {2.38, 4.62}
51. {−1.26, 0.26}

53 **a.** The time in which the firework explodes is the t-coordinate of the vertex.
$x = -\frac{b}{2a}$ — Equation of the axis of symmetry
$x = -\frac{(25)}{2(-1.5)}$ or $8\frac{1}{3}$ — $a = -1.5$ and $b = 25$
So, the firework explodes after $8\frac{1}{3}$ seconds.
b. The time in which the firework explodes is the d-coordinate of the vertex.
$d = -1.5t^2 + 25t$ — Original function
$d = -1.5\left(8\frac{1}{3}\right)^2 + 25\left(8\frac{1}{3}\right)$ — $t = 8\frac{1}{3}$
$d \approx 104.2$ — Simplify.
So, the firework explodes at a height of about 104.2 feet.

55. 2.56; $(x - 1.6)^2$

57a.
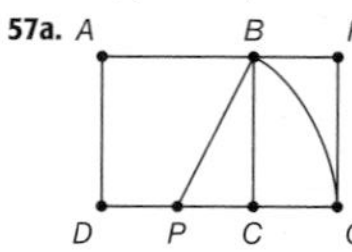

57b. $x = \frac{1 + \sqrt{5}}{2}$

57c.

CQ	x
2	$1 + \sqrt{5}$
3	$\frac{3 + 3\sqrt{5}}{2}$
4	$2 + 2\sqrt{5}$

57d. Sample answer: the x-values are multiples of $\frac{1 + \sqrt{5}}{2}$; $x = \frac{n(1 + \sqrt{5})}{2}$. **59.** $x = \frac{-b}{2} \pm \sqrt{\frac{b^2}{4} - c}$
61. Sample answer: $x^2 - \frac{2}{3}x + \frac{1}{9} = \frac{1}{4}$; $\left\{\frac{5}{6}, -\frac{1}{6}\right\}$
63. D **65.** 125 **67.** $39 + 80i$ **69.** $\frac{4}{39} - \frac{19}{39}i$
71. $5x^2 - 28x - 12 = 0$
73a.

	Evening	Matinee	Twilight
Adult	7.50	5.50	3.75
Child	4.50	4.50	3.75
Senior	5.50	5.50	3.75

73b. 3 × 3
75.
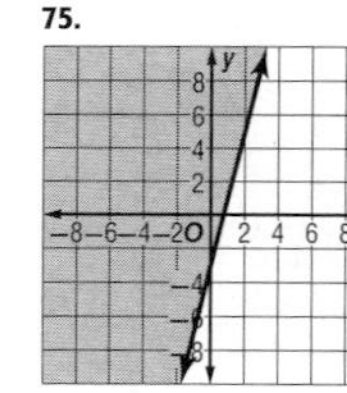

77.
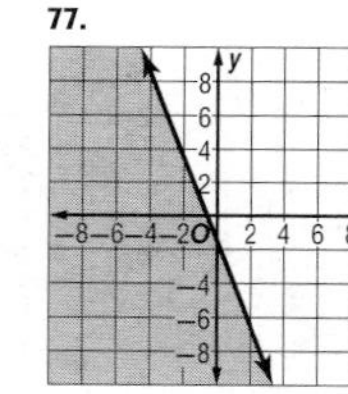

79. $f(x) = \begin{cases} -8 & \text{if } x \le -2 \\ 2x - 6 & \text{if } -2 < x \le 5 \\ 2x - 18 & \text{if } x > 5 \end{cases}$ **81.** −4 **83.** −136

Pages 297–300 Lesson 5-6

1 $x = \frac{-b \pm \sqrt{b^2 - 4ac}}{2a}$ — Quadratic Formula
$= \frac{-12 \pm \sqrt{12^2 - 4(1)(-9)}}{2(1)}$ — $a = 1$, $b = 12$, and $c = -9$
$= \frac{-12 \pm \sqrt{144 + 36}}{2}$ — Multiply.

For Homework Help, go to Hotmath.com

$= \frac{12 \pm \sqrt{180}}{2}$ Simplify.

$= \frac{-12 \pm 6\sqrt{5}}{2}$ $\sqrt{180} = 6\sqrt{5}$

$x = \frac{-12 + 6\sqrt{5}}{2}$ or $x = \frac{-12 - 6\sqrt{5}}{2}$ Write as two equations.

$= -6 + 3\sqrt{5}$ $= -6 - 3\sqrt{5}$ Simplify.

The solutions are $-6 + 3\sqrt{5}$ and $-6 - 3\sqrt{5}$.

3. $\left(\frac{5+\sqrt{57}}{8}, \frac{5-\sqrt{57}}{8}\right)$ **5.** (1.5, −0.2)

7. $\left(\frac{2+2\sqrt{7}}{3}, \frac{2-2\sqrt{7}}{3}\right)$ **9.** about 2.5 seconds

11a. −36 **11b.** 2 complex roots **13a.** −76

13b. 2 complex roots **15.** $\frac{-3 \pm \sqrt{15}}{2}$ **17.** $\frac{-7 \pm \sqrt{129}}{8}$

19. $\frac{-3 \pm i\sqrt{71}}{8}$

21 a. $b^2 - 4ac = 3^2 - 4(2)(-3)$ $a = 2, b = 3, c = -3$

$= 9 + 24$ or 33 Simplify.

b. The discriminate is positive and not a perfect square. So, there are 2 irrational roots.

c. $x = \frac{-b \pm \sqrt{b^2 - 4ac}}{2a}$ Quadratic Formula

$= \frac{-3 \pm \sqrt{3^2 - 4(2)(-3)}}{2(2)}$ $a = 2, b = 3$, and $c = -3$

$= \frac{-3 \pm \sqrt{9 + 24}}{4}$ Multiply.

$= \frac{-3 \pm \sqrt{33}}{4}$ Simplify.

23a. 49 **23b.** 2 rational **23c.** $\frac{1}{6}$, −1 **25a.** −87

25b. 2 complex **25c.** $\frac{3 \pm i\sqrt{87}}{6}$ **27a.** 36

27b. 2 rational **27c.** 1, $-\frac{1}{5}$ **29a.** 1 **29b.** 2 rational

29c. −1, $-\frac{4}{3}$ **31a.** −16 **31b.** 2 complex **31c.** $-1 \pm 2i$

33a. 0 **33b.** about 2.3 seconds **35a.** 64

35b. 2 rational **35c.** 0, $-\frac{8}{5}$ **37a.** 160 **37b.** 2 irrational

37c. $\frac{-1 \pm \sqrt{10}}{6}$ **39a.** 13.48 **39b.** 2 irrational

39c. $\frac{-0.7 \pm \sqrt{3.37}}{0.6}$

41 a. $y = -0.26x^2 - 0.55x + 91.81$ Original equation

$= -0.26(10)^2 - 0.55(10) + 91.81$ Replace x with 10.

$= 60.31$ Simplify.

$y = -0.26x^2 - 0.55x + 91.81$ Original equation

$= -0.26(15)^2 - 0.55(15) + 91.81$ Replace x with 15.

$= 25.06$ Simplify.

For 2010, the number of deaths per 100,000 is 60.31. For 2015, the number is 25.06.

b. $y = -0.26x^2 - 0.55x + 91.81$ Original equation

$50 = -0.26x^2 - 0.55x + 91.81$ Replace y with 50.

$0 = -0.26x^2 - 0.55x + 41.81$ Subtract 50 from each side.

$x = \frac{-b \pm \sqrt{b^2 - 4ac}}{2a}$ Quadratic Formula

$= \frac{-(-0.55) \pm \sqrt{(-0.55)^2 - 4(-0.26)(41.81)}}{2(-0.26)}$ $a = -0.26$, $b = -0.55$, and $c = 41.81$

$= \frac{0.55 \pm \sqrt{43.7894}}{-0.52}$ Simplify.

$x \approx -13.8$ or $x \approx 11.7$

Since the number of years after 2000 cannot be negative, the solution is 11.58. So, 11.7 years after 2000, or in 2011, the death rate will be 50 per 100,000.

c. $y = -0.26x^2 - 0.55x + 91.81$ Original equation

$0 = -0.26x^2 - 0.55x + 91.81$ Replace y with 0.

$x = \frac{-b \pm \sqrt{b^2 - 4ac}}{2a}$ Quadratic Formula

$= \frac{-(-0.55) \pm \sqrt{(-0.55)^2 - 4(-0.26)(91.81)}}{2(-0.26)}$ $a = -0.26$, $b = -0.55$, and $c = 91.81$

$= \frac{0.55 \pm \sqrt{95.7849}}{-0.52}$ Simplify.

$x \approx -19.78$ or $x \approx 17.76$

Since the number of years after 2000 cannot be negative, the solution is 17.76. So, 17.76 years after 2000, or in 2017, the death rate will be 0 per 100,000. Sample answer: This prediction is not reasonable because the death rate from cancer will never be 0 unless a cure is found. If and when a cure will be found cannot be predicted.

43. Jonathan is correct; you must first write the equation in the form $ax^2 + bx + c = 0$ to determine the values of a, b, and c. Therefore, the value of c is −7, not 7. **45a.** Sample answer: Always; when a and c are opposite signs, then ac will always be negative and $-4ac$ will always be positive. Since b^2 will also always be positive, then $b^2 - 4ac$ represents the addition of two positive values, which will never be negative. Hence, the discriminant can never be negative and the solutions can never be imaginary. **45b.** Sample answer: Sometimes; the roots will only be irrational if $b^2 - 4ac$ is not a perfect square.

47. −0.75 **49.** B **51.** 112.5 in² **53.** 42.25; $(x + 6.5)^2$

55. $\frac{4}{25}$; $\left(x + \frac{2}{5}\right)^2$ **57.** $4i$ **59.** 27 hours of flight instruction and 23 hours in the simulator

61. $y = x^2 + 1$ **63.** $y = |x + 3|$

Pages 308–310 Lesson 5-7

1. $y = (x + 3)^2 - 7$ **3.** $y = 4(x + 3)^2 - 12$

5.

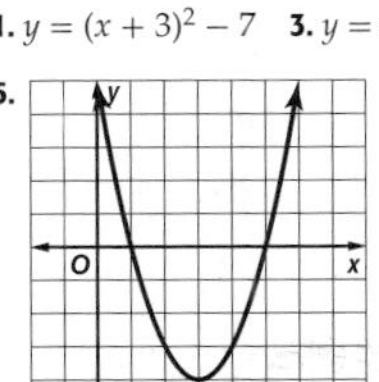

7.

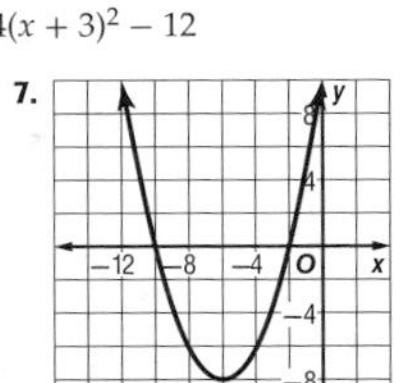

9. $y = (x - 3)^2 - 6$

11 $y = x^2 + 2x + 7$ Original equation.

$y = (x^2 + 2x + 1) + 7 - 1$ Complete the square by adding $\left(\frac{2}{2}\right)^2$ or 1. Balance the equation by subtracting 1.

$y = (x + 1)^2 + 6$ Write $x^2 + 2x + 1$ as a perfect square.

13. $y = (x + 4)^2$ **15.** $y = 3\left(x + \frac{5}{3}\right)^2 - \frac{25}{3}$

17. $y = -4(x + 3)^2 + 21$ **19.** $y = -(x + 2)^2 + 3$

21. $y = -15(x - 8.5)^2 + 4083.75$

23.

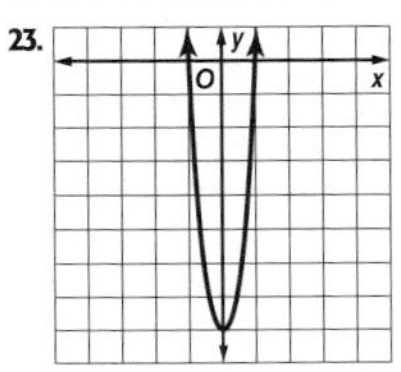

25.

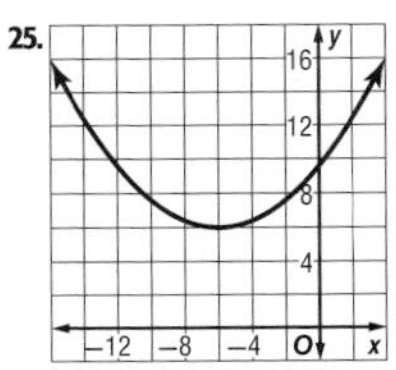

27.

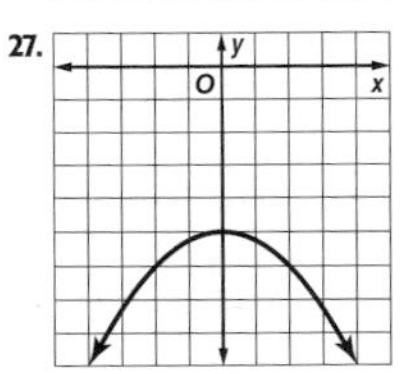

29.

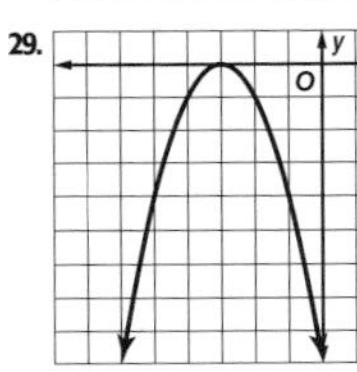

31.

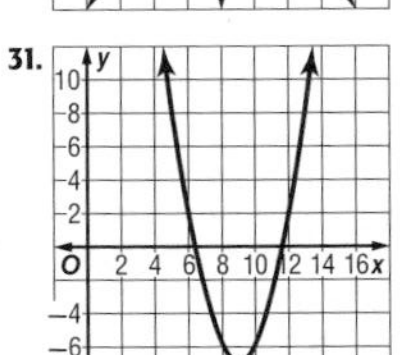

33.

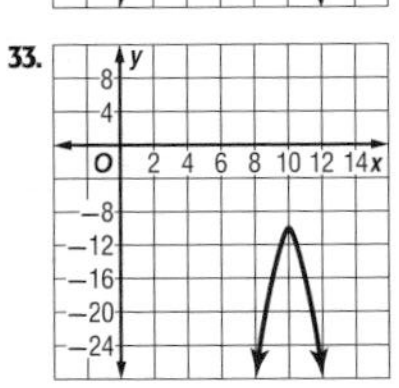

35. $y = 9(x - 6)^2 + 1$ **37.** $y = -\frac{2}{3}(x - 3)^2$

39. $y = \frac{1}{3}x^2 + 5$ **41.** $y = 3\left(x - \frac{2}{3}\right)^2 - \frac{10}{3}$; $\left(\frac{2}{3}, -\frac{10}{3}\right)$, $x = \frac{2}{3}$, opens up **43.** $y = -(x + 2.35)^2 + 8.3225$; $(-2.35, 8.3225)$, $x = -2.35$, opens down

45. $y = \left(x - \frac{1}{3}\right)^2 - 3$; $\left(\frac{1}{3}, -3\right)$, $x = \frac{1}{3}$, opens up

47 a. $S(t) = \frac{1}{2}at^2 + v_0t$ Original equation

$S(t) = \frac{1}{2}(0.002)t^2 + 0.0097t$ $a = 0.002$ and $v_0 = 0.0097$ m/s

$S(t) = 0.001t^2 + 0.0097t$ Simplify.

$S(t) = 0.001(t^2 + 9.7t)$ Group $ax^2 + bx$ and factor, dividing by a.

$S(t) = 0.001(t^2 + 9.7t + 4.86^2) - 0.024$ Complete the square by adding 4.86^2 inside the parentheses. This is an overall addition of 0.024. Balance the equation by subtracting 0.024.

$S(t) = 0.001(t + 4.86)^2 - 0.024$ Write as a perfect square.

b. $a \cdot t = v$ acceleration · time = velocity

$0.002 \text{ mi/s}^2 \cdot t = (68 - 35) \text{ mi/h}$ Substitution

$0.002 \text{ mi/s}^2 \cdot t = 33 \text{ m/h}$ Simplify.

$0.002 \text{ mi/s}^2 \cdot t = \frac{33 \text{ mi}}{1 \text{ h}} \cdot \frac{1 \text{ h}}{3600 \text{ s}}$ Convert hours to seconds.

$0.002 \text{ mi/s}^2 \cdot t = 0.009 \text{ mi/s}$ Simplify.

$t = \frac{0.009 \text{ mi}}{\text{s}} \div \frac{0.002 \text{ mi}}{\text{s}^2}$ Divide each side by 0.002 mi/s².

$t = \frac{0.009 \text{ mi}}{\text{s}} \cdot \frac{\text{s}^2}{0.002 \text{ mi}}$ Multiply by the reciprocal.

$t = 4.58$ s Simplify.

It will take about 4.58 seconds for Valerie to accelerate from 35 mi/h to 68 mi/h.

c. Yes; if we substitute $\frac{1}{8}$ for $S(t)$ and solve for t, we get 7.346 seconds. This is how long Valerie will be on the ramp. Since it will take her 4.58 seconds to accelerate to 68 mph, she will be on the ramp long enough to accelerate to match the average expressway speed.

49. The equation of a parabola can be written in the form $y = ax^2 + bx + c$ with $a \neq 0$. For each of the three points, substitute the value of the x-coordinate for x in the equation and substitute the value of the y-coordinate for y in the equation. This will produce three equations in three variables a, b, and c. Solve the system of equations to find the values of a, b, and c. These values determine the quadratic equation.

51. Sample answer: The variable a represents different values for these functions, so making $a = 0$ will have a different effect on each function. For $f(x)$, when $a = 0$, the graph will be a horizontal line, $f(x) = k$. For $g(x)$, when $a = 0$, the graph will be linear, but not necessarily horizontal, $g(x) = bx + c$.

53. B **55.** D **57.** $\frac{-15 \pm \sqrt{561}}{8}$ **59.** $\frac{3 \pm \sqrt{39}}{5}$

61. 0.0025 **63.** minimum, $9\frac{1}{3}$ **65.** minimum, −12

67a.

	Weekday	Weekend
Single	60	79
Double	70	89
Suite	75	95

67b.

	Single	Double	Suite
Weekday	60	70	75
Weekend	79	89	95

For Homework Help, go to Hotmath.com

69. 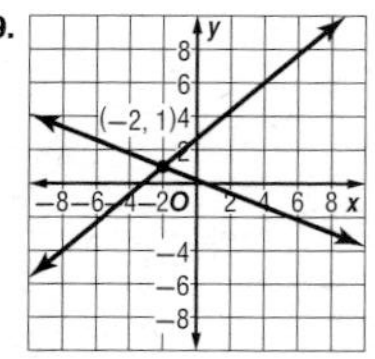 **71.** 9 **73.** 52 **75.** yes

Pages 315–318 Lesson 5-8

1. 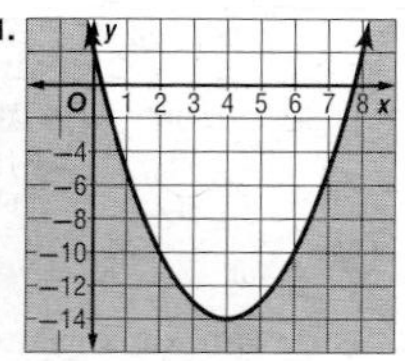

3. 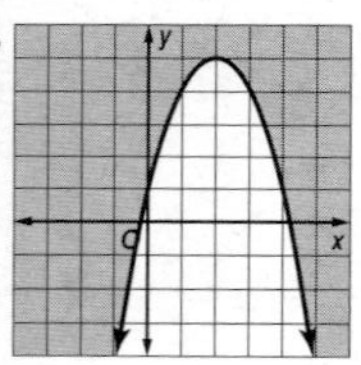

5. $\{x \mid -5 < x < -3\}$
7. $\{x \mid 0.29 \le x \le 1.71\}$
9. $\{x \mid -8 < x < 2\}$

11
$-x^2 + 12x = 28$ Related quadratic equation
$-x^2 + 12x - 28 = 0$ Subtract 28 from each side.
$x = \frac{-b \pm \sqrt{b^2 - 4ac}}{2a}$ Quadratic Formula
$= \frac{-12 \pm \sqrt{12^2 - 4(-1)(-28)}}{2(-1)}$ $a = -1$, $b = 12$, and $c = -28$
$x = \frac{-12 + \sqrt{32}}{-2}$ or $x = \frac{-12 - \sqrt{32}}{-2}$ Simplify and write as two equations.
≈ 3.17 ≈ 8.83 Simplify.

Plot 3.17 and 8.83 on a number line. Use dots since these values are solutions of the original inequality.

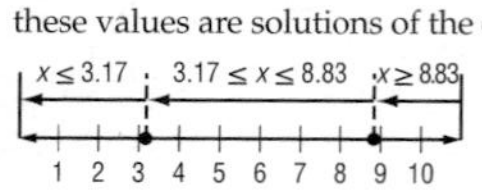

Test a value from each of the three intervals to see if it satisfies the original inequality.

$x \le 3.17$
Test $x = 0$.
$-x^2 + 12x \ge 28$
$-(0)^2 + 12(0) \ge 28$
$0 \not\ge 28$

$3.17 \le x \le 8.83$
Test $x = 5$.
$-x^2 + 12x \ge 28$
$-(5)^2 + 12(5) \ge 28$
$35 \ge 28$

$x \ge 8.83$
Test $x = 10$.
$-x^2 + 12x \ge 28$
$-(10)^2 + 12(10) \ge 28$
$20 \not\ge 28$

The solution set is $\{x \mid 3.17 \le x \le 8.83\}$.

13. 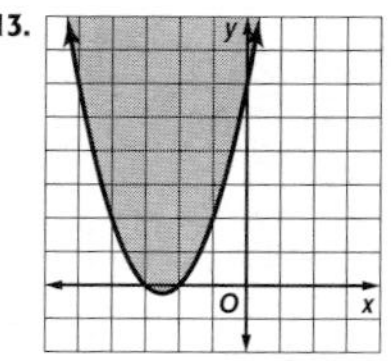

15. 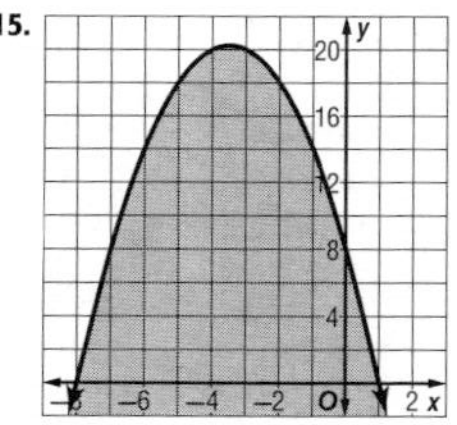

17. 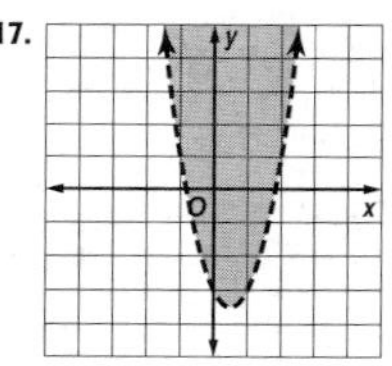

19. $\{x \mid 1.1 < x < 7.9\}$
21. $\{x \mid$ all real numbers$\}$
23. $\{x \mid x < -1.42$ or $x > 8.42\}$ **25.** $\varnothing$
27. $\{x \mid x < -0.73$ or $x > 2.73\}$
29. $\{x \mid -0.5 \le x \le 2.5\}$

31 The function describes the height of the arch. You want to find the values of x for which $f(x) \ge 7$.
$f(x) \ge 7$ Original inequality
$-x^2 + 6x + 1 \ge 7$ $f(x) = -x^2 + 6x + 1$
$-x^2 + 6x - 6 \ge 0$ Subtract 7 from each side.
Graph the related function $y = -x^2 + 6x - 6$ using a graphing calculator.

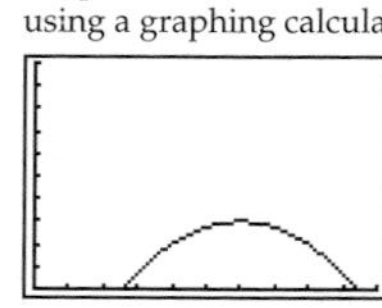

At $x \approx 1.26$ and $x \approx 4.73$, $f(x) \ge 7$. So, at about 1.26 ft to 4.73 ft from the sides of the arch, the height is at least 7 ft.

33. $\{x \mid 4 < x < 5\}$ **35.** $\{x \mid -1 < x < 2\}$ **37.** $\{x \mid x \le -2.32$ or $x \ge 4.32\}$ **39.** $\{x \mid x \le -1.58$ or $x \ge 1.58\}$
41. $\{x \mid$ all real numbers$\}$ **43.** $\{x \mid -2.84 < x < 0.84\}$

45a. 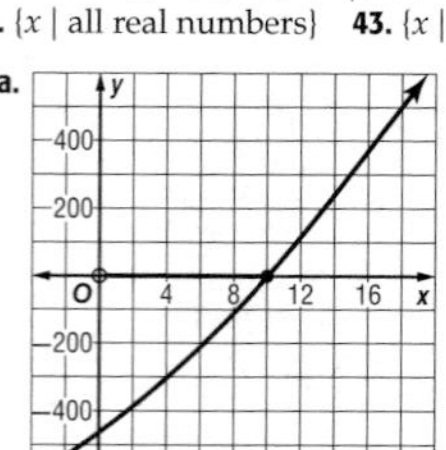

45b. greater than 0 ft but no more than 10.04 ft
47. $y \le -x^2 + 2x + 6$
49. $\{x \mid x < -1.06$ or $x > 7.06\}$

51 $11 = 4x^2 + 7x$ Related quadratic equation
$0 = 4x^2 + 7x - 11$ Subtract 11 from each side.
$x = \frac{-b \pm \sqrt{b^2 - 4ac}}{2a}$ Quadratic Formula
$x = \frac{-7 \pm \sqrt{7^2 - 4(4)(-11)}}{2(4)}$ $a = 4$, $b = 7$, and $c = -11$
$x = \frac{-7 + \sqrt{255}}{8}$ or $x = \frac{-7 - \sqrt{255}}{8}$ Simplify and write as two equations.
$= 1$ $= -2.75$ Simplify.

Plot −2.75 and 1 on a number line. Use dots since these values are solutions of the original inequality.

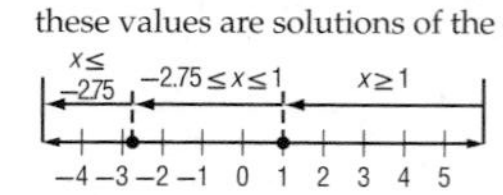

Test a value from each of the three intervals to see if it satisfies the original inequality.

$x \le -2.75$
Test $x = -3$.
$11 \le 4x^2 + 7x$
$11 \le 4(-3)^2 + 7(-3)$
$11 \le 15$

$-2.75 \le x \le 1$
Test $x = 0$.
$11 \le 4x^2 + 7x$
$11 \le 4(0)^2 + 7(0)$
$11 \not\le 0$

$x \ge 1$
Test $x = 2$.
$11 \le 4x^2 + 7x$
$11 \le 4(2)^2 + 7(2)$
$11 \le 30$

The solution set is $\{x \mid x \le -2.75$ or $x \ge 1\}$.

53. $\{x \mid x < 0.61$ or $x > 2.72\}$

55a. 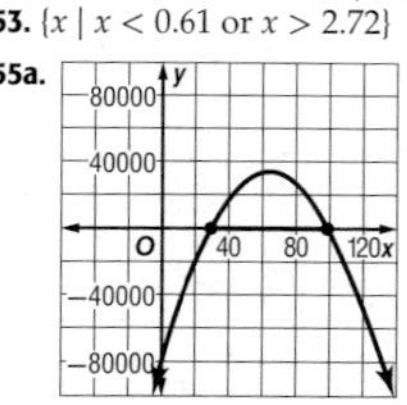

55b. from 30,000 to 98,000 digital audio players **55c.** The graph is shifted down 25,000 units. The manufacturer must sell from 48,000 to 81,000 digital audio players.

57a. Sample answer: $x^2 + 2x + 1 \ge 0$ **57b.** Sample answer: $x^2 - 4x + 6 < 0$ **59.** No; the graphs of the inequalities intersect the x-axis at the same points.

61. 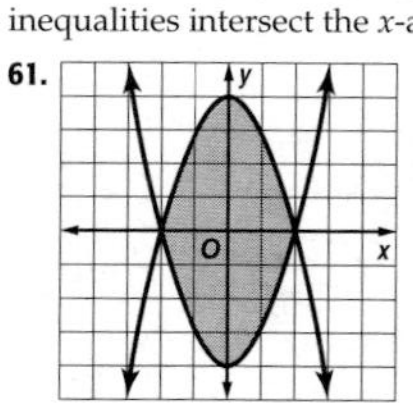

63. 15 **65.** G
67. $y = 2(x - 3)^2 - 4$
69. $y = 0.25(x + 4)^2 + 3$
71. −152; 2 complex roots **73.** (−8, 7), (−7, −8), and (8, −7)
75. $\begin{bmatrix} -28 & 60 \\ 20 & -70 \end{bmatrix}$
77. $-6x + 24$

79. $8y - 12z$ **81.** $2.5x + 3y$

Pages 320–324 Chapter 5 Study Guide and Review

1. false, standard form **3.** false, factored form
5. false, completing the square **7.** true
9a. y-int: 12; $x = -\frac{5}{2}$; $-\frac{5}{2}$

9b.

x	y
−3	6
−2	6
$-\frac{5}{2}$	$\frac{23}{4}$
−1	8
0	12

9c. 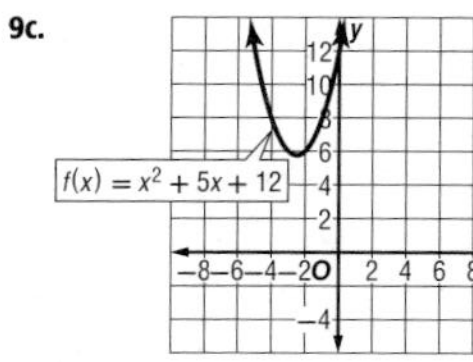

11a. y-int: −5; $x = \frac{9}{4}$; $\frac{9}{4}$

11b.

x	y
1	2
2	5
$\frac{9}{4}$	$\frac{41}{8}$
3	4
4	−1

11c. 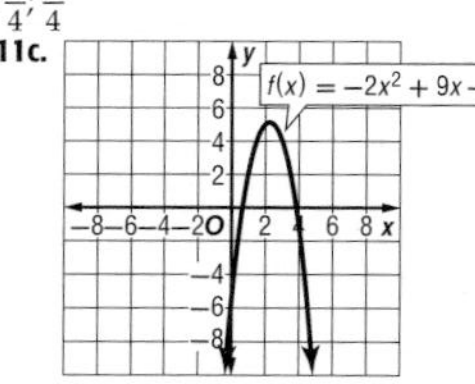

13. max; 1.25; D = {all real numbers}; R = $\{y \mid y \le 1.25\}$
15. 75 T-shirts at \$15 each **17.** $\left(-1, \frac{3}{2}\right)$ **19.** 7.5 seconds
21. $x^2 + 10x + 21 = 0$ **23.** $3x^2 - x - 2 = 0$
25. $4x^2 + 5x + 1 = 0$ **27.** $\left\{-\frac{1}{2}, 3\right\}$ **29.** $x = 12$; 9 ft by 14 ft **31.** $15 + 3i$ **33.** $28 + 3i$ **35.** $x = \pm 5i$
37. $x = \pm i\sqrt{5}$ **39.** $x = \pm \frac{1}{2}i$ **41.** 4; $(x - 2)^2$ **43.** 1.44; $(x + 1.2)^2$ **45.** $\frac{9}{25}$; $\left(x + \frac{3}{5}\right)^2$ **47.** $\{1 \pm i\sqrt{7}\}$
49. $\left\{1, -\frac{5}{2}\right\}$ **51a.** 0 **51b.** 1 real rational root **51c.** {5}
53a. 153 **53b.** 2 irrational real roots
53c. $\left\{\frac{-3 \pm 3\sqrt{17}}{4}\right\}$ **55a.** −32 **55b.** 2 complex roots
55c. $\{1 \pm 2i\sqrt{2}\}$ **57a.** −47 **57b.** 2 complex roots
57c. $\left\{\frac{-5 \pm i\sqrt{47}}{4}\right\}$
59. $y = -3(x - 1)^2 + 5$; (1, 5); $x = 1$; opens down

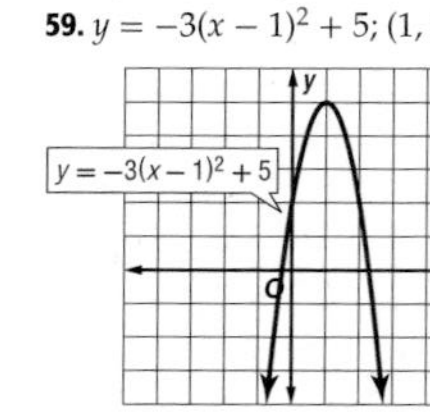

61. $y = -\frac{1}{2}(x + 2)^2 + 14$; (−2, 14); $x = -2$; opens down

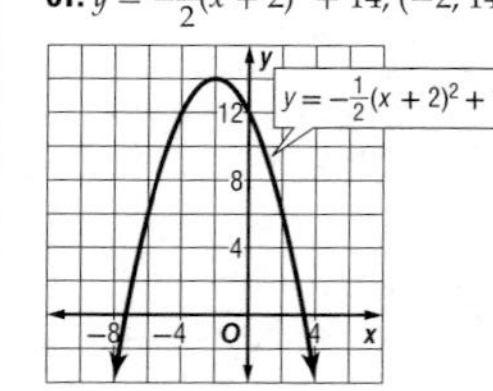

63. $f(x) = -x^2 + 10x$; 5 and 5

For Homework Help, go to Hotmath.com

65.

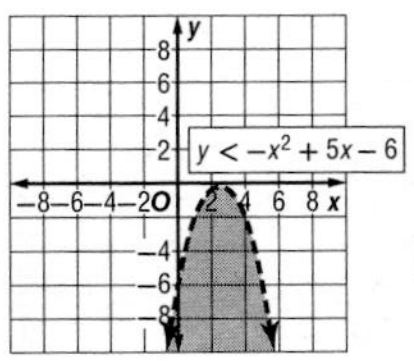

67.

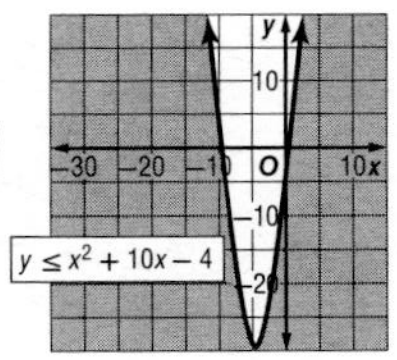

69. $\{x \mid x < -6 \text{ or } x > -2\}$ **71.** $\left\{x \,\middle|\, x < -4 \text{ or } x > \frac{5}{2}\right\}$
73. $\left\{x \,\middle|\, x < \frac{2}{3} \text{ or } x > 2\right\}$

Chapter 6 Polynomials and Polynomial Functions

Page 331 Chapter 6 Get Ready

1. $-5 + (-13)$ **3.** $5mr + (-7mp)$ **5.** $20 + (-2x)$ **7.** $-3b^2 - 2b + 1$ **9.** $-\frac{9}{4}z - \frac{15}{4}$ **11.** $-4, 2$ **13.** $-\frac{4}{3}, \frac{1}{2}$ **15.** about 1.77 seconds

Pages 337–339 Lesson 6-1

1. $-8a^5b^2$ **3.** $\frac{8a^6}{27b^3}$ **5.** yes, 1 **7.** no **9.** $-2x^2 - 6x + 3$ **11.** $8ab + 10a$ **13.** $n^2 - 2n - 63$ **15.** $750 - 2.5x$ **17.** $-8b^5c^3$ **19.** $-yz^2$ **21.** $\frac{a^2c^2}{2b^4}$ **23.** z^{18} **25.** yes; 3 **27.** no **29.** $3b^2 + 6b - 5$ **31.** $8x^3 + 4xy$

33 $(a + b)(a^3 - 3ab - b^2)$
$= a(a^3 - 3ab - b^2) + b(a^3 - 3ab - b^2)$ Distributive Property
$= a(a^3) - a(3ab) - a(b^2) + b(a^3) - b(3ab) - b(b^2)$ Distributive Property
$= a^4 - 3a^2b - ab^2 + a^3b - 3ab^2 - b^3$ Multiply.
$= a^4 + a^3b - 3a^2b - 4ab^2 - b^3$ Simplify.

35. $10c^3 - c^2 + 4c$ **37.** $12a^2b + 8a^2b^2 - 15ab^2 + 4b^2$ **39.** $4a^2x - 2a^2y + 10abx - 5aby + 6b^2x - 3b^2y$ **41.** $\frac{y^4}{81x^4}$ **43.** $\frac{x^6}{16y^{14}}$ **45.** b **47.** $\frac{2}{5}cd^4$ **49.** $\frac{1}{2}x^6y^3$

51 a. $d = rt$ distance = rate • time
$t = \frac{d}{r}$ Solve the formula for time.
$= \frac{2.367 \times 10^{21}\text{ m}}{3 \times 10^8\text{ m/s}}$ ← Distance from Andromeda to Earth ← Speed of light
$= \frac{2.367}{3} \cdot \frac{10^{21}}{10^8} \cdot \frac{\text{m}}{\text{m/s}}$ Separate to get powers of the same base.
$\approx 0.789 \cdot 10^{21-8}\text{ s}$ Subtract exponents.
$\approx 0.789 \times 10^{13}\text{ s}$ Simplify.
It takes about 0.789×10^{13} seconds or about 250,190.26 years.

b. $t = \frac{d}{r}$ Write the formula.
$= \frac{2.28 \times 10^{11}\text{ m}}{3 \times 10^8\text{ m/s}}$ ← Distance from the Sun to Mars ← Speed of light
$= \frac{2.28}{3} \cdot \frac{10^{11}}{10^8} \cdot \frac{\text{m}}{\text{m/s}}$ Separate to get powers of the same base.
$= 0.76 \times 10^{11-8}\text{ s}$ Subtract exponents.
$= 0.76 \times 10^3\text{ s}$ Simplify.
$= 760\text{ s}$ Simplify.
It takes 760 seconds or about 12.67 minutes.

53. $2n^4 - 3n^3p + 6n^4p^4$ **55.** $b^3 + \frac{b}{a} + \frac{1}{a^2}$ **57.** $2n^5 - 14n^3 + 4n^2 - 28$ **59.** $64n^3 - 240n^2 + 300n - 125$ **61a.** $0.155x^2 + 8.818x + 835.8$ **61b.** $0.061x^2 - 10.57x + 112.4$ **63.** 9 **65.** $\frac{1}{a^n} = \frac{a^0}{a^n} = a^{0-n} = a^{-n}$ **67.** Sample answer: We would have a 0 in the denominator, which makes the expression undefined. **69.** Sample answer: Astronomy deals with very large numbers that are sometimes difficult to work with because they contain so many digits. Properties of exponents make very large or very small numbers more manageable. As long as you know how far away a planet is from a light source, you can divide that distance by the speed of light to obtain how long it will take light to reach that planet. **71.** D **73.** C **75.** $x > 5$ or $x < -8$

77.

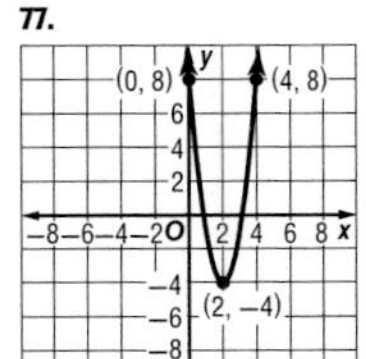

79.

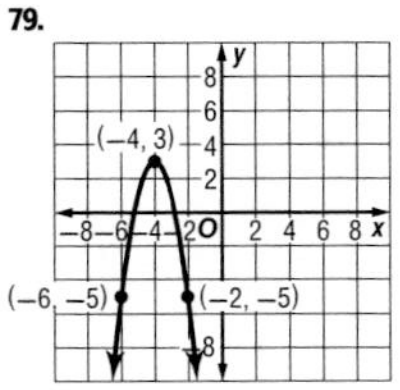

81. 42 **83.** 28 **85.** $\frac{7}{8}$ **87.** $\frac{1}{2}$ **89.** $\frac{5}{9}$ **91.** $4x(3ax^2 + 5bx + 8c)$ **93.** $(3y + 2)(4y + 3)$ **95.** $(2x - 3)(4a - 3)$

Pages 345–347 Lesson 6-2

1. $4y + 2x - 2$ **3.** $x - 8 - \frac{4}{x + 2}$ **5.** $3z^3 - 15z^2 + 36z - 105 + \frac{309}{z + 3}$ **7.** A **9.** $6a + 6 + \frac{21}{3a - 2}$ **11.** $3y + 5$ **13.** $x + 3y - 2$ **15.** $2a^2 + b - 3$ **17.** $3np - 6 + 7p$ **19.** $-w + 16 + \frac{1000}{w}$

21
$$\begin{array}{r} b^2 - 5b + 6 \\ b+1\overline{)b^3 - 4b^2 + b - 2} \\ (-)\,b^3 + b^2 \\ -5b^2 + b \\ (-)\,-5b^2 - 5b \\ 6b - 2 \\ (-)\,6b + 6 \\ -8 \end{array}$$
The quotient is $b^2 - 5b + 6$, and the remainder is -8. So, the expression equals $b^2 - 5b + 6 - \frac{8}{b + 1}$.

23. $x^4 + 4x^3 + 12x^2 + 52x + 208 + \frac{832}{x - 4}$ **25.** $g^3 + 2g^2 + g + 2 - \frac{14}{g - 2}$ **27.** $2x^4 + x^3 - x + \frac{2}{3} - \frac{2}{9x + 3}$ **29.** $b^2 - 4b + 8 - \frac{8}{b + 1}$ **31.** $2y^5 - y^4 + y^3 + y^2 - y - 3$ **33.** $V(t) = t^2 + 5t + 6$

35 a.
$$\begin{array}{r} 3500 \\ a^2+100\overline{)3500a^2} \\ (-)\,3500a^2 + 350{,}000 \\ -350{,}000 \end{array}$$
The quotient is 3500, and the remainder is −350,000. So, the expression equals $3500 - \frac{350{,}000}{a^2 + 100}$.

b. $n = 3500 - \frac{350{,}000}{a^2 + 100}$ Write the equation.
$= 3500 - \frac{350{,}000}{15^2 + 100}$ $a = 15$
$= 3500 - \frac{350{,}000}{325}$ Simplify.
≈ 2423 subscriptions

37. $\frac{4c^2d - 3d}{2}$ **39.** $n^2 - n - 1$ **41.** $3z^4 - z^3 + 2z^2 - 4z + 9 - \frac{13}{z + 2}$ **43.** Sample answer: Sharon; Jamal actually divided by $x + 3$. **45.** Sample answer: The degree of the quotient plus the degree of the divisor equals the degree of the dividend. **47.** $\frac{5}{x^2}$ does not belong with the other three. The other three expressions are polynomials. Since the denominator of $\frac{5}{x^2}$ contains a variable, it is not a polynomial. **49.** A **51.** 360 **53.** $3x^3 + 2x^2 + x + 4$ **55.** $23a^2 - 24a$ **57.** $8x^5y^8z^3$ **59.** 0 to 10 ft or 24 to 34 ft **61.** $4 \pm \sqrt{19}$ **63.** between −6 and −5; between −3 and −2 **65.** between −1 and 0; between 2 and 3 **67.** −21 **69.** −20 **71.** $-9d^2$

Pages 352–355 Lesson 6-3

1. degree = 6, leading coefficient = 11 **3.** not in one variable because there are two variables, x and y **5.** $w(5) = -247$; $w(-4) = 104$ **7.** $4y^9 - 5y^6 + 2$ **9.** $1536a^3 - 426a^2 - 144a + 82$ **11a.** $f(x) \to -\infty$ as $x \to -\infty$. $f(x) \to +\infty$ as $x \to +\infty$. **11b.** Since the end behavior is in opposite directions, it is an odd-degree function. **11c.** The graph intersects the x-axis at three points, so there are three real zeros. **13.** not in one variable because there are two variables, x and y **15.** degree = 6, leading coefficient = −12 **17.** degree = 4, leading coefficient = −5 **19.** degree = 2, leading coefficient = 3 **21.** degree = 9, leading coefficient = 2 **23.** $p(-6) = 1227$; $p(3) = 66$ **25.** $p(-6) = -156$; $p(3) = 78$

27 $p(x) = -x^3 + 3x^2 - 5$ Original function
$p(-6) = -(-6)^3 + 3(-6)^2 - 5$ Replace x with −6.
$= 216 + 108 - 5$ Simplify.
$= 319$ Simplify.
$p(x) = -x^3 + 3x^2 - 5$ Original function
$p(-6) = -(3)^3 + 3(3)^2 - 5$ Replace x with 3.
$= -27 + 27 - 5$ Simplify.
$= -5$ Simplify.

29. $18a^2 - 12a + 3$ **31.** $2b^4 - 4b^2 + 3$ **33.** $-64y^3 + 144y^2 - 104y + 25$ **35a.** $f(x) \to +\infty$ as $x \to -\infty$. $f(x) \to +\infty$ as $x \to +\infty$. **35b.** Since the end behavior is in the same direction, it is an even-degree function. **35c.** The graph intersects the x-axis at four points, so there are four real zeros. **37a.** $f(x) \to -\infty$ as $x \to -\infty$. $f(x) \to +\infty$ as $x \to +\infty$. **37b.** Since the end behavior is in opposite directions, it is an odd-degree function. **37c.** The graph intersects the x-axis at one point, so there is one real zero. **39a.** $f(x) \to -\infty$ as $x \to -\infty$. $f(x) \to -\infty$ as $x \to +\infty$. **39b.** Since the end behavior is in the same direction, it is an even-degree function. **39c.** The graph intersects the x-axis at two points, so there are two real zeros.

41 $KE(v) = 0.5mv^2$ Original function
$= 0.5(171)(11)^2$ Replace m with 171 and v with 11.
$= 10{,}345.5$ Simplify.
The kinetic energy is 10,345.5 kg-m/s or 10,345 joules.

43. $p(-2) = -16$; $p(8) = 1024$ **45.** $p(-2) = -0.5$; $p(8) = 3112$ **47.** D **49.** A **51.** $3a^3 - 24a^2 + 240a + 66$ **53.** $5a^6 - 298a^2 + 1008a - 928$

55a.

x	p(x)
−7	−585
−6	0
−4	240
−3	135
−2	0
0	−144
1	−105
2	0
4	240
6	0
7	−585

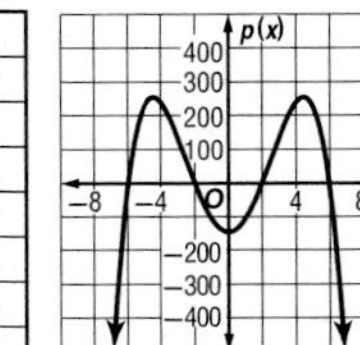

55b. −6, −2, 2, 6 **55c.** 2000 and 6000 items **55d.** Sample answer: The negative values should not be considered because the company will not produce negative items.

57 The degree, 4, is even and the leading coefficient, −5, is negative. So, $f(x) \to -\infty$ as $x \to -\infty$ and $f(x) \to -\infty$ as $x \to +\infty$.

59. $h(x) \to +\infty$ as $x \to -\infty$; $h(x) \to -\infty$ as $x \to +\infty$ **61.** $h(x) \to -\infty$ as $x \to -\infty$; $h(x) \to +\infty$ as $x \to +\infty$ **63.** Sample answer: Virginia is correct; an even function will have an even number of zeros and the double root represents 2 zeros. **65.** Sample answer: $f(x) \to +\infty$ as $x \to -\infty$; $f(x) \to +\infty$ as $x \to +\infty$; $\frac{f(x)}{g(x)}$ will become a 2-degree function with a positive leading coefficient. **67.** Sometimes; a polynomial function with four real roots may be a sixth-degree polynomial function with two imaginary roots. A polynomial function that has four real roots is at least a fourth-degree polynomial. **69.** Student A

71a.

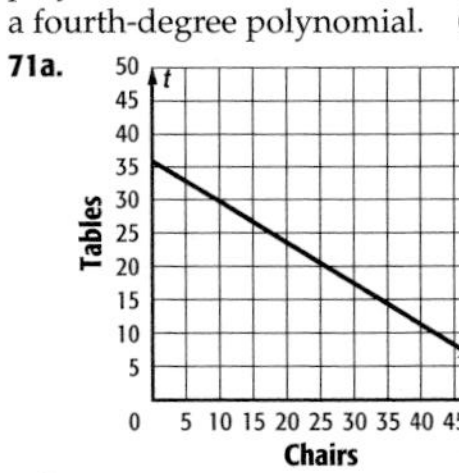

71b. $t = 0.5c$

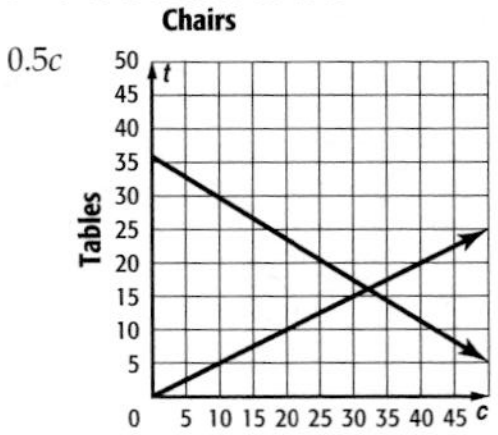

71c. 16 tables and 32 chairs **71d.** Sample answer: This can be determined by the intersection of the graphs. This point of intersection is the optimal amount of tables and chairs manufactured.
73. $2x^2y^2 + 4x^4y^4z^2$ **75.** $6c^3 - 1 + 4a^5cd^2$ **77.** yes; 6
79a. $h(d) = -2d^2 + 4d + 6$; The graph opens downward and is narrower than the parent graph, and the vertex is at (1, 8).
79b. $h(d) = -2(d - 1.25)^2 + 12.5$; it shifted the graph up 4.5 ft and to the right 3 in. **81.** $x \leq -\frac{2}{3}$ or $x \geq 2$
83. minimum; $-\frac{4}{3}$ **85.** maximum; 11

Pages 361–364 Lesson 6-4

1.

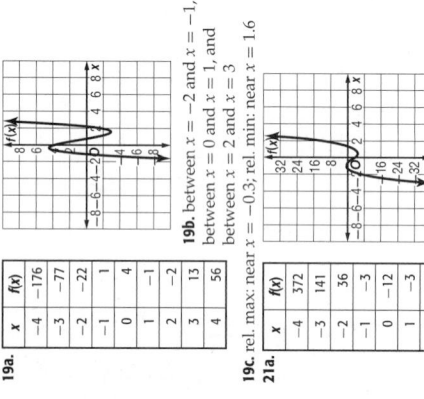

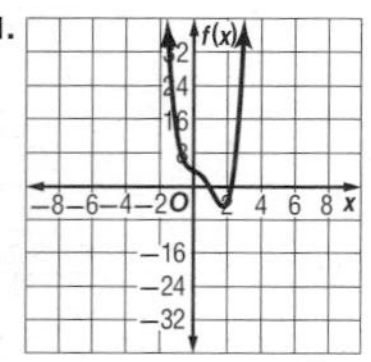

3.

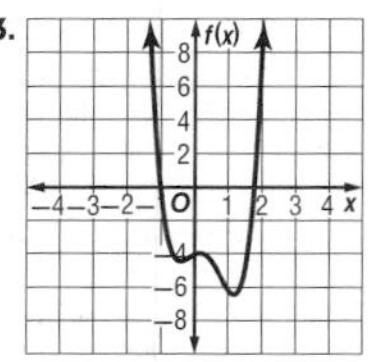

5. between −2 and −1 **7.** between 0 and 1 and between 2 and 3

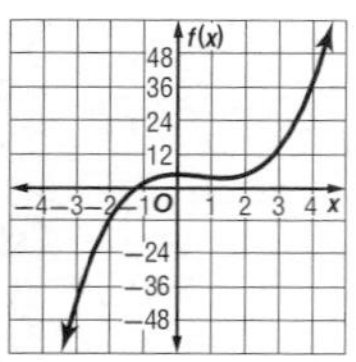

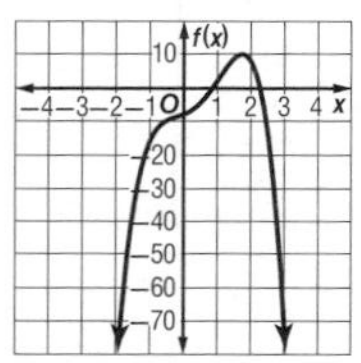

9. rel. max at $x \approx -1.8$; rel. min at $x \approx 1.1$; D = {all real numbers}, R = {all real numbers}

11. rel. max at $x \approx 2.4$; rel. min at $x \approx 0.3$; D = {all real numbers}, R = {all real numbers}

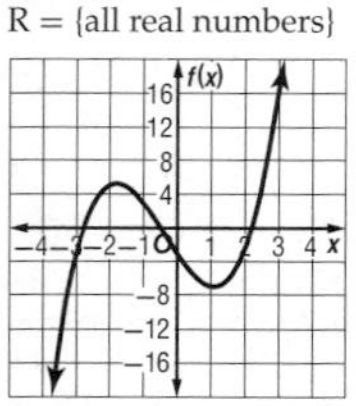

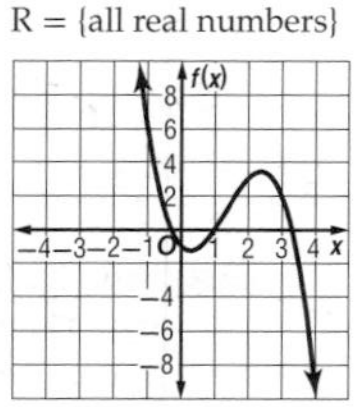

13a.

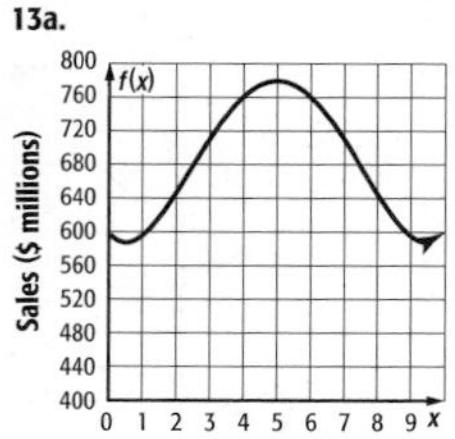

13b. Sample answer: The graph (music sales) increases until $x = 5$ (year 2000), then decreases until $x \approx 9.5$ (year 2004), and then increases indefinitely.

13c.

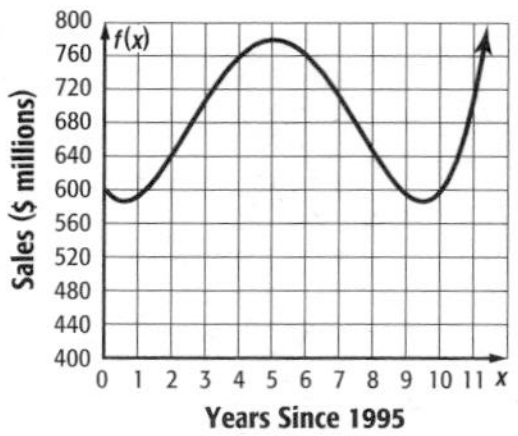

Sample answer: This suggests a dramatic increase in sales.

13d. Sample answer: No; with so many other forms of media on the market today, CD sales will not increase dramatically. In fact, the sales will probably decrease. The function appears to be accurate only until about 2005.

15 a. Since $f(x)$ is a third-degree polynomial function, it will have either 3 or 1 real zeros. Look at the values of $f(x)$ to locate the zeros. Then use the points to sketch the graph.

x	$f(x)$	
−4	92	
−3	41	
−2	12	← change in sign
−1	−1	
0	−4	
1	−3	
2	−4	
3	−13	
4	−36	

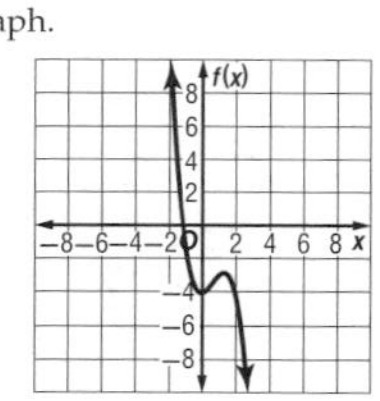

b. The value of $f(x)$ changes signs between $x = -2$ and $x = 1$. So, there is a zero between −2 and −1.
c. The value of $f(x)$ at $x = 0$ is less than the surrounding points, so there must be a relative minimum near $x = 0$. The value of $f(x)$ near $x = 1$ is greater than the surrounding points, so there must be a relative maximum near $x = 1$.

17a.

x	$f(x)$
−4	−155
−3	−80
−2	−33
−1	−8
0	1
1	0
2	−5
3	−8
4	−3
5	16

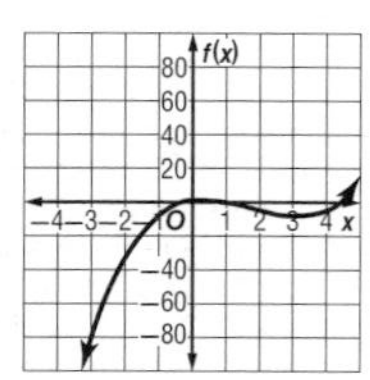

17b. at $x = 1$, between −1 and 0, and between $x = 4$ and $x = 5$ **17c.** rel. max: $x \approx \frac{1}{3}$, rel. min: $x = 3$

19a.

x	$f(x)$
−4	−176
−3	−77
−2	−22
−1	1
0	4
1	−1
2	−2
3	13
4	56

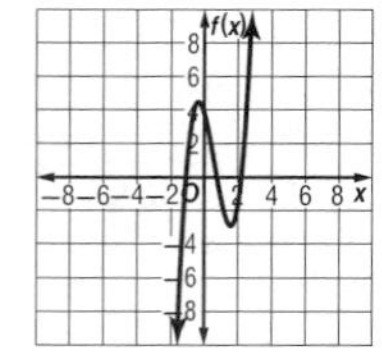

19b. between $x = -2$ and $x = -1$, between $x = 0$ and $x = 1$, and between $x = 2$ and $x = 3$
19c. rel. max: near $x = -0.3$; rel. min: near $x = 1.6$

21a.

x	$f(x)$
−4	372
−3	141
−2	36
−1	−3
0	−12
1	−3
2	36
3	141
4	372

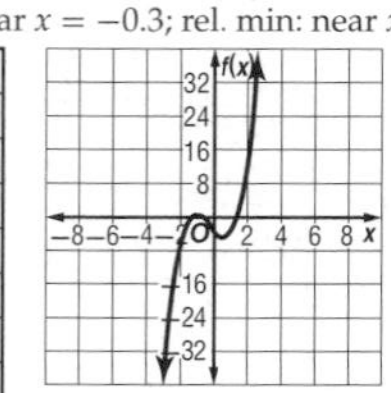

21b. between $x = -2$ and $x = -1$ and between $x = 1$ and $x = 2$ **21c.** min: near $x = 0$ **23.** rel. max: $x = -2.73$; rel. min: $x = 0.73$ **25.** rel. max: $x = 1.34$, no rel. min

27. Sample answer:

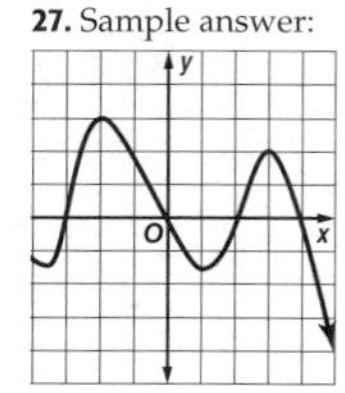

29. Sample answer:

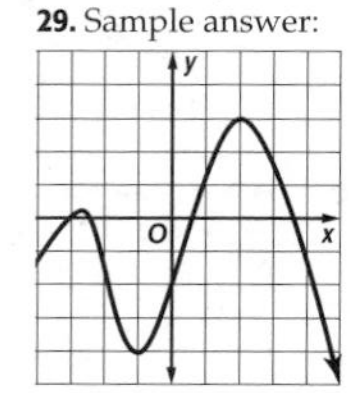

31. Sample answer:

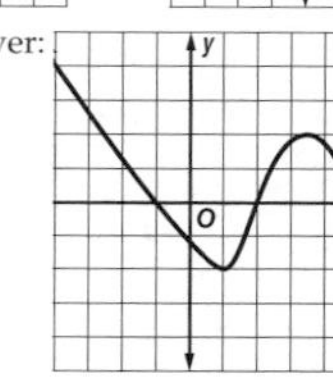

33 a.

x	$d(x)$
0	0
1	0.0145
2	0.056
3	0.1215
4	0.208
5	0.3125
6	0.432
7	0.5635
8	0.704
9	0.8505
10	1

b. Plot the points in the table and connect with a smooth curve.

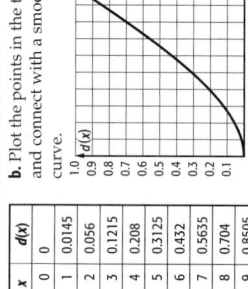

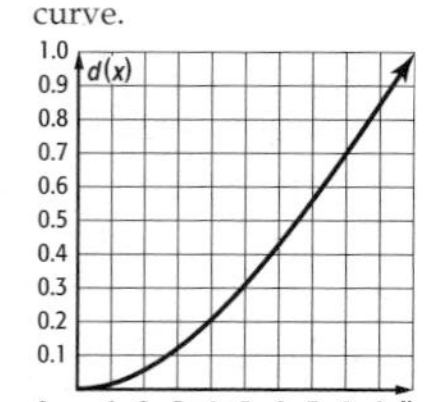

c. $d(x) \to +\infty$ as $x \to +\infty$; as x increases, $d(x)$ increases.
d. Sample answer: Since the diving board is only 10 feet long, x cannot be greater than 10. So, this trend cannot continue indefinitely.
35a. −2.5 (min), −0.5 (max), 1.5 (min) **35b.** −3.5, −1, 0, 3 **35c.** 4 **35d.** D = {all real numbers}; R = {y | $y \geq -3.1$} **37a.** −3.5 (min), −2.5(max), −2 (min), −1 (max), 1 (min) **37b.** −3.75, −3.25, −2, −1.75, −0.25, 2.9 **37c.** 6 **37d.** D = {all real numbers}; R = {y | $y \geq -5$} **39a.** −2 (max), 1 (min) **39b.** −3, −0.5, 2 **39c.** 3 **39d.** D = {all real numbers}; R = {all real numbers}

41.

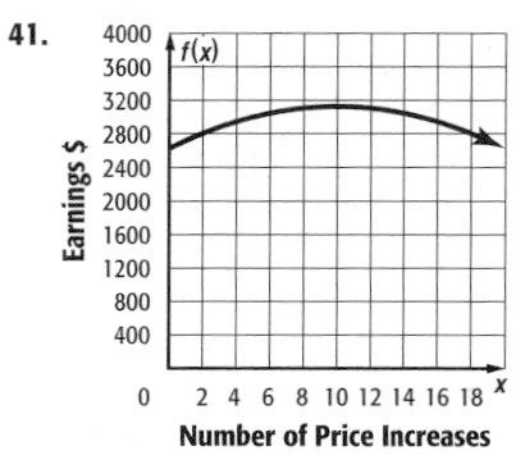

$1.25

43 a. Make a table of values and graph the function.

x	$f(x)$	
−2	−16	
−1.5	−4.5	
−1	−4	
−0.5	−4.6	
0	−4	
0.5	−3.3	
1	−4	
1.5	−3.5	← change in sign
2	8	

The value of $f(x)$ changes signs between $x = 1.5$ and $x = 2$. So, there is a zero between these values, at approximately 1.75. The x-intercept ≈ 1.75. The y-intercept is at −4. The value of $f(x)$ at $x \approx -1.25$ and at $x \approx 0.5$ is greater than the surrounding points, so $x \approx -1.25$ and $x \approx 0.5$ are turning points. The value of $f(x)$ at $x \approx -0.5$ and at $x \approx 1.25$ is less than the surrounding points, so $x \approx -0.5$ and $x \approx 1.25$ are turning points.
b. The function does not have an axis of symmetry because the graph is not a parabola.
c. The function is increasing in the intervals $x \leq -1.25$, $-0.5 \leq x \leq 0.5$, and $x \geq 1.25$. The function is decreasing in the intervals $-1.25 \leq x \leq -0.5$ and $0.5 \leq x \leq 1.25$.
45a. no zeros, no x-intercepts, y-intercept: 5; no turning points **45b.** no axis of symmetry **45c.** decreasing: $x \leq -4$; constant: $-4 < x \leq 0$; increasing: $x > 0$
47. As the x-values approach large positive or negative numbers, the term with the largest degree becomes more and more dominant in determining the value of $f(x)$.

49. Sample answer:

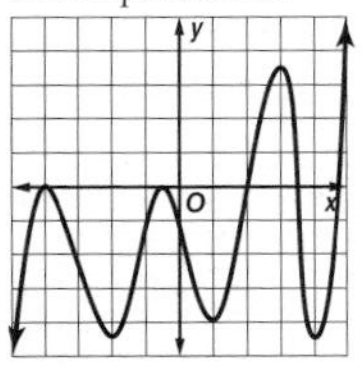

51. Sample answer: No; $f(x) = x^2 + x$ is an even degree, but $f(1) \neq f(-1)$. **53.** Sample answer: The degree will help determine whether the graph is even or odd and the maximum number of zeros and turning points for the graph. The leading coefficient determines the end behavior of the graph, and, along with the degree, builds the shape of the graph. The zeros and turning points allow for the plotting of specific points in the center of the graph. All of these things combine for an accurate sketch of the graph of a polynomial function. **55.** 95 **57.** C **59.** $f(x) \to -\infty$ as $x \to -\infty$. $f(x) \to -\infty$ as $x \to +\infty$. Since the end behavior is in the same direction, it is an even-degree function. The graph intersects the x-axis at six points, so there are six real zeros. **61.** $(x-2)(x+3)$ **63.** $2a^2 + a - 3 - \frac{3}{a-1}$ **65.** $(x+6)(x+3)$ **67.** $(a+8)(a-2)$ **69.** $(3x-4)(2x+1)$

Pages 372–375 Lesson 6-5

1. $(a+b)(3x+2y-z)$ **3.** prime **5.** $12q(w-q)(w^2+qw+q^2)$ **7.** $x^2(a+b)(a-b)(a^4+a^2b^2+b^4)$ **9.** $(2c-5d)(4c^2+12cd+25d^2)$ **11.** $4, -4, \pm\sqrt{3}$ **13.** $-3, \frac{3 \pm 3i\sqrt{3}}{2}$ **15.** 5 ft **17.** not possible **19.** $\sqrt{6}, -\sqrt{6}, 2\sqrt{3}, -2\sqrt{3}$ **21.** $x(4x+y)(16x^2-4xy+y^2)$ **23.** $y^3(x^2+y^2)(x^4-x^2y^2+y^2)$ **25.** prime **27.** $(6x^2-5y^2)(2a-3b+4c)$

29. $8x^5 - 25y^3 + 80x^4 - x^2y^3 + 200x^3 - 10xy^3$ Original expression

$= (8x^5 + 80x^4 + 200x^3) + (-25y^3 - x^2y^3 - 10xy^3)$ Group to find a GCF.

$= 8x^3(x^2 + 10x + 25) - y^3(25 + x^2 + 10x)$ Factor the GCF.

$= 8x^3(x+5)^2 - y^3(x+5)^2$ Perfect squares

$= (8x^3 - y^3)(x+5)^2$ Distributive Property

$= (2x-y)(4x^2+2xy+y^2)(x+5)^2$ Difference of cubes

31. $6, -6, \pm 2i\sqrt{5}$ **33.** $\pm\sqrt{7}, \pm i\sqrt{13}$ **35.** $-\frac{1}{4}, \frac{1 \pm i\sqrt{3}}{8}$ **37.** $-15(x^2)^2 + 18(x^2) - 4$ **39.** not possible **41.** $4(2x^5)^2 + 1(2x^5) + 6$ **43.** $\pm\sqrt{5}, \pm i\sqrt{2}$ **45.** $\pm\frac{2\sqrt{3}}{3}, \pm\frac{\sqrt{15}}{3}$ **47.** $\pm\frac{\sqrt{6}}{6}, \pm i\frac{\sqrt{3}}{2}$ **49.** $(x^2+25)(x+5)(x-5)$ **51.** $x(x+2)(x-2)(x^2+4)$ **53.** $(5x+4y+5z)(3a-2b+c)$ **55.** $x(x+3)(x-3)(3x+2)(2x-5)$ **57.** $x = 8; 5, 8, 11$ **59.** $\pm\frac{2\sqrt{3}}{3}, \pm i\frac{\sqrt{2}}{2}$ **61.** $\pm\frac{1}{3}, \pm i\frac{\sqrt{10}}{2}$ **63.** $3, -3, \pm i\frac{\sqrt{15}}{3}$

65
$x^6 - 26x^3 - 27 = 0$ Original equation
$(x^3)^2 - 26(x^3) - 27 = 0$ $(x^3)^2 = x^6$
$u^2 - 26u - 27 = 0$ Let $u = x^3$.
$(u-27)(u+1) = 0$ Factor.
$u - 27 = 0$ or $u + 1 = 0$ Zero Product Property
$x^3 - 27 = 0$ or $x^3 + 1 = 0$ Replace u with x^3.
$x^3 - 27 = 0$
$(x-3)(x^2+3x+9) = 0$ Difference of Two Cubes
$x - 3 = 0$ or $x^2 + 3x + 9 = 0$ Zero Product Property
$x = 3$ $\quad x = \frac{-3 \pm \sqrt{3^2 - 4(1)(9)}}{2(1)}$
$= \frac{-3 \pm 3i\sqrt{3}}{2}$
$x^3 + 1 = 0$
$(x+1)(x^2 - x + 1) = 0$ Sum of Two Cubes
$x + 1 = 0$ or $x^2 - x + 1 = 0$ Zero Product Property
$x = -1$ $\quad x = \frac{-(-1) \pm \sqrt{(-1)^2 - 4(1)(1)}}{2(1)}$
$= \frac{1 \pm i\sqrt{3}}{2}$

The solutions are $-1, 3, \frac{-3 \pm 3i\sqrt{3}}{2}$, and $\frac{1 \pm i\sqrt{3}}{2}$.

67. $-1, 1, \pm\frac{1}{2}$ **69.** $\pm i\sqrt{5}, \pm i\sqrt{3}$ **71a.** 2 ft **71b.** 176 ft^2 **71c.** 428 ft^2

73 a. $f(x) = (x+6)[x + x + (x+2) + (x+2)] + x[x + (x+2) + (x+2)] + x(x+2)$
$= (x+6)(4x+4) + x(3x+4) + x(x+2)$
$= 4x^2 + 24x + 4x + 24 + 3x^2 + 4x + x^2 + 2x$
$= 8x^2 + 34x + 24$

b. $f(x) = 8x^2 + 34x + 24$ Original function
$1366 = 8x^2 + 34x + 24$ Replace $f(x)$ with 1366.
$0 = 8x^2 + 34x - 1342$ Subtract 1366 from each side.
$0 = 2(4x^2 + 17x - 671)$ Factor.
$0 = 2(4x + 61)(x - 11)$ Perfect squares
$4x + 61 = 0$ or $x - 11 = 0$ Zero Product Property
$x = -15.25$ $\quad x = 11$ Simplify.

Since distance cannot be negative, $x = 11$ ft.

75. $(x+2)^3(x-2)^3$ **77.** $(x+y)^3(x-y)^3$ **79.** $(6x^n+1)^2$ **81.** Sample answer: $a = 1, b = -1$ **83.** Sample answer: The factors can be determined by the x-intercepts of the graph. An x-intercept of 5 represents a factor of $(x-5)$. **85.** D **87.** D **89.** rel max at $x \approx 1.5$, rel min at $x \approx 0.1$;

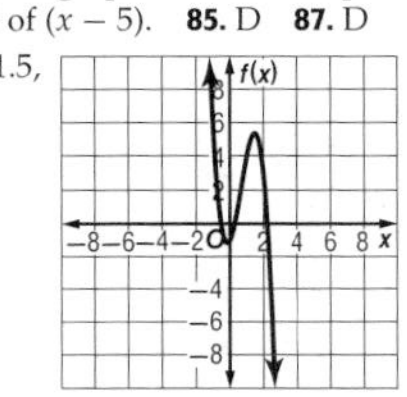

91. degree = 4; leading coefficient = 5 **93.** degree = 7; leading coefficient = −1 **95.** 18 skis and 10 snowboards **97.** $x + 2 - \frac{10}{x+4}$ **99.** $8x^2 - 12x + 24 - \frac{42}{x+2}$

Pages 380–382 Lesson 6-6

1. 58; −20 **3.** 12,526 **5.** $x+4, x-4$ **7.** $x-5, 2x-1$ **9.** 71; −6 **11.** −435; −15 **13.** −4150; 85 **15.** 647; −4 **17.** $(x-1)^2$ **19.** $x-4, x+1$ **21.** $x+6, 2x+7$ **23.** $x+1, x^2+2x+3$ **25.** $x-4, 3x-2$

27 a.

1	−0.04	0.8	0.5	−1	0
		−0.04	0.76	1.26	0.26
	−0.04	0.76	1.26	0.26	0.26

$f(1) = 0.26$ ft/s; At 1 second, the speed of the boat is 0.26 ft/s.

2	−0.04	0.8	0.5	−1	0
		−0.08	1.44	3.88	5.76
	−0.04	0.72	1.94	2.88	5.76

$f(2) = 5.76$ ft/s; At 2 seconds, the speed of the boat is 5.76 ft/s.

3	−0.04	0.8	0.5	−1	0
		−0.12	2.04	7.62	19.86
	−0.04	0.68	2.54	6.62	19.86

$f(3) = 19.86$ ft/s; At 3 seconds, the speed of the boat is 19.86 ft/s.

b.

6	−0.04	0.8	0.5	−1	0
		−0.24	3.36	23.16	132.96
	−0.04	0.56	3.86	22.16	132.96

$f(6) = 132.96$ ft/s; This means the boat is traveling at 132.96 ft/s when it passes the second buoy.

29. $x+2, x-3, x^2-x+4$ **31a.** $g(x) = 9x^4 + 50x^3 + 51x^2 - 150x - 72$

31b.

x	$g(x)$
−5	−9922
−4	−4160
−3	−1242
−2	−112
−1	70
0	−72
1	−130
2	88
3	558
4	1040
5	1078
6	0

31c. There is a zero between $x = -2$ and $x = -1$ because $f(x)$ changes sign between the two values. There are also zeros between $x = -1$ and Ø and between −1 and 0 and between $x = 1$ and $x = 2$ because $f(x)$ changes sign between the two values. There is also a zero at $x = 6$.

31d.

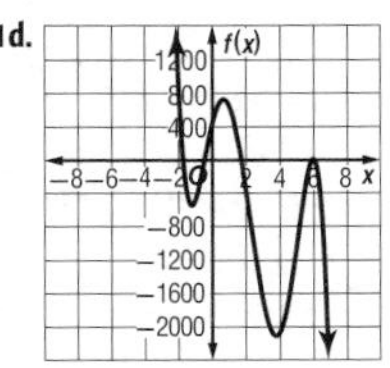

33

2	1	k	−17
		2	$2k + 4$
	1	$k + 2$	3

$-17 + 2k + 4 = 3$ Write an equation.
$-13 + 2k = 3$ Simplify.
$2k = 16$ Add 13 to each side.
$k = 8$ Divide each side by 2.

35. −3 **37.** $\pm\sqrt{6}, \pm\sqrt{3}$ **39a.** $x - c$ is a factor of $f(x)$. **39b.** $x - c$ is not a factor of $f(x)$. **39c.** $f(x) = x - c$ **41.** Sample answer: $f(x) = -x^3 + x^2 + x + 10$ **43.** Sample answer: A zero can be located using the Remainder Theorem and a table of values by determining when the output, or remainder, is equal to zero. For instance, if $f(6)$ leaves a remainder if 2 and $f(7)$ leaves a remainder of −1, then you know that there is a zero between $x = 6$ and $x = 7$. **45.** 4 **47.** B **49.** $\pm 3, \pm i\sqrt{3}$ **51a.** −1.5 (max), 0.5 (min), 2.5 (max) **51b.** −3.5, 3.75 **51c.** 4 **51d.** D = {all real numbers}; R = {$y \mid y \leq 4.5$} **53a.** −3 (min), −1 (max), 1 (min) **53b.** −0.25, 3 **53c.** 4 **53d.** D = {all real numbers}; R = {$y \mid y \geq -4.5$}

55.

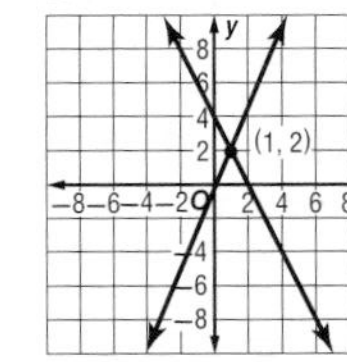

57.

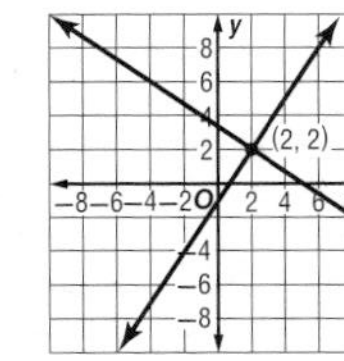

59. $4a^2 - 8a + 16$ **61.** $79a^2 - 58a + 12$ **63.** $-4a^4 - 24a^2 - 48a - 22$

Pages 388–390 Lesson 6-7

1. −2, 5; 2 real **3.** $-\frac{3}{2}, \frac{3}{2}, -\frac{3}{2}i, \frac{3}{2}i$; 2 real, 2 imaginary **5.** 3 or 1; 0; 0 or 2 **7.** 1 or 3; 0 or 2; 0, 2, or 4 **9.** −8, −2, 1 **11.** $-4, 6, -4i, 4i$ **13.** $x^3 - 9x^2 + 14x + 24$ **15.** $x^4 - 3x^3 - x^2 - 27x - 90$ **17.** $-2, \frac{3}{2}$; 2 real **19.** $-1, \frac{1 \pm i\sqrt{3}}{2}$; 1 real, 2 imaginary **21.** $-\frac{8}{3}$, 1; 2 real **23.** $-\frac{5}{2}, \frac{5}{2}, -\frac{5}{2}i, \frac{5}{2}i$; 2 real, 2 imaginary **25.** −2, −2, 0, 2, 2; 5 real

27 Find the number of sign changes for $f(x)$ and $f(-x)$.
$f(x) = x^4 - 5x^3 + 2x^2 + 5x + 7$
yes yes no no
Since there are 2 sign changes, the function has 0 or 2 positive real zeros.
$f(-x) = x^4 + 5x^3 + 2x^2 - 5x + 7$
no no yes yes
Since there are 2 sign changes, the function has 0 or 2 negative real zeros.
Since f(x) has degree 4, the function has 4 zeros.
So, the function could have the following.
2 positive real zeros, 2 negative real zeros, 0 imaginary zeros
2 positive real zeros, 0 negative real zeros, 2 imaginary zeros
0 positive real zeros, 0 negative real zeros, 4 imaginary zeros

29. 0 or 2; 1, 2 or 4 **31.** 0 or 2; 0 or 2; 2, 4, or 6 **33.** −6, −2, 1 **35.** $-4, 7, -5i, 5i$ **37.** $4, 4, -2i, 2i$ **39.** $\pm i\sqrt{\pi}$ **41.** $-\frac{1}{2}, \frac{1}{2}, -2i, 2i$ **43.** $f(x) = x^3 - 2x^2 - 13x - 10$ **45.** $f(x) = x^4 + 2x^3 + 5x^2 + 8x + 4$ **47.** $f(x) = x^4 - x^3 - 20x^2 + 50x$

49 a. Find the number of sign changes for $P(x)$ and $P(-x)$.
$P(x) = -0.006x^4 + 0.15x^3 - 0.05x^2 - 1.8x$
yes yes no
Since there are 2 sign changes, the function has 0 or 2 positive real zeros.
$P(-x) = -0.006x^4 - 0.15x^3 - 0.05x^2 + 1.8x$
no no yes
Since there is 1 sign change, the function has 1 negative real zero.
Since $f(x)$ has degree 4, the function has 4 zeros.
So, the function could have the following.

2 positive real zeros, 1 negative real zero, 1 imaginary zero
0 positive real zeros, 1 negative real zero, 3 imaginary zeros
b. Negative zeros do not make sense in the problem because the number of computers produced cannot be negative. Since the zeros are values of x for which $P(x) = 0$, nonnegative zeros represent numbers of computers produced per hour which lead to no profit for the manufacturer.
51. b **53a.** 3 or 1, 0, 2 or 0
53b.

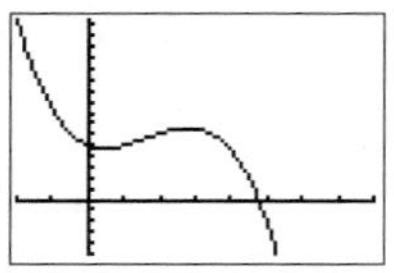

$[-10, 40]$ scl: 5 by $[-4000, 13{,}200]$ scl: 100

53c. 23.8; Sample answer: According to the model, the music hall will not earn any money after 2026.
55. 1 positive, 2 negative, 2 imaginary; Sample answer: The graph crosses the positive x-axis once, and crosses the negative x-axis twice. Because the degree of the polynomial is 5, there are 5 − 3 or 2 imaginary zeros. **57.** Sample answer: $f(x) = (x + 2i)(x - 2i)(3x + 5)(x + \sqrt{5})(x - \sqrt{5})$; Use conjugates for the imaginary and irrational values.
59a. Sample answer: $f(x) = x^4 + 4x^2 + 4$ **59b.** Sample answer: $f(x) = x^3 + 6x^2 + 9x$ **61.** C **63.** H **65.** $f(-8) = -1638$; $f(4) = 342$ **67.** $f(-8) = -63{,}940$; $f(4) = 1868$
69. $(a^2 + b^2)(a^4 - a^2b^2 + b^4)$ **71.** $(a - 4)(a - 2)(5a + 2b)$
73. 0.25 s **75.** $\pm1, \pm2, \pm4, \pm8, \pm\frac{1}{5}, \pm\frac{2}{5}, \pm\frac{4}{5}, \pm\frac{8}{5}$

Pages 393–396 Lesson 6-8

1. ±1, ±2, ±3, ±4, ±6, ±8, ±12, ±24
3. 5 in. × 9 in. × 28 in.
5 If $\frac{p}{q}$ is a rational zero, then p is a factor of 12 and q is a factor of 2.
p: ±1, ±2, ±3, ±4, ±6, ±12 q: ±1, ±2
possible rational zeros: $\frac{p}{q} = \pm1, \pm2, \pm3, \pm4, \pm6, \pm12, \pm\frac{1}{2}, \pm\frac{3}{2}$
There are no changes of signs for $f(x)$, so there are no positive real zeros. There are 4 changes of signs for $f(-x)$, so there are 0, 2, or 4 negative real zeros. Make a table for synthetic division and test the possible negative values.

$\frac{p}{q}$	2	11	26	29	12
−1	2	9	17	12	0
−2	2	7	12	5	2
−3	2	5	11	−4	24
−4	2	3	14	−27	120
−6	2	−1	32	−163	990
−12	2	−13	182	−2155	25,872
$-\frac{1}{2}$	2	10	21	18.5	2.75
$-\frac{3}{2}$	2	8	14	8	0

Because $f(-1) = 0$ and $f\left(-\frac{3}{2}\right) = 0$, there are zeros at $-\frac{3}{2}$ and −1. **7.** $-\frac{1}{2}, \frac{-5 \pm i\sqrt{23}}{8}$ **9.** $-\frac{1}{2}, \frac{3}{2}, 1 + 2i, 1 - 2i$
11. ±1, ±2, ±4, ±7, ±8, ±14, ±28, ±56
13 If $\frac{p}{q}$ is a rational zero, then p is a factor of 35 and q is a factor of 3.
p: ±1, ±5, ±7, ±35 q: ±1, ±3
possible rational zeros: $\frac{p}{q} = \pm1, \pm5, \pm7, \pm35, \pm\frac{1}{3}, \pm\frac{5}{3}, \pm\frac{7}{3}, \pm\frac{35}{3}$
15. $\pm1, \pm2, \pm3, \pm6, \pm7, \pm14, \pm21, \pm42, \pm\frac{1}{2}, \pm\frac{3}{2}, \pm\frac{7}{2}, \pm\frac{21}{2}, \pm\frac{1}{4}, \pm\frac{3}{4}, \pm\frac{7}{4}, \pm\frac{21}{4}, \pm\frac{1}{8}, \pm\frac{3}{8}, \pm\frac{7}{8}, \pm\frac{21}{8}$
17. $\pm1, \pm2, \pm4, \pm8, \pm16, \pm32, \pm64, \pm128, \pm\frac{1}{2}, \pm\frac{1}{4}, \pm\frac{1}{8}, \pm\frac{1}{16}$ **19.** −5, −3, −2 **21.** $-5, \frac{3}{4}, 5$ **23.** −1, 2
25. $-\frac{1}{4}$ **27.** −7, 1, 3 **29.** 2, −1, i, $-i$ **31.** 0, 3, $-i$, i
33. $-2, \frac{4}{3}, \frac{-3 \pm i}{2}$ **35.** $3, \frac{2}{3}, -\frac{2}{3}, \frac{-3 \pm \sqrt{13}}{2}$
37. $-\frac{1}{2}, \frac{1}{3}, \frac{1}{2}, \frac{3}{4}$ **39a.** $V(x) = 324x^3 + 54x^2 - 19x - 2$
39b. 3, 1.05i, −4.22i; 3 is the only reasonable value for x. The other two values are imaginary.
41 **a.** $V = \pi r^2 h$ Volume of a cylinder
$V = \pi r^2(r + 6)$ $h = r + 6$
$V = \pi r^2(r) + \pi r^2(6)$ Distributive Property
$V = \pi r^3 + 6\pi r^2$ Simplify.
b. $V = \pi r^3 + 6\pi r^2$ Volume of a cylinder
$160\pi = \pi r^3 + 6\pi r^2$ Substitute.
$0 = \pi r^3 + 6\pi r^2 - 160\pi$ Subtract 160π from each side.
$0 = r^3 + 6r^2 - 160$ Divide each side by π.
p: ±1, ±2, ±4, ±5, ±8, ±20, ±32, ±40, ±80, ±160
q: ±1
possible rational zeros: $\frac{p}{q} = \pm1, \pm2, \pm4, \pm5, \pm8, \pm20, \pm32, \pm40, \pm80, \pm160$
Make a table and test some possible rational zeros.

r	1	6	0	−160
1	1	7	7	−153
2	1	8	16	−128
3	1	9	27	−79
4	1	10	40	0

$V(r) = 0$, so there is a zero at $x = 4$. Use the Quadratic Formula to find zeros of the depressed polynomial $r^2 + 10r + 40$.

$x = \frac{-b \pm \sqrt{b^2 - 4ac}}{2a}$ Quadratic Formula
$= \frac{-10 \pm \sqrt{10^2 - 4(1)(40)}}{2(1)}$ $a = 1, b = 10$, and $c = 40$
$= \frac{-10 \pm \sqrt{100 - 160}}{2}$ Multiply.
$= \frac{-10 \pm \sqrt{-60}}{2}$ Simplify.
$= \frac{-10 \pm 2i\sqrt{15}}{2}$ $\sqrt{-60} = 2i\sqrt{15}$
$= -5 \pm 2i\sqrt{15}$
Since the radius cannot be an imaginary number, the only reasonable value is $r = 4$ in.
c. Since $r = 4$ in., $h = r + 6$ or 10 in.

43a. $30x^3 - 478x^2 + 1758x - 7608 = 0$ **43b.** 1, 2, 3, 4, 6, 8, 12, 24, 317, 634, 951, 1268, 1902, 2536, 3804, 7608
43c. 2010 **43d.** No; Sample answer: Music sales decline from 1997 to 2005, then increase indefinitely. It is not reasonable to expect sales to increase forever. **45.** 2, 3, 3, −3, −4 **47.** Sample answer: $f(x) = x^4 - 12x^3 + 47x^2 - 38x - 58$ **49.** Sample answer: $f(x) = 4x^5 + 3x^3 + 8x + 18$ **51.** Sample answer: For any polynomial function, the constant term represents p and the leading coefficient represents q. The possible zeros of the function can be found with $\pm\frac{p}{q}$ where the fraction is every combination of factors of p and q. For example, if p is 4 and q is 3, then $\pm4, \pm2, \pm1, \pm\frac{4}{3}, \pm\frac{2}{3}$, and $\pm\frac{1}{3}$ are all possible zeros. **53.** H **55.** 6 **57.** $f(x) = x^4 - 4x^3 + 11x^2 - 64x - 80$ **59.** $(x - 1)(x + 2)(x + 1)$
61. $(x - 3)(x + 4)(x - i)$ **63a.** about 3.5 s **63b.** 430 ft
65. $3x^3 + 12x$ **67.** 32 **69.** $18c + 2$

Pages 397–400 Chapter 6 Study Guide and Review

1. true **3.** false; depressed polynomial **5.** true
7. true **9.** true **11.** $\frac{7x}{y^4}$ **13.** $r^2 + 8r - 5$
15. $m^3 - m^2p - mp^2 + p^3$ **17.** $3x^3 + 2x^2y^2 - 4xy$
19. $a^3 + 3a^2 - 4a + 2$ **21.** $x^2 + 3x - 40$ units²
23. This is not a polynomial in one variable. It has two variables, x and y. **25.** $p(-2) = -3$; $p(x + h) = x^2 + 2xh + h^2 + 2x + 2h - 3$
27. $p(-2) = -25$; $p(x + h) = 3 - 5x^2 - 10xh - 5h^2 + x^3 + 3hx^2 + 3h^2x + h^3$
29a.

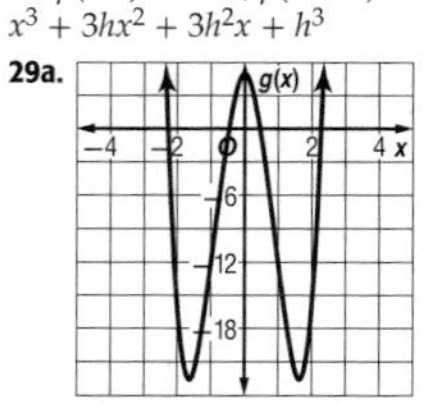

29b. between −3 and −2, between −1 and 0, between 0 and 1, between 2 and 3
29c. rel. max: $x \approx 0$; rel. min: $x \approx 1.62$ and $x \approx -1.62$
31a.

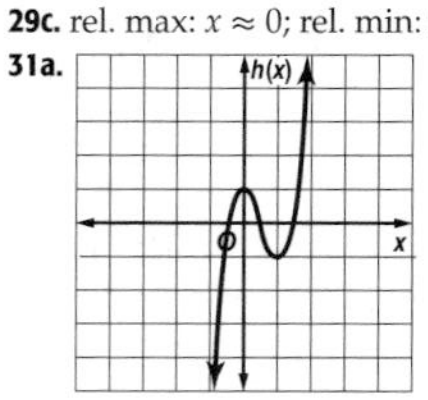

31b. between −1 and 0, between 0 and 1, and between 1 and 2
31c. rel. max: $x \approx 0$; rel. min: $x \approx 1$ **33.** 2 relative maxima and 1 relative minima
35. prime
37. $(2y + z)(3a + 2b - c)$ **39.** $\pm\frac{\sqrt{3}}{2}, \pm\frac{\sqrt{2}}{2}$
41. $f(-2) = 1$; $f(4) = 13$ **43.** $f(-2) = 16$; $f(4) = 118$
45. $x + 2$ and $3x - 1$ **47.** $x + 3, x + 4$
49. positive real zeros: 0
negative real zeros: 4, 2, or 0
imaginary zeros: 4, 2, or 0
51. positive real zeros: 2 or 0
negative real zeros: 1
imaginary zeros: 4 or 2
53. $-2, -1 \pm \sqrt{2}$ **55.** $-2, \pm2i$

Chapter 7 Inverses and Radical Functions and Relations

Page 407 Chapter 7 Get Ready

1. between 0 and 1, and between 3 and 4
3. between 1 and 2 seconds **5.** $3x + 2 - \frac{20}{x + 4}$
7. $3x^3 - 4x^2 + 5x - 3 + \frac{6}{x - 3}$

Pages 413–416 Lesson 7-1

1. $(f + g)(x) = 4x + 1$; $(f - g)(x) = -2x + 3$; $(f \cdot g)(x) = 3x^2 + 5x - 2$; $\left(\frac{f}{g}\right)(x) = \frac{x + 2}{3x - 1}, x \neq \frac{1}{3}$
3. $f \circ g$ is undefined; $g \circ f = \{(2, 8), (6, 13), (12, 11), (7, 15)\}$. **5.** $[f \circ g](x) = -15x + 18$; $[g \circ f](x) = -15x - 6$
7. Either way, she will have \$228.95 taken from her paycheck. If she takes the college savings plan deduction before taxes, \$76 will go to her college plan and \$152.95 will go to taxes. If she takes the college savings plan deduction after taxes, only \$62.70 will go to her college plan and \$166.25 will go to taxes.
9. $(f + g)(x) = 6x - 3$; $(f - g)(x) = -4x + 1$; $(f \cdot g)(x) = 5x^2 - 7x + 2$; $\left(\frac{f}{g}\right)(x) = \frac{x - 1}{5x - 2}, x \neq \frac{2}{5}$
11 $(f + g)(x) = f(x) + g(x)$ Addition of functions
$= (3x) + (-2x + 6)$ $f(x) = 3x$ and $g(x) = -2x + 6$
$= x + 6$ Simplify.
$(f - g)(x) = f(x) - g(x)$ Subtraction of functions
$= (3x) - (-2x + 6)$ Substitution
$= 5x - 6$ Simplify.
$(f \cdot g)(x) = f(x) \cdot g(x)$ Multiplication of functions
$= (3x)(-2x + 6)$ Substitution
$= -6x^2 + 18x$ Simplify.
$\left(\frac{f}{g}\right)(x) = \frac{f(x)}{g(x)}$ Division of functions
$= \frac{3x}{-2x + 6}, x \neq 3$ Substitution
13. $(f + g)(x) = x^2 + x - 5$; $(f - g)(x) = x^2 - x + 5$; $(f \cdot g)(x) = x^3 - 5x^2$; $\left(\frac{f}{g}\right)(x) = \frac{x^2}{x - 5}, x \neq 5$
15. $(f + g)(x) = 4x^2 - 8x$; $(f - g)(x) = 2x^2 + 8x - 8$; $(f \cdot g)(x) = 3x^4 - 24x^3 + 8x^2 + 32x - 16$; $\left(\frac{f}{g}\right)(x) = \frac{3x^2 - 4}{x^2 - 8x + 4}, x \neq 4 \pm 2\sqrt{3}$ **17.** $f \circ g = \{(-4, 4)\}$; $g \circ f = \{(-8, 0), (0, -4), (2, -5), (-6, -1)\}$ **19.** $f \circ g$ is undefined; $g \circ f$ is undefined. **21.** $f \circ g$ is undefined; $g \circ f = \{(-4, 0), (1, 2)\}$. **23.** $f \circ g = \{(4, 6), (3, -8)\}$; $g \circ f$ is undefined. **25.** $f \circ g = \{(3, -1), (6, 11)\}$; $g \circ f = \{(-4, 5), (-2, 4), (-1, 8)\}$
27 $[f \circ g](x) = f[g(x)]$ Composition of functions
$= f(x + 5)$ Replace $g(x)$ with $x + 5$.
$= 2(x + 5)$ Substitute $x + 5$ for x in $f(x)$.
$= 2x + 10$ Distributive Property

$[g \circ f](x) = g[f(x)]$ Composition of functions
$= g(2x)$ Replace f(x) with 2x.
$= 2x + 5$ Substitute 2x for x in g(x).

29. $[f \circ g](x) = 3x - 2$; $[g \circ f](x) = 3x + 8$
31. $[f \circ g](x) = x^2 - 6x - 2$; $[g \circ f](x) = x^2 + 6x - 8$
33. $[f \circ g](x) = 4x^3 + 7$; $[g \circ f](x) = 64x^3 - 48x^2 + 12x + 1$
35. $[f \circ g](x) = 128x^4 + 96x^3 + 18x^2$; $[g \circ f](x) = 32x^4 + 6x^2$
37a. $p(x) = 0.65x$; $t(x) = 1.0625x$
37b. Since $[p \circ t](x) = [t \circ p](x)$, either function represents the price. **37c.** \$1587.75 **39.** $2(g \cdot f)(x) = 2x^3 - 4x^2 - 30x + 72$; D = {all real numbers} **41.** 25 **43.** 483
45. −5 **47.** $-30a + 5$ **49.** $-10a^2 + 10a + 1$

51 a. Let $w(x)$ represent the function for women and $m(x)$ represent the function for men.
$(w + m)(x) = w(x) + m(x)$ Addition of functions
$= (1086.4x + 56{,}610) + (999.2x + 66{,}450)$ Substitution
$= 2085.6x + 123{,}060$ Simplify.
The equation $y = 2085.6x + 123{,}060$ models the total number.
b. $(f - g)(x)$ = the number of men employed in the U.S. − the number of women employed in the U.S. So, the function represents the difference in the number of men and women employed in the U.S.
53. 0 **55.** 1 **57.** 256 **59.** Sample answer: $f(x) = x - 9$, $g(x) = x + 5$ **61a.** D = {all real numbers} **61b.** D = $\{x \mid x \geq 0\}$ **63.** Compositions of functions are used when the value of a function is determined by another function. For example, the product of a manufacturing plant may have to go through several processes in a particular order, in which each process is described by a function.
65. G **67.** C **69.** −3, 2, 4 **71.** $-3, 5, \frac{1}{2}$ **73.** 1; 1; 2
75. 2 or 0; 2 or 0; 4, 2, or 0 **77.** (1, 2, 3) **79.** (3, −1, 5)
81. $x = \frac{12 + 7y}{5}$ **83.** $x = \frac{15 - 8yz}{4}$ **85.** $k = \pm\sqrt{A - b}$

Pages 420–422 Lesson 7-2

1. {(10, −9), (−3, 1), (−5, 8)}
3. $f^{-1}(x) = -\frac{1}{3}x$

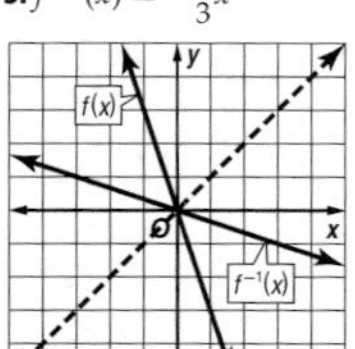

5. $y = \pm\sqrt{x + 3}$

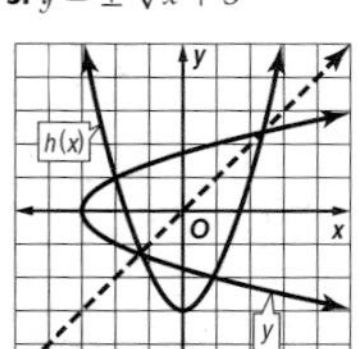

7. no **9.** {(6, −8), (−2, 6), (−3, 7)}
11. {(−1, 8), (−1, −8), (−8, −2), (8, 2)}
13. {(−5, 1), (6, 2), (−7, 3), (8, 4), (−9, 5)}

15. $f^{-1}(x) = x - 2$

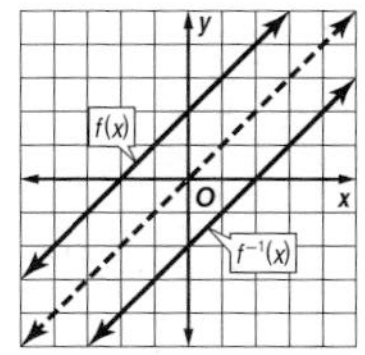

17. $y^{-1} = \frac{x - 1}{-2}$

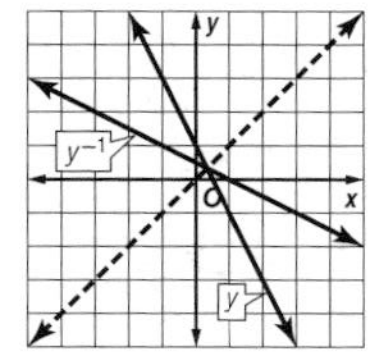

19. $y^{-1} = -\frac{3}{5}(x + 8)$

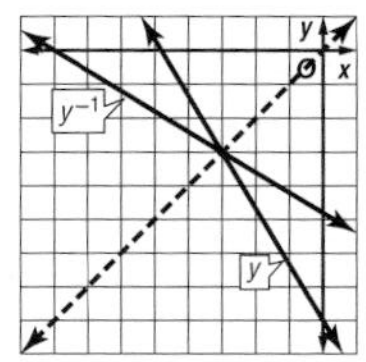

21. $f^{-1}(x) = \frac{1}{4}x$

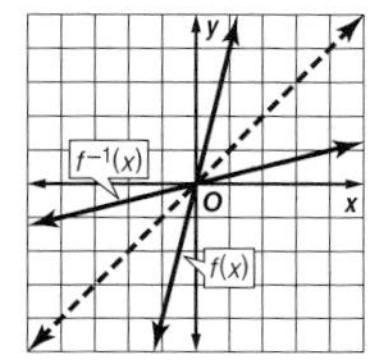

23. $y = \pm\sqrt{\frac{1}{5}x}$

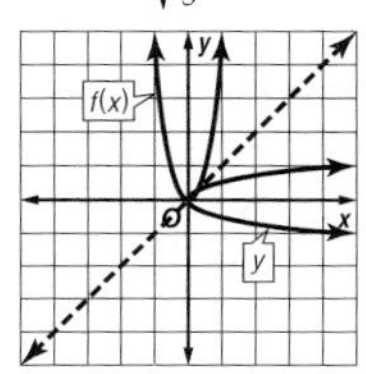

25. $y = \pm\sqrt{2x + 2}$

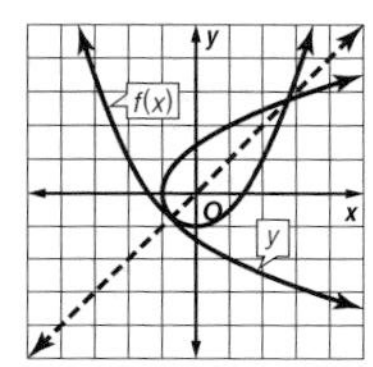

27. no **29.** yes **31.** yes **33.** yes

35 $[f \circ g](x) = f[g(x)]$ Composition of functions
$= f(x + 3)$ Replace g(x) with x + 3.
$= (x + 3)^2 - 9$ Substitute x + 3 for x in f(x).
$= x^2 + 6x + 9 - 9$ FOIL
$= x^2 + 6x$ Simplify.
$[g \circ f](x) = g[f(x)]$ Composition of functions
$= g(x^2 - 9)$ Replace f(x) with $x^2 - 9$.
$= (x^2 - 9) + 3$ Substitute $x^2 - 9$ for x in g(x).
$= x^2 - 6$ Simplify.
The functions are not inverses because $[f \circ g](x) \neq [g \circ f](x)$.
37. yes **39a.** $c(g) = 2.95g$ **39b.** $c(m) \approx 0.105m$

41 a. $A = \pi r^2$ Write the formula
$y = \pi x^2$ Write the formula using x and y.
$x = \pi y^2$ Exchange x and y in the equation.
$\frac{x}{\pi} = y^2$ Divide each side by π.
$\sqrt{\frac{x}{\pi}} = y$ Take the positive square root of each side.
So, replacing y with r and x with A, the inverse is $r = \sqrt{\frac{A}{\pi}}$.

b. $r = \sqrt{\frac{A}{\pi}}$ Write the inverse of the function.
$= \sqrt{\frac{36}{\pi}}$ A = 36
≈ 3.39 cm Simplify.
43. yes **45.** no **47.** no **49a.** $F^{-1}(x) = \frac{5}{9}(x - 32)$;
$F[F^{-1}(x)] = \frac{9}{5}\left[\frac{5}{9}(x - 32)\right] + 32 = x - 32 + 32 = x$;
$F^{-1}[F(x)] = \frac{5}{9}\left(\frac{9}{5}x + 32 - 32\right) = \frac{5}{9}\left(\frac{9}{5}x + 0\right) = x$.
49b. It can be used to convert Fahrenheit to Celsius.
51a.

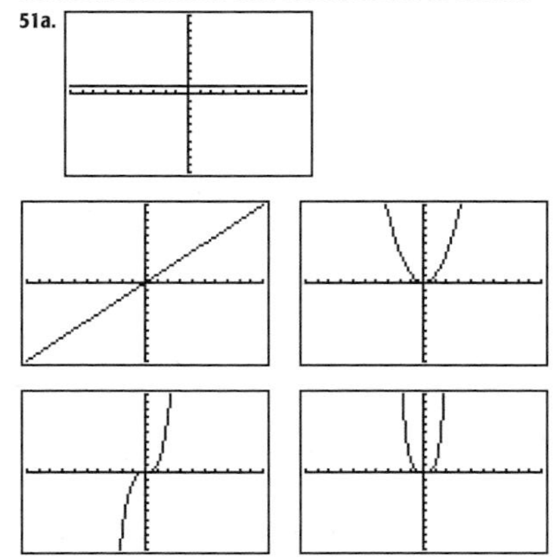

51b.

Function	Inverse a function?
$y = x^0$ or $y = 1$	no
$y = x^1$ or $y = x$	yes
$y = x^2$	no
$y = x^3$	yes
$y = x^4$	no

51c. n is odd. **53.** Sample answer: $f(x) = 2x$, $f^{-1}(x) = 0.5x$; $f[f^{-1}(x)] = f^{-1}[f(x)] = x$
55. $y^{-1} = \frac{x - b}{m}$ **57.** 30 in. **59.** I **61.** 12 **63.** 0
65. 289; $(x + 17)^2$ **67.** $23 + 14i$ **69.** i
71. $\begin{bmatrix} 2 & 4 & 2 & -3 \\ 3 & -3 & -5 & -2 \end{bmatrix}$; $\begin{bmatrix} -2 & -4 & -2 & 3 \\ -3 & 3 & 5 & 2 \end{bmatrix}$
73. 180° rotation
75.

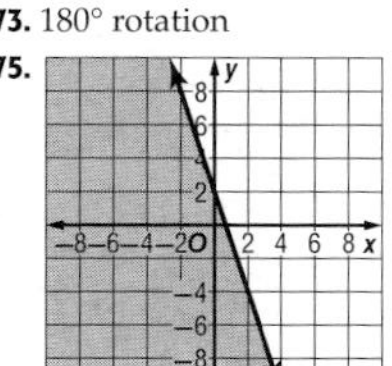

Pages 427–430 Lesson 7-3

1. D = $\{x \mid x \geq 0\}$; R = $\{f(x) \mid f(x) \geq 0\}$
3. D = $\{x \mid x \geq -8\}$; R = $\{f(x) \mid f(x) \geq -2\}$

5.

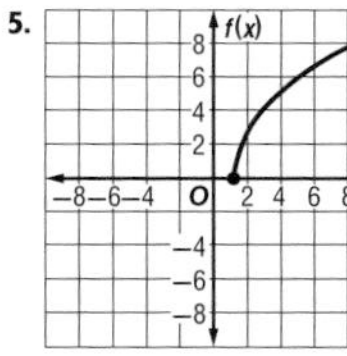

D = $\{x \mid x \geq 1\}$;
R = $\{f(x) \mid f(x) \geq 0\}$

7.

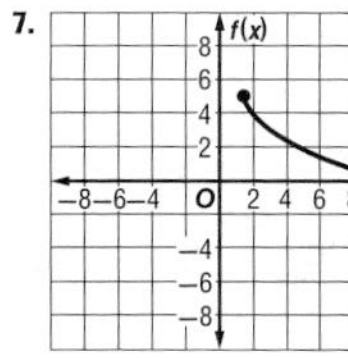

D = $\left\{x \mid x \geq \frac{5}{3}\right\}$;
R = $\{f(x) \mid f(x) \leq 5\}$

9.

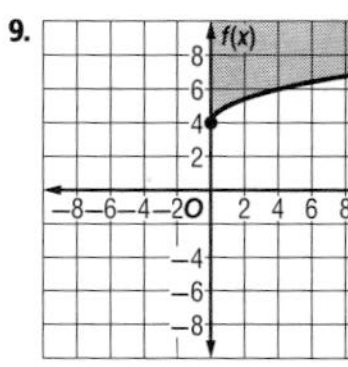

11.

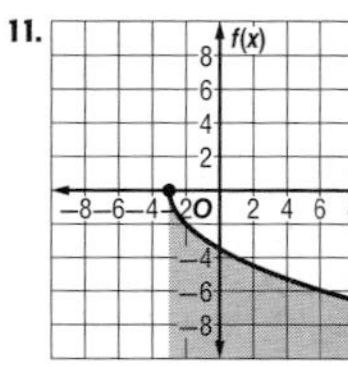

13. D = $\{x \mid x \geq 0\}$; R = $\{f(x) \mid f(x) \leq 2\}$

15 The domain only includes values for which the radicand is nonnegative.
$x - 2 \geq 0$ Write an inequality.
$x \geq 2$ Add 2 to each side.
The domain is $\{x \mid x \geq 2\}$. Find $f(2)$ to find the lower limit of the range.
$f(2) = 4\sqrt{2 - 2} - 8$
$= 0 - 8$ or -8
The range is $\{f(x) \mid f(x) \geq 2\}$.
17. D = $\{x \mid x \geq 4\}$; R = $\{f(x) \mid f(x) \geq -6\}$

19.

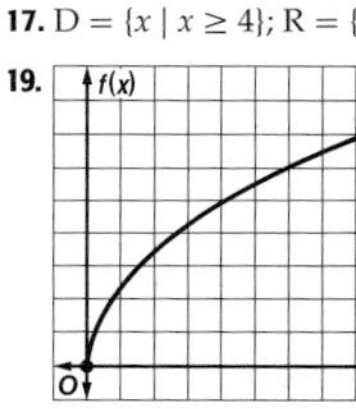

D = $\{x \mid x \geq 0\}$;
R = $\{f(x) \mid f(x) \geq 0\}$

21.

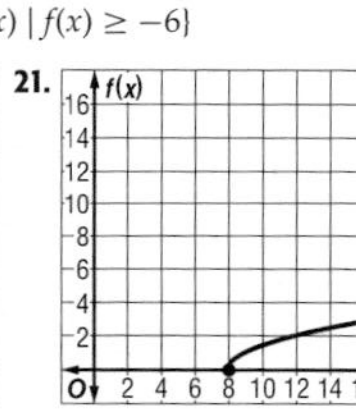

D = $\{x \mid x \geq 8\}$;
R = $\{f(x) \mid f(x) \geq 0\}$

23.

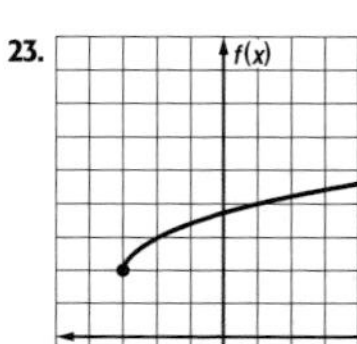

D = $\{x \mid x \geq -3\}$;
R = $\{f(x) \mid f(x) \geq 2\}$

25.

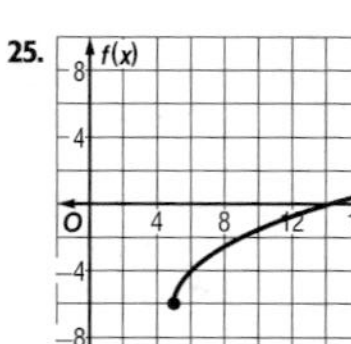

D = $\{x \mid x \geq 5\}$;
R = $\{f(x) \mid f(x) \geq -6\}$

27. 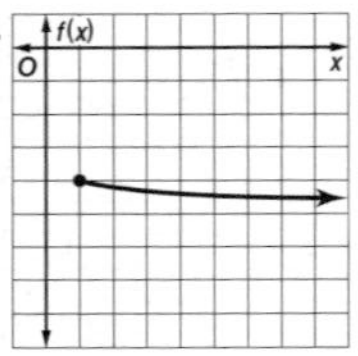

D = $\{x \mid x \geq 1\}$;
R = $\{f(x) \mid f(x) \leq -4\}$

29. 1936 ft

31. 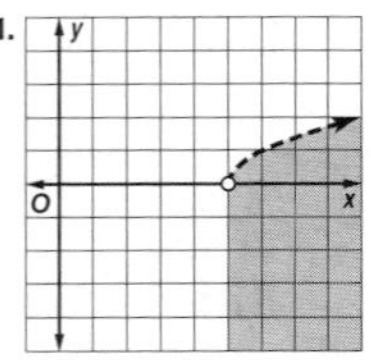

33 Graph the boundary $y = -4\sqrt{x+3}$. The domain is $\{x \mid x \geq -3\}$. Because y is *greater than*, the shaded region should be *above* the boundary and within the domain.

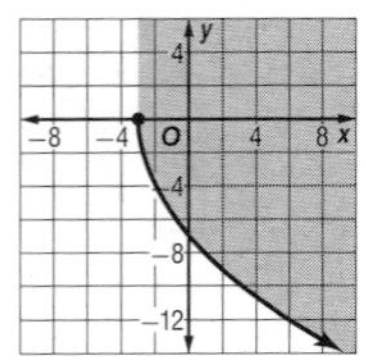

35. 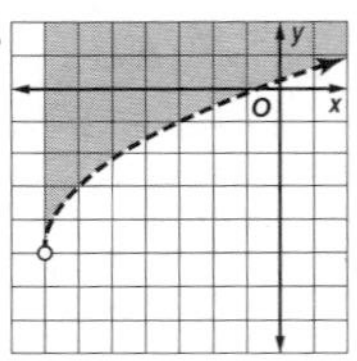

37. 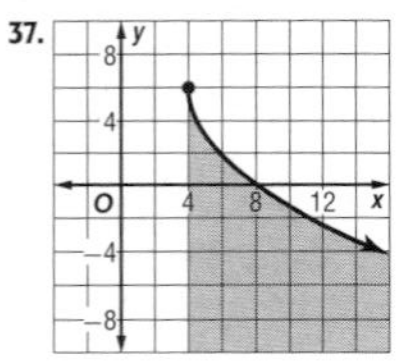

39a. $v = \sqrt{\frac{2E}{m}}$ **39b.** about 36.5 m/s **39c.** about 85,135 m/s **41.** $f(x) = \sqrt{x-4} - 6$

43. $f(x) = -\sqrt{x+6} - 6$

45 **a.** $T = 2\pi\sqrt{\frac{L}{g}}$ Original function

$T = 2\pi\sqrt{\frac{L}{32}}$ Replace g with 32.

Make a table of values for $0 \leq L \leq 10$. Graph the points and connect with a smooth curve.

L	T
0	0
1	1.11
2	1.57
3	1.92
4	2.22
5	2.48
6	2.72
7	2.94
8	3.14
9	3.33
10	3.51

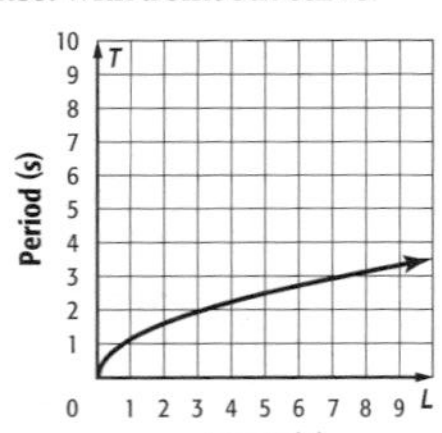

b. Use the table that you made in part a. (2, 1.57) means the period for a pendulum 2 feet long is about 1.57 seconds. (5, 2.48) means the period for a pendulum 5 feet long is about 2.48 seconds. (8, 3.14) means the period for a pendulum 8 feet long is about 3.14 seconds.

47. Sample answer: $y = -\sqrt{x+4} + 6$
49. Sample answer: $y = -\sqrt{x-8} + 14$
51. Molly is correct; Cleveland shaded incorrectly. He shaded above the graph when he should have shaded below. **53a.** Sample answer: The original is $y = x^2 + 2$ and inverse is $y = \pm\sqrt{x-2}$. **53b.** Sample answer: The original is $y = \pm\sqrt{x} + 4$ and inverse is $y = (x-4)^2$. **55.** G **57.** D **59.** no **61.** $[d \circ h](m) = \frac{m}{1440}$ **63.** rational **65.** rational

Pages 433–436 Lesson 7-4

1. $\pm 10y^4$

3 $\sqrt{(y-6)^8} = \sqrt{[(y-6)^4]^2}$
$= (y-6)^4$

5. $\pm 4iy^2$ **7.** 7.616 **9.** −2.122
11. about 4.088×10^8 m

13 $\pm\sqrt{225a^{16}b^{36}} = \pm\sqrt{(15a^8b^{18})^2}$
$= \pm 15a^8b^{18}$

15. $-4c^2|d|$ **17.** $-20x^{16}y^{20}$ **19.** $(x^2+6)^8$ **21.** $2a^2b^4$
23. $3b^6c^4$ **25.** $\pm i(x+2)^4$ **27.** $|x^3|$ **29.** a^4
31. $(4x-7)^8$ **33.** $4|(5x-2)^3|$ **35.** $2a^3b^2$ **37.** 8 cm
39. −12.247 **41.** 0.787 **43.** −5.350 **45.** 29.573
47. $14|c^3|d^2$ **49.** $-3a^5b^3$ **51.** $20x^8|y^3|$ **53.** $4(x+y)^2$
55. about 141 million mi

57 bald eagle:
$P = 73.3\sqrt[4]{m^3}$
$= 73.3\sqrt[4]{4.5^3}$
≈ 226.5 Cal/d

golden retriever:
$P = 73.3\sqrt[4]{m^3}$
$= 73.3\sqrt[4]{30^3}$
≈ 939.6 Cal/d

komodo dragon:
$P = 73.3\sqrt[4]{m^3}$
$= 73.3\sqrt[4]{72^3}$
≈ 1811.8 Cal/d

bottlenose dolphin:
$P = 73.3\sqrt[4]{m^3}$
$= 73.3\sqrt[4]{156^3}$
≈ 3235.5 Cal/d

Asian elephant:
$P = 73.3\sqrt[4]{m^3}$
$= 73.3\sqrt[4]{2300^3}$
$\approx 23{,}344.4$ Cal/d

59. Kimi is correct; Ashley's error was keeping the y^2 inside the absolute value symbol. **61.** Sample answer: Sometimes; when $x = -3$, $\sqrt[4]{(-x)^4} = |(-x)|$ or 3. When $x = 3$, $\sqrt[4]{(-x)^4} = |3|$ or 3.
63. Sample answers: 1, 64 **65.** $2\sqrt[3]{2xy}$ **67.** −0.1
69. $\frac{1}{625}$ **71.** G **73.** B

75. 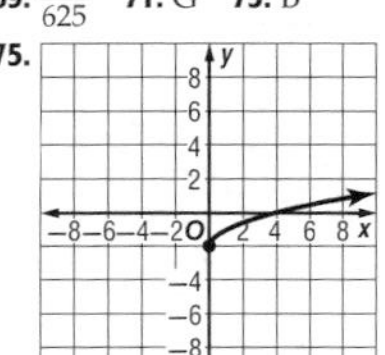

77. 3.41 kg and 49.53 cm
79. $4x^2 + 22x - 34$
81. $4a^4 + 24a^2 + 36$

83. $(-2, 3)$; $x = -2$; down

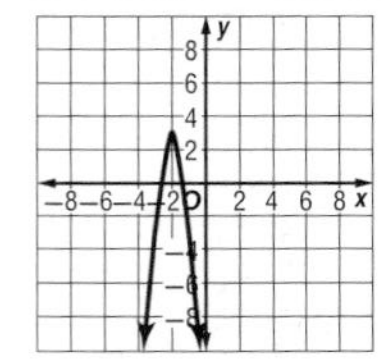

85. $(2, -2)$; $x = 2$; up

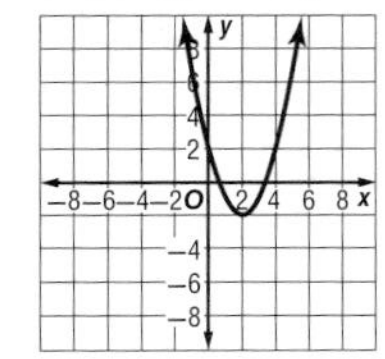

87. $x^2 + 9x + 20$ **89.** $a^2 - 7a - 18$ **91.** $x^2 + xy - 2y^2$

Pages 443–445 Lesson 7-5

1. $6b^2c^2\sqrt{ac}$ **3.** $\frac{c^2\sqrt{cd}}{d^5}$ **5.** $60x$ **7.** $36xy$
9. $20\sqrt{2} + 13\sqrt{3}$ **11.** $12\sqrt{3} + 16\sqrt{5} + 40 + 6\sqrt{15}$
13. $\frac{15 - 5\sqrt{2}}{7}$ **15.** $-2 - \sqrt{2}$ **17.** $32 - 2\sqrt{3}$ cm
19. $3a^7b\sqrt{ab}$ **21.** $3|a^3|bc^2\sqrt{2bc}$ **23.** $\frac{\sqrt{70xy}}{10y^2}$
25. $\frac{\sqrt[4]{28b^2x^3}}{2|b|}$ **27.** $32a^5b^3\sqrt{b}$ **29.** $25x^6y^3\sqrt{2xy}$
31. $18\sqrt{3} + 14\sqrt{2}$ **33.** $9\sqrt{6} + 72\sqrt{2} - 7\sqrt{3}$

35 $A = \ell w$ Area of a rectangle
$= (8 + \sqrt{3})(\sqrt{6})$ $\ell = 8 + \sqrt{3}$ and $w = \sqrt{6}$
$= 8 \cdot \sqrt{6} + \sqrt{3} \cdot \sqrt{6}$ Distributive Property
$= 8\sqrt{6} + \sqrt{18}$ Product Property
$= 8\sqrt{6} + 3\sqrt{2}$ ft^2 Simplify.

37. $56\sqrt{3} + 42\sqrt{6} - 36\sqrt{2} - 54$ **39.** 1260
41. $6\sqrt{3} + 6\sqrt{2}$ **43.** $\frac{20 - 7\sqrt{3}}{11}$ **45.** $2yz^4\sqrt[3]{2y}$

47. $3|a|b^3\sqrt[4]{2a^2bc}$ **49.** $\frac{\sqrt[4]{1500a^2b^3x^3y^2}}{5|a|b}$

51 $\frac{x+1}{\sqrt{x}-1} = \frac{x+1}{\sqrt{x}-1} \cdot \frac{\sqrt{x}+1}{\sqrt{x}+1}$ $\sqrt{x}+1$ is the conjugate of $\sqrt{x}-1$.
$= \frac{x(\sqrt{x}) + 1(x) + 1(\sqrt{x}) + 1(1)}{\sqrt{x}(\sqrt{x}) + 1(\sqrt{x}) + -1(\sqrt{x}) + (-1)(1)}$ Multiply.
$= \frac{x\sqrt{x} + x + \sqrt{x} + 1}{x + \sqrt{x} - \sqrt{x} - 1}$ Simplify.
$= \frac{x(\sqrt{x}+1) + (\sqrt{x}+1)}{x-1}$ Simplify.
$= \frac{(x+1)(\sqrt{x}+1)}{x-1}$ Simplify.

53. $\frac{\sqrt{x^3 - x}}{x^2 - 1}$ **55.** $|a|$ **57.** a^2

59a. $a^2 + b^2 = c^2$
$1^2 + 1^2 = c^2$
$2 = c^2$
$c = \sqrt{2}$

59b. 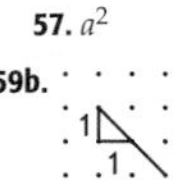

59c. $\sqrt{2} + \sqrt{2}$ units is the length of the hypotenuse of an isosceles right triangle with legs of length 2 units. Therefore, $\sqrt{2} + \sqrt{2} > 2$.

59d. 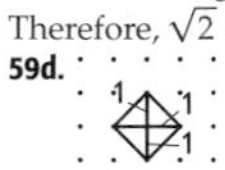

59e. The square creates 4 triangles with a base of 1 and a height of 1. Therefore the area of each triangle is $\frac{1}{2}bh = \frac{1}{2}(1)(1)$ or $\frac{1}{2}$. $4\left(\frac{1}{2}\right) = 2$. The area of the square is 2, so $\sqrt{2} \cdot \sqrt{2} = 2$.

61. $\left(\frac{-1 - i\sqrt{3}}{2}\right)^3 = \left(\frac{-1 - i\sqrt{3}}{2}\right) \cdot \left(\frac{-1 - i\sqrt{3}}{2}\right) \cdot \left(\frac{-1 - i\sqrt{3}}{2}\right)$
$= \frac{(-1 - i\sqrt{3})(-1 - i\sqrt{3})(-1 - i\sqrt{3})}{8}$
$= \frac{(1 + i\sqrt{3} + i\sqrt{3} + 3i^2)(-1 - i\sqrt{3})}{8}$
$= \frac{(2i\sqrt{3} - 2)(-1 - i\sqrt{3})}{8}$
$= \frac{-2i\sqrt{3} - 6i^2 + 2 + 2i\sqrt{3}}{8}$
$= \frac{-6i^2 + 2}{8} = \frac{8}{8}$ or 1

63. $\sqrt[1]{256} = 256$; $\sqrt[2]{256} = 16$; $\sqrt[4]{256} = 4$; $\sqrt[8]{256} = 2$
65. Sample answer: It is only necessary to use absolute values when it is possible that n could be odd or even and still be defined.
It is when the radicand must be nonnegative in order for the root to be defined that the absolute values are not necessary. **67.** G **69.** B **71.** $9ab^3$

73. 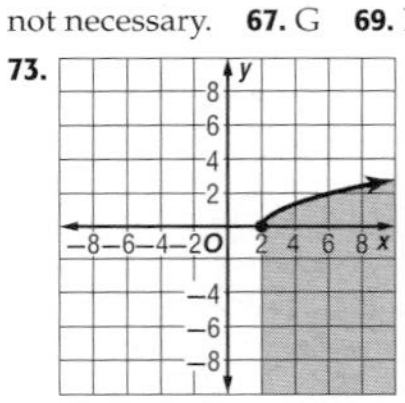

75. $-4, 4, -i, i$ **77.** $-4, 2 + 2i\sqrt{3}, 2 - 2i\sqrt{3}$
79. $\frac{3}{2}, \frac{-3 + 3i\sqrt{3}}{4}, \frac{-3 - 3i\sqrt{3}}{4}$ **81.** 9 small, 4 large **83.** $\frac{1}{3}$ **85.** $\frac{7}{12}$ **87.** $\frac{5}{12}$

Pages 449–452 Lesson 7-6

1. $\sqrt[4]{10}$ **3.** $15^{\frac{1}{3}}$ **5.** 7 **7.** 25

9 $\ell = A^{\frac{1}{2}}$ Write the formula.
$= 169^{\frac{1}{2}}$ $A = 169$
$= \sqrt{169}$ Write in radical form.
$= 13$ ft Simplify.

11. $x^{\frac{3}{5}}$ **13.** $\sqrt{3g}$ **15.** $\frac{g - 2g^{\frac{1}{2}} + 1}{g - 1}$ **17.** $\sqrt[7]{16}$ **19.** $\sqrt{x^9}$
21. $63^{\frac{1}{4}}$ **23.** $5x^{\frac{1}{2}}$ **25.** 4 **27.** $\frac{1}{3}$ **29.** about 2.64 cm
31. $a^{\frac{25}{36}}$ **33.** $\frac{y^{\frac{1}{5}}}{y}$

35 $\frac{\sqrt[4]{27}}{\sqrt[4]{3}} = \frac{27^{\frac{1}{4}}}{3^{\frac{1}{4}}}$ Rational exponents
$= \frac{(3^3)^{\frac{1}{4}}}{3^{\frac{1}{4}}}$ $27 = 3^3$
$= \frac{3^{\frac{3}{4}}}{3^{\frac{1}{4}}}$ Power of a power
$= 3^{\frac{3}{4} - \frac{1}{4}}$ Quotient of powers
$= 3^{\frac{2}{4}}$ Simplify.
$= 3^{\frac{1}{2}}$ Simplify.
$= \sqrt{3}$ Write in radical form.

37. $\sqrt[3]{9} \cdot \sqrt{g}$ **39.** $\frac{x + 4x^{\frac{3}{4}} + 8x^{\frac{1}{2}} + 16x^{\frac{1}{4}} + 16}{x - 16}$
41. $28.27x^{\frac{4}{3}}y^{\frac{2}{5}}z^4$ units^2 **43.** $6 - 2 \cdot 4^{\frac{1}{3}}$ **45.** $x^{\frac{10}{3}}$ **47.** $y^{\frac{3}{20}}$
49. $\sqrt{6}$ **51.** $\frac{w^{\frac{1}{8}}}{w}$

53 $\frac{f^{-\frac{1}{4}}}{4f^{\frac{1}{2}} \cdot f^{-\frac{1}{3}}} = \frac{f^{\frac{1}{3}}}{4f^{\frac{1}{2}} \cdot f^{\frac{1}{4}}}$ $f^{-\frac{1}{4}} = \frac{1}{f^{\frac{1}{4}}} \cdot \frac{1}{f^{-\frac{1}{3}}} = f^{\frac{1}{3}}$
$= \frac{f^{-\frac{1}{3}}}{4f^{\frac{3}{4}}}$ Add powers.
$= \frac{f^{\frac{1}{3}}}{4f^{\frac{3}{4}}} \cdot \frac{f^{\frac{1}{4}}}{f^{\frac{1}{4}}}$ Multiply to rationalize the denominator.
$= \frac{f^{\frac{7}{12}}}{4f}$ $f^{\frac{1}{3}} \cdot f^{\frac{1}{4}} = f^{\frac{1}{3} + \frac{1}{4}}$

55. $c^{\frac{1}{2}}$ **57.** $23\sqrt[6]{23}$ **59.** 3 **61.** $\frac{ab\sqrt{c}}{c}$ **63.** $2\sqrt{6} - 5$

65a.

x	f(x)	g(x)
−2	−8	−1.26
−1	−1	−1
0	0	0
1	1	1
2	8	1.26

65b.
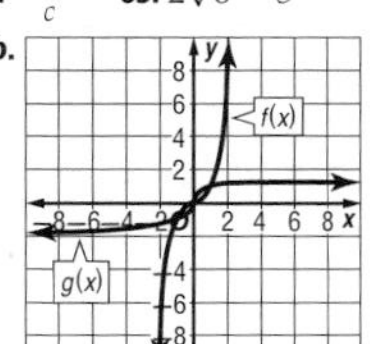

65c. It is a reflection of the line $y = x$. **67a.** Sample answer: $\sqrt[4]{(-16)^3} = \sqrt[4]{-4096}$; there is no real number that when raised to the fourth power results in a negative number. **67b.** Sample answer: $\sqrt[4]{-1}$
69. Sample answer: It may be easier to simplify an expression when it has rational exponents because all the properties of exponents apply. We do not have as many properties dealing directly with radicals. However, we can convert all radicals to rational exponents, and then use the properties of exponents to simplify. **71.** B **73.** C **75.** $9\sqrt{3}$ **77.** $6y^2z\sqrt[3]{7}$
79. -6; $x + h - 2$ **81.** -21; $6x + 6h + 3$
83. 20; $x^2 + 2xh + h^2 - x - h$ **85.** {0, 11} **87.** $\left\{-\frac{3}{4}, 4\right\}$
89. {3} **91.** 5 in. by 4 in. **93.** $3x - 4$ **95.** $x - 8\sqrt{x} + 16$
97. $9x + 6\sqrt{x} + 1$

Pages 456–459 Lesson 7-7

1. 20 **3.** 13
5 $\sqrt[3]{x - 2} = 3$ Original equation
$(\sqrt[3]{x - 2})^3 = 3^3$ Raise each side to the third power.
$x - 2 = 27$ Evaluate each side.
$x = 29$ Add 2 to each side.

7. 2 **9.** 49 **11.** $\frac{27}{2}$ **13a.** about 9.5 s **13b.** about 324 feet **15.** $-\frac{4}{3} \le x \le \frac{77}{3}$ **17.** $1 \le y \le 5$ **19.** $x > 1$
21. $x \le -11$ **23.** 22 **25.** 3 **27.** no real solution **29.** $\frac{1}{4}$
31. 9 **33.** $\frac{81}{16}$ **35.** 1 m **37.** 3 **39.** 83 **41.** 61 **43.** 3
45. 18 **47.** 2 **49.** F **51.** $x \ge 43$ **53.** no real solution

55 $\sqrt{d + 3} + \sqrt{d + 7} > 4$ Original inequality
$\sqrt{d + 3} > 4 - \sqrt{d + 7}$ Subtract $\sqrt{d + 7}$ from each side.
$d + 3 > 16 - 8\sqrt{d + 7} + d + 7$ Square each side.
$\frac{5}{2} < \sqrt{d + 7}$ Simplify.
$\frac{25}{4} < d + 7$ Square each side.
$-\frac{3}{4} < d$ Subtract 7 from each side.
$d > -\frac{3}{4}$ Rewrite inequality.

57. $-\frac{5}{2} \le y \le 2$ **59.** $a > 8$ **61.** $0 \le c < 3$
63. $M = \left(\frac{L}{0.46}\right)^3$

65 $A = \pi r^2$ Original formula
$250{,}000 = \pi r^2$ Replace A with 250,000.
$79{,}577.5 \approx r^2$ Divide each side by π.
$\sqrt{79{,}577.5} \approx r$ Take the square root of each side.
$282.1 \approx r$ Use a calculator.
The radius is about 282 ft.

67. $\sqrt{x + 2} - 7 = -10$
69. never
$\frac{\sqrt{(x^2)^2}}{-x} = x$
$\frac{x^2}{-x} = x$
$x^2 = (x)(-x)$
$x^2 \ne -x^2$

71. They are reciprocals of each other. **73.** 3
75. Sometimes; Sample answer: When the radicand is negative, then there will be extraneous roots. **77.** G
79. A **81.** 81 **83.** $4x^2y^2\sqrt{5}$ **85.** $y = \frac{-x - 3}{2}$
87. $y = \pm\frac{1}{2}\sqrt{x} - \frac{3}{2}$ **89a.** $f(x) \to +\infty$ as $x \to +\infty$, $f(x) \to +\infty$ as $x \to -\infty$ **89b.** even **89c.** 0 **91.** $\frac{1}{6}$
93. $\frac{5}{8}$ **95.** 16 **97.** $2\frac{1}{2}$

Pages 462–466 Chapter 7 Study Guide and Review

1. identity function **3.** composition of functions
5. rationalizing the denominator **7.** inverse relations
9. radical function
11. $[f \circ g](x) = x^2 - 14x + 50$; $[g \circ f](x) = x^2 - 6$
13. $[f \circ g](x) = 20x - 4$; $[g \circ f](x) = 20x - 1$
15. $[f \circ g](x) = x^2 + 4x$; $[g \circ f](x) = x^2 + 2x - 2$

17. $f^{-1}(x) = \frac{x + 6}{5}$
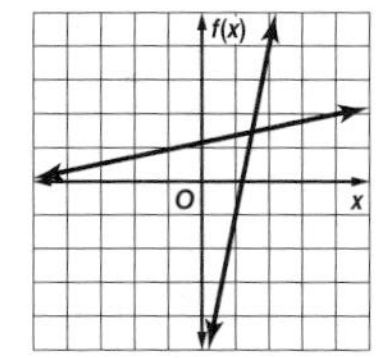

19. $f^{-1}(x) = 2x - 6$
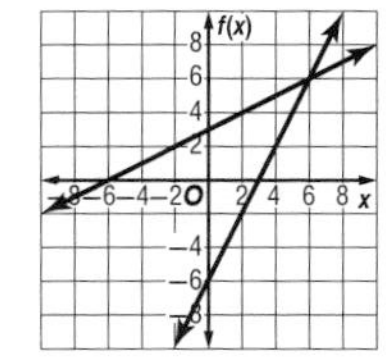

21. $y = \pm\sqrt{x}$
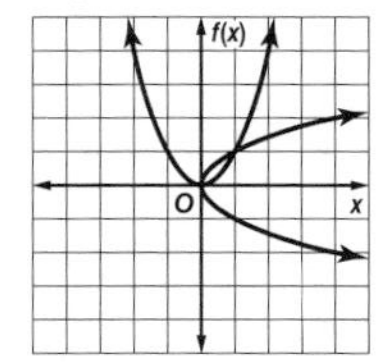

23. $1200 **25.** yes
27. no **29.** no

31.
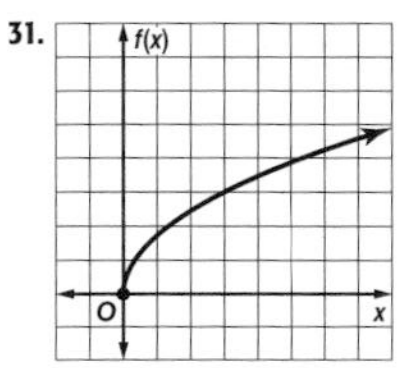

$D = \{x \mid x \ge 0\}$;
$R = \{f(x) \mid f(x) \ge 0\}$

33.
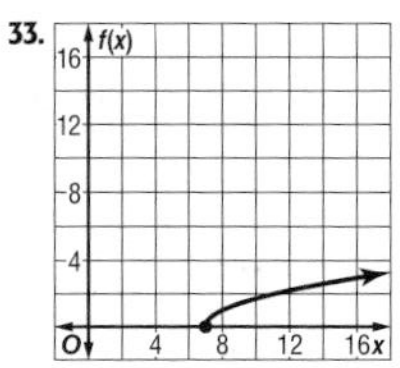

$D = \{x \mid x \ge 7\}$;
$R = \{f(x) \mid f(x) \ge 0\}$

35.
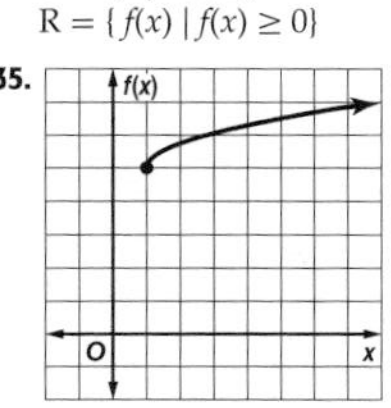

$D = \{x \mid x \ge 1\}$;
$R = \{f(x) \mid f(x) \ge 5\}$
37. about 9.8 in.

39.
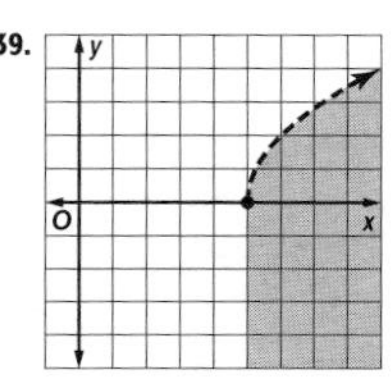

41. ±11 **43.** 6 **45.** $(x^2 + 2)^3$ **47.** $a^2|b^3|$ **49.** 10 m/s
51. $12ab^2\sqrt{ab}$ **53.** $80\sqrt{2}$ **55.** $\frac{m^2\sqrt{6mp}}{p^6}$
57. $-\sqrt{15} - 3\sqrt{2}$ **59.** $x^{\frac{7}{6}}$
61. $\frac{d^{\frac{5}{12}}}{d}$ **63.** 3 **65.** $4a^{\frac{2}{3}}b^{\frac{4}{5}}c^2\pi$ units^2 **67.** $\frac{100}{9}$

For Homework Help, go to Hotmath.com

69. 2 **71.** no solution **73.** 3 **75.** $\frac{1}{3} \le x < \frac{10}{3}$
77. $x \ge \frac{4}{3}$ **79.** no solution **81.** $x > \frac{5}{2}$

Chapter 8 Exponential and Logarithmic Functions and Relations

Page 473 Chapter 8 Get Ready

1. a^{12} **3.** $\frac{-3x^6}{2y^3z^5}$ **5.** 5 g/cm^3

7. $f^{-1}(x) = x + 3$
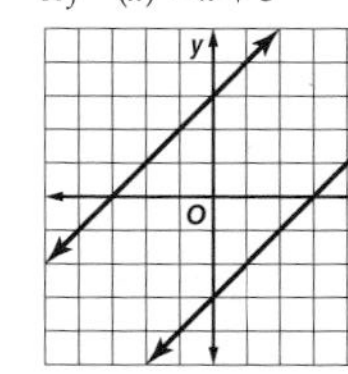

9. $f^{-1}(x) = 4x + 12$
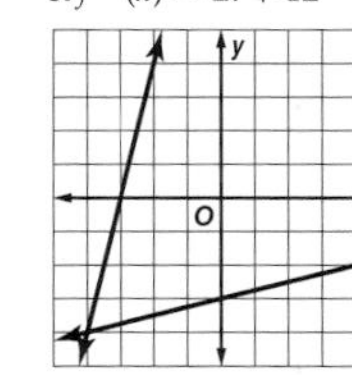

11. $f^{-1}(x) = 3x - 12$
13. no
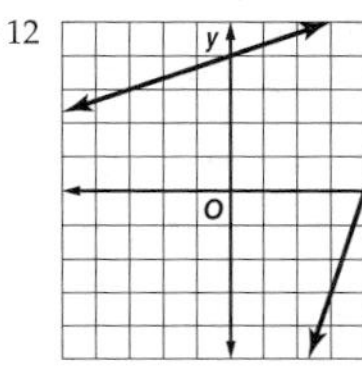

Pages 479–482 Lesson 8-1

1.
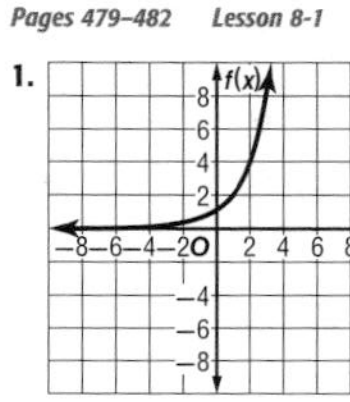

D = {all real numbers};
$R = \{f(x) \mid f(x) > 0\}$

3 Make a table of values. Then plot the points, and sketch the graph.

x	$f(x) = 3^{x-2} + 4$
−2	$3^{-2-2} + 4 = 4\frac{1}{81}$
−1	$3^{-1-2} + 4 = 4\frac{1}{27}$
0	$3^{0-2} + 4 = 4\frac{1}{9}$
1	$3^{1-2} + 4 = 4\frac{1}{3}$
2	$3^{2-2} + 4 = 5$
3	$3^{3-2} + 4 = 7$
4	$3^{4-2} + 4 = 13$

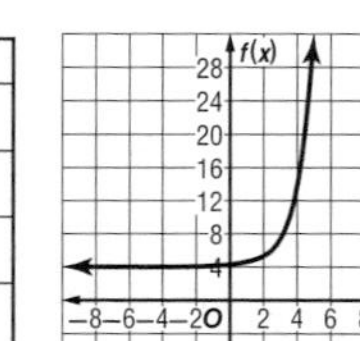

The domain is all real numbers and the range is all real numbers greater than 4.
D = {all real numbers}; $R = \{f(x) \mid f(x) > 4\}$

5. 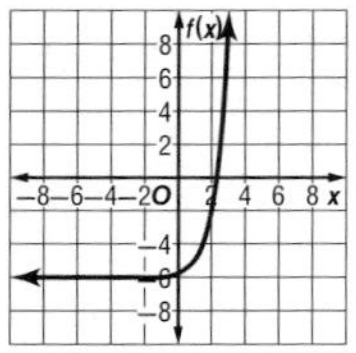
D = {all real numbers}; R = $\{f(x) \mid f(x) > -6\}$

7. 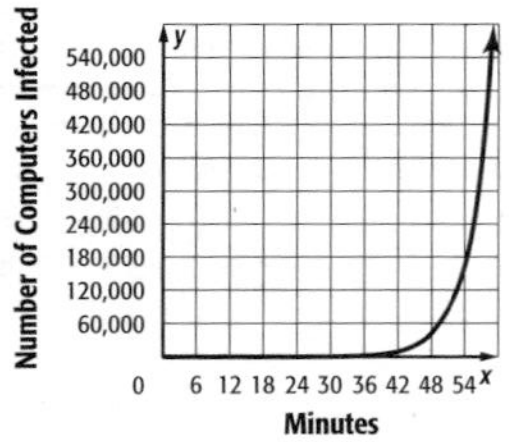

9. 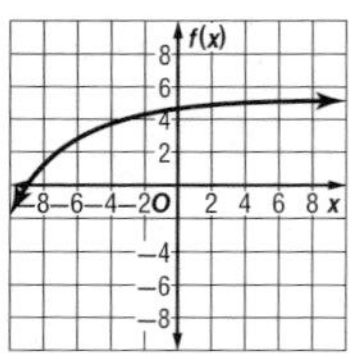
D = {all real numbers}; R = $\{f(x) \mid f(x) < 5\}$

11. 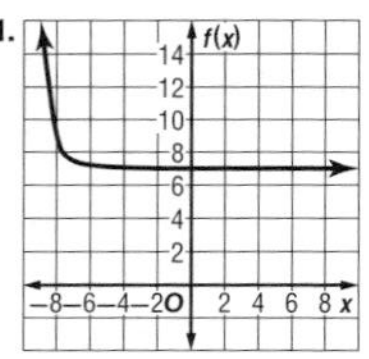
D = {all real numbers}; R = $\{f(x) \mid f(x) > 7\}$

13. 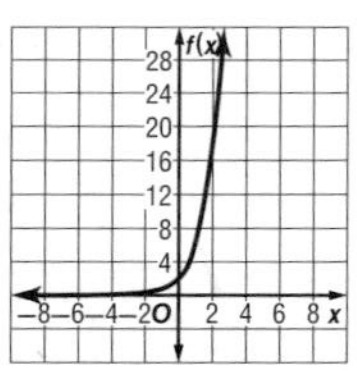
D = {all real numbers}; R = $\{f(x) \mid f(x) > 0\}$

15. 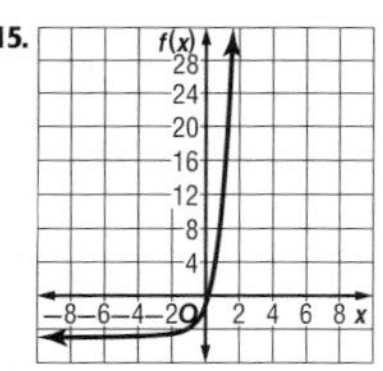
D = {all real numbers}; R = $\{f(x) \mid f(x) > -5\}$

17. 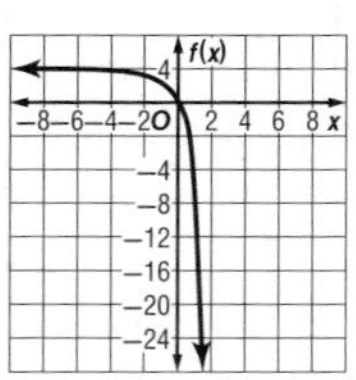
D = {all real numbers}; R = $\{f(x) \mid f(x) < 4\}$

19. $y = a(1 + r)^t$ Equation for exponential growth
$y = 65(1 + 0.3)^t$ $a = 65$ and $r = 0.3$
$y = 65(1.3)^t$ Simplify.

Make a table of values. Then plot the points, and sketch the graph.

t	$y = 65(0.3)^t$
0	$y = 65(1.3)^0 = 65$
2	$y = 65(1.3)^2 \approx 110$
4	$y = 65(1.3)^4 \approx 186$
6	$y = 65(1.3)^6 \approx 314$
8	$y = 65(1.3)^8 \approx 530$
10	$y = 65(1.3)^{10} \approx 896$

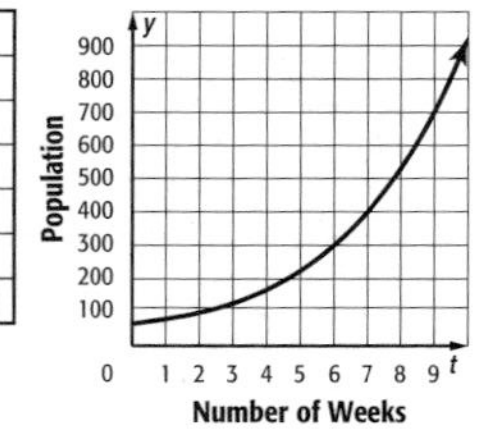

21. 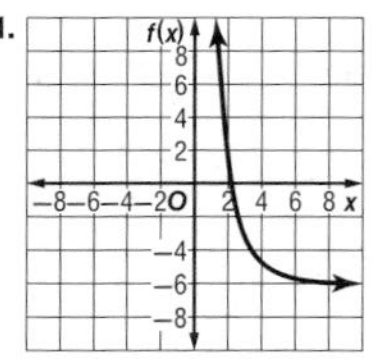
D = {all real numbers}; R = $\{f(x) \mid f(x) > -6\}$

23. 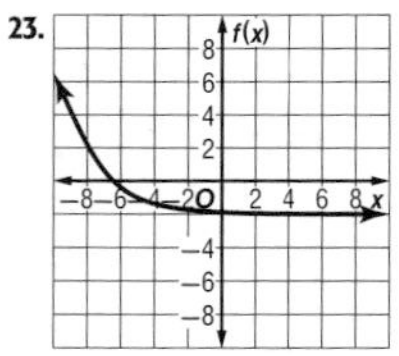
D = {all real numbers}; R = $\{f(x) \mid f(x) > -2\}$

25. 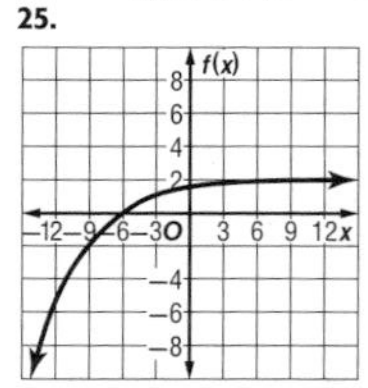
D = {all real numbers}; R = $\{f(x) \mid f(x) < 2\}$

27a. 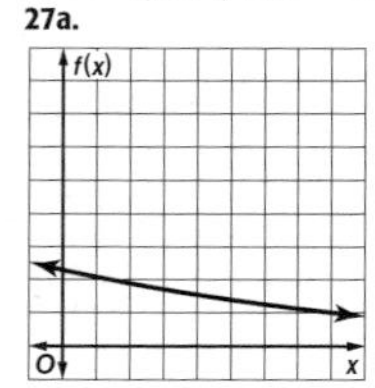

27b. The y-intercept represents the number of pay phones in 1999. The asymptote is the x-axis. The number of pay phones can approach 0, but will never equal 0. This makes sense as there will probably always be a need for some pay phones. **29a.** $f(x) = 18(1.25)^{x-1}$

29b. 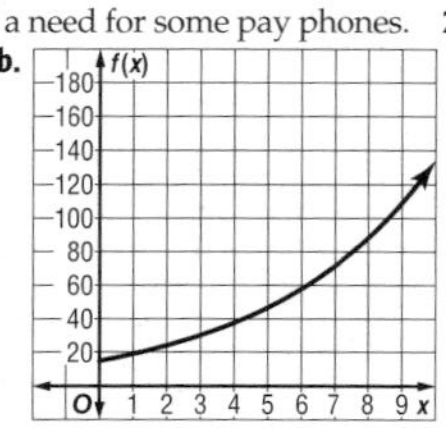

29c. 134
31. $g(x) = 4(2)^{x-3}$ or $g(x) = \frac{1}{2}(2^x)$

33 a. 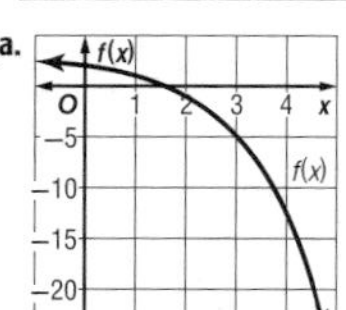

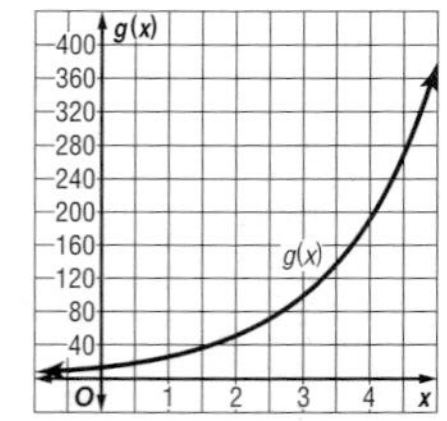
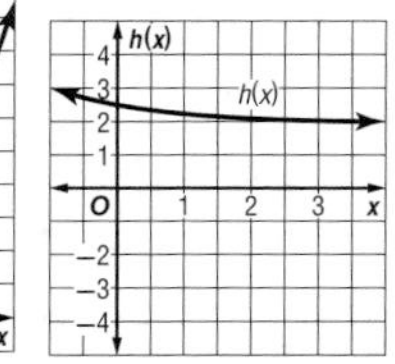

b. Sample answer: The graph of $f(x)$ appears to be the graph of $f(x) = b^x$ reflected across the x-axis. As the values of x increase, the output values decrease.
c. Sample answer: The graphs of $g(x)$ and $h(x)$ appear to be translated to the left.
d. Sample answer: $f(x)$ and $g(x)$ are growth and $h(x)$ is decay; the absolute value of the output is increasing for the growth functions and decreasing for the decay function.
35. Vince; Grady neglected to multiply by the negative sign. **37.** Sample answer: 10 **39.** 12 **41.** H

43. 8 **45.** $x \geq 21$ **47.** $d > -\frac{3}{4}$ **49.** $\frac{y^{\frac{3}{5}}}{y}$ **51.** $3x^{\frac{5}{3}} + 4x^{\frac{8}{3}}$ **53.** $\sqrt{3}$ **55.** about 204.88 ft **57.** $\frac{1}{f^3}$ **59.** $8xy^4$

Pages 488–491 Lesson 8-2

1. 12 **3.** −10 **5a.** $c = 2^{\frac{t}{15}}$ **5b.** 16 cells **7.** $x \geq 4.5$ **9.** 0

11
$81^{a+2} = 3^{3a+1}$ Original equation
$(3^4)^{a+2} = 3^{3a+1}$ Rewrite 81 as 3^4.
$3^{4(a+2)} = 3^{3a+1}$ Power of a Power
$3^{4a+8} = 3^{3a+1}$ Distributive Property
$4a + 8 = 3a + 1$ Property of Equality for Exponential Functions
$a + 8 = 1$ Subtract $3a$ from each side.
$a = -7$ Subtract 8 from each side.

13. $\frac{5}{3}$ **15a.** $y = 10{,}000(1.045)^x$ **15b.** about \$26,336.52 **17.** $y = 256(0.75)^x$ **19.** $y = 144(3.5)^x$ **21.** \$16,755.63 **23.** \$97,362.61 **25.** $b > \frac{1}{5}$ **27.** $d \geq -1$ **29.** $w < \frac{2}{5}$

31 a. $\frac{a}{w^{1.31}} = \frac{170}{45^{1.31}}$ Write a proportion
$a \cdot 45^{1.31} = w^{1.31} \cdot 170$ Cross Products Property
$a = \frac{w^{1.31} \cdot 170}{45^{1.31}}$ Divide each side by $45^{1.31}$.
$a = 1.16w^{1.31}$ Use a calculator.
b. $a = 1.16w^{1.31}$ Write the equation.
$= 1.16(430)^{1.31}$ $w = 430$
≈ 3268 Use a calculator.

33. $\frac{1}{7}$ **35.** $-\frac{4}{13}$ **37.** 1 **39a.** $d = 1.30h^{\frac{3}{2}}$ **39b.** about 1001 cm **41a.** 2, 4, 8, 16

41b.

Cuts	Pieces
1	2
2	4
3	8
4	16

41c. $y = 2^x$ **41d.** $y = 0.003(2)^x$ **41e.** about 3,221,225.47 in.

For Homework Help, go to Hotmath.com

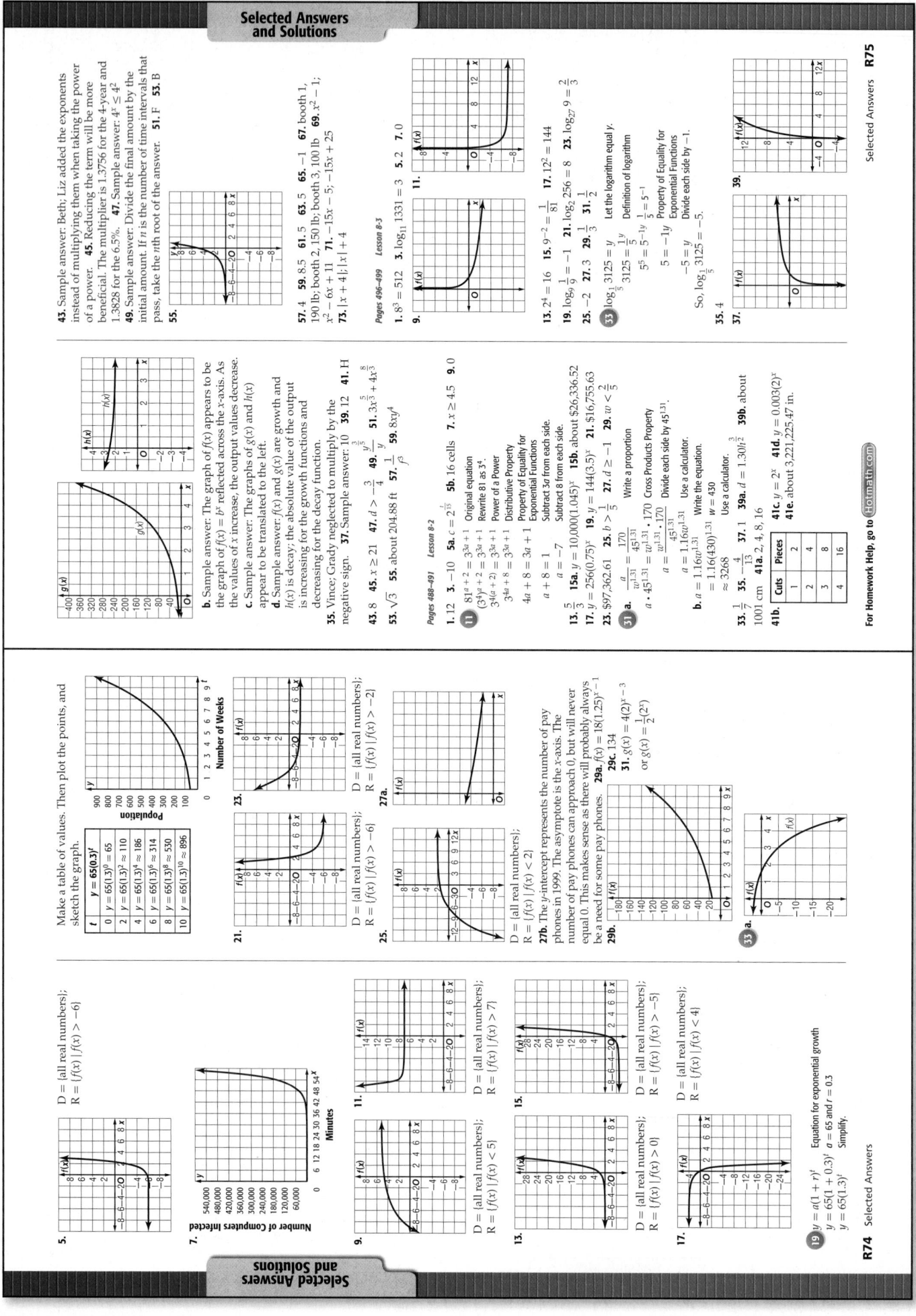

43. Sample answer: Beth; Liz added the exponents instead of multiplying them when taking the power of a power. **45.** Reducing the term will be more beneficial. The multiplier is 1.3756 for the 4-year and 1.3828 for the 6.5%. **47.** Sample answer: $4^x \leq 4^2$ **49.** Sample answer: Divide the final amount by the initial amount. If n is the number of time intervals that pass, take the nth root of the answer. **51.** F **53.** B

55. 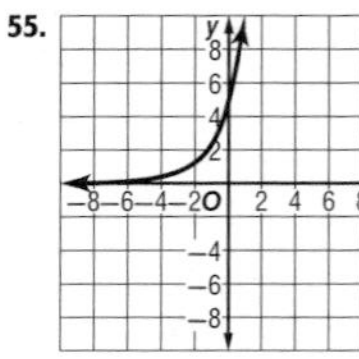

57. 4 **59.** 8.5 **61.** 5 **63.** 5 **65.** −1 **67.** booth 1, 190 lb; booth 2, 150 lb; booth 3, 100 lb **69.** $x^2 - 1$; $x^2 - 6x + 11$ **71.** $-15x - 5$; $-15x + 25$ **73.** $|x + 4|$; $|x| + 4$

Pages 496–499 Lesson 8-3

1. $8^3 = 512$ **3.** $\log_{11} 1331 = 3$ **5.** 2 **7.** 0

9. 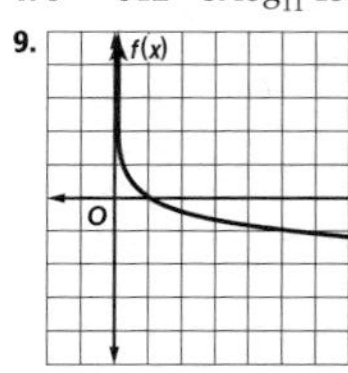

11. 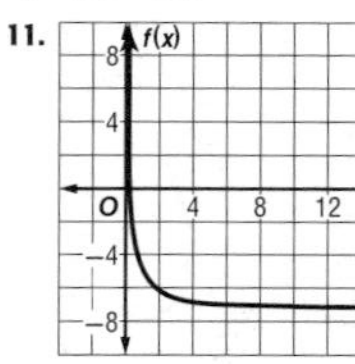

13. $2^4 = 16$ **15.** $9^{-2} = \frac{1}{81}$ **17.** $12^2 = 144$ **19.** $\log_9 \frac{1}{9} = -1$ **21.** $\log_2 256 = 8$ **23.** $\log_{27} 9 = \frac{2}{3}$ **25.** −2 **27.** 3 **29.** $\frac{1}{3}$ **31.** $\frac{1}{2}$

33 $\log_{\frac{1}{5}} 3125 = y$ Let the logarithm equal y.
$3125 = \frac{1}{5}^y$ Definition of logarithm
$5^5 = 5^{-1y}$ $\frac{1}{5} = 5^{-1}$
$5 = -1y$ Property of Equality for Exponential Functions
$-5 = y$ Divide each side by −1.
So, $\log_{\frac{1}{5}} 3125 = -5$.

35. 4

37. 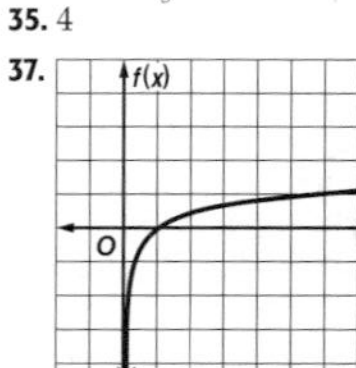

39. 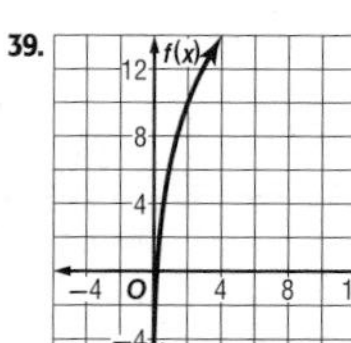

41. 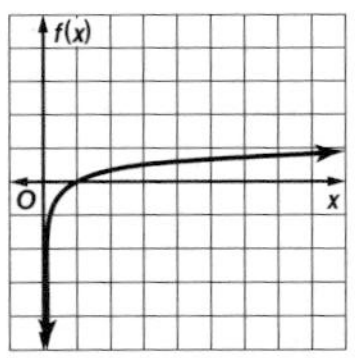
43. 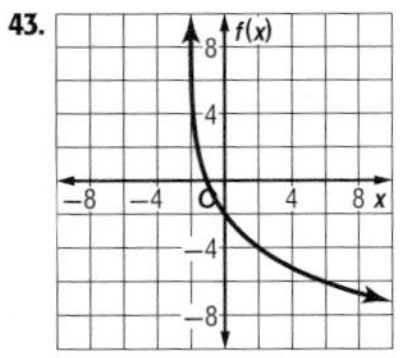
45. 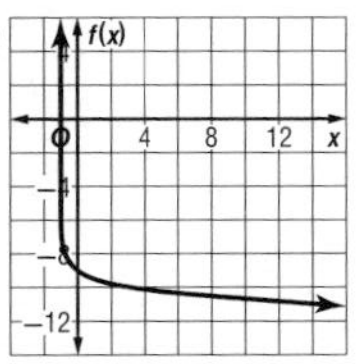
47. 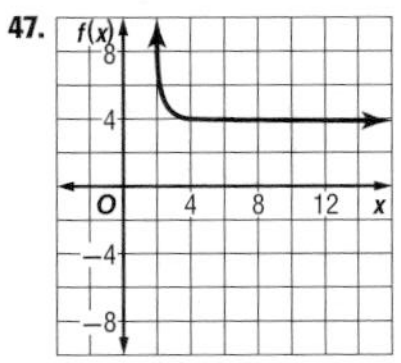

49a. 2 **49b.** 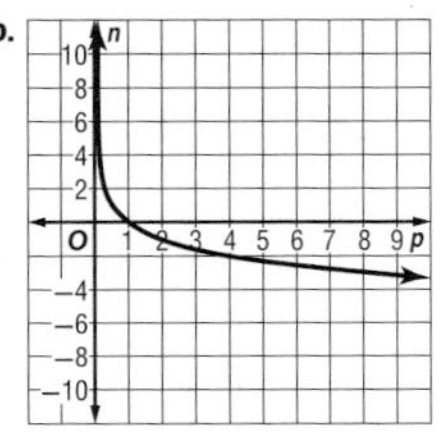

49c. less light; $\frac{1}{8}$

51 This represents a transformation of the graph of $f(x) = \log_2 x$.
$|a| = 4$: The graph expands vertically.
$h = 4$: The graph is translated 4 units to the right.
$k = 6$: The graph is translated 6 units up.

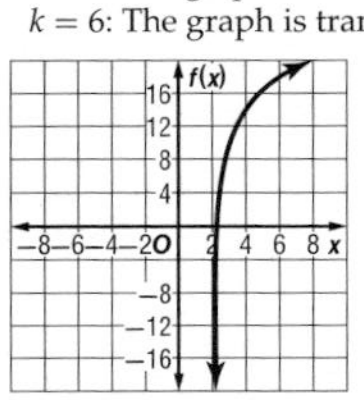

53. 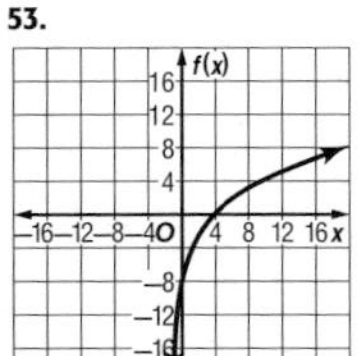

55. 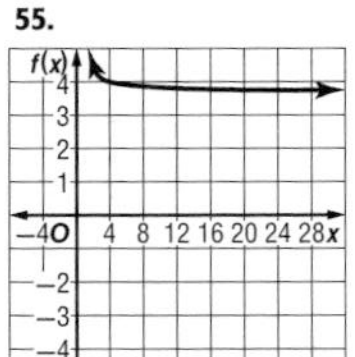

57a. $S(3) \approx 30$, $S(15) = 50$, $S(63) = 70$
57b. If \$3000 is spent on advertising, \$30,000 is returned in sales. If \$15,000 is spent on advertising, \$50,000 is returned in sales. If \$63,000 is spent on advertising, \$70,000 is returned in sales.

57c. **Sales versus Money Spent on Advertising**

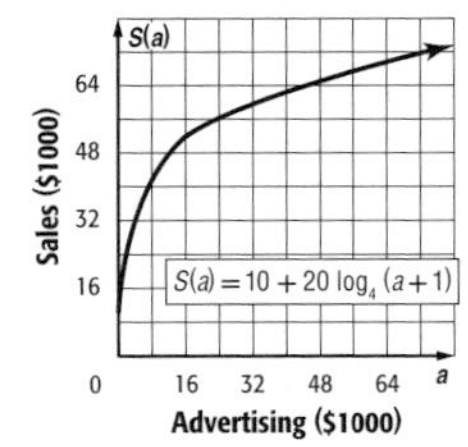

57d. Sample answer: Because eventually the graph plateaus, and no matter how much money you spend you are still returning about the same in sales.

59 a. $\log_{\left(1+\frac{0.24}{12}\right)} \frac{A}{2000} = 12t$ Original formula
$\log_{1.02} \frac{A}{2000} = 12t$ Simplify.
$\frac{A}{2000} = 1.02^{12t}$ Definition of logarithm
$A = 2000 \cdot 1.02^{12t}$ Multiply each side by 2000.

Make a table of values. Then plot the points, and sketch the graph.

t	$A = 2000 \cdot 1.02^{12t}$
0	$A = 2000 \cdot 1.02^{12(0)} = 2000$
2	$A = 2000 \cdot 1.02^{12(2)} \approx 3217$
4	$A = 2000 \cdot 1.02^{12(4)} \approx 5174$
6	$A = 2000 \cdot 1.02^{12(6)} \approx 8322$
8	$A = 2000 \cdot 1.02^{12(8)} \approx 13{,}386$
10	$A = 2000 \cdot 1.02^{12(10)} \approx 21{,}530$

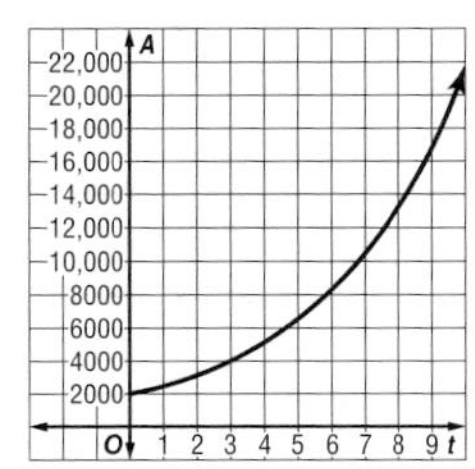

b. From the graph, $A = 4000$ at about $t = 3$. So, it will take approximately 3 years for the debt to double.
c. From the graph, $A = 6000$ at about $t = 4.5$. So, it will take approximately 4.5 years for the debt to triple.
61. Never; if zero were in the domain, the equation would be $y = \log_b 0$.
Then $b^y = 0$.
However, for any real number b, there is no real power that would let $b^y = 0$.
63. $\log_7 51$; Sample answer: $\log_7 51$ equals a little more than 2. $\log_8 61$ equals a little less than 2. $\log_9 71$ equals a little less than 2. Therefore, $\log_7 51$ is the greatest.

65. No; Elisa was closer. She should have $-y = 2$ or $y = -2$ instead of $y = 2$. Matthew used the definition of logarithms incorrectly. **67.** D
69. 80 **71.** $n > 5$ **73.** $n < 3$
75. 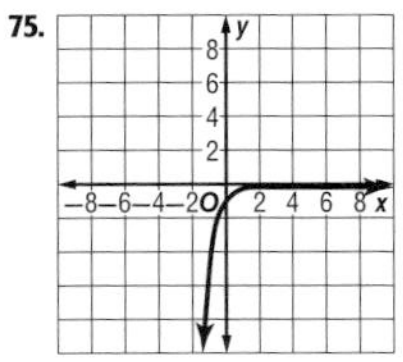
77. 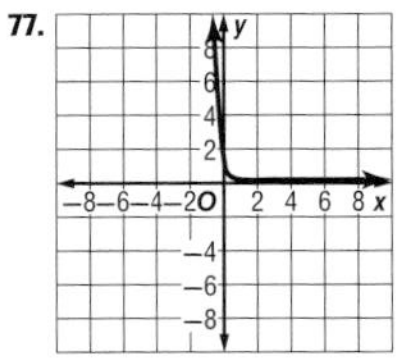

79. $\frac{27\sqrt{15}}{4}$ ft^2 **81.** batteries, \$74; spark plugs, \$58; wiper blades, \$48 **83.** -1 **85.** $x \le -\sqrt{6}$ or $x \ge \sqrt{6}$

Pages 504–507 Lesson 8-4

1. 16 **3.** C **5.** $\left\{x \,\middle|\, 0 < x \le \frac{1}{64}\right\}$ **7.** $\left\{x \,\middle|\, 2 > x > \frac{4}{3}\right\}$
9. 3125 **11.** -2 **13.** 9
15 $\log_{12}(x^2 - 7) = \log_{12}(x + 5)$ Original equation
$x^2 - 7 = x + 5$ Property of Equality for Exponential Functions
$x^2 - x - 7 = 5$ Subtract x from each side.
$x^2 - x - 12 = 0$ Subtract 5 from each side.
$(x - 4)(x + 3) = 0$ Factor.
$x - 4 = 0$ or $x + 3 = 0$ Zero Product Property
$x = 4$ $x = -3$ Solve each equation.
17. 5 **19.** -3 **21.** 318 mph **23.** $\{x \mid x \ge 256\}$
25 $\log_2 x \le -2$ Original inequality
$0 < x \le 2^{-2}$ Property of Inequality for Exponential Functions
$0 < x \le \frac{1}{4}$ Simplify.
The solution is $\left\{x \,\middle|\, 0 < x \le \frac{1}{4}\right\}$.
27. $\left\{x \,\middle|\, 0 < x < \frac{1}{7}\right\}$ **29.** $\left\{x \,\middle|\, \frac{1}{2} < x \le 1\right\}$
31. $\left\{x \,\middle|\, -\frac{5}{12} < x \le 1\right\}$ **33.** $\{x \mid x \ge 8\}$
35a. 37 **35b.** 61
37 a. $\beta = 10\log_{10}\left(\frac{I}{10^{-12}}\right)$ Original equation
$= 10\log_{10}\left(\frac{1}{10^{-12}}\right)$ $I = 10$
$= 10\log_{10}10^{12}$ Write $\frac{1}{10^{-12}}$ as 10^{12}.
$= 10(12)$ or 120 Definition of logarithm
b. $\beta = 10\log_{10}\left(\frac{I}{10^{-12}}\right)$ Original equation
$= 10\log_{10}\left(\frac{10^{-2}}{10^{-12}}\right)$ $I = 10^{-2}$
$= 10\log_{10}10^{10}$ Quotient of Powers Property
$= 10(10)$ or 100 Definition of logarithm
c. Sample answer: The power of the logarithm only changes by 2. The power is the answer to the logarithm. That 2 is multiplied by the 10 before the logarithm. So we expect the decibels to change by 20.
39. $6\frac{17}{20}$ **41.** The logarithmic function of the form $y = \log_b x$ is the inverse of the exponential function of the form $y = b^x$. The domain of one of the two inverse functions is the range of the other. The range of one of the two inverse functions is the domain of the other.
43a. less than **43b.** less than **43c.** no **43d.** infinitely many **45.** C **47.** B **49.** 4 **51.** 3 **53.** -3 **55.** $x \le 0$
57. $a \le -3$ **59.** -8 **61.** 5 ft **63.** x^8 **65.** $8p^6n^3$
67. x^3y^4

Pages 512–515 Lesson 8-5

1. 2.085 **3.** 0.3685 **5.** Mt. Everest: 26,855.44 pascals; Mt. Trisuli: 34,963.34 pascals; Mt. Bonete: 36,028.42 pascals; Mt. McKinley: 39,846.22 pascals; Mt. Logan: 41,261.82 pascals **7.** 2.4182 **9.** 2
11. 13.4403 **13.** 2.1610
15 $\log_4 \frac{4}{3} = \log_4 4 - \log_4 3$ Quotient Property
$= 1 - \log_4 3$ Inverse Property of Exponents and Logarithms
$\approx 1 - 0.7925$ Replace $\log_4 3$ with 0.7925.
≈ 0.2075 Simplify.
17. 1.5 **19.** 2.1606 **21.** 3.4818 **23.** 8 **25.** 2
27 a. $P = \log_{10}\left(1 + \frac{1}{d}\right)$ Original equation
$10^P = 1 + \frac{1}{d}$ Definition of logarithm
$10^P - 1 = \frac{1}{d}$ Subtract 1 from each side.
$d(10^P - 1) = 1$ Multiply each side by d.
$d = \frac{1}{10^P - 1}$ Divide each side by $10^P - 1$.
b. $d = \frac{1}{10^P - 1}$ Write the formula.
$= \frac{1}{10^{0.097} - 1}$ $P = 0.097$
≈ 4 Use a calculator.
c. $P = \log_{10}\left(1 + \frac{1}{d}\right)$ Original equation
$= \log_{10}\left(1 + \frac{1}{1}\right)$ $d = 1$
$= \log_{10} 2$ Simplify.
≈ 0.30103 Replace $\log_{10} 2$ with 0.30103.
The probability is about 30.1%.
29. 2.1133 **31.** 0.1788 **33.** 1.7228 **35.** 2.0478 **37.** 3
39. 5 **41.** $85\frac{1}{3}$ **43.** $\left(\frac{x-2}{256}\right)^{\frac{1}{6}}$ **45.** $\sqrt{6}, -\sqrt{6}$ **47.** 5
49. 12 **51.** false **53.** false **55.** true **57.** false
59a. 10^{12} **59b.** 10^4 or about 10,000 times **61a.** Sample answer: $\log_b \frac{xz}{5} = \log_b x + \log_b z - \log_b 5$ **61b.** Sample answer: $\log_b m^4p^6 = 4\log_b m + 6\log_b p$
61c. Sample answer: $\log_b \frac{j^8k}{h^5} = 8\log_b j + \log_b k - 5\log_b h$
63a. $\log_b 1 = 0$, because $b^0 = 1$. **63b.** $\log_b b = 1$, because $b^1 = b$. **63c.** $\log_b b^x = x$, because $b^x = b^x$.
65. $\log_b 24 \ne \log_b 20 + \log_b 4$; all other choices are equal to $\log_b 24$.
67. $x^{3\log_x 2 - \log_x 5} = x^{3\log_x 2 - \log_x 5}$
$= x^{\log_x 2^3 - \log_x 5}$
$= x^{\log_x 8 - \log_x 5}$
$= x^{\log_x \frac{8}{5}}$
$= \frac{8}{5}$

For Homework Help, go to Hotmath.com

69. D **71.** growing exponentially **73.** $\frac{1}{2}$, 1
75. no solution **77.** $2x$ **79.** 6.3 amps **81.** no **83.** $\frac{3}{5}$
85. 10 **87.** $x > 26$

Pages 519–522 Lesson 8-6

1. 0.6990 **3.** −0.3979 **5.** 3.55×10^{24} ergs **7.** 0.8442

9
$11^{b-3} = 5^b$ Original equation
$\log 11^{b-3} = \log 5^b$ Property of Equality for Logarithmic Functions
$(b-3)\log 11 = b \log 5$ Power Property of Logarithms
$b \log 11 - 3\log 11 = b\log 5$ Distributive Property
$-3\log 11 = b\log 5 - b\log 11$ Subtract $b \log 11$ from each side.
$-3\log 11 = b(\log 5 - \log 11)$ Distributive Property
$\frac{-3\log 11}{\log 5 - \log 11} = b$ Divide each side by log 5 − log 11.
$9.1237 \approx b$ Use a calculator.

11. $\{p \mid p \le 4.4190\}$ **13.** $\frac{\log 23}{\log 4} \approx 2.2618$
15. $\frac{\log 5}{\log 2} \approx 2.3219$ **17.** 1.0414 **19.** 0.9138 **21.** −1.3979
23. 1.7740 **25.** 5.9647 **27.** ±1.1691 **29.** $\{n \mid n > 0.6667\}$
31. $\{y \mid y \ge -3.8188\}$ **33.** $\frac{\log 18}{\log 7} \approx 1.4854$
35. $\frac{\log 16}{\log 2} = 4$ **37.** $\frac{\log 11}{\log 3} \approx 2.1827$

39 **a.** $n = 35[\log_4(t+2)]$ Original equation
$= 35[\log_4(10+2)]$ $t = 10$
$= 35[\log_4(12)]$ Simplify.
$= 35 \cdot \frac{\log_{10} 12}{\log_{10} 4}$ Change of Base Formula
≈ 62.737 Use a calculator.
In 2010, there are about 62.737 thousand, or 62,737 pet owners.
b. $n = 35[\log_4(t+2)]$ Original equation
$80 = 35[\log_4(t+2)]$ $n = 80$
$2.2857 \approx \log_4(t+2)$ Divide each side by 35.
$4^{2.2857} \approx t + 2$ Definition of logarithm
$22 \approx t$
In 22 years after 2000, or in 2022, there will be 80,000 pet owners.

41. 3.3578 **43.** −0.0710 **45.** 4.7393 **47.** $\{x \mid x \ge 2.3223\}$
49. $\{x \mid x \le 0.9732\}$ **51.** $\{p \mid p \le 2.9437\}$
53. $\frac{\log 12}{\log 4} \approx 1.7925$ **55.** $\frac{\log 2}{\log 8} = 0.3333$
57. $\frac{\log 7.29}{\log 5} \approx 1.2343$ **59a.** 113.03 cents
59b. about 218 Hz

61
$4^{x^2-3} = 16$ Original equation
$4^{x^2-3} = 4^2$ Rewrite 16 as 4^2.
$x^2 - 3 = 2$ Property of Equality for Exponential Functions
$x^2 = 5$ Add 3 to each side.
$x = \pm\sqrt{5}$ Take the square root of each side.
$\approx \pm 2.2361$ Use a calculator.

63. 3.5 **65.** −3.8188 **67a.** The solution is between 1.8 and 1.9. **67b.** (1.85, 13) **67c.** Yes; all methods produce the solution of 1.85. They all should produce the same result because you are starting with the same equation. If they do not, then an error was made.

69. $\log_{\sqrt{a}} 3 = \log_a x$ Original equation
$\frac{\log_a 3}{\log_a \sqrt{a}} = \log_a x$ Change of Base Formula
$\frac{\log_a 3}{\frac{1}{2}} = \log_a x$ $\sqrt{a} = a^{\frac{1}{2}}$
$2\log_a 3 = \log_a x$ Multiply numerator and denominator by 2.
$\log_a 3^2 = \log_a x$ Power Property of Logarithms
$3^2 = x$ Property of Equality for Logarithmic Functions
$9 = x$

71. $\log_3 27 = 3$ and $\log_{27} 3 = \frac{1}{3}$; Conjecture: $\log_a b = \frac{1}{\log_b a}$
Proof: $\log_a b \stackrel{?}{=} \frac{1}{\log_b a}$ Original statement
$\frac{\log_b b}{\log_b a} \stackrel{?}{=} \frac{1}{\log_b a}$ Change of Base Formula
$\frac{1}{\log_b a} = \frac{1}{\log_b a}$ Inverse Property of Exponents and Logarithms

73. B **75.** G **77.** 14 **79.** 15 **81.** 2 **83.** −4, 3
85. $32x^3 + 8x^2 - 24x + 16$ **87.** $2^x = 5$ **89.** $5^2 = 25$
91. $6^4 = x$

Pages 529–531 Lesson 8-7

1. $\ln 30 = x$ **3.** $\ln x = 3$ **5.** $7 \ln 2$ **7.** ln 17496
9. 2.0794 **11.** 0.1352 **13.** 993.6527 **15.** $\{x \mid -25.0855 < x < 15.0855, x \ne -5\}$ **17.** $\{x \mid x > 3.3673\}$
19. about 58 min **21.** $\ln 0.1 = -5x$ **23.** $5.4 = e^x$
25. $e^{36} = x + 4$ **27.** $e^7 = e^x$ **29.** 7 ln 10

31 $7\ln\frac{1}{2} + 5\ln 2 = 7\ln 2^{-1} + 5\ln 2$ Rewrite $\frac{1}{2}$ as 2^{-1}.
$= \ln 2^{-7} + \ln 2^5$ Power Property of Logarithms
$= \ln(2^{-7})(2^5)$ Product Property of Logarithms
$= \ln 2^{-2}$ Simplify.
$= -2\ln 2$ Power Property of Logarithms

33. $\ln 81x^6$ **35.** 3.7955 **37.** 0.6931 **39.** −0.5596
41. $\{x \mid x \le 2.1633\}$ **43.** $\{x \mid x > 8.0105\}$
45. $\{x \mid x < -239.8802$ or $x > 239.8802\}$

47 **a.** $A = Pe^{rt}$ Continuous Compounding Formula
$= 800e^{(0.045)(5)}$ $P = 800, r = 0.045, t = 5$
$= 800e^{0.225}$ Simplify.
≈ 1001.86 Use a calculator.
About $1001.86 will be in the account.
b. $A = Pe^{rt}$ Continuous Compounding Formula
$1600 = 800e^{(0.045)t}$ $A = 2 \cdot 800$ or 1600, $P = 800$, $r = 0.045$
$2 = e^{0.045t}$ Divide each side by 800.
$\ln 2 = \ln e^{0.045t}$ Property of Equality of Logarithms
$\ln 2 = 0.045t$ $\ln e^x = x$
$\frac{\ln 2}{0.045} = t$ Divide each side by 0.045.
$15.4 \approx t$ Use a calculator.
It would take about 15.4 years to double your money.

c. $A = Pe^{rt}$ Continuous Compounding Formula
$1600 = 800e^{r(9)}$ $A = 1600, P = 800, t = 9$
$2 = e^{9r}$ Divide each side by 800.
$\ln 2 = \ln e^{9r}$ Property of Equality of Logarithms
$\ln 2 = 9r$ $\ln e^x = x$
$\frac{\ln 2}{9} = r$ Divide each side by 9.
$0.077 \approx r$ Use a calculator.
You would need a rate of about 7.7%.
d. $A = Pe^{rt}$ Continuous Compounding Formula
$10{,}000 = Pe^{(0.0475)(12)}$ $A = 10{,}000, r = 0.0475, t = 12$
$10{,}000 = Pe^{0.57}$ Simplify.
$\frac{10{,}000}{e^{0.57}} = P$ Divide each side by $e^{0.57}$.
$5655.25 \approx P$ Use a calculator.
You would need to deposit about $5655.25.

49. $4\ln 2 - 3\ln 5$ **51.** $\ln x + 4\ln y - 3\ln z$
53. −0.8340 **55.** 1.1301

57a.

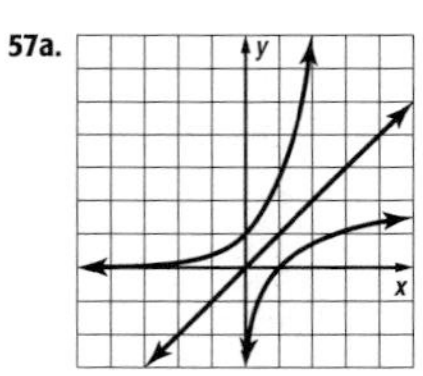

57b. y-axis; $a(x) = -e^x$

57c. $\ln(-x)$ is a reflection across the y-axis. $-\ln x$ is a reflection across the x-axis.

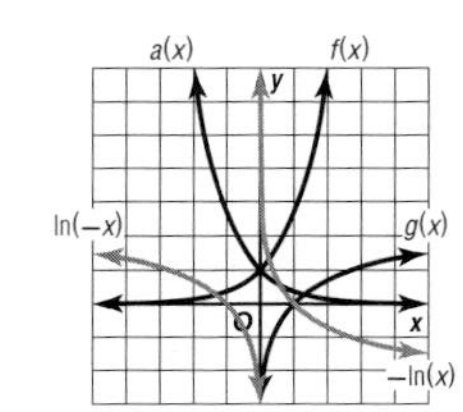

57d. Sample answer: No; these functions are reflections along $y = -x$, which indicates that they are not inverses.
59. Let $p = \ln a$ and $q = \ln b$. That means that $e^p = a$ and $e^q = b$.
$ab = e^p \times e^q$
$ab = e^{p+q}$ $\ln e^{(p+q)} = (p+q)\ln e = p + q$ $\ln e = 1$
$\ln(ab) = (p+q)$
$\ln(ab) = \ln a + \ln b$
61. Sample answer: $e^{\ln 3}$ **63.** B **65.** G **67.** 5.7279
69. $x < 7.3059$ **71.** $x \ge 5.8983$ **73.** 10 decibels
75. $x^2 + 2x + 3$ **77.** $\frac{2}{3}$ **79.** $-\frac{8}{3}$ **81.** $\frac{5}{3}$

Pages 537–539 Lesson 8-8

1a. 5.545×10^{-10} **1b.** 1,578,843,530 yr **1c.** about 30.48 mg **1d.** 3,750, 120,003 yr

3a.

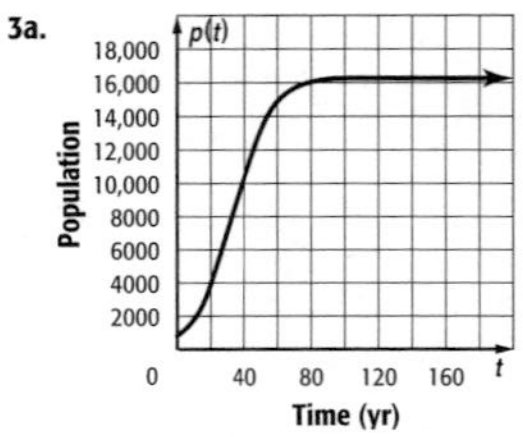

3b. $P(t) = 16{,}500$
3c. 16,500
3d. about 102 years

5 **a.** $y = 80e^{kt}$ Original formula
$675 = 80e^{k(30)}$ $y = 675, t = 30$
$8.4375 = e^{30k}$ Divide each side by 80.
$\ln 8.4375 = \ln e^{30k}$ Property of Equality for Logarithmic Functions
$\ln 8.4375 = 30k$ $\ln e^x = x$
$\frac{\ln 8.4375}{30} = k$ Divide each side by 30.
$0.071 \approx k$ Use a calculator.
b. $y = 80e^{kt}$ Original formula
$6000 = 80e^{(0.071)t}$ $y = 6000, k \approx 0.071$
$75 = e^{0.071t}$ Divide each side by 80.
$\ln 75 = \ln e^{0.071t}$ Property of Equality for Logarithmic Functions
$\ln 75 = 0.071t$ $\ln e^x = x$
$\frac{\ln 75}{0.071} = t$ Divide each side by 0.071.
$60.8 \approx t$ Use a calculator.
The bacteria will reach a population of 6000 cells in about 60.8 minutes.
c. $35e^{0.0978t} > 80e^{0.071t}$ Formula for exponential growth
$\ln 35e^{0.0978t} > \ln 80e^{0.071t}$ Property of Inequality for Logarithms
$\ln 35 + \ln e^{0.0978t} > \ln 80 + \ln e^{0.071t}$ Product Property of Logarithms
$\ln 35 + 0.0978t > \ln 80 + 0.071t$ $\ln e^x = x$
$0.0268t > \ln 80 - \ln 35$ Subtract $(0.071t + \ln 35)$ from each side.
$t > \frac{\ln 80 - \ln 35}{0.0268}$ Divide each side by 0.0268.
$t > 30.85$ Use a calculator.
The number of cells of this bacteria exceed the number of cells in the other bacteria in about 30.85 minutes.

7
$y = ae^{-0.00012t}$ Equation for the decay of Carbon-14
$0.85a = ae^{-0.00012t}$ $y = 0.85a$
$0.85 = e^{-0.00012t}$ Divide each side by a.
$\ln 0.85 = \ln e^{-0.00012t}$ Property of Equality for Logarithmic Functions
$\ln 0.85 = -0.00012t$ $\ln e^x = x$
$\frac{\ln 0.85}{-0.00012} = t$ Divide each side by −0.00012.
$1354 \approx t$ Use a calculator.
The bone is about 1354 years old.

9. about 14.85 billion yr **11.** about 20.1 yr

13a.
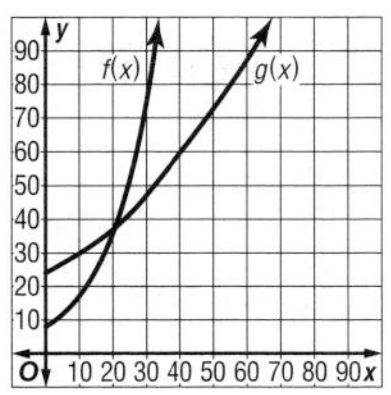

13b. The graphs intersect at $t = 20.79$. Sample answer: This intersection indicates the point at which both functions determine the same population at the same time.

13c. Sample answer: The logistic function $g(t)$ is a more accurate estimate of the country's population since $f(t)$ will continue to grow exponentially and $g(t)$ considers limitations on population growth such as food supply. **15.** $t \approx 113.45$ **17.** Sample answer: The spread of the flu throughout a small town. The growth of this is limited to the population of the town itself. **19.** C **21.** C **23.** $\ln y = 7$ **25.** $5x^4 = e^9$ **27.** $\frac{1}{6}$ **29.** $\frac{5}{8}$ **31.** 16 **33.** $2\frac{1}{2}$

Pages 541–544 Chapter 8 Study Guide and Review

1. exponential growth **3.** common logarithms **5.** change of base formula **7.** logarithmic function **9.** natural logarithm

11.
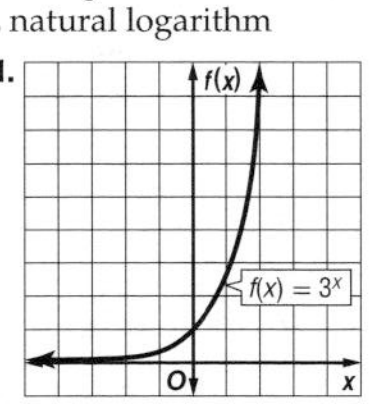

D = all real numbers
R = $\{f(x) \mid f(x) > 0\}$

13.
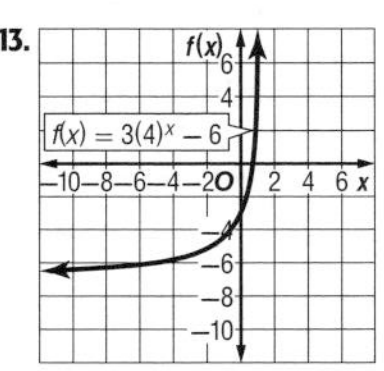

D = all real numbers
R = $\{f(x) \mid f(x) > -6\}$

15.
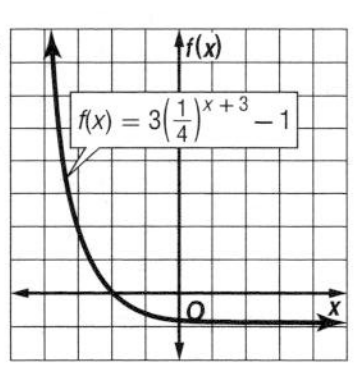

D = all real numbers
R = $\{f(x) \mid f(x) > -1\}$
17a. $f(x) = 120{,}000(0.97)^x$
17b. about 88,491
19. −7 **21.** $\frac{9}{41}$
23. $x \leq -\frac{2}{5}$
25. $2^{-4} = \frac{1}{16}$
27. 4

29.
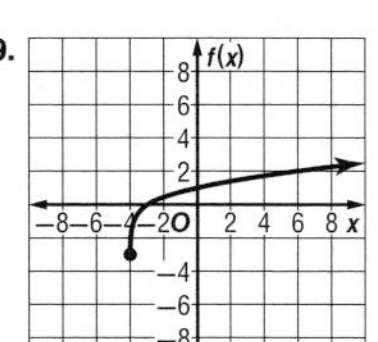

31. $x = 64$ **33.** $0 < x < 64$
35. no solution
37. no solution
39. 1.2920 **41.** 0.8614
43. −0.4307 **45.** $a = 3$
47. $n = 5$ **49.** $x \approx 2.4650$
51. $m \approx 0.6356$
53. $n > 0.5786$
55a. about 8.2 years

55b. about 13.9 years **57.** $x \approx -1.9459$ **59.** $x > 1.9459$ **61.** $x < -2.8904$ **63.** \$1054.69 **65.** about 4.2%

Chapter 9 Rational Functions and Relations

Page 551 Chapter 9 Get Ready

1. $x = \frac{15}{14}$ **3.** $k = \frac{32}{5}$ **5.** 27 gallons **7.** $\frac{1}{18}$ **9.** $\frac{43}{6}$ **11.** $p = 27$ **13.** $k = 17.5$

Pages 557–561 Lesson 9-1

1. $\frac{x+3}{x+8}$ **3.** D

5 $\frac{a^2x - b^2x}{by - ay} = \frac{x(a^2 - b^2)}{y(b-a)}$ Factor.
$= \frac{x(a-b)(a+b)}{y(b-a)}$ Factor.
$= \frac{-x(b-a)(a+b)}{y(b-a)}$ $a - b = -1(b-a)$
$= \frac{-x(b-a)(a+b)}{y(b-a)}$ Eliminate common factors.
$= \frac{-x(a+b)}{y}$ Simplify.

7. $\frac{2x^2}{3aby^2}$ **9.** $\frac{(a-b)(a+1)}{12(a-1)}$ **11.** 4 **13.** $\frac{x(x+6)}{x+4}$ **15.** $\frac{(x+3)(x-z)}{4}$ **17.** $\frac{x(x+2)}{6(x+5)}$ **19.** I **21.** $\frac{x^2}{x+6}$ **23.** $-\frac{c+4}{c+5}$ **25.** $\frac{c}{4ab^2f^2}$ **27.** $\frac{32b}{3ac^3f^2}$ **29.** $\frac{5a^4c}{3b}$

31 $\frac{y^2 + 8y + 15}{y - 6} \cdot \frac{y^2 - 9y + 18}{y^2 - 9}$
$= \frac{(y+3)(y+5)}{y-6} \cdot \frac{(y-3)(y-6)}{(y-3)(y+3)}$ Factor.
$= \frac{(y+3)(y+5)}{y-6} \cdot \frac{(y-3)(y-6)}{(y-3)(y+3)}$
$= y + 5$ Simplify.

33. $\frac{(x+4)(x+2)}{2(x-5)}$ **35.** $\frac{(x-3)(x+1)}{6(x+7)}$ **37.** $\frac{-a^2(a+b)}{b^4}$ **39a.** $\frac{33}{121}$ **39b.** $\frac{33+m}{121+a}$ **41a.** $T(x) = \frac{0.4}{x+3}$
41b. about 3.9 mm thick **43.** $\frac{1}{4}$ **45.** $\frac{x(x+2)(x-1)}{(x+3)(x-7)}$

47 $\frac{20x^2y^6z^{-2}}{3a^3c^2} \cdot \left(\frac{16x^3y^3}{9acz}\right)^{-1}$
$= \frac{20x^2y^6z^{-2}}{3a^3c^2} \cdot \frac{9acz}{16x^3y^3}$ $\left(\frac{16x^3y^3}{9acz}\right)^{-1} = \frac{9acz}{16x^3y^3}$
$= \frac{20x^2y^6}{3a^3c^2z^2} \cdot \frac{9acz}{16x^3y^3}$ $z^{-2} = \frac{1}{z^2}$
$= \frac{2 \cdot 2 \cdot 5 \cdot x \cdot x \cdot y \cdot y \cdot y \cdot y \cdot y \cdot y \cdot 3 \cdot 3 \cdot a \cdot c \cdot z}{3 \cdot a \cdot a \cdot a \cdot c \cdot c \cdot z \cdot z \cdot 2 \cdot 2 \cdot 2 \cdot 2 \cdot x \cdot x \cdot x \cdot y \cdot y \cdot y}$ Factor.
$= \frac{2 \cdot 2 \cdot 5 \cdot x \cdot x \cdot y \cdot y \cdot y \cdot y \cdot y \cdot y \cdot 3 \cdot 3 \cdot a \cdot c \cdot z}{3 \cdot a \cdot a \cdot a \cdot c \cdot c \cdot z \cdot z \cdot 2 \cdot 2 \cdot 2 \cdot 2 \cdot x \cdot x \cdot x \cdot y \cdot y \cdot y}$ Eliminate common factors.
$= \frac{5 \cdot y \cdot y \cdot y \cdot 3}{a \cdot a \cdot c \cdot z \cdot 2 \cdot 2 \cdot x}$ Simplify.
$= \frac{15y^3}{4a^2cxz}$ Simplify.

49. $\frac{2(4x+1)(2x+1)}{5(2x-1)(x+2)}$ **51.** $\frac{2x+1}{-9x(x+2)}$

53. $\frac{x(x-2)(x+8)}{2(2x-1)(3x+1)}$ **55.** $\frac{-2(x-8)(x+4)(x-2)(x+1)}{(2x+1)^2(x^2+2x-6)}$

57 **a.** 5 tracks $\cdot \frac{2 \text{ miles}}{1 \text{ track}} \cdot \frac{5280 \text{ feet}}{1 \text{ mile}} \cdot \frac{1 \text{ car}}{75 \text{ feet}}$
b. 5 tracks $\cdot \frac{2 \text{ miles}}{1 \text{ track}} \cdot \frac{5280 \text{ feet}}{1 \text{ mile}} \cdot \frac{1 \text{ car}}{75 \text{ feet}}$
$= 5 \text{ tracks} \cdot \frac{2 \text{ miles}}{1 \text{ track}} \cdot \frac{15 \cdot 352 \text{ feet}}{1 \text{ mile}} \cdot \frac{1 \text{ car}}{5 \cdot 15 \text{ feet}}$
$= \frac{1 \cdot 2 \cdot 352 \cdot 1 \text{ car}}{1 \cdot 1 \cdot 1 \cdot 1}$
$= 704$ cars
c. 704 cars $\cdot \frac{8 \text{ attendants}}{1 \text{ car}} \cdot \frac{45 \text{ s}}{1 \text{ attendant}} \cdot \frac{1 \text{ min}}{60 \text{ s}} \cdot \frac{1 \text{ h}}{60 \text{ min}}$
$= 704 \text{ cars} \cdot \frac{8 \text{ attendants}}{1 \text{ car}} \cdot \frac{45 \text{ s}}{1 \text{ attendant}} \cdot \frac{1 \text{ min}}{60 \text{ s}} \cdot \frac{1 \text{ h}}{60 \text{ min}}$
$= \frac{704 \cdot 8 \cdot 45 \cdot 1 \cdot 1 \text{ h}}{1 \cdot 1 \cdot 60 \cdot 60}$
$= 70.4$ hours

59. Sample answer: The two expressions are equivalent except that the rational expression is undefined at $x = 3$. **61.** $x^2 + x - 6$ **63.** Sample answer: Sometimes; with a denominator like $x^2 + 2$, in which the denominator cannot equal 0, the rational expression can be defined for all values of x. **65.** Sample answer: When the original expression was simplified, a factor of x was taken out of the denominator. If x were to equal 0, then this expression would be undefined. So, the simplified expression is also undefined for x. **67.** I **69.** 4π **71.** 0.2877 **73.** 0.2747 **75.** $10^{1.7}$ or about 50 times **77.** $2y\sqrt[3]{2}$ **79.** $2ab^2\sqrt{10a}$ **81.** $10a - 2b$ **83.** $-3y - 3y^2$ **85.** $x^2 + 9x + 18$

Pages 565–568 Lesson 9-2

1. $80x^3y^3$ **3.** $3y(y-3)(y-5)$ **5.** $\frac{48y^4 + 25x^2}{20xy^3}$ **7.** $\frac{21b^4 - 2}{36ab^3}$ **9.** $\frac{9x+15}{(x+3)(x+6)}$ **11.** $\frac{x-11}{3(x+2)(x-2)}$ **13.** $\frac{14x-10}{(x+1)(x-2)}$ **15.** $\frac{3y+2}{y+3}$ **17.** $\frac{2a+5b}{3b-8a}$ **19.** $180x^2y^4z^2$ **21.** $6(x+4)(2x-1)(2x+3)$ **23.** $\frac{28by^2z - 9bx}{105x^3y^4z}$ **25.** $\frac{20x^2y + 120y + 6x^2}{15x^3y}$ **27.** $\frac{15b^3 + 100ab^2 - 216a}{240ab^3}$

29 $\frac{6}{y^2 - 2y - 35} + \frac{4}{y^2 + 9y + 20}$
$= \frac{6}{(y-7)(y+5)} + \frac{4}{(y+4)(y+5)}$ Factor denominators.
$= \frac{6(y+4)}{(y-7)(y+5)(y+4)} + \frac{4(y-7)}{(y+4)(y+5)(y-7)}$ Multiply by missing factors.
$= \frac{6y + 24 + 4y - 28}{(y-7)(y+5)(y+4)}$ Add the numerators.
$= \frac{10y - 4}{(y-7)(y+5)(y+4)}$ Simplify.

31. $\frac{-10x - 10}{(2x-1)(x+6)(x-3)}$ **33.** $\frac{2x^2 + 32x}{3(x-2)(x+3)(2x+5)}$ **35.** $\frac{1000x + 800y}{x(x+2y)}$

37 $\frac{\frac{4}{x+5} + \frac{9}{x-6}}{\frac{5}{x-6} - \frac{8}{x+5}} = \frac{\frac{4(x-6)}{(x+5)(x-6)} + \frac{9(x+5)}{(x+5)(x-6)}}{\frac{5(x+5)}{(x+5)(x-6)} - \frac{8(x-6)}{(x+5)(x-6)}}$
$= \frac{\frac{4x - 24 + 9x + 45}{(x+5)(x-6)}}{\frac{5x + 25 - 8x + 48}{(x+5)(x-6)}}$ Simplify the numerator and denominator.
$= \frac{\frac{13x+21}{(x+5)(x-6)}}{\frac{-3x+73}{(x+5)(x-6)}}$ Combine like terms.
$= \frac{13x+21}{(x+5)(x-6)} \div \frac{-3x+73}{(x+5)(x-6)}$ Write as a division expression.
$= \frac{13x+21}{(x+5)(x-6)} \cdot \frac{(x+5)(x-6)}{-3x+73}$ Multiply by the reciprocal of the divisor.
$= \frac{13x+21}{-3x+73}$ Simplify.

39. $\frac{-x^2 + 33x + 16}{12x^2 + 11x - 27}$ **41.** $420x^5y^4z^3$ **43.** $(x+4)(x-4)(2x+1)(x-7)$ **45.** $\frac{360a^2 + 5a - 36}{60a^2}$ **47.** $\frac{42x+41}{6(3x-1)(x+8)(2x+3)}$ **49.** 0 **51.** $\frac{5a-11}{6}$ **53.** $(x-3)(x+2)$ to 1 **55.** $-\frac{3}{2}$ **57.** −1

59a. $y = \frac{70x}{x - 70}$ **59b.** Sample answer: When the object is 70 mm away, y needs to be 0, which is impossible.

61 **a.** $P_0\left(\frac{s_0}{s_0 - x}\right) - P_0\left(\frac{s_0}{s_0 - y}\right) = \frac{P_0s_0}{s_0 - x} - \frac{P_0s_0}{s_0 - y}$
$= \frac{P_0s_0(s_0 - y)}{(s_0 - x)(s_0 - y)} - \frac{P_0s_0(s_0 - x)}{(s_0 - x)(s_0 - y)}$
$= \frac{P_0s_0(s_0 - y) - P_0s_0(s_0 - x)}{(s_0 - x)(s_0 - y)}$
$= \frac{P_0s_0s_0 - P_0s_0y - P_0s_0s_0 - P_0s_0x}{(s_0 - x)(s_0 - y)}$
$= \frac{P_0s_0x - P_0s_0y}{(s_0 - x)(s_0 - y)}$
b. $\frac{P_0s_0x - P_0s_0y}{(s_0 - x)(s_0 - y)} = \frac{(500)(332)(70) - (500)(332)(45)}{(332 - 70)(332 - 45)}$
$P_0 = 500, s_0 = 332, x = 70, y = 45$
$= \frac{4{,}150{,}000}{75{,}194}$ Simplify.
≈ 55.2 Hz Simplify.

63. $\frac{-3x^3 - 2x^2 + 16x - 5}{4x^3 + 18x^2 - 6x}$ **65.** Sample answer: $20a^4b^2c$, $15ab^6$, $9abc$ **67.** D **69.** F **71.** $-\frac{4bc}{33a}$ **73.** $(n+3)(n-6)$

75. D = $\{x \mid x \geq -0.5\}$,
R = $\{y \mid y \leq 0\}$

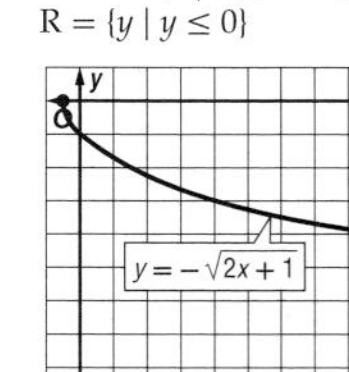

77. D = $\{x \mid x \geq -6\}$,
R = $\{y \mid y \geq -3\}$

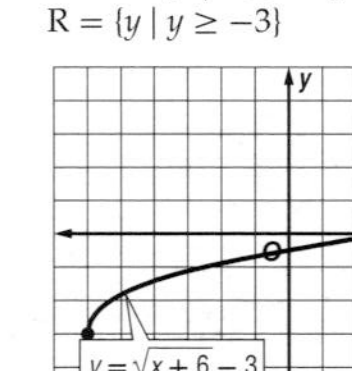

For Homework Help, go to Hotmath.com

79. D = {x | x ≥ 2}, R = {y | y ≥ 4}

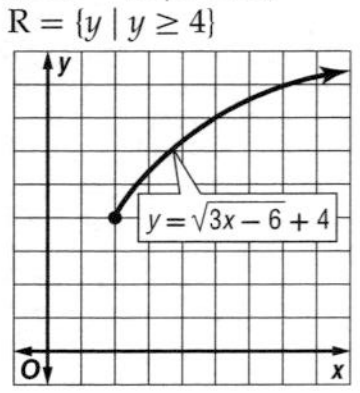

81. $-\frac{8}{3}$; 1 real **83.** 0, 3i, −3i; 1 real, 2 imaginary

85.

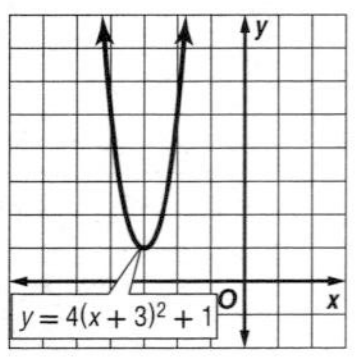

87.

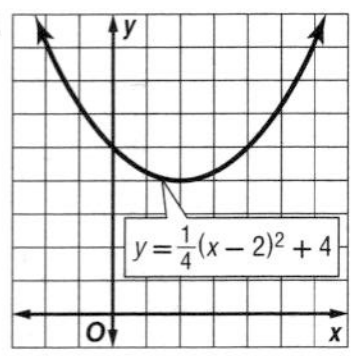

89.

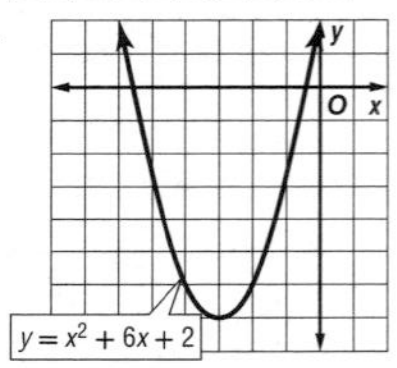

Pages 572–575 Lesson 9-3

1 $x - 1 = 0$

$x = 1$

$f(x)$ is not defined when $x = 1$. So, there is a vertical asymptote at $x = 1$.
From $x = 1$, as x-values decrease, $f(x)$ values approach 0, and as x-values increase, $f(x)$ values approach 0. So there is a horizontal asymptote at $f(x) = 0$. The domain is all real numbers not equal to 1 or D = {x | x ≠ 1}. The range is all real numbers not equal to 0 or R = {f(x) | f(x) ≠ 0}.

3.

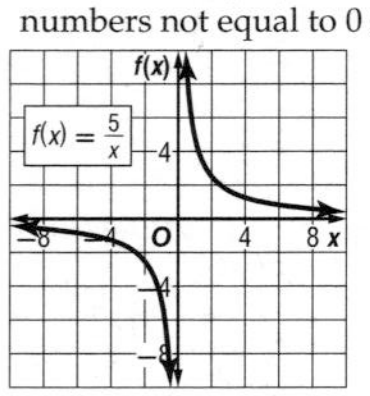

D = {x | x ≠ 0}; R = {f(x) | f(x) ≠ 0}

5.

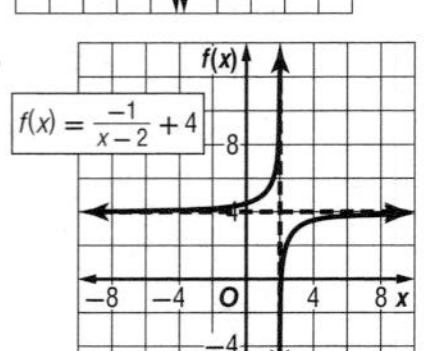

D = {x | x ≠ 2}; R = {f(x) | f(x) ≠ 4}

7. $x = -4, f(x) = 0$; D = {x | x ≠ −4}; R = {f(x) | f(x) ≠ 0} **9.** $x = -6, f(x) = -2$; D = {x | x ≠ −6}; R = {f(x) | f(x) ≠ −2}

11.

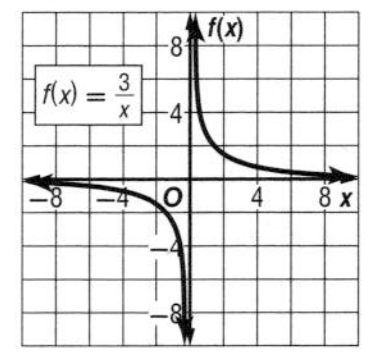

D = {x | x ≠ 0}; R = {f(x) | f(x) ≠ 0}

13.

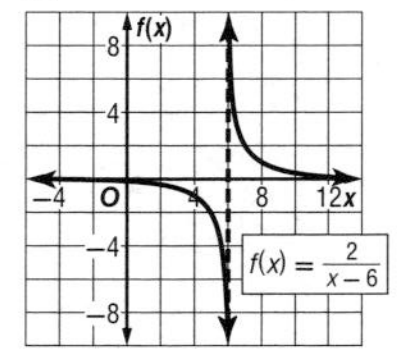

D = {x | x ≠ 6}; R = {f(x) | f(x) ≠ 0}

15 This represents a transformation of the graph of $f(x) = \frac{1}{x}$.
$a = 2$: The graph is expanded.
$k = 3$: The graph is translated 3 units up. There is a horizontal asymptote at $f(x) = 3$. Domain: D = {x | x ≠ 0}. Range: R = {f(x) | f(x) ≠ 3}.

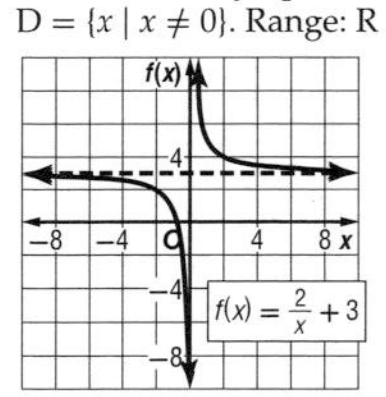

17.

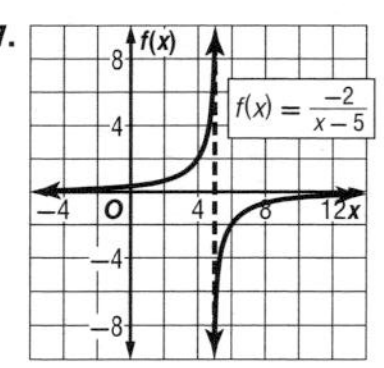

D = {x | x ≠ 5}; R = {f(x) | f(x) ≠ 0}

19.

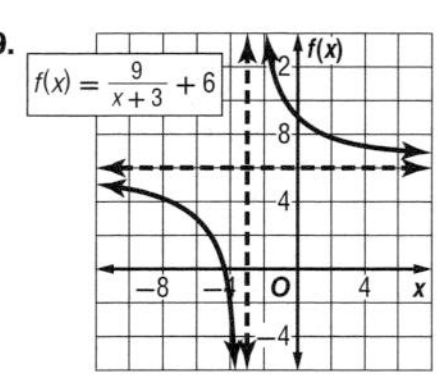

D = {x | x ≠ −3}; R = {f(x) | f(x) ≠ 6}

21.

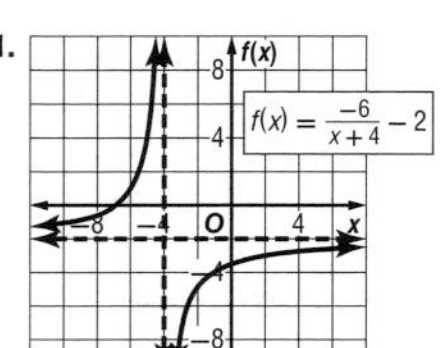

D = {x | x ≠ −4}; R = {f(x) | f(x) ≠ −2}

23a. $m = \frac{5000}{d}$

23b.

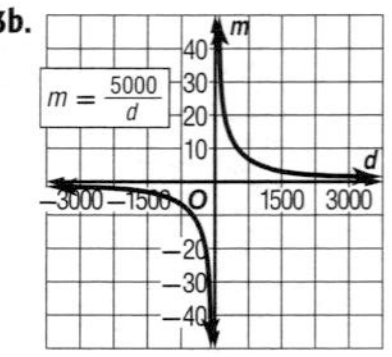

23c. 13.7 mi

25.

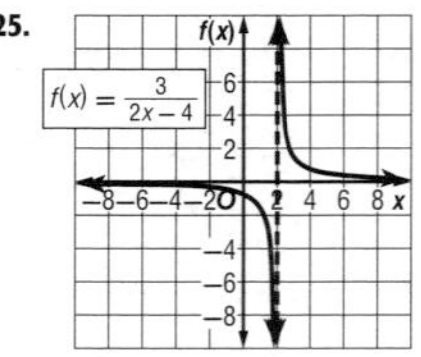

D = {x | x ≠ 2}; R = {f(x) | f(x) ≠ 0}

27.

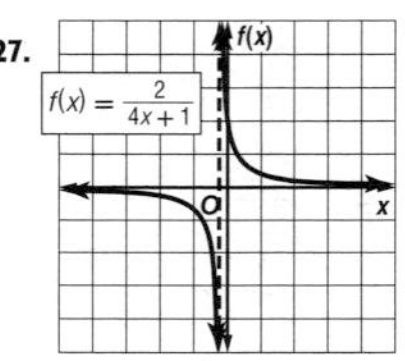

$D = \left\{x \mid x \neq \frac{1}{4}\right\}$; R = {f(x) | f(x) ≠ 0}

29 **a.** $rt = d$ rate · time = distance

$rt = 60.5$ $d = 60.5$

$r = \frac{60.5}{t}$ Divide each side by t.

b. This represents a transformation of the graph of $f(x) = \frac{1}{x}$. There are asymptotes at $t = 0$ and $r = 0$. Since $a = 60.5$, the graph is expanded.

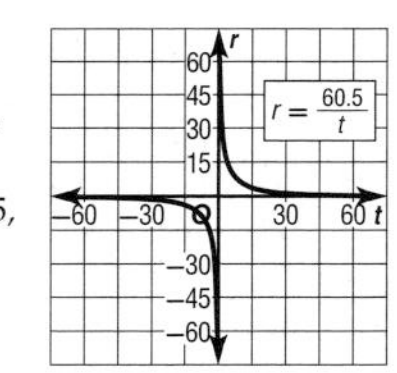

c. $r = \frac{60.5}{t}$ Write the equation.

$= \frac{60.5}{0.48}$ $t = 0.48$

≈ 126 ft/s   Use a calculator.

31. D = {x | x ≠ −2}; R = {f(x) | f(x) ≠ −5}; $x = -2, f(x) = -5$

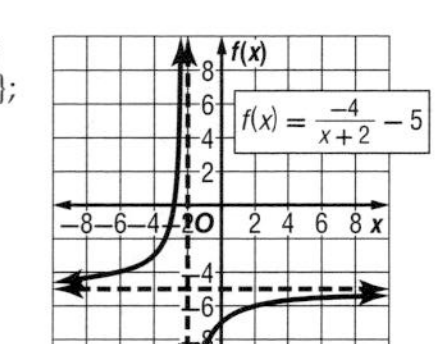

33. D = {x | x ≠ 4}; R = {f(x) | f(x) ≠ 3}; $x = 4, f(x) = 3$

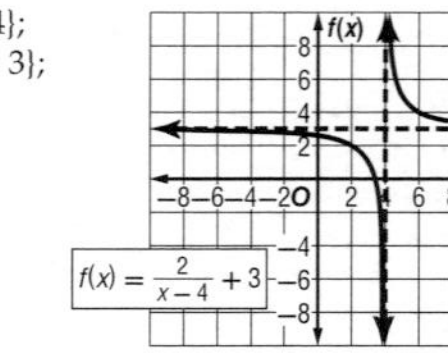

35. D = {x | x ≠ 7}; R = {f(x) | f(x) ≠ −8}; $x = 7, f(x) = -8$

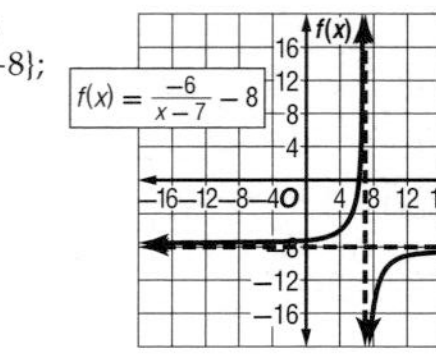

37a.

x	$f(x) = \frac{1}{x}$	x	$f(x) = \frac{1}{x^2}$
−3	$-\frac{1}{3}$	−3	$\frac{1}{9}$
−2	$-\frac{1}{2}$	−2	$\frac{1}{4}$
−1	−1	−1	1
0	undefined	0	undefined
1	1	1	1
2	$\frac{1}{2}$	2	$\frac{1}{4}$
3	$\frac{1}{3}$	3	$\frac{1}{9}$

37b.

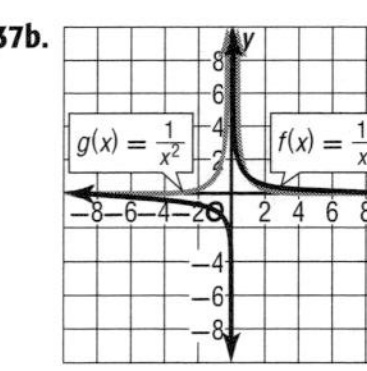

37c. The positive portion of $g(x) = \frac{1}{x^2}$ is similar to the graph of $f(x) = \frac{1}{x}$. Positive values of x produce positive values of $f(x)$. The negative portion of $g(x) = \frac{1}{x^2}$ appears to be a reflection of $f(x) = \frac{1}{x}$ over the x-axis. Negative values of x produce positive values of $g(x)$.
37d. Sample answer: When n is even, the graph will show symmetry with respect to the y-axis. When n is odd, the graph will show symmetry with respect to the origin. **39a.** The first graph has a vertical asymptote at $x = 0$ and a horizontal asymptote at $y = 0$. The second graph is translated 7 units up and has a vertical asymptote at $x = 0$ and a horizontal asymptote at $y = 7$.

39b. Both graphs have a vertical asymptote at $x = 0$ and a horizontal asymptote at $y = 0$. The second graph is stretched by a factor of 4. **39c.** The first graph has a vertical asymptote at $x = 0$ and a horizontal asymptote at $y = 0$. The second graph is translated 5 units to the left and has a vertical asymptote at $x = -5$ and a horizontal asymptote at $y = 0$.

39d.

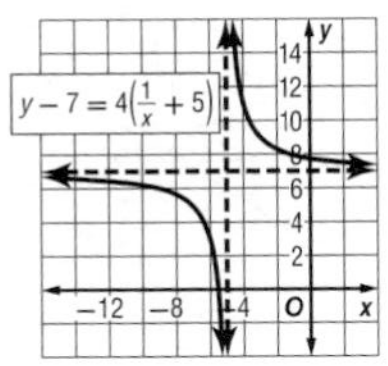

41. Sample answer: $f(x) = \frac{2}{x-3} + 4$ and $g(x) = \frac{5}{x-3} + 4$

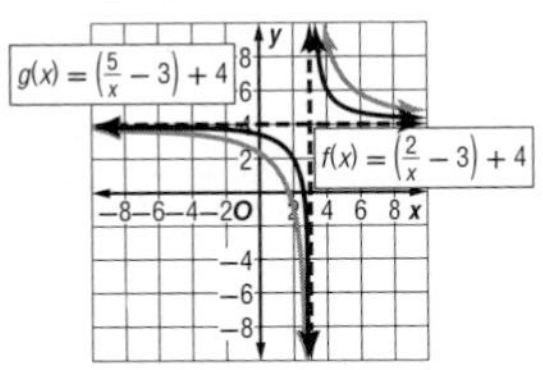

43. 4 **45.** B **47.** B **49.** $-2p$ **51.** $\frac{2x+y}{2x-y}$

53.

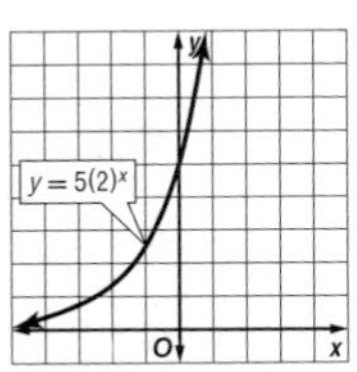

D = {all real numbers}, R = $\{y \mid y > 0\}$

55.

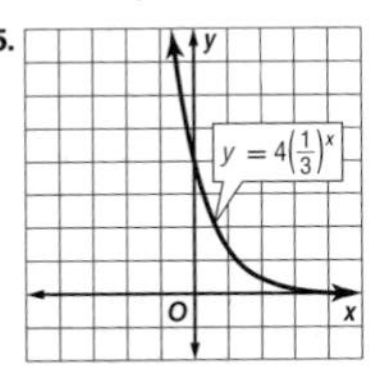

D = {all real numbers}, R = $\{y \mid y > 0\}$

57. $(f + g)(x) = 6x + 6$; $(f - g)(x) = -2x - 12$; $(f \cdot g)(x) = 8x^2 + 6x - 27$; $\left(\frac{f}{g}\right)(x) = \frac{2x-3}{4x+9}, x \neq -\frac{9}{4}$

59. $w = 4$ cm, $\ell = 8$ cm, $h = 2$ cm

61. rel. max at $x = 0$, rel. min at $x = -2$ and at $x = 2$; D = {all real numbers}, R = $\{f(x) \mid f(x) \geq -6\}$

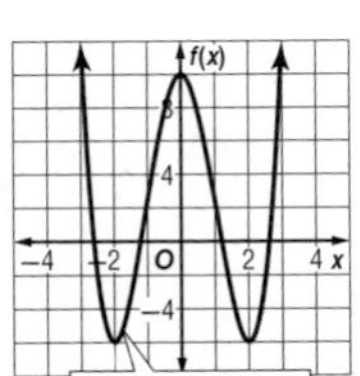

Pages 581–584 Lesson 9-4

1.

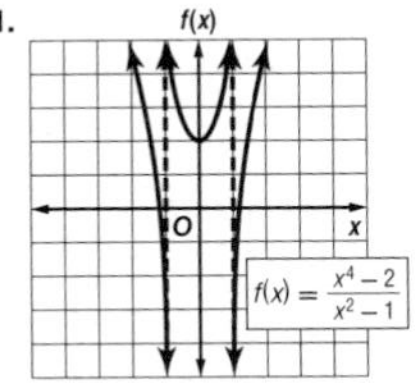

3a.

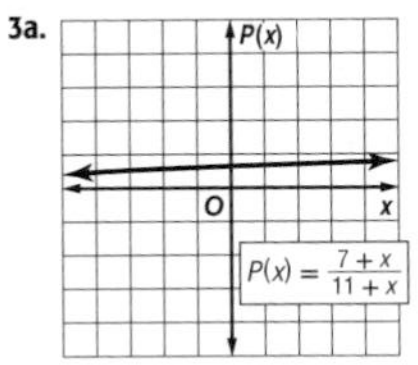

3b. The part in the first quadrant. **3c.** It represents his original field goal percentage of 63.6%. **3d.** $y = 1$; this represents 100% which he cannot achieve because he has already missed 4 field goals.

5 $x^2 + 8x + 20 = 0$ Set $a(x) = 0$.

Since $b^2 - 4ac = 8^2 - 4(1)(20)$ or -16, there are no real roots. So, there are no zeros.

$x + 2 = 0$ Set $b(x) = 0$.

$x = -2$ Subtract 2 from each side.

There is a vertical asymptote at $x = -2$. The degree of the numerator is greater than the degree of the denominator, so there is no horizontal asymptote. The difference between the degree of the numerator and the degree of the denominator is 1, so there is an oblique asymptote.

$$\begin{array}{r} x + 6 \\ x + 2\overline{)x^2 + 8x + 20} \\ (-)\ x^2 + 2x \\ 6x + 10 \\ (-)\ 6x + 12 \\ -2 \end{array}$$

The oblique asymptote is $y = x + 6$.

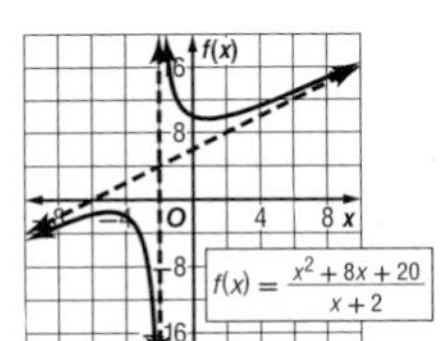

7.

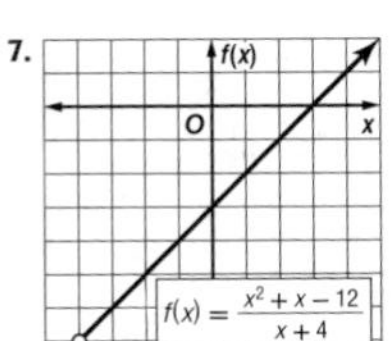

9.

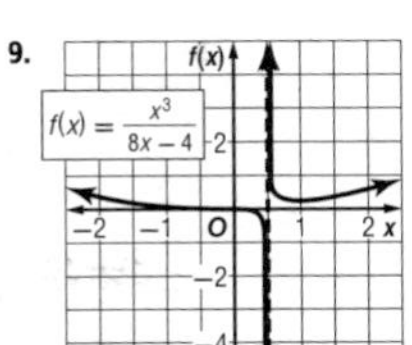

11.

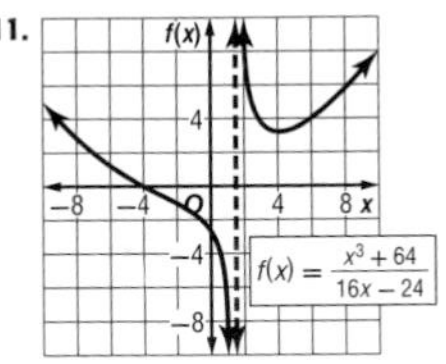

13.

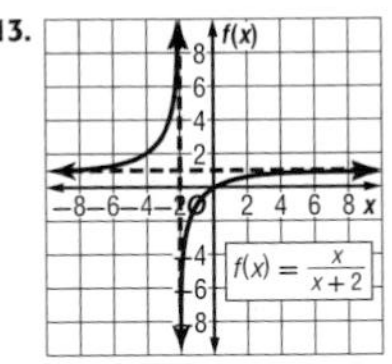

15 Since $a(x) = 4$, there are no zeros. The function is undefined for $x = 2$, so there is a vertical asymptote at $x = 2$. Since the degree of the numerator is less than the degree of the denominator, there is a horizontal asymptote at $f(x) = 0$. The difference between the degree of the numerator and the degree of the denominator is 2, so there is no oblique asymptote.

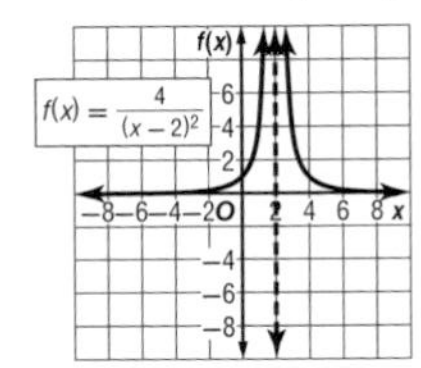

17.

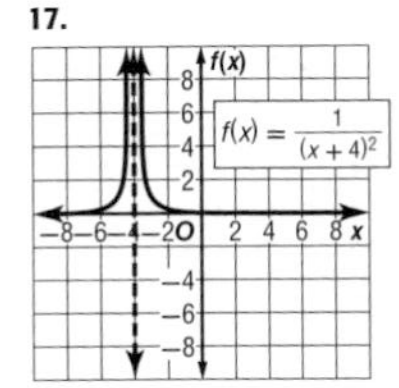

19.

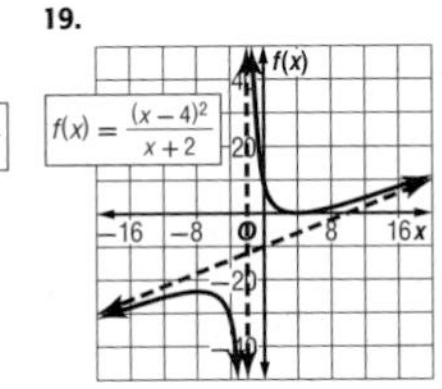

21.

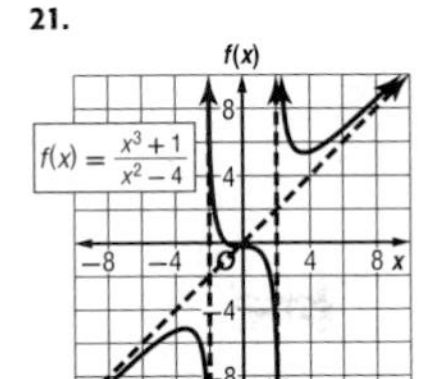

23.

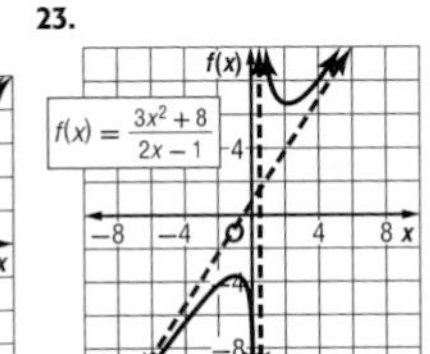

25.

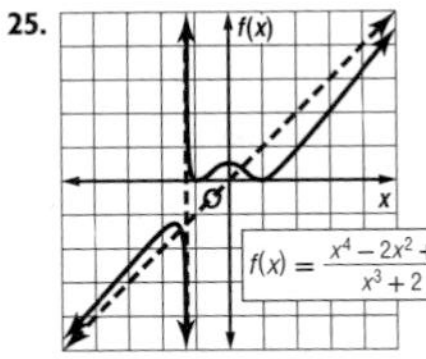

27a.

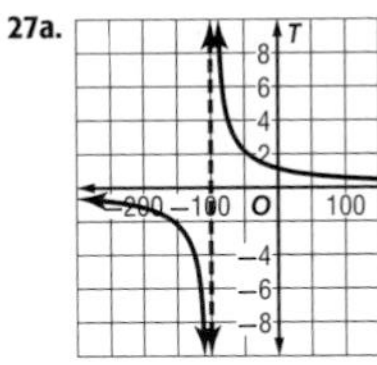

27b. $R_1 = -100$; no R_1-intercept; 1.2 **27c.** 0.5 amperes **27d.** $R_1 \geq 0$ and $0 < I \leq 1.2$

29.

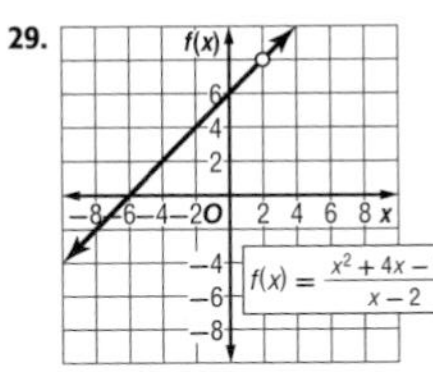

31.

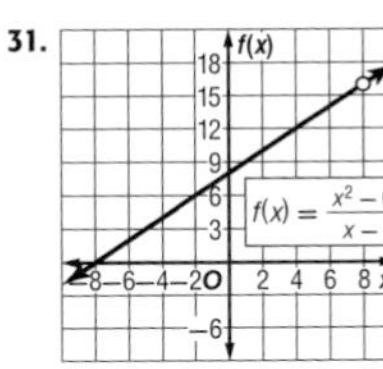

33.

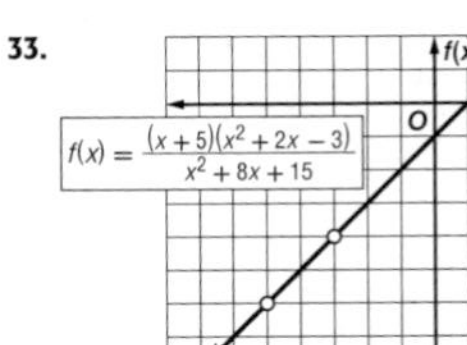

35.

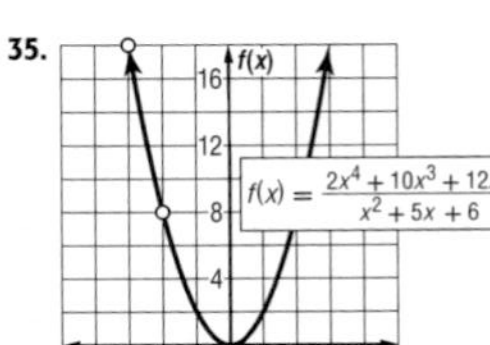

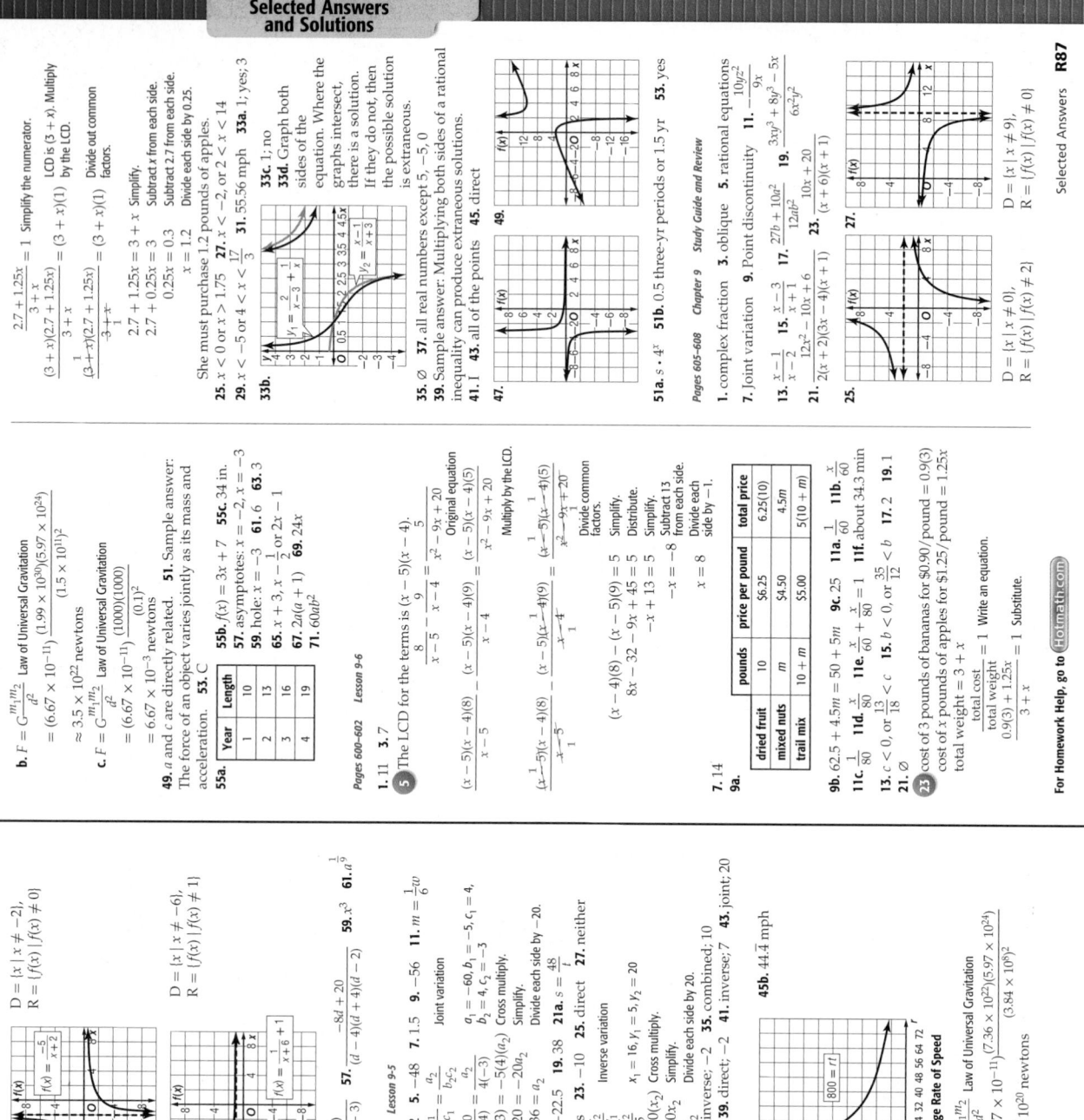

37 a. total cost = phone cost + monthly usage charge
$= 150 + 40x$
average monthly cost $= \frac{\text{total cost}}{\text{number of months}}$
$f(x) = \frac{150 + 40x}{x}$

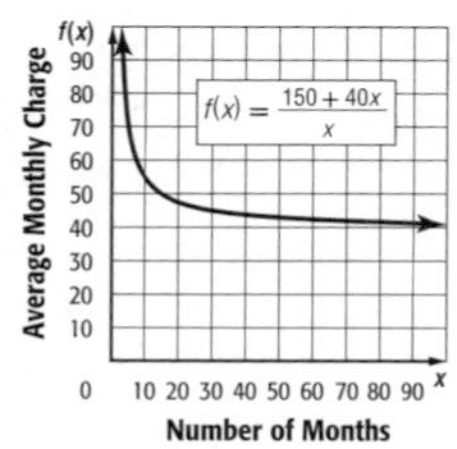

b. The vertical asymptote is $x = 0$. Since the degree of the numerator equals the degree of the denominator, the horizontal asymptote is at $f(x) = \frac{40}{1}$ or $f(x) = 40$.

c. Sample answer: The number of months and the average cost cannot have negative values.

d. $f(x) = \frac{150 + 40x}{x}$ Write the equation.
$45 = \frac{150 + 40x}{x}$ $f(x) = 45$
$45x = 150 + 40x$ Multiply each side by x.
$5x = 150$ Subtract $40x$ from each side.
$x = 30$ Divide each side by 5.

After 30 months, the average monthly charge will be $45.

39.
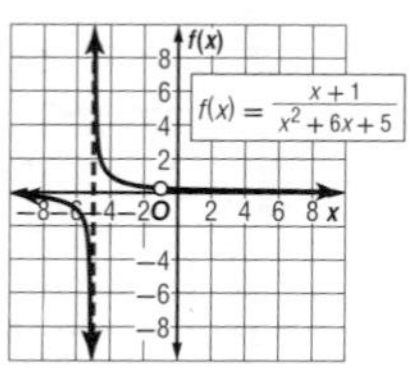

41.
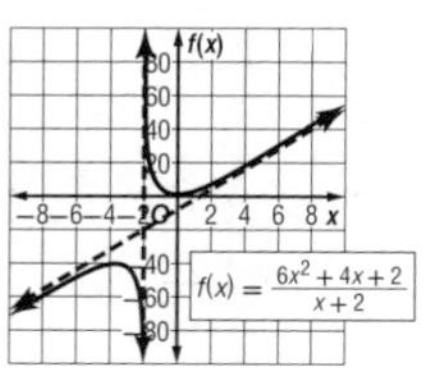

43. $f(x) = \frac{x^2 - 1}{x(x^2 - 1)}$

45. $f(x) = \frac{x}{a-b} + \frac{c(a-b)}{a-b}$
$= \frac{x + ca - cb}{a - b}$ **47.** C **49.** 4

51.
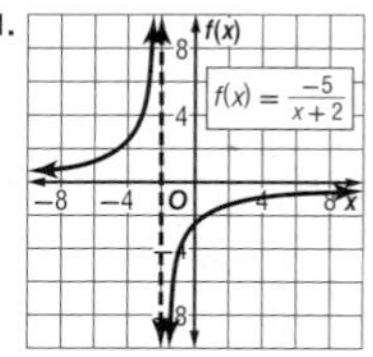

$D = \{x \mid x \neq -2\}$,
$R = \{f(x) \mid f(x) \neq 0\}$

53.
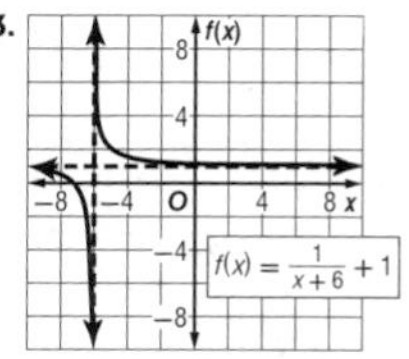

$D = \{x \mid x \neq -6\}$,
$R = \{f(x) \mid f(x) \neq 1\}$

55. $\frac{y(y-9)}{(y+3)(y-3)}$ **57.** $\frac{-8d+20}{(d-4)(d+4)(d-2)}$ **59.** x^3 **61.** $a^{\frac{1}{9}}$

Pages 590–593 Lesson 9-5

1. 21 **3.** −32 **5.** −48 **7.** 1.5 **9.** −56 **11.** $m = \frac{1}{6}w$

13 $\frac{a_1}{b_1c_1} = \frac{a_2}{b_2c_2}$ Joint variation
$\frac{-60}{-5(4)} = \frac{a_2}{4(-3)}$ $a_1 = -60, b_1 = -5, c_1 = 4, b_2 = 4, c_2 = -3$
$-60(4)(-3) = -5(4)(a_2)$ Cross multiply.
$720 = -20a_2$ Simplify.
$-36 = a_2$ Divide each side by −20.

15. −3 **17.** −22.5 **19.** 38 **21a.** $s = \frac{48}{t}$ **21b.** 3.2 hours **23.** −10 **25.** direct **27.** neither

29 $\frac{x_1}{y_2} = \frac{x_2}{y_1}$ Inverse variation
$\frac{16}{20} = \frac{x_2}{5}$ $x_1 = 16, y_1 = 5, y_2 = 20$
$16(5) = 20(x_2)$ Cross multiply.
$80 = 20x_2$ Simplify.
$4 = x_2$ Divide each side by 20.

31. −12 **33.** inverse; −2 **35.** combined; 10 **37.** direct; 4 **39.** direct; −2 **41.** inverse; 7 **43.** joint; 20

45a. $800 = rt$

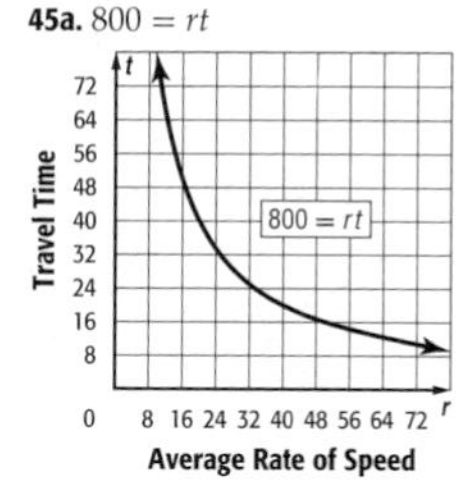

45b. $44.\overline{4}$ mph

47 a. $F = G\frac{m_1m_2}{d^2}$ Law of Universal Gravitation
$= (6.67 \times 10^{-11})\frac{(7.36 \times 10^{22})(5.97 \times 10^{24})}{(3.84 \times 10^8)^2}$
$\approx 2 \times 10^{20}$ newtons

b. $F = G\frac{m_1m_2}{d^2}$ Law of Universal Gravitation
$= (6.67 \times 10^{-11})\frac{(1.99 \times 10^{30})(5.97 \times 10^{24})}{(1.5 \times 10^{11})^2}$
$\approx 3.5 \times 10^{22}$ newtons

c. $F = G\frac{m_1m_2}{d^2}$ Law of Universal Gravitation
$= (6.67 \times 10^{-11})\frac{(1000)(1000)}{(0.1)^2}$
$= 6.67 \times 10^{-3}$ newtons

49. a and c are directly related. **51.** Sample answer: The force of an object varies jointly as its mass and acceleration. **53.** C

55a.

Year	Length
1	10
2	13
3	16
4	19

55b. $f(x) = 3x + 7$ **55c.** 34 in. **57.** asymptotes: $x = -2, x = -3$ **59.** hole: $x = -3$ **61.** 6 **63.** 3 **65.** $x + 3, x - \frac{1}{2}$ or $2x - 1$ **67.** $2a(a + 1)$ **69.** $24x$ **71.** $60ab^2$

Pages 600–602 Lesson 9-6

1. 11 **3.** 7

5 The LCD for the terms is $(x - 5)(x - 4)$.
$\frac{8}{x-5} - \frac{9}{x-4} = \frac{5}{x^2-9x+20}$ Original equation
$\frac{(x-5)(x-4)(8)}{x-5} - \frac{(x-5)(x-4)(9)}{x-4} = \frac{(x-5)(x-4)(5)}{x^2-9x+20}$ Multiply by the LCD.
$\frac{\overset{1}{(x-5)}(x-4)(8)}{\underset{1}{x-5}} - \frac{(x-5)\overset{1}{(x-4)}(9)}{\underset{1}{x-4}} = \frac{\overset{1}{(x-5)}\overset{1}{(x-4)}(5)}{\underset{1}{x^2-9x+20}}$ Divide common factors.
$(x-4)(8) - (x-5)(9) = 5$ Simplify.
$8x - 32 - 9x + 45 = 5$ Distribute.
$-x + 13 = 5$ Simplify.
$-x = -8$ Subtract 13 from each side.
$x = 8$ Divide each side by −1.

7. 14

9a.

	pounds	price per pound	total price
dried fruit	10	$6.25	6.25(10)
mixed nuts	m	$4.50	$4.5m$
trail mix	$10 + m$	$5.00	$5(10 + m)$

9b. $62.5 + 4.5m = 50 + 5m$ **9c.** 25 **11a.** $\frac{1}{60}$ **11b.** $\frac{x}{60}$ **11c.** $\frac{1}{80}$ **11d.** $\frac{x}{80}$ **11e.** $\frac{x}{60} + \frac{x}{80} = 1$ **11f.** about 34.3 min

13. $c < 0$, or $\frac{13}{18} < c$ **15.** $b < 0$, or $\frac{35}{12} < b$ **17.** 2 **19.** 1 **21.** ∅

23 cost of 3 pounds of bananas for \$0.90/pound = 0.9(3)
cost of x pounds of apples for \$1.25/pound = 1.25x
total weight = $3 + x$
$\frac{\text{total cost}}{\text{total weight}} = 1$ Write an equation.
$\frac{0.9(3) + 1.25x}{3 + x} = 1$ Substitute.
$\frac{2.7 + 1.25x}{3 + x} = 1$ Simplify the numerator.
$\frac{(3+x)(2.7+1.25x)}{3+x} = (3+x)(1)$ LCD is $(3 + x)$. Multiply by the LCD.
$\frac{\overset{1}{(3+x)}(2.7+1.25x)}{\underset{1}{3+x}} = (3+x)(1)$ Divide out common factors.
$2.7 + 1.25x = 3 + x$ Simplify.
$2.7 + 0.25x = 3$ Subtract x from each side.
$0.25x = 0.3$ Subtract 2.7 from each side.
$x = 1.2$ Divide each side by 0.25.

She must purchase 1.2 pounds of apples.

25. $x < 0$ or $x > 1.75$ **27.** $x < -2$, or $2 < x < 14$ **29.** $x < -5$ or $4 < x < \frac{17}{3}$ **31.** 55.56 mph **33a.** 1; yes; 3

33b.
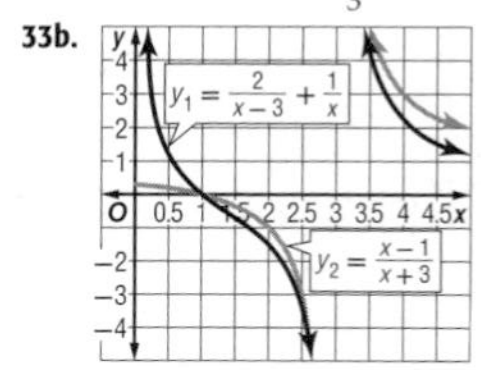

33c. 1; no **33d.** Graph both sides of the equation. Where the graphs intersect, there is a solution. If they do not, then the possible solution is extraneous.

35. ∅ **37.** all real numbers except 5, −5, 0 **39.** Sample answer: Multiplying both sides of a rational inequality can produce extraneous solutions. **41.** I **43.** all of the points **45.** direct

47.
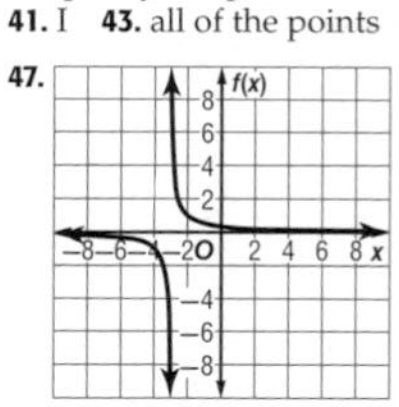

49.
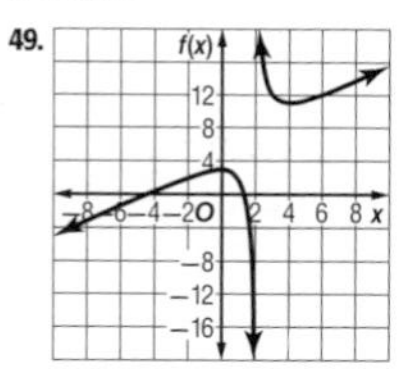

51a. $s \cdot 4^x$ **51b.** 0.5 three-yr periods or 1.5 yr **53.** yes

Pages 605–608 Chapter 9 Study Guide and Review

1. complex fraction **3.** oblique **5.** rational equations **7.** Joint variation **9.** Point discontinuity **11.** $-\frac{10yz^2}{9x}$ **13.** $\frac{x-1}{x-2}$ **15.** $\frac{x-3}{x+1}$ **17.** $\frac{27b + 10a^2}{12ab^2}$ **19.** $\frac{3xy^3 + 8y^3 - 5x}{6x^2y^2}$ **21.** $\frac{12x^2 - 10x + 6}{2(x+2)(3x-4)(x+1)}$ **23.** $\frac{10x + 20}{(x+6)(x+1)}$

25.
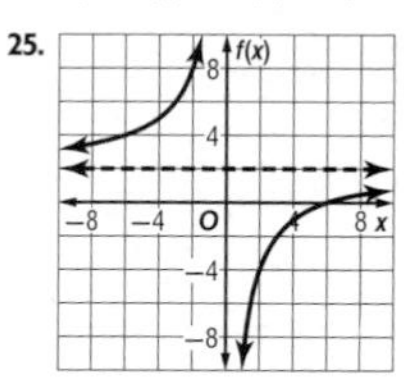

$D = \{x \mid x \neq 0\}$,
$R = \{f(x) \mid f(x) \neq 2\}$

27.
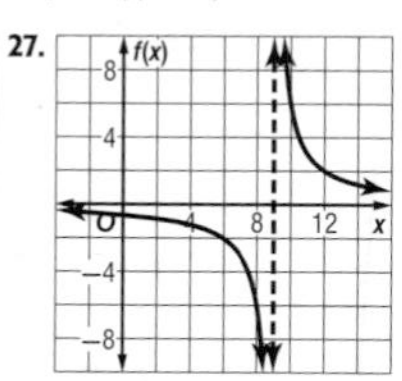

$D = \{x \mid x \neq 9\}$,
$R = \{f(x) \mid f(x) \neq 0\}$

For Homework Help, go to Hotmath.com

29. 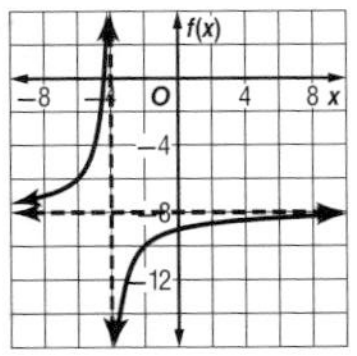
$D = \{x \mid x \neq -4\}$,
$R = \{f(x) \mid f(x) \neq -8\}$

31. $x = -4, x = 0$ **33.** $x = 8$; hole: $x = -3$

35. 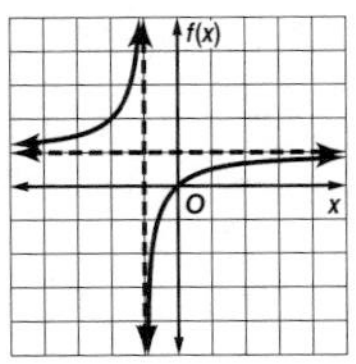

37. 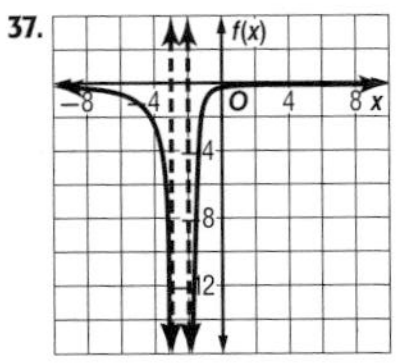

39. $a = 15$ **41.** $y = -\frac{1}{3}$ **43.** $y = \frac{48}{5}$ **45.** $x = \frac{46}{17}$
47. $x = -7$ **49.** $x = 8$ **51.** $-\frac{9}{10} < x < 0$

Chapter 10 Conic Sections

Page 615 ***Chapter 10*** ***Get Ready***

1. $\{-7, -1\}$ **3.** $\{3, 5\}$ **5.** $\left\{-5, \frac{3}{2}\right\}$ **7.** $\left\{\frac{3}{4} \pm \sqrt{2}\right\}$

9. $A'(-2, -5), B'(-1, -1), C'(5, -1), D'(4, -5)$ **11.** $J'(-3, 6), K'(-2, -3), L'(-10, -4)$

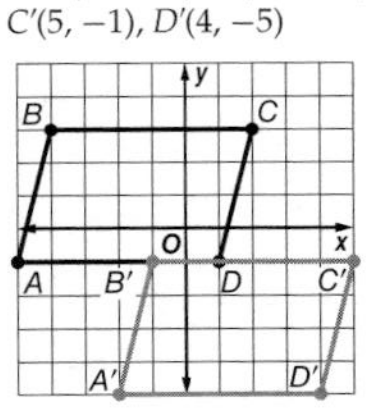

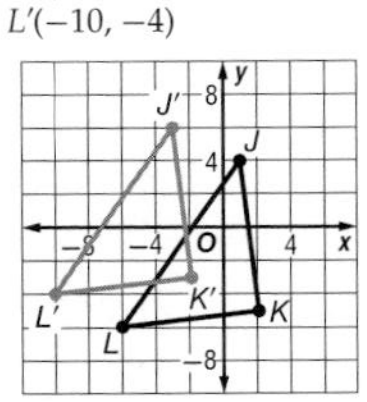

13. (115, 60), (125, 60), (125, 50), and (115, 50)

Pages 619–622 ***Lesson 10-1***

1. $\left(-\frac{1}{2}, 8\right)$ **3.** (14.5, 9.75) **5.** 11.662 units

7 $d = \sqrt{(x_2 - x_1)^2 + (y_2 - y_1)^2}$ Distance Formula
$= \sqrt{(3.5 - 0.25)^2 + (2.5 - 1.75)^2}$ $(x_1, y_1) = (0.25, 1.75)$ and $(x_2, y_2) = (3.5, 2.5)$
$= \sqrt{3.25^2 + 0.75^2}$ Simplify.
$= \sqrt{11.125}$ or about 3.335 units Simplify.

9. A **11.** $(-4, -1)$ **13.** (7.3, 1) **15.** $(-7.75, -4.5)$
17. 16.279 units **19.** 16.125 units **21.** 21.024 units
23. 55.218 units **25.** $(-1.5, 0)$; 185.443 units
27. $(-5.5, -50.5)$; 148.223 units **29.** (8, 15); 136.953 units **31.** $(-0.43, -2.25)$; 9.624 units

33 $\left(\frac{x_1 + x_2}{2}, \frac{y_1 + y_2}{2}\right)$ Midpoint Formula
$= \left(\frac{-\frac{5}{12} + \left(-\frac{17}{2}\right)}{2}, \frac{-\frac{1}{3} + \left(-\frac{5}{3}\right)}{2}\right)$ $(x_1, y_1) = \left(-\frac{5}{12}, -\frac{1}{3}\right)$ and $(x_2, y_2) = \left(-\frac{17}{2}, -\frac{5}{3}\right)$
$= \left(\frac{-\frac{107}{12}}{2}, \frac{-2}{2}\right)$ Simplify.
$\approx (-4.458, -1)$ Simplify.

$d = \sqrt{(x_2 - x_1)^2 + (y_2 - y_1)^2}$ Distance Formula
$= \sqrt{\left(-\frac{17}{2} - \left(-\frac{5}{12}\right)\right)^2 + \left(-\frac{5}{3} - \left(-\frac{1}{3}\right)\right)^2}$ $(x_1, y_1) = \left(-\frac{5}{12}, -\frac{1}{3}\right)$ and $(x_2, y_2) = \left(-\frac{17}{2}, -\frac{5}{3}\right)$
$= \sqrt{\left(-\frac{97}{12}\right)^2 + \left(-\frac{4}{3}\right)^2}$ Simplify.
≈ 8.193 units Use a calculator.

35. $(-4.719, 0.028)$; 17.97 units **37.** 14.53 km

39 $d = \sqrt{(x_2 - x_1)^2 + (y_2 - y_1)^2}$ Distance Formula
$= \sqrt{(254 - 132)^2 + (105 - 428)^2}$ $(x_1, y_1) = (132, 428)$ and $(x_2, y_2) = (254, 105)$
$= \sqrt{122^2 + (-323)^2}$ Simplify.
$= \sqrt{119{,}213}$ or about 345 units Simplify.
345 units • 0.316 mi/unit ≈ 109 mi

41a. 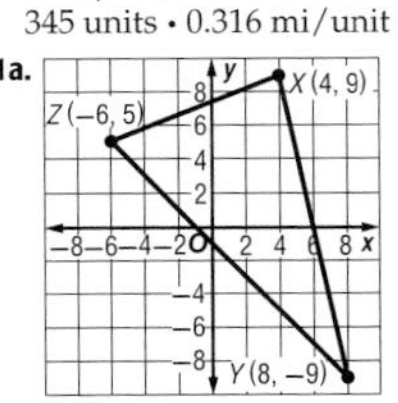

41b. midpoint of $\overline{XY} = (6, 0)$; midpoint of $\overline{YZ} = (1, -2)$; midpoint of $\overline{XZ} = (-1, 7)$ **41c.** The perimeter of $\triangle XYZ$ is $2\sqrt{29} + 14\sqrt{2} + 2\sqrt{85}$ units. perimeter $= \sqrt{29} + 7\sqrt{2} + \sqrt{85}$

41d. The perimeter of $\triangle XYZ$ is twice the perimeter of the smaller triangle. **43.** a circle and its interior with center at (5, 6) and radius 3 units **45.** The distance from *A* to *B* equals the distance from *B* to *A*. Using the Distance Formula, the solution is the same no matter which ordered pair is used first. **47.** 8.91
49. G **51.** $-6, -2$ **53.** $\frac{3}{2}$ **55.** 4.8362 **57.** 8.0086
59. $\{p \mid p \leq 1.9803\}$ **61.** -20 **63.** $\frac{1}{3}$
65. $y = (x - 3)^2 - 8$; $(3, -8)$; $x = 3$; up

Pages 627–629 ***Lesson 10-2***

1. $y = 2(x - 6)^2 - 32$; vertex $(6, -32)$; axis of symmetry: $x = 6$; opens upward **3.** $x = (y - 4)^2 - 27$; vertex $(-27, 4)$; axis of symmetry: $y = 4$; opens right

5. 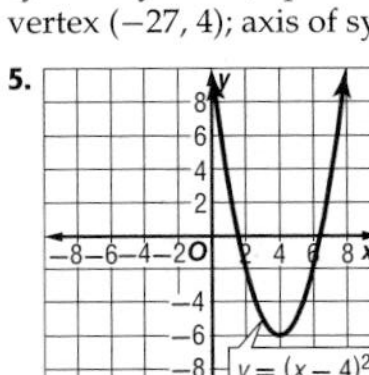

7. 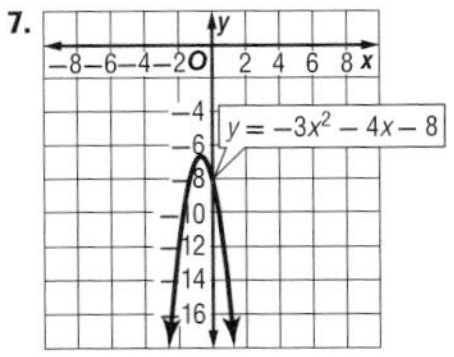

9. $y = \frac{1}{8}x^2 + 2$
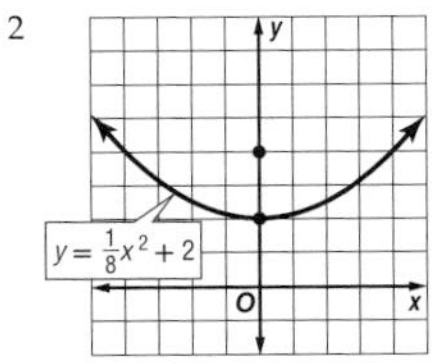

11. $y = -\frac{1}{12}(x - 3)^2 + 5$
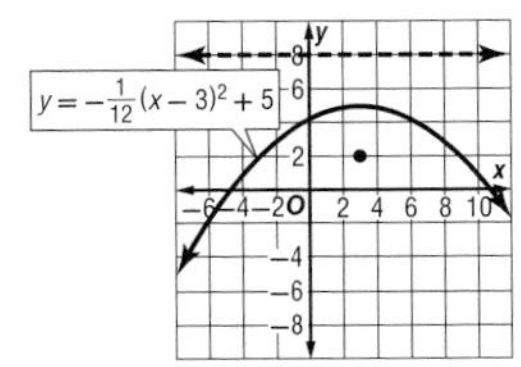

13a. $y = \frac{1}{24}x^2 - 6$
13b. 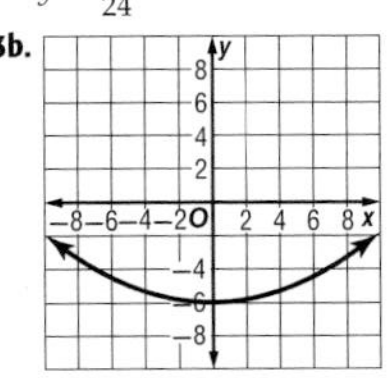

15. $y = 3(x + 7)^2 + 2$; vertex $= (-7, 2)$; axis of symmetry: $x = -7$; opens upward
17. $y = -3\left(x + \frac{3}{2}\right)^2 + \frac{3}{4}$; vertex $= \left(-\frac{3}{2}, \frac{3}{4}\right)$; axis of symmetry: $x = -\frac{3}{2}$; opens downward
19. $x = \frac{2}{3}(y - 3)^2 + 6$; vertex $= (6, 3)$; axis of symmetry: $y = 3$; opens right

21. 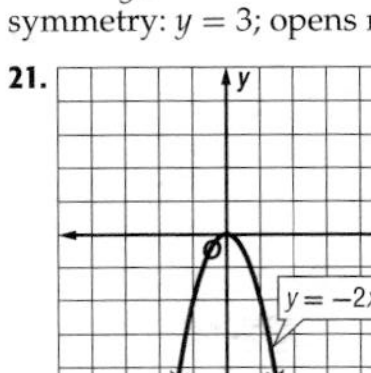

23. 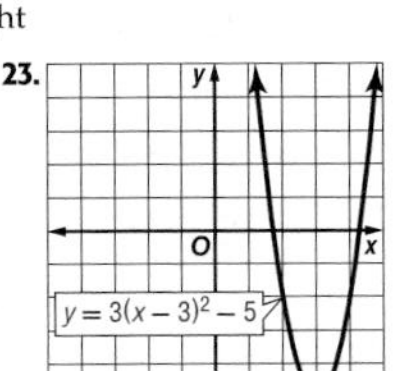

25. 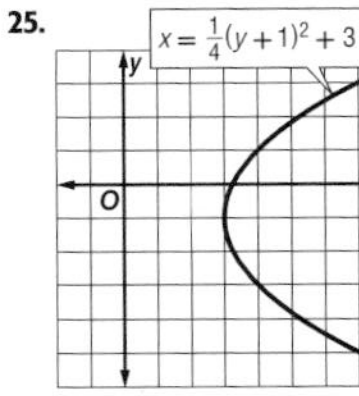

27. $y = \frac{1}{20}(x - 1)^2 + 8$
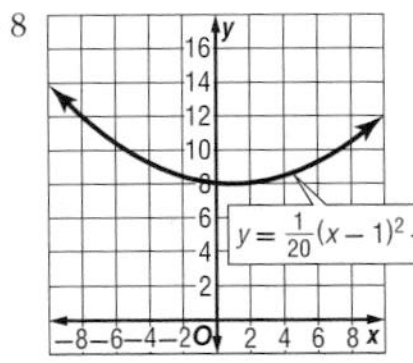

29 The directrix is a vertical line, so the equation of the parabola is of the form $x = a(y - k)^2 + h$. Since the vertex is equidistant from the focus and the directrix, the vertex is at (6, 4).
$x = h - \frac{1}{4a}$ Equation of directrix
$10 = 6 - \frac{1}{4a}$ $x = 10$ and $h = 6$
$4 = -\frac{1}{4a}$ Subtract 6 from each side.
$16a = -1$ Multiply each side by $4a$.
$a = -\frac{1}{16}$ Divide each side by 16.
$x = a(y - k)^2 + h$ Equation of a parabola
$x = -\frac{1}{16}(y - 4)^2 + 6$ $a = -\frac{1}{6}$, $(h, k) = (6, 4)$

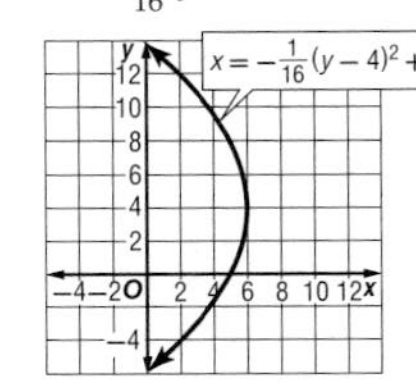

31. $y = -\frac{1}{4}(x - 9)^2 + 6$
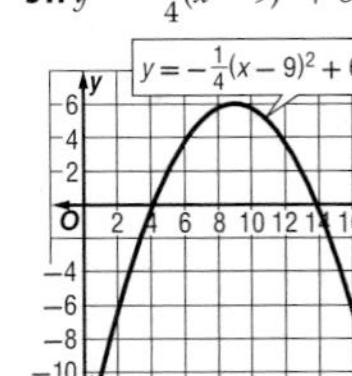

33a. 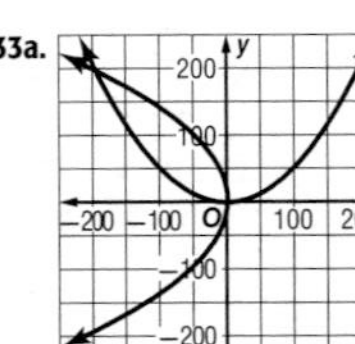

33b. $y = \frac{x^2}{192}$ and $x = \frac{y^2}{-192}$ **33c.** Sample answer: No; except for the direction in which they open, the graphs are identical.

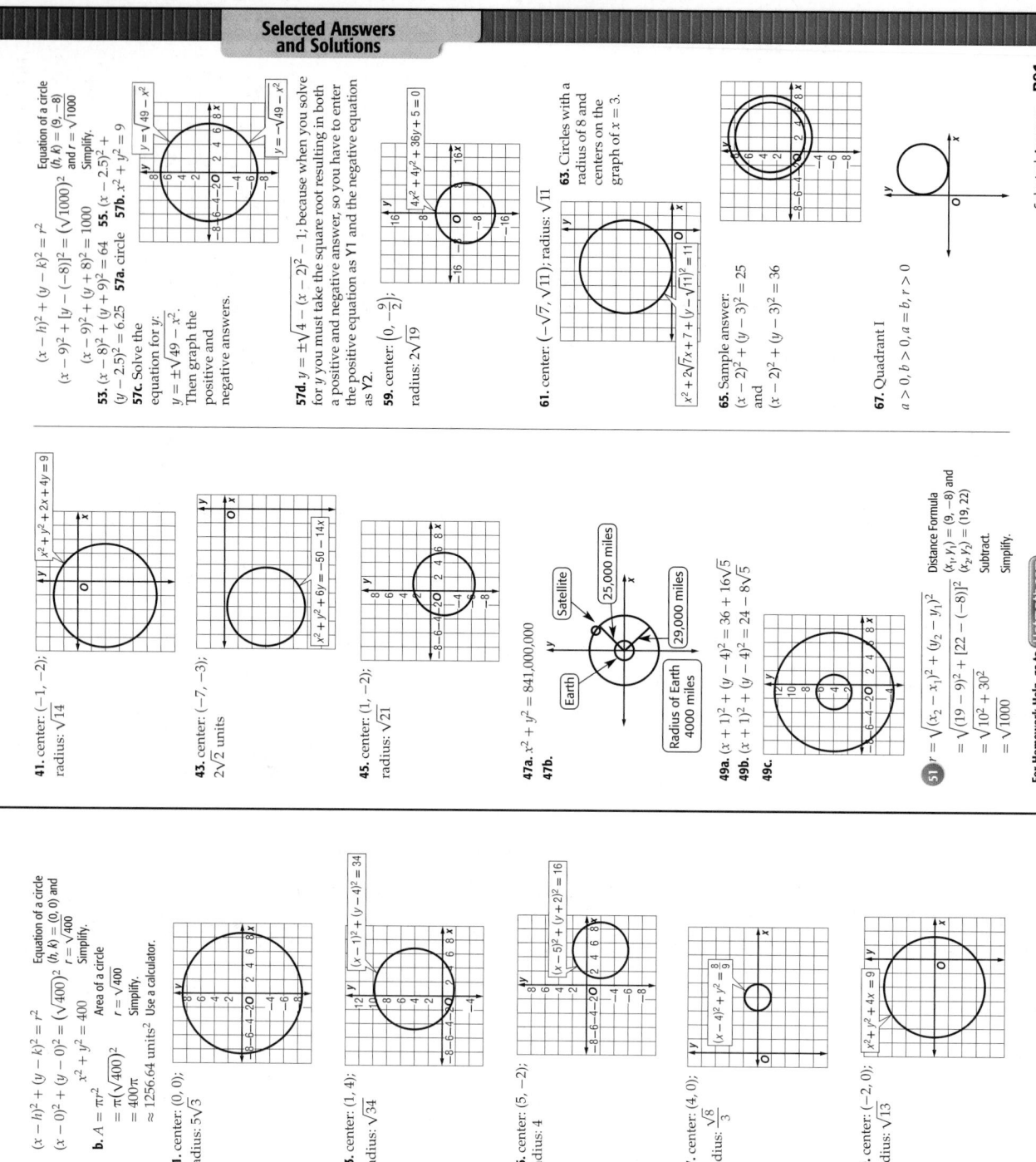

35 The high beams should be placed at the focus.
The y-coordinate of the focus is $k + \frac{1}{4a}$.

$k + \frac{1}{4a} = 0 + \frac{1}{4\left(\frac{1}{12}\right)}$ $k = 0, a = \frac{1}{2}$

$= \frac{12}{4}$ or 3   Simplify.

The filament for the high beams should be placed 3 units above the vertex.

37. Rewrite it as $y = (x - h)^2$, where $h > 0$. **39.** Russell; the parabola should open to the left rather than to the right. **41.** C **43.** D **45.** $5\sqrt{2} + 3\sqrt{10}$ units **47.** 1.7183 **49.** $x > 0.4700$ **51.** 0.5 **53.** z^2 **55.** $\pm1, \pm2, \pm3, \pm6$ **57.** $\pm1, \pm\frac{1}{3}, \pm\frac{1}{9}, \pm3, \pm9, \pm27$ **59.** $3\sqrt{5}$ **61.** $16\sqrt{2}$

Pages 634–637 Lesson 10-3

1. $(x - 72)^2 + (y - 39)^2 = 10{,}000$
3. $(x - 1)^2 + (y + 5)^2 = 9$ **5.** $(x + 5)^2 + (y + 3)^2 = 90$
7. $x^2 + (y + 4)^2 = 20$
9. center: (0, 7); radius: 3

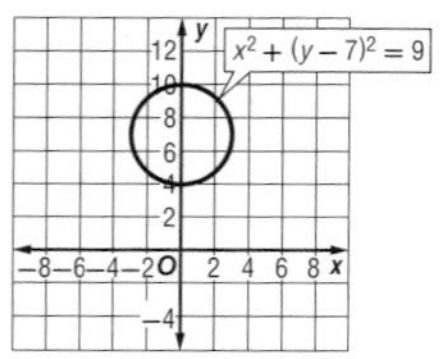

11. center: (2, −4); radius: 5

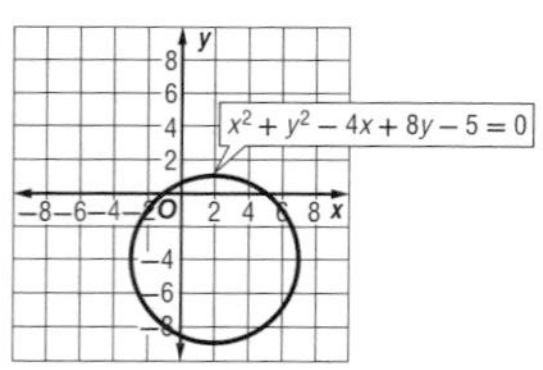

13. $(x + 3)^2 + (y - 1)^2 = 16$ **15.** $(x + 2)^2 + (y + 1)^2 = 81$

17 $(x - h)^2 + (y - k)^2 = r^2$ Equation of a circle

$(x - 0)^2 + [y - (-6)]^2 = (\sqrt{35})^2$ $(h, k) = (0, -6)$ and $r = \sqrt{35}$

$x^2 + (y + 6)^2 = 35$ Simplify.

19. $(x - 1)^2 + (y - 1)^2 = 4$ **21.** $x^2 + (y + 6) = 53$
23. $(x - 2)^2 + \left(y + \frac{3}{2}\right)^2 = \frac{25}{4}$ **25.** $\left(x - \frac{3}{2}\right)^2 + (y + 8)^2 = \frac{53}{4}$ **27.** $(x - 4)^2 + (y + 1)^2 = 20$

29 **a.** $(h, k) = \left(\frac{x_1 + x_2}{2}, \frac{y_1 + y_2}{2}\right)$ Midpoint Formula

$= \left(\frac{-12 + 12}{2}, \frac{16 + (-16)}{2}\right)$ $(x_1, y_1) = (-12, 16)$ and $(x_2, y_2) = (12, -16)$

$= (0, 0)$ Simplify.

$r = \sqrt{(x_2 - x_1)^2 + (y_2 - y_1)^2}$ Distance Formula

$= \sqrt{[0 - (-12)]^2 + (0 - 16)^2}$ $(x_1, y_1) = (-12, 16)$ and $(x_2, y_2) = (0, 0)$

$= \sqrt{12^2 + 16^2}$ Subtract.

$\approx \sqrt{400}$ Simplify.

$(x - h)^2 + (y - k)^2 = r^2$ Equation of a circle

$(x - 0)^2 + (y - 0)^2 = (\sqrt{400})^2$ $(h, k) = (0, 0)$ and $r = \sqrt{400}$

$x^2 + y^2 = 400$ Simplify.

b. $A = \pi r^2$ Area of a circle

$= \pi(\sqrt{400})^2$ $r = \sqrt{400}$

$= 400\pi$ Simplify.

≈ 1256.64 units^2 Use a calculator.

31. center: (0, 0); radius: $5\sqrt{3}$

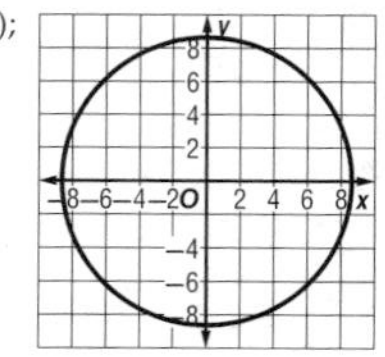

33. center: (1, 4); radius: $\sqrt{34}$

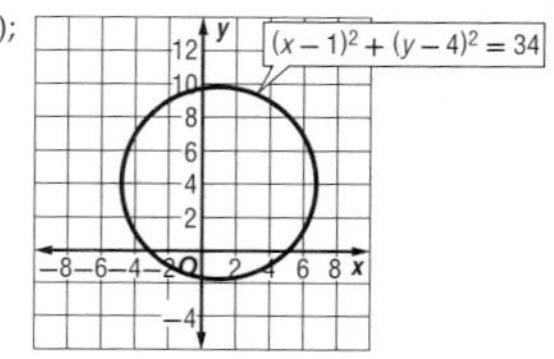

35. center: (5, −2); radius: 4

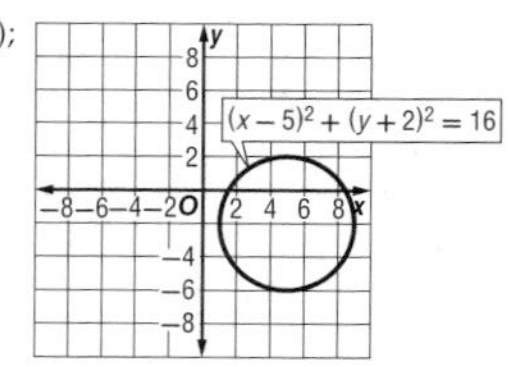

37. center: (4, 0); radius: $\frac{\sqrt{8}}{3}$

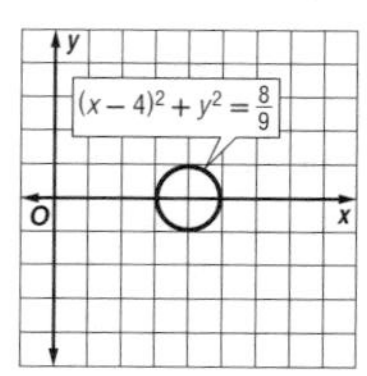

39. center: (−2, 0); radius: $\sqrt{13}$

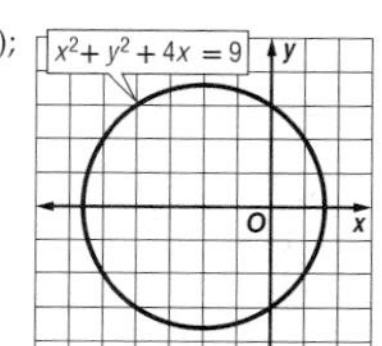

41. center: (−1, −2); radius: $\sqrt{14}$

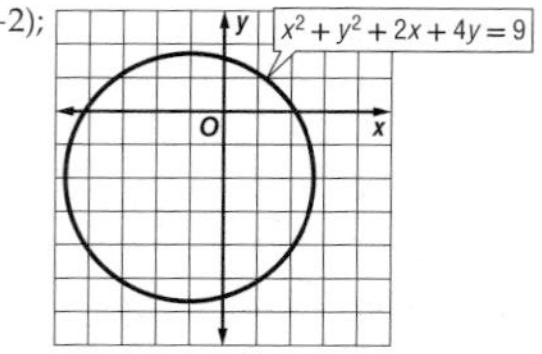

43. center: (−7, −3); $2\sqrt{2}$ units

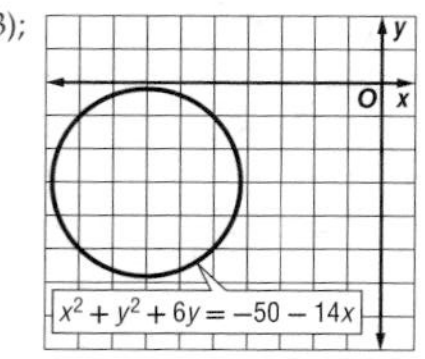

45. center: (1, −2); radius: $\sqrt{21}$

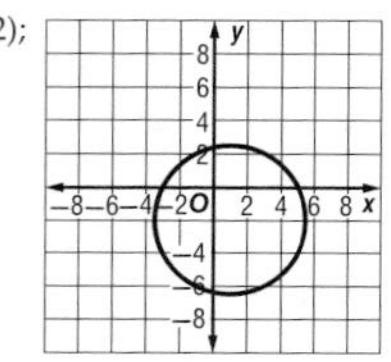

47a. $x^2 + y^2 = 841{,}000{,}000$
47b.

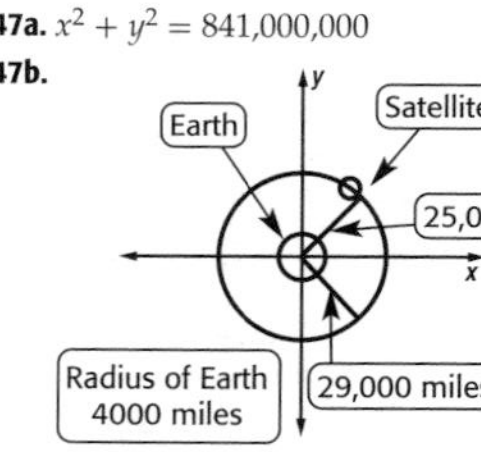

49a. $(x + 1)^2 + (y - 4)^2 = 36 + 16\sqrt{5}$
49b. $(x + 1)^2 + (y - 4)^2 = 24 - 8\sqrt{5}$
49c.

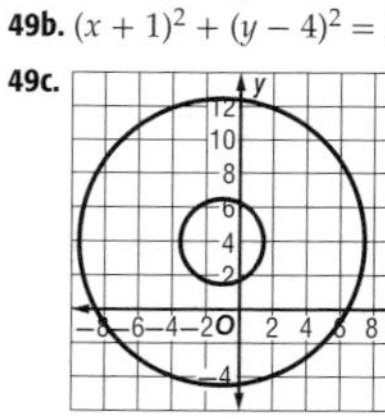

51 $r = \sqrt{(x_2 - x_1)^2 + (y_2 - y_1)^2}$ Distance Formula

$= \sqrt{(19 - 9)^2 + [22 - (-8)]^2}$ $(x_1, y_1) = (9, -8)$ and $(x_2, y_2) = (19, 22)$

$= \sqrt{10^2 + 30^2}$ Subtract.

$= \sqrt{1000}$ Simplify.

$(x - h)^2 + (y - k)^2 = r^2$ Equation of a circle

$(x - 9)^2 + [y - (-8)]^2 = (\sqrt{1000})^2$ $(h, k) = (9, -8)$ and $r = \sqrt{1000}$

$(x - 9)^2 + (y + 8)^2 = 1000$ Simplify.

53. $(x - 8)^2 + (y + 9)^2 = 64$ **55.** $(x - 2.5)^2 + (y - 2.5)^2 = 6.25$ **57a.** circle **57b.** $x^2 + y^2 = 9$

57c. Solve the equation for y: $y = \pm\sqrt{49 - x^2}$. Then graph the positive and negative answers.

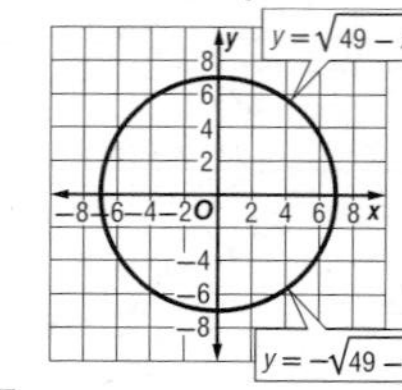

57d. $y = \pm\sqrt{4 - (x - 2)^2} - 1$; because when you solve for y you must take the square root resulting in both a positive and negative answer, so you have to enter the positive equation as **Y1** and the negative equation as **Y2**.

59. center: $\left(0, -\frac{9}{2}\right)$; radius: $2\sqrt{19}$

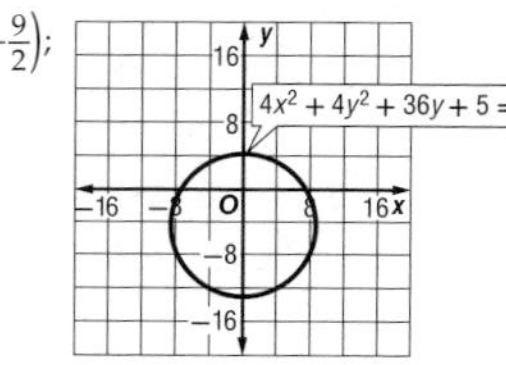

61. center: $(-\sqrt{7}, \sqrt{11})$; radius: $\sqrt{11}$

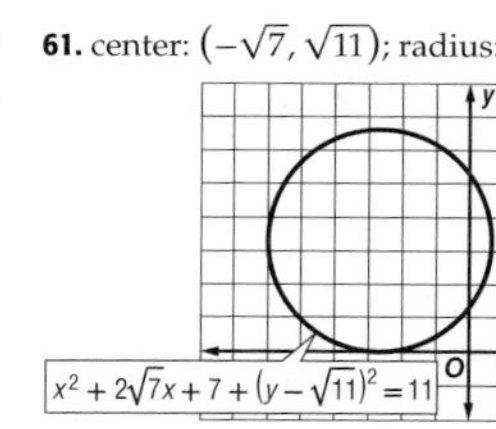

63. Circles with a radius of 8 and centers on the graph of $x = 3$.

65. Sample answer:
$(x - 2)^2 + (y - 3)^2 = 25$
and
$(x - 2)^2 + (y - 3)^2 = 36$

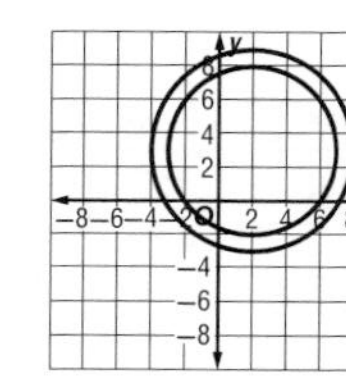

67. Quadrant I
$a > 0, b > 0, a = b, r > 0$

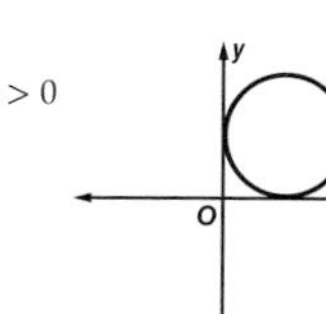

For Homework Help, go to Hotmath.com

Quadrant II

$a < 0, b > 0, a = -b, r > 0$

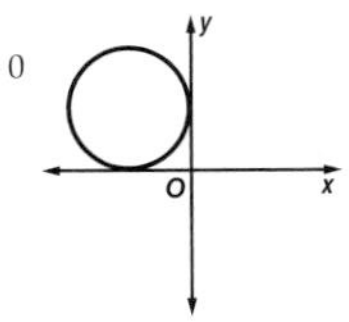

Quadrant III

$a < 0, b < 0, a = b, r > 0$

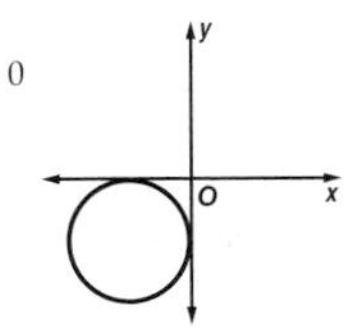

Quadrant IV

$a > 0, b < 0, a = -b, r > 0$

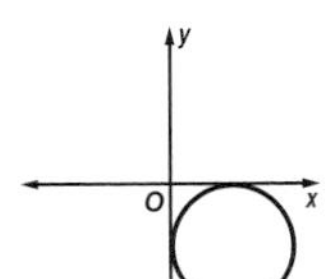

Sample answer: The circle is rotated 90° the origin from one quadrant to the next.

69. A **71.** C

73.

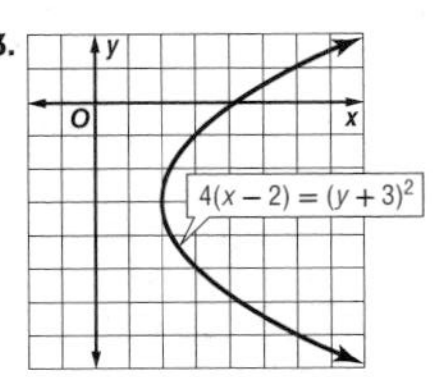

75. $\left(1, \frac{7}{22}\right)$; $\sqrt{65}$ units **77.** (0, 3); $\sqrt{29}$ units **79.** 64 **81.** $\frac{5}{2}$ **83.** −4 **85a.** The square root of a difference is not the difference of the square roots. **85b.** 34.1 ft/s

87. $\left\{\frac{3 \pm \sqrt{33}}{4}\right\}$

Pages 643–646 Lesson 10-4

1. $\frac{y^2}{25} + \frac{x^2}{9} = 1$ **3.** $\frac{(y+1)^2}{25} + \frac{(x+2)^2}{9} = 1$

5a. $a = 240, b = 160$ **5b.** $\frac{x^2}{57{,}600} + \frac{y^2}{25{,}600} = 1$

5c. about (179, 0) and (−179, 0)

7. center (5, −1); foci (5, 5) and (5, −7); major axis: 16; minor axis: ≈ 10.58

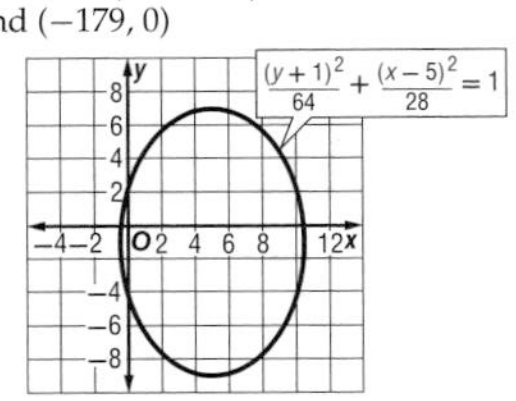

9 $4x^2 + y^2 - 32x - 4y + 52 = 0$ Original equation

$4x^2 - 32x + y^2 - 4y = -52$ Associative Property

$4(x^2 - 8x) + y^2 - 4y = -52$ Distributive Property

$4(x^2 - 8x + ■) + (y^2 - 4y + ■) = -52 + 4(■) + (■)$ Complete the squares.

$4(x^2 - 8x + 16) + (y^2 - 4y + 4) = -52 + 4(16) + (4)$

$(-4)^2 = 16$ and $(-2)^2 = 4$

$4(x - 4)^2 + (y - 2)^2 = 16$ Write as perfect squares.

$\frac{(x-4)^2}{4} + \frac{(y-2)^2}{16} = 1$ Divide each side by 16.

$h = 4$ and $k = 2$, so the center is at (4, 2). The ellipse is vertical. $a^2 = 16$, so $a = 4$, and $b^2 = 4$, so $b = 2$.

$c^2 = 16 - 4$ or 12, so $c \approx 3.46$.

foci: (4, 2 + 3.46) or (4, 5.46); (4, 2 − 3.46) or (4, −1.46)

major axis: 2 • 4 or 8

minor axis: 2 • 2 or 4

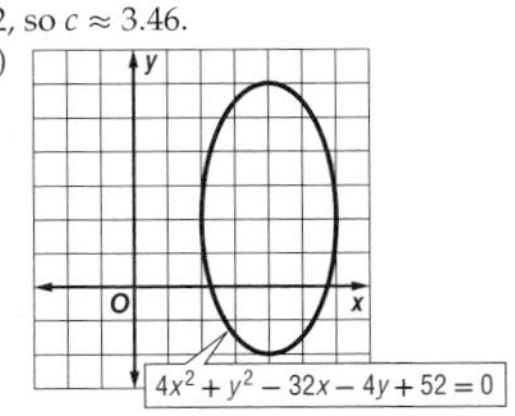

11. $\frac{y^2}{100} + \frac{x^2}{36} = 1$ **13.** $\frac{(x+5)^2}{49} + \frac{(y+4)^2}{25} = 1$

15. $\frac{(y-1)^2}{64} + \frac{(x+5)^2}{16} = 1$ **17.** $\frac{(x-3)^2}{81} + \frac{(y-4)^2}{64} = 1$

19 The x-coordinate is the same for both vertices, so the ellipse is vertical.

length of major axis: 16 − 6 or 10 units, so $a = 10$

length of minor axis: 1 − (−2) or 3 units, so $b = 3$

$\frac{(y-k)^2}{a^2} + \frac{(x-h)^2}{b^2} = 1$ Equation of a vertical ellipse

$\frac{(y-6)^2}{10^2} + \frac{[x-(-2)]^2}{3^2} = 1$ $(h, k) = (-2, 6), a = 10, b = 3$

$\frac{(y-6)^2}{100} + \frac{(x+2)^2}{9} = 1$ Simplify.

21. $\frac{(y-4)^2}{64} + \frac{(x-4)^2}{9} = 1$ **23.** $\frac{y^2}{73.96} + \frac{x^2}{53.29} = 1$

25. center (−6, 3); foci (−6, 7.69) and (−6, −1.69); major axis: ≈ 16.97; minor axis: ≈14.14

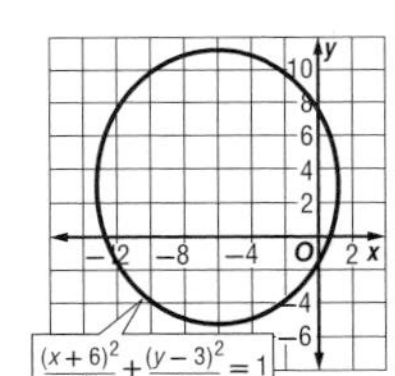

27. center (−4, 0); foci (−4, 7.68) and (−4, −7.68); major axis: ≈17.32; minor axis: 8

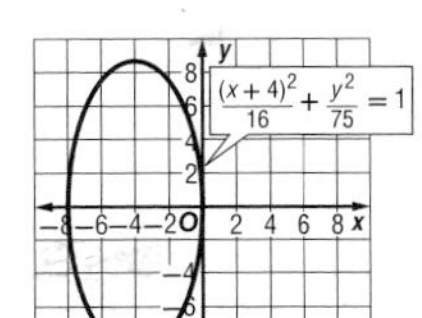

29. center (3, −3); foci (5.24, −3) and (0.76, −3); major axis: ≈8.94; minor axis: ≈7.75

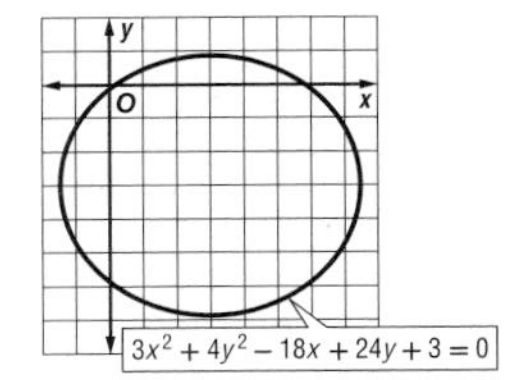

31. center (−2, 5); foci (−2, 7.83) and (−2, 2.17); major axis: ≈9.80; minor axis: 8

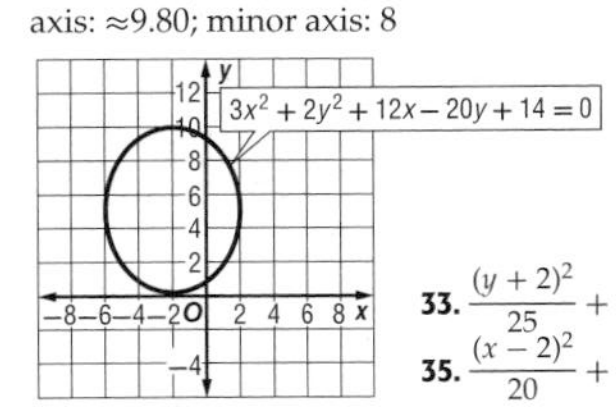

33. $\frac{(y+2)^2}{25} + \frac{(x+5)^2}{9} = 1$

35. $\frac{(x-2)^2}{20} + \frac{(y-8)^2}{4} = 1$

37 length of major axis $= 2a$

$10.9 = 2a$

$5.45 = a$

length of minor axis $= 2b$

$8.8 = 2b$

$4.4 = b$

$\frac{x^2}{a^2} + \frac{y^2}{b^2} = 1$ Equation of an ellipse

$\frac{x^2}{5.45^2} + \frac{y^2}{4.4^2} = 1$ Substitute.

$\frac{x^2}{29.7025} + \frac{y^2}{19.36} = 1$ Simplify.

39a.

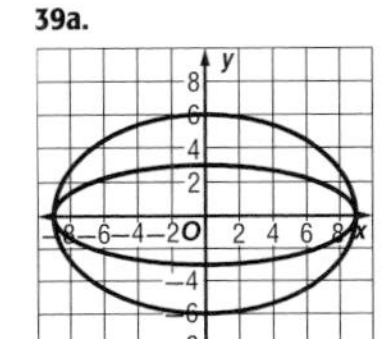

39b. Sample answer: The first graph is more circular than the second graph. **39c.** first graph: 0.745; second graph: 0.943 **39d.** Sample answer: The closer the eccentricity is to 0, the more circular the ellipse.

41. Sample answer: $\frac{(x+4)^2}{40} + \frac{y^2}{24} = 1$

43. $\frac{y^2}{9} + \frac{(x-2)^2}{3} = 1$

45. For any point on an ellipse, the sum of the distances from that point to the foci is constant by the definition of an ellipse. So, if (2, 14) is on the ellipse, then the sum of the distances from it to the foci will be a certain value consistent with every other point on the ellipse. The distance between (−7, 2) and (2, 14) is $\sqrt{(-7-2)^2 + (2-14)^2}$ or 15. The distance between (18, 2) and (2, 14) is $\sqrt{(18-2)^2 + (2-14)^2}$ or 20. The sum of these two distances is 35. The distance between (−7, 2) and (2, −10) is $\sqrt{(-7-2)^2 + [2-(-10)]^2}$ or 15. The distance between (18, 2) and (2, −10) is $\sqrt{(18-2)^2 + [2-(-10)]^2}$ or 15. The sum of these distances is also 35. Thus, (2, −10) also lies on the ellipse.

47. B **49.** 7 **51.** $(x-8)^2 + (y+9)^2 = 1130$

53. $(x+5)^2 + (y-4)^2 = 25$ **55.** $\frac{5d+16}{(d+2)^2}$

57. $\frac{x^2-5x+3}{(x-5)(x+1)}$ **59.** 4 **61.** $15a^3b^3 - 30a^4b^3 + 15a^5b^6$

63. $4x^2 - 3xy - 6y^2$ **65.** $y = -\frac{4}{5}x + \frac{17}{5}$

67. $y = -\frac{3}{5}x + \frac{16}{5}$

Pages 652–655 Lesson 10-5

1. $\frac{y^2}{36} - \frac{x^2}{28} = 1$ **3.** $\frac{x^2}{64} - \frac{y^2}{25} = 1$

5.

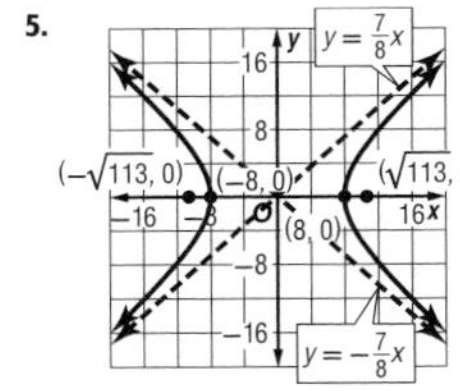

7.

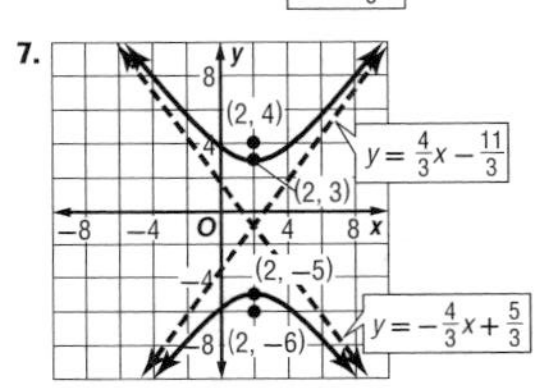

9. $\frac{x^2}{900} - \frac{y^2}{5500} = 1$

11 Since the vertices are equidistant from the center, the center is at (−8, 4). The value of a is the distance between a vertex and the center, or 4 units. The value of c is the distance between a focus and the center, or 8 units.

$c^2 = a^2 + b^2$ Equation relating a, b, and c for a hyperbola

$8^2 = 4^2 + b^2$ $c = 8$ and $a = 4$

$48 = b^2$ Subtract 4^2 from each side.

$\frac{(y-k)^2}{a^2} - \frac{(x-h)^2}{b^2} = 1$ Equation of a vertical hyperbola

$\frac{(y-4)^2}{4^2} - \frac{[x-(-8)]^2}{48} = 1$ $(h, k) = (-8, 4), a = 4, b^2 = 48$

$\frac{(y-4)^2}{16} - \frac{(x+8)^2}{48} = 1$ Simplify.

13. $\frac{(x+1)^2}{9} - \frac{(y-6)^2}{49} = 1$

15.

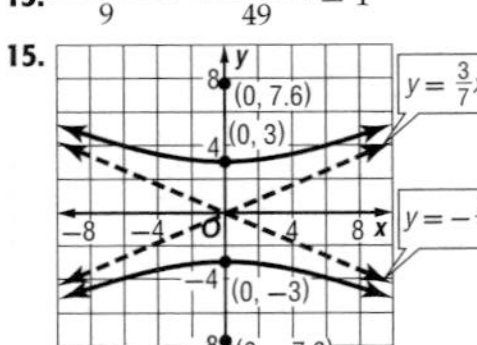

17.

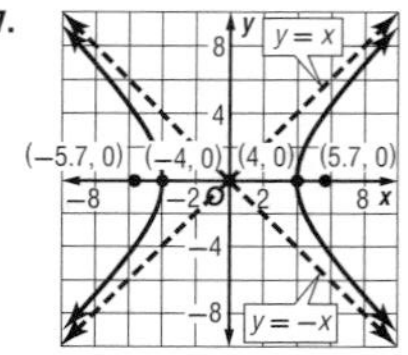

19.

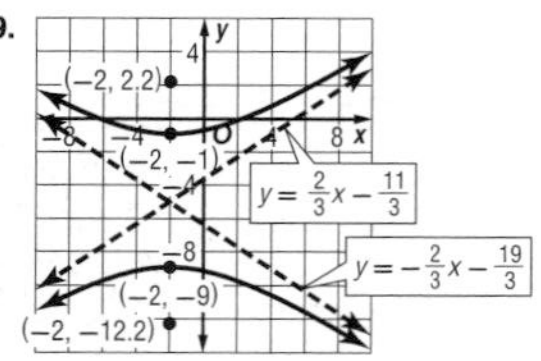

21.

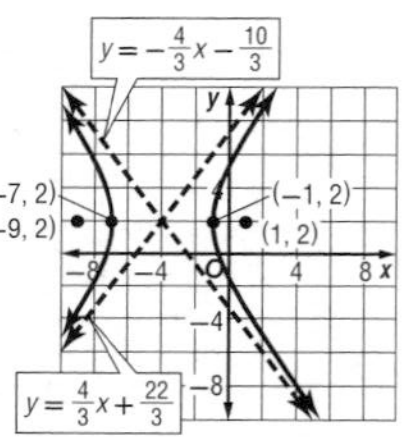

23.

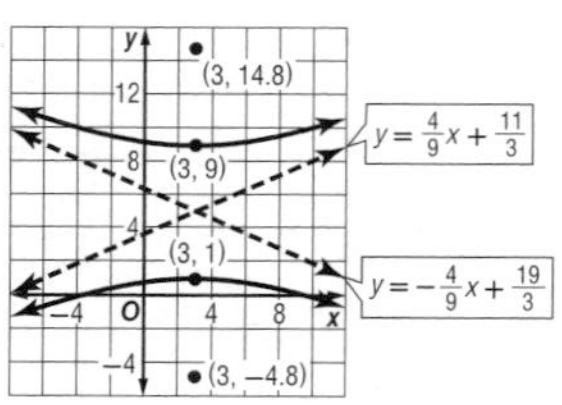

25. hyperbola **27.** ellipse **29.** ellipse

31 Because the center is at the origin, use the equation $\frac{x^2}{a^2} - \frac{y^2}{b^2} = 1$. The hyperbola intersects the x-axis at (10, 0), and one of the vertices is (10, 0). So, $a = 10$. The hyperbola also passes through (30, 100). Use $a = 10$, $x = 30$, and $y = 100$ to solve for b^2.

$\frac{x^2}{a^2} - \frac{y^2}{b^2} = 1$ Equation of an ellipse

$\frac{30^2}{10^2} - \frac{100^2}{b^2} = 1$ $a = 10, x = 30, y = 100$

$\frac{900}{100} - \frac{10{,}000}{b^2} = 1$ Evaluate exponents.

$9 - \frac{10{,}000}{b^2} = 1$ Simplify.

$-\frac{10{,}000}{b^2} = -8$ Subtract 9 from each side.

$-10{,}000 = -8b^2$ Multiply each side by b^2.

$\frac{-10{,}000}{-8} = b^2$ Divide each side by −8.

$1250 = b^2$ Simplify.

Substitute 1250 for b^2 in the equation $\frac{x^2}{a^2} - \frac{y^2}{b^2} = 1$. So, the equation of the path of the comet is $\frac{x^2}{100} - \frac{y^2}{1250} = 1$.

33a.

x	y
−12	−1.33
−10	−1.6
−8	−2
−6	−2.67
−4	−4
−2	−8
0	undef
2	8
4	4
6	2.67
8	2
10	1.6
12	1.33

33b.

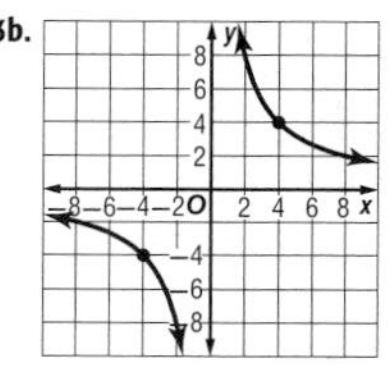

33c. The asymptotes are $y = 0$ and $x = 0$.

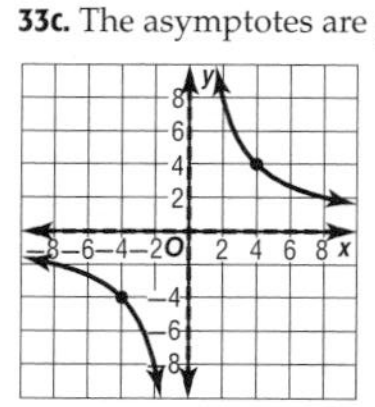

33d. They are perpendicular. **33e.** For $xy = 25$, the vertices will be at (5, 5) and (−5, −5), and for $xy = 36$, they will be at (−6, −6) and (6, 6).

35. $\frac{x^2}{2{,}722{,}500} - \frac{y^2}{1{,}277{,}500} = 1$ **37.** $\frac{x^2}{64} - \frac{y^2}{100} = 1$

39 The vertices are equidistant from the center. The center is at (2, −2). The value of a is the distance between a vertex and the center, or 4 units. The value of c is the distance between a focus and the center, or 8 units.

$c^2 = a^2 + b^2$ Equation relating a, b, and c for a hyperbola

$8^2 = 4^2 + b^2$ $c = 8$ and $a = 4$

$48 = b^2$ Subtract 4^2 from each side.

$\frac{(x-h)^2}{a^2} - \frac{(y-k)^2}{b^2} = 1$ Equation of a horizontal hyperbola

$\frac{(x-2)^2}{4^2} - \frac{[y-(-2)]^2}{48} = 1$ $(h, k) = (2, -2), a = 4, b^2 = 48$

$\frac{(x-2)^2}{16} - \frac{(y+2)^2}{48} = 1$ Simplify.

41. $\frac{x^2}{25} - \frac{y^2}{4} = 1$ **43.** (2308, 826) **45.** $\frac{(x-3)^2}{5} - \frac{(y+2)^2}{5} = 1$ **47.** Sample answer: When 36 changes to 9, the vertical hyperbola widens (splits out from the y-axis faster). This is due to a smaller value of y being needed to produce the same value of x. The vertices are moved closer together due to the value of a decreasing from 6 to 3. The foci move farther from the vertices because the difference between c and a increased.
49. Sample answer: The graphs of ellipses are closed in, while the branches of the hyperbolas extend without bound. There is always an upper and lower limit to the values of the coordinates of an ellipse, while maximum x- and y-values for the coordinates of hyperbolas are infinite. When both of the x^2 and y^2 terms are on the same side of the equation, the equation is for an ellipse if the signs of their coefficients are the same. Otherwise it is a hyperbola. (This is true only for conics that are not rotated.)

51. I **53.** D **55.** $\frac{y^2}{100} + \frac{x^2}{36} = 1$

57. (0, 3), 5 units

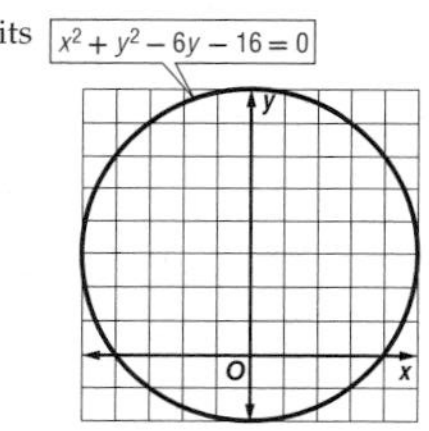

59a.

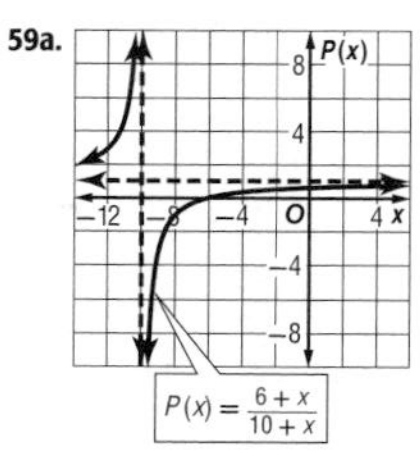

59b. the part in the first quadrant **59c.** It represents her original free-throw percentage of 60%. **59d.** $P(x) = 1$; this represents 100%, which she cannot achieve because she has already missed 4 free throws. **61.** $\frac{5}{3}$

63.

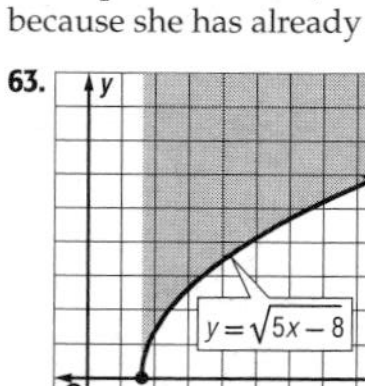

65.

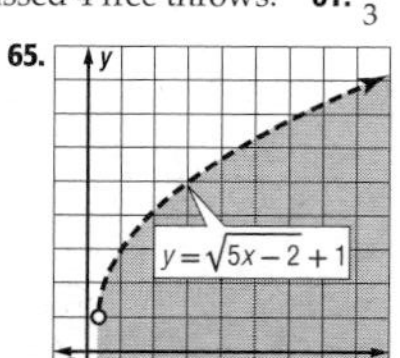

67. $y = \frac{4}{3}(x + 3)^2 - 4$

Pages 658–660 Lesson 10-6

1. $\frac{(x-3)^2}{36} + \frac{(y+2)^2}{9} = 1$; ellipse

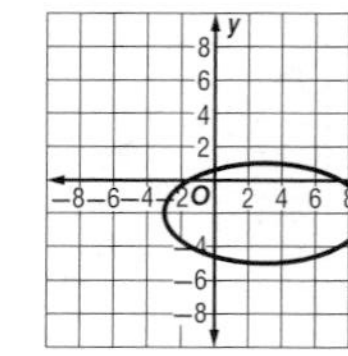

3. $\frac{(y-1)^2}{16} - \frac{(x+2)^2}{9} = 1$; hyperbola

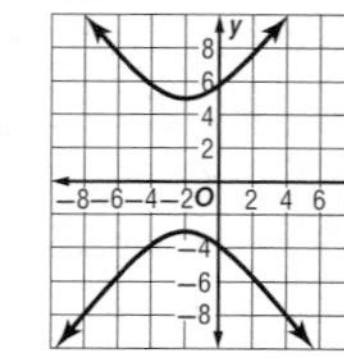

5. ellipse **7.** circle **9.** hyperbola **11.** ellipse
13a. parabola; $y = -0.024(x - 660)^2 + 10{,}500$
13b. about 1320 ft **13c.** 10,500 ft

15. $\frac{(x+4)^2}{32} + \frac{(y-5)^2}{24} = 1$; ellipse

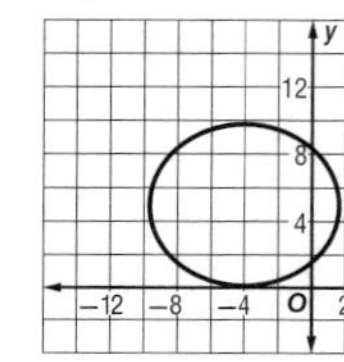

17. $y = 8(x + 2)^2 - 4$; parabola

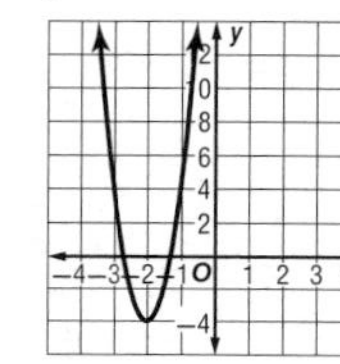

19. $(x - 3)^2 + (y + 4)^2 = 36$; circle

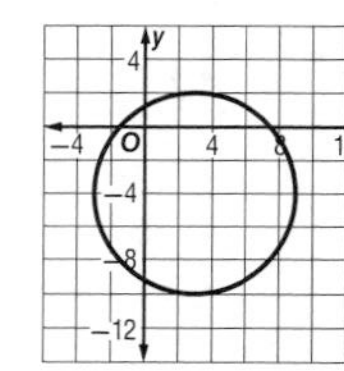

21. $\frac{(x+4)^2}{21} - \frac{(y-8)^2}{24} = 1$; hyperbola

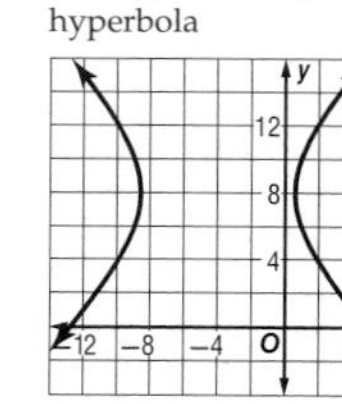

23. $\frac{(x+4)^2}{64} - \frac{(y-3)^2}{25} = 1$; hyperbola

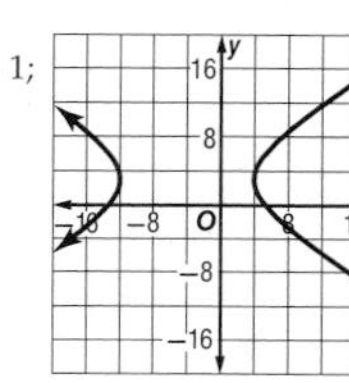

25. circle

27 $18x^2 - 16y = 12x - 4y^2 + 19$ Original equation

$18x^2 + 4y^2 - 12x - 16y - 19 = 0$ Standard form

$A = 18, B = 0$, and $C = 4$

$B^2 - 4AC = 0^2 - 4(18)(4)$ or -288

Since the discriminant is less than 0 and $A \neq C$, the conic is an ellipse.

29. hyperbola **31.** hyperbola **33.** hyperbola **35.** c

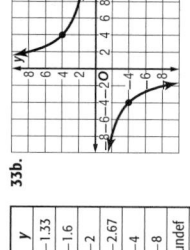

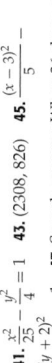

For Homework Help, go to Hotmath.com

37. b **39.** b

41 Equation *c* can be written as $y = -16x^2 + 90x + 0.25$. Since this is an equation of a parabola that opens downward, it could be used to represent the height of a football above the ground after being kicked.

43a. $\frac{(x-3)^2}{16} + \frac{(y+2)^2}{4} = 1$

43b. $x^2 + 4y^2 - 6x + 16y + 9 = 0$

43c.

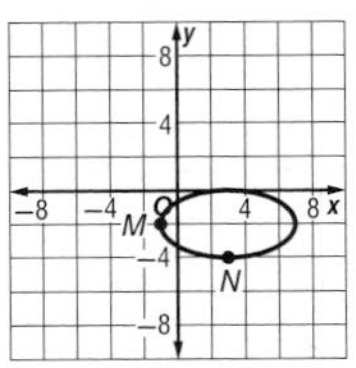

43d. $N(5, -2)$; 90° counterclockwise

45. Sample answer: Always; when a conic is vertical, $B = 0$. When this is true and $A = C$, the conic is a circle.

47. Sample answer: An ellipse is a flattened circle. Both circles and ellipses are enclosed regions, while hyperbolas and parabolas are not. A parabola has one branch, which is a smooth curve that never ends, and a hyperbola has two such branches that are reflections of each other. In standard form and when there is no *xy*-term: an equation for a parabola consists of only one squared term, an equation for a circle has values for *A* and *C* that are equal, an equation for an ellipse has values for *A* and *C* that are the same sign but not equal, and an equation for a hyperbola has values of *A* and *C* that have opposite signs. **49.** I **51.** B

53.

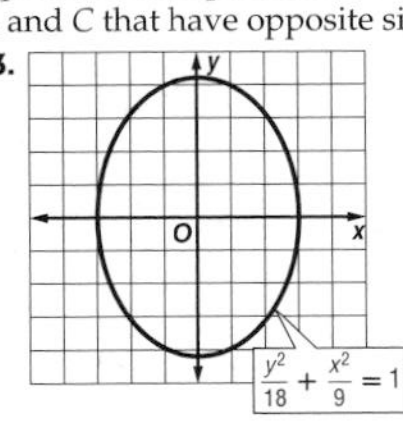

$(0, 0)$; $(0, \pm3)$; $6\sqrt{2}$; 6

55.

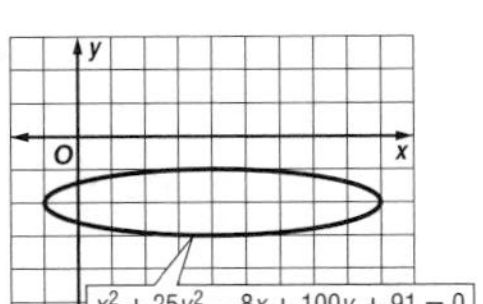

$(4, 2)$; $(4 \pm 2\sqrt{6}, -2)$; 10; 2

57.

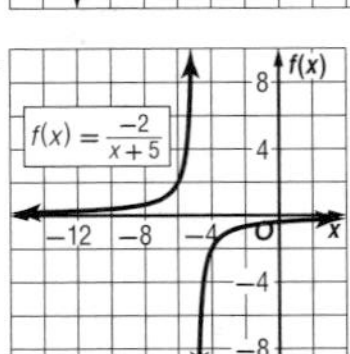

59a. Decay; the exponent is negative. **59b.** about 33.5 watts **59c.** about 402 days **61.** $\left(-\frac{1}{2}, \frac{3}{2}\right)$

Pages 664–667 Lesson 10-7

1. $(4, -5), (-4, 5)$ **3.** $(3, 6), (6, 42)$ **5.** no solution

7 Solve the second equation for x^2.

$y^2 - x^2 = 8 \rightarrow y^2 - 8 = x^2$

$x^2 + 2y = 7$ Write the first equation.

$y^2 - 8 + 2y = 7$ Substitute $y^2 - 8$ for x^2.

$y^2 + 2y - 15 = 0$ Subtract 7 from each side.

$(y - 3)(y + 5) = 0$ Factor.

$y - 3 = 0$ or $y + 5 = 0$ Zero Product Property

$y = 3$ $\quad y = -5$ Solve each equation.

Substitute 3 and −5 into one of the original equations and solve for *x*.

$x^2 + 2y = 7$ $\qquad x^2 + 2y = 7$

$x^2 + 2(3) = 7$ $\qquad x^2 + 2(-5) = 7$

$x^2 + 6 = 7$ $\qquad x^2 - 10 = 7$

$x^2 = 1$ $\qquad x^2 = 17$

$x = \pm1$ $\qquad x = \pm\sqrt{17}$

The solutions are $(-1, 3), (1, 3), (-\sqrt{17}, -5), (\sqrt{17}, -5)$.

9. $(40, 30)$ **11.**

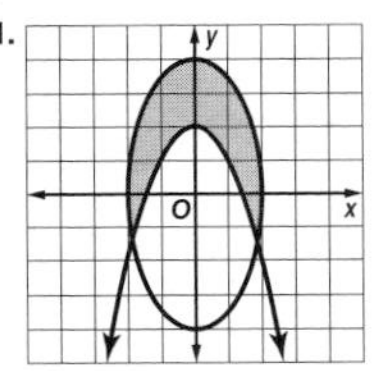

13.

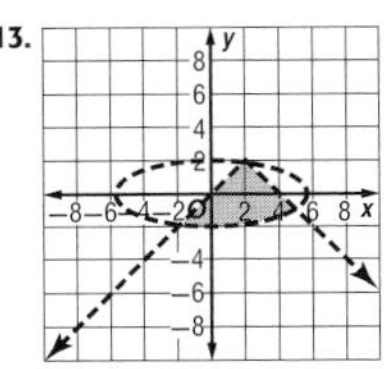

15. no solution
17. $(-3, -6), (3, 6)$
19. $(-1, -3), (8, 5)$
21. $(1, -\sqrt{15}), (1, \sqrt{15})$
23. $(-\sqrt{2}, 4), (\sqrt{2}, 4)$
25. $(5, -6), (5, 6), (-3, -2), (-3, 2)$

27.

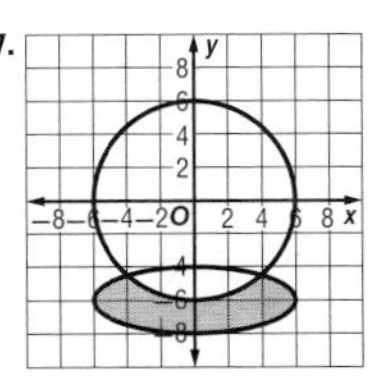

29.

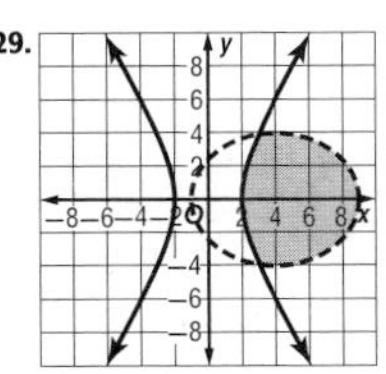

31.

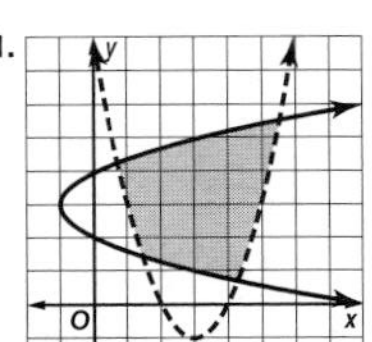

33.

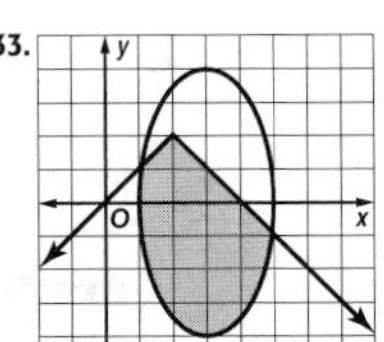

35.

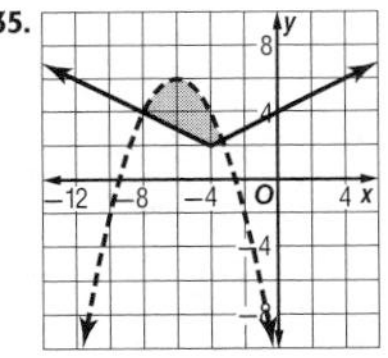

37. no solution

39a. $y = \pm900\sqrt{1 - \frac{x^2}{(300)^2}}$; $y = \pm690\sqrt{1 - \frac{x^2}{(600)^2}}$

39b. Sample answer: $(209, 647), (-209, 647), (-209, -647), (209, -647)$

39c. Sample answer: The orbit of the satellite modeled by the second equation is closer to a circle than the other orbit. The distance on the *x*-axis is twice as great for one satellite as for the other.

41 $y = -0.0037x^2 + 1.77x - 1.72$ Path of baseball equation

$\frac{3}{7}x - 128.6 = -0.0037x^2 + 1.77x - 1.72$ Substitute $\frac{3}{7}x - 128.6$ for *y*.

$-128.6 \approx -0.0037x^2 + 1.34x - 1.72$ Substitute $\frac{3}{7}x$ from each side.

$0 \approx -0.0037x^2 + 1.34x + 126.88$ Add 128.6 to each side.

$x = \frac{-b \pm \sqrt{b^2 - 4ac}}{2a}$ Quadratic Formula

$x = \frac{-1.34 \pm \sqrt{1.34^2 - 4(-0.0037)(126.88)}}{2(-0.0037)}$ $a = -0.0037$, $b = 1.34$, $c = 126.88$

$x \approx \frac{-1.34 \pm \sqrt{3.67}}{-0.0074}$ Simplify.

$x \approx -78$ or $x \approx 440$ Use a calculator.

Since the vertical distance cannot be negative, the ball landed about 440 ft from home plate.

$y = \frac{3}{7}x - 128.6$ Original equation

$y = \frac{3}{7}(440) - 128.6$ Replace *x* with 440.

$y \approx 60$ Use a calculator.

The ball was 60 ft above the playing surface.

43 Sample answer: A circle with the equation $(x + 10)^2 + y^2 = 36$ has its center at $(-10, 0)$ and contains the point $(-4, 0)$. An ellipse with the equation $\frac{x^2}{16} + \frac{y^2}{36} = 1$ has its center at $(0, 0)$ and contains the point $(-4, 0)$. The circle and ellipse intersect only $(-4, 0)$.

45. Sample answer: $x^2 + y^2 = 1$ and $\frac{x^2}{16} - \frac{y^2}{36} = 1$

47. Sample answer: $\frac{x^2}{64} + \frac{y^2}{100} = 1$ and $x^2 - y^2 = 1$

49. Sample answer: No; if one player is in one of the shaded areas and the other player is in the other shaded area, they will not be able to hear each other.

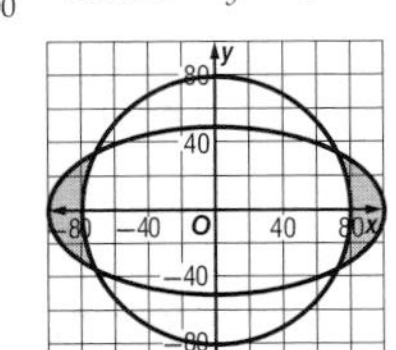

51. $k = a$ or $k = b$ **53.** Sample answer: $\frac{y^2}{128} + \frac{x^2}{32} = 1$ and $\frac{x^2}{8} - \frac{y^2}{64} = 1$ **55.** $(-3, -4), (3, 4)$ **57.** F **59.** b **61.** c

63. $(2, -2), (2, 8)$; $(2, 3 \pm \sqrt{41})$; $y - 3 = \pm\frac{5}{4}(x - 2)$

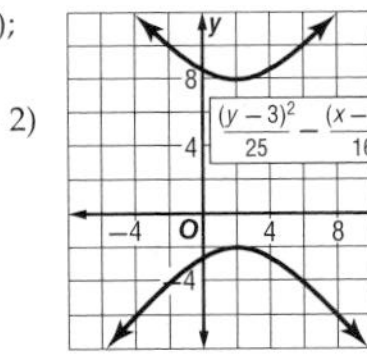

65. $\frac{p+5}{p+1}$ **67.** $\frac{3(r+4)}{r+3}$

69.

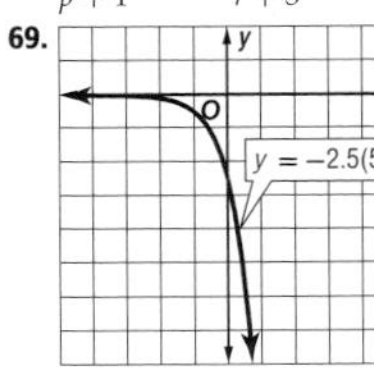

D = {all real numbers}, R = {$y \mid y < 0$}

71. $\frac{d}{t} = r$ **73.** $\frac{3V}{\pi r^2} = h$

Pages 668–672 Chapter 10 Study Guide and Review

1. false, center **3.** false, vertices **5.** true **7.** false, circle **9.** true **11.** $\left(-\frac{5}{2}, 5\right)$ **13.** $\left(\frac{5}{24}, \frac{5}{24}\right)$ **15.** $\sqrt{85}$ **17.** $\frac{\sqrt{34}}{4}$ **19a.** $\sqrt{89} \approx 9.4$ miles **19b.** $\left(4, -\frac{5}{2}\right)$

21.

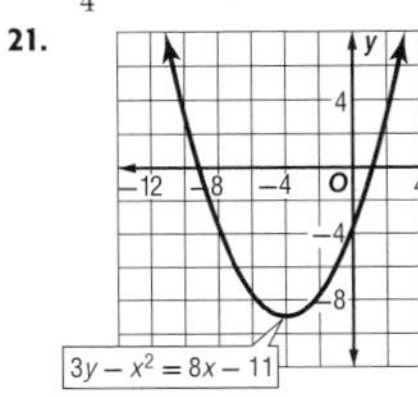

23.

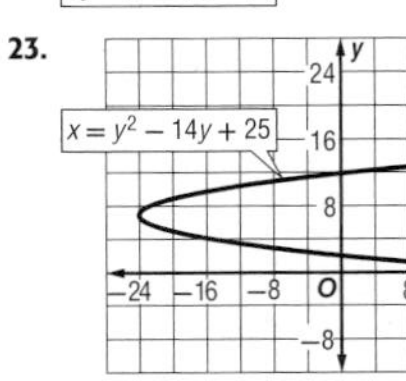

25. $y = 4(x - 2)^2 - 7$; vertex: $(2, -7)$; axis of symmetry: $x = 2$; opens up **27.** $x = (y + 7)^2 - 29$; vertex $= (-29, -7)$; axis of symmetry: $y = -7$; opens to the right **29.** $(x + 1) + (y - 6)^2 = 9$

31. $(x - 1)^2 + (y + 4)^2 = 13$

33. $(3, -1)$; $r = 5$

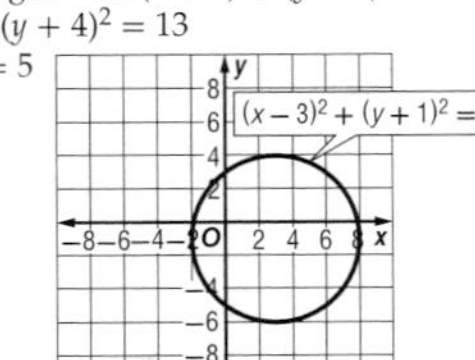

For Homework Help, go to Hotmath.com

35. $(-2, 1)$; $r = 4$

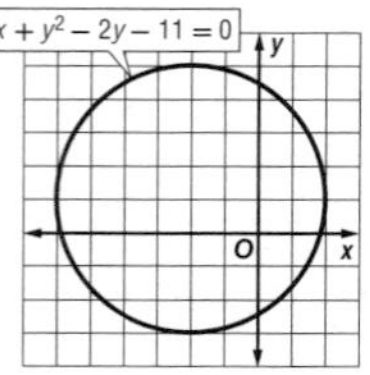

37. $(0, 0)$; $(0, \pm 3\sqrt{3})$; 12; 6

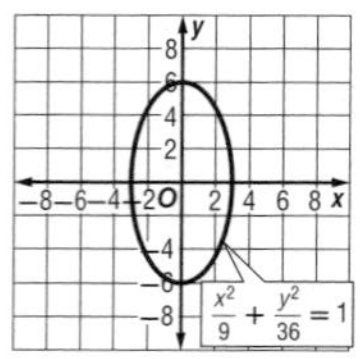

39. $(0, 4)$; $(\pm 4\sqrt{2}, 4)$; 12; 4

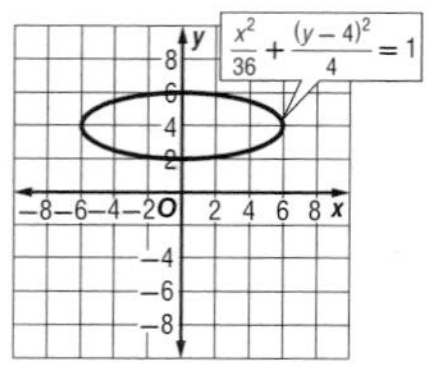

41. $(-1, 2)$; $(-4, 2)$; $(2, 2)$; 10; 8

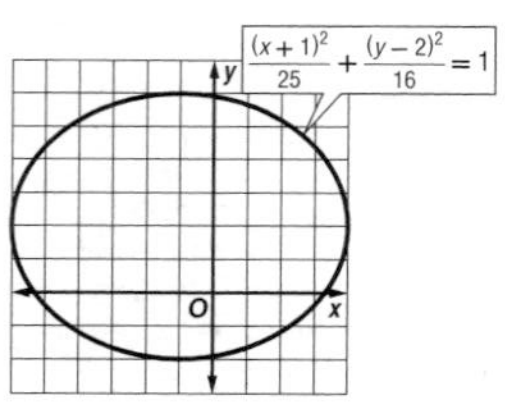

43. $(1, -1)$; $(-3, -1)$, $(5, -1)$; 10; 6

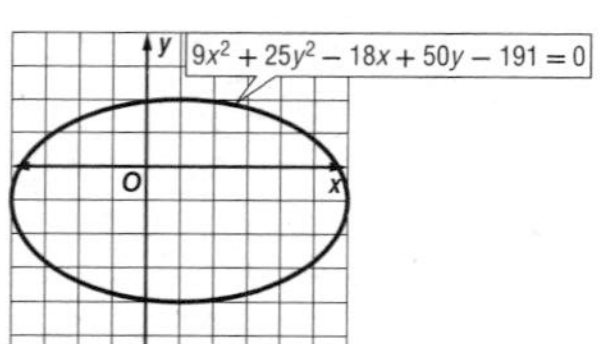

45. $\frac{x^2}{64} + \frac{y^2}{25} = 1$

47. $(2, -2)$, $(4, -2)$; $(3 \pm \sqrt{5}; -2)$; $y + 2 = \pm 2(x - 3)$

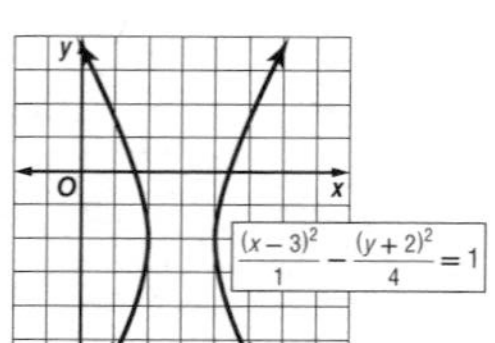

49. $(\pm 3, 0)$; $(\pm\sqrt{13}, 0)$; $y = \pm\frac{2}{3}x$

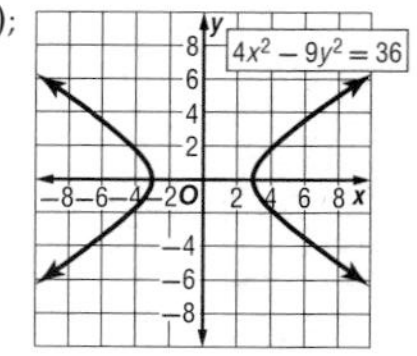

51. $\left(\frac{40 - 24\sqrt{5}}{5}, \frac{45 - 12\sqrt{5}}{5}\right)$

53. $\frac{x^2}{16} + \frac{y^2}{9} = 1$; ellipse

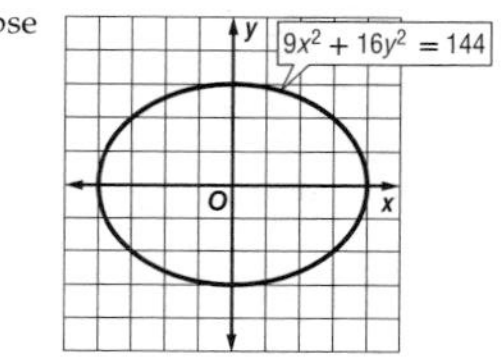

55. $\frac{y^2}{9} - \frac{(x-2)^2}{1} = 1$; hyperbola

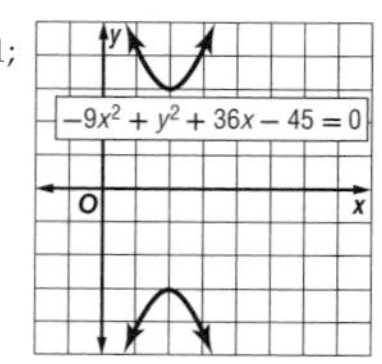

57. hyperbola **59.** circle **61.** $(2, -2)$, $(-2, 2)$

63. $(4, 0)$ **65.** $(1, \pm 5)$, $(-1, \pm 5)$

67a. 1.5 seconds

67b. 109 feet

69.

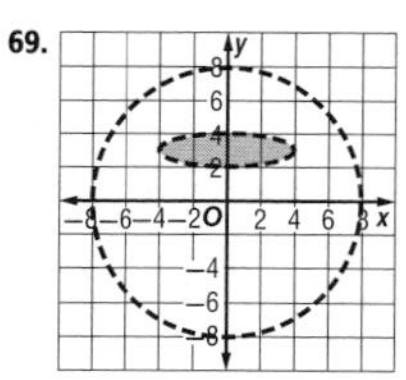

71.

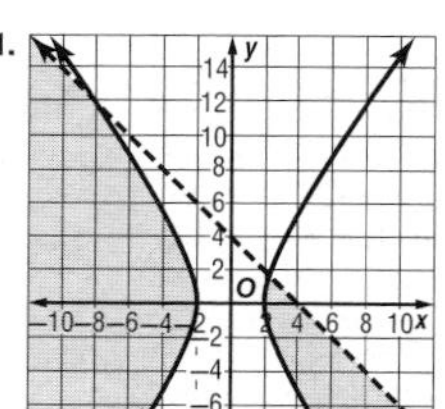

73.

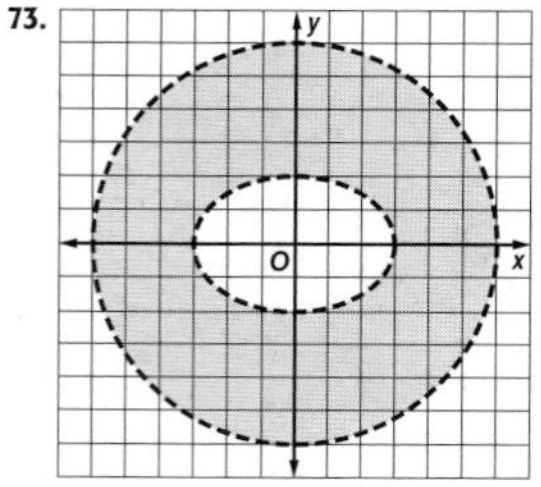

Chapter 11 Sequences and Series

Page 679 Chapter 11 Get Ready

1. $x = -12$ **3.** $x = 3$ **5.** 9 rows

7.

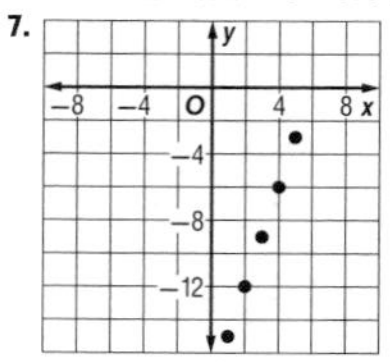

9.

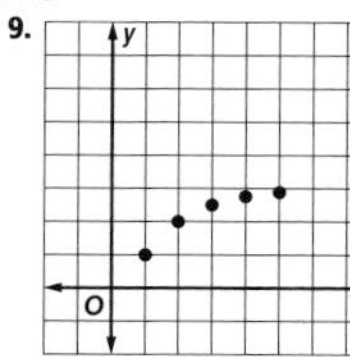

11. -30 **13.** $-\frac{2}{729}$

Pages 685–687 Lesson 11-1

1. yes **3.** no

5. 42, 54, 66, 78

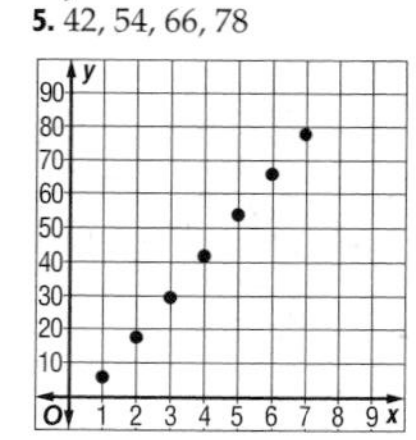

7. 5, 13, 21, 29

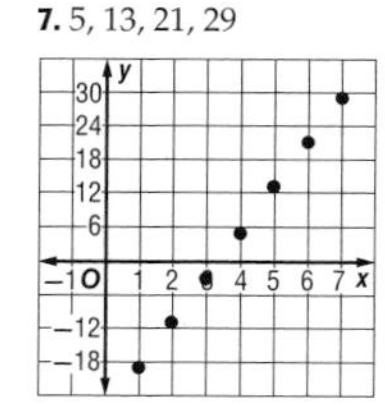

9a. \$850 **9b.** 24 wk **11.** yes **13.** no

15. 128, 256, 512

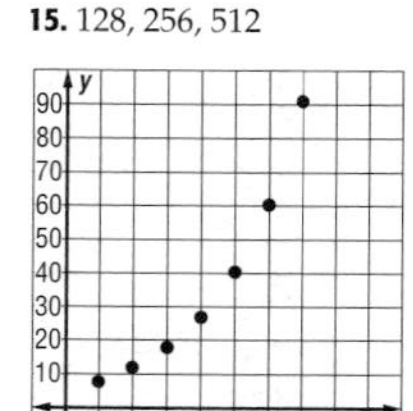

17. $\frac{1}{9}, -\frac{1}{27}, \frac{1}{81}$

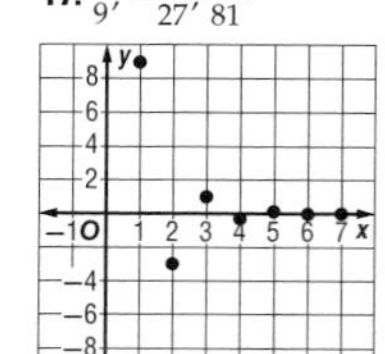

19. Geometric; the common ratio is $-\frac{1}{2}$. **21.** no **23.** no

25. 8, 11, 14, 17

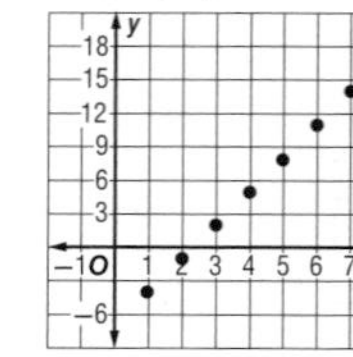

27. $-29, -35, -41, -47$

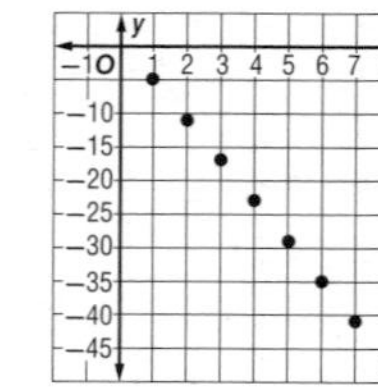

29. $2, \frac{13}{5}, \frac{16}{5}, \frac{19}{5}$

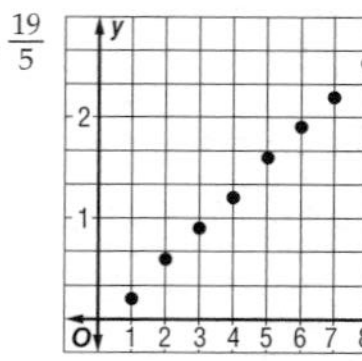

31 The difference between any two consecutive rows is 2, so the common difference is 2. Use point-slope form to write an equation for the sequence. Let $m = 2$ and $(x_1, y_1) = (1, 28)$. Solve for $x = 24$.

$(y - y_1) = m(x - x_1)$	Point-slope form
$(y - 28) = 2(x - 1)$	$m = 2$, $(x_1, y_1) = (1, 28)$
$y - 28 = 2x - 2$	Multiply.
$y = 2x + 26$	Add 28 to each side.
$y = 2(24) + 26$	Replace x with 24.
$y = 48 + 26$ or 74	Simplify.

There are 74 seats in the last row of the theater.

33. no

35 $\frac{18}{-27} = \frac{2}{3}$ and $\frac{-12}{18} = \frac{2}{3}$

Since the ratios of the consecutive terms are the same, the sequence is geometric.

37. no **39.** $-8, 32, -128$

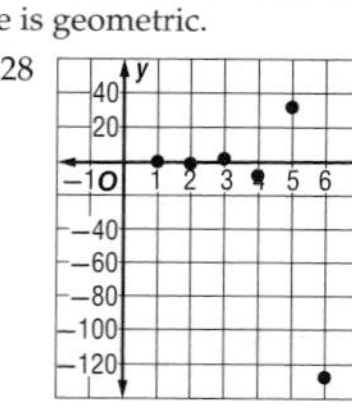

41. $27, \frac{81}{4}, \frac{243}{16}$

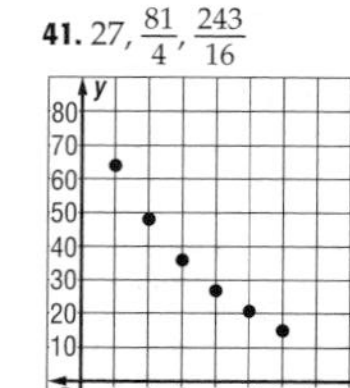

43. 27, 81, 243

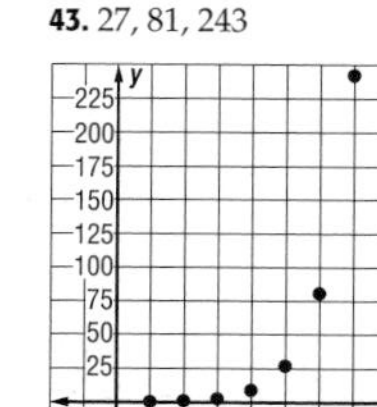

45. Neither; there is no common difference or ratio.

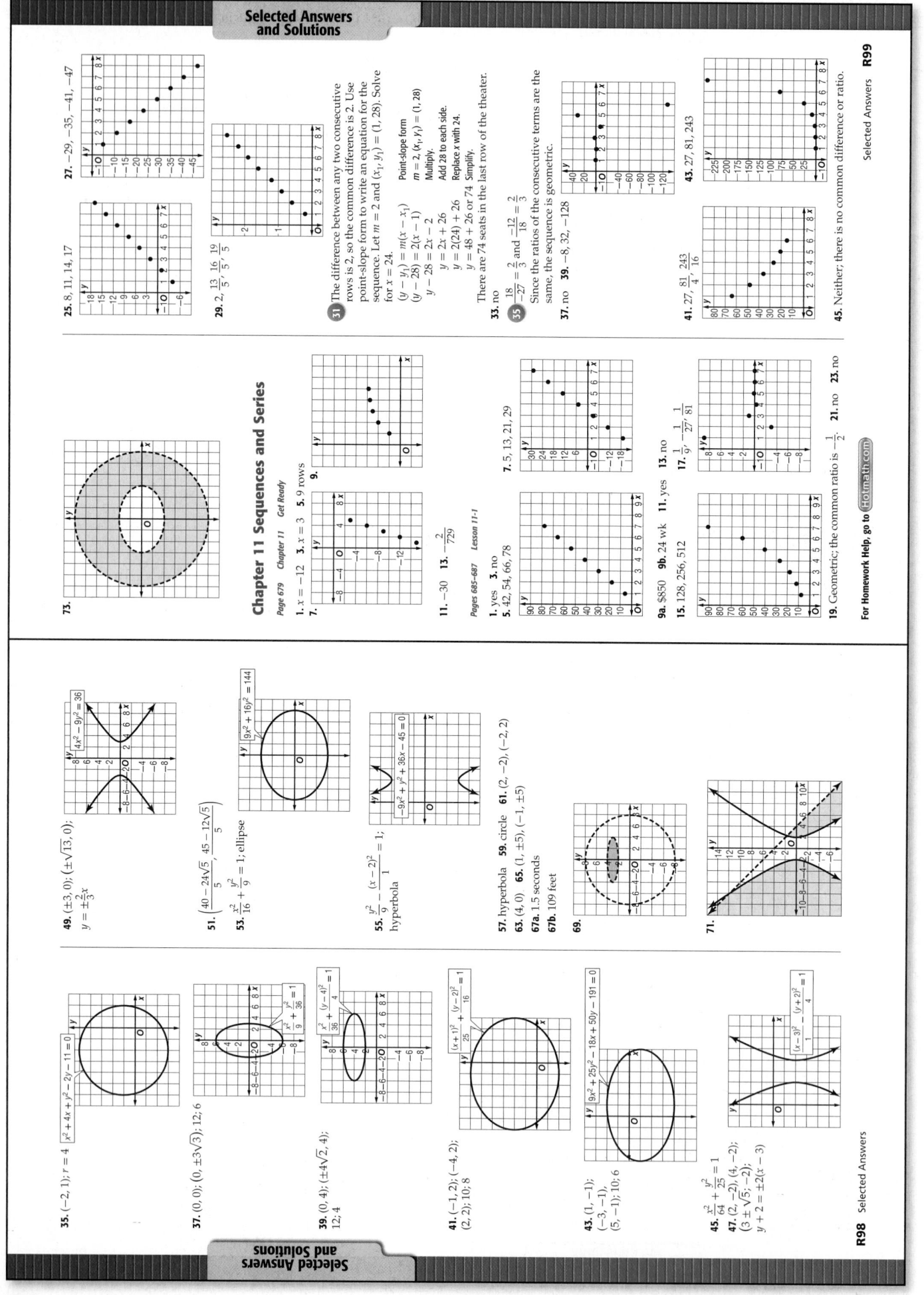

47. Geometric; the common ratio is 3. **49.** Arithmetic; the common difference is $\frac{1}{2}$. **51.** 86 pg/day **53.** about 13,744 km **55.** Sample answer: A babysitter earns $20 for cleaning the house and $8 extra for every hour she watches the children. **57.** Sample answer: Neither; the sequence is both arithmetic and geometric.
59. Sample answer: If a geometric sequence has a ratio r such that $|r| < 1$, as n increases, the absolute value of the terms will decrease and approach zero because they are continuously being multiplied by a fraction. When $|r| \geq 1$, the absolute value of the terms will increase and approach infinity because they are continuously being multiplied by a value greater than 1. **61.** $421.85
63. H **65.** $(\pm 4, 5)$ **67.** no solution
69. hyperbola; $\frac{x^2}{4} - \frac{y^2}{1} = 1$

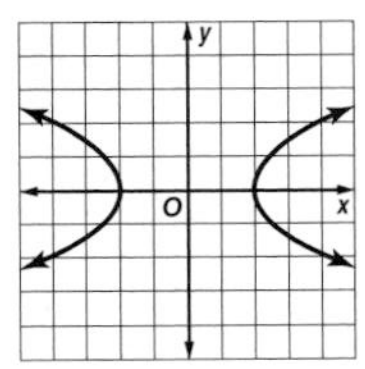

71.

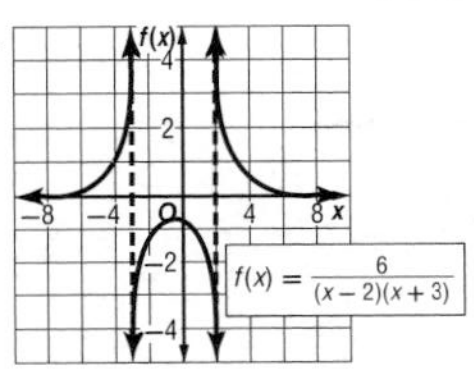

73.

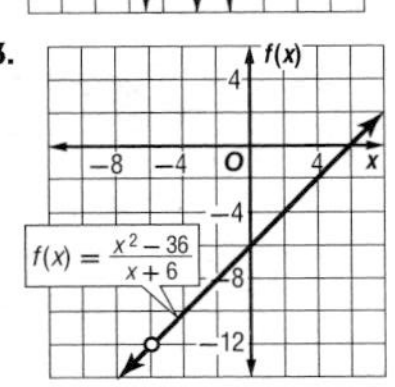

75. $y = 0.5x + 1$ **77.** $y = 3x - 6$ **79.** $y = -\frac{1}{2}x + \frac{7}{2}$

Pages 692–695 Lesson 11-2

1. 104 **3.** $a_n = 6n + 7$ **5.** 15, 24, 33 **7.** 1275 **9.** 4500 **11.** 8, 12, 16 **13.** C **15.** 248 **17.** −103 **19.** 14
21. $a_n = -14n + 45$

23
$a_n = a_1 + (n-1)d$ — nth term of an arithmetic sequence
$21 = a_1 + (7-1)5$ — $a_7 = 21$, $n = 7$, and $d = 5$
$21 = a_1 + 30$ — Multiply.
$-9 = a_1$ — Subtract 30 from each side.
$a_n = a_1 + (n-1)d$ — nth term of an arithmetic sequence
$a_n = -9 + (n-1)5$ — $a_1 = -9$ and $d = 5$
$a_n = -9 + (5n - 5)$ — Distributive Property
$a_n = 5n - 14$ — Simplify.

25. $a_n = 4.5n - 21$ **27.** $a_n = 9n - 32$ **29.** $a_n = \frac{2}{3}n - 3$
31. $a_n = \frac{1}{2}n - \frac{23}{10}$ **33.** 19, 14, 9, 4 **35.** −21, −14, −7, 0

37. −21, −30, −39, −48, −57 **39.** 10,100 **41.** 10,000 **43.** 696 **45.** 1272 **47.** $4400 **49.** 48, 60, 72

51
$S_n = n\left(\frac{a_1 + a_n}{2}\right)$ — Sum Formula
$2982 = 28\left(\frac{a_1 + 228}{2}\right)$ — $S_n = 2982$, $n = 28$, $a_n = 228$
$2982 = 14a_1 + 3192$ — Simplify.
$-210 = 14a_1$ — Subtract 3192 from each side.
$-15 = a_1$ — Divide each side by 14.
$a_n = a_1 + (n-1)d$ — nth term of an arithmetic sequence
$228 = -15 + (28-1)d$ — $a_n = 228$, $a_1 = -15$, $n = 28$
$243 = 27d$ — Add 15 to each side.
$9 = d$ — Divide each side by 27.
$a_1 = -15$, $a_2 = -15 + 9$ or -6, $a_3 = -6 + 9$ or 3
The first three terms are −15, −6, 3.

53. −44, −30, −16 **55.** −33, −21, −9 **57.** 512 **59.** 324 **61.** $2250 **63.** $a_n = 13n - 1055$ **65.** $a_n = 9n - 88$
67a. 14, 18, 22

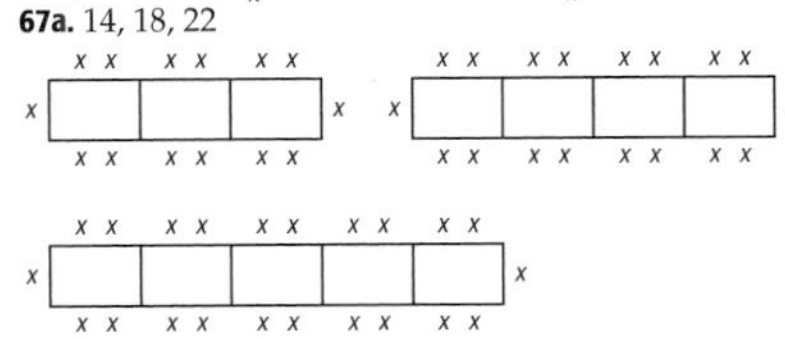

67b. $p_n = 4n + 2$ **67c.** No; there is no whole number n for which $4n + 2 = 100$.

69
$a_n = a_1 + (n-1)d$ — nth term of an arithmetic sequence
$100{,}000 = 28{,}000 + (n-1)4000$ — $a_n = 100{,}000$, $a_1 = 28{,}000$, $d = 4000$
$72{,}000 = (n-1)4000$ — Subtract 28,000 from each side.
$18 = n - 1$ — Divide each side by 4000.
$19 = n$ — Add 1 to each side.
He will have a salary of $100,000 in the 19th year.

71a.

n	S_n
1	4
2	10
3	18
4	28
5	40
6	54
7	70
8	88
9	108
10	130

71b.

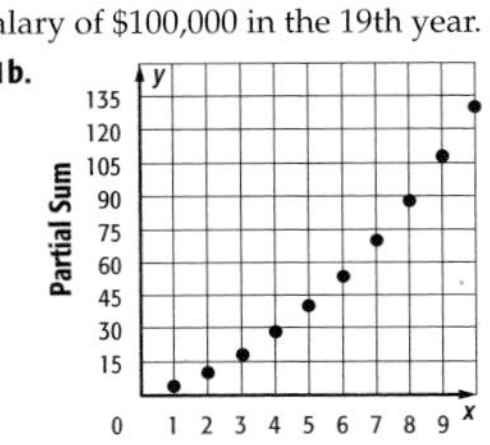

71c.

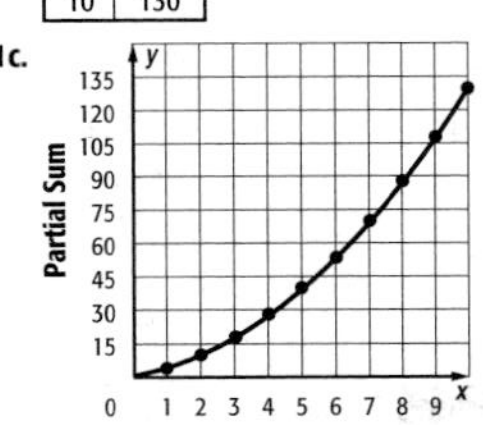

71d. Sample answer: The graphs cover the same range. The domain of the series is the natural numbers, while the domain of the quadratic function is all real numbers, $0 \leq x \leq 10$.

71e. Sample answer: For every partial sum of an arithmetic series, there is a corresponding quadratic function that shares the same range. **71f.** $\sum_{k=1}^{x} 2k + 7$

73. 16 **75.** $4b - 3a$ **77.** $S_n = nx + y\left(\frac{n^2 + n}{2}\right)$

79. Sample answer: An arithmetic sequence is a list of terms such that any pair of successive terms has a common difference. An arithmetic series is the sum of the terms of an arithmetic sequence.

81.
$S_n = (a_1 + a_n) \cdot \left(\frac{n}{2}\right)$ — General sum formula
$a_n = a_1 + (n-1)d$ — Formula for nth term
$a_n - (n-1)d = a_1$ — Subtract $(n-1)d$ from both sides.
$S_n = [a_n - (n-1)d + a_n] \cdot \left(\frac{n}{2}\right)$ — Substitution
$S_n = [2a_n - (n-1)d] \cdot \left(\frac{n}{2}\right)$ — Simplify.

83. B **85.** A **87.** yes **89.** no
91.

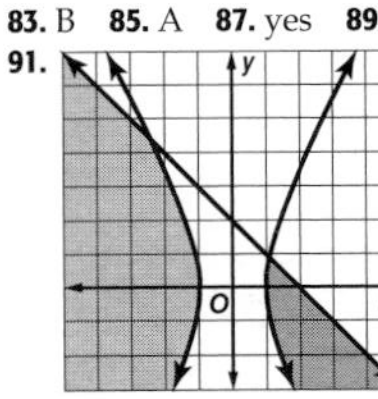

93a. 4.8 cm/g **93b.** 24 cm; The answer is reasonable. The object would stretch the first spring 60 cm and would stretch the second spring 40 cm. The object would have to stretch the combined springs less than it would stretch either of the springs individually.

95.

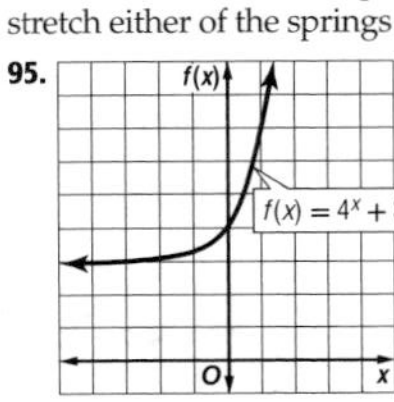

D = {all real numbers}, R = $\{f(x) \mid f(x) > 3\}$
97. 2.4550
99. 0.4341

Pages 699–702 Lesson 11-3

1. 2046 **3.** $a_n = 18 \cdot \left(\frac{1}{3}\right)^{n-1}$

5
$a_n = a_1 r^{n-1}$ — nth term of a geometric sequence
$4 = a_1(3^{2-1})$ — $a_n = 4$, $r = 3$, and $n = 2$
$4 = a_1(3)$ — Evaluate the power.
$\frac{4}{3} = a_1$ — Divide each side by 3.
$a_n = a_1 r^{n-1}$ — nth term of a geometric sequence
$a_n = \frac{4}{3}(3)^{n-1}$ — $a_1 = \frac{4}{3}$, $r = 3$

7. $a_n = 12(-8)^{n-1}$ **9.** 1, 5, 25 or −1, 5, −25 **11.** 4095 **13.** $\frac{1}{16}$ **15.** 512 **17.** 93 in. **19.** 25 **21.** 512 **23.** $a_n = (-3)(-2)^{n-1}$ **25.** $a_n = (-1)(-1)^{n-1}$
27. $a_n = 8 \cdot \left(\frac{1}{4}\right)^{n-1}$ **29.** $a_n = 7(2)^{n-1}$
31. $a_n = \frac{1}{15{,}552}(6)^{n-1}$ **33.** $a_n = 648\left(\frac{1}{3}\right)^{n-1}$

35. 270, 90, 30 or −270, 90, −30 **37.** $\frac{7}{3}, \frac{14}{9}, \frac{28}{27}$ or $-\frac{7}{3}, \frac{14}{9}, -\frac{28}{27}$ **39.** 15 and 75 **41.** 99.19% **43.** 31.9375 **45.** 9707.82 **47.** 2188 **49.** −87,381

51
$S_n = \frac{a_1 - a_1 r^n}{1 - r}$ — Sum formula
$-2912 = \frac{a_1 - a_1(3^6)}{1 - 3}$ — $S_n = -2912$, $r = 3$, and $n = 6$
$-2912 = \frac{a_1(1 - 3^6)}{1 - 3}$ — Distributive Property
$-2912 = \frac{-728a_1}{-2}$ — Subtract.
$-2912 = 364a_1$ — Simplify.
$-8 = a_1$ — Divide each side by 364.

53. 64 **55.** 0.25

57
$S_n = \frac{a_1 - a_1 r^n}{1 - r}$ — Alternate Sum formula
$= \frac{100 - 100(0.5)^5}{1 - 0.5}$ — Substitution
$= 193.75$ ft — Use a calculator.

59. 524, 288 **61.** about 471 cm **63a.** $11.79, $30.58, $205.72 **63b.** $7052.15 **63c.** Each payment made is rounded to the nearest penny, so the sum of the payments will actually be more than the sum found in part b.

65.
$S_n = \frac{a_1 - a_n r}{1 - r}$ — Alternate sum formula
$a_n = a_1 \cdot r^{n-1}$ — Formula for nth term
$\frac{a_n}{r^{n-1}} = a_1$ — Divide both sides by r^{n-1}.
$S_n = \frac{\frac{a_n}{r^{n-1}} - a_n r}{1 - r}$ — Substitution.
$= \frac{\frac{a_n}{r^{n-1}} - \frac{a_n r \cdot r^{n-1}}{r^{n-1}}}{1 - r}$ — Multiply by $\frac{r^{n-1}}{\frac{r^{n-1}}{1}}$.
$= \frac{\frac{a_n(1 - r^n)}{r^{n-1}}}{1 - r}$ — Simplify.
$= \frac{a_n(1 - r^n)}{r^{n-1}(1 - r)}$ — Divide by $(1 - r)$.
$= \frac{a_n(1 - r^n)}{r^{n-1} - r^n}$ — Simplify.

67. Sample answer: $n - 1$ needs to change to n, and the 10 needs to change to a 9. When this happens, the terms for both series will be identical (a_1 in the first series will equal a_0 in the second series, and so on), and the series will be equal to each other. **69.** 234
71. Sample answer: 4 + 8 + 16 + 32 + 64 + 128 **73.** B **75.** $32,000 **77.** $1550 **79.** Arithmetic; the common difference is $\frac{1}{50}$.
81. (3, 1), 5 units

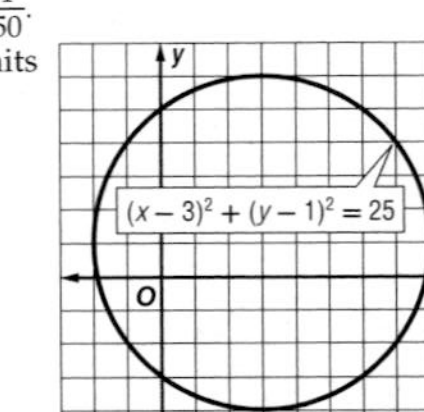

83. $(3, -7)$, $5\sqrt{2}$ units

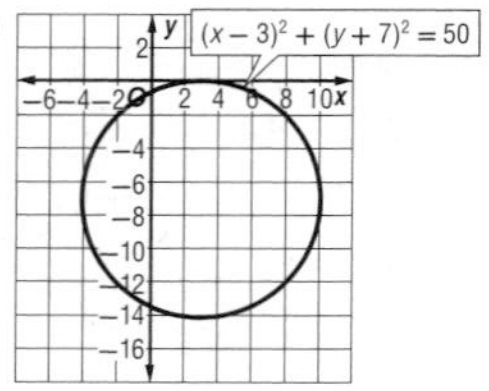

85. 731 customers **87.** $-\frac{5}{7}$ **89.** $\frac{27}{2}$

Pages 708–711 Lesson 11-4

1. convergent **3.** divergent **5.** 880 **7.** No sum exists. **9.** 12.5% **11.** −4 **13.** 2 **15.** $\frac{214}{333}$ **17.** convergent **19.** divergent **21.** divergent **23.** No sum exists.

25 $r = \frac{6}{5} \div \frac{12}{5}$ or $\frac{1}{2}$ Divide consecutive terms.

Since $\left|\frac{1}{2}\right| < 1$, the sum exists.

$S = \frac{a_1}{1-r}$ Sum formula

$= \frac{\frac{12}{5}}{1-\frac{1}{2}}$ $a_1 = \frac{12}{5}$ and $r = \frac{1}{2}$

$= \frac{12}{5} \div \frac{1}{2}$ or $\frac{24}{5}$ Simplify.

27. No sum exists. **29.** No sum exists. **31.** $\frac{35}{12}$ **33.** 16

35 $0.3\overline{21} = 0.3 + 0.021 + 0.00021 + \ldots$

$= \frac{3}{10} + \frac{21}{1000} + \frac{21}{100{,}000} + \ldots$

$S = \frac{a_1}{1-r} + \frac{3}{10}$ Sum formula

$= \frac{\frac{21}{1000}}{1-\frac{1}{100}} + \frac{3}{10}$ $a_1 = \frac{21}{1000}$ and $r = \frac{1}{100}$

$= \frac{2100}{99{,}000} + \frac{3}{10}$ Simplify.

$= \frac{107}{330} + \frac{3}{10}$ or $\frac{53}{165}$ Simplify.

37. $\frac{24}{11}$ **39.** $\frac{601}{4950}$ **41.** $\frac{40}{3}$ **43.** 8000 hrs **45.** $\frac{45}{4}$ **47.** No sum exists. **49.** $-\frac{54}{35}$ **51.** 200 ft **53.** 1170 ft

55 $S = \frac{a_1}{1-r}$ Sum formula

$= \frac{500}{1-0.8}$ $a_1 = 500$ and $r = 0.8$

$= \frac{500}{0.2}$ or \$2500 Simplify.

57. b **59.** a **61.** Sample answer: The sum of a geometric series is $S_n = \frac{a_1 - a_1r^n}{1-r}$. For an infinite series with $|r| < 1$, $r^n \to 0$ as $n \to \infty$. Thus, $S = \frac{a_1 - a_1(0)}{1-r}$ or $\frac{a_1}{1-r}$. **63.** Sample answer: An infinite geometric series has a sum when the common ratio is less than 1. When this occurs, the terms will approach 0 as n approaches infinity. With the future terms almost 0, the sum of the series will approach a limit. When the common ratio is 1 or greater, the terms will keep increasing and approach infinity as n approaches infinity and the sum of the series will have no limit. **65.** Sample answer: $3 + 2 + \frac{4}{3} + \ldots$ **67.** An arithmetic series has a common difference, so each term will eventually become more positive or more negative, but never approach 0. With the terms not approaching 0, the sum will never reach a limit and the series cannot converge. **69.** H **71.** C **73a.** 9, 18, 27, 36, 45, 54, 63, 72 **73b.** 42 meetings **75.** 12

Pages 717–719 Lesson 11-5

1. 16, 20, 24, 28, 32 **3.** 5, 17, 53, 161, 485 **5.** $a_{n+1} = 2a_n + 2$; $a_1 = 3$ **7a.** $a_n = 1.01a_{n-1} - 100$, $a_1 = 1500$ **7b.** \$1415, \$1329.15, \$1242.44, \$1154.87 **7c.** \$77.08 **9.** −18, 74, −294 **11.** −52, −420, −3364 **13.** −9, −10, −12, −16, −24 **15.** −4, −7, −12, −21, −38

17 $a_{n+1} = 5a_n + 2n$ Recursive formula

$a_{1+1} = 5a_1 + 2(1)$ $n = 1$

$a_2 = 5(-2) + 2(1)$ or -8 $a_1 = -2$

$a_3 = 5(-8) + 2(2)$ or -36 $a_2 = -8, n = 2$

$a_4 = 5(-36) + 2(3)$ or -174 $a_3 = -36, n = 3$

$a_5 = 5(-174) + 2(4)$ or -862 $a_4 = -36, n = 4$

The first five terms are −2, −8, −36, −174, and −862.

19. 4, 5, 6, 8, 8 **21.** 3, $2x$, $8x - 9$, $26x - 36$, $80x - 117$ **23.** 1, x, $3x + 6$, $15x + 18$, $63x + 90$ **25.** $a_{n+1} = 0.25a_n + 4$; $a_1 = 32$ **27.** $a_{n+1} = (a_n)^3 + 1$; $a_1 = 1$ **29.** $a_{n+1} = 0.25a_n + 8$; $a_1 = 480$ **31.** $a_{n+1} = 2a_n - 32$; $a_1 = 84$ **33.** 56, 680, 8168 **35.** −45, 273, −1635 **37.** −3, −18, −963 **39.** 43, 3484, 24,259,093 **41.** 4.25, 29.5625, 936.0664

43 **a.** The number of blue triangles is 1, 3, and 9. The sequence is geometric because each term after the first can be found after multiplying by a common ratio, 3.

$a_n = r \cdot a_{n-1}$ Recursive formula for geometric sequence

$a_n = 3a_{n-1}, a_1 = 1$ $r = 3$

b. $a_1 = 1, a_2 = 3, a_3 = 9$

$a_n = 3a_{n-1}$ Recursive formula

$a_4 = 3a_3$ $n = 4$

$= 3(9)$ or 27 $a_3 = 9$

$a_5 = 3a_4$ $n = 5$

$= 3(27)$ or 81 $a_4 = 27$

$a_6 = 3a_5$ $n = 6$

$= 3(81)$ or 243 $a_5 = 27$

There will be 243 blue triangles in the sixth figure.

45. No; the population of fish will reach 12,500. Each year, 20% of 12,500 or 2500 fish plus 10,000 additional fish yields 12,500 fish. **47a.** 11,000 **47b.** It converges to 7142.857. **47c.** Sample answer: They make it easier to analyze recursive sequences because they can produce the first 100 terms instantaneously; it would take a long time to calculate the terms by hand. **49.** Armando; Marcus included x_0 with the iterates and only showed the first 2 iterates. **51.** Sample answer: Sometimes; the recursive formula could involve the first three terms. For example, 2, 2, 2, 8, 20, … is recursive with $a_{n+3} = a_n + a_{n+1} + 2a_{n+2}$. **53.** Sample answer: In a recursive sequence, each term is determined by one or more of the previous terms. A recursive formula is used to produce the terms of the recursive sequence. **55a.** 160 m **55b.** 5.7 s **55c.** 11.4 s **57.** C **59.** $5\frac{14}{111}$ **61a.** 2, 3, 4.5, 6.75, 10.125 **61b.** the eighth session **61c.** during the ninth session **63.** dependent **65.** $x^2 + 4x - 12$ **67.** $4h^2 + 33h + 35$ **69.** $10g^2 + 19g - 56$

Pages 723–725 Lesson 11-6

1. $c^5 + 5c^4d + 10c^3d^2 + 10c^2d^3 + 5cd^4 + d^5$ **3.** $x^6 - 24x^5 + 240x^4 - 1280x^3 + 3840x^2 - 6144x + 4096$ **5.** $x^5 + 15x^4 + 90x^3 + 270x^2 + 405x + 243$ **7.** $\frac{3}{32}$ or 0.09375

9 $(x + 3y)^8 = \sum_{k=0}^{8} \frac{8!}{k!(8-k)!}x^{8-k}(3y)^k$

$\frac{8!}{k!(8-k)!}x^{8-k}(3y)^k = \frac{8!}{4!(8-4)!}x^{8-4}(3y)^4$ For the fifth term, $k = 4$.

$= 70x^4(81y^4)$ $C(8, 4) = 70$, $(3y)^4 = 81y^4$

$= 5670x^4y^4$ Simplify.

11. $-108{,}864c^3d^5$ **13.** $243a^5$ **15.** $a^6 - 6a^5b + 15a^4b^2 - 20a^3b^3 + 15a^2b^4 - 6ab^5 + b^6$ **17.** $x^6 + 36x^5 + 540x^4 + 4320x^3 + 19{,}440x^2 + 46{,}656x + 46{,}656$ **19.** $16a^4 + 128a^3b + 384a^2b^2 + 512ab^3 + 256b^4$

21 Let w represent the number of women and m represent the number of men.

$(w + m)^{10} = \sum_{k=0}^{10} \frac{10!}{k!(10-k)!}w^{10-k}m^k$

To find the probability that 7 members are women, find the term in which the exponent of w is 7. Since $10 - 3 = 7$, find the term in which $k = 3$, the fourth term.

$\frac{10!}{k!(10-k)!}w^{10-k}m^k = \frac{10!}{3!(10-3)!}w^{10-3}m^3$ For the fourth term, $k = 3$.

$= 120w^7m^3$ $C(10, 3) = 120$

The probability of choosing a woman is $\frac{1}{2}$ and the probability of choosing a man is $\frac{1}{2}$.

$120w^7m^3 = 120\left(\frac{1}{2}\right)^7\left(\frac{1}{2}\right)^3$ $w = \frac{1}{2}$ and $m = \frac{1}{2}$

$= 120\left(\frac{1}{2}\right)^{10}$ Product of Powers Property

$= \frac{120}{1024}$ $\left(\frac{1}{2}\right)^{10} = \frac{1}{1024}$

$= \frac{15}{128}$ Simplify.

The probability that 7 of the members will be women is $\frac{15}{128}$, or about 0.117.

23. $84x^5z^2$ **25.** $7168a^2b^6$ **27.** $32{,}256x^5$ **29.** $x^5 + \frac{5}{2}x^4 + \frac{5}{2}x^3 + \frac{5}{4}x^2 + \frac{5}{16}x + \frac{1}{32}$ **31.** $32b^5 + 20b^4 + 5b^3 + \frac{5}{8}b^2 + \frac{5}{128}b + \frac{1}{1024}$ **33a.** 0.121 **33b.** 0.121 **33c.** 0.309

35. Sample answer: While they have the same terms, the signs for $(x + y)^n$ will all be positive, while the signs for $(x - y)^n$ will alternate. **37.** Sample answer: $\left(x + \frac{6}{5}y\right)^5$ **39.** A **41.** G **43.** −2, 3, 8, 13, 18 **45.** 4, 6, 12, 30, 84 **47.** $1\frac{1}{8}$ **49a.** $\frac{150}{x}$; $\frac{130}{x-10}$ **49b.** $\frac{150}{x} + \frac{130}{x-10} = 4$; 75 mph, 65 mph **51.** true; $3(1) + 5 = 8$, which is even

Pages 729–731 Lesson 11-7

1. Step 1: When $n = 1$, the left side of the given equation is 1. The right side is 1^2 or 1, so the equation is true for $n = 1$.

Step 2: Assume that $1 + 3 + 5 + \cdots + (2k - 1) = k^2$ for some natural number k.

Step 3: $1 + 3 + 5 + \cdots + (2k - 1) + (2(k + 1) - 1)$

$= k^2 + (2(k + 1) - 1)$

$= k^2 + (2k + 2 - 1)$

$= k^2 + 2k + 1$

$= (k + 1)^2$

The last expression is the right side of the equation to be proved, where $n = k + 1$. Thus, the equation is true for $n = k + 1$. Therefore, $1 + 3 + 5 + \cdots + (2n - 1) = n^2$ for all natural numbers n.

3a. 3, 6, 10, 15, 21 **3b.** $a_n = \frac{n(n+1)}{2}$

3c. Step 1: When $n = 1$, the left side of the given equation is $\frac{1(1+1)}{2}$ or 1. The right side is $\frac{1(1+1)(1+2)}{6}$ or 1, so the equation is true for $n = 1$.

Step 2: Assume that $1 + 3 + 6 + \cdots + \frac{k(k+1)}{2} = \frac{k(k+1)(k+2)}{6}$ for some natural number k.

Step 3: $1 + 3 + 6 + \cdots + \frac{k(k+1)}{2} + \frac{(k+1)(k+1+1)}{2}$

$= \frac{k(k+1)(k+2)}{6} + \frac{(k+1)(k+1+1)}{2}$

$= \frac{k(k+1)(k+2)}{6} + \frac{3(k+1)(k+2)}{6}$

$= \frac{(k+1)(k+2)(k+3)}{6}$

$= \frac{(k+1)[(k+1)+1][(k+1)+2]}{6}$

The last expression is the right side of the equation to be proved, where $n = k + 1$. Thus, the equation is true for $n = k + 1$. Therefore, $1 + 3 + 6 + \cdots + \frac{n(n+1)}{2} = \frac{n(n+1)(n+2)}{6}$ for all natural numbers n.

5. Step 1: $4^1 - 1 = 3$, which is divisible by 3. The statement is true for $n = 1$.

Step 2: Assume that $4^k - 1$ is divisible by 3 for some natural number k. This means that $4^k - 1 = 3r$ for some whole number r.

Step 3: $4^k - 1 = 3r$

$4^k = 3r + 1$

$4^{k+1} = 12r + 4$

$4^{k+1} - 1 = 12r + 3$

$4^{k+1} - 1 = 3(4r + 1)$

Since r is a whole number, $4r + 1$ is a whole number. Thus, $4^{k+1} - 1$ is divisible by 3, so the statement is true for $n = k + 1$. Therefore, $4^n - 1$ is divisible by 3 for all natural numbers n. **7.** $n = 1$

9. Step 1: When $n = 1$, the left side of the given equation is 2. The right side is $\frac{1[3(1)+1]}{2}$ or 2, so the equation is true for $n = 1$.

Step 2: Assume that $2 + 5 + 8 + \cdots + (3k - 1) = \frac{k(3k+1)}{2}$ for some natural number k.

Step 3: $2 + 5 + 8 + \cdots + (3k - 1) + [3(k + 1) - 1]$

$= \frac{k(3k+1)}{2} + [3(k+1) - 1]$

$= \frac{k(3k+1) + 2[3(k+1) - 1]}{2}$

$= \frac{3k^2 + k + 6k + 6 - 2}{2}$

$= \frac{3k^2 + 7k + 4}{2}$

$= \frac{(k+1)(3k+4)}{2}$

$= \frac{(k+1)[3(k+1)+1]}{2}$

The last expression is the right side of the equation to be proved, where $n = k + 1$. Thus, the equation is true for $n = k + 1$. Therefore, $2 + 5 + 8 + \cdots + (3n - 1) = \frac{n(3n+1)}{2}$ for all natural numbers n.

11. Step 1: When $n = 1$, the left side of the given equation is 1. The right side is $1[2(1) - 1]$ or 1, so the equation is true for $n = 1$.

Step 2: Assume that $1 + 5 + 9 + \cdots + (4k - 3) = k(2k - 1)$ for some natural number k.

Step 3: $1 + 5 + 9 + \cdots + (4k - 3) + [4(k + 1) - 3]$

$= k(2k - 1) + [4(k + 1) - 3]$

$= 2k^2 - k + 4k + 4 - 3$

$= 2k^2 + 3k + 1$

$= (k + 1)(2k + 1)$

$= (k + 1)[2(k + 1) - 1]$

The last expression is the right side of the equation to be proved, where $n = k + 1$. Thus, the equation is true for $n = k + 1$. Therefore, $1 + 5 + 9 + \cdots + (4n - 3) = n(2n - 1)$ for all natural numbers n.

13 Step 1: When $n = 1$, the left side of the given equation is $4(1) - 1$ or 3. The right side is $2(1)^2 + 1$ or 3, so the equation is true for $n = 1$.

Step 2: Assume that $3 + 7 + 11 + \cdots + (4k - 1) = 2k^2 + k$ for some natural number k.

Step 3: $3 + 7 + 11 + \cdots + (4k - 1) + [4(k + 1) - 1]$

$= 2k^2 + k + [4(k + 1) - 1]$

$= 2k^2 + k + 4k + 3$

$= 2k^2 + 5k + 3$

$= 2k^2 + 4k + 2 + k + 1$

$= [2(k + 1)^2] + (k + 1)$

The last expression is the right side of the equation to be proved, where $n = k + 1$. Thus, the equation is true for $n = k + 1$. Therefore, $3 + 7 + 11 + \cdots + (4n - 1) = 2n^2 + n$ for all natural numbers n.

15. Step 1: When $n = 1$, the left side of the given equation is 1^2 or 1. The right side is $\frac{1[2(1) - 1][2(1) + 1]}{3}$ or 1, so the equation is true for $n = 1$.

Step 2: Assume that $1^2 + 3^2 + 5^2 + \cdots + (2k - 1)^2 = \frac{k(2k-1)(2k+1)}{3}$ for some natural number k.

Step 3: $1^2 + 3^2 + 5^2 + \cdots + (2k - 1)^2 + [2(k + 1) - 1]^2$

$= \frac{k(2k-1)(2k+1)}{3} + [2(k + 1) - 1]^2$

$= \frac{k(2k-1)(2k+1) + 3(2k+1)^2}{3}$

$= \frac{(2k+1)[k(2k-1) + 3(2k+1)]}{3}$

$= \frac{(2k+1)(2k^2 - k + 6k + 3)}{3}$

$= \frac{(2k+1)(2k^2 + 5k + 3)}{3}$

$= \frac{(2k+1)(k+1)(2k+3)}{3}$

$= \frac{(k+1)[2(k+1) - 1][2(k+1) + 1]}{3}$

The last expression is the right side of the equation to be proved, where $n = k + 1$. Thus, the equation is true for $n = k + 1$. Therefore, $1^2 + 3^2 + 5^2 + \cdots + (2n - 1)^2 = \frac{n(2n-1)(2n+1)}{3}$ for all natural numbers n.

17. Step 1: $5^1 + 3 = 8$, which is divisible by 4. The statement is true for $n = 1$.

Step 2: Assume $5^k + 3$ is divisible by 4 for some natural number k. This means that $5^k + 3 = 4r$ for some natural number r.

Step 3: $5^k + 3 = 4r$

$5^k = 4r - 3$

$5^{k+1} = 20r - 15$

$5^{k+1} + 3 = 20r - 12$

$5^{k+1} + 3 = 4(5r - 3)$

Since r is a natural number, $5r - 3$ is a natural number. Thus, $5^{k+1} + 3$ is divisible by 4, so the statement is true for $n = k + 1$. Therefore, $5^n + 3$ is divisible by 4 for all natural numbers n.

19. Step 1: $12^1 + 10 = 22$, which is divisible by 11. The statement is true for $n = 1$.

Step 2: Assume that $12^k + 10$ is divisible by 11 for some natural number k. This means that $12^k + 10 = 11r$ for some natural number r.

Step 3: $12^k + 10 = 11r$

$12^k = 11r - 10$

$12^{k+1} = 132r - 120$

$12^{k+1} + 10 = 132r - 110$

$12^{k+1} + 10 = 11(12r - 10)$

Since r is a natural number, $12r - 10$ is a natural number. Thus, $12^{k+1} + 10$ is divisible by 11, so the statement is true for $n = k + 1$. Therefore, $12^n + 10$ is divisible by 11 for all natural numbers n. **21.** $n = 2$ **23.** $n = 1$

25 In the sequence 1, 1, 2, 3, 5, 8, …, $f_1 = 1$, $f_2 = 1$, $f_3 = 2$, $f_4 = 3$, $f_5 = 5$, $f_6 = 8$, … .

$f_1 + f_2 + \cdots + f_n = f_{n+2} - 1$ Original equation

$f_1 = f_{1+2} - 1$ Let $n = 1$.

$f_1 = f_3 - 1$ Simplify.

Step 1: When $n = 1$, the left side of the given equation is f_1. The right side is $f_3 - 1$. Since $f_1 = 1$ and $f_3 = 2$, the equation becomes $1 = 2 - 1$ and is true for $n = 1$.

Step 2: Assume that $f_1 + f_2 + \cdots + f_k = f_{k+2} - 1$ for some natural number k.

Step 3: $f_1 + f_2 + \cdots + f_k + f_{k+1} = f_{k+2} - 1 + f_{k+1}$

$= f_{k+1} + f_{k+2} - 1$

$= f_{k+3} - 1$, since Fibonacci numbers are produced by adding the two previous Fibonacci numbers.

The last expression is the right side of the equation to be proved, where $n = k + 1$. Thus, the equation is true for $n = k + 1$. Therefore, $f_1 + f_2 + \cdots + f_n = f_{n+2} - 1$ for all natural numbers n.

27. Step 1: $18^1 - 1 = 17$, which is divisible by 17. The statement is true for $n = 1$.

Step 2: Assume that $18^k - 1$ is divisible by 17 for some natural number k. This means that $18^k - 1 = 17r$ for some natural number r.

Step 3: $18^k - 1 = 17r$

$18^k = 17r + 1$

$18^{k+1} = 18(17r + 1)$

$18^{k+1} = 306r + 18$

$18^{k+1} - 1 = 306r + 17$

$18^{k+1} - 1 = 17(18r + 1)$

Since r is a natural number, $18r + 1$ is a natural number. Thus, $18^{k+1} - 1$ is divisible by 17, so the statement is true for $n = k + 1$. Therefore, $18^n - 1$ is divisible by 17 for all natural numbers n. **29.** $n = 3$

31. Step 1: When $n = 1$, the left side of the given equation is $\frac{1}{1(1+1)(1+2)}$ or $\frac{1}{6}$. The right side is $\frac{1(1+3)}{4(1+1)(1+2)}$ or $\frac{1}{6}$, so the equation is true for $n = 1$.

Step 2: Assume that $\frac{1}{1 \cdot 2 \cdot 3} + \frac{1}{2 \cdot 3 \cdot 4} + \frac{1}{3 \cdot 4 \cdot 5} + \cdots + \frac{1}{k(k+1)(k+2)} = \frac{k(k+3)}{4(k+1)(k+2)}$ for some natural number k.

Step 3: $\frac{1}{1 \cdot 2 \cdot 3} + \frac{1}{2 \cdot 3 \cdot 4} + \cdots + \frac{1}{k(k+1)(k+2)} + \frac{1}{(k+1)(k+2)(k+3)}$

$= \frac{k(k+3)}{4(k+1)(k+2)} + \frac{1}{(k+1)(k+2)(k+3)}$

$= \frac{k(k+3)(k+3)}{4(k+1)(k+2)(k+3)} + \frac{4}{4(k+1)(k+2)(k+3)}$

$= \frac{k^3 + 6k^2 + 9k + 4}{4(k+1)(k+2)(k+3)}$

$= \frac{(k+1)(k^2 + 5k + 4)}{4(k+1)(k+2)(k+3)}$

$= \frac{(k+1)(k+4)}{4(k+2)(k+3)}$

$= \frac{(k+1)[(k+1)+3]}{4[(k+1)+1][(k+1)+2]}$

The last expression is the right side of the equation to be proved, where $n = k + 1$. Thus, the equation is true for $n = k + 1$. Therefore, $\frac{1}{1 \cdot 2 \cdot 3} + \frac{1}{2 \cdot 3 \cdot 4} + \frac{1}{3 \cdot 4 \cdot 5} + \cdots + \frac{1}{n(n+1)(n+2)} = \frac{n(n+3)}{4(n+1)(n+2)}$ for all natural numbers n. **33.** $n(n + 1)$

Step 1: When $n = 1$, the left side of the given equation is $2(1)$ or 2. The right side is $1(1 + 1)$ or 2, so the equation is true for $n = 1$.

Step 2: Assume that $2 + 4 + 6 + \cdots + 2k = k(k + 1)$ for some natural number k.

Step 3: $2 + 4 + 6 + \cdots + 2k + 2(k + 1)$

$= k(k + 1) + 2(k + 1)$

$= (k + 1)(k + 2)$

$= (k + 1)[(k + 1) + 1]$

The last expression is the right side of the equation to be proved, where $n = k + 1$. Thus, the equation is true for $n = k + 1$. Therefore, $2 + 4 + 6 + \cdots + n^2 = n(n + 1)$ for all natural numbers n. **35.** Sample answer: False; assume $k = 2$, just because a statement is true for $n = 2$ and $n = 3$ does not mean that it is true for $n = 1$.

37. $x = 3$ **39.** Sample answer: When dominoes are set up, after the first domino falls, the rest will fall as well. With induction, once it is proved that the statement is true for $n = 1$ (the first domino), $n = k$ (the second domino), and $n = k + 1$ (the next domino), it will be true for any integer value (any domino).

41. B **43.** 96 **45.** $160x^3y^3$ **47.** $-84x^6y^3$

49. $(6, -8)$, $(12, -16)$ **51.** 56 **53.** 665,280 **55.** 70

57. 132 **59.** 28 **61.** 24

Pages 732–736 Chapter 11 Study Guide and Review

1. true **3.** true **5.** true **7.** false, arithmetic sequence **9.** false, arithmetic means **11.** 48 **13.** -22 **15.** -7, -2, 3 **17.** 8, 4, 0, -4 **19.** \$480 **21.** 1040 **23.** -245

25. 629 **27.** -99 **29.** 99 **31.** $\frac{2187}{8}$ **33.** ± 24, 72, ± 216

35. \$1823.26 **37.** 12,285 **39.** 363 **41.** $-\frac{6305}{45,927}$ **43.** 32

45. 6 **47.** -3, 1, 5, 9, 13 **49.** 1, 6, 11, 16, 21 **51.** 7, 15, 31

53. 11, 65, 389 **55.** $a^3 + 3a^2b + 3ab^2 + b^3$

57. $-32z^5 + 240z^4 - 720z^3 + 1080z^2 - 810z + 243$

59. $x^5 - \frac{5}{4}x^4 + \frac{5}{8}x^3 - \frac{5}{32}x^2 + \frac{5}{256}x - \frac{1}{1024}$

61. $193{,}536x^2y^5$

63. Step 1: When $n = 1$, the left side of the equation is equal to 2. The right side of the equation is also equal to 2. So the equation is true for $n = 1$.

Step 2: Assume that $2 + 6 + 12 + \cdots + k(k + 1) = \frac{k(k+1)(k+2)}{3}$ for some positive integer k.

Step 3: $1{*}2 + 2{*}3 + \cdots + k(k + 1) + (k + 1)(k + 2) =$

$\frac{k(k+1)(k+2)}{3} + (k + 1)(k + 2)$

$= \frac{k(k+1)(k+2)}{3} + \frac{3(k+1)(k+2)}{3}$

$= \frac{(k+1)[k(k+2) + 3(k+2)]}{3}$

$= \frac{(k+1)(k+2)(k+3)}{3} = \frac{(k+1)[(k+1)+1][(k+1)+2]}{3}$

The last expression is the right side of the equation to be proved, where $n = k + 1$. Thus, the equation is true for $n = k + 1$.

Therefore, $2 + 6 + 12 + \cdots + k(k + 1) = \frac{k(k+1)(k+2)}{3}$ for all positive integers n.

65. Step 1: When $n = 1$, $5^1 - 1 = 5$ or 4. Since 4 divided by 4 is 1, the statement is true for $n = 1$.

Step 2: Assume that $5^k - 1$ is divisible by 4 for some positive integer k. This means that $5^k - 1 = 4r$ for some whole number r.

For Homework Help, go to Hotmath.com

Step 3: $5^k - 1 = 4r$

$5^k = 4r + 1$

$5^{k+1} = 20r + 5$

$5^{k+1} - 1 = 20r + 5 - 1$

$5^{k+1} - 1 = 20r + 4$

$5^{k+1} - 1 = 4(5r + 1)$

Since r is a whole number, $5r + 1$ is a whole number. Thus, $5^{k+1} - 1$ is divisible by 4, so the statement is true for $n = k + 1$.
Therefore, $5^n - 1$ is divisible by 4 for all positive integers n. **67.** $n = 2$ **69.** $n = 1$

Chapter 12 Probability and Statistics

Page 743 Chapter 12 Get Ready

1. independent **3.** independent **5.** permutation
7. $a^4 - 8a^3 + 24a^2 - 32a + 16$
9. $16b^4 - 32b^3 + 24b^2x^2 - 8bx^3 + x^4$ **11.** $243x^5 - 810x^4y + 1080x^3y^2 - 720x^2y^3 + 240xy^4 - 32y^5$
13. $\frac{a^5}{32} + \frac{5a^4}{8} + 5a^3 + 20a^2 + 40a + 32$

Pages 748–750 Lesson 12-1

1. No; the people surveyed would probably be more likely than others to love ice cream. **3.** b
5. observational study **7.** Survey; it is best to call random numbers throughout the country in order to get an unbiased sample. **9.** Causation; the Level 2 emergency is a direct cause of the school closing.
11. No; the people surveyed would probably be more likely than others to like science. **13.** Yes; everyone in the population has an equal chance to be part of the sample.
15 Question **a** is an unbiased question that will elicit the desired response. Questions **b** and **c** are unbiased questions that will not get the desired response.
17 This is an observational study because no attempt is made to influence the results.
19. observational study **21.** Experiment; the test subjects are gardens with deer. The treatment group of gardens gets the treatment, while the control gets a placebo.
23. Correlation; while the two may be related, reading does not directly increase intelligence.
25. Correlation; while there may be a relationship between the two, one does not cause the other.
27. Sample answer: Yes; the majority of employees who leave are not happy about some facet of their employment. The majority of employees who are happy will not leave, and will thus not complete the questionnaire. Biased or not, the goal of these questionnaires is to determine why the employee left.
29. Sample answer: A telephone survey can introduce bias because unlisted phone numbers are not called and people without phones are not called.
31a. Sample answer: Survey 50 students at school on their opinions about changing to block scheduling.
Sample: List all of the students at the school and randomly draw 50 names.
Subject of survey: "Rate your opinion about block scheduling at school from 1 to 5, 1 being strongly against and 5 being strongly in favor."
31b. Sample answer: Observe 20 students, half of whom have study halls, and compare their grades at the end of the semester. Control: no study hall; treatment: study hall. **31c.** Sample answer: Select a sample of 20 random students with the common cold. Give half of them a pill and the other half a placebo, and compare the results after 3 weeks.
Control: placebo; treatment: pill. **33.** C **35.** G
37. Step 1: $9^1 - 1 = 8$, which is divisible by 8. The statement is true for $n = 1$.
Step 2: Assume that $9^k - 1$ is divisible by 8 for some positive integer k. This means that $9^k - 1 = 8r$ for some whole number r.
Step 3: $9^k - 1 = 8r$

$9^k = 8r + 1$

$9^{k+1} = 72r + 9$

$9^{k+1} - 1 = 72r + 8$

$9^{k+1} - 1 = 8(9r + 1)$

Since r is a whole number, $9r + 1$ is a whole number. Thus, $9^{k+1} - 1$ is divisible by 8, so the statement is true for $n = k + 1$.Therefore, $9^n - 1$ is divisible by 8 for all positive integers n. **39.** $\left(\frac{3}{2}, \frac{9}{2}\right)$, $(-1, 2)$
41. no solution **43.** $(\pm 8, 0)$ **45.** $3\sqrt{17}$ units
47. 25 units **49.** $\sqrt{70.25}$ units **51.** $-5c^5d^3$ **53.** an
55. $-y^3z^2$ **57.** $x^2 - 6x - 27 = 0$ **59.** $x^2 + x - 20 = 0$
61. 63

Pages 755–758 Lesson 12-2

1. Mean; there are no extreme values. **3.** Median; there is one value that is much less than the rest of the data. **5.** sample **7.** sample
9 **a.** Margin of sampling error

$= \pm\frac{1}{\sqrt{n}}$ Margin of Sampling Error Formula

$= \pm\frac{1}{\sqrt{5824}}$ $n = 5824$

$\approx \pm 0.0131$ Simplify.

b. $0.29 + 0.0131 = 0.3031 \approx 30.3\%$
$0.29 - 0.0131 = 0.2769 = 27.7\%$
The likely interval that contains the percentage of the population that will watch the Summer Olympics on television is between 27.7% and 30.3%.
11. Median; there is one value that is much greater than the rest of the data, 66. **13.** sample
15. population **17.** sample **19.** population
21 **a.** Margin of sampling error

$= \pm\frac{1}{\sqrt{n}}$ Margin of Sampling Error Formula

$= \pm\frac{1}{\sqrt{5669}}$ $n = 5669$

$\approx \pm 0.0133$ Simplify.

b. $0.31 + 0.0133 = 0.3233 \approx 32.3\%$
$0.31 - 0.0133 = 0.2967 \approx 29.7\%$
The likely interval that contains the percentage of the population that goes to the movies at least once a month is between 29.7% and 32.3%.
23a. sample **23b.** 2.7 **25a.** The mean is 21.18, and the median is 21.4. They are very close.
25b. population **25c.** 1.02 **25d.** The new mean is 21.232, and the median is 21.45. The mean and median are each slightly greater.
27 Since 13 is much lower than the rest of the data and is lowering the mean, the median best represents the data.
13, 25, 25, 26, (28), 34, 35, 37, 42
The median is 28.
29. 2066 **31.** Sample answer: The median will also increase by 10. For example, in a data set with a middle or median value of 18, if all of the data are increased by 10, the 18 increases to 28 and remains in the middle. Thus, the new median is 18 + 10 or 28. The mean will also increase by 10 because all of the data have increased by 10. For example, the data set of 2, 2, 2, 2, 2 has a mean of 2. If they are all increased by 10, then the new data set will be 12, 12, 12, 12, 12 and the mean will be 2 + 10 or 12. The standard deviation will be unaffected because even though the data all increase by 10, they are still the same distance from the mean, which also increased by 10.
33. Sample answer: While the average heights of both teams are the same, the West team will have more players that are much taller than 6 feet as well as more players that are shorter than 6 feet. For the East team, most of the players will be between 5 ft 11 and 6 ft 1, while for the West team, most of the players will be between 5 ft 8 and 6 ft 4. **35.** $\frac{3}{2}$ **37.** C
39. No; basketball players are more likely to be taller than the average high school student, so a sample of basketball players would not give representative heights for the whole school. **41a.** $(39.2, \pm 4.4)$
41b. No; the comet and Pluto may not be at either point of intersection at the same time.
41c. $\left(-\frac{5}{3}, -\frac{7}{3}\right)$, $(1, 3)$ **41d.** $(3, \pm 4)$, $(-3, \pm 4)$
43. combination; 28 **45.** permutation; 120

Pages 761–763 Lesson 12-3

1. $\frac{5}{18}$ **3.** $\frac{5}{17}$ **5a.** $\frac{32}{41}$ **5b.** $\frac{2}{5}$ **5c.** $\frac{3}{7}$ **7.** $\frac{12}{27}$ **9.** 0
11 **a.** There is a total of 156 + 312 + 242 + 108 or 818 people in the study. Find the probability that a student is a club member C given that the student is a male M.

$P(C \mid M) = \frac{P(C \text{ and } M)}{P(M)}$ Conditional Probability Formula

$= \frac{156}{818} \div \frac{398}{818}$ $P(C \text{ and } M) = \frac{156}{818}$ and $P(M) = \frac{156 + 242}{818}$

$= \frac{156}{398}$ or $\frac{78}{199}$ Simplify.

The probability that a student is a member of a club given that he is male is $\frac{78}{199}$ or about 39.2%.
b. There is a total of 156 + 312 + 242 + 108 or 818 people in the study. Find the probability that a student is not a club member N given that the student is a female F.

$P(N \mid F) = \frac{P(N \text{ and } F)}{P(F)}$ Conditional Probability Formula

$= \frac{108}{818} \div \frac{420}{818}$ $P(N \text{ and } F) = \frac{156}{818}$ and $P(F) = \frac{312 + 108}{818}$

$= \frac{108}{420}$ or $\frac{9}{35}$ Simplify.

The probability that a student is not a member of a club given that she is female is $\frac{9}{35}$ or about 25.7%.
c. There is a total of 156 + 312 + 242 + 108 or 818 people in the study. Find the probability that a student is a male M given that he is not a member of a club N.

$P(M \mid N) = \frac{P(M \text{ and } N)}{P(N)}$ Conditional Probability Formula

$= \frac{242}{818} \div \frac{350}{818}$ $P(M \text{ and } N) = \frac{242}{818}$ and $P(N) = \frac{242 + 108}{818}$

$= \frac{242}{350}$ or $\frac{121}{175}$ Simplify.

The probability that a student is male given that he is not a member of a club is $\frac{121}{175}$ or about 69.1%.
13. $\frac{2}{5}$ **15.** $\frac{1}{15}$
17 The probability that she does not get a hit is $P(N) = 0.35$. The probability that she does not get a hit in five consecutive at-bats is $P(N) \cdot P(N) \cdot P(N) \cdot P(N) \cdot P(N) = 0.35 \cdot 0.35 \cdot 0.35 \cdot 0.35 \cdot 0.35 \approx 0.0053$, or about 0.5%.
19a. 37.3% **19b.** 14.3% **21.** 2% **23.** $\frac{43}{66}$
25. Sample answer: The final branches represent conditional probability. For example, consider the probabilities of students being sophomores and licensed to drive. The 0.4 represents the probability that a student is licensed given he or she is a sophomore.

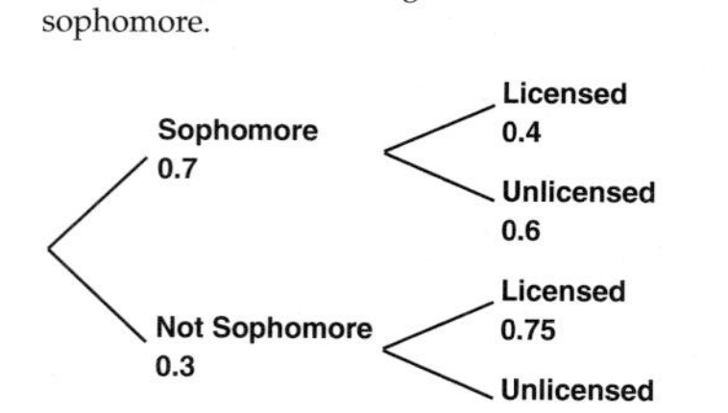

27. Sample answer:

Class	Male	Female
Freshman	6	9
Sophomore	8	5

the probability that a student is a female given she is a freshman: $\frac{3}{5}$

29. F **31.** −21 **33.** no **35.** $12,000 **37.** 8.9 **39.** 10 **41.** 15

Pages 767–771 Lesson 12-4

1. Determine the number of successes.
${}_8C_3$ 3 paintings chosen from 8 paintings
${}_{12}C_1$ 1 painting chosen from 20 − 8 or 12 paintings
${}_8C_3 \cdot {}_{12}C_1 = \frac{8!}{5!3!} \cdot \frac{12!}{11!1!}$ or 672 possible groups
Determine the total number of possibilities.
${}_{20}C_4 = \frac{20!}{16!4!}$ or 4845 ways to choose 4 paintings from 20 paintings
$P(3 \text{ Paul Gauguin paintings, 1 other painting}) = \frac{s}{s+f}$ Probability of success
$= \frac{672}{4845}$ $s = 672$ and $s + f = 4845$
≈ 0.139 Use a calculator.
The probability that 3 of the 8 Paul Gauguin paintings are selected is about 13.9%.
3. about 10.3% **5a.** 2.14 **5b.** 2.14 **5c.** 7.14
7. $\frac{69}{4900}$ or about 1.4% **9.** $\frac{1}{15,600}$

11 There are 12 red, 12 white, 12 blue, and 12 purple balloons.
Determine the number of successes.
${}_4P_2$ 2 colors chosen from 4 if order matters
${}_{12}C_3$ 3 red balloons chosen from a group of 12
${}_{12}C_4$ 4 blue balloons chosen from a group of 12
${}_4P_2 \cdot {}_{12}C_3 \cdot {}_{12}C_4 = 12 \cdot 220 \cdot 495$ or 1,306,800
Determine the total number of possibilities.
${}_{48}C_7 = 73,629,072$ ways to get 7 balloons from a package of 48
$P(3 \text{ red, 4 blue}) = \frac{s}{s+f}$ Probability of success
$= \frac{1,306,800}{73,629,072}$ Substitute.
≈ 0.2 Use a calculator.
The probability is $\frac{1,306,800}{73,629,072}$ or about 2%.

13. 0.36 **15a.** 7 **15b.** 2

17 $E(x) = (0 \cdot 0.1) + (1 \cdot 0.1) + (2 \cdot 0.15) + (3 \cdot 0.15) + (4 \cdot 0.25) + (5 \cdot 0.1) + (6 \cdot 0.08) + (7 \cdot 0.05) + (8 \cdot 0.02)$
$= 0 + 0.1 + 0.3 + 0.45 + 1 + 0.5 + 0.48 + 0.35 + 0.16$
$= 3.34$ snow days

19. 4.7 **21a.** Pablo; 30% **21b.** Damon and Tora or Damon and Fernando **21c.** Brett **21d.** 50% **21e.** 85%

23 ${}_{25}C_3$ 3 boys chosen from a group of 25
${}_{20}C_5$ 5 girls chosen from a group of 20
${}_{25}C_3 \cdot {}_{20}C_5 = 2300 \cdot 15,504 \cdot 495$ or 35,659,200

Determine the total number of possibilities.
${}_{45}C_8 = 215,553,195$ ways to choose 8 students from a group of 45
$P(3 \text{ boys, 5 girls}) = \frac{s}{s+f}$ Probability of success
$= \frac{35,659,200}{215,553,195}$ Substitute.
≈ 0.165 Use a calculator.
The probability is about 16.5%.

25a. Sample answer:

Color	Probability	Sector Area	Total Area	Sector Area / Total Area
red	$\frac{1}{6}$	3.27 in²	19.63 in²	0.166
orange	$\frac{1}{6}$	3.27 in²	19.63 in²	0.166
yellow	$\frac{1}{6}$	3.27 in²	19.63 in²	0.166
green	$\frac{1}{4}$	4.91 in²	19.63 in²	0.25
blue	$\frac{1}{4}$	4.91 in²	19.63 in²	0.25

25b. Sample answer: The probability is equal to the ratio of the sector area to the total area. **25c.** red: $\frac{1}{9}$; yellow: $\frac{1}{3}$; blue: $\frac{5}{9}$ **27.** Sample answer: False; experimental probability is based on experiments, and theoretical probability is based on mathematical methods and assumptions.
29. 2.4 **31.** H **33.** 0.39 **35.** population **37.** sample
39. 0.5, 1.25, 3.125, 7.8125, 19.53125 **41.** 12, 4, $\frac{4}{3}$, $\frac{4}{9}$, $\frac{4}{27}$
43. 80, 100, 125, $\frac{625}{4}$, $\frac{3125}{16}$ **45.** 27 **47.** 3 **49.** 106.8
51. 93.3 **53.** 14.4

Pages 775–778 Lesson 12-5

1. positively skewed

3 a.

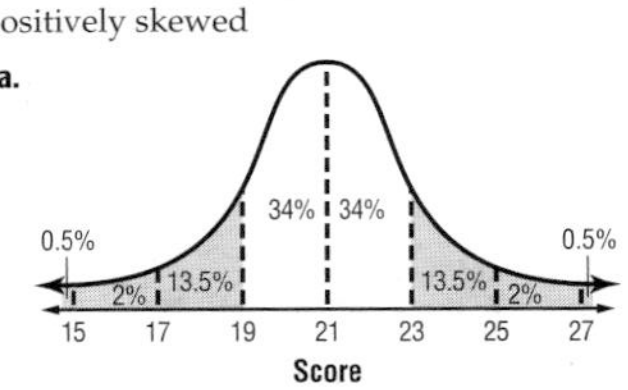

19 and 23 are 1σ away from the mean. Therefore, you would expect 34% + 34% or 68% to score between 19 and 23.
b. 23 and 25 are 1σ away from the mean and 2σ away from the mean, respectively. Therefore, you would expect 13.5% to score between 23 and 25.
c. 17 and 25 are 2σ away from the mean. Therefore, you would expect 13.5% + 34% + 34% + 13.5% or 95% to score between 17 and 25.
5. normally distributed

7

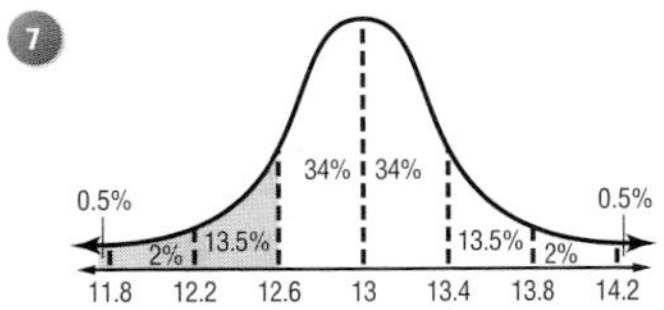

The probability that a randomly selected value in the distribution is less than $\mu - \sigma$, that is, 13 − 0.4 or 12.6, is the shaded area under the normal curve.
$P(x < 12.6) = 0.5\% + 2\% + 13.5\%$ or 16%

9. 97% **11a.** 16% **11b.** 855 **13a.** 50% **13b.** 50%
13c. 95%

15 **a.** $\bar{x} = \frac{9 + 12 + 8 + 7 + 17 + 20}{6}$
≈ 12.17 in.

b. $\sigma = \sqrt{\frac{\sum_{k=1}^{n}(x_n - \mu)^2}{n}}$ Standard Deviation Formula
$= \sqrt{\frac{(9 - 12.17)^2 + (12 - 12.17)^2 + \cdots + (17 - 12.17)^2 + (20 - 12.17)^2}{6}}$
≈ 4.81

c. 7.36 and 16.98 are 1σ away from the mean. Therefore, you would expect the annual precipitation to be between 7.36 in. and 16.98 in. 34% + 34% or 68% of the time.

17. 1600 **19.** Sample answer: True; according to the Empirical Rule, 68% of the data lie within 1 standard deviation of the mean. **21.** Sample answer: A discrete probability distribution can be the uniform distribution of the roll of a die. In this type of distribution, there are only a finite number of possibilities. A continuous probability distribution can be the distribution of the lives of 400 batteries. In this distribution, there are an infinite number of possibilities. **23.** D **25.** 32.5 **27.** 16.5% **29.** about $y = -0.00046x^2 + 325$ **31.** inverse variation or rational **33.** 9.6 **35.** 30.7

Pages 782–784 Lesson 12-6

1. $88.42 \le \bar{x} \le 91.58$ **3.** $83.36 \le \bar{x} \le 84.64$
5. $73.98 \le \bar{x} \le 76.02$ **7.** accept **9.** reject
11. $25.45 \le \bar{x} \le 26.55$

13 $CI = \bar{x} \pm 2 \cdot \frac{s}{\sqrt{n}}$ Confidence Interval Formula
$= 58 \pm 2 \cdot \frac{7.1}{\sqrt{225}}$ $\bar{x} = 58$, $s = 7.1$, and $n = 225$
$\approx 58 \pm 0.95$ Use a calculator.
The 95% confidence interval is $57.05 \le \mu \le 58.95$.

15. $91.03 \le \bar{x} \le 92.97$ **17a.** $\$6.30 \le \bar{x} \le \$6.80$
17b. $\$6.35 \le \bar{x} \le \$6.75$ **17c.** Sample answer: A larger sample decreases the range of the confidence interval. **19.** accept **21.** reject **23.** accept

25 State the hypothesis: H_0: $\mu = 28$ and H_1: $\mu < 28$.
$\bar{x} = 27.03$
$s \approx 1.28$
$CI = \bar{x} \pm 2 \cdot \frac{s}{\sqrt{n}}$ Confidence Interval Formula
$= 27.03 \pm 2 \cdot \frac{1.28}{\sqrt{30}}$ $\bar{x} = 27.03$, $s \approx 1.28$, and $n = 30$
≈ 26.5626 or 27.4974 Use a calculator.
This means that 95% of the time, the experiment will produce a mean between 26.5626 and 27.4974. The 95% confidence interval does not include H_0, so Diana can reject the null hypothesis. She can assume that the car averages less than 28 miles per gallon in the city.

27. reject **29.** 45 **31.** Sample answer: Always; if the null hypothesis falls within the confidence interval, then it is accepted, not rejected. **33.** 4.33 **35.** I
37. about 2.5% **39.** 729 **41.** 1
43. parabola

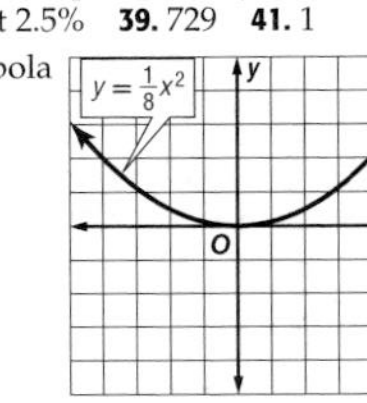

45. $y = 0.8x$ **47.** $y = -4$
49. $m^4 + 4m^3n + 6m^2n^2 + 4mn^3 + n^4$

Pages 790–793 Lesson 12-7

1.

K	-	-	-	-	-	A	-	-	-
-	-	-	A	K	-	K	-	-	-
-	-	K	A	-	-	A	-	-	-
-	A	-	-	-	-	-	-	-	K
-	K	-	-	-	-	-	-	-	K
-	-	K	-	-	A	-	-	-	K
-	-	-	-	-	-	-	-	-	-
-	-	-	-	-	-	-	-	-	-
-	-	-	-	-	-	-	-	-	-
-	-	-	-	-	A	-	-	-	-

An ace or a king was drawn at least once in 8 out of the 10 simulations, so the experimental probability of drawing at least one ace or king is 0.8.
3. 13.3%

5a.

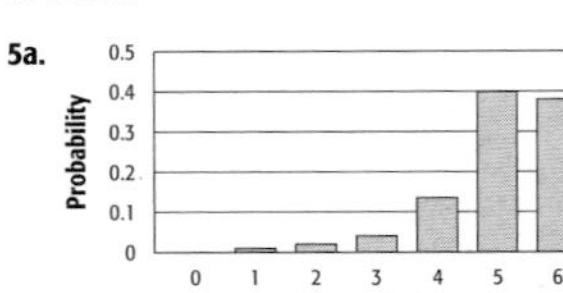

5b. 0.38

For Homework Help, go to Hotmath.com

7.

5	11	5	3	8	6	7	11	6	8
8	3	6	5	6	5	2	8	7	8
6	7	7	9	11	8	8	4	7	6
7	8	9	5	8	7	8	5	5	8
10	6	9	6	7	6	5	8	4	9
7	4	4	8	10	7	9	7	4	8
5	3	11	12	7	11	7	7	3	7
7	12	6	2	6	8	9	9	6	9
8	6	10	6	8	7	11	6	8	9
6	9	7	6	3	6	6	11	7	6

A 7 was rolled at least 2 out of 10 times in 8 of 10 simulations, so the experimental probability is 0.8.

9.

-	R	R	R	-	-	-	-	R	-
-	-	-	-	-	-	-	R	R	-
-	R	R	-	R	-	-	R	-	-
R	-	-	R	R	R	-	R	-	-
-	R	-	-	-	-	-	-	-	R
-	R	-	R	R	-	-	R	R	R
R	-	R	-	R	R	-	R	-	-
-	R	-	-	R	-	R	-	R	-
R	-	-	R	-	-	R	R	-	R
-	-	-	R	-	-	-	-	-	-

A red marble was pulled six times in 1 out of the 10 simulations, so the experimental probability of pulling a red marble 6 out of 10 times is 0.1.

11 $s = 0.92$ and $f = 1 - 0.92$ or 0.08
Calculate the probability of 8, 9, or 10 random high school students owning their own car, and then subtract that sum from 1.

$$\begin{aligned} &P(< 8 \text{ students}) \\ &= 1 - P(\geq 8 \text{ students}) \\ &= 1 - [P(8) + P(9) + P(10)] \\ &= 1 - [C(10, 8)(0.92)^8(0.08)^2 + C(10, 9)(0.92)^9(0.08)^1 \\ &\quad + C(10, 10)(0.92)^{10}(0.08)^0] \\ &= 1 - 0.9599 \\ &= 0.0401 \text{ or } 4.01\% \end{aligned}$$

13. 0.792 or 79.2% **15.** about 77.6%

17a.

Number of Students	Probability
0	0.00000000001%
1	0.000000002%
2	0.000002%
3	0.000008%
4	0.0003%
5	0.006%
6	0.1%
7	1.0%
8	7.5%
9	31.5%
10	59.9%

17b. 98.9%

19 $s = 0.65$ and $f = 1 - 0.65$ or 0.35

$$\begin{aligned} (s + f)^5 &= 1s^5 + 5s^4f + 10s^3f^2 + 10s^2f^3 + 5sf^4 + 1f^5 \\ &= (0.65)^5 + 5(0.65)^4(0.35) + 10(0.65)^3(0.35)^2 + \\ &\quad 10(0.65)^2(0.35)^3 + 5(0.65)(0.35)^4 + (0.35)^5 \\ &\approx 11.6\% + 31.2\% + 33.6\% + 18.1\% + 4.9\% + 0.5\% \end{aligned}$$

5 customers, 4 customers, 3 customers, 2 customers, 1 customer, 0 customers

$$\begin{aligned} P(\geq 4 \text{ customers}) &= P(4 \text{ customers}) + P(5 \text{ customers}) \\ &\approx 31.2\% + 11.6\% \text{ or } 42.8\% \end{aligned}$$

The probability that at least 4 customers will donate more than the minimum is 42.8%.

21a.

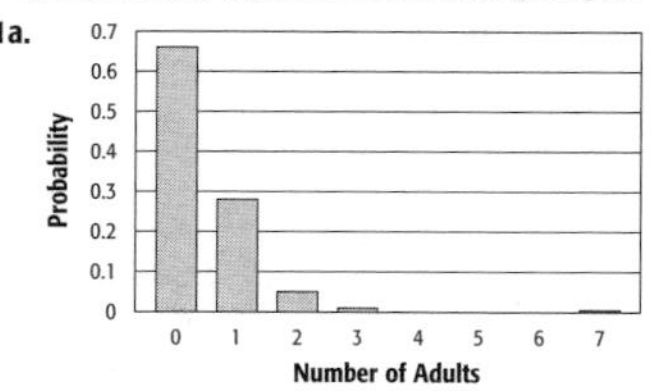

21b. 99.38% **23.** 16%

25

$$\begin{aligned} s &= 0.6 \text{ and } f = 1 - 0.6 \text{ or } 0.4 \\ P(\geq 12) &= P(12) + P(13) + P(14) + P(15) + P(16) + P(17) + P(18) \\ &= C(18, 12)(0.6)^{12}(0.4)^6 + C(18, 13)(0.6)^{13}(0.4)^5 + \\ &\quad \cdots + C(18, 18)(0.6)^{18}(0.4)^0 \\ &\approx 0.37 \text{ or } 37\% \end{aligned}$$

27. 10.8 **29.** 5 **31.** 5 **33.** 7 **35.** 60.3% **37.** 0.322 or 32.2% **39.** 0.99 or 99% **41.** 0.1109 or 11.09%
43. Sample answer: The poll will give you a percent of people supporting the addition. The percent of supporters represents the probability of success. You can use the formula for the expected number of successes in a binomial distribution with the total number of students in the school to predict the number that will support the science wing addition.
45. Sample answer: During May and June, lunches are held outside, weather permitting. Also during this time, there has historically been a 15% chance of rain. So, to determine the probability of not having rain for at least 24 of these 28 days, the binomial distribution would use $s = 0.85$, $f = 0.15$, and $n = 28$.
47. Sample answer: A binomial distribution shows the probabilities of the outcomes of a binomial experiment. **49.** C **51.** D **53.** accept **55.** accept **57.** 11 **59.** 15 **61.** −32

63a. Venus: $\frac{x^2}{4522.5625} + \frac{y^2}{4522.36} = 1$;

Jupiter: $\frac{x^2}{234{,}014.06} + \frac{y^2}{233{,}454.74} = 1$

63b. Venus **65.** $2 = \ln 6x$ **67.** $e^x = 5.2$ **69.** $-1 = \ln x^2$
71. $e^3 = e^x$

Pages 794–798 Chapter 12 Study Guide and Review

1. probability distribution **3.** biased **5.** margin of sampling error **7.** Yes; everyone in the population of customers has an equal chance to be part of the sample. **9.** No; the sample is biased towards the restaurant. **11.** experiment **13.** population

15. ±1.7% **17.** 0.005 **19.** $\frac{14}{575}$ **21.** $\frac{7}{115}$

23a.

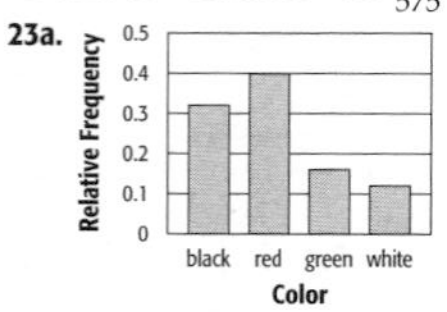

Color	black	red	green	white
Frequency	8	10	4	3

23b. red

23c. $\frac{12}{25}$ **25.** 97.5% **27.** 84% **29.** $22.8 \leq \bar{x} \leq 23.8$
31. $80.5 \leq \bar{x} \leq 82.3$ **33.** accept **35.** reject **37.** 21.5%
39. 38.2% **41.** 60% **43.** 97.5%

Chapter 13 Trigonometric Functions

Page 805 Chapter 13 Get Ready

1. 11.7 **3.** 20.5 **5.** $x = 9, y = 9\sqrt{2}$
7. $x = 12, y = 12\sqrt{3}$

Pages 813–816 Lesson 13-1

1. $\sin B = \frac{4}{5}$; $\cos B = \frac{3}{5}$; $\tan B = \frac{4}{3}$; $\csc B = \frac{5}{4}$; $\sec B = \frac{5}{3}$; $\cot B = \frac{3}{4}$ **3.** $\frac{\sqrt{33}}{7}$ **5.** 25.4 **7.** 8.3 **9.** 25.4
11. about 274.7 ft **13.** $\sin\theta = \frac{12}{13}$; $\cos\theta = \frac{5}{13}$; $\tan\theta = \frac{12}{5}$; $\csc\theta = \frac{13}{12}$; $\sec\theta = \frac{13}{5}$; $\cot\theta = \frac{5}{12}$
15. $\sin\theta = \frac{\sqrt{51}}{10}$; $\cos\theta = \frac{7}{10}$; $\tan\theta = \frac{\sqrt{51}}{7}$; $\csc\theta = \frac{10\sqrt{51}}{51}$; $\sec\theta = \frac{10}{7}$; $\cot\theta = \frac{7\sqrt{51}}{51}$

17 Since $\tan A = \frac{8}{15} = \frac{\text{opp}}{\text{adj}}$, label the opposite side 8 and the adjacent side 15.

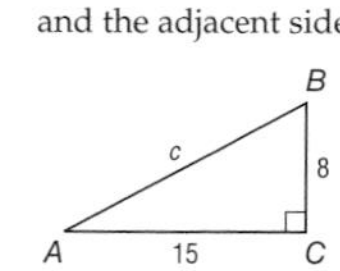

$$\begin{aligned} a^2 + b^2 &= c^2 && \text{Pythagorean Theorem} \\ 8^2 + 15^2 &= c^2 && a = 8 \text{ and } b = 15 \\ 289 &= c^2 && \text{Simplify.} \\ 17 &= c && \text{Take the positive square root of each side.} \\ \cos A &= \frac{\text{adj}}{\text{hyp}} && \text{Cosine function} \\ &= \frac{15}{17} && \text{Replace adj with 15 and hyp with 17.} \end{aligned}$$

19. $\frac{3\sqrt{10}}{10}$ **21.** 12.7

23

$$\begin{aligned} \tan\theta &= \frac{\text{opp}}{\text{adj}} && \text{Tangent function} \\ \tan 30° &= \frac{x}{18} && \text{Replace } \theta \text{ with } 30°\text{, opp with } x\text{, and adj with 18.} \\ \frac{\sqrt{3}}{3} &= \frac{x}{18} && \tan 30° = \frac{\sqrt{3}}{3} \\ \frac{18\sqrt{3}}{3} &= x && \text{Multiply each side by 18.} \\ 10.4 &\approx x && \text{Use a calculator.} \end{aligned}$$

25. 8.7 **27.** 132.5 ft **29.** 30 **31.** 36.9 **33.** 32.5
35. 25.3 ft higher **37.** $x = 21.9, y = 20.8$ **39.** $x = 19.3, y = 70.7$ **41.** 54.9 **43.** 20.5 **45.** 11.5

47

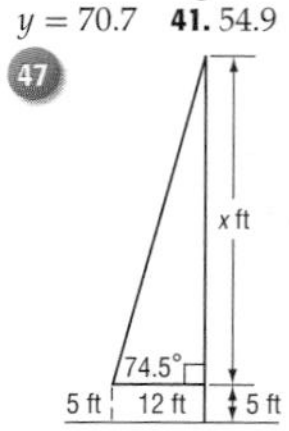

$$\begin{aligned} \tan\theta &= \frac{\text{opp}}{\text{adj}} && \text{Tangent function} \\ \tan 74.5° &= \frac{x}{12} && \text{Replace } \theta \text{ with } 74.5°\text{, opp with } x\text{, and adj with 12.} \\ 12 \cdot \tan 74.5° &= x && \text{Multiply each side by 12.} \\ 43 &\approx x && \text{Use a calculator.} \end{aligned}$$

So, the height of the bird's nest is 43 + 5 or 48 feet.
49a. about 647.2 ft **49b.** about 239.4 ft
51. $m\angle A = 59°, a = 31.6, c = 36.9$ **53.** $m\angle A = 38.7°$, $m\angle B = 51.3°, b = 7.5, c = 9.6$ **55.** True; $\sin\theta = \frac{\text{opp}}{\text{hyp}}$ and the values of the opposite side and the hypotenuse of an acute triangle are positive, so the value of the sine function is positive. **57.** Sample answer: The slope describes the ratio of the vertical rise to the horizontal run of the roof. The vertical rise is opposite the angle that the roof makes with the horizontal. The horizontal run is the adjacent side. So, the tangent of the angle of elevation equals the ratio of the rise to the run, or the slope of the roof; $\theta = 33.7°$. **59.** 24 **61.** F **63.** reject **65.** reject **67.** $\frac{1}{2}$
69. 22,704 feet **71.** 35 dollars **73.** $216\frac{2}{3}$ centimeters

Pages 820–823 Lesson 13-2

1.

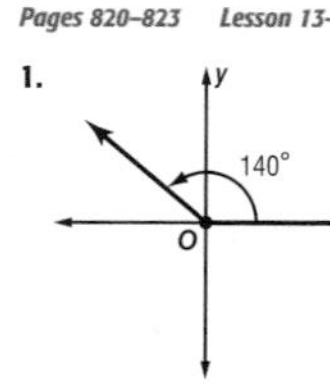

3.

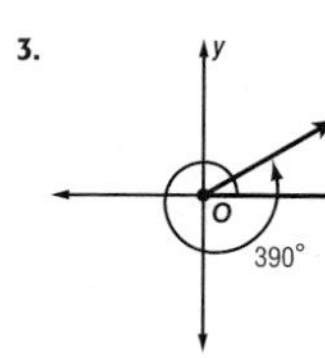

5 Sample answer:
positive angle: $175° + 360° = 535°$
negative angle: $175° - 360° = -185°$

7. 45° **9.** $-\frac{2\pi}{9}$

For Homework Help, go to Hotmath.com

11.

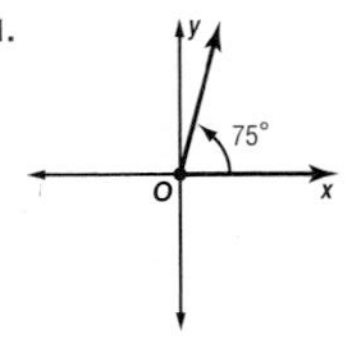

13.

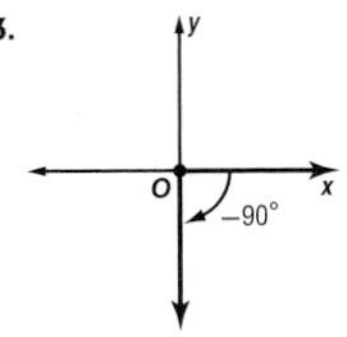

15.

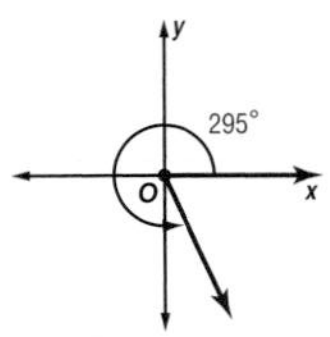

17.

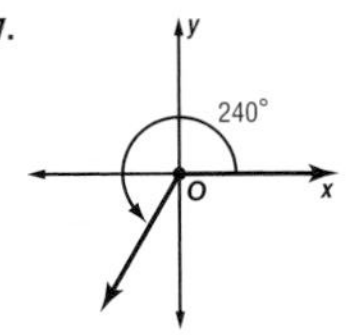

19. Sample answer: 410°, −310° **21.** Sample answer: 565°, −155° **23.** Sample answer: 280°, −440°

25 $330° = 330 \cdot \frac{\pi \text{ radians}}{180°}$

$= \frac{330\pi}{180}$ or $\frac{11\pi}{6}$ radians

27. −60° **29.** $\frac{19\pi}{18}$ **31.** about 12.6 ft **33.** 6.7 cm **35.** 1 h 15 min **37.** Sample answer: 260°, −100° **39.** Sample answer: $\frac{5\pi}{4}, -\frac{11\pi}{4}$

41 a.

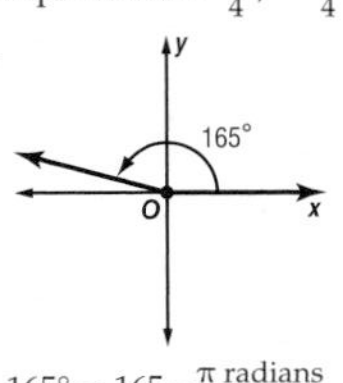

b. $165° = 165 \cdot \frac{\pi \text{ radians}}{180°}$

$= \frac{165\pi}{180}$ or $\frac{11\pi}{12}$ radians

c. $s = r\theta$ — Formula for arc length

$= 6.5 \cdot \frac{11\pi}{12}$ — $r = 6.5$ and $\theta = \frac{11\pi}{12}$

≈ 18.7 ft — Use a calculator.

d. The arc length would double. Since $s = r\theta$, if r is doubled and θ remains unchanged, then the value of s is also doubled.

43. 472.5° **45.** $-\frac{10\pi}{9}$ **47a.** $\frac{\pi}{6}$ **47b.** 2.1 ft **49.** $x = 2$

51. Sample answer: 440° and −280°

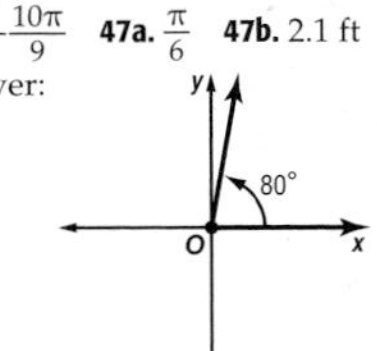

53. $\frac{\theta}{2\pi} = \frac{s}{2\pi r}$ — Substitute.

$2\pi r\theta = 2\pi s$ — Find the cross products.

$r\theta = s$ — Divide each side by 2π.

One degree represents an angle measure that equals $\frac{1}{360}$ rotation around a circle. One radian represents the measure of an angle in standard position that intercepts an arc of length r. To change from degrees to radians, multiply the number of degrees by $\frac{\pi \text{ radians}}{180°}$. To change from radians to degrees, multiply the number of radians by $\frac{180°}{\pi \text{ radians}}$.

55. *A* **57.** *B* **59.** $\sin\theta = \frac{\sqrt{259}}{22}$, $\cos\theta = \frac{15}{22}$, $\tan\theta = \frac{\sqrt{259}}{15}$, $\csc\theta = \frac{22}{\sqrt{259}}$ or $\frac{22\sqrt{259}}{259}$, $\sec\theta = \frac{22}{15}$, $\cot\theta = \frac{15}{\sqrt{259}}$ or $\frac{15\sqrt{259}}{259}$ **61.** 5.7%; 10.1% **63a.** 50% **63b.** 815 **63c.** 25 **65.** $3\sqrt{41}$ **67.** $\sqrt{317}$

Pages 829–831 Lesson 13-3

1. $\sin\theta = \frac{2\sqrt{5}}{5}$, $\cos\theta = \frac{\sqrt{5}}{5}$, $\tan\theta = 2$, $\csc\theta = \frac{\sqrt{5}}{2}$, $\sec\theta = \sqrt{5}$, $\cot\theta = \frac{1}{2}$ **3.** $\sin\theta = -1$, $\cos\theta = 0$, $\tan\theta =$ undefined, $\csc\theta = -1$, $\sec\theta =$ undefined, $\cot\theta = 0$

5. 65°

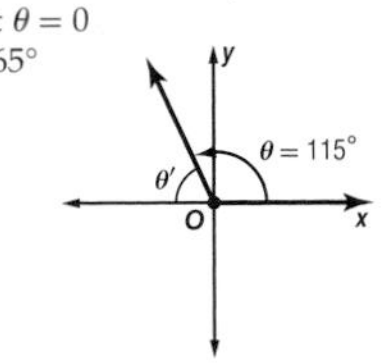

7. $\frac{\sqrt{2}}{2}$ **9.** −2

11a.

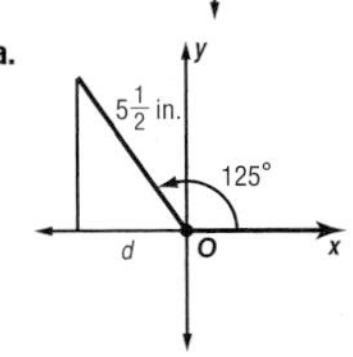

11b. 55°; $\cos 55° = \frac{d}{5\frac{1}{2}}$ **11c.** 3.2 in.

13

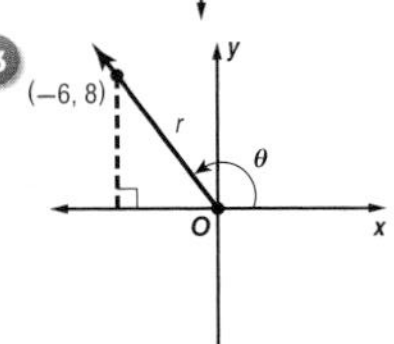

$r = \sqrt{x^2 + y^2}$

$= \sqrt{(-6)^2 + 8^2}$

$= \sqrt{100}$ or 10

Use $x = -6$, $y = 8$, and $r = 10$.

$\sin\theta = \frac{y}{r} = \frac{8}{10}$ or $\frac{4}{5}$ — $\cos\theta = \frac{x}{r} = \frac{-6}{10}$ or $-\frac{3}{5}$

$\tan\theta = \frac{y}{x} = \frac{8}{-6}$ or $-\frac{4}{3}$ — $\csc\theta = \frac{r}{y} = \frac{10}{8}$ or $\frac{5}{4}$

$\sec\theta = \frac{r}{x} = \frac{10}{-6}$ or $-\frac{5}{3}$ — $\cot\theta = \frac{x}{y} = \frac{-6}{8}$ or $-\frac{3}{4}$

15. $\sin\theta = -1$, $\cos\theta = 0$, $\tan\theta =$ undefined, $\csc\theta = -1$, $\sec\theta =$ undefined, $\cot\theta = 0$

17. $\sin\theta = -\frac{\sqrt{10}}{10}$, $\cos\theta = -\frac{3\sqrt{10}}{10}$, $\tan\theta = \frac{1}{3}$, $\csc\theta = -\sqrt{10}$, $\sec\theta = -\frac{\sqrt{10}}{3}$, $\cot\theta = 3$

19. 75°

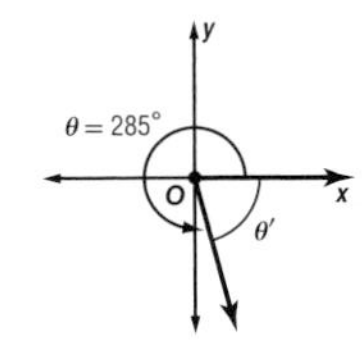

21. $\frac{\pi}{4}$

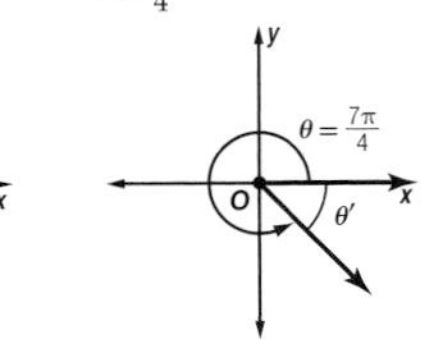

23. 40°

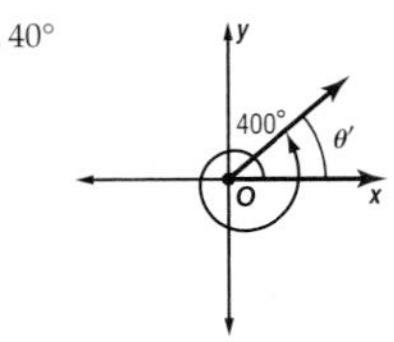

25. −1 **27.** $-\sqrt{2}$ **29.** $\frac{1}{2}$ **31.** $\frac{2\sqrt{3}}{3}$

33

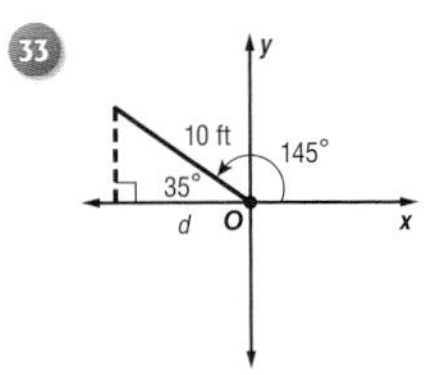

$\cos 35° = \frac{d}{10}$

$10 \cdot \cos 35° = d$

$8.2 \approx d$

The water reaches about 8.2 feet to the left of the sprinkler.

35. about 10.1 m **37.** $\cos\theta = -\frac{3}{5}$, $\tan\theta = -\frac{4}{3}$, $\csc\theta = \frac{5}{4}$, $\sec\theta = -\frac{5}{3}$, $\cot\theta = -\frac{3}{4}$ **39.** $\sin\theta = -\frac{15}{17}$, $\tan\theta = \frac{15}{8}$, $\csc\theta = -\frac{17}{15}$, $\sec\theta = -\frac{17}{8}$, $\cot\theta = \frac{8}{15}$

41. 0 **43.** $-\frac{1}{2}$ **45.** $\frac{\sqrt{3}}{2}$ **47.** No; for $\sin\theta = \frac{\sqrt{2}}{2}$ and $\tan\theta = -1$, the reference angle is 45°. However, for $\sin\theta$ to be positive and $\tan\theta$ to be negative, the reference angle must be in the second quadrant. So, the value of θ must be 135° or an angle coterminal with 135°. **49.** Sample answer: We know that $\cot\theta = \frac{x}{y}$, $\sin\theta = \frac{y}{r}$, and $\cos\theta = \frac{x}{r}$. Since $\sin 180 = 0$, it must be true that $y = 0$. Thus, $\cot\theta = \frac{x}{0}$, which is undefined. **51.** Sample answer: First, sketch the angle and determine in which quadrant it is located. Then use the appropriate rule for finding its reference angle θ'. A reference angle is the acute angle formed by the terminal side of θ and the x-axis. Next, find the value of the trigonometric function for θ'. Finally, use the quadrant location to determine the sign of the trigonometric function value of θ. **53.** C **55.** C **57.** 330° **59.** 40.1° **61.** 66.0° **63.** $10,737,418.23

65. $(x + 4)^2 + (y + 2)^2 = 73$ **67.** $\frac{x^2 + 7x - 35}{(x + 2)(x + 4)(x - 7)}$ **69.** $\frac{2(3x^2 + 2x - 12)}{3x(x + 4)(x - 6)}$ **71.** 2.5841 **73.** $\frac{1}{2}$ **75.** $\frac{1}{3125}$ **77.** 9

Pages 836–839 Lesson 13-4

1. 27.9 mm²

3 Area $= \frac{1}{2}bc \sin A$ — Area Formula

$= \frac{1}{2}(11)(6) \sin 40°$ — Substitution

≈ 21.2 cm² — Simplify.

5. $E = 107°$, $d \approx 7.9$, $f \approx 7.0$ **7.** $F = 60°$, $f \approx 12.3$, $h \approx 9.1$ **9.** no solution **11.** one; $B = 90°$, $C = 60°$, $c \approx 5.2$ **13.** 10.6 km² **15.** 36.8 m² **17.** 5.9 ft² **19.** 65.2 m² **21.** $C = 30°$, $b \approx 11.1$, $c \approx 5.8$ **23.** $L = 74°$, $m \approx 4.9$, $n \approx 3.1$

25 $m\angle K = 180 - (53 + 20)$ or 107°

$\frac{\sin H}{h} = \frac{\sin J}{j}$ — Law of Sines

$\frac{\sin 53°}{31} = \frac{\sin 20°}{j}$ — Substitution

$j = \frac{31 \sin 20°}{\sin 53°}$ — Solve for j.

$j \approx 13.3$ — Use a calculator.

$\frac{\sin H}{h} = \frac{\sin K}{k}$ — Law of Sines

$\frac{\sin 53°}{31} = \frac{\sin 107°}{k}$ — Substitution

$k = \frac{31 \sin 107°}{\sin 53°}$ — Solve for k.

$k \approx 37.1$ — Use a calculator.

27. $B \approx 63°$, $b \approx 2.9$, $c \approx 3.0$ **29.** one; $B \approx 25°$, $C \approx 55°$, $c \approx 5.8$ **31.** one; $B \approx 32°$, $C \approx 110°$, $c \approx 32.1$ **33.** two; $B \approx 53°$, $C \approx 85°$, $c \approx 7.4$; $B \approx 127°$, $C \approx 11°$, $c \approx 1.4$ **35.** no solution **37.** about 28°

39

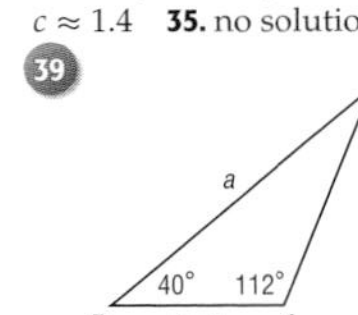

$m\angle C = 180 - (40 + 112)$ or 28°

$\frac{\sin A}{a} = \frac{\sin C}{c}$ — Law of Sines

$\frac{\sin 112°}{a} = \frac{\sin 28°}{8}$ — Substitution

$a = \frac{8 \sin 112°}{\sin 28°}$ — Solve for a.

$a \approx 15.8$ — Use a calculator.

Sirens B and C are about 15.8 miles apart.

41a. Sample answer:

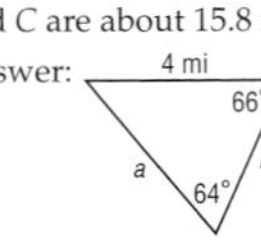

41b. Sample answer: $\frac{\sin 66°}{a} = \frac{\sin 64°}{4}$; $\frac{\sin 50°}{b} = \frac{\sin 64°}{4}$ **41c.** about 11.5 mi **43.** Cameron; R is acute and $r > t$, so there is one solution.

45. Sample answer:

Sin $A = \frac{opposite}{hypotenuse}$ Definition of sine

Sin $A = \frac{h}{c}$ h = opposite side, c = hypotenuse

$c \sin A = h$ Multiply both sides by c.

Area $= \frac{1}{2} \cdot$ base $\cdot$ height Area of a triangle

Area $= \frac{1}{2}bh$ b = base, h = height

Area $= \frac{1}{2}bc \sin A$ Substitution

47. Sample answer: In the triangle, $B = 115°$. Using the Law of Sines, $\frac{\sin 50°}{a} = \frac{\sin 115°}{b}$. This equation cannot be solved because there are two unknown sides. To solve a triangle using the Law of Sines, two sides and an angle must be given or two angles and a side opposite one of the angles must be given.

49. 2 **51.** G **53.** $-\frac{1}{2}$ **55.** $\frac{\sqrt{3}}{3}$ **57.** 328°, −392° **59.** 96 cm **61.** No sum exists. **63.** $\frac{x^2}{8.714 \times 10^{15}} + \frac{y^2}{8.710 \times 10^{15}} = 1$ **65.** $(y + 2)^2$ **67.** 56.25 **69.** 26

Pages 843–846 Lesson 13-5

1. $A \approx 36°, C \approx 52°, b \approx 5.1$ **3.** $A \approx 18°, B \approx 29°, C \approx 133°$ **5.** Sines; $B \approx 40°, C \approx 33°, c \approx 6.8$

7 Since the lengths of two sides and the measure of the included angle are known, first use the Law of Cosines to find the missing side length.

$r^2 = s^2 + t^2 - 2st \cos R$ Law of Cosines

$r^2 = 16^2 + 9^2 - 2(16)(9) \cos 35°$ $s = 16, t = 9, R = 35°$

$r^2 \approx 101.1$ Use a calculator.

$r \approx 10.1$ Take the positive square root of each side.

$\frac{\sin R}{r} = \frac{\sin T}{t}$ Law of Sines

$\frac{\sin 35°}{10.1} = \frac{\sin T}{9}$ Substitution

$\frac{9 \sin 35°}{10.1} = \sin T$ Multiply each side by 9.

$31° \approx T$ Use the $\sin^{-1}$ function.

$m\angle S = 180 - (35° + 31°)$ or 114°

9. $A \approx 70°, B \approx 40°, c \approx 3.0$ **11.** $A \approx 31°, B \approx 108°, C \approx 41°$ **13.** $a \approx 6.9, B \approx 41°, C \approx 23°$ **15.** $F \approx 65°, G \approx 94°, H \approx 21°$ **17.** Sines; $C \approx 45°, A \approx 85°, a \approx 18.2$ **19.** Cosines; $A \approx 27°, B \approx 115°, C \approx 38°$ **21.** Sines; $A \approx 17°, B \approx 79°, b \approx 6.9$

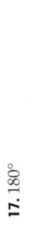

23 $d^2 = 338^2 + 520^2 - 2(338)(520) \cos 70°$

$d^2 \approx 264{,}417.1$

$d \approx 514.2$ m

25. 81°, 36°, 63° **27.** about 13,148 yd^2

29a. Sample answer:

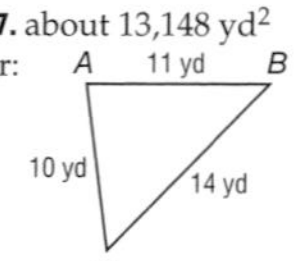

29b. Sample answer: Use the Law of Cosines to find the measure of $\angle A$. Then use the formula Area $= \frac{1}{2}bc \sin A$. **29c.** 54.6 yd^2

31

$\frac{\sin A}{a} = \frac{\sin B}{b}$ Law of Sines

$\frac{\sin 104°}{12.4} = \frac{\sin B}{8.1}$ Substitution

$\frac{8.1 \sin 104°}{12.4} = \sin B$ Multiply each side by 8.1.

$39° \approx B$ Use the $\sin^{-1}$ function.

$m\angle C \approx 180 - (39° + 104°)$ or 37°

$\frac{\sin A}{a} = \frac{\sin C}{c}$ Law of Sines

$\frac{\sin 104°}{12.4} = \frac{\sin 37°}{c}$ Substitution

$c = \frac{12.4 \sin 37°}{\sin 104°}$ Solve for c.

$c \approx 7.7$ Use a calculator.

33. $F \approx 42°, G \approx 72°, H \approx 66°$ **35.** The longest side is 14.5 centimeters. Use the Law of Cosines to find the measure of the angle opposite the longest side; 102°. **37.** When two angles and a side are given or when two sides and an angle opposite one of the sides are given, you can use the Law of Sines to solve a triangle. When two sides and an included angle are given or when three sides are given, you can use the Law of Cosines to solve a triangle. **39.** G **41.** 4, $\frac{23}{15}$

43. 7.5 yd^2 **45.** $\sin \theta = \frac{5\sqrt{89}}{89}$, $\cos \theta = \frac{8\sqrt{89}}{89}$, $\tan \theta = \frac{5}{8}$, $\csc \theta = \frac{\sqrt{89}}{5}$, $\sec \theta = \frac{\sqrt{89}}{8}$, $\cot \theta = \frac{8}{5}$

47. $\sin \theta = -\frac{3\sqrt{13}}{13}$, $\cos \theta = \frac{2\sqrt{13}}{13}$, $\tan \theta = -1.5$, $\csc \theta = \frac{-\sqrt{13}}{3}$, $\sec \theta = \frac{\sqrt{13}}{2}$, $\cot \theta = -\frac{2}{3}$ **49.** (40, 30)

51. hyperbola

53.

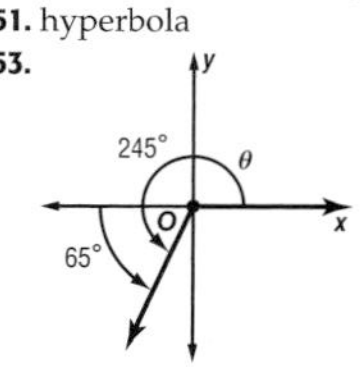

55.

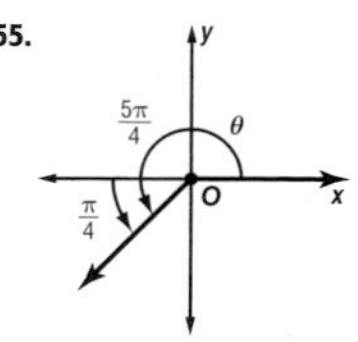

Pages 851–854 Lesson 13-6

1. $\cos \theta = \frac{15}{17}$, $\sin \theta = \frac{8}{17}$ **3.** 2 **5a.** 4 seconds

5b. Sample answer:

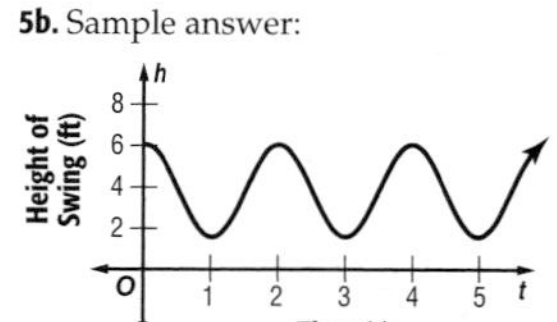

7. $-\frac{\sqrt{3}}{2}$ **9.** $\cos \theta = \frac{3}{5}$, $\sin \theta = -\frac{4}{5}$

11 $P\left(\frac{\sqrt{3}}{2}, \frac{1}{2}\right) = P(\cos \theta, \sin \theta)$

$\cos \theta = \frac{\sqrt{3}}{2}$ $\sin \theta = \frac{1}{2}$

13. 3 **15.** 12 **17.** 180°

19a.

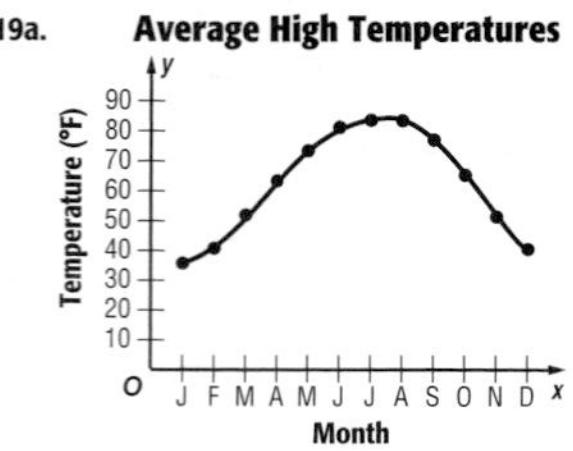

19b. 12 mo or 1 yr **21.** $\frac{1}{2}$ **23.** $\frac{\sqrt{2}}{2}$ **25.** $-\frac{\sqrt{3}}{2}$

27 **a.** The period is the time it takes to complete one rotation. So, the period is 60 seconds ÷ 2.5 or 24 seconds.

b. Since the siren is 1 mile from Ms. Miller's house and the beam of sound has a radius of 1 mile, then the minimum distance of the sound beam from the house is 0 miles and the maximum distance is 2 miles. Draw a sine curve with the pattern repeating every 24 seconds. Sample answer:

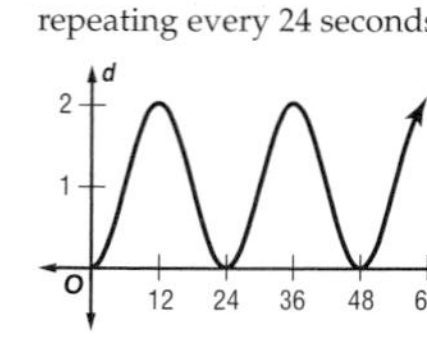

29a.

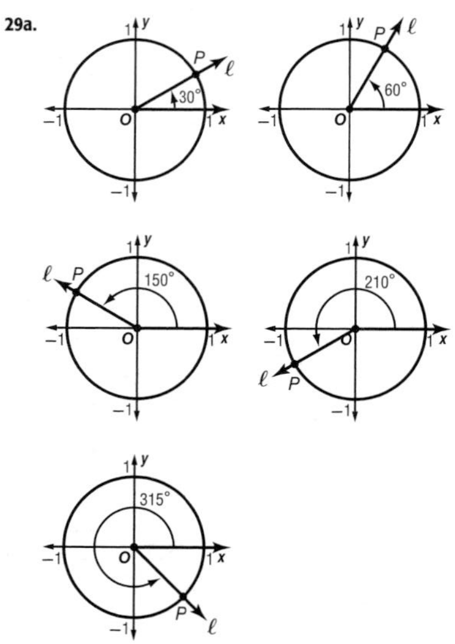

29b.

Angle	Slope
30	0.6
60	1.7
120	−1.7
150	−0.6
210	0.6
315	−1

29c. Sample answer: The slope corresponds to the tangent of the angle. For $\theta = 120°$, the x-coordinate of P is $-\frac{1}{2}$ and the y-coordinate is $\frac{\sqrt{3}}{2}$; slope $= \frac{\text{change in } y}{\text{change in } x}$. Since change in $x = -\frac{1}{2}$ and change in $y = \frac{\sqrt{3}}{2}$, slope $= \frac{\sqrt{3}}{2} \div \left(-\frac{1}{2}\right) = -\sqrt{3}$ or about −1.7.

31 $\cos 45° - \cos 30° = \frac{\sqrt{2}}{2} - \frac{\sqrt{3}}{2}$

$= \frac{\sqrt{2} - \sqrt{3}}{2}$

33. $-\frac{5\sqrt{3}}{2}$ **35.** 1 **37.** Benita; Francis incorrectly wrote $\cos \frac{-\pi}{3} = -\cos \frac{\pi}{3}$. **39.** Sometimes; the period of a sine curve could be $\frac{\pi}{2}$, which is not a multiple of π. **41.** The period of a periodic function is the horizontal distance of the part of the graph that is nonrepeating. Each nonrepeating part of the graph is one cycle. **43.** C **45.** A **47.** $A \approx 34°, C \approx 64°, c \approx 12.7$ **49.** $B \approx 33°, C \approx 29°, c \approx 9.9$ **51.** one solution; $B \approx 35°, C \approx 99°, c \approx 13.7$ **53.** 0.267 **55.** 7 **57.** $46,794.34 **59.** (5, 0), (−4, ±6) **61.** 108

Pages 859–861 Lesson 13-7

1. amplitude: 4; period: 360°

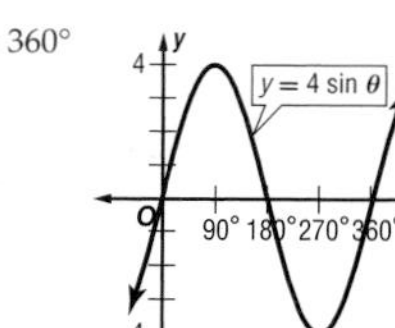

3. amplitude: 1; period: 180°

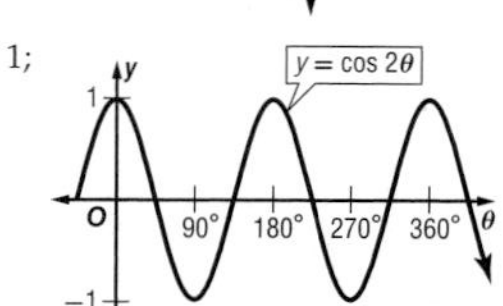

5a. $\frac{1}{14}$ or about 0.07 second

5b. $y = \sin 28\pi t$

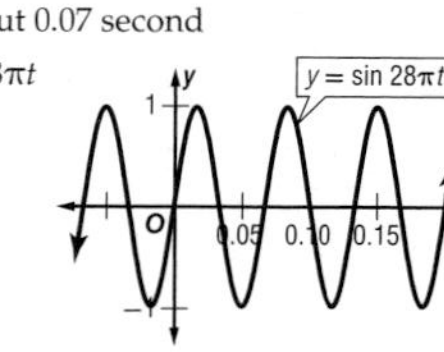

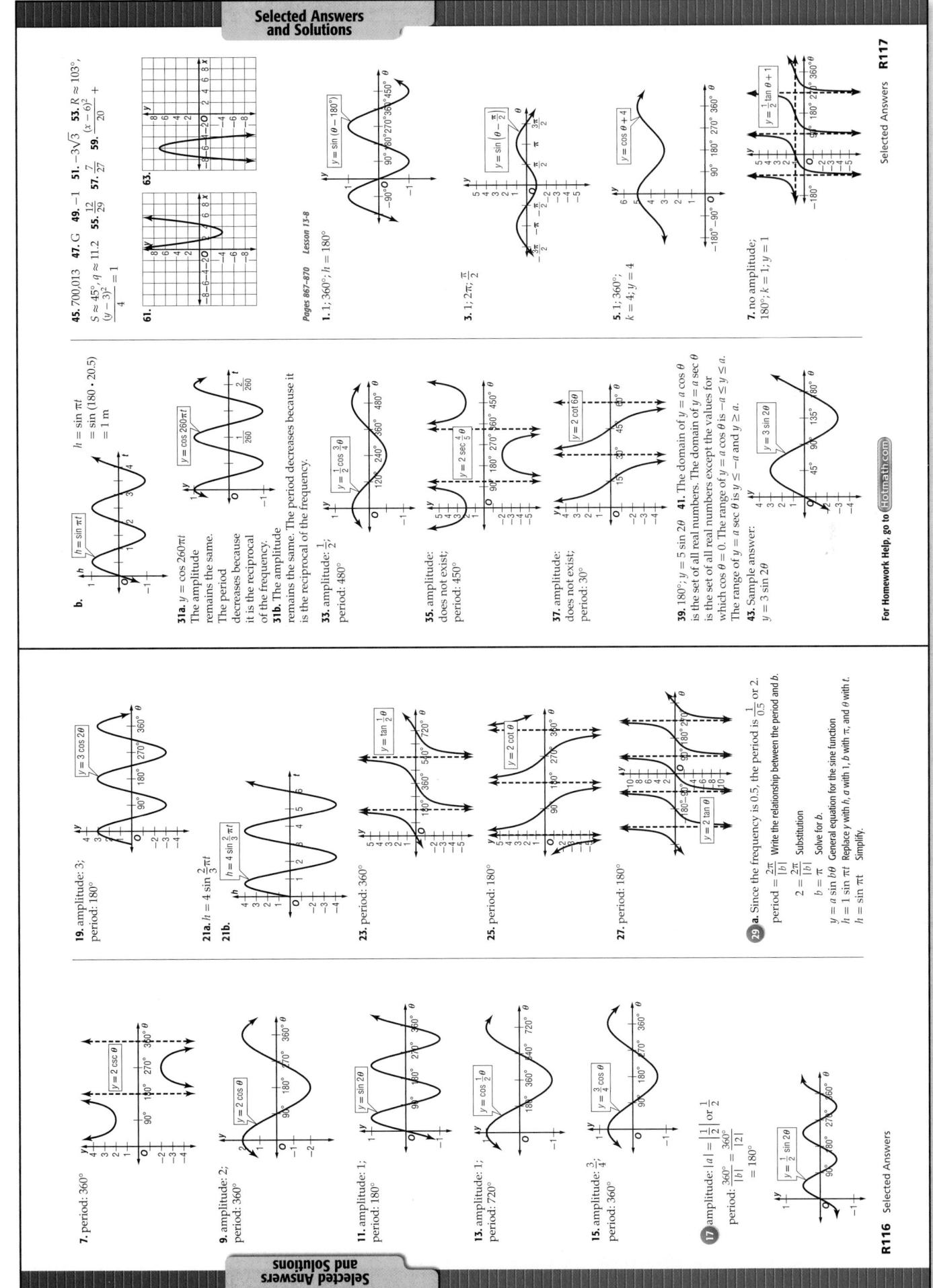

7. period: 360°

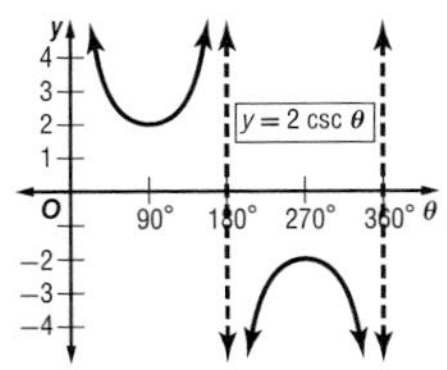

9. amplitude: 2; period: 360°

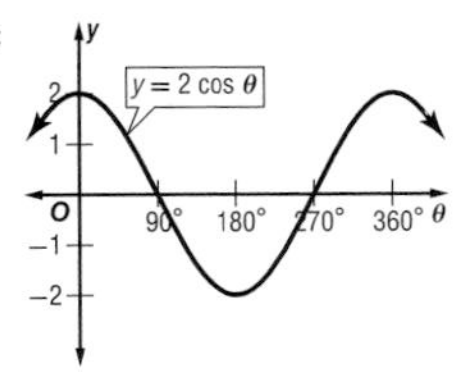

11. amplitude: 1; period: 180°

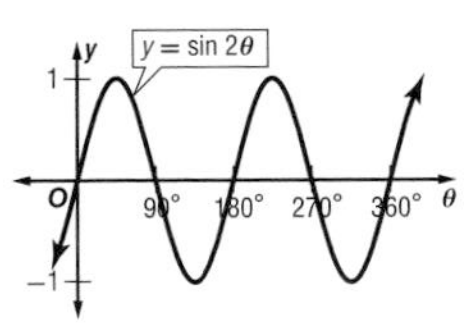

13. amplitude: 1; period: 720°

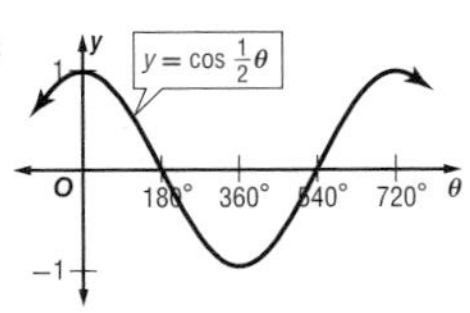

15. amplitude: $\frac{3}{4}$; period: 360°

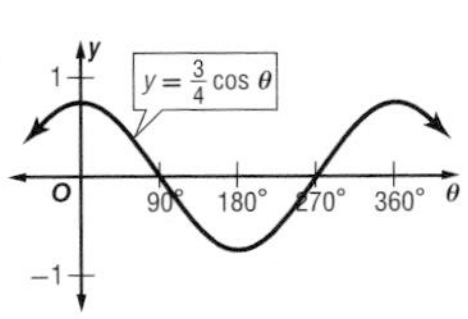

17 amplitude: $|a| = \left|\frac{1}{2}\right|$ or $\frac{1}{2}$

period: $\frac{360°}{|b|} = \frac{360°}{|2|}$
$= 180°$

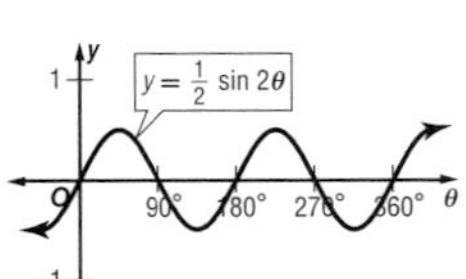

19. amplitude: 3; period: 180°

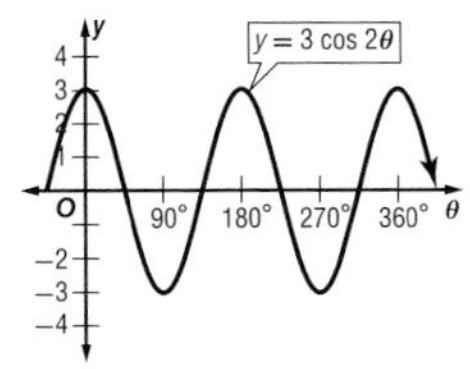

21a. $h = 4 \sin \frac{2}{3}\pi t$

21b.

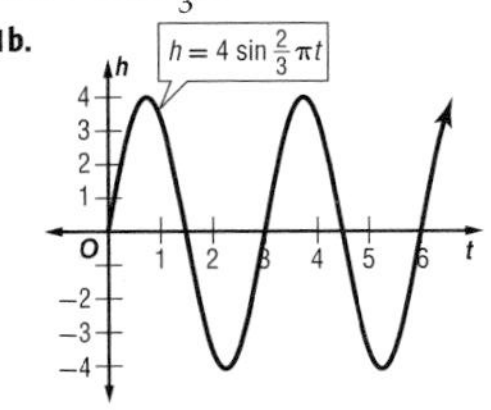

23. period: 360°

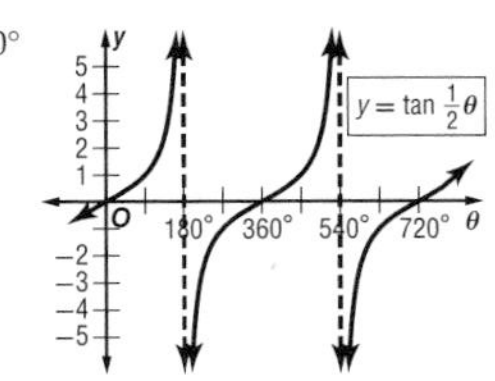

25. period: 180°

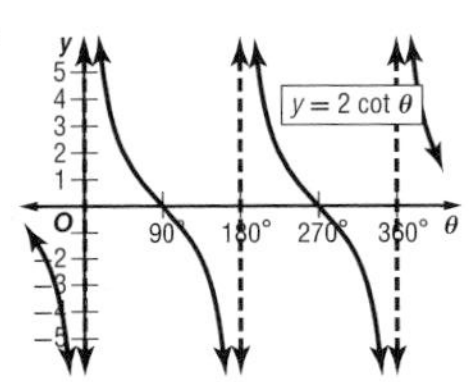

27. period: 180°

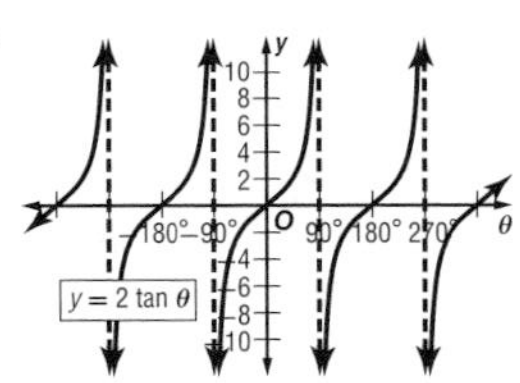

29 **a.** Since the frequency is 0.5, the period is $\frac{1}{0.5}$ or 2.

period $= \frac{2\pi}{|b|}$ Write the relationship between the period and *b*.
$2 = \frac{2\pi}{|b|}$ Substitution
$b = \pi$ Solve for *b*.
$y = a \sin b\theta$ General equation for the sine function
$h = 1 \sin \pi t$ Replace *y* with *h*, *a* with 1, *b* with π, and θ with *t*.
$h = \sin \pi t$ Simplify.

b.

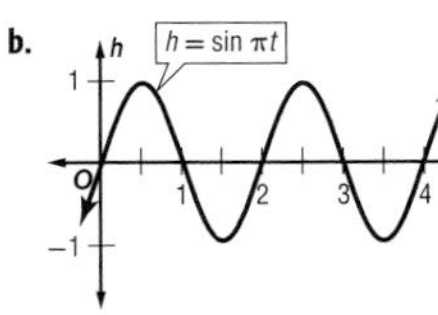

$h = \sin \pi t$
$= \sin (180 \cdot 20.5)$
$= 1$ m

31a. $y = \cos 260\pi t$
The amplitude remains the same. The period decreases because it is the reciprocal of the frequency.

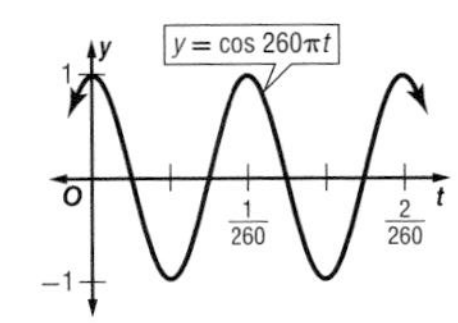

31b. The amplitude remains the same. The period decreases because it is the reciprocal of the frequency.

33. amplitude: $\frac{1}{2}$; period: 480°

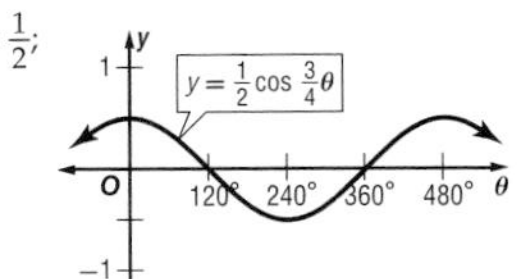

35. amplitude: does not exist; period: 450°

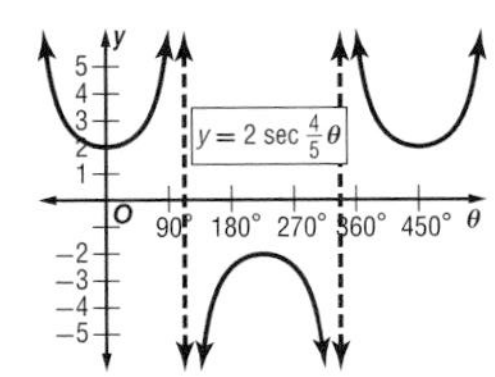

37. amplitude: does not exist; period: 30°

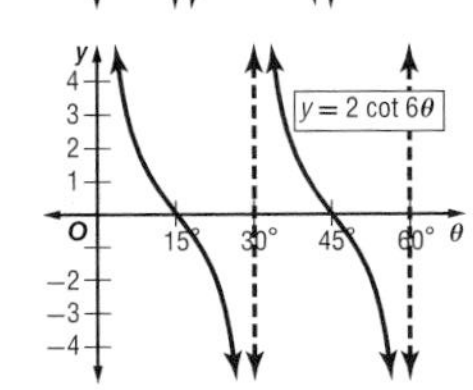

39. 180°; $y = 5 \sin 2\theta$ **41.** The domain of $y = a \cos \theta$ is the set of all real numbers. The domain of $y = a \sec \theta$ is the set of all real numbers except the values for which $\cos \theta = 0$. The range of $y = a \cos \theta$ is $-a \leq y \leq a$. The range of $y = a \sec \theta$ is $y \leq -a$ and $y \geq a$.

43. Sample answer: $y = 3 \sin 2\theta$

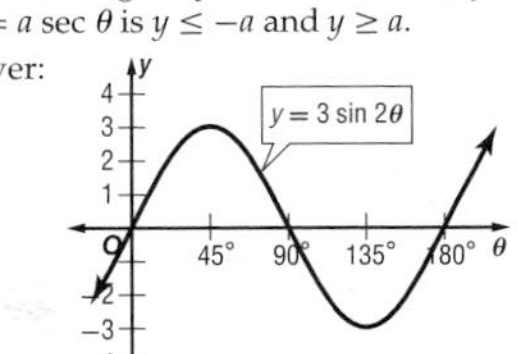

45. 700,013 **47.** G **49.** −1 **51.** $-3\sqrt{3}$ **53.** $R \approx 103°$, $S \approx 45°$, $q \approx 11.2$ **55.** $\frac{12}{29}$ **57.** $\frac{7}{27}$ **59.** $\frac{(x-6)^2}{20} + \frac{(y-3)^2}{4} = 1$

61.

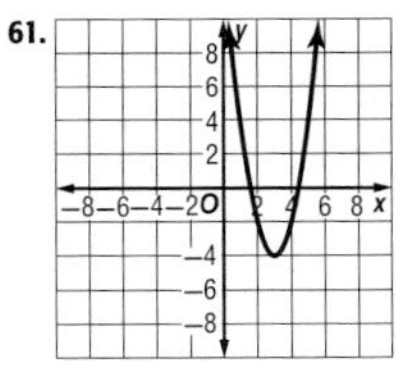

63.

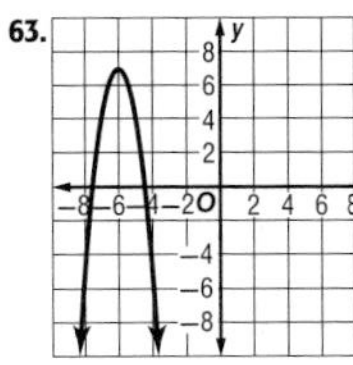

Pages 867–870 Lesson 13-8

1. 1; 360°; $h = 180°$

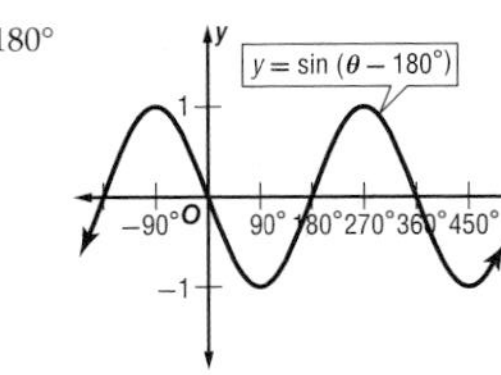

3. 1; 2π; $\frac{\pi}{2}$

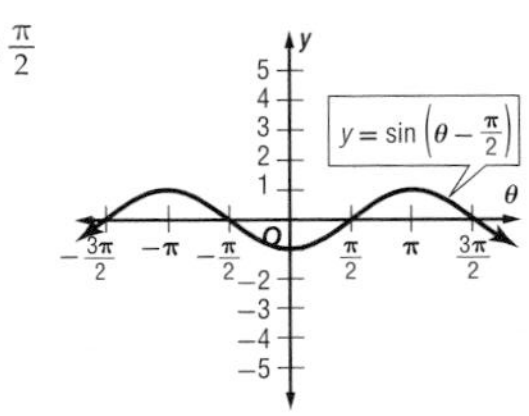

5. 1; 360°; $k = 4$; $y = 4$

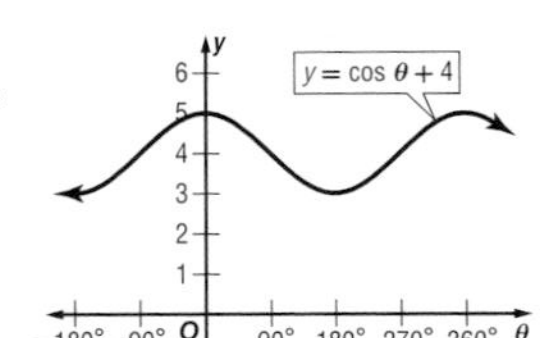

7. no amplitude; 180°; $k = 1$; $y = 1$

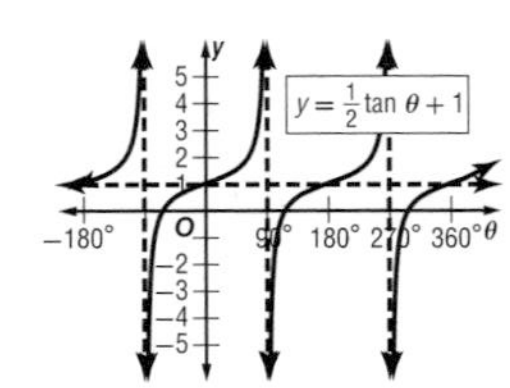

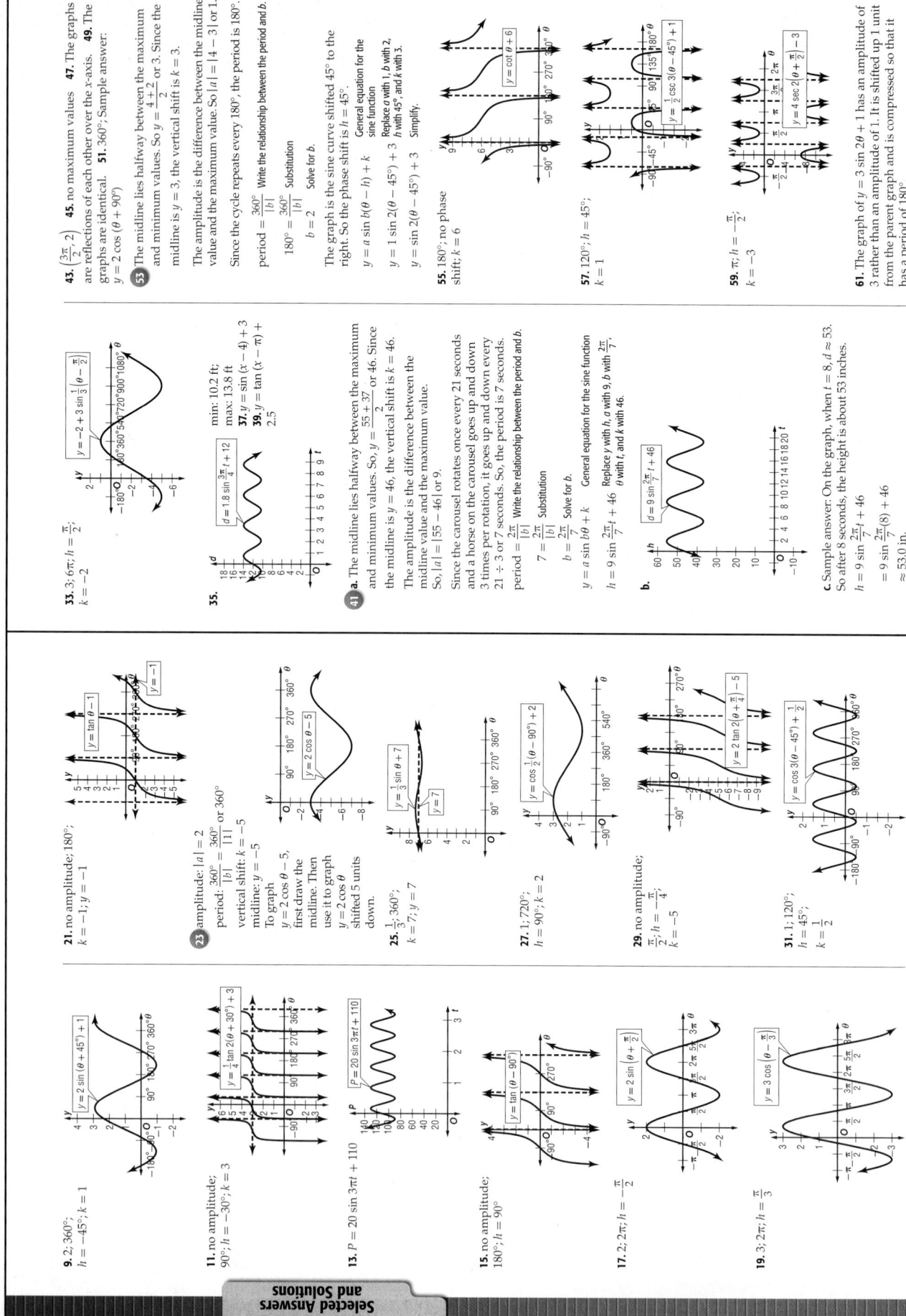

9. 2; 360°; $h = -45°$; $k = 1$

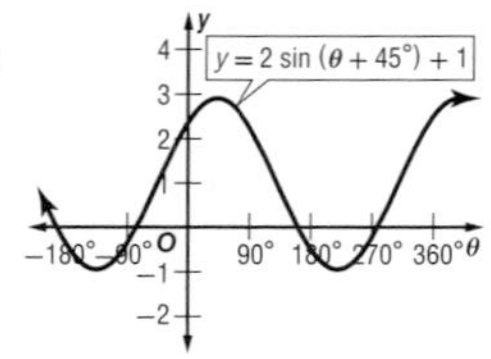

11. no amplitude; 90°; $h = -30°$; $k = 3$

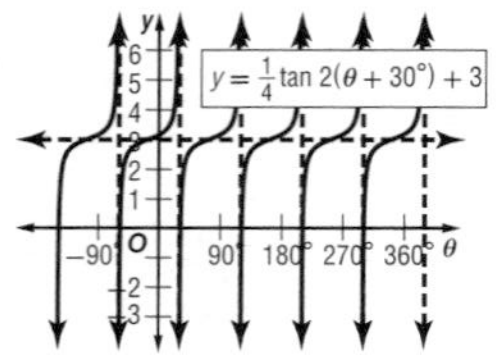

13. $P = 20 \sin 3\pi t + 110$

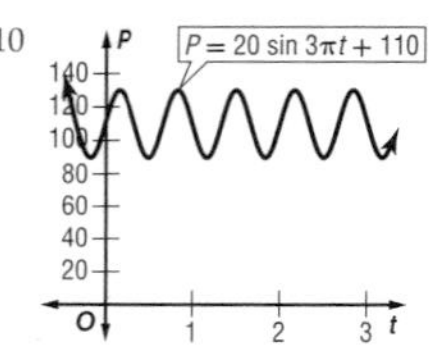

15. no amplitude; 180°; $h = 90°$

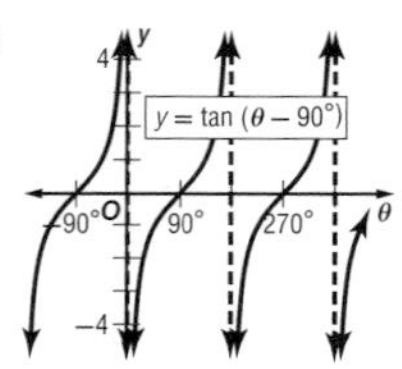

17. 2; 2π; $h = -\frac{\pi}{2}$

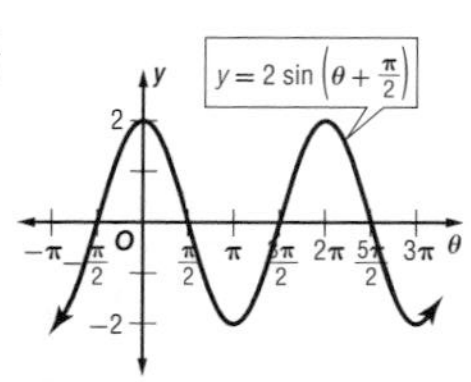

19. 3; 2π; $h = \frac{\pi}{3}$

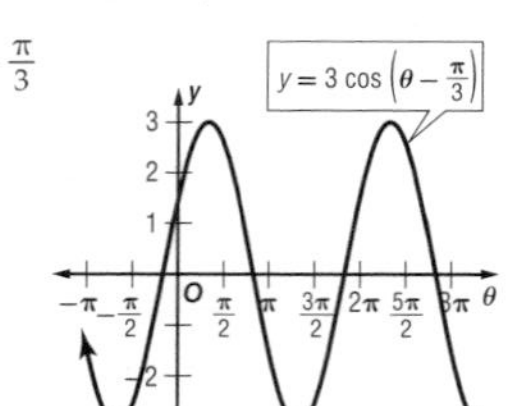

21. no amplitude; 180°; $k = -1$; $y = -1$

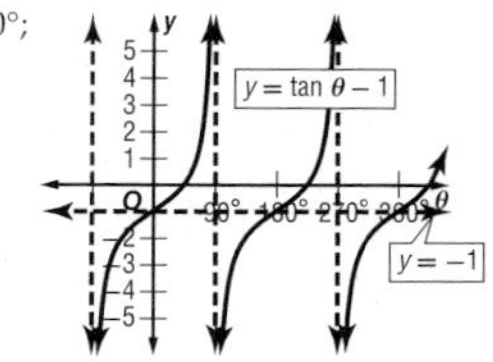

23 amplitude: $|a| = 2$

period: $\frac{360°}{|b|} = \frac{360°}{|1|}$ or 360°

vertical shift: $k = -5$

midline: $y = -5$

To graph $y = 2\cos\theta - 5$, first draw the midline. Then use it to graph $y = 2\cos\theta$ shifted 5 units down.

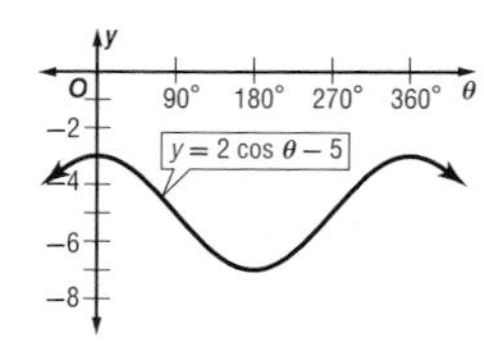

25. $\frac{1}{3}$; 360°; $k = 7$; $y = 7$

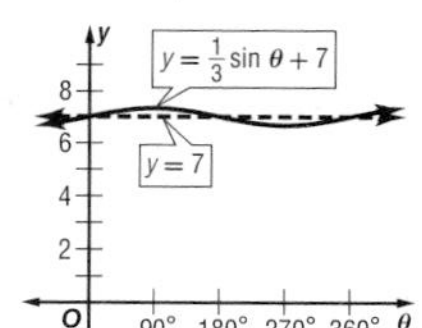

27. 1; 720°; $h = 90°$; $k = 2$

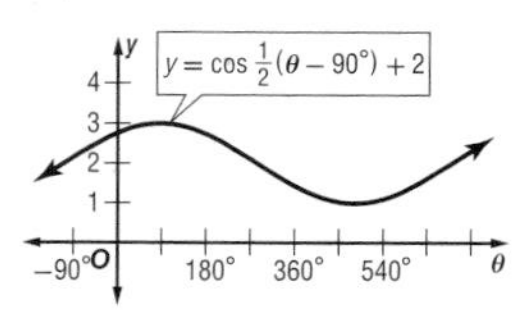

29. no amplitude; $\frac{\pi}{2}$; $h = -\frac{\pi}{4}$; $k = -5$

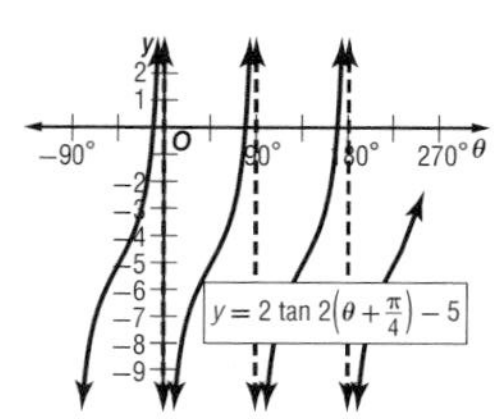

31. 1; 120°; $h = 45°$; $k = \frac{1}{2}$

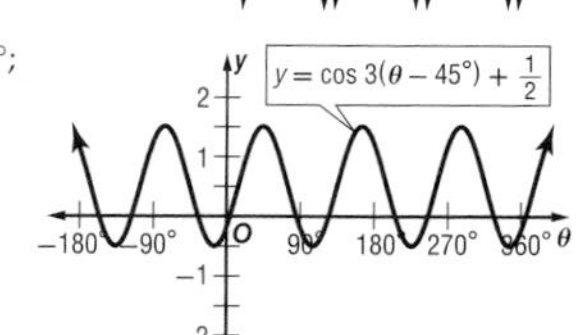

33. 3; 6π; $h = \frac{\pi}{2}$; $k = -2$

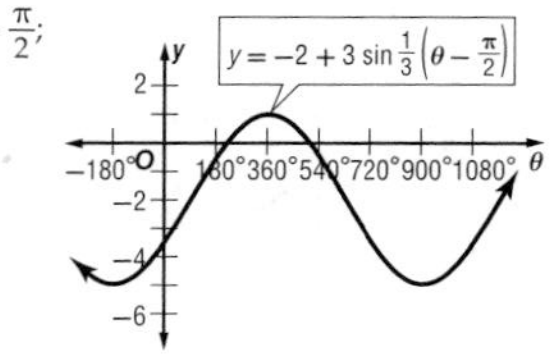

35.

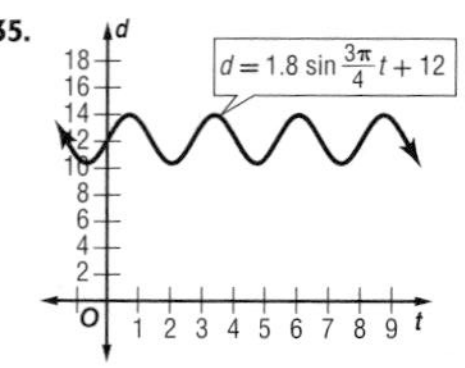

min: 10.2 ft; max: 13.8 ft

37. $y = \sin(x - 4) + 3$

39. $y = \tan(x - \pi) + 2.5$

41 **a.** The midline lies halfway between the maximum and minimum values. So, $y = \frac{55 + 37}{2}$ or 46. Since the midline is $y = 46$, the vertical shift is $k = 46$.

The amplitude is the difference between the midline value and the maximum value. So, $|a| = |55 - 46|$ or 9.

Since the carousel rotates once every 21 seconds and a horse on the carousel goes up and down 3 times per rotation, it goes up and down every $21 \div 3$ or 7 seconds. So, the period is 7 seconds.

period $= \frac{2\pi}{|b|}$ Write the relationship between the period and *b*.

$7 = \frac{2\pi}{|b|}$ Substitution

$b = \frac{2\pi}{7}$ Solve for *b*.

$y = a \sin b\theta + k$ General equation for the sine function

$h = 9 \sin \frac{2\pi}{7}t + 46$ Replace *y* with *h*, *a* with 9, *b* with $\frac{2\pi}{7}$, θ with *t*, and *k* with 46.

b.

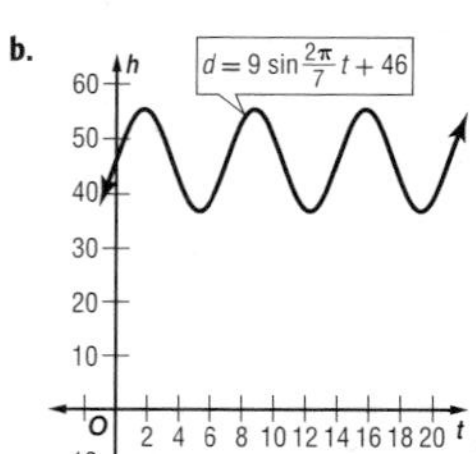

c. Sample answer: On the graph, when $t = 8$, $d \approx 53$. So after 8 seconds, the height is about 53 inches.

$h = 9 \sin \frac{2\pi}{7}t + 46$

$= 9 \sin \frac{2\pi}{7}(8) + 46$

≈ 53.0 in.

43. $\left(\frac{3\pi}{2}, 2\right)$ **45.** no maximum values **47.** The graphs are reflections of each other over the *x*-axis. **49.** The graphs are identical. **51.** 360°; Sample answer: $y = 2\cos(\theta + 90°)$

53 The midline lies halfway between the maximum and minimum values. So $y = \frac{4 + 2}{2}$ or 3. Since the midline is $y = 3$, the vertical shift is $k = 3$.

The amplitude is the difference between the midline value and the maximum value. So $|a| = |4 - 3|$ or 1.

Since the cycle repeats every 180°, the period is 180°.

period $= \frac{360°}{|b|}$ Write the relationship between the period and *b*.

$180° = \frac{360°}{|b|}$ Substitution

$b = 2$ Solve for *b*.

The graph is the sine curve shifted 45° to the right. So the phase shift is $h = 45°$.

$y = a \sin b(\theta - h) + k$ General equation for the sine function

$y = 1 \sin 2(\theta - 45°) + 3$ Replace *a* with 1, *b* with 2, *h* with 45°, and *k* with 3.

$y = \sin 2(\theta - 45°) + 3$ Simplify.

55. 180°; no phase shift; $k = 6$

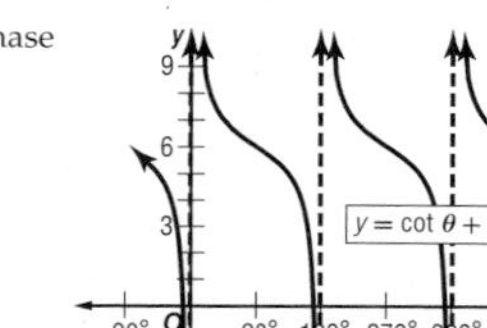

57. 120°; $h = 45°$; $k = 1$

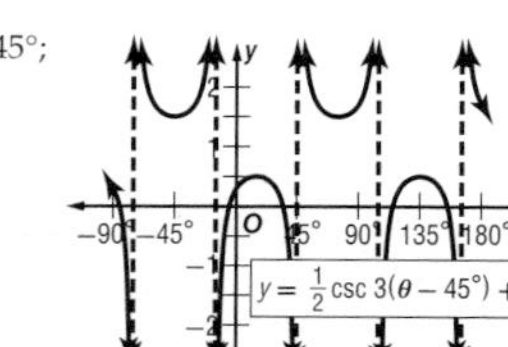

59. π; $h = -\frac{\pi}{2}$; $k = -3$

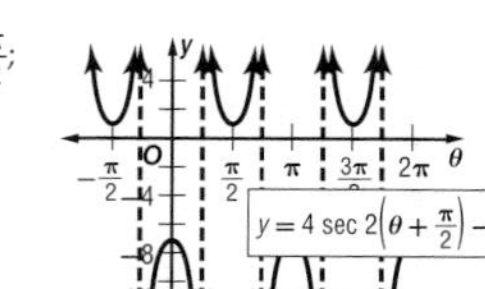

61. The graph of $y = 3 \sin 2\theta + 1$ has an amplitude of 3 rather than an amplitude of 1. It is shifted up 1 unit from the parent graph and is compressed so that it has a period of 180°.

For Homework Help, go to Hotmath.com

63. Sample answer: $y = 2\sin\theta - 3$

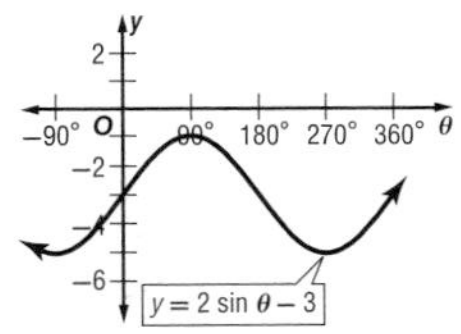

65. 1.25 **67.** F
69. amplitude: 2; period: 360°

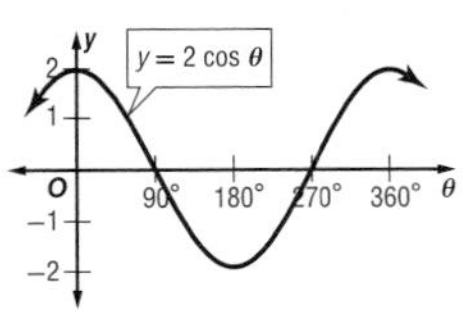

71. amplitude: 1; period: 180°

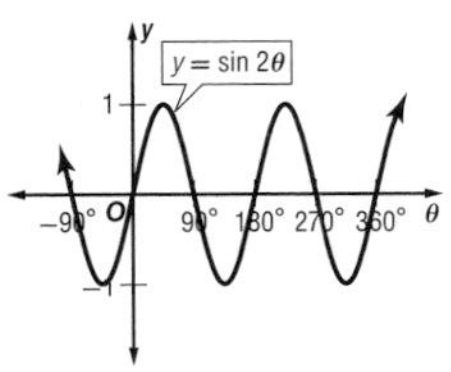

73. $-\frac{1}{2}$ **75.** Experiment; the people are put into groups at random. The treatment group is the exercisers, and the control is the other group. This is a biased experiment because the participants all know which group they are in. **77.** Observational study; the students who have part-time jobs are the treatment group, and the other students are the control; unbiased. **79.** 8 days **81.** 42° **83.** 37° **85.** 16°

Pages 874–876 Lesson 13-9

1. 30°; $\frac{\pi}{6}$ **3.** 180°; π **5.** 0 **7.** A **9.** −27.4°
11. Arctan $\frac{6.2}{18}$; 19°

13 KEYSTROKES: 2nd ENTER [COS⁻¹] 2nd [√] 3) ÷ 2) ENTER 30

So, $\text{Arccos}\left(\frac{\sqrt{3}}{2}\right) = 30°$ or $\frac{\pi}{6}$.

15. 60°; $\frac{\pi}{3}$ **17.** −30°; $-\frac{\pi}{6}$ **19.** −0.58 **21.** 0.87
23. 0.71 **25.** 64.2° **27.** 104.5° **29.** −11.3°
31. Arcsin $\frac{2.5}{24}$; 6°

33 $\frac{15 \text{ m/s} (\sin x)}{9.8 \text{ m/s}^2} = 1$ s — Maximum height equals 1.
$\sin x = \frac{9.8}{15}$ — Solve for sin x.
$x = \text{Sin}^{-1}\frac{9.8}{15}$ — Inverse sine function
$x \approx 40.8°$ — Use a calculator.

35. π **37.** no solution **39.** $\frac{\pi}{3}, \frac{5\pi}{3}$ **41.** false; $x = 2\pi$

43. The domain of $y = \text{Sin}^{-1} x$ is $-1 \le x \le 1$. This is the same as the range of $y = \text{Sin}\ x$. **45.** Sample answer: $y = \tan^{-1} x$ is a relation that has a domain of all real numbers and a range of all real numbers except odd multiples of $\frac{\pi}{2}$. The relation is not a function. $y = \text{Tan}^{-1} x$ is a function that has a domain of all real numbers and a range of $-\frac{\pi}{2} \le y \le \frac{\pi}{2}$.

47. A **49.** G **51a.** 164; 164; 360°, 90°
51b. $y = 100[\sin(x - 90°)] + 100$ **53.** 2 **55.** 4 **57.** −1
59. $-\frac{\sqrt{3}}{2}$

Pages 877–882 Chapter 13 Study Guide and Review

1. false, Law of Sines **3.** true **5.** false, Arcsin function **7.** $a = 10.9$; $A = 65°$; $B = 25°$ **9.** $A = 15°$; $a = 4.0$; $c = 15.5$ **11.** $B = 55°$; $a = 12.6$; $b = 18.0$
13. about 8.8 feet **15.** 450° **17.** $-\frac{7\pi}{4}$ **19.** 295°, −425°
21. $\frac{4\pi}{15}$ **23.** $-\frac{\sqrt{3}}{3}$ **25.** 0 **27.** $\sin\theta = \frac{12}{13}$, $\cos\theta = \frac{5}{13}$, $\tan\theta = \frac{12}{5}$, $\csc\theta = \frac{13}{12}$, $\sec\theta = \frac{13}{5}$, $\cot\theta = \frac{5}{12}$
29. about 17.1 meters **31.** two solutions; First solution: $C = 30°$, $B = 125°$, $b = 29.1$; second solution: $C = 150°$, $B = 5°$, $b = 3.1$ **33.** 105.5 ft **35.** Law of Sines; $B \approx 52°$, $C \approx 48°$, $c \approx 11.3$ **37.** Law of Sines; $B \approx 75°$, $C \approx 63°$, $c \approx 12.0$ or $B \approx 105°$, $C \approx 33°$, $c \approx 7.3$
39. 750.5 ft **41.** $\frac{-\sqrt{6}}{4}$ **43.** 0 **45.** 15 seconds

47. amplitude: 1, period: 720°

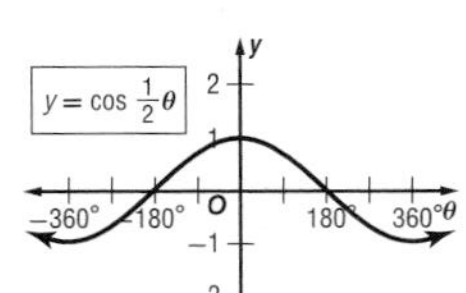

49. amplitude: not defined, period: 360°

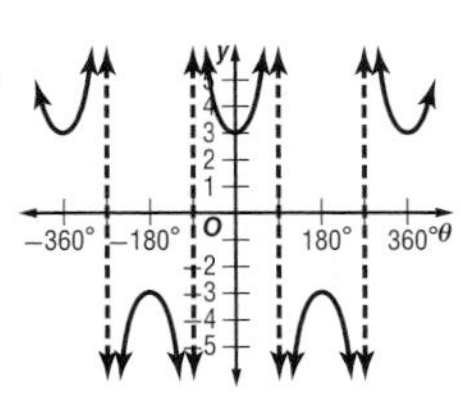

51. amplitude: not defined, period: 720°

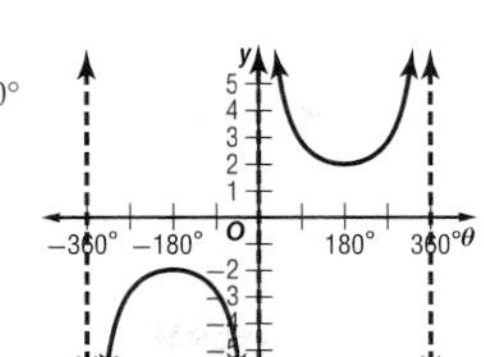

53. vertical shift: up 1; amplitude: 3; period 180°; phase shift: 90° right

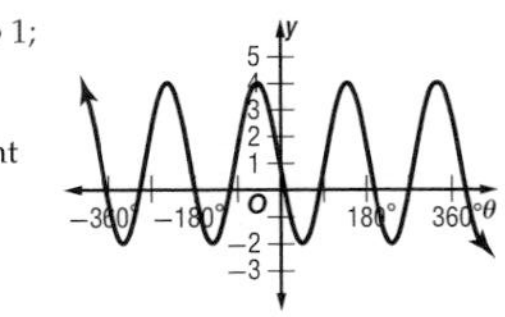

55. vertical shift: up 2 amplitude: not defined period: $\frac{2\pi}{3}$ phase shift: $\frac{\pi}{2}$° right

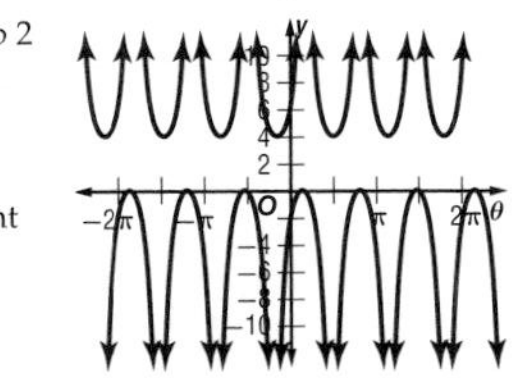

57. vertical shift: up 2 amplitude: $\frac{1}{3}$ period: 1080° phase shift: 90° right

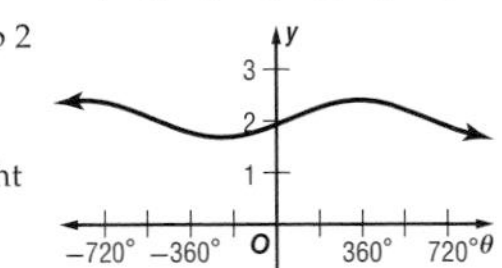

59. 90°, $\frac{\pi}{2}$ **61.** 60°, $\frac{\pi}{3}$ **63.** 45°, $\frac{\pi}{4}$ **65.** $\sin^{-1}\frac{5}{10} = \theta$; 30° **67.** −0.71 **69.** −55.0° **71.** 65.8°

Chapter 14 Trigonometric Identities and Equations

Page 889 Chapter 14 Get Ready

1. $-4a(a - 1)$ **3.** prime **5.** $(x + 2)$ in. **7.** {−7, 5}
9. {3, 4} **11.** $\frac{\sqrt{2}}{2}$ **13.** $-\frac{\sqrt{3}}{3}$ **15.** 45 ft

Pages 894–897 Lesson 14-1

1. $\frac{1}{2}$ **3.** $\frac{\sqrt{5}}{3}$ **5.** $\sin\theta\cos\theta$ **7.** $\cot^2\theta$ **9.** $\frac{5}{4}$ **11.** $\frac{4}{5}$
13. $-\frac{5}{4}$

15 $\cot^2\theta + 1 = \csc^2\theta$ — Pythagorean Identity
$\left(\frac{1}{4}\right)^2 + 1 = \csc^2\theta$ — Substitute $\frac{1}{4}$ for cot θ.
$\frac{1}{16} + 1 = \csc^2\theta$ — Square $\frac{1}{4}$.
$\frac{17}{16} = \csc^2\theta$ — Add.
$\pm\frac{\sqrt{17}}{4} = \csc\theta$ — Take the square root of each side.
Since θ is in the third quadrant, csc θ is negative.
So, $\csc\theta = -\frac{\sqrt{17}}{4}$.

17. $-\frac{12}{13}$ **19.** $\frac{3}{5}$ **21.** $\sec^3\theta$ **23.** $\csc\theta$ **25.** 1

27 $B = \frac{F\csc\theta}{I\ell}$ — Original equation
$I\ell \cdot B = F\csc\theta$ — Multiply each side by $I\ell$.
$I\ell B = F \cdot \frac{1}{\sin\theta}$ — $\frac{1}{\sin\theta} = \csc\theta$
$I\ell B\sin\theta = F$ — Multiply each side by sin θ.
The equation can be written as $F = I\ell B\sin\theta$.

29. $\sec\theta$ **31.** 2 **33.** $2\cos^2\theta$ **35a.** $\frac{\sqrt{65}}{9}$ **35b.** $\frac{4\sqrt{65}}{65}$

35c. $\frac{4}{9}, \frac{\sqrt{65}}{9}, \frac{4\sqrt{65}}{65}$ **37.** $\mu_k = \tan\theta$

39 $\frac{\cos\left(\frac{\pi}{2} - \theta\right) - 1}{1 + \sin(-\theta)} = \frac{\sin\theta - 1}{1 + \sin(-\theta)}$ — $\cos\left(\frac{\pi}{2} - \theta\right) = \sin\theta$
$= \frac{\sin\theta - 1}{1 - \sin\theta}$ — $\sin(-\theta) = -\sin\theta$
$= \frac{\sin\theta - 1}{-1(\sin\theta - 1)}$ — $1 - \sin\theta = -1(\sin\theta - 1)$
$= \frac{1}{-1}$ or -1 — Simplify.

41. $-\cot^2\theta$ **43.** Sample answer: $x = 45°$ **45.** The functions cos θ and sin θ can be thought of as the lengths of the legs of a right triangle, and the number 1 can be thought of as the measure of the corresponding hypotenuse. **47.** Sample answer: $\frac{\sin\theta}{\cos\theta} \cdot \sin\theta$ and $\frac{\sin^2\theta}{\cos\theta}$ **49.** $-\frac{4}{3}$ **51.** A **53.** D
55. 2.09 **57.** 0.52 **59.** 0.5 **61.** $h = 4 - \cos\frac{\pi}{2}t$ or $h = 4 - \cos 90°t$ **63.** $\frac{1093}{9}$ **65.** −3, 2 **67.** 2

Pages 900–903 Lesson 14-2

1. $\cot\theta + \tan\theta \stackrel{?}{=} \frac{\sec^2\theta}{\tan\theta}$
$\cot\theta + \tan\theta \stackrel{?}{=} \frac{\tan^2\theta + 1}{\tan\theta}$
$\cot\theta + \tan\theta \stackrel{?}{=} \frac{\tan^2\theta}{\tan\theta} + \frac{1}{\tan\theta}$
$\cot\theta + \tan\theta = \tan\theta + \cot\theta$ ✓

3. $\sin\theta \stackrel{?}{=} \frac{\sec\theta}{\tan\theta + \cot\theta}$
$\sin\theta \stackrel{?}{=} \frac{\frac{1}{\cos\theta}}{\frac{\sin\theta}{\cos\theta} + \frac{\cos\theta}{\sin\theta}}$
$\sin\theta \stackrel{?}{=} \frac{\frac{1}{\cos\theta}}{\frac{\sin^2\theta + \cos^2\theta}{\cos\theta\sin\theta}}$
$\sin\theta \stackrel{?}{=} \frac{\frac{1}{\cos\theta}}{\frac{1}{\cos\theta\sin\theta}}$
$\sin\theta \stackrel{?}{=} \frac{1}{\cos\theta} \cdot \frac{\cos\theta\sin\theta}{1}$
$\sin\theta = \sin\theta$ ✓

5. $\tan^2\theta\csc^2\theta \stackrel{?}{=} 1 + \tan^2\theta$
$\frac{\sin^2\theta}{\cos^2\theta} \cdot \frac{1}{\sin^2\theta} \stackrel{?}{=} \sec^2\theta$
$\frac{1}{\cos^2\theta} \stackrel{?}{=} \sec^2\theta$
$\sec^2\theta = \sec^2\theta$ ✓

7 $\frac{\tan^2\theta + 1}{\tan^2\theta} = \frac{\sec^2\theta}{\tan^2\theta}$ — $\tan^2\theta + 1 = \sec^2\theta$
$= \frac{\frac{1}{\cos^2\theta}}{\frac{\sin^2\theta}{\cos^2\theta}}$ — $\sec^2\theta = \frac{1}{\cos^2\theta}$ and $\tan^2\theta = \frac{\sin^2\theta}{\cos^2\theta}$
$= \frac{1}{\cos^2\theta} \cdot \frac{\cos^2\theta}{\sin^2\theta}$ — Invert the denominator and multiply.
$= \frac{1}{\sin^2\theta}$ — Simplify.
$= \csc^2\theta$ — $\csc^2\theta = \frac{1}{\sin^2\theta}$
The answer is D.

9. $\cot\theta(\cot\theta + \tan\theta) \stackrel{?}{=} \csc^2\theta$
$\cot^2\theta + \cot\theta\tan\theta \stackrel{?}{=} \csc^2\theta$
$\cot^2\theta + \frac{\sin\theta}{\cos\theta} \cdot \frac{\cos\theta}{\sin\theta} \stackrel{?}{=} \csc^2\theta$
$\cot^2\theta + 1 \stackrel{?}{=} \csc^2\theta$
$\csc^2\theta = \csc^2\theta$ ✓

For Homework Help, go to Hotmath.com

11. $\sin\theta \sec\theta \cot\theta \stackrel{?}{=} 1$

$\sin\theta \cdot \frac{1}{\cos\theta} \cdot \frac{\cos\theta}{\sin\theta} \stackrel{?}{=} 1$

$1 \stackrel{?}{=} 1$ ✓

13. $\frac{1 - 2\cos^2\theta}{\sin\theta\cos\theta} \stackrel{?}{=} \tan\theta - \cot\theta$

$\frac{(1-\cos^2\theta) - \cos^2\theta}{\sin\theta\cos\theta} \stackrel{?}{=} \tan\theta - \cot\theta$

$\frac{\sin^2\theta - \cos^2\theta}{\sin\theta\cos\theta} \stackrel{?}{=} \tan\theta - \cot\theta$

$\frac{\sin^2\theta}{\sin\theta\cos\theta} - \frac{\cos^2\theta}{\sin\theta\cos\theta} \stackrel{?}{=} \tan\theta - \cot\theta$

$\frac{\sin\theta}{\cos\theta} - \frac{\cos\theta}{\sin\theta} \stackrel{?}{=} \tan\theta - \cot\theta$

$\tan\theta - \cot\theta = \tan\theta - \cot\theta$ ✓

15. $\cos\theta \stackrel{?}{=} \sin\theta\cot\theta$

$\cos\theta \stackrel{?}{=} \sin\theta \frac{\cos\theta}{\sin\theta}$

$\cos\theta = \cos\theta$ ✓

17. $\cos\theta\cos(-\theta) - \sin\theta\sin(-\theta) \stackrel{?}{=} 1$

$\cos\theta\cos\theta - \sin\theta(-\sin\theta) \stackrel{?}{=} 1$

$\cos^2\theta + \sin^2\theta \stackrel{?}{=} 1$

$1 = 1$ ✓

19. $\sec\theta - \tan\theta \stackrel{?}{=} \frac{1 - \sin\theta}{\cos\theta}$

$\frac{1}{\cos\theta} - \frac{\sin\theta}{\cos\theta} \stackrel{?}{=} \frac{1-\sin\theta}{\cos\theta}$

$\frac{1-\sin\theta}{\cos\theta} = \frac{1-\sin\theta}{\cos\theta}$ ✓

21. $\sec\theta\csc\theta \stackrel{?}{=} \tan\theta + \cot\theta$

$\frac{1}{\cos\theta}\cdot\frac{1}{\sin\theta} \stackrel{?}{=} \frac{\sin\theta}{\cos\theta} + \frac{\cos\theta}{\sin\theta}$

$\frac{1}{\cos\theta\sin\theta} \stackrel{?}{=} \frac{\sin^2\theta}{\sin\theta\cos\theta} + \frac{\cos^2\theta}{\sin\theta\cos\theta}$

$\frac{1}{\cos\theta\sin\theta} \stackrel{?}{=} \frac{\sin^2\theta + \cos^2\theta}{\sin\theta\cos\theta}$

$\frac{1}{\cos\theta\sin\theta} = \frac{1}{\cos\theta\sin\theta}$ ✓

23. $(\sin\theta + \cos\theta)^2 \stackrel{?}{=} \frac{2 + \sec\theta\csc\theta}{\sec\theta\csc\theta}$

$(\sin\theta + \cos\theta)^2 \stackrel{?}{=} \frac{2 + \frac{1}{\cos\theta}\cdot\frac{1}{\sin\theta}}{\frac{1}{\cos\theta}\cdot\frac{1}{\sin\theta}}$

$(\sin\theta + \cos\theta)^2 \stackrel{?}{=} \left(2 + \frac{1}{\cos\theta\sin\theta}\right)\cdot\frac{\cos\theta\sin\theta}{1}$

$(\sin\theta + \cos\theta)^2 \stackrel{?}{=} 2\cos\theta\sin\theta + 1$

$(\sin\theta + \cos\theta)^2 \stackrel{?}{=} 2\cos\theta\sin\theta + \cos^2\theta + \sin^2\theta$

$(\sin\theta + \cos\theta)^2 = (\sin\theta + \cos\theta)^2$ ✓

25. $\csc\theta - 1 \stackrel{?}{=} \frac{\cot^2\theta}{\csc\theta + 1}$

$\csc\theta - 1 \stackrel{?}{=} \frac{\csc^2\theta - 1}{\csc\theta + 1}$

$\csc\theta - 1 \stackrel{?}{=} \frac{(\csc\theta - 1)(\csc\theta + 1)}{\csc\theta + 1}$

$\csc\theta - 1 = \csc\theta - 1$ ✓

27. $\sin\theta\cos\theta\tan\theta + \cos^2\theta \stackrel{?}{=} 1$

$\sin\theta\cos\theta\cdot\frac{\sin\theta}{\cos\theta} + \cos^2\theta \stackrel{?}{=} 1$

$\sin^2\theta + \cos^2\theta \stackrel{?}{=} 1$

$1 = 1$ ✓

29. $\csc^2\theta \stackrel{?}{=} \cot^2\theta + \sin\theta\csc\theta$

$\csc^2\theta \stackrel{?}{=} \cot^2\theta + \sin\theta\cdot\frac{1}{\sin\theta}$

$\csc^2\theta \stackrel{?}{=} \cot^2\theta + 1$

$\csc^2\theta = \csc^2\theta$ ✓

31. $\sin^2\theta + \cos^2\theta \stackrel{?}{=} \sec^2\theta - \tan^2\theta$

$1 \stackrel{?}{=} \tan^2\theta + 1 - \tan^2\theta$

$1 = 1$ ✓

33. yes

35 $\cot(-\theta)\tan(-\theta) = \frac{1}{\tan(-\theta)}\cdot\tan(-\theta)$ $\quad \frac{1}{\tan(-\theta)} = \cot(-\theta)$

$= 1$ Simplify.

37. 1 **39.** 1 **41.** $\cos\theta$ **43.** 2 **45.** $\sin\theta$ **47.** 1

49. $y = -\frac{gx^2}{2v_0^2}(1 + \tan^2\theta) + x\tan\theta$

51 **a.** $h = \frac{v_0^2\sin^2\theta}{2g} = \frac{47^2\sin^2\theta}{2(9.8)}$ Replace v_0 with 47 and g with 9.8.

$= \frac{2209\sin^2\theta}{19.6}$ Simplify.

$\frac{2209\sin^2 30°}{19.6} \approx 28.2$ m $\quad \theta = 30°$

$\frac{2209\sin^2 45°}{19.6} \approx 56.4$ m $\quad \theta = 45°$

$\frac{2209\sin^2 60°}{19.6} \approx 84.5$ m $\quad \theta = 60°$

$\frac{2209\sin^2 90°}{19.6} \approx 112.7$ m $\quad \theta = 90°$

b. Sample answer: Enter the equation $y = \frac{2209(\sin\theta)^2}{19.6}$. Use the window Xmin = −600, Xmax = 600, Xscl = 60, Ymin = −10, Ymax = 10, Yscl = 1, Xres = 1.

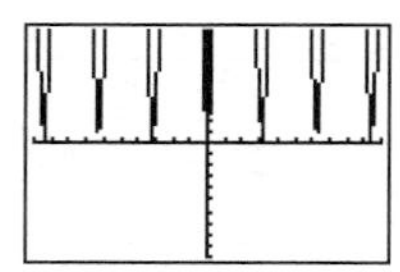

c. $\frac{v_0^2\tan^2\theta}{2g\sec^2\theta} \stackrel{?}{=} \frac{v_0^2\sin^2\theta}{2g}$

$\frac{v_0^2\left(\frac{\sin^2\theta}{\cos^2\theta}\right)}{2g\left(\frac{1}{\cos^2\theta}\right)} \stackrel{?}{=} \frac{v_0^2\sin^2\theta}{2g}$ $\quad \tan^2\theta = \frac{\sin^2\theta}{\cos^2\theta}$ and $\sec^2\theta = \frac{1}{\cos^2\theta}$

$\frac{v_0^2\sin^2\theta}{2g} = \frac{v_0^2\sin^2\theta}{2g}$ ✓ Simplify.

53. $\tan^2\theta = \frac{\sin^2\theta}{\cos^2\theta}$

$\tan^2\theta = \tan^2\theta$

$\tan^2\theta = \sec^2\theta - 1$

55. Sample answer: counterexample 45°, 30°

57. Sample answer: They are the trigonometric functions with which most people are familiar

59. Using the unit circle and the Pythagorean Theorem, we can justify $\cos^2\theta + \sin^2\theta = 1$.

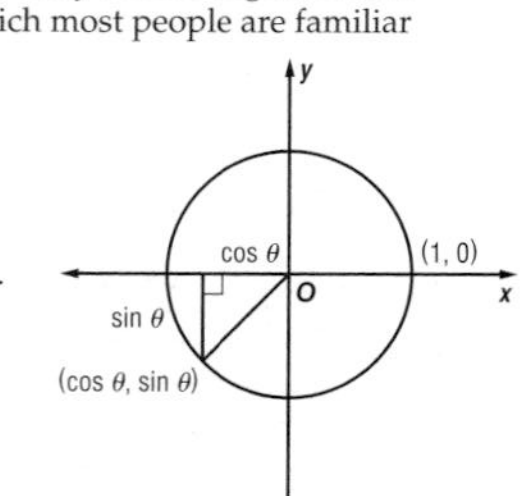

If we divide each term of the identity $\cos^2\theta + \sin^2\theta = 1$ by $\cos^2\theta$, we can justify $1 + \tan^2\theta = \sec^2\theta$.

$\frac{\cos^2\theta}{\cos^2\theta} + \frac{\sin^2\theta}{\cos^2\theta} = \frac{1}{\cos^2\theta}$

$1 + \tan^2\theta = \sec^2\theta$

If we divide each term of the identity $\cos^2\theta + \sin^2\theta = 1$ by $\sin^2\theta$, we can justify $\cot^2\theta + 1 = \csc^2\theta$.

$\frac{\cos^2\theta}{\sin^2\theta} + \frac{\sin^2\theta}{\sin^2\theta} = \frac{1}{\sin^2\theta}$

$\cot^2\theta + 1 = \csc^2\theta$

61. H **63.** G **65.** $\frac{\sqrt{5}}{3}$ **67.** $\frac{3}{5}$ **69a.** $\frac{1}{4200}$ **69b.** $\frac{1}{210}$

71. $(1, -6 \pm 2\sqrt{5})$; $(1, -6 \pm 3\sqrt{5})$; $y + 6 = \pm\frac{2\sqrt{5}}{5}(x - 1)$

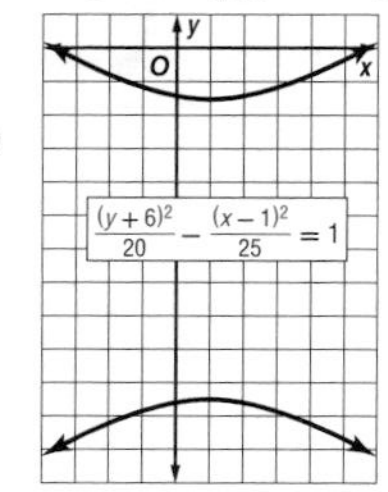

73. $\frac{12 + 7\sqrt{2}}{23}$

75. $\sqrt{x} + 1$

Pages 906–909 Lesson 14-3

1 $\cos 165° = \cos(120° + 45°)$

$= \cos 120°\cos 45° - \sin 120°\sin 45°$

$= \left(-\frac{1}{2}\cdot\frac{\sqrt{2}}{2}\right) - \left(\frac{\sqrt{3}}{2}\cdot\frac{\sqrt{2}}{2}\right)$

$= -\frac{\sqrt{2}}{4} - \frac{\sqrt{6}}{4}$

$= -\frac{\sqrt{2} + \sqrt{6}}{4}$

3. $\frac{\sqrt{6} - \sqrt{2}}{4}$ **5.** $\frac{\sqrt{2}}{2}$ **7a.** 0 **7b.** The interference is destructive. The signals cancel each other completely.

9. $\cos\left(\frac{3\pi}{2} - \theta\right) \stackrel{?}{=} -\sin\theta$

$\cos\frac{3\pi}{2}\cos\theta + \sin\frac{3\pi}{2}\sin\theta \stackrel{?}{=} -\sin\theta$

$0\cdot\cos\theta - 1\cdot\sin\theta \stackrel{?}{=} -\sin\theta$

$-\sin\theta = -\sin\theta$ ✓

11. $\sin(\theta + \pi) \stackrel{?}{=} -\sin\theta$

$\sin\theta\cos\pi + \cos\theta\sin\pi \stackrel{?}{=} -\sin\theta$

$(\sin\theta)(-1) + (\cos\theta)(0) \stackrel{?}{=} -\sin\theta$

$-\sin\theta = -\sin\theta$ ✓

13. $-\frac{\sqrt{2}}{2}$ **15.** $\frac{\sqrt{6} - \sqrt{2}}{4}$ **17.** $\frac{\sqrt{2} + \sqrt{6}}{4}$

19. $\cos\left(\frac{\pi}{2} + \theta\right) \stackrel{?}{=} -\sin\theta$

$\cos\frac{\pi}{2}\cos\theta - \sin\frac{\pi}{2}\sin\theta \stackrel{?}{=} -\sin\theta$

$(0)(\cos\theta) - (1)(\sin\theta) \stackrel{?}{=} -\sin\theta$

$-\sin\theta = -\sin\theta$ ✓

21. $\cos(180° + \theta) \stackrel{?}{=} -\cos\theta$

$\cos 180°\cos\theta - \sin 180°\sin\theta \stackrel{?}{=} -\cos\theta$

$-1\cdot\cos\theta - 0\cdot\sin\theta \stackrel{?}{=} -\cos\theta$

$-\cos\theta = -\cos\theta$ ✓

23a. $y = 30.9\sin\left(\frac{\pi}{6}x - 2.09\right) + 42.65$ **23b.** The new function represents the average of the high and low temperatures for each month. **25.** $\sqrt{2} - \sqrt{6}$

27. $-2 + \sqrt{3}$ **29.** $2 - \sqrt{3}$

31 **a.** Let X be the endpoint of the segment that is 8 inches long.

$\sin(m\angle BAC)$

$= \sin(m\angle BAX + m\angle XAC)$

$= \sin(m\angle BAX)\cos(m\angle XAC) + \cos(m\angle BAX)\sin(m\angle XAC)$

$= \frac{8\sqrt{3}}{16}\cdot\frac{8}{10} + \frac{8}{16}\cdot\frac{6}{10}$ $\quad \sin = \frac{\text{opp}}{\text{hyp}}$ and $\cos = \frac{\text{adj}}{\text{hyp}}$

$= \frac{4\sqrt{3}}{10} + \frac{3}{10}$ Multiply.

$= \frac{3 + 4\sqrt{3}}{10}$ Add.

b. Let X be the endpoint of the segment that is 8 inches long.

$\cos(m\angle BAC)$

$= \cos(m\angle BAX + m\angle XAC)$

$= \cos(m\angle BAX)\cos(m\angle XAC) - \sin(m\angle BAX)\sin(m\angle XAC)$

$= \frac{8}{16}\cdot\frac{8}{10} - \frac{8\sqrt{3}}{16}\cdot\frac{6}{10}$ $\quad \sin = \frac{\text{opp}}{\text{hyp}}$ and $\cos = \frac{\text{adj}}{\text{hyp}}$

$= \frac{4}{10} - \frac{3\sqrt{3}}{10}$ Multiply.

$\approx \frac{4 - 3\sqrt{3}}{10}$ Add.

c. $\cos(m\angle BAC) = \frac{4 - 3\sqrt{3}}{10}$

$m\angle BAC = \cos^{-1}\left(\frac{3 + 4\sqrt{3}}{10}\right)$

$\approx 96.9°$

d. Since $m\angle BAC \neq 90$, the triangle formed is not a right triangle.

33a.

A	B	sin A	sin B	sin (A + B)	sin A + sin B
30°	90°	$\frac{1}{2}$	1	$\frac{\sqrt{3}}{2}$	$\frac{3}{2}$
45°	60°	$\frac{\sqrt{2}}{2}$	$\frac{\sqrt{3}}{2}$	$\frac{\sqrt{2}+\sqrt{6}}{4}$	$\frac{\sqrt{2}+\sqrt{3}}{2}$
60°	45°	$\frac{\sqrt{3}}{2}$	$\frac{\sqrt{2}}{2}$	$\frac{\sqrt{2}+\sqrt{6}}{4}$	$\frac{\sqrt{2}+\sqrt{3}}{2}$
90°	30°	1	$\frac{1}{2}$	$\frac{\sqrt{3}}{2}$	$\frac{3}{2}$

33b.

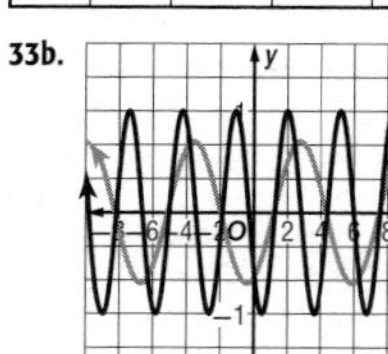

33c. No; a counterexample is: $\cos(30° + 45°) = \cos 30° + \cos 45°$, which equals $\frac{\sqrt{3}}{2} + \frac{\sqrt{2}}{2}$ or about 1.5731. Since a cosine value cannot be greater than 1, this statement must be false.

For Homework Help, go to Hotmath.com

35 $\cos(A+B) \stackrel{?}{=} \frac{1-\tan A\tan B}{\sec A\sec B}$

$\cos(A+B) \stackrel{?}{=} \frac{1-\frac{\sin A}{\cos A}\cdot\frac{\sin B}{\cos B}}{\frac{1}{\cos A}\cdot\frac{1}{\cos B}}$

$\cos(A+B) \stackrel{?}{=} \frac{1-\frac{\sin A}{\cos A}\cdot\frac{\sin B}{\cos B}}{\frac{1}{\cos A}\cdot\frac{1}{\cos B}}\cdot\frac{\cos A\cos B}{\cos A\cos B}$ $\frac{\cos A\cos B}{\cos A\cos B}=1$

$\cos(A+B) \stackrel{?}{=} \left(1-\frac{\sin A}{\cos A}\cdot\frac{\sin B}{\cos B}\right)\left(\frac{\cos A\cos B}{1}\right)\left(\frac{\cos A\cos B}{\cos A\cos B}\right)$

$\cos(A+B) \stackrel{?}{=} \frac{\cos A\cos B-\sin A\sin B}{1}$ Simplify.

$\cos(A+B) = \cos(A+B)$ ✓   Difference Identity

37. $\sin(A+B)\sin(A-B) \stackrel{?}{=} \sin^2 A - \sin^2 B$
$(\sin A\cos B+\cos A\sin B)(\sin A\cos B-\cos A\sin B) \stackrel{?}{=} \sin^2 A-\sin^2 B$
$(\sin A\cos B)^2-(\cos A\sin B)^2 \stackrel{?}{=} \sin^2 A-\sin^2 B$
$\sin^2 B\cos^2 B-\cos^2 A\sin^2 B \stackrel{?}{=} \sin^2 A-\sin^2 B$
$\sin^2 A\cos^2 B+\sin^2 A\sin^2 B-\sin^2 A\sin^2 B-\cos^2 A\sin^2 B \stackrel{?}{=} \sin^2 A-\sin^2 B$
$\sin^2 A(\cos^2 B+\sin^2 B)-\sin^2 B(\sin^2 A+\cos^2 A) \stackrel{?}{=} \sin^2 A-\sin^2 B$
$(\sin^2 A)(1)-(\sin^2 B)(1) \stackrel{?}{=} \sin^2 A-\sin^2 B$
$\sin^2 A-\sin^2 B = \sin^2 A-\sin^2 B$ ✓

39. Sample answer: To determine wireless Internet interference, you need to determine the sine or cosine of the sum or difference of two angles. Interference occurs when waves pass through the same space at the same time. When the combined waves have a greater amplitude, constructive interference results. When the combined waves have a smaller amplitude, destructive interference results.

41. $d=\sqrt{(\cos\alpha-\cos\beta)^2+(\sin\alpha-\sin\beta)^2}$
$d^2=(\cos\alpha-\cos\beta)^2+(\sin\alpha-\sin\beta)^2$
$d^2=(\cos^2\alpha-2\cos\alpha\cos\beta+\cos^2\beta)+(\sin^2\alpha-2\sin\alpha\sin\beta+\sin^2\beta)$
$d^2=\cos^2\alpha+\sin^2\alpha+\cos^2\beta+\sin^2\beta-2\cos\alpha\cos\beta-2\sin\alpha\sin\beta$
$d^2=1+1-2\cos\alpha\cos\beta-2\sin\alpha\sin\beta$ $\sin^2\alpha+\cos^2\alpha=1$ and $\sin^2\beta+\cos^2\beta=1$
$d^2=2-2\cos\alpha\cos\beta-2\sin\alpha\sin\beta$

Now find the value of d^2 when the angle having measure $\alpha-\beta$ is in standard position on the unit circle, as shown in the figure below.

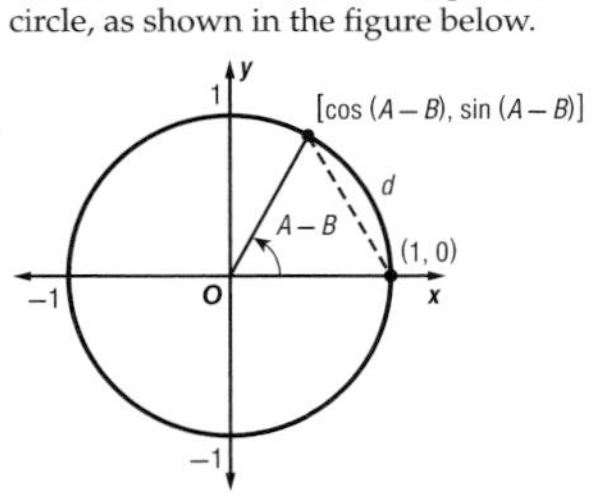

$d=\sqrt{[\cos(\alpha-\beta)-1]^2+[\sin(\alpha-\beta)-0]^2}$
$d^2=[\cos(\alpha-\beta)-1]^2+[\sin(\alpha-\beta)-0]^2$
$=[\cos^2(\alpha-\beta)-2\cos(\alpha-\beta)+1]+\sin^2(\alpha-\beta)$
$=\cos^2(\alpha-\beta)+\sin^2(\alpha-\beta)-2\cos(\alpha-\beta)+1$
$=1-2\cos(\alpha-\beta)+1$
$=2-2\cos(\alpha-\beta)$

43. 9 **45.** H

47. $\frac{\sin\theta}{\tan\theta}+\frac{\cos\theta}{\cot\theta} \stackrel{?}{=} \cos\theta+\sin\theta$
$\frac{\sin\theta}{\frac{\sin\theta}{\cos\theta}}+\frac{\cos\theta}{\frac{\cos\theta}{\sin\theta}} \stackrel{?}{=} \cos\theta+\sin\theta$
$\sin\theta\cdot\frac{\cos\theta}{\sin\theta}+\cos\theta\cdot\frac{\sin\theta}{\cos\theta} \stackrel{?}{=} \cos\theta+\sin\theta$
$\cos\theta+\sin\theta=\cos\theta+\sin\theta$ ✓

49. $\sin^2\theta$ **51.** $\sec\theta$

53. Step 1: $4^1-1=3$, which is divisible by 3. The statement is true for $n=1$.
Step 2: Assume that 4^k-1 is divisible by 3 for some positive integer k. This means that $4^k-1=3r$ for some whole number r.
Step 3: $4^k-1=3r$
$4^k=3r+1$
$4^{k+1}=12r+4$
$4^{k+1}-1=12r+3$
$4^{k+1}-1=3(4r+1)$
Since r is a whole number, $4r+1$ is a whole number. Thus, $4^{k+1}-1$ is divisible by 3, so the statement is true for $n=k+1$. Therefore, 4^n-1 is divisible by 3 for all positive integers n. **55.** –1 **57.** no solution

Pages 915–917 Lesson 14-4

1. $\frac{\sqrt{15}}{8}, \frac{7}{8}, \frac{\sqrt{8-2\sqrt{15}}}{4}, \frac{\sqrt{8+2\sqrt{15}}}{4}$ **3.** $-\frac{120}{169}, -\frac{119}{169}, \frac{3\sqrt{13}}{13}, \frac{2\sqrt{13}}{13}$ **5.** $-\frac{240}{289}, \frac{161}{289}, \frac{4\sqrt{17}}{17}, \frac{\sqrt{17}}{17}$ **7.** $\frac{\sqrt{2-\sqrt{2}}}{2}$

9a. $d=\frac{v^2\sin 2\theta}{g}$ **9b.** ≈ 81 ft

11. $(\sin\theta+\cos\theta)^2 \stackrel{?}{=} 1+2\sin\theta\cos\theta$
$(\sin\theta+\cos\theta)(\sin\theta+\cos\theta) \stackrel{?}{=} 1+2\sin\theta\cos\theta$
$\sin^2\theta+2\sin\theta\cos\theta+\cos^2\theta \stackrel{?}{=} 1+2\sin\theta\cos\theta$
$1+2\sin\theta\cos\theta=1+2\sin\theta\cos\theta$ ✓

13. $\frac{240}{289}, -\frac{161}{289}, \frac{5\sqrt{34}}{34}, -\frac{3\sqrt{34}}{34}$

15 $\sin^2\theta=1-\cos^2\theta$ $\sin^2\theta+\cos^2\theta=1$
$\sin^2\theta=1-\left(\frac{1}{5}\right)^2$ $\cos\theta=\frac{1}{5}$
$\sin^2\theta=\frac{24}{25}$ Subtract.
$\sin\theta=\pm\frac{2\sqrt{6}}{5}$ Take the square root of each side.
Since θ is in the fourth quadrant, sine is negative. So, $\sin\theta=-\frac{2\sqrt{6}}{5}$.
$\sin 2\theta=2\sin\theta\cos\theta$ Double-angle identity
$=2\left(-\frac{2\sqrt{6}}{5}\right)\left(\frac{1}{5}\right)$ $\sin\theta=-\frac{2\sqrt{6}}{5}$ and $\cos\theta=\frac{1}{5}$
$=-\frac{4\sqrt{6}}{25}$ Simplify.
$\cos 2\theta=1-2\sin^2\theta$ Double-angle identity
$=1-2\left(\frac{24}{25}\right)$ $\sin^2\theta=\frac{24}{25}$
$=-\frac{23}{25}$ Simplify.
$\sin\frac{\theta}{2}=\pm\sqrt{\frac{1-\cos\theta}{2}}$ Half-angle identity
$=\pm\sqrt{\frac{1-\frac{1}{5}}{2}}$ $\cos\theta=\frac{1}{5}$
$=\pm\sqrt{\frac{2}{5}}$ Simplify.
$=\pm\frac{\sqrt{2}}{\sqrt{5}}\cdot\frac{\sqrt{5}}{\sqrt{5}}$ or $\pm\frac{\sqrt{10}}{5}$ Rationalize the denominator.
If θ is between 270° and 360°, $\frac{\theta}{2}$ is between 135° and 180°. So, $\sin\frac{\theta}{2}$ is $\frac{\sqrt{10}}{5}$.
$\cos\frac{\theta}{2}=\pm\sqrt{\frac{1+\cos\theta}{2}}$ Half-angle identity
$=\pm\sqrt{\frac{1+\frac{1}{5}}{2}}$ $\cos\theta=\frac{1}{5}$
$=\pm\sqrt{\frac{3}{5}}$ Simplify.
$=\pm\sqrt{\frac{3}{5}}\cdot\frac{\sqrt{5}}{\sqrt{5}}$ or $\pm\frac{\sqrt{15}}{5}$ Rationalize the denominator.
If θ is between 270° and 360°, $\frac{\theta}{2}$ is between 135° and 180°. So, $\cos\frac{\theta}{2}$ is $-\frac{\sqrt{15}}{5}$.

17. $-\frac{4}{5}, -\frac{3}{5}, \sqrt{\frac{\sqrt{5}+1}{2\sqrt{5}}}, \sqrt{\frac{\sqrt{5}-1}{2\sqrt{5}}}$ **19.** $\frac{\sqrt{2+\sqrt{2}}}{2}$

21. $\sqrt{3}-2$ **23.** $\sqrt{2}-1$

25 $P=I_0^2R\sin^2\theta t$ Original equation
$P=I_0^2R(\cos^2\theta t-\cos 2\theta t)$ $\sin^2\theta t=\cos^2\theta t-\cos 2\theta t$
$P=I_0^2R\left(\frac{1}{2}\cos 2\theta t+\frac{1}{2}-\cos 2\theta t\right)$ $\cos^2\theta t=\frac{1}{2}\cos 2\theta t+\frac{1}{2}$
$P=I_0^2R\left(\frac{1}{2}-\frac{1}{2}\cos 2\theta t\right)$ Simplify.
$P=\frac{1}{2}I_0^2R-\frac{1}{2}I_0^2R\cos 2\theta t$ Distributive Property

27. $1+\frac{1}{2}\sin 2\theta \stackrel{?}{=} \frac{\sec\theta+\sin\theta}{\sec\theta}$
$\stackrel{?}{=} \frac{\frac{1}{\cos\theta}+\sin\theta}{\frac{1}{\cos\theta}}$
$\stackrel{?}{=} \frac{\frac{1}{\cos\theta}+\sin\theta}{\frac{1}{\cos\theta}}\cdot\frac{\cos\theta}{\cos\theta}$
$\stackrel{?}{=} 1+\frac{1}{2}\cdot 2\sin\theta\cos\theta$
$\stackrel{?}{=} 1+\frac{1}{2}\sin 2\theta$ ✓

29. $\tan\frac{\theta}{2} \stackrel{?}{=} \frac{\sin\theta}{1+\cos\theta}$
$\tan\frac{\theta}{2} \stackrel{?}{=} \frac{\sin 2\left(\frac{\theta}{2}\right)}{1+\cos 2\left(\frac{\theta}{2}\right)}$
$\tan\frac{\theta}{2} \stackrel{?}{=} \frac{2\sin\frac{\theta}{2}\cos\frac{\theta}{2}}{1+2\cos^2\frac{\theta}{2}-1}$
$\tan\frac{\theta}{2} \stackrel{?}{=} \frac{2\sin\frac{\theta}{2}\cos\frac{\theta}{2}}{2\cos^2\frac{\theta}{2}}$
$\tan\frac{\theta}{2} \stackrel{?}{=} \frac{\sin\frac{\theta}{2}}{\cos\frac{\theta}{2}}$
$\tan\frac{\theta}{2}=\tan\frac{\theta}{2}$ ✓

31. $\frac{24}{25}, \frac{7}{25}, \frac{24}{7}$ **33.** $-\frac{3}{5}, -\frac{4}{5}, \frac{3}{4}$ **35.** $-\frac{4\sqrt{21}}{25}, \frac{17}{25}, -\frac{4\sqrt{21}}{17}$

37. No; Teresa incorrectly added the square roots, and Nathan used the half-angle identity incorrectly. He used sin 30° in the formula instead of first finding the cosine. **39.** If you are only given the value of $\cos\theta$, then $\cos 2\theta=2\cos^2\theta-1$ is the best identity to use. If you are only given the value of $\sin\theta$, then $\cos 2\theta=1-2\sin^2\theta$ is the best identity to use. If you are given the values of both $\cos\theta$ and $\sin\theta$, then $\cos 2\theta=\cos^2\theta-\sin^2\theta$ works just as well as the other two.

41. $1-2\sin^2\theta=\cos 2\theta$ Double-angle identity
$1-2\sin^2\frac{A}{2}=\cos A$ Substitute $\frac{A}{2}$ for θ and A for 2θ.
$\sin^2\frac{A}{2}=\frac{1-\cos A}{2}$ Solve for $\sin^2\frac{A}{2}$.
$\sin\frac{A}{2}=\pm\sqrt{\frac{1-\cos A}{2}}$ Take the square root of each side.
Find $\cos\frac{A}{2}$.
$2\cos^2\theta-1=\cos 2\theta$ Double-angle identity
$2\cos^2\frac{A}{2}-1=\cos A$ Substitute $\frac{A}{2}$ for θ and A for 2θ.
$\cos^2\frac{A}{2}=\frac{1+\cos A}{2}$ Solve for $\cos^2\frac{A}{2}$.
$\cos\frac{A}{2}=\pm\sqrt{\frac{1+\cos A}{2}}$ Take the square root of each side.

43. 22.5 **45.** G **47.** $\frac{\sqrt{2}}{2}$ **49.** $\frac{-\sqrt{6}-\sqrt{2}}{4}$ **51.** $\frac{\sqrt{3}}{2}$

53. $\cot\theta+\sec\theta \stackrel{?}{=} \frac{\cos^2\theta+\sin\theta}{\sin\theta\cos\theta}$
$\cot\theta+\sec\theta \stackrel{?}{=} \frac{\cos^2\theta}{\sin\theta\cos\theta}+\frac{\sin\theta}{\sin\theta\cos\theta}$
$\cot\theta+\sec\theta \stackrel{?}{=} \frac{\cos\theta}{\sin\theta}+\frac{1}{\cos\theta}$
$\cot\theta+\sec\theta=\cot\theta+\sec\theta$

55. sines; $B\approx 102°$, $C\approx 44°$, $b\approx 21.1$ or $B\approx 10°$, $C\approx 136°$, $b\approx 3.7$ **57.** sines; $A=80°$, $a\approx 10.9$, $c\approx 5.4$ **59.** {–4, 7}

Pages 922–925 Lesson 14-5

1. 210°, 330° **3.** 60°, 180°, or 300° **5.** 150°, 210°

7 $\cos 2\theta=8-15\sin\theta$ Original equation
$\cos 2\theta+15\sin\theta-8=0$ Add $15\sin\theta-8$ to each side.
$1-2\sin^2\theta+15\sin\theta-8=0$ Double-angle identity
$-2\sin^2\theta+15\sin\theta-7=0$ Simplify.
$(-2\sin\theta+1)(\sin\theta-7)=0$ Factor.
$-2\sin\theta+1=0$ or $\sin\theta-7=0$ Zero Product Property
$\sin\theta=\frac{1}{2}$ $\sin\theta=7$
$\theta=30°$ or 150°   no solution since $0\le\sin\theta\le 1$

9. $\pm\frac{\pi}{6}+2k\pi$ or $\pm\frac{5\pi}{6}+2k\pi$ **11.** $\frac{3\pi}{2}+2k\pi$ **13.** $\pi+2k\pi$ **15.** $90°+k\cdot 180°$ **17.** $45°+k\cdot 90°$ **19.** $270°+k\cdot 360°$

21a. There will be $10\frac{1}{2}$ hours of daylight 213 and 335 days after March 21; that is, on October 20 and February 19. **21b.** Every day from February 19 to October 20; sample explanation: Since the longest day of the year occurs around June 22, the days between February 19 and October 20 must increase in length until June 22 and then decrease in length until October 20. **23.** $\frac{3\pi}{4} + \pi k$ **25.** $\frac{\pi}{2} + \pi k, \frac{\pi}{6} + 2\pi k, \frac{5\pi}{6} + 2\pi k$ **27.** $0° + k \cdot 45°$ or $0 + k \cdot \frac{\pi}{4}$

29. $90° + k \cdot 180°, 60° + k \cdot 360°, 300° + k \cdot 360°$

31. 135°, 225° **33.** $\frac{\pi}{6}$ **35.** 210°, 330°

37

$2\sin^2\theta = \cos\theta + 1$	Original equation
$2(1 - \cos^2\theta) = \cos\theta + 1$	$\sin^2\theta = 1 - \cos^2\theta$
$2 - 2\cos^2\theta = \cos\theta + 1$	Simplify.
$-2\cos^2\theta - \cos\theta + 1 = 0$	Subtract $\cos\theta + 1$ from each side and simplify.
$(-2\cos\theta + 1)(\cos\theta + 1) = 0$	Factor.
$-2\cos\theta + 1 = 0$ or $\cos\theta + 1 = 0$	Zero Product Property
$\cos\theta = \frac{1}{2}$ $\quad$ $\cos\theta = -1$	

The solutions of $\cos\theta = \frac{1}{2}$ are $\frac{\pi}{3} + 2k\pi$ and $\frac{5\pi}{3} + 2k\pi$.

The solution of $\cos\theta = -1$ is $\pi + 2k\pi$.

39. $0 + 2k\pi$ **41.** $0° + k \cdot 180°$ **43.** $30° + k \cdot 360°, 150° + k \cdot 360°$ **45.** $\frac{7\pi}{6} + 2k\pi, \frac{11\pi}{6} + 2k\pi$ or $210° + k \cdot 360°, 330° + k \cdot 360°$ **47.** $0 + 2k\pi, \frac{\pi}{2} + k\pi$ or $0° + k \cdot 360°, 90° + k \cdot 180°$ **49a.** 11 m **49b.** 7:00 A.M and 7:00 P.M. **51.** $\frac{\pi}{6} + 2\pi k, \frac{5\pi}{6} + 2\pi k, \frac{5\pi}{4} + 2\pi k, \frac{7\pi}{4} + 2\pi k$ **53.** $120° + 360°k, 240° + 360°k$

55. $\frac{\pi}{6} + 2\pi k, \frac{5\pi}{6} + 2\pi k$

57

$D = 0.5\sin(6.5x)\sin(2500t)$	Original equation
$0.01 = 0.5\sin(6.5 \cdot 500)\sin(2500t)$	$D = 0.01$ mm and $x = 0.5 \cdot 1000$ or 500 mm
$0.01 = 0.5\sin(3250)\sin(2500t)$	Simplify.
$0.1152 \approx \sin(2500t)$	Divide each side by 0.5 sin (3250).
$\text{Sin}^{-1}(0.1152) \approx 2500t$	Use the $\sin^{-1}$ function.
$6.6152 \approx 2500t$	Use a calculator.
$0.0026 \approx t$	Divide each side by 2500.

The time is about 0.0026 second.

59. $\frac{\pi}{3} < x < \pi$ or $\frac{5\pi}{3} < x < 2\pi$ **61.** All trigonometric functions are periodic. Adding the least common multiple of the periods of the functions that appear to any solution of the equation will always produce another solution. **63.** $2b$ **65.** A **67.** D

69. $\frac{\sqrt{2 - \sqrt{2}}}{2}$ **71.** $-\frac{\sqrt{2 - \sqrt{3}}}{2}$

73. $\cos(90° + \theta) \stackrel{?}{=} \cos 90° \cos\theta - \sin 90° \sin\theta$

c $0 - 1\sin\theta$

$= -\sin\theta$

75.

$\sin(90° - \theta) \stackrel{?}{=} \cos\theta$

$\sin 90° \cos\theta - \cos 90° \sin\theta \stackrel{?}{=} \cos\theta$

$1 \cdot \cos\theta - 0 \cdot \sin\theta \stackrel{?}{=} \cos\theta$

$\cos\theta - 0 \stackrel{?}{=} \cos\theta$

$\cos\theta = \cos\theta$ ✓

77. 17, 26, 35

79. −12, −9, −6

81.

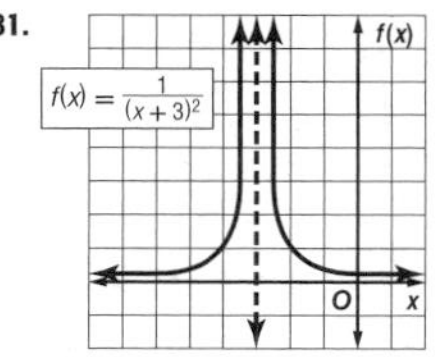

83.

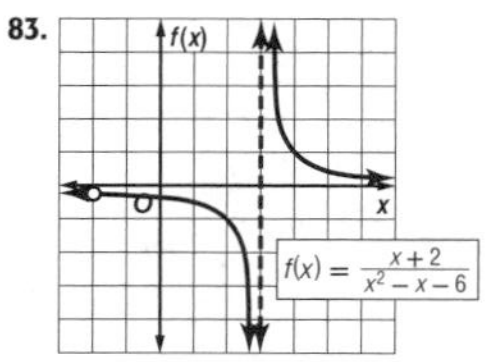

Pages 926–928 *Chapter 14* *Study Guide and Review*

1. difference of angles identity **3.** trigonometric identity **5.** trigonometric equation **7.** reciprocal identities **9.** Pythagorean identity **11.** $-\sqrt{3}$ **13.** $-\frac{4}{5}$

15. First find the length of the diagonal: $75^2 + 110^2 = c^2$; $5625 + 12{,}100 = c^2$; $17{,}725 = c^2$; $c = 5\sqrt{709}$;

$\sin\theta = \frac{75}{5\sqrt{709}} = \frac{15\sqrt{709}}{709}$ **17.** $\sec\theta$ **19.** $\sec\theta$

21.

$\frac{\cos\theta}{\cot\theta} + \frac{\sin\theta}{\tan\theta} \stackrel{?}{=} \sin\theta + \cos\theta$

$\cos\theta \div \frac{\cos\theta}{\sin\theta} + \sin\theta \div \frac{\sin\theta}{\cos\theta} \stackrel{?}{=} \sin\theta + \cos\theta$

$\cos\theta \cdot \frac{\sin\theta}{\cos\theta} + \sin\theta \cdot \frac{\cos\theta}{\sin\theta} \stackrel{?}{=} \sin\theta + \cos\theta$

$\sin\theta + \cos\theta = \sin\theta + \cos\theta$ ✓

23. $\tan^2\theta + 1 = \left(\frac{\sqrt{7}}{3}\right)^2 + 1 = \frac{7}{9} + 1 = \frac{7}{9} + \frac{9}{9} = \frac{16}{9}$;

$\sec^2\theta = \left(\frac{4}{3}\right)^2 = \frac{16}{9}$

25. $\frac{\sqrt{6} + \sqrt{2}}{4}$ **27.** $\frac{\sqrt{6} + \sqrt{2}}{4}$ **29.** $\frac{-\sqrt{6} + \sqrt{2}}{4}$

31.

$\sin\left(\frac{3\pi}{2} - \theta\right) \stackrel{?}{=} -\cos\theta$

$\sin\frac{3\pi}{2}\cos\theta - \cos\frac{3\pi}{2}\sin\theta \stackrel{?}{=} -\cos\theta$

$(-1)\cos\theta - (0)\sin\theta \stackrel{?}{=} -\cos\theta$

$-\cos\theta = -\cos\theta$ ✓

33. $\sin 2\theta = \frac{24}{25}, \cos 2\theta = \frac{7}{25}, \sin\frac{\theta}{2} = \frac{\sqrt{10}}{10}$, and $\cos\frac{\theta}{2} = \frac{3\sqrt{10}}{10}$ **35.** $\sin 2\theta = -\frac{4\sqrt{5}}{9}, \cos 2\theta = -\frac{1}{9}, \sin\frac{\theta}{2} = \frac{\sqrt{30}}{6}$, and $\cos\frac{\theta}{2} = \frac{\sqrt{6}}{6}$ **37.** 60°, 300°

39. 90°, 210°, 270°, 330° **41.** $\frac{\pi}{3}, \frac{5\pi}{3}$

Photo Credits

Cover Jason Reed/Getty Images, (bkgrnd)RubberBall Selects/Alamy; **iv** (tl tr bl)The McGraw-Hill Companies; **v** (tl tr)The McGraw-Hill Companies; **viii** Don Farrall/Getty Images; **ix** Thinkstock/CORBIS; **x** Tom Stewart/CORBIS; **xi** Kobal/The Picture Desk; **xii** Andrew Weeks/SuperStock; **xiii** Rodolfo Arpia/Alamy Images; **xiv** Masterfile; **xix** Digital Vision/Getty Images; **xv** Burgess Blevins/Getty Images; **xvi** Onne van der Wal/CORBIS; **xvii** Photodisc/Alamy Images; **xviii** Kim Karpeles/Alamy Images; **xx** Charlie Munsey/CORBIS; **xxi** Yellow Dog Productions/Getty Images; **P11** Photodisc/Getty Images; **P14** SW Productions/Getty Images; **2–3** Don Farrall/Getty Images; **5** moodboard/CORBIS; **8** Kevin Cooley/Getty Images; **13** Jon Riley/Getty Images; **15** CORBIS; **16** Glow Images/Alamy Images; **18** Bill Bachman/Alamy Images; **19** akg-images, London; **24** Mark Zylber/Alamy Images; **27** Onne van der Wal/CORBIS; **28** The Art Archive/Château de Beauregard Val de Loire/Gianni Dagli Orti/Picture Desk; **31** M. Timothy O'Keefe/Alamy Images; **36** Digital Vision/PunchStock; **37** Danita Delimont/Alamy Images; **38** Elise Amendola/AP Images; **41** Tom Stack/Tom Stack & Associates; **44** Jeff Greenberg/Index Stock Imagery; **46** Mark Scott/Alamy Images; **54** Comstock/PictureQuest; **58–59** Thinkstock/CORBIS; **63** Bernard Papon/AP Images; **65** image100/PunchStock; **66** Pixland/JupiterImages; **70** Akira Kaede/Getty Images; **73** David Young-Wolff / PhotoEdit; **77** Bonnie Kamin/PhotoEdit; **80** Phelan M. Ebenhack/AP Images; **81** (l)Brand X Pictures/PunchStock; **81** (r)Comstock Images/PictureQuest; **83** CORBIS; **87** Francois Gohier/Photo Researchers; **88** David Young-Wolff/PhotoEdit; **93** Jose Luis Pelaez Inc/Getty Images; **96** Michael Newman/PhotoEdit; **97** AP Images; **99** Jeff Cadge/Getty Images; **103** Jacques Boyer/Roger-Viollet/The Image Works; **106** Al Bello/Getty Images; **112** David Young-Wolff / PhotoEdit; **114** Mango Productions/CORBIS; **115** Bill Aron/PhotoEdit; **118** Thomas Barwick/Getty Images; **120** JupiterImages/Thinkstock/Alamy Images; **128** Rick Bowmer/AP Images; **132–133** Tom Stewart/CORBIS; **136** Jeff Greenberg/PhotoEdit; **140** George Silk/Time Life Pictures/Getty Images; **143** Adrian Sherratt/Alamy Images; **146** Brendan Hoffman/Alamy Images; **147** Alastair Grant/AP Images; **148** Visions of America, LLC/Alamy Images; **152** BananaStock/JupiterImages; **155** Jerry & Marcy Monkman/Earth Scenes; **156** Tracy Bennett/Bureau L.A. Collection/CORBIS; **162** Spencer Grant/PhotoEdit; **164** Brand X Pictures/PunchStock; **165** Thorsten Indra/Alamy Images; **170** Radius Images/Alamy Images; **172** Tony Freeman/PhotoEdit; **178** Christine Balderas/iStockphoto; **182–183** Kobal/The Picture Desk; **186** Stephen Dunn/Getty Images; **189** Scott T. Smith/CORBIS; **190** NASA, ESA, H. Weaver (JHU/APL), A. Stern (SwRI), and the HST Pluto Companion Search Team; **195** moodboard/CORBIS; **197** Kenneth Garrett/National Geographic Image Collection; **198** Darron Cummings/AP Images; **202** Stockbyte/Getty Images; **205** BananaStock/PunchStock; **206** Jose Fuste Raga/CORBIS; **209** CORBIS RF/Alamy Images; **215** Ian Timberlake/AFP/Getty Image; **216** Izzy Schwartz/Getty Images; **220** Moritsch, Marc (Via Hornocker, Maurice)/National Geographic Image Collection; **222** Digital Vision; **225** Photographers Choice RF/SuperStock; **226** Richard T. Nowitz/CORBIS; **227** BananaStock/PunchStock; **231** Courtesy Ichinoseki City Museum, Japan; **232** Ben Margo/AP Images; **234** (l)Ben Margot/AP Images; **234** (c)CORBIS/Punchstock; **234** (r)Andrew Hetherington/Getty Images; **246–247** Andrew Weeks/SuperStock; **253** Jennifer Page/AP Images; **255** Christopher Kerrigan/McGraw-Hill Companies; **256** Nice One Productions/CORBIS; **259** Bruce Laurance/Getty Images; **262** Emmanuel Duparcq/AFP/Getty Images; **265** StockShot/Alamy Images; **271** Stu Forster/Getty Images; **273** Randy Faris/CORBIS; **274** Eugene Hoshiko/AP Images; **279** Design Pics/Alamy Images; **281** Steve Allen/Getty Images; **284** Arthur S. Aubry/Getty Images; **289** Akira Kaede/Getty Images; **292** Amy Roh/AP Images; **294** British Library/akg-images, London; **299** Cris Haigh/Alamy Images; **309** Brand X Pictures; **312** Sharon Stabley/AP Images; **314** RubberBall/Alamy Images; **316** OJO Images Ltd/Alamy Images; **317** Keith Dannemiller/CORBIS; **319** Ed-Imaging; **326** Bobby Ristovski/iStockPhoto; **330–331** Rodolfo Arpia/Alamy Images; **333** Jerry Lodriguss/Photo Researchers; **336** ColorBlind Images/Getty Images; **338** Digital Vision/PunchStock; **346** Mark Kauffman/Sports Illustrated Set Number: X1388; **348** Tetra Images/Alamy Images; **349** Purestock/Alamy Images; **353** Bettmann/CORBIS; **354** David Young-Wolff/PhotoEdit; **357** Carnegie Library of Pittsburgh; **360** Randy Faris/CORBIS; **362** JupiterImages/Polka Dot/Alamy Images; **363** Rogelio V. Solis/AP Images; **369** Stock Montage/Getty Images; **373** Lawrence Migdale; **374** Jose Luis Pelaez, Inc./CORBIS; **377** blue jean images/Getty Images; **378** David Frazier/PhotoEdit; **380** Comstock/CORBIS; **383** Paul Sakuma/AP Images; **389** Ingram Publishing/SuperStock; **391** Blasius Erlinger/Getty Images; **394** Crystal Lagoons/www.crystal-lagoons.com; **395** J.Garcia/photocuisine/CORBIS; **402** KMITU/iStockphoto; **406–407** Masterfile; **412** Spencer Grant/PhotoEdit; **414** Tim Boyle/Getty Images; **415** BananaStock/PunchStock; **417** GeoStock/Getty Images; **421** Ryan McVay/Getty Images; **424** Ryan McVay/Getty Images; **426** Rob Wilkinson/Alamy Images; **428** Mikael Karlsson/Alamy Images; **429** Ken Reid/Getty Images; **431** JupiterImages; **433** Dennis Cox/Alamy Images; **435** Tom Uhlman/Visuals Unlimited; **439** akg-images, London; **442** The Granger Collection, NYC; **444** Paul Damien/Getty Images; **446** CORBIS; **447** Ariel Skelley/JupiterImages; **451** CORBIS; **453** John Swart/AP Images; **458** Duomo/CORBIS; **468** Superstudio/Getty Images; **472–473** Burgess Blevins/Getty Images; **475** Stockbyte/Alamy Images; **477** Creatas/SuperStock; **479** Core Imagery/Alamy Images; **480** Robert W. Ginn/PhotoEdit; **485** Bill Aron/PhotoEdit; **486** David Young-Wolff/PhotoEdit; **489** James Taylor/Alamy Images; **490** CORBIS; **492** Joe Tucciarone/Photo Researchers, Inc.; **495** Bettmann/CORBIS; **497** Andrew Paterson/Alamy Images; **498** David J. Green/Alamy Images; **505** Keren Su/CORBIS; **506** Ron Chapple/Thinkstock/Alamy Images; **510** Mark Leach/Alamy Images; **513** Digital Vision; **514** John Lund/Marc Romanelli/Getty Images; **517** Michael Newman/PhotoEdit; **518** The Granger Collection, New York; **520** Digital Vision; **521** Ingo Jezierski/CORBIS; **525** CORBIS; **528** Jose Luis Pelaez, Inc./CORBIS; **530** David Young-Wolff/PhotoEdit; **533** Nik Wheeler/CORBIS; **534** Tim White/AFP/Getty Images; **536** Lloyd Sutton/Masterfile; **538** (t)Oregon State Archive; **538** (b)Oregon State Archive; **540** Ed-Imaging; **546** ASP/Alamy Images; **550–551** Onne van der Wal/CORBIS; **553** Dave Fleetham/Tom Stack & Associates; **559** John Gaps III/AP Images; **560** Steve Allen Travel Photography/Alamy Images; **562** Philip Rostron/Masterfile; **566** Kenneth Garrett/National Geographic Image Collection; **567** Myrleen Ferguson Cate/PhotoEdit; **572** Bill Bachmann/PhotoEdit; **574** MLB Photos via Getty Images; **577** Myrleen Ferguson Cate/PhotoEdit; **579** PA1 Tom Sperduto, US Coast Guard; **583** Stefanie Weiss/AP Images; **589** RubberBall Productions; **591** Tim Fitzharris/Minden Pictures; **592** Tony West/Alamy Images; **594** Victor R. Caivano/AP Images; **595** Archive Photos/Getty Images; **596** Enigma/Alamy Images; **598** Paul Burns/Getty Images; **610** Stockbyte/Getty Images; **614–615** Photodisc/Alamy Images; **617** U.S. Department of Transportation; **618** Phil Noel/AP Images; **621** The McGraw-Hill Companies; **623** Chip Simons/Getty Images; **626** Brand X; **628** Derek Berwin/Getty Images; **631** Patrick Clark/Getty Images; **635** Brand X Pictures/PunchStock; **638** Ed-Imaging; **641** NASA-MSFC; **642** StockTrek/Getty Images; **644** James Houck/Alamy Images; **645** Wally McNamee/CORBIS SYGMA; **651** StockTrek/Getty Images; **653** R. Morley/PhotoLink/Getty Images; **654** Bettmann/CORBIS; **659** R. Morley/PhotoLink/Getty Images; **665** CLEO Photo/Alamy Images; **666** (l)Sean Murphy/Getty Images; **666** (r)Nick Ayliffe/Alamy Images; **674** Enrico Fianchini/iStockphoto; **678–679** Kim Karpeles/Alamy Images; **681** JupiterImages/Thinkstock / Alamy Images; **682** Thinkstock/JupiterImages; **686** Spencer Grant/PhotoEdit; **688** akg-images, London; **693** PhotoLink/Getty Images; **694** David Madison/Getty Images; **696** John Atashian/CORBIS; **697** Alinari Archives/The Image Works; **701** Nick Koudis/Getty Images; **709** Westend61/Alamy Images; **710** Blend Images/JupiterImages; **716** Thom Lang/CORBIS; **718** Stephen Alvarez/National Geographic Image Collection; **721** Somos/Veer/Getty Images; **724** Matt Slocum/AP Images; **727** Comstock Images/Alamy Images; **730** McGraw-Hill Companies; **738** Jose Luis Pelaez, Inc./CORBIS; **742–743** Digital Vision/Getty Images; **745** The McGraw-Hill Companies; **749** The McGraw-Hill Companies; **752** Brand X/JupiterImages; **753** image100/CORBIS; **754** Milk Photographie/CORBIS; **757** image100 Ltd; **759** Blend Images/SuperStock; **762** Kwame Zikomo/SuperStock; **764** Blend Images/SuperStock; **766** Dan Loh/AP Images; **769** Warren Westura/AP Images; **770** akg-images, London; **775** Ryan McVay/Getty Images; **776** Tony Freeman/PhotoEdit; **777** David Young-Wolff/PhotoEdit; **778** Noah Addis/Star Ledger/CORBIS; **780** Tony Anderson/Getty Images; **783** D. Hurst/Alamy Images; **785** Ed-Imaging; **786** Rim Light/PhotoLink/Getty Images; **787** Creative Expression/Alamy Images; **792** Skip Weisenburger/AP Images; **800** Charles Gupton/CORBIS; **804–805** Charlie Munsey/CORBIS; **808** isifa Image Service s.r.o./Alamy Images; **810** Edward Kinsman/Photo Researchers; **812** STAN HONDA/AFP/Getty Images; **815** Avico Ltd/Alamy Images; **817** Nick Koudis/Getty Images; **818** Grafton Marshall Smith/CORBIS; **821** Michael Burke/AP Images; **822** Digital Vision/Alamy Images; **825** Joseph Sohm/drr.net; **828** Jason Werling/AP Images; **830** age fotostock/SuperStock; **832** JPL/NASA; **836** Matthew Thayer/AP Images; **838** Image Source Black; **840** Ed-Imaging; **843** Federico Cabello/SuperStock; **845** CORBIS/SuperStock; **849** George S de Blonsky/Alamy Images; **852** Holger Otto/Reuters/CORBIS; **853** Kee Coleman/Courtesy of The Bancroft Library/University of California, Berkeley; **857** Digital Vision/PunchStock; **860** Brooke Fasani/CORBIS; **866** Stephen Frink Collection/Alamy Images; **868** Ingram Publishing/Alamy Images; **871** Pieter Estersohn/Beateworks/CORBIS; **875** Gene J. Puskar/PhotoEdit; **884** Cn Boon/Alamy Images; **888–889** Yellow Dog Productions/Getty Images; **891** Rubberball/JupiterImages; **893** Dinodia; **895** Thinkstock/CORBIS; **896** Jim West/Alamy Images; **898** S. Carmona/CORBIS; **901** George S de Blonsky/Alamy Images; **902** Marwood Jenkins/Alamy Images; **907** Balfour Studios/Alamy Images; **908** Thinkstock/Index Stock; **911** Steve Allen/Brand X/CORBIS; **914** Philip Scalia/Alamy Images; **916** Steve Kinderman/AP Images; **919** Wally McNamee/CORBIS; **924** JewelryStock/Alamy Images; **930** CORBIS/JupiterImages; **934** Eclipse Studios.

Glossary/Glosario

Math Online

A mathematics multilingual eGlossary is available at glencoe.com. The glossary includes the following languages:

Arabic	Haitian Creole	Russian	Vietnamese
Bengali	Hmong	Spanish	
Cantonese	Korean	Tagalog	
English	Portuguese	Urdu	

Cómo usar el glosario en español:

1. Busca el término en inglés que desees encontrar.
2. El término en español, junto con la definición, se encuentran en la columna de la derecha.

English

A

absolute value (p. 27) A number's distance from zero on the number line, represented by $|x|$.

absolute value function (p. 103) A function written as $f(x) = |x|$, where $f(x) \geq 0$ for all values of x.

algebraic expression (p. 5) An expression that contains at least one variable.

alternative hypothesis (p. 781) Mutually exclusive to the null hypothesis. It is stated as an inequality using $\neq$, $<$, $\leq$, $>$, or $\geq$.

amplitude (p. 855) For functions in the form $y = a \sin b\,\theta$ or $y = a \cos b\,\theta$, the amplitude is $|a|$.

angle of depression (p. 812) The angle between a horizontal line and the line of sight from the observer to an object at a lower level.

angle of elevation (p. 812) The angle between a horizontal line and the line of sight from the observer to an object at a higher level.

Arccosine (p. 871) The inverse of $y = \cos x$, written as $x = \text{Arccos } y$.

Arcsine (p. 871) The inverse of $y = \sin x$, written as $x = \text{Arcsin } y$.

Arctangent (p. 871) The inverse of $y = \tan x$ written as $x = \text{Arctan } y$.

arithmetic mean (p. 689) The terms between any two nonconsecutive terms of an arithmetic sequence.

arithmetic sequence (p. 681) A sequence in which each term after the first is found by adding a constant, the common difference d, to the previous term.

Español

valor absoluto Distancia entre un número y cero en una recta numérica; se denota con $|x|$.

función del valor absoluto Una función que se escribe $f(x) = |x|$, donde $f(x) \geq 0$, para todos los valores de x.

expresión algebraica Expresión que contiene al menos una variable.

hipótesis alternativa Mutuamente exclusiva a la hipótesis nula. Se indica como usar de la desigualdad $\neq$, $<$, $\leq$, $>$, o $\geq$.

amplitud Para funciones de la forma $y = a$ sen $b\,\theta$ o $y = a \cos b\,\theta$, la amplitud es $|a|$.

ángulo de depresión Ángulo entre una recta horizontal y la línea visual de un observador a una figura en un nivel inferior.

ángulo de elevación Ángulo entre una recta horizontal y la línea visual de un observador a una figura en un nivel superior.

arcocoseno La inversa de $y = \cos x$, que se escribe como $x = \arccos y$.

arcoseno La inversa de $y =$ sen x, que se escribe como $x =$ arcsen y.

arcotangente La inversa de $y = \tan x$ que se escribe como $x = \arctan y$.

media aritmética Cualquier término entre dos términos no consecutivos de una sucesión aritmética.

sucesión aritmética Sucesión en que cualquier término después del primero puede hallarse sumando una constante, la diferencia común d, al término anterior.

arithmetic series (p. 690) The indicated sum of the terms of an arithmetic sequence.

asymptote (pp. 475, 570) A line that a graph approaches.

augmented matrix (p. 238) A coefficient matrix with an extra column containing the constant terms.

axis of symmetry (p. 250) A line about which a figure is symmetric.

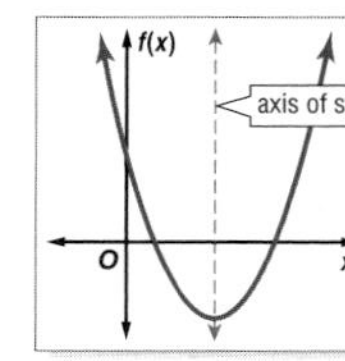

B

$b^{\frac{1}{n}}$ (p. 446) For any real number b and for any positive integer n, $b^{\frac{1}{n}} = \sqrt[n]{b}$, except when $b < 0$ and n is even .

bar graph (p. 1001) A graphic form using bars to make comparisons of statistics.

biased (p. 745) A sample or survey in which one or more parts of the population are favored over others.

binomial distribution (p. 786) A distribution that shows the probabilities of the outcomes of a binomial experiment.

binomial experiment (p. 786) An experiment in which there are exactly two possible outcomes for each trial, a fixed number of independent trials, and the probabilities for each trial are the same.

Binomial Theorem (p. 721) If n is a nonnegative integer, then $(a + b)^n = 1a^nb^0 + \frac{n}{1}a^{n-1}b^1 + \frac{n(n+1)}{1 \cdot 2}a^{n-2}b^2 + \cdots + 1a^0b^n$.

bivariate data (p. 92) Data with two variables.

boundary (p. 117) A line or curve that separates the coordinate plane into two regions.

bounded (p. 160) A region is bounded when the graph of a system of constraints is a polygonal region.

serie aritmética Suma específica de los términos de una sucesión aritmética.

asíntota Recta a la que se aproxima una gráfica.

matriz ampliada Matriz coeficiente con una columna extra que contiene los términos constantes.

eje de simetría Recta respecto a la cual una figura es simétrica.

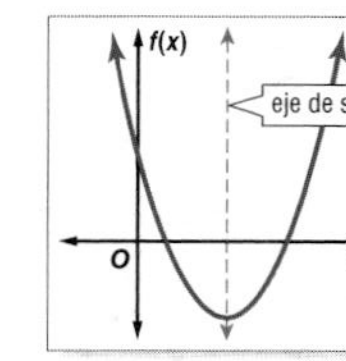

$b^{\frac{1}{n}}$ Para cualquier número real b y para cualquier entero positivo n, $b^{\frac{1}{n}} = \sqrt[n]{b}$, excepto cuando $b < 0$ y n es par.

gráfica de barras Tipo de gráfica que usa barras para comparar estadísticas.

sesgo Muestra o encuesta en la cual se prefiere una o más partes de la población sobre las otras.

distribución binómica Distribución que muestra las probabilidades de los resultados de un experimento binómico.

experimento binomial Experimento con exactamente dos resultados posibles para cada prueba, un número fijo de pruebas independientes y en el cual cada prueba tiene igual probabilidad.

teorema del binomio Si n es un entero no negativo, entonces $(a + b)^n = 1a^nb^0 + \frac{n}{1}a^{n-1}b^1 + \frac{n(n+1)}{1 \cdot 2}a^{n-2}b^2 + \cdots + 1a^0b^n$.

datos bivariados Datos con dos variables.

frontera Recta o curva que divide un plano de coordenadas en dos regiones.

acotada Una región está acotada cuando la gráfica de un sistema de restricciones es una región poligonal.

box-and-whisker plot (p. 1005) A diagram that divides a set of data into four parts using the median and quartiles. A box is drawn around the quartile values and whiskers extend from each quartile to the extreme data points.

break-even point (p. 136) The point at which the income equals the cost.

C

Cartesian coordinate plane (p. P4) A plane divided into four quadrants by the intersection of the x-axis and the y-axis at the origin.

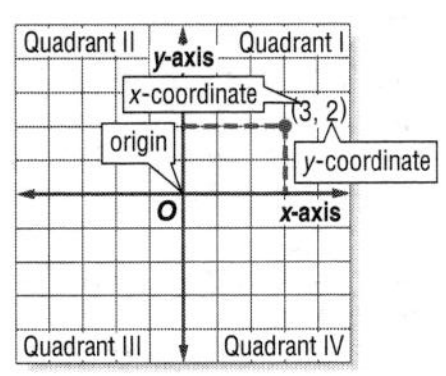

causation (p. 747) One event is shown to be the direct cause of another event.

census (p. 745) A survey in which every member of the population is polled.

center (pp. 631, 639)
1. circle—The given point on a plane from which the set of all points in the plane are equidistant.
2. ellipse—The point at which the axes are perpendicular.

center of a circle (p. 631) The point from which all points on a circle are equidistant.

center of a hyperbola (p. 648) The midpoint of the segment whose endpoints are the foci.

center of an ellipse (p. 639) The point at which the major axis and minor axis of an ellipse intersect.

central angle (p. 820) An angle with a vertex at the center of the circle and sides that are radii.

Change of Base Formula (p. 518) For all positive numbers a, b, and n, where $a \neq 1$ and $b \neq 1$, $\log_a n = \frac{\log_b n}{\log_b a}$.

diagrama de caja y bigotes Diagrama que divide un conjunto de datos en cuatro partes usando la mediana y los cuartiles. Se dibuja una caja alrededor de los cuartiles y se extienden patillas de cada uno de ellos a los valores extremos.

el punto de equilibrio Cuando el punto la renta iguala la causalidad del coste.

plano de coordenadas cartesiano Plano dividido en cuatro cuadrantes mediante la intersección en el origen de los ejes x y y.

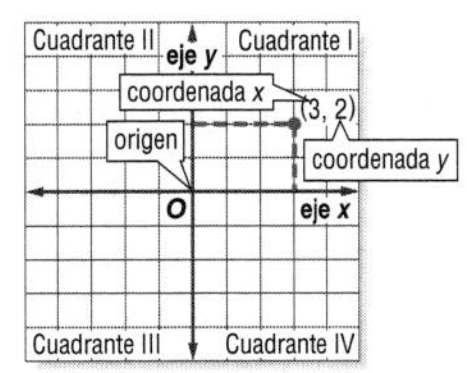

acontecimiento Un acontecimiento se demuestra para ser la causa directa de otro.

censo Examen en el cual voten a cada miembro de la población.

centro
1. círculo—El conjunto de todos los puntos de un plano que son equidistantes.
2. elipse—El punto en el cual las ejes son perpendiculares.

centro de un círculo El punto desde el cual todos los puntos de un círculo están equidistantes.

centro de una hipérbola Punto medio del segmento cuyos extremos son los focos.

centro de una elipse Punto de intersección de los ejes mayor y menor de una elipse.

ángulo central Ángulo cuyo vértice es el centro del círculo y cuyos lados son radios.

fórmula del cambio de base Para todo número positivo a, b y n, donde $a \neq 1$ y $b \neq 1$, $\log_a n = \frac{\log_b n}{\log_b a}$.

circle (p. 631) The set of all points in a plane that are equidistant from a given point in the plane, called the center.

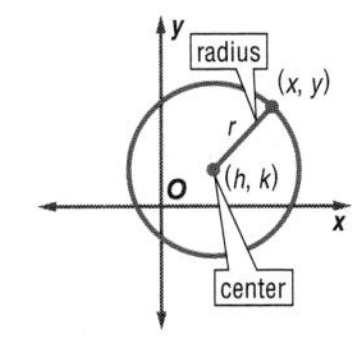

circular function (p. 848) A function defined using a unit circle.

coefficient matrix (p. 223) A matrix that contains only the coefficients of a system of equations.

column matrix (p. 186) A matrix that has only one column.

combination (p. P12) An arrangement of objects in which order is not important.

combined variation (p. 589) When one quantity varies directly and/or inversely as two or more other quantities.

common difference (p. 681) The difference between the successive terms of an arithmetic sequence.

common logarithms (p. 516) Logarithms that use 10 as the base.

common ratio (p. 683) The ratio of successive terms of a geometric sequence.

completing the square (p. 285) A process used to make a quadratic expression into a perfect square trinomial.

complex conjugates (p. 279) Two complex numbers of the form $a + bi$ and $a - bi$.

complex fraction (p. 556) A rational expression whose numerator and/or denominator contains a rational expression.

complex number (p. 277) Any number that can be written in the form $a + bi$, where a and b are real numbers and i is the imaginary unit.

composition of functions (p. 411) A function is performed, and then a second function is performed on the result of the first function. The composition of f and g is denoted by $f \circ g$, and $[f \circ g](x) = f[g(x)]$.

círculo Conjunto de todos los puntos en un plano que equidistan de un punto dado del plano llamado centro.

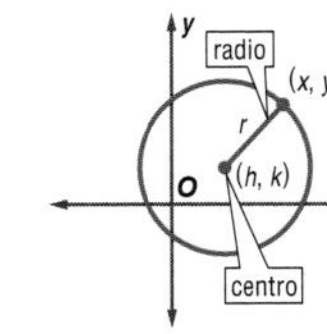

funciones circulares Funciones definidas en un círculo unitario.

matriz coeficiente Una matriz que contiene solamente los coeficientes de un sistema de ecuaciones.

matriz columna Matriz que sólo tiene una columna.

combinación Arreglo de elementos en que el orden no es importante.

variación combinada Cuando una cantidad varía directamente e inverso como dos o más otras cantidades.

diferencia común Diferencia entre términos consecutivos de una sucesión aritmética.

logaritmos comunes El logaritmo de base 10.

razón común Razón entre términos consecutivos de una sucesión geométrica.

completar el cuadrado Proceso mediante el cual una expresión cuadrática se transforma en un trinomio cuadrado perfecto.

conjugados complejos Dos números complejos de la forma $a + bi$ y $a - bi$.

fracción compleja Expresión racional cuyo numerador o denominador contiene una expresión racional.

número complejo Cualquier número que puede escribirse de la forma $a + bi$, donde a y b son números reales e i es la unidad imaginaria.

composición de funciones Se evalúa una función y luego se evalúa una segunda función en el resultado de la primera función. La composición de f y g se define con $f \circ g$, y $[f \circ g](x) = f[g(x)]$.

compound event (p. 998) Two or more simple events.

compound inequality (p. 41) Two inequalities joined by the word *and* or *or*.

compound interest (p. 486) Interest paid on the principal of an investment and any previously earned interest.

conditional probability (p. 759) The probability of an event given that another event has already occurred.

confidence interval (p. 780) An estimate of a population parameter stated as a range with a specific degree of certainty.

conic section (p. 656) Any figure that can be obtained by slicing a double cone.

conjugates (p. 442) Binomials of the form $a\sqrt{b} + c\sqrt{d}$ and $a\sqrt{b} - c\sqrt{d}$, where a, b, c, and d are rational numbers.

conjugate axis (p. 648) The segment of length $2b$ units that is perpendicular to the transverse axis at the center.

consistent (p. 137) A system of equations that has at least one solution.

constant difference (p. 651) The absolute value of the difference between the distances from any point on the hyperbola to the foci of the hyperbola.

constant function (p. 109) A linear function of the form $f(x) = b$.

constant matrix (p. 231) A matrix that contains the constants of a system.

constant of variation (pp. 90, 586) The constant k used with direct or inverse variation.

constant sum (p. 640) The sum of the distances from the foci to any point on the ellipse.

constant term (p. 249) In $f(x) = ax^2 + bx + c$, c is the constant term.

constraints (p. 160) Conditions given to variables, often expressed as linear inequalities.

contingency table (p. 760) Records data in which different possible situations result in different possible outcomes. Each value represents the relative frequency of an outcome.

evento compuesto Dos o más eventos simples.

desigualdad compuesta Dos desigualdades unidas por las palabras *y* u *o*.

interés compuesto Interés obtenido tanto sobre la inversion inicial como sobre el interes conseguido.

probabilidad condicional La probabilidad de un acontecimiento condicion que ha occurido un cierto acontecimiento precedente.

intervalo de la confianza Una estimación de un parámetro de la población indicado como gama con un grado específico de la certeza.

sección cónica Cualquier figura obtenida mediante el corte de un cono doble.

conjugados Binomios de la forma $a\sqrt{b} + c\sqrt{d}$ y $a\sqrt{b} - c\sqrt{d}$, donde a, b, c, y d son números racionales.

eje conjugado El segmento de $2b$ unidades de longitud que es perpendicular al eje transversal en el centro.

consistente Sistema de ecuaciones que posee por lo menos una solución.

diferencia constante El valor absoluto de la diferencia entre las distancias de cualquier punto en la hipérbola a los focos de la hipérbola.

función constante Función lineal de la forma $f(x) = b$.

matriz constante Una matriz que contiene las constantes de un sistema

constante de variación La constante k que se usa en variación directa o inversa.

suma constante La suma de las distancias de los focos a cualquier punto en la elipse.

término constante En $f(x) = ax^2 + bx + c$, c es el término constante.

restricciones Condiciones a que están sujetas las variables, a menudo escritas como desigualdades lineales.

table de contingencias Registra datos en que diferentes posibles situaciones resultan en distintos posibles resultados. Cada valor representa la frecuencia relative de un resultado.

continuous probability distribution (p. 773) The outcome can be any value in an interval of real numbers, represented by curves.

continuous relation (p. 62) A relation that can be graphed with a line or smooth curve.

control goup (p. 746) In an experiment, those given the placebo, or false treatment.

convergent series (p. 705) An infinite series with a sum.

correlation (p. 747) Two events ae related.

correlation coefficient (p. 94) A measure that shows how well data are modeled by a linear equation.

cosecant (p. 808) For any angle, with measure α, a point $P(x, y)$ on its terminal side, $r = \sqrt{x^2 + y^2}$, $\csc \alpha = \frac{r}{y}$.

cosine (p. 808) For any angle, with measure α, a point $P(x, y)$ on its terminal side, $r = \sqrt{x^2 + y^2}$, $\cos \alpha = \frac{x}{r}$.

cotangent (p. 808) For any angle, with measure α, a point $P(x, y)$ on its terminal side, $r = \sqrt{x^2 + y^2}$, $\cot \alpha = \frac{x}{y}$.

coterminal angles (p. 818) Two angles in standard position that have the same terminal side.

co-vertices (pp. 639, 648)
ellipse—The endpoints of the minor axis.
hyperbola—The endpoints of the conjugate axis.

Cramer's Rule (p. 223) A method that uses determinants to solve a system of linear equations.

cross products (p. 993) If $\frac{a}{c} = \frac{b}{d}$, then $ad = bc$. If $ad = bc$, then $\frac{a}{c} = \frac{b}{d}$, c and $d \neq 0$.

cycle (p. 849) One complete pattern of a periodic function.

distribución de probabilidad continua El resultado puede ser cualquier valor de un intervalo de números reales, representados por curvas.

relación continua Relación cuya gráfica puede ser una recta o una curva suave.

grupo de control En un experimento, ésos dados el placebo, o el tratamiento falso.

serie convergente Serie infinita con una suma.

corelacion Dos acontecimientos son relacionados.

coeficiente de correlación Una medida que demuestra cómo los datos bien son modelados por una ecuación linear.

cosecante Para cualquier ángulo de medida α, un punto $P(x, y)$ en su lado terminal, $r = \sqrt{x^2 + y^2}$, $\csc \alpha = \frac{r}{y}$.

coseno Para cualquier ángulo de medida α, un punto $P(x, y)$ en su lado terminal, $r = \sqrt{x^2 + y^2}$, $\cos \alpha = \frac{x}{r}$.

cotangente Para cualquier ángulo de medida α, un punto $P(x, y)$ en su lado terminal, $r = \sqrt{x^2 + y^2}$, $\cot \alpha = \frac{x}{y}$.

ángulos coterminales Dos ángulos en posición estándar que tienen el mismo lado terminal.

co-cimas
(elipse)—Puntos finales del eje de menor importancia.
(hipérbola)—Puntos finales del eje conyugal.

regla de Crámer Método que usa determinantes para resolver un sistema de ecuaciones lineales.

productos cruzados Si $\frac{a}{c} = \frac{b}{d}$, entonces $ad = bc$. Si $ad = bc$, entonces $\frac{a}{c} = \frac{b}{d}$, c y $d \neq 0$.

ciclo Un patrón completo de una función periódica.

D

decay factor (478) In exponential decay, the base of the exponential expression, $1 - r$.

degree of a polynomial (p. 335) The greatest degree of any term in the polynomial.

dependent (p. 137) When a system of linear equations has an infinite number of solutions.

factor de decaimiento En decaimiento exponencial, la base de la expresión exponencial, $1 - r$.

grado de un polinomio Grado máximo de cualquier término del polinomio.

dependiente Sistema de ecuaciones que posee un número infinito de soluciones.

dependent events (p. 998) The outcome of one event does affect the outcome of another event.

eventos dependientes El resultado de un evento afecta el resultado de otro evento.

dependent system (p. 137) A consistent system of equations that has an infinite number of solutions.

sistema dependiente Sistema de ecuaciones que posee un número infinito de soluciones.

dependent variable (p. 64) The other variable in a function, usually y, whose values depend on x.

variable dependiente La otra variable de una función, por lo general y, cuyo valor depende de x.

depressed polynomial (p. 379) The quotient when a polynomial is divided by one of its binomial factors.

polinomio reducido El cociente cuando se divide un polinomio entre uno de sus factores binomiales.

determinant (p. 220) A square array of numbers or variables enclosed between two parallel lines.

determinante Arreglo cuadrado de números o variábles encerrados entre dos rectas paralelas.

diagonal rule (p. 221) A method for finding the determinant of a third-order matrix.

regla diagonal Método para encontrar el determinante de una matriz third-order.

dilation (p. 111, 211) A transformation in which a geometric figure is enlarged or reduced.

homotecia Transformación en que se amplía o se reduce un figura geométrica.

dimensional analysis (p. 340) Performing operations with units.

análisis dimensional Realizar operaciones con unidades.

dimension (p. 185) A description of the number of rows and columns of a matrix.

dimensión Una descripción del número de filas y de columnas de una matriz.

dimensions of a matrix (p. 185) The number of rows, m, and the number of columns, n, of the matrix written as $m \times n$.

tamaño de una matriz El número de filas, m, y columnas, n, de una matriz, lo que se escribe $m \times n$.

directrix (p. 623) See parabola.

directriz Véase parábola.

direct variation (pp. 90, 586) y varies directly as x if there is some nonzero constant k such that $y = kx$. k is called the constant of variation.

variación directa y varía directamente con x si hay una constante no nula k tal que $y = kx$. k se llama la constante de variación.

discrete probability distributions (p. 767) Probabilities that have a finite number of possible values.

distribución de probabilidad discreta Probabilidades que tienen un número finito de valores posibles.

discrete relation (p. 62) A relation in which the domain is a set of individual points.

relación discreta Relación en la cual el dominio es un conjunto de puntos individuales.

discriminant (p. 295) In the Quadratic Formula, the expression $b^2 - 4ac$.

discriminante En la fórmula cuadrática, la expresión $b^2 - 4ac$.

Distance Formula (p. 618) The distance between two points with coordinates (x_1, y_1) and (x_2, y_2) is given by $d = \sqrt{(x_2 - x_1)^2 + (y_2 - y_1)^2}$.

fórmula de la distancia La distancia entre dos puntos (x_1, y_1) and (x_2, y_2) viene dada por $d = \sqrt{(x_2 - x_1)^2 + (y_2 - y_1)^2}$.

divergent series (p. 705) An infinite geometric series that does *not* have sum.

serie divergente Serie geométrica infinita que no tiene suma.

domain (p. P4) The set of all x-coordinates of the ordered pairs of a relation.

dominio El conjunto de todas las coordenadas x de los pares ordenados de una relación.

dot plot (p. 92) Two sets of data plotted as ordered pairs in a coordinate plane.

diagrama del punto Dos conjuntos de datos gráficados como pares ordenados en un plano de coordenadas.

double bar graph (p. 1001) Compares two sets of data by showing each as a bar whose length is related to the frequency.

gráfica de barras dobles Compara dos conjuntos de datos al mostrar cada uno de ellos como una barra cuya longitud se relaciona con la frecuencia.

E

e (p. 525) The irrational number 2.71828.... e is the base of the natural logarithms.

e El número irracional 2.71828.... e es la base de los logaritmos naturales.

element (p. 185) Each value in a matrix.

elemento Cada valor de una matriz.

elimination method (p. 144) Eliminate one of the variables in a system of equations by adding or subtracting the equations.

método de eliminación Eliminar una de las variables de un sistema de ecuaciones sumando o restando las ecuaciones.

ellipse (p. 639) The set of all points in a plane such that the sum of the distances from two given points in the plane, called foci, is constant.

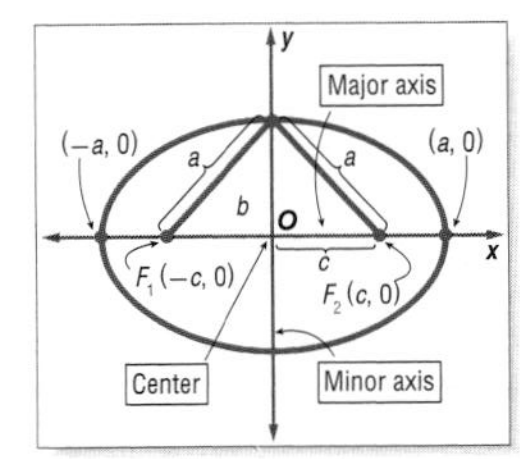

elipse Conjunto de todos los puntos de un plano en los que la suma de sus distancias a dos puntos dados del plano, llamados focos, es constante.

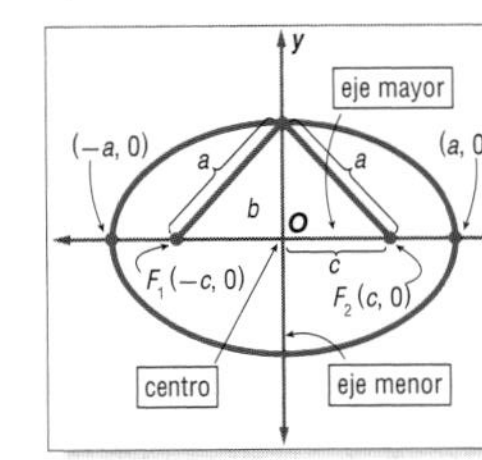

empty set (p. 28) The solution set for an equation that has no solution, symbolized by { } or ø.

conjunto vacío Conjunto solución de una ecuación que no tiene solución, denotado por { } o ø.

end behavior (p. 350) The behavior of the graph as x approaches positive infinity $(+\infty)$ or negative infinity $(-\infty)$.

comportamiento final El comportamiento de una gráfica a medida que x tiende a más infinito $(+\infty)$ o menos infinito $(-\infty)$.

equal matrices (p. 186) Two matrices that have the same dimensions and each element of one matrix is equal to the corresponding element of the other matrix.

matrices iguales Dos matrices que tienen las mismas dimensiones y en las que cada elemento de una de ellas es igual al elemento correspondiente en la otra matriz.

equation (p. 18) A mathematical sentence stating that two mathematical expressions are equal.

ecuación Enunciado matemático que afirma la igualdad de dos expresiones matemáticas.

event (pp. P5, 998) One or more outcomes of a trial.

evento Uno o más resultados de una prueba.

experiment (p. 746) Something that is intentionally done to people, animals, or objects, and then the response is observed.

experimento Algo se hace intencionalmente poblar, los animales, o los objetos, y entonces la respuesta se observa.

experimental probability (p. 786) What is estimated from observed simulations or experiments.

probabilidad experimental Qué se estima de simulaciones o de experimentos observados.

Glossary/Glosario

explicit formula (p. 714) Gives a_n as a function of n, such as $a_n = 3n + 1$.

exponential decay (p. 477) Exponential decay occurs when a quantity decreases exponentially over time.

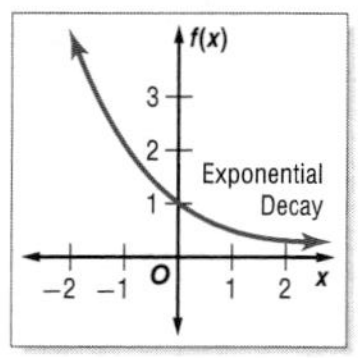

exponential equation (p. 485) An equation in which the variables occur as exponents.

exponential function (p. 475) A function of the form $y = ab^x$, where $a \neq 0$, $b > 0$, and $b \neq 1$.

exponential growth (p. 475) Exponential growth occurs when a quantity increases exponentially over time.

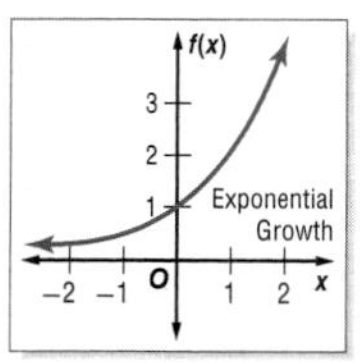

exponential inequality (p. 487) An inequality involving exponential functions.

extraneous solution (pp. 29, 453) A number that does not satisfy the original equation.

extrema (p. 358) The maximum and minimum values of a function.

un fórmula explícito Da en función de n, tal como $a_n = 3n + 1$.

desintegración exponencial Ocurre cuando una cantidad disminuye exponencialmente con el tiempo.

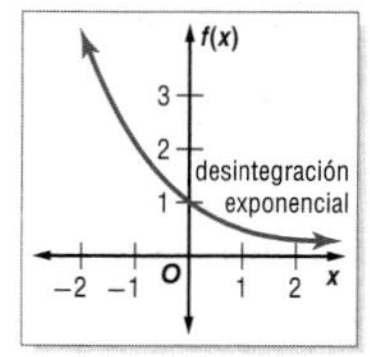

ecuación exponencial Ecuación en que las variables aparecen en los exponentes.

función exponencial Una función de la forma $y = ab^x$, donde $a \neq 0$, $b > 0$, y $b \neq 1$.

crecimiento exponencial El que ocurre cuando una cantidad aumenta exponencialmente con el tiempo.

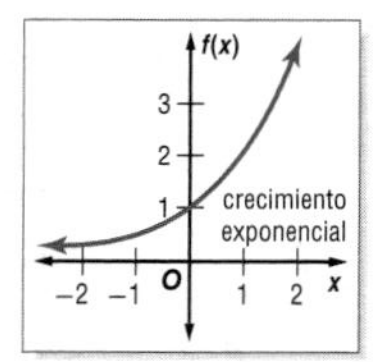

desigualdad exponencial Desigualdad que contiene funciones exponenciales.

solución extraña Número que no satisface la ecuación original.

extrema Son los valores máximos y mínimos de una función.

F

factored form (p. 268) The form of a polynomial showing all of its factors. $y = a(x - p)(x - q)$ is the factored form of a quadratic equation.

factorial (p. P10) If n is a positive integer, then $n! = n(n - 1)(n - 2) \ldots 2 \cdot 1$.

Factor Theorem (p. 379) The binomial $x - r$ is a factor of the polynomial $P(x)$ if and only if $P(r) = 0$.

failure (p. 764) Any outcome other than the desired outcome.

family of graphs (p. 109) A group of graphs that displays one or more similar characteristics.

forma reducida La forma de un polinomio que demuestra todos sus factores. $y = a(x - p)(x - q)$ es la forma descompuesta en factores de una ecuación cuadrática.

factorial Si n es un entero positivo, entonces $n! = n(n - 1)(n - 2) \ldots 2 \cdot 1$.

teorema factor El binomio $x - r$ es un factor del polinomio $P(x)$ si $P(r) = 0$.

fracaso Cualquier resultado distinto del deseado.

familia de gráficas Grupo de gráficas que presentan una o más características similares.

feasible region (p. 160) The intersection of the graphs in a system of constraints.

Fibonacci sequence (p. 714) A sequence in which the first two terms are 1 and each of the additional terms is the sum of the two previous terms.

finite sequence (p. 681) A sequence containing a limited number of terms.

foci (pp. 639, 648)
Ellipse—The two fixed points from which the sum of the distances from a set of all points in a plane is constant.
Hyperbola—The two fixed points from which the difference of the distances from a set of all points in a plane is constant.

focus (p. 623) See parabola, ellipse, hyperbola.

FOIL method (pp. P6, 268) The product of two binomials is the sum of the products of **F** the *first* terms, **O** the *outer* terms, **I** the *inner* terms, and **L** the *last* terms.

formula (p. 6) A mathematical sentence that expresses the relationship between certain quantities.

frequency (p. 856) The number of cycles in a given unit of time.

frequency table (p. 1002) A chart that indicates the number of values in each interval.

function (p. P4) A relation in which each element of the domain is paired with exactly one element in the range.

function notation (p. 64) An equation of y in terms of x can be rewritten so that $y = f(x)$. For example, $y = 2x + 1$ can be written as $f(x) = 2x + 1$.

Fundamental Counting Principle (p. P9) If event M can occur in m ways and is followed by event N that can occur in n ways, then event M followed by event N can occur in $m \cdot n$ ways.

región viable Intersección de las gráficas de un sistema de restricciones.

sucesión de Fibonacci Sucesión en que los dos primeros términos son iguales a 1 y cada término que sigue es igual a la suma de los dos anteriores.

secuencia finitas Una secuencia que contiene un número limitado de términos.

focos
(de elipse) Los dos puntos fijos de los cuales la suma de las distancias de un sistema de todos los puntos en un plano es constante.
(de hipérbola) Los dos puntos fijos de los cuales la diferencia de las distancias de un sistema de todos los puntos en un plano es constante.

foco Véase parábola, elipse, hipérbola.

método FOIL El producto de dos binomios es la suma de los productos de los primeros (***First***) términos, los términos exteriores (***Outer***), los términos interiores (***Inner***) y los últimos (***Last***) términos.

fórmula Enunciado matemático que describe la relación entre ciertas cantidades.

frecuencia El número de ciclos en una unidad del tiempo dada.

table de frecuencias Tabla que indica el número de valores en cada intervalo.

función Relación en que a cada elemento del dominio le corresponde un solo elemento del rango.

notación funcional Una ecuación de y en términos de x puede escribirse en la forma $y = f(x)$. Por ejemplo, $y = 2x + 1$ puede escribirse como $f(x) = 2x + 1$.

principio fundamental de conteo Si el evento M puede ocurrir de m maneras y es seguido por el evento N que puede ocurrir de n maneras, entonces el evento M seguido por el evento N pueden ocurrir de $m \cdot n$ maneras.

G

general form (p. 623) An equation of a parabola in the form $y = ax^2 + bx + c$.

geometric mean (p. 697) The terms between any two nonsuccessive terms of a geometric sequence.

forma general Una ecuación de una parábola en la forma $y = ax^2 + bx + c$.

media geométrica Cualquier término entre dos términos no consecutivos de una sucesión geométrica.

geometric sequence (p. 683) A sequence in which each term after the first is found by multiplying the previous term by a constant r, called the common ratio.

geometric series (p. 698) The sum of the terms of a geometric sequence.

greatest integer function (p. 102) A step function, written as $f(x) = [\![x]\!]$, where $f(x)$ is the greatest integer less than or equal to x.

growth factor (p. 477) In exponential growth, the base of the exponential expression, $1 + r$.

sucesión geométrica Sucesión en que cualquier término después del primero puede hallarse multiplicando el término anterior por una constante r, llamada razón común.

serie geométrica La suma de los términos de una sucesión geométrica.

función del máximo entero Una función etapa que se escribe $f(x) = [\![x]\!]$, donde $f(x)$ es el meaximo entero que es menor que o igual a x.

factor del crecimiento En el crecimiento exponencial, la base de la expresión exponencial, $1 + r$.

H

histogram (p. 1002) A histogram uses bars to display numerical data that have been organized into equal intervals.

horizontal asymptote (p. 577) A horizontal line which a graph approaches.

hyperbola (p. 569, 648) The set of all points in the plane such that the absolute value of the difference of the distances from two given points in the plane, called foci, is constant.

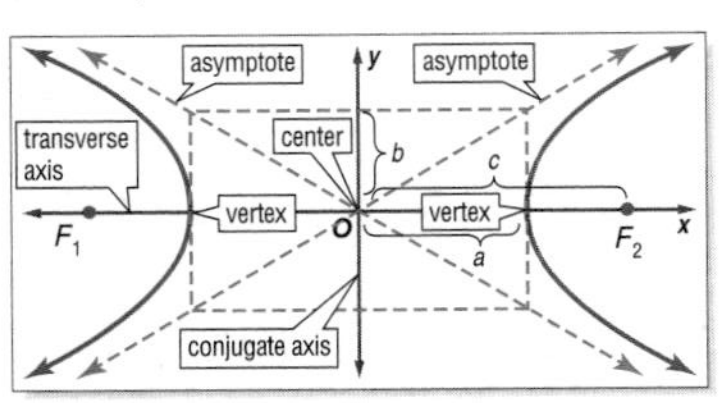

hypothesis (p. 781) An assumption about a population that can be verified by testing.

histograma Un histograma usa barras para exhibir datos numéricos que han sido organizados en intervalos iguales.

asíntota horizontal Una linea horizontal a que un gráfico acerca.

hipérbola Conjunto de todos los puntos de un plano en los que el valor absoluto de la diferencia de sus distancias a dos puntos dados del plano, llamados focos, es constante.

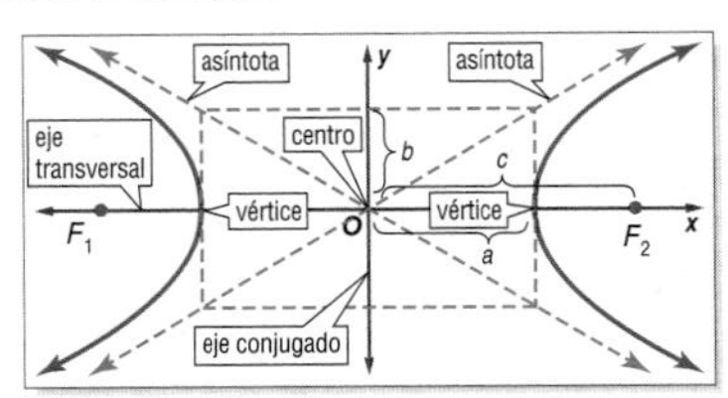

hipótesis Una asunción sobre una población que puede ser verificada probando.

I

identity function (p. 109) The function $I(x) = x$.

identity matrix (p. 229) A square matrix that, when multiplied by another matrix, equals that same matrix. If A is any $n \times n$ matrix and I is the $n \times n$ identity matrix, then $A \cdot I = A$ and $I \cdot A = A$.

image (p. 209) The graph of an object after a transformation.

imaginary unit (p. 276) i, or the principal square root of -1.

unción identidad La función $I(x) = x$.

matriz identidad Matriz cuadrada que al multiplicarse por otra matriz, es igual a la misma matriz. Si A es una matriz de $n \times n$ e I es la matriz identidad de $n \times n$, entonces $A \cdot I = A$ y $I \cdot A = A$.

imagen Gráfica de una figura después de una transformación.

unidad imaginaria i, o la raíz cuadrada principal de -1.

inclusive events (p. 999) Two events whose outcomes may be the same.

inconsistent (p. 137) A system of equations that has no solutions.

independent (p. 137) When a system of linear equations has exactly one solution.

independent events (p. 998) Events that do not affect each other.

independent system (p. 137) A system of equations that has exactly one solution.

independent variable (p. 64) In a function, the variable, usually x, whose values make up the domain.

index (p. 431) In nth roots, the value of n in the symbol $\sqrt[n]{}$. Indicates to what root the value under the radicand is being taken.

induction hypothesis (p. 727) The assumption that a statement is true for some positive integer k, where $k \geq n$.

inferential statistics (p. 780) Statistics like predictions and hypothesis testing are used to draw conclusions about a population by using a sample.

infinite geometric series (p. 705) A geometric series with an infinite number of terms.

infinite sequence (p. 681) A sequence that continues without end.

infinity (pp. 40, 707) Without bound, or continues without end.

initial side (p. 817) The fixed ray of an angle.

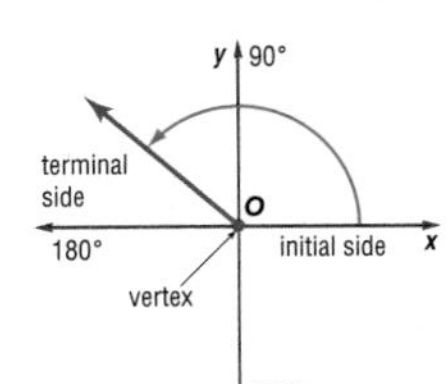

integer (p. 11) $\{\ldots, -3, -2, -1, 0, 1, 2, 3, \ldots\}$

inclusivo Dos eventos que pueden tener los mismos resultados.

inconsistente Sistema de ecuaciones que no tiene solución alguna.

independiente Cuando un sistema de ecuaciones lineares tiene exactamente una solución.

eventos independientes Eventos que no se afectan mutuamente.

sistema independiente Sistema de ecuaciones que sólo tiene una solución.

variable independiente En una función, la variable, por lo general x, cuyos valores forman el dominio.

indice (de un radical) En las nth raíces, el valor de n en el símbolo $\sqrt[n]{}$. Indica qué raíz se está llevando el valor bajo radicand.

hipótesis inductiva El suponer que un enunciado es verdadero para algún entero positivo k, donde $k \geq n$.

estadística deductiva La estadística como predicciones y la prueba de la hipótesis es utilizada para dibujar conclusiones sobre una población usando una muestra.

serie geométrica infinita Serie geométrica con un número infinito de términos.

secuencia infinita Una secuencia que continúa sin extremo.

infinito Sin límite, o continúa sin extremo.

lado inicial de un ángulo El rayo fijo de un ángulo.

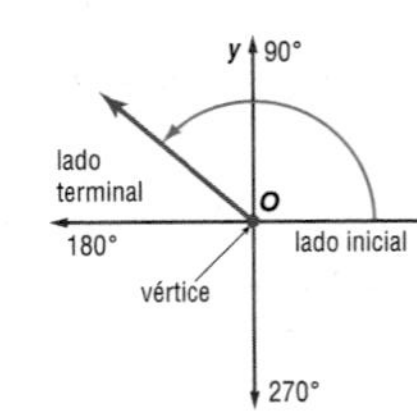

número entero $\{\ldots, -3, -2, -1, 0, 1, 2, 3, \ldots\}$

interquartile range (IQR) (p. 1006) The range of the middle half of a set of data. It is the difference between the upper quartile and the lower quartile.

amplitud intercuartílica Amplitud de la mitad central de un conjunto de datos. Es la diferencia entre el cuartil superior y el inferior.

intersection (p. 41) The graph of a compound inequality containing *and*.

intersección Gráfica de una desigualdad compuesta que contiene la palabra *y*.

interval notation (p. 40) A way to describe the solution set of an inequality.

notación del intervalo Una manera de describir el sistema de la solución de una desigualdad.

inverse function (p. 417) Two functions f and g are inverse functions if and only if both of their compositions are the identity function.

función inversa Dos funciones f y g son inversas mutuas si y sólo si las composiciones de ambas son la función identidad.

inverse of a trigonometric function (p. 871) The arccosine, arcsine, and arctangent relations.

inversa de una función trigonométrica Las relaciones arcocoseno, arcoseno y arcotangente.

inverse matrices (p. 229) Two $n \times n$ matrices are inverses of each other if their product is the identity matrix.

matrices inversas Dos matrices de $n \times n$ son inversas mutuas si su producto es la matriz identidad.

inverse relation (p. 417) Two relations are inverse relations if and only if whenever one relation contains the element (a, b) the other relation contains the element (b, a).

relaciones inversas Dos relaciones son relaciones inversas mutuas si y sólo si cada vez que una de las relaciones contiene el elemento (a, b), la otra contiene el elemento (b, a).

inverse variation (p. 588) y varies inversely as x if there is some nonzero constant k such that $xy = k$ or $y = \frac{k}{x}$, where $x \neq 0$ and $y \neq 0$.

variación inversa y varía inversamente con x si hay una constante no nula k tal que $xy = k$ o $y = \frac{k}{x}$, donde $x \neq 0$ y $y \neq 0$.

irrational number (p. 11) A real number that is not rational. The decimal form neither terminates nor repeats.

número irracional Número que no es racional. Su expansión decimal no es ni terminal ni periódica.

iteration (p. 716) The process of composing a function with itself repeatedly.

iteración Proceso de componer una función consigo misma repetidamente.

J

joint variation (p. 587) y varies jointly as x and z if there is some nonzero constant k such that $y = kxz$.

variación conjunta y varía conjuntamente con x y z si hay una constante no nula k tal que $y = kxz$.

L

latus rectum (p. 623) The line segment through the focus of a parabola and perpendicular to the axis of symmetry.

latus rectum El segmento de recta que pasa por el foco de una parábola y que es perpendicular a su eje de simetría.

Law of Cosines (p. 841) Let $\triangle ABC$ be any triangle with a, b, and c representing the measures of sides, and opposite angles with measures A, B, and C, respectively. Then the following equations are true.

$a^2 = b^2 + c^2 - 2bc \cos A$
$b^2 = a^2 + c^2 - 2ac \cos B$
$c^2 = a^2 + b^2 - 2ab \cos C$

Ley de los cosenos Sea $\triangle ABC$ un triángulo cualquiera, con a, b, y c las longitudes de los lados y con ángulos opuestos de medidas A, B y C, respectivamente. Entonces se cumplen las siguientes ecuaciones.

$a^2 = b^2 + c^2 - 2bc \cos A$
$b^2 = a^2 + c^2 - 2ac \cos B$
$c^2 = a^2 + b^2 - 2ab \cos C$

Law of Sines (p. 833) Let $\triangle ABC$ be any triangle with a, b, and c representing the measures of sides opposite angles with measurements A, B, and C, respectively. Then $\frac{\sin A}{a} = \frac{\sin B}{b} = \frac{\sin C}{c}$.

Ley de los senos Sea $\triangle ABC$ cualquier triángulo con a, b y c las longitudes de los lados y con ángulos opuestos de medidas A, B y C, respectivamente. Entonces $\frac{\sin A}{a} = \frac{\sin B}{b} = \frac{\sin C}{c}$.

leading coefficient (p. 348) The coefficient of the term with the highest degree.

coeficiente líder Coeficiente del término de mayor grado.

like radical expressions (p. 441) Two radical expressions in which both the radicands and indices are alike.

expresiones radicales semejantes Dos expresiones radicales en que tanto los radicandos como los índices son semejantes.

limit (p. 712) The value that the terms of a sequence approach.

límite El valor al que tienden los términos de una sucesión.

linear correlation coefficient (p. 96) A value that shows how close data points are to a line.

coeficiente de correlación lineal Valor que muestra la cercanía de los datos a una recta.

linear equation (p. 69) An equation that has no operations other than addition, subtraction, and multiplication of a variable by a constant.

ecuación lineal Ecuación sin otras operaciones que las de adición, sustracción y multiplicación de una variable por una constante.

linear function (p. 69) A function whose ordered pairs satisfy a linear equation.

función lineal Función cuyos pares ordenados satisfacen una ecuación lineal.

linear inequality (p. 117) Resembles a linear equation, but with an inequality symbol instead of an equals symbol.

desigualdad linear Se asemeja a una ecuación linear, pero con un símbolo de la desigualdad en vez de una relación linear del símbolo de los iguales.

linear permutation (p. P12) The arrangement of objects or people in a line.

permutación lineal Arreglo de personas o figuras en una línea.

linear programming (p. 160) The process of finding the maximum or minimum values of a function for a region defined by inequalities.

programación lineal Proceso de hallar los valores máximo o mínimo de una función lineal en una región definida por las desigualdades.

linear relation (p. 69) A relation that has straight line graphs.

notación del intervalo Una manera de describir el sistema de la solución de una desigualdad.

linear term (p. 249) In the equation $f(x) = ax^2 + bx + c$, bx is the linear term.

término lineal En la ecuación $f(x) = ax^2 + bx + c$, el término lineal es bx.

line graph (p. 1001) A type of statistical graph used to show how values change over a period of time.

gráfica lineal Tipo de gráfica estadística que se usa para mostrar cómo cambian los valores durante un período de tiempo.

line of fit (p. 92) A line that closely approximates a set of data.

recta de ajuste Recta que se aproxima estrechamente a un conjunto de datos.

line of reflection (p. 111) The line over which a reflection flips a figure.

línea de la reflexión La línea excedente que una reflexión mueve de un tirón una figura.

Location Principle (p. 357) Suppose $y = f(x)$ represents a polynomial function and a and b are two numbers such that $f(a) < 0$ and $f(b) > 0$. Then the function has at least one real zero between a and b.

principio de ubicación Sea $y = f(x)$ una función polinómica con a y b dos números tales que $f(a) < 0$ y $f(b) > 0$. Entonces la función tiene por lo menos un resultado real entre a y b.

logarithm (p. 492) In the function $x = b^y$, y is called the logarithm, base b, of x. Usually written as $y = \log_b x$ and is read "y equals log base b of x."

logaritmo En la función $x = b^y$, y es el logaritmo en base b, de x. Generalmente escrito como $y = \log_b x$ y se lee "y es igual al logaritmo en base b de x."

logarithmic equation (p. 502) An equation that contains one or more logarithms.

ecuación logarítmica Ecuación que contiene uno o más logaritmos.

logarithmic function (p. 493) The function $y = \log_b x$, where $b > 0$ and $b \neq 1$, which is the inverse of the exponential function $y = b^x$.

función logarítmica La función $y = \log_b x$, donde $b > 0$ y $b \neq 1$, inversa de la función exponencial $y = b^x$.

logarithmic inequality (p. 503) An inequality that contains one or more logarithms.

desigualdad logarítmica Desigualdad que contiene uno o más logaritmos.

logistic growth model (p. 536) A growth model that represents growth that has a limiting factor. Logistic models are the most accurate models for representing population growth.

modelo logístico del crecimiento Un modelo del crecimiento que representa el crecimiento que tiene un factor limitador. Los modelos logísticos son los modelos más exactos para representar crecimiento de la población.

lower quartile (p. 1005) The median of the lower half of a set of data, indicated by LQ.

cuartil inferior Mediana de la mitad inferior de un conjunto de datos, se denota con CI.

M

major axis (p. 639) The longer of the two line segments that form the axes of symmetry of an ellipse.

eje mayor El más largo de dos segmentos de recta que forman los ejes de simetría de una elipse.

mapping (p. P4) How each member of the domain is paired with each member of the range.

transformaciones La correspondencia entre cada miembro del dominio con cada miembro del rango.

margin of sampling error (p. 753) The limit on the difference between how a sample responds and how the total population would respond.

margen de error muestral Límite en la diferencia entre las respuestas obtenidas con una muestra y cómo pudiera responder la población entera.

mathematical induction (p. 727) A method of proof used to prove statements about positive integers.

inducción matemática Método de demostrar enunciados sobre los enteros positivos.

matrix (p. 185) Any rectangular array of variables or constants in horizontal rows and vertical columns.

matriz Arreglo rectangular de variables o constantes en filas horizontales y columnas verticales.

matrix equation (p. 231) A matrix form used to represent a system of equations.

ecuación matriz Forma de matriz que se usa para representar un sistema de ecuaciones.

maximum value (p. 252) The y-coordinate of the vertex of the quadratic function $f(x) = ax^2 + bx + c$, where $a < 0$.

valor máximo La coordenada y del vértice de la función cuadrática $f(x) = ax^2 + bx + c$, where $a < 0$.

measure of central tendency (p. 752) A number that represents the center or middle of a set of data.

medida de tendencia central Número que representa el centro o medio de un conjunto de datos.

measure of variation (p. 754) A representation of how spread out or scattered a set of data is.

medida de variación Número que representa la dispersión de un conjunto de datos.

midline (p. 864) A horizontal axis used as the reference line about which the graph of a periodic function oscillates.

recta central Eje horizontal que se usa como recta de referencia alrededor de la cual oscila la gráfica de una función periódica.

minimum value (p. 252) The y-coordinate of the vertex of the quadratic function $f(x) = ax^2 + bx + c$, where $a > 0$.

valor mínimo La coordenada y del vértice de la función cuadrática $f(x) = ax^2 + bx + c$, donde $a > 0$.

minor axis (p. 639) The shorter of the two line segments that form the axes of symmetry of an ellipse.

eje menor El más corto de los dos segmentos de recta de los ejes de simetría de una elipse.

mutually exclusive (p. 999) Two events that cannot occur at the same time.

mutuamente exclusivos Dos eventos que no pueden ocurrir simultáneamente.

N

***n*th root** (p. 431) For any real numbers a and b, and any positive integer n, if $a^n = b$, then a is an nth root of b.

raíz *enésima* Para cualquier número real a y b y cualquier entero positivo n, si $a^n = b$, entonces a se llama una raíz *enésima* de b.

natural base (p. 525) The value of e is 2.71828. The base used for the LN logarithmic function.

base natural El valor de e es 2.71828. La base usada para el número natural de la función logarítmica de LN.

natural base, e (p. 525) An irrational number approximately equal to 2.71828… .

base natural, e Número irracional aproximadamente igual a 2.71828… .

natural base exponential function (p. 525) An exponential function with base e, $y = e^x$.

función exponencial natural La función exponencial de base e, $y = e^x$.

natural logarithm (p. 525) Logarithms with base e, written ln x.

logaritmo natural Logaritmo de base e, el que se escribe ln x.

natural number (p. 11) {1, 2, 3, 4, 5, …},

número natural {1, 2, 3, 4, 5, …},

negative correlation (p. 92) When the values in a scatter plot are closely linked in a negative manner.

corelación negativo Cuando los valores en un diagrama de dispersión se ligan de cerca de una manera negativa.

negative exponent (p. 333) For any real number $a \neq 0$ and any integer n, $a^{-n} = \frac{1}{a^n}$ and $\frac{1}{a^{-n}} = a^n$.

exponente negativo Para cualquier número real $a \neq 0$ cualquier entero positivo n, $a^{-n} = \frac{1}{a^n}$ y $\frac{1}{a^{-n}} = a^n$.

nonproportional relationship (p. 993) A relationship in which two ratios are not equal.

relación no proporcional Relación en la que dos razones no son iguales.

normal distribution (p. 773) A frequency distribution that often occurs when there is a large number of values in a set of data: about 68% of the values are within one standard deviation of the mean, 95% of the values are within two standard deviations from the mean, and 99% of the values are within three standard deviations.

Normal Distribution

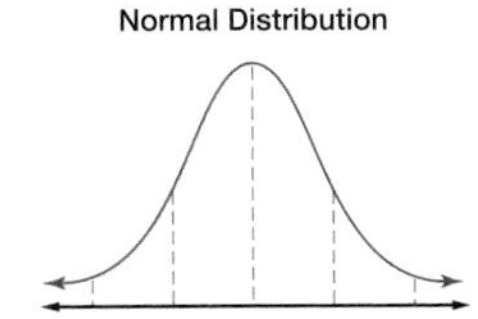

distribución normal Distribución de frecuencia que aparece a menudo cuando hay un número grande de datos: cerca del 68% de los datos están dentro de una desviación estándar de la media, 95% están dentro de dos desviaciones estándar de la media y 99% están dentro de tres desviaciones estándar de la media.

Distribución normal

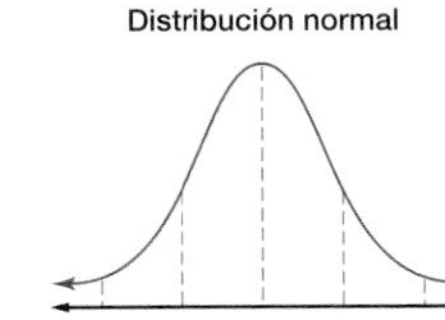

null hypothesis (p. 781) A specific hypothesis to be tested. It is expressed as an equality and is considered true until evidence indicates otherwise.

hipótesis nula Es una hipótesis específica que se probará. Se expresa como igualdad y se considera verdad hasta que la evidencia indica de otra manera.

O

oblique asymptote (p. 579) An asymptote that is neither horizontal nor vertical and is sometimes called a *slant asymptote.*

observational study (p. 746) Individuals are observed and no attempt is made to influence the results.

one-to-one function (p. 61) **1.** A function where each element of the range is paired with exactly one element of the domain **2.** A function whose inverse is a function.

onto function (p. 61) Each element of the range corresponds to an element of the domain.

open sentence (p. 18) A mathematical sentence containing one or more variables.

optimize (p. 162) To seek the optimal price or amount that is desired to minimize costs or maximize profits.

ordered triple (p. 167) **1.** The coordinates of a point in space **2.** The solution of a system of equations in three variables x, y, and z.

Order of Operations (p. 5)
Step 1 Evaluate expressions inside grouping symbols.
Step 2 Evaluate all powers.
Step 3 Do all multiplications and/or divisions from left to right.
Step 4 Do all additions and subtractions from left to right.

outcomes (p. P9) The results of a probability experiment or an event.

outlier (p. 93) A data point that does not appear to belong to the rest of the set.

asíntota oblicuo Una asíntota que es ni horizontal ni la vertical y a veces se llama una *asíntota inclinada.*

estudio de observación Observan a los individuos y no se hace ninguna tentativa de influenciar los resultados.

función biunívoca **1.** Función en la que a cada elemento del rango le corresponde sólo un elemento del dominio. **2.** Función cuya inversa es una función.

sobre la función Cada elemento de la gama corresponde a un elemento del dominio. Centro y un punto en el círculo. Índice del crecimiento continuo—la tarifa en la cual algo crece continuamente. El valor de k en la función exponencial del crecimiento, $f(x) = ae$.

enunciado abierto Enunciado matemático que contiene una o más variables.

optimice Buscar el precio óptimo o ascender que se desea para reducir al mínimo costes o para maximizar de los beneficios.

triple ordenado **1.** Las coordenadas de un punto en el espacio **2.** Solución de un sistema de ecuaciones en tres variables x, y y z.

orden de las operaciones
Paso 1 Evalúa las expresiones dentro de símbolos de agrupamiento.
Paso 2 Evalúa todas las potencias.
Paso 3 Ejecuta todas las multiplicaciones y divisiones de izquierda a derecha.
Paso 4 Ejecuta todas las adiciones y sustracciones de izquierda a derecha.

resultados Lo que produce un experimento o evento probabilístico.

valor atípico Dato que no parece pertenecer al resto el conjunto.

P

parabola (pp. 249, 623) The graph of a quadratic function. The set of all points in a plane that are the same distance from a given point, called the focus, and a given line, called the directrix.

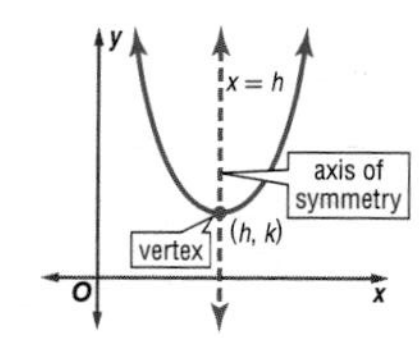

parallel lines (p. 85) Nonvertical coplanar lines with the same slope.

parameter (p. 752) A measure that describes a characteristic of a population.

parent function (p. 109) The simplest, most general function in a family of functions.

parent graph (p. 109) The simplest of graphs in a family.

partial sum (p. 690) The sum of the first n terms of a series.

Pascal's triangle (p. 721) A triangular array of numbers such that the $(n + 1)^{th}$ row is the coefficient of the terms of the expansion $(x + y)^n$ for $n = 0, 1, 2 \ldots$

period (p. 849) The least possible value of a for which $f(x) = f(x + a)$.

periodic function (p. 849) A function is called periodic if there is a number a such that $f(x) = f(x + a)$ for all x in the domain of the function.

permutation (p. P12) An arrangement of objects in which order is important.

perpendicular lines (p. 85) In a plane, any two oblique lines, the product of whose slopes is -1.

phase shift (p. 863) A horizontal translation of a trigonometric function.

piecewise-defined function (p. 101) A function that is written using two or more expressions.

piecewise-linear function (p. 102) Like a step function, it contains a single expression.

parábola La gráfica de una función cuadrática. Conjunto de todos los puntos de un plano que están a la misma distancia de un punto dado, llamado foco, y de una recta dada, llamada directriz.

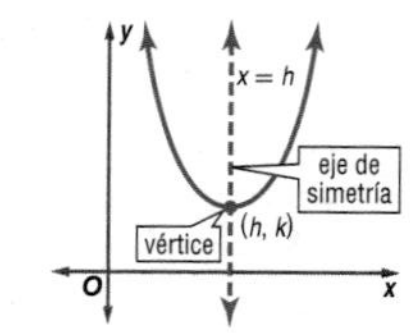

rectas paralelas Rectas coplanares no verticales con la misma pendiente.

parámetro Una medida que describe una característica de una población.

función del padre El más simple, la mayoría de la función general en una familia de funciones.

gráfica madre La gráfica más sencilla en una familia de gráficas.

suma parcial La suma de los primeros n términos de una serie.

triángulo de Pascal Arreglo triangular de números en el que la fila $(n + 1)^n$ proporciona los coeficientes de los términos de la expansión de $(x + y)^n$ para $n = 0, 1, 2 \ldots$

período El menor valor positivo posible para a, para el cual $f(x) = f(x + a)$.

función periódica Función para la cual hay un número a tal que $f(x) = f(x + a)$ para todo x en el dominio de la función .

permutación Arreglo de elementos en que el orden es importante.

rectas perpendiculares En un plano, dos rectas oblicuas cualesquiera cuyas pendientes tienen un producto igual a -1.

desvío de fase Traslación horizontal de una función trigonométrica.

función por trozos-definida Una función se escribe que usando dos o más expresiones.

función por partes lineal Como una función del paso, contiene una sola expression.

point discontinuity (p. 580) If the original function is undefined for $x = a$ but the related rational expression of the function in simplest form is defined for $x = a$, then there is a hole in the graph at $x = a$.

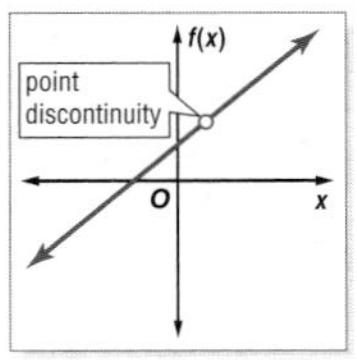

point-slope form (p. 84) An equation in the form $y - y_1 = m(x - x_1)$ where (x_1, y_1) are the coordinates of a point on the line and m is the slope of the line.

polynomial function (p. 349) A function that is represented by a polynomial equation.

polynomial in one variable (p. 348) $a_nx^n + a_{n-1}x^{n-1} + \cdots + a_2x^2 + a_1x + a_0$, where the coefficients $a_n, a_{n-1}, \ldots, a_0$ represent real numbers, and a_n is not zero and n is a nonnegative integer.

population (p. 745) An entire group of living things or objects.

positive correlation (p. 92) When the values in a scatter plot are closely linked in a positive manner.

power function (p. 349) An equation in the form $f(x) = ax^b$, where a and b are real numbers.

prediction equation (p. 92) An equation suggested by the points of a scatter plot that is used to predict other points.

preimage (p. 209) The graph of an object before a transformation.

prime polynomial (p. 368) A polynomial that cannot be factored.

principal root (p. 431) The nonnegative root.

principal values (p. 871) The values in the restricted domains of trigonometric functions.

probability distribution (p. 766) A function that maps the sample space to the probabilities of the outcomes in the sample space for a particular random variable.

discontinuidad evitable Si la función original no está definida en $x = a$ pero la expresión racional reducida correspondiente de la función está definida en $x = a$, entonces la gráfica tiene una ruptura o corte en $x = a$.

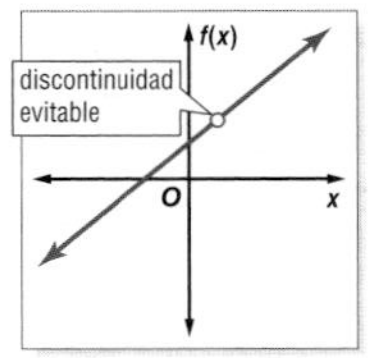

forma punto-pendiente Ecuación de la forma $y - y_1 = m(x - x_1)$ donde (x_1, y_1) es un punto en la recta y m es la pendiente de la recta.

función polinomial Función representada por una ecuación polinomial.

polinomio de una variable $a_nx^n + a_{n-1}x^{n-1} + \cdots + a_2x^2 + a_1x + a_0$, donde los coeficientes $a_n, a_{n-1}, \ldots, a_0$ son números reales, a_n no es nulo y n es un entero no negativo.

población Un grupo entero de cosas o de objetos vivos.

correlación positivo Cuando los valores en un diagrama de la dispersión se ligan de cerca de una manera positiva.

función potencia Ecuación de la forma $f(x) = ax^b$, donde a y b son números reales.

ecuación de predicción Ecuación sugerida por los puntos de una gráfica de dispersión y que se usa para predecir otros puntos.

preimagen Gráfica de una figura antes de una transformación.

polinomio primero Un polinomio que no puede ser descompuesto en factores.

raíz principal La raíz no negativa.

valores principales Valores en los dominios restringidos de las funciones trigonométricas.

distribución de probabilidad Función que aplica el espacio muestral a las probabilidades de los resultados en el espacio muestral obtenidos para una variable aleatoria particular.

proportion (p. 993) A statement of equality of two or more ratios.

proportional relationship (p. 993) The ratios of related terms are equal.

pure imaginary number (p. 276) The square roots of negative real numbers. For any positive real number b, $\sqrt{-b^2} = \sqrt{b^2} \cdot \sqrt{-1}$, or bi.

proporción Enunciado de la igualdad de dos o más razones.

relación proporcional Relación en la que la razón entre los términos relacionados permanece igual.

número imaginario puro Raíz cuadrada de un número real negativo. Para cualquier número (real positivo b, $\sqrt{-b^2} = \sqrt{b^2} \cdot \sqrt{-1}$, ó bi.

Q

quadrantal angle (p. 826) An angle in standard position whose terminal side coincides with one of the axes.

quadrants (p. P4) The four areas of a Cartesian coordinate plane.

quadratic equation (p. 259) A quadratic function set equal to a value, in the form $ax^2 + bx + c = 0$, where $a \neq 0$.

quadratic form (p. 371) For any numbers a, b, and c, except for $a = 0$, an equation that can be written in the form $u^2 + u + c = 0$, where u is some expression in x.

Quadratic Formula (p. 292) The solutions of a quadratic equation of the form $ax^2 + bx + c = 0$, where $a \neq 0$, are given by the Quadratic Formula, which is $x = \frac{-b \pm \sqrt{b^2 - 4ac}}{2a}$.

quadratic function (pp. 109, 249) A function described by the equation $f(x) = ax^2 + bx + c = 0$, where $a \neq 0$.

quadratic inequality (p. 312) A quadratic equation in the form $y > ax^2 + bx + c$, $y \geq ax^2 + bx + c$, $y < ax^2 + bx + c$, or $y \leq ax^2 + bx + c$.

quadratic term (p. 249) In the equation $f(x) = ax^2 + bx + c$, ax^2 is the quadratic term.

quartic function (p. 350) A fourth-degree function.

quartiles (p. 1005) The values that divide a set of data into four equal parts.

quintic function (p. 350) A fifth-degree function.

ángulo de cuadrante Ángulo en posición estándar cuyo lado terminal coincide con uno de los ejes.

cuadrantes Las cuatro regiones de un plano de coordenadas Cartesiano.

ecuación cuadrática Función cuadrática igual a un valor, de la forma $ax^2 + bx + c = 0$, donde $a \neq 0$.

forma de ecuación cuadrática Para cualquier número a, b, y c, excepto $a = 0$, una ecuación que puede escribirse de la forma $u^2 + u + c = 0$, donde u es una expresión en x.

fórmula cuadrática Las soluciones de una ecuación cuadrática de la forma $ax^2 + bx + c = 0$, donde $a \neq 0$, se dan por la fórmula cuadrática, que es $x = \frac{-b \pm \sqrt{b^2 - 4ac}}{2a}$.

función cuadrática Función descrita por la ecuación $f(x) = ax^2 + bx + c = 0$, donde $a \neq 0$.

desigualdad cuadrática Ecuación cuadrática de la forma $y > ax^2 + bx + c$, $y \geq ax^2 + bx + c$, $y < ax^2 + bx + c$, $y \leq ax^2 + bx + c$.

término cuadrático En la ecuación $f(x) = ax^2 + bx + c$, ax^2 el término cuadrático es ax^2.

función quartic Una función del cuarto-grado.

cuartiles Valores que dividen un conjunto de datos en cuatro partes iguales.

función quintic Una función del quinto-grado.

R

radian (p. 819) The measure of an angle θ in standard position whose rays intercept an arc of length 1 unit on the unit circle.

radián Medida de un ángulo θ en posición normal cuyos rayos intersecan un arco de 1 unidad de longitud en el círculo unitario.

Glossary/Glosario

radical equation (p. 453) An equation with radicals that have variables in the radicands.

radical function (p. 424) A function that contains the root of a variable.

radical inequality (p. 455) An inequality that has a variable in the radicand.

radical sign (p. 431) In *n*th roots, the symbol $\sqrt[n]{}$.

radicand (p. 431) In *n*th roots, the value inside in the symbol $\sqrt[n]{}$. Indicates the value that is being taken to the *n*th root.

radius (p. 631) Any segment whose endpoints are the center and a point on the circle.

random variable (p. 766) The outcome of a random process that has a numerical value.

range (p. P4) The set of all *y*-coordinates of a relation.

rate of change (p. 76) How much a quantity changes on average, relative to the change in another quantity, over time.

rate of continuous decay (p. 533) The rate at which something decays continuously. Represented by a constant *k* in the exponential decay function $f(x) = ae^{-kt}$, where *a* is the initial value, and *t* is time in years.

rate of continuous growth (p. 533) The rate at which something grows continuously. The value of *k* in the exponential growth function, $f(x) = ae^{kt}$.

rational equation (p. 594) Any equation that contains one or more rational expressions.

rational exponent (p. 447) For any nonzero real number *b*, and any integers *m* and *n*, with $n > 1$, $b^{\frac{m}{n}} = \sqrt[n]{b^m} = \left(\sqrt[n]{b}\right)^m$, except when $b < 0$ and *n* is even.

rational expression (p. 553) A ratio of two polynomial expressions.

rational function (p. 577) An equation of the form $f(x) = \frac{p(x)}{q(x)}$, where $p(x)$ and $q(x)$ are polynomial functions, and $q(x) \neq 0$.

rational inequality (p. 599) Any inequality that contains one or more rational expressions.

rationalizing the denominator (p. 440) To eliminate radicals from a denominator or fractions from a radicand.

ecuación radical Ecuación con radicales que tienen variables en el radicando.

función radical Una función que contiene la raíz de una variable.

desigualdad radical Desigualdad que tiene una variable en el radicando.

signo radical El símbolo $\sqrt[n]{}$, que se usa par indicar la raíz cuadrada no negative o el símbolo por raíz enésima.

radicando El número o la expressión que aparece debajo del signo radical.

radio Un segmento cuyos extremos son el centro y un punto del círculo.

variable aleatoria El resultado de un proceso aleatorio que tiene un valor numérico.

rango Conjunto de todas las coordenadas *y* de una relación.

tasa de cambio Lo que cambia una cantidad en promedio, respecto al cambio en otra cantidad, por lo general el tiempo.

índice de desintegración continúa Ritmo al cual algo se desintegra continuamente. Representado por la constante *k* en la función de desintegración exponencial $f(x) = ae^{-kt}$, donde *a* es el valor inicial y *t* es el tiempo en años.

el índice del crecimiento continuo Es la tasa en la cual algo crece continuamente. El valor de *k* en la función exponencial del crecimiento, $f(x) = ae^{kt}$. La tasa en la cual algo crece continuamente.

ecuación racional Cualquier ecuación que contiene una o más expresiones racionales.

exponent racional Para cualquier número real no nulo *b* y cualquier entero *m* y *n*, con $n > 1$, $b^{\frac{m}{n}} = \sqrt[n]{b^m} = \left(\sqrt[n]{b}\right)^m$, excepto cuando $b < 0$ y *n* es par.

expresión racional Razón de dos expresiones polinomiales.

función racional Ecuación de la forma $f(x) = \frac{p(x)}{q(x)}$, donde $p(x)$ y $q(x)$ son funciones polinomiales y $q(x) \neq 0$.

desigualdad racional Cualquier desigualdad que contiene una o más expresiones racionales.

racionalizar el denominador La eliminación de radicales de un denominador o de fracciones de un radicando.

rational number (p. 11) Any number $\frac{m}{n}$, where *m* and *n* are integers and *n* is not zero. The decimal form is either a terminating or repeating decimal.

Rational Zero Theorem (p. 391) Helps you choose some possible zeros of a polynomial function to test.

real numbers (p. 11) All numbers used in everyday life; the set of all rational and irrational numbers.

reciprocal function (pp. 569, 809) **1.** A function of the form $f(x) = \frac{1}{a(x)}$, where $a(x)$ is a linear function and $a(x) \neq 0$. **2.** Trigonometric functions that are reciprocals of each other.

recursive formula (p. 714) Each term is formulated from one or more previous terms.

recursive sequence (p. 714) A sequence in which each term is determined by one or more of the previous terms.

reference angle (p. 826) The acute angle formed by the terminal side of an angle in standard position and the *x*-axis.

reflection (p. 111) A transformation in which every point of a figure is mapped to a corresponding image across a line of symmetry.

reflection matrix (p. 212) A matrix used to reflect an object over a line or plane.

regression line (p. 94) A line of best fit.

relation (p. P4) A set of ordered pairs.

relative frequency (p. 760) In a contingency table, the frequency of occurrence for each data value.

relative frequency graph (p. 766) A table of probabilities or a graph to help visualize a probability distribution.

relative maximum (p. 358) A point on the graph of a function where no other nearby points have a greater *y*-coordinate.

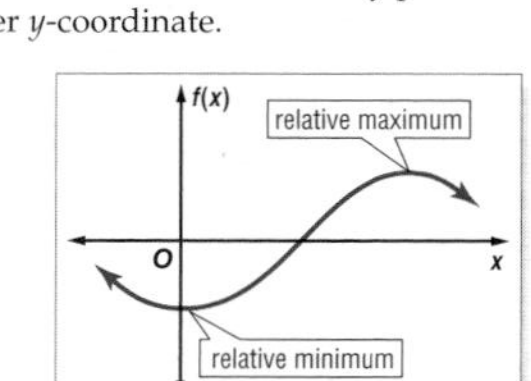

número racional Cualquier número $\frac{m}{n}$, donde *m* y n son enteros y n no es cero. Su expansión decimal es o terminal o periódica.

El teorema cero racional Ayudas usted elige algunos ceros posibles de una función polinómica para probar.

números reales Todos los números que se usan en la vida cotidiana; el conjunto de los todos los números racionales e irracionales.

funciones recíprocas **1.** Una función de la forma $f(x) = \frac{1}{a(x)}$, donde $a(x)$ es una función linear y $a(x) \neq 0$. **2.** Funciones trigonométricas de la función que son reciprocals de uno a.

fórmula recursiva Cada término proviene de uno o más términos anteriores.

sucesión recursiva Una secuencia en la cual cada término es determinado por uno o más de los términos anteriores.

ángulo de referencia El ángulo agudo formado por el lado terminal de un ángulo en posición estándar y el eje *x*.

reflexión Transformación en que cada punto de una figura se aplica a través de una recta de simetría a su imagen correspondiente.

matriz de reflexión Matriz que se usa para reflejar una figura sobre una recta o plano.

reca de regresión Una recta de óptimo ajuste.

relación Conjunto de pares ordenados.

frecuencia relativa En una tabla de la contingencia, la frecuencia de la ocurrencia para cada valor de los datos.

gráfica de frecuencia relativa Tabla de probabilidades o gráfica para asistir en la visualización de una distribución de probabilidad.

máximo relativo Punto en la gráfica de una función en donde ningún otro punto cercano tiene una coordenada *y* mayor.

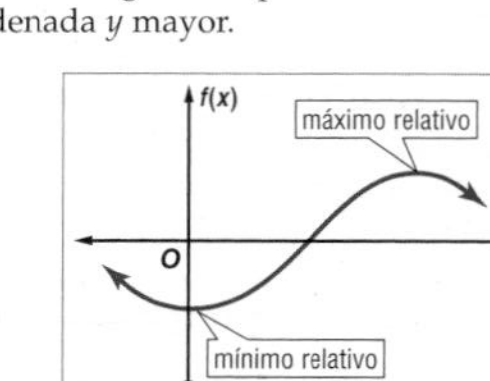

relative minimum (p. 358) A point on the graph of a function where no other nearby points have a lesser y-coordinate.

root (p. 259) The solutions of a quadratic equation.

rotation (p. 212) A transformation in which an object is moved around a center point, usually the origin.

rotation matrix (p. 212) A matrix used to rotate an object.

row matrix (p. 186) A matrix that has only one row.

mínimo relativo Punto en la gráfica de una función en donde ningún otro punto cercano tiene una coordenada y menor.

raíz Las soluciones de una ecuación cuadrática.

rotación Transformación en que una figura se hace girar alrededor de un punto central, generalmente el origen.

matriz de rotación Matriz que se usa para hacer girar un objeto.

matriz fila Matriz que sólo tiene una fila.

S

sample (p. 745) A part of a population.

sample space (p. P9) The set of all possible outcomes of an experiment.

scalar (p. 194) A constant.

scalar multiplication (p. 194) Multiplying any matrix by a constant called a scalar; the product of a scalar k and an $m \times n$ matrix.

scatter plot (p. 92) A set of data graphed as ordered pairs in a coordinate plane.

scientific notation (p. 997) The expression of a number in the form $a \times 10^n$, where $1 \leq a < 10$ and n is an integer.

secant (p. 808) For any angle, with measure α, a point $P(x, y)$ on its terminal side, $r = \sqrt{x^2 + y^2}$, $\sec \alpha = \frac{r}{x}$.

second-order determinant (p. 220) The determinant of a 2×2 matrix.

sequence (p. 681) A list of numbers in a particular order.

series (p. 690) The sum of the terms of a sequence.

set-builder notation (p. 35) The expression of the solution set of an inequality, for example $\{x \mid x > 9\}$.

sigma notation (p. 691) For any sequence $a_1, a_2, a_3, \ldots$, the sum of the first k terms may be written $\sum_{n=1}^{k} a_n$, which is read "the summation from $n = 1$ to k of a_n." Thus, $\sum_{n=1}^{k} a_n = a_1 + a_2 + a_3 + \cdots + a_k$, where k is an integer value.

muestra Parte de una población.

espacio muestral Conjunto de todos los resultados posibles de un experimento probabilístico.

escalar Una constante.

multiplicación por escalares Multiplicación de una matriz por una constante llamada escalar; producto de un escalar k y una matriz de $m \times n$.

gráfica de dispersión Conjuntos de datos graficados como pares ordenados en un plano de coordenadas.

notación científica Escritura de un número en la forma $a \times 10^n$, donde $1 \leq a < 10$ y n es un entero.

secante Para cualquier ángulo de medida α, un punto $P(x, y)$ en su lado terminal, $r = \sqrt{x^2 + y^2}$, $\sec \alpha = \frac{r}{x}$.

determinante de segundo orden El determinante de una matriz de 2×2.

sucesión Lista de números en un orden particular.

serie Suma específica de los términos de una sucesión.

notación de construcción de conjuntos Escritura del conjunto solucion de una desigualdad, por ejemplo, $\{x \mid x > 9\}$.

notación de suma Para cualquier sucesión $a_1, a_2, a_3, \ldots$, la suma de los k primeros términos puede escribirse $\sum_{n=1}^{k} a_n$, lo que se lee "la suma de $n = 1$ a k de los a_n." Así, $\sum_{n=1}^{k} a_n = a_1 + a_2 + a_3 + \cdots + a_k$, donde k es un valor entero.

simple event (p. 998) One event.

simplify (p. 333) To rewrite an expression without parentheses or negative exponents.

simulation (p. 785) The use of a probability experiment to mimic a real-life situation.

sine (p. 808) For any angle, with measure α, a point $P(x, y)$ on its terminal side, $r = \sqrt{x^2 + y^2}$, $\sin \alpha = \frac{y}{r}$.

skewed distribution (p. 773) A curve or histogram that is not symmetric.

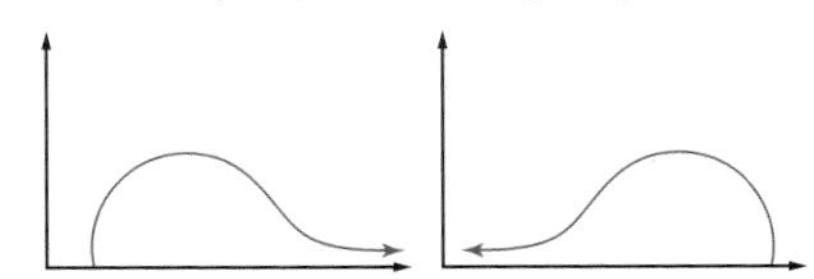

slope (p. 77) The ratio of the change in y-coordinates to the change in x-coordinates.

slope-intercept form (p. 83) The equation of a line in the form $y = mx + b$, where m is the slope and b is the y-intercept.

solution (p. 18) A replacement for the variable in an open sentence that results in a true sentence.

solving a right triangle (p. 833) The process of finding the measures of all of the sides and angles of a right triangle.

solving a triangle (p. 833) Using given measures to find all unknown side lengths and angle measures of a triangle.

square matrix (p. 186) A matrix with the same number of rows and columns.

square root (p. 995) For any real numbers a and b, if $a^2 = b$, then a is a square root of b.

square root function (p. 424) A function that contains a square root of a variable.

square root inequality (p. 426) An inequality involving the square root of a variable expression.

Square Root Property (p. 277) For any real number n, if $x^2 = n$, then $x = \pm\sqrt{n}$.

standard deviation (p. 754) The square root of the variance, represented by a.

evento simple Un solo evento.

reducir Escribir una expresión sin paréntesis o exponentes negativos.

simulación Uso de un experimento probabilístico para imitar una situación de la vida real.

seno Para cualquier ángulo de medida α, un punto $P(x, y)$ en su lado terminal, $r = \sqrt{x^2 + y^2}$, $\sin \alpha = \frac{y}{r}$.

distribución asimétrica Curva o histograma que no es simétrico.

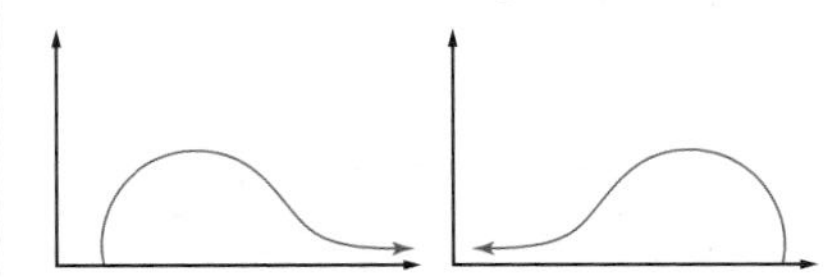

pendiente La razón del cambio en coordenadas y al cambio en coordenadas x.

forma pendiente-intersección Ecuación de una recta de la forma $y = mx + b$, donde m es la pendiente y b la intersección.

solución Sustitución de la variable de un enunciado abierto que resulta en un enunciado verdadero.

resolver un triángulo rectángulo Proceso de hallar las medidas de todos los lados y ángulos de un triángulo rectángulo.

resolver un triángulo Usar medidas dadas de hallar todas las medidas de las longitudes y laterales desconocidas del ángulo de un triángulo.

matriz cuadrada Matriz con el mismo número de filas y columnas.

raíz cuadrada Para cualquier número real a y b, si $a^2 = b$, entonces a es una raíz cuadrada de b.

función radical Función que contiene la raíz cuadrada de una variable.

desigualdad radical Desigualdad que presenta raíces cuadradas de un expresión con variables.

Propiedad de la raíz cuadrada Para cualquier número real n, si $x^2 = n$, entonces $x = \pm\sqrt{n}$.

desviación estándar La raíz cuadrada de la varianza, la que se escribe a.

standard form (pp. 70, 259, 623) **1.** A linear equation written in the form $Ax + By = C$, where A, B, and C are integers whose greatest common factor is 1, $A \geq 0$, and A and B are not both zero. **2.** A quadratic equation written in the form $ax^2 + bx + c = 0$, where a, b, and c are integers, and $a \neq 0$.

standard position (p. 817) An angle positioned so that its vertex is at the origin and its initial side is along the positive x-axis.

statistic (p. 752) A measure that describes a characteristic of a sample.

statistical inference (p. 780) Use inferential statistics like predictions and hypothesis testing. Use information from a sample to draw conclusions about a population.

stem-and-leaf plot (p. 1004) A system used to condense a set of data where the greatest place value of the data forms the stem and the next greatest place value forms the leaves.

step function (p. 102) A function whose graph is a series of line segments.

substitution method (p. 143) A method of solving a system of equations in which one equation is solved for one variable in terms of the other.

success (p. 764) The desired outcome of an event.

survey (p. 745) Used to collect information about a population.

synthetic division (p. 342) A method used to divide a polynomial by a binomial.

synthetic substitution (p. 377) The use of synthetic division to evaluate a function.

system of equations (p. 135) A set of equations with the same variables.

system of inequalities (p. 151) A set of inequalities with the same variables.

forma estándar **1.** Ecuación lineal escrita de la forma $Ax + By = C$, donde A, B, y C son enteros cuyo máximo común divisores 1, $A \geq 0$, y A y B no son cero simultáneamente. **2.** Una ecuación cuadrática escrita en la forma $ax^2 + bx + c = 0$, donde a, b, y c son números enteros, y $a \neq 0$.

posición estándar Ángulo en posición tal que su vértice está en el origen y su lado inicial está a lo largo del eje x positivo.

estadística Una medida que describe una característica de una muestra.

inferencia estadística Utiliza la estadística deductiva como las predicciones y la hipótesis que prueban información de uso de una muestra para dibujar las conclusiones acerca de una población.

diagrama de tallo y hojas Sistema que se usa para condensar un conjunto de datos, en que el valor de posición máximo de los datos forma el tallo y el segundo valor de posición máximo forma las hojas.

función etapa Función cuya gráfica es una serie de segmentos de recta.

método de sustitución Método para resolver un sistema de ecuaciones en que una de las ecuaciones se resuelve en una de las variables en términos de la otra.

éxito El resultado deseado de un evento.

encuesta Reunía información acerca de una población.

división sintética Método que se usa para dividir un polinomio entre un binomio.

sustitución sintética Uso de la división sintética para evaluar una función polinomial.

sistema de ecuaciones Conjunto de ecuaciones con las mismas variables.

sistema de desigualdades Conjunto de desigualdades con las mismas variables.

T

tangent (p. 808) **1.** A line that intersects a circle at exactly one point. **2.** For any angle, with measure α, a point $P(x, y)$ on its terminal side, $r = \sqrt{x^2 + y^2}$, $\tan \alpha = \frac{y}{x}$.

term (p. 681) **1.** The monomials that make up a polynomial. **2.** Each number in a sequence or series.

tangente **1.** Recta que interseca un círculo en un solo punto. **2.** Para cualquier ángulo, de medida α, un punto $P(x, y)$ en su lado terminal, $r = \sqrt{x^2 + y^2}$, $\tan \alpha = \frac{y}{x}$.

término **1.** Los monomios que constituyen un polinomio. **2.** Cada número de una sucesión o serie.

terminal side (p. 817) A ray of an angle that rotates about the center.

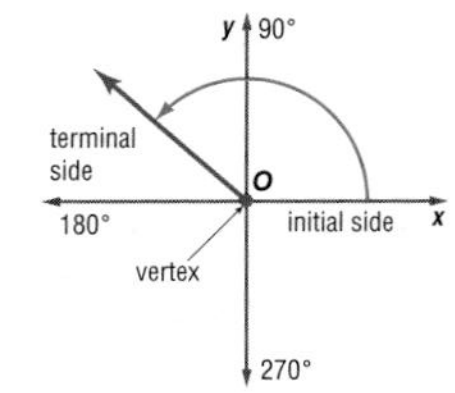

theoretical probability (p. 767) What should occur in a probability experiment.

third-order determinant (p. 221) Determinant of a 3×3 matrix.

transformation (p. 209) Functions that map points of a pre-image onto its image.

translation (p. 110) A figure is moved from one location to another on the coordinate plane without changing its size, shape, or orientation.

translation matrix (p. 209) A matrix that represents a translated figure.

transverse axis (p. 648) The segment of length $2a$ whose endpoints are the vertices of a hyperbola.

treatment group (p. 746) In an experiment, the people, animals, or objects given the treatment.

trigonometric equation (p. 921) An equation containing at least one trigonometric function that is true for some but not all values of the variable.

trigonometric functions (p. 808) For any angle, with measure α, a point $P(x, y)$ on its terminal side, $r = \sqrt{x^2 + y^2}$, the trigonometric functions of a are as follows.

$\sin \alpha = \frac{y}{r}$ $\quad \cos \alpha = \frac{x}{r}$ $\quad \tan \alpha = \frac{y}{x}$

$\csc \alpha = \frac{r}{y}$ $\quad \sec \alpha = \frac{r}{x}$ $\quad \cot \alpha = \frac{x}{y}$

trigonometric identity (p. 893) An equation involving a trigonometric function that is true for all values of the variable for which the function is defined.

trigonometric ratio (p. 808) Compares the side lengths of a right triangle.

trigonometry (p. 808) The study of the relationships between the angles and sides of a right triangle.

turning point (p. 358) Point at which a graph turns. The location of relative maxima or minima.

lado terminal Rayo de un ángulo que gira alrededor de un centro.

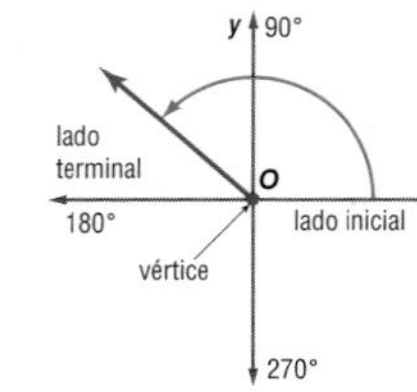

probabilidad teórica Lo que debería ocurrir en un experimento probabilístico.

determinante de tercer orden Determinante de una matriz de 3×3.

transformación Funciones que aplican puntos de una preimagen en su imagen.

traslación Se mueve una figura de un lugar a otro en un plano de coordenadas sin cambiar su tamaño, forma u orientación.

matriz de traslación Matriz que representa una figura trasladada.

eje transversal El segmento de longitud $2a$ cuyos extremos son los vértices de una hipérbola.

grupo tratamiento En un experimento, la gente, los animales, o los objetos dados el tratamiento.

ecuación trigonométrica Ecuación que contiene por lo menos una función trigonométrica y que sólo se cumple para algunos valores de la variable.

funciones trigonométricas Para cualquier ángulo, de medida α, un punto $P(x, y)$ en su lado terminal, $r = \sqrt{x^2 + y^2}$, las funciones trigonométricas de a son las siguientes.

$\sin \alpha = \frac{y}{r}$ $\quad \cos \alpha = \frac{x}{r}$ $\quad \tan \alpha = \frac{y}{x}$

$\csc \alpha = \frac{r}{y}$ $\quad \sec \alpha = \frac{r}{x}$ $\quad \cot \alpha = \frac{x}{y}$

identidad trigonométrica Ecuación que involucra una o más funciones trigonométricas y que se cumple para todos los valores de la variable en que el función es definido.

razón trigonometric Compara las longitudes laterales de un triángulo derecho.

trigonometría Estudio de las relaciones entre los lados y ángulos de un triángulo rectángulo.

momento crucial Un punto en el cual un gráfico da vuelta. La localización de máximos o de mínimos relativos.

U

unbiased (p. 745) When a sample is random, or not based on any predetermined characteristics of the population.

No sesgada Muestra que se selecciona de modo que sea representative de la poblacion entera.

unbiased sample (p. 745) A sample in which every possible sample has an equal chance of being selected.

muestra no sesgada Muestra en que cualquier muestra posible tiene la misma posibilidad de seleccionarse.

unbounded (p. 160) A system of inequalities that forms a region that is open.

no acotado Sistema de desigualdades que forma una región abierta.

uniform distribution (p. 766) A distribution where all of the probabilities are the same.

distribución uniforme Distribución donde todas las probabilidades son equiprobables.

union (p. 42) The graph of a compound inequality containing *or*.

unión Gráfica de una desigualdad compuesta que contiene la palabra *o*.

unit analysis (p. 340) The process of including unit measurement when computing.

análisis de la unidad Proceso de incluir unidades de medida al computar.

unit circle (p. 848) A circle of radius 1 unit whose center is at the origin of a coordinate system.

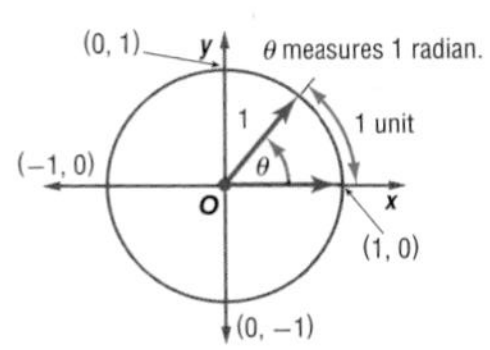

círculo unitario Círculo de radio 1 cuyo centro es el origen de un sistema de coordenadas.

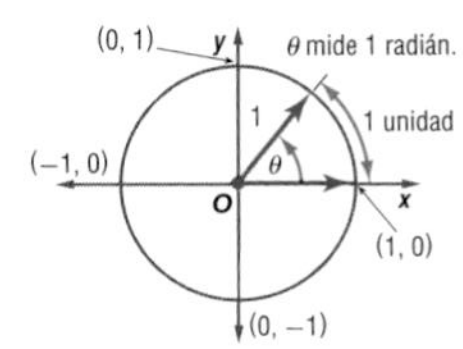

univariate data (p. 752) Data with one variable.

datos univariados Datos con una variable.

upper quartile (p. 1005) The median of the upper half of a set of data, indicated by UQ.

cuartil superior Mediana de la mitad superior de un conjunto de datos, denotada por CS.

V

variable (p. 5) Symbols, usually letters, used to represent unknown quantities.

variables Símbolos, por lo general letras, que se usan para representar cantidades desconocidas.

variable matrix (p. 231) A matrix that only contains the variables of a system of equations.

matriz variable Una matriz que contiene solamente las variables de un sistema de ecuaciones.

variance (p. 754) The mean of the squares of the deviations from the arithmetic mean.

varianza Media de los cuadrados de las desviaciones de la media aritmética.

vertex (pp. 160, 250) **1.** Any of the points of intersection of the graphs of the constraints that determine a feasible region. **2.** The point at which the axis of symmetry intersects a parabola. **3.** The point on each branch nearest the center of a hyperbola.

vértice **1.** Cualqeiera de los puntos de intersección de las gráficas que los contienen y que determinan una región viable. **2.** Punto en el que el eje de simetría interseca una parábola. **3.** El punto en cada rama más cercano al centro de una hipérbola.

vertex form (p. 305) A quadratic function in the form $y = a(x - h)^2 + k$, where (h, k) is the vertex of the parabola and $x = h$ is its axis of symmetry.

forma de vértice Función cuadrática de la forma $y = a(x - h)^2 + k$, donde (h, k) es el vértice de la parábola y $x = h$ es su eje de simetría.

vertex matrix (p. 209) A matrix used to represent the coordinates of the vertices of a polygon.

matriz de vértice Matriz que se usa para escribir las coordenadas de los vértices de un polígono.

vertical asymptote (p. 577) If the related rational expression of a function is written in simplest form and is undefined for $x = a$, then $x = a$ is a vertical asymptote.

asíntota vertical Si la expresión racional que corresponde a una función racional se reduce y está no definida en $x = a$, entonces $x = a$ es una asíntota vertical.

vertical line test (p. 62) If no vertical line intersects a graph in more than one point, then the graph represents a function.

prudba de la recta vertical Si ninguna recta vertical interseca una gráfica en más de un punto, entonces la gráfica representa una función.

vertical shift (p. 864) When graphs of trigonometric functions are translated vertically.

cambio vertical Cuando los gráficos de funciones trigonométricas son translado verticales.

vertices (pp. 639, 648) **Ellipse**—The endpoints of the major axis. **Hyperbola**—The endpoints of the transverse axis.

vértices **(de una elipse)** Son las puntos finales del eje principal. **(de una hipérbola)** Son las puntos finales del eje transversal.

W

weighted average (p. 596) A method for finding the mean of a set of numbers in which some elements of the set carry more importance, or weight, than others.

promedio ponderado Un método para encontrar el medio de un sistema de los números en los cuales algunos elementos del sistema llevan más importancia, o peso, que otros.

whole numbers (p. 11) {0, 1, 2, 3, 4, …}

números naturales {0, 1, 2, 3, 4, …}

X

x-intercept (p. 71) The x-coordinate of the point at which a graph crosses the x-axis.

intersección x La coordenada x del punto o puntos en que una gráfica interseca o cruza el eje x.

Y

y-intercept (p. 71) The y-coordinate of the point at which a graph crosses the y-axis.

intersección y La coordenada y del punto o puntos en que una gráfica interseca o cruza el eje y.

Z

zeros (p. 259) The x-intercepts of the graph of a function; the points for which $f(x) = 0$.

ceros Las intersecciones x de la gráfica de una función; los puntos x para los que $f(x) = 0$.

zero matrix (p. 186) A matrix in which every element is zero.

matriz nula matriz cuyos elementos son todos igual a cero.

Index

Index

A

Index

B

C

D

E

Index

Index

G

H

Index

I

Index

L

Index

M

N

Index

O

P

Q

R

Index

S

Index

Index

U

V

W

X

Y

Z

Formulas

Coordinate Geometry

Midpoint	$M = \left(\frac{x_1 + x_2}{2}, \frac{y_1 + y_2}{2}\right)$	**Distance**	$d = \sqrt{(x_2 - x_1)^2 + (y_2 - y_1)^2}$
		Slope	$m = \frac{y_2 - y_1}{x_2 - x_1}, x_2 \neq x_1$

Matrices

Adding	$\begin{bmatrix} a & b \\ c & d \end{bmatrix} + \begin{bmatrix} e & f \\ g & h \end{bmatrix} = \begin{bmatrix} a+e & b+f \\ c+g & d+h \end{bmatrix}$	**Multiplying by a Scalar**	$k\begin{bmatrix} a & b \\ c & d \end{bmatrix} = \begin{bmatrix} ka & kb \\ kc & kd \end{bmatrix}$
Subtracting	$\begin{bmatrix} a & b \\ c & d \end{bmatrix} - \begin{bmatrix} e & f \\ g & h \end{bmatrix} = \begin{bmatrix} a-e & b-f \\ c-g & d-h \end{bmatrix}$	**Multiplying**	$\begin{bmatrix} a & b \\ c & d \end{bmatrix} \cdot \begin{bmatrix} e & f \\ g & h \end{bmatrix} = \begin{bmatrix} ae+bg & af+bh \\ ce+dg & cf+dh \end{bmatrix}$

Polynomials

Quadratic Formula	$x = \frac{-b \pm \sqrt{b^2 - 4ac}}{2a}, a \neq 0$	**Square of a Difference**	$(a - b)^2 = (a - b)(a - b) = a^2 - 2ab + b^2$
Square of a Sum	$(a + b)^2 = (a + b)(a + b) = a^2 + 2ab + b^2$	**Product of Sum and Difference**	$(a + b)(a - b) = (a - b)(a + b) = a^2 - b^2$

Logarithms

Product Property	$\log_x ab = \log_x a + \log_x b$	**Power Property**	$\log_b m^p = p \log_b m$
Quotient Property	$\log_x \frac{a}{b} = \log_x a - \log_x b, b \neq 0$	**Change of Base**	$\log_a n = \frac{\log_b n}{\log_b a}$

Conic Sections

Parabola	$y = a(x - h)^2 + k$ or $x = a(y - k)^2 + h$	**Ellipse**	$\frac{x^2}{a^2} + \frac{y^2}{b^2} = 1$ or $\frac{y^2}{a^2} + \frac{x^2}{b^2} = 1, a, b \neq 0$
Circle	$x^2 + y^2 = r^2$ or $(x - h)^2 + (y - k)^2 = r^2$	**Hyperbola**	$\frac{x^2}{a^2} - \frac{y^2}{b^2} = 1$ or $\frac{y^2}{a^2} - \frac{x^2}{b^2} = 1, a, b \neq 0$

Sequences and Series

nth term, Arithmetic	$a_n = a_1 + (n - 1)d$	**nth term, Geometric**	$a_n = a_1 r^{n-1}$
Sum of Arithmetic Series	$S_n = n\left(\frac{a_1 + a_2}{2}\right)$ or $S_n = \frac{n}{2}[2a_1 + (n - 1)d]$	**Sum of Geometric Series**	$S_n = \frac{a_1 - a_1 r^n}{1 - r}$ or $S_n = \frac{a_1 - a_n r}{1 - r}, r \neq 1$

Trigonometry

Law of Sines	$\frac{\sin A}{a} = \frac{\sin B}{b} = \frac{\sin C}{c}, a, b, c \neq 0$		
Law of Cosines	$a^2 = b^2 + c^2 - 2bc \cos A$	$b^2 = a^2 + c^2 - 2ac \cos B$	$c^2 = a^2 + b^2 - 2ab \cos C$
Trigonometric Functions	$\sin \theta = \frac{\text{opp}}{\text{hyp}}$	$\cos \theta = \frac{\text{adj}}{\text{hyp}}$	$\tan \theta = \frac{\text{opp}}{\text{adj}} = \frac{\sin \theta}{\cos \theta}$
	$\csc \theta = \frac{\text{hyp}}{\text{opp}} = \frac{1}{\sin \theta}$	$\sec \theta = \frac{\text{hyp}}{\text{adj}} = \frac{1}{\cos \theta}$	$\cot \theta = \frac{\text{adj}}{\text{opp}} = \frac{\cos \theta}{\sin \theta}$
Pythagorean Identities	$\cos^2 \theta + \sin^2 \theta = 1$	$\tan^2 \theta + 1 = \sec^2 \theta$	$\cot^2 \theta + 1 = \csc^2 \theta$

	...se-defined function
	...lute value function
	...unction of greatest integer not greater than a
	f of x and y, a function with two variables, x and y
$\overrightarrow{AB}$	vector AB
i	the imaginary unit
$[f \circ g](x)$	f of g of x, the composition of functions f and g
$f^{-1}(x)$	inverse of $f(x)$
$b^{\frac{1}{n}} = \sqrt[n]{b}$	nth root of b
$\log_b x$	logarithm base b of x
$\log x$	common logarithm of x
$\ln x$	natural logarithm of x

$\sum$	sigma, summation
$\overline{x}$	mean of a sample
μ	mean of a population
s	standard deviation of a sample
σ	standard deviation of a population
$P(B\|A)$	the probability of B given that A has already occurred
nPr	permutation of n objects taken r at a time
nCr	combination of n objects taken r at a time
$\text{Sin}^{-1}\, x$	Arcsin x
$\text{Cos}^{-1}\, x$	Arccos x
$\text{Tan}^{-1}\, x$	Arctan x

Parent Functions

Linear Functions

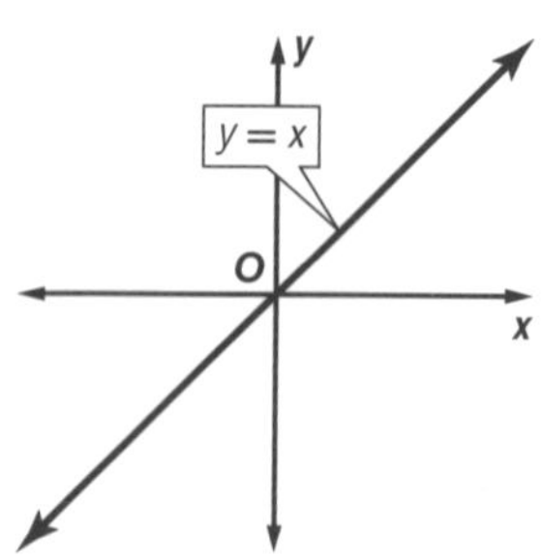

Absolute Value Functions

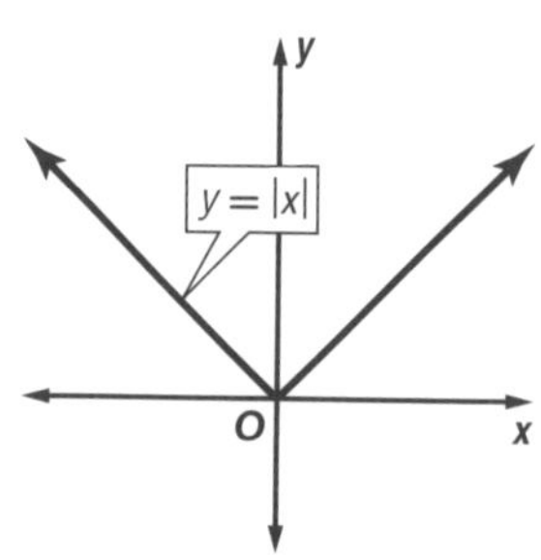

Quadratic Functions

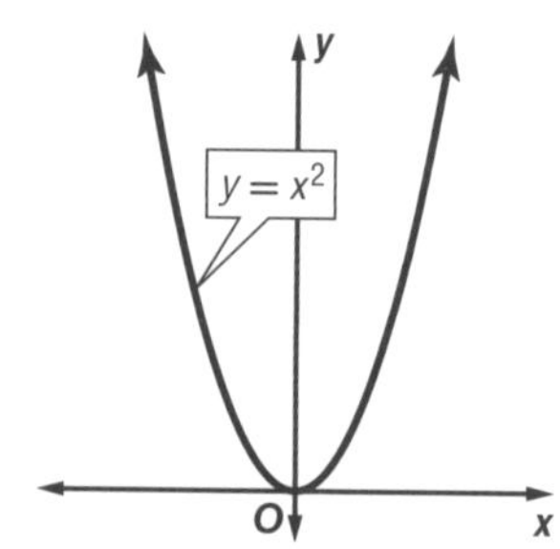

Exponential and Logarithmic Functions

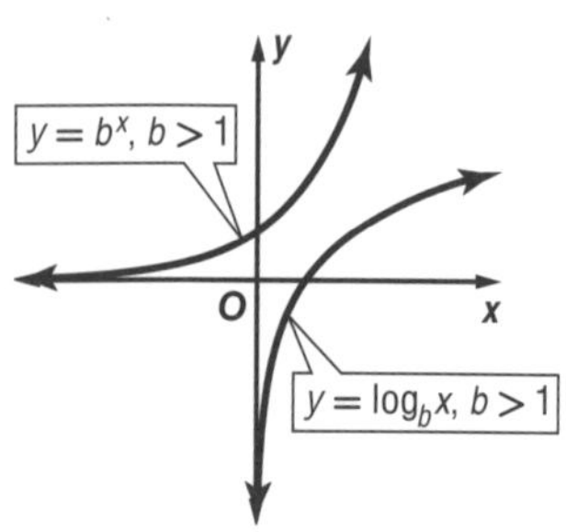

Square Root Functions

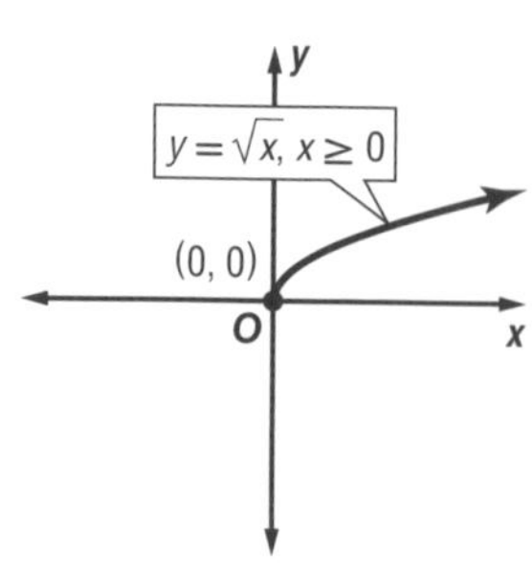

Reciprocal and Rational Functions

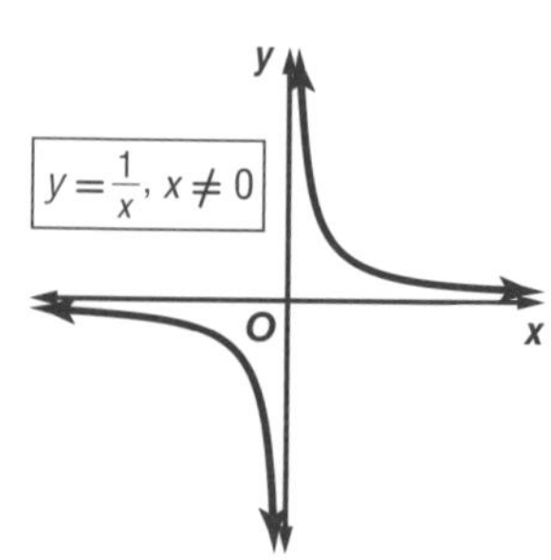